We've been saving money for years. And years. And years.

The Absa Group Museum houses the biggest collection of coins, notes, moneyboxes and related artefacts in the country, and traces the history of South African banking back to its inception. Come visit us. And while you may not always know where your money goes to, you'll certainly be able to see where it comes from.

Absa Group Museum: Ground Floor, 187 Fox Street, Johannesburg. Open 9:00 – 16:00 weekdays
Phone (011) 350 4167/6889, fax (011) 350 3435

ABSA

Today Tomorrow Together

ABSA Bank Ltd, Reg no 1986/004794/06

Y&R Gitam 123925

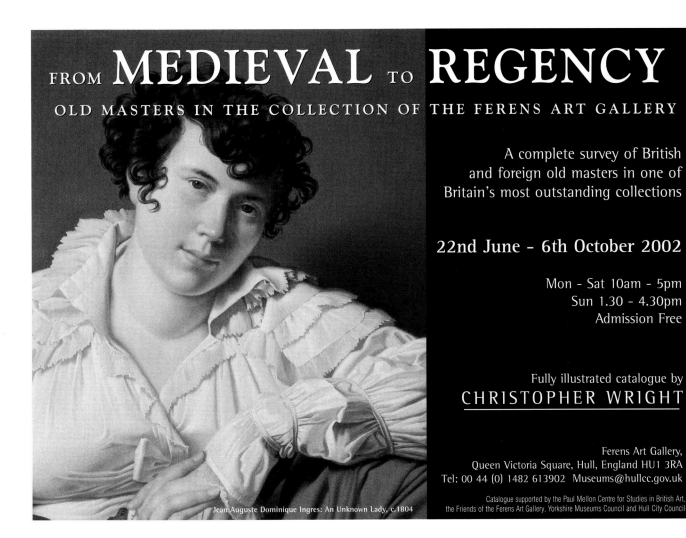

FROM **MEDIEVAL** TO **REGENCY**

OLD MASTERS IN THE COLLECTION OF THE FERENS ART GALLERY

A complete survey of British and foreign old masters in one of Britain's most outstanding collections

22nd June – 6th October 2002

Mon – Sat 10am – 5pm
Sun 1.30 – 4.30pm
Admission Free

Fully illustrated catalogue by
CHRISTOPHER WRIGHT

Ferens Art Gallery,
Queen Victoria Square, Hull, England HU1 3RA
Tel: 00 44 (0) 1482 613902 Museums@hullcc.gov.uk

Catalogue supported by the Paul Mellon Centre for Studies in British Art,
the Friends of the Ferens Art Gallery, Yorkshire Museums Council and Hull City Council

Jean-Auguste Dominique Ingres: An Unknown Lady, c.1804

Handbook of International Documentation and Information

Volume 16

Vol. I
Afghanistan
—
Swaziland

Vol. II
Sweden
—
Zimbabwe

Indices

Neues Stadtmuseum
Landsberg am Lech

Von-Helfensteingasse 426 · 86899 Landsberg · Tel. 0 81 91/ 94 23 26 · Fax: 0 81 91/ 94 23 27
BAB München-Lindau, Ausfahrt 26
e-mail : neues_stadtmuseum@landsberg.de
Geöffnet täglich, außer montags von 14 bis 17 Uhr, Februar und März geschlossen.

Museums of the World

9th revised and
enlarged edition

Volume I
Afghanistan – Swaziland

K·G·Saur München 2002

Editor/Redaktion:
Michael Zils

Editorial Office/Redaktionsbüro:
Luppenstr. 1b
D-04177 Leipzig (Germany)
Tel. +49 341 4869911
Fax +49 341 4869913

Die Deutsche Bibliothek - CIP-Einheitsaufnahme

Museums of the world
/ [ed.: Michael Zils]. - 9., rev and enl. ed. - München : Saur
(Handbook of international documentation and information ; Vol.16)
ISBN 3-598-20610-0

Vol. 1. Afghanistan - Swaziland. - 2002

Printed on acid-free paper

The publisher and editor do not assume and hereby disclaim
any liability to any party for any loss or damage caused by
errors or omissions in *Museums of the World*,
whether such errors or omissions result from negligence,
accident or any other cause.
Data preparation and automatic data processing by
bsix information exchange, Braunschweig
rinted and bound by Strauss Offsetdruck, Mörlenbach

Cover Art by William Pownall

ISSN 0939-1959 (Handbook)
ISBN 3-598-20610-0 (2 volumes)

Contents

Volume I

Volume II

Preface

Completely updated, this 9th edition of **Museums of the World** gives detailed information on 42,143 museums and museum associations in 199 countries. By sending out questionnaires throughout the world, all names, addresses, contact numbers (phone, fax, E-mail, etc.) were revised thoroughly.

Moreover a great many national and international museum associations provided us with their latest member lists which led to more than 1,300 new museum entries.

In order to make this handbook more user friendly, information on museum closings is given for the first time. If a place name has changed (e.g. in India), a cross reference leads to the new name.

Museums of the World is divided into five sections: Museums and Museum Associations, and three indexes providing access by museum name, by personalities, and by subject.

Museum Section
Organization: Countries are arranged alphabetically by the English name form. Within countries arrangement is by place name and finally by museum.

Modified letters as the Danish å or the Polish ł file in unmodified form as a or l, etc., in all sections.

Structure of entries
A typical entry consists of the following information:
- Name of the museum and/or institution to which the museum is subordinate, in the original language with an English translation when necessary
- Address, consisting of street and house number, post office box and mail address if appropriate, postal code, and town or city
- Telephone number *T*, area code in parentheses
- Telefax number *Fax*
- E-mail address and/or Internet address
- Type of museum
- Year museum was founded
- Name of director or head of museum
- Collections and facilities
- Entry number

Type of museums
Each museum has been assigned to at least one of the following categories:

Agriculture Museum	Military Museum
Archaeological Museum	Museum of Classical Antiquities
Association with Collection	Music Museum
Decorative Arts Museum	Natural History Museum
Ethnology Museum	Open Air Museum
Fine Arts Museum	Performing Arts Museum
Folklore Museum	Public Gallery
Historic Site	Religious Arts Museum
Historical Museum	Science & Tech Museum
Library with Exhibitions	Special Museum
Local Museum	University Museum

Museum Associations Section
Organization: Countries are arranged alphabetically by the English name form. Within countries arrangement is by association name.

A typical entry includes the complete address, phone and fax number, and the e-mail and internet address.

Indexes:

The *Alphabetical Index to Museums* lists museum and museum association names in the original language or in the English translation when given.

The *Personality Index* lists individuals whose works are featured in a given museum.

The *Subject Index* is arranged alphabetically by subject, within each subject by country and then by name of museum.

In all three indexes reference to the entry in the main section is by item number.

A reference book of this scope cannot be produced without the active support of countless people. The editors are particularly indebted to the curators, directors, secretaries, and other museum staff who have been unfailingly helpful and co-operative. Their contributions have made it possible to present in this edition complete and reliable information on museums all over the world. As always, the editors welcome any additional data, corrections, information on newly-founded museums, as well as comments and suggestions for improvements.

The editorial deadline for this edition was March 28th, 2002.

The editors

Museums
of the World

Volume I

Homo Pictor

Herausgeben von Gottfried Boehm, Redaktion: Stephan E. Hauser

2001. XIII, 390 Seiten und 61 Bildtafeln. Leineneinband
€ 57,– / sFr 98,–. ISBN 3-598-77418-4
(Colloquium Rauricum, Band 7)

Homo Pictor vereinigt die Beiträge der siebten Folge der alle zwei Jahre vom Colloquium Rauricum auf Castelen in Augst bei Basel veranstalteten Colloquia Raurica. Der Band enthält zwanzig Aufsätze von namhaften Fachvertretern, in denen das Thema des Menschen als Bilderzeuger aus der Sicht zahlreicher geistes- und kulturwissenschaftlicher Disziplinen, vorrangig kunsthistorischer, philosophischer, altertumswissenschaftlicher, historischer sowie sprachwissenschaftlicher bzw. germanistischer Prägung, behandelt wird. Der untersuchte Zeitraum reicht von der Prähistorie über die Zeit des Alten Ägyptens, der Antike, des Mittelalters und der Renaissance bis in die Gegenwart.

Basierend auf den Erfahrungen einer phasenweise überaus erfolgreichen und tonangebenden „Sprachwissenschaft" erkunden die in **Homo Pictor** versammelten Autoren und Autorinnen Grammatik und Syntax der visuellen Ausdrucksformen. Sie befragen die Möglichkeiten einer „Bildwissenschaft", die sich anthropologischer Argumente bedient, historiographische Erfahrungsweisen aber weder untergraben noch verdrängen, sondern fruchtbar erweitern möchte. In Anbetracht der Realität der Bilder und der Offenheit der Horizonte, vor denen sich diese manifestieren, dokumentieren die versammelten Beiträge Positionen einer Gesprächsgemeinschaft, die die Rolle des Bildes als Leitkategorie zum Anlass nimmt, die gemeinsamen Aufgaben angesichts einer zunehmend von Bildern durchsetzten Lebenswelt zu überdenken.

Die Publikation ist von besonderem Interesse für alle, die den Fragen, die aus der doppelten Eigenschaft der Bilder erwachsen, vergangen und gegenwärtig zugleich zu sein, offen gegenüberstehen.

 K·G·Saur Verlag
A Gale Group/Thomson Learning Company
Postfach 70 16 20 · 81316 München · Deutschland · Tel. (089) 7 69 02-232
Fax (089) 7 69 02-150/250 · e-mail: info@saur.de · http://www.saur.de

Afghanistan

Bamian

Bamian Museum, Bamian
Local Museum
Ethnography, local hist   00001

Ghazni

Ghazni Museum, Ghazni
Local Museum
Ethnography, local hist   00002

Herat

Herat Museum, Herat
Local Museum
Ethnography, local hist   00003

Kabul

Kabul Museum, Darul Aman, Kabul - T: 42656. Head:
Najibulla Popal
Ethnology Museum / Fine Arts Museum - 1922
Local and Far Eastern antiquities and objects d'art,
costumes and jewelry   00004

Pathology Museum, c/o Kabul University, Kabul
Special Museum
Pathological specimens   00005

Science Museum, c/o Faculty of Science, Kabul
University, Kabul
Natural History Museum
Zoological coll   00006

Kandahar

Kandahar Museum, Kandahar
Local Museum
Ethnography, local hist   00007

Maimana

Maimana Museum, Maimana
Local Museum
Ethnography, local hist   00008

Mazar-i-Sharif

Mazar-i-Sharif Museum, Mazar-i-Sharif
Local Museum
Ethnography, local hist   00009

Albania

Bérat

Architecture Museum, Bérat
Fine Arts Museum   00010

District Historical Museum, Bérat - T: (062) 32595.
Head: Arben Jaupaj
Historical Museum - 1958
Local hist, documents   00011

Ethnographic Museum, Bérat
Ethnology Museum   00012

Onufri Iconographic Museum, Town Castle, Bérat
Religious Arts Museum - 1986
Icons by medieval painter Onufri   00013

Butrint

Butrinti Museum, Butrint
Local Museum
Local history, archeology, prehistory   00014

Durrës

Archeological Museum of Durrës, Durrës - T: (052)
22253, Fax: 22253. Head: Prof. Afrim Hoti
Archaeological Museum - 1951
Coins, terracuits, pottery of black and red, figures,
glass vessels, grave stones   00015

Ethnographic Museum, Durrës
Ethnology Museum   00016

Elbasan

District Ethnographic Museum, Elbasan
Ethnology Museum   00017

Elbasan Museum, Festung, Elbasan. Head: Thomas
Konomi
Local Museum
Local and military hist, natural hist   00018

Museum of Education, Elbasan
Special Museum   00019

Fier

Fier Archaeological Museum, Fier. Head: Gori Sata
Archaeological Museum - 1958
Archaeological finds from Apollonia   00020

Muzeu Historik Fier (District Historical Museum), Fier
- T: (0642) 2583. Head: Petrit Malushi
Historical Museum - 1948   00021

Gjirokastër

Ethnographic Museum, Gjirokastër
Ethnology Museum   00022

Gjirokastër Museum, National Renaissance Museum,
Gjirokastër. Head: Lefter Dilo
Local Museum / Military Museum
Local and military hist   00023

Korçë

Fine Arts Gallery, Korçë
Fine Arts Museum   00024

Korçë Museum, Korçë. Head: Enin Selenitza
Local Museum / Ethnology Museum
Local hist, ethnography   00025

Museum of Education, Korçë
Special Museum
Development of education   00026

National Museum of Medieval Art, Korçë - T: (0824)
3022. Head: Lorenc Gliozheni
Fine Arts Museum - 1980
Stone, metal, paintings, icons, applied art,
textiles   00027

Kruja

Scanderbeg Museum, Kruja
Local Museum
Local history, natural history, archeology   00028

Përmet

District Historical Museum, Përmet
Historical Museum   00029

Pojani

Pojani Museum, Pojani
Archaeological Museum
Classical archeology   00030

Shkodër

Muzeu i Filmit Shkodër (Cinematographic Museum),
Qendre Kulturore Shkodër, Shkodër - T: (0224)
3217. Head: Gjergj Denelli
Special Museum - 1987
Three rolls of pathé-film (9,5mm) from 1920,
cinematographic projector from 1905   00031

Shkodër Museum, Shkodër. Head: Vasil Llazari
Local Museum
Hist of town and province from Neolithic times,
ethnography   00032

Tiranë

Fine Arts Gallery, Tiranë - T: (04) 226033,
Fax: 233975, E-mail: natgal@albaniaonline.net,
gquendro@albnet.com. Head: Gëzim Qëndro
Fine Arts Museum   00033

Museum of the Struggle for National Liberation,
Tiranë. Head: Vaso Bachniakon
Historical Museum
History of the Albanian people from the Ottoman
period to the present day   00034

Muzeu i Shkencave Natyrore (Museum of Natural
Sciences), Rr. e Kavajes 132, Tiranë. Head: Prof. Dr.
Idriz Haxhiu
Natural History Museum / University Museum
Zoology, botany, geology   00035

National Historical Museum, Skenderbe Sq, Tiranë -
T: (042) 28389, Fax: 28389. Head: Prof. Vilson Kuri
Agriculture Museum / Decorative Arts Museum /
Historical Museum - 1981
Agricultural tools of all periods, stock-breeding
equipment, interiors and exteriors, household
objects, textiles and customs, local crafts and
ceramics up to the present day   00036

National Museum of Archaeology, c/o Academy of
Science, Institute of Archaeology, Blvd Dëshmorët e
Kombit, Tiranë - T: (042) 26541. Head: Ilir Gjipali
Archaeological Museum - 1948
Prehistory, Illyrian culture and Middle ages in
Albania, household objects: ceramics, metal, stone,
marble, glass, bone - library   00037

Vlorë

District Historical Museum, Vlorë - T: 2646. Head:
Nail Sheku
Local Museum - 1953
Local history, archeology   00038

Algeria

Alger

History and Natural History Museum, People's
Palace, Av Franklin Roosevelt, Parc de la Liberté,
Alger
Historical Museum / Natural History Museum
Ottoman swords and jewellery, flora, fauna   00039

Musée Central de l'Armée, Riadh El Feth, Alger -
T: (021) 661612
Military Museum   00040

Musée des Arts Populaires, 9 Rue Mohamed Akli
Malek, Casbah, Alger - T: (021) 713414,
Fax: 713414. Head: Amamra Aziza Aicha
Folklore Museum - 1961
Popular arts and crafts   00041

Musée du Mont Riant (Children's Museum), Parc
Mont Riant, Alger - T: (021) 741708, Fax: 711820.
Head: Nedjma Serradj-Remili
Special Museum - 1966
Children's artefacts   00042

Musée National des Antiquités, Parc de la Liberté,
Alger - T: (021) 746686, Fax: 747471. Head: Drias
Lakhdar
Archaeological Museum / Fine Arts Museum - 1897
Classical and Islamic antiquities, ancient mosaics,
antique mosaics, Roman glass work and sculptures
- library   00043

Musée National des Beaux-Arts d'Alger, El-Hamma,
Pl Dar-El-Salem, Alger - T: (021) 664916,
Fax: 662054. Head: Dr. Dalila Orfali
Fine Arts Museum / Decorative Arts Museum - 1930
Contemporary and 16th c painting, drawing,
sculpture and graphics, 20th c Algerian miniature,
ceramics, medals, furniture - library   00044

Musée National du Bardo, 3 Av F.D. Roosevelt, Alger
16000 - T: (021) 747641, Fax: 742453. Head: Aïcha
Boukli
Ethnology Museum / Fine Arts Museum - 1930
Prehistoric and ethnographic coll, African art   00045

Musée National du Moudjahid, El Madania, Makam
Echahid, mail addr: BP 168, Alger - T: (021)
653488, Fax: 671974. Head: Zghidi Mohamed
Lahcéne
Historical Museum - 1983
Contemporary history   00046

Annaba

Musée d'Hippone (Hippo Regius Museum), Rte
d'Hippone, 23000 Annaba - T: (038) 837171
Museum of Classical Antiquities
Classical antiquities   00047

Béjaia

Musée d'Archéologie, Pl du 1er Novembre, Béjaia
Archaeological Museum
Roman and Hafsid finds   00048

Musée de Béjaia, Béjaia
Local Museum
Archaeology, natural sciences, fine arts   00049

Musée Emile Aubry, Rue Youcef Bouchebah, Béjaia
Fine Arts Museum
Contemporary paintings   00050

Bou Saada

Musée National Nasserdine Dinet, Bou Saada
Fine Arts Museum   00051

Cherchell

Musée Archéologique, El Asnam, Pl de la Mairie,
Cherchell - T: 799676
Archaeological Museum
Egyptian, Greek and Roman antiquities   00052

Constantine

Musée de Constantine, Plateau Coudiat, Pl des
Martyrs, Constantine
Fine Arts Museum / Museum of Classical Antiquities
Prehistoric antiquities, Islamic art, painting   00053

Musée National Cirta, Plateau Coudiat, Constantine -
T: (031) 923895, Fax: 923319,
E-mail: cirtamuseum@djazair-connect.com,
Internet: http://www.cirtamuseum.org. Head: Daho
Kelthoum Kitouni
Local Museum - 1853
library   00054

Palais du Bey, Constantine
Local Museum   00055

El-Oued

Musée d'El-Oued, Pl de la Jeunesse, El-Oued -
T: (032) 218849, Fax: 218799. Head: Nedjah Sadok
Local Museum - 1954
Prehistory, ethnography, crafts   00056

Ghardaia Oasis

Musée Folklorique de Ghardaia, Ghardaia Oasis
Folklore Museum
Crafts, folk arts   00057

Guelma

Musée Archéologique de Guelma, Rue du Théâtre
Romain, 24000 Guelma
Archaeological Museum
Sculpture, numismatics   00058

Oran

Musée National Zabana - Demaeght Museum, 19
Blvd Zabana, Oran - T: (041) 343781. Head: Dr.
Malki Nordine
Local Museum / Archaeological Museum - 1884
Prehist, modern art, ethnography, natural science,
classical antiquities, Roman and Byzantine
coins   00059

Ouargla

Musée Saharien de Ouargla, Ouargla
Local Museum
Prehist, ethnography, crafts   00060

Sétif

Musée de Sétif, El-Kala, Sétif, mail addr: c/o Musée
Marsa el-Kharez, BP 41, Sétif
Museum of Classical Antiquities - 1991
Roman antiquities   00061

Musée Régional d'Archéologie, Ancien Palais de
Justice, 102 Rue Bachi Abiel, Sétif - T: (036)
851112. Head: Kebbour Amor
Archaeological Museum - 1968   00062

National Archaeologic Museum, Rue de A.L.N. Sétif,
Sétif - T: (036) 851759, Fax: 854055. Head: Salima
Larguem
Archaeological Museum - 1985
Antique and Islamic coins, ceramics, mosaics
(Triumph of Bacchus)   00063

Skikda

Musée de Skikda, Centre Culturel, Rue Abdallah
Ghorsellah, 21000 Skikda - T: (038) 957819
Museum of Classical Antiquities / Fine Arts Museum
Punic and Roman antiquities, modern art   00064

Tazoult

Musée de Tazoult, Wilaya de Batna, Tazoult
Museum of Classical Antiquities
Classical antiquities   00065

Tebessa

Musée du Temple de Minerve, Pl de Minerve,
Tebessa - E-mail: med_houcine@yahoo.fr. Head:
Housine Med Cherif
Archaeological Museum / Museum of Classical
Antiquities / Fine Arts Museum
Local art, prehistoric finds, antiquities   00066

Tiemcen

Musée de Tiemcen, Pl Khemisti, Tiemcen - T: (043)
265506. Head: Brahim Chenoufi
Archaeological Museum - 1901
Islamic arts, natural science, classical
antiquities   00067

Timgad

Musée Archéologique de Timgad, Parc
Archéologique de Timgad, 05130 Timgad -
T: 811102. Head: Ali Guerbabi
Museum of Classical Antiquities - 1881
Classical antiquities, mosaics, coins   00068

Tipasa

Musée de Tipasa, Rue des Thermes, 42000 Tipasa -
T: (024) 477543. Head: Sabah Ferdi
Archaeological Museum - 1955
Mosaics, sculpture, archaeology   00069

Wilaya de Setif

Musée Archéologique de Djemila, Parc
Archéologique de Djemila-Cuicul, Rte d'El Eulma,
Wilaya de Setif. Head: Mona Arab
Archaeological Museum / Museum of Classical
Antiquities
Architecture, sculpture, classical antiquities   00070

American Samoa

Pago Pago

Jean P. Haydon Museum, POB 1540, Pago Pago, AS
96799 - T: (684) 633-5613, Fax: (684) 633-2059,
E-mail: ascah@Samoatelco.com. Head: Faailoilo J.
Lauvao
Fine Arts Museum / Local Museum / Folklore
Museum - 1969
Local hist, art   00071

Andorra

Encamp

Museu Nacional de l'Automòbil, Av Coprincep Episcopal 64, Encamp - T: 832266, Fax: 832266
Science&Tech Museum - 1988
Cars, motorbikes and bicycles from 1898 to 1950, exhibition of components, exhibition of miniature cars in porcelain and iron, steam machine Pinette (1885) 00072

Escaldes-Engordany

Museu Viladomat d'Escultura, Av Parc de La Mola s/n, Escaldes-Engordany - T: 829340, Fax: 829340, E-mail: museuviladomat@andorra.ad. Head: Gloria Pujol
Local Museum - 1987 00073

Ordino

Museu Casa d'Areny-Plandolit, Casa d'Areny-Plandolit, Ordino - T: 836908, Fax: 839660
Decorative Arts Museum - 1987
Typical 17th-c house, with later alterations, furniture, porcelain, costumes, family hist of Don Guillem d'Areny-Plandolit, Baron of Senaller and Gramenet 00074

Museu Postal d'Andorra, Borda del Raser, Ordino - T: 839760, 836908, Fax: 839660, E-mail: pca.gov@andorra.ad. Head: Marta Planas
Historical Museum - 1989
First-day covers, postcards, postal history 00075

Sispony

Museu Casa Rull, Carrer Major, Sispony - T: 836919, Fax: 835419, E-mail: casarull@andorra.ad
Historical Museum
Culture, family hist, argiculture, life in the parish of La Massana 00076

Angola

Benguela

Museu Nacional de Arqueologia, Rua Cerveira Pereira 1-3, Benguela, mail addr: CP 79, Benguela - T: (99) 3075. Head: Joaquim Pais Pinto
Archaeological Museum 00077

Cabinda

Museu Regional de Cabinda, CP 283, Cabinda. Head: Tadeu Domingos
Ethnology Museum
Ethnography 00078

Carmona

Museu do Congo, CP 11, Carmona
Local Museum - 1965
Items of material culture of the people of the area, indigenous art, wood carvings and ivories 00079

Chitato

Museu do Dundu, CP 54, Chitato - T: 64476. Head: Felizardo Jesus Gurgel
Ethnology Museum / Historical Museum - 1936
Ethnographic coll including art of the local Chokwe tribe, tape libr of North Eastern Angola folk music, local hist, photos from the 1880s 00080

Huambo

Museu Regional do Planalto Central, Av Feti, Huambo, mail addr: CP 2066, Huambo 945 - T: 2881. Head: Francisco Xavier Yambo
Local Museum 00081

Lobito

Museu de Etnografia do Lobito, CP 2152, Lobito - T: 3943. Head: Pedro Chacala Nuñulo
Ethnology Museum 00082

Luanda

Centro Nacional de Documentação e Investigação Histórica, Rua Pedro Felix Machado 49, Luanda - T: (2) 334410, 334416. Head: Aurora da Fonseca Ferreira
Historical Museum 00083

Museu Central das Forças Armadas, CP 1267, Luanda - T: (2) 339049. Head: Silvestre A. Francisco
Military Museum 00084

Museu da Escravatura, Museum of Slavery, Estrada da Barra do Kuanza, Luanda, mail addr: CP 1267, Luanda - T: (2) 371650. Head: Dr. Anicete do Amarel Gourgel
Historical Museum - 1977 00085

Museu de Geológia, Paleontológia e Mineralógia, Av Paulo Dias de Novais 105, Luanda, mail addr: CP 815, Luanda - T: (2) 322766, 323024. Head: Dr. Augusto C. de Aranjo
Natural History Museum / Archaeological Museum Geology and mineralogy, palaeontology, archaeology 00086

Museu do Café, Av 4 Fevereiro 107, Luanda, mail addr: c/o Instituto Nacional do Café de Angola, CP 342, Luanda. Head: Manuel Mateus de Almeida Dias
Special Museum
Historical and ethnographic artifacts related to the cultivation and preparation of coffee 00087

Museu Nacional de Antropologia, Frederico Engels 45, Luanda, mail addr: CP 2159, Luanda - T: (2) 337024. Head: Mamzambi Vuvu
Ethnology Museum - 1976
Ethnographical exhibits, African arts, agriculture, fishing, ceramics, iron industry, spiritual culture - library, restoration, ethnographic depot 00088

Museu Nacional de História Natural, Rua de Nossa Senhora da Muxima 47, Luanda, mail addr: CP 1267, Luanda - T: (2) 334054/55, 334028, Fax: 338907, E-mail: hist.nat@netangola.com. Head: Ana Paula dos Santos Correia Victor
Natural History Museum - 1938
Natural history exhibits - library 00089

Lumbango

Museu Regional da Huila, CP 445, Lumbango - T: 20744. Head: José Ferreira
Local Museum - 1956
History, natural history, ethnography, musical instruments 00090

Malange

Museu do Pioneiro, Delegação da S.E. Cultura, Malange
Local Museum 00091

Mbanza Koongo

Museu do Reino do Koongo, CP 49, Mbanza Koongo - T: 3943
Historical Museum 00092

Moçamedes

Museu da Pesca, Moçamedes
Local Museum
Hist of local fishing trade and industry 00093

Nova Lisboa

Museu Municipal, Av Paiva Couceiro, Nova Lisboa
Ethnology Museum
Historical and ethnologic coll, traditional and modern African sculpture 00094

Argentina

25 de Mayo

Museo Municipal Paula Florido, Calle 27 No 761, B6660 25 de Mayo
Local Museum / Natural History Museum - 1946
History and natural science 00095

9 de Julio

Museo Histórico General Julio de Vedia, Av Libertad 1191, B6500EVL 9 de Julio - T: (02317) 422392, 422498, Fax: 422697, E-mail: subcom@9julio.mun.gba.gov.ar. Head: Henry Aznar
Historical Museum - 1916
Local hist and culture, medals and seals, guns, musical instruments, religious art, paintings - archive 00096

Adrogué

Museo y Archivo Histórico Localista Almirante Guillermo Brown (Museum and Archive of Historical Localism Admiral William Brown), Calle Rosales 1521, 1846 Adrogué - T: (011) 42147112, Internet: http://www.todoadrogue.com.ar/cultura/castelforte. Head: Mónica Róncoli
Historical Museum - 1947
Documents, photographs and memorabilia of Admiral Brown, commemorative medals, town hist, subterranean gallery 00097

Aguilares

Museo Arqueológico, Calle Alberdi 1021, 4152 Aguilares - T: (03865) 481460
Archaeological Museum 00098

Albardón

Instituto de Investigaciones Arqueológicas y Museo Prof. Mariano Gambier, Termas La Laja, Casilla de Correo 13, J5419XAK Albardón - T: (0264) 6615033, Fax: 4223168,

E-mail: marianogambier@infovia.com.ar. Head: Prof. Mariano Gambier
Archaeological Museum - 1965
Archaeological artifacts, mummies 00099

Alpachiri

Museo Histórico Regional, Calle Urquiza 275, L6309BAE Alpachiri - T: (02953) 497102, Fax: 497464
Local Museum - 1980
Town history 00100

Alta Gracia

Museo Histórico Nacional Casa del Virrey Liniers, Av del Tajamar esq Solares, X5186KLA Alta Gracia - T: (03547) 421303, Fax: 421303, E-mail: mgorgas@siconet.com.ar. Head: Noemi Lozado de Solla
Historical Museum - 1969
Memorabilia of Virrey Liniers, furniture, paintings, tools, costume, religious art, regional history 00101

Museo Manuel de Falla, Av Carlos Pellegrini 1011, X5186KNK Alta Gracia - T: (03547) 421592. Head: Maria Christina Schutte
Music Museum - 1970
Memorabilia of the composer Manuel de Falla (1876-1946) 00102

Amaicha del Valle

Museo Centro Cultural Pachamama, Sobre la Ruta Provincial 307, 4137 Amaicha del Valle - T: (03892) 21004
Folklore Museum - 1998 00103

Andalgalá

Museo Arqueológico Provincial Andalgalá, Casilla de Correo 6, 4740 Andalgalá, mail addr: Av Libertad 50, 4740 Andalgalá - T: (03835) 422290. Head: Hugo Dante Coronel
Archaeological Museum - 1964
Historical and archeological artifacts 00104

Apóstoles

Museo Ucraniano, Calle Suipacha 57, N3350DTA Apóstoles - T: (03758) 422501
Local Museum
Local history, costume, traditions, religion 00105

Arenaza

Museo Histórico de Arenaza, Predio Estación Ferrocarril, B6075 Arenaza - T: (02355) 495150, E-mail: ferrari@cearenaza.com.ar
Local Museum 00106

Arequito

Museo General de Arequito, Calle E. Destéfanis 1178, S2183XBA Arequito - T: (03464) 4711106, 4711201
Local Museum
archive 00107

Aristóbulo del Valle

Museo El Alero, Cruce Pindayti, Lote 191, N3364 Aristóbulo del Valle
Special Museum
Regional mythology, local fauna, personalities 00108

Museo Faryluk, Ruta Nacional No 14 km 1215, N3364 Aristóbulo del Valle
Science&Tech Museum
Antique cars, phonographies, cameras 00109

Armstrong

Museo Histórico Municipal de Armstrong, Av Alberdi 1565, S2508ABE Armstrong - T: (03471) 461316/326, Fax: 461396, E-mail: muniarm@mrg.org.ar
Local Museum 00110

Arrecifes

Museo Histórico de Arrecifes, Calle Int. Gerardo Risso y España, B2740FMA Arrecifes - T: (02478) 451325 int 116, Fax: 454800, E-mail: - cultura_arrecifes@ed.gba.gov.ar
Local Museum - 1968
archives 00111

Avellaneda

Museo Histórico y Tradicional de Barracas al Sud, Calle Beruti 216, B1870CAF Avellaneda
Local Museum - 1962
Regional hist 00112

Museo Municipal de Artes Plásticas, Calle General San Martín 799, B1870APA Avellaneda
Fine Arts Museum - 1956
Painting, sculpture, drawing, and engraving by contemporary Argentine artists 00113

Ayacucho

Museo Histórico Regional de Ayacucho, Av Juan Domingo Perón 145, B7150BHB Ayacucho - T: (02296) 452085, Fax: 453551, E-mail: ayacucho@mun.gba.gov.ar
Local Museum
Local history, archaeology, coins and medals, trade, industry 00114

Azul

Museo Etnográfico y Archivo Histórico Enrique Squirru, Calle Bartolomé J. Ronco 654, B7300XXA Azul - T: (02281) 434811, E-mail: rosbar@hotmail.com
Ethnology Museum - 1945
Local hist and archeology, art and folklore, crafts 00115

Bahía Blanca

Museo de Arte Contemporáneo, Calle Sarmiento 450, B8000HQJ Bahía Blanca - T: (0291) 4594006, Fax: 4558803, E-mail: subcom@bb.mun.gba.gov.ar, Internet: http://www.gba.gov.ar/bahiablanca. Head: Andrés Duprat
Fine Arts Museum - 1995
Contemporary painting, sculpture, drawing, engraving 00116

Museo de la Aviación Naval, Base Aeronaval Cdte. Espora, B8107 Bahía Blanca - T: (0291) 4810510, E-mail: muan@rina.ara.mil.ar, Internet: http://www.ara.mil.ar/historia/museos
Science&Tech Museum - 1926
Airplanes and spips, naval aviation history, uniforms 00117

Museo Historico Municipal, Calle Dorrego 116, B8000FLD Bahía Blanca - T: (0291) 4563117, Fax: 4558803, E-mail: subcom@bb.mun.gba.gob.ar. Head: Emma R. Vila
Local Museum - 1951
Archeology and the hist of the city, its people and works 00118

Museo Municipal de Bellas Artes, Calle Alsina 65, B8000IHA Bahía Blanca - T: (0291) 4594000 int 2126, Fax: 4558803, E-mail: subcom@bb.mun.gba.gov.ar, Internet: http://www.gba.gov.ar/bahiablanca. Head: Andrés Duprat
Fine Arts Museum - 1931
Painting, sculpture, drawing, engraving 00119

Museo Municipal de Ciencias, Calle Juan José Castelli 3702, B8003APV Bahía Blanca - T: (0291) 4883266, Fax: 4883266, E-mail: mucie@bblanca.co.ar, Internet: http://www.gba.gob.ar/bahiablanca. Head: Viviana Mársico de Larribité
Natural History Museum
Paleontology, anatomy, physiology, botany, zoology, physics 00120

Balcarce

Museo del Automovilismo Juan Manuel Fangio, Calle Dardo Rocha esq Mitre, B7620 Balcarce - T: (02266) 425540, Fax: 425561, Internet: http://www.telefax.com.ar/balcarce/turismo/museo.html
Science&Tech Museum - 1958 00121

Balneario Claromecó

Museo Regional de Claromecó, Calle Juan Bellocq 345, B7505 Balneario Claromecó
Local Museum 00122

Banfield

Museo Pio Collivadino, Calle Medrano 165, B1828ICP Banfield - T: (011) 42025223
Fine Arts Museum 00123

Baradero

Museo Aeronáutico, c/o Aero Club, Av Jorge Newbery 1450, B2942EXR Baradero - T: (03329) 484540, Fax: 480643, E-mail: pberninger@pdm.com.ar, Internet: http://www.geocities.com/aeroclub_baradero
Science&Tech Museum 00124

Museo Histórico Municipal Juan Lavalle, Calle Fra. Santa María de Oro 761, B2942BKO Baradero
Local Museum 00125

Bariloche

De los Viejos Colonos, Calle Felix Goye s/n, Colonia Suiza, R8401GLA Bariloche - T: (02944) 448330
Historical Museum - 1997
Swiss first settlers in Argentina since 1895 00126

Museo de la Patagonia Dr. Francisco P. Moreno, Centro Cívico de San Carlos de Bariloche, R8400 Bariloche - T: (02944) 422309, Fax: 433839, E-mail: museo@bariloche.com.ar, Internet: http://www.bariloche.com.ar/museo. Head: Cecilia Girgenti
Local Museum - 1940
Regional hist, natural hist, archeology, ethnography 00127

Museo del Lago Gutiérrez, Bosque Petrificado 395, Villa Los Coihues, Lago Gutiérrez, R8400 Bariloche - T: (0268) 4308024
Natural History Museum
Marine invertebrates and reptiles, vertebrates, geology 00128

Belén

Museo Arqueológico Provincial Condor Huasi (interim), c/o Galería Misael, Calle San Martín 310, Planta Alta, K4750 Belén - T: (03833) 15688768. Head: Sergio Antonio Alvarez
Archaeological Museum - 1944
History, archaeology, folklore, colonial art, industry and cultures of different periods, numismatics and medals, Argentine Indian archaeology 00129

Benito Juárez

Museo Germán Guglielmetti, Calle Bernardino Rivadavia 165, B7020ARC Benito Juárez - T: (02292) 452447
Local Museum - 1913 00130

Bernal

Museo Municipal Histórico Regional Almirante Brown, Calle 25 de Mayo 198, Este, B1876AWD Bernal - T: (011) 42525508
Historical Museum - 1952
Memorabilia of Almirante Brown and national naval war hist 00131

Bolívar

Museo Florentino Ameghino, Av General San Martín 1065, B6550CGK Bolívar
Archaeological Museum - 1930
Regional archeology 00132

Boulogne

Museo Radiofónico de la Ciudad de Boulogne, Calle Bulnes 249, B1609AWE Boulogne - T: (011) 47665594
Science&Tech Museum 00133

Buenos Aires

Antiguo Recinto del Congreso Nacional, Calle Balcarce 139, C1064AAC Buenos Aires - T: (011) 43434416, 43315147, Fax: 43314633, E-mail: anhistoria_b@sinectis.com.ar. Head: Dr. Miguel Angel de Marco
Historical Museum - 1949
Documents and memorabilia of the National Congress (1864-1905), numismatics - library, archives 00134

Buque-Museo Fragata Presidente Sarmiento, Dique 3, Puerto Madero, C1106ACA Buenos Aires - T: (011) 43349336/386, Fax: 43349336
Historical Museum - 1964
Original flags, furnishings, armaments and instruments of the frigate Presidente Sarmiento 00135

Centro de Exposiciónes de Geologia y Mineria, Av Presidente General Julio A. Roca 651, C1067ABB Buenos Aires - T: (011) 43494450, Fax: 43493160, E-mail: mferre@secind.mecon.ar. Head: Marcelo Ferrero
Natural History Museum - 1904
Minerals, rocks, meteorites 00136

Centro de Exposiciones La Casona de los Olivera, Parque Avellaneda, Av Directorio y Lacarra, C1407JQA Buenos Aires - T: (011) 46712220, 46360904, Fax: 46712220, E-mail: - parqueavellaneda@buenosaires.gov.ar
Local Museum
Hist of the parc 00137

División Museo e Investigaciones Históricas de la Policía Federal, Calle San Martín 353, C1004AAG Buenos Aires - T: (011) 43946857
Historical Museum - 1967
History, technology and cases of crimonology 00138

Escuela Museo de Bellas Artes General Urquiza (Fine Arts School Museum), Calle Yerbal 2370, C1406GKB Buenos Aires - T: (011) 46120566, Fax: 46120566. Head: Prof. Alfredo Daniel Lamouret
Fine Arts Museum - 1963
Argentine painting and sculpture 00139

Fundación Banco Francés, Calle 11 de Septiembre 1990, C1428AID Buenos Aires - T: (011) 47833819, Fax: 47880494, E-mail: ajusto@bancofrances.com.ar
Public Gallery
Sculptures, paintings 00140

Fundación Federico Jorge Klemm, Calle Presidente Marcelo T. de Alvear 626, C1058AAH Buenos Aires - T: (011) 43122058, 43112527, Fax: 43122058, 43112527, E-mail: admin@fundacionfjklemm.org, Internet: http://www.fundacionfjklemm.org. Head: Federico Klemm
Public Gallery 00141

Fundación Solar Rietti, Calle Lezica 3948, C1202AAB Buenos Aires - T: (011) 49811241, Fax: 49822615
Natural History Museum
Memorabilia of Bernardo Houssay (Nobel prize physilogy) and Ciro Rietto 00142

Galerías Pacífico de Centro Cultural Borges, Calle General Juan José Viamonte esq San Martin, C1053ABA Buenos Aires - T: (011) 43195449/450, Fax: 43195451
Fine Arts Museum - 1999
Paintings, graphics, sculpture 00143

Itimuseum, Museo Itinerante de Arte Contemporaneo del Mercosur (Mercosur Itinerant Contemporary Art Museum), Av Caseros 2739, C1246AAH Buenos Aires - T: (011) 43082018, Fax: 49120997, E-mail: itimuseum@hotmail.com, Internet: http://www.itimuseum.com.ar. Head: Jorge Volpe
Fine Arts Museum - 2000
Mercosur artistic creation, paintings, engravings, drawings, mixed techniques art, photography, digital art, graphic humor, decorative art, tapestries 00144

Museo al Aire Libre (Open Air Museum), Calle Caminito, entre Magallanesy Lamadrid, C1160 Buenos Aires - T: (011) 45452073
Fine Arts Museum
Contemporary sculpture 00145

Museo Areneo de Estudios Históricos de Nueva Pompeya, Av Sáenz 1260, C1437DOR Buenos Aires
Historical Museum - 1971
Manuscripts, scores, photographs and memorabilia of Argentine artists, poets and musicians 00146

Museo Argentino de Ciencias Naturales Bernardino Rivadavia, Av Angel Gallardo 470, C1405DJR Buenos Aires - T: (011) 49820306, Fax: 49824494, E-mail: macn@musbr.org.secyt.gov.ar, Internet: http://www.macn.secyt.gov.ar. Head: Dr. Edgardo J. Romero
Natural History Museum - 1823
Comprehensive coll in all areas of natural science - library 00147

Museo Botanico, Av General Las Heras 4102, C1425ATS Buenos Aires
Natural History Museum - 1964
Herbarium, morphology and taxonomy of plants, botany 00148

Museo Casa de Alfredo Palacios, Calle Charcas 4741, C1425BNS Buenos Aires - T: (011) 47737122
Special Museum - 1971
Furnishings, documents, library and other personal belongings of A.L. Palacios 00149

Museo Casa de Bernardo A. Houssay, Calle General Juan José Viamonte 2790, C1213ACB Buenos Aires - T: (011) 49618748, Fax: 49618748, E-mail: museohoussay@vianw.com.ar, Internet: http://www.museohoussay.com.ar
Special Museum - 1977
Library, uniforms, documents, medals, correspondence and other memorabilia of B.A. Houssay, displayed in his former residence 00150

Museo Casa de Ricardo Rojas, Calle Charcas 2837, C1425BMG Buenos Aires - T: (011) 48244039
Special Museum - 1958
Furnishings, works of art, books, documents and memorabilia of Dr. Ricardo Rojas, displayed in his former residence 00151

Museo Casa de Yrurtia, Calle General O'Higgins 2390, C1428AGL Buenos Aires - T: (011) 47810385, Fax: 47810385, E-mail: info@ccec.org.ar, Internet: http://www.artesur.com.ar/yrurtia
Fine Arts Museum - 1942/1949
Furnishings, works of art and memorabilia of the sculptor Rogelio Yrurtia, in original setting 00152

Museo Criollo de los Corrales, Av de los Corrales 6436, C1440BBN Buenos Aires
Local Museum - 1963
Clothing, arms, lassos, domestic utensils, etc. representative of gaucho life 00153

Museo de Aduanas y Puerto, Calle Tte. de Fragata Benito Correa 1351, Darsena, C1107ALI Buenos Aires - T: (011) 43005829
Historical Museum - 1967
Artifacts and documents illustrating the history of the customs authority from the 16th c onward 00154

Museo de Animales Venenosos, Av Dr. Vélez Sársfield 563, C1282AFF Buenos Aires - T: (011) 43032492, Fax: 43032492, E-mail: adolab@anlis.gov.ar, Internet: http://www.anlis.gov.ar. Head: Dolab Jorge Adrian
Natural History Museum - 1954
Live poisonous animals 00155

Museo de Armas de la Nación, Av Santa Fé 702, C1059ABO Buenos Aires - T: (011) 43111071/79, Fax: 43129774. Head: Julio E. Soldaini
Military Museum / Science&Tech Museum - 1938
Firearms and other weapons from around the world 00156

Museo de Arte Español, Calle Juramento 2291, C1428DNK Buenos Aires - T: (011) 47844040, E-mail: larreta@dynamo.com.ar, Internet: http://www.buenosaires.gov.ar/cultura/museos/larreta. Head: Mercedes di Paola de Picot
Special Museum - 1962
Works of art, furnishings and memorabilia of writer Enrique Larreta 00157

Museo de Arte Hispanoamericano Isaac Fernández Blanco, Calle Suipacha 1422, C1011ACF Buenos Aires - T: (011) 43270272/228, E-mail: gcba@buenosaires.gov.ar, Internet: http://www.buenosaires.gov.ar/cultura/museos/f_blanco
Fine Arts Museum - 1947 00158

Museo de Arte Latinoamericano de Buenos Aires, Av Presidente J. Figueroa Alcorta 3415, C1425CLA Buenos Aires - Internet: http://www.malba.org.ar. Head: Agustín Arteaga
Fine Arts Museum 00159

Museo de Arte Moderno, Av Corrientes 1530, C1042AAO Buenos Aires - T: (011) 43749426
Fine Arts Museum 00160

Museo de Arte Moderno de la Ciudad de Buenos Aires, Av San Juan 350, C1147AAO Buenos Aires - T: (011) 43611121, Fax: 43001448, E-mail: mamba@xlnet.com.ar, Internet: http://www.buenosaires.gov.ar/cultura/museos/moderno. Head: Prof. Laura Buccellato
Fine Arts Museum - 1956
Painting, sculpture and media displays 00161

Museo de Artes Plásticas Eduardo Sívori, Av Infanta Isabel 555, C1425 Buenos Aires - T: (011) 47749452, Fax: 47783899, E-mail: gcba@buenosaires.gov.ar, Internet: http://www.buenosaires.gov.ar/cultura/museos/sivori. Head: Maria Isabel de Larrañaga
Fine Arts Museum - 1934
Argentine painting, sculpture, drawing and graphics (19th and 20th c) 00162

Museo de Bellas Artes de la Boca, Av Pedro de Mendoza 1835, C1169AAY Buenos Aires - T: (011) 4211080. Head: Dr. Guillermo C. de la Canal
Fine Arts Museum - 1936
Works of art by contemporary Argentine authors 00163

Museo de Calcos y Esculturas Compardas, Av Costanera Dr. Tristán Rodriguez 1701, C1107 Buenos Aires - T: (011) 43614419, E-mail: museodecalcos@yahoo.com.ar
Fine Arts Museum 00164

Museo de Centro Cultural Recoleta, Calle Junin 1930, C1113AAX Buenos Aires - T: (011) 48031041, 48039799, E-mail: ccprog@buenosaires.gov.ar, Internet: http://www.centroculturalrecoleta.org
Fine Arts Museum
Argentinian art 00165

Museo de Ciencia y Técnica, c/o Facultad de Ingeniería UBA, Av General Las Heras 2214, C1127AAR Buenos Aires - T: (011) 45143003
Natural History Museum / University Museum
Scientific instruments 00166

Museo de Esculturas Luis Perlotti, Calle Juan Pujol 644, C1405ALD Buenos Aires - T: (011) 44312825, Fax: 44333396, E-mail: gcba@buenosaires.gov.ar, Internet: http://www.buenosaires.gov.ar/cultura/museos/perlotti
Folklore Museum 00167

Museo de Gendarmería Nacional, Av Presidente Castillo y Calle 8, Edificio Centinela, C1433 Buenos Aires - T: (011) 43102642, Fax: 43102642
Historical Museum - 1990
Hist of police, uniforms, communication, transport 00168

Museo de Instituto Antártico Argentino, Av Angel Gallardo 470, C1405DJR Buenos Aires - T: (011) 48127327. Head: Dr. Ricardo Capdevila
Natural History Museum - 1956
Natural history of the Antarctic 00169

Museo de Instituto Nacional de Estudios de Teatro, Av Córdoba 1199, C1055AAB Buenos Aires - T: (011) 48167212, Fax: 48167212, E-mail: mclastra@fullzero.com.ar. Head: Cristina Lastra
Performing Arts Museum - 1938
Documents, original scripts, first editions, autographs, memorabilia, etc. illustrating the hist of the theater - library, archives 00170

Museo de Instrumentos Musicales, c/o Istituto Nacional de Musicología Carlos Vega, Calle México 564, C1097AAL Buenos Aires - T: (011) 43616520, Fax: 43616013
Music Museum 00171

Museo de la Administración Federal de Ingresos Públicos, Av de Mayo 1317, C1085ABD Buenos Aires - T: (011) 43840282, E-mail: museo@afip2.gov.ar, Internet: http://www.afip.gov.ar
Historical Museum
History of this institution, documents, photos 00172

Museo de la Caricatura Severo Vaccaro, Calle Lima 1037, C1073AAU Buenos Aires - T: (011) 43710350, 43719382, Fax: 43715001
Fine Arts Museum 00173

Museo de la Casa del Teatro, Av Santa Fé 1243, C1059ABG Buenos Aires - T: (011) 48117678, Fax: 48117678
Performing Arts Museum - 1976
History of the Argentine theater 00174

Museo de la Casa Rosada, Calle Presidente Hipólito Yrigoyen 219, C1086AAA Buenos Aires - T: (011) 43443802, Fax: 43443803. Head: Irma Arestizábal
Historical Museum / Fine Arts Museum - 1957
Argentine hist, memorabilia and documents of Argentine presidents, furniture, medals and objects of art 00175

Museo de la Ciudad, Calle Dr. A. Alsina 412, C1087AAF Buenos Aires - T: (011) 43319855, Fax: 43432123, E-mail: gcba@buenosaires.gov.ar, Internet: http://www.buenosaires.gov.ar/cultura/museos/ciudad
Local Museum - 1968
Momentos and artifacts illustrating the hist of the city 00176

Museo de la Dirección Nacional del Antártico, Av Angel Gallardo 470, C1405DJR Buenos Aires - T: (011) 48127327. Head: Dr. Ricardo Capdevila
Natural History Museum 00177

Museo de la Farmacia Dra. D'Alessio Bonino, c/o Facultad de Farmacia y Bioquímica, Universidad de Buenos Aires, Calle Junín 956, C1113AAD Buenos Aires - T: (011) 49648200 int 8339, 49648235, Fax: 49648200 int 8339, E-mail: rmora@ffyb.uba.ar. Head: Dr. Rafael A. Mora
Historical Museum / Science&Tech Museum / University Museum - 1969
Pharmacy and drugs - library 00178

Museo de la Policía Federal Argentina, Calle San Martín 353, C1004AAG Buenos Aires - T: (011) 43942017. Head: José A. Gutiérrez
Special Museum - 1899
Weapons, uniforms, documents and other exhibits illustrating the hist of the Argentine police force 00179

Museo de la Psicología Experimental Argentina Horacio G. Piñero, c/o Facultad de Psicología de la UBA, Av Independencia 3065, C1225AAM Buenos Aires - T: (011) 49574110, Fax: 49575886
Historical Museum / University Museum - 1990
Psychology science 00180

Museo de los Corrales Viejos de Parque de los Patricios, Calle Diego E. Zavaleta 140, C1437EYD Buenos Aires - T: (011) 43080056, Fax: 43086437, E-mail: info@indhor.com.ar. Head: Jorge Osvaldo Fernandez
Historical Museum
Argentine manners and customs, ornamental combs and fans, crafted cups, elements for daily life, medals and coins of Argentina, Whisky coll, telephone coll, indigenous items and weapons, fossils, dolls 00181

Museo de los Niños Abasto, Av Corrientes 3247, C1193AAE Buenos Aires - T: (011) 48612325, Fax: 48612325 int 115, E-mail: info@museoabasto.org.ar
Natural History Museum
Science interactive for children 00182

Museo de los Subterraneos, Calle Domingo Matheu, C1082ABB Buenos Aires
Science&Tech Museum - 1971
Busses, streetcars, subway trains and other municipal transportation equipment 00183

Museo de Motivos Argentinos José Hernández, Av del Libertador 2373, C1425AAJ Buenos Aires - T: (011) 48029967, 48032384, Fax: 48027294, E-mail: museohernandez@ciudad.com.ar, Internet: http://www.museohernandez.org.ar. Head: Ana María Cousillas
Decorative Arts Museum / Fine Arts Museum - 1948
Ceramics, decorative and applied arts, musical instruments, firearms, lithographs and paintings 00184

Museo de Patología, c/o Facultad de Medicina de la UBA, Calle Presidente José Evaristo Uriburu 950, C1114AAD Buenos Aires - T: (011) 45083600, Fax: 45083602, E-mail: mupa@fmed.uba.ar. Head: Prof. Dr. José Nápoli
Historical Museum - 1887
History of medicine and pathology 00185

Museo de SADAIC Vincente López y Planes, Calle General Juan Lavalle 1547, C1048AAK Buenos Aires - T: (011) 43798600, Internet: http://www.sadaic.org.ar
Music Museum
Musical instruments, scores 00186

Museo de Telecomunicaciones, Av de los Italianos 851, C1107 Buenos Aires - T: (011) 49683112/16, Fax: 49683120, E-mail: museo@ta.telecom.com.ar
Science&Tech Museum 00187

Museo de Urología, Calle Paraguay 1307, C1057AAU Buenos Aires - T: (011) 48118457, Fax: 48118457
Historical Museum
Specialize miedicine instruments - library, archive 00188

Museo del Automóvil, Calle Presidente Hipólito Yrigoyen 2261, C1089AAQ Buenos Aires - T: (011) 46440828, Fax: 46413969, E-mail: info@museodelautomovil.com.ar, Internet: http://www.museodelautomovil.com.ar
Science&Tech Museum 00189

Museo del Automóvil Club Argentino, Av del Libertador 1850, C1425AAR Buenos Aires - T: (011) 48011837, Fax: 48013972
Science&Tech Museum
Historic cars (Daimler 1892 to Dodge 1915) 00190

Museo del Cine Pablo C. Ducrós Hicken, Calle Defensa 1220, C1143AAB Buenos Aires - T: (011) 43612462, E-mail: gcba@buenosaires.gov.ar, Internet: http://www.buenosaires.gov.ar/cultura/museos/cine
Science&Tech Museum
Cinematography in Argentina 00191

Museo del Mundo, Calle Vicente Fidel López 2050, C1128ACF Buenos Aires - T: (011) 48070987
Ethnology Museum 00192

Museo del Patrimonio Histórico, Aguas Argentinas (Heritage Museum), Calle Ríobamba 750, C1025ABP Buenos Aires - T: (011) 63191104, 63191026, Fax: 63191104, E-mail: museo_patrimonio@aguasargentinas.com.ar, Internet: http://www.aguasargentinas.com.ar. Head: Jorge D. Tartarini
Historical Museum
Old sanatary devices and equipment 00193

Museo del Teatro Colón, Calle Tucumán 1165, C1049AAW Buenos Aires - T: (011) 4355414. Head: Carlos A. Martinez Saravia
Performing Arts Museum - 1939
Photographs, documents, programs and personal objects illustrating the hist of the Teatro Colon 00194

Museo Ethnográfico de las Obras Misionales Pontificias, Calle Medrano 735, C1179AAM Buenos Aires - T: (011) 48624136, Fax: 48631357, E-mail: ompar@sion.com
Ethnology Museum
Handicrafts, muscial instruments, textiles, weapons and ethnographic exhibits from Africa and Asia 00195

Museo Etnográfico Juán B. Ambrosetti, Calle Dr. Mariano Moreno 350, C1091AAH Buenos Aires - T: (011) 43458196, Fax: 43458196, E-mail: etnogra@mail.retina.ar. Head: Dr. José Antonio Perez Gollan
Ethnology Museum / Folklore Museum - 1904
Archeology, ethnography, anthropology and folklore - library and archive 00196

Museo Farmacobotánica, c/o Facultad de Farmacia y Bioquímica de la UBA, Calle Junín 956, C1113AAD Buenos Aires - T: (011) 49648235
Natural History Museum - 1900
Herbarium, useful plants, wood exhibits 00197

Museo Fundación Naum Komp, Calle Catamarca 1747, C1246AAK Buenos Aires - T: (011) 49412822, Fax: 43080925
Fine Arts Museum 00198

Museo General Belgrano, Calle Juan Antonio Saráchaga 4906, C1407EGP Buenos Aires - T: (011) 46716464, Fax: 43625978
Historical Museum
library, archive 00199

Museo Histórico de Cera (Historic Wax Museum), Calle del Valle Iberlucea 1261, C1160ABM Buenos Aires - T: (011) 43011497, 43030563, Fax: 43011497, E-mail: info@museo-cera.com, Internet: http://www.museo-cera.com. Head: Marcelo O. Juárez
Special Museum 00200

Museo Histórico de la Ciudad de Buenos Aires Brigadier-General Cornelio de Saavedra, Calle Crisólogo Larralde 6309, C1431AQG Buenos Aires - T: (011) 45720746, Fax: 45741328, Internet: http://www.buenosaires.org.ar/cultura/museos/saavedra. Head: Alberto Gabriel Piñeiro
Local Museum - 1921
History of Buenos Aires from the 18th c onward (numismatics, works of art, firearms, costumes, etc.) 00201

Museo Histórico de la Dirección General Impositiva, Av de Mayo 1317, C1085ABD Buenos Aires - T: (01) 375705
Historical Museum - 1974
Customs, taxes, internal revenue 00202

Museo Histórico de la Honorable Cámara de Diputados de la Nación, Av Bernardino Rivadavia 1860, C1033AAV Buenos Aires - T: (011) 49530843, 49532587, Internet: http://www.elbueno-saires.com.ar/mu_HCDN.htm
Historical Museum
Memorabilia of members of parliament 00203

Museo Histórico de la Iglesia, Calle San Martín 701, C1004AAO Buenos Aires
Religious Arts Museum - 1969
Religious objects and works of art from the colonial period onward 00204

Museo Histórico del Regimiento de Granaderos a Caballo General San Martín, Av General Luis María Campos 554, C1426BOQ Buenos Aires - T: (011) 45765666 int 211/213, Fax: 45765671. Head: Carol Edith Vitagliano
Military Museum - 1968
Military uniforms and artifacts used by Gen. San Martín in the Chile campaign, military documents and objects 00205

Museo Histórico Nacional, Calle Defensa 1600, C1143AAH Buenos Aires - T: (011) 43072301, 43073157, Fax: 43071182. Head: Dr. Alfredo I. Barbagallo
Historical Museum - 1889
Flags, arms, uniforms, medals, documents illustrating the history of Argentina 00206

Museo Histórico Nacional del Cabildo de Buenos Aires y de la Revolucion de Mayo, Calle General Simon Bolívar 65, C1066AAA Buenos Aires - T: (011) 43341782, Fax: 43426729
Historical Museum - 1940
Furnishings, arms, documents, religious art, revolution items from 22th May 1810 00207

Museo Histórico Sarmiento, Calle Juramento 2180, C1428DNJ Buenos Aires - T: (011) 47822354, Fax: 47812989 int 20, E-mail: mhs@mcmhs.gov.ar. Head: Marta Gaudencio de Germani
Historical Museum - 1938
Memorabilia of Domingo Faustino Sarmiento - library, archive 00208

Museo Histórico y de la Tradiciones Populares de la Boca, Av Pedro de Mendoza 1727, C1169AAB Buenos Aires - T: (011) 43117753
Folklore Museum / Local Museum
Archive Vaggi 00209

Museo Históricos del Banco de la Provincia de Buenos Aires, Calle Domingo F. Sarmiento 362, C1041AAH Buenos Aires - T: (011) 43311775, 43316600, Fax: 43316600, E-mail: bpmuseo@bapro.com.ar, Internet: http://www.bapro.com. Head: Alberto de Paula
Historical Museum - 1903
Exhibits depicting the hist of the bank 00210

Museo Houssay de Ciencia y Técnica, c/o Facultad de la Medicina UBA, Calle Paraguay 2155, C1121ABG Buenos Aires - T: (011) 49638612, Fax: 49638612
Natural History Museum 00211

Museo Judío de Buenos Aires Dr. Salvador Kibrick (Jewish Museum of Buenos Aires Dr. Salvador Kibrick), Calle Libertad 769, C1012AAO Buenos Aires - T: (011) 43722474, 43741955, Fax: 48143514, E-mail: ujsevi@mail.abaconet.com.ar. Head: Uriel J. Sevi
Religious Arts Museum / Historical Museum / Decorative Arts Museum - 1967
Religious and ceremonial Jewish art, hist of the Jews in Argentinia, Jewish art, documents, old books - archives, library 00212

Museo Maurice Minkowski, Calle Dr. Luis Pasteur 633, C1028AAM Buenos Aires - T: (011) 49530293, Fax: 49539614, E-mail: alicht1@einstein.com.ar
Fine Arts Museum - 1941
Memorabilia of the painter M. Minkowski 00213

Museo Metropolitano, Calle Castex 3217, C1425CDC Buenos Aires - T: (011) 48021911
Historical Museum 00214

Museo Mitre, Calle San Martín 336, C1004AAH Buenos Aires - T: (011) 43947659, 43948240, Fax: 43948240. Head: Dr. Jorge Carlos Mitre
Special Museum - 1906
Furnishings, works of art, weapons, uniforms, medals, books of Gen. Bartolomé Mitre, housed his former residence - library 00215

Museo Nacional de Aeronáutica, Av Rafael Obligado 4550, 1425 Buenos Aires - T: (011) 45141615, Fax: 45144268, E-mail: mna@faa.mil.ar
Science&Tech Museum - 1960
Documents and relics from the hist of Argentine and international aeronautics, aircraft exhibit 00216

Museo Nacional de Arte Decorativo, Av del Libertador 1902, C1425AAS Buenos Aires - T: (011) 48018248, 48068306, Fax: 48026606. Head: Alberto Guillermo Bellucci
Decorative Arts Museum - 1937
Furnishings, porcelain, tapestries, painting and sculpture 00217

Museo Nacional de Arte Oriental, Calle Ríobamba 985-991, C1116ABC Buenos Aires - T: (011) 48015988, Fax: 48015988. Head: Prof. Osvaldo Svanascini
Fine Arts Museum - 1966
Oriental and African art - library 00218

Museo Nacional de Bellas Artes, Av del Libertador 1473, C1425AAA Buenos Aires - T: (011) 48030802, Fax: 48038817, E-mail: mnba@museo.edu.ar, Internet: http://www.mnba.org.ar. Head: Alberto G. Bellucci
Fine Arts Museum - 1895
European painting (16th-20th c), sculpture, modern Argentine painting - library 00219

Museo Nacional de la Histórico del Traje, Calle Chile 832, C1098AAR Buenos Aires - T: (011) 43438427, Fax: 43438427
Historical Museum - 1972
Hist of Argentine fashion from Colonial times to the present, military and civilian costume 00220

Museo Nacional del Grabado, Calle Defensa 372, C1065AAF Buenos Aires - T: (011) 43455300, Fax: 43455300, E-mail: pasuco@ciudad.com.ar. Head: Prof. Oscar Carlos Peora
Fine Arts Museum - 1983
Engravings by Argentine and intnational artists, books with original engravings, lithographs - library 00221

Museo Nacional del Hombre, Calle 3 de Febrero 1370-1378, C1426BJN Buenos Aires - T: (011) 47827251, 47836554, Fax: 47843371, E-mail: museo@bibapl.edu.ar. Head: Liliana Ema Lorenzo
Ethnology Museum - 1964
Archeology, ethnography, folk art and crafts 00222

Museo Nacional y Centro de Estudios Históricos Ferroviarios, Av del Libertador 405, C1001ABE Buenos Aires - T: (011) 43125353
Science&Tech Museum - 1971
Documents and historic exhibits depicting the development of railway transportation in Argentina 00223

Museo Notarial Argentino, Calle Dr. A. Alsina 2280, C1090AAJ Buenos Aires - T: (011) 49515352
Historical Museum - 1965
Justice 17th-19th c 00224

Museo Numismático del Banco Naciónal, Calle Bartolomé Mitre 326, C1036AAF Buenos Aires - T: (011) 43424041
Historical Museum - 1966
Artifacts relating to the history of the National Bank of Argentina 00225

Museo Numismático Dr. José Evaristo Uriburu, c/o Banco Central, Calle San Martín 216, C1004AAF Buenos Aires - T: (011) 43483882, Fax: 43483699, E-mail: javiles@bcra.gov.ar
Special Museum - 1935
Numismatics, hist of Argentine money - library 00226

Museo Padre Coll, Calle Junín 1223, C1113AAI Buenos Aires - T: (011) 48218146, Fax: 48262506, E-mail: daqrosa@ciudad.com.ar, Internet: http://www.museosargentinos.org.ar/museos/museo.asp?codigo_427. Head: Susana Maria Arbucó
Religious Arts Museum - 1979
Religious hist, Pater Francisco Coll - library 00227

Museo Parlamentario, Calle Presidente Hipolito Yrigoyen 1708, C1089AAI Buenos Aires - T: (011) 49593000 int 3886/9, Fax: 49593000 int 3885, E-mail: museo@senado.gov.ar, Internet: http://www.senado.gov.ar. Head: Prof. Estela Masjoan
Historical Museum 00228

Museo Participativo de Ciencias, Calle Junín 1930, C1113AAX Buenos Aires - T: (011) 48073260, 48063456, Fax: 48063456, E-mail: museopar@giga.com.ar, Internet: http://www.mpc.giga.com.ar
Natural History Museum 00229

Museo Penitenciario Argentino, Calle Humberto Primo 378, C1103ACH Buenos Aires - T: (011) 43625803
Historical Museum - 1982
History of prison 00230

Museo Postal y Telegráfico Doctor Ramon J. Carcano, Calle Domingo F. Sarmiento 151, C1041AAC Buenos Aires
Special Museum / Science&Tech Museum - 1888
Hist of postal services 00231

Museo Roberto Noble, Calle Piedras 1743, C1140ABK Buenos Aires
Special Museum - 1970
Works of art, books, documents, furnishings and memorabilia of the journalist and politician Roberto Noble 00232

Museo Roca, Calle Vicente Fidel López 220, C1128ACJ Buenos Aires - T: (011) 48032798, Fax: 48032798
Historical Museum - 1961
Documents, photographs, books of Gen. Julio A. Roca 00233

Museo San Roque, Calle Dr. A. Alsina 340, C1087AAD Buenos Aires
Fine Arts Museum - 1967
Classical and contemporary Hispano-American art (18th-19th c) 00234

Museo Social Argentino de Universidad (Argentine Museum of Sociology), Av Corrientes 1723, C1042AAD Buenos Aires - T: (011) 43754601, Fax: 43754600. Head: Dr. Guillermo Garbarini Islas
Special Museum - 1911
library 00235

Museo Tecnológico Ingeniero Eduardo Latzina, Av Paseo Colón 650, C1063ACT Buenos Aires - T: (011) 43316444, 43315249, Fax: 43456886, E-mail: otokrause@impsat1.com.ar, Internet: http://www.nalyandria.com/01/otto-krause/museo_tecnologico. Head: Horacio Podestá
Science&Tech Museum - 1910
Beam machines, machines, tools, comunications, electronics, chemistry, phisiss 00236

El Museo Viajero, Calle Empedrado 2636, C1417GJD Buenos Aires - T: (011) 45839398, Fax: 45215879, E-mail: museoviajero@arnet.com.ar
Folklore Museum - 1998
Argentinas culture 00237

Museo Xul Solar, Calle Laprida 1212, C1425EKF Buenos Aires - T: (011) 48243302, Fax: 48215378, E-mail: xulsolar@ciudad.com.ar
Special Museum 00238

Museo y Biblioteca de la Literature Porteña, Calle Republica de Honduras 3784, C1180ACB Buenos Aires
Library with Exhibitions - 1977
Memorabilia of the poet Evaristo Carriego - library 00239

Museo y Centro Estudios Históricos de la Facultad de Odontologia, Calle Presidente Marcelo T. de Alvear 2142, C1122AAH Buenos Aires - T: (011) 49641271, Fax: 49620176
Historical Museum / University Museum 00240

Museum Oculorum, Av Bernardino Rivadavia 7047, C1406GMA Buenos Aires - T: (011) 46114808, Fax: 46116526, E-mail: museum@fibertel.com.ar
Historical Museum
Ophthalmologic history 00241

Palais de Glace, Calle Posadas 1725, C1112ADE Buenos Aires - T: (011) 48041163, 48044324, Fax: 48019014
Decorative Arts Museum / Fine Arts Museum
Paintings, sculptures, prints, drawings, textile art, ceramics, photography 00242

Primer Museo Permanente del Boxeo Argentino, Calle Bartolomé Mitre 2020, C1039AAF Buenos Aires
Special Museum - 1968
Materials from the history of boxing sport in Argentina 00243

Sala Historica General Savio, Av Cabildo 15, C1426AAA Buenos Aires - T: (011) 45765555, Fax: 45765681, E-mail: estbib@iese.edu.ar. Head: Guillermo A. Sevilla
Military Museum - 1977
Documents and relics pertaining to the life of Gen. don Manuel Nicolás Aristóbulo Savio and the military equipment industry 00244

Burzaco

Museo de Bellas Artes Claudio León Sempere, Calle Colón 581, B1852BSE Burzaco - T: (011) 42997279
Fine Arts Museum 00245

Cachi

Museo Arqueológico Pío P. Díaz, Calle Juan Calchaqui s/n, A4417XAD Cachi - T: (03868) 491080. Head: Miguel A. Xamena
Archaeological Museum - 1971
Regional archeology - library 00246

Cafayate

Museo de Arqueología Colonial Rodolfo I. Bravo, Calle Colón 191, 4427 Cafayate - T: (03868) 421054. Head: Helga Mazzoni de Bravo
Archaeological Museum - 1935
Local crafts, ceramics, metal, textiles 00247

Caleta Olivia

Museo del Hombre y su Entorno, Calle Saavedra y 25 de Mayo, Z9011AHA Caleta Olivia - T: (0297) 4852320, Fax: 4851189
Local Museum
Regional history, flora and fauna, archaeology, paleontology 00248

Campana

Museo Municipal de Bellas Artes de Campana, Calle San Martín 383, B2804GBG Campana
Fine Arts Museum - 1970
Painting, sculpture and graphics by Argentine artists 00249

Cañada de Gómez

Museo Histórico Municipal de Cañada de Gómez, Calle Ballesteros 991, S2500AZO Cañada de Gómez - T: (03471) 426029
Local Museum - 1981
Local history, railway, archaeology 00250

Cañuelas

Museo Histórico de Cañuelas, Calle San Martín 397, B1814FFG Cañuelas - T: (02226) 430327
Local Museum
archive 00251

Capilla del Señor

Museo del Periodismo Bonaerense, Calle Rivadavia 487, B2812DII Capilla del Señor - T: (02323) 491347
Local Museum 00252

Carcarañá

Museo Municipal de la Ciudad de Carcarañá, Calle Roca 1310, S2138 Carcarañá - T: (0341) 4941091, Fax: 4942366, E-mail: memedeca@arnet.com.ar, Internet: http://www.carcarania.gov.ar
Local Museum - 1997
archive, Newspaper-library 00253

Carhué

Museo Regional Dr. Adolfo Alsina, Calle Presidente Bernardino Rivadavia y Laprida, B6430DCA Carhué - T: (02936) 430575 int 122, Fax: 432632, E-mail: cultura_alsina@de.gba.gov.ar
Local Museum - 1963
Regional archeology, historical documents, weapons 00254

Carlos Casares

Exposición Roberto J. Mouras, Av 9 de Julio 127, B6530CLB Carlos Casares - T: (02395) 452667, E-mail: trauku@casaresnet.com.ar, Internet: http://www.mouras.com.ar
Special Museum - 1992 00255

Carmen de Patagonés

Museo Privado de Arqueología Regional Julio Gironde, Calle Villegas 416, B8504CLH Carmen de Patagonés - T: (0291) 154046275, E-mail: eneas1973@yahoo.com.ar. Head: Herberto Gironde
Archaeological Museum / Ethnology Museum
Local archaeology, primitive harvesting, fishing and hunting of the Fuéguidos and Láguidos tribes who settled in the lower Río Negro valley, Pampa indians 00256

Carro Quemado

Museo Atelier Antonio Ortiz Echagüe, L6319 Carro Quemado
Fine Arts Museum
Paintings 00257

Casilda

Museo de Antropología e Historia Natural Los Desmochados, Calle Remedios de Escalada 1321, S2170FMM Casilda - T: (03464) 422362
Local Museum
Anthropology, archaeology, ethnography, folklore, musical instruments of Southamerican villages, paleontology, fine art, mineralogy, minerals, rocks 00258

Museo Municipal Dr. Santos F. Tosticarelli, Blvd Ovidio Lagos 1208, S2170EYP Casilda - T: (03464) 426535, Fax: 422790, E-mail: gestion@casilda.datacop1.com.ar

Local Museum
Numismática, medals, furnishings, rural life, musical instruments, archaeology, ethnography, folklore - archives 00259

Castelli

Museo Regional Castelli, Calle Taillade y Av 25 de Mayo, B7114CJA Castelli
Local Museum
Natural science, history, archaeology, paleontology 00260

Chacabuco

Museo Tradicionalista El Rancho, Calle Pueyrredón 139, B6740EIC Chacabuco
Historical Museum
Arms, animal specimens, and artifacts of traditional ranch life and culture 00261

Chañar Ladeado

Museo Comunal de Chañar Ladeado, Calle Italia y Belgrano, S2643ATA Chañar Ladeado - T: (03468) 481221, 481256, Fax: 481221, E-mail: chladeado@islanet.com.ar
Local Museum 00262

Chascomús

Museo Pampeano de Chascomús, Av Lastra y Francisco Javier Muñiz, B7130FRA Chascomús - T: (02241) 430982, Fax: 431341
Archaeological Museum / Historical Museum / Folklore Museum - 1941
Archeology, hist and folklore 00263

Chasicó

Museo Arqueológico de Chasicó, Establecimiento, B8117XAF Chasicó - T: (02684) 4421688, Fax: (0291) 4548450
Archaeological Museum 00264

Chilecito

Museo de Chilecito, Calle Jamin Ocampo 55, Molino SAn Francisco, F5360DOA Chilecito
Local Museum
Archeology, botany and zoology, painting and sculpture, memorabilia of writer Joaquín V. González - library 00265

Chivilcoy

Complejo Histórico Chivilcoy, Calle 9 de Julio 177, B6620FKC Chivilcoy - T: (02346) 422185
Local Museum - 1943
Local hist, weapons and uniforms - library 00266

Museo Almacén El Recreo, Camino Real, Av de la Tradición s/n, B6620IAA Chivilcoy - T: (02346) 435314
Decorative Arts Museum 00267

Museo Municipal de Artes Plásticas Pompeo Boggio, Calle Bolívar 319, B6620HBG Chivilcoy - T: (02346) 430512, Fax: 430142
Fine Arts Museum - 1944
Argentine painting, sculpture, drawing, graphics and pottery 00268

Chos Malal

Museo Histórico Provincial Colonel Manuel José Olascoaga, Av 25 de Mayo y San Martín, Q8353AAA Chos Malal
Historical Museum
History, anthropology 00269

Cinco Saltos

Museo Regional de Cinco Saltos, Av General Manuel Belgrano 504, R8303BWS Cinco Saltos - T: (0299) 4980164
Local Museum 00270

Colón

Museo de la Ciudad de Colón, Calle 47 y 26, Estación del Ferrocarril, B2720AGD Colón
Local Museum - 1971
History, painting and sculpture, furnishings, crafts, costume 00271

Museo Natural Dr. Carlos A. Marelli, Calles 44 y 24, B2720CEA Colón - T: (02473) 422091, E-mail: carzoolco@hotmail.com, Internet: http://www.colonbaires.com.ar/museo.html
Natural History Museum - 1952
Zoology, botany and mineralogy 00272

Comodoro Rivadavia

Museo Nacional del Petróleo, Calle Carlos Calvo y San Lorenzo, U9005CGA Comodoro Rivadavia - T: (0297) 4559558, Fax: 4559558, E-mail: - museodelpetroleo@arnet.com.ar, Internet: http://www.mipatagonia.com/museodelpetroleo.htm
Special Museum - 1993 00273

Museo Paleontológico y Petrolero Astra, Ruta Nacional 3 km 20, U9000 Comodoro Rivadavia - T: (0297) 4475235, E-mail: urrezr@mb.astra.com.ar
Natural History Museum 00274

Museo Regional Patagónico, Av Rivadavia 1100, U9002AKZ Comodoro Rivadavia - T: (0297) 4477101, Fax: 4462374, E-mail: - claudiobarrientos@usa.net
Local Museum - 1948
Archeology, history, zoology, botany, anthropology 00275

Concepción del Uruguay

Museo Nacional Justo José de Urquiza, Palacio San José, Ruta 131, E3260 Concepción del Uruguay - T: (03442) 432620, Fax: 432620
Historical Museum - 1870
Confederation history, provincial history 00276

Salón Electo Brizuela, Biblioteca Popular El Porvenir, Calle San Martín 782, E3264ABB Concepción del Uruguay - T: (03442) 426540
Fine Arts Museum - 1872
Paintings, sculptures - library 00277

Concordia

Museo de Antropología y Ciencias Naturales (Museum of Anthropology and Natural Sciences), Ex-Estación Central, Av Robinson s/n, E3200 Concordia - T: (0345) 4213149, Fax: 4213491, E-mail: museoantropologia@concordia.com.ar. Head: Crsitina Vassallo de Cettour
Archaeological Museum / Natural History Museum
Regional and Argentinian archaeology, ceramics, paintings, textiles, natural history, fossils, animals and plants 00278

Museo Municipal de Artes Visuales, Calle Urquiza 638, 3200 Concordia - T: (03445) 4215973
Fine Arts Museum - 1948
Drawings, painting, sculpture, and engravings by Argentine artists 00279

Córdoba

Centro Cultural España Córdoba, Calle Entre Ríos 40, X5000AJB Córdoba - T: (0351) 4332721, Fax: 4332721, E-mail: info@ccec.org.ar, Internet: http://www.ccec.org.ar
Fine Arts Museum
Paintings, works by expressionistic artists 00280

Centro Mundo Aborigen, Calle Bernardino Rivadavia 155, X5000IPC Córdoba - T: (0351) 424-3278, E-mail: veronicaandrea@hotmail.com
Ethnology Museum / Folklore Museum 00281

Museo Botánico, Av Dr. Vélez Sarsfield y Duarte Quirós, X5000ALA Córdoba - T: (0351) 4332104, Fax: 4332104, E-mail: Postmaster@imbiv.edu.ar. Head: Armando T. Hunziker
Natural History Museum - 1870
Botany - library 00282

Museo de Antropología, Universidad Nacional de Córdoba, Pabellón Argentina, Cara Sur, Ciudad Universitaria, X5000 Córdoba - T: (0351) 4334061, Fax: 4334196, E-mail: proa@ffyh.unc.edu.ar
Archaeological Museum
Archaeology, etnography, bioanthropology 00283

Museo de Arte Religioso Juan de Tejeda, Calle Independencia 122, X5000IUD Córdoba. Head: Victor Manuel Infante
Religious Arts Museum
Religious art history, liturgical items, church treasure 00284

Museo de Ciencias Naturales Bartolomé Mitre, Av Hipólito Yrigoyen 115, X5000JHB Córdoba - T: (0351) 4332329. Head: Marta Cano de Martín
Natural History Museum - 1919
Zoology, mineralogy, anthropology, botany 00285

Museo de la Escuela Normal Alejandro Carbo, Calle Colón 959, X5000EPJ Córdoba
Local Museum
History, geography and natural science, firearms and antique items 00286

Museo de los Niños Barrilete, Calle La Rioja 1150, X5000EVX Córdoba - T: (0351)4252836, 4252828, Fax: 4245743, E-mail: vieja_usina@si.cordoba.com.ar, Internet: http://www.cordoba.com.ar/vieja_usina
Special Museum 00287

Museo de Mineralogía y Geología Dr. Alfredo Stelzner (Museum of Mineralogy and Geology Dr. Alfredo Stelzner), Av Dr. Vélez Sársfield 249, X5000JJC Córdoba - T: (0351) 4332100 ext 46, Fax: 4332090, E-mail: astelzner@com.uncor.edu, Internet: http://www.efn.uncor.edu/museos/mineralogia/index.html. Head: Hebe Dina Gay
Natural History Museum - 1871
Mineralogy, rocks (mainly minerals) 00288

Museo de Tecnología Aeronáutica y Espacial, c/o Instituto Universitario Aeronáutico, Av Fuerza Aérea km 6,5, X5022 Córdoba - T: (0351) 4650765, E-mail: newmuseum@hotmail.com
Science&Tech Museum
archive 00289

Museo de Zoología, Universidad de Córdoba, Av Dr. Vélez Sársfield 249, X5000JJC Córdoba - T: (0351) 4332090, 4332100 int 21, E-mail: pinifeijoo@yahoo.com
Natural History Museum - 1869
Zoology 00290

Museo del Teatro y la Música de Córdoba Cristobal de Aguilar, Av Dr. Vélez Sársfield 345, X5000JJD Córdoba
Performing Arts Museum / Music Museum - 1970
History of music and theater in Argentina 00291

Museo Histórico Provincial Marqués de Sobremonte, Calle Rosario de Santa Fé 218, X5000ACF Córdoba - T: (0351) 4331661, 4332354
Local Museum - 1887
Regional hist, art, weapons, jewelry - library 00292

Museo Independencia, c/o Colegio Léon XIII, Calle San Pedro Nolasco s/n, Villa Rivera Indarte, 5021 Córdoba - T: (03543) 420120, Fax: 440948, E-mail: leonxiii@si.cordoba.com.ar
Local Museum - 1916
Anthropology, hist and natural hist 00293

Museo Marcelo López del Instituto Hellen Keller, Calle Ingeniero Juan Marcelo López s/n, Ciudad Universitaria, X5002JMA Córdoba - T: (0351) 4334547
Natural History Museum
Animals, plants, minerals, physical and chemical elements, anatomy, geography, history 00294

Museo Meteorológico Nacional Dr. Benjamín A. Gould, Calle San Luis 801, X5000BBK Córdoba - T: (0351) 4768280, Fax: 4768280
Special Museum 00295

Museo Municipal de Bellas Artes Dr. Genaro Perez, Av General José María Paz 33, X5000JLA Córdoba - T: (0351) 4331512, Fax: 4332720, E-mail: museogp@agora.com.ar, Internet: http://www.agora.com.ar/museogp. Head: Gonzalo Biffarella
Fine Arts Museum - 1943
Argentine painting, sculpture and engraving by Genaro Pérez, Emilio Caraffa, Lino Spilimbergo, Antonio Berni, Marcelo Bonevardi - first restauration school of Argentina 00296

Museo Numismático del Banco de la Nación Argentina, Calle Gerónimo Cortes 40, X5001AEB Córdoba
Special Museum - 1970
Colonial Spanish and Argentine numismatics, history of money 00297

Museo Obispo Fray José Antonio de San Alberto, Calle Caseros 124, X5000AHD Córdoba
Religious Arts Museum
Various religious items 00298

Museo Pedro Ara, Calle Chubut 419, Barrio Alberdi, X5000LYI Córdoba - T: (0351) 4337024, Fax: 4337024
Historical Museum
Osteomioarticulary, skeletons, central nervous systen 00299

Museo Provincial de Bellas Artes Emilio A. Caraffa, Av Hipólito Yrigoyen 651, X5000JHG Córdoba - T: (0351) 4690786. Head: Dr. Graciela Elizabeth Palella
Fine Arts Museum - 1916
Argentine painting, drawing, sculpture and engraving (19th-20th c), foreign painting (17th-19th c) - library 00300

Museo Salesiano Ceferino Namuncura, Av Colón 1055, X5000EPK Córdoba
Local Museum - 1957
History, anthropology, archeology, ceramics, natural sciences, numismatics - library 00301

Museo San Antonio de Padua, Calle San Jeronimo 2051, San Vicente, X5006IJO Córdoba - T: (0351) 4554740, Fax: 4554740, E-mail: sdbacose@nt.com.ar
Local Museum
Local history, religious and cultural items 00302

Pinacoteca, c/o Escuela de Arte, Universidad Nacional de Córdoba, Calle Pabellón México, Universitaria, Estafeta 32, X5000BZB Córdoba - T: (0351) 4334079, Fax: 4334080, E-mail: esarte@ffyh.unc.edu.ar
Fine Arts Museum - 1950 00303

Pinacoteca de la Escuela Provincial de Bellas Artes Dr. Figueroa Alcorta, Calle Salta 74, X5000IHB Córdoba - T: (0351) 4332355, Fax: 4332355, E-mail: figueroa_educ@ciudad.com.ar. Head: Susana Bergero
Fine Arts Museum / University Museum 00304

Coronda

Museo Municipal José Manuel Maciel, Calle 25 de Mayo y Sarmiento, S2240 Coronda - T: (0342) 4911370
Local Museum
History of the province, archaeology, agriculture, social and cultural situation, fine art, natural history - laboratory 00305

Coronel Dorrego

Museo Regional Carlos Funes Derieul, Calle Juan Baltazar Maciel 555, B8150CSK Coronel Dorrego - T: (02921) 453989, Fax: 453989, E-mail: dorrego@mun.gba.gov.ar. Head: Enrique Román, Silvia Litvak
Local Museum / Natural History Museum - 1964
Historical exhibits, natural science 00306

Coronel Pringles

Museo de Bellas Artes de Coronel Pringles, Calle San Martín 857, B7530AAI Coronel Pringles
Fine Arts Museum - 1959
Contemporary Argentine painting, drawing, engraving and sculpture 00307

Museo Regional Histórico y de Ciencias Naturales, Calle Colón 425, B7530AII Coronel Pringles
Historical Museum / Natural History Museum - 1966
History and natural science 00308

Corrientes

Museo de Artesanías Tradicionales Folklóricas, Calle Fray José de la Quintana 905, W3400BGI Corrientes
Folklore Museum 00309

Museo de Bellas Artes Dr. Juan Ramón Vidal, Calle San Juan 634, W3400CBD Corrientes
Fine Arts Museum 00310

Museo de Ciencias Naturales Dr. Amado Bonpland, Calle San Martín 850, W3400APR Corrientes - T: (03783) 433092, Fax: 439799, E-mail: auroraarbelo@yahoo.com.ar. Head: Prof. Aurora Catalina Arbelo de Mazzaro
Natural History Museum - 1854
Botany, mineralogy, fossils, zoology and birds, geology of Argentina, archeology - library, video library 00311

Museo Histórico de Corrientes Manuel Cabral de Mayo y Alpoín, Calle 9 de Julio 1044, W3400AYR Corrientes. Head: Miguel Fernando Gonzalez Azcoaga
Local Museum - 1929
Religious and colonial art, weapons, furnishings, numismatics, painting and sculpture, history - library 00312

Museo Odontológico Dr. Jorge E. Dunster, Calle Paraguay 837, W3400CLG Corrientes
Special Museum - 1969
History of dentistry in Argentina 00313

Museo Provincial de Bellas Artes, Calle San Juan 634, W3400CBD Corrientes - T: (03783) 4436722
Fine Arts Museum - 1927
Painting, sculpture, and objects d'art 00314

Cruz Alta

Complejo Museológico La Estación, Av General San Martín, X2189CGA Cruz Alta - T: (03467) 421102, Fax: 421152
Local Museum / Science&Tech Museum
Local history, railways 00315

Curuzú Cuatiá

Casa de la Cultura, Museo Arqueológico, Museos Histórico y de la Ciudad, Calle Dr. Tomás Pozzi 560, W3460DQJ Curuzú Cuatiá - T: (03774) 424499
Local Museum / Archaeological Museum / Fine Arts Museum
National fine art, archaeology, local history 00316

Darregueira

Museo El Reencuentro, Calle Rivadavia 41, B8183CEA Darregueira - T: (02924) 420577, Fax: 420577, E-mail: egb7@cossma.com.ar
Local Museum 00317

Deán Funes

Museo Paleontológico, Arqueológico e Histórico de la Ciudad de Deán Funes, Calle 9 de Julio y Morandini, X5200CTA Deán Funes
Archaeological Museum / Local Museum 00318

Dolores

Museo de Escuela de Educación Técnica Número 1, Av B. Lamadrid 397, B7100DWD Dolores - T: (02245) 446108
Historical Museum 00319

Museo de la E.E.M. Número 3, Colegio Nacional, Calle Crámer 450, B7100ADJ Dolores
Historical Museum 00320

Museo Pedro Suro, CC 31, B7100 Dolores - T: (02245) 443020, Fax: 443020
Fine Arts Museum
Paintings, sculptures, antiques, photos 00321

Museo y Parque Libres del Sur, Calle Juan Bautista Selva 390, B7100BIH Dolores - T: (02245) 442730, Fax: 442730. Head: Hipólito S. del Blanco
Local Museum / Natural History Museum - 1940
Local history, natural sciences - library 00322

Don Torcuato

Paleorama - Museo Itinerante, Calle Guayaquil 2573, B1611HSO Don Torcuato - T: (011) 47480715, Fax: 47484944, E-mail: paleorama@galeon.com, Internet: http://www.galeon.com/paleorama
Archaeological Museum
Argentinian paleontology, especialy dinosaurios 00323

El Bolsón

Museo Ornitológico Patagónico, Calle Cornelio Saavedra 2759, R8430AGI El Bolsón - T: (02944) 492337
Natural History Museum 00324

El Calafate

Museo Regional Municipal de El Calafate, Av San Martin s/n, Z9405 El Calafate - T: (02902) 491081, Fax: 491020
Local Museum 00325

El Trébol

Museo Municipal de El Trébol, Av Libertad y Victoria, S2535AJA El Trébol - T: (03401) 420316, Fax: 422542
Local Museum
Local history, agriculture, agricultural devices, fine art, cameras, telephone - library 00326

Eldorado

Museo Cooperativo Eldorado, Av San Martin 1879, N3380ABF Eldorado - T: (03751) 421963, Fax: 421963, E-mail: museo@ceel.com.ar
Decorative Arts Museum - 1999
Ceramics, paintings, photography, books, baskets 00327

Museo Municipal de Eldorado, Parque Schwelm km 1, N3380 Eldorado - T: (03751) 430788, E-mail: beling@eldorado.com.ar
Local Museum
History of the settlement, antiques 00328

Embalse

Museo de la Energía, Barrio Casitas, X5856 Embalse
Special Museum 00329

Emilio Bunge

Museo Comunal Pedro Bargero, Calle Dr. Mantero y Gobernador Arias, B6241AIA Emilio Bunge - T: (03388) 493040, Fax: 493040, E-mail: bargero@servicoopsa.com.ar
Local Museum
Local history 00330

Ensenada

Museo Histórico Fuerte Barragan, Av Alte Brown y Camino a Club Regatas, B1925 Ensenada - T: (0221) 4694882, Fax: 4694882, E-mail: gespublica@munensenada.com.ar
Science&Tech Museum - 1969
Aeronautics 00331

Esperanza

Museo de Ciencias Naturales y Misional del Colegio San José, Calle Padre Arnoldo Janssen 2115, S3080IDQ Esperanza - T: (03496) 420083
Natural History Museum / Ethnology Museum
Mammals, reptiles, birds, missional items from China, Indonesia, Papua New Guinea and New Zealand 00332

Museo de la Colonización, Calle Dr. Rudolfo Lehmann 1566, S3080INZ Esperanza - T: (03496) 420009 ext 121, Fax: 420748, E-mail: muniespe@esperanza.gov.ar. Head: Graciela Russi
Historical Museum / Agriculture Museum - 1968
Local history of colonization 00333

Museo de la Máquina Agrícola, Calle Maestro Donnet s/n, Parque de la Agricultura, S3080 Esperanza - T: (03496) 420009, Fax: 420748, E-mail: muniespe@esperanza.gov.ar
Agriculture Museum 00334

Esquel

Museo Austral de Pintura Primitiva Moderna Naif, Calle Rivadavia 1065, U9200EJU Esquel - T: (02945) 451929, Fax: 451929, E-mail: webmaster@c.patagonia.com
Fine Arts Museum 00335

Museo Indigenista, Calle Belgrano 330, U9200BPH Esquel - T: (02945) 451929, Fax: 451929
Ethnology Museum 00336

Federación

Museo de los Asentamientos, Calle Presidente Hipólito Yrigoyen y Las Rosas, E3206BSA Federación
Local Museum
Founding of Mandisoví (1777), Pueblo de Federación (1847) and the new town 1979, religion, culture, military, economy, photography 00337

Firmat

Museo de Firmat, Calle San Martin 1546, S2630FXX Firmat - T: (03465) 423328, 423395, Fax: 423328, E-mail: municipalidad@firmat.gov.ar, Internet: http://www.firmat.gov.ar/gobierno/cultura/museodefirmat.html. Head: Nelson A. Rea
Local Museum 00338

Franck

Museo Particular Los Abuelos, Calle General Justo José de Urquiza 2557, S3009BJA Franck
Local Museum
Local history, flora and fauna, artists 00339

Fuerte Quemado

Museo Arqueológico y Colonial, K4141 Fuerte Quemado - T: (03833) 431734
Archaeological Museum 00340

Gaiman

Museo Histórico Regional de Gaiman, Calle 28 de Julio 705, U9105ABK Gaiman
Local Museum
library 00341

Gálvez

Museo Pedagógico de Artes Visuales, Calle San Martín 468, S2252IDH Gálvez
Fine Arts Museum - 1971
Painting, sculpture, engraving, and drawing 00342

General Alvear

Museo Municipal de Historia Natural, Calle San Rafael 48, M5620HFB General Alvear - T: (0265) 422100, Fax: 422661, Internet: http://www.pic.mendoza.gov.ar
Natural History Museum
Minerals, rocks, paleontology, archaeology - archive 00343

General Belgrano

Museo Histórico Municipal Alfredo E. Múlgura, Av Larrea 454, B7223GUO General Belgrano - T: (02243) 453060, Fax: 453059, Internet: http://www.belgrano.gba.gov.ar. Head: Marta Alicia Lombardo
Local Museum / Natural History Museum - 1997
Local and regional education, paleontology (quaternary megafauna), Salado river 00344

General Levalle

Museo Histórico Municipal General Levalle, Av Presidente General J.A. Roca 222, X6132AEO General Levalle - T: (03385) 480050, Fax: 480050, E-mail: muni.levalle@laboulaye.datacol9.com.ar
Local Museum
Local history since 1902 00345

General Pico

Museo Regional Maracó, Calle 17 No 560, L6360BAL General Pico - T: (02302) 431911, 421043, E-mail: museomaraco@hotmail.com. Head: Rosa Elba La Gioiosa
Local Museum - 1967
Regional hist and archeology 00346

General Pinto

Museo General Lavalle, Calle Fortin Ancaloo, B6050 General Pinto
Military Museum - 1969
Weapons, documents and other objects related to the hist of General Pinto 00347

Godoy Cruz

Museo Municipal de Bellas Artes, Calle Perito Moreno 16, M5501NGN Godoy Cruz
Fine Arts Museum - 1941
Painting, drawings, engravings and sculpture by Argentine artists 00348

Gregorio de Laferrere

Exposición de Gregorio de Laferrere, Calle Monseñor López May 4333, B1757DIS Gregorio de Laferrere - T: (011) 46987694, Fax: 46987694, E-mail: museo@laferrere.com.ar, Internet: http://www.laferrere.com.ar
Local Museum 00349

Gualeguay

Museo Histórico Regional, Calle San Antonio Norte 230, E2840DTF Gualeguay - T: (03444) 424595, Fax: 424595
Local Museum - 1949
Regional hist 00350

Gualeguaychú

Museo Arqueológico, Calle 25 de Mayo 734, E2822ABB Gualeguaychú - T: (03446) 432643
Archaeological Museum 00351

Museo de Instituto Magnasco, Calle Camila Nievas 78, E2822FED Gualeguaychú - T: (03446) 427287, Fax: 427287
Local Museum - 1898
History, sculpture, numismatics and medals, military hist, music, local art - archive, library 00352

Museo Ferroviario de Gualeguaychú, Calle 25 de Mayo 734, E2822ABB Gualeguaychú - T: (03446) 427989
Science&Tech Museum
Regional railway history 00353

Guatraché

Museo Histórico de Guatraché, Av Domingo F. Sarmiento 90, L6311BVN Guatraché - T: (02924) 492278. Head: Prof. Viviana Nuñes Laranjeira de Schroeder
Local Museum - 1995
Local history, native inhabitants, railway - archive 00354

Humahuaca

Estudio Museo Ramoneda, Calle Salta 214, Y4630DNF Humahuaca - T: (03887) 421066, E-mail: luisramoneda@hotmail.com. Head: Prof. Luis Alberto Ramoneda
Fine Arts Museum - 1936
Paintings, drawings, and engravings by Francisco Ramoneda 00355

Museo Folklórico Regional de Humahuaca, Calle Buenos Aires 435, Y4630BCI Humahuaca - T: (03887) 421064, Fax: 421064, E-mail: toqohumahuaca@yahoo.com, Internet: http://www.mfrhumahuaca.com.ar. Head: Sixto Vazquez Zuleta
Folklore Museum - 1969
Decorative and folk arts, wood sculpture, works from the colonial period, American art - restoration 00356

Ingeniero White

Museo del Puerto de Ingeniero White, Calle Guillermo Torres y Cárrega, B8103 Ingeniero White - T: (0291) 4573006, E-mail: cultura@bb.mun.gba.gob.ar
Local Museum 00357

Ischilín

Casa Museo Fernando Fader, Loza Corral, X5201XAD Ischilín - T: (03521) 422044
Fine Arts Museum
Paintings, memorabilia 00358

Isla del Cerrito

Museo Histórico Regional De la Isla, H3505XAA Isla del Cerrito - T: (03722) 496241
Local Museum 00359

Ituzaingó

Museo Clarisse Coulombie de Goyaud, Calle General José María Pirán 582, B1714LGL Ituzaingó - T: (011) 46244162, Fax: 46616661, 45857242, E-mail: museodeituzaingo@yahoo.com.ar, Internet: http://www.museodeituzaingo.8m.net. Head: Rolando Washington Goyaud
Local Museum
Local history, dewellers and inmigrants, weapons, costume, machinery - history institute, archive, Tango museum 00360

Museo Interactivo de Ciencias Naturales, Calle General Angel Pacheco 2280, B1714HEH Ituzaingó - T: (011)46249267, 46612897, E-mail: ecarletti@giga.com.ar, Internet: http://www.giga.com.ar/axxon/museo.htm
Natural History Museum
Natural history, insects, fosils 00361

Jesús María

Museo Nacional Jesútico de Jesús María, Convento e Iglesia de San Isidro, Calle Pedro de Oñate s/n, X5220 Jesús María - T: (03525) 420126, Fax: 420126, E-mail: mjn-jm@datacop5.com.ar. Head: Nelson Lenarduzzi
Fine Arts Museum / Decorative Arts Museum / Religious Arts Museum - 1946
European and American painting, religious sculpture, engravings, Colonial furniture, religious and colonial hist 00362

Museo Rural de la Posta de Sinsacate, Calle R.P. Pedro de Oñate s/n, 5220 Jesús María - T: (03525) 420126, Fax: 420126, E-mail: mjn-jm@datacop5.com.ar. Head: Nelson Lenarduzzi
Historical Museum / Fine Arts Museum - 1948
19th c paintings, 19th c vehicles, silver, stirrups, Colonial items, national hist, transport systems in the colnial time 00363

Junín

Museo Municipal de Arte Angel María de Rosa, Calle Roque Sáenz Peña 131, B6000FJC Junín - T: (02362) 422228, 443047, Fax: 444112. Head: Prof. María E. Telleria de Gallardo
Fine Arts Museum - 1944
Painting and sculpture - archive 00364

La Banda

Unidad Museológica Municipal de La Banda, Av Besares 222, El Veredón, G4300DOP La Banda - T: (0385) 4273419
Local Museum 00365

La Calera

Museo Municipal de Bellas Artes, Calle San Martín 425, M5151EMI La Calera - T: (03543) 466022, Fax: 466119
Fine Arts Museum
Oil paintings, watercolours, woodcuts, etchings, plaster casts 00366

La Carlota

Fuerte de la Punta del Sauce, Hilarión Abaca y España, X2670BFA La Carlota - T: (03584) 429687, Fax: 429682
Historical Museum
Artifacts relating to the history of Argentina 00367

La Cumbre

Casa de Manuel Mujica Láinez, Calle El Paraíso, Cruz Chica, X5180BGA La Cumbre - T: (03548) 451160, Fax: 451756
Special Museum - 1987
Company history, furniture, books, art objects, curiosity, historic documents 00368

Museo Cacique Balata, Calle 25 de Mayo 376, X5180DUH La Cumbre - T: (03548) 452055, 451479, Fax: 451097, 459940
Ethnology Museum
Ceramics, stones and bones of Comechingón culture 00369

La Falda

Museo de Ferrocarriles en Miniatura Werner Dura, Calle Las Murallas 200, X5172BDB La Falda - T: (03548) 423041, E-mail: trenesmuseo@coopvg.agora.com.ar
Science&Tech Museum 00370

Museo del Deporte Pierre de Coubertin (Sports Museum), Calle Dr. Meincke 32, X5172ABB La Falda - T: (03548) 470361047
Special Museum
History of the Olympic committee of Argentina 00371

La Gallareta

Museo Histórico La Gallareta Forestal, Calle General Justo José de Urquiza s/n, S3057APA La Gallareta - T: (03483) 496125
Local Museum
Local history, Argentina forest 00372

La Para

Museo Histórico Municipal La Para (La Para Municipal Historical Museum), Calle Presidente General J.A. Roca 551, X5137AWK La Para - T: (03575) 491001, 491488, Fax: 491001, E-mail: museolapara@hotmail.com, Internet: http://www.museolapara.gov.ar. Head: Prof. Carlos Alfredo Ferreyra
Local Museum
archives, library, research 00373

La Paz

Museo Municipal de Bellas Artes, Calle Italia 1043, 3190 La Paz - T: (03437) 421524, Fax: 421571
Fine Arts Museum 00374

Museo Regional de la Ciudad de La Paz, Parque Berón de Astrade, Calle 3 de Febrero s/n, 3190 La Paz - T: (03437) 421265, Fax: 421571. Head: Maria del Carmen Gorroño de Crespo
Local Museum - 1972
Documents, armaments and other artifacts from the early hist of the city, ancient religious artifacts, coins and medals, furnishings, agricultural implements 00375

La Plata

Museo Almafuerte, Av 66 Sur 530, B1904ASX La Plata
Special Museum - 1921
Personal objects, furnishings, manuscripts and memorabilia of the writer Almafuerte - library 00376

Museo Belgraniano, Av 13 y Calle 40, B1902CSN La Plata
Military Museum - 1971
Portraits, documents and numismatics connected with General Manuel Belgrano 00377

Museo Catedral de La Plata, Calle 14 e/ 51-53, B1902CTC La Plata - T: (0221) 4225026, 4273504, Fax: 4251772, E-mail: funcat@netverk.com.ar, Internet: http://catedral.laplata.net. Head: Oscar Angel Neaf
Religious Arts Museum 00378

Museo de Arte Contemporáneo Fra Angélico, Calle 47 entre 16 y Diagonal 73, B1900AJB La Plata
Fine Arts Museum 00379

Museo de Bellas Artes Bonaerense, Av 51 Centro 525, B1900AVK La Plata - T: (0221) 4218619, Fax: 4212206, E-mail: muspr@de.gba.gov.ar
Fine Arts Museum - 1928
Argentine art (17th-19th c), contemporary American and European painting - library 00380

Museo de Física de la Universidad Nacional de La Plata, Calle 49 y 115, B1900APA La Plata - T: (0221) 4239061, Fax: 4252006, E-mail: museo@venus.fisica.unlp.edu.ar, Internet: http://

www.exacta.unlp.edu.ar/museos/fisica. Head: Dr. Carlos García Canal
Science&Tech Museum / University Museum - 1994 00381

Museo de Instrumentos Musicales Emilio Azzarini, Av 44 Norte 775, B1902ABC La Plata
Music Museum - 1973
Antique musical instruments 00382

Museo de la Artesanía Tradicional Juan Alfonso Carrizo, Calle 2 No 417, B1902CHQ La Plata - T: (0221) 4244684, Fax: 4244684, E-mail: - casadelasprovinciasargentinas@speedy.com.ar, Internet: http://www.casadelasprovincias.cjb.net. Head: Prof. María Cristina Pozzuoli
Folklore Museum
Local folklore, traditional handicrafts - archives 00383

Museo de La Plata, c/o Universidao Nacional de La Plata, Paseo del Bosque s/n, B1900 La Plata - T: (0221) 4257744, 4259161, Fax: 4257527, E-mail: vicedecan@museo.fcnym.unlp.edu.ar, Internet: http://www.unlp.edu.ar/museo. Head: Dr. Marcelo Caballé
Local Museum / University Museum - 1884
Archeology, ethnography, botany, geology, mineralogy, paleontology, Patagonian and Pampean mammalia, zoology, anthropology, micology, ficology, entomology - library 00384

Museo Histórico Policial de La Plata, Calle 54 Centro 393, B1900BDO La Plata - T: (0221) 4231876, Fax: 4231876
Special Museum - 1951
Hist of the Argentine police 00385

Museo y Archivo Dardo Rocha, Calle 50 Centro 933, B1900ATK La Plata - T: (0221) 4211689. Head: Ana Maria Goycea
Fine Arts Museum - 1952
Local art, memorabilia of Dardo Rocha - library and archive 00386

La Rioja

Museo Arqueológico Regional Inca Huasi, Calle Juan Bautista Alberdi 650, F5300EFN La Rioja - T: (03822) 427310
Archaeological Museum - 1926
Regional archeology, religious art, weapons, anthropology, mineralogy, paleontology - library 00387

Museo de Arte Sacro de La Rioja, AvRivadavia 537, F5300ACF La Rioja
Religious Arts Museum
Religious art, books, antiques 00388

Museo de Bellas Artes Octavio de la Colina, Calle Copiapó 245, F5300DQE La Rioja
Fine Arts Museum - 1951
Paintings, sculpture, and book illustrations by contemporary artists 00389

Museo del Traje, Av Rivadavia 537, F5300ACF La Rioja - T: (03822) 426695, 428530, E-mail: beatrizfg@ciudad.com.ar
Folklore Museum
Traditional costume like sombreros , ranchos, capelinas 00390

Museo Folklórico, Calle Dr. Pelagio B. Luna 881, F5300EBQ La Rioja - T: (03822) 428500. Head: Raquel Corominas de Basso
Folklore Museum - 1969
Folklore and regional crafts 00391

Museo Histórico de La Rioja, Calle Adolfo E. Dávila 87, F5300DAA La Rioja
Historical Museum - 1916
Archeology, numismatics 00392

Laborde

Museo Histórico de Laborde, Calle General Simon Bolívar s/n, X2657AHA Laborde - T: (03534) 460215
Local Museum 00393

Laboulaye

Museo Histórico Manuel A. Moreira, Calle Bernardino Rivadavia 300, X6120EWF Laboulaye
Local Museum
library, archive 00394

Laguna Larga

Museo Polifacético Regional Vottero, Calle Cura Brochero 277, X5974ARE Laguna Larga - T: (03572) 480233, E-mail: museovottero@arnet.com.ar
Local Museum
Local history, natural history, religion, paleontology, numismatics 00395

Las Higueras

Museo Tecnológico Aeroespacial, Ruta 158 km 182, X5805 Las Higueras - T: (0358) 4979642, 4970822, Fax: 4979642, E-mail: museofaa@arnet.com.ar
Science&Tech Museum - 1999
Argentinian aviation 00396

Las Varillas

Museo Regional Las Varillas, Calle San Martín 127, X5992DXC Las Varillas - T: (03533) 420319 int 7, Fax: 420319 int 7
Local Museum 00397

Lavalle Villa Tulumaya

Museo Histórico y Natural de Lavalle, Calle Belgrano 62, M5533 Lavalle Villa Tulumaya - Internet: http://www.pic.mendoza.gov.ar
Local Museum / Natural History Museum 00398

Lincoln

Museo de Bellas Artes, Av Massey 1439, B6070 Lincoln
Fine Arts Museum - 1965
Contemporary Argentine art 00399

Lobería

Museo de História y Ciencias Naturales, Club de Pesca Loberia, Calle Alvear 181, B7635 Lobería
Natural History Museum - 1960
Paleontology, archeology, natural hist 00400

Lomas de Zamora

Museo Americanista, Calle Manuel Castro 254, B1832BSF Lomas de Zamora - T: 42399700, Fax: 42399536, E-mail: webmaster@ ilomas.zzn.com, Internet: http:// orbita.starmedia.com/~lomasdez/museo_americanista.htm
Historical Museum 00401

Museo Municipal de Lomas de Zamora, Calle Manuel Castro 254, B1832BSF Lomas de Zamora
Local Museum - 1958
Anthropology, hist, numismatics, natural hist, archeology, paleontology 00402

Los Toldos

Museo de Arte e História de Los Toldos, Av San Martín 972, B6015AIW Los Toldos - T: (02358) 443334
Historical Museum / Fine Arts Museum - 1975
Historical objects, pictorial art 00403

Museo del Indio, Monasterio Benedictino, Abadía Santa María, B6015 Los Toldos - T: (02358) 444146, Fax: 444211, E-mail: monjes@ infovia.com.ar. Head: P. Meinrado Hux
Ethnology Museum - 1962
Indian culture and culture Araucana 00404

Luján

Museo Colonial e Histórico, Complejo Museográfico Enrique Udaondo, Calle Lezica y Torrezuri 917, B6700CAQ Luján - T: (02323) 420245, Fax: 420245. Head: Carlos A. Scannapieco
Fine Arts Museum / Historical Museum - 1923
Regional hist (colonial period to 20th c), furnishings, jewellery, weapons, fine and applied arts - archive, library 00405

Museo de Bellas Artes, Parque Ameghino e San Martín y Lavalle, B6700ANH Luján
Fine Arts Museum - 1961
Contemporary Argentine art 00406

Museo de Transportes, Complejo Museográfico Enrique Udaondo, Lavalle entre Av Nuestra Señora de Luján y Lezica y Torrezuri, B6700CCA Luján - T: (02323) 420245, Fax: 420245. Head: Carlos A. Scannapieco
Science&Tech Museum - 1942
Hist of Argentine transport from Conquest times to 20th c 00407

Museo del Automóvil, Complejo Museográfico Enrique Udaondo, Av Nuestra Señora de Luján 751, B6700CCG Luján - T: (02323) 420245, Fax: 420245. Head: Carlos A. Scannapieco
Science&Tech Museum - 1992
Contains vintage car collection 00408

Museo Fernán Félix de Amador, Calle 9 de Julio 863, B6700CDM Luján - T: (02323) 420755
Fine Arts Museum 00409

Luján de Cuyo

Museo Nuestra Señora de Carrodilla, Calle San Martín y Carrodilla, M5507ETA Luján de Cuyo - T: (0261) 4361667
Historical Museum
Memorabilia from General San Martin 00410

Museo Provincial de Bellas Artes Emiliano Guiñazu - Casa de Fader, Calle San Martín 3651, M5507EVU Luján de Cuyo - T: (0261) 4960224, Fax: 4960224, Internet: http://www.pic.mendoza.gov.ar
Fine Arts Museum
Paintings of the Argentinian artist Fernando Fader (1882-1935) 00411

Luque

Museo Histórico Municipal de Luque, Av Santa Fé s/n, X5967 Luque - T: (03573) 480113
Local Museum - 1995 00412

Magdalena

Museo Histórico Regional Municipal de Magdalena, Calle Rivadavia esq Goenaga, B1913CZA Magdalena - T: (02221) 452144, Fax: 452217, E-mail: magdalena@stanet.com.ar
Local Museum 00413

Maipú

Ecomuseo Regional Maipú, Calle José Alberto Ozamis 988, M5515ECT Maipú - T: (02361) 44976435, Fax: 44973093, Internet: http:// www.pic.mendoza.gov.ar
Natural History Museum
Ecology, natural history, zoology, anthropology, paleontology, mineralogy, botany - library (also videos) 00414

Malargüe

Museo Regional Malargüe, Ruta 40 Norte s/n, M5613 Malargüe - T: (02627) 470369, Fax: 470369, Internet: http:// www.pic.mendoza.gov.ar
Local Museum
Local history, archaeology, natural history, paleontology 00415

Mar del Plata

Casa Museo Bruzzone, Calle Marie Curié 6193, B7605GCW Mar del Plata - T: (0223) 4790227, E-mail: casabruzzone@copetel.com.ar
Fine Arts Museum 00416

Museo del las Comunicaciones de Mar del Plata, Calle Castelli 2368, B7602HLX Mar del Plata - T: (0223) 4960763, Fax: 4960763, E-mail: - museocomunicaciones@educ.ar, Internet: http:// www.archivomdp.com.ar/comunicaciones
Science&Tech Museum
Postal service, telephone, broad casting, cinematography, television - library 00417

Museo Histórico Arqueológico Guillermo Magrassi, Calle 413 No750, Alfar, B7600 Mar del Plata - T: 0223 467-0369, E-mail: labase@ copefaro.com.ar. Head: Carlos Frederico Mertens
Archaeological Museum 00418

Museo Municipal de Arte Juan Carlos Castagnino, Calle Colón 1189, B7600FXE Mar del Plata - T: (0223) 4861636, Fax: 4519461, Internet: http:// www.culturamardelplata.com.ar. Head: Jorgelina Galicer
Fine Arts Museum - 1945
Painting, sculpture, engraving and drawing 00419

Museo Municipal de Ciencias Naturales Lorenzo Scaglia, Av Libertad 3099, Pl España, B7600HJB Mar del Plata - T: (0223) 4738791, Fax: 4738791, E-mail: scaglia@cultura-mgp.com.ar, Internet: http://www.culturamardelplata.com.ar. Head: Orlando Scaglia
Natural History Museum - 1938
Paleontology, zoology, geology, entomology, mastozoology - aquarium 00420

Museo y Centro Cultural Victoria Ocampo, Calle Domingo Matheu 1851, B7602GAK Mar del Plata - T: (0223) 4920569, Fax: 4920569, E-mail: scypu@ argenet.com.ar, Internet: http://www.culturamardelplata.com.ar
Special Museum - 1973 00421

María Teresa

Museo La Vieja Estación, Av San Martín s/n, S2609BFA María Teresa
Science&Tech Museum
Old railway station 00422

Martínez

Museo Chavin de Huantar, Calle Luis Sáenz Peña 2864, B1640ITF Martínez - T: (03792) 47981835. Head: Dr. Juan Carlos Columbano
Local Museum / Archaeological Museum - 1967
Archeology of the Americas, Argentine hist documents, contemporary Argentine painting, porcelain, bronze and ivory miniatures 00423

Mendoza

Eureka - Parque de la Ciencia, Calle Uriburu s/n, Parque General San Martín, M5500AAA Mendoza - T: (0261) 4250035, 4253688, Fax: 4253756, E-mail: eureka@lanet.com.ar
Special Museum / Science&Tech Museum 00424

Museo Argentino de Motos Antiguas, Calle Provincia de San Juan 646, M5500AFN Mendoza - T: (0261) 4291469, Fax: 4204038
Science&Tech Museum
Motorcycles (1904-1957) 00425

Museo Arqueológico del Instituto de Arqueología y Etnología, c/o Universidad Nacional de Cuyo, Facultad de Filosofía y Letras, Centro Universitario, M5500 Mendoza - T: (0261) 4230915, Fax: 4380457, E-mail: editor@logos.edu.ar. Head: Dr. Juan Schobinger
Archaeological Museum / University Museum - 1961
Archeology, ethnology, regional folklore 00426

Museo de Ciencias Naturales Juan Cornelio Moyano, Parque General San Martín, M5500AAA Mendoza - T: (0261) 4287666, Fax: 4287666, Internet: http://www.pic.mendoza.gov.ar. Head: Prof. Clara Abal de Russo
Natural History Museum / Ethnology Museum - 1911
Natural hist, archeology, anthropology, folklore, regional hist 00427

Museo del Area Fundacional, Calle Alberdi y V. Castillo, M5500CSA Mendoza - T: (0261) 4256927
Archaeological Museum
Archaeological finds (1989-91), ruins of San Francisco 00428

Museo del Pasado Cuyano, Calle Montevideo 544, M5500GGL Mendoza - T: (0261) 4236031
Historical Museum - 1961
Numismatics, weapons, religious art, hist of Cuyo province, petroleum 00429

Museo Histórico de la Policia de Mendoza, c/o Edificio Playas Serranas, Parque General San Martín, Av Prado Esp. s/n, M5500AAA Mendoza
Special Museum - 1961
Weapons and other objects of crime detection and prevention 00430

Museo Histórico Sanmartíniano, Calle Remedios Escalada de San Martín 1843, M5500ADC Mendoza - T: (0261) 4257947
Military Museum - 1913
Memorabilia of celebrated Argentinians, history of aeronautics in Argentina 00431

Museo Mineralógico Prof. Manuel Tellechea, Parque General San Martín, M5500AAA Mendoza, mail addr: CC 131, M5500 Mendoza
Natural History Museum - 1935
Geology and mineralogy, crystallography 00432

Museo Municipal de Arte Moderno de Mendoza, Plaza Independencia, M5500 Mendoza - T: (0261) 4257279
Fine Arts Museum 00433

Museo Universitario de Artes, c/o Facultad de Artes, Universidad Nacional de Cuyo, Parque General San Martín, M5500AAA Mendoza - T: (0261) 4494004 int. 2335, Fax: 4494059
Fine Arts Museum / University Museum 00434

Mercedes

Museo de Bellas Artes Domingo Faustino Sarmiento, Av Mitre 674, B6600AAA Mercedes
Fine Arts Museum - 1932
Archeology, fossils, hist, art - library 00435

Museo Histórico, Colonial y de Bellas Artes y Museo de Ciencias Naturales Regional Mesopotámico, Av Madariaga s/n, Parque Bartolomé Mitre, W3470DJA Mercedes - T: (03773) 420100 int 36
Local Museum 00436

Museo Histórico Municipal Víctor E. Míguez, Calle 12 No 542, B6600HTL Mercedes - T: (02324) 422442
Local Museum - 1973
Municipal hist 00437

Museo Municipal de Ciencias Naturales Carlos Ameghino, Calle 26 No 512, B6600GXL Mercedes - T: (02324) 420511
Natural History Museum - 1965
Paleontology, geology, archeology, zoology, botany, art of the Americas 00438

Metán

Museo Municipal de Bellas Artes Prof. Amelio Ronco Ceruti, Calle General Guemes y Layalle, S4440BNA Metán - T: (03876) 420737
Fine Arts Museum
Paintings, sculptures, graphics 00439

Miramar

Museo de la Región de Ansenuza Aníbal Montes, Calle Sarmiento y Urquiza, X5143 Miramar - T: (03563) 493279, Fax: 493078
Natural History Museum - 1958
Regional research, paleontology, archaeology, athropology, hydrobiology, ecology, botany, ornitology, herpetology, entemology etc 00440

Museo de la Selva Juan Forster, Calle 44 No 739, B7607CAS Miramar - T: (02291) 420317, E-mail: museodelaselva@yahoo.com
Natural History Museum - 1966
Geology, paleontology, ethnography, archaeology, herpetology, mastozoology, ornitology, hydrobiology, entomology, history of the institut 00441

Museo Municipal Punta Hermengo, Vivero Dunícola Florentino Ameghino, B7607 Miramar
Local Museum
Local history, natural history, paleontology, zoology, geology, archaeology 00442

Moisés Ville

Museo Histórico Comunal y de la Colonización Judía Rabino Aaron H. Goldman, Calle 25 de Mayo 188, S2313AAD Moisés Ville - T: (03409) 420665, Fax: 420042, E-mail: museo_mv@ interclass.com.ar, Internet: http://www.museomoisesville.com.ar. Head: Eva Guelbert de Rosenthal
Historical Museum
First organized Jewish agricultural settlement in Argentina - library 00443

Monte Caseros

Museo del Este, Calle Mendieta y Buenos Aires, W3220ASA Monte Caseros - T: (03775) 422740, E-mail: galantini@ciudad.com.ar
Local Museum 00444

Monte Grande

Museo Histórico Municipal Monte Grande, Calle Dean Funes 1221, B1842 Monte Grande - T: (011) 42900437, Fax: 42900437, E-mail: gustortiz@hotmail.com
Local Museum
Local history, paleontology, archeology - library 00445

Moreno

Museo Florencio Molina Campos, Calle Guemes esq Av Victorica, B1744BWA Moreno - T: (02228) 426904, E-mail: molinacampos@hotmail.com, Internet: http://habitantes.elsitio.com/molinaca. Head: Juan Carlos Ocampo
Fine Arts Museum - 1971
Originals and reproductions of the works of Molina Campos 00446

Museo Orlando Binaghi, Círculo Criollo El Rodeo, Av Puente Márquezy Mendoza, Paraje del Puente de Márquez, B1742 Moreno - T: (0237) 4685533, Fax: 4685533, E-mail: elrodeo@tradiciongaucha.com.ar, Internet: http://www.circuloelrodeo.com.ar/museo.htm
Local Museum
Tradition and history, military, antiques, religious coll 00447

Morón

Museo Histórico de Arte, Calle Presidente D.F. Sarmiento, B1708EKA Morón
Fine Arts Museum - 1951
National, provincial, local history and art 00448

Navarro

Museo Histórico de Navarro, Calle 22 No 332, B6605 Navarro - T: (02272) 430665, Fax: 430665
Local Museum 00449

Neuquén

Museo de Geología y Paleontología, c/o Universidad Nacional del Comahue, Calle Buenos Aires 1400, Q8300BCA Neuquén - T: (0299)4490300 int 247, Fax: 4490393, E-mail: wmuseo@ofco3.uncoma.edu.ar, Internet: http://www.uncoma.edu.ar
Archaeological Museum
Dinosaur 00450

Nono

Museo Rocsen, Area Rural, X5887 Nono - T: (03544) 498218, 498065, E-mail: email.rocsen@icox.com
Natural History Museum
Geology, minerals, paleontology, fosils, oceanography, antropology, history 00451

Oberá

Museo de Ciencias Naturales de Oberá, Calle Gobernador Barreyro y José Ingenieros, N3360AJA Oberá
Natural History Museum
Birds, mamals, reptiles, fishes 00452

Olavarría

Museo Etnográfico Municipal Dámaso Arce, Calle San Martín 2862, B7400KSK Olavarría - T: (02284) 421979, Fax: 424471. Head: Hugo Ratier
Ethnology Museum - 1963
Archeology and ethnography - library 00453

Museo Municipal de Artes Plásticas, Calle San Martín 2862, 7400 Olavarría - T: (02284) 421979, Fax: 427471. Head: Enrique Saisí
Fine Arts Museum - 1961
Argentine painting, silver work 00454

Oncativo

Museo Oncativo, Calle Las Heras 110, X5986CAB Oncativo - T: (03572) 466559, 460405
Local Museum 00455

Palmira

Museo Rauzi, Calle Belgrano 145, M5584APC Palmira - T: (02623) 462068, E-mail: rauzime@topmail.com.ar, Internet: http://www.rauzimuseo.edu.ar. Head: Prof. Estebar Rauzi
Archaeological Museum
Culture, gaucho, tradition, archaeology 00456

Paraná

Museo de Ciencias Naturales y Antropológicas Prof. Antonio Serrano, Calle Carlos Gardel 62, E3100FWB Paraná - T: (0343) 4208894, E-mail: biblioserrano@msn.com, Internet: http://www.museoserrano.8m.com. Head: María Luisa Adriana Rios de Saluso
Natural History Museum / Ethnology Museum / Archaeological Museum - 1917
Archeology and ethnography, birds, invertebrates, reptiles and insects, fishes, mineralogy and paleontology - library 00457

Museo de la Ciudad, Calle V. Sársfield y Av Laurencena, E3100IEA Paraná - T: (03443) 4201838
Local Museum 00458

Museo del Colegio Nacional Justo José de Urquiza, Calle General Justo José Urquiza, E3100FEC Paraná
Natural History Museum - 1949
Natural history 00459

Museo Histórico de Entre Ríos Martiniano Leguizamón, Calle Laprida y Buenos Aires, E3100FMA Paraná - T: (0343) 4207869, Fax: 4207829, E-mail: museoleguizamon@ciudad.com.ar. Head: Prof. Olga Mollano
Historical Museum - 1948
Local and regional history and nature, rural artists, numismatics 00460

Museo Interactivo de Ciencias, Blvd Racedo, entre Yrigoyen y P. Palma, E3100IDA Paraná - T: (0343) 4975100/101, Fax: 4975110, E-mail: museo@fi.uner.edu.ar. Head: Agustín Carpio
University Museum / Science&Tech Museum
General science, technology 00461

Museo Provincial de Bellas Artes Dr. Pedro E. Martínez, Calle Buenos Aires 355, E3100BQG Paraná - T: (03443) 4311527, Fax: 4311527
Fine Arts Museum - 1925
Painting, drawing, engraving and sculpture - library, archive 00462

Pedro Luro

Museo Regional Dr. José Luro, Calle Fortín Mercedes, B8148 Pedro Luro - T: (02928) 420125, Fax: 420125. Head: Vicente Enei
Local Museum - 1925
History, paleontology, natural history, Araucan arms and utensils, ethnographic, numismatic 00463

Pergamino

Museo Histórico Municipal de Pergamino, Calle Florida 629, B2700DFO Pergamino - T: (02477) 442374, E-mail: museoper@infovia.com.ar
Local Museum / Fine Arts Museum
Regional hist and arts 00464

Museo Municipal de Bellas Artes, Calle Florida 531, B2700DFM Pergamino
Fine Arts Museum
Painting, engraving and sculpture by Argentine artists 00465

Museo Pampeano del Pergamino, Estación Experimental Agropecuaria, B2700 Pergamino - T: (02477) 422057/58, 422779. Head: Jorge A. Josifovich
Agriculture Museum - 1963
Agricultural history of the Argentine pampa 00466

Pico Truncado

Museo Histórico y Regional Pico Truncado, Av Gobernador Gregores s/n, Z9015AWA Pico Truncado - T: (0297) 4990048, Fax: 4990098
Local Museum - 1991
Town history, archaeology 00467

Pigüé

Museo Coyug-Curá, Av Clemente Cabanettes 170, B8170CJO Pigüé - T: (02923) 472758, E-mail: coyugcura@hotmail.com
Local Museum
Archaeology, geology and minerlogy, paleontology, biology, antiques, coins, religious art 00468

Museo Regional de Pigüé, Parque Fortunato Chiappara, Rastreador Fournier s/n, B8170BOA Pigüé - T: (02923) 475001, Fax: 475580, E-mail: subcom@saavedra.mun.gba.gov.ar, Internet: http://www.pigüéonline.com. Head: Esther Andrieu
Local Museum - 1959 00469

Pirané

Museo del Pueblo, Calle Roque Sáenz Peña 761, P3606CYO Pirané - T: (03717) 460206, Fax: 460206
Local Museum 00470

Plaza Huincul

Museo Carmen Funes, Av Córdoba 55, Q8318EBA Plaza Huincul - T: (0299) 465486, Fax: 465486, E-mail: coriarod@neunet.com.ar
Local Museum
Local history and fauna, archaeology 00471

Porteña

Museo Municipal de Porteña, Estación del Ferrocarril G.B.M., X2415 Porteña - T: (03564) 450303, Fax: 450112
Local Museum
archive 00472

Posadas

Museo de Bellas Artes Juan Yapari, Calle Sarmiento 319, N3300 Posadas - T: (03752) 447375
Fine Arts Museum 00473

Museo de Ciencias Naturales e Historia, Instituto Superior del Profesorado Antonio Ruiz de Montoya, Calle San Luis 1962, N3300MXP Posadas - T: (03752) 423893, Fax: 425178, E-mail: isparm@misiones.com.ar
Natural History Museum / Local Museum
Regional history, culture, colonialization, natural history 00474

Museo Histórico de la Policía de la Provincia de Misiones, Calle Félix de Azara y Tucumán, N3300 Posadas - T: (03752) 447662, Fax: 447662
Historical Museum - 1976
Antique and modern weapons, historical objects related to law enforcement 00475

Museo Municipal de Bellas Artes Lucas Braulio Areco, Calle Bernardino Rivadavia 1846, N3300LDN Posadas - T: (03752) 449074 int 23
Fine Arts Museum - 1952
Painting, sculpture and engravings by Juan de Dios Mena, Bernardo Cesáreo de Quinós, Aida Carballo, hist and documentation of local missions 00476

Museo Regional Aníbal Cambas, Calle Alberdi 600, Parque República del Paraguay, N3300LWB Posadas
Local Museum - 1947
History, archeology, ethnography, natural history, culture of Guaraní, pre-jesuit time 00477

Palacio del Mate, Calle Bernardino Rivadavia 1846, N3300LDN Posadas - T: (03752) 428139
Fine Arts Museum / Decorative Arts Museum - 1952
Painting and sculpture, regional furniture 00478

Puan

Museo Municipal Ignacio Balvidares, Av General San Martín y Garay, B8180BGA Puan - T: (02923) 498022, Fax: 498001, E-mail: cultura_puan@ed.gba.gov.ar
Local Museum 00479

Puerto Belgrano

Museo Naval Puerto Belgrano, Av a la Estación s/n, B8111 Puerto Belgrano - T: (02932) 487526, Fax: 487151
Historical Museum
Military uniforms, antique navigation, photography, plans, documents 00480

Puerto Deseado

Museo Regional Provincial, Calle Colón y Belgrano, Z9050 Puerto Deseado - T: (0297) 4870220
Historical Museum
Argentinian archaeology, regional history 00481

Puerto Esperanza

Museo Arqueológico de Puerto Esperanza, Escuela de Frontera No 611, N3378 Puerto Esperanza - T: (03757) 480537, Fax: 480705
Archaeological Museum 00482

Puerto Madryn

Museo Provincial de Ciencias Naturales y Oceanográfico, Av Pedro Domeco García y Menéndez, U9120GLA Puerto Madryn - T: (02965) 451139, Fax: 451139, E-mail: musocpm@mcyech.org.ar
Natural History Museum
Naval mammals, invertebrates, fishes, geology, paleontology, botany, oceanography 00483

Puerto San Julián

Museo Regional y de Arte Marino, Calle Vieytes y Rivadavia, Z9310 Puerto San Julián - T: (02962) 452353, Fax: 452353
Local Museum / Fine Arts Museum - 1972 00484

Punta Alta

Museo Municipal de Ciencias Naturales Carlos Darwin, Calle Urquiza 123, B8109FWC Punta Alta - T: (02932) 432063, Fax: 432063
Natural History Museum 00485

Quilmes

Museo Histórico del Transporte Carlos Hillner Decoud, Calle Laprida y Ricardo Rojas, B1878BCA Quilmes - T: (011) 42805488, E-mail: aaapsega@mail.retina.ar
Historical Museum / Science&Tech Museum 00486

Museo Municipal de Artes Visuales, Calle Libertad 432, B1878 Quilmes, mail addr: Rivadavia 498, 1878 Quilmes - T: (011) 42245336, 42534173, E-mail: aaapsega@mail.retina.ar. Head: Alejo Apsega
Fine Arts Museum - 1965
Painting, sculpture, drawing, engraving 00487

Museo Municipal Histórico Fotográfico de Quilmes, Calle 25 de Mayo 218, B1878JZF Quilmes - T: (011) 42539162
Fine Arts Museum / Historical Museum 00488

Rafaela

Museo de la Fotografía, Calle Domingo F. Sarmiento 530, S2300QVL Rafaela - T: (03492) 431983, 423586, Fax: 429146, E-mail: muhisraf@arnet.com.ar. Head: Publio Parola
Fine Arts Museum - 1998
Regional photographic history, contemporary artists 00489

Museo Histórico Municipal y Colección de Arte Precolombino Arminio Weiss, Blv Santa Fe y 9 de Julio, S2300MHA Rafaela - T: (03492) 435050, E-mail: muhisraf@arnet.com.ar. Head: Norma Fenoglio
Local Museum / Ethnology Museum / Fine Arts Museum - 1959
Immigration objects (1881-1930), different cultures, ethnography, agricultural pottery, 00490

Museo Municipal de Bellas Artes Dr. Urbano Poggi, Calle Domingo F. Sarmiento 530, S2300QVL Rafaela - T: (03492) 431983, E-mail: muhisraf@arnet.com.ar. Head: Norma Fenoglio
Fine Arts Museum - 1969
Paintings, drawings and prints 00491

Ramallo

Museo Histórico Municipal Hércules J. Rabagliati, Calle Moreno 890, B2915BNR Ramallo - T: (03407) 421851, Fax: 421852
Local Museum 00492

Ranchos

Museo Histórico de Ranchos, Calle Leopoldo Casal 3059, B1987BDO Ranchos - T: (02241) 481477. Head: Maria Angélica Fernández
Local Museum - 1964
Local hist, artifacts of peasant culture, local fauna, Martin Gómez, "soguero" (making halters, reins, stirrups etc) and the silversmith Miguel Angel Ugalde (old colonial criollo style) - conference room 00493

Rauch

Museo Municipal de Arte, Av San Martín 252, 7203 Rauch. Head: Antonio A. Rizzo
Fine Arts Museum - 1962
Painting, drawings, engravings, and sculpture by Argentine artists 00494

Rawson

Museo Regional Salesiano de Rawson, Calle Don Bosco 248, U9103CAF Rawson - T: (02695) 482623, E-mail: donbosco-rw@cpsarg.com
Local Museum - 1941 00495

Realicó

Museo Patria Chica, Calle Gobernador Centeno 1566, L6200AQP Realicó - T: (02331) 462300
Local Museum / Decorative Arts Museum
Archaeology, historical documents, antique arms, colonial silver coll, marine items, curiosities, antiques 00496

Resistencia

El Fogon de los Arrieros, Calle Brown 350, 3500 Resistencia - T: (03722) 426418. Head: Hilda Torres Varela
Fine Arts Museum - 1943
Painting, sculpture (esp by Juan de Dios Mena) and engraving, photographs, crafts, documents, Emilio Pettoruti, Lucio Fontana, Lorenzo Domínguez - library 00497

Museo de Ciencias Naturales Augusto G. Schulz, Calle Carlos Pellegrini 802, H3500ENB Resistencia - T: (03722) 423864, Internet: http://www.ecomchaco.com.ar/cultura/ciencias.htm
Natural History Museum - 1992 00498

Museo de la Policía del Chaco, Calle Presidente General Julio A. Roca 233, H3500ASE Resistencia - T: (03722) 423504
Historical Museum - 1968
Weapons 00499

Museo de Medios de Comunicación, Calle Carlos Pellegrini 272, H3500CDF Resistencia - T: (03722)422649, Fax: 423954, E-mail: elterritorio@yahoo.com, Internet: http://www.ecomchaco.com.ar/cultura/medios.htm
Special Museum - 1999 00500

Museo Histórico Regional Ichoalay, Calle Donovan 425, H3500BQI Resistencia - T: (03722) 424200, E-mail: museoichoalay@hotmail.com.ar
Local Museum
Local history, culture, military 00501

Museo Regional de Antropología, Av Las Heras 727, H3500COI Resistencia - T: (03722) 446958, Fax: 446958, E-mail: historia@hum.unne.edu.ar. Head: Susana Colazo
Ethnology Museum / Archaeological Museum - 1968
Anthropology and archeology 00502

Río Cuarto

Museo Histórico Regional de Río Cuarto, Calle Fotheringham 178, X5800DGD Río Cuarto - T: (0358) 4671208
Local Museum - 1971
Local hist, archaeology, ceramics, colonial army, coins, religious art - library 00503

Museo Municipal de Bellas Artes Dr. Genaro Pérez, Calle Colón 149, X5800DKC Río Cuarto - T: (0358) 4671209, Fax: 4671207
Fine Arts Museum - 1933
Argentine sculpture, Argentine, European and North American painting, archeology 00504

Río Gallegos

Museo de Arte Eduardo Minnicelli, Calle Maipú 13, Z9400BFA Río Gallegos - T: (02966) 426769, E-mail: luciat@internet.siscotel.com
Fine Arts Museum 00505

Museo de los Pioneros, Calle Alberdi y El Cano, Z9400AYA Río Gallegos - T: (02966) 437763
Historical Museum
Pioneer settlers of the region 00506

Museo Malvinas Argentinas, Calle Dr. Luis Pasteur 74, Z9400BNB Río Gallegos - T: (02966) 420128
Historical Museum
History, justice, geography - library (also videos) 00507

Museo Marítimo y Naval de la Patagonia Austral, Calle Mariano Muratore y Alcorta, Z9400GRA Río Gallegos - T: (02966) 422600, Fax: 422600
Historical Museum
Maritime history 00508

Museo Regional Provincial Padre Manuel Jesús Molina, Calle Ramón y Cajal 51, Z9400BOA Río Gallegos - T: (02966) 423290, 426427, Fax: 423290, E-mail: museomolina@hotmail.com
Local Museum
Geology, paleontology, fauna, science, technology, fine arts, anthropology, archaeology, history, biology, minerals 00509

Sala Histórica del Regimiento de Infantería Mecanizado 24, Av San Martín 2300, Z9400ICW Río Gallegos - T: (02966) 420364 int 225, Fax: 420857
Military Museum
Regimental and military history 00510

Río Grande

Museo Monseñor José Fagnano, Misión Salesiana, Ruta Nacional 3 - km 2800, V9420 Río Grande - T: (02964) 421642, Fax: 421893, E-mail: candelaria@genesysrg.com, Internet: http://www.genesys.com.ar/mision
Local Museum / Religious Arts Museum - 1892
Local arts and crafts, weapons, zoology 00511

Río Mayo

Museo Regional Dr. Federico Escalada, Av Ejército Argentino s/n, U9030AFA Río Mayo - T: (02903) 420400, Fax: 420035
Local Museum 00512

Río Segundo

Museo Arqueológico Regional Anibal Montes, Calle Sarmiento 900, 5960 Río Segundo - T: (03572) 421455. Head: Marta Maria Bonofiglio
Archaeological Museum - 1970
Regional and local archeology and hist 00513

Rivadavia

Museo Hermanos Nacif Weiss, Av José Igacio de la Roza 1516, J5400 Rivadavia - T: (02364) 4332525, Fax: 4332526, E-mail: rectorado@uccuyo.edu.ar
Special Museum
Historicdocuments, furnishings, diploms, maps 00514

Museo Ramón Pérez Fernández, Ex-Estación, Calle Vitale s/n, M5577XAC Rivadavia - T: (02623) 443073, Internet: http://www.pic.mendoza.gov.ar
Historical Museum 00515

Rosario

Galería Monumento Histórico Nacional a la Bandera, Calle Santa Fé 581, S2000ATC Rosario - T: (0341) 4802238/39, Fax: 4802238, E-mail: general@rosario.gov.ar
Historical Museum - 1957 00516

Museo Activo del Pago de los Arroyos, Calle General Güermes 2311, S2000JBC Rosario - T: (0341) 4390395, Fax: 4402392, E-mail: cidac@uole.com
Local Museum
Archaeology, decorative art, photography, coins, railway, costume 00517

Museo de Ciencias Morfológicas, c/o Facultad de Ciencias Médicas de la UNR, Calle Santa Fé 3100, S2002KTR Rosario - T: (0341) 4804563, Fax: 4804563
Historical Museum / University Museum
Human anatomy, pathology - library 00518

Museo de la Partitura Historica, Calle Colonel Manuel Dorrego 2180, S2000GEJ Rosario - T: (0341) 4852062, Fax: 4852062, E-mail: m.dibella@museopartitura.com. Head: Miguel Angel di Bella
Music Museum
Musical history 00519

Museo Histórico Provincial de Rosario Dr. Julio Marc, Parque Independencia, S2001NRA Rosario - T: (0341) 4721457, Fax: 4721457, E-mail: museomarc@citynet.net.ar, Internet: http://www.santafe.gov.ar/cultura. Head: Eugenio A. Travella
Historical Museum - 1939
Local hist, crafts, coins and medals, furnishings, pre-Columbian ceramics and textiles, early Mexican ceramics, colonial art - library 00520

Museo Municipal de Arte Decorativo Firma y Odilo Estévez, Calle Sante Fé 748, S2000ATF Rosario - T: (0341) 4802547, Fax: 4802547, E-mail: museo@museoestevez.gov.ar, Internet: http://www.museoestevez.gov.ar. Head: P.A. Sinopoli
Decorative Arts Museum / Fine Arts Museum - 1968
Spanish and French furnishings (16th-18th c), ivories, glass, porcelain, ceramics, tapestries, American silver, paintings by Goya, Mattia Preti, Gerard, David, Magnasco, Albani, Monticelli, Hispanicamerican silver 00521

Museo Municipal de Bellas Artes Juan B. Castagnino, Av Carlos Pellegrini 2202, S2000QDN Rosario - T: (0341) 4217310, Fax: 4217310. Head: Prof. Miguel Ballesteros
Fine Arts Museum - 1937
Argentine art from independence to the present, sculpture, prints, paintings by El Greco, Goya, David and Titian - library 00522

Museo Municipal de la Ciudad de Rosario, Blvd Nicasio Oroño 2300, S2000GHS Rosario - T: (0341) 4802547
Local Museum
Local history, politics, social and economic conditons 00523

Museo Provincial de Ciencias Naturales Dr. Angelo Gallardo, Calle Dr. Mariano Moreno 750, Planta Alta, S2000DKP Rosario - T: (0341) 4257969, E-mail: museocng@satlink.com
Natural History Museum
Botany, zoology, paleontology, mineralogy, anthropology 00524

Museo Universitario Florentino y Carlos Ameghino, c/o Facultad de Ciencias Exactas, Universidad Nacional de Rosario, Calle Pellegrini 250, S2000BTP Rosario - T: (0341) 4802469, Fax: 4802654, E-mail: scornero@fceia.unr.edu.ar
Archaeological Museum / University Museum
Paleontoloy, archaeology 00525

Rueda

Museo Histórico Ferroviario Escribano Alfredo Rueda, Calle Urquiza y San Martín, S2921 Rueda - T: (03400) 496020, Fax: 496020
Science&Tech Museum 00526

Sacanta

Museo Regional de Sacanta, Ex-Estación, Av Bartolomé Mitre, X5945AVA Sacanta - T: (03533) 492178
Local Museum - 1985 00527

Salliqueló

Museo Histórico Regional Gabriel Campomar Cervera, Av 25 de Mayo y Italia, B6339ABA Salliqueló - T: (02394) 481366, Fax: 481366
Local Museum - 1952
History and archeology, natural history, Indian artifacts 00528

Salta

Museo Arqueológico de Salta, Av Ejército del Norte esq Calle Polo Sur, A4406BIA Salta - T: (0387) 4222960, E-mail: baresa@ciunsa.edu.ar. Head: Athos Barés
Archaeological Museum - 1974
Archaeology of northeast Argentina, esp Salta province, anthropology 00529

Museo de Arte Sacro San Francisco, Calle Córdoba 33, A4402EZA Salta - T: (0387) 4310830, Fax: 4213789, E-mail: basilica@cpsarg.com
Religious Arts Museum - 1969 00530

Museo de Ciencias Naturales, Calle Mendoza 2, A4402AHB Salta - T: (0387) 4210242. Head: Dr. Marissa Fabrezi
Natural History Museum - 1950
Biology, geology and archeology, zoology, mineralogy 00531

Museo de la Ciudad, Calle Florida 97, A4400FMA Salta - T: (0387) 4373352
Local Museum
History, numismatics, archeology, religious art, weapons, crafts and folklore 00532

Museo Presidente José Evaristo Uriburu, Calle Caseros 417, A4400DMI Salta
Historical Museum - 1943
Memorabilia of the generals José Evaristo Uriburu, San Martín y Alvarez de Arenales, Belgrano, and Alvarado, archeological and numismatic coll, books 00533

Museo Provincial de Bellas Artes, Calle Florida 20, A4402FMB Salta - T: (0387) 4214714. Head: Josefina Alvarez
Fine Arts Museum - 1982
Colonial period, 19th c art, contemporary coll of regional artists 00534

Salto

Museo del Tango Roberto Firpo, Calle Bolívar y Arredondo, B2741CQA Salto - T: (02474) 422723, E-mail: firpo@saltonline.com.ar, Internet: http://www.saltonline.com.ar/firpo
Music Museum 00535

Museo Municipal C.I.P.A.S., Av España y Antártida Argentina, B2741BHA Salto - T: (02474) 422004, E-mail: cipas2000@hotmail.com
Natural History Museum / Archaeological Museum 00536

Rincón de Historia, Calle Buenos Aires y Maipú, B2741AAA Salto - T: (02474) 423960, Fax: 425000, E-mail: scagnetti@imagen-net.com.ar
Local Museum - 1988 00537

San Antonio de Areco

Museo de Arte Gauchesco La Recova, Zapiola y Segundo Sombra, B2760CVA San Antonio de Areco - T: (02326) 454243
Fine Arts Museum 00538

Museo Escolar de Ciencias Naturales Carlos A. Merti, Calle Matheu 283, B2760BTC San Antonio de Areco - T: (02326) 4183
Natural History Museum - 1942
Paleontology, archeology - library 00539

Museo Evocativo y de Bellas Artes Osvaldo Gasparini, Calle Alvear 521, B2760 San Antonio de Areco - T: (02326) 453930
Fine Arts Museum 00540

Museo Gauchesco Ricardo Güiraldes, Calle Camino Güiraldes, B2760 San Antonio de Areco - T: (02326) 452061, E-mail: aircampo@areconet.com.ar. Head: Prof. Elba Esther Iriarte
Folklore Museum - 1937
Hist, arts and crafts, folklore (18th-20th c), memorabilia of Ricardo Guiraldes 00541

Museo La Cinacina, Calle B. Mitre y Pellegrini, B2760BVA San Antonio de Areco - T: (02326) 452045, Fax: 452773, E-mail: aircampo@areconet.com.ar, Internet: http://www.lacinacina.com.ar
Historical Museum / Folklore Museum
History of Campo Argentino, costume 00542

Museo Usina Vieja, Calle Alsina 66, B2760ACB San Antonio de Areco - T: (02326) 453804, Fax: 452101, E-mail: usinavieja@hotmail.com
Local Museum
Electricity, decorative art, local history, culture 00543

San Carlos Centro

Museo Histórico de la Colonia San Carlos, Av General San Martín 550, S3013CQS San Carlos Centro - T: (03404) 422047, Fax: 420667, E-mail: munmuseo@infovia.com.ar
Local Museum
Local history, industry and trade - library, archive 00544

San Cristóbal

Museo de Ciencias Naturales del Departamento San Cristóbal, Calle Alvear 646, S3070AHJ San Cristóbal - T: (03408) 422922, Fax: 422042
Natural History Museum 00545

San Fernando del Valle de Catamarca

Museo Arqueológico Adán Quiroga, Calle Sarmiento 450, K4751XAK San Fernando del Valle de Catamarca - T: (03833) 437413, Fax: 437420. Head: Adriana Russo de Fontela
Archaeological Museum - 1937
Regional archeology, colonial history, natural history, portraits, jewelry 00546

Museo de Bellas Artes Laureano Brizuela, Calle Mota Borello 239, K4751XAK San Fernando del Valle de Catamarca - T: (03833) 437563, Fax: 437561
Fine Arts Museum - 1935
Argentine art 00547

Museo Histórico de la Provincia de Catamarca, Calle Chacabuco 425, K4700BTI San Fernando del Valle de Catamarca - T: (03833) 437562
Historical Museum 00548

Museo Municipal del Deporte, Calle Ortiz de Ocampo 40, K4704DCB San Fernando del Valle de Catamarca - T: (03833) 437420, Fax: 437420
Special Museum 00549

Museos Integrales de Antofagasta de la Sierra y Laguna Blanca, Subsuelo Paseo General Navarro, K470ASA San Fernando del Valle de Catamarca - T: (03833) 437564, Fax: 427572
Historical Museum 00550

San Francisco

Fundación Archivo Gráfico y Museo Histórico de la Ciudad de San Francisco y la Región, Calle Santa Fé 374, X2400KRA San Francisco - T: (03564) 4421595, E-mail: archivograf@artesanfco.cjb.net, Internet: http://www.artesanfco.cjb.net
Local Museum
Politics, socials, sports, artists - Archive 00551

Museo de la Ciudad de San Francisco, Blvd 9 de Julio esq Avellaneda, X2400AIA San Francisco
Local Museum - 1967
Sculpture by Argentine artists 00552

San Genaro Norte

Museo Histórico Comunal de San Genaro Norte, Calle Santa Fé 467, S2147BEG San Genaro Norte - T: (03401) 493169, Fax: 493279
Local Museum
library 00553

San Guillermo

Museo Comunal Regional de San Guillermo, Calle Independencia s/n y General López, S2347AUA San Guillermo - T: (03562) 466881, Fax: 466050
Local Museum - 1991 00554

San Isidro

Exploratorio, Centro Científico Tecnológico Interactivo, Calle Roque Sáenz Peña 1400, B1642DBJ San Isidro - T: (011) 47431177, Fax: 47474605, E-mail: centro@exploratorio.com, Internet: http://www.exploratorio.com
Science&Tech Museum
Technology, physics, biology, chemistry, astromomy and information systems 00555

Museo Histórico Municipal Brigadier General Juan Martín de Pueyrredón, Calle Rivera Indarte 48, B1642IFB San Isidro - T: (011) 45123131, E-mail: museopuey@hotmail.com, Internet: http://members.xoom.com/museopuey
Local Museum - 1941
Art, weapons, historical documents and memorabilia of General Pueyrredón - library, archive 00556

San Javier

Museo del Libro, Las Chacras, X5879XAA San Javier - E-mail: museolibro@flasmail.com, Internet: http://www.museodellibro.cjb.net
Library with Exhibitions 00557

San José

Museo Histórico Regional de la Colonia San José, Calle Urquiza 1227, E3283DHO San José - T: (03447) 470088, Fax: 470088
Local Museum
Local history, agriculture, peace 00558

Museo Histórico San Ignacio de Loyola, Av Centenario y 9 de Julio, N3307AEA San José - T: (03758) 492012
Local Museum
Precolumbiana of the Aborigines, religion, local history 00559

San Juan

Casa Natal de Sarmiento, Calle Domingo Sarmiento Sur 21, J5402ECA San Juan - T: (0264) 4224603, Fax: 4224603, E-mail: Casnatsarm@impsat1.com.ar. Head: Beatriz Oviedo de Coria
Historical Museum - 1911
Memorabilia of Domingo Faustino Sarmiento and family - library 00560

Museo de Bellas Artes Franklin Rawson, Av Guillermo Rawson Sur 621, J5402EVG San Juan - T: (02364) 4229638
Fine Arts Museum - 1934
Argentine painting, drawing, sculpture, and engraving 00561

Museo El Hombre y la Naturaleza, Calle Pedro Echagüe 389, J5400ADG San Juan
Natural History Museum
Minerology, astronomy, archaeology, paleontology, coins and medals 00562

Museo Geográfico Einstein, Av Alem Norte 915, J5400DYD San Juan
Natural History Museum / Archaeological Museum - 1965
Astronomy, geology, botany, zoology, anthropology, archeology 00563

Museo Histórico Provincial, Av Rawson Sur 621, J5402EVG San Juan - T: (02364) 4229638
Local Museum
Local history, archaeology, costume, furnishings, silver, numismatics - library, archives 00564

Museo Tornambe de la Universidad Nacional de San Juan, Av Libertador San Martín Oeste 1654, J5400ASQ San Juan - T: (02364) 4234183, Fax: 4228577
University Museum / Decorative Arts Museum
Ceramics, paintings, prints 00565

San Lorenzo

Museo de Historia Reginal San Lorenzo y Galería del Libertador General San Martín (Museum of Regional History of San Lorenzo and Gallery of the Liberator General San Martín), Calle Entre Ríos 510, S2200CXJ San Lorenzo - T: (03476) 424540, Fax: 424540, E-mail: museosanlorenzo@yahoo.com.ar. Head: Angel Omar Nanzer
Local Museum / Fine Arts Museum
Regional history, paleomastozoology, anthropology, fine arts - puppet theatre, archives 00566

Museo Histórico Conventual San Carlos, Calle Belgrano 430, S2200CNH San Lorenzo - T: (03476) 424774, Fax: 424774, E-mail: -conventosancarlos_museo@arnet.com.ar. Head: José Carlos Magnago
Historical Museum - 1949
National history, items of 13 febuary 1813, San Martín, communication technology, polycrome sculptures, wood, paintings metals, architecture - library, archive 00567

San Luis

Museo Provincial Dora Ochoa de Masramón, Calle Colón y Ayacucho, D5700AVA San Luis
Local Museum
Provincial history, Spanish regiment, archaeology, fine art 00568

San Martín de los Andes

Museo Municipal Primeros Pobladores, Juan Manuel de Rosas, Q8370 San Martín de los Andes - T: (02972) 428676, Fax: 427700, E-mail: culturasmandes@yahoo.com.ar, Internet: http://www.smandes.gov.ar
Local Museum - 1919
Araucan art, regional coll 00569

San Miguel

Museo Entomológco Mariposas del Mundo, Calle Italia 650, B1663NXN San Miguel - T: (011) 46642108, Fax: 46642108, E-mail: museo@mariposasdelmundo.com, Internet: http://www.mariposasdelmundo.com
Natural History Museum 00570

San Miguel de Tucumán

Museo Casa Padilla, Calle Congreso de Tucumán 147, T4000IEC San Miguel de Tucumán
Decorative Arts Museum - 1976
Furnishings and objects d'art (17th-19th c) in an 1860 Italianate building 00571

Museo de Arqueología de la Universidad Nacional de Tucumán, Calle 25 de Mayo 265, T4000IIE San Miguel de Tucumán - T: (0381) 4233962, 4216024 int 211, Fax: 4233962, E-mail: iarqueo@unt.edu.ar
Archaeological Museum 00572

Museo de la Casa de Gobierno, Calle 25 de Mayo de 1810 y San Martín, T4000IIA San Miguel de Tucumán - T: (0381) 4212894
Historical Museum - 1976 00573

Museo de la Casa Histórica de la Independencia Nacional, Calle Congreso de Tucumán 141, T4000IEC San Miguel de Tucumán - T: (0281) 4310826, Fax: 4221335, E-mail: cshtc@tucbbs.com.ar, Internet: http://www.tucbbs.com.ar
Historical Museum / Local Museum
Furniture, documents, weapons, pictures, porcelain, domestic and military items 00574

Museo de la Facultad de Ciencias Naturales y del Instituto Miguel Lillo, Calle Miguel Lillo 251, T4000JFE San Miguel de Tucumán - T: (0381) 4330868, Fax: 4330868. Head: Dr. José Antonio Haedo
Special Museum / Natural History Museum - 1931
Biology, geology, zoology, fossils, minerals 00575

Museo Folklórico Provincial, Calle 24 de Septiembre 565, T4000CNK San Miguel de Tucumán
Folklore Museum - 1943
Regional history and archeology, crafts, folklore - library 00576

Museo Juan Carlos Iramaín, Calle Provincia de Entre Ríos 27, T4000IAB San Miguel de Tucumán - T: (0381) 4211874. Head: Margarita Tula Todd de Iramain
Fine Arts Museum - 1937
Painting, drawings, and sculpture by Juan Carlos Iramain 00577

Museo Provincial de Bellas Artes Timoteo Eduardo Navarro, Calle 9 de Julio 44, T4000IHB San Miguel de Tucumán - T: (0381) 4227300. Head: Prof. Mauricio Guzman
Fine Arts Museum - 1915
Painting, sculpture, engravings 00578

Museo Sacro de la Catedral, Calle 24 de Septiembre 416, T4000CNJ San Miguel de Tucumán - T: (0381) 4251366
Religious Arts Museum - 1977
Liturgical objects, furnishings, items used formerly in the cathedral and churches of Turcumán 00579

San Nicolás de los Arroyos

Museo de Ciencias Naturales Rvdo. P. Antonio Scasso, Colegio Don Bosco, Calle Don Bosco 580, B2900 San Nicolás de los Arroyos - T: (03461) 422230, Fax: 427329, E-mail: museoscasso@hotbot.com. Head: Jorge Liotta
Natural History Museum - 1956
Natural history, snails, neotropical freshwater fish coll 00580

Museo de la Casa de Acuerdo de San Nicolás, Calle de Nación 137-139, B2900AAC San Nicolás de los Arroyos - T: (03461) 421452, Fax: 428980
Local Museum
19th c hist, painting, furnishings - library 00581

Museo Municipal de Bellas Artes, Calle de Nación 346, B2900AAH San Nicolás de los Arroyos
Fine Arts Museum
Painting, engravings, and sculpture by Argentine artists 00582

Museo y Archivo Histórico de San Nicolás, Primer Combate Naval Argentino, Calle Francia 187, B2900HVC San Nicolás de los Arroyos
Local Museum - 1971
Regional art and folklore, coins and medals, documents and archives 00583

San Pedro de Jujuy

Museo Histórico, Arqueológico y de Arte Pedro Balduín, Calle Pedro Miguel Araoz 500, Y4500EZJ San Pedro de Jujuy - T: (03884) 4220533 int 52, E-mail: mspjujuy@sap-net.com.ar, Internet: http://www.mspjujuy.com.ar
Local Museum 00584

San Rafael

Museo Municipal de Historia Natural, Parque Mariano Moreno, M5600 San Rafael - T: (02627) 423095, Fax: 430688, E-mail: museo@msznrzfzel.com.ar, Internet: http://www.msznrzfzel.com.ar. Head: Dr. Humberto A. Lagiglia
Natural History Museum - 1956
Botany, zoology, mineralogy, geology, paleontology, archeology, folklore, regional hist 00585

San Salvador de Jujuy

Museo Arqueológico Provincial, Calle Lavalle 434, Y4600EAJ San Salvador de Jujuy - T: (03388) 4221343
Archaeological Museum - 1942
Local archeology 00586

Museo Histórico Franciscano, Calle Lavalle 325 y Belgrano, Y4600EAG San Salvador de Jujuy - T: (03388) 4233434
Religious Arts Museum - 1932
Regional archeology, antique firearms, colonial and religious painting 00587

Museo Jorge Pasquini López, Víctor Hugo 45, Barrio Alto la Viña, Y4602ETA San Salvador de Jujuy - T: (03388) 4262569, Fax: 4260596, E-mail: grupoyav@imagine.com.ar, Internet: http://www.grupoyavi.com.ar/. Head: Jorge Alberto Kulemeyer
Natural History Museum / Archaeological Museum - 1995
Ethnography, archeology, geology, biology, zoology, ethnobotany 00588

Sanagasta

Museo Regional Rumi Mayu (Río de Piedra), Ruta Nacional No 75 Km 18, Paraje El Secadal, F5301 Sanagasta - T: (03822) 432747
Local Museum 00589

Santa Catalina

Museo Regional Particular Epifanio Saravia, Calle Ernesto Padilla s/n, Y4655 Santa Catalina - T: (0388) 4224333
Local Museum
Fine art, antiques, musical instruments, gaucho items, ethnography, mining, religious art, furniture 00590

Santa Clara de Saguier

Museo Rafael Escriña, Calle 9 de Julio esq Castelli, S2405ACA Santa Clara de Saguier - T: (03492) 490078, E-mail: vainal@santafe.com.ar
Folklore Museum / Agriculture Museum
Italian immigrants, agricultural tools 00591

Santa Fé

Museo Biblioteca Municipal Cesar Fernández Navarro, Calle Defensa 7590, S3000JGV Santa Fé - T: (0342) 4578411, Fax: 4690058, E-mail: vanecarli@latinmail.com
Library with Exhibitions 00592

Museo del Médico, Calle 9 de Julio 2464, S3000FNB Santa Fé - T: (0342) 4520182/176, Fax: 4520177
Historical Museum 00593

Museo Etnográfico y Colonial Juan de Garay, Calle 25 de Mayo 1470, S3000FJL Santa Fé - T: (0342) 4573550, Fax: 4573550, E-mail: etnosfe@ceride.gov.ar, Internet: http://www.ceride.gov.ar/etnografico. Head: Luis María Calvo
Ethnology Museum / Historical Museum - 1940
Folklore, ethnography, archeology, historical documents - library 00594

Museo Histórico de San Francisco, Calle Amenábar 2557, S3000 Santa Fé
Religious Arts Museum - 1937
Sculpture, painting, religious art, and historical documents 00595

Museo Histórico Provincial Brig. Estanislao López, Calle General San Martín 1490, S3000FRH Santa Fé - T: (0342) 4593760, Fax: 4593760. Head: Prof. Alicia Talsky de Ronchi
Historical Museum / Fine Arts Museum - 1943
Peruvian painting (17th-18th c), colonial furnishings, art, weapons, regional hist and memorabilia of celebrated persons 00596

Museo López Claro, Calle Piedras 7352, S3004IVH Santa Fé - T: (0342) 461575, E-mail: lopez_claro@unl.edu.ar
Local Museum
library 00597

Museo Municipal de Artes Visuales, Calle General San Martín 2068, S3000FRT Santa Fé - T: (0342) 439696. Head: Prof. Aldo A. Groce
Fine Arts Museum - 1936
Painting 00598

Museo Provincial de Bellas Artes Rosa Galisteo de Rodríguez, Calle 4 de Enero 1510, S3000FHN Santa Fé - T: (0342) 4596142, Fax: 4596142. Head: Prof. Nydia Pereyra Salva de Impini
Fine Arts Museum - 1922
Painting, drawings, engravings, and sculpture (contemporary Argentine and modern) - library 00599

Museo Provincial de Ciencias Naturales Florentino Ameghino, Calle Primera Junta 2859, S3000CDI Santa Fé - T: (0342) 4523843, Fax: 4523843, E-mail: ameghino@alpha.arcride.edu.ar, Internet: http://www.unl.edu.ar/santafe/museocn.htm. Head: Carlos Alberto Virasoro
Natural History Museum - 1914
Paleontology, ornithology, mammals, ichthyology, botany, zoology, - Library, Documentation Center 'Dr Joaquin Frenguelli' 00600

Sala Josefa Rodriguez del Fresno, Calle Brigadier Estanislao López 2792, S3000DCJ Santa Fé - T: (0342) 4573029, Fax: 4506600 int 1597, E-mail: sipar@ceride.gov.ar, Internet: http://www.ceride.gov.ar/sipar. Head: Ana María Ceccini de Dallo
Historical Museum
Provincial history - Provincial general archives 00601

Santa María de Catamarca

Museo Provincial Arqueológico Eric Boman, Calle Belgrano y Sarmiento 180, K4139 Santa María de Catamarca - T: (03833) 421282
Archaeological Museum - 1960
Regional and local archeology 00602

Santa Rosa

Museo Provincial de Artes de La Pampa, Calle 9 de Julio y Villegas, L6300AUA Santa Rosa - T: (02954) 427332
Fine Arts Museum 00603

Museo Provincial de Historia Natural de La Pampa, Calle Carlos Pellegrini 180, L6300DRD Santa Rosa - T: (02954) 422693, E-mail: sc_mushnatlapampa@cpenet.com.ar. Head: Gustavo Bernardo Siegenthaler
Natural History Museum - 1935
Art and natural hist, archaeology, flora, fauna, mineralogy, palaeontology 00604

Santa Rosa de Río Primero

Museo Regional José G. Brochero, Calle Deán Funes, X5133ATA Santa Rosa de Río Primero - T: (03574) 480210, 480096
Historical Museum
Memorabilia, paintings, institutional history, religion 00605

Santa Teresita

Museo del Automóvil de Santa Teresita, Av 32 y 16, B7107ACA Santa Teresita - T: (02246) 430297, E-mail: sderossi@intramed.net.ar
Science&Tech Museum
Historic cars, camaras, radios, weapons 00606

Santiago del Estero

Museo de Ciencias Antropológicas y Naturales, Calle Avellaneda 355, G4200DBG Santiago del Estero - T: (0385) 4211380
Ethnology Museum / Natural History Museum
Ethnography, archaeology, anthropology, botany, zoology, mineralogy, paleontology 00607

Museo Histórico de la Provincia, Calle Urquiza 354, G4200DHH Santiago del Estero
Historical Museum - 1941
Hist, art, numismatics, folklore, weapons 00608

Museo Provincial de Arqueología Wagner, Calle Avellaneda, G4200DBA Santiago del Estero - T: (0385) 41064. Head: Olimpia L. Righetti
Archaeological Museum - 1917
Archeological finds from the Chaco-Santiagueno and later cultures, musical instruments and ceremonial objects, paleontology, folklore, anthropology 00609

Museo Provincial de Bellas Artes Ramón Gómez Cornet, Calle General M. Belgrano Sur 1554, G4200ABP Santiago del Estero - T: (0385) 4211839
Fine Arts Museum 00610

Santo Tomé

Museo de Artes y Artesanías Enrique Estrada Bello, Calle Libertad 1620, S3016JEL Santo Tomé - T: (0342) 4741588
Fine Arts Museum / Decorative Arts Museum
Arts, crafts, decorative art 00611

Museo Histórico Municipal Andrés A. Roverano, Calle Libertad 1620, S3016JEL Santo Tomé - T: (0342) 4741588, Internet: http://www.santotomeweb.com.ar. Head: Prof. Ernesto A. Grenon
Local Museum
exhibition hall of paleontology, archaeology and geoscience Dr. Joaquín Frenguelli 00612

Museo Histórico Regional Pablo Argilaga, Calle Víctor Navajas 844, W3340DKN Santo Tomé - T: (03756) 420275
Local Museum
Local history - library, archive 00613

Sastre

Museo Municipal Dr. Rodolfo Doval Fermi, Calle Sarmiento 1989, S2440BCO Sastre - T: (03406) 480173, E-mail: jsargi@sme.dataco30.com.ar
Local Museum - 1927
Mural paintings, local history, agriculture, technic 00614

Suipacha

Museo de Historia Natural Dr. Ricardo S. Vadell, Estancia Los Preludios, Cuartel 7, B6612 Suipacha - T: (011) 43742807, 43742758, Fax: 43742807, E-mail: rvadell@datamarket.com
Natural History Museum
Natural history 00615

Museo José Manuel Estrada, Calle Balcarce 645, B6612AKO Suipacha - T: (02324) 481073, Fax: 480218, E-mail: bibliotecaymuseoestrada@yahoo.com.ar. Head: Patricia Elena Rionda
Historical Museum / Local Museum - 1933
National and regional history, paleontology, coins, medals 00616

Tafí del Valle

Museo Arqueológico, El Bañado, Ruta Provincial 307, T4137 Tafí del Valle - T: (03892) 21075
Archaeological Museum - 1977 00617

Museo de Mitos y Leyendas, Casa Duende, Ruta 307 km 58, T4137 Tafí del Valle - T: (03867) 4807091
Local Museum
Local history, archaeology, sculpture, paintings, ceramics, costume 00618

Museo Runa de Antropología, Av Belgrano y Los Palenques, T4137 Tafí del Valle - T: (0376) 4807169
Ethnology Museum 00619

Tandil

Museo Fuerte Independencia, Calle 4 de Abril 845, B7000BAQ Tandil - E-mail: bonystaneck@arnet.com.ar, Internet: http://usuarios.arnet.com.ar/bonystaneck
Local Museum - 1963
National and regional history - library 00620

Museo Municipal de Bellas Artes, Calle B. de Chacabuco 357, B7000AKI Tandil - T: (02293) 432067, Fax: 432064. Head: E. Valor
Fine Arts Museum - 1920 00621

Tanti

Museo de Ciencias Naturales Luma, Calle El Paraíso 445, Villa Muñoz, X5155BXA Tanti - T: (0351) 4658863, E-mail: carssen@hotmail.com
Archaeological Museum / Natural History Museum - 1997
Minerals of the world, fosiils, archaeology 00622

Tigre

Museo de la Reconquista, Calle Liniers 818, B1648DAR Tigre - T: (011) 45124496, Fax: 45124496
Historical Museum - 1949
Argentine history 00623

Museo Histórico de la Prefectura Naval Argentina, Calle Liniers 1264, B1648DAZ Tigre - T: (011) 47496161, Internet: http://www.prefecturanaval.edu.ar
Historical Museum 00624

Museo Naval de la Nación, Paseo Victorica 602, B1648DVN Tigre - T: (011) 47490608, Fax: 47490608, Internet: http://www.ara.mil.ar. Head: Horacio Molina Pico
Historical Museum - 1892
Naval hist, model ships, paintings, documents, medals, weapons - library 00625

Tilcara

Museo Arqueológico de Tilcara, Calle Dr. Manuel Belgrano 445, Y4624AFI Tilcara - T: (0388) 4955006, Fax: 4955006
Archaeological Museum
Archaeological items from Argentina, Chile, Bolivia, Peru 00626

Museo Irureta, Calle Dr. Manuel Belgrano y Bolívar, Y4624AFA Tilcara - T: (0388) 4955124
Local Museum 00627

Museo Regional de Pintura José Antonio Terry, Av Bernardino Rivadavia 459, Y4624AYI Tilcara - T: (0388) 4955005, Fax: 4955005. Head: Francisco Tinte
Fine Arts Museum
Memorabilia of painter José Antonio Terry 00628

Tostado

Museo Historiador Hernández Galiano, Calle 6 de Caballería y Belgrano, S3060 Tostado - T: (03491) 471817
Military Museum
History of the regiment 6 of the Cavallery, uniforms, arms 00629

Trelew

Museo Paleontológico Egidio Feruglio, Av Fontana 140, U9100GYO Trelew - T: (02965) 432100, E-mail: info@mef.org.ar, Internet: http://www.cpatagonia.com/mef
Archaeological Museum 00630

Museo Regional Pueblo de Luis, Av 9 de julio y Fontana, U9100BYA Trelew - T: (02965) 424062. Head: Jacqueline Olive Garrard
Local Museum - 1984
Stone arrowheads, stone tools of Tehuelches indians, agriculture, immmigrants, railway trandport of farming products - library, photo coll 00631

Tres Arroyos

Museo Municipal José A. Mulazzi, Av San Martín 323, B7500IKD Tres Arroyos - T: (02983) 433154 int 20, Fax: 431648, E-mail: sub.com@tresa.mun.gba.gov.ar
Local Museum / Archaeological Museum
Local history, archaeology, paleontology 00632

Museo Regional de Ciencias Naturales Tomás Santa Coloma, Calle Lucio V. López 473, B7500 Tres Arroyos
Natural History Museum
Zoology, geology, paleontology, ethnology 00633

Trevelin

Cartref Taid, Calle El Malacara s/n, U9203AZB Trevelin - T: (02945) 480108, E-mail: clerycelta@cybersnet.com.ar, Internet: http://trevelin.itgo.com/cartref_taid.htm
Local Museum 00634

Museo Molino Nant Fach, Valle 16 de Octubre, Ruta 259, U9203 Trevelin - T: (0268) 4280836
Folklore Museum
Historic life 00635

Museo Regional Trevelin, Calle Molino Viejo 488, U9203 Trevelin - T: (02945) 480545, Fax: 480145
Local Museum 00636

Trisán Suárez

Museo de Historia Regional de Tristán Suárez, Calle 9 de Julio 133, B1806ECC Trisán Suárez - T: (011) 42348981, Fax: 42348981
Local Museum
Local history 00637

Unquillo

Museo Municipal Lino Enea Spilimbergo, Av Spilimbergo 290, X5109AUF Unquillo - T: (03543) 489033, Fax: 488653
Fine Arts Museum 00638

Urdinarrain

Museo Histórico Regional de Urdinarrain, Complejo Cultural Urdinarrain, E2826 Urdinarrain - T: (03446) 45631447, Fax: 480199, E-mail: dyc@urdi.com.ar, Internet: http://www.urdi.com.ar
Local Museum
Local history, railway, agriculture - archive 00639

Ushuaia

Museo del Fin del Mundo, Calle Maipú 172, V9410BJD Ushuaia - T: (02901) 421863, Fax: 431201. Head: Oscar Pablo Zanola
Local Museum / Natural History Museum - 1979
Regional museum of history and natural sciences - library 00640

Museo Marítimo de Ushuaia, Ex Presidio, Calle Yaganes y Gobernador Deloqui, V9410IHA Ushuaia - T: (02901) 437481, 436321, E-mail: cvairo@dynamo.com.ar, Internet: www.ushuaia.org. Head: Carlos Pedro Vairo
Historical Museum
Old jail Presidio, antarctic shipping, boats 00641

Uspallata

Museo y Monumento Histórico Las Bóvedas, Ruta 39, km 2, M5545 Uspallata - T: (0266) 4570755, Fax: 420045, Internet: http://www.pic.mendoza.gov.ar
Local Museum
Local history and culture, mineralogy 00642

Valcheta

Museo Regional Valcheta, Calle Gobernador Pagano y Roca, R8536APA Valcheta
Local Museum 00643

Valle Hermoso

Museo Capitán Juan de Zevallos, Av Juan Domingo Perón 199, X5168AVC Valle Hermoso - T: (03548) 470485, Fax: 470635
Local Museum
Local history, costume, minerals, biology, anthropology, numismatics, sculptures 00644

Venado Tuerto

Museo Regional Cayetano Alberto Silva, Calle Maipú 966, S2600IKT Venado Tuerto - T: (03462) 431163, Fax: 421417 int 297
Local Museum
archive 00645

Vicente López

Museo Rómulo Raggio, Calle Gaspar Campos 861, B1638ARO Vicente López - T: (011) 47910858, 47961456, E-mail: frraggio@smsi.com.ar
Fine Arts Museum
Argentinian art, paintings, prints, drawings, sculptures, artistic textiles, photographics 00646

Victoria

Museo de la Ciudad, Calle Congreso de 1816 No 593, E3153BEK Victoria - T: (03436) 421606, Fax: 421606, E-mail: eguiazu@bigfoot.com
Local Museum 00647

Viedma

Museo del Agua y del Suelo, Calle Colón 498, R8500FDJ Viedma - T: (02920) 431569, E-mail: ciliberto@impsat1.com.ar
Natural History Museum
Water, soil 00648

Villa Adelina

Museo de la Palabra, Calle Dr. Luís María Drago 2265, B1607CYC Villa Adelina - T: (011) 47668746
Historical Museum
History of the coutry and the world 00649

Villa Ballester

Museo de Bellas Artes Ceferino Carnacini, Calle 71 No 4400, América 151, B1653 Villa Ballester - T: (011) 47681189. Head: Juan B. Alberdi
Fine Arts Museum - 1974
Argentine painting and engraving 00650

Museo Histórico José Hernández-Chacra Pueyrredón, Calle Presbítero Carballo 5042, B1653IPD Villa Ballester - T: (011) 47687492
Special Museum - 1966
Memorabilia of the writer José Hernández (1834-1886) - library 00651

Villa Carlos Paz

Museo del Cielo (Open Air Museum), Calle Florencio Sánchez s/n, Estación, X5152GKA Villa Carlos Paz - T: (03541) 422254 int 110
Open Air Museum / Science&Tech Museum
Meteorits, paleontology, mining 00652

Salón de Artes Plásticas Antonia F. Rizzuto, Calle Cárcaraña 75, X5152BYA Villa Carlos Paz
Fine Arts Museum - 1969
Paintings, drawings, sculpture and ceramics by contemporary Argentine and foreign artists 00653

Villa Clara

Museo Histórico Municipal Villa Clara, Calle San Martin s/n, B3252 Villa Clara
Local Museum 00654

Villa Concepción del Tío

Museo Histórico Regional Padre Francisco Cremasco, Calle General Manuel Belgrano esq General San Martín, X2433ACA Villa Concepción del Tío - T: (03576) 493121, Fax: 493007
Local Museum
Local and religious history, archaeology, paleontology 00655

Villa Constitución

Museo Municipal Histórico Regional Santiago Lischetti, Calle Ingeniero Acevedo 650, S2919BHN Villa Constitución - T: (03461) 474180, Fax: 474435, E-mail: mvc-comp@satlink.com
Local Museum
Agro-export, village history, archaeology, culture of Goya-Malabrigo, Guaraní and Querandí 00656

Villa del Rosario

Museo Histórico Municipal Villa del Rosario, Calle Avola San Martín 780, X5963EMP Villa del Rosario - T: (03573) 422395, Fax: 422321, E-mail: - municipalidadvdr@covinter.com.ar. Head: Martha Beatriz Romagnoli
Historical Museum
Local hist, archaeology, art 00657

Villa Futalaufquen

Museo del Parque Nacional Los Alerces, Primeros Pobladores s/n, U9201XAK Villa Futalaufquen - T: (02945) 471020/015, Fax: 471020
Natural History Museum 00658

Villa General Belgrano

Museo del Carruaje El Tacu, Calle Paraná 785, X5194 Villa General Belgrano - T: (03546) 486019
Science&Tech Museum
40 carriages and vehicles 00659

Villa Gesell

Museo Histórico Municipal de Villa Gesell, Calle Alameda 201 y Calle 303, B7165 Villa Gesell - T: (02255) 468624, Fax: 462513
Local Museum - 1991
archive, library 00660

Villa La Angostura

Museo Histórico Regional de Villa La Angostura, Calle Laga Nahuel Huapi 1900, Q8407CAP Villa La Angostura
Local Museum 00661

Villa María

Museo Ramos Generales, Calle Dr. José Ingenieros 160, X5900JHD Villa María - T: (0353) 4534828
Science&Tech Museum / Special Museum
Antique cars 00662

Villa Mirasol

Museo Regional Rincón de Vida, Av San Martín 871, L6315XAD Villa Mirasol - T: (02333) 493031
Local Museum
archive 00663

Villa Regina

Museo Comunitario de Villa Regina, Calle Uruguay 161, R8336AWC Villa Regina
Special Museum
library 00664

Villa Trinidad

Museo Histórico Comunal, Calle General Manuel Belgrano 145, S2345ADC Villa Trinidad - T: (03491) 491036, E-mail: rcerutti@hersilia.dataco14.com.ar. Head: Lilia P. de Cerutti
Local Museum
Founder of the village José Guillermo Lehmann, local history, costume, agriculture - archive 00665

Yapeyú

Museo Jesuítico de Sitio, Calle Sargento Cabral y Obispo Romero, W3231BAA Yapeyú
Religious Arts Museum 00666

Zapala

Museo Histórico, Calle Frotín Regimiento 21, 8340 Zapala - T: (02942) 490139, Fax: 490131
Historical Museum - 1965
Araucan art, weapons, documents and historical photos 00667

Museo Prof. Dr. Juan Augusto Olsacher, Calle Martín Etcheluz 52, Q8340AUB Zapala - T: (02942) 430132, Fax: 430026, E-mail: neumin@zapala.com. Head: Sergio Eduardo Cocea
Natural History Museum - 1969
Paleontology, mineralogy, archeology, ethnography, reptiles, invertebrate and cephalopods 00668

Armenia

Erevan

Avetisians Museum, Ul Nalbandiana 29, Erevan
Fine Arts Museum
Paintings by the artist Avetisian 00669

Charents Literary Memorial Museum, Ul Arami 60, Erevan - T: (01) 535594, 531412. Head: Lilit Hakobyan
Historical Museum
Life and works of the Armenian poet Charents and of other artists 00670

Geological Museum of the Institute of Geology, Ul Pushkina 12, 375010 Erevan - T: (08852) 580663. Head: G.B. Mezhlumyan
Natural History Museum - 1937
Mineralogy, Geology, Fossils 00671

Isahakians Museum, Ul Zarobian 20, Erevan - T: (01) 562424, 587380. Head: Hasmik Melkonyan
Special Museum
Memorabilia of the poet Isahakian 00672

Jottos Museum-Workshop, Ul Zarobian 5, Erevan
Fine Arts Museum
Paintings by the artist Grigorian Gevork (Jotto) 00673

Khachatrians Museum, Ul Zarobian 3, Erevan
Music Museum
Memorabilia of the composer Khachatrian, his works and piano - Concert hall 00674

M. Sarians Museum, Sarian 3, Erevan - T: (02) 581762, Fax: 563661. Head: Shahen Khachatrian
Fine Arts Museum
Paintings and graphics by the Armenian artist M. Sarian (1880-1972) 00675

Matenadaran, Mashtots Av 111, Erevan
Historical Museum
More than 16000 ancient manuscripts 00676

Modern Art Museum, Ul Mashtots 12, Erevan
Fine Arts Museum
Modern Armenian artists 00677

National Art Gallery of Armenia, ul Aram 1, Erevan - T: (02) 580812, Fax: 563661. Head: Šahen Chačatrian
Fine Arts Museum
Coll of European, Russian, Armenian and Oriental Art, 20,000 pieces, works of Tintoretto, Rubens, Courbet, Kandinsky, Chagal, Serov, Repin, Ayvasovsky, Sarian, Yakoulov 00678

Sergei Paradjanov Museum, Dzoragiugh Ethnographic Centre, Bldgs 15-16, 375015 Erevan - T: (08852) 538473, E-mail: zaven@arm.r.am, Internet: http://www.paradjanov.com. Head: Zaven Sarkissian
Special Museum
Works by the film maker and director Parajanov, collages, graphics, drawings, documentation, antiques 00679

Spendiarians Museum, Ul Nalbandian 21, Erevan
Music Museum
Memorabilia of the composer Spendiarian incl his favourite violin 00680

State Folk Art Museum of Armenia, Ul Abovian 64, 375025 Erevan - T: (01) 569383, E-mail: - armfolkartmuseum@yahoo.com, Internet: http://www.armenian-folk-art-museum.com. Head: Saro Saruchanian
Folklore Museum / Decorative Arts Museum
Woodwork, carpets, works by silversmiths, metalworks, pottery, embroidery, paintings 00681

State Fretwork Museum, Ul Proshian 4, Erevan
Fine Arts Museum
Original woodworks by Armenian masters 00682

State History Museum of Armenia, Republik Sq, Erevan - T: (01) 582761, Fax: 506098. Head: Anelka Grigorian
Historical Museum / Archaeological Museum / Folklore Museum / Decorative Arts Museum / Religious Arts Museum - 1919
Culture and art of Armenia (paleolithic, neolithic, Bronce age, Urartu, Hellenistic, Christian art - library 00683

Tumanyans Museum, Moskovskaya ul 40, 375002 Erevan - T: (08852) 581271. Head: Tamar Tumanyan
Special Museum - 1953
Memorabilia of the poet and writer Ovanes Tumanyan, cultural and literary hist of Armenia 00684

Yerevan Children's Picture Gallery, Ul Abovian 13, Erevan - T: (08852) 527893. Head: H. Ikitian
Fine Arts Museum - 1970
Works of Armenian children as well as those of other nationalities 00685

Zoological Museum of the Institute of Zoology, Ul P. Sevaka 7, 375044 Erevan - T: (08852) 281502. Head: M.S. Adamyan
Natural History Museum 00686

Australia

Aberfoyle Park

Local History Collection, Civic Centre, The Hub, Aberfoyle Park, SA 5168 - T: (08) 83746222, Fax: 83705611
Local Museum
Local history, former city of Happy Valley 00687

Acland

Acland Coal Mine Museum, Francis St, Acland, Qld. 4352 - T: (07) 46915703
Science&Tech Museum
Machinery, items used by coal miners, lights from Tallow to modern electric, gas testing 00688

Acton

Art Collection, c/o Australian National University, Kingsley St, Acton, ACT 2601 - T: (02) 61252501, Fax: 62472595, E-mail: david.boon@anu.edu.au, Internet: http://www.anu.edu.au/pad/artcol. Head: Nancy Sever
Fine Arts Museum
Paintings, sculptures, Australian 20th-c art 00689

Canberra School of Art Gallery, Ellery Crescent, Liversidge St, Acton, ACT 2601, mail addr: GPOB 804, Acton, ACT 2601 - T: (02) 62495841, Fax: 62495722, E-mail: gallery.csa@anu.edu.au. Head: Merryn Gates
Fine Arts Museum - 1981
Contemporary art - library 00690

Drill Hall Gallery, c/o Australian National University, Kingsley St, Acton, ACT 2601 - T: (02) 61255832, Fax: 62472595, E-mail: nancy.sever@anu.edu.au, Internet: http://www.anu.edu.au/pad/drillhall.html. Head: Nancy Sever
Public Gallery
Art of the Canberra region 00691

Adamstown

Paterson Court House, 3 Lexington Parade, Adamstown, NSW 2289 - T: (02) 49434526, Fax: 49434526
Local Museum 00692

Adelaide

Adelaide Masonic Centre Museum, Rundle Mall, Adelaide, SA 5000, mail addr: POB 19, Adelaide, SA 5001 - T: (08) 82231633, Fax: 82240755, E-mail: myoll@eisa.net.au
Historical Museum
Freemasonry in South Australia and the Northern Territory 00693

Art Gallery of South Australia, North Terrace, Adelaide, SA 5000 - T: (08) 82077000, Fax: 82077070, E-mail: agsa.info@saugov.sa.gov.au, Internet: http://www.artgallery.sa.gov.au. Head: Ron Radford
Fine Arts Museum - 1881
Australian, British, Asian, European, Aboriginal art - library 00694

City of Adelaide Civic Collection, 128 King William St, Adelaide, SA 5000 - T: (08) 82037368, 82037203, Fax: 82037336, E-mail: city@adelaide.sa.gov.au. Head: Elizabeth Harris
Historical Museum
The life, history, traditions and role of the Council and the City 00695

Defence Services Museum, Kintore Av, Adelaide, SA 5000 - T: (08) 83056374, Fax: 83056689
Historical Museum 00696

Edmund Wright House, 59 King William St, Adelaide, SA 5000 - T: (08) 82268555, Fax: 82268580, E-mail: staff@history.sa.gov.au, Internet: http://www.history.sa.gov.au. Head: Margaret Anderson
Local Museum - 1978
Historic photos - library 00697

Flinders University Art Museum, Sturt Rd, Bedford Park, Adelaide, SA 5001, mail addr: c/o Flinders University of South Australia, GPOB 2100, Adelaide, SA 5001 - T: (08) 82012695, Fax: 82012543, E-mail: doreen.mellor@flinders.edu.au. Head: Doreen Mellor
Fine Arts Museum / University Museum - 1975
European graphics 15th c to present, 19th and 20th c Australian graphics, Contemporary graphics from developing countries and minority cultures, Aboriginal acrylic paintings and bark paintings, Koori art, Australian art (European tradition), European art, Post-Object and Documentation art, Aboriginal artefacts, Ethnographic coll from Asia, Africa and America - library 00698

Light Square Gallery, 39 Light Sq, Adelaide, SA 5000 - T: (08) 84635032, Fax: 84635001, E-mail: ygrass@adel.tafe.sa.edu.au. Head: Yasmin Grass
Public Gallery
Local artists' work 00699

Migration Museum, 82 Kintore Av, Adelaide, SA 5000 - T: (08) 82077580, Fax: 82077591, E-mail: migration@history.sa.gov.au, Internet: http://www.vianet.com.au/clients/MigrationMuseum/. Head: Viv Szekeres
Historical Museum - 1986
Hist of immigration, social hist, crafts 00700

Museum of Classical Archaeology, c/o University of Adelaide, Mitchell Bldg, North Tce, Adelaide, SA 5000 - T: (08) 83035344, E-mail: mohea@arts.adelaide.edu.au
Archaeological Museum
Artefacts from the Bronze Age to the Middle Ages, decorative pottery, terracotta, glassware, coins, bronze work, stone carving, oil lamps 00701

Museum of Exploration, Survey and Land Settlement (closed) 00702

North Adelaide School of Art Gallery → Light Square Gallery

Performing Arts Collection of South Australia, Adelaide Festival Centre, King William Rd, Adelaide, SA 5000 - T: (08) 82168769, Fax: 82127849, E-mail: jo.peoples@afct.org.au, Internet: http://www.pacsa.asn.au. Head: Jo Peoples
Performing Arts Museum - 1979
Luciana Arrighi costume designs for the opera "Death in Venice", Tanya Moiseiwitch's costumes and masks for "Oedipus" (1978), Agnes Dobson coll, Joanne Priest coll, Colin Balantyne Coll 00703

South Australian Museum, North Terrace, Adelaide, SA 5000 - T: (08) 82077500, Fax: 82077430, E-mail: museumed@www.saschools.edu.au, Internet: http://www.samuseum.sa.gov.au. Head: Prof. Tim Flannery
Ethnology Museum / Archaeological Museum / Natural History Museum / Ethnology Museum - 1856
Australian ethnology and archeology, zoology, minerals, Pacific culture, earth sciences - library, archives, information centre 00704

Union Gallery, Level 6, Union House, Adelaide University Union, Adelaide, SA 5000 - T: (08) 82285013, Fax: 82237165. Head: Paul Hewson
Fine Arts Museum - 1975
Australian art 1890s to present, mostly South Australian artists 1960s and 1970s 00705

University of South Australia Art Museum, 54 North Terrace, Adelaide, SA 5000 - T: (08) 83020870, Fax: 83020866, E-mail: Art.Museum@unisa.edu.au, Internet: http://www.unisa.edu.au/amu/index.htm. Head: Erica Green
Fine Arts Museum - 1991
SA paintings and drawings 1945 to present, SA prints, sculpture, photographs 1970 to present, SA, WA and NT Aboriginal paintings, 20th c, Australian paintings - library 00706

Zone Gallery, 80 Hindley St, Adelaide, SA 5000 - T: (08) 82314454
Public Gallery 00707

Adelaide River

Adelaide River Railway Station, Stuart Hwy, Adelaide River, NT 0846 - T: (08) 89767001
Science&Tech Museum 00708

Motorcycle Haven, Stuart Hwy, Adelaide River, NT 0846 - T: (08) 89767016
Science&Tech Museum
Motorcycles from 11 countries, 1939-1980's dirt road and competition models 00709

Airlie Beach

Heirloom Doll Museum, POB 116, Airlie Beach, Qld. 4800
Special Museum - 1970 00710

Albany

Albany Residency Museum, Residency Rd, Albany, WA 6330 - T: (08) 98414844, Fax: 98414027, E-mail: resmus@albanyis.com.au. Head: V. Milne
Local Museum - 1975
Regional natural history and specimens, pre-colonial history, aboriginals, relics of the local whaling industry, maritime history, optic from Eclipse lighthouse 00711

Cooperative Store Museum, 44 Frederick St, Albany, WA 6331 - T: (08) 98415403
Historical Museum 00712

Old Gaol Museum and Patrick Taylor Cottage Museum, Stirling Tce and Duke St, Albany, WA 6330, mail addr: POB 411, Albany, WA 6330 - T: (08) 98411401, Fax: 98415403. Head: Dr. J. Arnold
Historical Museum - 1962 00713

Vancouver Arts Centre, 85 Vancouver St, Albany, WA 6330, mail addr: POB 484, Albany, WA 6331 - T: (08) 98419260, Fax: 98419261, E-mail: vac@albany.wa.gov.au. Head: Caroline O'Neill
Fine Arts Museum / Public Gallery 00714

Whaleworld Museum, Frenchman Bay Rd, Albany, WA 6330 - T: (08) 98444021, Fax: 98444621, E-mail: whalewld@albanyis.com.au
Natural History Museum
Marine mammal paintings by Richard Ellis, Whaling relics, machinery, Whale skeleton 00715

Albion Park

Tongarra Museum, Russell St, Albion Park, NSW 2527 - T: (02) 42566698, Fax: 42562001, Internet: http://www.shellharbour.nsw.gov.au. Head: Diane Cranson
Local Museum
Local history, community culture 00716

Albury

Albury Regional Art Gallery, 546 Dean St, Albury, NSW 2640 - T: (02) 60238187, Fax: 60412482, E-mail: alburygallery@alburycity.nsw.gov.au, Internet: http://www.albury-gallery.bazar.com.au. Head: Audray M. Banfield
Fine Arts Museum - 1981
Albury City Coll, historical and contemporary photographic Coll, 16th to 20th c engravings, etchings, lithographs (Jacques Callot, Paul Signac, Raoul Dufy, Pierre Auguste Renoir, Marc Chagall), Drysdale, Dupain, Moffatt, Henson - library 00717

Albury Regional Museum, Wodonga Pl, Albury, NSW 2640 - T: (02) 60214550, Fax: 60413416, E-mail: hpithie@alburycity.nsw.gov.au, Internet: http://www.alburymuseum.nsw.gov.au. Head: Helen Pithie
Local Museum - 1967
Bonegilla - the Migrant Reception Centre coll 00718

Alexandra

Alexandra Timber Tramway and Museum, Station St, Alexandra, Vic. 3714, mail addr: POB 288, Alexandra, Vic. 3714 - T: (03) 57722392, Fax: 57721798
Open Air Museum / Science&Tech Museum
Technical, social, economic and ecological history of the timber industry in the Rubicon Forest 1900-1950 00719

Alfred Cove

Atwell House Gallery, 586 Canning Hwy, Alfred Cove, WA 6154 - T: (08) 93302800, Fax: 93309597
Public Gallery
Art and craft 00720

Alice Springs

Adelaide House Museum, Todd Mall, Alice Springs, NT 0870 - T: (08) 89521856, Fax: 89521856. Head: Lindsay Faulkner
Local Museum
Memorabilia of Revd. John Flynn DD, a set of Presbyterian Moderator General's Robes, first pedal radio built by Alfred Traeger 00721

Alice Springs RSL War Museum, Schwarz Crescent, Alice Springs, NT 0870 - T: (08) 89522868, Fax: 89534157, E-mail: rslalicesprings@octa4.net.au. Head: Michael Barrett
Military Museum
WWI, WWII air sea rescue, bombing of Darwin, Korea and Vietnam display, Peace signing in Europe and Pacific, East Timor 00722

Central Australian Aviation Museum, Stuart Terrace, Alice Springs, NT 5750 - T: (08) 89521129, Fax: 89530027
Science&Tech Museum - 1977
Aircrafts, flying doctor service items - library 00723

Museum of Central Australia, Alice Springs Cultural Precint, Larapinta Dr, Alice Springs, NT 0870 - T: (08) 89511121, Fax: 89511107, E-mail: -culturalprecinat.dam@nt.gov.au, Internet: http://www.nt.gov.au/dam. Head: Peter Murray
Natural History Museum
Natural wonders, fossils of extinct animals, minerals, meteorites, Strehlow display 00724

National Pioneer Women's Hall of Fame, Old Courthouse, 27 Hartley St, Alice Springs, NT 0870 - T: (08) 89529006, Fax: 89529406, E-mail: curator@pioneerwomen.com.au, Internet: http://www.pioneerwomen.com.au. Head: Pauline Cockrill
Historical Museum
Artefacts, photographs books, cassettes and other memorabilia related to pioneering Australian women 00725

Old Timers Traeger Museum, South Stuart Hwy, Alice Springs, NT 0871 - T: (08) 89522844, Fax: 89555225, E-mail: davidasp@ozemail.com.au
Local Museum
Cattle and camel industry, household paraphernalia, telegraphic equipment, gem and minerals, Aboriginal artefacts 00726

Spencer and Gillen Gallery, Ford Pl, Todd Mall, Alice Springs, NT 0870, mail addr: POB 2019, Alice Springs, NT 0871 - T: (08) 89527422, Fax: 89527452. Head: Dr. Peter Murray
Fine Arts Museum - 1988
Non-Aboriginal Australian art from First Settlement with emphasis on central Australia, Aboriginal art and material culture, and South-East Asian and Oceanic art and material culture 00727

Stuart Town Gaol Museum, Parsons St, Alice Springs, NT 0871 - T: (08) 89524516, Fax: 89522185, E-mail: heritage-as@octa4.net.au
Historical Museum
Local materials, history of law and order 00728

Allora

Allora Historical Museum, 27 Drayton St, Allora, Qld. 4362 - T: (07) 46663474, Fax: 46663474
Local Museum
Local and Darling Downs history 00729

Alpha

Beta Railway Station Historic Museum, Dryden St, Alpha, Qld. 4724 - T: (07) 9851213
Science&Tech Museum
Local railway establishment around 1890-1900 00730

Jane Neville-Rolfe Gallery, Dryden St, Alpha, Qld. 4724 - T: (07) 9851210
Fine Arts Museum
Art works by local artists 00731

Apollo Bay

Old Cable Station Museum, Great Ocen Rd, Apollo Bay, Vic. 3233 - T: (03) 52376505
Local Museum
Cable and shipping history, dairy and timber industries 00732

Applecross

Melville Discovery Centre, Almondbury Rd, Applecross, WA 6153 - T: (08) 93640659, Fax: 93640285, E-mail: charben@melville.wa.gov.au, Internet: http://www.melville.wa.gov.au
Local Museum
Local history 00733

Wireless Hill Telecommunications Museum, Almondbury Rd, Applecross, WA 6153, mail addr: POB 130, Applecross, WA 6953 - T: (08) 93640659, Fax: 93640285, E-mail: charben@melville.wa.gov.au, Internet: http://www.melville.wa.gov.au
Science&Tech Museum - 1979
Telecommunications equipment from the early radio to modern space exploration, bush pedal radio 00734

Ararat

Ararat Gallery, Town Hall, Vincent St, Ararat, Vic. 3377, mail addr: POB 72, Ararat, Vic. 3377 - T: (03) 53522836, Fax: 53524961, E-mail: araratag@netconnect.com.au
Fine Arts Museum - 1968
Contemporary textiles and fibre arts, costume coll 00735

Langi Morgala Museum, 48 Queen St, Ararat, Vic. 3377 - T: (03) 53523117. Head: Allan Wetton
Local Museum
Aboriginal name for 'home of yesterday', clothing and farm machinery, gold mining rush, photographs 00736

Archerfield

Australian Flying Museum, Airport, Archerfield, Qld. 4108, mail addr: POB 794, Archerfield, Qld. 4108 - T: (015) 120369, Fax: (07) 32774116
Science&Tech Museum
Lockheed Neptune Maritime Patrol aircraft, aviation memorabilia from the World War II period 00737

Ardrossan

Ardrossan Historical Museum, 9 Fifth St, Ardrossan, SA 5571 - T: (08) 88373213
Science&Tech Museum
Various types of farm machinery, original plans 00738

Armadale, Western Australia

History House, off Jull St, Armadale, Western Australia, WA 6112 - T: (08) 93996845, E-mail: curator@aiju.com.au. Head: Chantal Gurney-Pringle
Historical Museum - 1976
Items relating to early settlers in the district of Armadale-Kelmscott, local objects and photographs - library 00739

Armidale

Armidale and District Folk Museum, Corner Faulkner and Rusden Sts, Armidale, NSW 2350, mail addr: POB 75A, Armidale, NSW 2350
Folklore Museum - 1955
Domestic, social, and economic history of 19th century New England 00740

New England Regional Art Museum, Kentucky St, Armidale, NSW 2350, mail addr: POB 508, Armidale, NSW 2350 - T: (02) 67725255, 67725148, Fax: 67712397, E-mail: neram@northnet.com.au, Internet: http://www.neram.com. Head: Joseph Eisenberg
Fine Arts Museum - 1983
Howard Hinton Coll 1880-1948 Australian paintings, Chandler Coventry Coll 1960's-70's, watercolours, prints, drawings, contemp. australian art - library, audio-visual theatre 00741

Artarmon

Artarmon Galleries, 479 Pacific Hwy, Artarmon, NSW 2064 - T: (02) 94270322. Head: Philip Brackenreg
Fine Arts Museum - 1955 00742

Atherton

Hou Wang Miau, Corner of Herberton and Fong on Rd, Atherton, Qld. 4883 - T: (07) 32291788, Fax: 32290146, E-mail: nattrust@powerup.com.au
Open Air Museum / Historical Museum
Site of former Atherton Chinatown, religious furnishings and archaeological material 00743

Auburn

Police Station and Courthouse, Saint Vincent St, Auburn, SA 5451 - T: (08) 88492075, Fax: 88492228
Historical Museum 00744

Augusta

Augusta Historical Museum, POB 159, Augusta, WA 6290 - T: (08) 97581948. Head: Alan Kinson
Historical Museum - 1979
Pottery, textile, dolls, environment, personal belongings 00745

Bacchus Marsh

Blacksmith's Cottage, 100-102 Main St, Bacchus Marsh, Vic. 3340 - T: (03) 53671124
Local Museum
Blacksmith's pre-goldrush sandstone and weatherboard cottage 00746

Bairnsdale

Bairnsdale Museum, MacArthur St, Bairnsdale, Vic. 3875 - T: (03) 51526363
Local Museum
Farming machinery, a bark roof log cabin, historic domestic items, history of East Gippsland 00747

Balaklava

National Trust Museum, May Terrace, Balaklava, SA 5461 - T: (08) 88621467. Head: J. Zacher
Local Museum - 1971
Local artifacts 00748

Ballan

Ballan Shire Historical Museum, Stieglitz St, Ballan, Vic. 3342 - T: (03) 53681147
Local Museum - 1990
Local history 00749

Ballarat

Ballarat Fine Art Gallery, 40 Lydiard St N, Ballarat, Vic. 3350 - T: (03) 53205858, Fax: 53316361, E-mail: artgal@ballarat.vic.gov.au, Internet: http://www.balgal.com. Head: Margaret Rich
Fine Arts Museum - 1884
Colonial and Heidelberg School paintings, Australian

prints, watercolours, drawings 1770 to present, Medieval and Renaissance manuscripts, Oriental rugs, 19th c European paintings and decorative arts - library 00750

Eureka Museum, 111 Eureka St, Ballarat, Vic. 3350 - T: (03) 53322554, Fax: 53327400, E-mail: enquiries@eurekamuseum.com.au, Internet: http://www.eurekamuseum.com.au. Head: Laurel Johnson
Historical Museum
Weapons, tools, household pieces, irons, ironware, lighting 00751

Gold Museum, Bradshaw St, Ballarat, Vic. 3350 - T: (03) 53311944, Fax: 53329052, E-mail: goldmuseum@sovereignhill.austasia.net, Internet: http://www.sovereignhill.com.au. Head: Peter Hiscock
Local Museum / Special Museum - 1977
Local history: Paul Simon alluvial gold and gold coin coll, Ballarat Historical Society coll, postcard coll of Fitz Gerald - library 00752

Golden City Paddle Steamer Museum, Lake Wendouree, Ballarat, Vic. 3353 - T: (03) 53313100
Science&Tech Museum 00753

Old Curiosity Shop, 7 Queen St S, Ballarat, Vic. 3350 - T: (03) 53321854. Head: Barry McInerney
Decorative Arts Museum - 1855
Victorian furniture, ornaments, glassware and examples of needlework 00754

Sovereign Hill, Bradshaw St, Ballarat, Vic. 3350 - T: (03) 5311944, Fax: 5311528, E-mail: enquiries@sovereignhill.austasia.net, Internet: http://www.sovereignhill.com.au. Head: Peter Hiscock
Open Air Museum 00755

Ballina

Naval and Maritime Museum, Regatta Av, Ballina, NSW 2478 - T: (02) 66811002, Fax: 66811002
Historical Museum
Models of naval ships, sailing vessels, merchant shipping, paintings, uniforms, militaria 00756

Opal and Gem Museum, 8 Big Prawn Complex, Pacific Hwy, Ballina, NSW 2478 - T: (02) 66862559, Fax: 66866523
Decorative Arts Museum
Extensive range of opal in natural and cut slate 00757

Balwyn

Australian Freethought Heritage Library, 4 Alandale Av, Balwyn, Vic. 3103 - T: (03) 98579717, Fax: 98579466, E-mail: rayday@bigpond.net.au, Internet: http://www.vicnet.au/~humanist. Head: Ray Dahlitz
Library with Exhibitions
Book art, photographs 00758

Barcaldine

Barcaldine and District Historical Museum, Cnr Beech and Gidyea Sts, Barcaldine, Qld. 4725 - T: (07) 46512223, Fax: 46511564
Local Museum
Local history, horse-drawn transport, industry, steam machinery 00759

Barraba

Nandewar Historical Museum, 71 Queen St, Barraba, NSW 2347 - T: (02) 67821212
Local Museum
House clothing, household goods, some office equipment, machinery and tools 00760

Bass

Wildlife Wonderlands Giant Worm Museum, Bass Hwy, Bass, Vic. 3991 - T: (03) 56782222, Fax: 56782256, E-mail: giantworm@nex.net.au
Natural History Museum
Mysterious underworld, Wildlife 00761

Bassendean

Rail Transport Museum, 136 Railway Parade, Bassendean, WA 6054 - T: (08) 92797189, Fax: 93771588, E-mail: arhs_wa@yahoo.com.au, Internet: http://www.wantree.com.au/~ramjet/arhs/museum/. Head: Kim Tyler
Science&Tech Museum
Locomotives, carriages and wagons 00762

Bathurst

Bathurst and District Historical Museum, Russell St, Bathurst, NSW 2795 - T: (02) 63324755, Fax: 63325698
Local Museum
Local history 00763

Bathurst Regional Art Gallery, 70-78 Keppel St, Bathurst, NSW 2795 - T: (02) 63316066, Fax: 63325698, E-mail: brag@bathurst.nsw.gov.au. Head: Amanda Lawson
Fine Arts Museum - 1959
Australian 20th c oil, watercolours, drawings, prints, Australian ceramics 1970-present and the Lloyd Rees Coll - library 00764

Chifley Home, 10 Busby St, Bathurst, NSW 2795 - T: (02) 63321444, Fax: 63322333, E-mail: visitors@bathurst.nsw.gov.au, Internet: http://www.bathurst.nsw.gov.au
Historical Museum
Items to former Prime Minister of Australia Ben Chifley 00765

National Motor Racing Museum, Panorama Av, Mount Panorama, Bathurst, NSW 2795 - T: (02) 63321872, Fax: 63323349, E-mail: nmrm@ix.net.au
Special Museum
Motor sport history in Australia 00766

Battery Point

Narryna Heritage Museum, 103 Hampden Rd, Battery Point, Tas. 7004 - T: (03) 62342791, E-mail: aaashbolt@aol.com
Local Museum / Decorative Arts Museum
19th c furniture, china, glass, silver paintings, children's toys and domestic equipment 00767

Beachport

Aboriginal Artefacts Museum, McCourt St, Beachport, SA 5280 - T: (08) 87358029
Ethnology Museum 00768

Old Wool and Grain Store Museum, Railway Terrace, Beachport, SA 5280 - T: (08) 87358029, Fax: 87358309. Head: N. Brook
Local Museum - 1970
Whaling, Fishing, farming, relics of local wrecks, local memorabilia 00769

Beaconsfield

Grubb Shaft Gold and Heritage Museum, West St, Beaconsfield, Tas. 7270 - T: (03) 63831473, Fax: 63831540, Internet: http://www.wtc.tas.gov.au
Science&Tech Museum / Historical Museum
Relics of Tasmania's largest gold mine 1878-1914, local mineral coll, social history 00770

Beaudesert

Beaudesert Museum, 54 Brisbane St, Beaudesert, Qld. 4285 - T: (07) 55413740, 55411284, Fax: 55413740. Head: Maisie Lewis
Local Museum
Local history 00771

Beechworth

Beechworth Historic Court House, 94 Ford St, Beechworth, Vic. 3747 - T: (03) 57282721, Fax: 57282767
Historical Museum - 1991
Police, judiciary, bushrangers 00772

Burke Museum, Loch St, Beechworth, Vic. 3747 - T: (03) 57281420, Fax: 57282979, E-mail: burke_museum@indigoshire.vic.gov.au, Internet: http://www.beechworth.com/burkemus/. Head: Anna Robbins
Local Museum
Goldmining and life on the goldfields, Chinese, Aboriginal coll, natural history 00773

Carriage and Harness Museum, 29 Last St, Beechworth, Vic. 3747, mail addr: POB 288, Beechworth, Vic. 3747 - T: (03) 57281304, Fax: 57281957
Science&Tech Museum - 1969
Carriages ranging from 1875-1910, preserved locally made hearse, passenger drag, Cobb & Co. Coach 00774

Powder Magazine, Gorge Reserve, Beechworth, Vic. 3747, mail addr: POB 288, Beechworth, Vic. 3747 - T: (03) 57281370
Historical Museum - 1965
Completely restored magazine used for storing explosives during the gold rush (built 1859) 00775

Rockcavern, Ford St, Beechworth, Vic. 3747 - T: (03) 57281374. Head: Piers Foa, Robyn Foa
Natural History Museum - 1971
African stone carvings, fluorescent minerals 00776

Beenleigh

Beenleigh and District Museum, 189-199 Main St, Beenleigh, Qld. 4207 - T: (07) 33820608, Internet: http://home.quicknet.co.au/eastwind/historic
Local Museum
Local history, machinery, tools, household items, photographies 00777

Pioneer Rum Museum, Distillery Rd, Beenleigh, Qld. 4207 - T: (07) 38072307, Fax: 38072516
Science&Tech Museum
Oldest registered distillery in Australia 00778

Bega

Bega Valley Regional Art Gallery, Zingel Pl, Bega, NSW 2550, mail addr: POB 319, Bega, NSW 2550 - T: (02) 64992187, 64929487, Fax: 64992200, 64923323
Fine Arts Museum - 1988
Bega Valley Art and Craft Society's permanent coll including watercolours, paintings, pastels, drawings, prints 00779

Belair

Old Government House, Upper Sturt Rd, Belair, SA 5052 - T: (08) 82785477, Fax: 82788587, Internet: http://www.belair.sa.gov.au
Historical Museum 00780

Belmont

City of Belmont Museum, 61 Elizabeth St, Belmont, WA 6104 - T: (08) 92774879. Head: Peg Parkin
Local Museum
Local history 00781

Benalla

Benalla Costume and Pioneer Museum, 14 Mair St, Benalla, Vic. 3672 - T: (03) 57621749, Fax: 57621934, E-mail: benallamuseum@maxilink.com, Internet: http://www.maxilink.com/benallamuseum
Local Museum - 1967
Local history, Ned Kelly, costume 1770's to 1900's 00782

Benalla Regional Art Gallery, By the Lake, Bridge St, Benalla, Vic. 3672, mail addr: POB 108, Benalla, Vic. 3672 - T: (03) 57623027, Fax: 57625640, E-mail: benalla_art_gallery@dsc.mav.asn.au. Head: Simon Klose
Fine Arts Museum - 1968
19th and 20th c oil paintings and works on paper, Post-1965 art - library, gallery shop 00783

Bendigo

Bendigo Art Gallery, 42 View St, Bendigo, Vic. 3550 - T: (03) 54434991, Fax: 54436586, E-mail: bendigoartgallery@bendigo.vic.gov.au. Head: Karen Quinlan
Public Gallery - 1887
Extensive coll of paintings, furniture, works on paper, sculpture and decorative arts, European art of the 19th c incl. examples from the Romantic period, the Barbizon school and French Impressionism, Australian art from the 1800s onwards feat. the Colonial period, the Heidelberg School, Modernism and contemporary art 00784

Golden Dragon Museum, 5-11 Bridge St, Bendigo, Vic. 3550 - T: (03) 54415044, Fax: 54433127, E-mail: gdmb@netcon.net.au, Internet: http://users.netcon.net.au/gdmb. Head: Jack Russel
Ethnology Museum / Folklore Museum
History of Chinese people of Bendigo (1850's to the present) 00785

Tramway Museum, 1 Tramways Av, Bendigo, Vic. 3550 - T: (03) 54438322, Fax: 54438341, E-mail: bendigo.tram@impulse.net.au, Internet: http://www.bendigotramways.com. Head: Tim Borchers
Science&Tech Museum 00786

Bentley

Erica Underwood Gallery, c/o Curtin University of Technology, Kent St, Bentley, WA 6102 - T: (08) 93517347, Fax: 93512711. Head: Lisa Green
Fine Arts Museum / University Museum - 1968
Contemporary WA ceramics, fibre textiles, paintings, prints, sculpture, jewellery 00787

Berrima

Berrima District Museum, Market St, Berrima, NSW 2577 - T: (02) 48612072
Local Museum - 1991
Local history 00788

Berry

Berry Museum, 135 Queen St, Berry, NSW 2535 - T: (02) 44643097, E-mail: berrymuseum@virtualcity.com.au, Internet: http://www.berryhistory.org.au. Head: Dallas Rogers
Historical Museum
Local history, agriculture, dairying 00789

Beverley

Avondale Discovery Farm, Waterhatch Rd, Beverley, WA 6304 - T: (08) 96461004, Fax: 96461002, E-mail: dbarret@agric.wa.gov.au, Internet: http://www.beverleywa.com/avondale
Agriculture Museum
Social hist, Agricultural past, animal nursay, landcare farm drive trail, fifteen working tractors, clydesdale horses 00790

Biggenden

Biggenden Museum, Biggenden, Qld. 4621 - T: (07) 41271881
Local Museum
Local History, gold mining 00791

Binalong

Binalong Motor Museum, Oliver St, Binalong, NSW 2584 - T: (02) 62274406, Fax: 62824372
Science&Tech Museum
Assembly of cars driven over for the day, 1927 GP Bugatti, 1924 Tourer Bugatti, 1908 Chain drive aero-engined MAB, 1992 Norton FI Motorcycle, Ducati Motorcycle, 1961 Supercharged Jaguar Special 00792

Bingara

Bingara Museum, 16 Maitland St, Bingara, NSW 2404 - T: (02) 67241726
Local Museum
Local history, photo and gem-rock colls 00793

Birchip

Birchip Local History Museum, 2 Cumming Av, Birchip, Vic. 3483 - T: (03) 54922691. Head: Maureen Donnellon
Local Museum
Domestic and agricultural artefacts, war memorial room, photos, microfilms 00794

Birdsville

Birdsville Working Museum, Waddie Dr, Birdsville, Qld. 4482 - T: (07) 6563259
Local Museum
Roadside relics, tools, old shop, dairy, washing and ironing, household goods, old hospital, pottery, jewellery and toys 00795

Birdwood

National Motor Museum, Shannon St, Birdwood, SA 5234 - T: (08) 85685006, Fax: 85685195, E-mail: frontdesk@motormuseum.sa.gov.au, Internet: http://www.motormuseum.sa.gov.au
Science&Tech Museum 00796

Blackall

Historical Woolscour Blackall, Evora Rd, Blackall, Qld. 4472 - T: (07) 46574637, Fax: 46574637, E-mail: bhwa@b190.aone.net.au. Head: Kaye Wood
Historical Museum / Science&Tech Museum
Wool washing complex (steam driven) 00797

Blackburn

Australian Institute of Genealogical Studies, 41 Railway Rd, Ste 1, Blackburn, Vic. 3130 - T: (03) 98773789, Fax: 98779066
Historical Museum - 1973
Genealogy, heraldry, family history and allied subjects throughout Australia - archives 00798

Blackstone

Queensland Pioneer Steam Railway, Patrick St, Blackstone, Qld. 4305 - T: (07) 32889552
Science&Tech Museum
Railway memorabilia 00799

Blakehurst

Carss Cottage Museum, Carwar Av, Carss Park, Blakehurst, NSW 2221 - T: (02) 95467314
Local Museum
Australian history, particularly that of the Kogarah municipality 00800

Boolarra

Boolarra Historical Museum, Cnr Irving and Tarwin Sts, Boolarra, Vic. 3870 - T: (03) 51696210
Local Museum
Photographs from the 1880s onwards, local maps, school material, cemetery records, family albums 00801

Booleroo

Booleroo Steam and Traction Museum, Booleroo Centre, Booleroo, SA 5482, mail addr: POB 52, Booleroo, SA 5482 - T: (08) 86655032
Science&Tech Museum
Early steam power pastoral industry of South Australia, tractors 00802

Boonah

Templin Historical Village, Fassifern, Boonah, Qld. 4310, mail addr: POB 56, Boonah, Qld. 4310 - T: (07) 54631970, E-mail: templinvillage@hotmail.com, Internet: http://www.boonahservices.net.au
Open Air Museum / Folklore Museum - 1977
Crafts, books, costumes 00803

Booragul

Lake Macquarie City Art Gallery, 1a First St, Booragul, NSW 2310 - T: (02) 49210382, Fax: 49658733, E-mail: artgallery@lakemac.nsw.gov.au, Internet: http://www.lakemac.nsw.gov.au. Head: Debbie Abraham
Fine Arts Museum - 1980
20th c contemporary Australian paintings and drawings - The Water Coll, Ronaldo Cameron coll, Hunter Valley photographies 00804

Bordertown

Hawke House, Farquhar St, Bordertown, SA 5268 - T: (08) 87522569
Historical Museum
Former Prime Minister Mr Bob Hawke 00805

Mundulla National Trust Museum, 81 Macleod St, Bordertown, SA 5268 - T: (08) 87521717. Head: J.C. Guy
Local Museum 00806

Borroloola

Old Borroloola Police Station Museum, off Robinson Rd, Borroloola, NT 0854 - T: (08) 89759762, Fax: 89759761
Historical Museum
Oldest surviving outpost police station in the Northern Territory 00807

Bothwell

Thorpe Water Mill, Bothwell, Tas. 7411
Science&Tech Museum 00808

Boulia

Boulia Stone House Museum, Boulia, Qld. 4829 - T: (07) 47463386, Fax: 47463387. Head: Dick Suter
Local Museum
Local historical items, fossils, geology 00809

Bowen Hills

Miegunyah Pioneer Women's Memorial House Museum, 35 Jordan Tce, Bowen Hills, Qld. 4006 - T: (07) 32522979, Fax: 32574235. Head: Gloria Tehan
Local Museum / Ethnology Museum
Role of pioneer women in the development of the State 00810

Bowral

Berrima District Art Gallery, 1 Short St, Bowral, NSW 2576 - T: (02) 48614093
Public Gallery - 1994 00811

Bowraville

Bowraville Folk Museum, 84 High St, Bowraville, NSW 2449 - T: (02) 65648200, E-mail: withco@midcoast.com.au, Internet: http://www.holiday-coast.net.au/bowraville
Folklore Museum
Local history, crafts, drawings, furniture, minerals military, machinery 00812

Frank Partridge V.C. Military Museum, 29a High St, Bowraville, NSW 2449 - T: (02) 65647339, 65647056, E-mail: withco@midcoast.com.au, Internet: http://www.holidaycoast.net.au/bowraville
Military Museum
Military history 00813

Boyanup

Museum of Transportation and Rural Industries, Turner St, Boyanup, WA 6237 - T: (08) 97315250, Fax: 97315250
Science&Tech Museum
Vintage railway carriages and wagons, vintage and classic cars, restored farm machinery, a blacksmith shop, railway equipment 00814

Boyup Brook

Carnaby Collection of Beetles and Butterflies, Cnr Bridge and Abel Sts, Boyup Brook, WA 6244 - T: (08) 97651444, Fax: 97651444, E-mail: bbvisitor@wn.com.au, Internet: http://www.promaco.com.au/boyup. Head: Noreen Tuckett
Natural History Museum 00815

Braddon

Canberra Contemporary Art Space, Ainslie Av, Braddon, ACT 2612 - T: (02) 62470188, Fax: 62477357, E-mail: ccas@cyberone.com.au, Internet: http://www.ccas.com.au. Head: Jane Barney
Fine Arts Museum - 1987
Contemporary art 00816

Churchill House, National Museum of Australia, 218 Northbourne Av, Braddon ACT 2612 - T: (02) 62085000, Fax: 62085139. Head: Dr. Katy Gillette
Historical Museum 00817

Gorman House Arts Centre, Ainslie Av, Braddon, ACT 2612 - T: (02) 62497377, E-mail: thedirector@gormanhouse.org.au, Internet: http://www.gormanhouse.org.au
Public Gallery 00818

Mining Industry House, National Museum of Australia, 216 Northbourne Av, Braddon ACT 2612 - T: (02) 62085300, Fax: 62085099. Head: Dawn Casey
Fine Arts Museum
Aboriginal art 00819

Braidwood

Braidwood Museum, 186 Wallace St, Braidwood, NSW 2622 - T: (02) 48422310, E-mail: history@braidwood.net.au
Local Museum
Local and regional history, machinery shed, rural items 00820

Brewarrina

Brewarrina Aboriginal Cultural Museum, Cnr Bathurst and Darling Sts, Brewarrina, NSW 2839 - T: (02) 68392868, Fax: 68392850
Local Museum / Folklore Museum
Aboriginal fisheries, culture and life in Brewarrina, works of art 00821

Settlers Museum, Court House, Bathurst St, Brewarrina, NSW 2839 - T: (02) 68744940, Fax: 68744940
Local Museum / Folklore Museum
Local history 00822

Bribie Island

Bribie Island Community Arts Centre, Sunderland Dr, Banksia Beach, Bribie Island, Qld. 4507 - T: (07) 34089288, Fax: 34087900
Fine Arts Museum / Decorative Arts Museum
Artworks, contemporary arts and crafts, incl pottery, porcelain, painting, glass, wood turning, leatherwork 00823

Bridgetown

Bridgetown Old Gaol Museum, Hampton St, Bridgetown, WA 6255 - T: (08) 97611740, E-mail: tourist@mns.net.au
Historical Museum / Local Museum
archive 00824

Brierly Jigsaw Gallery, 154 Hampton St, Bridgetown, WA 6255 - T: (08) 97611740, Fax: 97611105
Fine Arts Museum / Special Museum - 1979
120 completed and framed jigsaws 00825

Brisbane

Anthropology Museum, c/o Dept. of Anthropology and Sociology, University of Queensland, Michie Bldg, Santa Lucia Campus, Brisbane, Qld. 4067 - T: (07) 33652674, E-mail: asmuseum@mailbox.uq.edu.au, Internet: http://www.uq.edu.au/about/campus-life/things-to-do/m-anthropology.html
Ethnology Museum
Culture, arts and crafts of the indigenous people of Oceania 00826

Brisbane City Gallery, City Hall, King George Sq, Brisbane, Qld. 4000, mail addr: GPOB 1434, Brisbane, Qld. 4001 - T: (07) 34034355, Fax: 34035325, E-mail: dbcg@brisbane.qld.com.au, Internet: http://www.brisbane.qld.gov.au. Head: Frank MacBride
Fine Arts Museum - 1977
Paintings, prints, drawings, ceramics, photographs, memorabilia reflecting Brisbane's history and development 1859 to present - library 00827

Metro Arts, 109 Edward St, Brisbane, Qld. 4000 - T: (07) 32211527, Fax: 32214375, E-mail: info@metroarts.com.au, Internet: http://www.metroarts.com.au. Head: Sue Benner
Public Gallery
Visual art, contemporary art and craft 00828

Museum of the Royal Historical Society of Queensland, 115 William St, Brisbane, Qld. 4002 - T: (07) 32214198, Fax: 32214198
Historical Museum
Colonial Queensland artefacts 00829

Old Government House, 2 George St, Brisbane, Qld. 4001 - T: (07) 32291788, Fax: 32290146
Historical Museum 00830

Physics Museum, c/o University of Queensland, Physics Department, Parnell Bldg, Santa Lucia Campus, Brisbane, Qld. 4067 - T: (07) 33653369, Fax: 33651242, E-mail: heckenberg@physics.uq.edu.au, Internet: http://www.physics.uq.edu.au/physics_museum/. Head: Dr. Norman Heckenberg
Science&Tech Museum / University Museum
Scientific instruments 00831

Queensland Air Museum, Caloundra Aerodrome, Brisbane, Qld. 4001 - T: (07) 54925930, Fax: 54925930, Internet: http://www.powerup.com.au/~qam. Head: Alan Graham
Science&Tech Museum - 1974
Aviation exhibits 00832

Queensland Police Museum, 200 Roma St, Brisbane, Qld. 4000 - T: (07) 33646425, Fax: 32360954, E-mail: JonesLisaA@police.qld.gov.au, Internet: http://www.brisbaneli-vingheritage.org/02_locations_museum/02_a_police-museum.htm. Head: Lisa Jones
Historical Museum
Police station histories and police personnel information 00833

Queensland Sciencentre, 110 George St, Brisbane, Qld. 4000 - T: (07) 32200166, Fax: 32200113, E-mail: info@sciencentre.qld.gov.au, Internet: http://www.sciencentre.qld.gov.au. Head: Dr. Graeme Potter
Science&Tech Museum
Interactive exhibits, non-formal learning programs 00834

University of Queensland Art Museum, c/o University of Queensland, Santa Lucia Campus, Brisbane, Qld. 4067 - T: (07) 33653046, Fax: 33659004, E-mail: artmuseum@mailbox.uq.edu.au. Head: Ross Searle
Fine Arts Museum / University Museum - 1973
Australian paintings, prints, drawings, sculpture 1780 to present 00835

Zoology Museum, c/o Dept. of Zoology, University of Queensland, Santa Lucia Campus, Brisbane, Qld. 4067 - T: (07) 33652474, Fax: 33651655
Natural History Museum / University Museum - 1911
Coll of vertebrate and invertebrate animals 00836

Broken Hill

Albert Kersten GeoCentre, Cnr Bromide and Crystal Sts, Broken Hill, NSW 2880 - T: (08) 80876538, Fax: 80876538, E-mail: geocentr@pcpro.net.au, Internet: http://www.pcpro.net.au/~geocentre
Natural History Museum
Mineralogy, metallurgy and geological times 00837

Broken Hill City Art Gallery, Corner Blende and Chloride St, Broken Hill, NSW 2880, mail addr: POB 448, Broken Hill, NSW 2880 - T: (08) 80885491, Fax: 80871411, E-mail: bhartgal@pcpro.net.au. Head: Gary Corbett
Fine Arts Museum - 1904
Extensive print and watercolour coll, Australian photographs, paintings, Aboriginal art, contemporary art - library 00838

Sulphide Street Station Railway and Historical Museum, Blende St, Broken Hill, NSW 2880 - T: (08) 80884660. Head: R. Carter
Science&Tech Museum
Steam and diesel locomotives, passenger coaches, machinery 00839

Brompton

Sagasco Historical Group Museum, Gas Works, Chief St, Brompton, SA 5007 - T: (08) 82175819, Fax: 82175855, E-mail: alan.miller@originenergy.com.au. Head: Alan Miller
Science&Tech Museum - 1978
Gas industry objects and data - South Australian Gas Company facilities 00840

Brooklyn Park

Wayville Latvian Museum, 29 Airport Rd, Brooklyn Park, SA 5032 - T: (08) 83522396. Head: M. Biezaitis
Historical Museum 00841

West Torrens Railway, Aviation and Signal Telegraph Museum, 112 Marion Rd, Brooklyn Park, SA 5032 - T: (08) 82345304, Internet: http://www.tne.net.au/wil/cahssa.html
Science&Tech Museum
Public transport 00842

Brookton

Old Police Station Museum Brookton, Robinson Rd, Brookton, WA 6306 - E-mail: jolu@wn.com.au. Head: Jan Eva
Historical Museum - 1986
Western Australian police memorabilia, local history 00843

Broome

Broome Historical Society Museum, Cnr Hamersley and Robinson Sts, Broome, WA 6725 - T: (08) 91922075, Fax: 91923597, E-mail: broomemuseum@winmail.com.au. Head: Val Burton
Local Museum
Town development, pearling and cattle industries, local government 00844

Broomehill

Broomehill Museum, Broomehill, WA 6318 - T: (08) 98241283
Local Museum
Local history, Agriculture 00845

Brooweena

Woocoo Museum, Smith Crescent, Brooweena, Qld. 4620 - T: (07) 41299235
Local Museum
Life, school, recreation, music and gracious living, machinery and horse-drawn vehicles 00846

Bruny Island

Bligh Museum of Pacific Exploration, 876 Main Rd, Adventure Bay, Bruny Island, Tas. 7150 - T: (03) 62931117, Fax: 62255295, E-mail: jontan@southcom.com.au, Internet: http://www.southcom.com.au/~jontan/index.html. Head: John Hamilton
Historical Museum - 1954
Exploration of the South Pacific, material on James Cook, William Bligh, Abdel Janszoon Tasman, Matthew Flinders, Tobias Furneaux - library 00847

Buderim

Buderim Pioneer Cottage, 5 Ballinger Crescent, Buderim, Qld. 4556 - T: (07) 54458005, Fax: 54458005, E-mail: jondos@ozemail.com.au, Internet: http://sites.archivenet.gov.au/bhsinc. Head: Oliver Close
Local Museum
Pioneer John Kerle Burnett, coll of household and personal items 00848

Bull Creek

Aviation Heritage Museum of Western Australia, RAAF Association, Air Force Memorial Estate, Bull Creek Dr, Bull Creek, WA 6149 - T: (08) 93114470, Fax: 933114455, E-mail: alclarke@raafawa.org.au, Internet: http://www.raafawa.org.au. Head: A.H. Clarke
Science&Tech Museum - 1979
60 aero engines, 31 aircraft, some extremely rare, relics and photos depicting the development of aviation - library, photographic library, archives 00849

Bulleen

Heide Museum of Modern Art, 7 Templestowe Rd, Bulleen, Vic. 3105 - T: (03) 98501500, Fax: 98520154, E-mail: moma@heide.com.au
Fine Arts Museum
Australian modern art from the 1930s to present 00850

Bunbury

Bunbury Regional Art Galleries, 64 Wittenoom St, Bunbury, WA 6230 - T: (08) 97218616, Fax: 97217423, E-mail: mail@brag.org.au, Internet: http://www.brag.org.au. Head: James Davies
Public Gallery - 1987
20th c Australian oil paintings, watercolours, drawings 00851

Bundaberg

Bundaberg Arts Centre, 1 Baroun St, Bundaberg, Qld. 4670, mail addr: POB 966, Bundaberg, Qld. 4670 - T: (07) 41523700, Fax: 41512725. Head: Joan G. Winter
Fine Arts Museum - 1996
Bundaberg City Art Coll 00852

Bundaberg Historical Museum, 6 Mount Perry Rd, Bundaberg, Qld. 4670 - T: (07) 41520101, Fax: 41520004
Local Museum
History of Bundaberg and district, agriculture, industry, commerce, home life, recreation and hobbies 00853

Bundaberg Railway Museum, 28 Station St, North Bundaberg, Bundaberg, Qld. 4670 - T: (07) 41521267. Head: Graham Cossart
Science&Tech Museum
Historical railway artefacts, buildings, rolling stock, plans and photographs 00854

Burnie

Burnie Regional Art Gallery, Civic Centre, Wilmot St, Burnie, Tas. 7320, mail addr: POB 973, Burnie, Tas. 7320 - T: (03) 64315918, Fax: 64314114, E-mail: gallery@burnie.net, Internet: http://www.burnie.net/artgallery. Head: Hugh J. Hassard
Fine Arts Museum - 1978
Contemporary Australian prints, drawings, watercolours, small but growing international coll 00855

Pioneer Village Museum, Little Alexander St, Burnie, Tas. 7320 - T: (03) 64305746, Fax: 64346123, E-mail: museum@burnie.net. Head: Patricia Boxhall
Local Museum 00856

Burra

Burra Mine Open Air Museum, Burra Mine Site, Burra, SA 5417, mail addr: 2 Market Sq, Burra, SA 5417 - T: (08) 88922154, Fax: 88922555, E-mail: bvc@capri.net.au, Internet: http://www.weblogic.com.au/burra
Open Air Museum / Science&Tech Museum - 1986
Mining relics, monster Burra Burra of this 'Monster mine' 00857

Morphett's Enginehouse Museum, Burra Mine Site, Burra, SA 5417 - T: (08) 88922154, Fax: 88922555, E-mail: bvc@capri.net.au, Internet: http://www.weblogic.com.au/burra
Science&Tech Museum 00858

Busselton

Wonnerup House and Old School, Layman Rd, Busselton, WA 6280 - T: (08) 97522039
Folklore Museum
Rural life in Western Australia 00859

Byfield

Byfield and District Museum, MS 142 Rasberry Creek, Byfield, Qld. 4703 - T: (07) 9351169, Fax: 9351169, E-mail: mobrien@opennet.net.au
Local Museum
Local history, Shoalwater Bay Military area 00860

Bylands

Victoria's Tramway Museum, 330 Union Ln, Bylands, Vic. 3762 - T: (03) 97986035, Fax: 97986035, E-mail: tmsv@optoshome.com.au, Internet: http://www.ozvisits.com. Head: G. Jordon
Science&Tech Museum - 1963
Horse, cable and electric tramcars, ancillary tramway vehicles, photographs, tickets, uniforms, tramway equipment, ride the 1km electric tramway 00861

Caboolture

Abbey Museum of Art and Archaeology, The Abbey Pl, Caboolture, Qld. 4510 - T: (07) 54951652, Fax: 54990081, E-mail: abbeymuseum@theforum.com.au, Internet: http://www.abbeymuseum.asn.au. Head: Michael Strong

Religious Arts Museum / Archaeological Museum
History of humankind over the last 500,000 years,
works of art, ceramics, glass, metalwork, textiles,
sculpture and paper   00862

Carboolture Historical Village and Museum,
Beerburrum Rd, Caboolture, Qld. 4510 - T: (07)
54954581, Fax: 54958746, E-mail: chv@
hotkey.net.au, Internet: http://www.historical-
village.com.au. Head: John Fenton
Local Museum
Displays of yesteryear, restored machinery, pioneer
life and buildings   00863

Cairns

Ben Cropp's Shipwreck Museum, Pier Marketpl,
Cairns, Qld. 4870 - T: (07) 40310102,
Fax: 40521197
Special Museum
Historic shipwreck relics form many ships, incl.
'Pandora', Cook's 'Endeavour'   00864

Cairns Museum, Shields St, Cairns, Qld. 4870 -
T: (07) 40515582, Fax: 40515586, Internet: http://
www.ozemail.com.au/~jsim
Local Museum
European, Aboriginal and Chinese artefacts, history
of Cairns   00865

Cairns Regional Gallery, Cnr Abbot and Shields Sts,
Cairns, Qld. 4870 - T: (07) 40316865,
Fax: 40316067, E-mail: info@cairnsregional-
gallery.com.au, Internet: http://www.cairnsregional-
gallery.com.au. Head: Louise Doyle
Fine Arts Museum
Art and culture, Australian and international
artworks   00866

Camberwell, Victoria

Organ Historical Trust of Australia, POB 200,
Camberwell, Victoria, Vic. 3124 - Internet: http://
www.vicnet.net.au/~ohta/
Music Museum
Historic organs and organ building records   00867

Camden

Camden Historical Museum, 40 John St, Camden,
NSW 2570 - T: (02) 465593400,
E-mail: camdenmuseum@yahoo.com. Head: Peter
Hayward
Local Museum - 1970
Social history of Camden   00868

Campbell

Australian War Memorial, Treloar Crescent, Ancac
Parade, Campbell, ACT 2601, mail addr: POB 345,
Canberra, ACT 2601 - T: (02) 62434211,
Fax: 62434325, E-mail: marketing@awm.gov.au,
Internet: http://www.awm.gov.au. Head: Steve
Grower
Military Museum - 1941
Military weapons and equipment, uniforms,
decorations and medals, paintings, drawings and
sculptures relating to both World Wars and to other
conflicts from the Sudan to Vietnam - library,
technology centre   00869

Campbelltown

Campbelltown City Bicentennial Art Gallery, Art
Gallery Rd, Campbelltown, NSW 2560 - T: (02)
46454333, Fax: 46454385, E-mail: art.gallery@
compbelltown.nsw.gov.au, Internet: http://
www.mycommunity.com.au/compbelltown. Head:
Michael Hedger
Fine Arts Museum - 1988
20th c Australian paintings, works on paper,
ceramics, sculpture, Aboriginal and Torres Strait
Islander art, Baycroft-Holt coll of contemporary
Scottish art - sculpture garden   00870

Camperdown

Camperdown and District Museum, 241 Manifold
St, Camperdown, Vic. 3260 - T: (03) 55931883
Local Museum
Coll of early photographs, maps, collectables,
historic documents   00871

H. B. Lamb Early Transport Buggy Museum, 26
Ower St, Camperdown, Vic. 3260 - T: (03)
55931119
Science&Tech Museum
Carriages, buggies and wagons, historic flour
mill   00872

The Museum of Nursing, c/o Royal Prince Alfred
Hospital, Missenden Rd, Camperdown, NSW 2050 -
T: (02) 95153009, E-mail: crollwilson@
bigpond.com. Head: Helen Croll
Historical Museum
Nurses and nursing, registers of all nurses at the
hospital, letter by Florence Nightingale   00873

Canberra

Canberra Museum and Gallery, Cnr London Circuit
and Civic Sq, Canberra, ACT 2608, mail addr: POB
939, Canberra, ACT 2608 - T: (02) 62073968,
Fax: 62072177, E-mail: jane.carter@act.gov.au,
Internet: http://www.arts.act.gov.au/cmag
Local Museum / Fine Arts Museum - 1996
Visual arts and social history of Canberra and
region, local history   00874

National Gallery of Australia, Parkes Pl, Canberra,
ACT 2601 - T: (02) 62406400, Fax: 62406426,
E-mail: marylou.lyon@nga.gov.au, Internet: http://
www.nga.gov.au. Head: Dr. Brian Kennedy
Fine Arts Museum / Public Gallery - 1982
Painting, sculpture, glass, pottery, textiles, books,
drawings, prints, multi-media, decorative
arts   00875

National Museum of Australia, Lawson Crescent,
Canberra, ACT 2600, mail addr: POB 1901,
Canberra, ACT 2601 - T: (02) 62085000,
Fax: 62085099, E-mail: information@nma.gov.au,
Internet: http://www.nma.gov.au. Head: Dawn
Casey
Historical Museum / Ethnology Museum - 1980
Aboriginal and Torres Strait Islander history,
Australian social history, enviromental
history   00876

Parliament House Art Collection, Parliament House,
Canberra, ACT 2600 - T: (02) 62775123,
Fax: 62773905
Fine Arts Museum
Contemporary art by Australian artists   00877

Cannington

Woodloes Homestead Folk Museum, 39 Woodloes
St, Cannington, WA 6107, mail addr: POB 606,
Cannington, WA 6107 - T: (08) 94518538. Head:
John Parker
Folklore Museum - 1978
Local Australian History exhibits and
memorabilia   00878

Captains Flat

Yesteryear Museum, 45 Blatchford St, Captains Flat,
NSW 2623 - T: (02) 62366295, Fax: 62366233
Local Museum
Bottles, calligraphy items, farm, mechanic and
carpentry tools, gemstones and minerals, Harley
Davidsons, knives, locks and keys, militaria, mining
equipment, motorcycles, pre-1960 household items,
petrolania, saddlery, swords, telephones,
typewriters   00879

Carcoar

Carcoar Historic Village, Carcoar, NSW 2791 -
T: (02) 63673154, Fax: 63673154
Historical Museum / Open Air Museum
Local artefacts coll of horse-drawn vehicles, local
family history research   00880

Carlton

Held Joan Museum, 113 Cardigan Rd, Carlton, Vic.
3053 - T: (03) 93492232
Special Museum   00881

Italian Historical Museum, 185 Faraday St, Carlton,
Vic. 3053 - T: (03) 93491063, Fax: 93470001
Historical Museum
History and heritage of Australians of Italian
origin   00882

Melbourne Museum, Carlton Gardens, Rathdowne St,
Carlton, Vic. 3053 - T: (03) 83417777,
Fax: 83417778, E-mail: webmaster@
museum.vic.gov.au, Internet: http://melbourne.mu-
seum.vic.gov.au. Head: James Dexter
Local Museum / Historical Museum - 2000
'Largest museum in the southern hemishere' with
Aboriginal Centre (Bunjilaka), children's museum,
forest gallery, human mind and body, science,
technology, environment   00883

Museum Victoria, Melbourne Museum, Carlton
Gardens, Rathdowne St, Carlton, Vic. 3053 - T: (03)
83417777, Fax: 83417778, E-mail: webmaster@
museum.vic.gov.au, Internet: http://melbourne.mu-
seum.vic.gov.au. Head: Harold Mitchell
Historical Museum / Science&Tech Museum /
Natural History Museum - 1854/1870
Natural science, indigenous cultures, social hist,
science, technology, Australian Aboriginal coll, Pru
Acton costumes, engineering, transportation,
communication, agriculture, electronics,
numismatics, arms, children's folklore, immigration,
working lives - Royal Exhibtion Building   00884

Tracy Maund Historical Collection, 132 Grattan St,
Carlton, Vic. 3053 - T: (03) 93442032,
Fax: 93481840
Historical Museum
Divers coll of the Royal Women's Hospital   00885

Carnarvon

Lighthouse Keepers Cottage, 2 Annear Pl,
Carnarvon, WA 6701 - T: (08) 99414309,
Fax: 99414309, E-mail: carnarvonheritage@
wn.com.au, Internet: http://www.wn.com.au/
carnarvonheritage. Head: Fred Heofler
Local Museum
Maritime, army, display, camel days, old
lighthouse   00886

Castlemaine

Castlemaine Art Gallery and Historical Museum,
Lyttleton St, Castlemaine, Vic. 3450 - T: (03)
54722292. Head: Peter Perry
Fine Arts Museum / Historical Museum - 1913
Australian Paintings, prints and drawings, records
and documents, photographs and articles
concerning the district   00887

Catherine Fields

Gledswood Farm Museum and Homestead, 900
Camden Valley Way, Catherine Fields, NSW 2567 -
T: (02) 96065111, Fax: 96065897, E-mail: info@
gledswood.com.au, Internet: http://
www.gledswood.com.au. Head: Theresa Testoni,
Marcus Testoni
Agriculture Museum / Historic Site   00888

Caulfield

Australian Racing Museum, Station St, Caulfield,
Vic. 3162, mail addr: POB 231, Caulfield, Vic. 3145 -
T: (03) 92577279, Fax: 95610294,
E-mail: racingmuseum@vatc.net.au,
Internet: http://www.racingmuseum.com.au. Head:
Annette Shiell
Special Museum - 1974
Horse racing   00889

Glen Eira City Gallery, Corner Glen Eira and
Hawthorn Rds, Caulfield, Vic. 3162, mail addr: POB
42, Caulfield, Vic. 3162 - T: (03) 95243214,
Fax: 95243399, E-mail: dohalloran@
gleneira.vic.gov.au, Internet: http://
www.citysearch.com.au/mel/gleneiraarts
Public Gallery - 1975
20th c Australian oil paintings, drawings, prints,
ceramics, textiles, sculpture   00890

Cessnock

Endeavour Museum, Maitland Rd, Wollombi,
Cessnock, NSW 2325 - T: (02) 49374927
Local Museum
Farming, mining, household items   00891

Charlesville

Charleville Historic House Museum, Alfred St,
Charlesville, Qld. 4470 - T: (07) 6543110
Local Museum
Old vintage vehicles, household furniture, domestic
artefacts   00892

Charters Towers

Zara Clarke Folk Museum, 36 Mosman St, Charters
Towers, Qld. 4820 - T: (07) 47874161
Folklore Museum   00893

Chelsea

Chelsea Court House Museum, The Strand, Chelsea,
Vic. 3196, mail addr: POB 377, Chelsea, Vic. 3196 -
T: (03) 97721897
Historical Museum
Original Woodwork and furnishings, local
government   00894

Cheltenham

Moorabbin Air Museum, Morrabbin Airport,
Cheltenham, Vic. 3192 - T: (03) 95807752,
Internet: http://www.netspace.net.au/~gridleys/
mam/
Military Museum / Science&Tech Museum
Civil and military aircraft   00895

Childers

Childers Pharmaceutical Museum, 90 Churchill St,
Childers, Qld. 4660 - T: (07) 1261994,
Fax: 1261604
Historical Museum   00896

Isis District Historical Complex, Taylor St, Childers,
Qld. 4660
Local Museum
Aboriginal artefacts, agriculture   00897

Chillagoe

Chillagoe Historical Centre, Hill St, Chillagoe, Qld.
4871 - T: (07) 40947109, Fax: 40947213
Local Museum
Local history, Aboriginal and New Guinea
artefacts   00898

Chiltern

Chiltern Athenaeum, 57 Conness St, Chiltern, Vic.
3683 - T: (03) 57261467, 567261280. Head: Rex
Fuge
Local Museum   00899

Chiltern Motor Museum, 13-17 Conness St, Chiltern,
Vic. 3683 - T: (02) 60267382
Science&Tech Museum
Automobilia, petrol pumps, signs, bottles and racks,
auto cycles, oil engines, tins   00900

Grapevine Museum, Cnr Conness and Main Sts,
Chiltern, Vic. 3683 - T: (03) 57261395
Special Museum   00901

Chinchilla

Chinchilla and District Historical Society Museum,
Villiers St, Chinchilla, Qld. 4413, mail addr: POB
250, Chinchilla, Qld. 4413 - T: (07) 46627014
Local Museum - 1970
Steam engines, authentic steam saw mill, slab
cottage (fully furnished) - library mainly of local
history   00902

Clare

Clare National Trust Museum, Old Police Station,
Cnr Victoria and Neagles Rock Rds, Clare, SA 5453,
mail addr: POB 251, Clare, SA 5453 - T: (08)
88422374, E-mail: valtil@capri.net.au,
Internet: http://www.chariot.net.au/~valtil/
museum.htm. Head: Val Tilbrook
Local Museum - 1970
Photos - library, archives   00903

Claremont, Tasmania

Alpenrail Swiss Model Village and Railway, 82
Abbotsfield Rd, Claremont, Tasmania, Tas. 7011 -
T: (03) 62493748, Fax: 62493748, E-mail: arail@
eisa.net.au. Head: Rudi Jenni
Special Museum / Ethnology Museum   00904

Claremont, Western Australia

Claremont Museum, 66 Victoria Av, Claremont,
Western Australia, WA 6010 - T: (08) 92854345,
Fax: 92854301, E-mail: museum@
claremont.wa.gov.au, Internet: http://
www.claremont.wa.gov.au/museum. Head: Lillian
Hankel
Local Museum - 1975
Local hist, transport, crafts, trade, contemporary
fashion coll 1970-90   00905

Edith Cowan University Museum of Childhood, c/o
Edith Cowan University, Goldsworthy Rd, Claremont,
Western Australia, WA 6010 - T: (08) 94421373,
Fax: 94421314, E-mail: b.shepherd@ecu.edu.au,
Internet: http://www.ecu.edu.au/ses/museum.
Head: Dr. Brian Shepherd
University Museum / Ethnology Museum / Historical
Museum
Coll of chilhood heritage, toys, games, items of
infant care   00906

Museum of Western Australian Sport, Challenge
Stadium, Stephenson Av, Claremont, Western
Australia, WA 6010 - T: (08) 93878542,
Fax: 93837972
Special Museum
Olympic medals, team blazers, sporting equipment,
awards and trophies   00907

Clarencetown

Clarencetown and District Historical Museum, Cnr
Grey and Prince St, Clarencetown, NSW 2321 -
T: (02) 49964267
Local Museum
Local history, navigation and river port   00908

Clayfield

Telstra Museum Brisbane, 3 Oriel Rd, Clayfield, Qld.
4011 - T: (07) 38622958, Fax: 32621199. Head:
Margaret Bartlett
Science&Tech Museum
History of telecommunications, telephone,
telegraphs, old photos and literature   00909

Clayton

Monash University Gallery → Monash University
Museum of Art

Monash University Museum of Art, off Wellington
Rd, Clayton Campus, Clayton, Vic. 3800 - T: (03)
99054217, Fax: 99054345, E-mail: muma@
adm.monash.edu.au, Internet: http://
www.monash.edu.au/muma. Head: Jenepher
Duncan
Fine Arts Museum / University Museum - 1975
Australian Art post 1960, contemporary art,
installations, photography, video   00910

School of Political and Social Inquiry Museum, c/o
Department of Anthropology and Sociology, Monash
University, Wellington Rd, Clayton, Vic. 3168 -
T: (03) 99052978, Fax: 99052410,
E-mail: catherine.thorpe@arts.monash.edu.au,
Internet: http://www.arts.monash.edu.au/schools/
psi/museum
Special Museum / Folklore Museum
Cultures of Aboriginal Ausgtralia, Melanesia and
Indonesia   00911

Cleve

Cleve National Trust Museum, Third St, Cleve, SA
5640, mail addr: POB 170, Cleve, SA 5640 - T: (08)
86282038. Head: A. Turnbull
Local Museum - 1972
Early pioneer's household and farming
implements   00912

Old Council Chambers Museum, Third St, Cleve, SA
5640 - T: (08) 86282038
Agriculture Museum / Science&Tech Museum
Farming, local industries, items of household,
bulldog tractors   00913

Cleveland

Redland Museum, 60 Smith St, Cleveland, Qld. 4163,
mail addr: POB 243, Cleveland, Qld. 4163 - T: (07)
32863494, Fax: 32869579, E-mail: museum@
redland.net.au
Local Museum / Historical Museum - 1970
Horse drawn vehicles, farm implements, steam
engine and stationary engines, fine china,
textiles   00914

Clifton

Clifton and District Historical Museum, King St S, Clifton, Qld. 4361 - T: (07) 6973383
Folklore Museum
Early farm machinery, tractors, wool presses, blacksmithing tools, dairy equipment   00915

Cloncurry

Cloncurry and District Museum, Gregory St, Cloncurry, Qld. 4824
Local Museum
Local history   00916

Clunes

Clunes Museum, 36 Fraser St, Clunes, Vic. 3370 - T: (03) 53453592
Local Museum
Victoria's first gold town   00917

Cobar

Great Cobar Heritage Centre, Barrier Hwy, Cobar, NSW 2835 - T: (02) 68362448, Fax: 68361818, E-mail: cobarmus@cobar.net.au
Local Museum
Industrial, pastoral, Aboriginal and social history   00918

Cobdogla

Cobdogla Irrigation and Steam Museum, Trussel Terrace, Cobdogla, SA 5346, mail addr: POB 208, Berri, SA 5343 - T: (08) 85822603, 85887055, Fax: 85822603, E-mail: austeam@riverland.net.au. Head: Bill Hewitt-Dower
Science&Tech Museum - 1988
Humphrey pump - only working example in world   00919

Coburg

Bluestone Cottage and Museum, 82 Bell St, Coburg, Vic. 3044 - T: (03) 93867121
Local Museum
Local history, early land transactions in Coburg and Pentridge   00920

Cohuna

Cohuna Historical Museum, Cnr Sampson and Cullen Sts, Cohuna, Vic. 3568 - T: (03) 54562713, 54567332, E-mail: cdhs@cybanet.net.au, Internet: http://www.cybanet.net.au/~cdhs
Local Museum   00921

Colac

Colac Otway Shire Hammerton Bottle Collection, Gellibrand St, Colac, Vic. 3250 - T: (05) 52314572. Head: Keith Chambers
Special Museum
Coll of 84 historic bottles   00922

Provan's Mechanical Museum, Princes Hwy, Colac, Vic. 3250
Science&Tech Museum - 1977
Motorcycles 1905-1951, steam engines 1875-1914, cars and trucks 1906-1930, farm implements, wireless sets, clocks, wind mills, oil and gas engines   00923

Coleraine

Coleraine Local History Museum, Court House, 78 Whyte St, Coleraine, Vic. 3315 - T: (03) 55752160
Local Museum
Local history   00924

Collie

Coalfields Museum, 161 Coalfields Hwy, Collie, WA 6225 - T: (08) 97341299, E-mail: - coalfieldsmuseum@wn.com.au. Head: Kaye Mavric
Local Museum
Collie's history   00925

Collingwood

Australian Toy Museum, 174-180 Smith St, Collingwood, Vic. 3066 - T: (03) 94194138
Special Museum   00926

Concord

Concord Heritage Museum, 5 Wellbank St, Concord, NSW 2137 - T: (02) 97448528, Fax: 97447591
Local Museum / Folklore Museum
Clothing, household items, furniture, war memorabilia, bric-a-brac, books, documents, photographs   00927

Coober Pedy

Umoona Opal Mine and Museum, Hutchison St, Coober Pedy, SA 5273, mail addr: POB 372, Coober Pedy, SA 5273 - T: (08) 86725288, Fax: 86725731, E-mail: umoona@ozemail.com.au, Internet: http://www.umoonopalmine.com.au. Head: Yanni Athanasiadis
Science&Tech Museum / Natural History Museum / Folklore Museum - 1977
Art and artifacts of Central Australian desert aboriginal tribes, opal deposits, preserved opal mine, Coober Pedy alluvial black opal   00928

Cooktown

Cooktown School of Art Gallery, Charlotte St, Cooktown, Qld. 4871 - T: (07) 40695629
Fine Arts Museum
Local artists   00929

James Cook Historical Museum, Cnr Helen and Furneaux Sts, Cooktown, Qld. 4871 - T: (070) 695386
Local Museum
Local history, Captian Cook's Endeavour voyage   00930

Coonabarabran

Crystal Kingdom, 16 Chappell Av, Coonabarabran, NSW 2357 - T: (02) 68421927, Fax: 68424135, E-mail: bredwolf@tpg.com.au, Internet: http://www.crystalkingdom.com.au. Head: Wolfgang Bredereck
Natural History Museum - 1974
Minerals, fossils   00931

Coraki

Mid-Richmond Historical Museum, Adam St, Coraki, NSW 2471 - T: (02) 66832116
Local Museum
Local history   00932

Corlette

Port Stephens Shell Museum, 92 Sandy Point Rd, Corlette, NSW 2315 - T: (02) 49811428
Decorative Arts Museum / Fine Arts Museum
Coll of shell, Native carvings, old prints and pictures, rocks, gems and minerals   00933

Coromandel Valley

Winns Historic Bakehouse Museum, 68 Winns Rd, Coromandel Valley, SA 5051 - T: (08) 82781034
Special Museum / Local Museum
Ovens, a bread trough and baking equipment, local history   00934

Corrigin

Corrigin Museum, Corner Kirkwood St and Kunjin Rd, Corrigin, WA 6375, mail addr: POB 203, Corrigin, WA 6375 - T: 90652048, Fax: 90652013. Head: Brian Parsons
Local Museum - 1970
Machinery, tools, local items   00935

Corryong

Man From Snowy River Folk Museum, 103 Hanson St, Corryong, Vic. 3707, mail addr: POB 127, Corryong, Vic. 3707 - T: (02) 60761363, Fax: 60762152. Head: Stewart Ross
Folklore Museum - 1963
Ski coll, folk art, costume room   00936

Cowra

Cowra Museums, Sydney Rd, Cowra, NSW 2794 - Fax: (02) 63422801
Local Museum
Nostalgia of railways, vintage farm machinery, tractors and engines, militaria, combat vehicles, weapons   00937

Crafers

Papua New Guinea Display Centre, 7 Old Mount Barker Rd, Crafers, SA 5152 - T: (08) 83394547
Natural History Museum
Fossils and artefacts from the Highlands of Papua New Guinea, rocks and minerals   00938

Crawley

Clarke Geological Museum, c/o University of Western Australia, School of Earth and Geological Sciences, 35 Stirling Hwy, Crawley, WA 6009 - T: (08) 93802681, Fax: 93801037, E-mail: jbevan@geol.uwa.edu.au, Internet: http://www.geol.uwa.edu.au/geology/museum. Head: Jennifer Bevan
Natural History Museum / University Museum
Devonian and Permian fossils of WA, lithology, mineralogy, economic geology   00939

Lawrence Wilson Art Gallery, c/o The University of Western Australia, 35 Stirling Hwy, Crawley, WA 6009 - T: (061) 893803707, Fax: 893801017, E-mail: lwzg@cyllene.uwa.edu.au, Internet: http://www.arts.uwa.edu.au/LW/LW.html. Head: John Barret Lennard
Fine Arts Museum / Public Gallery / University Museum - 1972
20th c Australian paintings, works on paper, mixed media, sculpture, ceramics   00940

Creswick

Creswick Historical Museum, 70 Albert St, Creswick, Vic. 3363 - T: (03) 53452329, E-mail: wendyohlsen@hotmail.com, Internet: http://www.ballaratgenealogy.org.au/chha/creswick. Head: Jack Sewell
Local Museum
Social life, mining records and memorabilia of gold rush and deep lead mining, artworks of Lindsays, Litherland, Tibbetts and Moyle, military history   00941

Crows Nest

Carbethon Folk Museum and Pioneer Village, New England Hwy, Crows Nest, Qld. 4355 - T: (07) 6984162
Folklore Museum / Local Museum
Local history, agriculture   00942

Sexton's Cottage Museum, 250 West St, Crows Nest, NSW 2065 - T: (02) 99571557, Fax: 99368440, E-mail: genmangr@northsydney.nsw.gov.au, Internet: http://www.northsydney.nsw.gov.au
Local Museum / Science&Tech Museum
Former St Thomas' Cemetery, social history   00943

Croydon

Old Court House, Samwell St, Croydon, Qld. 4871 - T: (07) 47456185, Fax: 47456147, E-mail: croydon@bigpond.com.au. Head: Lisa Wain
Historical Museum   00944

Old Jail House, Samwell St, Croydon, Qld. 4871 - T: (07) 47456185, Fax: 47456147, E-mail: croydon@bigpond.com.au. Head: Lisa Wain
Historical Museum
Jail house history, stark harsh reality of gaol life   00945

Crystal Brook

Bakehouse Museum → Crystal Brook Heritage Centre

Crystal Brook Heritage Centre, Brandis St, Crystal Brook, SA 5523 - T: (08) 86362396. Head: Kenneth C. Sawyer
Local Museum
Underground bakery, musical instruments, farming equipment   00946

Culcairn

Station House, 16 Balfour St, Culcairn, NSW 2660 - T: (02) 60298339, Fax: 60298607, E-mail: cul@peg.pegasus.oz.au
Special Museum / Science&Tech Museum
Railway heritage   00947

Cunderdin

Cunderdin Municipal Museum, Great Eastern Hwy, Cunderdin, WA 6407
Local Museum - 1972
Local rural history and development, farm tractors and other agricultural machinery   00948

Cunnamulla

Bicentennial Historical Museum, Cnr Stockyard and Louise Sts, Cunnamulla, Qld. 4490 - T: (07) 46551777, Fax: 46551647, E-mail: parooshire@bigpond.com.au
Local Museum
Local history   00949

Currie

King Island Historical Museum, Lighthouse St, Currie, Tas. 7256 - T: (03) 64621512
Local Museum - 1980
Island's history, shipwrecks   00950

Dalby

Dalby Regional Gallery, Cultural and Administrative Centre, 107 Drayton St, Dalby, Qld. 4405, mail addr: POB 551, Dalby, Qld. 4405 - T: (076) 625666, Fax: 624538. Head: Robert Alexander
Fine Arts Museum - 1991
Contemporary Australian paintings 1960 to present   00951

Lake Broadwater Natural History Museum, Lake Broadwater Rd, Dalby, Qld. 4405 - T: (07) 46633553
Natural History Museum
Plant-life, reptiles, insects, fossils, Aboriginal artefacts   00952

Dandenong

Benga Oral Historic Centre, 66 McCrea Rd, Dandenong, Vic. 3175 - T: (03) 97934511, Fax: 97945215, E-mail: lcondo@cgd.vic.gov.au, Internet: http://www.greaterdandenong.com.au. Head: Lena Condos
Local Museum   00953

Heritage Hill Museum, 51 Langhorne Rd, Dandenong, Vic. 3175 - T: (03) 97934511, Fax: 97945215, E-mail: lcondo@cgd.vic.gov.au, Internet: http://www.greaterdandenong.com.au. Head: Lena Condos
Historical Museum / Historic Site   00954

Walker Street Gallery, Cnr Robinson and Walker St, Dandenong, Vic. 3175 - T: (03) 97068441, Fax: 97067651, E-mail: walkerstgallery@cgd.vic.gov.au, Internet: http://www.greater-dandenong.com
Public Gallery   00955

Darlinghurst

Sydney Jewish Museum, 148 Darlinghurst Rd, Darlinghurst, NSW 2010 - T: (02) 93607999, Fax: 93314245, E-mail: admin@sjm.com.au, Internet: http://www.sydneyjewishmuseum.com.au. Head: John Roth, Toby Hammerman

Ethnology Museum / Historical Museum
Australian Jewish history, Jewish culture and continuity, the Holocaust, social justice, human rights - resource centre   00956

Dartmoor

Dartmoor District Coach House Museum, Greenham St, Dartmoor, Vic. 3304 - T: (03) 55281435, E-mail: Kyndalyn@hotmail.com
Local Museum - 1993
Historical items, Pine industry, rural community   00957

Darwin

Australian Pearling Exhibition, The Wharf Precinct, Darwin, NT 0820, mail addr: POB 4646, Darwin, NT 0801 - T: (08) 89996573, Fax: 89817625
Special Museum
Historic hard-hat days to modern day pearl farming   00958

Burnett House and Myilly Point Heritage Precinct, 4 Burnett Pl, Myilly Point, Darwin, NT 0800 - T: (08) 89812848, Fax: 89812379, E-mail: national.trust@octa4.net.au, Internet: http://www.northernexposure.com.au/nationaltrust.html. Head: Elisabeth Close
Local Museum
Works' architect, Burnett, tropical architecture pre WWII, cultural heritage, local and military history   00959

Museum and Art Gallery of the Northern Territory, Conacher St, Bullocky Point Fannie Bay, Darwin, NT 5790, mail addr: POB 4646, Darwin, NT 0820 - T: (08) 89898201, Fax: 89898289, E-mail: angela.keith@nt.gov.au, Internet: http://www.nt.gov.au/dam/magnt. Head: Anna Malgovzewicz
Fine Arts Museum / Natural History Museum - 1969
Natural history, Australian contemporary art Australian Aboriginal, Asian, Oceanic art, material culture and archaeology, Northern Territory, Indo-Pacific history, maritime history and archaeology, geology - library   00960

Daylesford

Daylesford and District Historical Museum, 100 Vincent St, Daylesford, Vic. 3460
Historical Museum - 1971
Local history - library   00961

Deloraine

Folk Museum, 98 Emu Bay Rd, Deloraine, Tas. 7304 - T: (03) 63622695. Head: Paul Challis, Liz Challis
Folklore Museum
Local artifacts, photographs, 'Jimmy Possum' chairs   00962

Denmark

Denmark Historical Museum, Mitchell St, Denmark, WA 6333 - T: (08) 98481781, Fax: 98481231, E-mail: history@denmarkwa.com.au, Internet: http://www.denmarkwa.com.au/his. Head: Ben McGuinness
Local Museum
European exploration, timber industry, pioneer settlement and cemetery records   00963

Devonport

Devonport Gallery and Arts Centre, 45-47 Stewart St, Devonport, Tas. 7310 - T: (03) 64248296, Fax: 64235305, E-mail: art_gallery@dcc.tas.gov.au. Head: Elizabeth Gleeson
Fine Arts Museum / Decorative Arts Museum - 1966
Glass and ceramics (20th c), Tasmanian paintings and works on paper   00964

Devonport Maritime Museum, Gloucester Av, Devonport, Tas. 7310 - T: (03) 64247100, Fax: 6424705. Head: Robert B. Vellacott
Historical Museum
Maritime and local history   00965

Don River Railway Museum, Forth Main Rd, Devonport, Tas. 7310 - T: (03) 64246335, Fax: 64246335, E-mail: drr@southcom.com.au. Head: Ray Howe
Science&Tech Museum
Coll of steam locomotives and passenger carriages (1869 to 1954)   00966

Tiagarra Aboriginal Culture Centre and Museum, Bluff Rd, Devonport, Tas. 7310 - T: (03) 64248250, Fax: 64270506
Folklore Museum / Fine Arts Museum
Cultures and art of Aboriginal people   00967

Dickson

Canberra Bicycle Museum, 2 Badham St, Dickson, ACT 2602 - T: (02) 62480999, Fax: 62305298, E-mail: BicycleMuseum@ctuc.asn.au, Internet: http://canberrabicyclemuseum.info. Head: Rod Driver
Science&Tech Museum
Technical and historical development of the bicycle (last 150 yrs)   00968

Old Canberra Tram Company Museum, 2 Badham St, Dickson, ACT 2602 - T: (02) 62480999, Fax: 62305298, E-mail: rdriver@ctuc.asn.au, Internet: http://www.ctuc.asn.au/

attracti.htm#trams. Head: Rod Driver
Science&Tech Museum
10 restored trams from Brisbane, Adelaide,
Melbourne, Sydney, Launceston   00969

Donald

Donald Agricultural Museum, Hammill St, Donald,
Vic. 3480 - T: (03) 54971555
Agriculture Museum
Historical agricultural machinery, machinery
manufactured by local blacksmiths   00970

Donnelly River

Donnelly River Timber Mill Museum (closed) 00971

Dorrigo

Dorrigo Steam Railway and Museum, Tallowood St,
Dorrigo, NSW 2453 - T: (02) 66572176,
Internet: http://www.dsrm.org.au. Head: Keith Jones
Science&Tech Museum - not yet open
61 locomotives, 300 carriages and wagons, 19
railmotors   00972

Dowerin

Dowerin District Museum, 16 Cotterell St, Dowerin,
WA 6461
Local Museum - 1914
Reconstructed pioneer's house with furniture (1900-
1920)   00973

Dromana

Dromana and District Museum, Old Shire Offices,
Dromana, Vic. 3936 - T: (03) 59810493,
Internet: http://avoca.vicnet.au/~dromana/
Local Museum   00974

Drysdale

Bellarine Historical Museum, High St, Drysdale, Vic.
3222 - T: (03) 52501783, Internet: http://
www.zades.com.au/bellhs/
Local Museum
Local history   00975

Dubbo

Dubbo Military Museum, Newell Hwy and Camp Rd,
Dubbo, NSW 2830 - T: (02) 68845550
Military Museum
Artefacts from the WW II era, incl planes, tanks,
guns, vehicles, uniforms and documents   00976

Dubbo Museum, 234 Macquarie St, Dubbo, NSW
2830 - T: (02) 68825359
Local Museum   00977

Dubbo Regional Gallery, 165 Darling St, Dubbo, NSW
2830, mail addr: POB 1495, Dubbo, NSW 2830 -
T: (02) 68814342, Fax: 68842615,
E-mail: rebeccap@dubbo.nsw.gov.au. Head: Rene
Sutherland
Fine Arts Museum - 1989
'Animals in Art', regional artists   00978

Old Dubbo Gaol, Macquarie St, Dubbo, NSW 2830 -
T: (02) 68828122, Fax: 68822422, E-mail: odg@
dubbo.nsw.gov.au
Historical Museum - 1974
Prison life, original set of gallows and a full
hangman's kit   00979

Dungog

Dungog Historical Museum, 105 Dowling St,
Dungog, NSW 2420
Local Museum
Local history   00980

Dunolly

Dunolly Museum, 77 Broadway, Dunolly, Vic. 3472 -
T: (03) 54681516
Local Museum
Local records   00981

Dunwich

North Stradbroke Island Historical Museum, 15-17
Welsby St, Dunwich, Qld. 4183 - T: (07) 34099699,
Fax: 34098548. Head: A. Rentoul
Local Museum   00982

Eagle Heights

Tamborine Mountain Heritage Centre, Wangawallan
Rd, Eagle Heights, Qld. 4271 - T: (07) 55451485
Folklore Museum / Local Museum
Wagons and farm machinery   00983

East Melbourne

Fire Services Museum of Victoria, 39 Gisborne St,
East Melbourne, Vic. 3002 - T: (03) 96622907,
Fax: 96622907, E-mail: fsmvic@alphalink.com.au,
Internet: http://www.alphalink.com.au/~fsmvic
Science&Tech Museum   00984

Goold Catholic Museum, 383 Albert St, East
Melbourne, Vic. 3002 - T: (03) 99265677,
Fax: 99265617
Religious Arts Museum
History of the Catholic Church in Victoria   00985

Johnston Collection, 152 Hotham St, East
Melbourne, Vic. 3002 - T: (03) 94162515,
Fax: 94162507, E-mail: wrjohnston@bigpond.com,
Internet: http://www.johnstoncollection.org. Head:
Nina Stanton
Decorative Arts Museum - 1990
Decorative arts   00986

East Perth

Geological Survey Museum, 100 Plain St, East
Perth, WA 6000 - T: (08) 92223333, Fax: 92223633
Natural History Museum
Rock, mineral and fossils   00987

Echuca

Alambee Auto and Folk Museum, 7-11 Warren St,
Echuca, Vic. 3625 - T: (03) 54824248,
Fax: 54826951
Folklore Museum / Science&Tech Museum - 1976
Vintage and veteran cars, model railway, folk items,
period costumes, guns, phonographs, wirelesses,
bottles and coins   00988

Echuca Gem Club Collection, Sturt St, Echuca, Vic.
3564, mail addr: POB 72, Moama, NSW 2731 -
T: (03) 54824642. Head: Alan Smith
Natural History Museum
Australian minerals, lapidary items, gem
stones   00989

Echuca Museum, 1-3 Dickson St, Echuca, Vic. 3564
- T: (03) 54801325, E-mail: ehsoc@
telstra.easymail.com.au. Head: Joan Mitchell
Local Museum   00990

Raverty's Motor Museum, 33 Ogilvie Av, Echuca,
Vic. 3564 - T: (03) 54822730, Fax: 54802036.
Head: Norm Raverty
Science&Tech Museum
Over 100 Vehicles since 1900, models of the
1950's/1960's   00991

World in Wax Museum, 630 High St, Echuca, Vic.
3625 - T: (03) 54823630, Fax: 54823630
Special Museum
Wax figures, famous historical and contemporary
figures   00992

Eden

Eden Killer Whale Museum, Imlay St, Eden, NSW
2551 - T: (02) 64962094, Fax: 64962024,
E-mail: orcaview@acr.net.au, Internet: http://
www.acr.net.au/~kwmuseum
Natural History Museum / Local Museum
Skeleton of the killer whale Old Tom, local folklore,
whaling industry   00993

Edge Hill

Royal Flying Doctor Service Visitors Centre, 1
Junction St, Edge Hill, Qld. 4870 - T: (07)
40535681, Fax: 40321776, E-mail: -
rfdscairnsviscentre@bigpond.com, Internet: http://
www.flyingdoctorqueensland.net. Head: Michael
Lacey
Science&Tech Museum
Radios (incl pedal radio), medical equipment and
aviation instruments, aircraft display   00994

Edithburg

Edithburgh Museum, Edith St, Edithburg, SA 5583 -
T: (08) 88526187
Local Museum
Local shipping history, salt industry, settlement,
agriculture   00995

Eidsvold

Eidsvold Historical Complex, POB 28, Eidsvold, Qld.
4627 - T: (07) 1651277
Local Museum / Open Air Museum
Local history   00996

Eldorado

Eldorado Museum, Main St, Eldorado, Vic. 3746 -
T: (03) 57251577
Local Museum
Domestic items, mining relics, farming machinery,
tools of trade   00997

Elizabeth Bay

Elizabeth Bay House, 7 Onslow Av, Elizabeth Bay,
NSW 2011 - T: (02) 93563022, Fax: 93577176,
E-mail: info@ho.hht.nsw.gov.au, Internet: http://
www.hht.nsw.gov.au. Head: Peter Watts
Historical Museum
Greek Revival architecture, English and Australian
colonial decorative arts   00998

Elmore

Elmore Progress Association Station Museum,
Railway Pl, Elmore, Vic. 3558 - T: (03) 54326559
Local Museum
Local history, farm accessories   00999

Elsternwick

Jewish Holocaust Centre, 13-15 Selwyn St,
Elsternwick, Vic. 3185 - T: (03) 95281985,
Fax: 95283758, E-mail: hc@sprint.com.au,
Internet: http://www.arts.manash.edu.au/affiliates/
hlc. Head: Johnathan Morris
Ethnology Museum / Historical Museum   01000

Rippon Lea House Museum, 192 Hotham St,
Elsternwick, Vic. 3185 - T: (03) 95236095,
Fax: 95236921, E-mail: rlnt@nattrust.com.au,
Internet: http://home.vicnet.net.au/~rlnt/
Decorative Arts Museum / Historical Museum
Last of Australia's great privately owned 19th c
suburban estates   01001

Emerald

Emerald Art Gallery, 44 Borilla St, Emerald, Qld.
4720 - T: (07) 9823101, Fax: 9821354
Fine Arts Museum   01002

Emerald Museum, Nobelius Heritage Park, Crichton
Rd, Emerald, Vic. 3782 - T: (03) 59682152,
Internet: http://www.skyfamily.com/emeraldvictoria/
j-museum.html
Historical Museum   01003

Emmaville

Emmaville Mining Museum, Wattle Grove,
Emmaville, NSW 2371 - E-mail: jen_body@
hotmail.com
Science&Tech Museum   01004

Emu Park

Emu Park Historical Museum, 17 Hill St, Emu Park,
Qld. 4702 - T: (07) 9396080
Local Museum - 1986
Photographs, artefacts, sea shells, rocks, crockery,
relics, coins, militaria, dolls and tools   01005

Emu Plains

Penrith Regional Gallery and The Lewers Bequest,
86 River Rd, Emu Plains, NSW 2750 - T: (02)
47351100, Fax: 47355663, E-mail: gallery@
penrithcity.nsw.gov.au, Internet: http://www.penrith-
city.nsw.gov.au/penrithgallery. Head: Michael
Crayford
Fine Arts Museum - 1981
1,200 works incl paintings, works on paper,
photographs, textiles and sculpture, special coll of
Sydney based artists between 1930-70 working in
abstraction, abstract expressionist paintings 1950-
70, outdoor sculpture garden - library   01006

Esperance

Esperance Municipal Museum, James St,
Esperance, WA 6450 - T: (08) 90711579,
Fax: 90711579, E-mail: museum@emerge.net.au
Local Museum - 1976
Weckage of Skylab, a WAGR steam locomotive, Sir
Douglas Mawson's Antarctic expedition, agricultural
machinery   01007

Eumundi

Eumundi Museum, 76 Memorial Dr, mail addr: POB
55, Eumundi, Qld. 4562 - T: (07) 54428762,
Fax: 54428181, E-mail: eumundimuseum@
dingoblue.net.au, Internet: http://
www.eumundimuseum.com. Head: Andy Reed
Local Museum
Social, natural history of Eumundi   01008

Euroa

Farmer's Arms Hotel Museum, 25 Kirkland Av,
Euroa, Vic. 3666 - T: (03) 57951330. Head: Loretta
McPherson
Local Museum - 1973
Furniture, furnishings, library, crockery, ornaments,
pictures, paintings, clothing, musical instruments,
farm implements, carriages, printing press, original
National Bank building c 1876, Eliza Forlonge
Cottage (wool mem.), Ned Kelly in Europa
memorabilia, militaria   01009

Ferny Grove

Brisbane Tramway Museum, 20 Tramway St, Ferny
Grove, Qld. 4055 - T: (07) 33511776
Science&Tech Museum - 1968
Brisbane trams and buses, archival holdings of the
Brisbane City Council Transport Department, 1885
horse tram truck built by John Stephenson, 1901
Californian combination car, four motor trams -
library, photographical archives   01010

Fitzroy

Centre for Contemporary Photography, 205
Johnston St, Fitzroy, Vic. 3065 - T: (03) 94171549,
Fax: 94171605, E-mail: info@ccp.org.au,
Internet: http://www.ccp.org.au. Head: Tessa Dwyer
Fine Arts Museum   01011

Mary MacKillop Pilgrimage Centre, 11 Brundwick
Rd, Fitzroy, Vic. 3065 - T: (03) 94199273
Religious Arts Museum   01012

Flaxton

**Miniature English Village and Brass Rubbing
Centre**, 340-342 Flaxton Dr, Flaxton, Qld. 4560 -
T: (07) 54457225
Fine Arts Museum / Music Museum
Models of original buildings in England, medieval
and Tudor brasses (13th-17th c)   01013

Flinders Island

Furneaux Museum, 8 Fowlers Rd, Flinders Island,
Tas. 7255 - T: (03) 63592010, Fax: 63592026,
E-mail: furneaux@tasmail.com, Internet: http://
www.flinders.tco.asn.au/pages/areas/area2.html.
Head: Lola Corbould
Historical Museum
Cultural history of the Furneaux group of islands
situated in Eastern Bass Strait   01014

Footscray

Melbourne Museum of Printing, 91 Moreland Rd,
Footscray, Vic. 3011 - T: (03) 93897555
Science&Tech Museum   01015

Forbes

Forbes Museum, Cross St, Forbes, NSW 2871 -
T: (02) 68523856, Fax: 68523856
Local Museum
Ben Hall (Bush Ranger) memorabilia, Aboriginal
display, agriculture, farming vehicle   01016

Fortitude Valley

Fusions Gallery, Cnr Brunswick and Malt Sts,
Fortitude Valley, Qld. 4006 - T: (07) 33585122,
Fax: 33584540
Fine Arts Museum / Decorative Arts Museum
Ceramic art and glass   01017

Queensland Military Memorial Museum, 28 Church
St, Fortitude Valley, Qld. 4006 - T: (07) 38523565,
Fax: 38523585, Internet: http://www.qmmm.org
Military Museum / Historical Museum
Military heritage   01018

Foster

Foster and District Historical Society Museum,
Main St, Foster, Vic. 3960 - T: (03) 56822817,
Fax: 56821340, E-mail: margie@dcsi.net.au,
Internet: http://www.promaccom.com.au/touring/
foster/museum. Head: Dr. M. Linton
Local Museum
Local history, discovery of gold, timber getting,
dairying   01019

South Gippsland Shire Museum → Foster and
District Historical Society Museum

Frankston

Frankston Primary Old School Museum, Davey St,
Frankston, Vic. 3199 - T: (03) 97833769,
Fax: 97814402
Historical Museum
Education from the past   01020

Fremantle

Fremantle Arts Centre, 1 Finnerty St, Fremantle, WA
6160, mail addr: POB 891, Fremantle, WA 6160 -
T: (08) 93358244, Fax: 94306613, E-mail: fac@q-
net.net.au. Head: Chris Girvan-Brown
Public Gallery - 1972   01021

Fremantle History Museum, 1 Finnerty St,
Fremantle, WA 6160 - T: (08) 94307966,
Fax: 94307458, E-mail: fhmsuper@
museum.wa.gov.au, Internet: http://
www.museum.wa.gov.au/. Head: Gary Morgan
Historical Museum
History of WA and Fremantle   01022

Fremantle Prison Precinct, The Terrace, Fremantle,
WA 6160 - T: (08) 93359473, Fax: 94306115,
E-mail: fremantleprison@cams.wa.gov.au,
Internet: http://www.fremantleprison.com
Historic Site - 1992
Convicts, prison life   01023

Western Australian Maritime Museum, Cliff St,
Fremantle, WA 6160 - T: (08) 94318444,
Fax: 94318490, E-mail: rept@museum.wa.gov.au,
Internet: http://www.mm.wa.gov.au. Head: Graeme
Henderson
Special Museum - 1979
Maritime archeology, maritime history   01024

World of Energy, 12 Parry St, Fremantle, WA 6160 -
T: (08) 94305655, Fax: 93358812,
E-mail: graham.horne@wpcorp.com.au,
Internet: http://www.wpcorp.com.au. Head: Graham
Horne
Science&Tech Museum - 1989
Electricity and gas industry in Western Australia,
alternative energy, new technologies for electricity
generation - library, photo library, archives   01025

Fryerstown

Herons Reef Historic Gold Diggings, Fryers Rd,
Fryerstown, Vic. 3451 - T: (03) 54734387,
Fax: 54705106, E-mail: lmsimmon@netcon.net.au,
Internet: http://www.genesis.net.au/~hrgold

Historic Site / Science&Tech Museum / Open Air Museum
Authentic alluvial gold diggings date from the 1850s to the 1930s, every known methods of gold extraction, lead mining 01026

Gascoyne Junction

Gascoyne Junction Museum, 4 Scott St, Gascoyne Junction, WA 6705 - T: (08) 99430988, Fax: 99430507
Local Museum
Work tools, household items, rocks, gemstones 01027

Gawler

Gawler Folk Museum, 59 Murray St, Gawler, SA 5118 - T: (08) 85222548
Folklore Museum
James Martin and other foundries in Gawler, local history 01028

Gayndah

Gayndah Museum, 3 Simon St, Gayndah, Qld. 4625 - T: (07) 41612226, Fax: 41611689. Head: David Berthelsen
Local Museum
Household and farm equipment 01029

Geelong

Geelong Gallery, Little Malop St, Geelong, Vic. 3220 - T: (03) 52293645, Fax: 52216441, E-mail: geelart@geelonggallery.org.au, Internet: http://www.geelong-gallery.org.au. Head: Geoffrey Edwards
Fine Arts Museum - 1896
Australian art (19th and 20th c), English paintings (late 19th c) 01030

Geelong Historical Records Centre, 51 Little Malop St, Geelong, Vic. 3220 - T: (03) 52217007, Fax: 52211328, E-mail: nhoughton@geelongcity.vic.gov.au, Internet: http://www.zades.com.au/geelong/ghre.html. Head: Tony Ansett
Local Museum
Family and local history 01031

National Wool Museum, 26 Moorabool St, Geelong, Vic. 3220 - T: (03) 52270701, Fax: 52221118, E-mail: nwminfo@geelongcity.vic.gov.au, Internet: http://www.mov.vic.gov.au/nwm
Special Museum
Story of wool in Australia, agriculture, textiles, manufacturing, science and technology, arts, craft 01032

Geeveston

Forest and Heritage Centre, Church St, Geeveston, Tas. 7109 - T: (03) 62971836, Fax: 62971839
Historical Museum
Timber industry, tools and equipment 01033

Geraldton

Garaldton Region Museum → Western Australian Museum Geraldton

Geraldton Regional Art Gallery, 24 Chapman Rd, Geraldton, WA 6530 - T: (08) 99647170, Fax: 99217453, E-mail: artgallery@geraldton.wa.gov. Head: Damian Kelly
Fine Arts Museum - 1984
Coll of 20th c Australian art 01034

Western Australian Museum Geraldton, Museum Pl, Geraldton, WA 6530 - T: (08) 99215080, Fax: 99215158, E-mail: museum@wa.com.au. Head: Dr. Rik Malhotra
Local Museum - 1980
Dutch shipwreck relics, Aboriginal heritage, natural hist, social hist 01035

Gerringong

Alne Bank (closed) 01036

Gerringong and District Museum, 10 Blackwood St, Gerringong, NSW 2534 - T: (02) 42342359
Local Museum - 1991 01037

Gilgandra

Gilgandra Museum, Newell Hwy, Gilgandra, NSW 2827 - T: (02) 68472716
Local Museum
Memorabilia of the Boer War, WW I, WW II 01038

Gisborne

Gisborne Steam Park, Webb Crescent, Gisborne, Vic. 3437
Science&Tech Museum
Railway, Fowler steam road roller and Ruston Hornsby portable steam engine 01039

Gladstone, Queensland

Gladstone Maritime History Museum, 6 Short St, Gladstone, Queensland, Qld. 4680
Historical Museum / Local Museum
Regions maritime and local history 01040

Gladstone Regional Art Gallery and Museum, Corner Goondoon and Bramston Sts, Gladstone, Queensland, Qld. 4680, mail addr: POB 29, Gladstone, Qld. 4680 - T: (07) 49701242, Fax: 49729097, E-mail: pamelaw@gladsonecc.qld.gov.au. Head: Pamela Whitlock
Fine Arts Museum / Local Museum - 1985
Australian art and craft, works on paper, paintings, and ceramics, artefacts pertaining to the history and development of Gladstone since 1847 - archives 01041

Gladstone, South Australia

Gladstone Gaol, Ward St, Gladstone, South Australia, SA 5473 - T: (08) 86622200, Fax: 86622240, E-mail: gladstonegaol@ozemail.com.au, Internet: http://gladstonegaol.com. Head: Ian Hogben, Barbara Hogben
Historical Museum - 1978
Gaol relics, former cells 01042

Glebe

Conservation Resource Centre, 61 Darghan St, Glebe, NSW 2037 - T: (02) 96928366, Fax: 96601426
Historical Museum
History of houses, furnishings and gardens in New South Wales 01043

Glen Innes

Land of the Beardies History House Museum, Cnr West Av and Ferguson St, Glen Innes, NSW 2370 - T: (02) 67321035
Local Museum
Early settlement in the 1840s, machinery 01044

Glenelg

HMS Buffalo, Adelphi Tce, Glenelg, SA 5045 - T: (08) 82947000, Fax: 82946847
Historical Museum 01045

Glenreagh

Glenreagh Memorial Museum, Coramba St, Glenreagh, NSW 2450 - T: (02) 66492001
Local Museum
Local history (Orara Valley) over the last 125 years 01046

Gloucester

Gloucester Folk Museum, 12 Church St, Gloucester, NSW 2422 - T: (02) 65581187
Local Museum
Australian domestic items, textiles, toys, militaria, geological specimens, tools and photographies 01047

Gloucester School Museum, Cnr Church and Oak Sts, Gloucester, NSW 2422 - T: (02) 65581187
Historical Museum 01048

Goolwa

Goolwa National Trust Museum, 11-13 Porter St, Goolwa, SA 5214, mail addr: POB 470, Goolwa, SA 5214 - T: (08) 85552221. Head: A.D. Presgrave
Local Museum - 1971 01049

Goombungee

Rosalie Shire Historical Museum, George St, Goombungee, Qld. 4354
Local Museum
Demestic and agricultural machinery, local history 01050

Gordon

Eryldene Heritage House, 17 McIntosh St, Gordon, NSW 2072 - T: (02) 94982271, Fax: 94992636. Head: Joseph Galscott
Decorative Arts Museum / Fine Arts Museum
Oriental art and artefacts from the T'ang dynasty, original furniture 01051

Gordonvale

Mulgrave Settlers Museum, Gordon St, Gordonvale, Qld. 4865 - T: (07) 40561810
Local Museum
The way of life from earlier times 01052

Gosford

Henry Kendall Cottage and Historical Museum, 27 Henry Kendall St, W, Gosford, NSW 2250 - T: (02) 43252270
Special Museum / Local Museum
Home of pioneer poet Henry Kendall, domestic items, musical instruments, early industries, farm implements 01053

Gosnells

City of Gosnells Museum, Orange Tee Farm, Homestead Rd, Gosnells, WA 6110 - T: (08) 94901575, Fax: 94901575
Historical Museum / Folklore Museum
Agricultural machinery, blacksmith shop, life of earlier times 01054

Goulburn

Goulburn Regional Art Gallery, Civic Centre, Corner Bourke and Church Sts, Goulburn, NSW 2580, mail addr: Locked Bag 22, Goulburn, NSW 2580 - T: (02) 48234443, Fax: 48234456, E-mail: goulbcc@goulburn.nsw.gov.au, Internet: http://www.goulburn.nsw.gov.au. Head: Jennifer Lamb
Fine Arts Museum - 1982
20th c Australian paintings and works on paper, contemporary textiles coll 01055

Grafton

Alumny Creek School Museum, Southgate Rd, Grafton, NSW 2460 - T: (02) 66422598
Historical Museum - 1988
Coll of early kindergarten and primary school text books, educational material, magazines 01056

Grafton Regional Gallery, 158 Fitzroy St, Grafton, NSW 2460 - T: (02) 66423177, Fax: 66432663, E-mail: mail@graftongallery.nsw.gov.au, Internet: http://www.graftongallery.nsw.gov.au. Head: Susi Muddiman
Public Gallery - 1988
Australian oil paintings, watercolours and drawing early 1960s, 1988 to present, regional artists, contemporary Australian drawings 01057

Schaeffer House Museum, 190 Fitzroy St, Grafton, NSW 2460 - T: (02) 66425212, Fax: 66422814
Local Museum
Local and family history 01058

Grange

Sturt House, Jetty St, Grange, SA 5022 - T: (08) 83568185, Fax: 83568185, E-mail: ronlobegeiger@optusnet.com.au, Internet: http://ronkay.mtx.net. Head: John Dyer
Special Museum - 1960
Residence of Captain Charles Sturt, whose voyage down river Murray, 1829-30, led to founding of South Australia, furniture of Sturt family, Union Jacks hoisted during voyage and northern expedition 01059

Grenfell

Grenfell Museum, Camp St, Grenfell, NSW 2810 - T: (02) 63431930. Head: Bruce Robinson
Local Museum
Local history, bushrangers, famous locals 01060

Griffith

Griffith Pioneer Park Museum, Cnr Remembrance and Scenic Drs, Griffith, NSW 2680 - T: (02) 69624196, Fax: 69642815, E-mail: darrellco@griffith.nsw.gov.au
Open Air Museum
Story of the Murrumbidgee Irrigation Area 01061

Griffith Regional Art Gallery, Banna Av, Griffith, NSW 2680, mail addr: POB 1076, Griffith, NSW 2680 - T: (02) 69625991, Fax: 69626119. Head: Kerry Creecy
Fine Arts Museum - 1983
Griffith Coll, Australian designer jewellery, Art and Craft Society Coll, Jack Carney Photography Coll 01062

Grove

Huon Valley and Heritage Museum, Main Rd, Grove, Tas. 7109 - T: (03) 63664345
Local Museum 01063

Gulgong

Henry Lawson Centre, 147 Mayne St, Gulgong, NSW 2852 - T: (02) 63742049
Special Museum
Books, writings and memorabilia 01064

Gumeracha

Gumeracha and District History Centre, Victoria St, Gumeracha, SA 5233 - Fax: (08) 83891025, E-mail: amber@chariot.com.au
Local Museum 01065

Gundagai

Gundagai Historical Museum, Homer St, Gundagai, NSW 2722 - T: (02) 69441995
Local Museum - 1968
Phar Lap's saddlecloth, the shirt worn by Banjo Patterson's Kiley of Kiley Run, bushrangers, Aboriginal hero 01066

Gungahlin

National Dinosaur Museum, Cnr Gold Creek Rd and Barton Hwy, Gungahlin, ACT 2912 - T: (02) 62302655, Fax: 62302357, E-mail: natdinom@contact.com.au, Internet: http://www.contact.com.au/dino-museum
Natural History Museum
Earth's Prehistoric past, fossils, largest display of dinosaur material in Australia 01067

Gunnedah

Water Tower Museum, South St, Gunnedah, NSW 2380 - T: (02) 67421519. Head: John Buchanan
Local Museum
Newspapers, militaria, books, kitchen implements, Aboriginal artefacts, clothing and school items 01068

Gympie

Gympie and District Historical and Gold Mining Museum, 215 Brisbane Rd, Gympie, Qld. 4570 - T: (07) 54823995, Fax: 54823995
Local Museum / Science&Tech Museum
Mining era, housing, dairy display, mining equipment 01069

Hahndorf

Hahndorf Academy Public Art Gallery and Museum, 68 Main St, Hahndorf, SA 5245 - T: (08) 83887611. Head: Ray Rothe
Fine Arts Museum / Historical Museum - 1967
German and Australian household items, literature and tools of the 19th century, small coll of original works by Sir Hans Heysen - library 01070

Tineriba Tribal Gallery and Museum, 77-79 Main St, Hahndorf, SA 5245 - T: (08) 83887218, Fax: 83887218, E-mail: tineriba@bukartilla.com.au, Internet: http://www.bukartilla.com.au. Head: Harold E. Gallasch
Ethnology Museum - 1955
Mask coll from the Baining tribe of New Britain (fully documented), contemporary New Ireland Malangans (documented with the legend), Tolai masks and carvings from New Britain, Australian aboriginal stone artifacts, contemporary aboriginal art - library 01071

Halls Gap

Brambuk Living Cultural Centre, Dunkeld Rd, Halls Gap, Vic. 3381 - T: (03) 53564452, Fax: 53564455
Folklore Museum
Past and present lifestyles of the Aboriginal people of south-west Victoria and the Wimmera 01072

Hamilton, Brisbane

Palma Rosa Museum, 9 Queens Rd, Hamilton, Brisbane, Qld. 4007 - T: (07) 32623769, Fax: 32561887, E-mail: esu@lrv.net.au. Head: Patricia Johnson
Fine Arts Museum
Memorabilia about Andre Stombuco, history of the English Speaking Union, Queensland Branch 01073

Hamilton, Tasmania

Hamilton Heritage Museum, Cumberland St, Hamilton, Tasmania, Tas. 7140 - T: (03) 62863218, Fax: 62863295, E-mail: GlenClyde@Southcom.com.au, Internet: http://www.tased.edu.au/tasonline/hamilton. Head: Lee Milne
Local Museum
Photo-displays of people, buildings and landscapes of the area 01074

Hamilton, Victoria

Hamilton Art Gallery, 107 Brown St, Hamilton, Victoria, Vic. 3300 - T: (03) 55730460, Fax: 55722910, E-mail: daniel_mcowan@sthgrampians.mav.asn.au. Head: Daniel McOwan
Fine Arts Museum - 1961
Oriental ceramics, Hogarth prints, European decorative arts, prints and gouaches by Paul Sandby, Australian paintings and prints 01075

Hampton

Melbourne Clocks Museum, 424 Bluff Rd, Hampton, Vic. 3188 - T: (03) 95533115, Fax: 95533115. Head: G.W.T. Brook
Science&Tech Museum
Clocks, towers, chronometers, brackets, carriage, regulators, electric synchrome and slaves, long cases - restoration workshop 01076

Harvey

Harvery Art Gallery, Above Post Office, Hayward St, Harvey, WA 6220 - T: (08) 97335121, Fax: 97335121
Public Gallery 01077

Hastings

Hastings-Western Port Historical Museum, Cnr Marine Parade and Skinner St, Hastings, Vic. 3915 - T: (03) 97702147, Fax: 97702146
Local Museum
Fishing Industry, Armstrong Gun, Pioneer's Cottage 01078

Hawker, South Australia

Hawker Museum, Wilpena Rd, Hawker, South Australia, SA 5434 - T: (08) 86484014, Fax: 86484283, E-mail: museum@hawkermotors.com.au, Internet: http://www.hawkermotors.com.au. Head: F. Teague
Local Museum 01079

Hay

Bishop's Lodge Museum, Rose St, Hay, NSW 2711 - T: (02) 69931727, Fax: 69932294, E-mail: HayVet@tpg.com.au
Religious Arts Museum
Social, cultural and religious history 01080

Hay Gaol Museum, Church St, Hay, NSW 2711 - T: (02) 69931003, Fax: 69931288
Folklore Museum
Clothing, hospital equipment, Aboriginal artefacts, bottles and jars, musical instruments, guns and pistols, tools 01081

Haymarket

Museum of Applied Arts and Sciences, POB K346, Haymarket, NSW 2007 - T: (02) 92170111, Fax: 92170333. Head: Terence Measham
Fine Arts Museum / Science&Tech Museum - 1880 01082

Herston

Marks-Hirshfeld Museum of Medical History, c/o Medical School, University of Queensland, Herston Rd, Herston, Qld. 4006 - T: (07) 33655423
Historical Museum
Medical instruments, medical history 01083

Hervey Bay

Hervey Bay Historical Society Museum, Queensland Museum, 13 Zephyr St, Hervey Bay, Qld. 4655 - T: (071) 284808, E-mail: ichristi@gil.com.au
Historical Museum - 1972
library 01084

Hobart

Hobart Heritage Museum, 103 Hampden Rd, Battery Point, Hobart, Tas. 7004 - T: (03) 62342791. Head: R. Banks
Local Museum - 1957
Ayrshire embroidery, clothing (mainly 19th c), needlework, colonial furniture 01085

John Elliott Classics Museum, c/o University of Tasmania, POB 252C-81, Hobart, Tas. 7001 - T: (03) 62262235, E-mail: classics.museum@classics.utas.edu.au, Internet: http://www.utas.edu.au/docs/classics/museum.html. Head: Dr. P.A. Gallivan
Museum of Classical Antiquities / Archaeological Museum / University Museum - 1954
Ancient art, archeology, Greek pottery, Greek and Roman coins 01086

Maritime Museum of Tasmania, 16 Argyle St, Hobart, Tas. 7001 - T: (03) 62341419
Historical Museum
Models, artefacts, artworks, photographs related to shipping operations 01087

Masonic Temple, 3 Sandy Bay Rd, Hobart, Tas. 7000 - T: (03) 62235814, Fax: 62238159
Local Museum
Coll of Masonic regalia, jewels 01088

Medical History Museum, 2 Gore St, S, Hobart, Tas. 7004 - T: (03) 62232047, Fax: 62236469
Historical Museum
Early medical curiosities and surgical instruments 01089

Museum of Fine Arts, c/o State Library of Tasmania, 91 Murray St, Hobart, Tas. 7001 - T: (03) 62337484, Fax: 62310927, Internet: http://www.tased.edu.au/cultural/allport
Fine Arts Museum / Decorative Arts Museum
Coll of 18th-19th c furniture, colonial paintings, silver and objet d'art, fine china, rare and antique books 01090

Plimsoll Gallery, c/o University of Tasmania, Centre for the Arts, Hunter St, Hobart, Tas. 7001 - T: (03) 62384309, Fax: 62384208. Head: Paul Zika
Fine Arts Museum / University Museum 01091

Salamanca Arts Centre, 77 Salamanca Pl, Hobart, Tas. 7004 - T: (03) 62348414, Fax: 62240245, E-mail: sacinc@salarts.org.au, Internet: http://www.salarts.org.au. Head: Rosemary Miller
Public Gallery 01092

Tasmania Distillery Museum, 2 Macquarie St, Hobart, Tas. 7000 - T: (03) 62310588, Fax: 62310590, E-mail: tasdist@south.com.au, Internet: http://www.tasdistillery.com.au. Head: Neville Parton
Special Museum
History and story of whisky making 01093

Tasmanian Museum and Art Gallery, 40 Macquarie St, Hobart, Tas. 7000 - T: (03) 62114177, Fax: 62114112, E-mail: tmagmail@tmag.tas.gov.au, Internet: http://www.tmag.tas.gov.au. Head: Patricia Sabine
Local Museum / Natural History Museum / Decorative Arts Museum / Public Gallery - 1843
Tasmanian paintings (particularly 19th c), Tasmanian geology, botany, zoology (vertebrate and invertebrate), aboriginal culture, photogr, hist, herbarium, decorative arts - library, information and visitor services 01094

Home Hill

Ashworths Treasures of the Earth, 170 Eight Av, Home Hill, Qld. 4806 - T: (07) 7821177, Fax: 7822490
Natural History Museum
Minerals 01095

Homebush

Westpac Museum, 6-8 Playfair St, The Rocks, Homebush, NSW 2140 - T: (02) 97635670, Fax: 97644950
Historical Museum
Beginnings in 1817 as the Bank of NSW to the present age of plastic cards and electric banking 01096

Horsham

Horsham Historical Museum, 33 Pynsent St, Horsham, Vic. 3402 - T: (03) 53821306
Local Museum
Locally made items, bottles, pottery 01097

Horsham Regional Art Gallery, 80 Wilson St, Horsham, Vic. 3400 - T: (03) 53825575, Fax: 53825407, E-mail: hrag@netconnect.com.au, Internet: http://www.horsham.net.au/gallery. Head: Merle Hathaway
Fine Arts Museum - 1969
Australian paintings, prints, drawings and photographs 01098

Horsley Park

Christmas Museum Gallery, Nativity House, 136-146 Garfield Rd, Horsley Park, NSW 2164 - T: (02) 96201218, Fax: 96201609
Special Museum
Over 600 nativity scenes (cribs) from 55 countries, antique Christmas cards, handcraft, paintings 01099

Hunters Hill

Hunters Hill Historical Museum, Town Hall, Alexandra St, Hunters Hill, NSW 2110
Local Museum
Local history 01100

Huntly

Huntly and Districts Historical Museum, 7693 Midland Hwy, Huntly, Vic. 3551 - T: (05) 4488287
Local Museum
History of the area 01101

Huonville

Huon Valley Apple and Heritage Museum, RSD, 2064 Grove, Huonville, Tas. 7109 - T: (03) 62664345, Fax: 62664109
Local Museum 01102

Hurstbridge

Allwood House, 901 Main Rd, Hurstbridge, Vic. 3099 - T: (03) 97182717
Local Museum
Memorabilia of the Hurst/Grey families, found objects of the Caledonia Goldfields 01103

Hurstville

Centennial Bakery Museum, 319-321 Forest Rd, Hurstville, NSW 2220 - T: (02) 95804040, Fax: 95804040, E-mail: rschulz@hurstville.nsw.gov.au
Special Museum / Local Museum
Baking and selling bread, general local history 01104

Huskisson

Lady Denman Heritage Complex, Dent St, Huskisson, NSW 2540 - T: (02) 44415675, Fax: 44417688, E-mail: ladydenman@shoalhaven.net.au, Internet: http://www.ladydenman.asn.au
Historical Museum
Maritime history, European discovery, early settlement, shipbuilding, shipwrecks, lighthouses, timbergetting, the Naval College and whaling, Lady Denman Ferry (1911) 01105

Ilfracombe

Ilfracombe Museum, Ilfracombe, Qld. 4727 - T: (07) 6581553
Local Museum 01106

Imbil

Museum of Wonders, Island Rd, Imbil, Qld. 4570 - T: (07) 44845294
Local Museum - 1972
Arms, helmets, local history, blacksmith's tools and motorcycles 01107

Inglewood

Inglewood District Historical Museum, Court House 56 Market St, Inglewood, Vic. 3517 - T: (03) 54383011
Local Museum
Photographs, books, costumes, various artefacts, records and micro-film 01108

Innisfail

Innisfail and District Historical Museum, 9 Edith St, Innisfail, Qld. 4860 - T: (070) 612731
Local Museum
Local history, facets of life 01109

Lit Sing Kwang Chinese Temple, 10 Owen St, Innisfail, Qld. 4860 - T: (070) 611527
Religious Arts Museum
Statues of the god of war, goddess of mercy, the god of harvest, Lao Tsu of Taoism, and Confucius and his disciples 01110

Ipswich

Global Arts Link, d'Arcy Doyle Pl, Nicholas St, Ipswich, Qld. 4305, mail addr: POB 191, Ipswich, Qld. 4305 - T: (07) 38139222, Fax: 38120428, E-mail: info@gal.org.au, Internet: http://www.gal.org.au. Head: Louise Denoon
Public Gallery - 1980
Early Queensland watercolours, contemporary Australian prints, paintings, drawings, sculpture, ceramics - library 01111

Jamestown

Jamestown National Trust Museum, Mannanarie Rd, Jamestown, SA 5491, mail addr: POB 232, Jamestown, SA 5491 - T: (08) 86640026. Head: David Box
Local Museum - 1971
Local and regional hist (Sir John Cockburn, politician), railways 01112

Jeparit

Wimmera Mallee Pioneers Museum, Dimboola Rd, Jeparit, Vic. 3423 - T: (03) 53972101
Local Museum 01113

Jerilderie

Jerilderie Doll World Museum, 57 Bolton St, Jerilderie, NSW 2716 - T: (03) 58861583
Special Museum 01114

Jolimont

Australian Gallery of Sport and Olympic Museum, Melbourne Cricket Ground, Yarra Park, Jolimont, Vic. 3002 - T: (03) 96578879, Fax: 96541387
Special Museum
Multi-sport museum, 1956 Olympic Games 01115

Junee

Junee Historical Museum, Peel St, Junee, NSW 2663 - T: (02) 69242185
Local Museum
History of Junee and district 01116

Kadina

Banking and Currency Museum, 3 Graves St, Kadina, SA 5554 - T: (08) 88212906, Fax: 88212901, Internet: http://www.yp-connect.net/~vortronald. Head: Michael P. Vort-Ronald
Special Museum - 1988
Bank signage, passbooks, 2600 moneyboxes, incl material from Credit unions and building societies, Australian uncut (sheet) notes, coinage notes and associated numismatic material, also on display, gems, minerals, fossils and meteorites, special ultraviolet displays 01117

Kadina Heritage Museum, 50 Maonta Rd, Kadina, SA 5554, mail addr: POB 232, Kadina, SA 5554 - T: (08) 88212721, Fax: 88214633, E-mail: spock@kadina.mtx.net.au
Agriculture Museum / Local Museum - 1967
Curiosities and furniture of the Victorian era, early agricultural machinery, native trees, old blacksmith's shop, printing, mining, domestic utensils, place where Caroline Carleton, authoress of the 'Song of Australia', died - Dry Land Farming Interpretive Center 01118

Kalamunda

Kalamunda History Village, 56 Railway Rd, Kalamunda, WA 6076 - T: (08) 92931371. Head: Brian Burgess
Folklore Museum / Open Air Museum
Largest folk museum in WA, horse-drawn vehicles, early agriculture 01119

Stirk Cottage, 12 Kalamunda Rd, Kalamunda, WA 6926 - T: (08) 92931371
Local Museum
Domestic life 01120

Kalgoorlie

Hannans North Tourist Mine, Broad Arrow Rd, Kalgoorlie, WA 6430, mail addr: POB 829, Kalgoorlie, WA 6430 - T: (08) 90914074, Fax: 90914075. Head: Don Montefiore
Historical Museum - 1992
Underground and surface mining methods used in the 'Golden Mile', replicas of homes and buildings of the goldfields, displays of machines used in goldmining in the past 100 years 01121

Kandos

Kandos Bicentennial Industrial Museum, 22 Buchanan St, Kandos, NSW 2848 - T: (02) 63794057, 63794595, Fax: 63794380. Head: Noel Costello
Historical Museum / Local Museum
Industry, agriculture, lifestyle, railway, communication, needlework, wartime, photo and postcard coll 01122

Kangaroo Ground

Andrew Ross Museum, Primary School, Main Rd, Kangaroo Ground, Vic. 3097 - T: (03) 97120668
Historical Museum
Writing of Andrew Ross, the district's first school master (1851-1876) 01123

Kapunda

Kapunda Museum, 11 Hill St, Kapunda, SA 5373, mail addr: POB 332, Kapunda, SA 5373 - T: (08) 85662214, Fax: 85662286, E-mail: wilmel@mail.kapunda.net. Head: M. Johncock
Local Museum - 1971
Hawke & Co Engineers and Foundary coll 01124

Katamatite

Katamatite Museum, Goorang St, Katamatite, Vic. 3649 - T: (03) 58651310
Local Museum
Local history, WWI and II veterans 01125

Katanning

Katanning Historical Museum, Cnr Taylor and Amabel Sts, Katanning, WA 6317 - T: (09) 98211543, Fax: 98211543
Local Museum
Local history 01126

Katherine

Katherine Museum, Gorge Rd, Katherine, NT 5780 - T: (08) 89723945, Fax: 89723946
Local Museum
Historical items 01127

Keith

Keith National Trust Museum, Heritage St, Keith, SA 5267 - T: (08) 87551391, Fax: 87551391
Local Museum 01128

Kelvin Grove

Queensland University of Technology Art Collection, Victoria Park Rd, Kelvin Grove, Qld. 4059, mail addr: GPOB 2434, Brisbane, Qld. 4001 - T: (07) 38643240, Fax: 38645548, E-mail: s.rainbird@qut.edu.au, Internet: http://www.qut.edu.au. Head: Stephen Rainbird
Fine Arts Museum / University Museum - 1945
Contemporary Australian paintings, post-1965, contemporary Australian prints, post-1960, contemporary Australian ceramics, post-1970, 20th c Queensland art, Oodgeroo coll of aboriginal and Torres Strait Islander art 01129

Kempsey

Kempsey Historical and Cultural Museum, Pacific Hwy, Museum Complex, South Kempsey Park, Kempsey, NSW 2440 - T: (02) 65627572, Fax: 65631537
Local Museum / Folklore Museum
History of the Macleay Valley, ships and shipping, telecommunications, agriculture, music, sports, leisure and entertainment 01130

Keswick

Army Museum of South Australia, Keswick Barracks, Anzac Hwy, Keswick, SA 5035 - T: (08) 83056374, Fax: 83056393. Head: Sven Kuusk
Military Museum - 1992
Service life - army, navy, air force and woman's services - from pre-Federation to the present day, Australian military badges 01131

Kew

Kew Historical Museum, Civic Dr, Kew, Vic. 3101 - T: (03) 98538758, Fax: 98538758
Local Museum
Artefacts, early scenes of Kew, costumes 01132

Kiama

Pilots Cottage Museum, Blowhole Point, Kiama, NSW 2533, mail addr: POB 79, Kiama, NSW 2533 - T: (02) 42321079, E-mail: pgall@telstra.easymail.com.au. Head: John Cornwell
Local Museum
Maritime and regional history, shipping, exploration, industry and farming, pioneer families 01133

Kilkivan

Kilkivan Historical Museum, 12 Bligh St, Kilkivan, Qld. 4600 - T: (07) 54841191
Local Museum
Local history, mining, agricultury 01134

Kimba

Kimba and Gawler Ranges Historical Society Museum, Eyre Hwy, Kimba, SA 5641, mail addr: POB 134, Kimba, SA 5641 - T: (08) 86272349. Head: M. Eatts
Historical Museum - 1978
Local history 01135

Kingaroy

Kingaroy Art Gallery, Civic Sq, Glendon St, Kingaroy, Qld. 4610 - T: (07) 1627149, Fax: 1624806
Public Gallery 01136

Kinglake

House of Bottles, 8 Parkland Rd, Kinglake, Vic. 3763 - T: (03) 57861328, Fax: 57861328, E-mail: housebottles@tsis.com.au. Head: Les Gray, Muriel Gray
Special Museum
House build from 13,569 bottles, rocks, minerals, fossils, 6,000 ornamental shoes, bottles, memorabilia 01137

Kingscote

Hope Cottage, Cenenary Av, Kingscote, SA 5223 - T: (08) 85532656, Fax: 85532881
Local Museum
Photography, books, shipwreck articles, tractors, engines and farm machinery 01138

Kingston

Australian Antarctic Division Display, Channel Hwy, Kingston, Tas. 7050 - T: (03) 62323209, Fax: 62323415, E-mail: maria_tur@antdiv.gov.au, Internet: http://www.antdiv.gov.au
Natural History Museum
Australian National Antarctic Research Expeditions (ANARE) from 1947 onwards and current Antarctic research 01139

Kingston Pioneer Museum, 23 Crooke St, Kingston, SA 5275 - T: (08) 87672114
Local Museum
Machinery, tools, clothing, photographs and household goods 01140

Koorda

Koorda Museum, Old Hospital Bldg, Ningham Rd, Koorda, WA 6475 - T: (08) 96841297, Fax: 96841379
Local Museum
Local artefacts 01141

Korumburra

Coal Creek Heritage Village, South Gippsland Hwy, Korumburra, Vic. 3950, mail addr: POB 193, Korumburra, Vic. 3950 - T: (03) 56551811, Fax: 56551480, E-mail: ccreek@tpg.com.au, Internet: http://www.coalcreekvillage.com.au
Open Air Museum / Local Museum - 1973
Hist of the South Gippsland area, black coal mining, railways and early rural hist 01142

Kurri Kurri

Sir Edgeworth David Memorial Museum, Deakin St opposite Greta St, Kurri Kurri, NSW 2327, mail addr: 36 Gillies St, Kurri Kurri, NSW 2327 - T: (02) 49374418, Fax: 49374418
Local Museum / Historical Museum
Rural and coal fields heritage of the region, classrooms - library 01143

Kurwongbah

Boiler House Steam and Engine Museum, North Pine Country Park, Dayboro Rd, Kurwongbah, Qld. 4503 - T: (07) 32856211, E-mail: sandave@bytesite.com.au
Science&Tech Museum
Coll of large steam engines, incl. a 1900 traction engine, tractors, trucks 01144

Fire Brigade's Museum, Dayboro Rd, Kurwongbah, Qld. 4503 - T: (07) 32655163
Historical Museum
Replica fire station, fire engines 01145

Kyneton

Kyneton Museum, 67 Piper St, Kyneton, Vic. 3444 - T: (03) 54221228, Fax: 54223623, E-mail: museum@macedon-ranges.vic.gov.au, Internet: http://www.macedon-ranges.vic.gov.au. Head: Dean Michael
Local Museum - 1968
Household items, linens, laces and costumes, artworks, photographs, farm equipment, horse drawn carriages 01146

Laidley

Laidley District Historical Village, Drayton St, Laidley, Qld. 4341 - T: (07) 54651166, Fax: 54651813
Open Air Museum
Original camping ground of the teamsters on the old Drayton 01147

Das Neumann Haus Museum, Cnr Patrick and William Sts, Laidley, Qld. 4341 - T: (07) 54653241, Fax: 54653592, E-mail: dnh@laidley.qld.gov.au
Special Museum
Making church furniture, grandfather clocks and violins, musical and other cultural pursuits 01148

Lake Tabourie

Lake Tabourie Museum, Princes Hwy, Lake Tabourie, NSW 2539 - T: (02) 44549615, Internet: http://www.shoalhaven.net.au/~cathyd/tabm.html
Local Museum
Snakes, spiders, minerals, Aboriginal artefacts, shells, war memorabilia, farm items 01149

Lakes Entrance

Griffiths Sea Shell Museum and Marine Display, 125 The Esplanade, Lakes Entrance, Vic. 3909 - T: (03) 51551538, Fax: 51551538
Natural History Museum 01150

Lancefield

Lancefield Court House Museum, 55 Main Rd, Lancefield, Vic. 3435 - T: (03) 54295584
Local Museum
District history 01151

Landsborough

Shire of Landsborough Historical Society, Maleny Rd, Landsborough, Qld. 4550 - T: (07) 54941755, Fax: 54948245, E-mail: museum@powerup.com.au, Internet: http://landsboroughhistorical.com.au. Head: Wendy M.C. Dixon
Local Museum - 1976
Local history displays, tools, laundry and kitchen implements, photographs 01152

Langwarrin

McClelland Gallery, 390 McClelland Dr, Langwarrin, Vic. 3910 - T: (03) 97891671, Fax: 97891610, E-mail: mcclell@corplink.com.au. Head: Jane Alexander
Fine Arts Museum / Public Gallery - 1971
Australian painting 1900-1940, contemporary sculpture, works on paper - library 01153

Latrobe

Latrobe Bicycle Race Club Museum, Recreation Ground, Gilbert St, Latrobe, Tas. 7307
Science&Tech Museum
100yrs of carnival programs, videos of races, bicycles used by wheelrace winners 01154

Latrobe Court House Museum, Gilbert St, Latrobe, Tas. 7307 - T: (03) 64267280. Head: R. Campbell
Local Museum - 1970
Pioneer and aboriginal artifacts, courtroom furniture, hospital articles, photographs of local hist (19th/20th c social and industrial development) 01155

Launceston

City Park Radio Museum, 43 Tamar St, Launceston, Tas. 7250 - T: (03) 63315049, Fax: 63346818, E-mail: citypark@microtech.com.au, Internet: http://www.tased.edu.au/tasonline/cpr/
Science&Tech Museum
Radio 7LTN, history of Australian radio 01156

Franklin House, Hobart Rd, Franklin Village, Launceston, Tas. 7250, mail addr: POB 711, Launceston, Tas. 7250 - T: (03) 63446233, Fax: 63444033, E-mail: nat_trust@vision.net.au. Head: Peter Fearn
Decorative Arts Museum - 1960
Restored house of early 19th c, 18th c furniture, lithographs 01157

National Automobile Museum of Tasmania, 86 Cimtiere St, Launceston, Tas. 7250 - T: (03) 63348888, Fax: 63348889, E-mail: automuseum@telstra.easymail.com.au, Internet: http://www.tased.edu.au/tasonline/namt. Head: Richard Moore
Science&Tech Museum
Motor vehicles and motorcycles from the 1900s to the 1990s 01158

Queen Victoria Museum and Art Gallery, Wellington St, Launceston, Tas. 7250 - T: (03) 63233777, Fax: 63233776, E-mail: library@qvmag.tased.edu.au, Internet: http://www.qvmag.tased.edu.au. Head: C.B. Tassell
Natural History Museum / Historical Museum / Fine Arts Museum - 1891
Tasmanian history, botany, geology, zoology, paleontology, Tasmanian and general anthropology 01159

Laurieton

Camden Haven Historical Museum, Cnr Lake and Laurie Sts, Laurieton, NSW 2443 - T: (02) 65599096, E-mail: plong@tsn.cc, Internet: http://www.angelfire.com/journal/chhsi
Local Museum
Early pioneer families, local history, early timber-working tools 01160

Learmonth

Learmonth Museum, High St, Learmonth, Vic. 3352 - T: (03) 53346330
Local Museum
Local history 01161

Lenah Valley

Lady Franklin Gallery, 268 Lenah Valley Rd, Lenah Valley, Tas. 7008 - T: (03) 62280076
Public Gallery 01162

Leongatha

Firelight Museum, Leongatha North Rd, Leongatha, Vic. 3953 - T: (03) 56686272
Decorative Arts Museum
Antique lamps (1860-1940), coins, pocket watches (1803 onwards), jewellery, firearms (1560-1935) 01163

Leonora

Gwalia Historical Museum, Tower St, Leonora, WA 6438 - T: (08) 90376176
Local Museum / Science&Tech Museum
Historical mining 01164

Lilydale

Museum of Lilydale, 33 Castella St, Lilydale, Vic. 3140 - T: (03) 97397230, Fax: 97397156, Internet: http://yarra.vicnet.net.au/~yranges. Head: Elizabeth Downes
Local Museum - 1976
Memorabilia of Helen Porter Mitchell (Dame Nellie Melba), Australian operatic soprano, local artifacts 01165

Linton

Linton and District Museum, Sussex St, Linton, Vic. 3360 - T: (03) 53447430
Local Museum
Local history, Linton cemetery records, Anglican Baptisms, Roman Catholic marriages, Presbyterian Church communion rolls 01166

Lismore

Lismore Regional Art Gallery, 131 Molesworth St, Lismore, NSW 2480 - T: (02) 66222209, Fax: 66222228, E-mail: artgallery@liscity.nsw.gov.au, Internet: http://www.liscity.nsw.gov.au/information/arts/artgallery.html. Head: Irena Dobrijevich
Fine Arts Museum - 1953
Australian paintings 1930s to 1950s - library 01167

Richmond River Historical Museum, 165 Molesworth St, Lismore, NSW 2480 - T: (02) 66219993, Fax: 66219992, E-mail: rrhsi@hotmail.com. Head: M. Henderson
Local Museum
Artefacts, maps, photographs relating to the Richmond River District, river shipping material, local industries 01168

Lithgow

Eskbank House, Cnr Inch and Bennett Sts, Lithgow, NSW 2790 - T: (02) 63513557
Local Museum
Coal industry, furnuture, pottery 01169

Littlehampton

Platform 1 Heritage Farm Railway, Junction Rd, Littlehampton, SA 5250 - T: (08) 83912696, Fax: 83916864, E-mail: liebelt@hotkay.net.au, Internet: http://www.platform1.com.au. Head: Glenn T. Liebelt
Science&Tech Museum - 1968
Old farm buildings, cattle and sheep, farm machinery, international railway coll with hands on exhibits 01170

Loftus

Sydney Tramway Museum, Pitt St, Loftus, NSW 2232 - T: (02) 95423646, Fax: 95453390, E-mail: suthergf@premiers.nsw.gov.au, Internet: http://www.railpage.org.au/tram/loftus.html
Science&Tech Museum
Australia's oldest tramway museum 01171

Logan

Logan Art Gallery, Cnr Wembley Rd and Jacaranda Av, Logan, Qld. 4114 - T: (07) 38265519, Fax: 32825350, E-mail: artgallery@logan.qld.gov.au, Internet: http://www.logan.qld.gov.au. Head: Annette Turner
Public Gallery 01172

Longreach

Australian Stockman's Hall of Fame and Outback Heritage Centre, Landsborough Hwy, Longreach, Qld. 4730, mail addr: POB 171, Longreach, Qld. 4730 - T: (07) 46582166, Fax: 46582495, E-mail: museum@outbackheritage.com.au, Internet: http://www.outbackheritage.com.au
Historical Museum
Aborigines, explorers, overlanders, stockman, pioneer settlers and many others, artefacts, memorabilia 01173

Longreach Power House Museum, 12 Swan St, Longreach, Qld. 4730 - T: (07) 6583933
Science&Tech Museum
Generating equipment 01174

QANTAS Founders Outback Museum, Longreach Airport, Longreach, Qld. 4730 - T: (07) 46583737, Fax: 46580707
Science&Tech Museum
History of the early days of QANTAS, manufactures their own planes 01175

Lord Howe Island

Lord Howe Island Museum, Cnr Lagoon and Middle Beach Rds, Lord Howe Island, NSW 2898 - T: (02) 65632111, Fax: 65632092
Local Museum
Cultural and natural history of Lord Howe Island 01176

Low Head

Maritime Museum, Pilot Station, Low Head, TAS 7253 - T: (03) 63821143, Fax: 63821143
Historical Museum 01177

Lower Snug

Channel Folk Museum, 2361 Channel Hwy, Lower Snug, Tas. 7054 - T: (03) 62679169. Head: G. von Bibra
Folklore Museum - 1976
Settlers' house with original tools and implements, timber, historical documents, boatbuilding, shipping, photos 01178

Loxton

Loxton District Historical Village, Riverfront Rd, Loxton, SA 5333 - T: (08) 85847194, Fax: 85846622, E-mail: dschliebs@loxtonwaikerie.sa.gov.au. Head: Des Schliebs
Local Museum - 1970
History of pioneer settlements, leather craft 01179

Mackay

Art and Local History Collections, Gordon St, Mackay, Qld. 4740 - T: (07) 9584516, Fax: 9535693
Local Museum / Fine Arts Museum
Local artists, local history, photography coll 01180

Pine Islet Lighthouse, Cnr Harbour Rd and Mulherin Dr, Mackay, Qld. 4740 - T: (07) 9558155, Fax: 9552868
Historical Museum
Maritime and naval history 01181

Maddington

Wyalong Park Private Museum, 14 River Av, Maddington, WA 6109 - T: (08) 94591129
Local Museum
Local history, McNamara family 01182

Maffra

Maffra Sugarbeet Museum, McMahon Dr, Maffra, Vic. 3860 - T: (03) 51472680, Fax: 51473032, E-mail: jjbpublishing@maffra.net.au, Internet: http://www.maffra.net.au/heritage/musmaf.htm
Agriculture Museum / Science&Tech Museum
Sugarbeet factory, agricultural machinery, sugarbeet growing 01183

Mahogany Creek

Mahogany Inn, Great Eastern Hwy, Mahogany Creek, WA 6072 - T: (08) 92951118, Fax: 92952900, E-mail: enquiries@mahoganyinn.com.au, Internet: http://www.mahoganyinn.com.au. Head: Laurie Bonini, Julia Bonini
Local Museum - 1842
Early Australian Inn, furniture and local historical items, early English and American home wear 01184

Main Ridge

Pine Ridge Car Museum, Purves Rd, Main Ridge, Vic. 3928 - T: (03) 59896320, Fax: 59896292
Science&Tech Museum
50 motor vehicles, model cars, motoring history 01185

Maitland, New South Wales

Maitland City Art Gallery, Brough House, Church St, Maitland, New South Wales, NSW 2320 - T: (02) 49336725, Fax: 49333209. Head: M.J. Sivyer
Fine Arts Museum - 1972/73
Contemporary Australian paintings and prints, African art, Aboriginal bark paintings, Photographic coll, Pottery 01186

Maitland, South Australia

Maitland Museum, Former School, Corner Kilkerran and Gardiner Terrace, Maitland, South Australia, SA 5573, mail addr: POB 106, Maitland, South Australia, SA 5573 - T: (08) 88322220. Head: B. Neumann
Local Museum - 1972 01187

Maldon

Maldon Museum, High St, Maldon, Vic. 3463 - T: (03) 54751633
Local Museum
Mining and domestic memorabilia, family and local history records - archives 01188

Mallala

Mallala and Districts Historical Museum, 9-10 Butler St, Mallala, SA 5502 - T: (08) 85272151. Head: L.M. Earl
Historical Museum - 1970 01189

Malvern, Victoria

Stonnington Local History Collection - Malvern, Northbrook House, Malvern, Victoria, Vic. 3144 - T: (03) 95297058, Fax: 95212255, E-mail: slis@vicnet.net.au
Local Museum
Local history 01190

Stonnington Stables Museum of Art, Deakin University, 336 Glenferrie Rd, Malvern, Victoria, Vic. 3144 - T: (03) 92445123, Fax: 92445254, E-mail: - stoningtonstables@deakin.edu.au, Internet: http://www.deakin.edu.au/stoningtonstables. Head: Caroline Field
University Museum / Fine Arts Museum
Artworks by professional artists 01191

Mandurah

Mandurah Community Museum, 1 Pinjarra Rd, Mandurah, WA 6210 - T: (08) 95359511, Fax: 95356218, E-mail: museum@mandurah.wa.gov.au
Local Museum
Local history 01192

Manilla

Manilla Historical Royce Cottage Museum, 197 Manilla St, Manilla, NSW 2346 - T: (02) 67851207
Local Museum
Historical artefacts, pictures of pioneers, local history, radios 01193

Manjimup

Manjimup Timber Museum, Cnr Rose and Edward Sts, Manjimup, WA 6258 - T: (08) 97711366, Internet: http://www.mns.net.au/~timberpark
Science&Tech Museum - 1977
Timber of Western Australia, equipment used in the timber industry, dining room suite (jarrah wood) 01194

Manly

Manly Art Gallery and Museum, West Esplanade Reserve, Manly, NSW 2095 - T: (02) 99491776, Fax: 99486938
Public Gallery 01195

Manunda

Doll and Bear Museum, 8 Mayers St, Manunda, Qld. 4870 - T: (07) 40537481
Special Museum
Dolls and bears from 100 countries 01196

Marburg

Rosewood Scrub Historical Museum, Edmond St, Marburg, Qld. 4346 - T: (07) 54644634, E-mail: rshs@gil.com.au, Internet: http://www.freeyellow.com/members2/rshs/. Head: Frank Snars
Historical Museum
Local district history, pioneer families 01197

Mareeba

Mareeba District Rodeo Museum, Kerribee Park, Dimbulah Rd, Mareeba, Qld. 4880 - T: (07) 40921583, Fax: 40921583
Local Museum
Local history, farm implements, tools and machinery 01198

Mareeba Heritage Museum, 345 Byrnes St, Mareeba, Qld. 4880 - T: (07) 40925674, Fax: 40925674, E-mail: mbainfo@fastinternet.net.au
Local Museum
History of the region, unique rail ambulance 01199

Maribyrnong

Melbourne's Living Museum of the West, Pipemakers Park, Van Ness Av, Maribyrnong, Vic. 3032 - T: (03) 93183544, Fax: 93181039, E-mail: lmwbriak@livingmuseum.org.au, Internet: http://livingmuseum.org.au. Head: Peter Haffenden
Local Museum / Open Air Museum
Ecomuseum, social history, industrial archaeology, Regional enviroment 01200

Marrickville

Local Studies Collection, Marrickville Town Hall, Cnr Marrickville and Petersham Rds, Marrickville, NSW 2204 - T: (02) 93352170, Fax: 95692829
Library with Exhibitions 01201

Maryborough

Bond Store Port of Maryborough Heritage Museum, 101 Wharf St, Maryborough, Qld. 4650 - T: (07) 41231523, Fax: 41231535, E-mail: bondstor@cyberalink.com.au
Local Museum
Port history, city developed 01202

Brennan and Geraghty's Store Museum, 64 Lennox St, Maryborough, Qld. 4650 - T: (07) 41212250
Special Museum - 1990
Operating grocery store, trading records, packagings and advertising material 01203

Old Ware House Gallery, 102 Wharf St, Maryborough, Qld. 4408 - T: (07) 1224408
Public Gallery
Local artists history 01204

Wide Bay and Burnett Historical Museum, Kent St, Maryborough, Qld. 4650, mail addr: c/o School of Arts, POB 84, Maryborough, Qld. 4650 - T: (07) 41217310, Fax: 41215562, E-mail: maryhistory@hotmail.com. Head: S.K. Taylor
Local Museum
Art, crafts, decorative arts, local history 01205

Wide Bay Hospital Museum, Yaralla St, Maryborough, Qld. 4650
Historical Museum
Medical profession, records of births and deaths, surgical instruments and apparatus, dental and pathology articles 01206

Maylands

Tranby House, Johnson St, Maylands, WA 6051 - T: (08) 92722630, Fax: 92722630
Local Museum - 1977
House furnished in mid-19th c style and depicting an early colonial farmhouse 01207

McCrae

McCrae Homestead Museum, 11 Beverly Rd, McCrae, Vic. 3938 - T: (03) 59865688, Internet: http://www.nattrust.com.au
Music Museum / Fine Arts Museum
Diarist and musician, water colours and oil paintings 01208

Meadows

Prospect Hill Museum, Meadows, SA 5201. Head: K. Griggs
Local Museum 01209

Melbourne

ANZ Banking Museum, 380 Collins St, Melbourne, Vic. 3000, mail addr: 170 Foster Rd, Mount Waverley, Vic. 3149 - T: (03) 95588522, Fax: 95588525, E-mail: kennedyp@anz.com
Historical Museum
Banking equipment, manuscripts and illustrations 01210

Australian Children's Folklore Collection, Museum of Victoria, 328 Swanston St, Melbourne, Vic. 3000 - T: (03) 92912179, Fax: 92912150
Folklore Museum
Games, rhymes, jokes, riddles, superstitions and other kinds of childlore 01211

Australian Railway Museum, Champion Rd, North Williamstown, Melbourne, Vic. 3001, mail addr: POB 5177AA, Melbourne, Vic. 3001 - T: (03) 93977412. Head: N. Pearson
Science&Tech Museum - 1961
Victorian railways, locomotives, carriages, wagons, photographic display 01212

Chinese Museum, 22 Cohen Pl, Melbourne, Vic. 3000 - T: (03) 96622888
Ethnology Museum 01213

City of Melbourne Collection, Town Hall, Swanston St, Melbourne, Vic. 3000, mail addr: POB 1603M, Melbourne, Vic. 3001 - T: (03) 96588789, Fax: 96588436, Internet: http://www.melbourne.vic.gov.au/
Fine Arts Museum
Open Air Sculptures, architectural plans, photographs, visual art coll 01214

Frances Burke Textile Resource Centre, 360 Swanson St, Melbourne, Vic. 3000 - T: (03) 99252784, Fax: 99252948, E-mail: kaye.ashton@rmit.edu.au, Internet: http://www.rmit.edu.au
Fine Arts Museum / Public Gallery - 1994
Fashion and textile design 01215

Geoffrey Kaye Museum of Anaesthetic History, 630 Saint Kilda Rd, Melbourne, Vic. 3004 - T: (03) 95106299, Fax: 95106786, E-mail: westhorr@cryptic.rch.unimelb.edu.au
Historical Museum
Coll of anaesthetic, development of anaesthesia 01216

George Adams Gallery, Victorian Arts Centre, 100 Saint Kilda Rd, Melbourne, Vic. 3004 - T: (03) 92818000, Fax: 92818530, E-mail: attractions@vact.vic.gov.au, Internet: http://www.artscentre.net.au. Head: Janine Barrand
Fine Arts Museum - 1984
Western Desert Coll, textiles coll, Viola Tait coll, Louis Kahan coll, Japanese print coll, works on paper coll, paintings coll, sculptures & three dimensional work coll, Celia Rosser Banksia prints coll 01217

Gold Treasury Museum, Spring St, Melbourne, Vic. 3000 - T: (03) 96512233, Fax: 96512288, E-mail: jcooper@oldtreasurymuseum.org.au, Internet: http://www.oldtreasurymuseum.org.au. Head: Jo-Ann Cooper
Historical Museum
Gold rush history of Melbourne 01218

Golf Australia House, 153-155 Cecil St S, Melbourne, Vic. 3205 - T: (03) 96997944, Fax: 96908510, Internet: http://www.agu.org.au
Special Museum 01219

Heide Museum of Modern Art, 7 Templestowe Rd, Bulleen, Melbourne, Vic. 3105 - T: (03) 98501500, Fax: 98520154, E-mail: moma@heide.com.au, Internet: http://www.heide.com.au. Head: Warwick Reeder
Fine Arts Museum - 1981
Australian art 1935 to present, Australian and intern sculpture 01220

Hellenic Antiquities Museum, Old Customs House, 400 Flinders St, Melbourne, Vic. 3000 - T: (03) 99272700, Fax: 99272728, Internet: http://www.mov.vic.gov.au/hellenic. Head: Anna Malgorzewicz
Museum of Classical Antiquities - 1998
Authentic antiquities from ancient Greece 01221

Immigration Museum, Old Customs House, 400 Flinders St, Melbourne, Vic. 3000 - T: (03) 99272700, Fax: 99272728, Internet: http://www.mov.vic.gov.au/immigration. Head: Anna Malgorzewicz
Historical Museum - 1998
Immigration expierience, Victoria's cultural diversity - library, tribute garden, Schiavello Access gallery 01222

La Trobe University Art Museum, c/o Glenn College, Bundoora, Melbourne, Vic. 3083 - T: (03) 94792111, Fax: 94795588, E-mail: r.noble@latrobe.edu.au, Internet: http://www.latrobe.edu.au/www./glenn/Museum/ArtMuseumHome.html. Head: Rhonda Noble
Fine Arts Museum / University Museum - 1984
Australian art post - library 01223

Medical History Museum, c/o University of Melbourne, Brownless Medical Library, Melbourne, Vic. 3010 - T: (03) 83445719, Fax: 93477762, E-mail: brothers@unimelb.edu.au, Internet: http://www.arts.unimelb.edu.au/general/projects/cshs/med_hist_museum.htm. Head: Dr. Janet McCalman
Historical Museum
Savory & Moore pharmacy (19th c), coll of apothecary bottles and decorative drug jars, historic microscope coll 01224

Military History Museum, 373 Queen St, Melbourne, Vic. 3000 - T: (03) 93283805
Military Museum
Militaria memorabilia 01225

National Gallery of Victoria (not completed during redevepment until late 2002), 180 Saint Kilda Rd, Melbourne, Vic. 3004 - T: (03) 92080222, Fax: 92080245, E-mail: enquiries@ngv.vic.gov.au, Internet: http://www.ngv.vic.gov.au. Head: Dr. Gerard Vaughan
Fine Arts Museum - 1859
Old master paintings, prints and drawings, Asian art, modern European and American painting and sculpture, decorative arts, antiquities, photogr, Australian art, Aboriginal art 01226

National Gallery of Victoria on Russel (only between November 2001 until late 2002), 285-321 Russel St, Melbourne, Vic. 3000 - T: (03) 92080222, Fax: 92080245, E-mail: enquiries@ngv.vic.gov.au, Internet: http://www.ngv.vic.gov.au. Head: Dr. Gerard Vaughan
Fine Arts Museum - 1859
International art 01227

Old Melbourne Gaol and Penal Museum, Russell St, Melbourne, Vic. 3000 - T: (03) 96637228, Fax: 96390119, E-mail: omgaol@vicnet.net.au, Internet: http://www.vicnet.net.au/~omgaol. Head: Amanda Baker
Historical Museum - 1972
Kelly Armour, phrenology exhibit, hangman's box and contents, particulars of execution book 01228

Performing Arts Museum, Victorian Arts Centre, 100 Saint Kilda Rd, Melbourne, Vic. 3004 - T: (03) 92818000, Fax: 92818530, E-mail: attractions@vact.vic.gov.au, Internet: http://www.artscentre.net.au/pam. Head: Janine Barrand
Performing Arts Museum - 1978
Dame Nellie Melba Memorial Coll, including Lohengrin cape 1891, Tait Coll of Costume Design, J.C. Williamson Program Coll, archives of St. Martins Theatre, Melbourne, Emerald Hill Theatre South Melbourne, National Theatre, Melbourne, Melbourne Repertory Theatre - library 01229

Rippon Lea Estate, 192 Hotham St, Elsternwick, Melbourne, Vic. 3185 - T: (03) 95236095, Fax: 95236921, E-mail: rlnt@vicnet.net.au, Internet: http://www.vicnet.net.au/rlnt. Head: Richard Heathcote
Historic Site - 1974
Historical home (created by Frederick Thomas Sargood 1860-1972) with furniture and an extensive garden 01230

RMIT Gallery, 344 Swanston St, Storey Hall, RMIT University, Melbourne, Vic. 3000 - T: (03) 99251717, Fax: 99251738, E-mail: sarah.morris@rmit.edu.au, Internet: http://www.rmit.edu.au/departments/gallery. Head: Suzanne Davies
Public Gallery 01231

Scienceworks Museum, 2 Booker St, Melbourne, Vic. 3015 - T: (03) 93924800, Fax: 93910100, Internet: http://www.museum.vic.gov.au/scienceworks. Head: Gaye Hamilton
Science&Tech Museum - 1992
Science, technology, historic Pumping Station - planetarium 01232

Westpac Gallery → George Adams Gallery

Melrose

Melrose Courthouse Museum, Stuart St, Melrose, SA 5483 - T: (08) 86662141
Historical Museum
Police history 01233

Mentone

Charles Ferguson Museum, Old Bakery Ln, Mentone, Vic. 3194 - T: (03) 95832310
Local Museum
Original bakery fittings, historical coll, local racing industry 01234

Mordialloc Historical Society Museum, Old Bakery Ln, Mentone, Vic. 3194 - T: (03) 95836353
Local Museum 01235

Menzies Creek

Puffing Billy Steam Museum, Menzies Creek Station, Menzies Creek, mail addr: POB 451, Belgrave, Vic. 3160 - T: (03) 97546800, Fax: 97542513, E-mail: pbr@pbr.org.au, Internet: http://www.pbr.org.au. Head: John A. Robinson
Science&Tech Museum - 1961
Steam locomotives and stationary engines - the museum is part of a fully restored 14 km narrow gauge line, traffic handled by four 1900-1910 vintage locomotives 01236

Merimbula

Old School Museum, Main St, Merimbula, NSW 2548 - T: (02) 64952114, Fax: 64952114
Historical Museum 01237

Merredin

Merredin Military Museum, East Barrack St, Merredin, WA 6415 - T: (08) 90411505, Fax: 90414505
Military Museum
Restored vehicles, weapons, uniforms, period from WW I to Vietnam 01238

Merredin Railway Station Museum, Great Eastern Hwy, Merredin, WA 6415 - T: (08) 90413370, Fax: 90412525
Science&Tech Museum
Railway history 01239

Merriwa

Merriwa Colonial Museum, Bettington St, Merriwa, NSW 2329 - T: (02) 65482607, Fax: 65482271
Local Museum 01240

Merrylands

Sydney Children's Museum, Cnr Pitt and Walpole Sts, Merrylands, NSW 2160 - T: (02) 98971414, Fax: 96827410
Science&Tech Museum
Science and technology 01241

Mildura

Mildura Arts Centre, 199 Cureton Av, Mildura, Vic. 3500, mail addr: POB 3206, Mildura, Vic. 3500 - T: (03) 50188330, Fax: 50211462, E-mail: arts_centre@mildura.vic.gov.au, Internet: http://www.milduraarts.net.au. Head: Julian Bowron
Fine Arts Museum - 1956
Australian sculpture post 1961, J.R. Bow memorial, c17-c19 English and European prints coll, R.D. Elliot coll of early 20th c English, Irish and Australian art 01242

Mile End

Embroiderers Guild Museum, 16 Hughes St, Mile End, SA 5031 - T: (08) 82341104. Head: Maureen Holbrook
Decorative Arts Museum - 1987 01243

Miles

Miles and District Historical Museum, Warrego Hwy, Miles, Qld. 4415 - T: (07) 46271492, Fax: 46271492
Local Museum
Local history, largest privately owned coll of shells in Australia, lapidary coll 01244

Murilla Shire Art Gallery, 81 Dawson St, Miles, Qld. 4415 - T: (07) 46271355, Fax: 46271782, E-mail: miles.library@bigpond.com
Public Gallery 01245

Millers Point

Garrison Gallery, Historical and Military Museum, 60 Lower Fort St, Millers Point, NSW 2000 - T: (02) 92472664, Fax: 92472664, E-mail: myradem@bigpond.com
Military Museum
First military settlement, maps, Boer War to Gulf War 01246

Millicent

Millicent National Trust Museum, 1 Mount Gambier Rd, Millicent, SA 5280, mail addr: GPOB 100, Millicent, SA 5280 - T: (08) 87331192, Fax: 87333205. Head: John Northwood
Local Museum - 1960
Horse drawn vehicles/agricultural and farming implements and machinery, shipwreck room (artefacts from local wrecks), replicas of deep cave Aboriginal art 01247

Mingenew

Mingenew Museum, Cnr Victoria and Irwin Sts, Mingenew, WA 6522 - T: (08) 99281146, Fax: 99281221
Agriculture Museum / Folklore Museum
Trucks and farm implements, Aboriginal artefacts 01248

Minlaton

Minlaton National Trust Museum, POB 120, Minlaton, SA 5575 - T: (08) 88532027. Head: T.B. Chambers
Local Museum 01249

Mitcham

Schwerkolt Cottage Museum, Deep Creek Rd, Mitcham, Vic. 3132 - T: (03) 98746592, Fax: 98742330
Local Museum 01250

Mitchell

National Motorcycle Museum, 26 Kemble Court, Mitchell, ACT 2911 - T: (02) 62418131, Fax: 62418106, E-mail: museum@ozemail.com.au, Internet: http://www.ozemail.com.au/~museum/
Science&Tech Museum
Largest coll vintage, veteran, classic and interesting motorcycles 01251

Moe

Gippsland Heritage Park, Princes Hwy, Moe, Vic. 3825, mail addr: POB 337, Moe, Vic. 3825 - T: (03) 51273082, Fax: 51278709. Head: Bill Harrington
Open Air Museum - 1969
Over 30 original buildings brought to the site from all over Gippsland now fully restored, incl 'Bushy Park' homestead of explorer Angus McMillan, 'Loren' early 19t h c portable home and extensive coll of fully restored horse drawn vehicles 01252

Moe Historical Museum, 2 High St, Moe, Vic. 3852 - T: (03) 56331326, 51271269
Local Museum
Industry and agricultural undertakings in the region, gold mining, timber milling, dairy farming, transport, coal mining 01253

Molong

Molong Historical Museum, 20 Riddell St, Molong, NSW 2866
Local Museum - 1970 01254

Mona Vale

Mona Vale Aero Nautical Museum, 5 Hunter St N, Mona Vale, NSW 2103 - T: (02) 99992662, Fax: 99992662
Science&Tech Museum
Armstrong Siddley and cylinder radial aircraft engine, badges, insignia, medals, uniforms, helmets, cameras, compasses, model aircraft/ships 01255

Moonah

Moonah Arts Centre, 65 Hopkins St, Moonah, Tas. 7009 - T: (03) 62281192, Fax: 62731056
Fine Arts Museum 01256

Moonta

Moonta Mines Museum, Verran Tce, Moonta, SA 5558 - T: (08) 88251891, 88252152, Fax: 88252930. Head: E. Woodward
Historical Museum
Cornish heritage and settlement of the district 01257

Moonta National Trust Museum, POB 23, Moonta, SA 5558 - T: (08) 88252152, 88251944, Fax: 88251944. Head: J. Bandt
Local Museum 01258

Moora

Berkshire Mill Museum, Berkshire Valley, Moora, WA 6510 - T: (08) 96549040
Local Museum / Science&Tech Museum
Coll of farming, domestic, sporting, educational and photographic articles 01259

Moorabbin

Moorabbin Air Museum, Airport, Moorabbin, Vic. 3189 - T: (03) 95807752
Science&Tech Museum 01260

Mooroopna

Historical Museum of Mooroopna, McLennan St, Mooroopna, Vic. 3629, mail addr: POB 206, Mooroopna, Vic. 3629 - T: (03) 58252403, Fax: 58252696, Internet: http://www.mooroopna.org.au/hsm.htm. Head: Dr. John MacKellar
Local Museum 01261

Morawa

Morawa Old Police Station Museum, Cnr Prater and Gill Sts, Morawa, WA 6623
Local Museum
Cells, local history, space debris, farm machinery, household and personal items, medical and dental equipment 01262

Moree

Moree Plains Gallery, 25 Frome St, Moree, NSW 2400, mail addr: POB 1108, Moree, NSW 2400 - T: (02) 67573320, Fax: 67527173, E-mail: gallery@northnet.com.au. Head: Bruce Tindale
Fine Arts Museum / Public Gallery - 1988
Australian landscapes 1980 to present, Australian sculpture 1988 to present, Aboriginal coll, Urban Aboriginal coll 1980 to present, artefacts from the Kamilaroi people - Kamilaroi Gallery 01263

Morgan

Nor West Bend Museum, Nor West Bend Station, Morgan, SA 5320 - T: (08) 85403329
Local Museum
Folk and local history 01264

Port of Morgan Historic Museum, River Front Rd, Morgan, SA 5320, mail addr: POB 98, Morgan, SA 5320 - T: (08) 82359266, 85402130, 85402136, Fax: 83536199, 85402130. Head: Dr. B. Douglas
Local Museum
River boat, rail and horse transport hist 1800-1900 01265

Morley

Ellis House, Neville St, Morley, WA 6062 - T: (08) 92720624, Fax: 92720665
Fine Arts Museum
Art centre 01266

Morningside

Queensland College of Art Gallery, Clearview Terrace, Morningside, Qld. 4170, mail addr: c/o Queensland College of Art, POB 84, Morningside, Qld. 4170 - T: (07) 38753140, Fax: 38753199, E-mail: s.myntyre@mailbox.gu.edu.au, Internet: http://www.gu.edu.au. Head: Sophie Myntyre
Fine Arts Museum / University Museum - 1982
Australian and Queensland oil paintings, prints, watercolours, ceramics 01267

Mornington

Mornington Peninsula Arts Centre, Dunns Rd, Mornington, Vic. 3931 - T: (059) 7543955, Fax: 770377. Head: Elizabeth Gleeson
Fine Arts Museum - 1969
Australian paintings, drawings and prints - library 01268

Old Mornington Post Office Museum, Corner Main St and Esplanade, Mornington, Vic. 3931
Local Museum - 1968
Local history, folklore, photos of historic homes 01269

Morwell

Latrobe Regional Gallery, 138 Commercial Rd, Morwell, Vic. 3840 - T: (03) 51341364, Fax: 51341874, E-mail: rodsc@latrobe.vic.gov.au, Internet: http://www.lvbusinessdirectory.com/lrg. Head: Rodney Scherer
Fine Arts Museum - 1971
Contemporary Australian paintings, prints, sculpture, glass, ceramics - library 01270

Mount Barker

Police Station Museum, Albany Hwy, Mount Barker, WA 6324 - T: (08) 98512505
Historical Museum - 1966
Household and farming artefacts 01271

Mount Gambier

Riddoch Art Gallery, 6 Commercial St E, Mount Gambier, SA 5290, mail addr: POB 980, Mount Gambier, SA 5290 - T: (08) 87239566, Fax: 87239161. Head: Louise Haigh
Fine Arts Museum - 1981
Contemporary Australian art, 'Art in Wood' Coll, 1970s Australian photography, Rodney Gooch Collection of Aboriginal art from Utopia - library 01272

Mount Hawthorn

Anzac Cottage Museum, 38 Kalgoorlie St, Mount Hawthorn, WA 6016
Military Museum
Memorial to the Great War, militaria, military history, weapons, arms 01273

Mount Morgan

Mount Morgan Historical Museum, 87 Morgan St, Mount Morgan, Qld. 4714 - T: (07) 49382122
Local Museum
Mining alcoves, Kitchen alcove 01274

Mount Victoria

Mount Victoria and District Historical Museum, Station St, Mount Victoria, NSW 2786 - T: (02) 47871190
Local Museum
Early Australian memorabilia, local artefacts 01275

Moven

Morven Historical Museum, Albert St, Moven, Qld. 4468 - T: (07) 46548131, Fax: 46548281
Local Museum
Old manual wool press, local artefacts 01276

Mudgee

Mudgee Colonial Inn Museum, 126 Market St, Mudgee, NSW 2850 - T: (02) 63723157
Local Museum
Iron foundry, farm machinery and horsedrawn vehicles, Mudgee's past 01277

Mullewa

Monsignor Hawes Priest House Museum, Dorey St, Mullewa, WA 6630 - T: (08) 99611165
Religious Arts Museum 01278

Murchison Settlement Museum, Gascoyne Rd, Mullewa, WA 6630 - T: (08) 99637680, Fax: 99637966
Local Museum 01279

Mullumbimby

Brunswick Valley Museum, Cnr Stuart and Myocum Sts, Mullumbimby, NSW 2482 - T: (02) 66884356, Fax: 66884356
Local Museum
Local history, machinery tools, local trades incl. timber cutting, coach building, plumbing and printing 01280

Mundubbera

Mundubbera and District Historical Museum, Frank McCauley St, Mundubbera, Qld. 4626
Local Museum
History of the district, farm machinery, sheds, tools, a slab shed and harness, dairy industry, butter factory 01281

Murray Bridge

Captain's Cottage Museum, 12 Thomas St, Murray Bridge, SA 5253 - T: (08) 85310049
Local Museum
History of Murray Bridge, dairy industry 01282

Murrumburrah

Murrumburrah-Harden Historical Museum, Albury St, Murrumburrah, NSW 2595
Local Museum
Local history 01283

Murrurundi

Murrurundi Museum, Mayne St, Murrurundi, NSW 2338 - T: (02) 65466142
Local Museum
Local history 01284

Murtoa

Murtoa Water Tower Museum, Concordia Complex, Comyn St and Soldier Av, Murtoa, Vic. 3390 - T: (03) 53852582, Fax: 53852790, E-mail: sydgreg@wimmera.com.au. Head: Peter Adler
Local Museum / Natural History Museum
Local history, coll of 130 year old James Hill's taxidermy (ca. 500 birds and animals from USA, New Guinea, Australia) 01285

Murwillumbah

Tweed River Regional Art Gallery, Tumbulgum Rd, Murwillumbah, NSW 2484, mail addr: POB 816, Murwillumbah, NSW 2484 - T: (02) 66702790, Fax: 66727585, E-mail: tweedart@tweed.nsw.gov.au, Internet: http://amol.org.au. Head: Gary Corbett
Fine Arts Museum - 1988
Australian portraits from all periods, work by regional artists and craftspeople - library 01286

Muswellbrook

Muswellbrook Regional Arts Centre, POB 122, Muswellbrook, NSW 2333 - T: (02) 65493880, Fax: 65493886, E-mail: artscentre@muswellbrook.nsw.gov.au, Internet: http://www.muswellbrook.nsw.gov.au/visitors/artscentre.html. Head: Rhonda Hunt
Fine Arts Museum - 1976
Paintings, drawings, photogr, Australian art 01287

Weidmann Cottage Heritage Centre, 132 Bridge St, Muswellbrook, NSW 2333 - T: (02) 65478143
Local Museum / Science&Tech Museum
Antiques, artefacts and items of local and historical interest 01288

Muttaburra

Dr. Arratta Memorial Museum, Old Hospital Rd, Muttaburra, Qld. 4732 - T: (07) 6585641, Fax: 6585665
Historical Museum 01289

Nambucca Heads

Headland Historical Museum, Headland Dr, Nambucca Heads, NSW 2448 - T: (02) 65686380, E-mail: jphil@midcoast.com.au. Head: Jean Philipson
Local Museum
Early days of timber and shipping, furniture, china, ceramics, craft, farming 01290

Nannup

Kealley's Gemstone Museum, 125 Warren Rd, Nannup, WA 6275 - T: (08) 97561182
Decorative Arts Museum
Information cards, most gemstones, stamps and shells 01291

Naracoorte

Naracoorte Art Gallery, 91 Ormerod, Naracoorte, SA 5271, mail addr: POB 45, Naracoorte, SA 5271 - T: (08) 87623390
Fine Arts Museum - 1968
Etchings by John Goodchild, Australian work on paper, regional art and craft 01292

Naracoorte Museum, Home of 100 Collections, 1 Jenkins Tce, Naracoorte, SA 5271 - T: (08) 87622059, E-mail: nctemuseum@optusnet.com.au, Internet: http://www.caveland.com.au/museum. Head: Barry Francis
Special Museum / Local Museum
Antiques, gemstones, butterflies, clocks,weapons, cameras, coins, birds eggs, badges, irons, bottles, fossils and shells, local reptiles 01293

Narembeen

Narembeen Historical Museum, Savage St, Narembeen, WA 6369 - T: (08) 90647299
Local Museum
Sporting, farming, education and household items 01294

Narooma

Narooma Lighthouse Museum, Princes Hwy, Narooma, NSW 2546 - T: (02) 44762881, Fax: 44761690, E-mail: narooma@naturecoast-tourism.com.au, Internet: http://www.naturecoast-tourism.com.au
Science&Tech Museum
Lighthouse mechanism from Montague Island and historical shipping 01295

Narrabri

Narrabri Old Gaol Heritage Centre, Cnr Bowen and Barwon Sts, Narrabri, NSW 2390 - T: (02) 67924742
Local Museum
Life in the town of Narrabri and surrounding agricultural lands 01296

Narrandera

Parkside Cottage Museum, Cnr Cadell and Twynam Sts, Narrandera, NSW 2700 - T: (02) 69591372
Historical Museum
World wide shell coll, 1000 years of monarchy, McArthur cloak (1816) 01297

Narre Warren North

Melbourne Tank Museum, 456 Belgrave-Hallam Rd, Narre Warren North, Vic. 3804 - T: (03) 97968188. Head: John Belfield
Military Museum
Tanks, jeeps, trucks, wreckers, artillery, trench art coll 01298

Narrogin

Narrogin Gallery, Town Hall Complex, Federal St, Narrogin, WA 6312, mail addr: POB 188, Narrogin, WA 6312 - T: (08) 98811944, Fax: 98813092
Fine Arts Museum - 1986
Australian art 01299

Narrogin Old Courthouse Museum, Old Courthouse Bldg, Loc 260, Cnr Egerton and Earl Sts, Narrogin, WA 6312, mail addr: POB 188, Narrogin, WA 6312 - T: (08) 98811944, Fax: 98813092
Local Museum - 1976
Local history, pottery - library 01300

Nathan

Griffith Artworks, Nathan Campus, Kessels Rd, Nathan, Qld. 4111 - T: (07) 38757414, Fax: 38757932, E-mail: artworks@gu.edu.au, Internet: http://www.gu.edu.au/centre/artworks
Fine Arts Museum / University Museum - 1975
Contemporary Australian art 1970 to present, new media - library 01301

Griffith University Gallery → Griffith Artworks

Nedlands

Berndt Museum of Anthropology, University of Western Australia, 35 Stirling Hwy, Nedlands, WA 6909 - T: (08) 93802854, Fax: 93801062, E-mail: bmuseum@cyllene.uwa.edu.au, Internet: http://www.berndt.uwa.edu.au. Head: Dr. J.E. Stanton
Ethnology Museum / University Museum - 1976
Australian Aboriginal crayon drawings on paper, children's art, photographs, bark paintings, sculpture, tape recordings 01302

Historic and Ethnic Instrument Collection, c/o School of Music, University of Western Australia, Nedlands, WA 6907 - T: (08) 93802051, Fax: 93801076, E-mail: jbelbin@cyllene.uwa.edu.au. Head: M. Coughlan
Music Museum / University Museum
Ethic (maily Asian) and historical European musical instruments, Japanese gamelan 01303

Royal Western Australian Historical Museum, Stirling House, 49 Broadway, Nedlands, WA 6009 - T: (08) 93863841, Fax: 93863309, E-mail: histwest@git.com.au, Internet: http://www.git.net.au/~histwest
Local Museum / Historical Museum
Social and domestic trends in the community, WA history, artworks of local cultural heritage, dolls, pioneer families, costumes 01304

Neutral Bay

Nutcote Museum, 5 Wallaringa Av, Neutral Bay, NSW 2089 - T: (02) 99534453, Fax: 99530302, Internet: http://www.maygibbs.com.au
Special Museum - 1994
Children's author and illustrator May Gibbs 01305

New Norcia

New Norcia Museum and Art Gallery, Great Northern Hwy, New Norcia, WA 6509 - T: (08) 96548056, Fax: 96548124, E-mail: museum_nn@yahoo.com.au, Internet: http://www.newnorcia.wa.edu.au. Head: Christopher Power
Historical Museum / Fine Arts Museum - 1951
European oil paintings, ecclesiastical vestments, aboriginal artifacts, rare books, local history - library 01306

Newcastle

Fort Scratchley Museum, Off Nobbys Rd, Newcastle, NSW 2300, mail addr: POB 971, Newcastle, NSW 2300 - T: (02) 49293066, Fax: 49270889
Historical Museum
Australia's coast defences 01307

Newcastle Region Art Gallery, 1 Laman St, Newcastle, NSW 2300 - T: (02) 49745100, Fax: 49745105, E-mail: nmitzevich@ncc.nsw.gov.au, Internet: http://www.ncc.nsw.gov.au. Head: Nick Mitzevich
Fine Arts Museum - 1956
Aboriginal bark, Australian art, Japanese ceramics, Australian ceramics 01308

Newcastle Region Maritime Museum, Fort Scratchley, off Nobbys Rd, Newcastle, NSW 2300 - T: (02) 49292588, Fax: 49295457, E-mail: nrmm@hunterlink.net.au. Head: Pip Linnerr
Historical Museum
Small boats, model ships, maritime artefacts of the Newcastle area 01309

Newcastle Regional Museum, 787 Hunter St, Newcastle, NSW 2300 - T: (02) 49741400, Fax: 49741405, E-mail: nrmuseum@ncc.nsw.gov.au, Internet: http://www.amol.org.au/newcastle
Local Museum
Local, natural, social and domestic or industrial material 01310

Newhaven

Churchill Island Agricultural Museum, Phillip Island Rd, Newhaven, Vic. 3925 - T: (03) 59567214
Agriculture Museum / Open Air Museum
Farm engines, machinery, tools 01311

Newtown

Camperdown Cemetery, 187 Church St, Newtown, NSW 2042 - T: (02) 95572043, Fax: 95165786, E-mail: rayeh@optushome.com.au
Historical Museum - 1848
Victorian funerary decoration and statuary, church of colonial architect Edmund Blacket 01312

Nile

Clarendon House, Nile, Tas. 7212 - T: (03) 63986220, Fax: 63986220. Head: R.M. Green
Decorative Arts Museum - 1962
Restored country house of early 19th c, late 18th and early 19th c English furniture, oil painting by John Glover, costumes 01313

Nimbin

Nimbin Museum, 62 Cullen St, Nimbin, NSW 2480 - T: (02) 66891123, Fax: 66891842, E-mail: hemp@nrg.com.au, Internet: http://www.nimbinaustralia.com/museum. Head: Michael Balderstone
Local Museum
Aboriginal, pioneer, and hippy eras 01314

Norman Park

Earlystreet, 75 McIlwraith Av, Norman Park, Qld. 4170
Open Air Museum - 1965
Early Queensland buildings, artifacts and gardens 01315

Norseman

Norseman Historical and Geological Collection, School of Mines Bldg, Battery Rd, Norseman, WA 6443, mail addr: POB 14, Norseman, WA 6443 - T: (08) 90391071
Natural History Museum - 1972
Artifacts from construction of Coolgardie-Dundas (Norseman) Balladonia-Eucla telegraph line (constructed 1896-97), household equipment and mining tools, mining books (1920-1970) - library 01316

North Geelong

Geelong Naval and Maritime Museum, Swinburne St, North Geelong, Vic. 3125 - T: (03) 52772260, Fax: 52772260, Internet: http://www.zades.comau/geelong/maritime.html
Historical Museum
Coll of ship models, maritime and naval artefacts, early navigation instruments, uniforms, medals 01317

North Rockhampton

Dreamtime Cultural Centre, Bruce Hwy, North Rockhampton, Qld. 4702 - T: (07) 9361655, Fax: 9361671
Folklore Museum
Aboriginal artefacts 01318

North Sydney

Don Bank Museum, 6 Napier St, North Sydney, NSW 2060 - T: (02) 99368440, Fax: 99368440, E-mail: genmangr@northsydney.nsw.gov.au, Internet: http://www.northsydney.nsw.gov.au
Historical Museum
Timber slab house construction, social history 01319

Mary Mackillop Place Museum, 7 Mount St, North Sydney, NSW 2060 - T: (02) 89124878, Fax: 89124835, E-mail: mackillop@sosj.org.au, Internet: http://www.marymackillopplace.org.au. Head: Scott Jessup
Historical Museum / Religious Arts Museum
Historical religious 01320

Northam

Old Railway Station Museum, Fitzgerald St, Northam, WA 6401 - T: (08) 96225487
Science&Tech Museum
Steam locomotive and carriages on static display 01321

Northampton

Chiverton House Museum, 80 Hampton Rd, Northampton, WA 6535 - T: (08) 99341215, Fax: 99341215. Head: P. Sellers
Folklore Museum
Changing lifestyles influenced by mining (1848-1950), restored agricultural machinery - genealogy research, herbarium 01322

Northcliffe

Northcliffe Pioneer Museum, Wheatley Coast Rd, Northcliffe, WA 6262
Local Museum 01323

Norton Summit

Old Council Chambers Museum, Main Lobethal Rd, Norton Summit, SA 5136
Special Museum
Local fruit growing and market, gardening industries 01324

Norwood

Adelaide Central Gallery, 45 Osmond Terrace, Norwood, SA 5067 - T: (08) 3642809, Fax: 3644865, E-mail: acsa@acsa.sa.edu.au, Internet: http://www.acsa.sa.edu.au. Head: Graham Ryan
Public Gallery 01325

Adelaide Lithuanian Museum and Archives, 6-8 Eastry St, Norwood, SA 5067 - T: (08) 83621074. Head: D. Pocius
Historical Museum - 1967
Lithuanian art, crafts, stamps, amber, artefacts and uniforms of free Lithuania's officials 01326

Nowra

Meroogal House, Cnr West and Worrigee Sts, Nowra, NSW 2541 - T: (02) 44218150, Fax: 44212747, Internet: http://www.hht.nsw.gov.au. Head: Peter Watts
Historical Museum
Women's history, daily routines, domestic chores, social life 01327

Nowra Museum, Cnr Plunkett and Kinghorne Sts, Nowra, NSW 2541 - T: (02) 44217008
Local Museum
Life in the Nowra district, watercolour paintings 01328

Nundah

Nundah and Districts Historical Museum, Sir William Knox Archives and Resource Centre, Nundah, Qld. 4012 - T: (07) 32606703, Fax: 32663617
Local Museum
History and heritage 01329

Oakey

Flypast Museum of Australian Army Flying, Army Airfield, Oakey, Qld. 4401 - T: (07) 6917666, Fax: 6917675
Military Museum / Science&Tech Museum 01330

Oaklands

Doug Kerr Vintage Museum, Coreen St, Oaklands, NSW 2646 - T: (02) 60354243, Fax: 60354226. Head: Peter Kerr
Agriculture Museum / Science&Tech Museum
History of agricultural and mining machinery 01331

Oakleigh

Oakleigh and District Museum, Mechanics Institute, Drummond St, Oakleigh, Vic. 3166
Local Museum
Local history 01332

One Tree Hill

Uleybury School Museum, Cornishman's Hill Rd, One Tree Hill, SA 5114 - T: (08) 82807396
Historical Museum / Fine Arts Museum
Children's art and craft 01333

Ongerup

Ongerup and Needilup District Museum, Eldridge St, Ongerup, WA 6336 - T: (08) 98282282, Fax: 98282281, E-mail: 100035.371@compuserve.com. Head: Vicki O'Neill
Local Museum
Local, natural history, agricultural machinery 01334

Onslow

Onslow Goods Shed Museum, Clarke Pl, Onslow, WA 6710 - T: (08) 91846165, Fax: 91846615
Science&Tech Museum
Camel Train, train and carriage used in transport of goods, wool ramps 01335

Orange

Orange Regional Gallery, Civic Sq, Byng St, Orange, NSW 2800, mail addr: POB 35, Orange, NSW 2800 - T: (02) 63615136, Fax: 63615100, E-mail: sisleya@ix.net.au, Internet: http://www.org.nsw.gov.au. Head: Alan Sisley
Fine Arts Museum / Decorative Arts Museum - 1986
Contemporary Australian ceramics, costume, jewellery, Australian painting 01336

Orroroo

Yesteryear Costume Gallery, 50 Second St, Orroroo, SA 5431 - T: (08) 86581032. Head: B.L. Catford
Special Museum
Costume and accessories (1870s to 1980s) 01337

Ouyen

Ouyen Local History Resource Centre, Oke St, Ouyen, Vic. 3490, mail addr: POB 131, Ouyen, Vic. 3490 - T: (03) 50921763, Fax: 50921107, E-mail: ouyenlhc@telstra.com.au, Internet: http://www.vicnet.net.au/ouyenlhc. Head: Merle Pole
Historical Museum 01338

Paddington

Army Museum, Victoria Barracks, Oxford St, Paddington, NSW 2021 - T: (02) 93393330, Fax: 93393068
Military Museum
Military heritage in New South Wales 01339

Australian Centre for Photography, 257 Oxford St, Paddington, NSW 2021 - T: (02) 93321455, Fax: 93316887, E-mail: info@acp.au.com, Internet: http://www.acp.au.com. Head: Alasdair Foster
Fine Arts Museum - 1974
Australian photography - library 01340

Ivan Dougherty Gallery, University of New South Wales, Selwyn St, Paddington, NSW 2021, mail addr: c/o College of Fine Arts, POB 259, Paddington, NSW 2021 - T: (02) 93850726, Fax: 93850603, E-mail: idg@unsw.edu.au, Internet: http://www.idg.cofa.unsw.edu.au. Head: Nick Waterlow Oam
Fine Arts Museum - 1977
College of Fine Arts Coll of Australian sculpture, prints, paintings, photographs, crafts 1970s to present - library 01341

Pakenham

Berwick Pakenham Historical Museum, John St, Pakenham, Vic. 3810, mail addr: 330 Officer S Rd, Officer, Vic. 3809 - T: (03) 59432271, Fax: 59431204. Head: William Ronald
Local Museum
Paintings, plans, photos, clothes, smaller artefacts and histories, models, large coll of Canes 01342

Palmyra

Miller Bakehouse Museum, Baal St, Palmyra, WA 6157, mail addr: POB 141, Melville, WA 6156 - T: (08) 93391390, Internet: http://www.nma.gov.au/amol
Special Museum - 1988
Bakers' trade 01343

Parkes

Blundell's Cottage, Wendouree Dr, Parkes, ACT 2600 - T: (02) 62732667
Open Air Museum / Folklore Museum
Farming life, history of Canberra's development, its social and working lifestyle 01344

Old Parliament House, King George Tce, Parkes, ACT 2600 - T: (02) 62708222, Fax: 62708111, E-mail: oph.info@dcita.gov.au, Internet: http://www.oldparliamenthouse.gov.au. Head: Craddock Morton
Historical Museum
Political and social history of Australia 01345

Questacon The National Science and Technology Centre, King Edward Tce, Parkes, ACT 2600 - T: (02) 62702800, Fax: 62702808, E-mail: info@questacon.edu.au, Internet: http://www.questacon.edu.au. Head: Annie Ghisalberti
Science&Tech Museum
Interactive exhibitions 01346

Parkside

Contemporary Art Centre of South Australia, 14 Porter St, Parkside, SA 5063 - T: (08) 82722682, Fax: 83734286, E-mail: cacsa@camtech.com.au
Public Gallery 01347

Parkville, Victoria

Cunningham Dax Collection of Psychiatric Art, 35 Poplar Rd, Parkville, Victoria, Vic. 3052 - T: (03) 93422394, Fax: 93812008, E-mail: j.morley@papyrus.mhri.edu.au, Internet: http://www.ozemail.com.au/~ecdax. Head: N. Gorman
Fine Arts Museum 01348

George Paton Gallery, c/o University of Melbourne, Union House, Parkville, Victoria, Vic. 3052 - T: (03) 93445418, Fax: 93494559, E-mail: gpg@musumail.union.unimelb.edu.au. Head: Susan Hewitt
Fine Arts Museum / University Museum - 1971 01349

Grainger Museum, c/o University of Melbourne, Gate 13, Royal Parade, Parkville, Victoria, Vic. 3052 - T: (03) 93445270, Fax: 93491707, E-mail: grainger@unimelb.edu.au, Internet: http://www.lib.unimelb.edu.au/collections/grainger/museum.home.html. Head: Geoffrey Down
Music Museum / University Museum - 1935
Grainger coll of 'free-music' machines (early synthesisers), music (manuscripts and published), sound archives, correspondence, furniture, costumes, works of art, ethnographic material and other personal items from Grainger's lifetime, archival records of the Royal Victorian Liedertafel,

music manuscripts of G.W.L. Marshall-Hall, Florence Ewart, Henry Tate, Ian Bonighton, smaller Australian coll, folk music from Great Britain, Denmark and the South Pacific 01350

Museum of Art, c/o University of Melbourne, Parkville, Victoria, Vic. 3052 - T: (03) 93445148, Fax: 93444484, Internet: http://www.arts.unimelb.edu.au/projects/gallery/. Head: Frances Lindsay
Fine Arts Museum / University Museum - 1971
Australian art, Leonhard Adams ethnographical coll (mainly Oceanic) 01351

Parramatta

New South Wales Lancers Memorial Museum, Linden House, Lancer Barracks, Smith St, Parramatta, NSW 2150 - T: (04) 14886461, Fax: (02) 47333873, E-mail: john.howells@lancers.org.au, Internet: http://www.lancers.org.au. Head: L.A. Koles
Military Museum - 1957
Australian Light Horse Memorabilia, armoured vehicles 01352

Pelaw Main

Richmond Main Mining Museum, Mulbring Rd, Pelaw Main, NSW 2327 - T: (02) 49913777, Fax: 49907237
Science&Tech Museum
Richmond Main Colliery, union/social history 01353

Richmond Vale Railway Museum, Mulbring Rd, Pelaw Main, NSW 2327 - T: (02) 49361891, Fax: 49362921, E-mail: PHBJM@alinga.newcastle.edu.au. Head: Chris Cleary
Science&Tech Museum / Open Air Museum
9 Steam locomotives, steam cranes, industrial diesel locomotives, Passenger carriages 01354

Penneshaw

Penneshaw Maritime and Folk Museum, Howard Dr, Penneshaw, SA 5222 - T: (08) 85531340, Fax: 85531340, E-mail: mycobscd@kin.net.au. Head: Graham Trethewey
Historical Museum / Folklore Museum
History and shipwrecks of Kangaroo Island, Aboriginal women, agriculture, industry, social and domestic life 01355

Perth

Army Museum of Western Australia, 2 Bulwer St, Perth, WA 6000
Military Museum - 1977
Memorabilia of Western Australian formations and units 01356

Art Gallery of Western Australia, Perth Cultural Centre, James St, Perth, WA 6000, mail addr: POB 8363, Perth, WA 6849 - T: (08) 94926600, Fax: 94926655, E-mail: admin@artgallery.wa.gov.au, Internet: http://www.artgallery.wa.gov.au. Head: Alan Dodge
Fine Arts Museum - 1895
Fine art and craft objects 01357

Western Australian Museum, Francis St, Perth, WA 6000 - T: (08) 94272700, Fax: 94272882, E-mail: reception@museum.wa.gov.au, Internet: http://www.museum.wa.gov.au. Head: Dr. Gary Morgan
Natural History Museum / Archaeological Museum / Science&Tech Museum / Historical Museum - 1891
Zoology, paleontology, mineralogy, meteorites, anthropology, archeology, technology, maritime archeology, Western Australian hist - library, discovery centre 01358

Pine Creek

Pine Creek Museum, Railway Tce, Pine Creek, NT 847 - T: (08) 89761221, Fax: 89761311
Local Museum
Development NT, Chinese relics, minerals, war years, communications, mining and social history 01359

Pinjarra

Old Blythewood, South West Hwy, Pinjarra, WA 6208 - T: (08) 95311485
Local Museum - 1976
Old Blythewood house furnished mid-19th c style and depicting and early colonial farm home 01360

Pinnaroo

D.A. Wurfel Grain Collection, Railway Tce, Pinnaroo, SA 5304 - T: (08) 85778115
Special Museum 01361

Pinnaroo Heritage Museum, Railway Tce S, Pinnaroo, SA 5304 - T: (08) 85778115
Local Museum / Science&Tech Museum
Local history, railway, pioneer days 01362

Pinnaroo Printing Museum, Soldiers Memorial Park, South Tce, Pinnaroo, SA 5304 - T: (08) 85778115
Science&Tech Museum / Fine Arts Museum
Old type, typesetting machines, letterpress printing machines 01363

Pittsworth

Pittsworth and District Historical Museum, Pioneer Way, Pittsworth, Qld. 4358 - T: (07) 6931997
Local Museum 01364

Point Cook

Royal Australian Air Force Museum, Point Cook Rd, Point Cook, Vic. 3029 - T: (03) 92561300, Fax: 92561692, E-mail: raafmus@ozemail.com.au, Internet: http://www.raafmuseum.com.au
Military Museum 01365

Pomona

Noosa Shire Museum, 29 Factory St, Pomona, Qld. 4568 - T: (02) 47851080
Local Museum
Local history 01366

Port Adelaide

National Railway Museum, Lipson St, Port Adelaide, SA 5015 - T: (08) 83411690, Fax: 83411626, E-mail: natrailmuseum@hotmail.com, Internet: http://www.natrailmuseum.org.au
Science&Tech Museum - 1988
Pullman Adelaide dining car, Webb locomotive, railway vehicles - archive, library 01367

Port Community Art Centre, 66 Commercial Rd, Port Adelaide, SA 5015 - T: (08) 83412430, E-mail: pcac@arcom.com.au
Public Gallery 01368

Port Dock Station Railway Museum → National Railway Museum

South Australian Aviation Museum, Cnr Ocean Steamers Rd and Honey St, Port Adelaide, SA 5015 - T: (08) 82401230, Fax: 82401230, E-mail: hillani@@adam.com.au, Internet: http://www.saam.org.au. Head: Pieter Van Dyk
Science&Tech Museum
Aircraft, engines, rockets, artefacts 01369

South Australian Maritime Museum, 126 Lipson St, Port Adelaide, SA 5015 - T: (08) 82076255, Fax: 82076266
Historical Museum
Maritime history, lighthouse (1869), three floating vessels 01370

Port Albert

Port Albert Maritime Museum, Tarraville Rd, Port Albert, Vic. 3971 - T: (03) 51825264
Historical Museum
Wreck of the Clonmel, navigational acids, charts and working models, a shell coll - archive 01371

Port Arthur

Port Arthur Historic Site, Port Arthur Historic Site, Port Arthur, Tas. 7182 - T: (03) 62512310, Fax: 62512311, E-mail: lesley.kirby@portarthur.org.au, Internet: http://www.portarthur.org.au
Historical Museum
Prison settlement, Asylum building 01372

Port Augusta

Homestead Park Pioneer Museum, 2 Elsie St, Port Augusta, SA 5700 - T: (08) 86422035
Local Museum
Local history 01373

Port Douglas

Treasure Trove Shipwreck Museum, 6 Dixie St, Port Douglas, Qld. 4871 - T: (07) 40995858, Fax: 40994300
Science&Tech Museum / Historical Museum
Coll of artefacts from ships and shipwrecks 01374

Port Elliot

Port Elliot Historical Museum, Railway Station, Port Elliot, SA 5212 - T: (08) 85542024, Fax: 85543331
Local Museum 01375

Port Fairy

Port Fairy Historic Lifeboat Station, Griffiths St, Port Fairy, Vic. 3284 - T: (03) 55682632, Fax: 55682632, E-mail: martange@bigpond.com, Internet: http://www.portfairy.vic.gov.au/lifeboat. Head: Noel Adamsom
Historical Museum
Maritime rescue equipment, sea-going lifeboat, pulling and sailing 01376

Port Fairy History Centre, Gipps St, Port Fairy, Vic. 3284 - T: (03) 55682263, E-mail: pfhs@ansonic.com.au. Head: D. Rearoon
Local Museum
Shipping and seafarers, local properties 01377

Port Lincoln

Axel Stenross Maritime Museum, 97 Lincoln Hwy, Port Lincoln, SA 5606 - T: (08) 86823624, E-mail: axelstenross@centralonline.com.au. Head: Philip Roe
Science&Tech Museum
Boat building, maritime technology 01378

Rosewall Memorial Shell Museum, Flinders Hwy, Port Lincoln, SA 5606 - T: (08) 86821868, Fax: 86833341. Head: H. Steven
Natural History Museum - 1978
Shells 01379

Port MacDonnell

Port MacDonnell and District Maritime Museum, 49 Meylin St, Port MacDonnell, SA 5291 - T: (08) 87387259, Fax: 87387340, E-mail: grandpa@dove.net.au, Internet: http://www.grandpa.mtx.net
Historical Museum 01380

Port Macquarie

Port Macquarie Historic Museum, 22 Clarence St, Port Macquarie, NSW 2444 - T: (02) 65831108, Fax: 65831108, E-mail: pmmuseum@midcoast.com.au, Internet: http://midcoast.com.au/~pmmuseum.htr. Head: Murray Thompson
Local Museum
Local history, 1821 Government house, Lake Innes house 01381

Port Phillip

Historical Society of Saint Kilda, 150 Carlisle St, Saint Kilda, Port Phillip, Vic. 3182 - T: (03) 95316127
Local Museum
Coll of costume and memorabilia 01382

Jewish Museum of Australia, Gandel Centre of Judaica, 26 Alma Rd, Saint Kilda, Port Phillip, Vic. 3182, mail addr: POB 117, Port Phillip, Vic. 3182 - T: (03) 95340083, Fax: 95340844, E-mail: info@jewishmuseum.com.au, Internet: http://www.jewishmuseum.com.au. Head: Dr. Helen Light
Historical Museum - 1978
Jewish ritual objects, documents, photographs, memorabilia, textiles, Holocaust art, Australian Jewish hist - library 01383

Linden Gallery and Arts Centre, 26 Acland St, Saint Kilda, Port Phillip, Vic. 3182 - T: (03) 92096560, Fax: 95254706, E-mail: linden@vicnet.net.au, Internet: http://www.portphillip.vic.gov.au
Public Gallery 01384

Port Phillip City Collection, Town Hall, Saint Kilda, Port Phillip, Vic. 3182 - T: (03) 92096215, Fax: 96451656, E-mail: assist@portphillip.vic.gov.au, Internet: http://www.portphillip.vic.gov.au
Fine Arts Museum / Local Museum 01385

Port Pirie

Port Pirie National Trust Museum, 429 Anzac Rd, Port Pirie, SA 5540 - T: (08) 86322272, Fax: 86322272. Head: Nancy Wood
Local Museum - 1970
Display of items from the Lead Smelters at Port Pirie, in a former railway station of unusual architectural design 01386

Port Victoria

Maritime Museum, Former Goods Smed, Main St, Port Victoria, SA 5573 - T: (08) 88342057. Head: G.K. Dutschke
Natural History Museum / Local Museum - 1975
Local maritime hist 01387

Port Victoria National Trust Museum, Victoria Terrace, Port Victoria, SA 5573 - T: (08) 88342057. Head: G.K. Dutschke
Local Museum 01388

Portland

History House, off Cliff St, Portland, Vic. 3305 - T: (03) 55222266
Historical Museum
Social history 01389

Portland 1889 Battery Museum, Victoria Parade, Portland, Vic. 3306 - T: (03) 55232450
Military Museum
Defend Victoria against Russian invasion in 1889 01390

Portland CEMA Arts Centre, Cnr Glenelg and Bentinck Sts, Portland, Vic. 3305 - T: (03) 55222263, Fax: 55222290, E-mail: portland@peg.pegasus.oz.au
Fine Arts Museum
Prints, drawings, watercolours and oil, selection of Botanical drawings 01391

Powerhouse House and Car Museum, Cnr Percy & Glenelg Sts, Portland, Vic. 3305 - T: (03) 55235795, Fax: 55231132
Science&Tech Museum
Vehicles, stationary engines, motorcycles, signs, models, trams, tractor, a fully set up workship 01392

Prahran

Stonnington Local History Collection - Prahran, 301 High St, Prahran, Vic. 3181 - T: (03) 82907160, Fax: 95212255, E-mail: dtuck@stonnington.vic.gov.au, Internet: http://www.stonnington.vic.gov.au/library
Local Museum 01393

Proserpine

Proserpine Historical Museum, 192 Main St, Proserpine, Qld. 4800 - T: (07) 49453969, Fax: 49451155. Head: J. Steel
Local Museum
Local history, sugar industry, mining and tourism 01394

Puckapunyal

Royal Australian Corps of Transport Museum, Tobruk Barracks, Puckapunyal, Vic. 3662 - T: (03) 57937253
Military Museum
Corps and related military memorabilia, restored vehicles 01395

Pyramid Hill

Pyramid Hill and District Historical Museum, McKay St, Pyramid Hill, Vic. 3575 - T: (03) 54557090. Head: Cliff Spowart
Local Museum 01396

Pyrmont

Sydney Heritage Fleet, Wharf 7, Pyrmont, NSW 2009 - T: (02) 92983888, Fax: 92983839, E-mail: museum@seaheritage.asn.au, Internet: http://www.seaheritage.asn.au. Head: Phil Renouf
Historical Museum
Sydney's maritime heritage 01397

Queanbeyan

Queanbeyan and District Historical Museum, 35 Stornoway Rd, Queanbeyan, NSW 2620 - T: (02) 62971978
Local Museum
Social life of this area 01398

Queenscliff

Fort Queenscliff Museum, King St, Queenscliff, Vic. 3225 - T: (03) 52581488, Fax: 52581788. Head: D.R. Lawrence
Military Museum
Victoria's first colonial defence initiatives 01399

Queenscliffe Historical Museum, Hesse St, Queenscliff, Vic. 3225 - T: (03) 52582253, Internet: http://www.zades.com.au/qcliffhs/
Local Museum
Photographs, paintings, newspapers, clothing, genealogy 01400

Queenscliffe Maritime Museum, Weeroona Parade, Queenscliff, Vic. 3225 - T: (03) 52583440, Fax: 52523440
Historical Museum
Dangers, wrecks, rescures 01401

Queenstown

Eric Thomas Galley Museum, 1-7 Driffield St, Queenstown, Tas. 7467 - T: (03) 64711483, Fax: 64711483. Head: Len Craig
Fine Arts Museum
Photographic coll from the 1890s 01402

Quilpie

Quilpie Museum, 51 Brolga St, Quilpie, Qld. 4480 - T: (07) 6562166, Fax: 6561016
Fine Arts Museum
Modern Architecture, Quilpie Artists 01403

Quirindi

Quirindi and District Historical Cottage and Museum, 44 Station St, Quirindi, NSW 2343
Local Museum 01404

Quorn

Quorn Mill Museum, 2 Railway Terrace, Quorn, SA 5433 - T: (08) 86486016, Fax: 86486279
Science&Tech Museum 01405

Ranelagh

Tasman Antique Motor Museum, Helen St, Ranelagh, Tas. 7108 - T: (03) 62641346
Science&Tech Museum 01406

Ravenshoe

Railco Museum, Grigg ST, Ravenshoe, Qld. 4872 - T: (070) 976005
Science&Tech Museum
Steam trains 01407

Ravensthorpe

Dance Cottage Museum, Morgans St, Ravensthorpe, WA 6346
Local Museum
Local history (late 1800's), farming, mining, CBH elevators, a railway carriage 01408

Redcliffe

Redcliffe Historical Museum, 75 Anzac Av, Redcliffe, Qld. 4020, mail addr: POB 370, Redcliffe, Qld. 4020 - T: (07) 38831898, Fax: 32844007
Historical Museum - 1969

Australiana, aboriginal relics, agriculture artifacts, monthly newsletters, first settlement in Queensland 1824, books for sale on hist of Redcliffe, Hornibrook Highway viaduct, longest wooden viaduct in Australia - library, archives 01409

Redfern

Performance Space, 199 Cleveland St, Redfern, NSW 2012 - T: (02) 96987235, Fax: 96991503, E-mail: admin@performancespace.com.au, Internet: http://www.performancespace.com.au. Head: Fiona Winning
Fine Arts Museum / Performing Arts Museum
Australia's contemporary art and performance 01410

Redhill

Redhill Museum, Bowman St, Redhill, SA 5521. Head: R. Wheaton
Local Museum 01411

Reid

Saint John's Schoolhouse Museum, Constitution Av, Reid, ACT 2601 - T: (02) 62496839, Fax: 62475481
Historical Museum 01412

Renmark

P.S. Industry Museum, POB 730, Renmark, SA 5341
Science&Tech Museum
Former riverboat relics, log books and photographs - Steamer in a specially constructed basin 01413

Richmond, Tasmania

Richmond Gaol Museum, 37 Bathurst St, Richmond, Tasmania, Tas. 7025 - T: (03) 62602127
Historical Museum
Oldest existing colonial gaol, coll of convict relics 01414

Richmond, Victoria

City of Richmond and Burnley Historical Museum, 415 Church St, Richmond, Victoria, Vic. 3121 - T: (03) 94286231
Local Museum 01415

Ringwood

Ringwood Miners Cottage, Ringwood Lake Reserve, Ringwood, Vic. 3134 - T: (03) 98797532
Local Museum
Local history 01416

Riverton

Scholz Park Museum, 20 Torrens Rd, Riverton, SA 5412 - T: (08) 88472128
Historical Museum 01417

Robe

Old Customs House Nautical Museum, Royal Circus, Robe, SA 5276 - T: (08) 87682195. Head: D. Shaw
Historical Museum
Ships, mines, maps, barometer, sextant, plate, spoon and other odds 01418

Rochester

Rochester Historical and Pioneer Museum, 96-98 High St, Rochester, Vic. 3561 - T: (03) 54841787
Local Museum
Local heritage 01419

Rockhampton

Rockhampton and District Historical Museum, Borough Chambers, Stapleton Park, Bridge St, Rockhampton, Qld. 4701, mail addr: POB 169, Rockhampton, Qld. 4700 - T: (07) 49278431. Head: Dr. L. McDonald
Local Museum
Local and family history 01420

Rockhampton City Art Gallery, 62 Victoria Parade, Rockhampton, Qld. 4700, mail addr: POB 243, Rockhampton, Qld. 4700 - T: (079) 311248, Fax: 211738. Head: Dianne Heenan
Fine Arts Museum - 1974
Australian paintings and works on paper 1970 to present, Australian ceramics 1970 to present, Regional paintings and works on paper Colonial to present - library 01421

The Rocks

Susannah Place Museum, 58-64 Gloucester St, The Rocks, NSW 2000 - T: (02) 92411893, Fax: 92412608, Internet: http://www.hht.nsw.gov.au. Head: Peter Watts
Local Museum
Community life 01422

Roebourne

Roebourne Old Goal Museum, Queen St, Roebourne, WA 6718 - T: (08) 91821060, Fax: 91821257, E-mail: sor@roebourne.wa.gov.au
Historical Museum / Local Museum
Social and cultural hist, pearling and mining industries 01423

Rosehill

Elizabeth Farm, 70 Alice St, Rosehill, NSW 2142 - T: (02) 96359488, Fax: 98913740, Internet: http://www.hht.nsw.gov.au. Head: Peter Watts
Open Air Museum - 1984
Oldest surviving European building in Australia, achitectural ideas and ambitions of the colony's first 50 yrs, Australian wool industry 01424

Roseworthy

Roseworthy Agricultural Museum, c/o University of Adelaide, Campus, Roseworthy, SA 5351 - T: (08) 83037739
Agriculture Museum
Development of dry land farming techniques, dairying, shearing and blacksmithing 01425

Ross

Tasmanian Wool Centre, Church St, Ross, Tas. 7209 - T: (03) 63815466, Fax: 63815407, E-mail: taswoolcentre@tassie.net.au, Internet: http://www.taswoolcentre.com.au. Head: R.A. Riggall
Historical Museum
Sheep and wool exhibition, industry 01426

Rottnest Island

Rottnest Island Museum, Rottnest Island, WA 6161 - T: (08) 93729753, Fax: 93729751, E-mail: enquiries@rottnest.wa.gov.au, Internet: http://www.rottnest.wa.gov.au. Head: Peggy Webb
Historical Museum / Local Museum - 1975
Native prison relics, local geology, flora and fauna, local and military history, pilot service (1838-1903) 01427

Rouse Hill

Rouse Hill Estate, Guntawong Rd, Rouse Hill, NSW 2155 - T: (02) 96276777, Fax: 96276776, Internet: http://www.hht.nsw.gov.au. Head: Peter Watts
Agriculture Museum
19th c farm, enterprising free settler Richard Rouse, family's chequered history 01428

Rushworth

Rushworth Museum, Old Rushworth Mechanic's Institute, Rushworth, Vic. 3612 - T: (03) 58561505. Head: John Graham
Local Museum
Lifestyle of the 1853 gold rush days up until more modern times, gold cradle, early farm implements, steam traction engine, horse drawn vehicles, music 01429

Ryde

Addington - Ryde House of Heritage, 813 Victoria Rd, Ryde, NSW 2112 - T: (02) 98074344
Local Museum
Australia's oldest remaining settlers cottage, pre-dating 1800, regional historic memorabilia 01430

Saint Helens

Saint Helens History Room, 59 Cecilia St, Saint Helens, Tas. 7216 - T: (03) 63761744, Fax: 63761099
Local Museum
Local history 01431

Saint Kilda, South Australia

Australian Electric Transport Museum, Saint Kilda Rd, Saint Kilda, South Australia, SA 5110, mail addr: GPOB 2012, Adelaide, SA 5001 - T: (08) 82808188, Fax: 82808528
Science&Tech Museum
Tramcars, trolleybuses, motorbuses, horsetram, electric locomotive and associated transportation artifacts, double-deck horsetram (builder: J. Stephenson, 1878), prototype Australian trolleybus (1932), Adelaide's No 1 electric tramcar (1908) 01432

Saint Kilda, Victoria → Port Phillip

Sale

Gippsland Art Gallery Sale, 68-70 Foster St, Sale, Vic. 3850, mail addr: POB 396, Sale, Vic. 3850 - T: (03) 51423372, Fax: 51423373, E-mail: michaely@wellington.vic.gov.au, Internet: http://www.wellington.vic.gov.au. Head: Michael Young
Fine Arts Museum - 1965
20th c Australian oil paintings, watercolours, mixed media, textiles, Coll of Wildlife Art, Coll of photographs and prints - library 01433

Sale Historical Museum, Foster St, Sale, Vic. 3850 - T: (03) 51445994
Local Museum
Portraits of local pioneers, early Sale, military objects, textiles and household devices 01434

Salisbury

Salisbury Folk Museum, Ann St, Salisbury, SA 5108 - T: (08) 82583016
Local Museum
General artefacts, farming relics, blacksmith's shop - library 01435

Waterwheel Museum, Commercial Rd, Salisbury, SA 5108 - T: (08) 82583016
Science&Tech Museum / Agriculture Museum
Pump water to irrigate a citrus orchard, citrus industry 01436

Samford

Samford and District Historical Museum, Station St, Samford, Qld. 4520 - T: (07) 32891282
Local Museum
Furniture, utensils, tools and goods donated by local residents - library 01437

San Remo

Vietnam Veterans Museum, 57 Phillip Island Rd, San Remo, Vic. 3925 - T: (03) 56785999, Fax: 56785995, E-mail: vvmuseum@nex.net.au, Internet: http://www.vietnamvetsmuseum.org. Head: John Methven
Historical Museum 01438

Sandgate

Sandgate and District Historical Museum, 150 Rainbow St, Sandgate, Qld. 4017 - T: (07) 38692283, E-mail: dneill@powerup.com.au
Local Museum
Local history 01439

Sandy Bay

University Fine Art Collection, c/o University of Tasmania, Churchill Av, Sandy Bay, Tas. 7001 - T: (03) 62262233, Fax: 62267172, E-mail: r.cameron@utas.edu.au. Head: Rosanna Cameron
Fine Arts Museum / University Museum - 1967
Contemporary Australian art 01440

Scone

Hunter Valley Museum of Rural Life, Bushy Hill, Scone, NSW 2337 - T: (02) 65437193
Local Museum / Folklore Museum
Rural life, carriages, carts, horse drawn hearse, poughing implements, wine making, butter making 01441

Scone and Upper Hunter Historical Museum, Kingdon St, Scone, NSW 2337 - T: (02) 65451218
Local Museum
Historical material to Scone and district, Australia Day, Horse Festival 01442

Semaphore Park

Fort Glanville, 359 Military Rd, Semaphore Park, SA 5019 - T: (08) 82421978, Fax: 82421978
Military Museum
19th c coastal artillery, guns, guard room, barracks 01443

Serpentine

Serpentine Vintage Tractors and Machinery Museum, Wellard St, Serpentine, WA 6125 - T: (08) 95252129, E-mail: jades@visionnet.com.au
Science&Tech Museum 01444

Serviceton

Serviceton Historic Railway Station, Elizabeth St, Serviceton, Vic. 3420 - T: (03) 53931220, Fax: 53931220
Local Museum / Science&Tech Museum
Local and railway memorabilia 01445

Seymour

Seymour and District Historical Museum, Tallarook St, Seymour, Vic. 3660 - T: (03) 57922311
Local Museum
Local history 01446

Shepparton

Bennetts Mineral and Fossil Collection, Verney Rd, Shepparton, Vic. 3630
Natural History Museum
Mineral specimens, coll of minerals, fossil coll incl Stromatolites, SA Archaeocytha, Eocene Horse skull, cast of Archaeopteryx, bones and teeth of Diprotodon 01447

Philippine House Museum, International Village, Parkside Dr, Shepparton, Vic. 3630 - T: (03) 58316637
Ethnology Museum
Material from the Philippines, incl books, paintings, sculpture, musical instruments, tapestries, crafts, costumes - library 01448

Shepparton Art Gallery, Civic Centre, Welsford St, Shepparton, Vic. 3632 - T: (03) 58329861, Fax: 58318480, E-mail: artgal@shepparton.vic.gov.au, Internet: http://www.shepparton.vic.gov.au/gallery. Head: Leanne Willis
Fine Arts Museum / Decorative Arts Museum - 1935
Australian pottery and ceramics (1820-1995), international ceramics Australian painting drawing and contemporary prints - library 01449

Silverton

Silverton Gaol Museum, Burke St, Silverton, NSW 2880 - T: (08) 80885317. Head: D. Morrison
Local Museum - 1968
Life in the homes, mining equipment, lodge religion of the area 01450

Singleton

Royal Australian Infantry Corps Museum, Lone Pine Barracks, Singleton, NSW 2331 - T: (02) 65703257, Fax: 65703427
Military Museum
Uniforms, weapons, medals, equipment and memorabilia 01451

Singleton Historical Museum, Burdekin Park, George St, Singleton, NSW 2330 - T: (02) 65778536, Fax: 65778536. Head: Kaye Stacy
Local Museum
Relics and other items of early Australia, lamps and lighting, bottles and Aboriginal artefacts, early farm machinery and vehicles 01452

Smithfield

Fairfield City Museum and Gallery, 632 The Horsley Dr, Smithfield, NSW 2164 - T: (02) 96093993, Fax: 97574357, E-mail: museum@fairfieldcity.nsw.gov.au, Internet: http://www.fairfieldcity.nsw.gov.au/museumgallery. Head: Susan Hutchinson
Local Museum
Social history, contemporary arts and crafts 01453

Sorrento

Nepean Historical Museum, 827 Melbourne Rd, Sorrento, Vic. 3943 - T: (03) 59840256, Fax: 59840935
Local Museum
Artefacts, aboriginal relics, photographs and documents, models, fashions (19th c) 01454

Victoria's First Hardware Museum, 80 - 98 Ocean Beach Rd, Sorrento, Vic. 3942 - T: (03) 59889000, Fax: 59888309
Science&Tech Museum
Hand tools 01455

South Bank

Queensland Museum, Grey and Melbourne Sts, South Bank, mail addr: POB 3300, Coorparoo, Qld. 4101 - T: (07) 38407555, Fax: 38461918, E-mail: InquiryCentre@qm.qld.gov.au, Internet: http://www.qmuseum.qld.gov.au. Head: Dr. Ian Galloway
Natural History Museum / Local Museum - 1862
Zoology, maritime archaeology, Australian aboriginal and Pacific Island ethnology, Geology, Social History 01456

South Brisbane

Queensland Art Gallery, Melbourne St, South Brisbane, Qld. 4101, mail addr: POB 3686, South Brisbane, Qld. 4101 - T: (07) 38407333, Fax: 38448865, E-mail: gallery@gag.qld.gov.au, Internet: http://www.qag.qld.gov.au. Head: Doug Hall
Fine Arts Museum - 1895
Paintings, prints, drawings, sculpture, installation, decorative arts, focus, on Australian, Aboriginal and Asian art, videos, photographs 01457

Queensland Maritime Museum, Sidon and Stanley Sts, South Brisbane, Qld. 4101, mail addr: POB 3098, South Brisbane, Qld. 4101 - T: (07) 38445361, Fax: 38461945, E-mail: qlbmaritime@ecn.net.au, Internet: http://www.qmma.ecn.net.au. Head: W.T. Foote
Science&Tech Museum - 1971
Steam tug 'Forceful' (built 1925, maintained and operated as part of the museum), frigate ex HMAS 'Diamantina', relics from the recently discovered HMS 'Pandora' - library, photographic library 01458

South Nanango

Berlins Gem and Historical Museum, Berlins Rd, South Nanango, Qld. 4615, mail addr: Mail Service 396, South Nanango, Qld. 4615 - T: (07) 41637145. Head: K.W. Berlin
Natural History Museum / Historical Museum - 1966
Minerals, gemstones, world wide general specimens, antique bottles, local hist items from 1848 Goodes Inn in Nanango's first school (1866), tektites - library 01459

South Perth

South Perth Heritage House, 111 Mill Point Rd, South Perth, WA 6151 - T: (08) 94741870, Fax: 94741870
Local Museum
Local and social history 01460

South Yarra

Australian Centre for Contemporary Art, Dallas Brooks Dr, South Yarra, Vic. 3141 - T: (03) 96546422, Fax: 96503438, E-mail: acca@connect.net.au, Internet: http://www.artnow.org.au. Head: Jenepher Duncan
Public Gallery - 1984 01461

Southbank

Polly Woodside Melbourne Maritime Museum, Lorimer St E, Southbank, Vic. 3006 - T: (03) 96999760, Fax: 96966117, E-mail: polly@nattrust.com.au, Internet: http://www.nattrust.com.au
Historical Museum
Historic ship 01462

Victorian College of the Arts Gallery, 234 Saint Kilda Rd, Southbank, Vic. 3006 - T: (03) 96859316, Fax: 96821841, E-mail: a.hull@vca.unimelb.edu.au, Internet: http://www.vca.unimelb.edu.au. Head: Prof. Andrea Hull
Fine Arts Museum / University Museum 01463

Spalding

Geralka Rural Farm, Hwy 83, 15k south of Spalding, Spalding, SA 5454 - T: (08) 88458081, Fax: 88458073. Head: D.E. Wilsdon
Agriculture Museum / Science&Tech Museum - 1972
Copper-mining history, various ploughs from the earliest to the modern day machine, likewise harrows, cultivators, seeding equipment, harvestors and headers, Clydesdale working horses, 1908 Daimler road train 01464

Spotswood

Scienceworks, Museum of Victoria, 2 Booker St, Spotswood, Vic. 3015 - T: (03) 96516777, Fax: 93910100, Internet: http://www.scienceworks.museum.vic.gov.au/
Science&Tech Museum
Art science and technology centre, sewage pumping station 01465

Spring Hill

Firearms Technology Museum, Lot 39 Broken Shaft Close, Spring Hill, NSW 2800 - T: (02) 63658681, Fax: 63658681, E-mail: guerin@netwit.net.au
Science&Tech Museum
Firearms from the matchlock to modern weapons 01466

Springfield

Carrick Hill Museum, 46 Carrick Hill Dr, Springfield, SA 5062 - T: (08) 83793886, Fax: 83797588, E-mail: smith.alanb@saugov.sa.gov.au, Internet: http://corrickhill.sa.gov.au. Head: Alan Smith
Fine Arts Museum / Decorative Arts Museum - 1986
20th c British paintings, 20th c Australian paintings, 19th and 20th c French paintings, 16th and 17th c English oak furniture, 19th c English porcelain, English silver, 20th c English sculpture 01467

Springsure

Brauhinia Shire Bicentennial Art Gallery, Eclipse St, Springsure, Qld. 4722 - T: (07) 9841166, Fax: 9841329
Public Gallery / Fine Arts Museum
Paintings 01468

Old Springsure Hospital Museum, POB 19, Springsure, Qld. 4722 - T: (07) 40841267, Fax: 40841640
Historical Museum
Beds, medical equipment and linen, nursery, operating equipment 01469

Springvale

Springvale and District Historical Museum, 7 Hlllcrest Grove, Springvale, Vic. 3171 - T: (03) 95482732, Fax: 95480519
Local Museum - 1990
History of the area 01470

Stansbury

Stansbury Museum, North Terrace, Stansbury, SA 5582, mail addr: POB 12, Stansbury, SA 5582 - T: (08) 88524391, E-mail: patti@bigpond.com, Internet: http://www.yorkeregion.on.net/stansbury. Head: John Eillott
Local Museum - 1975 01471

Stanthorpe

Stanthorpe Art Gallery, Weeroona Park, Locke St, Stanthorpe, Qld. 4380, mail addr: POB 211, Stanthorpe, Qld. 4380 - T: (07) 46811874, Fax: 46814021, E-mail: stanart@halenet.com.au. Head: Maurice Passmore, Ross McCorquodale
Fine Arts Museum - 1976
Australian art - library 01472

Stawell

Returned Services League War Museum, Stawell Sub-Branch, RSL Memorial Hall, Scallan St, Stawell, Vic. 3380 - T: (03) 53582332
Military Museum
Memorabilia from WWI and WWII 01473

Stawell Historical Museum, Longfield St, Stawell, Vic. 3380 - T: (03) 53583725, E-mail: cloats@netconnect.com.au
Local Museum 01474

Steiglitz

Steiglitz Court House, Stawell St, Steiglitz, Vic. 3331 - T: (03) 52841230
Local Museum / Religious Arts Museum
Early gold mining history, pastoral history 01475

Stratford

Stratford and District Museum, Hobson St, Stratford, Vic. 3862 - T: (03) 51458233
Local Museum
Local history 01476

Strathalbyn

Strathalbyn National Trust Museum, 1 Rankine St, Strathalbyn, SA 5255 - T: (08) 85362478. Head: B. Scott
Local Museum - 1974
Farm, domestic utensils, period furniture, costumes, town history, photographs, genealogy 01477

Streaky Bay

Old School Museum, Montgomerie Terrace, Streaky Bay, SA. 5680 - T: (08) 86261443. Head: Rae Brewster
Local Museum / Agriculture Museum - 1976
Local hist (early settlement of this district), kitchen household, furniture, school hist, Kelsh Pioneer Cottage, printing machinery, fishing, Nash car, farm machinery 01478

Stroud

Court House Museum, Cowper St, Stroud, NSW 2425 - T: (02) 49945400, Fax: 49945400
Local Museum / Agriculture Museum
Formation of the Australian Agricultural Company in London in 1824, local history 01479

Subiaco

Subiaco Museum, 241 Rokeby Rd, Subiaco, WA 6008, mail addr: POB 270, Subiaco, WA 6904 - T: (08) 92379227, Fax: 93814930, E-mail: c.bennett@subiaco.wa.gov.au. Head: Christobal Bennett
Historical Museum - 1975
Photographs, domestic furniture, costumes, documents, Subiaco memorabilia 01480

Western Australian Medical Museum, Harvey House, Cnr Barker and Railway Rds, Subiaco, WA 6008 - T: (08) 93401506, Fax: 93401236, E-mail: margaret.mann@health.wa.gov.au
Historical Museum
History ofmedicine, dentistry and public health in WA 01481

Surfers Paradise

Gold Coast City Art Gallery, 135 Bundall Rd, Surfers Paradise, Qld. 4217, mail addr: POB 6615, Gold Coast Mail Centre, Qld. 9726 - T: (07) 55816567, Fax: 55816594, E-mail: gallery@gcac.com.au, Internet: http://www.gcac.com.au. Head: John Walsh
Fine Arts Museum - 1986
Modern sculpture, contemporary aboriginal art, contemporary australian paintings, prints, drawings, mixed media, ceramics - library 01482

Surry Hills

Brett Whiteley Studio Museum, 2 Raper St, Surry Hills, NSW 2010 - T: (02) 92251881, Fax: 96901308
Fine Arts Museum
Art, photography, drawings, sculptures - workshops 01483

Swan Hill

Pioneer Settlement Museum, Horseshoe Bend, Swan Hill, Vic. 3585 - T: (03) 50362410, Fax: 50321096, E-mail: pioneersett@swanhill.vic.gov.au, Internet: http://www.pioneer-settlement.com.au
Historical Museum - 1963
Australiana, early agricultural machinery, Australia's largest inland paddle steamer P.S. 'Gem', stereoscopic theatre - library and education centre 01484

Swan Hill Regional Art Gallery, Horseshoe Bend, Swan Hill, Vic. 3585 - T: (03) 50329744, Fax: 50321133, E-mail: artgal@swanhill.vic.gov.au. Head: Helen Kaptein
Fine Arts Museum - 1967
Paintings, drawings, prints, naive art coll 01485

Swanbourne

Tom Collins House, 88 Wood St, Swanbourne, WA 6010 - T: (08) 93844771, Fax: 93844854, E-mail: fawwa@iinet.net.au, Internet: http://www.iinet.net.au/~fawwa. Head: Trisha Kotai-Ewers
Special Museum - 1949
House built in 1907 by Joseph Furphy (Tom Collins), a famous Australian author, Furphy memorabilia, rare Australian books - library 01486

Sydney

ANZAC Memorial, Hyde Park S, Sydney, NSW 2000, mail addr: 245 Castlereagh St, Sydney, NSW 2000 - T: (02) 92677668, Fax: 92671661
Historical Museum
Sculptures and bas relief panels by Raynor Hoff, WW I, servicemen and women in times of war 01487

Art Gallery of New South Wales, Art Gallery Rd, Domain, Sydney, NSW 2000 - T: (02) 92251744, Fax: 92216226, E-mail: artmail@ag.nsw.gov.au, Internet: http://www.artgallery.nsw.gov.au. Head: Edmund Capon
Public Gallery - 1874
Australian art, primitive and aboriginal art, incl notable burial posts and bark paintings, Melanesian art, British painting and sculpture, European painting, prints and drawings, Asian art, contemporary art, photography 01488

Australian Museum, 6 College St, Sydney, NSW 2010 - T: (02) 93206000, Fax: 93206050, E-mail: info1@austmus.gov.au, Internet: http://www.austmus.gov.au. Head: Prof. Michael Archer
Natural History Museum - 1827
Australian and Pacific anthropology, vertebrate and invertebrate zoology, earth sciences (mineralogy, palaeontology) - library, archives 01489

Australian National Maritime Museum, 2 Murray St, Darling Harbour, Sydney, NSW 2000, mail addr: POB 5131, Sydney, NSW 1042 - T: (02) 92983777, Fax: 92983780, E-mail: jmellefont@anmm.gov.au, Internet: http://www.anmm.gov.au. Head: Mary-Louise William
Natural History Museum - 1985
Maritime hist as exemplified by Colonial Navies, Royal Australian Navy, merchant shipping and trade, whaling and pearling, fishing industry, explorers and mapmakers, immigration, surfing, maritime activities of Aborigines, models, prints and drawings, glass plate negatives, uniforms, relics, fullsize vessels - library 01490

City Exhibition Space, 31 Alfred St, Circular Quay, Sydney, NSW 2000 - T: (02) 92428555, Fax: 92428556, E-mail: cbergman@cityofsydney.nsw.gov.au
Public Gallery
Urban planning issues, architectural models 01491

Government House, Macquarie St, Sydney, NSW 2000 - T: (02) 99315222, Fax: 99315208, Internet: http://www.hht.nsw.gov.au. Head: Peter Watts
Historical Museum
Furnishings and decoration (19th and early 20th c) 01492

Hyde Park Barracks Museum, Queens Sq, Macquarie St, Sydney, NSW 2000 - T: (02) 92238922, Fax: 92233368, Internet: http://www.hht.nsw.gov.au. Head: Peter Watts
Historical Museum
Female immigration depot, govermental asylum for women 01493

J.L. Shellshear Museum of Comparative Anatomy and Physical Anthropology, c/o Department of Anatomy and Histology, University of Sydney, Sydney, NSW 2006 - T: (02) 93514529, Fax: 93512813, E-mail: shellshear@anatomy.usyd.edu.au. Head: Prof. C.D. Shorey
Natural History Museum / University Museum - 1958
Human skulls, skeletons and brains, marsupials 01494

J.T. Wilson Museum of Human Anatomy, c/o Department of Anatomy, University of Sydney, Sydney, NSW 2006 - T: (02) 96922496, Fax: 95522026. Head: Prof. C.D. Shorey, K. Parsons
University Museum - 1886
Human anatomy and anthropology 01495

Justice and Police Museum, 8 Phillip St, Sydney, NSW 2000 - T: (02) 92521144, Fax: 92524860, Internet: http://www.hht.nsw.gov.au/frmuseums.html
Historical Museum - 1910
Crime, social history, Police and Water Police Court, gallery of mug shots, spine chilling weapons, police history, bushrangers, history of law 01496

Macleay Museum, c/o University of Sydney, Sydney, NSW 2006 - T: (02) 93512274, Fax: 93515646, E-mail: macleay@macleay.usyd.edu.au, Internet: http://www.usyd.edu.au/su/macleay. Head: Vanessa Mack
Natural History Museum / University Museum / Ethnology Museum - 1888
Macleay family natural hist and ethnographical coll, entomology, Miklouho-Maclay ethnographical coll, historic photographs, scientific instruments 01497

Museum of Contemporary Art Sydney, 140 George St, Circular Quay West, Sydney, NSW 2000 - T: (02) 92524033, Fax: 92524361, E-mail: publicitypr@mca.com.au, Internet: http://www.mca.com.au
Fine Arts Museum - 1989 01498

Museum of Pathology, c/o University of Sydney, Blackburn Bldg D06, Sydney, NSW 2006 - T: (02) 93512414, Fax: 93513429, E-mail: glenn@pathology.su.oz.au, Internet: http://www.med.su.oz.au/path/museum.html
Historical Museum - 1883
Historical medical istruments, develop today's medical technology 01499

Museum of Sydney, Cnr Bridge and Philip Sts, Sydney, NSW 2000 - T: (02) 92515988, Fax: 92515966, E-mail: info@ho.hht.nsw.gov.au, Internet: http://www.hht.nsw.gov.au/fmuseums.html. Head: Peter Watts
Historical Museum
First government place (1788), history of Australians Aboriginals 01500

Museum of the History of Science, c/o University of New South Wales, School of Chemistry, Barker St, Sydney, NSW 2052 - T: (02) 93855322, Fax: 93856141, E-mail: d.alderdice@unsw.edu.au, Internet: http://www.chem.unsw.edu.au/mhs. Head: Dr. David Alderdice
Science&Tech Museum / University Museum
Scientific and technical instruments, physical, chemical, navigational, optical and microscopes 01501

Nicholson Museum, University of Sydney, Sydney, NSW 2006 - T: (02) 93512812, Fax: 93514889, E-mail: Karin.Sowada@antiquity.usyd.edu.au, Internet: http://www.usyd.edu.au/nicholson. Head: Prof. Dan Potts
Archaeological Museum / University Museum - 1860
Egyptian, Greek, Roman, Cypriot, Middle Eastern and European antiquities 01502

S.H. Ervin Gallery, National Trust Centre, Watson Rd, The Rocks, Sydney, NSW 2000, mail addr: GPOB 518, Sydney, NSW 2001 - T: (02) 92580123, Fax: 92511110, E-mail: shervingallery@nsw.nationaltrust.org.au, Internet: http://www.nsw.nationaltrust.org.au/ervin/html. Head: Jane Watters
Fine Arts Museum - 1978
Australian art 01503

Sydney Harbour Bridge Pylon, Lower Fort St, Sydney, NSW 2148 - T: (02) 92473408, Fax: 98310926
Special Museum / Science&Tech Museum
Bridge built and harbour tunnel 01504

Sydney Observatory, Museum of Applied Arts and Sciences, Watson Rd, Sydney, NSW 2000 - T: (02) 92170485, Fax: 92170489, E-mail: nickl@phm.gov.au, Internet: http://www.phm.gov.au/observe. Head: Dr. Kevin Fewster
Science&Tech Museum
Telescopes 01505

University of Sydney Art Collection, c/o University of Sydney, Sydney, NSW 2006 - T: (02) 93514004, Fax: 93517785, E-mail: sgarside@mail.usyd.edu.au, Internet: http://www.usyd.edu.au. Head: S. Garside
Fine Arts Museum / University Museum - 1852
19th and 20th c Australian oil paintings and watercolours, sculpture, 19th c and Georgian silver, 19th and 20th c Australian and European portraits in oil, 20th c Australian ceramics, 19th c Persian Rugs, 17th and 18th c tapestries, Japanese and Chinese prints - library 01506

UNSW Art Collection, University of New South Wales, Sydney, NSW 2052 - T: (02) 93996521, Fax: 93851470, E-mail: belinda.webb@unsw.edu.au. Head: Belinda Webb
University Museum / Fine Arts Museum
Paintings, prints, drawings, sculpture, textiles, ceramics 01507

War Memorial Gallery of Fine Arts, c/o University of Sydney, Parramatta Rd, Sydney, NSW 2006 - T: (02) 93516883, Fax: 93517785, E-mail: sgarside@mail.usyd.edu.au, Internet: http://www.usyd.edu.au/su/uniart/artcolln/front.htm. Head: Sioux Garside
Fine Arts Museum / University Museum 01508

Westpac Museum, 6-8 Playfair St, The Rocks, Sydney, NSW 2000 - T: (02) 92511419, Fax: 97644950, Internet: http://www.westpac.com.au. Head: Kerrianne George
Historical Museum - 1987
Westpac Banking Corporation memorabilia 01509

Talbot

Talbot Arts and Historical Museum, Camp St, Talbot, Vic. 3371 - T: (03) 54632578
Local Museum / Fine Arts Museum
History of pioneers and settlers 01510

Tamworth

Calala Cottage, 142 Denison St, Tamworth, NSW 2340 - T: (02) 67657492
Local Museum
Memorabilia and bric-a-brac of historical interest 01511

Tamworth City Gallery, 203 Marius St, Tamworth, NSW 2340, mail addr: POB 555, Tamworth, NSW 2340 - T: (02) 67554459, Fax: 67554261, E-mail: gallery@tamworth.nsw.gov.au, Internet: http://www.tamworth.nsw.gov.au. Head: Brian Langer
Fine Arts Museum - 1919

Burdekin and Salvana coll, 19th c European oil paintings, 19th c and early 20th c Australian oil paintings and watercolours, Australian fibre/textile art, Utopian coll Bequest 01512

Tanunda

Barossa Valley Historical Museum, 47 Murray St, Tanunda, SA 5352, mail addr: POB 51, Tanunda, SA 5352 - T: (08) 85630501. Head: Donald A. Ross
Historical Museum - 1963
Local history, folk art, hand-made early pioneer tools and implements of german settlers - library 01513

Kev Rohrlach Technology and Heritage Museum (closed) 01514

Tara

Tara and District Pioneer Memorial Museum, Milne St, Tara, Qld. 4421 - T: (07) 46653758, Fax: 46653576. Head: Bruce Riethmuller
Local Museum
Coll of early day household items, original jail and railwagons, 1st permanent school, railway station 01515

Taralga

Taralga Historical Museum, Orchard St, Taralga, NSW 2580 - T: (02) 48402084. Head: Mary Chalker
Local Museum 01516

Taree

Manning Regional Art Gallery, 12 Macquarie St, Taree, NSW 2430, mail addr: POB 482, Taree, NSW 2430 - T: (02) 65510961, Fax: 65510961, E-mail: mrag@tpgi.com.au. Head: Sue Mitchell
Fine Arts Museum - 1988
Coll of Australian art 01517

Taroona

Beatties Historic Photograph Museum, 24 Flinders Esplanade, Taroona, Tas. 7053 - T: (03) 62858810
Science&Tech Museum / Special Museum
Life and work of Hobart photographer John Watt Beattie between 1890 and 1930 01518

Tatura

Tatura Irrigation and Wartime Camps Museum, 49 Hogan St, Tatura, Vic. 3616 - T: (03) 58241084, 58241867, E-mail: kneefam@mcmedia.com.au, Internet: http://www.maskell.com.au/museum.html. Head: Arthur Knee, Lurline Knee
Local Museum
Local history, history of irrigation, art gallery, WWII internment, POW camps 01519

Tea Tree Gully

Old Highercombe Museum, 3 Perserverance Rd, Tea Tree Gully, SA 5091
Local Museum - 1961
Interior of the old hotel furnished in the style of the 1850's, historic items of the district 01520

Tenterfield

Tenterfield Centenary Cottage, 136 Logan St, Tenterfield, NSW 2372 - T: (02) 67362844, E-mail: kenh1@telstra.easymail.com.au
Local Museum
Household items, farm machinery, tools, furniture, and books, Boer and World Wars 01521

Tewantin

Big Shell Museum, Gympie St, Tewantin, Qld. 4565 - T: (07) 54471268, Fax: 54471268
Natural History Museum
Wide variaty of (mainly Australian) shells, specimens from the sea 01522

House of Bottles and Bottle Museum, 19 Myles St, Tewantin, Qld. 4565 - T: (07) 54471277, Fax: 54471277
Special Museum - 1969 01523

Noosa Regional Art Gallery, Riverside, Pelican St, Tewantin, Qld. 4565 - T: (07) 54495297, Fax: 54471062, E-mail: agd@noosa.qld.gov.au, Internet: http://www.noosaregionalgallery.org. Head: Kevin Wilson
Public Gallery
International art in nature, Australian art 01524

Texas

Texas Historical Museum, 40 Flemming St, Texas, Qld. 4385 - T: (07) 46531204. Head: W. Glasser
Local Museum
Store/post office, blacksmith shop, jail, vehicle shed, machinery shed 01525

Tobacco Museum, 40 Flemming St, Texas, Qld. 4385 - T: (07) 46531204. Head: W. Glasser
Agriculture Museum
All implements unsed to produce tobacco leaf for market 01526

Tharwa

Nolan Gallery, Lanyon, Tharwa Dr, Tharwa, ACT 2620 - T: (02) 62375192, Fax: 62935342. Head: Angela Philp
Fine Arts Museum - 1980
20th c Australian paintings and works on paper by Sidney Nolan 01527

The Oaks

Wollondilly Heritage Centre, Edward St, The Oaks, NSW 2570 - T: (02) 46571796, Fax: 46572417, E-mail: tohs@mania.com.au, Internet: http://www.mania.com.au/~tohs
Local Museum
Local history 01528

Thebarton

Adelaide Gaol, Gaol Rd, Thebarton, SA 5031 - T: (08) 82314062, Fax: 82318975, E-mail: hanchant.deanne@saugov.sa.gov.au. Head: Deanne Hanchant
Historical Museum
Prisons and prison life in South Australia 01529

South Australian Police Museum, Police Barracks, Port Rd, Thebarton, SA 5001 - T: (08) 82074099
Historical Museum
History of crime and deviance, law enforcement 01530

Theodore

Dawson Folk Museum, Cnr Second Av and West Lane, Theodore, Qld. 4719 - T: (07) 49931482
Folklore Museum
Pioneer families, Aborigines, arts and crafts, coal and gold mining 01531

Thornbury

Northcote Pottery, 85 A Clyde St, Thornbury, Vic. 3071 - T: (03) 94844580, Fax: 94803075, E-mail: melb@northcote-pots.com.au, Internet: http://www.northcotepottery.com.au. Head: Peter Faulkner, Russ Porter
Decorative Arts Museum 01532

Thursday Island

Torres Strait Museum, Green Hill Fort, Thursday Island, Qld. 4875 - T: (07) 40691365
Historical Museum - 1994
Coll of gifts, souvenirs and collectables, defence Powder Magazine, Lighthouse, pearlshelling and shipping coll 01533

Tibooburra

Tibooburra Local Aboriginal Land Council Keeping Place, Briscoe St, Tibooburra, NSW 2880 - T: (08) 80913435, Fax: 80913446, E-mail: Halc@ruralnet
Folklore Museum
Aboriginal history, Tibooburra culture 01534

Timber Creek

Timber Creek Police Station Museum, Lot 48, O'Keele St, Timber Creek, NT 0852 - T: (08) 89750671, Fax: 89750652
Local Museum / Historical Museum / Museum of Classical Antiquities
Contact between Aborigines and Europeans, pastoral history, role of the police, Aboriginal artifacts 01535

Toodyay

Old Newcastle Gaol Museum, 129 Stirling Terrace, Toodyay, WA 6566 - T: (08) 95742435, Fax: 95742431, E-mail: toodyay@gidgenet.com.au
Historical Museum
Colonial building (1865) containing artifacts belonging to early settlers, historical maps, clothing and material relating to botanist James Drummonds in Toodyay 01536

Tooradin

Fisherman's Cottage, 13 Mickle St, Tooradin, Vic. 3977
Historical Museum
Farm machinery and fishing gear 01537

Toowoomba

Cobb and Co Museum, 27 Lindsay St, Toowoomba, Qld. 4350 - T: (07) 46391971, Fax: 46385791, E-mail: inquiries@cobbandco.qm.qld.gov.au
Science&Tech Museum
Coll of horse-drawn vehicles 01538

Milne Bay Military Museum, O'Quinn St, Toowoomba, Qld. 4350 - T: (07) 46393727, Fax: 46393717
Military Museum
Locally known as the 'Drill Hall', indoor sports 01539

Toowoomba Historical Museum, 49 Lindsay St, Toowoomba, Qld. 4350 - T: (07) 46387362, E-mail: history@tmba.design.net.au, Internet: http://www.toowoomba.qld.gov.au/histsoc. Head: Margaret McNally
Local Museum
Development of the city 01540

Toowoomba Regional Art Gallery, 531 Ruthven St, Toowoomba, Qld. 4350, mail addr: POB 3021, Toowoomba, Qld. 4350 - T: (07) 46886652, Fax: 46886895, E-mail: artgallery@toowoomba.qld.gov.au, Internet: http://www.toowoomba.qld.gov.au. Head: Diane Baker
Fine Arts Museum - 1938
18th to 20th c European and Australian paintings, drawings, prints, 17th to 20th c European, Australian and Oriental ceramics and porcelain, 18th to 19th c European glassware, 17th to 19th c European furniture, 18th to 20th c bronzes, 18th to 19th c works in silver and gold 01541

University of Southern Queensland Art Collection, Performance Centre Bldg, Toowoomba, Qld. 4350 - T: (07) 46313149, Fax: 46311855, E-mail: larner@usq.edu.au, Internet: http://www.usq.edu.au/faculty/arts/visarts
Fine Arts Museum / University Museum - 1967
Contemporary Australian works on paper, paintings, ceramics - library 01542

Torrens Park

Ukrainian Museum, 24a Fife Av, Torrens Park, SA 5062 - T: (08) 82714962. Head: L. Rostek
Historical Museum 01543

Townsville

Maritime Museum of Townsville, 42-68 Palmer St S, Townsville, Qld. 4810 - T: (07) 47215251, Fax: 47215759, E-mail: tmhs@bigpond.com. Head: Vivienne Moran
Historical Museum
Ship models, pearl diving equipment, marine radios, artefacts from the wreck of SS Yongala (1903-11) 01544

Museum of Tropical Queensland, 70-102 Flinders St, Townsville, Qld. 4810 - T: (07) 47260600, Fax: 47212093, E-mail: info@mtq.qld.gov.au, Internet: http://www.mtq.qld.gov.au. Head: Dr. C. Wallace
Natural History Museum / Archaeological Museum - 1987
Fossils, corals, marine biology, artefacts from HMS Pandora Shipwreck, Australian Aboriginal artefacts 01545

Perc Tucker Regional Gallery, Flinders Mall, Townsville, Qld. 4810, mail addr: POB 1268, Townsville, Qld. 4810 - T: (01) 47279011, Fax: 47723656, E-mail: ptrg@townsville.qld.gov.au. Head: Frances Thomson
Fine Arts Museum / Public Gallery - 1981
Art of tropical Queensland, traditional Aboriginal and Torres Strait Islander Art, contemporary art from Papua New Guinea - library 01546

School of Earth Sciences Museum, James Cook University of North Queensland, Townsville, Qld. 4811 - T: (07) 47814756, Fax: 47251501, E-mail: Susan.Cook@jcu.edu.au
Natural History Museum / University Museum
Rocks, minerals, fossils, thin sections and cores 01547

Townsville Museum, Cnr Surt and Stokes Sts, Townsville, Qld. 4810 - T: (07) 47725725, Fax: 47725725
Local Museum
Social history since 1864 01548

Vincent Art Gallery, c/o College of Music, Visual Arts and Theatre, James Cook University, 2 Ronan St, Townsville, Qld. 4814 - T: (07) 47813166, Fax: 47813169, E-mail: anne.lord@jcu.edu.au. Head: Anne Lord
Fine Arts Museum / University Museum 01549

Trentham

Trentham Agricultural and Railway Museum, Railway Station, Victoria St, Trentham, Vic. 3458 - T: (03) 54241598
Agriculture Museum / Science&Tech Museum
Railway Paraphernalia, freight handling, railway tickets, agricultural machinery 01550

Tully

Cardwell Shire Museum, 34 Bryant St, Tully, Qld. 4854 - T: (07) 40439100, Fax: 40681772
Local Museum
Historical photography, local Aboriginal artefacts, sugar industry 01551

Tumby Bay

C.L. Alexander Museum, 52 Harvey Dr, Tumby Bay, SA 5605 - T: (08) 86882760
Local Museum
Local history, agriculture, entertainment, sports, marine, schools, churches, transport, household items 01552

Excell Blacksmith and Engineering Workshop Museum, Barraud St, Tumby Bay, SA 5605 - T: (08) 86882101, Fax: 86882639
Science&Tech Museum 01553

Tumut

Tumut and District Historical Museum, Cnr Merivale and Capper Sts, Tumut, NSW 2720 - T: (02) 69471380. Head: Phyllis Dowling
Local Museum
Local history, incl furniture, clothing, books, china, machinery and photos, Miles Franklin coll 01554

Tuncurry

Great Lakes Historical Museum, Capel St, Tuncurry, NSW 2428 - T: (02) 65543012, Fax: 49976335, E-mail: mcneill@turboweb.net.au, Internet: http://greatlakeshistorical.museum.com
Historical Museum
Local history 01555

Tuncurry Museum → Great Lakes Historical Museum

Ubobo

Boyne Valley Historical Cottage, Railway Parade, Ubobo, Qld. 4680 - T: (07) 9741104
Local Museum
Timber, gold mining and railway history 01556

Ultimo

Powerhouse Museum, Museum of Applied Arts and Sciences, 500 Harris St, Ultimo, NSW 2007, mail addr: POB K346, Haymarket, NSW 1238 - T: (02) 92170111, Fax: 92170462, E-mail: info@phm.gov.au, Internet: http://www.phm.gov.au. Head: Dr. Kevin Fewster
Science&Tech Museum / Decorative Arts Museum / Historical Museum - 1880
Decorative arts and ceramics, communications, design, technology, hist of transportation, incl first train (1855), first Australian airmail aircraft (1911, Bleriot), an aeronautical steam beam engine by Boulton and Watt (1785), fashion, enviroment, information technology - library 01557

Ulverstone

Ulverstone Local History Museum, 50 Main St, Ulverstone, Tas. 7315 - T: (03) 64253835, E-mail: info@leven.tassie.net.au, Internet: http://www.leven.tassie.net.au/ulhm.htm
Local Museum 01558

Ungarie

Ungarie Museum, Wollongough St, Ungarie, NSW 2669 - T: (02) 69759338, Fax: 69759338
Local Museum 01559

Unley

City of Unley Museum, 80 Edmund Av, Unley, SA 5061 - T: (08) 83725117, Fax: 82714886, E-mail: kwalker@unley.sa.gov.av. Head: Kate Walker
Local Museum
Local histroy 01560

Uralla

Hassett's Uralla Military Museum, New England Hwy, Uralla, NSW 2358 - T: (02) 67784600, Fax: 67784600
Military Museum
Trucks, uniforms, weapons, coins and medals 01561

McCrossin's Mill Museum, Salisbury St, Uralla, NSW 2358 - T: (02) 67783022
Local Museum
Local history, artefacts, tools, machinery, horse drawn vehicles and steam engines 01562

New England Brass and Iron Lace Foundry Museum, 6 East St, Uralla, NSW 2358 - T: (02) 67785065
Special Museum
Production of iron lace, ornamental and other castings 01563

Vaucluse

Vaucluse House, Wentworth Rd, Vaucluse, NSW 2030 - T: (02) 93887922, Fax: 93374963, E-mail: info@ho.hht.nsw.gov.au, Internet: http://www.hht.nsw.gov.au. Head: Peter Watts
Historical Museum - 1911
Sydney home of William Charles Wentworth and Sarah Wentworth and their family, politics, Australian Constitution 01564

Victor Harbor

Port Victor Gallery, 7a Railway Tce, Victor Harbor, SA 5211 - T: (08) 85525988
Public Gallery
Paintings by local artist's 01565

Wagga Wagga

Charles Surt University Art Collection, Blakemore Building Healy Av, Wagga Wagga, NSW 2678 - T: (02) 69253666, Fax: 69253992, E-mail: tmiddlemost@csu.edu.au, Internet: http://www.csv.edu.au/. Head: Thomas A. Middlemost
Fine Arts Museum / University Museum
Fine early-modern, Aboriginal art 01566

City Art Gallery, 40 Gurwood St, Wagga Wagga, NSW 2650 - T: (02) 69235419, Fax: 69235409
Public Gallery
Art glass from 1975 to 1996, prints from the 1940s to the present, paintings, sculpture and other art media 01567

Wagga Wagga Regional Art Gallery, Civic Centre, Baylis St, Wagga Wagga, NSW 2650, mail addr: POB 20, Wagga Wagga, NSW 2650 - T: (02) 69269660, Fax: 69269669, E-mail: gallery@wagga.com.gov.au, Internet: http://www.waggaart-gallery.org
Fine Arts Museum - 1975
National Art Glass Collection, Margaret Carnegie Print Collection, Australian prints, Contemporgry art glass 01568

Wagin

Wagin Historical Village Museum, Kitchener St, Wagin, WA 6315 - T: (08) 98611232. Head: Glenys Ball
Historical Museum
Early history of Wagin, early style tractors, engines and shearing plants, buildings, furniture, records 01569

Wahroonga

Rose Seidler House, 71 Clissold Rd, Wahroonga, NSW 2076 - T: (02) 99898020, Fax: 94872761, Internet: http://www.hht.nsw.gov.au. Head: Peter Watts
Decorative Arts Museum
Architect Harry Seidler, modernist movement in Australia, post war design 01570

Walkaway

Walkaway Station Museum, Padbury Rd, Walkaway, WA 6528 - T: (08) 9261036. Head: Stan Gratte
Local Museum / Science&Tech Museum
Midland Railway room, local history, burials, gun, exploration 01571

Wallaroo

Wallaroo Heritage and Nautical Museum, Jetty Rd, Wallaroo, SA 5556, mail addr: POB 122, Wallaroo, SA 5556 - T: (08) 88233015. Head: Colin Boase
Historical Museum / Science&Tech Museum - 1969 01572

Wandin

Mont De Lancey Historical Museum, Wellington Rd, Wandin, Vic. 3139 - T: (03) 59642088, Fax: 59643855
Local Museum
Old vehicles and farm machinery, pioneer family histories 01573

Wangaratta

Wangaratta Exhibitions Gallery, 56-60 Ovens St, Wangaratta, Vic. 3677 - T: (03) 57220865, Fax: 57222969, E-mail: dianne.mangan@wangaratta.vic.gov.au. Head: Dianne Mangan
Fine Arts Museum / Public Gallery
Visual arts, crafts, design, heritage and social history 01574

Wangaratta Museum, Ford St, Wangaratta, Vic. 3677 - T: (03) 57222838, E-mail: arhall@netc.net.au
Local Museum
Local hist, household, industry, agriculture, military 01575

Warooka

Warooka and District Museum, Brentwood Rd, Warooka, SA 5577 - T: (08) 88545023
Local Museum 01576

Warracknabeal

North Western Agricultural Museum, Henty Hwy, Warracknabeal, Vic. 3393 - T: (03) 53981616
Agriculture Museum / Science&Tech Museum
Machinery pertaining to the wheat industry 01577

Warracknabeal Historical Centre, 81 Scott St, Warracknabeal, Vic. 3393 - T: (03) 53904236
Local Museum
Domestic items, documents, maps, pharmaceutical coll 01578

Warragul

Warragul and District Historical Museum, Old Shire Hall, Queen St, Warragul, Vic. 3820 - T: (03) 56295833
Local Museum
District's history, timber and dairy industries 01579

Warrandyte

Warrandyte Historical Museum, 111 Yarra St, Warrandyte, Vic. 3113 - T: (03) 98444176
Local Museum
Local history, gold mining history 01580

Warrnambool

Warrnambool Art Gallery, 165 Timor St, Warrnambool, Vic. 3280 - T: (03) 55647832, Fax: 55615136, E-mail: mbowes@warrnambool.vic.gov.au, Internet: http://www.artgallery.warrnambool.com. Head: Murray Bowes
Fine Arts Museum - 1886
Contemporary Australian prints, late 19th century Australian and European paintings, Melbourne Modernism 1930-1950, local works 01581

Warwick

Pringle Cottage Museum, 81 Dragon St, Warwick, Qld. 4370 - T: (07) 46612028
Local Museum
Historical items, farming equipment, vehicles and machinery 01582

Warwick Regional Art Gallery, 49 Albion St, Warwick, Qld. 4370 - T: (07) 46618588, Fax: 46618129, E-mail: artgallery@warwick.qld.gov.au. Head: Audrey Hoffmann
Fine Arts Museum 01583

Wauchope

Timbertown Museum, Oxley Hwy, Wauchope, NSW 2446, mail addr: POB 208, Wauchope, NSW 2446 - T: (02) 65852322, Fax: 65853588. Head: Louise Jamieson
Local Museum - 1976
Operating recreation of an 1880 logging and sawmilling community with craftsmen 01584

Wauchope District Historical Museum, Oxley Hwy, Wauchope, NSW 2446 - T: (02) 65853520
Local Museum 01585

Wayville

Latvian Museum, 34 Rose Tce, Wayville, SA 5034
Ethnology Museum / Decorative Arts Museum
Ethnic textile art, crafts and traditions, pottery, jewellery, lives of Latvian immigrants in Australia 01586

Wellington

Wellington Courthouse Museum, Old Punt Rd, Wellington, SA 5259 - T: (08) 85727330
Local Museum
Historical police station and courthouse, local history artifacts, early aboriginal and gold rush-related documents - special children's section 01587

Wembley Downs

Hale School Museum, Hale Rd, Wembley Downs, WA 6019 - T: (08) 93479777, Fax: 93479799, E-mail: bille@hale.wa.edu.au
Historical Museum
Convict era, the gold rushes, the Boer War, WW III, Korea and Vietnam, the Great Depression 01588

Werribee

Werribee and District Historical Museum, Cnr Watton St and Duncans Rd, Werribee, Vic. 3030 - T: (03) 97489333, Fax: 97489042
Local Museum 01589

West Perth

Alan Jones Scout Memorabilia Museum → W.A. Scout Museum

W.A. Scout Museum, 581 Murray St, West Perth, WA 6005 - T: (08) 93212814, Fax: 93212804. Head: G. Cargee
Historical Museum
Scout uniforms from 1914 to the present day, trophies, shields, memorial plaques, chinaware, wood carving, pennants, flags, badges, books, photographs 01590

West Wyalong

Bland District Museum, 16 Main St, West Wyalong, NSW 2671 - T: (02) 69723303
Local Museum
History of Wyalong and West Wyalong, early rural machinery, photos, colonial household furniture, a mineral, fossil and bottle coll - archive 01591

Westbury

Pearn's Steam World, Bass Hwy, Westbury, Tas. 7303 - T: (03) 63931414, Fax: 63973112, E-mail: bpheazlewood@vision.net.au. Head: Brenton Heazlewood
Agriculture Museum / Science&Tech Museum
Early agricultural heritage, steam traction engines, early wheel tractors, stationary engines, farm machinery and motorcycles 01592

White House, Village Green, Westbury, Tas. 7303 - T: (03) 63931171, Fax: 63330518, E-mail: clemons@bigpond.net.au
Fine Arts Museum / Decorative Arts Museum - 1970
English period furniture of the 17th and 18th centuries, early Tasmanian prints, paintings, copper and brass ware, toy exhibit, bicycles, cars, and horsedrawn vehicles 01593

Wheelers Hill

Monash Gallery of Art, 170 Jells Rd, Wheelers Hill, Vic. 3150, mail addr: POB 139, Wheelers Hill, Vic. 3150 - T: (03) 95621569, Fax: 95622433, E-mail: mga@monash.vic.gov.au. Head: Jane Scott
Fine Arts Museum - 1990
19th and 20th c Australian photography - library 01594

Waverley City Gallery → Monash Gallery of Art

Whyalla

Whyalla Maritime Museum, Lincoln Hwy, Whyalla, SA 5600 - T: (08) 86458900, Fax: 86453620, E-mail: paul.mazourek@whyalla.sa.gov.au, Internet: http://www.whyalla.sa.gov.au/tourism/maritime.htm. Head: Paul Mazourek
Historical Museum
Australian WW II anti-submarine and minesweeping vessels, BHP shipbuildig, natural history, maritime heritage of upper Spencer Gulf 01595

Whyalla Norrie

Mount Laura Homestead Museum, Ekblom St, Whyalla Norrie, SA 5608
Local Museum - 1975
Documents of the discovery of the area by Captain Matthew Flinders in 1802, early local exploration and pastoral activities following South Australia's founding in 1836, history of iron ore mining 01596

Whyte Yarcowie

Farming Through the Ages, Barrier Hwy, Whyte Yarcowie, SA 5420 - T: (08) 86653247, Fax: 86653247
Agriculture Museum / Science&Tech Museum
Coll of tractors, engines and steam engines from 1916 01597

Williamstown

HMAS Castlemaine - Museum Ship, Gem Pier, Nelson Pl, Williamstown, Vic. 3016 - T: (03) 93972363, 98530823, E-mail: hmascastlemaine@bigpond.com, Internet: http://www.hmascast-lemaine.com. Head: Peter J. Williams
Science&Tech Museum
Hist of WWII, Australian Navy vessel (Minesweeper) 01598

Williamstown Historical Museum, 5 Electra St, Williamstown, Vic. 3016 - T: (03) 93975423
Historical Museum - 1963
Model Ships, maritime artifacts, model of turret ship 'Cerberus' (1876), equipment from HMS 'Nelson' (1805), local history of European settlement in 1835 - library and education centre 01599

Williamtown

Fighter World, Medowie Rd, Williamtown, NSW 2314 - T: (02) 49651810, Fax: 49651940, E-mail: admin@fighterworld.com.au, Internet: http://www.fighterworld.com.au
Science&Tech Museum 01600

Monarch Historical Museum, 2-8 Slades Rd, Williamtown, NSW 2318 - T: (02) 49651641
Historical Museum
Social, military history, Japanese tank 01601

Winchelsea

Winchelsea and District Historical Records Centre, Hesse St, Winchelsea, Vic. 3241 - T: (03) 52889264, Fax: 52889246
Local Museum 01602

Windsor

Hawkesbury Museum, 7 Thompson Sq, Windsor, NSW 2756
Historical Museum - 1962 01603

Winton

Waltzing Matilda Centre and Qantilda Museum, 50 Elderslie St, Winton, Qld. 4735 - T: (07) 46571466, Fax: 46571886, E-mail: matilda@thehub.com.au, Internet: http://www.matildacentre.com.au
Local Museum / Music Museum / Science&Tech Museum - 1972
Waltzing Matilda song, QANTAS, pastoral properties, family history, Viscount crash, transport, war service, recreation, government, Winton history 01604

Wirrabara

Wirrabara Forestry Museum, Wirrabara Forest Headquartier, Wirrabara, SA 5481, mail addr: POB 91, Wirrabarra, SA 5481 - T: (08) 86684163
Natural History Museum 01605

Wodonga

National Museum of Australian Pottery, 66 South St, Wodonga, Vic. 3689 - T: (02) 60563152, Fax: 60563152
Decorative Arts Museum 01606

Wollongong

Illawarra Museum, 11 Market St E, Wollongong, NSW 2520 - T: (02) 42287770, Fax: 42287770, E-mail: sycado@bigpond.com, Internet: http://www.illawarramuseum.cjb.net. Head: J. McCarthy
Local Museum
Settlement, education, culture, agriculture, mining, transport and trade 01607

Wollongong East

Wollongong City Gallery, Corner Kembla and Burelli Sts, Wollongong East, NSW 2520, mail addr: POB 696, Wollongong East, NSW 2520 - T: (02) 42287500, Fax: 42265530, E-mail: gallery@wollongong.nsw.gov.au, Internet: http://www.wcg.1earth.net. Head: Peter O'Neill
Fine Arts Museum - 1978
Works of colonial Illawarra, contemporary Australian and Aboriginal art 01608

Wondai

Shire of Wondai Museum, Mackenzie St, Wondai, Qld. 4606 - T: (071) 685402, Fax: 685808
Local Museum
Dennis fire engine, bottle coll, steam traction engine, hospital operating theatre, shingle barn, manual telephone exchange, petrol pump, church organ, farm machinery 01609

Wongan Hills

Wongan Ballidu and District Museum, Camm St and Mitchell Sts, Wongan Hills, WA 6603, mail addr: POB 84, Wongan Hills, WA 6603 - T: (08) 96722026, Fax: 96722012. Head: Shirley O. Hewson
Local Museum - 1972
Local history, saddlery and blacksmithing tools including forge and bellows, photographic reproductions, horse-drawn farm machinery, reconstructed settler's hut - archives 01610

Wonthaggi

Railway Station Museum, Murray St, Wonthaggi, Vic. 3995 - T: (03) 56723053, Fax: 53724234
Local Museum / Science&Tech Museum
State coal mines, Wonthaggi history 01611

State Coal Mine Museum, Garden St, Wonthaggi, Vic. 3995 - T: (03) 56723053, Fax: 56724234
Science&Tech Museum
Models and mining artefacts 01612

Woodend

Woodend and District Local and Family History Resource Centre, Forest St, Woodend, Vic. 3442 - T: (03) 54272523, Fax: 54272523, E-mail: janeth@vicnet.net.au
Local Museum
Local and family history 01613

Woolloomooloo

Artspace, 43-51 Cowper Wharf Rd, Woolloomooloo, NSW 2011 - T: (02) 93681899, Fax: 93681705, E-mail: artspace@artspace.org.au, Internet: http://www.artspace.org.au. Head: Nicholas Tsoutas
Public Gallery
Contemporary visual art, conceptual works, installations, multi media, multidisciplinary works which explore technology, film, video and performance, new media 01614

Woomera

Woomera Heritage Centre, Cnr Banool and Dewrang Avs, Woomera, SA 5720 - T: (08) 86737042, Fax: 86743270
Local Museum
Rocket range, community lifestyle, history of Woomera 01615

Wowan

Wowan and District Museum, Leichhardt Hwy, Wowan, Qld. 4702 - T: (079) 371129, Fax: 371133
Local Museum
Former buttery factory, dairy industry, ambulance, dolls, railways 01616

Wyalkatchem

Wyalkatchem C.B.H. Agricultural Museum, Main St, Railway Tce, Wyalkatchem, WA 6485 - T: (08) 96381048, Fax: 96381078
Agriculture Museum
Tractor coll, variety of equipment 01617

Yackandandah

Bank of Victoria Museum, 21 High St, Yackandandah, Vic. 3749
Special Museum
Banking, business, gold, families and the town of Yackandandan 01618

Yamba

Story House Historical Museum, River St, Yamba, NSW 2464 - T: (02) 66461399
Local Museum
Lighthouse, the railway breakwater walls 01619

Yanchep

Gloucester Lodge Museum, Yanchep National Park, Yanchep, WA 6035, mail addr: Locked Bag 1, Wanneroo, WA 6946 - T: (08) 95611579, 94055000, Fax: 93001383, Internet: http://
www.wanneroo.wa.gov.au
Local Museum / Natural History Museum - 1979
Colonial artifacts, Gnangara mineral sands, speleological exhibits, shipwrecks off the Wannroo/
Yanchep Coast   01620

Yanco

Powerhouse Museum Yanco, Binya St, Yanco, NSW 2703 - T: (02) 69533663
Science&Tech Museum
Electricity   01621

Yankalilla

Yankalilla District Historical Museum, 169 Main Rd, Yankalilla, SA 5203 - T: (08) 85582048, Fax: 85582022
Local Museum
Industry and lifestyle of the district since settlement   01622

Yarra Glen

Gulf Station Historic Farm, Melba Hwy, Yarra Glen, Vic. 3775 - T: (03) 97301286, Fax: 97301820, Internet: http://www.vicnet.net.au/~nattrust/
prop.htm#gulf
Agriculture Museum
Farm complex of timber slab, farm tools, traditional breeds of farm animals   01623

Yarra Junction

Upper Yarra Valley Museum, Rte 175, Warburton Hwy, Yarra Junction, Vic. 3797 - T: (03) 59672167
Local Museum   01624

Yarraman

Yarraman Heritage Centre, 26 Millar St, Yarraman, Qld. 4614 - T: (07) 41638111, Fax: 41638999, E-mail: heritagehouse@glouzone.com.au. Head: John Barber
Historical Museum
Convent of the Sisters of Mercy, scrub/rainforest area, farm machinery, plant shade house, water wise garden and unique water tank system   01625

Yass

Cooma Cottage, Cnr Yass Valley Way and Dog Trap Rd, Yass, NSW 2582 - T: (02) 62261470, Fax: 62263024
Decorative Arts Museum
Original Hume furniture   01626

Hamilton Hume Museum, 247 Comur St, Yass, NSW 2582 - T: (02) 62263380
Local Museum
Development of Yass since the 1820's   01627

Yass Railway Museum, Lead St, Yass, NSW 2582 - T: (02) 62262169, E-mail: arhsact@
acslink.aone.net.au, Internet: http://
arhs.netsite1.net.au
Science&Tech Museum
Station buildings, locomotives and rolling stock of the type used on the tramway   01628

York

Old Gaol and Courthouse, 130 Avon Tce, York, WA 6302 - T: (08) 96412072, Fax: 96412072
Historical Museum   01629

Residency Museum, 4 Brook St, York, WA 6302 - T: (08) 96411751, E-mail: ResidencyMuseum@
YorkWA.com.au, Internet: http://
www.YorkWA.com.au/Residency.Museum
Local Museum - 1972
York's development, farming, tools, furniture, China, domestic utensils   01630

Young

Lambing Flat Museum, Community Arts Centre, Campbell St, Young, NSW 2594 - T: (02) 63822248, Fax: 63822248. Head: Bob Chandler
Local Museum - 1967
Trades and professions, instruments and phonographs, old armoury, radios, gramophones, telephones, dentistry display, old farm tools, original flags carried by miners in the Chinese Riots
1861   01631

Zeehan

West Coast Pioneer's Memorial Museum, Main St, Zeehan, Tas. 7469, mail addr: POB 70, Zeehan, Tas. 7469 - T: (03) 64716225, Fax: 64716650, E-mail: zeehanmuseum@tassie.net.au, Internet: http://www.tesed.edu.au/tasonline/
zeehanmus
Science&Tech Museum / Historical Museum - 1965
Minerals, railway locomotives, mining history 01632

Austria

Abfaltersbach

Museum Pfleggerichtshaus, Anras 27, 9913 Abfaltersbach - T: (04846) 65950, Fax: 65954
Historical Museum / Fine Arts Museum -
1997   01633

Absam

Gemeindemuseum Absam, Stainer Str 5, 6067 Absam - T: (05223) 44426, 564890, Fax: 5648983, E-mail: sekretariat@absam.at
Local Museum - 1988
Handicraft, hist, folklore   01634

Absdorf

Heimatmuseum Altlichtenwarth, Kindergartenstr 232, 2144 Absdorf - T: (02533) 801852
Local Museum - 1986   01635

Abtenau

Denkmalhof Arler, Markt 3, 5441 Abtenau - T: (06243) 2296
Agriculture Museum - 1982
Peasant life, agricultural tools, bee hive - bee museum   01636

Ach

Franz Xaver Gruber-Gedächtnishaus, Hochburg 44, 5122 Ach - T: (07727) 2561, Fax: 2561, E-mail: werner.suetzl@utanet.at. Head: Werner Sützl
Folklore Museum - 1976
Memorabilia of Franz Xaver Gruber (composer of "Stille Nacht, Heilige Nacht"), peasant life   01637

Obermühle Hochburg-Ach, Wanghausen 46, 5122 Ach - T: (07727) 2487. Head: Heinz Hübner
Open Air Museum / Agriculture Museum   01638

Achenkirch

Heimatmuseum Achental, Sixen-Hof, 6215 Achenkirch 29 - T: (05246) 6508, 5321
Local Museum - 1987
Peasant life   01639

Kunstpromenade Achensee, Nr 387, 6215 Achenkirch - T: (05246) 5300, Fax: 6780, E-mail: info@achensee.tirol.at, Internet: http://
www.achensee.com. Head: Markus Kofler
Fine Arts Museum - 1994   01640

Admont

Kunsthistorisches Museum, Benediktinerstift Admont, 8911 Admont - T: (03613) 2312601, Fax: 2312610, E-mail: kultur@stiftadmont.at, Internet: http://www.stiftadmont.at/kultur. Head: Dr. Michael Braunsteiner
Fine Arts Museum - 1959/1980
13th-20th c painting, sculpture, arts and crafts, pewter and glass, paraments (1640-1720)   01641

Naturhistorisches Museum, Benediktinerstift Admont, 8911 Admont - T: (03613) 2312, Fax: 2312610, E-mail: kultur@stiftadmont.at, Internet: http://www.stiftamont.at/kultur. Head: Dr. Jürgen Götze
Natural History Museum - 1866
Insects, birds, reptiles, amphibians, fish, shells, minerals and stones, fossils, herbarium   01642

Adnet

Marmormuseum, Nr 78, 5421 Adnet - T: (06245) 75964, 840410, Fax: 8404133. Head: Franz Kretschmer
Natural History Museum - 1992   01643

Aflenz

Heimatmuseum Aflenz, 8623 Aflenz - T: (03861) 2326
Local Museum - 1962   01644

Afritz

Mineralienschau, Berg ob Afritz 15, 9542 Afritz - T: (04247) 2279, Fax: 254016
Natural History Museum   01645

Aggsbach Dorf

Kartause Aggsbach, Nr 33, 3642 Aggsbach Dorf - T: (02753) 52101330, 8262, Fax: 52101309. Head: Karl Thir
Religious Arts Museum - 1985   01646

Aigen bei Raabs

Dokumentationraum Georg Matthäus Vischer, Ruine Kollmitz, 3814 Aigen bei Raabs - T: (02847) 80474. Head: Herbert Loskott
Special Museum
Topography   01647

Aigen im Mühlkreis

Vogelmuseum Die Vogelwelt des Böhmerwaldes, Kirchengasse 8, 4160 Aigen im Mühlkreis - T: (07281) 6395, Fax: 6395. Head: Emmerich Petz
Natural History Museum - 1993
650 exhibits of various kinds of birds   01648

Aigen-Schlägl

Kultur-Gut-Museum, Hauptstr 2, 4160 Aigen-Schlägl - T: (07281) 88010, 80510, Fax: 80516, E-mail: tv.aigen-schlaegl@netway.at, Internet: http://www.stift-schlaegl.at. Head: Johann Veit
Folklore Museum - 1997   01649

Stiftsmuseum Praemonstratenser-Chorherren Stift Schlägl, Schlägl 1, 4160 Aigen-Schlägl - T: (07281) 88010, Fax: 8801324, E-mail: stephanW@stift-schlaegl.at, Internet: http://www.stift-schlaegl.at. Head: Stephan W. Weber
Religious Arts Museum / Fine Arts Museum - 1902
Painting (late Gothic, Baroque, Danube School), manuscripts and incunabula (1463-1520), paraments, stamps - library   01650

Alberschwende

Heimatmuseum Alberschwende, Im Arzthaus, 6861 Alberschwende - T: (05579) 4233, 4182, Fax: 47386, E-mail: schwarzmann.erich@aon.at
Local Museum - 1974/77
Local hist, from flax to linen   01651

Alkoven

Gedenkräume im Schloß Hartheim, Hartheim 1, 4072 Alkoven - T: (07274) 536. Head: Petra Fosen-Schlichtinger
Historical Museum
Memorial site of the NS-extermination plan concerning people with mental and physical disabilities, gas chamber   01652

Allentsteig

Aussiedlermuseum im Schüttkasten, Hamerlingstr, 3804 Allentsteig - T: (02824) 23100, Fax: 23109, E-mail: gdeallentsteig@netway.at, Internet: http://
www.allensteig.net
Local Museum - 1989   01653

Alpbach

Bergbauernmuseum, 6236 Alpbach - T: (05336) 52240, Fax: 5990
Agriculture Museum - 1977   01654

Alpl

Österreichisches Wandermuseum, Waldschule, 8671 Alpl - T: (03855) 8230, 27662. Head: Wolfgang Riegler
Special Museum - 1982
History of hiking, hiking organizations, dress and equipment, symbolism and language, hiking maps, memorial to the writer Peter Rosegger   01655

Peter Roseggers Geburtshaus, Kluppenegger Hof, 8671 Alpl - T: (03855) 8230, Fax: 8230. Head: Stefan Leitner
Special Museum - 1927
Typical Styrian farmstead where the popular writer Peter Rosegger was born, memorabilia of Rosegger, 19th century furnishings, flax hut, historical implements for flax processing   01656

Altaussee

Literatur- und Heimatmuseum Altaussee, Kulturzentrum Steinberghaus, Lichtersberg 25, 8992 Altaussee - T: (03622) 71749
Special Museum / Local Museum - 1970
Lit, local hist, mining   01657

Salzbergwerk Altaussee, Steinberghaus, Lichtersberg 25, 8992 Altaussee - T: (06132) 2002551, Fax: 2004520, E-mail: info@
salzwelten.at, Internet: http://www.salzwelten.at. Head: Ernst Martin Gaisbauer
Science&Tech Museum - 1934
Salt mine, minerals, fossils, salt-mining tools, exhibits on salt mining   01658

Altenburg

Benediktinerstift und Stiftssammlungen, Benediktinerabtei 1, 3591 Altenburg - T: (02982) 3451, Fax: 345113, E-mail: info@stift-altenburg.at, Internet: http://www.stift-altenburg.at. Head: Dr. Albert Groiß
Fine Arts Museum / Religious Arts Museum / Archaeological Museum / Historic Site - 1144
12th-18th c art, esp Austrian Baroque painting, sculpture, furniture, historic 18th c buildings, manuscripts and documents from the 12th c - library   01659

Altenfelden

Trophäensaal und Erstes Oberösterreichisches Falknereimuseum, Atzesberg 8, 4121 Altenfelden - T: (07282) 5590, Fax: 5590, Internet: http://
www.rohrbach.at/wildpark
Natural History Museum - 1969
Trophies and stuffed native animals   01660

Altenhof am Hausruck

Galerie Hausruck, Hueb 10, 4674 Altenhof am Hausruck - T: (07735) 6631259, Fax: 6631333, E-mail: lebensraum@das-dorf.at, Internet: http://
www.das-dorf.at/kultur. Head: Ludwig Fotter
Fine Arts Museum - 1978   01661

Altenmarkt im Pongau

Heimatmuseum im alten Bruderhaus und in der Dechanathofscheune, Brunnbauerngasse 78, 5541 Altenmarkt im Pongau - T: (06452) 7373
Local Museum - 1972/82   01662

Altheim

Zeitspurenmuseum Altheim, Roßbacherstr 2, 4950 Altheim - T: (07723) 44231, 4225582, E-mail: i.bodingbauer@utanet.at, Internet: http://
www.ochzethaus.at
Archaeological Museum - 1995
Roman finds   01663

Altmünster

Radmuseum anno dazumal, Maria-Theresia-Str 3, 4813 Altmünster - T: (0664) 1521264, Fax: (07612) 87525, E-mail: h.denzel@gmx.at. Head: H. Denzel, W. Neumayer
Science&Tech Museum - 1994
Vehicles, motor bikes, historical bicycles   01664

Amstetten

Mostviertler Bauernmuseum, Ödhof, Gigerreith 39, 3300 Amstetten - T: (07479) 7334, Fax: 73344
Open Air Museum / Agriculture Museum / Folklore Museum - 1972
Peasant life   01665

Städtische Sammlungen, Rathausstr 1, 3300 Amstetten - T: (07472) 601, Fax: 601. Head: Alfred Grubbauer
Local Museum   01666

Andorf

Innviertler Freilichtmuseum Brunnbauerhof, Großpichl 4, 4770 Andorf - T: (07766) 225516, Fax: 2257, E-mail: gde.andorf@netway.at
Open Air Museum / Agriculture Museum -
1994   01667

Anger

Heimatmuseum Rauchstubenhaus Edelschachen, Anger 49, 8184 Anger - T: (03175) 2211, Fax: 2169
Local Museum - 1968   01668

Annaberg

Denkmalhof Gererhof, 5525 Annaberg - T: (06463) 8397
Agriculture Museum - 1982
Agricultural tools   01669

Ansfelden

ABC-Galerie, Carlonestr 2, 4052 Ansfelden - T: (07229) 7833310, Fax: 7833333. Head: Wolfgang Pfeiffer
Fine Arts Museum   01670

Anton Bruckner-Museum, Augustinerstr 3, 4052 Ansfelden - T: (07229) 87128, 82376. Head: Michael Mascherbauer
Special Museum - 1971
Birth house of Anton Bruckner, memorabilia   01671

Ardagger

Militärgeschichtliches Museum, Freizeithafen, 3321 Ardagger - T: (07479) 7239, Fax: 7239, E-mail: mitro@t-online.at, Internet: http://
www.mostviertel.direkt.at. Head: Harald Werner
Military Museum - 1973
Weapons, vehicles, uniforms   01672

Oldtimermuseum, Stift 3, 3321 Ardagger - T: (07479) 6565, 7433, Fax: 65658, E-mail: oldtimer@
mostgalerie.at, Internet: http://
www.oldtimermuseum.at. Head: Ferdinand Jandl
Science&Tech Museum
Motor-bikes since 1900   01673

Arnfels

Steirisches Uhren-, Musikalien- und Volkskundemuseum, Maltschach 3, 8454 Arnfels - T: (03458) 221. Head: Dominik Haindl
Science&Tech Museum / Music Museum / Ethnology Museum - 1945
Prehistory, paleontology, clocks, musical instruments, religious art, weapons, folk customs, stamps, herbarium - botanical garden   01674

Arnoldstein

Heimatmuseum, 9601 Arnoldstein - T: (04255) 2260, Fax: 226033
Local Museum   01675

Artstetten

Erzherzog Franz-Ferdinand Museum, Schloß Artstetten, 3661 Artstetten - T: (07413) 8006, Fax: 800615, E-mail: museum@schloss-arstetten.at, Internet: http://www.schloss-

arstetten.at. Head: Dr. Wladimir Graf Aichelburg, Anita Fürstin von Hohenberg
Historical Museum - 1982
archive 01676

Aspang

Automobilmuseum, Marienpl 4-6, 2870 Aspang - T: (02642) 52329, Fax: (01) 5244368. Head: Sonja Dirnbacher
Science&Tech Museum - 1987
Largest automobile museum in Austria 01677

Büromaschinen-Museum, Marienpl 4, 2870 Aspang - T: (02642) 931660. Head: Kurt Dirnbacher
Science&Tech Museum 01678

Volkskundliches Berufe- und Handwerker-Museum, z.Zt. geschlossen, Marienpl 4-6, 2870 Aspang - T: (02642) 52329. Head: Sonja Dirnbacher
Ethnology Museum - 1987 01679

Asparn an der Zaya

Museum für Urgeschichte des Landes Niederösterreich, Franz-Hampl-Pl 1, 2151 Asparn an der Zaya - T: (02577) 8039, Fax: 803920, E-mail: asparn.urgeschichte@utanet.at, Internet: http://www.urgeschichte.com. Head: Dr. Helmut Windl
Archaeological Museum / Open Air Museum - 1970
Prehistory of Lower Austria - open air museum, center of prehistory technology 01680

Niederösterreichisches Schulmuseum, Altes Schulhaus, Schulgasse 330, Michelstetten, 2151 Asparn an der Zaya - T: (02577) 8240, 8003, Fax: 824020, 800320, E-mail: schulmuseum@asn.netway.at. Head: Horst Hubinger
Historical Museum - 1979/80
School hist 01681

Weinlandmuseum, Nr 169, 2151 Asparn an der Zaya - T: (02577) 8240
Local Museum / Folklore Museum - 1950
History, history of law, crafts and guilds, religious art (Gothic to present), agricultural implements, peasant furniture and domestic tools, important local personalities/artists, stones - archive, documentation centre 01682

Atzenbrugg

Museum Franz Schubert und sein Freundeskreis, Schloß Atzenburg, Schloßpl 1, 3452 Atzenbrugg - T: (02275) 5900. Head: Rosl Schwab
Music Museum - 1986 01683

Auberg

Obermühlviertler Denkmalhof Unterkagerer, Oberes Mühlviertel, 4171 Auberg - T: (07289) 71603
Open Air Museum
Regional architecture 01684

Bad Aussee

Kammerhofmuseum Ausseerland, Chlumeckypl 1, 8990 Bad Aussee - T: (03622) 5251121, Fax: 5251127, E-mail: cornelia.koeberl@badaussee.at, Internet: http://www.badaussee.at. Head: Cornelia Köberl
Local Museum - 1951
Salt works, peasant costumes, fossils, cave findings, furniture, paintings - library, archive (paintings) 01685

Via Artis, Kurhauspl 55, 8990 Bad Aussee - T: (03622) 540400, Fax: 540407, E-mail: info@ausseerland.at
Fine Arts Museum 01686

Bad Bleiberg

Terra Mystica, Nötsch 91, 9531 Bad Bleiberg - T: (04244) 2255, Fax: 2434, E-mail: office@terra-mystica.at, Internet: http://www.terra-mystica.at. Head: Michael Grafenauer
Special Museum - 1995 01687

Bad Deutsch-Altenburg

Archäologisches Museum Carnuntinum, Badgasse 40-46, 2405 Bad Deutsch-Altenburg - T: (02165) 62480, Fax: 6248020, E-mail: - carnuntum.research@utanet.at, Internet: http://www.carnuntum.co.at. Head: Prof. Dr. Werner Jobst
Archaeological Museum - 1904
Roman art from the 1st to the 5th c - library 01688

Bad Eisenkappel

Obir-Tropfsteinhöhlen, Hauptpl 7, 9135 Bad Eisenkappel - T: (04238) 8239, 8253, Fax: 823910, E-mail: obir@hoehlen.at, Internet: http://www.hoehlen.at. Head: Walter Jerlich
Natural History Museum - 1991 01689

Bad Fischau

Blau-gelbe Viertelsgalerie, Industrieviertel, Schloss Fischau, Wiener Neustädter Str 3, 2721 Bad Fischau - T: (02639) 2324, 7675, Fax: 2329, E-mail: art@forum-bad-fischau.or.at, Internet: http://www.forum-bad-fischau.or.at. Head: Hannes Wöhrer
Public Gallery - 1998 01690

Höhlenmuseum Eisensteinhöhle, Obere Burg, 2721 Bad Fischau - T: (02639) 21033. Head: Gerhard Winkler
Natural History Museum
Geology, mineralogy 01691

Bad Gastein

Bad-Gasteiner Museum, Haus Austria, Kaiser-Franz-Josef-Str 1, 5640 Bad Gastein - T: (06434) 3488, 2591, 2110, Fax: 259185. Head: Fritz Kutter
Local Museum - 1936/1974 01692

Bad Goisern

Freilichtmuseum Anzenaumühle, Anzenau 1, 4822 Bad Goisern - T: (0664) 2528741, E-mail: jessica.jar@aon.at. Head: Jessica Jarosch
Open Air Museum 01693

Heimat- und Landlermuseum, Goisern 129, 4822 Bad Goisern - T: (06135) 7180, 8329
Local Museum - 1964
Literary estate of the peasant philosopher Konrad Deubler, local hist, violin construction, handicrafts, markmanship - Landlermuseum 01694

Holzknechtmuseum im Salzkammergut, Müllerwald, 4822 Bad Goisern - T: (06135) 8961, E-mail: r.zahler@eduhi.at. Head: Robert Zahler
Folklore Museum - 1976 01695

Bad Großpertholz

Heimatmuseum, Nr 138, 3972 Bad Großpertholz - T: (02857) 2253, 2710, Fax: 27103, E-mail: - gemeinde.grpertholz@wvnet.at, Internet: http://www.noel.gv.at/service/k/k1/museen/0102.htm
Local Museum - 1979 01696

Trift- und Holzfällermuseum, Nr 138, 3972 Bad Großpertholz - T: (02857) 2253, Fax: 27103, E-mail: gemeinde.grpertholz@wvnet.at, Internet: http://www.noel.gv.at/service/k/k1/museen/0165.htm
Special Museum - 1978 01697

Bad Hall

Forum Hall, Handwerk-Heimat-Haustüren, Eduard-Bach-Str 4, 4540 Bad Hall - T: (07258) 4888, Fax: 4888, Internet: http://www.badhall.com. Head: Franz Ehrenhuber
Local Museum - 1954
Local hist, peasant life, coll of front doors, 22 kinds of handicraft 01698

Bad Ischl

Haenel-Pancera-Familienmuseum, Concordiastr 3, 4820 Bad Ischl - T: (06132) 21689. Head: Johanna Haenel
Fine Arts Museum - 1959
Early 20th c villa, painting, sculpture, glass, porcelain, Oriental art, furniture from the Renaissance and Empire periods, autographs of famous composers, memorabilia of the pianist Ella Pančera 01699

Kaiservilla, Jainzen 38, 4820 Bad Ischl - Fax: (06132) 28285, Internet: http://www.herold.co.at/kaiservilla. Head: Markus Salvator
Historical Museum / Decorative Arts Museum - 1922
19th c villa of Kaiser Franz Josef I, 19th c interiors, paintings, sculpture, porcelain, arts and crafts, hunting trophies of Kaiser Franz Joseph I 01700

Lehár-Villa, Lehárkai 8, 4820 Bad Ischl - T: (06132) 26992, 30114, Fax: 30172, E-mail: msams@stadtamt-badischl.at. Head: Dr. Adam Sifkovits
Music Museum - 1948
Residence of the composer Franz Lehár, memorabilia of Lehár, the composer's art coll, original music scores, period furniture 01701

Museum der Stadt Bad Ischl, Esplanade 10, 4820 Bad Ischl - T: (06132) 25476, 30114, Fax: 30172, E-mail: msams@stadtamt-badischl.at. Head: Dr. Adam Sifkovits
Local Museum - 1989
Salt mining, cultural history, famous musicians and artists in Bad Ischl, theatre, balneology, Franz Joseph I 01702

Photomuseum des Landes Oberösterreich, Marmorschlößl, Jainzen 1, 4820 Bad Ischl - T: (06131) 24422, Fax: 244224. Head: Kurt Römer
Special Museum - 1978
History and development of photography, cameras, 19th century photographs, photos by Austrian photographers 01703

Bad Kreuzen

Burg Bad Kreuzen, Kreuzen 20a, 4362 Bad Kreuzen - T: (07266) 62550, Fax: 6254, 625575. Head: Gottfried Kranzl
Public Gallery 01704

Bad Leonfelden

Heimathaus Spitalskirche/Bürgerspital, Linzer Str, 4190 Bad Leonfelden - T: (07213) 6397, Fax: 641213, E-mail: info.bad-leonfelden@netway.at
Local Museum
Regional trade workshops, frescos 01705

Historischer Handblaudruck Wagner, Kurhausstr 11, 4190 Bad Leonfelden - T: (07213) 6588, Fax: 65884, E-mail: blaudrucke.wagner@netway.at. Head: Maria Wagner
Special Museum
Printing and indigo-dyeing of linen and silk 01706

Schulmuseum des Bezirkes Urfahr-Umgebung, Böhmerstr 1, 4190 Bad Leonfelden - T: (07213) 6397, Fax: 641213, E-mail: info.bad-leonfelden@netway.at, Internet: http://www.museumstrasse.at/schulmuseum
Historical Museum - 1988
School hist - library 01707

Bad Mitterndorf

Heimatkundliche Sammlung Strick, Nr 67, 8983 Bad Mitterndorf - T: (06153) 2217
Local Museum / Archaeological Museum - 1908
Archaeological finds, paleontology, religious folk art, domestic implements, coins, weapons, traditional costumes, masks of the local Nikolaus drama, pewter, archives - library 01708

Bad Pirawarth

Dokumentation des ehemaligen Heilbades, Plastiken-Freilichtmuseum Prof. Knesl, Prof.-Knesl-Pl 1, 2222 Bad Pirawarth - T: (02574) 2340, 2339, Fax: 23409
Local Museum / Fine Arts Museum - 1986
Scupltures, local hist, balneology 01709

Bad Radkersburg

Heimatmuseum, Emmenstr 9, 8490 Bad Radkersburg - T: (03476) 2545
Local Museum - 1927
Local hist, crafts 01710

Bad Tatzmannsdorf

Burgenländisches Brotmuseum, Joseph-Haydn-Pl 5, 7431 Bad Tatzmannsdorf - T: (03353) 8515. Head: Hans Gradwohl
Special Museum - 1990
Bread making, trade, traditions 01711

Freilichtmuseum, 7431 Bad Tatzmannsdorf - T: (03353) 8283. Head: Josef Hölzel
Open Air Museum - 1967
Original and reconstructed 17th-20th c farmhouses, stalls, wine cellar, smithy 01712

Kurmuseum, Quellenhof, 7431 Bad Tatzmannsdorf - T: (03353) 8283. Head: Helmut Sillner
Historical Museum - 1990
Balneology, traditions, early hist 01713

Bad Vöslau

Stadtmuseum mit Weinmuseum, Altes Rathaus, Kirchenpl 8, 2540 Bad Vöslau - T: (02252) 76135. Head: Robert Haininger
Local Museum / Special Museum - 1898
Geology of the eastern alpine zone, local industry, local history, general history, domestic implements, hunting trophies, weapons, viticulture 01714

Bad Wimsbach-Neydharting

Freilichtmuseum Hammerschmiede, Brückenweg 9, 4654 Bad Wimsbach-Neydharting - T: (07245) 25331, 25681, Fax: 25999
Science&Tech Museum - 1965 01715

Kurmuseum des Österreichischen Moorforschungsinstituts, Stiftungshaus, 4654 Bad Wimsbach-Neydharting - T: (07245) 5573, Fax: (0732) 77178125
Special Museum - 1955 01716

Notgeld-Sammlung 1918/20, Kurhaus, Stöber-Str 5, 4654 Bad Wimsbach-Neydharting - T: (07245) 5573, Fax: (0732) 77178125
Special Museum - 1945 01717

Baden bei Wien

Badener Puppen- und Spielzeugmuseum, Erzherzog-Rainer-Ring 23, 2500 Baden bei Wien - T: (02252) 41020, Fax: (01) 86800210, Internet: http://www.volkskunde.at/museen.htm. Head: Barbara Lorenz
Special Museum - 1990 01718

Beethovenhaus " Haus der Neunten", Rathausgasse 10, 2500 Baden bei Wien - T: (01) 86800231, Fax: 86800407, E-mail: kultur@baden-bei-wien.at, Internet: http://www.baden-bei-wien.at
Music Museum - 1965 01719

Frauenbad - Zentrum für zeitgenössische Kunst, Josefspl 5, 2500 Baden bei Wien - T: (02252) 86800522, Fax: 86800407, E-mail: kultur@baden-bei-wien.at, Internet: http://www.baden-bei-wien.at
Public Gallery - 1994 01720

Kaiser Franz-Josef-Museum für Handwerk und Volkskunst, Hochstr 51, 2500 Baden bei Wien - T: (02252) 41100, 44575. Head: Dr. Franziska Rampl
Folklore Museum - 1900
Handicrafts, folk art of Lower Austria, locksmith and forge, lamps, ceramics, wood crafts, coopery, weaving, clocks, musical instruments, religious folk art, weapons 01721

Rollettmuseum, Weikersdorfer Pl 1, 2500 Baden bei Wien - T: (02252) 48255. Head: Dr. Rudolf Maurer
Special Museum - 1810
Periods, maps, Dr. Gall skull coll, memorabilia of Grillparzer and Beethoven, coll of needlework 1790-1900 01722

Bärnbach

Burgenkundliches Museum des Steirischen Burgenvereins, Schloß Alt-Kainach, Hauptstr 68, 8572 Bärnbach - T: (03142) 48882. Head: Michael Schmeja
Historical Museum - 1968
Comparative history of fortresses, esp the Styrian fortresses, models, typology, paintings, maps, stamps with fortresses and castles, artists, commanders-in-chief, statesmen, and scientists in Styrian fortresses 01723

Steirisches Glaskunstzentrum und Glasmuseum Bärnbach, Hochtregisterstr 1, 8572 Bärnbach - T: (03142) 62950, Fax: 706804, E-mail: glascenter@stoelzle.com, Internet: http://www.glasmuseum.at. Head: Hans Martin Hittaller, Erhard Hohl
Special Museum - 1984 01724

Baldramsdorf

Erstes Kärntner Handwerksmuseum, Unterhaus 18, 9805 Baldramsdorf - T: (04762) 7140, 7658, Fax: 71147
Special Museum - 1977
Handicraft 01725

Bernhardsthal

Heimatmuseum, Alte Post, Museumspl 62, 2275 Bernhardsthal - T: (02557) 8302, 8800, E-mail: stratjelf@noe.wk.or.at
Local Museum - 1977 01726

Bernstein, Burgenland

Felsenmuseum, Hauptpl 5, 7434 Bernstein, Burgenland - T: (03354) 6620, Fax: 662014
Natural History Museum - 1981 01727

Sammlungen Burg Bernstein, Schloßweg 1, 7434 Bernstein, Burgenland - T: (03354) 6382, Fax: 6520. Head: Andrea Berger
Historical Museum - 1892
Historical interiors and inventory, weapons and armour, instruments of torture, pre- and ancient history, retorts and 17th c alchemist laboratory - library 01728

Bezau

Heimatmuseum, Ellenbogen 181, 6870 Bezau - T: (05514) 3230, 2559
Local Museum / Folklore Museum - 1920
Housing, costume, embroidery 01729

Wälderbähnle, Bahnhof 147, 6870 Bezau - T: (05514) 3174, Fax: (05513) 61924
Science&Tech Museum - 1985 01730

Bleiburg

Sudhaus Sorgendorf, Siebenhüttenweg, Sorgendorf, 9150 Bleiburg - T: (04235) 3622. Head: Franz Brandl
Fine Arts Museum - 1995 01731

Werner-Berg-Galerie der Stadt Bleiburg, 10. Oktober-Pl 4, 9150 Bleiburg - T: (04235) 2872, 21100, Fax: 211022, E-mail: bleiburg.markt@ktn.gde.at, Internet: http://www.berggalerie.at. Head: Gottfried Stöckl
Public Gallery / Fine Arts Museum - 1968
Woodprints, paintings, graphics, and sketches by Werner Berg 01732

Blindenmarkt

Oldtimermuseum im Schloß, Hubertendorf 32, 3372 Blindenmarkt - T: (07473) 2702. Head: Franz Mörtinger
Science&Tech Museum 01733

Bludenz

Museum der Stadt Bludenz, Kirchgasse 9, 6700 Bludenz - T: (05552) 63621237, Fax: 63621237, E-mail: creiter@bludenz.at. Head: Carmen Reiter
Local Museum - 1922
Local hist, pre- and early hist 01734

Böckstein

Böcksteiner Montanmuseum Hohe Tauern, Karl-Imhof-Ring 12, 5645 Böckstein - T: (06434) 5414, Fax: 5414, E-mail: montanmuseum_boeckstein@aon.at, Internet: http://www.boeckstein.at/montanmuseum. Head: Franz Haussteiner
Science&Tech Museum - 1979
library, archive 01735

Bramberg

Museum Bramberg - Wilhelmgut, Weichselsdorf Nr 27, 5733 Bramberg - T: (06566) 7237, 7214, Fax: 816685. Head: Prof. Hans Hönigschmid
Local Museum / Folklore Museum / Natural History Museum - 1960
Minerals from Hohe Tauern, zoology, religious art, mining - bee keeping 01736

Braunau am Inn

Museum Herzogsburg, Altstadt 10, 5280 Braunau am Inn - T: (07722) 808227, Fax: 87532, Internet: http://www.braunau.de. Head: Margarete Doppler
Local Museum - 1917
Folk art, painting, original bell-foundry, bakery 01737

Bregenz

Kunsthaus Bregenz, Karl-Tizian-Pl 1, 6900 Bregenz - T: (05574) 485940, Fax: 485948, E-mail: kub@kunsthaus-bregenz.at, Internet: http://www.kunsthaus-bregenz.at. Head: Eckhard Schneider
Fine Arts Museum - 1997 01738

Vorarlberger Landesmuseum, Kornmarkt 1, 6900 Bregenz - T: (05574) 46050, Fax: 4605020, E-mail: info@vlm.at, Internet: http://www.vlr.gv.at/landesregierung/iic/lmusver.htm. Head: Dr. Helmut Swozilek
Local Museum / Archaeological Museum / Decorative Arts Museum / Fine Arts Museum / Folklore Museum - 1857 01739

Vorarlberger Militärmuseum, Martinsturm, Martinsgasse 3b, 6901 Bregenz - T: (05574) 49223830, Fax: 49221708. Head: Erwin Fitz
Military Museum - 1986 01740

Zisterzienserabtei Mehrerau, Mehrerauer Str 66, Vorkloster, 6903 Bregenz - T: (05574) 714610, Fax: 7146117
Religious Arts Museum 01741

Breitenbrunn, Neusiedlersee

Turmmuseum, Prangerstr, 7091 Breitenbrunn, Neusiedlersee - T: (02683) 52130, 2205, Fax: 220511
Local Museum - 1969
Geology, local hist 01742

Brixlegg

Tiroler Bergbau- und Hüttenmuseum, Römerstr 30, 6230 Brixlegg - T: (05337) 62581, Fax: 62581, E-mail: tvb-brixlegg@magnet.at
Science&Tech Museum / Archaeological Museum - 1991
Old mining tools, metallurgy, archaeology 01743

Bruck an der Lafnitz

Kernstock-Museum, Festenburg 1, 8251 Bruck an der Lafnitz - T: (03331) 2255, 2489, Fax: 2255, E-mail: festenburg@aon.at, Internet: http://www.festenburg.at. Head: Dr. Ferdinand Hutz
Special Museum - 1928
Memorabilia of the poet Dr. Ottokar Kernstock in his former home, barogue frescos 01744

Bruck an der Leitha

Stadtmuseum Bruck an der Leitha, Burgenlandstr 22, 2460 Bruck an der Leitha - T: (02162) 65454, 6235440, Fax: 65454, 6235425. Head: Friedrich Petznek
Local Museum 01745

Bruck an der Mur

Stadtmuseum Bruck (temporary closed), Koloman Wallisch Pl 1, 8600 Bruck an der Mur - T: (03862) 890120, Fax: 890102, E-mail: stadtmarketing@bruckmur.at, Internet: http://www.bruckmur.at. Head: Inga Horny
Local Museum 01746

Waffensammlung Willibald Folger, Dr.-Karl-Renner-Str 42, 8601 Bruck an der Mur - T: (03862) 54864. Head: Willibald Folger
Military Museum - 1955
Arms and armour 01747

Brunn am Gebirge

Brunner Heimathaus mit Rudolf-Steiner-Gedenkstätte, Leopold-Gattringer-Str 34, 2345 Brunn am Gebirge - T: (02236) 33024, Fax: 3160139. Head: Reinhard Kluger
Local Museum
Memorabilia on the founder of anthroposophy 01748

Brunn an der Wild

Privatsammlung Ignaz Mann, Atzelsdorf 1, 3595 Brunn an der Wild - T: (02989) 2341
Local Museum 01749

Burgau

Schloß Burgau, Schloß 1, 8291 Burgau - T: (03383) 3380, 2111, Fax: 3380, E-mail: gde@burgau.steiermark.at. Head: Karl Fassl
Fine Arts Museum 01750

Dalaas

Klostertal-Museum, Wald am Arlberg 11, 6752 Dalaas - T: (05585) 7377, Fax: 7520, E-mail: christof.thoeny@a1.net. Head: Christof Thöny
Local Museum - 1994 01751

Deutsch Wagram

Eisenbahnmuseum, Bahnhofspl, 2232 Deutsch Wagram - T: (02247) 2303
Science&Tech Museum - 1987 01752

Napoleon- und Heimatmuseum, Erzherzog-Carl-Str 1, 2232 Deutsch Wagram - T: (02247) 3790. Head: Rupert Derbic
Historical Museum - 1959
Battle of Wagram 1809 01753

Deutschfeistritz

Museum Sensenwerk, Rudolf-Klug-Gasse 73, 8121 Deutschfeistritz - T: (03127) 41366, Fax: 42200
Special Museum 01754

Deutschkreutz

Goldmarkgedenkhaus Deutschkreutz, Hauptstr 54, 7301 Deutschkreutz - T: (02613) 80203
Special Museum 01755

Deutschlandsberg

Burgmuseum für Vor- und Frühgeschichte, Burg Deutschlandsberg, 8530 Deutschlandsberg - T: (03462) 2011. Head: Anton Steffan, Günther Steffan
Historical Museum 01756

Volkskundliches Museum, Unterer Steinwandweg 10, 8530 Deutschlandsberg - T: (03462) 34065. Head: Karl Trücher
Ethnology Museum - 1950
Peasant life, furniture, tools 01757

Dietmanns

Alte Huf- und Wagenschmiede, Hauptstr 81, 3813 Dietmanns - T: (02847) 4516, Fax: 4516
Science&Tech Museum - 1995 01758

Dobersberg

Naturkunde- und Feuerwehrmuseum, Schloßgasse 1, 3843 Dobersberg - T: (02843) 23320, Fax: 23326, E-mail: gemeinde.dobersberg@wvnet.at, Internet: http://www.tiscover.com/dobersberg. Head: Friedrich Goldnagl
Natural History Museum / Historical Museum 01759

Schloß Peigarten/Thaya, Peigarten 1, 3843 Dobersberg - T: (02843) 2702, 2973, Fax: (01) 4069363. Head: Dr. Martin Wolfer
Decorative Arts Museum - 1978
Style of home decor of 19th c nobility 01760

Dobl

Sendergalerie Dobl, Am Sendergrund 15, 8143 Dobl - T: (03136) 52085, Fax: 521119, E-mail: gde@dobl.steiermark.at, Internet: http://www.dobl.steiermark.at
Fine Arts Museum - 1998 01761

Dölsach

Museum Aguntum, Stribach 97, 9991 Dölsach - T: (04852) 61550, Fax: 6155505, E-mail: aguntum@aon.at. Head: Prof. Dr. Elisabeth Walde
Archaeological Museum - 1960
Roman finds 01762

Dornbirn

Kunst Raum Dornbirn, Achstr 1, 6850 Dornbirn - T: (05572) 55044, Fax: 550444838, E-mail: kunst.raum@dornbirn.at, Internet: http://www.kunstraumdornbirn.at
Public Gallery 01763

Stadtmuseum Dornbirn, Marktpl 11, 6850 Dornbirn - T: (05572) 330774911, Fax: 330774918, E-mail: stadtmuseum@dornbirn.at, Internet: http://www.stadtmuseum.dornbirn.at. Head: Hanno Platzgummer
Local Museum - 1991 01764

Vorarlberger Naturschau, Marktstr 33, 6850 Dornbirn - T: (05572) 23235, Fax: 232358, E-mail: naturschau@dornbirn.at, Internet: http://www.naturschau.at. Head: Dr. Margit Schmid
Natural History Museum - 1960
Geology, paleontology, insects, botany, zoology, ecology, climate, lakes and rivers - library 01765

Drosendorf an der Thaya

Galerie im Bürgerspital, Bürgerspitalgasse 17, 2095 Drosendorf an der Thaya - T: (02915) 2213, 23210. Head: Susanne Meiringer
Public Gallery - 1982 01766

Kunststube, Hauptpl 1, 2095 Drosendorf an der Thaya - T: (02915) 2213, Fax: 2213
Fine Arts Museum 01767

Städtisches Kießling-Museum, Bürgerspitalstr 11, 2095 Drosendorf an der Thaya - T: (02915) 2213, Fax: 2263, E-mail: gemeinde.drosendorf@nvnet.at, Internet: http://www.nvnet.at/gemeinden/drosendorf. Head: Hedwig Mayer
Local Museum / Archaeological Museum - 1925
Local and regional history, handicraft tools, archives and writings by Franz Kießling 01768

Dürnstein, Niederösterreich

Stift Dürnstein, Stift 1, 3601 Dürnstein, Niederösterreich - T: (02711) 375, Fax: 432
Religious Arts Museum / Fine Arts Museum 01769

Eben im Pongau

Tauernstraßen-Museum, Gasthofberg, 5531 Eben im Pongau - T: (06464) 8114, 7792, Fax: 8508. Head: Bruno Müller
Science&Tech Museum - 1977 01770

Ebenau

Heimatmuseum, Nr 2, 5323 Ebenau - T: (06221) 7229, 7257, Fax: 8167
Local Museum - 1965 01771

Ebene Reichenau

Mineralien-Museum Zirbenhof, Turracher Höhe 15, 9565 Ebene Reichenau - T: (04275) 8233, Fax: 82334. Head: Norbert Kranzelbinder
Natural History Museum - 1965 01772

Ebensee

Heimathaus Ebensee, Hauptstr 27, 4802 Ebensee - T: (06133) 705110, Fax: 5624
Local Museum - 1979
Local history, salt mines, forestry, folk customs 01773

KZ-Gedenkstätte und Zeitgeschichte-Museum Ebensee, Kirchengasse 5, 4802 Ebensee - T: (06133) 5601, Fax: 56014, E-mail: museum@utanet.at, Internet: http://www.ebensee.org. Head: Dr. Wolfgang Quatember
Historical Museum
Memorial site of the mining galleries of the concentration camp Mauthausen - subcamp Ebensee, exhibition, fotos, documents, modern Austrian hist, resistance, persecution, Austro-Faschism 01774

Ebental, Kärnten

Nostalgiebahnen in Kärnten, Museum für Technik und Verkehr, Lipizach 23, 9065 Ebental, Kärnten - T: (0463) 740368, Fax: 740208, E-mail: nostalgie.bahnen@utanet.at. Head: Jörg Prix
Science&Tech Museum 01775

Eberndorf

Galerie Stift Eberndorf, Kirchpl 1, 9141 Eberndorf - T: (04236) 2242-12, Fax: 2242-52, E-mail: eberndorf@ktn.gde.at, Internet: http://www.suedkaernten.at. Head: Robert Wlattnig
Fine Arts Museum 01776

Eckartsau

Barockjagdschloß Eckartsau, Schloß, 2305 Eckartsau - T: (02214) 2240, Fax: 224019, E-mail: fv.eckartsau@oebf.at, Internet: http://www.oebf.at/html/kunst_kultur.html. Head: Gottfried Pausch
Historical Museum - 1919 01777

Edelsbach bei Feldbach

Gsellmanns Weltmaschine, 8332 Edelsbach bei Feldbach - T: (03115) 2983
Special Museum
Perpetuum Mobile of phantasy 01778

Edlbach

Ramitscheder-Mühle, Mitterweng, 4580 Edlbach - T: (07562) 8768
Science&Tech Museum
Water mill and implements 01779

Eferding

Stadtmuseum und Fürstlich Starhembergisches Familienmuseum, Kirchenpl 1, 4070 Eferding - T: (07272) 55550, Fax: 555533, E-mail: gemeinde@eferding.ooe.gr.at. Head: Ingeborg Goldfuchs
Historical Museum - 1969
Memorabilia of the peasant wars, the Battle against the Turks 01780

Egg

Heimatmuseum Egg, Pfarrhof 5, 6863 Egg - T: (05512) 22160, Fax: 22169, E-mail: gemeinde@egg.cnv.at, Internet: http://www.egg.at. Head: Anton Pfeifer
Decorative Arts Museum - 1904 01781

Wälder Heimatschau → Heimatmuseum Egg

Eggenburg

Bürgerkorpsmuseum im Kanzlerturm, Judengasse, 3730 Eggenburg - T: (02984) 4878, E-mail: g.dafert@netway.at. Head: Dr. Wolfgang Dafert
Historical Museum / Military Museum - 1995 01782

Krahuletz-Museum, Krahuletz-Pl 1, 3730 Eggenburg - T: (02984) 34003, Fax: 34005, E-mail: gesellschaft@krahuletzmuseum.at. Head: Dr. Johannes M. Tuzar
Local Museum - 1866
Geology and paleontology, pre- and ancient history, Stone Age bone tools, ceramics, Roman provincial art, folklore, peasant tools, crafts, glass, porcelain, clocks, costumes, armaments, stones, stone masonry 01783

Museum Steinmetzhaus, Zogelsdorf 25, 3730 Eggenburg - T: (02984) 26530, Fax: 265315, E-mail: gemeinde.burgschleinitz_kuehnring@utanet.at. Head: Burghard Gaspar
Historical Museum - 1998 01784

Das Österreichische Motorradmuseum, Museumgasse 6, 3730 Eggenburg - T: (02984) 2151, Fax: 2151, E-mail: motorradmuseum@uta1002.at, Internet: http://www.motorradmuseum.at. Head: Prof. Friedrich Ehn
Science&Tech Museum - 1980
Motorbikes (esp. PUCH, BMW, British, Czech, Austrian) 01785

Ehrwald

Ehrwalder Heimatmuseum, Innsbrucker Str 16, 6632 Ehrwald - T: (05673) 2677, 3492. Head: Paul Richter
Local Museum / Folklore Museum - 1984
Local trade and craft, folklore, agriculture 01786

Gipfelmuseum, 6632 Ehrwald - T: (05673) 2309. Head: Josef Baumgartner
Natural History Museum - 1986 01787

Eibiswald

Galerie Kulturzentrum Lerchhaus, Nr 36, 8552 Eibiswald - T: (03466) 42307, Fax: 4221818, E-mail: gde@eibiswald.steiermark.at, Internet: http://www.eibiswald.steiermark.at
Public Gallery - 1992 01788

Heimatmuseum und Klöpferhaus, Nr 3682, 8552 Eibiswald - T: (03466) 43117, Fax: 4221818, E-mail: gde@eibiswald.steiermark.at, Internet: http://www.eibiswald.steiermark.at
Local Museum - 1954/1992
Prehistory, local and regional history, handicrafts and folk art, iron and coal, agriculture, manuscripts, letters, works of the popular writer Hans Klöpfer 01789

Einöde

Galerie im Bildhauerhaus und Skulpturenwanderweg, Kras 24, Krastal, 9541 Einöde - T: (04248) 3666, Fax: 3666, Internet: http://business.carinthia.com/krastal. Head: Helmut Machhammer
Fine Arts Museum / Open Air Museum - 1967 01790

Puppenmuseum, Winklern 14, 9541 Einöde - T: (04248) 2395
Special Museum - 1972
Dolls by Ellie Riehl 01791

Eisenerz

Eisenerzer Krippenhaus, Geyereggstr 1, 8790 Eisenerz - T: (03848) 4219
Decorative Arts Museum - 1988
Cribs 01792

Stadt- und Steirisches Eisenmuseum, Kammerhof, Schulstr 1, 8790 Eisenerz - T: (03848) 3615, Fax: 3505. Head: Dr. Sigrid Günther
Science&Tech Museum - 1986 01793

Eisenstadt

Burgenländische Landesgalerie, Schloss Esterházy, Stallungen, 7000 Eisenstadt - T: (02682) 6003607, 636750, Fax: 6271530. Head: Dr. Gertraud Klimesch
Fine Arts Museum - 1972
Loan exhibitions of contemporary art 01794

Burgenländisches Feuerwehrmuseum, Leithabergstr 41, 7000 Eisenstadt - T: (02682) 62105, Fax: 6210536. Head: Manfred Seidl
Science&Tech Museum - 1971
History of fire fighting 01795

Burgenländisches Landesmuseum, Museumgasse 1-5, 7000 Eisenstadt - T: (02682) 626520, 627150, Fax: 6271530, E-mail: bgld.lm@aon.at. Head: Dr. G. Schlag
Natural History Museum / Archaeological Museum / Local Museum / Folklore Museum - 1926
Geology and paleontology, archaeology, zoology and botany, folk customs, archives, manuscripts, Judaica, military arts, medaillons and orders, clocks - library, workshops, specimen workshops 01796

Diözesanmuseum Eisenstadt, Joseph-Haydn-Gasse 31, 7000 Eisenstadt - T: (02682) 629432, 777235, Fax: 777252, E-mail: brigitte.gerdenitsch@kath-kirche-eisenstadt.at, Internet: http://www.kath-kirche-eisenstadt.at. Head: Prof. Dr. Hans Peter Zelfel
Religious Arts Museum - 1980 01797

Haydn-Museum, Joseph-Haydn-Gasse 21, 7000 Eisenstadt - T: (02682) 62652, Fax: 6271530, E-mail: bgld.lm@aon.at. Head: Dr. G. Schlag
Music Museum - 1935
Haydn memorabilia, scores, instruments, medals and other artefacts of the period, housed in the composer's former residence 01798

Österreichisches Jüdisches Museum, Unterbergstr 6, 7000 Eisenstadt - T: (02682) 65145, Fax: 651454, E-mail: info@oejudmus.or.at, Internet: http://www.oejudmus.or.at/oejudmus. Head: Johannes Reiss
Special Museum - 1972
Judaica Austriaca - synagogue 01799

Eisgarn

Museumsstube, Nr 9, 3862 Eisgarn - T: (02863) 336, Fax: 7310
Local Museum - 1989 01800

Eitweg

Lavanttaler Heimatmuseum, Sankt Ulrich 17-18, 9421 Eitweg - T: (04355) 2547. Head: Leopoldine Deiser
Local Museum - 1959 01801

Elbigenalp

Falger-Museum, Dorf 55c, 6652 Elbigenalp - T: (05634) 6210, 6270, Fax: 6818, E-mail: lechtal@tirol.com. Head: Heribert Walch
Local Museum - 1887
Local hist 01802

Elsbethen-Glasenstein

Heimatmuseum Elsbethen, Johann-Herbst-Str 35, 5061 Elsbethen-Glasenstein - T: (0662) 621543, Fax: 629652
Local Museum - 1990 01803

Emmersdorf an der Donau

Kaiser Franz-Museum, Schloß Luberegg, 3644 Emmersdorf an der Donau - T: (02752) 71755, Fax: 830215. Head: Ulrich Graf Arco-Zinneberg
Historical Museum - 1991 01804

Engelhartsstetten

Schloß Niederweiden, 2292 Engelhartsstetten - T: (02214) 2803, Fax: (02285) 6580, Internet: http://www.schlosshof.at. Head: Brigitte Gawlik
Decorative Arts Museum
Formerly owned by Prince Eugen of Savoyen, Viennese 01805

Engelhartszell

Hufschmiedemuseum, 4090 Engelhartszell - T: (07717) 8059. Head: Gerlinde Maislinger
Science&Tech Museum
Hist smithy 01806

Engerwitzdorf

Urgeschichtliche Sammlung, Bürgerstr 2, 4210 Engerwitzdorf - T: (07235) 2307
Historical Museum
Early hist 01807

Enns

Museum Lauriacum, Hauptpl 19, 4470 Enns - T: (07223) 85362, Fax: 85362. Head: Dr. Herbert Kneifel
Archaeological Museum / Historical Museum / Folklore Museum - 1892
Roman art and archaeology, technology, art hist, folk customs, folklore, hist of lighting, Roman fresco, silver - library, archives 01808

Schmuckmuseum Gablonzer Industrie, Steyrer Str 18, 4470 Enns - T: (07223) 832360, Fax: 8323613, E-mail: office@gablonzer.com, Internet: http://www.gablonzer.com. Head: Harald Hohensinner
Special Museum - 1994 01809

Enzenkirchen

Heimathaus Richard Eichinger und Steinmuseum, Nr 29, 4761 Enzenkirchen - T: (07762) 3215, 3118, Fax: 3680, E-mail: gemeinde@enzenkirchen.ooe.gv.at
Local Museum / Natural History Museum 01810

Ernstbrunn

Ausgrabungsdokumentation 6000 Jahre Wohnberg Oberleis, Klement 79, 2115 Ernstbrunn - T: (02576) 2343, 80358. Head: Karl Nittmann
Historical Museum 01811

Fossilienschauraum, Beim Bahnhof, 2115 Ernstbrunn - T: (02576) 3238. Head: Ferdinand Weiß
Natural History Museum - 1982 01812

Falkenstein

Kellermuseum, Kellergasse, 2162 Falkenstein - T: (02554) 7883
Agriculture Museum - 1973
Hist of viticulture in Austria 01813

Feichten

Talmuseum Kaunertal, Pl 30, 6524 Feichten - T: (05475) 316, 204
Local Museum - 1986
Hist of the valley, mining, crafts 01814

Feistritz am Wechsel

Jagd- und Forstmuseum, Haus Nr. 17, 2873 Feistritz am Wechsel - T: (02641) 2163, Fax: 21635, E-mail: gdefeistritzwechsel@netway.at, Internet: http://www.netvillage.at/nv/feistritz-am-wechsel
Natural History Museum 01815

Feldbach

Bardeau'sches Kultur- und Ausstellungszentrum, Schloß Kornberg, Dörfl 2, 8330 Feldbach - T: (03152) 4213, Fax: 5824. Head: Andreas Graf Bardeau
Decorative Arts Museum / Fine Arts Museum 01816

Museum im Tabor, Franz-Josef-Str 3, 8330 Feldbach - T: (03152) 5856, Fax: 5856, E-mail: feldbach@styria.com, Internet: http://www.feldbach-tourismus.at. Head: Dr. Rudolf Grasmug
Local Museum - 1952
Fisheries, ethnography, early and prehist 01817

Museum im Troadkostn zu Giem, Untergiem 45, 8330 Feldbach - T: (03152) 4323. Head: Johann Praßl
Local Museum - 1983
Ethnography, handicraft, prisoner of war camp Mühldorf (1914-1918) 01818

Feldkirch

Galerie im Theater am Saumarkt, Mühletorpl 1, 6800 Feldkirch - T: (05522) 72895, Fax: 75578, E-mail: kulturkreis.feldkirch@vol.at, Internet: http://www.vol.at/kulturkreis.feldkirch
Public Gallery 01819

Palais Liechtenstein, Schlossergasse 8, 6800 Feldkirch - T: (05522) 3041272, Fax: 3041279, E-mail: kultur@feldkirch.at, Internet: http://www.feldkirch.at. Head: Albert Ruetz
Association with Coll 01820

Schattenburg Feldkirch, Burggasse 1, 6800 Feldkirch - T: (05522) 76001, Fax: 76002, Internet: http://www.feldkirch.com/kkf. Head: Markus Kevenhörster
Local Museum - 1912
Arms, coins, medals, items from the everyday life of the Biedermeier period up to now, frescos of the late-Gothic, Renaissance and Baroque 01821

Zimmerei-Museum, Naflastr 92b, 6800 Feldkirch - T: (05522) 78271. Head: Winfried Land
Historical Museum - 1994 01822

Feldkirchen bei Graz

Österreichisches Luftfahrtmuseum, Flughafen Graz-Thalerhof, 8073 Feldkirchen bei Graz - T: (0316) 291541. Head: Dr. Gerhard M. Dienes
Science&Tech Museum - 1979
Hist of Austrian aeronautics 01823

Feldkirchen in Kärnten

Galerie der Freien Akademie Feldkirchen, Heftgasse 2, 9560 Feldkirchen in Kärnten - T: (04276) 39030, Fax: 39030, E-mail: faf.kultur@aon.at, Internet: http://www.faf-kultur.org. Head: Dr. Richard Gangeler
Public Gallery 01824

Fels

Heimatmuseum Schloß Fels, Schulpl 1, 3481 Fels - T: (02738) 2381, Fax: 238122
Local Museum / Agriculture Museum - 1984
History, crafts, agriculture, viticulture 01825

Ferlach

Büchsenmacher- und Jagdmuseum, Sponheimerpl 1, 9170 Ferlach - T: (04227) 4920, Fax: 4970, E-mail: schloss.ferlach@carinthia.com. Head: Herbert Urbas
Science&Tech Museum - 1977
Hist of gunmaking in Ferlach, tools, machines, manufacturing techniques 01826

Finkenstein

Bauernmühle-Dorfmuseum, Warmbader Str, 9584 Finkenstein - T: (04254) 2020
Local Museum - 1982 01827

Fischamend

Heimatmuseum im alten Marktturm, Hauptpl 5, 2401 Fischamend - T: (02232) 7300
Local Museum - 1927
Folklore, local hist, Roman finds 01828

Fohnsdorf

Bergbaumuseum und Schaustollen, Schachthausweg 16, 8753 Fohnsdorf - T: (03573) 4647, Fax: 4647
Science&Tech Museum - 1983 01829

Forchtenstein

Freiraum, Wulkalände 32, 7212 Forchtenstein - T: (02626) 65180, Fax: 65180. Head: Josef Bernhardt
Fine Arts Museum - 1993 01830

Fürstlich Esterházy'sche Sammlungen Burg Forchtenstein, Melinda-Esterházy-Pl 1, 7212 Forchtenstein - T: (02626) 81212, 81511, Fax: 8151113, E-mail: kulturabteilung@burg-forchtenstein.at, Internet: http://www.burg-forchtenstein.at. Head: Dr. Gottfried Holzschuh
Fine Arts Museum / Military Museum / Historic Site - 1815
Hist of the Esterházy dynasty, treasury, armour, hunting, art 01831

Fornach

Troadkasten Fornach, Nr 3, 4892 Fornach - T: (07682) 5505, 5047, Fax: 550561, E-mail: gemeinde@fornach.ooe.gv.at, Internet: http://www.fornach.ooe.gv.at. Head: Josef Mayr
Agriculture Museum - 1975
Farming implements, tools and machines 01832

Frankenburg

Frankenburger Heimatstube, Schloß Frein, Frein 1, 4873 Frankenburg - T: (07683) 8574. Head: Gruber Helga
Local Museum - 1966
Crafts and old trades 01833

Frankenfels

Bergbauernmusem mit Galerie, Rosenbühelrotte 9, 3213 Frankenfels - T: (02725) 5218, Internet: http://www.noel.gv.at/service/k/k1/museen/0194.htm
Folklore Museum / Fine Arts Museum - 1989 01834

Frankenmarkt

Kulturhistorische Sammlung, Hauptstr 83, 4890 Frankenmarkt - T: (07684) 6255, 8855, Fax: 625521, E-mail: office@frankenmarkt.net, Internet: http://www.frankenmarkt.net. Head: Martin Wilhelm
Historical Museum - 1968
Local and trade hist 01835

Frauenkirchen

Schatzkammer, Kirchenpl 2, 7132 Frauenkirchen - T: (02172) 2224, Fax: 2224
Religious Arts Museum 01836

Freiland

Feld- und Industriebahnmuseum (FIM), Nr. 27, 3183 Freiland - T: (01) 9842354, Fax: 9842354, E-mail: fim@erlebnisbahn.at, Internet: http://www.erlebnisbahn.at/feldbahn/index.html. Head: Horst W. Kurdiovsky
Science&Tech Museum - 1965
Locomotives, carriages, tools - archive 01837

Freinberg

Troadkasten, Neudling 10, 4785 Freinberg - T: (07713) 8102, Fax: 810222. Head: Adolf Neulinger
Agriculture Museum
Agricultural implements, carpenter's wall paintings 01838

Freistadt, Oberösterreich

Brauhaus-Galerie, Promenade 7, 4240 Freistadt, Oberösterreich - T: (07942) 4485, 75037. Head: Herbert Wagner
Public Gallery - 1988 01839

Mühlviertler Schlossmuseum Freistadt, Schloßhof 2, 4240 Freistadt, Oberösterreich - T: (07942) 72274, Fax: 722744, E-mail: - schlossmuseum.freistadt@aon.at, Internet: http://www.museumsstrasse.at/schlossmuseum
Local Museum - 1926
Pre- and ancient history, geology, local history, folk customs of the Mühlviertel, glass paintings, peasant furniture and tools, history of the guilds, history of law and defence, traditional costumes, textiles, jewellery - library, archives 01840

Fresach

Evangelisches Diözesanmuseum, Nr 60, 9712 Fresach - T: (04245) 4849, 6149. Head: Oskar Sakrausky
Religious Arts Museum - 1960
History of Reformation and Protestantism in Austria and countries of former K.u.K. Monarchy, documents, archives, books and Bibles, hymnals 01841

Friedberg

Thonet-Museum, Bahnhofstr 63, 8240 Friedberg - T: (03339) 25110, 25121, Fax: 2511020, E-mail: stadtgemeinde@friedberg.at, Internet: http://www.friedberg.at. Head: Adolf Reinbacher
Decorative Arts Museum - 1994
Thonet wooden furniture 01842

Friedburg

Franz Winkelmeier-Gedenkraum, 5211 Friedburg - T: (06218) 2214
Historical Museum 01843

Friesach

Stadtmuseum Friesach, Petersbergweg 18, 9360 Friesach - T: (04268) 22139, 2600, Fax: 221350, E-mail: friesach@ktn.gde.at. Head: Ewald Supanz
Local Museum - 1987
Medieval hist 01844

Frohnleiten

Burg Rabenstein, Adriach 41, 8130 Frohnleiten - T: (03126) 2303, Fax: 23034, E-mail: burgrabenstein@yahoo.com
Historical Museum
Castle complex from the 12th-15th c 01845

Frojach

Schmalspurbahn-Museum, Katsch, 8841 Frojach, mail addr: Club 760-Verein der Freunde der Murtalbahn, 8850 Murau. Head: August Zopf
Science&Tech Museum - 1978
Locomotives, waggons, narrow gauge (760 mm) 01846

Fügen

Heimatmuseum, Bahnhofstr 109, 6263 Fügen - T: (05288) 2209
Local Museum - 1975 01847

Fürstenfeld

Museum der Stadt Fürstenfeld, Klostergasse 18, 8280 Fürstenfeld - T: (03382) 52401, Fax: 5240130, E-mail: gde@fuerstenfeld.-steiermark.at, Internet: http://www.fuerstenfeld.de. Head: Dieter Raidl
Local Museum
Trade, craftmanship, sacral exhibits 01848

Fulpmes

Schmiedemuseum, Schmelzhüttengasse 20, 6166 Fulpmes - T: (05225) 696024, 62240, Fax: 64105
Science&Tech Museum - 1970
Old tools, ancient hammer smithy 01849

Furth bei Göttweig

Kunstsammlungen und Graphisches Kabinett, Stift Göttweig, 3511 Furth bei Göttweig - T: (02732) 85581226, Fax: 85581266, 71848, E-mail: graph.kab.gtw@eunet.at, Internet: http://www.stiftgoettweig.or.at/stiftgoettweig. Head: Dr. Gregor Martin Lechner, Prof. Michael Grünwald
Fine Arts Museum - 1960
Historical rooms and interiors, Roman art, 16th-18th c German, Dutch, Italian, and French graphic arts and drawings, 17th-18th c copper plaques, numismatics, painting, weapons, paraments, portraits, topography, in 11th c religious foundation - library, music archives 01850

Gaaden

Heimatmuseum, Siegenfelder Str 6, 2531 Gaaden - T: (02236) 47522, (02237) 8521, E-mail: gdegaaden@netway.at
Local Museum - 1957/1984
Handicraft, agricultural tools, local hist 01851

Gablitz

Heimatmuseum, Linzer Str 62, 3003 Gablitz - T: (02231) 39554
Local Museum - 1986
Local hist 01852

Gallneukirchen

Heimathaus Gallneukirchen, Dienergasse 2, 4210 Gallneukirchen - T: (07235) 64801, E-mail: - johann.hofstadler@telering.at, Internet: http://www.gallneukirchen.at
Local Museum - 1973
Crafts, prehist coll 01853

Gallspach

Institut Zeileis, Valentin-Zeileis-Str 33, 4713 Gallspach - T: (07248) 62351
Special Museum
Hist of electrophysical cure institute and high frequence therapy 01854

Gaming

Kartause Gaming, Kartause, 3292 Gaming - T: (07485) 98682, Fax: 986824. Head: Walter Hildebrand
Religious Arts Museum - 1984 01855

Gamlitz

Galerie und Weinmuseum Schloß Gamlitz, Nr 32, 8462 Gamlitz - T: (03453) 4848, Fax: 4550
Special Museum / Fine Arts Museum 01856

Gars am Kamp

Befestigungsanlagen von Thunau, Grabungsdokumentation, Hauptpl 83, 3571 Gars am Kamp - T: (02985) 2225. Head: Prof. Dr. Herwig Friesinger
Historical Museum - 1979 01857

Franz von Suppé-Gedenkstätte, Rathaus, Hauptpl 82, 3571 Gars am Kamp - T: (02985) 22250, Fax: 222524. Head: Anton Ehrenberger
Music Museum 01858

Freilichtmuseum, Thunau, 3571 Gars am Kamp - T: (02985) 2680. Head: Prof. Dr. Herwig Friesinger
Open Air Museum 01859

Handelsmuseum, Rathaus, Hauptpl 82, 3571 Gars am Kamp - T: (02985) 22250, Fax: 222524. Head: Emil Becker
Historical Museum - 1989 01860

Heimatmuseum, Horner Str 155, 3571 Gars am Kamp - T: (02985) 2225, 2680
Local Museum
Local hist, folklore, school hist 01861

Garsten

Schattleitenmühle, Mühlbachstr 42, 4451 Garsten - T: (07252) 46652. Head: Alfred Bramberger
Science&Tech Museum - 1992
Thatched mill made from natural stones 01862

Stiftsmuseum, Am Platzl 2, 4451 Garsten - T: (07252) 54196, Fax: 5419623. Head: Josef Nöhammer
Religious Arts Museum - 1970
Sacral art objects from the Baroque 01863

Gaschurn

Montafoner Tourismusmuseum Gaschurn, Kirchdorf 2, 6793 Gaschurn - T: (05558) 8201, 8270, Fax: (05556) 74723/24, E-mail: andi.gier@eunet.at, Internet: http://www.fiscaves.com/gaschurn
Special Museum - 1992
Development of tourism in photographs, prospecti, sports equipment and guest rooms 01864

Gasen

Stoani Haus der Musik, Nr 35, 8616 Gasen - T: (03171) 5000, Fax: 5005, E-mail: stoanihaus@kom.at, Internet: http://www.stoakogler.at. Head: Wilhelm Schwaiger
Music Museum 01865

Geras

Prämonstratenser-Chorherrenstift mit Stiftssammlungen, Hauptstr 1, 2093 Geras - T: (02912) 345286, Fax: 345299, E-mail: stiftgeras@netway.at, Internet: http://www.stiftgeras.at. Head: Prof. Dr. Joachim Angerer
Religious Arts Museum / Fine Arts Museum 01866

Gerersdorf

Freilicht-Museum Ensemble Gerersdorf, Nr 66b, 7542 Gerersdorf - T: (03328) 32255, 32272, Fax: 3227216, E-mail: freilichtmuseum.gerersdorf@aon.at, Internet: http://www.freilichtmuseum-gerersdorf.at. Head: Gerhard Kisser
Open Air Museum - 1973
18th and 19th c wood architecture, peasant furniture, agricultural tools 01867

Gläsermuseum, Güssinger Str 1, Sulz, 7542 Gerersdorf - T: (03322) 42121, Fax: 4212112
Special Museum 01868

Gföhl

Märchenhain Gföhl, Hauptpl 3, 3542 Gföhl - T: (02716) 63260, 8968, Fax: 632626, Internet: http://www.gfoehl.at
Special Museum - 1996 01869

Waldviertler Bauernhof-Museum, Gföhleramt 23, 3542 Gföhl - T: (02716) 6470. Head: Franz Fux
Agriculture Museum - 1974
Flax processing, agricultural implements 01870

Glaubendorf

Museum Schloß Wetzdorf, Kleinwetzdorf 1, Heldenberg, 3704 Glaubendorf - T: (02956) 2341, Fax: 2162. Head: Anton Fichtl
Historical Museum - 1979
Life of Napoleon I, copper engravings 01871

Gleisdorf

Heimatmuseum, Rathaus, Florianpl 14, 8200 Gleisdorf - T: (03112) 2601, 2735, Fax: 273515
Local Museum - 1954
Prehistoric and Roman artefacts, local and regional history, peasant life, tools, history of the post 01872

Museum für Sozialkunde und Geschichte des Möbels, Schloß Freiberg, 8200 Gleisdorf
Ethnology Museum / Historical Museum
Social sciences and hist of furniture 01873

Globasnitz

Archäologisches Museum, 9142 Globasnitz - T: (04230) 310, Fax: 630, E-mail: globasnitz@ktn.gde.at. Head: Dr. Franz Glaser
Archaeological Museum - 1982
Early Christian findings, mosaics, church buildings 01874

Gloggnitz

Bergbau- und Heimatmuseum, Berggasse 122, 2640 Gloggnitz - T: (02662) 45407, 45243
Local Museum / Science&Tech Museum - 1986
Mining, agriculture, geology 01875

Brot- und Mühlen-Lehrmuseum, Hauptstr 49, 2640 Gloggnitz - T: (02662) 42242, Fax: 422424. Head: Karl Dirnbacher
Special Museum - 1979 01876

Burgenmuseum Kranichberg, 2640 Gloggnitz - T: (02662) 8242. Head: Dr. Johannes Hübner
Historical Museum - 1981
Photos and models of fortresses 01877

Museum in der Schloßkirche, Kirchensteig 3, 2640 Gloggnitz - T: (02662) 42275. Head: Ernst Stranz
Religious Arts Museum - 1978 01878

Zeitreise - Renner Villa Gloggnitz, Rennergasse 4, 2640 Gloggnitz - T: (02662) 42498, Fax: 43430. Head: Friedrich Brettner
Historical Museum / Military Museum - 1978
Former villa of the politician Dr. Renner, exhibits of his private and public life - archives 01879

Gmünd, Kärnten

Eva Faschaunerin-Heimatmuseum, Hintere Gasse 56, 9853 Gmünd, Kärnten - T: (04732) 221518, Fax: 221521, E-mail: gmuend@ktn.at
Historical Museum 01880

Galerie Gmünd, Hintere Gasse 36, 9853 Gmünd, Kärnten - T: (04732) 221524, Fax: 221521, E-mail: gmuend@ktn.at
Public Gallery 01881

Galerie im Stadtturm, Hauptpl 20, 9853 Gmünd, Kärnten - T: (04732) 221524, Fax: 221521
Public Gallery 01882

Museum der Stadt Gmünd, Hauptpl 13, 9853 Gmünd, Kärnten - T: (04732) 221524, Fax: 221521
Local Museum - 1961 01883

Porsche Automuseum Helmut Pfeifhofer, Riesertratte 4a, 9853 Gmünd, Kärnten - T: (04732) 2471, 2971, Fax: 2454, E-mail: 911@porschemuseum.at, Internet: http://www.erlebnis.net. Head: Helmut Pfeifhofer, Elisabeth Pfeifhofer
Science&Tech Museum - 1982
Memorabilia of Prof. Ferdinand Porsche and his family 01884

Gmünd, Niederösterreich

Geologisches Freilichtmuseum, Naturpark Blockheide Eibenstein-Gmünd, 3950 Gmünd, Niederösterreich, mail addr: Schremser Str 6, 3950 Gmünd, Niederösterreich - T: (02852) 53817, 5250628, Fax: 54514, E-mail: stadtgemeinde@gmuend.at, Internet: http://www.blockheide.gmuend.at
Natural History Museum / Open Air Museum - 1964
Stones from Lower Austria, geology 01885

Schaumuseum Alte Schmiede, Stadtpl 11, 3950 Gmünd, Niederösterreich - T: (02852) 52506, Fax: 52506500, E-mail: stadtgemeinde@gmuend.at, Internet: http://www.gmuend.at. Head: Erika Achatz
Special Museum 01886

Stadt-, Glas- und Steinmuseum, Stadtpl 34, 3950 Gmünd, Niederösterreich - T: (02852) 52506, Fax: 52506500, E-mail: stadtgemeinde@gmuend.at, Internet: http://www.gmuend.at. Head: Walter Mair
Local Museum / Special Museum - 1965/1968
Local history, minerals and stones, guilds, weapons, handicrafts, religious art, history of glass production, glass-making tools, glasses (17th-19th c), masonry 01887

Gmunden

Hipp-Halle, Theresientalstr 68, 4810 Gmunden - T: (07612) 765770, Fax: 76577200, E-mail: vincent.leroy@hipp.de. Head: Vincent Leroy
Public Gallery - 1987 01888

Kammerhofgalerie der Stadt Gmunden, Museumspl, 4810 Gmunden - T: (07612) 794244, Fax: (07617) 2977, E-mail: linschin@ufg.ac.at. Head: Josef Linschinger
Fine Arts Museum - 1928 01889

Kammerhofmuseum der Stadt Gmunden, Kammerhofgasse 8, 4810 Gmunden - T: (07612) 794244, Fax: 794244, E-mail: museum@gmunden.ooe.gv.at. Head: Ingrid Spitzbart
Local Museum - 1907
Local history, history of the salt trade, geology, local ceramics, archaeology, Brahms and Hebbel rooms, Brahms coll, Himlaya-showroom 01890

Oldtimer-Museum, Mühlwangstr 20, 4810 Gmunden - T: (07612) 3665. Head: Karl Marschhofe
Science&Tech Museum
Hist of cars, motorbikes, scooters 01891

Schloß Weyer, Karl-Josef von Frey Gasse 27, 4810 Gmunden - T: (07612) 650180, Fax: 6560531
Decorative Arts Museum
Porcellain, silver 01892

Gnas

Heimatmuseum, Hauptpl 46, 8342 Gnas - T: (03151) 2260, Fax: 226018
Local Museum 01893

Göpfritz

Rudolf Weinwurm-Museum, Scheideldorf 36, 3800 Göpfritz - T: (02825) 8535. Head: Adolf Auska
Music Museum - 1990 01894

Göstling an der Ybbs

Familienmuseum im Altbauernhaus, Hochreit 5, 3345 Göstling an der Ybbs - T: (07484) 2422. Head: Ernest Zettel
Folklore Museum 01895

Holztriftanlage Mendlingtal, Schluchtweg, 3345 Göstling an der Ybbs - T: (07484) 502019, Fax: 502018, E-mail: goestling.hochkar@aon.at, Internet: http://www.goestling-hochkar.at
Science&Tech Museum 01896

Götzis

Kinder-Knürstl-Museum, Zielstr 19, 6840 Götzis - T: (0650) 5885510, Fax: 58855, E-mail: knuerstle@aon.at, Internet: http://www.knuerstle.at. Head: Herbert Rath
Special Museum - 1995 01897

Goldegg

Pongauer Heimatmuseum im Schloß Goldegg, Hofmark 1, 5622 Goldegg - T: (06415) 8171. Head: Hubertus Droste-Vischering-Galen
Local Museum - 1975
Castle complex with four wings, Renaissance frescos, painted wall and ceiling panels 01898

Golling an der Salzach

Museum Burg Golling, Markt 1, 5440 Golling an der Salzach - T: (06244) 5360, 43560, Fax: 422320, E-mail: Golling@ping.at, Internet: http://www.sbg.at/leiblfinger.proemer. Head: Erich Urbanek
Local Museum - 1969
Local hist, paleontology 01899

Gollrad

Jagdmuseum Brandhof, 8635 Gollrad - T: (03884) 207
Special Museum
Memorial site of Archduke Johann of Tyrol 01900

Grafenwörth

Heimatmuseum, Kirchpl, 3484 Grafenwörth - T: (02738) 2212
Local Museum - 1978
Viticulture and oenology 01901

Museum für landwirtschaftliche Geräte, Hauptstr 68, 3484 Grafenwörth - T: (02738) 2212, Fax: 221221, E-mail: grafenw@noet.at
Agriculture Museum 01902

Gratwein

Stiftssammlungen des Zisterzienserstiftes Rein, Am Grünanger 94, 8112 Gratwein - T: (03124) 53754, Fax: 53754, E-mail: zwicker.music@styria.com. Head: Jörg Zwicker
Religious Arts Museum / Music Museum
Coll of historic music instruments 01903

Graz

Alte Galerie, Landesmuseum Joanneum, Neutorgasse 45, 8010 Graz - T: (0316) 80179770, Fax: 80179847, E-mail: post@lmj-ag.stmk.gv.at, Internet: http://www.museum-johanneum.at. Head: Dr. Gottfried Biedermann
Fine Arts Museum - 1941
Medieval paintings, sculptures, stained glass windows, European Renaissance, Mannerisme, Baroque, first of all paintings, Austrian and Southern German Baroque, Baroque oil sketches - library, archives, workshops 01904

Bild- und Tonarchiv, Landesmuseum Joanneum, Sackstr 17, 8010 Graz - T: (0316) 830335, Fax: 8303359422, E-mail: post@lmj-bt-nt1.stmk.gv.at, Internet: http://www.museum-joanneum.at
Library with Exhibitions
Documents of Steyrian history by photos, audio and film - archive, audio visually museum 01905

Diözesanmuseum Graz, Mariahilfer Pl 3, 8020 Graz - T: (0316) 7139940, Fax: 710224, E-mail: dioezesanmuseum@graz-sekau.at, Internet: http://www.graz-seckau.at/dioezesanmuseum. Head: Heimo Kaindl
Religious Arts Museum - 1932
Religious fine art of Styria, liturgical instruments, old musical instruments 01906

Druckmuseum Graz, Hans-Brandstetter-Gasse 12, 8010 Graz - T: (0316) 471468, Fax: 4714684, E-mail: berufsschule7@computerhaus.at, Internet: http://www.lbs-stmk.ac.at/graz7/lbs7.htm. Head: Dr. Karlpeter Elis
Science&Tech Museum - 1982 01907

Grazer Kunstverein, Bürgergasse 4, 8010 Graz - T: (0316) 834141, Fax: (0316) 834142, E-mail: -grazerkunstverein@xarch.tu-graz.ac.at, Internet: http://www.xarch.tu-graz.ac.at/grazerkunstverein
Association with Coll 01908

Grazer Stadtmuseum, Sackstr 18, 8010 Graz - T: (0316) 822580, Fax: 8225806, E-mail: stadtmuseum@stadt.graz.at, Internet: http://www.stadtmuseum-graz.at. Head: Dr. Gerhard M. Dienes
Local Museum - 1928
Local and cultural hist of Graz, art and chemist's store - archive, library 01909

Hanns Schell-Collection, Österreichisches Museum für Schloß, Schlüssel, Kästchen, Kassetten und Eisenkunstguß, Wiener Str 10, 8020 Graz - T: (0316) 71565638, 321182, Fax: 71565638, E-mail: -hanns.schell.colletion@cybertron.at, Internet: http://hsc.multiservers.com. Head: Ewald Berger
Science&Tech Museum - 1972
Historic locks and keys from antiquity to the present from around the world, tools, metal mountings, cascets, cassettes, cast-iron objects 01910

Hans Mauracher-Museum, Hans-Mauracher-Str 29, 8044 Graz - T: (0316) 392394
Fine Arts Museum - 1960
Works of the sculptor Hans Mauracher in wood, plaster and bronze 01911

Künstlerhaus Graz, Burgring, 8010 Graz - T: (0316) 827391, Fax: 828952. Head: Charlotte Urschitz
Fine Arts Museum - 1952 01912

Kulturhistorische Sammlung, Landesmuseum Joanneum, Neutorgasse 45, 8010 Graz - T: (0316) 80179780, Fax: 80179849, E-mail: a21-khs@stmk.gv.at, Internet: http://www.museum-joanneum.at. Head: Dr. Eva Marko
Decorative Arts Museum - 1891
Arts and crafts, glass, ceramics, furniture, clocks, wrought iron 01913

Landesmuseum Joanneum, Raubergasse 10, 8010 Graz - T: (0316) 80179700, Fax: 80179800, E-mail: A21@stmk.gv.at, Internet: http://www.museum-joanneum.at. Head: Dr. Odo Burböck
Local Museum - 1811
library, workshops 01914

Landeszeughaus, Landesmuseum Joanneum, Herrengasse 16, 8010 Graz - T: (0316) 828796, 80179818, Fax: 815967, E-mail: daniela.lex@stmk.gv.at, Internet: http://www.museum-joanneum.at. Head: Prof. Dr. Peter Krenn
Military Museum - 1644
16th-18th c weapons, handarms, armour - arsenal 01915

Lebende Galerie, Körblergasse 111-113, 8010 Graz - T: (0316) 6010. Head: Johannes Koren
Fine Arts Museum - 1970 01916

Münzensammlung, Landesmuseum Joanneum, Eggenberger Allee 90, 8020 Graz - T: (0316) 5832649513, Fax: 5832649530, E-mail: burboeck@lmj-egg-ntl, Internet: http://www.museum-joanneum.at. Head: Dr. Odo Burböck
Historical Museum 01917

Museum der Wahrnehmung, Friedrichgasse 41, 8010 Graz - T: (0316) 8115990, Fax: 829121, E-mail: muwa@styria.com. Head: Werner Wolf
Fine Arts Museum / Performing Arts Museum - 1990 01918

Neue Galerie, Landesmuseum Joanneum, Sackstr 16, 8010 Graz - T: (0316) 829155, Fax: 815401, E-mail: neuegalerie@stmk.gv.at, Internet: http://www.neuegalerie.at. Head: Dr. Christa Steinle
Fine Arts Museum - 1941
Austrian art of the 19th and 20th c, 19th and 20th c graphic art, international art of the 90s (Richard Artschwager, Günter Brus, Marcel Duchamp, Valie Export, Sol LeWitt, Ad Reinhardt, Donald Judd) - library, archive 01919

Provinzialrömische Sammlung und Antikenkabinett, Landesmuseum Joanneum, Eggenberger Allee 90, 8020 Graz - T: (0316) 5832649521, Fax: 5832649518, Internet: http://www.museum-joanneum.at. Head: Dr. Erich Hudeczek
Archaeological Museum 01920

Referat Botanik, Landesmuseum Joanneum, Raubergasse 10, 8010 Graz - T: (0316) 80179750, Fax: 80179670, E-mail: A21-bot@stmk.gv.at, Internet: http://www.museum-joanneum.at. Head: Dr. Detlef Ernet
Natural History Museum - 1811
European and non-European flowering plants, ferns, algae, mushrooms, European wood types, fruits and seeds - alpine botanical garden 01921

Referat Communication & Education, Landesmuseum Joanneum, Raubergasse 10, 8010 Graz - T: (0316) 80179727, Fax: 80179846, E-mail: post@lmj-kom.stmk.gv.at, Internet: http://www.museum-joanneum.at. Head: Christiane Holler
Local Museum 01922

Referat Geologie und Paläontologie, Landesmuseum Joanneum, Raubergasse 10, 8010 Graz - T: (0316) 80179730, Fax: 80179842, E-mail: A21-8@stmk.gv.at, Internet: http://www.museum-joanneum.at. Head: Odo Burböck
Natural History Museum
Paleontology(evertebraten, vertebraten), paleobotanic, geology, mining 01923

Referat Mineralogie, Landesmuseum Joanneum, Raubergasse 10, 8010 Graz - T: (0316) 80179740/ 43, Fax: 80179672, E-mail: walter.postl@ stmk.gv.at, Internet: http://www.museum-joanneum.at. Head: Dr. Walter Postl
Natural History Museum - 1811
Minerals, precious stones, meteorites, rocks 01924

Referat Volkskunde, Landesmuseum Joanneum, Paulustorgasse 11-13a, 8010 Graz - T: (0316) 830416, Fax: 815233, E-mail: lmj@lmj-nt1.at, Internet: http://www.museum-joanneum.at. Head: Dr. Roswitha Orač-Stipperger
Folklore Museum 01925

Referat Zoologie, Landesmuseum Joanneum, Raubergasse 10, 8010 Graz - T: (0316) 80179760, Fax: 80179800, E-mail: a21-zoo@stmk.gv.at, Internet: http://www.museum-joanneum.at. Head: Dr. Karl Adlbauer
Natural History Museum - 1811
Styrian animals, extinct animals, exotic fauna 01926

Robert Stolz Museum Graz, Mehlpl 1, 8010 Graz - T: (0316) 815951, E-mail: stadtmuseum@ stadt.graz.at, Internet: http://www.stadtmuseum-graz.at. Head: Dr. Gerhard M. Dienes
Music Museum - 1980
Hist of the composer Robert Stolz 01927

Sammlung Jagdkunde, Landesmuseum Joanneum, Eggenberger Allee 90, 8020 Graz - T: (0316) 5832649516, Fax: 5832649548, E-mail: - karlheinz.wirnsberger@stmk.gv.at, Internet: http:// www.museum-joanneum.at. Head: Karlheinz Wirnsberger
Natural History Museum 01928

Schauräume im Glockenturm, Schloßberg 6, 8010 Graz - T: (0316) 8724902, Fax: 8724909, E-mail: kulturamt@stadt.graz.at, Internet: http:// www.graz.at. Head: Dr. Peter Grabensberger
Historical Museum / Historic Site - 1950
History of the castle hill 01929

Schloß Eggenberg, Landesmuseum Joanneum, Eggenberger Allee 90, 8020 Graz - T: (0316) 5832640, Fax: 58326455, E-mail: andrea.hauser@ stmk.gv.at, Internet: http://www.museum-johanneum.at. Head: Dr. B. Kaiser
Historic Site / Decorative Arts Museum - 1947
Artefacts, gardens and interiors from the 17th c, allegorical paintings by Hans Adam Weissenkircher, 14th c Gothic chapel, 18th c church - library, workshops, coin coll 01930

Tramway-Museum Graz, Maria Troster Str 204, 8044 Graz - T: (0316) 8871411, 887401, Fax: 887788. Head: Dr. Antony Scholz
Science&Tech Museum / Special Museum - 1971
34 old trollies, carriages, motor cars from Graz, Innsbruck, Vienna, Hungary, and Yugoslavia, wagons from the Graz Castle mountain cable railway 01931

Ur-und frühgeschichtliche Sammlungen, Landesmuseum Joanneum600= Eggenberger Allee 90, 8020 Graz - T: (0316) 5832649571, Fax: 5832649577, E-mail: diether.kramer@ stmk.gv.at, Internet: http://www.museum-joanneum.at. Head: Dr. Diether Kramer
Archaeological Museum 01932

Greifenstein

Burg Greifenstein, 3422 Greifenstein - T: (02242) 32353, Fax: 31396. Head: Dr. John Hübner
Historical Museum - 1919
11th c fortress, historic period rooms, weapons, folk customs and art, hist of fortress - library 01933

Grein an der Donau

Oberösterreichisches Schiffahrtsmuseum, c/o HSCG Forstverwaltung Greinburg, Greinburg 1, 4360 Grein an der Donau - T: (07268) 7007, Fax: 700715, E-mail: mail@sachsen-coburg-gotha.at, Internet: http://www.schloss-greinburg.at. Head: Franz Gruber
Science&Tech Museum - 1970
Navigation from antiquity to present, Danube, Inn, Salzach, and Enns ship transportation, rafts, hist of rowboat navigation 01934

Gressenberg

Heimatmuseum, Volksschule, 8541 Gressenberg - T: (03461) 640
Local Museum - 1982
Folklore, tourism, tools 01935

Gresten

Proviant-Eisen Museum, Unterer Markt 33, 3264 Gresten - T: (07487) 2310, Fax: 231020
Local Museum - 1954 01936

Gries im Pinzgau

Unser kleines Museum, Altes Zeughaus, 5662 Gries im Pinzgau - T: (06543) 8256
Special Museum - 1995 01937

Grieskirchen

Bienen- und Wagnereimuseum, Bezirksheimathaus, Tollet 1, 4710 Grieskirchen - T: (07248) 68665
Special Museum / Science&Tech Museum
Renaissance castle, folk art 01938

Griffen

Peter Handke-Ausstellung, Stift Griffen 1, 9112 Griffen - T: (04233) 2345, Fax: (0463) 5135468. Head: Bernd Liepold-Moser
Special Museum - 1996 01939

Gröbming

Heimatmuseum Gröbming, 8962 Gröbming
Local Museum 01940

Grödig

Untersbergmuseum Fürstenbrunn, Kugelmühlweg 4, 5082 Grödig - T: (06246) 76411, 721060
Science&Tech Museum - 1990 01941

Groß-Enzersdorf

Heimatmuseum, Rathausstr 5, 2301 Groß-Enzersdorf - T: (02249) 2314, Fax: 4240
Local Museum - 1976 01942

Groß Sankt Florian

Steirisches Feuerwehrmuseum, Gross Sankt Florian Kunst und Kulturzentrum, Marktstr 1, 8522 Groß Sankt Florian - T: (03464) 8820, Fax: 8836, E-mail: st.feuerwehrmuseum@aon.at, Internet: http://www.feuerwehrmuseum.at. Head: Hannes Weinelt
Science&Tech Museum / Historical Museum / Fine Arts Museum - 1995 01943

Groß Schweinbarth

Niederösterreichisches Museum für Volkskultur, Hauptstr 15, 2221 Groß Schweinbarth - T: (02289) 2687
Folklore Museum - 1985 01944

Groß Siegharts

Lebendes Textilmuseum, Museumgasse 2, 3812 Groß Siegharts - T: (02847) 23710, Fax: 237128, E-mail: gemeinde.gross-siegharts@wvnet.at
Special Museum - 1987
Weaving, social hist 01945

Sakraler Austellungsraum, Hauptpl 10, 3812 Groß Siegharts - T: (02847) 2426, 2365. Head: Franz Schuster
Religious Arts Museum - 1989
Religious items 01946

Großarl

Denkmalhof Kösslerhäusl, Eben 32, 5611 Großarl - T: (06414) 340
Historical Museum - 1972 01947

Großengersdorf

Heimatmuseum Großengersdorf, Neustift 24, 2212 Großengersdorf - T: (02245) 88201, 88410, Fax: 88404
Local Museum 01948

Großgmain

Salzburger Freilichtmuseum, Hasenweg 2, 5084 Großgmain - T: (0662) 8500110, Fax: 8500119, E-mail: salzburger@freilichtmuseum.com, Internet: http://www.freilichtmuseum.com. Head: Dr. Michael Becker
Open Air Museum - 1978
Buildings, household articles, agricultural tools 01949

Großkirchheim

Schloß- und Goldbergbaumuseum, Schloß Großkirchheim, Döllach 36, 9843 Großkirchheim - T: (04825) 226. Head: Josef F. Lindsberger
Science&Tech Museum / Historical Museum - 1956
In 16th c gold miner's castle, historical furnishings, sculpture and paintings, glass, pewter, copper and bronze, gold mining, minerals, ore samples, tools, gold amalgamation 01950

Großklein

Bauernmuseum Großklein, Schloß Ottersbach, Mantrach 20, 8452 Großklein - T: (03456) 320
Agriculture Museum
Old farming equipment 01951

Museum Großklein, Hallstattmuseum, Nr 10, 8452 Großklein - T: (03456) 2289, Fax: 22896, E-mail: gde@grossklein.steiermark.at, Internet: http://www.grossklein.steiermark.at. Head: Georg Zöhrer
Local Museum - 1990
Hallstatt period 01952

Nostalgie auf Rädern - Fahrzeugmuseum, Nestelbach 94, 8452 Großklein - T: (03456) 2300, Fax: 23004
Science&Tech Museum - 1997 01953

Großkrut

Kellermuseum Das Preßhaus, Kapellenberg Althöflein, 2143 Großkrut - T: (02556) 7200, 5383, Fax: 720022, E-mail: gemeinde.grosskrut@ direkt.at, Internet: http://www.grosskrut.at
Local Museum - 1995 01954

Großraming

Heimatstube Großraming, Kirchenpl 3, 4463 Großraming - T: (07254) 84143
Local Museum - 1977
Farming and trade implements 01955

Krippensammlung, Lumplgraben 106, 4463 Großraming - T: (07254) 317. Head: Rosina Gruber
Religious Arts Museum
Christmas cribs 01956

Kutschen- und Schlittenmuseum, Rodelsbach 36, 4463 Großraming - T: (07254) 8283, Fax: 828314. Head: Franz Gruber
Science&Tech Museum - 1986
Restored coaches, sleighs, commercial and agricultural vehicles 01957

Großreifling

Österreichisches Forstmuseum, Nr 23, 8931 Großreifling - T: (03633) 2455, 2201, Fax: 2405, E-mail: tourismus@landl.steiermark.at, Internet: http://www.landl.at/region/ reg.eisenwurzen/orte/landl/home.htm. Head: Adolf Grabner
Natural History Museum - 1979
Wood types, wood processing, vehicles for wood transport, exhibits on forestry, documentation 01958

Großschönau

Heimatmuseum Großschönau, Nr 80, 3922 Großschönau - T: (02815) 6252, 6582, Fax: 6252
Local Museum - 1982 01959

Großweikersdorf

Pleyel-Geburtshaus, Ruppersthal, Nr 108, 3701 Großweikersdorf - T: (02955) 70645, Fax: (01) 330384710, E-mail: adolf.ehrentraud@post.at. Head: Adolf Ehrentraud
Music Museum - 1998 01960

Grünbach am Schneeberg

Bergbaumuseum, Am Neuschacht 12, 2733 Grünbach am Schneeberg - T: (02638) 2225
Science&Tech Museum 01961

Gündorf

Rauchstubenhaus, Haus Nr. 11, 8453 Gündorf - T: (03455) 306. Head: Friedrich Krieger
Local Museum 01962

Günselsdorf

Heimatmuseum Schönau, Kirchengasse 12, Schönau, 2525 Günselsdorf - T: (02256) 635720
Local Museum - 1987
Local hist and art 01963

Güssing

Burgmuseum, Battyánystr 10, 7540 Güssing - T: (03322) 43400, Fax: 43400, E-mail: hubert.janics@bgld.gv.at, Internet: http:// www.bnet.co.at/guessing. Head: Dr. Hunert Janics
Historical Museum - 1870
Baroque and Renaissance art, instruments of torture 01964

Weinmuseum, Pinkataler Weinstr 162, Moschendorf, 7540 Güssing - T: (03324) 6317, 7527, Fax: 7243. Head: Stefan Behm
Special Museum - 1982 01965

Gumpoldskirchen

Bergerhaus, Schrannenpl 5, 2352 Gumpoldskirchen - T: (02252) 621010, Fax: 6210133
Public Gallery - 1970 01966

Guntersdorf

Bauernmuseum Guntersdorf, Kalladorf 26, 2042 Guntersdorf - T: (02951) 3358
Agriculture Museum - 1979
Agricultural machinery 01967

Guntramsdorf

Heimatmuseum Guntramsdorf, Schulgasse 2, 2353 Guntramsdorf - T: (02236) 869769, 53501143, Fax: 5350132
Local Museum - 1927
Prehistory, tombs with burial objects 01968

Gurk

Salvatorianerkloster, Dom zu Gurk, Dompl 11, 9342 Gurk - T: (04266) 82360, Fax: 823616, E-mail: domkustodie@dom-zu-gurk.at, Internet: http://www.dom-zu-gurk.at
Religious Arts Museum 01969

Gußwerk

Montanhistorisches Museum, Zur Waldpromenade 4, 8632 Gußwerk - T: (03882) 3701, Fax: 4152. Head: Richard Pichler
Science&Tech Museum - 1998 01970

Gutau

Färbermuseum, Sankt-Leonharder Str 3, 4293 Gutau - T: (07946) 62550, Fax: 6755, E-mail: info.kernland@netway.at, Internet: http:// www.tiscover.com/kernland
Special Museum - 1982
Hist of dyeing works 01971

Mühlviertler Vogelkundeweg, Lehen 65, 4293 Gutau - T: (07946) 6720
Natural History Museum
Different biotops for various kinds of birds 01972

Gutenstein

Raimund-Gedenkstätte, Markt 21, 2770 Gutenstein - T: (02634) 7487. Head: Anna Kellerer
Special Museum - 1966 01973

Stiftung Aratym, Markt 2, 2770 Gutenstein - T: (02634) 7220, Fax: 8500, Internet: http:// www.gutenstein.at
Fine Arts Museum 01974

Waldbauernmuseum, Alte Hofmühle, Markt 31, 2770 Gutenstein - T: (02634) 7313, Fax: 7313, E-mail: pawelak-ast@aon.at, Internet: http:// www.gutenstein.at. Head: Hiltraud Ast
Agriculture Museum / Folklore Museum - 1965
Woodworking tools and equipment, 1767 sawmill, dioramas, drawings, paintings, photos, and etchings, wood production and its by-products 01975

Haag am Hausruck

Haager Heimatstuben, Schloß Starhemberg, 4680 Haag am Hausruck - T: (07732) 2255, 2404, Fax: 225520, E-mail: marktgemeinde@haag-hausruck.ooe.gv.at, Internet: http://www.haag-hausruck.at
Local Museum - 1964
2th c fortress and later Renaissance building, local history, mining, local handicrafts, guilds, agriculture, peasant live 01976

Haag, Niederösterreich

Mostviertelmuseum Haag, Volksfestpl, 3350 Haag, Niederösterreich - T: (07434) 4242317, Fax: 4242321, E-mail: stadtamt@stadthaag.at, Internet: http://www.stadthaag.at. Head: Hans Steinwendtner
Local Museum - 1968
Peasant life, local culture 01977

Niederösterreichisches Freilichtmuseum, Weißpark, 3350 Haag, Niederösterreich - T: (07434) 4242317, Fax: 4242321, E-mail: stadtamt@ stadthaag.at, Internet: http://www.stadthaag.at. Head: Hans Steinwendtner
Open Air Museum - 1979
Trad architecture, agricultural tools, medical plants 01978

Hadersdorf

Heimatmuseum, Rathaus, Landsknechtpl 1, 3493 Hadersdorf - T: (02735) 2309
Local Museum - 1971
Locqal hist, arms 01979

Weinbau- und Landwirtschaftsmuseum, Preßhaus, Weinstr, 3493 Hadersdorf - T: (02735) 5525
Agriculture Museum - 1982 01980

Hadres

Franz Daurach-Sammlung, Pfarramt, Untermarkersdorf, 2061 Hadres - T: (02943) 2288
Special Museum 01981

Pulkautaler Weinbaumuseum, Unter-Markersdorf, 2061 Hadres - T: (02943) 2344. Head: Alfred Seidl
Agriculture Museum - 1982 01982

Hafnerbach

Heimatmuseum mit Raimund von Montecuccoli-Gedenkraum, Volksschule, 3385 Hafnerbach - T: (02749) 2320, Fax: 22789
Local Museum - 1982
Local history, archaeology 01983

Hainburg an der Donau

Stadtmuseum Wienertor Hainburg, Hauptpl 23, 2410 Hainburg an der Donau - T: (02165) 62111, Fax: 62410. Head: Kurt Svoboda
Local Museum / Agriculture Museum - 1928
Hist of town and tobacco 01984

Haitzendorf

Schloßmuseum, Grafenegg 10, 3485 Haitzendorf - T: (02735) 220522, Fax: 220511, E-mail: kultur@ grafenegg.at, Internet: http://www.grafenegg.at. Head: Yasmin Göker
Local Museum - 1971
Metalwork of the Historicism 01985

Halbturn

Österreichische Galerie Belvedere, Schloß, 7131 Halbturn - T: (02172) 8577, Fax: 8577, E-mail: schlosshalbturn@netway.at, Internet: http:// www.netway.at/schlosshalbturn. Head: Gerbert Frodl
Fine Arts Museum 01986

Hall in Tirol

Bergbaumuseum, Oberer Stadtpl, Fürstengasse, 6060 Hall in Tirol - T: (05223) 584541, Fax: 41286
Science&Tech Museum - 1926
Reconstructed salt mine with gallery, shaft and slide, minerals 01987

Kunsthalle Tirol, Autobahnauffahrt Mitte, 6060 Hall in Tirol - T: (05223) 523220, Fax: 523229, E-mail: info@kunsthalle-tirol.at, Internet: http://www.kunsthalle-tirol.at. Head: Hubert Salden
Fine Arts Museum - 1993 01988

Sammlung Flörl, Kugelanger 12-14, 6060 Hall in Tirol - T: (05223) 56716, 41504, Fax: 56717. Head: Johann Flörl
Science&Tech Museum - 1945 01989

Stadtmuseum Hall in Tirol, Burg, Hasegg 3, 6060 Hall in Tirol - T: (05223) 584541, Fax: 41286
Local Museum - 1933
History of guilds, mining, fine arts, coins, arms and armour, prehistoric artefacts 01990

Hallein

Bindereimuseum Hofbräu Kaltenhausen, Salzachtal-Bundesstr Nord 37, 5400 Hallein - T: (06245) 795, Fax: 79572, Internet: http://www.brauunion.com
Science&Tech Museum - 1986
Brewery 01991

Keltenmuseum, Pflegerpl 5, 5400 Hallein - T: (06245) 80783, 89880, Fax: 8078314, E-mail: keltenmuseum@netway.de, Internet: http://www.keltenmuseum.at. Head: Kurt Zeller
Archaeological Museum - 1970
Pre- and ancient history, Laténe findings, prehistoric salt mining, topography, town history - library 01992

Salzbergwerksmuseum und Schaustollen, Ramsaustr 3, 5422 Hallein - T: (06245) 85285, Fax: 8528518
Science&Tech Museum - 1991
Prehistorical finds, minerals 01993

Stille Nacht-Museum, Franz-Xaver-Gruber-Pl 1, 5400 Hallein - T: (06245) 80783, Fax: 8078314, E-mail: keltenmuseum@netway.at, Internet: http://www.keltenmuseum.at. Head: Kurt W. Zeller
Special Museum - 1993
Hist of the Christmas carol "Stille Nacht", cribs, regional Christmas traditions, "Halleiner Liedertafel" - archive 01994

Hallstatt

Heimatmuseum Hallstatt, Dr.-F.-Morton-Weg 27, 4830 Hallstatt - T: (06134) 8280, Fax: 8280, E-mail: r.gamsjaeger@eduhi.at, Internet: http://www.museum-hallstadt.at
Local Museum - 1884 01995

Kulturerbe Hallstatt, Seestr 56, 4830 Hallstatt - T: (06134) 8280, Fax: 8280, E-mail: r.gamsjaeger@eduhi.at, Internet: http://www.museum-hallstatt.at. Head: Rudolf Gamsjäger
Archaeological Museum - 1884
Folkore, local finds from Hallstatt and Laténe periods, local salt mining, Roman provincial art, ornithology, wood cross-sections, geology - library 01996

Prähistorisches Museum → Kulturerbe Hallstatt

Hard, Vorarlberg

Textildruckmuseum Mittelweiherburg, Erikastr 6, 6971 Hard, Vorarlberg - T: (05574) 69720, Fax: 69754. Head: Ernst Köhlmeier
Science&Tech Museum / Local Museum - 1962
Exhibits from the beginning of cloth printing, making of wooden hand-printing stamps 01997

Hardegg

Emperor Maximilian of Mexico Museum, Burg Hardegg 1, 2082 Hardegg - T: (02949) 8225, Fax: 7003, E-mail: pilati@eunet.at. Head: Francesca Gräfin Pilati von Thassul-Filo della Torre
Historical Museum - 1905
Weappons coll of the Princes Khevenhüller-Metsch, hist of French intervension in Mexico (1864-67) - archive 01998

Hartberg

Stadtmuseum Hartberg, Herrengasse 6, 8230 Hartberg - T: (03332) 60336, Fax: 60351, E-mail: gem@hartberg.at, Internet: http://www.hartberg.at. Head: Josef Strauß
Local Museum - 1968
Local hist, Roman exhibition, folklore, school history 01999

Haslach

Heimathaus des Heimatvereins Haslach, Pflaster 13, 4170 Haslach - T: (07289) 72203
Local Museum - 1921
Hist of the weavers' market 02000

Heimatstube der Deutsch-Reichenauer, Sankt Oswald 18, 4170 Haslach - T: (07289) 715550, Fax: 715559
Local Museum 02001

Kaufmannsmuseum des Heimatvereins Haslach, Windgasse 17, 4170 Haslach - T: (07289) 72173. Head: Peter Anderle
Special Museum - 1988
Old grocer's, education of the grocer's trade people 02002

Museum für mechanische Musik und Volkskunst, Windgasse 9, 4170 Haslach - T: (07289) 71379, E-mail: erwin.rechberger@iris.at, Internet: http://www.iris.at/mech.musik_und_volkskunst. Head: Erwin Rechberger
Music Museum / Folklore Museum - 1994
Mechanical musical instruments (musical boxes, barrel-organs, gramophones etc.), cribs, 70 mechanical figures 02003

Webereimuseum, Kirchpl 3, 4170 Haslach - T: (07289) 71593, Fax: 71593. Head: Alfred Eggerstorfer
Science&Tech Museum - 1970
Flax processing, thread, hand and mechanized weaving, printing and dying, starch and linseed oil, history of linen production 02004

Haus

Dekanatsmuseum, Nr 1, 8967 Haus - T: (03686) 2316, 2681. Head: Prof. Walter Stipperger
Religious Arts Museum - 1964
Hist of the Upper Inn Valley, religious customs, Christian art, Peasant War, Reformation and Counter-Reformation, folk beliefs, pilgrimages, ecclesiastical art 02005

Heidenreichstein

Franz Zeh-Museum, Kleinpertholz 2, 3860 Heidenreichstein - T: (02862) 52604. Head: Manfred Zeh
Fine Arts Museum - 1999 02006

Moor- und Torfmuseum, Kleinpertholz 36, 3860 Heidenreichstein - T: (02862) 52506, Fax: 5233629, E-mail: gdeheidenreichstein@netway.at, Internet: http://www.heidenreichstein.at
Natural History Museum - 1989 02007

Museum Burg Heidenreichstein, Schremser Str 1, 3860 Heidenreichstein - T: (02862) 52268, Fax: 522685, E-mail: kinskysches.forstamt@wvnet.at
Decorative Arts Museum
Interior 02008

Stadt- und Heimatmuseum, Kleinpertholz 36, 3860 Heidenreichstein - T: (02862) 52506, Fax: 5233629, E-mail: gaesteservice@heidenreichstein.gv.at, Internet: http://www.heidenreichstein.at. Head: Romana Kranner
Local Museum 02009

Webermuseum, Bahnhofstr 4, 3860 Heidenreichstein - T: (02862) 52455, Fax: 52455151
Historical Museum - 1992 02010

Heiligenblut

Freilichtmuseum Apriacher Stockmühlen, Apriach 10, 9844 Heiligenblut - T: (04824) 2354, 2628. Head: Matthias Schmidl
Open Air Museum - 1975 02011

Mentlhof-Bergbauernmuseum, Apriach 23, 9844 Heiligenblut - T: (04824) 2527, Fax: 2527, E-mail: vms@utanet.at
Agriculture Museum / Folklore Museum - 1985 02012

Heiligenbrunn

Kellerviertel Heiligenbrunn, Freilichtmuseum, Haus Nr. 40, 7522 Heiligenbrunn - T: (03324) 228
Open Air Museum - 1963
Tools, viticulture, early hist 02013

Helfenberg

Schmiede im Hammergraben, Ahorn 9, 4184 Helfenberg - T: (07216) 6359
Science&Tech Museum 02014

Hellmonsödt

Freilichtmuseum Pelmberg, Denkmalhof Mittermayer, Pelmberg 2, 4202 Hellmonsödt - T: (07215) 39110
Open Air Museum - 1970
Thatched farm house 02015

Hengsberg

Hengistburgmuseum, Hengsberg 4, 8411 Hengsberg - T: (03185) 2203, Fax: 22039, E-mail: gde@hengsberg.steiermark.at, Internet: http://www.hengsberg.at
Local Museum - 1977 02016

Volkskundliche Sammlung, Hengsberg 4, 8411 Hengsberg - T: (03185) 2203, Fax: 22039, E-mail: gde@hengsberg-steiermark.at, Internet: http://www.hengsberg.at
Folklore Museum 02017

Herberstein

Schloßmuseum, Buchberg 1, 8222 Herberstein - T: (03176) 8825, 8775, Fax: 877520, E-mail: herberstein@mail.styria.com. Head: Andrea Gräfin Herberstein
Fine Arts Museum / Decorative Arts Museum - 1920
Paintings, arms, Chinese porcelain 02018

Hermagor

Gailtaler Heimatmuseum Georg Essel, Möderndorf 1, 9620 Hermagor - T: (04282) 3060, 240163820, Fax: 240163810, Internet: http://www.karnische-museen.at
Local Museum - 1983
Pre- and ancient history, natural history, peasant life during the Baroque and Biedermeier periods, glass paintings, traditional costumes, musical instruments, Hafner Ceramics, painting, Gothic wooden statuettes, religious books and ancient Bibles - library 02019

Hernstein

Pechermuseum, Pfarrgasse 2, 2560 Hernstein - T: (02633) 47205, Fax: 47209
Special Museum 02020

Herrnbaumgarten

Dorfmuseum, Poysbrunner Str 9, 2171 Herrnbaumgarten - T: (02555) 2290, 2867
Local Museum - 1994
Prehist, agricultural tools, Nonseum (Museum for Useless Inventions) 02021

Herzogenburg

Heimatkundesammlung Inzersdorf, Inzersdorf 60, 3130 Herzogenburg - T: (02782) 83166, Fax: 85445, E-mail: gdelnzersdorf@netway.at, Internet: http://netvilleage.at/nv/inzersdorf-getzersdorf
Local Museum - 1983 02022

Kunstausstellung Stift Herzogenburg, Stiftsgasse 3, 3130 Herzogenburg - T: (02782) 83113, Fax: 83113, E-mail: stift-fuehrungen@herzogenburg.at, Internet: http://www.herzogenburg.at/stift. Head: Wolfgang Payrich
Fine Arts Museum / Religious Arts Museum - 18th c
12th c cloister, medieval art, Baroque painting, sculpture, arts and crafts, paraments, prehistoric items, coins, incunabula, late-Gothic panel painting - library 02023

Hieflau

Montanmuseum, Lend 2a, 8920 Hieflau - T: (03634) 294, 5050, Fax: 545, E-mail: gde@hieflau.steiermark.at, Internet: http://www.hieflau.-steiermark.at
Science&Tech Museum - 1998 02024

Hinterbrühl

Schaubergwerk Seegrotte, Grutschgasse 2a, 2371 Hinterbrühl - T: (02236) 26364, Fax: 26364, E-mail: seegrotte@kapsi.at, Internet: http://www.tourist-net.co.at/seegr1.htm
Science&Tech Museum - 1932
Plaster mine, Europe's largest subterranean lake, former airplane factory 02025

Hirschbach

Hirschbacher Bauernmöbelmuseum, Unterhirschgraben 18, 4242 Hirschbach - T: (07948) 541, 243, Fax: 541. Head: Robert Himmelbauer
Decorative Arts Museum - 1992
Historical development of farmhouse furniture 02026

Hirschwang

Museumseisenbahn Payerbach-Hirschwang, Bahnhof, 2652 Hirschwang - T: (02666) 52552, E-mail: oeglb@byronny.at, Internet: http://www.erlebnisbahn.at/hoellentalbahn. Head: Wolfgang Thier
Science&Tech Museum - 1977 02027

Volkskundliches Museum Alois Alphons, Gasthof Hirschwangerhof, 2652 Hirschwang - T: (02666) 2491. Head: Alois Alphons
Ethnology Museum - 1980 02028

Hittisau

Alpsennereimuseum, Altes Schulhaus, 6952 Hittisau - T: (05513) 6354, Fax: 63544, 62133
Agriculture Museum - 1980 02029

Ausstellung Hittisauer Lebensbilder aus dem 19. Jahrhundert, Pl 183, 6952 Hittisau - T: (05513) 6354, 6209, Fax: 62133. Head: Elisabeth Stöckler
Historical Museum - 1996 02030

Hochwolkersdorf

Gedenkraum 1945, Gemeindehaus, Nr 37, 2802 Hochwolkersdorf - T: (02645) 8222, Fax: 8222, Internet: http://www.hochwolkersdorf.at. Head: Dr. Johann Hagendorfer
Historical Museum - 1981 02031

Hof bei Salzburg

Denkmalhof Rauchhaus Mühlgrub, Vorderelsenwang 7, 5322 Hof bei Salzburg - T: (06229) 22040, 2249, Fax: 220424, E-mail: tourist@hofonline.at, Internet: http://www.hofonline.at. Head: Dr. Werner Berktold
Historical Museum - 1965 02032

Hofstetten, Pielach

Galerie Hofstetten → Galerie im Bürger- und Gemeindezentrum Hofstetten-Grünau

Galerie im Bürger- und Gemeindezentrum Hofstetten-Grünau, Hauptpl 3-5, 3202 Hofstetten, Pielach - T: (02723) 82420, Fax: 824230, E-mail: gertrud.kirchner@ktp.at, Internet: http://www.tiscover.com/hofstetten-gruenau. Head: Ingrid Fuchssteiner
Public Gallery - 1995 02033

Hohe Wand-Stollhof

Alpin- und Heimatmuseum, Hohe Wand 118, 2724 Hohe Wand-Stollhof - T: (02638) 883481, Fax: 883482
Local Museum / Natural History Museum - 1991 02034

Hohenau an der March

Museum Hohenau an der March, Hauptstr 12, 2273 Hohenau an der March - T: (02535) 23070, Fax: 230918, E-mail: gemeindeamt@hohenau-an-der-march.at, Internet: http://www.hohenau-an-der-march.at. Head: Ernst Springer, Wilhelm Swatschina
Local Museum - 1936 02035

Hohenems

Erstes Österreichisches Rettungsmuseum, Kaiserin-Elisabeth-Str 4, 6845 Hohenems - T: (05576) 7032202, Fax: 73563, E-mail: -rettungsmuseum.h.ems@gmx.de. Head: Ernst Schwarz
Historical Museum - 1994
Red cross history, rescue devices, items of police, mountain and cave rescue, fire fighting 02036

Jüdisches Museum Hohenems, Schweizer Str 5, 6845 Hohenems - T: (05576) 73989, Fax: 77793, E-mail: office@jm-hohenems.at, Internet: http://www.jm-hohenems.at. Head: Dr. Johannes Inama
Historical Museum - 1991
History of the Jewish community in Hohenems, everyday life and religion (17th-20th c) - library, archives 02037

Museum Stoffels Säge-Mühle, Sägerstr 11, 6845 Hohenems - T: (05576) 72434, Internet: http://www.hohenems.at. Head: Bernd Amann
Science&Tech Museum / Open Air Museum - 1981
Tools, mills 02038

Hohenzell

Kaplanstöckl, Nr 23, 4921 Hohenzell - T: (07750) 3514, Fax: (07752) 85706. Head: August Fisecker
Religious Arts Museum - 1994
Old working tools, pilgrimage souvenirs 02039

Hollabrunn

Museum Schöngrabern, Pfarrhof 174, Schöngrabern, 2020 Hollabrunn - T: (02952) 2132, Fax: 5448. Head: Alois Hörker
Local Museum - 1978
Lapidarium 02040

Neues Museum, Alte Hofmühle, Mühlenring 2, 2020 Hollabrunn - T: (02952) 210217, Fax: (02742) 900512052, E-mail: ernst.bezemek@noel.gv.at, Internet: http://www.altehofmuehle.at. Head: Dr. Ernst Bezemek
Local Museum - 1903
Pre- and ancient hist, local hist, folk customs and art, numismatics, medaillons 02041

Holzgau

Heimatmuseum, Nr 35, 6654 Holzgau - T: (05633) 5726, 5356, Fax: 5726, E-mail: oberlechtal@tirol.com, Internet: http://www.oberlechtal.com
Local Museum - 1986 02042

Horn

Archiv für die Waldviertler Urgeschichtsforschung, Frauenhofnerstr 17, 3580 Horn - T: (02982) 30123
Library with Exhibitions / Historical Museum 02043

Höbarth- und Madermuseum der Stadt Horn, Wiener Str 4, 3580 Horn - T: (02982) 23721, Fax: 23724, E-mail: stadtgemeinde@wvnet.at, Internet: http://www.stadtgemeindehorn.at. Head: Prof. Dr. Erich Rabl
Natural History Museum - 1930/1983
Local prehistory, geology and mineralogy, art and folk art, agricultural machines and utensils - library 02044

Hüttenberg

Ausstellungszentrum Heft, Bahnhofstr 12, 9375 Hüttenberg - T: (04263) 8108, Fax: 8109, E-mail: harrermuseum@aon.at, Internet: http://www.huettenberg.at. Head: Rudolf Schratter
Open Air Museum - 1983 02045

Bergbaumuseum mit Mineralienschau und Schaubergwerk, Bahnhofstr 12, 9375 Hüttenberg - T: (04263) 427, Fax: 8109, E-mail: harrermuseum@aon.at, Internet: http://www.huettenberg.at
Science&Tech Museum - 1979/80 02046

Heinrich Harrer-Museum, Bahnhofstr 12, 9375 Hüttenberg - T: (04263) 8108, Fax: 1983, E-mail: harrermuseum@aon.at, Internet: http://www.harrermuseum.at. Head: Rudolf Schratter
Special Museum / Ethnology Museum
Memorabilia of the traveller and writer Heinrich Harrer, Tibetan culture and religion, pilgrim path Lingkor 02047

Puppenmuseum Kärntner Eisenwurzen, Bahnhofstr 12, 9375 Hüttenberg - T: (04263) 8108, Fax: 8109, E-mail: harrermuseum@aon.at, Internet: http://www.huettenberg.at. Head: Rudolf Schratter
Special Museum - 1990 02048

Ilz

Museum Ilz, Nr 58, 8262 Ilz - T: (03385) 37714, Fax: 37719, E-mail: gde@ilz.steiermark.at, Internet: http://www.ilz.at
Local Museum - 1991 02049

Imst

Heimatmuseum → Museum im Ballhaus

Museum für bäuerliche Arbeitsgeräte, Meraner Str 6, 6460 Imst - T: (05412) 66346, Fax: 6634645, E-mail: lla_imst@tsn.at, Internet: http://www.lla-imst.tsn.at. Head: Josef Gstrein
Agriculture Museum - 1956 02050

Museum im Ballhaus (closed until 2002/03), Ballgasse 1, 6460 Imst - T: (05412) 698041, Fax: 63500. Head: Anton Stecher
Local Museum - 1909
Prehistoric finds, works of local artists, manger scenes, country furniture and utensils 02051

Innervillgraten

Bäuerliches Gerätemuseum und Venezianer-Gatter, Nr 93, 9932 Innervillgraten - T: (04843) 5240
Agriculture Museum / Science&Tech Museum 02052

Innsbruck

Alpenverein-Museum, Wilhelm-Greil-Str 15, 6020 Innsbruck - T: (0512) 5954719, Fax: 575528, E-mail: museum@alpenverein.at. Head: Monika Gärtner
Fine Arts Museum / Special Museum - 1911
Reliefs of the East and Westalps, history of the Alpenverein, mountaineering, paintings - photo archive 02053

Anatomisches Museum, Institut für Anatomie der Universität Innsbruck, Müllerstr 59, 6020 Innsbruck - T: (0512) 5073051/60, Fax: 5072862. Head: Dr. Karl Mager
Natural History Museum / Special Museum - 1889
Human anatomy and animal anatomy comparison, anthropology, art history, embryology, human diversity 02054

Berg-Isel-Museum der Tiroler Kaiserjäger mit Andreas Hofer-Galerie, Bergisel 1, 6020 Innsbruck - T: (0512) 582312, Fax: 588675. Head: Paul Hoffmann
Military Museum - 1880
Hist of the War of Independence (1809), memorabilia of Andreas Hofer, hist of the former Tyrolean Imperial Regiments 02055

Einsiedelei Erzherzog Maximilians des Deutschmeisters, Kaiserjägerstr 6, 6020 Innsbruck - T: (0512) 24914
Historical Museum 02056

Fotoforum, Adolf-Pichler-Pl 8, 6020 Innsbruck - T: (0512) 572236, Fax: 5722364, E-mail: fotoforum@aon.at, Internet: http://www.fotoforum.at. Head: Rupert Larl
Public Gallery - 1989
Contempoary photographies - workshops 02057

Galerie im Taxispalais, Maria-Theresien-Str 45, 6020 Innsbruck - T: (0512) 5083171, Fax: 5083175, E-mail: taxis.galerie@tirol.gv.at, Internet: http://www.galerieimtaxispalais.at. Head: Dr. Silvia Eiblmayr
Public Gallery - 1964 02058

Glockenmuseum der Glockengiesserei, Leopoldstr 53, 6020 Innsbruck - T: (0512) 5941637, Fax: 5941622, E-mail: info@grassmayr.at, Internet: http://www.grassmayr.at. Head: Johannes Grassmayr
Science&Tech Museum / Special Museum - 1993
From ore to the bell 02059

Historisches Stadtmuseum Innsbruck, Badgasse 2, 6020 Innsbruck - T: (0512) 587380, Fax: 5873808, E-mail: stadtarchiv@magibk.at. Head: Dr. Lukas Morscher
Historical Museum - 1966 02060

Hofingers Rahmenmuseum, Templstr 8, 6010 Innsbruck - T: (0512) 577182, Fax: 577182, E-mail: atelier-hofinger@tyrol.at, Internet: http://www.tyrol.at/atelier-hofinger. Head: Franz Hofinger
Decorative Arts Museum
Frames 02061

Kaiserliche Hofburg zu Innsbruck, Rennweg 1, 6020 Innsbruck - T: (0512) 587186, Fax: 58718613, E-mail: hofburg.ibk@tirol.com, Internet: http://www.tirol.com/hofburg-ibk. Head: Waltraud Schreilechner
Decorative Arts Museum
Late 18th c furnishings and decorations in former imperial residence, built by Maximilian I, ceiling paintings, portraits and tapestries 02062

Kunstkammer des Innsbrucker Servitenkloster, Maria-Theresien-Str 42, 6010 Innsbruck - T: (0512) 588881/83, Fax: 588883/84. Head: Johann Paul M. Müller
Religious Arts Museum
Paintings in baroque style, paintings 19th c 02063

Kunstraum Innsbruck, Maria-Theresien-Str 34, 6020 Innsbruck - T: (0512) 584000, Fax: 58400015, E-mail: kunstraum-innsbruck@tyrol.net, Internet: http://www.kunstraum-innsbruck.at. Head: Elisabeth Thoman-Oberhofer
Public Gallery 02064

Localbahnmuseum, Tiroler Museums Bahnen, Stubaitalbahnhof, Pater-Reinisch-Weg 4, 6020 Innsbruck - T: (0512) 345321, Fax: 930005711, E-mail: erich.gruber@pv.oebb.at, Internet: http://www.tmb.at. Head: Erich Gruber
Science&Tech Museum - 1983 02065

Maximilianeum - Goldenes Dachl, Herzog-Friedrich-Str 15, 6020 Innsbruck - T: (0512) 581111, Fax: 581111, E-mail: sekretariat@tiroler-landesmuseum.at, Internet: http://www.tiroler-landesmuseum.at. Head: Prof. Dr. Gert Ammann
Historical Museum - 1996 02066

Museum im Zeughaus, Zeughausgasse, 6020 Innsbruck - T: (0512) 587439, Fax: 58743918, E-mail: zeughaus@tiroler-landesmuseum.at, Internet: http://www.tiroler-landesmuseum.at. Head: Dr. Meinrad Pizzinini
Local Museum - 1973
Geology and mineralogy, mining in Tyrol 15th/16th c, social history since 1500, sound room of musical history of Tyrol, exhibition of time 02067

Museum von Abgüssen und Originalsammlung, Institut für Klassische Archäologie der Universität, Innrain 52, 6020 Innsbruck - T: (0512) 5074271, Fax: 5072989, E-mail: klass-archaeologie@uibk.ac.at, Internet: http://www.info.uibk.ac.at/c/c6/c614. Head: Prof. Elisabeth Walde
Archaeological Museum / University Museum - 1869 02068

Riesenrundgemälde Schlacht am Bergisel, Rennweg 39, 6020 Innsbruck, mail addr: A. Gisinger, Kaiser-Franz-Josef-Str 14, 6020 Innsbruck - T: (0512) 584434, Fax: 53053980, Internet: http://www.panorama-innsbruck.at/platform.htm. Head: Christoph Schlenk
Fine Arts Museum - 1948 02069

Schloß Ambras, Kunsthistorisches Museum, Schloßstr 20, 6020 Innsbruck - T: (0512) 348446, Fax: 361542, E-mail: schloss.ambras@khm.at, Internet: http://www.khm.at/ambras. Head: Dr. Alfred Auer
Fine Arts Museum - 1580
Painting, weapons, period furnishings, arms and armour 02070

Stiftssammlungen Wilten, Klostergasse 7, 6020 Innsbruck - T: (0512) 5830480, Fax: 58304822
Religious Arts Museum 02071

Tiroler Kaiserschützenmuseum (temporary closed), Klostergasse 1, 6020 Innsbruck - T: (0512) 583386, 587439, Fax: 58743918, E-mail: zeughaus@tiroler-landesmuseum.at, Internet: http://www.tiroler-landesmuseum.at. Head: Dr. Meinrad Pizzinini
Military Museum - 1931
History of the Tyrolean marksmen, national defence of Tyrol during WW I 02072

Tiroler Kunstpavillon Kleiner Hofgarten, Rennweg 8a, 6020 Innsbruck - T: (0512) 581133, Fax: 585971, E-mail: pavillon@kuenstlerschaft.at, Internet: http://www.kuenstlerschaft.at. Head: Ingeborg Erhart
Public Gallery - 1951 02073

Tiroler Landesmuseum Ferdinandeum (closed until May 2003), Museumstr 15, 6020 Innsbruck - T: (0512) 59489, Fax: 5948988, E-mail: sekretariat@tiroler-landesmuseum.at, Internet: http://www.tiroler-landesmuseum.at. Head: Prof. Dr. Gert Ammann
Decorative Arts Museum / Historical Museum - 1823
Prehistory, European painting and sculpture (Romanesque to present), decorative arts 02074

Tiroler Volkskunstmuseum, Universitätsstr 2, 6020 Innsbruck - T: (0512) 584302, Fax: 58430270, E-mail: tiroler@volkskunstmuseum.cnt.at. Head: Dr. Hans Gschnitzer
Folklore Museum - 1888
Tyrolean folk arts, original farmhouse parlours and furniture 02075

Irdning

Studiensammlung historischer Ziegel, Ringgasse 27, 8952 Irdning - T: (03682) 22559. Head: Manfred Hofer
Special Museum - 1982 02076

Jedenspeigen

Urgeschichtssammlung und Heimtmuseum, Sierndorf a.d. M. Haus Nr. 80, 2264 Jedenspeigen - T: (02536) 8224. Head: Alfred Schultes
Local Museum - 1950
Local history, folklore, wine production, farm implements and household utensils, artworks, weapons, masonry coll - library 02077

Jenbach

Bäuerliche Gerätesammlung, Landeslehranstalt Rotholz, 6200 Jenbach - T: (05244) 2161. Head: Martin Widschwendter
Agriculture Museum 02078

Jenbacher Museum, Achenseestr 21, 6200 Jenbach - T: (05244) 61409, Fax: 61409, E-mail: erika.felkel@utanet.at, Internet: http://members.tripod.de/jenbachermuseum. Head: Otto Scheifinger
Science&Tech Museum / Natural History Museum / Local Museum - 1995
Railroads, scythe industry, mining, butterflies, birds, skiing, winter sports, regional history 02079

Schloß Tratzberg mit Sammlungen, Tratzberg 1, 6200 Jenbach - T: (05242) 6356215, Fax: 6356211, E-mail: tratzberg@tirol.com, Internet: http://www.schloss-tratzberg.at. Head: Ulrich Graf Goess-Enzenberg
Fine Arts Museum / Historical Museum
Historic period rooms, furnishings and crafts (late Gothic to early Renaissance), painting, armour, weapons, 15th c castle, chapel 02080

Jetzelsdorf

Weinviertler Naturmuseum, Jetzelsdorf 12-14, 2053 Jetzelsdorf - T: (02944) 2301, Fax: 2301. Head: Robert Würthner
Natural History Museum - 1919/1969 02081

Jochberg

Bergbau- und Heimatmuseum, Altes Schulhaus, 6373 Jochberg - T: (05355) 5416
Science&Tech Museum / Local Museum - 1978 02082

Schaubergwerk Kupferplatte, Bergwerksweg 10, 6373 Jochberg - T: (05355) 5615, 5779, Fax: 5459, E-mail: info@bergbau.kupferplatte.at, Internet: http://www.schaubergwerk.kupferplatte.at
Science&Tech Museum - 1990 02083

Jois

Ortskundliches Museum Jois, Untere Hauptstr 23, 7093 Jois - T: (02160) 7121
Local Museum - 1978
Folklore, local hist, handicraft 02084

Judenburg

Stadtmuseum Judenburg, Kaserngasse 27, 8750 Judenburg - T: (03572) 85053, E-mail: museum@ainet.at. Head: Dr. Michael Schiestl
Local Museum - 1948
Local and regional history, mineralogy, crafts and trades, art works, folklore, coins, contemporary history 02085

Julbach

Heimathaus Julbach, Bräuerau 11, 4162 Julbach - T: (07288) 8223
Local Museum
Flax and wood processing 02086

Kaindorf an der Sulm

Bauernmuseum im Grottenhof, Grottenhof 1, 8430 Kaindorf an der Sulm, mail addr: Seggauberg 1, 8430 Leibnitz - T: (03452) 824350, Fax: 8243510, E-mail: gutsverwaltung@seggau.com, Internet: http://www.seggau.com
Agriculture Museum 02087

Kals am Großglockner

Heimatmuseum, Ködnitz 18, 9981 Kals am Großglockner - T: (04876) 8277, Fax: 821017, E-mail: gemeindeamt.kals@tirol.com
Local Museum - 1974 02088

Kapfenberg

Museum der Stadt Kapfenberg, Mürzgasse 3, 8605 Kapfenberg - T: (03862) 225011240, Fax: 225011210, E-mail: museum@kapfenberg.at, Internet: http://www.kapfenberg.at. Head: Peter Kobald
Local Museum - 1989
Town hist 02089

Kapfenstein

Geologische Sammlung Schloß Kapfenstein, Schloßmuseum, 8353 Kapfenstein - T: (03157) 2202. Head: Burkhardt Winkler-Hermaden
Natural History Museum - 1965 02090

Kaprun

Museum Kaprun, Hohenwarterpark, 5710 Kaprun - T: (06547) 8462
Local Museum - 1968
Local hist, early hist 02091

Karlstift

Stierhübelteichhaus, Trift- und Holzfällermuseum, 3973 Karlstift - T: (02857) 2253, Fax: 27103, E-mail: gemeinde.grpertholz@wvnet.at, Internet: http://www.noel.gv.at/service/k/k1/museen/0165.htm
Special Museum
Wood, wood cutting 02092

Katsdorf

Heimatmuseum → Karden-und Heimatmuseum

Karden-und Heimatmuseum, Kirchenpl 1, 4223 Katsdorf - T: (07237) 2533, E-mail: eva.reichl@aon.at, Internet: http://www.webland.lion.cc/ooe/240064. Head: Leo Reichl
Local Museum - 1986
Early and prehistory, local hist 02093

Katzelsdorf, Leitha

Dorfmuseum, Hauptstr 47, 2801 Katzelsdorf, Leitha - T: (02622) 782000, 78471, Fax: 7820015
Local Museum 02094

Kaumberg

Heimatmuseum Kaumberg, Pfarrgasse 5, 2572 Kaumberg - T: (02765) 282, Fax: 544, Internet: http://www.kaumberg.at
Local Museum - 1985 02095

Kautzen

Heimatmuseum Kautzen, Waidhofner Str 9, 3851 Kautzen - T: (02864) 2980, 2959, Fax: 224111, E-mail: gemeinde.kautzen@wvnet.at, Internet: http://www.kautzen.com
Local Museum - 1987 02096

Kematen an der Ybbs

Heimatmuseum, Erste Str 31, 3331 Kematen an der Ybbs - T: (07448) 2312
Local Museum - 1979
Roman times 02097

Kierling

Kierlinger Heimatmuseum, Hauptstr 114, 3412 Kierling - T: (02243) 83882, Fax: 83882. Head: Friedrich Chlebecek
Local Museum - 1987
Local history, Austrian largest coll of silhouettes, field baking and cooking, crafts, gastronomy, agriculture 02098

Kindberg

Heimat- und Montanmuseum in Schloß Oberkindberg, Schloßallee 9, 8650 Kindberg - T: (03865) 3764, 4114, Fax: 3763
Local Museum - 1980
Coins 02099

Kirchbach

Heimatmuseum, Sammlung Fuchs, 8082 Kirchbach - T: (03116) 27130
Local Museum 02100

Kirchberg am Walde

Robert Hamerling - Museum, Hauptpl 14, 3932 Kirchberg am Walde - T: (02854) 249, 7010, Fax: 70104, E-mail: gdekirchbergwalde@wvnet.at. Head: Elmar Peter
Special Museum - 1992 02101

Kirchberg am Wechsel

Ludwig Wittgenstein-Dauerausstellung, Markt 63, 2880 Kirchberg am Wechsel - T: (02641) 2557, Fax: 2557, E-mail: alws@nextra.at, Internet: http://www.sbg.ac.at/phs/alws/alws.htm
Special Museum - 1974
Photos, works and memorabilia of the philosopher Ludwig Wittgenstein 02102

Kirchbichl

Rittersaalmuseum, Burg Mariastein, 6322 Kirchbichl - T: (05332) 56474. Head: Rudolf Ludwig
Historical Museum / Religious Arts Museum - 1960 02103

Kirchham

Heimatmuseum, 4656 Kirchham - Fax: (07619) 201520, E-mail: gemeinde@kirchham.ooe.gv.at, Internet: http://www.kirchham.ooe.gv.at
Local Museum - 1985
Handicraft, agricultural and farming implements 02104

Kirchschlag

Heimatmuseum, Kirchenpl 1, 2860 Kirchschlag - T: (02646) 2213
Local Museum - 1984 02105

Kirchstetten

Josef Weinheber-Museum, Nr 28, 3062 Kirchstetten - T: (02743) 8989. Head: Brigitte Weinheber-Janota
Special Museum
Memorabilia of the poet J. Weinheber 02106

Wystan Hugh Auden-Dokumentationsräume, Gemeindeamt, 3062 Kirchstetten - T: (02743) 8206, 8989, Fax: 872018, E-mail: gdekirchstetten@netway.at, Internet: http://www.homepages.at/kstetten. Head: Maria Rollenitz
Library with Exhibitions 02107

Kittsee

Ethnographisches Museum Schloss Kittsee, Dr.-Ladislaus-Batthyany-Pl 1, 2421 Kittsee - T: (02143) 2304, Fax: 2025, E-mail: office@schloss-kittsee.at, Internet: http://www.schloss-kittsee.at. Head: Dr. Klaus Beitl, Dr. Franz Grieshofer
Folklore Museum - 1974
East and Southeast European folklore 02108

Kitzbühel

Museum Kitzbühel, Hinterstadt 32, 6370 Kitzbühel - T: (05356) 64588, 67274, Fax: 64588, E-mail: info@museum-kitzbuehel.at, Internet: http://www.museum-kitzbuehel.at. Head: Dr. Wido Sieberer
Local Museum / Historic Site - 1932
Skiing, mining, old Tower 02109

Tiroler Bauernhausmuseum, Hinterobernau, 6370 Kitzbühel - T: (05356) 49884. Head: Erwin Steidl
Agriculture Museum - 1978 02110

Kitzeck im Sausal

Weinmuseum Kitzeck, Steinriegel 11, 8442 Kitzeck im Sausal - T: (03456) 2243
Special Museum - 1979
Presses and other implements used in viticulture 02111

Klagenfurt

Alpen-Adria Galerie im Stadthaus, Theaterpl 3, 9020 Klagenfurt - T: (0463) 537532, Fax: 537537, 593022, E-mail: stadtgalerie@teleweb.at, Internet: http://www.galerie.klagenfurt.at. Head: Dr. Karl Princic, Beatrix Obernosterer
Public Gallery 02112

Bergbaumuseum Klagenfurt, Prof.-Dr.-Kahler-Pl 1, 9020 Klagenfurt - T: (0463) 511252, Fax: 51125215, E-mail: bbm@bergbaumuseum.at, Internet: http://www.bergbaumuseum.at. Head: Gerhard Finding
Science&Tech Museum - 1973
Mining equipment, documentation on history of mining in Carinthia, mineralogy 02113

Bischöfliches Diözesanmuseum Klagenfurt, Lidmanskygasse 10, 9020 Klagenfurt - T: (0463) 502498. Head: Dr. Eduard Mahlknecht
Religious Arts Museum - 1917/1974
Religious art from Carinthia (12th-18th c) 02114

Großer Wappensaal im Landhaus, Kärntner Landtag, 9020 Klagenfurt - T: (0463) 577570; 53630556, Fax: 57757233, 53630540, E-mail: e.pirker@ktn.gv.at, Internet: http://www.buk.ktn.gv.at/landesmuseum. Head: Jörg Freuenschlag
Decorative Arts Museum 02115

Kärntner Landesgalerie, Burggasse 8, 9020 Klagenfurt - T: (0463) 53630542/43, Fax: 53630544, E-mail: helga.schreyer@ktn.gv.at, Internet: http://www.landesgalerie.ktn.gv.at. Head: Dr. Arnulf Rohsmann
Fine Arts Museum - 1933
19th and 20th c art from Carinthia 02116

Koschatmuseum, Viktringer Ring 17, 9020 Klagenfurt - T: (0463) 599633. Head: Norbert Egger
Music Museum - 1934
Memorabilia of the composer Koschat 02117

Kunstverein Kärnten, Künstlerhaus, Goethepark 1, 9020 Klagenfurt - T: (0463) 55383, Fax: 504046, E-mail: office@kunstvereinkaernten.at, Internet: http://www.kunstvereinkaernten.at. Head: Dr. Fred Dickermann
Association with Coll - 1908 02118

Landesmuseum für Kärnten, Museumgasse 2, 9021 Klagenfurt - T: (0463) 53630552, Fax: 53630540, E-mail: info@landesmuseum-knt.at, Internet: http://www.landesmuseum-knt.at. Head: Dr. Friedrich W. Leitner
Natural History Museum / Local Museum - 1844/1884
Archaeology and prehistory, cultural history, zoology, geology, botany, folklore 02119

Landwirtschaftsmuseum Schloß Ehrental, Ehrentaler Str 119, 9020 Klagenfurt - T: (0463) 43540, Fax: 48176510, E-mail: landw_museum@lfs-ktn.at, Internet: http://www.landwirtschaftsmuseum.at. Head: Heimo Schinnerl
Agriculture Museum / Science&Tech Museum - 1993
Farmers life 1850 to 1950 02120

Minimundus, Villacher Str 241, 9020 Klagenfurt - T: (0463) 211940, Fax: 2119460, E-mail: info@minimundus.at, Internet: http://www.minimundus.at. Head: Diethard Humer
Special Museum - 1959
Models of famous buildings 1:25 02121

Museum der Trauerarbeitsplätze, Institut für Philosophie und Gruppendynamik, Universitätsstr 65, 9020 Klagenfurt - T: (0463) 27002117, E-mail: -helmut.stockhammer@uni-klu.ac.at, Internet: http://www.uni-klu.ac.at/~hstockha. Head: Dr. Helmut Stockhammer
Fine Arts Museum / Association with Coll - 1997 02122

Robert Musil-Literatur-Museum, Bahnhofstr 50, 9020 Klagenfurt - T: (0463) 501429, Fax: 5014291, E-mail: klagenfurt@musilmuseum.at, Internet: http://www.musilmuseum.at. Head: Dr. Heimo Strempfl
Special Museum - 1961
Bequest of Robert Musil (photos, documents, first editions, literature) 02123

Stadtgalerie Klagenfurt, Theatergasse 4, 9020 Klagenfurt - T: (0463) 537532, 537545, Fax: 593022, E-mail: stadtgalerie@teleweb.at, Internet: http://www.galerie.klagenfurt.at. Head: Beatrix Obernosterer
Public Gallery - 1996 02124

Klam

Burgmuseum Clam, Burg Clam, Sperken 1, 4352 Klam - T: (07269) 72170, Fax: 72175. Head: Dr. M.C.D. Clam-Martinic
Local Museum - 1967
Chapel, pharmacy, coll of porcelain, weapons 02125

Klein Sankt Paul

Talmuseum Lachitzhof, Sittenbergstr 2, 9373 Klein Sankt Paul - T: (04264) 2069. Head: Otto Leitgeb
Local Museum - 1985
Iron, industry 02126

Kleinwetzdorf

Radetzky-Gedenkstätte Heldenberg, Heldenbergstr 50, 3704 Kleinwetzdorf - T: (02956) 2372, 2553, Fax: 255314, E-mail: gdeheldenberg@netway.at
Military Museum - 1849 02127

Klostermarienberg

KiK - Kultur im Kloster, Feldgasse 1, 7444 Klostermarienberg - T: (02611) 3248, 2204, Fax: 22044, E-mail: antonschoberwalter@yahoo.de, Internet: http://www.kulturimkloster.at. Head: Kurt Vogel
Religious Arts Museum / Special Museum / Natural History Museum - 1991
Forrest and wood museum, European dogs museum 02128

Klosterneuburg

Archäologisches Museum, Pfarrkirche Sankt Martin, Martinstr 38-42, 3400 Klosterneuburg - T: (02243) 32568, Fax: 38158, E-mail: st.martin-klosterneuburg@utanet.at. Head: Prof. Dr. Johannes Wolfgang Neugebauer
Archaeological Museum / Religious Arts Museum - 1985
Church hist 02129

Mährisch-Schlesisches Heimatmuseum, Schießstattgasse 2, 3400 Klosterneuburg - T: (02243) 444287, Internet: http://www.volkskulturnoe.at/museum/0214.htm. Head: Hans-Peter Kauder
Folklore Museum / Local Museum / Library with Exhibitions / Historical Museum - 1957
Folklore of East/West Silesia and Moravia 02130

Museum des Chorherrenstifts Klosterneuburg, Stiftspl 1, 3400 Klosterneuburg - T: (02243) 411154, Fax: 411156, E-mail: kultur@stift-klosterneuburg.at, Internet: http://www.stift-klosterneuburg.at. Head: Prof. Dr. Dr. Floridus Röhrig
Religious Arts Museum - 1773
Medieval panel painting, decorative arts - library 02131

Sammlung Essl - Kunst der Gegenwart, An der Donau-Au 1, 3400 Klosterneuburg - T: (02243) 37050, Fax: 3705022, E-mail: hoffer@sammlung-essl.at, Internet: http://sammlung-essl.at. Head: Dr. Gabriele Bösch
Fine Arts Museum - 1999 02132

Stadtmuseum Klosterneuburg, Kardinal-Piffl-Pl 8, 3400 Klosterneuburg - T: (02243) 444286, 444299, Fax: 444404, E-mail: stadtmuseum@klosterneuburg.at, Internet: http://www.klosterneuburg.at/kultur. Head: Michael Duscher
Local Museum - 1930/1998
Town hist, pre and early hist, art 02133

Kobersdorf

Heimathaus im alten Zollhaus, Waldgasse 15, 7332 Kobersdorf - T: (02618) 8200, Fax: 8511
Local Museum - 1971
Local hist, peasant life 02134

Koblach

Museum für Urgeschichte, Werben 9, 6842 Koblach - T: (05523) 62875, Fax: 6287520, E-mail: gemeinde@koblach.at, Internet: http://www.koblach.at. Head: Fritz Maierhofer, Reinold Madlener
Historical Museum - 1990 02135

Köflach

Museum der Stadt Köflach, Bahnhofstr 24, 8580 Köflach - T: (03144) 2519710, Fax: 2519111. Head: Bernhard Stangl
Local Museum - 1967
Local and prehistory, agricultural tools, regional writer Hans Kloepfer 02136

Vor- und Frühgeschichtliche Privatsammlung, Kautschitschstr 2, 8580 Köflach - T: (03144) 8924, 29243. Head: Walter Muley
Archaeological Museum 02137

Königswiesen

Heimathaus Königswiesen, Marktpl 12, 4280 Königswiesen - T: (07955) 625532, Fax: 625532, E-mail: marktgemeinde@koenigswiesen.at, Internet: http://www.koenigswiesen.at
Local Museum - 1992
Kitchen, bakery, flax processing, weaver's workshop, motorbike exhibition 02138

Köstendorf

Heimatmuseum Kohbauernhaus, Museumstr 2, 5203 Köstendorf - T: (06216) 6554, 53130, Fax: 531310
Local Museum - 1984
Hunting, fishery, crafts 02139

Kötschach-Mauthen

Freilichtmuseum des Gebirgskrieges, Plöckenpaß, 9640 Kötschach-Mauthen - T: (04715) 851332, Fax: 851337, E-mail: museum@dolomitenfreunde.at, Internet: http://www.dolomitenfreunde.at. Head: Prof. Walther Schaumann
Open Air Museum / Military Museum - 1992 02140

Museum 1915-1918, Rathaus, 9640 Kötschach-Mauthen - T: (04715) 851332, Fax: 851337, E-mail: museum@dolomitenfreunde.at, Internet: http://www.dolomitenfreunde.at. Head: Prof. Walther Schaumann
Historical Museum / Military Museum - 1992 02141

Korneuburg

Museum der Stadt Korneuburg, Dr.-Max-Burckhard-Ring 11, 2100 Korneuburg - T: (02262) 72553, Fax: 72553. Head: Peter Langhammer
Local Museum - 1961 02142

Kramsach

Freilichtmuseum Tiroler Bauernhöfe, Angerberg 10, 6233 Kramsach - T: (05337) 62636, Fax: 63578, E-mail: office@museum-tb.at, Internet: http://www.museum.tb.at
Open Air Museum / Agriculture Museum - 1974
Farmhouses and farm buildings typical of North, South and East Tyrol 02143

Museumsfriedhof Tirol, Hagau 240, 6233 Kramsach - T: (05337) 62447, Fax: 64154. Head: Hans Guggenberger
Open Air Museum 02144

Skulpturenpark Kramsach, Achenrain 453, 6233 Kramsach - T: (05337) 65656, Fax: 65656, E-mail: troadkastn@tirol.com. Head: Michael Geiger
Fine Arts Museum - 1993 02145

Krems

Beethovenhaus, Schloßstr 19, Gneixendorf, 3500 Krems - T: (02732) 86876. Head: Maria Gettinger
Music Museum - 1827 02146

Karikaturmuseum Krems, Steiner Landstr 3a, 3500 Krems - T: (02732) 908020, Fax: 908021, E-mail: office@karikaturmuseum.at, Internet: http://www.karikaturmuseum.at. Head: Dr. Severin Heinisch
Fine Arts Museum - 2001 02147

Kunsthalle Krems, Franz-Zeller-Pl 3, 3500 Krems - T: (02732) 908010, Fax: 908011, E-mail: office@kunsthalle.at, Internet: http://www.kunsthalle.at. Head: Carl Aigner
Fine Arts Museum 02148

Moderne Galerie im Weinstadtmuseum Krems, Körnermarkt 14, 3500 Krems - T: (02732) 801567, 801570, Fax: 801576, E-mail: museum@krems.gv.at, Internet: http://www.weinstadtmuseum.at. Head: Dr. Franz Schönfellner
Public Gallery 02149

Motorrad-Museum Krems-Egelsee, Ziegelofengasse 1, 3500 Krems - T: (02732) 41624, Fax: 41378, E-mail: motorrad.museum@aon.at, Internet: http://www.motorrad-museum.at. Head: Herbert Kirchmayer, Christian Kirchmayer
Science&Tech Museum - 1984
200 engines, prospects, posters, sparking plugs, carburettors 02150

Weinstadtmuseum Krems, Dominikanerkirche, Körnermarkt 14, 3500 Krems - T: (02732) 801570, 801567, Fax: 801576, E-mail: museum@krems.gv.at, Internet: http://www.Weinstadtmuseum.at. Head: Dr. Franz Schönfellner
Local Museum - 1892
History of the Krems region from prehistoric to modern times, crafts and trades, furnishings and folklore, viticulture, contemporary arts 02151

Kremsmünster

Kunstsammlungen des Stiftes Kremsmünster, Benediktinerstift, 4550 Kremsmünster - T: (07583) 5275151, Fax: 5275159, E-mail: stift@kremsmuenster.at, Internet: http://www.kremsmuenster.at/stift. Head: Klaudius Wintz
Fine Arts Museum / Natural History Museum
Zoology, mineralogy, geology, paleontology and anthropology, physics and astronomy, Gothic, Renaissance, Baroque and Biedermeier art works, armour - library 02152

Musica Kremsmünster, Musikinstrumentenmuseum, Schloss Kremsegg, Kremsegger Str 59, 4550 Kremsmünster - T: (07583) 5247, Fax: 6830, E-mail: info@schloss-kremsegg.at, Internet: http://www.schloss-kremsegg.at. Head: Prof. Heinz Preiss, Franz Fellinger
Music Museum - 1996
Wind instruments, pianos, string instruments 02153

Krenglbach

Museum - Begegnung der Kulturen, Schmiding 27, 4631 Krenglbach - T: (07249) 46272, Fax: 46566, E-mail: zooschmiding@i-one.at, Internet: http://www.museumschmiding.at. Head: Dr. Artmann
Ethnology Museum - 1987
Anthropology, ethnology 02154

Museum der Begegnung → Museum - Begegnung der Kulturen

Krieglach

Heimatmuseum, Peter-Rosegger-Str 46, 8670 Krieglach - T: (03855) 3425
Local Museum - 1968
Memorabilia of Peter Rosegger, hunting, musical instruments, tools 02155

Peter Rosegger-Museum, Peter-Rosegger-Str 44, 8670 Krieglach - T: (03855) 2375, Fax: 2375. Head: Sabine Maketz-Anderle
Special Museum - 1947
Photos, documents, first editions and memorabilia of Peter Rosegger in rooms he occupied, typical country furniture and furnishings from the Styria region 02156

Kronstorf

Brucknerzimmer, Brucknerpl 4, 4484 Kronstorf - T: (07225) 8256, Fax: 825625
Music Museum - 1989
Memorabilia of Anton Bruckner 02157

Krumbach

Museumsdorf Krumbach, Bürgerspital 2, 2851 Krumbach - T: (02647) 42238, Fax: 4223822, E-mail: gemeinde@krumbach-noe.gv.at, Internet: http://www.krumbach-noe.at. Head: Ernst Dorner
Local Museum - 1976
Local hist, folklore, agricultural tools 02158

Kuchl

Heimatmuseum, c/o Marianne Siller, Severinpl, 5431 Kuchl - T: (06244) 4686
Local Museum - 1960
Folklore, Roman finds 02159

Kufstein

Inn-Galerie, Arkadenpl 4, 6330 Kufstein - T: (05372) 64001, Fax: 62045, E-mail: georg.hoeck@i-one.at. Head: Johann Scheiber, Georg Höck
Public Gallery - 1984 02160

Kukmirn

Erstes Südburgenländisches Schnapsbrennereimuseum, c/o Brennerei Lagler, Nr 137, 7543 Kukmirn - T: (03328) 32003, Fax: 320034
Special Museum 02161

Kulm bei Weiz

Erstes Urgeschichtliches Freilichtmuseum der Steiermark, Kulmkeltendorf, 8212 Kulm bei Weiz - T: (03113) 2352, Fax: 2352. Head: Dr. Titus Lanto
Open Air Museum 02162

Laa an der Thaya

Biermuseum, Burgpl 23, 2136 Laa an der Thaya - T: (02522) 250129, 85142, Fax: 250199, E-mail: laa@nanet.at, Internet: http://www.laa.at
Special Museum - 1972
Coll of beer bottles 02163

Burggalerie Laa, Burgpl 23, 2136 Laa an der Thaya - T: (02522) 250129, 85142, Fax: 250199, E-mail: Laa@nanet.at, Internet: http://www.laa.at. Head: F. Gruber
Fine Arts Museum - 1972 02164

Kutschenmuseum, Hanfthaler Str, 2136 Laa an der Thaya - T: (02522) 250129. Head: Wolfgang Satzer, Walter Gröger
Science&Tech Museum - 1994 02165

Südmährer Heimatmuseum, Altes Rathaus, Stadtpl 17, 2136 Laa an der Thaya - T: (02522) 501
Local Museum - 1986
Local traditions 02166

Längenfeld

Ötztaler Freilichtmuseum, Lehn Nr. 24, 6444 Längenfeld - T: (05253) 5540
Open Air Museum - 1968
Historic farmhouses and outbuildings of the Ötztal region, farm implements and household utensils 02167

Lainbach

Wastlmühle, Mooslandl 60, 8921 Lainbach - T: (03637) 346
Science&Tech Museum 02168

Lambach

Stiftssammlungen Lambach, Klosterpl 1, 4650 Lambach - T: (07245) 21710, Fax: 21710302, E-mail: archiv@stift-lambach.at, Internet: http://www.stift-lambach.at. Head: P. Maximilian Neulinger
Religious Arts Museum - 1056
Romanesque frescos from the 11th c, medieval mannscripts - library, Baroque theatre 02169

Lamprechtshausen

Franz Xaver Gruber-Museum, Arnsdorf, Stille-Nacht-Pl 1, 5112 Lamprechtshausen - T: (06274) 7453, 6937, Internet: http://members.magnet.at/f.x.gruber-museum-arnsdorf. Head: Ottilie Aigner
Music Museum - 1959
Memorabilia of the Composer Franz Xaver Gruber 02170

Landeck

Schloßmuseum Landeck, Schloßweg 2, 6500 Landeck - T: (05442) 63202, 65307, Fax: 653074, E-mail: office@schlosslandeck.at, Internet: http://www.tirol.com/schlossmuseum/landeck. Head: Eva Lunger-Valentini
Local Museum / Fine Arts Museum / Folklore Museum
Folklore, furniture, peasant life 02171

Landsee

Burgenländisches Steinmuseum, Markt Sankt Martin, 7341 Landsee - T: (02618) 7216. Head: Dr. H. Schmid
Natural History Museum - 1976
Geology of the Burgenland 02172

Gedächtnisstätte Mida Huber, Sankt Martin, 7341 Landsee - T: (02618) 7205. Head: Josefine Schuh
Historical Museum 02173

Langenlois

Heimatmuseum, Rathausstr 9, 3550 Langenlois - T: (02734) 210139, 210110, Fax: 210139
Local Museum - 1906
Prehistory, folklore, archaeology 02174

Maurermuseum und Dachdeckermuseum, Franziskanerpl 9-11, 3550 Langenlois - T: (02734) 2460, 2502, Fax: 250230, E-mail: lbs.bau.noe@asn.netway.at
Special Museum / Science&Tech Museum 02175

Mineralien-Fossilien-Bergbau, Privat-Museum Helmut und Monika Steininger, Zwettler Str 11, 3550 Langenlois - T: (02734) 3594
Natural History Museum - 1997 02176

Langenzersdorf

Anton Hanak-Museum, Obere Kirchengasse 23, 2103 Langenzersdorf - T: (02244) 29473, E-mail: museum@langenzersdorf.or.at, Internet: http://www.xpoint.at/xpt/Hanakmuseum/Langenzersdorfer-Museen/Langenzersdorfer-Museen.html. Head: Erich Gusel
Fine Arts Museum - 1970
Sculpture, sketches and drawings by Prof. Anton Hanak (local resident 1901-1923), room with Hanak-scholars - sculpture garden 02177

Heimatmuseum, Obere Kirchengasse 23, 2103 Langenzersdorf - T: (02244) 29473, E-mail: museum@langenzersdorf.or.at, Internet: http://www.xpoint.at/xpt/Hanakanmuseum/Langenzersdorfer-Museen/Langenzersdorfer-Museen.html
Historical Museum - 1955 02178

Siegfried Charoux-Museum, Obere Kirchengasse 23a, 2103 Langenzersdorf - T: (02244) 29473, E-mail: museum@langenzersdorf.or.at, Internet: http://www.xpoint.at/xpt/Hanakmuseum/Langenzersdorfer-Museen/Langenzersdorfer-Museen.html. Head: Erich Gusel
Fine Arts Museum - 1982
Works by Prof. Siegfried Charoux (drawings, paintings, sculptures), coll of the sculptor Alois Heidel - sculpture garden 02179

Lanzenkirchen

Bauernmuseum Lanzenkirchen, Hauptstr 5, 2821 Lanzenkirchen - T: (02627) 45417
Agriculture Museum - 1981 02180

Lasberg

Alte Marktschmiede, Markt 18, 4291 Lasberg - T: (07947) 5923, 72550, Fax: 725533, E-mail: tourismuskern@lasberg.at, Internet: http://www.tiscover.com/lasberg
Science&Tech Museum
Originally equipped cart smithy 02181

Freilichtmuseum Fürstenhammer, Siegelsdorf 25, 4291 Lasberg - T: (07947) 7255
Open Air Museum
Smithy from the 16th c 02182

Volkskundemuseum Spiralschmiede, Grieb 7, 4291 Lasberg - T: (07947) 7391, 72550, Fax: 725533. Head: Richard Kreindl
Ethnology Museum
Coal mining, steel processing 02183

Lauffen

Museum Fahrzeug-Technik-Luftfahrt, Sulzbach 178, 4821 Lauffen - T: (06132) 26658, Fax: 23934. Head: Josef Loidl
Science&Tech Museum
Agricultural and military vehicles 02184

Launsdorf

Sammlungen der Burg Hochosterwitz, Hochosterwitz 1, 9314 Launsdorf - T: (04213) 2010, 2020, Fax: 202016, E-mail: Burg@hochosterwitz.or.at, Internet: http://www.hochosterwitz.or.at/burg. Head: Maximilian Khevenhüller-Metsch
Historical Museum / Historic Site - 1875
Arms and armour, family portraits, housed in medieval fortress 02185

Laussa

Großmitterberger Troadkasten, Großmitterberg 87, 4461 Laussa 87 - T: (07255) 26113. Head: Josef Felbauer, Maria Felbauer
Agriculture Museum - 1983
Silo for 2.000-3.000 kg grain from 1663 02186

Lauterach

Alte Seifenfabrik, Bahnhofstr 3, 6923 Lauterach - T: (05574) 680245, Fax: 68025, E-mail: lauterach@aon.at. Head: Werner Hagen
Public Gallery - 1992 02187

Laxenburg

Filmsammlungen Laxenburg, Forsthaus, Parkweg 26, 2361 Laxenburg - T: (02236) 71449, Fax: 714404
Special Museum 02188

Franzensburg, Schloßpl 1, 2361 Laxenburg - T: (02236) 712260, 71422, Fax: 72730, E-mail: office@schloss-Laxenburg.at, Internet: http://www.schloss-laxenburg.at. Head: Prof. Josef Rauchenberger, Robert Dienst
Historical Museum / Historic Site / Fine Arts Museum - 1945 02189

Museum der Freiwilligen Feuerwehr, Herbert-Rauch-Gasse 2, 2361 Laxenburg - T: (02236) 71390
Science&Tech Museum - 1979 02190

Museum Laxenburg, Herzog-Albrecht-Str 9, 2361 Laxenburg - T: (02236) 76174. Head: Walter Heidenreich
Local Museum / Historical Museum - 1988 02191

Lech

Walsermuseum Lech-Tannberg, Dorf 16, 6764 Lech - T: (05583) 2935, 3825, Fax: 221341, E-mail: Archiv@gemeinde.lech.at, Internet: http://www.gemeinde.lech.at. Head: Herbert Sauerwein
Folklore Museum / Agriculture Museum - 1984
Religious folk art, fossiles, skiing, mountain farming, crafts 02192

Leiben

Landtechnikmuseum, Europaschloss Leiben, 3652 Leiben - T: (02752) 70043, Fax: 700434, E-mail: -oekoregio.schloss.leiben@wvnet.at, Internet: http://www.schloss-leiben.at. Head: Karl Krischka
Science&Tech Museum 02193

Leibnitz

Tempelmuseum Frauenberg, Seggauberg 17, 8430 Leibnitz - T: (03452) 6320
Archaeological Museum - 1955
Roman temple ruins (1st c AD) and finds from former Roman settlement Flavia Solva (lamps, ceramics, glass, coins, inscriptions) 02194

Leithaprodersdorf

Gschlößl Leithaprodersdorf-Freilichtanlage, Parzelle Nr. 2703/1, 2443 Leithaprodersdorf - T: (02682) 2652
Open Air Museum - 1979
Medieval and Roman hist 02195

Lembach

Heimatmuseum Lembach, Schulstr 2, 4132 Lembach - T: (07286) 8255, Fax: 825534
Local Museum
Local hist (Peasants' War in 1626) 02196

Lendorf

Römermuseum Teurnia, Sankt Peter in Holz 1a, 9811 Lendorf - T: (04762) 33807, Fax: 33807, E-mail: teurnia@landesmuseum-ktn.at, Internet: http://www.landesmuseum-ktn.at/Teurnia.htm. Head: Prof. Dr. Franz Glaser
Archaeological Museum - 1959/1999
Early Christian mosaics, Roman monuments and inscriptions, and small grave finds from local ancient settlement, two early Christian basilicas (episcopal church and memorial church) 02197

Lengenfeld bei Krems

Privatsammlung Silvester Berner, Kremser Str 21, 3552 Lengenfeld bei Krems - T: (02719) 5073
Local Museum 02198

Leoben

Brauereimuseum im Stift Göß, 8707 Leoben - T: (03842) 22621. Head: Dr. Alfred Weitzendorfer
Science&Tech Museum - 1970
Old brewery tools and implements, housed in former malt house 02199

Kunsthalle Leoben, Kirchgasse 6, 8700 Leoben - T: (03842) 4062400, Fax: 4062410, E-mail: kunsthalle@leoben.at, Internet: http://www.leoben.gv.at. Head: Susanne Leitner-Böchzelt
Fine Arts Museum 02200

Museum der Stadt Leoben, Kirchgasse 6, 8700 Leoben - T: (03842) 4062227, Fax: 4062410, E-mail: kunsthalle@leoben.at. Head: Susanne Leitner-Böchzelt
Local Museum - 1883/1970
Early history, zoology, mineralogy and mining, art works (Gothic to Baroque), incunabula, old tools, decorative arts, weapons (18th-19th c) - library and archive 02201

Schauraum im ehemaligen Benediktinerinnenstift Göß, Turmgasse 4, 8700 Leoben - T: (03842) 22148, Fax: 221484, E-mail: leoben.goess@graz-seckau.at. Head: Matthias Keil
Religious Arts Museum
Sacral works of art, oldest monstery of Styria founded around 1000 BC 02202

Leogang

Bergbaumuseum Leogang, Hütten, Nr 10, 5771 Leogang - T: (06583) 7105, Fax: 822383, E-mail: office@gem-leogang.salzburg.at, Internet: http://www.leogang.at
Science&Tech Museum / Fine Arts Museum - 1992
Minerals, coins, Gothic sculptures (saints of mining) 02203

Schaubergwerk Barbarastollen, Nr 4, 5771 Leogang - T: (06583) 8223, Fax: 822383, E-mail: office@gem-leogang.salzburg.at, Internet: http://www.leogang.at
Science&Tech Museum - 1989 02204

Leonding

Galerie im 44er Haus, Stadtpl 7, 4060 Leonding - T: (0732) 68780, Fax: 6878266, E-mail: stadtamt@leonding.at, Internet: http://www.leonding.at. Head: Bärbel Füsselberger
Public Gallery - 1998 02205

Stadtmuseum Leonding - Turm 9, Daffingerstr 55, 4060 Leonding - T: (0732) 68780, 674746, Fax: 6878266, E-mail: stadtmuseum@leonding.at, Internet: http://www.leonding.at. Head: Bärbel Füsselberger
Local Museum - 1999 02206

Leopoldschlag

Mühlviertler Keramikwerkstätte Hafnerhaus, Hafnerstr 5, 4262 Leopoldschlag - T: (07949) 825515, Fax: 825514, E-mail: galli@leopoldschlag.ooe.gv.at
Decorative Arts Museum - 1995
Earthenware, ceramics 02207

Leopoldsdorf im Marchfelde

Österreichisches Spiele Museum, Raasdorfer Str 28, 2285 Leopoldsdorf im Marchfelde - T: (02216) 70006, Fax: 70003, E-mail: office@spielen.at, Internet: http://www.spielemuseum.at. Head: Ferdinand de Cassan, Dagmar de Cassan
Special Museum - 1996 02208

Lichtenau

Künstlergarten Alfred Kurz, Wietzen 11, 3522 Lichtenau
Fine Arts Museum 02209

Lienz

Archäologisches Museum Lavant, Lavant 61, 9900 Lienz - T: (04852) 68175, Fax: 681756, E-mail: gemeinde.lavant@aon.at. Head: Prof. Dr. Elisabeth Walde
Archaeological Museum - 1996 02210

Museum der Stadt Lienz, Schloß Bruck, Schloßberg 1, 9900 Lienz - T: (04852) 62580, Fax: 625804, Internet: http://www.1500circa.net. Head: Dr. Lois Ebner
Local Museum - 1907
Natural history, folklore and folk arts, farm implements, costumes and domestic utensils, painting 02211

Städtische Galerie, Johannespl 10a, 9900 Lienz - T: (04852) 600530, Fax: 71280. Head: Gerhard Wassnig
Fine Arts Museum - 1964 02212

Ligist

Heimatmuseum und Keltenhaus, Schloß Ligist, 8563 Ligist - T: (03143) 2911, 2229, Fax: 222924
Local Museum - 1973
Local hist, peasant culture 02213

Lilienfeld

Bezirksheimatmuseum mit Zdarsky-Skimuseum, Babenberger Str 3, 3180 Lilienfeld - T: (02762) 52478, 5221217, Fax: 52478. Head: Franz Josef Klaus
Local Museum / Special Museum - 1958
Skiing coll - Zdarsky-Archiv 02214

Zisterzienserstift, Klosterrotte 1, 3180 Lilienfeld - T: (02762) 5242038, Fax: 522924. Head: Eugen Müller
Religious Arts Museum
Baroque interior, cloister, library, picture gallery and copperplate etchings 02215

Linz

Adalbert-Stifter-Haus, Oberösterreichisches Literaturmuseum, Adalbert-Stifter-Pl 1, 4020 Linz - T: (0732) 77201295, Fax: 77201780, E-mail: office@stifter-haus.at, Internet: http://www.stifter-haus.at. Head: Dr. Johann Lachinger
Special Museum - 1950
Literature by and on Adalbert Stifter, Upper Austrian literature from the Middle Ages to the 20th c, literary history of Upper Austria - library, archives, Adalbert Stifter memorial room 02216

Ars Electronica Center, Hauptstr 2, 4041 Linz - T: (0732) 72720, Fax: 72722, E-mail: info@aec.at, Internet: http://www.aec.at. Head: Gerfried Stocker
Public Gallery / Science&Tech Museum / Fine Arts Museum - 1996 02217

Außenstelle Wegscheid des Oberösterreichischen Landesmuseums, Bäckermühlweg 41, 4030 Linz - T: (0732) 384585, Fax: 3845859. Head: Dr. Peter Assmann
Historical Museum 02218

Automobilhistorisches Museum, Schloß Ebelsberg, 4033 Linz - T: (0732) 42008. Head: Wolfgang Prinz zu Schaumburg-Lippe
Science&Tech Museum - 1977
Cars, motorbikes 02219

Biologiezentrum des Oberösterreichischen Landesmuseums, Johann-Wilhelm-Klein-Str 73, 4040 Linz - T: (0732) 759733, Fax: 75973399, E-mail: bio-linz@landesmuseum-linz.ac.at, Internet: http://www.biologiezentrum.at. Head: Dr. Peter Assmann, Dr. Franz Speta
Natural History Museum - 1993
Worldwide colls an botany and zoology 02220

Cowboy-Museum Fatsy, Traundorferstr 266, 4030 Linz - T: (0732) 791855, Fax: 7890491. Head: Hans-Jörg Ratzenböck
Special Museum
Hist of the life of the cowboys 02221

Diözesanmuseum Linz, Petrinumstr 12, 4020 Linz - T: (0732) 73658130, Fax: 700405, E-mail: kunstref@mail.asn-linz.ac.at, Internet: http://www.dioezese-linz.or.at/kunst. Head: Dr. Conrad Lienhardt
Religious Arts Museum - 1906 02222

Galerie der Begegnung, Verein zur Förderung zeitgenössischer Kunst, Ursulinenhof, Landstr 31, 4020 Linz - T: (0732) 774007, E-mail: CDB83@hotmail.com
Public Gallery 02223

Galerie der Mitte, Steingasse 21a, 4020 Linz - T: (0732) 797818. Head: Dr. Hans Peter Stecher
Public Gallery - 1950 02224

Galerie im Adalbert Stifter-Haus, Adalbert Stifter-Pl 1, 4020 Linz - T: (0732) 77205469, Fax: 77201786, E-mail: martin.hochleitner@ooe.gv.at, Internet: http://www.is.co.at/MuNe/iHV/StifterHaus
Public Gallery - 1992 02225

BURGMUSEUM

A-9314 Launsdorf-Hochosterwitz
Kärnten

Tel.: 04213 - 2020 und 2010
Fax: 04213 - 2020 - 16

HOCHOSTERWITZ

Kunst Raum Goethestraße, Goethestr 22, 4020 Linz - T: (0732) 651346-16, Fax: 651346-16, E-mail: kunstraum@servus.at, Internet: http://www.kunstraum.at
Public Gallery 02226

Landesgalerie Oberösterreich, Oberösterreichisches Landesmuseum, Museumstr 14, 4010 Linz - T: (0732) 77448243, Fax: 77448266, E-mail: galerie@landesgalerie.at, Internet: http://www.landesgalerie.at. Head: Dr. Peter Assmann, Martin Hochleitner
Fine Arts Museum - 1833
Upper Austrian art from 1945 to the present, colls of Alfred Kubin, Klemens Brosch, Franz Sedlacek, Arnulf Rainer a.s.o. 02227

LinzGenesis, Hauptpl 1-5, 4041 Linz - T: (0732) 70701920, Fax: 70702955, E-mail: nordico@mag.linz.at, Internet: http://www.nordico.at. Head: Dr. Willibald Katzinger
Local Museum - 1999
Development of Linz 02228

Moviemento-Art-Galerie, Centrum für Gegenwartskunst, Dametzstr 30, 4020 Linz - T: (0732) 784178, Fax: 78409040. Head: Wilhelm Schwind
Fine Arts Museum - 1989 02229

Neue Galerie der Stadt Linz, Wolfgang-Gurlitt-Museum, Blütenstr 15, 4040 Linz - T: (0732) 70703600, Fax: 736190, E-mail: Neue.Galerie@mag.linz.at, Internet: http://neuegalerie.linz.at. Head: Prof. Peter Baum
Fine Arts Museum - 1947
19th and 20th c, works by Alfred Kubin, Hrdlicka, Corinth, Liebermann, Makart, Kokoschka, Schiele, Nolde, Art Brut, photography, German expressionsm, Austrian and international contemporary art - library 02230

Nordico - Museum der Stadt Linz, Dametzstr 23, 4020 Linz - T: (0732) 70701900, Fax: 793518, E-mail: nordico@mag.linz.at, Internet: http://www.nordico.at. Head: Dr. Willibald Katzinger
Local Museum - 1974
Graphic coll (European master drawings), bequests of architects, archaeological coll 02231

Oberösterreichische Fotogalerie, Landstr 31, 4020 Linz - T: (0732) 7819120, 252923, Fax: 252923. Head: Manfred Puchner
Fine Arts Museum - 1990
archives 02232

Schlossmuseum, Oberösterreichisches Landesmuseum, Tummelpl 10, 4010 Linz - T: (0732) 774419, Fax: 77441929, E-mail: schloss@landesmuseum-linz.ac.at, Internet: http://www.schlossmuseum.at. Head: Dr. Peter Assmann, Dr. Bernhard Prokisch
Local Museum
History art, crafts, numismatics, musical instruments, folklore, arms, Museum Physikum, archaeology (reopen 2003) 02233

Vermessungskundliche Sammlung, Prunerstr 5, 4020 Linz - T: (0732) 773881, Fax: 795478. Head: Helmut Ranftl
Special Museum - 1962
Hist of maps and cartography 02234

Zoll- und Finanzgeschichtliche Sammlung, Oberösterreichisches Landesmuseum, Zollamtstr 7, 4010 Linz - T: (0732) 76052040, 76052453, Fax: 76052668, E-mail: b.prokisch@landesmuseum-linz.ac.at, Internet: http://www.schlossmuseum.at. Head: Dr. Bernhard Prokisch
Special Museum - 1950
Hist of the Upper Austrian customs office 02235

Litschau

Heimatmuseum, Stadtpl 21, 3874 Litschau - T: (02865) 5385, 5521, Fax: 538514, E-mail: info.litschau@wvnet.at, Internet: http://www.tiscover.com/litschau
Local Museum - 1987 02236

Litzelsdorf

Heimathaus Litzelsdorf, Obere Bergen 108, 7532 Litzelsdorf - T: (03358) 2234, Fax: 2235
Local Museum - 1983
Peasant life 02237

Lockenhaus

Burgenländisches Schulmuseum, Hauptstr 29, 7442 Lockenhaus - T: (02616) 2051
Special Museum - 1985 02238

Paul Anton Keller-Museum, Burg Lockenhaus, 7442 Lockenhaus - T: (02616) 2394, Fax: 239480, E-mail: burg.lockenhaus@wellcom.at, Internet: http://www.tiscover.com/burg.hotel.lockenhaus. Head: Eugen Horvath
Special Museum / Historical Museum / Historic Site - 1980 02239

Lölling

Heimatmuseum Lölling, Schattseite 1, 9335 Lölling - T: (04263) 724, Fax: 724
Local Museum - 1996 02240

Schmiedemuseum, Graben 6, 9335 Lölling - T: (04263) 407
Science&Tech Museum 02241

Lohnsburg

Heimatmuseum am Kobernaußerwald, Nr 28, 4923 Lohnsburg - T: (07754) 4110, Fax: 411085
Local Museum 02242

Loosdorf, Bez. Melk

Schloß Schallaburg, Schallaburg 1, 3382 Loosdorf, Bez. Melk - T: (02754) 63170, Fax: 631755, E-mail: office@schallaburg.at, Internet: http://www.schallaburg.at. Head: Franz Strohmaier
Fine Arts Museum 02243

Spielzeugmuseum, Schallaburg 1, 3382 Loosdorf, Bez. Melk - T: (02754) 63170, Fax: 631755, E-mail: office@schallaburg.at, Internet: http://www.schallaburg.at. Head: Franz Strohmaier
Special Museum
Toys 02244

Loosdorf, Bez. Mistelbach

Schloß Loosdorf mit Prunkräumen und Zinnfigurensammlung, Nr 1, 2133 Loosdorf, Bez. Mistelbach - T: (02524) 822217, Fax: 822219, E-mail: verena.piatti@nanet.at, Internet: http://www.schloss-loosdorf.at. Head: Verena Piatti
Special Museum / Decorative Arts Museum / Fine Arts Museum - 1960 02245

Losenstein

Heimatmuseum Losenstein, Eisenstr 45, 4460 Losenstein - T: (07255) 60000, Fax: 600020, E-mail: gemeinde.losenstein@gemeinde-losenstein.at, Internet: http://gemeinde-losenstein.at
Local Museum - 1998 02246

Ludesch

Volkskundliche Sammlung alter bäuerlicher Geräte, Volksschule, Kirchstr 19, 6713 Ludesch - T: (05550) 3160, Fax: 3160, E-mail: vs.ludesch@cable.vol.at. Head: Christine Streitberger
Agriculture Museum - 1968 02247

Lunz

Heimatmuseum im Amonhaus, Amonstr 16, 3293 Lunz - T: (07486) 80810, Fax: 808120, E-mail: info@lunz.at
Local Museum - 1914
Prehistory, wrought iron, folklore, natural hist, coal mining 02248

Lustenau

Galerie Stephanie Hollenstein, Pontenstr 20, 6890 Lustenau - T: (05577) 8181301, Fax: 86868, E-mail: w.oberfrank@lustenau.at, Internet: http://www.lustenau.at. Head: Wilhelm Oberfrank
Fine Arts Museum - 1971 02249

Mailberg

Malteser-Museum Mailberg, Schloß Mailberg, 2024 Mailberg - T: (02943) 2251, Fax: 2251. Head: Robert Hofferer
Historical Museum - 1975
Hist of Order of the Knights of Malta 02250

Malta

Bauernmöbelmuseum Propstkeusche, 9854 Malta - T: (04732) 3183
Decorative Arts Museum - 1989 02251

Mank

Heimatmuseum, Hauptpl 3, 3240 Mank - T: (02755) 2782
Local Museum
Crafts, agricultural tools 02252

Mannersdorf

Edmund Adler-Galerie, Sommereiner Str 35, 2452 Mannersdorf - T: (02168) 20534. Head: Rosa Adler
Public Gallery 02253

Museum Mannersdorf, Jägerzeile 9, 2452 Mannersdorf - T: (02168) 62680, Internet: http://www.noel.gv.at/service/k/k1/museen. Head: Heribert Schutzbier
Local Museum - 1979
Archaeology, minerals, folk art, stone mason technics 02254

Marchegg

Heimatmuseum, Schloß, 2293 Marchegg - T: (02285) 64165
Local Museum - 1984
Folklore, archaeology, toys, aeronautics 02255

Niederösterreichisches Landesjagdmuseum und Afrikamuseum (closed) 02256

Maria Enzersdorf am Gebirge

Wallfahrtsmuseum, Franziskanerkloster, Hauptstr 5, 2344 Maria Enzersdorf am Gebirge - T: (02236) 2253116, 29830, Fax: 225314, E-mail: pfarre-ma.enzersdorf@netway.at. Head: Thomas Lackner
Religious Arts Museum 02257

Maria Laach am Jauerling

Kräutermuseum - Naturpark Jauerling Wachau, Hoch Jauerling, 3620 Maria Laach am Jauerling - T: (02713) 2406
Natural History Museum - 1986
Local herbs, mushrooms 02258

Maria Luggau

Alte Wassermühlen und Museum Des Bauern Sach und Zeug, Trattenbach 15, Oberluggau, 9655 Maria Luggau - T: (04716) 269, Fax: 269. Head: Leopold Lugger
Agriculture Museum - 1970 02259

Maria Saal

Kärntner Freilichtmuseum, Dompl 3, 9063 Maria Saal - T: (04223) 31660, 2812, Fax: 316620, E-mail: freilichtmuseum-mariasaal@aon.at, Internet: http://www.freilichtmuseum-mariasaal.at. Head: Dr. Johann Schwertner
Open Air Museum - 1952
Carinthian farm houses and interiors, peasant furniture (16th-19th c) 02260

Maria Schmolln

Bauernmuseum Sollinger-Bauer, Sollach 1, 5241 Maria Schmolln - T: (07743) 2430
Agriculture Museum
Agricultural and trade implements, tools 02261

Maria Schutz am Semmering

Schatzkammer der Wallfahrtskirche Maria Schutz, Passionistenkloster, Göstritz 4, 2642 Maria Schutz am Semmering - T: (02663) 8208, Fax: 920116
Religious Arts Museum
Treasure chamber 02262

Maria Taferl

Volksschulmuseum, Nr. 32, 3672 Maria Taferl - T: (07413) 7040, 266, Fax: 704014, E-mail: gde.mariataferl@wvnet.at, Internet: http://www.mariataferl.at. Head: Gertrude Feyertag
Historical Museum - 1994 02263

Wallfahrtsmuseum, Basilika, 3672 Maria Taferl - T: (07413) 2780. Head: Helmut Hofmann
Religious Arts Museum
Religious art, Baroque wall and ceiling painting 02264

Mariazell

Heimathaus mit Photographiemuseum, Wiener Str 35, 8630 Mariazell - T: (03882) 2366, 224531, Fax: 3245, E-mail: heimathaus@mariazell.at
Local Museum - 1973
Peasant furniture and household utensils, votive offerings, glass paintings, prayer books and other items of religious folk art, decorative cast iron works, crafts 02265

Österreichisches Straßenbahn- und Lokalbahnbetriebsmuseum, Museumstramway Mariazell-Erlaufsee, An der Museumsbahn 5, 8630 Mariazell - T: (03882) 3014, Fax: 3393, E-mail: mt-eisenbahn@nextra.at, Internet: http://www.mt-eisenbahn.at. Head: Alfred Fleissner
Science&Tech Museum
100 vehicles, oldest steam tramway engine 02266

Schatzkammern, Galerien und Reliquienkammer der Wallfahrtsbasilika Mariazell, Kardinal-Eugene-Tisserant-Pl 1, 8630 Mariazell - T: (03882) 25950/60, Fax: 259520. Head: Karl Schauer
Religious Arts Museum / Folklore Museum 02267

Markt Piesting

Heimatmuseum Markt Piesting, Marktpl 1, 2753 Markt Piesting - T: (02633) 422410, Fax: 4224122, E-mail: piesting@netway.at, Internet: http://www.piesting.at
Local Museum - 1996 02268

Museum in der Gaststätte Scherrerwirt, Gaststätte Scherrerwirt, Dreistätten, 2753 Markt Piesting - T: (02633) 2590. Head: Franz Hager
Local Museum - 1888 02269

Mathon

Paznauner Bauernmuseum, Haus Nr 12, 6562 Mathon - T: (05444) 5931, Fax: 20013, E-mail: ischgel@restaurant-walserstube.at, Internet: http://www.restaurant-walserstube.at. Head: Elmar Kurz
Agriculture Museum 02270

Matrei in Osttirol

Heimatkundliches Museum Medaria, Rathaus, 9971 Matrei in Osttirol - T: (04875) 680528
Local Museum 02271

Mattersburg

Artbox, Wulkalände 2, 7210 Mattersburg - T: (02626) 62096, Fax: 65019, E-mail: mattersburg@bgld-kulturzentren.at, Internet: http://bgld-kulturzentren.at. Head: Dr. Josef Wiedenhofer
Public Gallery 02272

Mattighofen

Zinngießerhäusl, Stadtpl 8a, 5230 Mattighofen - T: (07742) 2285. Head: Dr. Thomas Steidl
Local Museum
Pewtery and pewterware 02273

Mattsee

Stiftsmuseum, Seestr 2, 5163 Mattsee - T: (06217) 52020, Fax: 520224, E-mail: office@stiftmattsee.at, Internet: htp://www.stiftmattsee.at. Head: Vinzenz Baldemair
Religious Arts Museum - 1977
library 02274

Mautern in Steiermark

Heimatmuseum, Mooswiese 11, 8774 Mautern in Steiermark - T: (03845) 2469
Local Museum - 1976
Agricultural tools, archaeology, minerals 02275

Mautern, Niederösterreich

Römermuseum, Schloßgasse 12, 3512 Mautern, Niederösterreich - T: (02732) 81155, 83151, Fax: 8315112, E-mail: stadtgemeinde@mautern.at, Internet: http://www.mautern.at. Head: Werner Kristament
Archaeological Museum - 1961
Roman finds 02276

Mauterndorf

Lungauer Landschaftsmuseum, Lungau, Burg, 5570 Mauterndorf - T: (06472) 7425, 7393, Fax: 7425, E-mail: helga.gappmayer@iclz.surfnet.at. Head: Helga Gappmayer
Natural History Museum / Local Museum - 1971
Local landscape, flora, fauna, mineralogy 02277

Sammlungen Schloß Moosham, 5570 Mauterndorf - T: (06476) 305. Head: Alexander Wilezek
Fine Arts Museum - 1886
Painting, sculpture, frescoes, faience, antique stoves, arms and armour, local folk and decorative arts 02278

Mauthausen

Heimatmuseum Schloß Pragstein, Rathausstr 2, 4310 Mauthausen - T: (07238) 2228, Fax: 22284
Local Museum - 1910
Local hist, early and prehist, shipping 02279

KZ-Gedenkstätte Mauthausen, Erinnerungsstr 1, 4310 Mauthausen - T: (07238) 22690, Fax: 226940, E-mail: mauthausen-memorial@mail.bmi.gv.at, Internet: http://www.mauthausen-memorial.gv.at
Historical Museum / Historic Site - 1948
History of the concentration camp Mauthausen, resistance and persecution in the Third Reich 02280

Prof. Gerstmayr-Museum, Vormarktstr 13, 4310 Mauthausen - T: (07238) 2255, 3916, Fax: 225530
Special Museum
Steel cutting by Prof. Hans Gerstmayr, granite processing 02281

Melk

Heimatmuseum, Linzer Str 3-5, 3390 Melk - T: (02752) 2307
Local Museum - 1958
Prehistory 02282

Stift Melk, Stiftsmuseum, Dietmayrstr 1, 3390 Melk - T: (02752) 52312-232, Fax: 52312-249, E-mail: kultur.tourismus@stiftmelk.at, Internet: http://www.stiftmelk.at. Head: Martin P. Rotheneder
Religious Arts Museum - 1960
Medieval and Baroque religious art and crafts - library 02283

Michaelbeuern

Klostersammlung der Benediktinerabtei, Stift, 5152 Michaelbeuern - T: (06274) 81162017, Fax: 81161003, E-mail: museum@abtei-michaelbeuern.at, Internet: http://www.abtei-michaelbeuern.at. Head: Berthold Egelseder
Religious Arts Museum - 1957
Religious and folk art, including paintings and sculpture by Austrian Baroque artists, clocks, porcelain, glass and pewter - library 02284

Micheldorf

Oberösterreichisches Sensen-Schmiede-Museum, Gradnstr 10, 4563 Micheldorf - T: (07582) 3407, Fax: 521106, E-mail: wir@serafin.at, Internet: http://www.serafin.at
Open Air Museum / Special Museum
Scythe forging, wellnes, recreatien 02285

Michelhausen

Heimatmuseum Michelhausen, Tullner Str 16, 3451 Michelhausen - T: (02275) 5241, Fax: 6107
Local Museum - 1993 02286

Leopold Figl-Museum, Rust im Tullnerfeld 55, 3451 Michelhausen - T: (02275) 5241, Fax: 524120, E-mail: gemeinde.michaelhausen@michaelhausen.at, Internet: http://www.michaelhausen.at
Special Museum - 1984
Life of Austrian politician Leopold Figl 02287

Miesenbach

Gauermann-Museum, Scheuchenstein 127, 2761 Miesenbach - T: (02632) 8267, Fax: 82353. Head: Helmut Weissenberger
Fine Arts Museum - 1976 02288

Millstatt

Heimat-Museum, Altes Schulhaus, Obermillstatt 7, 9872 Millstatt - T: (04766) 2263, Fax: 3637
Local Museum - 1990 02289

Stiftsmuseum, Stiftgasse 1, 9872 Millstatt - T: (06246) 75035, Fax: 75035. Head: Dr. Franz Nikolasch
Religious Arts Museum / Fine Arts Museum - 1980
Minerals, history of Millstatt, Order of the Knights of St. George 02290

Mistelbach an der Zaya

Aktion Museum M, Museumsgasse 4, 2130 Mistelbach an der Zaya - T: (02572) 3844, Fax: 38443, E-mail: kulturbund@utanet.at. Head: Dr. Franz Schwelle
Local Museum - 1980
Local hist 02291

Blau-gelbe Viertelsgalerie Niederösterreich, Weinviertel, Barockschlößl, Museumgasse 4, 2130 Mistelbach an der Zaya - T: (02572) 3844, Fax: 384433, E-mail: kulturbund@utanet.at. Head: Ferdinand Altmann
Association with Coll - 1988 02292

Puppentheatermuseum, Franz-Josef-Str 43, 2130 Mistelbach an der Zaya - T: (02572) 2515253, Fax: 2515217, E-mail: helga.ruso@mistelbach.noe.gv.at, Internet: http://www.nanet.at/mistelbach/
Special Museum - 1997 02293

Mitterkirchen

Urgeschichtliches Freilichtmuseum Keltendorf Mitterkirchen, Lehen, 4343 Mitterkirchen - T: (07269) 6611, 82550, Fax: 825525, E-mail: -Marktgemeindeamt.Mitterkirchen@vpn.at, Internet: http://www.mitterkirchen.at. Head: Josef Riesenberger
Open Air Museum / Archaeological Museum - 1991
Reconstructed village site from the Hallstatt period, barrow, pottery, bakery 02294

Mitterndorf an der Fischa

Automobil- und Motorradmuseum Austria, Heinrich Löri-Gasse 1, 2441 Mitterndorf an der Fischa - T: (02234) 79600, Fax: 79666, E-mail: museum@oldtimertreff.com, Internet: http://www.oldtimertreff.com. Head: Dr. Jackob Barnea
Science&Tech Museum - 1997
Motor cars 02295

Mittersill

Nationalparkmuseum, Im Felberturm, 5730 Mittersill - T: (06562) 4444. Head: Hans Brennsteiner
Natural History Museum - 1960
Farm and country culture, including tools, furniture and domestic utensils, minerals, crafts, skiing exhibit, local and regional history 02296

Mödling

Anton Wildgans-Haus, Anton-Wildgans-Weg 4, 2340 Mödling - T: (02236) 23433, Fax: 23433. Head: Gottfried Wildgans, Ilse Wildgans
Special Museum - 1934
Memorabilia of the poet Anton Wildgans 02297

Galerie Sala Terrena, Pfarrgasse 9, 2340 Mödling - T: (02236) 40021, Fax: 23373. Head: Jörg Miggitsch
Fine Arts Museum - 1980 02298

Missions-Ethnographisches Museum St. Gabriel, Gabrieler Str 171, 2340 Mödling - T: (02236) 803221, Fax: 8034, E-mail: hochschule.stgabriel@steyler.at, Internet: http://www.steyler.at. Head: Prof. Dr. Andreas Bsteh
Ethnology Museum / Religious Arts Museum - 1909
Artefacts from Papua New Guinea 02299

Mödlinger Stadtverkehrsmuseum, Thomas-Tamussino-Str 3, 2340 Mödling - T: (02236) 46375. Head: Peter Standenat
Science&Tech Museum
Public traffic 02300

Museum der Stadt Mödling, Josef-Deutsch-Pl 2, 2340 Mödling - T: (02236) 24159, Fax: 24159, E-mail: museum.moedling@i-one.at, Internet: http://www.moedling.at.tf. Head: Dr. Walter Chiba
Local Museum - 1904
Artefacts from local Avarian burial site, botanical and mineralogical coll, local hist (from prehistory to the 19th c) - library, archive, Beethoven-Gedenkstätte Hauptstr 79 02301

Schönberg-Haus in Mödling, Bernhardgasse 6, 2340 Mödling - T: (02236) 42223, Fax: (01) 712188888, E-mail: office@schoenberg.at, Internet: http://www.schoenberg.at. Head: Dr. Christian Meyer
Music Museum - 1974
Apartment where the composer lived between 1918 and 1925, permanent exhibition presents his furniture, musical instruments, manuscripts 02302

Volkskundemuseum, Klostergasse 16, 2340 Mödling - T: (02236) 48759, Fax: 24159, E-mail: museum.moedling@i-one.at, Internet: http://www.museum.moedling.at.tf. Head: Gudrun Foelsche
Folklore Museum - 1984
Folklore, agriculture, viticulture, smithy, garden 02303

Möllersdorf

Stadtmuseum Traiskirchen, Wolfstr 18, 2513 Möllersdorf - T: (02252) 52611, Fax: 56924. Head: Franz Schlögl
Local Museum - 1987
Vehicles, viticulture, cap coll 02304

Mönchhof

Dorfmuseum Mönchhof, Bahngasse 62, 7123 Mönchhof - T: (02173) 80642
Agriculture Museum - 1990
Agricultural tools 02305

Mörbisch

Heimathaus Mörbisch, Hauptstr 55, 7072 Mörbisch - T: (02682) 62652, Fax: 62715, E-mail: bgld.lm@aon.at
Local Museum - 1972
Local ethnography 02306

Mogersdorf

Kreuzstadelmuseum, Türkenschlacht-Gedenkraum, Nr 77, 8382 Mogersdorf - T: (03325) 8200, 8217, Fax: 8766, E-mail: post@mogersdorf.bgld.gv.at, Internet: http://www.mogersdorf.at. Head: Gerhard Granitz
Historical Museum - 1975
Battle of Mogersdorf (1664) 02307

Mondsee

Freilichtmuseum Mondseer Rauchhaus, Hilfbergstr 7, 5310 Mondsee - T: (06232) 2270. Head: Prof. Dr. Walter Kunze
Open Air Museum - 1960
Renovated historic smokehouse and other buildings, peasant furnishings, tools and implements 02308

Österreichisches Pfahlbaummuseum und Museum Mondseeland, Marschall-von-Wrede-Pl 1, 5310 Mondsee - T: (06232) 2270. Head: Prof. Dr. Walter Kunze
Local Museum / Archaeological Museum - 1953/1981
Early local history, art works from the Mondsee monastery, folk art, book illumination, costume coll, hunting coll, young stone age (pole constructions) 02309

Salzkammergut-Lokalbahn-Museum, Seebadstr 2, 5310 Mondsee - T: (06232) 2270, 4270, Fax: 4470. Head: August Zopf
Science&Tech Museum - 1996
Hist of the narrow-gauge railway that linked up Salzburg with Bad Ischl until 1957, locomotives, wagons, model railway etc. 02310

Schloßgalerie Mondseeland, Schloßhof 5, 5310 Mondsee - T: (06232) 7744, Fax: 7711, E-mail: info@schlossgalerie.at, Internet: http://www.schlossgalerie.at. Head: Dr. Peter Bönsch
Public Gallery - 1998 02311

Mühlbach am Hochkönig

Bergbaumuseum, Nr 203, 5505 Mühlbach am Hochkönig - T: (0676) 7733182, Fax: 720918, 781018, E-mail: museum.muehlbach@sbg.at. Head: Heinz Gottfried
Science&Tech Museum - 1980 02312

Mühlbach am Mannhartsberg

Joseph Misson-Gedenkstätte, Nr 23, 3473 Mühlbach am Mannhartsberg - T: (02272) 6268633. Head: Judith Prillinger
Special Museum - 1953 02313

Mühlen

Prähistorische Privatsammlung, Noreia 23, 8822 Mühlen - T: (03586) 388. Head: Herwig Walzer
Archaeological Museum 02314

Mürzzuschlag

Bergbaumuseum Heilige Barbara, Wiener Str 80, 8680 Mürzzuschlag - T: (03852) 3579
Science&Tech Museum 02315

Internationales Wintersport- und Heimatmuseum, Wiener Str 79, 8680 Mürzzuschlag - T: (03852) 3504, Fax: 3504, E-mail: int.wintersportmuseum@netway.at
Special Museum - 1946
History and development of winter sports, farm implements, folklore - archive 02316

Johannes Brahms-Museum, Wiener Str 4, 8680 Mürzzuschlag - T: (03852) 3434, Fax: 3434, E-mail: brahms.museum@netway.at, Internet: http://www.brahmsmuseum.at. Head: Elisabeth Fuchs, Ronald Fuchs
Special Museum - 1991 02317

Kunsthaus Mürzzuschlag, Wiener Str 54-56, 8680 Mürzzuschlag - T: (03852) 56200, Fax: 56209, E-mail: kunst@kunsthausmuerz.at. Head: Ursula Horvath
Fine Arts Museum 02318

Murau

Eisenmuseum, Schloßberg 1, 8850 Murau - T: (03532) 23020, Fax: 230222, E-mail: schwarzenberg-murau@aon.at. Head: Heike Kellner
Science&Tech Museum - 1957
Local iron ore mining and heavy industry 02319

Evangelisches Diözesanmuseum, Evang. Elisabethkirche, Marktpl 4, 8850 Murau - T: (03532) 3380, Fax: 3380
Religious Arts Museum - 1981 02320

Heimatmuseum der Stadt Murau, Kapuzinerkloster, Grazer Str 19, 8850 Murau - T: (03532) 222810, Fax: 222810
Local Museum 02321

Mureck

Heimatmuseum, Hauptpl 29, 8480 Mureck - T: (03472) 210523, Fax: 21056, E-mail: k.baeck@mureck.steiermark.at
Local Museum
Local hist, trade, crafts 02322

Nagelberg

Glasmuseum Zalto, Neu-Nagelberg 58, 3871 Nagelberg - T: (02859) 72370, Fax: 72374, E-mail: glasstudio.zalto@wvnet.at
Decorative Arts Museum 02323

Sammlung der Neuen Stölzle Kristall, Alt-Nagelberg 45, 3871 Nagelberg - T: (02859) 75310, Fax: 753153
Science&Tech Museum 02324

Nassereith

Fastnachtmuseum, Sachsengasse 81a, 6465 Nassereith - T: (05265) 52120, Fax: 521216. Head: Ludwig Thurner
Folklore Museum / Fine Arts Museum - 1947
Carnival exhibits, bear group, larvas from the painter and sculptor Kranewitter 02325

Naßwald

Huebmer-Gedächtnisstätte, 2661 Naßwald - T: (02667) 7220, 238, 7256. Head: Josef Flug
Folklore Museum 02326

Nauders

Schloß Naudersberg, 6543 Nauders - T: (05473) 87242, 87252, Fax: 8725260. Head: Ludwig Thoma
Historical Museum - 1980
Trespassing of Reschenpass, judiciary 02327

Neuberg an der Mürz

Museum Kaiser Franz Joseph I. und die Jagd, Jagdschloß, Hauptstr 13, 8692 Neuberg an der Mürz - T: (03857) 8182, Fax: 820274, E-mail: marktgemeinde@neuberg.at, Internet: http://www.neuberg.at
Historical Museum / Fine Arts Museum - 1990 02328

Naturmuseum, Sammlung Schliefsteiner, Kaplanweg 11, 8692 Neuberg an der Mürz - T: (03857) 8774, 8890, Fax: 8890. Head: Herbert Schliefsteiner
Natural History Museum - 1966
European insects and birds, watercolours, oil paintings 02329

Neufelden

Heimathaus Neufelden, Leinengasse 2, 4120 Neufelden - T: (07282) 6255
Local Museum - 1983
Everyday life objects, smithy, pharmacy 02330

Neuhofen an der Ybbs

Ostarrichi-Kulturhof, Nr 130, 3364 Neuhofen an der Ybbs - T: (07475) 590650, Fax: 5906520, E-mail: office@ostarrichi-kulturhof.at, Internet: http://www.ostarrichi-kulturhof.at
Historical Museum - 1980
Ostarrichi document from 996 02331

Neukirchen am Großvenediger

Tauriska-Galerie, Leopold Kohr Akademie, Kammerlanderstall, Nr 15a, 5741 Neukirchen am Großvenediger - T: (06565) 6145, Fax: 6794, E-mail: office@tauriska.at, Internet: http://www.tauriska.at. Head: Susanna Vötter-Dankl
Local Museum - 1986 02332

Neukirchen an der Vöckla

Freilichtmuseum Stehrerhof - Dreschmaschinenmuseum, Haid 7, 4872 Neukirchen an der Vöckla - T: (07682) 7033, 7017, Fax: 703420, E-mail: stehrerhof@netway.at, Internet: http://www.stehrerhof.at. Head: Johann Pillichshammer
Open Air Museum / Agriculture Museum - 1978
Agricultural tools and machinery, threshing machines 02333

Neukirchen bei Altmünster

Heimathaus Neukirchen, Kapellenweg, 4814 Neukirchen bei Altmünster - T: (07618) 238
Local Museum
Hist of farm life 02334

Neulengbach

Heimatmuseum und Schiele Museum, Gerichtsgebäude, 3040 Neulengbach - T: (02772) 5210552, Fax: 5210555, E-mail: ilomuhr@neulengbach.com, Internet: http://www.neulengbach.com
Local Museum - 1960
Local hist 02335

Neumarkt am Wallersee

Heimatmuseum Feuerwehrzeugstätte, Hauptstr 10, 5202 Neumarkt am Wallersee - T: (06216) 5704
Science&Tech Museum - 1984 02336

Neumarkt im Mühlkreis

Mostmuseum, Trosselsdorf 9, 4212 Neumarkt im Mühlkreis - T: (07941) 8217. Head: Martin Miesenberger
Special Museum - 1994
Stone fruit press and must production 02337

Neumarkt in Steiermark

Bergbaumuseum Pöllau, 8820 Neumarkt in Steiermark - T: (03584) 2554
Science&Tech Museum 02338

Novum Forum, Schulgasse, 8820 Neumarkt in Steiermark - T: (03584) 2005, Fax: 2126. Head: Matth. Edlinger
Decorative Arts Museum - 1996
Old cups and mugs - Schule-Häferl 02339

Neunkirchen, Niederösterreich

Heimatmuseum der Stadt Neunkirchen, Dr.-Emil-Stockhammer-Gasse 13, 2620 Neunkirchen, Niederösterreich - T: (02635) 61147, 62324, Fax: 62324
Local Museum - 1910
Local hist, religious art, folk art 02340

Motorradmuseum, Pernersdorfer Str 6, 2620 Neunkirchen, Niederösterreich - T: (02635) 62364. Head: Walter Schuh
Science&Tech Museum - 1980 02341

Neupölla

Erstes Österreichisches Museum für Alltagsgeschichte, Nr 10, 3593 Neupölla - T: (02988) 6220, Fax: 6220-4, E-mail: gemeinde.poella@wvnet.at, Internet: http://www.regionalberatung.at/museum
Folklore Museum - 1997 02342

Neusiedl am See

Pannonisches Heimatmuseum, Kasernengasse 40, 7100 Neusiedl am See - T: (02167) 8173, 2229
Local Museum - 1981
Local hist, handicraft 02343

Neusiedl an der Zaya

Erdölmuseum, Erholungszentrum, Bahnstr, 2183 Neusiedl an der Zaya - T: (02533) 255
Special Museum - 1980 02344

Niederleis

Heimatmuseum, Hauptstr 153, 2116 Niederleis - T: (02576) 2228, Fax: 2345
Local Museum - 1977
Local postal hist, vehicles (photo documentation) 02345

Schloßmuseum Niederleis, Schloß, 2116 Niederleis - T: (02576) 3184, Fax: 318431, E-mail: office@schaffgotsch.at. Head: Marie-Elise Gräfin Schaffgotsch
Fine Arts Museum - 1964
Sculpture, painting, tapestries, faience, glass, etc in Renaissance moated castle 02346

Niederndorf

Heimatmuseum, Nr 37, 6342 Niederndorf - T: (05373) 61296, Fax: 612966
Local Museum - 1981 02347

Niedersulz

Weinviertler Museumsdorf, 2224 Niedersulz - T: (02534) 333, Fax: 33320, E-mail: museumsdorf@xpoint.at, Internet: http://www.museumsdorf.at. Head: Josef Geissler
Open Air Museum - 1979
Crafts, furniture, religious art, textiles, vinotheque 02348

Niederwaldkirchen

Prof. Eidenberger-Museum, Nr 76, 4174 Niederwaldkirchen - T: (07231) 252713, Fax: 25274, E-mail: kapfer@netway.at. Head: Otto Kapfer
Fine Arts Museum - 1994
Landscape painting, copper engravings and etchings by Josef Eidenberger 02349

Nikitsch

Dorfmuseum, Hauptstr 25, 7302 Nikitsch - T: (02614) 8314, Fax: 83144
Agriculture Museum / Local Museum - 1981
Agricultural tools, ceramics 02350

Nötsch im Gailtal

Museum des Nötscher Kreises, Haus Wiegele, Nr 39, 9611 Nötsch im Gailtal - T: (04256) 3664, Fax: 29069, E-mail: office@noetscherkreis.at, Internet: http://www.noetscherkreis.at. Head: Dr. Otmar Rychlik
Fine Arts Museum - 1998 02351

Obdach

Heimatmuseum Obdach, 8742 Obdach - T: (03578) 202
Local Museum 02352

Oberdrauburg

Oberkärntner Brauchtums- und Maskenmuseum, Marktstr 3, 9781 Oberdrauburg - T: (04710) 2001, 2695. Head: Franz Jochum
Folklore Museum / Local Museum - 1990
Wooden masks, folklore 02353

Oberhofen

Heimatmuseum, Haus Nr. 202, 6405 Oberhofen - T: (05262) 6274720, Fax: 6274717, E-mail: gemeinde-oberhofen@tira.com
Local Museum - 1986
Agriculture, folklore 02354

Oberlienz

Freilichtmuseum Oberlienz, 9900 Oberlienz - T: (04852) 3475, 64488. Head: Dr. Lois Ebner
Open Air Museum - 1964 02355

Obernberg am Inn

Heimathaus Obernberg am Inn, Marktpl 22, 4982 Obernberg am Inn - T: (07758) 223525, 2255
Local Museum - 1927
Local hist, agriculture, ethnography, crafts, rafting and shipping 02356

Oberndorf bei Salzburg

Georg Rendl-Museum, Au 10, Sankt Georgen, 5110 Oberndorf bei Salzburg - T: (06272) 29290, Fax: 292978. Head: Josef Erbschwendtner
Special Museum
Memorabilia of the poet Rendl 02357

Stille-Nacht- und Heimatmuseum Bruckmannhaus, Stille-Nacht-Pl 7, 5110 Oberndorf bei Salzburg - T: (0676) 6375219, Fax: (06272) 44224, E-mail: stillenacht.oberndorf@gmx.at, Internet: http://www.oberndorf.co.at/museum. Head: Manfred W.K. Fischer
Local Museum / Historical Museum / Special Museum - 1960
Local and regional hist, hist of the Christmas carol "Silent Night, Holy Night", Salzach river navigation - library, archive 02358

Oberneukirchen

Schnopfhagen-Stüberl, Marktpl 43, 4181 Oberneukirchen - T: (07212) 7197. Head: Karl Weichselbaum
Music Museum
Memorabilia of the composer of the Upper Austrian antheme, Hans Schnopfhagen, musical instruments 02359

Oberperfuss

Peter Anich-Museum, Schulhaus, 6173 Oberperfuss - T: (05232) 81313. Head: Dr. Ernst Madersbacher
Special Museum - 1906
Memorabilia of the cartographers Peter Anich and Blasius Heuber, astronomical instruments, maps and globes 02360

Oberpullendorf

Ur- und frühgeschichtliche Eisenindustrie im Bezirk Oberpullendorf - Schauraum, Hauptstr 9, 7350 Oberpullendorf - T: (02612) 42207, Fax: 4220710, E-mail: post@oberpullendorf.bgld.gv.at, Internet: http://www.burgenland.at. Head: Dr. Gerald Schlag
Science&Tech Museum - 1975 02361

Obertilliach

Bäuerliche Sammlung, Dorf 1, 9942 Obertilliach - T: (04847) 5202. Head: Theresia Weilter
Agriculture Museum 02362

Obertraun

Höhlenmuseum, Winkl 14, 4831 Obertraun - T: (06134) 84001830, Fax: 84004343, E-mail: s.gamsjaeger@oebf.at, Internet: http://www.dachsteinregion.at. Head: Siegfried Gamsjäger
Natural History Museum - 1984
Ice caves 02363

Obertrum am See

Heimatmuseum, Kirchstättstr 23, 5162 Obertrum am See - T: (06219) 6582, 6305, Fax: 6582
Local Museum - 1982
Farming implements, tools 02364

Oberwölbling

Robert Hytha-Museum, Internationales Sonder-Museum Wildtiere der Welt, Landersdorf 47, 3124 Oberwölbling - T: (02786) 2420. Head: Prof. Dr. Robert K. Hytha
Natural History Museum - 1980
Behaviourism, Asian and African mammals, insects, minerals, mollusks, shells 02365

Oberwölz

Stadtmuseum Oberwölz, Vorstadt 49, 8832 Oberwölz - T: (03581) 324. Head: Herta Haas
Local Museum - 1946
Exhibits from the times of the reign of the bishops of Freising 02366

Oberzeiring

Historische Silbergruben - Schaubergwerk und Museum, Münzgasse 1, 8762 Oberzeiring - T: (03571) 2979, 2811
Science&Tech Museum - 1958
Reconstructed 13th c silver mine, history of mining, minerals, folklore 02367

Tabakmuseum, Hauptstr 17, 8762 Oberzeiring - T: (03571) 2891, 891308
Special Museum - 1987
Pipes, tobacco industry 02368

Oetz

Galerie zum alten Ötztal, Piburger Str 4, 6433 Oetz - T: (05252) 6485. Head: Hans Jäger
Local Museum - 1980
Art, local hist 02369

Offenhausen

Paläontologisches Museum, Schloß Würting, 4625 Offenhausen - T: (07247) 6232, E-mail: - claudia.nessizius@aon.at. Head: Dr. Herbert Schaffer
Natural History Museum - 1975
Fossils, paleontology, minerals 02370

Ort im Innkreis

Bauernmuseum Osternach, Osternach 18, 4974 Ort im Innkreis - T: (07751) 414
Agriculture Museum
Agricultural tools and machinery, cart smithy 02371

Orth an der Donau

Heimat- und Bienenzuchtmuseum, Schloßpl 1, 2304 Orth an der Donau - T: (02212) 2555, Fax: 2208/17, E-mail: info@orth.at, Internet: http://www.orth.at
Local Museum / Agriculture Museum - 1957
Local and regional history, domestic utensils, weapons, natural history, development of bee keeping in Austria from earliest times to present 02372

Österreichisches Donau- und Fischereimuseum, Schloßpl 1, 2304 Orth an der Donau - T: (02212) 2555, Fax: 220817, E-mail: info@orth.at, Internet: http://www.orth.at
Special Museum - 1961
Development of international fresh water and deep sea fishing industry, local fishes and fishing, fresh water aquarium 02373

Ostermiething

Gotischer Freskenraum, Bezirksalten- und Pflegeheim, 5121 Ostermiething - T: (06278) 222. Head: Josef Maier
Fine Arts Museum 02374

Privatsammlung Hermine Brandstetter, Timmelkamer Str 42, 5121 Ostermiething - T: (06278) 7216
Special Museum
35.000 different lighters and other colls 02375

Pabneukirchen

Heimatmuseum Pabneukirchen, Markt 16, 4363 Pabneukirchen - T: (07265) 5245, Fax: 5720
Local Museum
Agricultural implements, documents, scripts, sacral objects 02376

Passail

Heimatmuseum Arzberg, Arzberg 16, 8162 Passail - T: (03179) 23277
Local Museum
Folklore 02377

Payerbach

Kunststätte Kuenburg, Karl-Feldbacher-Str 4-8, 2650 Payerbach - T: (02666) 53135, Fax: 53135, E-mail: p.fischer@magnet.at, Internet: http://members.magnet.at/p.fischer. Head: Hanspeter Stein
Public Gallery - 1994 02378

Schaubergwerk Grillenberg, Hauptstr 20, 2650 Payerbach - T: (02666) 52611, Fax: 52930, E-mail: geoinert.umwelttechnik@netway.at
Science&Tech Museum - 1996 02379

Peggau

Höhlenmuseum in der Lurgrotte, Lurgrottenstr 1, 8120 Peggau - T: (03127) 2580, Fax: 2580, E-mail: lurgrotte.peggau@networld.at, Internet: http://Lurgrotte-Peggau.networld.at
Natural History Museum - 1894
Paleontology, mineralogy 02380

Penk

Fotohistorische Sammlung, Nr 65, 9816 Penk - T: (04762) 2464, Fax: 2464, Internet: http://www.kinogeschichte.at/foto.htm. Head: Stavros Diamantakis
Science&Tech Museum 02381

Perchtoldsdorf

Feuerwehrmuseum, Donauwörther Str 29, 2380 Perchtoldsdorf - T: (01) 8692334, Fax: 8694860
Science&Tech Museum - 1969 02382

Floristisches Museum, Wiener Gasse, 2380 Perchtoldsdorf - T: (01) 860289
Special Museum 02383

Hugo Wolf-Haus, Brunner Gasse 26, 2380 Perchtoldsdorf - T: (01) 8655932, 86683211, Fax: 86683133, E-mail: gemeinde@markt-perchtoldsdorf.at, Internet: http://www.markt-perchtoldsdorf.at. Head: Dr. Christine Mitterwenger
Music Museum - 1973
Memorabilia of composer Hugo Wolf (1860-1903), in originally furnished rooms 02384

Museen im Rathaus, Marktpl 10, 2380 Perchtoldsdorf - T: (01) 86683210, Fax: 86683133, E-mail: gemeinde@markt-perchtoldsdorf.at, Internet: http://www.markt-perchtoldsdorf.at. Head: Dr. Christine Mitterwenger
Local Museum - 1981
Ottoman Museum, Deutschmeister, Hans Fronius 02385

Museen im Wehrturm, Marktpl, 2380 Perchtoldsdorf - T: (01) 86683210, Fax: 86683133, E-mail: gemeinde@markt-perchtoldsdorf.at, Internet: http://www.markt-perchtoldsdorf.at. Head: Dr. Christine Mitterwenger
Local Museum - 1973/1995
Local hist, archaeology 02386

Perg

Heimathaus und Stadtmuseum, Stifterstr 1, 4320 Perg - T: (07262) 53535, Fax: 53535, E-mail: fra.moser@eduhi.at, Internet: http://www.perg.at. Head: Anton Baumann
Local Museum / Open Air Museum - 1993
Prehistory, New Stone Age, grave findings from 800 BC, High Middle Age, findings from the castle ruin Mitterberg, pottery from Perg, mill-stone and granite industry, caolin mining 02387

Pernegg

Destillier- und Drogenmuseum, Kirchdorf 3, 8132 Pernegg - T: (03867) 207
Special Museum 02388

Perschling

Heimatmuseum der Gemeinde Weißenkirchen, Hauptstr 21, 3142 Perschling - T: (02784) 7103, Fax: 71036, E-mail: gemeinde@weissenkirchen-perschling.noe.gv.at
Local Museum - 1989
Crafts, furniture, household articles, Stone Age 02389

Persenbeug

Heimatmuseum Persenbeug-Gottsdorf, Rathauspl 1, 3680 Persenbeug - T: (07412) 522060, Fax: 53530, E-mail: gde.persenbeug@wvnet.at, Internet: http://www.tiscover.com/persenbeug-gottsdorf
Local Museum - 1900 02390

Perwang

Zoll- und Heimatmuseum, Nr 1, 5163 Perwang - T: (06217) 82470, 8565, Fax: 824715, E-mail: perwang@netway.at, Internet: http://www.netvillage.at/perwang_am_grabensee.htd
Special Museum / Local Museum - 1979
Former customs border, uniforms, documents, local and natural history 02391

Petronell

Archäologischer Park Carnuntum, Freilichtmuseum Petronell, Hauptstr 465, 2404 Petronell - T: (02163) 33770, Fax: 33775, E-mail: info@carnuntum.co.at, Internet: http://www.carnuntum.co.at. Head: Dr. Markus Wachter
Archaeological Museum / Open Air Museum / Historic Site
Excavations of parts of a Roman town, reconstruction of Diana temple, paved Roman roads 02392

Archäologischer Park Carnuntum, Legionslage und Lagerstadt, Hauptstr 296, 2404 Petronell - T: (02163) 33770, Fax: 33775, E-mail: info@carnuntum.co.at, Internet: http://www.carnuntum.co.at. Head: Dr. Petra Bohuslav
Archaeological Museum / Open Air Museum - 1996
Roman art from the 1st to the 5th c 02393

Pettenbach

Schrift- und Heimatmuseum Bartlhaus, Mittendorf 99, 4643 Pettenbach - T: (07586) 815512, 7455, Fax: 815525. Head: Reinhold Braunegger
Local Museum - 1992
Regional culture, ex libris, art of writing 02394

Peuerbach

Schlossmuseum mit Bauernkriegsmuseum, Oberösterreichischer Landeskrippe und Georg-von-Peuerbach-Ausstellung, Rathauspl 2, 4722 Peuerbach - T: (07276) 2014, Fax: 29159, E-mail: stadt@peuerbach.ooe.gv.at, Internet: http://www.peuerbach.at. Head: Hubert Haslehner
Historical Museum - 1981
Artefacts from the period of the Peasants' War 02395

Pfaffstätten

Heimatmuseum, Dr.-Josef-Dolp-Str 1, 2511 Pfaffstätten - T: (02252) 88985
Local Museum - 1950
Local hist, viticulture 02396

Pfunds

Heimatmuseum, Nr 103, 6542 Pfunds - T: (05474) 5221, 5938
Local Museum - 1982 02397

Pichling

Privatsammlung Franz Pinteritsch, Geisslerstr 67, 8581 Pichling - T: (03144) 8470
Local Museum 02398

Pillichsdorf

Turmmuseum, Kirchenpl 1, 2211 Pillichsdorf - T: (02245) 6269, Internet: http://www.noel.gv.at/service/k/k1museen/index.htm
Local Museum - 1984
Geology, prehistory, medieval coll 02399

Pinkafeld

Stadtmuseum Pinkafeld, Rathauspl 1, 7423 Pinkafeld - T: (03357) 4235112, 43307, Fax: 4235185. Head: Rudolf Köberl
Local Museum - 1924
Archaeology, town hist, folk art 02400

Pischeldorf, Kärnten

Archäologischer Park Magdalensberg, Landesmuseum für Kärnten, Magdalensberg 15, 9064 Pischeldorf, Kärnten - T: (04224) 2255, Fax: 29529, E-mail: magdalensberg@schatzsuche.at, Internet: http://www.buk.ktn.gv.at/landesmuseum. Head: Dr. Heimo Dolenz
Open Air Museum / Archaeological Museum - 1948
Early Roman art and architectural remains, housed in reconstructed antique buildings 02401

Pischelsdorf in Steiermark

Landschaftsmuseum der Kulmregion, Färberturm, 8212 Pischelsdorf in Steiermark - T: (03113) 2352, Fax: 2352. Head: Titus Lantos
Local Museum - 1965
Regional life and culture 02402

Podersdorf

Windmühle, Mühlstr 26, 7141 Podersdorf - T: (02177) 2286, 2227, 2291
Local Museum 02403

Pöchlarn

Dokumentationszentrum Prof. Sepp Mayrhuber, Ulmenstr 10, 3380 Pöchlarn - T: (02757) 3458, Fax: 7768. Head: Anton Mühlbacher
Fine Arts Museum - 1989 02404

Erstes Österreichisches Tischler-Museum, Oskar-Kokoschka-Str 5, 3380 Pöchlarn - T: (02757) 8903, Fax: 8904
Historical Museum 02405

Oskar Kokoschka Geburtshaus, Regensburger Str 29, 3380 Pöchlarn - T: (02757) 7956, Fax: 7956. Head: Hans Klimmer, Anette Eisler
Fine Arts Museum - 1973
Life and work of Oskar Kokoschka - library, archive 02406

Stadtmuseum Arelape-Bechelaren, Gernotstr 49, 3380 Pöchlarn - T: (02757) 23100, Fax: 231066, E-mail: stadtgemeinde.poechlarn@aon.at. Head: Franz Wimmer
Local Museum - 1927
Roman and prehistorical artefacts, local peasant artefacts 02407

Pöggstall

Folterkammer mit Heimatmuseum, Schloß Pöggstall, Hauptpl 1, 3650 Pöggstall - T: (02758) 3310, Fax: 3140, E-mail: gde.poeggstall@wvnet.at, Internet: http://www.wvnet.at/gemeinden/poeggstall. Head: Ernst Schöbl
Local Museum - 1920 02408

Franz Traunfellner-Dokumentation, Schloß Rogendorf, Hauptpl 1, 3650 Pöggstall - T: (02758) 3310, Fax: 3140, E-mail: gde.poeggstall@wvnet.at, Internet: http://www.poegstall.at. Head: Irmgard Linke
Fine Arts Museum - 1994
Graphic arts and paintings 02409

Imkereimuseum, Schloß Rogendorf, Hauptpl 1, 3650 Pöggstall - T: (0664) 1618944, Fax: (0664) 1662700, E-mail: gde.poeggstall@wvnet.at. Head: Herbert Kolm
Agriculture Museum - 1989 02410

Museum für Rechtsgeschichte, Schloß Rogendorf, Hauptpl 1, 3650 Pöggstall - T: (02758) 3310, 23830, Fax: 3140, E-mail: gde.poeggstall@wvnet.at, Internet: http://www.wvnet.at/gemeinden/poeggstall
Historical Museum - 1988
Lapidarium 02411

Rogendorfer-Ausstellung, Sonderausstellung des Museumsvereins, Schloß Pöggstall, Hauptpl 1, 3650 Pöggstall - T: (02758) 3310, 23830, Fax: 3140, E-mail: gde.poeggstall@wvnet.at, Internet: http://www.poeggstall.at. Head: Herbert Neidhart
Historical Museum
Ruling dynasty of Rogendorfer (1478-1601) 02412

Pölfing-Brunn

Bergbauschaustollen, Brunn 191, 8544 Pölfing-Brunn - T: (03465) 3000, Fax: 300022, E-mail: gde@@poelfing-brunn.steiermark.at, Internet: http://www.poelfing-brunn.at. Head: Dr. Siegfried W. Hermann
Science&Tech Museum - 1988
Coal mining 02413

Pöllau

Museum Schloß Pöllau, Schloß 1, 8225 Pöllau - T: (03335) 2433, 4210, Fax: 4235, E-mail: tv.poellau@ito.at
Local Museum - 1908
Folklore, guilds 02414

Schloßgalerie Pöllau, Schloß 1, 8225 Pöllau - T: (03335) 2433, 4210, Fax: 4235, E-mail: tv.poellau@ito.at
Fine Arts Museum 02415

Pöls

Husslik-Heimatmuseum, 8761 Pöls
Local Museum 02416

Pörtschach am Wörther See

Galerie Loisel Grafik, Karlstr 11, 9210 Pörtschach am Wörther See - T: (04272) 3712, Fax: 3350, Internet: http://www.loisel.at. Head: Dr. Ulrike Loisel
Fine Arts Museum 02417

Pöttelsdorf

Dorfmuseum, Zemendorf, 7023 Pöttelsdorf - T: (02626) 5242
Agriculture Museum - 1979
Agricultural tools, peasant furniture 02418

Poppendorfberg

Winzerhaus, 8330 Poppendorfberg. Head: Karl Sand
Agriculture Museum 02419

Pottendorf

Heimatmuseum Rother Hof, Hauptstr 25, 2486 Pottendorf - T: (02623) 73755, 722780, Fax: 7227824
Local Museum - 1997 02420

Pottenstein

Sterbehaus Ferdinand Raimunds, Gedenk- und Informationsstätte, Hauptpl 6, 2563 Pottenstein - T: (02672) 87212. Head: Hans Buczkowski
Historical Museum - 1985 02421

Potzneusiedl

Österreichisches Ikonenmuseum, Schloß Potzneusiedl, 2473 Potzneusiedl - T: (02145) 2249, Fax: (01) 5354680. Head: Gerhard Egermann
Religious Arts Museum - 1974 02422

Zsolnay-Keramik-Porzellan-Museum, Schloß, 2473 Potzneusiedl - T: (02145) 2249. Head: Gerhard Egermann
Decorative Arts Museum - 1984 02423

Poysdorf

Galerie im Nachtwächterhaus, Berggasse 6, 2170 Poysdorf - T: (02552) 2816, 20371, Fax: 2200-11, E-mail: gemeinde@stadt-poysdorf.at, Internet: http://www.hspoysdorf1.ac.at/Fm_ohm_d.htm. Head: Elfriede Lenk
Fine Arts Museum 02424

Museum der Stadt Poysdorf, Brünner Str 9, 2170 Poysdorf - T: (02552) 3209. Head: Josef Preyer
Local Museum - 1958
Local folklore, viticulture, geology 02425

Weinviertler Oldtimermuseum Poysdorf, Liechtensteinstr 68, 2170 Poysdorf - T: (02552) 2316, Fax: 266819, E-mail: oldtimerclub@a1.net, Internet: http://www.veltinerland.at. Head: Manfred Parisch
Science&Tech Museum
Hist of cars, motorbikes, tractors and train driver, gyroplane, radio 02426

Prägarten

Heimatmuseum Oberbichl, Bichl 9, 9974 Prägarten - T: (04877) 5361
Local Museum - 1968 02427

Pram

Galerie im Troadkasten, Schloß Feldegg, 4742 Pram - T: (07736) 62611, Fax: 62614, E-mail: schlossfeldegg@lion.cc, Internet: http://www.galerie-im-troadkasten.com. Head: Liselotte Hanreich, Georg Hanreich
Fine Arts Museum - 1994 02428

Museum Furthmühle, Nr 45, 4742 Pram - T: (07736) 6457, 6170, Fax: 6457, E-mail: meinrad@aon.at, Internet: http://members.tripod.de/furthmuehle. Head: Meinrad Mayrhofer
Science&Tech Museum / Open Air Museum 02429

Schloß und Gurschner Museum, Schloß Feldegg, 4742 Pram - T: (07736) 62611, Fax: 62614, E-mail: georg.hanreich@a1plus.at, Internet: http://www.cosy.sbg.ac.at/gurschner. Head: Georg Hanreich
Fine Arts Museum - 1971
Sketches, tools and reliefs by the sculptor Gustav Gurschner, castle hist 02430

Pramet

Franz Stelzhamer-Geburtshaus, Großpiesenham 26, 4874 Pramet - T: (07754) 8387. Head: Georg Seifriedsberger, Anna Seifriedsberger
Special Museum
Memorabilia on the Upper Austrian dialect poet Franz Stelzhamer 02431

Imkereimuseum, Gemeindeamt, Haus Nr 42, 4874 Pramet - T: (07754) 8443. Head: Josef Zeillinger, August Rauscher
Agriculture Museum - 1988
Apiculture, honeymaking 02432

Preding

Kürbismühlenmuseum, Nr 231, 8504 Preding - T: (03185) 2222, 3412, Fax: 222212
Special Museum - 1995 02433

Pregarten

Burgmuseum Reichenstein, Reichenstein 30, 4230 Pregarten - T: (07236) 3277
Local Museum / Archaeological Museum - 1984
Early finds, coins, jewellery 02434

Heimathaus Pregarten, Marktpl 13, 4230 Pregarten - T: (07236) 22550, 22560, Fax: 225527
Local Museum - 1995
Hist of settlement and trades 02435

Prellenkirchen

Weinmuseum Prellenkirchen, Kellergasse, 2472 Prellenkirchen - T: (02145) 2202, Fax: 2949. Head: Heribert Mitterer
Agriculture Museum 02436

Pressbaum

Heimatmuseum, Hauptstr 79, 3021 Pressbaum - T: (02233) 33445, 55855
Local Museum - 1959 02437

Private Lebzelt- und Buttermodelab-drucksammlung, Dr.-Niedermayr-Gasse 14, 3021 Pressbaum - T: (02233) 2639
Special Museum - 1960 02438

Prigglitz

Heimat-Jagdmuseum, Auf der Wiese 53, 2640 Prigglitz - T: (02662) 3524
Local Museum / Special Museum - 1973 02439

Prinzendorf

Landwirtschaftliches Museum und Pfarrer Franz Engel-Museum, Alter Pfarrhof, Am Schulberg 8, 2185 Prinzendorf - T: (02533) 89732, 8520. Head: Norbert Pallan
Agriculture Museum / Special Museum - 1973
Agricultural machinery 02440

Prottes

Freilichtmuseum Erdöl- und Erdgaslehrpfad, Hauptpl 11, 2242 Prottes - T: (02282) 2182, Fax: 218222, E-mail: gdeprottes@netway.at. Head: Manfred Grünwald
Open Air Museum - 1979 02441

Puch bei Weiz

Steirisches Obstbaumuseum, Haus des Apfels, Harl 25, 8182 Puch bei Weiz - T: (03177) 3117, 2222, Fax: 3117, E-mail: kelz@utanet.at
Special Museum - 1990 02442

Puchberg

Zahnradbahnschuppen, Pfenningbachstr 10, 2734 Puchberg - T: (02636) 2225, Fax: 3262, Internet: http://www.puchberg.schneeberg.at. Head: Gerhard Zenz
Science&Tech Museum - 1992 02443

Pürgg

Heimathaus Fahringer, 8981 Pürgg - T: (03682) 2272, 3245
Local Museum 02444

Pulkau

Heimatmuseum Pulkau, Pöltingerhof, Bahnstr 2, 3741 Pulkau - T: (02946) 2995, 22760, Fax: 227630
Local Museum - 1988 02445

Pulkauer Gewerbemuseum, Bahnstr 4, 3741 Pulkau - T: (02946) 2248. Head: Erwin Röck
Historical Museum - 1999 02446

Purgstall an der Erlauf

Erlauftaler Feuerwehrmuseum, Pöchlarner Str 56, 3251 Purgstall an der Erlauf - T: (07489) 2914, 406243, Fax: 2914. Head: Franz Wiesenhofer
Science&Tech Museum - 1970
History of fire fighting - library 02447

Museum im Ledererhaus, Mariazeller Str 2, 3251 Purgstall an der Erlauf - T: (07489) 271117, Fax: 271144, E-mail: gemeinde@purgstall.at, Internet: http://www.purgstall.at. Head: Anna Hofmacher
Local Museum - 1996 02448

Weg des Friedens, Schauboden, Gasthaus Schager, 3251 Purgstall an der Erlauf - T: (07489) 2914, 2245, Fax: 2914. Head: Franz Wiesenhofer
Historical Museum - 1998
Events at the imperial and royal prisoner camps in the Erlauf Valley - archive 02449

Purkersdorf

Heimatmuseum, Hauptpl 6, 3002 Purkersdorf - T: (02231) 63374, 636010, Fax: 63159
Local Museum - 1967
Local hist, crafts, religious art 02450

Josef Hoffmann-Sanatorium, Hauptpl 1, 3002 Purkersdorf - T: (02231) 636010, Fax: 62267
Fine Arts Museum 02451

Putzleinsdorf

Hanrieder-Gedenkraum, Nr 7, 4134 Putzleinsdorf - T: (07286) 82760, Fax: 82769, E-mail: -marktgemeinde.putzleinsdorf@resi.at, Internet: http://www.resi.at/putzleinsdorf. Head: Franz Höfler
Special Museum - 1992
Memorial room for the dialect poet Norbert Hanrieder 02452

Raab

Bräustüberlmuseum, Marktstr 101, 4760 Raab - T: (07762) 225521, Fax: 22551, E-mail: gde.raab@netway.at, Internet: http://www.netvillage.at
Special Museum
Hist of beer brewing 02453

Heimathaus Raab, Hofgarten 16, 4760 Raab - T: (07762) 225521, 2392, Fax: 22551, E-mail: gde.raab@netway.at, Internet: http://www.netvillage.at
Local Museum - 1995
Trade workshops, exhibits of bourgeois culture of living 02454

Raabs an der Thaya

Grenzlandmuseum Raabs an der Thaya, Hauptpl 11, 3820 Raabs an der Thaya - T: (02846) 3650, Fax: 36521, E-mail: gemeinde.raabs@wvnet.at, Internet: http://www.tiscover.com/raabs.thaya
Local Museum - 1984
Stone Age tools 02455

Rabensburg

Richard-Simoncic-Museum, Volkskundemuseum, Hauptstr 73, 2274 Rabensburg - T: (02535) 3685
Folklore Museum 02456

Rabenstein an der Pielach

Heimatmuseum Rabenstein, Marktpl 6, 3203 Rabenstein an der Pielach - T: (02723) 225015, Fax: 225022, E-mail: gemeinde@rabenstein.cc, Internet: http://www.rabenstein.cc
Local Museum - 1954
Agricultural tools, household implements 02457

Pielachtaler Heimatmuseum → Heimatmuseum Rabenstein

Radenthein

Galerie Günther Frey, Fischerstr 16, 9545 Radenthein - T: (04246) 28212, 29895. Head: Richard Bertl, Othmar Schmölzer
Fine Arts Museum - 1979 02458

Radstadt

Heimatmuseum, Schloß Lerchen, Schloßstr 1, 5550 Radstadt - T: (06452) 6374, 42920
Local Museum - 1985
Local history, sacrial art objects 02459

Kapuzinerturm, Schießstatt 3, 5550 Radstadt - T: (06452) 7083, 42920. Head: Max Walter
Agriculture Museum / Historical Museum - 1990
Agriculture, crafts 02460

Raiding

Lisztmuseum, Lisztstr 46, 7321 Raiding - T: (02619) 7220. Head: Dr. Hanns Schmid
Music Museum - 1911
Documents, scores, photos, autographs and memorabilia of Franz Liszt (1811-1886), displayed in the composer's birth place 02461

Rainbach im Mühlkreis

Pferde-Eisenbahn, Kerschbaum 61, 4261 Rainbach im Mühlkreis - T: (07949) 6800, 6118, Fax: 68004, E-mail: pferdeeisenbahn@netway.at, Internet: http://www.pferdeeisenbahn.at. Head: Walter Mayr
Science&Tech Museum - 1996 02462

Wäschepflegemuseum, Prager Str 2, 4261 Rainbach im Mühlkreis - T: (07949) 6880, Fax: 6870, E-mail: waschmuseum@tm1.at, Internet: http://www.bez-freistadt.at/waschmuseum. Head: Helmut Knogler
Special Museum - 1996 02463

Ramsau am Dachstein

Alpinmuseum Dachstein, Austriahütte Ramsau-Türlwand, Schildlehen 48, 8972 Ramsau am Dachstein - T: (03687) 81522, Fax: 810853
Natural History Museum 02464

Heimatmuseum Grahhof, 8972 Ramsau am Dachstein - T: (03687) 8181211
Local Museum - 1982
Peasant life, church hist 02465

Ramsauer Getreidemühle, 8972 Ramsau am Dachstein - T: (03687) 81812, Fax: 810853
Science&Tech Museum 02466

Rankweil

Freilichtmuseum Römervilla in Brederis, Römerweg, 6830 Rankweil - T: (05522) 4050, Fax: 405600, E-mail: marktgemeinde@rankweil.at, Internet: http://www.rankweil.at
Open Air Museum / Archaeological Museum 02467

Rannersdorf

Heimatmuseum Rothmühle, Rothmühlstr 5, 2324 Rannersdorf - T: (01) 7078159
Local Museum 02468

Rappottenstein

Dorfmuseum Roiten, Roiten 20, 3911 Rappottenstein - T: (02828) 8501, Fax: 75793
Local Museum - 1990
Local hist, hunting, costume, crafts 02469

Museum Alte Brettersäge, Kirchbach 50, 3911 Rappottenstein - T: (02828) 7589
Science&Tech Museum 02470

Ratten

Blasmusik-Museum, Kirchenviertel 104, 8673 Ratten - T: (03173) 221316, Fax: 221318, E-mail: friesenbichler.gerh.@netway.at. Head: Gerhard Friesenbichler
Music Museum - 1993 02471

Rattenberg, Inn

Augustinermuseum, Pfarrgasse 8, 6240 Rattenberg, Inn - T: (05337) 64831, Fax: 65679, E-mail: hermann.drexel@telecom.at, Internet: http://www.augustinermuseum.at. Head: Hermann Drexel
Religious Arts Museum / Fine Arts Museum - 1993
Treasure chamber with silver- and goldsmith artefacts 02472

Rauris

Rauriser Talmuseum, Marktstr 59, 5661 Rauris - T: (06544) 6253, 6237. Head: Hans Viehhauser
Local Museum - 1937
Rural life, gold mining, mineralogy 02473

Rechberg

Stein- und Bauernmuseum Großdöllnerhof, Nr 18, 4322 Rechberg - T: (07264) 465516, Fax: 46554, E-mail: tourismusverband@rechberg.at, Internet: http://www.tiscover.com/rechberg
Open Air Museum / Agriculture Museum
Agricultural implements 02474

Rechnitz

Heimatmuseum Rechnitz, Steinamangerstr 16, 7471 Rechnitz - T: (03363) 79176, Fax: 79176
Local Museum 02475

Stiefelmachermuseum, Hauptpl 10, 7471 Rechnitz - T: (03363) 79202, Fax: 7920222, E-mail: post@rechnitz.bgld.gv.at
Special Museum - 1989 02476

Reichenau an der Rax

Wasserleitungsmuseum, Kaiserbrunn 53, Höllental, 2651 Reichenau an der Rax - T: (02666) 52548, Fax: 525489931765, Internet: http://www.magwien.gv.at/ma53/museen/kaiser.htm. Head: Josef Donner
Science&Tech Museum / Special Museum 02477

Reichenthal

Grasselmühle, Allhut 10, 4193 Reichenthal - T: (07214) 4067
Science&Tech Museum
Mill next to the Bohemian border, linseed press 02478

Reichersberg

Museum des Augustiner-Chorherrenstifts, 4981 Reichersberg - T: (07758) 2313, Fax: 231332, E-mail: office@stift-reichersberg.co.at, Internet: http://www.stift-reichersberg.co.at. Head: Dr. Gregor Schauber
Religious Arts Museum - 1966
Paintings, sculpture, documents displayed in historic monastery rooms - library 02479

Reichraming

Forstmuseum, Nr 263, 4462 Reichraming - T: (07255) 8201, 8257. Head: Karl Garstenauer
Natural History Museum - 1985
Wood workers' implements, coll of stones 02480

Reidling

Barockmuseum, Schloß Heiligenkreuz-Gutenbrunn, 3454 Reidling - T: (02782) 84097, Fax: 840974, E-mail: anna-marie.figdor@gmx.at. Head: Dr. Joachim Rössl
Fine Arts Museum - 1964
Baroque art, Dr. Albert Figdor coll 02481

Imkereiausstellung Einst-Jetzt, Immenweg 1, 3454 Reidling - T: (02276) 2885. Head: Karl Schäffel, Brigitte Schäffel
Agriculture Museum 02482

Weinbaumuseum, Ahrenberger Kellergasse, 3454 Reidling - T: (0663) 9794770
Agriculture Museum - 1996 02483

Rein

Sammlungen des Zisterzienserstiftes Rein, Nr 1, 8103 Rein - T: (03124) 516210, Fax: 5162134, E-mail: zwicker.music@styria.com. Head: Stephan Ellmeyer, Jörg Zwicker
Religious Arts Museum
12th c Cistercian cloister, incunabula, musical instruments, chapel with sepulchres, treasure items - library, archive 02484

Reingers

Neubistritzer Heimatstube, Reingers 81, 3863 Reingers - T: (02863) 8208, Fax: 82084, E-mail: gemeinde.reingers@wvnet.at, Internet: http://www.reingers.at. Head: Frasl Erich
Local Museum - 1982 02485

Reith im Alpbachtal

Heimatmuseum Reith, Bergfried von Schloß Matzen, 6235 Reith im Alpbachtal - T: (05337) 622120, Fax: 64060, E-mail: martin.reiter@tirol.com
Local Museum / Public Gallery - 1976 02486

Rennweg

Arsenik-Schauhütte des Bezirksheimatmuseums Spittal im Pöllatal, Haus Sonnblick, Gries 46, 9863 Rennweg - T: (04734) 5603. Head: Prof. Helmut Prasch
Science&Tech Museum - 1975 02487

Katschtaler Heimatmuseum, Sankt Peter 34, 9863 Rennweg - T: (04734) 243. Head: Norbert Loquenz
Local Museum - 1948
Local hist, mining 02488

Retz

Österreichs größter historischer Weinkeller, Hauptpl 30, 2070 Retz - T: (02942) 2700, Fax: 2700, E-mail: tourismus@retz.at, Internet: http://www.retz.at. Head: Reinhold Griebler
Special Museum / Historic Site - 1976 02489

Windmühle, Kalvarienberg 1, 2070 Retz - T: (02942) 2700, E-mail: tourismus-retz@eunet.at
Science&Tech Museum - 1976 02490

Reutte

Dengel-Galerie, Obermarkt, 6600 Reutte - T: (05672) 72304. Head: Veronika Kunz, Hartmut Kunz
Public Gallery - 1984 02491

Heimatmuseum der Marktgemeinde Reutte, Untermarkt 25, 6600 Reutte - T: (05672) 72304, Fax: 72305, E-mail: gruenes.haus@tirol.com, Internet: http://www.tirol.com/reutte-kultur
Local Museum - 1934
Religious folk art, guilds (17th-19th c) - library, archive 02492

Ried im Innkreis

Museum Innviertler Volkskundehaus und Galerie der Stadt Ried, Kirchenpl 13, 4910 Ried im Innkreis - T: (07752) 901244, 901245, Fax: 901253, E-mail: museum-volkskundehaus@ried-innkreis.ooe.gv.at, Internet: http://www.ried.at/museum/home.htm. Head: Dr. Sieglinde Baumgartner
Public Gallery / Fine Arts Museum / Folklore Museum - 1933
Religious folk art, Baroque sculptures - library 02493

Riegersburg, Niederösterreich

Barockschloß Riegersburg, Nr 1-3, 2092 Riegersburg, Niederösterreich - T: (02916) 400, Fax: 40032, E-mail: pilati@schloss.de. Head: Francesca Gräfin Pilati von Thassul-Filo della Torre
Decorative Arts Museum - 1967
Original 18th c furnishings in a Baroque palace (Franz Anton Pilgram 1735-1775), permanent exhibit on aristocratic taste in the 18th c 02494

Perlmuttdrechslerei, Felling 37, 2092 Riegersburg, Niederösterreich - T: (02916) 203, Fax: 424. Head: Bruno Marchart
Special Museum - 1942 02495

Riegersburg, Steiermark

Hexenmuseum, Nr 1, 8333 Riegersburg, Steiermark - T: (03153) 82130, Fax: 8513. Head: Friedrich Liechtenstein
Military Museum / Historical Museum
Weapons, instruments of torture, history of the Liechtenstein family, Asian and African exhibits 02496

Rietz

Heimatmuseum, Lußrain 1, 6421 Rietz - T: (05262) 64621
Local Museum - 1984
Folklore, Gothic sculpture 02497

Riezlern

Walsermuseum, Walser Str 52, 6991 Riezlern - T: (05517) 53150. Head: Margarethe Hippe
Local Museum - 1969
History and geology of the Wals Valley, folk art and customs, farm implements, sculpture and painting 02498

Röhrenbach

Renaissance Schloss Greillenstein, Greillenstein 1, 3592 Röhrenbach - T: (02989) 821621, 808021, Fax: 808013, E-mail: schloss.greillenstein@aon.at, Internet: http://www.greillenstein.at. Head: Elisabeth Gräfin Kuefstein
Historical Museum - 1959
16th c caste with Baroque sandstone balustrades and grotesque stone dwarves (fragments of the baroque gardens of 1720, parts of the balustrades are designed by Fischer von Erlach), hist period rooms, portraits and paintings, weapons,coll of items on ancient law, docs on crime and police, court room 02499

Schloßmuseum → Renaissance Schloss Greillenstein

Rohr im Gebirge

Freilichtmuseum Historische Volkskunde Kalte Kuchl, Innerhalbach 42, 2663 Rohr im Gebirge - T: (02766) 8538, 8522. Head: Rudolf Thron, Josef Rittmann
Folklore Museum / Open Air Museum - 1985 02500

Rohrau

Graf Harrach'sche Familiensammlung, Schloß, 2471 Rohrau - T: (02164) 225318, Fax: 225320, E-mail: arco-zinneberg@direkt.at, Internet: http://harrach.nwy.at. Head: Ulrich Graf Arco-Zinneberg
Fine Arts Museum - 1850
Spanish and Neapolitan Baroque painting, 19th c furniture, period furnishings 02501

Haydn-Geburtshaus, Obere Hauptstr 25, 2471 Rohrau - T: (02164) 2268. Head: Dr. Alfred Willander
Music Museum - 1959
Pictures, scores and memorabilia of Joseph Haydn (1732-1809) and Michael Haydn (1737-1806) 02502

Rohrbach an der Lafnitz

Sammlung Schloß Aichberg, 8234 Rohrbach an der Lafnitz - T: (03338) 3425, Fax: 34254, E-mail: aichberg@t-online.at. Head: Cajetán Gril
Historical Museum - 1980 02503

Rohrbach in Oberösterreich

Buchdruckermuseum, Linzer Str 6, 4150 Rohrbach in Oberösterreich - T: (07289) 6815026, Fax: 681522. Head: Peter Kumpfmüller, Franz Bauer
Historical Museum 02504

Rosegg

Figurencabinett Madamme Lucrezia, Nr 1, 9232 Rosegg - T: (04274) 3009, Fax: 300913, E-mail: info@rosegg.at, Internet: http://www.rosegg.at
Fine Arts Museum 02505

Rosenau Schloß

Blau-gelbe Viertelsgalerie, Waldviertel, Rosenau 1, 3924 Rosenau Schloß - T: (02822) 582210, Fax: 582218. Head: Edeltraud Thier
Association with Coll - 1988 02506

Österreichisches Freimaurermuseum, Schloß 1, 3924 Rosenau Schloß - T: (02822) 5822115, Fax: 5822115, E-mail: schloss.rosenau@wvnet, Internet: http://www.schlosshotel.rosenau.at. Head: Dr. Michael Kraus
Historical Museum - 1975
Hist of Freemasonry 02507

Rosenburg am Kamp

Schloßmuseum Rosenburg, 3573 Rosenburg am Kamp - T: (02982) 2911, 2303, Fax: 4512, 4511, E-mail: fvhoyoshorn@via.at, Internet: http://www.rosenburg.at. Head: Hans Hoyos
Historical Museum - 1859
Arms, furniture, prehistoric coll, painting 02508

Rothenthurn

Frühmittelaltermuseum Carantana, Pfarrhof Molzbichl, 9701 Rothenthurn - T: (04767) 666, E-mail: carantana@netway.at, Internet: http://www.spittal-drau.at/carantana. Head: Kurt Karpf
Historical Museum - 1991 02509

Rust, Burgenland

Seevogel-Museum Neusiedlersee, Am Hafen 2, 7071 Rust, Burgenland - T: (02685) 6868, Fax: 6868. Head: Herbert Vargyas
Natural History Museum - 1975 02510

Rutzenmoos

Bibelmuseum, Nr 62, 4845 Rutzenmoos - T: (07672) 23314
Religious Arts Museum
Bibles, praying books, religious literature portraying the Protestant belief during and since the Counter-Reformation 02511

Saalfelden

Pinzgauer Heimatmuseum, Schloß Ritzen, 5760 Saalfelden - T: (06582) 72759, 72458, Fax: 72759, Internet: http://www.hib.salzburg.at/museum/museum.htm
Local Museum - 1965
Cribs, geology, mineralogy, agriculture, votive tablets 02512

Salzburg

Domgrabungsmuseum, Salzburger Museum Carolino Augusteum, Residenzpl, 5020 Salzburg - T: (0662) 6208080, Fax: 620808120, E-mail: office@smca.at, Internet: http://www.smca.at. Head: Dr. Erich Marx
Archaeological Museum 02513

Dommuseum zu Salzburg, Dompl, 5010 Salzburg - T: (0662) 8047127, 844189, Fax: 840442, E-mail: - dommuseum.salzburg@kirchen.net, Internet: http:// www.kirchen.net/dommuseum. Head: Dr. Johann Kronbichler
Religious Arts Museum - 1974
Cathedral treasure, Rupertus cross (8th c), religious painting and sculpture 14th and 19th c from the archbishopric Salzburg, Art and Rarity Chamber 02514

Festungsmuseum, Salzburger Museum Carolino Augusteum, Festung Hohensalzburg, 5020 Salzburg - T: (0662) 844145, Fax: 620808120, E-mail: office@smca.at, Internet: http:// www.smca.at. Head: Dr. Erich Marx
Historical Museum / Historic Site 02515

Galerie 5020, Sigmund-Haffner-Gasse 12, 5020 Salzburg - T: (0662) 848817, Fax: 848817, E-mail: galerie5020@salzburg.co.at
Public Gallery 02516

Galerie der Stadt Salzburg im Mirabellgarten, Bernhard-Paumgartner-Weg 2, 5024 Salzburg - T: (0662) 80723443/46, Fax: 80723423
Public Gallery 02517

Galerie im Traklhaus, Waagpl 1a, 5020 Salzburg - T: (0662) 80422149, Fax: 80423078, E-mail: traklhaus@salzburg.gv.at, Internet: http:// www.salzburg.gv.at/kultur/traklhaus. Head: Dietgard Grimmer
Public Gallery - 1973 02518

Galerie Kunst der Gegenwart, Rudolfskai 32, 5020 Salzburg - T: (0662) 846519, Fax: 846519, E-mail: gredler@salzburg.co.at, Internet: http:// lithowerkstatt.at/gredler. Head: Martin Gredler
Fine Arts Museum - 1952 02519

Georg Trakl-Forschungs- und Gedenkstätte, Waagpl 1a, 5020 Salzburg - T: (0662) 845289, Fax: 842665, E-mail: kulturvereinigung@ salzburg.co.at. Head: Dr. Hans Weichselbaum
Historical Museum - 1973
Furnishings, letters, documents, works and memorabilia of Georg Trakl (1887-1914), displayed in the poet's birthplace, secondary literature on Trakl 02520

Johann Michael Haydn-Gedenkstätte, c/o Institut für Musikwissenschaft der Universität, Erzabtei Sankt Peter, Bergstr 10, 5020 Salzburg - T: (0662) 80444650, 84457619, Fax: 80444660, 84457619, E-mail: ernst.hintermaier@sbg.ac.at, Internet: http://www.sbg.ac.at/mus/ MHaydnGes.htm. Head: Prof. Dr. Gerhard Croll
Music Museum - 1984 02521

Kunstraum Sankt Virgil, Ernst-Grein-Str 14, 5026 Salzburg - T: (0662) 659010, Fax: 65901509, E-mail: office@virgil.at, Internet: http:// www.virgil.at. Head: Peter Braun
Public Gallery 02522

Mozart Wohnhaus, Makartpl 8, 5020 Salzburg - T: (0662) 87422740, Fax: 872924, E-mail: archiv@ mozarteum.at, Internet: http://www.mozarteum.at. Head: Dr. Gabriele Ramsauer
Music Museum - 1955
Historical musical instruments, Mozart autographs, portraits 02523

Mozarts Geburtshaus, Getreidegasse 9, 5020 Salzburg - T: (0662) 844313, Fax: 840693, E-mail: archiv@mozarteum.at, Internet: http:// www.mozarteum.at. Head: Dr. Gabriele Ramsauer
Music Museum - 1880
Portraits, scores, books, musical instruments and other memorabilia of W.A. Mozart, displayed in the composer's birthplace 02524

Naturkundemuseum Haus der Natur, Museumspl 5, 5020 Salzburg - T: (0662) 8426530, 8423220, Fax: 847905, E-mail: hausdernatur@salzburg.co.at, Internet: http://www.salzburg.co.at/hausdernatur. Head: Prof. Dr. Eberhard Stüber
Natural History Museum - 1924
Mineralogy, geology, paleontology, human biology, nature and environment in various continents, marine biology, man and space, entomology, ornithology, domestic animals - aquarium, reptile zoo, ecological institute, national-park institute, observatory 02525

Pater Peter Singer-Museum, Franziskanerkloster, Franziskanergasse 5, 5020 Salzburg - T: (0662) 8436290
Religious Arts Museum
Music instruments building, paintings 02526

Rainermuseum Salzburg, Festung Hohensalzburg, 5020 Salzburg - T: (0662) 647050
Military Museum - 1924
History of the Imperial "Archduke Rainer" Regiment, uniforms and equipment of the Austrian alpine troops in WWII, history of the Austrian Army in both World Wars 02527

Residenzgalerie Salzburg, Salzburger Landessammlungen, Residenzpl 1, 5010 Salzburg - T: (0662) 80404510, Fax: 8040451 16, E-mail: residenzgalerie@salzburg.gv.at, Internet: http://www.residenzgalerie.at. Head: Dr. Roswitha Juffinger
Fine Arts Museum - 1923
European paintings from 16th to 19th c 02528

Rupertinum, Museum für moderne Kunst Salzburg, Wiener Philharmoniker-Gasse 9, 5010 Salzburg - T: (0662) 80422541, Fax: 80423074, E-mail: rupertinum@salzburg.gv.at, Internet: http:// www.rupertinum.at. Head: Dr. Agnes Husslein
Fine Arts Museum - 1983
Modern art (Oskar Kokoschka, Otto Dix, Marc Chagall; Klimt, Gustav) Austrian art since 1945, photos, graphics 02529

Salzburger Barockmuseum, Sammlung Rossacher, Orangerie des Mirabellgartens, 5024 Salzburg - T: (0662) 877432, Fax: 87743217, E-mail: office@ barockmuseum.at, Internet: http:// www.barockmuseum.at. Head: Regina Kaltenbrunner
Fine Arts Museum - 1973
Sketches and drawings for monumental works in the European Baroque style - Sammlung Rossacher 02530

Salzburger Museum Carolino Augusteum, Museumspl 1, 5020 Salzburg - T: (0662) 620808200, Fax: 620808220, E-mail: office@ smca.at, Internet: http://www.smca.at. Head: Dr. Erich Marx
Fine Arts Museum - 1834
Prehist and Early Hist, archaeology, graphic arts, arts and crafts, numismatics, toy coll, folklore 02531

Spielzeugmuseum, Salzburger Museum Carolino Augusteum, Bürgerspitalgasse 2, 5020 Salzburg - T: (0662) 620808300, Fax: 620808320, E-mail: office@smca.at, Internet: http:// www.smca.at. Head: Dr. Erich Marx
Special Museum / Music Museum - 1978 02532

Universitätsbibliothek Salzburg, Hofstallgasse 2-4, 5010 Salzburg - T: (0662) 8044775/50, Fax: 8044103, E-mail: christine.unterrainer@ sbg.ac.at, Internet: http://www.ubs.sbg.ac.at. Head: Dr. Christine Unterrainer
Library with Exhibitions
Salzburg hist, Mozart, Paracelsus 02533

Volkskundemuseum, Salzburger Museum Carolino Augusteum, Monatsschlößl in Hellbrunn, 5020 Salzburg - T: (0662) 620808500, Fax: 620808120, E-mail: office@smca.at, Internet: http:// www.smca.at. Head: Dr. Erich Marx
Folklore Museum 02534

Sandl

Hinterglasmuseum, Nr 4, 4251 Sandl - T: (07944) 81107, Fax: 82504. Head: Hannes Braun
Decorative Arts Museum - 1989
Verre églomisé pictures from Sandl/Buchers 02535

Sankt Aegyd am Neuwalde

Heimatmuseum und Pfeifenmuseum, Waldgasse 14, 3193 Sankt Aegyd am Neuwalde - T: (02768) 7276, 22900, Fax: 2270, E-mail: staegyd@ netway.at, Internet: http://www.tiscover.com/ staegyd
Local Museum / Special Museum - 1991 02536

Sankt Agatha

Stefan Fadinger-Museum, Stauffstr 2, 4084 Sankt Agatha - T: (07277) 825515. Head: Fritz Erlinger
Historical Museum
Memorial site for the leader of the Upper Austrian rebellion against the Bavarians (1626), Stefan Fadinger 02537

Sankt Anton

Ski- und Heimatmuseum, Villa Koutzouglou, 6580 Sankt Anton - T: (05446) 22690
Special Museum / Local Museum - 1978 02538

Sankt Florian

Feuerwehrmuseum, Stiftsstr 3, 4490 Sankt Florian - T: (07224) 4219. Head: Wilhelm Hackhofer, August Schicklberger
Science&Tech Museum - 1984
Hist of the institution of the fire brigade 02539

Florianerbahn, Alter Bahnhof, 4490 Sankt Florian - T: (0732) 243292, Fax: 243292, E-mail: info@ florianerbahn.at, Internet: http:// www.florianerbahn.at
Science&Tech Museum - 1994
Historic trams 02540

Oberösterreichisches Freilichtmuseum Sumerauerhof, Samesleiten 15, 4490 Sankt Florian - T: (07224) 8031, 8498, Fax: 8031, E-mail: info@ sumerauerhof.at, Internet: http:// www.sumerauerhof.at. Head: Hermann Zangenfeind
Open Air Museum - 1973
Farm houses with peasant's furniture, agricultural machinery and implements 02541

Oberösterreichisches Jagdmuseum, Schloß Hohenbrunn, Hohenbrunn 1, 4490 Sankt Florian - T: (07224) 20083, Fax: 20083, E-mail: h.moosbauer@jagdverb-ooe.at, Internet: http://www.jagdverb-ooe.at. Head: Hans Reisetbauer
Special Museum - 1967
Historic weapons, tapestries, porcelain and faience, glass and silver with hunting motives, 18th c hunting paintings, memorabilia of Emporer Franz Joseph I 02542

Sammlungen des Augustiner Chorherrenstifte, Stiftstr 1, 4490 Sankt Florian - T: (07224) 890254, Fax: 890260, E-mail: bibliothek@stift-st-florian.at. Head: Prof. Dr. Dr. Karl Rehberger
Religious Arts Museum - 1071
Historic rooms, painting and sculpture, decorative arts, graphic coll, minerals and natural history coll, panel painting by Albrecht Altdorfer - library, archive 02543

Sankt Georgen an der Gusen

Heimathaus Sankt Georgen an der Gusen, Mauthausener Str 14, 4222 Sankt Georgen an der Gusen - T: (07237) 3946, 3148, Fax: 227877, E-mail: rahd@magnet.at, Internet: http://linz.orf.at/ orf/gusen/pf/ahdg.htm
Historical Museum - 1986
Archival mat concerning the former KZ Gusen complex, incl Holocaust and Shoah mats of that camps within the KZ Mauthausen complex, coll of mat concerning the German underground installation of the KZ Gusen II "Bergkristall" - Memorial room concentration camp Mauthausen-Gusen 02544

Sankt Georgen an der Stiefing

Paul Ernst-Gedenkstätte, Schloß, 8413 Sankt Georgen an der Stiefing - T: (03183) 468. Head: Christine Reinisch
Special Museum - 1934
Memorial and sepulchre of the writer Paul Ernst 02545

Sankt Georgen bei Salzburg

Heimatmuseum Siglhaus, Holzhausen 29, 5112 Sankt Georgen bei Salzburg - T: (06274) 4069
Local Museum - 1981
Tools, prehistory 02546

Sankt Georgen im Attergau

Eisstockmuseum, Pausingergasse 26, 4880 Sankt Georgen im Attergau - T: (07667) 8962
Special Museum
Hist of the curling stone 02547

Sankt Gilgen

Heimatkundliches Museum Wetzlhäusl, Pichlerpl 6, 5340 Sankt Gilgen - T: (06227) 2642, Fax: 8175
Local Museum - 1980
Laces, fauna, religious items, glass, insects - Archive 02548

Mozart-Gedenkstätte im Bezirksgericht, Ischler Str 15, 5340 Sankt Gilgen - T: (06227) 401, Fax: (0662) 840693. Head: Dr. Gabriele Ramseuer
Music Museum - 1983 02549

Sankt Jakob-Breitenau

Votivschatz der Wallfahrtskirche, Sankt Erhard 21, 8614 Sankt Jakob-Breitenau - T: (03866) 2235, Fax: 22354
Religious Arts Museum 02550

Sankt Johann am Walde

Heimathaus Beandhaus, Geisereck 1, 5242 Sankt Johann am Walde - T: (07743) 8295
Local Museum
Small originally equipped and furnished farm house 02551

Sankt Johann am Wimberg

Mühlviertler Kulturgütermuseum, Petersberg 50, 4172 Sankt Johann am Wimberg - T: (07217) 7194
Local Museum
Old steam engine, agricultural implements 02552

Sankt Johann im Saggautal

Rauchstubenhaus, Gündorf 11, 8453 Sankt Johann im Saggautal - T: (03456) 266
Local Museum
Peasant life and furnishings, tools, in 18th c smoke house 02553

Sankt Johann in Tirol

Galerie der Marktgemeinde Sankt Johann in Tirol, Bahnhofstr 8, 6380 Sankt Johann in Tirol - T: (05352) 690013, 65888, Fax: 690023, E-mail: fischer@st.johann.net, Internet: http:// www.museum.stjohann.at. Head: Peter Fischer
Fine Arts Museum - 1996 02554

Museum der Marktgemeinde Sankt Johann in Tirol, Bahnhofstr 8, 6380 Sankt Johann in Tirol - T: (05352) 65888, 690013, Fax: 690023, E-mail: fischer@st.johann.net, Internet: http:// www.museum-stjohann.at. Head: Peter Fischer
Local Museum - 1994 02555

Sankt Kanzian

Keltenmuseum Gracarca, Klopeiner See-Unterburg, Römerweg 11, 9122 Sankt Kanzian - T: (0664) 3400138, E-mail: a-eberhart@aon.at
Archaeological Museum 02556

Sankt Koloman

Heimatmuseum, 5423 Sankt Koloman - T: (06241) 225
Local Museum - 1968
Minerals, peasant life, hunting 02557

Sankt Lambrecht

Sammlungen des Stiftes Sankt Lambrecht, Volkskundemuseum, Galerie und Vogelsammlung, Hauptstr 1, 8813 Sankt Lambrecht - T: (03585) 2305, Fax: 230520. Head: P. Benedikt Plank
Religious Arts Museum / Folklore Museum / Natural History Museum - 1848
Historical period rooms, religious art, in particular Gothic and 17th-18th c panel paintings and sculpture, ornithology, stuffed mammals, minerals, natural science, religious folk art, peasant furniture and household utensils from Upper Styria, in 11th c cloister 02558

Sankt Leonhard am Forst

Mostmuseum, Hauptpl 1, 3243 Sankt Leonhard am Forst - T: (02756) 2204, Fax: 220430
Special Museum - 1947 02559

Sankt Margarethen

Freilichtmuseum Römersteinbruch, Römersteinbruch, 7062 Sankt Margarethen - T: (02680) 21880, 22070, Fax: 218822, E-mail: office@roemersteinbruch.at, Internet: http:// www.roemersteinbruch.at. Head: Reinhard Gossy
Open Air Museum / Fine Arts Museum / Historic Site - 1959
Stone sculpture, fossils, legends depicted in sculptures and paintings 02560

Sankt Marien

Heimatkundehaus und Münzkabinett, Kurzenkirchen 2, 4502 Sankt Marien - T: (07227) 8360
Local Museum - 1980
Local hist, coins, tools 02561

Sankt Marienkirchen an der Polsenz

Mostmuseum und Heimathaus, Kirchenpl 10, 4076 Sankt Marienkirchen an der Polsenz - T: (07249) 47112, Fax: 471126, E-mail: mostmuseum@st-marienkirchen-polsenz.ooe.gv.at. Head: Johann Kaltenberger
Local Museum - 1981 02562

Sankt Marienkirchen bei Schärding

Richard Billinger-Gedenkraum, Nr 140, 4774 Sankt Marienkirchen bei Schärding - T: (07711) 2638. Head: Erhard Maier
Special Museum
Memorabilia of the Upper Austrian poet Richard Billinger 02563

Sankt Martin am Tennengebirge

Heimatstube Sankt Martin am Tennengebirge, 5522 Sankt Martin am Tennengebirge - T: (06463) 7225
Local Museum 02564

Sankt Martin am Wollmißberg

Heimatmuseum Sankt Martin am Wöllmißberg, Sankt Martin 9, 8580 Sankt Martin am Wollmißberg - T: (03140) 202, Fax: 2024, E-mail: gde@st-martin-woellmissberg.steiermark.at
Local Museum
Weaving, tools, household articles 02565

Sankt Martin bei Lofer

Votivsammlung der Wallfahrtskirche Maria Kirchental, 5092 Sankt Martin bei Lofer - T: (06588) 8528. Head: Michael Hecht
Religious Arts Museum - 1962
Votive tablets donated by pilgrims since 1690, 17th c church 02566

Sankt Michael

Werkhof Bistrica, Feistritz 31, 9143 Sankt Michael - T: (04235) 2838, Fax: 2838. Head: Alfred Pototschnig
Public Gallery 02567

Sankt Oswald bei Freistadt

Brennereimuseum am Hitzlhammer, Wippl 6, 4271 Sankt Oswald bei Freistadt - T: (07945) 7203, Fax: 7825, E-mail: mittholz@aon.at. Head: Gabriele Mittendorfer
Science&Tech Museum - 1983
Fruit schnapps distillery 02568

Freilichtmuseum Ledermühle, Am Sportpl 24, 4271 Sankt Oswald bei Freistadt - T: (07945) 7312, 75090, Fax: 78239. Head: Karl Narzt
Open Air Museum / Science&Tech Museum - 1991
Leather mill 02569

Kirchenhäusl, Markt 1c, 4271 Sankt Oswald bei Freistadt - T: (07945) 227. Head: Josef Friesenecker
Religious Arts Museum
Portrayal of social contributions by the church to the poor, sacral objects 02570

Sankt Pantaleon

Bauern- und Heimatmuseum Haigermoos, Haigermoos 5, 5120 Sankt Pantaleon - T: (06277) 8129
Agriculture Museum / Local Museum
Hey barn from 1872, farming implements 02571

Museum für zeitgenössische Metallplastik, Riedersbach 109, 5120 Sankt Pantaleon - T: (06277) 79790, Fax: 79798200
Fine Arts Museum 02572

Sankt Paul

Lavanttaler Obstbaumuseum, 9470 Sankt Paul - T: (04357) 201960. Head: Dr. Cölestin Spendel
Agriculture Museum - 1990 02573

Stiftsmuseum Schatzhaus Kärntens, Benediktinerstift, Hauptstr 1, 9470 Sankt Paul - T: (04357) 201922, Fax: 201923, E-mail: schatzhaus@carinthia.com, Internet: http://www.stift-stpaul.at. Head: Dr. Gerfried Sitar
Religious Arts Museum - 1991
11th c cloister, 17th-18th c ecclesiastical items, paintings, graphics, porcelain, coins, paraments, archives, incunabula - library 02574

Sankt Peter am Wimberg

Schulstub'n-Glockenhäusl, Kasten 44, 4171 Sankt Peter am Wimberg - T: (07289) 71957
Special Museum
Historical school building, farm house parlour 02575

Sankt Peter im Sulmtal

Heimathaus Sankt Peter im Sulmtal, Nr 99, 8542 Sankt Peter im Sulmtal - T: (03467) 8302, Fax: 830217, E-mail: gde@st-peter-sulmtal.steiermark.at
Local Museum - 1980 02576

Sankt Pölten

Diözesan-Museum, Dompl 1, 3100 Sankt Pölten - T: (02742) 324331, Fax: 324309, E-mail: dioezesanmuseum.stpoelten@kirche.at. Head: Herbert Berndl
Religious Arts Museum / Fine Arts Museum - 1888/1984
Panel paintings, sculpture, Gothic glass painting and copper etchings, religious art, liturgical items, Baroque paintings and sculptures, Roman finds, coins and medaillons 02577

Museum im Hof, Heßstr 4, 3100 Sankt Pölten - T: (02742) 353477, 3332800, Fax: 3332809, E-mail: sinasko@st-poelten.gv.at. Head: Siegfried Nasko
Historical Museum - 1990
History of labour movement 02578

Niederösterreichisches Dokumentationszentrum für Moderne Kunst, c/o Landesverband der niederösterreichischen Kunstvereine, Prandtauer Str 2, 3100 Sankt Pölten - T: (02742) 353336, Fax: 353336, E-mail: noedok@aon.at, Internet: http://www.kunstnet.at/NOEDOK. Head: Prof. Erich Steininger
Fine Arts Museum / Library with Exhibitions - 1978
Contemporary Lower Austrian art 02579

Niederösterreichisches Landesmuseum, Franz-Schubert-Pl 5, 3109 Sankt Pölten - T: (02742) 9080900, Fax: 908091, E-mail: office@landesmuseum.net, Internet: http://www.landesmuseum.net. Head: Dr. Erich Steiner, Carl Aigner
Fine Arts Museum / Natural History Museum / Local Museum - 1997 02580

Stadtmuseum Sankt Pölten, Prandtauer Str 2, 3100 Sankt Pölten - T: (02742) 3332643, Fax: 3332609, E-mail: heplatzer@st-poelten.gy.at, Internet: http://www.st-poelten.gv.at. Head: Thomas Pulle
Local Museum - 1879
Pre- and ancient hist, local and regional hist, economics, post-1820 theatre, coins, late medieval art in St. Pölten, Baroque sculpture and painting, 20th c Austrian painting (Ernst Stöhr, Ferdinand Andri) 02581

Sankt Roman

Sauwald-Heimathaus, Schnürberg 3, 4793 Sankt Roman - T: (07716) 7372, 7359, Fax: 7372, 73594. Head: Matthias Fuchs
Local Museum - 1974
300-year-old farm house portraying peasant life, agricultural implements 02582

Sankt Ruprecht

Steirisches Holzmuseum, 8862 Sankt Ruprecht - T: (03534) 2202, Fax: 22024, E-mail: steirischesholzmuseum@direkt.at, Internet: http://www.holzmuseum.at. Head: Hans Edler
Natural History Museum - 1988 02583

Sankt Thomas am Blasenstein

Ateliersammlung Herbert Hiesmayr, Mitter-Sankt Thomas 57, 4364 Sankt Thomas am Blasenstein - T: (07265) 5856. Head: Herbert Hiesmayr
Archaeological Museum - 1985
Early and pre-historic finds and objects 02584

Sankt Valentin

Geschichtliches Museum Enns-Donauwinkel, Hauptpl 5, 4300 Sankt Valentin - T: (07435) 58660, Fax: 58660. Head: Dieter Matschiner
Local Museum - 1964
Local hist 02585

Museum Schloß Erla, Erla 47, 4300 Sankt Valentin - T: (07435) 7463, 7292
Local Museum - 1996 02586

Sankt Veit an der Glan

Justinus Mulle-Museum, Unterer Pl 20, 9300 Sankt Veit an der Glan - T: (04212) 2210
Folklore Museum 02587

Münzkabinett, Burggasse 9, 9300 Sankt Veit an der Glan - T: (04212) 5555, 2210
Special Museum 02588

Rathausgalerie, Hauptpl 1, 9300 Sankt Veit an der Glan - T: (04212) 555531, Fax: 5555666, E-mail: city@stveit.carinthia.com
Fine Arts Museum - 1961 02589

Stadtmuseum Sankt Veit, Burggasse 9, 9300 Sankt Veit an der Glan - T: (04212) 555591, 2210, Fax: 5555112, 71266. Head: Heinz Ellersdorfer
Local Museum - 1886 02590

Verkehrsmuseum Sankt Veit an der Glan, Hauptpl 29, 9300 Sankt Veit an der Glan - T: (04212) 555564, Fax: 5555112, E-mail: citystveit.carinthia.at. Head: Willy Marschnig
Science&Tech Museum - 1982
Railroads, postal services, traffic 02591

Sankt Veit im Mühlkreis

Heinrich Suso Waldeck und Hans Schnopfhagen-Gedenkraum, Stiftstr 1, 4173 Sankt Veit im Mühlkreis - T: (07217) 6013. Head: Dr. Herbert Traxler
Special Museum - 1973
Memorabilia on Hans Schnopfhagen, composer of the Upper Austrian antheme and Heinrich Suso Waldeck, priest and poet 02592

Ortsmuseum Sankt Veit, Schnopfhagenpl 4, 4173 Sankt Veit im Mühlkreis - T: (07217) 6013
Local Museum 02593

Sankt Veit im Pongau

Seelackenmuseum, Langmoos 41, 5621 Sankt Veit im Pongau - T: (06415) 5177, Fax: 6362. Head: Alois Reiter
Local Museum - 1988 02594

Sankt Wolfgang im Salzkammergut

Internationale Puppenausstellung, Josef-Stern-Allee 101, 5360 Sankt Wolfgang im Salzkammergut - T: (06138) 2323. Head: Margit Bachler-Rix
Special Museum - 1970
More than 300 dolls from various countries, accessories 02595

Michael Pacher-Haus, Markt 28, 5360 Sankt Wolfgang im Salzkammergut - T: (06138) 23120, Fax: 231281, E-mail: gemeindeamt@st-wolfgang.ooe.gv.at. Head: Johannes Peinsteiner
Public Gallery 02596

Schatzkammer - Turmmuseum der Pfarrkirche, Pfarrkirche, 5360 Sankt Wolfgang im Salzkammergut - T: (06138) 2321, Fax: 3169
Religious Arts Museum
Famous site of pilgrimage, sacral objects 02597

Saxen

Strindberg-Museum Saxen, Nr 7, 4351 Saxen - T: (07269) 284, Fax: 60204, E-mail: ch.lettner@eduhi.at. Head: Christoph Lettner
Special Museum 02598

Schärding

Städtisches Museum, Schloßgasse 5, 4780 Schärding - T: (07712) 6303, 3154. Head: Norbert Leitner
Local Museum - 1906
Town and regional hist, prehistoric finds, folk customs and art, peasant and town-dweller furnishings, arts and crafts, Gothic and Baroque painting and sculpture, superstitions, memorabilia of the poets M. Denis and R. Billinger and the chronicler J.E. Lamprecht 02599

Schalchen

Heimathaus Schalchen, Hauptstr 23, 5231 Schalchen - T: (07742) 4130
Local Museum
Hist of the skythe smithy, hey barn 02600

Schardenberg

Troadkasten, Haus Nr. 57, 4784 Schardenberg - T: (07713) 6518. Head: Cäcilia Doppermann
Agriculture Museum
Agricultural implements 02601

Scharnstein

Museum für Österreichische Zeitgeschichte, Schloss, 4644 Scharnstein - T: (0664) 3005677, Fax: 21446784. Head: Harald Seyrl
Historical Museum 02602

Museum Geyerhammer, Grubbachstr 10, 4644 Scharnstein - T: (07615) 2365, 2381, Fax: 236575, E-mail: s.pesendorfer@eduhi.at, Internet: http://www.welcome.to/museum.geyerhammer. Head: Walter Luckeneder
Science&Tech Museum - 1991
Skythe production site 02603

Österreichisches Kriminalmuseum, Schloßberg 12, 4644 Scharnstein - T: (0664) 3005677, Fax: (01) 21446384, E-mail: kriminalmuseum@aon.at. Head: Harald Seyrl
Special Museum - 1973
Exhibits on criminal law 02604

Scheibbs

Heimatmuseum, Rathauspl 1, 3270 Scheibbs - T: (07482) 2511
Local Museum - 1952
Handicraft, docs, instruments of torture, arms 02605

Schützenscheibenmuseum, Rathauspl 10, 3270 Scheibbs - T: (07482) 42511, 46072
Special Museum - 1991 02606

Scheifling

Heimatmuseum des Heimatkreises Scheiflingertal, Bahnhofstr 67, 8811 Scheifling - T: (03582) 286
Local Museum - 1982
Local hist, pipes, tobacco 02607

Schladming

Stadtmuseum Schladming, Bruderladenhaus, Talbachgasse 110, 8970 Schladming - T: (03687) 2250832, Fax: 2250840. Head: Rudolf Nebl
Local Museum - 1989
Minerals, mining equipment, history of Schladming, folk sagas, geology 02608

Schleinbach

Museum Kunst-Kultur-Kellerromantik, Himmelkeller, Kronberg 157, 2123 Schleinbach - T: (02245) 4377, Fax: (02246) 34243. Head: Hermann Bauch
Historical Museum - 1965 02609

Schlierbach

Museum des Zisterzienserstifts mit Margret Bilger-Galerie, Stift, Schlierbach 1, 4553 Schlierbach - T: (07582) 83013123, Fax: 83013176, E-mail: office@stift-schlierbach.at, Internet: http://www.stift-schlierbach.at. Head: Alfred Strigl
Religious Arts Museum / Fine Arts Museum - 1973
Historical interiors, religious arts and crafts, in 14th c Cistercien cloister - library 02610

Schlosshof

Schloss Schlosshof, Nr 1, 2294 Schlosshof - T: (02285) 6580, Fax: 6580, E-mail: info@schlosshof.at, Internet: http://www.schlosshof.at. Head: Brigitte Gawlik
Decorative Arts Museum
Formerly owned by Prince Eugen of Savoyen, Viennese 02611

Schnifis

Militärgeschichtliche Ortssammlung, Gemeindeamt, 6822 Schnifis - T: (05524) 8515, Fax: 851520, E-mail: gemeinde@schnifis.at. Head: Heinrich Erhart
Military Museum - 1986 02612

Schörfling

Heimathaus Schörfling, Gmundner Str, 4861 Schörfling - T: (07662) 2543, 2259, Fax: 5570, E-mail: v_heimatpflege@yahoo.de
Local Museum 02613

Schoppernau

Franz Michael Felder-Stube, Unterdorf 2, 6886 Schoppernau - T: (05515) 21130, 2495, Fax: 211319, E-mail: gemeindeamt@schoppernau.at, Internet: http://www.schoppernau.at
Local Museum - 1969 02614

Schrattenberg

Alte Mühle Schrattenberg, Schafzeile 23, 2172 Schrattenberg - T: (02555) 2332, Fax: 23324, Internet: http://tiscover.com/schrattenberg.noe
Science&Tech Museum - 1921 02615

Schrems

Heimatmuseum, Kirchenpl, Schulgasse 4, 3943 Schrems - T: (02853) 774540, 76502, Fax: 7745444, E-mail: gemeinde@schrems.at
Local Museum - 1966
Local hist, textiles, agricultural tools 02616

Schruns

Montafoner Heimatmuseum Schruns, Kirchpl 15, 6780 Schruns - T: (05556) 74723, Fax: 74723/24, E-mail: andi.gier@eunet.at
Local Museum - 1906
Folklore, furniture, Alpine dairy farming 02617

Schwanenstadt

Heimathaus Schwanenstadt, Stadtpl 54, 4690 Schwanenstadt - T: (07673) 3521, Fax: 225539
Local Museum - 1949
Agricultural tools, crafts, Roman finds 02618

Schwarzenberg am Böhmerwald

Heimatstube Schwarzenberg am Böhmerwald, Nr 113, 4164 Schwarzenberg am Böhmerwald - T: (07280) 306, 82550, Fax: 82554, E-mail: schwarzenberg@netway.at
Local Museum - 1976
Glas production and various types of farm house styles, tomb of Schwarzenberg 02619

Schwarzenberger Skulpturenpark, Nr 113, 4164 Schwarzenberg am Böhmerwald - T: (07280) 306, 2550, Fax: 2554, E-mail: schwarzenberg@netway.at, Internet: http://www.tiscover.com/schwarzenberg.boemerwald. Head: Franz Deutschbauer
Fine Arts Museum - 1976 02620

Schwarzenberg in Vorarlberg

Heimatmuseum, Brand 34, 6867 Schwarzenberg in Vorarlberg - T: (05512) 2967, 2084, Fax: 2902, E-mail: schw@fh-vorarlberg.ac.at
Fine Arts Museum / Local Museum - 1913
Housing, costume, paintings by Angelika Kauffmann 02621

Schwaz

Erstes Tiroler Feuerwehrmuseum, Marktstr 19, 6130 Schwaz - T: (05242) 62371, Fax: 71419, E-mail: k.rinnergschwentner@schwaz.at, Internet: htpp://www.schwaz.at/feuerwehr
Science&Tech Museum / Special Museum - 1984 02622

Galerie der Stadt Schwaz, Palais Enzenberg, Franz Josef-Str 27, 6130 Schwaz - T: (05242) 73983, Fax: 66896, E-mail: galerie.stadt.schwaz@netway.at. Head: Martin Janda
Fine Arts Museum - 1993 02623

Haus der Völker, Museum für Kunst und Ethnographie, Chr.-Anton Mayr-Weg 7, 6130 Schwaz - T: (05242) 66090, Fax: 66091, E-mail: haus.d.voelker@chello.at, Internet: http://www.hausdervoelker.com. Head: Prof. Gert Chesi
Fine Arts Museum / Ethnology Museum - 1995
African and Asian folk art 02624

Museum der Stadt Schwaz, Schloß Freundsberg, Burggasse 55, 6130 Schwaz - T: (05242) 63967. Head: Ferdl Angerer
Science&Tech Museum / Local Museum - 1930
Silver mining exhibits, coll of costumes and wooden masks 02625

Schwazer Silberbergwerk, Alte Landstr 3a, 6130 Schwaz - T: (05242) 72372, Fax: 723724, E-mail: info@silberbergwerk.at, Internet: http://www.silberbergwerk.at. Head: Alexander Sarlay
Historical Museum - 1990 02626

Schwechat

Neues Museum Schwechat, Neukettenhofer Str 6-8, 2320 Schwechat - T: (01) 70108-284, Fax: 7073223, E-mail: stadtgemeinde@schwechat.gv.at, Internet: http://www.schwechat.gv.at. Head: Adolf Ezsöl
Local Museum 02627

Schweiggers

Gemeindemuseum, Marktpl 74, 3931 Schweiggers - T: (02829) 8234, Fax: 7348
Local Museum - 1973 02628

Seckau

Benediktinerabtei und Abteimuseum, Abtei, 8732 Seckau - T: (03514) 234. Head: Dr. Stephan Chr. Dorner
Religious Arts Museum
Historical interiors, religious art and liturgical items, coins, 12th c cloister - library 02629

Kunsthistorisches Museum, 8732 Seckau - T: (03514) 205
Fine Arts Museum / Historical Museum 02630

Seebenstein

Burgmuseum, 2824 Seebenstein - T: (02627) 47017
Historical Museum
Items of furniture from various epochs, Chinese and Japanese porcelain, armoury 02631

Seeham

Freilichtmuseum Kugelmühle, Wildkarwasserfall, 5164 Seeham - T: (06217) 525. Head: Matthias Hemetsberger
Open Air Museum / Science&Tech Museum - 1981
Local hist, production of marbles 02632

Seitenstetten

Kunstsammlung des Benediktinerstifts Seitenstetten, Am Klosterberg 1, 3353 Seitenstetten - T: (07477) 423000, Fax: 4230050, E-mail: stift@stift-seitenstetten.at, Internet: http://www.stift-seitenstetten.at. Head: Martin Mayrhofer
Fine Arts Museum - 1819
Historical buildings from 12th-18th c, interiors, Gothic to Baroque painting and sculpture, natural hist, graphics, mss, archaeology - library, music archives 02633

Serfaus

Tiroler Kaiserjägermuseum Obergricht, Sankt Zeno 3, 6534 Serfaus - T: (05476) 6327, Fax: 632865. Head: Barbara Drucha-Graber
Historical Museum - 1991
Culture of living, Tyrolean folk customs, agricultural trades - archive 02634

Siegendorf

Freilichtmuseum Spätbronzezeitlicher Hügelgräber, Im Schuschenwald, 7011 Siegendorf - T: (02682) 62652, Fax: 6271530, E-mail: Bgld.LM@aon.at. Head: Dr. Gerald Schlag
Open Air Museum / Archaeological Museum - 1974
Excavated and reconstructed mound grave of a warrior from 1200 BC, grave finds 02635

Siget

Heimatmuseum, 7501 Siget - T: (03352) 2501
Local Museum - 1956 02636

Sigharting

Schloßmuseum, Nr 1, 4771 Sigharting - T: (07766) 24050, Fax: 240515, E-mail: gemeinde@sigharting.ooe.at. Head: Eberhard Pöstinger
Local Museum / Science&Tech Museum - 1984
Agricultural tools 02637

Sigmundsherberg

Waldviertler Eisenbahnmuseum, Bahnhof, 3751 Sigmundsherberg - T: (02983) 2307360, Fax: 2307313. Head: Rupert Öhlknecht
Science&Tech Museum - 1987 02638

Sillian

Kutschen- und Heimatmuseum, Nr 17, 9920 Sillian - T: (04842) 6657, 6666. Head: Herbert Troyer, Eva Bernatzky
Local Museum / Folklore Museum - 1993 02639

Simonsfeld

Bauernhaus 1809 vor der Industrialisierung, Haus Nr. 41, 2115 Simonsfeld - T: (02576) 2965
Agriculture Museum 02640

Sonntag

Heimatmuseum Großes Walsertal, Flecken 17, 6731 Sonntag - T: (05554) 5110
Local Museum - 1981
Crafts, agriculture 02641

Spannberg

Bauernmuseum Spannberg, Hauptstr 55, 2244 Spannberg - T: (02538) 87782
Agriculture Museum - 1981
Peasant life, tools 02642

Spital am Pyhrn

Österreichisches Felsbildermuseum, Nr 1, 4582 Spital am Pyhrn - T: (07563) 318, Fax: 318, Internet: http://www.felsbildermuseum.at. Head: Christine Eggl
Fine Arts Museum - 1979
Photos and graphics of rock art in Austria and other rock carving localities 02643

Spittal an der Drau

Galerie im Schloß Porcia, Burgpl 1, 9800 Spittal an der Drau - T: (04762) 3420, Fax: 3237, Internet: http://www.spittal-drau.at. Head: Klaus Zlattinger, Ingrid Weichselberger
Public Gallery - 1980 02644

Museum für Volkskultur Spittal an der Dau, Schloß Porcia, Burgpl 1, 9800 Spittal an der Drau - T: (04762) 2890, Fax: 565067, E-mail: museum@spittal-drau.at, Internet: http://www.buk.ktn.gv.at/museumspittal. Head: Dr. Hartmut Prasch
Folklore Museum - 1958
Period rooms of the 16th c castle, hunting, folk art, handicrafts, toys, customs, religious art, paintings by Karl Truppe, glass production in Upper Carinthia, mining, pottery, history of education, alpine farming, wintersports, mountaineering - archives, library 02645

Spitz

Schiffahrtsmuseum, Auf der Wehr 21, 3620 Spitz - T: (02713) 2246. Head: Reinhold Nothnagl
Science&Tech Museum - 1969
History and development of navigation of the Danube, rowboat and raft navigation, tools and equipment used in ship building, models of old ships and rafts, open air museum with two historical wooden ships - archive, library 02646

Stadl-Paura

Schiffleutmuseum, Fabrikstr 13, 4651 Stadl-Paura - T: (07245) 4651
Special Museum - 1934
History of navigation of the Traun, models, local history, peasant furnishings 02647

Stadtschlaining

Burg Schlaining mit Museum → Europäisches Museum für Frieden

Europäisches Museum für Frieden, Rochuspl 1, 7461 Stadtschlaining - T: (03355) 2306, Fax: 2306, E-mail: orthofer@aspr.ac.at, Internet: http://wwwaspr.ac.at. Head: Dr. Manfred Hainzl
Historical Museum / Fine Arts Museum - 2001
Artefacts in the contex of violence, conflict and peace 02648

Stainz

Volkskundlich-Landwirtschaftliche Sammlung, Landesmuseum Joanneum Graz, Schloss Stainz, 8510 Stainz - T: (03463) 27720, Fax: 277220, E-mail: kuegerl@lmj.nt1.stlrg.gv.at, Internet: http://www.museum-joanneum.at. Head: Dr. Roswitha Orac-Stipperger
Agriculture Museum / Folklore Museum - 1968
Styrian peasant life, furniture, domestic utensils, tools, 16th-18th c peasant rooms, cookbooks, archives on "Baumkuchen", carrying frames, farming sledges and cars, agricultural machines of the 19th and 20th c - workshop, library 02649

Stams

Zisterzienserstift und Stiftssammlungen, Stiftshof 1, 6422 Stams - T: (05263) 624253, Fax: 6080, E-mail: stift.stams@tirol.com, Internet: http://www.tirol.com/stift-stams. Head: Norbert Schnellhammer-Ocist
Religious Arts Museum - 1973
Ornate historical rooms, religious art, artistic locks, inlaid work, 13th c Cistercian cloister 02650

Stegersbach

Regional- und Telegrafenmuseum, Sparkassenpl 2, 7551 Stegersbach - T: (03326) 54489, 52230, Fax: 52242. Head: Dr. G. Schlag
Local Museum / Science&Tech Museum - 1969
Costume, furniture, biology, geology, archaeology, folklore 02651

Steinach

Alfons Graber-Museum, Brennerstr 28, 6150 Steinach - T: (05272) 6006, Fax: 6251. Head: Fritz Plattner
Fine Arts Museum - 1990
Paintings and drawings by Alfons Graber 02652

Steinbach am Attersee

Hausmühle, Bei der Kaisingerbrücke, 4853 Steinbach am Attersee - T: (07663) 259. Head: Johann Zopf
Science&Tech Museum
Former mill 02653

Heimathaus Steinbach am Attersee, Seefeld 26, 4853 Steinbach am Attersee - T: (07663) 401
Local Museum
Production and transport of wood 02654

Komponierstube Gustav Mahlers, Hotel-Gasthof, Seefeld 14, 4853 Steinbach am Attersee - T: (07663) 8100, Fax: 810042, E-mail: hotel-foettinger@salzkammergut.at, Internet: http://www.foettinger.at. Head: Franz Föttinger
Music Museum - 1985
Little house in which Mahler composed his 2nd and 3rd symphonies 02655

Steyr

Eisenuhren- und Antikuhrenmuseum, Grünmarkt 2, 4400 Steyr - T: (07252) 530910, Fax: 5309118, E-mail: office@schmollgruber.at, Internet: http://www.schmollgruber.at. Head: Friedrich Schmollgruber
Science&Tech Museum - 1958 02656

Galerie Schloß Lamberg, Stadtpl 27, 4400 Steyr - T: (07252) 5750, Fax: 48386
Public Gallery 02657

Kunsthalle Steyr, Pyrachstr 1, 4401 Steyr - T: (07252) 46163, Fax: 47746, E-mail: office@kunsthallesteyr.com, Internet: http://www.kunsthallesteyr.com. Head: Reinhold Rebhandl
Public Gallery - 1997 02658

Museum Arbeitswelt Steyr, Wehrgrabengasse 7, 4400 Steyr - T: (07252) 77351, Fax: 7735111, E-mail: office@museum-steyr.at, Internet: http://www.museum-steyr.at. Head: Gabriele Heger
Science&Tech Museum - 1987
Industrial hist 02659

Museum der Stadt Steyr, Grünmarkt 26, 4400 Steyr - T: (07252) 575348. Head: Dr. Volker Lutz
Local Museum - 1913
Historical armour and weapons, Baroque interiors, knife coll (500 exhibits from 4 continents), folklore, metallurgy 02660

Museumsbahn Steyrtal, Redtenbachergasse 14, 4400 Steyr - T: (07252) 46569
Science&Tech Museum
Local railway and its hist, utensils 02661

Sammlung Bodingbauer, Schuhbodengasse 1, 4400 Steyr - T: (07252) 70035. Head: Prof. Adolf Karl Bodingbauer
Decorative Arts Museum - 1963
Baroque painting, graphics, religious art, glass, furniture 02662

Sommerhuber-Kachelofenmuseum, c/o Sommerhuber Keramik GmbH, Resthofstr 69, 4400 Steyr - T: (07252) 8930, Fax: 893210, E-mail: keramik@sommerhuber.co.at, Internet: http://www.sommerhuber.co.at. Head: Rudolf Christian Sommerhuber
Decorative Arts Museum - 1984
From the campfire site to the tiled stove 02663

Steyr-Gleink

Bauern-Technik-Museum, Thannstr 22, Dietach, 4407 Steyr-Gleink - T: (07252) 38294, Fax: 38294
Science&Tech Museum / Folklore Museum
Farming implements, must presses, folk costumes, vehicles 02664

Stiftsmuseum Steyr-Gleink, Gleinker Hauptstr 20, 4407 Steyr-Gleink - T: (07252) 80901, Fax: 8090150, E-mail: spz-gleink@caritas-linz.or.at. Head: Ute Hünninghaus-Böckmann
Religious Arts Museum
Sacral objects from the Baroque, chalices, candelabras, reliquaries 02665

Steyregg

Heimatmuseum Steyregg, Stadtturmgasse 11, 4221 Steyregg - T: (0732) 640677
Local Museum
Early and prehist, geology 02666

Steyrermühl

Feuerwehrmuseum, Museumspl 1, 4662 Steyrermühl - T: (07613) 3951, Fax: 8834
Historical Museum - 1997 02667

Papiermachermuseum, Museumspl 1, 4662 Steyrermühl - T: (07613) 3951, Fax: 8834. Head: Karl Neuwirth
Historical Museum - 1999 02668

Stillfried

Museum für Ur- und Frühgeschichte, Im Schulhaus, 2262 Stillfried - T: (02283) 2493. Head: Prof. Gerhard Antl
Historical Museum - 1914/1979 02669

Stinatz

Heimatmuseum Stinatz, 7552 Stinatz - T: (03358) 2433
Local Museum - 1975
Peasant life 02670

Stockerau

Automobil-Museum Siegfried Marcus, Schießstattgasse 9, 2000 Stockerau - T: (02266) 645642, Fax: 645644, E-mail: siegfried.marcus@xpoint.at, Internet: http://www.siegfried-marcus.at. Head: Peter Malek
Science&Tech Museum - 1986 02671

Bezirksmuseum Stockerau, Belvederegasse 3, 2000 Stockerau - T: (02266) 65188. Head: Dr. Günter Sellinger
Local Museum - 1910
Paleontology, prehistory, early history, numismatics, natural history 02672

Stockern

Schatzkammer der Wallfahrtskirche Maria Dreieichen, Pfarramt, 3744 Stockern - T: (02982) 8253, Fax: 825318. Head: Robert Boesner
Religious Arts Museum - 1780
Votive pictures 02673

Stoob

Evangelisches Diözesanmuseum im Burgenland, Hauptstr 140, 7344 Stoob - T: (02612) 43491, Fax: 43491. Head: Wolfgang Klietmann
Religious Arts Museum - 1982 02674

Töpfermuseum, Hauptstr 85-87, 7344 Stoob - T: (02612) 42436, 42197
Decorative Arts Museum - 1979 02675

Strass

Truppenmuseum, Hauptstr 75, 8472 Strass - T: (03453) 261184. Head: Christian Lichenecker
Military Museum - 1970
History of the Archduke Johann Barracks from 1900 until today 02676

Straßburg

Volkskundliche und kirchliche Sammlungen, Schloß Straßburg, 9341 Straßburg - T: (04266) 23750, 223612
Religious Arts Museum / Folklore Museum - 1991
Peasant household and farming utensils 02677

Strasshof

Eisenbahnmuseum Strasshof - Das Heizhaus, Sillerstr 123, 2231 Strasshof - T: (01) 6035301, Fax: 6022196/22, E-mail: museum@heizhaus.com, Internet: http://www.heizhaus.com. Head: Jan A. Janu
Science&Tech Museum - 1984
Historical railroads, tools, and machines - workshop 02678

Strobl

Aberseer Heimathaus, Lipphaus-Museum, Nr 3-4, 5350 Strobl - T: (06137) 6594. Head: Sigmund Eisl
Local Museum - 1978
Local culture, household implements, agriculture 02679

Stübing bei Graz

Österreichisches Freilichtmuseum Stübing, Enzenbach 32, 8114 Stübing bei Graz - T: (03124) 53700, Fax: 5370018, E-mail: service@freilichtmuseum.at, Internet: http://www.freilichtmuseum.at. Head: Prof. DDr. V.H. Pöttler
Open Air Museum - 1962
93 farm houses and village buildings with their original equipment, agricultural vehicles and tools 02680

Sulz

Motorradmuseum, Sammlung Waldmann, Lange Seite 132, 2392 Sulz - T: (02238) 8708, Fax: (01) 5233386, E-mail: erich.waldmann@tgm.ac.at, Internet: http://www.drive.to/motorradmuseum. Head: Erich Waldmann
Science&Tech Museum - 1987
Motorbikes, bicycles, motorcycles 02681

Tainach

Galerie des Bildungshauses Sodalitas, Nr. 119, 9121 Tainach - T: (04239) 26420, Fax: 264276, E-mail: office@sodalitas.at, Internet: http://www.sodalitas.at. Head: Josef Kopeinig
Public Gallery - 1980 02682

Tamsweg

Lungauer Heimatmuseum Tamsweg, Kirchengasse 133, 5580 Tamsweg - T: (06474) 6504, Fax: 6504
Local Museum - 1962
Peasant life, costume, archaeology, religious art 02683

Schloß Moosham, Unternberg, 5580 Tamsweg - T: (06476) 305, 368, Fax: 305. Head: Alexander Graf Wilczek jun.
Decorative Arts Museum - 1256 02684

Tannheim

Heimatmuseum Tannheimer Tal, Kienzen 7, 6675 Tannheim - T: (05675) 6532
Local Museum - 1981
Crafts, trade, local housing and economy 02685

Tarrenz

Heimatmuseum, Schulgasse 19, 6464 Tarrenz - T: (05412) 66008, 68722, Fax: 65709
Local Museum - 1981
Peasant culture 02686

Taufkirchen an der Pram

Heimatmuseum, Hauptschule, Nr 80, 4775 Taufkirchen an der Pram - T: (07719) 7388, 7378, Fax: 7388, E-mail: hs.taufkirchen.pram@eduhi.at
Local Museum - 1953
Tools, lamps, musical instruments 02687

Teesdorf

Franz Jonas-Gedenkraum, 2524 Teesdorf - T: (02253) 81444. Head: Anna Seitz
Local Museum 02688

Heimatmuseum, Schulstr 11, 2524 Teesdorf - T: (02253) 81444
Local Museum - 1966
Crafts, viticulture 02689

Hermann Broch-Museum, Schulstr 11, 2524 Teesdorf - T: (02253) 81444. Head: Anna Seitz
Special Museum - 1966
Memorabilia of the writer Hermann Broch, his pipe coll 02690

Telfs

Bergbauernmuseum, Ropferhof, 6410 Telfs - T: (05262) 64490, Fax: 5801896
Agriculture Museum 02691

Heimatmuseum, Sparkassenpl 1, 6410 Telfs - T: (05262) 31752
Local Museum - 1966
Folk art, tools and domestic utensils, manger scenes, masks worn in local folk festival 02692

Textilmuseum Firma Franz Pischl, Niedere-Munde-Str 9, 6410 Telfs - T: (05262) 2312. Head: Rupert Pischl
Special Museum - 1978 02693

Ternberg

Museum in der Wegscheid, Kirchenpl 12, 4452 Ternberg - T: (07256) 6005, Fax: 600580, Internet: http://www.tiscover.com/ternberg
Local Museum / Folklore Museum - 1998 02694

Ternitz

Stadtgalerie im alten Herrenhaus, Franz-Dinhobl-Str 2, 2630 Ternitz - T: (02630) 3824058, Fax: 3824074, E-mail: gemeinde@ternitz.at, Internet: http://www.ternitz.at. Head: Gerhard Hainfellner
Fine Arts Museum - 1997 02695

Texing

Dr. Engelbert Dollfuß-Museum, Großmaierhof 1, 3242 Texing - T: (02755) 7228, Fax: 72284, E-mail: gemeindetexingtal@netway.at, Internet: http://www.tiscover.com/texingtal. Head: Karl Franc
Special Museum / Historical Museum - 1998 02696

Schloßmuseum, Schloß Plankenstein, 3242 Texing - T: (02755) 7254, Fax: 7468. Head: Hans-Peter Trimbacher
Local Museum - 1978
Folklore, carpets, ceramics 02697

Thalgau

Hundsmarktmühle, Thalgauegg 24, 5303 Thalgau - T: (06235) 6417, Fax: 6363. Head: Christiana Nussbaumer
Science&Tech Museum / Local Museum - 1990 02698

Thaya

Ausgrabungen Wüstung Hard, Bahnhofstr 1a, Wüstungsareal, 3842 Thaya - T: (02842) 52663, Fax: 54354, E-mail: gde.thaya@netway.at, Internet: http://www.wvnet.at/gemeinden/thaya. Head: Prof. Dr. Sabine Felgenhauer-Schmiedt
Archaeological Museum 02699

Heimatmuseum, Bahnhofstr 1a, 3842 Thaya - T: (02842) 52663, Fax: 54354, E-mail: gde.thaya@netway.at, Internet: http://www.wvnet.at/gemeinden/thaya
Local Museum - 1977
Folklore, traditions, local hist 02700

Thernberg

Erzherzog Johann-Dokumentationsstätte, Mesnerhaus, Markt 2, 2832 Thernberg - T: (02629) 3412, Fax: 2334, 3188, E-mail: -marktgem.scheiblingkirchen@compufit.at, Internet: http://www.thernberg.at/erzherzog. Head: Martin Lechner
Historical Museum - 1990 02701

Thomatal

Hochofen-Museum Bundschuh, Bundschuh, 5591 Thomatal - T: (06476) 250, Fax: 25022, E-mail: eisen@hochofen-bundschuh.at, Internet: http://www.hochofen-bundschuh.at
Science&Tech Museum - 1974 02702

Traiskirchen

Stadtmuseum Traiskirchen, Hauptpl 13, 2514 Traiskirchen - T: (02252) 52611, Fax: 56924, E-mail: office@traiskirchen.gv.at. Head: Franz Schlögl
Local Museum - 1986 02703

Traismauer

Heimatmuseum, Florianipl 13, 3133 Traismauer - T: (02783) 6120, 8555, Fax: 6120
Local Museum - 1931 02704

Museum für Frühgeschichte des Landes Niederösterreich, Schloß, Hauptpl 1, 3133 Traismauer - T: (02783) 8555, 6272, Fax: 6272. Head: Dr. Helmut Windl
Historical Museum - 1989 02705

Urzeitmuseum Nußdorf ob der Traisen, Schloßgarten, 3133 Traismauer - T: (02783) 7465, Fax: 7464. Head: Dr. J.-W. Neugebauer
Historical Museum - 1993 02706

Traun

Galerie der Stadt Traun, Hauptpl 1, 4050 Traun - T: (07229) 688117, 688105, Fax: 68899105, E-mail: alexandra.wolf@traun.at, Internet: http://www.traun.at. Head: Prof. Gertrude Haider
Fine Arts Museum - 1985 02707

Heimatvertriebenen-Stuben, Schloß Traun, 4050 Traun - T: (07582) 51793, Fax: (07229) 688170
Historical Museum / Folklore Museum
Memorabilia of the expellees from the South-East of Europe, folk art and costumes 02708

Trautenfels

Landschaftsmuseum im Schloß Trautenfels, Steiermärkisches Landesmuseum Joanneum, 8951 Trautenfels - T: (03682) 222330, Fax: 2223344, E-mail: post@museumtrautenfels.at, Internet: http://www.museumtrautenfels.at. Head: Dr. Volker Hänsel
Folklore Museum - 1951
Folk art, forestry, alpine pastures, weaving, apiculture, furniture 02709

Treffen bei Villach

Elli Riehl-Puppenmuseum, Winklern 14, Einöde, 9521 Treffen bei Villach - T: (04248) 2395. Head: Elfriede Berger
Special Museum - 1977 02710

Trofaiach

Heimatmuseum, Rebenburggasse 2, 8793 Trofaiach - T: (03847) 2255
Local Museum - 1975
Costume, crafts, local hist 02711

Türnitz

Feuerwehrmuseum, Nr 38, 3184 Türnitz - T: (02769) 7258, Fax: 7160
Historical Museum - 1986 02712

K & K-Museum, Schafluckmühle, Anthofrotte 7, 3184 Türnitz - T: (02769) 7472. Head: Andreas Leitner
Historical Museum - 1990
Items of Kaiser Karl 02713

Tulln

Egon Schiele-Museum, Donaulände 28, 3430 Tulln - T: (02272) 64570, Fax: 690400, E-mail: stadtamt@tulln.at, Internet: http://www.tulln.at/stadt/bildung/b_mus06.htm. Head: Hermann Kramer
Fine Arts Museum
Biographical dep, 90 original works by Schiele 02714

Limesmuseum, Marc-Aurel-Park 5, 3430 Tulln - T: (02272) 61915, Fax: 6191534, E-mail: stadtamt@tulln.at, Internet: http://www.tulln.at/stadt/bildung/b_mus00.htm. Head: Dr. Roderich Geyer, Prof. Dr. Hansjörg Ubl
Local Museum / Special Museum 02715

Niederösterreichisches Feuerwehrmuseum, Minoritenpl 1, 3430 Tulln - T: (02272) 6073206, 3170, Fax: 6073135, E-mail: joerg.wuerzelberger@noel.gv.at, Internet: http://www.feuerwehr-noe-ov.at. Head: Jörg Würzelberger
Science&Tech Museum - 1979 02716

Österreichisches Zuckermuseum, Minoritenpl 1, 3430 Tulln - T: (02272) 602230, 61915, Fax: 602225, E-mail: gerhard.hammerschmied@agrana.at. Head: Gerhard Hammerschmied
Special Museum - 1982
Hist of sugar production 02717

Tullner Museen im Minoritenkloster, Minoritenpl 1, 3430 Tulln - T: (02272) 61915, Fax: 6191534, E-mail: stadtamt@tulln.at, Internet: http://www.tulln.at. Head: Dr. Roderich Geyer
Local Museum / Archaeological Museum - 1993 02718

Tullnerbach-Lawies

Metallmuseum, Hauptstr 39, 3013 Tullnerbach-Lawies - T: (02233) 52442. Head: Ernst Zoubek
Special Museum / Natural History Museum - 1970 02719

Tumeltsham

Feuerwehrsmuseum, Haus Nr. 30, 4910 Tumeltsham - T: (07752) 82904
Science&Tech Museum
Hist of the fire brigade, implements, uniforms 02720

Ulmerfeld-Hausmening

Sammlungen der Stadt Amstetten auf Schloß Ulmerfeld, Burgweg 1, 3363 Ulmerfeld-Hausmening - T: (07475) 5232611, Fax: 5232615, E-mail: l.naderer@amstetten.noe.gv.at
Local Museum 02721

Ulrichsberg

Galerie in der Hauptschule, Schulgasse 6, 4161 Ulrichsberg - T: (07288) 70292, Fax: 70294, E-mail: woge@utanet.at. Head: Gerhard Wöß
Public Gallery - 1996 02722

Heimathaus Ulrichsberg, Markt 28, 4161 Ulrichsberg - T: (07288) 7005, Fax: 700515, E-mail: ulrichsberg@netway.at, Internet: http://www.tiscover.com/ulrichsberg
Local Museum / Historical Museum - 1992
Economic and cultural hist of the Bohemian Forest, glas manufacture - Glass-museum 02723

Unken

Festung Kniepaß, Unkenberg 1, 5091 Unken - T: (06589) 42020. Head: Helmut Adler
Local Museum - 1968
Fortress 02724

Heimatmuseum Kalchofengut, Nr 25, 5091 Unken - T: (06589) 202
Agriculture Museum / Local Museum - 1968
Original farmyard (400 yrs old) 02725

Unterwart

Unterwarter Heimathaus, Nr. 208, 7501 Unterwart - T: (03352) 34179, 34020. Head: Ernst Szabo
Local Museum - 1970 02726

Unterweißenbach

Karlinger-Schmiede, Grafenschlag 16, 4273 Unterweißenbach - T: (07956) 7354. Head: Friedrich Karlinger
Science&Tech Museum
Hammer mill, farrier from the 17th c 02727

Villach

Archäologische Sammlung Warmbad-Villach, Kurzentrum Thermalheilbad Warmbad-Villach, 9504 Villach - T: (04242) 37000, Fax: 37000309. Head: H. Lukeschitsch
Archaeological Museum 02728

Galerie Freihausgasse, Galerie der Stadt Villach, Leiningengasse 12, 9500 Villach - T: (04242) 2053450, Fax: 2053499, E-mail: renate.obud@villach.at, Internet: http://www.villach.at. Head: Renate Obud
Public Gallery - 1993 02729

Museum der Stadt Villach, Widmanngasse 38, 9500 Villach - T: (04242) 205349, Fax: 205361, E-mail: museum@villach.at. Head: Dr. Dieter Neumann
Local Museum - 1873
Local archaeology, municipal history, local landscape painting (19th c), local minerals and fossils, large-scale topographical map of Carinthia 02730

Othmar Jaindl-Museum, Enzenbergstr 36, 9500 Villach - T: (04242) 52909. Head: Franz Jaindl
Fine Arts Museum - 1982 02731

Pilz-Lehrschau, Burgpl 4, 9500 Villach - T: (04242) 23501/278
Natural History Museum 02732

Puppenmuseum Hintermann, Vassacher Str 65, 9500 Villach - T: (04242) 22855, Fax: 2285575, E-mail: taupe@netway.at, Internet: http://www.netway.at/doll. Head: Georg & Ingrid Taupe
Decorative Arts Museum - 1994 02733

Villacher Fahrzeugmuseum, Draupromenade 12, 9500 Villach - T: (04242) 25530, Fax: 2553078, E-mail: uhren-pirker@carinthia.at, Internet: http://www.oldtimermuseum.at. Head: Rudolf Pirker
Science&Tech Museum - 1987 02734

Vils

Galerie Alte Schule, Bahnhofstr 10, 6682 Vils - T: (05677) 8852, Fax: 8852. Head: Sylvia Natterer
Fine Arts Museum - 1993 02735

Museum der Stadt Vils, Kapellenhof, 6682 Vils - T: (05677) 8290, 8522, Fax: (05672) 6248814. Head: Reinhold Schrettl
Local Museum - 1993 02736

Vöcklabruck

Galerie der Stadt Vöcklabruck, Hinterstadt 13-15, 4840 Vöcklabruck - T: (07672) 760217, Fax: 76081, E-mail: franz.huber@voecklabruck.at, Internet: http://www.voecklabruck.at. Head: Franz Huber
Public Gallery 02737

Heimathaus Vöcklabruck, Hinterstadt 15, 4840 Vöcklabruck - T: (07672) 5249
Local Museum
Pre and early hist, buildings on stilts, memorabilia of Bruckner, folklore 02738

Vöcklamarkt

Kinderweltmuseum, Schloß Walchen, 4870 Vöcklamarkt - T: (07682) 6246
Special Museum - 1979
The world of the child in all its aspects (education, clothing, play, food, etc) 02739

Völkermarkt

Bezirksheimatmuseum, Faschinggasse 1, 9100 Völkermarkt - T: (04232) 257139, Fax: 257128, E-mail: voelkermarkt@ktn.gde.at, Internet: http://www.suedkaernten.at. Head: Robert Wlattnig
Local Museum - 1984
Hist of Carinthia 1918-1920, local hist, local art 02740

Volders

Freilichtmuseum Himmelreich, Museum Wattens, Höralstr, 6112 Volders - T: (05224) 5002415, Fax: 5012415. Head: Guido Mark
Open Air Museum 02741

Schloß Friedberg, 6111 Volders - T: (0512) 588189, Fax: 577581. Head: Dr. Oswald Graf Trapp, Gaudenz Graf Trapp
Decorative Arts Museum 02742

Vomp

Stiftsmuseum, Benediktinerabtei Sankt Georgenberg-Fiecht, 6134 Vomp - T: (05242) 63276, Fax: 632767, E-mail: anselm@tirol.com, Internet: http://www.tirol.com/st-georgenberg-fiecht. Head: Anselm Zeller
Ethnology Museum / Religious Arts Museum / Local Museum - 1968
South Korea, Manchuria, East Africa, local hist 02743

Vorau

Freilichtmuseum Vorau, Nr 226, 8250 Vorau - T: (03337) 2342, 3466. Head: Alois Koschatko
Open Air Museum - 1979
Tools, mill, smithy, domestic utensils 02744

Vorchdorf

Emailmuseum Gertrude Stöhr, Fischerturm, Schloßpl 7, 4655 Vorchdorf - T: (07614) 8245. Head: Alfred Hollinetz
Decorative Arts Museum - 1980
Enamel works by Gertrude Stöhr 02745

Heimatmuseum Schloß Hochhaus, Schloßpl 1, 4655 Vorchdorf - T: (07614) 6444
Local Museum - 1985
Economic and settler's hist, portrayal of the watch-making family Krumphuber 02746

Oberösterreichischer Steingarten, Schulstr 8, 4655 Vorchdorf - T: (07614) 6444. Head: Rudolf Hüttner
Open Air Museum / Natural History Museum
Geology 02747

Vordernberg

Erzbergbahn- und Wintersportmuseum, Bahnhofstr 5, 8794 Vordernberg - T: (03849) 6004, Fax: 20618
Science&Tech Museum / Special Museum - 1980 02748

Hochofenmuseum Radwerk IV, Peter-Tunner-Str 2, 8794 Vordernberg - T: (03849) 283, Fax: 21995. Head: Prof. Dr. Herbert Hiebler
Science&Tech Museum - 1959
Mining implements, costumes, forging tools, metallurgy 02749

Wagna

Museum Flavia Solva (closed) 02750

Wagrain

Karl Heinrich Waggerl-Haus, Karl-Heinrich-Waggerl-Str 1, 5602 Wagrain - T: (06413) 821318, 8203, Fax: 821317, E-mail: kulturverein@wagrain.salzburg.at. Head: Margareta Kühhas
Special Museum - 1994
Literature, furniture, Karl Heinrich Waggerl, daily culture - archive 02751

Waidhofen an der Thaya

Erstes Waldviertler Webereimuseum, Moriz-Schadek-Gasse 4, 3830 Waidhofen an der Thaya - T: (02842) 51500, 53401
Science&Tech Museum - 1978/1990 02752

Heimathaus Waidhofen, Wiener Str 1, 3830 Waidhofen an der Thaya - T: (02842) 505112, Fax: 505168
Folklore Museum 02753

Heimatmuseum Waidhofen, Neues Museum, Moritz-Schadek-Gasse 4, 3830 Waidhofen an der Thaya - T: (02842) 53401, 54298
Local Museum - 1978 02754

Silomuseum, Raiffeisenstr 14, 3830 Waidhofen an der Thaya - T: (02842) 2535. Head: Johannes Jeitler
Agriculture Museum 02755

Waidhofen an der Ybbs

Heimatmuseum Waidhofen an der Ybbs, Oberer Stadtpl 32, 3340 Waidhofen an der Ybbs - T: (07442) 511247, Fax: 511247, E-mail: museum@waidhofen.at
Local Museum - 1905
Iron industry, paintings 02756

Privatsammlung Piaty, Untere Stadt 39, 3340 Waidhofen an der Ybbs - T: (07442) 53110, Fax: 5311040, E-mail: k.piaty@aon.at, Internet: http://www.members.aon.at/konditorei. Head: Karl Piaty
Folklore Museum - 1962
Folklore, 17th c farm house parlour 02757

Rathausgalerie, Oberer Stadtpl 28, 3340 Waidhofen an der Ybbs - T: (07442) 511222, Fax: 51199, E-mail: galerie@waidhofen.at, Internet: http://www.waidhofen.at. Head: Gabriele Rieser
Public Gallery - 1997
Contemporary art 02758

Waizenkirchen

Wilhelm Kienzl-Museum, Kienzlstr 1, 4730 Waizenkirchen - T: (07277) 2009. Head: Petra & Gerti Mayrhuber
Music Museum - 1957
Memorabilia and birth place of the composer of the "Evangelimannes" 02759

Waldkirchen

Museum Humanum, Fratres 11, 3844 Waldkirchen - T: (02843) 2874, 26625, Fax: 2874. Head: Peter Coreth
Historical Museum - 1997 02760

Waldviertler Puppenmuseum, Rudolz 26, 3844 Waldkirchen - T: (02843) 2858, 2282
Special Museum - 1985 02761

Wallsee

Römermuseum Wallsee-Sindelburg, Nr 27, 3313 Wallsee - T: (07433) 221622, Fax: 221620, Internet: http://www.netvillage.at/wallsee-sindelburg.htd. Head: Elmar Tscholl
Archaeological Museum - 1997 02762

Wartberg an der Krems

Heimathaus Wartenberg an der Krems, Kirchenpl 4, 4552 Wartberg an der Krems - T: (07587) 7451, Fax: 716129
Local Museum / Agriculture Museum
Fruit-juice production, agriculture, cultural items 02763

Wartberg im Mürztal

Heimatmuseum, Burgruine Lichtenegg, 8661 Wartberg im Mürztal - T: (03858) 2287, 2502, Fax: 228777
Local Museum - 1929
Tools, crafts 02764

Wattens

Industrie- und Vorgeschichtemuseum, Freilichtmuseum Himmelreich, 6112 Wattens - T: (05224) 585856
Science&Tech Museum / Open Air Museum 02765

Museum Wattens, Höraltstr 4, 6112 Wattens - T: (05224) 585856. Head: Guido Mark
Local Museum
Prehistory, industry 02766

Swarovski Kristallwelten, Kristallweltenstr 1, 6112 Wattens - T: (05224) 510800, Fax: 5108031, E-mail: swarovski.kristallwelt@swarovski.com, Internet: http://www.swarovski.kristallwelt.com. Head: Dr. Andreas Braun
Fine Arts Museum - 1995 02767

Weikendorf

Marchfeldmuseum, 2253 Weikendorf - T: (02282) 2218, Fax: 5418. Head: Johannes Rathfelder
Local Museum 02768

Weikertschlag

Ortsmuseum, Staufferweg 118, 3823 Weikertschlag - T: (02845) 282
Local Museum - 1994 02769

Weinburg

Dorfmuseum Weinburg, Kirchenstr 15, 3200 Weinburg - T: (02747) 26160, Fax: 26168, E-mail: gem.weinburg@direkt.at, Internet: http://www.weinburg.at
Local Museum 02770

Weissenbach an der Triesting

Triestingtaler Heimatmuseum, Kirchenpl 3, 2564 Weissenbach an der Triesting - T: (02674) 87822, Fax: 86339. Head: Wolfgang Stiawa
Local Museum - 1987 02771

Weißenkirchen im Attergau

Museum Freudenthaler Glassammlung, Nr. 3, 4890 Weißenkirchen im Attergau - T: (07684) 6355, 8279, Fax: 6355, E-mail: gemeinde@weissenkirchen.gemeinde.web.at. Head: Herbert Saminger
Decorative Arts Museum - 1981
Glas manufacture, vessels 02772

Weißenkirchen in der Wachau

Galerie im Teisenhoferhof der Malschule Motiv Wachau, Teisenhoferhof, 3610 Weißenkirchen in der Wachau - T: (02715) 22314, Fax: 223222, E-mail: gem.weissenkirchen@wvnet.at, Internet: http://www.weissenkirchen-wachau.at. Head: Stefan Jawurek
Fine Arts Museum - 1997 02773

Wachaumuseum, Nr 177, 3610 Weißenkirchen in der Wachau - T: (02715) 2268, Fax: 223222. Head: Dr. Joachim Rössl
Fine Arts Museum - 1965
Painting of the Wachau School (late 19th c) 02774

Weistrach

Blau-gelbe Viertelsgalerie, Mostviertel, Pfarrhofsiedlung 1, 3351 Weistrach - T: (07477) 42363, Fax: 43875, E-mail: gemeinde@weistrach.at, Internet: http://www.weistrach.at. Head: Leopold Kogler
Fine Arts Museum - 1988 02775

Weitensfeld im Gurktal

Schauraum über Geschichte und Brauchtum, Weitensfelder Kranzelreiten, Marktgemeindeamt, 9344 Weitensfeld im Gurktal - T: (04265) 2420, Fax: 7452. Head: Franz Stromberger
Local Museum 02776

Weitra

Museum Alte Textilfabrik, Brühl, Nr 13, 3970 Weitra - T: (02856) 2973, 2998, Fax: 2432, E-mail: -museum.alte.textilfabrik@aon.at, Internet: http://www.members.aon.at/textilmuseum. Head: Prof. Dr. A. Hackl
Science&Tech Museum / Historic Site - 1990 02777

Schlossmuseum Weitra, Schloss, 3970 Weitra - T: (02856) 3311, 2998, Fax: 33114, E-mail: schloss.weitra@aon.at, Internet: http://www.viaimperialis.at
Special Museum / Fine Arts Museum / Local Museum 02778

Waldviertler Bauernhaus-Museum, Moorbad Harbach, Lauterbach 11, 3970 Weitra - T: (02858) 3352, 5214, Fax: 5271
Agriculture Museum - 1982
Household equipment, tools 02779

Weiz

Galerie Weberhaus, Südtiroler Pl 1, 8160 Weiz - T: (03172) 6690, Fax: 669014, E-mail: weberhaus@weiz.steiermark.at, Internet: http://www.welz.at. Head: Georg Köhler
Public Gallery - 1990 02780

Wels

Agrargeschichtliche Sammlung, Burggasse 13, 4600 Wels - T: (07242) 235735, Fax: 235697, E-mail: ma03@wels.gv.at. Head: Dr. Renate Miglbauer
Agriculture Museum - 1958
Rural furniture, agricultural equipment and tools 02781

Galerie der Stadt Wels, Pollheimer Str 17, 4600 Wels - T: (07242) 235693, Fax: 235773, E-mail: galerie.wels@aon.at. Head: Günter Mayer, Lienhard Dinkhauser
Public Gallery - 1976 02782

Heidegalerie, Oberhartstr 7, 4600 Wels - T: (07242) 67567. Head: Waltraud Gabat
Fine Arts Museum - 1993 02783

Museum der Heimatvertriebenen, Burggasse 13, 4600 Wels - T: (07242) 235735, Fax: 235697, E-mail: ma03@wels.gv.at. Head: Dr. Renate Miglbauer
Historical Museum
Hist of the Swabian, Transilvania-Saxon, Sudeten-German, Carpathian-German and Buchenwald-German expellees from South-East Europe, costumes, folk customs 02784

Österreichisches Gebäckmuseum, Burggasse 13, 4600 Wels - T: (07242) 235735, Fax: 235697, E-mail: ma03@wels.gv.at. Head: Dr. Renate Miglbauer
Special Museum - 1983
Folk bakings 02785

Stadtmuseum Wels, Pollheimer Str 17, 4600 Wels - T: (07242) 235694, 235735, Fax: 235697, 235773, E-mail: ma03@wels.gv.at. Head: Dr. Renate Miglbauer
Local Museum - 1904
Early and pre-hist, Roman finds 02786

Welser Puppenweltmuseum, Stelzhamer Str 14, 4600 Wels - T: (07242) 44631, Fax: 44631. Head: Reingard Ecker
Special Museum - 1986
Dolls, dollhouses, teddy bears, tin soldiers - Playing corner 02787

Wendling

Traktorveteranensammlung Dorf an der Pram, Oberparz 4, 4741 Wendling - T: (07764) 7684. Head: Ernst Stelzhamer
Science&Tech Museum
Coll of old tractors 02788

Weng im Innkreis

Heimatmuseum Weng im Innkreis, Hauptstr 25, 4952 Weng im Innkreis - T: (07723) 5055, Fax: 50554
Local Museum
Portrayal of farmers' daily lives and work 02789

Wenigzell

Heimathaus Wenigzell, 8254 Wenigzell - T: (03336) 2436
Local Museum - 1964
Functional old grinding mill and equipment, ceramics, street lamp coll, religious folk art, peasant furniture 02790

Werfen

Museum Kuenburggewölbe, Burg Hohenwerfen, Burgstr 2, 5450 Werfen - T: (06468) 7159, Fax: 523188. Head: Peter Mayr
Fine Arts Museum / Local Museum - 1984 02791

Werfenweng

Salzburger Landes-Skimuseum, Ortspl, 5453 Werfenweng - T: (06466) 7670, Fax: 7674. Head: Hans Müller
Special Museum - 1995 02792

Wernstein am Inn

Burg Wernstein, Burgpl 1, 4783 Wernstein am Inn - T: (07713) 70780
Local Museum 02793

Kubin-Haus, Zwickledt 7, 4783 Wernstein am Inn - T: (07713) 6603. Head: Jutta Mairinger
Fine Arts Museum - 1997 02794

Weyer

Ennsmuseum Kastenreith, Steyrer Str 27, 3335 Weyer - T: (07355) 7305, Fax: 7305. Head: Dr. Werner Kortschak
Local Museum - 1974
Rafting, nature, folk art, cultural hist and economy of the Enns region 02795

Freilichtmuseum Katzensteiner Mühle, Am Gaflenzbach, 3335 Weyer - T: (07447) 6593, Fax: 7305. Head: Peter Katzensteiner
Science&Tech Museum
Hist of the mill 02796

Weyregg am Attersee

Bruckbacher Hoarstubn, Reichholz 7, 4852 Weyregg am Attersee - T: (07664) 2236
Science&Tech Museum
Flax processing, tools and implements 02797

K.u.k. Hausmuseum, Nr 47, 4852 Weyregg am Attersee - T: (07664) 2202, 2653, Fax: 265355, E-mail: k.u.k.landgasthof@aon.at, Internet: http://www.tiscover.com/k.u.k.-landgasthof. Head: Georg Eichhorn jun.
Historical Museum
Austrian-Hungarian Monarchy 02798

Wien

Adalbert Stifter-Gedenkstätte, Nußdorferstr 54, 1090 Wien - T: (01) 3173601, Fax: 50587477201, E-mail: post@m10.magwien.gv.at, Internet: http://museum.vienna.at. Head: Dr. Günter Düriegl
Special Museum - 1918
Life and work of the writer Adalbert Stifter, his paintings, drawings, manuscripts, and first editions - archives, library 02799

Albertina, Albertinapl 1, 1010 Wien - T: (01) 534830, Fax: 5337697, E-mail: info@albertina.at, Internet: http://www.albertina.at. Head: Dr. Klaus Albrecht Schröder
Fine Arts Museum - 1919
Drawings and graphics from the 15th c to the present, water colour painting, copperplate engravings, works by artists such as Raphael, Michelangelo, Leonardo da Vinci, Albrecht Dürer, Rembrandt, Pieter Paul Rubens, Claude Lorrain, Nicolas Poussin, Jean Honoré de Fragonard - library, photo laboratory, workshops 02800

Anna Bahr-Mildenburg-Gedenkraum & Hermann Bahr-Gedenkraum, Österreichisches Theatermuseum, Hanuschgasse 3, 1010 Wien - T: (01) 5122427, Fax: 512880045, E-mail: a-pistorius@othm.org. Head: Dr. Helga Dostal
Special Museum 02801

Architektur im Ringturm, Schottenring 30, 1010 Wien - T: (01) 531391336, Fax: 531393134
Fine Arts Museum - 1998
Architecture 02802

Architekturzentrum Wien, Museumsquartier, Museumspl 1, 1070 Wien - T: (01) 5223115, Fax: 5223117, E-mail: office@azw.at, Internet: http://www.azw.at. Head: Dietmar Steiner
Special Museum - 1993/2001 02803

Archiv der Universität Wien, Schausammlung, Postgasse 9, 1010 Wien - T: (01) 427717201, Fax: 42779172, E-mail: archiv@univie.ac.at, Internet: http://www.univie.ac.at/archiv. Head: Dr. Kurt Mühlberger
University Museum - 1365
History of the University of Vienna, history of science 02804

Arnold Schönberg Center, Schwarzenbergpl 6, 1030 Wien - T: (01) 7121888, Fax: 712188888, E-mail: office@schoenberg.at, Internet: http://www.schoenberg.at. Head: Dr. Christian Meyer
Music Museum / Library with Exhibitions - 1997
The legacy of Arnold Schönberg 02805

Art Cult Center - Tabakmuseum, Museumsquartier, Museumspl 1, 1070 Wien - T: (01) 52617160, Fax: 526171610, E-mail: artcult@austriatabak.com, Internet: http://www.austriatabak.com. Head: Günther Mayer
Special Museum / Fine Arts Museum - 1873/1959
Porcelain pipes and snuff boxes, antique pipes, meerschaum pipes, tobacco jars, paintings, drawings, documents - library 02806

Artothek-Galerie, Schönlaterngasse 7a, 1010 Wien - T: (01) 5129476, Fax: 51319629, E-mail: artothek-galerie@alte-schmiede.at, Internet: http://www.alte-schmiede.at
Public Gallery - 1990 02807

Atelier Augarten - Zentrum für zeitgenössische Kunst der Österreichischen Galerie Belvedere, Gustinus Ambrosi-Museum, Scherzergasse 1a, 1020 Wien - T: (01) 795570, Fax: 79557134, E-mail: belvedere@belvedere.at, Internet: http://www.belvedere.at. Head: Dr. Gerbert Frodl
Fine Arts Museum - 1978
Life and works of the sculptor G. Ambrosi 02808

Ausstellungszentrum Heiligenkreuzer Hof, Universität für Angewandte Kunst Wien, Grashofgasse 3, 1010 Wien - T: (01) 711336300, Fax: 711336309, E-mail: ausstellungsreferat@uni-ak.qc.at, Internet: http://www.uni-ak.ac.at. Head: Alexandra Goldbacher
Public Gallery 02809

Bäckermuseum, Florianigasse 13, 1080 Wien - T: (01) 4055396, Fax: 405539619, E-mail: Kurt.Schebesta@wkw.at. Head: Dr. Kurt Schebesta
Special Museum - 1898 02810

Bank Austria Kunstforum, Freyung 8, 1010 Wien - T: (01) 5373312, Fax: 5373327, E-mail: office@kunstforum-wien.at, Internet: http://www.kunstforum-wien.at. Head: Dr. Ingried Brugger
Fine Arts Museum - 1989
Fotographis coll 02811

Basis Wien, Museumsquartier, Museumspl 1, 1070 Wien - T: (01) 5226795, Fax: 5225389, E-mail: basis@t0.or.at, Internet: http://www.basis-wien.at. Head: Lioba Reddeker
Public Gallery
archive 02812

BAWAG Foundation, Tuchlauben 7a, 1010 Wien - T: (01) 534532296, Fax: 534533096. Head: Christine Kintisch
Fine Arts Museum - 1974
International contemporary art 02813

Beethoven-Gedenkstätte, Haus des Heiligenstädter Testaments, Probusgasse 6, 1190 Wien - T: (01) 3188608. Head: Elfriede Rührnschopf
Music Museum - 1954
Photographs of the" Heiligenstädter Testament" written by Beethoven in 1802, pictures of Heiligenstadt and environs 02814

Beethoven-Gedenkstätte Eroicahaus, Döblinger Hauptstr 92, 1190 Wien - T: (01) 3691424, Fax: 50587477201, E-mail: post@m10.magwien.at, Internet: http://museum.vienna.at. Head: Dr. Günter Düriegl
Music Museum - 1970
Beethoven's flat in summer 1803, music scores 02815

Beethoven-Gedenkstätte in Floridsdorf, Jeneweingasse 17, 1210 Wien - T: (01) 2785267, Fax: 2785267, E-mail: beethoven-gedenkstaette@gmx.net, Internet: http://come.to/beethoven-gedenkstaette. Head: Eva Krapf
Music Museum - 1971
Documents, letters, photos 02816

Beethoven-Wohnung im Pasqualati-Haus, Mölker Bastei 8, 1010 Wien - T: (01) 5358905, Fax: 50587477201. Head: Dr. Günter Düriegl
Music Museum - 1941
Memorabilia of Beethoven, room in which he died, portraits of Beethoven and his friends, music scores 02817

Bezirksgalerie Alsergrund, Markthalle, Nußdorfer Str, 1090 Wien - T: (01) 40034127, 3281306, Fax: 4003499120. Head: Wilhelm Urbanek
Public Gallery - 1999 02818

Bezirksmuseum Alsergrund, Währinger Str 43, 1090 Wien - T: (01) 4003409127, Fax: 4003499120. Head: Dr. Wilhelm Urbanek
Local Museum - 1958
Topography, district hist, memorial to the writer Heimito von Doderer and Erich Fried, incl study, original furnishings, documentation, Jews on the Alsergrund - library 02819

Bezirksmuseum Brigittenau, Dresdner Str 79, 1200 Wien - T: (01) 3305068, Fax: 3305068, Internet: http://www.wien.gv.at/ma53/museen/bmlo. Head: Prof. Roland Herold
Local Museum - 1950
Local hist, Robert Blum doc (revolution 1848), regulation of Danube (1869-1875), department for Eastern - history and Glagolistik 02820

Bezirksmuseum Döbling, Villa Wertheimstein, Döblinger Hauptstr 96, 1190 Wien - T: (01) 3686546, Fax: 3686546. Head: Prof. Kurt Apfel
Local Museum - 1963
Historic interiors in 19th c Villa Wertheimstein, memorials to the writers Ferdinand von Saar and Eduard von Bauernfeld, district hist incl maps, medaillons, music, geology, local artists, viniculture - archives, library, wine-museum 02821

Bezirksmuseum Donaustadt, Kagraner Pl 53-54, 1220 Wien - T: (01) 2032126, Fax: 2032126. Head: Helmut Just
Local Museum - 1976 02822

Bezirksmuseum Favoriten, Ada-Christen-Gasse 2c, 1100 Wien - T: (01) 6898193, 6040124. Head: Werner Schubert
Local Museum - 1934
Roman finds, geology 02823

Bezirksmuseum Floridsdorf, Prager Str 33, 1210 Wien - T: (01) 2705194
Local Museum - 1935 02824

Bezirksmuseum Hernals, Hernalser Hauptstr 72-74, 1170 Wien - T: (01) 4619572, 4034338, Fax: 4034338. Head: Prof. Stephanie Zabusch
Local Museum 02825

Bezirksmuseum Hietzing, Am Platz 2, 1130 Wien - T: (01) 8777688. Head: Prof. Harry Glöckner
Local Museum - 1954
Hist, Ethiopia coll of Friedrich Julius Bieber, docs on Egon Schiele 02826

Bezirksmuseum Innere Stadt, Wipplinger Str 8, 1010 Wien - T: (01) 5343601127. Head: Prof. Alois Mucnjak
Local Museum - 1985 02827

Bezirksmuseum Josefstadt, Schmidgasse 18, 1080 Wien - T: (01) 4036415, Fax: 4036415, E-mail: elfriede.faber@everyday.com. Head: Dr. Elfriede Faber
Local Museum - 1938
Memorabilia on Stefan Zweig, Friedrich Hebbel 02828

Bezirksmuseum Josefstadt, Außenstelle Alte Backstube mit Museum, Lange Gasse 34, 1080 Wien - T: (01) 4061101, Fax: (02264) 5173, E-mail: office@backstube.at, Internet: http://www.backstube.at. Head: Sabine Wallner
Special Museum
Baking trade 02829

Bezirksmuseum Landstraße, Sechskrügelgasse 11, 1030 Wien - T: (01) 7113403127, Fax: 711349935040, E-mail: vkhauer@gmx.at. Head: Karl Hauer
Local Museum / Historic Site - 1936 02830

Bezirksmuseum Leopoldstadt, Karmelitergasse 9, 1020 Wien - T: (01) 21106127. Head: Franz Kratochwil, Josef König
Local Museum - 1963 02831

Bezirksmuseum Margareten, Schönbrunner Str 54, 1050 Wien - T: (01) 5463405127
Local Museum - 1977
Topography 02832

Bezirksmuseum Mariahilf, Mollardgasse 8, 1060 Wien - T: (01) 5697965, 5867868
Local Museum - 1954 02833

Bezirksmuseum Meidling mit Galerie, Längenfeldgasse 13-15, 1120 Wien - T: (01) 8176598, Fax: 817659812, E-mail: bezmus12@utanet.at, Internet: http://www.magwien.gv.at/ma53/museen/bm12. Head: Prof. Dr. Vladimira Bousska
Local Museum - 1923
Documents on local hist, fire brigade, trade workshops, Meidling theatre - gallery 02834

Bezirksmuseum Neubau, Stiftgasse 8, 1070 Wien - T: (01) 5245052
Local Museum - 1979 02835

Bezirksmuseum Ottakring, Richard-Wagner-Pl 19b, 1160 Wien - T: (01) 4919616127, Fax: 491969916111. Head: Prof. Robert Medek
Local Museum - 1935 02836

Bezirksmuseum Penzing, Penzinger Str 59, 1140 Wien - T: (01) 8972852. Head: Karl Koller
Local Museum - 1962
library, archive 02837

Bezirksmuseum Simmering, Enkpl 2, 1110 Wien - T: (01) 743586226, 74034127
Local Museum 02838

Bezirksmuseum Währing, Währinger Str 124, 1180 Wien - T: (01) 4763418127. Head: Prof. Dr. Helmuth Haas
Local Museum - 1965 02839

Bezirksmuseum Wieden, Klagbaumgasse 4, 1040 Wien - T: (01) 5817811, 6508905. Head: Dr. Peter Zawrel
Local Museum - 1983
Tröpferlbadmuseum 02840

Billardmuseum → Museum für Billard- und Kaffeehauskultur

Carl Michael Ziehrer-Gedenkraum, Österreichisches Theatermuseum, Hanuschgasse 3, 1010 Wien - T: (01) 5122427, Fax: 512880045, E-mail: a-pistorius@othm.org. Head: Dr. Helga Dostal
Special Museum 02841

Caspar Neher-Gedenkraum, Österreichisches Theatermuseum, Hanuschgasse 3, 1010 Wien - T: (01) 5122427, Fax: 512880045, E-mail: a-pistorius@othm.org. Head: Dr. Helga Dostal
Special Museum 02842

Depot - Kunst und Diskussion, Museumsquartier, Museumspl 1, 1070 Wien - T: (01) 5227613, Fax: 5226642, E-mail: depot@depot.or.at, Internet: http://www.depot.or.at
Public Gallery 02843

Dokumentationsarchiv des österreichischen Widerstandes, Wipplinger Str 6-8, 1010 Wien - T: (01) 5343601779, Fax: 534369901771, E-mail: docarch@email.adis.at, Internet: http://www.doew.at. Head: Prof. Dr. Wolfgang Neugebauer
Historical Museum
Resistance and persecution in Austria during the Third Reich, Austrian Emigrés, Austrian right-wing extremism, Spanish Civil War, newspaper clippings, post war trials 02844

Elektropathologisches Museum, Gomperzgasse 1-3, 1160 Wien - T: (01) 4892080, Fax: 48920804, E-mail: epm@xpoint.at, Internet: http://www.user.xpoint.at/epm. Head: Gerhard Rabitsch
Special Museum - 1904
Exhibits on damage to organic and anorganic objects caused by electricity, protective measures and first aid, electropathology - archives, library 02845

Emmerich Kálmán-Gedenkraum, Österreichisches Theatermuseum, Hanuschgasse 3, 1010 Wien - T: (01) 5122427, Fax: 512880045, E-mail: a-pistorius@othm.org. Head: Dr. Helga Dostal
Special Museum 02846

Ephesos-Museum, Antikensammlung des Kunsthistorischen Museums Wien, Burgring 5, 1010 Wien - T: (01) 52524431, Fax: 52524531, E-mail: info.as@khm.at, Internet: http://www.khm.at. Head: Dr. Kurt Gschwantler
Archaeological Museum - 1978
Finds from the Austrian excavations in Ephesos (1895-1906) and Samothrace (1873-75), Greek and Roman architecture and sculpture 02847

Ernst Fuchs-Privatmuseum, Hüttelbergstr 26, 1140 Wien - T: (01) 9148575, Fax: 914857518, E-mail: - ernst.fuchs.privatstiftung@netway.at, Internet: http://www.ernstfuchs-zentrum.com. Head: Dr. Emanuel Fuchs
Fine Arts Museum - 1988
Former summer residence (built 1888) of the archictect Otto Wagner, architectural works of Otto Wagner, drawings, sculptures, paintings of Ernst Fuchs, member of the "Schule des Phantastischen Realismus" 02848

Erstes Österreichisches Funk- und Radiomuseum, Eisvogelgasse 4-5, 1060 Wien - T: (01) 5971230, E-mail: radiomuseum.wien@chello.at, Internet: http://members.chello.at/peter.braunstein/radiomuseum.htm. Head: Arthur Bauer
Science&Tech Museum - 1974 02849

Erzbischöfliches Dom- und Diözesanmuseum, Stephanspl 6, 1010 Wien - T: (01) 515523689, Fax: 515523599, E-mail: dommuseum@edw.or.at. Head: Gerhard Eederndorfer
Religious Arts Museum - 1932
Sacral art from the Middle Ages to the present 02850

Evangelisches Museum in Wien, Hamburger Str 3, 1050 Wien - T: (01) 5873141, Fax: 587314122, E-mail: wien@evang.at. Head: Prof. Dr. Karl Schwarz
Religious Arts Museum - 1974 02851

Fiakermuseum, Veronikagasse 12, 1170 Wien - T: (01) 401060, Fax: 4010625, E-mail: taxi.mietwagen@wkw.at. Head: Dr. Andreas Curda
Special Museum - 1963
Development and hist of the Viennese coachman profession, models, fiaker cabs in pictures, originals, flags - archives, library 02852

Foltermuseum, Museum für mittelalterliche Rechtsgeschichte, Fritz-Grünbaum-Pl 1, 1060 Wien - T: (01) 5857185, Fax: 5868259, E-mail: folter@netway.at, Internet: http://www.folter.at. Head: Frank Riegler
Special Museum
Torture, execution and punish tool 02853

Fritz Wotruba-Gedenkraum, Hanuschgasse 3, 1010 Wien - T: (01) 5122427, Fax: 512880045, E-mail: a-pistorius@othm.org. Head: Dr. Helga Dostal
Special Museum 02854

Gemäldegalerie der Akademie der Bildenden Künste, Schillerpl 3, 1010 Wien - T: (01) 58816228, Fax: 5863346, E-mail: GemGal@akabild.ac.at, Internet: http://www.akademiegalerie.at. Head: Dr. Renate Trnek
Fine Arts Museum - 1822
European master paintings (Bosch, Cranach, Titian, Rubens, Guardi), 17th c Dutch and Flemish painting, "Last Judgement" Triptych by Bosch 02855

Generali Foundation, Wiedner Hauptstr 15, 1040 Wien - T: (01) 5049880, Fax: 5049883, E-mail: foundation@generali.at, Internet: http://www.foundation.generali.at. Head: Dr. Sabine Breitwieser
Association with Coll / Library with Exhibitions - 1988
Contemporary sculpture, film, video, photography and installations 02856

Gesellschaft der Musikfreunde in Wien, Archiv, Bibliothek und Sammlungen, Bösendorfer Str 12, 1010 Wien - T: (01) 505868144, Fax: 505868166. Head: Prof. Dr. Otto Biba
Library with Exhibitions 02857

Geymüller Schlössel, Sammlung Sobek, Khevenhüllerstr 2, 1180 Wien - T: (0431) 4793139, 71136232, Fax: 47931393, E-mail: office@mak.at, Internet: http://www.mak.at. Head: Dr. Christian Witt-Dörring
Decorative Arts Museum - 1965
Empire and Biedermeier furniture (1800-1850), Viennese clocks from the Biedermeier period 02858

Globenmuseum der Österreichischen Nationalbibliothek, Josefspl 1, 1015 Wien - T: (01) 53410297, Fax: 53410319, E-mail: jan.mokre@onb.ac.at, Internet: http://www.sammlungen/globen/index.htm. Head: Jan Mokre
Special Museum - 1956
Old globes 02859

Gold- und Silberschmiedemuseum, Zieglergasse 22, 1070 Wien - T: (01) 5234096, 5233388, Fax: 5239910, E-mail: silbervaugoin@aon.at, Internet: http://www.wien.gr.at. Head: Prof. Leopold Rössler
Decorative Arts Museum - 1986 02860

Grillparzer-Gedenkzimmer, c/o Österreichisches Finanz- und Hofkammerarchiv, Johannesgasse 6, 1010 Wien - T: (01) 5125434. Head: Dr. Gottfried Mraz
Special Museum
Grillparzer study with original furniture 02861

Haus Wittgenstein, Bulgarisches Kulturinstitut, Parkgasse 18, 1030 Wien - T: (01) 7133164, Fax: 7134340, E-mail: bki.wittgenstein@europe.com. Head: Nikolai Kateliev
Public Gallery
International artists showing paintings, graphics, sculptures 02862

Haydn-Gedenkstätte mit Brahms-Gedenkraum, Haydngasse 19, 1060 Wien - T: (01) 5961307, 50587470, Fax: 50587477201. Head: Dr. Günter Düriegl
Music Museum - 1899
Memorabilia of the composer Joseph Haydn, housed in his former residence 02863

Heeresgeschichtliches Museum im Arsenal, Arsenal, Ghegastr, 1032 Wien - T: (01) 7956160000, Fax: 7956117707, E-mail: bmlv.hgm@magnet.at, Internet: http://www.hgm-wien.at. Head: Univ.-Doz. Dr. Manfried Rauchensteiner
Military Museum - 1869
Military artefacts, hist of the Austrian army, archives, models, hist of the Austrian navy, oldest state museum building of Vienna, hist of the World War II - library 02864

Heizungsmuseum Wien, Längenfeldgasse 13-15, 1120 Wien - T: (01) 400074494, Fax: 4000998032, E-mail: ind@m32.magwien.gv.at. Head: Reinhard Indrak
Science&Tech Museum - 1987 02865

Heraldisch-Genealogische Gesellschaft Adler, Universitätsstr 6-9b, 1096 Wien, mail addr: Postfach 220, 1096 Wien - Fax: (01) 8775493, E-mail: - society.adler.vienna@chello.at. Head: Dr. Georg Johannes Kugler
Library with Exhibitions - 1870 02866

Hermesvilla, Lainzer Tiergarten, 1130 Wien - T: (01) 8041324, 50587470, Fax: 50587477201, E-mail: post@m10.magwien.gv.at, Internet: http://www.museum.vienna.at. Head: Dr. Günter Düriegl
Fine Arts Museum / Historic Site
Villa of Empress Elisabeth of Austria, paintings by Gustav Klimt and Hans Makart 02867

Historisches Museum der Stadt Wien, Karlspl, 1040 Wien - T: (01) 50587470, Fax: 50587477201, E-mail: post@m10.magwien.gv.at, Internet: http://www.museum.vienna.at. Head: Dr. Günter Düriegl
Historical Museum - 1888
Hist of art and cultural life of Vienna from prehistoric to present times, topography, graphics, portraits, hist of theatre, numismatics, arts and crafts, furniture, folk customs, painting, sculpture, architecture, weapons - archives, library, workshop 02868

Hofjagd- und Rüstkammer des Kunsthistorischen Museums, Neue Burg, Heldenpl, 1010 Wien - T: (01) 52524460/461, Fax: 52524358, E-mail: info.hjrk@khm.at, Internet: http://www.khm.at. Head: Dr. Christian Beaufort
Military Museum - 15th c
Imperial armoury, imperial hunting cabinet, arms coll of Ambras Castle, late Gothic tournament armour - library 02869

Hugo Thimig-Gedenkraum, Österreichisches Theatermuseum, Hanuschgasse 3, 1010 Wien - T: (01) 5122427, Fax: 512880045, E-mail: a-pistorius@othm.org. Head: Dr. Helga Dostal
Special Museum 02870

Instituts- und Studiensammlung des Instituts für Ur- und Frühgeschichte, Franz-Klein-Gasse 1, 1190 Wien - T: (01) 427740473, Fax: 42779404, E-mail: alexandra.krenn-leeb@univie.ac.at, Internet: http://www.univie.ac.at/urgeschichte. Head: Dr. Alexandra Krenn-Leeb
Archaeological Museum 02871

Internationales Esperanto-Museum der Österreichischen Nationalbibliothek, Sammlung für Plansprachen, Hofburg, Michaelerkuppel, 1010 Wien - T: (01) 5355145, E-mail: plansprachen@onb.ac.at, Internet: http://www.onb.ac.at/sammlungen/plansprachen/index.htm. Head: Herbert Mayer
Special Museum - 1929
Photos, picture postcards, sound films in Esperanto, posters, exhibits depicting Esperanto movement, literature on language planning - archives, library 02872

Johann Strauß-Gedenkstätte, Praterstr 54, 1020 Wien - T: (01) 2140121, Fax: 50587477201, E-mail: post@m10.magwien.gv.at, Internet: http://www.museum.vienna.at. Head: Dr. Günter Düriegl
Music Museum
Furniture, paintings, musical instruments which belonged to Johann Strauß and to members of his family 02873

Josef Kainz-Gedenkraum, Österreichisches Theatermuseum, Hanuschgasse 3, 1010 Wien - T: (01) 5122427, Fax: 512880045, E-mail: a-pistorius@othm.org. Head: Dr. Helga Dostal
Special Museum 02874

Jüdisches Museum der Stadt Wien, Dorotheergasse 11, 1010 Wien - T: (01) 5350431, Fax: 5350424, E-mail: info@jmw.at, Internet: http://www.jmw.at. Head: Dr. Karl Albrecht-Weinberger
Historical Museum - 1990
Berger coll, Jewish life and culture in Vienna and in the Austrian-Hungarian monarchy - library, archive 02875

Kaiserappartments und Ehemalige Hofsilber- und Tafelkammer, Hofburg, Michaelerkuppel-Batthyanytor, 1010 Wien - T: (01) 5337570, Fax: 533757033, E-mail: kotvojs@schoenbrunn.at, Internet: http://www.hofburg-wien.at, http://www.silberkammer.athttP://www.kaiserappartements.at. Head: Dr. Franz Sattlecker, Dr. Wolfgang Kippes
Decorative Arts Museum / Historical Museum - 1922
Living and official rooms of Emperor Franz Joseph I and Empress Elisabeth, silver tableware 02876

Kaisergruft, Tegetthoffstr 2, 1010 Wien - T: (01) 5126853, Fax: 512685319, Internet: http://www.kaisergruft.at. Head: Gottfried Undesser
Historical Museum / Historic Site
Family vault of the Habsburg imperial family, 140 sarcophagi including those of 12 emperors and 17 empresses 02877

Kaiserliches Hofmobiliendepot, Museen des Mobiliendepots, Andreasgasse 7, 1070 Wien - T: (01) 5243357601, Fax: 5243357666, E-mail: barta-fliedl@magnet.at. Head: Dr. Peter Parenzan
Decorative Arts Museum - 1924
Austrian early Baroque, Biedermeier period furniture from imperial estate, modern Austrian furniture - workshops 02878

Karst- und Höhlenkundliche Abteilung, Naturhistorisches Museum Wien (Dept. of Carst and Caves, Museum of Natural History), Museumsquartier, Museumspl 1, 1070 Wien - T: (01) 5230418, Fax: 523041919, E-mail: speleo.austria@netway.at, Internet: http://www.nhm-wien.ac.at/nhm/hoehle. Head: Dr. Karl Mais
Natural History Museum 02879

Kindermuseum Zoom, Museumsquartier, Museumspl 1, 1070 Wien - T: (01) 5226748/1815, Fax: 52267484, E-mail: info@kindermuseum.at, Internet: http://www.kindermuseum.at. Head: Claudia Haas
Special Museum - 1993/2001 02880

Die Kleine Galerie, Kundmanngasse 30, 1030 Wien - T: (01) 7103403, Fax: 710340313, E-mail: kleine.galerie@vhs.at, Internet: http://www.vhs.at/kleine.galerie
Public Gallery 02881

Konventmuseum der Barmherzigen Brüder, Große Mohrengasse 9, 1020 Wien - T: (01) 211211305
Religious Arts Museum 02882

Kopiergerätemuseum, Reichsratsstr 5, 1010 Wien - T: (01) 50506060, Fax: 505060623. Head: Viktor Pavlu
Science&Tech Museum - 1983 02883

Künstlerhaus Wien, Karlspl 5, 1010 Wien - T: (01) 5879663, Fax: 5878736, E-mail: office@k-haus.at, Internet: http://www.k-haus.at. Head: Manfred Nehrer
Public Gallery
Hausgalerie, Passagegalerie 02884

Kunstforum Ebendorf, Ebendorfer Str 8, 1010 Wien - T: (01) 4083587, Fax: 408358731, E-mail: y1031uab@rs6000.univie.ac.at, Internet: http://www.univie.ac.at/khg
Public Gallery 02885

Kunstforum Wien → Bank Austria Kunstforum

Kunsthalle Wien, Museumspl 1, 1070 Wien - T: (01) 521891201, Fax: 521891260, E-mail: office@kunsthallewien.at, Internet: http://www.kunsthallewien.at. Head: Dr. Gerald Matt
Public Gallery 02886

Kunsthalle Wien, Projekt Sapace, Karlspl, Treitlstr 2, 1040 Wien - T: (01) 521891201, Fax: 521891260, E-mail: office@kunsthalle.wien.at, Internet: http://www.kunsthallewien.at. Head: Dr. Gerald Matt
Public Gallery 02887

KunstHausWien, Untere Weissgerberstr 13, 1030 Wien - T: (01) 7120495, Fax: 7120496, E-mail: pressoffice@kunsthauswien.com, Internet: http://www.kunsthauswien.at. Head: Joram Harel
Fine Arts Museum - 1991
Works by Hundertwasser 02888

Kunsthistorisches Museum im Palais Harrach, Freyung 3, 1010 Wien - T: (01) 5321230, Fax: 5358427, E-mail: info.harrach@khm.at. Head: Annita Mader
Fine Arts Museum - 1994 02889

Kunsthistorisches Museum Wien, Burgring 5, 1010 Wien - T: (01) 525240, Fax: 5232770, E-mail: annita.mader@khm.at, Internet: http://www.khm.at. Head: Dr. Wilfried Seipel, Dr. Karl Schütz
Archaeological Museum / Fine Arts Museum - 1871-91
Coll of Egyptian and Oriental art, Greek and Roman antiquities, coll of sculptures and decorative art (incl tapestries, cut stones, jewellery and treasury), coin cabinet, picture gallery (14th-18th c), coll of historical musical instruments, coll of arms and armour, coll of historical carriages, paintings such as works by Dürer, Rubens, Rembrandt, Titian, Breughel 02890

Kunstsammlung Volpinum, Theresiengasse 25-27, 1180 Wien - T: (01) 4055626, Fax: 3284724, E-mail: office@volpinum.com, Internet: http://www.volpinum.at. Head: Ernfried Fuchs
Public Gallery
Paintings, photography, video, sculpture and graphik 02891

Kunstsammlungen Palais Schwarzenberg, Rennweg 2, 1030 Wien - T: (01) 7134699. Head: Karl Johann von Schwarzenberg
Fine Arts Museum
Historic period rooms in late 17th c palace, Baroque art, sculpture - park 02892

Kupferstichkabinett, Akademie der bildenden Künste, Makartgasse 3, 1010 Wien - T: (01) 5813040, Fax: 581304031, E-mail: M.Knofler@akbild.ac.at, Internet: http://www.akbild.ac.at. Head: Dr. Monika Knofler
Fine Arts Museum - 1692/1773
Drawings and graphic arts (15th-21st c) architectural designs, sketches, water colour paintings, photography - library 02893

Kynologisches Museum, Johann-Teufel-Gasse 8, 1230 Wien - T: (01) 8887092, Fax: 8892621. Head: Dr. Michael Kreiner
Natural History Museum - 1956
Hist and origin of the dog, breeding, photos, engravings, and paintings - library 02894

Lehár-Schlößl, Schikaneder-Schlößl, Hackhofergasse 18, 1190 Wien - T: (01) 3185416. Head: Hermine Kreuzer
Special Museum
Historical interiors, architecture 02895

Leopold Museum, Museumsquartier, Museumspl 1, 1070 Wien - T: (01) 525700, Fax: 525701500, E-mail: leopoldmuseum@leopoldmuseum.org, Internet: http://www.leopoldmuseum.org. Head: Prof. Dr. Rudolf Leopold
Fine Arts Museum - 1994
Austrian modern art 02896

Lichtentaler Pfarrmuseum, Marktgasse 40, 1090 Wien - T: (01) 3152646, Fax: 315264624
Religious Arts Museum - 1978
Local history, paraments, memorabilia of Franz Schubert and the parish Lichtental 02897

Lipizzaner Museum, Reitschulgasse 2, 1010 Wien - T: (01) 5338659, 5337811, Fax: 5333853, E-mail: lipizzaner@khm.at, Internet: http://www.lipizzaner.at. Head: Georg Kugler
Special Museum - 1997 02898

Lobaumuseum, Lobau 256, 1220 Wien - T: (02214) 2781. Head: Anton Klein
Natural History Museum - 1972
Environmental protection 02899

MAK - Österreichisches Museum für angewandte Kunst, Stubenring 5, 1010 Wien - T: (01) 711360, Fax: 7131026, E-mail: office@MAK.at; presse@MAK.at, Internet: http://www.mak.at. Head: Peter Noever
Decorative Arts Museum - 1864
European and East Asian decorative arts, Oriental carpets, textiles, furniture, metal items, glass, ceramics and porcelain, art prints, design, contemporary art - library, workshops, photo laboratory, bookbinding 02900

Max Reinhardt-Gedenkraum, Österreichisches Theatermuseum, Hanuschgasse 3, 1010 Wien - T: (01) 5122427, Fax: 512880045, E-mail: a-pistorius@othm.org. Head: Dr. Helga Dostal
Special Museum 02901

Medizinhistorisches Museum, Institut für Geschichte der Medizin der Universität Wien, Währinger Str 25, 1090 Wien - T: (01) 427763401, Fax: 42779634, Internet: http://www.univie.ac.at/medizingeschcihte. Head: Dr. Manfred Skopec
University Museum / Historical Museum - 1920
18th c anatomical and obstetrical wax models, history of medicine in Vienna, manuscripts, coins and medaillons - library 02902

Mittelalterliches Museum, Tuchlauben 19, 1010 Wien - T: (01) 5359065, Fax: 50587477201. Head: Dr. Günter Düriegl
Fine Arts Museum
Frescos from 1398 02903

Modeschauraum des Historischen Museums der Stadt Wien, Schloß Hetzendorf, Hetzendorfer Str 79, 1120 Wien - T: (01) 8021657, Fax: 8040468, E-mail: post@m10.magwien.gv.at, Internet: http://museum.vienna.at. Head: Dr. Günter Düriegl
Special Museum 02904

Mozart-Gedenkstätte Figarohaus, Domgasse 5, 1010 Wien - T: (01) 5136294, 50587470, Fax: 50587477201. Head: Dr. Günter Düriegl
Music Museum - 1941
Memorabilia of the composer Wolfgang A. Mozart, housed in his former residence (1784-1787), exhibits on Mozart and Vienna, illustrations in Mozart's works, Mozart's circle of friends 02905

Museum 15, Bezirksmuseum Rudolfsheim-Fünfhaus, Rosinagasse 4, 1150 Wien - T: (01) 8913415127, Fax: 8937045, E-mail: museum15@hotmail.com. Head: Monika Griebl
Local Museum - 1972
library for children 02906

Museum Alte Schmiede, Schönlaterngasse 9, 1010 Wien - T: (01) 5128329, Fax: 51319629, E-mail: info@alte-schmiede.at, Internet: http://www.alte-schmiede.at. Head: Joanna Lukaszuk-Ritter
Science&Tech Museum / Fine Arts Museum / Special Museum - 1970
Forging trade 02907

Museum Aspern-Essling 1809, Asperner Heldenpl 9, 1220 Wien - T: (01) 7742184, Fax: 7742184. Head: Helmut Tiller
Historical Museum / Local Museum - 1979
Battle of Aspern in 1809, 8500 figure 02908

Museum auf Abruf, Makartgasse 1, 1010 Wien - T: (01) 400084758, Fax: 40009984758, E-mail: post@m07.magwien.gv.at, Internet: http://www.wien.gv.at/ma07/veran_ka.htm. Head: Dr. Berthold Ecker, Dr. Wolfgang Hilger
Public Gallery 02909

Museum der Gewerkschaft Agrar-Nahrung-Genuß, Albertgasse 35, 1080 Wien - T: (01) 40149, Fax: 4014920. Head: Gerhard Riess
Historical Museum - 1980
Historical flags 02910

Museum der Mechitharisten-Congregation, Mechitaristengasse 4, 1070 Wien - T: (01) 52364170, Fax: 5237018, E-mail: -mechitaristenkloster@chello.at, Internet: http://www.mekhitarist.org. Head: Vahan Hovagimian, Augustin Sekulian
Religious Arts Museum / Historical Museum - 1811
History of Armenia, numismatics, philology, ethnology - archives, library 02911

Museum des Blindenwesens, Bundes-Blindenerziehungsinstitut, Wittelsbachstr 5, 1020 Wien - T: (01) 7280866, Fax: 7280866, E-mail: museum@bbi.asn-wien.ac.at, Internet: http://www.bbi.asn-wien.ac.at. Head: Prof. Susanne Altmeder
Special Museum - 1830
Development and hist of education for the blind, the Braille script, Braille book printing, typewriters, the blind person in art - historical archives, library 02912

Museum des Instituts für gerichtliche Medizin, Sensengasse 2, 1090 Wien - T: (01) 427765701, Fax: 42779657. Head: Georg Bauer
Historical Museum 02913

Museum des Veterinäramtes, Henneberggasse 3, 1030 Wien - T: (01) 7951497955, Fax: 7951497955. Head: Dr. Peter Hasitschka
Special Museum - 1924
Pathology, anatomy 02914

Museum des Wiener Männergesang-Vereins, Bösendorfer Str 12, 1010 Wien - T: (01) 5057362, Fax: 5045450, E-mail: office@wienermaennergesang-verein.at, Internet: http://www.wienermaennergesang-verein.at. Head: Kurt Schuh
Music Museum - 1843
Memorabilia of famous composers (Beethoven, Bruckner, Schubert) 02915

Museum für Beschirrung und Besattelung, Hufbeschlag und Veterinär-Orthopädie, Josef-Baumann-Gasse 1, 1210 Wien - T: (01) 250775501, Fax: 250775590, E-mail: christian.stanek@vu-wien.ac.at. Head: Dr. Christian Stanek
Agriculture Museum / Special Museum - 1767
Horsehoes, tools, treatment of hoof and claw diseases, harnesses for horses and cattle, saddles, bits and bridles, training and care, reindeer sleds, trotter and troika harnesses, Ostrich saddle - library, workshop 02916

Museum für Billard- und Kaffeehauskultur, Goldschlagstr 1, 1150 Wien - T: (01) 9852150, 9824399, Fax: 9826948, E-mail: -billard.weingartner@aon.at. Head: Heinrich Weingartner
Special Museum - 1993 02917

Museum für Bodyart und Videoart, Kurrentgasse 4, 1010 Wien - T: (01) 5359854, Fax: 5359854. Head: Friederike Pezold
Performing Arts Museum 02918

Museum für Völkerkunde, Neue Hofburg, Heldenpl, 1014 Wien - T: (01) 534300, Fax: 53430230, E-mail: direktion@ethno-museum.ac.at, Internet: http://www.ethno-museum.ac.at
Ethnology Museum - 1928
Ethnographical and partly archaeological objects from Asia, Africa, Oceania, Australia and Amerika - archives, library, photoarchive 02919

Museum im Schottenstift, Freyung 6, 1010 Wien - T: (01) 53498600, Fax: 53498955, E-mail: klosterladen@schottenstift.at, Internet: http://www.schottenstift.at. Head: Stephan Szinai, Michael Wiehart
Fine Arts Museum / Music Museum - 1994
Library, archive 02920

Museum in Progress, Fischerstiege 1, 1010 Wien - T: (01) 5335840, Fax: 5353631, E-mail: office@mip.at, Internet: http://www.mip.at. Head: Kathrin Messner, Josef Ortner
Historical Museum - 1990 02921

Museum Judenplatz Wien, Judenpl 8, 1010 Wien - T: (01) 5350431, Fax: 5350424, E-mail: info@jmw.at, Internet: http://www.jmw.at. Head: Dr. Karl Albrecht-Weinberger
Historical Museum - 2000
Jewish life and culture in the Middle age 02922

Museum moderner Kunst Stiftung Ludwig Wien, Museumspl 1, 1070 Wien - T: (01) 52500, Fax: 525001300, E-mail: info@mumok.at, Internet: http://www.mumok.at. Head: Edelbert Köb
Fine Arts Museum - 1962/2001
Art of the 20th c 02923

Museum und Schatzkammer des Deutschen Ordens, Singerstr 7, 1010 Wien - T: (01) 5121065, Fax: 5121552, E-mail: hochmeisteramt@deutscher-orden.at, Internet: http://www.deutscher-orden.at. Head: Dr. Bernhard Demel
Decorative Arts Museum / Religious Arts Museum - 1956
Goldsmith work, crystal, mountings of semi-precious stones esp from the 15th-17th c, documents, coins, badges, ornate goblets, tableware, weapons, clocks, portraits 02924

Naturhistorisches Museum, Burgring 7, 1014 Wien - T: (01) 52177, Fax: 5235254, 52177578, E-mail: bernd.lotsch@nhm-wien.ac.at, Internet: http://www.nhm-wien.ac.at. Head: Prof. Dr. Bernhard Lötsch
Natural History Museum - 1748
Mineralogy and petrography, geology and paleontology, botany, zoology, anthropology, prehistory - archives, library, laboratories, workshops, bookbinding 02925

Österreichische Galerie Belvedere, Oberes Belvedere, Prinz Eugen-Str 27, 1037 Wien - T: (01) 79557134, Fax: 79557134, E-mail: public@belvedere.at, Internet: http://www.belvedere.at. Head: Dr. Gerbert Frodl
Fine Arts Museum - 1903
19th-20th c coll - library, artist's archive 02926

Österreichische Galerie Belvedere, Unteres Belvedere, Rennweg 6a, 1030 Wien - T: (01) 79557134, Fax: 79557134, E-mail: public@belvedere.at, Internet: http://www.belvedere.at. Head: Dr. Gerbert Frodl
Fine Arts Museum - 1903
Medieval and Baroque art 02927

Österreichische Nationalbibliothek, Josefspl 1, 1015 Wien - T: (01) 534100, Fax: 53410280, E-mail: onb@onb.ac.at, Internet: http://www.onb.ac.at. Head: Dr. Johanna Rachinger
Library with Exhibitions / Historic Site - 14th c
Department of manuscripts, autographs and closed collections, department of incunabula, old and rare books, department of maps and globe museum, department of music, department of portraits, pictures and fideicommis library, department of papyri and papyrus museum, department of broadsheets, posters and exlibris, Austrian literary archives, department of artificial languages and International Esperanto Museum, Austrian Folk Song Institute - institute of conservation 02928

Österreichisches Circus- und Clown-Museum, Sammlung Unterhaltungskunst, Karmelitergasse 9, 1020 Wien - T: (01) 3691111, Fax: 3691111. Head: Prof. Berthold Lang
Performing Arts Museum - 1968
International clown coll, circus photos and posters, costumes and props - archives, library 02929

Österreichisches Filmmuseum, Albertina, Augustinerstr 1, 1010 Wien - T: (01) 5337054, Fax: 533705625, E-mail: office@filmuseum.at, Internet: http://www.filmmuseum.at. Head: Alexander Horwath
Special Museum - 1964
Presentation of international classical movies, conservation of Austrian and international film-avantgarde, documentaries, advert clips, New American Cinema 02930

Österreichisches Gartenbaumuseum
(closed) 02931

Österreichisches Gesellschafts- und Wirtschaftsmuseum, Vogelsanggasse 36, 1050 Wien - T: (01) 54525510, Fax: 545255155, E-mail: wirtschaftsmuseum@oegwm.ac.at, Internet: http://www.wirtschaftsmuseum.at. Head: Hans Hartweger
Historical Museum - 1925
Contemporary Austrian history, business and economy in Austria 02932

Österreichisches Museum für Volkskunde, Gartenpalais Schönborn, Laudongasse 15-19, 1080 Wien - T: (01) 4068905, Fax: 4085342, E-mail: office@volkskundemuseum.at, Internet: http://www.volkskundemuseum.at. Head: Prof. Dr. Franz Grieshofer
Folklore Museum - 1895
Furniture, household articles, ceramics, masks, folk art, religious folk art, musical instruments, glass, textiles - archives, library, workshops 02933

Österreichisches Olympia- und Sportmuseum, Eduard-Klein-Gasse 2, 1130 Wien - T: (01) 8776259. Head: Kurt Heller
Special Museum - 1976
Books, photographs, pennants, posters and magazines 02934

Österreichisches Sprachinselmuseum, Semperstr 29, 1180 Wien - T: (01) 4796083, Fax: 4796083. Head: Prof. Dr. Maria Hornung
Special Museum - 1982 02935

Österreichisches Theatermuseum, Lobkowitzpl 2, 1010 Wien - T: (01) 51288000, Fax: 5128800645, E-mail: info@theatermuseum.at, Internet: http://www.theatermuseum.at. Head: Dr. Ulrike Dembski
Performing Arts Museum
Manuscripts, photos, books, drawings, paintings, costumes, films, phonograph records etc, depicting the world of the theatre, esp in Austria, children theatre museum - library 02936

Österreichisches Tonbandmuseum, Beingasse 3, 1150 Wien - T: (01) 9822162, Fax: 9822162, Internet: http://members.get.at/tbm. Head: Helmut Böhm
Science&Tech Museum - 1984 02937

Otto Wagner-Pavillion, Museen der Stadt Wien, Schönbrunner Schloßstr, 1013 Wien - T: (01) 505874784059, Fax: 50587477201, E-mail: post@m10.magwien.gv.at, Internet: http://www.museum.vienna.at. Head: Dr. Günter Düriegl
Historical Museum 02938

Palais Palffy, Palais Palffy, Josefspl 6, 1010 Wien - T: (01) 512568115, Fax: 512568118, E-mail: office@palais-palffy.at, Internet: http://www.palais-palffy.at. Head: Dr. Tobias Reinisch
Public Gallery - 1950 02939

Papyrusmuseum und Papyrussammlung, Heldenpl, Neue Hofburg, 1010 Wien, mail addr: Josefspl 1, 1015 Wien - T: (01) 53410323, Fax: 53410395, E-mail: harrauer@onb.ac.at, Internet: http://www.onb.ac.at. Head: Prof. Dr. Hermann Harrauer
Museum of Classical Antiquities - 1883 02940

Pathologisch-anatomisches Bundesmuseum, Spitalgasse 2, 1090 Wien - T: (01) 4068672, Fax: 4076262, E-mail: pat@via.at, Internet: http://www.pathomus.or.at. Head: Dr. B. Patzak
Natural History Museum - 1796
Moulage coll (ca 2 500 exhibits), prepared specimen, mainly human objects, bones and skeletons 02941

Pratermuseum, Oswald-Thomas-Pl 1, Planetarium, 1020 Wien - T: (01) 7267683, Fax: 50587477201, E-mail: post@m.10.magwien.gr.at, Internet: http://www.museum.vienna.at. Head: Dr. Günter Düriegl
Historical Museum - 1964
History of the Viennese amusement park "Prater" 02942

Privatsammlung A.F. Fleischer, Jägerstr 3, 1200 Wien. Head: Alexander Franz Fleischer
Local Museum 02943

Provinzmuseum der Franziskaner, Franziskanerpl 4, 1010 Wien - T: (01) 5124578, Fax: 5121555, E-mail: ofm.vienna@magnet.at, Internet: http://www.franziskaner.at. Head: Franz Lackner
Religious Arts Museum
History of the Franciscan Order, paintings, liturgical items, reliquaries 02944

Puppen- und Spielzeugmuseum, Schulhof 4, 1010 Wien - T: (01) 5356860, Fax: 5329385, E-mail: -puppenmuseumwien@everyday.com. Head: Vaclav Sladky
Special Museum - 1989 02945

Rauchfangkehrermuseum, RFK-Innung, Klagbaumgasse 4, 1040 Wien - T: (01) 222254, Fax: 7343789. Head: Günter Stern
Historical Museum - 1985 02946

Richard Teschner-Gedenkraum, Theatersammlung der österreichischen Nationalbibliothek, Josefspl 1, 1015 Wien - T: (01) 53410341. Head: Dr. Oskar Pausch
Performing Arts Museum 02947

Römische Baureste Am Hof, Museen der Stadt Wien, Am Hof 9, 1010 Wien - T: (01) 50587470, Fax: 50587477201, E-mail: post@m10.magwien.gv.at, Internet: http://www.museum.vienna.at. Head: Dr. Günter Düriegl
Archaeological Museum - 1953
Roman remains, sketches, charts and pictures illustrating Vienna's Roman past 02948

Römische Ruinen unter dem Hohen Markt, Museen der Stadt Wien, Hoher Markt 3, 1010 Wien - T: (01) 5355606, Fax: 50587477201. Head: Dr. Günter Düriegl
Archaeological Museum - 1950
Excavations, architectural fragments, casts, and reliefs from Roman times 02949

Salvador Dali im Palais Pallavicini, Josefspl 5a, 1010 Wien - T: (01) 5032690, 5122549, Fax: 5032691, Internet: http://www.dali-wien.at. Head: Dagmar Kalista
Fine Arts Museum - 1997 02950

Sammlung der Universität für angewandte Kunst Wien mit Oskar Kokoschka Zentrum, Postgasse 6, 1010 Wien - T: (01) 711333250, Fax: 5130616, E-mail: sammlung@uni-ak.ac.at, Internet: http://www.uni-ak.ac.at. Head: Erika Patka
Fine Arts Museum / Decorative Arts Museum / University Museum - 1981
Fine arts, decorative/ applied arts, architecture, autographs, photographs 02951

Sammlung historischer Prägestempel, c/o Österreichisches Hauptmünzamt, Am Heumarkt 1, 1030 Wien - T: (01) 52524380, Fax: 52524353, E-mail: guenther.dembski@khm.at, Internet: http://www.khm.at/. Head: Prof. Dr. Günther Dembski
Special Museum 02952

Sammlung Oskar Kokoschka → Sammlung der Universität für angewandte Kunst Wien mit Oskar Kokoschka Zentrum

Sammlung Religiöser Volkskunst, Johannesgasse 8, 1010 Wien - T: (01) 5121337, Fax: 4085342. Head: Dr. Franz Grieshofer, Klaus Beitl
Religious Arts Museum - 1966
Historic monastery pharmacy, religious folk art (esp 17th and 18th c), religious decorative arts and liturgical items 02953

Sammlungen des Marktamtes, Am Modenapark 1-2, 1030 Wien - T: (01) 400087921, Fax: 40009987919, E-mail: blr@m59.magwien.gv.at, Internet: http://adv.magwien.gv.at/ma53/museen/markt.htm. Head: Hubert Vyskocil, Peter Tuschell
Historical Museum - 1939
Photo archive 02954

Sanitärmuseum, Mollardgasse 87, 1060 Wien - T: (01) 59916, Fax: 59916, 9995670. Head: Kurt Pant
Special Museum - 1986
Hygiene, sanitary equipment, technical development 02955

Schloß Schönbrunn, 1130 Wien - T: (01) 811130, Fax: 8121106, E-mail: info@schoenbrunn.at, Internet: http://www.schoenbrunn.at. Head: Dr. Franz Sattlecker, Dr. Wolfgang Kippes
Local Museum
Summerresidence of the imperial family 02956

Schlumberger Wein- und Sektkellerei, Heiligenstädter Str 35-43, 1190 Wien - T: (01) 3686038, Fax: 3686034, E-mail: services@schlumberger.co.at, Internet: http://www.schlumberger.co.at. Head: Dr. Rudolf Kobatsch
Special Museum - 1919
Hist of the production of wine and champagne, Austrian wine trade, hist of the Schlumberger family - archives, library 02957

Schubert-Gedenkstätte Geburtshaus, Nußdorfer Str 54, 1090 Wien - T: (01) 3173601, Fax: 50587477201, E-mail: post@m10.magwien.gv.at, Internet: http://www.museum.vienna.at. Head: Dr. Günter Düriegl
Music Museum - 1912
Memorabilia of the composer Franz Schubert, housed in his birthplace, portraits of his circle of friends and family, scores and compositions, historical documents 02958

Schubert-Gedenkstätte Sterbewohnung, Kettenbrückengasse 6, 1040 Wien - T: (01) 5816730, 50587470, Fax: 50587477201, E-mail: post@m10.magwien.gv.at, Internet: http://www.museum.vienna.at. Head: Dr. Günter Düriegl
Music Museum
Memorabilia of the last years of the composer Franz Schubert 02959

Sigmund Freud-Museum, Berggasse 19, 1090 Wien - T: (01) 3191596, Fax: 3170279, Internet: http://www.freud-museum.at. Head: Inge Scholz-Strasser
Special Museum - 1971
Original furniture, books, antique coll and memorabilia of Freud housed in his appartment and office (1891-1938), archives on the hist of psychoanalysis, foundation 'Modern Art' - library, archive 02960

Sparkassen-Museum der Erste Bank, Gersthofer Str 143, 1180 Wien - T: (01) 4782136, 531001095, Fax: 531001094. Head: Richard Heinzl
Special Museum - 1956
Money boxes, purses, documents, medals, savings books 02961

Spielkartensammlung Piatnik, Hütteldorfer Str 229-231, 1141 Wien - T: (01) 9144151, Fax: 9111445. Head: Dieter Strehl
Special Museum - 1978 02962

Technisches Museum Wien, Mariahilfer Str 212, 1140 Wien - T: (01) 899980, Fax: 899983333, E-mail: mbox@tmw.ac.at, Internet: http://www.tmw.ac.at. Head: Dr. Gabriele Zuna-Kratky
Science&Tech Museum - 1908/1999
Development of technology from ancient times to the present, exhibits on chemistry and physics, models 02963

Teo Otto-Gedenkraum, Hanuschgasse 3, 1010 Wien - T: (01) 5122427, Fax: 512880045, E-mail: a-pistorius@othm.org. Head: Dr. Helga Dostal
Special Museum 02964

Uhrenmuseum der Stadt Wien, Schulhof 2, 1010 Wien - T: (01) 5332265, Fax: 50587477201. Head: Dr. Günter Düriegl
Science&Tech Museum - 1921
Hist of measuring time, clocks 02965

Universitätsbibliothek Wien, Dr. Karl Lueger Ring 1, 1010 Wien - T: (01) 427715001, Fax: 42779150, E-mail: ilse.dosoudil@univie.ac.at, Internet: http://www.univie.ac.at/ubunivie.ac.at. Head: Dr. Ilse Dosoudil
Library with Exhibitions 02966

Wagenburg im Schloß Schönbrunn, Kunsthistorisches Museum, Schloß Schönbrunn, 1130 Wien - T: (01) 8773244, Fax: 52524524, E-mail: info.wb@khm.at, Internet: http://www.khm.at. Head: Dr. Monica Kurzel-Runtscheiner
Science&Tech Museum / Decorative Arts Museum - 1922
Transport pool of the Viennese court (ca 1700-1918), state carriages, everyday's vehicles, harnesses and saddles of the Australian imperial family 02967

Wiener Bestattungsmuseum, Goldeggasse 19, 1041 Wien - T: (01) 501954227, Fax: 501954320, E-mail: direktion@bestattungwien.co.at, Internet: http://www.bestattungwien.co.at. Head: Arno Molinari
Special Museum - 1967
Funeral ceremonies, palls, orders and awards, paraments, old Viennese cemeteries, historic funerals, hearses, death announcements, uniforms, cremation, documents on the history of burials, death mask of Joseph Haydn - archives, library 02968

Wiener Feuerwehrmuseum, Am Hof 9, 1010 Wien - T: (01) 531991, Fax: 53199690, E-mail: gom@m68.magwien.gv.at, Internet: http://www.magwien.gv.at/feuerwehr/. Head: Manfred Görlich
Science&Tech Museum - 1901
Fire fighting and civil defense work 02969

Wiener Glasmuseum, Sammlung Lobmeyr, Kärntner Str 26, 1010 Wien - T: (01) 5120508, Fax: 512050885, E-mail: office@lobmeyer.at, Internet: http://www.lobmeyr.com. Head: Harald Rath
Decorative Arts Museum 02970

Wiener Kriminalmuseum, Museum der Bundespolizeidirektion Wien, Große Sperlgasse 24, 1020 Wien - T: (01) 2144678, Fax: 21446784. Head: Harald Seyrl
Special Museum - 1991
Hist of the judicial and police systems and the crime hist from the Middle Ages to the recent times - archive 02971

Wiener Phonomuseum, Mollardgasse 8, 1060 Wien - T: (01) 5811159, Fax: 5811159. Head: Gerhard Jagodic
Science&Tech Museum - 1982 02972

Wiener Porzellanmanufaktur Augarten, Schloß Augarten, 1020 Wien - T: (01) 211240, Fax: 2166833
Decorative Arts Museum 02973

Wiener Secession, Vereinigung bildender Künstler und Küntlerinnen, Friedrichstr 12, 1010 Wien - T: (01) 5875307, Fax: 587530734, E-mail: presse@secession.at, Internet: http://www.secession.at. Head: Matthias Herrmann
Fine Arts Museum - 1897
Changing exhibitions of contemporary art (founded by Josef Hoffmann, Gustav Klimt and Kolo Moser) 02974

Wiener Stadt- und Landesbibliothek, Rathaus, 1082 Wien - T: (01) 400084815, Fax: 40007219, E-mail: post@m09.magwien.gv.at, Internet: http://www.stadtbibliothek.wien.at. Head: Dr. Walter Obermaier
Library with Exhibitions 02975

Wiener Straßenbahnmuseum, Ludwig-Koeßler-Pl, 1030 Wien - T: (01) 790943700, Fax: 790943709, E-mail: strassenbahnmuseum@wienerlinien.at. Head: Harald Marincig
Science&Tech Museum - 1986 02976

Wiener Teddybärenmuseum, Drahtgasse 3, 1010 Wien - T: (01) 5334755
Special Museum 02977

Wiener Tramwaymuseum, Holochergasse 24, 1150 Wien - T: (01) 9854553, Fax: 9824124, E-mail: info@wiener-tramwaymuseum.org, Internet: http://www.wiener-tramwaymuseum.org. Head: Helmut Portele
Science&Tech Museum 02978

Wiener Ziegelmuseum, Penzinger Str 59, 1140 Wien - T: (01) 8972852. Head: Karl Koller
Special Museum - 1978
Development of masonry - library, archive 02979

Wiener Neudorf

Gemeindegalerie, Rathauspl 1, 2351 Wiener Neudorf - T: (02236) 6250140, Fax: 6250136, E-mail: kultur@noe.gv.at
Public Gallery 02980

Wiener Neustadt

Das Comic-Museum, Museumspl 1, 2700 Wiener Neustadt - T: (02622) 88550, Fax: 885505. Head: Peter P. Habarta
Special Museum 02981

Fabrikmuseum Johann Nemetz, Pernerstorfer Str 29, 2700 Wiener Neustadt - T: (02622) 3154. Head: Johann Nemetz
Science&Tech Museum - 1976 02982

Flugmuseum Aviaticum, Ferdinand-Graf-von-Zeppelin-Str 1, 2700 Wiener Neustadt - T: (02622) 88630, Fax: 88670, E-mail: aviaticum@utanet.at, Internet: http://www.aviaticum.at. Head: Claudia Cunia
Science&Tech Museum
Airplanes, motors of Austro Daimler, parachutes, instruments 02983

Industrieviertel-Museum, Museum für Industrie und Arbeitsgeschichte, Anna-Rieger-Gasse 4, 2700 Wiener Neustadt - T: (02622) 26015, Fax: 26015, Internet: http://www.wiener-neustadt.at/kultur/museen1_3htm/. Head: Gerhard Geissl
Special Museum / Historical Museum 02984

Das McDonald's Junior-Tüten & Pin Museum, Museumspl 1, 2700 Wiener Neustadt - T: (02622) 88550, Fax: 885505. Head: Peter P. Habarta
Special Museum 02985

Die Museumswelt, Museumspl 1, 2700 Wiener Neustadt - T: (02622) 88550, Fax: 885505. Head: Peter P. Habarta
Special Museum - 1998 02986

Reckturm, Stadtmuseum Wiener Neustadt, Reyergasse 23, 2700 Wiener Neustadt - T: (02236) 23531341. Head: Dr. Gertrud Buttlar-Elberberg
Local Museum - 1958 02987

Stadtmuseum Wiener Neustadt, Petersgasse 2a, 2700 Wiener Neustadt - T: (02622) 373440/41, Fax: 89104, E-mail: n.koppensteiner@wiener-neustadt.at, Internet: http://www.stadtmuseum.wrn.at. Head: Norbert Koppensteiner
Local Museum - 1824/1994
Prehist, archaeology, local hist, painting, sculpture, frescos, arts and crafts, coins 02988

Wienerbruck

Feuerwehrmuseum, Langseitenrotte 42, 3223 Wienerbruck - T: (02728) 263
Historical Museum - 1990 02989

Holzknechtmuseum Trübenbach im Naturpark Ötscher-Tormäuer, Trübenbach 5, 3223 Wienerbruck - T: (02728) 392
Special Museum 02990

Wieselburg an der Erlauf

Braumuseum, c/o Brauerei Wieselburg, Dr.-Beurle-Str 1, 3250 Wieselburg an der Erlauf - T: (07416) 501140, Fax: 501211
Science&Tech Museum 02991

Museum für Ur- und Frühgeschichte, Marktschloß, Hauptpl 7, 3250 Wieselburg an der Erlauf - T: (07416) 523190, Fax: 5231930, E-mail: wieselburg@eunet.at, Internet: http://www.wieselburg.at
Archaeological Museum - 1952
Prehistoric finds, artefacts from the Ice Age to modern times 02992

Wildalpen

Heimat- und Pfarrmuseum, Säusenbach 14, 8924 Wildalpen - T: (03636) 4510, Fax: 261
Local Museum / Religious Arts Museum - 1983
Local history 02993

Wasserleitungsmuseum, Säusenbach 14, 8924 Wildalpen - T: (03636) 4510, Fax: 451472637. Head: Josef Donner
Science&Tech Museum / Special Museum - 1985
History of Vienna water supply 02994

Wildbad-Einöd

Burgmuseum Ruine Dürnstein, Dürnstein 29, 9323 Wildbad-Einöd - T: (04268) 3189, 28200, Fax: 4912
Historical Museum 02995

Wildschönau

Bergbauernmuseum, 6311 Wildschönau - T: (05339) 8110
Agriculture Museum - 1971
Peasant life, wooden machines, tools for flax and hemp production, domestic utensils, furnishings, butter molds, mangers, weapons, traditional costumes, superstition and witchery 02996

Wildschönau-Auffach

Erstes Tiroler Holzmuseum, Auffach 148, Wildschönau, 6313 Wildschönau-Auffach - T: (05339) 8842, Fax: 8842, E-mail: info@wildschoenau.tirol.at, Internet: http://www.holzmuseum.com
Special Museum - 1996 02997

Wilfersdorf

Heimatmuseum und Sammlung Liechtenstein, Schloß, Hauptstr 1-5, 2193 Wilfersdorf - T: (02573) 2453, 2366, Fax: 236618, E-mail: museum.wilfersdorf@utanet.at, Internet: http://www.liechtensteinzentrum.at
Local Museum - 1984
Hist of the princely family of Liechtenstein 02998

Wilhering

Fritz Fröhlich-Sammlung im Stift Wilhering, Linzer Str 4, 4073 Wilhering - T: (07226) 231146, Fax: 231111. Head: Prof. Gabriel Weinberger
Religious Arts Museum - 1984
Paintings by Fritz Fröhlich 02999

Windhaag bei Freistadt

Alte Anton Bruckner-Schule, Markt 7, 4263 Windhaag bei Freistadt - T: (07943) 408, 220. Head: Alois Quaß
Special Museum
Hist of the school system and building 03000

Freilichtmuseum Handwerkerhaus Stegwagner, Nr 14, 4263 Windhaag bei Freistadt - T: (07943) 6111, Fax: 61114, E-mail: waldschule@windhaag-freistadt-ooe.gv.at, Internet: http://www.tiscover.com/kernland. Head: Dr. Hubert Roiß
Open Air Museum - 1984
Portrayal of various trades 03001

Freilichtmuseum Sägehammer Hofwies, Nr 11, 4263 Windhaag bei Freistadt - T: (07943) 404, Fax: 61114, E-mail: waldschule@windhaag-freistadt-ooe.gv.at, Internet: http://www.tiscover.com/kernland. Head: Dr. Hubert Roiß, Johann Haider
Open Air Museum / Science&Tech Museum - 1984
Iron processing, smithy 03002

Freilichtmuseum Venetianersäge, Felbermühle, 4263 Windhaag bei Freistadt - T: (07943) 6111, Fax: 61114, E-mail: waldschule@windhaag-freistadt-ooe.gv.at, Internet: http://www.tiscover.com/kernland. Head: Dr. Hubert Roiß
Open Air Museum / Science&Tech Museum
Hist of the saw mill 03003

Leithenmühle, Riemetschlag 27, 4263 Windhaag bei Freistadt - T: (07943) 495, 255, Fax: 495
Science&Tech Museum - 1990
Water mill 03004

Mühlviertler Waldhaus, Nr 5, 4263 Windhaag bei Freistadt - T: (07943) 611115, Fax: 61114, E-mail: waldschule@windhaag-freistadt-ooe.gv.at, Internet: http://www.tiscover.com/kernland
Natural History Museum
Forest hist and its various functions, biotops and symbiosis 03005

Zimmermannshaus Lackinger, Pieberschlag 18, 4263 Windhaag bei Freistadt - T: (07943) 6111, Fax: 61114, E-mail: waldschule@windhaag-freistadt-ooe.gv.at, Internet: http://www.tiscover.com/kernland. Head: Dr. Hubert Roiß
Local Museum
Trade and farm life hist 03006

Windischgarsten

Heimatmuseum Windischgarsten, Nr 7, 4580 Windischgarsten - T: (07562) 5007, 5266, Fax: 5397, E-mail: hvwdg@netway.at
Local Museum - 1987
Local and Roman hist 03007

Wörgl

Heimatmuseum, Brixentaler Str 1, 6300 Wörgl - T: (05332) 77239, 71365, E-mail: heimatmuseum@woergl.netwing.at
Local Museum - 1932/1988 03008

Wolfsberg, Kärnten

Lavanttaler Heimatmuseum, Tanglstr 1-7, 9400 Wolfsberg, Kärnten - T: (04352) 54357, 72001. Head: Cölestin Spendel
Local Museum - 1987
Tools, crafts, local traditions 03009

Stadtgalerie am Minoritenplatz, Minoritenpl 1, 9400 Wolfsberg, Kärnten - T: (04352) 537246, Fax: 537444, E-mail: werner.rink@wolfsberg.at, Internet: http://wolfsberg.at. Head: Max Koschu
Public Gallery - 1993 03010

Wolfsegg

Erstes Österreichisches Friedensmuseum und Heimatstube, Schulstr 18, 4902 Wolfsegg - T: (07676) 73550, Fax: 73550, E-mail: Gem@Wo.ooe.gv.at, Internet: http://www.ooevbw.org/friedensmuseum/friedensmuseum.htm. Head: Franz Deutsch
Local Museum - 1993
Farm house parlour and museum on questions of peace and war 03011

Ybbs

Fahrradmuseum, Herrengasse 12, 3370 Ybbs - T: (07412) 52612121, E-mail: margot.liernberger@ybbs.at
Science&Tech Museum - 1999
Bicycles since 1896 03012

Ybbsitz

Museum Kremayr, Markt 24, 3341 Ybbsitz - T: (07443) 86601, Fax: 8660160, E-mail: ybbsitz@netway.at, Internet: http://www.tiscover.com/ybbsitz. Head: Erika Helm
Local Museum - 1989 03013

Yspertal

Heimatmuseum Altenmarkt, Alte Schule, 3683 Yspertal - T: (07415) 492
Local Museum - 1979
Early hist, local hist 03014

Zederhaus

Denkmalhof Maurerbauernhof, Haus Nr. 94, 5584 Zederhaus - T: (06478) 288
Agriculture Museum - 1984
Agricultural tools 03015

Zell am Moos

Irrseer Heimathaus, Sammlung Hans Mairhofer-Irrsee, Dorfstr 20, 4893 Zell am Moos - T: (06234) 7025. Head: Monika E. Mayrhofer
Local Museum - 1965
Housing, handicraft, folk art, smoke kitchen 03016

Zell am See

Heimatmuseum Vogtturm, Kreuzgasse 2, 5700 Zell am See - T: (06542) 47034
Local Museum - 1973
Local hist, mining, crafts 03017

Zellerndorf

Bacher-Museum, Weinviertlerhof, 2051 Zellerndorf - T: (02945) 7252. Head: Josef Graf
Special Museum - 1934 03018

Zeltweg

Schloß Farrach, Schlossweg 13, 8740 Zeltweg - T: (03577) 25257, Fax: 2239720, E-mail: info@schlossfarrach.at, Internet: http://www.schlossfarrach.at. Head: Silvia Waltraud Hartleb
Public Gallery 03019

Zirl

Heimat- und Krippenmuseum, Dorfpl 2, 6170 Zirl - T: (05238) 54382, 540010
Local Museum / Religious Arts Museum - 1977
Cribs, early and prehistory of Zirl, local artists (Franz Plattner) 03020

Zistersdorf

Stadtmuseum Zistersdorf, Im Meierhof, 2225 Zistersdorf - T: (02532) 24010, Fax: 240115, E-mail: stadtgemeinde@zisterdorf.com. Head: Dr. Rudolf Streihammer
Local Museum - 1995 03021

Zurndorf

Sammlung Friedrichshof, Römerstr 1, 2424 Zurndorf - T: (02147) 7000171, (0676) 7497682, Fax: 7000116, E-mail: kunst@friedrichshof.at, Internet: http://www.friedrichshof.at. Head: Magdalena Stumpf
Fine Arts Museum - 1989 03022

Zwentendorf

Ortsmuseum, Amtshaus, 3435 Zwentendorf - T: (02277) 2209
Local Museum - 1962
Roman finds, early Christian cemetery (10th-11th c), medieval finds 03023

Zwettl, Niederösterreich

Anton-Museum, Landstr 65, 3910 Zwettl, Niederösterreich - T: (02822) 2343
Folklore Museum / Local Museum - 1927
Folk art and handicrafts, 18th-19th c sculpture, glass painting, peasant furnishings, tools, and weapons 03024

Museum für Medizin-Meteorologie, Museum Dürnhof, Dürnhof, Stift Zwettl 8, 3910 Zwettl, Niederösterreich - T: (02822) 53180, E-mail: funterst@mail.zserv.tuwien.ac.at. Head: Eva Untersteiner
Natural History Museum / Special Museum - 1984 03025

Stadtmuseum Zwettl, Hauptpl 4, 3910 Zwettl, Niederösterreich - T: (02822) 52564, Internet: http://www.zwettl.simplenet.com/stadtmuseum. Head: Franz Fichtinger
Local Museum - 1904/1992
Georg Ritter von Schönerer, city model, jurisdiction 03026

Stiftsmuseum, Zisterzienserstift, 3910 Zwettl, Niederösterreich - T: (02822) 55017, Fax: 55050, E-mail: info@stift-zwettl.co.at, Internet: http://www.stift-zwettl.co.at
Religious Arts Museum
Cloister, church, paintings 03027

Zwingendorf

Dorfmuseum Zwingendorf, Museumspl 1, Alte Schrotmühle, 2063 Zwingendorf - T: (02526) 7315, Fax: 73154, E-mail: adhai@jet2web.cc, Internet: http://www.members.e-media.at/dorfmuseum-zwingendorf. Head: Adolf Haider
Local Museum / Natural History Museum - 1990
Natural scientific documentation of salty,soils and plants and animal life there, local and regional history 03028

Joslowitzer Heimatstube, Museumspl 6, 2063 Zwingendorf - T: (02526) 7315, Fax: 73154, E-mail: adhai@jet2web.cc, Internet: http://www.members.e-media.at/dorfmuseum-zwingendorf. Head: Adolf Haider
Local Museum
Local regional history of the village Joslowitz (Jaroslavice) in South Moravia (Czech Republic) 03029

Azerbaijan

Baku

Azerbaijan State Museum of Fine Arts, Niyazi ul 9, 370001 Baku - T: (012) 925217
Fine Arts Museum 03030

Baku Museum of Education, ul Niazi 11, 370001 Baku - T: (012) 920453. Head: T.Z. Ahmedzade
Special Museum - 1940
Pedagogics, hist of education - library 03031

Museum of the History of Azerbaijan, ul Malygina 4, 370005 Baku - T: (012) 933648. Head: P.A. Azizbekova
Historical Museum - 1920
Traditional life and hist of Azerbaijan, furniture, popular art, - library 03032

Nizami Ganjavi, Azerbaijan National Academy of Sciences (Nizami Ganjavi State Museum of Azerbaijan Literature), Istiglaliyyat 53, 370001 Baku - T: (012) 921864. Head: I.R. Israfilovglu
Special Museum - 1939
Manuscripts and early editions of works by Azerbaijan writers, portraits, memorabilia, handwritings, classic and modern Azerbaijan literature - library 03033

State Art Museum R. Mustafaev, ul Čkalova 9, Baku. Head: K.M. Kyazim
Fine Arts Museum - 1936
Paintings, sculpture, contemporary art - library 03034

State Historical and Architectural Museum-preserve Shirvan Shah's Palace, Gala Dongesi 76, Baku - T: (012) 928304, Fax: 928304, E-mail: -shirvanshahmuseum@bakililar.az, Internet: http://www.geocities.com/tokyo/fountain/2411. Head: Dadasheva Sevda
Historical Museum - 1964
Weapons coll, art, palace decorations, carpets, copper ware, photos, graphics - library, archive 03035

State Museum of Azerbaijan Carpets and Applied Art Letif Kerimov, Neftçiler pr 123A, 370000 Baku - T: (012) 930501, 936685, Fax: 930501, E-mail: azcarpetmuseum@azeurotel.com, Internet: http://www.azcarpetmuseum.a-zeurotel.com. Head: Roya Taghiyeva
Decorative Arts Museum
Azerbaijan carpets, copperware, silver, embroidery, national costumes 03036

State Museum of the Dzabarey Theatre, Dzabarey Theatre, Baku
Performing Arts Museum
Paintings, photographs, stage and costume designs - library 03037

Bahamas

Hope Town

Wyannie Malone Historical Museum, Gillam St, Hope Town, Abaco - T: (242) 366-0107, E-mail: macmcaleer@aol.com
Historical Museum - 1977
Genealogy of early American loyalist settlers, chronology of Hope Town's hist, daily life of the past, sponging, boatbuilding, wrecking (salvaging ship wrecks) 03038

Nassau

Angelo Roker's Art Centre and Museum, Harold Rd, Nassau, mail addr: POB SS 6230, Nassau
Fine Arts Museum 03039

Bahamas Historical Society Museum, Elizabeth Av, Nassau, mail addr: POB SS-6833, Nassau - T: (242) 322-4231, E-mail: bahistsoc@batelnet.bs, Internet: http://www.bahamas.net.bs/history. Head: Dr. Gail Saunders, David L. Cates
Historical Museum - 1959
Bahamas history, anthropology and archaeology, maps, prints, photographs, shells, marine salvage coll - library 03040

Bahamas Museum, POB N1510, Nassau
Local Museum 03041

Nassau Public Library and Museum, POB N3210, Nassau
Library with Exhibitions
Maps, prints, coins, stamps, paintings 03042

Pompey Museum of Slavery and Emancipation, Ar Vendue House, Bay St, Nassau, mail addr: POB SS-6341, Nassau - T: (242) 326-2566, Fax: (242) 393-2855. Head: Dr. Gail Saunders
Historical Museum / Ethnology Museum / Folklore Museum - 1992
Ethnology, folk art 03043

Bahrain

Manama

Bahrain National Museum, Diplomatic Area, SH Ahmed Al-Fatih Rd, Manama, mail addr: POB 2199, Manama - T: 292977, Fax: 293820. Head: Nayla Al-Khalifa
Archaeological Museum - 1970
Archaeological display on the rise of the Dilmun civilization, Dilmun seals, costumes, tools, weapons, etc. of historic Bahrain 03044

Bangladesh

Chittagong

Chittagong University Museum, c/o Chittagong University, Chittagong - T: (031) 616547, Fax: 682030. Head: Shamsul Hossain
Local Museum - 1973
Ethnography, archeology, folk art, documents of Liberation War 03045

Ethnological Museum, Agrabad, Chittagong 4100 - T: (031) 721734. Head: M. Mosharraf Hossain
Ethnology Museum - 1966
Ethnic objects of Bangladesh and foreign countries 03046

Comilla

Ram Mala Museum, Comilla. Head: Rasmohan Chakravarti
Local Museum
Local history 03047

Dhaka

Ahsan Manzil Museum, Nawab Ahsanullah Rd, Shadarghat, Dhaka - T: (02) 282790. Head: Dr. Enamul Haque
Decorative Arts Museum / Fine Arts Museum - 1986
Crafts, art 03048

Bangla Academy Folklore Museum, Bangla Academy, Dhaka - T: (02) 502286. Head: Dr. Mahmud Kuraishi
Folklore Museum - 1978
Folkart, crafts 03049

Bangladesh National Museum, Shahbagh, Dhaka, mail addr: POB 355, Dhaka 2 - T: (02) 500300. Head: Dr. Enamul Haque
Museum of Classical Antiquities / Decorative Arts Museum / Historical Museum / Ethnology Museum - 1913
Classical and decorative art, history, ethnography, natural history - library 03050

Bangladesh Shamorik Jadughar, Mirpur Cantonment, Mirpur, Dhaka - T: (02) 80251120 ext 257. Head: Muhammad Ziauddin
Natural History Museum / Fine Arts Museum - 1987
Natural hist, art 03051

Dhaka Museum, Ramna Rd, Dhaka
Fine Arts Museum / Archaeological Museum - 1913
Art and archaeology of Bengal, Buddhist and Brahmanical iconography, coins 03052

Geological Survey Museum, 153 Pinoeer Rd, Segunbagicha, Dhaka 1000 - T: (02) 408483, Fax: 9339309, E-mail: gsb@dhaka.agni.com. Head: Pradip Kumar Sen Gupta
Natural History Museum - 1967 03053

Lala Bagh Fort Museum, Mughal Fort, Dhaka - T: (02) 507262. Head: Dr. Shamsul Alam
Historical Museum - 1974
Historical collections housed in 18th c pavillon 03054

Dinajpur

Dinajpur Museum, Dinajpur. Head: Mahmud Mokarram Hossain
Archaeological Museum - 1968
Material from excavations in the Dinajpur region 03055

Mahastangarh

Archaeological Museum, Bogra District, Mahastangarh. Head: Dr. Shamsul Alam
Archaeological Museum - 1965 03056

Mainamati

Archaeological Museum, Comilla District, Mainamati
Archaeological Museum - 1966
Remains of Buddhist monastery, terracotta plaques 03057

Paharpur

Archaeological Museum, Rajshahi District, Paharpur. Head: Dr. Shamsul Alam
Archaeological Museum - 1956 03058

Rajshahi

Varendra Research Museum, c/o University of Rajshahi, Aksaya Kumar Maitra Rd, Rajshahi - T: 3455. Head: Dr. Saifuddin Chowdhury
Archaeological Museum / Fine Arts Museum - 1910
Architectural fragments from the Kushan, Gupta, Pala and Sena periods, articles from the Muslim period (c 1200-1857), stone and metal images, paintings, arms, manuscripts and inscriptions, coins - library, conservation 03059

Rangpur

Rangpur Archaeological Museum, Old Public Library Building, Rangpur - T: (0521) 3879. Head: Dr. Shamsul Alam
Archaeological Museum - 1965 03060

Sonargaon

Sonargaon Folk Art and Craft Museum, P.O. Aminpur, Sonargaon - T: 72080 ext 331. Head: Shamsul Hug
Folklore Museum - 1975 03061

Sylhet

Osmani Museum, Nairopul, Sylhet - T: (0821) 4361. Head: Dr. Enamul Haque
Fine Arts Museum / Decorative Arts Museum - 1985
Art, glass, books 03062

Barbados

Bridgetown

Iron Garden, Perry Gap, Roebuck St, Bridgetown - T: (246) 429-5137, Fax: (246) 429-1336
Special Museum 03063

Christ Church

Mallalieu Motor Museum, Pavillion Court, Hastings, Christ Church - T: (246) 426-4640, Fax: (246) 426-0660, E-mail: billm@sunbeach.net. Head: William P. Mallalieu
Science&Tech Museum 03064

Saint James

Portobello Gallery, Saint James - T: (246) 424-1687, Fax: (246) 424-1687, E-mail: portobel@caribsurf.com
Public Gallery 03065

Sir Frank Hutson Sugar Museum, Portvale Sugar Factory, Saint James - T: (246) 432-0100, 436-9033, Fax: (246) 429-9055
Special Museum
Producing sweets, sugar, molasses and rum 03066

Saint Michael

Barbados Museum, Saint Ann's Garrison, Saint Michael - T: (246) 427-0201, 436-1956, Fax: (246) 429-5946, E-mail: museum@caribsurf.com, Internet: http://www.barbmuse.org.bb. Head: Alissandra Cummins
Local Museum - 1933
Historical coll, natural hist, furniture, silver, glass and china, Cunard coll of West Indian prints, paintings, archaeology, postcards, maps, books - library 03067

Saint Phillip

Rum Factory and Heritage Park, Four Sq, Saint Phillip - T: (246) 420-1977, Fax: (246) 420-1976
Science&Tech Museum 03068

Sunbury Great House, Sunbury Planatation, Saint Phillip - T: (246) 423-6270, Fax: (246) 423-5863
Historical Museum / Decorative Arts Museum
Antiques, old prints, china, glassware, horsedrawn carriages 03069

Belarus

Beloveżskaja Pušča

Beloveżskaja Pušča Muzej, 225063 Beloveżskaja Pušča - T: (01631) 56267, 56396, 56169, Fax: 21283, E-mail: box@npbprom.belpak.brest.by. Head: M.N. Žuravlev
Natural History Museum
Natural hist, flora and faune of the Beloveżskaja Pušča forest, preservation of the bison and other rare species 03070

Grodno

Grodnenski Gosudarstvennyj Istoričeskij Muzej (Grodno State Historical Museum), Zamkovaja vul 22, Grodno - T: (0152) 449431. Head: E.A. Solovëva
Historical Museum / Archaeological Museum - 1920
History, economy, natural hist, archeology, ethnography, fine arts, decorative arts, religious arts - library, dept of amateur and folk arts 03071

Kobrin

Kobrinski Voenno-istoričeski Muzej im. A.V. Suvorova, ul Suvorova 18, 225860 Kobrin - T: 23794
Military Museum
Military hist, memorial to Aleksandr Vasilevich Suvorov - library 03072

Minsk

Belorusskij Gosudarstvennyj muzej Istorii Velikoj Otečestvennoj Vojny (Belorussian State Museum of the History of World War II), pr Skaryny 25a, 220030 Minsk - T: (017) 2271166, 2277635, Fax: 2271166, Internet: http://www.beltelecom.minsk.by/~war-museum. Head: Gennady Barkoun
Military Museum - 1943
Coll of small arms and artillery pieces, standards, documents and photos, newspapers, soviet orders and medals, military equipment, etc - library, archives 03073

Fire Museum, ul Kozlova 28, Bldg 8, 220000 Minsk - T: (017) 2369122
Historical Museum / Science&Tech Museum
Hist of Minsk's fire brigade 03074

Gallery of Traditional Ornamental Art, ul Oktjabrskaja 5, Minsk - T: (015) 2768980
Folklore Museum 03075

Gosudarstvennyj Muzej Istorii i Kultury Belarusa (National Museum of the History and Culture of Belarus), ul Karla Marksa 12, 220050 Minsk - T: (0172) 2273665, Fax: 2273665. Head: P.S. Khotko
Historical Museum - 1957
Hist of Belorussia - library 03076

Litaraturny muzej Janki Kupaly (Yanka Kupala Literary Museum), vul Kupaly 4, 220030 Minsk - T: (017) 277943, Fax: 277943, E-mail: kupalamuseum@hotmail.com, Internet: http://www.belarus.net/museum/y_index.htm. Head: Jeanne Dapkyunas
Special Museum - 1945
Literary hist, coll of manuscripts and works of the poet Yanka Kupala 03077

Literary History Museum, ul Bogdanoviča 15, 220000 Minsk - T: (017) 2345621/9932
Special Museum 03078

Maksim Bogdanovich Literature Museum, ul Rabkorauskaja 14, 220000 Minsk - T: (017) 2206213
Special Museum 03079

Muzej Staražytna Belaruskaj Kultury (Ancient Belarusian Culture Museum), ul Surganova 1-2, 220072 Minsk - T: (017) 2842732, Fax: 2842381, E-mail: secr@mserv.bas-net.by. Head: Victor Šmatov
Ethnology Museum / Archaeological Museum / Religious Arts Museum
Archaeology, religious art 16th-19th c, folk art, decorative art 17th-19th c 03080

Nacionalnyj Chudožestvennyj Muzej Respubliki Belarus (National Art Museum of the Republic of Belarus), ul Lenina 20, 220030 Minsk - T: (0172) 2275672, Fax: 2275672, E-mail: NMMRB@mail.ru, Internet: http://www.nacbibl.org.by. Head: Vladimir I. Prakapcov
Fine Arts Museum - 1939
Russian, Belorussian, Soviet and foreign art - library 03081

National Art Gallery, ul Kozlova 3, Minsk - T: (015) 2330549
Public Gallery / Fine Arts Museum 03082

Vitebsk

Chagall Museum, Putna 2, 210026 Vitebsk - T: (0212) 360387, 372737, Fax: 372737, E-mail: chagall@chagall.belpak.vitebsk.by, Internet: http://www.chagall.vitebsk.by. Head: Ljudmila Chmelnickaja
Fine Arts Museum / Special Museum
Marc Chagall Memorial House; graphic works by Marc Chagall; coll of modern paintings 03083

Belgium

Aalst

Daensmuseum en Archief van de Vlaamse Sociale Strijd, Oude Vismarkt 1, 9300 Aalst - T: 053776906, 053772094, Fax: 053778450. Head: M. Van de Perre
Special Museum
Museum of the first Belgian trade-unionist Daens 03084

Stedelijk Museum Aalst, Oude Vismarkt 13, 9300 Aalst City Museum Aalst - T: 053732340, Fax: 053732319, E-mail: musea@aalst.be. Head: Luc Geeroms
Local Museum - 1903
Works of art, archaeology, history of art and traditions 03085

Aarschot

Stedelijk Museum voor Heemkunde en Folklore, Begijnhof 25, 3200 Aarschot - T: 016568451. Head: A. Coeck
Local Museum - 1967
Documents on Joseph Cuypers (composer) and the Meulemans family (musicians), iconography, prehistory, local history, folklore 03086

Affligem

Archeologisch Museum Abdij, Abdijstr 6, 1790 Affligem - T: 053667025
Archaeological Museum
Ancient history, archaeology, memorabilia on local painters and composers 03087

Amel

Wurzel- und Heimatmuseum, Kirchweg 169, 4770 Amel - T: 080349408, 080340263
Natural History Museum / Local Museum 03088

Andenne

Musée de la Céramique d'Andenne, 29 Rue Charles Lapierre, 5300 Andenne - T: 085844181, Fax: 085845631. Head: Robert Mordant
Decorative Arts Museum - 1930
Pottery from 2nd-14th c, 12th c candelabra, rare pipes, faience and porcelain (18th-19th c), stoneware artefacts, tiles, bricks, oven, plastic earth mine, ceramic workshop 03089

Trésor de la Collegiale Sainte-Begge, Pl du Chapitre, 5300 Andenne - T: 085841344
Religious Arts Museum 03090

Annevoie-Rouillon

Château et Jardin d'Annevoie, 5537 Annevoie-Rouillon - T: 081611555
Decorative Arts Museum 03091

Anthisnes

Musée de la Cervoise, du Gruyt et des Bières Mediévales, 19 Av de l'Abbaye, 4160 Anthisnes - T: 043836390, Fax: 043836390. Head: S. Eggen
Special Museum - 1994
Folklore and regional art, implements, beer and gin implements 03092

Antoing

Musée Château des Princes de Ligne et Musée Lapidaire, Pl Bara, 7640 Antoing - T: 069441729, E-mail: tourismeantoing@swing.be. Head: Didier Dudant
Decorative Arts Museum 03093

Musée de la Pierre, Stade d'Antoing, 7640 Antoing - T: 069441729, Fax: 069444572, E-mail: tourismeantoing@swing.be. Head: Didier Dudant
Natural History Museum 03094

Parc Archéologique, Hameau de Guéronde, 7640 Antoing - T: 069441729, Fax: 069444572, E-mail: tourismeantoing@swing.be. Head: Didier Dudavt
Archaeological Museum 03095

Antwerpen

Archief en Museum voor het Vlaamse Cultuurleven, Minderbroedersstr 22, 2000 Antwerpen - T: 032229320, Fax: 032229321, E-mail: amvc@cs.antwerpen.be, Internet: http://www.antwerpen.be. Head: Leen Van Dijck
Special Museum - 1933
Literature, music, theater, architecture, paintings 03096

Bormshuis, Volkstr 30, 2000 Antwerpen - T: 032383399, 036454291
Historical Museum 03097

Brouwershuis, Adriaan Brouwerstr 20, 2000 Antwerpen - T: 032326511, Fax: 032326511. Head: Rita Jalon
Historical Museum - 1933
Installations for the supply of water to breweries (16th c), rich council chamber, industrial archeology 03098

Centrum voor de Vlaamse Kunst van de 16de en de 17de Eeuw, Kolveniersstr 20, 2000 Antwerpen - T: 032011577, Fax: 032319387. Head: F. Baudouin
Fine Arts Museum 03099

Dagbladmuseum Abraham Verhoevenhuis, Lombardevest 6, 2000 Antwerpen - T: 038870178, E-mail: info@dagbladmuseum.be. Head: Georges Blommaert
Special Museum
Newspaper Museum 03100

Etnografisch Museum, Suikerrui 19, 2000 Antwerpen - T: 032208600, Fax: 032270871, E-mail: jan.vanalphen@cs.antwerpen.be, Internet: http://www.antwerpen.be/cultuur/etnografisch_museum/. Head: Jan Van Alphen
Ethnology Museum - 1952
Arts and crafts of pre-literate and non-European peoples 03101

Eugeen Van Mieghem Museum, Beatrijslaan 8, 2000 Antwerpen - T: 032110330
Fine Arts Museum
Paintings 03102

Filmmuseum, Centrum voor Beeldcultuur, Koninklijk Paleis, Meir 50, 2000 Antwerpen - T: 032338571, Fax: 032262764, E-mail: cvb@pandora.be, Internet: http://www.antwerpen.be/cvb. Head: Marc Holthof
Performing Arts Museum
Film hist 03103

Heemmuseum van Borgerhout, Turnhoutsebaan 110, 2200 Antwerpen - T: 031364917
Local Museum
Local history, crafts, popular religious art, costumes 03104

Jordaenshuis, Reyndersstr 4, 2000 Antwerpen - T: 032343985
Fine Arts Museum
Jacob Jordaens Museum (1593-1678) 03105

Koninklijk Museum voor Schone Kunsten, Leopold de Waelpl 1-9, 2000 Antwerpen, mail addr: Plaatsnijdersstr 2, 2000 Antwerpen - T: 032387809, Fax: 032480810, E-mail: postmaster@kmska.be, Internet: http://www.dma.be/cultuur/kmska. Head: Dr. Paul Huvenne
Fine Arts Museum - 1810
Flemish paintings, sculpture - library 03106

Koninklijke Maatschappij voor Dierkunde van Antwerpen, Koningin Astridplein 26, 2018 Antwerpen - T: 032024540, Fax: 032310018, E-mail: jacques@zooantwerpen.be, Internet: http://www.zooantwerpen.be. Head: F.J. Daman
Natural History Museum - 1843
Zoology, botany, Dr. H. Van Heurck coll - aquarium, nocturnal house, winter garden, planetarium, education dept 03107

Maagdenhuismuseum, Lange Gasthuisstr 33, 2000 Antwerpen - T: 032235620, Fax: 032235331, E-mail: maggy.anthonissen@ocmw.antwerpen.be. Head: M. Beets-Anthonissen
Fine Arts Museum / Decorative Arts Museum
Paintings, sculptures, decorative art, painted glass, furniture, metal works, ceramics 03108

Miniatuurstad, Cockerillkaai 50, Hangar 15, 2000 Antwerpen - T: 032370329
Special Museum 03109

Museum Mayer van den Bergh, Lange Gasthuisstr 19, 2000 Antwerpen - T: 032324237, Fax: 032317335, E-mail: hans.nieuwdorp@cs.antwerpen.be, Internet: http://www.antwerpen.be/cultuur/museum_mvdb. Head: Hans Nieuwdorp
Fine Arts Museum - 1904
Gothic painting and sculpture, 17th c painting, Pieter Bruegel I 'Dulle Griet' (Mad Margot), Meester Heinrich of Konstanz, Jezus-Johannes-groep 03110

Museum Plantin-Moretus, Vrijdagmarkt 22, 2000 Antwerpen - T: 032211450, 032211451, Fax: 032211471, E-mail: - museum.plantin.moretus@antwerpen.be, Internet: http://www.antwerpen.be/culture/museum_plantin-moretus/. Head: Dr. Francine de Nave
Science&Tech Museum - 1877
Old printing office and foundry of Christopher Plantin and his successors (1555-1876), typographical material, old bindings, paintings (incl Rubens) - city print room 03111

Museum Smidt van Gelder, Belgiëlei 91, 2018 Antwerpen - T: 032390652, Fax: 032302281, E-mail: museumsmidtvangelder@stad.antwerpen.be. Head: Clara Vanderhenst
Decorative Arts Museum / Fine Arts Museum - 1950
Chinese, Japanese and European porcelain, 18th c interior, furniture, paintings 03112

Museum van de Sint-Jakobskerk, Lange Nieuwstr 73, 2000 Antwerpen - T: 032321032, Fax: 032321032, E-mail: jacobus.antverpiae@yucom.be, Internet: Http://www.topa.be. Head: Louis Leclef
Religious Arts Museum 03113

Museum van Hedendaagse Kunst Antwerpen (Museum of Contemporary Art of Antwerp), Leuvenstr 32, 2000 Antwerpen - T: 032385960, Fax: 032162486, E-mail: muhka@skynet.be, Internet: http://www.artsite.be/musea/muhka. Head: Florent Bex
Fine Arts Museum - 1987
Gordon Matta-Clark Foundation, Flemish art - library, educational service 03114

Museum Vleeshuis, Vleeshouwersstr 38-40, 2000 Antwerpen - T: 032336404, Fax: 032314705, E-mail: vleeshuis@antwerpen.be, Internet: http://www.antwerpen.be/cultuur/musea/mvlee.htm. Head: W. Porttier
Local Museum - 1913
Local history museum 03115

Museum voor Anesthesie Verantare, Louizastr 8, 2000 Antwerpen - T: 032383878. Head: Dr. P.M. Desbarax
Historical Museum
Apparatus and drugs about anasthesia and blood transfusion 03116

Museum voor Binnenscheepvaart, Bonapartedok, Nieuwepoortkade Kaai 10, 2000 Antwerpen - T: 032250015
Historical Museum 03117

Museum voor Kerkelijke Kunst Sint-Carolus, Hendrik Consciencepl 12, 2000 Antwerpen - T: 032338433
Religious Arts Museum 03118

Nationaal Centrum voor de Plastische Kunsten van de 16de en de 17 de Eeuw → Centrum voor de Vlaamse Kunst van de 16de en de 17de Eeuw

Nationaal Museum en Archief van Douane en Accijnzen, Kattendijkdok, Oostkaai 22, 2000 Antwerpen - T: 032292242
Historical Museum 03119

Nationaal Scheepvaartmuseum (National Maritime Museum), Steenpl 1, 2000 Antwerpen - T: 032019340, Fax: 032019341, E-mail: scheepmus@stad.antwerpen.be, Internet: http://www.dma.be/cultuur/scheepvaartmuseum. Head: Rita Jalon
Science&Tech Museum - 1952
Ship models, navigational instruments, charts - library 03120

Natuurhistorisch Museum, Koningin Astridplein 26, 2018 Antwerpen - T: 032311640
Natural History Museum 03121

Natuurhistorisch Museum Boekenbergpark, Boekenbergpark, 2100 Antwerpen - T: 033215438
Natural History Museum
Speleology, mineralogy, prehist, archaeology, paleontology 03122

Natuurwetenschappelijk Museum, Leopoldstr 24, 2000 Antwerpen - T: 032324087. Head: J. Lauwers
Natural History Museum 03123

New International Cultural Center, Pourbusstr 5, 2000 Antwerpen - T: 032160771, E-mail: nicc@thepentagon.com
Public Gallery 03124

Openluchtmuseum voor Beeldhouwkunst Middelheim (Open Air Museum of Sculpture Middelheim), Middelheimlaan 61, 2020 Antwerpen - T: 038271534, Fax: 038252835, E-mail: - MiddelheimOpenluchtmuseum@cs.antwerpen.be, Internet: http://www.dma.be/cultuur/museum_middelheim. Head: Menno Meewis
Fine Arts Museum / Open Air Museum - 1950
Sculpture (incl Moore, Rodin, Maillol, Zadkine, Marini) - library 03125

Pelgrom Museum Poorterswoning, Pelgrimstr 15, 2000 Antwerpen - T: 032340809, Fax: 032319335, Internet: http://www.pelgrom.be. Head: Johan Snoeys
Folklore Museum 03126

Poldermuseum, Tolhuisstr 10-16, Lillo-Fort, 2040 Antwerpen - T: 033216186. Head: Daniël Graaf Le Grelle
Local Museum - 1959
Costumes, agricultural implements, furniture, kitchen utensils, objects and documents in connection with popular superstition and customs, photographs of old sites and buildings no longer existing, concerning the region north of Antwerpen 03127

Politiemuseum Oudaan, Oudaan 5, 2000 Antwerpen - T: 032025511
Historical Museum 03128

Provinciaal Diamantmuseum, Koningin Astridplein 19-23, 2018 Antwerpen - T: 032024890, Fax: 032024898, E-mail: info@diamant.provant.be, Internet: http://www.diamantmuseum.be. Head: Sabine Denissen
Science&Tech Museum - 1972
Technique of diamond cutting and the craft of diamond jewelry, historical tools for diamond cutting - library 03129

Provinciaal Museum Sterckshof - Zilvercentrum, Hooftvunderlei 160, 2100 Antwerpen - T: 033605250, Fax: 033605253, E-mail: info@sterckshof.provant.be, Internet: http://www.provant.be/sterckshof. Head: Leo de Ren
Decorative Arts Museum - 1954
Historical arts and crafts, an outstanding coll of Belgian silver, Renaissance painted wooden ceiling (about 1545) - library 03130

Provinciaal Museum voor Fotografie, Waalse Kaai 47, 2000 Antwerpen - T: 032429300, Fax: 032429310, E-mail: info@fotografie.provant.be, Internet: http://www.provant.be/fotomuseum. Head: Dirk Berkvens
Science&Tech Museum / Fine Arts Museum - 1986
Historical cameras, photos 03131

Provinciaal Veiligheidsinstituut, Jezusstr 28-30, 2000 Antwerpen - T: 032034200, Fax: 032034250, E-mail: info@pvi.be, Internet: http://www.provant.be/pvi. Head: Albert Voet
Science&Tech Museum - 1942
All kinds of items about work safety, safety at home - library 03132

Rockoxhuis, Keizerstr 12, 2000 Antwerpen - T: 032019250, Fax: 032019251. Head: Dr. K. Vanderhoeght
Fine Arts Museum - 1977
Painting (Rubens, Van Dyck, Jordaens, Teniers), furniture - audio-visual, audioguides 03133

Rubenianum, Kolveniersstr 20, 2000 Antwerpen - T: 032011577, Fax: 032319387
Library with Exhibitions 03134

Rubenshuis, Wapper 9-11, 2000 Antwerpen - T: 032011555, Fax: 032273692, E-mail: carl.depauw@cs.antwerpen.be, Internet: http://www.antwerpen.be/cultuur/rubenshuis. Head: Carl Depauw
Fine Arts Museum - 1946
Reconstructed home and studio of Pieter Paul Rubens (1577-1640), Flemish furniture (17th c), paintings and sketches by Rubens and some of his contemporaries 03135

Stadhuis van Antwerpen, Grote Markt 1, 2000 Antwerpen - T: 032208211
Local Museum
City hall with a coll paintings and portraits (16th-19th c) 03136

Stedelijk Prentenkabinet, Vrijdagmarkt 22-23, 2000 Antwerpen - T: 032211450, Fax: 032211460, E-mail: prentenkab@stad.antwerpen.be, Internet: http://www.antwerpen.be/cultuur/stedelyk_prentenkabinet. Head: Dr. Francine de Nave
Fine Arts Museum - 1938
Drawings by P.P. Rubens, A. van Dyck, J. Jordaens a.o. 16th-17th c Flemish masters, prints, graphic arts and drawings from early 16th c to present (Ensor, Masereel, Jan Fabre a.o.) - library 03137

Tentoonstellingzaal Hessenhuis, Falconroi 53, 2000 Antwerpen - T: 032060350, E-mail: hessenhuis@stad.antwerpen.be, Internet: http://www.antwerpen.be/cultuur/hessenhuis
Public Gallery 03138

Theater Poesje, Gildekamersstr 2-6, 2000 Antwerpen - T: 032329409
Performing Arts Museum
Puppets 03139

Vleeshuis, Vleeshouwerstr 38, 2000 Antwerpen - T: 032336404, Fax: 032314705, E-mail: vleeshuis@stad.antwerpen.be, Internet: http://www.dma.be/cultuur/vleeshuis. Head: Karel Moens
Fine Arts Museum / Music Museum / Archaeological Museum - 1913
Musical instruments, archeology, art - library 03140

Volkskundemuseum, Gildekamersstr 2-6, 2000 Antwerpen - T: 032208666, Fax: 032208368, E-mail: werner.vanhoof@antwerpen.be, Internet: http://www.dma.be/cultuur/musea/vlkmus.htm
Folklore Museum - 1907
The Pageants and the Giants, Antwerpen figures, popular beliefs, magic, popular medicine (pharmacy), Flemish folk art, popular prints, popular customs, puppet theatre, the head of the Giant Druon Antigon - library 03141

Volksmuseum Deurne, Koraalpl 2, 2100 Antwerpen - T: 033244880, Fax: 033267598. Head: L. Peeters
Local Museum - 1970
Coll local hist and paleontology (whalebones), wage earners, the industrial revolution, paintings and decoration - library, archives 03142

Arendonk

Het Arendonks Heemmuseum, Huis Deroissart, Vrijheid 21, 2370 Arendonk - T: 014678726
Local Museum
Local hist 03143

Arlon

Musée de la Basilique et des Thermes Romains, Rue des Thermes Romains, 6700 Arlon, mail addr: 6700 Arlon - T: 063216360. Head: Lucette Graas
Archaeological Museum
Remainders of a 4th c basilica, burial place for christianized Merovingians, Roman thermae, bath and canalization 03144

Musée de la Tour Romaine, Grand Pl, 6700 Arlon - T: 063216360, Fax: 063216360, E-mail: si@ping.be, Internet: http://www.ial.be
Archaeological Museum - 1954
Remainders of a fortress tower (3rd c.), Roman sepulchral monuments 03145

Musée Luxembourgeois, 13 Rue des Martyrs, 6700 Arlon - T: 063221236, 063226192, Fax: 063228412, E-mail: info@ial.be, Internet: http://www.ial.be. Head: Louis Lejeune
Museum of Classical Antiquities / Archaeological Museum 03146

Asse

Heemkundig Museum, Oud Gasthuis, Mollestr 5, 1730 Asse - T: 024528740
Local Museum / Archaeological Museum
Local hist and archeological finds 03147

Ath

Espace Gallo-Romain, 2 Rue de Nazareth, 7800 Ath - T: 068269233, Fax: 068282763, E-mail: espace.gallo-romain@ath.be. Head: Karine Bausier, Jean-Pierre Ducastelle
Archaeological Museum - 1997
Gallo-Roman ships of Pommeroeul (2nd c BC), memorabilia on the Gallo-Roman life and work (shipping, tanner's and butcher's workshop, ceramics) 03148

Musée Athois, 16 Rue du Bouchain, 7800 Ath - T: 068269232, Fax: 068269239, E-mail: musee.d.histoire@ath.be. Head: Jean-Pierre Ducastelle
Local Museum / Archaeological Museum / Decorative Arts Museum - 1966
Prehistoric archaeology, local hist, clay models about evolution of the town, ceramics, pottery, lace, furnishings, tapestries, stitching, crafts (stone, woodworkings), medieval and Renaissance sculpture, Grablegung Christi (Notre-Dame du Refuge, Ath, 1400-1410) - library 03149

Attre

Collection du Château d'Attre, 8 Av du Château, 7941 Attre - T: 068454460, Fax: 068454460, E-mail: chateau.de.attre@skynet.be. Head: B. de Meester de Heyndonck
Fine Arts Museum 03150

Aubechies

Archéosite, Rue de l'Abbaye, 7972 Aubechies - T: 069671116. Head: Leonce Demarez
Open Air Museum / Archaeological Museum 03151

Domus Romana, 17 Rue de Leuze, 7672 Aubechies - T: 069664727, 069662938. Head: Leonce Demarez
Archaeological Museum - 1977
Prehistoric and protohistoric objects, fragments of mural painting 03152

Awirs

Musée Château d'Aigremont, 12 Rue du Château, 4400 Awirs - T: 041751971, 041714238
Local Museum 03153

Aywaille

Musée de la Liberation, Château de Dieupart, 4920 Aywaille - T: 041845972
Local Museum 03154

Baasrode

Scheepvaartmuseum, Sint-Ursmarusstr 137, 9200 Baasrode - T: 052333426, Fax: 052332308, E-mail: fieldcarlos@skynet.be. Head: Jan Annemans
Archaeological Museum / Historic Site 03155

Balen

Kruiermuseum, Vaartstr 29, 2490 Balen - T: 014812266
Local Museum 03156

Basècles

Musée de la Pierre et du Marbre, Grand Pl, 7971 Basècles - T: 069577480, 069575933
Natural History Museum 03157

Bastogne

Au Pays d'Ardenne - Original Museum, 20 Rue de Neufchâteau, 6600 Bastogne - T: 062214911
Local Museum 03158

Bastogne Historical Center, American Memorial Hill of the Mardasson, 6650 Bastogne - T: 062211413
Military Museum - 1976
Uniforms, guns, vehicles of World War II in special context with Bastogne, diorama, audio-visual program, cinema 03159

Musée de la Parole au Pays de Bastogne, 103 Lutrebois, 6600 Bastogne - T: 062213700
Local Museum 03160

Musée en Piconrue, 24 Pl Saint-Pierre, 6600 Bastogne - T: 062212929
Local Museum 03161

Musée Maison Mathelin, 1 Rue Gustave Delperdange, 6600 Bastogne - T: 061211758, 061213287, Fax: 061213287. Head: Patrick Hilgers
Historical Museum / Archaeological Museum / Military Museum 03162

Bazel

Heemkundig Kring Wissekerke, Koningin Astridplein 28, 9150 Bazel - T: 0307741971
Local Museum 03163

Beaumont

Musée de la Tour Salamandre, 10 Grand Pl, 6500 Beaumont - T: 071588191, Fax: 071588191, E-mail: otbeaumont@swing.be
Local Museum
Regional history, iconography, regional arts and crafts 03164

Beauraing

Musée Marial de Beauraing, 21 Rue de l'Eglise, 5570 Beauraing - T: 082711218
Religious Arts Museum - 1964
Religious folklore, puppets 03165

Beauvechain

Musée du Passé Agricole de Beauvechain, 8 Rue de Wavre, 1320 Beauvechain - T: 010866314
Agriculture Museum 03166

Beauvoorde

Kasteel Beauvoorde, Wulveringemstr, 8486 Beauvoorde - T: 058299229
Historic Site 03167

Beernem

Provinciaal Museum van het Bulskampveld, Kasteel-Bulskampveld, 8730 Beernem - T: 050789176, Fax: 050403105. Head: Ludo Valcke
Agriculture Museum 03168

Beerse

Heemkundig Museum Tempelhof, Bisschopslaan 1, 2340 Beerse - T: 014612874, Fax: 014612874. Head: Leo Dignef
Folklore Museum 03169

Beersel

Herman Teirlinckhuis, Duwenberg 14, 1650 Beersel - T: 023764557
Local Museum 03170

Kasteel van Beersel, 1650 Beersel
Historic Site 03171

Beloeil

Château de Beloeil, Rue du Château, 7970 Beloeil - T: 069689426, Fax: 069688782, E-mail: fondation.ligne@skynet.be. Head: Michel Prince de Ligne
Decorative Arts Museum
Castle with tapestries, furniture (18th c), paintings, Chinese porcelain, archives (since 13th c) and library with works of the Belgian writer Ch.-J. de Ligne (18th c) 03172

Berchem

Andre Garitte Foundation, Ringlaan 16-18, 2600 Berchem - T: 034496614
Fine Arts Museum 03173

Antwerps Tram- en Autobusmuseum → Vlaams Tram- en Autobusmuseum

Vlaams Tram- en Autobusmuseum, Diksmuidelaan 42, 2600 Berchem - T: 033224462, Fax: 033227242, E-mail: info@vlatam.be. Head: Eric Keutgens
Science&Tech Museum 03174

Beringen

Mijnmuseum, Koolmijnlaan, 3580 Beringen - T: 011422001
Science&Tech Museum 03175

Berlare

Museum Huize Bareldonk, Donklaan 123, 9290 Berlare - T: 091675321
Local Museum 03176

Museum van de Boerenkrijg, Gemeentehuis, 9290 Berlare
Historical Museum 03177

Bernissart

Musée de l'Iguanodon, 2 Rue du Château, 7320 Bernissart - T: 069577029, 069576487
Local Museum 03178

Binche

Musée International du Carnaval et du Masque, 10 Rue Saint-Moustier, 7130 Binche - T: 064335741, Fax: 064341430, E-mail: administrationamuseedumasque.be, Internet: http://www.museedumasque.be. Head: Michel Revelard
Ethnology Museum - 1975
Masks and disguises from Latin America, Asia, Oceania, Africa, Europe, carnival in Europe, Belgium and especially at Binche - library 03179

Bissegem

Landbouwmuseum, Kruiskouter 52, 8501 Bissegem - T: 056353677, 056410379
Agriculture Museum 03180

Blicquy

Musée du Poitier Gallo-Romain, Maison Communale, Grand Pl, 7922 Blicquy - T: 069662495, 069664727. Head: Leonce Demarez
Archaeological Museum
Iron and bronze objects, gravestones, vases 03181

Bocholt

Bocholter Brouwerij Museum (Brewery Museum Bocholt), Dorpsstr 53, 3950 Bocholt - T: 089481676, Fax: 089481679, E-mail: -bocholterbrouwerijmuseum@yucom.be, Internet: http://www.bocholterbrouwerijmuseum.be. Head: Jean Martens
Science&Tech Museum - 1979
Brewing 03182

Geologisch Museum, Kloosterstr 10, 3950 Bocholt - T: 011472169
Natural History Museum 03183

Boekhoute

Heemkundig Museum Boekhoute, Boekhoutedorp 3, 9961 Boekhoute - T: 093736541. Head: Edgard Stockman
Local Museum
Crafts, agriculture, folklore, fishing 03184

Bon-Secours

Galerie Permanente, c/o Centre Culturel de Bon-Secours, 10 Rue des Sapins, 7603 Bon-Secours. Head: André Lamblin
Fine Arts Museum 03185

Maison de la Forêt, Plaine des Sapins, 2 Allée Max Quintart, 7603 Bon-Secours - T: 069772045, Fax: 069772045. Head: A. Quintart
Natural History Museum - 1979
Exhibits pertaining to ecology, esp forest - diorama 03186

Booischot

Museum en oud Kempisch Dorp, Liersesteenweg 15, 2221 Booischot - T: 015222469
Local Museum 03187

Boom

Ecomuseum en Archief van de Boomse Baksteen, Noeveren 196, 2850 Boom - T: 038881558, Fax: 038433402, Internet: http://www.conservare.be/emabb. Head: Luc Verbeeck
Historic Site 03188

Borgerhout

Heemkundig Museum, Turnhoutsebaan 110, 2140 Borgerhout - T: 032701721
Local Museum
Local history 03189

Bornem

Havesdonckhoeve, Museum van Oud Landbouwalaam en Volkshuisraad, Nattenhaesdonckstr 13, 2880 Bornem - T: 038891847. Head: Frans Spiessens
Agriculture Museum 03190

Kasteel van Bornem, Kasteelstr 34, 2880 Bornem - T: 038892430
Local Museum 03191

Monumental Gallery Sculpturama, Luipegem 77, 2880 Bornem - T: 038890169, Fax: 038890169, E-mail: lannoye@pandora.be, Internet: http://www.portofantwerp.be/lannoye. Head: Henri Lannoye
Public Gallery 03192

Scheepvaartmuseum, Omgangstr 34, 2880 Bornem - T: 052342625
Historical Museum 03193

Scheldemuseum de Notelaer, Notelaersdreef 2, 2880 Bornem - T: 038896920
Local Museum 03194

Bouillon

Château Fort, 6830 Bouillon, mail addr: BP 13, 6830 Bouillon - T: 061466257, Fax: 061466257
Local Museum 03195

Musée Ducal, 1-3 Rue du Petit, 6830 Bouillon - T: 061464189, Fax: 061464199, E-mail: museeducal@swing.be, Internet: http://www.swing.be/musee.ducal. Head: Christine Serson
Historical Museum / Fine Arts Museum / Religious Arts Museum - 1947
Buildings (17th-18th c), crafts, costumes, local history, history of the crusades, medieval weapons and documents from the Orient and Occident, Byzantine goldsmith art, Limoges enamelware, Persian ceramics, fine Arts, industrial history 19th-20th c 03196

Bouvignes

Musée Communal (closed) 03197

Braine-l'Alleud

Centre d'Art Nicolas de Staël, 83 Chaussée de Mont-Saint-Jean, 1420 Braine-l'Alleud - T: 071879877, Fax: 071879877
Fine Arts Museum 03198

Centre du Visiteur, 252-254 Rte du Lion, 1420 Braine-l'Alleud - T: 023851912, Fax: 023850052, E-mail: info@waterloo1815.be, Internet: http://www.waterloo1815.be. Head: Isabelle Baecker-Renard
Historical Museum / Military Museum 03199

Panorama de la Bataille de Waterloo, 252-254 Rte du Lion, 1420 Braine-l'Alleud - T: 023851912, Fax: 023850052, E-mail: info@waterloo1815.be, Internet: http://www.waterloo1815.be. Head: Isabelle Baecker-Renard
Military Museum - 1911
Documentation on the battle of Waterloo, circular painting 110m x 12m representing the battle of Waterloo 03200

Braine-le-Château

Musée de la Meunerie, 20 Grand-Pl, 1440 Braine-le-Château - T: 023669349, Fax: 023669349, E-mail: tourisme@braine-le-chateau.org, Internet: http://www.braine-le-chateau.org. Head: Baron E. de Wykerslooth
Science&Tech Museum 03201

Braine-le-Comte

Musée Communal de la Ville de Braine-le-Comte, Ancient Convent des Dominicains, Rue des Dominicains, 7490 Braine-le-Comte - T: 067552330
Local Museum
Local history and folklore, local writers, documents of the period 1914-1948 03202

Brecht

Kempisch Museum, Mudeusstr 1, 2160 Brecht - T: 0313138596
Local Museum - 1904
Ancient crafts, agricultural materials, prehistory, folklore 03203

Bredene

Turkeyenhof, Zegelaan, 8450 Bredene - T: 059330830
Local Museum 03204

Bree

Heemkundig Museum, Oud Stadhuis, Markt, 3960 Bree - T: 089462514, Fax: 089462514. Head: Marie-Jeanne Cardinaels
Decorative Arts Museum / Natural History Museum - 1975
Arts and crafts, local flora and fauna, photos 03205

Natuurhistorisch Museum, Stadhuis, Markt, 3960 Bree - T: 011472169
Natural History Museum 03206

Brugge

Archeologisch Museum, Stedelijke Musea, Mariastr 36a, 8000 Brugge, mail addr: Dijver 12, 8000 Brugge - T: 050448711, Fax: 050448778, E-mail: musea@brugge.be, Internet: http://www.brugge.be. Head: Manfred Sellink
Archaeological Museum 03207

Arentshuis, Stedelijke Musea, Dijver 16, 8000 Brugge - T: 050448711, Fax: 050448778, E-mail: musea@brugge.be, Internet: http://www.brugge.be. Head: Manfred Sellink
Fine Arts Museum / Decorative Arts Museum - 1987/1990
Art Nouveau and Art Deco carpets, pottery, furniture, engravings, watercolours, drawings and paintings by Frank Brangwyn (1867-1956) 03208

Begijnhuisje Monasterium De Wijngaard, Begijnhof 30, 8000 Brugge - T: 050330011, Fax: 050331881, E-mail: begijnhof.brugge@yucom.be, Internet: http://www.monasteria.org. Head: Rita Dericum
Religious Arts Museum
Reconstruction of a 17th c Beguine house 03209

Belfort, Stedelijke Musea, Markt 7, 8000 Brugge - T: 050448711, Fax: 050448778, E-mail: musea@brugge.be, Internet: http://www.brugge.be. Head: Walter Rycquart
Historic Site 03210

Gotische Zaal, Stadhuis, Stedelijke Musea, Burg 12, 8000 Brugge - T: 050448711, Fax: 050448778, E-mail: musea@brugge.be, Internet: http://www.brugge.be. Head: Manfred Sellink
Historic Site / Fine Arts Museum - 20th c
Gothic hall of the Town Hall (14th-15th c, and 19th c), town history 03211

Groeningemuseum, Stedelijke Musea, Dijver 12, 8000 Brugge - T: 050448711, Fax: 050448778, E-mail: musea@brugge.be, Internet: http://www.brugge.be. Head: Manfred Sellink
Fine Arts Museum - 1929/30
Fine arts (Flemish Primitives to 20th c Modern art) 03212

Gruuthusemuseum, Stedelijke Musea, Dijver 17, 8000 Brugge - T: 050448711, Fax: 050448778, E-mail: musea@brugge.be, Internet: http://www.brugge.be. Head: Walter Rycquart
Decorative Arts Museum / Fine Arts Museum / Historic Site
Decorative arts, sciences, manufacturing, musical instruments, numismatics, weights and measures, tapestries, textiles, glass 03213

Guido Gezelle Museum, Stedelijke Musea, Rolweg 64, 8000 Brugge - T: 050448711, Fax: 050448778, E-mail: musea@brugge.be, Internet: http://www.brugge.be. Head: Manfred Sellink
Special Museum - 1926
Birthplace of Guido Gezelle (1830-1899; his library and all his manuscripts and other archival documents are held in safekeeping at the City Library Brugge) 03214

Kantcentrum, Peperstr 3, 8000 Brugge - T: 050330072
Local Museum 03215

Koninklijke Hoofdgilde Sint-Sebastiaan, Carmersstr 174, 8000 Brugge - T: 050331626, E-mail: hoofdman@sebastiaansgilde.be, Internet: http://www.sebstiaansgilde.be
Historical Museum
Documents and archives relating to the guild of Saint Sebastian (since 1400), documents on royal families of Belgium and England 03216

Memlingmuseum, Stedelijke Musea, Mariastr 38, 8000 Brugge - T: 050448711, Fax: 050448778, E-mail: musea@brugge.be, Internet: http://www.brugge.be. Head: Walter Rycquart
Fine Arts Museum / Historical Museum / Historic Site - 19th c
Paintings by Hans Memling, portraits, archeology, old furniture, old pharmacy 03217

Museum Grootseminarie, Abdij ter Duinen, Potterierei 72, 8000 Brugge - T: 050330362, Fax: 050330521, E-mail: gootseminarie.brugge@kerknet.be. Head: E. Vanden Berghe
Religious Arts Museum 03218

Museum Onze-Lieve-Vrouw ter Potterie, Stedelijke Musea, Potterierei 79, 8000 Brugge - T: 050448703, Fax: 050448778, E-mail: musea@brugge.be, Internet: http://www.brugge.be. Head: Hilde Lobelle-Caluwé
Religious Arts Museum / Fine Arts Museum
Museum of the historic charitable institution Our Lady of the Potterie in the old hospital building (14th-17th c) 03219

Museum van de Kruisbooggilde Sint-Joris, Stijn Streuvelsstr 59, 8000 Brugge - T: 050335408, E-mail: didier.deforche@pandora.be, Internet: http://www.brugge.be/musea/nl/mjorn.htm. Head: C. Heyneman
Military Museum 03220

Museum van de Onze-Lieve-Vrouwkerk, Mariastr, 8000 Brugge - T: 050345314
Religious Arts Museum 03221

Museum van de Sint-Salvatorskathedraal (reopen autumn 2002), Steenstr, 8000 Brugge, mail addr: Sint-Salvatorkoorstr 8, 8000 Brugge - T: 050336841, Fax: 050336841
Religious Arts Museum
Old Flemish painting, sculptures, embroidery, goldsmith art, tombstones, frescoes on 13th century graves 03222

Museum van het Heilig Bloed, Baseliek van het Heilig Bloed, Burg 13, 8000 Brugge - T: 05031399
Religious Arts Museum
Paintings (Pourbus, Van Dyck), works of goldsmith Jan Crabbe (1617), tapestries (1637), reliquaries 03223

Museum voor Volkskunde, Stedelijke Musea Brugge, Rolweg 40, 8000 Brugge - T: 050330044, Fax: 050335489, E-mail: musea@brugge.be, Internet: http://www.brugge.be. Head: Willy P. Dezutter
Folklore Museum - 1939/1973
Folklore, regional ethnology, folk art, religious traditions, interiors of a 19th c inn and drugstore, kitchen utensils, grocery shop, cooper, hatmaker, confectioner, shoemaker 03224

Renaissancezaal van Het Brugse Vrije, Burg 11a, 8000 Brugge - T: 050448711, Fax: 050448778, E-mail: musea@brugge.be, Internet: http://www.brugge.be. Head: Manfred Sellink
Fine Arts Museum / Historic Site 03225

Rijksarchief, Academiestr 14, 8000 Brugge - T: 050337288, Fax: 050337288, E-mail: - rijksarchief.brugge@arch.be, Internet: http://www.arch.arch.be/brugge.html. Head: M. Nuyttens
Special Museum 03226

Sint-Janshuismolen en Koeleweimolen, Stedelijke Musea Brugge, Kruisvest, 8000 Brugge - T: 050330044, Fax: 050335489, E-mail: musea@brugge.be, Internet: http://www.brugge.be. Head: Willy P. Dezutter
Science&Tech Museum - 1770
Windmill exhibits, demonstration of cornmilling 03227

Steinmetzkabinet, Stedelijke Musea, Mariastr 36bis, 8000 Brugge - T: 050448704, Fax: 050448778, E-mail: musea@brugge.be, Internet: http://www.brugge.be. Head: Manfred Sellink
Fine Arts Museum
Prints and drawings 03228

Brûly-de-Pesche

Bunker d'Hitler, Musée de la Resistance, Pl Saint-Méen, 5660 Brûly-de-Pesche - T: 060345454
Military Museum 03229

Bruxelles

Archief en Museum van het Vlaams Leven te Brussel, Visverkopersstr 13, 1000 Bruxelles - T: 025124281, Fax: 025028321, E-mail: amvb@skynet.be, Internet: http://amvb.vgc.be. Head: Patricia Quintens
Historical Museum / Folklore Museum 03230

Archives et Musée de la Littérature, c/o Bibliothèque Royale Albert I, 4 Blvd de l'Empereur, 1000 Bruxelles - T: 025195584, Fax: 025195583, E-mail: aml@cfwb.be, Internet: http://www.aml.cfwb.be. Head: Marc Quaghebeur
Special Museum / Performing Arts Museum - 1958
Manuscripts and documentation on Belgian literature in French, documents on theatre history, archives of the Royal Academy of French Language and Literature - library 03231

Atomium, Blvd du Centenaire, 1020 Bruxelles - T: 024748977, Fax: 024748398, E-mail: info@atomium.be, Internet: http://www.atomium.be. Head: Etienne Claude
Special Museum / Historic Site - 1958
The Atomium in comic strips 03232

Autoworld, 11 Parc du Cinquantenaire, 1000 Bruxelles - T: 027364165, Fax: 027365136, E-mail: autoworld@skynet.be, Internet: http://www.autoworld.be. Head: Sylvain Demaerschalk
Science&Tech Museum - 1986
450 automobiles and motorcycles from 1886 to 1980 03233

Béguinage d'Anderlecht, 8 Rue du Chapelain, 1070 Bruxelles - T: 025211383, Fax: 025271269, E-mail: erasmushuis.maisonerasme@skynet.be
Folklore Museum / Religious Arts Museum / Local Museum - 1930
Folklore, religious interiors 03234

Bibliothèque d'Art, 21 Abbaye de la Cambre, 1000 Bruxelles - T: 026489619, Fax: 026409693, E-mail: ensav.lacambre@sup.cfwb.be, Internet: http://www.lacambre.be. Head: Régine Carpentier
Library with Exhibitions 03235

Bibliothèque Royale Albert Ier, 4 Blvd de l'Empereur, 1000 Bruxelles - T: 025195311, Fax: 025195533
Library with Exhibitions 03236

Bruxella 1238, Musée de la Ville de Bruxelles, Rue de la Bourse, 1000 Bruxelles, mail addr: 1 Rue du Poivre, 1000 Bruxelles - T: 022794355, 022794350, Fax: 022794362. Head: Anne Vandenbulcke
Archaeological Museum 03237

Cabinet des Estampes, c/o Bibliothèque Royale Albert Ier, 4 Blvd de l'Empereur, 1000 Bruxelles
Fine Arts Museum - 1876
Engravings, drawings, prints, woodcuts, documentation 03238

Cabinet des Médailles, c/o Bibliothèque de Belgique, 4 Blvd de l'Empereur, 1000 Bruxelles - T: 025195603/08, Fax: 025195533, E-mail: callatay@duke.kbr.be, Internet: http://www.kbr.be/coll/coin/coin1_fr.html. Head: François de Callatay
Historical Museum / Archaeological Museum - 1835
Coins, medals and instruments for coinage, De Hirsch Coll - numismatic library 03239

CCNOA (Center for Contemporary Non Objective Art), 2 Rue Notre Dame du Sommeil, 1000 Bruxelles - T: 025026912, Fax: 025026912, E-mail: ccnoa.annex@belgacom.net. Head: Petra Bungert
Public Gallery 03240

Centre Belge de la Bande Dessinée, 20 Rue des Sables, 1000 Bruxelles - T: 027338664, 026731506
Special Museum 03241

Centre d'Art Contemporain, 63 Av des Nerviens, 1040 Bruxelles - T: 027350531, Fax: 027355190. Head: Fabienne Dumont
Public Gallery 03242

Centre de Recherches et d'Etudes Technologiques des Arts Plastiques, Av F. Roosevelt 50, 1050 Bruxelles - T: 026503922/2419, Fax: 026504349, E-mail: art-tech@ulb.ac.be, Internet: http://www.ulb.ac.be/recherche/home. Head: C. Périer-d'Ieteren
University Museum 03243

Centre d'Histoire et de Traditions de la Gendarmerie, 33 Av de la Force Aérienne, 1040 Bruxelles - T: 026426929, Fax: 026426369. Head: Denis Guido
Special Museum 03244

CIAFMA, 19 Av Houzeau, 1180 Bruxelles. Head: Aubin Pasque
Public Gallery 03245

Cinquantenaire Museum, Musées Royaux d'Art et d'Histoire, 10 Parc du Cinquantenaire, 1000 Bruxelles - T: 027417211, Fax: 027337735, E-mail: info@kmkg-mrah.be, Internet: http://www.kmkg-mrah.be. Head: Francis Van Noten
Archaeological Museum / Ethnology Museum / Folklore Museum / Fine Arts Museum / Decorative Arts Museum - 1835 03246

Exposition Permanente de Documents d'Archives, c/o Archives Générales du Royaume, 2-6 Rue de Ruysbroeck, 1000 Bruxelles - T: 025137680. Head: E. Persoons
Historical Museum
Archives of Belgium 03247

Fondation et Musée René Carcan, 122-126 Rue Champ du Roi, 1040 Bruxelles - T: 027357355, Fax: 027357355
Local Museum 03248

Fondation pour l'Architecture, 55 Rue de l'Ermitage, 1050 Bruxelles - T: 026490259, Fax: 026404623, E-mail: fondation.architecture@skynet.be
Fine Arts Museum 03249

Horta-Lambeaux Pavilion, Musées Royaux d'Art et d'Histoire, Parc du Cinquantenaire, 1000 Bruxelles - T: 027417211, Fax: 027337735, E-mail: karin.theunis@kmkg-mrah.be, Internet: http://www.kmkg-mrah.be. Head: Francis Van Noten
Historic Site 03250

Institut Royal des Sciences Naturelles de Belgique (Royal Belgian Institute of Natural Sciences), 29 Rue Vautier, 1000 Bruxelles - T: 026274211, 026274238, Fax: 026274113, Internet: http://www.naturalsciences.net. Head: Daniel Cahen
Natural History Museum - 1846
Skeletons of the Iguanodons of Bernissart, Belgian fossils, Neanderthal skeletons, insects, shells, skeletons of whales, terrestrial animals - library 03251

Kunstraum Bruxelles, 27 Pl Saint-Géry, 1000 Bruxelles - T: 025020012, Fax: 025020012, E-mail: kunstraum@t-online.de. Head: Christoph Anselm Huber
Public Gallery 03252

Maison d'Erasme, 31 Rue du Chapitre, 1070 Bruxelles - T: 025211383, Fax: 025271269, E-mail: erasmushuis.maisonerasme@skynet.be
Historical Museum / Fine Arts Museum - 1932
Art and history of humanism, paintings by Hieronymus Bosch, Albrecht Dürer, Hans Holbein - library 03253

Maison du Roi, Musées de la Ville de Bruxelles, Grand-Pl, 1000 Bruxelles, mail addr: c/o Musées Communaux, 1 Rue du Poivre, 1000 Bruxelles - T: 022794350, Fax: 022794362. Head: Anne Vandenbulcke
Historical Museum / Decorative Arts Museum / Folklore Museum
Brussels tapestries (16th-18th c), paintings (17th-20th c), town history, models, maps, manuscripts 03254

Maison du Spectacle La Bellone, 46 Rue de Flandre, 1000 Bruxelles - T: 025133333. Head: Serge Creuz, Anne Molitor
Fine Arts Museum 03255

Musée Antoine Wiertz, Musées Royaux des Beaux-Arts de Belgique, 62 Rue Vautier, 1050 Bruxelles - T: 025083211, Fax: 025083232, E-mail: brita_velghe@fine-arts-museum.be, Internet: http://www.fine-arts-museum.be. Head: Brita Velghe
Fine Arts Museum - 1868
Works by the 19th c romantic painter Antoine Wiertz (paintings, sculptures, drawings) 03256

Musée Bruxellois de la Gueuze, Brasserie Cantillon, 56 Rue Gheude, 1070 Bruxelles - T: 025214928
Special Museum - 1978
Hist of beer brewing 03257

Musée Camille Lemonnier, 150 Chaussée de Wavre, 1050 Bruxelles - T: 025122968, Fax: 025024373. Head: Emile Kesteman, France Bastia
Fine Arts Museum - 1946
Reconstruction of Camille Lemonnier's (1844-1913) working room with library, manuscripts and documents, paintings by Belgian masters of the second half of the 19th c, drawings, a work of Rodin 03258

Musée Charlier, 16 Av des Arts, Saint-Josse-ten-Noode, 1210 Bruxelles - T: 022185382, Fax: 022202819, E-mail: musee_charlier-museum@yahoo.fr, Internet: http://www.musee-charlier-museum.be
Fine Arts Museum 03259

Musée Communal de Jette, 24 Rue Jean Tiebackx, 1090 Bruxelles - T: 024790052
Decorative Arts Museum / Archaeological Museum
Figurines of tin, lead, plastic and other materials, archeology 03260

Musée Communal de Woluwe-Saint-Lambert, 40 Rue de la Charrette, 1200 Bruxelles - T: 027612765, Fax: 027612757. Head: Daniel J. Frankignoul
Local Museum - 1950
History of country and Woluwe valley, music bands of the 19th c, Frisian (North Holland) furniture and tiles 03261

Musée Constantin Meunier, Musées Royaux des Beaux-Arts de Belgique, 59 Rue de l'Abbaye, 1050 Bruxelles - T: 026484449
Fine Arts Museum
Paintings, drawings and sculptures by Constantin Meunier 03262

Musée d'Art Ancien, Musées Royaux des Beaux-Arts de Belgique, 3 Rue de la Régence, 1000 Bruxelles, mail addr: 9 Rue du Musée, 1000 Bruxelles - T: 025083211, Fax: 025083232, E-mail: info@fine-arts-museum.be, Internet: http://www.fine-arts-

museum.be. Head: Dr. Eliane de Wilde
Fine Arts Museum - 1801
15th-18th c Flemish and foreign art, painting, sculpture, Pieter Bruegel the elder, Rubens - library 03263

Musée d'Art Moderne, Musées Royaux des Beaux-Arts de Belgique, 1-2 Pl Royale, 1000 Bruxelles, mail addr: 9 Rue du Musée, 1000 Bruxelles - T: 025083211, Fax: 025083232, E-mail: info@fine-arts-museum.be, Internet: http://www.fine-arts-museum.be. Head: Dr. Eliane de Wilde
Fine Arts Museum - 1801
19th-20th c paintings, sculptures and drawings, Belgian and International art 03264

Musée David et Alice Van Buuren, 41 Av Léo Errera, 1180 Bruxelles - T: 023434851, Fax: 023476689, E-mail: museumvanbuuren@skynet.be. Head: Françoise Lechien Durant
Fine Arts Museum
Paintings by Pieter Bruegel the elder, Seghers, Fantin-Latour, Joachim Patenier, Rik Wouters, Constant Permeke, James Ensor, Van de Woestijne, Max Ernst, P. Signac, F. Guardi, Fujita, sculptures and drawings 03265

Musée de Chine, Mission Van Scheut, 548 Chausée de Ninove, 1070 Bruxelles - T: 025214729, 025261400, Fax: 025233048, E-mail: - missiehuis.van.scheut@skynet.be. Head: Paul Lissens
Ethnology Museum
Everyday life of Chinese people, traditional religions (Lamaism, Buddhism) 03266

Musée de la Brasserie, C.B.B. Museum (Belgian Brewers Museum), 10 Grand Pl, 1000 Bruxelles - T: 025114987, Fax: 025113259, E-mail: belgian.brewers@beerproduire.be, Internet: http://www.beerparadise.be. Head: Michel Brichet
Science&Tech Museum - 1952
Brewery (18th c) with original equipment and inn and Center of the latest brewing technology 03267

Musée de la Médecine (Museum of Medical History), Campus Erasme, 808 Rte de Lennik, 1070 Bruxelles - T: 025553431, Fax: 025553471, E-mail: dgasparo@ulb.ac.be, Internet: http://medicmuseum.org. Head: Prof. Thiérry Appelboom
Historical Museum / University Museum / Science&Tech Museum
Spitzner Coll. of Anatomical Waxes, 500 pcs. of Art and Archaeology 03268

Musée de la Porte de Hal, Porte de Hal, Blvd de Waterloo, 1000 Bruxelles - T: 025381834
Military Museum
Arms and armors, history of arms and objects relating to the Belgian dynasty 03269

Musée de la Radiodiffusion et Télévision Belge, 52 Blvd A. Reyers, 1030 Bruxelles - T: 027372852, 027372844
Special Museum 03270

Musée de la Reliure et du Hochet, 21 Rue du Bemel, 1150 Bruxelles - T: 027705333, Fax: 027622139. Head: Annie de Coster
Special Museum 03271

Musée de la Serrure, 70 Rue des Bouchers, 1000 Bruxelles - T: 025113591
Special Museum 03272

Musée de l'Assistance Publique, Hôpital Saint-Pierre, 298a Rue Haute, 1000 Bruxelles - T: 025436055, Fax: 025436106
Fine Arts Museum / Decorative Arts Museum
Paintings, sculptures, tin, goldsmith work, furniture, tapestries, contemporary painting 03273

Musée de l'Ecole, 161 Rue de l'Aqueduc, 1050 Bruxelles - T: 025119084
Special Museum 03274

Musée de l'Escrime Charles Debeur, 12 Rue Général Thys, 1050 Bruxelles - T: 026486932
Special Museum 03275

Musée de l'Histoire Industrielle et Sociale de la Région Bruxelloise, 27 Rue Ransfort, 1080 Bruxelles - T: 025223080
Historical Museum 03276

Musée de l'Hôtel Bellevue (closed) 03277

Musée de Minéralogie et de Géologie, Musées de l'Université, 30 Av Antoine Depage, 1000 Bruxelles - T: 026502236, Fax: 026502226, E-mail: mspronck@ulb.ac.be. Head: A. Bernard
Natural History Museum / University Museum 03278

Musée de Zoologie Auguste Lameere, c/o Université Libre de Bruxelles, 50 Av Fr. Roosevelt, 1050 Bruxelles - T: 026503678, 026502412, Fax: 026502796, E-mail: mjangoux@ulb.ac.be. Head: Prof. M. Jangoux
Natural History Museum 03279

Musée des Archives d'Architecture Moderne, 86 Rue de l'Ermitage, 1050 Bruxelles - T: 026498665, Fax: 026499045, E-mail: musee@aam.be, Internet: http://www.aam.be. Head: Maurice Culot
Special Museum 03280

Musée des Chemins de Fer Belges, Gare Bruxelles-Nord, 76 Rue du Progrès, 1030 Bruxelles - T: 022246279, Fax: 022246243. Head: J. Thys
Science&Tech Museum - 1951
Railroad history, architecture of railway stations, uniforms and medals 03281

Le Musée des Enfants- Het Kindermuseum, 15 Rue du Bourgmestre, 1050 Bruxelles - T: 026400107, Fax: 026468007, E-mail: - childrenmuseum.brussels@skynet.be, Internet: http://www.museedesenfants.be. Head: Kathleen Lippens
Special Museum 03282

Musée des Instruments de Musique, Musées Royaux d'Art et d'Histoire, 2 Rue Montagne de la Cour, 1000 Bruxelles - T: 025450130, Fax: 025450178/79, E-mail: info@mim.fgov.be, Internet: http://www.mim.fgov.be. Head: Prof. Dr. Malou Haine
Music Museum - 1877
Musical instruments (16th c to present) from European and non-European countries - Educational services (workshops for children), library, concerts 03283

Musée des Plantes Médicinales et de la Pharmacie, Musées de l'Université Libre de Bruxelles, Campus de la Plaine, Blvd du Triomphe, Bâtiment B/C, Niveau 2, 1050 Bruxelles - T: 026505279, Fax: 026505282, E-mail: vanhaele@ulb.ac.be, Internet: http://www.ulb.ac.be/docs/musees. Head: M. Vanhaelen
University Museum 03284

Musée d'Ixelles, 71 Rue Jean Van Volsem, 1050 Bruxelles - T: 025156421, Fax: 025156424, E-mail: musee.ixelles@skynet.be, Internet: http://www.musee-ixelles.be. Head: Nicole d' Huart
Fine Arts Museum - 1892
Art (17th-20th c), drawings by Rembrandt, Dürer, Bandinelli, Fragonard, Boucher, Flemish and Dutch painting (16th-18th c), French and Belgian painting (19th c), posters of Toulouse-Lautrec, Steinlein, Cheret, Mucha - library 03285

Musée d'Orgues de Kermesse, 104 Rue Waelhem, 1030 Bruxelles - T: 022412791
Music Museum 03286

Musée du Cinéma, 9 Rue Baron Horta, 1000 Bruxelles - T: 025078370, Fax: 025131272
Special Museum - 1962
History of cinema - 2 screening rooms 03287

Musée du Costume et de la Dentelle, Musées de la Ville de Bruxelles, 4-6 Rue de la Violette, 1000 Bruxelles, mail addr: c/o Musées Communaux, 6 Rue de la Violette, 1000 Bruxelles - T: 025127709, Fax: 025130265. Head: Anne Vandenbulcke
Decorative Arts Museum - 1977
Traditional and contemporary lace from Belgium and Brussels, costumes from the 18th-20th c - library 03288

Musée du Crime, Palais de Justice, 1000 Bruxelles - T: 025086233
Special Museum 03289

Musée du Jouet, 24 Rue de l'Association, 1000 Bruxelles - T: 022196168. Head: André Raemdonck
Special Museum
Thousands of old toys, dolls, trains, wooden toys, theatres, toy forts, mechanical toys - Toy library, places to play 03290

Musée du Livre et Cabinets de Donations de la Bibliothèque Royale de Belgique (closed for restauration), Mont des Arts, 1000 Bruxelles - T: 025195357, Fax: 025195533, E-mail: serveduc@kbr.be; educdien@kbr.be, Internet: http://www.kbr.be. Head: Pierre Cockshaw
Library with Exhibitions - 1970
History of books from the early beginnings 03291

Musée du Théâtre de Toone, 21 Rue des Bouchers, 1000 Bruxelles - T: 025117137
Performing Arts Museum 03292

Musée du Théâtre Royal de la Monnaie, Pl de la Monnaie, 1000 Bruxelles - T: 022172211
Performing Arts Museum - 1962
Documents about the Théâtre Royal de la Monnaie and about the opera and ballet in general 03293

Musée du Transport Urbain Bruxellois (Public Transportmuseum Brussel), 364b Av de Tervueren, 1150 Bruxelles - T: 025153108, Fax: 025153109, E-mail: mtub_msvb@yahoo.com, Internet: http://www.mtub.be. Head: M. Willem Draps
Science&Tech Museum 03294

Musée en Petit, 47 Rue Rouge, 1180 Bruxelles - T: 023740495
Local Museum 03295

Musée Horta, 25 Rue Americaine, 1060 Bruxelles - T: 025430490, Fax: 025387631, E-mail: musee.horta@horta.irisnet.be, Internet: http://www.bruxelles-art-nouveau.be. Head: Françoise Aubry
Decorative Arts Museum - 1969
Furniture of the architect Victor Horta - library 03296

Musée International des Marionnettes, 50 Av de la Fôret, 1050 Bruxelles - T: 026738730
Performing Arts Museum 03297

Musée Léon Leclère, Fondation Archéologique de l'Université Libre de Bruxelles, 50 Av F. Roosevelt, 1000 Bruxelles - T: 02486510
University Museum / Archaeological Museum 03298

Musée Maurice Carême, 14 Av Nellie Melba, 1070 Bruxelles - T: 025216775, Fax: 025202086. Head: Jeannine Burny
Special Museum
archives, library 03299

Musée National de la Résistance, 14 Rue Van Lint, 1070 Bruxelles - T: 025224041
Historical Museum
History of the national resistance movement during German occupation in WW I and II 03300

Musée Numismatique et Historique de la Banque Nationale de Belgique (Money Museum of the National Bank of Belgium), 9 Rue du Bois Sauvage, 1000 Bruxelles - T: 022212206, Fax: 022213160, E-mail: museum@nbb.be
Special Museum / Historical Museum 03301

Musée Postal, 40 Pl du Grand Sablon, 1000 Bruxelles - T: 025117740, Fax: 025027177. Head: M. Mary
Science&Tech Museum - 1931
Postal history, stamp coll of Belgium and foreign countries, telecommunications - library 03302

Musée Privé de la Documentation Ferroviaire-Mupdofer, 63 Rue du Houblon, 1000 Bruxelles - T: 026723967
Science&Tech Museum 03303

Musée Royal de l'Armée et d'Histoire Militaire, 3 Parc du Cinquantenaire, 1000 Bruxelles - T: 027377811, Fax: 027377802, E-mail: piet.de.gryse@klm-mra.be, Internet: http://www.klm-mra.be. Head: Prof. Patrick Lefèvre
Military Museum - 1910
Militaria from the Middle Ages up to now, Belgian Army uniforms and weapons, Russian Imperial uniforms (1812-1915) - library; iconographic service 03304

Musée Schott, 27 Rue du Chêne, 1000 Bruxelles
Fine Arts Museum - 1967
Works and coll of painter Philippe Schott, sculptures (15th-18th c), furniture (16th-18th c) 03305

Musées Royaux d'Art et d'Histoire (Royal Museums of Art and History), 10 Parc du Cinquantenaire, 1000 Bruxelles - T: 027417211, Fax: 027337735, E-mail: info@kmkg-mrah.be, Internet: http://www.kmkg-mrah.be. Head: Eliane de Wilde
Decorative Arts Museum / Historical Museum / Fine Arts Museum / Music Museum - 1835
Sculpture, decorative arts, archaeology, history, ethnology, folklore, scientific material, ceramics, costumes, textiles, lace, jewelry, stained glass, goldsmith art, musical instruments, tapestries, treasury, altar pieces - library 03306

Palais des Beaux-Arts, 23 Rue Ravenstein, 1000 Bruxelles - T: 025078211, Fax: 025143044, E-mail: info@pbapsk.be, Internet: http://www.pbapsk.be. Head: Etienne Davignon
Fine Arts Museum 03307

Pavillon Chinois et Tour Japonaise (Chinese Pavilion and Japanese Tower), 44 Av Van Praet, 1020 Bruxelles, mail addr: c/o Musées Royaux d'Art et d'Histoire, 10 Parc du Cinquantenaire, 1000 Bruxelles - T: 022681608, Fax: 022681608, E-mail: info@kmkg-mrah.be, Internet: http://www.kmkg-mrah.be. Head: Anne Cahen-Delhaye
Decorative Arts Museum - 1913
Chinese and Japanese export porcelain (17th to 19th c) 03308

Porte de Halle, Musées Royaux d'Art et d'Histoire, Blvd du Midi, 1000 Bruxelles - T: 025341518. Head: Francis Van Noten
Local Museum - 2000 03309

Buggenhout

Den Ast, Brouwerij Bosteels, Kerkstr 92, 9255 Buggenhout - T: 052332282, 052332323
Special Museum 03310

Buzenol

Musée et Parc Archéologiques de Montauban, 6743 Buzenol - T: 063570315
Archaeological Museum
Fortresses of the Iron Age and the Roman period, fortress tower of the Middle Ages, Roman sculpture found in situ 03311

Carnières

Musée Alexandre-Louis Martin, 52 Pl Communale, 7141 Carnières - T: 064442035. Head: Jean-Marie Tassignon
Fine Arts Museum
Works and personal remembrances of the painter Alexandre-Louis Martin 03312

Celles

Château de Véves, 5 Noisy, 5561 Celles - T: 082666393, Fax: 082666036, E-mail: veves-maisy@skynet.be, Internet: http://www.chateau-de-veves.be. Head: Comte Hadelin de Liedekerke Beaufort
Decorative Arts Museum 03313

Cerfontaine

Musée de la Vie Régionale, Ancienne Gare, 5630 Cerfontaine - T: 071644850, E-mail: - musee.cerfontaine@skynet.be, Internet: http://users.skynet.be/cerfontaine. Head: André Lépine
Local Museum - 1973
History, archeology, folklore, crafts, shoemaker's shop for wooden shoes 03314

Charleroi

Musée de la Photographie, 11 Av Paul Pastur, 6032 Charleroi - T: 071435810, Fax: 071364645, E-mail: museephoto@infonie.be, Internet: http://musee.photo.infonie.be. Head: Xavier Canonne
Special Museum 03315

Musée de la Société Royale d'Archéologie et de Paléontologie de Charleroi, 10 Blvd Defontaine, 6000 Charleroi - T: 071310838
Archaeological Museum - 1979
Prehistory, Greek and Roman archeology, medieval and post-medieval wooden sculptures - library 03316

Musée des Beaux-Arts Charleroi, Pl Charles II, 6000 Charleroi - T: 071861136, 071861134, Fax: 071861133, E-mail: mba@charleroi.be, Internet: http://www.charleroi-museum.org. Head: Chantal Lemal Mengeot
Fine Arts Museum - 1953
Works by local artists (19th-20th c), paintings by François-Joseph Navez, Pierre Paulus, Fernand André, works by foreign artists 03317

Musée des Chasseurs à Pied, Blvd Général Michel, 6000 Charleroi - T: 071300748, Fax: 071300748, E-mail: ancap@chasseurs-a-pied.com
Military Museum 03318

Musée du Verre Art et Technique, 10 Blvd Defontaine, 6000 Charleroi - T: 071310838, Fax: 071334480. Head: Isabelle Laurent
Decorative Arts Museum
History, art and technics of glass, engraved glass (17th-18th c), Venetian glass (16th-20th c), Roman glass, Belgian glass - technical division 03319

Musée Jules Destrée, Hôtel de Ville, Pl Charles II, 6000 Charleroi - T: 071861138, Fax: 071861133, E-mail: mjd@charleroi.be, Internet: http://www.charleroi-museum.org. Head: Patricia Vanerck
Local Museum 03320

Palais des Beaux-Arts, Pl du Manège, 6000 Charleroi - T: 071314420, Fax: 071334297, E-mail: info@pba.be, Internet: http://www.pba.be. Head: Guy Rassel
Fine Arts Museum 03321

Chaudfontaine

Musée Hydrogéologique, Thermal de Chaudfontaine, 4930 Chaudfontaine
Natural History Museum
Geology 03322

Chimay

Collection du Château des Princes, Château des Princes, 6460 Chimay - T: 060212823
Fine Arts Museum 03323

Comblain-au-Pont

Musée d'Ourthe-Ambléve, 1 Grand Pl, 4170 Comblain-au-Pont - T: 041731013
Local Museum - 1933/1977
Prehistory, fossils, history, folklore, craftmen's tools - library 03324

Comines

Musée de la Rubanerie Cominoise, 50 Rue du Fort, 7780 Comines - T: 056555600, Fax: 056555608, E-mail: office.tourisme.comines.warneton@belgacom.net. Head: Remi Broucke
Special Museum 03325

Corroy-le-Château

Château Feodal, 4 Rue du Château de Corroy, 5032 Corroy-le-Château - T: 081633232, Fax: 081633375, E-mail: hamal.trazegnies@skynet.be. Head: Marquis de Trazegnies
Decorative Arts Museum 03326

Cortil-Noirmont

Musée Français - Armée Française Mai 1940, 3 Rue Tansoul, 5861 Cortil-Noirmont - T: 081613140. Head: Albert Noel
Military Museum
Canons, guns and various arms, history of WW 2 May 1940, libraries, battle of Gembloux 03327

Couvin

Cavernes Préhistoriques de l'Abime, Rue de la Falaise, 5660 Couvin - T: 060311954
Historic Site 03328

Crupet

Donjon-Château Carondolet, 5332 Crupet - T: 083699093
Decorative Arts Museum 03329

Cuesmes

Maison Vincent Van Gogh, 3 Rue du Pavillon, 7033 Cuesmes - T: 065335580
Fine Arts Museum 03330

Cul-des-Sarts

Musée des Riezes et des Sarts, 1 Rue de Rocroi, 6404 Cul-des-Sarts - T: 060377003, 060377074. Head: Dr. Georges André
Decorative Arts Museum / Military Museum - 1968
Crafts, arms, furniture 03331

Dalhem

Musée du Général Thys, 27 Rue Général Thys, 4607 Dalhem
Military Museum 03332

Damme

Oudheidkundig Museum Sint-Janshospitaal, Kerkstr 33, 8340 Damme - T: 050461080, Fax: 050461081, E-mail: mieke.dejonghe@publilink.be, Internet: http://www.flanderstourist.be/musea/sintjan. Head: Mieke de Jonghe
Decorative Arts Museum / Historical Museum - 1901
Local hist, religious hist, silver, pewter, furniture - hospital archives 03333

Stedelijk Museum, Stadhuis, Markt 1, 8340 Damme - T: 050353319, Fax: 050370021, E-mail: toerismedamme@village.uunet.be. Head: Bert Van Haecke
Archaeological Museum / Local Museum / Folklore Museum - 1950
Medieval archeology, local hist and folklore 03334

Uilenspiegel-Maerlantmuseum, Huyze de Grote Sterre, Jacob van Maerlantstr 3, 8340 Damme - T: 050288610, Fax: 050370021, E-mail: toerismedamme@village.uunet.be. Head: Bert Van Haecke
Special Museum - 1977
Cultural and historic aspects on the figure of Tijl Uilenspiegel since 1500 (books, statues, computer-animation etc.), life and work of Jacob van Maerlant, Flemish poet, who lived at the end of 13th c 03335

Dampicourt

Musée de la Vie Paysanne, Montquintin, 6763 Dampicourt - T: 063570315
Local Museum
Country life 03336

De Panne

Koningin Astridmuseum, Zeelaan 9, 8470 De Panne - T: 058234005
Historical Museum - 1977
World War I documentation, Queen Astrid of Belgium and King Albert coll, Red Cross, sculptures 03337

Deerlijk

Heemkundig Museum vat het Gaverdomein (closed) 03338

Deinze

Kasteel Ooidonk, Ooidonkdreef 9, 9800 Deinze - T: 092823570, 092826123, Fax: 092825282, E-mail: info@ooidonk.be, Internet: http://www.ooidonk.be. Head: Juan Graaf T'Kint de Roodenbeke
Historic Site 03339

Museum van Deinze en de Leiestreek, Lucien Matthyslaan 3-5, 9800 Deinze - T: 093819670, Fax: 093819679, E-mail: museum@deinze.be, Internet: http://www.museumdeinze.be. Head: Veerle Van Doorne
Fine Arts Museum / Local Museum - 1928
Paintings and sculptures of the Latemgroup and by regional painters - library (art books), archive 03340

Dendermonde

Begijnhofmuseum, Begijnhof 11, 9200 Dendermonde - T: 052211679, Fax: 052214736. Head: Dr. A. Stroobants
Religious Arts Museum 03341

Museum voor Volkskunde, Begijnhof 24-25, 9200 Dendermonde - T: 052211679, Fax: 052214736. Head: Dr. A. Stroobants
Folklore Museum 03342

Vleeshuismuseum, Grote Markt 32, 9200 Dendermonde - T: 052220465, Fax: 052214736. Head: Dr. A. Stroobants
Archaeological Museum / Historical Museum / Folklore Museum - 1895
Archeology, history, folklore, iconography 03343

Zwijvekemuseum, Nijverheidsstr 1, 9200 Dendermonde - T: 052213018, Fax: 052214736. Head: Dr. A. Stroobants
Local Museum 03344

Deurle

Gemeentelijk Museum Gustaaf de Smet, Gustaaf de Smetdreef 1, 9831 Deurle - T: 091827742
Fine Arts Museum - 1950
House of the painter Gustaaf de Smet (1877-1943) and parts of his works, antiquities 03345

Musée Léon de Smet, Museumlaan 18, 9831 Deurle - T: 091823090. Head: Rafael Lingier
Fine Arts Museum - 1969
Works of the painter Léon de Smet and personal effects 03346

Museum Dhondt-Dhaenens, Museumlaan 14, 9831 Deurle - T: 092825123, Fax: 092810853, E-mail: info@museumdd.be, Internet: http://www.museumdd.be
Fine Arts Museum - 1967
Paintings of Flemish expressionist and modern art 03347

Deurne

Volkskundemuseum Deurne, Koraalpl 2, 2100 Deurne - T: 033267598, Fax: 033267598, E-mail: Ludo.Peeters3@yucom.be. Head: Ludo Peeters
Local Museum / Folklore Museum 03348

Diest

Kanthuisje Monika, Begijnhof, 3290 Diest - T: 013333800
Local Museum 03349

Stedelijk Museum Diest, Stadhuis, Grote Markt 1, 3290 Diest - T: 013312121. Head: E. Peeters Saenen
Local Museum / Historical Museum / Decorative Arts Museum - 1957
Local art and hist, decorative arts, painting 'The last Judgement' (1420-1450) - library 03350

Diksmuide

Dodengang en Oorlogsmuseum, 8600 Diksmuide - T: 050445418, Fax: 050445423, E-mail: 5Kdr@mil.be
Military Museum / Historical Museum 03351

IJzertoren-Museum Oorlog-Vrede-Vlaamse Ontvoogding, IJzerdijk 49, 8600 Diksmuide - T: 051500286, Fax: 051502258, E-mail: ijzertoren@unicall.be, Internet: http://www.ijzertoren.org. Head: Dirk Demeurie
Historical Museum - 1965
Memorials and documents relating to World War I, peace, Flemish emanzipation 03352

Museum Inter-Filac, Kerkhofstr 27, 8600 Diksmuide - T: 051500658. Head: Roger Vantoortelboom
Special Museum 03353

Stedelijk Museum Diksmuide, Wilgendijk 55, 8600 Diksmuide - T: 051503675. Head: Joris Vlaemynck
Historical Museum - 1927
Objects recalling World War I, rural life, paintings and postcards, remainders of the Gothic sculptures 'Het Doksaal', destructed in World War I - library 03354

Dilsen-Stokkem

Heemkundig Museum, Brugwachterskade 1, 3650 Dilsen-Stokkem - T: 011757352, 011756089
Local Museum 03355

Dinant

Maison Espagnole de Bouvignes, 16 Pl du Baillage, 5500 Dinant - T: 082222152, 082224910
Local Museum 03356

Musée de la Citadelle et Armes de Guerre, 22 Le Prieuré, 5500 Dinant - T: 082223670, 082222119
Military Museum 03357

Dison

Musée Adolphe Hardy, 79 Pl du Sablon, 4820 Dison - T: 087332508
Special Museum 03358

Dranouter

Pottekarie, Lettingstr 60, 8951 Dranouter - T: 057444406, Fax: 057447486
Folklore Museum 03359

Drogenbos

Museum Felix de Boeck, Gemeentehuis, Grote Baan 222, 1620 Drogenbos - T: 023782426. Head: Jan de Kelver
Fine Arts Museum
Works of painter Felix de Boeck 03360

Duffel

Domein De Locht, Liersesteenweg 44-46, 2570 Duffel - T: 015307210, Fax: 015315401
Folklore Museum 03361

Durbuy

Musée Archéologique, Science, Pêche et Folklore, Halle aux Blés, Grand Rue, 5480 Durbuy
Local Museum
Archeology, hunting, folklore, local flora and fauna, religious objects (15th-18th c), domestic utensils 03362

Eben-Emael

Musée d'Eben, Rue du Geer, 4690 Eben-Emael - T: 041862790. Head: Freddy Close
Archaeological Museum 03363

Musée du Silex, Eben-Ezer, 4690 Eben-Emael - T: 041861240
Local Museum 03364

Ecaussinnes-Lalaing

Musée du Château-Fort, 1 Rue de Seneffe, 7191 Ecaussinnes-Lalaing - T: 067442490, Fax: 067442490. Head: Robert d'Ursel
Historic Site / Local Museum
Furniture, paintings, glasses, porcelain, sculptures, portraits, ceramics, ancient weapons 03365

Edegem

Huis Hellemans, Strijdersstr 14, 2650 Edegem - T: 032892246, Fax: 032892244, E-mail: huis.hellemans@edegem.be, Internet: http://intranet.edegem.be. Head: Kristel Kussé
Public Gallery
Paintings, sculptures, photography 03366

Karrenmuseum Den Doem, Fort V-Str, 2650 Edegem - T: 0313600621
Science&Tech Museum 03367

Eeklo

Heemmuseum Eeklo, Gentsesteenweg 80, 9900 Eeklo - T: 093781222, Fax: 093781222, E-mail: eeklo@toerismevlaanderen.be. Head: A. Vertenten
Local Museum - 1967
Folklore, trade, old toys, old printing-presses - watch-makers workshop 03368

Elouges

Musée Communal Georges Mulpas, Sq des Combattants, Rue du Commerce, 7370 Elouges
Archaeological Museum / Local Museum - 1968
Local archeology (prehistoric, Gallo-Roman, Merovingian), documents, regional industries, numismatics, folklore 03369

Embourg

Ancienne Position Fortifiée de Liège, Fort d'Embourg, 4053 Embourg - T: 041659947, 041652635
Local Museum 03370

Enghien

Musée de la Tapisserie, Maison Jonathan, 7 Rue Montgomery, 7850 Enghien - T: 023955906
Decorative Arts Museum
Five locally made 16th-c tapestries, hist of the tapestry industry in Enghien 03371

Engis

Musée Minéralogique et Paléontologique Jean-Marie Souplet, 9bis Rue Vinâve, 4480 Engis - T: 041753885
Natural History Museum 03372

Erezée

Grange Musée Li Vile Gregne, 7a Rue Général Borlon, 6997 Erezée - T: 086477301, Fax: 086477301
Local Museum / Folklore Museum 03373

Essen

Heemkundig Museum Gerard Meeusen, Gemeentehuis, Heuvelplein 23, 2910 Essen, mail addr: Moerkantsebaan 48, 2910 Essen - T: 036677390, Fax: 036677390, E-mail: heemhuis@busmail.net. Head: Jan Hectors
Local Museum - 1954
Farm implements, religious objects, costumes 03374

Karrenmuseum, Moerkantsebaan 48, 2910 Essen - T: 036677390, Fax: 036677390, E-mail: karrenmuseum@busmail.net. Head: Jan Hectors
Agriculture Museum - 1971
Coll of carts, cars, restored coaches, funeral carts, farm and trade workshop implements (cartwright's, tanner's, peat house) - library 03375

Kempisch Bosmuseum, Wildertse Duintjes 18, 2910 Essen - T: 036672440
Special Museum 03376

Molen- en Bakkerijmuseum, Sint-Jansstr 184, 2910 Essen - T: 036672026
Special Museum 03377

Open Veld Museum, Horendonk 350, 2910 Essen - T: 036675468
Open Air Museum 03378

Eupen

Stadtmuseum Eupen, Gospertstr 52, 4700 Eupen - T: 087740005. Head: Prof. Dr. Alfred Minke
Local Museum 03379

Falaên

Château Ferme, 13 Rue du Château Ferme, 5522 Falaên - T: 082699224, 082699626
Local Museum 03380

La Forge, Rue de Chertin, 5522 Falaên - T: 082699626
Local Museum 03381

Fernelmont

Château de Fernelmont, 47 Rue Saint-Roch, 5380 Fernelmont - T: 081833825
Archaeological Museum 03382

Ferrières

Musée du Jouet et de l'Enfant, 6 Rte de Lognoûle, 4190 Ferrières - T: 086400823, 086400198, Fax: 086400700, Internet: http://www.plug.in.be/plug.in/museum/toy.html. Head: Francis Colla
Special Museum 03383

Flémalle

Musée de la Préhistoire en Wallonie, 128 Rue de la Grotte, 4400 Flémalle - T: 041336474. Head: Jules Haeck
Archaeological Museum / Natural History Museum - 1907
Prehistoric archeology, paleontology, mineralogy, biospeleology 03384

Musée de la Société Royale Belge d'Etudes Géologiques et Archéologiques "Les Chercheurs de la Wallonie", 128 Rue de la Grotte, 4400 Flémalle. Head: Jules Haeck
Natural History Museum 03385

Fontaine-l'Evêque

Musée de la Mine et Musée du Clou, Château, 6140 Fontaine-l'Evêque - T: 071525005, 071524354
Science&Tech Museum
Mining 03386

Fosses-la Ville

Galerie-Musée Le Petit Chapitre, 11 Pl du Chapitre, 5070 Fosses-la Ville - T: 071711202. Head: Lilette Arnould
Decorative Arts Museum / Ethnology Museum 03387

Franc-Waret

Château Franc-Waret, 50 Rue du Village, 5380 Franc-Waret - T: 081833404
Local Museum 03388

Fronville

Château de Deulin, 6990 Fronville - T: 084466616
Decorative Arts Museum 03389

Gaasbeek

Kasteel van Gaasbeek, Kasteelstr 40, 1750 Gaasbeek - T: 025310130, Fax: 025310143. Head: Dr. H. Vandormael
Fine Arts Museum / Decorative Arts Museum - 1924
Medieval and Renaissance architecture, antiquities, paintings, sculptures (15th-18th c), furniture, tapestries - library; archives 03390

Geel

Sint-Dimpna en Gasthuismuseum, Gasthuisstr 1, 2440 Geel - T: 014591443
Special Museum / Historical Museum
Folkloristic furniture, household articles in pewter, copper and earthenware, details about the cult of Sint-Dimpna and the boarding out of mental patients, treasures of the Geel parish churches 03391

Gembloux

Musée de la Vie Locale et de la Coutellerie, Maison du Bailli, 5030 Gembloux - T: 081611725
Local Museum 03392

Genappe

Dernier Quartier Général de Napoléon, 66 Chaussée de Bruxelles, 1472 Genappe - T: 023842424, Fax: 023872264, E-mail: dernier.qg.napoleon@belgacom.net. Head: Gilbert Menne
Historical Museum
Memorials of Napoleon I, weapons, furniture, documents, Napoleonic library 03393

Genk

Arboretum, Domein Bokrijk, 3600 Genk - T: 011224575
Natural History Museum 03394

Gemeentelijk Museum en Cultuurhuis Emiel Van Doren, H. Decleenestr 21, 3600 Genk - T: 011355766
Fine Arts Museum - 1976
Works of the painter Emiel Van Doren (1865-1949), studio, furniture and personal effects 03395

Museum Het Alaam, Horstenstr 54, 3600 Genk - T: 011361629
Local Museum 03396

Provinciaal Openluchtmuseum Bokrijk (Provincial Open-Air Museum), Domein Bokrijk, 3600 Genk - T: 011265300, Fax: 011265310, E-mail: bokrijk@limburg.be, Internet: http://www.limburg.be/bokrijk. Head: Annick Boesmans
Open Air Museum - 1953
Popular rural and urban life of Flanders, architecture, culture, agriculture, textiles, clothing, handicrafts, trade, religion 03397

Gent

Archeologisch Museum van de Universiteit, Blandijnberg 2, 9000 Gent - T: 092257571. Head: Prof. Dr. J. Nenquin
Archaeological Museum / University Museum
Prehistory, Gallo-Roman period, Middle Ages, mainly objects from Belgium but also from Italy, Spain, France, Switzerland, the Netherlands and Germany 03398

Bijlokemuseum, Godshuizenlaan 2, 9000 Gent - T: 092251106, Fax: 092333459, E-mail: museum.Bijloke@Gent.be, Internet: http://www.gent.be. Head: Jeannine Baldewijns
Decorative Arts Museum / Historical Museum - 1833
Hist of Gent (from the Middle Ages to the French Revolution), paintings, watercolours, prints of historical events in Gent, sculptures, liturgical objects, silver pottery, brass and bronze, iron and pewter, tapestries, finery dresses, arms, municipal life 03399

Centrale Bibliotheek van de Universiteit Gent, Rozier 9, 9000 Gent - T: 092643851, Fax: 092643852, E-mail: guido.vanhooydonk@rug.ac.be. Head: G. Van Hooydonk
Library with Exhibitions 03400

Design Museum Gent, Jan Breydelstr 5, 9000 Gent - T: 092679999, Fax: 092244522, E-mail: museum.design@gent.be, Internet: http://www.design.museum.gent.be. Head: L. Daenens
Decorative Arts Museum - 1903
Art objects and decorations (15th-20th c), furniture, dining room and lustre by J.F. Allaert (1703-1779), writing desk of Louis XVIII, Art Nouveau, Art Deco, modern design - library, educational service 03401

Energeia, Langerbrugge Kaai 3, 9000 Gent - T: 091531641
Science&Tech Museum
Hist of EBES electricity supply 03402

Etnografische Collecties van de Universiteit Gent, Blandijnberg 2, 9000 Gent - T: 092644129, Fax: 092644195, E-mail: elze.bruyninx@rug.ac.be, Internet: http://www.flwi.rug.ac.be/etnischekunst. Head: Prof. Dr. E. Bruyninx
Ethnology Museum / University Museum - 1968
Ethnological objects from Africa, America and Melanesia 03403

Gravensteen, Sint-Veerleplein 11, 9000 Gent - T: 092259306
Special Museum 03404

Het Huis van Alijn, Kraanlei 65, 9000 Gent - T: 092692350, Fax: 092692358, E-mail: huis.alijn@gent.be, Internet: http://www.museum.al-pijn.gent.be. Head: Sylvie Dhaene
Folklore Museum - 1962
Crafts, industries and folklore from around 1900 03405

Kasteel Achtendries, Orchideestr 51, 9041 Gent - T: 093552218, Fax: 093556960. Head: Dr. Jean-Pierre de Bruyn
Historic Site
Flemish and Dutch paintings, 17th-19th century, small coll of space-objects and meteorites, 18th century building 03406

Kunsthal Sint-Pietersabdij, Sint-Pietersplein 9, 9000 Gent - T: 092439730, Fax: 092439734, E-mail: -drr.sintpietersabdij@gent.be/spr, Internet: http://www.gent.be. Head: Johan Van de Wiele
Historic Site / Public Gallery - 1958
Hist of Saint Peter's Abbey, exhibitions 03407

Meerhemmuseum, c/o Instituut Sint-Jan de Deo, Fratersplein 9, 9000 Gent - T: 092337624, Fax: 092255733. Head: Dr. Georges Pieters
Science&Tech Museum / Religious Arts Museum - 1974
History of the local textile industry and religious traditions 03408

Museum Arnold Vander Haeghen, Veldstr 82, 9000 Gent - T: 092698460, Fax: 092698479, E-mail: directie.cultuur@gent.be. Head: Dr. Johan Decavele
Special Museum - 1975
Maurice Maeterlinck (1862-1942) room, Victor Stuyvaert (1897-1974) room - library 03409

Museum Dr. Guislain, Jozef-Guislainstr 43, 9000 Gent - T: 092163595, Fax: 092163535, E-mail: -museum.dr.guislain@fracarita.org, Internet: http://www.fracarita.org/nl/europa/belgie/museum. Head: Dr. R. Stockman
Special Museum
History of psychiatry 03410

Museum van Hedendaagse Kunst → Stedelijk Museum voor Actuele Kunst

Museum voor de Geschiedenis van de Wetenschappen, c/o Universiteit Gent, Krijgslaan 281, Gebouw 30, 9000 Gent - T: 092644930, Fax: 092644973, E-mail: jozef.uyttenhove@rug.ac.be, Internet: http://mhsgent.rug.ac.be. Head: Prof. Dr. J. Uyttenhove
Historical Museum / Science&Tech Museum - 1965
Original instruments and archives of J. Plateau, physics: optics and electricity from 1800-1950, microscopes, calculators, photography - library 03411

Museum voor Geschiedenis van de Geneeskunde, Onderbergen 1, 9000 Gent - T: 092230832, Fax: 092648396. Head: Prof. Dr. A.K. Eyrard
Historical Museum 03412

Museum voor Industriele Archeologie en Textiel, Minnemeers 9, 9000 Gent - T: 092694200, Fax: 092330739, E-mail: museum.miat@gent.be, Internet: http://www.miat.gent.be. Head: René De Herdt
Science&Tech Museum / Archaeological Museum / Historical Museum - 1976
Textile machinery, soft drink machinery coll, coll of coffee machinery, shoemaking, distillery, steam engines, metal industry, textile machines, industrial archaeology - library, archives, photo coll 03413

Museum voor Schone Kunsten Gent, Citadelpark, 9000 Gent - T: 092400700, Fax: 092400790, E-mail: museum.msk@gent.be, Internet: http://finearts.museum.gent.be. Head: Dr. Robert Hoozee
Fine Arts Museum - 1798/1902
Flemish Old Masters (15th-17th c), Belgian Art (19th-20th c) 03414

Museum voor Sierkunst en Vormgeving → Design Museum Gent

Museum voor Stenen Voorwerpen, Gandastr 7, 9000 Gent - T: 092251585
Fine Arts Museum - 1887
Stone sculptures (15th-18th c) 03415

Oudheidkundig Museum van de Bijloke → Bijlokemuseum

Schoolmuseum Michel Thiery, Sint-Pietersplein 14, 9000 Gent - T: 092447373, Fax: 092447374, E-mail: schoolmuseum.mt@gent.be, Internet: http://www.geocities.com/schoolmuseum/. Head: A.M. Van Gijseghem
Natural History Museum - 1924
Minerals, molluscs, insects, fossils, birds and mammals, invertebrates, human evolution and biology - library, educational service for schools and children; plantentuin and hortusmuseum: botanic garden, greenhouse, beehive 03416

Sint-Baafskathedraal Gent, Sint-Baafsplein, 9000 Gent - T: 092251626, Fax: 092233959, E-mail: ludo.collin@kerknet.be. Head: Ludo Collin
Religious Arts Museum
Crypt of the former Sint-Janskerk with wall paintings (12th c), Justus van Gent 'Calvarie' (15th c), the life of Saint Andreas Pourbus (16th c), frescoes (15th c), 'the Mystic Lamb' (Van Eyck 1432) 03417

Stadhuis, Botermarkt 1, 9000 Gent - T: 092665251, Fax: 092665259, E-mail: -secretarie.gemeenteraad@gent.be, Internet: http://www.gent.be. Head: Geert Van Doorne
Historical Museum
Historic halls with various art objects, place of the peace treaty between Protestants and Catholics in 1576 03418

Stedelijk Museum voor Actuele Kunst (Museum for Contemporary Art), Citadelpark, 9000 Gent - T: 092211703, Fax: 092217109, E-mail: museum.smak@gent.be, Internet: http://www.smak.be. Head: Jan Hoet
Fine Arts Museum - 1976
Art since 1945 03419

Gentinnes

Musée d'Art Africain Religieux, 140 Rue du Couvent, 1450 Gentinnes - T: 071877075, Fax: 071877338, E-mail: spirgent@pophost.eunet.be. Head: Joseph Burgraff
Religious Arts Museum 03420

Genval

Musée de la Fontaine et de l'Eau, Les Masures, 63 Av Hoover, 1332 Genval - T: 026541923, Fax: 067647386, E-mail: musee-eau-fontaine@belgacom.net, Internet: http://www.pixelsbw.com/musee-eau-fontaine. Head: Jean-Pierre Courtois
Special Museum 03421

Geraardsbergen

Manneken-Pis-Museum, Markt 1, Stadhuis, 9500 Geraardsbergen - T: 054419287, 054437289, Fax: 054419287, E-mail: nevraumont.fleur@busmail.net, Internet: http://home.tiscalinet.be/manneken-pis. Head: Marcel Nevraumont
Folklore Museum 03422

Museum van het Abtenhuis, Abdijstr 10, 9500 Geraardsbergen - T: 054411394. Head: Johan Quintelier
Decorative Arts Museum - 1962
Japanese and Chinese faience, Louis XV and Renaissance furniture, paintings by Dutch masters and the Laguillère-school, Sèvre vases, once the property of a French king, representing the battle of Fontenoy, a 'boudoir', identical to the Salle des Glaces of Versailles 03423

Museum voor Oudheidkunde, Gasthuisstr, 9500 Geraardsbergen
Archaeological Museum 03424

Gerpinnes

Musée des Marches Folkloriques de l'Entre-Sambre-et-Meuse, Rue de la Régence, 6280 Gerpinnes - T: 071503565
Folklore Museum 03425

Gesves

Musée de la Préhistoire, Cavernes Préhistoriques de Goyet, Vallée du Samson, 5340 Gesves - T: 083588545. Head: Jean Kindt
Archaeological Museum
Caves, Paleolitic human fossils, traces of human existence tools, arms, ornaments, fossils of animals from the surroundings of Wurm glaciation 03426

Gistel

Sint-Godelievemuseum, Abdijstr 84, 8470 Gistel - T: 059278671, Fax: 059277791
Religious Arts Museum - 1972
Religious objects and traditions 03427

Grez-Doiceau

Musée du Peruchet, 36 Rue de Morsaint, 1390 Grez-Doiceau - T: 010844513
Local Museum 03428

Grimbergen

Museum voor de Oudere Technieken, Guldendal 20, 1850 Grimbergen - T: 022708111, Fax: 022700983, E-mail: info@mot.be, Internet: http://www.mot.be. Head: Johan David
Science&Tech Museum - 1982
Transport, craft skills, agricultural techniques 03429

Grobbendonk

Archaeologisch Museum, Boudewijnstr 2, 2280 Grobbendonk - T: 014511020
Archaeological Museum
Results of archeological excavations 1200 BC - 300 AC 03430

Diamantmuseum, Bovenpad 3a, 2280 Grobbendonk
Science&Tech Museum / Natural History Museum
Different kinds of diamonds and diamond treatment, diamond polishers at work 03431

Groot-Bijgaarden

Bakkerijmuseum, Industrialaan 25, 1720 Groot-Bijgaarden - T: 024671211, Fax: 024662581
Special Museum 03432

Halen

Museum Slag der Zilveren Helmen (Museum Battle of the Silver Helmets), Rotem 14, 3545 Halen - T: 013441014, Fax: 013461156. Head: Didier de Witte de Haelen
Military Museum - 1958
Belgium and German Uniforms from 1870 to 1914, arms, documents, paintings by James Thiriair 03433

Halle

Hallerbosmuseum, Vlasmarktdreef 4, 1500 Halle - T: 023661870
Local Museum 03434

Klokkenmuseum van de Sint-Martinusbasiliek, Grote Markt, 1500 Halle - T: 023564174
Music Museum - 1973
Historic bells and chimes 03435

Krypte en Schatkamer van de O.L.V. Basiliek, Sint-Martinuskerk, Grote Markt, 1500 Halle - T: 023601098
Religious Arts Museum
Religious treasury 03436

Zuidwestbrabants Museum, Kardinaal Cardijnstr 7, 1500 Halle - T: 023659415, Fax: 023659415. Head: Dr. R. Borremans
Local Museum 03437

Ham-sur-Heure

Musée de la Vie Rurale et Artisanale, Château, 11 Beau Chemin, 6120 Ham-sur-Heure - T: 071213683. Head: Andrée Schelfhaut
Folklore Museum 03438

Hamme

Archeologisch Museum Van Bogaert-Wauters, Museumstr 3, 9220 Hamme - T: 052474151
Archaeological Museum - 1955
Archeology, hist - library 03439

Hamont-Achel

Gemeentemuseum, 3930 Hamont-Achel - T: 011445040
Local Museum 03440

Museum Grevenbroek, Generaal Dempseylaan 1, 3930 Hamont-Achel - T: 011646070
Local Museum 03441

Han-sur-Lesse

Musée du Monde Souterrain, 3 Pl Théo Lannoy, 5580 Han-sur-Lesse - T: 084377007
Archaeological Museum / Natural History Museum
Archeology, geology 03442

Harelbeke

Archeologisch Museum, Koning Leopold III-Plein 71, 8530 Harelbeke - T: 056733470, Fax: 056733470, E-mail: museoharelbeke@yucom.be. Head: Ann Matton
Archaeological Museum 03443

Peter Benoitmuseum, Marktstr 55-57, 8530 Harelbeke - T: 056733470, Fax: 056733470, E-mail: museaharelbeke@yucom.be. Head: A. Matton
Music Museum
Archives, manuscripts, furniture and personal effects of the Flemish composer Peter Benoit 03444

Stedelijk Museum voor Pijp en Tabak, Marktstr 100, 8530 Harelbeke - T: 056733470, Fax: 056733470, E-mail: museaharelbeke@yucom.be. Head: A. Matton
Special Museum / Agriculture Museum / Science&Tech Museum 03445

Harzé

Musée de la Meunerie, Château de Harzé, Rue de Bastogne, 4920 Harzé - T: 041844125
Science&Tech Museum 03446

Hasselt

Fashion Museum, Gasthuisstr 11, 3500 Hasselt - T: 011239621, Fax: 011221066, E-mail: modemuseum@hasselt.be, Internet: http://www.modemuseum.be
Special Museum 03447

Literair Museum, Bampsplaan 35, 3500 Hasselt - T: 011261787, Fax: 011232297, E-mail: literairmuseum@skynet.be
Special Museum - 1997 03448

Museum Pater Valentinus, Minderbroedersstr 19, 3500 Hasselt - T: 011241063. Head: Georges Hermans
Religious Arts Museum 03449

Museum Stellingwerff-Waerdenhof, Maastrichterstr 85, 3500 Hasselt - T: 011241070, Fax: 011262398, E-mail: stellingwerffwaerdenhof@hasselt.be, Internet: http://www.stellingwerffwaerdenhof.be. Head: Myriam Lipkens
Local Museum 03450

Nationaal Jenevermuseum, Witte Nonnenstr 19, 3500 Hasselt - T: 011241144, Fax: 011211050, E-mail: jenevermuseum@hasselt.be, Internet: http://www.jenevermuseum.be. Head: Ann Vandeput
Special Museum - 1981
History of spirits 03451

Nationaal Museum van Oorlog en Vrede, Kuringersteenweg 4, 3500 Hasselt - T: 011252317
Military Museum 03452

Provinciaal Centrum voor Beeldende Kunsten-Begijnhof, Zuivelmarkt 33, 3500 Hasselt - T: 011295960, Fax: 011295961, E-mail: pcbk@limburg.be, Internet: http://www.limburg.be/pcbk. Head: Steven Dusoleil, Jan Boelen
Fine Arts Museum
Contemporary art and design 03453

Hastière-par-Delà

Musée et Patrimoine Hastière, Tour de l'Eglise Romane, Rue Moussia, 5541 Hastière-par-Delà - T: 082644266. Head: Albert Pirotte
Archaeological Museum / Local Museum
Archeological objects (prehistoric, Roman and medieval), coins, tools, religious traditions, photos and documents 03454

Hechtel

Bosmuseum, Kamperbaan 149, 3940 Hechtel - T: 011734150
Natural History Museum 03455

Klokkenmuseum, Lommelsebaan 11, 3940 Hechtel - T: 011734102, Fax: 011734520, E-mail: scheelen@online.be. Head: J. Scheelen
Special Museum 03456

Heist-Op-Den-Berg

Heemmuseum Die Swane, Kerkplein 25, 2220 Heist-Op-Den-Berg - T: 015241259
Local Museum / Folklore Museum - 1956
Local history and folklore 03457

Spoorwegmuseum van Miniaturmodellen, Kerkplein 24, 2220 Heist-Op-Den-Berg - T: 015241486. Head: Pieter Nombluez
Science&Tech Museum - 1971
Hist and models of steam locomotives 03458

Henri-Chapelle

Villa Pelsser, 2 Chausée de Liège, 4841 Henri-Chapelle - T: 087880214, Fax: 087880214, E-mail: info@villapelsser.com, Internet: http:www.-villapelsser.com. Head: Wolfgang Schulte, Liana Zantfrisco
Fine Arts Museum 03459

Herentals

Begijnhofmuseum, Begijnhof 13, 2200 Herentals - T: 014219068, Fax: 014307747, E-mail: convent@ocmwherentals.be. Head: Louisa Ceulemans
Folklore Museum 03460

Herenthout

Heemkundig Museum Sandelijn, Zwanenberg 3, 2270 Herenthout - T: 014512453
Local Museum 03461

Herk-de-Stad

Museum van de Gelukzalige Amandina van Schakkebroek, Amandinaweg 74, 3540 Herk-de-Stad - T: 013551982. Head: J. Dreezen
Local Museum 03462

Herstal

Musée Communal Herstalien d'Archéologie et de Folklore, 25 Pl Licour, 4040 Herstal - T: 042406515, Fax: 042406576. Head: Marcella Colle
Local Museum - 1971
Arms, folklore, archeology, paintings and sculpture of local artists, Merovingian gravestone 03463

Herve

Espace des Saveurs, 36b Av Dewandre, 4650 Herve - T: 087693670
Decorative Arts Museum 03464

Heule

Het Heuls Curiosamuseum, Peperstr 24, 8501 Heule - T: 056350490
Special Museum 03465

Heverlee

Kasteel van Arenberg, Kardinaal Mercierlaan, 3001 Heverlee - T: 016324015
Historic Site 03466

Hoegaarden

Museum 't Nieuwhuys Hoegaarden, Ernest Ourystr 2-4, 3320 Hoegaarden - T: 016766294
Archaeological Museum / Local Museum / Folklore Museum / Science&Tech Museum - 1965
Archeology, local history, folklore, crafts and industries 03467

Hoeilaart

Bosmuseum van Het Zonienwoud, Duboislaan 6, 1560 Hoeilaart - T: 026572203. Head: Dr. J. Zwaenepoel
Natural History Museum 03468

Gemeentelijk Heemkundig Museum, Jan van Ruusbroeckpark, Gemeentehuis, 1560 Hoeilaart - T: 026574190, Internet: http://www.hoeilaart.be/infogids/gidscultuur.htm
Local Museum
Local hist and archeology 03469

Honnelles

Musée Rural de Plein Air, 1 Pl F. Masson, 7387 Honnelles - T: 065759143, 065759222
Open Air Museum 03470

Hoogstraten

Stedelijk Ostmuseum, Begijnhof 10, 2320 Hoogstraten - T: 033146588, Fax: 033142381
Fine Arts Museum - 1976
Works by the painter Alfred Ost, archeological objects, local furniture, Albert Poels, Maurits Bilcke - archives 03471

Hornu

Musée des Arts Contemporains de la Communauté Française (open September 2002), Site du Grand-Hornu, 82 Rue Sainte-Louise, 7301 Hornu - T: 065652121, Fax: 065765669, E-mail: mac.grandhornu@freebel.net, Internet: http://www.mac-s.be. Head: Laurent Busine
Fine Arts Museum - 2002 03472

Houdeng-Aimeries

Musée de la Mine, Rue Saint-Patrice, Bois-du-Luc, 7110 Houdeng-Aimeries - T: 064225448, 064226418, Fax: 064225448. Head: Paule Dupont
Science&Tech Museum 03473

Houffalize

Musée d'Archéologie, 1 Pl du Crucifix, 6660 Houffalize - T: 062288629
Archaeological Museum 03474

Houthalen

Bijenmuseum Hengelhoef (closed) 03475

Tysmans Museum, Vredelaan 36, 3530 Houthalen - T: 011524980
Local Museum 03476

Huissignies

Musée de la Vie Rurale, 34 Rue J Lizon, 7950 Huissignies - T: 069689427, 069689400
Folklore Museum 03477

Hulste

Nationaal Volkssportmuseum voor de Vinkensport, Hazestr 4, 8531 Hulste - T: 056308082
Special Museum 03478

Huy

Musée Communal de Huy, Ancien Couvent des Frères Mineurs, 20 Rue Vankeerberghen, 4500 Huy - T: 085232435
Local Museum / Archaeological Museum
Prehistoric archeology, local history, sculpture, folklore, medieval pottery, arts and crafts, religious art 03479

Musée du Fort de Huy, Citadel, Quai de Namur, 4500 Huy - T: 085215334
Military Museum - 1967
Arms 03480

Trésor de la Collégiale, Quai de Namur, 5200 Huy - T: 085212005, Fax: 085212005
Religious Arts Museum
Goldsmith art, reliquary of Gedefroi de Huy, sculpture, textiles, paintings 03481

Ieper

Herinneringsmuseum Ypres Salient 1914-1918, Grote Markt, 8900 Ieper - T: 057228555, Fax: 057218589. Head: Jan Dewilde
Military Museum 03482

Hotel-Museum Merghelynck, Merghelynckstr 2, 8900 Ieper - T: 057228582, Fax: 057205880, E-mail: stedelijke.musea@ieper.be, Internet: http://www.ieper.be. Head: Jan Dewilde
Decorative Arts Museum - 1894
Patrician house with period furniture and decorative art, Chinese and Japanese porcelain 03483

In Flanders Fields Museum, Lakenhallen, Grote Markt 34, 8900 Ieper - T: 057228584, Fax: 057205880, E-mail: stedelijke.musea@ieper.be, Internet: http://www.inflandersfields.be. Head: Jan Dewilde
Military Museum - 1927/1948
Hist of WWI - library 03484

Museum Godshuis Belle, Rijselsestr 38, 8900 Ieper - T: 057228582, Fax: 057205880, E-mail: stedelijke.musea@ieper.be, Internet: http://www.ieper.be. Head: Jan Dewilde
Local Museum - 1962
Ypres scabinal seals of 14th and 15th c, Ypres painters (15th-18th c) 03485

Stedelijk Museum Ieper, Ieperleestr 31, 8900 Ieper - T: 057228582, Fax: 057205880, E-mail: stedelijke.musea@ieper.be, Internet: http://www.ieper.be. Head: Jan Dewilde
Decorative Arts Museum / Fine Arts Museum / Historical Museum - 1828
Louise de Hem (1866-1922) 03486

Stedelijk Onderwijsmuseum Ieper (Museum of Education in Flanders), G. de Stuersstr 6A, 8900 Ieper - T: 057228582, Fax: 057205880, E-mail: stedelijke.musea@ieper.be, Internet: http://www.ieper.be. Head: Jan Dewilde
Special Museum / Historical Museum - 1990
Hist of education in Belgium from 1253 until now - library 03487

Ingooigem

Provinciaal Museum Stijn Streuvels, Het Lijsternest, Stijn Streuvelsstr 24, 8570 Ingooigem - T: 056778958
Special Museum - 1980
Library, furniture, paintings, household effects of Streuvels' lifetime, photographic exhibition about the author's life, general view of bookprinting from the 15th to the 20th c, paintings by Constant Permeke, Albert Saverys, Rik Slabbinck 03488

Ittre

Musée de la Forge, 11 Rue Basse, 1460 Ittre - T: 067646300, 067647372
Science&Tech Museum 03489

Musée du Folklore, 14 Rue Basse, 1460 Ittre - T: 067646832. Head: Jean-Paul Cayphas
Folklore Museum 03490

Izegem

Nationaal Borstelmuseum (National Museum of Brushware), Baron de Pélichystr 5, 8870 Izegem - T: 051316446, Fax: 051314867, E-mail: info@izegem.be, Internet: http://www.izegem.be. Head: Hilde Colpaert
Science&Tech Museum 03491

Nationaal Schoeiselmuseum (National Museum for Footwear), Wijngaardstr 9, 8870 Izegem - T: 051316543, Fax: 051314867, E-mail: info@izegem.be, Internet: http://www.izegem.be. Head: Hilde Colpaert
Science&Tech Museum - 1968
Footwear, techniques of shoemaking in former times, shoemakers workshop 03492

Izenberge

Openluchtmuseum Bachten de Kupe, Sint-Mildredaplein, 8691 Izenberge - T: 058298090. Head: Marcel Messiaen
Open Air Museum 03493

Petite Blaevoet Museum, Groenestr 33, 8691 Izenberge - T: 058299244
Local Museum 03494

Regionale Heemmusea Bachten de Kupe, Sint-Mildredaplein, 8991 Izenberge - T: 058298090. Head: Marcel Messiaen
Local Museum / Archaeological Museum / Science&Tech Museum - 1970
Crafts, regional archeology, religious customs, textile industry, peasant life 03495

Jabbeke

Museum Constant Permeke, Gistelsteenweg 341, 8490 Jabbeke - T: 059508118, Fax: 059805626. Head: W. Van den Bussche
Fine Arts Museum - 1969
Paintings, drawings and sculpture by C. Permeke, documents, photos and correspondence of Permeke, works of P. Devos, F. Van den Berghe, O. Jespers, L. Peire 03496

Jandrain-Jandrenouille

Musée du Premier Corps de la Cavalerie Française, Ecole Communale, Chaussée de Hannut, 1350 Jandrain-Jandrenouille - T: 019634063, 019633403
Military Museum 03497

Jehay-Amay

Musée Historique et Préhistorique Van den Steen, Château de Jehay, 4540 Jehay-Amay - T: 085311716. Head: Comte Guy Van den Steen de Jehay
Decorative Arts Museum / Historical Museum / Archaeological Museum - 1958
Prehistoric relics, Greek and Roman objects, memorials of the Duke and the Duchess of Marlborough, silver, furniture, tapestries, paintings, sculptures 03498

Jemeppe-sur-Sambre

Musée de la Préhistoire, 3 Rue de la Poste, 5190 Jemeppe-sur-Sambre - T: 071786041, 071786701
Historical Museum 03499

Jodoigne

Musée de la Vie Regionale et des Metiers Disparus, 5a Chaussée de Charleroi, 1370 Jodoigne - T: 010810182
Local Museum 03500

Jupille-sur-Meuse

Galerie des Peintres, Maison Communale, 4020 Jupille-sur-Meuse
Fine Arts Museum 03501

Kalmthout

Bijenteeltmuseum Kalmthout, Heikantstr 51a, 2920 Kalmthout - T: 0316669698. Head: M. Schoofs
Special Museum 03502

Kanne

Ondergronds Museum, Davergat, 3770 Kanne - T: 012451100
Archaeological Museum
Paintings of prehistoric animals and plants, fossils, grottos 03503

Keerbergen

De Botermolen, Haachtsebaan 85, 3140 Keerbergen - T: 015511973, 015512577
Folklore Museum
Folklore, church furniture, toys 03504

Kerniel

Museum Klooster Marienlof, Kolenstr 1, 3840 Kerniel - T: 012741467
Religious Arts Museum 03505

Kessel-Lo

Lokomotiefdepot Leuven, Brugberg, 3010 Kessel-Lo - T: 0165238080
Science&Tech Museum 03506

Knokke-Heist

Heemkundig Museum Sincfala, Pannenstr 140, 8300 Knokke-Heist - T: 050630872, Fax: 050630872, E-mail: sincfala@online.be
Archaeological Museum / Agriculture Museum / Local Museum / Folklore Museum - 1960
Archeology, folklore, agricultural equipment, fishing - library 03507

Koersel

Maquettenmuseum, Spechtenstr 5, 3582 Koersel - T: 011431845, 011422001
Special Museum 03508

Koksijde

Abdijmuseum Ten Duinen 1138, Koninklijke Prinslaan 8, 8670 Koksijde - T: 058521686, Fax: 058510061, E-mail: duinenabdij@koksijde.be
Historical Museum / Archaeological Museum / Historic Site - 1959
Regional history and archeology, cistercian history, architecture 03509

Rariteiten- en Ambachtenmuseum 't Krekelhof, Koninklijke Baan 237, 8670 Koksijde - T: 058512332, Fax: 058519132, E-mail: hadisof@mail.com, Internet: http://www.koksijde.be/krekelhof. Head: Van Damme
Folklore Museum 03510

Kontich

Museum voor Heem- en Oudheidkunde, Duivenstr 22, 2550 Kontich - T: 034578604, Fax: 034575468, E-mail: heemkundekontich@hotmail.com. Head: Guido Theys
Folklore Museum / Historical Museum / Archaeological Museum - 1959
Folklore, prehist, pottery and ceramics, textiles, religious art and traditions, craftman's tools and samplers - library 03511

Kortrijk

Begijnhofmuseum, Begijnhofstr, 8500 Kortrijk - T: 056244802, Fax: 056244848
Historical Museum / Folklore Museum / Religious Arts Museum 03512

Nationaal Vlas-Kant- en Linnenmuseum, Etienne Sabbelaan 4, 8500 Kortrijk - T: 056210138, Fax: 056200483
Special Museum - 1982
Handicraft and folklore related to flax and linen, example of industrial archeology, 60 life-size polyester replicas of farmers, flax dressers, spinners and weavers placed in reconstructions of authentic work rooms, tools and pre-industrial machines, original clothing and old utensils - library 03513

Stedelijke Musea Kortrijk, Broelkaai 4, 8500 Kortrijk - T: 056240870, Fax: 056240871, E-mail: musea.stadkortrijk@kortrijk.be. Head: Isabelle de Jaegere
Fine Arts Museum / Historical Museum
Old and modern painting, objects of the Stone and Bronze Ages, Gallo-Roman antiquities, ceramics, works by Roeland Savery and 19th c animal painters, hist of Kortrijk, linnen, damask 03514

Kruishoutem

Stichting Veranneman, Vandevoordeweg 2, 9770 Kruishoutem - T: 093835287, Fax: 093838215, E-mail: veranneman.art@unicall.be, Internet: http://www.gallery-veranneman.be
Public Gallery 03515

La Louvière

Centre de la Gravure et de l'Image Imprimée de la Communauté Française de Belgique, 10 Rue des Amours, 7100 La Louvière - T: 064278727, Fax: 064278729, E-mail: accueil@centredelagravure.be. Head: Catherine de Braekeleer
Fine Arts Museum - 1984
Coll of more than 10,000 works of contemporary Belgian and international artists (Pierre Avechinsky, Pat Andrea, Eduardo Chillida, Sol LeWitt, Takesada Matsutani, Antonio Segui, Roland Topor) - Library 03516

Musée Ianchelevici, 21 Pl Communale, 7100 La Louvière - T: 064282530, Fax: 064216793, E-mail: ianchelevici@t:scalimet.be. Head: Valerie Formery
Fine Arts Museum 03517

Laarne

Kasteelmuseum Slot van Laarne, Eekhoek 5, 9270 Laarne - T: 092309155, Fax: 092316614. Head: Paul de Pessemier 's Gravendries
Decorative Arts Museum - 1965
Silverware (15th-18th c), furniture (17th-18th c.), tapestries (15th-17th c), pictures (16th-17th c), coll Dallemagne 03518

Lahamaide

Musée de l'Agriculture Traditionnelle et de l'Artisanat de nos Campagnes, 3 Rue Plada, 7890 Lahamaide - T: 068645049
Agriculture Museum
Ancient agricultural methods and rural handicrafts 03519

Lanaye

Musée de la Montagne Saint-Pierre, Pl du Roi Albert, 4600 Lanaye - T: 043792803, 043748494, Fax: 043748481, Internet: http://www.ful.ac.be/hotes/savoeur/msp/musee.htm
Natural History Museum 03520

Landen

Museum Rufferdinge, Molenberg 2, 3400 Landen - T: 011883468, Fax: 011885505, E-mail: ecresis@vl-brabant.be. Head: Eric Crésis
Agriculture Museum / Archaeological Museum 03521

Lasne-Chapelle-Saint-Lambert

Musée d'Art Naif, 140 Rue de la Lasne, 1380 Lasne-Chapelle-Saint-Lambert - T: 026541933
Fine Arts Museum 03522

Musée Ribauri, 4 Rue du Musée, 1330 Lasne-Chapelle-Saint-Lambert - T: 026537259
Ethnology Museum
Primitive art from Africa, Oceania, Indian and Chinese art, shells 03523

Latour

Musée Baillet-Latour, 26 Rue Baillet-Latour, 6761 Latour - T: 063577758. Head: Jean Dauphin
Historical Museum - 1964
Hist of the castle of Latour and its inhabitants 03524

Lavaux-Sainte-Anne

Musée de la Chasse, de la Vénerie et de la Protection de la Nature, Château de Lavaux-Sainte-Anne, 5580 Lavaux-Sainte-Anne - T: 084388362, Fax: 084387302. Head: René Martin
Natural History Museum - 1958
Castle (15th c), hunting and hunting costumes, ornithology, botany, furniture, art objects 03525

Leers-et-Fosteau

Château du Fosteau, 1 Rue du Marquis, 6530 Leers-et-Fosteau - T: 071592344, Fax: 071594900, E-mail: albin.vanhoonacker1@yucom.be, Internet: http://www.chateaufosteau.be. Head: Marie-Henriette Van Hoonacker, Albin Van Hoonacker
Decorative Arts Museum 03526

Lembeke

Bardelaere Museum, Ledestr 42, 9971 Lembeke - T: 093770422, Fax: 093770422. Head: Marc Dauwe
Agriculture Museum / Local Museum - 1974
Agricultural implements, handicrafts, domestic utensils, religious art, toys 03527

Lens

Musée de la Vie Lensoise, 102 Rue Vallaville, 7870 Lens - T: 065229515
Local Museum 03528

Leopoldsburg

Museum van het Kamp van Beverlo, Militair Hospitaal, Hechtelse Steenweg, 3970 Leopoldsburg - T: 011344804, E-mail: muskvb@belgacom.net. Head: S. Weuts
Military Museum - 1972 03529

Lessines

Hôpital Notre-Dame de la Rose, Pl Alix de Rosoit, 7860 Lessines - T: 068332403, Fax: 068332403, E-mail: info@notredamealarose.com, Internet: http://www.notredamealarose.com. Head: Raphaël Debruyn
Local Museum / Religious Arts Museum / Historic Site / Science&Tech Museum - 1242
Historic site, medical and pharmaceutical collections, religious life 03530

Leuven

Museum van het Vlaams Studentenleven, c/o Katholieke Universiteit Leuven, Mgr. Ladeuzeplein 21, 3000 Leuven - T: 016324642, Fax: 016324709, E-mail: archief@bib.kuleuven.ac.be, Internet: http://www.kuleuven.ac.be/archief/index.htm. Head: Prof. Dr. Jan Roegiers
University Museum - 1975
Documents and manuscripts, books and journals concerning student life - archive 03531

Nationaal Scoutsmuseum, Sint-Geertruiabdij 5, 3000 Leuven - T: 016257270, Fax: 016813287. Head: Roger Quintens
Special Museum 03532

Sportmuseum Vlaanderen, c/o Vlaamse Volkssport Centrale, Tervuursevest 101, 3001 Leuven - T: 016225438, 016220445, Fax: 016201595, E-mail: sportimonium@sportimonium.be, Internet: http://www.sportimonium.be. Head: Eric de Vroede
Special Museum - 1985
Traditional games (worldwide), gymnastics, modern sports (Flanders, Belgium) - archive, library, lending service 03533

Stedelijk Brouwerijmuseum, Stadhuis, Grote Markt, 3000 Leuven - T: 016226906, Fax: 016211800. Head: Lutgarde Bessemans
Special Museum - 1978
Local economic and social history in connection with the brewing industry 03534

Stedelijk Museum Van der Kelen-Mertens, Savoyestr 6, 3000 Leuven - T: 016226906, Fax: 016238930
Fine Arts Museum / Decorative Arts Museum - 1823
Paintings (Rogier van der Weyden, Albrecht Bouts, Quentin Metsys, Pieter Coecke van Aelst, Michel Coxie), late Gothic sculpture, decorative arts (porcelain, stained glass, silver, goldsmith's work, furniture), local finds from prehist to the Middle Ages 03535

Liège

Aquarium Dubuisson et Musée de Zoologie de l'Université de Liège, c/o Institut de Zoologie, 22 Quai Van Beneden, 4020 Liège - T: 043665021, Fax: 043665093, E-mail: aquarium@ulg.ac.be, Internet: http://www.ulg.ac.be/aquarium. Head: Dr. J. Voss
University Museum / Natural History Museum - 1962
Stuffed animals and skeletons, living fishes and aquatic organisms 03536

Cabinet des Estampes et des Dessins, 3 Parc de la Boverie, 4020 Liège - T: 043423923, Fax: 043414404, E-mail: mamac@skynet.be. Head: Régine Rémon
Fine Arts Museum - 1951
Copper engravings and drawings by artists from the 16th c to present days - library 03537

Collections Artistiques de l'Université de Liège, 7 Pl du 20 Août, 4000 Liège - T: 043665329, Fax: 043665854, E-mail: wittert@ulg.ac.be, Internet: http://www.ulg.ac.be/wittert/a_accveil.html. Head: Prof. Jean-Patrick Duchesne
Fine Arts Museum / University Museum - 1968
Paintings and engravings, medals, arms and masks from Africa 03538

Galerie Lapidaire du Palais, Palais de Justice, Pl Saint-Lambert, 4000 Liège - T: 042232068, 042221600
Archaeological Museum 03539

Maison de la Metallurgie et de l'Industrie de Liège, 17 Blvd R. Poincaré, 4020 Liège - T: 043426563, Fax: 043447023. Head: Pascal Lefebvre
Science&Tech Museum - 1960
Metalworking industries, reconstruction of Walloon iron foundry (18th c), blast furnace using charcoal, melting iron techniques, bar iron production, kitchen utensils, steam engines, gas engines, olynamos, old computers - library 03540

Maison de la Science, 22 Quai Van Beneden, 4020 Liège - T: 043434918
Special Museum 03541

Musée Curtius (closed for restauration), 13 Quai de Maastricht, 4000 Liège - T: 042219404, Fax: 042219432. Head: Ann Chevalier, Marie-Claire Gueury
Archaeological Museum / Decorative Arts Museum - 1909
Gallo-Roman archeology, Frankish gold jewels, glass, numismatics of Liège from the Merovingian period to the 18th c, decorative arts, Mosan art (11th-13th c), furniture (16th-18th c), silverware, ivory, French miniatures, European and Oriental ceramics (medieval-19th c) - library 03542

Musée d'Ansembourg, 114 Féronstrée, 4000 Liège - T: 042219402, Fax: 042219432. Head: Ann Chevalier, Marie-Claire Gueury
Decorative Arts Museum - 1905
Applied and decorative arts of the 18th c at Liège, especially furniture 03543

Musée d'Archéologie Préhistorique de l'Université de Liège, 7 Pl du 20 Août, 4000 Liège - T: 043665341, 043665331, Fax: 043665551
Archaeological Museum / University Museum
Prehistoric coll from Belgium excavations made by University of Liège - library 03544

Musée d'Armes de Liège, Halles du Nord, 4 Rue de la Boucherie, 4000 Liège - T: 042219416/17, Fax: 042219401, E-mail: claude.gaier@museedarmes.be, Internet: http://www.museesdarmes.be. Head: Dr. Claude Gaier
Special Museum - 1885
Over 20000 Firearms and mechanism of firearms (14th-20th c), edged and defensive weapons (Prehistory-20th c), medals, decorations and orders of Chivalry, only fourteen-barrelled flintlock rifle ever made, only surviving example of Chambers seven-barrelled swivel-gun (224 shots), double wheellock pistol, which belonged to Louis XIII of France - library 03545

Musée d'Art Differencie, Parc d'Avroy, 4000 Liège - T: 042223295, Fax: 042223970, E-mail: mad@skynet.be
Fine Arts Museum 03546

Musée d'Art Moderne et d'Art Contemporain, 3 Parc de la Boverie, 4020 Liège - T: 043430403, Fax: 043441907, E-mail: mamac@skynet.be, Internet: http://www.mamac.org
Fine Arts Museum - 1903
Modern Belgian painting, French painting from Boudin to Picasso, sculpture, Coll Graindorge - library 03547

Musée d'Art Religieux et d'Art Mosan, 11 Rue Mère-Dieu, 4000 Liège - T: 042214225, 042214279, Fax: 042214283, E-mail: maramliege@multimania.com, Internet: http://www.multimania.com/maramliege. Head: Albert Lemeunier
Religious Arts Museum / Fine Arts Museum / Decorative Arts Museum - 1880
Medieval sculpture, textiles, goldsmith art, Flemish and Italian painting (16th c), German and Dutch painting (15th c.), Mosan art, iconography of Saint-Lambert - Library, archives 03548

Musée de la Vie Wallonne, Cour des Mineurs, 4000 Liège - T: 042236094, Fax: 042211035. Head: Maurice Remouchamps, Alain-Gérard Krupa
Folklore Museum / Ethnology Museum - 1912
Ethnography, folklore, rural crafts and agriculture, puppets, glass, religion and science, Max Elskamp sun-dials coll - library, research dept 03549

Musée de l'Art Différencié, Parc d'Avroy, 4000 Liège - T: 042223295, Fax: 042223970, E-mail: mad@skynet.be. Head: Anne-Sophie Dejace
Fine Arts Museum 03550

Musée de l'Art Wallon, Ilot Saint-Georges, 86 Féronstrée, 4000 Liège - T: 042219231, 042218911, Fax: 042219232, E-mail: maw@liege.be, Internet: http://www.liege.be
Fine Arts Museum - 1952
Wallon artists, paintings and sculpture (16th-20th c), works by L. Lombard, L. Defrance, R. Magritte, P. Delvaux, P. Bury - library 03551

Musée des Transports en Commun du Pays de Liège, 9a Rue Richard Heintz, 4020 Liège - T: 043670064
Science&Tech Museum 03552

Musée du Verre (closed for restoration), 13 Quai de Maastricht, 4000 Liège - T: 042219404, Fax: 042219432. Head: Pauline Bruy, Marie-Claire Gueury
Science&Tech Museum / Decorative Arts Museum - 1959
Glass production from the beginnings to 20th c - library 03553

Musée en Plein Air du Sart-Tilman, Centre d'Animation et d'Intégration des Arts Plastiques de la Communauté française de Belgique, Domaine Universitaire du Sart-Tilman, Bâtiment B25, 4000 Liège 1 - T: 043662220, Fax: 043662221, E-mail: musee.pleinair@ulg.ac.be, Internet: http://www.ulg.ac.be/museepla/. Head: Jean-Patrick Duchesne
Open Air Museum / University Museum
Paintings and sculptures 03554

Musée Grétry, 34 Rue des Recollets, 4020 Liège - T: 042230627, Fax: 042230627
Special Museum 03555

Musée Tchantches - Musée de la République Libre d'Outre-Meuse, 56 Rue Surlet, 4020 Liège - T: 043427575
Local Museum 03556

Lier

Museum Wuyts-Van Campen en Baron Caroly, Fl. Van Cauwenberghstr 14, 2500 Lier - T: 034911396, Fax: 034892654, E-mail: musea@lier.be, Internet: http://www.museumsite.be. Head: Luc Coenen
Fine Arts Museum - 1892
Paintings, including works by Rubens, Brueghel the Younger, Snyders, Floris, prints, decorative arts, furnishing, porcelain 03557

Timmermans-Opsomerhuis, Netelaan 4, 2500 Lier - T: 034911394, Fax: 034892654, E-mail: musea@lier.be, Internet: http://www.museumsite.be. Head: L. Coenen
Fine Arts Museum - 1968
Paintings, drawings of Baron I. Opsomer, paintings, drawings, books, manuscripts, letters of Felix Timmermans, iron works by Lodewijk Van Boeckel, room devoted to musical composer Renaat Veremans 03558

Zimmertoren, Zimmerpl 18, 2500 Lier - T: 03489111, Fax: 034881357
Special Museum - 1930
Astronomical Clocks 03559

Liernu

Musée Agricole de la Haute Hesbaye, 4 Rue du Gros Chêne, 5310 Liernu - T: 081657070
Agriculture Museum 03560

Ligny

Musée Napoleonien, 23 Rue Pont Pirau, 5140 Ligny - T: 071888057. Head: Léon Ruquoy
Historical Museum - 1968
Objects relating to the emperor and his epoch, battle of Ligny (last victory of Napoléon) 03561

Limal

Musée Vivant de la Plante Aquatique, 11 Rue Léon Deladrière, 1300 Limal - T: 02414230
Natural History Museum 03562

Lo-Reninge

Automuseum Old Timer, Tempelare 12, Weg Ypres-Furnes, 8647 Lo-Reninge - T: 057400442, Fax: 057401164. Head: N. Bossaert
Science&Tech Museum 03563

Lokeren

Stedelijk Museum Lokeren, Markt 15a, 9160 Lokeren - T: 093405064, 093405059, Fax: 093405053, E-mail: cclokeren@village.uunet.be, Internet: http://www.lokeren.-belgamedia.be. Head: Dr. Rik Van Daele
Historical Museum - 1896
Reconstruction of a baker's and a butcher's shop as it was in 1900, folklore, ethnology, archeology (Egypt), paintings, furniture 03564

Lommel

Museum Kempenland, Dorp 16, 3920 Lommel - T: 011541335. Head: Veerle Leysen
Archaeological Museum / Special Museum - 1958
Archeology, travelling merchants 03565

Museum Wateringhuis, Oude Maai 80, 3920 Lommel - T: 011540221
Local Museum 03566

Longueville

Musée de la Ligne Koningshooikt-Wavre, Maison Communale, 1325 Longueville - T: 010840270
Local Museum 03567

Loppem

Groot Kasteel van Loppem, Steenbrugsestr 26, 8210 Loppem - T: 050822245
Local Museum 03568

Kunsthalle Loppen, Torhoutsesteenweg 52a, 8210 Loppem - T: 075344840
Fine Arts Museum 03569

Louvain-la-Neuve

Musée de Louvain-la-Neuve, 1 Pl Blaise Pascal, 1348 Louvain-la-Neuve - T: 010474841/45, Fax: 010472413, E-mail: acc@muse.ucl.ac.be, Internet: http://www.muse.ucl.ac.be. Head: I. Vandevivere
Fine Arts Museum / University Museum - 1979
Contemporary art, African art, Greek & Roman, ancien art (European) 03570

Louvignies

Château de Louvignies, 1 Rue de Villegas, 7063 Louvignies - T: 027710895
Decorative Arts Museum 03571

Loverval

Musée d'Histoire et d'Archéologie, 76 Rte de Philippeville, 6280 Loverval - T: 071433158. Head: Paul Eloy
Historical Museum / Archaeological Museum 03572

Maaseik

Museactron, Lekkerstr 5, 3680 Maaseik - T: 089566890, Fax: 089560561. Head: Dr. Hubert Heymans
Archaeological Museum / Science&Tech Museum / Fine Arts Museum - 1962/1987
Prehistoric and Roman artifacts, medieval and post-medieval archeologica, oldest chemistry of Belgium, Delft and tin chemist's pots, old chemist's instruments, spice cultivation, two restored watermills and a Van Eyck exhibition 03573

Museum Kerkschat Sint-Katharinakerk, Mgr Koningsstr 1, 3680 Maaseik
Religious Arts Museum 03574

Maffle

Musée de la Pierre et Site des Carrières, 419 Chaussée de Mons, 7810 Maffle - T: 068269236, Fax: 068269239. Head: Jean-Pierre Ducastelle
Archaeological Museum - 1989
Iconographic coll, implements and machines connected with stone masonry - library 03575

Malmédy

Musée du Cwarmê, Maison Cavens, 11 Pl de Rome, 4960 Malmédy - T: 080337058, Fax: 080339232. Head: Thierry Lambert
Folklore Museum 03576

Musée National du Papier, Maison Cavens, 11 Pl de Rome, 4960 Malmédy - T: 080337058, Fax: 080339232. Head: Thierry Lambert
Science&Tech Museum 03577

Marche-en-Famenne

Musée de la Tourelle, Rempart des Jésuites, 6900 Marche-en-Famenne, mail addr: c/o Syndicat d'Initiative, 52 Rue de Luxembourg, 5400 Marche-en-Famenne - T: 084312135. Head: Pierre Pestiaux
Special Museum - 1968/1989
Hist of lace 03578

Musée des Francs et de la Famenne, 17 Rue du Commerce, 6900 Marche-en-Famenne - T: 084327060, E-mail: musee.famenne@marche.be, Internet: http://musee.marche.be. Head: Muriel Linon Van Ruymbeke
Archaeological Museum / Decorative Arts Museum
Art history 03579

Marchienne-au-Pont

Musée Marchiennois d'Histoire et d'Archéologie Industrielle, 36 Pl des Martyrs, 6030 Marchienne-au-Pont - T: 071436363. Head: Marcelle Letroye
Historical Museum / Archaeological Museum - 1976
Local history from Gallo-Roman times to the present, regional industrial development 03580

Marchin

Musée de la Vie d'Autrefois, Pl du Grand-Marchin, 4570 Marchin - T: 027347130
Folklore Museum 03581

Mariembourg

Chemin de Fer à Vapeur des Trois Vallées, Remise des Locomot ives, 49 Chaussée de Givet, 5660 Mariembourg - T: 060344985, 060312440. Head: R. Maegerman
Science&Tech Museum - 1979
Steam engines and steam locomotives 03582

Martelange

Musée de la Haute Sûre, 17 Rue du Musée, 6630 Martelange - T: 063600860, 063600773
Local Museum
Reconstruction of the interior of a slater's house of 1600, furniture, kitchen utensils 03583

Mechelen

Archeologisch Museum, Sint-Romboutskerkhof 2, 2800 Mechelen - T: 015206638. Head: Jean Willems
Archaeological Museum 03584

Internationaal Apimondia Bijenteelt-Museum (International Apimondia Beekeeping Museum), Nekkerspoelstr 21, 2800 Mechelen - T: 015557075, E-mail: vanlaere@uia.ua.ac.be
Natural History Museum
Life history of honey-bees, hives from all over the world, philately, bee products 03585

Joods Museum van Deportatie en Verzet (Jewish Museum of Deportation and Resistance), Goswin de Stassartstr 153, 2800 Mechelen - T: 015290660, Fax: 015290876, E-mail: infos@cicb.be, Internet: http://www.cicb.be. Head: Nathan Ramet
Historical Museum 03586

Museum Woning voor antieke Horlogerie, Lange Schipstr 13, 2800 Mechelen - T: 015211894, Fax: 015212515, E-mail: clock@skynet.be, Internet: http://www.users.skynet.be/horlogerie. Head: Jozef Op de Beeck
Science&Tech Museum - 1983
Mystery clocks 03587

Speelgoedmuseum Mechelen, Nekkerspoel 21, 2800 Mechelen - T: 015557075, Fax: 015552085, E-mail: info@speelgoedmuseum.be, Internet: http://www.speelgoedmuseum.be
Special Museum 03588

Stedelijk Museum Brusselport, Hoogstr, 2800 Mechelen - T: 015274425, Fax: 015294031, E-mail: dienstmusea@mechelen.be. Head: Heidi de Nijn
Archaeological Museum
Urban development, archaeology, markets, fishing 03589

Stedelijk Museum Hof van Busleyden, Fred de Merodestr 65, 2800 Mechelen - T: 015202004, Fax: 015294031, E-mail: dienstmusea@mechelen.be, Internet: http://www.mechelen.be/stedelijkemusea. Head: Heidi de Nijn
Decorative Arts Museum / Fine Arts Museum / Historical Museum - 1844
Hist of crafts and guilds, former Mechlin industrial arts (copper, bronze, goldleather, lace), sculpture 15th-20th c 03590

Stedelijk Museum Schepenhuis, Steenweg 1, 2800 Mechelen - T: 015211602, Fax: 015294031, E-mail: dienstmusea@mechelen.be. Head: Heidi de Nijn
Local Museum / Religious Arts Museum / Fine Arts Museum
City life 1400-1600, sculptures, religious wood-carving, reliefs 03591

Technopolis, Technologielaan, 2800 Mechelen - T: 015342000, Fax: 015342001, E-mail: info@technopolis.be, Internet: http://www.technopolis.be. Head: Erik Jacquemyn
Science&Tech Museum
Science, technology 03592

De Wit - Royal Manufacturers of Tapestries, Schoutetstr 7, 2800 Mechelen - T: 015202905, Fax: 015204888, E-mail: info@dewit.be, Internet: http://www.dewit.be. Head: Yvan Maes de Wit
Science&Tech Museum / Fine Arts Museum
Tapestries production,cleaning and restoration 03593

Melle

Gemeentelijk Museum, Brusselsesteenweg 395, 9090 Melle - T: 092522647. Head: A. de Baets
Archaeological Museum / Folklore Museum - 1973
Archeology, folklore - genealogical documentation center 03594

Merksem

Museum De Kijkuit, Terlindenhofstr 265, 2170 Merksem - T: 036451677
Local Museum
Folklore, local hist 03595

Mesen

Geschiedkundig Museum Mesen, Stadhuis, Markt 1, 8957 Mesen - T: 057445040, Fax: 057445040, E-mail: museum.mesen@yvcom.be. Head: Louis Menu
Historical Museum - 1972
Folklore, ancient Mesen abbey, history of World War I referring to the Battle of Messines, June 7, 1917 and the Victory of the ANZACS 03596

Mesvin

L'Amusette, Musée Interactif pour Enfants, 33 Rue Brunehaut, 7022 Mesvin - T: 065338233, Fax: 065338233, E-mail: amusette@swing.be, Internet: http://www.gal.ac.be/hotes/amusette
Special Museum 03597

Mettet

Musée du Bois - Musée de la Vie Rurale, 10 Rue des Artisans, 5640 Mettet - T: 071699253
Natural History Museum / Agriculture Museum
All kinds of wooden objects 03598

Modave

Musée du Château des Comtes de Marchin, 4577 Modave - T: 085411369, Fax: 085412676, E-mail: info@modave-castle.be
Decorative Arts Museum / Fine Arts Museum 03599

Mol

Museum Jakob Smits, Sluis 155, 2400 Mol - T: 014317435. Head: F. Van Gompel
Fine Arts Museum - 1977
Graphic art and painting by the Belgian artist Jakob Smits, documentation on his life, works of contemporaries 03600

Natuurhistorisch Museum Provinciaal Domein Zilvermeer, Zilvermeerlaan 2, 2400 Mol - T: 014313811. Head: D. Vermeulen
Natural History Museum
Regional flora and fauna, ornithology 03601

Monceau-Imbrechies

Musée 40-44, 100 Rue d'Imbrechies, 6592 Monceau-Imbrechies - T: 060512496, 060511252
Historical Museum 03602

Mons

Musée de la Route, Casemate 4, Pl Nervienne, 7000 Mons - T: 3265379211, Fax: 3265352284, E-mail: bvanmol@met.wallonie.be. Head: Bruno Van Mol
Science&Tech Museum 03603

Musée des Beaux-Arts de la Ville de Mons, 8 Rue Neuve, 7000 Mons - T: 065405306, Fax: 065347763, E-mail: musees.mons@swing.be. Head: Michel de Reymaeker
Fine Arts Museum - 1913/1970
Belgian coll: mostly 19th to 20th c, Walloon school, international coll: abstract and figurative art from early 60's to late 80's 03604

Musée d'Histoire Naturelle de Mons, 7 Rue des Gailliers, 7000 Mons - T: 065401140, Fax: 065348675, E-mail: monsmuseum.dnf.dgrne@mrw.wallonie.be
Natural History Museum - 1839
Natural hist, skeleton of giant Constantin 03605

Musée du Folklore et de la Vie Montoise, Maison Jean Lescarts, 9 Rue Neuve, 7000 Mons - T: 065349555, 065314357, Fax: 065347763, E-mail: musees.mons@swing.be. Head: Michel de Reymaeker
Folklore Museum
Paintings, ancient arms, statues, furniture, weights and measures, folklore especially handicrafts and carnivals, archeology 03606

Musée du Vieux Nimy, 31 Rue Mouzin, 7000 Mons - T: 065335771. Head: Pierre Coppieters
Local Museum - 1973
Pipes, ancient tools used in the local crafts, local folklore, hist of the battle of Mons in 1914, ceramics 03607

Trésor de la Collegiale Sainte-Waudru, Pl du Châpitre, 7000 Mons - T: 065335580, 065353488, Fax: 065356336, E-mail: otz@mons.be
Religious Arts Museum - 1958
Goldsmith art, religious vestments, documents 03608

Le Vieux Logis, Musée du Chanoine Edmond Puissant, 22 Rue de Notre-Dame Rébounaire, 7000 Mons - T: 065336670. Head: Christiane Pierard
Historical Museum / Decorative Arts Museum - 1934
Furniture, crafts objects, wrought iron work, weapons, modern ceramics by Sars-La-Bruyère, drawings, religious objects, goldsmith art, wood sculptures, vestments, old textiles, manuscripts, books (15th-18th c), Gutenberg bible - library 03609

Montignies-sur-Roc

Château de Montignies-sur-Roc, 7387 Montignies-sur-Roc - T: 065586523, 065756194
Decorative Arts Museum 03610

Moorslede

Oorlogsmuseum, Beselarestr 18, 8890 Moorslede - T: 056500545
Military Museum 03611

Morlanwelz-Mariemont

Musée Royal de Mariemont, 100 Chaussée de Mariemont, 7140 Morlanwelz-Mariemont - T: 064212193, Fax: 064262924. Head: Patrice Dartevelle
Archaeological Museum / Museum of Classical Antiquities - 1920
Antiquities from Egypt, the Middle East, Greece, Rome, China, Japan, local Gallo-Roman and Merovingian archeology, porcelain of Tournai, bookbindings - library 03612

Mouscron

Musée Communal de Folklore Léon Maes, 3 Rue des Brasseurs, 7700 Mouscron - T: 056860466, 056860467, Fax: 056860469, E-mail: mouscron.musee@innet.be. Head: Veronique Van de Voorde
Folklore Museum - 1954
Folklore, arts and crafts - archives 03613

Mozet

Musée de la Préhistorique, Cavernes Préhistoriques de Goyet, 5340 Mozet - T: 081588545, 081589651
Archaeological Museum 03614

Munkzwalm

Zwalmmuseum, Rekegemstr 28, 9630 Munkzwalm - T: 055498933
Local Museum 03615

Muno

Musée de la Pierre, 35 Rue d' Enfer, 6820 Muno - T: 061320019, E-mail: si.muno@swing.be, Internet: http://www.chez.com/muno
Natural History Museum 03616

Namur

Musée Africain, Ancienne Caserne Léopold, 1 Rue du 1er Lancier, 5000 Namur - T: 081231383, 081226401
Local Museum / Ethnology Museum
Central Africa 03617

Musée Archéologique, Halle des Bouchers, Rue du Pont 21, 5000 Namur - T: 081231631. Head: J. Plumier
Archaeological Museum
Prehistoric and Roman archeology, hist, decorative arts 03618

Musée d'Armes et d'Histoire Militaire du Comte de Namur, Citadelle de Namur, Rte Merveilleuse, 5000 Namur - T: 081224826
Military Museum 03619

Musée de Groesbeeck de Croix, 3 Rue Joseph Saintraint, 5000 Namur - T: 081237510, Fax: 081237517. Head: M. Arickx-George
Decorative Arts Museum - 1935
Furniture, paintings, history, ceramics, glass, art objects from Namur and his county, 17th to 19th c silver - library 03620

Musée des Archives de l'Etat à Namur, 45 Rue d'Arquet, 5000 Namur - T: 081223498, Fax: 081223498. Head: Daniel Van Overstraeten
Historical Museum - 1931
Historical documents (8th-20th c) 03621

Musée des Arts Anciens du Namurois, Hôtel de Gaiffier d'Hestroy, 24 Rue de Fer, 5000 Namur - T: 081220065, 081224362, Fax: 081227251, E-mail: musee.arts.anciens@province.namur.be. Head: Jacques Toussaint
Fine Arts Museum - 1964
Regional art objects from the Middle Ages to Renaissance 03622

Musée Diocésain et Trésor de la Cathédrale Saint-Aubain, 1 Pl du Châpitre, 5000 Namur - T: 081221701, Fax: 081444285. Head: Jacques Jeanmart
Religious Arts Museum - 1896
Medieval goldsmith art, portable altar with ivory decoration, crown reliquary of Saint Doornen, sculpture (11th-18th c), vestments, glass 03623

Musée du Donjon, 4 Rte Merveilleuse, 5000 Namur - T: 081222859
Military Museum 03624

Musée Félicien Rops, 12 Rue Fumal, 5000 Namur - T: 081220110, Fax: 081225447, E-mail: rops@ciger.be, Internet: http://www.ciger.be/rops. Head: Bernadette Bonnier
Fine Arts Museum - 1964
Paintings and engravings by Félicien Rops, temporary exhibitions of engravings and art of the 19th c 03625

Musée Provincial de la Forêt, 7 Rte Merveilleuse, 5000 Namur - T: 081743894
Natural History Museum - 1901
Fauna and flora of Walloon forests, exotic insects, arboretum, wood technology 03626

Trésor du Frère Hugo d'Oignies, c/o Institut des Soeurs de Notre-Dame, 17 Rue Julie Billiart, 5000 Namur - T: 081230342, 081230449, Fax: 081231144. Head: Suzanne Vandecan
Religious Arts Museum
Medieval goldsmith art (13th c) 03627

Nandrin

Musée de la Vie Rurale Condruze, Rue F. Godinasse, 4550 Nandrin - T: 041511157
Local Museum 03628

Neu-Moresnet

Gohltalmuseum, Maxstr 11, 4721 Neu-Moresnet - T: 087657504
Local Museum 03629

Nevele

Rietgaverstede, Streekmuseum van het Land van Nevele, C. Van der Cruyssenstr 60, 9850 Nevele - T: 093715166, 093718339, Fax: 093714695. Head: Jan Janssens
Local Museum / Historical Museum / Folklore Museum - 1963
Archeology, local hist, crafts and guilds, transport and industry, military hist, local literature, agriculture, natural hist, folklore, historical films 03630

Nieuwpoort

Museum voor Plaatselijke Geschiedenis (closed) 03631

Nismes

Maison des Bailles, 1 Rue d'Avignon, 5670 Nismes - T: 060311625
Local Museum - 1972
Local hist, folklore, local archeology, genealogy, works of painter Fernand Charlier 03632

Musée de Folklore, Château Communal, 5670 Nismes
Folklore Museum 03633

Musée du Cinema, Ferme de la Maladrerie, 64 Rue Saint-Roch, 5670 Nismes - T: 060311934, 060346038
Special Museum 03634

Nivelles

Musée d'Archéologie, 27 Rue de Bruxelles, 1400 Nivelles - T: 067882280, Fax: 067840533. Head: Jean-Luc Delattre
Archaeological Museum - 1956
Art hist, archeology, ceramics 03635

Oelegem

Provinciaal Textiel- en Kostuummuseum Vrieselhof, Schildesteenweg 79, 2520 Oelegem - T: 033834680, Fax: 033852164. Head: Frieda Sorber
Special Museum - 1977
Lace, costumes, textile craft techniques, recent Flemish textile art - library 03636

Olsene

Gemeentelijk Museum, Kerkstr 36, 9870 Olsene - T: 09889076
Decorative Arts Museum - 1978
Ancient furniture, porcelain, tapestries, paintings, tin 03637

Onoz

Musée d'Iconographie Historique, Château de Mielmont, 5190 Onoz - T: 081633344
Fine Arts Museum 03638

Oostduinkerke

Folkloremuseum Florishof, Koksijdesteenweg 72, 8670 Oostduinkerke - T: 058511257, Fax: 0585111257. Head: Jan Florizoone
Folklore Museum - 1972
Holy-water vases, Romanesque vases, ancient documents, tools, crafts, old inn, chapel (1660), shed with ancient agricultural implements 03639

Nationaal Visserijmuseum van Oostduinkerke, Pastoor Schmitzstr 6, 8670 Oostduinkerke - T: 058512468, Fax: 058510817, Internet: http://www.visserijmuseum.be. Head: Willem Lanszweert
Special Museum - 1975
Tombstones with the names of 358 fishermen, documents on fishery, ship models since the 2nd c, porcelain with ornaments relating to fishing, house of a fisherman with interiors, aquariums, video-projection, harbour model - library 03640

Oostende

Museum Ensorhuis, Vlaanderenstr 27, 8400 Oostende - T: 059805335, Fax: 059802891, Internet: http://www.Artsite.be/musea/MSKOostende.htm. Head: Norbert Hostyn
Fine Arts Museum - 1949
Reconstitution of the last home of James Ensor (1860-1949) 03641

Museum voor Moderne Kunst, Romestr 11, 8400 Oostende - T: 059508118, Fax: 059805626, E-mail: willy.van_den_bussche@west-vlaanderen.be, Internet: http://www.pmmb.be. Head: W. Van den Bussche
Fine Arts Museum - 1986
Belgian 20th c art, from the beginning of this c up to the present day - workshop, educational dept, temporary exhibitions 03642

Museum voor Moderne Religieuze Kunst, Sint-Sebastiaanstr 41, 8400 Oostende - T: 059708687. Head: J. Ghekiere
Religious Arts Museum - 1974
Religious art of James Ensor, Constant Permeke, Léon Spillaert, Jan De Clerck, Jacob Smits, Gustave Van de Woestijne, Paul Vermere and others 03643

Museum voor Schone Kunsten, Wapenpl, 8400 Oostende - T: 059805335, Fax: 059802891, Internet: http://www.Artsite.be/musea/MSKOostende.htm. Head: Norbert Hostyn
Fine Arts Museum - 1893
Belgian Art from romantic period till post-Impressionism, contemporary foreign artists, James Ensor, Leon Spilliaert 03644

Oostends Historisch Museum De Plate, Voormalig Koninklijk Paleis, Langestr 69, 8400 Oostende - T: 059805335, 059507145, Fax: 059802891. Head: Norbert Hostyn
Local Museum - 1907
Folklore, local hist 03645

Zeilopleidingsschip Mercator, Mercator-Yachthaven, Leopold II Laan, 8400 Oostende - T: 059705654, Fax: 0597200139
Science&Tech Museum 03646

Opglabbeek

Legermuseum, Schrijversweg 9b, 3660 Opglabbeek - T: 089854130, 089854723
Military Museum 03647

Opheylissem

Musée de Folklore et d'Histoire Armand Pellegrin, Ancienne Ecole Communale des Garçons, 15 Rue de Moulin, 1357 Opheylissem - T: 019655100. Head: Maurice de Wolf
Folklore Museum / Historical Museum - 1930
Local hist, crafts, pottery, pipes, ancient machinery, religious documents 03648

Musée de la Boite à Biscuits, 2 Rue Dewolf, 1357 Opheylissem - T: 019655491
Special Museum 03649

Orp-le-Grand

Musée Archéologique Régional d'Orp-le-Grand, 2 Pl Communale, 1350 Orp-le-Grand - T: 019633403, 019633779. Head: Eugène Mottart
Archaeological Museum
Prehistory, Iron Age pottery, Gallo-Roman and Merovingian finds 03650

Oudenaarde

Archeologisch Museum → Provinciaal Archeologisch Museum-Ename

Huis de Lalaing, Bourgondiestr 9, 9700 Oudenaarde - T: 055314863
Local Museum 03651

Provinciaal Archeologisch Museum-Ename, Lynwaadmarkt 20, 9700 Oudenaarde - T: 055309040, Fax: 055309901, E-mail: museum@ename974.org, Internet: http://www.ename974.org. Head: Marie-Claire Van der Douckt
Archaeological Museum 03652

Stedelijk Museum, Stadhuis, Markt, 9700 Oudenaarde - T: 055317251, Fax: 055309248, E-mail: toerisme@oudenaarde.be, Internet: http://www.oudenaarde.be. Head: Geertrin Van Kerkhoven
Decorative Arts Museum
Flemish and Dutch paintings (15th-19th c), sculptures, tapestries, silver 03653

Streekmuseum, Liedtskasteel, Parkstr, 9700 Oudenaarde - T: 055313121
Local Museum 03654

Oudenburg

Stedelijk Museum, Marktstr 25, 8460 Oudenburg - T: 059266027, Fax: 059265406, Internet: http://www.oudenburg.be. Head: Jean Luc Meulemeester
Archaeological Museum - 1972
Remains of a fortress from the Roman period 03655

Oupeye

Musée Archéologique Regional, 127 Rue du Roi Albert, 4680 Oupeye - T: 041655800, 041642714
Archaeological Museum 03656

Overijse

Het Wijnmuseum, Justus Lipsiusplein, 3090 Overijse - T: 026877722
Special Museum 03657

Overmere

Boerenkrijgmuseum (closed for rebuilding until 2003), Baron Tibbautstr 2, 9290 Overmere - T: 052432340
Military Museum - 1960
Memorials of the Peasants' War, which started at Overmere in 1798, local folklore 03658

Peer

Muziekinstrumenten-Museum, Oud Stadhuis, Markt, 3990 Peer - T: 011611602, Fax: 011611605, E-mail: peer@toerismevlaanderen.be
Music Museum 03659

Pessoux

Château de Jannée, 5590 Pessoux - T: 083688207, 083688368
Decorative Arts Museum 03660

Poperinge

Nationaal Hopmuseum De Stadsschaal, Gasthuisstr 71, 8970 Poperinge - T: 057346676/7, Fax: 057335703, E-mail: poperinge@toerismerlaanderen.be, Internet: http://www.poperinge.be. Head: Luk Dequidt
Agriculture Museum / Folklore Museum - 1978
Hist of hop cultivation 03661

Talbot House, Gasthuisstr 43, 8970 Poperinge - T: 057333228, Fax: 057332183, E-mail: talbot.house@skynet.be. Head: N. Cornick
Historical Museum - 1930
Drawings by Eric Kennington, original WW I mementoes and relics 03662

Porcheresse

Musée du Sabot, Rue de Graide, 6929 Porcheresse - T: 061511201, Fax: 061511201. Head: Fernand Bernard
Local Museum 03663

Quevaucamps

Musée de la Bonneterie et du Negoce de la Toile, 46 Rue Paul Pastur, 7972 Quevaucamps - T: 069575571
Special Museum 03664

Raeren

Pottenbakkerijmuseum Raeren, Burgstr 103, 4730 Raeren - T: 087850903, Fax: 087850932. Head: R. Mennicken
Decorative Arts Museum - 1963
Hist of local pottery (12th-19th c), Rhenish stoneware - library, archive 03665

Rance

Musée de la Chasse, 21 Grand-Rue, 6470 Rance - T: 060411085
Special Museum 03666

Ranst

Procinciaal Textiel- en Kostuummuseum Vrieselhof, Schildesteenweg 79, 2520 Ranst - T: 033834680, Fax: 033852164. Head: Frieda de Booser, Lutgard Van Houtven, Frieda Sorber
Decorative Arts Museum 03667

Rebecq-Rognon

Musée d'Arenberg, 6 Rue Docteur Colson, 1430 Rebecq-Rognon - T: 067638232
Local Museum 03668

Rekem

Gemeentelijk Museum, Groenplaats, 3620 Rekem - T: 089718621. Head: Mathieu Maeten
Local Museum - 1956
Church furniture (17th-18th century) 03669

Reuland

Musée Paul Gerardy, Kulturhaus, 4790 Reuland - T: 080329712
Fine Arts Museum 03670

Rêves

Musée Rodava, 15 Rue de Bruxelles, 6210 Rêves - T: 067843129
Local Museum 03671

Rijkevorsel

Gemeentelijk Heemkundig Museum, Molenstr 5, 2310 Rijkevorsel - T: 0313146395
Local Museum 03672

Rijmenam

Museum August Gille, Plaastr 7, 2820 Rijmenam - T: 015511141
Local Museum 03673

Smiske Museum, Hoogstr 52a, 2820 Rijmenam - T: 015513688, Fax: 015520994, E-mail: -verstraeten.herman@belgacom.net. Head: Walter Van Looy
Local Museum / Folklore Museum 03674

Rixensart

Château de Rixensart, 40 Rue de l'Eglise, 1330 Rixensart - T: 026536505, Fax: 026541756
Decorative Arts Museum 03675

Robertville

Château de Reinhardstein, Burg Metternich, 4950 Robertville - T: 080446868
Decorative Arts Museum 03676

Rochefort

Musée du Pays de Rochefort et de la Famenne, 5 Av d'Alost, 5580 Rochefort - T: 084214409. Head: Pierre Herbay
Local Museum - 1965
Cultural hist of the region 03677

Rochehaut

Musée Vivant de la Moisson, 6830 Rochehaut - T: 061496970
Local Museum 03678

Roeselare

Nationaal Wielermuseum, Polenplein 15, 8800 Roeselare - T: 051268740, Fax: 051268741
Science&Tech Museum - 1998
Bicycles 03679

Pauselijk Zouavenmuseum, Zuidstr 27, 8800 Roeselare - T: 051221524, Fax: 051243766, E-mail: college@kleinseminarie.be. Head: Johan Strobbe
Military Museum / Historical Museum
Letters, decorations, announcements of death and mourning cards, portraits, military equipment and uniforms, flags, maps and documentation which illustrate the struggle of the Papal Zouaves 03680

Stedelijk Museum Alfons Blomme, Ooststr 84, 8800 Roeselare - T: 051221414
Local Museum 03681

Stedelijke Academie voor Schone Kunsten, Leenstr 14, 8800 Roeselare - T: 051203029, Fax: 051203029, E-mail: sask.roeselare@pandora.be
Public Gallery 03682

Villa 't Eksternest, Bergstr 27, Zilverberg, 8800 Roeselare - T: 051243388, Fax: 051203393, E-mail: eksternest@callebert.be, Internet: http://www.eksternest.be. Head: Fernand Callebert
Association with Coll 03683

Roisin

Centre Provincial d'Hébergement Le Caillou, Maison Emile Verhaeren, 23 Rue E. Verhaeren, 7386 Roisin - T: 065759352/59. Head: G. Cornez
Special Museum
Study of poet E. Verhaeren (1855-1916) and affiliated documents 03684

Roly

Musée des Fagnes, Château de Roly, 6371 Roly
Archaeological Museum / Historical Museum / Natural History Museum
Archeology, geology, paleontology, history, local flora and fauna, folklore 03685

Romedenne

Musée Européen de la Brasserie, 2a Fontaine Saint-Pierre, 5600 Romedenne - T: 082677275
Special Museum 03686

Ronse

Kryptemuseum onder de Sint-Hermeskerk, Kaatsspelplein, 9600 Ronse - T: 055211735, 055232812, Fax: 055232819. Head: E. Devos
Religious Arts Museum 03687

Stedelijk Museum voor Folklore en Regionale Geschiedenis, Bruulpark, 9600 Ronse - T: 055211730, 055232812, Fax: 055232819. Head: E. Devos
Folklore Museum / Local Museum - 1937
Local hist, folklore, interiors of middle-class houses, trades and guilds, archeology of the Roman period and early Middle Ages, stone objects 03688

Ruisbroek, Antwerpen

Museum De Bres, Oud Gemeentehuis, Dorp, 2870 Ruisbroek, Antwerpen - T: 038866069
Historical Museum - 1976
Memorabilia of the flood on January 3rd 1976 - library 03689

Rumes

Musée Gallo-Romain, Ecole Communale, Rue H. Delaissé, 7610 Rumes - T: 069649144
Archaeological Museum - 1965
Prehistoric tools, Gallo-Roman ceramics, Merovingian vases, Roman safe 03690

Rumst

Steenbakkerijmuseum van de Rupelstreek, Steenberghoekstr 20, 2840 Rumst - T: 038444974. Head: Ania Schaaf
Special Museum 03691

Rupelmonde

Mercator Graventoren-Watermolen, Mercatoreiland, Kasteelstr, 9150 Rupelmonde - T: 037441013, Fax: 037441013, Internet: http://www.kruibeke.be
Local Museum - 1994
Water mill 03692

Saint-Ghislain

Musée de la Foire, 11a Onzième Rue, 7330 Saint-Ghislain - T: 065791334
Special Museum 03693

Saint-Hubert

Musée de la Vie Rurale en Wallonie, Fourneau Saint-Michel, 6870 Saint-Hubert - T: 084210890, 084210613, Fax: 084221936, E-mail: fsm@skynet.be. Head: Damien Watteyne
Open Air Museum - 1971
Peasant houses with furniture and domestic utensils from different parts of the region, ancient crafts - library 03694

Musée de l'Histoire de la Forêt d'Ardenne, Fourneau Saint-Michel, 6870 Saint-Hubert - T: 084210613, 084210890, Fax: 084221936, E-mail: fsm@skynet.be. Head: Damien Watteyne
Natural History Museum 03695

Musée des Archives, c/o Archives de l'Etat Saint-Hubert, 12 Pl de l'Abbaye, 6870 Saint-Hubert - T: 061611455
Historical Museum - 1978
Regional archives 03696

Musée du Fer et de la Métallurgie Ancienne, Fourneau Saint-Michel, 6870 Saint-Hubert - T: 084210613, 084210890, Fax: 084221936, E-mail: fsm@skynet.be. Head: Damien Watteyne
Science&Tech Museum / Historic Site - 1959
Ancient metallurgy (12th-18th c) - library 03697

Musée P.-J. Redouté et de l'Illustration Botanique, Fourneau Saint-Michel, 6870 Saint-Hubert - T: 084210613, Fax: 084221936, E-mail: fsm@skynet.be. Head: Damien Watteyne
Special Museum - 1989
Books and illustrations of P.-J. and H.-J. Redouté - library 03698

Saint-Vith

Zwischen Venn und Schneeifel, Schwarzer Weg 6, 4780 Saint-Vith - T: 080229209
Local Museum - 1967
Ancient habitation and country life, sacred art, ancient crafts, historical documents on the region of Saint-Vith 03699

Sainte-Marie-sur-Semois

Musée du Potier Gallo-Romain, Huombois, 6740 Sainte-Marie-sur-Semois - T: 063570315
Archaeological Museum 03700

Schelle

Heemmuseum Bijsterveld, Peperstr 48, 2627 Schelle - T: 038874796
Local Museum
Religious art, interiors (1900-1910), agricultural implements, machinery (1900-1910) 03701

Schepdaal

Buurtspoorweg-Museum, Ninoofsesteenweg 184, 1703 Schepdaal - T: 025691614
Science&Tech Museum 03702

Trammuseum, Ninoofsesteenweg 955, 1703 Schepdaal - T: 025691614, E-mail: mario.lopez@ping.be. Head: Günter Pfeiffer
Science&Tech Museum - 1962
Steamlocomotives, Dieselrailcar and electric railway trams of the former National Light Railway Company of Belgium 03703

Scherpenheuvel

Stedelijk Museum Huize Ernest Claes, Ernest Claesstr 152, Zichem, 3271 Scherpenheuvel - T: 013772081, Fax: 013782554. Head: Harry Beerts
Special Museum - 1967
Works of the writer Ernest Claes, manuscripts, photos and personel effects, furniture, domestic utensils 03704

Schoten

Mineralogisch Museum, Churchilllaan 57, 2900 Schoten, mail addr: c/o Academy for Mineralogy, Wapenhaghestr 16, 2600 Berchem - T: 036586283, 032392876, Fax: 036517926, E-mail: info@acam.be, Internet: http://www.acam.be. Head: A. Harre Hérin
Natural History Museum - 1971
Fluorescent minerals, stones, fossils - library 03705

Seneffe

Musée de l'Orfevrerie de la Communaute Française, Château de Seneffe, 6 Rue Plasman, 7180 Seneffe - T: 064556913
Ethnology Museum 03706

Seraing

Château d'Aigremont, 82 Rue de la Forière, 4100 Seraing, mail addr: 12 Rue du Château, 4400 Awirs - T: 043361687, Fax: 043370801, E-mail: - anne.renard.ortmans@skynet.be
Decorative Arts Museum - 1972
Painting (18th c), tapestries (17th c), furniture (18th c) 03707

Musée du Verre chez Val-Saint-Lambert Château (during restoration), Esplanade de l'Europe, 4100 Seraing - T: 043303620, Fax: 043303640
Science&Tech Museum / Decorative Arts Museum
Glass production from the beginnings to 20th c - library 03708

Seraing-le-Château

Musée Valery Stuyver, Château, 4537 Seraing-le-Château
Local Museum 03709

Sinaai-Waas

Tinelmuseum, Tinelstr 31, 9112 Sinaai-Waas - T: 031723279
Local Museum 03710

Sint-Amands

Emile Verhaeren Museum, Emile Verhaerenstr 71, 2890 Sint-Amands - T: 052330805, Fax: 052336861, E-mail: verhaeren@sink-amands.org, Internet: http://www.provant.be/cultur. Head: Dr. Sophie Van Outryve
Special Museum - 1955
Works, portraits and documents of the poet E. Verhaeren 03711

Molenmuseum, Verhaerenstr 7, 2890 Sint-Amands - T: 052332338
Science&Tech Museum 03712

Sint-Amandsberg

Museum van het Groot Begijnhof, Groot Begijnhof 63, 9040 Sint-Amandsberg - T: 0912281913
Folklore Museum 03713

Sint-Gillis

E. Hielmuseum, Weggevoerdenstr 1, 9330 Sint-Gillis - T: 02213018. Head: Dr. A. Stroobants
Local Museum 03714

Sint-Idesbald

Museum Paul Delvaux, Paul Delvauxlaan 42, 8670 Sint-Idesbald - T: 058521229, 058510908, Fax: 058521273, Internet: http://www.pauldelvaux.be. Head: Charles Van Deun
Fine Arts Museum - 1982
Paintings, drawings, etchings and lithographs by Delvaux, personal objects 03715

Sint-Martens-Latem

Museum Minne-Gevaert, Kappiteldreef 45, 9830 Sint-Martens-Latem - T: 091823129
Local Museum 03716

Sint-Niklaas

Internationaal Exlibriscentrum, Regentiestr 61-63, 9100 Sint-Niklaas - T: 037772942, Fax: 037665057, E-mail: stedelijke.musea@sint-niklaas.be, Internet: http://www.sint-niklaas.be. Head: Tony Oost
Public Gallery 03717

Kerkmuseum, Sint-Niklaaskerk, 9100 Sint-Niklaas - T: 037763718
Religious Arts Museum 03718

Mercator Museum, Zamanstr 49, 9100 Sint-Niklaas, mail addr: Regentiestr 61, 9100 Sint-Niklaas - T: 037772942, Fax: 037665057, E-mail: stedelijke.musea@sint-niklaas.be, Internet: http://www.sint-niklaas.be. Head: T. Oost
Special Museum - 1861
Maps, atlases and globes of Gerard Mercator (1512-1594) 03719

Salons voor Schone Kunsten, Stationsstr 85, 9100 Sint-Niklaas, mail addr: Regentiestr 61, 9100 Sint-Niklaas - T: 037772942, Fax: 037665057, E-mail: stedelijke.musea@sint-niklaas.be, Internet: http://www.sint-niklaas.be. Head: T. Oost
Fine Arts Museum - 1988
Paintings, sculptures, furniture, applied arts (16th-20th c), Henri Evenepoel 03720

Stedelijke Musea, Zwijgershoek, Regentiestr 61-63, 9100 Sint-Niklaas, mail addr: Regentiestr 61, 9100 Sint-Niklaas - T: 037772942, Fax: 037665057, E-mail: stedelijke.musea@sint-niklaas.be, Internet: http://www.sint-niklaas.be. Head: T. Oost
Music Museum / Special Museum - 1979
Barbierama (hist of barber's and hairdresser's profession), gramophones, jukeboxes, musicboxes, Thomas Alva Edison, bookplates, knitting machines, mediaeval archaeology 03721

Het Wase Pijprokerssalon, Regentiestr 29, 9100 Sint-Niklaas - T: 037666060
Special Museum 03722

Sint-Pieters-Rode

Kasteel van Horst, Horststr 28, 3220 Sint-Pieters-Rode - T: 016623345, 016621112, Fax: 016621112, E-mail: sve.horst@pi.be, Internet: http://www.monument.vlaanderen.be
Historic Site 03723

Sint-Stevens-Woluwe

Gemeentelijk Streekmuseum De Veste, Kleine Kerkstr 13, 1932 Sint-Stevens-Woluwe - T: 027201856, Fax: 027257277
Agriculture Museum / Historical Museum / Folklore Museum 03724

Sint-Truiden

Astronomisch Compensatieuurwerk Kamiel Festraets, Begijnhof, 3800 Sint-Truiden - T: 011701818, Fax: 011701820. Head: Hilde Hendricx
Natural History Museum / Science&Tech Museum - 1974
Restraets clock, the Foucault pendulum, rotation of the earth round the sun 03725

Brustempoort Museum, Luikerstr, 3800 Sint-Truiden - T: 011701818, Fax: 011701820. Head: H. Hendricx
Military Museum - 1969
Medieval gate, ammunition chambers, weapons, plans and maps 03726

Hoevemuseum, Sint-Trudo Abdij, Abdijstr 1, 3800 Sint-Truiden - T: 011671993
Special Museum 03727

Museum van Hedendaagse Kantwerken, Naamsestr 5, 3800 Sint-Truiden - T: 011672356
Fine Arts Museum 03728

Museum Vlaamse Minderbroeders V.Z.W., Capucienessenstr 1-3, 3800 Sint-Truiden - T: 011672971, Fax: 011684705, E-mail: - musea.vlaamse.minderbroeders@skynet.be. Head: E.P.H. Hansen
Religious Arts Museum - 1988
Paintings (16th-19th c), silver (17th-20th c), relics, textiles 03729

Provinciaal Museum Begijnhofkerk Sint-Truiden, Begijnhof, 3800 Sint-Truiden - T: 011688579, Fax: 011237585, E-mail: pcce@limburg.be. Head: Marc Laenen
Religious Arts Museum 03730

Provinciaal Museum voor het Industrieel Erfgoed, Begijnhof 59, 3800 Sint-Truiden - T: 011688579. Head: Bert Van Doorslaer
Science&Tech Museum 03731

Sint-Franciscusmuseum, Minderbroederstr 5, 3800 Sint-Truiden
Fine Arts Museum
Medieval sculpture and painting (Rubens, Rembrandt) 03732

Sivry

Musée de la Nature, 1 Rue des Ecoles, 6470 Sivry - T: 060455684
Natural History Museum 03733

Soignies

Centre d'Art et de Culture, 23 Rue de la Régence, 7060 Soignies - T: 067347376, Fax: 067334693. Head: Jean Gautier
Fine Arts Museum 03734

Musée du Vieux-Cimetière, 17 Rue Henry Leroy, 7060 Soignies - T: (067) 340666, Fax: 340666, E-mail: maritony@compaqnet.be. Head: Jean-Pol Van den Abeele
Fine Arts Museum / Archaeological Museum / Decorative Arts Museum - 1895
Prehistoric and medieval archeology, paintings (16th-18th c), sculpture (14th-19th c) ceramics, porcelain, 'Christ au Golgatha' (sculpture, 15th c.), 'Adoration des Mages' (painting, 1520) 03735

Solre-sur-Sambre

Château de Solre-sur-Sambre, 6560 Solre-sur-Sambre - T: 071556746
Decorative Arts Museum 03736

Sombreffe

Château de Sombreffe, Rue du Château, 5140 Sombreffe - T: 071889860
Local Museum 03737

Soumagne

Musée de la Vie Populaire, 4 Rue des Déportés, 4630 Soumagne - T: 041771288, 041772182
Folklore Museum 03738

Spa

Musée de la Forêt, Domaine de Bérinsenne, 4900 Spa - T: 087776300, Fax: 087775035, E-mail: - berinzen.rens.reserv@swing.be, Internet: http://www.berinsenne.be. Head: Pierre Noe
Natural History Museum 03739

Musée de la Ville d'Eaux, 77b Av Reine Astrid, 4900 Spa - T: 087774486, Fax: 087774486. Head: M.T. Ramaekers
Fine Arts Museum
Drawings, engravings, wood painting 03740

Musée Spadois du Cheval, 77 Av Reine Astrid, 4900 Spa - T: 087774486, Fax: 087774486. Head: M.T. Ramaekers
Special Museum
Documents on horse racing 03741

Spontin

Château de Spontin, 5530 Spontin - T: 083699055, 083639306
Decorative Arts Museum 03742

Sprimont

Musée Communal de la Pierre de Sprimont, Rue J. Potier 54, 4140 Sprimont - T: 0413822195, Fax: 0413823268. Head: V. Brancaleoni
Science&Tech Museum
Industrial and artistic treatment of stone, extracting methods and tools, fossils, shells, minerals 03743

Musée de la Ferme, 23 Rue Abbé Demasteau, 4140 Sprimont - T: 041821561
Agriculture Museum 03744

Stavelot

Musée de l'Ancienne Abbaye, 4970 Stavelot - T: 080862706, Fax: 080862706. Head: Theodore Galle
Local Museum - 1926
History of the tanning industry, local history documents, painting (17th-18th c), sculpture, goldsmith art, contemporary paintings (Spilliaert, Mambour, Claus, Malfait, Tytgat), works of Degouve de Nuncques, regional religious art 03745

Musée du Circuit de Spa-Francorchamps, Abbaye de Stavelot, 4970 Stavelot - T: 080864261, Fax: 080880877, E-mail: p.erler@abbayedestavelot.be, Internet: http://www.abbayedestavelot.be. Head: Francis Mourant
Historical Museum 03746

Musée Guillaume Apollinaire, Abbaye, 4970 Stavelot - T: 080862766, E-mail: janhysmans@yucom.be
Special Museum - 1954
Works (various editions), manuscripts and biography of G. Apollinaire (1880-1918), letters from his friends, reconstruction of his room, paintings by Marie Laurencin, bronze figure by O. Zadkine - archives 03747

Trésor de l'Eglise Primaire de Saint-Sebastien, 7 Rue de l'Eglise, 4970 Stavelot - T: 080862284
Religious Arts Museum
Religious goldsmith art, sacerdotal vestment 03748

Strépy-Bracquegnies

Musée du Canal du Centre, 2 Rue Noulet, 7110 Strépy-Bracquegnies - T: 064662561
Special Museum 03749

Temploux

Musée de la Vie Rurale, 7 Rue Lieut. Colonel Manniette, 5020 Temploux
Agriculture Museum 03750

Temse

Gemeentemuseum, Kasteelstr 16, 9140 Temse - T: 037101330, 037714818, Fax: 037110101, E-mail: burgemeester@temse.be
Local Museum
Archeology, painting and sculpture by local artists, local hist - library 03751

Museum Heraldiek Benelux, Kasteelstr 74, 9140 Temse - T: 037109751, Fax: 037719434, E-mail: heraldiek@temse.be
Historical Museum
Collection of coats of arms (heraldry), flags and marks of honour - library 03752

Terhagen

Museum Rupelklei, Korte Veerstr 43, 2840 Terhagen - T: 0318880057
Local Museum 03753

Museum van de Baksteennijverheid, Steenbakkerijk Heylen, Nieuwstr, 2840 Terhagen
Science&Tech Museum - 1978
Briquet manufacturing 03754

Tervuren

Africa-Museum, Leuvense Steenweg 13, 3080 Tervuren - T: 027695211, Fax: 027670242, E-mail: info@africamuseum.be, Internet: http://www.africamuseum.be. Head: Ph. Marechal
Ethnology Museum / Natural History Museum / Historical Museum - 1898
Ethnography, mainly African art and technology, musical instruments, prehistory and archeology of tropical Africa, zoology, African vertebrates and invertebrates, wood of tropical regions, European involvement in Africa, geology and minerals of Africa, Statue of King Kata Mbula Kuba, Congo, statue of Ndengeze, Congo, Luba helmet-mask, Congo, wood sculpture of 8th-9th c, Angola - library, archives 03755

Heemkundig Museum, Nieuwstr 15, 3080 Tervuren - T: 02766863, E-mail: vic-mdte@hotmail.com, Internet: http://home-5.worldonline.be/~gaijmarc. Head: Vic Motte
Historical Museum / Folklore Museum 03756

Tessenderlo

Bosmuseum, Zandberg, 3980 Tessenderlo - T: 013663448
Natural History Museum 03757

Theux

Musée du Château de Franchimont, 24 Rte de Sassor, 4910 Theux - T: 087541027
Decorative Arts Museum 03758

Thuillies

Musée du Cheval, de la Vie Rurale et du Tabac, 84 Rue de la Victoire, 6536 Thuillies - T: 071533742, 071533834, E-mail: jc.fissiaux@worldonline.be. Head: Claude Hennuy
Agriculture Museum 03759

Thy-le-Château

Château Médiéval et Musée Delporte, Pl de l'Eglise, 5651 Thy-le-Château - T: 071611319, 071613102
Local Museum 03760

Tienen

Stedelijk Museum Het Toreke, Grote Markt 6, 3300 Tienen - T: 016805666, Fax: 016810479, E-mail: museum.toreke@skynet.be. Head: S. Thomas
Archaeological Museum / Fine Arts Museum / Folklore Museum - 1978
Gallo-Roman archeology, medieval and baroque sculpture, silver ornaments, folklore - library 03761

Tilff

Musée de l'Abeille, 4 Rue Blandot, 4130 Tilff - T: 041882263
Local Museum 03762

Tongeren

Basilica Museum, Schatkamer van de Onze-Lieve-Vrouwbasiliek, Grote Markt, 3700 Tongeren - T: 012231417. Head: L. Noelmans
Religious Arts Museum 03763

Gallo-Romeins Museum, Kielenstr 15, 3700 Tongeren - T: 012670330, Fax: 012670333, E-mail: grm@limburg.be, Internet: http://www.limburg.be/gallo. Head: Carmen Willems
Archaeological Museum - 1954
Prehistory, Gallo-Roman archeology, Merovingian archeology - library 03764

Munt- en Penningkabinet van de Provincie Limburg, Kielenstr 15, 3700 Tongeren - T: 012670330, Fax: 012670333, E-mail: grm@limburg.be. Head: R. Van Laere
Special Museum - 1985
Roman coins, coins of the Low Countries, medals 03765

Tongerlo

Da Vinci-Museum, Norbertijnenabdij, Abdijstr 40, 2260 Tongerlo - T: 014541001, Fax: 014539908, E-mail: abdij@tongerlo.org, Internet: http://www.tongerlo.org. Head: M. Meeusen
Religious Arts Museum - 1966
Replica of L. da Vinci's 'The Last Supper' with documentation 03766

Torhout

Kasteel van Wijnendale, Oostendestr, 8820 Torhout - T: 050220770, Fax: 050221504, E-mail: toerisme@torhout.cevi.be, Internet: http://www.torhout.be. Head: Marc Logghe
Decorative Arts Museum / Historic Site 03767

Landbouwmuseum en Kinderboerderij, Ieperse Heirweg 7, 8820 Torhout - T: 050216703
Agriculture Museum 03768

Museum voor Torhouts Aardewerk, Kasteel Ravenhof, 8820 Torhout - T: 050220770, Fax: 050221504, E-mail: torhout@toerismevlaanderen.be, Internet: http://www.torhout.be. Head: Marc Logghe
Decorative Arts Museum / Fine Arts Museum 03769

Stedelyke Musea, Ravenhofstr 1, 8820 Torhout - T: 050220770, Fax: 050220580, E-mail: torhout@toerismevlaanderen.be, Internet: http://www.torhout.be. Head: Marc Logghe
Local Museum
Pottery and local history 03770

Tournai

Het Huis Van Alijn, 8 Rue des Carmes, 7500 Tournai - T: 0692692350, Fax: 0692692358, E-mail: huis.alijn@gent.be, Internet: http://museum.alijn.gent.be. Head: Sylvie Dhaene
Archaeological Museum 03771

Maison Tournaisienne, Reduit des Sions, 7500 Tournai - T: 069224069, Fax: 069216221, E-mail: - bureau.tourisme.tournai@skynet.be
Folklore Museum 03772

Musée d'Archéologie Industrielle, 84 Rue Jean Cousin, 7500 Tournai - T: 069212664
Archaeological Museum 03773

Musée de la Tour Henri VIII, Rue des Remparts, 7500 Tournai
Military Museum
Military history, arms and weapons, documents of resistence during World War II 03774

Musée des Beaux-Arts de Tournai, 8 Enclos Saint-Martin, 7500 Tournai - T: 069222043. Head: Serge Baron Le Bailly de Tilleghem
Fine Arts Museum
Old Flemish Masters (including Rogier van der Weyden, Jaques Danet, Mabuse, Pieter Huys, Jordaans), modern art, painting, sculpture, drawings, prints, French and Belgian paintings (19th-20th c), Belgian and French impressionists 03775

Musée d'Histoire et d'Archéologie, 8 Rue des Carmes, 7500 Tournai - T: 069221672. Head: Dr. Marianne Delcourt-Vlaeminck
Historical Museum / Archaeological Museum - 1953
Geology, Prehistory, Gallo-Roman and Merovingian objects from Tournai 03776

Musée d'Histoire Naturelle de la Ville de Tournai, Hôtel de Ville, 7500 Tournai - T: 069233939, Fax: 069841445. Head: Ph. Brunin
Natural History Museum - 1828
Zoology, botany, fauna of Madagascar 03777

Musée Militaire, Rue du Rempart, 7500 Tournai
Military Museum 03778

Trésor de la Cathedrale Notre-Dame, 1 Pl de l'Evêché, 7500 Tournai - Fax: 069211535
Religious Arts Museum
Ivory, goldsmith art, tapestries, vestements, lace, coat of Emperor Charles, Byzantine cross 03779

Trazegnies

Château de Trazegnies, 6183 Trazegnies - T: 071451046
Decorative Arts Museum 03780

Treignes

Musée de la Vie et des Technologies Rurales et Musée du Machinisme Agricole, 63 Rue Eugène Defraire, 5670 Treignes - T: 060399624, 060399450, Fax: 060399450, E-mail: wquinet@ulb.ac.be. Head: Y.-C. Verhaeghe
Science&Tech Museum / Agriculture Museum 03781

Musée du Malgré-Tout, 28 Rue de la Gare, 5670 Treignes - T: 060390243, Fax: 060390470, E-mail: cedarc@skynet.be, Internet: http://www.users.skynet.be/cedarc. Head: P. Cattelain
Archaeological Museum 03782

Trois-Ponts

Musée de Logbiermé, Logbiermé, 4980 Trois-Ponts - T: 080880163, 080862068
Local Museum 03783

Trooz

Musée Auto-Retro, 216 Grand Rue, 4870 Trooz - T: 041516100, 041517198. Head: R. Pirenne
Science&Tech Museum 03784

Tubize

Musée de la Porte, 64 Rue de Bruxelles, 1480 Tubize - T: 023555539, Fax: 023555539
Local Museum - 1968
Folklore, art objects, ancient pharmaceutical laboratory, paintings by Jules Gonthier, religious traditions crafts, local history, archeology 03785

Turnhout

Kempisch Vogelmuseum, Graatakker 11, 2300 Turnhout - T: 014412252, Fax: 014439651. Head: Peter Sterkens
Natural History Museum - 1962
Stuffed birds 03786

Nationaal Museum van de Speelkaart, Druivenstr 18, 2300 Turnhout - T: 014415621, Fax: 014414324. Head: Guido Landuyt
Special Museum - 1965
Playing cards and archives of Turnhout, engines for the production of cards - library 03787

Oudheidkundig Museum van het Begijnhof, Beguinage 56, 2300 Turnhout - T: 014412343
Historical Museum
History of the Beguines (12th-17th c) 03788

Taxandriamuseum, Begijnenstr 28, 2300 Turnhout - T: 014436335, Fax: 014436335. Head: Harry de Kok
Local Museum - 1903
Regional hist, furniture (17th-18th c), sculpture, archaeology (prehistoric-7th c), folklore, numismatics, decorative arts, paintings - library 03789

Velzeke-Ruddershove

Gallo-Romeins Museum, Paddestr 7a, 9620 Velzeke-Ruddershove
Archaeological Museum 03790

Verviers

Musée d'Archéologie et Folklore, 42 Rue des Raines, 4800 Verviers - T: 087331695. Head: Marie-Paule Deblanc Magnée
Archaeological Museum / Folklore Museum - 1959
Prehistoric, Egyptian, Greek, Roman, Gallo-Roman and Frankish archeology, folklore, history, furniture (17th-19th c), weapons (18th-19th c.), lace, Roman coins 03791

Musée de la Laine, 8 Rue de Séroule, 4800 Verviers - T: 087331695. Head: Marie-Paule Deblanc Magnée
Science&Tech Museum - 1985
Wool work and industry up to 1800 - documentation center 03792

Musée des Beaux-Arts et Céramique, 17 Rue Renier, 4800 Verviers - T: 087331695. Head: Marie-Paule Deblanc Magnée
Fine Arts Museum / Decorative Arts Museum - 1884
Paintings of Liège, Flemish, Dutch, French and Italian masters, 19th-20th c paintings, modern Belgian and French prints, 15th-16th c sculptures, porcelain, Raeren sandstones 03793

Veurne

Bakkerijmuseum, Albert I Laan 2, 8630 Veurne - T: 058313897, 058312154
Special Museum 03794

Baretta-Museum, Grote Markt 29, 8630 Veurne - T: 058312154
Fine Arts Museum 03795

Vielsalm

Musée de l'Histoire et de la Vie Salmiennes, 3 Tienne Messe, 6690 Vielsalm - T: 080216252. Head: Charles Legros
Local Museum 03796

Musée du Coticule, 12 Rue du Coticule, 6690 Vielsalm - T: 080215768, Fax: 080215768
Science&Tech Museum
Razor-stone production, tools, machinery 03797

Vieuxville

Musée Archéologique et Historique du Comte de Logne, Ferme de la Bouverie, 4190 Vieuxville - T: 086212033, Fax: 086214559, E-mail: dtvl@euronet.be
Archaeological Museum / Historical Museum 03798

Villers-devant-Orval

Musée de l'Abbaye d'Orval, Abbaye Notre-Dame d'Orval, 6823 Villers-devant-Orval
Religious Arts Museum - 1935
Ruins of medieval abbey (from 12th c on), sculptures, paintings, manuscripts, medical utensils, garden of medical plants 03799

Vilvoorde

Tyndalemuseum, Lange Molenst 58, 1800 Vilvoorde - T: 022513945
Local Museum 03800

Virton

Musée Gaumais, 38 Rue d'Arlon, 6760 Virton - T: 063570315. Head: C. Chariot
Special Museum
Stoves, cast-iron hearth plates, wrought iron, pot hangers, firedogs, locks, furniture (17th-19th c), reconstruction of 18th and 19th c interiors and workshops, prehistorc, Gallo-Roman, Merovingian archeology, watercolours by Nestor Outer, wood sculpture (16th c), Boch faience (18th c.) 03801

Visé

Musée de la Compagnie Royale des Anciens Arquebusiers de Visé, 11 Rue Haute, 4600 Visé - T: 041797837
Military Museum
History of firearms, documents on local history 03802

Musée Régional d'Histoire et d'Archéologie, 31 Rue du Collège, 4600 Visé - T: 0413748563, Fax: 041795281, E-mail: jplensen@infonie.be, Internet: http://www.visearc.org. Head: Jean-Pierre Lensen
Historical Museum / Archaeological Museum / Folklore Museum - 1921
Prehistorical objects, Roman pottery, Belgian guilds, World War I and II, folklore, architecture 03803

Vlijtingen

Heemkundig Museum Slag van Lafelt, Oud Gemeentehuis, Mheerplaats, 3770 Vlijtingen - T: 012451138
Archaeological Museum / Historical Museum
Prehistory, Iron Age, Roman and Merovingian period, medieval pottery, documents on the Battle of Lafelt 03804

Waasmunster

Museum van de Abdij van Roosenberg, Oudeheerweg-Heide 3, 9250 Waasmunster - T: 037723392
Religious Arts Museum - 1237
Religious hist, documents on the hist of Abbey Roosenberg, maps (17th-18th c), iconography, religious books, paintings, furniture - library 03805

Wachtebeke

Moervarststede, Kalve 70, 9185 Wachtebeke - T: 093450444. Head: Georges Delaender
Local Museum - 1976
Historical arms, coins, folklore, popular religious objects, relics from World War I and II 03806

Provinciaal Molenmuseum, Puyenbrug 5, 9185 Wachtebeke - T: 093424240, Fax: 093424256, E-mail: molenmuseum@oost-vlaanderen.be, Internet: http://www.oost-vlaanderen.be. Head: Walter Van den Branden
Science&Tech Museum - 1976
Water and wind mills, mill construction, documentation on milling 03807

Walcourt

Trésor de la Basilique Saint-Materne, 20 Rue de la Basilique, 5650 Walcourt - T: 071611966, 071611935
Religious Arts Museum 03808

Wanfercée-Baulet

Musée Vivant du Cinema, 47 Rue des Dames, 6224 Wanfercée-Baulet - T: 071811291. Head: Claude Deloge
Special Museum 03809

Waregem

The Museum of Museums, Jan Bouckaertstr 8, 8790 Waregem - T: 056601661, Fax: 056602680. Head: Johan Van Geluwe
Fine Arts Museum - 1970
Architecture, contemporary art, folk art, unusual works of art, artist's museums 03810

Warneton

Musée de la Brasserie, La Poste, Rue Pierre de Simpel, 7784 Warneton - T: 056557966
Special Museum 03811

Musée d'Histoire et d'Archéologie, Hôtel de Ville, Pl de l'Abbaye, 7784 Warneton - T: 056557966, Fax: 056557966
Historical Museum / Archaeological Museum 03812

Waterloo

Musée de Cire, 315 Rte du Lion, 1410 Waterloo - T: 023846740
Local Museum 03813

Musée de Waterloo, 147 Chaussée de Bruxelles, 1410 Waterloo - T: 023547806, Fax: 023542223
Historical Museum
Hist of the town and the battle of Waterloo 03814

Musée Wellington, 147 Chaussée de Bruxelles, 1410 Waterloo - T: 023547806, Fax: 023542223/831, Internet: http://www.museewellington.euronet.be. Head: Françoise Dupriez
Military Museum - 1954
Quarters of General Wellington at the time of the victory against Napoleon in June 1815, personal objects of Wellington and Colonel Gordon, arms, engravings 03815

Wavre

Musée Cantonnal, 2 Rue de l'Escaille, 1300 Wavre
Archaeological Museum - 1964
Archeology (prehistory to Gallo-Roman period) 03816

Musée Historique et Archéologique de Wavre et de la Region, 23 Rue de l'Ermitage, 1300 Wavre - T: 010223548
Historical Museum / Archaeological Museum 03817

Weert

Streekmuseum van Klein-Brabant De Zilverreiger, Scheldestr 18, 2880 Weert - T: 0318890603, Fax: 0318991617
Local Museum - 1969
Crafts, regional flora and fauna, schildtfishery, flax industry, basketmakers, wooden shoemakers 03818

Welkenraedt

Musée de la Route, Village, 4840 Welkenraedt - T: 087880854
Open Air Museum 03819

Wenduine

Museum voor Heem- en Volkskunde, Gemeentehuis, Markt 2, 8420 Wenduine - T: 050415001
Local Museum 03820

Wépion

Musée de la Fraise et du Terror Wépionnais, 1037 Chaussée de Dinant, 5100 Wépion - T: 081460113, 081460313
Natural History Museum 03821

Wervik

Tobacco Museum, Koestr 63, 8940 Wervik - T: 056314929, Fax: 056315676, E-mail: - tabaksmuseum.wervik@skynet.be, Internet: http://www.wervik.be. Head: John Samyn
Agriculture Museum 03822

Westerlo

Heemmuseum de Zuiderkempen, Sint-Michielsstr 2, 2260 Westerlo - T: 014234127, E-mail: jef_thys@hotmail.com, Internet: http://www.heemkringansfried.org. Head: Joseph Thys
Local Museum - 1970
Local hist, iconography, tools from local arts and crafts 03823

Wetteren

Heemkundig Museum Wetteren, Gemeentehuis, Markt 1, 9230 Wetteren - T: 093660733, 024673326, Fax: 024673334, E-mail: vanderhaegen@shelfservice.com. Head: Erik Van der Haegen
Historical Museum - 1954
Folklore, popular religious objects, ancient crafts, old kitchen, class room (1890), pub, pharmacy, archeology of Wetteren - library, photo archives 03824

Poppenmuseum Christus Koning, Parochiaal, Oude Aardeweg, 9230 Wetteren. Head: Alfons Willems
Religious Arts Museum
Religious traditions, puppets with religious vestments 03825

Wezemaal

Lampenmuseum, Aarschotsesteenweg 196, 3111 Wezemaal - T: 016445365
Special Museum
Lamps from various centuries and countries 03826

Willebroek

Breendonk Fort National Memorial, Brandstr 52, 2830 Willebroek - T: 038866209, Fax: 038665391, E-mail: info@breendonk.be, Internet: http://www.breendonk.be. Head: Prof. R. Coekelbergs
Military Museum / Historical Museum
Fort occupied during World War I and World War II, concentration camp (World War II), Jacques Ockx coll, Wilchar coll, concentration camp for PP 03827

Herman de Cuyper Museum, Mechelsesteenweg 249, 2830 Willebroek - T: 038863907. Head: Chris de Cuyper
Fine Arts Museum 03828

Museum van de Willebroekse Vaart, Sashuis, Sasplein, 2830 Willebroek - T: 038609791, 038443945, Fax: 038609799, Internet: http://www.willebroek.de. Head: Gerda Goossens
Local Museum 03829

Wilrijk

Heemkundig Museum, Sint-Bavostr 20, 2610 Wilrijk - T: 038288551
Local Museum
Local history 03830

Wommelgem

Heemmuseum De Kaeck, Dasstr 25, 2160 Wommelgem - T: 0313538361
Local Museum
Agricultural machinery, domestic utensils, guilds, photos 03831

Politiemuseum, Mortelmansstr 116A, 2160 Wommelgem - T: 033221266
Special Museum 03832

Xhoris

Musée Communal, 34 Rte de Hamoir, 4190 Xhoris - T: 041692520, 041433874
Local Museum
Reconstructed ancient kitchen, tools used in the local handicrafts, agricultural implements 03833

Zillebeke

Queen Victoria Rifles Museum, Zwarteleenstr 40, 8902 Zillebeke - T: 057206276
Military Museum 03834

Sanctuary Wood - Hill 62, Canadalaan 26, 8902 Zillebeke
Military Museum
Photos and various materials from World War I 03835

Zolder

Heemkundig Museum, Woutershof, Dekenstr 28, 3550 Zolder - T: 011534958
Local Museum 03836

Zonhoven

Voorhistorisch Museum, Kleine Hemmen 4, 3520 Zonhoven
Archaeological Museum
Prehistory, geology 03837

Zottegem

Kasteel van Leeuwergem, 9620 Zottegem - T: 093602216, Fax: 093610138. Head: B. Baron della Faille d'Huysse
Decorative Arts Museum 03838

Museum voor Folklore, Grotenbergestr 162, 9620 Zottegem - T: 093601263, 093646500, Fax: 093646479, E-mail: zottegem@tourismevlaanderen.be, Internet: http://www.zottegem.be
Folklore Museum - 1951 03839

Provinciaal Archeologisch Museum van Zuid-Oost-Vlaanderen, Paddestr 7, 9620 Zottegem - T: 093606716, Fax: 093612841. Head: M. Rogge
Archaeological Museum - 1986
Local finds: prehistory to the early medieval period, coin treasure from the Roman vicus of Velzeke 03840

Zulte

Museum Modest Huys, Modest Huyslaan 44, 9780 Zulte - T: 091602447
Fine Arts Museum - 1960
Paintings and drawings of Modest Huys (1874-1932) 03841

Zwijndrecht

Alfred Ost Museum, Gemeentehuis, 2070 Zwijndrecht - T: 032504800, Fax: 032504809
Fine Arts Museum
Works by the painter Alfred Ost 03842

Benin

Abomey

Musée Historique, Institut Français d'Afrique Noire, Ancien Palais des Rois, Abomey, mail addr: BP 25, Abomey - T: 500314, Fax: 500314, E-mail: musabome@bow.intnet.bj
Historical Museum / Decorative Arts Museum
History, thrones, jewelry, costumes, carpets, weapons 03843

Musée National d'Abomey, Abomey. Head: R.-Ph. Assogba
Historical Museum 03844

Cotonou

Musée de Cotonou, Institut Français d'Afrique Noire, Cotonou
Ethnology Museum
Ethnographic coll 03845

Natitingou

Musée de Natitingou, BP 157, Natitingou - T: 822021. Head: Noanti M. Constant
Local Museum / Ethnology Museum 03846

Ouidah

Musée d'Histoire, Ex-Fort Portugais, Ouidah - T: 341021, E-mail: mhom@hotmail.com. Head: Micheline Egounlety
Historical Museum
History of the colonial period (1420-1960) and the discovery of the Gulf of Guinea, history of the slave trade in Ouidah and the resolting cultural connection with the Americas 03847

Porto-Novo

Musée d'Homme, BP 299, Porto-Novo - T: 213566, Fax: 212525
Local Museum 03848

Musée Ethnographique, BP 299, Porto-Novo - T: 212554, Fax: 212525
Ethnology Museum
Exhibits on the tribes of Dahomey, musical instruments, pottery, masks, weapons 03849

Musée National, c/o IRA, BP 6, Porto-Novo. Head: Martin Akabiamu
Historical Museum 03850

Bermuda

Flatts

Bermuda Natural History Museum, 40 N Shore Rd, Flatts FL BX, mail addr: POB FL 145, Flatts FL BX - T: (441) 293-2727, Fax: (441) 293-3176, Internet: http://www.bamz.org. Head: Jack Ward
Natural History Museum - 1928
Bermuda natural hist, geology, botany and ornithology - library 03851

Hamilton

Bermuda Historical Society Museum, Par-la-Ville, 13 Queen St, Hamilton - T: 2952487. Head: Colin Benbow
Local Museum
Local history 03852

Bermuda National Gallery, City Hall, Church St, Hamilton - T: (441) 295-9428, Fax: 295-2055
Fine Arts Museum 03853

Bermuda Society of Arts, Church Str, mail addr: c/o West Gallery, City Hall, POB HM 1202, Hamilton HM FX - T: (441) 292-3824, Fax: 2960699, E-mail: bsoa@ibl.bm, Internet: http://www.bermuda.bm/bsoa
Fine Arts Museum / Decorative Arts Museum / Public Gallery 03854

The Masterworks Foundation Collection, 7 Front St, Bermuda House Ln, Hamilton - T: (441) 295-5580, 295-2379, Fax: (441) 295-2619, E-mail: mworks@ibl.bm, Internet: http://www.masterworks.bm
Fine Arts Museum 03855

Mangrove Bay

Bermuda Maritime Museum, POB MA 133, Mangrove Bay - T: (441) 234-1333, Fax: (441) 234-1735, E-mail: marmuse@ibl.bm. Head: Dr. E.C. Harris
Historical Museum - 1975
Bermuda maritime hist, archaeology, history 03856

Saint George's

Bermuda National Trust Museum, King's Sq, Saint George's - T: 4412971423, Fax: 4412360617, E-mail: palmetto@bnt.bm, Internet: http://www.bnt.bm. Head: Amanda Outerbridge
Historical Museum - 1961
Ship models, hist of Bermuda's role in the American Civil War, furniture - video presentation "Bermuda - Centre of the Atlantic" 03857

Carriage Museum, 22 Water St, Saint George's - T: 2971367. Head: Henry Laing
Science&Tech Museum
Coaches and carriages 03858

Saint George's Historical Society Museum, Duke of Kent St, Saint George's. Head: Freda Olivey
Historical Museum - 1920
Bermuda cedar furniture, silver coins, local historical objects 03859

Tucker House Museum, Water St, Saint George's - T: (441) 297-0545, Fax: (441) 236-0617. Head: Amanda Outerbridge
Local Museum - 1955
Paintings by Blackburn, furniture, archaeological coll, decorative arts coll 03860

Smith's Parish

Verdmont Historic House Museum, Collector's Hill, Smith's Parish - T: (441) 236-7639, Fax: (441) 236-0617. Head: Amanda Outerbridge
Local Museum / Decorative Arts Museum
John Green portraits and Bermuda cedar furniture 03861

Bhutan

Paro

National Museum of Bhutan, Tag Dzong, Paro - T: (2) 29138, Fax: 29103. Head: Mynak R. Tulku
Religious Arts Museum / Folklore Museum / Decorative Arts Museum / Natural History Museum - 1968
Northern Buddhism and Bhutanese religious art objects, textiles, decorative art, history and animals of Bhutan 03862

Bolivia

Cochabamba

Museo Universitario, Calle Jordán E-199, Cochabamba, mail addr: c/o Universidad Mayor de San Simón, CP 992, Cochabamba - T: (04) 250010, Fax: 232545. Head: David M. Pereira Herrera
Ethnology Museum / Archaeological Museum - 1953
Archaeology, precolumbian ceramics, textiles, mummies metal 03863

La Paz

Casa Pedro Domingo Murillo, Parque Riosinhio, La Paz. Head: José de Mesa
Special Museum - 1950
Archaeology, objects of Kallwaya civilization, pre-Columbian masks, ceramics of Tihuanaco, Inca and Mollo, colonial and Bolivian folk art, silver 18th and 19th c, 18th c painting 03864

Museo Costumbristá, Parque Riosinhio, La Paz. Head: José de Mesa
Local Museum - 1979
Hist of La Paz 03865

Museo del Litoral Boliviano, Parque Riosinhio, La Paz. Head: José de Mesa
Natural History Museum
Bolovian coast 03866

Museo del Oro y Metales Preciosos, Parque Riosinhio, La Paz. Head: José de Mesa
Decorative Arts Museum - 1983
Gold, metal art 03867

Museo Mineralogico, Banco Minero de Bolivia, Calle Comercio 1290, La Paz
Natural History Museum
Minerals of Bolivia and other countries 03868

Museo Nacional de Arqueología, Calle Tihuanaco 93, La Paz - T: (02) 311621, Fax: 329624. Head: Max Portugal Ortiz
Archaeological Museum - 1846/1961
Archaeology, anthropology, ethnology, zoology, numismatics, traditional native arts and crafts, colonial art, Lake Titicaca district exhibitions - library 03869

Museo Nacional de Arte, Calle Socabaya, esp Calle Comerció, La Paz - T: (02) 375016, Fax: 371177. Head: Teresa Villegas de Aneiva
Fine Arts Museum - 1961
Folklore 03870

Museo Nacional de Etnografía y Folklore, Calle Ingavi 916, La Paz - T: (02) 340791, Fax: 392241
Ethnology Museum / Folklore Museum 03871

Museo Nacional Tihuanacu, Calle Tihuanacu 93, La Paz, mail addr: Apdo 64, La Paz. Head: Prof. Gregorio Cordero Miranda
Fine Arts Museum / Decorative Arts Museum
Ancient art and craft of Tihuanacu 03872

Potosí

Museo de la Casa Nacional de la Moneda, Calle Ayacucho, Potosí, mail addr: Casilla 39, Potosí. Head: Luis Alfonso Fernández
Local Museum - 1938
Silver mint machinery (1750), history, mineralogy, numismatics, regional ethnography, archaeology, modern art - library, archives 03873

Sucre

Casa de la Libertad, Calle 25 de Mayo, Sucre, mail addr: CP 101, Sucre - T: (064) 54200, Fax: 52690, E-mail: caslib@mara.entelnet.bo. Head: Dr. Jorge Querejazu Calvo
Historical Museum - 1939
Historical coll concerned with Independence, including Bolivian Declaration of Independence, Republica epoch coll 1825 - library, archive 03874

Galería de Arte Moderna, Museos Universitarios, Calle Bolívar 698, Sucre - T: (064) 3285. Head: Dr. Manuel Giménez Carrazana
Fine Arts Museum / University Museum 03875

Museo Antropológico, Museos Universitarios, Palacio de Gran Poder, Calle Bolívar 698, Sucre - T: (064) 3285. Head: Dr. Manuel Giménez Carrazana
Ethnology Museum / University Museum - 1944
Ethnography, folklore, archaeology, items of pre-Inca civilization 03876

Museo Charcas, Universidad Boliviana Mayor, Calle Bolívar 401, Sucre - T: (064) 3285. Head: Jaime Urioste Avana, Elizabeth Rojas Toro, Dr. Manuel Giménez Carrazana
Folklore Museum / University Museum - 1944
Colonial art, folklore 03877

Museo del Ateneo de Bellas Artes, Sucre
Fine Arts Museum
Bolivian art 03878

Bosnia and Herzegovina

Banja Luka

Muzej Bosanske Krajine → Muzej Republike Srpske

Muzej Republike Srpske (Museum of Bosnian Serb Republic), Djure Daničića, 78000 Banja Luka - T: (078) 35486, Fax: 47318. Head: Milica Radojčić
Local Museum - 1930
Archaeology, history, ethnography and natural hist of north-west Bosnia, national revolutionary hist - library 03879

Umjetnička Galerija (Art Gallery), trg 27 Marta br 2, 78000 Banja Luka - T: (078) 34090. Head: Besim Karabegović
Fine Arts Museum
Sculpture and paintings by Yugoslav artists 03880

Bar

Umjetnička Galerija Velimir A. Leković, Setalište kralja Nikole 1, 85000 Bar - T: (085) 27949
Public Gallery 03881

Bihać

Regionalni Muzej, ul AVNOJ-a 2, 77000 Bihać - T: (077) 229743. Head: Enisa Jusić
Local Museum
Archaeology, ethnography, national revolutionary history 03882

Bileća

Zavičajni Muzej (Local Museum), Dvorišta BB, 79320 Bileća - T: 73018
Local Museum 03883

Bosansko Grahova

Memorijalni Muzej Gavrila Principa u Obljaju (Gavrilo Princip Memorial Museum), 77270 Bosansko Grahova - T: 810067. Head: Nikola Babić
Historical Museum
Birthplace and memorabilia of Gavrilo Princip 03884

Brčko

Umjetnička Galerija Rizah Stetić (Art Gallery Rizah Stetić), trg Maršala Tita 8, 76100 Brčko - T: (076) 28309. Head: Aziz Isaković
Fine Arts Museum 03885

Ljubuški

Humačka Arheološko Zbirka, Franjevački Samostan (Archaeological Collection), trg sv Ante 1, 88320 Ljubuški - T: (088) 835000, Fax: 833000. Head: Mate Dragićević
Archaeological Museum
Archaeological finds from local excavations 03886

Mostar

Muzej Hercegovine (Museum of Herzegovina), ul Glavna br. 172A, 88000 Mostar - T: (088) 551602. Head: Prof. Sabit Hodžić
Historical Museum
Archaeology, ethnography, labour movement, National Liberation War 03887

Umjetnička Galerija (Art Gallery), Dom Kulture-Rondo, 79000 Mostar
Fine Arts Museum
Sculpture and paintings by regional artists 03888

Mrkonjić Grad

Spomen Muzej Prvog Zasjedanja ZAVNOBiH-a, Maršala Tita 1, 70260 Mrkonjić Grad - T: (070) 12708
Local Museum 03889

Prijedor

Zavičajni Muzej (Local Museum), ul Partizanska 21, 78300 Prijedor - T: (079) 21334
Local Museum
Archaeology, ethnography, history 03890

Sarajevo

Muzej Jevreja Bosne i Hercegovine (Jewish Museum), ul Maršala Tita 98, 71000 Sarajevo
Historical Museum
Jewish history in Bosnia and Hercegovina 03891

Muzej Književnosti i Pozorišne Umjetnosti Bosne i Hercegovine i Galerija MAK (Museum of Literature and the Art Theatre and Gallery MAK), ul Sime Milutinovića-Sarajlije 7, 71000 Sarajevo - T: (033) 471828, Fax: 471828, E-mail: iljak@gih.net.ba. Head: Aleksandar Ljiljak
Special Museum / Performing Arts Museum - 1961
National literature of Bosnia and Herzegovina and portrait of writers and actors from Bosnia and Herzegovina 03892

Muzej-riznica Stare Srpske Pravoslavne Crkve (Museum Collection of the Old Orthodox Church), ul Maršala Tita 87, 71000 Sarajevo - T: (033) 22221. Head: Slobodan Radović
Religious Arts Museum
Art, religious items 03893

Svrzina Kuća (Svrzo's House), ul Dr. Jovana Kršića 5, 71000 Sarajevo
Historic Site
Feudal Turkish house, local history 03894

Umjetnička galerija Bosne i Hercegovine (Art Gallery), Zelenih beretki 8, 71000 Sarajevo - T: (033) 266550, Fax: 664162, E-mail: ugbih@yahoo.com. Head: Meliha Husedžinović
Fine Arts Museum - 1946
Modern and contemporary art (painting, sculpture, droving, graphic, installations) collection of icons 03895

Zemaljski Muzej (National Museum), Zmaja od Bosne 3, 71000 Sarajevo - T: (033) 668025, Fax: 668025, E-mail: muzej@citynet.ba, Internet: http://www.zemaljskimuzej.ba. Head: Dr. Djenana Buturović
Archaeological Museum / Ethnology Museum / Natural History Museum - 1888
Prehistoric, Roman, Greek and medieval archaeology, ethnography, natural hist, geology, anthropology, folklore, economics, transportation, jewellery, customs, mineralogy, petrography, botany, zoology - library, botanical garden 03896

Travnik

Zavičajni Muzej (Local Museum), trg Republike br 1, 72270 Travnik - T: (072) 813494. Head: Nikola Lovrinović
Local Museum
Mineralogy, petrography, natural history, archaeology, ethnography, numismatics, National Liberation War 03897

Trebinje

Zavičajni Muzej Trebinje, Alekse Santića 1, 89101 Trebinje - T: (089) 20220
Local Museum 03898

Tuzla

Galerija Portreta Tuzla, Slavka Mičića 25b, 75000 Tuzla - T: (075) 31245. Head: Ekmečić Mevludin
Fine Arts Museum 03899

Muzej Istične Bosně, Mije Keroševića 9, 75000 Tuzla - T: (075) 282111. Head: Nikola Panjević
Local Museum - 1947
Hist, archaeology, ethnology, art, natural hist - library 03900

Visoko

Etnografska Zbirka i Lapidarij Franjevačke Gimnazije, Franciscan Secondary School at Visoko (Ethnographic and Archeological Collection), Kadije Uvejsa 4, 71300 Visoko - T: (032) 738277 lok 105, Fax: 735826. Head: Dr. Ignacije Gavran
Ethnology Museum / Archaeological Museum 03901

Zavičajni Muzej (Local Museum), ul Ognjena Price 119, 71300 Visoko - T: (071) 731267. Head: Nataša Schinović
Local Museum
Local history 03902

Zenica

Muzej Grada Zenice (City Museum), ul F. Spanca 1, 72000 Zenica. Head: Zdravko Balta
Local Museum
Archaeology, ethnography, local history, art 03903

Botswana

Francistown

Supa-Ngwao Museum Centre, Plot 1310, Francistown, mail addr: POB 766, Francistown - T: 203088, Fax: 203088. Head: Stella Rundle
Local Museum - 1986
Ethnographic material, natural hist, local and regional hist - archives 03904

Gaborone

Botswana National Museum and Art Gallery, 331 Independence Av, Gaborone, mail addr: Private Bag 00114, Gaborone - T: 374616, Fax: 302797, E-mail: national.museum@gov.bw. Head: Tickey Pule
Local Museum / Fine Arts Museum - 1968
Local history and customs, art of Africa south of the Sahara, loan exhibitions, archaeology, etnology, natural history - library, national herbarium 03905

Postal Museum Botswana, POB 100, Gaborone - T: 353131, Fax: 313599, E-mail: - botspostEmcis.co.za. Head: M. Ruda
Special Museum - 1991
National historical stamp coll, items related to history of national postal services 03906

Kanye

Kgosi Bathoen II (Segopotso) Museum, POB M1304, Kanye - T: (0267) 342552, Fax: 342552, E-mail: bathoen@info.bw. Head: Oarabilke J. Noko
Local Museum
Ethnology, archaeology and natural history, arts, crafts, history, old district commisioner's office 03907

Mochudi

Phuthadikobo Museum, POB 367, Mochudi - T: 377238. Head: Pat Kollars
Local Museum - 1976
Photography, ethnography, screenprinting, blacksmithy - art training facility 03908

Brazil

Belém

Museu Paraense Emílio Goeldi, Av Magalhães Barata 376, Belém 66040-170, mail addr: CP 399, Belém 66017-970 - T: (091) 2491233, Fax: 2490466, E-mail: postmaster@museu-goeldi.br. Head: Adélia E. de Oliveira Rodrigues
Ethnology Museum / Natural History Museum - 1866
Anthropology, ethnography, zoology, botany, natural sciences of Amazonia - library 03909

Belo Horizonte

Fundação Clóuis Salgado - Palácio das Artes, Av Afonso Pena 1537, Belo Horizonte 30130-004 - T: (02131) 32377333, 32377264, Fax: 32377298, Internet: http://www.palaciodasartes.com.br. Head: Mauro Werkema
Public Gallery - 1970
Brazialian and European paintings, drawings, sculpture 03910

Galeria de Arte Prof. Sylvio Vasconcellos, Instituto Cultural Brasil-Estados Unidos, Rua da Bahia 1723, Belo Horizonte 30160-011 - T: (031) 2267633
Fine Arts Museum 03911

Museu de Arte e História Racioppi, Rua Padre Eustáquio 1442, Belo Horizonte 30710-580
Fine Arts Museum / Religious Arts Museum / Historical Museum - 1931
Profane and religious art from Antiquity to the present 03912

Museu Histórico Abílio Barreto, Rua Bernardo Mascarenhas, Barrio Cidade Jardim, Belo Horizonte 30380-010 - T: (031) 2963896, Fax: 2774800. Head: Arnaldo Augusto Godoy
Historical Museum - 1943
Local history 03913

Brasília

Fundação Cultural do Distrito Federal, Av W-3, 508, Lote 47, Brasília
Historical Museum
Documentation on the evolution and construction of Brasília 03914

Museu Vivo da Memória Candanga, Via Epia Sul, Lote D, HJKO, Núcleo Bandeirante, Brasília 71735-900 - T: (061) 3011009, Fax: 3013590, E-mail: museuvivo@terra.com.br. Head: Raquel Cavalcante
Local Museum / Fine Arts Museum - 1990
Popuar art, handicraft - library 03915

Cachoeira

Museu das Alfaias da Paróquia da Cachoeira, Igreja Matriz de Nossa Senhora do Rosário da Cachoeira, Cachoeira 44300-000
Religious Arts Museum
Objects of gold, silver and precious stones, paintings (17th and 18th c) 03916

Caeté

Casa Setecentista de Caeté, Rua Monsenhor Domingos s/n, Caeté 34800-000
Local Museum - 1979
Colonial furniture and religious art, musical instruments, objects from the coll of novelist Cornélio Pena 03917

Campanha

Museu Dom Inocencio, Rua João Luiz Alvez 76, Campanha 37400-000
Local Museum
Coins, minerals, books and manuscripts 03918

Campinas

Museu Carlos Gomes, Centro de Ciências, Letras y Artes, Rua Bernardino de Campos, 989-Centro, Campinas 13010-151 - T: (019) 32312561/67, Fax: 32312567, E-mail: ccla@correionete.com.br, Internet: http://www.museu-carlosgome-s.cosmo.com.br. Head: Simao Podolsky
Music Museum - 1904
Documents and personal belongings of Gomes family 03919

Museu de História Natural, Rua Coronel Quirino 2, Campinas 13025-000 - T: (019) 32310555 ext 372. Head: Tereza Cristina Silva Mello Borges
Natural History Museum - 1938
Anthropology, zoology, mineralogy, fossils 03920

Museu Ferroviário da Cia. Mogiana de Estradas de Ferro, Rua Dr. Sales de Oliveira 1380, Campinas 13035-270
Science&Tech Museum - 1965
Historic photographs, uniforms, furnishings and equipment used by the railroads 03921

Campo Grande

Museu Regional D. Bosco, Rua Barão do Rio Branco 1885, Campo Grande 79002-173, mail addr: CP 415, Campo Grande 79002-970 - T: (067) 3833994. Head: João Falco
Local Museum - 1951
History, ethnography, insects, shells 03922

Campos do Jordão

Coleção do Palácio do Governo de Campos do Jordão, Palácio Boa Vista, Campos do Jordão 12460-000
Fine Arts Museum / Decorative Arts Museum - 1964
Painting and sculpture, antique furniture, porcelain, religious objects, Persian carpets 03923

Carpina

Museu do Instituto Histórico, Praça Carlos Pena 94, Carpina 55810-000
Historical Museum - 1962
Antique weapons, numismatics, religious objects 03924

Cataguases

Museu de Belas-Artes, Chácara da Granjaria, Cataguases 36770-000
Fine Arts Museum
Brazilaian paintings and sculpture 03925

Cuiabá

Museu de Arte e Cultura Popular Coordenação de Cultura, Av Fernando Côrrea da Costa, Cuiabá 78000
Folklore Museum
Popular art 03926

Curitiba

Casa de Alfredo Andersen, Museu e Escola de Arte, Rua Mateus Leme 336, Curitiba 80510-190
Special Museum - 1971
Paintings, drawings, and personal belongings of Alfredo Andersen 03927

Museu de Arte do Paranà, Av Iguaçu 1317, Curitiba 80250-190. Head: Eduardo da Rocha Virmond
Fine Arts Museum 03928

Museu do Homem, c/o Dept do Antropologia, Universidade Federal do Praná, Rua General Carneiro 460, Curitiba 80060-150
Ethnology Museum / University Museum - 1957
Indian ethnography, paleontology and prehistoric archeology, folklore 03929

Museu Paranaense, Praça Generoso Marques s/n, Curitiba 80020-230 - T: (041) 3231411, 3228570, Fax: 2225824, E-mail: museupr@pr.gov.br, Internet: http://www.pr.gov.br/museupr. Head: Jayme Antonio Cardoso
Historical Museum / Ethnology Museum / Archaeological Museum - 1876
History, anthropology, ethnology, prehistory, sculpture, graphic arts, metalwork arms, numismatics - library 03930

Diamantina

Museu do Diamante, Rua Direita 14, Diamantina 39100-000
Natural History Museum - 1954
Minerals, furniture and altar pieces, paintings and ceramics 03931

Feira de Santana

Museu Regional de Feira de Santana, Rua Prof. Geminiano Costa s/n, Feira de Santana 44025-070
Fine Arts Museum - 1967
Local and national art, particularly contemporary works, English contemporary art 03932

Florianópolis

Museu de Arte de Santa Catarina, Av Governador Irineu Bornhausen 5000, Florianópolis 88025-202, mail addr: CP 1471, Florianópolis 88010-970 - T: (0482) 342166. Head: Harry Laus
Fine Arts Museum 03933

Fortaleza

Museu de Arte da Universidade do Ceara, Av Visconde de Cauipé 2854, Fortaleza 60020-180. Head: Floriano Teixeira
Fine Arts Museum / University Museum 03934

Museu do Ceará, Rua São Paulo 51, Fortaleza 60030-100 - T: (085) 2511502, Fax: 2614733. Head: Valéria Laena Bezerra Rolim
Historical Museum - 1935
Archives and documents 03935

Museu Gustavo Barroso, c/o Colégio Militar de Fortaleza, Praça da Bandeira s/n, Fortaleza 60150-320
Archaeological Museum / Military Museum
Classical archaeology, history of the Military College 03936

Goiânia

Museu de Ornitologia, Av Pará 381-395, Goiânia 74520-100 - T: (062) 2335773. Head: Prof. José Hidasi
Natural History Museum - 1968
Ornithology - library, archive, laboratory 03937

Museu Goiano Zoroastro Artiaga, Praça Cívica 13, Goiânia 74003-010 - T: (062) 2231763, Fax: 2231763, E-mail: museuzoroastro@agepel.go.gov.br. Head: Dr. Henrique de Freitas
Historical Museum - 1946
Ethnography and anthropology, natural history, archeology, items of local history, geology, folklore 03938

Goiás

Museu das Bandeiras, Praça Dr. Brasil, Goiás 76600-000 - T: (062) 3711087. Head: Maria Luiza Brandaó
Historical Museum - 1950
Artifacts, mostly from the 18th c, from the history of the region, objects from the local churches, ceramics 03939

Guarapuava

Museu Municipal Visconde de Guarapuava, Rua Visconde de Guarapuava 288, Guarapuava 85010-240
Local Museum - 1956
Indian agricultural and domestic utensils, local history 03940

Itatiaia

Museu Parque Nacional do Itatiaia, Rodovia Presidente Dutra, km 155, Itatiaia 27580-000 - T: (0243) 521461
Natural History Museum - 1942
Local flora 03941

Itu

Museu Republicano Convenção de Itu, Rua Barão de Itaim 67, Itu 13300-000 - T: (011) 40230240, Fax: 40236533, E-mail: jonasouz@usp.br, Internet: http://www.mp.usp.br/mr. Head: Prof. Jonas Soares de Souza
Historical Museum - 1923 03942

João Pessoa

Museu-Escola Esacro do Estado da Paraiba, Praça São Francisco s/n, João Pessoa 58010-650 - T: (083) 2212840
Ethnology Museum / Archaeological Museum / Natural History Museum - 1970
Anthropology and ethnography, archeology, geography, religious art, local history, natural history 03943

Juazeiro do Norte

Museu Civico-Religioso Padre Cicero, Rua São José 224, Juazeiro do Norte 63010-450
Ethnology Museum / Folklore Museum / Natural History Museum - 1951
Artifacts of Amazon Indians, local folklore and folk art, natural history 03944

Juiz de Fora

Museu do Banco de Crédito Real de Minas Gerais, Rua Halfeld 504, Juiz de Fora 36010-001
Special Museum - 1964
Numismatics and banking 03945

Museu Mariano Procópio, Rua Dom Pedro II s/n, Bairro Mariano Procópio, Juiz de Fora 36035-090 - T: (032) 2111145, Fax: 2150721. Head: Arthur Arcuri
Decorative Arts Museum / Fine Arts Museum / Natural History Museum - 1921
Porcelain, furniture, and painting (19th-20th c), natural hist - archives, library 03946

Lavras

Museu Bi Moreira, Campus Universitário, Lavras 37200-000, mail addr: CP 37, Lavras 37200-000 - T: (035) 8213700. Head: Angelo Alberto de Moura Delphim
Historical Museum / University Museum 03947

Museu Histórico, Escola Superior de Agricultura de Lavras, Lavras 37200-000
Historical Museum - 1949
Local history, furnishings, instruments of torture, documents and maps 03948

Macapá

Museu Territorial do Amapá, Fortaleza de San José de Macapá, Macapá
Local Museum - 1948
Zoology, archaeology, ethnography, and numismatics of Amapá territory 03949

Maceió

Museu Comercial e Arqueológico do Sindicato dos Empregados, Rua João Pessoa 418, Maceió
Archaeological Museum 03950

Museu de Arte Sacra Dom Ranulfo, Igreja do Rosário, Rua João Pessoa 270, Maceió
Religious Arts Museum - 1966
Paintings and icons, religious books and objects 03951

Manaus

Museu do Índio, Rua Duque de Caxias 356, Manaus 69020-140 - T: (092) 6351922, Fax: 6352091, E-mail: visitadoria@auxiliadora.g12.br
Local Museum / Ethnology Museum - 1952
Music instruments, hunting and fishing tools, weaving, ceramics, arts and crafts - library, auditorium 03952

Museu e Biblioteca do Instituto Geográfico e Histórico do Amazonas, Rua Bernardo Ramos 131, Manaus 69005-310
Historical Museum / Natural History Museum - 1917
History, natural history - library 03953

Seção de Numismática do Estado do Amazonas, Palácio Rio Branco, Av Dom Pedro I, Manaus 69040-040
Special Museum
World-wide coll of antique coins 03954

Mariana

Museu Arquidiocesano de Mariana, Rua Frei Durão 49, Mariana 35420-000. Head: Prof. Pedro Terra
Religious Arts Museum 03955

Natal

Museu Câmara Cascudo, Av Hermes da Fonseca 1398, Natal 59022-001
Local Museum - 1961
Regional archeology, natural history, Brazilian ethnology 03956

Museu de Arte e História, Rua da Conceição 601, Natal 59025-270
Fine Arts Museum / Historical Museum
Fine arts and folk art, Indian art, domestic utensils characteristic of the region, arms, various historical artifacts 03957

Museu de Arte Popular da Fortaleza dos Reis Magos, Fortaleza dos Reis Magos, Rua Trairi 558, Natal 59020-150
Folklore Museum - 1966
Furnishings, sculpture, applied arts 03958

Museu do Instituto de Antropologia Câmara Cascudo, Av Hermes da Fonseca 1398, Natal 59022-001
Ethnology Museum
Coll in anthropology, natural history, paleontology, etc 03959

Museu do Instituto Histórico e Geográfico do Rio Grande do Norte, Rua da Conceição, Natal 59070-270
Historical Museum
History, geography 03960

Niterói

Museu Antonio Parreiras, Rua Tiradentes 47, Niterói 24210-510 - T: (021) 7198728. Head: Prof. Maria Auxiliadora Silveira
Fine Arts Museum - 1941
Paintings and drawings from Antônio Parreiras, European paintings, Brazilian contemporary art 03961

Museu de Arte Contemporânea - MAC Niterói, Rua Almirante de Boa Viagem s/n -Boa Viagem, Niterói 24210-390 - T: (021) 6202400/81
Fine Arts Museum
Coll of contemporary Brazilian art 03962

Nova Era

Museu Municipal de Arte e História, Praça da Matriz, Nova Era 35920-000
Fine Arts Museum / Historical Museum - 1965
Profane and sacred art coll demonstrating the history of art 03963

Olinda

Museu Regional de Olinda, Rua do Amparo 128, Olinda, PE
Historical Museum / Fine Arts Museum - 1934
History, art 03964

Ouro Prêto

Museu da Inconfidência, Praça Tiradentes 139, Ouro Prêto 35400-000 - T: (031) 5511121. Head: R. Mourão
Local Museum - 1944
Colonial art, history, objects related to the 1789 revolutionaires of Minos Gerais, wood carvings, furniture, paintings, religious art, silver - library, historical archives, laboratory, research center 03965

Museu de Arte e Historia, Casa de Gonzaga, Rua do Ouvidor 9, Ouro Prêto 35400-000
Fine Arts Museum / Historical Museum
Art, history 03966

Museu de Ciência e Técnica da Escola de Minas, Praça Tiradentes 20, Ouro Prêto 35400-000 - T: (031) 5515257, Fax: 5515261, E-mail: museuct@ouropreto.feop.com.br. Head: Leonardo Barbosa Godefroid
Science&Tech Museum / Natural History Museum - 1995 03967

Museu Mineralógico da Escola de Minas, Praça Tiradentes 20, Ouro Prêto 35400-000 - T: (031) 551110, Fax: 5511689. Head: Antônio M. Claret de Gouvêia
Science&Tech Museum - 1876
Mining and metallurgy 03968

Paranaguá

Museu de Arqueologia e Artes Populares, Rua Quinze de Novembro 567, Paranaguá 83203-010 - T: (041) 4220228. Head: Verginia Andersen
Archaeological Museum / Folklore Museum - 1965
Prehistoric archeology (Brazil, Asia, Africa and Europe), Brazilian arts and crafts 03969

Pelotas

Museu e Biblioteca Pública Pelotense, Praça Coronel Pedro Osório 103, Pelotas 96015-010
Local Museum / Natural History Museum
Zoology, botany, mineralogy, palaeontology, local history, archaeology, ethnography, coins 03970

Petrópolis

Museu de Armas Ferreira da Cunha, Rodovia Washington Luiz, km 84, Petrópolis 25655-001 - T: (0242) 426564, Fax: 2743140, E-mail: sergioh@fund.cepel.br. Head: Sergio Henrique Ferreira da Cunha
Military Museum - 1957
Brazilian, European, African and Asiatic arms 03971

Museu Imperial, Rua da Imperatriz 220, Petrópolis 25610-320 - T: (0242) 378000, Fax: 378540, E-mail: musim@npoint.com.br, Internet: http://www.museuimperial.gov.br. Head: Maria de Lourdes Parreiras Horta
Decorative Arts Museum / Historical Museum - 1940
Brazilian Empire 1808-1889, imperial clothing, jewelry, furniture, glass, china, applied arts, iconography, photogr (19th c) - library, archives 03972

Piratini

Museu Histórico Farroupilha, Rua Coronel Manoel Pedroso 77, Piratini 96490-000 - T: (053) 2571481, Fax: 2571481. Head: Angélica Barroso Panatieri
Fine Arts Museum / Historical Museum - 1953
Art, history 03973

Porto Alegre

Galeria de Arte do Instituto de Artes da Universidade Federal do Rio Grande do Sul, Rua Senhor dos Passos 248, Porto Alegre 90020-180 - T: (0512) 240464. Head: Luiz Fernando Barth
Fine Arts Museum / University Museum 03974

Museu Anchieta, Av Dr. Nilo Peçanha 1521, Porto Alegre 91330-000
Natural History Museum - 1908
Entomology and ornithology, local minerals, fossils, shells, etc - library 03975

Museu da Curia Metropolitana, Arcebispado, Porto Alegre
Religious Arts Museum
Religious art 03976

Museu de Arte do Rio Grande do Sul, Praça da Alfândega, Porto Alegre 90010-150 - T: (051) 2272311, Fax: 2272311. Head: Paulo Cesar Brasil do Amaral
Fine Arts Museum - 1954 03977

Museu Julio de Castilhos, Rua Duque de Caxias 1205, Porto Alegre 90010-283 - T: (051) 32215933, Fax: 32215933. Head: Mariana Casseminho Meira
Historical Museum - 1903
National history, militaria, Indian coll, armaments, old furniture, ethnology 03978

Museu Particular de Armas de Arlindo Pedro Zatti, Av Mostardeiro 938, Porto Alegre 90430-000
Military Museum - 1920
Arms and weapons from various periods and parts of the world (over 2000 exhibits) 03979

Pinacoteca Barão de Santo Angelo, Rua Senhor dos Passos 248, Porto Alegre 90020-180 - T: (0512) 240464
Fine Arts Museum 03980

Porto Velho

Museu da Estrada de Ferro Madeira-Mamoré, Praça da EFMM, Porto Velho
Science&Tech Museum - 1971
Restored railroad cars and equipment, restored railway station 03981

Recife

Museu de Antropologia do Instituto Joaquim Nabuco de Pesquisas Sociais, Av 17 de Agosto 2187, Recife 52061-540
Ethnology Museum
Ceramics, furnishings domestic and agricultural utensils and implements, folklore, etc 03982

Museu de Arte Sacra da Irmandade de Nossa Senhora da Conceição dos Militares, Rua Nova 309, Recife
Religious Arts Museum 03983

Museu de Ciências Naturais, c/o Universidade Federal Rural de Pernambuco, Horto Zoobotânico de Dois Irmãos, Recife 52071-030. Head: Gustavo Pacheco
Natural History Museum / University Museum - 1973
Brazilian fauna, particularly of the Amazon and central Brazilian regions, mineralogy 03984

Museu do Estado de Pernambuco, Av Rui Barbosa 960, Recife 52011-040 - T: (081) 4270766, Fax: 4279322. Head: Sylvia Pontual
Local Museum - 1929
Local history, art history, ethnology, weapons, furniture, paintings, indian coll - library 03985

Museu do Instituto Arqueológico, Histórico e Geográfico Pernam Bucano, Rua do Hospício 130, Boa Vista, Recife 50060-080 - T: (081) 2224952. Head: Dr. Leonardo D. Silva
Archaeological Museum / Historical Museum
History, archaeology 03986

Museu Dom Vital, Convento da Penha, Praça Dom Vital, Recife 50020-280
Religious Arts Museum
Religious art 03987

Rio de Janeiro

Academia Brasileira de Letras, Av Presidente Wilson 203, Rio de Janeiro 20030-021 - T: (021) 2205441
Special Museum 03988

Açude Museum, Museus de Castro Maya, Estrada do Açude 764, Alto da Boa Vista, Rio de Janeiro 20531-330 - T: (021) 4922119, 4925443, Fax: 4922119, E-mail: cmaya01@visualnet.com.br, Internet: http://www.visualnet.com.br/cmayo. Head: Vera de Alencar
Decorative Arts Museum / Natural History Museum - 1964
Antique Portuguese, French, Dutch and Spanish tiles, 19th c china, furniture, Oriental art, enviromental education - gardens 03989

Army Museum and Fort Copacabana, Praça Cel. Eugênio Franco, Copacabana, Rio de Janeiro 22070-020 - T: (021) 2471242
Military Museum 03990

Arquivo Nacional, Rua Azeredo Coutinho 77, Rio de Janeiro 20230-170 - T: (021) 38066175/76, Fax: 22328430, E-mail: diretorirgeral@arquivonacional.gov.br, Internet: http://www.arquivonacional.gov.br. Head: Jaime Antunes da Silva
Library with Exhibitions 03991

Casa de Deodoro, Campo de Santana 197, Rio de Janeiro 20211-360 - T: (021) 2310688
Local Museum 03992

Casa de José Bonifácio, Praia da Guarda 119, Rio de Janeiro 20397-010
Local Museum 03993

Casa de Osório, Rua do Riachuelo 303, Rio de Janeiro 20230-001 - T: (021) 2429370
Military Museum
Weapons, heraldic shields, military insignia from the 18th and 19th c coll 03994

Centro de Pesquisas Folclóricas, Rua do Passeio 98, Rio de Janeiro 20021-290 - T: (021) 2401541, Fax: 2401441. Head: Samuel M. Araujo
Music Museum - 1943
Folklore music, early brazilian popular music - library 03995

Chácara do Céu Museum, Museus Castro Maya, Rua Murtinho Nobre 93, Santa Teresa, Rio de Janeiro 20241-050 - T: (021) 22248981, 25071932, Fax: 22248524, E-mail: cmaya01@visualnet.com.br, Internet: http://www.visualnet.com.br/cmaya. Head: Vera de Alencar
Fine Arts Museum - 1972
Works by modern Brazilian and European masters, Oriental art, Brasiliana coll - library, archives 03996

Espaço Cultural da Marinha, Av Alfredo Agache s/n, Rio de Janeiro 20021-000
Military Museum
Historical shipping exhibition, underwater archeology coll, models of regional vessels and tools - Galeota de Dom João VI built in 1808 03997

Espaço Museu da Vida, Av Brasil 4365, Rio de Janeiro 21040-360 - T: (021) 5984343, 5984341, Fax: 2608342, 5984437
Science&Tech Museum
History of science since 19th c 03998

Estrada do Açude Museum, Fundação Raymundo Ottoni de Castro Maya, Estrada do Açude 764, Rio de Janeiro 20531-330
Fine Arts Museum / Decorative Arts Museum - 1962
Water colors and drawings by Jean Baptiste Debret, porcelain and tiles (18th-20th c) 03999

Fundação Eva Klabin Rappaport, Av Epitácio Pessoa 2480, Lagoa, Rio de Janeiro 22471-000 - T: (021) 2873509, Fax: 5233471
Fine Arts Museum
Private coll of paintings, sculptures, furniture, ceramics and silverware from several centuries 04000

Fundação Nacional Pró-Memória, Rua da Imprensa 16, Rio de Janeiro 20030-120 - T: (021) 2209991, 2205540
Natural History Museum 04001

Fundaçao Oscar Niemeyer, Rua Conde Lages 25, Rio de Janeiro 20241-080 - T: (021) 5091844, Fax: 2226445
Special Museum / Fine Arts Museum
Silk-screens, mock-ups and furniture by Oscar Niemeyer coll 04002

Museu Aeroespacial, Av Marechal Fontenella 2000, Rio de Janeiro 21470-000 - T: (021) 3575214/13
Science&Tech Museum
Historic weapons coll, exhibition of documents and aircrafts 04003

Museu Amsterdam Suer de Pedras Preciosas, Rua Garcia D'Avila 105, Rio de Janeiro 22421-010 - T: (021) 5121132, Fax: 2944728. Head: Daniel Sauer
Special Museum 04004

Museu Angelo Agostini / Casa de Cultura Laura Alvim, Av Vieira Souto 176, Rio de Janeiro 22420-000 - T: (021) 2671647
Local Museum 04005

Museu Antonio Lago, Rua Andradas 96, Rio de Janeiro 20051-000 - T: (021) 2877567
Special Museum
Pharmacy 04006

Museu Antropológico do Instituto Superior de Cultura Brasileira, Av Mem de Sá s/n, Rio de Janeiro 20230-000
Ethnology Museum 04007

Museu Biblioteca da Academia de Polícia, Rua Frei Caneca 162, Rio de Janeiro 20211-040 - T: (021) 2246058
Special Museum
Jurisdiction, police 04008

Museu Carmen Miranda, Parque Brigadeiro Eduardo Gomes, Av Rui Barbosa frente a 560, Rio de Janeiro 22250-020 - T: (021) 5512597
Music Museum
Memorabilia of the celebrated popular singer Carmen Miranda 04009

Museu Carpológico do Jardim Botânico do Rio de Janeiro, Rua Pacheco Leão 915, Rio de Janeiro 22460-030 - T: (021) 25112749, 25112588, Fax: 25112749, E-mail: rb@graziela.jbrj.gov.br, Internet: http://www.jbrj.gov.br. Head: Ronaldo Marquete
Natural History Museum - 1915
Dry fruits of Brazilian and exotic plants, botany - herbarium 04010

Museu Casa de Benjamin Constant, Rua Monte Alegre 255, Rio de Janeiro 20240-190 - T: (021) 5091248
Special Museum
Home of Benjamin Constant, introducer of positivism in Brazil 04011

Museu Casa de Rui Barbosa, Rua São Clemente 134, Botafogo, Rio de Janeiro 22260-000 - T: (021) 5370036, Fax: 5371114
Special Museum - 1930
Rui Barbosa's personal belongings, furniture, silver, porcelain, sculptures, paintings, ceramics, jewelry, medals, carpets, books, drawing, documents - library 04012

Museu Casa do Pontal, Estrada do Pontal 3295, Rio de Janeiro 22785-560 - T: (021) 4376278, Fax: 2053008, E-mail: pontal@openlink.com.br. Head: Guy van de Beuque
Folklore Museum
Brazilian folk art coll 04013

Museu Clube dos Caçadores, Rua São Geraldo 38, Rio de Janeiro
Special Museum
Hunting 04014

Museu da Companhia Independente do Palácio Guanabara, Rua Cardoso Júnior 479, Laranjeiras, Rio de Janeiro 22245-000
Historical Museum
Police, militaria 04015

Museu da Eletricidade, c/o Centro Cultural Light, Av Marechal Floriano 168, Rio de Janeiro 20080-002 - T: (021) 2114822
Science&Tech Museum
Items, equipment, photographs and documents portray the history of electricity in Rio de Janeiro 04016

Museu da Escola Naval, Av Almirante Silvio de Noronha s/n, Rio de Janeiro 20021-010 - T: (021) 2921252 ext 297
Historical Museum - 1962
Marine history - library 04017

Museu da Farmácia, Rua Santa Luzia 206, Rio de Janeiro 20020-020 - T: (021) 2976611 ext 592
Special Museum
Pharmacy 04018

Museu da Fauna (Wildlife Museum), Parque Quinta da Boa Vista, Rio de Janeiro 20940-040 - T: (021) 2280556
Natural History Museum - 1939
Birds and mammals of the Brazilian fauna 04019

Museu da Fazenda Federal, Av Presidente Antônio Carlos 375a, Rio de Janeiro 20020-010 - T: (021) 2405990, 2973939. Head: Leticia Mainieri Piedade
Historical Museum - 1970
Historical financial documentation, machines, coins, numismatics - library 04020

Museu da Força Expedicionária Brasileira - FEB, Rua das Marrecas 35, Rio de Janeiro 20031-000 - T: (021) 2405990, 2623609
Military Museum - 1976
Military weapons, uniforms, decorations and equipment used by the Brazilian Expeditionary Force and other units in World War II 04021

Museu da Imagem e do Som, Praça Rui Barbosa 1, Rio de Janeiro 20021-320 - T: (021) 2620309
Music Museum - 1965
Brazilian musical heritage 04022

Museu da Limpeza Urbana - Casa de Banhos de Dom João VI, Praia do Caju 385, Rio de Janeiro 20931-340 - T: (021) 5800699
Local Museum / Historic Site
History of modern Rio de Janeiro 04023

Museu da Polícia do Rio de Janeiro, Rua Marquês de Pombal 128, Rio de Janeiro 20230-240
Special Museum 04024

Museu da República, Rua do Catete 153, Rio de Janeiro 22220-000 - T: (021) 2659747, Fax: 2856320, E-mail: musrepublica@uol.com.br, Internet: http://www.museudarepublica.org.br. Head: Anelise Pacheco
Historical Museum - 1960
Relics of presidents of the republic, furniture, paintings, engravings, drawings, watercolours, sculptures, silverware, jewels, weapons, crystals, coins, medals, documents - library, archive 04025

Museu da Secção de Tecnologia do Serviço Florestal, Rua Major Rubéns Vaz 122, Gávea, Rio de Janeiro 22470-070. Head: Dr. Nearch Azevedo de Silva
Science&Tech Museum - 1938
Wood technology, products of the wood industry 04026

Museu da Venrável Ordem Terceira de São Francisco da Penitência, Largo da Carioca, Rio de Janeiro 20050-020 - T: (021) 5716242, Fax: 5714500. Head: Eckart Hermann Höfling
Religious Arts Museum - 1933
Religious art and traditions 04027

Museu de Arte Moderna do Rio de Janeiro, Av Infante Dom Henrique 85, Rio de Janeiro 20021-140, mail addr: CP 44, Rio de Janeiro 20001-970 - T: (021) 22404944, Fax: 22404899, E-mail: mam@mamrio.org.br, Internet: http://www.mamrio.org.br. Head: M.F. do Nacimento Brito
Fine Arts Museum - 1948
Paintings, engravings, sculptures, drawings/pictures of foreign and national artists - library, film archive 04028

Museu de Arte Sacra, Santa Casa da Misericórdia do Rio de Janeiro, Rua Santa Luzia 206, Rio de Janeiro
Religious Arts Museum
Religious art 04029

Museu de Astronomia e Ciências Afins, Rua General Bruce 586, Rio de Janeiro 20921-030 - T: (021) 5807010
Science&Tech Museum 04030

Museu de Ciências da Terra - DNPM (Earth Science Museum), Av Pasteur 404, Rio de Janeiro 22290-240 - T: (021) 2956673, Fax: 2954896. Head: Diogenes de Almeida Campos
Natural History Museum - 1907
Minerals, rocks, gems and fossils 04031

Museu de Esportes Mané Garrincha, Rua Prof. Eurico Rabelo, Portão 18, Rio de Janeiro 20271-150
Special Museum 04032

Museu de Folclore Édison Carneiro, Rua Catete 181, Rio de Janeiro 22220-000 - T: (021) 22798451, Fax: 22050090, E-mail: folclore@funarte.gov.br, Internet: http://www.funarte.gov.br. Head: Claudia Marcia Ferreira
Folklore Museum - 1969
Wood handicrafts, ceramics, toys, theatre, folk music, religions - library 04033

Museu de Images do Inconsciente, Rua Ramiro Magalhães 521, Rio de Janeiro 20730-460 - T: (021) 25968460, Fax: 25968460, E-mail: - museu.inconsciente@bol.com.br, Internet: http://www.museuimagensdoinconsciente.org.br. Head: Luiz Carlos Mello
Special Museum
Art works done by psychatric patients at the Instituto Nise da Silveira 04034

Museu de Nossa Senhora da Glória do Outeiro, Praça Nossa Senhora da Glória 135, Rio de Janeiro 22211-110
Religious Arts Museum
Religious art 04035

Museu de Odontologia Professor Salles Cunha (Odontology Museum Prof. Salles Cunha), Rua Barão de Sertório 75, Rio de Janeiro 20261-050 - T: (021) 25040002, Fax: 25043859, E-mail: aborj@aborj.org.br, Internet: http://www.aborj.org.br. Head: Thales Ribeiro de Magalhães
Special Museum
Equipments, books and items related to the history of odontology 04036

Museu de Patologia do Instituto Oswaldo Cruz, Rua Manguinhos, Rio de Janeiro
Special Museum
Public health 04037

Museu de Valores, Banco Central do Brasil, SBS, Quadra 3, Bloco A, Rio de Janeiro 70074-900 - T: (021) 2530226. Head: João Carlos A. Ferreira
Special Museum - 1966
Brazilian and foreign countries coins, bank notes, medals, documents 04038

Museu do Banco de Brasil, Rua Primeiro de Março 66, Rio de Janeiro 20010-000 - T: (021) 2160259
Special Museum
Coins and banknotes throughout the history of Brazil 04039

Museu do Bonde (Tram Museum), c/o Oficina dos Bondes de Santa Teresa, Rua Carlos Brant 14, Largo dos Guimarães, Rio de Janeiro 20240-220 - T: (021) 2221003, 2422354, Fax: 2221003, E-mail: - bondesantateresa@domain.com.br. Head: Bernardo Stille Neto
Science&Tech Museum
Trams, equipment, tools, seats, clocks, bells, uniforms 04040

Museu do Carnaval, Praça de Apoteose - entrada Rua Frei Caneca s/n - Centro, Rio de Janeiro 20211-020 - T: (021) 2937122, 5026996
Special Museum 04041

Museu do Gás, Av Presidente Vargas 2610, Rio de Janeiro 20210-031 - T: (021) 589-5622
Science&Tech Museum 04042

Museu do Indio, Rua das Palmeiras 55, Botafogo, Rio de Janeiro 22270-070 - T: (021) 2862097, Fax: 2868899, E-mail: museudoindio@ax.apc.org.br. Head: José Carlos Levinho
Ethnology Museum - 1953
History, ethnography of Indians, basket and feather handicrafts, weapons, garments, ceramics, musical instruments, pictures, films and recordings of Indian music - library, archives 04043

Museu do Instituto Histórico e Geográfico Brasileiro, Av Augusto Severo 8, Glória, Rio de Janeiro 20021-040 - T: (021) 2321312 ext 23, Fax: 2524430, E-mail: ihgbiresidencia@unikey.com.br. Head: Arno Wehling
Historical Museum / Ethnology Museum - 1838
History, geography, ethnography 04044

Museu do Jardim Botânico, Rua Jardim Botânico 1008, Rio de Janeiro 22470-051
Natural History Museum 04045

Museu do Monumento Nacional aos Mortos da Segunda Guerra Mundial, c/o Parque Brigadeiro Eduardo Gomes, Av Infante Dom Henrique 75, Rio de Janeiro 20021-140 - T: (021) 2401283
Historical Museum
Uniforms, weapons, medals, stamps and documents beloging to Brazilian, American and German World War II soldiers 04046

Museu do Porto do Rio, Av Rodrigues Alves, Rio de Janeiro
Local Museum 04047

Museu do Primeiro Reinado, Av Pedro II 293, Rio de Janeiro 20941-070
Historical Museum 04048

Museu do Telephone, Rua Dois de Dezembro 63, Rio de Janeiro 22220-040 - T: (021) 5563189, Fax: 2054872
Special Museum
History of the telecomunication in Brazil coll 04049

Museu Dom João VI, Av Pasteur 250, Rio de Janeiro 22290-240 - T: (021) 2902112
Local Museum 04050

Museu dos Teatros do Rio de Janeiro, Rua São João Batista 103-105, Rio de Janeiro 22270-030 - T: (021) 2863234
Special Museum
Paintings, photographs and scenic art documents coll. Opera's Manuscripts and wardrobe coll - Library including rare books 04051

Museu e Arquivo Histórico do Centro Cultural Banco do Brasil, Rua Primeiro de Março 66, Rio de Janeiro 20010-000 - Fax: (021) 38082304, E-mail: ccbbrio@com.br, Internet: http://www.cultura-e.com.br. Head: Walter Nunes de Vasconcelos junior
Historical Museum - 1955
Numismatics, Brazilian coins - library 04052

Museu Ferroviário do Rio de Janeiro, Rua Arquias Cordeiro 1046, 20770-001 Rio de Janeiro 20770-001 - T: (021) 2695545
Science&Tech Museum
Train wagons and locomitives coll including the "Baronesa" 04053

Museu H. Stern, Rua García D'Ávila 113, Rio de Janeiro 22421-010 - T: (021) 22597442 ext 297/240, Fax: 25112598, E-mail: tmk@hstern.com.br. Head: Hans Stern
Special Museum
Prize winning Jewelery coll, rare minerals coll - workshop 04054

Museu Histórico da Cidade do Rio de Janeiro, Estrada Santa Marinha s/n, Gávea, Rio de Janeiro 22451-240 - T: (021) 5122353. Head: Beatriz de Vicq Carvalho
Local Museum - 1934
Rio de Janeiro art and history, furniture, weapons, coins and medals, paintings, engravings, watercolors, drawings, sculptures, chinaware, religious images, historical documents, banners, flags, jewels, instruments of torture of the black slaves - library 04055

Museu Histórico do Corpo de Bombeiros, Praça da República 45, Rio de Janeiro 20211-350 - T: (021) 2818103/1746
Special Museum 04056

Museu Histórico do Exército e Forte de Copacabana, Praça Coronel Eugênio Franco 01, Rio de Janeiro 22070-020 - T: (021) 5226136
Military Museum / Historic Site
Fort built in 1914 with military weapons coll 04057

Museu Histórico e Diplomático do Itamaraty, Av Marechal Floriano 196, Rio de Janeiro 20080-002 - T: (021) 2537691, Fax: 2633053. Head: J. Hermes Pereira de Araujo
Historical Museum / Fine Arts Museum - 1955
Art coll of the Baron of Rio Branco and Esteves Brandão coll - library, archives 04058

Museu Histórico Nacional, Praça Marechal Ancora, Rio de Janeiro 20021-200 - T: (021) 2409529, Fax: 2206290, E-mail: mhn02@visualnet.com.br, Internet: http://www.museuhistóricona-cional.com.br. Head: Vera Lúcia Bottrel Tostes
Historical Museum - 1922
National history, painting, prints, and ivories, porcelain, arms, numismatics, weapons 04059

Museu Inaldo de Lyra Neves-Manta, Academia Nacional de Medicina, Av General Justo 365, Castelo, Rio de Janeiro 20021-130 - T: (021) 25242034 ramal 40, Fax: 25242034, E-mail: musanm@uol.com.br, Internet: http://www.anm.org.br. Head: Glaciomar Machado
Science&Tech Museum / Historical Museum - 1898
Memorabilia of physicians who devoted themselves to the progress of medicine in Brazil, hist of medicine, equipment - medicine library 04060

Museu Internacional de Arte Naïf do Brasil (International Museum of Naive Art of Brazil), Rua Cosme Velho 561, Rio de Janeiro 22241-090 - T: (021) 22058612, 22058547, Fax: 2058884, E-mail: mian@museunaif.com.br, Internet: http://www.museunaif.com.br. Head: Jacqueline A. Finkelstein
Fine Arts Museum
Naïve art coll from Brazilian and International artists 04061

Museu Nacional, Parque Quinta da Boa Vista, Rio de Janeiro 20940-040 - T: (021) 2544320, Fax: 5688262 ext 232, E-mail: museu@acd.ufrj.br, Internet: http://www.acd.ufrj.br/museu. Head: Luiz Fernando Dias Duarte
Natural History Museum / Historical Museum / Archaeological Museum / Ethnology Museum - 1818
Archaeology, ethnology, natural history, anthropology, geology, botany, zoology, fossils, Egyptian and American antiquities - library 04062

Museu Nacional de Belas Artes, Av Rio Branco 199, Rio de Janeiro 20040-008 - T: (021) 2409869, Fax: 2626067, E-mail: diretoria@mmba.gov.br. Head: Prof. Heloisa A. Lustosa
Fine Arts Museum - 1937
Brazilian and European paintings, sculpture, graphic arts, furniture, primitive art, numismatics, posters - library 04063

Museu Naval e Oceanográfico (Naval Museum), Rua Dom Manuel 15, Rio de Janeiro 20010-090 - T: (021) 25337626, Fax: 25249360, E-mail: sdm30@sdm.mar.mil.br, Internet: http://www.sdm.mar.mil.br. Head: Paulo Roberto Oliveira Mesquita Spränger
Historical Museum / Military Museum - 1884
Maritime hist, navigation, maps, weapons, paintings, battleships and regional boat's models, medals, orders and decorations, nautical instruments, under-water archaeology - library 04064

Museu Navio Comandante Bauru, c/o Marina da Glória s/n, Pier da Praça Mauá, Rio de Janeiro 20021-000 - T: (021) 2539236
Military Museum 04065

Museu Numismático e Filatélico, Praça da República 173, Rio de Janeiro 20211-350 - T: (021) 2405267
Special Museum 04066

Museu Sitio Arqueológico Casa dos Pilões, Rua Jardim Botânico 1008, Rio de Janeiro 22460-010
Archaeological Museum / Special Museum 04067

Museu Teatro, Teatro Municipal, Av Rio Branco, Rio de Janeiro
Performing Arts Museum
Theater, dance 04068

Museu Universitário Gama Filho, Rua Manoel Vitorino 625 - Prédio ON, Rio de Janeiro 20740-280 - T: (021) 5997117
University Museum 04069

Museu Villa-Lobos, Rua Sorocaba 200, Botafogo, Rio de Janeiro 22271-110 - T: (021) 2663894, 2863097, Fax: 2663845, 5391715, E-mail: mvillalobos@museuvillalobos.org.br, Internet: http://www.museuvillalobos.org.br. Head: Turibio Santos
Music Museum - 1960
Memorabilia of the composer Heitor Villa-Lobos (1887-1959), books, documents, recordings 04070

Oficina Museu da Universidade Estácio de Sá, Rua do Bispo 83, Rio de Janeiro 20261-000 - T: (021) 5037000/7121
University Museum 04071

Paço Imperial, Praça XV de Novembro 48, Rio de Janeiro 20010-010
Local Museum 04072

Palácio das Laranjeiras, Rua Paulo César de Andrade 407, Rio de Janeiro 22221-090 - T: (021) 2850066
Local Museum 04073

Palácio Guanabara, Rua Pinheiro Machado s/n, Rio de Janeiro 22231-090
Local Museum 04074

Palácio Gustavo Capanema, Rua da Imprensa 16, Rio de Janeiro 20030-120 - T: (021) 2204139/1740
Local Museum 04075

Panteão Duque de Caxias, Praça Duque de Caxias 25, Rio de Janeiro 20221-260 - T: (021) 5185300
Military Museum / Special Museum
Belongings, insignia, ducal crown, sabers and tombstone of the Duque de Caxias 04076

Quartel de Santa Cruz, Praça Ruão 35, Rio de Janeiro 23570-200 - T: (021) 3951022
Military Museum 04077

Sítio Roberto Burle Marx, Estrada Barra de Guaratiba 2019, Rio de Janeiro 23020-240 - T: (021) 24101412, Fax: 24101412, E-mail: srburlemarx@iphan.gov.br. Head: Robério Dias
Local Museum / Fine Arts Museum / Open Air Museum 04078

Solar de Dom João VI, Rua Príncipe Regente 55, Rio de Janeiro 20397-010
Local Museum 04079

Solar Grandjean de Montigny, Rua Marquês de São Vicente 225, Rio de Janeiro 22453-900 - T: (021) 5299380/478
Local Museum 04080

Rio Grande

Museu Oceanográfico Prof. Eliézer de C. Rios, Rua Heitor Perdigão 10, Rio Grande, mail addr: CP 379, Rio Grande 96200-970 - T: (0532) 323496, Fax: 329633. Head: Lauro Barcellos
Natural History Museum - 1953
Largest seashell coll of Latin America, oceanography, ichthyology, malacology, algology, bentology - library 04081

Rio Pardo

Museo Municipal Barão de Santo Angelo, Rua Andrade Neves 324, Rio Pardo 96640-000
Local Museum - 1940
Costumes and traditions, arms and armor - library 04082

Sabará

Museu do Ouro, Rua da Intendência, Sabará 34505-480 - T: (031) 6711848, Fax: 6711848. Head: Selma Melo Miranda
Historical Museum - 1945
History and technology of gold mining, 18th c silver furniture, crafts of the mining regions - library 04083

Salvador

Casa dos Sete Candeeiros, Rua São Francisco 32, Salvador
Decorative Arts Museum
Furnishings, goldwork and objects d'art, portraits 04084

Museu Carlos Costa Pinto, Av Sete de Setembro 2490, Salvador 40080-001 - T: (071) 3366081, Fax: 3362702, E-mail: mccp@museucostapinto.com.br, Internet: http://www.museucostapinto.com.br. Head: Mercedes Rosa
Decorative Arts Museum - 1969
Brazilian jewelry, silver, porcelain, crystal, painting, furniture (17th-19th), Chinese and European porcelain (18th-19th c), jewelry and art objects, painting, silver, ivory, oriental rugs, drawings, sculpture, medals 04085

Museu Casa de Rui Barbosa, Rua Rui Barbosa 12, Salvador 40020-070
Special Museum
Books, photographs, documents and personal objects of Rui Barbosa 04086

Museu Castro Alves, Colégio Ipiranga, Rua do Sodré, Salvador 40060-240
Special Museum
Documents and personal objects of Castro Alves 04087

Museu de Arte Antiga → Museu Henriqueta Catharino

Museu de Arte da Bahia, Av 7 de Setembro 2340, Vitória, Salvador 40080-001 - T: (071) 3365642, Fax: 3364583. Head: Sylvia Athayde
Fine Arts Museum / Decorative Arts Museum - 1918
Furniture and porcelain, Bahian colonial art - library 04088

Museu de Arte Moderna da Bahia, Av Contorno s/n, Solar do Unhão, Salvador 40015-230 - T: (071) 2436174, Fax: 2412851. Head: Heitor Reis
Fine Arts Museum - 1959
Modern Brasilian art 04089

Museu de Arte Popular, Rua Desembargador Castelo Branco 1, Solar do Unhão, Salvador 40060-060
Folklore Museum - 1966
Popular arts and crafts 04090

Museu de Arte Sacra, Rua do Sodré 25, Salvador 40060-240 - T: (071) 2436110. Head: Prof. Pedro Moacir Maia
Religious Arts Museum
Religious art objects 04091

Museu de Arte Sacra da Catedral-Basílica, Praça Terreiro de Jesus, Salvador 40025-010
Religious Arts Museum
Icons and other religious art and artifacts from the 17th to 18th c 04092

Museu do Estado da Bahia, Convento do Carmo, Rua do Carmo s/n, Salvador 40030-130. Head: Gisélia Antonia Gomes Leite
Historical Museum / Fine Arts Museum - 1918
History and art 04093

Museu do Instituto Geografico e Historico da Bahia, Av Sete de Setembro 94, Salvador 40060-001. Head: Gisélia Antonia Gomes Leite
Historical Museum / Folklore Museum - 1894
Geography and history, folklore and mineralogy of Bahia 04094

Museu do Instituto Nina Rodrigues, Rua Alfredo Brito, Salvador 40025-040
Ethnology Museum - 1896
Anthropology, forensic medicine 04095

Museu Henriqueta Catharino, Instituto Feminino da Bahia, Rua Monsenhor Flaviano 2, Salvador 40080-150 - T: (071) 3295522, Fax: 3295681, E-mail: institutofemino@svn.com.br. Head: Henriqueta Martins Catharino
Decorative Arts Museum - 1933
Religious, decorative and popular art, national art, crafts in gold and silver, costumes, armaments, sea shells, human hair, slave liberation in 1888 04096

Santa Leopoldina

Museu do Colono, Rua Presidente Vargas s/n, Santa Leopoldina 29640-000
Decorative Arts Museum - 1968
Maps, rare Bibles, furniture, musical instruments, and other items of colonial domestic culture 04097

Santa Maria

Museu Victor Bersani, Rua Venâncio Aires 1934, Santa Maria 97100-004
Local Museum
Local history 04098

Santana do Ipanema

Museu Histórico e de Artes, Av Nossa Senhora de Fátima 181, Santana do Ipanema 57500-000
Local Museum - 1959
Popular culture, costumes, and art 04099

São Cristóvão

Museu Histórico de Sergipe, Praça São Francisco s/n, São Cristóvão 49100-000
Historical Museum - 1960
Arms and armor, sculptures, numismatics, furniture, porcelain - library 04100

São Gabriel

Museu João Pedro Nunes, Rua Cel. Sezefredo 536, São Gabriel 97300-000
Historical Museum / Decorative Arts Museum
Relics relating to the Revolutions of 1893 and 1923, applied art 04101

São João del Rei

Museu Municipal, Praça Frei Orlando 90, São João del Rei 36300-000
Local Museum - 1959
Antique telephones, lamps, paintings and portraits, period furniture, instruments of torture, natural history exhibits 04102

São Leopoldo

Museu Histórico Visconde de São Leopoldo, Rua Independência 111, São Leopoldo 93010-001 - T: (0512) 924557
Local Museum - 1959
History, geography, folklore - library 04103

São Paulo

Fundação Bienal de São Paulo, Arquivo Wanda Svevo, Parque Ibirapuera, São Paulo 04094-000, mail addr: CP 7832, 01064-970 São Paulo - T: (011) 5727722
Library with Exhibitions 04104

Museu da Cidade, Rua Roberto Simonsen 136, São Paulo 01017-020
Ethnology Museum - 1980
Ethnographic objects from Brazilian Indian tribes, 19th c household objects 04105

Museu da Imigração Japonesa no Brasil, Rua São Joaquim 381, São Paulo 01508-001 - T: (011) 2795465
Historical Museum
Documents relating to Japanese in Brasil 04106

Museu de Arqueologia e Etnologia da Universidade de São Paulo, Av Prof. Almeida Prado 1466, São Paulo 05508-900 - T: (011) 2124001, Fax: 8184904, Internet: http://www.mae.urp.br. Head: Prof. Paula Montero
Archaeological Museum / Ethnology Museum / University Museum - 1964
Classical, Mesopotamian, and pre-Columbian, pre-historical and Brazilian archaeology 04107

Museu de Arte Contemporânea da Universidade de São Paulo, Rua de Reitoria 160, São Paulo 05508-900 - T: (011) 38183538, Fax: 38120218, E-mail: mac@edu.usp.br, Internet: http://www.usp.br/mac. Head: Prof. Dr. José Teixeira Coelho Netto
Fine Arts Museum / University Museum - 1963
Painting, sculptures, prints and drawings by modern masters of the international school and Brazilian art (Amedeo Modigliani, Giorgio De Chirico, Umberto Boccioni, Di Cavalcanti, Tarsila do Amaral, Anita Malfatti, Massimo Campigli, Joseph Beuys, Fernand Léger, Max Bill) - library, art education department, archiv 04108

Museu de Arte de São Paulo Assis Chateaubriand, Av Paulista 1578, São Paulo 01310-200 - T: (011) 2515644, Fax: 32840574, E-mail: atemasp@masp.art.br, Internet: http://www.masp.art.br. Head: Julio Neves
Fine Arts Museum - 1947
Italian, Spanish, Dutch, Flemish, and French painting (classical and modern) - library 04109

Museu de Arte Moderna de São Paulo, Parque Ibirapuera em Frente à Bienal, São Paulo 04094-000 - T: (011) 50851300, Fax: 55492342, E-mail: curadoria@mam.org.br, Internet: http://www.mam.org.br. Head: Milu Villela
Fine Arts Museum - 1946
Modern and contemporary Brazilian art 04110

Museu de Arte Sacra, Av Tiradentes 676, São Paulo 01102-000 - T: (011) 2277694, Fax: 2277687, E-mail: Museu@artesacra.com.br, Internet: http://www.artesacra.com.br. Head: Mari Marino
Religious Arts Museum - 1970
Gold liturgical objects, religious art, ornaments, sculpture - library 04111

Museu de Etnografia Plinio Ayrosa, Universidade de São Paulo, São Paulo 05340-901, mail addr: CP 8105, São Paulo 01065-970
Ethnology Museum / University Museum - 1934
Relics of Brazilian Indian cultures, Tupi ceramics, Rio Negro wooden signal drums, Canella and Bororo coll 04112

Museu de Zoologia, Av Nazaré 481, São Paulo 04263-000, mail addr: c/o Universidade de São Paulo, CP 42694, São Paulo 04299-970 - T: (011) 61658121, Fax: 61658116, E-mail: crfbrand@usp.br, Internet: http://www.mz.usp.br. Head: Dr. Carlos Roberto Ferreira Brandão
Natural History Museum / University Museum - 1892
Animals of the neotropical region - library 04113

Museu Florestal Octávio Vecchi, Rua do Horto 931, Bairro Horto Florestal, São Paulo 02377-000 - T: (011) 9528555 ext 263/64, Fax: 2048067. Head: Dalmo Dippold Vilar
Natural History Museum - 1931
Forestry science and technology - Archeology and History Section 04114

Museu Folclorico da Divisão de Discoteca e Biblioteca de Música de São Paulo, Rua Catão 611, São Paulo 05049-000
Folklore Museum / Music Museum - 1935
Folklore, folk music 04115

Museu José Bonifácio, Instituto Histórico e Geográfico de São Paulo, Rua Benjamin Constant 158, São Paulo 01005-000 - T: (011) 2328064, Fax: 2323582. Head: Amélia Franzolin Trevisan, Brás Ciro Galotta
Historical Museum / Military Museum - 1958
Military equipment linked with the revolution of 1932 and the Paraguayan war, historical documents and objects, old coins from Brazil and other countries 04116

Museu Lasar Segall, Rua Berta 111, São Paulo 04120-040 - T: (011) 55747322, Fax: 55723586, E-mail: mlsegall.info@mls.gov.br, Internet: http://www.museusegall.org.br. Head: Carlos Magalhães, Marcelo Araujo
Fine Arts Museum - 1967
Books, paintings, prints and drawings, sculptures, photographies, docs - library 04117

Museu Paulista da Universidade de São Paulo, Parque da Independência, Ipiranga, São Paulo 04218-970, mail addr: CP 42503, São Paulo 04218-970 - T: (011) 2154588, Fax: 2154588, E-mail: mp@edu.usp.br, Internet: http://www.mp.usp.br. Head: Raquel Gleizer
Historical Museum / Local Museum / Religious Arts Museum / Decorative Arts Museum / University Museum - 1895
History, museology, philatelics, numismatics, material culture, furniture - library, archives 04118

Pinacoteca do Estado do São Paulo, Av Tiradentes 141, Luz, São Paulo 01101-010 - T: (011) 2276329, Fax: 2289637. Head: Emmanoel Araújo
Fine Arts Museum - 1906
Painting 04119

São Paulo Telephone Museum, Av Ipiranga 200, São Paulo 01046-010 - T: (011) 2857007, Fax: 2145919, E-mail: museu@telesp.com.br. Head: Elza Maria Vasques La Farina
Science&Tech Museum - 1977
Telecommunications, including videophone and facsimile equipment 04120

Sobral

Museu Diocesano, Av Dom José 878, Sobral 62100-290 - T: (085) 6113525. Head: Manoel Valdeny da Rocha
Religious Arts Museum - 1952
Furnishings, coins, objects d'art, rare books, religious art, and items of ethnographic interest 04121

Teresina

Museu do Piauí, Praça Marechal Deodoro, Teresina 64000-160 - T: (086) 2226027. Head: Selma Duarte Ferreira
Fine Arts Museum / Local Museum - 1980
Art, history 04122

Museu Histórico do Piaú, Casa Anísio de Brito, Rua Coelho Rodrigues 1016, Teresina 64000-080
Historical Museum - 1947
Numismatics (Brazil and Portugal), ethnography, fossils, arms, porcelain, furniture, and objects d'art 04123

Teresópolis

Museu von Martius, Av Rotariana s/n, Teresópolis
Natural History Museum - 1971
Botany, manuscripts 04124

Triunfo

Museu Farroupilha, Av Luis Barreto 23, Triunfo 95840-000 - T: (051) 6511299. Head: Rodrigo Fernando Casagrande
Local Museum 04125

Vitória

Museu Capela Santa Luzia, c/o Universidade Federal do Espírito Santo, Rua José Marcelino, Vitória 29015-120
Decorative Arts Museum / Fine Arts Museum / University Museum
Furniture, jewellery, religious art, paintings 04126

Museu de Arte e Historia da Universidade Federal do Espírito Santo, Av 15 de Novembro, Jucutuquara, Vitória 29020-260 - T: (027) 2270798
Fine Arts Museum / Historical Museum / University Museum - 1939
Religious art, archeology, folklore and history 04127

Museu de Arte Religiosa, Rua José Marcelino s/n, Vitória 29015-120
Religious Arts Museum 04128

Museu Solar Monjardim, c/o Universidade Federal do Espirito Santo, Av Paulino Muller, Jucutuquara, Vitória 29042-571 - T: (027) 2223788. Head: Prof. Calebe Pires Martins
Historical Museum / University Museum - 1939
Furniture, archeology, items of local historical interest, locale folklore, instruments of torture, clocks and watches, etc 04129

Brunei

Bandar Seri Begawan

Bangunan Alat Kebesaran Diraja (Royal Regalia Gallery), Jalan Sultan, Bandar Seri Begawan BS 8811 - T: (02) 238358, 238360, Fax: 242727, E-mail: bmexhib@brunet.bn. Head: Mohamed Jadid Hashim Bin
Fine Arts Museum - 1992 04130

Constitutional History Gallery, Jalan Sultan, Bandar Seri Begawan 2085 - T: (02) 238362, Fax: 242727. Head: Mohamed Jadid Hashim Bin
Historical Museum - 1971
Constitutional hist and development of Brunei 04131

Exhibition Gallery of the Islamic Dáwah Centre, Kampong Pulaie, Bandar Seri Begawan BB4310 - T: (02) 383996, Fax: 381293, Internet: http://www.pusat-dakwah.gov.bn. Head: Awang Haji Adam bin Haji Ahmad
Religious Arts Museum - 1985
Hist of Islam in Brunei 04132

Muzium Brunei (Brunei Museum), Jalan Kota Batu, Bandar Seri Begawan BD 1510 - T: (02) 244545/6, Fax: 242727, E-mail: bmdir@brunet.bn, Internet: http://www.museums.gov.bn. Head: Matassim Bin Haji Jibah
Local Museum - 1965
Archaeology, ethnography, Borneo hist, photographs - library, archives 04133

Muzium Teknologi Melayu (Malay Technology Museum), Jalan Kota Batu, Bandar Seri Begawan BD 1510 - T: (02) 244545 ext 150, 242862, Fax: 242727, E-mail: bmethno@brunet.bn
Science&Tech Museum / Agriculture Museum / Ethnology Museum - 1988
Traditional industries 04134

Pusat Latihan Kesenian & Pertukangan Tangan Brunei (Brunei Arts and Handicrafts Training Centre), Jalan Residency, Bandar Seri Begawan BS 8110 - T: (02) 240676, 240391, Fax: 241909, E-mail: plphead@brunet.bn
Decorative Arts Museum / Fine Arts Museum - 1975
Arts, crafts 04135

Royal Brunei Armed Forces Museum, Bolkiah Camp, Jalan Berakas, Bandar Seri Begawan 1110 - T: (02) 30531
Military Museum - 1977
Small warships, including the world's fastest patrol boat, helicopters, armored vehicles, small arms, regiment insignia - library 04136

Sungai Liang

Brunei Forestry Museum, Sungai Liang KC 1135 - T: (03) 230385, E-mail: jphq@brunet.bn. Head: Haji Abdul Rahman Bin Haji Chuchu
Natural History Museum - 1986
Natural hist, forestry 04137

Tutong

Taman Warisan Merimbun (Merimbun Heritage Park), Tutong TH 1349 - T: (04) 261179, Fax: (02) 242727, E-mail: bmnahis@brunet.bn
Local Museum 04138

Bulgaria

Asenovgrad

Gradski Istoričeski Muzej (Municipal Historical Museum), ul Georgi Dimitrov 27, 4230 Asenovgrad - T: 2150. Head: Dafina Karaivanova
Local Museum
Archeology, history of the 18th-19th c Bulgarian National Revival period and liberation movement, history of capitalism and the revolutionary labour movement 04139

Babuk

Kašta-muzej Došo Mihajlov, 7573 Babuk - T: 98521379
Special Museum 04140

Bachkovo

Bachkovski Manastir muzej (Bachkovo Monastery Museum), 4251 Bachkovo
Religious Arts Museum
History of the monastery, religious art, icons, folk art, jewelry 04141

Balčik

Gradski Istoričeski Muzej (Municipal Historical Museum), pl Deveti Septemvri, kulturen dom, 9600 Balčik - T: (0579) 2177. Head: Darin Kanarov
Local Museum
Thracian, Greek and Roman archeology, hist of the Bulgarian National Revival period (18th-19th c), contemporary history, art 04142

Bansko

Kašta-muzej Nikola Ënkov Vapcarov (N.Y. Vaptsarov Memorial House), pl Vapcarov 9, 2770 Bansko - T: (07443) 2345. Head: Elena Erinina
Special Museum
Memorabilia on the poet and revolutionist N.Y. Vaptsarov (1909-1942) in his birthplace, manuscripts, first editions of his poems, personal possessions, history of the anti-Fascist movement in Bulgaria 04143

Batak

Istoričeski Muzej (Historical Museum), Pl Osvoboždenie 3, 4580 Batak - T: (03553) 2339, Fax: 2030. Head: Chaterina Peičinova
Historical Museum / Ethnology Museum - 1956
Hist of the 18th-19th c Bulgarian National Revival period and liberation movement, esp hist of the April 1876 Uprising, ethnological expo 04144

Belogradčik

Municipal Muzei Belogradčik (Municipal Historical Museum), pl Colo Todorov, 3900 Belogradčik - T: 3469. Head: Angel Malkočev
Local Museum - 1960
Hist of the Belogradchik Uprising (1850) and liberation movement, agriculture, animal husbandry, smithwork, tools, copper smithery, pottery, textiles, a house built 1810, goldsmith's trade 04145

Prirodonaučen Muzej (Natural History Museum), Loven park, 3900 Belogradčik - T: 3231. Head: Emil Džuninski
Natural History Museum 04146

Berkovica

Etnografski Muzej (Ethnographical Museum), ul Poručik Grozdanov, 3500 Berkovica - T: (0953) 2235. Head: Christo Paškulev
Ethnology Museum - 1974
Ethnography, folk art, crafts, folk costumes, in a 19th c house 04147

Gradska Chudožestvena Galerija (City Art Gallery), 3500 Berkovica - T: (0953) 2244. Head: Christo Michailov
Fine Arts Museum
Bulgarian fine art 04148

Kašta-muzej Ivan Vazov (Ivan Vazov Memorial House), ul Poruchik Grozdanov 2, 3500 Berkovica - T: (0953) 2289. Head: Anna Apostolova
Special Museum
Memorabilia on the Bulgarian national writer Ivan Vazov (1850-1921) and his stay in Berkovitsa 1879-1880, in a 19th c house 04149

Bjala

Voenno-istoričeski Muzej Osvoboditelna Vojna 1877-1878 (Military History Museum War of Liberation 1877-1878), ul Julija Vrevskaja 2, 7200 Bjala - T: 2466. Head: Mariya Bogdanova
Military Museum
History of the Russo-Turkish War 1877-1878, documents, uniforms, weapons, banner, lithographs 04150

Bjala Čerkva

Kašta-muzej Canko Cerkovski, ul Canko Cerkovski 6, 5220 Bjala Čerkva - T: 633. Head: Angel Petrov
Local Museum 04151

Blagoevgrad

Istoričeski Muzej (Historical Museum), Rila 1, 2700 Blagoevgrad - T: 29020, Fax: 29020. Head: Kamelia Grančarova
Historical Museum - 1951
Archeology, natural hist, ethnology, art, hist of Bulgaria 15th c-1912, 1912 till now, public relations, numismatics, record office 04152

Nacionalen Park-muzej Samuiulova krepost, 2700 Blagoevgrad - T: 997427
Open Air Museum 04153

Botevgrad

Gradski Istoričeski Muzej (Municipal Historical Museum), Cherven ploshtad, 2140 Botevgrad - T: 2080. Head: Tedor Valtchev
Local Museum
Div: archeology, history of the Bulgarian National Revival period and liberation movement, ethnography, history of capitalism and the revolutionary labour movement, contemporary history 04154

Boženci

Muzej-rezervat, 5349 Boženci - T: 34462. Head: Boganil Boev
Open Air Museum
The village is an architectonic and ethnographic reserve, representing the life of the Bulgarian National Revival period, several 18th-19th c houses, original interiors, traditional Bulgarian wood-carved ceilings, ironworks, domestic utensils, carpets, textiles, embroideries 04155

Bradvari

Kašta-muzej Nikola P. Karadžchata, 7568 Bradvari - T: 98510889
Special Museum 04156

Brazigovo

Istoričeski Muzej (Historical Museum), ul Kostur 2, 4579 Brazigovo - T: 2139. Head: Stoianka Iordanova
Local Museum
Hist of the Bulgarian National Revival period and liberation movement, hist of the April 1876 Uprising, weapons, banners, documents, contemporary hist 04157

Burgas

Etnografski muzej, Okräžen Istoričeski Muzej (Ethnographical Museum), Jana Lăskova 31, 8000 Burgas - T: (056) 47596. Head: Krali Kralev
Ethnology Museum
Folk costumes, domestic utensils, interiors, crafts, in a 19th c house 04158

Istoričeski Muzej (Historical Museum), Slavjanska 69, 8000 Burgas - T: (056) 40293. Head: C. Draževa
Local Museum - 1947
Archaeology of the Black-Sea Greek colonies Apolonia, Messembria and Anchialos, ceramics, gold jewelry, tombstones, hist of the national liberation movement, natural hist, ethnography 04159

Okräžna Chudožestvena Galerija (Regional Art Gallery), ul Saint Vodenicharov 24, 8000 Burgas - T: (056) 42803. Head: Nenko Tokmaktčiev
Fine Arts Museum - 1966
Paintings by I. Mrkvichka, Z. Todorov, N. Mikhailov, V. Dimitrov-Maistora, G. Mitev, G. Baev, T. Atanasov, Yani Khristopulos etc, icon coll 04160

Čepelare

Muzej na Rodopskija Karst (Cave Museum of the Rhodopes), ul Shina Andreeva 7A, 4850 Čepelare - T: 3041, E-mail: mus_speleologia@yahoo.com. Head: Maria Barzakova
Natural History Museum - 1980
Geology of the region, caves minerals, biospeleology coll, paleontology and anthropology coll 04161

Chaskovo

Muzej Chaskovski Zatvor 1923-1944, 6300 Chaskovo - T: (038) 32067. Head: Georgi Gramatikov
Local Museum 04162

Okräžen Istoričeski Muzej (Regional Historical Museum), ul Car Osvoboditel 10, 6300 Chaskovo - T: (038) 32067. Head: G. Gramatikov
Local Museum - 1952
Archaeology, Bulgarian National Revival period and liberation movement, ethnography, hist of capitalism and the labour movement 04163

Čirpan

Gradski Istoričeski Muzej (Municipal Historical Museum), ul Tanyo Peev, 6200 Čirpan
Local Museum
Regional history 04164

Kašta-muzej Peë K. Javorov, ul Kračolovi 28, 6200 Čirpan - T: 4019. Head: Dimitar Danajlov
Special Museum 04165

Muzej na Revoljucionnoto Dviženie, ul Tanjo Peev 7, 6200 Čirpan - T: 2230. Head: Ganka Slabakova
Historical Museum 04166

Čurek

Muzej na Partizanskij Otrjad Chavdar (Museum of the Partisan Brigade Chavdar), mestnost Žerkovo, 2126 Čurek
Historical Museum
History of the partisan struggle during World War II, weapons, documents 04167

Dalgopol

Gradski Istoričeski Muzej (Municipal Historical Museum), 9250 Dalgopol - T: 2181. Head: Ivan Ivanov
Local Museum
Ethnography, local history 04168

Dimitrovgrad

History Museum, ul Kliment Ohridski 7, 6400 Dimitrovgrad - T: (0391) 23787, E-mail: - dimitrovgrad_museum@yahoo.com. Head: Elene Georgieva
Historical Museum 04169

Dobrič

Art Gallery Dobrič, ul Bulgaria 14, 9300 Dobrič - T: (058) 28215. Head: Evelina Handzhieva
Fine Arts Museum - 1964
Foreign print works, graphic art, contemporary Bulgarian fine art, coll 'Paper Art', Albin Brunovski, Rolf Escher, Kounito Nagaoka, Atsouo Sakatsoume, Paul Wunderlich, Rolf Münzner 04170

Ethnographical Museum, 24, 25 Septemvri, 9300 Dobrič, mail addr: PK 131, 9300 Dobrič - T: (058) 24717, Fax: 28256, E-mail: museum@dobrich.net. Head: Diana Borisova
Ethnology Museum - 1970
Bulgarian folk costumes and spiritual culture of the Bulgarians, handwoven materials, clothes, ornaments, jewels, copper vessels, tools 04171

Istoričeski Muzej (Museum of History), 18 Konstantin Stoilov, 9300 Dobrič - T: (058) 28256, Fax: 28256, E-mail: museum@dobrich.net. Head: Diana Borisova
Local Museum - 1953
Archaeology, hist of the Bulgarian National Revival period, ethnography, cemetery from WWI, hist of capitalism and National liberation movement against Romanian domination, contemporary hist, natural hist 04172

Kašta-muzej s Dom Pametnik Jordan Jovkov (House Museum and Memorial House of Jordan Jovkov), 4 Gurko, 9300 Dobrič, mail addr: PK 131, 9300 Dobrič - T: (058) 28213, Fax: 28213, E-mail: dobrichmuseum@abv.bg. Head: Kremena Miteva
Special Museum - 1980
Literature and theatre, works by J. Jovkov 04173

Open Air Museum Old Dobrich, ul Konstantin Stoilov 18, 9300 Dobrič, mail addr: PK 131, 9300 Dobrič - T: (058) 22642, E-mail: museum@dobrich.net. Head: Diana Borisova
Open Air Museum / Local Museum 04174

Draganovo

Kašta-muzej Asen Razcvetnikov, ul Oboriste, 5137 Draganovo - T: (0618) 41464. Head: Natalia Sovaudjieva
Local Museum - 1976 04175

Drjanovo

Dryanovski Manastir Muzej (Dryanovo Monastery Museum), 5370 Drjanovo - T: 2097. Head: Tonja Beltcheva
Historical Museum
History of the monastery, history of the April 1876 Uprising against Ottoman rule, documents, photographs, arms 04176

Istoričeski Muzej (Historical Museum), ul Lipka 59, 5370 Drjanovo - T: 2097. Head: Tonja Belčeva
Historical Museum 04177

Muzej Kolju Fičevo (Kolja Fichev Museum), ul Šipka 59, 5370 Drjanovo - T: 2097. Head: Tonja Beltcheva
Historical Museum
History of Bulgarian architecture during the National Revival period (18th-19th c), tools, models, memorabilia on the architect Nikola Fichev, also known as Kolyu Ficheto 04178

Elčovo

Etnografski Muzej (Ethnographical Museum), ul Šipka 4, 8700 Elčovo - T: (0478) 2217. Head: Christo Christov
Ethnology Museum - 1959
Ethnography, folk art 04179

Elena

Văzroždendki Muzej Ilarion Makariopolski (I. Makariopolski Museum of Bulgarian National Revival Period), ul Dojčo Gramatik 2, 5070 Elena - T: 2214. Head: Georgi Stefanov
Historical Museum
Memorabilia of Ilarion Makariopolski, religious history, local history, history of education, memorabilia of the poet P.J. Todorov, icon coll, paintings, history of the labour movement 04180

Etropole

Obščinski Istoričeski Muzej (Municipal Historical Museum), ul christo Botev, 2170 Etropole - T: 2124. Head: Natalija Cvetkova
Local Museum - 1958
Archeology, hist of the Bulgarian National Revival period and the liberation movement, ethnography, hist of capitalism and the revolutionary labour movement, contemporary hist, renaissance house 04181

Gabrovo

Architekturno-etnografski Muzej Etara (Open-Air Museum of Ethnography), Kvartal Etar, 5300 Gabrovo - T: (066) 42023, Fax: 42023, E-mail: etar@gb.bia-bg.com. Head: Karamfila Grudova
Ethnology Museum / Open Air Museum - 1963
Old crafts of the Bulgarian National Revival Period (18th-19th c), several workshops, equipped with original tools and still in operation, show the development of various crafts: goldsmithery, weaving, mills, dyeing, pottery, ironwork, cutlery, shoemaking, carpet manufacturing, bakery 04182

Dom na Humora i Satirata (House of Humour and Satire), ul Brjanska 68, 5300 Gabrovo, mail addr: PK 104, 5300 Gabrovo - T: (066) 27229, 29300, Fax: 26989, E-mail: humorhouse@mbox.stemo.bg, Internet: http://www.humorhouse.org. Head: Tatjana Cankova
Special Museum 04183

Istoričeski Muzej (Historical Museum), ul Opalstenska 19, 5300 Gabrovo - T: (066) 25218, Fax: 25218. Head: Peter Totzev
Local Museum - 1883
Archaeology, hist of the Bulgarian National Revival Period and liberation movement, ethnography, industry and labour movement, nature coll 04184

Kašta-muzej Mitko Palauzov, Okräžen muzej Gabrovo (Mitko Palauzov Memorial House), ul Veselie 3, 5300 Gabrovo - T: (066) 25218. Head: Stansho Stanshev
Special Museum
Memorabilia of the child partisan Dimităr Trifonov Palauzov, also known as Mitko, who was killed by the fascists at the age of eleven 04185

Muzej na Narodnoto Obrazovanie (Museum of Public Education), ul Aprilovska 15, 5300 Gabrovo - T: (066) 27011. Head: Tsanko Denkov
Special Museum - 1973
History of education in Bulgaria 04186

Georgi Damianovo

Kašta-muzej Georgi Damianovo, 3470 Georgi Damianovo - T: 364
Special Museum 04187

Gorna Studena

Voenno-istoričeski Muzej (Museum of Military History), 5294 Gorna Studena - T: 620. Head: Lili Apostolova
Military Museum 04188

Gorni Dabnik

Park-muzej General V.Z. Lavrov, 5880 Gorni Dabnik - T: 2264, 22623. Head: Michail Grantčarov
Open Air Museum / Military Museum - 1954
Place in Lavrov Park where the fiercest battle of the war of liberation was fought in 1877 (Russian-Turkish War for Bulgaria), documents, memorabilia of General Lavrov and other fallen warriors 04189

Haskovo

Regional Museum of History, pl Svoboda, 6300 Haskovo - T: 32067. Head: G. Gramatikov
Local Museum - 1952 04190

Hisar

Gradski Archeologičeski Muzej (Municipal Archeological Museum), ul Aleksandăr Stambolijski 8, 4180 Hisar - T: (0337) 2796. Head: Mitko Madjarov
Archaeological Museum - 1953
Prehistoric archeology, Roman finds 04191

Ichtiman

Istoričeski Muzej (History Museum), ul Car Osvoboditel 84, 2050 Ichtiman - T: (0724) 2226. Head: Julia Jankova
Historical Museum
Ethnography, local hist, hist of the revolutionary labour movement, hist of the September 1923 Uprising and anti-Fascist struggle (1941-1944) 04192

Jambol

Nacionalen Archeologičeski Rezervat Kabile (National Archaeological Reserve Cabyle), 8600 Jambol - T: (046) 62736,, Fax: 63376, E-mail: thor@descom.com, Internet: http://www.descom.com/museum. Head: Dr. Dimitar Draganov
Open Air Museum / Archaeological Museum 04193

Oblasten Istoričeski Muzej (Museum of History), Bjalo more 2, 8600 Jambol - T: (046) 62736, 63403, 63416, Fax: 63376, E-mail: thor@descom.com, Internet: http://www.descom.com/museum. Head: Dr. Dimitar Draganov
Historical Museum - 1952
Archeology, hist of the Jambol region, ethnography, numismatics 04194

Okräžna Chudožestvena Galerija (Regional Art Gallery), ul M. Rubenova 10, 8600 Jambol - T: (046) 21010. Head: Ivan Ivanov
Fine Arts Museum - 1980
Contemporary Bulgarian fine art 04195

Jeravna

Chudožestvena Galerija, ul G. Dimitrov 2, 8988 Jeravna - T: 202. Head: Galia Nedeva
Fine Arts Museum 04196

Gradski Istoričeski Muzej (Municipal Historical Museum), 8988 Jeravna - T: 286. Head: Plamen Merdjanov
Local Museum
Local hist, archaeology, hist of the Bulgarian Revival period 04197

Kalipetrovo

Etnografski Kompleks (Ethnographical complex), 7500 Kalipetrovo - T: 23855, 42815
Ethnology Museum 04198

Kalofer

Kašta-muzej Christo Botev (Cristo Botev Memorial House), ul Christo Botev 15, 4370 Kalofer - T: 2271. Head: A. Nikolova
Special Museum - 1945
Memorabilia on Khristo Botev, Bulgarian national poet, publicist and revolutionist, manuscripts, books, documents on his revolutionary activity in Romania, hist of the Bulgarian national liberation movement against the Ottoman rule 04199

Kardžali

Okražna Chudožestvena Galerija, ul Republikanska 5, 6600 Kardžali - T: (0361) 264654, 23619, Fax: 24785, E-mail: hmuzkj@infotel.bg. Head: Pavel Petkov
Open Air Museum / Local Museum 04200

Regionalen Istoričeski Muzej (Regional Museum of History), ul Republikanska 4, 6600 Kardžali - T: (0361) 24785, Fax: 24785, E-mail: hmuzkj@infotel.bg. Head: Pavel Petkov
Local Museum - 1960
Div: archeology, Bulgarian National Revival period and liberation movement, ethnography, history of capitalism and the revolutionary labour movement, development of socialism, local nature 04201

Karlovo

Istoričeski Muzej (Municipal Historical Museum), Vazrozhdenska 4, 4300 Karlovo - T: (0335) 4728. Head: Pepa Tododrova
Local Museum
Archeology, history of the Bulgarian National Revival period and liberation movement, ethnography, contemporary history 04202

Muzej Vasil Levski (Vasil Levski Museum), Gen. Karcov 57, 4300 Karlovo - T: (0335) 3489, E-mail: v_levski_museum@orbitel.bg. Head: D. Čauševa
Historical Museum - 1937
Birthplace of Vasil Levski (1837-1873), founder and organizer of the Intternal Revolutionary Committee for the liberation of Bulgaria, hist of the 19th c liberation movement against Ottoman rule, documents 04203

Karnobat

Gradski Istoričeski Muzej (Municipal Historical Museum), blvd Lenin 18, 8400 Karnobat - T: (0559) 7143. Head: Dimkho Momkhilov
Local Museum - 1921
Archeology, local history, ethnography, nature 04204

Kašta-muzej Dimitǎr Polyanov (Memorial House of Dimitar Poljanov), ul Dimitar Polianov 4, 8400 Karnobat - T: (0559) 2206. Head: Natasha Chakarova Krasteva
Special Museum - 1973
Hist, literature 04205

Kavarna

Gradski Istoričeski Muzej (Municipal Historical Museum), ul Dobroticsa 24, 9650 Kavarna - T: (0570) 2150. Head: Asen Salkin
Local Museum
Local history 04206

Kazanlǎk

Chudožestvena Galerija (Art Gallery), ul P.R. Slaveikov 8, 6100 Kazanlǎk - T: (0431) 63104, 63762, E-mail: kagal@mail.bg. Head: Hristo Genev
Fine Arts Museum - 1901
Icons, decorative arts, ex-libris 04207

Dom-pametnik na Vrach Buzludža, ul Skobelev 3, 6100 Kazanlǎk - T: (0431) 24418, 23852
Special Museum 04208

Gradski Istoričeski Muzej (Municipal Historical Museum), ul Sloveykov 8, 6100 Kazanlǎk - T: (0431) 23741. Head: Dr. Kossio Zarev
Historical Museum - 1901
Div: archeology, hist of the Bulgarian National Revival period and liberation movement, ethnography, hist of capitalism and the labour movement, contemporary hist 04209

Kašta-muzej Dimitǎr Čorbadžiski-Čudomir, ul Trapezica 8, 6100 Kazanlǎk - T: (0431) 24449. Head: Metodi Takhev
Local Museum 04210

Kazanlǎshka Roza, Gradski istoričeski muzej (Museum of the Rose), ul Slovejkov 8, 6100 Kazanlǎk - T: (0431) 25170. Head: Dr. Kossio Zarev
Ethnology Museum - 1968
Hist of the production of rose oil, a fragrant essential oil, obtained from special roses and used chiefly in perfumery and in flavoring, old tools, destillation equipment 04211

Nacionalen Park-muzej Šipka-Buzludža (National Park Museum Shipka-Budloudzha), ul P.R. Slavejkov 8, 6100 Kazanlǎk - T: (0431) 62495, Fax: 64787, E-mail: shipkamuseum@mail.bg. Head: Dancho Danchev
Open Air Museum / Military Museum / Religious Arts Museum - 1956
Military hist, religious art, scene of major battles during Russian-Turkish war (1877-1878), hist of national liberation movement against Otoman rule 04212

Kjustendil

Okražen Istoričeski Muzej (Regional Museum of History), Av Bulgaria 55, 2500 Kjustendil, mail addr: PK 258, 2500 Kyustendil - T: (078) 26396, Fax: 26396. Head: Ilia Simeonov Prokopov
Historical Museum - 1897
Archeology, ethnology, Bulgarian National Revival, modern hist - library, archives 04213

Okražna Chudožestvena Galerija Vladimir Dimitrov-Maistora, ul Lyuben Karavelov 1, 2500 Kjustendil - T: (078) 22503. Head: Nedko Kableshkov
Fine Arts Museum
Bulgarian painting, especially works of Vladimir Dimitrov-Majstora 04214

Klisura

Gradski Istoričeski Muzej (Municipal Historical Museum), ul 20 April 27, 4341 Klisura - T: (0313) 72004. Head: Penka Docheva
Local Museum
Hist of the April 1876 Uprising, documents, maps, arms 04215

Koprivštica

Etnografski Muzej Oslekova kǎšta (Ethnographic Museum in the Oslekov House), ul Generiloto 6, 2090 Koprivštica
Ethnology Museum - 1958
Ethnography, folk art, wood carvings, mural paintings, original interiors, in a house built in 1856 04216

Kašta-muzej Dimcho Debelyanov (Dimcho Debelyanov Memorial House), 2090 Koprivštica
Special Museum - 1958
Memorabilia of the poet Dimcho Debelyanov (1887-1916), books, first editions, in his birthplace built in 1830 04217

Kašta-muzej Ljuben Karavelov (Lyuben Karavelov Memorial House), 2090 Koprivštica
Special Museum - 1958
Memorabilia of the writer and revolutionist Lyuben Karavelov (1837-1879), history of the Bulgarian National Revival period, in his birthplace built in 1810 04218

Kašta-muzej Todor Kableškov (Todor Kableshkov Memorial House), 2090 Koprivštica
Special Museum - 1958
Memorabilia of the revolutionist Todor Kableshkov, history of the Bulgarian National Revival period and the April 1876 Uprising against Ottoman rule, in his birthplace built in 1845 04219

Muzej na Gradskij Bit Oslekova Kašta, pl 20 April 6, 2090 Koprivštica - T: 2180. Head: J. Dorosiev
Historical Museum 04220

Kotel

Izložba na Stari Kotlenski Kilimi, Muzej na Kotlenskite Vazroždenci i Panteon na Georgi S. Rakowski (Exposition of Old Bulgarian Carpets), Isvorska ul 17, 8970 Kotel - T: (0453) 2316, Fax: 2540, E-mail: obkotel@mbox.infotel.bgf. Head: Stefan Ivanov
Decorative Arts Museum - 1990
Old original Kotel carpets, woven materials and demonstration of weaving 04221

Kěrpeeva Kašta (Kyorpeev's House), ul Kěrpeev, 8970 Kotel - T: (0453) 2315. Head: Plamen Merdjanov
Ethnology Museum / Decorative Arts Museum
19th c Kotel architecture, original interiors, Kotel carpets, textiles, jewelry, costumes 04222

Muzej na Kotlenskite Vazroždenci i Panteon na Georgi S. Rakovski (Kotel Enlighteners Museum and Rakovski Pantheon), pl Vazraždane 3, 8970 Kotel - T: (0453) 2549. Head: Plamen Merdjanov
Historical Museum - 1981
Local and regional hist, hist of the Bulgarian National Revival period and liberation movement in the 18th-19th c, memorabilia on the revolutionist and publicist Georgi S. Rakovski (1821-1867), memorabilia on Neofit Bozveli, organizer of the fight for Independent Orthodox Bulgarian Church, documents on literary and pedagogic activities of Dr Petǎr Beron etc 04223

Prirodonaučen Muzej (Natural History Museum), Louda Kamčija 3, 8970 Kotel - T: (0453) 2355, Fax: 2540, E-mail: obkotel@mbox.infotel.bg. Head: Veselin Talazov
Natural History Museum
Natural history, geological science, invertebrate fossiles, plants, amphibians, reptiles, fishes 04224

Kovačevci

Kašta-muzej Georgi Dimitrov (Georgi Dimitrov Memorial House), ul Georgi Dimitrov 1, 2450 Kovačevci. Head: Ognian Asprov
Special Museum
Memorabilia on the politician Georgi Dimitrov (1882-1949) in his birthplace, history of the international labour movement 04225

Kozloduj

Nacionalen Muzej Korab Radecki, ul Radecki 1, 3320 Kozloduj - T: 20373
Historical Museum 04226

Lom

Gradski Istoričeski Muzej (Municipal Historical Museum), ul Eremiya Bǎlgarov 6, 3600 Lom - T: (0971) 2489. Head: Aleksandar Mihailov
Local Museum
Archeology, history of the Bulgarian National Revival Period and liberation movement, ethnography, contemporary history 04227

Loveš

Muzej Vasil Levski (Vasil Levski Memorial House), ul Marin Pop Lukanov 14, 5500 Loveš - T: (068) 27990. Head: Ivan Lalev
Special Museum
Memorabilia on Vasil Levski (1837-1873), founder and organizer of the Revolutionary Committee the for Liberation of Bulgaria, history of the 19th c liberation movement against Ottoman rule 04228

Okražen Istoričeski Muzej (Regional Museum of History), pl Todor Kirkov 1, 5500 Loveš - T: (068) 26259. Head: I. Lalev
Local Museum - 1895
Div: archeology, hist of the Bulgarian National Revival Period (18th-19th c) and liberation movement, ethnography, hist of capitalism and the revolutionary labour movement, development of socialism 04229

Madan

Muzej na Rudodobiva i Minnoto Delo, ul Republikanska 3, 4900 Madan - T: 2465
Special Museum 04230

Muzej na Socialističeskoto Stroitelstvo (Museum of Socialist Development), ul Republika 3, 4900 Madan - T: 2465. Head: Ivan Ivanov
Historical Museum
Contemporary history 04231

Madara

Muzej Rafail Popov (Rafail Popov Museum), 9750 Madara - T: 57410. Head: Dečko Lečev
Archaeological Museum
Archaeological material from local excavations, prehistory, flint tools, weapons 04232

Medven

Kašta-muzej Zahari Stojanov, ul Zahari Stojanov 9, 8987 Medven. Head: Plamen Merdjanov
Historical Museum 04233

Melnik

Gradski Istoričeski Muzej (Municipal Historical Museum), ul G. Dimitrov 2, 2820 Melnik - T: 229. Head: Georgi Stoyanov
Local Museum - 1953
Archeology, ethnography, national liberation movement, history of the Bulgarian National Revival Period (19th c) 04234

Pashova Kǎshta, ul Ivan Ivanov 1, 2820 Melnik - T: 229. Head: Georgi Stoyanov
Historical Museum 04235

Mezdra

Chudožestvena Galerija (Art Gallery), ul Christo Botev 50, 3100 Mezdra - T: 2417. Head: Veneta Balkanska
Fine Arts Museum 04236

Michajlovgrad

Chudožestvena Galerija (Art Gallery), blvd Aleksandar Stamboliski 12, 3400 Michajlovgrad - T: (096) 25216. Head: Teodosi Antonov
Fine Arts Museum 04237

Kašta-muzej Christo i Ivan Michailovi, ul Ivan Bobanov 17, 3400 Michajlovgrad - T: (096) 22589. Head: Radka Nikolova
Historical Museum 04238

Muzej na Septemvrijskoto Văstanie (Museum of the September Uprising), ul Vasil Kolarov 3, 3400 Michajlovgrad - T: (096) 22489. Head: Uljana Darakčijska
Historical Museum
History of the September 1923 Uprising, revolutionary movement (1925-1944) and anti-Fascist struggle (1941-1944), documents, photographs, maps, weapons, memorabilia on the politicians Vasil Kolarov (1877-1950) and Georgi Dimitrov (1882-1949) 04239

Montana

Okražen Istoričeski Muzej (Regional Museum of History), Tsar Boris III 2, 3400 Montana - T: 28481, Fax: 22536. Head: U. Derakčiiaska
Local Museum - 1935 04240

Nesebâr

Gradski Archeologičeski Muzej (Archaeological Museum), 8230 Nesebâr - T: (0554) 46018, Fax: 46018. Head: Dimo Kozhukharov
Archaeological Museum - 1956
Archeology, Greek ceramics and statues, tombstones, ethnography, medieval art, icons, finds from Ottoman period, coins 04241

Nova Zagora

Gradski Istoričeski Muzej (Municipal Historical Museum), ul Ivan Pašov 1, 8900 Nova Zagora - T: 2154. Head: Ivan Želev
Local Museum - 1926
Archeology, contemporary history, fine art 04242

Orjachovo

Gradski Istoričeski Muzej (Municipal Historical Museum), ul Vasil Levski 13, 3300 Orjachovo - T: 2467. Head: Eugeniya Naidenova
Local Museum
Archeology, ethnography, local history 04243

Panagjurište

Gradski Istoričeski Muzej (Municipal Historical Museum), ul Racho Ralchev 1, 4500 Panagjurište - T: 2012. Head: Atanas Atanasov
Local Museum
History of the Bulgarian National Revival period and liberation movement, history of the April 1876 Uprising against Ottoman rule and the Russo-Turkish War (1877-1878), contemporary history 04244

Kašta-muzej Rajna Popgeorgieva, ul Oborište 5, Panagjurište - T: 3832
Special Museum
History of the Bulgarian National Revival period and liberation movement, memorabilia of the folk heroine Rayna Popgeorgieva, also known as Rayna Knyaginya, history of the April 1876 Uprising, historical banner sewn by R. Popgeorgieva in 1876 04245

Pazardžik

Kašta-muzej Stanislav Dospevski (Stanislav Dospevski Memorial House), Maria-Luisa 54, 4400 Pazardžik - T: (034) 444830. Head: Natalia Tocheva
Fine Arts Museum
Life and work of the painter Stanislav Dospevski (1823-1876) in his former house, documents on the role of the painter in the 19th c National Liberation Movement, personal effects, icons, paintings 04246

Okražen Istoričeski Muzej (Regional Historical Museum), pl K. Veličkov 15, 4400 Pazardžik - T: (034) 443113. Head: Dimitar Mitrev
Local Museum - 1923
Archaeology, ethnography, folk art, folk costumes, interiors, arts and crafts, folk architecture, history (18-19th c), liberation movement period (19-20th c), modern and contemporary hist - library 04247

Stanislav Dospevsky Art Gallery, pl K. Veličkov 15, 4400 Pazardžik - T: (034) 27152. Head: Neichev
Fine Arts Museum - 1966
Art works of Bulgarian artists from the Pazardzhik region: Stanislav Dospevski, Konstantin Velichkov, Elisaveta Konsulova-Vazova, Georgi Mashev, Stoyan Vasilev, Todor Hadzhinikolov, Mana Parpulova, Zlatka Dǎbova etc 04248

Pernik

Chudožestvena Galerija (City Art Gallery), 1 Krakra Sq, 2300 Pernik - T: (076) 25983. Head: Erika Nikolova
Fine Arts Museum - 1957
Contemporary Bulgarian art 04249

Okražen Istoričeski Muzej (Regional Historical Museum), Fizkulturna 2, 2300 Pernik - T: (076) 3118. Head: Ognian Asprov
Local Museum - 1954
Div: archaeology, Bulgarian National Revival Period (18th-19th c) and liberation movement, ethnography, modern hist, mining development 04250

Peruštica

Gradski Istoričeski Muzej (Municipal Historical Museum), Gradski ploshtad, 4225 Peruštica - T: 2205. Head: Kresa Todorova
Local Museum
History of 18th-19th c Bulgarian National Revival period and liberation movement, especially history of the April 1876 Uprising, history of capitalism and the revolutionary labour movement 04251

Pleven

Chudožestvena Galerija Darenie Kollekcia Svetlin Russev (Pleven Art Gallery - Donation Svetlin Russev Collection), Doiran ul 75, 5800 Pleven - T: (064) 38342. Head: Maria Meskin
Fine Arts Museum 04252

Chudožestvena Galerija Ilija Beškov, bul Skobelev 1, 5800 Pleven - T: (064) 30090. Head: Nikola Popov
Fine Arts Museum 04253

Kašta-muzej Stojan i Vladimir Zaimovi, Skobelev park, 5800 Pleven - T: (064) 22919
Special Museum 04254

Muzej na Ikonata v Carkvata Sv. Nikolai, ul Dr. Zamenchov 6, 5800 Pleven - T: (064) 37208. Head: Nikola Bošnakov
Religious Arts Museum 04255

Muzej Osvoboždenieto na Pleven 1877 (Museum of the Liberation of Pleven 1877), V. Levsky 157, 5800 Pleven - T: (064) 20130. Head: Michail Grančarov
Historical Museum - 1907
Hist of the Russo-Turkish War 1877-78 and the liberation of Pleven, documents on the meeting between the commander of the Turkish army Osman Pasha and the Russian Emperor Alexander II, arms, weapons 04256

Okražna Chudožestvena Galerija (Regional Art Gallery), ul Dr. Zamenchov 13, 5800 Pleven - T: (064) 36192
Fine Arts Museum
Painting, sculpture, graphics, works by I. Mrkvička, S. Spiridonov, I. Lazarov, K. Zonev. D. Uzunov, G. Popov, N. Petkov, S. Rusev, I. Nenov etc, icon coll 04257

Panorama Plevenska Epopeia 1877, ul Plevenska epopeia 2, 5800 Pleven - T: (064) 37308, 37306
Special Museum 04258

Regionalen Istoričeski Muzej (Regional History Museum), ul Stojan Zaimov 3, 5800 Pleven - T: (064) 22691, Fax: 22623, E-mail: plevenmuseum@dir.bg, Internet: http://www.plevenmuseum.dir.bg. Head: Michail Grančarov
Historical Museum - 1953
History, archaeology,nature, ethnography, Bulgarian National Revival and liberation movement, Russo-Turkish War 1877-78 and the liberation of Pleven, hist of capitalism till WWI - library, restoration studio, archives, funds 04259

Skobelev Park-muzej (Park-Museum Skobelev), Park Skobelev, 5800 Pleven - T: (064) 22919. Head: Michail Grančarov
Historical Museum - 1907 04260

Pliska

Muzej, 9920 Pliska - T: 57410. Head: Rečko Lečev
Local Museum / Archaeological Museum
History of Pliska, capital city of Bulgaria (681-893), medieval archeology, arms, ceramics 04261

Plovdiv

Archeologičeski Muzej (Archeological Museum), pl Săedinenie 1, 4000 Plovdiv - T: (032) 631760, Fax: 633106, E-mail: arch_mus_plov@dir.bg. Head: Kostadin Kissiov
Archaeological Museum - 1882
Prehistoric, classical and medieval archeology, finds from the Thracian, Roman, Byzantine and Bulgarian period, numismatics 04262

Etnografski Muzej (Ethnographical Museum), ul Dr. Čomakov 2, 4000 Plovdiv - T: (032) 625257, E-mail: ethnograph_plovdiv@www.com. Head: Dr. A. Yankov
Ethnology Museum - 1945
Agriculture, handicrafts, costumes, textiles, interiors, jewelry, musical instruments, games and customs, architecture, in a 19th c house decorated with frescoes 04263

Gradska Chudožestvena Galerija (City Gallery of Fine Arts), Saborna 14a, 4000 Plovdiv - T: (032) 263790, Fax: 448809, E-mail: ghgplart@ mail.techno-link.com. Head: Krasimir Linkov
Fine Arts Museum - 1952
Art of the Bulgarian National Revival period (18th-19th c), 20th c art, current art, graphics, 18th-19th c icons 04264

Kašta-muzej Lamartine (Lamartine Memorial House), ul Zora 3, 4000 Plovdiv - T: (032) 224339. Head: Zdravko Karov
Special Museum
Memorabilia on the French poet Alphonse de Lamartine and his stay in Plovdiv, documents, manuscripts, books, in a house where the poet lived 1833 04265

Naciolna Chudozestvena Galerija → Gradska Chudožestvena Galerija

Okrăžen Istoričeski Muzej (Regional Museum of History), pl Săedinenie 1, 4000 Plovdiv - T: (032) 269955. Head: Stefan Šivačev
Historical Museum - 1948
Historical documents, contemporary hist 04266

Okrăžen Muzej na Văzraždaneto i Nacionalno-osvoboditelnite Borbi (Regional Museum of the Bulgarian National Revival period and Liberation Movement), ul Starinna 1, 4000 Plovdiv - T: (032) 225923. Head: Dimitar Stančev
Historical Museum - 1956
17th-19th c Bulgarian hist, economic hist, cultural hist, in a house built 1848 04267

Prirodonaučen Muzej (Natural Science Museum), ul Chr.G. Danov 34, 4000 Plovdiv - T: (032) 633096. Head: Ilko Basamakov
Natural History Museum - 1955
Soil science, flora, fauna, history of evolution, invertebrates, reptiles, vertebrates, birds, mammals - library 04268

Pordim

Muzej Glavna Kvartira na Ruskata Armija 1877-1878 (Museum Headquarters of the Russian Army 1877-1878), 5898 Pordim - T: 22623. Head: Nikola Bochnakov
Military Museum
History of the Russo-Turkish War 1877-1878, documents, uniforms, weapons 04269

Provadia

Kašta-muzej Svetoslav Obretenov, ul Svetoslav Obretenov 14, 9200 Provadia - T: 3263. Head: Ivan Ivanov
Historical Museum 04270

Razgrad

Istoričeski Muzej (Historical Museum), ul G. Dimitrov 2, 7200 Razgrad, mail addr: POB 162, 7200 Razgrad - T: (084) 660851, Fax: 660090, E-mail: abritus_rz@hotmail.com, Internet: http:// www.geocities.com/abritus_rz. Head: Ivan Ivanov
Historical Museum - 1887
Archaeology, hist of Bulgaria (15th-19th c), ethnology, modern and contemporary hist, regional music hist, ethnography - library, archives, funds 04271

Okrăžna Chudožestvena Galerija (Regional Art Gallery), ul Kiril i Metodi 3, 7200 Razgrad - T: (084) 27067. Head: Nenko Metev
Fine Arts Museum - 1962
Contemporary Bulgarian art 04272

Razlog

Kašta-muzej Nikola Parapunov (Nikola Parapunov Memorial House), pl 15. Septemvri 1903, 2760 Razlog - T: 2060. Head: Emilija Kadurina
Special Museum
Memorabilia on the revolutionist Nikola Parapunov (1909-1943), history of the anti-Fascist partisan struggle during World War II 04273

Rilski Manastir

Nacionalen Muzej Rilski Manastir (Rila Monastery National Museum), 2643 Rilski Manastir - T: (0771) 22208. Head: P. Mitev
Historical Museum / Fine Arts Museum - 1961
History and art hist of the Bulgarian National Revival period, hist of the monastery, architecture, mural paintings, wood carving, arts and crafts 04274

Rožen

Nacionalen Muzej Roženski Manastir, 2820 Rožen - T: 270. Head: Georgi Stoianov
Historical Museum 04275

Ruse

Okrăžen Istoričeski Muzej (Regional Historical Museum), pl Kniaz A. Batemberg 3, 7000 Ruse - T: (082) 236115. Head: R. Gančev
Local Museum - 1904
Natural hist, hist of the Bulgarian National Revival period and liberation movement, archaeology, ethnography, modern hist - library 04276

Okrăžna Chudožestvena Galerija (Regional Art Gallery), ul Sredets 6, 7000 Ruse - T: (082) 26657. Head: Stefan Katsarov
Fine Arts Museum - 1947
Bulgarian painting especially of the 30's (Ivan Milev, Pencho Georgiev, Iliya Beshkov, Dechko Uzunov, Kiril Tsonev, Zlatyu Boyadzhiev, Danail Dechev, coll of works of Vladimir Dimitrov-Maystora), sculpture (Ivan Lazarov, Ivan Funev) 04277

Transporten Muzej (Museum of Transportation), ul Bratja Obretenovi 5, 7000 Ruse - T: (082) 222012. Head: Enčo Enev
Science&Tech Museum - 1966
Railway transportation, Danube River navigation, communications, post and telecommunications 04278

Samakov

Gradski Istoričeski Muzej (Municipal Historical Museum), 4 Ichtimansko shosse, 2000 Samakov - T: (0722) 22194. Head: Dimitar Balabanov
Local Museum - 1949
Archaeology, hist of Bulgarian National Revival period and liberation movement, ethnography, hist of capitalism and labour revolutionary movement, socialist development, art (examples of the famous 18th-19th c Samakov Art School and Samakov Wood-Carving School), national costumes, jewellery, icons, modern art - library, mosque, Saraff house, art gallery 04279

Sandanski

Gradski Archeologičeski Muzej (Municipal Archaeological Museum), blvd Georgi Dimitrov 12, 2800 Sandanski - T: (0746) 188. Head: Vladimir Petkov
Archaeological Museum
Roman finds from the middle Struma Valley, mosaics from the Byzantine period (3rd-4th c) 04280

Selo Černi Osam

Prirodonaučen Muzej (Natural History Museum), 5620 Selo Černi Osam - T: 371. Head: Christo Iliev
Natural History Museum - 1976
Mammals, wild life in Stara Planina, birds, flies, butterflies, snakes 04281

Selo Gavril Genovo

Memorialen Kompleks Balova Shuma, 3469 Selo Gavril Genovo - T: 364. Head: Emiliya Grigorova
Historical Museum 04282

Selo Nikjup

Nikopolis ad Istrum-Antičen grad, Archeologičeski razkopki, 5068 Selo Nikjup - T: 415, 369. Head: Petko Machkovski
Archaeological Museum 04283

Selo Orešak

Nacionalen Panair i Izložba na Narodnite Chudožestveni Zanajati i Priložnite Izkustva (National exhibition of popular crafts), 5630 Selo Orešak - T: 2317. Head: Stoyan Stoyanov
Decorative Arts Museum 04284

Troyanski Manastir (Trojanski monastery), 5630 Selo Orešak - T: 2480
Religious Arts Museum 04285

Sevlievo

Gradski Istoričeski Muzej (Municipal Historical Museum), ul G. Dimitrov 2, 5400 Sevlievo - T: (0675) 4765. Head: Totyu Grozev
Local Museum
History of the region, ethnography 04286

Silistra

Archeologičeska Ekspozicija Kreposta, ul G. Dimitrov 6, 7500 Silistra - T: (086) 27040. Head: Ivan Bachvarov
Archaeological Museum 04287

Chudožestvena Galerija (Art Gallery), pl Karl Marks, 7500 Silistra - T: (086) 26838. Head: Ĕrdan Kisĕv
Fine Arts Museum 04288

Chudožestvena Galerija Zname na Mira, 7500 Silistra - T: (086) 23628. Head: Ditimar Kulev
Fine Arts Museum 04289

Etnografski Muzej (Ethnographical Museum), ul Otec Paisi 37, 7500 Silistra - T: (086) 23855. Head: Donka Sabotinova
Ethnology Museum 04290

Okrăžen Istoričeski Muzej (Regional Historical Museum), ul Docho Mikhailov 18, 7500 Silistra - T: (086) 23894. Head: Sava Christov
Local Museum - 1954
Archeology, history of the Bulgarian National Revival period and liberation movement, ethnography, history of capitalism and labour movement, contemporary history, natural history 04291

Rimska Grobnitsa Silistra (Roman grave), ul 7-mi Septemvri 10, 7500 Silistra - T: (086) 27040. Head: Ivan Bachvarov
Archaeological Museum 04292

Slavovica

Muzej Aleksandăr Stambolijski, 4460 Slavovica - T: 28113. Head: Dimitar Mitrev
Special Museum - 1958 04293

Sliven

Kašta-muzej Chadži Dimităr, Okrăžen Istoričeski Muzej (Khadzhi Dimităr Memorial House), ul Asenovska 2, 8800 Sliven - T: (044) 22496. Head: Vasil Rečev
Special Museum
Memorabilia on the revolutionist Dimităr Khadzhi (1840-1868) in his birthplace, hist of the Bulgarian liberation movement against Ottoman rule in 19th c, documents, original interiors 04294

Kašta-muzej Dobri Čintulov (Dobri Chintulov Memorial House), ul Mesta 5, 8800 Sliven - T: (044) 25198. Head: Georgi Kjuptčupov
Special Museum
Memorabilia of the poet and pedagogue Dobri Chintulov (1822-1886), author of several popular revolutionary songs in the 19th c 04295

Kašta-muzej na Slivenskija Bit ot 19 Vek, ul Simeon Tabakov 5, 8800 Sliven - T: (044) 23149. Head: Georgi Kyupchupov
Historical Museum 04296

Kašta-muzej Panaĕt Chitov, Okrăžen istoričeski muzej (Panaĕt Chitov Memorial House), ul Černo more 7, 8800 Sliven - T: (044) 25392. Head: Georgi Kjuptčupov
Special Museum
Memorabilia on the revolutionist Panayot Khitov in his birthplace, hist of the Bulgarian liberation movement against Ottoman rule in 19th c 04297

Muzej na Tekstilnata Industrija (Museum of Textile Industry), Pl Stoil Voivoda 3, 8800 Sliven - T: (044) 26759. Head: Nezabravka Petrova
Science&Tech Museum - 1986 04298

Muzej Slivenski Zatvor, ul Dobrudja 2, 8800 Sliven - T: (044) 25392. Head: Georgi Kiupčupov
Historical Museum 04299

Okrăžen Istoričeski Muzej (Regional Historical Museum), ul Lenin 4, 8800 Sliven - T: (044) 22495. Head: Georgi Kyupchupov
Local Museum - 1948
Div: archeology, history of the Bulgarian National Revival period and liberation movement, ethnography, history of capitalism and the labour movement, socialist development 04300

Okrăžna Chudožestvena Galerija (Regional Art Gallery), bul Lenin 7, 8800 Sliven - T: (044) 22083. Head: Petar Shtilyanov
Fine Arts Museum
19th c art of the Bulgarian National Revival Period (D. Dobrovich, G. Danchov, N. Pavlovich), 20th c art (J. Kjuvliev, S. Ivanov, Khristo Stanchev, Vladimir Dimitrov-Maystora, Z. Lavrenov, N. Marinov, D. Dechev, N. Tanev, I. Beshkov, L. Dalchev, K. Zonev etc) 04301

Smoljan

Chudožestvena Galerija, ul Veslec 8, 4700 Smoljan - T: (0301) 23268. Head: Valko Gajdarov
Fine Arts Museum 04302

Okrăžen Istoričeski Muzej (Regional Historical Museum), bul Lenin 5, 4700 Smoljan - T: (0301) 24601. Head: Nikola Damianov
Local Museum - 1952
Div: archeology, history of the Bulgarian National Revival period and liberation movement, ethnography, history of capitalism and the labour movement, socialist development 04303

Sofia

Alexander Nevski Cathedral - Crypt - Museum of Old Bulgarian Art, National Art Gallery, Pl Katedrala Alexandar Nevskij 1, 1000 Sofia - T: (02) 9815775, Fax: 9810071, E-mail: nag@office1.bg. Head: Dr. Rouja Marinska
Fine Arts Museum - 1965
Bulgarian iconography (9th-19th c), Bulgarian iconography school 04304

Centralen Muzej na Fizičeskata Kultura i Sport, ul Angel Kantchev 4, 1000 Sofia
Special Museum 04305

Earth and Man Museum, Černij Vruch bul 4, 1421 Sofia - T: (02) 656639, Fax: 656942, E-mail: emnm@web.bg. Head: Dr. Michail Maleev
Natural History Museum / Science&Tech Museum - 1986
Giant crystals, regional coll of minerals, minerals and mineral resources of Bulgaria and of the earth - Library, X-ray lab, gem cutting facilities 04306

Gradska Chudožestvena Galerija (Municipal Art Gallery), ul Gurko 1, 1000 Sofia - T: (01) 872181
Fine Arts Museum - 1957
Paintings, sculpture, graphics 04307

Kašta-muzej Christo Smirnenski, Nacionalen muzej na bălgarskata literatura (Khristo Smirenski Memorial House), ul Emil ŠekerdzB3ijski 116, 1303 Sofia - T: (02) 318060. Head: Svetla Točeva
Special Museum - 1953
Memorabilia on the revolutionary poet Khristo Smirnenski (1898-1923) 04308

Kašta-muzej Dimităr Blagoev (Dimităr Blagoev Memorial House), ul Lajoš Košut 34, 1606 Sofia - T: (02) 523145. Head: R. Russev
Special Museum - 1948
Memorabilia on Dimităr Blagoev (1856-1924), founder of the Bulgarian Workers' Social Democratic Party, hist of the Bulgarian labour movement 04309

Kašta-muzej Dimităr Dimov, ul Krastju Sarafov 26, 1421 Sofia - T: (02) 661664. Head: Ani Svitkova
Local Museum 04310

Kašta-muzej Georgi Karaslavov, ul Zachari Zograf 4, 1715 Sofia - T: (02) 882493. Head: Georgi Svežin
Local Museum 04311

Kašta-muzej Georgi Kirkov (Georgi Kirkov Memorial House), ul Bacho Kiro 53, 1205 Sofia - T: (02) 835118. Head: Dina Rustčeva
Special Museum - 1964
Memorabilia on the revolutionist and politician Georgi Kirkov, hist of the Bulgarian labour movement 04312

Kašta-muzej Ivan Lazarov, Nacionalnata chudožestvena galerija, bul Vassil Levski 49, 1000 Sofia - T: (02) 655325, Fax: 9800071, E-mail: nag@office1.bg. Head: Rouja Marinska
Local Museum 04313

Kašta-muzej Ivan Vazov, Nacionalen muzej na bălgarskata literatura (Ivan Vazov Memorial House), ul Ivan Vazov 10, 1000 Sofia - T: (02) 881270. Head: I. Bačeva
Special Museum - 1926
Memorabilia on the Bulgarian national poet and writer Ivan Vazov (1850-1921) in his former house 04314

Kašta-muzej Nikola Vapcarov, Nacionalen muzej na bălgarskata literatura (Nikola Vaptsarov Memorial House), ul Angel Kănchev 37, 1000 Sofia - T: (02) 872933
Special Museum - 1956
Memorabilia on the revolutionary poet Nikola Vaptsarov (1909-1942), manuscripts, documents, letters 04315

Kašta-muzej Pejo Javorov, Nacionalen muzej na bălgarskata literatura (Peyo Yavorov Memorial House), ul Rakovski 136, 1000 Sofia - T: (02) 880887
Special Museum - 1956
Memorabilia on the poet Peyo Kracholov Yavorov (1877-1914) in his former house 04316

Kašta-muzej Petko i Pencho Slavejkovi, Nacionalen muzej na bălgarskata literatura (Petko and Pencho Slaveykov Memorial House), ul Rakovski 138, 1000 Sofia - T: (02) 871945. Head: Mariya Lovdyieva
Special Museum - 1949
Memorabilia on the Bulgarian writers Petko Racho Slaveykov (1828-1895) and his son Pencho Slaveykov (1866-1912), original interiors, documents, library 04317

Muzej na Naroden Teatar Ivan Vazov, ul V. Levski 5, 1000 Sofia - T: (02) 874831 ext 276. Head: Rumjana Vasileva
Performing Arts Museum 04318

Muzej na Narodnata Opera (Museum of the National Opera), bul Kniaz Dondukov 58, 1000 Sofia - T: (02) 877011/203. Head: Bojanka Arnaudova
Performing Arts Museum / Music Museum
History of the National Opera, scores, programmes, posters, costumes 04319

Nacionalen Archeologičeski Muzej (National Archeological Museum), Saborna ul 2, 1000 Sofia - T: (02) 882405/06, Fax: 882405. Head: M. Vaklinova
Archaeological Museum - 1879
Prehistoric archeology, finds from the Neolithic, Copper and Iron Ages, Thracian period exhibits, coll of Greek tombstones and ceramics, Roman sculptures, medieval archeology, Slav and Bulgarian material culture and art, epitaphs, proto-Bulgarian inscriptions, in a 15th c Buyuk Mosque 04320

Nacionalen Cărkoven Istoriko-archeologičeski Muzej (National Museum of Ecclesiastical History and Archaeology), pl Sveta Nedelja 19, 1000 Sofia - T: (02) 890115, 881343. Head: N. Chadžiev
Religious Arts Museum - 1922
Valuable 15th-19th c Bulgarian icons, manuscripts, religious hist and art, archeology, crafts, decorative arts 04321

Nacionalen Etnografski Muzej na Bălgarskata Akademija na Naukite (National Ethnographical Museum of the Bulgarian Academy of Sciences), ul Moskovska 6a, 1000 Sofia - T: (02) 9874191, Fax: 9801162. Head: Prof. N. Teneva
Ethnology Museum - 1906
18th-20th c folk art, fishing, hunting, apiculture, agriculture, rose-growing, wine-producing, domestic utensils, handicrafts, weaving, textiles, interiors, carpets, folk costumes, embroideries, jewelry, ceramics - library 04322

Nacionalen Istoričeski Muzej (National History Museum), bul Vitoša 2, 1000 Sofia - T: (02) 9802258, 9816600, Fax: 9804260, E-mail: nim@einet.bg, Internet: http://www.historymuseum.org. Head: Prof. Ilja Prokopov
Historical Museum - 1973 04323

Nacionalen Muzej Bojanska Crkva (Boyana Church National Museum), ul Bojansko ezero 1-3, 1616 Sofia - T: (02) 687434, 685304, Fax: 687266, E-mail: nmbc@bitex.com. Head: Mariana Hristova
Religious Arts Museum - 1947
Valuable frescoes from 1259, examples of Bulgarian medieval art in a church built in the 11th-13th c, various painted scenes belonging to the precious heritage of Bulgarian painting during the time of the Second Bulgarian Kingdom, Zemen monastery church (10th c), murals (14th c) 04324

Nacionalen Muzej Georgi Dimitrov (Georgi Dimitrov National Museum), ul Opălčenska 66, 1303 Sofia - T: (02) 320149. Head: Vera Dičeva
Special Museum - 1951
Memorabilia on the politician and Communist Party leader G. Dimitrov (1882-1949) in his former house, library, political documents, hist of the Bulgarian labour movement and international labour and antifascist movement 04325

Nacionalen Muzej na Dekorativno-priložnite Izkustva (National Museum of Decorated and Applied Arts), Vasil Levski 56, 1000 Sofia - T: (02) 654172. Head: Zdravko Navrodiev
Decorative Arts Museum - 1976 04326

Nacionalen Muzej na Literatura (National Museum of Literature), ul Rakovski 138, 1000 Sofia - T: (02) 9882493. Head: Džordan Kamenov
Special Museum - 1976
Art objects and illustrations connected with Bulgarian classical writers, first editions of books of Bulgarian writers, documents and records about Bulgarian literature, creative unions of writers, periodicals - library, archives 04327

Nacionalen Politechničeski Muzej (National Polytechnical Museum), ul Opalčenska 66, 1303 Sofia - T: (02) 313004, Fax: 314036, E-mail: polytechnic@web.bg. Head: A. Valčev
Science&Tech Museum - 1957
library 04328

Nacionalen Prirodonaučen Muzej (National Museum of Natural History), Tsar Osvoboditel bul 1, 1000 Sofia - T: (02) 9885115, Fax: 9882897, E-mail: nmnhpb@bgcict.acad.bg. Head: Prof. Petar Beron
Natural History Museum - 1889
Fauna of Bulgaria and the world, osteological and paleontological coll, minerals, botanical coll - library 04329

Nacionalen Selskostopanski Muzej (National Agricultural Museum), ul Suchodolska 30, 1373 Sofia - T: (02) 230275. Head: Prof. Georgi Ralčev
Agriculture Museum 04330

Nacionalen Voennoistoričeski Muzej (National Museum of Military History), ul Gen. Skobelev 23, 1463 Sofia - T: (02) 521596. Head: P. Jotov
Military Museum - 1916
Slav and Bulgarian medieval arms from the 7th-14th c, national liberation movement against Ottoman rule, documents on the Russo-Turkish War (1877-1878), 20th c military hist (orders, medals, badges, seals, uniforms etc) - library 04331

Nacionalna Chudožestvena Galerija (National Art Gallery), pl Aleksănder Battenberg 1, 1000 Sofia - T: (02) 9803320, Fax: 9810071, E-mail: nag@office1.bg. Head: Dr. Rouja Marinska
Fine Arts Museum - 1948
19th c secular art of the Bulgarian National Revival period, Modern and Contemporary Bulgarian art, Dept of old Bulgarian art in the crypt of Saint Alexander Nevski Cathedral - branch of old Bulgarian art in the crypt of the Alexander Nevski Cathedral 04332

Nacionalna Galerija za Čuždestranno Izkustvo (National Gallery for Foreign Art), pl Aleksandar Nevski 1, ul 19 Fevruari, 1504 Sofia - T: (02) 9807262, Fax: 9806081, E-mail: ngfa@abv.bg, Internet: http://www.ngfa.abv.bg. Head: Georgi Lipovanski
Fine Arts Museum 04333

Sofijski Istoričeski Muzej (Historical Museum of Sofia), ul Ekzarch Josif 27, 1000 Sofia - T: (02) 9835351, 9833799, Fax: 9835351, E-mail: Kiravall@web.bg. Head: Peter Mitanov
Historical Museum - 1952
Archaeology, ethnography, new (before WWII) and contemporary (after WWII) hist, art 04334

Sopot

Ivan Vazov Museum, 4330 Sopot - T: (03134) 2070. Head: C. Nedelčeva
Special Museum - 1935
Birth-place of the writer Ivan Vazov 04335

Sozopol

Gradski Istoričeski Muzej (Municipal Historical Museum), ul N. Popov 2, 8130 Sozopol - T: (05514) 47596. Head: Krali Kralev
Local Museum / Archaeological Museum - 1961
Archeological finds from the antique Greek town Apollonius (Apolonia), vases, coll of antique and medieval amphorae 04336

Stanke Dimitrov

Gradski Muzej (Municipal Museum), ul Hristo Botev 10, 2600 Stanke Dimitrov - T: 2208. Head: Vasilka Tcherveniakova
Local Museum
Local history 04337

Stara Zagora

Kašta-muzej Geo Milev (Geo Milev Memorial House), ul Geo Milev 35, 6000 Stara Zagora - T: (042) 23450. Head: Petar Vasilev
Special Museum
Memorabilia of the poet and revolutionist Geo Milev (1893-1925) in his birthplace, original interiors, historical documents on the September 1923 Uprising 04338

Okrăžna Chudožestvena Galerija (Regional Art Gallery), ul Bajer, 6000 Stara Zagora - T: (042) 22843. Head: Ivan Poptschev
Fine Arts Museum - 1960
Contemporary Bulgarian fine art, paintings by B. Mitov, G. Mitov, N. Kozhukharov, D. Gyudzhenev, A. Michov, M. Zhekov etc 04339

Regionalen Istoričeski Muzej (Regional Museum of History), Graf Ignatiev 11, 6000 Stara Zagora - T: (042) 600299, Fax: 600299, E-mail: histmuseumsz@mbox.digsys.bg. Head: Petar Kalčev
Local Museum - 1907
Div: archeology, hist of the Bulgarian National Revival period and liberation movement, ethnography, numismatics, contemporary hist - dep of neolithic dwellings 04340

Stražica

Chudozhestvena Galerija, ul Ivan Kirov 1, 5150 Stražica - T: (06161) 33804, Fax: 2568
Public Gallery 04341

Šumen

Archeologičeski Rezervat Starijat Grad Šumen, 9700 Šumen - T: (054) 55383. Head: Dečko Lečev
Archaeological Museum 04342

Galerija s Darenija Fond 13 Veka Bălgarija (Gallery 13 Centuries Bulgaria), ul Car Osvoboditel 66, 9700 Šumen - T: (054) 55353. Head: Dečko Lečev
Historical Museum 04343

Istoričeski Muzej (Historical Museum), Bul Slavjanski 17, 9700 Šumen - T: (054) 57410. Head: Dečko Lečev
Local Museum / Historical Museum - 1904
Archaeology: prehistory, finds from Thracian necropolis, medieval Bulgarian burial remains, ethnography, folk art, handicrafts, Bulgarian National Revival period, cultural hist, guilds and crafts 04344

Kašta-muzej Dobri Voinikov, ul Car Osvoboditel 87, 9700 Šumen - T: (054) 56897. Head: Dečko Lečev
Historical Museum 04345

Kašta-muzej Laëš Košut (Layos Kossuth Memorial House), ul Car Osvoboditel 35, 9700 Šumen - T: (054) 57209. Head: Dečko Lečev
Special Museum
Memorabilia on the Hungarian revolutionist and politician Lajos Kossuth (1802-1894) and his stay in Shumen in 1848, historical documents, in a 19th c house 04346

Kašta-muzej Panaët Volov, ul E. Markovski 42, 9700 Šumen - T: (054) 63429. Head: Dečko Lečev
Historical Museum 04347

Kašta-muzej Pančo Vladigerov, ul Car Osvoboditel 62, 9700 Šumen - T: (054) 52123. Head: Dečko Lečev
Historical Museum 04348

Kašta-muzej Vasil Kolarov (Vasil Kolarov Memorial House), ul I. Ikonomov 11, 9700 Šumen - T: (054) 55062. Head: Dečko Lečev
Special Museum
Memorabilia of the politician Vasil Kolarov (1877-1950) in his birthplace, personal library 04349

Okrăžna Chudožestvena Galerija (Regional Art Gallery), 9700 Šumen - T: (054) 51227. Head: Dian Evtimov
Fine Arts Museum - 1969
Contemporary Bulgarian fine art 04350

Svištov

Gradski Istoričeski Muzej Aleko Konstantinov (Aleko Konstantinov Municipal Historical Museum), ul Klokotnica 6, 5250 Svištov - T: (0631) 25452. Head: Peti Donevski
Local Museum
Local hist, memorabilia on the writer Aleko Konstantinov (1863-1897), archaeology, ethnology 04351

Targovište

Chudožestvena Galerija Nikola Marinov, ul Murgach 6, 7700 Targovište - T: (0601) 27760. Head: Angel Gadev
Fine Arts Museum 04352

Istoričeski Muzej Targovište (Regional Historical Museum), ul Rakovski 1, 7700 Targovište - T: (0601) 43978. Head: Ilka Angelova
Archaeological Museum / Ethnology Museum - 1959
Archaeology, ethnography, folk arts and crafts, costumes, 19th c interiors 04353

Teteven

Gradski Istoričeski Muzej (Municipal Historical Museum), pl Sava Mladenov, 5700 Teteven - T: 2005. Head: Yosho Yoshev
Local Museum
Local history, revolutionary and resistance movements during World War II in the neighbouring mountains 04354

Trjavna

Muzej na Rezbarskoto i Zografsko Izkustvo (Museum of Wood Carving and Icon Paintings), pl Kapitan Nikola 7, 5350 Trjavna - T: (0677) 2278, Fax: 2278. Head: Cvetan Kolev
Decorative Arts Museum - 1963
Valuable examples of the art of the Bulgarian National Revival Period (18th-19th c), exhibits from the 19th c Tryavna School of wood carving and painting, old icons, wood-carved ceilings and altar pieces, original tools, original interiors, in a Daskalov house, built in 1808, paintings by Dimitar Kazakov, Nikolai Maistorov, Ivan Gazdov 04355

Trojan

Muzej na Chudožestvenite Zanajati i Priložni Izkustva (Museum of Folk Craft and Applied Arts), pl Vazraždane, 5600 Trojan - T: 22062/63. Head: Totju Totevski
Decorative Arts Museum - 1962
19th c pottery workshop interior, copper, silver and goldsmith work, jewelry, tanners' and furriers' trade, wood working, folk costumes, textiles, Trojan carpets 04356

Tutrakan

Etnografski Muzej Dunavski Ribolov i Lodkostroenie (Ethnographical Museum Dunabian Fishing and Boatbuilding), ul Transmariška 5, 7600 Tutrakan - T: (0857) 5235, Fax: 5110, E-mail: tnmuseummail@yahoo.com. Head: Petr Boychev
Ethnology Museum
Danubian fishing and boatbuilding, ethnography 04357

Istoričeskij Muzej (Historical Museum), ul Suvorov 1, 7600 Tutrakan - T: (0857) 5235, Fax: 5110, E-mail: tnmuseummail@yahoo.com. Head: Petr Boychev
Historical Museum
Archeology, Bulgarian hist, military hist, ethnology 04358

Varna

Archeologičeski Muzej (Archaeological Museum), bul maria Luiza 41, 9000 Varna - T: (052) 681030, 681014, Fax: 681025, E-mail: archeoiv@mail.vega.bg. Head: Ivan Ivanov
Archaeological Museum - 1906
Ancient gold (ca. 5000 B.C.), bronze age pottery and metalworks, ancient jewellery, pottery and glass, coins (5th c B.C. - 18th c), medieval Bulgarian pottery, metalworks and jewellery - library, Roman baths (2nd-3d c A.C.), Rock monastery (12 - 14th c.) 04359

Etnografski Muzej (Ethnographical Museum), ul Panagjurište 22, 9000 Varna - T: (052) 630588. Head: Lidia Petrova
Ethnology Museum
Crafts, copper smithery, folk costumes, embroidery, textiles, 19th c interiors, farming, tools, sea and river fishing 04360

Istoriko-chudožestven Muzej, ul Dimitar Blagoev 41, 9000 Varna - T: (052) 237256. Head: Kostadin Stojanov
Historical Museum 04361

Kartinna Galerija (Art Gallery), bul Lenin 65, 9000 Varna - T: (052) 237256. Head: Stefan Kirov
Fine Arts Museum
Painting, graphics, sculpture, works by I. Mrkvichka, S. Ivanov, Z. Todorov, Z. Boyadzhiev, D. Usunov, D. Dechev, A. Mikhov, A. Mutafov 04362

Muzej Družba na Narodite ot 1944 g., ul Vitoša 5, 9023 Varna - T: (052) 440302
Special Museum 04363

Muzej na Văzraždaneto (Museum of the Bulgarian National Revival Period), ul 27. Juli 9, 9000 Varna - T: (052) 223585. Head: Kostadin Stojanov
Historical Museum
19th c Bulgarian religious art, icons, history of the Bulgarian National Revival period (18th-19th c) 04364

Muzej na Văzroždenskata Ikona, Okražen Istoričeski Muzej (Museum of Icons), ul Graf Ignatiev 19, 9000 Varna - T: (052) 237256. Head: Stefan Kirov
Religious Arts Museum / Fine Arts Museum
North Bulgarian icon coll, especially examples from the 19th c Tryavna School of woodcarving and painting, in the church Sveti Anastas 04365

Muzej za Istorija na Varna (Museum of History of Varna), ul 8. Noemvri 5, 9000 Varna - T: (052) 230423. Head: Alexander Mintčev
Historical Museum / Fine Arts Museum - 1952/1991
19th-20th c fine arts, industrial and handicraft samples, books, postcards, cultural memorabilia from and on Varna, photographs and documents 04366

Park-Muzej Vladislav Varnenčik, blvd Janoš Huniady 3, 9000 Varna, mail addr: PK 110, 9000 Varna - T: (052) 440302. Head: Šanko Apostolov
Historical Museum - 1935 04367

Regionalen Istoričeski Muzej Varna (Regional Museum of History), Maria Luiza 41, 9000 Varna - T: (052) 681011, 681012, Fax: 681025, E-mail: archeoiv@mail.vega.bg., Internet: http://www.varna-bg.com. Head: Alexander Minchev
Local Museum - 1906
Archaeology, ethnography, Bulgarian National Revival Period (16th-19th c), hist of Varna natural hist, historic sites and open air museum G. Velchev Fine Arts Museum Ancient and medieval, jewellery, gold, ceramics, metalworks, icons, sculptures - library 04368

Voenno-morski Muzej (Museum of Maritime History), bul Primorski 2, 9000 Varna - T: (052) 632018, Fax: 258783. Head: Todor Parušev
Historical Museum - 1885
Navigation hist, navigation during the Ottoman period, Bulgarian maritime history, documents on World War III, coll of ship-models and war-ships, coll of mines , guns and anchors 04369

Veliki Preslav

Nacionalen Istoriko-archeologičeski Rezervat s Muzej Veliki Preslav (National Historical-Archaeological Reserve with Museum Veliki Preslav), 9850 Veliki Preslav - T: (0538) 2630, 3243, Fax: 4537, E-mail: preslavcap@yahoo.com. Head: Dr. Todor Balabanov
Archaeological Museum / Decorative Arts Museum - 1981
Hist of Preslav, capital city of Bulgaria (893-972), medieval archaeology (9th-13th c), pottery, ceramic icons, architectural details, decorations and ornaments, medieval Bulgarian art, metal work, glass, proto-Bulgarian, Cyrilic and Glagolic inscriptions, masterpieces of medieval art as Preslav Gold Treasure and ceramic icon of Saint Theodor 04370

Veliko Tărnovo

Archaeological Preserve Nicopolis ad Istrum, 18 km from Veliko Tărnovo, 5000 Veliko Tărnovo, mail addr: ul 2 N. Picolo, 5000 Veliko Tărnovo. Head: Petio Penkov
Open Air Museum / Archaeological Museum 04371

Archeologičeski Muzej (Archaeological Museum), ul Ivanka Boteva 1, 5000 Veliko Tărnovo - T: (062) 34946, Fax: 36954. Head: Petio Penkov
Archaeological Museum - 1915
Thracian period archaeological finds, ceramics, gold jewelry, exhibits from the period of the Second Bulgarian State (1186-1396) 04372

Architekturno-muzeen Rezervat Arbanassi, Architectural Museum Preserve Arbanassi, Arbanassi, 5000 Veliko Tărnovo, mail addr: ul 2 N. Picolo, 5000 Veliko Tărnovo - T: (062) 30229, Fax: 36954. Head: Petio Penkov
Open Air Museum
Houses resembling small fortresses and fine churches (from the 16th-17th c) 04373

Architekturno-muzeen Rezervat Carevec (Architectural Museum Preserve Carevec), Carevec, 5000 Veliko Tărnovo - T: (062) 38841, Fax: 36954. Head: Petio Penkov
Open Air Museum
In the years 1186-1396 Tărnovo was main fortress and capital of Bulgaria, night show on the hill in sound and light 04374

Kašta-muzej Emiliian Stanev, ul Nikola Zlatarski 20, 5000 Veliko Tărnovo - T: (062) 21925. Head: Radka Pencheva
Special Museum - 1987
Books, photos - archive 04375

Muzeen Kat Kooperativna Pečatnica Rabotnik (Museum Collection Co-operative printing-house Rabotnik), ul Tchitalishtna 10, 5000 Veliko Tărnovo - T: (062) 23847
Local Museum 04376

Muzeen Kat Parva Socialističeska Sbirka (Museum Collection First Socialist Meeting), ul Nikola Gabrovski 20, 5000 Veliko Tărnovo - T: (062) 23847. Head: Petko Machkovski
Historical Museum 04377

Muzej Vazraždane i Učreditelno Sabranie (National Revival and Constituent Assembly), ul Ivan Vazov 2, 5000 Veliko Tărnovo - T: (062) 29821, Fax: 36954, E-mail: rimtv@yahoo.com. Head: Christo Charitonov
Religious Arts Museum / Historical Museum - 1985
About 250 icons and church vessels from the Bulgarian Revival period (18th-19th c), hist of the

Bulgarian National Revival period, economical and cultural hist, development of education, arts and crafts, ethnography, tools, handicrafts, architecture, in an administrative building built 1872 by Kolju Ficheto 04378

Nacionalen Architekturno Muzej (National Museum of Architecture), Ivan Vazov 35, 5000 Veliko Tărnovo - T: (062) 30587. Head: Teofil Teofilov
Fine Arts Museum - 1979
library 04379

Nova Istoria na Veliko Tărnovo (New History of Veliko Tărnovo), pl Săedinenie, 5000 Veliko Tărnovo - T: (062) 23847, Fax: 36954. Head: Petio Penkov
Historical Museum - 1969 04380

Okrăžen Istoričeski Muzej (Regional History Museum), ul Nikola Picolo 2, 5000 Veliko Tărnovo - T: (062) 20256, 33805, Fax: 36954. Head: Petio Penkov
Historical Museum - 1871 04381

Okrăžna Chudožestvena Galerija (Regional Art Gallery), ul Karaminkov 6, 5000 Veliko Tărnovo - T: (062) 30390. Head: Georgi Kostov
Fine Arts Museum - 1957
Paintings, graphics, sculpture, works by Ivan Khristov, B. Denev, N. Tanev, A. Terziev, J. Popov etc 04382

Sarafkina Kašta Gradski Bit, ul Gurko 88, 5000 Veliko Tărnovo - T: (062) 35802, Fax: 36954. Head: Petio Penkov
Historical Museum - 1972
Urban lifestyle, late 19th-early 20th c 04383

Zatvor-muzej (Prison Museum), pl Săedinenie, 5000 Veliko Tărnovo - T: (062) 22864, Fax: 36954. Head: Petio Penkov
Historical Museum - 1960
Hist of the 18th-19th c liberation movement against Ottoman rule, memorabilia on Vasil Levski, Bacho Kiro, T. Kableškov, S. Karada, hist of the anti-Fascist struggle 04384

Velingrad

Istoričeski Muzej (History Museum), ul Vl. Chernozemski 4, 4602 Velingrad - T: (0359) 22591. Head: Iljana Maslarova
Historical Museum
Archaeology, ethnology, art 04385

Vidin

Istoričeski Muzej Krastata Kazarma, ul Bojan Chonos 34, 3700 Vidin - T: (094) 23855. Head: F. Filipova
Historical Museum 04386

Kašta-muzej Bojan Chonos, ul Gavril Genov 1, 3700 Vidin - T: (094) 27528. Head: Teodora Georgieva
Historical Museum 04387

Muzej-krepost Baba Vida, pl Baba Vida 1, 3700 Vidin - T: (094) 22884. Head: Neven Ilev
Local Museum 04388

Okrăžen Istoričeski Muzej (Regional Historical Museum), ul S. Veliki 13, 3700 Vidin - T: (094) 24421. Head: A. Banova
Local Museum - 1910
Div of archeology, hist of the Bulgarian National Revival period and liberation movement, Div of ethnology, hist of capitalism, revolutionary labour movement and socialist development (ul Bojan Chonos 36) - library 04389

Okrăžna Chudožestvena Galerija (Regional Art Gallery), pl Dimităr Blagoev 1, 3700 Vidin - T: (094) 24421. Head: Georgi Petrov
Fine Arts Museum
Paintings, sculpture, graphics, works by I. Mrkvichka, B. Mitov, Vladimir Dimitrov-Maystora, Z. Boyadzhiev, L. Dalchev 04390

Peštera Rabiša Muzej (Rabiša Cave Museum), 3700 Vidin
Archaeological Museum / Natural History Museum
Prehistoric archaeology, cave art, natural hist 04391

Vraca

Okrăžen Istoričeski Muzej (Regional Historical Museum), ul Chr. Boteva 10, 3000 Vraca - T: (092) 20373. Head: Ivan Rajkinski
Local Museum - 1952
Archaeology, Bulgarian National Revival period and liberation movement, ethnography, modern and contemporary hist 04392

Okrăžna Chudožestvena Galerija (Regional Art Gallery), ul Georgi Dimitrov, 3000 Vraca - T: (092) 22513. Head: Ilja Bechirov
Fine Arts Museum
Contemporary Bulgarian art 04393

Otdel Etnografiya, Istoričeski Muzej (Ethnographic Division, Historical Museum), pl Christo Botev 2, 3000 Vraca - T: (092) 20373. Head: Ivan Raykinsky
Ethnology Museum - 1953
Goldsmith tools and work, folk costumes, embroidery, crafts 04394

Zemen

Pametnik na Kulturata Zemenski Manastir, 2440 Zemen - T: (07741) 2029
Religious Arts Museum 04395

Žeravna

Kašta-muzej Ěrdan Ěovkov (Yordan Yovkov Memorial House), 8988 Žeravna - T: 286. Head: Plamen Merdjanov
Special Museum
Memorabilia of the writer Yordan Yovkov in his birthplace, original interiors, documents, books 04396

Burkina Faso

Bobo-Dioulasso

Musée Provincial du Houet, BP 126, Bobo-Dioulasso - T: 972080, Fax: 316808. Head: Prosper Tiendrebeogo
Music Museum / Folklore Museum - 1990
Music instruments, drums, costumes 04397

Gaoua

Musée des Civilisations du Sud Ouest, Haut Commissariat du Poni, Gaoua, mail addr: BP 24, Gaoua - T: 870169
Ethnology Museum 04398

Ouagadougou

Musée National de Burkina Faso, Av Oubritenga, Ouagadougou, mail addr: BP 55, Ouagadougou - T: 307389, Fax: 312509
Ethnology Museum
Ethnology, ethnography 04399

Pobe

Musée Pobe Mengao, Dép. de Mengao Province Soum, Pobe - T: 551160. Head: Konfé Salam
Local Museum - 1974
Traditional objects, stone tools, ceramic pots, early metal work, pre-colonial history 04400

Burundi

Bujumbura

Musée Vivant de Bujumbura, BP 1095, Bujumbura - T: (022) 26852. Head: Emmanuel Niragira
Natural History Museum - 1977
Natural history, zoology 04401

Gitega

Musée National de Gitega, 223 Pl de la Révolution, Gitega, mail addr: BP 110, Gitega - T: (040) 2359, 3378. Head: Jacques Mapfarakora
Local Museum - 1955
Musical instruments, weapons, witchcraft utensils, basket works - library 04402

Cambodia

Battambang

Musée d'Archéologie, Battambang
Archaeological Museum 04403

Musée Poveal, Battambang
Archaeological Museum - 1956
Archeological fragments, sculpture 04404

Kampong Thom

Musée, Kampong Thom
Archaeological Museum 04405

Phnom Penh

Musée du Palais Royal, Palais Royal, Phnom Penh
Decorative Arts Museum 04406

Musée National de Phnom Penh, BP 2341, Phnom Penh - T: (023) 24369. Head: Pich Keo
Fine Arts Museum / Decorative Arts Museum - 1917
Khmer art from 5th to 13th c including specimens from Angkor Wat, Angkor Thom and Bantea Srei, decorative arts 04407

Siem Reap

The Angkor Conservation, Angkor Wat, nr Grand Hotel d'Angkor, Siem Reap
Historical Museum / Religious Arts Museum
Statues from the temples (8th-13th c), Angkor Wat, Bakong, Banteaisrei, The Baphuon, The Bayon, Preah Ko, Preah Khan, Ta Prohm, Ta Keo 04408

Cameroon

Bamenda

Musée International de Akum, POB 389, Bamenda. Head: Peter S. Atanga
Ethnology Museum - 1948
Local and foreign artefacts, anthropolgy, archaeology 04409

Douala

Cameroon Maritime Museum, POB 1588, Douala - T: 423206, Fax: 428901. Head: Patrick Achaah Ndumbi
Special Museum - 1984
Maritime history, maritime athnography, marine biology, slave trade, colonial coins, bank notes, antique currency - library, archives 04410

Musée de Douala, BP 1271, Douala. Head: Esther Jemba
Ethnology Museum / Fine Arts Museum
Ethnography, traditional art 04411

Dschang

Musée Bamilike, BP 152, Dschang
Folklore Museum
Sculpture, masks, pottery 04412

Foumban

Musée des Arts et des Traditions Bamboun, BP 50, Foumban - T: 220956. Head: Jean Bayard
Fine Arts Museum / Ethnology Museum
Art and handicrafts, ethnography 04413

Musée du Palais, Palais du Sultanat Bamoun, Foumban, mail addr: BP 246, Foumban. Head: Pierre Bayard
Local Museum
Archaeology, history, ethnology, handicrafts 04414

Maroua

Musée de Diamare, Maroua. Head: Irène Ottou Onana
Ethnology Museum / Decorative Arts Museum
Handicraft, musical instruments, regional ethnography 04415

Musée de Maroua, Mallet Hamadou, Maroua, mail addr: BP 36, Maroua
Local Museum
Local history, ethnography 04416

Mokolo

Musée Municipal de Mokolo, Mokolo
Ethnology Museum
Pottery, musical instruments, local ethnography, weapons 04417

Yaoundé

Musée d'Art Nègre, Centre Catholique Universitaire de Yaoundé, Yaoundé, mail addr: BP 876, Yaoundé - T: 232667. Head: Engelbert Mveng
Folklore Museum
Traditional art, archaeology, Ethiopian coins, ceramics, African antiquities 04418

Petit Musée d'Art Camerounais, Monastère Bénédictin de Mont Fébé, Yaoundé, mail addr: BP 1178, Yaoundé - T: 220947
Religious Arts Museum - 1979
Works of sacred art 04419

Canada

Abbotsford

Matsqui Sumas Abbotsford Museum, 2313 Ware St, Abbotsford, B.C. V2S 3C6 - T: (604) 853-0313, Fax: (604) 853-3722, E-mail: mail@msa.museum.bc.ca, Internet: http://www.abbotsford.net/msamuseum. Head: Lynne Wright
Local Museum - 1969
Local history, 1920's heritage home - archives 04420

Abernethy

Abernethy Nature Heritage Museum, POB 125, Abernethy, Sask. S0A 0A0 - T: (306) 333-2113, E-mail: mcken.j@sk.sympatico.ca
Natural History Museum 04421

Motherwell Homestead, POB 247, Abernethy, Sask. S0A 0A0 - T: (306) 333-2116, Fax: (306) 333-2210
Special Museum 04422

Agassiz

Agassiz-Harrison Historical Museum, 6947 Lougheed Hwy, Agassiz, B.C. V0M 1A1 - T: (604) 796-3545, Fax: (604) 796-3572, E-mail: avogstad@dowco.com
Local Museum 04423

Ainsworth Hot Springs

Silver Ledge Hotel Museum, POB 1314, Ainsworth Hot Springs, B.C. V0G 1A0 - T: (403) 243-6302, Fax: (403) 243-3672, E-mail: eduff@acs.ucalgary.ca, Internet: http://members.home.net/silverledge/
Science&Tech Museum / Historical Museum 04424

Airdrie

Nose Creek Valley Museum, POB 3351, Airdrie, Alta. T4B 2B6 - T: (403) 948-6685, Fax: (403) 948-6685, E-mail: museum@cadvision.com. Head: Al Sivertson
Local Museum 04425

Alberta Beach

Alberta Beach District Museum, Alberta Beach, Alta. T0E 0A0. Head: Barb Goode
Local Museum 04426

Garden Park Farm Museum, POB 639, Alberta Beach, Alta. T0E 0A0 - T: (780) 9243391. Head: David Oselies
Local Museum - 1967
Historical artifacts, geological material, dinosaur bones 04427

Alberton

Alberton Museum, 451 Church St, Alberton, P.E.I. C0B 1B0 - T: (902) 853-4048, Fax: (902) 853-4048, E-mail: ahf@isn.net. Head: Linda Curtis
Local Museum / Historic Site - 1965
Local hist, genealogy 04428

Alert Bay

U'Mista Cultural Centre, Kwakwaka'wakw museum, POB 253, Alert Bay, B.C. V0N 1A0 - T: (250) 974-5403, Fax: (250) 974-5499, E-mail: umista@north.island.net, Internet: http://www.swifty.com/umista/
Folklore Museum 04429

Alexandria

Glengarry Pioneer Museum, RR 1, Dunvegan Rd, Alexandria, Ont. K0C 1A0, mail addr: POB 416, Alexandria, Ont. K0C 1A0
Local Museum - 1962
Local history including farm implements and domestic utensils of the Scottish settlers 04430

Alida

Gervais Wheels Museum, POB 40, Alida, Sask. S0C 0B0 - T: (306) 443-2303. Head: Alex Gervais
Science&Tech Museum - 1972
Automobiles of North America, pioneer artifacts, music boxes 04431

Alix

Wagon Wheel Regional Museum, 4912 50th St, Alix, Alta. T0C 0B0 - T: (403) 747-3119, 747-3540, Fax: (403) 747-3119, E-mail: awwm@incentre.com. Head: Eve Keates
Local Museum - 1970
Local historical artifacts - archives 04432

Allanburg

Ball's Falls Historical Park, Centre St, Allanburg, Ont. L0S 1A0 - T: (905) 788-3135, Fax: (905) 788-1121, Internet: http://www.conservation-niagara.on.ca/conservation-areas/ballsfalls.html
Open Air Museum - 1963
Buildings and artifacts related to early industrial activities of the Niagara area including grist mill (1809), blacksmith shop (1880), log cabins (1740-1777) 04433

Alliance

Alliance and District Museum, POB 101, Alliance, Alta. T0B 0A0
Local Museum
Local hist, machinery, blacksmith shop, barn 04434

Alliston

South Simcoe Pioneer Museum, Riverdale Park, Fletcher Crescent, Alliston, Ont. L9R 1A1, mail addr: POB 910 Alliston, Ont. L9R 1A1 - T: (705) 435-0167, Fax: (705) 434-3006, E-mail: sspmchin@bcconnex.net
Local Museum - 1959
Pioneer history including agricultural implements and tools, guns, musical instruments, historical log cabin 04435

Alma

Langage Plus, 750 Rue Scott, Alma, P.Q. G8B 5W1 - T: (418) 668-6635
Fine Arts Museum 04436

Almonte

Mississippi Valley Textile Museum, 3 Rosamond St E, Almonte, Ont. K0A 1A0 - T: (613) 256-3754, Fax: (613) 256-3754, E-mail: mvtm@magma.ca, Internet: http://www.textilemuseum.mississippimills.com
Science&Tech Museum 04437

North Lanark Regional Museum, POB 218, Almonte, Ont. K0A 1A0 - T: (613) 256-1805. Head: Dawn Leduc
Local Museum 04438

Alonsa

Alex Robertson Museum, Alonsa, Man. R0H 0A0 - T: (204) 767-2095
Special Museum 04439

Altona

Schwartz Heritage House, POB 1391, Altona, Man. R0G 0B0 - T: (204) 324-5901, Fax: (204) 324-8918
Special Museum 04440

Ameliasburgh

Ameliasburgh Historical Museum, Main St, Ameliasburgh, Ont. K0K 1A0 - T: (613) 968-9678, Fax: (613) 962-1514, Internet: http://www.pec.on.ca/ameliasburghmuseum. Head: Marion Casson
Local Museum 04441

Amherst

Cumberland County Museum, 150 Church St, Amherst, N.S. B4H 3C4 - T: (902) 667-2561, Fax: (902) 667-0996, E-mail: ccmuseum@istar.ca, Internet: http://business.auracom.com/madhouse/ccm. Head: Barb Thompson
Local Museum 04442

Amherstburg

Fort Malden, 100 Laird Av, Amherstburg, Ont. N9V 2Z2, mail addr: POB 38, Amherstburg, Ont. N9V 2Z2 - T: (519) 736-5416, Fax: (519) 736-6603, E-mail: ont_fort-malden@pch.gc.ca, Internet: http://parkscanada.gc.ca/malden. Head: Robert Watt
Historic Site / Military Museum - 1939
General history including Indian and military history - resource centre 04443

North American Black Historical Museum, 277 King St, Amherstburg, Ont. N9V 2C7 - T: (519) 736-5433, Fax: (519) 736-5433. Head: Elise Harding-Davis
Ethnology Museum / Folklore Museum 04444

Park House Museum, 214 Dalhousie St, Amherstburg, Ont. N9V 1W4 - T: (519) 736-2511, Fax: (519) 736-2511. Head: Valerie Buckie
Natural History Museum 04445

Amos

Centre d'Exposition d'Amos, 222 Première Av, Amos, P.Q. J9T 1H3 - T: (819) 732-6070, Fax: (819) 732-3242, E-mail: exposition@ville.amos.qc.ca, Internet: http://www.ville.amos.qc.ca. Head: Marianne Trudel
Fine Arts Museum / Local Museum 04446

Ancaster

Fieldcote Museum, 300 Wilson St E, Ancaster, Ont. L9G 2B9 - T: (905) 648-8144, Fax: (905) 648-8144, E-mail: bradleyj@currentthinking.com, Internet: http://www.currentthinking.com/fieldcote
Local Museum 04447

Hermitage Gatehouse Museum, POB 7099, Ancaster, Ont. L9G 3L3 - T: (905) 648-4427, Fax: (905) 648-4622, Internet: http://www.hamrca.on.ca
Historical Museum 04448

Valens Log Cabin, POB 7099, Ancaster, Ont. L9G 3L3 - T: (905) 659-7715, Internet: http://www.hamrca.on.ca. Head: Gord Costie
Decorative Arts Museum 04449

Andrew

Andrew and District Local History Museum, POB 180, Andrew, Alta. T0B 0C0 - T: (780) 365-3687. Head: Verna Topolinsky
Local Museum - 1973
Local historical artifacts and records 04450

Angusville

Ukrainian Peoples Home of Ivan Franco, POB 77, Angusville, Man. R0J 0A0 - T: (204) 773-2764, Fax: (204) 773-2449
Special Museum 04451

Annapolis Royal

Fort Anne, 323 Saint George St, Annapolis Royal, N.S. B0S 1A0 - T: (902) 532-2321, Fax: (902) 532-2232, E-mail: atlantic_parksinfo@pch.gc.ca, Internet: http://parkscanada.pch.gc.ca. Head: Theresa Bunbury
Historical Museum - 1917
Fort Anne heritage tapestry, 1621 copy of Royal Charter of Nova Scotia, colonization, Vauban fort 04452

O'Dell Inn, POB 503, Annapolis Royal, N.S. B0S 1A0 - T: (902) 532-2041. Head: Dr. Barry Moody
Local Museum 04453

Port Royal National Historic Site, Port Royal, Annapolis Royal, N.S. B0S 1A0 - T: (902) 532-2321, Fax: (902) 532-2232, E-mail: atlantic_parksinfo@pch.gc.ca, Internet: http://parkscanada.pch.gc.ca
Historical Museum / Historic Site - 1939
Reconstruction of one of the earliest European settlements North of the Spanish possessions, French culture, commerce and colonization manifest in North America (1605-1613), fur trade 04454

Anola

Anola and District Community Museum, PTH 12 and Hwy 15, Anola, Man. R0E 0A0, mail addr: POB 153, Anola, Man. R0E 0A0 - T: (204) 866-2922
Local Museum - 1975
Local history 04455

Anse-au-Griffon

Manoir Leboutillier, CP 37, Anse-au-Griffon, P.Q. G4X 6A4 - T: (418) 892-5150, Fax: (418) 892-5189, E-mail: manoir.leboutillier@globeroor.net. Head: Johanne Murray
Historical Museum 04456

L'Anse-au-Loup

Labrador Straits Museum, POB 98, L'Anse-au-Loup, Nfld. A0K 3L0 - T: (709) 927-5659
Local Museum 04457

Antigonish

Antigonish Heritage Museum, 20 East Main St, Antigonish, N.S. B2G 2B2 - T: (902) 863-6160, Internet: http://www.grassroots.ns.ca/tour/ahm.htm
Local Museum 04458

Appin

Ekfrid Township Museum, Appin, Ont. N0L 1A0 - T: (519) 289-2016
Local Museum 04459

Arcola

Arcola Museum, POB 279, Arcola, Sask. S0C 0G0 - T: (306) 455-2480. Head: JoAnne Martin
Local Museum 04460

Arctic Bay

Sod House Museum, Arctic Bay, N.T. X0A 0A0 - T: (867) 439-9918
Historical Museum 04461

Arichat

Le Noir Forge, Arichat, N.S. B0E 1A0 - T: (902) 226-9364, Fax: (902) 226-1919. Head: Donna Boudrot
Local Museum - 1967
Local crafts and trades, blacksmith forge and tools 04462

Arkona

Arkona Lion's Museum, c/o Ausable-Bayfield Conservation Authority, RR 3, Arkona, Ont. N0M 1S5 - T: (519) 828-3071, Fax: (519) 235-1963, E-mail: abca@execulink.com
Ethnology Museum - 1972
Indian artifacts including arrowheads, skinning stones, ceremonial stones, fossils and petrified wood, minerals and semi-precious stones 04463

Armstrong

Armstrong-Spallumcheen Museum, POB 308, Armstrong, B.C. V0E 1B0 - T: (250) 546-8318
Fine Arts Museum 04464

Arnprior

Arnprior and District Museum, 35 Madawaska St, Arnprior, Ont. K7S 1R6 - T: (613) 623-4902, Fax: (613) 632-8091. Head: Helen MacMaster
Local Museum - 1967
Indian artifacts, lumbering industry, furnishings, antique jewelry, documents dating back to the 1820's 04465

Asbestos

Musée Minéralogique d'Asbestos, 345 Blvd Saint-Luc, Asbestos, P.Q. J1T 2W4 - T: (819) 879-6444, 879-5308. Head: A.J. Millen
Natural History Museum
Minaeralogy of the Jeffrey mine 04466

Ashcroft

Ashcroft Museum, 404 Fourth St, Ashcroft, B.C. - T: (250) 453-9232, Fax: (250) 453-9664. Head: Helen Forster
Local Museum - 1960
History, agricultural implements, native Indian and Chinese items, mineralogy - archives 04467

Ashern

Ashern Pioneer Museum, First St SW, off PTH 6, Ashern, Man. R0C 0E0, mail addr: POB 642, Ashern, Man. R0C 0E0 - T: (204) 768-3147
Local Museum 04468

Ashville

Drifting River Museum, Farm in Gilbert Plains Municipality, RR 2, Ashville, Man. R0E A0A
Local Museum 04469

Assiniboia

Assiniboia and District Historical Society Museum, POB 1211, Assiniboia, Sask. S0H 0B0 - T: (306) 642-3003, 642-4216
Local Museum 04470

Saint Mary's Museum of Maxstone, POB 1693, Assiniboia, Sask. S0H 0B0
Local Museum
Restored church 04471

Astra

Royal Canadian Air Force Memorial Museum, 8 Wing Trenton, Astra, mail addr: POB 1000, Stn Forces, Astra, Ont. K0K 3W0 - T: (613) 965-2140, 2208, Fax: (613) 965-7352, E-mail: rcafmail@reach.net, Internet: http://www.rcafmuseum.on.ca. Head: Jeffrey C. Brace
Military Museum 04472

Atikokan

Atikokan Centennial Museum, Civic Centre, Atikokan, Ont. P0T 1C0 - T: (807) 597-6585, Fax: (807) 597-6186, E-mail: warren.paulson@athydro.com. Head: Warren Paulson
Local Museum - 1966
Local history, local art, Indian artifacts, lumbering and mining 04473

Quetico Provincial Park Heritage Pavilion, Dawson Trail Campground, Quetico Park, Atikokan, Ont. P0T 1C0 - T: (807) 929-2571, Fax: (807) 929-2123
Local Museum
research library 04474

Atlin

Atlin Historical Museum, Third & Trainor Sts, Atlin, B.C. V0W 1A0, mail addr: POB 111, Atlin, B.C. V0W 1A0 - T: (250) 651-7522, Fax: (250) 651-7522, E-mail: heritage@atlin.net. Head: R. Anttila
Local Museum - 1972
Local history, natural history, material from the Gold Rush era - archives 04475

Aulac

Fort Beauséjour National Historic Site, 111 Fort Beauséjour Rd, Aulac, N.B. E4L 2W5 - T: (506) 364-5080, Fax: (506) 536-4399, E-mail: fort_beausejour@pch.gc.ca, Internet: http://www.parkscanada.gc.ca
Historic Site / Historical Museum - 1936
Documentation on French-British battles, military items, local hist 04476

Aurora

Aurora Museum, 22 Church St, Aurora, Ont. L4G 1G4 - T: (905) 727-8991, E-mail: AuroraMuseum@aci.on.ca. Head: Jacqueline Stuart
Local Museum 04477

Hillary House and Koffler Museum of Medicine, 15372 Yonge St, Aurora, Ont. L4G 1N8 - T: (905) 727-4015
Historical Museum 04478

Austin

Manitoba Agricultural Museum, S of the Junction of Hwys 1 and 34, Austin, Man. R0H 0C0 - T: (204) 637-2354, Fax: (204) 637-2395, E-mail: info@ag-museum.mb.ca, Internet: http://www.ag-museum.mb.ca
Agriculture Museum - 1953
Antique agricultural equipment, household utensils (1880-1920) 04479

Authier

École du Rang II, 269 Rang II, Authier, P.Q. J0Z 1C0 - T: (819) 782-3289, Fax: (819) 782-3456
Historical Museum 04480

Avonlea

Avonlea and District Museum, 201 Railway Av, mail addr: POB 401, Avonlea, Sask. S0H 0C0 - T: (306) 868-2101, Fax: (306) 868-2221, E-mail: avonlea@sk.sympatico.ca, Internet: http://www3.sk.sympatico.ca/avonlea. Head: Jean E. Kincaid
Local Museum - 1980
Coll of pionier artifacts, paintings, agriculture 04481

Aylmer

Aylmer and District Museum, 14 East St, Aylmer, Ont. N5H 1W2 - T: (519) 773-9723. Head: Patricia Zimmer
Local Museum 04482

Canadian Golf Museum, 1461 Mountain Rd, RR 2, Aylmer, P.Q. J9H 5E1 - T: (819) 827-0330. Head: W. Lyn Stewart
Special Museum - 1967
Golf equipment, books, prints, and other related artifacts 04483

Centre d'Exposition l'Imagier, 9 Rue Front, Aylmer, P.Q. J9H 4W8 - T: (819) 684-1445, Fax: (819) 684-4058, E-mail: limagier@qc.aira.com, Internet: http://www.limagier.qc.ca. Head: Yvette Debain
Fine Arts Museum 04484

Musée d'Aylmer, POB 311, Aylmer, P.Q. J9H 5E6 - T: (819) 682-0291, Fax: (819) 682-6594
Local Museum 04485

Ontario Police College Museum, POB 1190, Aylmer, Ont. N5H 2T2 - T: (519) 773-5361, Fax: (519) 773-5762. Head: M. Brown
Historical Museum 04486

Baddeck

Alexander Graham Bell National Historic Site, Rte 205, 559 Chebucto St, Baddeck, N.S. B0E 1B0 - T: (902) 295-2069, Fax: (902) 295-3496, E-mail: agbellhs@auracom.com, Internet: http://www.parkscanada.gc.ca. Head: Aynsley MacFarlane
Historical Museum - 1956
Photographs, films, artifacts, models, A.G. Bell's life and experiments, incl his use of Visible Speech to teach deaf people to speak, development of the telephone, photophone and graphophone, medical experiments, man-carrying tetrahedal kites, airplanes and hydrofoil boats 04487

Gaelic College of Celtic Arts and Crafts, POB 9, Baddeck, N.S. B0E 1B0 - T: (902) 295-3411, Fax: (902) 295-2912, E-mail: gaelcoll@atcon.com, Internet: http://www.gaeliccollege.edu. Head: S.D. Mac Phee
Ethnology Museum / Historical Museum 04488

Highland Pioneers Museum, POB 9, Baddeck, N.S. B0E 1B0 - T: (902) 295-3411
Local Museum 04489

Victoria County Museum, Gilbert Grosvenor Bldg, Baddeck, N.S. B0E 1B0, mail addr: POB 75, Baddeck, N.S. B0E 1B0 - T: (902) 295-3397. Head: Margot MacAulay, Donald MacAulay
Agriculture Museum - 1971
Agricultural implements, domestic utensils - archives 04490

Baie Comeau

Musée de Baie Comeau, 43 Rue Mance, Baie Comeau, P.Q. G4Z 2H1 - T: (418) 296-9690. Head: Raphael Hovington
Ethnology Museum / Archaeological Museum - 1952
Ethnological and archeological exhibits, domestic utensils, natural history specimens 04491

Baie-Saint-Paul

Centre d'Art, 4 Blvd Fafard, Baie-Saint-Paul, P.Q. G0A 1B0 - T: (418) 435-3681
Fine Arts Museum 04492

Baie-Sainte-Catherine

Pointe-Noire - Parc Marin du Saguenay, Rte 138 Est, Baie-Sainte-Catherine, P.Q. G1N 4L8 - T: (418) 237-4383, 235-4703, Fax: (418) 235-4325, 235-4686
Historical Museum 04493

Baie Verte

Baie Verte Peninsula Miners' Museum, POB 122, Baie Verte, Nfld. A0K 1B0 - T: (709) 532-8090, Fax: (709) 532-4166, E-mail: baievertpeda@nf.aibn.com
Science&Tech Museum 04494

Bancroft

Art Gallery of Bancroft, POB 1360, Bancroft, Ont. K0L 1C0 - T: (613) 332-1542, Fax: (613) 332-2119. Head: Diana Gurley
Fine Arts Museum 04495

Bancroft Mineral Museum, 8 Hastings Heritage Way, Bancroft, Ont. K0L 1C0 - T: (613) 332-1513, Fax: (613) 332-2119, E-mail: chamber@commerce.bancroft.on.ca, Internet: http://www.commerce.bancroft.on.ca. Head: Chris Fouts
Natural History Museum 04496

North Hastings Heritage Museum, Station St, Bancroft, Ont. K0L 1C0, mail addr: POB 239, Bancroft, Ont. K0L 1C0 - T: (613) 332-1884, Fax: (613) 332-1884. Head: Rob Walker
Local Museum - 1967
Original log house (1859) with pioneer artifacts, historical documents 04497

Banff

Banff Park Museum, Banff National Park, 91 Banff Av, Banff, Alta. T1L 1K2 - T: (403) 762-1558, Fax: (403) 762-1565, E-mail: banff-vrc@pch.gc.ca, Internet: http://www.worldweb.com/ParksCanada-Banff/museum.html. Head: Michael Gair
Natural History Museum - 1903
Brewster coll, geology, wild life 04498

Cave and Basin, Banff National Park, 311 Cave Av, Banff, Alta. T1L 1K2 - T: (403) 762-1566, Fax: (403) 762-1565, E-mail: banff-vrc@pch.gc.ca, Internet: http://www.worldweb.com/parkscanada-banff/cave.html
Historic Site / Historical Museum - 1885
Birthplace of National Parks in Canada, hot springs, geology, endangered snails 04499

Luxton Museum of the Plains Indian, 1 Birch Av, Banff, Alta. T0L 0C0 - T: (403) 762-2388, Fax: (403) 762-2803, E-mail: luxton@telusplanet.net, Internet: http://www.collections.ic.gc.ca/luxton. Head: Pete Brewster
Ethnology Museum - 1952
Plains Indian costumes, tipis, weapons, tools and utensils, North American natural history specimens, paintings 04500

Walter Phillips Gallery, The Banff Centre, 107 Tunnel Mountain Dr, Banff, Alta. T1L 1H5 - T: (403) 762-6281, Fax: (403) 762-6659, E-mail: walter-phillips-gallery@banffcentre.ca, Internet: http://www.banffcentre.ca/wpg. Head: Anthony Kiendl
Fine Arts Museum 04501

Whyte Museum of the Canadian Rockies, 111 Bear St, Banff, Alta. TIL IA3 - T: (403) 762-2291, Fax: (403) 762-8919, E-mail: info@whyte.org, Internet: http://www.whyte.org. Head: Douglas Leonard
Fine Arts Museum / Ethnology Museum - 1968
Coll of human history artifacts relating to the Canadian Rockies, paintings, prints, drawings, manuscripts, photographs - library, archives 04502

Barkerville

Barkerville Historic Town, 88 km E of Quesnel on Hwy 26, Barkerville, B.C. V0K 1B0, mail addr: POB 19, Barkerville, B.C. V0K 1B0 - T: (250) 994-3302, Fax: (205) 994-3435, E-mail: bill.quackenbush@gems4.gov.bc.ca, Internet: http://www.heritage.gov.bc.ca
Open Air Museum / Historic Site - 1958
130 buildings including a church, saloon, store, blacksmith and cabinet makers shops, bakery, print shop, gold mining, commerce and transportation, Chinese documents, photographs, original archival material - library, archives 04503

Lac La Hache Museum, POB 252, Barkerville, B.C. V0K 1T0 - T: (250) 396-7332
Local Museum - 1972 04504

Barrhead

Barrhead and District Centennial Museum, 5629 49th St, Barrhead, Alta. T7N 1A1, mail addr: POB 4122, Barrhead, Alta. T7N 1A1 - T: (780) 674-5203. Head: Wally Steinbring, Mabel Gravel
Local Museum - 1967
Local historical artifacts and archives 04505

Barrie

MacLaren Art Centre, 147 Toronto St, Barrie, Ont. L4N 1V3 - T: (705) 721-9696, E-mail: maclaren@mcw.on.ca
Fine Arts Museum 04506

Barriere

North Thompson Museum, POB 228, Barriere, B.C. V0E 1E0 - T: (250) 672-5583, Fax: (250) 672-9311
Local Museum 04507

Barrington

Barrington Woolen Mill Museum, Hwy 103, Barrington, N.S. B0W 1E0 - T: (902) 637-2185, E-mail: maxwelbm@gov.ns.ca
Science&Tech Museum - 1968
Water-powered woolen mill (1882) with carding and spinning machinery, hist of woolen cloth production 1890-1960, wall mural depicting seasons of Nova Scotia, first piece of Nova Scotia Tartan 04508

Old Meeting House Museum, Hwy 103, Barrington, N.S. B0W 1E0 - T: (902) 637-2185, E-mail: maxwelbm@gov.ns.ca
Local Museum - 1979
Oldest non-Conformist house of worship extant in Canada, sole survivor of five Congregationalist church buildings in Nova Scotia prior to 1770, erected by Cape Cod families which had founded Barrington Township and opened in 1765 04509

Seal Island Light Museum, Hwy 103, Barrington, N.S. B0W 1E0 - T: (902) 637-2185, E-mail: maxwelbm@gov.ns.ca
Local Museum - 1985
35-foot replica of the original lighthouse on Seal Island, with the original 1902 Fresnel Lens capping the top 04510

Barss Corner

Parkdale-Maplewood Community Museum, 3005 Barss Corner Rd, RR 1, Barss Corner, N.S. B0R 1A0 - T: (902) 644-3288, Fax: (902) 644-3422, E-mail: rosmith@fox.nstn.ns.ca, Internet: http://www.ednet.ns.ca/educ/museum/other_ns/parkdale/museum1.html. Head: Donna M. Smith
Local Museum - 1951
German heritage and local history 04511

Bateman

Bateman Historical Museum, POB 89, Bateman, Sask. S0H 0E0 - T: (306) 648-3548
Local Museum 04512

Bath

Loyalist Cultural Centre, Adolphustown Park, Box 112, RR1, Bath, Ont. K0H 1G0 - T: (613) 373-2196, E-mail: ruswrite@kingston.net, Internet: http://www.freeyellow.com/members6/loyal-ists. Head: Barry Russell
Military Museum / Historical Museum
United empire loyalists, genealogy 04513

Bathurst

Memorial War Museum, c/o Royal Canadian Legion Branch 18, 575 Saint Peters Av, Bathurst, N.B. E2A 2Y5 - T: (506) 546-3135, Fax: (506) 546-1011, E-mail: hjgoodvc@nbnet.nb.ca. Head: Cy Comeau
Historical Museum 04514

Batiscan

Vieux Presbytère de Batiscan, 340 Rue Principale, Batiscan, P.Q. G0X 1A0, mail addr: CP 76, Batiscan, P.Q. G0X 1A0 - T: (418) 362-2051, Fax: (418) 362-3174, E-mail: shcheminduroy@multimania.com, Internet: http://www.mediat-muse.qc.ca. Head: Alain Bourbonnais
Historic Site - 1816
Furniture dating back to the 18th19th c, some local geological specimens and manuscripts pertaining to Canada's hist 04515

Batoche

Batoche National Historic Site, Batoche, Sask. S0K 0K0 - T: (306) 937-2621
Historical Museum - 1961
Cultural history, military exhibits, historic buildings - outdoor interpretive satellite 04516

Battleford

Battleford National Historic Site, POB 70, Battleford, Sask. S0M 0E0 - T: (306) 937-2621, Fax: (306) 937-3370, E-mail: battleford_info@pch.gc.ca, Internet: http://parkscanada.pch.gc.ca. Head: Glenn Ebert, M.A. Simpson
Historical Museum / Military Museum - 1951
Military buildings, Indian ethnology, pioneer artifacts, anthropology, agriculture, North West Mounted Police and Canadian militia 04517

Fred Light Museum, POB 40, Battleford, Sask. S0M 0E0 - T: (306) 937-7111, Fax: (306) 937-2450
Local Museum
Pioneer artifacts 04518

Saskatchewan Baseball Hall of Fame and Museum, 121 20th St, Battleford, Sask. S0M 0E0 - T: (306) 445-8485, Fax: (306) 446-0509
Special Museum 04519

Beachville

Beachville District Museum, 584371 Beachville Rd, Beachville, Ont. N0J 1A0 - T: (519) 423-6497, Fax: (519) 423-6935, E-mail: bmchin@execulink.com. Head: Melissa Wakeling
Local Museum 04520

Bear River

River View Ethnographic Museum, RR 1, 18 Chute Rd, Bear River, N.S. B0S 1B0, mail addr: POB 3, Bear River, N.S. B0S 1B0 - T: (902) 467-3762, Fax: (902) 467-3762, E-mail: costumeshop.the@ns.sympatico.ca, Internet: http://www3.ns.sympatico.ca/costumeshop.the. Head: Sarah Elizabeth Glover
Ethnology Museum / Folklore Museum / Library with Exhibitions - 1980
Farming, logging and shipping equipment (19th-early 20th c) 04521

Beaumont

Moulin de Beaumont, 2 Rte du Fleuve, Beaumont, P.Q. G0R 1C0 - T: (418) 833-1867. Head: Gilles Sheedy
Science&Tech Museum 04522

Beauport

Galerie des Sculptures, 907 Blvd Rochette, Beauport, P.Q. G1C 1C7
Fine Arts Museum 04523

Beauséjour

Pioneer Village Museum, Brokenhead Centennial Park, Beauséjour, Man. R0E 0C0 - T: (204) 268-3048. Head: Peter H. Kozyra
Open Air Museum - 1973
Local pioneer artifacts, agricultural implements, restored school, railroad station and community hall 04524

Beauval

Frazer's Museum, Hwy 155 N, 2 Miles S of Beauval Forks, Beauval, Sask. S0M 0G0. Head: John Frazer
Local Museum - 1970
Native and pioneer artifacts, missionary and MÚtis culture, northern technology 04525

Beaverlodge

South Peace Centennial Museum, NW of Beaverlodge on Hwy 43, Beaverlodge, Alta. T0H 0C0 - T: (780) 354-8869, Fax: (780) 354-8869. Head: Lois Dueck
Agriculture Museum - 1967
Pioneer farm equipments, household artifacts, antique cars 04526

Beaverton

Beaver River Museum, 284 Simcoe St, Beaverton, Ont. L0K 1A0 - T: (705) 426-9641, E-mail: bte.hist.soc@on.aibn.com. Head: Julienne Everett
Local Museum 04527

Bedfords

Atlantic Canada Aviation Museum, 1658 Bedford Hwy, Bedfords, N.S. B4A 4J7 - T: (902) 873-3773, E-mail: acam@ednet.ns.ca, Internet: Http://acam.ednet.ca. Head: Mark Peapell
Science&Tech Museum 04528

Bella Coola

Bella Coola Museum, POB 726, Bella Coola, B.C. V0T 1C0 - T: (250) 799-5767, Fax: (250) 982-2328, E-mail: rmorton@belco.bc.ca
Local Museum 04529

Belleville

Glanmore National Historic Site, 257 Bridge St E, Belleville, Ont. K8N 1P4 - T: (613) 962-2329, Fax: (613) 962-6340, E-mail: glanmore@suckercreek.on.ca, Internet: http://www.suckercreek.on.ca/glanmore. Head: Rona Rustige
Local Museum / Fine Arts Museum / Historic Site - 1973
Local hist, Couldery coll of European and Oriental furniture and paintings, Dr. Paul lighting coll - archives 04530

O'Hara Mill Museum, c/o Moira River Conservation Authority, POB 698, Belleville, Ont. K8N 5B3 - T: (613) 968-8240
Science&Tech Museum 04531

Belmont

Belmont and District Museum, POB 69, Belmont, Man. R0K 0C0 - T: (204) 537-2252
Local Museum 04532

Evergreen Firearms Museum, Belmont, Man. R0K 0C0 - T: (204) 537-2647
Historical Museum 04533

Bergonnes

Cap-de-Bon-Désir, 14 Ch du Cap-de-Bon-Désir, Bergonnes, P.Q. G0T 1G0 - T: (418) 232-6751, 235-4703, Fax: (418) 232-6414, 235-4703
Science&Tech Museum 04534

Berthierville

Musée Gilles-Villeneuve, 9601 Av Gilles-Villenueve, Berthierville, P.Q. J0K 1A0 - T: (450) 836-2714, Fax: (450) 836-3067, E-mail: museegv@pandore.qc.ca, Internet: http://www.villeneuve.com. Head: Alain Bellehumbur
Special Museum
Formula 1 sport 04535

Big Beaver

Big Beaver Nature Centre and Museum, Big Beaver, Sask. S0H 0G0 - T: (306) 267-6017
Natural History Museum 04536

Big River

Big River Memorial Museum, POB 220, Big River, Sask. S0J 0E0 - T: (306) 469-2112
Local Museum - 1976 04537

Biggar

Biggar Museum and Gallery, 105 Third Av, Biggar, Sask. S0K 0M0 - T: (306) 948-3451, Fax: (306) 948-5134, E-mail: bgmc@sk.sympatico.ca, Internet: http://www.sasktourism.com/biggarmuseum
Local Museum / Decorative Arts Museum - 1972
Local hist from the time of the native people to the early thirties, artifacts used in early photography, medicine and drug stores, applied arts, clothing 04538

Homestead Museum, POB 542, Biggar, Sask. S0K 0M0 - T: (306) 948-3427. Head: Roger Martin
Local Museum 04539

Binscarth

Binscarth and District Gordon Orr Memorial Museum, 152 2nd Av, Binscarth, Man. R0J 0G0 - T: (204) 532-2217, Fax: (204) 532-2153
Local Museum 04540

Birtle

Birdtail Country Museum, POB 508, Birtle, Man. R0M 0C0 - T: (204) 842-3363, E-mail: mmoulson@escape.ca
Natural History Museum 04541

Blackville

Blackville Historical Museum, Rte 8, Blackville, N.B. E0C 1C0 - T: (506) 843-7761
Local Museum 04542

Blaine Lake

Blaine Lake Museum, POB 10, Blaine Lake, Sask. S0J 0J0
Local Museum 04543

Blind River

Timber Village Museum, Hwy 17, 13 Michigan Av, Blind River, Ont. P0R 1B0 - T: (705) 356-7544, Fax: (705) 356-7343, E-mail: timberv@onlink.net, Internet: http://www.blindriver.com/briver. Head: Nathalie Morsch
Local Museum - 1966
History of lumbering, blacksmith shop, rocks and minerals, agriculture, woodcarvings 04544

Bloomfield

Quinte Educational Museum, POB 190, Bloomfield, Ont. K0K 1G0 - T: (613) 393-3752
Historical Museum 04545

United Empire Loyalist Museum, Adolphustown Park, RR 1, Bloomfield, Ont. K0K 2T0. Head: W.J. Van Koughnett
Local Museum - 1962
History of Loyalist settlers, pioneer tools, costumes, furniture and documents 04546

Bobcaygeon

Kawartha Settlers' Village, 85 Dunn St, Bobcaygeon, Ont. K0M 1A0 - T: (705) 738-6163, Fax: (705) 738-6824
Open Air Museum / Local Museum 04547

Boiestown

Central New Brunswick Woodmen's Museum, 6342 Rte 8, Boiestown, N.B. E6A 1Z5 - T: (506) 369-7214, Fax: (506) 369-9081, E-mail: museum@woodsmenmuseum.com, Internet: http://www.woodsmenmuseum.com. Head: Francis Smith
Historical Museum
Local culture of the Miramichi River Valley, lumbering, fishing 04548

Boissevain

Beckoning Hills Museum, POB 670, Boissevain, Man. R0K 0E0 - T: (204) 534-6544, Fax: (204) 534-3710
Historical Museum - 1967
Early agricultural tools, pioneer household utensils, clothing, pictures, books and documents, Indian artifacts 04549

Moncur Gallery, Civic Centre, Boissevain, Man. R0K 0E0 - T: (204) 534-2433, Fax: (204) 534-3710, E-mail: gmay@mail.techplus.com, Internet: http://www.town.boissevain.mb.ca/moncur
Public Gallery 04550

Bolton

Canadian Museum of Animal Art, POB 500, Bolton, Ont. L7E 5T4 - T: (905) 859-0651
Fine Arts Museum 04551

Bonaventure

Musée Acadien du Québec, 95 Av Port-Royal, Bonaventure, P.Q. G0C 1E0 - T: (418) 534-4000, Fax: (418) 534-4105. Head: Jean-Claude Cyr
Historical Museum 04552

Bonavista

Bonavista Museum, POB 882, Bonavista, Nfld. A0C 1B0 - T: (709) 468-2575. Head: Marguerite Linthorne
Local Museum - 1968
Local history 04553

Cape Bonavista Lighthouse, Hwy 230, Bonavista, Nfdl. A0C 1B0 - T: (709) 729-0592, 468-7444, E-mail: capebonavista@nf.aibn.com, Internet: http://www.nfmuseum.com
Science&Tech Museum 04554

Mockbeggar Plantation, Mockbeggar Rd, Bonavista, Nfdl. A0C 1B0 - T: (709) 729-0592, 468-7300, E-mail: capebonavista@nf.aibn.com, Internet: http://www.nfmuseum.com
Local Museum / Historical Museum
The way of Newfoundland to Canada, period costumes, old fish store, carpentry shop, cod liver oil factory 04555

Bonne Bay

Wiltondale Pioneer Village, Woody Point, Bonne Bay, Nfld. A0K 1P0 - T: (709) 453-2470, Fax: (709) 453-7214. Head: Glenda Aubert
Historical Museum 04556

Bonshaw

Car Life Museum, 45 Oak Dr, Bonshaw, P.E.I. C1A 6T6 - T: (902) 675-3555, 892-1754. Head: Kevin MacKay
Science&Tech Museum - 1966
Restored early cars, pioneer farm machinery 04557

Borden

Base Borden Military Museum, Canadian Forces Base Borden, Borden, Ont. L0M 1C0 - T: (705) 423-3531, Fax: (705) 423-3623. Head: Stuart Beaton
Military Museum - 1955
Military hist and equipment, WWI/II fighting vehicles and guns, large coll consisting of 9 military museums, WWI air hanger, post Korea aircraft WWII, training air craft, on Maj. Gen. Worthington (RCAC) 04558

Bothwell

Fairfield Museum, 14878 Longwoods Rd, Bothwell, Ont. N0P 1C0 - T: (519) 692-4397
Local Museum - 1960
Life of Moravian missionaries, Indian artifacts, Bibles and handbooks translated into the Algonquin language of the Delaware Indians 04559

Botwood

Botwood Heritage Centre, POB 490, Botwood, Nfld. A0H 1E0 - T: (709) 257-2839, Fax: (709) 257-3330. Head: Ed Evans
Local Museum 04560

Boucherville

Maison Louis-Hippolyte Lafontaine, 314 Rue Marie Victorin, Boucherville, P.Q. J4B 7J9 - T: (450) 449-8347, Fax: (450) 449-4709. Head: Nathalie Routhier
Historical Museum 04561

Bowden

Bowden Pioneer Museum, 2011 20th Av, Bowden, Alta. T0M 0K0 - T: (403) 224-2122, Fax: (403) 224-2366. Head: Ellie Nelson
Local Museum - 1967
Local pioneer hist, Bob Hoare photography 04562

Bowmanville

Bowmanville Museum, 37 Silver St, Bowmanville, Ont. L1C 3K9, mail addr: POB 188, Bowmanville, Ont. L1C 3K9 - T: (905) 623-2734, Fax: (905) 623-5684, E-mail: bm-chin@durham.net, Internet: http://www.bowmanville-museum.org. Head: Charles D. Taws
Local Museum - 1961
Local history, trades and crafts before 1900, toys, furnishings, music instruments, textiles, tools 04563

Darlington Province Park Pioneer Home, RR 2, Bowmanville, Ont. L1C 3K3 - T: (416) 723-4341. Head: B.D. Swaile
Local Museum 04564

Bowsman

McKays Museum, RR 1, Bowsman, Man. R0L 0H0 - T: (204) 238-4412
Local Museum - 1959
Local history 04565

Boyd's Cove

Boyd's Cove Beothuk Interpretation Centre, Off Hwy 340, Boyd's Cove, Nfld. A0G 1G0 - T: (709) 729-0592, 656-3114, E-mail: boydscove@nf.aibn.com, Internet: http://www.nfmuseum.com
Historical Museum
Life in a thriving Beothuk village, artifacts from the site forster 04566

Bracebridge

Chapel Gallery, 15 King St, Bracebridge, Ont. P1L 1T7 - T: (705) 645-5501, Fax: (705) 645-0385, E-mail: mac@surenet.net, Internet: http://www.muskokaartsandcrafts.com. Head: Elene J. Freer
Fine Arts Museum 04567

Woodchester Villa, POB 2231, Bracebridge, Ont. P1L 1W1 - T: (705) 645-8111. Head: Elene J. Freer
Historical Museum 04568

Ziska Gallery, Ziska Rd, RR1, Bracebridge, Ont. P1L 1W8 - T: (705) 645-2587, Fax: (705) 645-1779, Internet: http://www.ziskgallery.on.ca. Head: Jack MacCallum
Fine Arts Museum 04569

Bracken

Bracken Community Museum, CPR Station, Main St, Bracken, Sask. S0N 0G0 - T: (306) 293-2878
Local Museum - 1957
Ammonites, Indian artifacts, household items 04570

Braeside

Waba Cottage Museum, RR1, Braeside, Ont. K0A 1G0 - T: (613) 623-4341
Local Museum 04571

Bralorne

Bralorne Pioneer Museum, SS1 Goldbridge, Bralorne, B.C. V0K 1P0 - T: (250) 238-2240. Head: Gail Goudry
Local Museum 04572

Brampton

Art Gallery of Peel, 9 Wellington St E, Brampton, Ont. L6W 1Y1 - T: (905) 791-4055, Fax: (905) 451-4931, E-mail: david.somers@region.peel.on.ca, Internet: http://www.region.peel.on.ca/heritage/hcomplex.htm
Fine Arts Museum 04573

Lorne Scots Regimental Museum, 48 John St, Brampton, Ont. L6W 2H1 - T: (416) 451-5724. Head: A. Goodman
Military Museum 04574

Peel Heritage Complex, 9 Wellington St E, Brampton, Ont. L6W 1Y1 - T: (905) 791-40#5, Fax: (905) 451-4931051, E-mail: david.somersd@region.peel.on.ca, Internet: http://www.region.peel.on.ca/heritage/hcomplex.htm. Head: David Somers
Fine Arts Museum / Historical Museum
Archiv 04575

Brandon

26th Field Artillery Regiment Museum, 116 Victoria Av, Brandon, Man. R7A 1B2 - T: (204) 728-2559, Fax: (204) 725-1766
Military Museum 04576

Art Gallery of Southwestern Manitoba, 638 Princess Av, Brandon, Man. R7A 0P3 - T: (204) 727-1036, Fax: (204) 726-8139, E-mail: agsm@mb-sympatico.ca, Internet: http://www.docker.com/~agsm. Head: Glenn Allison
Public Gallery 04577

Assiniboine Historical Society Museum, 609 McDiarmid Dr, Brandon, Man.
Historical Museum 04578

B.J. Hales Museum of Natural History, c/o Brandon University, McMaster Hall, Basement Concourse 270 18th St, Brandon, Man. R7A 6A9 - T: (204) 727-7307, Fax: (204) 728-7346. Head: Maureen Rodgers
Natural History Museum / University Museum - 19th c
Mounted birds and mammals, geology, archeology 04579

Chapman Museum, RR 2, Brandon, Man. R7A 5Y2 - T: (204) 728-7396. Head: A.T. Chapman
Local Museum 04580

Commonwealth Air Training Plan Museum, Group 520, RR5, Brandon, Man. R7A 5Y5 - T: (204) 727-2444, Fax: (204) 725-2334, E-mail: airmuseum@mb.sympatico.ca, Internet: http://www.airmuseum.ca. Head: Stephen Hayter
Military Museum 04581

Daly House Museum, 122 18 St, Brandon, Man. R7A 5A4 - T: (204) 727-1722, Fax: (204) 727-1722, E-mail: dalymus@mb.sympatico.ca. Head: Sandra Head
Historical Museum 04582

Manitoba Agricultural Hall of Fame Inc., 1129 Queens Av, Brandon, Man. R7A 1L9 - T: (204) 728-3736, Fax: (204) 726-6260, E-mail: agrifame@mts.net, Internet: http://www.mts.net/~agrifame
Agriculture Museum 04583

Manitoba Amateur Radio Museum, 25 Queens Cres., Brandon, Man. R7B 1G1 - T: (204) 728-2463, Fax: (204) 728-2463, E-mail: dsnydal@mb.sympatico.ca, Internet: http://www.mts.net/~dsnydal/austin.html. Head: Dave Snydal
Science&Tech Museum 04584

Brantford

Bell Homestead, 94 Tutela Heights Rd, Brantford, Ont. N3T 1A1 - T: (519) 756-6220, Fax: (519) 759-5975, E-mail: bwood@city.brantford.on.ca, Internet: http://www.city.brantford.on.ca. Head: Brian Wood
Science&Tech Museum / Historic Site - 1917
Restored home of Alexander G. Bell and his family incl original 1870s furnishings, extensive telephone coll, working 1920's telephone exchange 04585

Brant County Museum, 57 Charlotte St, Brantford, Ont. N3T 2W6 - T: (519) 752-2483, Fax: (519) 752-2483, E-mail: bcma@bfree.on.ca. Head: Stacey McKellar
Local Museum / Historical Museum - 1908
First nation, pioneer and local history, industrial, commerial, social and family hist, Harrison M. Scheak fine arts coll 04586

Glenhyrst Art Gallery of Brant, 20 Ava Rd, Brantford, Ont. N3T 5G9 - T: (519) 756-5932, Fax: (519) 759-5910, E-mail: glenhyrst@bfree.on.ca, Internet: http://bfree.on.ca/comdir/musgal/glenhyrst. Head: Mary-Ellen Heiman
Public Gallery - 1971
Contemporary Canadian prints and drawings, European and American prints, works by Robert Whale of Brant 04587

Myrtleville House Museum, 34 Myrtleville Dr, Brantford, Ont. N3V 1C2 - T: (519) 752-3216, Fax: (519) 752-9550, E-mail: myrtleville@bfree.on.ca, Internet: http://www.bfree.on.ca/comdir/musgal/myrtle/. Head: Tanya Wiegand
Historical Museum 04588

Bridgetown

James House Museum, POB 373, Bridgetown, N.S. B0S 1C0 - T: (902) 665-4530, 665-4215
Historical Museum 04589

Tupperville School Museum, RR3, Bridgetown, N.S. B0S 1C0 - T: (902) 665-2427. Head: Marion L. Inglis
Historical Museum 04590

Bridgewater

Desbrisay Museum and Exhibition Centre, 130 Jubilee Rd, Bridgewater, N.S. B4V 2W9 - T: (902) 543-4033, Fax: (902) 543-4713, E-mail: desbrisaymuseum@town.bridgewater.ns.ca. Head: Gary D. Selig
Local Museum - 1902
Morris porcupine-quill decorated cradle, Alice Hagen ceramics, 18th-19th c European artifacts, regional natural and human hist 04591

Wile Carding Mill Museum, 242 Victoria Rd, Bridgewater, N.S. B4V 2W9 - T: (902) 543-8233, Fax: (902) 543-4713, E-mail: desbrisaymuseum@town.bridgewater.ns.ca. Head: Gary D. Selig
Science&Tech Museum - 1974
Wool carding mill with waterwheel (1860) 04592

Briercrest

Briercrest and District Museum, POB 216, Briercrest, Sask. S0H 0K0 - T: (306) 799-4406, Fax: (306) 799-2115
Local Museum 04593

Brighton

Presqu'ile Provincial Park Museum, Presqu'ile Provincial Park, RR 4, Brighton, Ont. K0K 1H0 - T: (613) 475-4324, Fax: (613) 475-4324, E-mail: presquil@parks.kosone.com
Local Museum / Natural History Museum - 1957
Natural history, ecology, early hist of the area 04594

Proctor House Museum, 96 Young St, Brighton, Ont. K0K 1H0 - T: (613) 475-2144, E-mail: -proctorhousemuseum@sympatico.ca, Internet: http://www.3.sympatico.ca/proctorhouse.museum/index.html. Head: Roy Rittwage
Historical Museum 04595

Britannia Beach

British Columbia Museum of Mining, Hwy 99 N, Britannia Beach, mail addr: POB 188, Britannia Beach, B.C. V0N 1J0 - T: (604) 896-2233, Fax: (604) 896-2260, E-mail: general@bcmuseumofmining.org, Internet: http://www.bcmuseumogmining.org. Head: Terry Johnson
Science&Tech Museum / Historic Site - 1975 04596

Broadview

Broadview Museum, POB 556, Broadview, Sask. S0G 0K0 - T: (306) 696-2533, Fax: (306) 696-3573, E-mail: townofbroadview@sk.sympatico.ca, Internet: http://townwelcome.to/broadview
Local Museum 04597

Brocket

Oldman River Cultural Centre, POB 70, Brocket, Alta. T0K 0H0 - T: (403) 965-3939. Head: Jo-Ann Yellow Horn
Public Gallery / Local Museum 04598

Brockville

Brockville Museum, 5 Henry St, Brockville, Ont. K6V 6M4 - T: (613) 342-4397, Fax: (613) 342-7345, E-mail: mbchin@cybertap.com, Internet: http://www.cybertap.com/bmchin. Head: Bonnie Burke
Local Museum 04599

Brooks

Brooks and District Museum, 568 Sutherland Dr, Brooks, Alta. T0J 0J0 - T: (403) 362-5073
Local Museum - 1975
History, ethnology - archives 04600

Brownvale

Brownvale North Peace Agricultural Museum, POB 3, Brownvale, Alta. T0H 0L0 - T: (780) 597-3950, Fax: (780) 597-2388. Head: George Musa
Agriculture Museum 04601

Bruce Mines

Bruce Mines Museum, Taylor St, Hwy 17, Bruce Mines, Ont. P0R 1C0 - T: (705) 785-3426, Fax: (705) 785-3170. Head: Tina Peppler
Local Museum - 1956
Local hist, first commercially successful copper mine in Canada (1848), Yakaboo Canoe, Puddingstone - Jasper Conqlomerate - archives 04602

Bulyea

Lakeside Museum, 4 miles S and 10 1/2 miles W of Bulyea, RR 1, Bulyea, Sask. S0G 0L0 - T: (306) 725-4558. Head: Robert Swanson
Local Museum - 1945
Pioneer, Indian and war relics, prehistoric bones 04603

Burgessville

Oxford County Museum School, POB 37, Burgessville, Ont. N0J 1C0 - T: (519) 424-9964, Fax: (519) 242-9964, E-mail: museschl@execulink.com
Historical Museum 04604

Burin

Burin Heritage House, POB 326, Burin, Nfld. A0E 1E0 - T: (709) 891-2217, Fax: (709) 891-2069, E-mail: -burinheritagemuseum@nf.aibn.com. Head: Claudine Prior
Local Museum 04605

Burlington

Burlington Art Centre, 1333 Lakeshore Rd, Burlington, Ont. L7S 1A9 - T: (905) 632-7796, Fax: (905) 632-0278, E-mail: info@BurlingtonArtCentre.on.ca, Internet: http://www.BurlingtonArtCentre.on.ca. Head: Ian D. Ross
Public Gallery
Contemporary Canadian ceramic art 04606

Ireland House Museum, 2168 Guelph Line, Burlington, Ont. L7P 4M3 - T: (905) 332-9888
Historical Museum 04607

Joseph Brant Museum, 1240 North Shore Blvd E, Burlington, Ont. L7S 1C5 - T: (905) 634-3556, Fax: (905) 634-4498, E-mail: barbt@worldchat.com. Head: Barbara E. Teatero
Local Museum - 1942
Iroquois Indian artifacts, local history, 19th c costumes, mementos of Captain Joseph Brant and the Brant family - library 04608

Burnaby

Burnaby Art Gallery, 6344 Deer Lake Av, Burnaby, B.C. V5G 2J3 - T: (604) 291-9441, Fax: (604) 291-6776, E-mail: can-bag-bb@immedia.ca. Head: Karen A. Henry
Public Gallery - 1967
Contemporary and historical Canadian works of art, prints 04609

Burnaby Village Museum, 6501 Deer Lake Av, Burnaby, B.C. V5G 3T6 - T: (604) 293-6500, Fax: (604) 293-6525
Local Museum - 1971
Regional hist (1890-1925), ethnic hist, transportation, industrial machinery, medicine - archives 04610

Museum of Archaeology and Ethnology, c/o Department of Archaeology, Simon Fraser University, Burnaby, B.C. V5A 1S6 - T: (604) 291-3325, Fax: (604) 291-5666, E-mail: bwinter@sfu.ca, Internet: http://www.sfu.ca/archaeology/museum/index.htm. Head: Dr. B. Winter
Archaeological Museum / Ethnology Museum - 1971
Prehistory, ethnography, cultural material from North America, Africa, Asia, Australia, Central and South America 04611

Simon Fraser Gallery, Simon Fraser University, Burnaby, B.C. V5A 1S6 - T: (604) 291-4266, Fax: (604) 291-3029, E-mail: janet_menzies@sfu.ca, Internet: http://www.sfu.ca/artgallery. Head: Dr. Grazia Merler
Fine Arts Museum / Decorative Arts Museum - 1965
Contemporary and eskimo art, international graphics 04612

Burns Lake

Lakes District Museum, POB 266, Burns Lake, B.C. V0J 1E0 - T: (250) 692-7450
Local Museum 04613

Burwash Landing

Kluane Museum of Natural History, Mile 1093, Alaska Hwy, Burwash Landing, Y.T. Y0B 1V0 - T: (867) 841-5561, Fax: (867) 841-5605, E-mail: klvanemus@yknet.yk.ca
Natural History Museum 04614

Cabri

Cabri and District Museum, 102 First St, Cabri, Sask. S0N 0J0 - T: (306) 587-2915
Local Museum 04615

Cache Creek

Historic Hat Creek Ranch, POB 878, Cache Creek, B.C. V0K 1H0 - T: (250) 457-9722, Fax: (250) 457-9311, E-mail: explore@hatcreekranch.com, Internet: http://www.heritage.gov.bc.ca
Historical Museum 04616

Cadillac

Cadillac Museum, Cadillac, Sask. S0N 0K0 - T: (306) 785-2128
Local Museum   04617

Caledon East

Yaneff International Art, 18949 Centreville CRK. Rd, Caledon East, Ont. L0N 1E6 - T: (905) 584-9398, Fax: (905) 584-9569, E-mail: posters@yaneff.com, Internet: http://www.yaneff.com. Head: Greg Yaneff
Fine Arts Museum   04618

Caledonia

Edinburgh Square Heritage and Cultural Centre, 80 Caithness St E, Caledonia, Ont. N3W 2G6 - T: (905) 765-3134, Fax: (905) 765-3009, E-mail: eschin@interlynx.com, Internet: http://www.headstartcomp.on.ca/heritage/square. Head: Barbra Lang Walker
Local Museum   04619

Calgary

Aero Space Museum of Calgary, 4629 McCall Way NE, Calgary, Alta. T2E 8A5 - T: (403) 250-3752, Fax: (403) 250-8399, E-mail: aerospace@lexicom.ab.ca, Internet: http://www.asmac.ab.ca. Head: Keith Toone
Science&Tech Museum   04620

Alberta Wheat Pool Grain Museum, POB 2700, Calgary, Alta. T2P 2P5 - T: (403) 290-4701, Fax: (403) 290-5528. Head: Tim Kennedy
Special Museum   04621

Art Gallery of Calgary, 117 8th Av SW, Calgary, Alta. T2P 1B4 - T: (403) 266-2764, Fax: (403) 264-8077. Head: Greg Elgstrand
Fine Arts Museum   04622

Calgary Chinese Cultural Centre, 197 1 St SW, Calgary, Alta. T2P 4M4 - T: (403) 262-5071, Fax: (403) 232-6387, E-mail: ccca@globalserve.net, Internet: http://www.cultural-centre.ab.ca
Folklore Museum   04623

Calgary Highlanders Museum, 4520 Crowchild Trail SW, Calgary, Alta. T3E 1T8 - T: (403) 974-2855, Fax: (403) 974-2855, Internet: http://db.nucleus.com/highmus. Head: Brian King
Military Museum   04624

Calgary Police Service Interpretive Centre, 316 Seventh Av SE, Calgary, Alta. T2G 0J4 - T: (403) 206-4566, 268-4565, Fax: (403) 974-0508, E-mail: pol7753@calgarypolice.ca. Head: Janet Pieschel
Historical Museum
Police and social history   04625

Calgary Science Centre, 701 11th St SW, Calgary, Alta. T2P 2M5 - T: (403) 268-8300, Fax: (403) 237-0186, E-mail: discover@calgaryscience.ca, Internet: http://www.calgaryscience.ca. Head: W. Peters
Science&Tech Museum - 1967   04626

Fort Calgary, 750 Ninth Av SE, Calgary, Alta. T2P 2M5 - T: (403) 290-1875, Fax: (403) 265-6534, E-mail: info@fortcalgary.com, Internet: http://www.fortcalgary.com. Head: Sara Jane Gruetzner
Open Air Museum / Local Museum - 1977
Historic buildings (Hunt House, 1876; Deane House, 1906; Fort Calgary archaeology, 1875-1914)   04627

Glenbow Museum, 130 Ninth Av SE, Calgary, Alta. T2G 0P3 - T: (403) 268-4100, Fax: (403) 265-9769, E-mail: glenbow@glenbow.org, Internet: http://www.glenbow.org. Head: Michael Robinson
Local Museum / Fine Arts Museum / Military Museum - 1966
Ethnology, cultural hist, arms and armor, mineralogy, historical paintings, modern and contemporary Canadian art - art gallery, library, archives   04628

Grain Academy, Museum, 505 2nd St SW, Calgary, Alta. T2P 2P5 - T: (403) 263-4594, Fax: (403) 290-5528. Head: Dale Riddell
Agriculture Museum   04629

Heritage Park - Historical Village, 1900 Heritage Park Dr SW, Calgary, Alta. T2V 2X3 - T: (403) 268-8500, Fax: (403) 268-8501, E-mail: info@heritagepark.ab.ca, Internet: http://www.heritagepark.ab.ca. Head: R. Smith
Open Air Museum - 1964
Pioneer life from the days of early fur traders to 1914, historic buildings, steam locomotive, passenger paddle wheel steamer, antique midway   04630

Illingworth Kerr Gallery, c/o Alberta College of Art and Design, 1407 14 Av NW, Calgary, Alta. T2N 4R3 - T: (403) 284-7680, Fax: (403) 289-6682, E-mail: gallery@acad.ab.ca, Internet: http://www.acad.ab.ca. Head: Ronald Moppett
Fine Arts Museum / University Museum - 1958
Regional contemporary art   04631

Leighton Foundation Collection, Box 9, Site 31, RR8, Calgary, Alta. T2J 2T9 - T: (403) 931-3633, Fax: (403) 931-3633, Internet: http://www.sharcom.ca/leighton/. Head: Ann Harp
Fine Arts Museum   04632

Lord Strathcona's Horse Museum, 4520 Crowchild Trail SW, Calgary, Alta. T2T 5J4 - T: (403) 242-6610, Fax: (403) 974-2858, E-mail: ldsh@nucleus.com, Internet: http://www.nucleus.com/idsl. Head: Darryl Crowell
Military Museum - 1970
Military artifacts, archives   04633

Mount Royal College Gallery, 4825 Richard Rd SW, Calgary, Alta. T3E 6K6 - T: (403) 246-6344
Fine Arts Museum   04634

Museum of the Regiments, 4520 Crowchild Trail SW, Calgary, Alta. T2T 5J4 - T: (403) 974-2853, Fax: (403) 974-2858, E-mail: regiments@nucleus.com, Internet: http://www.nucleus.com/~regiments. Head: Ian Gray
Military Museum - 1990
Military artifacts of 4 founding regiments (Lord Straathcona's Horse Museum, Princess Patricia's Canadian Light Infantry, Calgary Highlanders, King's Own Calgary Regiment), military history of Alberta since 1874 - library, archives   04635

Naval Museum of Alberta, 1820 24 St SW, Calgary, Alta. T2T 0G6 - T: (403) 242-0002, Internet: http://www.lexicom.ab.ca/~navalmuseum/
Historical Museum   04636

The Nickle Arts Museum, c/o University of Calgary, 2500 University Dr NW, Calgary, Alta. T2N 1N4 - T: (403) 220-7234, Fax: (403) 282-4742, E-mail: nickle@ucalgary.ca, Internet: http://www.ucalgary.ca/~nickle. Head: Dr. Ann Davis
Fine Arts Museum / University Museum - 1972
Modern and contemporary art, numismatics   04637

Olympic Hall of Fame and Museum, 88 Canada Olympic Rd SW, Calgary, Alta. T3B 5R5 - T: (403) 247-5454, Fax: (403) 286-7213, E-mail: twest@coda.ab.ca, Internet: http://www.coda.ab.ca. Head: J. Thomas West
Special Museum   04638

Princess Patricia's Canadian Light Infantry Museum, 4520 Crowchild Trail SW, Calgary, Alta. T2T 5J4 - T: (403) 974-2860, Fax: (403) 974-2864, E-mail: ppcli@nucleus.com, Internet: http://www.ppcli.com. Head: Ted Giradeau
Military Museum - 1954
Regimental history from 1914 to the present   04639

Sarcee People's Museum, 3700 Anderson Rd SW, Calgary, Alta. T2W 3C4 - T: (403) 238-2677
Religious Arts Museum   04640

University of Calgary Museum of Zoology, c/o Department of Biology, University of Calgary, 2500 University Dr, Calgary, Alta. T2N 1N4 - T: (403) 220-5269, Fax: (403) 289-9311, E-mail: fitch@acs.ucalgary.ca. Head: Dr. H.I. Rosenberg
Natural History Museum / University Museum - 1966
Osteological specimens, skin coll, vertebrate material   04641

Calixa-Lavallée

Musée-Atelier Calixa-Lavallée, 310 Ch Beauce, Calixa-Lavallée, P.Q. J0L 1A0 - T: (450) 583-3191, Fax: (450) 583-6729
Fine Arts Museum   04642

Callander

Callander Bay Heritage Museum, 107 Lansdowne St E, Callander, Ont. P0H 1H0 - T: (705) 752-2282, Fax: (705) 752-3116, E-mail: callandermuseum@yahoo.ca, Internet: http://www.township.-callander.ca/museum/. Head: Carol Anne Pretty
Historic Site
Former home and practice of the physician Dr. A.R. Dafoe   04643

Cambellcroft

Dorothy's House Museum, 3632 Ganaraska Rd, Cambellcroft, Ont. L0A 1B0 - T: (905) 797-1170, Fax: (905) 797-3379, E-mail: edhs@nhb.com, Internet: http://www.nhb.com/edhs.htm
Historical Museum   04644

Cambridge

Cambridge Galleries, 20 Grand Av N, Cambridge, Ont. N1S 2K6 - T: (519) 621-0460, Fax: (519) 621-2080, E-mail: mmisner@library.cambridge.on.ca. Head: Mary Misner
Fine Arts Museum   04645

Campbell River

Campbell River and District Public Art Gallery, 1235 Shoppers Row, Campbell River, B.C. V9W 2C7 - T: (250) 287-2261, Fax: (250) 287-2268, E-mail: art.gallery@crcn.net, Internet: http://crartgal.ca. Head: Jeanette Taylor
Public Gallery   04646

Campbell River Museum, 470 Island Hwy, Campbell River, B.C. V9W 4Z9 - T: (250) 287-3103, Fax: (250) 286-0109, E-mail: general.inquiries@crmuseum.ca, Internet: http://www.crmuseum.ca. Head: Lesia Davis
Ethnology Museum / Historical Museum - 1958
Northwest Coast Indian ethnography, local hist, social and industrial hist - library, archives   04647

Campbell River Optical Maritime Museum, 250 Dogwood St, Campbell River, B.C. V9W 2X9 - T: (250) 287-2052, Fax: (250) 287-2052. Head: Robert Somerville
Historical Museum   04648

Campbellford

Campbellford-Seymour Heritage Centre, 113 Front St N, Campbellford, Ont. K0L 1L0 - T: (705) 653-2634, E-mail: csheritage@kawartha.com. Head: Ann Rowe
Local Museum   04649

Campbellton

Restigouche Gallery, 39 Andrew St, Campbellton, N.B. E3N 3H1 - T: (506) 753-5750, Fax: (506) 759-9601. Head: Colette Bourgoin
Fine Arts Museum   04650

Canmore

Centennial Museum of Canmore, 907 7th Av, Canmore, Alta. T1W 2A9 - T: (403) 678-2462, Fax: (403) 678-2216, E-mail: info@cmags.org. Head: Kathy Jones
Local Museum   04651

Cannington

Cannington Centennial Museum, POB 196, Cannington, Ont. L0E 1E0 - T: (705) 432-2558. Head: Edna Eastman
Local Museum   04652

Canso

Canso Museum, Union St, Canso, N.S. B0H 1H0 - T: (902) 366-2170, Fax: (902) 366-3093, Internet: http://www.schoolnet.ca/collections/canso/. Head: Martha Kavanaugh
Local Museum   04653

Canwood

Canwood Museum, Village, Canwood, Sask. S0J 0K0 - T: (306) 468-2616
Local Museum   04654

Canyon

The Alfoldy Gallery, POB 57, Canyon, B.C. V0B 1C0 - T: (250) 428-7473, E-mail: alfoldy@kootenay.com, Internet: http://www.alfoldy.com
Fine Arts Museum   04655

Cape Sable Island

Archelaus Smith Museum, 915 Hwy 330, Cape Sable Island, N.S. B0W 1P0 - T: (902) 745-3361, Internet: http://www.bmhs.ednet.ns.ca/tourism/smith.htm. Head: Kent Blades, Margaret Messenger
Local Museum - 1970
Marine history, fishing industry, boatbuilding, local history   04656

Caraquet

Le Musée Acadien, 15 Blvd Saint-Pierre E, Caraquet, N.B. E1W 1B6 - T: (506) 727-2727, Fax: (506) 726-2660. Head: Graham LeBlanc
Folklore Museum   04657

Village Historique Acadien, 14311 Rte 11, Caraquet, N.B. E1W 1B7, mail addr: CP 5626, Caraquet, N.B. E1W 1B7 - T: (506) 726-2600, Fax: (506) 726-2601, E-mail: vha@gnb.ca, Internet: http://www.villagehi-storiqueacadien.com. Head: Louis LeBouthillier
Historic Site - 1977
Historical village of the Acadians (1770-1939), furnishings, farm implements, fishing equipment   04658

Carberry

Carberry Plains Museum, 520 4th Av, Carberry, Man. R0K 0H0 - T: (204) 834-2195, 834-3295
Local Museum   04659

Seton Centre, 116 Main St, Carberry, Man. R0K 0H0 - T: (204) 834-2059
Special Museum   04660

Carbonear

Carbonear Railway Station, POB 64, Carbonear, Nfld. A0A 1T0 - T: (709) 596-2267
Science&Tech Museum   04661

Shades of the Past, POB 496, Carbonear, Nfld. A0A 1T0 - T: (709) 596-1977. Head: Stan Deering
Local Museum   04662

Victoria Hydro Station Museum, 30 Goff Av, Carbonear, Nfld. A1Y 1A6 - T: (709) 945-4403, Fax: (709) 945-4490, E-mail: dbutt@newfoundlandpower.com
Science&Tech Museum   04663

Cardston

C.O. Card Home, 337 Main St, Cardston, Alta. T0K 0K0 - T: (403) 653-3391, 653-4322. Head: Tom Matkin
Historic Site - 1967
Local hist in restored 1887 home, artifacts, furniture of pioneer days   04664

Remington-Alberta Carriage Centre, 623 Main St, Cardston, Alta. T0K 0K0 - T: (403) 653-5139, Fax: (403) 653-5160, E-mail: info@remingtoncentre.com, Internet: http://www.remingtoncentre.com
Science&Tech Museum   04665

Carleton

Centre d'Artistes Vaste et Vague, 756 Blvd Perron, Carleton, P.Q. G0C 1J0 - T: (418) 364-3123
Fine Arts Museum   04666

Musée Carleton, Rte 132, Carleton, P.Q. G0C 1J9
Local Museum - 1970
Coins and stamps, weapons, domestic utensils, history of Baie-des-Chaleurs navigation   04667

Carleton Place

Robert Tait McKenzie Memorial Museum and Mill of Kintail, NW of Almonte, Carleton Place, Ont. K7C 3P5, mail addr: c/o Mississipi Valley Conservation, POB 268, Lanark, Ont. K0G 1K0 - T: (613) 256-3610, Fax: (613) 259-3468, E-mail: mississippi@superage.com, Internet: http://www.mvc.on.ca
Fine Arts Museum   04668

Victoria School Museum, 267 Edmund St, Carleton Place, Ont. K7C 3E8 - T: (613) 253-1395
Historical Museum   04669

Carlyle

Rusty Relics Museum, Railway Av and 3rd St West, Carlyle, Sask. S0C 0R0 - T: (306) 453-2812, Fax: (306) 453-2938, 453-2812, E-mail: joe.emond@sk.sympatico.ca. Head: J. Wilbert Hume
Local Museum / Folklore Museum - 1974
Pioneer artifacts, old dentist's office, 1943 Canadian Pacific Railway motor car and tool shed complete with railway tools, 1905 one-room country school, agricultural machinery, 1943 Canadian Pacific Railway caboose, church   04670

Carman

Dufferin Historical Museum, 44 King's Park Rd, Carman, Man. R0G 0J0 - T: (204) 745-3597
Local Museum - 1954
Watercolors depicting rural life about 1900, clothing, Indian artifacts, household and farm utensils   04671

Heaman's Antique Autorama, Hwy 3, Carman Man. R0G 0J0, mail addr: POB 105, Carman, Man. R0G 0J0 - T: (204) 745-2981
Science&Tech Museum - 1967
Canadian and American automobiles from 1912 to the present   04672

Carstairs

Roulston Museum, 1138 Nanton St, Carstairs, Alta. T0M 0N0, mail addr: POB 1067, Carstairs, Alta. T0M 0N0 - T: (403) 337-3710, Fax: (403) 337-3343, E-mail: cdhs@telusplanet.net. Head: Betty Ayers
Local Museum
archives   04673

Cartwright

Badger Creek Museum, 350 Broadway Av, Cartwright, Man. R0K 0L0 - T: (204) 529-2363, Fax: (204) 529-2288
Agriculture Museum - 1975
Agricultural and domestic tools and utensils - archives   04674

Castlegar

Kootenay Gallery of Art, History and Science, 120 Heritage Way, Castlegar, B.C. V1N 3M5 - T: (250) 365-3337, Fax: (250) 365-3822, E-mail: kgal@netidea.com, Internet: http://www.kootenay-gallery.com. Head: Sherry Cournoyer
Public Gallery / Historical Museum / Science&Tech Museum - 1975
Art, hist, science, ethnography, local, national and international   04675

Railway Station Museum, 400 13th Av, Castlegar, B.C. V1N 1G2. Head: Myrna Cobb
Local Museum - 1994
Regional hist, ethnography, mining equipment   04676

Selkirk Local History Collection, 301 Frank Beinder Way, Castlegar, B.C. V1N 3J1 - T: (250) 365-1229, Fax: (250) 365-7259, Internet: http://library.selkirk.bc.ca. Head: Elizabeth Ball
Historical Museum / University Museum - 1970
Printed material, photographs, films and sound recordings relating to the Doukhobours of Western Canada - library, archives   04677

Castor

Castor and District Museum, 5101 49th Av, Castor, Alta. T0C 0X0 - T: (403) 882-3435. Head: Verna Pickles
Local Museum - 1969
Local history   04678

Cayuga

Haldimand-Norfolk County Museum, 8 Echo St, Cayuga, Ont. N0A 1E0 - T: (905) 772-5880, Fax: (905) 772-1725, E-mail: hcmachin@interlynx.net, Internet: http://haldimand-norfolk.on.ca/h-nmuseum.htm
Local Museum - 1930
Pioneer coll, restored log cabin (1835), military coll, pre-historic Indian material, genealogy - archives 04679

Central Butte

Central Butte District Museum, POB 165, Central Butte, Sask. S0H 0T0 - T: (306) 796-2146
Local Museum / Agriculture Museum 04680

Cereal

Cereal Prairie Pioneer Museum, Old Railway Station, Cereal, Alta. T0J 0N0 - T: (403) 326-3899. Head: F. Adams
Local Museum - 1974
Local history 04681

Chambly

Fort-Chambly, 2 Rue Richelieu, Chambly, P.Q. J3L 2B9 - T: (450) 658-1585. Head: Claude Picher
Military Museum
Ruins of Fort Chambly, exhibits concerning military life 04682

Channel-Port-aux-Basques

Channel-Port-aux-Basques Museum, 118 Main St, Channel-Port-aux-Basques, Nfld. A0M 1C0 - T: (709) 695-7604, 956-2170, Fax: (709) 956-2170, Internet: http://www.gatewaytonewfoundland.com
Local Museum 04683

Chapleau

Chapleau Centennial Museum, Monk St, Chapleau, Ont. P0M 1K0, mail addr: POB 129, Chapleau, Ont. P0M 1K0 - T: (705) 864-1211, Fax: (705) 864-2138, E-mail: salvador@township.chapleau.on.ca, Internet: http://www.township.chapleau.on.ca. Head: Fred Salvador
Local Museum - 1967
Mineralogy, mounted animals, historical pictures and booklets 04684

Charlottetown

Beaconsfield Historic House, Prince Edward Island Museum and Heritage Foundation, 2 Kent St, Charlottetown, P.E.I. C1A 1M6 - T: (902) 368-6600, Fax: (902) 368-6608, E-mail: peimuse@bud.peinet.pe.ca. Head: Nonie Fraser
Local Museum - 1984
Artifacts, displays and archives pertaining to local history, largest coll of genealogical material on the island in a 1877 shipbuilder's home 04685

Confederation Centre Art Gallery and Museum, Confederation Centre of the Arts, 145 Richmond St, Charlottetown, P.E.I. C1A 1J1 - T: (902) 628-6111, Fax: (902) 566-4648, E-mail: jsimpson@confederationcentre.com, Internet: http://www.confederationcentre.com. Head: Jon Tupper
Fine Arts Museum - 1964
Canadian paintings, graphics, decorative arts, porcelain (1780-1880), Robert Harris coll 04686

Green Gables House, 2 Palmers Lane, Charlottetown, P.E.I. C1A 5V6 - T: (902) 963-3370
Historical Museum 04687

Lord Selkirk Settlement, off Trans-Canada Hwy near Eldon, Charlottetown, P.E.I. C1A 7N7
Local Museum - 1973
Replicas of the first shelters of the Selkirk settlers 04688

Lucy Maud Montgomery Birthplace, New London, Charlottetown, P.E.I. C1A 4N6, mail addr: POB 491, Kensington, P.E.I. C0B 1M0 - T: (902) 436-7329. Head: Dr. Francis Bolger
Special Museum - 1965
Furniture of 1870's-1880's, scrapbooks, pretaining to L.M. Montgomery 04689

Port-la-Joye-Fort Amherst, 2 Palmers Ln, Charlottetown, P.E.I. C1A 5V6 - T: (902) 566-8287, Fax: (902) 566-8295, E-mail: sharon_larter@pch.gc.ca, Internet: http://www.parkscanada.pch.gc.ca
Historical Museum
Social, political and military history of the vicinity 04690

Prince Edward Island Museum, 2 Kent St, Charlottetown, P.E.I. C1A 1M6 - T: (902) 368-6600, Fax: (902) 368-6608, E-mail: peimuse@pei.sympatico.ca, Internet: http://metamedia.pe.ca/museum. Head: Christopher C. Severance
Historical Museum / Public Gallery 04691

The Prince Edward Island Regiment Museum, c/o Queen Charlotte Armouries, 3 Haviland St, Charlottetown, P.E.I. C1A 7N1 - T: (902) 368-0108, Fax: (902) 368-3034. Head: Greg Gallant
Military Museum 04692

Province House, 165 Richmond St, Charlottetown, P.E.I. C1A 1J1 - T: (902) 566-7626, Fax: (902) 566-8295
Historical Museum
Confederation of Canada, first conference in 1864 04693

Spoke Wheel Car Museum, RR3, Charlottetown, P.E.I. C1A 7J7. Head: Clarence Foster
Science&Tech Museum 04694

Chase

Chase and District Museum, 1042 Shuswap Av, Chase, B.C. V0E 1M0 - T: (250) 679-8847
Local Museum 04695

Château-Richer

Musée de l'Abeille, 8862 Blvd Sainte-Anne, Château-Richer, P.Q. G0A 1N0 - T: (418) 824-4411, Fax: (418) 824-4411, E-mail: rhayes@musee-abeille.qc.ca, Internet: http://www.musee-abeille.qc.ca
Natural History Museum 04696

Chatham, New Brunswick

Saint Michael's Historical Museum, 12 Alexandra St, Chatham, New Brunswick, N.B. E1N 1V2 - T: (506) 773-3277, Fax: (506) 778-5156, E-mail: mmuseum@nbnet.nb.ca, Internet: http://www.nibc.nb.ca/st-mikes/default.htm. Head: John Connell
Religious Arts Museum - 1975
Church related artifacts, documents written by the local clergy (1816-1900), genealogical records from parish registers (1801) 04697

Chatham, Ontario

Chatham-Kent Museum, 75 William St N, Chatham, Ontario, Ont. N7M 4L4 - T: (519) 360-1998, Fax: (519) 354-4170, E-mail: daveb@city.chatham-kent.on.ca, Internet: http://www.city.chatham-kent.on.ca/ccc
Local Museum - 1945
History, natural history, orntihological coll, Indian artifacts, Australian and Egyptian displays, 2000 years old mummy 04698

Chatham Railroad Museum, 2 McLean St, Chatham, Ontario, Ont. N7M 5K5 - T: (519) 352-3097
Science&Tech Museum 04699

Firefighting Museum, 5 Second St, Chatham, Ontario, Ont. K7M 5X2 - T: (519) 436-3295, Fax: (519) 352-8620
Science&Tech Museum / Historical Museum 04700

Milner House, c/o Chatham-Kent Museum, 75 William St N, Chatham, Ontario, Ont. N7M 4L4 - T: (519) 360-1998, Fax: (519) 354-4170, E-mail: daveb@city.chatham-kent.on.ca, Internet: http://www.city.chatham-kent.on.ca/ccc. Head: Dave Benson
Special Museum
Life of Robert Milner, a carriage maker, his hamily, period funishings, accessories, original artwork by his wife Emma, trophy room of exotic animal spacimens 04701

Thames Art Gallery, 75 William St N, Chatham, Ontario, Ont. N7M 4L4 - T: (519) 360-1998, Fax: (519) 354-4170, E-mail: carll@city.chatham-kent.on.ca, Internet: http://www.city.chatham-kent.on.ca/ccc. Head: Carl L. Lavoy
Public Gallery 04702

Cheltenham

Great War Flying Museum, Brampton Airport, RR1, Cheltenham, Ont. L0P 1C0 - T: (905) 838-1400
Science&Tech Museum 04703

Cheticamp

Galerie Elizabeth LeFort, CP 430, Cheticamp, N.S. B0E 1H0 - T: (902) 224-2642, Fax: (902) 224-1579, E-mail: pignons3@atcon.com, Internet: http://www.lestroispignons.com. Head: Lisette Cormier
Fine Arts Museum 04704

Musée Acadien, 114 Main St, Cheticamp, N.S. B0E 1H0, mail addr: CP 98, Cheticamp, N.S. B0E 1H0 - T: (902) 224-2170, Fax: (902) 224-2170. Head: Luce Marie Boudreau, Diane Poirier
Local Museum - 1967
History of wool carding, fishing implements, agricultural tools, domestic utensils 04705

Chetwynd

Little Prairie Heritage Museum, POB 1777, Chetwynd, B.C. V0C 1J0 - T: (250) 788-3358
Local Museum 04706

Chicoutimi

Espace Virtuel, 534 Rue Jacques-Cartier, Chicoutimi, P.Q. G7H 5B7 - T: (418) 549-3618
Public Gallery 04707

La Pulperie de Chicoutimi, 300 Rue Dubuc, Chicoutimi, P.Q. G7J 4M1 - T: (418) 698-3100, Fax: (418) 698-3158, E-mail: jlapointe@pulperie.com, Internet: http://www.pulperie.com. Head: Yolande Racine
Local Museum - 1896
Pulp Mill site (former Chicoutimi Pulp Company), art, ethnology 04708

Chilliwack

Chilliwack Museum, 45820 Spadina Av, Chilliwack, B.C. V2P 1T3 - T: (604) 795-5210, Fax: (604) 795-5291, E-mail: cm_chin@dowco.com, Internet: http://www.chilliwack.museum.bc.ca/cm. Head: Ron Denman
Local Museum 04709

Church Point

Musée Sainte-Marie, POB 28, Church Point, N.S. B0W 1M0 - T: (902) 769-2832, Fax: (902) 769-0048
Religious Arts Museum 04710

Churchill

Eskimo Museum, 242 La Verendrye, Churchill, Man. R0B 0E0 - T: (204) 675-2030, Fax: (204) 675-2140
Folklore Museum - 1944
Eskimo material including archeology, ethnology and fine arts, pre-Dorset, Thule and Eskimo artifacts 04711

Parks Canada Visitor Reception Centre, Lawerendrye St, Churchill, Man. R0B 0E0, mail addr: POB 127, Churchill, Man. R0B 0E0 - T: (204) 675-8863, Fax: (204) 675-2026, E-mail: mannorth_nhs@pch.gc.ca, Internet: http://parkscanada.pch.gc.ca/parks/manitoba/prince_wales_fort/prince_walesforte.htm
Historical Museum - 1922
Partially restored Hudson Bay Company Fort, built in 1731-1771, York factory, Wapusk National Park 04712

Prince of Wales Fort, POB 127, Churchill, Man. R0B 0E0 - T: (204) 675-8863
Historical Museum 04713

Clair

Petit Musée, POB 401, Clair, N.B. E0L 1B0 - T: (506) 992-3637
Local Museum 04714

Claresholm

Appaloosa Horse Club of Canada Senior Citizens Museum, POB 940, Claresholm, Alta. T0L 0T0 - T: (403) 625-3326
Special Museum 04715

Claresholm Museum, 5126 1st St, Hwy 2, Claresholm, Alta. T0L 0T0 - T: (403) 625-3131, Fax: (403) 625-3869
Local Museum - 1967
Local history 04716

Clementsport

Old Saint Edward's Anglican Church, RR 2, Annapolis Royal, Clementsport, N.S. B0S 1E0
Religious Arts Museum - 1961
18th c Anglican church, ecclesiastical artifacts, artefacts of the surrounding area 04717

Climax

Climax Community Museum, POB 59, Climax, Sask. S0N 0N0 - T: (306) 293-2051. Head: Victor van Allen
Local Museum 04718

Clinton

South Cariboo Historical Museum, 1419 Cariboo Hwy, Clinton, B.C. V0K 1K0 - T: (250) 459-2442, Fax: (250) 459-0058. Head: Janet Lowe
Local Museum - 1953
Local historical artifacts, transportation equipment used in the Cariboo - archives 04719

Cloyne

Cloyne Pioneer Museum, POB 228, Cloyne, Ont. K0H 1K0 - T: (613) 336-2203, E-mail: margion@mazinaw.on.ca
Local Museum 04720

Coaticook

Musée Beaulne, Château Norton, 96 Rue Union, Coaticook, P.Q. J1A 1Y9 - T: (819) 849-6560, Fax: (819) 849-9519, E-mail: bonjour@museebeaulne.qc.ca, Internet: http://www.museebeaulne.qc.ca. Head: Mario Leandry
Fine Arts Museum - 1964
Costumes, textiles, fine and decotative arts 04721

Cobalt

Cobalt's Northern Ontario Mining Museum, 24 Silver St, Cobalt, Ont. P0J 1C0, mail addr: POB 215, Cobalt, Ont. P0J 1C0 - T: (705) 679-8301, Fax: (705) 679-8301, E-mail: cnomchin@ntl.sympatico.ca, Internet: http://www.nt.net/cobalt. Head: Anne Fraboni
Science&Tech Museum / Local Museum - 1953
Mining hist, rock samples and mineral specimens, silver specimens, photographs, newspapers, social life, fluorescent rock display - archives 04722

Cobourg

Art Gallery of Northumberland, Victoria Hall, 55 King St W, Cobourg, Ont. K9A 2M2 - T: (905) 372-0333, Fax: (905) 372-1587, E-mail: agn@eagle.ca, Internet: http://www.artgalleryofnorthumberland.com. Head: Godfray DeLisle
Public Gallery - 1961/1977
Canadian, European and American paintings, arts and crafts, Eskimo artifacts, ceramics and sculpture 04723

Cochrane

Cochrane Railway and Pioneer Museum, 210 Railway St, Cochrane, Ont. P0L 1C0 - T: (705) 272-4361, Fax: (705) 272-6068, E-mail: lisel@puc.net, Internet: http://www.town.cochrane.on.ca. Head: Paul Latondress
Science&Tech Museum / Local Museum 04724

Coldwater

Coldwater Canadiana Heritage Museum, POB 125, Coldwater, Ont. L0K 1E0 - T: (705) 835-5032, Fax: (705) 835-2295
Local Museum 04725

Cole Harbour

Cole Harbour Heritage Farm Museum, 471 Poplar Dr, Cole Harbour, N.S. B2W 4L2 - T: (902) 462-0154, Fax: (902) 434-0222, E-mail: farmmuseum@ns.sympatico.ca, Internet: http://www3.ns.sympatico.ca/farmmuseum/. Head: Elizabeth Corser
Agriculture Museum 04726

Coleman

Crowsnest Museum, 7701 18 Av, Coleman, Alta. T0K 0M0 - T: (403) 563-5434, Fax: (403) 563-5434, E-mail: cnmuseum@telusplanet.net, Internet: http://www.telusplanet.net/public/cnmuseum. Head: Wendy Zack
Local Museum 04727

Collingwood

Collingwood Museum, Memorial Park, 1 Saint Paul St, Collingwood, Ont. L9Y 4B2, mail addr: POB 556, Collingwood, Ont. L9Y 4B2 - T: (705) 445-4811, Fax: (705) 445-9004, E-mail: cm-chin@georgian.net, Internet: http://www.town.collingwood.on.ca. Head: Tracy Marsh
Local Museum - 1904
Local hist incl shipbuilding industry, railway and Collingwood hist 04728

Comber

Comber and District Historical Society Museum, 8840 Hwy 77, S of Comber, Comber, Ont. N0P 1J0 - T: (519) 687-3332
Agriculture Museum - 1967
Agricultural development of the region 04729

Tilbury West Agricultural Museum → Comber and District Historical Society Museum

Combermere

Madonna House Pioneer Museum, Combermere, Ont. K0J 1L0 - T: (613) 756-0103. Head: Linda Lambeth
Local Museum 04730

Commanda

Commanda General Store Museum, 4077 Hwy 522, Commanda, Ont. P0H 1J0 - T: (705) 729-2113, Fax: (705) 729-5470
Historical Museum 04731

Connors

Connors Museum, 3614 Rte 205, Connors, N.B. E7A 1S3 - T: (506) 992-2500, Fax: (506) 992-2500, E-mail: armandb@nb.sympatico.ca. Head: Suzie Bernier
Local Museum 04732

Pioneer Historical Connors Museum, 1352 Rte 205, Connors, N.B. E7A 1S3 - T: (506) 992-2500, Fax: (506) 992-2500, E-mail: darmandb@nb.sympatico.ca. Head: Suzie Bernier
Historical Museum 04733

Corner Brook

Humber-Bay of Islands Museum, 65 Central St, Corner Brook, Nfld. A2H 2M7 - T: (709) 634-7907, Fax: (709) 634-7907
Local Museum 04734

Sir Wilfred Grenfell College Art Gallery, Memorial University of Newfoundland, Corner Brook, Nfld. A2H 6P9 - T: (709) 637-6357, Fax: (709) 637-6383, E-mail: coneill@beothuk.swgc.mun.ca, Internet: http://www.swgc.mun.ca. Head: Colleen O'Neill
Fine Arts Museum / University Museum 04735

Sticks and Stones House, 12 Riverhead Rd, Corner Brook, Nfld. A2H 1J6 - T: (709) 634-3275. Head: Ruby MacDonald
Special Museum 04736

Cornwall

Cornwall Regional Art Gallery, 168 Pitt St, Cornwall, Ont. K6H 6P4 - T: (613) 938-7387, Fax: (613) 938-9619
Fine Arts Museum 04737

Museum of the North American Indian Travelling College, RR3, Cornwall, Ont. K6H 5R7 - T: (613) 932-9454, Fax: (613) 932-0092, E-mail: nnatc@glen-net.ca
Special Museum / Historical Museum 04738

United Counties Museum, 731 Second St W, Cornwall, Ont. K6H 5T5 - T: (613) 932-2381, Fax: (613) 830-8741
Local Museum - 1956
Cornwall and Eastern Ontario manufactured household goods c 1850-1930 04739

Coronach

Coronach District Museum, 240 First St W, Coronach, Sask. S0H 0Z0 - T: (306) 267-5724
Local Museum - 1987
Artifacts and records depicting early settlements in this area - archives 04740

Côteau-du-Lac

Lieu Historique National de Côteau-du-Lac, 308 Ch du Fleuve, Côteau-du-Lac, P.Q. J0P 1B0 - T: (450) 763-5631, Fax: (450) 763-1654
Local Museum - 1967
Ruins of a military fort, model of the fort as it existed in 1812, military artifacts, exhibits on 19th c transportation 04741

Courtenay

Courtenay and District Museum and Paleontology Centre, 207 4th St, Courtenay, B.C. V9N 1G7 - T: (250) 334-0686, Fax: (250) 338-0619, E-mail: Museum@island.net, Internet: http://www.courtenaymuseum.ca. Head: A. Shopland
Natural History Museum - 1961
Paleontology, First Nations, pioneer - archives 04742

Cow Head

Dr. Henry N. Payne Community Museum, POB 47, Cow Head, Nfld. A0K 2A0 - T: (709) 243-2023, Fax: (709) 243-2622. Head: Glenda Reid-Bavis, Elizabeth Payne
Folklore Museum 04743

Cowansville

Centre d'Art de Cowansville, 225 Rue Principale, Cowansville, P.Q. J2K 1J4
Fine Arts Museum - 1967
Canadian paintings 04744

Cowichan Bay

Cowichan Bay Maritime Centre, POB 22, Cowichan Bay, B.C. V0R 1N0 - T: (250) 746-4955, Fax: (250) 746-9989, E-mail: cwbs@island.net, Internet: http://www.classicboats.org. Head: Paul Mitchell
Historical Museum 04745

Craik

Prairie Pioneer Museum, Old 11 Hwy, Craik, Sask. S0G 0V0 - T: (306) 734-2480. Head: R. Meshke
Local Museum - 1967
Restored pioneer house (1904), furnished in the style of that period, dolls, jewelry, Elizabethan Bible 04746

Cranbrook

Aasland Museum Taxidermy, 220 Kimberley Hwy NE, Cranbrook, B.C. V1C 4H4 - T: (250) 426-3566. Head: Odd Aasland
Natural History Museum 04747

Canadian Museum of Rail Travel, 1 Van Horne St N, Cranbrook, mail addr: POB 400, Cranbrook, B.C. V1C 4H9 - T: (250) 489-3918, Fax: (250) 489-5744, E-mail: mail@trainsdeluxe.com, Internet: http://www.trainsdeluxe.com. Head: Garry Anderson
Science&Tech Museum / Local Museum - 1976
13 restored railway cars, complete set of the 1929 luxury train "Trans-Canada Ltd" and 1907 "Soo Spokane Train Deluxe", royal cars, cars of state, buisness cars, railway gardens, 1900 Elko station, decorative arts 04748

Creighton

Frames Northern Museum, c/o Lawrence Frame, 436 First St W, Creighton, Man. R8A 1M3
Natural History Museum - 1966
Mounted animals, birds, and fish indigenous to the North 04749

Creston

Creston and District Museum, 219 Devon St, Creston, B.C. V0B 1G3 - T: (250) 428-9262, Fax: (250) 428-3324, E-mail: crvmchin@kootenay.com
Local Museum 04750

Crofton

Old Crofton School Museum, POB 159, Crofton, B.C. V0R 1R0 - T: (250) 246-3804
Historical Museum 04751

Crowsnest Pass

Frank Slide Interpretive Centre, 1.5 km off Hwy 3, Crowsnest Pass, mail addr: POB 959, Stn Blairmore, Crowsnest Pass, Alta. T0K 0E0 - T: (403) 562-7388, Fax: (403) 562-8635, E-mail: info@frankslide.com, Internet: http://www.frankslide.com. Head: Monica Field
Local Museum
Local history, incl Frank Slide, science 04752

Leitch Collieries, off Hwy 3, Crowsnest Pass, mail addr: POB 959, Stn Blairmore, Crowsnest Pass, Alta. T0K 0E0 - T: (403) 562-7388, Fax: (403) 562-8635, E-mail: info@frankslide.com, Internet: http://www.frankslide.com. Head: Monica Field
Science&Tech Museum
Coal mining history in the Crossnest Pass, technology 04753

Crystal City

Crystal City Community Museum, 218 Broadway, Crystal City, Man. R0K 0N0 - T: (204) 873-2293
Local Museum 04754

Cumberland, British Columbia

Cumberland Museum, 2680 Dunsmuir Av, Cumberland, British Columbia, B.C. V0R 1S0 - T: (250) 336-2445, Fax: (250) 336-2321, E-mail: CMA_chin@island.net, Internet: http://cumberland.museum.bc.ca. Head: Barbara Lemky
Local Museum - 1965
Mining equipment, old hospital equipment, Chinese items, multi cultural displays, family research - archives 04755

Cumberland, Ontario

Cumberland Heritage Village Museum, 2940 Queen St, Cumberland, Ontario, Ont. K4C 1E6, mail addr: BP 159, Cumberland, Ontario, Ont. K4C 1E6 - T: (613) 833-3059, Fax: (613) 833-3061, E-mail: chumchin@cyberplus.ca
Open Air Museum / Local Museum - 1976
Local history, historic buildings 04756

Cupar

Cupar and District Heritage Museum, POB 164, Cupar, Sask. S0G 0Y0 - T: (306) 723-4324
Local Museum 04757

Cupids

Cupids Museum, Seaforest Dr, Cupids, Nfld. A0A 2B0 - T: (709) 528-3500, E-mail: cupidshistorical@nf.sympatico.ca, Internet: http://www3.nf.sympatico.ca/cupidshistorical. Head: Linda Kane
Local Museum 04758

Curve Lake

Whetung Craft Centre and Art Gallery, Curve Lake, Ont. K0L 1R0 - T: (705) 657-3661, Fax: (705) 657-3412, Internet: http://www.whetung.com
Fine Arts Museum / Decorative Arts Museum 04759

Cutknife

Clayton McLain Memorial Museum, Cutknife, Sask. S0M 0N0 - T: (306) 398-2590
Local Museum 04760

Czar

Prairie Panorama Museum, Shorncliffe Park, Czar, Alta. T0B 0Z0 - T: (780) 857-2155. Head: Helena Lawrason
Fine Arts Museum / Decorative Arts Museum / Local Museum - 1962
Fine and decorative arts, local archival material 04761

Dalhousie

Musée Restigouche, 437 Rue George, Dalhousie, N.B. E0K 1B0 - T: (506) 684-7490, Fax: (506) 684-7613, E-mail: qurrm@nbnet.nb.ca
Local Museum 04762

Darlingford

Darlingford School Heritage Museum, Darlingford, Man. R0G 0L0 - T: (204) 246-2026
Historical Museum 04763

Dartmouth

Black Cultural Centre for Nova Scotia, 1149 Main St, Dartmouth, N.S. B2Z 1A8 - T: (902) 434-6223, Fax: (902) 434-2306, E-mail: mail@bccns.com, Internet: http://www.bccns.com. Head: Henry Bishop
Folklore Museum 04764

Evergreen Historic House, 26 Newcastle St, Dartmouth, N.S. B2Y 3M5 - T: (902) 464-2301, Fax: (902) 464-8210. Head: Anita Price
Local Museum 04765

Regional Museum of Cultural History, 100 Wyse Rd, Dartmouth, N.S. B3A 1M1 - T: (902) 464-2300, Fax: (902) 464-8210, Internet: http://www.region.halifax.ns.ca
Local Museum - 1968
History of the Micmac Indians, local history, whaling, local industry 04766

William Ray House, 57 Ochterloney St, Dartmouth, N.S. B2Y 1C3 - T: (902) 464-2253, Fax: (902) 464-8210, E-mail: pricea@region.halifax.ns.ca. Head: Anita Price
Historical Museum 04767

Dauphin

Dr. V.L. Watson Allied Arts Centre, 104 First Av NW, Dauphin, Man. R7N 1G9 - T: (204) 638-6231, Fax: (204) 638-6231, E-mail: art6231@mb.sympatico.ca. Head: Dr. Veron L. Watson, Nina Crawford
Fine Arts Museum 04768

Fort Dauphin Museum, 140 Jackson Av, Dauphin, Man. R7N 2V1 - T: (204) 638-6630, Fax: (204) 629-2327, E-mail: fortdphn@mb.sympatico.ca, Internet: http://www.city.dauphin.mb.ca. Head: Lori Bicklmeier
Local Museum / Archaeological Museum - 1973
Archeology, fur trade, pioneer artifacts, military, agricultural, historical, natural hist 04769

McCallum's Museum, Hwy 5, Dauphin, Man. R7N 2V1
Local Museum 04770

Trembowla Cross of Freedom Museum, 121 7 Av SE, Dauphin, Man. R7N 2E3 - T: (204) 638-9641, Fax: (204) 638-5746. Head: John Slobodzian
Historical Museum / Religious Arts Museum
Art and culture of the Ukrainian people who settled in the Trembowla area, 1st Ukrainian divine liturgy in Canada, 1st Ukrainian Catholic church in Canada, 1st settlers leader Wasyl Ksionzyk - archives 04771

Dawson City

Dawson City Museum, 595 Fifth Av, Dawson City, Y.T. Y0B 1G0 - T: (867) 993-5291, Fax: (867) 993-5839, E-mail: dcmuseum@yknet.yk.ca, Internet: http://www.gold-rush.org. Head: Paul C. Thistle
Local Museum - 1959
Local history exhibits, especially concerning the Klondike Gold Rush 04772

Klondike National Historic Sites, POB 390, Dawson City, Y.T. Y0B 1G0 - T: (867) 993-5462, Fax: (867) 993-5683
Local Museum / Historical Museum 04773

Dawson Creek

Dawson Creek Art Gallery, 816 Alaska Av, Dawson Creek, B.C. V1G 4T6 - T: (250) 782-2601, Fax: (250) 782-3352, E-mail: dcag@pris.bc.ca, Internet: http://www.islandnet.com/~bcma/museums/dawsoncreek. Head: Loris Martin
Fine Arts Museum / Decorative Arts Museum - 1962
Fine and decorative arts 04774

Dawson Creek Station Museum, 900 Alaska Av, Dawson Creek, B.C. V1G 4K8 - T: (250) 782-9595, Fax: (250) 782-9538, E-mail: dctourin@pris.bc.ca, Internet: http://www.pris.bc.ca/dcsm. Head: Day Roberts
Local Museum - 1962
Natural history of the region, historical artifacts of pioneer era 04775

Walter Wright Pioneer Village, c/o Dawson Creek Station Museum, 900 Alaska Av, Dawson Creek, B.C. V1G 4T6
Open Air Museum 04776

DeBolt

DeBolt and District Pioneer Museum, POB 447, DeBolt, Alta. T0H 1B0 - T: (780) 957-3957, Fax: (780) 957-2934. Head: Fran Moore
Local Museum 04777

Deer Lake

Roy Whalen Regional Heritage Centre, 44 Trans Canada Hwy, Nfld. A8A 2E4 Deer Lake - T: (709) 635-4440, Fax: (709) 635-5103, Internet: http://www.town.deerlake.nf.ca. Head: D. Kelly
Local Museum 04778

Delburne

Anthony Henday Museum, POB 374, Delburne, Alta. T0M 0V0 - T: (403) 749-2711
Local Museum 04779

Delhi

Delhi Ontario Tobacco Museum & Heritage Centre, 200 Talbot Rd, Delhi, Ont. N4B 2A2 - T: (519) 582-0278, Fax: (519) 582-0122, E-mail: tobacco.museum@norfolkcounty.on.ca. Head: Judy A. Livingstone Cowan
Special Museum 04780

Teeterville Pioneer Museum, 200 Talbot Rd, Delhi, Ont. N4B 2A2 - T: (519) 582-0278, Fax: (519) 582-0122, E-mail: teeterville.museum@norfolkcounty.on.ca. Head: Ivoy A. Livingstone
Local Museum 04781

Windham Township Pioneer Museum → Teeterville Pioneer Museum

Deloraine

Deloraine Museum, POB 327, Deloraine, Man. R0M 0M0
Local Museum 04782

Delta

Delta Mill and Old Stone Mill Museum, POB 172, Delta, Ont. K0E 1G0 - T: (613) 928-2584, Fax: (613) 928-2584, E-mail: thedeltamillsociety@recorder.ca, Internet: http://www.rideau-info.com/delta/stonemill.html
Science&Tech Museum 04783

Delta Museum, 4858 Delta St, Delta, B.C. V4K 2T8 - T: (604) 946-9322, Fax: (604) 946-5791, E-mail: mail@delta.museum.bc.ca. Head: Donna Bryman
Local Museum - 1969
Turn-of-the-century street scene, Victorian period rooms of pioneer home, First Nations artifacts, early, fishing, farming, canning industry, duck hunting, decoys, photographs and cartography - archives 04784

Denare Beach

Northern Gateway Museum, Denare Beach, Sask. S0P 0B0 - T: (306) 362-2054, Fax: (306) 362-2251, E-mail: denarebch@sask.sympatico.ca, Internet: http://www.quantumlynx.com/denarebeach. Head: Norma Barr
Local Museum - 1956
Local beadwork, Inuit carvings, trade goods, fossils, primitive tools 04785

Denman Island

Denman Island Museum, 1111 Northwest Rd, Denman Island, B.C. V0R 1T0 - T: (250) 335-0880. Head: Rhoda Millard
Local Museum 04786

Denmark

Sutherland Steam Mill, Rte 326, Denmark, N.S. B3H 3A6 - T: (902) 657-3365, Fax: (902) 657-3016, Internet: http://museum.gov.ns.ca
Science&Tech Museum
Motive force for industry in N.S., rough-sawn wood, dressed lumber, wagons, carriages 04787

Desbiens

Centre d'Interpretation de la Métabetchouane, 243 Rue Hébert, Desbiens, P.Q. G0W 1N0 - T: (418) 346-5341
Local Museum 04788

Dewberry

Dewberry Valley Museum, POB 30, Dewberry, Alta. T0B 1G0 - T: (780) 847-3053
Local Museum 04789

Didsbury

Didsbury and District Museum, POB 1175, Didsbury, Alta. T0M 0W0 - T: (403) 335-9295. Head: Katie Harder
Local Museum 04790

Digby

Admiral Digby Museum, 95 Montague Row, Digby, N.S. B0V 1A0 - T: (902) 245-6322, Fax: (902) 245-5196, E-mail: bryder@ns.sympatico.ca, Internet: http://www3.ns.sympatico.ca/admuseum
Historical Museum 04791

Dingwall

North Highland Community Museum, RR1, Dingwall, N.S. B0C 1G0 - T: (902) 383-2579, E-mail: museum@nscn.ns.ca, Internet: http://www.nscn.ns.ca/museum. Head: Kathleen MacLeod
Local Museum 04792

Dinsmore

Yester-Years Community Museum, POB 216, Dinsmore, Sask. S0L 0T0
Local Museum 04793

Doaktown

Atlantic Salmon Museum on the Miramichi River, 263 Main St, Doaktown, N.B. E9C 1A9 - T: (506) 365-7787, Fax: (506) 365-7359, E-mail: museum@nbnet.nb.ca
Fine Arts Museum 04794

Doak House, Rte 8, Doaktown, N.B. E0C 1G0 - T: (506) 365-4363
Local Museum 04795

Dodsland

Dodsland Museum, POB 203, Dodsland, Sask. S0L 0V0 - T: (306) 356-4700. Head: Weldon Bacon
Local Museum 04796

Donalda

Donalda and District Museum, POB 40, Donalda, Alta. T0B 1H0 - T: (403) 883-2100, Fax: (403) 883-2022, E-mail: lamps@village.donalds.ab.ca, Internet: http://village.donalda.ab.ca. Head: Georgina Brown
Local Museum 04797

Dorchester

Bell Inn, The Square, Dorchester, N.B. E0A 1M0 - T: (506) 379-2237. Head: Sylvia Yeoman
Local Museum 04798

Keillor House Museum, 4974 Main St, Dorchester, N.B. E4K 2X2 - T: (506) 379-6633, Fax: (506) 379-3033, E-mail: keillorhouse@nb.aibn.com, Internet: http://www.keillorhousemuseum.com. Head: Alice Folkins
Local Museum - 1967
Stone farmhouse (1813) furnished in the period style of 1813 to 1900, costumes, tools, maps, antique vehicles 04799

Dorval

Dorval Art Gallery and Cultural Centre, 1401 Lakeshore Dr, Dorval, P.Q. H9S 2E5 - T: (514) 633-4040, Fax: 6334016, E-mail: citédedorval@city.dorval.gc.ca, Internet: http://www.city.dorval.gc.ca
Fine Arts Museum / Decorative Arts Museum - 1967
Paintings, sculpture, crafts, jewelry 04800

Drayton Valley

Drayton Valley Museum, POB 5099, Drayton Valley, Alta. T7A 1R3
Local Museum 04801

Dresden

Uncle Tom's Cabin Historic Site, 29251 Uncle Tom's Rd, Dresden, Ont. N0P 1M0 - T: (519) 683-2978, Fax: (519) 683-1256, E-mail: parkway@ebtech.net, Internet: http://www.uncletomscabin.org. Head: Garry McDonald
Historical Museum / Historic Site - 1963
Black history 04802

Drumheller

Drumheller Dinosaur and Fossil Museum, 335 First St E, Drumheller, Alta. T0J 0J0, mail addr: POB 2135, Drumheller, Alta. T0J 0Y0 - T: (403) 823-2593. Head: Dorothy Farmer
Natural History Museum - 1957
Fossils, Indian artifacts, local history 04803

Homestead Antique Museum, 901 Dinosaur Trail, Drumheller, mail addr: POB 3154, Drumheller, Alta. T0J 0Y0 - T: (403) 823-2600, Fax: (403) 823-5479. Head: Steven Kempling
Local Museum - 1963 04804

Royal Tyrrell Museum of Palaeontology, Midland Provincial Park, Drumheller, mail addr: POB 7500, Drumheller, Alta. T0J 0Y0 - T: (403) 823-7707, Fax: (403) 823-7131, E-mail: info@tyrrellmuseum.com, Internet: http://www.tyrrellmuseum.com. Head: Dr. Bruce G. Naylor
Natural History Museum - 1985 04805

Drummondville

Galerie d'Art l'Union-Vie, 175 Rue Ringuet, Drummondville, P.Q. J2C 2P7 - T: (819) 477-5518 ext 225, Fax: (819) 477-5723, E-mail: nblanchette@centre-culturel.qc.ca. Head: Normand Blanchette
Fine Arts Museum 04806

Musée de la Cuisine, Parc des Voltigeurs, Drummondville, P.Q. J2B 6V6 - T: (819) 472-3662, Fax: (819) 472-1628, Internet: http://www.drummond.com/trent
Special Museum 04807

Village Québecois d'Antan, 1425 Rue Montplaisir, Drummondville, P.Q. J2B 7T5 - T: (819) 478-1441, Fax: (819) 478-8155
Local Museum 04808

Dryden

Dryden and District Museum, 15 Van Horne Av, Dryden, Ont. P8N 2A5 - T: (807) 223-4671, Fax: (807) 223-3999. Head: Edna Libbus Boon
Local Museum 04809

Duck Lake

Duck Lake Regional Interpretive Centre, POB 328, Duck Lake, Sask. S0K 1J0 - T: (306) 467-2057, Fax: (306) 467-2257, E-mail: duckmuf@sk.sympatico.ca, Internet: http://www.dlric.org. Head: Shirley Perillat
Local Museum - 1960
First nations and Métis beadwork, pioneer artifacts, events of uprising of 1885, Almightyvoice story 04810

Duff

Duff Community Heritage Museum, POB 57, Duff, Sask. S0A 0S0 - T: (306) 728-3592
Local Museum 04811

Dufresne

Aunt Margaret's Museum of Childhood, Trans-Canada Hwy, Dufresne, Man. R0A 0J0 - T: (204) 422-8426
Special Museum - 1968
Toys 04812

Dugald

Cooks Creek Heritage Museum, Hwy 212, RR 2, Cooks Creek, Dugald, Man. R0E 0K0 - T: (204) 444-4448, Fax: (204) 444-4224, Internet: http://www.blazeinet.com/st-michaels. Head: Jane Burpee
Local Museum - 1969
Slavic pioneer material, religious artifacts, Galician log house, farm machinery, blacksmith barn 04813

Costume Museum of Canada, POB 38, Dugald, Man. R0E 0K0 - T: (204) 853-2166, Fax: (204) 853-2077, E-mail: info@costumemuseum.com, Internet: http://www.costumemuseum.com. Head: Monique Brandt
Decorative Arts Museum 04814

Duncan

B.C. Forest Discovery Centre, 2892 Drinkwater Rd, Duncan, B.C. V9L 6C2 - T: (250) 715-1113, Fax: (250) 715-1170, E-mail: bcfm@islandnet.com
Local Museum / Open Air Museum - 1964
Forest industry incl buildings, machinery and photos, First Nations display, locomotives and narrow-gauge operating railroad with steam trains - forestry education 04815

British Columbia Forest Museum → B.C. Forest Discovery Centre

Cowichan Valley Museum, Duncan Train Station, Canada Av., mail addr: POB 1014, Duncan, B.C. V9L 3W2 - T: (250) 746-6612, Fax: (250) 746-6612, E-mail: cvm_chin@island.net. Head: Priscilla Davis
Historical Museum 04816

Dundas

Dofasco Gallery, Dandas Valley School of Art, 21 Ogilvie St, Dundas, Ont. L9H 2S1 - T: (905) 628-6357
Public Gallery - 1967
Contemporary Canadian sculpture and works of art 04817

Dundas Historical Society Museum, 139 Park St W, Dundas, Ont. L9H 1X8 - T: (905) 627-7412
Local Museum - 1956
Local history, Indian artifacts, costumes and textiles, porcelain and glass, furnishings, children's section 04818

Dunvegan, Ontario

Glengarry Pioneer Museum, POB 27, Dunvegan, Ontario, Ont. K0C 1J0 - T: (613) 527-5230
Local Museum 04819

Durham

Durham Art Gallery, POB 1021, Durham, Ont. N0G 1R0 - T: (519) 369-3692. Head: Bear Epp
Fine Arts Museum 04820

Durrell

Durrell Museum, Arm Lads' Brigade Armoury, Durrell, Nfld. A0G 1Y0 - T: (709) 884-5537. Head: Lloyd Bulgin
Local Museum - 1978
Fishery 04821

Ear Falls

Ear Falls District Museum, Hwy 105, Ear Falls, mail addr: POB 309, Ear Falls, Ont. P0V 1T0 - T: (807) 222-3198, Fax: (807) 222-2384, E-mail: eftownship@town.earfalls.on.ca, Internet: http://www.town.earfalls.on.ca. Head: J. Morand
Local Museum 04822

East Coulee

East Coulee School Museum, POB 539, East Coulee, Alta. T0J 1B0 - T: (403) 822-3970, Fax: (403) 822-2111, Internet: http://www.virtuallydrumheller.com/tour/east.htm
Historical Museum 04823

Historic Atlas Coal Mine, 110 Century Av, East Coulee, Alta. T0J 1B0 - T: (403) 822-2220, Fax: (403) 822-2220, E-mail: hacm@telusplanet.net, Internet: http://www.atlascoalmine.ab.ca. Head: Linda Digby
Science&Tech Museum
Coal mining technology, life of coal miners, the coal age 04824

Eastend

Eastend Museum, POB 214, Eastend, Sask. S0N 0T0 - T: (306) 295-3819
Local Museum 04825

Eastend School Museum, First Av, Eastend, Sask. S0N 0T0 - T: (306) 295-3508
Local Museum - 1930
Fossils, local history, rocks, photographs 04826

Eaton Corner

Compton County Historical Museum, 374 Route 253, Eaton Corner, P.Q. J0B 1M0, mail addr: CP 967, Cookshire, P.Q. J0B 1M0 - T: (819) 875-5256, 875-5776, Fax: (819) 875-5776, E-mail: elaberee@abacom.com. Head: E.F. Laberee
Local Museum - 1959
Farm implements, household items, old medical instruments, wooden articles 04827

Edam

Harry S. Washbrook Museum, POB 182, Edam, Sask. S0M 0V0 - T: (306) 397-2260. Head: Harry Washbrook
Local Museum 04828

Edgerton

Edgerton and District Museum, POB 64, Edgerton, Alta. T0B 1K0 - T: (780) 755-3963. Head: J.H. Withnell
Local Museum 04829

Edmonton

Alberta Art Foundation Collection, 10158 103rd St, Edmonton, Alta. T5J 0X6 - T: (780) 427-9968, Fax: (780) 422-1162, Internet: http://www.affta.ab.ca. Head: John C. Oslen
Association with Coll 04830

Alberta Association of Registered Nurses Museum, 11620 168 St, Edmonton, Alta. T5M 4A6 - T: (780) 453-0534, Fax: (780) 482-4459, E-mail: lmycha@nurses.ab.ca, Internet: http://www.nurses.ab.ca. Head: Lorraine Mychajlunow
Historical Museum 04831

Alberta Aviation Museum, 11410 Kingsway Av, Edmonton, Alta. T5C 3R6 - T: (780) 453-1078, Fax: (780) 453-1885, Internet: http://www.discover-edmonton.com/AviationMuseum
Science&Tech Museum - 1973
Hall of fame dedicated to individuals who have made contributions to aviation history in Canada 04832

Alberta Railway Museum, POB 70014, Edmonton, Alta. T5C 3R6 - T: (780) 472-6229, Fax: (780) 487-8705, Internet: http://www.discoveredmonton.com/railwaymuseum/
Science&Tech Museum 04833

Beaver House, 10158 103 St, Edmonton, Alta. T5J 0X6 - T: (780) 427-2031, Fax: (780) 422-9132
Historical Museum 04834

Calgary and Edmonton Railway Museum, 10447 86 Av, Edmonton, Alta. T6E 2M4 - T: (780) 433-9739, Fax: (780) 431-0138, E-mail: jledm@ecn.ab.caet.ab.ca, Internet: http://www.canderail-way.museum.com
Science&Tech Museum 04835

Dental Museum, c/o Faculty of Medicine and Dentistry, University of Alberta, 89 Avenue, Edmonton, Alta. T6G 2N8 - T: (780) 492-5194, Fax: (780) 492-1624, E-mail: gsperber@ualberta.ca. Head: Dr. G. Sperber
Special Museum / Historical Museum / University Museum - 1952
Antique and historic dental instruments and furniture, natural hist, animal skulls, palaeoanthropology coll of early fossil hominids - archives 04836

Edmonton Art Gallery, 2 Sir Winston Churchill Sq, Edmonton, Alta. T5J 2C1 - T: (403) 422-6223, Fax: (403) 426-3105, E-mail: info@eag.org, Internet: http://www.eag.org. Head: Virginia Stephen
Fine Arts Museum - 1924
Western Canadian art, Canadian art from Krieghoff and his time to the present, contemporary international art 04837

Edmonton Public Schools Museum, 10425 99 Av, Edmonton, Alta. T5K 0E5 - T: (780) 422-1970, Fax: (780) 426-0192, E-mail: -archivesandmuseum@psb.edmonton.ab.ca, Internet: http://museum.epsb.net
Historical Museum 04838

Edmonton Telephone Historical Centre, 10437 83rd Av, Edmonton, Alta. T6E 2C7, mail addr: POB 4459, Edmonton, Alta. T6E 4T5 - T: (780) 433-1010, Fax: (780) 433-4068, E-mail: thc@planet.eon.net, Internet: http://www.telephonehistoricalcentre.com. Head: Robert Yeudall
Science&Tech Museum - 1981
Development of the telephone industry, antique telephones, switchboards, test gear, tools, insulators 04839

Fort Edmonton Park, Fox and Whitemud Drives, Edmonton, Alta. T5J 2R7 - T: (780) 496-8787, Fax: (780) 496-8797, Internet: http://www.gov.edmonton.ab.ca/fort. Head: Bryan Monaghan
Open Air Museum - 1974
Historical buildings from the mid-18th c to the 1920s, reconstruction of a fur-trading fort (1846), pre-railway settlement (1885), city of 1905, 1919 steamtrain, streetcars, automobiles 04840

Front Gallery, 12306 Jasper Av NW, Edmonton, Alta. T5N 3K5 - T: (403) 488-2952
Public Gallery 04841

Latitude 53 Gallery, 10137 104th St, Edmonton, Alta. T5J 0Z9 - T: (780) 423-5353, Fax: (780) 424-9117, E-mail: latitude53@compusmart.ab.ca. Head: Todd Janes
Public Gallery - 1978 04842

Loyal Edmonton Regiment Military Museum, Prince of Wales Armoury, 10440 108 Av, Ste 118, Edmonton, Alta. T5H 3Z9 - T: (780) 421-9943. Head: Dustin Covey
Military Museum 04843

Man and Telecommunication Museum, 10020 100th St, Edmonton, Alta. T5J 0N5 - T: (403) 425-3978
Science&Tech Museum 04844

Museum of Geology, c/o Department of Earth & Atmospheric Sciences, University of Alberta, Edmonton, Alta. T6G 2E3 - T: (780) 4923265, Fax: 4922030, Internet: http://www.ualberta.ca/EAS/. Head: Prof. B. Jones
Natural History Museum / University Museum - 1913
Geology, paleontology, mineralogy, meteorites 04845

Museum of Ukrainian Arts and Culture, 10951 107th St, Edmonton, Alta. T5R 3R7
Fine Arts Museum 04846

Museum of Zoology, University of Alberta, Biological Sciences, Edmonton, Alta. T6G 2E9 - T: (780) 492-4622, Fax: (780) 492-9234, E-mail: uamz@ualberta.ca, Internet: http://www.biology.ualberta.ca/uamzhp/uamz.html. Head: Cindy Paszowski
Natural History Museum 04847

Provincial Museum of Alberta, 12845 102nd Av, Edmonton, Alta. T5N 0M6 - T: (780) 453-9100, Fax: (780) 454-6629, E-mail: pstepney@mcd.gov.ab.ca, Internet: http://www.pma.edmonton.ab.ca. Head: Dr. Philip Stepney
Local Museum - 1967
Geology, quaternary paleontology, botany, ornithology, mammalogy, invertebrates, government hist, folk life, Western Canadian hist, archaeology, ethnology and fine art coll, Blackfoot, Athapaskan, Avian skeletal, mineralogy, egg coll, international hymenoptera coll, militaria, numismatics, ichthyology, herpetology, firearms 04848

Rutherford House, 11153 Saskatchewan Dr, Edmonton, Alta. T6G 2S1 - T: (780) 427-3995, Fax: (780) 422-4288, Internet: http://www.gov.ab.ca/~mcd/mcd.htm
Historical Museum - 1974
Home of the first Premier of Alberta, A.C. Rutherford, furnished in the style of the early 20th c 04849

Stephansson House, 8820 112 St, Edmonton, Alta. T6G 2P8 - T: (780) 427-3995
Special Museum 04850

Strathcona Archaeological Centre, 8820 112 St, Edmonton, Alta. T6G 2P8
Archaeological Museum 04851

Ukrainian Canadian Archives and Museum of Alberta, 9543 110th Av, Edmonton, Alta. T5H 1H3 - T: (780) 424-7580, Fax: (780) 420-0562. Head: Khrystyna Hohut
Historical Museum / Fine Arts Museum - 1972
History of Ukrainians in Alberta, Ukrainian arts and crafts 04852

Ukrainian Catholic Women's League Museum, 10825 97th St, Edmonton, Alta. T5H 2M4 - T: (780) 466-7210. Head: Nadia Cyncar
Folklore Museum - 1952
Ukrainian artifacts and textiles, historical costumes 04853

Ukrainian Cultural Heritage Village, Trans Canada Hwy 16, 50 km E of Edmonton, Edmonton, Alta., mail addr: c/o Historic Sites Service, 8820 112 St, Alberta, Alta. T6G 2P8 - T: (780) 662-3640, Fax: (780) 662-3273, E-mail: uchv@mcd.gov.ab.ca, Internet: http://www.cd.gov.ab.ca/uchv. Head: Barry Manchak
Open Air Museum / Ethnology Museum / Historical Museum / Agriculture Museum - 1976
Buildings including churches, homesteads, stores restored and furnished in the style of the period from 1890-1930 04854

Ukrainian Museum of Canada - Alberta Branch, 10611 110th Av, Edmonton, Alta. T5H 1H7 - T: (780) 483-5932, Fax: (780) 423-6738. Head: D. Ensslen
Ethnology Museum - 1953
Ethnography, folk art, textiles - library 04855

University of Alberta Museums, Ring House 1, Edmonton, Alta. T6G 2E1 - T: (780) 492-5834, Fax: (780) 492-6185, E-mail: museums@ualberta.ca, Internet: http://www.museums.ualberta.ca. Head: Janine Andrews
University Museum 04856

Victoria School Museum, 10210 108 Av, Edmonton, Alta. T5H 1A8 - T: (780) 426-3010, Fax: (780) 425-4626, E-mail: jcalkins@epsb.edmonton.ab.ca. Head: Jack Calkins
Historical Museum 04857

West End Gallery, 12308 Jasper Av NW, Edmonton, Alta. T5N 3K5 - T: (780) 488-4892
Public Gallery 04858

Edmundston

Galerie Colline, 165 Blvd Herbert, Edmundston, N.B. E3V 2S8 - T: (506) 737-5050. Head: Jacques Martin
Fine Arts Museum / Decorative Arts Museum - 1969
Painting, sculpture, graphic arts and decorative arts 04859

Musée Historique du Madawaska, 165 Blvd Hébert, Edmundston, N.B. E3V 2S8 - T: (506) 735-8804, Fax: (506) 739-5373. Head: Richard Therrien
Local Museum 04860

Edson

Galloway Station Museum, 5425a 3 Av, Edson, Alta. T7E 1L5 - T: (780) 723-3582
Local Museum 04861

Red Brick Arts Centre and Museum, 4818 7 Av, Edson, Alta. T7E 1K8 - T: (780) 723-3582
Fine Arts Museum 04862

Elbow

Elbow Museum, POB 207, Elbow, Sask. S0H 1J0 - T: (306) 854-2285, Fax: (306) 854-2229. Head: James Wankel
Local Museum - 1968
Local historical items, Indian artifacts, arrowhead coll, sod house 04863

Elgin

Kingston Mills Blockhouse, POB 10, Elgin, Ont. K0G 1E0 - T: (613) 359-5377, Fax: (613) 359-6042
Science&Tech Museum 04864

Elk Lake

Elk Lake Heritage Museum, Rosedale, Elk Lake, mail addr: POB 70, Elk Lake, Ont. P0J 1G0 - T: (705) 678-2237, Fax: (705) 678-2495. Head: Mel Giles
Local Museum
Local histiory, woods industry, mining, farming, trapping 04865

Elk Point

Fort George Museum, POB 66, Elk Point, Alta. T0A 1A0 - T: (780) 724-3654. Head: Steve Andrishak
Local Museum - 1952
Local history, archeology 04866

Elkhorn

Manitoba Automobile Museum, POB 477, Elkhorn, Man. R0M 0N0 - T: (204) 845-2604, Fax: (204) 845-2312. Head: Ted Stremel
Science&Tech Museum - 1966
Automobiles from 1908 to 1958, picture walls, agricultural machinery, household utensils, Indian artifacts 04867

Elliot Lake

Elliot Lake Nuclear and Mining Museum, Hwy 108, Lester B. Pearson Civic Center, Elliot Lake, Ont. P5A 2T1 - T: (705) 848-2084, Fax: (705) 461-7244, 848-2987, E-mail: paradise@inorth.on.ca. Head: F.J. Mann
Science&Tech Museum - 1965
Northern home of the "Canadian mining hall of fame", models of uranium mine bldgs, Dr. Franc Joubin mineral colls 04868

Elmira

Elmira Railway Museum, Prince Edward Island Museum and Heritage Foundation, Elmira, P.E.I. C0A 1K0 - T: (902) 357-7234. Head: Nonie Fraser
Science&Tech Museum
Railway station, 1930 mailcar 04869

Elrose

Elrose Heritage Museum, 116 Fourth Av E, Elrose, Sask. S0L 0Z0, mail addr: POB 458, Elrose, Sask. S0L 0Z0 - T: (306) 378-2202, Fax: (306) 378-2966, E-mail: townofelrose@sk.sympatico.ca. Head: Elizabeth Dinsmoie
Local Museum 04870

Emo

Rainy River District Women's Institute Museum, POB 511, Emo, Ont. P0W 1E0 - T: (807) 482-2007. Head: Tina Visser
Historical Museum 04871

Enderby

Enderby and District Museum, 901 George St, Enderby, B.C. V0E 1V0 - T: (250) 838-7170, Fax: (250) 838-0123, E-mail: edms@jetstream.net, Internet: http://www.enderbymuseum.ca. Head: Joan Cowan
Local Museum 04872

Englehart

Englehart and Area Historical Museum, 67 6th Av, Englehart, Ont. P0J 1H0 - T: (705) 544-2400, Fax: (705) 544-8737, E-mail: eahmchin@ntl.sympatico.ca. Head: Susan Noakes
Local Museum 04873

Eriksdale

Creamery Museum, Creamery Rd, Eriksdale, Man. R0C 0W0 - T: (204) 739-2140, E-mail: dmysmith@mb.sympatico.ca. Head: Donna Smith
Special Museum - 2000
Story of butter making 04874

Eriksdale Museum, Railway Av S, Eriksdale, Man. R0C 0W0 - T: (204) 739-2621, E-mail: dmysmith@mb.sympatico.ca. Head: Donna Smith
Local Museum - 1974
Pioneer artifacts, local newspapers (1961-present) 04875

Esterhazy

Esterhazy Community Museum, Hwy 22, Esterhazy, mail addr: POB 149, Esterhazy, Sask. S0A 0X0 - T: (306) 745-6761, 745-2988, Fax: (306) 896-2233. Head: A.M. Provick
Local Museum 04876

Kaposvar Historic Site, Our Lady of Assumption Church Museum, 3 miles S of Esterhazy, Esterhazy, Sask. S0A 0X0 - T: (306) 745-2715
Local Museum - 1975
Exhibit concerning the first Hungarian colony in Saskatchewan, habits of local Grey Nuns, church artifacts 04877

Estevan

Estevan National Exhibition Centre, Art Gallery and Museum, 118 Fourth St, Estevan, Sask. S4A 0T4 - T: (306) 634-7644, Fax: (306) 634-2490, E-mail: enec@cableestevan.com, Internet: http://www.cap.estevan.sk.ca/enec. Head: Brenda Barry Byrne
Local Museum / Fine Arts Museum - 1978
Local artifacts, paintings, prints, archive 04878

Eston

Prairie West Historical Centre, 946 Second St SE, Eston, Sask. S01 1A0 - T: (306) 962-3772, E-mail: pwhs@sk.sympatico.ca
Local Museum 04879

Etobicoke

Art Gallery, 56 Neilson Dr, Etobicoke, Ont. M9C 1V7 - T: (416) 622-5294, Fax: (416) 622-0892, E-mail: npcc@idirect.com, Internet: http://www.webhoem.idirect.com/~npcc
Fine Arts Museum 04880

Montgomery's Inn, 4709 Dundas St W, Etobicoke, Ont. M9A 1A8 - T: (416) 394-8113, Fax: (416) 394-6027, Internet: http://www.montgomerysinn.com. Head: U. Ernest Buchner
Historical Museum 04881

Etzikom

Museum of South East Alberta, POB 585, Etzikom, Alta. T0K 0W0 - T: (403) 666-3737, Fax: (403) 666-2002. Head: June Mitzel
Local Museum / Historical Museum 04882

Evansburg

Pembina Lobstick Historical Museum, POB 85, Evansburg, Alta. T0E 0T0 - T: (780) 727-3861, Fax: (780) 727-3861. Head: Hazel B. Fausak
Local Museum - 1970
Local historical artifacts and archives 04883

Fairview

RCMP Centennial Celebration Museum, POB 326, Fairview, Alta. T0H 1L0 - T: (780) 835-2467. Head: Viola Evans
Military Museum 04884

Fenelon Falls

Fenelon Falls Museum, 50 Oak St, Fenelon Falls, Ont. K0M 1N0 - T: (705) 887-1044
Local Museum / Folklore Museum - 1963
Local history and folklore, gun coll 04885

Fergus

Wellington County Museum, Wellington Pl, RR 1, Fergus, Ont. N1M 2W3 - T: (519) 846-0916, Fax: (519) 846-9630, E-mail: info@wcm.on.ca, Internet: http://www.wcm.on.ca. Head: Bonnie Callen
Local Museum - 1952
General hist relating to the county, local artists and crafts persons - archives 04886

Fernie

Fernie and District Historical Museum, POB 1527, Fernie, B.C. V0B 1M0 - T: (250) 423-7016, E-mail: fdhs_chin@elkvalley.net
Local Museum 04887

Ferryland

Historic Ferryland Museum, Old Courthouse, Ferryland, Nfld. A0A 2H0 - T: (709) 432-2711. Head: Maxine Dunne
Local Museum 04888

Flat Rock

Flat Rock Museum, 663 Windpag Rd, Flat Rock, Nfld. A1K 1C7 - T: (709) 437-6312, Fax: (709) 437-6311
Local Museum 04889

Flesherton

South Grey Museum, Memorial Park, 40 Sydenham St, Flesherton, Ont. N0C 1E0 - T: (519) 924-2843. Head: Doriann Seifried
Local Museum - 1973
Farm tools, quilts, military, railway exhibit, pioneer life 04890

Flin Flon

Flin Flon Museum, 529a South Hudson St, Flin Flon, Man. - T: (204) 687-2946, Fax: (204) 687-5133, E-mail: brussell@city.flinflon.mb.ca. Head: Brenda Russell
Local Museum 04891

Foam Lake

Foam Lake Museum, POB 1041, Foam Lake, Sask. S0A 1A0 - T: (306) 272-4292. Head: Ruth Gushulak
Local Museum - 1967
Local pioneer items, various household articles 04892

Fogo Island

Bleakhouse Museum, Fogo, Fogo Island, Nfld. A0G 2B0 - T: (709) 266-2237
Historical Museum 04893

Forest

Forest-Lambton Museum, 59 Broadway, Forest, Ont. N0N 1J0 - T: (519) 786-3239, Fax: (519) 786-1151. Head: Clarence Hodgson
Local Museum - 1963
Ornithology, fossils, religious artifacts, lighting and telephone systems, furnishings, local history - library 04894

Forestburg

Forestburg and District Museum, 4707 50 St, Forestburg, Alta. T0B 1N0 - T: (780) 582-3768, Fax: (780) 582-4203
Local Museum 04895

Forestville

Petite Anglicane, 22e Rue, Forestville, P.Q. G0T 1E0 - T: (418) 587-2109, Fax: (418) 587-6212
Local Museum 04896

Fort Chipewyan

Fort Chipewyan Bicentennial Museum, POB 203, Fort Chipewyan, Alta. T0P 1B0 - T: (780) 697-3844, Fax: (780) 697-2389. Head: Mary Bourque
Local Museum 04897

Fort Erie

Mildred M. Mahoney Silver Jubilee Dolls' House Gallery, 657 Niagara Blvd, Fort Erie, Ont. L2A 3H9 - T: (905) 871-5833, Fax: (905) 871-2447, E-mail: yvonne@iaw.on.ca, Internet: http://www.angelfire.com/biz/DollHouseGallery/. Head: June Spear
Decorative Arts Museum 04898

Fort Frances

Fort Frances Museum, 259 Scott St, Fort Frances, Ont. P9A 1G8 - T: (807) 274-7891, Fax: (807) 274-4103, E-mail: ffmus@fort-frances.lakeheadu.ca, Internet: http://www.fort-frances.com/museum
Local Museum - 1978
Logging equipment, Indian artifacts, farm implements 04899

Fort Saint Pierre, Pither's Point Park, Fort Frances, Ont. P9A 1G8 - T: (807) 274-7891, Fax: (807) 274-7891, E-mail: ffmus@ff.lakeheadu.ca, Internet: http://www.fort-frances.com/museum. Head: Pam Hawley
Local Museum 04900

Fort Good Hope

Dene Museum, Fort Good Hope, N.T. X0E 0H0 - T: (867) 598-2331
Local Museum 04901

Fort Langley

British Columbia Farm Machinery and Agricultural Museum, 9131 King St, Fort Langley, B.C. V0X 1J0 - T: (604) 888-2273, E-mail: margaret@direct.ca, Internet: http://webit.simplenet.com/museum. Head: Carel Jongs
Agriculture Museum - 1966
Farm machinery used in British Columbia from 1880 to 1960's, historic photogr, heavy horse breeders photodisplay - library, photograph coll 04902

Fort Langley, 23433 Mavis Av, Fort Langley, B.C. V1M 2R5, mail addr: POB 129, Fort Langley, B.C. V1M 2R5 - T: (604) 513-4777, Fax: (604) 513-4788, E-mail: fort_langley@pch.gc.ca, Internet: http://www.parkscanada.gc.ca/langley. Head: Bryan Jackson
Historical Museum - 1955
Artifacts illustrating fur trade and settlement, reconstructed trading fort (1840-1860) 04903

Langley Centennial Museum and National Exhibition Centre, 9135 King St, Fort Langley, B.C. V1M 2S2, mail addr: POB 800, Fort Langley, B.C. V1M 2S2 - T: (604) 888-3922, Fax: (604) 888-7291, E-mail: museum@township.langley.bc.ca, Internet: http://www.langleymuseum.org. Head: Sue Morhun
Local Museum - 1958/1974
Pioneer artifacts, handiwork and native artifacts 04904

Fort Macleod

Fort Museum, 219 25th St, Fort Macleod, Alta. T0L 0Z0, mail addr: POB 776, Fort Macleod, Alta. T0L 0Z0 - T: (403) 553-4703, Fax: (403) 553-3451, E-mail: ftmuseum@telusplanet.net, Internet: http://www.discoveralberta.com/fortmuseum. Head: Ron Ulrich
Open Air Museum / Local Museum - 1957
Historic buildings, Indian and pioneer artifacts, N.W.M.P. artifacts and archives, history of the N.W.M.P. later to become the Royal Canadian Mounted Police 04905

Head-Smashed-In Buffalo Jump, POB 1977, Fort Macleod, Alta. T0L 0Z0 - T: (403) 553-2731, Fax: (403) 553-3141, E-mail: info@head-smshed-in.com, Internet: http://www.head-smashed-in.com
Historical Museum 04906

Fort McMurray

Fort McMurray Oil Sands Discovery Centre, 515 MacKenzie Blvd, Fort McMurray, Alta. T9H 4X3 - T: (780) 743-7167, Fax: (780) 791-0710, E-mail: osdc@home.com
Local Museum 04907

Heritage Park, 1 Tolen Dr, Fort McMurray, Alta. T9H 1G7 - T: (780) 791-7575, Fax: (780) 791-5180, E-mail: heritage@ccinet.ab.ca, Internet: http://www.fortmcmurrayhistory.com
Open Air Museum 04908

Fort Nelson

Fort Nelson Heritage Museum, POB 716, Fort Nelson, B.C. V0C 1R0 - T: (250) 774-3536, Fax: (250) 774-3536. Head: Marlin Brown
Local Museum 04909

Fort Qu'appelle

Fort Qu'appelle Museum, 198 Bay Av N, Fort Qu'appelle, Sask. S0G 1S0 - T: (306) 332-6033
Local Museum - 1967
Indian artifacts, pioneer life, items relating to the Anti-Tuberculosis League, fur trading post Hudson Bay 04910

Fort Saint James

Fort Saint James National Historic Site, Kwah Rd, Fort Saint James, B.C. V0J 1P0 - T: (250) 996-7191, Fax: (250) 966-8566
Open Air Museum / Local Museum - 1977
Historic buildings furnished according to the 1890 period, history (pre-European to 1896) 04911

Fort Saint John

Fort Saint John-North Peace Museum, 9323 100 St, Fort Saint John, B.C. V1J 4N4 - T: (250) 787-0430, Fax: (250) 787-0405, E-mail: fsjnpmuseum@ocol.com, Internet: http://collections.ic.gc.ca/north_peace
Historical Museum 04912

Fort Saskatchewan

Fort Saskatchewan Museum, 10104 101st St, Fort Saskatchewan, Alta. T8L 1V9 - T: (780) 998-1750, Fax: (780) 998-1750, E-mail: museum@fortsaskinfio.com, Internet: http://www.fortsaskinfo.com/museum
Local Museum - 1967
History, archeology, archives of the Historical Society, 1909 courthouse, Northwest Mounted Police hist 04913

Fort Smith

Northern Life Museum and National Exhibition Centre, 110 King St, Fort Smith, N.T. X0E 0P0 - T: (867) 872-2859, Fax: (867) 872-5808, E-mail: nlm@gardtal.com, Internet: http://www.northernlifemuseum.org. Head: Clarence Rhymer
Ethnology Museum - 1974
Natural history, ethnology, minerals and fossils 04914

Fort Steele

Fort Steele Heritage Town, 9851 Highway 93-95, Fort Steele, B.C. V0B 1N0 - T: (250) 417-6006, Fax: (250) 489-2624, E-mail: dwwhite@fortsteele.bc.ca, Internet: http://

www.fortsteele.bc.ca. Head: Martin J.E. Ross
Historical Museum / Historic Site - 1967
History, Kutenai Indians, transportation, industrial archeology, Kootenaiana archives - archives 04915

Fort Vermilion

Rocky Lane School Museum, POB 9000, Fort Vermilion, Alta. T0H 1N0 - T: (780) 927-3297, Fax: (780) 927-4344. Head: M. Nugent
Historical Museum 04916

Frankford

Orval Berry Museum, 46 Belleville St, Frankford, Ont. K0K 2C0 - T: (613) 398-6531
Special Museum 04917

Fraser Lake

Fraser Lake Museum, POB 430, Fraser Lake, B.C. V0J 1S0 - T: (250) 699-6257, Fax: (250) 699-6469, E-mail: fraserlk@flk.auracom.com, Internet: http://www.village.fraserlk.bc.ca
Local Museum 04918

Fredericton

Beaverbrook Art Gallery, 703 Queen St, Fredericton, N.B. E3B 5A6 - T: (506) 458-8545, Fax: (506) 459-7450, E-mail: chant@nbnet.nb.ca, Internet: http://www.beaverbrookartgallery.org. Head: Laurie Glenn
Fine Arts Museum - 1959
British and Canadian painting, paintings by Salvador Dalí, English porcelain, sculpture - Marion McCain Atlantic Gallery 04919

Brydone Jack Observatory Museum, 8 Bailey Av, Fredericton, N.B. E3B 5A3, mail addr: c/o University of New Brunswick, POB 4400, Fredericton, N.B. E3B 5A3 - T: (506) 453-4841, Fax: (506) 453-3570, E-mail: science@unb.ca. Head: Dr. E. Parr-Johnston
Science&Tech Museum 04920

Electrical Engineering Museum, c/o Department of Electrical Engineering, University of New Brunswick, Head Hall, Fredericton, N.B. E3B 5A3 - T: (506) 453-4561, Fax: (506) 453-3589, E-mail: eeoffice@unb.ca, Internet: http://www.unb.ca
Science&Tech Museum - 1968
Electronic tubes, demonstration apparatuses, measuring instruments, radios from the 1920's, old books on electronical phenomena 04921

Gallery Connexion, POB 696, Fredericton, N.B. E3B 5B4 - T: (506) 454-1433, Fax: (506) 454-1401, E-mail: connex@nbnet.nb.ca
Fine Arts Museum 04922

Guard House and Soldiers Barracks, Carleton St, Fredericton Military Compound, Fredericton, N.B. E3B 5H1 - T: (506) 460-2041, Fax: (506) 460-2474, E-mail: tourism@city.fredericton.nb.ca, Internet: http://www.city.fredericton.nb.ca. Head: Wendy Betts
Military Museum
Restored British military guard house with period rooms 04923

House of International Dolls, 214 Cedar Av, Fredericton, N.B. E3A 2C6 - T: (902) 658-2449
Decorative Arts Museum 04924

New Brunswick Craft School Gallery, POB 6000, Fredericton, N.B. E3B 5H1 - T: (506) 453-2305, Fax: (506) 457-7352, E-mail: lneveu@gov.nb.ca. Head: Luc Paulin
Fine Arts Museum 04925

New Brunswick Healthcare Museum, 384 Smythe St, Fredericton, N.B. E3B 3E4 - T: (506) 453-0747, Fax: (506) 459-0503
Historical Museum 04926

New Brunswick Sports Hall of Fame, 503 Queen St, Fredericton, N.B. E3B 5H1 - T: (506) 453-3747, Fax: (506) 459-0481, E-mail: deborah.williams@gnb.ca, Internet: http://www.nbssportshalloffame.nb.ca. Head: Kathy Meagher
Special Museum 04927

Old Government House, 51 Woodstock Rd, Fredericton, N.B. E3B 5H1 - T: (506) 453-2505, Fax: (506) 444-5280, E-mail: ogh@gnb.ca, Internet: http://www.gov.nb.ca/mch/culaff/heritage/
Historical Museum 04928

University of New Brunswick Art Centre, Memorial Hall, Bailey Dr, Fredericton, N.B. E3B 5A3, mail addr: POB 4400, Fredericton, N.B. E3B 5A3 - T: (506) 453-4623, Fax: (506) 453-5012, E-mail: mem@unb.ca, Internet: http://www.unb.ca/web/FineArts/. Head: Marie E. Maltais
Fine Arts Museum / University Museum - 1942
Approx 1500 Canadian artworks primarily drawn from the Atlantic Region 04929

Wulastook Museums, 108 Queen St, Fredericton, N.B. E3B 5B4 - T: (506) 451-7777, Fax: (506) 451-1029
Historical Museum 04930

York Sunbury Historical Society Museum, 571 Queen St, Fredericton, N.B. E3B 5C8, mail addr: POB 1312, Fredericton, N.B. E3B 5C8 - T: (506) 455-6041, E-mail: yorksun@nbnet.nb.ca. Head: Kate Mossman
Local Museum / Military Museum - 1932
Military and local hist 04931

Frenchman Butte

Frenchman Butte Museum, POB 114, Frenchman Butte, Sask. S0M 0W0 - T: (306) 344-4478, Fax: (306) 344-4613. Head: Gwen Zweifel
Local Museum - 1979
Agricultural, guns, native artifacts, books, domestic, CNR station and memorabilia, log cabin Tea House, historic Minigolf, playground, original school house 04932

Frobisher

Frobisher Thresherman's Museum, POB 194, Frobisher, Sask. S0C 0Y0 - T: (306) 486-2162
Science&Tech Museum - 1976
Steam engines, wooden threshing separators (1912), tractors, 19th c household items 04933

Gagetown

Queens County Museum, Tilley House and Court House, 69 Front St, Gagetown, N.B. E5M 1A4 - T: (506) 488-2966, Fax: (506) 488-2966, E-mail: gbt@nbnet.nb.ca, Internet: http://www.geocities.com/heartland/lake/334. Head: Bruce Thomson
Local Museum - 1967
Home of Sir Leonard Tilley, 'Father of the Confederation', period rooms, local history 04934

Gananoque

Gananoque Museum, 10 King St E, Gananoque, Ont. K7G 2T7 - T: (613) 382-4024, Fax: (613) 382-8587
Local Museum - 1964
Indian artifacts, pioneer tools, glass and china, industrial artifacts, Victorian furniture, militaria 04935

Gander

North Atlantic Aviation Museum, Trans-Canada Hwy, Gander, Nfld. A1V 1W6, mail addr: POB 234, Gander, Nfld. A1V 1W6 - T: (709) 256-2923, Fax: (709) 256-2124
Science&Tech Museum - 1967
Aeronautical models, photographs of pioneer aviation 04936

Ganges

Salt Spring Island Museum, POB 961, Ganges, B.C. V0S 1E0 - T: (250) 537-9567
Agriculture Museum 04937

Garibaldi Heights

Squamish Valley Museum, POB 166, Garibaldi Heights, B.C. V0N 1T0 - T: (604) 898-3273
Local Museum 04938

Gaspé

Hyman and Sons General Store, 122 Blvd de Gaspé, Gaspé, P.Q. G4X 1A9 - T: (418) 892-5553, Fax: (418) 892-5951, Internet: http://www.parkscanada.gc.ca/forillon
Historical Museum 04939

Musée de la Gaspésie, 80 Blvd Gaspé, Gaspé, P.Q. G4X 1A9 - T: (418) 368-1534, Fax: (418) 368-1535, E-mail: musee@globetrotter.qc.ca
Local Museum 04940

Musée d'Histoire et de Traditions Populaires, Baie de Gaspé, Gaspé, P.Q. G0C 1R0
Historical Museum / Folklore Museum - 1972
Historical, ethnographical, and archeological exhibits, works of art 04941

Gatineau → Outaouais

Gibsons

Elphinstone Pioneer Museum, 716 Winn Rd, Gibsons, B.C. V0N 1V0 - T: (604) 886-8232, E-mail: e_p_museum@uniserve.com, Internet: http://www.gibsonslibrary.bc.ca. Head: Jim Malyea
Local Museum - 1965
Pioneer materials, Salish Coast artifacts, shells - Library, archives 04942

Sunshine Coast Maritime Museum, POB 1912, Gibsons, B.C. V0N 1V0 - T: (604) 886-4114, Fax: (604) 886-9058, E-mail: scmm@sunshine.net, Internet: http://www.sunshine.net. Head: Lilian Kunstler
Historical Museum 04943

Gilbert Plains

Wasyl Negrych Pioneer Homestead, 10 miles N and 2 miles E of Gilbert Plains, Gilbert Plains, Man. R0L 0X0 - E-mail: skrahn@techplus.com. Head: Susan Krahn
Local Museum - 1992
Ukrainian homestead, original buildings dating back to 1899, Ukrainian handicrafts 04944

Gillam

Gillam Community Museum, 236 Mattonnabee Av, Gillam, Man. R0B 0L0 - T: (204) 652-2206
Local Museum 04945

Gimli

New Iceland Heritage Museum, 108-94 First Av, Gimli, Man. R0C 1B0 - T: (204) 642-4001, E-mail: safn@mb.sympatico.ca
Historical Museum 04946

Girouxville

Musée Girouxville, CP 276, Girouxville, Alta. T0H 1S0 - T: (780) 323-4252
Local Museum - 1969
History and archives, natural history, agriculture and industries 04947

Glace Bay

Cape Breton Miners' Museum, 42 Birkley St, Glace Bay, N.S. B1A 5T8 - T: (902) 849-4522, Fax: (902) 849-8022, E-mail: cbminers@cbnet.ns.ca, Internet: http://www.cbnet.ns.ca/cbnet/mainmenu.html. Head: Tom Miller
Historical Museum - 1967
Coal mining in the late 19th to early 20th c, coal formation, transportation and company history, steam locomotive 04948

Gladstone

Gladstone and District Museum, Williams Park on Sixth St, Gladstone, Man. R0J 0T0 - T: (204) 385-2551. Head: O.E. Whitten
Local Museum
Local pioneer artifacts 04949

Glen Ewen

Glen Ewen Community Antique Centre, Glen Ewen, Sask. S0C 1C0 - T: (306) 925-2221. Head: Arne Hansen
Museum of Classical Antiquities / Local Museum 04950

Glenora

Claude Crayston Museum, 20 km SE of Baldur, Glenora, Man. R0K 0Y0, mail addr: POB 95, Glenora, Man. R0K 0Y0 - T: (204) 535-2283
Local Museum
Pioneer artifacts 04951

Glentworth

Glentworth Museum, POB 174, Glentworth, Sask. S0H 1V0
Local Museum 04952

Gloucester

Gloucester Museum, 4550 Bank St, Gloucester, Ont. K1G 3N4 - T: (613) 822-2076
Local Museum 04953

Musée Acadien, Caraquet, Gloucester, N.B. E0B 1K0 - T: (506) 727-3269
Folklore Museum - 1967
Folklore 04954

Goderich

Huron County Museum, 110 N St, Goderich, Ont. N7A 2T8 - T: (519) 524-2686, Fax: (519) 524-5677, E-mail: hcm-chin@odyssey.on.ca, Internet: http://www.odyssey.on.ca/~hcm-chin. Head: Claus Breede
Local Museum - 1950
Local trades and crafts, Victorian furnishings and costumes, natural history, transportation, toys 04955

Golden

Golden and District Museum, 1302 11th Av, Golden, B.C. V04 1H0 - T: (250) 344-5169, Fax: (250) 344-5169. Head: Colleen Columbo
Local Museum - 1974
Pioneer artifacts from 1865 - archives 04956

Golden Lake

Algonquin Culture and Heritage Centre, 1674 Mishomis Inamo, Golden Lake, Ont. K0J 1X0 - T: (613) 625-2823
Historical Museum - 1954
Pioneer hist and folklore, Indian artifacts, natural hist, costumes, paintings, mineralogy 04957

Goodsoil

Goodsoil Historical Museum, POB 57, Goodsoil, Sask. S0M 1A0 - T: (306) 238-2084, Fax: (306) 238-2039
Local Museum 04958

Goose Bay

Northern Lights Military Museum, Hamiliton River Rd, Goose Bay, Nfld. A0P 1E0, mail addr: POB 2168, Stn B, Goose Bay, Nfld. A0P 1E0 - T: (709) 896-5939. Head: Bruce Haynes
Military Museum 04959

Gore Bay

Manitoulin Historical Society Museum, Dawson St, Gore Bay, Ont. P0P 1H0 - T: (705) 282-2040, Fax: (705) 282-3076
Local Museum - 1954
Agriculture, archeology, botany, local history, Indian artifacts, transportation and industries, medical equipment, textiles and costumes, ornithology - library 04960

Gormley

Whitchurch-Stouffville Museum, 14732 Woodbine Av, Gormley, Ont. L0H 1G0 - T: (905) 727-8954, Fax: (905) 727-1282, Internet: http://www.townof.ws.com/museum.php. Head: Dorie Billich
Folklore Museum 04961

Govan

Govan and District Museum, Govan, Sask. S0G 1Z0
Local Museum 04962

Gowganda

Gowganda and Area Museum, Gowganda, Ont. P0J 1J0 - T: (705) 624-3171. Head: David Ford
Local Museum - 1974
History of the silver mining area, mining equipment, hand tools and implements used by the early trappers and loggers 04963

Grafton

Barnum House Museum, Hwy 2, Cherry Hill Rd, Grafton, Ont. K0K 2G0 - T: (905) 349-2656, Fax: (905) 373-1838
Local Museum - 1940
Historic mansion (1813-17) furnished to represent the home of a country gentleman 04964

Grand-Anse

Musée des Papes, 184 Rue Acadie, Grand-Anse, N.B. E8N 1A6 - T: (506) 732-3003, Fax: (506) 732-5491, E-mail: museedespapes@nb.aibn.com. Head: Edmond Landry
Religious Arts Museum 04965

Grand Bank

Southern Newfoundland Seamen's Museum, Marine Dr, Grand Bank, Nfld. A0E 1W0 - T: (709) 832-1484, Fax: (709) 832-2053, E-mail: gwcrews@nf.aibn.com, Internet: http://www.nfmuseum.com
Local Museum - 1972
Fishing hist on the Grand Banks 04966

Grand Bend

Lambton Heritage Museum, RR 2, Grand Bend, Ont. N0M 1T0 - T: (519) 243-2600, Fax: (519) 243-2600, E-mail: lhmchin@htl.net
Local Museum 04967

Grand Falls

Grand Falls Museum, 142 Court St, Grand Falls, N.B. E3Z 2R2 - Fax: (506) 473-7160. Head: Patrick McCooey
Local Museum - 1973
Pioneer and early Victorian artifacts, farm and lumbering implements, newspapers 04968

Grand Falls-Windsor

Beothuck Village, Saint Catherine St, Grand Falls-Windsor, Nfld. A2A 1W9 - T: (709) 489-9629
Open Air Museum 04969

Mary March Regional Museum and Logging Exhibition, 22 Catherine St, Grand Falls-Windsor, Nfld. A2A 1W9 - T: (709) 292-4522, 486-0492, Fax: (709) 292-4526, E-mail: demasduit@thezone.net, Internet: http://www.delweb.com/nfmuseum. Head: Penny Wells
Local Museum / Natural History Museum - 1970/1977
Logging, pulp and paper industry of this region, native people who once lived in this area 04970

Grand Forks

Boundary Museum, 108 Ninth St SE, Grand Forks, B.C. V0H 1H0 - T: (250) 442-3737, Fax: (250) 442-3737, E-mail: jomiller@wkpowerlink.com
Local Museum - 1958
Regional artifacts and history, pictures of the area and descriptive literature 04971

Grand Forks Art Gallery, 7340 Fifth St, Grand Forks, B.C. V0H 1H0 - T: (250) 442-2211, Fax: (250) 442-0099, E-mail: gfagchin@direct.ca, Internet: http://www.galleries.bc.ca/grandforks. Head: Richard Reid
Fine Arts Museum 04972

Mountain View Doukhobor Museum, Hardy Mountain Rd, Grand Forks, B.C. V0H 1H0 - T: (250) 442-8855
Natural History Museum 04973

Grand Manan

Grand Manan Museum, 1141 Rte 776, Grand Manan, N.B. E5G 4E9 - T: (506) 662-3524, Fax: (506) 662-3009, E-mail: ava@nb.sympatico.ca. Head: Ava Sturgeon
Local Museum - 1967
Local history, geology, Moses coll of birds of Grand Manan, Walter B. McLaughlin Marine Gallery - archives 04974

Grand-Pré

Fort Edward, POB 150, Grand-Pré, N.S. B0P 1M0 - T: (902) 542-3631
Military Museum 04975

Grand-Pré National Historic Site of Canada, 2242 Grand-Pré Rd, Grand-Pré, N.S. B0P 1M0 - T: (902) 542-3631, Fax: (902) 542-1691, E-mail: info@grand-pre.com, Internet: http://www.grand-pre.com. Head: Donna Doucet
Local Museum / Historic Site - 1907
Hist of Acadians and their deportation from N.S., blacksmith shop, formal gardens, Evangeline monument 04976

Grande Prairie

Grande Prairie Museum, POB 687, Grande Prairie, Alta. T8V 3A8 - T: (780) 532-5482, Fax: (780) 831-7371, Internet: http://www.telusplanet.net/public/amassee/gpmuseum.html. Head: Peter Goertzen
Natural History Museum 04977

Prairie Gallery, 10209 99 St, Grande Prairie, Alta. T8V 2H3 - T: (780) 532-8111, Fax: (780) 539-1991, E-mail: pag@telusplanet.net, Internet: http://www.prairieartgallery.ab.ca. Head: Donna White
Public Gallery 04978

Grandview

Watson Crossley Community Museum, Railway Av N, Grandview, Man. R0L 0Y0, mail addr: POB 396, Grandview, Man. R0L 0Y0 - T: (204) 546-2661. Head: Gerald Morran
Local Museum - 1975
Human and natural history of the area, Ukrainian tools and handicrafts, Indian artifacts, pioneer furnishings, antique tractors, machinery and cars 04979

Granville Ferry

North Hills Museum, 5065 Granville Rd, Granville Ferry, N.S. B0S 1K0 - T: (902) 532-2168, Fax: (902) 532-7707, Internet: http://museum.gov.ns.ca. Head: John Kirby
Decorative Arts Museum
18th c paintings, furniture, furnishings, Worchester and Spode china, glass 04980

Gravelbourg

Gravelbourg and District Museum, POB 862, Gravelbourg, Sask. S0H 1X0 - T: (306) 648-2332, Fax: (306) 648-3400
Local Museum 04981

Gravenhurst

Bethune Memorial House, 235 John St N, Gravenhurst, Ont. P1P 1G4 - T: (705) 687-4261, Fax: (705) 687-4935, E-mail: ont_bethune@pc.gc.ca, Internet: http://parkscanada.gc.ca/bethune. Head: Scott Davidson
Historic Site
Birthplace of Dr. Norman Bethune 04982

Segwun Heritage Centre, Gravenhurst Bay, Gravenhurst, Ont. P1P 1V4 - T: (705) 687-6667, Fax: (705) 687-7820. Head: Al Smitten, G. Coates
Historical Museum - 1962
Marine and lumbering hist documented in the last remaining steamboat on the Muskoka Lakes, and Heritage Centre 04983

Greenspond

Greenspond Court House, POB 99, Greenspond, Nfld. A0G 2N0 - T: (709) 269-3591, E-mail: feblack@hotmail.com. Head: Frank E. Blackwood
Local Museum - 1974
Local history 04984

Greenwood

Greenwood Military Aviation Museum, Ward Rd, Greenwood, N.S. B0P 1N0 - T: (902) 765-1494 ext 5955, Fax: (902) 765-1261, E-mail: gmam001@hotmail.com, Internet: http://gmam.ednet.ns.ca. Head: Bryan Nelson
Military Museum 04985

Greenwood Museum, 214 Copper St S, Greenwood, B.C. V0H 1J0 - T: (250) 445-6355, Fax: (250) 445-6355, E-mail: museum@sunshinecable.com, Internet: http://www.greenwoodheritage.bc.ca. Head: Marge Maclean
Local Museum - 1967
Pioneer artifacts including mining and logging equipment, photographic archives, information about the internment of Japanese-Canadians 04986

Grenfell

Grenfell Community Museum, Wolseley Av, Grenfell, Sask. S0G 2B0 - T: (306) 697-2930, Fax: (306) 697-2500. Head: Lloyd Arthur
Local Museum - 1973
Pioneer artifacts, Victorian house furnished in a Victorian style 04987

Grimsby

Grimsby Museum, 6 Murray St, Grimsby, Ont. L3M 4G5 - T: (905) 945-5292, Fax: (905) 945-0715, E-mail: amchin@interlynx.net
Local Museum 04988

Grimsby Public Art Gallery, 25 Adelaide St, Grimsby, Ont. L3M 1X2 - T: (905) 945-3246, Fax: (905) 945-1789, E-mail: gpag@town.grimsby.on.ca, Internet: http://www.town.grimsby.on.ca/art_gallery. Head: Rhona Wenger
Public Gallery - 1975
20th c Canadian art 04989

Stone Shop Museum, 271 Main St W, Grimsby, Ont. L3M 1G3
Decorative Arts Museum - 1963
Textiles, glass and china, pottery, tools, historical pictures - archives 04990

Grimshaw

Lac Cardinal Regional Pioneer Village Museum, POB 325, Grimshaw, Alta. T0H 1W0 - T: (780) 332-4863
Local Museum 04991

Groundbirch

Groundbirch Museum, POB 149, Groundbirch, B.C. V0C 1T0 - T: (250) 780-2383, Fax: (250) 780-2248
Local Museum 04992

Guelph

Guelph Civic Museum, Guelph Museums, 6 Dublin St S, Guelph, Ont. N1H 4L5 - T: (519) 836-1221, Fax: (519) 836-5280, E-mail: info@museum.guelph.on.ca, Internet: http://www.museum.guelph.on.ca. Head: Laurence Grant
Local Museum - 1967
Local hist, agricultural and industrial development, textiles and costumes, military, archives, historical photogr, John McCrae archival material 04993

McCrae House, Guelph Museums, 108 Water St, Guelph, Ont. N1G 1A6 - T: (519) 836-1221, Fax: (519) 836-5280, E-mail: info@museum.guelph.on.ca, Internet: http://www.museum.guelph.on.ca. Head: Laurence Grant
Local Museum - 1968
Birthplace of John McCrae, literary works, drawings and personal articles of Lieutenant-Colonel J. McCrae, author of the poem "In Flanders Fields" 04994

Macdonald Stewart Art Centre, 358 Gordon St, Guelph, Ont. N1G 1Y1 - T: (519) 837-0010, Fax: (519) 767-2661, E-mail: msac@uoguelph.ca, Internet: http://www.uoguelph.ca/msac. Head: Judith M. Nasby
Fine Arts Museum - 1980
Canadian art (18th c - present), international prints, Inuit art, outdoor sculpture 04995

Guysborough

Old Court House Museum, POB 232, Guysborough, N.S. B0H 1N0 - T: (902) 533-4008, E-mail: kavery@ns.sympatico.ca. Head: Kim Avery
Historical Museum 04996

Hague

Saskatchewan River Valley Museum, POB 630, Hague, Sask. S0K 1X0
Local Museum 04997

Haileybury

Haileybury Heritage Museum, 451 Meridian Av, Haileybury, Ont. P0J 1K0 - T: (705) 672-1922, Fax: (705) 672-3200. Head: Christopher Oslund
Local Museum 04998

Temiskaming Art Gallery, 545 Lakeshore Rd, Haileybury, Ont. P0J 1K0 - T: (705) 672-3706, Fax: (705) 672-5966, E-mail: tag@ntl.sympatico.ca. Head: Maureen Steward
Fine Arts Museum 04999

Haliburton

Haliburton Highlands Museum, POB 535, Haliburton, Ont. K0M 1S0 - T: (705) 457-2760. Head: Thomas Ballantine
Local Museum 05000

Rail's End Gallery, POB 912, Haliburton, Ont. K0M 1S0 - T: (705) 457-2330, Fax: (705) 457-2338. Head: Laurie Carmount
Fine Arts Museum 05001

Halifax

Anna Leonowens Gallery, c/o Nova Scotia College of Art and Design, 5163 Duke St, Halifax, N.S. B3J 3J6 - T: (902) 494-8223, Fax: (902) 425-3997, E-mail: peterd@nscad.ns.ca, Internet: http://www.nscad.ns.ca/~gallery. Head: Peter Dykhuis
Fine Arts Museum / Decorative Arts Museum / University Museum - 1968
Contemporary art, craft and design 05002

Army Museum, Halifax Citadel, Halifax, N.S. B3J 3K6 - T: (902) 422-5979, Fax: (902) 422-4228, E-mail: roderick_maclean@pch.gc.ca. Head: Roderick MacLean
Military Museum - 1953
Arms and armour, swords since the 16th c, uniforms (18th c), models of fortifications, paintings and prints 05003

Art Gallery of Nova Scotia, 1741 Hollis St, Halifax, N.S. B3J 3C8 - T: (902) 424-7542, Fax: (902) 424-7359, E-mail: riordb@gov.ns.ca. Head: Bernard Riordon
Fine Arts Museum - 1975
Historical and contemporary Nova Scotian art, folk art 05004

Cavalier Block, Halifax Citadel, Halifax, N.S. B3H 3A6
Ethnology Museum / Historical Museum / Decorative Arts Museum - 1960
Human history, Micmac Indian artifacts, history of explorations and local history, furniture, silver and glass 05005

Centre for Art Tapes, 5600 Sackville St, Ste 207, Halifax, N.S. B3J 3S9 - T: (902) 420-4580, Fax: (902) 420-5481, Internet: http://chebucto.ns.ca/Culture/CFAT/. Head: Catherine Phoenix
Fine Arts Museum 05006

Dalhousie Art Gallery, 6101 University Av, Halifax, N.S. B3H 3J5 - T: (902) 494-2403, Fax: (902) 494-2890, E-mail: gallery@dac.cohn.dal.ca, Internet: http://is.dal.ca/~gallery. Head: Susan Gibson Garvey
Fine Arts Museum / University Museum - 1954
Canadian paintings and drawings, Canadian, American and European prints, Inuit sculpture, contemporary Nova Scotia works 05007

Fisherman's Life Museum, Jeddore Oyster Ponds, 58 Navy Pool Loop, Halifax, N.S. B0J 1W0 - T: (902) 889-2053, Fax: (902) 889-2053, E-mail: monkma@gov.ns.ca
Folklore Museum 05008

Halifax Citadel, Halifax, N.S. B3J 3K6 - T: (902) 426-5080, Fax: (902) 426-4228, E-mail: denise_graham@pch.gc.ca, Internet: http://parkscanada.pch.gc.ca/citadel
Military Museum - 1953 05009

Halifax Police Museum, Halifax City Police Headquarters, 1975 Gottingen St, Halifax, N.S. B3J 2H1 - T: (902) 421-6840, E-mail: hpd@atcon.com. Head: Dan Young
Special Museum - 1964
Historical police equipment, items used in unusual crimes 05010

HMCS Sackville, POB 99000, Stn Forces, Halifax, N.S. B3K 5X5 - T: (902) 429-7966, 429-0550, Fax: (902) 424-1346, E-mail: nstn1674@fox.nstn.ca, Internet: http://www.hmcssackville-cnmt.ns.ca
Historical Museum / Military Museum 05011

Maritime Command Museum, Admiralty House, Halifax, mail addr: POB 99000, Stn Forces, Halifax, N.S. B3K 5X5 - T: (902) 427-0550, 427-8250, Fax: (902) 427-0550, 427-6726, E-mail: museum@marlant.dlfx.dnd.ca. Head: Marilyn Gurney
Military Museum / Historical Museum 05012

Maritime Museum of the Atlantic, 1675 Lower Water St, Halifax, N.S. B3J 1S3 - T: (902) 424-7490, Fax: (902) 424-0612, E-mail: murraymr@gov.ns.ca, Internet: http://maritime.museum.gov.ns.ca. Head: M. Murray
Historical Museum - 1948
Photographic coll, Eastern Canadian shipping and fishing, small crafts, charts, and vessel plans, maritime and Titanic artifacts, Canadian naval history - library, museum ship CSS Acadia 05013

Mount Saint Vincent University Art Gallery, Seton Academic Centre, 166 Bedford Hwy, Halifax, N.S. B3M 2J6 - T: (902) 457-6160, Fax: (902) 457-2447, E-mail: art.gallery@msvu.ca, Internet: http://www.textstyle.net/msvuart. Head: Ingrid Jenkner
Fine Arts Museum / University Museum - 1971
Canadian art, painting, sculpture, graphics, crafts, ceramics and paintings by Alice Hagen 05014

Museum of Natural History, 1747 Summer St, Halifax, N.S. B3H 3A6 - Internet: http://museum.gov.ns.ca
Natural History Museum
Ancient fossils, glittering, gold, deadly mushrooms, frogs and snakes, whale skeletons, dinosaurus 05015

Nova Scotia Centre for Craft and Design, 1683 Barrington St, Halifax, N.S. B3J 1Z9 - T: (902) 424-4062, Fax: (902) 424-0670, E-mail: tylercd@gov.ns.ca, Internet: http://www.craft-design@ednet.ns.ca
Decorative Arts Museum 05016

Nova Scotia Museum, 1747 Summer St, Halifax, N.S. B3H 3A6 - T: (902) 424-6471, Fax: (902) 424-0560, E-mail: nsmwebmaster@gov.ns.ca, Internet: http://museum.gov.ns.ca. Head: David Newlands
Natural History Museum / Historical Museum / Decorative Arts Museum / Agriculture Museum - 1868
Geology, botany, zoology, marine history, history, furniture, glass, silver, agricultural implements 05017

Prince of Wales Martello Tower, POB 9080, Stn A, Halifax, N.S. B3K 5M7 - T: (902) 426-5080, Fax: (902) 426-4228, E-mail: denise_graham@pch.gc.ca, Internet: http://parkscanada.pch.gc.ca
Military Museum 05018

Ross Thomson Museum, 1747 Summer St, Halifax, N.S. B3H 1Z9 - T: (902) 875-2698. Head: Dr. T.L. Rogers
Local Museum 05019

Saint Mary's University Art Gallery, Robie St, Halifax, N.S. B3H 3C3 - T: (902) 420-5445, Fax: (902) 420-5060, E-mail: gordon.laurin@stmarys.ca. Head: Gordon Laurin
Fine Arts Museum / University Museum 05020

Telephone Historical Collection, Maritime Centre, Halifax, N.S. B3J 2W3
Science&Tech Museum - 1967
Telephone equipment including Bell's experimental models as well as the latest models in use 05021

Thomas McCulloch Museum, c/o Dalhousie University, Biology Dept., 1355 Oxford St, Halifax, N.S. B3H 4J1 - T: (902) 494-3515, 494-3530, Fax: (902) 494-3736, E-mail: biology@dal.ca, Internet: http://is.dal.ca/~biology2/museum.html. Head: Stephen Fry
Natural History Museum
Mounted birds prepared by T. McCulloch 18th c, coll of shells, insects, ceramic mushroom models 05022

William D. Lawrence House, Nova Scotia Museum, 1747 Summer St, Halifax, N.S. B3H 3A6 - T: (902) 429-4610
Local Museum - 1970
Home of William D. Lawrence, builder of the largest square-rigged sailing ship ever built in Canada, period furniture, shipbuilding in the "Golden Age of sail" 05023

Hamilton

Art Gallery of Hamilton, 123 King St W, Hamilton, Ont. L8P 4S8 - T: (905) 527-6610, Fax: (905) 577-6940, E-mail: larissa@artgalleryofhamilton.com. Head: Louise Dompierre
Fine Arts Museum - 1914
Historical and contemporary Canadian art, American, British and European art - library 05024

Canadian Football Hall of Fame and Museum, 58 Jackson St W, Hamilton, Ont. L8P 1L4 - T: (905) 528-7566, Fax: (905) 528-9781, E-mail: fhfchin@interlynx.net, Internet: http://www.footballhof.com. Head: Janice Smith
Special Museum - 1972
Development of football over the past 100 years 05025

Dundurn Castle, 610 York Blvd, Dundurn Park, Hamilton, Ont. L8R 3HI - T: (905) 522-5313, Fax: (905) 522-4535, E-mail: dcchin@interlynx.net, Internet: http://www.city.hamilton.on.ca/cultureandrecreation
Local Museum - 1967 05026

The Hamilton Children's Museum, 1072 Main St E, Hamilton, Ont. L8M 1N6 - T: (905) 546-4848, Fax: (905) 546-4851, E-mail: hcmchin@interlynx.net, Internet: http://www.city.hamilton.on.ca/cultureandrecreation. Head: Ellen Hobin
Special Museum
Natural science and history, social science, arts, multiculturalsm 05027

Hamilton Military Museum, Dundurn Park, York Blvd, Hamilton, Ont. L8R 3H1 - T: (905) 546-4974, Fax: (905) 546-2016, E-mail: can-hmm@immedia.ca
Military Museum - 1976
Military history from 1812 to World War II 05028

Hamilton Museum of Steam and Technology, 900 Woodward Av, Hamilton, Ont. L8H 7N2 - T: (905) 549-5225, Fax: (905) 549-1156, E-mail: hmstchin@interlynx.net, Internet: http://www.city.hamilton.on.ca/cultureandeducation. Head: Ian Kerr-Wilson
Science&Tech Museum 05029

Hamilton Psychiatric Hospital Museum & St. Joseph's Mountain Site, 100 W 5th St, Hamilton, Ont. L8N 3K7 - T: (905) 388-2511, Fax: (905) 381-5601, E-mail: l.muirhea@stojsham.on.ca
Historical Museum 05030

McMaster Museum of Art, c/o McMaster University, 1280 Main St W, Hamilton, Ont. L8S 4L6 - T: (905) 525-9140 ext 23081, 27573, Fax: (905) 527-4548, E-mail: museum@mcmaster.ca, Internet: http://www.mcmaster.ca/museum. Head: Kim G. Ness
Fine Arts Museum / Public Gallery / University Museum - 1967
15th-20th c European prints, early 20th c German art, historical and contemporary Canadian art, modern and contemporary European and North American art 05031

Ontario Workers Arts and Heritage Centre, 51 Stuart St, Hamilton, Ont. L8L 1B5 - T: (905) 522-3003, Fax: (905) 522-5424, E-mail: owahc@web.net, Internet: http://www.web.net/~owahc
Local Museum / Fine Arts Museum 05032

Royal Hamilton Light Infantry Heritage Museum, 200 James St N, Hamilton, Ont. L8R 2L1 - T: (905) 572-2742, Fax: (905) 528-5443. Head: D. Wentworth
Military Museum 05033

Whitehern Historic House and Garden, 41 Jackson St W, Hamilton, Ont. L8P 1L3 - T: (905) 546-2018, Fax: (905) 546-4933, E-mail: whchin@interlynx.net. Head: Ken Heaman
Historic Site 05034

Hamiota

Clegg's Museum of Horse-Drawn Vehicles, Lilac Residence, Ste 1, Hamiota, Man. R0M 0T0 - T: (204) 764-2791. Head: R.E. Clegg
Science&Tech Museum 05035

Hamiota Pioneer Club Museum, Centennial Park, Hamiota, Man. R0M 0T0 - T: (204) 764-2222, 764-2434. Head: John L. Rankin
Local Museum - 1966
Regional history, farm machinery, wildlife display 05036

Hampton

Kings County Museum, 27 Centennial Rd, Hampton, N.B. E5N 6N3 - T: (506) 832-6009, Fax: (506) 832-6007, E-mail: kingscm@nbnet.nb.ca, Internet: http://www3.nbnet.nb.ca/kingcm. Head: A. Faye Pearson
Local Museum - 1968
Pioneer artifacts, early handicrafts, old china, jewelry - archives 05037

Hanna

Hanna Pioneer Museum, E End of Hanna Townsite, Hanna, Alta. T0J 1P0 - T: (403) 854-4244, Fax: (403) 854-3381. Head: W.J. McFalls
Local Museum / Agriculture Museum - 1966
Pioneer village, antique farm machinery, furnished household, church, school, country store, 1st hospital, blacksmith, railway station, caboose - archives 05038

Hants County

Avon River Heritage Museum, POB 17, Hants County, N.S. B0N 2A0 - T: (902) 757-1869, Fax: (902) 757-3669
Historical Museum 05039

Happy Valley

Labrador Heritage Museum, POB 729, Stn B, Happy Valley, Nfld. A0P 1E0 - T: (709) 896-2762. Head: Elsie Johnson
Historical Museum 05040

Harbour Grace

Conception Bay Museum, Water St, Harbour Grace, Nfld. A0A 2M0 - T: (709) 596-5465. Head: Peggy Fahey
Local Museum - 1974
Historical pirate fort (1610), 19th c furniture, history of early aviation, local art objects, fishermens, pictures, Peter Easton exhibit 05041

Harris

Harris Heritage and Museum, Railway Av, Harris, Sask. S0L 1K0 - T: (306) 652-2158
Local Museum 05042

Harrison Mills

Kilby Historic Store and Farm, 215 Kilby Rd, Harrison Mills, B.C. V0M 1L0 - T: (604) 796-9576, Fax: (604) 796-9592, E-mail: khsfchin@ntoaline.com
Agriculture Museum 05043

Harrow

John R. Park Homestead, 915 County Rd 50 E, Harrow, Ont. N0R 1G0 - T: (519) 738-2029, Fax: (519) 776-8688, E-mail: jrph@erca.org, Internet: http://www.erca.org. Head: Janet Cobban
Historic Site 05044

Hartney

Hart-Cam Museum, Hartney, Man. R0M 0X0 - T: (204) 858-2590, Fax: (204) 858-2681, E-mail: hartney@techplus.com, Internet: http://www.techplus.com/towns/towns.htm
Local Museum
Local artifacts 05045

Havre-Aubert

Musée de la Mer, Havre-Aubert, P.Q. G0B 1J0 - T: (418) 937-5711, Fax: (418) 937-2449, E-mail: museemer@cancom.net, Internet: http://www.ilesdelamadeleine.com. Head: Frédéric Landry
Special Museum - 1969
Articles pertaining to fishing, navigation, and shipwrecks, domestic art - archives 05046

Hazelton

Ksan Historical Village and Museum, Hwy 62, Highlevel Rd, Hazelton, B.C. V0J 1Y0, mail addr: POB 326, Hazelton, B.C. V0J 1Y0 - T: (250) 842-5544, Fax: (250) 842-6533, E-mail: ksan@ksan.org, Internet: http://www.ksan.org. Head: Laurel Mould
Ethnology Museum / Local Museum - 1970/1976
Gitksan regalia and artifacts 05047

Northwestern National Exhibition Centre, POB 333, Hazelton, B.C. V0J 1Y0 - T: (250) 842-5723. Head: Eve Hope
Fine Arts Museum / Historical Museum 05048

Hazenmore

Heritage Hazenmore, POB 103, Hazenmore, Sask. S0N 1C0 - T: (306) 264-5105
Local Museum 05049

Heart's Content

Heart's Content Cable Station, Hwy 80, Heart's Content, Nfld. A0B 1Z0, mail addr: POB 8700, Saint John's, Nfld. A1B 4J6 - T: (709) 729-0592, 583-2160, Fax: (709) 729-0870, 583-2373, E-mail: heartscontent@nf.aibn.com, Internet: http://www.nfmuseum.com
Science&Tech Museum 05050

High Prairie

High Prairie and District Museum, POB 1442, High Prairie, Alta. T0G 1E0 - T: (780) 523-2601, Fax: (780) 523-2601, E-mail: hpdmchin@telusplanet.net, Internet: http://www.inetnorth.net/org/museum. Head: Maxine Nordin
Local Museum - 1967
Indian artifacts, pioneer items, archival material, geological specimens 05051

High River

Museum of the Highwood, 406 First St SW, High River, Alta. T1V 1R9 - T: (403) 652-7156, Fax: (403) 652-7660, E-mail: moth@caduision.com. Head: Dianne Vallee
Local Museum - 1961
Material related to early trading, ranching and farming, Indian artifacts, fossils 05052

Hillsborough

Hillsborough Railway Museum, 2847 Main St, Hillsborough, N.B. E4H 2X7 - T: (506) 734-3195, Fax: (506) 734-3711, Internet: http://www3.ns.sympatico.ca/othen/shrr.htm
Science&Tech Museum 05053

William Henry Steeves House, 40 Mill St, Hillsborough, N.B. E4H 2Z8 - T: (506) 734-3102, Fax: (506) 734-3711, E-mail: stevesmuseum@nb.aibn.com, Internet: http://www.steeveshousemuseum.ca
Historical Museum 05054

Hines Creek

End of Steel Heritage Museum, POB 686, Hines Creek, Alta. T0H 2A0 - T: (780) 494-3522
Science&Tech Museum 05055

Hinton

Alberta Forestry Service Museum, 1176 Switzer Dr, Hinton, Alta. T7V 1V3 - T: (780) 865-8200, Fax: (780) 865-8266, E-mail: - environmental.training@gov.ab.ca
Special Museum - 1971
Historical coll related to the management and use of the forest 05056

Hodgeville

Hodgeville Community Museum, Third Rd NW, Hodgeville, Sask. S0H 2B0 - T: (306) 677-2693, Fax: (306) 677-2707. Head: Faye Rister
Local Museum 05057

Holden

Holden Historical Society Museum, 4920 50 Holden Av, Holden, Alta. T0B 2C0 - T: (780) 688-2464, Fax: (780) 688-2464, E-mail: dgmarusz@telusplanet.net. Head: Dave Maruszeczka
Local Museum 05058

Holland Centre

Comber Pioneer Village, Rte 3, Holland Centre, Ont. N0H 1R0 - T: (519) 794-3467. Head: Robert James Comber
Local Museum / Open Air Museum 05059

Hope

Hope Museum, 919 Water St, Hope, B.C. V0X 1L0, mail addr: POB 26, Hope, B.C. V0X 1L0 - T: (604) 869-7322, Fax: (604) 869-2160. Head: Inge Wilson
Local Museum - 1965
Pioneer implements, domestic utensils, Indian artifacts, historical photos, native rocks 05060

John Weaver Sculpture Museum, POB 1723, Hope, B.C. V0X 1L0 - T: (604) 869-5312, Fax: (604) 869-5117. Head: Henry Weaver
Fine Arts Museum 05061

Remember When Doll Museum, RR2, Hope, B.C. V0X 1L0 - T: (604) 869-2923
Special Museum 05062

Horsefly

Jack Lynn Memorial Museum, POB 71, Horsefly, B.C. V0L 1L0 - T: (604) 620-3304. Head: Ernie Gruhs
Local Museum - 1973
Gold mining artifacts, farm implements and domestic utensils 05063

Hudson Bay

Hudson Bay Museum, POB 931, Hudson Bay, Sask. S0E 0Y0 - T: (306) 865-2170, Fax: (306) 865-3120
Local Museum - 1978
Native artifacts, ukraine coll, fina arts coll 05064

Hudson's Hope

Hudson's Hope Museum, 10508 105th Av, Hudson's Hope, B.C. V0C 1V0 - T: (250) 783-5735, E-mail: hhmuseum@hhcn.prn.bc.ca. Head: Ida Saraver
Local Museum / Archaeological Museum - 1967
Prehistory, incl ichthyosaur fossil, Aboriginal coll, regional artefacts, police hist, mining, photographies of the Dam construction by W.A.C. Bennett 05065

Hull → Outaouais

Humboldt

Humboldt and District Museum and Gallery, Cnr Main St and Sixth Av, Humboldt, Sask. S0K 2A0, mail addr: POB 2349, Humboldt, Sask. S0K 2A0 - T: (306) 682-5226, Fax: (306) 682-3144, E-mail: hblt.museum@sk.sympatico.ca. Head: Jennifer Hoesgen
Local Museum 05066

Hunter River

Royal Atlantic Wax Museum, Rte 6 and Cavendish Beach Rd, Hunter River, P.E.I. C0A 1N0 - T: (902) 963-2350, Fax: (902) 963-3213, Internet: http://www.cavendishpei.com
Fine Arts Museum 05067

Huntsville

Muskoka Heritage Place, 88 Brunel Rd, Huntsville, Ont. P1H 1R1 - T: (705) 789-7576, Fax: (705) 789-6169, E-mail: village@muskokaheritageplace.org, Internet: http://www.muskokaheritageplace.org. Head: Teri Souter
Local Museum - 1958
Local hist, Natural Interpretation, steam train, pioneer village 05068

Iddesleigh

Rainy Hills Historical Society Pioneer Exhibits, c/o Margaret Harahus, Iddesleigh, Alta. T0J 1T0 - T: (306) 898-2173, Fax: (306) 898-2270
Local Museum 05069

Ignace

Ignace Heritage Centre, 36 Hwy 17 W, Ignace, Ont. P0T 1T0 - T: (807) 934-2280, Fax: (807) 934-6452
Local Museum 05070

Iles-de-la-Madeleine

Musée de la Mer, 1023 Rte 199, Iles-de-la-Madeleine, P.Q. G0B 1J0 - T: (418) 937-5711, Fax: (418) 937-5711. Head: Fréderic Landry
Historical Museum 05071

Imperial

Imperial and District Museum, POB 269, Imperial, Sask. S0G 2J0 - T: (306) 963-2280
Local Museum 05072

Nels Berggran Museum, POB 125, Imperial, Sask. S0G 2J0 - T: (306) 963-2033
Decorative Arts Museum / Music Museum - 1955
Hanging lamps, musical instruments, clocks, art 05073

Indian Head

Indian Head Museum, POB 155, Indian Head, Sask. S0G 2K0 - T: 306-695-3800
Local Museum 05074

Ingersoll

Ingersoll Cheese Factory Museum, 130 Oxford St, Ingersoll, Ont. N5C 2V5 - T: (519) 485-0120, 485-5510, Fax: (519) 485-3543. Head: Shirley Lovell
Science&Tech Museum 05075

Inglis

Saint Elie Pioneer Church Museum, POB 203, Inglis, Man. R0J 0X0 - T: (204) 564-2228, Fax: (204) 564-2643. Head: Barry Sawchuk
Local Museum 05076

Innisfail

Innisfail and District Historical Museum, 52nd Av and 42nd St, Innisfail, Alta. T0M 1A0, mail addr: POB 6042, Innisfail, Alta. T4G 1S7 - T: (403) 227-2906. Head: L. Boyd
Local Museum 05077

Innisville

Innisville and District Museum, Hwy 7 N, Innisville, Ont. K0A 1J0 - T: (613) 253-1604
Local Museum / Folklore Museum - 1969
Local history and folklore 05078

Inukjuak

Musée et Centre de Transmission de la Culture Daniel Weetaluktuk, Inukjuak, P.Q. J0M 1M0 - T: (819) 254-8277, Fax: (819) 254-1042. Head: Susie K. Moreau
Ethnology Museum / Fine Arts Museum 05079

Invermere

Windermere District Historical Museum, 7th Av and 9th St, Invermere, B.C. V0A 1K0, mail addr: POB 2315, Invermere, B.C. V0A 1K0 - T: (604) 342-6859. Head: Dorothy Blunden
Local Museum - 1964
Pioneer and Indian artifacts, local mining and mineral coll, archeology - archives 05080

Inverness

Inverness Miners Museum, 62 Lower Railway St, Inverness, N.S. B0E 1N0, mail addr: POB 598, Inverness, N.S. B0E 1N0 - T: (902) 258-3822, 258-3291, E-mail: invhistsoc@ns.sympatico.ca. Head: Ned MacDonald
Historical Museum
Early settlement, coal mining, railway history 05081

Musée du Bronze d'Inverness, 1760 Ch Dublin, Inverness, P.Q. G0S 1K0 - T: (418) 453-2101, Fax: (418) 453-7711, E-mail: info@museedubronze.com. Head: Michelle Joannette
Special Museum 05082

Iona

Highland Village Living History Museum, Rte 223, Iona, N.S. B0A 1L0 - Internet: http://museum.gov.ns.ca/hv
Open Air Museum / Folklore Museum 05083

Iqaluit

Nuantta Sunakkutaangit Musuem, Bldg 212, Iqaluit, mail addr: POB 1900, Iqaluit, N.T. X0A 0H0 - T: (867) 979-5537, Fax: (867) 979-4533, E-mail: museum@nunanet.com. Head: Brian Lunger
Local Museum 05084

Iroquois

Carman House Museum, Carman Rd S, Iroquois, Ont. K0E 1K0 - T: (613) 652-4422, Fax: (613) 652-4636
Decorative Arts Museum / Fine Arts Museum - 1967
Arts and crafts (early 19th c), original period furnishings 05085

Iroquois Falls

Iroquois Falls Pioneer Museum, 245 Devonshire Av, Iroquois Falls, Ont. P0K 1E0 - T: (705) 258-3730, Fax: (705) 258-3730, E-mail: sonya@ntl.sympatico.ca, Internet: http://members.tripod.com/lhussey/iqf_museum. Head: Sonya Hodgins-Wollan
Local Museum 05086

Islay

Morrison Museum of the Country School, POB 120, Islay, Alta. T0B 2J0 - T: (780) 744-2271. Head: Allen Ronaghan
Historical Museum 05087

Ituna

Ituna Cultural and Historical Museum, POB 282, Ituna, Sask. S0A 1N0
Local Museum 05088

Jasper

Jasper-Yellowhead Museum and Archives, 400 Pyramid Lake Rd, Jasper, Alta. T0E 1E0 - T: (780) 852-3013, Fax: (780) 852-3240, E-mail: jymachin@telusplanet.net, Internet: http://jasper-alberta.com/Museum&Arch/index1.htm. Head: Herb Robinson
Special Museum 05089

Jeddore Oyster Ponds

Fishermen's Life Museum, Jeddore Oyster Ponds, N.S. B0A 1W0 - Internet: http://museum.gov.ns.ca
Folklore Museum
Rural living, parlour pump organ, hooked mats, wood stove 05090

Joliette

Musée d'Art de Joliette, 145 Rue Wilfrid-Corbeil, Joliette, P.Q. J6E 4T4 - T: (450) 756-0311, Fax: (450) 756-6511, E-mail: musee.joliette@citenet.net, Internet: http://www.bw.qc.ca/musee.joliette. Head: France Gascon
Fine Arts Museum - 1967
Religious and medieval art, Canadian and European paintings and sculpture, contemporary art 05091

Jonquière

Centre National d'Exposition, 4160 Rue du Vieux Pont, Jonquière, P.Q. G7X 7W4, mail addr: CP 605, Succ A, Jonquière, P.Q. G7X 7W4 - T: (418) 546-2177, Fax: (418) 546-2180, E-mail: cne@videotron.ca, Internet: http://pages.infinit.net/cne.

Head: Jacqueline Caron
Public Gallery - 1978
Sculpture, paintings, engravings, sketches, history, science 05092

Jordan

Jordan Historical Museum of the Twenty, 3802 Main St, Jordan, Ont. L0R 1S0 - T: (905) 562-5242, Fax: (905) 562-7786, E-mail: jhmtchin@vaxxine.com, Internet: http://tourismniagara.com/jordan.museum. Head: Helen Booth
Local Museum - 1953
Pioneer history, farm implements, kitchenware and furniture, letters and books, fraktur folk art 05093

Kahnawake

Musée Kateri Tekakwitha, Mission Saint-François Xavier, Kahnawake, P.Q. J0L 1B0 - T: (450) 632-6030. Head: Léon Lajoie
Religious Arts Museum - 1925
Exhibits devoted to the only Iroquois Indian to be declared blessed, religious relics made of gold, Indian belts, sculpture 05094

Kakabeka Falls

Hymers Museum, RR1, Kakabeka Falls, Ont. P0T 1W0. Head: M. Petryshyn
Local Museum 05095

Kamloops

Kamloops Art Gallery, 465 Victoria St, Ste 101, Kamloops, B.C. V2C 2A9 - T: (250) 828-3543, Fax: (250) 828-0662, E-mail: kamloopsartgallery@kag.bc.ca, Internet: http://www.galleries.bc.ca/kamloops. Head: Jann L.M. Bailey
Fine Arts Museum
Canadian contemporary art 05096

Kamloops Museum, 207 Seymour St, Kamloops, B.C. V2C 2E7 - T: (250) 828-3576, Fax: (250) 314-2016
Local Museum - 1937
Prehistory, fur trading, pioneer and Chinese artifacts, geological specimens - archives 05097

Rocky Mountain Rangers Museum, 1221 McGill Rd, Kamloops, B.C. V2C 6B8 - T: (250) 851-4890, Fax: (250) 851-4891. Head: Wendy McKenzie
Military Museum 05098

Secwepemc Museum, 35 Yellowhead Hwy, Kamloops, B.C. V2H 1H1 - T: (250) 828-9801, Fax: (250) 372-1127, E-mail: museum@secwepemc.org, Internet: http://www.secwepemc.org. Head: Ken Favrholdt
Folklore Museum 05099

Kamouraska

Musée de Kamouraska, 69 Av Morel, Kamouraska, P.Q. G0L 1M0 - T: (418) 492-3144, Fax: (418) 492-3144. Head: Yvette Raymond
Local Museum 05100

Kamsack

Kamsack and District Museum, POB 991, Kamsack, Sask. S0A 1S0 - T: (306) 542-4415
Local Museum 05101

Kapuskasing

Ron Morel Memorial Museum, 88 Riverside Dr, Kapuskasing, Ont. P5N 1B3 - T: (705) 335-5443, Fax: (705) 337-1741
Special Museum 05102

Kaslo

Artery Gallery of Photography (closed) 05103

Langham Cultural Centre Galleries, 447 A Av, Kaslo, B.C. V0G 1M0 - T: (250) 353-2661, Fax: (250) 366-4325, E-mail: langham@pop.kin.bc.ca, Internet: http://www.kin.bc.ca/langham. Head: Margot McKague
Public Gallery / Historical Museum
History of Japanese Canadian Internment in WWII, art 05104

S.S. Moyie National Historic Site, 324 Front St, Kaslo, B.C. V0G 1M0, mail addr: POB 537, Kaslo, B.C. V0G 1M0 - T: (250) 353-2525, Fax: (250) 353-2525, E-mail: ssmoyie@pop.kin.bc.ca, Internet: http://www.kin.bc.ca/moyie/moyiehome1.html. Head: Jack Morris
Local Museum / Historic Site - 1957
Kootenay area, shipwright's tools, restored steam powered sternwheeler (1898), Canadian Pacific railway, lake and river service memorabilia - archives 05105

Keene

Lang Pioneer Village, 16 kms SE of Peterborough, 3.2 kms North of Keene at Lang, Keene, Ont. K0L 2G0, mail addr: 470 Water St, Peterborough, Ont. K9H 3M3 - T: (705) 295-6694, Fax: (705) 295-6644, E-mail: ptbocnty@county.peterborough.on.ca
Local Museum - 1967
Artifacts from 1800-1900 displayed in their historical setting in a museum village, village homes, store, church blacksmith shop, cider barn, and shingle mill, early farm machinery 05106

Kelliher

Kelliher and District Heritage Museum, POB 8, Kelliher, Sask. S0A 1V0 - T: (306) 675-4514, Fax: (306) 675-4538
Local Museum 05107

Kelowna

British Columbia Orchard Industry Museum, 1304 Ellis St, Kelowna, B.C. V1Y 1Z8 - T: (250) 763-0433, Fax: (250) 868-9272, E-mail: orchardm@pacificcoast.net. Head: Wayne Wilson
Historical Museum / Agriculture Museum / Historic Site 05108

Father Pandosy Mission, 3685 Benvoulin Rd, Kelowna, B.C. V1Y 8R3, mail addr: POB 1532, Kelowna, B.C. V1Y 7V8 - T: (250) 860-8369
Historic Site - 1958
Restorated buildings of the Oblate Mission (1859), domestic utensils, furnishings, farm machinery, transportation equipment 05109

Kelowna Art Gallery, 1315 Water St, Kelowna, B.C. V1Y 9R3 - T: (250) 762-2226, Fax: (250) 762-9875, E-mail: dona.kag@shaw.ca, Internet: http://www.kelownaartgallery.com. Head: Dona Moore
Fine Arts Museum
Modern and contemporary Canadian art 05110

Kelowna Museum, 470 Queensway Av, Kelowna, B.C. V1Y 6S7 - T: (250) 763-2417, Fax: (250) 763-5722, E-mail: kmuseum@pacificcoast.net. Head: Wayne Wilson
Natural History Museum / Agriculture Museum - 1951
Local, general and natural hist, ethnography, decorative art, tree fruit agriculture, wine related material 05111

The Wine Museum, 1304 Ellis St, Kelowna, B.C. V1Y 1Z8 - T: (250) 868-0441, Fax: (250) 868-9272, E-mail: winem@pacificcoast.net. Head: Lorna Gunn
Agriculture Museum 05112

Keno City

Keno City Mining Museum, Keno City, Y.T. Y0B 1J0 - T: (867) 995-2792, 995-3103, Fax: (867) 995-2730, Internet: http://www.kenocity.yk.ca. Head: Mike Mancini
Science&Tech Museum / Local Museum 05113

Kenora

Lake of the Woods Museum, Memorial Park, Main and Water Sts, Kenora, Ont. P9N 3X5 - T: (807) 467-2105, Fax: (807) 467-2109, E-mail: lwmchin@voyageur.ca, Internet: http://www.lakeofthe-woodsmuseum.ca. Head: Lori Nelson
Local Museum - 1964
Mineralogy, Indian and pioneer artifacts, period costumes, documents 05114

Kensington

Anne of Green Gables Museum, Silver Bush Park Cnr Rte 20, Kensington, P.E.I. C0B 1M0, mail addr: POB 491, Kensington, P.E.I. C0B 1M0 - T: (902) 436-7329, Fax: (902) 436-1787, E-mail: kindredspirits@annesociety.org, Internet: http://www.annesociety.org/anne. Head: George Campbell
Special Museum - 1971
Furniture, books 05115

Keir Memorial Museum, POB 177, Kensington, P.E.I. C0B 1M0 - T: (902) 836-3054, Fax: (902) 836-4801, E-mail: ygillespie@auracom.com
Historical Museum 05116

Veterans'Memorial Military Museum, Legion Branch 9, Kensington, P.E.I. C0B 1M0 - T: (902) 836-3600
Military Museum 05117

Kentville

Blair House Museum, Agricultural Centre, Kentville, N.S. B4N 1J5 - T: (902) 678-1093, Fax: (902) 678-1567, E-mail: derith@nsapples.com
Agriculture Museum 05118

Old Kings Courthouse Museum, 37 Cornwallis St, Kentville, N.S. B4N 2E2 - T: (902) 678-6237, Fax: (902) 679-0066, E-mail: khs@glinx.com, Internet: http://www.go.ednet.ns.ca/~ip960031. Head: Bria Stokesbury
Historical Museum 05119

Keremeos

Grist Mill, Upper Bench Rd, RR1, Keremeos, B.C. V0X 1N0 - T: (250) 499-2888, Fax: (250) 499-2434
Science&Tech Museum 05120

South Similkameen Museum, POB 135, Keremeos, B.C. V0X 1N0 - T: (250) 499-5445
Local Museum 05121

Kerrobert

Kerrobert and District Museum, POB 401, Kerrobert, Sask. S0L 1R0 - T: (306) 834-2744
Local Museum 05122

Keswick

Georgina Pioneer Museum, Civic Centre Rd, Keswick, Ont. L4P 3E9 - T: (905) 476-4301, Fax: (905) 476-7492, Internet: http://www.town.georgina.on.ca
Local Museum 05123

Killarney

J.A.V. David Museum, 414 Williams Av, Killarney, Man. R0K 1G0 - T: (204) 523-7325
Local Museum - 1960
Pioneer history and textiles, Indian artifacts, natural history - archives 05124

Killarney Centennial Museum, 32 Commissioners St, Killarney, Ont. P0M 2A0 - T: (705) 287-2424, Fax: (705) 287-2660
Local Museum 05125

Kimberley

Kimberley Heritage Museum, POB 144, Kimberley, B.C. V1A 2Y5 - T: (250) 427-7510
Local Museum 05126

Kincaid

Kincaid Museum, POB 177, Kincaid, Sask. S0H 2J0 - T: (306) 264-3910
Local Museum 05127

Kindersley

Kindersley Plains Museum, First St W and Princess Av, Baker Park, Kindersley, Sask. S0l 1S0 - T: (306) 463-6620. Head: Cecilia Pincemin
Local Museum - 1968
Local geological specimens, Indian artifacts, pioneer history, genealogical records 05128

King City

King Township Historical Museum, 2920 King Rd, King City, Ont. L7B 1L6 - T: (905) 727-6322. Head: Helen Poulis
Local Museum 05129

Kingsbury

Centre d'Interpretation de l'Ardoise, 289 Rue Prinicipale, Kingsbury, P.Q. J0B 1X0 - T: (819) 826-5329, Fax: (819) 826-5329
Local Museum 05130

Kingston

Agnes Etherington Art Centre, c/o Queens University, University Av and Queen's Crescent, Kingston, Ont. K7L 3N6 - T: (613) 533-2190, Fax: (613) 533-6765, E-mail: agnes@post.queensu.ca, Internet: http://www.queensu.ca/ageth. Head: Dorothy Farr
Fine Arts Museum / University Museum - 1957
Canadian and European paintings, drawings, and sculpture, decorative arts, ethnology 05131

Bellevue House National Historic Site, 35 Centre St, Kingston, Ont. K7L 4E5 - T: (613) 545-8666, Fax: (613) 545-8721, E-mail: Bellevue_house@pch.gc.ca, Internet: http://parkscanada.pch.gc.ca. Head: John H. Grenville
Local Museum - 1967
The home of Canada's first Prime Minister, Sir John A. Macdonald, furnished in the style of the 1840's 05132

Correctional Service of Canada Museum, 555 King St W, Kingston, Ont. K7L 4V7 - T: (613) 530-3122, Fax: (613) 536-4815, E-mail: stongedc@csc.scc.gc.ca
Special Museum - 1969
Contraband items made by prison inmates, such as escape devices and weapons, old restraint devices, drug apparatus and stills - archives 05133

Fort Henry, Junction of Hwys 2 and 15, 1 Mile E of Kingston, Kingston, Ont. K7L 4V8 - T: (613) 542-7388, Fax: (613) 542-3054, E-mail: john.robertson@forthenry.com, Internet: http://www.forthenry.com
Military Museum - 1938
An original 19th c fort, military and naval artifacts (1750-1919), displays depicting the life of the British garrison 1867, uniforms, medals 05134

Frontenac County Schools Museum, 559 Bagot St, Kingston, Ont. K7K 3E1 - T: (613) 544-9113
Historical Museum 05135

International Ice Hockey Federation Museum, York and Alfred Sts, Kingston, Ont. K7L 4V6 - T: (613) 544-2355, Fax: (613) 544-2355, Internet: http://www.kingston.org/ihm. Head: Edward Grenda
Special Museum - 1965
Hockey hist displays (1886 to the present day), equipment, mementoes of early teams and hockey stars, memorabilia coll 05136

John Fisher Memorial Museum, 3950 Rte 845, Kingston, N.B. E5N 1E9 - T: (506) 763-2101
Historical Museum 05137

Kingston Archaeological Centre, 370 King St W, Kingston, Ont. K7L 2X4 - T: (613) 542-3483, Fax: (613) 542-3483, E-mail: carf@kos.net, Internet: http://www.carf.info. Head: Sue Bazely
Archaeological Museum 05138

Kingston Fire Department Museum, 271 Brock St, Kingston, Ont. K7L 1S5 - T: (613) 542-9727
Historical Museum 05139

Marine Museum of the Great Lakes, 55 Ontario St, Kingston, Ont. K7L 2Y2 - T: (613) 542-2261, Fax: (613) 542-0043, E-mail: mmuseum@stauffer.queensu.ca, Internet: http://www.MarMus.ca. Head: Maurice Smith
Special Museum
archives, library, museum ship 05140

Military Communications and Electronics Museum, Canadian Forces Base, Kingston, Ont. K7K 7B4, mail addr: POB 17000, Station Forces, Kingston, Ont. K7K 7B4 - T: (613) 541-5395, Fax: (613) 540-8111, E-mail: staff@c-and-e-museum.org, Internet: http://www.c-and-e-museum.org. Head: Jack Magilton
Military Museum / Science&Tech Museum
Communications equipment, uniforms, signals, troops, times, military technology - archives 05141

Miller Museum of Geology, c/o Queen's University, Miller Hall, Kingston, Ont. K7L 3N6 - T: (613) 533-6767, Fax: (613) 533-6592, E-mail: Badham@Geolserv.geol.queensu.ca, Internet: http://geol.queensu.ca/museum/museum.html. Head: Mark Badham
Natural History Museum / University Museum - 1841
Minerals, rocks, fossils 05142

Murney Tower Museum, King and Barrie Sts, Kingston, Ont. K7L 1X0 - T: (613) 544-9925, Fax: (613) 544-3715
Military Museum - 1925
Handweapons 1840-1900, light canons, heavy canon 05143

Museum of Health Care, Ann Baillie Bldg, George St, Kingston, Ont. K7L 2V7 - T: (613) 548-2419, Fax: (613) 548-6042, E-mail: museum@kgh.kari.net, Internet: http://www.museumof-healthcare.ca. Head: Dr. James Low
Historical Museum / Science&Tech Museum 05144

Pump House Steam Museum, 23 Ontario St, Kingston, Ont. K7L 2Y2 - T: (613) 546-4696, Fax: (613) 542-0043, E-mail: mmuseum@stauffer.queensu.ca, Internet: http://www.marmus.ca. Head: Maurice Smith
Science&Tech Museum 05145

Royal Military College of Canada Museum, 4 Point Frederick Dr, RMC Campus, Kingston, Ont. K7L 7B4, mail addr: POB 17000, Station Forces, Kingston, Ont. K7K 7B4 - T: (613) 541-6000 ext 6652, Fax: (613) 542-3565, E-mail: mckenzie-r@rmc.ca, Internet: http://www.rmc.ca/museum. Head: J.P. Pike
Military Museum - 1961
RMC hist, military articles of national interest, Douglas coll of weapons, small arms once the property of General Dias, President of Mexico, Naval dockyard Point Frederick artifacts - archives 05146

Saint Lawrence College Art Gallery, Portsmouth Av, Kingston, Ont. K7L 5A6. Head: D. Gordon
Fine Arts Museum 05147

Kingsville

Jack Miner Museum, c/o The Jack Miner Migratory Bird Foundation, Kingsville, Ont. N9Y 2E8 - T: (519) 733-4034. Head: Beth Shaughnessy
Science&Tech Museum 05148

Southwestern Ontario Heritage Village, Kingsville, Ont. N9Y 2E5 - T: (519) 776-6909, Fax: (519) 776-8321, E-mail: swoheritagevillage@on.aibn.com, Internet: http://www.cnls.com/swo_heritage_village
Local Museum / Open Air Museum / Science&Tech Museum 05149

Kinistino

Kinistino District Pioneer Museum, POB 10, Kinistino, Sask. S0J 1H0 - T: (306) 864-2838, 864-2474, Fax: (306) 864-2880
Local Museum - 1971
Indian artifacts, Hudson Bay Company trade goods, rural life in the 1880's 05150

Kipling

Kipling District Historical Society Museum, Kipling, Sask. S0G 2S0 - T: (306) 736-2488
Local Museum 05151

Kirkland Lake

Moose Factory Centennial Museum, c/o Roy Thomson, 521 Government Rd W, Kirkland Lake, Ont. P2N 3H6 - T: (705) 567-4500. Head: Roy Thompson
Local Museum 05152

Museum of Northern History, Sir Harry Oakes Château, 2 Château Dr, Kirkland Lake, Ont. P2N 3M7 - T: (705) 568-8800, Fax: (705) 567-6611, E-mail: mnhchin@nt.net. Head: Robin Ormerod
Historical Museum - 1967
Early trades and crafts, mining exhibits, minerals and ore, agriculture, lumbering, pioneer artifacts 05153

Kitchener

Doon Heritage Crossroads, Homer Watson Blvd, Kitchener, Ont. N2G 3W5 - T: (519) 748-1914, Fax: (519) 748-0009, E-mail: rtom@region.waterloo.on.ca, Internet: http://www.region.waterloo.on.ca/doon. Head: Thomas A. Reitz
Open Air Museum - 1956
Various pioneer homes and buildings, such as a church (1861), general store (1840), and Mennonite farm, interpretation of rural hist 1900-1914 05154

Homer Watson House and Gallery, 1754 Old Mill Rd, Kitchener, Ont. N2P 1H8 - T: (519) 748-4377, Fax: (519) 748-6808, E-mail: educator@homerwatson.on.ca, Internet: http://www.homerwatson.on.ca. Head: Faith Hieblinger
Public Gallery 05155

Joseph Schneider Haus, 466 Queen St S, Kitchener, Ont. N2G 1W7 - T: (519) 742-7752, Fax: (519) 742-0089, E-mail: bususan@region.waterloo.on.ca, Internet: http://www.region.waterloo.on.ca. Head: Susan M. Burke
Decorative Arts Museum / Folklore Museum - 1981
Quilts, folk art, hand weaving, furniture and furnishings 05156

Kitchener-Waterloo Art Gallery, 101 Queen St N, Kitchener, Ont. N2H 6P7 - T: (519) 579-5860, Fax: (519) 578-0740, E-mail: mail@kwag.on.ca. Head: Alfred M. Bogusky
Fine Arts Museum - 1956 05157

Woodside National Historic Site, 528 Wellington St N, Kitchener, Ont. N2H 5L5 - T: (519) 571-5684, Fax: (519) 571-5686, E-mail: ont_woodside@pch.gc.ca, Internet: http://parkscanada.pch.gc.ca/parks/ontario/woodside. Head: Kim Seward Hannam
Local Museum - 1954
Restored boyhood home of William Lyon Mackenzie King, 10th Prime Minister of Canada, reflecting the middle upper class Victorian era 05158

Kitimat

Kitimat Centennial Museum, 293 City Centre, Kitimat, B.C. V8C 1T6 - T: (250) 632-8990, Fax: (250) 632-7429, E-mail: kitmuse@sno.net, Internet: http://www.sno.net/kitmuse. Head: Louise Avery
Local Museum - 1969
Indian and pioneer material, Haisla Nation Kemano-Kitimat Project - archives 05159

Kitwanga

Meanskinisht Village, Cedarvale, Kitwanga, B.C. V0J 2A0 - T: (250) 849-5732. Head: Mary G. Dalen
Local Museum / Open Air Museum 05160

Kleinburg

Kleinburg Doll Museum, 10489 Islington Av N, Kleinburg, Ont. L0J 1C0 - T: (905) 893-1358
Decorative Arts Museum 05161

McMichael Canadian Art Collection, 10365 Islington Av, Kleinburg, Ont. L0J 1C0 - T: (905) 893-1121, Fax: (905) 893-2588, E-mail: info@mcmichael.on.ca, Internet: http://www.mcmichael.on.ca. Head: Vincent J. Varga
Public Gallery - 1965
Works of the Group of Seven, Tom Thomson, Emily Carr, David Milne, J.W. Morrice, Clarence Gagnon and others, Inuit, First Nations and Native art - library 05162

Knowlton

Brome County Historical Society Museum, 130 Lakeside Rd, Knowlton, P.Q. J0E 1V0 - T: (450) 243-6782, E-mail: bchs@endirect.qc.ca. Head: Gail Gibbs
Local Museum - 1903
Pioneer artifacts, Victorian furniture, original 1918 Fokker DVII aircraft, nature exhibits - archives 05163

Komoka

Komoka Railway Museum, 133 Queen St, Komoka, Ont. N0L 1R0 - T: (519) 657-1912, Fax: (519) 657-6791, E-mail: railmus@komokarail.ca, Internet: http://www.komokarail.ca. Head: Ron Davis
Science&Tech Museum 05164

La Baie

Musée du Fjord, 3346 Blvd de la Grande-Baie S, La Baie, P.Q. G7B 1G2 - T: (418) 697-5077, Fax: (418) 697-5079, E-mail: mfjord@videotron.ca, Internet: http://www.museedufjord.com. Head: Guylaine Simard
Local Museum 05165

La Broquerie

Musée Saint-Joachim, Baie Normandeau, La Broquerie, mail addr: BP 314, La Broquerie, Man. R0A 0W0 - T: (204) 424-9442. Head: Rhéal Gagnon
Local Museum 05166

La Have

Fort Point Museum, POB 99, La Have, N.S. B0R 1C0 - T: (902) 688-2696, E-mail: lchs-fortpoint@ns.sympatico.ca
Historical Museum 05167

La Have Islands Marine Museum, RR 1, Bldg 100, Bell's Island, La Have, N.S. B0R 1C0 - T: (902) 688-2565, Internet: http://www.lunco.com/heritage/lehaveisl.htm. Head: Wade Hirtle
Special Museum - 1978
Marine artifacts, life of the inshore fishermen of the LaHave Islands 05168

La Pocatière

Musée François Pilote, 100 Av Painchaud, La Pocatière, P.Q. G0R 1Z0 - T: (418) 856-3145, Fax: (418) 856-5611, E-mail: mfprcip@globetrotter.net, Internet: http://www.kam.qc.ca. Head: Paul-André Leclerc
Local Museum - 1974
Former rural parish life, agricultural exhibits, mammalia, ornithology, entomology, local hist, antique furniture, crafts 05169

La Rivière

Archibald Historical Museum, 2 Miles E and 4 Miles N of La Rivière, La Rivière, Man. R0G 1A0, mail addr: POB 97, La Rivière, Man. R0G 1A0 - T: (204) 242-2825, 242-2554, 242-2235. Head: Wilma K. Wallcraft
Local Museum / Historical Museum / Historic Site / Agriculture Museum - 1973
2 furnished homes of author, politician and suffragette Nellie McClung, CPR Station with famous roof design, Pioneer artifacts, farm machinery, heritage Archibald church 05170

La Ronge

Lac La Ronge Museum, City Center, La Ronge, Sask. S0J 1L0
Natural History Museum - 1965
Mounted animals, birds and fish, Indian artifacts 05171

La Sarre

Musée d'Histoire et d'Archéologie, Ecole Polyno de La Sarre, Av Principale, La Sarre, P.Q. J9Z 2X4 - T: (514) 333-2512. Head: Dominique Godbout
Historical Museum / Archaeological Museum - 1969
Prehistoric utensils made of stone 05172

Lac Mégantic

Musée Namesokanjik, 5527 Rue Frontenac, Lac Mégantic, P.Q. G8B 1H6 - T: (819) 583-2441, Fax: (819) 583-5920, E-mail: greffier@ville.lac-megantic.qc.ca, Internet: http://www.lac-megantic.qc.ca. Head: Jean-François Grandmont
Local Museum 05173

Lachine

Lieu Historique National du Commerce de la Fourrure, 1255 Saint-Joseph, Lachine, P.Q. H8S 2M2 - T: (514) 637-7433, Fax: (514) 637-5325
Historical Museum 05174

Musée de la Ville de Lachine, 110 Chemin de LaSalle, Lachine, P.Q. H8S 2X1 - T: (514) 634-3471 ext 346, Fax: (514) 637-6784, E-mail: museedelachine@ville.lachine.qc.ca, Internet: http://www.cum.qc.ca/lachine/fr/musee.htm. Head: Marc Pitre
Local Museum / Fine Arts Museum / Open Air Museum - 1948
Jewelry, costumes and accessories, furniture, domestic utensils, religious items, actual and contemporary art, archaeological artefacts 05175

Musée des Soeurs de Sainte-Anne, 1300 Blvd Saint-Joseph, Lachine, P.Q. H8S 2M8 - T: (514) 637-4616, Fax: (514) 637-2746. Head: Colette Masson
Religious Arts Museum 05176

Ladysmith

Black Nugget Museum, 12 Gatacre St, Ladysmith, B.C. V0R 2E0 - T: (250) 245-4846, Fax: (250) 246-2441. Head: Kurt Guilbride
Science&Tech Museum 05177

Ladysmith Railway Museum, POB 777, Ladysmith, B.C. V0R 2E0 - T: (250) 245-4454
Science&Tech Museum 05178

Ladywood

Atelier Ladywood Museum, RR3, Ladywood, Man. R0E 0C0 - T: (204) 265-3226. Head: Lenard Anthony
Fine Arts Museum 05179

Lake Cowichan

Kaatza Station Museum, POB 135, Lake Cowichan, B.C. V0R 2G0 - T: (250) 749-6142, Fax: (250) 749-3900, E-mail: khs@island.net. Head: Barbara Simkins
Science&Tech Museum 05180

Lakefield

Christ Church Museum, c/o Doug Twist, POB 427, Lakefield, Ont. K0L 2H0 - T: (705) 652-3176. Head: Peter Bishop
Religious Arts Museum 05181

Lamaline

Lawn Heritage Museum, POB 39, Lamaline, Nfld. A0E 2C0 - T: (709) 857-2555, Fax: (709) 857-2021, E-mail: ahillier@porthole.nl.ca. Head: Ellen Mary Drake
Special Museum 05182

Lanark

Middleville Museum, RR2, Lanark, Ont. K0G 1K0 - T: (613) 259-5462
Local Museum 05183

Lancer

Lancer Centennial Museum, c/o Bertha E. Hopfauf, POB 3, Lancer, Sask. S0N 1G0 - T: (306) 689-2925, Fax: (306) 689-2890. Head: Cliff Murch
Local Museum - 1967
Models of Lancer as it was in 1915 and in 1965, early homestead items 05184

Langham

Langham and District Heritage Village Museum, POB 516, Langham, Sask. S0K 2L0 - T: (306) 283-4342
Local Museum 05185

Langley

Canadian Museum of Flight, 5333 216th St, Ste 200, Langley, B.C. V2Y 2N3 - T: (604) 532-0035, Fax: (604) 532-0056, E-mail: museum@canadianflight.org, Internet: http://www.canadianflight.org
Science&Tech Museum 05186

Langruth

Heritage Museum, Langruth, Man. R0H 0N0
Local Museum 05187

LaSalle

Moulin Fleming, 9675 Blvd LaSalle, LaSalle, P.Q. H8R 2W8 - T: (514) 367-6486, Fax: (514) 367-6439
Science&Tech Museum 05188

Lashburn

Lashburn Centennial Museum, Lashburn, Sask. S0M 1H0 - T: (306) 285-3860
Local Museum 05189

Latchford

House of Memories, POB 82, Latchford, Ont. P0J 1N0 - T: (705) 676-2417, Fax: (705) 676-2121. Head: Helen LaRose
Local Museum 05190

Laval

Cercle d'Art, 2159 Blvd Saint-Martin, Laval, P.Q. H7E 4X6 - T: (514) 384-2551
Public Gallery 05191

Cosmodôme, 2150 Autoroute des Laurentides, Laval, P.Q. H7T 2T8 - T: (450) 978-3600, Fax: (450) 978-3601, E-mail: cosmodome@sim.qu.ca, Internet: http://www.cosmodome.org
Science&Tech Museum 05192

Maison André-Benjamin-Papineau, 5475 Blvd Saint-Martin W, Laval, P.Q. H7T 1C6 - T: (450) 681-1157
Historical Museum 05193

Musée Écologique Vanier, 3995 Blvd Lévesque, Laval, P.Q. H7E 2R3 - T: (450) 661-9320. Head: Alfred Rioux
Natural History Museum 05194

Salle Alfred Pellan, 1395 Blvd de la Concorde, Laval, P.Q. H7N 5W1 - T: (450) 662-4440
Fine Arts Museum 05195

Lazo

Comox Air Force Museum, CFB Comox, Lazo, B.C. V0R 2K0 - T: (250) 339-8162, Fax: (250) 339-8162, E-mail: camuseum@mars.ark.com, Internet: http://mars.ark.com/~camuseum. Head: Bob Richter
Military Museum 05196

Leaf Rapids

Leaf Rapids National Exhibition Centre, POB 220, Leaf Rapids, Man. R0B 1W0 - T: (204) 473-8682, Fax: (204) 437-2707, E-mail: excentre@mail.cancom.net. Head: Joan Seddon
Public Gallery 05197

Leamington

The Arts Centre, South Essex Arts Association, 72 Talbot St W, Leamington, Ont. N8H 1M4 - T: (519) 326-2711, Fax: (519) 326-6491, E-mail: arts_centre@hotmail.com, Internet: http://www.town.leamington.on.ca. Head: Maureen Sutherland
Fine Arts Museum - 1971
Contemporary arts 05198

Point Pelee Natural History Museum, 1118 Point Pelee Dr, Leamington, Ont. N8H 3V4 - T: (519) 322-2365, Fax: (519) 322-1277, E-mail: pelee_info@pch.gc.ca, Internet: http://parkcanada.pch.gc.ca/Pele
Natural History Museum 05199

Leduc

Dr. Woods House Museum, 4801 49 Av, Leduc, Alta. T9E 6L6 - T: (780) 986-1517
Special Museum 05200

Lennoxville

Bishop's Art Gallery, Bishop's University, Lennoxville, P.Q. J1M 1Z7 - T: (819) 822-9600 ext 2687, Fax: (819) 822-9703, E-mail: gverna@ubishops.ca, Internet: http://www.ubishops.ca. Head: Gaëtane Verna
University Museum / Fine Arts Museum 05201

Leross

Kellross Heritage Museum, POB 46, Leross, Sask. S0A 2C0 - T: (306) 675-6144
Local Museum 05202

Leroy

Leroy and District Heritage Museum, POB 47, Leroy, Sask. S0K 2P0 - T: (306) 286-3464
Local Museum 05203

Lethbridge

Fort Whoop-Up Centre, Indian Battle Park, West End Third Av S, Lethbridge, mail addr: POB 1074, Lethbridge, Alta. T1J 4A2 - T: (403) 329-0444, Fax: (403) 329-0645, E-mail: admin@fortwhoopup.com, Internet: http://www.fortwhoopup.com. Head: Richard Shockley
Historical Museum
Indian artifacts, North West mounted police, fur trade 05204

Lethbridge Community College Gallery, Buchanan Resource Centre, Lethbridge, Alta. T1K 1L6 - T: (403) 320-3352
Fine Arts Museum / University Museum 05205

Sir Alexander Galt Museum, 910 Fourth Av S, Lethbridge, Alta. T1J 0P6 - T: (403) 320-3898, 320-4258, Fax: (403) 329-4958, E-mail: museum@galtmuseum.com, Internet: http://www.galtmuseum.com. Head: Wilma Wood
Historical Museum - 1965
Human history of Southern Alberta - archives 05206

Southern Alberta Art Gallery, 601 Third Av S, Lethbridge, Alta. T1J 0H4 - T: (403) 327-8770, Fax: (403) 328-3913, E-mail: saag@uleth.ca, Internet: http://www.home.uleth.ca/~saag. Head: Marilyn Smith
Public Gallery - 1976
Works by local, national and international artists - library 05207

University of Lethbridge Art Gallery, 4401 University Dr, Lethbridge, Alta. T1K 3M4 - T: (403) 329-2666, Fax: (403) 382-7115, Internet: http://home.uleth.ca/sfa-gal. Head: Jeffrey Spalding
Fine Arts Museum / University Museum
20th c art 05208

Lévis

Centre d'Art de Lévis, 33 Rue Wolfe, Lévis, P.Q. G6V 8T2 - T: (418) 833-8831
Public Gallery 05209

Musée du College de Lévis, 9 Rue M. Gosselin, Lévis, P.Q. G6V 5K1 - T: (418) 837-8600, Fax: (418) 839-7592. Head: Loic Bernard
Historical Museum 05210

Lewisporte

By the Bay Museum, Women's Institute Bldg, Lewisporte, Nfld. A0G 3A0 - T: (709) 535-2844
Local Museum 05211

Lillooet

Lillooet District Museum, Main St, Lillooet, B.C. V0K 1V0, mail addr: POB 441, Lillooet, B.C. V0K 1V0 - T: (250) 256-4308, Fax: (250) 256-0043
Local Museum
Pioneer history, period room, Indian artifacts, farm machinery 05212

Limehouse

Canadian Military Studies Museum, RR1, Limehouse, Ont. L0P 1H0 - T: (905) 877-6522. Head: Frank F. Grant
Military Museum 05213

Lindsay

Lindsay Gallery, 190 Kent St W, Lindsay, Ont. K9V 2Y6 - T: (705) 324-1780. Head: Rodney Malham
Fine Arts Museum 05214

Victoria County Historical Society Museum, 322 Kent St W, Lindsay, Ont. K9V 4R8 - T: (705) 324-6756. Head: Lorraine Petzold
Local Museum - 1959
Pioneer home furnishings, clothing, farming tools, Indian artifacts 05215

Linigan

Lanigan and District Heritage Centre, 75 Railway Av, Linigan, Sask. S0K 2M0 - T: (306) 365-2569, Fax: (306) 365-2960, E-mail: linigan.dist.heritage@sk.sympatico.ca, Internet: http://www3.sk.sympatico.ca/ldha. Head: Isabelle Nixon
Local Museum
Canadian Pacific Railway, potash, farming, development of Lanigan 05216

L'Islet-sur-Mer

Musée Maritime du Québec, 55 Rue des Pioniers Est, L'Islet-sur-Mer, P.Q. G0R 2B0 - T: (418) 247-5001, Fax: (418) 247-5002, E-mail: info@mmq.qc.ca. Head: Sonia Chassé
Local Museum - 1968
Models of ships and of a shipyard, navigational instruments, personal possessions of Capt. J.E. Bernier, traditional small craft 05217

Liverpool

Hank Snow Country Music Centre, 148 Bristol Av, Liverpool, N.S. B0T 1K0 - T: (902) 354-4675, Fax: (902) 345-5199, E-mail: info@hanksnow.com, Internet: http://www.hanksnow.com
Music Museum 05218

Queens County Museum, POB 1078, Liverpool, N.S. B0T 1K0 - T: (902) 354-4058, Fax: (902) 354-2050, E-mail: rafusela@ednet.ns.ca, Internet: http://www.geocities.com/Paris/2669/. Head: Linda Rafuse
Local Museum 05219

Simeon Perkins House, Queens County Museum, 105 Main St, Liverpool, N.S. B0T 1K0 - T: (902) 354-4058, Fax: (902) 354-2050, E-mail: rafusela@ednet.ns.ca. Head: Linda Rafuse
Local Museum - 1947
Historic house in Cape Cod style (1766), home of Colonel Simeon Perkins, the diarist of Liverpool, period furniture, local history 05220

Lloydminster

Barr Colony Heritage Cultural Centre, 5011 49th Av, Lloydminster, Sask. S9V 0T8 - T: (403) 825-5655, Fax: (403) 825-7170
Local Museum - 1964
Pioneer artifacts, history of the Barr Colony 05221

Lockeport

Little School Museum, Lockeport, N.S. B0T 1L0 - T: (902) 656-2238
Historical Museum 05222

London

Eldon House, 421 Ridout St N, London, Ont. N6A 2P8 - T: (519) 672-4580, Fax: (519) 660-8397, E-mail: bmeehan@city.london.on.ca, Internet: http://www.londonmuseum.on.ca. Head: Brian Meehan
Local Museum - 1960
House built in 1834 by John Harris, original Harris furniture (19th c) 05223

Fanshawe Pioneer Village, 2609 Fanshawe Park Rd E, London, Ont. N5X 4A1 - T: (519) 457-1296, Fax: (519) 457-3364, E-mail: fpv@wwdc.com, Internet: http://www.pioneer.wwdc.com. Head: Kim Shipp
Open Air Museum 05224

First Hussars Citizen Soldiers Museum, 399 Ridout St N, London, Ont. N6A 2P1 - T: (519) 471-1538. Head: Alastair Neely
Military Museum 05225

Gibson Gallery, 181 King St, London, Ont. N6A 1C9 - T: (519) 439-0451
Fine Arts Museum 05226

Gratton's Weldwood Museum, Hwy 2 S, RR 4, London, Ont.
Science&Tech Museum / Music Museum / Folklore Museum - 1969
Antique and classic cars (1914-1940), arms, mounted animals, musical instruments, Indian and pioneer artifacts 05227

Grosvenor Lodge, 1017 Western Rd, London, Ont. N6G 1G5 - T: (519) 645-2845, Fax: (519) 645-0981
Historical Museum 05228

Guy Lombardo Museum, 205 Wonderland Rd S, London, Ont. N6K 2T3 - T: (519) 473-9003, Fax: (519) 473-9003
Music Museum 05229

London Historical Museum, 1017 Western Rd, London, Ont. N6G 1G5 - T: (519) 661-5165. Head: R. Osborne
Historical Museum 05230

London Museum of Archaeology, c/o University of Western Ontario, 1600 Attawandaron Rd, London, Ont. N6G 3M6 - T: (519) 473-1360, Fax: (519) 473-1363, E-mail: rpearce@uwo.ca, Internet: http://www.uwo.ca/museum. Head: Robert J. Pearce
Archaeological Museum / University Museum - 1933
Archeological, ethnographic, and historical artifacts of southwestern Ontario 05231

London Regional Children's Museum, 21 Wharncliffe Rd S, London, Ont. N6J 4G5 - T: (519) 434-5726, Fax: (519) 434-1443. Head: Leigh-Anne Stradeski
Special Museum - 1976
Indian and Inuit artifacts, clothing, esp used for cave exploration, games, Victorian life-style artifacts, crafts, multi-cultural artifacts, dinosaurs 05232

McIntosh Gallery, c/o The University of Western Ontario, London, Ont. N6A 3K7 - T: (519) 661-3181, Fax: (519) 661-3059, E-mail: mcisus@uwoadmin.uwo.ca, Internet: http://www.uwo.ca/uwocom/McIntosh. Head: Arlene Kennedy
Fine Arts Museum / University Museum - 1942
19th-20th c Canadian paintings, sculpture, drawings, and prints, multimedia 05233

Museum London, 421 Ridout St N, London, Ont. N6A 5H4 - T: (519) 661_0333, Fax: (519) 661-2559, E-mail: bmeehan@city.london.on.ca, Internet: http://www.museumlondon.ca. Head: Brian Meehan
Fine Arts Museum / Historical Museum / Decorative Arts Museum - 1940
Canadian paintings, sculpture, prints, and graphics, architecture, decorative arts, photos, artifacts of 18th-21st c 05234

The Royal Canadian Regiment Museum, Wolseley Hall, 750 Elizabeth St, London, Ont. N5Y 4T7 - T: (519) 660-5102, Fax: (519) 660-5344, E-mail: rcr.museum@dnd.ca, Internet: http://www.army.dnd.ca/rcr_rhq/english/museum. Head: R. Smyth
Military Museum - 1962
Military displays pertaining to the Regiment (1883 to the present) - library, archives 05235

Londonderry

Londonderry Mines Museum, RR1, Londonderry, N.S. B0M 1M0 - T: (902) 668-2043. Head: Trueman Matheson
Local Museum 05236

Longueuil

Centre d'Exposition Plein Sud, 100 Rue de Gentilly, Longueuil, P.Q. J4H 4A9 - T: (450) 679-2966, Fax: (450) 679-4480
Public Gallery 05237

Musée Historique Charles Le Moyne, 4 Rue Saint-Charles Est, Longueuil, P.Q. J4H 1A9
Local Museum 05238

Musée Marie-Rose Durocher, 80 Rue Saint-Charles E, Longueuil, P.Q. J4H 1A9 - T: (450) 651-8104, Fax: (450) 651-8636, E-mail: SNJMGA@total.net. Head: Stella Plante
Religious Arts Museum 05239

Loon Lake

Big Bear Trails Museum, Loon Lake, Sask. S0M 1L0 - T: (306) 837-2070. Head: John W. Simpson
Local Museum 05240

Loretteville

Musée Kio-Warini, Village Huron, Loretteville, P.Q. G2B 3W5 - T: (418) 843-5515. Head: François Vincent
Ethnology Museum - 1972
Photographs and artifacts pertaining to the Huron culture and mythology - archives 05241

Lougheed

Iron Creek Museum, POB 294, Lougheed, Alta. T0B 2V0 - T: (780) 386-3984
Local Museum 05242

Louisbourg

Atlantic Statiquarium Marine Museum, POB 316, Louisbourg, N.S. B0A 1M0 - T: (902) 733-2721. Head: Alex Storm
Historical Museum 05243

Fortress of Louisbourg, 259 Park Service Rd, Louisbourg, N.S. B1C 2L2 - T: (902) 733-2280, Fax: (902) 733-2362. Head: Carol Whitfield
Decorative Arts Museum / Natural History Museum / Archaeological Museum / Local Museum - 1928
Partly reconstructed fortress, 18th c French and provincial furnishings, history, geography, biology, industry, archeology, decorative arts - archives 05244

Sydney and Louisburg Railway Museum, Main St, Louisbourg, N.S. B0A 1M0 - T: (902) 733-2720, Fax: (902) 733-2157
Science&Tech Museum - 1972
Restored station (1895), local history, marine commerce and railroading - archives 05245

Lower Sackville

Fultz House Museum, POB 124, Lower Sackville, N.S. B4C 2S8 - T: (902) 865-3794, Fax: (902) 865-6940, E-mail: fultz.house@ns.sympatico.ca, Internet: http://users.andara.com/~zx2
Historical Museum 05246

Lucan

Donnelly Homestead, 34937 Roman Line, RR3, Lucan, Ont. N0M 2J0 - T: (519) 227-1244, E-mail: rsalts@quadro.net, Internet: http://www.quadro.net/~donnelly
Special Museum 05247

Lumsden

Lumsden Heritage Museum, Qu'Appelle Dr, Lumsden, Sask. S0G 3C0 - T: (306) 731-2905
Local Museum 05248

Lundar

Lundar Museum, POB 265, Lundar, Man. R0C 1Y0 - T: (204) 762-5689. Head: Sigfus Johannson
Local Museum 05249

Lunenburg

Fisheries Museum of the Atlantic, 68 Bluenose Dr, Lunenburg, N.S. B0J 2C0 - T: (902) 634-4794, Fax: (902) 634-8990, E-mail: fma@gov.ns.ca, Internet: http://fisheries.museum.gov.ns.ca. Head: J.A. Tupper
Natural History Museum - 1967
Fresh and salt water fishes, bluenose, Bank Fishery Gallery, inshore fisheries, whaling, shipbuilding, rumrunning, life in fishing communities, marine engines, schooner Theresa E. Connor - library, archives, aquariums 05250

Lunenburg Art Gallery, 19 Pelham St, Lunenburg, N.S. B0J 2C0 - T: (902) 634-3305, Fax: (902) 634-9544, E-mail: aloha@tallships.istar.ca
Fine Arts Museum 05251

Luseland

Luseland and Districts Museum, Grand Av, Luseland, Sask. S0L 2A0 - T: (306) 372-4258. Head: Valerie Finley
Local Museum 05252

Lynn Lake

Lynn Lake Mining Town Museum, 470 Cobalt Pl, Lynn Lake, Man. R0B 0W0 - T: (204) 356-8302. Head: Neil Campbell
Local Museum 05253

Lytton

Lytton Museum, 420 Fraser St, Lytton, B.C. V0K 1Z0 - T: (250) 455-2254, Fax: (250) 455-2394. Head: Richard Forrest
Local Museum
archives 05254

McBride

Valley Museum, POB 775, McBride, B.C. V0J 2E0 - T: (250) 569-2411
Local Museum 05255

McCord

McCord and District Museum, 1 Main St, McCord, Sask. S0H 2T0 - T: (306) 478-2522, Fax: (306) 478-2403, E-mail: ba.wilson@sk.sympatico.ca. Head: Audrey Wilson, Joy Jones
Local Museum / Folklore Museum - 1969
Pioneer artifacts, rock coll, historical church, railway artifacts 05256

Mackenzie

Mackenzie and District Museum, POB 934, Mackenzie, B.C. V0J 2C0 - T: (250) 997-4323, E-mail: chris@perf.bc.ca
Local Museum 05257

Macklin

Macklin and District Museum, 5002 Herald St, Macklin, Sask. S0L 2C0 - T: (306) 753-2610
Local Museum 05258

Macrorie

Macrorie Museum, POB 58, Macrorie, Sask. S0L 2E0 - T: (306) 243-4327
Local Museum 05259

Magnetawan

Magnetawan Historical Museum, Hwy 520, Biddy St, Magnetawan, Ont. P0A 1P0 - T: (705) 387-3308
Local Museum / Science&Tech Museum - 1972
Restored machinery and turbine that supplied the first electricity for the village, local artifacts, log cabin (1880) 05260

Mahone Bay

Settlers' Museum, 578 Main St, Mahone Bay, N.S. B0J 2E0 - T: (902) 624-6263, Fax: (902) 624-6263. Head: Wilma Stewart
Historical Museum 05261

Main Centre

Main Centre Heritage Museum, POB 42, Main Centre, Sask. S0H 2V0
Local Museum 05262

Maitland

East Hants Historical Museum, RR1, Maitland, N.S. B0N 1T0 - T: (902) 261-2627
Local Museum 05263

Lawrence House Museum, 8660 Rte 215, RR1, Maitland, N.S. B0N 1T0 - T: (902) 424-6478, Fax: (902) 424-0560
Historical Museum
Shipbuilders home, William D. Lawrence's shipbuilding yard on Cobequid Bay 05264

Malartic

Musée Régional des Mines et des Arts de Malartic, 650 Rue de la Paix, Malartic, P.Q. J0Y 1Z0 - T: (819) 757-4677, Fax: (819) 757-4140. Head: Jean Massicotte
Science&Tech Museum - 1972
Mining specimens and equipment 05265

Manitowaning

Assiginack Historical Museum and Norisle Heritage Park, Arthur St, Manitowaning, Ont. P0P 1N0 - T: (705) 859-3905, Fax: (705) 859-3010, E-mail: assigmuse@amtelecom.net. Head: David Smith
Local Museum - 1955
Former local jail housing historical artifacts, early farm implements, Indian artifacts, restored pioneer buildings, 1946 steamship 05266

Maniwaki

Château Logue, 8 Rue Comeau, Maniwaki, P.Q. J9E 2R8 - T: (819) 449-7999, Fax: (819) 449-7078. Head: François Ledoux
Historical Museum 05267

Manor

Manor Museum, Newcombe St, Manor, Sask. S0C 1R0 - T: (306) 448-2055
Local Museum 05268

Manotick

Swords and Ploughshares Museum, POB 520, Manotick, Ont. K0A 2N0 - T: (613) 837-0149
Science&Tech Museum / Decorative Arts Museum 05269

Watson's Mill, 5525 Dickinson St, Manotick, Ont. K4M 1A2 - T: (613) 692-6455, 692-4436, Fax: (613) 692-5486, E-mail: bgray@magma.ca, Internet: http://www.watsonsmill.com. Head: Bonnie Gray
Science&Tech Museum - 1974
Water-powered flour and gristmill (1860) 05270

Maple Creek

Antique Tractor Museum and Frontier Village, Maple Creek, Sask. S0N 1N0 - T: (306) 667-2964. Head: John Stewart
Science&Tech Museum / Agriculture Museum 05271

Fort Walsh, 34 Miles SW of Maple Creek in Cypress Hills, Maple Creek, Sask. S0N 1N0 - T: (306) 662-2645, Fax: (306) 662-2711, E-mail: fort_walsh@pch.gc.ca, Internet: http://parkscanada.pch.gc.ca/parks/saskatchewan/fort_walsh
Historic Site - 1972
North West Mounted Police fort (1880), Farwell's Trading Post (1873), hist of the NWMP and the Cypress Hills Massacre 05272

Jasper Cultural and Historical Centre, POB 1504, Maple Creek, Sask. S0N 1N0 - T: (306) 662-2434, Fax: (306) 662-4359, E-mail: jaspercentre@sk.sympatico.ca
Local Museum 05273

Southwestern Saskatchewan Oldtimer's Museum, POB 1540, Maple Creek, Sask. S0N 1N0 - T: (306) 662-2474
Local Museum
Early settlement, ranching, NW-Mount police, metis, first nations - archive 05274

Maple Ridge

Maple Ridge Art Gallery, 11995 Haney Pl, Maple Ridge, B.C. V2X 6G2 - T: (604) 467-5855
Fine Arts Museum / Public Gallery 05275

Maple Ridge Museum, 22520 116th Av, Maple Ridge, B.C. V2X 0S4 - T: (604) 463-5311, E-mail: mrmuseum@axion.net. Head: Val Patenaude
Local Museum 05276

Thomas Haney House, 11012 224 St, Maple Ridge, B.C. V2X 5Z7 - T: (604) 463-1377
Special Museum 05277

Markerville

Historic Markerville Creamery, POB 837, Markerville, Alta. T0M 1M0 - T: (403) 728-3006, Fax: (403) 728-3106. Head: Fay Schatschneider
Decorative Arts Museum 05278

Markham

Markham Museum and Historic Village, 9350 Hwy 48, Markham, Ont. L3P 3J3 - T: (905) 294-4576, Fax: (905) 294-4590, E-mail: beasey@city.markham.on.ca, Internet: http://www.markham.on.ca
Local Museum 05279

Marten River

Marten River Logging Museum, Marten River, Ont. P0H 1T0 - T: (705) 892-2200
Local Museum 05280

Maryfield

Maryfield Museum, POB 262, Maryfield, Sask. S0G 3K0 - T: (306) 646-2201
Local Museum 05281

Marystown

Marystown Museum, POB 688, Marystown, Nfld. A0E 2M0 - T: (709) 279-1507, Internet: http://www.schooner.nf.ca
Local Museum 05282

Massey

Massey Area Museum, 160 Sauble St, Massey, Ont. P0P 1P0 - T: (705) 865-2266, Fax: (705) 865-2266, E-mail: massey@etown.net. Head: Florence Erickson
Local Museum - 1968
Pioneer and Indian artifacts, lumbering, fur-trading, fluorescent minerals, miniatures, costumes 05283

Matane

Galerie d'Art de Matane, 520 Av Saint-Jérôme, Matane, P.Q. G4W 3B5 - T: (418) 566-6687, Fax: (418) 566-2115, E-mail: gartm@globetrotter.qc.ca
Fine Arts Museum 05284

Musée du Vieux-Phare, 968 Av du Phare, Matane, P.Q. G4W 1V7 - T: (418) 562-9766. Head: Dr. Robert Fournier
Local Museum 05285

Matheson

Thelma Miles Museum, POB 601, Matheson, Ont. P0K 1N0 - T: (705) 273-2325, Fax: (705) 273-2140. Head: Dianne Bush
Local Museum 05286

Mattawa

Mattawa and District Museum, 285 First St, Mattawa, Ont. P0H 1V0 - T: (705) 744-5495
Local Museum 05287

Voyageur Heritage Centre, Samuel de Champlain Provincial Park, Hwy 17, 8 Miles W of Mattawa, Mattawa, Ont. P0H 1V0 - T: (705) 744-2276, Fax: (705) 744-0587
Local Museum - 1971
History and construction of birch bark canoes, fur-trading 05288

Maxville

Glengarry Sports Hall of Fame, POB 282, Maxville, Ont. K0C 1T0 - T: (613) 527-1044
Special Museum 05289

Mayne Island

Mayne Island Museum, Mayne Island, B.C. V0N 2J0 - T: (250) 539-2283. Head: M.W. Haggart
Agriculture Museum 05290

Meadow Lake

Meadow Lake Museum, POB 610, Meadow Lake, Sask. S0M 1V0 - T: (306) 236-3622. Head: Vincent Huffman
Local Museum 05291

Meaford

Meaford Museum, 111 Bayfield St, Meaford, Ont. N4L 1H1 - T: (519) 538-5974, Internet: http://www.meaford.com
Local Museum 05292

Medicine Hat

Clay Products Interpretive Centre, 703 Wood St SE, Medicine Hat, Alta. T1A 7E9 - T: (403) 529-1070, Fax: (403) 529-1070, Internet: http://www.medalta.org
Decorative Arts Museum 05293

Medicine Hat Museum and Art Gallery, 1302 Bomford Crescent SW, Medicine Hat, Alta. T1A 5E6 - T: (403) 507-8580, Fax: (403) 502-8589, E-mail: mhmag@city.medicine-hat.ab.ca, Internet: http://www.medicine-hat.ab.ca/cityservices/museum/index.html. Head: Donny White
Local Museum / Fine Arts Museum - 1951/1978
Pioneer home furnishings and clothing prior to 1900, farm machinery, Indian artifacts, paleontology material - art gallery, archives 05294

Melbourne

Richmond County Historical Society Museum, 1296 Route 243, Melbourne, P.Q. J0B 2B0 - T: (819) 845-2303, Internet: http://www.interlinx.qc.ca/~e-dhealy. Head: Robin Barrington
Local Museum - 1968
Genealogy, old tools, photographs, newspapers 05295

Meldrum

Mississagi Strait Lighthouse Museum, Meldrum, Ont. P0P 1R0 - T: (705) 283-3011, Fax: (705) 283-3209
Science&Tech Museum 05296

Meldrum Bay

The Ned Shed Museum, Water St, Meldrum Bay, Ont. P0P 1R0 - T: (705) 283-3385. Head: Dawn McKinlay
Local Museum 05297

Melfort

Melfort and District Museum, 401 Melfort St W, Melfort, Sask. S0E 1A0 - T: (306) 752-5870, Fax: (306) 752-5556, E-mail: melfort.museum@sk.sympatico.ca. Head: Frances Westlund
Local Museum 05298

Melita

Antler River Historical Society Museum, Ash St, Melita, Man. R0M 1L0 - T: (204) 522-3919, 522-3438, Fax: (204) 522-3168. Head: William H. Critchlow
Local Museum 05299

Melocheville

Parc Archéologique de la Pointe-du-Buisson, 333 Rue Émond, Melocheville, P.Q. J0S 1J0 - T: (450) 429-7857, Fax: (450) 429-5921
Archaeological Museum 05300

Melville

Melville Heritage Museum, Heritage Dr, Melville, Sask. S0A 2P0, mail addr: POB 2528, Melville, Sask. S0A 2P0 - T: (306) 728-2070, Fax: (306) 728-2038. Head: Marj Redenbach
Local Museum
Chapel furnishings, military (WW I&II), railways - library 05301

Melville Railway Museum, Melville Regional Park, Melville, Sask. S0A 7P0 - T: (306) 728-4177, Fax: (306) 728-5911, E-mail: chamber@spreda.sk.ca. Head: Adeline Kolodziejak
Science&Tech Museum - 1978
Railway artifacts 05302

Memramcook

Monument Lefebvre, 480 Rue Centrale, Memramcook, N.B. E4K 3S6 - T: (506) 758-9783, Fax: (506) 758-9813, E-mail: monument@nbnet.nb.ca
Historical Museum 05303

Merrickville

Blockhouse Museum, Corner Saint Lawrence and Main Sts, Merrickville, Ont. K0G 1N0 - T: (613) 269-4034
Local Museum / Agriculture Museum - 1966
Blockhouse built in 1832 as a defence for the Rideau Canal, military items, agriculture, local heritage 05304

Merrit

Nicola Valley Museum, 2202 Jackson Av, Merrit, B.C. V1K 1B8 - T: (250) 378-4145, Fax: (250) 378-4145
Local Museum 05305

Miami

Miami Museum, POB 153, Miami, Man. R0G 1H0 - T: (204) 435-2305, Fax: (204) 435-2067
Local Museum 05306

Middelton

Annapolis Valley Macdonald Museum, 21 School St, Middelton, N.S. B0S 1P0 - T: (902) 825-6116, Fax: (902) 825-0531
Local Museum 05307

Middle Lake

Middle Lake Museum, POB 157, Middle Lake, Sask. S0K 2X0. Head: Susan Bauer
Local Museum 05308

Midland

Huron-Ouendat Village, 549 Little Lake Park Rd, Midland, Ont. L4R 4P4 - T: (705) 526-2844, Fax: (705) 527-6622, E-mail: hmchin@bconnex.net, Internet: http://www.georgianbaytourism.on.ca. Head: Ralph Lynn, Jamie Hunter
Open Air Museum / Folklore Museum / Historical Museum - 1954
Huron Village restored to its original appearance prior to European contact, 17th c Indian artifacts, Huron people, village hist 05309

Huronia Museum, 549 Little Lake Park Rd, Midland, Ont. L4R 4P4 - T: (705) 526-2844, Fax: (705) 527-6622, E-mail: hmchin@bconnex.net, Internet: http://www.georgianbaytourism.on.ca. Head: Ralph Lynn, Jamie Hunter
Local Museum / Fine Arts Museum - 1947
Pioneer and Indian artifacts, Great Lakes, shipping, photography, archaeological and general hist coll, lighthouses, art coll (W.J. Wood, F. Johnston, L. Oille-Wells, T. Lord, B. Watson, J. Bald) 05310

Martyrs' Shrine, 16163 Hwy 12 W, Midland, Ont. L4R 4K5 - T: (705) 526-3788, Fax: (705) 526-1546, E-mail: shrine@jesuits.ca, Internet: http://www.jesuits.ca/martyrs-shrine. Head: Robert K.L. Wong
Religious Arts Museum 05311

Midway

Kettle River Museum, POB 149, Midway, B.C. V0H 1M0 - T: (250) 449-2614, Fax: (250) 449-2614
Science&Tech Museum 05312

Milden

Milden Community Museum, Milden, Sask. S0L 2L0 - T: (306) 935-2199. Head: Brenda Latsay
Local Museum 05313

Milford

Mariners' Park Museum, Junction of County 1349 and RR 2, Milford, Ont. K0K 2P0 - T: (613) 476-4695, Fax: (613) 476-8392
Natural History Museum / Historical Museum - 1967
Marine artifacts from surrounding waters of Prince Edward County, false ducks lighthouse, showing marine commerce, shipwrecks 05314

Millet

Millet and District Museum, 5120 50 St, Millet, Alta. T0C 1Z0 - T: (780) 387-5558, Fax: (780) 387-5548, E-mail: mdhs@glink2.com. Head: Tracey Leavitt
Local Museum 05315

Milton

Halton Region Museum, 6 Miles NW of Milton in Kelso Park, RR 3, Milton, Ont. L9T 2X7 - T: (905) 875-2200, Fax: (905) 876-4322, E-mail: museum@region.halton.on.ca
Local Museum / Natural History Museum - 1962
History of Halton County from 1808 to 1920, ornithology 05316

Milton Blacksmith Shop Museum, POB 572, Milton, N.S. B0T 1P0 - T: (902) 350-0268, Internet: http://www.qcis.ns.ca. Head: Christine Tupper
Local Museum / Historical Museum 05317

Ontario Agricultural Museum, 3 Miles W of Milton, Milton, Ont. L9T 2Y3 - T: (905) 878-8151, Fax: (905) 876-4530. Head: John Wiley, R.W. Carbert
Agriculture Museum - 1979
Agricultural machinery, farm home equipment and furnishings, tools - library, archives 05318

Streetcar and Electric Railway Museum, 13629 Guelph Line Rd, mail addr: POB 578, Milton, Ont. L9T 5A2 - T: (519) 856-9802, Fax: (519) 856-1399, E-mail: streetcar@hcry.org, Internet: http://www.hcry.org. Head: Gordon McOuat
Science&Tech Museum 05319

Minden

Agnes Jamieson Gallery, POB 648, Minden, Ont. K0M 2K0 - T: (705) 286-3763
Fine Arts Museum 05320

Minesing

Simcoe County Museum, RR 2, Minesing, Ont. L0L 1Y0 - T: (705) 728-3721, Fax: (705) 728-9130, E-mail: museum@bar.imag.net, Internet: http://www.county.simcoe.on.ca. Head: Gloria Taylor
Local Museum - 1928
Archeology, ethnology, pioneer and Victorian exhibits, domestic items, early agricultural material, hist buildings - library, archives 05321

Miniota

Miniota Municipal Museum, RR 1, Miniota, Man. R0M 1M0, mail addr: POB 189, Miniota, Man. R0M 1M0 - T: (204) 567-3675, 567-3789
Local Museum 05322

Minnedosa

Minnedosa and District Co-Coperative Museum, 49 Second Av NW, Minnedosa, Man. R0J 1E0 - T: (204) 867-3444, Fax: (204) 867-5171. Head: Margaret Shorrock
Local Museum - 1962
Local history 05323

Minto

Minto Museum, 71 Main St, Minto, N.B. E0E 1J0 - T: (506) 327-3383
Local Museum 05324

Miramichi

Miramichi Natural History Museum, 149 Wellington St, Miramichi, N.B. E1N 3A5 - Fax: (506) 773-7305
Natural History Museum - 1880
Geology, paleontology, vertebrate zoology, Indian artifacts - archives 05325

Rankin House Museum, 2224 King George Hwy, Miramichi, N.B. E1V 6N3 - T: (506) 773-3448. Head: Jack Ullock
Historical Museum 05326

Mirror

Mirror and District Museum, POB 246, Mirror, Alta. T0B 3C0 - T: (403) 788-3828
Local Museum 05327

Miscouche

Musée Acadien, Prince Edward Island Museum and Heritage Foundation, 23 Main Dr, Miscouche, P.E.I. C0B 1T0 - T: (902) 432-2880, 436-6237. Head: Cécile Gallant
Local Museum / Folklore Museum - 1964
Objects used by the Acadians, carpentry, blacksmith and kitchen items, old books, photographs 05328

Mission

Mission Museum, 33201 Second Av, Mission, B.C. V2V 1J9 - T: (604) 826-1011, Fax: (604) 826-1017, E-mail: muse@mission.museum.bc.ca, Internet: http://www.mission.museum.bc.ca. Head: Kim Allen
Local Museum - 1972
Local hist, First Nations artifacts, farm equipment, period rooms, railway, hist of minority groups - archives 05329

XA Ytem Museum, 35087 Lougheed Hwy, Mission, B.C. V2V 6T1 - T: (604) 820-9725, Fax: (604) 820-9735, E-mail: xaytem@dowco.com, Internet: http://www.xaytem.museum.bc.ca/
Archaeological Museum 05330

Mississauga

Art Gallery of Mississauga, 300 City Centre Dr, Mississauga, Ont. L5B 3C1 - T: (905) 896-5088, Fax: (905) 615-4167, E-mail: fred.troughton@city.mississauga.on.ca, Internet: http://www.city.mississauga.on.ca/agm
Fine Arts Museum 05331

Benares Historic House, 1507 Clarkson Rd N, Mississauga, Ont. L5J 2W8 - T: (905) 822-2347, Fax: (905) 822-5372, E-mail: scott.gillies@city.missisauga.on.ca, Internet: http://www.museumsofmississauga.com. Head: Annemarie Hagan
Special Museum 05332

Blackwood Gallery, University of Toronto, Erindale College, 3359 Mississauga Rd N, Mississauga, Ont. L5L 1C6 - T: (905) 828-3789, Fax: (905) 828-5202, E-mail: blackwood_gallery@utm.utoronto.ca, Internet: http://www.erin.utoronto.ca. Head: Barbara Fischer
Fine Arts Museum / University Museum 05333

Bradley Museum, 1620 Orr Rd, Mississauga, Ont. L5J 4T2 - T: (905) 822-1569, Fax: (905) 823-3591, E-mail: scott.gillies@city.mississauga.on.ca, Internet: http://www.museumsofmississauga.com. Head: Annemarie Hagan
Agriculture Museum 05334

The Gallery, 1900 Dundas St W, Mississauga, Ont. L5K 1P9 - T: (905) 823-7323
Fine Arts Museum 05335

Harbour Gallery, 1697 Lakeshore Rd W, Mississauga, Ont. L5J 1J4 - T: (905) 822-5495
Fine Arts Museum 05336

Lithuanian Museum-Archives of Canada, 2185 Stavebank Rd, Mississauga, Ont. L5C 1T3 - T: (905) 566-8755, Fax: (905) 275-1336, E-mail: litharch@the-wire.com, Internet: http://daryl.chin.gc.ca/Museums/. Head: Dr. Rasa Mazeika
Historical Museum / Military Museum
Immigration history, textiles, military medals, fine and decorative arts, rare books - archive 05337

Springbank Visual Arts Centre, 3057 Mississauga Rd N, Mississauga, Ont. L5L 1C8 - T: (905) 828-9151
Fine Arts Museum 05338

Moncton

Atelier Imago, 140 Rue Botsford, Moncton, N.B. E1C 4X5 - T: (506) 388-1431
Fine Arts Museum 05339

Galerie d'Art, Université de Moncton, Edifice Clément Cormier Bldg, Moncton, N.B. E1A 3E9 - T: (506) 858-4088, Fax: (506) 858-4043, E-mail: charetl@umoncton.ca, Internet: http://www.umoncton.ca/gaum. Head: Luc A. Charette
Fine Arts Museum / University Museum - 1964
Contemporary Canadian art 05340

Galerie Georges-Goguen, 250 Av Université, Moncton, N.B. E1C 8N8 - T: (506) 853-6666, Fax: (506) 853-6739
Fine Arts Museum 05341

Galerie Sans Nom, 140 Rue Botsford, Ste 16, Moncton, N.B. E1C 4X4 - T: (506) 854-5381, Fax: (506) 857-2064
Fine Arts Museum 05342

Lutz Mountain Meeting House, 3030 Mountain Rd, Moncton, N.B. E1G 2W8 - T: (506) 384-4967, Fax: http://personal.nbnet.nb.ca/lutzmtn, E-mail: lutzmtn@nbnet.nb.ca. Head: Eleanor Weldon
Local Museum - 1976
Furniture, clothing, household utensils, farm implements, genealogical files on the first settlers (1766) 05343

Moncton Museum, 20 Mountain Rd, Moncton, N.B. E1C 2J8 - T: (506) 856-4383, Fax: (506) 856-4355, E-mail: info.museum@moncton.org, Internet: http://www.moncton.org. Head: Brenda P. Orr
Local Museum - 1973
Human history, local history since 1850 05344

Musée Acadien, Université de Moncton, Edifice Clément Cormier, Moncton, N.B. E1A 3E9 - T: (506) 858-4088, Fax: (506) 858-4043, E-mail: leblanbc@umoncton.ca, Internet: http://www.umoncton.ca/maum. Head: Bernard LeBlanc
Historical Museum / University Museum - 1886
History and culture of the Acadians, evangeline, furniture, trade, agriculture, architecture, fishing, tools, textiles, costumes, religion 05345

Mont-Laurier

Centre d'Exposition Mont-Laurier, 385 Rue Du Pont, Mont-Laurier, P.Q. J9L 3N7 - T: (819) 623-2441, Fax: (819) 623-7262, E-mail: orcentex@sympatico.ca. Head: Reine Charbonneau
Public Gallery 05346

Mont-Saint-Hilaire

Musée d'Art de Mont-Saint-Hilaire, 150 Rue du Centre-Civique, Mont-Saint-Hilaire, P.Q. J3H 5Z5 - T: (450) 536-3033, Fax: (450) 536-3032, E-mail: mamsh@mamsh.qc.ca, Internet: http://www.mamsh.qc.ca. Head: Marie-Andrée Leclerc
Fine Arts Museum 05347

Montague

Garden of the Gulf Museum, POB 1237, Montague, P.E.I. C0A 1R0 - T: (902) 838-2467. Head: Donna Collings
Natural History Museum 05348

Montebello

Lieu Historique National du Manoir-Papineau, 500 Notre-Dame, Montebello, P.Q. J0V 1L0 - T: (819) 423-6965, Fax: (819) 423-6455
Historical Museum 05349

Montmagny

Maison de l'Accordéon, 301 Blvd Taché E, Montmagny, P.Q. G5V 3S3 - T: (418) 248-9196
Music Museum 05350

Montréal

Alcan Aluminium Corporate Art Collection, 1188 Sherbrooke St W, Montréal, P.Q. H3A 3G2 - T: (514) 848-8000
Fine Arts Museum / Decorative Arts Museum - 1967
Objects, documents and photographs related to the company's founding and growth, early and unusual uses of aluminum 05351

Art Cannon Gallery, 4885 Av du Parc, Montréal, P.Q. H2V 4E7 - T: (514) 274-9118, E-mail: art@artcannon.com, Internet: http://www.artcannon.com. Head: Misha Gostick
Public Gallery 05352

Bank of Montreal Museum, 129 Saint Jacques St, Montréal, P.Q. H2Y 1L6, mail addr: POB 6002, Montréal, P.Q. H2Y 1L6 - T: (514) 877-6810, Fax: (514) 877-1140, E-mail: yolaine.toussaint@bmo.com. Head: Yolaine Toussaint
Special Museum - 1963
Numismatic and banking memorabilia 05353

Basilique Notre-Dame de Montréal, 110 Rue Notre-Dame W, Montréal, P.Q. H2Y 1T2 - T: (514) 842-2925, Fax: (514) 842-3370, E-mail: basndm@globetrotter.net
Religious Arts Museum 05354

Beaulieu Collection, 3157 Lacombe, Montréal, P.Q. H3T IL6
Fine Arts Museum 05355

Bell Canada Telephone Historical Collection, 1050 Beaver Hall Hill, Room 1436, Montréal, P.Q. H2Z 1S3
Science&Tech Museum - 1936
Telecommunications history 05356

Biodôme de Montréal, 4777 Av Pierre-de-Coubertin, Montréal, P.Q. H1V 1B3 - T: (514) 868-3000, Fax: (514) 868-3065, E-mail: biodome@ville.montreal.qc.ca, Internet: http://www.ville.montreal.qc.ca/biodome. Head: Jean-Pierre Doyon
Natural History Museum - 1992 05357

Black Watch of Canada Regimental Memorial Museum, 2067 Bleury St, Montréal, P.Q. H3A 2K2 - T: (514) 4961686, Fax: 4962758, E-mail: info@blackwatchcanada.com, Internet: http://www.blackwatchcanada.com. Head: Bruce Bolton
Military Museum - 1949
Medals, weapons, uniforms, paintings and other military memorabilia - library 05358

Canadian Centre for Architecture, 1920 Rue Baile, Montréal, P.Q. H3H 2S6 - T: (514) 939-7000, Fax: (514) 939-7020, E-mail: ref@cca.qc.ca, Internet: http://cca.qc.ca. Head: Nicholas Olsberg
Fine Arts Museum - 1989
65,000 Master drawings and prints, 50,000 photographs, 100 archival fonds - research library 05359

Centre Commémoratif de l'Holocauste à Montréal, 1 Carré Cummings, Montréal, P.Q. H3W 1M6 - T: (514) 345-2605, Fax: (514) 344-2651, E-mail: mhmc@total.net
Historical Museum 05360

Centre d'Art du Mont-Royal, 1260 Chemin Remembrance, Montréal, P.Q. H3H 1A2
Fine Arts Museum - 1963
Painting, sculpture, engravings 05361

Centre des Arts Contemporains du Québec à Montréal, 4247 Saint-Dominique, Montréal, P.Q. H2W 2A9 - T: (514) 842-4300
Public Gallery 05362

Centre d'Histoire de Montréal, 335 Pl d'Youville, Montréal, P.Q. H2Y 3T1 - T: (514) 872-3207, Fax: (514) 872-9645, E-mail: chm@ville.montreal.qc.ca, Internet: http://www.ville.montreal.qc.ca/chm
Local Museum 05363

Centre International d'Art Contemporain de Montréal, 760 Pl du Parc, Montréal, P.Q. H2X 4A6 - T: (514) 288-0811, Fax: (514) 288-5021, E-mail: courrier@ciac.ca, Internet: http://www.ciac.ca. Head: Claude Gosselin
Public Gallery 05364

Centre Missionnaire Sainte-Therèse, 4387 Esplanade, Montréal, P.Q. H2W 1T3
Fine Arts Museum / Decorative Arts Museum / Natural History Museum - 1967
Mounted animals, arts and crafts, Indian, African and Ethiopian art - archives 05365

Cinémathèque Québécoise - Musée du Cinéma, 335 de Maisonneuve Est, Montréal, P.Q. H2X 1K1 - T: (514) 842-9763, Fax: (514) 842-1816, E-mail: info@cinematheque.qc.ca, Internet: http://www.cinematheque.qc.ca. Head: Robert Daudelin
Special Museum - 1963
Kaleidoscopes, optical tricks, cinema apparatus such as cameras from various lands - archives 05366

Galerie Dominion, 1438 Rue Sherbrooke Ouest, Montréal, P.Q. H3G 1K4 - T: (514) 845-7833
Public Gallery 05367

Galerie l'Industrielle-Alliance, 680 Rue Sherbrooke, Montréal, P.Q. H3A 2S6 - T: (514) 499-3768, Fax: (514) 284-2655. Head: Danielle Brunelle
Fine Arts Museum 05368

Gallery of the Saidye Bronfman Centre for the Arts, 5170 Chemin Côte Sainte-Catherine, Montréal, P.Q. H3W 1M7 - T: (514) 739-2301, Fax: (514) 739-9340, E-mail: sbcgallery@sbca.qc.ca, Internet: http://www.sbca.qc.ca. Head: Sylvie Gilbert
Fine Arts Museum - 1967
Exhibits of national and international works of contemporary art 05369

Insectarium de Montréal, 4581 Rue Sherbrooke E, Montréal, P.Q. H1X 2B1 - T: (514) 872-0663, Fax: (514) 872-0662, E-mail: insectarium@ville.montreal.qc.ca. Head: Guy Bélair
Natural History Museum - 1990 05370

Lake Saint Louis Historical Society Museum, POB 1024, Station A, Montréal, P.Q. H3C 2W9
Historical Museum 05371

Leonard and Bina Ellen Art Gallery, c/o Concordia University, 1400 Blvd de Maisonneuve Ouest, Montréal, P.Q. H3G 1M8 - T: (514) 848-4750, Fax: (514) 848-4751, E-mail: ellengal@alcor.concordia.ca, Internet: http://ellen-gallery.concordia.ca. Head: Lynn Bearis
Fine Arts Museum / University Museum - 1966
Modern and contemporary Canadian art and small coll of ancient 05372

McCord Museum, 690 Sherbrooke St W, Montréal, P.Q. H3A 1E9 - T: (514) 398-7100, Fax: (514) 398-5045, E-mail: info@mccord.lan.mcgill.ca, Internet: http://www.musee-mccord.qc.ca. Head: Victoria Dickenson
Ethnology Museum - 1921
Ethnological material pertaining to the First Nations of Canada, drawings, prints and paintings by Canadian artists, antique costumes, accessories, furniture, crafts, and historical photos - archives 05373

Maison de la Poste, 1035 Rue Saint-Jacques, Montréal, P.Q. H3C 1H0 - T: (514) 283-4602
Special Museum 05374

Maison du Calvet, 401 Rue Bonsecours, Montréal, P.Q. H2Y 3C3
Decorative Arts Museum - 1966
Antique furniture 05375

Marguerite d'Youville Museum, 1185 Rue Saint-Mathieu, Montréal, P.Q. H3H 2H6 - T: (514) 932-7724
Historical Museum 05376

Montréal Museum of Fine Arts, 1379-1380 Rue Sherbrooke, Ouest, Montréal, P.Q. H2X 3X5, mail addr: POB 3000, Station H, Montréal, P.Q. H3G 2T9 - T: (514) 285-1600, Fax: (514) 844-6042, E-mail: webmaster@mbamtl.org, Internet: http://www.mmfa.qc.ca
Fine Arts Museum - 1860 05377

Musée d'Art Contemporain de Montréal, 185 Rue Sainte-Catherine Ouest, Montréal, P.Q. H2X 3X5 - T: (514) 847-6226, Fax: (514) 847-6291, E-mail: info@macm.org, Internet: http://www.macm.org. Head: Marcel Brisebois
Fine Arts Museum - 1964 05378

Musée d'Art Néo-Byzantin, 10025 Blvd l'Acadie, Montréal, P.Q. H4N 2S1
Fine Arts Museum / Decorative Arts Museum - 1975
Icons, wood sculpture, textiles 05379

Musée de l'Eglise Notre-Dame (temporary closed), 424 Rue Saint-Sulpice, Montréal, P.Q. H2Y 2V5 - T: (514) 842-2925, Fax: 8423370, E-mail: basndm@globetrotter.net. Head: M. Joland Tremblay
Religious Arts Museum - 1937
Furniture, silver and ceramic items, religious ornaments, paintings, statues - archives 05380

Musée de l'Oratoire Saint-Joseph, 3800 CH Reine-Marie, Montréal, P.Q. H3V 1H6 - T: (514) 733-8211, Fax: (514) 733-9735. Head: André Bergeron
Religious Arts Museum 05381

Musée des Arts Décoratifs de Montréal, 2200 Rue Crescent, Montréal, P.Q. H1W 3W2 - T: (514) 284-1252, Fax: (514) 284-0123, Internet: http://www.madm.org. Head: Dr. Luc d' Iberville-Moreau
Decorative Arts Museum - 1979
Extensive coll of decorative arts from the period of 1935 to the present, incl textiles, glass and jewellery, important coll of modernist jewellery and Canadian studio glass, from 1970 to today 05382

Musée des Beaux-Arts de Montréal, 3400 Av du Musée, Montréal, P.Q. H3G 1K3 - T: (514) 285-1600, Fax: (514) 844-6042, Internet: http://www.mbam.qc.ca. Head: Guy Cogeval
Fine Arts Museum / Decorative Arts Museum - 1860
European, African and Canadian sculpture, Asian, European, Islamic, Pre-Columbian, and American Indian art, furniture, silver and ceramic items - library 05383

Musée des Soeurs Grises de Montréal, 1185 Rue Saint-Mathieu, Montréal, P.Q. H3H 2H6 - T: (514) 937-9501 poste 335, Fax: (514) 937-0503. Head: Marie Lemire
Religious Arts Museum 05384

Musée du Château Ramezay, 280 Rue Notre-Dame Est, Montréal, P.Q. H2Y 1C5 - T: (514) 861-7182, 861-3708, Fax: (514) 861-8317, E-mail: mcrm1@globetrotter.qc.ca. Head: André J. Delisle
Decorative Arts Museum / Historical Museum - 1895
Coll and exhibition of the hist of Montreal and the province of Quebec, from pre-contact Native society to 1900 05385

Musée du Frère André, Oratoire Saint-Joseph, 3800 Chemin Queen Mary, Montréal, P.Q. H3V 1H6 - T: (514) 733-8211. Head: André Bergeron
Religious Arts Museum - 1952
Church windows, mosaics, frescoes, sculpture 05386

Musée Juste Pour Rire, 2111 Blvd Saint Laurent, Montréal, P.Q. H2X 2T5 - T: (514) 845-3155, Fax: (514) 849-5462, E-mail: rmichaud@hahaha.com, Internet: http://www.hahaha.com. Head: Raynald Michaud
Special Museum - 1992 05387

Musée Maison Saint-Gabriel, 2146 Pl Dublin, Montréal, P.Q. H3K 2A2 - T: (514) 935-8136, Fax: (514) 935-5692, E-mail: msgrcip@globetrotter.qc.ca, Internet: http://www.maisonsaint-gabriel.qc.ca. Head: Madeleine Juneau
Local Museum 05388

Musée Marc-Aurèle Fortin, 118 Rue Saint-Pierre, Montréal, P.Q. H2Y 2L7 - T: (514) 845-6108, Fax: (514) 845-6100, E-mail: mafortin@globetrotter.net. Head: René Buisson
Historical Museum 05389

Musée Marguerite Bourgeoys, 400 Rue Saint-Paul Est, Montréal, P.Q. H2Y 1H4 - T: (514) 282-8670, Fax: (514) 282-8672, E-mail: museemb@videotron.ca, Internet: http://www.marguerite-bourgeoys.com. Head: Danielle Dubois
Historical Museum / Historic Site / Religious Arts Museum / Archaeological Museum - 1998
History of Montréal and of the life of Marguerite Bourgeoys, archaeology, architecture, art, history 05390

Musée Stewart au Fort de Ile Sainte-Hélène (Stewart Museum at the Fort of Ile Sainte-Hélène), 20 Chemin Tour de l'Isle, Montréal, P.Q. H3C 4G6 - T: (514) 861-6701, Fax: (514) 284-0123, E-mail: courriel@stewart-museum.org, Internet: http://www.stewart-museum.org. Head: Bruce D. Bolton
Historical Museum - 1955
Military, maritime and social hist exhibits, rare maps, domestic utensils, fire arms and scientific instruments - library 05391

Pointe-à-Callière - Musée d'Archéologie et d'Histoire de Montréal, 350 Pl Royale, Montréal, P.Q. H2Y 3Y5 - T: (514) 872-9150, Fax: (514) 872-9151, E-mail: info@musee-Pointe-a-Calliere.qu.ca, Internet: http://www.musee-Pointe-a-Calliere.qc.ca
Archaeological Museum 05392

Redpath Museum, c/o McGill University, 859 Sherbrooke St West, Montréal, P.Q. H3A 2K6 - T: (514) 348-4086, Fax: (514) 398-3185, Internet: http://www.mcgill.ca/redpath. Head: Dr. Graham A.C. Bell
University Museum - 1882 05393

Royal Canadian Ordnance Corps Museum, 6560 Rue Hochlega, Montréal, P.Q. H1N 3R9 - T: (514) 252-2241. Head: Ivan Burch
Military Museum 05394

Saint-Laurent Art Museum, 615 Av Sainte-Croix, Montréal, P.Q. H4L 3X6 - T: (514) 747-7367, Fax: (514) 747-8892, E-mail: Masl01@globetrotter.qc.ca. Head: Johane Canning-Lacroix
Fine Arts Museum / Religious Arts Museum 05395

Univers Maurice Rocket Richard, 2800 Rue Viau, Montréal, P.Q. H1V 3J3 - T: (514) 251-9930, Internet: http://www.Rocket9.org
Special Museum 05396

Mooretown

Moore Museum, 94 Moore Line, Mooretown, Ont. N0N 1M0 - T: (519) 867-2020, Fax: (519) 867-2020, E-mail: lmason@twp.stclair.on.ca, Internet: http://www.timewellspent.ca. Head: Laurie Mason
Local Museum - 1975
Hist of Moore Township, including schoolhouse, log cabin, marine and agricultural equipment 05397

Moose Jaw

History of Transportation, Western Development Museum, 50 Diefenbaker Dr, Moose Jaw, Sask. S65 IL9 - T: (306) 693-5989, Fax: (306) 691-0511, E-mail: wdm.mj-wdm@sasktel.net, Internet: http://www.wdmuseum.sk.ca. Head: David Klatt
Local Museum / Science&Tech Museum - 1949
Transportation exhibits, aviation, railway, only snowbirds gallery, dedicated to 431 squadron snowbirds in the world, only restored Avro Anson MK I in North America 05398

Moose Jaw Art Museum and National Exhibition Centre → Moose Jaw Museum and Art Gallery

Moose Jaw Museum and Art Gallery, 461 Langdon Crescent, Moose Jaw, Sask. S6H 0X6 - T: (306) 692-4471, Fax: (306) 694-8016, E-mail: mjamchin@sk.sympatico.ca, Internet: http://www.mjmag.ca. Head: Heather Smith
Public Gallery / Local Museum - 1966
Regional history, visual art by local/ provincial artists 05399

Sukanen Ship Pioneer Village and Museum of Saskatchewan, on Hwy 2, 8 miles S, Moose Jaw, mail addr: POB 2071, Moose Jaw, Sask. S6H 7T2 - T: (306) 693-3506. Head: R. Jones
Local Museum / Historical Museum
Village, prairie, animal farming 05400

Moosehorn

Moosehorn Heritage Museum, Cnr Railway and First Sts, Moosehorn, Man. R0C 2E0 - T: (204) 768-2087. Head: Lois Metner
Local Museum / Ethnology Museum - 1974
History, ethnology - archives 05401

Moosomin

Jamieson Museum, 306 Gertie St N, Moosomin, Sask. S0G 3N0 - T: (306) 435-3156. Head: P.M. Jamieson
Historical Museum / Military Museum - 1972
Large military coll, farm implements, house built before 1900 and furnished in the style of the period, hospital, barbershop, country church, school, Indian artifacts 05402

Moosonee

Revillon Frères Museum, POB 127, Moosonee, Ont. P0L 1Y0 - T: (705) 336-2933
Special Museum 05403

Morden

Morden and District Museum, 111B Gilmour St, Morden, Man. R6M 1N9 - T: (204) 822-3406, Fax: (204) 822-9414, E-mail: morden_museum@mb.sympatico.ca, Internet: http://www.mordenmuseum.com. Head: Shawn Bugden
Local Museum - 1971
Marine fossils (cretaceous era), pioneer artifacts 05404

Pembina Hills Regional Art Gallery, 352 Stephen St, Morden, Man. R6M 1T5 - T: (204) 822-6026
Public Gallery 05405

Moreton's Harbour

Moreton's Harbour Museum, POB 28, Moreton's Harbour, Nfld. A0G 3H0 - T: (709) 684-2355
Local Museum 05406

Morpeth

Rondeau Provincial Park Visitor Centre, RR 1, Morpeth, Ont. N0P 1X0 - T: (519) 674-1772, Fax: (519) 674-1755. Head: Pamela Burns
Natural History Museum / Local Museum - 1965
Zoology, entomology, ornithology, archeology, history - library, herbarium 05407

Morris

Morris and District Centennial Museum, POB 344, Morris, Man. R0G 1K0 - T: (204) 746-2169, Fax: (204) 746-8801, E-mail: liljakern@hotmail.com. Head: Peter Unraw
Local Museum 05408

Morrisburg

Upper Canada Village, Hwy 2, 11 Miles East of Morrisburg, Morrisburg, Ont. K0C 1X0 - T: (613) 543-3704, Fax: (613) 543-4098, Internet: http://www.uppercanadavillage.ca. Head: Dave Dobbie
Open Air Museum - 1961
Recreated 19th c village of 40 buildings moved from original sites, portraying an Upper Canadian Saint Lawrence River Valley community, furnishings, decorative arts, textiles - library 05409

Morse

Morse Museum, POB 308, Morse, Sask. S0H 3C0 - T: (306) 629-3230, Fax: (306) 629-3230
Local Museum 05410

Mossbank

Mossbank and District Museum, POB 278, Mossbank, Sask. S0H 3G0 - T: (306) 354-2889, E-mail: mossbankmuseum@sk.sympatico.ca. Head: Roy Tollefson
Local Museum 05411

Mount Brydges

Ska-Nah-Doht Iroquoian Village and Museum, 8358 Longwoods Rd, Mount Brydges, Ont. N0L 1W0 - T: (519) 264-2420, Fax: 264-1562, E-mail: lowerthames@odyssey.on.ca, Internet: http://www.lowerthames-conservation.on.ca. Head: Karen Mattila
Open Air Museum - 1973
Education facility of recreated Iroquoian settlement, two archeological sites 05412

Mount Hope

Canadian Warplane Heritage Museum, Hamilton Airport, 9280 Airport Rd, Mount Hope, Ont. L0R 1W0 - T: (905) 679-4183, Fax: (905) 679-4186, E-mail: museum@warplane.com, Internet: http://www.warplane.com
Science&Tech Museum / Military Museum 05413

Mount Uniacke

Uniacke Estate Museum, Mount Uniacke, N.S. B3H 3A6 - T: (902) 866-0032, Fax: (902) 866-2560, Internet: http://museum.gov.ns.ca. Head: Candace Stevenson
Military Museum - 1949
Home of Richard John Uniacke, attorney general of Nova Scotia 1797-1830, with original furnishings 05414

Mundare

Basilian Fathers Museum, 5420 Sawchuth St, Mundare, Alta. T0B 3H0 - T: (780) 764-3887, Fax: (780) 764-3961, E-mail: paulosbm@catholic.org. Head: Paul Chomnycky
Folklore Museum / Religious Arts Museum - 1953
Ukrainian folklore and Eastern rite religious artefacts - archives 05415

Murray Harbour

Log Cabin Museum, Murray Harbour, P.E.I. C0A 1V0 - T: (902) 962-2201. Head: Preston Robertson
Historical Museum 05416

Musgrave Harbour

Fisherman's Museum, 4 Marine Dr, Musgrave Harbour, Nfld. A0G 3J0 - T: (709) 684-2355
Special Museum - 1974
Fishery, ship models, engines, logbooks (1902) containing accounts of local shipwrecks 05417

Musquodoboit Harbour

Musquodoboit Railway Museum, POB 303, Musquodoboit Harbour, N.S. B0J 2L0 - T: (902) 889-2689
Science&Tech Museum 05418

Naicam

Naicam Museum, POB 93, Naicam, Sask. S0K 2Z0 - T: (306) 874-2280, Fax: (306) 874-5444, E-mail: naicam@sk.sympatico.ca, Internet: http://www3.sk.sympatico.ca/naicom
Local Museum 05419

Nain

Piulimatsivik - Nain Museum, POB 247, Nain, Nfld. A0P 1L0 - T: (709) 922-2821
Local Museum 05420

Nakusp

Bonnington Arts Centre, 6th Av W and 4th St N, Nakusp, B.C. V0G 1R0 - T: (250) 265-4234, Fax: (250) 265-3808
Fine Arts Museum 05421

Nakusp Museum, POB 584, Nakusp, B.C. V0G 1R0 - T: (604) 265-4518. Head: Frances Walmsley
Local Museum - 1968
Local history, Indian artifacts - archives 05422

Nanaimo

Bastion, Front St, Nanaimo, B.C. V9R 5S5 - T: (250) 753-1821, Fax: (250) 518-0125, E-mail: ndmuseum@nanaimo.museum.bc.ca. Head: Debbie Trueman
Science&Tech Museum - 1930
Log fortification (1853) containing pioneer, mining and nautical material, ethnography, coins, rifles 05423

Centennial Museum of the Nanaimo Regional General Hospital, 1200 Dufferin Cres, Nanaimo, B.C. V9S 2B7 - T: (250) 755-7637, Fax: (250) 755-7947, E-mail: Lynne.Tourond@cvihr.bc.ca
Historical Museum 05424

Nanaimo Art Gallery and Exhibition Centre, c/o Malaspina College, 900 5 St, Nanaimo, B.C. V9R 5S5 - T: (250) 755-8790, Fax: (250) 755-8725. Head: Jane Cole
Fine Arts Museum 05425

Nanaimo District Museum, 100 Cameron Rd, Nanaimo, B.C. V9R 2X1 - T: (250) 753-1821, Fax: (250) 518-0125, E-mail: ndmuseum@nanaimo.museum.bc.ca, Internet: http://www.nanaimo.museum.bc.ca/ndm. Head: Debbie Trueman
Local Museum - 1967
Local history, coal mining 05426

Nanton

Nanton Lancaster Air Museum, POB 1051, Nanton, Alta. T0L 1R0 - T: (403) 646-2270, Fax: (403) 646-2270, E-mail: nanton@lexicom.ab.ca, Internet: http://www.lexicom.ab.ca/~nanton/. Head: Bob Evans
Science&Tech Museum 05427

Napanee

Alan Macpherson House, 180 Elizabeth St, Napanee, Ont. K7R 3M3 - T: (613) 354-5982, Fax: (613) 354-5285, Internet: http://www.ihorizons.net/macpherson. Head: Marten Lewis
Decorative Arts Museum - 1967
Restored home built in 1826 by Allan Macpherson period furniture and furnishings 05428

Lennox and Addington County Museum and Archives, 97 Thomas St E, Napanee, Ont. K7R 3S9 - T: (613) 354-1005, Fax: (613) 354-3112, E-mail: museum@fox.nstn.ca, Internet: http://fox.nstn.ca/~museum
Local Museum 05429

Naramata

Naramata Museum, POB 95, Naramata, B.C. V0H 1N0 - T: (250) 496-5866. Head: Jean Smith
Local Museum 05430

Neepawa

Beautiful Plains Museum, 80 Hamilton St W, Neepawa, Man. R0J 1H0 - T: (204) 476-3896. Head: Allan Drysdale
Local Museum
Masonic and Eastern Star regalia and hist, military, agricultural and historical exhibits 05431

Margaret Laurence Home, 312 First Av, Neepawa, Man. R0J 1H0 - T: (204) 476-3612, E-mail: mlh@mb.sympatico.ca, Internet: http://www.town.neepawa.mb.ca/mlh
Special Museum 05432

Murray's Museum of History, POB 489, Neepawa, Man. R0J 1H0 - T: (204) 476-2460
Archaeological Museum / Historical Museum - 1972
Archeology - archives 05433

Neilburg

Manitou Pioneer Museum, POB 160, Neilburg, Sask. S0M 2C0
Local Museum 05434

Nelson

Nelson Museum, 402 Anderson St, Nelson, B.C. V1L 3Y3 - T: (250) 3529813, Fax: (250) 3529810, E-mail: nmchin@direct.ca, Internet: http://www.kics.bc.ca/museum. Head: Alan R. Ramsden
Local Museum / Public Gallery - 1957
Indian artifacts, pioneer and explorer material, Doukhobour arts and crafts, geology and mining, 54th Kty Battalion WWI, pleasure-boats, hist of West Kootenay forrest - archives, art gallery 05435

Nepean

Algonquin College Museum, 1385 Woodroffe Av, Nepean, Ont. K2G 1V8 - T: (613) 727-4723, Fax: (613) 727-1759, E-mail: pattilk@algonquincollege.com
Historical Museum 05436

The Log Farm, 670 Cedarview Rd, Nepean, Ont. K2R 1E5 - T: (613) 825-4352, 239-5188
Agriculture Museum 05437

Nepean Museum, 16 Rowley Av, Nepean, Ont. K2G 1L9 - T: (613) 723-7936, Fax: (613) 723-7936. Head: DAn Hoffman
Local Museum 05438

New Denmark

New Denmark Memorial Museum, c/o New Denmark Historical Society, 710 Rte 380 New Denmark, N.B. E7G 2Y6 - T: (506) 553-6464. Head: Sterling Jensen
Local Museum - 1972
Household articles, tools, machinery and documents of the Danish settlers 05439

New Denver

Sandon Museum, POB 52, New Denver, B.C. V0G 1S0 - Fax: (250) 358-2607
Science&Tech Museum 05440

Silvery Slocan Museum, 202 Main St, New Denver, B.C. V0G 1S0 - T: (250) 358-2201, Fax: (250) 358-7251
Science&Tech Museum 05441

New Glasgow

Carmicheal-Stewart House, 100 Churchill Dr, New Glasgow, N.S. B2H 1V2 - T: (902) 752-5583
Historical Museum 05442

MacPherson's Mill and Farm Homestead, POB 403, New Glasgow, N.S. B2H 5E5 - T: (902) 752-7828. Head: Dr. H. Locke
Agriculture Museum / Science&Tech Museum 05443

Pictou County Historical Museum, 86 Temperance St, New Glasgow, N.S. B2H 3A7 - T: (902) 752-5583. Head: Graham Holman
Local Museum - 1964
Agricultural equipment, household utensils, pictures and documents relating to the area, early native glassware 05444

New Richmond

Gaspesian British Heritage Village, 351 Blvd Perron W, New Richmond, P.Q. G0C 2B0 - T: (418) 392-4487, Fax: (418) 392-5907, E-mail: gbhc@globetrotter.net. Head: J. Robert Bradbury
Historical Museum / Open Air Museum / Agriculture Museum 05445

New Ross

Ross Farm Museum, Rte 12, New Ross, N.S. B0J 2M0 - T: (902) 689-2210, Fax: (902) 689-2264. Head: A. Hiltz
Agriculture Museum - 1970
Old agricultural methods and implements, rural crafts, plow coll 05446

New Westminster

Amelia Douglas Gallery, POB 2503, New Westminster, B.C. V3L 5B2 - T: (604) 527-5528
Fine Arts Museum 05447

Canadian Lacrosse Hall of Fame, 302 Royal Av, New Westminster, B.C. V3L 1H7 - T: (604) 527-4640, Fax: (604) 527-4641, E-mail: allan@lacrosse.ca. Head: Allan Blair
Special Museum 05448

Irving House Historic Centre and New Westminster Museum, 302 Royal Av, New Westminster, B.C. V3L 1H7 - T: (604) 527-4640, Fax: (604) 527-4641, E-mail: amiller@city.new-westminster.bc.ca, Internet: http://www.city.new-westminster.bc.ca.cityhall.museam
Local Museum - 1950/1964
Indian artifacts, general history of the town, furnished pioneer home - archives 05449

Museum of The Royal Westminster Regiment Historical Society, The Armoury, 530 Queens Av, New Westminster, B.C. V3L 1K3 - T: (604) 526-5116, Fax: (604) 666-4042. Head: B.V. Morgan
Military Museum - 1973
Military artifacts and memorabilia of The Royal Westminster Regiment and its antecedents (1863) 05450

Samson V Maritime Museum, c/o Royal Agricultural and Industrial Society of BC, 1005 Columbia St, Ste 105, New Westminster, B.C. V3M 6H5 - T: (604) 522-6894, Fax: (604) 522-6094
Historical Museum 05451

Newmarket

Elman W. Campbell Museum, 134 Main St S, Newmarket, Ont. L3Y 3Y7 - T: (905) 953-5314, Fax: (905) 898-2083, E-mail: elmanmuseum@rogers.com. Head: Elizabeth Sinyard
Local Museum 05452

Niagara Falls

Daredevil Hall of Fame, 5651 River Rd, Niagara Falls, Ont. L2E 6V8 - T: (905) 356-2151, Fax: (905) 356-2151, E-mail: nfmuseum@aol.com. Head: Jacob Sherman
Local Museum / Natural History Museum 05453

Guinness Museum of World Records, 4943 Clifton Hill, Niagara Falls, Ont. L2G 3N5 - T: (905) 356-2299
Special Museum 05454

Laura Secord Homestead, 7555 Montrose Rd, Niagara Falls, Ont. L2H 2E9
Special Museum 05455

Louis Tussaud's Waxworks Museum, 4915 Clifton Hill, Niagara Falls, Ont. L2G 3N5 - T: (905) 374-6601, Fax: (905) 374-7345, E-mail: nfalls@ripleys.com
Special Museum 05456

Lundy's Lane Historical Museum, 5810 Ferry St, Niagara Falls, Ont. L2G 1S9 - T: (905) 358-5082, Fax: (905) 358-0920, E-mail: llmuseum@city.niagara-falls.on.ca, Internet: http://www.lundyslanemuseum.com
Local Museum - 1961
Pioneer utensils and tools, Indian and military artifacts, children's toys 05457

McFarland House, Niagara Parkway, Niagara Falls, mail addr: POB 150, Niagara Falls, Ont. L2E 6T2 - T: (905) 371-0254, Fax: (905) 354-6041, E-mail: npinfo@niagaraparks.com, Internet: http://www.niagaraparks.com. Head: John Kernhan
Historical Museum
War of 1812, furnishings 05458

Movieland Wax Museum, 4950 Clifton Hill, Niagara Falls, Ont. L2G 3N4 - T: (905) 358-3061, Fax: (905) 358-9456, E-mail: info@cliftonhill.com, Internet: http://www.cliftonhill.com
Special Museum 05459

Niagara Falls Art Gallery - Kurlek Collection, 8058 Oakwood Dr, RR 2, Niagara Falls, Ont. L2E 6S5 - T: (905) 356-1514. Head: Brian Smylski
Fine Arts Museum 05460

Oak Hall, 7400 Portage Rd, Niagara Falls, Ont. L2E 6T2 - T: (905) 356-2241, Fax: (905) 354-6041, E-mail: npinfo@niagaraparks.com, Internet: http://www.niagaraparks.com
Fine Arts Museum / Decorative Arts Museum - 1964
Home and furniture of Sir Harry Oakes, Canadian paintings 05461

Old Fort Erie, POB 150, Niagara Falls, Ont. L2E 6T2 - T: (905) 871-0540
Military Museum 05462

Ripley's Believe It or Not Museum, 4960 Clifton Hill, Niagara Falls, Ont. L2G 3N4 - T: (905) 356-2238, Fax: (905) 374-7545, E-mail: nfalls@ripleys.com, Internet: http://www.ripleys.com. Head: Tim Parker
Fine Arts Museum
Cartoons, oddities, curiosities 05463

Willoughby Historical Museum, 9935 Niagara Pkwy, Niagara Falls, Ont. L2E 6S6 - T: (905) 295-4036, Fax: (905) 295-4036, E-mail: willomus@becon.org. Head: Emma Chambers
Local Museum 05464

Niagara-on-the-Lake

Fort George, POB 787, Niagara-on-the-Lake, Ont. L0S 1J0 - T: (905) 468-4257, Fax: (905) 468-4638
Military Museum - 1950
Reconstructed fort built in 1799, furnishings of the period from 1797 to 1812, relics of the War of 1812 05465

Niagara Apothecary, c/o Ontario College of Pharmacists, 5 Queens St, Niagara-on-the-Lake, Ont. L0S 1J0 - T: (416) 962-4861, Fax: (416) 703-3118, E-mail: awlosek@ocpharma.com, Internet: http://www.ocpharma.com. Head: Connie Campbell
Special Museum - 1971
Restored pharmacy (1866), original glass and ceramic apothecary ware 05466

Niagara Fire Museum, c/o Fire Department, POB 498, Niagara-on-the-Lake, Ont. L0S 1J0 - T: (905) 468-7279
Science&Tech Museum - 1972
Exhibits of local firefighting equipment dating back 140 years 05467

Niagara Historical Museum, 43 Castlereagh St, Niagara-on-the-Lake, Ont. L0S 1J0 - T: (905) 468-3912, Fax: (905) 468-1728, E-mail: nhs@niagara.com, Internet: http://www.niagara.com/~nhs. Head: Clark Bernat
Local Museum 05468

Perfume Museum, 393 York Rd, Niagara-on-the-Lake, Ont. L0S 1J0 - T: (905) 685-6666, Fax: (905) 984-8226, E-mail: jerry@perfumefactory.ca, Internet: http://www.perfumefactory.ca. Head: Jerry Youssoufian
Special Museum
19th c perfumery techniques, labels coll, contemporary perfumery, art objects 05469

River Brink, The Samuel E. Weir Collection, 116 Queenston St, Niagara-on-the-Lake, Ont. L0S 1J0 - T: (905) 262-4510, Fax: (905) 262-4477, E-mail: weirlib@becon.org, Internet: http://www.riverbrink.org. Head: Mary Albers
Fine Arts Museum 05470

Nicolet

Musée des Religions, 900 Blvd Louis-Fréchette, Nicolet, P.Q. J3T 1V5 - T: (819) 293-6148, Fax: (819) 293-4161, E-mail: musee@museedesreligions.qc.ca, Internet: http://www.museedesreligions.qc.ca. Head: Michèle Paradis
Religious Arts Museum - 1831 05471

Nipawin

Nipawin and District Living Forestry Museum, Second Av W and old Hwy 35 E, Nipawin, Sask. S0E 1E0 - T: (306) 862-9299, Fax: (306) 862-4717
Local Museum - 1972
Historical exhibits, especially of regional lumbering industries 05472

Nipigon

Nipigon Museum, POB 208, Nipigon, Ont. P0T 2J0 - T: (807) 887-2727. Head: Roland Choiselat
Local Museum 05473

Nipissing

Nipissing Township Museum, Nipissing, Ont. P0H 1W0 - T: (705) 724-2938, Fax: (705) 724-5385. Head: Joe Steele
Local Museum 05474

Nokomis

Nokomis and District Museum, POB 56, Nokomis, Sask. S0G 3R0 - T: (306) 528-2979. Head: Karen Lee
Local Museum 05475

Norman Wells

Colville Lake Museum, Norman Wells, N.T. X0E 1L0 - T: (867) 709-2500, Fax: (867) 709-2500. Head: Bern Will Brown
Public Gallery / Local Museum 05476

Norman Wells Historical Centre, POB 56, Norman Wells, N.T. X0E 0V0 - T: (867) 587-2415, Fax: (867) 587-2469
Local Museum 05477

North Battleford

Allen Sapp Gallery, 1 Railway Av E, North Battleford, Sask. S9A 2Y6 - T: (306) 445-1760, Fax: (306) 445-0411, E-mail: sapp@allyssa.com, Internet: http://www.allensapp.com. Head: Dean Bauche
Fine Arts Museum 05478

Chapel Gallery, 891 99th St, North Battleford, Sask. S9A 2Y6 - T: (306) 445-1757, 445-1760, Fax: (306) 445-1009, E-mail: thechapel_ca@yahoo.ca
Fine Arts Museum - 1973
Paintings by local artists 05479

Heritage Farm & Village, Western Development Museum, Junction of Hwys 16 and 40, North Battleford, Sask. S9A 2Y1 - T: (306) 445-8033, Fax: (306) 445-7211, E-mail: wdm.nb@sk.sympatico.ca, Internet: http://www.wdmuseum.sk.ca. Head: David Klatt
Agriculture Museum / Local Museum - 1949
Pioneer village displaying household items and agricultural machinery 05480

North Battleford Art Centre → Chapel Gallery

Saskatchewan Wildlife Federation Museum, POB 35, North Battleford, Sask. S9A 2X6
Natural History Museum 05481

North Bay

Dionne Homestead Museum, POB 747, North Bay, Ont. P1B 8J8 - T: (705) 472-8480, Fax: (704) 472-8027. Head: Sharon Clark-Bedard
Historical Museum 05482

North Bay and Area Museum, 171 Mian St W, North Bay, Ont. P1B 8J5 - T: (705) 476-2323. Head: Pamela Handley
Local Museum 05483

White Water Gallery, 114 Main St E, North Bay, Ont. P1B 1A8 - T: (705) 476-2444, Fax: (705) 476-9243. Head: Claire Powers
Fine Arts Museum 05484

W.K.P. Kennedy Gallery, 150 Main St E, North Bay, Ont. P1B 1A8 - T: (705) 474-1944, Fax: (705) 474-8431, E-mail: geden@capitolcentre.ca, Internet: http://capitolcentre.efni.com. Head: Dennis Geden
Fine Arts Museum / Public Gallery 05485

North Buxton

Buxton Museum, c/o Raleigh Township Centennial Museum, 21975 A.D. Shadd Rd, North Buxton, Ont. N0P 1Y0 - T: (519) 352-4799, Fax: (519) 352-8561, E-mail: buxton@ciaccess.com, Internet: http://www.buxtonmuseum.com. Head: Shannon Prince
Local Museum
Local and Black history, underground railway 05486

North East Margaree

Margaree Salmon Museum, North East Margaree, N.S. B0E 2H0 - T: (902) 248-2848. Head: Brooks Hart
Special Museum - 1965
Historic fishing tackles and books an angling 05487

Museum of Cape Breton Heritage, North East Margaree, N.S. B0E 2H0 - T: (902) 248-2551
Decorative Arts Museum - 1972
Cape Breton crafts, china and glass, locally-made furniture, hand-hooked rugs 05488

North Vancouver

Bernadette's Galleries, 1321 Pemberton Av, North Vancouver, B.C. V7P 2R6 - T: (604) 980-7216, Fax: (604) 983-9978, E-mail: bernadette@xl.ca
Fine Arts Museum 05489

Lynn Canyon Ecology Centre, 3663 Park Rd, North Vancouver, B.C. V7J 3G3 - T: (604) 981-3103, Fax: (604) 981-3154
Natural History Museum - 1971
Ecological education for all age groups, ecological displays on forests, wildlife, etc and human impact 05490

North Vancouver Museum, 209 W Fourth St, North Vancouver, B.C. V7M 1H8 - T: (604) 987-5618, Fax: (604) 987-5609, E-mail: info@northvan.museum.bc.ca, Internet: http://www.district.north-van.bc.ca/nvma. Head: R.R. Inglis
Local Museum - 1976
Shipbuilding, logging, waterfront industry, North Vancouver community - archives 05491

Pacific Great Eastern Station, c/o North Vancouver Museum, Foot of Londsdale Av, North Vancouver, B.C. V7M 1H8 - T: (604) 987-5618, Fax: (604) 987-5609, E-mail: pge@northvan.museum.bc.ca, Internet: http://www.dnv.org/nvma. Head: Robin Inglis
Science&Tech Museum 05492

Presentation House Gallery, 333 Chesterfield Av, North Vancouver, B.C. V7M 3G9 - T: (604) 986-1351, Fax: (604) 986-5380, E-mail: -presentationhousegall@telus.net, Internet: http://www.presentationhousegall.com. Head: Bill Jeffries
Fine Arts Museum 05493

Seymour Art Gallery, 4360 Gallant Av, North Vancouver, B.C. V7G 1L2 - T: (604) 924-1378, Fax: (604) 924-3786, E-mail: seymourg@vcn.bc.ca, Internet: http://www.deepcove.bc.com/SeymourArtGallery. Head: Carole Badgley
Public Gallery 05494

North York

Black Creek Pioneer Village, 1000 Murray Ross Pkwy, North York, Ont. M3J 2P3 - T: (416) 736-1733, Fax: (416) 661-6610, E-mail: bcpuinfo@trca.on.ca, Internet: http://www.trca.on.ca. Head: Marty Brent
Open Air Museum - 1960
Canadian folklore, agriculture, furniture, textiles, blacksmith tools, toys and dolls, handicrafts, restored Ontario village (1793-1867) 05495

Gibson House, 5172 Yonge St, North York, Ont. M2N 5P6 - T: (416) 395-7432, Fax: (416) 395-7442. Head: Karen Edwards
Local Museum - 1971
Local hist 05496

Glendon Gallery, Glendon College, York University, 2275 Bayview Av, North York, Ont. M4N 3M6 - T: (416) 487-6721, Fax: (416) 487-6779, E-mail: gallery@glendon.yorku.ca, Internet: http://www.glendon.yorku.ca
Fine Arts Museum / University Museum 05497

Irving E. and Ray Kanner Heritage Museum, 3560 Bathurst St, North York, Ont. M6A 2E1 - T: (416) 789-2500, Fax: (416) 785-2378
Special Museum 05498

Museum of Contemporary Canadian Art, 5040 Yonge St, North York, Ont. M2N 6R8 - T: (416) 395-0067, Fax: (416) 395-7598, E-mail: beyre@city.north-york.on.ca, Internet: http://www.mocca.com. Head: Glen E. Cumming
Fine Arts Museum 05499

Norwich

Norwich and District Museum, RR 3, Norwich, Ont. N0J 1P0 - T: (519) 863-3101
Religious Arts Museum - 1969
Former Quaker meeting house, displays portraying pioneer life and Quaker culture, farm implements and machinery 05500

Notre-Dame-de-Lourdes

Museum Dom Benoît, Notre-Dame-de-Lourdes, Man. R0G 1M0 - T: (204) 248-2372
Religious Arts Museum 05501

Oakville

Canadian Golf Hall of Fame, 1333 Dorval Dr, Oakville, Ont. L6J 4Z3 - T: (905) 849-9700, Fax: (905) 844-3366, E-mail: cghf@cghf.org, Internet: http://www.cghf.org. Head: Karen E. Hewson
Special Museum 05502

Oakville Galleries, Centennial, 120 Navy St, Oakville, Ont. L6J 2Z4, mail addr: 1306 Lakeshore Rd E, Oakville, Ont. L6J 1L6 - T: (905) 844-4402, Fax: (905) 844-7968, E-mail: oakgalleries@idirect.com, Internet: http://www.oakville-galleries.com. Head: Francine Périnet
Fine Arts Museum - 1967
Canadian contemporary art 05503

Oakville Galleries, Gairloch, 1306 Lakeshore Rd E, Oakville, Ont. L6J 1L6 - T: (905) 844-4402, Fax: (905) 844-7968, E-mail: oakgalleries@idirect.com, Internet: http://www.oakville-galleries.com. Head: Francine Périnet
Fine Arts Museum - 1967
Canadian contemporary art 05504

Oakville Museum at Erchless Estate, 8 Navy St, Oakville, Ont. L6J 2Y5 - T: (905) 338-4400, Fax: (905) 815-5973, E-mail: iknight@town.oakville.on.ca, Internet: http://www.oakvillemuseum.com. Head: Irene Knight
Local Museum / Historic Site 05505

Odanak

Musée des Abénakis, Réserve Indienne des Abénakis, 108 Waban-Aki, Odanak, P.Q. J0G 1H0 - T: (514) 568-2600, Fax: (514) 568-5959, E-mail: abenaki@enter-net.com. Head: Nicole O'Bomsawin
Ethnology Museum - 1962
Sculpture portraiting the culture of the Abénakis, items made by other Canadian Indian tribes, religious objects made by Québec goldsmiths, baskets 05506

Odessa

Historic Babcock Mill, 100 Bridge St, Odessa, Ont. K0H 2H0 - T: (613) 389-8314, Fax: (613) 634-4045, E-mail: pbeyer@loyalist-township.on.ca, Internet: http://www.loyalist-township.on.ca. Head: Patrick Beyer
Science&Tech Museum 05507

Ohsweken

Chiefswood Museum, POB 5000, Ohsweken, Ont. N0A 1M0 - T: (519) 752-5005, Fax: (519) 752-9578. Head: Paula Whitlow
Special Museum 05508

Two Turtle Iroquois Fine Art Gallery, RR1, Ohsweken, Ont. N0A 1M0 - T: (519) 751-2774, E-mail: twoturtl@wchat.on.ca, Internet: http://wchat.on.ca/tom/2turtle.htm
Fine Arts Museum 05509

Oil Springs

Oil Museum of Canada, 22 Miles SE Sarnia, RR 2, Oil Springs, Ont. N0N 1P0 - T: (519) 834-2840, Fax: (519) 834-2840, E-mail: OMCCHIN@ebtech.net
Special Museum - 1960
Hist of the discovery and development of oil in the area, life in an oil town of the 1860's, working wells with antique equipment - library, archives 05510

Okanagan

Lake Country Museum, 11255 Okanagan Centre Rd, Okanagan, B.C. V4V 2J7
Local Museum 05511

Okanagan Falls

Bassett House Museum, 1145 Main St, Okanagan Falls, B.C. V0H 1R0 - T: (250) 497-5445, Fax: (250) 497-7047, Internet: http://www.mypageuniserve-ofhms.com. Head: Eleanor Walker
Special Museum 05512

Old Perlican

Howard House of Artifacts, POB 100, Old Perlican, Nfld. A0A 3G0 - T: (709) 587-2172. Head: Jerome Howard
Local Museum
History of Newfoundland, 100 years of fishing tradition 05513

Olds

Mountain View Museum, 5038 50th St, mail addr: POB 3882, Olds, Alta. T4H 1P6 - T: (403) 556-8464, E-mail: ohschin@telusplanet.net, Internet: http://www.telusplanet.net.public/ohschin. Head: Darlene McMullen
Historical Museum 05514

O'Leary

Prince Edward Island Potato Museum, 1 Heritage Ln, O'Leary, P.E.I. C0B 1V0 - T: (902) 859-2039, Fax: (902) 859-3364, E-mail: oleary.guardian@pei.sympatico.ca, Internet: http://www.peipotatomuseum.com
Agriculture Museum 05515

West Point Lighthouse Museum, RR2, O'Leary, P.E.I. C0B 1V0 - T: (902) 859-3605, Fax: (902) 859-3117
Science&Tech Museum 05516

Oliver

Vaseaux Lake Galleries, Hwy 97 N, RR2, Oliver, B.C. V0H 1T0 - T: (250) 498-3522, Fax: (250) 498-3546
Fine Arts Museum 05517

Orangedale

Orangedale Railway Museum, Orangedale, N.S. B0E 2K0 - T: (902) 756-3384, Fax: (902) 756-2547
Science&Tech Museum 05518

Orillia

Orillia Museum of Art and History, 30 Peter St S, Orillia, Ont. L3V 5A9 - T: (705) 326-2159, Fax: (705) 326-7828, E-mail: sirsam@bconnex.net. Head: C. Gay Guthrie
Fine Arts Museum / Local Museum 05519

Stephen Leacock Museum, Old Brewery Bay, Orillia, Ont. L3V 6K5, mail addr: POB 625, Orillia, Ont. L3V 6K5 - T: (705) 329-1908, Fax: (705) 326-5578, E-mail: leacock@mail.transdata.ca, Internet: http://www.transdata.ca/leacock. Head: Craig Metcalf
Special Museum - 1958
Furniture belonging to Stephen Leacock, his manuscripts, letters, and personal library - library, archives 05520

Oromocto

Canadian Force Base Gagetown Military Museum, Bldg A-5, Oromocto, N.B. E2V 4J5, mail addr: POB 17000 Station Forces, Oromocto, N.B. E2V 4J5 - T: (506) 422-1304, Fax: (506) 422-1304, E-mail: museum_gagetown@brunnet.net, Internet: http://www.brunnet.net/museum_gagetown. Head: M.L. Richard
Military Museum - 1973
Weapons, uniforms, artifacts, memorabilia, vehicles, documents - archive 05521

Orono

Clarke Museum, POB 152, Orono, Ont. L0B 1M0 - T: (905) 983-9243, E-mail: cma-chin@durham.net.ca. Head: Mark Jackman
Local Museum 05522

Orwell

Orwell Corner Historic Village, Prince Edward Island Museum and Heritage Foundation, Vernon RR 2, Orwell, P.E.I. C0A 2E0 - T: (902) 651-8510, Fax: (902) 368-6608, E-mail: orwellcorner@gov.pe.ca, Internet: http://www.orwellcorner.isn.net. Head: Wendell Boyle
Open Air Museum / Agriculture Museum - 1973
Restored rural crossroads, buildings of a late 19th c rural community 05523

Oshawa

Canadian Automotive Museum, 99 Simcoe St S, Oshawa, Ont. L1H 4G7 - T: (905) 576-1222, Fax: (905) 576-1223. Head: J.F. Innes, I. Bathe
Science&Tech Museum - 1962
Over 60 antique cars and trucks on display, related memorabilia - library, archives 05524

Oshawa Sydenham Museum, Lakeview Park, 7 Henry St, Oshawa, Ont. L1H 7V5 - T: (905) 436-7624. Head: Laura Suchan
Local Museum 05525

Robert McLaughlin Gallery, Civic Centre, Oshawa, Ont. L1H 3Z3 - T: (905) 576-3000, Fax: (905) 576-9774, E-mail: communications@rmg.on.ca, Internet: http://www.rmg.on.ca. Head: David Avrandt
Fine Arts Museum - 1967
Contemporary Canadian coll, works of the "Painters Eleven", Japanese wood-block prints, drawings, sculpture - library 05526

Osler

Osler Historical Museum, POB 54, Osler, Sask. S0K 3A0 - T: (306) 239-2155
Local Museum 05527

Osoyoos

Osoyoos Art Gallery, 89th and Main St, Osoyoos, B.C. V0H 1V0 - T: (250) 495-2800
Fine Arts Museum 05528

Osoyoos Museum, Main St, Community Park 2, Osoyoos, B.C. V0H 1V0, mail addr: POB 791, Osoyoos, B.C. V0H 1V0 - T: (250) 495-2582, Fax: (250) 495-6723. Head: Doris McDonald
Local Museum - 1963
Reconstructed log cabin furnished in pioneer style, Indian artifacts and handicrafts 05529

Ottawa

Billings Estate Museum, 2100 Cabot St, Ottawa, Ont. K1H 6K1 - T: (613) 247-4830, Fax: (613) 247-4832, E-mail: billingsestatemuseum@city.ottawa.on.ca
Historical Museum 05530

Bytown Historical Museum, Driveway, near Junction of Rideau Canal and Ottawa River, Ottawa, Ont. K1P 5P6, mail addr: POB 523, Station B, Ottawa, Ont. K1P 5P6 - T: (613) 234-4570, Fax: (613) 234-4846, E-mail: ah294@freenet.carleton.ca. Head: Lana Shaw
Historical Museum - 1917
Artifacts relating to Colonel By, the Rideau Canal, Ottawa, and the vicinity 05531

Cameron Highlanders of Ottawa Regimental Museum, The Drill Hall, Cartier Sq, Ottawa, Ont. K1A 0K2 - T: (613) 990-3507, Fax: (613) 825-7020, E-mail: pyms.min.reg@sympatico.ca, Internet: http://www.cameronsottawa.net. Head: Peter Pym-Hember
Military Museum 05532

Canada Agriculture Museum, Cnr Prince of wales and Experimental Farm Dr, Ottawa, mail addr: POB 9724, Stn T, Ottawa, Ont. K1G 5A3 - T: (613) 991-3044, Fax: (613) 947-2374, E-mail: ttarasoff@nmstc.ca, Internet: http://www.agriculture.nmstc.ca. Head: Michelle Dondo-Tardiff
Agriculture Museum - 1983
National agricultural coll, animal husbandry, agricultural technology, food production 05533

Canada Aviation Museum, Aviation and Rockcliffe Pwy S, Ottawa, Ont. K1G 5A3, mail addr: POB 9724, Stn T, Ottawa, Ont. K1G 5A3 - T: (613) 993-2010, Fax: (613) 990-3655, E-mail: aviation@mus.ca, Internet: http://www.aviation.mus.ca. Head: Christopher J. Terry
Science&Tech Museum - 1960
Approx. 120 aircraft (esp from the World War I and II and from the bush flying era of the 1920s to the 1950s), 360 aircraft engines, several thousand associated aviation artifacts and 160,000 aviation images, hist of aviation - library, archives 05534

Canada Science and Technology Museum, 1867 Saint Laurent Blvd, Ottawa, Ont. K1G 5A3 - T: (613) 991-3044, Fax: (613) 990-3654, E-mail: scitech@nmstc.ca, Internet: http://www.science-tech.nmstc.ca. Head: Christopher J. Terry
Agriculture Museum / Science&Tech Museum - 1967
National exhibits in the physical sciences and all technologies, agriculture, astronomy, industry, space, transportation, communication, energy etc - library, observatory 05535

Canadian Museum of Contemporary Photography, National Gallery of Canada, 1 Rideau Canal, Ottawa, Ont. K1N 9N6 - T: (613) 990-8257, Fax: (613) 990-6542, E-mail: cmcp@gallery.ca, Internet: http://www.cmcp.gallery.ca. Head: Martha Hanna
Fine Arts Museum - 1967
Canadian photography as art form and form of social documentation 05536

Canadian Museum of Nature, Victoria Memorial Museum Bldg, McLeod and Metcalfe Sts, Ottawa, Ont. K1P 6P4, mail addr: POB 3443, Station D, Ottawa, Ont. - T: (613) 566-4700, Fax: (613) 364-4021, E-mail: questions@mus-nature.ca, Internet: http://www.nature.ca. Head: Joanne DiCosimo
Natural History Museum - 1842
Vascular plants, lichens, algae, bryophytes, fossil plants, fungi and pollen, minerals, gems, vertebrate fossils, annelids, molluscs, crustaceans, insects, parasites, faunal assemblage, general invertebrates, fish, general invertenrates, fish, amphibians, reptiles, birds, mammals - library, archives 05537

Canadian Scouting Museum, Boy Scouts of Canada National Headquarters, 1345 Baseline Rd, Ottawa, Ont. K2C 3G7 - T: (613) 224-5131, Fax: 224-3571, E-mail: bhallett@scouts.ca. Head: Bob Hallett
Special Museum - 1953
Memorabilia of the founder of Scouting, Lord Baden-Powell, Canadian Scouting items, such as badges, equipment, and books 05538

Canadian Ski Museum, 1960 Scott St, Ste 200, Ottawa, Ont. K1Z 8L8 - T: (613) 722-3584
Special Museum 05539

Canadian War Museum, 330 Sussex Dr, Ottawa, Ont. K1A 0M8 - T: (819) 776-8600, Fax: (819) 776-8623, Internet: http://www.warmuseum.ca. Head: Joe Geurts
Military Museum - 1880
Weapons, uniforms, photographs, war art, and medals, peacekeeping - library 05540

Canadian Wildlife and Wilderness Art Museum, POB 98, Stn B, Ottawa, Ont. K1P 6C3 - T: (613) 237-1581, Fax: (613) 237-1581, E-mail: cawa@magma.ca, Internet: http://www.magma.ca/cawa. Head: Gary Slimon
Fine Arts Museum 05541

Carleton University Art Gallery, Saint Patrick's Bldg, 1125 Colonel By Dr, Ottawa, Ont. K1S 5B6 - T: (613) 520-2120, Fax: (613) 520-4409, E-mail: mbell@ccs.carleton.ca, Internet: http://www.carleton.ca/gallery. Head: Michael Bell
Fine Arts Museum / University Museum 05542

Currency Museum of the Bank of Canada, 245 Sparks St, Ottawa, Ont. K1A 0G9 - T: (613) 782-8914, Fax: (613) 782-7761, E-mail: museum-musee@bankofcanada.ca, Internet: http://www.currencymuseum.ca. Head: Shirley Betts
Special Museum 05543

Gallery 101, 236 Nepean St, Ottawa, Ont. K2P 0B8 - T: (613) 230-2799, Fax: (613) 230-3253, E-mail: oneoone@web.net, Internet: http://www.gallery101.org. Head: François Dion
Fine Arts Museum 05544

Governor General's Foot Guards Regimental Museum, Drill Hall, Cartier Sq, Ottawa, Ont. K1A 0K2 - T: (613) 990-0620, E-mail: elane@storm.ca. Head: Martin Lane
Military Museum - 1955
Artifacts of regimental interest over the past 125 years, located in the Drill Hall (1879), weapons, uniforms, medals, war souvenirs 05545

Laurier House, 335 Laurier Av E, Ottawa, Ont. K1N 6R4 - T: (613) 992-8142, Fax: (613) 992-9233, E-mail: bernie_roche@pch.gc.ca. Head: Doug Stewart
Local Museum - 1951
House built in 1878, the residence of two Canadian Prime Ministers, furnishings, books, paintings, manuscripts - library 05546

Mackenzie King Estate, 40 Elgin St, Ste 202, Ottawa, Ont. K1P 1C7 - T: (819) 827-6026, Fax: (819) 827-3337, E-mail: dmessier@ncc.ccn.ca, Internet: http://www.capcan.ca
Historical Museum 05547

National Aviation Museum → Canada Aviation Museum

National Gallery of Canada, 380 Sussex Dr, Ottawa, Ont. K1N 9N4 - T: (613) 990-1985, Fax: (613) 993-4385, E-mail: info@gallery.ca, Internet: http://national.gallery.ca. Head: Pierre Théberge
Fine Arts Museum - 1880
Old Masters - Italian, Dutch, French, Flemish, and German, modern European and American paintings and sculptures, medieval art, Canadian art from the 18th c to the present, decorative arts - library 05548

SAW Gallery, 67 Nicholas St, Ottawa, Ont. K1N 7B9 - T: (613) 236-6181, Fax: (613) 564-4428, E-mail: saw@magi.com, Internet: http://www.artengine.ca/saw. Head: Marcus Milller
Fine Arts Museum 05549

Temple de la Renommée Olympique du Canada (Canadian Olympic Hall of Fame), c/o Canadian Olympic Association, 85 Albert St, Ste 1400, Ottawa, K1P 6A4 - T: (613) 244-8181, Fax: (613) 244-0169, E-mail: sholloway@ottawa.coa.ca, Internet: http://www.coa.ca. Head: Sue Holloway
Special Museum 05550

Outaouais

Axe Néo-7 Art Contemporain, 205 Rue Montcalm, Outaouais, P.Q. J8Y 3B7 - T: (819) 771-2122, Fax: (819) 771-0696, E-mail: axeneo7@axeneo7.qc.ca, Internet: http://www.axeneo7.qc.ca
Fine Arts Museum 05551

Centre d'Exposition Art-Image, 855 Blvd de la Gappe, Outaouais, P.Q. J8T 8H9 - T: (819) 243-2325, Fax: (819) 243-2527, E-mail: artimage@ville.gatineau.qc.ca, Internet: http://www.ville.gatineau.qc.ca/artimage
Public Gallery 05552

Galerie Montcalm, Maison du Citoyen, 25 Rue Laurier, Outaouais, P.Q. J8X 4C8 - T: (819) 595-7488, Fax: (819) 595-7425, E-mail: galeriemontcalm@ville.hull.qc.ca, Internet: http://www.wille.hull.qc.ca. Head: Dominique Laurent
Fine Arts Museum 05553

Musée Canadien de la Poste (Canadian Postal Museum), 100 Rue Laurier, Outaouais, P.Q. J8X 4H2 - T: (819) 776-8200, Fax: (819) 776-7062, Internet: http://www.civilisations.ca. Head: Francine Brousseau
Special Museum - 1974
Postal communications, post office equipment, writing tools, artworks, philatelic colls 05554

Musée Canadien des Civilisations, 100 Rue Laurier, Outaouais, P.Q. J8X 4H2 - T: (819) 776-7000, Fax: (819) 776-8300, Internet: http://www.civilization.ca. Head: Victor Rabinovitch, Sylvie Morel, Stephen Inglis, Joe Geurts
Ethnology Museum / Folklore Museum / Archaeological Museum - 1967
Folkculture, archaeology, ethnology 05555

Outlook

Outlook and District Heritage Museum and Gallery, 100 Railway Av, Outlook, Sask. S0L 2N0 - T: (306) 867-8285
Local Museum / Fine Arts Museum 05556

Owen Sound

Billy Bishop Heritage Museum, 948 3rd Av W, Owen Sound, Ont. N4K 4P6 - T: (519) 371-0031, Fax: (519) 371-5310, E-mail: info@billy-bishop.org, Internet: http://www.billbishop.org
Special Museum / Military Museum 05557

County of Grey-Owen Sound Museum, 975 Sixth St E, Owen Sound, Ont. N4K 1G9 - T: (519) 376-3690, Fax: (519) 376-7970, E-mail: museum@greycounty.on.ca, Internet: http://www.greycounty.on.ca. Head: A. Wayne Landen
Local Museum - 1967
Ojibway Indian and emigrant European culture artifacts, log cabins, blacksmith shop - library 05558

Owen Sound Marine-Rail Museum, 1165 First Av W, Owen Sound, Ont. N4K 4K8 - T: (519) 371-3333, Fax: (519) 371-8628, E-mail: marinerail@bmts.com, Internet: http://www.bmts.com/~marinerail
Science&Tech Museum 05559

Tom Thomson Memorial Art Gallery, 840 First Av W, Owen Sound, Ont. N4K 4K4 - T: (519) 376-1932, Fax: (519) 376-3037, E-mail: ttmag@city.owen-sound.on.ca, Internet: http://www.tomthomson.org
Public Gallery - 1967
Paintings and drawings by Tom Thomson, memorabilia of his life, works of the 'Group of Seven' and their contemporaries, contemporary Canadian artists, fine crafts - library 05560

Oxbow

Ralph Allen Memorial Museum, 802 Railway Av, Oxbow, Sask. S0C 2B0 - T: (306) 483-5082, E-mail: m.bartolf@sk.sympatico.ca. Head: M. Bartolf
Local Museum - 1973
Oil field and railway displays, pioneer and Indian artifacts, early pictures of the district 05561

Oyen

Crossroads Museum, First Av, Oyen, Alta. T0J 2J0 - T: (403) 664-3850. Head: Nellie Eaton
Local Museum - 1973
Local history, farm machinery, settler's effects, restored prairie home 05562

Pangnirtung

Sipalaseequtt Museum, Angmarlik Visitor Centre, Pangnirtung, N.T. X0A 0R0 - T: (867) 473-8737, Fax: (867) 473-8685
Local Museum 05563

Parksville

Craig Heritage Park Museum, Franklin Gull Rd and Island Hwy, Parksville, B.C. V9P 2H4, mail addr: POB 1452, Parksville, B.C. V0R 2S0 - T: (250) 248-6966, E-mail: dbghs@island.net. Head: Trevor Batchelor
Local Museum
Parksville and Nanoose artefacts - archives 05564

Parrsboro

Fundy Geological Museum, 162 Two Islands Rd, Parrsboro, N.S. B0M 1S0 - T: (902) 254-3814, Fax: (902) 254-3666, E-mail: fundyg@ns.sympatico.ca, Internet: http://www.fundygeomuseum.com. Head: Kenneth Adams
Natural History Museum - 1993
Lower Carboniferous fossils, Upper Carboniferous plant and animal fossils, Triassic - Jurassic fossils, prosauropod material, minerals, ores, agate, jewelry, amethyst, zeolites - lab, specimen preparation 05565

Mineral and Gem Geological Museum, POB 297, Parrsboro, N.S. B0M 1S0 - T: (902) 254-2627. Head: Marilyn Smith
Natural History Museum 05566

Parry Sound

West Parry Sound District Museum, 17 George St, Parry Sound, Ont. P2A 2X4 - T: (705) 746-5365, Fax: (705) 746-8775, E-mail: wpschin@zeuter.com, Internet: http://www.zeuter.com/wpschin/
Local Museum 05567

Paspébiac

Site-Historique du Banc-de-Paspébiac, 3e Rue, Rte du Banc, Paspébiac, P.Q. G0C 2K0 - T: (418) 752-6229, Fax: (418) 752-6408, E-mail: shbp@globetrotter.net. Head: Marie-Josée Lebrasseur
Historical Museum 05568

Patricia

Dinosaur Provincial Park, Royal Tyrrell Museum of Palaeontology Field Station, 28 Miles NE of Brooks, Patricia, Alta. T0J 2K0, mail addr: POB 60, Patricia, Alta. T0J 2K0 - T: (403) 378-4587, Fax: (403) 378-4342, Internet: http://www.gov.ab.ca/env/parks/prov_parks/dinosaur
Natural History Museum - 1955
Partial dinosaur skeletal remains, hadrosaurian and young ceratopsian dinosaur, displays of animal life in the present, geology, pioneer hist 05569

Paynton

Bresaylor Heritage Museum, Hamlet of Bresaylor, Paynton, Sask. S0M 2J0, mail addr: POB 33, Paynton, Sask. S0M 2J0 - T: (306) 895-4813. Head: Velma Foster
Local Museum 05570

Peace River

Peace River Centennial Museum, 10302 99th St, Peace River, Alta. T8S 1K1 - T: (780) 624-4261, Fax: (780) 624-4270, E-mail: prmcaa@ccinet.ca. Head: Victoria Barsalou
Local Museum - 1967
Artifacts relating to the fur trade, early settlement and agriculture, navigation on the Peace River - archives, films 05571

Peachland

Peachland Museum, 5890 Beach Av, Peachland, B.C. V0H 1X0 - T: (250) 767-3441
Local Museum 05572

Pelly

Fort Pelley and Livingston Museum, POB 33, Pelly, Sask. S0M 2J0 - T: (306) 595-2030. Head: Mabel Campbell
Local Museum 05573

Pemberton

Pemberton Museum, POB 267, Pemberton, B.C. V0N 2L0 - T: (604) 894-6765. Head: Florence Bilenduke
Local Museum 05574

Pembroke

Champlain Trail Museum, 1032 Pembroke St E, Pembroke, Ont. K8A 7M5 - T: (613) 735-0517
Local Museum - 1958
Exhibits pertaining to Champlain's exploration (1613), fur trade, lumbering, pioneer household items, agricultural implements, costumes, uniforms, steam engines, pioneer home (1872) - library, archives 05575

Penetanguishene

Discovery Harbour, 93 Jury Dr, Penetanguishene, Ont. L9M 1G1 - T: (705) 549-8064, Fax: (705) 549-4858, E-mail: hhp@hhp.on.ca, Internet: http://www.hhp.on.ca/discover/. Head: Bill Brodeur
Historic Site / Military Museum 05576

Penetanguishene Centennial Museum, 13 Burke St, Penetanguishene, Ont. L9M 1C1 - T: (705) 549-2150, Fax: (705) 549-7542, E-mail: pcmchin@mid.igs.net, Internet: http://www.town.penetanguishene.on.ca. Head: Doug Leroux
Local Museum - 1967
1875 General Store, lumber industry, local artifacts from 19th c, replica fire hall and 1879 Baldwin steam engine, fire fighting 05577

Penticton

Art Gallery of the South Okanagan, 199 Front St, Penticton, B.C. V2A 1H3 - T: (250) 493-2928, Fax: (250) 493-3992, E-mail: agso@vip.net, Internet: http://www.galleries.bc.ca/agso/. Head: Geraldine Parent
Fine Arts Museum 05578

R.N. Atkinson Museum, 785 Main St, Penticton, B.C. V2A 5E3 - T: (250) 4902451, Fax: (604) 492-0440, E-mail: museum@city.penticton.bc.ca. Head: R.S. Manuel
Local Museum / Natural History Museum - 1958
Salish artifacts, military insignia and arms, mineralogy, railway, natural hist, birds, pioneers, historic transport-Stern Wheel Ships - archives 05579

Percé

Centre d'Interpretation du Parc de l'île-Bonaventure-et-du Rocher-Percé, Percé, P.Q. G0C 2L0 - T: (418) 782-2721
Natural History Museum - 1974
Characteristic biological specimens of the Atlantic coast region 05580

Musée Le Chafaud, 145 Rte 132, Percé, P.Q. G0C 2L0 - T: (418) 782-5100
Special Museum 05581

Peribonka

Musée Louis-Hemon, 700 Maria Chapdelaine, Peribonka, P.Q. G0W 2G0 - T: (418) 374-2177, Fax: (418) 374-2516. Head: Lynn Boisselle
Fine Arts Museum 05582

Perth

Perth Museum, 11 Gore St E, Perth, Ont. K7H 1H9 - T: (613) 267-1947, Fax: (613) 267-5635, E-mail: pmchin@superaje.com, Internet: http://www.superaje.com/~perth.museum. Head: A. Quattrocchi
Local Museum 05583

Petawawa

Canadian Airborne Forces Museum, Canadian Forces Base Petawawa, Petawawa, Ont. K8H 2X3 - T: (613) 588-6238, Fax: (613) 588-5886
Military Museum 05584

Canadian Forces Military Museum, Canadian Forces Base Petawawa, Petawawa, Ont. K8H 2X3 - T: (613) 588-6238, Fax: (613) 588-5886
Military Museum 05585

Peterborough

Art Gallery of Peterborough, 2 Crescent St, Peterborough, Ont. K9T 2G1 - T: (705) 743-9179, Fax: (705) 743-8168, E-mail: gallery@agp.on.ca, Internet: http://www.agp.on.ca. Head: Illi-Maria Tamplin
Public Gallery - 1978
European and Canadian paintings and prints 05586

Artspace, 129a Hunter St W, Peterborough, Ont. K9J 7X6 - T: (705) 748-3883, Fax: (705) 748-3224, E-mail: artspace@nexicom.net. Head: Heather Webb
Fine Arts Museum 05587

Hope Water Powered Saw Mill, 250 Milroy Dr, Peterborough, Ont. K9H 7M9 - T: (705) 745-5791, Fax: (705) 745-7488, E-mail: otonabeca@otonabee.com, Internet: http://www.otonabee.com
Science&Tech Museum 05588

Hunter West Gallery, 131 Hunter St W, Peterborough, Ont. K9H 2K7 - T: (705) 876-9623
Fine Arts Museum 05589

Lang Water Powered Grist Mill, 250 Milroy Dr, Peterborough, Ont. K9H 7M9 - T: (705) 745-5791, Fax: (705) 745-7488, E-mail: otonabeeca@otonabee.com
Science&Tech Museum 05590

Perkins Bull Collection, 361 Park St N, Peterborough, Ont. - T: (705) 742-0146. Head: Prof. T.H.B. Symons
Historical Museum / Fine Arts Museum 05591

Peterborough Centennial Museum and Archives, Armour Hill, Hunter St E and Armour Rd, Peterborough, Ont. K9J 6Y5 - T: (705) 743-5180, Fax: (705) 743-2614. Head: Susan Neale
Local Museum - 1967
Pioneer and 19th c furniture, utensils, clothing, tools, dolls, and toys, natural history - archives 05592

Russell Gallery of Fine Art, 138 Simcoe St, Peterborough, Ont. K9H 2H5 - T: (705) 743-0151, Fax: (705) 743-8010, E-mail: russelgallery@sympatico.ca, Internet: http://www.russell-gallery.com
Fine Arts Museum 05593

Petit-Rocher

New Brunswick Mining and Mineral Interpretation Centre, Rte 134, Petit-Rocher, N.B. E0B 2E0 - T: (506) 783-8714
Natural History Museum / Science&Tech Museum 05594

Petrolia

Petrolia Discovery, POB 1480, Petrolia, Ont. N0N 1R0 - T: (519) 882-0897, Fax: (519) 882-4209, E-mail: petdisc@xcelco.on.ca, Internet: http://www.petroliadiscovery.com. Head: Betty Popelier
Local Museum 05595

Pickering

Pickering Museum Village, One The Esplanade, Pickering, Ont. L1V 6K7 - T: (905) 420-4620, 683-8401, Fax: (905) 420-2596
Local Museum 05596

Picton

Macaulay Heritage Park, 35 Church St, Picton, Ont. K0K 2T0 - T: (613) 476-3833, Fax: (613) 476-8356, E-mail: predmus@kos.net, Internet: http://www.pec.on.ca/macaulay
Local Museum 05597

Rose House Museum, POB 3530, Picton, Ont. K0K 2T0 - T: (613) 476-5439, Fax: (613) 476-0013, E-mail: predmus@kos.net, Internet: http://wwws.pec.on.ca
Historical Museum
First German settlement in Ontario 05598

Pictou

McCulloch House Museum and Hector Exhibit Centre, POB 1210, Pictou, N.S. B0K 1H0 - T: (902) 485-4563, 485-5213, Fax: (902) 485-5213, E-mail: pcghs@ednet.ns.ca, Internet: http://www.rootsweb.com/~spcghs
Local Museum / Library with Exhibitions - 1974
Home of Thomas McCulloch, founder of a liberalized system of education, genealogical material, early 19th c period furniture - library 05599

Northumberland Fisheries Museum, POB 1489, Pictou, N.S. B0K 1H0 - T: (902) 485-4972
Historical Museum 05600

Pilot Mound

Marringhurst Pioneer Park Museum, RR 2, Pilot Mound, Man. R0G 1P0 - T: (204) 825-2697
Local Museum 05601

Pilot Mound Cenntenial Museum, Centennial Bldg, 219 Broadway Av W, Pilot Mound, Man. R0G 1P0 - T: (204) 825-2784
Local Museum - 1967
Household and agricultural tools and equipment - library 05602

Pincher Creek

Kootenai Brown Pioneer Village, 1037 Bridge Av, Pincher Creek, Alta. T0K 1W0 - T: (403) 627-3684, Fax: (403) 627-5850, E-mail: kootenai@telusplanet.net, Internet: http://telusplanet.net/public/kootenai. Head: George Sinnott
Local Museum 05603

Pincher Creek Museum → Kootenai Brown Pioneer Village

Pitt Meadows

Pitt Meadows Museum, 12294 Harris Rd, Pitt Meadows, B.C. V3Y 2E9 - T: (604) 465-4322, E-mail: pimhs@direct.ca
Local Museum 05604

Placentia

Castle Hill National Historic Park, Jerseyside, Placentia Nfld. A0B 2G0 - T: (709) 227-2401, Fax: (709) 227-2452, E-mail: kelly-healy@pch.gc.ca. Head: Heather MacLellan
Open Air Museum - 1968
French fortifications (1692-1713), cannons from the English period, French and English flags 05605

Placentia Area Museum, O'Reilly House, 48 Riverside Dr, Placentia, Nfld. A0B 2Y0 - T: (709) 227-5568
Local Museum 05606

Plamondon

Plamondon and District Museum, 9735 99 St, Plamondon, Alta. T0A 2T0 - T: (780) 798-3896, Fax: (780) 798-3909, E-mail: acfapl@canoemail.com. Head: Marie Bourassa
Local Museum - 1976
Local history and culture 05607

Plaster Rock

Plaster Rock Museum, 157 Main St, Plaster Rock, N.B. E7G 2H2 - T: (506) 356-6077, Fax: (506) 356-6081, E-mail: vilprock@nb.sympatico.ca
Local Museum 05608

Plenty

Carscadden's Museum, POB 149, Plenty, Sask. S0L 2R0 - T: (306) 932-2226. Head: William Olson
Local Museum 05609

Plum Coulee

Plum Coulee and District Museum, POB 36, Plum Coulee, Man. R0G 1R0 - T: (204) 829-3419, Fax: (204) 829-3436. Head: Ben Bergman
Local Museum 05610

Pointe-à-la-Croix

Lieu Historique National du Canada de la Bataille-de-la-Ristigouche, Rte 132, Pointe-à-la-Croix, P.Q. G0C 1L0 - T: (418) 788-5676, Fax: (418) 788-5895, E-mail: parcscanada-que@pch.gc.ca, Internet: http://www.parcscanada.gc.ca/ristigouche. Head: Michel Bujold
Historical Museum 05611

Pointe-au-Père

Musée de la Mer de Rimouski, 1034 du Phare, Pointe-au-Père, P.Q. G5M 1L8 - T: (418) 724-6214. Head: Serge Guay
Historical Museum 05612

Pointe-au-Pic

Musée de Charlevoix, 1 Chemin du Havre, Pointe-au-Pic, P.Q. G0T 1M0, mail addr: CP 549, Pointe-au-Pic, P.Q. G0T 1M0 - T: (418) 665-4411, Fax: (418) 665-4560, E-mail: mcpprcip@cite.net. Head: Patrice Giroux
Folklore Museum / Ethnology Museum - 1975
Folk art and hist, tomahawks and 18th c weapons, photographs and documents retracing the colonization of Charlevoix county, ethnology - archives 05613

Pointe-Claire

Galerie d'Art Stewart Hall, 176 Bord du Lac, Pointe-Claire, P.Q. H9S 4J7 - T: (514) 630-1254, Fax: (514) 630-1285, E-mail: millarj@ville.pointe-claire.qc.ca. Head: Joyce Millar
Public Gallery - 1963
Temporary exhibitions of visual expression painting, sculpture, printmaking, national and international 05614

Ponoka

Alberta Hospital Museum, POB 1000, Ponoka, Alta. T0C 2H0 - T: (403) 783-7600
Special Museum - 1969
Artifacts showing changes in the practices of the hospital since 1910 including instruments, clothing and photographs 05615

Fort Ostell Museum, 5320 54 St, Ponoka, Alta. T4J 1L8 - T: (403) 783-5224. Head: Connie Pugh
Historical Museum 05616

Porcupine Plain

Porcupine Plain and District Museum, Cultural Centre Bldg, Elm St W, Porcupine Plain, Sask. S0E 1H0 - T: (306) 278-2317. Head: Joyce Logan
Local Museum - 1976
Local historic items, Indian artifacts, Inuit display, lace pillows, pioneer log cabin 05617

Port Alberni

Alberni Valley Museum, 4255 Wallace St, Port Alberni, B.C. V9Y 3Y6 - T: (250) 723-2181, Fax: (250) 723-1035, E-mail: avmuseum@city.port-alberni.bc.ca. Head: Jean McIntosh
Local Museum - 1973
Regional hist, Nootkan Indian artifacts, prehistoric artifacts, photogr coll (historical and ethnographical), industrial heritage, regional folk art 05618

McLean Mill, 5633 Smith Rd, Port Alberni, B.C. V9Y 7L5 - T: (250) 723-8284, Fax: (250) 723-5910, E-mail: email@alberniheritage.com, Internet: http://www.alberniheritage.com
Science&Tech Museum 05619

Rollin Art Centre, 3061 8th Av, Port Alberni, B.C. V9Y 2K5 - T: (250) 724-3412, Fax: (250) 724-3472, E-mail: communityarts@alberni.net, Internet: http://www.alberni.net/communityarts
Fine Arts Museum 05620

Port-au-Port

Our Lady of Mercy Museum, POB 239, Port-au-Port, Nfld. A0N 1T0 - T: (709) 648-2632
Special Museum 05621

Port-aux-Basques

Gulf Museum, POB 1299, Port-aux-Basques, Nfld. A0M 1C0 - T: (709) 695-7604
Historical Museum 05622

Port-aux-Basques Railway Heritage Centre, POB 1299, Port-aux-Basques, Nfld. A0M 1C0 - T: (709) 695-7560, 956-2170, Fax: (709) 956-2170, Internet: http://www.gatewaytonewfoundland.com
Science&Tech Museum 05623

Port Carling

Muskoka Lakes Museum, Island Park, by the Locks, Port Carling, Ont. P0B 1J0 - T: (705) 765-5367, Fax: (705) 765-6271, E-mail: musklake@muskoka.com. Head: Lindsay Hill
Local Museum - 1961
Articles used by settlers in the Muskoka area dating back to 1865, locally-built boats, Indian artifacts 05624

Port Carling Pioneer Museum, Island Park, Port Carling, Ont. P0B 1J0 - T: (705) 765-5367
Local Museum 05625

Port Clements

Port Clements Museum, POB 417, Port Clements, B.C. V0T 1R0 - T: (250) 557-4576
Local Museum 05626

Port Colborne

Port Colborne Historical and Marine Museum, 280 King St, Port Colborne, Ont. L3K 5X8, mail addr: POB 572, Port Colborne, Ont. L3K 5X8 - T: (905) 834-7604, Fax: (905) 834-6198, E-mail: pcmchin@niagara.com, Internet: http://www.chin.gc.ca. Head: Virginia Anger
Historical Museum - 1974
Local history, marine navigational and Welland Canal artifacts, log school and home, blacksmith 05627

Port-de-Grave

Fishermen's Museum, Porter House and School, Port-de-Grave, Nfld. A0A 3J0 - T: (709) 786-3912. Head: Herman Porter
Historical Museum 05628

Port Dover

Port Dover Harbour Museum, 44 Harbour St, Port Dover, Ont. N0A 1N0 - T: (519) 583-2660, E-mail: can-pdhm@immedia.ca
Historical Museum 05629

Port Edward

North Pacific Cannery Village Museum, 1889 Skeena Dr, Port Edward, B.C. V0V 1G0 - T: (250) 628-3538, Fax: (250) 628-3540
Local Museum 05630

Port Hardy

Port Hardy Museum, POB 2126, Port Hardy, B.C. V0N 2P0 - T: (250) 949-8143. Head: William F. Reeve
Local Museum 05631

Port Hastings

Port Hastings Museum, POB 115, Port Hastings, N.S. B0E 2T0 - T: (902) 625-1295. Head: Beryl MacDonald-MacLeod
Local Museum 05632

Port Hill

Green Park Shipbuilding Museum and Yeo House, Prince Edward Island Museum and Heritage Foundation, Tyne Valley, RR 1, Port Hill, P.E.I. C0B 2C0 - T: (902) 831-7947. Head: Linda Arsenault
Science&Tech Museum / Local Museum - 1973
Wooden shipbuilding yard, 19th c furniture 05633

Port Hood

Chestico Museum, POB 144, Port Hood, N.S. B0E 2W0 - T: (902) 787-2244, 787-3104
Local Museum 05634

Port Moody

Mountain View Gallery, 2720 Saint Johns St, Port Moody, B.C. V3H 2B7 - T: (604) 936-3472
Fine Arts Museum 05635

Port Moody Station Museum, 2734 Murray St, Port Moody, B.C. V3H 1X2 - T: (604) 939-1648, Fax: (604) 939-1647, E-mail: pmmuseum@vcn.bc.ca, Internet: http://www.vcn.bc.ca/pmmuseum
Local Museum - 1967
Regional 1907 Canadian Pacific Railway station, 1920 CPR sleeping car, hist of Port Moody 05636

Port Perry

Scugog Shores Historical Museum, 16210 Island Rd, Port Perry, Ont. L9L 1B4 - T: (905) 985-3589, Fax: (905) 985-3492, E-mail: ssh-chin@durham.net, Internet: http://www.durham.net/~ssh-chin. Head: Susan Neale
Local Museum 05637

Port Rowan

Backus Heritage Village, c/o Long Point Authority, 1 Mile E of Hwy 59 and 1 Mile N of Port Rowan, Port Rowan, Ont. N0E 1M0 - T: (519) 586-2201, Fax: (519) 586-7333, E-mail: backus@lprca.on.ca, Internet: http://www.lprca.on.ca
Open Air Museum / Local Museum - 1956
Agricultural tools, horse-drawn vehicles, sawmill, windmill, ciderpress, threshing barn, heritage village 05638

Port Union

Port Union Museum, POB 98, Port Union, Nfld. A0C 2J0 - T: (709) 464-3315, 469-2728. Head: Rosella Hiscock
Local Museum 05639

Port Williams

Prescott House Museum, Starr's Point, off Rte 358, Port Williams, N.S. B0P 1T0 - T: (902) 542-3984, Fax: (902) 542-3984, Internet: http://museum.gov.ns.ca
Decorative Arts Museum
Oriental rugs, early needlework 05640

Portage-la-Prairie

Fort La Reine Museum and Pioneer Village, Junction Hwys 1a and 26, Portage-la-Prairie, Man. R1N 3C2 - T: (204) 857-3259, Fax: (204) 857-3259, E-mail: edwards@cpnet.net
Local Museum / Decorative Arts Museum - 1967
Late 19th c village with furnishings, vehicles, local history 05641

Portage and District Arts Council, 160 Saskatchewan Av W, Portage-la-Prairie, Man. R1N 0M1 - T: (204) 239-6029, Fax: (204) 239-1472, E-mail: pdac@portage.net. Head: Eveline Mauws
Public Gallery 05642

Pouce Coupe

Pouce Coupe Museum, 5006 49th Av, Pouce Coupe, B.C. V0C 2C0 - T: (250) 786-5555, Fax: (250) 786-5257. Head: Ellen de Wetter
Local Museum - 1972
Pioneer artifacts, railway car, old Railway Station - archives 05643

Pouch Cove

Pouch Cove Museum, POB 59, Pouch Cove, Nfld. A0A 3L0 - T: (709) 335-2848, Fax: (709) 335-2840
Local Museum 05644

Powell River

Powell River Historical Museum, Across from Willington Beach, Powell River, B.C. V8A 4Z5, mail addr: POB 42, Powell River, B.C. V8A 4Z5 - T: (604) 485-2222, Fax: (604) 485-2327, E-mail: museum@aisl.bc.ca, Internet: http://armourtech.com/~museum. Head: P. Bird
Historical Museum - 1968
Hist of Regional area 1890's till present, negative photograph coll, First Nations artifacts, replica of a Powell Lake Recluses cabin, extensive archival coll - archives 05645

Prairie River

Prairie River Museum, Railway Av, Prairie River, Sask. S0E 1J0 - T: (306) 889-4220, Fax: (306) 889-4220, E-mail: lmwaskowic@hotmail.com. Head: Lorraine Waskowic
Local Museum 05646

Prelate

Saint Angela's Museum, Saint Angela's Convent, Prelate, Sask. S0N 2B0 - T: (306) 673-2200, Fax: (306) 673-2635, E-mail: st.angela.acad01@sk.sympatico.ca, Internet: http://

www3.sk.sympatico.ca/stangela. Head: Philomena Marte
Religious Arts Museum - 1969
Hist of the Ursuline Order in Saskatchewan, Blumenfeld Saint Peter Paul church in rural area 05647

Prescott

Fort Wellington, 400 Dibble St, Prescott, Ont. K0E 1T0 - T: (613) 925-2896, Fax: (613) 925-1536. Head: D.J. Delaney
Military Museum - 1926
Restored British fort built in 1838 to guard the Upper Saint Lawrence, period furnishings, small arms, uniforms and accoutrements 05648

Forwarders' Museum, POB 2179, Prescott, Ont. K0E 1T0 - T: (613) 925-5788. Head: Marg Solomatenko
Historical Museum 05649

Prince Albert

Diefenbaker House, 10 River St E, Prince Albert, Sask. S6V 8A9. Head: Ron Smith
Historical Museum 05650

Grace Campbell Gallery, 125 12th St E, Prince Albert, Sask. S6V 1B7 - T: (306) 763-8496, Fax: (306) 763-3816, E-mail: library@jmc.panet.pa.sk.ca. Head: Eleanor Acorn
Fine Arts Museum 05651

Little Gallery, 575 12th St E, Prince Albert, Sask. S6V 1C5
Fine Arts Museum 05652

Prince Albert Historical Museum, 10 River St E, Prince Albert, Sask. S6V 8A9 - T: (306) 764-2992. Head: R.E.G. Smith
Local Museum - 1923
Local hist, early settlement, pioneers, Indian life - archives 05653

Rotary Museum of Police and Corrections, POB 3008, Prince Albert, Sask. S6V 6J9 - T: (306) 922-3313
Historical Museum 05654

Prince George

Fraser-Fort George Regional Museum, 333 Becott Pl, Prince George, B.C. V2L 4V7 - T: (250) 562-1612, Fax: (250) 562-6395, E-mail: info@theexplorationplace.com, Internet: http://www.theexplorationplace.com. Head: George Phillips
Local Museum / Natural History Museum / Science&Tech Museum / Historic Site - 1972
Indian artifacts, local history, photos, Wally West and Simonssen coll, paleontology 05655

Prince George Railway and Forestry Museum, 850 Rivai Rd, Prince George, B.C. L2L 5S8 - T: (250) 563-7351, Fax: (250) 563-3697, E-mail: trains@pgrfm.bc.ca, Internet: http://www.pgrfm.bc.ca. Head: Trudy Swaan
Science&Tech Museum / Natural History Museum / Open Air Museum 05656

Prince Rupert

Kwinitsa Station Railway Museum, Waterfront, next to Rotary Waterfront Park, Prince Rupert, mail addr: POB 669, Prince Rupert, B.C. V8J 3S1 - T: (250) 627-1915, 627-3207, Fax: (250) 627-8009, E-mail: mnbc@citytel.net, Internet: http://www.museumodnorthernbc.com. Head: Susan Marsden
Science&Tech Museum 05657

Museum of Northern British Columbia, 100 First Av W, Prince Rupert, B.C. V8J 1A8 - T: (250) 624-3207, Fax: (250) 627-8009, E-mail: mnbc@citytel.net, Internet: http://www.museumofnorthernbc.com. Head: Robin Weber
Local Museum - 1924
Local history, natural history including Northwest Coast First Nations material, fossils and rocks, coins, historic photographs 05658

Prince Rupert Fire Museum, 200 1st Av W, Prince Rupert, B.C. V8J 1A8 - T: (250) 624-2211, 627-4475, Fax: (250) 624-3407. Head: Brian Hadland
Historical Museum 05659

Prince William

Kings Landing Historical Settlement, 20 Kings Landing Service Rd, Prince William, N.B. E6K 3W3 - T: (506) 363-4999, Fax: (506) 363-4989, E-mail: office@kingslanding.nb.ca, Internet: http://www.kingslanding.nb.ca. Head: Alida Visbach
Historic Site - 1974
History of the Saint John River valley (1790-1910), historical farm, saw mill, various buildings 05660

Princeton

Princeton and District Museum, 167 Vermilion Av, Princeton, B.C. V0X 1W0 - T: (604) 295-7588, E-mail: pdma@nethop.net. Head: D.C. Coyle
Local Museum - 1958
Indian and Chinese material, pioneer items, period rooms, fossils, "Bill Miner", minerals, mining exhibits 05661

Qualicum Beach

Old School House Arts Centre, 122 Fern Rd W, Qualicum Beach, B.C. V9K 1T2 - T: (250) 752-6133, Fax: (250) 752-2600, E-mail: tosh@macn.bc.ca, Internet: http://macn.bc.ca/~tosh
Fine Arts Museum 05662

Quathiaski Cove

Kwagiulth Museum, POB 8, Quathiaski Cove, B.C. V0P 1N0 - T: (250) 285-3733, Fax: (250) 285-2400, E-mail: kmccchin@island.net, Internet: http://www.island.net/~kmccchin/
Local Museum / Folklore Museum 05663

Québec

Centre Muséographique de l'Université Laval, Université Laval, Pavillon Louis-Jacques-Casault, Québec, P.Q. G1K 7P4 - T: (418) 656-7111, Fax: (418) 656-7925, E-mail: -centre.museographique@cmus.ulaval.ca, Internet: http://www.ulaval.ca/cmus. Head: Nicole Brindle
Natural History Museum / University Museum
Astronomy, geology, biology, prehistory 05664

Fort-Numéro-Un de la Pointe-de-Lévy, 41 Ch du Gouvernement, Québec, P.Q. G1K 7R3 - T: (418) 835-5182, Fax: (418) 835-5443
Historical Museum 05665

Fortifications-de-Québec, 2 Rue d'Auteuil, Québec, P.Q. G1K 7R3 - T: (418) 648-7016, Fax: (418) 648-4825, E-mail: parcscanada-que@pch.gc.ca
Historical Museum 05666

Galerie de l'UQAM, 1400 Rue Berri, Québec P.Q. H3C 3P8, mail addr: c/o Université du Québec, CP 8888, Montréal, P.Q. H3C 3P8 - T: (514) 987-6150, Fax: (514) 987-3009. Head: Chantal Bouthat
Fine Arts Museum / Decorative Arts Museum / University Museum - 1972
Furniture, sculpture, more than 1,000 engravings, Egyptian art, French ceramics 05667

Galerie Municipale au Palais Montcalm, 995 Pl d'Youville, Québec, P.Q. G1R 3P1
Fine Arts Museum 05668

Maison Maillou, 17 Rue Saint-Louis, Québec, P.Q. G1R 3Y8
Decorative Arts Museum - 1959
Furniture of the 18th c, military drums 05669

Musée Bon-Pasteur, 14 Rue Couillard, Québec, P.Q. G1R 3S9 - T: (418) 694-0243, Fax: (418) 694-6233
Religious Arts Museum 05670

Musée de la Civilisation, 85 Rue Dalhousie, Québec, P.Q. G1K 7A6, mail addr: CP 155, Succ. B, Québec, P.Q. G1K 7A6 - T: (418) 643-2158, Fax: (418) 646-9705, E-mail: mcq@mcq.orgca, Internet: http://www.mcq.org. Head: Roland Arpin
Ethnology Museum / Historical Museum - 1984
Ethnohistoric coll, scientific coll, art, archaeology, iconography, stamps, coins - archives, library 05671

Musée de l'Amérique Française, 9 Rue de l'Université, Québec, P.Q. G1R 7A6, mail addr: CP 460, Succ. Haute-Ville, Québec, P.Q. G1K 7A6 - T: (418) 692-2843, Fax: (418) 646-5206, E-mail: mcq@mcq.org, Internet: http://www.mcq.org. Head: Roland Arpin
Ethnology Museum - 1806/1983
Ethnohistoric coll, scientific coll, art coll, archeological coll, iconographic coll, stamps, coins - archives, library 05672

Musée des Augustines de l'Hôpital Général de Québec, Monastère des Augustines, 260 Blvd Langelier, Québec, P.Q. G1K 5N1
Religious Arts Museum - 1930
Paintings, sculpture, gildings and embroidery made by the Jesuits, goldsmith workshop 05673

Musée des Ursulines, 12 Rue Donnacona, Québec, P.Q. G1R 4T1 - T: (418) 694-0694, Fax: (418) 694-2136, E-mail: murq@globetrotter.net, Internet: http://www.museocapitale.qc.ca/014.htm. Head: Christine Turgeon
Religious Arts Museum - 1964
Local history, dwelling of Madame de la Peltrie, first institute of learning for girls in New France, paintings, stamps, embroidery, lace, furniture, craft objects - archives, library 05674

Musée du Québec, 1 Av Wolfe-Montcalm, Parc des Champs de Bataille, Québec, P.Q. G1R 5H3 - T: (418) 643-2150, Fax: (418) 646-3330, E-mail: webmdq@mdq.org, Internet: http://www.mdq.org. Head: John R. Porter
Fine Arts Museum - 1933
Old, modern and contemporary art by Québec artists, works representing all schools of art from the 17th c to the present - library 05675

Musée du Royal 22e Régiment, Côte La Citadelle, Québec, P.Q. G1R 4V7 - T: (418) 694-2815, Fax: (418) 694-2853, E-mail: information@lacitadelle.qc.ca, Internet: http://www.lacitadelle.qc.ca. Head: Robert Girard
Military Museum / Historic Site - 1949
Guns, machine guns and canons, uniforms, documents 05676

Musée Place-Royale, 225 Grande-Allée E, Bloc C, Québec, P.Q. G1R 5K5 - T: (418) 643-9314. Head: André Couture
Decorative Arts Museum 05677

Parc de l'Artillerie, 2 Rue d'Auteuil, Québec, P.Q. G1K 7R3 - T: (418) 648-4205, Fax: (418) 648-4825, E-mail: parcscanada-que@pch.gc.ca, Internet: http://www.upc.qc.ca/pch/artillerie
Military Museum 05678

Vieille Maison des Jésuites, 2320 Chemin des Foulons, Québec, P.Q. G1T 1X4
Religious Arts Museum - 1926
Exhibits depicting the work of Jesuits in Québec, old books and engravings, Indian artifacts 05679

VU Centre de Diffusion et de Production de la Photographie, 523 Rue Saint-Vallier E, Québec, P.Q. G1K 3P9 - T: (418) 640-2585, Fax: (418) 640-2586, E-mail: vuphoto@meduse.org, Internet: http://www.meduse.org/vuphoto. Head: André Gilbert
Fine Arts Museum 05680

Queen Charlotte

Kitwanga Fort, c/o Gwaii Haanas National Park Reserve, POB 37, Queen Charlotte, B.C. V0T 1S0 - T: (250) 559-8818, Fax: (250) 559-8366, E-mail: gwaiicom@island.net
Local Museum 05681

Queenston

MacKenzie Heritage Printery Museum, 1 Queenston St, Queenston, Ont. L0S 1L0 - T: (905) 262-5676, Fax: (905) 262-5676, E-mail: npinfo@npc.com, Internet: http://www.niagaraparks.com
Special Museum 05682

Quesnel

Quesnel and District Museum, 405 Barlow Av, Quesnel, B.C. V2J 2C3 - T: (250) 992-9580, Fax: (250) 992-9680, E-mail: stubbsr@sd28.bc.ca, Internet: http://www.sd28.bc.ca/museum. Head: Ruth Stubbs
Local Museum / Agriculture Museum / Ethnology Museum - 1963
Local history, mining, Chinese and Indian artifacts - archives 05683

Rapid City

Rapid City Museum, Fourth Av, Rapid City, Man. R0K 1W0 - T: (204) 826-2597. Head: J. Northam
Local Museum - 1973 05684

Raymore

Raymore Pioneer Museum, POB 453, Raymore, Sask. S0A 3J0
Local Museum 05685

Readlyn

Thompson Museum, W of Readlyn, Readlyn, Sask. S0H 3N0, mail addr: POB 40, Readlyn, Sask.
Historical Museum - 1955
Antique tractors and cars, historical artifacts 05686

Red Bay

Red Bay Historic Site, POB 103, Red Bay, Nfld. A0K 4K0 - T: (709) 920-2142, Fax: (709) 920-2144, E-mail: cindy_gibbons@pch.gc.ca, Internet: http://parkscanada.pch.gc.ca/parks/newfoundland/red_bay. Head: Cindy Gibbons
Archaeological Museum / Historic Site
Artifacts from underwater and terrestrial archaeology of a 16th c Basque whaling station 05687

Red Deer

Alberta Sports Hall of Fame and Museum, 30 Riverview Park, Red Deer, Alta. T4N 1E3 - T: (403) 341-8614, Fax: (403) 341-8619
Special Museum 05688

Fort Normandeau, 6300 45 Av, Red Deer, Alta. T4N 3M4 - T: (403) 347-7550, Fax: (403) 347-2550, E-mail: kwnc@telusplanet.net, Internet: http://www.city.red-deer.ab.ca/kerry/
Military Museum 05689

Red Deer and District Museum, 4525 47a Av, Red Deer, Alta. T4N 6Z6 - T: (403) 309-8405, Fax: (403) 342-6644, E-mail: museum@museum.red-deer.ab.ca, Internet: http://www.museum.red-deer.ab.ca. Head: Wendy Martindale
Local Museum - 1973
Local natural hist, artifacts of native peoples, agriculture, manufacturing, trade, transport, textiles, contemporary First Nation art, Inuit art 05690

Red Lake

Red Lake Museum, 55 Highway 105, mail addr: POB 64, Red Lake, Ont. P0V 2M0 - T: (807) 727-3006, Fax: (807) 727-2686, E-mail: rlmchin@sunsetcountry.com, Internet: http://www.red-lake.com/museum. Head: Michéle Alderton
Local Museum 05691

Redcliff

Redcliff Museum, POB 758, Redcliff, Alta. T0J 2P0 - T: (403) 548-6260
Local Museum 05692

Redwater

Redwater and District Museum, POB 355, Redwater, Alta. T0A 2W0 - T: (780) 942-2512
Local Museum 05693

Regina

Alex Youck School Museum, 1600 4th Av, Regina, Sask. S4R 8C8 - T: (306) 791-8200
Historical Museum 05694

Assiniboia, 2429 11th Av, Regina, Sask. S4P 0K4 - T: (306) 522-0997
Public Gallery 05695

Cannington Manor, 26 km E of Moose Mountain Provincial Park, Regina, mail addr: c/o Sk. Environment and Resource Management, 3211 Albert St, Regina, Sask. S4S 5W6 - T: (306) 787-9571, Fax: (306) 787-7000, E-mail: jhamilton@serm.gov.sk.ca, Internet: http://www.serm.gov.sk.ca/parks
Historic Site - 1965
Artifacts used by the English and Canadian settlers during the 1880's and 1890's, original photographs 05696

Cumberland House, 3211 Albert St, Ste 530, Regina, Sask. S4S 5W6 - T: (306) 787-9571, Fax: (306) 787-7000, E-mail: jhamilton@serm.gov.sk.ca, Internet: http://www.serm.gov.sk.ca/parks
Historic Site
Fur trade, transportation 05697

Diefenbaker Homestead House, 2900 Wascana Dr, Regina, Sask. S4P 2S7, mail addr: POB 7111, Regina, Sask. S4P 2S7 - T: (306) 522-3661, Fax: (306) 565-2742, E-mail: wca@sk.sympatico.ca, Internet: http://www.wascana.sk.ca. Head: Blair Paterson
Local Museum - 1967
Restored boyhood home of Canada's 13th Prime Minister, memorabilia of the family, pioneer artifacts 05698

Dunlop Art Gallery, 2311 12th Av, Regina, Sask. S4P 0N3, mail addr: c/o Regina Public Library, POB 2311, Regina, Sask. S4P 3Z5 - T: (306) 949-7264, Fax: (306) 777-6221, E-mail: dunlop@rpl.regina.sk.ca, Internet: http://www.dunlopart-gallery.org. Head: Anthony Kiendl
Fine Arts Museum - 1946
Saskatchewan art, Canadian prints, drawings, paintings and photographs 05699

Fifth Parallel Gallery, c/o University of Regina, College Av at Cornwall St, Regina, Sask. S4S 0A2 - T: (306) 585-5741
University Museum / Fine Arts Museum 05700

Fort Carlton, 3211 Albert St, Ste 530, Regina, Sask. S4S 5W6 - T: (306) 787-9571, Fax: (306) 787-7000, E-mail: jhamilton@serm.gov.sk.ca, Internet: http://www.serm.gov.sk.ca/parks
Historic Site
Fur trade, first nations 05701

Gallery on the Roof, 2025 Victoria Av, Regina, Sask. S4P 0S1 - T: (306) 566-2553, Fax: (306) 566-2548, Internet: http://www.saskpower.com
Fine Arts Museum 05702

Government House Museum, 4607 Dewdney Av, Regina, Sask. S4P 3V7 - T: (306) 787-5773, Fax: (306) 787-5714, E-mail: blawrence@iaa.gov.sk.ca, Internet: http://www.iaa.gov.sk.ca/govhouse. Head: Brad Lawrence
Historic Site
Antiques, government, political history, heritage 05703

Legislative Building Art Galleries, Legislative Bldg, 2405 Legislative Dr, Regina, Sask. S4S 0B3 - T: (306) 787-5358, Fax: (306) 787-8217, E-mail: visitorserv@legassembly.sk.ca, Internet: http://www.legassembly.sk.ca
Fine Arts Museum - 1911
Pastel sketches of famous prairie Indians, portraits of former Lieutenant Governors, Premiers and speakers, coll of paintings depicting the North West Mounted Police 05704

McIntyre Street Gallery, 2347 McIntyre St, Regina, Sask. S4P 2S3 - T: (306) 757-4323, Fax: (306) 359-0280, E-mail: mcintyre.gallery@sk.sympatico.ca, Internet: http://www.quantumlynk.com/mcintyregallery. Head: Louise Durnford
Public Gallery 05705

MacKenzie Art Gallery, 3475 Albert St S, Regina, Sask. S4S 6X6 - T: (306) 584-4250, Fax: (306) 569-8191, E-mail: mackenzie@uregina.ca, Internet: http://www.mackenziegallery.sk.ca. Head: Kate Davis
Fine Arts Museum / University Museum - 1953
15th to 19th c European paintings, drawings and prints, historical and contemporary Canadian and American art - library 05706

Regina Firefighters Museum, 3845 Cameron St, Regina, Sask. S4S 3E6
Science&Tech Museum 05707

Regina Plains Museum, 1835 Scarth St, Regina, Sask. S4P 2G9 - T: (306) 780-9435, Fax: (306) 565-2979, E-mail: rp.museum@sk.sympatico.ca, Internet: http://www.reginaplainsmuseum.com. Head: S.L. Massey
Local Museum - 1960
Civic and community coll 05708

Rosemount Art Gallery, 2420 Elphinstone St, Regina, Sask. S4T 7S7 - T: (306) 522-5940. Head: Karen Schoonover
Public Gallery 05709

Royal Canadian Mounted Police Museum, POB 6500, Regina, Sask. S4P 3J7 - T: (306) 780-5558, Fax: (306) 780-6349, E-mail: friends@sk.sympatico.ca, Internet: http://www.rcmpmuseum.com. Head: W.A.F. Mackay
Special Museum - 1933
Artifacts of the Mounted Police's influence on the history of Canada 05710

Royal Saskatchewan Museum, Wascana Park, College Av and Albert St, Regina, Sask. S4P 3V7 - T: (306) 787-2815, Fax: (306) 787-2820, E-mail: dbaron@mach.gov.sk.ca, Internet: http://www.gov.sk.ca/govt/rsm. Head: David Baron
Natural History Museum / Archaeological Museum - 1906
Saskatchewan wildlife exhibits, geology, paleontology, archaeology, human hist, conservation, zoology 05711

Saskatchewan Arts Board Collection, 2135 Broad St, Regina, Sask. S4P 3V1 - T: (306) 787-4056, Fax: (306) 787-4199, E-mail: sab@artsboard.sk.ca, Internet: http://www.artsboard.sk.ca. Head: Jeremy Morgan
Association with Coll - 1949
Works by contemporary Saskatchewan artists (1950 to the present) 05712

Saskatchewan Military Museum, 1600 Elphinstone St, Regina, Sask. S4T 3N1 - T: (306) 347-9349, Fax: (306) 586-5525
Military Museum 05713

Saskatchewan Pharmacy Museum, 4010 Pasqua St, Ste 700, Regina, Sask. S4S 6S4 - T: (306) 584-2292, Fax: (306) 584-9695, E-mail: saskpharm@sk.sympatico.ca
Historical Museum 05714

Saskatchewan Science Centre, Wascana Centre, College and Albert, Regina, Sask. S4P 3V7 - T: (306) 791-7900
Science&Tech Museum 05715

Saskatchewan Sports Hall of Fame and Museum, 2205 Victoria Av, Regina, Sask. S4P 0S4 - T: (306) 780-9232, Fax: (306) 780-9427, E-mail: sshfm@dlcwest.com, Internet: http://www.dlcwest.com/~sshfm. Head: Sheila Kelly
Special Museum - 1967
Portraits of regional sports personalities, sports items, Saskatchewan Roughriders Football Club coll 05716

Telorama, 2350 Albert St, Regina, Sask. S4P 2Y4
Science&Tech Museum - 1965
Communications history 05717

Wood Mountain Post, 3211 Albert St, Regina, Sask. S4K 5W6 - T: (306) 787-9571, Fax: (306) 787-7000, E-mail: jhamilton@serm.gov.sk.ca, Internet: http://www.serm.gov.sk.ca/parks
Historical Museum
North West Mounted Police, Sioux first nation - Sitting Bull 05718

Renfrew

McDougall Mill Museum, POB 544, Renfrew, Ont. K7V 4B1 - T: (613) 432-2129. Head: Marie Henderson
Science&Tech Museum 05719

Reston

Reston and District Historical Museum, Reston Memorial Park, Ninth St, Reston, Man. R0M 1X0 - T: (204) 877-3960. Head: Art Smith
Local Museum - 1967
Regional history - archives 05720

Revelstoke

Revelstoke Court House, 1100 2nd St W, Revelstoke, B.C. V0E 2S0 - T: (250) 837-7636, Fax: (250) 836-7640
Historical Museum 05721

Revelstoke Museum, 315 First St W, Revelstoke, B.C. V0E 2S0, mail addr: POB 1908, Revelstoke, B.C. V0E 2S0 - T: (250) 837-3067, Fax: (250) 837-3094, E-mail: rm_chin@revelstoke.net. Head: Catherine English
Historical Museum - 1964
Local history including lumbering, mining, farming, railroading and early settlement - archives 05722

Revelstoke Railway Museum, 719 Track St W, Revelstoke, B.C. V0E 2S0 - T: (250) 837-6060, Fax: (250) 837-3732, E-mail: railway@junction.net, Internet: http://www.railwaymuseum.com. Head: Martin Fransen
Science&Tech Museum 05723

Richards Landing

Fort Saint Joseph, POB 220, Richards Landing, Ont. P0R 1J0 - T: (705) 246-2664, 942-6262, Fax: (705) 246-1796, Internet: http://www.parcsczaten.ge.ca/joseph
Military Museum 05724

Saint Joseph Island Museum Village, RR 2, Richards Landing, Ont. P0R 1J0 - T: (705) 246-2672, E-mail: sjimuseum@canada.com, Internet: http://www.stjosephisland.net
Local Museum 05725

Richibucto

Richibucto River Museum, Old Post Office, Town Hall, Richibucto, N.B. E0A 2M0 - T: (506) 523-4408. Head: John McCleave
Local Museum - 1968
Local history 05726

Richmond

12 Vancouver Service Battalion Museum, Sherman Armoury, 5500 4th Rd, Richmond, B.C. V6X 3L5 - T: (604) 666-4086
Military Museum 05727

Britannia Heritage Shipyard, 3811 Moncton St, Richmond, B.C. V7E 3A0 - T: (604) 241-9453, Fax: (604) 241-4118, E-mail: britannia@city.richmond.bc.ca
Historical Museum 05728

Gulf of Georgia Cannery, 12138 4th Av, Richmond, B.C. V7E 3J1 - T: (604) 664-9009, Fax: (604) 664-9008, E-mail: gogcs@portal.ca, Internet: http://www.netlink2000.com/villager. Head: Connie Baxter
Historical Museum 05729

Les Maisons de Bouteilles, CP 72, Richmond, P.E.I. C0B 1Y0 - T: (902) 854-2987, 854-2254, E-mail: actionstourisme@pei.sympatico.ca, Internet: http://www.teleco.org/maisonsdebouteilles
Decorative Arts Museum 05730

Richmond Art Gallery, 7700 Minoru Gate, Richmond, B.C. V6Y 1R9 - T: (604) 231-6457, Fax: (604) 231-6423, E-mail: gallery@city.richmond.bc.ca, Internet: http://www.city.richmond.bc.ca/artgallery. Head: Coreen Corry
Public Gallery - 1987
Local history, fishing and navigation, aviation agriculture, religion, education 05731

Richmond Museum, 7700 Minoru Gate, Richmond, B.C. V6Y 1R9 - T: (604) 231-6457, Fax: (604) 231-6423, E-mail: museum@city.richmond.bc.ca, Internet: http://www.city.richmond.bc.ca. Head: Kate Bourdon
Local Museum 05732

Steveston Museum, 3811 Moncton St, Richmond, B.C. V7E 3A0 - T: (604) 271-6868, Fax: (604) 271-5919
Special Museum 05733

Trev Deeley Motorcycle Museum, 13500 Verdun Pl, Richmond, B.C. V6V 1V4 - T: (604) 273-5421, Fax: (604) 273-2029
Science&Tech Museum 05734

Ridgetown

Ridge House Museum, 53 Erie St S, Ridgetown, Ont. N0P 2C0 - T: (519) 674-2223, Fax: (519) 674-0660. Head: Elsie Reynolds
Local Museum 05735

Ridgeway

Fort Erie Historical Museum, 402 Ridge Rd, Ridgeway, Ont. L0S 1N0 - T: (905) 894-5322, Fax: (905) 894-6851. Head: Jane Davies
Local Museum 05736

Fort Erie Railroad Museum, Central Av, Ridgeway, Ont. L0S 1N0 - T: (905) 871-1412, Fax: (905) 894-6851. Head: Jane Davies
Science&Tech Museum 05737

Ridgeway Battlefield Museum, Owy 3, nr Cnr Ridge Rd, Ridgeway, Ont. L0S 1N0 - T: (905) 894-5322, Fax: (905) 894-6851. Head: Jane Davies
Military Museum 05738

Rigaud

Musée du Collège Bourget (closed) 05739

Rimouski

Maison Lamontagne, 707 Blvd du Rivage E, Rimouski, P.Q. G5L 1H2 - T: (418) 722-4038, Fax: (418) 722-4038, E-mail: mlamon@globetrotter.qc.ca. Head: Robert Malenfant
Special Museum 05740

Musée Régional de Rimouski, 35 Rue Saint-Germain Ouest, Rimouski, P.Q. G5L 4B4 - T: (418) 724-2272, Fax: (418) 725-4433, E-mail: mrdr@globetrotter.net, Internet: http://www.museeri-mouski.qc.ca. Head: Carl Johnson
Local Museum
Local history, contemporary art, sciences and technology 05741

River Herbert

King Seaman School Museum, RR2, River Herbert, N.S. B0L 1G0 - T: (902) 251-2041
Historical Museum 05742

Riverhurst

F.T. Hill Museum, Riverhurst, Sask. S0H 3P0 - T: (306) 353-2112
Local Museum - 1967
Pioneer and Indian artifacts, fossils 05743

Riverport

Ovens Museum, POB 38, Riverport, N.S. B0J 2W0 - T: (902) 766-4621, Fax: (902) 766-4344, E-mail: dreamer@interactive.net, Internet: http://www.overspark.com. Head: Angela Chapin
Natural History Museum 05744

Riverside-Albert

Old Bank of New Brunswick Museum, 5985 Rte 114, Riverside-Albert, N.B. E4H 2B8 - T: (506) 882-2015, E-mail: maryspt@nbnet.nb.ca, Internet: http://personal.nbnet.nb.ca/maryspt/ACHT/
Historical Museum 05745

Riverton

Hecla Island Heritage Home Museum, POB 70, Riverton, Man. R0C 2R0 - T: (204) 279-2056, 378-2945
Local Museum 05746

Rivière-du-Loup

Musée du Bas Saint-Laurent, 300 Rue Saint-Pierre, Rivière-du-Loup, P.Q. G5R 3V3 - T: (418) 862-7547, Fax: (418) 862-3019, E-mail: mbsl@qc.aira.com, Internet: http://www.mbsl.qc.ca. Head: Guy Bouchard
Ethnology Museum / Fine Arts Museum / Archaeological Museum 05747

Roblin

Keystone Pioneer Museum, E of Roblin, Hwy 5, Roblin, Man. R0L 100 - T: (204) 937-2935. Head: Art McIntyre
Agriculture Museum - 1972
Agricultural equipment 05748

Rocanville

Rocanville and District Museum, Corner of Qu'Appelle Av and Saint Albert St, Rocanville, Sask. S0A 3L0 - T: (306) 645-2605, Fax: (306) 645-4492, E-mail: roc.cap@sk.sympatico.ca, Internet: http://www3.sk.sympatico.ca/roccap. Head: Phyllis Ore
Local Museum - 1967
Steam and gas engines, machinery, tools, pioneer furnishings, local hist 05749

Rockton

Westfield Heritage Village, Regional Rd 552, off Hwy 8, Rockton, Ont. L0R 1X0 - T: (519) 621-8851, Fax: (519) 621-6897, E-mail: west@nonline.net, Internet: http://www.westfieldheritage.com. Head: Rondalyn Brown
Open Air Museum - 1964
Various buildings recreating a mid 19th c rural community in Central Canada incl a blacksmith, harness, and printing and bookbinding shop, general store, locomotive, native Canadian log church 05750

Rose Valley

Rose Valley and District Heritage Museum, POB 232, Rose Valley, Sask. S0E 1M0
Local Museum 05751

Rosebud

Rosebud Centennial Museum, POB 601, Rosebud, Alta. T0J 2T0 - T: (403) 677-2208, Fax: (403) 677-2065
Local Museum 05752

Rosemont

Dufferin County Museum, POB 120, Rosemont, Ont. L0N 1R0 - T: (705) 435-1881, Fax: (705) 435-9876, E-mail: dcmchin@planeteer.com, Internet: http://www.dufferincounty.on.ca/departments. Head: Wayne Townsend
Local Museum 05753

Rosetown

Rosetown Museum and Art Center, Centennial Library, Rosetown, Sask. S0L 2V0 - T: (306) 882-3566. Head: Frank Glass
Local Museum / Fine Arts Museum 05754

Rossburn

Rossburn Museum, POB 487, Rossburn, Man. R0J 1V0 - T: (204) 859-2762, Fax: (204) 859-2959
Local Museum 05755

Rossland

Rossland Historical Museum, Hwy Junction at Rossland, Rossland, B.C. V0G 1Y0 - T: (250) 362-7722, Fax: (250) 362-5379
Local Museum / Science&Tech Museum - 1967
Regional hist, mining industry, Western Canada Hall of Fame housing trophies and equipment of Nancy Greene, Olaus Jeldness and Kerrin Lee-Gartner 05756

Rosthern

Batoche National Historic Site, POB 999, Rosthern, Sask. S0K 3R0 - T: (306) 423-6227, Fax: (306) 423-5400, E-mail: batoche.info@pch.gc.ca, Internet: http://parkscanada.pch.gc.ca/parks/saskatchewan/batoche. Head: Cheryl Penny
Local Museum - 1963 05757

Mennonite Heritage Museum, Rosthern, Sask. S0K 3R0 - T: (306) 232-5353, Fax: (306) 232-5518
Religious Arts Museum - 1963
German and Russian Mennonite artifacts dating back to the 1890's 05758

Rouleau

Rouleau and District Museum, POB 132, Rouleau, Sask. S0G 4H0 - T: (306) 776-2363
Local Museum 05759

Rouyn-Noranda

Centre d'Exposition de Rouyon-Noranda, 425 Blvd du Collège, Rouyn-Noranda, P.Q. J9X 5C4 - T: (819) 762-6600. Head: Céline Rivard
Public Gallery 05760

Maison Dumulon, CP 242, Rouyn-Noranda, P.Q. J9X 5C3 - T: (819) 797-7125, Fax: (819) 762-3367. Head: Diane Tremblay
Historical Museum 05761

Rowley

Yester-Year Artifacts Museum, Rowley, Alta. T0J 2X0 - T: (403) 368-3816, Fax: (403) 368-2239
Local Museum 05762

Rustico

Farmers Bank of Rustico, Hunter River, RR3, Rustico, P.E.I. C0A 1N0 - T: (902) 963-2304. Head: P.E. Blanchard
Historical Museum 05763

Saanichton

Saanich Historical Artifacts Society, 7321 Lockside Dr, Saanichton, B.C. V8M 1W4 - T: (250) 652-5522, Fax: (250) 652-5999, E-mail: shas@horizon.bc.ca, Internet: http://www.horizon.bc.ca/~shas. Head: Maurice Michell
Local Museum / Agriculture Museum - 1967
Agricultural machinery and equipment 05764

Saanich Pioneer Log Cabin Museum, 7910 E Saanich Rd, Saanichton, B.C. V8M 1T4 - T: (250) 656-2572, Fax: (250) 656-2533, E-mail: spma@victoria.tc.ca, Internet: http://www.museumassn.bc.ca. Head: Norma Sealey
Local Museum
Agricultural, commercial, family and social history of the Saanich Peninsula 05765

Sachs Harbour

Sachs Harbour Museum, Sachs Harbour, N.T. X0E 0Z0 - T: (867) 690-4361
Local Museum 05766

Sackville

Owens Art Gallery, c/o Mount Allison University, 61 York St, Sackville, N.B. E4L 1E1 - T: (506) 364-2574, Fax: (506) 364-2575, E-mail: gkelly@mta.ca, Internet: http://www.mta.ca/owens. Head: Gemey Kelly
Public Gallery / University Museum - 1893
European (19th c), Canadian historical and contemporary art 05767

Struts Gallery, 7 Rue Lorne, Sackville, N.B. E4L 3Z6 - T: (506) 536-1211, Fax: (506) 536-4565, E-mail: struts@nb.sympatico.ca, Internet: http://www.tantramar.com/struts. Head: Donna Wawzonek
Fine Arts Museum 05768

Saint-Albert

Musée Héritage, 5 Sainte-Anne St, Saint-Albert, Alta. T8N 3Z9 - T: (780) 459-1528, Fax: (780) 459-1546, E-mail: museum@compusmart.ab.ca. Head: Alexandra Hatcher
Local Museum 05769

Saint-André-Avelin

Musée des Pioneers, 20 Rue Bourgeois, Saint-André-Avelin, P.Q. J0V 1W0 - T: (819) 983-2624
Historical Museum 05770

Saint-André-d'Argenteuil

Musée Regional d'Argenteuil, 44 Rte du Long-Sault, Saint-André-d'Argenteuil, P.Q. J0V 1X0 - T: (514) 387-3861, Fax: (450) 566-0975, E-mail: nlowe@aiservice.com. Head: Luc A. Lépine
Folklore Museum / Local Museum - 1938
Indian artifacts, domestic utensils, farming equipment, furniture, textiles, natural science, fine and decorative arts, musical instruments - archive, library 05771

Saint Andrews

Ross Memorial Museum, 188 Montague St, Saint Andrews, N.B. E5B 1J2 - T: (506) 529-5124, Fax: (506) 529-5129, E-mail: rossmuse@nbnet.ca, Internet: http://www.townsearch.com/rossmuseum. Head: Margot Magee Sackett
Decorative Arts Museum 05772

Sunbury Shores Arts and Nature Centre, 139 Water St, Saint Andrews, N.B. E0G 2X0 - T: (506) 529-3386, Fax: (506) 529-4779, E-mail: sunshore@ngnet.nb.ca, Internet: http://www.sunburyshores.org. Head: Debbie Nielsen
Public Gallery 05773

Saint Anthony

Grenfell House Museum, POB 93, Saint Anthony, Nfld. A0K 4S0 - T: (709) 454-3333, Fax: (709) 454-3171
Historical Museum 05774

Saint-Basile

Saint Basile Chapel Museum, Saint-Basile Parish, Saint-Basile, N.B. E7C 1H7 - T: (506) 263-5971. Head: Romain Tripanier
Local Museum / Folklore Museum - 1956
Local history and folklore 05775

Saint-Boniface

Musée de Saint-Boniface, 494 Av Taché, Saint-Boniface, Man. R2H 2B2 - T: (204) 237-4500, Fax: (204) 986-7964, E-mail: stbmus1@mb.sympatico.ca, Internet: http://www.franco-manitobain.org/msbm. Head: Philippe R. Mailhot
Local Museum / Historic Site - 1967
Pioneer history and furnishings of French Canadians and Grey Nuns, Louis Riel 05776

Saint-Brieux

Musée Saint-Brieux, 300 Barbier Dr, Saint-Brieux, Sask. S0K 3V0 - T: (306) 275-2229. Head: Chantel Schur
Local Museum 05777

Saint Catharines

Mountain Mills Museum, POB 3012, Saint Catharines, Ont. L2R 7C2
Science&Tech Museum 05778

Rodman Hall Arts Centre, 109 Saint Paul Crescent, Saint Catharines, Ont. L2S 1M3 - T: (905) 684-2925, Fax: (905) 682-4733, E-mail: rodman_hall@aibn.com. Head: David Aurandt
Fine Arts Museum - 1960
19th and 20th c Canadian paintings, sculpture, prints, and drawings, American and European art - library 05779

Saint Catharines Museum, 1932 Government Rd, Saint Catharines, Ont. L2R 7C2 - T: (905) 984-8880, Fax: (905) 984-6910, E-mail: muslk3@niagara.com, Internet: http://www.lock3.com
Local Museum 05780

Saint Claude

Saint Claude Museum, Saint Claude, Man. R0G 1Z0 - T: (204) 379-2405. Head: Henri Bellec
Local Museum
History of the first settlers 05781

Saint Constant

Canadian Railway Museum, 120 Saint-Pierre St, Saint Constant, P.Q. J5A 2G9 - T: (450) 638-1522, Fax: (450) 638-1563, E-mail: mfed@globetrotter.qc.ca. Head: Marie-Claude Reid
Science&Tech Museum - 1965
Steam and diesel locomotives, streetcars, model railway, restored railway station - library, archives 05782

Saint-Denis

Maison Chapais, CP 70, Saint-Denis, P.Q. G0L 2R0 - T: (418) 498-2353, Fax: (418) 856-5611
Special Museum 05783

Saint-Eustache

Moulin Légaré, 232 Rue Saint-Eustache, Saint-Eustache, P.Q. J7R 2L7 - T: (514) 472-4440, 433-1762
Science&Tech Museum 05784

Musée Jean-Hotte, 405 Grande-Côté, Saint-Eustache, P.Q. J7P 1H6 - T: (450) 473-4370
Science&Tech Museum 05785

Saint-Evariste

Écomusée de la Haute-Beauce, Musée Territoire, 325 Rue Principale, Saint-Evariste, P.Q. G0M 1G0 - T: (418) 459-3195, Fax: (418) 459-3122. Head: Nicole Lamontagne
Local Museum / Natural History Museum 05786

Saint George

Adelaide Hunter Hoodless Homestead, 359 Blue Lake Rd, RR 1, Saint George, Ont. N0E 1N0 - T: (519) 448-1130, Fax: (519) 448-1150. Head: Sue Doiron
Local Museum - 1961
Birthplace of the founder of the Federated Women's Institutes, furnishings of the 1850-1881 period 05787

Saint-Georges, Manitoba

Musée Saint-Georges, 19 Baie Caron, Saint-Georges, Manitoba, Man. R0E 1V0, mail addr: POB 171, Saint-Georges, Manitoba, Man. R0E 1V0 - T: (204) 367-8001, 367-2927
Local Museum 05788

Saint-Georges, Quebec

Centre d'Art de Saint-Georges, 250 18e Rue, Saint-Georges, Quebec, P.Q. G5Y 4S9 - T: (418) 228-2027, Fax: (418) 226-4669
Public Gallery 05789

Saint-Hyacinthe

Centre d'Exposition de Saint-Hyacinthe, 495 Av Saint-Simon, Saint-Hyacinthe, P.Q. J2S 5C3 - T: (450) 773-4209, Fax: (450) 773-5270, E-mail: expression@expression.qc.ca, Internet: http://www.expression.qc.ca. Head: Michel Groleau
Public Gallery 05790

Musée du Séminaire de Saint-Hyacinthe, 650 Rue Girouard Est, Saint-Hyacinthe, P.Q. J2S 7B7 - T: (450) 774-0203, Fax: (450) 774-7101. Head: Jean-Noël Dion
Local Museum / Natural History Museum - 1875
Ornithology, entomology, antiques of historical interest, portraits, stamps, medals 05791

Saint Jacobs

Maple Syrup Museum, Princess St, Saint Jacobs, Ont. N0B 2N0 - T: (519) 669-2423, Fax: (519) 669-4259
Special Museum 05792

Saint-Jacques

Musée Automobile, Les Jardins, Saint-Jacques, N.B. E0L 1K0, mail addr: CP 1567, Saint-Jacques, N.B. E7B 1H3 - T: (506) 735-2525, Fax: (506) 735-7262
Science&Tech Museum - 1972
Automotive and other mechanical inventions of the past seventy years 05793

Saint-Jean

Manoir Mauvide-Jenest, 1451 Av Royale, Saint-Jean, P.Q. G0A 3W0
Decorative Arts Museum - 1928
English Victorian furniture, 18th c furniture 05794

Musée du Fort Saint-Jean, c/o Collège Militaire Royal, Rte 223, Saint-Jean, P.Q. J0J 1R0 - T: (450) 346-2131. Head: D. Landry
Military Museum / Archaeological Museum - 1966
History of Fort Saint-Jean from 1666 to the present, uniforms, weapons, archeological discoveries 05795

Saint-Jean-Port-Joli

Maison Médard-Bourgault, 322 de Gaspé W, Saint-Jean-Port-Joli, P.Q. G0R 3G0 - T: (418) 598-3880
Special Museum 05796

Musée des Anciens Canadiens, 332 Av de Gaspé W, Saint-Jean-Port-Joli, P.Q. G0R 3G0 - T: (418) 598-3392, Fax: (418) 598-3392
Historical Museum 05797

Musée les Retrouvailles, 248 Av de Gaspé, Saint-Jean-Port-Joli, P.Q. G0R 3G0 - T: (418) 598-3531
Science&Tech Museum 05798

Saint-Jean-sur-Richelieu

Musée du Haut-Richelieu, 182 Jacques-Cartier N, Saint-Jean-sur-Richelieu, P.Q. J3B 7W3 - T: (450) 347-0649, Fax: (450) 347-9994, E-mail: mrhr@globetrotter.net. Head: Suzanne Lavoie
Local Museum 05799

Saint John

Barbour's General Store Museum, City Hall, King St E and Carmarthen, Saint John, N.B. E2L 4L1 - T: (506) 658-2939, Fax: (506) 632-6118
Local Museum - 1967
Historical country store with original furnishings (1867) and equipment, fully equipped barber shop 05800

City of Saint John Gallery, 20 Hazen Av, Saint John, N.B. E2L 3G8 - T: (506) 649-6040, Fax: (506) 632-6118, E-mail: bernard.cormier@city.saint-john.nb.ca
Fine Arts Museum 05801

Loyalist House Museum, 120 Union St, Saint John, N.B. E2L 1A3 - T: (506) 652-3590. Head: Dennis Knibb
Local Museum / Decorative Arts Museum 05802

New Brunswick Museum, 277 Douglas Av, Saint John, N.B. E2K 1E5 - T: (506) 643-2300, Fax: (506) 643-2360, E-mail: agraham@nb.aibn.com, Internet: http://www.gnb.ca/0130. Head: Jane Fullerton
Local Museum / Natural History Museum - 1842
Ornithology, mammals, fish, geology, paintings, especially works by New Brunswick artists (19th-20th c), decorative art, history including social hist - archives, library 05803

Partridge Island Museum (closed) 05804

Saint John Firefighters Museum, 24 Sydney St, Saint John, N.B. E2L 2L3 - T: (506) 633-1840
Historical Museum 05805

Saint John Jewish Historical Museum, 29 Wellington Row, Saint John, N.B. E2L 3H4 - T: (506) 633-1833, Fax: (506) 642-9926, E-mail: sjjhm@nbnet.nb.ca. Head: Katherine Biggs-Craft
Historical Museum 05806

Saint John Sports Hall of Fame, Harbour Station, Saint John, N.B. E2L 4L1 - T: (506) 658-2909, Fax: (506) 658-2902
Special Museum 05807

Telephone Pioneer Museum, Saint John, N.B. E2L 4K2
Science&Tech Museum 05808

Saint John's

Anglican Cathedral Museum, 68 Queen's Rd, Saint John's, Nfld. A1C 2A8 - T: (709) 726-5677, Fax: (709) 726-2053, E-mail: cathedral@nf.aibn.com, Internet: http://www.infonet.st-johns.nf.ca/cathedral. Head: Julia Mathieson
Religious Arts Museum 05809

Art Gallery of Newfoundland and Labrador, c/o Memorial University of Newfoundland, Arts and Culture Centre, Prince Philip Dr, Saint John's, Nfld. A1C 5S7 - T: (709) 737-8210, Fax: (709) 737-2007, E-mail: agnl@morgan.ucs.mun.ca, Internet: http://www.mun.ca/agnl. Head: Patricia Grattan
Fine Arts Museum / Folklore Museum / University Museum - 1961
Contemporary Canadian art, Newfoundland art, folk art 05810

Cape Spear Historic Site, POB 1268, Saint John's, Nfld. A1C 5M9 - T: (709) 772-5367, Fax: (709) 772-6302, E-mail: cape_spear@pch.gc.ca, Internet: http://www.parkscanada.gc.ca/parks/nfld_hse.htm. Head: Jewel Cunningham
Local Museum - 1975
Lightkeeping in the 1840's, historic structure, WW II coastal defense battery 05811

CBC Radio Museum, 344 Duckworth St, Saint John's, Nfld. A1B 3T8 - T: (709) 737-4207, Fax: (709) 737-4954. Head: John F. O'Mara
Science&Tech Museum 05812

Commissariat House, King's Bridge Rd, Saint John's, Nfld. A1B 4J6, mail addr: POB 8700, Saint John's, Nfld. A1B 4J6 - T: (709) 729-0592, 729-6730, Fax: (709) 729-0870, 729-6745, E-mail: lbadcock@mail.gov.nb.ca, Internet: http://www.nfmuseum.com
Historical Museum 05813

Eastern Edge Art Gallery, POB 2641, Stn C, Saint John's, Nfld. A1C 6K1 - T: (709) 739-1882, Fax: (709) 579-1636
Fine Arts Museum 05814

James J. O'Mara Pharmacy Museum, Apothecary Hall, 488 Water St, Saint John's, Nfld. A1E 1B3 - T: (709) 753-5877, Fax: (709) 753-8615, E-mail: npha@nf.sympatico.ca
Historical Museum 05815

Lillian Stevenson Nursing Archives Museum, Dr. Miller Centre, Forest Rd, Saint John's, Nfld. A1A 1E5 - T: (709) 777-7682, Fax: (709) 777-6969
Historical Museum 05816

Newfoundland Museum, 285 Duckworth St, Saint John's, Nfld. A1C 1G9 - T: (709) 729-6007, Fax: (709) 729-2179, E-mail: cjoyce@mail.gov.nf.ca, Internet: http://www.nfmuseum.com. Head: Penny Houlden
Local Museum - 1849
Hist of early settlers, navigation, natural hist, archaeology, ethnology, aviation, material hist, military hist, Beothuk, Innu, Inuit, Mi'kmaq 05817

Point Amour Lighthouse, L'Anse Amour Rd, off Hwy 510, Saint John's, Nfld. A1B 4J6, mail addr: POB 8700, Saint John's, Nfld. A1B 4J6 - T: (709) 729-0592, 729-5826, Fax: (709) 729-0870, 927-5833, E-mail: lbadcock@mail.gov.nf.ca, Internet: http://www.nfmuseum.com
Science&Tech Museum / Historical Museum 05818

Port Au Choix, 150 Miles N of Deer Lake on the Great Northern Peninsula, Saint John's, Nfld. A1C 5X4, mail addr: POB 140, Port au Choix, Nfld. A0K 4C0 - T: (709) 861-3522, Fax: (709) 861-3827, E-mail: pac-historic-site@pch.gc.ca, Internet: http://parkscanada.pch.gc.ca. Head: Millie Spence
Archaeological Museum / Historical Museum - 1969
Maritime archaic Indian culture (2000 B.C.) including excavations from burial grounds, Dorste and Groswater palaeoeskimo cultures 05819

Quidi Vidi Battery, Cuckhold's Cove Rd, Saint John's Nfld. A1B 4J6, mail addr: POB 8700, Saint John's, Nfld. A1B 4J6 - T: (709) 729-0592, 729-2977, Fax: (709) 729-0870, 729-6745, E-mail: commissariat@nf.aibn.com, Internet: http://www.nfmuseum.com
Historic Site 05820

Regatta Museum → Royal Saint John's Regatta Museum

Royal Newfoundland Constabulary Museum, POB 7247, Saint John's, Nfld. A1E 3Y4 - T: (709) 729-8151, Fax: (709) 729-8214, E-mail: gbrownw@rnc.gov.nt.ca
Historical Museum 05821

Royal Saint John's Regatta Museum, POB 214, Saint John's, Nfld. A1C 5J3 - T: (709) 753-9448. Head: Gail Malone
Special Museum 05822

Saint Thomas' Old Garrison Church Museum, 8 Military Rd, Saint John's, Nfld. A1C 2C4 - T: (709) 576-6632, Fax: (709) 576-2541, E-mail: st.thomas@nf.sympatico.ca, Internet: http://www3.nf.sympatico.ca/st.thomas/. Head: Dr. John Netten
Religious Arts Museum 05823

Signal Hill Historic Site, Signal Hill Rd, Saint John's, Nfld. A1C 5M9 - T: (709) 772-5367, Fax: (709) 772-6302, E-mail: signal_hill@pch.gc.ca, Internet: http://www.parkscanada.gc.ca. Head: Jewel Cunningham
Local Museum - 1958
History of Newfoundland from the early Vikings (ca 1000) to Confederation with Canada in 1949 05824

Saint-Joseph

Musée Saint-Joseph, CP 47, Saint-Joseph, Man. R0G 2C0 - T: (204) 737-2241. Head: Jean L. Perron
Local Museum / Agriculture Museum - 1975
Minerals, historic house with furnishings (1915-1925), antiquities, agricultural, implements, houses, workshops 05825

Saint-Joseph-de-Beauce

Musée Marius Barbeau, CP 1081, Saint-Joseph-de-Beauce, P.Q. G0S 2V0 - T: (418) 397-4039
Special Museum 05826

Saint-Joseph-de-Sorel

Musée du Navigateur Flottant, La Goelette, 425 Rue Désirée, Saint-Joseph-de-Sorel, P.Q. J3I 3E2
Special Museum - 1977
Ship with displays of items once used by seamen 05827

Saint Joseph Island

Fort Saint Joseph National Historic Park, Richard's Landing, Saint Joseph Island, Ont.
Historical Museum - 1972
Ruins of a fort built after 1796 to serve as a centre for the fur trade, British military, and the Indian department in the Upper Great Lakes 05828

Saint-Lambert

Galarie du Centre, 250 Rue Saint-Laurent, Saint-Lambert, P.Q. J4P 3R8 - T: (450) 672-4772. Head: Jacqueline Beaudry Dion
Fine Arts Museum 05829

Musée Marsil, 349 Riverside, Saint-Lambert, P.Q. J4P 1A8 - T: (450) 671-3098, Fax: (450) 465-8694, E-mail: mars@quebectel.com. Head: Louise Séguin
Special Museum 05830

Saint-Laurent

Musée d'Art de Saint-Laurent, 615 Av Sainte-Croix, Saint-Laurent, P.Q. H4L 3X6 - T: (514) 747-7367, Fax: (514) 747-8892. Head: Johane Canning-Lacroix
Fine Arts Museum / Decorative Arts Museum - 1962/79
18th and 19th c works of art and artifacts, prehistoric items, American Indian artifacts, Québec art and cultural exhibits 05831

Yorkshire Air Museum, Canada Branch, 470 Petit St, Saint-Laurent, P.Q. H4N 2H6 - E-mail: webmaster@yorksairmuseum.-freeserve.co.uk, Internet: http://www.yorksairmu-seum.freeserve.co.uk
Science&Tech Museum / Military Museum
Aircraft 05832

Saint Lawrence

Saint Lawrence Memorial Miner's Museum, Rte 220, Saint Lawrence, mail addr: POB 128, Saint Lawrence, Nfld. A0E 2V0 - T: (709) 873-2222, Fax: (709) 873-3352, E-mail: townofst.lawrence@nf.albn.com. Head: Wayde Rowsell
Science&Tech Museum 05833

Saint-Léonard

Galerie Port-Maurice, 8420 Blvd Lacordaire, Saint-Léonard, P.Q. H1R 3G5 - T: (514) 328-8585
Fine Arts Museum 05834

Saint-Lunaire-Griquet

L'Anse aux Medows National Historic Site, POB 70, Saint-Lunaire-Griquet, Nfld. A0K 2X0 - T: (709) 623-2608, Fax: (709) 623-2028, E-mail: viking_lam@pch.gc.ca, Internet: http://parkscanada.pch.ac.ca/parks/newfoundland/anse_meadows
Historic Site 05835

Saint-Malo

Musée Le Pionnier, Saint-Malo, Man. R0A 1T0 - T: (204) 347-5767. Head: Maurice Comeault
Local Museum 05836

Saint Martins

Quaco Museum and Archives, 246 Main St, Saint Martins, N.B. E5R 1B8 - T: (506) 833-4740, Fax: (506) 833-2594, E-mail: bar@nbnet.nb.ca, Internet: http://www.fundytrailparkway.com. Head: Barbara McIntyre
Local Museum - 1978
Historical artifacts, furnishings and family treasures, lumbering and farming implements, shipbuilding - archives 05837

Saint Marys

Saint Marys Museum, 177 Church St S, Saint Marys, Ont. N4X 1A9, mail addr: POB 98, Saint Marys, Ont. N4X 1A9 - T: (519) 284-3556, Fax: (519) 284-2881, E-mail: stmmchin@quadro.net, Internet: http://www.stonetown.net. Head: M. Smith
Local Museum - 1959
Old stone house displays, antique furniture, glassware, local historical artifacts, research resources for genealogy and local hist 05838

Saint Paul

Fort George and Buckingham House, 5025 49 Av, Ste 318, Saint Paul, Alta. T0A 3A4 - T: (780) 645-6256, Fax: (780) 645-4760, E-mail: FtGeorge@mcd.gov.ab.ca
Archaeological Museum 05839

History Museum of Saint Paul, POB 1925, Saint Paul, Alta. T0A 3A0 - T: (780) 645-4800
Local Museum 05840

Saint-Paul-de-Ile-aux-Noix

Fort Lennox, 1 61st Av, Saint-Paul-de-Ile-aux-Noix, P.Q. J0J 1G0 - T: (450) 291-5700, Fax: (450) 291-4389, Internet: http://parkscanada.pch.gc.ca/parks/Quebec/Fortlennox. Head: Daniel Langlois
Historic Site - 1921
Various artifacts from Fort Lennox such as weapons and ceramics, several refurnished rooms 05841

Saint Peters

Nicolas Denys Museum, POB 249, Saint Peters, N.S. B0E 3B0 - T: (902) 535-2379. Head: Donna Cotie
Historical Museum - 1967
History of settlement (French including Huguenots and Acadians, Micman Indians, Scottish and Irish), artifacts from Denys settlement 1650-1683 05842

Saint-Pierre-Jolys

Musée de Saint-Pierre-Jolys, 432 Rue Joubert, Saint-Pierre-Jolys, Man. R0A 1V0 - T: (204) 433-7226, Fax: (204) 433-7181
Local Museum 05843

Saint Stephen

Charlotte County Museum, 443 Milltown Blvd, Saint Stephen, N.B. E3L 1J9 - T: (506) 466-3295, Fax: (506) 466-7701, E-mail: - charlotteco.museum@nb.aibn.com. Head: Irene Ritch
Local Museum 05844

Saint Thomas

Elgin County Pioneer Museum, 32 Talbot St, Saint Thomas, Ont. N5P 1A3 - T: (519) 631-6537, Fax: (519) 631-3884, E-mail: ecpmchin@execulink.com, Internet: http://www.execulink.com/~ecpmchin. Head: Linda Louwagie-Neyens
Historical Museum - 1957
Historic building (1848), first medical school in Upper Canada (1824) 05845

Elgin Military Museum, 30 Talbot St, Saint Thomas, Ont. N5P 1A3 - T: (519) 633-7641. Head: Sterling Ince
Military Museum 05846

Elgin Public Art Centre → Saint Thomas-Elgin Public Art Centre

Saint Thomas-Elgin Public Art Centre, 301 Talbot St, Saint Thomas, Ont. N5P 1B5 - T: (519) 631-4040, Fax: (519) 631-4057, E-mail: info@stepac.ca, Internet: http://www.stepac.ca. Head: Lori Chamberlain
Public Gallery 05847

Saint Victor

Beau Village Museum, POB 58, Saint Victor, Sask. S0H 3T0 - T: (306) 642-4016
Local Museum 05848

McGillis Pioneer Home, Saint Victor, Sask. S0H 3T0 - T: (306) 642-3155
Local Museum - 1972
Log home (1889), furnishings, Indian and Métis artifacts 05849

Saint Walburg

Imhoff Art Gallery, 4 Miles S and 1 Mile W of Saint Walburg, Saint Walburg, Sask. S0M 2T0, mail addr: POB 313, Saint Walburg, Sask. S0M 2T0 - T: (306) 248-3812, Fax: (306) 248-3812, E-mail: bpimhoff@sk.sympatico.ca, Internet: http://www.imhoff-art.com. Head: Bert C. Imhoff
Fine Arts Museum - 1920
Paintings by Berthold von Imhoff (1884-1939) 05850

Saint Walburg and District Historical Museum, POB 336, Saint Walburg, Sask. S0M 2T0 - T: (306) 248-3359
Local Museum 05851

Sainte-Anne

Musée Pointe des Chênes, 208 Av Centrale, Sainte-Anne, Man. R5H 1C9 - T: (204) 422-5639, Fax: (204) 422-5514, E-mail: norbrit@mb.sympatico.ca. Head: Gilles Nault
Local Museum 05852

Sainte-Anne-de-Beaupré

Musée de Sainte-Anne, 9803 Blvd Sainte-Anne, Sainte-Anne-de-Beaupré, P.Q. G0A 3C0 - T: (418) 827-6873, Fax: (418) 827-6870. Head: Julie Simard
Fine Arts Museum - 1997
Goldsmith work, 17th and 18th c votive pictures, sculptures - archives 05853

Sainte-Foy

Maison Hamel-Bruneau, 2608 Ch Saint-Louis, Sainte-Foy, P.Q. G1V 4E1 - T: (418) 654-4325, Fax: (418) 654-4151
Public Gallery 05854

Musée de Geologie, c/o Université Laval, Pavillion pouliot, Sainte-Foy, P.Q. G1K 7P4 - T: (418) 656-2193, Fax: (418) 656-7339, E-mail: alevesqu@ggl.ulaval.ca
Natural History Museum / University Museum - 1852
Haüy coll, Miguasha fishes coll 05855

Sainte-Marie

Maison J.A. Vachon, 383 Rue de la Coopérative, Sainte-Marie, P.Q. G6E 3B6 - T: (418) 387-4052, Fax: (418) 387-2454
Special Museum
Snack and cake factory 05856

Salmo

Salmo Museum, 104 4th St, Salmo, B.C. V0G 1Z0 - T: (250) 357-2200. Head: Gloria Currie
Local Museum 05857

Salmon Arm

Salmon Arm Museum, POB 1642, Salmon Arm, B.C. V1E 4P7 - T: (250) 832-5243, Fax: (250) 832-5291, E-mail: haney_park@telus.net
Local Museum - 1962
Indian and pioneer material - films 05858

Salvage

Salvage Fisherman's Museum, Bishop Dr, Salvage, Nfld. A0G 3X0 - T: (709) 677-2414. Head: Marion Heffern
Local Museum - 1969
Local history, tools, ship and fishing vessel equipment, household utensils and furniture, crafts, firearms 05859

Sandy Lake

Ukrainian Cultural Heritage Museum, Sandy Lake, Man. R0J 1X0 - T: (204) 585-2168
Local Museum 05860

Sangudo

Lac Sainte-Anne and District Pioneer Museum, POB 525, Sangudo, Alta. T0E 2A0 - T: (780) 785-2398
Local Museum / Ethnology Museum / Agriculture Museum - 1959
History, ethnology, farm equipment and tools - archives 05861

Sarnia

Gallery Lambton, 150 South Christina St N, Sarnia, Ont. N7T 2M6 - T: (519) 336-8127, Fax: (519) 336-8128, E-mail: glchin@ebtech.net
Public Gallery - 1903 05862

Sarnia Public Library and Art Gallery, 124 Christina St S, Sarnia, Ont. N7T 2M6 - T: (519) 337-3291. Head: H. Ford
Fine Arts Museum - 1903
Canadian paintings, prints, and sculpture, mainly works of the 'Group of Seven', Eskimo carvings 05863

Saskatoon

1910 Boomtown, Western Development Museum, 2610 Lorne Avenue South, Saskatoon, Sask. S7J 0S6 - T: (306) 931-1910, Fax: (306) 934-0525, E-mail: s_wdm@sasktel.net, Internet: http://www.wdmuseum.sk.ca. Head: David Klatt
Local Museum / Science&Tech Museum - 1949
Indoor 1910 prairie town, agricultural gallery, automotive galleries 05864

A.K.A. Gallery, 12 23rd St E, Saskatoon, Sask. S7K 0H5 - T: (306) 652-0044, Fax: (306) 652-9924, E-mail: aka@quadrat.net, Internet: http://www.quadrat.net/aka
Public Gallery 05865

Biology Museum (closed) 05866

Diefenbaker Canada Centre, University of Saskatchewan, 101 Diefenbaker Pl, Saskatoon, Sask. S7N 5B8 - T: (306) 966-8384, Fax: (306) 966-6207, E-mail: bruce.shepard@sask.usask.ca, Internet: http://www.usask.ca/diefenbaker. Head: Bruce Shepard
Historical Museum / University Museum 05867

Gordon Snelgrove Art Gallery, c/o University of Saskatchewan, 191 Murray Bldg, Saskatoon, Sask. S7N 5A4 - T: (306) 966-4208, Fax: (306) 966-4266, E-mail: gary.young@usask.ca, Internet: http://www.usask.ca./snelgrove. Head: Gary Young
Public Gallery / University Museum 05868

Kenderdine Art Gallery, c/o University of Saskatchewan, Thorvald Bldg, 110 Science Pl, Saskatoon, Sask. S7N 5C9 - T: (306) 966-4571, Fax: (306) 978-8340, E-mail: kent.archer@usask.ca, Internet: http://www.usask.ca/kenderdine. Head: Kent Archer
Fine Arts Museum / University Museum - 1964 05869

Memorial Library and Art Gallery, Nutana Collegiate Institute, 411 11th St E, Saskatoon, Sask. S7N 0E9 - T: (306) 653-1677. Head: Philip Listoe
Historical Museum / Fine Arts Museum / University Museum - 1925
Memorial to the collegiate students who died in WW I, Canadian paintings - library 05870

Mendel Art Gallery, 950 Spadina Crescent E, Saskatoon, Sask. S7K 3L6, mail addr: POB 569, Saskatoon, Sask. S7K 3L6 - T: (306) 975-7610, Fax: (306) 975-7670, E-mail: mendel@mendel.saskatoon.sk.ca, Internet: http://www.mendel.saskatoon.sk.ca. Head: Gilles Hébert
Fine Arts Museum - 1964
Canadian paintings, drawings, sculpture, prints, Inuit sculpture and prints 05871

Museum of Antiquities, c/o University of Saskatchewan, 237 Murray Bldg, 3 Campus Dr, Saskatoon, Sask. S7N 5A4 - T: (306) 966-7818, Fax: (306) 966-1954, E-mail: gundersn@duke.usask.ca, Internet: http://www.usask.ca/antiquities. Head: Catherine F. Gunderson
Museum of Classical Antiquities / University Museum 05872

Museum of Natural Sciences, c/o Department of Geological Sciences, University of Saskatchewan, 114 Science Rd, Saskatoon, Sask. S7N 5E2 - T: (306) 966-5683, Fax: (306) 966-8593, E-mail: weiman@admin.usask.ca, Internet: http://www.usask.ca/geology/museum.html
Natural History Museum / University Museum - 1977
Fossils, incl horse skeletons, dinosaur skeletons, meteorites, rocks and minerals, and some live displays 05873

Photographers Gallery, 12 23rd St E, Saskatoon, Sask. S7K 0H5 - T: (306) 244-8018, Fax: (306) 665-6568, E-mail: tpg@sk.sympatico.ca. Head: Donna Jones
Fine Arts Museum - 1973
Contemporary Canadian photography, electronic arts 05874

Saint Thomas More Art Gallery, c/o University of Saskatchewan, 1437 College Dr, Saskatoon, Sask. S7N 0W6 - T: (306) 966-8900, Fax: (306) 966-8904. Head: Colleen Fitzgerald
Fine Arts Museum / University Museum - 1968
Traditional, impressionistic and abstract art, photography 05875

Saskatchewan Craft Gallery, 813 Broadway Av, Saskatoon, Sask. S7N 1B5 - T: (306) 653-3616, Fax: (306) 244-2711
Public Gallery 05876

Ukraina Museum, 202 Av M South, Saskatoon, Sask. S7M 2K4 - T: (306) 244-4212, Fax: (306) 244-4212, E-mail: info@mum.ca, Internet: http://www.mum.ca. Head: Emilia Panamaroff
Ethnology Museum - 1951
Ethographic coll representing the spiritual, material and folkloric cultural heritage of Ukraine, Ukrainian civilization from prehist to the commencement of emigration - archives 05877

Ukrainian Museum of Canada, 910 Spadina Crescent E, Saskatoon, Sask. S7K 3H5 - T: (306) 244-3800, Fax: (306) 652-7620, E-mail: ukrmuse@sk.sympatico.ca, Internet: http://www.umc.sk.ca. Head: Janet Prebushewsky Danylink
Ethnology Museum - 1936
Ukrainian heritage objects, especially textiles, William Kurelek, Peter Rupchan - archives, resource center 05878

Wanuskewin Heritage Park, RR4, Saskatoon, Sask. S7K 3J7 - T: (306) 931-6767, Fax: (306) 931-4522
Local Museum 05879

Western Development Museum, 2935 Melville St, Saskatoon, Sask. S7J 5A6 - T: (306) 934-1400, Fax: (306) 934-4467, E-mail: swdm@sk.sympatico.ca, Internet: http://www.wdmuseum.sk.ca. Head: David Klatt
Local Museum 05880

Sault Sainte Marie

Art Gallery of Algoma, 10 East St, Sault Sainte Marie, Ont. P6A 3C3 - T: (7059 949-9067, Fax: (705) 949-6261, E-mail: artgala@age.net, Internet: http://www.angelfire.com/on/ArtGalleryofAlgoma. Head: Michael Burtch
Fine Arts Museum 05881

Ermatinger, Clergue Heritage Site, 831 Queen St E, Sault Sainte Marie, Ont. P6A 5N1, mail addr: POB 580, Sault Sainte Marie, Ont. P6A 5X6 - T: (705) 759-5443, Fax: (705) 541-7023, E-mail: old.stone.house@cityssm.on.ca
Local Museum - 1969
Oldest stone house west of Toronto (1814), period furnishings, exhibits describing the fur trade and local historical events 05882

Saint Mary's River Marine Centre, Museum Ship Norgoma, Station Mall, Sault Sainte Marie, Ont. P6A 6W6, mail addr: POB 23099, Sault Sainte Marie, Ont. P6A 6W6 - T: (705) 256-7447, Fax: (705) 942-6368, E-mail: budcampbell@sympatico.ca. Head: Bill Polnick
Special Museum - 1976
Motor ship Norgoma, 188 foot passenger vessel built in 1950, historical artifacts 05883

Sault Sainte Marie Museum, 690 Queen St E, Sault Sainte Marie, Ont. P6A 2A4 - T: (705) 759-7278, Fax: (705) 759-3058, E-mail: ssmmchin@vianet.on.ca. Head: Kathryn Fisher
Local Museum 05884

Sayward

Link and Pin, Loggin and Pioneer Museum, Sayward, B.C. V0P 1R0 - T: (604) 282-3678
Local Museum 05885

Scarborough

Scarborough Historical Museum, 1007 Brimley Rd, Scarborough, Ont. M1P 3E8 - T: (416) 431-3441, Fax: (416) 431-3441
Local Museum - 1962
Historic house furnished to present the era of Scarborough's Centennial in 1896, pioneer (1850) log house, 19th c carriage shop 05886

Sceptre

Great Sandhills Museum, POB 29, Sceptre, Sask. S0N 2H0 - T: (306) 623-4345, Fax: (306) 623-4612
Local Museum / Natural History Museum 05887

Sechelt

Téms Swíya Museum, POB 740, Sechelt, B.C. V0N 3A0 - T: (604) 885-8991, Fax: (604) 885-3490. Head: Bee Jackson
Local Museum 05888

Sedgewick

Sedgewick Museum and Gallery, POB 508, Sedgewick, Alta. T0B 4C0 - T: (780) 384-3741
Local Museum / Public Gallery 05889

Selkirk

Kennedy House, 1 Keystone Dr, Selkirk, Man. R1A 2H5 - T: (204) 334-2498, 785-5080, Fax: (204) 785-5082, E-mail: dhallam@nr.gov.mb.ca. Head: Doug Hallam
Historical Museum 05890

Lower Fort Garry, 35 km N of Winnipeg on Hwy 9, RR 3, Selkirk, Man. R1A 2A8, mail addr: POB 37-343, Selkirk, Man. R1A 2A8 - T: (204) 785-6050, Fax: (204) 482-5887, E-mail: LFGNH_Info@pch.gc.ca, Internet: http://parkscanada.pch.gc.ca/garry
Local Museum / Open Air Museum / Historic Site - 1963
Euro-Canadian artifacts, fur trade, Red River settlement, ethnographic material, Hudson Bay Company coll, mainly ethnographic, incl Athapaskan and Algonquian beadwork and quillwork 05891

Marine Museum of Manitoba, Selkirk Park, Mercy Av, Selkirk, Man. R1A 2B1 - T: (204) 482-7761, Fax: (204) 785-2452. Head: Ted Francis
Special Museum - 1972
Marine history of the Red River and Lake Winnipeg, fishing, two vessels on land 05892

Wilson MacDonald Memorial School Museum, RR1, Selkirk, Ont. N0A 1P0 - T: (905) 776-3319, Fax: (905) 776-3319, E-mail: wmcdmemorial@hotmail.com
Historical Museum 05893

Sept-Iles

Musée Régional de la Côte-Nord, 500 Blvd Laure, Sept-Iles, P.Q. G4R 4K9 - T: (418) 968-2070, Fax: (418) 968-8323, E-mail: mrcn@mrcn.qc.ca. Head: Micheline Huard
Local Museum / Fine Arts Museum 05894

Seven Sisters Falls

Nutimik Lake Museum, Seven Sisters Falls, Man. R0E 1Y0 - T: (204) 348-2203
Local Museum 05895

Whiteshell Natural Historic Museum, c/o Department of Natural Resources, Seven Sisters Falls, Man. R0E 1Y0 - T: (204) 348-2846, Fax: (204) 348-7141
Natural History Museum 05896

Shag Harbour

Chapel Hill Museum, Shag Harbour, N.S. B0W 3B0 - T: (902) 723-2830, Fax: (902) 723-2919
Local Museum 05897

Shamrock

Shamrock Museum, POB 106, Shamrock, Sask. S0H 3W0 - T: (306) 648-2909
Local Museum 05898

Sharon

Sharon Temple Museum, 18974 Leslie St, Sharon, Ont. L0G 1V0 - T: (905) 478-2389, E-mail: info@sharontemple.ca, Internet: http://www.sharontemple.ca. Head: Janet Emonson
Religious Arts Museum / Local Museum - 1918
Wooden temple built between 1825-1832 by the Children of Peace, artifacts of this religious sect and the York County area, hist of early settlers in Canada, religious hist of Children of Peace, a Quaker sect 05899

Shaunavon

Grand Coteau Heritage and Cultural Centre, Center St, Shaunavon, Sask. S0N 2M0 - T: (306) 297-3882, Fax: (306) 297-3668, E-mail: gchcc@sk.sympatico.ca. Head: Ingrid Cazakoff
Local Museum - 1932
Natural hist, archaeology and pioneer artifacts - art gallery 05900

Shawinigan

Centre des Arts de Shawinigan, 2100 Blvd des Hetres, Shawinigan, P.Q. G9N 6V3, mail addr: CP 400, Shawinigan, P.Q. G9N 6V3 - T: (819) 539-1888, Fax: (819) 539-2400, E-mail: cas01@videotron.ca, Internet: http://www.cdas.ca. Head: Robert Y. Desjardins
Fine Arts Museum - 1967
Paintings by local artists, photography 05901

Cité de l'Énergie, CP 156, Shawinigan, P.Q. G9N 6T9 - T: (819) 536-4992, Fax: (819) 536-2982, E-mail: citedelenergie@qc.aira.com, Internet: http://www.mauricie.net/citeenergie
Science&Tech Museum 05902

Shawnigan Lake

Shawnigan Lake Historical Museum, POB 331, Shawnigan Lake, B.C. V0R 2W0 - T: (250) 748-5707, Fax: (250) 748-2493
Local Museum 05903

Shearwater

Shearwater Aviation Museum, 12 Wing, Bonaventure Av, Shearwater, N.S. B0J 3A0 - T: (902) 460-1083, Fax: (902) 460-2037, E-mail: awmuseum@ns.sympatico.ca, Internet: http://www.shearwateraviation-museum.ns.ca. Head: D.A. Mason
Military Museum 05904

Sheguiandah

Little Current-Howland Centennial Museum, Hwy 68, S of Little Current, Sheguiandah, Ont. P0P 1W0 - T: (705) 368-2367, Fax: (705) 368-2361, E-mail: lindakelly@compuserv.com. Head: Linda Kelly
Local Museum - 1967
Hist of the pioneers of Manitoulin Island following the signing of the Treaty in 1862 permitting white settlement 05905

Shelburne

Dory Shop Museum, Shelburne, N.S. B0T 1W0 - Internet: http://museum.gov.ns.ca
Special Museum
Dory building factory, Banks fishery 05906

Ross Thomson House Museum, 9 Charlotte Ln, Shelburne, N.S. B0T 1W0, mail addr: POB 39, Shelburne, N.S. B0T 1W0 - T: (902) 875-3141, Fax: (902) 875-4141, E-mail: shelburne.museum@ns.sympatico.ca, Internet: http://www.historics-helburne.com/. Head: David Huddleston
Historical Museum - 1957
History of the Loyalists, documents relating to George and Robert Ross and Robert Thompson 05907

Shelburne County Museum, 8 Maiden Ln, Shelburne, N.S. B0T 1W0, mail addr: POB 39, Shelburne, N.S. B0T 1W0 - T: (902) 875-3219, Fax: (902) 875-4141, E-mail: shelburne.museum@ns.sympatico.ca, Internet: http://www.historics-helburne.com. Head: Finn Bower
Local Museum 05908

Shell Lake

Shell Lake Museum, POB 280, Shell Lake, Sask. S0J 2G0 - T: (306) 427-2272
Local Museum 05909

Sherbrooke, Nova Scotia

Sherbrooke Village, POB 285, Sherbrooke, Nova Scotia, N.S. B0J 3C0 - T: (902) 522-2400, Fax: (902) 522-2974, E-mail: svillage@gov.ns.ca, Internet: http://sherbrooke.museum.gov.ns.ca. Head: Craig MacDonald
Open Air Museum / Local Museum / Historic Site - 1971
Restoration of a lumbering and goldmining town (1860-1890) 05910

Sherbrooke, Québec

Centre d'Interpretation de l'Histoire de Sherbrooke, 275 Rue Dufferin, Sherbrooke, Québec, P.Q. J1H 4M5 - T: (819) 821-5406, Fax: (819) 821-5417, E-mail: societehistoire@sympatico.ca, Internet: http://shs.ville.sherbrooke.qc.ca. Head: Johanne Lacasse
Historical Museum 05911

Galerie d'Art du Centre Culturel, c/o Université de Sherbrooke, 2500 Blvd de l'Université, Sherbrooke, Québec, P.Q. J1K 2R1 - T: (819) 821-7748, Fax: (819) 820-1361, E-mail: j.brouill@courrier.usherb.ca. Head: Johanne Brouillet
Fine Arts Museum / University Museum - 1964
Contemporary art 05912

Musée des Beaux-Arts de Sherbrooke, 241 Rue Dufferin, Sherbrooke, Québec, P.Q. J1H 4M3 - T: (819) 821-2115, Fax: (819) 821-4003, E-mail: mbas@interlinx.qc.ca, Internet: http://mba.ville.sherbrooke.qc.ca. Head: Cécile Gélinas
Fine Arts Museum 05913

Musée du Séminaire de Sherbrooke, 195 Rue Marquette, Sherbrooke, Québec, P.Q. J1H 1L6 - T: (819) 564-3200, Fax: (819) 564-7388, E-mail: mss1@microtec.net, Internet: http://www.mss.ville.sherbrooke.qc.ca. Head: Yves Lauzière
Natural History Museum - 1879
Natural history, ethnology, archeology - archives 05914

Musée Régimentaire les Fusiliers de Sherbrooke, 64 Rue Belvédère S, Sherbrooke, Québec, P.Q. J1H 4B4 - T: (819) 564-5940, Fax: (819) 564-5641
Military Museum 05915

Sherwood Park

Strathcona County Heritage Foundation Museum, 913 Ash St, Sherwood Park, Alta. T8A 2G3 - T: (780) 467-8189
Local Museum 05916

Shilo

Royal Canadian Artillery Museum, Canadian Forces Base, Shilo, Man. R0K 2A0, mail addr: POB 5000, Shilo, Man. R0K 2A0 - T: (204) 765-3000 ext 4066, Fax: (204) 765-3289, E-mail: rcamuse@escape.ca, Internet: http://www.artillery.net. Head: R. Sanderson
Military Museum - 1962
Regimental history, uniforms, medals, documents and technical books, WWII vehicles - archives 05917

Shoal Lake

Police and Pioneer Museum, Lakeside Park, Shoal Lake, Man. R0J 1Z0
Local Museum - 1970
Pioneer artifacts, prints and paintings, shells, fossils, petrified wood 05918

Sicamous

Sicamous and District Museum, POB 944, Sicamous, B.C. V0E 2V0 - T: (250) 836-4456
Local Museum 05919

Sidney

British Columbia Aviation Museum, Victoria Airport, 1910 Norseman Rd, Sidney, B.C. V8L 5V5 - T: (250) 655-3300, Fax: 655-1611, E-mail: bcam@bcam.net, Internet: http://www.bcam.net. Head: Stan Henderson
Science&Tech Museum 05920

Sidney Historical Museum, Society of Saanich Peninsula Museums, 2423 Beacon Av, Sidney, B.C. V8L IX5 - T: (250) 655-6355, Fax: (250) 655-6366, E-mail: sspm@island.net, Internet: http://www.sidneymuseum.ca. Head: Peter Garnham
Historical Museum - 1971
LOcal and regional history 05921

Sidney Marine Museum, Society of Saanich Peninsula Museums, 9801 Seaport Pl, Sidney, B.C. V8L 4X3 - T: (250) 656-1322, Fax: (250) 656-2847, E-mail: sspm@pacificcoast.net, Internet: http://www.sidneymuseum.ca. Head: Peter Garnham
Special Museum - 1990
Ocean science, marine mammals, marine ecology 05922

Sidney Museum → Sidney Historical Museum

Sidney Museum → Sidney Marine Museum

West Coast Museum of Flying, 10137 W Saanich Rd, Sidney, B.C. V8L 5T6 - T: (250) 656-9339, Fax: (250) 655-3993
Science&Tech Museum 05923

Siksika

Siksika Nation Museum, POB 1730, Siksika, Alta. T0J 3W0 - T: (403) 734-5361, Fax: (403) 264-9659
Local Museum 05924

Sillery

Domaine Cataraqui, 2141 Ch Saint-Louis, Sillery, P.Q. G1T 1P9 - T: (418) 681-3010, Fax: (418) 681-3865, E-mail: cataraqui@globetrotter.net, Internet: http://www.cataraqui.qc.ca
Historical Museum 05925

Villa Bagatelle, 1563 Ch Saint-Louis, Sillery, P.Q. G1S 1G1 - T: (418) 688-8074, Fax: (418) 681-3865, E-mail: cataraqui@globetrotter.net, Internet: http://www.www.cataraqu.qc.ca
Historical Museum 05926

Silverton

Frank Mills Outdoor Mining Machinery Museum, POB 69, Silverton, B.C. V0G 1S0 - T: (250) 358-2485, Fax: (250) 358-2485
Open Air Museum / Science&Tech Museum 05927

Simcoe

Eva Brook Donly Museum, 109 Norfolk St S, Simcoe, Ont. N3Y 2W3 - T: (519) 426-1583, Fax: (519) 426-1584, E-mail: office@norfolklore.com, Internet: http://www.norfolklore.com. Head: William Yeager
Local Museum - 1929
Brick house with Victorian and pioneer furnishings, fossils, Indian artifacts, Van Norman forge exhibit, local history, paintings by Edgar Cantelon - archives 05928

Lynnwood Arts Centre, 21 Lynnwood Av, Simcoe, Ont. N3Y 4K8 - T: (519) 428-0540, Fax: (519) 428-0549, E-mail: lynnwood@kwic.com. Head: Rod Demerling
Fine Arts Museum 05929

Sioux Lookout

Sarah Vaughan Museum, Fifth Av, Sioux Lookout, Ont. P0V 2T0
Historical Museum / Science&Tech Museum - 1967
Early aviation artifacts, paintings by Carl Roy, Indian crafts, pioneer displays, replica of skis used by Byrd on his South Pole exploration 05930

Sioux Lookout Museum, 75 Wellington St, Sioux Lookout, Ont. P8T 1B9 - T: (807) 737-1562, Fax: (807) 737-4624, E-mail: slrec@slkt.net, Internet: http://www.municipalityofsiouxlookout.ca
Local Museum 05931

Skidegate

Haida Gwaii Museum at Qay'llnagaay, RR 1, Second Beach, Skidegate, B.C. V0T 1S1, mail addr: POB 1373, Skidegate, B.C. V0T 1S1 - T: (250) 559-4643, Fax: (250) 559-4662, E-mail: muse@qcislands.net. Head: Nathalie MacFarlane
Local Museum / Ethnology Museum - 1976
Haida ethnology and archeology, natural history, local history, totem pole coll - photo archives 05932

Smithers

Adams Igloo Wildlife Museum, Comp. 1, Site 9, RR1, Smithers, B.C. V0J 2N0 - T: (250) 847-3188
Natural History Museum 05933

Bulkley Valley Museum, POB 2615, Smithers, B.C. V0J 2N0 - T: (250) 847-5322, Fax: (250) 847-3337, E-mail: bvmuseum@mail.bulkley.net. Head: Lillian Weedmark
Local Museum 05934

Smithers Public Art Gallery, Central Park Bldg, Smithers, B.C. V0J 2N0 - T: (250) 847-3898
Public Gallery 05935

Smith's Cove

Smith's Cove Historical Museum, RR1, Smith's Cove, N.S. B0S 1S0
Local Museum 05936

Smiths Falls

Heritage House Museum, Old Slys Rd, Smiths Falls, Ont. K7A 4T6 - T: (613) 283-8560, Fax: (613) 283-4764, E-mail: hhmchin@falls.igs.net, Internet: http://www.town.smiths.falls.on.ca. Head: Susan McNichol
Local Museum 05937

Industrial Heritage Complex, 34a Beckwith St S, Smiths Falls, Ont. K7A 2A8 - T: (613) 283-5170, Fax: (613) 283-0677
Science&Tech Museum 05938

Smiths Falls Railway Museum of Eastern Ontario, 90 William St W, Smiths Falls, Ont. K7A 5A5 - T: (613) 283-5696, Fax: (613) 283-7211, E-mail: sfrmchin@superaje.com, Internet: http://www.magma.ca/~sfrm. Head: George Margita
Special Museum / Historic Site 05939

Snowflake

Star Mound School Museum, 2 Miles W and 1 Mile N of Snowflake, Snowflake, Man. R0G 2K0 - T: (204) 876-4749. Head: Alvin Findley
Special Museum 05940

Sombra

Sombra Township Museum, 146 Saint Clair St, Sombra, Ont. N0P 2H0 - T: (519) 892-3982, 892-3631
Local Museum - 1959
Exhibits pertaining to the Saint Clair River, kitchen utensils, crafts, local historical artifacts - library 05941

Sooke

Sooke Region Museum, Art Gallery and Historic Moss Cottage, 2070 Phillps Rd, Sooke, B.C. V0S 1N0 - T: (604) 642-6351, Fax: (604) 642-7089, E-mail: info@sooke.museum.bc.ca, Internet: http://www.island.net/~scm_chin. Head: Terry Malone
Local Museum / Fine Arts Museum - 1977
Local history - archives 05942

Sorel-Tracy

Centre d'Interprétation du Patrimoine de Sorel, 6 Rue Saint-Pierre, Sorel-Tracy, P.Q. J3P 3S2 - T: (450) 780-5740, Fax: (450) 780-5734, E-mail: cips@globetrotter.net, Internet: http://www.centrart.qc.ca/cips. Head: Marc Mineau
Natural History Museum
Nature, environment 05943

Souris

Basin Head Fisheries Museum, Prince Edward Island Museum and Heritage Foundation, RR 2, Souris, P.E.I. C0A 2B0 - T: (902) 357-7233. Head: Anne Garrett
Special Museum - 1973
Fishing industry 05944

Hillcrest Museum, 26 Crescent E, Souris, Man. R0K 2C0 - T: (204) 483-2008. Head: Harvey Harltow
Local Museum - 1967
Furnished period rooms (1912), pioneer artifacts including tools and toys, native artifacts, history room, pictures 05945

South Porcupine

Timmins Museum, National Exhibition Centre, 70 Legion Dr, South Porcupine, Ont. P0N 1H0 - T: (705) 235-5066, Fax: (705) 235-9631, E-mail: tmnec@city.timmins.on.ca. Head: Karen Bachmann-Tonelli
Local Museum
Local history and folklore, fine arts - archives 05946

South Rawdon

South Rawdon Museum, 1761 S Rawdon Rd, Hwy 202, South Rawdon, N.S. B0N 1Z0 - T: (902) 757-2344, 757-2341, E-mail: hbhaley@ns.sympatico.ca, Internet: http://www.rawdonmuseum.com. Head: Helen Haley
Local Museum - 1967 05947

Southampton

Bruce County Museum, 33 Victoria St N, Southampton, Ont. N0H 2L0 - T: (519) 797-2080, Fax: (519) 797-2191, E-mail: museum@brucecounty.on.ca, Internet: http://museum.brucecounty.on.ca. Head: Barbara Ribey
Local Museum 05948

Southey

Southey and District Museum, Southey, Sask. S0G 4P0
Local Museum 05949

Spalding

Reynold Rapp Museum, First St S, Spalding, Sask. S0K 4C0 - T: (306) 872-2295. Head: Velma Spizauka
Local Museum 05950

Springdale

Harvey Grant Heritage Centre Community Museum, POB 57, Springdale, Nfld. A0J 1T0 - T: (709) 673-4313, Fax: (709) 673-4969
Local Museum 05951

Springhill

Anne Murray Centre, Main St, Springhill, N.S. B0M 1X0 - T: (902) 597-8614, Fax: (902) 597-2001, Internet: http://www.grtplaces.com/ac/anne
Special Museum 05952

Springhill Miner's Museum, Black River Rd, Springhill, N.S. B0M 1X0 - T: (902) 597-3449, 597-8614, Fax: (902) 597-2001, Internet: http://www.grtplaces.com/ac/mine. Head: Shelagh F. Rayworth
Science&Tech Museum - 1972
Mining history 05953

Spruce Home

Buckland Heritage Museum, Hwy 2, Spruce Home, Sask. S0J 2N0 - T: (306) 764-8470
Local Museum 05954

Spruce View

Dickson Store Museum, POB 146, Spruce View, Alta. T0M 1V0 - T: (403) 728-3331
Historical Museum 05955

Spy Hill

Wolverine Hobby and Historical Society Museum, 108 Main St, Spy Hill, Sask. S0A 3W0 - T: (306) 534-2252. Head: Glenn Walz
Local Museum - 1954
Local history exhibits, pioneer and Indian artifacts, violins, early gramophones 05956

Stanbridge East

Missisquoi Museum, 2 River St, Stanbridge East, P.Q. J0J 2H0 - T: (514) 248-3153, Fax: (514) 248-0420, E-mail: sochm@globetrotter.net, Internet: http://www.geocities.com/Heartland/lake/8392
Local Museum - 1964
Farm machinery, model Victorian village, workshops of various trades, handicrafts, antique weapons, furniture, china, toys, glass, tools - library, archives 05957

Star City

Star City Museum, 217 Fifth St, Star City, Sask. S0E 1P0 - T: (306) 863-2309, Fax: (306) 863-2255
Local Museum 05958

Steinbach

Mennonite Heritage Village, Hwy 12, N of Steinbach, Steinbach, Man. R0A 2A0 - T: (204) 326-9661, Fax: (204) 326-5046, E-mail: mennovil@mb.sympatico.ca, Internet: http://www.mennonite-heritagevillage.mb.ca. Head: Gary Snider
Open Air Museum / Agriculture Museum - 1966
Reconstructed Mennonite village including school, church, windmill, blacksmith shop, printery, pioneer and Mennonite artifacts - library, archives 05959

Stellarton

Museum of Industry, 147 North Ford St, Stellarton, N.S. B0K 1S0 - T: (902) 755-5425, Fax: (902) 755-7045, E-mail: industry@gov.ns.ca, Internet: http://www.industry.museum.gov.ns.ca. Head: Debra McNabb
Historical Museum 05960

Stettler

Stettler Town and Country Museum, 44th Av W, Stettler, Alta. T0C 2L0 - T: (403) 742-4534. Head: Wilda V. Gibbon
Open Air Museum - 1974
Historic buildings with furnishings and artifacts from pioneer days 05961

Stewart

Stewart Historical Museum, Columbia and Sixth Av, Stewart, B.C. V0T 1W0 - T: (250) 636-2568, Fax: (250) 636-2568. Head: Karin Hanhart
Science&Tech Museum / Local Museum - 1975
Mining equipment, mineralogy, natural history, pioneer items - archives 05962

Stoney Creek

Battlefield House Museum, 77 King St W, Stoney Creek, Ont. L8G 5E5 - T: (905) 662-8458, Fax: (905) 662-0529, E-mail: curator@battlefieldhouse.ca, Internet: http://www.battlefieldhouse.ca. Head: Susan Ramsay
Historical Museum 05963

Erland Lee Home, 552 Ridge Rd, Stoney Creek, Ont. L8J 2Y6 - T: (905) 662-2691, Fax: (905) 662-2045, E-mail: erlandlh@fwio.on.ca, Internet: http://www.fwio.on.ca/fwio/promo.html. Head: Michael Gemmell
Historic Site / Historical Museum
Household furnishings 19th c, quilts - archive 05964

Stony Plain

Multicultural Heritage Centre, 5411 51st St, Stony Plain, Alta. T7Z 1X7, mail addr: POB 2188, Stony Plain, Alta. T7Z 1X7 - T: (780) 963-2777, Fax: (780) 963-0233, E-mail: multihc@telusplanet.net, Internet: http://www.heritag.ab.ca. Head: Judy Unterschultz
Local Museum - 1974
Local hist, photo coll, pioneer artifacts, cabin, 1910 house, 1925 school, farming, art - library, archives 05965

Stony Plain and District Pioneer Museum, 5120 43 Av, Stony Plain, Alta. T7Z 1X2 - T: (780) 963-9825
Local Museum 05966

Stoughton

Stoughton and District Museum, 327 Main St, Stoughton, Sask. S0G 4T0 - T: (306) 457-2662
Local Museum 05967

Strasbourg

Strasbourg and District Museum, CPR Station, Railway Av, Strasbourg, Sask. S0G 4V0 - T: (306) 725-3443. Head: Ingrid Youck
Local Museum - 1973
Local pioneer and Indian artifacts, mounted birds and animals indigenous to Saskatchewan 05968

Stratford

Brocksden Country School Museum, 87 Nile St, Stratford, Ont. N5A 4C7
Historical Museum 05969

Gallery Stratford, 54 Romeo St S, Stratford, Ont. N5A 4S9 - T: (519) 271-5271, Fax: (519) 271-1642, E-mail: clee@gallerystratford.on.ca, Internet: http://www.gallerystratford.on.ca. Head: Robert Windrum
Fine Arts Museum - 1966
Contemporary Canadian and American prints and drawings, sculpture 05970

Minnie Thomson Memorial Museum, 138 Vivian St, Stratford, Ont. N5A 4C7 - T: (519) 271-1138
Agriculture Museum / Science&Tech Museum - 1960
Household items, antique automobiles, farm machinery and tractors, steam caliope (1897), steam locomotive and coach 05971

Perth Regiment Museum, c/o Stratford Armoury, 80 Waterloo St S, Stratford, Ont. N5A 4A9. Head: John Blue
Military Museum 05972

Strathclair

Strathclair Museum, Main St, Strathclair, Man. R0J 2C0 - T: (204) 365-5201/02
Local Museum 05973

Strathroy

A.W. Campbell House Museum, 205 Mill Pond Cres., Strathroy, Ont. N7G 3P9 - T: (519) 245-3710, Fax: (519) 245-3348, E-mail: stclair@scrca.on.ca, Internet: http://www.scrca.on.ca
Historical Museum 05974

Strathroy Middlesex Museum, 84 Oxford St, Strathroy, Ont. N7G 3A5 - T: (519) 245-0492. Head: Muriel Kew
Local Museum - 1971
Local history exhibits, period rooms, computer room, tools 05975

Strome

Sodbuster Archives Museum, POB 151, Strome, Alta. T0B 4H0 - T: (780) 376-3688
Historical Museum 05976

Sturgeon Falls

Sturgeon River House, 250 Chemin Fort, Sturgeon Falls, Ont. P0H 2G0 - T: (705) 753-4716, Fax: (705) 753-5476, E-mail: srhchin@onlink.net, Internet: http://www.sturgeonriverhouse.com. Head: Irene Guenette
Local Museum
Artifacts pertaining to the furtrade, local history, trapping equipments 05977

Sturgis

Sturgis Station House Museum, POB 255, Sturgis, Sask. S0A 4A0 - T: (306) 548-5565, Fax: (306) 548-2948
Local Museum 05978

Sudbury

Art Gallery of Sudbury, 251 John St, Sudbury, Ont. P3E 1P9 - T: (705) 675-4871, Fax: (705) 674-3065, E-mail: gallery@artsudbury.org, Internet: http://www.artsudbury.org. Head: Bill Huffman
Fine Arts Museum - 1967
Canadian historical and contemporary work including painting,video and installation,sculpture,Eskimo prints, sculpture and artifacts 05979

Centre Franco-Ontarien de Folklore, Maison d'Youville, 38 Rue Xavier, Sudbury, Ont. P3C 2B9 - T: (705) 675-8986, Fax: (705) 675-5809. Head: Germain Lemieux
Folklore Museum 05980

Copper Cliff Museum, BP 5000, Stn A, Sudbury, Ont. P3A 5P3 - T: (705) 674-3141 ext 457, Fax: (705) 671-8145
Local Museum 05981

Flour Mill Museum, 514 Rue Notre Dame, Sudbury, Ont. P3A 5P3 - T: (705) 674-2391, Fax: (705) 671-8145. Head: Peter Philipon
Science&Tech Museum 05982

Greater Sudbury Heritage Museum, POB 6400, Sudbury, Ont. P3A 3B7 - T: (705) 692-4448, Fax: (705) 692-4448, E-mail: jim.fortin@city.greatersudbury.on.ca, Internet: http://www.city.greatersudbury.on.ca. Head: James Fortin
Agriculture Museum / Local Museum 05983

Science North, 100 Ramsey Lake Rd, Sudbury, Ont. P3E 5S9 - T: (705) 522-3701, Fax: (705) 522-4954, Internet: http://sciencenorth.on.ca
Science&Tech Museum / Natural History Museum 05984

Summerland

Summerland Museum, 9521 Wharton St, Summerland, B.C. V0H 1Z0, mail addr: POB 1491, Summerland, B.C. V0H 1Z0 - T: (250) 494-9395, Fax: (250) 494-9326, E-mail: smhschin@vip.net, Internet: http://www.chin.gc.ca. Head: Merlin Rosser
Local Museum - 1969
Historical photos of pioneers and the district, early 20th c archival material, household utensils, agricultural tools, railway history 05985

Summerside

Eptek National Exhibition Centre, Prince Edward Island Museum and Heritage Foundation, Waterfront Properties, 130 Harbour Dr, Summerside, P.E.I. C1N 1A9 - T: (902) 888-8373, Fax: (902) 888-8375. Head: Nonie Fraser
Local Museum - 1978 05986

International Fox Museum, 286 Fitzroy St, Summerside, P.E.I. C1N 1J2 - T: (902) 436-2400
Science&Tech Museum / Agriculture Museum 05987

Sundre

Historical Museum and Pioneer Village, POB 314, Sundre, Alta. T0M 1X0 - T: (403) 638-3233
Local Museum 05988

Sundridge

Maple Sugar Museum, Art Gallery and Pioneer Home, Sundridge, Ont. P0A 1Z0 - T: (705) 384-7764
Special Museum / Fine Arts Museum / Local Museum 05989

Surrey

Historic Stewart Farmhouse, 13723 Crescent Rd, Surrey, B.C. V4A 2W3 - T: (604) 574-5744, Fax: (604) 574-7338. Head: B.A. Sommer
Agriculture Museum 05990

Surrey Art Gallery, 13750 88th Av, Surrey, B.C. V3W 3L1 - T: (604) 501-5566, Fax: (604) 501-5581, E-mail: artgallery@city.surrey.bc.ca, Internet: http://www.city.surrey.bc.ca/ParksRecCulture/artgallery. Head: Liane Davison, Ingrid Kolt
Fine Arts Museum - 1975
Contemporary visual art 05991

Surrey Museum, 6022 176th St, Surrey, B.C. V3S 4E8 - T: (604) 502-6456, E-mail: LMPanko@city.surrey.bc.ca
Ethnology Museum / Archaeological Museum / Local Museum - 1958
First Nations, agriculture, business, transportation, domestic life, furnishings, military, textiles - archives, education 05992

Sussex

Agricultural Museum of New Brunswick, Rte 1, Sussex, N.B. E0E 1P0 - T: (506) 433-6799
Agriculture Museum 05993

Sutton, Ontario

Eildon Hall Sibbald Memorial Museum, Sibbald Point Provincial Park, RR 2, Sutton, Ontario, Ont. L0E 1R0 - T: (905) 722-3268, Fax: (905) 722-5416
Local Museum - 1957
Pioneer home of the Sibbald family (1837), portraits and military and naval paraphernalia primarily of the Victorian era 05994

Swan River

Swan Valley Museum, POB 2078, Swan River, Man. R0L 1Z0 - T: (204) 734-3585. Head: Glynn Donaldson
Local Museum 05995

Swift Current

Art Gallery of Swift Current National Exhibition Centre, 411 Hebert St E, Swift Current, Sask. S9H 1M5 - T: (306) 778-2736, Fax: (306) 778-2198, E-mail: k.houghtling@city.swift-current.sk.ca, Internet: http://www.city.swift-current.sk.ca/arts/nec. Head: Kim Houghtling
Fine Arts Museum - 1974 05996

Sydney

Cape Breton Centre for Heritage and Science, The Lyceum, 225 George St, Sydney, N.S. B1P 1J5 - T: (902) 539-1572, Fax: (902) 539-1572, E-mail: maltby.janet@ns.sympatico.ca. Head: Janet Maltby
Local Museum / Natural History Museum - 1988
Regional natural and cultural heritage exhibitions and programming, travelling exhibitions, children's discovery corner - Archive 05997

Cossit House Museum, Cape Breton Centre for Heritage and Science, 75 Charlotte St, Sydney, N.S. B1P 1J5 - T: (902) 539-7973/1572, Fax: (902) 539-1572, E-mail: maltby.janet@ns.sympatico.ca. Head: Janet Maltby
Historical Museum / Historic Site - 1977
Early colonial hist, 18th c furnishings, 18th c period rooms, Reverend Ranna Cossit, Loyalist and first permanent Anglican minister in Sydney 05998

Jost House Museum, 54 Charlotte St, Sydney, N.S. B1P 6J4, mail addr: POB 912, Sydney, N.S. - T: (902) 539-0366/1572. Head: Joan Harriss, Janet Maltby
Historical Museum - 1991
Local and marine hist, 18th-19th c period rooms, antiques, early apothecary's shop, photographs, Jost family hist 05999

Saint Patrick's Museum, Cape Breton Centre for Heritage and Science, 89 Esplanade, Sydney, N.S. B1P 1J5 - T: (902) 562-8237, 539-1572, Fax: (902) 539-1572, E-mail: maltby.janet@ns.sympatico.ca. Head: Janet Maltby
Local Museum - 1967
Local history, artifacts - library 06000

University College of Cape Breton Art Gallery, 1250 Grand Lake Rd, mail addr: POB 5300, Sydney, N.S. B1P 6L2 - T: (902) 563-1342, Fax: (902) 563-1142, E-mail: bdavis@uccb.ns.ca, Internet: http://www.uccb.ns.ca/artgallery. Head: Beryl Davis
Fine Arts Museum / University Museum 06001

Taber

Taber and District Museum, 4702 50 St, Taber, Alta. T1G 2B6 - T: (403) 223-5708
Local Museum 06002

Tabusintac

Tabusintac Centennial Museum, 4490 Rte 11, Tabusintac, N.B. E9H 1J3 - T: (506) 779-8045
Local Museum 06003

Tadoussac

Chapelle des Indiens, Tadoussac, P.Q. G0T 2A0 - T: (418) 235-4324
Religious Arts Museum - 1747
Religious items, missal (1600), Virgin Mary statue (1760), paintings, Indian necklace 06004

Poste de Traite Chauvin, 157 Rue du Bord-de-l'Eau, Tadoussac, P.Q. G0T 2A0 - T: (418) 235-4657, Fax: (418) 235-4149
Special Museum 06005

Tatamagouche

Balmoral Grist Mill, RR4, Tatamagouche, N.S. B0K 1V0 - T: (902) 657-3016
Science&Tech Museum 06006

Sunrise Trail Museum, Main St, Tatamagouche, N.S. B0K 1V0 - T: (902) 657-2433. Head: Ellen Millard
Local Museum - 1958
Local history, artifacts of early settlers, household and kitchen utensils, farming 06007

Tatla Lake

Tatla Lake Centennial Museum, Tatla Lake, B.C. V0L 1V0
Historical Museum / Natural History Museum - 1967
Human history, natural history - archives 06008

Teeterville

Teeterville Pioneer Museum, POB 85, Teeterville, Ont. N0E 1S0 - T: (519) 443-4400, 582-0218, Fax: (519) 582-0122
Local Museum - 1967
Agricultural implements, furnished pioneer log house (1849) - archives 06009

Tehkummah

Tehkummah Township Museum, Municipal Office, Tehkummah, Ont. P0P 2C0 - T: (705) 859-3293, Fax: (705) 854-2605, E-mail: twptehk@amtelecom.ca
Local Museum 06010

Telkwa

Telkwa Museum, POB 595, Telkwa, B.C. V0J 2X0 - T: (250) 846-9656
Local Museum 06011

Terrace

Heritage Park Museum, 4113 Sparks St, Terrace, B.C. V8G 4B5 - T: (250) 635-4546, Fax: (250) 615-3010, E-mail: museum@terracetourism.bc.ca. Head: Bruce Martindale
Local Museum 06012

Teslin

George Johnston Tlingit Indian Museum, Mile 804, Alaska Hwy, Teslin, Y.T. Y0A 1B0 - T: (867) 390-2550, Fax: (867) 390-2828
Local Museum / Historical Museum 06013

Teulon

Teulon and District Museum, Owen Acres Park, Teulon, Man. R0C 3B0 - T: (204) 886-2792, Fax: (204) 886-3787
Local Museum - 1976
Local history 06014

The Pas

Sam Waller Museum, 306 Fischer Av, The Pas, Man. R9A 1K4 - T: (204) 623-3802, Fax: (204) 623-5506, E-mail: museum@cancom.net, Internet: http://www.cancom.net/~museum. Head: Ron Scott
Historical Museum / Natural History Museum - 1958
Indian artifacts, mineralogy, natural hist, numismatics, local hist - archives 06015

Thetford Mines

Musée Minéralogique et Minier de Thetford Mines, 711 Blvd Smith Sud, Thetford Mines, P.Q. G6G 5T3 - T: (418) 335-2123, Fax: (418) 335-5605, E-mail: mmmtm@mmmtm.qc.ca, Internet: http://www.mmmtm.qc.ca. Head: François Cinc-Mars
Natural History Museum / Science&Tech Museum
Story of the Appalachian Mountains, their exeptional mineral deposits, talc, copper and chrome, minerals and crystals 06016

Three Hills

Kneehill Historical Museum, POB 653, Three Hills, Alta. T0M 2A0 - T: (403) 443-5348
Local Museum 06017

Thunder Bay

Centennial Park 1910 Logging Museum, 111 Syndicate Av S., Thunder Bay, Ont. P7E 6S4 - T: (807) 625-2113, Fax: (807) 625-3258. Head: Dwight Gessie
Open Air Museum - 1967
Restored typical local logging camp (1910) including cookery, bunkhouse, sauna, blacksmith's shop, and stable, logging artifacts 06018

Northwestern Ontario Sports Hall of Fame, 219 May St S, Thunder Bay, Ont. P7E 1B5 - T: (807) 622-2852, Fax: (807) 622-2736, E-mail: nwosport@air.on.ca
Special Museum 06019

Old Fort William Historical Park, King Rd, Thunder Bay, Ont. P0T 2Z0 - T: (807) 577-8461, Fax: (807) 473-2327, E-mail: info@oldfortwilliam.on.ca, Internet: http://www.oldfortwilliam.on.ca. Head: Elaine Nemeth
Historical Museum / Historic Site - 1973
Reconstruction of Fort William as it existed in 1815, a living historical community, including a farm, cottages, artisan's square, canoe building areas, jail, Council House, Native encampment, fur trade themes, explorers Alexander MacKenzie and Simon Fraser (North West Company 1774-1821) - library 06020

Paipoonge Historical Museum, RR6, Thunder Bay, Ont. P7C 5N5 - T: (807) 939-1262, Fax: (807) 939-4132. Head: Lois Garrity
Local Museum 06021

Thunder Bay Art Gallery, 1080 Keewatin St, Thunder Bay, Ont. P7B 6T7 - T: (807) 577-6427, Fax: (807) 577-3781, E-mail: tbagchin@tbaytel.net, Internet: http://thunderbayculture.com. Head: Sharon Godwin
Fine Arts Museum 06022

Thunder Bay Historical Society Museum, 425 Donald St E, Thunder Bay, Ont. P7E 5V1 - T: (807) 623-0801, Fax: (807) 622-6880, E-mail: tbhms@tbaytel.net, Internet: http://www.tbaytel.net/tbhms. Head: Thorold Tronrud
Historical Museum - 1908
Indian and pioneer artifacts, marine and military items, Canadian hist, urban hist - archives 06023

Thunder Bay Military Museum, The Armoury, 317 Park Av, Thunder Bay, Ont. P7C 1C7 - T: (807) 343-5175, Fax: (807) 345-1961, E-mail: jjyoung@norlink.net. Head: John J. Young
Military Museum
Navy, army and airforce history, military art, German prisoner of war coll 06024

Tighish

Dalton Centre Museum, POB 160, Tighish, P.E.I. C0B 2B0. Head: J. Henri Gaudet
Local Museum 06025

Tillsonburg

Annandale National Historic Site, 30 Tillson Av, Tillsonburg, Ont. N4G 2Z8 - T: (519) 842-2294, Fax: (519) 842-9431, E-mail: rcorner@town.tillsonburg.on.ca, Internet: http://www.town.tillsonburg.on.ca. Head: Rita Corner
Local Museum / Decorative Arts Museum - 1972
Displays pertaining to local hist, aesthetic house interior and furnishings incl painted ceilings, stained art glass, carved and moulded woodwork, clothing and textiles, documentary artifacts 06026

Tobermory

Peninsula and Saint Edmunds Township Museum, RR 1, Tobermory, Ont. N0H 2R0 - T: (519) 596-2479
Local Museum 06027

Tofield

Tofield Historical Museum, 5020 46th Av, Tofield, Alta. T0B 4J0 - T: (780) 662-3191, Fax: (780) 662-3929, E-mail: tofield@supernet.ab.ca, Internet: http://www.tenap.tofield.ab.ca. Head: Ron

Taylor
Local Museum - 1962
Indian artifacts, agricultural tools and implements, minute books, historic Bibles 06028

Tofino

West Coast Maritime Museum, POB 249, Tofino, B.C. V0R 2Z0 - T: (250) 725-3346. Head: Olivia Mal
Historical Museum 06029

Tompkins

Tompkins Museum, POB 393, Tompkins, Sask. S0N 2S0 - T: (306) 622-2024
Local Museum 06030

Torbay

Torbay Museum, 1288 Torbay Rd, Torbay, Nfld. A1K 1K4 - T: (709) 437-6571, Fax: (709) 437-1309, E-mail: torbayheritage@nf-mail.net, Internet: http://www.torbay.publib.ng.ca/. Head: Jerri Pellegrinetti
Local Museum 06031

Toronto

A Space, 401 Richmond St W, Toronto, Ont. M5T 2R7 - T: (416) 979-9633, Fax: (416) 979-9683, E-mail: aspace@interlog.com, Internet: http://www.interlog.com/~aspace
Public Gallery 06032

Academy of Spherical Arts, 38 Hanna Av, Toronto, Ont. M6K 1X5 - T: (416) 532-2782, Fax: (416) 532-3075
Fine Arts Museum 06033

Annex Art Centre Gallery, 1073 Bathurst St, Toronto, Ont. M5R 3G8 - T: (416) 516-0110. Head: Deborah Harris
Fine Arts Museum 06034

Art Gallery of Ontario, 317 Dundas St W, Toronto, Ont. M5T 1G4 - T: (416) 979-6648, Fax: (416) 979-6646, E-mail: director@ago.net, Internet: http://www.ago.net. Head: Matthew Teitelbaum
Fine Arts Museum - 1900
Italian 15th-18th c, Dutch 17th c, French 17th-20th c, British 18th-20th c, Canadian and American 19th-20th c paintings, drawings, sculptures, and prints, Henry Moore sculpture and graphics - library 06035

Art Gallery of York University, 145 Ross Bldg, 4700 Keele St, North York, Toronto, Ont. M3J 1P3 - T: (416) 736-5169, Fax: (416) 736-5985, E-mail: agyu@yorku.ca, Internet: http://www.yorku.ca/agyu. Head: Loretta Yarlow
Fine Arts Museum / University Museum - 1970
Contemporary Canadian and international paintings, sculpture, drawings and prints, historic and modern carvings 06036

Bata Shoe Museum, 327 Bloor St W, Toronto, Ont. M5S 1W7 - T: (416) 979-7799, Fax: (416) 979-0078, Internet: http://www.batashoemuseum.ca. Head: Sonja Bata
Special Museum
Over 4,500 years shoe history, 10,000 shoes, 20th c coll 06037

Beth Tzedec Reuben and Helene Dennis Museum, 1700 Bathurst St, Toronto, Ont. M5P 3K3 - T: (416) 781-3514 ext. 32, Fax: (416) 781-0150, E-mail: btmuseum@cpol.com
Religious Arts Museum / Ethnology Museum - 1962
Silver, pewter, and bronze Judaic objects, torah scroll ornaments in silver and textiles, illuminated marriage contracts (17th-19th c) 06038

Campbell House, 160 Queen St W, Toronto, Ont. M5H 3H3 - T: (416) 597-0227, Fax: (416) 597-1588, Internet: http://www.advsoc.on.ca/campbell
Local Museum - 1974
Built in 1822, Campbell House was the home of William Campbell, the Chief Justice of Upper Canada from 1825-1829, furnishings of the period, model of the town of York 06039

Canada's Sports Hall of Fame, Exhibitions Pl, Toronto, Ont. M6K 3C3 - T: (416) 260-6789, Fax: (416) 260-9347, E-mail: cshof@inforamp.net, Internet: http://www.inforamp.net/~cshof
Special Museum 06040

Canadian Baseball Hall of Fame, c/o Ontario Place, 955 Lake Shore Blvd W, Toronto, Ont. M6K 3B9 - T: (416) 965-7917, Fax: (416) 598-0056
Special Museum 06041

Canadian Museum of Health and Medicine, 595 University Av, Bell Wing 1-651, Toronto, Ont. M5G 2C4 - T: (416) 340-4800, Fax: (416) 340-4896, E-mail: krumbold@torhosp.toronto.on.ca, Internet: http://www.cmhm.org
Historical Museum 06042

Canadiana Gallery, Royal Ontario Museum, 14 Queen's Park Crescent W, Toronto, Ont. M5S 2C6 - T: (416) 586-5704
Public Gallery 06043

Casa Loma, 1 Austin Terrace, Toronto, Ont. M5R 1X8 - T: (416) 923-1171, Fax: (416) 923-5734, E-mail: info@casaloma.org, Internet: http://www.casaloma.org. Head: Virginia Cooper
Historical Museum 06044

CBC Museum, 250 Front St W, Toronto, Ont. M5W 1E6 - T: (416) 205-5574, Fax: (416) 205-7583. Head: Ivan Harris
Science&Tech Museum 06045

Centre for Experimental Art and Communication, 15 Duncan St, Toronto, Ont. M5H 3H1
Fine Arts Museum - 1973
Canadian and international art in the form of performances, discussions, interviews and installations, artists' books - archives 06046

Century Schoolhouse, 502 Sammon Av, Toronto, Ont. M4C 2V3 - T: (416) 396-2074, Fax: (416) 396-2238
Historical Museum 06047

Children's Own Museum, 90 Queen's Park, Toronto, Ont. M5S 2C5 - T: (416) 542-1492, Fax: (416) 542-1495
Historical Museum 06048

City of York Museum, 2694 Eglinton Av W, Toronto, Ont. M6M 1V1 - T: (416) 394-2513, Fax: (416) 394-2803
Local Museum - 1969
Tools dating back to the pioneer days in the Old Town of Weston and vicinity, equipment used by the local Police Department 06049

Colborne Lodge, c/o Culture Division, City of Toronto, 55 John St, Toronto, Ont. M5V 3C6 - T: (416) 392-6916, Fax: (416) 392-0375, E-mail: clodge@city.toronto.on.ca, Internet: http://www.toronto.on.ca/culture. Head: Rita Davies
Historical Museum 06050

Creative Spirit Art Centre, 1071 Bathurst St, Toronto, Ont. M5R 3G8 - T: (416) 588-8801, Fax: (416) 588-8801, E-mail: csac@interlog.com, Internet: http://www.creativespirit.on.ca. Head: Ellen Anderson
Public Gallery 06051

Enoch Turner Schoolhouse, 106 Trinity St, Toronto, Ont. M5A 3C6 - T: (416) 863-0010. Head: Dean Malloy
Special Museum - 1971
School articles and textbooks of the 1800's 06052

Fire Fighting Museum, 895 Eastern Av, Toronto, Ont. M4L 1A2
Historical Museum 06053

Gallery 44, 401 Richmond St W, #120, Toronto, Ont. M5V 3A8 - T: (416) 979-3941, Fax: (416) 340-8458, E-mail: G44@interlog.com, Internet: http://www.interlog.com/~g44
Public Gallery 06054

Gallery Arcturus, 80 Gerrard St E, Toronto, Ont. M5B 1G6 - T: (416) 977-1077, Fax: (416) 977-1066, E-mail: ob-art@arcturus.ca, Internet: http://www.arcturus.ca. Head: James S. Anthony
Public Gallery 06055

George R. Gardiner Museum of Ceramic Art, 111 Queen's Park, Toronto, Ont. M5S 2C7 - T: (416) 586-8080, Fax: (416) 586-8085, E-mail: mail@gardinermuseum.on.ca, Internet: http://www.gardinermuseum.on.ca. Head: Alexander Montgomery
Decorative Arts Museum - 1984
Precolombian, European and contemporary ceramic art, Syz coll of European porcelain - Clay Pit Studio 06056

Hart House, c/o University of Toronto, 7 Hart House Circle, Toronto, Ont. M5S 3H3 - T: (416) 978-2453, Fax: (416) 978-8387, E-mail: judi.schwartz@utoronto.ca, Internet: http://www.utoronto.ca/gallery. Head: Judith Schwartz
Fine Arts Museum / University Museum - 1919
Canadian art from 1919 to the present 06057

Historic Fort York, 100 Garrison Rd, Toronto, Ont. M5V 3K9 - T: (416) 392-6907, Fax: (416) 392-6917, E-mail: fortyork@city.toronto.on.ca, Internet: http://www.city.toronto.on.ca/culture. Head: Jo Ann Pynn
Historic Site
Largest coll of war of 1812 buildings in Canada 06058

History of Contraception Museum, 19 Green Belt Dr, Toronto, Ont. M3C 1L9 - T: (416) 449-9444, Fax: (416) 382-5986
Historical Museum 06059

HMCS Haida Naval Museum, 955 Lakeshore Blvd W, Toronto, Ont. M6K 3B9 - T: (416) 314-9755, Fax: (416) 314-9878, E-mail: hnmchin@planeteer.com, Internet: http://www3.sympatico.ca/hrc/haida. Head: Carla Morse
Military Museum - 1971
WWII and Korean War Royal Canadian Navy destroyer, the last remaining Tribal Class Destroyer in the world, commissoned 1943, decommissioned 1963, uniforms 06060

Hockey Hall of Fame, BCE Pl, 30 Yonge St, Toronto, Ont. M5E 1X8 - T: (416) 360-7765, Fax: (416) 360-7765, E-mail: ppritchard@hhof.com, Internet: http://www.hhof.com. Head: Philip Pritchard
Special Museum - 1993
Artifacts relevant to the history of hockey, trophies, skates, sticks and other instruments - library 06061

Joseph D. Carrier Art Gallery, 901 Lawrence Av W, Toronto, Ont. M6A 1C3 - T: (416) 789-7011
Fine Arts Museum 06062

Justina M. Barnicke Gallery, Hart House, University of Toronto, 7 Hart House Circle, Toronto, Ont. M5S 3H3 - T: (416) 978-8398, Fax: (416) 978-8387, E-mail: judi.schwartz@utoronto.ca, Internet: http://www.utoronto.ca/gallery. Head: Judith Schwartz
Fine Arts Museum / University Museum
Canadian art 06063

Koffler Gallery, 4588 Bathurst St, Toronto, Ont. M2R 1W6 - T: (416) 636-1800 ext 268, Fax: (416) 636-5813, E-mail: koffler@bjcc.ca, Internet: http://www.bjcc.ca. Head: Diane Uslaner
Fine Arts Museum 06064

Latvian History Museum, 125 Broadview Av, Toronto, Ont. M4M 2E9 - T: (416) 889-0472. Head: Andrew Brumelis
Folklore Museum 06065

Mackenzie House, 82 Bond St, Toronto, Ont. M5B 1X2 - T: (416) 392-6915, Fax: (416) 392-0114, E-mail: machouse@city.toronto.on.ca, Internet: http://www.city.toronto.on.ca/culture. Head: Janet Schwartz
Historical Museum / Historic Site - 1960
Home of W.L. Mackenzie, Toronto's first mayor and leader of the rebellion of 1837, furnishings, and memorabilia of the period from 1820-1860 06066

Marine Museum of Upper Canada, Exhibition Pl, Toronto, Ont. M6K 3C3 - T: (416) 392-1765, Fax: (416) 392-1767. Head: John Summers
Special Museum - 1959
Hist of shipping and transportation of the Great Lakes-Saint Lawrence region, exhibits describing the role of inland waterways in defence and fur trade settlement through the days of paddle, sail, and steam 06067

Market Gallery, Culture Division, City of Toronto, Lawrence Market, 95 Front St E, Toronto, Ont. M5E 1C2 - T: (416) 392-7604, Fax: (416) 392-0572, E-mail: pwachna@city.toronto.on.ca, Internet: http://www.city.toronto.on.ca. Head: Pamela Wachna
Fine Arts Museum
Art collection 06068

Mercer Union - Centre for Contemporary Visual Art, 37 Lisgar St, Toronto, Ont. M6J 3T3 - T: (416) 536-1519, Fax: (416) 536-2955, E-mail: info@mercerunion.org, Internet: http://www.mercerunion.org. Head: Thea Demetrakopoulos, Natalie De Vito
Fine Arts Museum 06069

Metropolitan Toronto Police Museum and Discovery Centre, 40 College St, Toronto, Ont. M5G 2J3 - T: (416) 808-7020, Fax: (416) 808-7052, Internet: http://www.ntps.on.ca
Historical Museum 06070

Museum for Textiles, 55 Centre Av, Toronto, Ont. M5G 2H5 - T: (416) 599-5321, Fax: (416) 599-2911, E-mail: info@museumfortextiles.on.ca, Internet: http://www.museumfortextiles.on.ca. Head: Jennifer Kaye
Decorative Arts Museum - 1975
Canadian hooked rugs, Central Asian textiles, Chinese embroidery, South East Asian batik, 9000 artifacts from all parts of the world featuring traditional textiles - contemporary gallery, library, gift and book stores 06071

Museum of Childhood, 55 Mill St, Toronto, Ont. M5A 3C4 - T: (416) 368-2866, Fax: (416) 964-2716
Ethnology Museum 06072

Museum of Mental Health Services, 1001 Queen St W, Toronto, Ont. M6J 1H4 - T: (416) 535-8501, Fax: (416) 583-1308, Internet: http://www.camh.net. Head: Vivienne W. Gibbs
Historical Museum
History of Canadian psychiatry 06073

OCAD Gallery, c/o Ontario College of Art and Design, 100 McCaul St, Toronto, Ont. M5T 1W1 - T: (416) 977-6000 ext 262, Fax: (416) 977-4080, E-mail: cswiderski@ocad.on.ca, Internet: http://www.ocad.ca. Head: Christine Swiderski
Fine Arts Museum / University Museum 06074

Ontario Science Centre, 770 Don Mills Rd, Toronto, Ont. M3C 1T3 - T: (416) 429-4100, Fax: (416) 696-3124, Internet: http://www.osc.on.ca. Head: Lesley Lewis
Science&Tech Museum - 1965
Over 800 exhibits in all fields of science and technology - library 06075

Power Plant Contemporary Art Gallery, Harbourfront Centre, 231 Queen's Quay West, Toronto, Ont. M5J 2G8 - T: (416) 973-4949, Fax: (416) 973-4933, E-mail: powerplant@harbourfront.on.ca, Internet: http://www.thepowerplant.org. Head: Wayne Baerwaldt
Fine Arts Museum 06076

Puppet Centre, 171 Avondale Av, Toronto, Ont. M2N 2V4 - T: (416) 222-9029. Head: Julia von Flotow
Decorative Arts Museum 06077

Queen's Own Rifles of Canada Regimental Museum, Casa Loma, 1 Austin Terrace, Toronto, Ont. M5R 1X8 - T: (905) 826-6138
Military Museum - 1970
Artifacts pertaining to the regiment's activities in times of war and peace, medals, weapons 06078

Queen's York Rangers Regimental Museum, 660 Fleet St, Toronto, Ont. M5V 1A9 - T: (416) 203-4642, Fax: (416) 203-3675, E-mail: qyrang@connection.com, Internet: http://www.connection.com/~qarang/. Head: R.H. Kennedy
Military Museum 06079

Redpath Sugar Museum, 95 Queen's Quay E, Toronto, Ont. M5E 1A3 - T: (416) 366-3561, Fax: (416) 366-7550
Special Museum 06080

Royal Canadian Military Institute Museum, 426 University Av, Toronto, Ont. M5G 1S9 - T: (416) 597-0286. Head: Gregory Loughton
Military Museum 06081

Royal Ontario Museum, 100 Queen's Park, Toronto, Ont. M5S 2C6 - T: (416) 586-5549, Fax: (416) 586-5863, E-mail: info@rom.on.ca, Internet: http://www.rom.on.ca. Head: Dr. Lindsay Sharp
Fine Arts Museum / Natural History Museum / Ethnology Museum / Decorative Arts Museum - 1912
Greek, Roman, Near and Far Eastern, European and Canadian art and applied art, Chinese art and archeology, ethnology esp. of American Indians, North American archeology, ethnology esp. of American Indians, North American archeology, entomology, invertebrate zoology, geology, ichthyology and herpetology, invertebrate paleontology, mammalogy, mineralogy, ornithology, vertebrate paleontology, Canadian textiles and costumes - library 06082

Royals Museum, Fort York Armoury, 54 Meighen Av, Toronto, Ont. M4B 2G9 - T: (416) 757-3955, 369-3677. Head: W. Bennett
Military Museum 06083

Salvation Army George Scott Railton Heritage Centre and Museum, 2130 Bayview Av, Toronto, Ont. M4N 3K6 - T: (416) 481-4441, Fax: (416) 481-6096, E-mail: ira.barrow@sallynet.org. Head: Ira E. Barrow
Historical Museum / Religious Arts Museum
Hist of Salvation army in Canada, religion, social services, emigration coll of ships logs (1912-1930) 06084

Scadding Cabin, 2482 Yonge St, Toronto, Ont. M4P 3E3 - T: (416) 481-8648
Historical Museum 06085

Sesquicentennial Museum, c/o Toronto District School Board, 155 College St, Toronto, Ont. M5T 1P6 - T: (416) 397-3680, Fax: (416) 397-3685, E-mail: donald.nethery@tdsb.on.ca. Head: Gail Gregory
Historical Museum 06086

Show Gallery, 978 Queen W, Toronto - T: (416) 533-4276
Fine Arts Museum
Therapeutic art for disabled and disadvantaged, art of psychatric patients and physically disabilities 06087

Silverman Heritage Museum, Baycrest Centre for Geriatric Care, 3560 Bathurst St, Toronto, Ont. M6A 2E1 - T: (416) 785-2500, Fax: (416) 785-4228, E-mail: pdickinson@baycrest.org. Head: Pat Dickinson
Religious Arts Museum - 1972
Jewish ceremonial and domestic objects, mostly European, late 19-early 20th c 06088

Spadina Historic House Museum, 285 Spadina Rd, Toronto, Ont. M5B - T: (416) 392-6827, Fax: (416) 392-6834, E-mail: spadina@city.toronto.on.ca, Internet: http://www.torontohistory.on.ca
Historical Museum 06089

Todmorden Mills Heritage Museum and Arts Centre, 67 Pottery Rd, Toronto, Ont. M4J 2H2, mail addr: East York Civic Centre, 850 Coxwell Av, Toronto, Ont. M4C 5R1 - T: (416) 396-2819, E-mail: tomorden@city.toronto.on.ca, Internet: http://www.city.toronto.on.ca/todmorden
Science&Tech Museum 06090

Toronto Aeropspace Museum, 65 Carl Hall Rd, Toronto, Ont. M3K 2B6 - T: (416) 638-6078, Fax: (416) 638-5509, E-mail: contact@torontoaerospacemuseum.com, Internet: http://www.torontoaerospacemuseum.com. Head: Paul Cabot
Science&Tech Museum 06091

Toronto Center for Contemporary Art, 2211-40 Homewood Av, Toronto, Ont. M4Y 2K2 - T: (416) 975-5296, E-mail: kazimirglaz@idirect.com. Head: Kazimir Glaz
Fine Arts Museum 06092

Toronto Dominion Gallery of Inuit Art, Aetna Tower, T-D Centre, Toronto, Ont. M5K 1A2 - T: (416) 982-8473
Fine Arts Museum 06093

Toronto Scottish Regimental Museum, Fort York Armoury, 660 Fleet St, Toronto, Ont. M5V 1A9
Military Museum 06094

Toronto Sculpture Garden, 115 King St E, Toronto, Ont. M4T 2L7 - T: (416) 515-9658, E-mail: rcg@sympatico.ca. Head: Rina Greer
Fine Arts Museum / Open Air Museum 06095

Toronto's First Post Office, 260 Adelaide St E, Toronto, Ont. M5A 1N1 - T: (416) 865-1833, Fax: (416) 865-9414, E-mail: tfpo@total.net, Internet: http://www.townofyork.com. Head: Louise Bridge
Historical Museum 06096

Toronto's Waterfront Museum, 205 Yonge St, Toronto, Ont. M5B 1N2 - T: (416) 392-6827, Fax: (416) 392-6834, E-mail: thepier@city.toronto.on.ca, Internet: http://www.torontohistory.on.ca
Historical Museum / Science&Tech Museum 06097

Ukrainian Museum of Canada - Ontario Branch, 620 Spadina Av, Toronto, Ont. M5S 2H4 - T: (416) 923-3318, Fax: (416) 923-8266, E-mail: svi@stvladimir.on.ca
Ethnology Museum / Decorative Arts Museum - 1944
Textiles and costumes, wooden artifacts, ethnographical books, kylyms 06098

University of Toronto Art Centre, 15 King's College Circle, Toronto, Ont. M5S 3H7 - T: (416) 978-1838, Fax: (416) 971-2059. Head: David Silcox
Public Gallery / University Museum 06099

Ydessa Hendeles Art Foundation, 778 King St W, Toronto, Ont. M5V 1N6 - T: (416) 413-9400, Fax: (416) 969-9889, E-mail: ydessa@yhaf.org, Internet: http://www.yhaf.org. Head: Ydessa Hendeles
Fine Arts Museum 06100

York Quay Gallery at Harbourfront Centre, 235 Queen's Quay W, Toronto, Ont. M5J 2G8 - T: (416) 973-5379, Fax: (416) 973-4859, E-mail: info@harbourfront.on.ca, Internet: http://www.habourfront.on.ca. Head: William J.S. Boyle
Public Gallery 06101

YYZ Artists' Outlet, 401 Richmond St W, Ste 410, Toronto, Ont. M5V 3A8 - T: (416) 598-4546, Fax: (416) 598-2282, E-mail: yyz@yyzartistsoutlet.org, Internet: http://www.yyzartistsoutlet.org. Head: Lisa Deanne Smith, Dionne McAffee
Public Gallery 06102

Trail

Sports Hall of Memories, 3775 Dogwood Dr, Trail, B.C. V1R 2V4
Special Museum 06103

Trail Museum, 1051 Victoria St, Trail, B.C. V1R 4L7 - T: (250) 364-1262, Fax: (250) 364-0830, E-mail: jdforbes@cityoftrail.com. Head: Jamie Forbes
Local Museum 06104

Treherne

Treherne Museum, 183 Van Zile St, Treherne, Man. R0G 2V0 - T: (204) 723-2621. Head: L.A. Darling
Local Museum - 1978 06105

Trepassey

Trepassey Area Museum, POB 63, Trepassey, Nfld. A0A 4B0 - T: (709) 436-2044, E-mail: s.deveraux@publib.nf.ca
Local Museum 06106

Trinity

Hiscock House, Church St, Trinity, Nfdl. A0C 2S0, mail addr: POB 8700, Saint John's, Nfld. A1B 4J6 - T: (709) 729-0592, 464-2042, Fax: (709) 729-0870, 464-2349, E-mail: trinity@nf.aibn.com
Decorative Arts Museum 06107

Trinity Interpretation Centre, West St, Trinity, Nfld. A0C 2S0, mail addr: POB 8700, Saint John's, Nfld. A1B 4J6 - T: (709) 729-0592, 464-2042, Fax: (709) 729-0870, 464-2349, E-mail: trinity@nf.aibn.com, Internet: http://www.nfmuseum.com
Local Museum 06108

Trinity Museum, POB 32, Trinity, Nfld. A0C 2S0 - T: (709) 464-3706, Fax: (709) 464-3706. Head: David White
Local Museum / Science&Tech Museum - 1967
Hist of early settlers, sealing and whaling, shipbuilding, sports, English fire engine (1811) - archives 06109

Trochu

Trochu and District Museum, POB 538, Trochu, Alta. T0M 2C0 - T: (403) 442-2220. Head: George O. Braham
Local Museum 06110

Trois-Rivières

Centre d'Exposition Raymond-Lasnier, Maison de la Culture de Trois-Rivières, 1425 Pl de l'Hôtel-de-Ville, Trois-Rivières, P.Q. G9A 5H3 - T: (819) 372-4611, Fax: (819) 372-4632, E-mail: cdcTR@V3R.net, Internet: http://www.v3r.net. Head: Michel Jutras
Public Gallery 06111

Centre d'Exposition sur l'Industrie des Pâtes et Papiers, CP 368, Trois-Rivières, P.Q. G9A 5H3 - T: (819) 372-4633, Fax: (819) 374-1900
Historical Museum 06112

Galerie d'Art du Parc, 864 Rue des Ursulines, Trois-Rivières, P.Q. G9A 5J9 - T: (819) 374-2355, Fax: (819) 374-1758, E-mail: galerie@galeriedartduparc.qc.ca, Internet: http://www.galeriedartduparc.qc.ca. Head: Christiane Simoneau
Fine Arts Museum 06113

Lieu Historique National des Forges du Saint-Maurice, 10000 Blvd des Forges, Trois-Rivières, P.Q. G9C 1B1 - T: (819) 378-5116, Fax: (819) 378-0887. Head: Carmen Desfossés Le Page
Local Museum - 1973
Reproductions of paintings, exhibits of objects made in forges 06114

Musée d'Archéologie de l'Université du Québec à Trois-Rivières, 3351 Blvd des Forges, Trois-Rivières, P.Q. G9A 5H7 - T: (819) 376-5032
Archaeological Museum / University Museum - 1963
Prehistoric objects found in the Mauricie, Lac Abitibi, Lotbinière and Lanoraie regions, prehistoric items found in southern France (paleolithic to Iron Age) 06115

Musée des Arts et Traditions Populaires du Québec, 200 Rue Laviolette, Trois-Rivières, P.Q. G9A 5L2 - T: (819) 372-0406, Fax: (819) 372-9907, E-mail: musee@matpq.qc.ca
Folklore Museum 06116

Musée des Ursulines, 734 Rue des Ursulines, Trois-Rivières, P.Q. G9A 5B5 - T: (819) 375-7922, Fax: (819) 375-0238, E-mail: mutr@globetrotter.net, Internet: http://www.musee-ursulines.qc.ca. Head: Josée Granomont
Historical Museum - 1982
Historic sculpture, paintings, porcelain, embroidery 06117

Musée Militaire du 12e Régiment Blindé du Canada, 574 Rue Saint-François-Xavier, Trois-Rivières, P.Q. G9A 1R6 - T: (819) 371-5290, Fax: (819) 371-5292
Military Museum 06118

Musée Pierre Boucher, Séminaire Saint-Joseph, 858 Rue Laviolette, Trois-Rivières, P.Q. G9A 5S3 - T: (819) 376-4459, Fax: (819) 378-0607, E-mail: MPB01@quebectel.com. Head: Françoise Chainé, Jean Panneton
Fine Arts Museum - 1934
Exhibits describing the life and livelihood of the 'petite patrie', the forges of Saint Maurice, agricultural and navigational displays 06119

Pavillon Saint-Arnaud, Parc Pie XXII, Trois-Rivières, P.Q. G9A 5L2
Decorative Arts Museum - 1955
Batiks, gouaches, pottery, enamels, embroidery 06120

Truro

Colchester Historical Museum, 29 Young St, Truro, N.S. B2N 5C5 - T: (902) 895-6284, Fax: (902) 895-9530, E-mail: colhismus@auracom.com, Internet: http://www.genealogynet.com/colchester. Head: Beverley Withers
Local Museum - 1976
Local hist including agriculture, forestry, shipbuilding, railroading and education, Mi'kmag first peoples's culture, photographs - archives 06121

Little White Schoolhouse, 20 Arthur St, Truro, N.S. B2N 5N2 - T: (902) 895-5170, E-mail: lwsm@auracom.com, Internet: http://www.lwsm.ednet.ns.ca. Head: Tom Acker
Historical Museum 06122

Turner Valley

Turner Valley Gas Plant, Turner Valley, mail addr: POB 959, Stn Blairmore, Crowsnest Pass, Alta. T0K 0E0 - T: (403) 562-7388, Fax: (403) 562-8635, E-mail: info@frankslide.com, Internet: http://www.frankslide.com. Head: Monica Field
Science&Tech Museum
Petroleum history, discovery, development, regulation, processing, transportation 06123

Tweed

Tweed and Area Heritage Centre, 40 Victoria St N, Tweed, Ont. K0K 3J0 - T: (613) 478-3989, Fax: (613) 478-6457, E-mail: tweedheritageinfo@on.aibn.com, Internet: http://www.twp.tweed.on.ca/around/houstonhouse.htm. Head: E. Morton
Local Museum 06124

Twillingate

Twillingate Museum, Twillingate, Nfld. A0G 4M0 - T: (709) 884-2825. Head: Lorna Stuckless
Local Museum - 1971
Victorian period furniture, medical instruments, guns, printing press (1834), Dorset Eskimo and Beothuck Indian artifacts 06125

Two Hills

Two Hills and District Museum, POB 566, Two Hills, Alta. T0B 4K0 - T: (780) 657-2224
Local Museum 06126

Tyne Valley

Ellerslie Shellfish Museum, POB 24, Tyne Valley, P.E.I. C0B 2C0 - T: (902) 831-2933. Head: Nan Kernaghan
Historical Museum 06127

Unity

Unity and District Heritage Museum, POB 12, Unity, Sask. S0K 4L0 - T: (306) 228-4464
Local Museum 06128

Uxbridge

Thomas Foster Memorial Temple, c/o Uxbridge-Scott Museum, POB 1301, Uxbridge, Ont. L9P 1N5 - T: (905) 852-5854, E-mail: museum@interhop.net, Internet: http://www.uxlib.com/museum
Historical Museum 06129

Uxbridge-Scott Museum, 7239 Concession 6, Uxbridge, Ont. L9P 1N5, mail addr: POB 1301, Uxbridge, Ont. L9P 1N5 - T: (905) 852-5854, E-mail: museum@interhop.net, Internet: http://www.uxlib.com/museum. Head: Allan McGillivray
Local Museum - 1972
Local artifacts, local Quaker hist, family tree files - archives 06130

Val d'Or

Centre d'Exposition de Val d'Or, 600 7e Rue, Val d'Or, P.Q. J9P 3P3 - T: (819) 825-0942. Head: Lilse Gagné
Public Gallery 06131

Village Minier de Bourlamaque, La Cité de l'Or, 90 Av Perreault, Val d'Or, P.Q. J9P 4P3 - T: (819) 825-7616, Fax: (819) 825-9853, E-mail: courriel@citedelor.qc.ca, Internet: http://www.citedelor.qc.ca. Head: Pierre Dufour
Science&Tech Museum 06132

Val Marie

Perrault's Museum, First St N, Val Marie, Sask. S0N 2T0 - T: (306) 298-2241. Head: Lise Perrault
Fine Arts Museum / Special Museum
Art and authors of westerns, buffalo coll, paintings, Wiel Jannes coll 06133

Valcourt

Musée J. Armand Bombardier, 1001 Av J.A. Bombardier, Valcourt, P.Q. J0E 2L0 - T: (514) 532-5300, Fax: (514) 532-2260, E-mail: musee@fjab.qc.ca, Internet: http://www.museebombardier.com. Head: M. Sylvain Lainesse
Science&Tech Museum - 1971
Prototypes and original vehicles, tools and machines that commemorate the inventive genius of J. Armand Bombardier and a large coll of snowmobiles that chronicle the evolution of the industry around the world 06134

Valemount

Valemount and Area Museum, POB 850, Valemount, B.C. V0E 2Z0 - T: (250) 566-4177, Fax: (250) 566-8411, E-mail: museum@valemount.com
Local Museum 06135

Valleyfield

Écomusée des Deux-Rives, 111 Rue Ellice, Valleyfield, P.Q. J6T 1E7 - T: (450) 371-6772
Natural History Museum 06136

Vancouver

15th Field Artillery Regiment Museum, 2025 11th Av W, Vancouver, B.C. V6J 2C7 - T: (604) 666-4370, Fax: (604) 666-4083. Head: Victor Stevenson
Military Museum 06137

Biblical Museum of Canada, 5800 University Blvd, Vancouver, B.C. V5R 6A8 - T: (604) 432-6122, Fax: (604) 435-8181. Head: Frederick W. Metzger
Religious Arts Museum 06138

British Columbia Congenital Heart Museum, c/o Department of Paediatrics, Faculty of Medicine, University of Britsh Columbia, 4480 Oak St, Vancouver, B.C. V6H 3V4 - T: (604) 875-2296, Fax: (604) 875-3463
Special Museum / University Museum - 1967
Specimens of human hearts with congenital heart defects 06139

British Columbia Golf House Museum, 2545 Blanca St, Vancouver, B.C. V6R 4N1 - T: (604) 222-4653, Fax: (604) 222-4654, E-mail: mashie@intergate.ca, Internet: http://www.bcgolfmuseum.org. Head: Dorothy Brown
Special Museum 06140

British Columbia Medical Association Museum, 1665 Broadway W, Vancouver, B.C. V6J 1X1 - T: (604) 736-5551, Fax: (604) 736-4556
Special Museum - 1965
Medical instruments, equipment and related items from the 19th and 20th centuries 06141

British Columbia Regiment Museum, 620 Beatty St, Vancouver, B.C. V6B 2L9 - T: (604) 666-4368. Head: W.D. Edgar
Military Museum 06142

British Columbia Sports Hall of Fame and Museum, British Columbia Place Stadium, 777 Pacific Blvd S, Vancouver, B.C. V6B 4Y8 - T: (604) 687-5520, Fax: (604) 687-5510. Head: Don Taylor
Special Museum - 1966
Sports and sports hist 06143

British Columbia Sugar Museum, 123 Rogers St, Vancouver, B.C. V6B 3V2 - T: (604) 253-1131, Fax: (604) 253-2517
Special Museum 06144

Canadian Craft and Design Museum, 639 Hornby St, Vancouver, B.C. V6C 2G3 - T: (604) 687-8266, Fax: (604) 684-7174, E-mail: info@ccdm.org. Head: Angela Brayham
Decorative Arts Museum 06145

Charles H. Scott Gallery, c/o Emily Carr Institute of Art and Design, 1399 Johnston St, Granville Island, Vancouver, B.C. V6H 3R9 - T: (604) 844-3809, Fax: (604) 844-3801, E-mail: scottgal@eciad.bc.ca, Internet: http://chscott.eciad.bc.ca. Head: Greg Bellerby
Fine Arts Museum 06146

Circle Craft Gallery, 1666 Johnston St, Vancouver, B.C. V6H 3S2 - T: (604) 669-8021, Fax: (604) 669-8585, E-mail: circraft@direct.ca
Public Gallery 06147

Contemporary Art Gallery, 555 Nelson St, Vancouver, B.C. V6B 6R5 - T: (604) 681-2700, Fax: (604) 683-2710, E-mail: info@contemporaryartgallery.ca, Internet: http://www.contemporaryartgallery.ca. Head: Christina Ritchie
Public Gallery - 1972
Works of Vancouver artists in the 1970s 06148

Cowan Vertebrate Museum, c/o Department of Zoology, University of British Columbia, 6270 University Blvd, Vancouver, B.C. V6T 1Z4 - T: (604) 822-4665, Fax: (604) 822-2416, E-mail: vertmus@zoology.ubc.ca. Head: Dr. James N.M. Smith
Natural History Museum / University Museum - 1951
Specimens of mammals, birds, reptiles and amphibians 06149

Exposure Gallery, 851 Beatty St, Vancouver, B.C. V6B 2M6 - T: (604) 688-6853, Fax: (604) 688-6853, E-mail: exposuregallery@bc.sampatico.ca. Head: Ian McGuffie
Public Gallery 06150

Gallery of British Columbia Ceramics, 1359 Cartwright St, Vancouver, B.C. V6H 3R7 - T: (604) 669-5645, Fax: (604) 669-5627, E-mail: bcpguild@intouch.bc.ca, Internet: http://www.bcpotters.com. Head: Kimcha Rajkumar
Public Gallery 06151

Grunt Gallery, 116-350 East 2nd Av, Vancouver, B.C. V5T 4R8 - T: (604) 875-9516, Fax: (604) 877-0073, E-mail: grunt@telus.net, Internet: http://www.grunt.bc.ca. Head: Glenn Alteen
Fine Arts Museum 06152

Heffel Gallery, 2247 Granville St, Vancouver, B.C. V6H 3G1 - T: (604) 732-6505, Fax: (604) 732-4245, E-mail: mail@heffel.com, Internet: http://www.heffel.com
Public Gallery 06153

Horizon Art Galleries, 665 Hove St, Vancouver, B.C. V6C 2E5 - T: (604) 689-5360
Public Gallery 06154

H.R. MacMillan Space Centre, 1100 Chestnut St, Vancouver, B.C. V6J 3J9 - T: (604) 738-7827, Fax: (604) 736-5665, E-mail: ddodge@pacific-space-centre.bc.ca, Internet: http://www.hrmacmillanspacecentre.com
Science&Tech Museum - 1988 06155

Marion Scott Gallery, 481 Howe St, Vancouver, B.C. V6C 2X6 - T: (604) 685-1934, Fax: (604) 685-1890, E-mail: art@marionscottgallery.com, Internet: http://www.marionscottgallery.com. Head: Judy Kardosh
Fine Arts Museum
Inuit art 06156

Morris and Helen Belkin Art Gallery, University of British Columbia, 1825 Main Mall, Vancouver, B.C. V6T 1Z2 - T: (604) 822-2759, Fax: (604) 822-6689, E-mail: nsawada@interchange.ubc.ca, Internet: http://www.belkin-gallery.ubc.ca. Head: Scott Watson
Fine Arts Museum 06157

Museum of Anthropology, c/o University of British Columbia, 6393 Marine Dr NW, Vancouver, B.C. V6T 1Z2 - T: (604) 822-5087, Fax: (604) 822-2974, E-mail: jenwebb@interchange.ubc.ca, Internet: http://www.moa.ubc.ca. Head: Prof. Ruth B. Phillips
Ethnology Museum / University Museum - 1948
Ethnography, archeology 06158

M.Y. Williams Planet Earth Museum, c/o Dept. of Earth and Ocean Sciences, University of British Columbia, 6339 Stores Rd, Vancouver, B.C. V6T 1Z4 - T: (604) 822-2449, Fax: (604) 822-6088, E-mail: ssutherland@eos.ubc.ca. Head: Dr. Stuart Sutherland
Natural History Museum / University Museum - 1924
Minerals, ore deposits, paleontology, petrology, atmospheric sciences, oceanography, geophysics 06159

Old Hastings Mill Store Museum, 1575 Alma Rd, Vancouver, B.C. V6R 3P3 - T: (604) 734-1212
Local Museum - 1931
Mill store (1865), pioneer and Indian artifacts, furniture and furnishings, textiles, maps and pictures 06160

Raymond Chow Art Gallery, 1618 W 75th Av, Vancouver, B.C. V6P 6G2 - T: (604) 263-5439, Fax: (604) 263-1568
Fine Arts Museum 06161

Roedde House Museum, 1415 Barclay St, Vancouver, B.C. V6G 1J6 - T: (604) 684-7040, Fax: (604) 684-7027, E-mail: roeddehs@roeddehouse.org, Internet: http://www.roeddehouse.org. Head: T. Brunette
Historical Museum 06162

Seaforth Highlanders of Canada Regimental Museum, Seaforth Armoury, 1650 Burrard St, Vancouver, B.C. V6J 3G4 - T: (604) 733-3836, Fax: (604) 666-4078
Military Museum - 1972
Artifacts, documents and photos relating to Seaforth Highlanders and affiliated regiments, uniforms, weapons 06163

Sidney and Gertrude Zack Gallery, 950 W 41st Av, Vancouver, B.C. V5Z 2N7 - T: (604) 257-5111, Fax: (604) 257-5121
Fine Arts Museum 06164

Spencer Entomological Museum, c/o Department of Zoology, University of British Columbia, 6270 University Blvd, Vancouver, B.C. V6T 1Z4 - T: (604) 822-3379, Fax: (604) 822-2416, E-mail: scudder@zoology.ubc.ca, Internet: http://www.insecta.com. Head: G.G.E. Scudder
Natural History Museum / University Museum - 1953
Insects 06165

UBC Fish Museum, c/o Department of Zoology, University of British Columbia, 6270 University Blvd, Vancouver, B.C. V6T 1Z4 - T: (604) 822-4803, 822-9152, Fax: (604) 822-2416, E-mail: etaylor@zoology.ubc.ca, Internet: http://www.zoology.ubc.ca/~etaylor/nfrg/fishmuseum.html
Natural History Museum / University Museum - 1953
Preserved fish, skeletons, fossils 06166

Ukrainian Museum of Canada, 154 Tenth Av E, Vancouver, B.C. V5T 1Z4 - T: (604) 327-7725. Head: Savelia Stasiuk
Folklore Museum - 1957
Ukrainian costumes, textiles, ceramics, woodcarvings, embroidery and embroidery patterns - archives 06167

Vancouver Art Gallery, 750 Hornby St, Vancouver, B.C. V6Z 2H7 - T: (604) 662-4700, Fax: (604) 682-1086, E-mail: webmaster@vanartgallery.bc.ca, Internet: http://www.vanartgallery.bc.ca. Head: Joseph McHugh
Fine Arts Museum - 1931
Canadian paintings and graphics, works by Emily Carr (1871-1945), modern American prints, British watercolors, British paintings (18th-20th c) 06168

Vancouver Holocaust Education Centre, 950 W 41st Av, Ste 50, Vancouver, B.C. V5Z 2N7 - T: (604) 264-0499, Fax: (604) 264-0497, E-mail: info@vhec.org, Internet: http://www.vhec.org. Head: Dr. Roberta Kremer
Historical Museum 06169

Vancouver Maritime Museum, 1905 Ogden Av, Vancouver, B.C. V6J 1A3 - T: (604) 257-8300, Fax: (604) 737-2621, E-mail: jdelgado@vmm.bc.ca, Internet: http://www.vmm.bc.ca. Head: James P. Delgado
Special Museum - 1958
Maritime hist including models, uniforms, paintings, photogr, documents, engines, tools, communications equipment, fishing gear, small craft - archives, library 06170

Vancouver Museum, 1100 Chestnut St, Vanier Park, Vancouver, B.C. V6J 3J9 - T: (604) 736-4431, Fax: (604) 736-5417, E-mail: marketing@vanmuseum.bc.ca, Internet: http://vanmuseum.bc.ca. Head: Pauline Thompson
Archaeological Museum / Ethnology Museum / Historical Museum - 1894
Regional archaeology, ethnology, history, decorative arts 06171

Vancouver Police Centennial Museum, 240 Cordova St E, Vancouver, B.C. V6A 1L3 - T: (604) 665-3346, Fax: (604) 665-3585, E-mail: vphscm@dextor.com, Internet: http://www.city.vancouver.bc.ca/police/museum/
Historical Museum
Hist of Vancouver Police Dept 06172

Wickaninnish Gallery, 1666 Johnston St, Vancouver, B.C. V6H 3S2 - T: (604) 681-1057
Public Gallery 06173

Vanderhoof

Vanderhoof Community Museum, POB 1515, Vanderhoof, B.C. V0J 3A0 - T: (250) 567-2991, Fax: (250) 567-2931, E-mail: museum@hwy16.com
Local Museum 06174

Vanguard

Vanguard Centennial Museum, Vanguard, Sask. S0N 2V0 - T: (306) 582-2244
Local Museum 06175

Vaudreuil

Musée des Sciences Naturelles, Pavillon Vaudreuil, Cité des Jeunes, Vaudreuil, P.Q. J7V 6B1
Natural History Museum - 1972
Mammalia, ornithology, herpetology, ichthyology, entomology, mollusks, minerals, fossils, plants 06176

Musée Régional de Vaudreuil-Soulanges, 431 Av Saint-Charles, Vaudreuil, P.Q. J7V 2N3 - T: (450) 455-2092, Fax: (450) 455-6782, E-mail: danielbi@mrvs.qc.ca, Internet: http://www.mrvs.qc.ca. Head: Daniel Bissonnette
Local Museum
Paintings, sculpture and engravings, armory and locksmith items, costumes, textiles and tapestries, furniture, applied arts 06177

Vegreville

Vegreville Regional Museum, POB 328, Vegreville, Alta. T9C 1R3 - T: (780) 632-7650, Fax: (780) 632-6756, E-mail: vrmuseum@vegnet.com, Internet: http://www.vegreville.com. Head: L. Giebelhaus, J. Komick
Local Museum 06178

Verdun

Centre Culturel de Verdun, 5955 Rue Bannantyne, Verdun, P.Q. H4G 1H6 - T: (514) 765-7150, Fax: (514) 765-7263, E-mail: nancy.raymond@ville.verdun.qc.ca, Internet: http://www.cum.qc.ca/verdun. Head: Nancy Raymond
Fine Arts Museum - 1967
Paintings, sculptures, theatre exhibits 06179

Verigin

National Doukhobour Heritage Village, POB 99, Verigin, Sask. S0A 4H0 - T: (306) 542-4441, Fax: (306) 542-2017, E-mail: barhar@sk.sympatico.ca
Ethnology Museum / Local Museum - 1969
Tools, handicrafts, costumes and literature pertaining to Doukhoubor history 06180

Vernon, British Colombia

Greater Vernon Museum, 3009 32 Av, Vernon, British Colombia, B.C. V1T 2L8 - T: (250) 542-3142, Fax: (250) 542-5358, E-mail: mail@vernon.museum.bc.ca. Head: Ron Candy
Local Museum 06181

Historic O'Keefe Ranch, 12 km N of Vernon on Hwy 97, Vernon, British Colombia, B.C. V1T 6M8 - T: (250) 542-7868, Fax: (250) 542-7868, E-mail: okr_chin@junction.net, Internet: http://www.okeeferanch.bc.ca. Head: Jamie Kidston
Agriculture Museum - 1977
Historic ranch (1867), furnishings, farm equipment, early cattle ranching, cowboys, farming 06182

Vernon Public Art Gallery, 3228 31st Av, Vernon, British Colombia, B.C. V1T 2H3 - T: (250) 545-3173, Fax: (250) 545-9096, E-mail: vernonartgallery@shawbiz.ca, Internet: http://www.galleries.bc.ca/vernon. Head: Susan Brandoli
Public Gallery 06183

Vernon, Ontario

Osgoode Township Museum, POB 74, Vernon, Ontario, Ont. K0A 3J0 - T: (613) 821-4062, E-mail: oths@magma.ca, Internet: http://www.magma.ca/~oths
Local Museum - 1974
Local history, clothing, agricultural tools, family bibles and books, old machinery 06184

Verona

Bell Rock Mill Museum, Verona, Ont. K0H 2W0 - T: (613) 374-1458, 478-1195. Head: Richard Tosswill
Science&Tech Museum 06185

Verwood

Verwood Community Museum, Verwood, Sask. S0H 4G0 - T: (306) 642-5767
Local Museum 06186

Victoria

Art Gallery of Greater Victoria, 1040 Moss St, Victoria, B.C. V8V 4P1 - T: (250) 384-4101, Fax: (250) 361-3995, E-mail: aggv@aggv.bc.ca, Internet: http://www.aggv.bc.ca. Head: Pierre Arpin
Fine Arts Museum - 1951
Canadian art (1860-present), contemporary art of British Columbia, prints and drawings from Europe, North America and Japan, decorative arts and textiles, Japanese and Chinese ceramics 06187

British Columbia Forest Service Museum, 1675 Douglas St, Victoria, B.C. V8W 3E7 - T: (604) 387-5255, Fax: (604) 387-8495. Head: D.E. Adderley
Special Museum - 1951
Forestry, historical books and tools 06188

British Columbia Mineral Museum, 30 Douglas Bldg, 617 Government St, Victoria, B.C. V8V 1X4 - T: (604) 387-5538
Natural History Museum 06189

Canadian Scottish Regiment Museum, Bay Street Armoury, 715 Bay St, Victoria, B.C. V8T 1R1 - T: (250) 363-8753, Fax: (250) 363-3593, E-mail: csrmuse@islandnet.com, Internet: http://www.islandnet.com/~csrmuse. Head: John R. Wigmore
Military Museum 06190

Carr House, 207 Government St, Victoria, B.C. V8V 2K8 - T: (250) 383-5843, Fax: (250) 383-5843, E-mail: ch.chin@island.net. Head: Jan Ross
Historical Museum 06191

CFB Esquimalt Naval Museum and Military Museum, POB 17000, Stn Forces, Victoria, B.C. V9A 7N2 - T: (250) 363-4312, 5655, Fax: (250) 363-4252, E-mail: nadenmuseum@pacificcoast.net. Head: Debbie Towell
Historical Museum / Military Museum 06192

Craigdarroch Castle Historical Museum, 1050 Joan Cres., Victoria, B.C. V8S 3L5 - T: (250) 592-5323, Fax: (250) 592-1099, E-mail: ccastle@islandnet.com
Historical Museum 06193

Emily Carr Arts Centre Museum, 207 Government St, Victoria, B.C. V8V 2K8
Fine Arts Museum - 1972
Birthplace of Emily Carr (1871-1945), reproductions of her paintings, personal articles and letters 06194

Fort Rodd Hill Museum, 501 Belmont Rd, Victoria, B.C. V9C 1B5 - T: (250) 380-4662
Local Museum 06195

Goldstream Region Museum, 697 Goldstream Av, Victoria, B.C. V9B 2X2 - T: (250) 474-6113
Local Museum 06196

Helmcken House Pioneer Doctor's Residence, 638 Elliott St, Victoria, B.C. V8V 1W1 - T: (250) 387-4697, Fax: (604) 387-5129. Head: John D. Adams
Historical Museum - 1941
Furniture (1860), medical instruments of Dr. J.S. Helmcken 06197

Lieutenant General Ashton Armoury Museum, 724 Vanalman Av, Victoria, B.C. V8Z 3B5 - T: (250) 477-1117
Military Museum 06198

Maltwood Art Museum and Gallery, c/o University of Victoria, University Campus, 3800 Finnerty Rd, Victoria, B.C. V8W 3P2 - T: (250) 721-8298, Fax: (250) 721-8997, E-mail: msegger@uvic.ca, Internet: http://www.maltwood.ca. Head: Martin Segger
Fine Arts Museum / Decorative Arts Museum - 1977
Katharine Maltwood coll, British Columbia art, decorative arts, paintings, sculpture, graphics, archeology, costumes, glass, textiles, ceramics, furniture - library 06199

Maritime Museum of British Columbia, 28 Bastion Sq, Victoria, B.C. V8W 1H9 - T: (250) 385-4222, Fax: (250) 382-2869, E-mail: info@mmbc.ca, Internet: http://mmbc.bc.ca. Head: Yvonne Sharpe
Historical Museum / Military Museum - 1955
Maritime history including models, documents and pictures, ship plans - library, photographic archives 06200

Metchosin School Museum, 4475 Happy Valley Rd, Victoria, B.C. V9C 4B1 - T: (250) 478-3451. Head: Ron Bradley
Special Museum 06201

Open Space Gallery, 510 Fort St, Victoria, B.C. V8W 1E6 - T: (250) 383-8833, Fax: (250) 383-8841, E-mail: openspace@openspace.ca, Internet: http://www.openspace.ca. Head: Todd A. Davis
Public Gallery
Contemorary Art - performance space 06202

Point Ellice House, 2616 Pleasant St, Victoria, B.C. V8T 4V3 - T: (250) 385-3837
Decorative Arts Museum - 1968
Victorian and Edwardian furniture and furnishings 06203

Royal British Columbia Museum, 675 Belleville St, Victoria, B.C. V8W 9W2, mail addr: POB 9815, Station Provincial Government, Victoria, B.C. V8W 9W2 - T: (250) 356-7226, Fax: (250) 387-5674, E-mail: reception@royalbcmuseum.bc.ca, Internet: http://www.royalbcmuseum.bc.ca. Head: Pauline Rafferty
Historical Museum / Ethnology Museum / Archaeological Museum / Natural History Museum - 1886
British Columbia natural and human hist, incl modern hist, ethnology and archaeology 06204

Royal London Wax Museum, 470 Belleville St, Victoria, B.C. V8V 1W9 - T: (250) 388-4461, Fax: (250) 388-4493, E-mail: khl@pinc.com, Internet: http://www.waxworld.com
Special Museum 06205

Victoriaville

Musée Laurier, 16 Rue Laurier Ouest, Victoriaville, P.Q. G6P 6P3 - T: (819) 357-8655, Fax: (819) 357-8655, E-mail: mlaurier@ivic.qc.ca. Head: Richard Pedneault
Local Museum - 1929
Home of Wilfred Laurier from 1867-1896, furniture 06206

Viking

Viking Historical Museum, 5024 58th Av, Viking, Alta. T0B 4N0 - T: (780) 336-3066. Head: J.H. Roddick
Local Museum - 1967
Local history, land maps of the area and photographs 06207

Ville des Laurentides

Lieu Historique National de Sir Wilfrid Laurier, 12e Av Laurier, Ville des Laurentides, P.Q. J0R 1C0 - T: (450) 439-3702, Fax: (450) 439-5721. Head: Thomas Piché
Local Museum - 1941

Restored house, furnished in the style of the period from 1840-1950, Wilfrid Laurier (first French-Canadian to become Prime Minister of Canada) 06208

Virden

Currahee Military Museum, POB 729, Virden, Man. R0M 2C0 - T: (204) 748-2454, Fax: (204) 748-1805. Head: John Hipwell
Military Museum 06209

River Valley School Museum, POB 729, Virden, Man. R0M 2C0 - T: (204) 748-2454
Historical Museum 06210

Virden Pioneer Home Museum, 390 King St W, Virden, Man. R0M 2C0 - T: (204) 748-1659, Fax: (204) 748-2501, E-mail: cao@town.virden.mb.ca, Internet: http://town.virden.mb.ca. Head: Helen Boulton Elliott
Local Museum - 1969
Historic brick house (1888) furnished in Victorian style 06211

Wabowden

Wabowden Historical Museum, Wabowden, Man. R0B 1S0 - T: (204) 689-2362, Fax: (204) 689-2284, 689-2212
Local Museum 06212

Wadena

Wadena and District Museum and Gallery, POB 1208, Wadena, Sask. S0A 4J0 - T: (306) 338-3454, Fax: (306) 338-3804, Internet: http://wsd.inet.wadena.sk.ca/wadena
Local Museum / Fine Arts Museum 06213

Wainwright

Wainwright Museum, POB 2994, Wainwright, Alta. T9W 1S9 - T: (780) 842-3115, Fax: (780) 842-4910
Local Museum 06214

Wakaw

John G. Diefenbaker Replica Law Office, POB 760, Wakaw, Sask. S0K 4P0 - T: (306) 233-5157. Head: William Kindrachuk
Historical Museum 06215

Wakaw Heritage Museum, POB 475, Wakaw, Sask. S0K 4P0 - T: (306) 233-4257
Local Museum 06216

Wallace Bridge

Wallace Area Museum, 13440 Rte 6, Wallace Bridge, N.S. B0K 1Y0 - T: (902) 257-2191, Fax: (902) 257-2191
Local Museum 06217

Wanham

Grizzly Bear Prairie Museum, POB 68, Wanham, Alta. T0H 3P0 - T: (780) 694-3933. Head: Stanley Sather
Natural History Museum 06218

Warner

Devil's Coulee Dinosaur Heritage Museum, Royal Tyrrell Museum of Paleontology, 300 County Rd, Warner, Alta. T0K 2L0 - T: (403) 642-2118, Fax: (403) 642-3660, E-mail: dinoegg@telusplanet.net. Head: Judy Greeno
Archaeological Museum / Local Museum
Paleontology ,dinosaur fossils, heritage 06219

Wasaga Beach

Nancy Island Historic Site, Wasaga Beach Provincial Park, Mosley St, Wasaga Beach, Ont. L0L 2P0, mail addr: POB 183, Wasaga Beach, Ont. L0L 2P0 - T: (705) 429-2728, Fax: (705) 429-7983. Head: Mark Shoreman
Local Museum / Science&Tech Museum - 1969
Remains of the British Schooner Nancy, marine aspects of the War of 1812, replics of an early Upper Lakeslighthouse, war of 1812, 1800's water travel 06220

Wasagaming

Pinewood Museum, 154 Wasagaming Dr, Wasagaming, Man. R0J 2H0 - T: (204) 735-2205, 848-7622
Natural History Museum 06221

Waskada

Waskada Museum, Railway Av, Waskada, Man. R0M 2E0, mail addr: POB 27, Waskada, Man. R0M 2E0 - T: (204) 673-2503, Fax: (204) 673-2663, E-mail: normr@mail.com, Internet: http://www.techplus.com/was/history/museum.html. Head: Hilt Wallace
Local Museum - 1967
Historic house, local history, pioneer artifacts 06222

Waskesiu Lake

Prince Albert National Park Nature Centre, POB 100, Waskesiu Lake, Sask. S0J 2Y0 - T: (306) 663-4515, Fax: (306) 663-5424, E-mail: panp_info@pch.gc.ca, Internet: http://www.parkscanada.pch.gc.ca
Natural History Museum 06223

Waterford

Spruce Row Museum, 159 Nichol St, Waterford, Ont. N0E 1Y0 - T: (519) 443-4211, Fax: (519) 443-4211. Head: Alan Whyte
Local Museum 06224

Waterloo

Brubacher House Museum, c/o Conrad Grebel College, Waterloo, Ont. N2L 3G6 - T: (519) 886-3855, Fax: (519) 885-0014, E-mail: bhouse@uwaterloo.ca, Internet: http://grebel.uwaterloo.ca/bhouse. Head: E. Paul Penner
Historical Museum / Decorative Arts Museum 06225

Canadian Clay and Glass Gallery, 25 Caroline St N, Waterloo, Ont. N2L 2Y5 - T: (519) 746-1882, Fax: (519) 746-6396, E-mail: glenn@canadianclayandglass.ca. Head: Glenn Allison
Fine Arts Museum 06226

Earth Sciences Museum, c/o University of Waterloo, 200 University Av W, Waterloo, Ont. N2L 3G1 - T: (519) 888-4567 ext 2469, Fax: (519) 746-0183, E-mail: esmuseum@sciborg.uwaterloo.ca, Internet: http://www.science.uwaterloo.ca/earth/museum/museum.html. Head: Jocelyne Legault
Natural History Museum / University Museum - 1968
Ornithology, minerals, fossils, dinosaur display, rock garden 06227

Elliott Avedon Museum and Archives of Games, c/o University of Waterloo, 200 University Av W, Waterloo, Ont. N2L 3G1 - T: (519) 888-4424, Fax: (519) 746-6776, E-mail: museum@healthy.uwaterloo.ca, Internet: http://www.ahs.uwaterloo.ca/~museum. Head: Dr. Ron Johnson
Special Museum / University Museum - 1971
Artifacts depicting the history and development of games throughout the world - archives 06228

Enook Galleries, 29 Young St E, Waterloo, Ont. N2J 4A4 - T: (519) 884-3221, Fax: (519) 744-6740, E-mail: hns20@cam.ac.uk
Fine Arts Museum 06229

Museum of Visual Science and Optometry, c/o University of Waterloo, School of Optometry, 200 University Av W, Waterloo, Ont. N2L 3G1 - T: (519) 885-1211 ext 3405, Fax: (519) 725-0784, E-mail: eyemuse@quark.uwaterloo.ca, Internet: http://quark.uwaterloo.ca/~museum. Head: Lauren Walker
Science&Tech Museum / University Museum - 1974
Early instruments, antique spectacles, books, diplomas, documents on optometry, visual science and optics 06230

Robert Langen Gallery, c/o Wilfrid Laurier University, 75 University Av W, Waterloo, Ont. N2L 3C5 - T: (519) 884-1970 ext 3801, Fax: (519) 888-9721, E-mail: sluke@wlu.ca, Internet: http://www.wlu.ca. Head: Suzanne Luke
Public Gallery / University Museum 06231

University of Waterloo Art Gallery, 200 University Av W, Waterloo, Ont. N2L 3G1 - T: (519) 888-4567 ext 3575, Fax: (519) 746-4982, E-mail: cpodedwo@uwaterloo.ca, Internet: http://www.artgallery.uwaterloo.ca. Head: Carol Podedworny
Fine Arts Museum / University Museum - 1962
Contemporary Canadian art 06232

Wawa

Agawa Bay Exhibition Centre, Agawa Campground, 58 Miles S of Wawa on Hwy 17, Wawa, Ont. P0S 1K0
Natural History Museum - 1965
Mounted mammals, reptiles, birds, and butterflies 06233

Wawanesa

Sipiweske Museum, Wawanesa, Man. R0K 2J0 - T: (204) 824-2244
Historical Museum 06234

Wawota

Wawota and District Museum, Wawota, Sask. S0G 5A0 - T: (306) 739-2110
Local Museum 06235

Weekes

Dunwell and Community Museum, Weekes Recreation Centre, Weekes, Sask. S0E 1V0 - T: (306) 278-2906
Local Museum - 1971
Local pioneer artifacts representing several countries of origin 06236

Welland

Welland Historical Museum, 65 Hooker St, Welland, Ont. L3C 5G9 - T: (905) 732-2215, Fax: (905) 732-9169, E-mail: whmchin@niagara.com, Internet: http://www.niagara.com/~whmchin. Head: Angela Dyck
Local Museum - 1977
Local historical artifacts, displays related to the Welland Canal, Indian, military, and pioneer relics 06237

Wellington, Ontario

Wellington Community Historical Museum, 290 Main St, Wellington, Ontario, Ont. K0K 3L0 - T: (613) 399-5015, 476-8112, E-mail: pecwmus@kos.net. Head: Diane Wenn
Historical Museum - 1967
Local hist, glass, stamps, farm implements, buttons, Quaker heritage, pioneer life, agricultural products, canning industry 06238

Wellington, Prince Edward Island

Musée d'Art Religieux, Rte 11, 802 Rue Eau Est, Wellington, Prince Edward Island, P.E.I. C1N 4J6 - T: (902) 854-2260. Head: Ulric Poirier
Religious Arts Museum 06239

Wells

Island Mountain Arts Public Gallery, 2323 Pooley St, Wells, B.C. V0K 2R0 - T: (250) 994-3466, Fax: (250) 994-3433, E-mail: info@imarts.com, Internet: http://www.imarts.com. Head: Cheryl Peebles
Public Gallery 06240

Wells Museum, Pooley St, Wells, B.C. V0K 2R0 - T: (250) 994-3342, Fax: (250) 994-3342, E-mail: wellsmsm@uniserve.com, Internet: http://www.wellsbc.com. Head: Bill Quackenbush
Local Museum - 1975
Local historical artifacts, mining 06241

Welshpool

Campobello Island Museum, Welshpool, N.B. E0G 3H0 - T: (506) 752-2268
Local Museum 06242

Roosevelt Campobello International Park, Campobello Island, Welshpool, N.B. E5E 1A4 - T: (506) 752-2922, Fax: (506) 752-6000, E-mail: info@fdr.net, Internet: http://www.fdr.net. Head: Paul B Cole
Local Museum - 1964
Summer home and furnishings of Franklin Delano Roosevelt, park 06243

Wendake

Musée Arouane, 10 Rue Alexandre-Duchesneau, Wendake, P.Q. G0A 4V0 - T: (418) 845-1241
Local Museum 06244

Wesleyville

Bonavista North Regional Memorial Museum, Wesleyville, Nfld. A0G 4R0 - T: (709) 536-2402. Head: Naboth Winsor
Fine Arts Museum / Decorative Arts Museum - 1976
Fine and decorative arts 06245

West Bay

Marble Mountain Community Museum, RR 1, West Bay, N.S. B0E 3K0 - T: (902) 756-2638. Head: Jean McNicol
Local Museum 06246

West Pubnico

Musée Acadien de Pubnico-Ouest, CP 92, West Pubnico, N.S. B0W 3S0 - T: (902) 762-3380, Fax: (902) 762-0726, E-mail: musee.acadien@ns.sympatico.ca, Internet: http://www.ccfne.ns.ca/~museum
Local Museum 06247

West Vancouver

Ferry Building Gallery, 1414 Argyle Av, West Vancouver, B.C. V7T 1C2 - T: (604) 925-7290, Fax: (604) 925-5913
Fine Arts Museum 06248

Vancouver Naval Museum, POB 91399, West Vancouver, B.C. V7V 3P1 - T: (604) 913-3363, Fax: (604) 926-3126. Head: Foster K. Dennison
Military Museum
Canadian naval history, battle of the Atlantic, men and women of the Canadian Navy and merchantmen 06249

West Vancouver Museum, 680 17th St, West Vancouver, B.C. V7V 3T2 - T: (604) 925-7295, Fax: (604) 925-5915, E-mail: ipatton@westvancouver.net, Internet: http://www.westvancouver.net. Head: Deborah Tuyttens
Local Museum
archives 06250

Westport

Rideau District Museum, 29 Bedford St, Westport, Ont. K0G 1X0, mail addr: POB 305, Westport, Ont. K0G 1X0 - T: (613) 273-2502, E-mail: bwlaird@rideau.net, Internet: http://www.rideaulakes.net/museum
Historical Museum - 1961
Pioneer history 06251

Wetaskiwin

Alberta Central Railway Museum, RR2, Wetaskiwin, Alta. T9A 1W9 - T: (780) 352-2257, Fax: (780) 352-2257, E-mail: abcentral@incentre.net, Internet: http://www.abcentralrailway.com
Science&Tech Museum
Canadian Pacific passenger cars and freight, railyard equipment 06252

Canada's Aviation Hall of Fame, Hwy 13 W, Wetaskiwin, mail addr: POB 6360, Wetaskiwin, Alta. T9A 2G1 - T: (780) 361-1351, Fax: (780) 361-1239, E-mail: cahf@telusplanet.net, Internet: http://www.cahf.ca. Head: Jennifer Romanko
Science&Tech Museum 06253

Reynolds Museum, 4110-57 St, Wetaskiwin, Alta. T9A 2B6 - T: (780) 352-6201, Fax: (780) 352-4666, E-mail: srsl@incentre.net. Head: Stanley G. Reynolds
Science&Tech Museum / Military Museum - 1955
Antique and vintage cars and trucks, gas tractors, steam engines, gas engines, fire engines, 100 military vehicles, war relics, surplus antique cars, trucks, tractors, steam engines are available for sale to allow for expansion of other colls 06254

Wetaskiwin and District Museum, 5010 53 Av, Wetaskiwin, Alta. T9A 0Y7 - T: (780) 352-0227, Fax: (780) 352-0226. Head: Silvia Larson
Local Museum 06255

Weyburn

Allie Griffin Art Gallery, 45 Bison Av, Weyburn, Sask. S4H 1L8 - T: (306) 848-3278, Fax: (306) 848-3271. Head: Helen Mamer
Fine Arts Museum - 1970
Realistic art by contemporary artists 06256

Prairie Gallery → Signal Hill Gallery

Signal Hill Gallery, Signal Hill Arts Centre, 424 10th Av S, Weyburn, Sask. S4H 2A1 - T: (306) 848-3278, Fax: (306) 848-3271, E-mail: shac@city.weyburn.sk.ca. Head: Alice Neufeld
Fine Arts Museum 06257

Soo Line Historical Museum, 411 Industrial Ln, Hwy 39 E, Weyburn, Sask. S4H 2L2 - T: (306) 842-2922, Fax: (306) 842-2977, E-mail: slhm@dlc.west.com. Head: A. Wallace
Local Museum - 1960
Pioneer and Indian artifacts, farm and household items, musical instruments, silver 06258

Turner Curling Museum, POB 370, Weyburn, Sask. S4H 2K6 - T: (306) 848-3217, Fax: (306) 842-2001
Special Museum 06259

Whitbourne

Whitbourne Museum, Whitbourne, Nfld. A0B 3K0 - T: (709) 759-2345, Fax: (709) 759-2242
Local Museum 06260

Whitby

The Station Gallery, Henry and Victoria St W, Whitby, Ont. L1N 5R7 - T: (905) 668-4185. Head: Linda Paulocik
Fine Arts Museum - 1970
Historical and contemporary prints and drawings, contemporary sculpture 06261

White Fox

White Fox Museum, POB 68, White Fox, Sask. S0J 3B0 - T: (306) 276-2170
Local Museum 06262

White Rock

Arnold Mikelson Mind and Matter Gallery, 13743 16 Av, White Rock, B.C. V4A 1P7 - T: (604) 536-6460, E-mail: mindandmatterart@show.ca, Internet: http://www.mindandmatterart.com. Head: Mary Mikelson
Fine Arts Museum 06263

White Rock Museum, 14970 Marine Dr, White Rock, B.C. V4B 1C4 - T: (604) 541-2222, Fax: (604) 541-2223, E-mail: mail@whiterock.museum.bc.ca, Internet: http://www.whiterock.museum.bc.ca. Head: Kathleen Tsang
Local Museum
Regional history - archives 06264

Whitehorse

Fort Selkirk, POB 2703, Whitehorse, Y.T. Y1A 2C6 - T: (867) 667-5386, Fax: (867) 667-8844, E-mail: doug.olynyk@gov.yk.ca
Historical Museum 06265

MacBride Museum, First Av and Wood St, Whitehorse, Y.T. Y1A 3S9, mail addr: POB 4037, Whitehorse, Y.T. Y1A 3S9 - T: (867) 667-2709, Fax: (867) 633-6607, E-mail: macbridemus@yknet.yk.ca, Internet: http://

www.macbridemuseum.com. Head: Clifford Evans
Historical Museum / Natural History Museum - 1951
Prehistoric items, Klondike Gold Rush, pioneer articles, wildlife display 06266

Yukon Beringia Interpretive Centre, POB 2703, Whitehorse, Y.T. Y1A 2C6 - T: (867) 667-3516, Fax: (867) 667-8854, E-mail: ekrahn@gov.yk.ca, Internet: http://www.beringia.com
Archaeological Museum
Ice age items 06267

Yukon Transportation Museum, 30 Electra Cres, Whitehorse, Y.T. Y1A 6E6 - T: (867) 668-4792, Fax: (867) 633-5547, E-mail: ytranmus@yknet.yk.ca, Internet: http://www.yukontransport-museum.homestead.com. Head: Shannon Poelman, Jocelyn Laveck
Science&Tech Museum 06268

Whitemouth

Whitemouth Municipal Museum, Whitemouth Community Grounds, Whitemouth, Man. R0E 2G0 - T: (204) 348-2641, Fax: (204) 348-7731. Head: Tom Cowell
Agriculture Museum - 1974
Agricultural equipment, blacksmith shop, pioneer farm artifacts 06269

Whitewood

Old George's Authentic Collectibles, POB 118, Whitewood, Sask. S0G 5C0 - T: (306) 735-2255, Fax: (306) 735-4399. Head: George C. Chopping
Local Museum 06270

Whitewood Historical Museum, POB 752, Whitewood, Sask. S0G 5C0 - T: (306) 735-4388
Local Museum 06271

Whitney

Algonquin Park Logging Museum, POB 219, Whitney, Ont. K0J 2M0 - T: (613) 637-2828, Fax: (613) 637-2138, Internet: http://www.algonquin.on.ca. Head: Dan Strickland
Local Museum
Logging history of region 06272

Wilcox

Athol Murray College of Notre Dame Museum, POB 100, Wilcox, Sask. S0G 5E0 - T: (306) 732-2080, Fax: (306) 732-2075, Internet: http://www.notredame.sk.ca. Head: Colleen Kvisle
Historical Museum 06273

Wilkie

McLurg Museum, POB 489, Wilkie, Sask. S0K 4W0 - T: (306) 843-2288, Fax: (306) 843-2664
Natural History Museum
Bird, wildlife 06274

Wilkie and District Museum, POB 868, Wilkie, Sask. S0K 4W0 - T: (306) 843-2717
Local Museum 06275

Williams Lake

Museum of the Cariboo Chilcotin, 113 N 4 Av, Williams Lake, B.C. V2G 2C8 - T: (250) 392-7404, Fax: (250) 392-7404, E-mail: mccwl@uniserve.com, Internet: http://www.cowboy-museum.com
Local Museum / Agriculture Museum - 1987
Chilcotin, Chinese and First Nations artifacts, ranching, rodeo, BC Cowboy Hall of Fame - archives 06276

Stationhouse Gallery, 1 N Mackenzie Av, Williams Lake, B.C. V2G 1N4 - T: (250) 392-6113, Fax: (250) 392-6184, Internet: http://sos-connect.com/station/
Public Gallery 06277

Williams Lake Museum, RR2, Williams Lake, B.C. V2G 2C8 - T: (250) 392-5573, Fax: (250) 392-7404
Local Museum 06278

Williamstown

Nor' Wester and Loyalist Museum, 19651 John St Williamstown, Ont. K0C 2J0 - T: (613) 347-3547
Historical Museum - 1967
Fur trade equipment, Indian and Inuit artifacts, history of Loyalists, genealogical records, geology 06279

Willingdon

Historical Village and Pioneer Museum, Willingdon, Alta. T0B 4R0 - T: (780) 367-2428, E-mail: mereska@vegnet.com. Head: Wilson Zukiwski
Local Museum / Open Air Museum 06280

Willow Bunch

Willow Bunch Museum, 8 5th St E, Willow Bunch, Sask. S0H 4K0, mail addr: POB 39, Willow Bunch, Sask. S0H 4K0 - T: (306) 473-2806, Fax: (306) 473-2866, E-mail: fts@sk.sympatico.ca, Internet: http://www.quantumlynx.com/fts/musee
Local Museum 06281

Windsor, Nova Scotia

Haliburton House Museum, 414 Clifton Av, Windsor, Nova Scotia, N.S. B3M 3A6 - T: (902) 798-2915, Fax: (902) 798-5619, Internet: http://museum.gov.ns.ca
Historical Museum
Home of Thomas Chandler Haliburton 06282

Shand House Museum, Avon St, Windsor, Nova Scotia, N.S. B0N 2T0 - T: (902) 798-8213, Fax: (902) 798-5619, Internet: http://museum.gov.ns.ca
Historical Museum
Nova Scotia's industrial and economic history 06283

Windsor, Ontario

Art Gallery of Windsor, 401 Riverside Dr W, Windsor, Ontario, Ont. N9A 7J1 - T: (519) 977-0013, Fax: (519) 977-0776, E-mail: email@artgalleryof-windsor.com, Internet: http://www.artgalleryof-windsor.com. Head: Glen Cumming
Fine Arts Museum - 1943
Canadian art: paintings, drawings, prints, sculpture and graphic art, Inuit art 06284

Serbian Heritage Museum of Windsor, 6770 Tecumseh Rd E, Windsor, Ontario, Ont. N8T 1E6 - T: (519) 944-4884, Fax: (519) 974-3963. Head: Svetlana Miskovic
Historical Museum / Folklore Museum 06285

Willistead Manor, 1899 Niagara St, Windsor, Ontario, Ont. N8Y 1K3 - T: (519) 255-6545
Historical Museum 06286

Windsor's Community Museum, 254 Pitt St W, Windsor, Ontario, Ont. N9A 5L5 - T: (519) 253-1812, Fax: (519) 253-0919, E-mail: wcmchin@mnsi.net, Internet: http://www.city.windsor.on.ca/wpl/museum
Local Museum 06287

Windsor, Québec

Centre Culturel et Patrimonial la Poudrière de Windsor, 342 Saint-Georges, Windsor, Québec, P.Q. J1S 2Z5 - T: (819) 845-5284, Fax: (819) 845-5284, E-mail: poudriere@interlinx.qc.ca. Head: Denise Savard
Folklore Museum 06288

Wingham

North Huron District Museum, 275 Josephine St, Wingham, Ont. N0G 2W0 - T: (519) 357-1096
Local Museum - 1977
Pioneer history, paintings of the late George A. Reid, Artifacts from the early days of the CKNX radio and TV station, Canadian writers Alice Munro and Harry Boyle, Canadian painter George A. Reid, local geneology 06289

Winkler

Pembina Threshermen's Museum, POB 1103, Winkler, Man. R6W 4B2 - T: (204) 822-5369, Fax: (204) 325-9021
Agriculture Museum / Local Museum 06290

Winnipeg

Ace Art, 290 McDermot Av, Winnipeg, Man. R3B 0T2 - T: (204) 944-9763, Fax: (204) 944-9763, E-mail: aceart@escape.ca. Head: Sigrio Dahle, Grant Guy
Public Gallery 06291

Air Command Headquarters Museum and Air Park, Bishop Bldg, 17 Wing, Winnipeg, Man. R3J 0T0 - T: (204) 833-2500, Fax: (204) 833-2512, E-mail: jpickett@escape.ca, Internet: http://www.airforce.dnd.ca. Head: Don Pearsons
Military Museum 06292

Centre Culturel Franco-Manitobain, 340 Blvd Provencher, Winnipeg, Man. R2H 0G7 - T: (204) 233-8972, Fax: (204) 233-3324, E-mail: ccfm@ccfm.mb.ca. Head: Christian Delaquis
Public Gallery 06293

Clothing and Textiles Museum, University of Manitoba, Human Ecology Bldg, 35 Chancellor's Circle, Winnipeg, Man. R3T 2N2 - T: (204) 474-8138, Fax: (204) 275-7592, E-mail: turnbull@ms.umanitoba.ca
Special Museum / University Museum 06294

Dalnavert Museum, 61 Carlton St, Winnipeg, Man. R3C 1N7 - T: (204) 943-2835, E-mail: dalnavert@escape.ca, Internet: http://www.mhs.mb.ca. Head: Tim Worth
Decorative Arts Museum - 1974
House of Hugh John MacDonald with furniture and furnishings (1840-1905), English, Canadian, American, Chinese and German artifacts 06295

Floating Gallery, 100 Arthur St, Winnipeg, Man. R3B 1H3 - T: (204) 942-8183, Fax: (204) 942-1555, E-mail: floatgal@pangea.ca. Head: Charles Shilliday
Public Gallery 06296

Forest Sandilands Centre and Museum, 900 Corydon Av, Winnipeg, Man. R3M 0Y4 - T: (204) 453-3182
Natural History Museum 06297

Fort Garry Horse Regimental Museum, 551 Machray Av, Winnipeg, Man. R2W 1A8 - T: (204) 586-6298, Fax: (204) 582-0370, E-mail: fgh@escape.ca, Internet: http://www.escape.ca/~fgh
Military Museum - 1976
Regimental history incl archival material - archives 06298

Gallery I.I.I., c/o School of Art, University of Manitoba, 211 FitzGerald Bldg, Winnipeg, Man. R3T 2N2 - T: (204) 474-9322, Fax: (204) 474-7605, Internet: http://www.umanitoba.ca/schools/art/info/gallery.html. Head: Prof. Dale Amundson
Fine Arts Museum / University Museum - 1965
Contemporary Canadian, American and European paintings, prints, drawings and sculptures 06299

Gallery One One One, University of Manitoba, Fort Garry Campus, 203 Fitzgerald Bldg, Winnipeg, Man. R3T 2N2 - T: (204) 474-9322, Fax: (204) 474-7605, E-mail: eylandc@hotmail.com, Internet: http://www.umanitoba.ca/schools/art. Head: Cliff Eyland
University Museum / Fine Arts Museum / Public Gallery
Fitzgerald study coll 06300

Historical Museum of Saint James-Assiniboia, 3180 Portage Av, Winnipeg, Man. R3K 0Y5 - T: (204) 888-8706. Head: Grant Tyler
Ethnology Museum - 1971
Indian and Eskimo artifacts, pioneer history 06301

Ivan Franko Museum, 595 Pritchard Av, Winnipeg, Man. R2W 2K4 - T: (204) 589-4397, Fax: (204) 589-3404. Head: Z. Nykolyshyn
Special Museum - 1956
Documents on the life and work of the Ukrainian writer, poet and statesman Ivan Franko (1856-1916), including photocopies of manuscripts, Ukrainian costumes and embroidery - library 06302

J.B. Wallis Museum of Entomology, c/o Dept. of Entomology, University of Manitoba, 424 University Centre, Winnipeg, Man. R3T 2N2 - T: (204) 474-6023/24, Fax: (204) 275-0402. Head: Dr. R.E. Roughley
Natural History Museum 06303

Living Prairie Museum, 2795 Ness Av, Winnipeg, Man. R3J 3S4 - T: (204) 832-0167, Fax: (204) 986-4172, E-mail: prairie@city.winnipeg.mb.ca, Internet: http://www.city.winnipeg.mb.ca/cms-prod/parks/envserv/living.html
Natural History Museum 06304

Manitoba Children's Museum, 45 Forks Market Rd, Winnipeg, Man. R3C 4T6 - T: (204) 924-4000, Fax: (204) 956-2122, E-mail: general@childrensmuseum.com, Internet: http://www.childrensmuseum.com. Head: Diane Doth
Special Museum 06305

Manitoba Electrical Museum, 680 Harrow St, Winnipeg, Man. R3M 3A3 - T: (204) 284-9439, Fax: (204) 475-4820, E-mail: publicaffairs@hydro.mb.ca, Internet: http://hydro.mb.ca. Head: Jenett Richter
Science&Tech Museum
education centre 06306

Manitoba Museum of Man and Nature, 190 Rupert Av, Winnipeg, Man. R3B 0N2 - T: (204) 956-2830, Fax: (204) 942-3679, E-mail: info@manitobamuseum.mb.ca, Internet: http://www.manitobamuseum.mb.ca. Head: Claudette Leclerc
Natural History Museum / Historical Museum / Science&Tech Museum - 1970
Hudson Bay Company Museum Coll, anthropology, archaeology, hist, textiles and costumes, ethnology, geology, herpetology, entomology, biology, mineralogy, natural hist, paleontology, botany, ornithology - planetarium, science centre, library 06307

Manitoba Sports Hall of Fame and Museum, 200 Main St, Ste 210, Winnipeg, Man. R3C 4M2 - T: (204) 925-5735, Fax: (204) 925-5792, Internet: http://www.sport.mb.ca
Special Museum 06308

Museum of Canada, Aquatic Hall of Fame, Pan-Am Pool, 25 Poseidon Bay, Winnipeg, Man. R3M 3E4 - T: (204) 957-1700, Fax: (204) 942-2325, Internet: http://www.city.winnipeg.mb.ca/cms-prod/aquatics/aquaticshall. Head: Luke Small
Special Museum - 1967
Aquatic sports, swimming, diving, syncronized swimming, waterpolo - archives 06309

Ogniwo Polish Museum, 1417 Main St, Winnipeg, Man. R2W 3V3 - T: (204) 586-5070, E-mail: ogniwo@mb.sympatico.ca, Internet: http://www.polishmuseum.com. Head: Christine Tabbernor
Local Museum
Folklore, history, military, ethnology, pioneers 06310

Oseredok Ukrainian Art Gallery and Museum, 184 Alexander Av E, Winnipeg, Man. R3C 0L6 - T: (204) 942-0218, Fax: (204) 943-2851. Head: Ernest Cicierski
Historical Museum / Fine Arts Museum / Folklore Museum - 1944
Fine and decorative art, history of the Ukrainians in Canada and the Ukrainian Nationalist Movement 06311

Queen's Own Cameron Highlanders of Canada Regimental Museum, 230 Minto Armoury, 969 Saint Matthew's St, Winnipeg, Man. R3G 0J7 - T: (204) 786-4330. Head: Grant Tyler
Military Museum - 1973
Regimental uniforms and equipment (1910-present) 06312

R.B. Ferguson Museum of Mineralogy, c/o Department of Geological Sciences, University of Manitoba, Winnipeg, Man. R3T 2N2 - T: (204) 474-8765, Fax: (204) 474-7623, E-mail: p_cerny@umanitoba.ca. Head: Dr. P. Cerny
Natural History Museum / University Museum - 1922
Mineralogical specimens from granitic pegmatites 06313

Riel House, 330 River Rd, Winnipeg, Man. R2M 3Z8 - T: (204) 257-1783, 233-4888, Fax: (204) 233-4888. Head: Janelle Reynolds
Special Museum 06314

Ross House Museum, 140 Meade St N, Winnipeg, Man. R2W 3K5 - T: (204) 943-2835, Internet: http://www.mhs.mb.ca. Head: Tim Worth
Historical Museum 06315

Royal Canadian Mint, 520 Lagimodiere Blvd, Winnipeg, Man. R2J 3E7 - T: (204) 983-6400, Fax: (204) 255-5203, E-mail: west@rcmint.ca, Internet: http://www.rcmint.ca. Head: Patrick Cunningham
Historical Museum 06316

Royal Winnipeg Rifles Museum, 208 Minto Armoury, 969 Saint Matthew's Av, Winnipeg, Man. R3G 0J7 - T: (204) 786-4392. Head: Win Anders
Military Museum - 1970
Weapons, medals, bagdes, uniforms, pictures, hist of the regiment - archives, library 06317

Saint Norbert Provincial Heritage Park, 40 Turnbull Dr, Winnipeg, Man. R3J 3W3 - T: (204) 945-4375, Fax: (204) 945-0012, E-mail: kporteous@mb.gov.mb.ca, Internet: http://manitobaparks.com. Head: Ken Porteous
Natural History Museum / Local Museum 06318

Saint Volodymyr Museum, Ukrainian Catholic Archeparchy of Winnipeg, 233 Scotia St, Winnipeg, Man. R2V 1V7 - T: (204) 338-7801, Fax: (204) 339-4006, E-mail: archepar@escape.ca, Internet: http://www.archeparchy.ca. Head: Natalia Radawetz
Religious Arts Museum - 1967
Church artifacts incl Gospel books, icons, crosses, vestments, candleholders, Ukrainian catholic church diorama, tabernacles, liturgical items - library, archives, education centre 06319

Seven Oaks House Museum, 1650 Main St, Winnipeg, Man. R2V 4C8 - T: (204) 339-7429
Local Museum - 1976
Historic house (1851) with furniture and household articles, period furnishings 06320

Site Gallery, 55 Arthur St, Winnipeg, Man. R3B 1H1 - T: (204) 942-1618, Fax: (204) 943-7980, E-mail: site@pangea.ca, Internet: http://www.pangea.ca/site. Head: Keith Oliver
Public Gallery 06321

Sounds of Yesteryear, 71 De Bourmont Bay, Winnipeg, Man. R2J 1K2
Music Museum - 1974
Antique automatic musical instruments including player pianos, nickelodians, orchestrions, music boxes 06322

Transcona Historical Museum, 141 Regent Av W, Winnipeg, Man. R2C 1R1 - T: (204) 222-0423, Fax: (204) 222-0208, E-mail: Transcon@istar.ca, Internet: http://members.xoom.com/Transcona. Head: Pat Dance
Local Museum - 1967
Ethnology, lepidoptera, firearms, bird eggs, community hist - archives 06323

Ukrainian Museum of Canada - Manitoba Branch, 1175 Main St, Winnipeg, Man. R2W 3S4 - T: (204) 582-7345
Decorative Arts Museum / Religious Arts Museum - 1954
Ukrainian national costumes and embroidery, tapestries, ceramics and woodwork 06324

Upstairs Gallery, 266 Edmonton St, Winnipeg, Man. R3C 1R9 - T: (204) 943-2734, Fax: (204) 943-7726, Internet: http://www.upstairsgallery.mb.ca. Head: Faye Settler
Public Gallery 06325

UVAN Historical Museum, 205 456 Main St, Winnipeg, Man. R3B 1B6 - T: (204) 942-5095, Fax: (204) 947-3882. Head: Prof. M. Tarnawesky
Historical Museum / Ethnology Museum - 1970
History, ethnology - archives 06326

Western Canada Aviation Museum, Hangar T-2, 958 Ferry Rd, Winnipeg, Man. R3H 0Y8 - T: (204) 786-5503, Fax: (204) 775-4761, E-mail: info@wcam.mb.ca, Internet: http://www.wcam.mb.ca. Head: George Elliott
Science&Tech Museum - 1974
Civil and military aircraft - library, archives 06327

Winnipeg Art Gallery, 300 Memorial Blvd, Winnipeg, Man. R3C 1V1 - T: (204) 786-6641, Fax: (204) 788-4998, E-mail: inquiries@wag.mb.ca, Internet: http://www.wag.mb.ca. Head: Patricia E. Bovey
Fine Arts Museum - 1912

Canadian contemporary art, Canadian paintings and prints (19th-20th c), Inuit sculpture and prints, Gothic panel painting (15th-16th c), English porcelain, silver and glass (18th-19th c) 06328

Winnipeg Police Museum, 130 Allard Av, Winnipeg, Man. R3K 0T4 - T: (204) 986-3976, Fax: (204) 986-6101. Head: Jack Templeman
Historical Museum 06329

Zoology Museum, c/o Department of Zoology, University of Manitoba, Duff Roblin Bldg, Winnipeg, Man. R3T 2N2
Natural History Museum / University Museum - 1960
Mammals, birds, fish, reptiles, amphibians, crustaceans, mollusks, casts of fossils, snakes 06330

Winnipegosis

Winnipegosis Museum, POB 4, Winnipegosis, Man. R0L 2G0 - T: (204) 656-4791. Head: Stephen Lytwyn
Local Museum 06331

Wolfville

Acadia University Art Gallery, POB 1269, Wolfville, N.S. B0P 1X0 - T: (902) 585-1373, Fax: (902) 585-1070, E-mail: fran.kruschen@acadiau.ca, Internet: http://ace.acadiau.ca/arts/artgal/home.htm. Head: Franziska Kruschen
Fine Arts Museum / University Museum - 1978
20th c Canadian drawings, paintings from maritime region, Eskimo sculpture, Alex Colville serigraphs 06332

Randall House Museum, 171 Main St, Wolfville, N.S. B0P 1X0 - T: (902) 542-9775. Head: Heather A. Davidson
Local Museum - 1941
Historic house (built 1815-16) with original period furniture and kitchen utensils, toys, portraits 06333

Wolseley

Wolseley Community Museum, Wolseley, Sask. S0G 5H0 - T: (306) 698-2543. Head: Eileen Isman
Local Museum 06334

Wood Mountain

Wood Mountain Ranch and Rodeo Museum, 3 Miles S of Wood Mountain, Wood Mountain, Sask. S4P 0M8, mail addr: POB 53, Wood Mountain, Sask. S0H 4L0 - T: (306) 266-4539. Head: Pat Fitzpatrick
Agriculture Museum / Folklore Museum - 1965
Artifacts of the North West Mounted Police and Sioux Indians (c 1885) 06335

Woodbridge

Kortright Centre Museum, Pine Valley Dr, Woodbridge, Ont. M3N 1S4 - T: (905) 832-2289, Fax: (905) 832-8238, E-mail: info@kortright.org, Internet: http://www.kortright.org. Head: Dr. Allan Foster
Natural History Museum - 1978
Management of the renewable natural resources land, water, forest and wildlife for sustainable living 06336

Woodlands

Woodlands Pioneer Museum, Woodlands, Man. R0C 3H0 - T: (204) 383-5584, Fax: (204) 383-5685. Head: Opal Langrell
Local Museum 06337

Woodstock

Old Carleton County Court House, 128 Connell St, Woodstock, N.B. E7M 1L5 - T: (506) 328-9706, Fax: (506) 328-2942, E-mail: jtribe@nb.sympatico.ca
Historical Museum 06338

Woodstock Art Gallery, 447 Hunter St, Woodstock, Ont. N4S 4G7 - T: (519) 539-6761, Fax: (519) 539-2564, E-mail: gallery@city.woodstock.on.ca, Internet: http://www.city.woodstock.on.ca. Head: Maria Ricker
Fine Arts Museum 06339

Woodstock Museum, 466 Dundas St, Woodstock, Ont. N4S 1C4 - T: (519) 537-8411, Fax: (519) 537-7235, E-mail: museum@city.woodstock.on.ca, Internet: http://www.city.woodstock.on.ca. Head: Sheila A. Johnson
Local Museum / Historic Site 06340

Wynyard

Wynard and District Museum, POB 734, Wynyard, Sask. S0A 4T0 - T: (306) 554-2898, Fax: (306) 554-3224. Head: Dave Cross
Local Museum - 1974 06341

Yale

Historic Yale Museum, 31179 Douglas St, Yale, B.C. V0K 2S0 - T: (604) 863-2324
Local Museum 06342

Yarmouth

Firefighters' Museum of Nova Scotia and National Exhibition Centre, 451 Main St, Yarmouth, N.S. B5A 1G9 - T: (902) 742-5525, Fax: (902) 742-5525. Head: Daniel Darby
Science&Tech Museum - 1968
Firefighting history - library 06343

Yarmouth County Museum, 22 Collins St, Yarmouth, N.S. B5A 3C8 - T: (902) 742-5539, Fax: (902) 749-1120, E-mail: yemuseum@ns.sympatico.ca. Head: Eric J. Ruff
Local Museum - 1958
Ship models and ship portraits, paintings, dolls, musical instruments, period rooms of the Victorian era, costumes, local industries and local hist, genealogy - archives 06344

Yellowknife

Prince of Wales Northern Heritage Centre, Frame Lake N, Yellowknife, N.T. X1A 2L9 - T: (867) 873-7551, Fax: (867) 873-0205, E-mail: charles_arnold@ece.learnnet.nt.ca, Internet: http://www.pwnhc.learnnet.nt.ca. Head: Dr. Charles D. Arnold
Local Museum - 1979
Archeology, ethnology, history, the natural sciences and arts, primarily of the Canadian Arctic and subarctic - Northwest Territories archives 06345

Ymir

Ymir Museum, POB 65, Ymir, B.C. V0G 2K0 - T: (250) 357-9600
Local Museum 06346

Yorkton

Saskatchewan Western Development Museum, Hwy 16 W, Yorkton, Sask. S3N 2V6 - T: (306) 783-8361, Fax: (306) 782-1027, E-mail: wem.y@sk.sympatico.ca, Internet: http://www.sdmuseum.sk.ca. Head: David Klatt
Local Museum - 1949 06347

Story of People, Western Development Museum, Hwy 16 W, Yorkton, Sask. S3N 2V6 - T: (306) 783-8361, Fax: (306) 782-1027, E-mail: wdm.y@sk.sympatico.ca, Internet: http://www.wdmuseum.sk.ca. Head: David Klatt
Local Museum / Agriculture Museum - 1949
Immigration and pioneer household artifacts, early agricultural equipment 06348

Yorkton Arts Council, 49 Smith St E, Yorkton, Sask. S3N 0H4 - T: (306) 783-8722, Fax: (306) 786-7667. Head: Lori Glauser
Public Gallery - 1966
Local artists' exhibits, graphics, pottery, serigraphs 06349

Cape Verde

Praia

Museu de Documentos Esperciais, Arquivio Historico Nacional, Cha de Areia, Praia, mail addr: CP 321, Praia - T: 612125, Fax: 613900
Historical Museum 06350

Central African Republic

Bangassou

Musée Labasso, Maison des Jeunes, Bangassou, mail addr: BP 89, Bangassou
Ethnology Museum / Historical Museum - 1975
Archaeology from Nzakara and Zandé districts, historical maps and documents, ethnology 06351

Bangui

Musée National Barthélémy Boganda, Rues Languédoc et Industrie, Bangui, mail addr: BP 349, Bangui - T: 613533. Head: Maurice Licky
Ethnology Museum - 1964
Ethnography 06352

Bouar

Musée Ethnographique Regional, Bouar
Ethnology Museum / Folklore Museum
Ethnography, folklore 06353

M'Baiki

Musée Botanique de Wakombo, M'Baiki
Natural History Museum
Botany 06354

Musée Scientifique de Boukoko, M'Baiki
Natural History Museum 06355

Chad

Abeche

Musée d'Abeche, Abeche
Local Museum 06356

N'Djamena

Musée National, Institut National des Sciences Humaines, 1 Pl de l'Indépendance, N'Djamena, mail addr: BP 503, N'Djamena - T: 3686. Head: Djamil Moussa Nene
Natural History Museum / Historical Museum - 1963
Paleontology, archeology, ethnography, handicrafts, natural sciences, arms, musical instruments 06357

Musée N'Djamena, Fort Archambault, N'Djamena, mail addr: BP 638, N'Djamena - T: 513375
Local Museum
Local history, archeology, ethnography 06358

Sarh

Musée National de Sarh, BP 244, Sarh - T: 681394, Fax: 681468, 681243. Head: Kloumtouin Baitchiba-Afalna
Local Museum - 1968
Protohistory, prehistory, archaeology, ethnographic, ethnomusic, folk-art 06359

Chile

Angol

Museo Dillmann S. Bullock, CP 8-D, Angol - T: 711142, Fax: 712395. Head: Alberto E. Montero
Natural History Museum / Historical Museum - 1946
Local flora and fauna, birds, mammals, reptiles, insects, archaeology, anthropology, colonial weapons, 80 funeral urns of the Kofkeche culture - library 06360

Antofagasta

Museo Antropológico de Antofagasta, c/o Universidad de Antofagasta, CP 170, Antofagasta - T: (055) 222528
Ethnology Museum / University Museum - 1973
Exhibits on the prehistory, ethnohistory and mestizo communities of Northern Chile, includes Instituto de Investigaciones Antropológicas - library 06361

Museo Regional de Antofagasta, Calle Bolívar 188, Antofagasta, mail addr: CP 746, Antofagasta - T: (055) 227016. Head: Ivo Kuzmanić Pierotić
Local Museum - 1984
Archaeology, history, ethnography, geology - library 06362

Arica

Museo Arqueológico San Miguel de Azapa, Calle 18 Septiembre No 2222, Arica, mail addr: c/o Universidad de Tarapacá, CP 6-D, Arica - T: (058) 205555, Fax: 224248, E-mail: ichacama@vision.facsae.uta.cl. Head: Juan Chacama Rodríguez
Archaeological Museum / University Museum - 1959
Archaeology, ceramics, anthropology, textiles, the oldest mummification in the world: the Chinchorro culture mummies, all types of organic material (plants, animals etc) - library, lab 06363

Cañete

Museo Folklórico Araucano de Cañete Juan A. Ríos M., CP 28, Cañete - T: (041) 611093, Fax: 611093. Head: Gloria Cardenas Troncoso
Folklore Museum - 1968
Exhibits of the Mapuche culture from its origins to contact with Spanish culture, environment which Vladivia saw in 1552 when he built the Tucapel Fort (near the museum), anthropological research of still existing Mapuche settlements - library 06364

Chiu Chiu

Museo Arqueológico de Chiu Chiu, Calle Central, Chiu Chiu
Archaeological Museum - 1980
Archeological artifacts found in the Chiu Chiu region 06365

Concepción

Casa del Arte de la Universidad de Concepción, Calle Chacabuco esq de Paicavi, Concepción, mail addr: CP 2737, Concepción - T: (041) 234985 ext 2126. Head: Dr. Antonio Fernández
Fine Arts Museum / University Museum
Paintings 06366

Museo de Historia Natural de Concepción, Calle Maipú 2359 Plaza Luis Acevedo, Concepción - T: (041) 310932, Fax: 310932, E-mail: musconce@ctcreuna.cl, Internet: http://www.dibam.renib.cl. Head: Marco Sánchez Aguilera
Natural History Museum - 1902
Archaeology, natural history - library 06367

Museo de Hualpén, Parque Pedro del Río Zañ, Casilla 2656, Concepción - T: (041) 227305. Head: Victor Lobos Lápera
Archaeological Museum / Ethnology Museum / Folklore Museum - 1882
Coll of Greek, Roman and Egyptian archaeology, Oriantal art, Chilean and American folk art, Chilea arms, numismatics and archaeology 06368

Pinacoteca de la Universidad de Concepción, Casa del Arte, Barrion Universitario Frente a Plaza Perú, Concepción - T: (041) 27455. Head: Prof. Tole Peralta
Fine Arts Museum
Paintings 06369

Copiapó

Museo Regional de Atacama, Calle Atacama 98, Copiapó - T: (052) 212313, Fax: 212313. Head: Miguel Cervellino
Archaeological Museum / Historical Museum - 1973
Archaeology, mineralogy, ecology and history - library 06370

Iquique

Museo Antropológico de Iquique, Campus Pedro Lagos, Calles Pedro Lagos y Grumete Bolados, Iquique, mail addr: c/o Universidad Arturo Prat de Iquique, CP 121, Iquique. Head: Alvaro Carevic Rivera
Ethnology Museum - 1987
Permanent exhibition showing the cultural development of the people of the region from 10,000 BC to 1535, research in archaeology, physical anthropology, history and ethnography - library 06371

Museo Regional de Iquique, Calle Baquedano 951, Iquique - T: (057) 411034, 472061, Fax: 413278. Head: Cora Romy Moragas
Local Museum - 1960
Permanent exhibition of regional archaeology, Aymara ethnical handicrafts, hist of nitrate period (19th-20th c) 06372

La Serena

Museo Arqueológico de La Serena, Calle Cordovez esq Cienfuego, La Serena, mail addr: CP 617, La Serena - T: (051) 224492, Fax: 225398. Head: Gonzalo Ampuero
Archaeological Museum - 1943
Archaeology, prehistory, colonial history, ethnography and anthropology, paleontology, pottery of Molle, Diaguita and Inca culture, feather embroided costumes - library 06373

Linares

Museo de Arte y Artesanía de Linares, Av Valentín Letelier 580, Linares, mail addr: CP 272, Linares - T: 662. Head: Pedro Olmos Muñoz
Local Museum - 1966
Agriculture, birds, weaving, ceramics, Araucan arms and masks 06374

Osorno

Auto Museum Moncopulli, Km 25 Ruta 215 Puyehue, Osorno - T: (064) 204200, Fax: 204200, E-mail: automuseum@moncopulli.cl, Internet: http://www.moncopulli.cl. Head: Bernardo Eggers
Science&Tech Museum 06375

Museo Histórico de Osorno, Calle Matta 809, Osorno, mail addr: CP 42-0, Osorno - T: (064) 238615, Fax: 255988, E-mail: museosorno@telsur.cl, Internet: http://www.osornochile.cl. Head: Gabriel Peralta Vidal
Historical Museum - 1946
Fossils, ceramics 06376

Ovalle

Museo del Limari, Calle Independencia 329, Ovalle, mail addr: CP 59, Ovalle. Head: Marcos Biskupovic Mazzei
Archaeological Museum - 1963
1200 archaeological exhibits, valuable pottery and ceramics of the local Indian culture 06377

Puerto Williams

Museo Martín Gusinde, Puerto Williams. Head: Maurice Van de Maele
Historical Museum / Natural History Museum - 1975
History and geography of the southern most archipelagos of America, aboriginal culture, flora, fauna and minerals of the area - library 06378

Punta Arenas

Museo Histórico Regional de Magallanes, Centro Cultural Braun-Menéndez, Hernando de Magallanes 949, Punta Arenas - T: (061) 244216, Fax: 221387. Head: Desanka Ursić
Historical Museum - 1983
Patagonian history - library 06379

Museo Regional Salesiano Maggiorino Borgatello, Instituto Don Bosco, Av Bulness 374, Punta Arenas - T: (061) 221096, Fax: 241242. Head: Prof. Sergio Lausič Glasinovič
Natural History Museum / Ethnology Museum - 1893
Natural history, ethnography, relics of Indian tribes 06380

San Pedro de Atacama

Museo Arqueológico R.P. Gustavo Le Paige S.J., Universidad Católica del Norte, San Pedro de Atacama - T: (055) 851002, Fax: 851066, E-mail: museospa@tie.cl. Head: Dr. Agustín Llagostera Martínez
Archaeological Museum - 1963
Archaeology, physical Anthropology, stone tools, snuffing boxes, ceramics - library 06381

Santiago

Luis E. Peña G. Collection, CP 2974, Santiago - T: (02) 7455066, Fax: 7455176, E-mail: ugartepena@ltn.cl. Head: Alfredo Ugarte-Peña
Natural History Museum - 1940
Entomology 06382

Museo Chileno de Arte Precolombino, Calle Bandera 361, Santiago, mail addr: CP 3687, Santiago - T: (02) 6953851, Fax: 6972779. Head: Carlos Aldunate del Solar
Archaeological Museum - 1981
2000 items of Pre-Columbian art, 1,000 ethnographic items from Mapuche and Aymara cultures, textiles, ceramics, metal work, stone sculptures, photographs, slides, video and audio cassettes, research on precolumbian music, rock art, Tiahuanaco, Aymara, Atacama and Araucanian cultures, prehistoric architecture, Andean textiles and symbolism, educational programmes - library, lab for textile and pottery conservation, lab for archaeological research 06383

Museo de Arte Colonial de San Francisco, Calle Alameda Bernardo O'Higgins 834, Santiago - T: (02) 6398737, Fax: 6398737, Internet: http://www.museosanfrancisco.cl. Head: Rosa D. Puga
Fine Arts Museum / Decorative Arts Museum - 1968
Paintings 17th-19th c, locksmith's craft, wrought iron grills from Chile (17th c), silversmith's works (16th c) - library 06384

Museo de Arte Contemporáneo, c/o Universidad de Chile, Facultad de Artes, Parque Forestal s/n, Centro, Santiago - T: (02) 6395486, 6396488, Fax: 6394945, E-mail: mac.uchile@entelchile.net, Internet: http://www.mac.uchile.cl. Head: Francisco Brugnoli Bailoni
Fine Arts Museum / University Museum - 1947
Contemporary art 06385

Museo de Arte Popular Americano, Parque Forestal s/n, Santiago, mail addr: c/o Universidad de Chile, CP 2100, Santiago - T: (02) 6821480, Fax: 6821481, E-mail: museopop@abello.dic.uchile.cl. Head: Sylvia Ríos Montero
Folklore Museum - 1943
Folk art, crafts, trades, folklore, Araucanian silver - library 06386

Museo de Historia Natural de San Pedro Nolasco, Av Kennedy 5850 Vitacura, Santiago, mail addr: CP 525, Santiago - T: (02) 6330438, E-mail: cspn@ctcinternet.cl. Head: Carlos A. Espinoza
Natural History Museum - 1912
library 06387

Museo de la Solidaridad Salvador Allende, Calle Virginia Opazo 38, Santiago - T: (02) 6971033
Historical Museum 06388

Museo del Carmen de Maipú, CP 895, Santiago - T: (02) 9429669, Fax: 5310359. Head: German Domínguez
Historical Museum / Decorative Arts Museum / Religious Arts Museum - 1956
Coll of antiques, historical documents and coaches 06389

Museo Histórico Nacional, Plaza de Armas 951, Santiago - T: (02) 6381411, Fax: 6331815. Head: Dr. Sofía Correa Sutil
Historical Museum - 1911
Militaria, arms, painting, furniture, silver, porcelain, textiles, engravings, coins and medals, photogr - library, textile dept, numismatic cabinet, iconographic archive 06390

Museo Nacional de Bellas Artes de Santiago de Chile, Parque Forestal s/n, Santiago, mail addr: CP 3209, Santiago - T: (02) 6330655, Fax: 6393297, E-mail: mivelic@oris.renib.cl, Internet: http://www.dibam.renib.cl/isc160. Head: Milan Ivelic
Fine Arts Museum - 1880
History of Chilean painting from colonial times to today, Dutch and Spanish baroque items, Italian drawings of the 15th, 16th and 17th c, photography, sculptures, prints - library 06391

Museo Nacional de Historia Natural, Quinta Normal, Santiago, mail addr: CP 787, Santiago - T: (02) 6404603, Fax: 6804602, E-mail: eramirez@mnhn.cl, Internet: http://www.mnhn.cl. Head: María Eliana Ramirez Casali
Natural History Museum - 1830
Vertebrates, invertebrates, entomology, biology, botany, mineralogy, geology, paleontology, anthropology - library 06392

Museo Pedagógico Carlos Stuardo Ortiz, Calle Compañía 3150, Santiago - T: (02) 91938. Head: David Vergara Torres
Historical Museum - 1941
History of education in Chile, numismatics - library 06393

Museo Ralli, Calle Alonso de Sotomayor 4110, Santiago - T: (02) 6816022
Music Museum 06394

Proed, Calle General del Canto 426, Santiago - T: (02) 2640689
Local Museum 06395

Sala Sergio Larrain, Calle El Comendador 1926, Santiago, mail addr: c/o Escuela de Arte, Pontificia Universidad Católica de Chile, CP 114-D, Santiago - T: (02) 2224516 (2682). Head: Edgar Pfennings
Fine Arts Museum / University Museum 06396

Talca

Museo O'Higginiano y de Bellas Artes de Talca, Calle Uno Norte 875, Talca, mail addr: CP 189, Talca - T: (071) 227330. Head: Sergio Ulloa Rojos
Fine Arts Museum - 1964
Paintings, stainded glass, armaments, sculptures, history 06397

Temuco

Museo Regional de la Araucania, Av Alemanía 084, Temuco, mail addr: CP 481, Temuco - T: (045) 211108, Fax: 234881. Head: Hector Zumaeta Zúñiga
Ethnology Museum / Folklore Museum - 1943
Arts and crafts of Araucanian Indians, folklore, history, pre-Araucanian ceramics, crania, fossiles trees, lithic tombs - library 06398

Valdivia

Museo de Arte Contemporaneo, Av Los Laureles s/n, Valdivia - T: (063) 221968, E-mail: mac@uach.cl, Internet: http://www.macvaldivia.uach.cl
Fine Arts Museum 06399

Museo Histórico y Antropológico de la Universidad Austral de Chile, CP 586, Valdivia - T: (063) 212872, Fax: 212872, E-mail: museo@entelchile.net. Head: Jorge E. Inostroza Saavedra
Ethnology Museum / Historical Museum / University Museum - 1967
Part of University Centre for Conservation of Historical Monuments, Archaeology, Museums and Historical Archives, undertakes teaching, research, training of museum staff, conservation, museology - library, historical archive 06400

Valparaíso

Casa-Museo La Sebastiana, Fundación Pablo Neruda, Ferrari 692, Cerro Bellavista, Valparaíso - T: (032) 256606, 233759, Fax: 233759, E-mail: lasebastiana-neruda@entelchile.net, Internet: http://www.lasebastiana-neruda.cl. Head: Elisa Figueroa
Special Museum
Pablo Neruda's home in Valparaiso, antiquities, furniture, paintings, curious objects 06401

Museo de Historia Natural de Valparaíso, Calle Condell 1546, Valparaíso, mail addr: CP 3208, Valparaíso - T: (032) 257441, Fax: 220846, E-mail: mhnv@ctcinternet.cl. Head: Ana Avalos Valenzuela
Natural History Museum - 1876
Invertebrates, mollusks, fishes, birds, vertebrates, minerals, fossils, archaeology - library 06402

Museo Municipal de Bellas Artes de Valparaíso, Palacio Baburizza, Paseo Yugoslavo Cerro Algere, Valparaíso - T: (032) 252332, Fax: 223329. Head: Jacob Ahumada Valencia
Fine Arts Museum - 1941
Chile: Camilo Mori, Juan Francisco Gaonzalez, Tomás Somerscales, Romero de Torres (España), Europa: Luis Gabriel Isabey, Henry Rosseau, Daniel Hidalgo, Julio Romero de Torres, Eugene Galien L., Francisco Pradilla 06403

Vicuña

Museo Gabriela Mistral de Vicuña, Gabriela Mistral 759, Vicuña - T: (051) 411223, Fax: 412524, E-mail: mgmistral@entelchile.net. Head: Rodrigo Iribarren Avilés
Special Museum - 1971
Cultural legacy of the poetess, Gabriela Mistral (Nobel prize for Literature 1945), documents, photographs and personal effects, replica of birthplace of poetess, talks, films, music - library 06404

Viña del Mar

Museo Comparativo de Biología Marina, Av Borgoño s/n, Mar, Viña del Mar, mail addr: c/o Instituto de Oceanología, CP 13-D, Viña del Mar - T: (032) 832702, Fax: 833214. Head: Isabel Solis
Natural History Museum - 1955
Marine invertebrates, sea birds, fishes, shells 06405

Museo de Bellas Artes, Quinta Vergara, Calle Errázuriz 596, Viña del Mar - T: (032) 680618. Head: Mónica Pino Morán
Fine Arts Museum
Paintings by South American artists 06406

Museo Naval de Viña del Mar, Castillo Wulf, Av Marina 37, Viña del Mar
Science&Tech Museum 06407

China, People's Republic

Anqing

Anqing Municipal Museum, Yingjiang Temple, Anqing
Local Museum / Archaeological Museum
History, archaeology 06408

Anshan

Anshan City Museum, 45 Xinhua St, Tiedong, 114001 Anshan - T: (0412) 5536210
Local Museum 06409

Anyang

Anyang Yin Xu Bo Wu Yuan (Anyang City Museum), Xijiao Small Tun, 455004 Anyang - T: (0372) 3932171
Local Museum 06410

Archaeological Museum, Anyang 455000
Archaeological Museum 06411

Bangbu

Bangbu City Museum, 79 Sheng Li Rd, Zhongshi, 233000 Bangbu - T: (0552) 2042312
Local Museum 06412

Baoding

Zhi Li Victory Museum, Yu Hua Rd, 071000 Baoding - T: (0312) 2038020, Fax: 2038020
Historical Museum 06413

Baoji

Municipal Museum, Jintai Temple, Baoji 721000 - T: 2861
Archaeological Museum
Archeological finds including bronzes 06414

Beijing

Ancient Architecture Museum, 21 Dongjing Rd, Xuanwu, 100050 Beijing - T: (010) 63045608 (010) 63039760
Fine Arts Museum 06415

Ancient Coins Museum, Deshengmen Jian Floor, Xicheng, 100011 Beijing - T: (010) 62018073
Special Museum 06416

Anthropological Museum, c/o Institute of Vertebrate Paleontology and Paleoanthropology, Beijing 100000
Ethnology Museum 06417

Astronautics Museum, South Garden, Zhonghua, 100000 Beijing - T: (010) 68384455
Science&Tech Museum 06418

Aviation Museum of the Air Force, Datangshan, Changping, Xiaotangshan, Beijing 102211, mail addr: POB 5806, Beijing 102211 - T: (010) 61784882, 61781054, Fax: 61784883
Military Museum - 1987
Aircraft, guided missiles, radar, airborne armament, aeroengine, survival equipment, antiaircraft gun, aerocamera 06419

Beijing Animation Art Museum, 24 Wutasi Bai Shi Qiao Rd, Haidian, 100081 Beijing - T: (010) 62172945, Fax: 62174709
Performing Arts Museum 06420

Beijing Art Museum, Wanshou Temple, Haidian, 100081 Beijing - T: (010) 68413380, 68413382
Fine Arts Museum 06421

Beijing Capital Museum, 13 Guozijian St, Dongcheng, 100007 Beijing - T: (010) 64012118
Local Museum 06422

Beijing Changcheng Hua Ren Huai, Sanbao Village, Yanqing, Beijing - T: (010) 69121245
Open Air Museum 06423

Beijing Cultural Relic Protection Foundation, 5 Lu Micang, Dongcheng, 100010 Beijing - T: (010) 65123478
Folklore Museum 06424

Beijing Folklorish Museum, 141 Chaowai Av, Chaoyang, 100020 Beijing - T: (010) 65510150
Folklore Museum 06425

Beijing Gu Guanxiang Station, Jianguomen, 100000 Beijing - T: (010) 65242202
Science&Tech Museum 06426

Beijing Natural History Museum, 126 Tianqiao South Av, Tian Bridge, 100050 Beijing - T: (010) 67024431, Fax: 67021254, E-mail: bnhm@public3bta.net.cn. Head: Ai Chunchu
Natural History Museum - 1951
Botany, zoology, paleontology, anthropology, fossils, dioramas of fauna - library 06427

Beijing Opera Museum, Hufang Rd, 100000 Beijing - T: (010) 63518284
Performing Arts Museum 06428

Big Bell Gu Zhon Museum, Beisanhuan Rd W, Haidian, 100086 Beijing - T: (010) 62550843
Special Museum 06429

Central Nation University Museum, Baishi Bridge Rd, 100000 Beijing - T: (010) 68932760
Historical Museum / University Museum 06430

China Art Gallery, 1 Wu Si St, E City District, Beijing 100000 - T: (010) 442152. Head: Liu Kaiqu
Fine Arts Museum / Folklore Museum - 1958
10,000 items of traditional Chinese paintings, oils, wood-block painting and sculpture, 30000 items of folk art - library 06431

China Contemporary Literature Museum, Xisanhuan Rd N, 100000 Beijing - T: (010) 68464451
Special Museum 06432

China First History Archive Museum, Nanchizi, 100000 Beijing - T: (010) 65253774
Library with Exhibitions 06433

China Great Wall Museum, Badaling Special Zone,Yanqing County, 102102 Beijing - T: (010) 69121394
Historical Museum 06434

China Museum of Buddhist Literature and Heritage, Fa Yuan Si Hou Jie St, Xuan Wu District, Beijing 100000
Religious Arts Museum - 1979 06435

China National Museum, Men 20 Beichang St, Xicheng, 100031 Beijing - T: (010) 66068100, Fax: 66067900
Historical Museum 06436

China Sports Museum, Anding Rd, Chaoyang, 100029 Beijing - T: (010) 64912167, Fax: 64912164
Special Museum 06437

China Stamp Museum, Hepingmen, Xuanwu, 100051 Beijing - T: (010) 63022394
Special Museum 06438

Da Bao Taixi Tombs of Western Han Dynasty Museum, Guo Gong Village, Beijing - T: (010) 63736427
Special Museum 06439

Dabaotai Xihanmu Museum, South, Shi Jie Park, Fengtai, 100070 Beijing - T: (010) 63816688
Local Museum 06440

Dingling Museum, 13 Ling Dingling, Changping County, 102213 Beijing 102200 - T: (010) 60761049, 84358642
Archaeological Museum
Items from the catacomb of Zhu Yijun or the Emperor Shen Zong and his two Empresses (Ming dynasty) 06441

Gianfu Classic Art Museum, 80 Nanzhugan Alley, Beijing 100010 - T: (010) 65265566111, 65263208, Fax: 65250558, E-mail: guanfu@public.east.net.cn. Head: Weidi Ma
Fine Arts Museum - 1997 06442

Gutao Wenming Museum, Nancai Garden, 100070 Beijing - T: (010) 63538811
Special Museum 06443

Jiaozhuang Hu Didao Station, Hu Village, Jiao Village, Shunyi County, 100000 Beijing - T: (010) 60461906
Science&Tech Museum 06444

Kang Xicao Museum, West, Dawang Village, 100000 Beijing - T: (010) 69131639
Local Museum 06445

Liao Jincheng Yuan (Liao-Jin Dynasty City Walls Museum), Youanmen, Yulin Li Zone, Fengtai, 100054 Beijing - T: (010) 63054992/988
Historical Museum 06446

Lugouqiao Display Center, 88 St N,Fengtai, 100072 Beijing - T: (010) 63815981
Local Museum 06447

Mao Dun Former Residence, Kou Nansan Ln, Jiao Rd, 100000 Beijing - T: (010) 64040520
Decorative Arts Museum 06448

Mentougou Museum, Av Mentougou, New Bridge, 100000 Beijing - T: (010) 69852446
Special Museum 06449

Museum in Memory of Lu Xun, Fuchengmeinnei St, Xicheng, 100034 Beijing - T: (010) 66162462, 66165654, Fax: 66162462, E-mail: yuekan@263.net. Head: Zhang Quanguo
Special Museum - 1949
Documents, texts, and memorabilia of the writer Lu Xun (1881-1936) 06450

Museum of Fine Arts, Chaoyan Men St, Beijing 100000
Fine Arts Museum
Modern Chinese painting and graphics 06451

Museum of International Friendship, Lane, Xi Floor, 100007 Beijing - T: (010) 64040710
Special Museum 06452

Museum of the Chinese People's Revolutionary Military Affairs, 9 Fuxing Rd, Haidian, 100038 Beijing - T: (010) 8014441. Head: Xinghan Qin
Military Museum - 1958
Weapons relating to different periods of revolutionary wars 06453

Museum of the Chinese Revolution, Tiananmen Sq East, 16 Dongchangan St, 100006 Beijing - T: (010) 65263355, Fax: 65256774, E-mail: zggmbwg@sohu.com. Head: Xia Yangue
Historical Museum - 1950 06454

Museum of the Cultural Palace of National Minorities, Chang'an St, Beijing 100000
Ethnology Museum
Documents on the national minorities of China, characteristic music instruments, ornaments, costumes, agricultural tools and products, displays, mannequins, and models 06455

Nation Museum, Nationality Garden Rd, Zhonghua, 100000 Beijing - T: (010) 64263646
Historical Museum 06456

National Geological Museum of China, 15 Yangrou Hutong Ln, Xicheng, 100034 Beijing - T: (010) 66168132, 66168870, Fax: 66168870. Head: Qiang Ji
Natural History Museum - 1916
Minerals, rocks, fossils displayed in three halls 06457

National Museum of Chinese History, Tiananmen Sq East, 100006 Beijing - T: (010) 65128986, 65266604, Fax: 65128986. Head: Zhu Fenghan
Historical Museum - 1912
History of China from the very beginnings to the Opium War of 1840, archeological finds, models and display charts 06458

National Museum of Music, c/o National Music Institute, Xue Yuang St, Beijing 100000
Music Museum
History of music, music instruments 06459

The Palace Museum, 4 Jing Shan Qianjie, 100009 Beijing - T: (010) 65132255, Fax: 65123119, E-mail: ggwaishi@public3.bta.net.cn, Internet: http://www.dpm.org.cn. Head: Zhu Chengru
Local Museum / Decorative Arts Museum - 1925
Furnishings of the Imperial Palace, bronzes of the Shang and Zhou dynasties, scroll paintings, traditional crafts (jade and goldsmith works), porcelain, jade, bronze, steles, calligraphy, paintings, seals, lacquer, cloisonné, goldware, silverware, jewelry, embroidery, stationery, weaponry, furniture, sculpture, scripture, architecture, books, toys, clocks, musical instruments, costume 06460

Peking Man in Zhoukoudian, Exhibition Centre, Fangshan District, Beijing 102400
Ethnology Museum - 1953
Remains of Pekingensis, paleoanthropological coll, world cultural heritage exhibit 06461

Pinggu Shangzhai Cultural Display Center, Jin Haihu,Pinggu County, 101201 Beijing - T: (010) 69991268
Folklore Museum 06462

Quaternary Period Qlacier Traces Exhibition Hall, Moshikou, 100041 Beijing - T: (010) 68802585
Historical Museum 06463

Renmin Kang Ri Zhan Zhen Memorial Hall, Wanping, Fengtai, 100072 Beijing - T: (010) 83893163
Historical Museum 06464

Shan Rong Cultural Display Center, Sheng Li St, Yu Huangmiao Village, Yanqing, 102100 Beijing - T: (010) 69143788, 69189534
Folklore Museum 06465

Song Qingling Tongzhi Former Residence, Houhai N, Yan, 100000 Beijing - T: (010) 64044205
Decorative Arts Museum 06466

Stone Engraving Art Museum, 24 Wuta Temple Village, Haidian, 100081 Beijing - T: (010) 62172894, 62186081, Fax: 68320305
Fine Arts Museum 06467

Tongxian Museum, 9 Tongzhou Av W, Tongzhou, 101100 Beijing - T: (010) 69546442
Folklore Museum
Cultural Relic,Lin Shi 06468

Tongzhou District Museum, 9 Tongzhou Av W,Huguo Temple, Tongzhou, 100000 Beijing - T: (010) 69555161, 66180351
Local Museum 06469

Wen Tianxiang Temple, 63 Fuxue Ln, Dongcheng, 100007 Beijing - T: (010) 64014968
Religious Arts Museum 06470

Xizhou Yandu Yi Zhi Museum, Shan Zhou Museum, Liulihe Shan, Fangshan, 102403 Beijing - T: (010) 89381435
Historical Museum 06471

Xu Bei-Hong Memorial Hall, Kou Av N, New St, 100000 Beijing - T: (010) 62252042
Special Museum 06472

Yanhuang Art Center, 9 Hui Zhon Rd, Yayun Village, Chaoyang, 100101 Beijing - T: (010) 64910909
Public Gallery 06473

Zhan Tianyou Memorial Hall, Badaling,Yanqing County, 102100 Beijing - T: (010) 69121006
Special Museum 06474

Zhonghua Nation Museum, 1 Minzu Garden Rd, Chaoyang, 100101 Beijing - T: (010) 62063640, Fax: 62063650
Historical Museum 06475

Benxi

Benxi City Museum, 18 Sheng Li Rd, 117000 Benxi - T: (0414) 2843350
Local Museum 06476

Bole

Boer Tala Zhou Museum, Boer Tower, Lazhou, Meng Gu, 833400 Bole - T: (0909) 2222765
Local Museum 06477

Bozhou

Bozhou City Museum, 1 Xianning St, Fuyang Di, 236800 Bozhou - T: (0558) 5522493
Local Museum 06478

Changchun

Jilin Museum, 3 Guang Fu Rd N, Kuancheng, 130051 Changchun - T: (0431) 2954025
Historical Museum / Archaeological Museum
Prehistory, industrial development of the city and province, archaeology, workers' and revolutionary movements 06479

Jilin Natural Museum, 3 Guan Fu Rd N, Kuancheng, 130051 Changchun - T: (0431) 2954287
Natural History Museum 06480

Jilin Revolutionary Museu, 7 Xian Rd, Chaoyang, 130061 Changchun - T: (0431) 2930048
Historical Museum - 1979
History of the revolutionary struggle in modern China 06481

Wei Huanggong Display Center, 5 Guan Fu Rd N, Kuancheng, 130051 Changchun - T: (0431) 2958516
Special Museum 06482

Changji

Changji Mulei County Museum, Changji Mulei Hasake, 831900 Changji - T: (0994) 4822209
Local Museum 06483

Changjizhou Museum, 831100 Changji - T: (0994) 2722497
Local Museum 06484

Changping

Museum near the Ming Tombs, North of Beijing, Changping
Archaeological Museum
Burial offerings from the 17th c grave of the Emperor Shen Zong (Wan Li) and his two wives Xiao Duan and Xiao Jing, in the tomb complex 06485

Changsha

Changsha City Museum, 126 First 8 Rd N, 410011 Changsha - T: (0731) 4414613
Local Museum 06486

Hunan Museum, 3 Dongfeng Rd, North, Lieshi Gongyuan Park, 410005 Changsha - T: (0731) 2223866, Fax: 4447649. Head: Chuan Xin Xiong
Archaeological Museum - 1956
Archeological finds from the tombs at Mawangdui (2nd c BC), over 3,000 items incl the mummy of the wife of the Duke of Dai, 14 silk gowns, embroidery, wood statuettes, lacquer items, texts on silk and bamboo, musical instruments, bronze wares of the Shang and Zhou Dynasties, cultural relics of 'Chu', ceramics from the Han to Tang Dynasties, paintings and calligraphy 06487

Hunan Revolutionary Cemetery, 4 Wangyue Village S, 410002 Changsha - T: (0731) 3332857
Historical Museum / Historic Site 06488

Changshu

Changshu City Museum, 13 Bei Men Av, 215500 Changshu - T: (0520) 2776855
Local Museum 06489

Changshu Engraved Stone Museum, 7-1 Houta St, 215500 Changshu - T: (0520) 2774297
Fine Arts Museum 06490

Changshu Mausoleum of Fallen Heroes, 21 Yushan Rd N, 215500 Changshu - T: (0520) 2891468
Historical Museum 06491

Changzhou

Lingtong Exhibition, 63 Linjin Rd, Yaoguan, 213102 Changzhou - T: (0519) 8702328, Fax: 8701653, E-mail: lintong@public.cz.js.cn, Internet: http://www.ling-tong.com
Special Museum 06492

Chaoyang

Chaoyang City Museum, Xinhua Road, 122000 Chaoyang - T: (0421) 2831891
Local Museum 06493

Kazuo County Museum, Qingan Rd, Kazuo County, 122300 Chaoyang - T: (0421) 4822436
Local Museum 06494

Chengde

Bi Shu Country Villa Museum, Li Palace Yard, Shuangqiao, 067000 Chengde - T: (0314) 2023489
Historical Museum - 1953 06495

Pu Le Temple, Open Air Museum, Chengde
Open Air Museum / Religious Arts Museum - 1703-1790
The summer resort of the Qing emperors, palaces in various architectural styles, furnishings, stone-carved poems, lake center pavilions, sculpture, stone tablets - teahouse, exhibition hall 06496

Chengdu

Chengdu City Museum, 23 Dacisi Rd, Jinjiang, 610016 Chengdu - T: (028) 6656624
Local Museum 06497

Chengdu Du Pu Museum, Caotang Rd W, Quinyang, 610072 Chengdu - T: (028) 7769258
Special Museum
Home and memorabilia of the poet Du Pu (770), paintings which inspired his poems 06498

Li Ren Former Residence, Shangsha Hepu, Jinjiang, 610066 Chengdu - T: (028) 4790320
Decorative Arts Museum 06499

Longquanyi District Museum, Luodai Town, Longquanyi, 610108 Chengdu - T: (028) 4893201
Local Museum 06500

Ming Shu Wangling Museum, 8 Group, Daliang Village, Longquanyi, 610106 Chengdu - T: (028) 4600460
Local Museum 06501

Sichuan Museum, 3-4 Segment, Renmin Rd S, Wuhou, 610041 Chengdu - T: (028) 5224586, Fax: 5222324
Archaeological Museum / Historical Museum - 1941
Excavations including Buddhist sculptures from the Tang and Sung periods, Shang bronze, Han stone figures, Sung and Ming porcelain, tile reliefs from the Han period 06502

Sichuan University Museum, c/o Sichuan University, 29 Wangjiang Rd, Chengdu 610064 - T: (028) 55838752313, Fax: 5417157. Head: Prof. Wei Huo
Archaeological Museum - 1914
Tang figures from the Qionglai area, stone carvings (Han dynasty), Chengdu Shadow puppets (Quing dynasty), Tibet and Daoism figures - library 06503

Sui Tangyao Zhi Display Center, 31 Xier Segment, Yihuan Rd, Qingyang, 610072 Chengdu - T: (028) 7769266
Folklore Museum 06504

Wang Jian Mu Museum, 5 Fuqin Rd E, Jinniu, 610031 Chengdu - T: (028) 7768245
Special Museum 06505

Wuhou Museum, 231 Wuhou Ci Av, Wuhou, 610041 Chengdu - T: (028) 5561579
Local Museum 06506

Zhua Yuan Display Center, Minan Village, Dayi County, 611331 Chengdu - T: (028) 8315113
Historical Museum 06507

Chinchow

Liaoning Provincial Museum, Chinchow
Local Museum 06508

Chongqing

China Tradition Medicine Museum, 101 Pipa Shan Zhen St, Yu Zhong District, 400013 Chongqing - T: (023) 63528755, Fax: 63527067, E-mail: museum@public.cta.cq.cn. Head: Guang Rui Liu
Special Museum / Folklore Museum 06509

Chongqing Museum, 72 Pipa Shan Zhen St, 400013 Chongqing - T: (023) 63501268. Head: Yuchuan Liu
Archaeological Museum / Decorative Arts Museum / Natural History Museum - 1951
Burial finds from Ba and Shu areas, stone reliefs of the Han dynasty, ceramics, coins, paintings, natural history, fossils 06510

Chongqing Natural Museum, Pipa Shan Zhen St, Yu Zhong, 400013 Chongqing - T: (023) 63500681
Natural History Museum 06511

Stone Engraving Art Museum, Beishan Rd, Dazu County, 400000 Chongqing - T: (023) 43722268
Fine Arts Museum 06512

Wan Zhou District Museum, Yuanjia Dun, Wan State, 400000 Chongqing - T: (023) 58123187
Local Museum 06513

Dalian

Dalian Museum of Natural History, 3 Yuntai St, Xigang, 116001 Dalian - T: (0411) 2635996, Fax: 2633581. Head: Zuwen Tan
Natural History Museum - 1926
Mineralogy, fauna and flory 06514

Jinzhou District Museum, Jiefang Plaza, 116000 Dalian - T: (0411) 7805231
Local Museum 06515

Lushun Museum, 42 Liening St, 116041 Dalian - T: (0411) 6383006, Fax: 6382247, E-mail: lumuseum@mail.dlptt.in.cn. Head: Guang Tang Liu
Archaeological Museum / Decorative Arts Museum / Fine Arts Museum - 1917
Archaeology, finds from the Liadong Peninsula, bronze ware, inscriptions, pottery, clay, figurines, porcelain, paintings, calligraphy 06516

Lushun Snakes Dao Natural Museum, 2 Youyi Rd, Lushunkou, 116041 Dalian - T: (0411) 6612480
Natural History Museum 06517

Lushun Su Jun Mausoleum of Fallen Heroes, Village, Sanli Bridge, Lushunkou, 116041 Dalian - T: (0411) 6611527
Historical Museum 06518

Pulandian City Museum, 4 Nanshan Park, 116200 Dalian - T: (0411) 9614521
Local Museum 06519

Dandong

Dandong Museum on the War to resist U.S. Aggression and Aid Korea, Dandong 118000
Military Museum - 1958 06520

Datong

Museum of Datong, Huayan Temple, Datong 037000
Archaeological Museum / Historical Museum - 1952
Palaeontology, archaeology, history 06521

Dayi

Landlord's Manor House Museum, Anren Town, Dayi 611331 - T: (08238) 315113. Head: Hung Yuen Wu
Decorative Arts Museum / Fine Arts Museum - 1958
Furniture, decorations, calligraphy, paintings, tools, sculptures 06522

Dongguan

Ya Pian Zhan Zhen Museum, 88 Jiefang Rd, Humen Town, 511761 Dongguan - T: (0769) 5512065, Fax: 5512065
Local Museum 06523

Donghuang

Beijing Telephone History Museum, Gen St.N, Donghuang Beijing - T: (010) 64041099
Science&Tech Museum 06524

Dujiangyan

Wangmiao Display Center, Libing St, 611830 Dujiangyan - T: (028) 7283285
Folklore Museum 06525

Enjiang

Yongfeng County Museum, 331500 Enjiang - T: (0796) 2511392
Local Museum 06526

Fenghua

Fenghua Xikou Museum, 33 Wuling Rd, 315502 Fenghua - T: (0574) 8850311
Local Museum 06527

Foshan

Foshan City Museum, 21 Zumiao Rd, 528000 Foshan - T: (0757) 2280000
Local Museum 06528

Nanhai Museum, Qiao Jiangpu W, 528000 Foshan - T: (0757) 6886919
Local Museum 06529

Fu

Stone Engraving Museum, South Rd, Fu Beijing - T: (010) 68356240
Fine Arts Museum 06530

Fufeng

County Museum, Main St, Fufeng 722200
Archaeological Museum
Excavations including Shang bronzes and a Hu gui bronze vessel (9th c B.C.) 06531

Fushun

Fushun City Museum, Nanchang 17 Pingshan St, Lutian, 113008 Fushun - T: (0413) 2636382
Decorative Arts Museum / Archaeological Museum / Local Museum - 1970
Bronzes, porcelain, pottery, gold and silver vessels, ironware, stone inscriptions from prehistory to the Ming and Quin dynasties, 800 skeletons of victims during the Japanese invasion 06532

Fuxin

Fuxin City Museum, Industry St, 123000 Fuxin - T: (0418) 2813967
Local Museum 06533

Fuyang

Fuyang Museum, 78 Xin Rd N, 311400 Fuyang - T: (0571) 3322669
Local Museum 06534

Fuzhou

Fujian Province Museum, 2 Xihu, West Lake Park, 350001 Fuzhou - T: (0591) 3725750
Local Museum / Archaeological Museum / Folklore Museum - 1953
Prehistory, archaeology, tea growing and export, coll illustrating Fuzhou as a treaty-port, popular art and handicrafts of the region 06535

Fuzhou City Hualin Si, Hua Da 78, 350003 Fuzhou - T: (0591) 7822672
Folklore Museum 06536

Ganzhou

Nankang County Museum, Rongjiang, Nankang County, 341400 Ganzhou - T: (0797) 7812451
Local Museum 06537

Shicheng County Museum, Qinjiang, Shicheng County, 342700 Ganzhou - T: (0797) 8725055
Local Museum 06538

Guangzhou

Guangdong Folk Arts and Crafts Museum, 34 En Long Li, 7th Zhongshan Rd, Liwan, 510170 Guangzhou - T: (020) 81814371, 81814559, Fax: 81723994
Folklore Museum 06539

Guangdong Museum, 215 Wenming Rd, Dongshan, 510110 Guangzhou - T: (020) 83838432, Fax: 83858600
Archaeological Museum / Fine Arts Museum / Historical Museum
Prehistory, bronzes from the Shang period (16th-11th c B.C.), tomb figures from the Han period (206 B.C.-220 A.D.), painting, calligraphy 06540

Guangzhou Art Gallery, Yuexiushan,Hongqiao St, Yuexiu, 510030 Guangzhou - T: (020) 83559412
Fine Arts Museum / Public Gallery 06541

Guangzhou Art Museum, Luhu Rd, 510400 Guangzhou - T: (020) 83507904, Fax: 83588095
Fine Arts Museum 06542

Guangzhou Liwan District Museum, 84 Fengyuan St N, Longjin Rd W, 510150 Guangzhou - T: (020) 81939917
Local Museum 06543

Guangzhou Lu Xun Museum, Wen Ming Rd, Guangzhou 510110 - T: (020) 83802780, 83815803. Head: Jing Zhang
Special Museum
Documentation on the life and work of the writer Lu Xun (1881-1936) 06544

Guangzhou Museum, Hai Rd, Yuexiushan, 510040 Guangzhou - T: (020) 83550627, Fax: 83541030
Local Museum / Archaeological Museum
Local history, maps, models, excavation finds, photos, documents 06545

Guangzhou Yi Tai Yuan, 986 Jiefang Rd N, Yuexiu, 510030 Guangzhou - T: (020) 86666988, Fax: 86666988
Special Museum
Ernst Komrowski facilities 06546

Gungdong Revolution History Museum, 2 West Rd, Ling Garden, Changzhou Dao, Dongshan, 510055 Guangzhou - T: (020) 82203564, 83341321
Historical Museum 06547

Memorial Museum of the Peasant Movement Institute by Comrade Mao Zedong, 42 Zhongshan Rd, Guangzhou 510000
Historical Museum 06548

Nan Yue Wang Palace Museum, 316 Fourth Zhongshan Rd, 510030 Guangzhou - T: (020) 83361029
Decorative Arts Museum 06549

Revolutionary History Museum, 200 Qiyi Rd, 510075 Guangzhou - T: (020) 83374048
Historical Museum 06550

Xihan Nan Yue Wang Mu Museum, 867 Jiefang Rd N, Yuexiu, 510040 Guangzhou - T: (020) 86693868, Fax: 86678030
Special Museum 06551

Guilin

Guangxi Provincial Museum, Guilin 541000
Local Museum
Sculptures, industrial development of the province (especially textiles, timber and sugar), archaeology, history 06552

Guilin City Museum, 4 Xishan Rd, Xiufeng, 541001 Guilin - T: (0773) 2824862
Local Museum 06553

Li Zong Ren Display Center, Xiangshan District, 541002 Guilin - T: (0773) 2831749
Folklore Museum 06554

Pi Yandong Xue Yi Zhi Display Center, Zeng Pi Yan 3, Xiangshan, 541003 Guilin - T: (0773) 3835368
Special Museum 06555

Guiyang

Guizhou Provincial Museum, Beijing Rd, Guiyang 550004 - T: (0851) 6822210, Fax: 6822210. Head: Qianbin Li
Local Museum - 1953
Finds from excavations in the province, cultural history of ethic minorities, handicrafts, calligraphy, paintings, animals and plant specimens 06556

Gunan

Qijiang Stone Engraving Museum, Houshan Rd, Gunan, Chongqing - T: (023) 48652941
Fine Arts Museum 06557

Haikou

Hainan Museum, 58 Haikou Xinhua Haixiu Rd, 570206 Haikou - T: (0898) 6778942
Historical Museum 06558

Hangzhou

China Silk Museum, 73-1 Yuhuangshan Rd, Xihu, 310002 Hangzhou - T: (0571) 7062079, 7068134, Fax: 7068136
Special Museum / Fine Arts Museum 06559

China Tea Museum, Ji Long Rd, Xihu, 310013 Hangzhou - T: (0571) 7964778, 7964551, Fax: 7982096
Special Museum 06560

China Yin Xue Museum, 1 Hou Gushan Rd, 310013 Hangzhou - T: (0571) 7977149
Local Museum 06561

Chinese Medicine Museum, c/o Huqing Yutang Pharmaceutical Co., Huqing, Hangzhou - T: (0571) 7815209
Historical Museum 06562

Liangzhu Cultural Museum, Liangzhu Xun Shan,Yuhang, 311113 Hangzhou - T: (0571) 8770700
Folklore Museum 06563

Linan Museum, Plaza Rd, Linan, 311300 Hangzhou - T: (0571) 3722765
Local Museum 06564

Nansong Guanyao Museum, 42 Shijiashan, Hangzhou - T: (0571) 6082594
Special Museum 06565

Nansong Qian Currency Museum, 12 Jiang Yuan Long, 310003 Hangzhou - T: (0571) 87911087, 87075701, Fax: 87911087, 87919829, E-mail: kenlucky@hotmail.com
Special Museum
Ancient Chinese coins and coins worldwide 06566

Zhejiang Museum, 10 Gushan Houshan Rd, Xihu, 310007 Hangzhou - T: (0571) 7980281
Historical Museum / Folklore Museum / Natural History Museum / Decorative Arts Museum
History, folk art, geography, botany, zoology, documents on the Great Chanel, porcelain, whale skeleton (13th c) 06567

Zhejiang Natural Museum, 10 Jiao Gong Rd, Xihu, 310012 Hangzhou - T: (0571) 8840702, Fax: 8838819
Natural History Museum 06568

Harbin

Heilongjiang Province Nation Museum, 25 Wenmiao St, Nangang, 150001 Harbin - T: (0451) 8348352
Historical Museum - 1923
Development of man and the animal world, 130,000 historical artifacts, 100,000 animals 06569

Heilongjiang Province Revolutionary Museum, 2 Yiman St, Nangang, 150001 Harbin - T: (0451) 3627135
Historical Museum 06570

Northeast Martyrs Memorial Hall, 241 Yi Man St, Harbin 150001 - T: (0451) 3627135, Fax: 3627135
Historical Museum - 1947
reference library 06571

Hefei

Anhui Sheng Bo Wu Guan (Museum of Anhui Province), 268 Anqing Rd, Zhongshi, 230061 Hefei - T: (0551) 2654655
Local Museum / Archaeological Museum - 1953
History of the region, palaeontology, archaeology 06572

Hejing

Zhou Hejing County Museum, Meng Gu, Bayinguoleng, 841300 Hejing - T: (0996) 5020471
Local Museum 06573

Hong Kong

Art Museum of the Chinese Univertity of Hong Kong, Sha Tin, New Territories, Hong Kong - T: (00852) 26097416, Fax: 26035366, E-mail: artmuseum@cuhk.edu.hk, Internet: http://www.cuhk.edu.hk/ics/amm. Head: Prof. Peter Y.K. Lam
Fine Arts Museum / University Museum
Chinese paintings, calligraphies, ceramics, decorative art 06574

Flagstaff House Museum of Tea Ware, 10 Cotton Tree Dr, Central, Hong Kong Island, Hong Kong - T: (00852) 28690690, Fax: 28100021, Internet: http://www.lcsd.gov.hk/hkma. Head: Dr. Christina Chu
Special Museum
Home of the British Commander-in-Chief, rare ceramics, Chinese teaware, Yixing pottery, Chinese seals 06575

Hong Kong Art Centre Pao Galleries, 2 Harbour Rd, Wan Chai, Hong Kong Island, Hong Kong - T: (00852) 25820200
Fine Arts Museum
Contemporary Art, paintings, photography, crafts, design 06576

Hong Kong Heritage Museum, 1 Man Lam Rd, Shatin, New Territories, Hong Kong
Historical Museum / Local Museum - 2000
History, art and culture of Hong Kong 06577

Hong Kong Lepidopterists' Society Museum, Kin Ga Industrial Bldg, Tuen Mun, Hong Kong - T: (00852) 24638599
Special Museum 06578

Hong Kong Museum of Art, 10 Salisbury Rd, Tsim Sha Tsui, Kowloon, Hong Kong - T: (00852) 27210116, Fax: 27237666, Internet: http://www.lcsd.gov.hk/hkma. Head: Gerard C.C. Tsang
Fine Arts Museum - 1962
Chinese antiquities, historical pictures, Chines fine art, Xubaizhai paintings and calligraphy coll, seal and tea ware, crafts, contemporary Hong Kong art 06579

Hong Kong Museum of History, 100 Chatham Rd S, Tsim Sha Tsui, Kowloon, Hong Kong - T: (00852) 27249042, Fax: 27249090, E-mail: hkmh@lcsd.gov.hk, Internet: http://lcsd.gov.hk/hkmh. Head: Joseph S.P. Ting
Historical Museum - 1975
Local hist, Fr.D. Finn archaeological coll, Fr.R. Maglioni archaeological coll, ethnography and natural hist 06580

Hong Kong Racing Museum, 2/F Happy Valley Stand, Racecourse, Happy Valley, Hong Kong Island, Hong Kong - T: (00852) 29668065, Fax: 29667057, E-mail: hkjcmuse@netvigator.com, Internet: http://www.hongkongjockeyclub.com. Head: Helen Lee
Historical Museum - 1996
Story of horse racing in Hong Kong (1840s to today's) 06581

Hong Kong Railway Museum, 13 Shung Tak St, Tai Po Market, New Territories, Hong Kong - T: (00852) 26533455
Science&Tech Museum - 1913
H.K.'s rail hist, old coaches, models, electric' train compartment 06582

Hong Kong Science Museum, 2 Science Museum Rd, Tsim Sha Tsui East, Kowloon, Hong Kong - T: (00852) 27323232, Fax: 23112248, E-mail: science@lcsd.gov.hk, Internet: http://www.lcsd.gov.hk/hkscm. Head: Chee-Kuen Yip
Science&Tech Museum - 1991 06583

Hong Kong Space Museum, 10 Salisbury Rd, Tsim Sha Tsui, Kowloon, Hong Kong - T: (00852) 27210226, Fax: 23115804, E-mail: spacem@space.lcsd.gov.hk, Internet: http://www.lcsd.gov.hk/CE/Museum/Space. Head: Kim-Fung Chow
Science&Tech Museum / Natural History Museum - 1980
Graphics, exhibits, models, and displays concerning astronomy and space science, space suit - planetarium, library, IMAX-Dome 06584

Law Uk Folk Museum, 14 Kut Shing St, Chai Wan, Hong Kong Island, Hong Kong - T: (00852) 28967006, Fax: 27249090, Internet: http://www.lcsd.gov.hk/hkmh
Folklore Museum
Hakka village house, rural furniture, farm implements 06585

Lei Cheng Uk Han Tomb Museum, Hong Kong Museum of History, 41 Tonkin St, Sham Shui Po, Kowloon, Hong Kong - T: (00852) 23862863
Special Museum - 1988
Tomb findings, calligraphy, content of the inscriptions on tomb bricks, built in the Eastern Han dynasty (25-220AD) 06586

Museum of Medical Sciences, 2 Caine Ln, Mid-Levels, Hong Kong Island, Hong Kong - T: (00852) 25495123
Historical Museum - 1996
Traditional Chinese and Western approaches to medicine, development of medical science 06587

Museum of Site, Most I, Block 54, Ln 3, Shing Mun Tsuen, Kam Tin, Yuen Long, Hong Kong - T: (00852) 24494417, 98029440, E-mail: artopia-net@yahoo.com, Internet: http://www.geocities.com/tokyo/flats/3435. Head: Andrew Lam
Fine Arts Museum 06588

Museum of Site, Most II, Block 115, Ln 5, Kat Hing Wai, Kam Tin, Yuen Long, Hong Kong - T: (00852) 24494417, 98029440, E-mail: artopia-net@yahoo.com, Internet: http://www.geocities.com/tokyo/flats/3435. Head: Andrew Lam
Fine Arts Museum 06589

Para/Site Art Space, 2 Po Yan St, Sheung Wan, Hong Kong - T: (00852) 25174620, Fax: 25176850, E-mail: info@para-site.org.hk, Internet: http://www.para-site.org.hk
Public Gallery - 1996 06590

Police Museum, 27 Coombe Rd, Mid-Levels, Hong Kong Island, Hong Kong - T: (00852) 28497019
Historical Museum
Wan Chai Gap Police station, history of H.K. Police Force 06591

Sam Tung Uk Museum, 2 Kwu Uk Ln, Tsuen Wan, New Territories, Hong Kong - T: (00852) 24112001, Fax: 24139271, E-mail: stum@lcsd.gov.hk, Internet: http://www.heritagemuseum.gov.uk/english/branch_sel_syf.htm
Folklore Museum - 1786
Rural Hakka walled village 18th c, period furniture, farming tools 06592

Sheung Yiu Folk Museum, Pak Tam Chung Nature Trail, Sai Kung, New Territories, Hong Kong - T: (00852) 27926365, Fax: 21944776, E-mail: stum@lcsd.gov.hk, Internet: http://www.heritagemuseum.gov.uk/english/branch_sel_syf.htm
Folklore Museum
Rural Hakka village, lime kiln, period furniture and farming tools 06593

Tsui Museum of Art, Henley Bldg, 5 Queen's Rd, Central, Hong Kong - T: (00852) 28682688, Fax: 28682663
Fine Arts Museum 06594

University Museum and Art Gallery, c/o University of Hong Kong, Pokfulam, 94 Bonham Rd, Hong Kong Island, Hong Kong - T: (00852) 22415500, Fax: 25469659, E-mail: museum@hkusua.hku.hk, Internet: http://www.hku.hk/hkumag. Head: C.T. Yeung
Fine Arts Museum / Decorative Arts Museum / University Museum - 1953
Chinese ceramics, bronzes, sculpture and painting 06595

Huaian

Museum of the former Residence of Premier Zhou En-Lai, Fuma Ln, Huaian 223200
Historical Museum 06596

Huangshan

Huangshan City Museum, 29 Xi Huishan Rd, Xiaqu Tun, 245000 Huangshan - T: (0559) 2514539
Local Museum 06597

Huangshi

Huangshi Municipal Museum, Huangshi 435000
Historical Museum / Archaeological Museum - 1950
History, ancient mining and metallurgy, a vertial bronze melting furnace of the period 770-476 B.C., a ground smelting furnace of the Song dynasty, archaeology, history 06598

Huhehot

Huhehot City Museum, 1 Gongzhufu St, Xincheng, 010051 Huhehot - T: (0471) 6924793
Local Museum
Zhan Chu coll 06599

Inner Mongolia Museum, 2 Xinhua Av, Xincheng, 010020 Huhehot - T: (0471) 6918805, 6964924, Fax: 6918763
Historical Museum / Ethnology Museum - 1957
Ethnic minorities tools, Song Dynasty tomb relics, Red Army documents and weapons, dinosaur fossils and artifacts 06600

Huichang

Huichang County Museum, 342600 Huichang - T: (0797) 5622189
Local Museum 06601

Huludao

Huludao City Museum, Yongchang Rd, 125001 Huludao - T: (0427) 2124084
Local Museum 06602

Jian

Jian City Museum, 88 Ying Bin Rd, 134200 Jian - T: (0435) 6222796
Local Museum 06603

Jiangmen

Jiangmen Museum, Av West-District, 529000 Jiangmen - T: (0750) 3527027
Local Museum 06604

Jiangyin

Jiangyin City Museum, 159 Park Rd, Chengjiang, 214431 Jiangyin - T: (0510) 6805684
Local Museum 06605

Rongyu Guan, 6 Renmin Rd E, 214432 Jiangyin - T: (0510) 6286772
Special Museum
International Communication 06606

Jiaonan

Jiaonan City Museum, Zhong Segment,Wen Hua Rd, 266400 Jiaonan - T: (0532) 6163775
Local Museum 06607

Jilin

Jilin City Wenmiao Museum, 2 Nanchang Rd, Wenmiao St, Changyi, 132001 Jilin - T: (0432) 2454333
Historical Museum / Ethnology Museum
History of primitive societies in the Jilin area, bronze ware, stone implements, specimens of the meteorite shower in the area 06608

Jimo

Jimo City Museum, 145 Zhongshan St, 266200 Jimo - T: (0532) 8512844
Local Museum 06609

Jinan

Changqing County Museum, 5 Dongguan St, Changqing County, 250300 Jinan - T: (0531) 7227571
Local Museum 06610

Jinan City Museum, 6 Zhong Min Kang Li, Lixia, 250014 Jinan - T: (0531) 2959204
Local Museum 06611

Jinan Revolutionary Mausoleum of Fallen Heroes, 18 Yinxongshan Rd, Zhong, 250002 Jinan - T: (0531) 2011226
Historical Museum 06612

Licheng District Museum, Licheng, 250115 Jinan - T: (0531) 2991038
Local Museum 06613

Shandong Provincial Museum, 14 Jing 11th Rd, 250014 Jinan - T: (0531) 2967179, Fax: 2943694. Head: Wensheng Lu
Archaeological Museum / Historical Museum - 1954
Bronze axes from the Shang period, Longshan Rhyton vessels, Bamboo writing (219 B.C.), earthen figures from a grave and stone reliefs of the Western Han dynasty, grave painting from the Sui dynasty, burial remains of Prince of Lu, son of the first Ming Emperor, Buddhist stone sculptures 06614

Shandong Stone Engraving Art Museum, 6 Qing Nian Rd E, Lixia, 250011 Jinan - T: (0531) 2953873
Fine Arts Museum 06615

Jingdezhen

Jingdezhen Porcelain Museum, 12 Lianshe Rd N, Zhushan, 333000 Jingdezhen - T: (0789) 8229783
Decorative Arts Museum - 1980
Porcelain and history of porcelain making 06616

Jinggang Mountains

Revolutionary Museum of the Jinggang Mountains, Ciping, Jinggang Mountains
Historical Museum
History of the Revolution, some of the buildings were occupied by the the Revolutionary Army in December 1927 06617

Jinzhou

Jinzhou City Museum, 56 North 3 Li, 121001 Jinzhou - T: (0416) 3138530
Local Museum 06618

Jishou

Museum of the Tujia and Miao Autonomous Prefecture in Western Hunan, Jishou 416000
Archaeological Museum / Folklore Museum - 1957
Archaeology, palaeontology, folklore of the Tujia and Miao minorities 06619

Jiuquan

Municipal Museum, Jiuquan 735000 - T: (0937) 2613307, 2616129
Local Museum - 1978
From New Stone Age, Han dynasty, Jin dynasty to Ming and Ching dynasties cultural relics, special valuables like Han, Jin and Tang dynasties mural painting tomb, brick-painting tomb, mould brick-relief tomb and painted-relief tomb 06620

Jixian

Jixian Display Center, 41 Wuding St,Guan, 301900 Jixian - T: (022) 29142904
Local Museum 06621

Kaifeng

Kaifeng Municipal Museum, Front St, State Bridge, Gulou, 475000 Kaifeng - T: (0378) 3931800
Local Museum / Archaeological Museum - 1961
Prehistory, history, archaeology, local excavations, furnishings, paintings, agricultural history, history of the cotton production 06622

Kueiyang

Kweichow Provincial Museum, Kueiyang
Local Museum 06623

Kuerle

Bayin Guoleng Zhou Museum, Plaza Rd, Meng Gu, Bayinguoleng, 841000 Kuerle - T: (0996) 2024656
Local Museum 06624

Kunming

Museum of Yunnan Province, 118 Wuyi Rd, 650032 Kunming - T: (0871) 3611548, 3629694, Fax: 3629694. Head: Kunsheng Li
Archaeological Museum - 1951
Finds from the Han grave of Shi Zhai Shan, Han bronze from graves near Jinning, Buddhist artifacts found in Dali area belong to Nahzhad and Dali periods (Tang and Song dynasties), fossils - Palaeoanthropological Research Office 06625

Lanzhou

Gansu Provincial Museum, West Xijin Rd, 730050 Lanzhou - T: (0931) 33300, 33847. Head: Gao You Xun
Historical Museum / Archaeological Museum
History of the province, archaeology, arts, applied arts, handicrafts, industries, agriculture 06626

Lanzhou City Museum, 110 Quingyang Rd, Guan, 730030 Lanzhou - T: (0931) 8828555
Local Museum / Archaeological Museum
Ceramics from Yangshao, tomb with paintings from the Han period (206 B.C.-220 A.D.), the bronze 'Flying Horse' from the East Han dynasty (2nd c A.D.) 06627

Lhasa

Museum of the History of Revolution, Lhasa 850000
Historical Museum
History of traditional Tibet and the period since 1959 06628

Liaoyang

Liaoyang City Museum, Center Rd, 111000 Liaoyang - T: (0419) 3132297
Local Museum 06629

Lingyuan

Lingyuan City Museum, West St, 122500 Lingyuan - T: (0421) 6822842
Local Museum 06630

Linxia

Museum of the Linxia Autonomous Region, Prefecture of the Hui Nationality, Linxia 731100
Local Museum / Archaeological Museum
Regional history, archaeology 06631

Liquan Xian

Zhaoling Museum, Liquan Xian 713200
Archaeological Museum
Archeological finds including Ding bronze vessel (14th c B.C.), painted ceramic figures from the grave of Li Zhen depicting various officials 06632

Liucheng

Liuhe County Display Center, 44 Xiaobeimen, 211500 Liucheng - T: (025) 7759942
Local Museum 06633

Luchou

Luchou Museum, Luchou
Local Museum
Local history, handicrafts, furnishings, development of the area since 1920 06634

Luoyang

Baimasi Han Wei Gucheng Display Center, 401 Zhongzhou Rd, Xigong, 471450 Luoyang - T: (0379) 3931053
Folklore Museum 06635

Ducheng Museum, 21 Dingding Rd S, Xigong, 471450 Luoyang - T: (0379) 3934880
Local Museum 06636

Luoyang City Folklorish Museum, 133 New St, Chanhe Hui Zu, 471452 Luoyang - T: (0379) 3951064
Folklore Museum 06637

Luoyang City Museum, 298 Zhongzhou Rd, Center, Xigong, 471450 Luoyang - T: (0379) 3937107
Archaeological Museum / Local Museum
Prehistoric finds from Er li tou, Yangshao ceramics, bronzes from the Shang and Zhou dynasties (16th c-771 B.C.), Sung porcelain (960-1279), stone lions from the Sui dynasty, Han tomb figures (206 B.C.-220 A.D.), fossils, jade objects, development of society from prehistory to feudal times 06638

Macau

Dr. Sun Yat Sen Memorial House, Av Sidonio Pais, Macau
Historical Museum
Great Chinese revolutionary, books, memorabilia, documents and pictures from his life 06639

Galeria de Exposições Temporárias da CMMP, Pavilhão Chon Chao, Jardim de Lou Lim Ioc, Macau - T: (00853) 9884000, Fax: 322127, E-mail: src@cmmp.gov.mo, Internet: http://www.cmmp.gov.mo/src. Head: José Luís de Sales Marques, Eric Choi
Public Gallery - 1986 06640

Grand Prix Museum, Rua Luis Gonzaga Gomes, Macau - Internet: http://www.macau.grandprix.gov.mo
Special Museum
Racecars from the last 45 years of Macau Grand Prix 06641

Macau Museum of Art, Av Xian Xing Hai, Macau - T: (00853) 7919800, Fax: 751317, E-mail: artmuseu@macau.ctm.net, Internet: http://www.cityguide.gov.mo/mg/mam_c.htm. Head: Ung Vai Meng
Fine Arts Museum - 1999
Chinese trade paintings, Chinese ceramics from Shiwan, painters' work, Macau fine art 06642

Macau Wine Museum, Rua Luis Gonzaga Gomes, Macau
Special Museum
Portugese wine, over 1100 wine bands, wine development 06643

Maritime Museum of Macau, Largo do Pagode da Barra 1, Macau - T: (00853) 595481, Internet: http://www.museumaritimo.gov.mo
Historical Museum
Maritime history of Macau and the world 06644

Military Museum, Calçada dos Quarteis, Macau - T: (00853) 559999, Fax: 559998, E-mail: info@fsm.gov.mo, Internet: http://www.fsm.gov.mo. Head: Peng Sam Chan
Military Museum
Hist of Macau Security Forces, police, fire fighting 06645

Museum of Macau, Monte Fort, Praceta do Museu de Macau, Macau - T: (00853) 357911, Internet: http://www.macaumuseum.gov.mo
Historical Museum
History of Macau for the past century 06646

Museum of Sacred Art, Av Sidonio Pais, Macau
Religious Arts Museum / Fine Arts Museum
Sacred relicts and Macau art works 06647

Saint Dominic Church Museum, Largo de São Domingos, Senate Sq, Macau
Religious Arts Museum
Sacred art 06648

Taipa House Museum, Av de Paria, Taipa, Macau
Historical Museum
Typical colonial houses, combination of European and Asian style 06649

Nanchang

Museum of Fine Arts, Wujiaotong St, Nanchang 330000
Fine Arts Museum
Modern Art 06650

Museum of the Revolution, Bayi Da Dao St, Nanchang 330000
Historical Museum
Documentation on the rebellion and battles of 1927/28 06651

Nanchang City Museum, 104 Bayi Av, Donghu, 330006 Nanchang - T: (0791) 6221207
Local Museum - 1952
History, geography, antique ceramics 06652

Old Zhi Display Center, Xing Si Army, 7 You Zhu Ln, Xihu, 330003 Nanchang - T: (0791) 6221297
Military Museum 06653

Yuzhang Bo Wu Yuan (Folklorish Museum), 95 Zigu Rd,Donghu, 330008 Nanchang - T: (0791) 6782024
Folklore Museum 06654

Nanjing

History Museum of the Taiping Heavenly Kingdom in Nanjing, 128 Zhanyuan Rd, 210001 Nanjing - T: (025) 2202345, Fax: 2202345. Head: Yi Jia Sheng
Historical Museum 06655

Jiangnan Gongyuan History Display Center, 1 Jin Ling Rd, Qinhuai, 210001 Nanjing - T: (025) 6626556
Historical Museum 06656

Jiangning County Museum, Zhushan Lin Garden, Jiangning County, 211100 Nanjing - T: (025) 2286102
Local Museum 06657

Li Xian Jun Former Residence, 38 Chaoku St, Qinhuai, 210001 Nanjing - T: (025) 2201629
Decorative Arts Museum 06658

Lishui County Museum, 60 Zhong Av, Lishui County, 210000 Nanjing - T: (025) 7212084
Local Museum 06659

Mingcheng Yuan Shi Museum, 8 Jiefang Men, 210018 Nanjing - T: (025) 3608359
Local Museum 06660

Nanjing Folklorish Museum, 19 South Bu Hall, Jianye, 210001 Nanjing - T: (025) 6628704
Folklore Museum 06661

Nanjing Museum, 321 Zhongshan E Rd, 210016 Nanjing - T: (025) 4802977, Fax: 4802061. Head: Qian Ji
Fine Arts Museum / Local Museum / Archaeological Museum - 1950 06662

Nanjingdi Zhen Science Museum, Zhongshan Lingshui Xie Nandong, New Village, 210014 Nanjing - T: (025) 4432772
Science&Tech Museum 06663

Nanjingdi Zhi Museum, 700 Zhujiang Rd, 210018 Nanjing - T: (025) 4813754, Fax: 4825745, E-mail: njdzbwg@yahoo.cn. Head: Gu Guohua
Special Museum 06664

Shi Liao Display Center, 116 Chao Yue Floor, 210011 Nanjing - T: (025) 8802973
Local Museum 06665

Taiping Museum, Taiping St, near Southern Gate of the Town, Nanjing 210000 - T: (025) 623024. Head: Guo Cui Xiae
Historical Museum
Documentation on the Taiping Rebellion 06666

Nanning

Guangxi Natural Museum, 1-1 Renmin Rd E, Xincheng, 530012 Nanning - T: (0771) 2820904, Fax: 2612347. Head: Huang Zhitao
Natural History Museum 06667

Museum of the Guangxi Province, Qiyi Guangdhang Sq, Nanning 530000
Archaeological Museum / Historical Museum - 1934
Excavation finds from the Guiangxi province, ancient bronze drums, history of the Taiping Rebellion 06668

Nanning City Museum, 79 Minsheng Rd, Xingning, 530012 Nanning - T: (0771) 2435718
Local Museum 06669

Xincheng District Museum, 34 Min Zu Av, New City, 530022 Nanning - T: (0771) 2423072
Archaeological Museum 06670

Nantong

Nantong Museum, 23 Ren Min Rd, Chongchuan, 226001 Nantong - T: (0513) 5512956
Historical Museum / Archaeological Museum / Fine Arts Museum - 1905
History, archaeology, stone tools, handicrafts, pottery, jade, paintings, calligraphy, fossils, history of the salt and cotton industries 06671

Nanyang

Nanyang Hanhua Guan (Nanyang City Museum), Meixi Office, Wolong Rd, 473055 Nanyang - T: (0377) 3133097, 3131511. Head: Xiao Jun Zhang
Local Museum / Fine Arts Museum / Decorative Arts Museum
Stone relics of the Han dynasty, archaeology, history, porcelain, coins, calligraphy, paintings 06672

Ningbo

Ningbo Baoguo Si Display Center, Anshan, Jiangbei, 315033 Ningbo - T: (0574) 7586317
Local Museum 06673

Ningbo Museum, 117 Yaohang St, Haishu, 315000 Ningbo - T: (0574) 7317712
Local Museum 06674

Tianyi Ge Museum, 10 First Tian St, Haishu, 315010 Ningbo - T: (0574) 7293526
Historical Museum 06675

Pingdu

Pingdu City Museum, 91 Hongqi Rd, 266700 Pingdu - T: (0532) 7363114
Local Museum 06676

Pixian

Pixian Museum, Wangcong St, Pi County, 611730 Pixian - T: (028) 7862236
Local Museum 06677

Qian Xian

Qianling Museum, Grave of Princess Yong Tai, Qian Xian
Archaeological Museum
Grave findings from Tang period including ceramic figures 06678

Qingdao

Nanji Guan (Seafood Museum), 2 Laiyang Rd, Qingdao - T: (0532) 2866614, 2962897
Special Museum 06679

PLA Naval Museum, 8 Laiyang Rd, 266100 Qingdao - T: (0532) 2888409, 2874308
Historical Museum - 1949
History of shipping, trade, commerce between the former treaty-port and the outside world 06680

Qingdao City Folklorish Museum, 19 Tai Ping Rd, 266000 Qingdao - T: (0532) 2964914
Folklore Museum 06681

Qingdao City Museum, 7 University Rd, Qingdao 266003 - T: (0532) 2870473. Head: Lijing Yan
Archaeological Museum / Historical Museum / Decorative Arts Museum / Fine Arts Museum - 1959
Archaeology, local history, Shandong provincial history, porcelain, jade, paintings, calligraphy, rare tools, sculptures 06682

Quanzhou

Oversea Transport Shi Museum, Donghu, Licheng District, 362000 Quanzhou - T: (0595) 2286655. Head: Wang Lianmao
Historical Museum - 1959
History of regional navigation, ship from the Sung dynasty, Islamic, Nestorian, Manichean, Brahmanic and Buddhist inscription stones, Hindu Vishnu statue 06683

Shanghai

Changning District Revolutionary Display Center, 34 Lane 1376, Yuyuan Rd,Changning, 200050 Shanghai - T: (021) 62511515
Historical Museum 06684

Children's Museum, Song Garden Rd, 200000 Shanghai - T: (021) 62754145
Historical Museum 06685

Chongming County Museum, Ao Shan Rd, Chongming, 202150 Shanghai - T: (021) 59623827
Local Museum 06686

Fahua Ta Tayuan Museum, State Bridge,Jiading, 201800 Shanghai - T: (021) 59927867
Special Museum 06687

Fengxian Museum, Jiefang Rd E, Fengxian County, 201400 Shanghai - T: (021) 57413539
Local Museum 06688

Hong Kong Haigang Chen Yuan (Architectural Material Exhibition), 1809 Rd W, 200000 Shanghai - T: (021) 62531777, Fax: 62567809
Special Museum 06689

Jiading District Museum, 183 Av S, Jiading, 201800 Shanghai - T: (021) 59533789, Fax: 59528816
Local Museum 06690

Jinshan Museum, 200 Luoxing Rd, Jinshan County, 201500 Shanghai - T: (021) 57320267
Local Museum 06691

Longhua Mausoleum of Fallen Heroes, 2887 Longhua Rd, Xuhui, 200232 Shanghai - T: (021) 64382252, Fax: 64382775
Special Museum 06692

Museum at the Site of the First National Congress of the Communist Party of China, 374 Huangpi S Rd, Shanghai 200000 - T: (021) 260664. Head: Cheng Zhi Zhang
Historical Museum - 1921 06693

Museum of Medical History, c/o Shanghai University of Traditional Chinese Medicine, 530 Lingling Rd, Shanghai 200032 - T: (021) 54231350, 54231376, E-mail: museum@msproxy.shutcm.edu.cn. Head: Hongzhou Wu
Historical Museum - 1938
Acupuncture techniques, medical instruments and books 06694

Qingpu Museum, Park Rd, Qingpu County, 201700 Shanghai - T: (021) 59728341
Local Museum 06695

Shanghai History Museum, 1286 Hongqiao Rd, Changning, 200336 Shanghai - T: (021) 62755595, Fax: 62192030
Historical Museum 06696

Shanghai Luxun House, 2288 Sichuan Rd, Shanghai 200081 - T: (021) 56961181. Head: Xi Rong Wang
Special Museum - 1951
Documents, letters, manuscripts, books, photos of the writer Luxun (1881-1936) - Luxun's mausoleum and his former residence 06697

Shanghai Museum, 201 Ren Min Av, Huangpu, 200003 Shanghai - T: (021) 63728503, 63723500, Fax: 63728522. Head: Ma Chengyuan
Historical Museum / Local Museum
Cultural hist of China - library 06698

Shanghai Natural History Museum, 260 Yanan Rd E, 200002 Shanghai - T: (021) 63213548, Fax: 63210595, E-mail: mpdsmnh@ms.stn.sh.cn, Internet: http://www.snhm.sh.cn. Head: Song Nian Yang
Natural History Museum - 1956
Biological abnormalities, Chinese medicinal herbs and plants 06699

Song Qingling Former Residence, 1843 Huaihai Rd, Center, 200030 Shanghai - T: (021) 64376268
Decorative Arts Museum 06700

Songjiang County Museum, Zhongshan E Rd, Songjiang County, 201600 Shanghai - T: (021) 57833314
Local Museum 06701

Yi Zhi Shi Liao Guan, 145 Duolun Rd, Hongkou, 200081 Shanghai - T: (021) 56960558
Special Museum 06702

Zhabei Revolutionary Shi Liao Display Center, 1667 Gonghexin Rd, Zhabei, 200072 Shanghai - T: (021) 56639667
Historical Museum 06703

Shantou

Shantou Archaeology Museum, 17 Dongsha Rd, Jinyuan, 515041 Shantou - T: (0754) 8618977, Fax: 8618971
Archaeological Museum 06704

Shaoguan

Book Cultural Museum, Maba Town, Qujiang County, 512100 Shaoguan - T: (0751) 6666154
Library with Exhibitions 06705

Shaoguan City Museum, 32 Fengcai Rd, Beijiang, 512000 Shaoguan - T: (0751) 8883032
Local Museum 06706

Shaoshan

Museum of the former Residence of Comrade Mao Zedong at Shaoshan, Shao Shan Chong, Shao Shan District, Shaoshan 411301 - T: 25752121. Head: Dang Wei Wu
Historical Museum - 1952
Farmhouse where Mao Zedong was born 1893, original furnishings, memorabilia of Mao 06707

Shaoxing

Lu Xun Museum In Shaoxing, 393 Lu Xun Middle Rd, Shaoxing 312000 - T: 5132084. Head: Qiu Shi Xiong
Special Museum - 1953
Memorabilia of the writer Lu Xun 06708

Shenyang

Jin Contemporary Shi Museum, Shao Shuaifu Ln, Chaoyang St, 110011 Shenyang - T: (024) 24845465
Fine Arts Museum 06709

Liaoning Museum, 26 Shiwei Rd, Heping, 110003 Shenyang - T: (024) 22821316, Fax: 22821316. Head: Mian Hou Wang
Archaeological Museum / Fine Arts Museum / Historical Museum - 1948
Bronze, painting and calligraphy from Neolithic period to Qing dynasty, Qi Bai-shi painting 06710

Shenyang Palace Museum, 171 Shenyang Rd, Shenhe, 110011 Shenyang - T: (024) 24843809, Fax: 24864188. Head: Yunting Zhi
Archaeological Museum - 1926
Historical objects and arts and crafts from the Qing dynasty, Jade seal for the Qing Emperor Nurhachi, Imperial sword for the Emperor Nurhachi, deer antler chair for Emperor Huang Tai Ji 06711

Xinle Yi Zhi Museum, 1 Longshan Road, Av Hebei Huan, 110031 Shenyang - T: (024) 86809440, 86807381
Local Museum 06712

Shenzhen

Dapeng Gucheng Museum, Peng City Village, Dapeng Town,Longgang, 518120 Shenzhen - T: (0755) 4302269
Local Museum 06713

Longgang Ke Jia Folklorish Museum, 1 St N, Luo Rui He Village,Longgang, 518116 Shenzhen - T: (0755) 8835108
Folklore Museum 06714

Shenzhen Museum, 6 Tongxin Rd, Shennan Rd, Futian, 518027 Shenzhen - T: (0755) 2244044
Local Museum 06715

Xi Bao Opaque Porcelain Museum, 2095 Baoan Rd S, Luohu, 518008 Shenzhen - T: (0755) 5563935
Decorative Arts Museum 06716

Shihezi

Shihezi Junken Museum, 832000 Shihezi - T: (0993) 2012111
Local Museum 06717

Shijiazhuang

Hebei Museum, Changan, 050011 Shijiazhuang - T: (0311) 6043529
Historical Museum 06718

Shijiazhuang City Museum, 7 Jian She Av NE, Bridge, 050011 Shijiazhuang - T: (0311) 6042117
Local Museum 06719

Zhengding County Display Center, Dong Men Li, Zhengding County, 051800 Shijiazhuang - T: (0311) 8022560
Local Museum 06720

Siping

Siping City Museum, 60 Ying Xion Av, Tiexi, 136000 Siping - T: (0434) 3223161
Local Museum 06721

Suzhou

Suzhou Art Gallery, 4 Ting Hou, Canglang, 215007 Suzhou - T: (0512) 5201214
Fine Arts Museum
Arts, crafts coll 06722

Suzhou Engraved Stone Museum, 45 Canglang District Rd, 215007 Suzhou - T: (0512) 5194343
Fine Arts Museum 06723

Suzhou Museum, 204 Hang St, Pingjiang, 215007 Suzhou - T: (0512) 7271231
Historical Museum / Archaeological Museum
Archeological finds (prehistory to present), history of silk weaving since the Sung dynasty, bronze, porcelain, historic geography of the Great Chanel 06724

Suzhou National Treasure Numismatics Museum, 640 Ren Min Rd, 215005 Suzhou 215001 - T: (0512) 7271530, Fax: 7271530. Head: Zu-E Chen
Special Museum
Antique money currency, Gu currency, memory currency 06725

Suzhou Silk Museum, 661 Min Rd, Pingjiang, 215001 Suzhou - T: (0512) 7536506, Fax: 7276539
Special Museum 06726

Zhan Tai Yan Former Residence, 17 Jinfan Rd, Canglang, 215006 Suzhou - T: (0512) 5221350
Decorative Arts Museum 06727

Taichang

Taichang City Museum, 8 Xi Men St, Xian-Town, 215400 Taichang - T: (0520) 3523354
Local Museum 06728

Taigu

Sanduo Tang Museum, Beiguang, 030800 Taigu - T: (0354) 4613002
Local Museum 06729

Taiping

Memorial Hall of the People's Resistance against British Invasion at Humen During the Opium War, Taiping
Historical Museum 06730

Taiyuan

Museum of Shanxi Province, Confucian Temple, Di Liang Gong St, Taiyuan 030000
Archaeological Museum - 1955
Buddhist sculptures from the Tang period, sitting Guanyin statue from the Yuan period, painting and calligraphy, Sutra texts from the Jin period, Tang grave from Dongrucun near Taiyuan (696) 06731

Tang Xian

Dr. Norman Bethune Memorial Hall of Tang Xian, Tang Xian 072350 - T: 2440
Historical Museum 06732

Tianjin

Dagu Paotai Yi Zhi Museum, Haifang Rd, Tanggu, 300452 Tianjin - T: (022) 25888544
Local Museum 06733

Santiaoshi History Museum, 16 Shixiao Rd, Hongqiao, 300092 Tianjin - T: (022) 27270970
Historical Museum 06734

Tianjin Art Museum, 77 Jiefang Rd N, Heping, 300041 Tianjin - T: (022) 23315878
Fine Arts Museum - 1957
Chinese paintings from the Yuan, Ming and Qing dynasties, contemporary arts, local handicrafts, terracotta figurines 06735

Tianjin Drama Museum, Av Nan Men Li, Nankai, 300090 Tianjin - T: (022) 27273443
Performing Arts Museum 06736

Tianjin Folklorish Museum, 82 Front Plaza, Guwenhua St, Nankai, 300090 Tianjin - T: (022) 27275074
Folklore Museum 06737

Tianjin History Museum, 4 Guan Hua Rd, Hedong, 300170 Tianjin - T: (022) 24314630
Local Museum 06738

Tianjin Museum of Natural History, 206 Machang Dao Rd, Hexi, 300074 Tianjin - T: (022) 23359807, 23353562, Fax: 23359807, E-mail: tjnhm@public.tpt.tj.cn
Natural History Museum - 1914
Palaeontology, zoology, botany, anthropology 06739

Tianjin People's Science Hall, Tianjin
Natural History Museum 06740

Wenmiao Museum, Dongle Rd, Dong Men Li, Nankai, 300090 Tianjin - T: (022) 27272978
Local Museum 06741

Yangliuqing Museum, Yangliuqing, Tianjin - T: (022) 27391617
Local Museum 06742

Tieling

Tieling City Museum, South Rd, 112000 Tieling - T: (0410) 2823205
Local Museum 06743

Tongliao

Museum of the Zhelimu League, Tongliao 028000
Historical Museum / Archaeological Museum - 1957
History of the ethnic tribes of northern China, mural paintings, porcelain Buddhas, excavations from a princess' grave of the Qing dynasty 06744

Tongzhou

Minbing Weapon Equipment Display Center, Guan Town, Tongzhou Beijing - T: (010) 89590766
Decorative Arts Museum 06745

Urumchi

Xinjiang Museum, 132 West Rd N, Wulumuqi, 830000 Urumchi - T: (0991) 4510413
Historical Museum 06746

Urumqi

Urumqi City Museum, Qianjin Rd, Tianshan, 830830 Urumqi - T: (0991) 2627325, 2828708
Archaeological Museum / Local Museum - 1953
Local archeological finds and customs from the Stone Age to the Qing dynasty 06747

Wafangdian

Wafangdian City Museum, Xincheng Group, 116300 Wafangdian - T: (0411) 5613596
Local Museum 06748

Weihai

China Jia Wu Zhan Zhen Museum, Liugongdao, 264200 Weihai - T: (0631) 5226357, Fax: 5226357
Local Museum 06749

Wuhan

Bo Te Guan Museum, New St, Jiangxia, 430200 Wuhan - T: (027) 87952056
Local Museum 06750

Caidian District Museum, 10 New St, Caidian, 430100 Wuhan - T: (027) 84948759
Local Museum 06751

Hebei Provincial Museum, Western Lake, Wuhan
Local Museum / Archaeological Museum
Local history following the Opium War, new excavations, ceramics, ancient chimes, burial offerings from Jin Zhou, burial remains from a 5th c grave 06752

Old Zhi National Government, 708 Zhongshan Av, Jianghan, 430020 Wuhan - T: (027) 85893790
Historical Museum 06753

Wuhan City Museum, 13 Hong Ln, Wuchang, 430061 Wuhan - T: (027) 88873616
Local Museum 06754

Xin Hai Shouyi Mausoleum of Fallen Heroes, 2 Qiuchang St, Jiangan, 430016 Wuhan - T: (027) 82410639
Historical Museum 06755

Zhan Tianyou Former Residence, 51 Dongting St, Jiangan, 430014 Wuhan - T: (027) 82835804
Decorative Arts Museum 06756

Wujiang City

Wujiang Museum, Park, Songling, 215200 Wujiang City - T: (0512) 3486091/92. Head: Linyan Dai
Local Museum
Local history 06757

Wuxi

Folklorish Museum, 109 Huishan Zhi St, Beitang, 214001 Wuxi - T: (0510) 2725256
Folklore Museum 06758

Wuxi City Museum, 71 Huihe Rd, 214062 Wuxi - T: (0510) 5804355
Local Museum 06759

Wuxi Engraved Stone Display Center, 3 Mu Qin Ln, Chongan, 214001 Wuxi - T: (0510) 2723138
Fine Arts Museum 06760

Wuxi Revolutionary Display Center, 1 Chen Lie Museum Rd, Nanchang, 214023 Wuxi - T: (0510) 5757348
Historical Museum 06761

Xiamen

Anthropological Museum of Xiamen University, c/o Xiamen University, Xiamen 361000
Ethnology Museum / Archaeological Museum - 1926
Relics of the Stone Age, bronzes, jade, seals, coins, ceramics, sculptures, paintings, calligraphy, costumes of the She and Gaoshan minorities 06762

China Xiamen Huaqiao Museum, 493 Siming Rd S, Siming, 361005 Xiamen - T: (0592) 2085345, Fax: 2093032
Local Museum 06763

Tongan County Museum, Nan Men, Tongan County, 361100 Xiamen - T: (0592) 7022478
Local Museum 06764

Xiamen City Museum, 43 Guxin Rd, Gulangyu, 361002 Xiamen - T: (0592) 2060364
Local Museum 06765

Xian

China Calligraphy Art Museum, Nanmencheng Floor, Beilin, 710001 Xian - T: (029) 5231120, Fax: 5253015
Fine Arts Museum 06766

Lintong County Museum, Lintong County, 710600 Xian - T: (029) 3812071
Local Museum 06767

Qin Dai Zhan Guan (Fine Piece Museum), Lintong County, 710600 Xian - T: (029) 3813029
Fine Arts Museum 06768

Qin Shi Huan Bingmayong Museum, Xia He Villige, Quinling town, Lintong, 710600 Xian - T: (029) 3911961
Archaeological Museum / Historical Museum - 1979
Bing Horse, Yong imitate, arts, crafts, calligraphies, paintings, Emperor's army 06769

Shaanxi History Museum, 12 East St, Xingshan Temple, Yanta, 710054 Xian - T: (029) 5217141, Fax: 5262216
Historical Museum 06770

Tang Dai Art Museum, 1 Yanyin Rd, Yanta, 710061 Xian - T: (029) 5525652
Fine Arts Museum 06771

Xian Banpo Museum, 1 Banpo Rd, Baqiao, 710038 Xian - T: (029) 3512796, 3512807, Fax: 3512807. Head: Wei Guang
Archaeological Museum - 1958
Excavated Neolithic settlement (6,000 B.C.) including residential district, cemetary and pottery, documentation 06772

Xian Beilin Museum, 15 Sanxue St, Beilin, 710001 Xian - T: (029) 7210764, Fax: 7282184
Local Museum 06773

Xian Forest of Stone Tablets Museum, 15 San Xue St, Xian 710001 - T: (029) 7210764, Fax: 7282184
Fine Arts Museum - 1911
Former temple of Confucius, history including excavations and reproductions of the Tang Emperors' graves of Qian Xian, sculptures including animal sculptures and Buddhist sculptures from the Tang period, inscriptions beginning with the Han dynasty, including Confucian classical philosophers (9th c), gold treasure from Hejiacun (Tang dynasty) 06774

Xian Highway Display Center, 10 Huaqing Rd, Lintong County, 710600 Xian - T: (029) 3813401, Fax: 3813401
Special Museum 06775

Xiaoyanta Bag Guan Museum, 76 Youyi Rd W, Beilin, 710068 Xian - T: (029) 5252070
Local Museum 06776

Xiangtan

Xiangtan City Museum, Yuhu, 411100 Xiangtan - T: (0732) 8264775
Local Museum 06777

Xianyang

Xianyang City Museum, 53 Zhongshan St, Weicheng, 712000 Xianyang - T: (0910) 3213015. Head: Shi Yu Kuo
Archaeological Museum / Local Museum - 1962
Archeological finds including earthen figurines of warriors and horsemen from Yangjiawan (Western Han dynasty), jade figures 06778

Xingping Maoling Museum, Nanwei Rd, Zhan Village, Xingping County, 713100 Xianyang - T: (0910) 8822416
Local Museum 06779

Xiaoshan

Xiaoshan City Museum, 104 Culture Rd, 311200 Xiaoshan - T: (0571) 2623084
Local Museum 06780

Xichang

Museum of the Liangshan Autonomous Prefecture of the Yi Nationality, Xichang
Historical Museum / Archaeological Museum - 1960
Regional history, slavery of the Yi people, earthquakes, handicrafts, finds from tomb excavations 06781

Xinhui

Regional Museum, Confucius Temple, Xinhui 529100
Archaeological Museum
Prehistory, ceramics of the Sung to Ming dynasties 06782

Xuchang

Xuchang City Museum, 32 Wenfeng Rd, Weidu, 461000 Xuchang - T: (0374) 2334772
Local Museum 06783

Xuzhou

Xuzhou Museum, Heping Rd, Yunlong, 221000 Xuzhou - T: (0516) 3728414
Local Museum / Archaeological Museum / Decorative Arts Museum - 1959
History, archaeology, stone implements, jade, bronzes, pottery, porcelain, fossils, paintings, relief stone carvings from the Han dynasty 06784

Yanan

Museum of the Revolution, Wangjiaping, Yanan 716000
Historical Museum
Documentation on Mao Zedong, who lived here for some time 06785

Yangliuqing

Ping Jin Zhan Yi, Old Zhi Display Center, Av East, Yaowang Temple, 300380 Yangliuqing - T: (022) 27391551
Folklore Museum 06786

Yangzhou

Yangzhou Museum, 3 Fengleshang St, Guangling, 221002 Yangzhou - T: (0514) 7344383
Local Museum 06787

Yanji

Yanbian Autonomous Prefecture Museum, 11 Canhua St, Yanbian, 133000 Yanji - T: (0433) 2512869
Folklore Museum - 1960
Korean folklore and customs 06788

Yao Xian

Yao Xian Museum, E of Yao Xian, Yao Xian 727100
Archaeological Museum
Stelae dating back to the Northern Wei dynasty 06789

Yichang

Yichang City Museum, Yi Ling Rd, Xiling, 443000 Yichang - T: (0717) 6444269
Local Museum 06790

Yinchuan

Museum of Ningxia Autonomous Region of the Hui Nationality, West Pagoda Compound, Yinchuan - T: (0951) 25480. Head: Zhung Kan
Archaeological Museum / Historical Museum - 1960
Archaeology, history, tools, finds from tombs of the Song dynasty and of the Western Xia regime 06791

Yingkou

Yingkou City Museum, Democracy St, Kou, 115000 Yingkou - T: (0417) 2835170
Local Museum 06792

Yixing

Yixing Porcelain Corporation Museum, Dingshu Town, 214221 Yixing - T: (0510) 7403451
Decorative Arts Museum 06793

Yuyao

Simingshan Revolutionary Martyr Memory, Xiao East, 315430 Yuyao - T: (0574) 2367022
Historical Museum 06794

Zaicheng

Lishui County Museum, 46 Zhong Av, 211200 Zaicheng - T: (025) 7212084
Local Museum 06795

Zengcheng

Zengcheng City Museum, Fenghuangshan, 31 Qianjin Rd, 511300 Zengcheng - T: (020) 82753949
Local Museum 06796

Zhangqiu

Zhangqiu Museum, Ming 2 Village, 250200 Zhangqiu - T: (0531) 3213028
Local Museum 06797

Zhengzhou

Dahe Village Yi Zhi Museum, Liulin Village, Jinshui, 450045 Zhengzhou - T: (0371) 5946074
Local Museum 06798

Henan Provincial Museum, 11 People Rd, Zhengzhou 450000 - T: 24214
Archaeological Museum / Decorative Arts Museum - 1927
Items from the Stone and Bronze Ages, ceramics from the period of the Warring States (475-221 B.C.), Han burial offering and porcelain, clay model of an ornate tower house from the Han period, bronze vases (4th c B.C.), archeological finds from Anyang, items from a grave of the Warring States period, burial remains from the Sung dynasty 06799

Huanghe Museum, Renmin Road St, Jinshui, 450003 Zhengzhou - T: (0371) 6222971
Local Museum 06800

Zhengzhou Museum, Song, Linshanzhai St, Zhong Yuan District, 450052 Zhengzhou - T: (0371) 7447301
Local Museum 06801

Zhenjiang

Zhenjiang Museum, 1 Xiaomatou St, Zhenjiang 212000 - T: 22143, 26517
Archaeological Museum / Decorative Arts Museum - 1960
Archaeology, silk fabrics from the Southern Song dynasty, porcelain from the Yuan dynasty, gold and silver vessels 06802

Zhongshan

Museum of Dr. Sun Yat-Sen, Cuiheng, 528454 Zhongshan - T: (0760) 5501691, Fax: 5503738, E-mail: sys@sunyat-sen.org, Internet: http://www.sunyat-sen.org. Head: Runjun Xiao
Historical Museum
Dr. Sun and his social conditions in his early years, folk customs and culture in the Pearl River Delta 06803

Zhongshan Museum, Sunwen Rd, Center, 518400 Zhongshan - T: (0760) 8825249
Local Museum 06804

Zhoukou

Tai Hao Ling Museum, Tai Hao Ling, Huaiyang, 466700 Zhoukou - T: (0394) 2661610
Local Museum 06805

Zhuhai

Doumen County Museum, Kou, Meiwan Rd,Doumen, 519100 Zhuhai - T: (0756) 5534458
Local Museum 06806

Zhuhai Museum, Jiuzhou Av, Xiangzhou, 519015 Zhuhai - T: (0756) 3359842
Local Museum 06807

Zhujiang

Lin San Zhi Art Display Center, Qiu Yushan, 211800 Zhujiang - T: (025) 8882034
Fine Arts Museum
Calligraphy and Painting, Zhan Chu 06808

Zibo

Qi Guo Gucheng Yi Zhi Museum, Qi Du, Linzi, 255422 Zibo - T: (0533) 7981929
Local Museum 06809

Zibo City Museum, 1 Zhangdian, 255000 Zibo - T: (0533) 2287817
Local Museum 06810

Zigong

Museum of the History of the Salt Industry, Zigong 643000
Science&Tech Museum - 1959
Local salt industry from the 14th-20th c, ancient salt well, local history 06811

Zunyi

Memorial Hall of the Zunyi Conference, East Red Flag Rd, Zunyi
Historical Museum 06812

China, Republic

Ali Shan

Ali Shan Museum, Ali Shan
Local Museum
Local history coll 06813

Taichung

Taiwan Museum of Art, 2 Wuchuan West Rd, Taichung - T: (04) 3723552, Fax: 3721195, E-mail: artnet@art.tmoa.gov.tw, Internet: http://www.tmoa.gov.tw. Head: Tsai-Chin Ni
Fine Arts Museum - 1986
Works of Taiwan and Chinese artist working abroad - library 06814

Taipei

Armed Forces Museum, 243 Kuien Yang St, Section 1, Taipei - T: (02) 3716832
Military Museum - 1961
Military documents and history 06815

Chang Foundation Museum, 63 Jenai Rd, Section 2, Taipei - T: (02) 23569575, Fax: 23569579, E-mail: museum@changfound.org.tw, Internet: http://www.changfound.org.tw. Head: Kui-Yin Liao
Fine Arts Museum
18th-20th c Chinese Paintings, works of art, Chinese ceramic and porcelain 06816

Chung-Cheng Aviation Museum, Chiang Kai-Shek Airport, Taipei
Science&Tech Museum 06817

Hwa Kang Museum, c/o Chinese Culture University, 55 Hwa-kang Rd, Yang-Ming-Shan, Taipei - T: (02) 28610511 ext 409, Fax: 28621918, E-mail: margcl@staff.pccu.edu.tw, Internet: http://w3.pccu.edu.tw. Head: Margaret Chen-Lee
Fine Arts Museum / Folklore Museum / University Museum - 1971
Chinese folk art, paintings, calligraphy, photography, ceramics, Aboriginal art 06818

Museum of the Institute of History and Philology, Academia Sinica, Nankang, Taipei - T: (02) 26523180, Fax: 27868834, E-mail: museum@gate.sinica.edu.tw, Internet: http://museum.sinica.edu.tw. Head: Dr. Kwang-Tzuu Chen
Archaeological Museum / Ethnology Museum / Historical Museum
Artifacts from capital site of late Shang dynasty, Han dynasty wooden slips, ethnography coll, Mortillet's paleolithic coll - Mortillet coll 06819

National Museum of History, 49 Nan Hai Rd, Taipei 100 - T: (02) 23610270, Fax: 23610171, E-mail: service@moe.nmh.gov.tw, Internet: http://www.nmh.gov.tw. Head: Kuang-Nan Huang
Historical Museum / Museum of Classical Antiquities - 1955
Coll of nearly 60,000 pieces classified in bronze, jade, ceramics, coinage, calligraphy, painting, craft, folk art etc., from prehistory to present - library 06820

National Palace Museum, Wai-shuang-hsi, Shih-lin, Taipei - T: (02) 28812021, Fax: 28821440, E-mail: service01@npm.gov.tw, Internet: http://www.npm.gov.tw. Head: Cheng Sheng Tu
Fine Arts Museum / Decorative Arts Museum - 1925
Traditional Chinese objets d'art from the various dynasties, such as: works of calligraphy and painting, jades, bronzes, ceramics and porcelains, oracle bones and artifacts from the Shang Royal tombs, costume and jewelry, Buddhist statues, enamel ware, tapestries and embroideries, lacquer ware, carvings, miniature curio cabinets, rare books and documents - library, archives 06821

National Taiwan Art Gallery, Nan Hai Rd, Taipei
Public Gallery 06822

National Taiwan Science Education Center, 41 Nan Hai Rd, Taipei - T: (02) 23116734. Head: Shih-Bey Chen
Natural History Museum - 1958
Natural science exhibits - planetarium 06823

Postal Museum, 45 Chungking South Rd, Section 2, Taipei 10741 - T: (02) 23945185, Fax: 23518773, E-mail: musol@mail.post.gov.tw, Internet: http://www.post.gov.tw/museum.htm. Head: Hsien-Dar Chen
Special Museum - 1966
Hist of Chinese postal services, stamps - library 06824

Ran-In-Ting Museum, 11-124 Fulin Rd, Shilin, Taipei
Fine Arts Museum
Works and memorabilia of the painter Ran-In-Ting 06825

Taipei Fine Arts Museum, 181 Chungshan N Rd, Sec. 3, Taipei - T: (02) 5957656
Fine Arts Museum 06826

Taiwan Craft Center, 110 Yenping S Rd, Taipei - T: (02) 3315701
Decorative Arts Museum 06827

Taiwan Folk Arts Museum, 32 Yuya Rd, Peitou, Taipei - T: (02) 8931787
Folklore Museum / Fine Arts Museum 06828

Taiwan Museum, 2 Siangyang Rd, Taipei - T: (02) 3613925, Fax: 3979514, E-mail: ckku@eden.tpm.gov.tw. Head: Minfa Shih
Natural History Museum - 1908
Zoology and botany, fossils, mineral specimens, fishes and other marine organisms, prehistoric culture, ethnology and culture of Taiwan aborigines, local hist, Chieh Kuang Ku 06829

Colombia

Barranquilla

Museo de Antropología, Universidad del Atlántico-Facultad de Ciencias Humanas- Departamento de Historia, Calle 68 No. 53-45, Barranquilla - T: (953) 341477. Head: Margarita Galindo Steffens
Folklore Museum
Folklore 06830

Belencito

Museo Siderúrgico de Colombia, Calle 15 No. 10-26, Belencito
Science&Tech Museum - 1969
Mining, metallurgy, geology 06831

Bucaramanga

Casa de Bolívar, Calle 37 No. 12-15, Bucaramanga. Head: Lucila Gonzalez Aranda
Local Museum
Archaeology, history and documents 06832

Museo de Arte Moderno de Bucaramanga (Modern Art Museum of Bucaramanga), Calle 37 26-16, Bucaramanga - T: (97) 6450483, Fax: 6450483, E-mail: mamb@reymoreno.net.co, Internet: http://www.telefonica-data.net.co/mamb. Head: Lucilia González Aranda
Fine Arts Museum - 1989 06833

Cali

Museo Arqueológico Julio César Cubillos, c/o Universidad del Valle, Sede Meléndez, Biblioteca Central, Cali - T: (92) 3315278, Fax: 3315278. Head: Carlos Armando Rodriguez
Archaeological Museum / University Museum - 1967
Archaeological finds of the region 06834

Museo de Arte Moderno La Tertulia, Av Colombia No. 5-105 Oeste, Cali - T: (92) 825642. Head: Gloria Delgado Restrepo
Fine Arts Museum - 1968
Paintings, sculptures, graphic arts, drawings - library 06835

Museo Manuel Maria Buenaventura, Av 4 No. 10-42, Cali
Local Museum 06836

Cartagena

Museo Casa Rafael Núñez, Carrera 2 No. 41-89, Barrio El Cabrero, Cartagena - T: (95) 6649440, Fax: 6649440. Head: Teresita Roman de Zurek
Special Museum - 1950
Memorabilia on president Rafael Núñez 06837

Museo de Arte Moderno de Cartagena, Plaza de San Pedro Claver, Cartagena - T: (95) 6645815, Fax: 6645815. Head: Yolanda Pupo de Mogallón
Fine Arts Museum - 1959
Modern art, Latin American paintings from 1950 - library 06838

Museo de Arte Religioso, Casa de San Pedro Claver, Carrera 4 No. 30-01, Cartagena, mail addr: Apdo Aéreo 620, Cartagena - T: (095) 6644991, Fax: 6647256, E-mail: tafi39@hotmail.com. Head:

Tulio Aristizábal Giraldo
Religious Arts Museum
Archaeology, ethnography, paintings and sculptures, religious art 06839

Museo Histórico de Cartagena Casa de la Inquisición, Academia de la Historia de Cartagena de Indias, Plaza de Bolívar, La Inquisition, Cartagena - T: (95) 6645432. Head: Donaldo Bossa Herazzo
Folklore Museum / Archaeological Museum
Folklore, colonial architecture, history and archaeology 06840

Cartago

Museo de Ciencias y Antropología, Colegio Nacional Académico, Cartago
Natural History Museum / Ethnology Museum
Ethnography, natural sciences 06841

Museo Trajes Regionales de Colombia, Calle 13 No. 4-53, Cartago
Folklore Museum - 1971
Regional costumes 06842

Cúcuta

Museo de la Ciudad, Calle 13 No. 3-67, Cúcuta
Fine Arts Museum
Modern art, paintings, sculptures, engravings, drawings 06843

Duitama

Museo de Arte Religioso, Palacio Episcopal, Duitama - T: 2811, 2275. Head: Carlos Chaparro
Religious Arts Museum - 1965
Colonial art, ethnography, religious art 06844

Museo de Ciencias Naturales, Calle 13 No. 14-41, Duitama
Natural History Museum
Botany, zoology 06845

El Retiro

Museo Arqueológico La Puma de Oro, Hacienda Los Potreros, El Retiro
Archaeological Museum 06846

Envigado

Museo Colegio de la Salle, Calle 24 Sur No. 42B-45, Envigado
Historical Museum
Education 06847

Ibagué

Museo de Arte Moderno de Ibagué, Extensión Cultural del Tolima, Ibagué - T: (982) 633618. Head: Mario Arbelaez Martinez
Fine Arts Museum
Modern art 06848

Museo del Hombre Tolimense, c/o Universidad del Tolima, Ibagué
Archaeological Museum - 1967
Pre-Colombian ceramics, goldwork and lithic funeral statuary - library 06849

Ipiales

Museo Arqueológico, Calle Batallón Cabal, Ipiales
Archaeological Museum
Archaeology, ethnography 06850

Manizales

Exposición Permanente de Cerámica Indigena, Banco de la República, Manizales - T: (968) 8845534, Fax: 8846101, E-mail: alopezfr@banrep.gov.co, Internet: http://www.banrep.gov.co. Head: Amparo López Franco
Ethnology Museum / Archaeological Museum
Indian ceramics, crafts, folklore 06851

Museo Arqueológico, Antiquo Seminario Mayor, Carrera 23 No. 58-65, Manizales, mail addr: c/o Universidad de Caldas, Apdo Aéreo 275, Manizales - T: (968) 851374. Head: María Cristina Moreno
Archaeological Museum / University Museum - 1955 06852

Museo de Historia de Caldas, Colegio de Cristo, Manizales
Historical Museum
Local history 06853

Medellín

Museo de Antioquia, Carrera 52 No 52-43, Antiguo Palacio Municipal, Medellín, mail addr: Apdo Aéreo 12256, Medellín - T: (94) 2513636, 2512222, Fax: 2510874, E-mail: museodeantioquia@epm.net.co, Internet: http://www.museodeantioquia.org. Head: Pilar Velilla Moreno
Fine Arts Museum - 1881
Collections of the Botero Donation: paintings and sculptures of Fernando Botero and international contemporary artists, 19th and 20th c art collection, prehispanic and colonial art collection, works of Luis Caballero - Free museum school, library, museum shop 06854

Museo de Arte Moderno de Medellín, Carrera 64b No 51-64, Medellín - T: (94) 2600203, 2302622, Fax: 2302723, E-mail: museoam@md.impsat.net.co. Head: Carlos E. Restrepo
Fine Arts Museum - 1980 06855

Museo de Ciencias Naturales del Colegio de San José, Calle 50a No. 22-4, Medellín, mail addr: Apdo 1180, Medellín. Head: Marco A. Serna
Natural History Museum - 1913
Zoology, botany, mineralogy, fossils, archaeology, mollusks, insects - library 06856

Museo El Castillo Diego Echavarría, Calle 9 sur No.32-269 Loma de Los Balsos El Poblado, Medellín - T: (94) 2660900, Fax: 2686040, E-mail: cmescobar@epm.net.co
Decorative Arts Museum
Furniture, porcelain, sculptures, colombian and european paintings and tapestries 06857

Museo Etnográfico Madre Laura, Carrera 92 No. 34D-21, Barrio Belencito, Medellín - T: (94) 2523017. Head: Hermana Martha Lucía Galvis
Ethnology Museum - 1964
Ethnography and folklore, archaeology 06858

Museo Etnográfico Miguel Angel Builes, Carrera 81 No. 52B-120, Medellín - T: (94) 4716259, Fax: 2642299
Ethnology Museum
Ethnography 06859

Museo Filatélico del Banco de la República, Edificio Banco de la República, Parque de Berrio, Medellín - T: (94) 2515579, Fax: 2515488, E-mail: filatelic@banrep.gov.co, Internet: http://www.banrep.gov.co/blaavirtual/coleccionfilat. Head: Hernán Gil Pantoja
Special Museum - 1977
Coll of Colombian postage stamps, and stamps from other countries 06860

Museo Folklórico de Tejicóndor, Carrera 65 No. 45A-23, Medellín. Head: Dr. Dario Isaza Franco
Folklore Museum
Folklore, costumes, textiles 06861

Museo Histórico de Antioquia, Palacio de la Cultura "Rafael Uribe Uribe", Carrera 51 No. 52-03, Medellín - T: (94) 2513654, Fax: 2518461. Head: Rubén Darío García Vanegas
Local Museum
History of Medellín 06862

Museo Mineralógico Salón Tulio Ospina, Carrera 80 No. 65-223, Medellín - T: (94) 4220022 ext 5412, Fax: 2341002, E-mail: decminas@perseus.unalmed.edu.co. Head: Dr. Martha Henao Vásquez
Natural History Museum - 1888
Ornamental rocks, Colombian fossils, Colombian emeralds, Colombian coals, cristals and imitated shapes, types of rocks, Colombian minerals resources, fluorescent minerals 06863

Museo Universitario, Calle 67 No. 53-108, Ciudad Universitaria Bl 15, Medellín, mail addr: c/o Universidad de Antioquía, Apdo Aéreo 1226, Medellín - T: (94) 2105180/81, Fax: 2638282, 2334406, E-mail: museo@quimbaya.udea.edu.co, Internet: http://museo.udea.edu.co. Head: Roberto Ojalvo Prieto
University Museum - 1942
Anthropology, natural science, arts, history, antiquities 06864

Mongua

Museo Arqueológico, Mongua
Archaeological Museum
Finds from local excavations 06865

Ocaña

Museo de Bellas Artes, Palacio de Bellas Artes, Ocaña
Fine Arts Museum
Sculpture, paintings, graphic art 06866

Pamplona

Museo Casa Colonial, Calle 6 No. 2-56, Pamplona. Head: Dr. Alfredo Lamus Giron
Local Museum
Paleography, history, anthropology, archaeology, folklore 06867

Pasca

Museo Arqueológico, Casa Parroquial, Pasca
Archaeological Museum - 1969
Lithic and ceramics objects, colonial paintings, documents, numismatics - library 06868

Pasto

Museo Escobar María Goretti, Av de Las Américas, Pasto
Local Museum
Archaeology, history, folklore, natural history 06869

Museo Maridiaz, Calle 18, Pasto, mail addr: Apdo Aéreo 319, Pasto
Local Museum - 1940
Archaeology, ethnography, folklore, mineralogy, botany, zoology, geography, art 06870

Popayán

Museo Arquidiocesano de Arte Religioso de Popayán, Calle 4a No. 4-56, Popayán
Religious Arts Museum
Religious art, vestments 06871

Museo Casa Valencia, Calle 3a, Carrera 6a, Popayán
Special Museum
Memorabilia on the poet Guillermo Valencia 06872

Museo de Arte Colonial e Historia Casa Mosquera, Calle 3 No. 5-14, Popayán - T: (928) 2684. Head: Helena M. de Casiao
Fine Arts Museum / Decorative Arts Museum / Historical Museum - 1970
Colonial art, paintings, ceramics, porcelain, furniture, Isis statuette from the Sais excavation 06873

Museo de Historia Natural, c/o Universidad del Cauca, Popayán - T: (928) 234115, 231730, Fax: 235516. Head: Santiago Ayerbe
Natural History Museum / University Museum
Archaeology, folklore, animals (esp. birds), geology, mammals, insects, fossils 06874

Museo Efrain Martínez, Carrera 3, Via Sur, El Refugio, Popayán
Fine Arts Museum
Works of the painter Efrain Martínez 06875

Museo San Francisco, Calle 4a, Carrera 9a, Popayán
Religious Arts Museum
Cult objects, colonial art 06876

Ráquira

Museo de Arte Religioso del Desierto de la Candelaria, Ráquira
Religious Arts Museum
Objects of religious and colonial art, incunabula 06877

Rionegro

Museo de Arte Religioso de la Catedral de San Nicolás, Catedral de San Nicolás, Parque Central, Rionegro - T: (94) 2710718
Religious Arts Museum 06878

Museo Histórico Casa de la Convención de Rionegro, Calle 51 No 47-67, Rionegro - T: (94) 2710710. Head: Elvira Tobón Arbeláez
Historical Museum - 1941
History, paintings 06879

Roldanillo

Museo Omar Rayo, Calle 8a No. 8-53, Roldanillo - T: (92) 2298623. Head: Omar Rayo Reyes
Fine Arts Museum - 1981
Specializes in modern works on or with paper, fundamentally graphic art and design, by Latin American artists or those working in Latin America, a large coll has been donated by the artist Omar Rayo - library 06880

San Augustin

Parque Arqueológico, Vereda de Mesitas, San Augustin - T: (91) 3330535, Fax: 2330960, E-mail: scolican@col1.telecom.com.co. Head: Alvaro Muñoz
Archaeological Museum / Open Air Museum - 1950 06881

Santa Marta

Museo Bolivariano de Arte Contemporáneo, Fundación Museo Bolivariano, Avenida Libertador, Namatoco, Santa Marta - T: (95) 4330589, 4332994, Fax: 4330589, E-mail: museobol@telesantamarta.net.co. Head: Javier Mejia
Fine Arts Museum - 1986
Picture, sculptures from Latin-American artists 06882

Museo Quinta de San Pedro Alejandrino, Fundación Museo Bolivariano, Avenida Libertador, Mamatoco, Santa Marta - T: (95) 4330589, 4332994, Fax: 4330589, E-mail: museobol@telesantamarta.net.co. Head: Javier Mejia
Historical Museum / Open Air Museum
Memorabilia on Simón Bolívar, furniture, pictures, books 06883

Santafé de Bogotá

Casa-Museo 20 de Julio de 1810, Calle 11 No. 6-94, Santafé de Bogotá - T: (91) 3344150. Head: Carmen Ortega Ricaurte
Historical Museum
Documents, printing press, furniture 06884

Casa-Museo Jorge Eliécer Gaitán, Calle 42 No. 15-23, Santafé de Bogotá - T: (91) 2450368, Fax: 2879093. Head: Claudia Gaitán
Local Museum - 1948
Local history, memorabilia of Jorge Eliécer Gaitán 06885

Casa Museo Quinta de Bolívar, Calle 20 No 1-91 Este, Santafé de Bogotá - T: (91) 3366410/19, Fax: 3366410, E-mail: quintadebolivar@excite.com. Head: Daniel Castro Benítez
Historical Museum - 1922
Memorabilia on South America national hero Simón Bolívar (1783-1830) 06886

Colección de Arte y Museo Botero, Banco de la República, Calle 11 No. 4-41, Santafé de Bogotá - T: (91) 3431202, Fax: 2863551, E-mail: wbiblic@banrep.gov.co, Internet: http://www.lablaa.org. Head: Jorge Orlando Melo
Fine Arts Museum
Painting, sculpture, paper - library 06887

Colección Numismática, Banco de la República, Calle 11 No. 4-93, Santafé de Bogotá - T: (91) 3431202, Fax: 2863551, E-mail: wbiblio@banrep.gov.co, Internet: http://www.lablaa.org. Head: Jorge Orlando Melo
Special Museum
Coins, bills - Luis Angel Arango library 06888

Galeria del Colegio Mayor de Nuestra Señora del Rosario, Colegio Mayor de Nuestra Señora del Rosario, Santafé de Bogotá
Fine Arts Museum 06889

Museo Arqueologico Casa del Marqués de San Jorge, Carrera 6a No 7-43, Santafé de Bogotá - T: (91) 2433619, Fax: 2430442, E-mail: fpc@polcola.com.co, Internet: http://www.bancopopular.com.co/fpc. Head: Maria Cristina Vargas
Archaeological Museum - 1973
Ceramics, relics of Colombian, Mexican, Peruvian and Ecuadorian civilization 06890

Museo Arqueológico Nacional, Carrera 7A No. 28-66, Santafé de Bogotá, mail addr: Apdo Nacional 407, Santafé de Bogotá
Archaeological Museum
Archaeology of Colombia 06891

Museo Colonial Don Juan del Corral, Calle 11 No. 9-77, Santafé de Bogotá
Local Museum - 1970
Religious art, colonial furnishings, implements, objects of Indian handicraft 06892

Museo de Armas, Escuela de Cadetes, Calle 81, Carrera 38, Santafé de Bogotá
Military Museum
Arms, uniforms, insignia 06893

Museo de Arte Colonial, Carrera 6 No. 9-77, Santafé de Bogotá - T: (91) 2866768, 3416017, Fax: 2841373, E-mail: colonial@mincultura.gov.co. Head: Roberto Burgos Cantor
Fine Arts Museum / Decorative Arts Museum - 1942
Paintings, sculptures, decorative objects and graphic arts from the Spanish colonial period (16th to 18th c), miniatures, goldsmith work, furniture 06894

Museo de Arte Contemporáneo, Minuto de Dios, Carrera 73 No. 81-27, Santafé de Bogotá - T: (91) 523599. Head: German Ferrer Barrera
Fine Arts Museum - 1966
Colombian, Latin American, European contemporary art, paintings, engravings, sculptures, drawings, ceramics - library 06895

Museo de Arte Moderno de Bogotá, Calle 26 No. 6-05, Santafé de Bogotá - T: (91) 2858098, Fax: 2817710, E-mail: mam1@multi.net.co. Head: Gloria Zea de Uribe
Fine Arts Museum - 1958
Colombian art since 1900, graphics, paintings, sculptures, contemporary art of Latin America, International coll - library, auditorium 06896

Museo de Arte Moderno de Bogotá II, Calle 24 No. 6-00, Santafé de Bogotá - T: (91) 2858098, Fax: 2817710, E-mail: mam2@multi.net.co. Head: Gloria Zea de Uribe
Fine Arts Museum - 1958
International coll 06897

Museo de Arte y Tradiciones Populares, Carrera 8 No. 7-21, Santafé de Bogotá - T: (91) 2845319, Fax: 2840524. Head: Cecilia Duque
Folklore Museum - 1971
Colombian popular art and traditional handicrafts 06898

Museo de Artes Gráficas, Carrera 15 No. 56 Sur, Santafé de Bogotá - T: (91) 463603. Head: Tarcisio Higuera
Fine Arts Museum
Graphic arts, printing presses 06899

Museo de Desarollo Urbano de Bogotá, Calle 10 No. 4-21, Santafé de Bogotá
Historical Museum
Maps, plans, photography 06900

Museo de Historia de la Medicina, c/o Facultad de Medicina, Ciudad Universitaria, Santafé de Bogotá
Historical Museum / University Museum
Medical science, medical instruments 06901

Museo de Historia Natural, Carrera 30 y Calle 45, Ciudad Universitaria, Santafé de Bogotá, mail addr: c/o Instituto de Ciencias Naturales, Universidad Nacional de Colombia, Apdo 7495, Santafé de Bogotá - T: (91) 3165305, 3165316, Fax: 3165365, E-mail: myundrad@ciencias.unal.edu.co, Internet: http://www.icn.unal.edu.co. Head: M. Ganzalo Andrade
Natural History Museum / University Museum - 1936
Anthropology, botany, geology, zoology 06902

Museo de Minerales del Instituto Geofísico, Universidad Javeriana, Carrera 7 No 40-76, Santafé de Bogotá, mail addr: Apdo Aéreo 56710, Santafé de Bogotá - T: (91) 3208320 ext 4731, Fax: 3208320 ext 4733, E-mail: insgeo@javeriana.edu.co, Internet: http://ainsuca.javeriana.edu.co/geofisico. Head: Andrés Alfaro
Natural History Museum - 1941
Colombian minerals 06903

Museo de Museos Colsubsidio, Calle 26 No. 25-50, Santafé de Bogotá - T: (91) 3432669, 3432686, Fax: 3402690, 3432782, E-mail: museo@colsubsidio.com, Internet: http://

www.colsubsidio.com. Head: Adelaida Espinoza Mella
Fine Arts Museum
Reproductions of engravings 06904

Museo de Santa Clara, Carrera 8 No. 8-91, Santafé de Bogotá - T: (91) 3376762. Head: Pilar Zuleta
Religious Arts Museum
Religious art, painting 06905

Museo del Instituto de la Salle, Calle 11 No. 1-69, Santafé de Bogotá
Natural History Museum / Religious Arts Museum
Natural history, religious art 06906

Museo del Mar, Calle 23 No. 4-47, Santafé de Bogotá
Natural History Museum - 1969
Marine specimens of the Atlantic and Pacific coast of Colombia - library 06907

Museo del Oro, Banco de la República, Calle 16 No. 5-41, Parque de Santander, Santafé de Bogotá - T: (91) 3348748, Fax: 2847450, E-mail: wmuseo@banrep.gov.co, Internet: http://www.banrep.gov.co/museo. Head: Dr. Clara Isabel Botero
Archaeological Museum - 1939
Pre-Colombian gold coll, native Indian tribal culture, hist, religions, customs, ceramics, textiles - library 06908

Museo Etnográfico de Colombia, Calle 34 No. 6-61, Santafé de Bogotá, mail addr: Apdo Aéreo 10511, Santafé de Bogotá
Ethnology Museum - 1966
Folklore, religious art, applied arts, relics of Indian tribes - library 06909

Museo Geológico José Royo y Gómez, Diagonal 53, No. 35-53, Santafé de Bogotá - T: (91) 2221811, Fax: 2220797, E-mail: museo@trilobite.ingeomin.gov.co. Head: Maria E. Páramo Fonseca
Natural History Museum - 1939
Minerals, fossils, skeletons and emeralds of Colombia 06910

Museo Mercedes Sierra de Pérez El Chico, Carrera 7a No. 94-17, Santafé de Bogotá
Fine Arts Museum / Decorative Arts Museum
Art, furniture, applied arts 06911

Museo Nacional de Antropología, Calle 8 No. 8-87, Santafé de Bogotá, mail addr: Apdo Nacional 407, Santafé de Bogotá - T: (91) 2462481, Fax: 2330960. Head: Myriam Jimeno Santoyo
Ethnology Museum - 1941
Colombian ethnography, archaeology, anthropology, paintings, folklore, textiles, carvings, ceramics, crafts 06912

Museo Nacional de Colombia, Carrera 7, Calles 28 y 29, Santafé de Bogotá - T: (91) 3348366, Fax: 3347447, E-mail: museo2@colciencias.gov.co, Internet: http://www.latino.net.co/arte/mnal/mhome.html. Head: Elvira Cuervo de Jaramillo
Archaeological Museum / Ethnology Museum / Historical Museum / Fine Arts Museum - 1823
Archaeological material of prehispanic societies, ethnographic objects of native and Afro-Colombian communities, historical coll from 16th-20th c, and art works since Spanish colonial times until contemporary Colombian art, Simón Bolívar, Fernando Botero, Andrés de Santa María - documentation center, educative and cultural division 06913

Museo Organológico Folklórico Musical, Conservatorio de Música, Ciudad Universitaria, Santafé de Bogotá. Head: Prof. Guillermo Abadia
Music Museum / University Museum
Organs 06914

Museo Taurino de Bogotá, Plaza de Toros de Santa Maria, Santafé de Bogotá
Special Museum
Bullfighting 06915

Socorro

Museo Casa de la Cultura, Calle 14 No. 12-35, Socorro
Local Museum
History, archaeology, ethnography, documents 06916

Sogamoso

Museo Arqueológico, Sogamoso - T: (987) 3122. Head: Prof. Eliecer Silvy Celis
Archaeological Museum
Archaeology, anthropology, folklore, botany 06917

Sonsón

Casa de los Abuelos, Museo Folclórico, Calle 9 No. 7-30, Sonsón - T: (948) 275752. Head: Susana Cadavid López
Folklore Museum - 1956
Folklore 06918

Museo de Arte Religioso Tiberio de J. Salazar y Herrera, Parroquia de la Catedral de Sonsón, Carrera 8 No 5-67, Catedral de Sonsón, Sonsón - T: (948) 275186. Head: Helmer de Jesús Flórez
Religious Arts Museum
Jewelry, pictures 06919

Tunja

Casa Museo Don Juan de Vargas, Calle 20, Carreras 8 y 9, Tunja
Archaeological Museum 06920

Museo de Museos, Carrera 10 No. 19-17, Tunja
Fine Arts Museum
Paintings, sculpture casts 06921

Villa de Leyva

Museo de Arte Colonial, Alcaldía Municipal, Villa de Leyva
Fine Arts Museum - 1971
Colonial paintings 06922

Museo del Carmen, Plazuela del Carmen, Villa de Leyva - T: (987) 320214. Head: Rafael Mejía Maya
Religious Arts Museum - 1971
Religious art, cult objects 06923

Congo, Democratic Republic

Butemo

Musée de Butemo, Butemo
Local Museum 06924

Jadotville

Musée Geologique Sengier-Cousin, c/o Générale Congolaise des Minerals, Jadotville
Natural History Museum
Geology, minerals 06925

Kananga

Musée National de Kananga, 159-160 Av Kinkole, Kananga, mail addr: BP 612, Kananga - T: 2299
Ethnology Museum 06926

Kinshasa

Musée d'Anthropologie, c/o Université Lovanium, BP 139, Kinshasa
Ethnology Museum
Anthropological handicrafts, pottery, and woodcarvings, musical instruments, traditional agricultural, fishing, and hunting methods, sculptures, coins 06927

Musée de Mayombe, Kangu, Kinshasa
Local Museum 06928

Musée de Préhistoire, c/o Université Nationale du Zaire, Campus de Kinshasa, Kinshasa - T: (12) 30123
Archaeological Museum
Prehistory exhibits 06929

Musée des Beaux-Arts, Av des Victimes de la Rébellion, Kinshasa, mail addr: BP 8249, Kinshasa
Fine Arts Museum
Modern sculptures 06930

Musée Universitaire, Kinshasa, mail addr: c/o Université de Kinshasa, BP 802, Kinshasa - T: (12) 23274
University Museum 06931

Kisangani

Musée Regional, Kisangani
Ethnology Museum
Ethnography 06932

Lubumbashi

Musée National de Lubumbashi, BP 2375, Lubumbashi. Head: Roger de Poerck
Ethnology Museum / Archaeological Museum
Ethnology, ethnography, archeology 06933

Luluabourg

Musée de Luluabourg, 159 Av Général Gillain, Luluabourg
Folklore Museum 06934

Mbandaka

Musée de Mbandaka, 16 Av du Commerce, Mbandaka, mail addr: BP 344, Mbandaka. Head: Louis Bamala
Ethnology Museum / Archaeological Museum
Ethnography, archeology, antiquities 06935

Mushenge

Musée du Roi de Cuba, Cour Royale de Mushenge, Mushenge, mail addr: BP 55, Mweka, Mushenge. Head: Nyimi Kuete Mbokashanga
Ethnology Museum
Ethnography of Kasai, statues, goblets 06936

Tshikappa

Musée Ethnolopique Provincial, Tshikappa
Ethnology Museum 06937

Congo, Republic

Brazzaville

Musée National, Av Patrice Lumumba, Brazzaville, mail addr: BP 459, Brazzaville - T: 883713. Head: Joseph Ngoubeli
Local Museum - 1965
National history, ethnography, ivory sculptures - library 06938

Kinkala

Musée Régional André Grenard Matsoua, BP 85, Kinkala - T: 852014. Head: Bivingou-Nzeingui
Ethnology Museum - 1978
Ethnography - library 06939

Pointe-Noire

Musée Régional Ma-Loango Diosso, BP 1225, Pointe-Noire - T: 941579, Fax: 946337. Head: Joseph Kimfoko-Madoungou
Historical Museum / Ethnology Museum - 1982
Historical, ethnographical, artisanal, artistic materials as a source of information on Congolese culture 06940

Costa Rica

Alajuela

Museo Histórico Cultural Juan Santamaría, Av 3, Calle Central y 2, Alajuela - T: (506) 4414775, 4421838, Fax: 4416926, E-mail: mhcjscr@racsa.co.cr. Head: Raúl Aguilar Piedra
Historical Museum - 1974
Hist of Costa Rica since the 19th c 06941

San José

Galeria Facultad de Bellas Artes, c/o Universidad de Costa Rica, San José
Fine Arts Museum / University Museum
Painting, sculpture, drawings, graphics 06942

Galeria Teatro Nacional Enrique Echandi y Joaquín García Monge, Av 2, Calle 5, San José 1000, mail addr: Apdo 5015, San José - T: 2111329, Fax: 2234990. Head: Graciela Moreno Ulloa
Performing Arts Museum
Costumes, posters, programmes, history of the National Theatre 06943

Museo de Arte Costarricense, Calle Fecosa, San José 1009, mail addr: Apdo 378, San José 1009 - T: 2227155, Fax: 2227247, E-mail: musarco@raosa.co.cr. Head: Amalia Chaverri
Fine Arts Museum
Paintings, sculpture, drawings, prints and photographs 06944

Museo de Jade, c/o Instituto Nacional de Seguros, San José
Decorative Arts Museum
Objects made of jade, jade production 06945

Museo de Numismática, Museos del Banco Central de Costa Rica, Calle 5, Av 0 y 2, San José 1000, mail addr: Apdo 12388, San José 1000 - T: 2434202, Fax: 2434220, E-mail: museoro@sol.racsa.co.cr, Internet: http://www.museosdelbancocentral.org. Head: Dora Sequeira
Special Museum - 1950
Spanish empire coins from 1516, Costa Rican coins from 1821, Banknotes from 1858, coffee tokeus from 1850, counterfeits from 1841 06946

Museo de Oro Precolombino, Museos del Banco Central de Costa Rica, Calle 5, Av 0 y 2, San José 1000 - T: 2434202, Fax: 2434220, E-mail: museoro@sol.racsa.co.cr, Internet: http://www.bccr.fi.cr/museos.htm. Head: Dora María Sequeira
Archaeological Museum - 1950
Precolombian gold 06947

Museo Indigeno (Native Museum), Seminario Central, San José. Head: Walter E. Jovel Castro
Folklore Museum - 1890
Native arts and crafts - library 06948

Museo Nacional de Costa Rica, Calle 17, Av Central y 2, San José 1000, mail addr: Apdo 749, San José 1000 - T: 2214429, Fax: 2337427, E-mail: museonac@sol.racsa.co.cr. Head: Melania Ortiz Volio
Fine Arts Museum / Natural History Museum / Historical Museum - 1887
Pre-Colombian, colonial and republican religious art, botany, history, entomology, ornithology, herbarium and birds - library 06949

Sala de Exhibitiones Temporales, Museos del Banco Central de Costa Rica, Calle 5, Av 0 y 2, San José 1000 - T: 2434202, Fax: 2434220, E-mail: museoro@sol.racsa.co.cr, Internet: http://www.museosdelbancocentral.org. Head: Dora Sequeira
Public Gallery - 1998
Paintings, sculptures 06950

Côte d'Ivoire

Abengourou

Musée Régional Bieth d'Abengourou, BP 701, Abengourou
Local Museum 06951

Abidjan

Musée de la Côte d'Ivoire, BP 1600, Abidjan - T: 20222056. Head: Dr. B. Holas
Local Museum
Ethnography, sociology, art and science 06952

Bingerville

Musée Régional Charles Combes, BP 15, Bingerville - T: 303270
Local Museum 06953

Bondoukou

Musée Régional de Bondoukou, Mairie, Bondoukou, mail addr: BP 433, Bondoukou
Local Museum 06954

Bonoua

Musée de Bonoua, Mairie, Bonoua, mail addr: BP 195, Bonoua
Local Museum 06955

Duekoue

Musée Don Bosco, Mairie, Duekoue, mail addr: BP 271, Duekoue
Local Museum 06956

Grand Bassam

Musée National du Costume, BP 311, Grand Bassam - T: 301370, 301415, Fax: 213359. Head: Barro Aminata
Folklore Museum
Costumes, photos, masks, jewellery, model traditional house 06957

Korhogo

Musée Régional Gbon Coulibaly, BP 133, Korhogo - T: 860466
Local Museum - 1992 06958

Vavoua

Musée de Vavoua, BP 18, Vavoua
Local Museum 06959

Musée du Prophète Djouman Mihin, BP 18, Vavoua
Historical Museum 06960

Musée K. Raphaël, BP 432, Vavoua - T: 754202
Local Museum - 1960 06961

Croatia

Bakar

Bakar Local History Museum, Donja Zagrada 212, 51222 Bakar. Head: Ivan Kavrečić
Local Museum
Local history, navigational instruments 06962

Baška

Zavičajni Muzej, Kralja Zvonimira, 51523 Baška - T: 856544, Fax: 856544, E-mail: tz-baska@ri.tel.hr, Internet: http://www.tz-baska.hr. Head: Majda Šale
Historical Museum / Ethnology Museum - 1970
Navigation hist, ethnographical coll of native costumes, memorial room of Dr Zdenke Čermakove, Baška Tablet (plaster copy of a precious artifact in Croatian glagolithic culture and Croatian language) 06963

Belišće

Muzej Belišće, Vijenae S.H. Gutmanna 26, 31551 Belišće - T: (031) 663111, 663215, Fax: 663215. Head: Stjepan Krznarić
Local Museum - 1971
Local history, traffic 06964

Beran

Spomen-Kuća Vladimira Gortana, Beran
Special Museum
Memorabilia of Vladimir Gortan 06965

Biograd na Moru

Zavičajni Muzej, Krešimirova Obala 22, 23210 Biograd na Moru - T: (023) 383721, Fax: 383721. Head: Vegar Mira
Local Museum - 1969
Archaeology, ethnology, cultural hist, hist, coll of paintings - library 06966

Bjelovar

Gradski Muzej, trg Eugena Kvaternika 1, 43000 Bjelovar - T: (043) 244207, Fax: 244207. Head: Goran Jakovljevič
Local Museum - 1949
Archaeology, numismatics, cultural hist, hist, ethnology - library 06967

Bol

Branko Deškovič Art Gallery, 21420 Bol - T: (021) 635270. Head: Ive Marinković
Public Gallery 06968

Muzej Dominikanskog Samostana (Museum Collection of the Dominican Monastery), Dominikanski samostan, 21420 Bol. Head: Ivo Plenković
Religious Arts Museum 06969

Brijuni

Archeological and Natural History Museum, Nacionalni Park Brijuni, Brijuni - T: (052) 525822, Fax: 525918, E-mail: mira_pavletic@yahoo.com. Head: Mira Pavletić
Special Museum
Prehistoric, antique, middle ages finds and sites, roman villa from 1 ct.; photo exhibition of Jozop Broz Tito on Brioni Island, exhibition about Paul Kupelwieser (owner of the island in 19th/20th cc.; mineral collection; coll of stuffed animals 06970

Brseč

Memorijalna Zbirka Eugena Kumičića, 51418 Brseč - T: (051) 211785, Fax: 211785, E-mail: maja.frankovic@ri.hinet.hr. Head: Dr. Bernard Franković
Special Museum
Memorabilia of Eugen Kumičić, art, ethnology - library 06971

Buzet

Zavičajni Muzej, trg Rašporskih Kapetana 1, 52420 Buzet - T: (052) 662792, Fax: 662836. Head: Mirjana Pauletić
Local Museum - 1961
Local history 06972

Čakovec

Muzej Medjimurja, trg Republike 5, 40000 Čakovec - T: (040) 313285, 313499, Fax: 312820. Head: Prof. Ljubica Ramušćak
Local Museum - 1954
Archaeology, ethnography, cultural history, history, art - library, restoration and conservation workshop 06973

Cavtat

Bukovac Art Gallery, Vlahe Bukovca 5, 20210 Cavtat - T: (020) 88038. Head: Antun Karaman
Public Gallery 06974

Knežev Dvor, Obala 18, 20210 Cavtat - T: (020) 478556, Fax: 478556, E-mail: hazu.bogisic@du.tel.hr. Head: Nenad Vecarić
Local Museum - 1909
Cultural hist, graphics, ethnography, numismatics, Baldo Bogisic coll - library, archives 06975

Čazma

Muzejska Zbirka (Museum Collection), trg Pobjede 7, 43240 Čazma
Local Museum
Ethnography, history of the revolution 06976

Zavičajni Muzej, trg Pobjede 10, 43240 Čazma. Head: Mihajlo Bradić
Local Museum
Ethnography, history of revolution, archaeology - library 06977

Cres

Creski Muzej (Museum of Cres), Palača Arsan, Ribarska ul 7, 51557 Cres - T: (051) 571127, Fax: 571127, E-mail: creski-muzej@ri.tel.hr, Internet: http://www.srce/art-collections-losinj. Head: Jasminka Čus Rukonić
Historical Museum / Archaeological Museum / Ethnology Museum - 1910
Hist of the island of Cres - library 06978

Dakovo

Dakovština Museum (Local Museum), Preradović 17Zl, 31400 Dakovo - T: (054) 843254. Head: Ivo Pavlović
Local Museum 06979

Muzej Džkovštine, P. Preradovića, 31440 Dakovo
Ethnology Museum
Ethnography 06980

Delekovec

Delekovec Local History Collection, ul Pavleka Miškine 1, 48316 Delekovec - T: 823391. Head: Venija Bobnjarić
Special Museum
Life and work of the peasant writer Mihovila Pavleka Miškinde (1889-1942) and the naive painter Mirka Viriusa (1889-1943), ethnography 06981

Dubrovnik

Biskupska Pinakoteka (Diocesan Art Gallery), Biskupski Ordinarijat Dubrovnik, trg Marina Držića 2, 20000 Dubrovnik - T: (020) 26445. Head: Mirko Talajić
Religious Arts Museum
Paintings by 15th-16th c Dubrovnik artists, 13th c Byzantine icons, 16th-17th c Italian paintings, works of Venetian goldsmiths 06982

Galerija Sebastijan, Atlas Art Agencija, Pile 1, 20000 Dubrovnik - T: (020) 27333. Head: Ljuba Gamulin
Fine Arts Museum 06983

Galerija Zavjetnih Slika Brodova (Gallery of Sailor's Votive Paintings), Kapucinski Samostan Gospe od Milosrda, Liechtensteinov Put 16, 20000 Dubrovnik. Head: Stanislav Novak
Religious Arts Museum
18th-19th c sailor's votive paintings 06984

Memorijalna Zbirka Antuna Masle (Antun Masla Memorial Collection), ul N. Božidarevića 11, 20000 Dubrovnik
Fine Arts Museum
Memorabilia of the painter Antun Masla 06985

Museum Collection and Old Pharmacy of the Friars Minor, Placa 2, 20000 Dubrovnik - T: (020) 321410, Fax: 321029, E-mail: mala.braca@du.hinet.hr, Internet: http://www.mala-braca.cjb.net. Head: Vojko Šikić
Religious Arts Museum 06986

Muzej Srpske Pravoslavne Crkve (Museum of the Serbian Orthodox Church), Od Puča 2, 20000 Dubrovnik - T: (020) 26260. Head: Ranko Gunjić
Religious Arts Museum / Fine Arts Museum - 1953
Icons from Serbia, Crete, Corfu, Venice, Russia, Greece, Dubrovnik, Boka-Kotorska, coll of portraits - library 06987

Pomorski Muzej, Dubrovački Muzeji (Maritime Museum), Tvrdava sv. Ivana, 20000 Dubrovnik - T: (020) 426465, Fax: 322096. Head: Anica Kisić
Science&Tech Museum / Archaeological Museum - 1872
Navigation hist, archaeology, submarine archaeology - library 06988

Riznica Katedrala (Treasury of the Cathedral Saint Vlaho), Poljana M. Držića 2, 20000 Dubrovnik - T: (020) 26445. Head: Mirko Talajić
Religious Arts Museum 06989

Umjetnička Galerija (Museum of Modern Art), Put Frana Supila 23, 20000 Dubrovnik - T: (020) 426590, Fax: 432114. Head: Antun Karaman
Fine Arts Museum - 1945
19th-20th c paintings, park sculptures 06990

Gornja Stubica

Muzej Seljackih Buna, Muzeji Hrvatskog Zagorja (Museum of the Peasant Revolt), Samci 62, 49245 Gornja Stubica - T: (049) 289125, 290107, Fax: 500165, E-mail: muzeji-hrvatskog-zagorja@kr.tel.hr. Head: Goranka Kovačić
Historical Museum - 1973
Hist of the 1573 peasant revolt in Croatia and Slovenia, ethnography, fine arts - art gallery 06991

Hlebine

Galerija Hlebine-Muzejska Zbirka, Filipovićeva bb, 48323 Hlebine - T: (048) 822554. Head: Oka Ričko
Public Gallery
Naive art 06992

Hvar

Arheološka Zbirka i Lapidarij Dr. Grga Novak (Archaeological Collection and Lapidarium Dr. Grga Novak), 21450 Hvar - T: (021) 741009, Fax: 741009. Head: Nives Tomasović
Archaeological Museum - 1966
Prehistoric, ancient and Christian archaeology, medieval and postmedieval stone sculptures and decorative artefacts 06993

Centar za Zaštitu Kulturne Baštine Otoka Hvara (Center for the Protection of the Cultural Heritage), Vila H. Lucića, 21450 Hvar - T: (021) 741009, Fax: 741009. Head: Nives Tomasović
Local Museum - 1950
Ethnology, archaeology, archives, prehistoric cave of Gračeva Špilja - library, archives, collections 06994

Katedralna Zbirka (Cathedral Collection), Biskupovi Dvori, 21450 Hvar - T: (021) 741152, Fax: 741152. Head: Slobodan Štambuk
Religious Arts Museum
Religious art, 16th-18th c lace vestments, Baroque chalices and vessels 06995

Zbirka Umjetnina Franjevačkog Samostana (Art Collection of the Franciscan Monastery), Franjevački Samostan, 21450 Hvar - T: (021) 74193. Head: Karlo Bošnjak
Religious Arts Museum
Paintings, numismatics, vestments, Glagolitic books 06996

Imotski

Muzejska Zbirka (Museum Collection), K. Zvonimira 1, 21260 Imotski - T: (021) 841273. Head: Snježana Tonković
Local Museum - 1988
Local history, ethnography, archaeology, paintings 06997

Muzejska Zbirka Franjevačkog Samostana (Museum Collection of the Franciscan Monastery), Vladimira Nazora 19, 21260 Imotski - T: (021) 841178, Fax: 842165. Head: Vjeko Vrčic
Religious Arts Museum - 1962
Liturgical objects, religious art (19th-20th c), liturgical books 06998

Jastrebarsko

Muzejska Zbirka Jastrebarsko, Dvorac Erdödi, 10450 Jastrebarsko - T: (01) 831126. Head: Dragica Cvetaw
Local Museum
Local history, ethnography 06999

Karlobag

Muzejska Zbirka Kapucinskog Samostana (Museum Collection of the Capuchin Monastery), 53288 Karlobag
Religious Arts Museum 07000

Karlovac

Gradski Muzej Karlovac (Karlovac Municipal Museum), Strossmayerov trg 7, 47000 Karlovac, mail addr: PP 59, 47000 Karlovac - T: (047) 615980, 412381, Fax: 615981, E-mail: gradski-muzej@ka.tel.hr, Internet: http://mdc.hr/karlovac. Head: Višnja Lasić
Local Museum / Public Gallery - 1904
Cultural hist, ethnography, archaeology, natural hist, history 07001

Kaštel Lukšić

Kaštela Gradski Muzej (Kaštel Town Museum), Brce 1, 21215 Kaštel Lukšić - T: (021) 260245, Fax: 260245. Head: Anikca Babin
Public Gallery / Local Museum
Archeology (hellenistic pottery, paleolithic findings); etnology, religious and contemporary art; sculptures of Marin Studin 07002

Klanjec

Galerija Antuna Augustinčića, trg Antuna Mihanovića 10, 49290 Klanjec - T: (049) 550343, Fax: 550343. Head: Božidar Pejković
Fine Arts Museum - 1970
Portrait busts by the sculptor Antun Augustinčić, coll of paintings and sculptures from Franciscan monastery 07003

Knin

Muzej Kninske Krajine, Tvrdjava bb, 23400 Knin, mail addr: PP 61, Knin - T: (023) 60773. Head: Ljubica Radić
Local Museum
Local history 07004

Komiža

Memorijalna Galerija Djure Tiljka (Djuro Tiljak Memorial Gallery), 21485 Komiža
Fine Arts Museum
Paintings of Djuro Tiljak (1895-1965) 07005

Koprivnica

Muzej Grada Koprivnice, trg L. Brozovića 1, 48000 Koprivnica - T: (048) 823391. Head: Franjo Horvatić
Local Museum
Archaeology, cultural hist, ethnography, naive art, hist 07006

Podravka Museum, Starogradska ul bb, 48000 Koprivnica - T: (048) 824085, Fax: 827169
Local Museum 07007

Koprivnički

Etnografska Zbirka (Ethnological Collection), Zupni Dvor, 48324 Koprivnički
Ethnology Museum
Ethnography, local hist 07008

Korčula

Izložbena Dvorana Sv. Mihovila, Sv. Mihovil, 20260 Korčula
Religious Arts Museum 07009

Muzej Korčula (City Museum of Korčula), trg Sv. Marka, 20260 Korčula - T: (020) 711420. Head: Marija Kraljević
Local Museum
Archaeology, ethnography, shipbuilding, history, painting, music, contemporary art, old cards, development of Korčula 07010

Opatska Riznica Sv. Marka, Biskupska Palača, trg Sv. Marka, 20260 Korčula - T: (020) 81049. Head: Ivo Matijaca
Decorative Arts Museum / Fine Arts Museum
Embroidered vestments, 15th-18th c church plate and jewelry, medals and coins, Italian Renaissance paintings, 17th-18th c drawings 07011

Zbirka Bratovštine Gospe od Utjehe (Collection of the Fraternity of Our Lady of Consolation), 20260 Korčula
Religious Arts Museum
Religious art, decorative art, numismatics 07012

Zbirka Bratovštine Sv. Roka, Bratoviština Sv. Roka, 20260 Korčula
Religious Arts Museum
Religious art, decorative art 07013

Zbirka Ikona Bratovštine Svih Svetih, Grad 156, 20260 Korčula
Religious Arts Museum
Religious art, decorative art 07014

Krapina

Dr. Ljudevit Gaj Museum, Gajeva ul 14, 49000 Krapina - T: (049) 70561. Head: Boris Uhernik
Local Museum
Memorabilia of Ljudevit Gaj, leader of the 19th Illyric Movement, which campaigned for the Croatian language, local history 07015

Muzej Krapinskog Pračovjeka (Museum of the Krapina Prehistoric Man), Šetalište Vilibalda Sluge bb, 49000 Krapina - T: (049) 371491, Fax: 371491, E-mail: vkrklec@globalnet.hr, Internet: http://www.krapina.net. Head: Vesna Gregurović
Natural History Museum / Archaeological Museum - 1969
Palaeontology, geology, achaeology 07016

Muzejska Zbirka Krapina i Okolica, Stari Grad, Perivoj Matije Gupca 1, 49000 Krapina
Ethnology Museum
Ethnography, cultural history 07017

Križevci

Gradski Muzej (City Museum), ul Sermaggeva 2, 48260 Križevci - T: (048) 841036, Fax: 841036. Head: Prof. Zoran Homen
Local Museum - 1952
Local history 07018

Kumrovec

Spomen Park-Kumrovec (Kumrovec Memorial Park), 49295 Kumrovec - T: (049) 53122. Head: Ivica Hrastović
Special Museum
Personal possessions and other memorabilia of Tito in his former family home 07019

Staro Selo Kumrovec, Maršala Tita, 49295 Kumrovec - T: (049) 53107, Fax: 53107. Head: Branka Sprem Lovrić
Open Air Museum - 1952
Ethnology, local hist, paintings 07020

Kutina

Muzej Moslavine, trg Kralja Tomislava 13, 44320 Kutina - T: (044) 21145. Head: Rastko Pražic
Local Museum
Archaeology, ethnography, history 07021

Labin

Narodni Muzej Labin (People's Museum of Labin), ul 1. Maja 6, 52220 Labin, mail addr: PP 44, 52220 Labin - T: (052) 855477, Fax: 852477, E-mail: tullio.vorano@pu.hinet.hr. Head: Tullio Vorano
Local Museum - 1960
Archaeology, ethnography, mining, art, Matthias Flacius Illyricus, coll of sacred art - library 07022

Lopud

Zupski Muzej Lopud (Church Museum Lopud), Zupni Ured, 20222 Lopud - T: (020) 87038. Head: Jure Ladišić
Religious Arts Museum
11th-19th c religious paintings 07023

Makarska

Gradski Muzej Makarska, Obala Kralya Tomislava 17/1, 21300 Makarska - T: (021) 612302, Fax: 612302, E-mail: gradski-muzej-makarska@st.tel.hr, Internet: http://www.mdc.hr/makarska. Head: Sanja Bozek
Local Museum
Archaeology, ethnology, modern and art hist 07024

Malakološki Muzej (Malacological Museum), Franjevački put 1, 21300 Makarska - T: (021) 611256, Fax: 611256. Head: Dr. Marija-Edita Šolić
Natural History Museum
Seashells, paleontology, botany 07025

Mali Lošinj

Općinski Muzej (Public Museum), ul Brdina 13, 51550 Mali Lošinj
Local Museum
Local history 07026

Metković

Arheološka Zbirka (Archaeological Collection), Vid, 20350 Metković - T: (020) 683693. Head: Dr. Emilio Marin
Archaeological Museum - 1820
Finds from excavations in the area 07027

Motovun

Galerija Slika, 52424 Motovun
Fine Arts Museum
Yugoslavian painting 07028

Našice

Zavičajni Muzej Našice (Local Museum), Pejačevićev trg 5, 31500 Našice - T: (034) 613414, Fax: 613414. Head: Silvija Lučevnjak
Local Museum
Local hist, memorial room of Dora Pejačević 07029

Nerezine

Arheološka Zbirka Osor (Archaeological Collection Osor), Gradska Loggia, 51554 Nerezine - T: (051) 237346. Head: Jasminka Čus Rukonić
Archaeological Museum - 1889
Material from local excavations 07030

Nin

Arheološka Zbirka (Archaeological Collection), 23232 Nin - T: (023) 64160. Head: Radomir Jurić
Archaeological Museum - 1960
Material found during excavations of the ancient Roman town of Aenona, two Croatian ships from 11th c 07031

Riznica Župne Crkve (Treasury of the Parish Church), Zupna Crkva, 23232 Nin - T: (023) 64162. Head: Pavao Zubčie
Religious Arts Museum
18th-20th c liturgical items, 8th-16th c religious paintings 07032

Nova Gradiška

Zavičajni Muzej, trg Oslobodjenja, 35400 Nova Gradiška - T: (035) 64205. Head: Predrag Drlić
Local Museum
Ethnography, local history 07033

Novi Vinodolski

Novi Vinodolski Regional Museum, trg Palih Boraca 1, 51250 Novi Vinodolski - T: (051) 791266. Head: Ognjana Janović
Local Museum / Natural History Museum
Natural history, archaeology, ethnography, cultural history, numismatics, art, history 07034

Ogulin

Zavičajni Muzej (Local Museum), trg Žrtava Fašizma 2, 47300 Ogulin - T: (047) 2502. Head: Ivan Tironi
Local Museum
Archaeology, ethnography, history 07035

Orebić

Fine Arts Collection of the Franciscan Monastery, Celestinov Put 6, 20250 Orebić - T: (020) 83075. Head: Andrija Vlašić
Religious Arts Museum
Ethnography, archaeology, religious art 07036

Orebić Maritime Museum, trg Mimbelli bb, 20250 Orebić - T: (020) 713009
Special Museum
Navigational instruments, history of Orebić's merchant fleet, models, charts 07037

Osijek

Muzej Slavonije Osijek (Museum of Slavonia Osijek), Trg svetog Trojstva 6, 31000 Osijek - T: (031) 208501, Fax: 208502, E-mail: muzej-slavonije@os.tel.hr, Internet: http://www.mdc.hr/osijek/hr/home.html. Head: Mladen Radić
Historical Museum / Decorative Arts Museum / Archaeological Museum / Local Museum - 1877
Archaeology, ethnography, history, artistic craft, numismatics, natural science, technology - library, restoration and conservation workshop 07038

Otočac

Spomen Muzej Stojana Araliče (Stojan Aralič Memorial Museum), Spomen Dom ZAVNOH-a, 53220 Otočac - T: (053) 71143. Head: Nikola Pejnović
Fine Arts Museum
Works by the painter Stojan Aralič 07039

Zavičajni Muzej (Local Museum), Narodno Sveučilište, 53220 Otočac
Historical Museum / Archaeological Museum
Archaeology, history 07040

Ozalj

Zavičajni Muzej Ozlja (Local Museum Ozalj), Zrinskih i Frankopana 3, 47280 Ozalj - T: (047) 731170, Fax: 731170. Head: Zdenka Stupić
Local Museum - 1971
Ethnology, archaeology, local hist, religious art, hist monument 07041

Pazin

Ethnographic Museum of Istria, trg Istarskog Razvoda 127, 52000 Pazin - T: (052) 21851. Head: Marija Ivetić
Ethnology Museum
12th-18th c bells, local history, ethnography, anthropology 07042

Poreč

Zavičajni Muzej Poreštine (Local Museum Poreč), ul Dekumanska 9, 52440 Poreč - T: (052) 431585, 452738, Fax: 452119, E-mail: muzej-porec@pu.tel.hr, Internet: http://www.culture-vision.com
Local Museum - 1884
Local hist, archaeology, National Liberation War - library 07043

Požega

Gradski Muzej (Regional Muzeum of the Požeška Valley), ul Matice hrvatske 1, Požega - T: (034) 272130, Fax: 272130. Head: Prof. Dubravka Sokač-Štimac
Local Museum - 1924
Palaeontology, archaeology, cultural hist, ethnography, hist of revolution, memorabilia of Miroslav Kraljević - library 07044

Pula

Arheološki Muzej Istre (Archaeological Museum of Istria), Mate Balote 3, 52100 Pula - T: (052) 33488, Fax: 212415. Head: Kristina Mihovilić
Archaeological Museum - 1902
Roman and medieval archaeology, carved stones, inscriptions, prehistory 07045

Museum of Istrian History, Uspon Muzeju 14, 52100 Pula - T: (052) 41740, 41566. Head: Herman Bursić
Historical Museum
National Liberation War 07046

Punat

Muzej Franjevačkog Samostana Košljun, Košljun, 51521 Punat - T: (051) 854017. Head: Anselmo Stulić
Local Museum - 1926
Archaeology, ethnography, natural history, art, archives - library 07047

Rijeka

Moderna Galerija Rijeka - Muzej Moderne i Suvremene Umjetnosti, Museum of Modern ans Contemporary Art, Dolac 1/II, 51000 Rijeka - T: (051) 334280, 335252, Fax: 330982, E-mail: moderna-galerija-rijeka@ri.tel.hr, Internet: http://www.mgr.hr. Head: Ljubica Dujmović-Kosovac
Fine Arts Museum - 1948
Croatian art of the 20th c. (paintings, sculptures, graphics, drawings, mixed media), paintings from Rijeka 19th c., art from abroad 20zh c., posters, photographs - library 07048

Muzej Grada Rijeke (Town Museum Rijeka), Muzejski trg 1, 51000 Rijeka - T: (051) 336711, Fax: 336521, E-mail: muzej-grada-rijeke@ri.tel.hr. Head: Ervin Dubrović
Local Museum / Historical Museum
History of World War II, cultural hist of Rijeka - archives 07049

Muzej Narodne Revolucije → Muzej Grada Rijeke

Permanent Exhibition of Votive Pictures Sanctuary of our Lady of Trsat, Frankopanski trg 12, 51000 Rijeka - T: (051) 443018. Head: Dr. Franjo Emanuel Hoško
Religious Arts Museum 07050

Pomorski i Povijesni Muzej Hrvatskog Primorja (Maritime and Historical Museum of Croatian Littoral), Muzejski trg 1, 51000 Rijeka - T: (051) 213578, Fax: 213578. Head: Željko Barbalić
Historical Museum / Fine Arts Museum - 1961
Maritime hist, ethnology, archaeology, seperated coll of works by old great painters 07051

Prirodoslovni Muzej (Natural History Museum), Lorenzov Prolaz 1, 51000 Rijeka - T: (051) 334988, Fax: 334988, E-mail: primuzri@ri.tel.hr. Head: Milvana Arko-Pijevac
Natural History Museum - 1946
Natural history, geology, paleontology, entomology, biology - library 07052

Rovinj

Muzej Franjevačkog Samostana (Museum of the Franciscan Monastery), ul De Amicis 36, 52210 Rovinj - T: (052) 811938. Head: Hilar Lukšić
Religious Arts Museum
1th-19thc sculpture, icons, illuminated manuscripts, liturgical items 07053

Zavičajni Muzej Grada Rovinja (Museum of Rovinj's Heritage), trg Maršala Tita 11, 52210 Rovinj - T: (052) 816720, Fax: 830650, E-mail: muzej-rovinj@pu.tel.hr. Head: Argeo Curto
Local Museum / Fine Arts Museum - 1954
Paintings, old masters and modern art, ethnology, cultural history, archeology - library 07054

Samobor

Samobor Museum, Livadićeva ul 7, 10430 Samobor - T: (01) 781014. Head: Miroslav Milonjić
Local Museum / Fine Arts Museum
Local history, archaeology, 18th-19th c paintings, memorabilia of the composer Ferde Livadića 07055

Savski Marof

Muzej Brdovec, Ilije Gregorica 13, Savski Marof - T: 70550. Head: Mario Lenković
Local Museum 07056

Senj

Sakralna Baština Muzej, Cimiter 7, 53270 Senj - T: (053) 882109, Fax: 882109. Head: Milena Rogić
Religious Arts Museum - 1970
Vestments, lapidary coll, church plate, Gothic silver cross, portraits of bishops - library, archives 07057

Senj Municipal Museum, Milana Ogrizovića 5, 53270 Senj - T: (053) 881141, Fax: 881141. Head: Prof. Blaženka Ljubović
Local Museum
Archaeology, ethnography, glagolitic literature, hist of the revolution, maritime trade - library 07058

Sesvete

Muzej Prigorja-Sesvete, trg D. Domjanića 5, 10360 Sesvete - T: (01) 201601. Head: Vladimir Sokol
Local Museum
Local history 07059

Šibenik

Muzej Grada (Town Museum), Gradska Vrata 3, 22000 Šibenik - T: (022) 213880, Fax: 213355, E-mail: muzej.sibenik@public.srce.hr, Internet: http://pubwww.srce.hr/muzej_sibenik. Head: Gojko Lambaša
Local Museum - 1925
Archaeology, cultural hist, local hist, ethnography 07060

Zbirka Crkvene Umjetnosti (Collection of Religious Art), pri Biskupskom Ordinarijatu, 22000 Šibenik - T: (022) 201010, Fax: 201017, E-mail: biskupski-ordinarijat-si@si.tel.hr. Head: Franko Čeko
Religious Arts Museum
Religious art 07061

Sinj

Muzej Cetinjske Krajine, ul Duše Čikare 5, 21230 Sinj - T: (021) 821569. Head: Prof. Ante Milošević
Archaeological Museum / Ethnology Museum
Archaeology, ethnography 07062

Zbirka Franjevačkog Samostana (Collection of the Franciscan Monastery), Šestalište A. Stepinca 1, 21230 Sinj - T: (021) 821374, Fax: 824301. Head: Josip Ante Saldo
Archaeological Museum - 1860
Prehistory, Roman and Christian archaeology, numismatics - library, archive 07063

Sisak

Gradski Muzej Siska, Tomislavova 10, 44000 Sisak - T: (044) 520294, Fax: 543225. Head: Zoran Burojević
Local Museum
Archaeology, ethnography, cultural hist, new hist - art gallery 07064

Škrip

Brački Muzej (Regional Museum), SIZ ul Oblasti Kulture Općine Brač, Škrip. Head: Hrvoje Gjurašin
Historical Museum / Natural History Museum
History of the island of Brač, prehistory, natural history 07065

Slavonski Brod

Brlić House (Ivana Brlić-Mažuranić House), Titov trg, 55000 Slavonski Brod. Head: Viktor Ružić
Local Museum - 1933
Evolution over 300 years of a Croatian middle-class family, Ivana Brlić (1874-1938), writer and first woman member of the Yugoslavian Academy of Sciences and Arts - archives, library 07066

Muzej Radničkog Pokreta i NOB za Slavoniju i Baranju, ul Starcevićeva 8, 35000 Slavonski Brod - T: (035) 232415. Head: Nikola Bogdanović
Local Museum
Labour Movement 07067

Split

Arheološki Muzej u Splitu (Split Archaeological Museum), Zrinsko-Frankopanska 25, 21000 Split - T: (021) 318762, 318721, Fax: 318714, E-mail: arheoloski-muzej-st@st.tel.hr. Head: Prof. Emilio Marin
Archaeological Museum - 1820
Finds from Greek, Roman and Christian sites, 9th-10th c Croatian monuments, numismatics - library 07068

Cathedral Treasury, Cathedral of Saint Dujo, Kraj Sv. Duje 5, 21000 Split - T: (021) 42589. Head: Ivan Cvitanović
Religious Arts Museum
Treasury, religious items 07069

Etnografski Muzej Split (Split Ethnographical Museum), Iza Lože 1, 21000 Split, mail addr: PP 261, 21000 Split - T: (021) 344164, 343108, Fax: 344164, 343108, E-mail: etnografski-muzej-st@st.tel.hr. Head: Silvio Braica
Folklore Museum - 1910
Dalmatian costumes, jewellery, weapons, ceramics - library, archives 07070

Galerija Umjetnina (Gallery of Fine Arts), ul Lovretska 11, 21000 Split - T: (021) 480149, 480150, Fax: 480149, E-mail: galerija-umjetnina@ct.tel.hr, Internet: http://www.galum.hr. Head: Prof. Božo Majstorovic
Fine Arts Museum - 1931
Ancient and modern paintings and sculptures - library 07071

Ivan Meštrović Gallery, Ivan Mestrovič Foundation, Šetalište Ivana Meštrovića 46, 21000 Split - T: (021) 358719/450, Fax: 358719, E-mail: galerija-mestrovic@st.tel.hr. Head: Prof. Guidoa Quien
Fine Arts Museum - 1952
Works of sculptor Ivan Meštrović (1883-1962) - library 07072

Muzej Grada Splita (Museum of the City of Split), ul Papalićeva 1, 21000 Split - T: (021) 341240, Fax: 341240, E-mail: muzej-grada-st@st.tel.hr. Head: Goran Borčić
Historical Museum - 1946
Political and cultural hist from medieval times on up to the 20th c - library 07073

Muzej Hrvatskih Arheoloških Spomenika (Museum of Croatian Archaeological Monuments), Stjepana Gunjače bb, 21000 Split - T: (021) 358455, 358420, Fax: 358411, E-mail: muzej-has1@st.hinet.hr, Internet: http://www.mhas-split.hr. Head: Prof. Ante Milošević
Archaeological Museum
Finds mainly from the 9th-12th c in Croatia, jewelry, weapons, inscriptions in sone 07074

Prirodoslovni Muzej (Natural Science Museum), Vrh Marjana 2, 21000 Split - T: (021) 46773. Head: Dr. Antun Cvitanić
Natural History Museum - 1924
Mineralogy, palaeontology, zoology, botany - library 07075

Riznica Franjevačkog Samostana Split, Poljud, Topuska 4, 21000 Split - T: (021) 42254. Head: Dr. Ante Budimir
Religious Arts Museum 07076

Stari Grad

Collection of the Dominican Priory, Dominican Priory, 21460 Stari Grad - T: (021) 665442. Head: Bernard Dedic
Archaeological Museum - 1948
Material from excavations in the district 07077

Galerija Jerolim, Priko bb, 21460 Stari Grad
Fine Arts Museum 07078

Zbirka Umjetnina Juraj Plančić, Biankinieva 2, 21460 Stari Grad - T: (021) 765022. Head: Aldo Cavić
Public Gallery 07079

Ston

Zupski Ured (Archeological Collection), T. Setalište 17, 20230 Ston. Head: Josip Barišić
Archaeological Museum 07080

Trakošćan

Dvor Trakošćan (Castle Museum), Dvorac, 42254 Trakošćan - T: (042) 796422, Fax: 796420. Head: Adam Pintarić, Ivan Mravlinčić
Decorative Arts Museum / Fine Arts Museum - 1953
15th-19th c furniture, weapons, paintings, crafts 07081

Trogir

Lapidarij - Klaustar Samostana Sv. Domenika, Partizanska 1, 21220 Trogir - T: (021) 73960. Head: Veselko Begić
Archaeological Museum 07082

Muzej Grada Trogira, Gradska Vrata 4, 21220 Trogir - T: (021) 881406, Fax: 796046/48, E-mail: muzej-grada-trogira@st.hinet.hr. Head: Fani Celio Cega
Local Museum - 1963
Local hist - library 07083

Riznica Katedrala (Cathedral Treasury), Narodni trg 3, 21220 Trogir. Head: Ivo Djurdjević
Religious Arts Museum
Treasury, religious items, art 07084

Zbirka Umjetnina KAIROS, Benediktinski Samostan Sv. Nikole, Kohl-Genscher 2, 21220 Trogir - T: (021) 881631, Fax: 881631. Head: Ivana Šeravić
Religious Arts Museum / Performing Arts Museum - 1969
Religious items, art, archaeology, music, performing arts 07085

Varaždin

Gradski Muzej Varaždin (Varaždin Municipal Museum), Strossmayerovo Šetalište 7, 42000 Varaždin - T: (042) 212918/19, Fax: 310519, E-mail: gradski-muzej-vz@vz-tel.hr, Internet: http://www.varazdin.hr. Head: Ljerka Šimunić
Local Museum
Local hist, aristical crafts, works of Croatian and European old and modern masters, local archeological, ethnological and entomological coll 07086

Varaždinske Toplice

Yaraždinske Toplice Local History Museum, trg Slobode 16, 42223 Varaždinske Toplice - T: (042) 631339. Head: Stjepan Hajduk
Local Museum
Archaeology, balneology, cultural history, ethnography   07087

Velika Gorica

Muzej Turopolja (Museum of Turopolja), trg Kralja Tomislava 1, 10410 Velika Gorica - T: (01) 6221325, Fax: 6225077, E-mail: muzej-turopolja@muzej-turopolja.hr, Internet: http://www.muzej-turopolja.hr. Head: Prof. Igor Maroević
Local Museum - 1960
Local hist, ethnography, archaeology   07088

Virje

Virje Local History Museum and Fine Arts Gallery, trg S. Radića 1, 48326 Virje - T: (048) 818053. Head: Josip Ljubić
Local Museum
Ethnology, local history, cultural traditions   07089

Virovitica

Gradski Muzej Virovitica (Virovitica Municipal Museum), Dvorac Pejačević, 33000 Virovitica - T: (033) 722127, Fax: 722127, E-mail: gradski-muzej-virovitica@vt.hinet.hr, Internet: http://www.mhi/virovitica. Head: Prof. Dubravka Sabolic
Local Museum
Archaeology, ethnography, cultural hist, visual arts, Branislav Glumac coll   07090

Visovac

Zbirka Franjevačkog Samostana Visovac (Collection of the Franciscan Monastery), Franjevački Samostan, Visovac - T: 75416, Fax: 75755. Head: Dr. Šime Samac
Religious Arts Museum
17th-18th c paintings   07091

Vrpolje

Spomen Galerija Ivana Meštrovića (Ivan Meštrović Memorial Gallery), trg Ivana Meštrovića 1, 35210 Vrpolje - T: (035) 76375. Head: Ljubica Dumančić
Fine Arts Museum
Works and memorabilia of the sculptor Ivan Meštrović   07092

Zadar

Archaeological Museum, trg Opatice Cike bb, 23000 Zadar - T: (023) 23950. Head: Radomir Jurić
Archaeological Museum - 1830
Roman architecture, Roman epigraphy and archaeology, medieval archaeology   07093

Narodni Muzej (National Museum), ul Poljana V. Gortana, 23000 Zadar - T: (023) 33239. Head: Valentin Uranija
Local Museum
History, folk art, folklore, contemporary arts, 15th-17th c glass and ceramics, natural history, crafts   07094

Pomorski Muzej (Maritime Museum), Obala Kneza Trpimira 8, 10000 Zadar - T: (023) 443094, 443095, Fax: 443095. Head: Seid Traljić
Historical Museum
Sailing and navigation, prehistory, antiquities 07095

Riznica Samostana Svetog Frane (Saint Francis Art Collections), trg Svetog Frane 1, 23000 Zadar. Head: Alfons Orlić
Religious Arts Museum
Sculpture, religious art   07096

Zagreb

Arheološki Muzej Zagreb, Zrinski trg 19, 10000 Zagreb, mail addr: PP 13, 10000 Zagreb - T: (01) 4873100, Fax: 4873102, E-mail: amz@zg.tel.hr, Internet: http://www.arheoloski.hr. Head: Prof. Ante Rendić-Miočević
Archaeological Museum - 1846
Prehistory, Egyptian Coll, Greco-Roman Coll: stone monuments, painted Greek vases, the longest written text in the Etruscan language on a linen cloth (Liber linteus Zagrebiensis), Medieval Coll, numismatics - library   07097

Atelier Ivan Meštrović, Ivan Meštrović Foundation, Mletačka 8, 10000 Zagreb - T: (01) 428586, Fax: 428966. Head: Guido Quien
Fine Arts Museum - 1952
Studio of the sculptor Ivan Meštrović (1883-1962)   07098

Dijecezanski Muzej Zagrebačke Nadbiskupije, Kaptol 31, 10000 Zagreb - T: (01) 4894846, 4666897, 4814727, Fax: 4667338. Head: Dr. Juraj Kolarić
Religious Arts Museum / Special Museum - 1939
Religious sculptures, pictures, westments, art 07099

Etnografski Muzej (Ethnographical Museum), Mažuranićev trg 14, 10000 Zagreb - T: (01) 4826220, Fax: 4826221, E-mail: EMZ@etnografskij-muzej.hr, Internet: http://www.etnografskij-muzej.hr. Head: Damodar Frlan
Ethnology Museum - 1919
National costumes of the three ethnographic regions

of Croatia: Pannonic, Dinaric, Adriatic, coll of pottery, carpets, kerchiefs, laces, musical instruments of Croatia, coll of non-European cultures - library   07100

Galerija Klovićevi Dvori, Jezuitski trg 4, 10000 Zagreb - T: (01) 4851926, Fax: 4852116, E-mail: info@galerijaklovic.hr, Internet: http://www.galerijaklovic.hr. Head: Prof. Zvonko Festini
Fine Arts Museum   07101

Glyptothèque, Medvedgradska 2, 10000 Zagreb - T: (01) 276005. Head: Miro Montani
Fine Arts Museum / Archaeological Museum - 1937
Archaeology, ancient, medieval and modern frescos, castings, 19th-20th c sculptures   07102

Grafička Zbirka Nacionalne i Sveučilišne Knjižnice (Print Collection of the National and University Library), Hrvatske Bratske Zajednice bb, 10000 Zagreb - T: (01) 6164101, Fax: 6164128, E-mail: mmastrovic@nsk.hr, Internet: http://www.nsk.hr
Fine Arts Museum
Graphics, documents   07103

Hrvatski Muzej Naivne Umjetnosti (Croatian Museum of Naive Art), ul sv. Ćirila i Metoda 3, 10000 Zagreb - T: (01) 4851911, Fax: 4852125, E-mail: hmnu@zg.tel.hr, Internet: http://www.hmnu.org. Head: Prof. Franjo Mrzljak
Fine Arts Museum - 1994
Croatian naive art, international naive art - library   07104

Hrvatski Muzej Pošte i Telekomunikacija (Croatian Museum of Post and Telecommunications), Jurišićeva 13, 10000 Zagreb - T: (01) 4818957, Fax: 420616, E-mail: kata.sutalo@hpt.hr, Internet: http://www.mdc.hr/www-hpt-hr/index.html. Head: Kata Šutalo
Special Museum - 1953
Postal hist, philately, telecommunication hist - library, archives   07105

Hrvatski Narodni Zoološki Muzej (Croatian Zoological Museum), Demetrova 1, 10000 Zagreb - T: (01) 428596, Fax: 424998, E-mail: hpm@hpm.hr. Head: Dr. Nikola Tvrtković
Natural History Museum - 1846
Zoology, malacology, entomology, Krapina's man coll - library   07106

Hrvatski Povijesni Muzej (Croatian Historical Museum), Matoševa ul 9, 10000 Zagreb - T: (01) 431065, Fax: 425515, E-mail: HISMUS@Zg.tel.hr. Head: Ankica Pandžić
Historical Museum - 1846
Croatian hist from the 14th c to the present day - library   07107

Hrvatski Prirodoslovni Muzej (Croatian Natural History Museum), Demetrova 1, 10000 Zagreb - T: (01) 428615, Fax: 424998, E-mail: hpm@hpm.hr. Head: Dr. Nikola Tvrtković
Natural History Museum - 1846
Geology, palaeontology, fossils, neogene malacological fauna of the Pannonian region (ca. 20000 specimens), the Krapina Neandertal remains (680 specimens) - library   07108

Hrvatski Školski Muzej (Croatian School Museum), trg Maršala Tita 4, 10000 Zagreb - T: (01) 4855716, Fax: 4855825, E-mail: hrskolski.muzej@inet.hr, Internet: http://www.hrskolski-muzej.hr. Head: Elizabeta Serdar
Special Museum - 1901
Hist of education in Croatia - library   07109

Hrvatski Sportski Muzej (Croatian Sports Museum), Ilica 13, 10000 Zagreb - T: (01) 4833483, 4831379, Fax: 4833483, E-mail: hr-sportski-muzej@zq.tel.hr. Head: Zdenko Jajčević
Special Museum / Historical Museum   07110

Kabinet Grafike HAZU (HAZU Print Room), Hebrangova 1, 10000 Zagreb - T: (01) 4922374, Fax: 4922374, E-mail: kabgraff@hazu.hr, Internet: http://www.hazu.hr/kabinet_grafike.html. Head: Prof. Slavica Marković
Fine Arts Museum - 1951
Prints, drawings and posters   07111

Lovački Muzej (Museum of Hunting), Vladimira Nazora 63, 10000 Zagreb - T: (01) 433410, Fax: 271044. Head: Andjelko Stažić
Special Museum - 1954   07112

Mineraloško-Petrografski Muzej, ul Demetrova 1, 10000 Zagreb - T: (01) 428615. Head: Dr. Nikola Tvrtković
Natural History Museum - 1846
Mineralogy, petrography   07113

Moderna Galerija (Gallery of Modern Art), Andrije Hebranga 1, 10000 Zagreb - T: (01) 433802, Fax: 433802. Head: Igor Zidić
Fine Arts Museum - 1905
19th-20th c Croatian art, painting, sculpture (Vlaho Bukovac, Josip Račić, Miroslav Kraljević) - library   07114

Muzej Grada Zagreba (City Museum of Zagreb), Opatička 20-22, 10000 Zagreb - T: (01) 4851362, Fax: 4851359, E-mail: muzej-grada-zagreba@mgz.tel.hr, Internet: http://www.mdc.hr/mgz. Head: Prof. Vinko Ivić
Historical Museum - 1907
Sculpture (14th-18th c), paintings and drawings of Zagreb, portraits of Zagreb personalities (18th-19th c), guild articles, furniture, applied arts, plans and old photos of the city, stone sculpture from the Cathedral (14th-17th c) - library   07115

Muzej Hrvatske Književnosti i Kazališne Umjetnosti (Croatian Museum of Literature and Theatre), Opatička 18, 10000 Zagreb - T: (01) 274884. Head: Jure Kaštelan
Special Museum
History of Croatian literature and theater   07116

Muzej Kliničke Psihijatrijske Bolnice Vrapče, Bolnička 32-36, 10000 Zagreb - T: (01) 156211. Head: Dr. Ante Sila
Special Museum   07117

Muzej Suvremene Umjetnosti, Museum of Contemporary Art, Habdelićeva 2, 10000 Zagreb - T: (01) 4851930, 4851931, Fax: 4851930, 4851931, E-mail: msu@msu.tel.hr, Internet: http://www.mdc.hr/msu. Head: Snježanda Pintarić
Fine Arts Museum - 1954
Coll of modern and of contemporary art, coll of international art, coll of outsider art, coll of design and posters, coll of photography, film, video art - library, documentation, publishing dept, audio-visual dept   07118

Muzej za Umjetnost i Obrt (Museum of Arts and Crafts), Trg maršala Tita 10, 10000 Zagreb - T: (01) 4826922, Fax: 4828088, E-mail: muo@muo.hr, Internet: http://www.muo.hr. Head: Vladimir Maleković
Decorative Arts Museum / Fine Arts Museum - 1880
Furniture, ceramics, glass, metalware, textile, paintings, sculptures, clocks and watches, industrial and graphic design, photography, architecture - library   07119

Muzejski Dokumentacijski Centar (Museum Documentation Centre), Mesnička 5, 10000 Zagreb, mail addr: PP 539, 10000 Zagreb - T: (01) 4847897, 4847913, Fax: 4847913, E-mail: info@mdc.hr, Internet: http://www.mdc.hr. Head: Višnja Zgaga
Association with Coll   07120

Riznica Zagrebačke Katedrala (Treasury of Zagreb Cathedral), Kaptol 31, 10000 Zagreb - T: (01) 4812032, 4814727, Fax: 4812038. Head: Josip Klarić
Religious Arts Museum
Religious objects of metals, missal-codices, paraments in all liturgical colours   07121

Strossmayerova galerija starih majstora (Strossmayer Gallery of Old Masters), trg Nikole Šubića Zrinskoga 11, 10000 Zagreb - T: (01) 4813344, 4569082/083, Fax: 4819979, E-mail: sgallery@hazu.hr, Internet: http://www.mahazu.hazu.hr. Head: Djuro Vandura
Fine Arts Museum - 1884
13th-19th c art   07122

Tehnički Muzej (Technical Museum), Savska cesta 18, 10000 Zagreb - T: (01) 4844050, Fax: 4843568, E-mail: tehnicki-muzej@tehnicki-muzej.hinet.hr, Internet: http://www.mdc.hr. Head: Božica Škulj
Science&Tech Museum - 1954
Astronomy, mineralogy, petrography, firefighting, steam machines, motors, acroplanes, motorcars, photo-equipment, medicine equipment, radioappliances, gramophones, measurement equipment - library   07123

Tiflološki Muzej (Museum of the Blind - Typhlology), ul Draškovićeva 80, 10000 Zagreb - T: (01) 433351, Fax: 433351. Head: Vjeskolav Mršić
Special Museum - 1953
Exhibits relating to the blind, tactile gallery - library   07124

Umjetnički Paviljon, Tomislavob trg 22, 10000 Zagreb - T: (01) 276135. Head: Lea Ukrainček
Fine Arts Museum   07125

Zbirka Anke Gvozdanović, Museum of Arts and Crafts (Anka Gvozdanović Collection), Visoka 8, 10000 Zagreb - T: (01) 4826922, Fax: 4828088, E-mail: muo@muo.hr. Head: Vladimir Maleković
Fine Arts Museum / Decorative Arts Museum - 1968
Applied arts   07126

Zaostrog

Etnografska Zbirka Franjevačkog Samostana (Ethnographical Collection of the Franciscan Monastery), Franjevački Samostan, 21334 Zaostrog - T: (021) 629048. Head: Nikola Radić
Ethnology Museum / Religious Arts Museum
Ethnography, religious art, paintings, archives   07127

Zlatar

Gallery of Naive Art, Zagrebačka 3, 49250 Zlatar - T: (049) 61823, 61845. Head: Josip Simunec
Public Gallery   07128

Županja

Stjepan Gruber Museum, Savska 2, 32270 Županja - T: (032) 71581. Head: Branko Sinčić
Local Museum
Paleontology, archaeology, ethnography   07129

Cuba

Banes

Museo Chorro de Maita, Chorro de Maita, Banes
Archaeological Museum
Aboriginal funerary archeology coll, idols and ceramics coll   07130

Bayamo

Museo Casa Natal de Carlos Manuel de Céspedes, Calle Maceo 57, Bayamo
Local Museum
Local and Cuban History coll, Carlos Manuel de Céspedes's personal belongings and objects, art and archaeology coll   07131

Museo de la Provincia de Granma, Calle Maceo 58, Bayamo
Local Museum
Cuban history, archaeology and natural sciences coll   07132

Camagüey

Museo Ignacio Agramonte, Av de los Martires 2, Camagüey - T: 7231
Fine Arts Museum / Decorative Arts Museum / Historical Museum
Colonial paintings, furniture, history   07133

Cardenas

Museo Oscar María de Rojas, Calle Calzada 4, Cardenas. Head: Oscar M. de Rojas y Cruzat
Local Museum - 1900
Shells and insects coll, furniture, decorative arts, coins, weapons, arms, snails, butterflies, archaeology, history   07134

La Habana

Centro de Desarrollo de las Artes Visuales, Calle San Ignacio 352 esq Teniente Rey, 10100 La Habana - T: (07) 623533, 629295, 625279, Fax: 623533, E-mail: avisual@cubarte.cult.cu. Head: Margarita González Lorente
Public Gallery   07135

Centro de Diseño Ambiental, Calle 15 No 1074, Vedano, La Habana - T: (07) 301283, 300974, Fax: 338121
Public Gallery   07136

Centro Wilfredo Lam, Calles Oficios y Acosta, La Habana
Fine Arts Museum
Works by Wilfredo Lam and other 20th c Third-World artists. Bibliographical and documentary collection.   07137

Depósito del Automóvil (Deposit of Cars), Calle Oficios 13, La Habana - T: (07) 615868, Fax: 619080, E-mail: automovil@cultural.ohch.cu. Head: Eduardo Mesejo Maestre
Science&Tech Museum
Old American cars such as a Cadillac from 1905   07138

Haydee Santamaría Galería Latino Americana, Calle G entre 3ra y 5ta, Vedado, La Habana
Fine Arts Museum
Latin American Art. Sculptures, paintings, Photographs and popular art collections   07139

Morro-Cabaña Parque Histórico Militar, Carretera de la Cabaña, La Habana
Historic Site / Military Museum
Antique weapons, history of navigation   07140

Museo Antropológico Montané, c/o Universidad de La Habana, Facultad de Biología, Plaza Ignacio Agramonte, La Habana 4 - T: (07) 329000, Fax: 321321. Head: Dr. Antonio J.F. Martínez Fuentes
Ethnology Museum / University Museum - 1903
Cuban primitive archeology, American, European archeology, objects of the Cuban prehistorical cultures Ciboney and Taino, Cuban prehistorical physical anthropology - library, laboratory   07141

Museo Arabe, Calle Oficios esq Obispo y Obrapia, La Habana
Historical Museum
Arab architecture and ornamental objects   07142

Museo Casa Natal José Martí, Calle Leonor Pérez 314, La Habana - T: (07) 68852. Head: Maria de la Luz Ramirez Estrada
Special Museum - 1925
Works, iconography and bibliography of writer and Cuban hero José Martí (1853-1895) in the house where he was born   07143

Museo de Arte Colonial de la Habana, Plaza de la Catedral, La Habana. Head: Margarita Suárez
Historical Museum
Cuban life during the Colonial period, furniture   07144

Museo de Arte Popular, Plaza de la Catedral, La Habana
Folklore Museum
Cuban and foreign art   07145

Museo de Artes Decorativas, Calle 1 No 502 D-E, Vedado, La Habana 10400 - T: (07) 320924, 308037, Fax: 613857, E-mail: musna@artsoft.cult.cu. Head: Katia Varela
Decorative Arts Museum - 1964
Decorative art in gold, silver, bronze, ivory, barn stone, tapestries, pottery, costumes, clocks - library, conservation and restauration departments 07146

Museo de Etnologia, Palacio Aldama, Reina y Amistad, La Habana
Ethnology Museum / Folklore Museum
Folklore, especially in connection with Africa 07147

Museo de Historia Natural Felipe Poey, c/o Universidad de la Habana, Plaza Ignacio Agramonte, La Habana
University Museum
Preserve animals and birds 07148

Museo de la Ciudad de la Habana (Museum of the City of Havana), Palacio de los Capitanes Generales, Calle de Tacón 1, La Habana. Head: Eusebio Leal Spengler
Historical Museum - 1938
History of the city since aboriginal times, memorabilia of Martí Gómez and Maceo, foundation of La Habana - library 07149

Museo de la Revolución y Granma Memorial, Calle Refugio 1, La Habana
Local Museum
History of the cuban revolution. Weapons collection, recordings, videos and films. Painting and sculptures. Landing Yacht used by Fidel Castro 07150

Museo Ernest Hemingway, Finca La Vigía, San Francisco de Paula, La Habana 19180 - T: (07) 910809, Fax: 558090. Head: Danilo M. Arrate Hernandez
Special Museum - 1962
Personal memorabilia of writer Ernest Hemingway (1899-1961) 07151

Museo Etnográfico, Pueblo de Madruga, La Habana
Ethnology Museum 07152

Museo Histórico Municipal, Palacio de Lombillo, Plaza de la Catedral, La Habana
Historical Museum
Local history 07153

Museo Municipal de Guanabacoa, Calle Martí 108, Guanabacoa 11, La Habana - T: (07) 979117. Head: Maria Cristina Peña Reigosa
Historical Museum - 1964
19th c relics, Afro-Cuban coll 07154

Museo Municipal de Regla, Calle Martí 158, La Habana
Local Museum
Foundings and development of the town of Regla 07155

Museo Nacional de la Campana de Alfabetización, Ciudad Libertad Mariano, La Habana
Historical Museum
History of Cuban literacy campaign 07156

Museo Nacional de la Cerámica, Castillo de la Real Fuerza, Calle O'Reilly 2, 10100 La Habana, mail addr: CP 10200, La Habana - T: (07) 616130, Fax: 613857. Head: Alejandro G. Alonso
Decorative Arts Museum - 1977 07157

Museo Nacional de Música (National Music Museum), Calle Cárcel 1, La Habana
Music Museum
Music and musical instruments from 16th c to present 07158

Museo Napoleónico, Calle San Miguel y Ronda, La Habana
Historical Museum - 1961
Artworks, furniture, porcelain, armaments, costumes, history of France in Revolutionary, Imperial and Directorate periods 07159

Museo Numismático, c/o Banco Central de Cuba, La Habana 1 - T: (07) 615811, Fax: 615811. Head: Inés Gutiérrez Carcia
Historical Museum - 1975
Cubian coins fron 1536, medals, orders and decorations, Spanish, French, US and Latin american coins, counterfeits, and revolutionary bonds, sugar mill tokens, lottery tickets - numismatics library 07160

Museo Postal Cubano, Av Rancho Boyeros, Plaza de la Revolución, La Habana
Special Museum
Cuban and world stamps, History of the postal service 07161

Museo y Biblioteca de Zoología, Calle 42 No 3307, La Habana
Natural History Museum - 1933
Zoology, mollusks - library 07162

Sala de Artes, c/o Departamento de Servicios al Publico, Biblioteca Nacional José Martí, Plaza de la Revolución, La Habana - T: (07) 708029
Fine Arts Museum 07163

Habana Vieja

Fototeca de Cuba, Calle Mercaderes 307, Habana Vieja
Fine Arts Museum 07164

Museo Nacional de Bellas Artes (National Museum of Fine Arts), Trocadero, Calle Zulueta y Monserrate, Habana Vieja, mail addr: CP 10200, La Habana - T: (07) 639042, Fax: 629626, E-mail: musna@artsoft.cult.cu. Head: Moraima Clavijo Colom
Fine Arts Museum
Egyptian, Greek and Roman art, Renaissance and 17th-18th c Italian art, Netherlands, French, English and Spanish art, Cuban art since colonial times - library, conservation department, restauration department 07165

Holguín

Museo Provincial de Holguín, Calle Frexes 198, Holguín
Local Museum
History of Holguín coll, historical documents and objects, visual art and aboriginal archaeology coll 07166

Matanzas

Museo Farmacéutico, Calle Milanes 4951, Matanzas
Special Museum - 1964
Medicines, porcelain jars and tools of a 1882 founded French Pharmacy 07167

Museo Municipal de Matanzas, Plaza de la Virgía, Matanzas - T: 3195. Head: Gonzalo Domínguez Cabrera
Local Museum - 1959
Local history, archaeology, ethnography, art 07168

Museo Playa Girón, Playa Girón, Zapata Marshes, Matanzas
Historical Museum / Local Museum
Documents, objects, pictures, weapons related to the Invasion in 1961 07169

Nueva Gerona

Museo Prisión Modelo, Peparto Chacón, Nueva Gerona, Isla de la Juventud
Special Museum
Replica of Joliet prison in Illinois, U.S.A. 07170

Pinar del Río

Museo Provincial de la Historia de Pinar del Río (Provincial Museum of History of Pinal del Río), Calle Martí 58, Pinar del Río
Local Museum 07171

Tranquilino Sandalio de Noda Museo de Ciencias Naturales (Tranquilino Sandalio de Noda Museum of Natural Science), Calle Martí 202, Pinar del Río
Science&Tech Museum 07172

Remedios

Museo de las Parrandas de Remedios, Calle Máximo Gómez 71, Remedios
Folklore Museum
Objects, models, costumes and history of the Remedios Parrandas 07173

Museo de Remedios José Maria Espiñosa, Calle Maceo 32, Remedios. Head: Alberto Vigil y Colomba
Fine Arts Museum / Historical Museum / Natural History Museum - 1933
Local art, history, natural history 07174

San Antonio de los Baños

Museo del Humor, Calle 60 esq. Av 45, San Antonio de los Baños
Local Museum - 1979
Graphic and literary humor 07175

Sancti-Spiritus

Museo Colonial Palacio Valle Iznaga, Calle Placido 74, Sancti-Spiritus 60100 - T: 25455. Head: Elizabet Melgarejo Cabrera
Historical Museum / Decorative Arts Museum / Fine Arts Museum - 1967
Colonial period, furniture, art coll 07176

Santa Clara

Museo de Artes Decorativas de Santa Clara, Calle María Abreu esq. a Luis Estevez, Santa Clara
Decorative Arts Museum
Colonial objects and ornamental pieces coll in a colonial Mansion 07177

Museo Provincial de Villaclara, Ciudad Escolar Abel Santamaria, Reparto Osvaldo Herrera, Santa Clara
Local Museum / Fine Arts Museum
Halls devoted to the 19th and 20th c Independence wars, art works by local artist, natural history coll 07178

Santiago de Cuba

Casa Natal de Antonio Maceo, Calle Los Maceos 207, Santiago de Cuba
Local Museum
Antonio Maceo's biography, history of the wars for independence coll 07179

Museo de la Piratería, Castillo del Morro, Santiago de Cuba
Local Museum / Historic Site
History of piracy in the Caribbean, coll of weapons 07180

Museo del Ambiente Histórico Cubano, Calle Felix Pena 612, Santiago de Cuba
Local Museum
Furniture, china, crystal and decorative elements coll 07181

Museo Histórico 26 de Julio, 26th of July School City, Santiago de Cuba
Historic Site
Historical panorama of the revolution 07182

Museo La Isabelica, Carretera de La Gran Piedra, km 14, Santiago de Cuba
Local Museum / Archaeological Museum
History of the French ssettlements, objects, furniture and farming implements coll 07183

Museo Municipal Emilio Bacardí Moreau, Calle Pio Rosado y Aguilera, Santiago de Cuba - T: (0226) 8402. Head: José A. Arocha Rovira
Fine Arts Museum / Archaeological Museum / Natural History Museum - 1899
Art, archaeology, natural and local history 07184

Siboney Farm, Carretera de Siboney, km 13,5, Santiago de Cuba
Historic Site
Documents, objects and belongings of revolutionaries 07185

Trinidad

Museo Arqueológico Guamuhaya, Calle Simón Bolívar 457, Trinidad
Archaeological Museum
Cuban pre-history from 3,500 BC to the conquest coll 07186

Museo de los Combates contra los Bandidos, Calle del Cristo, esq. a Boca, Trinidad
Local Museum
Documents, objects and weapons coll 07187

Museo Municipal de Trinidad, Calle Simón Bolívar 423, Trinidad
Local Museum
Works of art, archaeology, natural science coll, local history coll 07188

Museo Romántico, Calle Fernando Hernández Echemendía 52, Trinidad
Local Museum
Jewelry, furniture, china, silverware, sculptures coll 07189

Cyprus

Aghia Napa

Museum of Marine Life of Cyprus → Tornaritis-Pierides Municipal Museum of Marine Life

Tornaritis-Pierides Municipal Museum of Marine Life, 5330 Aghia Napa - T: (23) 723409, Fax: 722607. Head: Antonia Kallicas
Natural History Museum - 1992
Marine life, fossils, ammonites, paleontological finds, birds, turtles, fish, shells - aquarium 07190

Episkopi

Kourion Museum, Episkopi
Archaeological Museum
Archaeological finds 07191

Koukila

Temple of Aphrodite, Palaepaphos, Koukila
Archaeological Museum 07192

Kouklia

Palaepaphos Museum, Kouklia - T: (26) 432180
Museum of Classical Antiquities 07193

Larnaka

Larnaca District Archaeological Museum, Kalogera Sq, Larnaka - T: (24) 630169
Archaeological Museum 07194

Larnaca District Museum, M. Parides Sq, Larnaka, mail addr: POB 534, Larnaka - T: (24) 630169, Fax: 304578. Head: Dr. Sophocles Hadjisavvas
Archaeological Museum - 1969 07195

Pierides Museum, Popular Bank's Cultural Centre, Zenon Kitiefs 4, 6300 Larnaka, mail addr: POB 40025, 6300 Larnaka - T: (24) 652495, Fax: 657227. Head: Yannis A. Toumazis
Archaeological Museum - 1839
Archaeological finds from all periods of Cypriot history, from Neolithic to Roman and Byzantine, Minoan and Mycenaean coll, Roman glass, cartography, folk art - library 07196

Limassol

Cyprus Medieval Museum, Limassol Castle, Limassol - T: (25) 330419. Head: Dr. Sophocles Hadjisavvas
Historical Museum / Archaeological Museum - 1987
Local and imported pottery from the Early Christian, Byzantine and medieval periods, medieval tombstones 07197

Folk Art Museum, Saint Andrew St 253, Limassol - T: (25) 63103, 62303
Folklore Museum
National costumes, tapestry, embroidery 07198

Limassol District Museum, Lord Byron St, 3401 Limassol - T: (25) 305157, Fax: 305173. Head: Dr. Sophocles Hadjisavvas
Archaeological Museum - 1974
Pottery, glass, bronze, jewelry, sculpture from Limassol district 07199

Nikos Nikolaides Theatrical Archives, Aghiou Andrea 253, Limassol - T: (25) 463028
Performing Arts Museum - 1992
Theatre manuscripts, photos, costumes, posters and literature 07200

Nicosia

Byzantine Museum and Art Galleries, Archbishop Kyprianos Sq, Nicosia 1016, mail addr: POB 21269, Nicosia 1505 - T: (229 430008, Fax: 430667, E-mail: makarios@logos.cy.net
Religious Arts Museum - 1978
Byzantine icons, frescoes,sacred vestments, consecrated vessels, European paintings 15th - 19th c, engravings, maps, Greek and Cypriot Contemporary art 07201

Cyprus Folk Art Museum, Archbishop Kyprianos Sq, Nicosia, mail addr: POB 1436, Nicosia - T: (22) 463205. Head: Dr. Eleni Papademetriou
Folklore Museum - 1950
Cypriot arts and crafts from early to recent times, ecclesiastical items, Cypriot folk art 07202

Cyprus Historical Museum, Pentelis 50, Strovolos, Nicosia. Head: Petros Stylianou
Historical Museum - 1975
library 07203

Cyprus Jewellers Museum, 7-9 Praxippou, Laiki Yatonia, Nicosia
Decorative Arts Museum
Display of the jewellery tradition from the end of 19th c to 20th c, incl ornaments, religious items, silver utensils and old tool 07204

Cyprus Museum, Museum Av, Nicosia, mail addr: POB 22024, Nicosia 1516 - T: (22) 865801, Fax: 303148, E-mail: roctarah@cytanet.com.cy. Head: Dr. Sophacles Hadjisavvas
Museum of Classical Antiquities / Archaeological Museum - 1882
Pottery from the Neolithic and Chalcolithic periods to the Roman age, terra cotta figures, limestone and marble sculpture, Bronze Age jewelry, Mycenaean finds, coins, inscriptions, glass 07205

Cyprus National Struggle Museum, Archbishop Kyprianos Sq, Nicosia - T: (22) 302465
Historical Museum - 1963 07206

Cyprus Olympic Committee Museum, 19 Nikitaras St, Nicosia
Special Museum 07207

House of Hadjigeorgakis Kornesios, POB 2024, Nicosia - T: (22) 302191, Fax: 303148. Head: Dr. Sophocles Hadjisavvas
Historical Museum 07208

Leventis Municipal Museum of Nicosia, 17 Hippocrates St, Nicosia, mail addr: POB 21015, 1500 Nicosia - T: (22) 661475, Fax: 662285, E-mail: lemuseum@spidernet.com.cy. Head: Loukia Loizou Hadjigavriel
Historical Museum - 1989
First historical museum of Cyprus, exhibits from 3000 BC until today, hist of Nicosia, the last divided capital in Europe, Greek-Roman, medieval, Renaissance, Ottoman and British Empire art and antiquities, colonial hist - educational dept 07209

Museum of the History of Cypriot Coinage, Bank of Cyprus Head Office, 51 Stassinos St, Ayia Paraskevi, 2002 Nicosia - T: (22) 677134, Fax: 662898, E-mail: info@cultural.bankofcyprus.com, Internet: http://www.bankofcyprus.com. Head: Michaelidou Lefki
Historical Museum
2600 years of the hist of Cyprus, local coinage from the classical City-Kingdoms via the Hellenistic, Roman, Byzantine, Frankish and Venetian periods to the times of Ottoman occupation, British colonialism and independence 07210

Nicosia Municipal Arts Centre, 19 Apostolou St, Nicosia - T: (22) 432577
Fine Arts Museum - 1993 07211

State Gallery of Contemporary Cypriot Art, Cnr Stassinou Av and Kritis St 1, Nicosia - T: (22) 22304947/992. Head: Elena S. Nikita
Fine Arts Museum - 1990
Paintings and sculptures by Cypriot artists (1910-1990) - library 07212

Paphos

Byzantine Museum, In the Premises of the Bichopric, Paphos
Fine Arts Museum
Icons 07213

Ethnographical Museum, 1 Exo Vrisy, Paphos - T: (26) 232010
Ethnology Museum 07214

Paphos District Archaeological Museum, Grivas-Dighenis Av, Paphos - T: (26) 240215, Fax: 306297, E-mail: nicolas5@cytanet.com.cy. Head: Dr. Eustathios Raptou
Museum of Classical Antiquities
Cypriot antiquities 07215

Yeroskipos

Folk Art Museum, Yeroskipos - T: (26) 240216,
Fax: (22) 303148. Head: Dr. Demos Christou
Folklore Museum - 1978
Folk art, household utensils and agricultural
implements (19th-20th c)　　　　　　07216

Cyprus, Turkish Republic

Famagusta → Gazimagusa

Gazimagusa

Gazimagusa Municipal Art Gallery, 16th June St,
Gazimagusa, via Mersin 10, Turkey - T: (0090-392)
62345. Head: G. Pierides
Public Gallery　　　　　　　　　　07217

Icon Museum, Agios Ioannis Church, Gazimagusa, via
Mersin 10, Turkey
Fine Arts Museum　　　　　　　　07218

Namik Kemal Dungeon Museum, Venetian Palace,
Gazimagusa, via Mersin 10, Turkey
Special Museum
Life and work of the poet Namik Kemal and his time
after criticising the Sultan　　　　　07219

Girne

Decorative Arts Museum, Pasabahce Av, Girne, via
Mersin 10, Turkey - T: (0090-392) 8152142
Decorative Arts Museum　　　　　07220

Folk Art Museum, Back St behind the Harbour, Girne,
via Mersin 10, Turkey - T: (0090-392) 8152143
Folklore Museum　　　　　　　　07221

Icon Museum, Girne, via Mersin 10, Turkey
Fine Arts Museum　　　　　　　　07222

Shipwreck Museum, Girne, via Mersin 10, Turkey
Science&Tech Museum　　　　　　07223

Güzelyurt

Archaeological and Natural Science Museum,
Güzelyurt, via Mersin 10, Turkey
Archaeological Museum / Natural History Museum -
1979　　　　　　　　　　　　07224

Icon Museum, Saint Mamas Church, Güzelyurt, via
Mersin 10, Turkey
Fine Arts Museum　　　　　　　　07225

Kyrenia → Girne

Lefkoşa

Ethnographical Museum, Dervish Pasha Mansion,
Lefkoşa, via Mersin 10, Turkey
Ethnology Museum　　　　　　　07226

Lapidari Museum, nr Selimiye Mosque, Lefkoşa, via
Mersin 10, Turkey
Archaeological Museum　　　　　07227

Mevlevi Tekke Museum, nr Girna Gate, Atatürk Sq,
Lefkoşa, via Mersin 10, Turkey
Ethnology Museum
Costumes, dresses, cooking utensils, musical
instruments, manuscripts　　　　　07228

Museum of Barbarism, Kumsal District, Lefkoşa, via
Mersin 10, Turkey
Historical Museum
House of Dr. Nihat Ilhan　　　　　07229

Morphou → Güzelyurt

Nicosia → Lefkoşa

Czech Republic

Adamov

Stará Huť v Josefovském Údolí, 679 04 Adamov -
T: (0506) 446671
Science&Tech Museum　　　　　　07230

Aš

Městské Muzeum, Mikulášská 3, 352 01 Aš -
T: (0166) 925195. Head: Josef Borsig
Local Museum - 1892
Art, crafts, porcelain, textiles, mineralogy,
ornithology, Oriental arms, exhibits illustrating the
anti-Fashist struggle in World War II　　07231

Bechyně

Muzeum Keramiky (Ceramics Museum), nám T.G.
Masaryka 140, 391 65 Bechyně
Decorative Arts Museum - 1911
Ceramics, folk art, local history, archeology　07232

Bělá pod Bezdězem

Vlastivědné Muzeum, zámek 1, 294 21 Bělá pod
Bezdězem
Local Museum - 1906
Local geology, ethnography, social and cultural
history of the region　　　　　　07233

Benátky nad Jizerou

Okresní Muzeum, Přírodovědecké odd., Zámek 1,
294 71 Benátky nad Jizerou - T: (0326) 916102,
916682, Fax: 916389. Head: Jana VerberováStifter
Local Museum - 1937
Paleontology, botany, ornithology, archeology,
ethnography, local history, coll illustrating the life
and work of the composer Bedřich Smetana (1824-
1884), astronomer Tycho Brahe (1546-1601),
General Johann von Werth (1590-1652), composer
Georg Benda (1722-1795), and Franz Benda (1709-
1786)　　　　　　　　　　　　07234

Benešov

Muzeum Umění, Malé nám 1, 256 01 Benešov -
T: (0301) 24601
Local Museum　　　　　　　　　07235

Beroun

Muzeum Českého Krasu v Berouně (Museum of
Bohemian Karst in Beroun), Husovo nám 87-88, 266
01 Beroun 1 - T: (0311) 621084, 621462, 624101,
E-mail: petr.kminek@c-box.cz, Internet: http://
www.muzeum.ceskykras.cz. Head: Petr Kmínek
Local Museum - 1892
Palaeontology, mineralogy, archeology, local hist,
ethnography, memorabilia of the conductor Václav
Talich (1883-1961) and the painter Jan Preisler
(1872-1918)　　　　　　　　　　07236

Bílá Třemešná

Památník Jana Ámoše Komenského (Memorial of
Jan Amos Comenius), 544 72 Bílá Třemešná -
T: (0437) 68210
Special Museum - 1958
Life and work of the pedagogue, philosopher and
theologist Jan Ámos Komenský (J.A. Comenius,
1592-1670), during his stay in Bílá Třemešná (1626-
1628) on the estate of Jiří Sádovský of Sloupno -
library　　　　　　　　　　　　07237

Bilovec

Městské Muzeum, Zámecká ul 5, 743 01 Bilovec -
T: (0655) 2417
Local Museum - 1905
Local history, archeology, ethnography　07238

Blansko

Galerie Města Blanska, Dvorská 2, 678 01 Blansko -
T: (0506) 415781, Fax: 415781, E-mail: zpravodaj@
blansko.cz, Internet: http://www.blansko.cz. Head:
Ivana Mašátová
Fine Arts Museum　　　　　　　07239

Muzeum Blansko, Zámek 1, 678 01 Blansko -
T: (0506) 417221, Fax: 418780, E-mail: muzeum@
bk.cz, Internet: http://www.muzeum.bk.cz. Head:
Eva Nečasová
Local Museum - 1959
Local history, industrial history, archeology, iron
casts - library, archive　　　　　　07240

Blovice

Okresní Muzeum, Hradištská 148, 336 01 Blovice -
T: (0185) 2208
Local Museum - 1953
Archeology, history, ethnography, literature　07241

Boskovice

Muzeum Boskovicka (Regional Museum of
Boskovice), Hradní ul 1, 680 01 Boskovice -
T: (0501) 452077, 452090, 454601, Fax: 452077,
E-mail: muzeum@boskovice.cz, Internet: http://
www.boskovice.kultura.cz
Local Museum - 1905
Archeology, local hist, (hist of Boskovice and its
region, Jewish city in Boskovice), ethnology,
weapons, agriculture　　　　　　07242

Bouzov

Státní hrad Bouzov (Bouzov castle), 783 25 Bouzov -
T: (068) 5446201, Fax: 5446202. Head: R. Váňa
Decorative Arts Museum / Fine Arts Museum - 1912
Interiors in neo-Gothic style, paintings,
handicrafts　　　　　　　　　　07243

Brandýs nad Labem

Okresní Muzeum Praha-východ (District Museum
Prague-East), Masarykovo nám 97, 250 01 Brandýs
nad Labem - T: (0202) 802688. Head: Dr. Ivan
Krutina
Local Museum - 1911
Regional natural hist, prehist, medieval archeology,
ethnography, fine and decorative arts　07244

Památník Františka Ondříčka a Českého kvarteta,
Kpt. Jaroše 734, 250 01 Brandýs nad Labem. Head:
Vilém Černík
Music Museum - 1962
Memorial to the violinist František Ondříček and
Czech quartet in Brandýs n.L.　　　07245

Zámek Brandýs, 250 01 Brandýs nad Labem -
T: (0202) 804629
Fine Arts Museum　　　　　　　07246

Brandýs nad Orlicí

Pamětní Síň Jana Ámoše Komenského, Náměstí
203, 561 12 Brandýs nad Orlicí - T: (0465) 544211
Special Museum - 1957
Memorabilia of the pedagogue, philosopher and
theologist Jan Amos Komenský (J.A. Comenius,
1592-1670)　　　　　　　　　　07247

Břeclav

Archeologické Muzeum, Pohansko zámeček, 690 00
Břeclav - T: (0627) 374248, Fax: 322878,
E-mail: bvmuz@bvnet.cz. Head: Dr. Evženie
Klanicová
Local Museum - 1998
Regional folklore, history, archeology, excavation of
one of the most important slavic sattlements in
central Europe　　　　　　　　07248

Městské Muzeum a Galerie (Municipal Museum and
Gallery Breclav), U Tržiště 10, 690 01 Břeclav -
T: (0627) 371488, Fax: 322878, E-mail: bvmuz@
bvnet.cz, Internet: http://www.breclav-city.cz. Head:
Dr. Evženie Klanicová
Local Museum
Jewish Synagogue　　　　　　　07249

Březnice

Galerie Ludvíka Kuby, Zámek, 262 72 Březnice -
T: (0306) 982179, Fax: 982179
Historical Museum / Fine Arts Museum - 1897
Archeology, local history, ethnography, paintings by
Ludvík Kuba　　　　　　　　　07250

Brno

Biskupský Dvůr, Moravské Zemské Museum,
Muzejní 2, 602 00 Brno - T: (05) 42321205 kl 282,
Internet: http://www.mzm.cz/mzm
Natural History Museum
Moravian fauna　　　　　　　　07251

Blindness Museum → Technické Muzeum v Brně

Design Centrum České Republiky, Jakubské mám
5, 601 00 Brno - T: (05) 42211423
Decorative Arts Museum　　　　　07252

Dům Umění Města Brna, Malinovského nám 2, 601
00 Brno - T: (05) 42211662
Public Gallery　　　　　　　　　07253

Etnografický Ústav, Moravské Zemské Museum
(Ethnographical Institute of the Moravian Museum),
Kobližná 1, 659 37 Brno - T: (05) 42211161,
Fax: 42212792, E-mail: hdvorakova@mzm.cz,
Internet: http://www.mzm.cz. Head: Dr. Hana
Dvořáková
Ethnology Museum - 1961
Costumes and textiles, ceramic, folk art, toys, films,
photographs, graphics, agricultural and craft
implements, contemporary craft ritual
objects　　　　　　　　　　　07254

Janáčkovo Muzeum, Moravské zemské museum
(Janaček Museum), Smetanova 14, 602 00 Brno -
T: (05) 41212811, 41249084, Fax: 42212792,
E-mail: fmaly@mzm.cz. Head: Dr. František Malý
Music Museum - 1919
Music, musicology, musical instruments,
manuscripts, memorabilia of the composer Leoš
Janáček (1854-1928)　　　　　　07255

Mendelianum - Památník Gregora Mendela,
Moravské Zemské Museum (Gregor Mendel
Memorial), Údolní 39, 602 00 Brno - T: (05)
42216216, Fax: 42212792, E-mail: genetika@
mzm.cz, Internet: http://www.mzm.cz/mendel.htm.
Head: Jiří Sekerák
Natural History Museum - 1965
Memorabilia of the geneticist Gregor Mendel (1822-
1884), botany, genetics, evolution,
informatics　　　　　　　　　　07256

Měnínská Brána, Muzeum města Brna, Měnínská 7,
662 00 Brno - T: (05) 42214946, Fax 42211584,
E-mail: muzeum.brno@spilberk.cz, Internet: http://
www.spilberk.cz. Head: Dr. Jiří Vanek
Archaeological Museum
History of local theatre, archeological coll　07257

Moravská Galerie Brno (Moravian Gallery Brno),
Pražákův Palác, Husova 18, 662 26 Brno - T: (05)
32169111, Fax: 42215758, E-mail: m-gal@
moravska-galerie.cz, Internet: http://moravska-
galerie.cz. Head: Dr. Kaliopi Chamonikola
Fine Arts Museum / Decorative Arts Museum
European and Czech visual and applied art 20th
century, arts and crafts - library　　07258

Moravská Galerie Brno Místodrzitelsky Palác

Moravská Galerie Brno Místodrzitelsky Palác
(Moravian Gallery), Místodrzitelsky Palác, Moravské
nám. 1a, 662 26 Brno - T: (05) 42321100,
Fax: 42215758, E-mail: m-gal@moravska-
galerie.cz, Internet: http://www.moravska-
galerie.cz. Head: Dr. Kaliopi Chamonikola
Fine Arts Museum / Decorative Arts Museum /
Public Gallery　　　　　　　　07259

Moravské Zemské Muzeum (Moravian Museum),
Dietrichsteinský palác, Zelný trh 6-8, 659 37 Brno -
T: (05) 42321205, Fax: 42212792, E-mail: mzm@
mzm.cz, Internet: http://www.mzm.cz. Head: Dr.
Petr Šuleř
Natural History Museum / Archaeological Museum /
Historical Museum - 1817
Janáček archive, Gregor Mendel coll, mineralogy,
geology, anthropology, entomology, zoology, botany,
history, archaeology, ethnography, hist of theatre,
musicology, hist of literature, numismatics - puppet
theatre, library, documentation department　07260

Muzeum Města Brna (Brno Municipal Museum),
Spilberk Castle, 662 24 Brno - T: (05) 42214145,
Fax: 42211584, E-mail: muzeum.brno@spilberk.cz,
Internet: http://www.spilberk.cz. Head: Dr. Jiří
Vaněk
Local Museum - 1904
Archeology, applied arts, fine arts, local history,
history of the Italian, Hungarian and Polish
revolutionary prisoners in the Špilberk fortress,
resistance movement in World War II　07261

Obec Architektů, Starobrněská 16-18, 601 00 Brno
Fine Arts Museum　　　　　　　07262

Technické Muzeum v Brně (Brno Museum of
Technology), Purkyňova 99, 612 00 Brno - T: (05)
41214410, Fax: 41214418, E-mail: info@
technicalmuseum.cz, Internet: http://
www.technicalmuseum.cz. Head: Vlastimil Vykydal
Science&Tech Museum - 1953
Metallurgy, energy, mechanical engieering,
precission mechanics, handicraft, industrial
heritage, Computers, optics, windmill, watermill,
ironworks - library, documentation dept,
laboratories, workshops dep of blindness　07263

U Zlaté Koruny, Muzeum města Brna, Radnická 5,
662 00 Brno - T: (05) 42214145
Historical Museum
Medical history　　　　　　　　07264

Vila Tugendhat, Muzeum města Brna, Černopolní 45,
613 00 Brno - T: (05) 45212118, Fax: 45212118,
E-mail: muzeum.brno@spilberk.cz, Internet: http://
www.tugendhat-villa.cz. Head: Dr. Jiří Vaněk
Fine Arts Museum
Modern architecture, Ludwig Mies Van der
Rohe　　　　　　　　　　　　07265

Broumov

Vlastivědné Muzeum, Muzeum Broumovska, Klášter,
550 01 Broumov
Local Museum - 1945
History and natural history of the region,
ethnography　　　　　　　　　07266

Brtnice

Expozice Josef Hoffmann, Nám Svobody, 588 32
Brtnice - T: (066) 7216128
Fine Arts Museum　　　　　　　07267

Bruntál

Muzeum v Bruntále (Museum in Bruntal), Zámecké
nám 7, 792 01 Bruntál - T: (0646) 717947/49,
Fax: 718558, E-mail: muzeumbruntal@iol.cz,
Internet: http://www.bruntal-zamek.cz. Head: Hana
Garncarzová
Local Museum - 1907
Natural hist and hist of the region　07268

Bučovice

Muzeum Bučovice, Muzeum Vyškovska (Regional
Museum), zámek 1, 685 01 Bučovice - T: (0507)
383190. Head: Jiří Setinský
Local Museum - 1914
Local archeology, history, ethnography,
numismatics　　　　　　　　　07269

Budyně nad Ohří

Městské Muzeum, Zámek, 411 18 Budyně nad Ohří
Local Museum - 1945
Paleontology, archeology, art, handicrafts,
ethnography　　　　　　　　　07270

Bystřice nad Pernštejnem

Městské Muzeum, nám T. G. Masaryka 1, 593 01
Bystřice nad Pernštejnem - T: (0505) 2180,
Fax: 2254
Local Museum - 1955
Local natural history and history in general,
handicrafts, ethnography, archeology　07271

Bzenec

Muzeum, nám 75, 696 81 Bzenec
Local Museum
Local history　　　　　　　　　07272

Čáslav

Městské Muzeum, Husova 291, 286 01 Čáslav - T: (0322) 312207, Fax: 312207, E-mail: muzeumc@pvtnet.cz, Internet: http://www.acein.cz. Head: Soňa Dedíková
Local Museum - 1864/1884
Geology, mineralogy, zoology, botany, archeology, numismatics, ethnography, art, handicrafts, literary archives of the writer Jiří Mahen 07273

Čáslavice

Památník Bedřicha Václavka, 675 24 Čáslavice
Special Museum - 1942
Memorabilia of the literary historian Bedřich Václavek in his former home 07274

Čechy pod Košířem

Památník Josefa Mánesa (Memorial House of Josef Mánes), Zámek, 798 58 Čechy pod Košířem
Special Museum
Memorabilia of the painter Josef Mánes (1820-1871) 07275

Čejkovice

Muzeum T.G. Masaryk's House, Templárská, 696 15 Čejkovice - T: (0628) 362602, Fax: 362704, E-mail: OU@cejkovice.cz, Internet: http://www.cejkovice.cz
Special Museum
Childhood house of T.G. Masaryk, documents of his live 07276

Čelákovice

Městské Muzeum, Na Hrádku 464, 250 88 Čelákovice - T: (0202) 891556, 891192, Fax: 891192. Head: Jaroslav Spaček
Local Museum - 1903
Local archeology, history, natural history of the Polabí region, basketry 07277

Červený Kostelec

Památník Boženy Němcové (Memorial House of Božena Němcová), ul Boženy Němcové 127, 549 41 Červený Kostelec
Special Museum
Memorabilia of the writer Božena Němcová (1820-1862) 07278

Česká Lípa

Okresní Vlastivědné Muzeum a Galerie (Regional Museum and Gallery), nám Osvobození 297, 470 34 Česká Lípa - T: (0425) 824145, 823843, Fax: 824146, E-mail: ovmcl@clnet.cz, Internet: http://www.muzeum.clnet.cz. Head: Zdeněk Vitáček
Local Museum - 1900
Geology, mineralogy, paleontology, zoology, archeology, ethnography, numismatics, applied art, fine art, old prints, history of labour movement, military, history of Bohemian glass, botany - library, photo lab, conservation lab 07279

Česká Skalice

Muzeum Boženy Němcové (Museum of Božena Němcová), Maloskalická 47, 552 03 Česká Skalice - T: (0441) 451285, Fax: 452933, E-mail: muzeumbn@atlas.cz, Internet: http://www.bozenanemcova.cz. Head: Milan Horký
Special Museum - 1931
Memorabilia of the writer Božena Němcová (1820-1862), porcelain, textiles, ethnography, history, painting 07280

Textilní Muzeum TIBA (Textile Museum of TIBA), Maloskalická 123, 552 03 Česká Skalice - T: (0441) 452933, Fax: 452933, E-mail: textilmuz@atlas.cz, Internet: http://freeweb.bohemia.net/mbn-tm
Science&Tech Museum - 1936
Summary of development of textile pinting (blueprinting, calico-printing, screenprinting), Czech textile designers, coptic textiles 07281

Česká Třebová

Městské Muzeum, Klácelova 11, 560 02 Česká Třebová - T: (0465) 534516, E-mail: muzeum.ct@worldonline.cz. Head: Jiří Pištora
Local Museum - 1888
Folk art, local history, guild relics, development of railway transportation, hist of Esperanto in the Czech Republic 07282

České Budějovice

Dům Umění, Nám Přemysla Otakara II. č 38, 370 01 České Budějovice - T: (038) 636539
Public Gallery 07283

Jihočeské Muzeum v Českých Budějovicích (South-Bohemian Museum in České Budějovice), Dukelská 1, 370 51 České Budějovice - T: (038) 7311528, Fax: 56447, E-mail: muzeumcb@muzeumcb.cz, Internet: http://www.muzeumcb.cz. Head: Pavel Šafr
Local Museum - 1877
Natural sciences, archeology, theatre and music, local history, ethnography, numismatics, regional literature, manuscripts, prints 07284

Český Brod

Podlipanské Museum, Regionální Kolín, ul 5. Května 761, 282 01 Český Brod - T: (0203) 42321, 22988. Head: Zbyněk Sedláček
Local Museum - 1896
Local archeology, ethnography, history of the town 07285

Český Dub

Podještědské Muzeum Karoliny Světlé, PMKS 32, 463 43 Český Dub
Local Museum - 1919
Local ethnography, archeology, geology and mineralogy, literary history and memorabilia of the writer Karolina Světlá; P. Dillinger; Czech painting of 20th cent. 07286

Český Krumlov

Egon Schiele Art Centrum, Široka 70-72, 381 01 Český Krumlov - T: (0337) 70401114, Fax: 711191, E-mail: schiele.art.centrum@ck.ipex.cz, Internet: http://www.schieleartcentrum.org. Head: Gerwald Sonnberger, Hana Jirmusová
Fine Arts Museum - 1993
Egon Schiele, Vienna at the turn of the c 07287

Okresní Vlastivědné Muzeum, Horní ul 152, 381 01 Český Krumlov
Local Museum - 1946
Natural history, archeology, local history, ethnography, Gothic and Renaissance sculpture 07288

Český Těšín

Muzeum Těšínska, Hlavní třída 13, 737 27 Český Těšín - T: (0659) 761211, Fax: 761223, E-mail: muzeum@muzeumct.cz, Internet: http://www.muzeumct.cz. Head: Jaroslav Keller
Local Museum - 1948
Local hist, ethnography, botany, geology coll of folk costume, silver jewels - Library, exhibition halls in Havířov, Orlová and Karviná, Technology Museum, Kotula's Timber House, Monument of the Tragedy of Životice 07289

Výstavní síň Muzea Těšínska, Muzeum Těšínska (Exhibition Hall), Hlavní 3, 737 01 Český Těšín - T: (0659) 711087, Fax: 761223, E-mail: muzeum@muzeumct.cz, Internet: http://www.muzeumct.cz. Head: Jana Byrtusová
Historical Museum / Ethnology Museum - 2001
Exhibitions of the hist of Těšín area, folk culture, archeology of of the Slavic castle Chotěbuz-Podobora 07290

Cheb

Chebské Museum (Cheb Museum), nám Krále Jiřího z Podebrad 3, 350 11 Cheb - T: (0166) 4223867, 422246, Fax: 422292, E-mail: muzeumch@ch.cesnet.cz. Head: Dr. Eva Dittertová
Local Museum - 1874
Archeology, ethnography, natural sciences, history, memorabilia of Albrecht Valdsten (Albrecht von Wallenstein, Duke of Friedland, 1583-1634), Wallenstein portrait gallery - library 07291

Státní Galerie Výtvarného Umění (State Gallery of Fine Arts), nám krále Jiřího z Poděbrad 16, 350 46 Cheb - T: (0166) 422450, Fax: 22163. Head: Dr. Jiří Vykoukal
Fine Arts Museum - 1961
Czech Gothic sculpture from 14th to 16th c, 16th-17th c Cheb relief intarsia, contemporary Czech art 07292

Chlumec nad Cidlinou

Kinski Castle, Zámek Karlova Koruna, 503 51 Chlumec nad Cidlinou - T: (0448) 926119. Head: Martiner Lubomir
Decorative Arts Museum / Historical Museum - 1992
Interior, hist of Kinsky family, portraits, furniture, glass, library 07293

Chlumec u Ústi nad Labem

Památník Bitvy 1813, 403 39 Chlumec u Ústi nad Labem - T: 91385
Historical Museum - 1913
Mementoes of the Battle of Ústí nad Labem (Aussig) in 1813, historical documents 07294

Ústecká Bus Historické Muzeum (Historical Transport Museum), Ústecká ul 130, 403 39 Chlumec u Ústi nad Labem - T: (047) 5102307, Fax: 5101078, E-mail: info@prirodnisvet.cz. Head: David Griffiths
Special Museum
Omnibusses, trucks, trolleybusses, tramcars 07295

Choceň

Orlické Muzeum, Pardubická 1, Zámek, 565 00 Choceň - T: (0468) 972624. Head: Dr. Zdeňek Staffen
Local Museum - 1909
Ornithology, paleontology, archeology, ethnography, history of the Resistance Movement 1939-1945 07296

Chomutov

Okresní Muzeum (Regional Museum), nám 1. Máje 1, 430 00 Chomutov - T: (0396) 651570. Head: Dr. Antonín Kallista
Local Museum - 1923
Geology, mineralogy, flowers, archeology, production of lace and trimmings, 15th-20th c art - archive, library, conservation workroom 07297

Chotěboř

Městské Muzeum (Municipal museum), Riegrova 1, Zámek, 583 01 Chotěboř - T: (0453) 3293. Head: Miloslav Janků
Local Museum - 1885
Geology, mineralogy, local hist, applied art, paintings, graphics by Jindřich Prucha, Zdeněk Rykr, sculpture by Karel Opatrný - library 07298

První České Muzeum Velocipédu (Czech Private Bicycle Museum), Riegrova 401, 583 01 Chotěboř - T: (0453) 3220
Science&Tech Museum 07299

Chrast u Chrudimě

Městské Muzeum, Zámek, Náměstí 1, 538 51 Chrast u Chrudimě - T: (0455) 667194
Local Museum - 1893
Geology, local history, handicrafts, paintings 07300

Chrastava

Městské Muzeum, 463 31 Chrastava
Local Museum 07301

Chropyně

Památnik Dr. Emila Axmana, nám 30, Zámek, 768 11 Chropyně - T: (0634) 355074, Fax: 343297, E-mail: muzeum@muzeum-km.cz, Internet: http://www.muzeum-km.cz. Head: Jiří Stránsky
Music Museum - 1960
Memorabilia of the composer Dr. Emil Axman and the painter Emil Filla, local history and ethnography 07302

Chrudim

Muzeum Loutkářských Kultur (Museum of Puppetry), Břetislavova 74, 537 60 Chrudim - T: (0455) 620310, Fax: 620650, E-mail: puppets@cps.cz, Internet: http://www.puppets.cz. Head: Alena Exnarová
Special Museum - 1972
Hist of puppets and puppetry 07303

Okresní Muzeum (District Museum), Široká ul 86, 537 01 Chrudim - T: (0455) 620434, 620330, Fax: 620330, E-mail: chrudim.muzeum@worldonline.cz. Head: Milena Burdychová
Local Museum - 1865
Mineralogy, zoology, archeology, local hist and ethnography, applied art 07304

Chudenice

Muzeum Josefa Dobrovského a pamětní síň Jaroslava Kvapila, Stary Zámek čp 1, 340 14 Chudenice - T: (0186) 98100, 98245, Fax: 98245
Special Museum - 1948
Memorabilia of the Slavicist Josef Dobrobský (1753-1829) and the writer Jaroslav Kvapil, local hist 07305

Chýnov u Tábora

Bílkův Dům v Chýnově, Galerie Hlavního Města Prahy, Údolní 133, 391 55 Chýnov u Tábora - T: (0361) 801230
Fine Arts Museum
Art of the Czech symbolist František Bílek (1872 - 1941) 07306

Dačice

Městské Muzeum, Havlíčkovo nám 85, 270 35 Dačice - T: (0332) 2493
Local Museum - 1893
Local and regional archeology, history, art from the Middle Ages to the 20th c, contemporary Czech painting and graphics 07307

Dašice

Památník Josefa Hybeše, Na Zářečí 2, 271 01 Dašice
Special Museum - 1971
Memorabilia of the politician and workers' leader Josef Hybeš 07308

Děčín

Okresní Muzeum, Tř Československé mládeže 1, 405 02 Děčín - T: (0412) 531549, Fax: 532560, E-mail: muzeum.dc@space.cz. Head: Milan Rosenkranc
Local Museum - 1923
Local history, shipping on the Elbe River, geology, entomology, paintings, sculpture, graphics, art, handicrafts, relicts and history of the German concentration camp at Rabštejn 07309

Diváky

Památník Bratří Mrštíků (Mrštík Brothers Memorial House), 691 71 Diváky - T: 95927. Head: Jaroslav Němeček
Special Museum - 1960
Memorabilia of the Mrštík brothers, 19th c writers, in their former house 07310

Dobřiv

Muzeum Dr. Bohuslava Horáka, Pobočka vodni hamr Dobřiv, 338 44 Dobřiv - T: (0181) 722160, Fax: 723548, E-mail: muzeum@ro.cesnet.cz, Internet: http://www.jonas.ro.cesnet.cz/~romuzeum. Head: Dr. Miroslava Šandová
Science&Tech Museum - 1529/1971
Forge with water-driven hammer (ca. 1702) 07311

Dobruška

Městské Muzeum (Museum of Dobruška), Šubertovo 45, 518 01 Dobruška - T: (0443) 21982. Head: Jiří Mach
Local Museum - 1931
Local and regional history, documents on the period of rebirth of the nationalist movement in the 19th c, pictures of František Kupka 07312

Doksy

Památnik Karla Hynka Máchy, c/o Okresní vlastivědné muzeum, Valdšstejnské nám 150, 472 01 Doksy - T: (0425) 872137. Head: Zdeněk Vitáček
Special Museum - 1960
Memorabilia of the poet Karel Hynek Mácha (1810-1836) 07313

Dolní Domaslavice

Památnik, Škola, 739 38 Dolní Domaslavice
Ethnology Museum
Handicrafts, folk furniture, costumes, local history 07314

Domažlice

Muzeum Chodska (Museum of Chodsko), Chodské nám 96, Hrad, 344 00 Domažlice - T: (0189) 776009, 725952, Fax: 720515, E-mail: muzeum.chodska@seznam.cz, Internet: http://www.kultinfo.cz. Head: Josef Nejdl
Local Museum - 1889
Local history, ethnography, regional archeology, 07315

Muzeum Jindřicha Jindřicha (Museum of Jindřich Jindřich), nám Svobody 61, 344 00 Domažlice - T: (0189) 722974, E-mail: kejval@cmail.cz. Head: Josef Haas
Special Museum - 1972
Ethnography, regional painting, literary and musical manuscripts by the musician and ethnography collector Jindřich Jindřich - library, archives 07316

Duchcov

Muzeum G. Casanovy, Zámek, 419 01 Duchcov - T: (0417) 835301
Special Museum 07317

Nábytek jako umění a řemeslo, Uměleckoprůmyslové muzeum Praha (Furniture Collection), Zámek, 419 01 Duchcov - T: (0417) 835301. Head: Dagmar Hejdová
Decorative Arts Museum 07318

Dvůr Králové nad Labem

African Safari and Veteran Car Museum, Štefánikova 1029, pod Zoo, 544 01 Dvůr Králové nad Labem
Special Museum / Science&Tech Museum 07319

Městské a Textilni Muzeum (City Museum and Museum of Textiles), Sladkovského 530, 544 00 Dvůr Králové nad Labem - T: (0437) 623800
Science&Tech Museum / Local Museum - 1936
History of textile manufacturing in Czech lands, laces 07320

Františkovy Lázně

Městské Muzeum, Dr. Pohoreckého 8, 351 01 Františkovy Lázně - T: (0166) 542344, E-mail: muzeum_fl@iol.cz. Head: Stanislav Macek
Local Museum - 1913
Local history concerning the development of the town as a spa, balneology 07321

Frenštát pod Radhoštěm

Městské Muzeum, nám Míru 1, 744 01 Frenštát pod Radhoštěm - T: (0656) 835936
Local Museum - 1951
Local history, folk art, ethnography, weaving 07322

Frýdek-Místek

Muzeum Beskyd Frýdek-Místek (The Museum of the Beskydy), ul Hluboká 66, 738 01 Frýdek-Místek - T: (0658) 621924, Fax: 630452, E-mail: muzeumbeskyd@telecom.cz, Internet: http://web.telecom.cz/muzeumbeskyd.. Head: Zuzana Břízová
Local Museum - 1929

Natural hist, ethnography, folk art, memorabilia of the composer Leoš Janáček, the poet Petr Bezruč and the poet and philosopher Ondra Lysohorsky - library 07323

Frýdlant v Čechách

Státní Hrad a Zámek, Zámek, 464 01 Frýdlant v Čechách - T: (0427) 21382
Local Museum - 1899
Geology, botany, local history, applied arts, documents of the Peasant Revolt of 1679 and 1775 07324

Fulnek

Památník Jana Ámoše Komenského, Vlastivědné Mmuzeum Nový Jičín, Sborová 1, 742 45 Fulnek - T: (0656) 741015
Special Museum - 1954
Memorabilia of the pedagogue, philosopher and theologist Jan Ámos Komenský (Comenius) 07325

Harrachov v Krkonoších

Muzeum Skla (Glass Museum), Sklárna Novosad & Syn, 512 46 Harrachov v Krkonoších - T: (0432) 528141, Fax: 528148. Head: K. Pipek
Decorative Arts Museum - 1972
Blown glass from one of the oldest Czechoslovakian glass works, founded in 1712, modern glass examples 07326

Havířov

Kotulova Dřevěnka, Muzeum Těšínska (Kotula's Timber House), Hálkova 4, 736 01 Havířov - T: (0602) 709731, Fax: 761223, E-mail: muzeum@muzeumct.cz, Internet: http://www.muzeumct.cz. Head: Hana Palzerová
Ethnology Museum / Open Air Museum - 1979
Exposition of folk housing and traditional agriculture 07327

Muzeum Těšínska, Dělnická 14, 735 64 Havířov - T: (069) 6813456
Local Museum 07328

Památník Životické Tragedie, Muzeum Těšínska (Monument of Životice's Tragedy), Padlých hrdinů, 736 01 Havířov - T: (069) 6434138, Fax: 761223, E-mail: muzeum@muzeumct.cz, Internet: http://www.muzeumct.cz. Head: Hana Palzerová
Historical Museum - 1963
Hist of the German occupation and the local resistance movement 07329

Havlíčkův Brod

Galerie Výtvarného Umění (Art Gallery), Malinův dům, Havlíčkov nam 50, 580 01 Havlíčkův Brod - T: (0451) 22035. Head: Zdeněk Pokorný
Fine Arts Museum - 1965
Czech drawings, graphics and illustrations 07330

Památník Karla Havlíčka Borovského, Okresní vlastivědné muzeum Havlíčkův Brod (Memorial Karel Havlíček Borovský), Havlíčkovo nám 19, 580 01 Havlíčkův Brod - T: (0451) 429151, Fax: 429987, E-mail: muzeum@muzeum.hb.net.cz. Head: Dr. Jana Beránková
Special Museum - 1924
Memorabilia on the life and work of the journalist and writer Karel Havlíček Borovský in the house where he lived 07331

Památník Otakara Štáfla, Okresní muzeum (Memorial of Otakar Štáfl), Havlíčkovy sady, bašta, 580 01 Havlíčkův Brod - T: (0451) 24092, Fax: 22683. Head: Dr. Jana Pajskrová
Fine Arts Museum - 1957
Memorabilia of the painter Otakar Štáfl, coll of his paintings 07332

Hlinsko v Čechách

Městské Muzeum a Galerie, Havlíčkova 675, 539 01 Hlinsko v Čechách
Local Museum
Natural history, especially, mineralogy, geology, regional history, ethnography, archeology, art 07333

Hluboká nad Vltavou

Alšova Jihočeská Galerie (Aleš South Bohemian Gallery), Zámek, 373 41 Hluboká nad Vltavou - T: (038) 7967041, Fax: 7965436, E-mail: ajghluboka@volny.cz, Internet: http://www.www.volny.cz/ajghluboka. Head: Dr. Hynek Rulíšek
Fine Arts Museum - 1952
Gothic art of South Bohemia, 16th-18th Czech and European art, 19th-20th c Czech art, modern Czech and world ceramics - department of ceramics, exhibition hall 07334

Lesnické, Myslivecké a Rybářské Muzeum, Národní Zemědělské Muzeum Praha (Museum of Forestry, Hunting and Fisheries), Zámek Ohrada, 373 41 Hluboká nad Vltavou - T: (038) 7965340, Fax: 7965791, E-mail: ohrada@raz-dva.cz. Head: Václav Kasal
Agriculture Museum - 1842
Sallač's coll of the antlers of deer - library 07335

Hodonín

Galerie Výtvarného Umění (Fine Art Gallery), Úprkova 2, 695 00 Hodonín - T: (0628) 21701
Fine Arts Museum - 1907
Modern Czech art, contemporary paintings 07336

Masarykovo Muzeum (Masaryk-Museum), Zámecké nám 9, 695 01 Hodonín - T: (0628) 21834, Fax: 22568. Head: T. Martonová
Local Museum / Historical Museum - 1903
Life of T. G. Masaryk, local history 07337

Hodslavice

Památník Františka Palackého (Memorial House of František Palacký), 742 71 Hodslavice
Special Museum - 1946
Memorabilia of the historian and politician František Palacký (1789-1876) in his former home 07338

Holešov

Městské Muzeum, Okresní muzeum Kroměřížska, nám F.X. Richtera 190, 769 01 Holešov
Local Museum - 1941
Furniture production, local history and ethnography 07339

Holice v Čechách

Památník Dr. Emila Holuba, Holubova ul I/768, 534 01 Holice v Čechách - T: (0456) 520476, 820154, Fax: 520364, E-mail: kd@holice.cz, Internet: http://www.kd.holice.cz. Head: Luděk Kaplan
Special Museum - 1966
Memorabilia of the explorer Dr. Emil Holub, natural history, art and ethnography of Africa 07340

Horažďovice

Městské Muzeum (City Museum), Zámek 11, 341 00 Horažďovice - T: (0187) 512271. Head: Irena Kratochvílová
Local Museum - 1895
Local history, agriculture, archeology, ethnography - library, archives, gallery, concert hall 07341

Hořice v Pokrkonoší

Městské Muzeum a Galerie (City Museum and Gallery), nám Krále Jiřího 160, 508 01 Hořice v Pokrkonoší - T: (0435) 624497, 622961, Fax: 624497, E-mail: mag@ebox.cz. Head: Václav M. Bukač
Fine Arts Museum / Archaeological Museum / Ethnology Museum / Local Museum - 1887
Czech sculptors of the beginning of 20th c, contemporary sculptures, achaeology, ethnography, toy making 07342

Horní Branná

Památník Jana Ámoše Komenského, Zámek, 512 36 Horní Branná - T: 8431. Head: Věra Hyšková
Special Museum
Coll illustrating life and work of the pedagogue, philosopher and theologist Jan Ámos Komenský (Comenius, 1592-1670) 07343

Horní Planá

Rodný Domek Adalberta Stiftera, Okresní muzeum Český Krumlov (Memorial House of Adalbert Stifter), Palackého 21, 382 26 Horní Planá - T: (0337) 97473
Special Museum
Memorabilia of the Austrian writer Adalbert Stifter (1805-1868) in his former house 07344

Hořovice

Okresní Muzeum, Zámek 1, 268 01 Hořovice - T: (0316) 512479. Head: Dr. Jana Čapková
Local Museum - 1912
Geology, paleontology, mineralogy, zoology, archeology, ethnography, applied art 07345

Horšovský Týn

Vlastivědné Muzeum, Zámek, nám Republiky 1, 346 01 Horšovský Týn - T: (0188) 425111
Local Museum - 1945
Local history and archeology, numismatics, ethnography, applied art 07346

Hostinné

Muzeum Antického Umění (Museum of Classical Art), Františkánský klášter, 543 71 Hostinné
Museum of Classical Antiquities - 1969
Casts from Greek and Roman sculpture 07347

Muzeum s Historickou Expozicí, nám 1. Máje 69/70, 543 71 Hostinné - T: (0438) 441333, Fax: 942702
Historical Museum 07348

Hrabyně

Památník Národní Svobody, 747 63 Hrabyně - T: (0653) 922309
Historical Museum 07349

Hradec Králové

Krajská Galerie, Galerie moderniho umění (Regional Gallery of Modern Art), Žižkovo nám 130-140, 500 00 Hradec Králové - T: (049) 27078
Fine Arts Museum - 1953
20th c Czech art 07350

Muzeum Východních Čech v Hradci Králové, Oddělení Archeologické, Historické, Přírodovědecké (Museum of Eastern Bohemia in Hradec Kralove), Eliščino nábřeží 465, 500 01 Hradec Králové - T: (049) 5514624, Fax: 5512899, E-mail: info@muzeumhk.cz, Internet: http://www.muzeumhk.cz. Head: Dr. Zdeněk Zahradník
Local Museum - 1879
Regional archeology, history, medieval ceramics, illuminated manuscripts, numismatics, applied art, arms, mineralogy, palaeontology, geology, botany, entomology, zoology - Memorial of the battle 1866 at Chlum 07351

Hradec nad Moravicí

Zámek, Městečko 2, 747 41 Hradec nad Moravicí - T: (0653) 783444, Fax: 783485, E-mail: zamek.hradec@iol.cz. Head: Radomír Přibyla
Historical Museum 07352

Hranice

Muzeum a Galerie, Okresní vlastivědné muzeum Přerov, Zámecká 118, 753 01 Hranice - T: (0642) 201390
Local Museum - 1905
Local natural history and history in general, archeology, ethnography, pottery from the 18th c 07353

Hronov

Muzeum Aloise Jiráska, Jungmannova 277, 549 31 Hronov - T: (0441) 81538. Head: Dr. Jana Weiserová
Special Museum - 1951
Memorabilia of the writer Alois Jirásek and the painter Mikoláš Aleš, local and natural history - library 07354

Hukvaldy

Památník Leoše Janáčka (Memorial House of Leoš Janáček), 739 46 Hukvaldy - T: (065897) 97252. Head: Bohumír Volný
Special Museum
Memorabilia of the composer Leoš Janáček (1854-1928) 07355

Humpolec

Muzeum Dr. Aleše Hrdličky, Horní nám 273, 396 01 Humpolec - T: (0367) 532115
Special Museum - 1895
Memorabilia of the anthropologist Dr. Aleš Hrdlička (1869-1943), Gustav Mahler, local history, textile production, ethnography 07356

Husinec

Památník Mistra Jana Husa (Memorial House of Jan Hus), Husova 36, Rodný domek, 384 21 Husinec
Religious Arts Museum - 1952
Memorabilia of the reformer Jan Hus (1370-1415) in his former home 07357

Ivančice

Okresní Muzeum, Palackého nám 6, 664 91 Ivančice - T: (0502) 921131
Local Museum - 1894
Archeology, local history, ethnography, ceramics 07358

Jabkenice

Památník Bedřicha Smetany (Memorial House of Bedřich Smetana), 294 45 Jabkenice 33 - T: (0326) 989154, 989127. Head: Dr. Olga Mojžíšová
Music Museum - 1937
Memorabilia of the composer Bedřich Smetana (1824-1884) concerning his life here in the years 1876-1884 07359

Jablonec nad Nisou

Muzeum Skla a Bižuterie (Museum of Glass and Jewellry), U Muzea 398/4, 466 00 Jablonec nad Nisou - T: (0428) 710544, Fax: 710035, E-mail: msbjbc@quick.cz, Internet: http://web.quick.cz/msbjbc. Head: Jaroslava Slabá
Decorative Arts Museum - 1900
16th-19th c European, especially Northern Bohemian glass, glass products of all kinds, jewelry, Czech coins and medals (1922 - 1997) - library 07360

Jablonné v Podještědí

Expozice Dominikánský Klášter, Klašterní 33, 471 25 Jablonné v Podještědí - T: (0424) 762105
Religious Arts Museum 07361

Zámek Lemberk, Bredovský zámeček, 471 25 Jablonné v Podještědí - T: (0424) 762305
Local Museum / Natural History Museum 07362

Jablunkov

Výstavní síň Muzeum Těšínska, Muzeum Těšínska (Exhibition Hall), Mariánské nám 14, Těšín, 739 91 Jablunkov - T: (0659) 359533, Fax: 761223, E-mail: muzeum@muzeumct.cz, Internet: http://www.muzeumct.cz. Head: Jiřina Ježowitzová
Historical Museum / Ethnology Museum - 1948
Hist of the Jablunkov town, folk culture of the region 07363

Jáchymov

Muzeum Jáchymovského Hornictví a Lázeňství (Museum of Mining and Balneology in Jáchymov), Hornické nám 37, 362 51 Jáchymov - T: (017) 911379
Historical Museum - 1923
Numismatics, library of the 16th c Latin school at Jáchymov, history of the spa, uranium mining 07364

Jaroměř

Městské Muzeum a Galerie Otakara Spaniela a Josefa Wágnera, Husova tř 259, 551 00 Jaroměř - T: (0442) 812731
Fine Arts Museum - 1883
Archeology, ethnography, numismatics, exhibits on the life and work of the sculptor Otakar Španiel, paintings and sculpture by O. Španiel and Josef Wágner 07365

Jemnice

Západomoravské Muzeum v Třebíči - Muzeum Jemnice (West-Moravian Museum in Třebíč - Museum Jemnice), nám Svobody 75, 675 31 Jemnice - T: (0617) 450767. Head: Jaroslav Martinek
Local Museum - 1928
Local history, history of mining, old crafts, medieval ceramics, cultural history of the town 07366

Jesenice u Rakovnika

Městské Muzeum, Morové nám 15, 270 33 Jesenice u Rakovnika - T: (0313) 599359
Local Museum
Archeology, old crafts, ethnography, natural history 07367

Jeseník

Muzeum Jeseník → Vlastivědné Muzeum Jesenícka

Vlastivědné Muzeum Jesenícka, Zámecké nám 1, 790 00 Jeseník - T: (0645) 401070, Fax: 411748, E-mail: vmjesenik@iol.cz, Internet: http://www.vmjesenik.hyperlink.cz. Head: Petr Košacký
Local Museum - 1901
Geology, mineralogy, local archeology, history of the region and spa, history of mining; biology 07368

Jevišovice

Starý Zámek, 671 53 Jevišovice - T: (0624) 231141
Local Museum 07369

Jičín

Okresní Muzeum a Galerie (Museum and Regional Art Gallery), Valdštejnovo nám 1, 506 01 Jičín - T: (0433) 22204, Fax: 24242. Head: Jaromir Gottlieb
Fine Arts Museum - 1895
Contemporary Czech art, regional art, graphic arts of Josef Váchal and Anna Macková, Kablík's coll of Czech birds 07370

Jihlava

Expozice Mladý Gustav Mahler a Jihlava, Kosmákova 9, 586 01 Jihlava - T: (066) 7309147
Fine Arts Museum 07371

Muzeum Vysočiny (Museum of Highlands), Masarykovo nám 55, 586 01 Jihlava - T: (066) 7309728, 7300838, Fax: 7300828, E-mail: muzeum.vysociny@post.cz. Head: Jitka Hošková
Local Museum - 1892
Botany, mineralogy, zoology, entomology, handicrafts, ceramics, porcelain, glass, numismatic, art, nativity scene - library 07372

Oblastní Galerie Vysočiny I (Regional Art Gallery), Masarykovo nám 24, 586 00 Jihlava - T: (066) 29721
Fine Arts Museum - 1948
Czech artists 19th-20th c 07373

Oblastní Galerie Vysočiny II (Regional Art Gallery), Komenského 10, 586 00 Jihlava - T: (066) 21680
Fine Arts Museum - 1948
Czech modern art 07374

Jilemnice

Krkonošské Muzeum (Museum of Krkonoše Region), Zámek 75, 514 01 Jilemnice - T: (0432) 543041. Head: Jan Luštinec
Folklore Museum / Natural History Museum - 1891
Geology of the region of Krkonoše, old crafts, folk art, history, paintings by František Kaván 07375

Jílové u Prahy

Regionální Muzeum v Jílovém u Prahy (Regional Museum Specialized in Gold), Masarykovo nám 16, 254 01 Jílové u Prahy - T: (02) 41950791, Fax: 41950877, E-mail: regmuz@cbox.cz, Internet: http://www.muzeumjilove.cz. Head: Otakar Vorel
Science&Tech Museum / Special Museum - 1891
Hist and technology of local gold mining, archaeology, local natural hist 07376

Jindřichův Hradec

Okresní Muzeum (District Museum), Balbínovo nám 19, 377 01 Jindřichův Hradec - T: (0331) 363660. Head: Dr. Jan Dolák
Local Museum - 1882
Local hist, memorabilia of E. Destinnová, B. Smetana, ethnography, folk art, Bohemian glass, Gothic and baroque art, Czech art of 19th and 20th c, sharp-shooting targets, archeology, guild materials, book culture, nativity scenes - library 07377

Jirkov

Zámek, Okresní muzeum Chomutov, Červený Hrádek, 431 11 Jirkov - T: (0396) 684560
Historical Museum - 1969
Palace interior, wood-sculptures, historical exhibition on the agreement (1938) on Sudetenland and anti-fascist resistance in World War II 07378

Kačina

Národní Zemědělské Muzeum Praha, Muzeum Českého Venkova (Museum of the Czech Countryside), Zámek Kačina, 285 31 Kačina - T: (0327) 571170, Fax: 571274, E-mail: kacina@kacina.cz, Internet: http://www.kacina.cz. Head: Dr. Pavel Novák
Agriculture Museum / Science&Tech Museum - 1891 07379

Kadaň

Muzeum - Františkánský klaster, Švermova 474, 432 01 Kadaň - T: (0398) 344482, Fax: 342126, E-mail: galerie@mesto.kadan.cz, Internet: http://www.mesto.kadan.cz
Local Museum
Local history, ethnography, geology, archeology, mining in the Kadan region 07380

Kamenice nad Lipou

Vlastivědné Muzeum, Palackého 75, 394 70 Kamenice nad Lipou - T: (0364) 434168. Head: Olga Bělochová
Local Museum - 1940
Mineralogy, zoology, local history, applied art, ethnography, numismatics, memorabilia of the composer Vítězslav Novák 07381

Kamenický Šenov

Sklářské Muzeum (Glass Museum), Osvobození 69, 471 14 Kamenický Šenov - T: (0424) 292206, Fax: 791500. Head: Helena Braunová
Decorative Arts Museum - 1923
Old Bohemian glass, modern glass products, 17th-20th c engravings 07382

Karlovy Vary

Galerie Umění Karlovy Vary (Karlovy Vary Art Gallery), Goethova stezka 6, 360 01 Karlovy Vary - T: (017) 3224387, Fax: 3224388. Head: Miroslav Lepší
Fine Arts Museum - 1953
20th c Czech and Slovak art 07383

Karlovarské Muzeum (Museum of Karlovy Vary), Nová Louka 23, 360 01 Karlovy Vary - T: (017) 26252. Head: Květoslav Kroča
Local Museum - 1870
Natural sciences, art, applied arts, industry, history and documents of the Karlovy Vary Spa 07384

Muzeum Porcelánu Pirkenhammer (Museum of Carlsbad Porcelain), 362 15 Karlovy Vary - T: (017) 26695
Decorative Arts Museum - 1964
History of the porcelain factory at Březová 07385

Muzeum Sklářské Manufactury - Moser, a.s. (Moser Glass Museum), Kpt. Jaroše 19, 360 06 Karlovy Vary 6 - T: (017) 3449455, Fax: 3449619, E-mail: customerservice@moser-glass.com, Internet: http://www.moser-glass.com. Head: Antonin Vlk
Decorative Arts Museum
Hist of Moser glass 07386

Zlaty Klíč Muzeum (Golden Key Museum), Lázeňská 3, 360 01 Karlovy Vary - T: (017) 23888. Head: K. Kroča
Local Museum - 1960
Art nouveau paintings 07387

Karlštejn

Muzeum Betlémů, Hrad, 267 18 Karlštejn - T: (0311) 684385, 684617
Fine Arts Museum / Local Museum 07388

Kašperské Hory

Muzeum Historických Motocyklů, Vimperská 12, 341 92 Kašperské Hory
Science&Tech Museum 07389

Muzeum Šumavy, Náměstí 140, 341 92 Kašperské Hory - T: (0187) 582226. Head: Dr. Vladimír Horpeniak
Local Museum - 1924
Natural history of Šumava region, art glass, coll illustrating the glass industry, paper industry, mining, lumbering, plant and animal coll, mineralogy and geology 07390

Kelč

Památník Bratří Křičků, Vsetín, 756 43 Kelč
Special Museum - 1948
Memorabilia of the writer Petr Křička (1884-1949) and his brother Jaroslav Křička, local archeology, paleontology, numismatics, coll of pipes 07391

Kladno

Muzeum Strojíren Poldi, 272 01 Kladno
Historical Museum 07392

Okresní Muzeum Kladno, Záduśní 1841, 272 80 Kladno - T: (0312) 628045, Internet: http://www.oku-kl.cz. Head: Zdeněk Kuchyňka
Local Museum - 1899
Geology, mineralogy, archeology, etnography, decorative arts, hist of district Kladno 07393

Klášterec nad Ohří

Muzeum Českého Porcelánu (Museum of Czech Porcelain), Zámek, Chomutovska 1, 431 51 Klášterec nad Ohří - T: (0398) 375436
Decorative Arts Museum - 1953
Oriental and European porcelain, documents on the production of Czech porcelain since 1792 07394

Klatovy

Okresní Muzeum v Klatovech, Hostašova 1, 339 01 Klatovy - T: (0186) 313109, Fax: 316011. Head: Luboš Smolík
Local Museum - 1882
Local hist, ethnography, archeology, medicine and pharmacy, cultivation of carnations, history of the labour movement - library, archives 07395

Klenčí pod Čerchovem

Muzeum Jindřicha Simona Baara, nám J. Jindřicha 140, 345 34 Klenčí pod Čerchovem
Special Museum - 1925
Memorabilia of the writer J.Š. Baar, composer Jindřich Jindřich and the physician Prof. Dr. Josef Thomayer, ethnography of the region Chodsko, local history 07396

Klimkovice

Muzeum Klimkovice, Lidická 1, 742 83 Klimkovice
Local Museum 07397

Klobouky u Brna

Městské Muzeum (City Museum), Zámecká 8, 691 72 Klobouky u Brna - T: (0626) 419254, Fax: 419122, E-mail: klobouky.ubrna@kloboucko.cz, Internet: http://www.kloboucko.cz. Head: Jarmila Švachová
Local Museum - 1906
Ethnography, local archeology 07398

Kojetín

Muzeum Marie Gardavské, Husova 64, 752 01 Kojetín
Local Museum - 1933
Local history, archeology, ceramics, glass 07399

Kolín

Regionální Muzeum v Kolíně (Kolín Regional Museum), Karlovo nám 8, 280 02 Kolín - T: (0321) 722988, Fax: 722988, E-mail: muzeum@kolin.cz, Internet: http://www.kolin.cz/muzeum/. Head: Dr. Jarmila Valentová
Local Museum - 1895
Archeology, literature, numismatics, history, natural history, art of the town Kolín, memorabilia of J.G. Debureau - library 07400

Komárov u Horovic

Železářské Muzeum (Museum of Ironwork), Zámek, 267 62 Komárov u Horovic
Science&Tech Museum
History of Komárov ironwork and smithwork, cast iron 07401

Kopidlno

Mistní Muzeum, 507 32 Kopidlno
Local Museum
History, archeology, numismatics 07402

Kopřivnice

Muzeum Fojtství, Záhumenní 1, 742 21 Kopřivnice - T: (0656) 812601, Fax: 821415, E-mail: fojstvi@tatramuseum.cz, Internet: http://www.tatramuseum.cz. Head: Lenka Hodslavská
Local Museum - 1990
Local hist - archives, library 07403

Technické Muzeum Tatra (Tatra Technical Museum), Záhumenni 369, 742 21 Kopřivnice - T: (0656) 821415, Fax: 821415, E-mail: regmuko@tatramuseum.cz, Internet: http://www.tatramuseum.cz. Head: Lenka Hodslaská
Science&Tech Museum - 1947
Hist of automobiles and automotive engineering, esp of the Tatra works; cars, trucks, railway vehicles, aircraft 07404

Kostelec na Hané

Pámatník Petra Bezruče (Memorial House of Petr Bezruč), Bezručova 256, 798 41 Kostelec na Hané - T: (0508) 92247. Head: Marta Bartoníková
Special Museum
Memorabilia of the poet Petr Bezruč (1867-1958), letters, original interiors 07405

Kostelec nad Černými lesy

Muzeum Hrnčířství a Keramiky (Museum of Pottery and Çeramics), nám Smířických, 281 63 Kostelec nad Černými lesy - T: (0203) 42321, 22988. Head: Dr. Alena Pospisilova
Decorative Arts Museum - 1935
Pottery and ceramics 07406

Kouřim

Muzeum Kouřimska, Mírové nám 1, 281 61 Kouřim - T: (0321) 83380. Head: Dr. Jarmila Valemtová
Local Museum - 1906
Geology, paleontology, archeology, ethnography, local history, fine arts 07407

Muzeum Lidových Staveb (Village Museum), 281 61 Kouřim. Head: Zbyněk Sedláček
Open Air Museum - 1972
Examples of folk architecture, expositions of the traditional technical equipments and hand-made products 07408

Kožlany

Městské Muzeum, 331 44 Kožlany
Local Museum - 1946
Pottery, local history, ethnography 07409

Kralice nad Oslavou

Památník Kralické Tiskárny, 675 72 Kralice nad Oslavou - T: (0509) 663619
Local Museum
Local history, culture 07410

Králíky

Městské Muzeum, Velké nám 365, 561 69 Králíky - T: (0446) 631117, E-mail: muzeumkra@orlicko.cz. Head: Ivo Pecháček
Local Museum - 1907
Local history, natural history of the region Kralický Sněžník 07411

Kralovice

Muzeum a Galerie Severního Plzeňska (Museum and Gallery of Northern Pilsen Region), Mariánská Tynice 1, 331 41 Kralovice - T: (0182) 396410, Fax: 396410, E-mail: Mtynice@iol.cz. Head: Dr. Irena Bukačová
Local Museum - 1952
Cast iron, national costumes, argricultural implements, baroque pictures 07412

Kralupy nad Vltavou

Muzeum Kralupy, Vrchlického 590, 278 01 Kralupy nad Vltavou - T: (0205) 23035
Local Museum
Local history 07413

Křečovice

Památník Josefa Suka (Josef Suk Memorial), Křečovice u Sedlčan 3, 257 48 Křečovice - T: (0301) 941308. Head: Dr. Markéta Hallová
Music Museum - 1935
Memorabilia of the composer Josef Suk (1874-1935) in his former home 07414

Krnov

Muzeum Krnov, Muzeum v Bruntále (Museum Krnov), Revoluční 20, 794 00 Krnov - T: (0652) 2301. Head: Dr. Tomáš Niesner
Local Museum - 1890
Hist of the town with special reference to the development of the textile industry, local natural hist 07415

Kroměříž

Okresní Muzeum Kroměřížska, Velké nám 38, 767 00 Kroměříž - T: (0634) 21457
Local Museum - 1933
15th-19th c paintings and graphics, music archives, baroque music, numismatics, medals - library 07416

Krupka

Muzeum Krupka, Regionální muzeum Teplice (Museum Krupka), Husitská 21, 417 41 Krupka - T: (0417) 862042, Fax: 41461, E-mail: muzeum@tep.cesnet.cz, Internet: http://www.teplice.cz/muzeum. Head: Dr. Dušan Spička
Local Museum - 1919
Hist of the town, applied art, tin ore mining and processing, nature of North Western Bohemia 07417

Kutná Hora

Galerie Felixe Jeneweina, Vlašský Dvůr, 284 00 Kutná Hora - T: (0327) 512347, Fax: 512347, E-mail: galerie@mira.cz, Internet: http://www.kutnahora. Head: Aleš Rezler
Fine Arts Museum
Paintings, bequest of the painter Felix Jenewein, drawings, studies and early works of the painter Felix Jenewein 07418

Kamenný Dům, Okresní muzeum v Kutné Hoře, Václavské nám 183, 284 01 Kutná Hora - T: (0327) 512821, Fax: 513813, E-mail: muzeum.kh@muzeum.zde.cz, Internet: http://www.muzeum.zde.cz. Head: Dr. Světlana Hrabánková
Archaeological Museum / Decorative Arts Museum - 1877
Medieval art and handicraft from 16th-19th c, archeology 07419

Okresní Muzeum v Kutné Hoře - Hradek (Kutná Hora Regional Museum), Barborská 28, Hrádek, 284 80 Kutná Hora - T: (0327) 512159, Fax: 513813, E-mail: muzeum@kutnohorsko.cz, Internet: http://www.muzeum.kutnohorsko.cz. Head: Dr. Světlana Hrabánková
Local Museum - 1877
Geology, 14th-15th c mining tools, medieval ceramics, art history, 14th-16th c mining tools, geology mining of silver, history of Kutná Hora, archeology, ceramics and art archeology, ceramics and art 07420

Zemědělská Sbírka na Zámku Kačina (Agricultural Collection in the Castle of Kačina), Zámek Kačina, 284 00 Kutná Hora - T: (0327) 71170, Fax: 71274. Head: Dr. Pavel Novák
Agriculture Museum - 1891
Agriculture, food industry 07421

Kyjov

Vlastivědné Muzeum, Palackého 70, 697 01 Kyjov - T: (0629) 612338
Local Museum - 1904
Local nature, history and ethnography 07422

Lanškroun

Městské Muzeum, Nám A. Jiráska 1, Zámek, 563 01 Lanškroun - T: (0467) 6328
Local Museum
Paleontology, geology, local history, applied arts, ethnography 07423

Lázně Bělohrad

Fričovo Muzeum, Nám K.V. Raise, 507 81 Lázně Bělohrad - T: (0434) 92208
Local Museum
History, art by Františka Šormy 07424

Památník Karla Václava Raise (Memorial House of Karel V. Rais), Barákova 3, 507 81 Lázně Bělohrad - T: (0434) 692208, Fax: 692484, E-mail: belohrad@ultranet.cz. Head: Ladislav Stuchlík
Special Museum - 1959
Memorabilia of the writer Karel Václav Rais 07425

Ledeč nad Sázavou

Městské Muzeum (Town Museum), Hradní 1, 584 01 Ledeč nad Sázavou - T: (0452) 621128, Fax: 621507, E-mail: is@ledec-net.cz. Head: Dr. Jana Beránková
Local Museum - 1911
History, ethnography, ceramics 07426

Lešany u Týnce nad Sázavou

Vojenské Technické Muzeum (Military Technology Museum), Lešany u Týnce nad Sázavou - T: (02) 20204926
Military Museum / Science&Tech Museum
Hardware for ground warfare 1890-1990 07427

Lesná u Znojma

Muzeum Motocyklů, 671 27 Lesná u Znojma - T: (0624) 291077
Science&Tech Museum
Bikes 07428

Letohrad

Památník Petra Jilemnického (Memorial House of Petr Jilemnický), Zámek, 561 51 Letohrad
Special Museum - 1958
Memorabilia of the writer Peter Jilemnický (1901-1949) 07429

Libáň

Místní Muzeum, 507 23 Libáň 96
Local Museum - 1937
Local history, applied arts, arms 07430

Liběchov

Náprstek Museum of Asian, African and American Cultures, Zámek Liběchov, 277 21 Liběchov - T: (0206) 697036, Fax: 697134, Internet: http://www.aconet.cz/npm. Head: Dr. Jana Součková
Historical Museum / Fine Arts Museum
Asian fine and decorative art, sculpture, wood carving, metal casting and beating, paintings, textiles, musical instruments, tribal and folk art 07431

Liberec

Oblastní Galerie (Regional Art Gallery), U Tiskárny 1, 460 01 Liberec - T: (048) 5106325, Fax: 5106321, E-mail: oblgal@ogl.cz, Internet: http://www.ogl.cz. Head: Dr. Věra Laštovková
Fine Arts Museum - 1945
16th-18th c Dutch painting, 19th c French, German and Austrian paintings, 19th-20th c Czech art 07432

Severočeské Muzeum v Liberci (North Bohemian Museum Liberec), Masarykova 11, 460 01 Liberec 1 - T: (048) 5108252/83, Fax: 5108319, E-mail: muzeumlb@proactive.cz. Head: Alois Čvančara
Local Museum / Decorative Arts Museum / Natural History Museum / Archaeological Museum - 1873
Historical and contemporary coll of European and Bohemian glass and industrial arts, geology, paleontology, botany, local hist, archeology 07433

Libochvice

Zámek Libochovice, 411 17 Libochvice - T: (0419) 591443
Historical Museum 07434

Lidice

Památník Lidice (Museum Lidice), 273 54 Lidice - T: (0312) 253063, Fax: 253088. Head: Miroslav Čermák
Historical Museum - 1947
Hist of Lidice, photographs and other material illustrating the destruction of the town in the Nazi period 07435

Liten

Památník Václava Beneše Třebízského a Svatopluka Čecha (Memorial House of Václav Beneš Třebízský and of Svatopluk Čech), ul Litenského zámku, 267 27 Liten
Special Museum - 1965
Memorabilia of the writers V.B. Třebízský and Svatopluk Čech (1846-1908) 07436

Litoměřice

Galerie a Muzeum Litoměřické Diecéze (Diozesan Museum), Mírové nám 24, 412 01 Litoměřice
Religious Arts Museum 07437

Galerie Výtvarného Umění Litoměřice (Gallery of Fine Arts Litoměřice), Michalská 7, 412 01 Litoměřice - T: (0416) 732382, Fax: 732383, E-mail: gvu.ltm@worldonline.cz, Internet: http://www.galerie-ltm.cz. Head: Dr. Jan Štíbr
Fine Arts Museum - 1956
13th-20th c painting and sculpture, special coll of Roman, Gothic and Bohemian art, naive painting and sculpture - library 07438

Okresni Muzeum, Mirové nám 171/40, 412 01 Litoměřice - T: (0416) 731339, Fax: 731327. Head: Eva Štíbrová
Local Museum - 1874
Local history, botany, archeology, ethnography, vine cultivation, fruit growing, ceramics 07439

Litomyšl

Muzeum České Hudby (Museum of Czech Music), Zámek, 570 01 Litomyšl - T: (0464) 2067. Head: Josef Holub
Music Museum
Coll illustrating the development of Czech music 07440

Vlastivědné Muzeum, Městske muzeum i galerie, Jiráskova 9, 570 01 Litomyšl - T: (0464) 2287
Local Museum - 1890
Paleontology, zoology, history, ethnography, numismatics, applied art, crafts 07441

Litovel

Muzeum Litovel, ul Dr. J. Smyčky 149, 784 01 Litovel - T: (068) 5441510
Local Museum - 1893
Local history, pottery 07442

Litvínov

Muzeum, Tr. Sovetské Armády 1, 436 00 Litvínov
Local Museum - 1896
Local geology, botany, entomology, industry, labour movement in the region of Most and Litvínov, ethnography 07443

Lomnice nad Popelkou

Městské Muzeum a Galerie, Husovo nám 43-44, 512 51 Lomnice nad Popelkou - T: (0431) 671872, Fax: 671335, E-mail: ddmlom@mikroservis.cz, Internet: http://www.adam.cz/win1250/ddm/lom/lom.htm. Head: Jan Drahoňovský
Local Museum - 1891
Ethnography, mineralogy, zoology, paintings by regional artists, contemporary room interiors of the Šlechta family 07444

Loštice

Havelkovo Muzeum, ul U muzea 8, 789 83 Loštice
Decorative Arts Museum / Historical Museum - 1928
Pottery, stove making from the 15th-19th c, local history 07445

Památník Adolfa Kaspara, Palackého 343, 789 83 Loštice - T: (0648) 52256
Fine Arts Museum - 1970
Memorabilia of the painter Adolf Kašpar, his paintings 07446

Louny

Archeological Open Air Museum in Březno u Loun, Okresni muzeum, Pivovarská 28, 440 01 Louny - T: (0395) 652456. Head: Dr. Bedřich Štauber
Archaeological Museum
Archeology, medieval archeology 07447

Galerie Benedikta Rejta v Lounech, Pivovarská 29-34, 440 01 Louny - T: (0395) 652634, Fax: 3247. Head: Dr. Alica Štefančíková
Fine Arts Museum - 1966
20th c Czech art - library 07448

Okresni Muzeum, Pivovarská 28, 440 01 Louny - T: (0395) 652456, 653037. Head: Dr. Bedřich Štauber
Local Museum - 1889
Local geology, archeology, medieval archeology, ethnography, local hist 07449

Luhačovice

Oddělení Oblastního Muzea Jihovychodní Moravy, Zlín (Branch of the Regional Museum of South-Eastern Moravia in Zlín), Villa Lipová, 763 26 Luhačovice - T: (067) 932883
Folklore Museum
Regional folk art 07450

Lysá nad Labem

Muzeum Starých Orientálních Kultur v Díle Akademika Bedřicha Hrozného (Museum of old oriental cultures in the work of Bedřich Hrozný), nám Dr. B. Hrozného 265, 289 22 Lysá nad Labem
Archaeological Museum
Archeology, oriental art, coll illustrating the work of the Czech Orientalist Dr. Bedřich Hrozný 07451

Lysice

Zámek Lysice, 679 71 Lysice - T: (0501) 472235
Historical Museum 07452

Malé Svatoňovice

Muzeum Bratří Čapků (Museum of the Čapek Brothers), nám K. Čapka 147, 542 34 Malé Svatoňovice - T: 934295. Head: Eva Hylmarsová
Special Museum - 1946
Coll illustrating the life and work of the writer Karel Čapek (1890-1938) and his brother the painter Josef Čapek (1887-1945) 07453

Manětín

Zámek Manětín, Muzeum a galerie severního Plzeňska, Zámek Manětín, 331 62 Manětín - T: (0182) 92283. Head: Dr. Irena Bukačová
Local Museum
Local history, baroque art 07454

Mariánské Lázně

Městské Muzeum v Mariánských Lázních (Mariánské Lázně Municipal Museum), Goethovo nám 11, 353 01 Mariánské Lázně - T: (0165) 622740, Fax: 621753, E-mail: muzeumml@telecom.cz. Head: Petr Bouše
Local Museum - 1887
Mineralogy, geology, ethnography, applied arts, porcelain coll, local history of the town and the spa, memorabilia of J.W. von Goethe's, F. Chopin's and M. Gorkij's stays at Mariánské Lázně 07455

Mělník

Okresní Muzeum, Svatováclavská 9, Zámek 19, 276 01 Mělník - T: (0206) 621917, Fax: 622158. Head: Dr. Miloslava Havlíčková
Local Museum - 1888
Archeology, ethnography, art, handicrafts, local wine industry, manuscripts of the politician and writer Victor Dyk 07456

Městec Králové

Místní Muzeum, nám 74-75, 289 03 Městec Králové
Local Museum - 1909
Local history, archeology, ethnography, handicrafts 07457

Mikulčice

Národní Kulturní Památník - Valy (Old Slavonic Ringwall - National Cultural Monument), Valy, 696 19 Mikulčice, mail addr: POB 189, 695 01 Hodonín - T: (0628) 357293. Head: Dr. Josef Šolc
Archaeological Museum - 1963
Archeological finds from excavations at local Slavonic sites (8th-9th c) 07458

Mikulov na Moravě

Regionální Muzeum, Zámek, 692 15 Mikulov na Moravě - T: (0625) 2255, 3575. Head: Dobromila Brichtová
Local Museum - 1913
Local hist, natural hist, archeology, ethnography, applied arts - library 07459

Miletin

Památník Karla Jaromira Erbena (Memorial House of Karel J. Erben), ul Barbory Linkové 142, 507 71 Miletin - T: (0435)693124/224, Fax: 693224, E-mail: obec.miletin@iol.cz. Head: Lenka Kožiškova
Special Museum - 1911
Memorabilia of the poet Karel Jaromír Erben (1811-1870) in his former home 07460

Milevsko

Milevské Muzeum, Klášter, 399 01 Milevsko - T: (0368) 521093
Local Museum - 1926
Local archeology, history, handicrafts 07461

Mirotice

Památnik Mikoláše Alše (Memorial House of Mikuláš Aleš), 398 01 Mirotice
Fine Arts Museum - 1962
Memorabilia of the painter Mikoláš Aleš (1852-1913) 07462

Mladá Boleslav

Okresní Muzeum, Staroměstské nám 1, 293 01 Mladá Boleslav - T: (0326) 25616/22542, Fax: (0326) 22542, E-mail: ludek.benes@oku-mb.cz, Internet: http://www.aa.cz/muzeum. Head: Dr. Luděk Beneš
Local Museum - 1885
Archeology, ceramics and glass especially from the 19th c, numismatics, ethnography - archives 07463

Škoda Auto Museum, Václava Klementa 294, 293 60 Mladá Boleslav - T: (0326) 831134, 831139, Fax: 832028, E-mail: museum@skoda-auto.cz, Internet: http://www.skoda-auto.cz. Head: Margit Černá
Science&Tech Museum - 1995 07464

Mladá Vožice

Místní Muzeum, Žižkovo nám 80, 391 43 Mladá Vožice - T: (0361) 201911, 201921, Fax: 201920. Head: Alexej Salzman
Local Museum - 1912
Ethnography, local hist, memorabilia of the historian August Sedláček and Jan Jeník z Bratřic, coll of oil paintings, particularly by Otta Bubeníček 07465

Mnichovo Hradiště

Městské Muzeum, Zámek 148, 295 01 Mnichovo Hradiště - T: (0329) 771001
Local Museum - 1894
Regional archeology, history, ethnography, anti-Fashist struggle in World War II, memorabilia of the politician Jan Šverma 07466

Mohelnice

Muzeum Mohelnice, Kostelní nám 3, 789 85 Mohelnice - T: (0648) 51234. Head: Dr. Miloš Melzer
Archaeological Museum - 1923
Archeology, local history 07467

Moravská Třebová

Městské Muzeum (Town Museum), Svitavská 18, 571 01 Moravská Třebová - T: (0462) 311203, Fax: 316202, E-mail: muzeummtr@iol.cz, Internet: http://www.ksmt.wz.cz. Head: Jana Martínková
Science&Tech Museum / Fine Arts Museum - 1872
Textile industry, Holzmaister's Coll of Non-European applied art 07468

Moravské Budějovice

Expozice Řemesel, nám Míru 1, 676 02 Moravské Budějovice - T: (0617) 421100, Fax: 421100. Head: Jaroslav Martínek
Special Museum / Historical Museum - 1893 07469

Moravský Krumlov

Městské Muzeum, Jihomoravské Muzeum Znojmo, Hlavni nám 321, 672 01 Moravský Krumlov - T: (0621) 322225
Local Museum - 1905
Local archeology and history 07470

Zámek Moravský Krumlov, Galerie Hlavního Města Prahy, 672 01 Moravský Krumlov - T: (0621) 322789
Fine Arts Museum 07471

Most

Okresni Muzeum, Čs. Armády 1360, 434 00 Most - T: (035) 213445. Head: Libuše Pokorná
Local Museum - 1888
Mineralogy, geology, paleontology, archeology, local history, mining, art, handicrafts 07472

Mšeno u Mělníka

Památník Josefa Ladislava Piče, nám Miru 21, 277 35 Mšeno u Mělníka - T: (0206) 80. Head: Frantisek Vitous
Special Museum
Memorabilia of the historian and archeologist Jan Ladislav Píč 07473

Náchod

Galerie Výtvarného Umění (Fine Arts Gallery), Státní Zámek, Smiřických 272, 547 01 Náchod - T: (0441) 423245, Fax: 423245, E-mail: gvun@gvun.cz, Internet: http://www.gvun.cz. Head: Jan Kapusta
Fine Arts Museum - 1966
19th-20th c Russian and Soviet paintings and graphics, contemporary Czech art 07474

Okresní Muzeum, Zámek 1284, 547 00 Náchod
Local Museum - 1879
Archeology, local history, ethnography, handicrafts, numismatics, glass, ceramics 07475

Napajedla

Odděleni Oblastni Muzeum Jihovýchodni Moravy (Regional Museum of South-Eastern Moravia), 763 61 Napajedla
Local Museum
Local history 07476

Nejdek

Městské Muzeum, Nám Karla IV. 238, 362 21 Nejdek
Local Museum 07477

Nelahozeves

Památník Antonína Dvořáka (Antonín Dvořák Memorial), Proti nádraží 12, 277 51 Nelahozeves - T: (0205) 785099. Head: Dr. Markéta Hallová
Music Museum - 1951
Memorabilia of the composer Antonín Dvořák (1841-1904) in his native house 07478

Zámek Nelahozeves, 277 51 Nelahozeves - T: (0205) 22995
Historical Museum 07479

Nepomuk

Městské Muzeum, nam. A. Němejce 126, 335 01 Nepomuk - T: (0185) 592546, Fax: 591422, E-mail: muzeum.nepomuk@wo.cz, Internet: http://www.nepomucko.cz
Local Museum - 1957
Local and natural hist, baroque art, memorabilia of the painter Augustin Němejc, St. Jan Nepomuk 07480

Netolice

Místní Muzeum, Muzeum JUDr. Otakara Kudrny, nám 248, 384 11 Netolice - T: (0338) 324251, Fax: 324251
Local Museum - 1909
Local archeology, ethnography, hist of the town 07481

Netvořice

Místní Muzeum, 257 44 Netvořice 46
Local Museum - 1931
18th-19th c ceramics, local archeology, history 07482

Nová Paka

Městské Muzeum Klenotnice, F.F. Procházky 70, 509 01 Nová Paka - T: (0434) 621943, Fax: 621928, E-mail: novapaka@muzeum.cz. Head: Ivo Chocholáč
Natural History Museum - 1952
Regional geology, mineralogy, semi-precious stones (agate, jasper etc.), spiritism and its paintings (l'art brute) 07483

Sucharduv Dům, Městské Muzeum, Suchardova 283, 509 01 Nová Paka - T: (0434) 623542, Fax: 621928, E-mail: novapaka@muzeum.cz. Head: Miloslav Barina
Local Museum - 1908
History of the region, ethnography, memorabilia of the sculptor Vojtěch Sucharda 07484

Nové Město na Moravě

Horácka Galerie, Vratislavovo nám 1, 592 31 Nové Město na Moravě - T: (0616) 618025, Fax: 618025. Head: Josef Chalupa
Fine Arts Museum - 1964
Painting, sculpture 07485

Horácké Muzeum (Museum of the Moravian Heights), Vratislavovo nám 114, 592 31 Nové Město na Moravě - T: (0616) 650216. Head: Jaroslava Pelikánová
Local Museum - 1892
Regional hist, ethnography, hist of skiing in the region, coll illustrating the life and work of the painter Karel Němec 07486

Nové Město nad Metují

Městské Muzeum, Na Zádomí 1226, 549 01 Nové Město nad Metují - T: (0441) 470289
Local Museum 07487

Zámek, Husovo nám 1201, 549 01 Nové Město nad Metují - T: (0441) 73568
Historical Museum 07488

Nové Strašecí

Městské Muzeum, ul Školy 123, 271 01 Nové Strašecí
Local Museum - 1895
Local archeology, ethnography, folk art 07489

Nový Bor

Sklářské Muzeum (Glass Museum), nám Míru 105, 473 01 Nový Bor - T: (0424) 222196, Fax: 723862. Head: Eva Ranšová
Science&Tech Museum - 1893
Hist and technology of glass production, optical glass 07490

Nový Bydžov

Městské Muzeum, ul B. Němcové 507, 504 01 Nový Bydžov - T: (0448) 23086. Head: J. Prokop
Local Museum - 1888
Local history, ethnography, memorabilia of the writer Božena Němcová (1820-1862) and her stay at Nový Bydžov 07491

Nový Jičín

Kloboučnické Muzeum (Hat-Making Museum), ul 28. Října 12, 741 00 Nový Jičín
Science&Tech Museum - 1949
History of the local hat-making industry 07492

Muzeum Svitidel a Chladičů (Ligthing and Refrigerator Museum), ul 28. Října 12, 741 00 Nový Jičín
Science&Tech Museum - 1969
History of lighting and the local production of refrigerators 07493

Okresni Vlastivědné Muzeum, ul 28. Října 12, 741 00 Nový Jičín - T: (0656) 701156
Local Museum / Natural History Museum - 1887
Mineralogy, paleontology, entomology, botany, zoology, local history, ethnography, handicrafts, art 07494

Nymburk

Vlastivědné Muzeum, Tyršova 9, 288 00 Nymburk - T: (0325) 2473. Head: Dr. Kamila Beštáková
Local Museum - 1885
Local botany, zoology, entomology, archeology, medieval archeology, ethnography, local economic history - library 07495

Obříství

Památnik Svatopluka Čecha, Obříství 83, 277 42 Obříství - T: 612
Special Museum - 1956
Memorabilia of the writer and poet Svatopluk Čech (1846-1908) 07496

Ohrada

Zemědělské Muzeum Ohrada (Agricultural Museum Ohrada), Ohrada - T: (038) 965340. Head: Dr. Václav Kasal
Agriculture Museum - 1858 07497

Olomouc

Muzeum Umění Olomouc (Olomouc Museum of Art), Denisova 47, 771 11 Olomouc - T: (068) 5228470, Fax: 5223166, E-mail: info@olmuart.cz, Internet: http://www.olmuart.cz. Head: Dr. Pavel Zatloukal
Fine Arts Museum - 1952
19th-20th c Bohemian art, old European art - archive, library 07498

Vlastivědné Muzeum v Olomouci, nám Republiky 5, 771 73 Olomouc - T: (068) 5222741, Fax: 5222743, E-mail: muzeumol@power.ol.cesnet.cz, Internet: http://risc.upol.cz/muzeumol
Local Museum - 1874
Natural science in Northern Moravia, history, archeology, art hist, decorative arts, military art, numismatics, agriculture, trades, transportation, ethnography, graphics 07499

Olomučany

Muzeum Olomučanské Keramiky (Museum of the Olomučany ceramics), 679 03 Olomučany 123 - T: (0506) 2550. Head: Jiří Kratochvíl
Decorative Arts Museum - 1960
Local ceramics 07500

Opava

Archeologické Pracoviště, Slezské zemské muzeum (Archeology Department of the Silesian Museum), Komenského 8, 746 01 Opava - T: (0653) 214862, Fax: 622999. Head: Dr. Jaromír Kalus
Archaeological Museum - 1814
Archaeology of the Silesian region, prehistory 07501

Muzikologické Pracoviště, Slezské Zemské Muzeum (Musicological Department of the Silesian Museum), Tyršova 1, 746 01 Opava - T: (0653) 623540, Fax: 622999, E-mail: szmored@opanet.cz, Internet: http://www.muopava.cz/szmo. Head: Petr Koukal
Music Museum - 1814
Hist of music of the Silesian region 07502

Památnik Petra Bezruče, Slezské zemské muzeum (Silesian Museum), Ostrožná ul 35, 746 01 Opava - T: (0653) 625024, Fax: 622999, E-mail: szmored@opanet.cz. Head: Dr. Jaromír Kalus
Special Museum - 1956
Memorabilia of the poet Petr Bezruč (1867-1958) and other Silesian literary figures 07503

Přírodovědecké Sbirky, Slezské zemské muzeum (Natural Science Dept. of the Silesian Museum), Masarykova 35, 746 46 Opava - T: (0653) 212870, Fax: 622999, E-mail: szmoprir@opanet.cz. Head: Dr. Jindřich Roháček
Natural History Museum - 1814
Geological sciences, mineralogy, paleontology, botany, zoology 07504

Slezské Zemské Muzeum (Silesian Museum), Ostrožná ul 42, 746 01 Opava - T: (0653) 623540, Fax: 622999. Head: Dr. Jaromír Kalus
Local Museum - 1814
Hist of the Silesian region, Bohemian/Moravian money coll, sculptures, paintings, applied art, glass, ceramic, theater hist, ethnography 07505

Zámecké Muzeum, Alejní 24, Kravaře ve Slezsku, 746 01 Opava - T: (0653) 671201, E-mail: Mesto@Kravare.cz. Head: Erich Šefčík
Historical Museum 07506

Orlová

Výstavní Síň Muzea Těšínska, Staré nám 74, 735 11 Orlová - T: (069) 6531205
Science&Tech Museum 07507

Ostrava

Galerie Výtvarného Umění (Fine Arts Gallery), Jurečkova 9, 702 00 Ostrava - T: (069) 6112566, Fax: 6126445. Head: Petr Beránek
Fine Arts Museum - 1926
European paintings and graphics, modern Czech art 07508

Hornické Muzeum OKD (Mining Museum), Pod Landekem 64, 725 29 Ostrava, Petřkovice - T: (069) 6131804/1847, Fax: 6131847, E-mail: hornicke.muzeum@okd.cz, Internet: http://www.hgf.vsb.cz/kat545/landek. Head: Miroslav Fojtík
Science&Tech Museum 07509

Museum of Vítkovice, Výstavní 99, Zámek, 706 02 Ostrava - T: (069) 2926057. Head: Tomaš Moravec
Science&Tech Museum - 1971
Metallurgy, technology, local labour movement 07510

Ostravské Muzeum, Masarykovo nám 1, 702 00 Ostrava 1 - T: (069) 6123760, 6125338, Fax: 6114449, E-mail: ostrmuz@iol.cz, Internet: http://www1.osu.cz/omuzeum/index.htm. Head: Jiřina Kábrtova
Local Museum - 1872
Geology, mineralogy, paleontology, ornithology, archeology, art hist, ethnography, folk sculpture, glass painting 07511

Výtvarné Centrum Chagall (The Art Center Chagall), Repinova 16, 702 00 Ostrava - T: (069) 6112019, Fax: 234344
Public Gallery 07512

Ostředek

Památnik Svatopluka Čecha (Memorial House of Svatopluk Čech), Zámek, Ostředek
Special Museum - 1898
Memorabilia of the writer Svatopluk Čech (1846-1908) 07513

Ostrov nad Ohří

Galerie Umění, Zámek, 363 01 Ostrov nad Ohří - T: (0164) 2883. Head: Vladimír Přibil
Fine Arts Museum - 1961
20th c Czech drawings and graphics, regional art 07514

Pacov

Městské Muzeum Antonína Sovy, Hronova 273, 395 01 Pacov - T: (0365) 442193. Head: Eliška Stejskalová
Special Museum - 1908
Memorabilia of the poet Antonín Sova and other local artists, local history 07515

Pardubice

Dům u Jonáše, Východočeská Galerie (East Bohemian Gallery), Pernštýnské nám 50, 530 02 Pardubice - T: (040) 6510003. Head: Dr. Hana Řeháková
Fine Arts Museum - 1954
Czech modern art, especially regional art 07516

Východočeská Galerie (East Bohemian Gallery), Zámek 3, 530 00 Pardubice - T: (040) 6501897, E-mail: vcg.rehakova@wo.cz. Head: Dr. Hana Řeháková
Fine Arts Museum - 1954
Czech modern art, especially regional art 07517

Východočeské Muzeum (East Bohemian Museum), Zámek 2, 530 02 Pardubice - T: (040) 6513263, Fax: 6513056, E-mail: vcm@vcm.cz, Internet: http://www.vcm.cz. Head: Dr. F. Šebek
Local Museum - 1880
Ornithology, zoology, botany, mineralogy, numismatics, archeology of Eastern Bohemia, arms, uniforms, applied arts, ethnography, regional literature, history, picture postcard coll, glass coll - library 07518

Paseky nad Jizerou

Krkonošské Muzeum, Památník Zapadlých vlastenců, ul Kostela, 512 47 Paseky nad Jizerou - T: (0432) 92609. Head: J. John
Special Museum
Memorabilia of the teacher Metelka and the writer K.V. Rais 07519

Pelhřimov

Muzeum Rekordů a Kuriozit, Jihlavská brána, 393 01 Pelhřimov - T: (0366) 321327
Special Museum
About 50 Czech entries in the Guinness book 07520

Okresní Muzeum, Masarykova nám 10, 393 01 Pelhřimov - T: (0366) 21535
Local Museum - 1901
Archeology, medieval archeology, local history, ethnography, art handicrafts, (embroidery, wood carving), folk art 07521

Petřvald u Karviné

Technické Muzeum, Muzeum Těšínska (Technology Museum), K muzeu 89, 735 41 Petřvald u Karviné - T: (069) 6541092, Fax: 76122333, E-mail: muzeum@muzeumct.cz, Internet: http://www.muzeumct.cz. Head: Miluše Malinová
Science&Tech Museum - 1997
Hist of the tram transport, hist of mining in the Karviná region 07522

Písek

Galerie Portyč, Čechova 406, 397 01 Písek - T: (0362) 271277
Fine Arts Museum
Local hist 07523

Prácheňské Muzeum, Velké nám 114, 397 01 Písek - T: (0362) 214731
Local Museum
Local hist 07524

Plánice

Památnik Dr. Františka Křižíka, Křižíkova 86, 340 34 Plánice
Science&Tech Museum - 1957
Memorabilia on the electrical engineer Dr. František Křižík and his inventions 07525

Plzeň

Archeologické Sbirky, Západočeské muzeum (Archaeological Collection of the West Bohemian Museum), Koterovská 162, 300 00 Plzeň - T: (019) 7444483, Fax: 7224115, E-mail: zpcm@pm.cesnet.cz, Internet: http://www.zcu.cz/plzen/org/museum/index-cz.html
Archaeological Museum
Prehistory and medieval archeology of Western Bohemia 07526

Národopisné Muzeum Plzeňska, Západočeské Muzeum (Ethnographical Collection of the West Bohemian Museum in Pilsen), nám Republiky 13, 301 13 Plzeň - T: (019) 7236054/980, 7324028, Fax: 7236541, E-mail: zpcm@pm.cesnet.cz. Head: Dr. František Frýda
Ethnology Museum - 1915
Cultural hist and ethnography of Western Bohemia (19th-20th c) 07527

Pivovarské Muzeum, Západočeské Muzeum (Brewery Museum), Veleslavínova 6, 301 14 Plzeň - T: (019) 7235574, Fax: 7235574. Head: Jaroslav Křivanec
Science&Tech Museum - 1959
History of brewing, original equipment, coll of beer labels - video projection 07528

Velká Synagoga, Klstovská tř, 301 00 Plzeň - T: (0609) 441943
Public Gallery 07529

Západočeská Galerie v Plzni (West Bohemian Gallery in Plzeň), Praszká 16, 301 14 Plzeň - T: (019) 222970, Fax: 222970. Head: Dr. Jana Potužáková
Fine Arts Museum - 1954
Czech art, painting and sculpture from the 14th c to the present 07530

Západočeské Muzeum (West Bohemian Museum), Kopeckého sady 2, 301 50 Plzeň - T: (019) 7237311, Fax: 7236541, E-mail: zpcm@pm.cesnet.cz, Internet: http://www.zcu.cz/plzen/org/museum/index-cz.html. Head: Dr. František Frýda
Natural History Museum / Historical Museum - 1878
Natural history of Western Bohemia, geology, petrography, paleontology, mineralogy, botany, entomology, zoology, history, applied art - museum library 07531

Počátky

Městské Muzeum, Palackého nám 27, 394 64 Počátky - T: (0364) 493037
Local Museum - 1892
Local archeology, history, ethnography, memorabilia on local writers and artists 07532

Rodný Domek Otokara Březiny, Městské muzeum, Otokara Březiny 224, 394 64 Počátky - T: (0364) 493037, E-mail: museum.pocatky@c-mail.cz. Head: Maria Filipová
Special Museum
Memorabilia on the poet Otokar Březina 07533

Poděbrady

Památnik Krále Jiřího z Poděbrad a Lapidarium, Oblastni muzeum (Memorial House of King Jiří z Poděbrad and Lapidarium), Zámek, 290 01 Poděbrady
Special Museum
Lapidary 07534

Polabské Muzeum (Museum of the Elbe Region), Palackého trg 68, 290 01 Poděbrady - T: (0324) 2640
Local Museum - 1902
Paleontology, zoology, herbarium, art, especially works by the French sculptor J.P. Dantan (1800-1869), ethnography, numismatics, literature 07535

Police nad Metuji

Památnik Města, Komenského nám 1, 549 54 Police nad Metuji
Local Museum - 1949
Local and regional history, folk handicrafts 07536

Polička

Městská Galerie, Palackého nám 2, 572 01 Polička - T: (0463) 22769
Public Gallery 07537

Městské Muzeum, Tylova ul 112-113, 572 01 Polička - T: (0463) 22769, Fax: 724056, E-mail: muzeum@policka-city.cz. Head: David Junek
Local Museum - 1880
Local history, ethnography, glass making, folk art, memorabilia on local artists, old handicrafts 07538

Památnik Bohuslava Martinů, Městské muzeum a galerie, 572 01 Polička - T: (0463) 22769, Fax: 724056, E-mail: bmartinu@policka-city.cz. Head: David Junek
Music Museum
Memorabilia on the composer Bohuslav Martinů (1890-1959) 07539

Svojanov Hrad, 569 73 Polička - T: (0463) 91824
Historical Museum 07540

Polná

Muzeum Polná, Zámek 1, 588 13 Polná - T: (066) 7212336. Head: Jitka Hošková
Local Museum - 1895
Old Czech school, pharmacy, watch, handicrafts 07541

Potštejn

Památnik Jiráskova Pokladu, Muzeum Orlických Hor, Rychnov nad Kněžnou, 517 43 Potštejn
Local Museum
History of the linen manufacture at Potštejn (18th c), documentation on the novel Poklad by Alois Jirásek 07542

Prace u Brna

Památnik Mohyla míru, 664 58 Prace u Brna - T: (05) 91724. Head: Antonín Reček
Military Museum - 1909
History of the Napoleonic wars, especially the Battle of Slavkov (Austerlitz) 07543

Prachatice

Muzeum Krajky (Lace Museum), Poštovní 178, 383 01 Prachatice
Decorative Arts Museum 07544

Prachatické Muzeum, Velké nám 13, 383 01 Prachatice - T: (0338) 311419, Fax: 316652, E-mail: muzeum@prachatice.cz, Internet: http://www.prachatice.cz/muzeum. Head: Zuzana Polanská
Local Museum - 1904
Local history, ethnography, handicrafts, industry, art 07545

Praha

Armádní Muzeum Žižkov (Army Museum Žižkov), ul Památníku 2, 130 05 Praha 3 - T: (02) 20204926, Fax: 6279657. Head: Dr. Zdeněk Jelínek
Military Museum - 1918
Development of the Czechoslovak army from 1917 onwards 07546

Automuseum E.R. Prihoda, Hrozenkovska 13, 150 00 Praha - T: (02) 740444, Fax: 777644
Science&Tech Museum 07547

Bílkova Vila, Galerie Hlavního Města Prahy, Mickiewiczova 1, Praha 6 - T: (02) 24322021, Fax: 33323664, E-mail: ghmp@volny.cz, Internet: http://www.citygalleryprague.cz. Head: Jaroslav Fatka
Fine Arts Museum
Coll of the Czech sculptor, graphic artist and architect František Bílek, symbolism, mysticism 07548

České Centrum Fotografie (Czech Center of Photography), Náplavni 1, Praha 2 - T: (02) 24922726, Fax: 24922726, E-mail: jas.gal@telecom.cz
Fine Arts Museum / Public Gallery 07549

České Muzeum Výtvarných Umění (Czech Museum of Fine Arts), Husova 19-21, 110 01 Praha 1 - T: (02) 22220218, Fax: 22221190, E-mail: cmvu@ecn.cz, Internet: http://www.ecn.cz/cmvu. Head: Dr. Jan Sekera
Fine Arts Museum - 1964
European art of 14th to 19th c, Czech modern art 07550

České Zdravotnické Muzeum (Museum of Czech Health Sciences), Sokolská 31, 120 00 Praha
Special Museum - 1934
History of the health sciences, documents, numismatics, stamps 07551

Císařská Konírna, Prague Castle Gallery (Imperial Stables), Pražsky Hrad, 119 01 Praha - T: (02) 24373368, Fax: 24373238, E-mail: Frantisek.Kadlec@hrad.cz, Internet: http://www.hrad.cz. Head: Dr. František Kadlec
Fine Arts Museum / Public Gallery
Coll of old art 07552

Dům u Černé Matky Boží, Celetná 34, Praha 1 - T: (02) 24211732
Fine Arts Museum / Public Gallery
Coll of Czech kubism and expressionsim 07553

Dům u Kamenného Zvonu, Galerie Hlavního Města Prahy, Staroměstské nám 13, 110 00 Praha 1 - T: (02) 24827526, Fax: 2327693, E-mail: upsv@volny.cz, Internet: http://www.citygalleryprague.cz. Head: Jaroslav Fatka
Public Gallery 07554

Dům u Zlatého Prstenu, Galerie Hlavního Města Prahy, Týnská 6, 110 00 Praha 1 - T: (02) 24827022/24, Internet: http://www.citygalleryprague.cz. Head: Jaroslav Fatka
Fine Arts Museum
Coll of Cech art 20th c 07555

Entomologické Oddělení, Národní Muzeum (National Museum, Department of Entomology), Golčova 1, 148 00 Praha - T: (02) 44911374. Head: Dr. J. Jelínek
Natural History Museum - 1952
Entomology - Library 07556

Expozice Asijského Uměni Národní Galerie v Praze (Exposition of Asian Art of the National Gallery of Prague), Zámek Zbraslav, Praha 5 - T: (02) 57921638, Fax: 57921929, E-mail: asiainfo@ngprague.cz
Fine Arts Museum - 1952
Coll of Asian art, coll of Dr. R. Kreissl 07557

Expozice České Lidové Armády, Vojenské muzea, ul Památníku 2, 130 05 Praha 3 - T: (02) 272665
Military Museum - 1924
Czech military history 07558

Galerie Hlavního Města Prahy (Prague City Gallery), Mickiewiczova 3, 160 00 Praha 6 - T: (02) 33321200, Fax: 33323664, E-mail: ghmp@volny.cz, Internet: http://www.citygalleryprague.cz. Head: Jaroslav Fatka
Fine Arts Museum - 1963
19th-20th c Czech art 07559

Galerie Křižovníků (Gallery of the Knights of the Cross), Křižovnické nám 3, 110 00 Praha 1 - T: (02) 21108226, 21108227, Fax: 21108248. Head: Vanda Bočanová
Religious Arts Museum / Public Gallery 07560

Galerie Rudolfinum, Alšovo náb 12, 110 00 Praha 1 - T: (02) 24893205, Fax: 2319293, E-mail: -galerie.rudolfinum@telecom.cz. Head: Petr Nedoma
Public Gallery
Modern art 20th c and current Czech and international art 07561

Historické Muzeum, Národní Muzeum (Historical Museum of the National Museum in Prague), Václavské nám 68, 115 79 Praha 1 - T: (02) 24497111, Fax: 24226488, E-mail: nm@nm.cz. Head: Dr. Eduard Šimek
Historical Museum - 1818
Prehistoric, historic and classical archaeology, hist, numismatics, theatre coll, ethnography, hist of sports - archives 07562

Hrdličkovo Muzeum Člověka (Hrdlička's Museum of Man), c/o Universita Karlova, Viničná 7, 120 00 Praha - T: (02) 21953214, Fax: 21953214, E-mail: hmc@natur.cuni.cz, Internet: http://www.natur.cuni.cz/~hmc. Head: Božena Škvařilová
Special Museum / University Museum - 1930
Evolution of man, comparative anatomy, primatology, ontogenetic evolution, racial differences, skull formations, postmortal cast, anthropology, osteology 07563

Jízdárna Pražskeho Hradu (Riding School Exhibition Hall), Pražsky Hrad, 119 01 Praha - T: (02) 24373368, Fax: 24373238, E-mail: Frantisek.Kadlec@hrad.cz, Internet: http://www.hrad.cz. Head: Dr. František Kadlec
Public Gallery 07564

Kaple Sv. Kříže, Pražsky Hrad, 119 01 Praha - T: (02) 24373368, Fax: 24373238, E-mail: Frantisek.Kadlec@hrad.cz, Internet: http://www.hrad.cz. Head: Dr. František Kadlec
Public Gallery 07565

Klášter Sv. Anežky České, Národní Galerie v Praže (Convent of Saint Agnes of Bohemia), U Milosrdných 17, Praha 1 - T: (02) 21879214/16, 20514595, Fax: 20513180, Internet: http://www.ngprague.cz. Head: Dr. Vit Vlnas
Fine Arts Museum
Medieval art in Bohemia and Central Europe 07566

Klašter Sv. Jiří, Národní galerie v Praze (Convent of Saint George), Jiřske nám 33, 11 000 Praha - T: (02) 57320536, Internet: http://www.ngprague.cz
Fine Arts Museum
Coll of old Czech masters 07567

Královsky Letohradek (Royal Summer Palace), Pražsky Hrad, 119 01 Praha - T: (02) 24373368, Fax: 24373238, E-mail: Frantisek.Kadlec@hrad.cz, Internet: http://www.hrad.cz. Head: Dr. František Kadlec
Public Gallery
Creative art, artistic crafts 07568

Letecké Muzeum, Historický Ústav Armády České Republiky (Aviation Museum), Kbely, Mladoboleslavská, 190 00 Praha 9 - T: (02) 20207504, Fax: 20204933. Head: Petr Klučina
Military Museum - 1968
History of Czech military air force, aviation, space cooperation 07569

Lobkovicky Palác, National Museum (Lobkovicz Palace), Pražsky Hrad, 119 01 Praha - T: (02) 24373368, Internet: http://www.hrad.cz
Historical Museum
Older Czech history 07570

Městská Knihovna, Galerie Hlavního Města Prahy, Mariánské nam 1, Praha 1 - T: (02) 2310489
Public Gallery 07571

Micovna (Ball Game Hall), Pražsky Hrad, 119 01 Praha - T: (02) 24373368, Fax: 24373238, E-mail: Frantisek.Kadlec@hrad.cz, Internet: http://www.hrad.cz. Head: Dr. František Kadlec
Public Gallery
Creative art 07572

Museum Hraček (Toy Museum Prag & Barbie Museum), Pražski hrad, Jiřská 6, 11901 Praha - T: (02) 24372294, Fax: 24372295. Head: Ivan Steiger
Special Museum
Coll of toys and Barbies 07573

Muzeum Aloise Jiráska a Mikoláše Alše, Letohrádek Hvězda, 160 00 Praha 6 - T: (02) 367938. Head: Dr. Jana Weiserová
Special Museum - 1951
Memorabilia of the Czech writer Alois Jirásek (1851-1930) and the painter Mikoláš Aleš (1852-1913) - library 07574

Muzeum Antonína Dvořáka (Antonín Dvořák Museum), Ke Karlovu 20, 120 00 Praha - T: (02) 24923363, Fax: 24923363, E-mail: a.dvorak.museum@nm.cz, Internet: http://www.nm.cz. Head: Dr. Jarmila Tauerová
Music Museum - 1932
Autographs and documents relating to the composer Antonín Dvořák (1841-1904), memorabilia (his viola, piano and other personal things) 07575

Muzeum Bedřicha Smetany (Bedřich Smetana Museum), Novotného lávka 1, 110 00 Praha 1 - T: (02) 22220082, Fax: 22220082, Internet: http://www.nm.cz. Head: Dr. Olga Mojžíšová
Music Museum - 1926
Memorabilia on the composer Bedřich Smetana (1824-1884), compositions, diaries, drawings, works of art, documents, correspondence, iconography, playbills and posters, personal belongings 07576

Muzeum české hudby, Národní muzeum (Museum of Czech Music), Novotného lávka 1, 110 00 Praha 1 - T: (02) 24229075. Head: Dr. Markéta Hallová
Music Museum - 1946
History of music, musical instruments from the 16th to 19th c 07577

Muzeum Hlavniho Města Prahy (The City of Prague Museum), Na Poříčí 52, 110 00 Praha 1 - T: (02) 24223696, Fax: 24214306, E-mail: muzeum@muzeumprahy.cz, Internet: http://www.muzeumprahy.cz. Head: Z. Strnadová
Local Museum - 1883
History of the city, fine art, archeology, architecture - library 07578

Muzeum Tělovýchovy a Sportu, Historické Muzeum (Muzeum of Sport Education and Sport), Ujezd 450, Tyrštův dům, 110 00 Praha
Special Museum - 1924
Documents about the development of physical training and sport, history of physical culture 07579

Náprstkovo Muzeum Asijských, Afrických a Amerických Kultur, Národní muzeum (Náprstek Museum of Asian, African and American Culture), Betlémské nám 1, 110 00 Praha 1 - T: (02) 22221416/17, 22220017, Fax: 22221418, E-mail: npm@aconet.cz, Internet: http://www.aconet.cz/npm. Head: Dr. Jana Součková
Ethnology Museum / Decorative Arts Museum / Fine Arts Museum - 1862
Ethnology, archaeology, oriental art, handicraft, numismatics, musical instruments, historical photographs, folk art - library, archives 07580

Národni Dům na Smíchově, nam 14. října 16, Praha 5 - T: (02) 57324605
Fine Arts Museum
Paintings of Miro, Dali, Picasso, Gaudi et al 07581

Národní Muzeum (National Museum), Václavské nám 68, 115 79 Praha 1 - T: (02) 24497111, Fax: 24226488, E-mail: nm@nm.cz, Internet: http://www.nm.cz. Head: Dr. Milan Stloukal
Local Museum / Ethnology Museum / Library with Exhibitions / Archaeological Museum / Historical Museum / Museum of Classical Antiquities / Folklore Museum / Music Museum / Natural History Museum - 1818
Natural history, history, Asian, African and American cultures, Czech music - library, archive 07582

Národní Technické Muzeum (National Technical Museum), Kostelní 42, 170 78 Praha 7 - T: (02) 20399111, Fax: 33371801, E-mail: info@ntm.cz, Internet: http://www.ntm.cz. Head: Dr. Ivo Janoušek
Science&Tech Museum - 1908
Permanent exhibition of engineering, transport, mining, metallurgy, cinematography, photography, broadcasting, television, astronomy, acoustics, telecommunication technology - library, educational and documentation section 07583

Národní Zemědělské Muzeum (National Museum of Agriculture), Kostelní 44, 170 00 Praha - T: (02) 33379025, Fax: 33372561, E-mail: nzm.praha@telecom.cz. Head: A. Hájek
Agriculture Museum - 1891
library 07584

Národopisné Odděleni, Historické Muzeum, Národní Muzeum v Praze (Ethnographical Department of the Historical Museum), Kinského zahrada 97, 150 00 Praha - T: (02) 57325766, 57327893, Fax: 57323063. Head: Dr. Jiřina Langhammerová
Ethnology Museum - 1895
Ethnography, development of Czech folk culture (textiles, costumes, furniture, ceramics, folk art), coll of Slavic folk culture and folk culture of Europe 07585

Nejvyssi Purkrabstvi (Supreme Burgrave's House), Pražsky Hrad, 119 01 Praha - T: (02) 24373368, Internet: http://www.hrad.cz
Public Gallery
Creative art, photography 07586

Obecní Dům, nám Republiky 5, 111 21 Praha 1 - T: (02) 22002101, Fax: 22002100, E-mail: info@obecni-dum.cz, Internet: http://www.obecnidum.cz. Head: František Laudat
Public Gallery 07587

Obrazárna Pražského Hradu (Prague Castle Gallery), Pražsky Hrad, 119 01 Praha - T: (02) 24373368, Fax: 24373238, E-mail: Frantisek.Kadlec@hrad.cz, Internet: http://www.hrad.cz. Head: Dr. František Kadlec
Fine Arts Museum / Public Gallery
Coll of European, esp Czech art 16th - 18th c 07588

Palác Kinských, Národní galerie v Praze, Staroměstske nám 12, 110 15 Praha 1 - T: (02) 24810758, Internet: http://www.ngprague.cz
Fine Arts Museum
Prints, drawings, graphic art 07589

Památník Národního Písemnictví (Muzeum České Literatury) (Museum of Czech Literature), Strahovské nádvoří 132, 118 38 Praha 1 - T: (02) 20516695, Fax: 20517277, E-mail: post@pamatniknarodnihopisemnictvi.cz, Internet: http://www.pamatniknarodnihopisemnictvi.cz. Head: Dr. Eva Wolfová
Special Museum - 1953
Coll of the development of Czech literature of the 19th and 20th c: literary archives containing 6 million objects, library of Czech Literature containing 500,000 books, art coll containing ca 400,000 objects 07590

Památník W.A. Mozarta a Manželů Duškových, Bertramka, Mozartova ul 169, 150 00 Praha 5 - T: (02) 57316753, 57318461, Fax: 57316753, E-mail: mozart@bertramka.cz, Internet: http://www.bertramka.cz. Head: Dr. Vlasta Cibulová
Music Museum - 1927
Memorabilia on W.A. Mozart, his visits in Prague (1786-1791) and his hosts the Dušeks 07591

Pedagogické Muzeum Jana Ámoše Komenského (Jan Amos Comenius Pedagogical Museum), Valdštejnská ul 20, 118 00 Praha 1 - T: (02) 57320039, Fax: 530997, E-mail: pmjak@bon.cz, Internet: http://www.pmjak.cz. Head: Ludovít Emanuel
Special Museum - 1891
Documents illustrating the development of Czechoslovak education and the life and work of Jan Amos Comenius 07592

Poštovní Muzeum (Postal Museum), Nové Mlýny 2, 110 00 Praha 1 - T: (02) 2312006, Fax: 2311930, E-mail: museumcp@pha.pvtnet.cz, Internet: http://www.cpost.cz. Head: Dr. Pavel Čtvrtník
Historical Museum - 1918
Documents of postal history, stamp coll 07593

Přírodovědecké muzeum, Národní muzeum (Natural History Museum of the National Museum), Václavské nám 68, 115 79 Praha 1 - T: (02) 24497271, 24222550, Fax: 24226488, E-mail: jirí.cejka@nm.cz, Internet: http://www.nm.cz. Head: Dr. Jiří Čejka
Natural History Museum - 1818
Mineralogy, petrography, geology, paleontology, botany, mycology, entomology, zoology, anthropology - research chemistry division, bird ringing centre 07594

Starý Královsky Palác (Old Royal Palace), Pražsky Hrad, 119 01 Praha - T: (02) 24373368, Fax: 24373238, E-mail: Frantisek.Kadlec@hrad.cz, Internet: http://www.hrad.cz. Head: Dr. František Kadlec
Public Gallery
Creative art 07595

Šternberský Palác, Národní Galerie v Praže (National Gallery in Prague), Hradčanské nám 15, 119 04 Praha 1 - T: (02) 2329331, Fax: 2324641, Internet: http://www.ngprague.cz. Head: Dagmar Šefčíková, Milan Knizak
Fine Arts Museum - 1796
Coll of Old Masters (early Czech art, early European art, 19th c Czech art), coll of Asian art, coll of prints and drawings, coll of modern and contemporary art (Czech modern art 1900-1960, Czech art 1969-1995, 19th/20th c French art, 20th c European art) - archive, library, conservation 07596

Strahovská Obrazárna (Strahov Gallery), Strahovské nádvoří 1, 118 00 Praha 1 - T: (02) 20517278, Fax: http://www.strahovmonastery.cz, E-mail: art.strahov@volny.cz. Head: Libor Šturc
Fine Arts Museum
Czech and European painting of the gothic, mannerism and baroque periods 07597

Středoevropská Galerie a Nakladatelství, Masarykovo nábřeží 250, 110 00 Praha - T: (02) 291807, 90001044/45, Fax: 90001044/45. Head: Simeona Hošková
Public Gallery 07598

Uměleckoprůmyslové Muzeum v Praze (Museum of Decorative Arts in Prague), ul 17 Listopadu 2, 110 01 Praha 1 - T: (02) 5109311, Fax: 24811666, E-mail: upm.direct@volny.cz, Internet: http://www.upm.praha. Head: Dr. Helena Koenigsmarková
Decorative Arts Museum - 1885
One of the largest coll of glass in the world, ceramics, porcelain, textiles, furniture, gold and silver works, prints, photography, metal works, posters, clocks - library, Josef Sudek's Gallery 07599

Veletržní Palác, Národní galerie v Praze, Dukelských hrdinů 47, 170 00 Praha 7 - T: (02) 24301111, Fax: 33376243, E-mail: smsu@ngprague.cz, Internet: http://www.ngprague.cz. Head: Milan Knížák
Fine Arts Museum
European and esp. Czech art of the 19th, 20th and 21st cc 07600

Vojenské Historické Muzeum (Military Historical Museum), Hradčanské nám 2, 110 00 Praha 1 - T: (02) 536488
Military Museum - 1918
Development of Czech and Slovak military history from the 10th c onwards 07601

Zámek Troja, Galerie Hlavního Města Prahy, U Trojského Zámku 1, 170 00 Praha 7 - T: (02) 83851627, Fax: 83851626, E-mail: troja-ghmp@volny.cz, Internet: http://www.citygalleryprague.cz. Head: Jaroslav Fatka
Fine Arts Museum
Coll of Czech art 19th c 07602

Zámek Zbraslav, Národní galerie v Praze (Zbraslav Castle, National Gallery, Collection of Asian Art), Bartoňova 2, 156 00 Praha 5 - T: (02) 57921638/39, Fax: 57921929, E-mail: asiainfo@ngprague.cz, Internet: http://www.ngprague.cz. Head: Dr. Filip Suchomel
Fine Arts Museum
Asian art 07603

Židovské Muzeum v Praze (Jewish Museum in Prague), U stare školy 1, 110 01 Praha 1 - T: (02) 24819456, Fax: 24819458, E-mail: office@jewishmuseum.cz, Internet: http://

www.jewishmuseum.cz. Head: Dr. Leo Pavlát
Historical Museum / Fine Arts Museum / Religious Arts Museum / Ethnology Museum / Public Gallery - 1906
Coll of Jewish art from Bohemia and Moravia: silver and other metal liturgical objects, synagogue textiles, rare manuscripts and prints, books, archives of Bohemian and Moravian Jewish communities, works of Czech Jewish painters children's drawings from the concentration camp in Terezín/Theresienstadt, Historical buildings and sites: Maisel, Spanish, Klausen and Pinkas Synagogue, Old Jewish Cemetery, Ceremonial Hall (Chevra Kaddishah) - Robert Guttmann Gallery, library, educational and cultural centre, reservation centre 07604

Přelouč

Městské Muzeum, Pardubická ul, 535 01 Přelouč - T: (0457) 2628. Head: Martina Matoušková
Local Museum - 1902
Ornithology, archeology, local history, ethnography, handicrafts, numismatics 07605

Přerov

Muzeum Komenského v Přerově (Comenius Museum Přerov), Horní nám 1, 751 52 Přerov - T: (0641) 307295, Fax: 219380, E-mail: muzeum.prerov@telecom.cz, Internet: http://muzeum.prerov.net. Head: Dr. František Hýbl
Local Museum - 1888
Archeology, history, folklore, natural history, education - Helfštýn-Castle; Moravian Ornitological Station 07606

Polabské Národnopisné Muzeum (Ethnographic Museum of the Elbe Region), Skanzen, 750 00 Přerov
Ethnology Museum - 1896
Ethnography, folk architecture, peasant furniture, household equipment 07607

Příbor

Okresní Vlastivědné Muzeum Nový Jičín, Městské Muzeum (Town Museum of Příbor), Lidická 50, 742 58 Příbor - T: (0656) 911252
Local Museum - 1912
History of the town and school education, coll depicting the life and work of Sigmund Freud (1856-1939) 07608

Příbram

Okresní Muzeum Příbram, Hornické Muzeum (Mining Museum), nám Hynka Kličky 293, 261 02 Příbram - T: (0306) 626675, 626307, Fax: 622566, E-mail: muzeum_pribram@volny.cz, Internet: http://www.pb.cz/muzeum. Head: Dr. Josef Velfl
Local Museum - 1886
Mining hist, ethnography, handicrafts, Prokop Schaft, mine's machine-room, steam-engine from 1914, geology, mineralogy 07609

Přibyslav

Hasičské Muzeum, Zámek, Husova 300, 582 22 Přibyslav
Public Gallery 07610

Městské Muzeum, Vyšehrad 271, 582 22 Přibyslav - T: (0451) 82361
Local Museum 07611

Proseč u Skutče

Památník Terezy Novákové, nám 61, 539 44 Proseč u Skutče - T: (0454) 321137, Fax: 321327, E-mail: prosec@unet.cz. Head: Stanislava Češková
Special Museum - 1961
Coll illustrating the life and work of the writers Tereza Novákova and Thomas and Heinrich Mann, pipes production, old architecture, folklore 07612

Prostějov

Muzeum Prostějovska, nám T.G. Masaryka 2, 796 01 Prostějov - T: (0508) 330991, Fax: 344798, E-mail: muzeum@muzeumpv.cz, Internet: http://www.muzeumpv.cz. Head: Václav Hruška
Local Museum - 1894
Local history, natural history (especially botany, entomology, geology), archeology, ethnography, handicrafts, numismatics, literary archive, memorabilia on the poet Jiří Wolker, coll of clocks 07613

Protivín

Městské Muzeum, nám 19, 398 11 Protivín - T: (0362) 92471. Head: Václav Bartoš
Local Museum - 1932
Local history, archeology, ethnography, handicrafts 07614

Průhonice

Botanické Oddělení Národniho Muzea (Botany Department of the National Museum), Zámek Průhonice u Prahy, 252 43 Průhonice - T: (02) 67750024, Fax: 67750024, E-mail: museum@ibot.cas.cz. Head: Jindřich Chrtek
Natural History Museum - 1818
Vascular plants and mosses - herbarium, botanical library 07615

Radnice u Rokycan

Městské Muzeum (City Museum), nám K. Šternberka 2, 338 28 Radnice u Rokycan - E-mail: MK.Radnice@seznam.cz. Head: Alena Kratochvílová
Local Museum - 1892
Paleobotany, mineralogy, history, ethnography, library (e.g. library of first book-club in Bohemia, medical library from 18.-19. c, books from Czech Natinal Revival, etc.), coll of Václav Kočka - Amort, archeology, theatrical coll (amateur theatricals in Radnice) - library 07616

Rakovník

Okresní Muzeum, Vysoká 95, 269 00 Rakovník - T: (0313) 513953
Local Museum - 1894
Mineralogy, paleontology, archeology, ethnography, local history, handicrafts, art 07617

Říčany u Prahy

Městské Vlastivědné Mudruňkovo Muzeum, Rýdlova 271, 251 01 Říčany u Prahy - T: (0204) 603161
Local Museum 07618

Rokycany

Muzeum Bicyklů, Jiráskova 208, 337 01 Rokycany - T: (0181) 725224
Science&Tech Museum 07619

Muzeum Dr. Bohuslava Horáka (Regional Museum of Dr. Bohuslav Horák), Urbanovo nám 141, 337 01 Rokycany - T: (0181) 722160, Fax: 723548, E-mail: muzeumro@proactive.cz, Internet: http://www.proactive.cz/muzeumro. Head: Dr. Miroslava Šandová
Local Museum - 1905
Paleontology, history of the regional iron industry, handicrafts - library, water hammer 07620

Ronov nad Doubravou

Galerie Antonína Chittussiho (Gallery of Antonín Chittussi), Čáslavská 309, 538 42 Ronov nad Doubravou - T: (0455) 90102, Fax: 690276, E-mail: ronov@zde.cz, Internet: http://www.ronov.zde.cz. Head: Zdeněk Sejček
Fine Arts Museum - 1961
Memorabilia on the painter Antonín Chittussi 07621

Roudnice nad Labem

Galerie Výtvarného Umění (Fine Art Gallery), Očkova 5, 413 01 Roudnice nad Labem - T: (0411) 837301, Fax: 837301. Head: Dr. Miroslava Hlaváčková
Fine Arts Museum - 1910
19th-20th c Czech paintings, currant art 07622

Roždalovice

Památník Jiřího Melantricha z Aventýna, Polabské muzeum Poděbrady, 289 34 Roždalovice
Special Museum - 1952
Memorial to Jiří Melantrich z Aventýna, history of letter printing 07623

Rožmitál pod Třemšínem

Městské Muzeum a Památník Jakuba Jana Ryby, Old School, 262 42 Rožmitál pod Třemšínem - T: (0306) 965339. Head: Miloš Zvelebil
Local Museum - 1920
Local history, memorabilia on the schoolmaster and musician Jakub Jan Ryba, heraldic coll - gallery 07624

Rožnov pod Radhoštěm

Valašské Muzeum v Přírodě (Vallachian Open-Air Museum), Palackého 147, 756 61 Rožnov pod Radhoštěm - T: (0651) 757111, Fax: 654712, E-mail: muzeum@applet.cz. Head: Dr. Jaroslav Štika, Dr. Vitezlaw Koukal
Open Air Museum
17th-19th c life of the Carpathian population, trades, folk art, agriculture, apiculture, sheep breeding, in 42 original buildings - library 07625

Roztoky u Prahy

Středočeské Muzeum (Museum of Central Bohemia), Zámek 1, 252 63 Roztoky u Prahy - T: (02) 209100167, Fax: 20911015, E-mail: smr@smr.anet.cz. Head: Eva Balaštíková
Local Museum - 1957
Local natural hist, archeology from Central Bohemia, local ethnology, history, art - conservation radiation facility, plasmachemical laboratory 07626

Rtyně v Podkrkonoší

Památník Selského Povstání, Městske muzeum, Býv. Rychta č 1775, 542 33 Rtyně v Podkrkonoší - T: 936414
Historical Museum - 1963
Coll depicting the peasant revolt of 1775 07627

Rudice

Větrný Mlýn, Radniční 7, Rudice - T: (0506) 443528
Science&Tech Museum 07628

Rumburk

Muzeum Rumburk, Na Valech 401, 408 01 Rumburk - T: (0413) 332194
Local Museum 07629

Rychnov nad Kněžnou

Muzeum Orlických Hor, Zámek 1, Javornická 12, 516 01 Rychnov nad Kněžnou - T: (0445) 21450
Local Museum - 1892
Local history, ethnology, ethnography, zoology, herpetology, handicrafts 07630

Orlická Galerie, Státni Zámek, 516 01 Rychnov nad Kněžnou - T: (0445) 21015
Fine Arts Museum - 1965
20th c Czech art 07631

Rýmařov

Městské Muzeum (City Museum), Nám Míru 6, 795 01 Rýmařov - T: (0647) 211770, E-mail: museum.n@worldonline.cz. Head: Jiří Karel
Local Museum
Geology and history of the Rýmařov region, seasonal exhibitions of art 07632

Sadská

Městské Muzeum, Palackého nám 257, 289 12 Sadská - T: (0325) 594521. Head: Drahomíra Krátká
Historical Museum - 1909/1910
Local history, archeology and ethnography 07633

Sedlčany

Městské Muzeum, nám T.G. Masaryka 34, 264 01 Sedlčany - T: (0304) 822742, 582, Fax: 875666. Head: Jiří Páv
Local Museum - 1894
Archeology, local history, memorabilia on Josef Suk 07634

Semily

Muzeum a Pojizerská Galerie, Husova 2, 513 01 Semily - T: (0431) 622528. Head: Igor Činovec
Local Museum / Fine Arts Museum - 1960
Regional labour movement, memorabilia on the writers Antal Stašek and Ivan Olbracht 07635

Skuteč

Městské Muzeum (Town Museum), Rybičkova 364, 539 73 Skuteč - T: (0454) 350131. Head: Jana Zemanová
Local Museum - 1910
Geological coll, ornithological coll, shoemaker's coll, production of pipes and toys 07636

Slany

Vlastivědné Muzeum, Masarykovo nám 159, 274 01 Slany - T: (0314) 522209, E-mail: muzeum@slansko.cz, Internet: http://www.slansko.cz/muzeum. Head: Božena Franková
Local Museum - 1885
Local geography, paleontology, entomology, ornithology, archeology, medieval ceramics, handicrafts, ethnography of the region, folk art, art coll 07637

Slapanice

Městské Muzeum, Masarykovo nám 4, 664 51 Slapanice - T: (05) 442228029
Local Museum - 1933
Geology, local history, ethnology, handicrafts, paintings by Alois Kalvoda 07638

Slatiňany

Hippologické Muzeum (Hippological Museum), Zámek, 538 21 Slatiňany - T: (0455) 681112, Fax: 681112. Head: Jaroslav Havlíček
Special Museum - 1947
Anatomy, engravings, oil-paintings, pictures, china, books (hippological library), saddles, harnesses, horseshoes coll, farriery 07639

Slavkov u Brna

Historické Muzeum (Historical Museum), Palackého nám 1, Zámek, 684 01 Slavkov u Brna - T: (05) 44221635, Fax: 44221685. Head: Jan Špatný
Historical Museum / Military Museum - 1935
Coll from the Napoleonic wars with a special exhibition of the battle of Slavkov (Austerlitz), local hist, ethnography, furniture, Baroque Château with Baroque picture gallery - gallery 07640

Soběslav

Rožmberský Dům, Husitske Muzeum v Táboře (Rozmberk's House - Hussite Museum), Petra Voka 152, 392 01 Soběslav - T: (0363) 524425, E-mail: muzeum.sobeslav@quick.cz, Internet: http://www.tabor.cz/muzeum. Head: Dr. Miloš Drda
Natural History Museum - 1896
Mineralogy, geology, botany, zoology, entomology, ichthyology 07641

Smrčkův Dům, Husitske Muzeum v Táboře (Smrcka's House - Hussite Museum), nám Republiky 107, 392 01 Soběslav - T: (0363) 524853. Head: Dr. Miloš Drda
Historical Museum - 1896
Ethnography, local and regional history 07642

Sokolov

Okresní Muzeum Sokolov (Regional Museum), Zámecká 1, 356 00 Sokolov - T: (0168) 623930, Fax: 602217, E-mail: muzeum@omks, Internet: http://www.volny.cz/muzeumsokolov. Head: Pavel Beran
Local Museum / Science&Tech Museum - 1934
Mineralogy, petrology, botany, entomology, local hist, hist of the local mining industry, local archeology, ecology 07643

Stará Huť u Dobříše

Památník Karla Čapka (Memorial House of Karel Čapek), Na Strži 125, 262 02 Stará Huť u Dobříše - T: (0305) 522265, Fax: 520649, E-mail: pamatnik.vanova@worldonline.cz, Internet: http://www.capek-karel-pamatnik.cz. Head: Kristina Váňová
Special Museum - 1963
Memorabilia on the writer Karel Čapek, his brother the painter Josef Čapek and his wife Olga Scheinflugová, in Čapek's former summer house 07644

Šternberk

Muzeum Hodin (Horology Museum), Státní Hrad Šternberk, 785 01 Šternberk - T: (0643) 2714. Head: Dr. Anežka Simková
Science&Tech Museum - 1907
History of watch-making, historical clocks and watches, present watch-making industry at Šternberk 07645

Strakonice

Muzeum Středniho Pootavi (Museum of the Middle Otava Area), Hrad 1, 386 00 Strakonice - T: (0342) 321537, Fax: 333391, E-mail: muzeu@strakonice.cz, Internet: http://www.muzeum.strakonice.cz. Head: Dr. Ivana Říhová
Local Museum - 1895
Coll of bagpipes from Czech and the world; geology, archeology, historical documents, trades, industry, art history, numismatics, literary history, memorabilia of the poet František L. Čelákovsky 07646

Štramberk

Muzeum ve Štramberku, Náměstí 31, 742 66 Štramberk - T: (0656) 852284
Local Museum - 1899
Local geology and paleontology, ethnography, history 07647

Strážnice

Městské Muzeum, 692 62 Strážnice - T: (0631) 334155
Local Museum 07648

Stříbro

Městské Muzeum (Town Museum), Masarykovo nám 21, 349 01 Stříbro - T: (0183) 622214. Head: Ivona Lojdová
Local Museum - 1930
Mineralogy, paleontology, local archeology and history, local mining 07649

Studénka

Vagonářské Muzeum (Museum of Carriages), Panská 229, 742 13 Studénka - T: (0655) 401285. Head: Dr. Svatomír Černín
Science&Tech Museum - 1956
History of carriages and coaches 07650

Šumperk

Okresní Vlastivědné Muzeum, Hlavní tr 22, 787 31 Šumperk - T: (0649) 214070, 214908, Fax: 214909, E-mail: ovmsumperk@seznam.cz, Internet: http://ovmsumperk.webpark.cz. Head: Miloš Melzer
Local Museum / Natural History Museum - 1896
Local botany, entomology and zoology, history, handicrafts, labour movement 07651

Sušice

Muzeum Šumavy, nám Svobody 40, 342 01 Sušice 1 - T: (0187) 8850. Head: Dr. Vladimír Horpeniak
Local Museum - 1880
Local archeology and history, handicrafts, ethnography, local glass making, match industry 07652

Švihov

Švihov Hrad, 340 12 Švihov - T: (0186) 693378
Historical Museum 07653

Svitavy

Městské Muzeum a Galerie, Máchova alej 1, 568 02 Svitavy - T: (0461) 21704, E-mail: muzeum@booksy.cz, Internet: http://www.muzeum.svitavy.cz. Head: Blanka Čuhelová
Local Museum / Historical Museum / Science&Tech Museum
Local history, Hist. of washing machines; Oskar Schindler 07654

Okresni Vlastivedné Muzeum → Městské Muzeum a Galerie

Sychrov

Zámek Sychrov, 463 44 Sychrov - T: (048) 5146079
Historical Museum 07655

Tábor

Husitské Muzeum v Táboře (Hussite Museum in Tabor), nám Mikoláse z Husi 44, 390 01 Tábor - T: (0361) 252242, 251884, Fax: 252245, E-mail: muzeum@tabor.cz, Internet: http://www.tabor.cz/muzeum. Head: Dr. Miloš Drda
Historical Museum - 1878
Ancient history, medieval archeology, Hussite movement in Southern Bohemia, local architectural history, numismatics - library; expositions in Žižkovo nam.čp. 1 07656

Tachov

Okresní Muzeum (District Museum), Třída Míru 447, 347 01 Tachov - T: (0184) 722171. Head: Ivona Lojdová
Local Museum - 1933
Regional ethnography, natural history, handicrafts, Hussite movement 07657

Telč

Hrad Roštejn, Doupě 1, 588 56 Telč - T: (066) 962738. Head: Jitka Hošková
Decorative Arts Museum - 1964
Porcelain, ceramics, pewter, arms, nativity scene 07658

Muzeum Telč (Museum of Highlands), Zámek, nám Míru 1, 588 56 Telč - T: (066) 962918. Head: Jitka Hošková
Ethnology Museum / Decorative Arts Museum - 1886
Furniture, ceramics, arms, African sculputre by F.V. Foit, regional ethnography, folk art, historical crafts 07659

Teplice

Regionální Muzeum v Teplicích (Regional Museum in Teplice), Zámecké nám 14, 415 01 Teplice - T: (0417) 537869, Fax: 572300, E-mail: info@muzeum-teplice.cz, Internet: http://www.muzeum-teplice.cz. Head: Dr. Dušan Špička
Local Museum - 1894
Archeology, palaeontology, nature of North Western Bohemia, history, balneology, graphics, numismatics, porcelain, ceramics, glass, paintings (gothic to today), historical clocks - library 07660

Teplice nad Metují

Památník Románu Aloise Jiráska Skály, Zámek Skály, 549 57 Teplice nad Metují
Special Museum
Life and work of the writer Alois Jirásek, especially concerning his novel 'Skály' 07661

Terezín

Magdeburská Kasárna, Tyršova ul, 411 55 Terezín
Historical Museum 07662

Památník Terezín (Terezín Memorial), Alej Principova 304, 411 55 Terezín - T: (0416) 782225, Fax: 782245, E-mail: munk@pamatnik-terezin.cz. Head: Dr. Jan Munk
Historical Museum - 1947
Documents and materials illustrating the hist of the Nazi persecution policy in Bohemia and Moravia during WWII, esp the hist of the Gestapo prison in the Small Fortress and the Jewish ghetto in the town of Terezín as well as the concentration camp in Litoměřice 07663

Tišnov

Galerie Jamborův Dům, Kulturní Středisko, 666 01 Tišnov - T: (0504) 410082
Fine Arts Museum 07664

Podhorácké Muzeum, Porta Coeli 1, 666 02 Tišnov 2 - T: (0504) 412293. Head: Antonín Řeček
Local Museum
Local geology and mineralogy, paleontology 07665

Tovačov

Etnografické muzeum, Zámek, 751 01 Tovačov
Ethnology Museum / Archaeological Museum - 1936
Local archeology, ethnography, ceramics, glass, furniture, weapons 07666

Třeběchovice pod Orebem

Třebechovické Muzeum Betlémů (Museum of Nativity), Masarykovo nám 24, 503 46 Třeběchovice pod Orebem - T: (049) 5592053, Fax: 5592677, E-mail: tmb@wo.cz, Internet: http://www.betlem.cz. Head: Zita Zemanova
Special Museum - 1907
Cribs from Czech and Slovakia 07667

Třebenice

Muzeum Českého granátu (Museum of Czech Garnet), nám Loucké, 411 13 Třebenice
Science&Tech Museum - 1872
History of mining, processing and utilisation of garnets, mining techniques, mining ethnography 07668

Třebíč

Galerie Malovaný Dům, Karlovo nám 53, 647 01 Třebíč - T: (0618) 846153, 840459
Public Gallery 07669

Západomoravské Muzeum v Třebíči (West-Moravian Museum in Třebíč), Zámek 1, 674 01 Třebíč - T: (0618) 840518, Fax: 840518, E-mail: muzeum@zmm.cz, Internet: http://www.zmm.cz. Head: Jaroslav Martínek
Local Museum / Natural History Museum - 1898
Botany, geology, mineralogy of Western Moravia, zoology, archeology, ethnography, art, hist, nativity scenes, pipes 07670

Třebíz

Národopisné Muzeum Třebíz, 273 75 Třebíz - T: (0314) 522209. Head: Božena Franková
Open Air Museum / Folklore Museum
Rural buildings from the Slánsko region, furnishings, domestic utensils 07671

Památník Václava Beneše Třebízského, 273 75 Třebíz 19
Special Museum
Memorabilia on the priest and writer V.B. Třebízský in his former home 07672

Třešt

Muzeum Třešť' (Museum of Highlands), nám T.G. Masaryka 103, 589 01 Třešt - T: (066) 7224128. Head: Jitka Hošková
Local Museum - 1933
Nativity scenes, handicrafts, manufacture of matches 07673

Třinec

Muzeum Třineckých Železáren, Frýdecká 389, 739 61 Třinec - T: (0659) 435501
Local Museum 07674

Trutnov

Muzeum Podkrkonoší, Školní, 541 00 Trutnov - T: (0439) 811897, Fax: 811897, E-mail: muzeum@muzeumtrutnov.cz, Internet: http://www.muzeumtrutnov.cz. Head: Dr. Milada Ryšánková
Local Museum - 1890
Ethnography, local archeology, history, regional arts, military, clocks - library, archive 07675

Turnov

Expozice Historického Nábytku 16.-19. a Oděvů 19. Století (Historical Collection of Furnishings 16th-19th c and Costumes 19th c), Zámek Hrubý Rohozec, 511 01 Turnov - T: (02) 24811241, Fax: 24811666. Head: Dr. Helena Koenigsmarková
Decorative Arts Museum - 1885
Furnishings, interiors, costumes, fashion 07676

Muzeum Českého Ráje (Museum of the Bohemian Paradise), Skálova 71, 511 01 Turnov - T: (0436) 322106, Fax: 325277, E-mail: jakoubeova@museum-turnov.cz. Head: Dr. Vladimíra Jakoubeová
Natural History Museum / Special Museum - 1886
Mineralogy, precious stone processing, jewellery of the 19th and 20th c, ethnology, prehistory, local cultural history 07677

Týn nad Bečvou

HelfštybOn Hrad, 751 31 Týn nad Bečvou - T: (0641) 797073
Historical Museum 07678

Týn nad Vltavou

Muzeum Týn nad Vltavou, nám Míru 1, 375 01 Týn nad Vltavou - T: (0334) 22659. Head: Marie Rychlíková
Local Museum / Natural History Museum - 1932
Local natural history, ethnography, popular musical instruments, construction of rafts and ships 07679

Týnec nad Sázavou

Muzeum Tynecké Keramiky (Ceramics Museum), Nádvoří Adama Hodějovského 48, 257 41 Týnec nad Sázavou - T: (0301) 901431. Head: Václav Stejskal
Decorative Arts Museum - 1955
History of ceramics manufacture (18th-19th c), history of the spinning mill at Brodce, labour movement 07680

Uherské Hradiště

Slovácké Muzeum (Slovácko Museum), Smetanovy sady 179, 686 11 Uherské Hradiště - T: (0632) 551370, Fax: 551059. Head: Dr. Ivo Frolec
Ethnology Museum / Archaeological Museum - 1914
Ethnography of Moravian Slovakia, archeology, local history, fine arts, folk costumes - library 07681

Uherský Brod

Muzeum Jana Ámoše Komenského v Uherském Brodě, Přemysla Otakara II 37, 688 12 Uherský Brod - T: (0633) 632288, Fax: 634078, E-mail: muzeum@muzeum.ub.brod.cz, Internet: http://www.muzeum.uh.brod.cz. Head: Dr. Pavel Popelka
Special Museum - 1898
Ethnography, archaeology, applied arts, memorabilia of Jan Amos Comenius (1592-1670) - library 07682

Unhošt

Melicharovo Městské Muzeum, Dr. Beneše 1, 273 51 Unhošt
Local Museum - 1913
Prehistory and medieval archeology, local history, ethnography, handicrafts 07683

Úpice

Městské Muzeum, nám Vaduice, 542 32 Úpice
Local Museum - 1895
Regional ethnography, local history, local labour movement, memorabilia on the brothers Karel and Josef Čapek 07684

Úsov

Muzeum Úsov, 789 73 Úsov - T: (0648) 41287. Head: Dr. Miloš Melzer
Natural History Museum - 1900
Zoology, forestry, hunting - archives 07685

Ústí nad Labem

Muzeum Města Ústí nad Labem (Municipal Museum of Ústí nad Labem), Masarykova třída 3, 400 01 Ústí nad Labem - T: (047) 5210937, 5201116, Fax: 5211260, E-mail: muzeum.usti@ecn.cz, Internet: http://www.muzeumusti.cz. Head: Tomáš Wiesner
Local Museum - 1876
Archeology, local hist and industry, biology, geology, numismatics, prints, regional literature, art, weapons, Gothic sculptures, battles of Napoleon's wars 07686

Ústí nad Orlicí

Výstavní Síň Muzea, Mírové nám 7, 562 01 Ústí nad Orlicí - T: (0465) 524687
Fine Arts Museum 07687

Valašské Klobouky

Městské Muzeum (Town Museum), Masarykovo nám 276, 766 01 Valašské Klobouky - T: (0636) 320095. Head: Petr Odehnal
Local Museum / Natural History Museum - 1933
Local natural history, archeology, ethnography, handicrafts, local history 07688

Valašské Meziříčí

Okresní Vlastivědné Muzeum Vsetín, Zamek Kinských, Zámecká 3, 757 00 Valašské Meziříčí - T: (0651) 611764, Fax: 611764. Head: Dr. Tomáš Mikulaštík
Local Museum / Natural History Museum - 1884
Local geology, botany, paleontology, zoology, prehist, ceramics, numismatics, militaria, literary hist, handicraft, ethnography - Lapidarium Saint Trinity Church 07689

Valtice

Národní Zemědělské Muzeum v Praze, Úsek Valtice (National Museum of Agriculture), nám Svobody 8, 691 42 Valtice - T: (0627) 352037, 352144, Fax: 352144, E-mail: nzm@email.cz. Head: Jaroslav Pokorný
Agriculture Museum - 1954
Ecology, horticulture in Czech Republic, hunting - libraries 07690

Vamberk

Muzeum Krajky (Lace museum), Husovo nám 88, 517 54 Vamberk - T: (0445) 541518, E-mail: omoh@rychnov.czcom.cz, Internet: http://www.vkm.net. Head: Irena Krejčí
Decorative Arts Museum - 1929
History of Czech lace 07691

Velká Bíteš

Městské Muzeum (Museum of Velká Bíteš), Masarykovo nám 5, 595 01 Velká Bíteš - T: (0619) 532383, Fax: 532383. Head: Silva Smutná
Local Museum - 1925
Local history 07692

Velké Březno

Zámek Velké Březno, Zámek, 691 02 Velké Březno - T: (047) 5145331
Historical Museum 07693

Velké Karlovice

Karlovské Muzeum, 756 06 Velké Karlovice - T: (0657) 644019. Head: Karel Vašut
Local Museum - 1971
Local history, ethnography 07694

Velké Losiny

Papírna Muzeum, 788 15 Velké Losiny - T: (0649) 248433
Fine Arts Museum 07695

Velké Meziřiči

Muzeum Silnic a Dálnic ČR (Museum of roads and motorways of the ČR), Zámek, 594 01 Velké Meziřiči - T: (0619) 522773, 522206, Fax: 522773. Head: Dr. Marie Ripperová
Special Museum - 1893
Shells, fishes, birds, sculptures, history, transport 07696

Veltrusy

Zámek Veltrusy, Zámek, 277 46 Veltrusy - T: (0205) 781144
Historical Museum 07697

Velvary

Městské Muzeum a Galerie J. Karse, Pražska 109, 273 24 Velvary - T: (0205) 761419. Head: Vilma Sklenářová
Archaeological Museum / Ethnology Museum / Historical Museum / Fine Arts Museum - 1913
Local archeology, ethnography, history, applied art 07698

Veselí nad Lužnicí

Weisův Dům, Husitské Muzeum v Táboře (Hussite Museum - Weis' House), nám T.G. Masaryka 111, 391 81 Veselí nad Lužnicí - T: (0363) 583376. Head: Dr. Miloš Drda
Local Museum - 1926
Local history, applied art, paintings, sculpture 07699

Veselí nad Moravou

Městské Muzeum, Bartolomějské nám 41, 698 01 Veselí nad Moravou - T: (0631) 322412
Local Museum - 1907
Archeology, paleontology, ethnography, history 07700

Vimperk

Městské Muzeum, Zámek 20, 385 01 Vimperk
Local Museum - 1956
Regional natural history, history of the town, history of glass making, lumbering, local printing 07701

Vizovice

Zámek Vizovice, Palackého 376, 763 12 Vizovice - T: (067) 7452762, Fax: 7452762, E-mail: zaamek.vizovice@volny.cz, Internet: http://www.hyperlink.cz/zamek-viz. Head: Jana Pluhařová
Historical Museum 07702

Vlašim

Okresní Muzeum, Zámek, 258 01 Vlašim - T: (0303) 42927
Local Museum
Hist of Bebešov county 07703

Vodňany

Městské Muzeum a Galerie, nám Svobody 18, 389 01 Vodňany - T: (0342) 382075
Local Museum / Fine Arts Museum - 1895
Local history, archeology, handicrafts, fishery, ethnography, memorabilia on Július Zeyer and František Herites, art, literary history 07704

Vodochody

Malé Máslovické Muzeum Másla, Máslovice č 3, 250 69 Vodochody - T: (02) 20940235, Fax: 20940235
Local Museum 07705

Volyně

Městské Muzeum, Školní 112, 387 01 Volyně - T: (0342) 372481
Local Museum - 1912
Local mineralogy, archeology, history 07706

Vrchlabí

Krkonošské Muzeum (Museum of the Krkonoše Mts.), nám Míru 222, 543 01 Vrchlabí - T: (0438) 456704, Fax: 422095, E-mail: muzeum@krnap.cz, Internet: http://www.krnap.cz/krnap/aktivity/muzeum/index.phpß. Head: Dr. Jana Sojková

Local Museum / Natural History Museum - 1883
Regional natural history, folk handicrafts, folk art, local history, plastic arts and painting, glass and porcelain - library, archive 07707

Muzeum Správy Krnap, Husva 213, 543 01 Vrchlabí - T: (0438) 285708
Science&Tech Museum 07708

Vrchotovy Janovice

Zámek, 257 53 Vrchotovy Janovice - T: (0302) 595181
Historical Museum 07709

Všeborice

Památník Zdeňka Fibicha, Dolní Kralovice, 257 68 Všeborice
Music Museum
Memorabilia on the composer Zdeněk Fibich in his former house 07710

Všestary

Památník Bitvy 1866 na Chlumu (1866 Battle of Chlum Memorial), Chlum 66, 503 12 Všestary - T: (049) 5951058, Fax: 5512899, E-mail: info@muzeumhk.cz, Internet: http://www.muzeumhk.cz. Head: Dr. Zdeněk Zahradník
Military Museum - 1936
Mementoes of the Austro-Prussian War and the Battle of Hradec Králové (Königgrätz) 07711

Vsetín

Okresní Vlastivědné Muzeum (District Museum in Vsetín), Horní nám 2, 755 01 Vsetín - T: (0657) 611690, Fax: 611689. Head: Dr. Tomáš Mikulaštík
Local Museum - 1924
History of the region, ethnography, archeology, art 07712

Vyškov

Muzeum Vyškovska, nám Čs. Armády 2, 682 01 Vyškov - T: (0507) 21040, Fax: 21040. Head: Dr. František Jordán
Local Museum / Natural History Museum - 1893
Regional geology, zoology, botany, paleontology, history, ethnography, art, archaeology, numismatics, folk ceramics, orientalist Alois Musil 07713

Vysoká u Příbrami

Památník Antonína Dvořáka (Antonin Dvořak Memorial House), Zámeček 69, Vysoká u Příbrami, mail addr: 262 42 Rožmitál pod Třemšínem - T: (0306) 918115, Fax: 618115, E-mail: pamatnik@antonindvorak.cz, Internet: http://www.antonindvorak.cz. Head: Vladimíra Šplíchalová
Music Museum
Memorabilia on A. Dvořák, especially concerning his opera 'Rusalka' 07714

Vysoké Mýto

Okresní Muzeum, Šemberova 125, 566 01 Vysoké Mýto - T: (0468) 522850/51, Fax: 522852, E-mail: muzeum@vysokemyto.cz. Head: Marcela Halouzková
Local Museum - 1884
Local archeology, ethnology, folk art, local history, literary archive, memorabilia an corresp. of the philologist Otmar Vanorny 07715

Vysoké nad Jizerou

Vlastivědné Muzeum, Dr. K. Farskeho nám 130, 512 11 Vysoké nad Jizerou - T: (0432) 593118
Folklore Museum / Historical Museum - 1930
Regional and folk art, history of skiing in the Krkonoše Mountains 07716

Vyšší Brod

Poštovní Muzeum (Post Museum), Former Convent, 382 73 Vyšší Brod
Special Museum
History of postal services and telecommunications in Czechoslovakia 07717

Zábřeh na Moravě

Muzeum, Žižkova 1, 789 00 Zábřeh na Moravě. Head: Miloš Melzer
Historical Museum / Ethnology Museum - 1930
History of the textile industry, local ethnography 07718

Žamberk

Městské Muzeum (Municipal Museum), Č. Armády 472, 564 01 Žamberk - T: (0446) 611678. Head: Marie Otavová
Special Museum / Local Museum - 1911
Memorabilia on the naturalist Prokop Diviš (1698-1765) and Eduard Albert (1841-1900), local ethnography 07719

Žatec

Regionální Muzeum K.A. Polánka, Husova 678, 438 01 Žatec - T: (0397) 749466, Fax: 749466, E-mail: rmz@oasanet.cz, Internet: http://www.zatecko.cz/muzeum.htm. Head: Dr. Radmila Holodňáková
Local Museum - 1896
Regional prehist, hist of the town, handicrafts 07720

Zámek Líčkov, Líčkov 1, 438 01 Žatec - T: (0397) 765022
Historical Museum 07721

Zbiroh

Městské Muzeum (Town Museum), Masarykovo nám 28, 338 08 Zbiroh - T: (0181) 794078. Head: Dagmar Viletová
Local Museum / Ethnology Museum - 1933
Local ethnography and history, handicrafts 07722

Muzeum J.V. Sládka (Museum of J.V. Sládek), Masarykovo nám 28, 338 08 Zbiroh - T: (0181) 794078. Head: Dagmar Viletová
Special Museum - 1952
Memorabilia on the poet Josef Václav Sládek (d. 1912) 07723

Zbraslav nad Vltavou

Sbírka Českého Sochařství (Museum of Czech Sculpture), 225 01 Zbraslav nad Vltavou
Fine Arts Museum
Sculpture 07724

Ždánice

Městské Vrbasovo Muzeum, Zámek 1, 696 32 Ždánice - T: (0629) 633665
Local Museum - 1942
Local archeology, ceramics, folk art, handicrafts 07725

Žďár nad Sázavou

Muzeum Knihy, Národní muzeum Praha (Book Museum Prague), Zámek, 591 02 Žďár nad Sázavou - T: (0616) 25370, Internet: http://www.nm.cz. Head: Helga Turkova, Alena Skwarlová
Special Museum - 1957
Invention and history of book printing, technical development of printing presses, book illustration, bookbinding, book art 07726

Regionální Muzeum, Tvrz 8, 591 00 Žďár nad Sázavou - T: (0616) 25687
Local Museum - 1934
Regional geology, mineralogy, botany, ethnography, local history, glass making, production of iron 07727

Žebrák

Muzeum Českého Krasu v Berouně - pobačka muzeum v Žebráku (Museum of Bohemian Karst Beroun, Branch Žebrák), Náměstí 89, 267 53 Žebrák - T: (0316) 533342. Head: Petr Kmínek
Local Museum - 1925
Local history and archeology, handicrafts, memorabilia on local writers and artists 07728

Železnice

Městské Muzeum a Galerie T.F. Simona, Muzejní nám 94, 507 13 Železnice
Local Museum / Fine Arts Museum - 1917
Local geology, mineralogy, paleontology, archeology, folk art, ethnography, paintings by T.F. Simon, F. Kaván, P. Zikmund etc 07729

Železný Brod

Městské Muzeum v Železném Brodě (Municipal Museum of Železný Brod), Běliště 57, 468 22 Železný Brod - T: (0428) 391149, 389081. Head: Jaroslava Jelinková
Historical Museum - 1998
Old crafts, folk architecture, old school 07730

Městské Muzeum v Železném Brodě (Municipal Museum Železný Brod), nám 3. května, 468 22 Železný Brod - T: (0428) 389081, 389770. Head: Jaroslava Jelinková
Decorative Arts Museum - 1870
Glass production illustrating the development of local glass-making 07731

Žirovnice

Vlastivědné Muzeum, Zámek, Branka 1, 394 68 Žirovnice - T: (0364) 494095
Local Museum / Fine Arts Museum - 1926
Local history, applied art 07732

Zlín

Muzeum Jihovýchodní Moravy (Museum of South-Eastern Moravia), Zámek Zlín, Soudní 1, 762 57 Zlín - T: (067) 7004611, Fax: 7004632, E-mail: info@muzeum.zlin.cz, Internet: http://www.muzeum.zlin.cz. Head: Dr. Ivan Plánka
Local Museum / Natural History Museum - 1953
Natural sciences, archaeology, ethnography, hist, historical shoes - library 07733

Obuvnické Muzeum (Shoe Museum), tř Tomáše Bati 1970, 762 57 Zlín, mail addr: POB 175, 762 57 Zlín - T: (067) 7213978, Fax: 7213978, E-mail: muzeum@mbox.vol.cz. Head: Miroslava Štýbrová
Science&Tech Museum - 1959
Hist of shoe production and technology 07734

Státní Galerie ve Zlíně (State Gallery of Fine Arts), nám T.G. Masaryka 2570, 762 27 Zlín - T: (067) 7210662, Fax: 32735, E-mail: sgz@avonet.cz, Internet: http://www.avonet.cz/sgz. Head: Dr. Ludvík Ševeček
Fine Arts Museum - 1953
Modern Czech art (19th-20th c), design, architecture 07735

Zlonice

Památník Antonína Dvořáka (Muzeum of A. Dvořák), Liehmannova 20, 273 71 Zlonice - T: (0314) 591244. Head: Zdenka Kuklová
Music Museum - 1954
Memorabilia on the composer Antonín Dvořák (1841-1904) 07736

Žlutice

Muzeum Husitstvi (Museum of the Hussite), Velké nám 1, 364 52 Žlutice - T: (089) 93357. Head: Květoslav Kroča
Local Museum - 1900
Local archeology, local history, especially Hussite period 07737

Znojmo

Dům Umění, Jihomoravské Muzeum ve Znojmě (House of Arts, South Moravian Museum), nám T.G. Masaryka 11, 669 45 Znojmo - T: (0624) 226529, Fax: 225210, E-mail: dumumenizn@volny.cz, Internet: http://www.znojmuz.cz. Head: Dr. Pavel Ciprian
Public Gallery / Fine Arts Museum
Fine art, works of J.T. Fischer 07738

Jihomoravské Muzeum ve Znojmě (South Moravian Museum), Minoritský klášter, Přemyslovců 6,, 669 45 Znojmo - T: (0624) 224961, Fax: 225210, E-mail: znojmuz@znojmuz.cz, Internet: http://www.znojmuz.cz. Head: Dr. Pavel Ciprian
Local Museum / Natural History Museum - 1878
Natural sciences and hist, ceramics, furniture, archeology, handicrafts, art, in a castle with 11th c chapel 07739

Památník Prokopa Diviše, Jihomoravské Muzeum ve Znojme (The Prokop Diviš Memorial), Přímětice 19, 66945 Znojmo, mail addr: Přemyslovců 6, 66945 Znojmo - T: (0624) 225210, 241914, Fax: 225210, E-mail: znojmuz@znojmuz.cz, Internet: http://www.znojmuz.cz. Head: Dr. Pavel Ciprian
Special Museum
Memorabilia on the naturalist Prokop Diviš (1698-1765) 07740

Znojemský Hrad, Jihomoravské Muzeum ve Znojmě (Castle of Znojmo, South Moravian Museum), Hradní 1, 669 45 Znojmo - T: (0624) 222311, Fax: 225210, E-mail: znojmuz@znojmuz.cz, Internet: http://www.znojmuz.cz. Head: Dr. Pavel Ciprian
Historical Museum / Decorative Arts Museum / Local Museum
Historical interior of the Znojmo castle, furniture, archeology, handicrafts and art from Znojmo 07741

Žumberk

Památník Venkovského Lidu, 538 36 Žumberk - T: (0335) 362124
Local Museum 07742

Denmark

Aabenraa

Aabenraa Museum, H.P. Hanssens G 33, 6200 Aabenraa - T: 74622645, Fax: 74632950. Head: Birgitte Kragh
Local Museum - 1887
Shipping and shipbuilding, foreign treasures brought home by sailors from travels abroad, local handicrafts, painted panels, furniture, silver, pottery - library 07743

Egnsmuseet Ll. Kolstrupgaard, Toften 37a, 6200 Aabenraa - T: 74622645
Local Museum - 1961
Furnishings, tools, peasant furniture 07744

Aalborg

Aalborg Historiske Museum, Alg 48, 9100 Aalborg, mail addr: Postboks 1805, 9100 - T: 96310410, Fax: 98161131, E-mail: aahm@aahm.dk, Internet: http://www.aahm.dk
Historical Museum / Archaeological Museum - 1863
Archaeological finds, local historical artefacts, applied art, silver, glass, panelled room from 1602, industrial period - library 07745

Danmarks Tekniske Museum Kommunikationsmuseet, Riihimäkivej 6, 9200 Aalborg - T: 98183711, Fax: 98183367. Head: Jens Breinegaard
Science&Tech Museum
All types of communication devices, old typewriters, telegraphs, radios 07746

Nordjyllands Kunstmuseum, Kong Christians Allé 50, 9000 Aalborg - T: 98138088, Fax: 98162820, E-mail: nord-kunst@aalborg.dk, Internet: http://www.nordjyllandskunstmuseum.dk. Head: Nina Hobolth
Fine Arts Museum - 1877
International and Danish art from the 20th c onwards, especially of Danish modernism, COBRA and Fluxus, museum building designed by Finnish architects Elissa and Alvar Aalto and Danish architect Jean-Jacques Baruël - library, lecture rooms 07747

Ærøskøbing

Ærø Museum, Brog 3-5, 5970 Ærøskøbing - T: 62522950, Fax: 62522920. Head: Karen M. Fabricius
Agriculture Museum
18th c farm house, artifacts of peasant life, traditional peasant costumes, textiles, navigation history, apothecary 07748

Flaske-Peters-Samling, Smedeg 22, 5970 Ærøskøbing - T: 62522951, Fax: 62522920. Head: Karen M. Fabricius
Fine Arts Museum - 1943
Coll of roughly 200 ship models in bottles 07749

Hammerichs Hus, Gyden 22, 5970 Ærøskøbing - T: 62522950, Fax: 62522920. Head: Karen M. Fabricius
Decorative Arts Museum
Coll by G. Hammerich, tiles, pottery, glass, 17th-19th c 07750

Ålestrup

Danmarks Cykelmuseum, 9620 Ålestrup
Science&Tech Museum
Motorcycles and motorcycle equipment from 1865 to the present 07751

Århus

Århus Bymuseum, Carl Blochs G 28, 8000 Århus C - T: 86132862. Head: Lars Holleufer
Local Museum 07752

Århus Kunstmuseum (Århus Art Museum), Vennelystparken, 8000 Århus C - T: 86135255, Fax: 86133351, E-mail: info@aarhuskunstmuseum.dk, Internet: http://www.aarhuskunstmuseum.dk. Head: Jens Erik Sørensen
Fine Arts Museum - 1858
Danish art from 1750 to the present, paintings, sculpture, graphic arts, modern international art, prints - library 07753

Den Gamle By, Danmarks Købstadmuseum (The Old Town), Viborgvej 2, 8000 Århus C - T: 86123188, Fax: 86760687, E-mail: mail@dengamleby.dk, Internet: http://www.dengamleby.dk. Head: Thomas Bloch Ravn
Historical Museum / Open Air Museum / Folklore Museum / Decorative Arts Museum - 1914
Den Gamle By (The Old Town) is Denmark's National Museum of Urban History and Culture watches, clocks, textiles, toys, silver, delftware, 75 historical houses from 20 Danish towns - theatre 07754

Kvindemuseet i Danmark (Women's Museum in Denmark), Domkirkepl 5, 8000 Århus C - T: 86136144, Fax: 86192235, E-mail: kvindemuseet@post5.tele.dk, Internet: http://www.kvindemuseet.dk
Special Museum
Culture and history of women 07755

Naturhistorisk Museum (Natural History Museum), Universitetsparken, Bygning 210, 8000 Århus C - T: 86129777, Fax: 86130882, E-mail: nm@nathist.dk, Internet: http://www.naturhistoriskmuseum.dk. Head: Dr. Thomas Secher Jensen
Natural History Museum - 1921
Exhibits on geological development of Denmark after the last Ice Age, zoological section with habitats of Northern and African animals, geology, biology, ecology - children's section, mini museums, field station 07756

Steno Museet (Steno Museum), C.F. Møllers Allé, Bygn 100, 8000 Århus C - T: 89423975, Fax: 89423995, E-mail: stenomus@au.dk, Internet: http://www.stenomuseet.dk. Head: Kurt Moller-Pedersen
Science&Tech Museum - 1994
Original and reconstructed apparatuses used to illustrate the hist of astronomy, physics, maths, chemistry and medicine - planetarium, medicinal herb garden 07757

Vikingemuseet Moesgaard (The Viking Museum), Sct. Clemens Torv 2-6, 8000 Århus C - T: 89421100, Fax: 86272378, E-mail: moesgaard@moes.hum.aau.dk, Internet: http://www.vikingemuseet.dk. Head: Jan Skamby Madsen
Archaeological Museum
Weapons, tools, and other findings from Viking times, reconstructed Viking community 07758

Års

Vesthimmerlands Museum, Sønderg 44, 9600 Års - T: 98623577. Head: Mogens Hansen
Archaeological Museum
Prehistoric hunters, vikings, bronze age finds, amber 07759

Årslev

Carl Nielsens Barndomshjem, Odensevej 2a, 5792 Årslev C - T: 66148814 lokal 4601, Fax: 65908600, E-mail: museum@odmus.dk, Internet: http://www.odmus.dk. Head: Torben Grøngaard Jeppesen
Special Museum - 1956
House where Carl Nielsen, the composer, lived as a child, documents pictures 07760

Asnæs

Odsherreds Kunstmuseum, Storeg 51-53, 4550 Asnæs - T: 59652423, Fax: 59652824, E-mail: ohk@odsherreds-kunstmuseum.dk, Internet: http://www.odsherreds-kunstmuseum.dk. Head: Gitte Valentiner
Fine Arts Museum 07761

Odsherreds Museum, Høvevej 57, 4550 Asnæs - T: 53413325
Local Museum - 1935
Geology, cultural hist, archaeology, local hist 07762

Assens

Familien Ernsts Samlingers Fond, Østerg 57, 5610 Assens - T: 64711132. Head: John Koppel
Local Museum 07763

Willemoesgårdens Mindestuer, Østerg 36, 5610 Assens - T: 4564713190. Head: H. Erhardt Clausen
Local Museum 07764

Auning

Dansk Landbrugsmuseum (Danish Agricultural Museum), Gamle Estrup, Randersvej 4, 8963 Auning - T: 86483001, 86483444, Fax: 86484182, E-mail: dansklandbrugsmuseum@gl-estrup.dk, Internet: http://www.gl-estrup.dk. Head: Peter Barnskøj
Agriculture Museum - 1889
Farming equipment and models 07765

Gammel Estrup Jyllands Herregaardsmuseum, Randersvej 2, 8963 Auning - T: 86483001, Fax: 86483181, E-mail: - gl.estrup.herregaardsmuseum@euroconnect.dk, Internet: http://www.kulturnet.dk/homes/dlmuseum. Head: Britta Andersen
Decorative Arts Museum - 1930
Manor house furnishings and interiors, European paintings 07766

Ballerup

Ballerup Egnsmuseet, Pederstrupvej 51-53, 2750 Ballerup - T: 44971113, Fax: 44772718, E-mail: info@ballerupegnsmuseum.de, Internet: http://www.ballerupegnsmuseum.de. Head: Jørgen O. Bjerregaard
Local Museum / Fine Arts Museum - 1936
Domestic utensils, personal items of village life, Grand Duchess Olga Alexandrovna exhibition with paintings 07767

Bjerringbro

Elmuseet, Danmarks Museum for Elektricitetens Fysik, Teknologi og Kulturhistorie (Danish Museum of Electricity), Bjerringbrovej 44, 8850 Bjerringbro - T: 86684555, Fax: 86680470, E-mail: elmus@elmus.dk, Internet: http://www.elmus.dk. Head: Keld Nielsen
Science&Tech Museum - 1984 07768

Blåvand

Blåvand Museum, Varde Museum, Blåvandsvej, 6857 Blåvand, mail addr: Lundvej 4, 6800 Varde - T: 75220877, Fax: 75220716. Head: Ole Faber
Special Museum - 1974
Exhibits on fishing and navigation, shipwrecks and lifesaving, thatchedroofed church (1891), division of natural history with exhibits on ornithology, botany, and geology, archives and photos 07769

Blåvand Redningsbådsmuseum, Fyrvej 25, 6857 Blåvand - T: 75220877, Fax: 75220716, E-mail: vam@vardemuseum.dk. Head: Ole Faber
Special Museum
Rescue station from 1851, life boat and rocket equipment 07770

Tirpitz-Stillingen, Varde Museum, Tane Hedevej, 6857 Blåvand, mail addr: Lundvej 4, 6800 Varde - T: 75278427, Fax: 75220716. Head: Ole Faber
Military Museum - 1991
WW II, The Atlantic Wall, Film: The Atlantic Wall in Danish or German 07771

Bogense

Nordfyns Museum, Vesterg 16, 5400 Bogense - T: 64811884. Head: Anders Jaeger
Local Museum 07772

Borre

Liselund Gamle Slot, Langebjergvej 4, 4791 Borre - T: 55812178. Head: Villads Villadsen
Decorative Arts Museum - 1938
Historic castle built in 1792-95, items and interior decorations from period of Louis XVI, parks 07773

Brande

Brande Museum, Aktivcentret, 7330 Brande - T: 97180059. Head: Ellen Becken
Local Museum - 1928
Items of local historical interest, domestic utensils and tools, pottery and faience, glass - library 07774

Broager

Cathrinesminde Teglværksmuseum, Illerstrandvej 7, 6310 Broager - T: 74449474, Fax: 74441720, E-mail: CMT@mail.tele.dk. Head: Peter Dragsbo
Historical Museum
Handicraft, industrial heritage 07775

Brønshøj

Brønshøj Museum, Brønshøj Rytterskole, Brønshøj Torv, 2700 Brønshøj - T: 38282722, Fax: 31284722, E-mail: lcp@kff.kk.dk, Internet: http://www.netby.dk/oest.opollogade/brhmns. Head: Lars Cramer-Petersen
Local Museum - 1988
Danish-Swedish War 1657-60, Swedish town "Carlstad" 07776

Brørup

Museet på Sønderskov, Sønderskovgårdsvej 2, 6650 Brørup - T: 75383866, Fax: 75383865, E-mail: post@sonderskov.dk, Internet: http://www.sonderskov.dk. Head: Svend Aage Knudsen
Historic Site
1620 renaissance stronghold with moat, cultural hist 07777

Charlottenlund

Ordrupgaard, Vilvordevej 110, 2920 Charlottenlund - T: 39641183, Fax: 39641005, E-mail: ordrupgaard@ordrupgaard.dk, Internet: http://www.ordrupgaard.dk. Head: Anne-Birgitte Fonsmark
Fine Arts Museum - 1918
19th and early 20th c Danish and French art, French impressionists 07778

Dannewerk

Museet ved Danevirke, Danevirkegården, Ochsenweg 5, 24867 Dannewerk, mail addr: Postboks 369, 6330 Padborg - T: 462137814, Fax: 462131025, E-mail: kuehl@sydslesvigsk-forening.de, Internet: http://www.sydslesvigsk-forening.de. Head: Dr. Jørgen Kühl
Local Museum - 1990 07779

Dianalund

Tersløsegaard, Holbergsvej 101, Tersløse, 4293 Dianalund - T: 58264384. Head: Bodil Panild
Special Museum
Mansion from 1736 where poet Ludvig Holberg spent his last years 1745-1754 07780

Dragør

Amagermuseet, Hovedgaden 412, 2791 Dragør - T: 32539307, Fax: 32530268, E-mail: amagermuseet@museum.dk, Internet: http://www.dragoer-information.dk. Head: Jan Vejle
Local Museum - 1901
Oldest half-timbered house in Denmark, local historical items, period of Dutch colonization, interior and furnishings, drawings and paintings of local artists, peasant costumes 07781

Dragør Museum, Havnepl 2-4, 2791 Dragør - T: 32534106, Fax: 32534116, E-mail: dragorin@post10.tele.dk, Internet: http://www.dragoer-information.dk. Head: Jan Vejle
Local Museum - 1930
Local history, textiles, crafts, Vikings, navigation 07782

Mølsteds Museum, Dr. Dichs Pl 1, 2791 Dragør - T: 32534106, Fax: 32534116, E-mail: dragorin@post10.tele.dk, Internet: http://www.dragoer-information.dk. Head: Jan Vejle
Fine Arts Museum - 1971
Coll of marine paintings and drawings of Christian Mølsted (1862-1930) in his atelier 07783

Dronninglund

Try Museum, Højskolevej 1, 9330 Dronninglund - T: 98843105, Fax: 98844105. Head: Anna Kathrine Nielsen
Local Museum - 1929
7000 years local hist, handicrafts, domestic industries, milling, hunting, wood 07784

Voergård Slot, Flauenskjold, 9330 Dronninglund - T: 98867108, 98469072, Fax: 72211650, E-mail: dbj@hjulmand-kaptain.dk, Internet: http://www.voergaardslot.dk. Head: H.J. Kaptain
Decorative Arts Museum
Medieval castle, artifacts from feudal times, sculpture, porcelain, furnishings, paintings by Rubens, Rafael, Goya, etc. 07785

Dronningmølle

Rudolph Tegners Museum, Museumsvej 19, 3120 Dronningmølle - T: 49719177, E-mail: evategner@hansen.mail.dk, Internet: http://www.rudolph.degner.dk. Head: Kirsten Bjerregaard
Fine Arts Museum - 1938
Coll of Rudolf Tegner's sculpture, busts, and drawings and paintings from his travels - sculpture park 07786

Ebeltoft

Ebeltoft Museum, Torvet og Juulsbakke 1, 8400 Ebeltoft - T: 86345599. Head: Jakob Vedsted
Local Museum - 1909
Historic town hall from 1789, items from historical times, ethnographic coll from Thailand, old handicrafts 07787

Fregatten Jylland, Strandvejen 4, 8400 Ebeltoft - T: 86341099, Fax: 86342714, E-mail: info@fregatten-jylland.dk, Internet: http://www.fregatten-jylland.dk. Head: Jørgen Pedersen
Science&Tech Museum - 1978
Ship equipment, unique 19th c wooden naval ship 07788

Glasmuseet Ebeltoft, Strandvejen 8, 8400 Ebeltoft - T: 86341799, Fax: 86346060, E-mail: glasmuseet@glasmuseet.dk, Internet: http://www.glasmuseet.dk. Head: Dagmar Brendstrup
Decorative Arts Museum - 1986
600 international glass artists, modern and contemporary international glass art - library 07789

Engesvang

Klosterlund Museet, Klosterlundvej 27, 7442 Engesvang - T: 86865043. Head: Ulla Thyrring
Archaeological Museum - 1933
Palaeolitithic culture of Klosterlund 07790

Esbjerg

Bogtrykmuseet (Printing Museum), Borgerg 6, 6700 Esbjerg - T: 75127811, Fax: 75135949. Head: Michael Lauenborg
Science&Tech Museum - 1981
Printing hist, equipment, presses and typesetting machines 07791

Esbjerg Kunstmuseum (Esbjerg Art Museum), Havneg 20, 6700 Esbjerg - T: 75130211, Fax: 75126812. Head: Inge Merete Kjeldgaard
Fine Arts Museum - 1962
20th c Danish and foreign paintings, sculptures, installations and graphics 07792

Esbjerg Museum, Torveg 45, 6700 Esbjerg - T: 75127811, Fax: 75135949, E-mail: esm@esbjergmuseum.dk. Head: Ulla Mejdahl
Archaeological Museum / Ethnology Museum / Local Museum - 1941
Prehistory, neolithic battle-ax culture and funnel-neck beaker culture, Roman, Iron Age, and Viking times, local hist, early industrial revolution, farming implements, Danish amber - library 07793

Fiskeri- og Søfartsmuseet (Fishing and Maritime Museum), Tarphagevej, 6700 Esbjerg V - T: 76122000, Fax: 76122010, E-mail: fimus@fimus.dk, Internet: http://www.fimus.dk. Head: Morten Hahn Pedersen
Special Museum / Science&Tech Museum - 1962
Historical material on development of fisheries from Viking times to the present, shipping, research on harbour seal, seawater aquarium, sealarium 07794

Den Rosendahlske Bibelsamling, Oddesundvej 1, 6715 Esbjerg N, mail addr: Postboks 3069, 6715 Esbjerg, N - T: 76101112, Fax: 76101122, E-mail: rosendahl@rosendahls.dk, Internet: http://www.rosendahls.dk
Religious Arts Museum
150 Bibles from different periods and countries, several 500 years old, fragment of the Gutenberg Bible 07795

Eskildstrup

Lolland-Falsters Traktor- og Motormuseum, Nørreg 17b, 4863 Eskildstrup - T: 54437007, Fax: 54437797. Head: Mogens Sommer
Science&Tech Museum 07796

Espergærde

Flynderupgård Museet, Agnetevej 9, 3060 Espergærde - T: 49281900, Fax: 49281901. Head: Kenno Pedersen
Local Museum 07797

Fåborg

Brahetrolleborg Skolemuseum, Sybillesvej 3, 5600 Fåborg
Local Museum
School from 1783, archives, paintings, domestic utensils, local history 07798

Fåborg Museum for Fynsk Malerkunst, Grønneg 75, 5600 Fåborg - T: 62610645, Fax: 62610665, E-mail: faaborgmuseum@faaborgmuseum.dk, Internet: http://www.faaborgmuseum.dk. Head: Susanne Thestrup Truelsen
Fine Arts Museum - 1910
Painting and sculpture 07799

Den Gamle Gaard, Holkeg 1-3, 5600 Fåborg - T: 62613338, Fax: 62613358, E-mail: fkm@post7.tele.dk, Internet: http://home7.inet.tele.dk/fkm. Head: Anders Rehde
Folklore Museum / Local Museum - 1932
Historic farmstead, furnishings from 1750-1850, East Indian porcelain, Delft faience, glass, pottery, ship models and paintings 07800

Haastrup Folkemindesamling, Haastrup Skole, Byg 14, 5600 Fåborg - T: 62681104
Folklore Museum - 1966
Folklore, documents and records, tools, horse-drawn fire engine 07801

Kaleko Mølle (Kaleko Mill), Priceshavevej 38, 5600 Fåborg - T: 62613338, Fax: 62613358, E-mail: fkm@post7.tele.dk, Internet: http://home7.inet.tele.dk/fkm. Head: Anders Rehde
Science&Tech Museum - 1917
Denmark's oldest working watermill in its original surroundings with mill brook and millpond (since the middle of the 15th c) 07802

Fanø

Fanø Kunstsamling, Sønderho, 6720 Fanø
Fine Arts Museum
Paintings and watercolors inspired by local mileau, ceramics, maps, etchings, and lithographs of Fanø 07803

Fanø Museum, Skolevej, Nordby, 6720 Fanø - T: 75166137, Fax: 75166900, E-mail: stineberg@centrum.dk. Head: Ida Bjerg
Local Museum 07804

Fanø Skibsfarts- og Dragtsamling, Hovedg 28, Nordby, 6720 Fanø - T: 75162272. Head: Svend Kallesen
Folklore Museum - 1966
Traditional peasant costumes of Fanø, items from sailors' lifes, model ships 07805

Hannes Hus og Fonden Gamle Sønderho, Sønderho, 6720 Fanø - T: 75164429, E-mail: - fgsvibeheschoett@post.tele.dk. Head: Vibehe Schøtt
Special Museum 07806

Farsø

Digterhuset, Sønderg 48, 9640 Farsø - T: 631686
Special Museum
Birth place of the Nobel Prize writer Johannes Vilhelm Jensens, furnishings, paintings by his brother, the artist Hans Deurs, books by Jensens and his sister Thit, photographs, excerpts from articles on Jensens, local archives 07807

Landbrugs- og Interiørmuseet, Herregården Hessel, 9640 Farsø - T: 98638125, Fax: 98638727. Head: Johnny Højgaard
Agriculture Museum 07808

Farum

Farums Arkiver og Museer, Kulturhuset, 3520 Farum - T: 77434356, Fax: 77434103, E-mail: info@famus.dk, Internet: http://www.famus.dk. Head: Cathrine Kyø Hermansen
Local Museum
Local hist, immigration hist of civilization 07809

Fjerritslev

Fjerritslev Bryggeri- og Egnsmuseum, Gamle Bryggergaard, 9690 Fjerritslev
Science&Tech Museum
Rural brewery in operation from 1897 to 1968, exhibits on brewing, brewery equipment 07810

Fredericia

Museerne i Fredericia, Jernbaneg 10, 7000 Fredericia - T: 72106981, Fax: 72106981, E-mail: museerne@fredericiakom.dk. Head: Bodil Schelde-Jensen
Local Museum - 1916
Religious, ethnography, Frederician personalities, market, harbour, silversmith farmer's life, historical crops 07811

Frederiksberg

Bakkemuseet, Rahbeks Allé 23, 1801 Frederiksberg C - T: 33314362, E-mail: info@bakkehusmuseet.dk, Internet: http://www.bakkehusmuseet.dk. Head: Inge Nørballe
Special Museum
Culture, literature 1760-1850, the Golden Age 07812

P. Storm Museet, Frederiksberg Runddel, 2000 Frederiksberg - T: 31860523, Fax: 31860529. Head: Jens Bing
Fine Arts Museum
Drawings of Danish humourist Storm P. (1882-1949), garden for children 07813

Frederikshavn

Bangsbo Museum, Dr. Margrethesvej 6, 9900 Frederikshavn - T: 98423111, Fax: 98430597, E-mail: bangsbo@bangsbo-museum.dk, Internet: http://www.bangsbo-museum.dk. Head: Hans Munk Pedersen
Local Museum - 1948
Local hist, military art and science, navigation, Viking period, Viking trade ships, coll of historic gallion figureheads, artefacts from the occupation

period, marine archaeology dept, hair works textiles, maritime department, World War II department, vehicle coll from the oast 400 years, hair trinkets, textiles - regional archive 07814

Bunker Museet, Nordre Strandvej 19, 9900 Frederikshavn - T: 98424548, Fax: 98430597, Internet: http://www.bangsbo-museum.dk/bunkermuseet. Head: Hans Munk Pedersen
Military Museum - 1990
Bunker as used in the German Atlantic Wall 07815

Frederikshavn Kunstmuseum- og Exlibrissamling, Parallelvej 14, 9900 Frederikshavn - T: 96225625, Fax: 98439180, E-mail: kunstmuseum@frederikshavn.dk, Internet: http://www.fredrikshavn-kunstmuseum.dk. Head: Klaus Rödel
Fine Arts Museum
Ex-libris or bookplates, one of the biggest coll in Europe 07816

Krudttaarnsmuseet, Kragholmen 2, 9900 Frederikshavn - T: 98431919, Fax: 98430597, Internet: http://www.bangsbo-museum.dk/krudttaernet. Head: Hans Munk Pedersen
Military Museum - 1948
National and local history, small arms and cannons from 1600 to the present, 17th c gunpowder tower, the Great Nordic Wars (17th c), the Napoleonic Wars (18th c) 07817

Frederikssund

J.F. Willumsens Museum, Jenriksvej 4, 3600 Frederikssund - T: 47310773, Fax: 47385473, E-mail: ifwmus@frederikssund-kom.dk, Internet: http://www.frederikssund-kom.dk/Willumsens. Head: Leila Krogh
Fine Arts Museum - 1957
J.F. Willumsen's paintings, drawings, sculpture, prints 07818

Frederiksværk

Frederiksværk Bymuseum, Torvet 18, 3300 Frederiksværk - T: 42120605, Fax: 42120693, E-mail: frm@frm.dk, Internet: http://www.frederiksvaerk.dk. Head: Inge Bodilsen
Local Museum - 1932
Historical items related to the construction of canals in the 18th c, industrial equipment, coins and paper currency, war medals, prehistoric finds - Krudtverksamuseet, garden 07819

Frøstrup

Kirsten Kjærs Museum, Langvadvej 64, 7741 Frøstrup - T: 97991052, Fax: 97991052, E-mail: kkmuseum@dadu.net. Head: John Andersen, Harald Fuglsang
Local Museum 07820

Fur

Fur Museum, Nederby 28, 7884 Fur - T: 97593411, Fax: 97593917, Internet: http://www.fur-museum.dk. Head: Georg Stenstrop
Natural History Museum - 1954
Prehist, archaeology, fossilized fish, plants, insects, turtle from lower Eocene - library, archives 07821

Gilleleje

Gilleleje Fiskerimuseum, Rostgaardsvej 2, 3250 Gilleleje - T: 48301631, Fax: 48301671. Head: Søren Frandsen
Special Museum - 1929
Exhibits on fisheries, including tools, models, panoramas, peasant implements and furniture, items from the Stone and Bronze Ages 07822

Give

Give-Egnens Museum, Donneruplundvej 2, 7323 Give - T: 75739375, Fax: 75735520, E-mail: GEM@GEM.dk, Internet: http://www.gem.dk. Head: Falk Mikkelsen
Local Museum
Coll of different tools used in wood workshop, agriculture, kitchen, moor, etc., which visitors can use 07823

Gjern

Jysk Automobilmuseum, Skovvejen, 8883 Gjern - T: 86875050. Head: Aage Louring
Science&Tech Museum - 1967
140 vehicles, 68 different types from the period 1900-1948, primarily cars and motorcycles, also trucks and fire engines 07824

Glamsbjerg

Vestfyns Hjemstavnsgård, Klareg 23, 5620 Glamsbjerg - T: 64721600. Head: Sven Rask
Agriculture Museum - 1931
Old farm with period interiors, wagons, tools 1750-1950 07825

Gram

Midtsønderjyllands Museum, Gram Slot, Slotsvej, 6510 Gram - T: 74821000, Fax: 74820423, E-mail: msm@sja.dk. Head: Flemming Roth
Natural History Museum - 1976
Geology and paleontology of Southern Jutland, fossils of the Upper Miocene Gram clay from Denmark, well-preserved baleen whale skeletons 07826

Grenå

Djurslands Museum - Dansk Fiskerimuseum, Sønderg 1, 8500 Grenå - T: 86324800, Fax: 86320302, E-mail: djm_dfm@post2.tele.dk. Head: Brita Mosdal
Special Museum / Ethnology Museum / Archaeological Museum
Archeology, ethnological exhibits 07827

Greve

Greve Museum, Grevegård, Bækgårdsvej 9, 2670 Greve - T: 43404036, Fax: 43404018, E-mail: adm@grevemuseum.dk, Internet: http://www.grevemuseum.dk. Head: Ena Hvidberg
Local Museum 07828

Grindsted

Besættelsessamlingen 1940-45, Vestre Skole, Fælledvej 3, 7200 Grindsted - T: 75310166, Fax: 75310399, E-mail: museum@grindsted.dk. Head: Mogens Hansen
Military Museum
Occupation and resistance 1940-45 07829

Grindsted Museum, Borgerg 25-27, 7200 Grindsted - T: 75310166, Fax: 75310399, E-mail: museum@grindsted.dk. Head: Mogens Hansen, Mogens Hansen
Local Museum - 1923
Exhibits showing life of heath dwellers from prehistoric times to the present, runic inscription, black earthenware, 1930s original farm 07830

Zoologisk Museum, Mellemvej 16, Dal, 7200 Grindsted
Natural History Museum - 1965
Approximately 1,100 different birds, 250 mammals, antler coll, snail houses, Indian elephant 07831

Gudhjem

Bornholms Kunstmuseum, Helligdommen, Rø, 3760 Gudhjem - T: 56484386, Fax: 56484358, E-mail: post@bornholms-kunstmuseum.dk, Internet: http://www.bornholms-kunstmuseum.dk. Head: Lars Kærulf Møller
Fine Arts Museum 07832

Landbrugsmuseet Melstedgård, Melstedvej 25, 3760 Gudhjem - T: 56485598
Agriculture Museum
Old farm, furnished house, demonstrations of old farming methods 07833

Museet på Gudhjem Station, 3670 Gudhjem - T: 56485067. Head: Inge Madsen
Science&Tech Museum 07834

Haderslev

Haderslev Museum, Dalg 7, 6100 Haderslev, mail addr: Postboks 122, 6100 Haderslev - T: 74527566, Fax: 74534014, E-mail: mail@haderslev-museum.dk, Internet: http://www.haderslev-museum.dk. Head: Orla Madsen
Archaeological Museum - 1887
Prehistoric finds of North Schleswig, local historical artifacts - library 07835

Slesvigske Vognsamling - Dansk Vognmuseum, Seijstensgyde, 6100 Haderslev. Head: Per Ole Schovsbo
Historical Museum 07836

Hadsten

Nielstrup Museum, Steng 17, 8370 Hadsten
Local Museum 07837

Hadsund

Als Hjemstavnsmuseum, Kirkevej 17, 9560 Hadsund, mail addr: Rosendalsallé 8, 9560 Hadsund - T: 98574388, Fax: 96520515, E-mail: hem@mail.tele.dk, Internet: http://www.hadsund-museum.dk. Head: Lise Andersen
Local Museum - 1950
Reconstructed peasant home from the mid-19th c, typical furniture, tools, and domestic utensils of the period 07838

Hadsund Egns Museum (Regional Museum of Hadsund), Rosendalsallé 8, 9560 Hadsund - T: 98574388, Fax: 96520515, E-mail: hem@mail.tele.dk, Internet: http://www.hadsund-museum.dk. Head: Lise Andersen
Local Museum - 1962
Handicraft, commerce and transport of the town Hadsund and surroundings - archive, Als Hjemstavnsmuseum, Havnø Windmill 07839

Hanstholm

Museumscenter Hanstholm, Molevej 29, 7730 Hanstholm - T: 97961736, Fax: 97960595, E-mail: MCHkanon@post8.tele.dk. Head: Jens Andersen
Natural History Museum / Military Museum
Harbour construction, fishing, fauna and flora, geology, world war II fortification 07840

Haslev

Haslev Museum, Frederiksg 6, 4690 Haslev - T: 56313700. Head: Margit Baad Pedersen
Local Museum 07841

Hellerup

Blindehistorisk Museum (Museum of the History of the Blind), Rymarksvej 1, 2900 Hellerup - T: 39452545, Fax: 39452525, E-mail: ibos@ibos.dk. Head: Mogens Bang
Special Museum - 1977 07842

Experimentarium, Tuborg Havnevej 7, 2900 Hellerup - T: 39273333, Fax: 39273395, E-mail: info@experimentarium.dk, Internet: http://www.experimentarium.dk. Head: Asger Høeg
Science&Tech Museum 07843

Øregaard-Museum, Ørehøj Allé 2, 2900 Hellerup - T: 39611107, Fax: 39611107
Local Museum - 1920
Hegel coll 07844

Telefonmuseet, Svanemøllevej 112a, 2900 Hellerup - T: 33994050, Fax: 39623770, E-mail: blackp@telefonmuseet.dk. Head: S. Black Petersen
Science&Tech Museum - 1981
Exhibition in a fully authentic large manual operated telephone exchange showing telephone sets, switchboards and related items of the history of telephony from 1876 until today 07845

Helsingør

Danmarks Tekniske Museum, Nordre Strandvej 23, 3000 Helsingør - T: 49222611, Fax: 49226211, E-mail: jb@tekniskmuseum.dk, Internet: http://www.tekniskmuseum.dk. Head: Jens Breinegaard
Science&Tech Museum - 1911
Industry, technology, inventions, motorcars, navigation, fire prevention, aviation - library 07846

Handels- og Søfartsmuseet paa Kronborg, Kronborg Slot, 3000 Helsingør - T: 49280200, Fax: 49213440, E-mail: info@soefartsmuseet.dk, Internet: http://www.soefartsmuseet.dk. Head: Hans Jeppesen
Historical Museum - 1914
Hist of the Danish merchant marine, ship models, shipbuilding and under-water-archaeology - library, archive (photos, drawings) 07847

Helsingør Bymuseum (The Local Museum of Helsingør), Hestemøllestræde 1, 3000 Helsingør - T: 49281800, Fax: 49281801, E-mail: museer@helsingor.dk. Head: Kenno Pedersen
Local Museum 07848

Kronborg Slot (Kronborg Castle), Kronborg, 3000 Helsingør - T: 49213078, Fax: 49213052, E-mail: kronborg@ses.dk, Internet: http://www.ses.dk. Head: Lars Holst
Decorative Arts Museum / Fine Arts Museum - 1934
16th c castle with fortress and casemates used as setting by Shakespeare in 'Hamlet', furnishings, paintings, and tapestries from the 15th-16th c, well-preserved castle chapel with art objects 07849

Hemmet

Fahl Kro, Oblingvej 34, 6893 Hemmet - T: 75280143, E-mail: museum@skjern-egvald-museum.dk, Internet: http://www.skjern-egvald-museum.dk. Head: Kim Clausen
Local Museum 07850

Herning

Blichermuseet på Herningsholm, Viborgvej 72, 7400 Herning - T: 97222299. Head: Ulla Thyrring
Special Museum - 1980
Coll of works of the heath poet, Steen Steensen Blicher, paintings from the heath, hist of the estate Herningsholm 07851

Carl-Henning Pedersen og Else Alfelts Museum, Birk, 7400 Herning - T: 97221079, E-mail: museum@chpeamuseum.dk, Internet: http://www.chpe@museum.dk
Fine Arts Museum
4000 paintings by Carl-Henning Pedersen and Else Alfelt 07852

Danmarks Fotomuseum, Museumsg 28, 7400 Herning - T: 97225322, Fax: 97225322, E-mail: -danmarks.fotomuseum@mail.tele.dk, Internet: http://www.fotomuseum.dk. Head: Bjarne Meldgård
Special Museum - 1984 07853

Herning Kunstmuseum, Angligården, Birk Centerpark 3, 7400 Herning - T: 97121033, Fax: 97127912, E-mail: herningkunstmuseum@mail.tele.dk, Internet: http://www.herning-kunstmuseum.dk. Head: Holger Reenberg
Fine Arts Museum - 1977
Modern Danish and international art and sculptures (1930-), COBRA art, Constructive art, Conceptual art (Gruppe Zero, Piero Manzoni), architecture, modern Danish landscape (C.Th. Sørensen) 07854

Herning Museum, Museumsg 32, 7400 Herning - T: 97123266, Fax: 97127518. Head: Ulla Thyrring
Special Museum / Agriculture Museum / Archaeological Museum / Local Museum / Open Air Museum - 1892
Historic farm house, exhibits on the heath, peasant life, prehist exhibits - craft workshops 07855

Søby Brunkulslejer og Brunkulsmuseet, Brunkulsvej 29, 7400 Herning - T: 97147529. Head: S.E. Jakobsen
Science&Tech Museum - 1977
Photo documentation of work in the brown coal mines (1940-1970), the apartment of a miner in 1940 07856

Textilforum, Vesterg 20, 7400 Herning - T: 97122980, Fax: 97127518, E-mail: textilforum@textilforum.dk. Head: Ulla Thyrring
Special Museum 07857

Hillerød

Æbelholt Museum, Æbelholt 4, 3400 Hillerød - T: 48210351. Head: Erna Christaffersen
Special Museum - 1957
Monastery from 1175, numerous skeletons with signs of illnesses, medicinal herbs 07858

Det Nationalhistoriske Museum på Frederiksborg, Frederiksborg Slot, 3400 Hillerød - T: 48260439, Fax: 48240966, E-mail: frederiksborgmuseet@frederiksborgmuseet.dk, Internet: http://www.frederiksborgmuseet.dk. Head: Jesper Knudsen
Historical Museum / Decorative Arts Museum - 1878
Portraits and paintings illustrating the hist of Denmark, Norway (until 1814) and Schleswig-Holstein (until 1864), the chapel of the Renaissance castle where the Danish kings were crowned, furniture - library 07859

Nordsjaellandsk Folkemuseum, Helsingørsg 65, 3400 Hillerød - T: 48243448, Fax: 48243442, E-mail: nfh@get2net.dk, Internet: http://hjem.get2net.dk/nfh. Head: Finn Erik Kramer
Local Museum - 1925 07860

Hinnerup

Socialmuseet Det Gamle Syge-Plejehjem, Nørrerisvej 4, 8382 Hinnerup - T: 86964580. Head: Christian Siegumfeldt
Special Museum 07861

Hirtshals

Nordsømuseet (North Sea Museum), Willemoesvej 2-4, 9850 Hirtshals - T: 98944844, Fax: 98945480, E-mail: info@nordsoemuseet.dk, Internet: http://www.nordsoemuseet.dk. Head: Susanne Fibiger
Natural History Museum - 1984
North sea museum, aquarium, fishery, environment 07862

Hjørring

Vendsyssel Historiske Museum, Museumsg 3, 9800 Hjørring - T: 96241050, Fax: 96241051, E-mail: vhm@vhm.dk, Internet: http://www.vhm.dk. Head: Mogens Thøgersen
Local Museum - 1889
Stone, Bronze, and Iron Ages, Viking times to recent times, ceramics, textiles, religious art, prehistoric graves, furniture and handicraft - archives, library, herb garden 07863

Vendsyssel Kunstmuseum, Brinck Seidelinsg 10, 9800 Hjørring - T: 98924133, Fax: 98921695, E-mail: info@vkm.de, Internet: http:www.vkm.dk. Head: Marianne Ilkjær
Fine Arts Museum - 1963
Art from 1935 to present, frescoes with local history as theme, contemporary Danish artists, modern graphics 07864

Hobro

Hobro Museum, Sydhimmerlands Museum, Vesterg 21-23, 9500 Hobro, mail addr: Postboks 980999, 9500 Hobro - T: 98510555, Fax: 98524367. Head: Birte Friis
Local Museum - 1910
Archeology, silver, faience and china, finds from the Viking fortress Fyrkat located nearby - local archives 07865

Højbjerg

Moesgård Museum, Moesgård, 8270 Højbjerg - T: 89421100, Fax: 86272378, E-mail: moesgaard@moes.hum.aau.dk, Internet: http://www.moesmus.dk. Head: Jan Skamby Madsen
Archaeological Museum - 1861
Archaeological coll from the Stone Age to the Viking Age, the Grauballe Man: only preserved bog body from the Iron Age, coll of runic stones, ethnographic exhibition from Nuristan and the Hindukush 07866

Højby

Stenstrup Museum, Stenstrup, 4573 Højby - T: 59302027, Fax: 59302075. Head: Jan Steen Jacobsen
Local Museum - 1907
Items of the peasant culture over the last 200-300 years, domestic implements, agricultural tools, traditional peasant costumes, military items, navigation 07867

Højer

Højer Mølle- og Marskmuseum, Skoleg, 6280 Højer - T: 74782911. Head: Inger Lauridsen
Local Museum 07868

Holbæk

Museet for Holbæk og Omegn, Klosterstræde 18, 4300 Holbæk - T: 59432353, Fax: 59432452, E-mail: Holbaek@museum.dk, Internet: http://www.holbaek.dk. Head: Lene Floris
Local Museum - 1910
Folk culture, archeology, Holbaek pottery, 19th c merchant shop - library 07869

Museum for Zone-Redningskorpsets, Skyttensvej 2, 4300 Holbæk - T: 53430194, Fax: 59445955. Head: Frederik Madsen
Historical Museum 07870

Holme-Olstrup

Sparresholm Vognsamling, Sparresholm, 4684 Holme-Olstrup
Science&Tech Museum
Exhibits of transportation facilities from 1750 to 1945, 100 horse-drawn carriages, including Frederik XII's gala carriage and everyday models, sleds, fire engine 07871

Holstebro

Dragon- og Frihedsmuseet (Dragoon and Freedom Museum), Museumsvej 2, 7500 Holstebro - T: 97422933, Fax: 97428109, E-mail: homuseum@post1.tele.dk, Internet: http://www.holstebro-museum.dk. Head: Torben Skov
Military Museum - 1959
Weapons, documents and books on the resistance of 1940-1945, concentration camps, equipment of Jutland Dragoon Regiment since 1679 - library 07872

Hjemmevaernsmuseet, Sydbanevej 20, 7500 Holstebro
Military Museum - 1975
Material from the wars of 1848-50, 1864, WW I, WW II, and the Resistance, historical weapon coll from 30 countries 07873

Holstebro Kunstmuseum, Museumsvej 2, 7500 Holstebro - T: 97424518, Fax: 97414171, E-mail: info@holstebrokunstmuseum.dk, Internet: http://www.holstebrokunstmuseum.dk. Head: Folke Kjems
Fine Arts Museum - 1967
Modern Danish art, African art, preColumbian ceramics, Balinese art, modern international grafics 07874

Holstebro Museum, Museumsvej 2, 7500 Holstebro - T: 97422933, Fax: 97428109, E-mail: homuseum@holstebro-museum.dk, Internet: http://www.holstebro-museum.dk. Head: Torben Skov
Local Museum - 1930
Local historical artifacts, crafts, silver smithy, prehistoric tools, Viking artifacts, dolls and tin toys 07875

Jens Nielsens og Olivia Holm-Møller Museet, Nørrebrog 1, 7500 Holstebro - T: 97421824. Head: Folke Kjems
Fine Arts Museum - 1971
Works of the painters Jens Nielsen and Olivia Holm-Møller, drawings, graphic art, sculpture 07876

Holte

Søllerød Museum, Mothsgaarden, Søllerødvej 25, 2840 Holte - T: 45802046, Fax: 45805360. Head: Niels Peter Stilling
Local Museum - 1930/1974
Prehistoric items from the Stone and Bronze Ages, items illustrating development of the district through fishing and agriculture, local historical paintings - township and local historical archives 07877

Hornslet

Rosenholm Slot, 8543 Hornslet - T: 86994010, E-mail: info@rosenholmslot.dk, Internet: http://www.rosenholmslot.dk. Head: Baron Erik Christian Rosenkrantz
Decorative Arts Museum
Renaissance castle from 1560, art objects from 16th c to the present 07878

Horsens

Arbejder-, Håndværker- og Industrimuseet, Gasvej 17-19, 8700 Horsens - T: 75620788, Fax: 75601277. Head: Ole Puggaard
Science&Tech Museum
Machinery, handicrafts 07879

Fængselshiststoriske Museum (Jail Museum), Fussingsvej 8, 8700 Horsens - T: 79254100. Head: Aage Egholm
Historical Museum 07880

Glud Museum, Glud, 8700 Horsens - T: 75683082, E-mail: post@gludmuseum.dk, Internet: http://www.gludmuseum.dk. Head: Dr. Jacob B. Jensen
Agriculture Museum - 1912
Exhibits on agriculture through the ages, domestic utensils, farm tools over a period of 300 years, 17th c half-timbered house 07881

Horsens Kunstmuseum (Horsens Museum of Modern Art), Carolinelundsvej 2, 8700 Horsens - T: 75611311, Fax: 75613242, E-mail: kunstmuseum@horsens.dk, Internet: http://www.horsenskunstmuseum.dk. Head: Claus Hagedorn Olsen
Fine Arts Museum - 1906
Danish art 18-21st c 07882

Horsens Museum, Sundvej 1a, 8700 Horsens - T: 75622933, Fax: 75618621, E-mail: horsensmuseum@horsens.dk, Internet: http://www.horsensmuseum.dk. Head: Ole Schiørring
Archaeological Museum - 1906
Prehistoric coll, specially rich gravefinds from Early Roman Ironage, Vikingage from Horsens town. Handcraft with a large silvercoll from the town, textiles, a section about the adventures of Vitus Bering, born in Horsens 1681 - archive 07883

Hørsholm

Dansk Jagt- og Skovbrugsmuseum (Danish Museum of Hunting and Forestry), Folehavevej 15-17, 2970 Hørsholm - T: 45860572, Fax: 45762002, E-mail: museum@jagtskov.dk, Internet: http://www.jagtskov.dk. Head: Jette Baagøe
Natural History Museum - 1942
Hunting weapons, trophies, game mammals and birds, traps, wood samples, forestry tools and implements, forestry industry 07884

Hørsholm Egns Museum, Sdr Jagtvej 2, 2970 Hørsholm - T: 42860711. Head: Lisbet Hein
Local Museum - 1944
Local history, industry, agriculture, royal castle 07885

Horslunde

Reventlow-Museet Pederstrup, Pederstrupvej 124, 4913 Horslunde - T: 54935154, Fax: 54935155, E-mail: reventlow@museum.dk, Internet: http://www.reventlow-museet.dk. Head: John Erichsen
Special Museum - 1940
Coll of paintings, furniture and personal effects regarding the Danish county and statesman C.D.F. Reventlow, reforms of Danish society - 19th c garden 07886

Humlebæk

Louisiana Museum of Modern Art, Gl. Strandvej 13, 3050 Humlebæk - T: 49190719, Fax: 49193505, E-mail: curatorial@louisiana.dk, Internet: http://www.louisiana.dk. Head: Poul Erik Toejner
Fine Arts Museum - 1958
Modern Danish and international sculptures and paintings by Alberto Giacometti, Hans Arp, Henry Moore, Francis Bacon, Pablo Picasso, Alexander Calder - sculpture garden, concert hall, film auditorium, children's wing 07887

Hundested

Knud Rasmussens Hus, Knud Rasmussensvej 9, 3390 Hundested - T: 47937161
Special Museum - 1933
Former home of the polar explorer and Eskimo ethnograph, Knud Rasmussen, memorabilia, information on his expeditions 07888

Hurup Thy

Heltborg Museum, Sydthy Kunst- og Kulturcenter, Skårhøjvej 15, Heltborg, 7760 Hurup Thy - T: 97952077, Fax: 97952717. Head: Jytte Nielsen
Fine Arts Museum 07889

Hvalsø

Tadre Mølle, Tadre Møllevej 23, 4330 Hvalsø - T: 59194001, Fax: 59194001
Science&Tech Museum
archives 07890

Ishøj

Arken Museum of Modern Art, Skovvej 100, 2635 Ishøj - T: 43540222, Fax: 43540522, E-mail: reception@arken.dk, Internet: http://www.arken.dk. Head: Christian Gether
Fine Arts Museum 07891

Jægerspris

Jægerspris Slot, Slotsgården 15, 3630 Jægerspris - T: 47531004, Fax: 47503073, E-mail: kf@kongfrederik.dk, Internet: http://www.kongfrederik.dk. Head: Nils Sættem
Decorative Arts Museum - 1873
Medieval castle, parks, sculptures by J. Wiedewelt, interiors and furnishings from 1700-1800, memorial for King Frederik VII and Grevinde Danners 07892

Museet Færgegaarden, Færgelundsvej 1, 3630 Jægerspris - T: 47312511, Fax: 47312967, E-mail: mufae@get2net.dk, Internet: http://www.egnsmuseet-faergegaarden.dk. Head: Carsten Hess
Local Museum - 1984 07893

Jyllinge

Fjordmuseet, Bygaden 28, 4040 Jyllinge - T: 46731728, Fax: 46731728, E-mail: FJORDMUS@image.dk. Head: Alan H. Rasmussen
Ethnology Museum - 1982
Fishing, agricultural implements 07894

Jystrup Midtsj

Sporvejsmuseet, Skjoldenæsvej 107, 4174 Jystrup Midtsj - T: 31635401, Fax: 31554393. Head: Mikael Lund
Science&Tech Museum - 1978
Tramcars from Denmark 07895

Kalundborg

Kalundborg og Omegns Museum, Lindegaarden, Adelg 23, 4400 Kalundborg - T: 59512141, Fax: 59517315, E-mail: kalundborgmuseum@kalmus.dk, Internet: http://www.kalmus.dk. Head: Lisbeth Pedersen
Local Museum - 1908
Local history, 19th c peasant costumes, apothecary, textiles, handicrafts, agriculture, archaeology 07896

Kastrup

Kastrupgaardsamlingen, Kastrupvej 339, 2770 Kastrup - T: 32515180, Fax: 32503609
Fine Arts Museum - 1977
Coll of graphics of living artists 07897

Kerteminde

Farvergården, Langeg 8, 5300 Kerteminde - T: 65323727, Fax: 65324707, E-mail: kert_mus@post4.tele.dk, Internet: http://www.kert-mus.dk. Head: Kurt Risskov Sørensen
Local Museum / Folklore Museum
Handicraft exhibitions, workshops 07898

Johannes Larsen Museet, Møllebakken, 5300 Kerteminde - T: 65323727, Fax: 65324707, E-mail: kert_mus@post4.tele.dk, Internet: http://www.kert-mus.dk. Head: Erland Porsmose
Fine Arts Museum - 1985
Home and works by J. Larsen, 50 other local painters represented 07899

Kerteminde Egnens Museer, Strandg 7, 5300 Kerteminde - T: 65323727, Fax: 65324707, E-mail: kert_mus@post4.tele.dk, Internet: http://www.kert-mus.dk. Head: Erland Porsmose
Local Museum 07900

Ladbyskibsmuseet, Vikingevej 123, 5300 Kerteminde - T: 65321667, Fax: 65323469, E-mail: ladmus@post.tele.dk, Internet: http://www.kert-mus.dk. Head: Bodil Holm Sørensen
Archaeological Museum - 1937
Ship burial from Viking period preserved in a vault under burial mound and a small museum with exhibition informing about Viking finds from the area 07901

Kirke Hyllinge

Bramsnæs Museum, Hornsherredsvej 430, Sæby, 4070 Kirke Hyllinge - T: 46404506, Fax: 46404506
Agriculture Museum 07902

Kjellerup

Blicheregnens Museum, Blichersvej 30, Thorning, 8620 Kjellerup - T: 86880877, Fax: 86880859. Head: Hans Kruse
Natural History Museum - 1979
Coll of stuffed birds - archive 07903

Knebel

Fuglsøcentret, Mols, 8420 Knebel - T: 86351355, Fax: 86352669
Local Museum 07904

København

Amalienborg, Danske Kongers Kronologiske Samling, Christian VIII Palace, 1257 København K - T: 33122186, Fax: 33933203, E-mail: amalienborgmuseet@c.dk. Head: Niels-Knud Liebgott
Historical Museum - 1994
Memorabilia and treasures of the Royal family 07905

Arbejdermuseet (Worker's Museum), Rømersg 22, 1362 København K - T: 33933388, Fax: 33145258, E-mail: am@arbejdermuseet.dk, Internet: http://www.arbejdermuseet.dk. Head: Peter Ludvigsen
Historical Museum / Ethnology Museum / Fine Arts Museum - 1982
Work and working conditions, housing and food 07906

Børnenens Museum, Nationalmuseet (Children's Museum), Ny Vesterg 10, 1220 København K - T: 33134411, Fax: 33473330, Internet: http://www.natmus.dk. Head: Steen Hvass
Special Museum 07907

Botanisk Museum, Gothersg 130, 1123 København K - T: 35322200, Fax: 35322210, E-mail: bm@bot.ku.dk. Head: Henning Knudsen
Natural History Museum
Main botanical museum of Denmark, herbarium - library 07908

Burmeister & Wain's Museum, Strandg 4, 1401 København K - T: 32540227
Science&Tech Museum
Industry, propulsion technology, full-scale steam and diesel engines, models of old and new ships, historical display and developments, working models 07909

Danmarks Bogmuseum (Danish Museum of Books), c/o Kongelige Bibliotek, Postboks 2149, 1016 København K - T: 33474747, Fax: 33146133, E-mail: cmb@kb.dk, Internet: http://www.kb.dk. Head: Dr. Ivan Boserup
Library with Exhibitions
Origins of the art of printing, incunabula (around 4500 works printed before 1501), post-incunabula (6500 vols printed 1501-1530), parchment coll, art of illustration and bookbinding, book provenance and related library hist 07910

Det Danske Filmmuseum, Vognmagerg 10, 1120 København K - T: 33743400, Fax: 33743599. Head: Dan Nissen
Special Museum - 1941
Danish film hist from the silent and sound era, coll of Asta Nielsen's stills and films, Carl T. Dreyer's films, literature on film and television - library 07911

Det Danske Kunstindustrimuseum (Danish Museum of Decorative Art), Bredg 68, 1260 København - T: 33149452, Fax: 33113072, E-mail: info@mus-kim.dk, Internet: http://www.mus-kim.dk. Head: Bodil Busk Laursen
Decorative Arts Museum
European, Chinese, and Japan art and applied art from medieval times through the present - library 07912

Davids Samling (The David Collection), Kronprinsesseg 30-32, 1306 København K - T: 33734949, Fax: 33734948, E-mail: museum@davidmus.dk, Internet: http://www.davidmus.dk. Head: Dr. Kjeld von Folsach
Decorative Arts Museum / Fine Arts Museum - 1945
7th-19th c Islamic art, European decorative art (mainly 18th c) 07913

Frihedsmuseet (Museum of Danish Resistance 1940-1945), Churchillparken, 1263 København K - T: 33137714, Fax: 33140314, E-mail: frihedsmuseet@natmus.dk, Internet: http://www.frihedsmuseet.dk. Head: Esben Kjeldbæk
Historical Museum - 1957
Archives, photos, and documents concerning Denmark during Nazi occupation 1940-1945 - library, archives, photo archives 07914

Fyrskib Nr. XVII, Ud for Nyhavn 2, 1051 København K
Science&Tech Museum
Lightship built in 1895 with all signaling and warning devices intact 07915

Geologisk Museum (Geological Museum), Øster Voldg 5-7, 1350 København K - T: 35322345, Fax: 35322325, E-mail: rcp@savik.geomus.ku.dk, Internet: http://www.geological-museum.dk. Head: M. Rosing
Natural History Museum / University Museum - 1770
Minerals and rocks, meteorites, fossils, geology of Denmark and Greenland - library, archives 07916

Den Hirschsprungske Samling, Stockholmsg 20, 2100 København Ø - T: 35420336, Fax: 35433510, E-mail: dhs@hirschsprung.dk, Internet: http://www.hirschsprung.dk. Head: Marianne Saabye
Fine Arts Museum - 1911
Hirschsprung Coll of 19th and early 20th c Danish art 07917

København Museum for Moderne Kunst, Nikolajg 22, 1068 København K - T: 33136970, Fax: 33339969, E-mail: Knud_Pedersen@vip.cybercity.dk, Internet: http://www.kunstbiblioteket.dk. Head: Knud Pedersen
Fine Arts Museum - 1957
Avantgarde art - art library 07918

Københavns Bymuseum (Copenhagen City Museum), Vesterbrog 59, 1620 København V - T: 33210772, Fax: 33250772, E-mail: sekr@kbhbymuseum.dk, Internet: http://www.kbhbymuseum.dk. Head: Jørgen Selmer
Historical Museum - 1901
Hist of city's development, paintings, memorabilia of the philosopher S. Kierkegaard, photograph archives, archaeology (medieval), cultural hist 07919

Den Kongelige Mønt- og Medaillesamling, Nationalmuseet (Royal Collection of Coins and Medals), Frederiksholms Kanal 12, 1220 København K - T: 33134411, Fax: 33155521, E-mail: joergen.steen.jensen@natmus.dk, Internet: http://www.natmus..dk/moentsamling. Head: Jørgen Steen Jensen
Special Museum - 1780/81
Ancient Greek and Roman coins, full coll of Danish coins from 10th c and medals from 1541 to present, important coll of European medieval and modern coins, representative coll of coins of the world, especially Islamic, India, China, Japan, and Latin America - library 07920

Kunstakademiets Bibliotek, Kongelige Danske Kunstakademi, Kongens Nytorvej 1, 1050 København K, mail addr: Postboks 3053, 1021 København K - T: 33744800, Fax: 33744888, E-mail: kab@kb.dk, Internet: http://www.kunstbib.dk. Head: Patrick Kvagelund
Public Gallery / Library with Exhibitions - 1997 07921

Kunsthallen, Gothersg 9, 1123 København K - T: 33325200, Fax: 33324670, E-mail: nr@kunsthallen.dk, Internet: http://www.kunsthallen.dk
Fine Arts Museum 07922

Louis Tussaud Wax Museum, H.C. Andersens Blvd 22, 1553 København V - T: 33142922
Special Museum - 1974
Wax models of famous historical and contemporary personalities, horror chamber 07923

Medicinisk-Historisk Museum, Bredg 62, 1260 København K - T: 35323800, Fax: 35323816, E-mail: med.hist.museum@mhm.ku.dk, Internet: http://www.pubhealth.ku.dk/mhm. Head: Thomas Söderqvist
Historical Museum - 1907
Hist of medicine, exhibits on radiography, pharmacy, dentistry, and psychiatry, surgery amphitheater - library, archives 07924

Museet for Dansk Bladtegning (Museum of Danish Cartoon Art), c/o Kongelige Bibliotek, Postboks 2149, 1016 København K - T: 33474747, Fax: 33329846, E-mail: kobj@kb.dk, Internet: http://www.kb.dk. Head: Ingrid Fischer Jonge
Special Museum
Origins drawings/prints of political comments and satire 07925

Museet ved Sct. Ansgar Kirke, Bredg 64, 1260 København K - T: 33133762. Head: Dietrich Timmermann
Religious Arts Museum - 1968
History of the Catholic church from 1654 to the present, articles used in the mass, textiles, liturgical items, religious paintings 07926

Musikhistorisk Museum og Carl Claudius' Samling, Åbenrå 30, 1124 København K - T: 33112726, Fax: 33116044, E-mail: info@musikhistoriskmuseum.dk, Internet: http://www.musikhistoriskmuseum.dk. Head: Lisbet Torp
Music Museum - 1898
Folk and classical music instruments from Europe, Asia, Africa, and South America 07927

Det Nationale Fotomuseum, Søren Kierkegaards Pl 1, København, mail addr: c/o Kongelige Bibliotek, Postboks 2149, 1016 København K - T: 33474747, Fax: 33329846, E-mail: ifj@kb.dk, Internet: http://www.kb.dk/dept/nbo/dnf. Head: Ingrid Fischer Jonge
Fine Arts Museum - 1996
Danish and foreign photography since 1839 (W.H. Fox Talbot, Maxime du Camp, John Thomson, Man Ray, A. Renger-Patzsch, Bill Brandt, Duane Michals, Paul Graham) 07928

Nationalmuseet (National Museum), Prinsens Palais, Frederiksholms Kanal 12, 1220 København K - T: 33134411, Fax: 33473330, Internet: http://www.natmus.dk. Head: Steen Hvass
Historical Museum / Archaeological Museum - 1807
Danish prehist, Middle Ages, Renaissance, modern hist, ethnography, classical antiquities, coins and medals 07929

Ny Carlsberg Glyptotek, Dantes Pl 7, 1556 København V - T: 33418141, Fax: 33912058, Internet: http://www.glyptoteket.dk. Head: Søren Dietz
Archaeological Museum / Fine Arts Museum - 1888
Egyptian, Greek, Etruscan and Roman art, classical archeology, French and Danish art of the 19th and 20th c - library 07930

Orlogsmuseet (Royal Danish Naval Museum), Overg oven Vandet 58, 1415 København K - T: 31546363, Fax: 31542980, E-mail: info@orlogsmuseet.dk, Internet: http://www.orlogsmuseet.dk. Head: Ole Lisberg Jensen
Military Museum - 1957
Hist of the Danish Navy, ships' models covering three c, painting and photograph coll of ships, naval artillery, mines and torpedos, swords and firearms, uniforms, ships' decorations - library 07931

Post & Tele Museum (PTT Museum of Denmark), Købmagerg 37, 1012 København K - T: 33410900, Fax: 33410909, E-mail: museum@ptt-museum.dk, Internet: http://www.ptt-museum.dk. Head: Birgitte Wistoft
Science&Tech Museum / Historical Museum - 1907
Hist of the post and telegraph, commerce and communication, Valdemar Poulsen's generator and telegrafon 07932

Rosenborg Slot, Danske Kongers Kronologiske Samling (Rosenborg Castle), Øster Voldg 4a, 1350 København K - T: 33153286, Fax: 33152046, E-mail: museum@dkks.dk, Internet: http://www.kulturnet.dk/homes/rosenb. Head: Niels Eilschou Holm
Historical Museum - 1833
Crown jewels, memorabilia and treasures of the Royal Family, 16th-20th c 07933

Statens Museum for Kunst, Sølvg 48-50, 1307 København K - T: 33748494, Fax: 33748404, E-mail: smk@smk.dk, Internet: http://www.smk.dk. Head: Allis Helleland
Fine Arts Museum - 1760
Danish painting and sculpture, Scandinavian art, modern French art and Old Master paintings, prints, drawings and etchings - library 07934

Teatermuseet (The Theatre Museum), Christiansborg Ridebane 18, 1218 København K - T: 33115176, Fax: 33125022, E-mail: teatermuseet@teliamail.dk, Internet: http://www.teatermuseet.dk. Head: Lisbet Grandjean
Performing Arts Museum - 1912
Danish theatre hist from 1700 to present, costumes, manuscripts, paintings, drawings, set drawings 07935

Thorvaldsens Museum, Porthusg 2, 1213 København K - T: 33321532, Fax: 33321771, E-mail: thm@thorvaldsensmuseum.dk, Internet: http://www.thorvaldsensmuseum.dk. Head: Dr. Stig Miss
Fine Arts Museum - 1848
Sculptures and drawings by the Danish sculptor Bertel Thorvaldsen (1770-1844), paintings, graphics, classical antiquities, international art in Rome about 1800 - library 07936

Tøjhusmuseet (Royal Danish Arsenal Museum), Tøjhusg 3, 1214 København, mail addr: Frederiksholms Kanal 29, 1220 København K - T: 33116037, Fax: 33937152, E-mail: thm@thm.dk, Internet: http://www.thm.dk. Head: Ole L. Frantzen
Military Museum - 1838
Private and military arms of Western civilization since 1400, international military art and science, uniforms, models 07937

Wesselstuerne, Graabrødretorv 3, 1154 København K - T: 33148923. Head: Dr. Harald Langberg
Special Museum - 1945
Home of the Danish poet Johan Herman Wessel, original editions of his work 07938

Zoologisk Museum, c/o Københavns Universitet, Universitetsparken 15, 2100 København Ø - T: 35321000, Fax: 35321010, E-mail: henghoff@zmuc.ku.dk, Internet: http://www.zmuc.kn.dk/zmuc/zmuc.htm. Head: Dr. Henrik Enghoff
Natural History Museum - 1770
Terrestrial and aquatic animals from all regions - library 07939

Køge

Køge Museum, Nørreg 4, 4600 Køge - T: 56634242, Fax: 56634232, Internet: http://www.dmol.dk. Head: Michael Teisen
Local Museum - 1896
Development of area from the Stone Age to the medieval period, peasant culture, half-timbered houses, model reconstructions 07940

Kunstmuseet Køge Skitsesamling, Nørreg 29, 4600 Køge - T: 53662414, Fax: 56632414. Head: Ellen Tange
Fine Arts Museum 07941

Kokkedal

Karlebo Museum, Rytterskolen, Avderødvej 19, 2980 Kokkedal - T: 48280176, Internet: http://www.isberthelsen.suite.dk/karlebo.htm. Head: Mogens de Neergaard
Local Museum 07942

Kolding

Museet på Koldinghus, Postbox 91, 6000 Kolding - T: 76338100, Fax: 76338199, E-mail: museum@koldinghus.dk, Internet: http://www.koldinghus.dk. Head: Poul Dedenroth-Schou
Decorative Arts Museum / Historical Museum / Historic Site - 1890
Danish fine arts and decorative arts since Renaissance, silver, porcelain, military hist 07943

Trapholt, Museum of Modern Danish Art, Applied Art and Furniture Design, Æblehaven 23, Strandhuse, 6000 Kolding - T: 76300530, Fax: 76300533, E-mail: kunstmuseum@trapholt.dk, Internet: http://www.trapholt.dk. Head: Peter S. Meyer
Decorative Arts Museum / Fine Arts Museum - 1981
Modern Danish Art, applied art and furniture design 07944

Korsør

Arkaeologisk Museum, Søbatteriet 5, 4220 Korsør - T: 53574235, 53581010. Head: Helge Torm
Archaeological Museum 07945

Korsør By- og Overfartsmuseum, Fæstningen, Søbatteriet 3, 4220 Korsør - T: 53574755. Head: P.J. Bell
Local Museum 07946

Sparekassemuseet, Korsør Lystskovej 44, 4220 Korsør - T: 53571919. Head: Lizette Koefoed
Special Museum 07947

Kværndrup

Egeskov Veteranmuseum, Egeskov G 18, 5772 Kværndrup - T: 62271016, Fax: 62271404, E-mail: info@egeskov.dk, Internet: http://www.egeskov.com. Head: Michael Ahlefeldt Laurvig Bille
Science&Tech Museum - 1967
Motorcars, motorcycles, coaches, aeroplanes, models, Piet Hein, the Golden Egg and the Mazes castle 07948

Læsø

Læsø Museum, Gl. Østerby Skole, 9940 Læsø - T: 98498045, Fax: 98498545, E-mail: laesoemu@image.dk, Internet: http://www.worldonline.dk/~laesoemu. Head: Kirsten Gjedsted
Agriculture Museum / Local Museum - 1938
Local farm museum, fishing, ship building 07949

Museumsgården, Museumsvej 3, Byrum, 9940 Læsø - T: 98498045, Fax: 98408545, E-mail: laesoemu@image.dk, Internet: http://www.worldonline.dk/~laesoemu. Head: Kirsten Gjedsted
Local Museum 07950

Søfarts og Fiskerimuseet, Vesterø Havneg 5, 9940 Læsø - T: 98498045, Fax: 98498545, E-mail: laesoemu@image.dk, Internet: http://www.worldonline.dk/~laesoemu. Head: Kirsten Gjedsted
Historical Museum 07951

Lejre

Lejre Forsøgscenter, Slangealleen 2, 4320 Lejre - T: 46480878, Fax: 46481405, E-mail: lejre@lejre-center.dk, Internet: http://www.lejre-center.dk. Head: Lars Holten
Historical Museum / Archaeological Museum / Open Air Museum 07952

Lemvig

Jens Søndergaard Museet, Transvej 4, Ferring, 7620 Lemvig - T: 97895254, Fax: 97811511, E-mail: jsm@mail.tele.dk, Internet: http://www.lemvigmuseum.dk. Head: Ellen Damgaard
Fine Arts Museum - 1958
Paintings, sculptures and watercolours of Jens Søndergaard in the summer house which he inhabited from 1930-57 07953

Lemvig Museum Vesterhus, Vesterg 44, 7620 Lemvig - T: 97820025, Fax: 97811511, E-mail: lemvigmuseum@post.tele.dk, Internet: http://www.lemvigmuseum.dk. Head: Ellen Damgaard
Local Museum - 1932
Exhibits on local history, items from shipwrecks, lifesaving services, furnishings from the ship 'Alexander Newskij', painted peasant furniture, paintings by local artists, manuscripts and book coll from the poet Thoger Larsen - "Planetary Path" (a scale model of the solar system 1:1 milliard) 07954

Museet for Religiøs Kunst og Bodil Kaalund Samlingerne, Strandvejen 13, 7620 Lemvig - T: 97810371, Fax: 97810371. Head: Kirsten Schjødt Villadsen
Fine Arts Museum / Religious Arts Museum 07955

Lintrup

Mejlby Kunsthaus → Wellings Landsbymuseum

Wellings Landsbymuseum, Mejlbyvej 10, 6660 Lintrup - T: 855286. Head: Torsten Østervig
Natural History Museum / Agriculture Museum / Folklore Museum
Geology, fossils, old agricultural machines and tools, artifacts from the Stone Age 07956

Løgstør

Limfjordsmuseet, Kanalfogedhuset, 9670 Løgstør - T: 98671805, Fax: 98674052, E-mail: limfjordsmuseet@nethotel.dk, Internet: http://www.limfjordsmuseet.dk. Head: Finn Rindom Madsen
Special Museum
Sailing, fishery, canal bailift's house 07957

Løgumkloster

Museet Holmen, Østerg 13, 6240 Løgumkloster - T: 74744165. Head: Kurt Andersen
Fine Arts Museum 07958

Løkken

Løkken Museum, Johanne Grønbechs Hus, Nørreg 12, 9840 Løkken - T: 98991847, Fax: 98991847. Head: Peter Ussing Olsen
Local Museum 07959

Lundby

Grundtvigs Mindestuer i Udby, Udby, 4750 Lundby. Head: Holger Jepsen
Special Museum - 1926
Effects of N.F.S. Grundtvig, Danish historian, theologian, and educator, his desk, books, and Bible with notes, photos of family and friends, manuscripts and original editions of his works 07960

Lyngby

Brede Værk (Brede Works), Kongevejen 100, 2800 Lyngby, mail addr: Postboks 260, 2800 Lyngby - T: 33134411, Fax: 33473317, Internet: http://www.natmus.dk
Local Museum / Open Air Museum - 1879
Costumes, furniture, domestic utensils 07961

Frilandsmuseet (Open Air Museum), Kongevejen 100, 2800 Lyngby, mail addr: Postboks 250, 2800 Lyngby - T: 33134411, Fax: 33473397, Internet: http://www.natmus.dk. Head: Inger Tolstrup
Open Air Museum - 1901
Rural buildings from the 18th and 19th c, peasant life and handicrafts 07962

Mariager

Mariager Museum, Kirkeg 3-5, 9550 Mariager - T: 98541287. Head: Vagn Andreasen
Archaeological Museum - 1922
Tools and ceramics from the Stone Age, swords from the Bronze Age, furniture from 1700 to 1800, peasant life, domestic implements, handicrafts 07963

Maribo

Frilandsmuseet i Maribo, Meinckesvej, 4930 Maribo - T: 54781101, Fax: 54781181, E-mail: maribo@museum.dk, Internet: http://www.aabne-samlinger.dk. Head: Thomas W. Lassen
Open Air Museum / Agriculture Museum
Exhibits on agriculture in the 19th c, farmstead with six houses, a smithy, mill, and school, medieval curative plants and fruit trees 07964

Lolland-Falsters Stiftsmuseum, Museumsg 1, 4930 Maribo - T: 54781101, Fax: 54781181, E-mail: maribo@museum.dk, Internet: http://www.aabne-samlinger.dk. Head: Thomas W. Lassen
Local Museum - 1884
Historic finds, ceramics, folk art, work tools, exhibit on Polish migrant workers, 14th c crucifixes - library 07965

Storstrøms Kunstmuseum, Banegårdspl, 4930 Maribo - T: 54781414, Fax: 54781214, E-mail: post@stkm.dk, Internet: http://www.storstroems-kunstmuseum.dk. Head: Anne Højer Petersen
Fine Arts Museum - 1890
Danish paintings and sculpture from the Golden Age (19th c) to the present, watercolours, drawings, graphics, Olaf Rude (1886-1957), Oluf Hartmann (1879- 1910), Danish painter - archive, reference library 07966

Marstal

Marstal Søfartsmuseum (Marstal Maritime Museum), Prinsensg 2-4, 5960 Marstal, mail addr: Postboks 36, 5960 Marstal - T: 62532331, Fax: 62533166, E-mail: info@marstal-maritime-museum.dk, Internet: http://www.marstal-maritime-museum.dk. Head: Erik Kromann
Science&Tech Museum - 1929
200 models of various ships, bottleship coll, navigation instruments and log books, weapons, model of 19th c shipyard, paintings on sea themes and personalities, local coll of costumes, furnishings, and porcelain - library 07967

Middelfart

Middelfart Museum, Knorreg 2, 5500 Middelfart - T: 64414741, Fax: 64418786, E-mail: info@middelfart-museum.dk. Head: Peter Dragsbo
Local Museum - 1919
Renaissance house, local items dating from the Middle age to our days (town and country), women's hat coll 1850-1960, history of ships, exhibition conc. the Little Belt bridge (1935), local industry (cast iron) - archive, old shipyard 07968

Næstved

Næstved Museum, Ringstedg 4, 4700 Næstved - T: 55770811, Fax: 55771854, E-mail: post@naestved-museum.dk, Internet: http://www.aabne-samlinger.dk/naestved. Head: Palle Birk Hansen
Decorative Arts Museum - 1917
Handicrafts and applied arts, Holmegaard glass, Kähler ceramics, 15th c houses - library 07969

Nexø

Nexø Museum, Kirkestræde 30, 3730 Nexø - T: 56492554. Head: Bent Sonne Jacobsen
Local Museum - 1969
WW II and the Russian liberation 07970

Nivå

Nivaagaards Malerisamling, Gammel Strandvej 2, 2990 Nivå - T: 49141017, Fax: 49141057, E-mail: museum@nivaagaard.dk, Internet: http://www.nivaagaard.dk. Head: Nils Ohrt
Fine Arts Museum - 1908
19th c Danish art, 17th c Dutch art, and 16th c Italian art 07971

Nørager

Sydhimmerlands Museum, Ørnbjergvej 13, Boldrup, 9610 Nørager, mail addr: Vesterg 23, 9500 Hobro - T: 98510555, Fax: 98524367. Head: Birte Friis
Agriculture Museum - 1965
Agriculture, handicrafts, small holders - library 07972

Nørre Nebel

Blaabjerg Egnsmuseum, Varde Museum, Sønder Allé 21, 6830 Nørre Nebel, mail addr: Lundvej 4, 6800 Varde - T: 75220877, Fax: 75220716. Head: Ole Faber
Local Museum - 1976
Reconstruction of "Lønne girl" burial find from about Christs' birth, local hist 07973

Nørresundby

Lindholm Høje Museet, Vendilavej 11, 9400 Nørresundby - T: 96310428, Fax: 98175562, E-mail: Lhm@aahm.dk, Internet: http://www.aahm.dk. Head: Torben Witt
Archaeological Museum - 1992
Late Iron Age, Viking Age 07974

Sundby Samling Bryggergården, Gamle Østerg 8, 9400 Nørresundby - T: 98174755. Head: Ketty Johansson
Local Museum - 1967
Local historical items 07975

Sundby Samling Raschgården, Frederik Raschsvej 9, Lindholm, 9400 Nørresundby - T: 98173346. Head: Ketty Johansson
Local Museum - 1967
Local historical items, 18th-19th furnishings, paintings, domestic utensils, agricultural tools 07976

Nyborg

Nyborg og Omegns Museer, Slotsg 11, 5800 Nyborg - T: 65310207, Fax: 65310229, E-mail: museer@nyborg.dk, Internet: http://www.museer-nyborg.dk. Head: Knud Hornbeck
Local Museum 07977

Nykøbing Falster

Museum Falsters Minder, Langg 2, 4800 Nykøbing Falster - T: 54852671, Fax: 54852602, E-mail: falsters-minder@museum.dk, Internet: http://www.aabne-samlinger.dk/falsters-minder
Local Museum - 1913
Textiles, peasant costumes, handicrafts, historic house from 1700, the Old Grocer's Shop - local archive 07978

Skovbrugsmagasinet på Corselitze, Tromnæs Alléen 2, 4800 Nykøbing Falster - T: 54851262. Head: Thyge Andersen
Special Museum 07979

Nykøbing Mors

Landbrugsmuseet Skarregaard, Feggesundvej 53, Sejerslev, 7900 Nykøbing Mors - T: 97751609. Head: Per Noe
Agriculture Museum 07980

Molermuseet, Skarrehagevej 8, Hesselbjerg, 7900 Nykøbing Mors - T: 97751716. Head: Per Noe
Archaeological Museum
Fossils, viking and middle age houses 07981

Morslands Historiske Museum, Dueholm Kloster, Dueholmg, 7900 Nykøbing Mors - T: 97723421, Fax: 97722623, E-mail: dueholm@museum.dk, Internet: http://www.dueholmkloster.dk. Head: Per Noe
Historical Museum - 1901
Local hist and archeology, iron casting, fisheries, religious art, peasant culture, Viking era, navigation, military objects, fossils, local art - library, archives 07982

Nykøbing Sjælland

Anneberg-Samlingerne, Anneberg, 4500 Nykøbing Sjælland
Decorative Arts Museum - 1965
Greek and Roman glass, Bohemian glass, Spanish glass, decorated glass, sculpture, handicrafts, paintings 07983

Odsherreds Museum, Kirkestræde 12, 4500 Nykøbing Sjælland - T: 59913325, Fax: 59913320, E-mail: ods-museum@get2net.dk. Head: Kirsten Strandgaard
Local Museum - 1912
Archaeology, ethnology, hist 07984

Nysted

Aalholm Automobil Museum, Aalholm Parkvej 17, 4880 Nysted - T: 54871200, Fax: 54871158, E-mail: gods@aalholm.dk, Internet: http://www.aalholm.dk
Science&Tech Museum - 1964
Motor cars, model railroad system 07985

Odder

Odder Museum, Rosensgade 84, 8300 Odder - T: 86540175, Fax: 86541390, E-mail: os@oddermuseum.dk, Internet: http://www.oddermuseum.dk. Head: Ove Sørensen
Local Museum - 1929
Excavations of medieval manor houses, 19th c peasant furniture, folklore, beekeeping, oldest distillery in Scandinavia, 13th c distillery equipment, textiles 07986

Odense

Bymuseet Møntergaarden, Overg 48, 5000 Odense C - T: 66148814 lokal 4601, Fax: 65908600, E-mail: museum@odmus.dk, Internet: http://www.odmus.dk. Head: Torben Grøngaard Jeppesen
Local Museum
Local hist, town culture, peasant costumes, handicrafts 07987

Carl Nielsen Museet, Claus Bergs G 11, 5000 Odense C - T: 66148814 lokal 4601, Fax: 65908600, E-mail: museum@.odmus.dk, Internet: http://www.odmus.dk. Head: Torben Grøngaard Jeppesen
Special Museum - 1988
Presentation of the composer's life and work (furniture, works of art, personal items) 07988

Danmarks Grafiske Museum, Dansk Pressemuseum, Brandts Passage 37, 5000 Odense C - T: 66121020, Fax: 66121063, E-mail: info@mediemuseum.dk, Internet: http://www.mediemuseum.dk. Head: Ervin Nielsen
Science&Tech Museum - 1981
Hist of graphic and press industry, bookbinding, paper making 07989

Danmarks Jernbanemuseum (The Danish Railway Museum), Dannebrogsg 24, 5000 Odense C - T: 66136630, Fax: 66190220, E-mail: jbmuseum@dsb.dk, Internet: http://www.railmuseum.dk. Head: Poul Thestrup
Science&Tech Museum - 1975
Steam locomotives, passenger coaches, royal saloons, ferry models 07990

Fyns Kunstmuseum, Jernbaneg 13, 5000 Odense C - T: 66148814 lokal 4601, Fax: 65908600, E-mail: museum@odmus.dk, Internet: http://www.odmus.dk. Head: Torben Grøngaard Jeppesen
Fine Arts Museum - 1885
Danish art from ca 1750 until the present - library 07991

Den Fynske Landsby (Funen Village), Sejerskovvej 20, 5260 Odense SØ - T: 66148814 lokal 4601, Fax: 66127956, E-mail: museum@odmus.dk, Internet: http://www.odmus.dk. Head: Torben Grøngaard Jeppesen
Open Air Museum - 1946
Peasant culture, farms and peasant houses, domestic animals, dept of architectural hist 07992

Hans Christian Andersen Hus, Hans Jensens Straede 37-45, 5000 Odense C, mail addr: Bangs Boder 5, 5000 Odense - T: 66131372, Fax: 65908600, E-mail: museum@odmus.dk, Internet: http://www.odmus.dk. Head: Torben Grøngaard Jeppesen
Special Museum - 1905
Letters and manuscripts of Andersen, drawings and graphics inspired by his work, personal items, editions of his books 07993

H.C. Andersens Barndomshjem, Munkemöllestr 3-5, 5000 Odense C - T: 66131372, Fax: 65908600, E-mail: museum@odmus.dk, Internet: http://www.odmus.dk. Head: Torben Grønnegaard Jeppesen
Special Museum - 1931
House where Andersen lived as a child (1807-19), paintings and other materials on his life and the city of that time 07994

Hollufgård - Arkeologi og Landskab, Hestehaven 201, 5220 Odense SØ, mail addr: Bangs Boder 5, 5000 Odense - T: 66131372, Fax: 65959135, E-mail: museum@odmus.dk, Internet: http://www.odmus.dk. Head: Torben Grøngaard Jeppesen
Archaeological Museum - 1860
Prehistoric findings, Viking artifacts, items from Bronze and Iron Ages, coins and medals 07995

Kunsthallen Brandts Klaedefabrik, Brandts Passage 37-43, 5000 Odense C - T: 66137897, Fax: 66137310, E-mail: kunsthallen@brandts.dk, Internet: http://www.brandts.dk. Head: Karsten Ohrt
Fine Arts Museum - 1987
Graphic arts, fine arts exhibition hall 07996

Museet for Fotokunst (Museum of Photographic Art), Brandts Passage 37-43, 5000 Odense - T: 66137816, Fax: 66137310, E-mail: mff@brandts.dk, Internet: http://www.brandts.dk. Head: Finn Thrane
Fine Arts Museum 07997

Oksbøl

Blaavandshuk Egnsmuseum, Varde Museum, Kirkeg 1, 6840 Oksbøl, mail addr: Lundvej 4, 6800 Varde - T: 75272159, Fax: 75220716. Head: Ole Faber
Local Museum - 1972
Agricultural implements, domestic utensils, military items from the Occupation and WW II, local archives 07998

Ravmuseet (Danish Amber Museum), Vesterg 25, 6840 Oksbøl - T: 75270703, 75220877, Fax: 75220716, E-mail: vam@vardemuseum.dk. Head: Ole Faber
Decorative Arts Museum / Natural History Museum - 1998
Amber - natural and cultural hist from Europe and other parts of the world, esp from Denmark 07999

Ølgod

Hjedding Mejerimuseum, Hjeddingvej 2, 6870 Ølgod - T: 75245011, Fax: 75246330. Head: Jens Sørensen
Special Museum / Science&Tech Museum - 1948
First community dairy from 1882, various dairy machines, centrifuge, etc 08000

Ølgod Museum, Vesterg 5-7, 6870 Ølgod - T: 75245011, Fax: 75246330, E-mail: post@oelgodmuseum.dk. Head: Jens Sørensen
Local Museum - 1954
Items of local historical interest 08001

Øster-Assels

Smedemuseet, Kongehøjvej 33, Ørding, 7990 Øster-Assels - T: 97723421, Fax: 97722623, E-mail: dueholm@museum.dk, Internet: http://www.dueholmkloster.dk. Head: Per Noe
Science&Tech Museum 08002

Otterup

Otterup Museum, Bakkevej 3, 5450 Otterup - T: 65954035. Head: Herluf Knudsen
Local Museum - 1930
Local exhibits 08003

Padborg

Bov Museum, Bovvej 2, 6330 Padborg - T: 74675150, Fax: 74675037
Local Museum - 1979
Old uniforms, pictures of the frontier gendarmery, agricultural tools, old fire engines, regional poetry 08004

Frøslevlejrens Museum, Lejrvej 83, 6330 Padborg - T: 74676557, Fax: 74676077, E-mail: - froeslevlejrensmuseum@mail.tele.dk. Head: Henrik Skov Kristensen
Local Museum
Prison camp (World War II) 08005

Præstø

Dansk Brandværnshistorisk Museum, Havnevej 4, 4720 Præstø - T: 55991844. Head: Søren Laursen
Science&Tech Museum 08006

Thorvaldsens Samlingen på Nysø, Østerbro 2, 4720 Præstø - T: 55909200, 53799393. Head: Agathe Ohmann
Fine Arts Museum - 1926
Sculpture, reliefs, busts, and statuettes by the Danish sculptor Bertel Thorvaldsen, including his self-portrait and the bust of Martin Luther, several memorabilia of the artist 08007

Randers

Kulturhistorisk Museum, Stemannsg 2, 8900 Randers - T: 86428655, Fax: 86418649, E-mail: khm@khm.dk, Internet: http://www.khm.dk. Head: Jørgen Smidt-Jensen
Historical Museum - 1872
Prehistoric and medieval archeology, numismatics, regional crafts, textiles, furniture, and household utensils, woodcuts by Dürer and etchings by Rembrandt and Ostade - library, study room 08008

Randers Kunstmuseum, Stemannsg 2, 8900 Randers - T: 86422922, Fax: 86432954, E-mail: kunst1@post2.tele.dk, Internet: http://www.randers-kunstmuseum.dk. Head: Finn Terman Frederiksen
Fine Arts Museum - 1887
Danish painting from 1770 to the present, modern international art, painting, graphics, and sculpture 08009

Ribe

Den Antikvariske Samling, Overdammen 12, 6760 Ribe - T: 76881122, Fax: 76881135, E-mail: asr.qg@post.tele.dk, Internet: http://www.ribesvikinger.dk. Head: Jakob Kieffer-Olsen
Archaeological Museum / Local Museum - 1855
Excavation finds, religious art, Renaissance furniture, decorative arts, porcelain and glass, archaeological objects from the 7th to the 17th c - Museet Ribes Vikinger, Quedens Gård, Rådhussamlingen 08010

Museums-Everten Johanne Dan (closed) 08011

Ribe Kunstmuseum, Sankt-Nikolajg 10, 6760 Ribe - T: 75420362, Fax: 75422182. Head: Claus Olsen
Fine Arts Museum - 1891
Coll of Danish art with emphasis on art from the Golden Age (19th c) 08012

Ribe Raadhussamling, V. Støckensplads, 6760 Ribe - T: 76881122, Fax: 76881135, E-mail: asr.qg@post.tele.dk. Head: Jakob Kieffer-Olsen
Local Museum
Town hall from 1528, old debtor's prison, equipment of a medieval executioner, e.g., thumb screws, branding irons 08013

Ringe

Ringe Museum, Kirkepladsen 6, 5750 Ringe - T: 62623538. Head: Jørgen Havelund
Local Museum 08014

Ringkøbing

Ringkøbing Museum, Kongevejen 1, 6950 Ringkøbing - T: 97321615, 97321615, Fax: 97321621. Head: J. Aarup Jensen
Archaeological Museum - 1908
Prehist and hist of W. Jutland, coll from expedition to NE Greenland 1906-08 08015

Ringsted

Ringsted Museum, Køgevej 41, 4100 Ringsted - T: 57626900, Fax: 57626906, E-mail: ringstedmuseum@ringsted.dk. Head: Kirsten Bøge Henriksen
Local Museum
Cultural hist of central Seeland 08016

Risskov

Museet Psykiatrisk Hospital i Århus, Skovagervej 2, 8240 Risskov - T: 77893680, Fax: 77893099, E-mail: mpr@mobilixnet.dk, Internet: http://www.aaa.dk/musph. Head: Johannes Nielsen
Special Museum
Psychiatric hist, outsider art 08017

Rødovre

HTs-Museum, Islevdalvej 119, 2610 Rødovre - T: 42912391
Local Museum 08018

Rødvig Stevns

Lille Heddinge Rytterskole, Stormarksvej 1, 4673 Rødvig Stevns - T: 53702556
Historical Museum 08019

Rønne

Bornholms Museum, Sdr. Strandvej 95, 3700 Rønne, mail addr: Postboks 126, 3700 Rønne - T: 56950735, Fax: 56950745. Head: Henrik Vensild
Fine Arts Museum - 1893
Art and applied art 08020

Erichsens Gaard, Bornholms Museum, Lakseg 7, 3700 Rønne - T: 56958735. Head: Ann Vibeke Knudsen
Local Museum
19th c farm, furnishings of period 08021

Forsvarsmuseet på Bornholm, Arsenal Vej, 3700 Rønne - T: 56956583, E-mail: FpB@post9.tele.dk, Internet: http://home9.inet.dk/fpb. Head: J.C. Skaarup
Military Museum - 1979
Military uniforms, weapons, and equipment from the Bornholm forces, weapons and items from the German Occupation and the Russian forces in 1945-46 - library 08022

Roskilde

Museet for Samtidskunst (Museum of Contemporary Art), Stændertorvet 3, 4000 Roskilde - T: 46368874, Fax: 46360190, E-mail: museet@mfsk.dk, Internet: http://www.mfsk.dk. Head: Marianne Bech
Fine Arts Museum 08023

Palæsamlingerne (Palace Collection), Stændertorvet 3e, 4000 Roskilde - T: 46357880, Fax: 46321647, E-mail: romu@post7.tele.dk, Internet: http://www.roslkildemuseum.dk. Head: Frank Birkebæk
Folklore Museum
Culture of the middleclass 08024

Roskilde Domkirkemuseum, Cathedral, Great Hall, 4000 Roskilde - T: 46351624, 46328348, Fax: 46322527, E-mail: museum@roskildedomkirke.dk, Internet: http://www.roskilde.dk. Head: Anette Kruse
Religious Arts Museum 08025

Roskilde Museum, Sankt Ols Gade 18, 4000 Roskilde - T: 46366044, Fax: 46321647, E-mail: romu@post7.tele.dk, Internet: http://www.roskildemuseum.dk. Head: Frank A. Birkebaek
Local Museum 08026

Roskilde Museums Købmandsgård (Grocer's Shop of Roskilde Museum), Ringstedg 6-8, 4000 Roskilde - T: 46350061
Special Museum 08027

Slagterbutikken anno 1920 (Butcher's Shop from 1920), Ringstedg 8, 4000 Roskilde - T: 46356140
Special Museum 08028

Vikingeskibsmuseet (Viking Ship Museum), Vindeboder 12, 4000 Roskilde, mail addr: Postboks 298, 4000 Roskilde - T: 46300200, Fax: 46300201, E-mail: museum@vikingeskibsmuseet.dk, Internet: http://www.vikingeskibsmuseet.dk. Head: Tinna Damgaard Sørensen
Historical Museum / Science&Tech Museum - 1969
Original Viking ships of various types, displays of Viking activities and culture - film room 08029

Roslev

Jenle Museum, 7870 Roslev
Special Museum
Farm and home of the Danish writer Jeppe Aakjær and his wife Nanna, his books, effects, and paintings and sculpture of his friends 08030

Rudkøbing

Langelands Museum, Jens Winthersvej 12, 5900 Rudkøbing - T: 63511010, Fax: 63511011, E-mail: - LangelandsMuseum@rudkom.dk, Internet: http://www.rudkom.dk/museum. Head: Jørgen Skaarup
Local Museum - 1900
Famous Stone Age settlement finds from late Stone Age, Viking chieftain graves, a 16th c fisherman's settlement, furniture from manor houses, religious artifacts, sailing, gardens, mills - library, conservation department 08031

Rungsted Kyst

Karen Blixen Museet, Rungsted Strandvej 111, 2960 Rungsted Kyst - T: 45571057, Fax: 45571058, E-mail: karen-blixen@dinesen.dk, Internet: http://www.isak-dinesen.dk. Head: Marianne Wirenfeldt Asmussen
Historical Museum - 1991 08032

Ry

Danmarks Kloster Museum (The Monastic Museum of Denmark), Munkevej 8, 8680 Ry - T: 86898194, E-mail: cara.insula@ecomuseum.dk, Internet: http://www.klostermuseet.dk. Head: Bo Gregersen
Archaeological Museum / Religious Arts Museum - 1911
Medieval cloister ruin (1172), medieval archeological findings, medicine coll of pathological bones from the graveyard, medieval herbgarden, monastic hist, Cistercan Order 08033

Sæby

Sæby Museum and Sæbygaard Manor Museum, Alg 1-3, 9300 Sæby - T: 98461077, Fax: 98401349, Internet: http://www.kulturnet.dk. Head: Bent Bang Larsen
Local Museum - 1919/90
18th c half-timbered house, artefacts from the prehistorical period to the present, early 20th c school room with physics equipment, a merchant's shop, photographer's studio, 16th c manor house, furnished rooms from the periods 1700-1900 08034

Samsø

Økomuseum Samsø, Museumsvej 10, Tranebjerg, 8305 Samsø - T: 86592150, Fax: 86592277, E-mail: info@ecomuseum-samso.dk, Internet: http://www.ecomuseum-samso.dk. Head: Lis Nymark
Local Museum / Archaeological Museum
Cultural hist, archaeology 08035

Silkeborg

Silkeborg Kulturhistoriske Museum, Hovedgaarden, 8600 Silkeborg - T: 86821499, Fax: 87205190, E-mail: info@silkeborgmuseum.dk, Internet: http://www.silkeborgmuseum.dk. Head: Christian Fischer
Historical Museum - 1900
Items from the Stone Age to the present, 2400-year old prehistoric corpses (The Tollund Man and the Elling Woman), pottery and wooden shoe workshops, glass 08036

Silkeborg Kunstmuseum (Silkeborg Museum of Art), Gudenaavej 7-9, 8600 Silkeborg, mail addr: Postboks 940, 8600 Silkeborg - T: 86825388, Fax: 86815131, E-mail: silkeborg.kunstmuseum@get2net.dk, Internet: http://www.silkeborg-kunstmuseum.dk. Head: Troels Andersen
Fine Arts Museum - 1966
Modern art, European paintings from the late 19th-20th c, graphics, ceramics 08037

Skagen

Drachmanns Hus, Hans Baghs Vej 21, 9990 Skagen - T: 98445188, 98442822, Fax: 98445362, E-mail: hnielsen@ofir.dk, Internet: http://www.skagen.dk/skagib/drach.html. Head: Hans Nielsen
Special Museum - 1911
Summer house of the writer Holger Drachmann, paintings by Drachmann, Krøyer, Ancher, Tuxen 08038

Grenen Kunstmuseum, Fyrvej 40, Grenen, 9990 Skagen - T: 98442288, Fax: 98451788, Internet: http://www.grenenkunstmuseum.org. Head: Axel Lind
Fine Arts Museum 08039

Michael og Anna Anchers Hus og Saxilds Gaard, Markvej 2-4, 9990 Skagen - T: 98443009, Fax: 98450235, E-mail: museum@anchershus.dk, Internet: http://www.anchershus.dk. Head: Steffen Inne
Fine Arts Museum / Decorative Arts Museum - 1964
House where the Anchers lived, interior furnishings, paintings by the artists and other scandinavian artists 08040

Skagen By- og Egnsmuseum (Town and Regional Museum of Skagen), P.K. Nielsens Vej 8-10, 9990 Skagen - T: 98444760, Fax: 98446730, E-mail: info@skagen-bymus.dk, Internet: http://www.skagen-bymus.dk. Head: Michael Ax
Open Air Museum / Local Museum - 1927
Ship models, town history - archive, ship smith's workshop, fishing vessel 08041

Skagens Museum, Bröndumsvej 4, 9990 Skagen, mail addr: Postboks 171, 9990 Skagen - T: 98446444, Fax: 98441810, E-mail: museum@skagensmuseum.dk, Internet: http://www.skagensmuseum.dk. Head: Annette Johansen
Fine Arts Museum - 1908
Fine art by the artists' colony painters at Skagen, applied art by Th. Bindesbøll, the famous diningroom of the Brøndum Hotel (1870-1910) 08042

Skanderborg

Skanderborg Museum, Adelg 5, 8660 Skanderborg - T: 86522499, Fax: 86521198
Local Museum - 1913
Local historical items dating from the Stone Age to the present, artifacts from the Viking era, peasant culture - archive 08043

Skive

Skive Kunstmuseum, Havnevej 14, 7800 Skive - T: 97526933, Fax: 97513933, E-mail: skivkuns@post5.tele.dk, Internet: http://www.kulturnet.dk/homes/skivekunst. Head: Lisbet Astrup Mogensen
Fine Arts Museum - 1964
Expressive landscape-painting and Neo-realist art 08044

Skive Museum, Havnevej 14, 7800 Skive - T: 97526933, Fax: 97513933. Head: Gudrun Gormsen
Local Museum - 1910
Prehistoric amber coll, exhibits on local ethnography and archeology 08045

Skjern

Bymuseet (Village Museum), Bredg 73-77, 6900 Skjern - T: 97351900, E-mail: museum@skjern-egvald-museum.dk, Internet: http://www.skjern-egvald-museum.dk. Head: Kim Clausen
Local Museum 08046

Dansk Veteranflysamling, Stauning Lufthavn, 6900 Skjern - T: 97369333, Internet: http://www.flymuseum.dk. Head: Karsten Knudsen
Science&Tech Museum 08047

Dejbjerg Jernalder, Bundsbækvej 4a, 6900 Skjern - T: 97362343, Fax: 97362480, E-mail: museum@skjern-egvald-museum.dk, Internet: http://www.skjern-egvald-museum.dk. Head: Kim Clausen
Local Museum 08048

Skjern-Egvad Museum, Bundsbækvej 25, 6900 Skjern - T: 97362343, Fax: 97362480, E-mail: museum@skjern-egvald-museum.dk, Internet: http://www.skjern-egvald-museum.dk. Head: Kim Clausen
Open Air Museum / Ethnology Museum / Archaeological Museum - 1929
Findings from the Iron ages, pottery, domestic utensils, peasant furniture, fishing implements, religious objects, watermill, windmill, rock music 08049

Skjern Vindmølle, Langagervej 25, 6900 Skjern - T: 97352973, E-mail: museum@skjern-egvald-museum.dk, Internet: http://www.skjern-egvald-museum.dk. Head: Kim Clausen
Science&Tech Museum 08050

Skørping

Spillemands-Jagt og Skovbrugsmuseet i Rebild, Cimbrervej 2, Rebild, 9520 Skørping - T: 98391604, Fax: 98392604, E-mail: spillemandsmuseet@mail.dk, Internet: http://www.roldskovmuseum.dk. Head: Niels Jøan, Østargård
Local Museum / Folklore Museum - 1951
Forestry, hunting, local history, folk music and instruments, folk dancing, blacksmith shop, peasants' furniture, pottery, and kitchen utensils 08051

Thingbaek Kalkminer Bundgaards Museum, Røde Møllervej 4, 9520 Skørping - T: 98375112, E-mail: hanne.bach-nielsen@get2net.dk, Internet: http://www.roldskovmuseerne.dk. Head: Hanne Bach-Nielsen
Fine Arts Museum - 1969
Coll of the sculpture of Anders Bundgaard and Carl Johan Bonnesens exhibited in a mine 08052

Slagelse

Flakkebjerg Skolemuseum, Gimlingevej 2, Flakkebjerg, 4200 Slagelse - T: 53586077. Head: C. Nicolaisen
Historical Museum 08053

Museet ved Trelleborg, Trelleborg Allé 4, Hejninge, 4200 Slagelse - T: 58549506, Fax: 58549516, E-mail: trelleborg@mobilixnet.dk, Internet: http://www.vikingeborg.dk. Head: Kåre Johannessen
Historical Museum - 1995
Viking age monument, fortress 08054

Slagelse Museum for Handel, Håndværk og Industri, Bredg 11, 4200 Slagelse - T: 53524238. Head: Poul Bryde Nielsen
Historical Museum 08055

Slangerup

Historisk Museum, Postboks 98, 3550 Slangerup. Head: Jens Westerlund
Local Museum 08056

Søby Ærø

Søbygård, Søbymarksvej 2, 5985 Søby Ærø - T: 62581676. Head: Karen M. Fabricius
Special Museum
Manor house build by Duke Hans the Younger 1580 08057

Sønderborg

Museet på Sønderborg Slot, Sønderborg Slot, 6400 Sønderborg - T: 74422539, Fax: 74430655, E-mail: MSS@sja.dk. Head: Peter La Cour Dragsbo
Historical Museum / Folklore Museum / Open Air Museum - 1908
Castle, history of Sleswig, local historical items, handicrafts, paintings, military weapons and uniforms, medieval art 08058

Sorø

Hauchs Physiske Cabinet, Sorø Akademis, Vaenget Soeg 17a, 4180 Sorø - T: 57821335, Fax: 57820136, E-mail: bgsbroby@inet.uniz.dk, Internet: http://www.awhauch.dk
Science&Tech Museum - 1827
Scientific instruments late 18th c 08059

Sorø Amts Museum, Storg 17, 4180 Sorø - T: 57834063, Fax: 57820740, E-mail: sam@soroe-amts-museum.dk. Head: Helge Torm
Local Museum - 1916
Peasant costumes and culture, development of town culture in the 18th and 19th c, archeological findings from the Stone Age to the present, furniture, glass, silver, paintings 08060

Vestsjællands Kunstmuseum, Storg 9, 4180 Sorø - T: 57832229, Fax: 57820018, E-mail: museum@vestkunst.dk, Internet: http://www.vestkunst.dk. Head: Charlotte Sabroe
Fine Arts Museum - 1943
Danish art (1780-1850), Russian art (1870-1930), contemporary art 08061

Spøttrup

Borgmuseum, Bogen 6a, 7860 Spøttrup - T: 97561606, Fax: 97561899, E-mail: spottrup-borg@mail.tele.dk, Internet: http://www.spottrup.dk/borgen. Head: Thomas Høvsgaard
Historical Museum 08062

Stege

Møns Museum, Storeg 75, 4780 Stege - T: 55814067, Fax: 55814057. Head: Edith Marie Rosenmeier
Local Museum - 1914
Religious art, local history, archeological findings from 10,000 BC to Bronze Age, peasant costumes, furniture 08063

Store Heddinge

Østsjællands Museum, Stevns Museum, Højerup Bygade 38, 4660 Store Heddinge - T: 56502806, Fax: 56502865, E-mail: oestsjaellands@museum.dk, Internet: http://www.aabne-samlinger.dk/oestsjaellands. Head: Helle Schummel
Local Museum 08064

Struer

Struer Museum og Johs. Buchholtz Hus, Sønderg 23, 7600 Struer - T: 97851311, Fax: 97840922, E-mail: mail@struermuseum.dk, Internet: http://www.struermuseum.dk. Head: Torben Holm
Local Museum - 1929
Local hist of art and culture, hist of radio- and TV company Bang & Olufsen, Struer as a railway junction, local marine coll, and a fine coll of topographical art from the area, home of Danish author Johannes Buchholtz with interior from the 1920's and 1930's 08065

Stubbekøbing

Radio- og Motorcykel Museet, Nykøbingvej 52, 4850 Stubbekøbing - T: 54442222. Head: Erik Nielsen
Science&Tech Museum - 1977 08066

Svendborg

Anne Hvides Gaard, Fruestræde 3, 5700 Svendborg - T: 62210261, Fax: 62202161, E-mail: info@svendborgmuseum.dk, Internet: http://www.svendborgmuseum.dk. Head: Esben Hedegaard
Local Museum - 1908
Oldest worldly building in Svendborg, 18th and 19th c middle class interiors, Svendborg silver- and brasswork 08067

Johannes Jørgensens Mindestuer, Fruestræde 15, 5700 Svendborg - T: 62210559, Fax: 62220539
Special Museum
Private coll of books of the Danish writer Johannes Jørgensen, personal furniture brought from Assisi, coll of letters 08068

Ofenmuseum L. Lange & Co., Vesterg 45, 5700 Svendborg - T: 62210261, Fax: 62202161, E-mail: info@svendborgmuseum.dk, Internet: http://www.svendborgmuseum.dk. Head: Esben Hedegaard
Science&Tech Museum - 1986
Coll of stoves 08069

Søfartssamlingerne i Troense (Maritime Collections at Troense), Strandg 1, Troense, 5700 Svendborg - T: 62210261, Fax: 62202161, E-mail: info@svendborgmuseum.dk, Internet: http://www.svendborgmuseum.dk. Head: Esben Hedegaard
Science&Tech Museum - 1956
Navigation, wooden ship industry 08070

Svendborg og Omegns Museum, Grubbemøllevej 13, 5700 Svendborg - T: 62210261, Fax: 62202161, E-mail: info@svendborgmuseum.dk, Internet: http://www.svendborgmuseum.dk. Head: Esben Hedegaard
Local Museum - 1908
Items from prehistory through the Middle Ages, folklore, social history, handicrafts, maritime history 08071

Taasinge Skipperhjem og Folkemindesamling, Kirkebakken, Bregninge, Tåsinge, 5700 Svendborg - T: 62227144, Fax: 62514484, E-mail: Jytte.Per@get2net.dk. Head: Jytte Munch
Folklore Museum - 1958
Half-timbered house (1770), agricultural implements, navigation, articles from the Stone Age to the present, traditional peasant costumes, maritime paintings, music of the common people in Tåsinge 08072

Viebæltegaard, Grubbemøllevej 13, 5700 Svendborg - T: 62210261, Fax: 62202161, E-mail: info@svendborgmuseum.dk, Internet: http://www.svendborgmuseum.dk. Head: Esben Hedegaard
Local Museum - 1974
Exhibits of 19th c indigents' home and labour institute items from prehistory through the Middle Ages, social hist, handicrafts 08073

Zoologisk Museum Svendborg, Dronningemaen 30, 5700 Svendborg - T: 62210650, Fax: 62218417, Internet: http://www.zoomus.dk. Head: Jakob Salvig
Natural History Museum - 1935
Denmark's fauna from the Ice Age to the present, panoramas of environmental habitats of each species, whales, fossils, bird coll 08074

Taastrup

Ole Rømer Museet, Kroppedals Allé 3, 2630 Taastrup - T: 43353680, Fax: 43353686, E-mail: mail@oleroemer.dk, Internet: http://www.oleroemer.dk. Head: Claus Thykier
Science&Tech Museum - 1979
History of Danish astronomy, Ole Rømer discovery of the velocity of light, and his deeds concerning astronomy 08075

Thisted

Museet for Thy og Vester Hanherred, Jernbaneg 4, 7700 Thisted - T: 97920577, Fax: 97912377, E-mail: thistedmuseum@mail.tele.dk, Internet: http://www.thistedmuseum.dk. Head: Jette Kjær
Local Museum - 1903
Handicrafts, local history from Viking times to present, coll of bronzes, memorial to the Danish poet Jens Peter Jacobsen 08076

Tikøb

Museet Tikøb Frysehus, Helsingør Kommunes Museer, Søgårdsvej, Harreshøjvej, 3080 Tikøb. Head: Kenno Pedersen
Local Museum 08077

Tønder

Sønderjyllands Kunstmuseum, Kongevej 51, 6270 Tønder - T: 74722657, Fax: 74720850, E-mail: museerne_toender@sja.dk. Head: Ove Mogensen
Fine Arts Museum - 1972
Danish art from the 20th c 08078

Tønder Museum, Kongevej 51, 6270 Tønder - T: 74722657, Fax: 74720850, E-mail: Museerne_Toender@sja.dk. Head: Inger Lauridsen
Decorative Arts Museum - 1923
Silver, tiles, lace, Renaissance and Baroque furniture, faience and porcelain, glass, tower with large coll of chairs made by the designer Hans J. Wagner 08079

Ulfborg

Strandgaarden Museum, Ringkøbing Museum, Husby Klitvej 5, 6990 Ulfborg - T: 97331020, Fax: 97331020. Head: J. Aarup Jensen
Agriculture Museum
Farm in dunes, coast protection, first editions of Munks works 08080

Strandingsmuseum St. George, Ringkøbing Museum, Vesterhavsg 1e, Thorsminde, 6990 Ulfborg - T: 4597497366, Fax: 4597497382, E-mail: post@strandingsmuseum.dk, Internet: http://www.strandingsmuseum.dk. Head: Morten Sylvester
Historical Museum / Military Museum - 1992
Relics from HMS St. George and HMS Defence wrecked on the coast of W. Jutland Dec 24th 1811, the Battle of Jutland in WW I 08081

Væggerløse

Bøtø Nor Gl. Pumpestation, Møllesøvej, Marrebæk, 4873 Væggerløse - T: 53848009. Head: Otto Jensen
Science&Tech Museum 08082

Værløse

Værløse Museum, Mosegården, Skovgaards Allé 37, 3500 Værløse - T: 42480070. Head: Jørgen Seit Jespersen
Local Museum - 1968
Local history, items from the Middle Ages and Viking times, peasant culture, furniture, tools, textiles, rope, historical photographs, ceramics from medieval times to the Renaissance - library 08083

Valby

Carlsberg Museum Valby, Valby Langg 1, 2500 Valby - T: 33271273, Fax: 33274814, E-mail: mogens.kragh@carlsberg.com. Head: Mogens Kragh
Special Museum - 1916
Technology, industry, brewery, hist of founders 08084

Varde

Jugendhuset (House of Modern Style), Lundvej 39, 6800 Varde - T: 75221518, Fax: 75220716. Head: Ole Faber
Fine Arts Museum / Decorative Arts Museum - 1997
Paintings of Otto Frello, pottery 08085

Museet for Varde By og Omegn (Varde Museum), Lundvej 4, 6800 Varde - T: 75220877, Fax: 75220716. Head: Ole Faber
Local Museum / Decorative Arts Museum / Archaeological Museum - 1912
Exhibits on town and region from prehistoric times to the present, furniture, weapons, applied art, Danish paintings, Jutland pottery, silver, textiles - library 08086

Varde Artillerimuseum, Varde Museum, Vestervold 11a, 6800 Varde, mail addr: Lundvej 4, 6800 Varde - T: 75221594, Fax: 75220716. Head: Ole Faber
Military Museum - 1992
Hist of Danish Artilleri, 1500-1985 08087

Vejen

Vejen Kunstmuseum, Østerg 4, 6600 Vejen - T: 75360482, Fax: 75360482, E-mail: conniej@vejenkommune.dk, Internet: http://www.kulturnet.dk/homes/vejenk. Head: Teresa Nielsen
Fine Arts Museum - 1924
Sculptures and ceramics of Niels Hansen Jacobsen, drawings of Jens Lund, mosaics of Ejnar Nielsen, paintings of Ring, Hammershøj, Anna Ancher, and Danish symbolism 08088

Vejle

Vejle Kunstmuseum, Flegborg 16, 7100 Vejle - T: 75723199, Fax: 75723135, E-mail: vkm@vejle.dk, Internet: http://www.vejlekunstmuseum.dk. Head: Nina Damsgaard
Fine Arts Museum - 1899
Danish drawings from the 19th and 20th c, Danish and European graphic arts, including 500 prints from 16th c Netherlands, Danish painting from especially the 20th c 08089

Vejle Museum, Flegborg 18, 7100 Vejle - T: 75824322, Fax: 75825922. Head: Per Kristian Madsen
Local Museum - 1899
Prehist, town hist, handicrafts 08090

Vesløs

Skjoldborgs Barndomshjem, Øsløs, 7742 Vesløs - T: 97920577
Special Museum
Birth place of the Danish writer Johan Skjoldborg, exhibit on cobbler's trade, personal effects of the writer 08091

Viborg

Bruunshåb Gamle Papfabrik, Vinkelvej 93b, 8800 Viborg - T: 86675900. Head: Ingrid Mortensen
Science&Tech Museum
Cardboard, original machines 08092

Det Danske Hedeselskabs Museum, Klostermarken, 8800 Viborg, mail addr: Postboks 110, 8800 Viborg - T: 86676111, Fax: 86675101, E-mail: hedeselskabet@hedeselskabet.dk, Internet: http://www.hedeselskabet.dk
Agriculture Museum
Exhibits on the cultivation of the heath beginning in 1850 08093

E. Bindstouw, Lysgaard, Blichersvej 40, 8800 Viborg - T: 86667579, Fax: 87252620, E-mail: vibmus@viborgkommune.dk. Head: Henning Ringgaard Lauridsen
Special Museum - 1952
Exhibits on literature up to the novelist and poet Steen Steensen Blicher (1782-1848) and his times 08094

Kongenhus Mindeparks Museum, c/o Hedeselskabet, Klostermarken 12, Postboks 110, 8800 Viborg - T: 87281000, Fax: 87281001, E-mail: kongenshus@kongenshus.dk, Internet: http://www.kongenshus.dk. Head: Ove Kloch
Natural History Museum 08095

Skovgaard Museet i Viborg, Domkirkestræde 2-4, 8800 Viborg - T: 86623975, Fax: 87254179, E-mail: skovgaardmuseet@mail.tele.dk, Internet: http://www.dmol.dk. Head: Dr. Thomas Bullinger
Fine Arts Museum - 1937
Paintings, drawings, graphics, ceramics, and sculptures by the artist family Skovgaard - library 08096

Viborg Stiftsmuseum, Hjultorvet 4, 8800 Viborg - T: 87252610, Fax: 87252620, E-mail: vibmus@viborgkommune.dk, Internet: http://www.viborgstiftsmuseum.dk. Head: Henning Ringgaard Lauridsen
Archaeological Museum / Ethnology Museum / Historical Museum - 1861
Artifacts from Stone Age and Bronze Age, finds from medieval town excavations, costumes, toys, large bird coll - library, local archive 08097

Vinderup

Hjerl Hedes Frilandsmuseum, Hjerl Hedevej 14, 7830 Vinderup - T: 97448060, Fax: 97448502, E-mail: frilandmuseum@hjerlhede.dk, Internet: http://www.hjerlhede.dk. Head: Poul Buskov
Open Air Museum / Natural History Museum 08098

Vorbasse

Vorbasse Museum, Kirkeg 3, 6623 Vorbasse - T: 75333717, Fax: 75310399, E-mail: museum@grindsted.dk. Head: Mogens Hansen
Natural History Museum
Forestry science, lumber industry, hunting 08099

Vordingborg

Sydsjællands Museum, Ruinterraenet, 4760 Vordingborg - T: 53772554, Fax: 53771954. Head: Lars Buus Eriksen
Archaeological Museum - 1915
Local historical artifacts from the Stone Age to the present, medieval religious art, traditional costumes and textiles, ruin of medieval fort - library 08100

Dominican Republic

Santo Domingo

Casa-Fuerte de Ponce de León (Ponce de León's Fort), Calle San Rafael de Yuma, Higuëy, Santo Domingo
Special Museum - 1972
Residence of Ponce de León who discovered Florida and Puerto Rico, authentic furniture and household items from a 16th-c house 08101

Fortaleza de San Felipe (Saint Philip's Fortress), Av Gregorio Luperón, Puerto Plata, Santo Domingo
Archaeological Museum - 1972
16th-c fort, archaeological objects found during restoration 08102

Galería Nacional de Bellas Artes (National Fine Arts Gallery), Av Independencia, Santo Domingo - T: 6873300. Head: Dr. José J. de Alvarez Valverde
Fine Arts Museum - 1943
Paintings, sculptures 08103

Museo Alcázar de Colón, Calle Las Damas, Plaza de España, Santo Domingo - T: 6824750. Head: Nora Pérez Ornes
Decorative Arts Museum - 1967
Furniture (16th c) 08104

Museo de Arte Moderno, Plaza de la Cultura Juan Carlos Duarte, Santo Domingo - T: 6852153, Fax: 6828280. Head: Sara Hermann-Szabó
Fine Arts Museum - 1976
Contemporary art 08105

Museo de la Familia Dominicana Siglo XIX, Calle Las Atarazanas 2, Santo Domingo - T: 6824750. Head: Esteban Prieto Vicioso
Local Museum - 1967
16th c house 08106

Museo de las Atarazanas, Calle Colón 4, Santo Domingo - T: 6825834
Local Museum 08107

Museo de las Casas Reales (Museum of the Royal Houses), Calle Las Damas esq. Mercedes, mail addr: Apdo 2664, Santo Domingo - T: 6824202, Fax: 6886925. Head: Frank Moya Pons
Local Museum - 1976
Buildings used to be the headquarters of the colonial government, exhibition of items from that period (1492-1821), arms and armour, ceramics and items from shipwrecks - library 08108

Museo del Hombre Dominicano, Plaza de la Cultura Juan Pablo Duarte, Santo Domingo - T: 6873622, Fax: 6829112. Head: Dr. Fernando Morbán Laucer
Ethnology Museum / Archaeological Museum - 1973
Indian archaeology, colonial armour, ship parts 08109

Museo Juan Pablo Duarte, Calle Isabela La Católica 308, Santo Domingo. Head: Eduardo Fiallo Hernández
Special Museum
Memorabilia of the nobleman Juan Pablo Duarte in his birthplace 08110

Museo Natural de Historia y Geografía, Calle Pedro Henríquez Ureña, Plaza de la Cultura, Santo Domingo - T: 6890106. Head: José Chez Checor
Natural History Museum / Ethnology Museum - 1927
Archeology, Colonial and Republican history, anthropology, Indian ethnography, pre-Columbian period, crafts, armaments, Spanish relics, also modern paintings, drawings, photos, numismatics 08111

Sala de Arte Prehispánico, Apdo 723, Santo Domingo. Head: Manuel Antonio García Arévalo
Fine Arts Museum - 1973
Studies and exhibits of pre-Hispanic culture - library 08112

East Timor

Dili

Museum Negeri of Timor-Timur, Jalan Lecue Kotak Pos 48, Dili - T: (0390) 2756
Local Museum 08113

Ecuador

Ambato

Museo Quinta Casa de Juan Montalvo, Calle Mantalvo y Bolívar, Ambato, Tungurahua - T: (03) 824248
Local Museum
Local history 08114

Museo Quinta Juan Leon Mera, Av de los Capulíes, Ambato, Tungurahua - T: (03) 284014
Local Museum
Local history 08115

Museo Zoológico, Colegio Bolívar, Calle Sucre 8-39, Ambato
Natural History Museum
Natural history of Ecuador 08116

Atacames

Museo del Colegio Stella Maris, Atacames, Esmeraldas - T: (06) 731084
Archaeological Museum
Archaeology 08117

Azogues

Museo de Sitio de Ingapirca, Carretera Cañar, Azogues, Cañar
Archaeological Museum
Archaeology 08118

Bahia de Carácluez

Museo Arqueologico del Banco Central de Bahia, Calle Alberto F. Santos y Malecón, Bahia de Caráclues, Manabi - T: (05) 960361 ext 37
Archaeological Museum
Archaeology, antique photographies 08119

Baños

Museo de Arte Religioso la Concepción, Calle Argentines s/n y Larrea, Baños, Tungurahua - T: (03) 965212
Fine Arts Museum
Colonial religious art 08120

Museo del Santuario de la Virgen de Agua Santa, Calle Ambato 2840, Baños, Tungurahua - T: (03) 740451
Natural History Museum
Archaeology, mineralogy, zoology 08121

Chordeleg

Museo de la Comunidad de Chordeleg, 24 de Mayo 232, Chordeleg, Azuay - T: (07) 255261
Local Museum 08122

Cotocollao

Museo Aurelio Espinoza Polit, Calle José Nogales y Francisco Arcos, Cotocollao, Pichincha - T: (02) 530420
Local Museum
Archaeology, cartography, ethnology - library 08123

Cuenca

Museo Azuayo del Folklore, Calle Luis Cordero 722, Edificio CCk, Cuenca, Azuay - T: (07) 830016
Folklore Museum / Ethnology Museum
Ethnology, folk art, folklore 08124

Museo de la Inmaculada Concepción, Calle Hermano Miguel 633 y Juan Jaramillo, Cuenca, Azuay - T: (07) 830625
Fine Arts Museum / Folklore Museum
Colonial and folk art, ethnology 08125

Museo de las Artes Populares Cidap, Calle Hermano Miguel 323 y Calle Largo, Cuenca, Azuay - T: (07) 828878
Folklore Museum / Fine Arts Museum
Ethnology, art and folk art 08126

Museo del Banco Central, Calle Larga y Av Huayna Cápac, Cuenca, Azuay - T: (07) 831255, Fax: 823461, E-mail: aabad@uio.bce.fin.ec, Internet: http://www.bce.fin.ec. Head: Dr. Andres Abad
Local Museum
Archaeology, colonial art, history, ethnology, numismatics 08127

Museo Historico Casa de los Tratados, Calle Bolivar y Córdoba, Cuenca, Azuay
Historical Museum 08128

Museo Municipal de Arte Moderno, Sucre 1E-27 y Coronel Tálbot, Cuenca, Azuay - T: (07) 831027
Fine Arts Museum 08129

Museo Municipal Remigio Crespo Toral, Calle Larga 7-07 y Borrero, Cuenca
Local Museum
Ethnography, local history, handicrafts of colonial period, paintings, furniture 08130

Esmeraldas

Museo Arqueologico Carlos Aiiercado, Sucre 513 y Salinas, Esmeraldas - T: (06) 710393
Archaeological Museum
Archaeology 08131

Museo Sala de Exposición Banco Central de Esmeraldas, Av Libertad y Bolívar, Esmeraldas
Archaeological Museum
Archaeology - library 08132

Guaranga

Museo Cultural Iijdio Guaranga, Cruz Loma, Guaranga, Bolivar - T: 980757, 980327
Local Museum
Archaeology, history, ethnology 08133

Guayaquil

Museo Antropológico del Banco Central, Banco Central del Ecuador, Guayaquil - T: (04) 327707, Fax: 322792. Head: Freddy Olmedo
Ethnology Museum / Fine Arts Museum / Archaeological Museum - 1974
Archaeology of the Ecuadorian coast, gallery of contemporary Latin American art - library 08134

Museo Banco del Pacifico, Pl Icaza 113 y Pichincha, Guayaquil, Guayas - T: (04) 566010
Archaeological Museum
Archaeology 08135

Museo Colonel Felix Luque Plata, Pl Colón s/n, Guayaquil, Guayas - T: (04) 303572
Military Museum
History of the bomb corps 08136

Museo de la Casa de la Cultura Ecuatoriana, Av 9 de Octubre, Guayaquil
Archaeological Museum
Archaeology 08137

Museo de Sitio Arqueologico el Mongote Real Alto, Carretera a Salinas Chanduy, Guayaquil, Guayas - T: (04) 306683
Archaeological Museum
Archaeology, anthropology 08138

Museo Franciiscos Campos, Calle Lizardo García 225 y Vélez, Guayaquil, Guayas - T: (04) 360790
Natural History Museum
Zoology, paleontology, mineralogy, archaeology 08139

Museo Historico Bae Calderon, Calle Cañar y 5 de Junio, Guayaquil, Guayas - T: (04) 345317
Local Museum
History, military, astromomy 08140

Museo Municipal, Av 10 de Agosto, Calle Pedro Carbo, Guayaquil
Local Museum - 1862
Art, history, archeology, ethnography, paleontology, geology, paintings and numismatics of colonial and modern periods - library 08141

Museo Nahim Isaias B., Calle Clemente Ballén y Pichincha, Guayaquil, Guayas - T: (04) 329099
Fine Arts Museum / Archaeological Museum
Archaeology, art 08142

Latacunga

Museo de la Casa de la Cultura Ecuatoriana, Latacunga
Local Museum
Applied arts, handicrafts, local history 08143

Loja

Museo del Banco Central, 10 de Agosto 1330, Loja - T: (07) 963004
Local Museum
Archaeology, colonial art, history ,ethnography 08144

Museo Diocesano de Arte Religioso Nuestra Señora del Cisne, Santuario del Cisne, Loja - T: (07) 961805
Religious Arts Museum
Religious history and art 08145

La Magdalena

Museo Santuario Nuestra Señora Natividad del Guayco, El Guayco, La Magdalena, Bolívar, mail addr: Apdo 02-01-033, Guaranda, Bolívar - T: (03) 972150, E-mail: phdgda@uio.satnet.net. Head: Javier Catta
Archaeological Museum / Fine Arts Museum /

Religious Arts Museum
Ecuadorian archaeology esp. Panzaleo, Puruha and Inca, religious art, history of the sanctuary, exhibition of the devotedly of Turín - library 08146

Manta

Museo del Banco Central de Manta, Calle 9 y Av 2, alto del Municipio, Manta, Manabi - T: (05) 612878
Archaeological Museum
Archaeology 08147

Montecristi

Museo Arqueologico Largacha Ceballos Marlac, 9 de Julio 303 y Manta, Montecristi, Manabi
Archaeological Museum 08148

Museo Municipal Casa de Alfaro, Calle Eloy Alfaro 608 y Roca Fuerte, Montecristi, Manabi
Local Museum
Local history - library 08149

Puerto López

Museo de la Comunidad de Agua Blanca, Carretera Río Buenavista km 5, Machalilla, Puerto López, Manabi
Local Museum
Local history 08150

Quito

Museo Aeronautico y del Espacio, Av La Prensa 3570, Base Aérea Mariscal Sucre, Quito - T: (02) 445046
Science&Tech Museum 08151

Museo Antropológico, c/o Universidad Central del Ecuador, Av 12 de Octubre 1430 y Wilson, Quito - T: (02) 562633. Head: Dr. Holguer Jara
Ethnology Museum / University Museum - 1925
Archeology, ethnography, anthropology 08152

Museo Arqueología y Etnología, Instituto Ecuatoriano de Antropología y Geografía, Quito, mail addr: CP 2258, Quito
Archaeological Museum / Ethnology Museum - 1950
Precious stones, prehistoric sculpture, ceramics 08153

Museo Camilo Egas del Banco Central, Calle Venezuela 1312 y Esmeraldas, Quito - T: (02) 514511
Fine Arts Museum
Contemporary art 08154

Museo Casa de Benalcazar, Calle Olmedo y Benalcázar, Quito - T: (02) 215838, 218102
Fine Arts Museum
Colonial art 08155

Museo Casa de Sucre, Calle Venezuela 573 y Sucre, Quito - T: (02) 512860
Historical Museum
Republical history, colonial art 08156

Museo Convento de San Diego, Calle Calicuchima 117 y Farfán, Quito - T: (02) 212616, 514026
Fine Arts Museum
Colonial art 08157

Museo Cultural del Instituto Geografico Militar, Calle Sernierger s/n, El Dorado, Quito - T: (02) 502091, 542617
Historical Museum / Fine Arts Museum
History, colonial and contemporary art 08158

Museo de Arte Alberto Mena Caamaño, Calle Garcia Moreno 751 y Sucre, Quito, mail addr: Apdo 17013346, Quito - T: (02) 584363, 287694, Fax: 584362, E-mail: dpc@boy.net. Head: Alfonso Ortiz Crespo
Fine Arts Museum / Historical Museum - 1959
History archeology, painting, sculpture 08159

Museo de Arte Colonial, Calles Cuenca 901 y Mejía, Quito, mail addr: Apdo 2555, Quito - T: (02) 212297. Head: Carlos Rodriguez
Fine Arts Museum - 1914
16th-18th c art, colonial art, Miguel de Santiago's and Caspicara's coll 08160

Museo de Artesanias Cefa, Av 12 de Octubre 1738 y Lizardo García, Quito - T: (02) 503873, 501631
Decorative Arts Museum
Arts and crafts, ceramics, textiles, wood carvings - library 08161

Museo de Etnografía, Calle Mitad del Mundo, Quito - T: (02) 527077 ext 272
Ethnology Museum
Anthropology of Central and South America 08162

Museo de Instrumentos Musicales Pablo Traversari, Av 6 de Diciembre 332, Quito, mail addr: Apdo 67, Quito - T: (02) 527440. Head: Corsino Durán
Music Museum
Musical instruments of European, pre-Inca and colonial cultures 08163

Museo de la Casa de la Cultura Ecuatoriana, Av 12 de Octubre 555 Patria, Quito - T: (02) 527440 ext 40
Fine Arts Museum / Folklore Museum
Art photography, ethnography 08164

Museo de la Fundación Guayasamín, Calle José Bosmediano 543, Quito - T: (02) 446277, 446455, Fax: 446277, E-mail: guayasam@hoy.net, Internet: http://www.guayasamin.com. Head: Pablo Guayasamín
Fine Arts Museum
Art, archaeology 08165

Museo Ecuatoriano de Ciencias Naturales, Calle Rumipamba s/n, Parque La Carolina, Quito - T: (02) 449824/25
Natural History Museum
Mineralogy, botany, zoology, paleontology 08166

Museo Etnografico del Cologio Nacional Mejia, Calle Venezuela s/n y Ante, Quito - T: (02) 213418
Ethnology Museum
Ethnology 08167

Museo Guillermo Perez Chiriboga del Banco Central, Av 10 de Agosto y Briceño, Quito - T: (02) 510302, 519651
Fine Arts Museum / Archaeological Museum
Archaeology, art (colonial and contemporary) 08168

Museo Jacinto Jijón y Caamaño, Av 12 de Octubre y Carrión, Quito, mail addr: c/o Pontifícia Universidad Católica, Apdo 17-01-2184, Quito - T: (02) 565627 ext 1317, Fax: 544995, E-mail: museo-jjc@puceuio.puce.edu.ec. Head: Ernesto Salazar
Archaeological Museum / Fine Arts Museum - 1969
Peruvian mummies, Ecuadorian archaeology/colonial furniture, art - library 08169

Museo La Salle, Calle Caldas 587, Quito, mail addr: Apdo 329, Quito
Natural History Museum
Natural history 08170

Museo Nacional de Historia de la Medicina Eduardo Estrella, Calle García Moreno 524 y Av 24 de Mayo, Quito - T: (02) 573792, E-mail: ccmedica@ecnet.ec. Head: Dr. Antonio Crespo-Burgos
Historical Museum
Medical history, art - library, archives 08171

Museo Nacional de la Dirección Regional del Banco Central del Ecuador, Calle Reina Victoria y Jorge Washington, Quito, mail addr: Apdo 339, Quito - T: (02) 220547, Fax: 568972. Head: Juan Fernando Pérez
Archaeological Museum - 1969
Archeology, numismatics, Quitenian art, Latin American modern art, pre-Columbiam gold coll from la Tolita culture, ceramic coll (3200 B.C.-1500 A.D.) - library 08172

Museo Petrográfico del Servicio Nacional de Geología y Minería, Calle Carrión 1016, Quito - T: (02) 232087, 261380. Head: Horacio Rueda
Natural History Museum
Mineralogy 08173

Museo Templete de los Heros Nacionales, Colegio Militar Eloy Alfaro, Av Orellana y Amazonas, Quito - T: (02) 547555
Military Museum - 1937
History, army 08174

Museo Templo de la Patria, Camino a la Cima de la Libertad, Quito - T: (02) 512860
Historical Museum / Military Museum
History, colonial army 08175

Museo Weilbauer, Av 12 de Octubre y Ladrón de Guevara, Quito - T: (02) 230577
Archaeological Museum
Archaeology 08176

Vivarium, Museo de Historia Natural, Av Shyris 1130 y Portugal, Quito - T: (02) 432915
Natural History Museum
Natural history of Ecuador, zoology, herpetology 08177

Riobamba

Museo de Arte Religioso Concepción, Calle argentina s/n y Larrea, Riobamba, Chimborazo - T: (03) 965212
Fine Arts Museum
Colonial art 08178

Museo del Banco Central, Primera Constituyente y Carabobo, Riobamba, Chimborazo - T: (03) 960817
Fine Arts Museum
Colonial art 08179

Museo del Colegio Nacional Pedro Vicente Maldonado, Primera Constituyente 2436 y España, Riobamba, Chimborazo - T: (03) 960211
Archaeological Museum / Natural History Museum
Archaeology, mineralogy, botany 08180

Museo Historico, 2 de Agosto 1426, Sicalpa, Riobamba, Chimborazo
Local Museum
Local hist 08181

Salango

Museo Balseros del Mar del Sur (River Museum of the Southern Sea), Pl Municipal, Salango, Manabi
Local Museum
Archaeology, history 08182

San Antonio

Museo de Sitio del Rumicucho, San Antonio, Pichincha - T: (02) 514877
Archaeological Museum
Archarology 08183

Tulcán

Museo Carlos Emilio Grijalva, Calle Argentina 81, Tulcán, Carchi - T: (06) 980266
Archaeological Museum
Archaeology 08184

Museo David Paltan, Calle Montufar 708, Gabriel, Tulcán, Carchi - T: (06) 990112
Archaeological Museum
Archaeology, paleontology 08185

Egypt

Abbasieh

Criminology Museum, Abbasieh
Special Museum
Crime prevention, history of criminology 08186

Al-Matariyya

Obelisk Museum, Masalet, Al-Matariyya
Special Museum 08187

Al-Uqsur

Luxor Museum of Ancient Art, Corniche el-Nil St, Al-Uqsur - T: (095) 380269
Museum of Classical Antiquities 08188

Alexandria

Al-Muntaza Palace Museum, Al-Muntaza, Alexandria
Decorative Arts Museum 08189

Anatomy and Pathology Museum, c/o University of Alexandria, Alexandria
Special Museum / University Museum 08190

Greco-Roman Museum, Sharia Museum 51, 21521 Alexandria - T: (03) 4825820. Head: Doreya Said
Archaeological Museum - 1892
Greek, Roman and Coptic coll - library 08191

Hydrobiological Museum, Qaytbay's Citadel, Alexandria
Natural History Museum 08192

Library of the Greek Orthodox Patriarchate of Alexandria and All Africa, Sharia Mosque Attarine 104, Alexandria - T: (03) 4868595, 4861744, Fax: 4875684, Internet: http://www.greece.org/gopatalex
Library with Exhibitions
Manuscripts (since 9th c), rare old books 08193

Municipal Museum, Alexandria
Local Museum
Ethnography, local history 08194

Museum of Fine Arts and Cultural Center, Sharia Menascha 18, Alexandria
Fine Arts Museum
Painting and sculpture by traditional and contemporary artists 08195

Museum of the Faculty of Arts, c/o University of Alexandria, Alexandria - T: (03) 4864249, Fax: 4873088, E-mail: arts@maktoob.com, Internet: http://www.geocities.com/arts_alex. Head: Prof. Dr. Mohamed Abdo Mahgoub
University Museum / Historical Museum / Fine Arts Museum
Sculpture, paintings, drawings, prints 08196

National Maritime Museum, Qaytbay's Citadel, Alexandria. Head: Dr. Mehrez El-Husseini
Special Museum 08197

Aswan

Elephantine Island's and Aswan Museum, Elephantine Island, Aswan - T: (097) 322066
Museum of Classical Antiquities
Egyptian antiquities, mummies, sarcophagi, monumental sculpture 08198

Bulaq-el-Dakrur

Royal Carriage Museum, 82 26th-July St, Bulaq-el-Dakrur - T: (02) 774437
Special Museum 08199

Cairo

Abdeen Palace Museum, Midan Gumhouria, Abdeen, Cairo - T: (02) 857938
Decorative Arts Museum 08200

Airport Museum, Cairo Airport, Cairo - T: (02) 2914288, 2914277
Science&Tech Museum 08201

Anderson Museum, Beit El-Kretlia, Cairo. Head: Younes Mahran
Fine Arts Museum - 1936
Oriental art objects, 18th c coll 08202

Arabic Museum, Midan Bab El Khalk, Cairo
Ethnology Museum / Fine Arts Museum
Ethnography and art coll 08203

Cairo Geological Museum, Cornish El-Nil, Maadi Rd, Cairo - T: (02) 3187056, Fax: 820128. Head: Mohammed Ahmed El-Bedawi
Natural History Museum - 1904
Geology, fossils, rocks and minerals, gemstones, meteorites, Arsinoitherium skulls - library 08204

Coptic Museum, Mari Girgis St, Old Cairo, Misr-al-Qadimah, Cairo - T: (02) 3628766, 3639742. Head: Dr. Mahar Salib
Museum of Classical Antiquities / Decorative Arts Museum / Religious Arts Museum - 1908
Architecture, classical antiquities, icons, ivory, pottery, glass and textiles, papyrus manuscripts - library 08205

Cotton Museum, Sharia Khediv Ismael, Cairo, mail addr: c/o Egyptian Agricultural Society, POB 63, Cairo. Head: M. El-Bahtimi
Agriculture Museum - 1923
Displays of Egyptian agricultural techniques 08206

Education Museum, Sharia Manour 3, Cairo
Special Museum
Materials and methods of education, documents 08207

Egyptian Museum, Midan-el-Tahrir, Kasr El Nil, Sharia Selim Hassan, 11556 Cairo - T: (02) 5782448, 5782452, Fax: 5796974, E-mail: egymus@idsc.net.eg, Internet: http://www.egyptianmuseum.gov.eg. Head: Dr. Mamdouh Eldematy
Archaeological Museum - 1902
Egyptian antiquities from prehistoric times to the 3rd c A.D. - library 08208

Egyptian National Railways Museum, Cairo Station Bldg, Ramses Sq, Bab al-Hadid St, 11669 Cairo - T: (02) 763793, 977393, Fax: 5740000. Head: Ali Ibrahim Saleh
Science&Tech Museum - 1932/33
Locomotives and other rolling stock, railroad signal and other equipment, bridges, documents and maps illustrating the development of railway transport 08209

Entomological Museum, Sharia Milika Nazli 14, Cairo
Natural History Museum
Entomology and ornithology 08210

Ethnological Museum, Geographical Society Bldg, 109 Qasr al-Ayni St, Cairo - T: (02) 3545450
Ethnology Museum 08211

Folklore Museum, 19 Borsa al-Tawfiqiya St, Cairo - T: (02) 5752460
Folklore Museum 08212

Gazirah Museum, Gazirah Exhibition Grounds, Cairo - T: (02) 806982
Local Museum 08213

Manastirli Palace and Nilometer, Southern end of Rawdah, Cairo
Historical Museum 08214

Manyal Palace Museum, 1 Saray St, Manial, Cairo - T: (02) 987495
Decorative Arts Museum 08215

Military Museum, The Citadel, Cairo - T: (02) 5129619
Military Museum
Firearms, swords, daggers, orders, medals, and other military artifacts 08216

Mukhtar Museum, Sharia Ismail, Gazirah, nr Galaa Bridge, Cairo - T: (02) 3402519
Fine Arts Museum
Works of Egyptian sculptor Mahmoud Mokhtar (1891-1934) 08217

Musafir-Khana, Darb al-Tablawi, Gamaliyyah, Cairo - T: (02) 920472
Special Museum 08218

Museum of Hygiene, Midan-el-Sakakini, Daher, Cairo. Head: Dr. Fawzi Sweha
Special Museum
Medical and hygiene coll 08219

Museum of Islamic Art, 352 Ahmed Maher Sq, Bab al-Khalq, 11638 Cairo - T: (02) 901930, 3909930. Head: Dr. Nemat M. Abu-Bakr
Museum of Classical Antiquities / Decorative Arts Museum - 1881
Classical antiquities, bronzes, lamps ceramics, carpets - library 08220

Museum of Modern Art, Sharia Kasr El-Nil 4, Cairo - T: (02) 3416667. Head: Salah E. Taher
Fine Arts Museum - 1920
Painting and sculpture, copper plate engravings 08221

Museum of the History of Medicine, Saray El Sakakini, Ghamra, Cairo
Special Museum 08222

Museum of the People's Assambly, Meglis ash-Shaab Bldg, Meglis al-Shaab St, Cairo
Ethnology Museum / Historical Museum 08223

Mustafa Kamil Museum, Maydan Salah ad-Din, Cairo - T: (02) 919943
Special Museum 08224

Nagi Museum, Alexandria Desert Rd, Cairo - T: (02) 3853484
Special Museum 08225

National Museum for Civilization, Sharia Ismail Abu El Fetouh 18, Cairo - T: (02) 3405198
Historical Museum
Displays from Palaeolithic, Neolithic and historical periods of Egyptian civilization 08226

National Police Museum and Ancient Police Museum, Citadel, Cairo
Historical Museum 08227

Ornithology and Entomology Museum, Sharia Ramses and Av Nahdet Misv 14, Cairo
Natural History Museum 08228

Pharaonic Museum, c/o Cairo University, Cairo
Archaeological Museum / University Museum
Egyptian archaeology 08229

Postal Museum, Al Ataba Sq, Cairo
Special Museum - 1943
Postage stamps from Egypt and other countries 08230

Qasr Al-Gawharah (Gawharah Palace Museum), The Citadel, Cairo - T: (02) 926187, 5116187
Decorative Arts Museum / Fine Arts Museum - 1954
Oriental and French furniture, Turkish paintings, clocks, glass, and 19th c costumes housed in 19th c Ottoman-style palace 08231

Qasr Al-Ibrahim (Amr Ibrahim Palace), Gezira and Shaykh-al-Marsafi Sts, Zamalek, Cairo - T: (02) 987495
Historical Museum 08232

Scientific Researches Museum, Kasr El Eini, Cairo
Natural History Museum
Botany, zoology, natural history 08233

Sharia Museum, Sharia Ismail, next to National Culture Centre, Cairo - T: (02) 806982
Local Museum 08234

Shawqi Museum, 6 Ahmed Shawqi St, Cairo - T: (02) 729479
Local Museum 08235

Transportation Museum, Ahmed Maher Pacha, Cairo
Science&Tech Museum
Automobile coll 08236

U.A.R. Geological Museum, Sharia Sheikh Rian 15, Cairo
Natural History Museum 08237

Daqahlia

Al-Mansora Museum Dar-ibn-Luqman, Moafi Sq, Daqahlia
Special Museum 08238

El-Alamein

Military Museum, El-Alamein
Military Museum
Military equipment, documents of Battle of El Alamein (1945) 08239

Giza

Agricultural Museum, c/o Ministry of Agriculture, Doqqi, Giza - T: (02) 700063, 3608681/82. Head: Samir M. Sultan
Agriculture Museum - 1938
Horticulture, botany and zoology, irrigation - library 08240

Giza Zoological Museum, Zoological Garden, Giza - T: 736233. Head: Mervat Morcos Gayyed
Natural History Museum
Egyptian birds, reptiles and amphibians, ancient mummified crocodile 08241

Museum of Mohamed Mahmoud Khalil and his wife, 1 Kafour St, Orman, Giza - T: (02) 3401538, Fax: 3410650, E-mail: mkhalil@idsc.gov.eg
Special Museum 08242

Solar Boats Museum, nr Cheop's Pyramids, Giza - T: (02) 3857928
Science&Tech Museum 08243

Haram

Taha Hussien Museum, Taha Hussien Madkour St, Haram - T: (02) 852818
Special Museum 08244

Helwan

Helwan Corner Museum, Farouq's Corner, Helwan - T: (02) 3405198, 783573
Local Museum 08245

Ismailia

Ismailia Museum, Matthaf and Salah Salem St, Ismailia - T: (064) 22749
Museum of Classical Antiquities / Local Museum
Classical antiquities, Darius monument 08246

Mallawy

Mallawy Museum, Galaa St, Mallawy - T: (086) 652061
Local Museum 08247

Munira

Saad Zaghlul Museum, Bayt-al-Umma, 2 Saad Zaghlul St, Munira - T: (02) 3545399
Local Museum 08248

Port Said

Port Said Museum, 23rd of July St, Port Said
Local Museum / Military Museum
History of the Suez Canal, documents on the Battle of Port Said (1956), military equipment and flags 08249

Ras-al-Tin

Ras-al-Tin Palace Museum, Ras-al-Tin
Decorative Arts Museum 08250

Saint Catherine, Sinai

Monastery of Saint Catherine, Jabal Katrina, Saint Catherine, Sinai - T: (062) 470355/343, Fax: 470349
Religious Arts Museum
Codex Sinaiticus, Codex Syriacus, numerous manuscripts, scrolls and documents, Dayr Katrina hist 08251

Sharqiya

San el-Haggar Museum, San el-Haggar, Sharqiya
Local Museum 08252

Suez

Aquatics Museum - Institute of Oceanography and Fisheries, Attapa, al-Ghardaqa, Suez, mail addr: POB 128, Suez
Natural History Museum
Marine biology, flora and sauna of the Red Sea and Gulf of Suez 08253

Tanta

Tanta Museum, Mustafa el-Gendy St, Tanta - T: (040) 319003
Local Museum 08254

Zamalek

Bayet Aisha Fahmi (Mogamaa el-Fonoon), Maahad el-Swissry St, Zamalek - T: (02) 3408211
Museum of Classical Antiquities 08255

Hadiqat al-Asmak Museum, Gabalaya St, Hadiqat al-Asmak, Zamalek
Local Museum 08256

Zaqaziq

Hariya Razna and Ahmed Urabi Museum, Hariya Razna, Zaqaziq - T: (055) 322373
Local Museum 08257

Zizinia

Palace of Royal Jewelleries, Kasr al-Mogawharat, al-Malakiya, Zizinia
Decorative Arts Museum 08258

El Salvador

San Salvador

Museo de Historia Natural de El Salvador, Final Calle Los Viveros, Colonia Nicaragua, San Salvador - T: 2709228 ext 15, Fax: 2701387
Natural History Museum - 1976
library 08259

Museo Nacional David J. Guzmán, Av La Revolución, Colonia San Benito, San Salvador. Head: Manuel R. López
Archaeological Museum / Ethnology Museum / Historical Museum - 1883
Archaeology, ethnography, history, anthropology, linguistics 08260

Equatorial Guinea

Santa Isabel

Museo Etnológico Misional C.M.F., Apdo 10, Santa Isabel
Ethnology Museum
Prehistory and ethnology, native art of the Bubus, wooden bells, sculpture Druid stones 08261

Eritrea

Asmara

Archaeological Museum, c/o Department of Culture, POB 5284, Asmara - T: (4) 114666, Fax: (1) 124847. Head: Yacob Misghina
Archaeological Museum - 1992
Archaeology of Eritrea Province - archive 08262

Estonia

Tallinn

Adamson-Eric Museum, Art Museum of Estonia, Lühike jalg 3, 10130 Tallinn - T: 6445838, Fax: 6442094, E-mail: muuseum@ekm.estnet.ee, Internet: http://www.ekm.ee. Head: Marika Valk, Ülle Kruus
Fine Arts Museum / Decorative Arts Museum 08263

Eesti Kunstimuuseum (Art Museum of Estonia), Kiriku pl 1, 10130 Tallinn - T: 6449340, Fax: 6442094, E-mail: muuseum@ekm.estnet.ee, Internet: http://www.ekm.ee. Head: Marika Valk
Fine Arts Museum - 1919
Estonian art and applied art, medieval art, European art, Russian art - library, archives, restoration dept 08264

Eesti Teatri-ja Muusikamuuseum (Estonian Theatre and Music Museum), Müürivahe 12, 0001 Tallinn - T: (02) 442132. Head: A. Saar
Music Museum / Performing Arts Museum - 1924
Theatrical art and music in Estonia, musical instruments, musical manuscripts - library 08265

Estonian History Museum, Pikk 17, 10123 Tallinn - T: 6411630, Fax: 6443446, E-mail: post@eam.ee, Internet: http://www.eam.ee. Head: Toomas Tamla
Historical Museum - 1864
Estonian hist from ancient times to the present - library 08266

Estonian Open Air Museum, Vabaöhumuuseumi tee 12, 0035 Tallinn - T: (02) 6560230, Fax: 6560227, E-mail: e.v.m.@online.ee. Head: Merike Lang
Open Air Museum / Fine Arts Museum / Ethnology Museum - 1957
Architecture and ethnography 18th-20th c 08267

Kristjan Raud Museum, Art Museum of Estonia, Kristjan Raud 8, 0016 Tallinn - T: (02) 449340, Fax: 442094. Head: Marika Valk, Renate Riibak
Fine Arts Museum 08268

Museum of Estonian Architecture, 2 Ahtri St, 10151 Tallinn - T: 6257000, Fax: 6257003, E-mail: - architekuurimuuseum@architektuurimuuseum.ee, Internet: http://www.archtiktuurimuuseum.ee. Head: Karin Hallas-Murula
Fine Arts Museum 08269

Niguliste Muuseum, Art Museum of Estonia (Saint Nicolais Church Museum), Niguliste 3, 10146 Tallinn - T: 6314330, Fax: 6314327, E-mail: nigulite.ekm@mail.ee, Internet: http://www.ekm.ee. Head: Marika Valk, Tarmo Saaret
Fine Arts Museum 08270

Tallinna Linnamuuseum (Tallinn City Museum), Vene t 17, 10123 Tallinn - T: (02) 6441829, Fax: 6441574, E-mail: lmuuseum@tonilne.ee. Head: Maruta Varrak
Local Museum / Fine Arts Museum - 1937
Local hist, fine art - library 08271

Tarbekunstimuuseum, Eesti Kunstimuuseum (Applied Art Museum), Lai 17, 10133 Tallinn - T: 6411927, Fax: 5277123, E-mail: trkunst@tarbekunst.ee, Internet: http://www.ekm.ee. Head: Merike Alber
Decorative Arts Museum 08272

Tartu

Art Museum of Tartu University, Ülikooli 18, 50090 Tartu - T: (07) 375384, Fax: 375440, E-mail: kmm@ut.ee, Internet: http://www.ut.ee/artmuseum. Head: Inge Kukk
Fine Arts Museum / University Museum - 1803
Plaster reproductions of ancient sculpture, gems and coins, Greek and Roman antiquities, engravings, paintings, Russian icons, applied art, photographies 08273

Eesti Kirjandusmuuseum (Estonian Literary Museum), Vanemuise 42, 51003 Tartu, mail addr: POB 368, 50002 Tartu - T: (07) 430035, Fax: 420426, E-mail: krista@kirmus.ee, Internet: http://www.kirmus.ee. Head: Krista Aru
Special Museum 08274

Estonian National Museum, Veski 32, 51014 Tartu - T: (07) 421279, Fax: 422254, E-mail: erm@erm.ee, Internet: http://www.erm.ee. Head: Jaanus Plaat
Ethnology Museum - 1909
Life of Estonian and other Finno-Ugric People - library, archives 08275

Estonian Sports Museum, Rii 27a, 51010 Tartu
Special Museum 08276

Tartu Art Museum, Valikraavi 14, 2400 Tartu - T: (07) 441143, Fax: 441143. Head: Enriko Taluistu
Fine Arts Museum - 1940
Western European painting of the 17th-18th c, Estonian and Baltic-German painting, sculpture and graphics of the 19th-20th c, Russian painting of the turn of the 19th/20th c, Estonian applied art of the 1950s-70s - library, archives 08277

Tartu Linnamuuseum, Tartu Linnamuuseum Orut 2, 2400 Tartu - T: (07) 422022, Fax: 422693. Head: Helvi Pullerits
Local Museum 08278

Ethiopia

Addis Ababa

Ethnographic Museum, 12 Yekatit Sq, Addis Ababa, mail addr: c/o Institute of Ethiopian Studies, Addis Ababa University, POB 1176, Addis Ababa - T: (1) 550844, Fax: 552688, E-mail: ies@padis.gn.apc.org. Head: Ahmed Zekaria
Ethnology Museum / University Museum - 1963
Ethnography, traditional art, liturgical items, stamps, numismatics 08279

Museum of the Holy Trinity Church of Ethiopia, POB 3137, Addis Ababa
Religious Arts Museum 08280

National Museum, Sudan St, Addis Ababa, mail addr: POB 76, Addis Ababa - T: (1) 117150, Fax: 553188
Local Museum - 1967
Palaeontology, archaeology, costumes, modern art 08281

Natural History Museum, 12 Yekatit Sq, Addis Ababa, mail addr: c/o Addis Ababa University, POB 1176, Addis Ababa - T: (1) 192110
Natural History Museum / University Museum
Zoology, ornithology, entomology, conchology 08282

War Museum, Unity Sq, Addis Ababa, mail addr: c/o Ministry of Defence, POB 1373, Addis Ababa
Military Museum
Weapons, uniforms and historical photos 08283

Aksum

Aksum Archaeology Museum, POB 15, Aksum - T: (04) 750228. Head: Fisseha Zibelo
Archaeological Museum
Archaeology 08284

Gonder

Castle Museum, POB 81, Gonder - T: (8) 110308. Head: Fasil Ayehu Zeleke
Historic Site - 1970
Historical castles 08285

Makale

City Museum, Makale
Local Museum
Ethnography, costumes 08286

Yirgalem

City Museum, POB 54, Yirgalem - T: (06) 250603. Head: Keder Nuri
Local Museum
Ethnography - library 08287

Faroe Islands

Tórshavn

Føroya Fornminnissavn (National Museum), Hoyvík, Tórshavn, mail addr: PB 1155, 110 Tórshavn - T: 310700, Fax: 312259, E-mail: fornminndl@natmus.fo, Internet: http://www.natmus.fo. Head: Arne Thorsteinsson
Archaeological Museum / Ethnology Museum - 1898
Archaeology, ethnology 08288

Føroya Náttúrugripasavn (The Faroese Museum of Natural History), V.U. Hammerhaimbsg 13, 100 Tórshavn - T: 312306, Fax: 318438, E-mail: ngs@ngs.fo, Internet: http://www.ngs.fo. Head: Dorete Bloch
Natural History Museum - 1955 08289

Savnid 1940-45 (Faeroe-British Museum), Brekkuni 7, 100 Tórshavn - T: 13813
Military Museum - 1983
Militaria from British occupation 08290

Fiji

Suva

Fiji Museum, Government Bldgs, Suva, mail addr: POB 2023, Suva - T: 315944, Fax: 305143, E-mail: fijimuseum@is.com.fj. Head: Kate Vusoniwailala
Local Museum - 1906
Cultural material from Fiji and other Pacific Island countries, archaeological, rare book and document, photographic natural hist coll 08291

Finland

Äänekoski

Äänekosken Kaupunginmuseo (Äänekoski Town Museum), Siltakatu 8, 44100 Äänekoski - T: (014) 5297308
Local Museum   08292

Ähtäri

Ähtärin Kotiseutumuseo, 63700 Ähtäri - T: (06) 5330291, E-mail: pakkala@pp.inet.fi, Internet: http://www.mtp.ahtari.fi/ahtseura. Head: Matti Teerimäki, Taru Pakkala
Local Museum - 1960   08293

Ala-Philaja

Salpalinjan Bukkerialue (Bunker Museum), Yläpihlaja, 49960 Ala-Philaja - T: (05) 71610
Military Museum   08294

Alajärvi

Nelimarkka Museo . Etelä-Pohjanmaan Aluetaidemuseo ja Nelimarkka-resedenssi (Nelimarkka Museum, Regional Art Museum of Southern Ostrobothnia), Pekkolantie 123, 62900 Alajärvi - T: (06) 5572129, Fax: 5573889, E-mail: lepassi@japo.fi, Internet: http://www.alajarvi.fi/museo/index.html. Head: Leena Passi
Fine Arts Museum - 1964
Paintings by Eero Nelimarkka, Finnish graphics, Eero Nelimarkkas's personal letters (ca. 5000), artist's residence - archives   08295

Anjalankoski

Anjalan Kartanomuseo (Anjala Manor), Ankkapurhantie 5, 46910 Anjalankoski - T: (05) 3674994, Fax: 3674990, Internet: http://www.nba.fi. Head: Lea Värtinen
Fine Arts Museum / Decorative Arts Museum - 1955
19th c interiors, household articles, Mathilda Wrede collection, Anjala Manor (18th - 19th c) - library   08296

Ankkapurhan Teollisuusmuseo (Ankkapurha Industrial Museum), Koskitie 2, 46900 Anjalankoski - T: (0204) 626248, Fax: 626550, E-mail: annikki.nayho@storaenso.com. Head: Hannu Karppinen
Science&Tech Museum
Finland's first continuously running paperboard machine from 1897   08297

Museotalo Warpunen (Varpunen House Museum), Reunatie 3, 46900 Anjalankoski - T: (0204) 626248, Fax: 626550, E-mail: Annikki.Nayho@storaenso.com. Head: Hannu Karppinen
Local Museum   08298

Arkkukari

Saloisten Kotiseutumuseo (Saloinen Local History Museum), 92210 Arkkukari - T: (08) 228570. Head: Osmo Tamminen
Open Air Museum - 1966
Peasant culture, equipment for seal hunting, public granaries, farm buildings, fishermen's huts, boat sheds and buildings connected with fish salting   08299

Artjärvi

Artjärven Kotiseutumuseo (Artjärvi Museum), Kotiseutuyhdistys, 16230 Artjärvi - T: (03) 7602224, 48. Head: Jouko Hovi
Local Museum - 1921   08300

Asikkala

Asikkalan Kotiseutumuseo (Asikkala Museum), 17320 Asikkala - T: (03) 7666329, 7665137. Head: Erkki Raunio
Folklore Museum   08301

Urajärven Kartanomuseo (Urajärvi Manor), Kartanontie, 17150 Asikkala, mail addr: PL 913, 00101 Helsinki 10 - T: (03) 7667191, (09) 40501, Fax: (09) 4050442. Head: Lea Värtinen
Historical Museum - 1915
Furnishings, household articles, English garden, 20th c interiors, home of Lilly and Hugo von Heideman, buildings from 18th and 19th c   08302

Askainen

Louhisaaren Kartanolinna (Louhisaari Manor), Louhisaarentie 244, 21240 Askainen - T: (02) 4312555, Fax: 4358056, Internet: http://www.nba.. Head: Lea Värtinen
Historical Museum / Historic Site - 1967
17th-19th c interiors, furnishings and household articles, portrait coll, main building built in 1655, childhooh home of the Marshal of Finland C.G.E. Mannerheim, landscape garden   08303

Dalsbruk

Taalintehtaan Ruukinmuseo (Dals Ironworks Museum), Tullbacksvägen 7, 25900 Dalsbruk - T: (02) 4662200, 4661496
Local Museum   08304

Degerby

Föglo Museet (Föglö Museum), 22710 Degerby - T: (018) 50348, 51234, Fax: 50047. Head: Marlene Sjöblom
Local Museum   08305

Dragsfjärd

Söderlångvikin Museo (Söderlångvik Museum), 25870 Dragsfjärd - T: (02) 424662, 424549, Fax: 68444622, E-mail: museum@amosanderson.fi, Internet: http://www.amosanderson.fi
Decorative Arts Museum / Fine Arts Museum - 1965
Original interiors, Finnish 20th c art collection and library of the statesman and philanthropist Amos Anderson   08306

Ekenäs

Ekenäs Museum, Gustaf Wasas g 11, 10600 Ekenäs - T: (019) 26311, Fax: 2633150, E-mail: ekenasmuseum@ekenas.fi, Internet: http://www.ekenas.fi. Head: Ivar Nordlund
Local Museum - 1906
Local hist and artifacts, homes of wealthy craftsmen (early 19th c)   08307

Finlandssvenskt Konstcentrum, Villa Ormnäs, 10600 Ekenäs - T: (019) 2412663, Fax: 2412661, E-mail: kansli@proartibus.fi, Internet: http://www.proartibus.fi
Association with Coll   08308

Tammiharjun Sairaalamuseo, 10600 Ekenäs - T: (019) 21213, Fax: 2414776. Head: Kaj Palmgren
Special Museum   08309

Elimäki

Elimäen Kotiseutumuseo ja Koulumuseo (Elimäki District Museum and Schoolmuseum), Vanhamaantie, 47200 Elimäki - T: (05) 3776462, Fax: 3776024, E-mail: marju.myllymaa@elimaki.fi, Internet: http://www.elimaki.fi. Head: Marju Myllymaa
Local Museum / Historic Site   08310

Elimäen Koulumuseo (Elimäki School Museum), Mustilan Koulu, 47200 Elimäki - T: (05) 7790243, Fax: 3776024
Historical Museum   08311

Espoo

Espoon Kaupunginmuseo (Espoo City Museum), Ahertajantie 5, 02100 Espoo - T: (09) 81657033, Fax: 81657031, E-mail: kaupunginmuseo@espoo.fi, Internet: http://www.espoo.fi/museo. Head: Mariliina Perkko
Local Museum - 1958
Household articles, agricultural equipment, carriage coll, costume coll, glass coll - library, photo archives   08312

Gallen-Kallela Museum, Gallen-Kallelantie 27, 02600 Espoo 60 - T: (09) 5413388, Fax: 5416426, E-mail: tarvaspaa@gallen-kallela.fi, Internet: http://www.gallen-kallela.fi. Head: Kerttu Karvonen-Kannas
Fine Arts Museum / Decorative Arts Museum - 1957
Akseli Gallen-Kallela's works, paintings, sculpture, drawings, graphics, studio furniture, textile designs, illustrations to the epic 'Kalevala', handicraft, ethnographic coll from Africa, special exhibitions on varied themes, contemporary art - library, archives   08313

Geologian Tutkimuskeskuksen Kivimuseo (Geological Survey of Finland, Mineralogical Museum), Kivimiehentie 1, Otaniemi, 02150 Espoo, mail addr: PL 96, 02151 Espoo - T: (0205) 502243, Fax: 5012, E-mail: pentti.karhunen@gsf.fi, Internet: http://www.gsf.fi/info/museoeng.htm. Head: Pentti Karhunen
Natural History Museum - 1956
Minerals, rocks, sediments, ores, fossils, crystals, old prospecting equipment, gems, obicular rocks   08314

Glims Talomuseo, Espoon Kaupinginmuseo (Espoo City Museum, Glims Farmstead Museum), Glimsintie 1, 02740 Espoo - T: (09) 8696980, 8632979, Fax: 8696979, E-mail: kaupunginmuseo@espoo.fi, Internet: http://www.espoo.fi/museo. Head: Mariliina Perkko
Local Museum - 1958
Former stagecoach inn and official residence of the rural police chiefe, special exhibitions   08315

Suomen Kellomuseo (Finnish Museum of Horology), Opinkuja 2, 02100 Espoo - T: (09) 4520688, Fax: 45205656, E-mail: tuulia.tuomi@kelloseppaliitto.fi, Internet: http://www.kelloseppaliitto.fi. Head: Tuulia Tuomi
Science&Tech Museum - 1944
Finnish watch and clock making, tools and apparatus of horology   08316

Fiskars

Fiskars Museum, 10470 Fiskars - T: (019) 237013, Fax: 237013, E-mail: lokalhistoriska.arkivet@kolumbus.fi, Internet: http://www.kolumbus.fi/lokalhistoriska.arkivet. Head: M. Gripenberg
Special Museum - 1949
Fiskars cutlery - archive   08317

Forssa

Forssan Luonnonhistoriallinen Museo (Forssa Natural History Museum), Wahrenkatu 11, 30101 Forssa 10 - T: (03) 4354949, 846, E-mail: flhm@surffi.net, Internet: http://www.surffi.net/~flhm. Head: Prof. A. Brander
Natural History Museum - 1951
Vertebrates, insects, specimens of plants and stones, wild life conservation   08318

Lounais-Hämeen Museo (Southwestern Häme Museum), Wahreninkatu 12, 30100 Forssa - T: (03) 4355998, Fax: 4355998, Internet: http://www.forssa.fi/matkailu/nähtävyydet. Head: Lauri Pohjakallio
Local Museum - 1923
Agricultural implements, household articles, handicrafts, furniture, costumes, textiles, photographs   08319

Tieteelliset Kokoelmat (Scientific Collections), Vapaudenkatu 5b, 30101 Forssa 10 - T: (03) 4354949, E-mail: flhm@surffi.net. Head: Prof. A. Brander
Natural History Museum - 1951
11.000 botanical specimens, 34.000 insects and invertebrates   08320

Hämeenlinna

Artillery Museum of Finland, Linnankasarmi, 13100 Hämeenlinna - T: (03) 6824600, Fax: 6824601, E-mail: tykistomuseo@virpi.net, Internet: http://www.hameenlinna.fi/Artillery. Head: Raimo Vilhu
Military Museum - 1977
Hist of the Finnish field artillery since 15th c, gun coll, coll of ammunition - library   08321

Hämeenlinnan Kaupungin Historiallinen Museo (Hämeenlinna Historical Museum), Lukiokatu 6, 13100 Hämeenlinna 10 - T: (03) 142840, Fax: 142851. Head: Maria-Liisa Ripatti
Local Museum - 1910
Articles connected with the history of Hämeenlinna and the peasant culture of the province of Häme, handicrafts, textiles, furniture, 18th and 19th c silverware from Hämeenlinna, coins and medals, research archives and photographs, articles connected with Jean Sibelius (composer) - library   08322

Hämeenlinnan Taidemuseo (Hämeenlinna Art Museum), Viipurintie 2, 13200 Hämeenlinna 20 - T: (03) 6212669, 6212668, Fax: 6212860, E-mail: taidemuseo@hameenlinna.fi, Internet: http://www.hameenlinna.fi/artmuseum. Head: Taina Lammassaari
Fine Arts Museum - 1952
Finnish art, paintings, sculptures, graphics, drawings, design - library   08323

Vanajan Kotiseutumuseo (Vanaja Local History Museum), Vanajan Kirkonkylä, 13100 Hämeenlinna 10 - T: (03) 121547. Head: Pekka Lampinen
Local Museum - 1958
Ethnographical and ecclesiastical objects   08324

Hailuoto

Hailuodon Kotiseutumuseo Kniivilä (Hailuoto Museum Kniivilä), 90480 Hailuoto - T: (08) 8100473, Fax: 8100473, E-mail: kirjasto@hailuoto.oulu.net
Local Museum / Open Air Museum
Area of 27 buildings   08325

Halikko

Halikkon Museo (Halikko Local Museum), Kirkkorinne 7, 24801 Halikko - T: (02) 7743320, Fax: 7743266, Internet: http://www.halikko.fi/matkailu/nahtavyydet.htm
Local Museum - 1955
Ethnography, tanner, shoemaker and carpenter workshops, 18th c inn with furnishings, coins, weapons   08326

Hamina

Haminan Kaupunginmuseo (Hamina Town Museum), Kadettikoulunkatu 2, 49400 Hamina - T: (05) 7495242, 43, Internet: http://www.hamina.fi/matkailu/museot.htm. Head: Markku Jaakkola
Local Museum - 1903
Social, political and military history of the town and its surroundings, navigation and trade instruments, period interiors, costumes and textiles, numismatic collection - archives   08327

Reserviupseerikoulun Museo (Reserve Officer School Museum), Kadettikoulunkatu 8, 49400 Hamina - T: (05) 18166498, 6291, Fax: 18166522, Internet: http://www.hamina.fi/matkailu/museot.htm. Head: Hannu Kaukiainen
Military Museum - 1975
Objects connected with the traditions of the Reserve Officer School, uniforms, weapons, fighting, equipment, teaching aids   08328

Hankasalmi

Hankasalmen Kotiseutumuseo (Hankasalmi Local History Museum), 41520 Hankasalmi - T: (014) 841149, 079
Decorative Arts Museum / Ethnology Museum - 1954
Furnishings, ethnographical material   08329

Hanko

Hangon Museo, Kaupungintalo, Bulevardi 6, 10900 Hanko - T: (019) 2203223, Fax: 2203261, E-mail: birgitta.ekstrom@hanko.fi, Internet: http://www.hanko.fi. Head: Birgitta Ekström Söderlund
Decorative Arts Museum - 1909
Handicrafts, interiors, textiles - archive, no exhibitions at the moment   08330

Hanko Front Museum, Lappohja, 10820 Hanko - T: (019) 231301, Fax: 231301. Head: Stig Häggström
Military Museum   08331

Linnoitusmuseo (Fortress Museum), Nycander 4, 10900 Hanko - T: (019) 2203223, Fax: 2203261, E-mail: birgitta.ekstrom@hanko.fi, Internet: http://www.hanko.fi. Head: Birgitta Ekström Söderlund
Historic Site / Historical Museum - 1971   08332

Harjavalta

Emil Cedercreutzin Museo, Museotie 1, 29200 Harjavalta - T: (02) 5351200, Fax: 5351220, E-mail: cedercreutzin.museo@harjavalta.fi, Internet: http://www.harjavalta.fi. Head: Ritva Kava
Fine Arts Museum / Ethnology Museum - 1916
Emil Cedercreutz' silhouettes and sculptures, folk art, handicraft, rugs, item of peasantry, carriages and sledges, fishing gear - library   08333

Hartola

Itä-Hämeen Museo (Eastern Häme Museum), Koskipää, 19600 Hartola - T: (03) 7161252, Fax: 7161252, E-mail: ihmuseo@cc.jyu.fi, Internet: http://www.http.jyu.fi/~ihmuseo. Head: Vesa Järvinen
Local Museum
Local ethnography and cultural history material, furniture, textiles, agricultural implements, household articles, tools of gunsmiths and tanners, Koskipää Manor and chimneyless dwelling (early 19th c), room dedicated to authoress Maila Talvio (1871 - 1952)   08334

Hauho

Hauhon Esinemuseo (Hauho Museum), 14700 Hauho - T: (03) 6751146, Fax: 491931. Head: Vesa Leppala
Local Museum   08335

Hausjärvi

Hausjärven Kotiseutumuseo (Hausjärvi Museum), Kurvatie 550, 12210 Hausjärvi - T: (019) 768966, 785240, Fax: 7861298
Local Museum
Local hist, rural life   08336

Heinola

Heinolan Kaupunginmuseo (Heinola Town Museum), Kauppakatu 14, 18100 Heinola - T: (03) 8493651, Fax: 7152137, E-mail: museo@heinola.fi, Internet: http://www.heinola.fi/museo.html. Head: Kari-Paavo Kokki
Local Museum - 1964
Economic and social hist of the town, ecclesiastical mat, manorial furniture, textiles, handicrafts, numismatic coll, photograph coll, colls of Hynnien Art Foundation (Baltic silver) - art gallery, Aschan residence   08337

Lääninkivalteri Aschanin Talo (Aschan Residence), Kauppakatu 3b, 18100 Heinola - T: (03) 8493655/51, Fax: 7152137, E-mail: museo@heinola.fi, Internet: http://www.heinola.fi/museo.html. Head: Kari-Paavo Kokki
Historical Museum   08338

Helsinki

Amos Andersonin taidemuseo (Amos Anderson Art Museum), Yrjönkatu 27, 00101 Helsinki 10 - T: (09) 6844460, Fax: 68444622, E-mail: museum@amosanderson.fi, Internet: http://www.amosanderson.fi. Head: Bengt von Bonsdorff
Fine Arts Museum - 1965
Contemporary Finnish art, 15th-19th c European art, graphics, medals - library   08339

Arabia Museum-Gallery, Hämeentie 135, 00560 Helsinki - T: (020) 43911, Fax: 4395180, E-mail: marjut.kumela@designor.com. Head: Marjut Kumela
Decorative Arts Museum - 1948
Products of the Arabia porcelain works   08340

Ateneumin Taidemuseo, Valtion Taidemuseo (Ateneum Art Museum - Finnish National Gallery), Kaivokatu 2, 00100 Helsinki - T: (09) 173361, Fax: 17336226, Internet: http://www.fng.fi. Head: Soili Sinisalo
Fine Arts Museum   08341

Bank Museum of Kansallis-Osake-Pankki, Aleksanterinkatu 42, 00100 Helsinki - T: (09) 1633452. Head: Risto Varjonen
Special Museum 08342

Cygnaeuksen Galleria (Cygnaeus Gallery), Kalliolinnantie 8, 00140 Helsinki 14 - T: (09) 40509628, Fax: 40509627, E-mail: - cygnaeuksengalleria@nba.fi, Internet: http://www.nba.fi/museums/cygn/cygnaeng.htm. Head: Riitta Ailonen
Fine Arts Museum - 1882
Fredrik Cygnaeus coll of foreign and especially Finnish 19th c art 08343

Didrichsenin Taidemuseo (Didrichsen Art Museum), Kuusilahdenkuja 1, 00340 Helsinki - T: (09) 489055, Fax: 489167, E-mail: office@didrichsenmuseum.fi, Internet: http://www.didrichsenmuseum.fi. Head: Peter Didrichsen
Fine Arts Museum - 1965
Modern art incl sculptures by Henry Moore and Jean Arp, and paintings by Kandinsky and Picasso, pre-Columbian art, old Chinese art, (Shang to Tang), small collection of Persian and East-Asiatic art 08344

Ehrensvärd-Museo (Ehrensvärd Museum), Suomenlinna B 40, 00190 Helsinki 19 - T: (09) 6841850, Fax: 668348, Internet: http://www.suomenlinna.fi/suomi/mus/emuseo.html
Historical Museum - 1921
Articles pertaining to the history of the Suomenlinna naval installation (1748), commandant's residence 08345

Eläinlääketieteen Historian Museo (Museum of the History of Veterinary Medicine), Hämeentie 57, 00580 Helsinki - T: (09) 19149750, Fax: 19149762, E-mail: museo@vetmed.helsinki.fi, Internet: http://www.vetmed.helsinki.fi/museo.htm. Head: Teodora Oker-Blom
Historical Museum - 1973
Instruments used by veterinarians, photographs and documents, history of veterinary medicine 08346

Eläinmuseo, Luonnontieteellinen Keskusmuseo (Zoological Museum), P. Rautatiekatu 13, 00100 Helsinki 10 - T: (09) 19128830, Fax: 19128843, E-mail: olof.bistrom@helsinki.fi, Internet: http://www.fmnh.helsinki.fi. Head: Prof. Olof Biström
Natural History Museum - 1923
Mammals, birds, skeletons, birds, fishes, amphibians and reptiles, insects and other invertebrates - library 08347

Hakasalmen Huvila, Helsingin Kaupunginmuseo (Hakasalmi Villa - Helsinki City Museum), Karamzininkatu 2, 00100 Helsinki, mail addr: PB 4300, 00099 Helsinki - T: (09) 1693444, Fax: 667665, E-mail: kaupunginmuseo@hel.fi, Internet: http://www.hel.fi/kaumuseo. Head: Leena Arkio-Laine
Local Museum - 1911 08348

Helsingin Kaupungin taidemuseo, Mejlahti (Helsinki City Art Museum), Tamminientie 6, 00250 Helsinki, mail addr: Simonkatu 3, 00250 Helsinki - T: (09) 31087031, Fax: 31087030, E-mail: artmuseum@hel.fi, Internet: http://www.hel.fi/artmuseum. Head: Tuula Karsalainen
Fine Arts Museum - 1976
Bäcksbacka, Becker, Laaksonen, Lindeberg Roos-Hasselblatt coll, Finnish and French 20th c art, photograph coll 08349

Helsingin Kaupungin Taidemuseo, Tennispalatsi (Helsinki City Art Museum), Salomonkatu 15, 00250 Helsinki, mail addr: Simonkatu 3, 00250 Helsinki - T: (09) 31087001, 7002, Fax: 31087000, E-mail: artmuseum@hel.fi, Internet: http://www.hel.fi/artmuseum. Head: Tuula Karsalainen
Fine Arts Museum - 1999
Finnish and foreign art 08350

Helsingin Kaupunginmuseo (Helsinki City Museum), Sofiankatu 4, 00170 Helsinki, mail addr: PB 4300, 00099 Helsinki - T: (09) 1693422, Fax: 667665, E-mail: kaupunginmuseo@hel.fi, Internet: http://www.hel.fi/kaumuseo. Head: Leena Arkio-Laine
Local Museum - 1911
Social, economic, cultural and political hist of the Finnish capital - photographic archive 08351

Helsingin Taidehalli (Kunsthalle Helsinki), Nervanderinkatu 3, 00100 Helsinki 10 - T: (09) 4542060, Fax: 45420610, E-mail: info@taidehalli.fi, Internet: http://www.taidehalli.fi. Head: Maija Tanninen-Mattila
Public Gallery - 1928 08352

Helsingin Yliopiston Lääketieteen Historian Laitos ja Museo (University of Helsinki Museum of Medical History), Hämeentie 153c, 00560 Helsinki 13 - T: (09) 1914823, Fax: 1914824, E-mail: - Hindrik.Strandberg@helsinki.fi, Internet: http://www.helsinki.fi/museo/laakhis.html. Head: Prof. Ismo Virtanen
University Museum - 1937
Examination implements, instruments and furniture of the medical and nursing sciences, veterinary medicine, odontology and pharmacy - library 08353

Helsingin Yliopiston Maatalousmuseo (University of Helsinki Agricultural Museum), Viikin Koetila, 00710 Helsinki 71 - T: (09) 647677. Head: Teppo Korhoven
Agriculture Museum / University Museum - 1946
Peasant farm tools, old mechanized agricultural implements, dairy farming, farm vehicles, carpenter's tools, miniature statues of domestic animals 08354

Herttoniemen Museo (Herttoniemi Museum), Linnanrakentajantie 14, 00810 Helsinki 81 - T: (09) 789874
Historic Site
Peasant culture, carriages and charts, photograph collections, Herttoniemi manor house (18th-19th c), Knusbacka peasant farmhouse and outbuildings 08355

Hotelli- ja Ravintolamuseo (Hotel and Restaurant Museum), Tallberginkatu 1g, 00180 Helsinki, mail addr: PL 133, 00181 Helsinki - T: (09) 68593700, Fax: 68593766, E-mail: hrm@kaapeli.fi. Head: Kirsti Grönholm
Special Museum - 1971
Hist of hotels, restaurants and cafés in Finland, alcoholic beverages and sales in Finland, traditional Finnish cooking 08356

Kansallis-Osake-Pankin Rahanäyttely (closed) 08357

Kasvimuseo, Luonnontieteellinen Keskusmuseo (Botanical Museum), Unioninkatu 44, 00170 Helsinki, mail addr: PL 7, 00014 Helsingin Yliopisto - T: (09) 1911, Fax: 19124456, Internet: http://www.fmnh.helsinki.fi. Head: Dr. Pertti Uotila
Natural History Museum - 1750
Herbarium, about 3 mill specimens - library 08358

Katumuseo, Helsingin Kaupunginmuseo (Street Museum of Heslinki City Museum), Sofiankatu, 00100 Helsinki, mail addr: PB 4300, 00099 Helsinki - T: (09) 1693422, Fax: 667665, E-mail: kaupunginmuseo@hel.fi, Internet: http://www.hel.fi/kaumuseo. Head: Leena Arkio-Laine
Open Air Museum / Special Museum - 1998
Street pavement, street furniture (18th c to 1930's) 08359

Kivimuseo, Luonnontieteellinen Keskusmuseo (Geology Museum of the Finnish Museum of Natural History) (closed until 2003), Snellmaninkatu 3, 00170 Helsinki, mail addr: PL 64, 00014 Helsingin Yliopisto - T: (09) 19150833, Fax: 19150826, E-mail: martti.lehtinen@helsinki.fi, Internet: http://www.fmnh.helsinki.fi. Head: Dr. Martti Lehtinen
Natural History Museum - 1829
Crystallographic coll, Gadolin's coll, Sahama's coll, meteorite coll (the Finnish meteorites), Parainen (Pargas) coll, Outokumpu coll, Pitkäranta coll 08360

Kluuvin Galleria, Helsingin Kaupungin Taidemuseo, Unioninkatu 28b, 00100 Helsinki 10 - T: (09) 31087039, Fax: 31087038, Internet: http://www.hel.fi/artmuseum
Fine Arts Museum - 1895
Modern art 08361

Koulumuseo, Helsingin Kaupunginmuseo (School Museum of Helsinki City Museum), Kalevankatu 39-43, 00180 Helsinki, mail addr: PB 4300, 00099 Helsinki - T: (09) 31087066, 1693422, Fax: 667665, E-mail: kaupunginmuseo@hel.fi, Internet: http://www.hel.fi/kaumuseo. Head: Leena Arkio-Laine
Historical Museum - 2000
History of schools in Helsinki, class rooms, teaching material 08362

Kulttuurien Museo (Museum of Cultures), Eteläinen Rautatienkatu 8, 00100 Helsinki, mail addr: PL 913, 00101 Helsinki - T: (09) 40509805, Fax: 40509821, E-mail: kulttuurienmuseo@nba.fi, Internet: http://www.nba.fi/museums/kultmus/tennisp.html. Head: Eija-Maija Kotilainen
Ethnology Museum - 1896/1998
Ethnography, Finno-Ugrian coll, Arctic coll, Central Asian colls 08363

Kuurojen Museo (Museum of the Deaf), Ilkantie 4, 00400 Helsinki - T: (09) 58031, 5803525, Fax: 5803770, E-mail: tiina.naukkarinen@kl-deaf.fi, Internet: http://www.kl-deaf.fi. Head: Tiina Naukkarinen
Special Museum 08364

Lähetysmuseo (Mission Museum), Tähtitorninkatu 18, 00140 Helsinki - T: (09) 1297252, 1297343, Fax: 1297337, E-mail: museo@mission.fi, Internet: http://www.mission.fi/museo. Head: Liisa Helminen
Ethnology Museum / Religious Arts Museum
African and Asian ethnology 08365

Lastenmuseo, Helsingin Kaupunginmuseo (Children's Museum of Helsinki City Museum), Tuomarinkylän Kartano, 00690 Helsinki, mail addr: PB 4300, 00099 Helsinki - T: (09) 7287458, 1693422, Fax: 667665, E-mail: kaupunginmuseo@hel.fi, Internet: http://www.hel.fi/kaumuseo. Head: Leena Arkio-Laine
Historical Museum - 1992
Historical education of children 08366

Mannerheim Museo, Kalliolinnantie 14, 00140 Helsinki - T: (09) 635443, Fax: 636736, E-mail: info@mannerheim-museo.fi, Internet: http://www.mannerheim-museo.fi. Head: Vera von Fersen
Historical Museum - 1951
Field Marshall Gustaf Mannerheim: commander-in-chief of the Finnish army, regent and president of Finland, explorer and chair of the Finnish Red Cross 08367

Metsämuseo (Museum of Forestry), c/o Helsingin Yliopisto, Viikki, 00014 Helsinki - T: (09) 70851. Head: Prof. Matti Leikola
Natural History Museum 08368

Military Museum Manege, Iso-Mustasaari C 77, 00190 Helsinki, mail addr: PL 266, 00171 Helsinki - T: (09) 18145296, Fax: 18126390, E-mail: markku.melkko@mil.fi, Internet: http://www.mpkk.fi. Head: Markku Melkko
Military Museum - 1989
Heavy equipment mostly dating from 1939-45 in a manége originally built in 1881 for the Suomenlinna Artillery 08369

NIFCA - Nordic Institute for Contemporary Art, Suomenlinna B 28, 00190 Helsinki - T: (09) 686430, Fax: 668594, E-mail: information@nifca.org, Internet: http://www.nifca.org. Head: Søren Friis Møller
Fine Arts Museum 08370

Nordiskt Institut för Samtidskonst → NIFCA - Nordic Institute for Contemporary Art

Nukke- ja Lelumuseo (Doll and Toy Museum), Suomenlinna C 66, 00190 Helsinki - T: (09) 669417
Special Museum 08371

Nykytaiteen Museo (Museum of Contemporary Art), Mannerheiminaukio 2, 00100 Helsinki - T: (09) 17336501, Fax: 17336503, E-mail: info@kiasma.fi, Internet: http://www.kiasma.fi. Head: Tuula Karjalainen
Fine Arts Museum - 1990
Finnish and Scandinavian contemporary art 08372

Osuuspankkimuseo (Okubank Group Museum), Arkadiankatu 23, 00101 Helsinki 82 - T: (09) 4042053, 2298, Fax: 407309. Head: Heikki Vitie
Historical Museum - 1954
20th c bank equipment, photogr, documents, hist of co-operative banking 08373

Postimuseo (Post Museum), Asema-Aukio 5H, 00101 Helsinki - T: (0204) 514908, Fax: 514777, E-mail: postimuseo@posti.fi, Internet: http://www.posti.fi/postimuseo. Head: Jari Karhu
Special Museum - 1926
History of the Finnish postal service, Finnish and international stamps, stamp designs - library, photo archives 08374

Raha- ja Mitalikokoelma (Coin and Medal Collection of the University of Helsinki), Mannerheimintie 34, 00100 Helsinki, mail addr: c/o National Museum of Finland, PL 913, 00100 Helsinki - T: (09) 40509540, Fax: 40509437, E-mail: tuukka.talvio@nba.fi, Internet: http://www.nba.fi/natmus/kmeng.html. Head: Tuukka Talvio
Special Museum / University Museum - 18th c 08375

Raitioliikennemuseo, Helsingin Kaupunginmuseo (Tram Museum of Helsinki City Musuem), Töölönkatu 51a, 00250 Helsinki, mail addr: PB 4300, 00099 Helsinki - T: (09) 1693576, 1693422, Fax: 667665, E-mail: kaupunginmuseo@hel.fi, Internet: http://www.hel.fi/kaumuseo. Head: Leena Arkio-Laine
Science&Tech Museum - 1994
Public transport in Helsinki, tram depot from 1900, scale model of Helsinki from 1870's 08376

Rannikkotykistömuseo (Coast Artillery Museum), Suomenlinna, Kustaanmiekka, Rakennus A 2, 00190 Helsinki, mail addr: PL 266, 00171 Helsinki - T: (09) 18145295, Fax: 18126390, E-mail: markku.melkko@mil.fi, Internet: http://www.mpkk.fi. Head: Markku Melkko
Military Museum - 1948
Finnish coastal defence equipment from Viking time to present in the fortress of Suomenlinna 08377

Ruiskumestarin Talo, Helsingin Kaupunginmuseo (Burgher's House - Helsinki City Museum), Kristianinkatu 12, 00170 Helsinki, mail addr: PB 4300, 00099 Helsinki - T: (09) 1351065, 1693422, Fax: 667665, E-mail: kaupinginmuseo@hel.fi, Internet: http://www.hel.fi/kaumuseo. Head: Leena Arkio-Laine
Historical Museum / Decorative Arts Museum - 1980
Oldest suviving wooden house in the city 08378

Sederholmin Talo, Helsingin Kaupunginmuseo (Sederholm House of Helsinki City Museum), Aleksanterinkatu 16-18, 00170 Helsinki, mail addr: PB 4300, 00099 Helsinki - T: (09) 1693625, 1693422, Fax: 667665, E-mail: kaupunginmuseo@hel.fi, Internet: http://www.hel.fi/kaumuseo. Head: Leena Arkio-Laine
Special Museum - 1995
Oldest stone building in downtown Helsinki (1757) 08379

Seurasaaren Ulkomuseo (Seurasaari Open Air Museum), Seurasaari, 00250 Helsinki, mail addr: PL 913, 00101 Helsinki - T: (09) 40501, Fax: 40509579, E-mail: seurasaarenulkomuseo@nba.fi, Internet: http://www.nba.fi. Head: Riita Ailonen
Open Air Museum - 1909
Peasant and upper class buildings from different areas of Finland, a church, sauna, cattle shelters, storehouses, mills, a smithy, 'church boats', furnishings, tools 08380

Sinebrychoffin Taidemuseo, Valtion Taidemuseo (Sinebrychoff Art Museum - Finnish National Gallery) (closed until end of 2002), Bulevardi 40, 00120 Helsinki 12 - T: (09) 173361, Fax: 17336476, E-mail: eija.pekkanen@fng.fi, Internet: http://www.fng.fi. Head: Ulla Huhtamäki
Fine Arts Museum - 1921
Old Dutch, Flemish, Italian and French paintings, Swedish portraits, Russian and Karelian icons, furniture, silver and porcelain 08381

Sotamuseo (Military Museum of Finland), Maurinkatu 1, 00170 Helsinki - T: (09) 18126381, Fax: 18126390, E-mail: markku.melkko@mil.fi, Internet: http://www.mpkk.fi. Head: Markku Melkko
Military Museum - 1929
Military items, weapons, ammunition, Coast Artillery Museum, submarine Vesikko, Manege in the Fortress of Suomenlinna - photo archives, library 08382

Sukellusvene Vesikko (Submarine Vesikko), Suomenlinna, Susisaari, 00190 Helsinki, mail addr: PL 266, 00171 Helsinki - T: (09) 18146238, Fax: 18126390, E-mail: markku.melkko@mil.fi, Internet: http://www.mpkk.fi. Head: Markku Melkko
Military Museum - 1973
A 250-ton coastal submarine of WWII 08383

Suomen Kansallismuseo (National Museum of Finland), Mannerheimintie 34, 00100 Helsinki, mail addr: PL 913, 00101 Helsinki - T: (09) 40501, Fax: 40509400, E-mail: ritva.ware@nba.fi, Internet: http://www.nba.fi/natmus/kmeng.html. Head: Dr. Ritva Wäre
Archaeological Museum / Historical Museum / Ethnology Museum - 1893
Finnish prehistory, medieval art, historical colls, folk culture, Sami coll, coins and medals 08384

Suomen Merimuseo, National Board of Antiquities (Maritime Museum of Finland), Hylkysaari, 00570 Helsinki - T: (09) 40501, Fax: 40509060, E-mail: suomenmerimuseo@nba.fi, Internet: http://www.nba.fi/museums/maritime/merimeng.htm. Head: Marja Pelanne
Historical Museum - 1981
Boats and shipping, maps, drawings of ships, maritime hist, underwater archaeology - conservation laboratory 08385

Suomen Rakennustaiteen Museo (Museum of Finnish Architecture), Kasarmikatu 24, 00130 Helsinki 13 - T: (09) 85675100, Fax: 8567501, E-mail: mfa@mfa.fi, Internet: http://www.mfa.fi. Head: Marja-Riitta Norri
Fine Arts Museum - 1956
Finnish architecture, drawings, and photographs - library 08386

Suomen Urheilumuseo (Sports Museum of Finland), Olympic Stadium, 00250 Helsinki 25 - T: (09) 4342250, Fax: 43422550, E-mail: urheilumuseo@stadion.fi, Internet: http://www.stadion.fi. Head: Pekka Honkanen
Special Museum - 1938
History of Finnish sports, ski collection, sports equipment, clothes, flags, prizes - library, photographic archives, archives, information service 08387

Suomen Valokuvataiteen Museo (The Finnish Museum of Photography), Tallberginkatu 1G, 00180 Helsinki - T: (09) 68663613, 6866360, Fax: 68663630, E-mail: fmp@fmp.fi, Internet: http://www.fmp.fi. Head: Asko Mäkelä
Special Museum - 1969
Coll of photographs and photographic apparatus, temporary exhibitions of photographic art - photographic archive 08388

Suomenlinna-Museo (Suomenlinna Museum), Suomenlinna C 74, 00190 Helsinki - T: (09) 40509691, Fax: 40509690, E-mail: riitta.ailonen@nba.fi, Internet: http://www.nba.fi. Head: Riitta Ailonen
Historical Museum / Military Museum - 1998
Hist of Suomenlinna fortress 08389

Suomenlinna-Sveaborg (Suomenlinna Island Fortress), Suomenlinna C 40, 00190 Helsinki - T: (09) 41323300, Fax: 41323280, E-mail: hoitokunta@suomenlinna.fi, Internet: http://www.suomenlinna.fi. Head: Jaakko Antti-Poika
Historic Site - 1973 08390

Taidekoti Kirpilä (Kirpilä Art Collection), Pohjoinen Hesperiankatu 7, 00260 Helsinki - T: (09) 494436, Fax: 447658, E-mail: al@skr.fi, Internet: http://www.skr.fi. Head: Anneli Lindström
Fine Arts Museum - 1992
Finnish art collected by Dr. Kirpilä in his home 08391

Taideteollisuusmuseo (Museum of Art and Design), Korkeavuorenkatu 23, 00130 Helsinki 13 - T: (09) 6220540, Fax: 62205455, E-mail: info@designmuseum.fi, Internet: http://www.designmuseum.fi. Head: Pekka Saarela
Decorative Arts Museum - 1873
Objects connected with the development of industrial art, artistic handicrafts and industrial design in Finland from the second half of the 19th c to the present day, examples of industrial art and artistic handicrafts from abroad - library, lecture room with audio-visual equipment, archives 08392

Teatterimuseo (Theatre Museum), Tallberginkatu 1g, 00180 Helsinki - T: (09) 68509100, Fax: 68509121, E-mail: teatterimuseo@teatterimuseo.fi, Internet: http://www.teatterimuseo.fi. Head: Hanna-Leena Helavuori
Performing Arts Museum - 1962
Photographs, costumes, sets, programs, posters, archives 08393

Tekniikan Museo (Museum of Technology), Viikintie 1, 00560 Helsinki 56 - T: (09) 797066, Fax: 7571617. Head: Lea Väkeväinen
Science&Tech Museum - 1969
Printing, coinage and bank-note printing, surveying, meteorology, power engines, chemical industry, sugar industry, communications, forest industry, building construction, mining industry, metal industry, electricity, household technology and dataprocessing technology - library 08394

Tiemuseo (Road Museum), Opastinsilta 12 A, 00521 Helsinki - T: (09) 14872493, Fax: 14872471. Head: Leena Sälejoki-Hiekkanen
Science&Tech Museum - 1980
Road construction, cars, traffic 08395

Tuomarinkylän Museo, Helsingin Kaupunginmuseo (Tuomarinkylä Museum - Helsinki City Museum), Tuomarinkylän Kartano, 00690 Helsinki, mail addr: PB 4300, 00099 Helsinki - T: (09) 7287458, 1693422, Fax: 667665, E-mail: kaupunginmuseo@hel.fi, Internet: http://www.hel.fi/kaumuseo. Head: Leena Arkio-Laine
Historical Museum / Agriculture Museum - 1962
Manor house (1790), manor life 08396

Työväenasuntomuseo, Helsingin Kaupunginmuseo (Worker Housing Museum of Helsinki City Museum), Kirstinkuja 4, 00510 Helsinki, mail addr: PB 4300, 00099 Helsinki - T: (09) 1461039, 1693422, Fax: 667665, E-mail: kaupunginmuseo@hel.fi, Internet: http://www.hel.fi/kaumuseo. Head: Leena Arkio-Laine
Decorative Arts Museum / Historical Museum - 1989
Lifes of worker families (1909-1985) 08397

Urho Kekkonen Museo Tamminiemi, Seurasaarentie 15, 00250 Helsinki - T: (09) 40509653, Fax: 40509653, E-mail: urhokekkonenmuseo@nba.fi, Internet: http://www.nba.fi. Head: Riitta Ailonen
Historical Museum - 1987
Home of the President of Finland Urho Kekkonen 1900 - 1986) Finish art and design, interior 08398

Voimalamuseo, Helsingin Kaupunginmuseo (Power Station Museum of Helsinki City Museum), Hämeentie 163, 00560 Helsinki, mail addr: PB 4300, 00099 Helsinki - T: (09) 31087064, 1693422, Fax: 667665, E-mail: kaupunginmuseo@hel.fi, Internet: http://www.hel.fi/kaumuseo. Head: Leena Arkio-Laine
Science&Tech Museum - 2000
Water board's turbine pumping station, steampower plant, mill, industrial traditions 08399

Hollola

Hollolan Kotiseutumuseo (Hollola Local History Museum), Rälssintie, 16710 Hollola - T: (03) 888014081, 7803298
Decorative Arts Museum / Agriculture Museum - 1969
Peasant furniture, textiles, costumes, household articles, agricultural implements, early 19th c Hentilä and Ylä-Kölli farmhouses 08400

Huittinen

Huittisten Museo, Kirkkotie 4, 32700 Huittinen - T: (02) 5604319, 5604111, Fax: 5604215, E-mail: museo@huittinen.fi, Internet: http://www.huittinen.fi/nahtavyydet/museo.html. Head: Irma Keski-Vakkuri
Fine Arts Museum / Local Museum
Works by sculptor and teacher L. Leppänen, department of President Risto Ryti 08401

Hyrynsalmi

Kaunislehdon Talomuseo (Kaunislehto Farmhouse), 89400 Hyrynsalmi - T: (08) 749111, Fax: 742086, E-mail: kunta@hyrynsalmi.fi, Internet: http://www.hyrynsalmi.fi/kaunisl.htm
Open Air Museum - 1966
Furnishings, tar-burning equipment, Kaunislehto farm 08402

Hyvinkää

Suomen Rautatiemuseo (Finnish Railway Museum), Hyvinkäänkatu 9, 05800 Hyvinkää - T: (0307) 25241, Fax: 25240, E-mail: info@rautatie.org, Internet: http://www.rautatie.org. Head: Matti Bergström
Science&Tech Museum / Open Air Museum - 1898
Models of railways vehicles, networks and buildings, train of Russian Czar and Grand Duke of Finland (1870), oldest preserved steam engine of Finland (1868), passenger coaches, steam engines and oldest track motor car, furnished railway station buildings (1870), railway equipment - library, photo archive 08403

Iisalmi

Juhani Ahon Museo, Ouluntie 37, Mansikkaniemi, 74120 Iisalmi - T: (017) 81771, 8303248, Fax: 8303248, Internet: http://www.iisalmi.fi/iisalmi/kulttur. Head: Arvo Polvi
Special Museum
Childhood home of the author Juhani Aho (1861 - 1921) 08404

Ylä-Savon Kotiseutumuseo (Museum of Ylä-Savo), Kivirannantie 5, 74100 Iisalmi - T: (017) 825865. Head: Hannes Kuosmanen
Local Museum 08405

Iittala

Iittalan Tehtaan Museo (Iittala Glass Museum), 14500 Iittala - T: (0204) 396230, Fax: 393516, E-mail: iittala.museum@designor.com
Decorative Arts Museum - 1971
Articles produced by the Iittala glass works since 1881, art pieces by Tapio Wirkkala, Timo Sarpaneva, Alvar Aalto 08406

Kalvolan Kunnan Kotiseutumuseo, Iittalantie 284, 14500 Iittala - T: (03) 67371, Fax: 6737225
Local Museum 08407

Ilmajoki

Ilmajoen Museo (Ilmajoki Museum), Ilkan puisto, 60800 Ilmajoki - T: (06) 4248474, Fax: 4246401. Head: Lea Värtinen
Local Museum - 1909
Folk art, furniture, textiles, carriages, agricultural equipment, numismatics, church museum (housed in a reconstruction of the 1638 building), photographs, tradition of Aalto's artillery battalion - research archives 08408

Yli-Lauroselan Talomuseo (Yli-Laurosela Farmhouse Museum), Könnintie 2, 60800 Ilmajoki 7 - T: (06) 4246719, Fax: 4246739, Internet: http://www.nba.fi. Head: Lea Värtinen
Local Museum - 1978
19th and 20th c interior, furnishing and household articles, main building (1848) in typical archuteczure of this part of Finland (Ostrobothnia) 08409

Imatra

Imatran Taidemuseo (Imatra Art Gallery), Virastokatu 1, 55100 Imatra 10 - T: (05) 6817602, Fax: 6816610, E-mail: eero.laajo@imatra.fi, Internet: http://www.imatra.fi. Head: Eero Laajo
Fine Arts Museum - 1951
Modern Finnish paintings, sculptures, medals, drawings, graphic arts 08410

Karjalainen Kotitalo (Karelian Farmhouse), Kotipolku 1, 55120 Imatra 10 - T: (05) 6816711, 6703
Agriculture Museum / Open Air Museum - 1959
Peasant objects, handicrafts, textiles, farm buildings (19th c) 08411

Teollisuustyöväen Asuntomuseo (Museum of Industrial Worker's Dwellings), Ritikanranta, 55120 Imatra 40 - T: (05) 6816712, 6703
Historical Museum - 1975
Wooden dwelling of industrial workers and outbuilding, four tenements of the building demonstrate how the workers lived at the beginning of the c and in the 1920's 1940's and 1960's 08412

Inari

Saamelaismuseo Siida (Sámi Museum and Northern Lapland Nature Centre), Inarintie, 99870 Inari - T: (016) 665212, Fax: 671486, E-mail: siida@samimuseum.fi, Internet: http://www.siida.fi. Head: Tarmo Jomppanen
Ethnology Museum / Open Air Museum - 1961
Dwellings of non-nomadic Lapps, Lappish fishermen and Fjeld Lapps together with important outbuildings such as storehouses, drying racks for fish, fishing nets, animal shelters, Lapp's house from Petsamo, gold prospector's dwelling and washing equipment, courtroom, furnishings, household articles, textiles, hunting equipment 08413

Isokyrö

Isonkyrön Kotiseutumuseo (Isokyrö Local History Museum), Museotie, Taipale, 61500 Isokyrö 5 - T: (06) 4713253. Head: Helvi Markko
Open Air Museum / Historical Museum - 1947
Relocated farm buildings, windmill, granaries (18th and 19th c), furnishings of buildings, textiles, handicrafts, carpenter's and shoemarker's shops 08414

Järvenpää

Ainola, 04400 Järvenpää - T: (050) 3503819, E-mail: hilkka.helminen@maaseutukeskus.fi, Internet: http://www.ainola.fi. Head: Hilkka Helminen
Music Museum - 1972
Home of composer Jean Sibelius, designed by Lars Sonck (1904), with furnishings 08415

Jakobstad

Arktisk Museum Nanoq, Färbodavägen, 68620 Jakobstad - T: (06) 7293679, Fax: 7293679
Special Museum 08416

Jakobstads museum, Storg 2, 68600 Jakobstad - T: (06) 7851111, Fax: 7851440, Internet: http://www.jakobstad.fi. Head: Pekka Toivanen
Local Museum - 1904
Maritime coll, ship paintings and drawings, sea charts, trade, ship building, maritime commerce, town culture, textiles, dolls and toys - library, archive, photo archive 08417

Malmska gården, Jakobstads Museum, Storg 2, 68600 Jakobstad - T: (06) 7851373, 7851111, Fax: 7851440
Local Museum
Interior, local hist 08418

Runebergs stugan (Runeberg's Cottage), Östanpåvägen, 68600 Jakobstad - T: (06) 7231627, 7851371, Fax: 7851440
Special Museum
Hunting and fisher house of Lorenz Ulrik Runeberg 08419

Westmansmors stugan (Westman's Cottage), Visabacken 4, 68600 Jakobstad - T: (06) 7851531, 7851371, Fax: 7851440
Special Museum
First school of the national poet Johan Ludvig Runeberg 08420

Jalasjarvi

Jalasjärven Museo, 61600 Jalasjarvi 2 - T: (06) 4560332, Fax: 4560540. Head: Vilho Pienimaa
Local Museum 08421

Janakkala

Laurinmäen Torpparimuseo (Crofter's Museum of Laurinmäki), 14240 Janakkala - T: (03) 6801280
Open Air Museum / Local Museum - 1963
Croft buildings (19th and 20th c) and objects belonging to them 08422

Joensuu

Joensuun Taidemuseo (Joensuu Art Museum), Kirkkokatu 23, 80100 Joensuu 10 - T: (013) 2675385, Fax: 2675390, E-mail: ann-mari.karvinen@qjns.fi, Internet: http://www.jns.fi/taidemuseo. Head: Ann-Mari Karvinen
Fine Arts Museum - 1962
Finnish art since the Late 19th c, paintings, sculpture (Manzú, Marini), drawings, graphics, European Classical, and Chinese art objects, Iris ceramics - library 08423

Pohjois-Karjalan Museo (North Karelian Museum), Carelicum, Koskikatu 5, 80100 Joensuu 10 - T: (013) 2675222, Fax: 2675320, E-mail: auli.patjas@jns.fi, Internet: http://www.carelicum.fi. Head: Auli Patjas
Historical Museum / Folklore Museum - 1917
Hist and folk culture of Northern and Ladoga Carelia, cultural hist of Joensuu city - library, photo archive 08424

Jokioinen

Jokioisten Museorautatie ja Kapearaidemuseo (Jokioinen Railway Museum and Narrow Gauge Museum), 31601 Jokioinen - T: (03) 4333235, Fax: 0425861976, E-mail: info@jokioistenmuseo-rautatie.fi, Internet: http://www.jokioistenmuseo-rautatie.fi. Head: Antti Välicki
Science&Tech Museum - 1976
Old locomotives, small items and pictures of Finnish narrow gauge railways - library 08425

Jokioisten Pappilamuseo (Jokioinen Parsonage Museum), 31600 Jokioinen, mail addr: PL 46, 30101 Forssa - T: (03) 83386. Head: Alli Brander
Historic Site - 1959
Storehouse, smokehouse (1800), interiors (1850) - library 08426

Jomala

Ålands Jakt och Fiske Museum, Ulfsby, 22150 Jomala - T: (018) 31147, 22450
Special Museum 08427

Joroinen

Joroisten Kotiseutumuseo (Joroinen Local Arts and Crafts Museum), Golftie 14, 79600 Joroinen - T: (017) 572222, Fax: 572555
Local Museum
Local hist and culture 08428

Joutsa

Joutsan Kotiseutumuseo (Joutsa Museum), Häntäläntie 5, 19650 Joutsa - T: (014) 882748, 882470
Local Museum 08429

Joutseno

Pitäjäntupa-Museo, Imatrantie, 54101 Joutseno - T: (05) 6326727, Fax: 6326275
Local Museum
Textiles from the region 08430

Jurva

Kotiseutumuseo, Haapalantie 3, 66300 Jurva - T: (06) 3632253, Fax: 3632253, Internet: http://www.jurva.fi/museo. Head: Ritva Anttila
Local Museum 08431

Juuka

Juuan Pitäjänmuseo, Vuorentie, 83900 Juuka - T: (013) 470773, Fax: 472015
Local Museum 08432

Myllymuseo (Mill Museum), Huttulantie, 83900 Juuka - T: (013) 470773, Fax: 472015
Science&Tech Museum 08433

Juva

Juvan Karjalaisten Museo (Karelians Museum), Partala, Huttulantie 1, 51900 Juva - T: (015) 7551297, 1224, Fax: 7551555, E-mail: leena.orro@juva.fi, Internet: htp://www.juva.fi
Local Museum 08434

Juvan Museo, Huttulantie 1, 51900 Juva - T: (015) 75511, Fax: 7551555, E-mail: leena.orro@juva.fi, Internet: http://www.juva.fi. Head: Leena Orro
Local Museum - 1951
Handicrafts 08435

Jyväskylä

Alvar Aalto Museum, Alvar Aallon katu 7, 40600 Jyväskylä, mail addr: PL 461, 40101 Jyväskylä - T: (014) 624809, Fax: 619009, E-mail: museum@alvaraalto.fi, Internet: http://www.alvaraalto.fi. Head: Markku Lahti
Decorative Arts Museum / Special Museum - 1966
Building designed by architect Alvar Aalto (1973), Alvar Aalto collection, sketches, drawings, designs, photostat reproductions, furniture, experiments with bent wood - archives 08436

Jyväskylän Lyseon Museo (Jyväskylä School Museum), Yliopistonkatu 13, 40100 Jyväskylä - T: (014) 624919, 928, Fax: 624933
Special Museum 08437

Jyväskylän Yliopiston Museo (Jyväskylä University Museum), c/o Jyväskylä Yliopisto, Seminaarinkatu 15, 40100 Jyväskylä 10 - T: (014) 2603800, 3881, 3810, Fax: 2603801, 3811, Internet: http://www.jyu.fi/tdk/museo. Head: Janne Vilkuna
Historical Museum / University Museum - 1900
Cultural-historical section, objects, related to the hist of Jyväskylä Teacher's Training College, College of Education and University, incl Uno Cygnaeus' room, classrooms, women's dormitory and teaching implements from 1863, natural science section, zoological, botanical, and geological coll 08438

Keski-Suomen Museo (Museum of Central Finland), Alvar Aallon katu 7, 40101 Jyväskylä - T: (014) 624930, 624928, Fax: 624936, E-mail: ksmuseo.info@jkl.fi, Internet: http://www.jkl.fi/ksmuseo. Head: Risto Koskinen
Local Museum / Ethnology Museum - 1931
Ethnographic material, native art, rug coll, Finnish medals - library 08439

Suomen Käsityön Museo (Craft Museum of Finland), Kauppakatu 25, 40100 Jyväskylä - T: (014) 624946, Fax: 624947, E-mail: craftmuseum@jkl.fi, Internet: http://www.craftmuseum.fi. Head: Seija Heinänen
Historical Museum - 1888
Textiles, esp embroidery, lacework, national costumes, table linen, woven clothings, Markku-Piri coll of industrial design, handicraft and craft industry - conservation centre, National Costume Center of Finland 08440

Suomen Kansallispukukeskus (National Costume Center of Finland), Gummeruksenkatu 3 E, 40100 Jyväskylä - T: (014) 626840, Fax: 626841. Head: Seija Heinänen
Special Museum - 1992 08441

Kaarina

Kuusiston Kartano, 20780 Kaarina - T: (02) 557038
Local Museum 08442

Kaarlela

Kaarlelan Kotiseutumuseo (Kaarlela Local History Museum), 67700 Kaarlela
Local Museum - 1928
Furnished farmhouse, windmill, tanner's workshop (18th c), handicrafts 08443

Kaavi

Eloaitta, Kaavin Kotiseutumuseo, 73600 Kaavi - T: (017) 662697, 662188
Local Museum 08444

Kälviä

Kälviän Kotiseutumuseo, 68300 Kälviä - T: (06) 50135
Local Museum 08445

Talonpojanmuseo (Peasant Museum), 68300 Kälviä - T: (06) 8351190, 8350034, Fax: 8350034, Internet: http://www.kpnet.com/elainpuisto
Local Museum 08446

Kärsämäki

Kärsämäen Kotiseutumuseo, Toimisto Kunnantoimisto, 86710 Kärsämäki - T: (08) 61770
Local Museum 08447

Kajaani

Ämmäkosken Kanava → Tervakanava

Kainuun Museo (Museum of Kainuu), Asemakatu 4, 87100 Kajaani - T: (08) 6155407, Fax: 6155672, E-mail: heidi.komulainen@kajaani.fi, Internet: http://www.kajaani.fi/kainuunmuseo. Head: Antti Mäkinen
Local Museum - 1930
Articles and equipment for hunting, fishing, dairy farming, tar burning and logging, articles connected with the history of Kajaani castle, watercolors, paintings and drawings by Louis Sparre (1863-1964) 08448

Kajaanin Taidemuseo (Kajaani Art Museum), Linnankatu 14, 87100 Kajaani - T: (08) 6155415, Fax: 6155581, E-mail: taidemuseo@kajaani.fi, Internet: http://www.kajaani.fi/taidemuseo. Head: Heikki Aranne
Fine Arts Museum - 1993
Modern art from WW II
08449

Tervakanava (Tar Boat Canal), Ämmäkosken Ranta, 87100 Kajaani - T: (08) 6155410, 6155407, Fax: 6155672
Local Museum
08450

Kalajoki

Kalajoen Kalastusmuseo (Kalajoki Fishing Museum), Plassintie 47, 85100 Kalajoki - T: (08) 462389, 460591
Special Museum
08451

Kalajoen Kotiseutumuseo, Siltasaari, 85100 Kalajoki - T: (08) 46911, Fax: 4691317, Internet: http://www.kalajoki.fi
Local Museum
08452

Kalanti

Kalannin Kotiseutumuseo (Kalanti Local History Museum), Kuriirikuja 1, 23600 Kalanti - T: (02) 874118, Fax: 155442. Head: Mari Jalava
Local Museum - 1951
18th and 19th c farm buildings, furnishings, wooden vessel collection
08453

Kangasala

Kangasalan Museo, 36200 Kangasala - T: (03) 771323, 772335
Local Museum
08454

Mobilia (Car and Traffic Museum), Kustaa Kolmannentie 75, 36270 Kangasala - T: (03) 31404000, Fax: 31404050, E-mail: mobilia@fi, Internet: http://www.mobilia.fi. Head: Kimmo Levä
Science&Tech Museum
08455

Kangaslampi

Kangaslammin Koti- ja Koulumuseo (Kangaslampi Home and School Museum), Kirkonkylä, 79480 Kangaslampi - T: (017) 86231
Special Museum
08456

Kangasniemi

Kangasniemen Museo (Kangasniemi Museum), 51200 Kangasniemi - T: (015) 2133
Local Museum - 1954
Objects connected with peasant culture, public granary (1908-13)
08457

Pitkänpellon Talomuseo, Paappala, 51200 Kangasniemi - T: (015) 2858
Local Museum
08458

Kannonkoski

Kannonkosken Kotiseutukokoelma, Kannonkosken Kunta, 43300 Kannonkoski - T: (014) 51211
Local Museum
08459

Kannus

Kannuksen Museo, 69101 Kannus - T: (06) 71451
Local Museum
08460

Karhula

Karhulan Lasimuseo (Karhula Glass Museum), 48600 Karhula - T: (05) 63100
Decorative Arts Museum
08461

Karijoki

Karijoen Kotiseutumuseo, Marttusen Mäki, 64350 Karijoki - T: (06) 2680405
Historical Museum
08462

Karjaa

Hangon Rintamamuseo, Stabsgatan 10, 10300 Karjaa - T: (019) 231301, 2443068, Fax: 231301. Head: Dr. Stig Häggström
Military Museum
08463

Karjaan Museo (Karis Museum), Keskuskatu 90, 10300 Karjaa - T: (019) 2786540, Fax: 232346, E-mail: jan.fast@karis.fi, Internet: http://www.karis.fi/karis
Ethnology Museum / Archaeological Museum - 1936
Cultural history, ethnography, photographs, archaeology
08464

Karkkila

Karkkila Högforsin Työläismuseo (Karkkila Worker's Museum), PL 50, 03601 Karkkila - T: (09) 22505251, Fax: 22505208, E-mail: tommi-kuutsa@karkkila.fi. Head: Tommi Kuutsa
Historical Museum - 1986
Worker's culture, local hist - archives
08465

Suomen Valimomuseo ja Högforsin Masuuni (Finnish Foundry Museum and Högfors Blast Furnace), Tehtaanpuisto, 03601 Karkkila - T: (09) 22505261, E-mail: suomen.valimomuseo@co.inet.fi, Internet: http://www.karkkila.fi
Science&Tech Museum - 1989
Foundry techniques and traditions
08466

Karstula

Karstulan Kotiseutumuseo, 43500 Karstula - T: (014) 469511
Local Museum
08467

Karttula

Karttulan Kotiseutumuseo, Kirkkotie, 72100 Karttula - T: (017) 49511, Fax: 495495
Local Museum
08468

Riuttalan Talonpoikaismuseo, Riuttala, 72100 Karttula
Local Museum
08469

Karvia

Karvian Museo, 39930 Karvia - T: (02) 43122
Local Museum
08470

Karvion Kanava

Varistaipaleen Kanavamuseo (Canal Museum), Heinäveden Kanavat, 79810 Karvion Kanava - T: (017) 63509
Science&Tech Museum
08471

Kaskinen

Fiskemuseet i Kaskö, Sjöbobacken, 64260 Kaskinen - T: (06) 2227711, 2227286, Fax: 2227235
Special Museum
08472

Kaskö Hembygdsmuseum, Rådhusg 48, 64260 Kaskinen - T: (06) 27575, Internet: http://www.museum.svof.fi
Local Museum
08473

Kastelholm

Kronohäktet Vita Björn (Crown Jail Vita Björn), 22520 Kastelholm - T: (018) 43820, 43822
Historical Museum
08474

Kauhajoki

Eduskuntasalimuseo (Parliament In-Exile Museum), Koulupolku, 61800 Kauhajoki - T: (063) 18339, 18314
Historical Museum
08475

Kauhajoen Museo, 61800 Kauhajoki - T: (06) 2312713, E-mail: kaalha@kauhajoki.fi, Internet: http://www.kauhajoki.fi/kulttuuri/museo. Head: Kari M. Alhaainen
Open Air Museum - 1933
19th c farmhouse and outbuildings, public granary, household articles, furniture, textiles, carpenter's tanner's and shoemaker's tools, numismatics
08476

Kauhava

Kauhavanmuseo, 62200 Kauhava - T: (06) 80573, 340024
Local Museum
08477

Kaukonen

Särestöniemi Museo, Särestöntie 880, 99110 Kaukonen - T: (016) 654480, 654489, Fax: 654489, E-mail: liisa.tervahauta-kauppala@kittila.fi. Head: Liisa Tervahauta-Kauppala
Fine Arts Museum
08478

Kaustinen

Kaustisen Kotiseutumuseo, Kirkonkylä, 69600 Kaustinen - T: (06) 61170162
Local Museum
08479

Suomen Kansansoitinmuseo (Finnish Folk Instrument Museum), Pelimannitori, 69600 Kaustinen, mail addr: PL 10, 69601 Kaustinen - T: (06) 8611252, Fax: 8612352. Head: Risto Känsälä
Music Museum
Finnish folk instruments
08480

Kauttua

Kauttuan Tehtaan Museo (Kauttua Factory Museum), 27500 Kauttua - T: (02) 283922306, 2561, Fax: 283922020, E-mail: eino.poukka@ahlstrom.com
Science&Tech Museum
08481

Keikyä

Keikyän Kotiseutumuseo, 32730 Keikyä - T: (03) 31432
Local Museum
08482

Keitele

Aholan Talomuseo, 72601 Keitele - T: (017) 52751
Local Museum
08483

Kello

Haukiputaan Koulumuseo (Haukipudas School Museum), Oravan Koulu, 90820 Kello - T: (08) 5401314, Fax: 5401314
Special Museum
08484

Kellokoski

Kellokosken Sairaalan Museo (Hospital Museum), 04500 Kellokoski - T: (09) 27161
Special Museum
08485

Kemi

Jalokivi Galleria (Gemstone Gallery), Kauppakatu 29, 94100 Kemi - T: (016) 220300, 259690, Fax: 259675, E-mail: Anja.Holpainen@kemi-fi, Internet: http://www.kemi.fi/jalokivigalleria. Head: Anja Holpainen
Decorative Arts Museum - 1986
The Crown of King of Finland, Prix Arctica competitions best works
08486

Kemin Museo (Kemin Museum), Meripuisto, 94100 Kemi 10 - T: (016) 14813
Open Air Museum - 1938
Chimneyless dwelling (1796) farmhouse (1849), storehouses and customs hall (1873), furniture, textiles, household articles, equipment used for fishing in the Kemi river
08487

Kemin Taidemuseo (Kemi Art Museum), Marina Takalon Katu 3, 94100 Kemi - T: (016) 258247, Fax: 258243, E-mail: pekka.ronkko@kemi.fi, Internet: http://www.kemi.fi/taidemuseo/taidem.htm. Head: Unto Käyhkö
Fine Arts Museum - 1947
Older and modern Finnish art, especially from Northern Finland
08488

Kemin Työläismuseo (Worker's Museum), Leinosenpolku, 94200 Kemi - T: (016) 62808, 14813
Historical Museum
08489

Suomen Värimuseo (Finnish Paint Museum), Sankarikatu 12, 95410 Kemi - T: (016) 17122, 14813
Special Museum
08490

Kemijärvi

Kemijärven Kotiseutumuseo, Sepänkatu 4, 98120 Kemijärvi - T: (016) 21494, 21464. Head: Marita Liekonen
Local Museum
08491

Keminmaa

Keminmaan Museo, 94400 Keminmaa - T: (016) 23253, 53509
Local Museum
08492

Kempele

Kempeleen Kotiseutumuseo, 90440 Kempele - T: (08) 555222/441
Local Museum
08493

Kerava

Keravan Museo, Museopolku 1, 04200 Kerava - T: (09) 29492162/66, Fax: 29492082, E-mail: matti.karttunen@kerava.fi, Internet: http://www2.kerava.fi/index2.htm. Head: Matti Karttunen
Local Museum - 1957
Heikkilä farmhouse and outbuildings (18thc), domestic items and furnishings, agricultural equipment, handicrafts, photographs, local hist
08494

Keravan Taidemuseo (Kerava Art Museum), Klondyketalo, 04260 Kerava - T: (09) 2948090
Fine Arts Museum
08495

Kerimäki

Suomen Järvikalastusmuseo ja Kerimäen Ulkomuseoalue, Kirkonkylä, Puruvedentie 65, 58200 Kerimäki - T: (015) 57541. Head: Heikki Pylkkänen
Open Air Museum
08496

Kesälahti

Kesälahden Museo, 59800 Kesälahti - T: (015) 371087. Head: Kyllikki Paajanen
Local Museum
08497

Keuruu

Einari Vuorelan Kirjailijakoti (Vuorela's Author Home), Runoilijantie, Jukojärvi, 42791 Keuruu - T: (014) 7517276, Fax: 771872
Special Museum
08498

Keuruun Kotiseutumuseo (Keuruu Open Air Museum), Museotie 3, 42700 Keuruu - T: (014) 7512541, Fax: 7512542, Internet: http://www.keuruu.fi/matkailu/nahtavyydet. Head: Anna-Riikka Hirvonen
Open Air Museum - 1959
Early 19th c farm buildings, peasant household articles
08499

Keuruun Museo, Kamana, Kangasmannilantie 4, 42700 Keuruu - T: (014) 7512541, Fax: 7512542, E-mail: anna-riikka-hirvonen@keuruu.fi, Internet: http://www.keuruu.fi/matkailu/kamana/museo. Head: Anna-Riikka Hirvonen
Fine Arts Museum / Historical Museum
08500

Kihniö

Aitonevan Turvemuseo, 39829 Kihniö - T: (03) 49246, 49252
Local Museum
08501

Kihniön Museo (Open Air Museum), Kankarin Paikallistie, 39820 Kihniö - T: (03) 84391, 84252
Open Air Museum
08502

Kiihtelysvaara

Kiihtelysvaaran Museo, 82140 Kiihtelysvaara - T: (013) 79046
Local Museum
08503

Kiikala

Kiikalan Kotiseutumuseo, Porvarinpolku 10, 25390 Kiikala - T: (02) 7288200, Fax: 7288228, E-mail: riitta.manni@kiikaala.fi, Internet: http://www.kiikala.fi
Local Museum
08504

Kiikoinen

Kiikoisten Kotiseutumuseo, Torpparimuseum, 38360 Kiikoinen - T: (03) 531097, 531227
Local Museum
08505

Kiiminki

Kiimingin Museo, Toimisto Kunnanvirasto, 90900 Kiiminki - T: (08) 863111
Local Museum
08506

Kimito

Sagalunds Museum (Sagalund Museum), Museiv 7, 25700 Kimito - T: (02) 421738, Fax: 421847, E-mail: info@sagalund.fi, Internet: http://www.sagalund.fi. Head: Li Näse
Open Air Museum - 1900
Ethnography, cultural and school history, Linné coll, nautical books, teacher's quarters, courthouse and schoolbuilding, peasant buildings, archives building (18th and 19th c)
08507

Kinnula

Kinnulan Kotiseutumuseo, 43900 Kinnula - T: (014) 85307, 85512
Local Museum
08508

Kintaus

Keski-Suomen Tieliikennemuseo (The Road & Traffic Museum of Central Finland), Museotie 18, 41920 Kintaus - T: (014) 855199, 859511, Fax: 854271, E-mail: risto.raivio@petajavesi.fi. Head: Risto Raivio
Science&Tech Museum
08509

Kirkkonummi

Gesterbyn Kartano - Kirkkonummen Kunnan Museoalue (Gesterby Manor), Gesterby Tie, 02410 Kirkkonummi - T: (09) 2967263, 2981539, Internet: http://www.kirkkonummi.fi
Local Museum / Historic Site
Manor house, windmill, barn and smithy
08510

Hvitträsk, Hvitträskintie 166, 02440 Kirkkonummi - T: (09) 40509630, Fax: 40509631, E-mail: hvittrask@nba.fi, Internet: http://www.nba.fi
Fine Arts Museum / Decorative Arts Museum
Studio of the three architects Eliel Saarinen, Armas Lindgren and Herman Gesellius, designed (1903) in National Romantic style, interior, furniture, textile design, garden
08511

Kisko

Kiskon Kotiseutumuseo, Toimisto Kulttuurilautakunta, 25470 Kisko - T: (02) 391400
Local Museum
08512

Kitee

Kiteen Kotiseutumuseo, Kitee Local History and Crafts Museum, Kiteentie 23, 82500 Kitee - T: (013) 6841214, Fax: 411342, E-mail: matkailutoimisto@kitee.fi
Local Museum
08513

Kittilä

Kittilän Kotiseutumuseo, Pakattiojantie 1, 99100 Kittilä - T: (016) 642356, E-mail: riitta.maukonen@kittila.fi
Local Museum
08514

Kiuruvesi

Kiuruveden Kotiseutumuseo, Kirkkoharjuntie 2, 74700 Kiuruvesi - T: (017) 768111, 752613, Fax: 750222, Internet: http://www.iisalmi.fi/www/kiuruvesi/yleispal/elinkein/nahta/museo.html
Local Museum
08515

Kodisjoki

Kodisjoen Kotiseutumuseo, Toimisto Kunnanvirasto, 27310 Kodisjoki - T: (02) 42345
Local Museum
08516

Kokemäki

Kokemäen Maatalousmuseo (Kokemäki Agricultural Museum), 32800 Kokemäki - T: (03) 68627. Head: Esko Pertola
Agriculture Museum - 1925
Agricultural equipment, household articles, textiles, numismatics, documents, old literature, public granary (1838) 08517

Kokemäen Ulkomuseo (Kokemäki Open Air Museum), 32800 Kokemäki. Head: Esko Pertola
Open Air Museum - 1962
18 peasant buildings (17th-19th c), smithy (17th c), furnishings 08518

Kokkola

Historiallinen Museo ja Näyttelyhalli, Pitkänsillankatu 28, 67100 Kokkola - T: (06) 289474, 289476
Historical Museum 08519

Kaarlelan Kotiseutumuseo, Kirkkopolku 4, 67700 Kokkola - T: (06) 15578
Local Museum 08520

K.H. Renlundin Museo (K.H. Renlund Museum), Pitkänsillankatu 39, 67100 Kokkola 10 - T: (06) 8289474, Fax: 8289389. Head: Paul Stenman
Historical Museum - 1909
Articles connected with navigation, shipbuilding, trade, handicrafts, school and military history 08521

Luontomuseo (Nature Museum), Pitkänsillankatu 1-13, 67100 Kokkola - T: (06) 289497
Natural History Museum 08522

Taidemuseo, K.H. Renlund Museum (Art Museum), Pitkänsillankatu 39, 67100 Kokkola 10 - T: (06) 289474. Head: Paul Stenman
Fine Arts Museum - 1909
Finnish paintings, including works from Albert Edelfelt, Pekka Halonen and Magnus Enckell, Roos House (1813), Veikko Vionoja coll, Kerttu meriläinen Shilhouet coll 08523

Kolkanlahti

Säätyläiskotiseutumuseo (Upperclass Home Museum), 43250 Kolkanlahti - T: (014) 439688, 4291411, Fax: 455117, E-mail: museo@saarijarvi.fi
Local Museum 08524

Konginkangas

Konginkankaan Kotiseutumuseo, Konginkankaan Kunta, 44400 Konginkangas - T: (014) 5297308
Local Museum 08525

Konnevesi

Konneveden Kotiseutumuseo, Kauppatie 25, 44300 Konnevesi - T: (014) 559291, Fax: 559213, Internet: http://www.konnevesi.fi
Local Museum
Local history 08526

Kontiolahti

Kontiolahden Museo, 81100 Kontiolahti - T: (013) 731257
Local Museum 08527

Koria

Pioneerimuseo (Sapper Museum), Varuskunta, 45610 Koria - T: (05) 820321. Head: Jorma Viita
Military Museum - 1954
Field equipment from fortifications used in World War II in the Finnish front lines, sapper equipment, military uniforms, miniature models - library 08528

Korkeakoski

Kallenaution Kievari, Hyytiälä, 35500 Korkeakoski - T: (03) 81915, 48002
Local Museum 08529

Korpilahti

Korpilahden Kotiseutumuseo, 41800 Korpilahti - T: (014) 821126
Local Museum 08530

Korppoo

Korppoon Kotiseutumuseo, 21710 Korppoo - T: (02) 31246
Local Museum 08531

Korsnäs

Korsnäs Hembygdsmuseum, 66200 Korsnäs - T: (06) 641059
Local Museum 08532

Kvarnbackmuseet i Harrström (Windmill Museum), 66200 Korsnäs - T: (06) 645141. Head: Anita Svartgrund
Science&Tech Museum 08533

Kortesjärvi

Kortesjärven Museo, 62420 Kortesjärvi - T: (06) 85100, 85105
Local Museum 08534

Koski

Kosken Kotiseutumuseo, 16800 Koski - T: (03) 7641202, Fax: 7641345
Local Museum 08535

Yrjö Liipolan Taidekokoelma (Yrjö Liipola Art Collection), Museokaari, 31500 Koski - T: (02) 4841969, Fax: 48441511, E-mail: kosken.kunta@koski.fi, Internet: http://www.koski.fi. Head: Olli Urmas
Fine Arts Museum - 1968
Sculptures and drawings by Yrjö Liipola 08536

Kotka

Ahtausmuseo (Stevedoring Museum), Vuorikatu 2, 48100 Kotka - T: (05) 2344438, Fax: 2344277, E-mail: museo@kotka.fi, Internet: http://www.kotka.fi/museo. Head: Eira Karppinen
Special Museum 08537

Kymenlaakson maakuntamuseo (Provincial Museum of Kymenlaakso), Kotkankatu 13, 48100 Kotka 10 - T: (05) 2344438, Fax: 2344277, E-mail: museo@kotka.fi, Internet: http://www.kotka.fi/museo. Head: Eira Karppinen
Historical Museum - 1927
Objects connected with the naval battle of Ruotsinsalmi, maritime archaeology and life on the islands, hist of Ruotsinsalmi fort and Kotka, Icebreaker Tarmo and museum boat hall - photo archives 08538

Langingkoski Imperial Fishing Lodge, Langinkoski, 48230 Kotka - T: (05) 2281050, 2283300, Fax: 2283300. Head: Ragnar Backström
Historical Museum - 1933
Fishing lodge (1889) built for Czar Alexander III and Czarina Maria Feodorovna, furnishings, fishing equipment 08539

Kouvola

Apteekkimuseo (Pharmacy Museum), Varuskuntakatu 9, 45100 Kouvola - T: (05) 8296323, Fax: 3751605, E-mail: kaukiainen.heli@kouvola.fi, Internet: http://www.kouvola.fi/matkailija. Head: Heli Kaukiainen
Special Museum 08540

Kouvolan Taidemuseo (Art Museum of Kouvola), Varuskuntakatu 11, 45100 Kouvola - T: (05) 8296323, Fax: 3751605, E-mail: kaukiainen.heli@kouvala.fi, Internet: http://www.kouvola.fi/matkailija. Head:
Fine Arts Museum 08541

Nygrenin Talo, Kiskonraitti, Kaunisnurmi, 45100 Kouvola - T: (05) 296325
Local Museum 08542

Puolakan Talomuseo, Museomutka, 45100 Kouvola - T: (05) 8296323, Fax: 3751605, E-mail: kaukiainen.heli@kouvola.fi, Internet: http://www.kouvola.fi/matkailija
Ethnology Museum 08543

Putkiradiomuseo (Tube Receiver Museum), Pajaraitti 1, 45100 Kouvola - T: (05) 8296558
Science&Tech Museum 08544

Rautatieläiskotimuseo, Veturimiehenraitti 5, 45100 Kouvola - T: (05) 8296323, Fax: 3751605, E-mail: kaukiainen.heli@kouvola.fi, Internet: http://www.kouvola.fi/matkailija. Head: Heli Kaukiainen
Ethnology Museum 08545

Kovjoki

Kovjoki Museo, 66930 Kovjoki - T: (06) 18120
Local Museum 08546

Kråkö

Kråkö Båtbyggarmuseum (Boatbuilding Museum), Posti Thure Lindström, 07410 Kråkö - T: (019) 44009, 44002
Science&Tech Museum 08547

Kristiinankaupunki

Carlsro Museum, Carksrovägen 181, 64100 Kristiinankaupunki - T: (06) 2223144, 2216343, Fax: 2216241, E-mail: helena.karhu@krs.fi, Internet: http://www.krs.fi
Historical Museum 08548

Lebell Residence, Rantakatu 51, 64100 Kristiinankaupunki - T: (06) 2212159. Head: Carl-Anders Lundberg
Decorative Arts Museum / Folklore Museum - 1940
18th and 19th c Southern Ostrobothnian merchant's residence with furnishings, folk art 08549

Sjöfartsmuseet (Maritime Museum), Kauppatori 1, 64100 Kristiinankaupunki - T: (06) 2212859, 2216343, Fax: 2216241, E-mail: helena.karhu@krs.fi, Internet: http://www.krs.fi. Head: Jouni Harju
Historical Museum 08550

Kruunupyy

Tolvmansgården, Hopsala, 68500 Kruunupyy - T: (08) 45361
Local Museum 08551

Kuhmalahti

Kuhmalahden Kotiseutumuseo, 36810 Kuhmalahti - T: (03) 74132
Local Museum 08552

Kuhmo

Talvisotanäyttely, Kalevalakylä Hiitola, 88900 Kuhmo - T: (08) 6556368, Fax: 6556368
Military Museum 08553

Tuupalan Museo, Tervatie 1, 88900 Kuhmo - T: (08) 6556283
Local Museum 08554

Kuhmoinen

Kuhmoisten Kotiseutumuseo, Toritie 34a, 17800 Kuhmoinen - T: (03) 5521227, Fax: 5551340, E-mail: marja-leena.kovanen@kuhmoinen.fi. Head: Marja-Leena Kovanen
Local Museum 08555

Kuivaniemi

Kuivaniemen Kotiseutumuseo, Kirkkotie, 95100 Kuivaniemi - T: (016) 743308, 741095
Local Museum 08556

Kullaa

Kullaan Kotiseutumuseo, 29340 Kullaa - T: (02) 5591551, Fax: 5591302, E-mail: - kullaan.kotiseutuyhdistys@kotiseutumuseo.inet.fi
Local Museum 08557

Kuninkaankylä

Viirilän Kotiseutumuseo, 07980 Kuninkaankylä - T: (05) 78104
Local Museum 08558

Kuopio

J.V. Snellmanin Kotimuseo (J.V. Snellman Home Museum), Snellmaninkatu 19, 70100 Kuopio - T: (017) 182624, Fax: 182600, E-mail: kuopionmuseo.kut@kuopio.fi, Internet: http://www.kulttuuri.kuopio.fi/museo. Head: Tapio Laaksonen
Special Museum 08559

Kuopion Korttelimuseo (Old Kuopio Museum), Kirkkokatu 22, 70100 Kuopio - T: (017) 182625, Fax: 182630, E-mail: kuopionmuseo.kut@kuopio.fi, Internet: http://www.kulttuuri.kuopio.fi/korttelimuseo. Head: Tapio Laaksonen
Open Air Museum / Local Museum - 1972
Buildings and interiors of old Kuopio 08560

Kuopion Luonnontieteellinen Museo, Kuopion Kulttuurihistoriallinen Museo (Kuopio Natural History Museum), Kauppakatu 23, 70100 Kuopio, mail addr: Myhkyrinkatu 22, 70100 Kuopio - T: (017) 182652, Fax: 182654, E-mail: seija.kuronen@kuopio.fi, Internet: kuopio.fi/ymp/museo/i_museo.htm. Head: Dr. Matti Haapasaari
Natural History Museum / Ethnology Museum - 1897
Finnoscandinavian animals, plants, fungi, stones and minerals - library 08561

Kuopion Taidemuseo (Kuopio Art Museum), Kauppakatu 35, 70100 Kuopio - T: (017) 182633, Fax: 182642, Internet: http://www.kulttuuri.kuopio.fi/taidemuseo. Head: Aija Jaatinen
Fine Arts Museum 08562

Ortodoksinen Kirkkomuseo (Orthodox Church Museum of Finland), Karjalankatu 1, 70110 Kuopio 11 - T: (017) 2872244, Fax: 2872211, E-mail: church.museum@ort.fi, Internet: http://www.ort.fi/autonom/museo/museo.htm. Head: Kristina Thomenius
Religious Arts Museum - 1957
Icons, sacred objects, liturgical textiles, all objects from Finnish monasteries and churches, manuscripts - library, photo archive 08563

Savupirttimuseo (Smoke Cabin Museum), Pohjois-Savon Kansanopisto, Pitkälahti, 70800 Kuopio - T: (017) 3611334, Fax: 3616375
Special Museum
Chimneyless dwelling, built in 1821 08564

Kuortane

Klemettimuseo, 63100 Kuortane - T: (06) 54473
Local Museum 08565

Talomuseo, 63100 Kuortane - T: (06) 54473
Local Museum 08566

Kurikka

Kurikan Museo (Kurikka Museum), 61300 Kurikka 5 - T: (06) 52372. Head: Viljo Myllymäki
Local Museum - 1939
Agricultural and household articles, equipment and tools of carpenters, shoemakers, tailors, and constructors of musical instruments, objects pertaining to emigration to Canada and North America, films and photographs, farmhouse and cart maker's workshop 08567

Kuru

Kurun Ulkomuseo, Kauppatie 7-9, 34300 Kuru - T: (03) 3172
Local Museum 08568

Kustavi

Kustavin Kotiseutumuseo, Etelä-Varstala, 23360 Kustavi - T: (02) 37522
Local Museum 08569

Kuusamo

Kuusamon Kotiseutumuseo, Kitronintie, 93600 Kuusamo - T: (08) 2046027
Local Museum 08570

Kuusankoski

Kettumäen Ulkomuseo ja Kotiseututalo (Kettumäki Local History Museum), Kettumäki, 45700 Kuusankoski - T: (05) 46822
Local Museum - 1957
Local history collection, ethnographical objects, farm dwellings and school building (19th c) 08571

Palomuseo (Fire Museum), Kansantie, 45701 Kuusankoski - T: (05) 404464, 4043365
Science&Tech Museum 08572

Työväenasuntomuseo (Workers' Museum), Kettumäki, 45701 Kuusankoski - T: (05) 404336, 404306
Historical Museum 08573

Kuusjoki

Iloniemen Pajamuseo, Raatala, 25330 Kuusjoki - T: (02) 842073
Local Museum 08574

Kvevlax

Kvevlax Hembygdsmuseum, Koivulahden Kirkolla, 66530 Kvevlax - T: (06) 360105
Local Museum 08575

Kyyjärvi

Kyyjärven Kotiseutumuseo, 43700 Kyyjärvi - T: (014) 71284
Local Museum 08576

Längelmäki

Längelmäen Kirkkomuseo, 35480 Längelmäki - T: (03) 31255, 33433
Religious Arts Museum 08577

Länkipohja

Längelmäen Pellavamuseo (Linen Museum), 35400 Länkipohja - T: (03) 51215
Special Museum 08578

Lahti

Askon Museo, Askonkatu 3, 15101 Lahti - T: (03) 81511, 8152246, Fax: 8152301, E-mail: tanja.paksunen@askokiinteistot.fi
Special Museum
History of Asko (f. in 1918) and Upo (f. in 1938) fctories, industrial-made design furniture 08579

Hiihtomuseo, Lahden Kaupunginmuseo (Ski Museum), Urheilukeskus, Vuorikatu 27, 15110 Lahti 11, mail addr: PL 113, 15111 Lahti - T: (03) 8144520/23, Fax: 8144525, E-mail: museo@lahti.fi, Internet: http://www.lahti.fi/kulttuuri/museot. Head: Jouko Heinonen
Special Museum - 1974
Old skis, stamps, trophies - library 08580

Julistemuseo, Lahden Kaupunginmuseo (Lahti Poster Museum), Vesijärvenkatu 11u 27, 15111 Lahti - T: (03) 8144546, 01, Fax: 8144545, E-mail: museo@lahti.fi, Internet: http://www.lahti.fi/kulttuuri/museot/juliste
Special Museum
Finnish posters since 1900, foreign poster since 1970's 08581

Lahden Historiallinen Museo, Lahden Kaupunginmuseo (Lahti Historical Museum), Lahdenkatu 4, 15110 Lahti 11, mail addr: PL 113, 15111 Lahti - T: (03) 8144534/36, Fax: 8144535, E-mail: museo@lahti.fi, Internet: http://www.lahti.fi/kulttuuri/museot. Head: Jouko Heinonen
Historical Museum - 1914
Local collections, peasant furniture, coins, modern Finnish medals, French and Italian paintings, sculpture and furniture from the Middle Ages to the 18th c - library 08582

Lahden Kaupunginmuseo (Lahti City Museum), Vuorikatu 27, 15110 Lahti, mail addr: PL 113, 15111 Lahti - T: (03) 8144500, Fax: 8144505, E-mail: museo@lahti.fi, Internet: http://www.lahti.fi/kulttuuri/museot. Head: Jouko Heinonen
Local Museum 08583

Lahden Taidemuseo (Lahti Art Museum), Vesijärvenkatu 11, 15140 Lahti, mail addr: PL 113, 15111 Lahti - T: (03) 8144542/47, Fax: 8144545, E-mail: museo@lahti.fi, Internet: http://www.lahti.fi/kulttuuri/museot. Head: Jouko Heinonen
Fine Arts Museum - 1949
Modern Finnish paintings, graphics, drawings, posters - library 08584

Radio- ja TV-Museo (Radio and TV Museum), Radiomäki, 15110 Lahti 11, mail addr: PL 113, 15111 Lahti - T: (03) 81410, 8144511/12, Fax: 8144515, E-mail: museo@lahti.fi, Internet: http://www.lahti.fi/kulttuuri/museot. Head: Jouko Heinonen
Science&Tech Museum - 1968
History of Finnish broadcasting and radio technology 08585

Sotilaslääketieteen Museo (Museum of Military Medicine), PL 5, 15701 Lahti - T: (03) 7824844, 18146111, Fax: 18146297, E-mail: jorma.jokela@kolumbus.fi, Internet: http://www.lahti.fi/kulttuuri/museot/sotilaslaaketieteenmuseo. Head: Jorma Jokela
Military Museum 08586

Laihia

Laihian Kirkkomuseo (Church Museum), 66400 Laihia - T: (06) 770098
Religious Arts Museum 08587

Laihian Museo, Kupparla, 66400 Laihia - T: (06) 771050
Local Museum 08588

Laitila

Kaariaisten Mäkitupalaismuseo, Ojanperä, 23800 Laitila - T: (02) 53234, 41700
Local Museum 08589

Kaivolan Museo, Kaivola, 23800 Laitila - T: (02) 52623, 52733
Local Museum 08590

Kauppilan Umpipiha, Koukkela, 23800 Laitila - T: (02) 855208, 85011, Fax: 856790, E-mail: jokka.rehmas@laitila.fi, Internet: http://www.laitila.fi
Open Air Museum 08591

Nolhin Torppa, Pato, 23800 Laitila - T: (02) 53938, 53033
Local Museum 08592

Untamalan Kotiseutumuseo, Untamala, 23800 Laitila - T: (02) 54335, 54762
Local Museum 08593

Lammi

Kotiseutumuseo Pellava ja Sahti Lammin Ajokalumuseo, 16900 Lammi - T: (03) 32544
Local Museum 08594

Lapinjärvi Porlammi

Porlammin Kotiseutumuseo (Porlammi Local History Museum), Porlammi, 07820 Lapinjärvi Porlammi - T: (019) 62051, 62033. Head: Anja Varjola
Local Museum - 1943
Peasant culture, public granary and croft (19th c) 08595

Lapinkylä

Alisgården, 02520 Lapinkylä - T: (09) 264776, 266296
Local Museum 08596

Lapinlahti

Halosen Museo → Lapinlahden Taidemuseo ja Eemil Halonen Museo

Lapinlahden Taidemuseo ja Eemil Halonen Museo, Halonten Museosäätiö (Eemil Halonen Museum and Museum of Modern Art), Suistamontie 3, 73100 Lapinlahti - T: (017) 732288, Fax: 733178, E-mail: lltm@eemil.inet.fi. Head: Olli Lähdesmäki
Fine Arts Museum - 1973
Works by the sculptor Eemil Halonen (1875-1950), Arne Paldanius collection, two slide collections, modern Finnish art, art park surrounding the art center and Eemil Halonen Museum - library 08597

Lappeenranta

Etelä-Karjalan Museo, Kristiinankatu 15, 53101 Lappeenranta - T: (05) 6162255, Fax: 6162911, E-mail: museot@lappeenranta.fi, Internet: http://www.lappeenranta.fi/museot. Head: Olli Immonen
Local Museum - 1963
Miniature model of Viipuri (Vyborg) in 1939, now in Russia 08598

Etelä-Karjalan Taidemuseo (South Carelian Artmuseum), Linnoitus, 53100 Lappeenranta - T: (05) 6162256, Fax: 6162911, 6162253, Internet: http://www.lappeenranta.fi/museot. Head: Olli Immonen
Fine Arts Museum - 1965
Finnish art, since 1850, changing exhibitions 08599

Kymen Läänin Aluetaidemuseo, Etelä-Karjalan Taidemuseo (Regional Art Museum of the Kymi Province), Kristiinankatu 8-10, 53101 Lappeenranta - T: (05) 6162256, Fax: 6162911, Internet: http://www.lappeenranta.fi/museot. Head: Olli Immonen
Fine Arts Museum - 1965
Finnish art, since 1850, changing exhibitions 08600

Laura Korpikaivo Tammisen Käsityömuseo, Etelä-Karjalan Museo (Handicraft Museum), Kantokatu 1, 53100 Lappeenranta - T: (05) 6162270, 2261, Fax: 6162911. Head: Leena Stenberg
Decorative Arts Museum - 1983
Finnish textile art and craftmanship 08601

Ratsuväkimuseo, Etelä-Karjalan Museo (Cavalry Museum), Kristiinankatu 2, 53900 Lappeenranta, mail addr: PL 239, 53101 Lappeenranta - T: (05) 6162257, Fax: 6162911, E-mail: museot@lappeenranta.fi, Internet: http://www.lappeenranta.fi/museot. Head: Olli Immonen
Military Museum - 1973
Cavalry uniforms and equipment, photograph collection 08602

Saimaan Kanavan Museo (Saimaa Canal Museum), Sulkuvartijankatu 16, 53300 Lappeenranta - T: 0204483115, 0204483104, Fax: 0204483110, E-mail: paivi.vattulainen@fma.fi, Internet: http://www.fma.fi/saimaacanal/kanavamuseo
Science&Tech Museum 08603

Wolkoffin Talomuseo, Etelä-Karjalan Museo (Wolkoff House Museum), Kauppakatu 26, 53101 Lappeenranta - T: (05) 6162258, Fax: 6162911, E-mail: museot@lappeenranta.fi, Internet: http://www.lappeenranta.fi/museot. Head: Olli Immonen
Local Museum - 1993
The Wolkoff family lived in the house from 1870s to 1983 and all of their personal belongings and their home is exhibited 08604

Lappi

Lapin Tl. Kotiseutumuseo, 27230 Lappi - T: (02) 8261619
Local Museum 08605

Lappoby-Åland

Skärgårdsmuseet (Museum of the Archipelago), 22840 Lappoby-Åland - T: (018) 56689, Fax: 56689, Internet: http://www.kulturfonden.fi/skargardsmuseet
Ethnology Museum
Fishermen's tools, ethnographics 08606

Lapua

Ränkimäen Ulkomuseo, Ränkimäentie, 62100 Lapua - T: (06) 4384580, 4331364, E-mail: esa.sivonen@city.lapua.fi. Head: Esa Sivonen
Open Air Museum 08607

Larsmo

Larsmo Hembygdsmuseum, 68570 Larsmo - T: (06) 81017
Local Museum 08608

Laukaa

Museokylä Kalluntalo (Kalluntalo Museum), 41340 Laukaa - T: (014) 831342. Head: Paavo Tammenoksa
Local Museum - 1959
Peasant dwellings, two 'church boats', school equipment, farm buildings, windmill, public granary 08609

Lavia

Lavian Kotiseutumuseo, 38600 Lavia - T: (03) 571883
Local Museum 08610

Lehtimäki

Lehtimäen Museo, 63500 Lehtimäki - T: (06) 71115
Local Museum 08611

Lemi

Lemin Kotiseutumuseo, Lemi Heritage Museum, Viinikkalantie 6, 54710 Lemi - T: (05) 4146370, Fax: 4146497. Head: Pertti Haiko
Local Museum 08612

Lempäälä

Kuokkalan Museoraitti, 37550 Lempäälä - T: (03) 752643
Local Museum 08613

Rantalan Riihimuseo (Threshing Museum), 37500 Lempäälä - T: (03) 751028, 752872
Agriculture Museum 08614

Sotavallan Tuulimylly, 37500 Lempäälä - T: (03) 751028, 752872
Local Museum 08615

Tapulimuseo, 37500 Lempäälä - T: (03) 750822, 751028
Local Museum 08616

Lemu

Lemun Kotiseutumuseo, 21230 Lemu - T: (02) 716704
Local Museum 08617

Leppäkoski

Ida Aalbergin Lapsuudenkoti (Ida Aalberg's CXhildhood Home), 12380 Leppäkoski - T: (03) 6801280
Local Museum
Childhood home of the actress Ida Aalberg (19th c) 08618

Leppävirta

Leppävirran Kotiseutumuseo (Leppävirta Local History Museum), 79100 Leppävirta - T: (017) 4092210, 40921. Head: Kari Viinikainen
Local Museum - 1956
Ethnographical material, mining equipment and minerals connected with the Kotalahti nickel mine, samples of the art of precision forging in Sorsakoski factory, wooden public granary 08619

Lestijärvi

Lestijärven Kotiseutumuseo, 69440 Lestijärvi - T: (06) 637274
Local Museum 08620

Liedenpohja

Liedenpohjan Museo, 34930 Liedenpohja - T: (03) 561151
Local Museum 08621

Lieksa

Pielisen Museo, Pappilantie 2, 81720 Lieksa 2 - T: (013) 6894151, Fax: 6894916, E-mail: museo@lieksa.fi, Internet: http://www.lieksa.fi/lieksa/matkailu/museo.htm. Head: Hilke Liisa Himanen
Open Air Museum - 1948
18th-20th c farm buildings, croft, water- and windmills, agriculture, forestry, ethnographic material from the district - archives 08622

Lieto

Nautalankosken Museo, Nautelankoskentie 40, 21360 Lieto - T: (02) 4892400, Fax: 4892413, E-mail: museo@nautelankoski.net, Internet: http://www.nautelankoski.net. Head: Leena Viskari
Historical Museum 08623

Liljendal

Embom-Garpom Backstugusittarstuga, Posti Garpom, 07880 Liljendal - T: (019) 66030, 66324
Local Museum 08624

Liljendal Hembygdsmuseum, Sävträsk, 07880 Liljendal - T: (019) 66559, 66459
Local Museum 08625

Lillby

Kulturgården på Lassfolk, Lillbyvägen, 68940 Lillby - T: (06) 7271198, 7271121. Head: Per Sjöskog
Folklore Museum 08626

Liminka

Abraham Ojanperän Museo, Rantatie, 91900 Liminka - T: (08) 5203655, Fax: 5203612, E-mail: raija.palsa@liminka.fi, Internet: http://www.liminka.fi. Head: Raija Palsa
Local Museum 08627

Lampi-Museo (Lampi Museum), Rantatie, 91900 Liminka - T: (08) 5203655, Fax: 5203612, E-mail: raija.palsa@liminka.fi, Internet: http://www.liminka.fi. Head: Raija Palsa
Fine Arts Museum - 1972
Finnish art, works of Vilho Lampi, Tyko Sallinen, Marcus Collin, Ellen Thesleff, modern art from Northern Finland, former school building (1868) 08628

Limingan Kotiseutumuseo, Rantatie, 91900 Liminka - T: (08) 5203655, Fax: 5203612
Local Museum 08629

Liperi

Enwald-Museo, Tuomelan Talo, Maatalousmuseo, Koulutie, 83100 Liperi. Head: Juhani Kosonen
Local Museum 08630

Littoinen

Kaarinan Koulumuseo (School Museum), Nipsikatu 1, 20660 Littoinen - T: (02) 2461047, 2462213. Head: Jukka A. Tamminen
Special Museum 08631

Liuksiala

Liuksialan Maatalousmuseo (Agricultural Museum), 5 km Kirkolta Valkeakosken Suuntaan, 36200 Liuksiala - T: (03) 771004
Agriculture Museum 08632

Lohiranta

Posion Kotiseutumuseo, Kitkajärven Eteläranta, 97940 Lohiranta - T: (016) 424216
Local Museum 08633

Lohja

Lohjan Museo, Iso-Pappila, 08100 Lohja - T: (019) 3204201, Fax: 3204326. Head: Eero Ahtela, Eira Mikkola Huk
Local Museum 08634

Tytyrin Kalkkikaivosmuseo (Limestone Mine Museum), 08100 Lohja - T: (019) 201218
Science&Tech Museum 08635

Lohtaja

Lohtajan Kotiseutumuseo, 68230 Lohtaja - T: (06) 8812111, Fax: 8812217, E-mail: lohtajan.kirjasto@lohtaja.fi, Internet: http://www.lohtaja.fi
Local Museum 08636

Loimaa

Loimaan Kotiseutumuseo, 32210 Loimaa - T: (02) 27312, 86156
Local Museum 08637

Vesikosken Mylly, Hirvikoskentie, 32200 Loimaa - T: (02) 203288
Local Museum 08638

Lokalahti

Lottan Torppa, Lokalahti kk, 23450 Lokalahti - T: (02) 70346
Local Museum 08639

Loppi

Kotiseutumuseo Lukkarin Puustelli (Verger's Museum), 12700 Loppi - T: (019) 40450
Local Museum 08640

Loviisa

Loviisan Kaupungin Museo (Loviisa Town Museum), Puistokatu 2, 07900 Loviisa - T: (019) 555357, Fax: 535791, E-mail: pia.wilhelmson@loviisa.fi, Internet: http://www.loviisa.fi. Head: Pia Wilhelmson
Local Museum - 1904
Articles dealing with the history of Loviisa, military history, navigation, commerce, costumes, furniture, tin collection and workshop, stationer's shop (19th c), commandant's residence (1775) 08641

Lovisa

Hardom Sädesmagasin och Stenkulla Torp, Pl 245a, 07900 Lovisa - T: (019) 562115, 60340
Local Museum 08642

Lurens, Pl 245a, 07900 Lovisa - T: (019) 562114
Local Museum 08643

Luopioinen

Luopioisten Museo (Luopioinen Museum), 36760 Luopioinen - T: (03) 61141
Open Air Museum - 1952
Wooden public granary and croft museum area containing 18th-19th c buildings, windmill (1867) 08644

Luopioisten Torpparimuseo, Mikkelinmäki, 36760 Luopioinen - T: (03) 61145
Local Museum 08645

Luumäki

Kotkaniemi - Presidentti P.E. Svinhufvudin koti (Kotkaniemi - The Home of President P.E. Svinhufvud), Lappeenrannantie 455, 54530 Luumäki - T: (05) 4573101, Fax: 40509579, Internet: http://www.nba.fi. Head: Lea Värtinen
Historical Museum - 2000
20th c interior, furnishing and household articles, home of Presiden of Finland Pehr Evind Svinhufvud (1861 - 1944) 08646

Luusua

Luusuan Kylämuseo, 98230 Luusua - T: (016) 87185
Local Museum 08647

Luvia

Luvian Kotiseutumuseo, Hanninkylä, 29100 Luvia - T: (03) 581070
Local Museum 08648

Lyly

Lylyn Viestivarikon Museo (Lyly Signal Depot Museum), Varikontie 235, 35531 Lyly - T: (03) 18156111, E-mail: lyvv@mil.fi
Military Museum 08649

Mäntsälä

Mäntsälän Kotiseutumuseo, 04600 Mäntsälä - T: (019) 6890214, Fax: 6890276, E-mail: sepanmaki@mantsala.fi, Internet: http://www.mantsala.fi. Head: Sirkku Mäkelä
Local Museum 08650

Sepänmäen Käsityömuseo (Sepänmäki Handicraft Museum), 04600 Mäntsälä - T: (019) 6890214, Fax: 6890276, E-mail: sepanmaki@mantsala.fi, Internet: http://www.mantsala.fi. Head: Sirkku Mäkelä
Open Air Museum - 1969
Smithy, shoemaker's and tailor's workshops, repair shop for bicycles and cars 08651

Mänttä

Gösta Serlachiuksen Taidemuseo (Gösta Serlachius Museum of Fine Arts), Joenniemi Manor, 35800 Mänttä - T: (03) 4745515, Fax: 4748260, E-mail: maritta.pitkanen@serlachiusartmuseum.fi, Internet: http://www.serlachiusartmuseum.fi. Head: Maritta Pitkänen
Fine Arts Museum - 1945
19th and early 20th c Finnish art, works of Akseli Gallen-Kallela, Albert Edelfelt, Helene Schjerfbeck, Hugo Simberg, Wäinö Aaltonen and Hannes Autere, works of Italian and Spanish Renaissance and baroque masters, coll of 17th c Dutch art, works of Ribera, Zurbaran, Eeckhout, Vrancx, Fragonard and Ruysdael - library, archives 08652

Mäntyharju

Mäntyharjun Museo (Mäntyharju Museum), 52710 Mäntyharju - T: (015) 95621/870
Local Museum / Ethnology Museum - 1970
Ethnography and cultural history, Mäntyharju Mansion (1811) 08653

Malax

Brinkens Museum, 66100 Malax - T: (06) 3654344, E-mail: siri@pp.inet.fi. Head: Siri Hagback
Open Air Museum 08654

Kvarkens Båtmuseum (Boat Museum), Åminne, 66100 Malax - T: (06) 3651123, E-mail: goran.stromfors@pp.inet.fi. Head: Göran Strömfors
Special Museum 08655

Mariehamn

Ålands Konstmuseum (Åland Art Museum), PL 60, 22101 Mariehamn - T: (018) 25426, Fax: 17440, E-mail: konst.info@aland-museum.aland.fi, Internet: http://www.aland-museum.aland.fi/konst. Head: Julia von Hellens
Fine Arts Museum - 1963
Art of the Åland Islands 08656

Ålands Museum, Stadshusparken, 22100 Mariehamn - T: (018) 25000, Fax: 17440, E-mail: info@aland-museum.aland.fi, Internet: http://www.aland-museum.aland.fi. Head: Kjell Ekström
Local Museum - 1934
Prehist, cultural hist, hist, art - library, film and multivision center 08657

Ålands Sjöfartsmuseum (Åland Maritime Museum), Hamngatan 2, 22101 Mariehamn - T: (018) 19930, Fax: 19936, E-mail: staff@maritime-museum.aland.fi, Internet: http://www.maritime-museum.aland.fi. Head: Henrik Karlsson
Science&Tech Museum / Historical Museum - 1954
Ships, tools, photo exhibition from old times - library 08658

Museifartyget Pommern (The Museumship Pommern), PL 5, 22101 Mariehamn - T: (018) 531421, 531420, Fax: 531479, E-mail: pommern@mariehamn.aland.fi, Internet: http://www.pommern.aland.fi. Head: Jyrki Abrahamsson
Science&Tech Museum 08659

Önningebymuseet (Önningeby Colony Museum), Önningeby 31, 22100 Mariehamn - T: (018) 33710, Fax: 33804, E-mail: kjell.ekstrom@aland.fi, Internet: http://www.aland-museum.aland.fi/onningeby/museum.html. Head: Kjell Ekström
Fine Arts Museum - 1992
Art by the artists around Victor Westerholm and his colony 1886-1914 08660

Marttila

Marttilan Kirkkomuseo, 21490 Marttila - T: (02) 768134
Religious Arts Museum 08661

Marttilan Kotiseutumuseo, Marttilan Kunta, 21490 Marttila - T: (02) 845256
Local Museum 08662

Masku

Maskun Museo, Maskuntie, 21250 Masku - T: (02) 4388260, Fax: 4320464, E-mail: pekka.karenmaa@masku.fi, Internet: http://www.masku.fi/vapaaaika/kultuuri
Local Museum 08663

Mellilä

Mellilän Museoriihi (Threshing Museum), 32300 Mellilä - T: (02) 27312, 86156
Agriculture Museum 08664

Merijärvi

Merijärven Kotiseutumuseo, 86220 Merijärvi - T: (08) 71443
Local Museum 08665

Merikarvia

Matilda Roslin-Kalliolan Kirjailijakoti, 29900 Merikarvia - T: (02) 540333, Fax: 5512074, Internet: http://www.merikarvia.fi
Local Museum 08666

Merikarvian Kalastusmuseo (Fishing Museum), Toimisto Kunnanvirasto, 29900 Merikarvia - T: (02) 540333, Fax: 5512074, Internet: http://www.merikarvia.fi
Historical Museum 08667

Miehikkälä

Salpalinja-Museo (Bunker Museum), 49700 Miehikkälä - T: (05) 74901, Fax: 7490219
Military Museum 08668

Suur-Miehikkälän Kylämuseo, Suur-Miehikkälä, 49700 Miehikkälä - T: (05) 77270
Local Museum 08669

Mietoinen

Tavastilan Kotiseutumuseo, 23120 Mietoinen - T: (02) 711942
Local Museum 08670

Mikkeli

Harjukosken Vesimylly (Water Mill), 30 km Mikkelistä, Ihastjärvelle, 50600 Mikkeli - T: (05) 18881
Science&Tech Museum 08671

Jalkaväkimuseo (Infantry Museum), Jääkärinkatu 6-8, 50100 Mikkeli - T: (015) 369666, Fax: 369666. Head: Reijo Mäkeläinen
Military Museum 08672

Kirkkomuseo (Stone Sacristy), Porrassalmenkatu 32a, 50100 Mikkeli, mail addr: Hallituskatue 8e, 50100 Mikkeli - T: (05) 1942424, Fax: 366161, E-mail: pentti.nousiainen@mikkeli.fi, pirjo.julkunen@mikkeli.fi, Internet: http://www.mikkeli.fi/palvelut/museot/sakasti.htm. Head: Pirjo Julkunen
Religious Arts Museum - 1931
Objects from nearby churches 08673

Mikkelin Taidemuseo (Mikkeli Art Museum), Ristimäenkatu 5, 50100 Mikkeli 10, mail addr: Hallituskatu 8e, 50100 Mikkeli - T: (015) 1942424, Fax: 366161, Internet: http://www.mikkeli.fi/palvelut/museot/taide.htm. Head: Pirjo Julkunen
Fine Arts Museum - 1970
Johannes Haapasalo's sculptures, Martti Airion art coll 08674

Päämajamuseo (Headquarters Museum), Päämajankuja 1-3, 50100 Mikkeli 10, mail addr: Hallituskatu 8e, 50100 Mikkeli - T: (015) 1942424, Fax: 366161, E-mail: pentti.nousiainen@mikkeli.fi, pirjo.julkunen@mikkeli.fi, Internet: http://www.mikkeli.fi/palvelut/museot/paamaja.htm. Head: Pirjo Julkunen
Military Museum - 1974
Headquarters of Marshall C.G. Mannerheim during World War II 08675

Suur-Savon Museo, Otavankatu 11, 50100 Mikkeli 10, mail addr: Hallituskatu 8e, 50100 Mikkeli - T: (015) 1942424, Fax: 366161, E-mail: -pentti.nousiainen@mikkeli.fi, Internet: http://www.mikkeli.fi/palvelut/museot/suursavo.htm. Head: Pirjo Julkunen
Local Museum / Ethnology Museum - 1912
Local history, ethnography 08676

Viestikeskus Lokki (Communications Centre Lokki), Naisvuori, Vuorikatu/Ristimäenkatu, 50100 Mikkeli - T: (015) 1942429
Military Museum
Second World War communication centre 08677

Möhkö

Möhkön Ruukkimuseo, Ilomantsin Museosäätiö (Möhkö Ironworks Museum), Möhköntie 209, 82980 Möhkö - T: (013) 6893192, 844111, Fax: 6893910, E-mail: ulla.vartiainen@ilomantsi.fi, Internet: http://www.pogosta.com/mohkonruukki. Head: Ulla Vartiainen
Historical Museum
Iron making, logging traditions, Möhkö during WW I 08678

Muhniemi

Korvenkylän Nuorisoseuran Museo (Youth Club Museum), Korvenkylä, 46960 Muhniemi - T: (05) 3675079
Special Museum
Farming implements 08679

Muhos

Muhoksen Kotiseutumuseo, 91500 Muhos - T: (08) 5334200, Fax: 5330433, E-mail: Pirkko.Tiepuoli@muhos.fi
Local Museum 08680

Multia

Multian Kotiseutumuseo, Museotie 2, 42600 Multia - T: (014) 752124, 754111, Fax: 754211, E-mail: multia.kunta@multia.fi, Internet: http://www.multia.fi/multian.kylat. Head: Kalevi Hakasalo
Local Museum 08681

Uitamonkosken Myllymuseo, Tie 627, 3 km Multian Keskustasta, 42600 Multia - T: (014) 752124, 754111, Fax: 754211, E-mail: multia.kunta@multia.fi, Internet: http://www.multia.fi/multiankylaet. Head: Kalevi Hakasalo
Local Museum 08682

Munsala

Finlands Svenska Skolmuseum (School Museum), Storsved, 66950 Munsala - T: (06) 20854
Special Museum 08683

Munsala Hembygdsmuseum, 66950 Munsala - T: (06) 44529
Local Museum 08684

Muonio

Muonion Kotiseutumuseo, Lahenrannantie 51, 99300 Muonio, mail addr: PL 25, 99301 Muonio - T: (016) 534315, Fax: 534320, E-mail: maritta.vimpari@muonio.fi, Internet: http://www.muonio.fi. Head: Maritta Vimpari
Local Museum 08685

Mustiala

Mustialan Maataloushistoriallinen Museo (Mustiala Agricultural Museum), Mustialantie 105, 31310 Mustiala - T: (03) 6465519, Fax: 6465500, E-mail: mustiala@qhamk.fi, Internet: http://www.mustiala.hamk.fi. Head: Ari Mikkola
Agriculture Museum 08686

Muurla

Muurlan Kotiseutumuseo (Muurla Arts and Crafts Museum), Muurlantie, 25130 Muurla - T: (02) 7281100, Fax: 7281111, E-mail: hanna-maija-saarimaa@hammas-syke.finnet.fi, Internet: http://www.muurla.fi. Head: Hanna-Maija Saarimaa
Folklore Museum 08687

Muuruvesi

Muuruveden Kotiseutumuseo, 73460 Muuruvesi - T: (017) 621490
Local Museum 08688

Mynämäki

Karjalan Kotiseutumuseo, 23100 Mynämäki - T: (02) 709041
Local Museum 08689

Korvensuun Museo (closed) 08690

Korvensuun Voimalaitos- ja Konepajamuseo (Power Station- and Engineering Museum), Korvensuu, 23100 Mynämäki - T: (02) 4310283, Fax: 4376619, E-mail: matti.nepponen@mynamaki.fi, Internet: http://www.mynamaki.fi. Head: Tiina Sivusaari
Science&Tech Museum 08691

Munnuisten Museo (closed) 08692

Myrskylä

Myrskylän Kotiseutumuseo, 07600 Myrskylä - T: (019) 70211, 70249
Local Museum 08693

Naantali

Maatilamuseo Luhdinsola (Farm Museum), Lapilantie, Luonnonmaa, 21100 Naantali - T: (02) 759172
Agriculture Museum 08694

Naantalin Museo (Naantali Museum), Katinhäntä 1, 21100 Naantali - T: (02) 4345321, Fax: 4345433. Head: Marja Salkoranta
Local Museum - 1920
Town history, home furnishings, textiles, silversmith work, carpentry, atifacts of the 15th c nunnery at Naantali, numismatics, three wooden town residences with outbuildings (18th-19th c) 08695

Naarva

Asesepän Paja (Narva Gunsmith's Shop), 81470 Naarva - T: (013) 21707
Science&Tech Museum 08696

Närpes

Närpes Hembygdsmuseum, Kaskövägen 23, 64200 Närpes - T: (06) 2249111, Fax: 2241285. Head: Peter Andersén
Special Museum - 1955
pharmacy museum 08697

Öjskogsparkens Museiområde, 64200 Närpes - T: (06) 41221
Open Air Museum 08698

Nakkila

Nakkilan Kotiseutumuseo, Juustomeijerimuseo (Cheesemaking-Museum), 29250 Nakkila - T: (03) 374557
Special Museum 08699

Nampa

Alanamman Koulumuseo (School Museum), 97520 Nampa - T: (016) 293377
Special Museum 08700

Nastola

Nastolan Kotiseutumuseo, Anttilantie 7, 15560 Nastola - T: (03) 885111, Fax: 8851207, E-mail: nastolan.kunta@nastola.fi
Local Museum 08701

Nauvo

Nagu hembyggdsmuseum/Nauvon Kotiseutumuseo, Local Heritage Museum of Nagu/Nauvo, 21660 Nauvo - T: (02) 4654382
Local Museum 08702

Nedervetil

Nedervetil Hembygdsgård, Klockarbacken, 64410 Nedervetil - T: (06) 48567
Local Museum 08703

Nickby

Sibbesgården, Gästerby, 04130 Nickby - T: (09) 237004, 234046
Local Museum 08704

Sibbo Jordbruksmuseum (Agricultural Museum), Posti Hembygdsforskningsför. Borgby, 04130 Nickby - T: (09) 237004, 237017
Agriculture Museum 08705

Niemisjärvi

Pienmäen Talomuseo (Pienmäki Farm Buildings Museum), 41490 Niemisjärvi - T: (014) 845497, 624928, Fax: 624936, E-mail: ksmuseo.info@jkl.fi, Internet: http://www.jkl.fi/ksmuseo. Head: Risto Koskinen
Open Air Museum - 1969
Farmhouse and outbuildings, 18th-19th c interiors 08706

Niinisalo

Kankaanpään Kaupunginmuseo, 38840 Niinisalo - T: (02) 5787454, Fax: 5787459, E-mail: kaupunginmuse@kankaanpaa.fi, Internet: http://www.pori.fi/art/satakunta. Head: Leena Sivula
Local Museum 08707

Nilsiä

Nilsiän Kotiseutumuseo, Nilsiän Simola, 73300 Nilsiä - T: (017) 431022/316
Local Museum 08708

Nivala

Kyösti- ja Kalervo Kallion Museo, Ruojantie 11, 85500 Nivala - T: (08) 440814, 440346, Fax: 4439220, E-mail: nivala-seura@nivala-lehti.fi, Internet: http://www.nivala-lehti.fi
Historical Museum / Fine Arts Museum
Coll of Kalervo Kallio's sculptures, coll of President Kyösti Kallio's life 08709

Nivalan Museo Katvala (Nivala Museum Katvala), 85500 Nivala - T: (08) 4439200, Fax: 4439220, E-mail: nivala-seura@nivala-lehti.fi, Internet: http://www.nivala-lehti.fi
Folklore Museum / Decorative Arts Museum - 1936
Furnishings, household objects, precentor's house with outbuildings 08710

Nokia

Nokian Kotiseutumuseo (Nokia Local History Museum and Museum of Workers' Homes), Nokianvaltatie, 37100 Nokia - T: (03) 414030
Open Air Museum - 1954
Furnishings, household articles, agricultural equipment, Hinttala military residence and outbuildings, workers' homes (early 19th c) 08711

Noormarkku

Kotiseututalo, 29600 Noormarkku - T: (03) 550356
Open Air Museum 08712

Nousiainen

Nousiaisten Kotiseutumuseo, Nousiainen kk, 21270 Nousiainen - T: (02) 715256
Local Museum 08713

Topoisten Ulkomuseoalue, Topoinen, 21270 Nousiainen - T: (02) 715265
Open Air Museum 08714

Nukari

Nukarin Koulumuseo (School Museum), Nukarin Kylä, 05450 Nukari - T: (09) 20881
Special Museum 08715

Nummi

Nummen Kotiseutumuseo, Nummi kk, 09810 Nummi - T: (019) 73118
Local Museum 08716

Numminen

Alikartano (Alikartano Manor), Nummistentie 48, 04660 Numminen - T: (019) 6883398, Fax: 40509579, Internet: http://www.nba.fi. Head: Lea Värtinen
Historical Museum - 1982
19th c interiors, home of the explorer Adolf Erik Nordenskiöld 08717

Nurmes

Nurmeksen Kaupunginmuseo (Town Museum), Kotiniementie 2, 75530 Nurmes - T: (013) 6895152, Fax: 6895902, E-mail: meri.rossander@nurmes.fi, Internet: http://www.nurmes.fi. Head: Niko Saatsi
Local Museum 08718

Nurmijärvi

Rajamäen Tehtaiden Museo (closed) 08719

Nurmo

Nurmon Museo, Tepontie, 60550 Nurmo - T: (06) 46143, 149388
Local Museum 08720

Nuutajärvi

Pykäri Nuutajärven Lasimuseo, Designor Oy Ab (Nuutajärvi Glass Museum), 31160 Nuutajärvi - T: (0204) 396504, Fax: 393531
Science&Tech Museum / Decorative Arts Museum - 1977
History of Nuutajärvi glass manufacture since 1850, glassware 08721

Nyslott

Nyslotts Landskapsmuseum, Riihisaari, 57130 Nyslott - T: (0159) 5714712, Fax: 5714717, E-mail: museo@savonlinna.fi, Internet: http://www.savonlinna.fi/sivistys/museo. Head: Mirja Kosunen
Local Museum 08722

Öja

Öjan Kotiseutumuseo, 68550 Öja - T: (06) 40410
Local Museum 08723

Öllölä

Koskenniskan Mylly- ja Kievarimuseo, Koskenniska, 83750 Öllölä - T: (013) 55176
Local Museum 08724

Övermark

Övermark Hembygdsmuseum, 64610 Övermark - T: (06) 53412, 53314
Local Museum 08725

Olavinlinna

Linnan Museo ja Ortodoksinen Kirkkomuseo (Castle and Orthodox Church Museum), 57170 Olavinlinna - T: (015) 531164, Fax: 510585, E-mail: olavinlinna@nba.fi, Internet: http://www.nba.fi
Historical Museum / Religious Arts Museum 08726

Olavinlinna Castle, 57150 Olavinlinna - T: (015) 531164, Fax: 510585, E-mail: olavinlinna@nba.fi, Internet: http://www.nba.fi. Head: Kirsi Loikkanen
Historical Museum 08727

Oravais

Kimo Bruks Museum and Gallery, Kimovägen 38-39, 66800 Oravais - T: (06) 3850204. Head: Gunvor Häggman
Ethnology Museum / Fine Arts Museum 08728

Virgo Labour Museum, Oravaisfabrik, 66800 Oravais - T: (06) 3825550, 3850310, Internet: http://www.oravais.fi/kimobruk. Head: Ulf Johansson
Ethnology Museum 08729

Orimattila

Orimattilan Kotiseutumuseo (Orimattila Local History Museum), 16300 Orimattila - T: (03) 8881370/389, Fax: 8881336, Internet: http://www.orimattila.fi
Open Air Museum / Decorative Arts Museum - 1949
Furnishings, agricultural equipment, photographs, farm buildings (18th-19th c), water mill (18th c) 08730

Orimattilan Taidemuseo (Orimattilas Art Museum), Lahdentie 65, 16300 Orimattila - T: (03) 8881369/370, Fax: 8881336, Internet: http://www.orimattila.fi
Fine Arts Museum 08731

Oripää

Hartmanin Mökki, Posti Oripään Kunta, 32500 Oripää - T: (02) 6309
Local Museum 08732

Oripään Museo, Posti Oripään Kunta, 32500 Oripää - T: (02) 6309
Local Museum 08733

Orivesi

Oriveden Paltanmäen Museo (Orivesi Paltanmäki Museum), 35300 Orivesi - T: (03) 57243. Head: Veli Paavola
Open Air Museum / Military Museum - 1932
Peasant house (19th c), windmill and water mill, furnishings, household articles, agricultural and military equipment, uniforms of riflemen 08734

Oulainen

Oulaisten Kotiseutumuseo, Kaarikatu 38, 86300 Oulainen - T: (08) 70721
Local Museum 08735

Oulu

Merimiehenkotimuseo, Pohjois-Pohjanmaan Museo (Northern Ostrobothnia Museum - SailorS Home), Pikisaarentie 6, 90015 Oulu - T: (08) 55847185, Fax: 55847199, Internet: http://www.ouka.fi/ppm/merimies
Local Museum
Home of a sailor in the 18th c 08736

Oulun Automuseo, Rajalantie, 90420 Oulu - T: (08) 521600, 145590
Science&Tech Museum 08737

Oulun Taidemuseo (Oulu City Art Museum), Kasarmintie 7, 90100 Oulu - T: (08) 55847463, Fax: 55847499, E-mail: keskus.taidemuseo@ouka.fi, Internet: http://www.ouka.fi/taidemuseo. Head: Ullamaria Pallasmaa
Fine Arts Museum - 1963
Contemporary art from Finland, naive art coll - library, archives 08738

Oulun Yliopiston Eläinmuseo (University of Oulu, Zoological Museum), Linnanmaa, 90014 Oulu - T: (08) 5531253, Fax: 5531227, E-mail: - zoological.museum@oulu.fi, Internet: http://www.oulu.fi/english/services.html. Head: Juhani Itämies
Natural History Museum / University Museum - 1960
70,000 vertebrate and 1,5 mio invertebrate zoological specimens from Northern Scandinavia 08739

Oulun Yliopiston Geologinen Museo (Geological Museum), Linnanmaa, 90570 Oulu - T: (08) 5531430, 40, Fax: 5531484, E-mail: geomuseo@ouli.fi, Internet: http://cc.oulu.fi/~geomuwww
Natural History Museum 08740

Oulun Yliopiston Kasvimuseo (Botanical Museum), Linnanmaa, 90401 Oulu, mail addr: c/o Oulun yliopisto, POB 3000, 90014 Oulu - T: (08) 5531551/559, Fax: 5531560, E-mail: pehalone@sun3oulu.fi, Internet: http://cc.oulu.fi/~herboulu. Head: Pekka Halonen
Natural History Museum / University Museum
Vascular plants, bryophytes, lichens, fungi, Northern Finland 08741

Pateniemen Sahamuseo, Pohjois-Pohjanmaan Museo (Pateniemi Sawmill Museum), Sahantie 21, 90015 Oulu - T: (08) 55867196, 551847150, Fax: 55847199, Internet: http://www.ouka.fi/ppm/paten
Special Museum 08742

Pohjois-Pohjanmaan Museo (Northern Ostrobothnia Museum), Ainolan puisto, 90015 Oulu - T: (08) 55847150, Fax: 55847199, Internet: http://www.ouka.fi/ppm. Head: Ilse Juntikka
Local Museum - 1896
Local history, ethnology, tar burning, shipping, trade, weapons, coins, Lappish coll - library, photograph and document archives 08743

Turkansaaren Ulkomuseo, Pohjois-Pohjanmaan Museo (Turkansaari Open Air Museum), Turkansaarientie 165, 90310 Oulu 31 - T: (08) 55867191, 55847154, Fax: 55867190, E-mail: anneli.syrjanen@ouka.fi, Internet: http://www.ouka.fi/ppm/turkans. Head: Anneli Syrjänen
Open Air Museum - 1961
Furnishings of buildings, equipment for tar burning, Turkansaari church (1694), Särkilahti mansion (17th-18th c), various farm buildings (17th-18th c) 08744

Oulunsalo

Oulunsalon Kotiseutumuseo, Kirkkotie, 90460 Oulunsalo - T: (08) 481673
Open Air Museum 08745

Outokumpu

Outokummun Kaivosmuseo (Mining Museum), Kaivosmiehenpolku 1, 83500 Outokumpu - T: (013) 555356, Fax: 555294. Head: Johanna Junno-Pennanen
Science&Tech Museum
Mine technology hist, working conditions, ore-prospecting 08746

Paakkola

Tervolan Kotiseutumuseo, 37 km Kemistä, 4-tien Varressa, 95325 Paakkola - T: (016) 787868
Local Museum 08747

Paattinen

Paattisten Kotiseutumuseo (Paattinen District Museum), 21300 Paattinen - T: (02) 2620111, Fax: 2620444, E-mail: maakuntamuseo@turku.fi, Internet: http://www.turku.fi/museo. Head: Juhani Kostet
Local Museum 08748

Paavola

Paavolan Kotiseutumuseo, Posti Paavolan Kotiseutuyhdistys, 92430 Paavola - T: (08) 76125
Local Museum 08749

Padasjoki

Padasjoen Museo, Nyystölä, 17501 Padasjoki - T: (03) 12931
Local Museum 08750

Paimio

Paimion Kotiseutumuseo, Hiihtomaja, 21530 Paimio - T: (02) 804511
Local Museum 08751

Palojoki

Aleksis Kiven Syntymäkoti (Aleksis Kivi's Birth-Place), Palojoen Kylä, 01940 Palojoki - T: (09) 25002500, Fax: 25002503, E-mail: museo@nurmijarvi.fi, Internet: http://www.nurmijarvi.fi/kirku/museot.htm. Head: Riitta Manka
Local Museum - 1951
Some personal things of our national author Aleksis Kivi (1834-1872) 08752

Paltamo

Paltamon Kotiseutumuseo, Lepikontie, 88300 Paltamo - T: (08) 405380078, Fax: 6898425, E-mail: raimo.kantola@koulu.paltamo.fi, Internet: http://www.paltamo.fi/~yritys/pseura. Head: Senja Säkkinen
Local Museum 08753

Parainen

Parainen District Museum, Storgårdinkatu 11, 21600 Parainen - T: (02) 4581452, Fax: 4585793, E-mail: pargas.hembygdsmuseum@parnet.fi, Internet: http://www.wakkanet.fi/museot. Head: Anne Bergström
Open Air Museum 08754

Parainen Industrial Museum, Skräbbölentie, 21600 Parainen - T: (02) 4581452, Fax: 4585793, E-mail: pargas.hembygdsmuseum@parnet.fi, Internet: http://www.wakkanet.fi/museot. Head: Anne Bergström
Science&Tech Museum 08755

Skyttalan Museo, Posti Kulttuuritoimisto, 21600 Parainen - T: (02) 4585794, Fax: 4585793, E-mail: pargas.hembygdsmuseum@parnet.fi, Internet: http://www.wakkanet.fi/museot. Head: Anne Bergström
Local Museum 08756

Parikkala

Parikkalan Kotiseutumuseo, Kirkonkylä, 59100 Parikkala - T: (015) 61641
Local Museum 08757

Parkano

Parkanon Kotiseutumuseo, Museokuja, 39700 Parkano - T: (03) 4433276
Local Museum 08758

Parkanon Metsämuseo, Rännärinmuseotie, 39700 Parkano - T: (03) 4433276
Natural History Museum 08759

Parola

Panssarimuseo (Tank Museum), PL 31, Hattulantie 334, 13721 Parola - T: (03) 18144524, Fax: 18144522. Head: Maunu Uoti
Military Museum - 1961
Tank equipment, anti-tank equipment used during World War II in the Finnish front lines, post war armoured vehicles 08760

Pattijoki

Olkijoen Rauhanpirtti (Treaty Museum), Olkijoki, Posti Kunnanvirasto, 92140 Pattijoki - T: (08) 64581/249
Special Museum 08761

Pattijoen Kotiseutumuseo Ojala, Ojalantie, Posti Kunnanvirasto, 92140 Pattijoki - T: (08) 64581/249
Local Museum 08762

Pelkosenniemi

Pelkosenniemen Kotiseutumuseo, Kirkonmäki, 98500 Pelkosenniemi - T: (016) 51411
Local Museum 08763

Pello

Pellon Kotiseutumuseo, Museotie, 95700 Pello - T: (016) 13841
Local Museum 08764

Peräseinäjoki

Riihimuseo (Threshing Museum), Toimisto Peräseinäjoen kunta, 61100 Peräseinäjoki - T: (06) 181111
Agriculture Museum 08765

Perho

Perhon Kotiseutumuseo, 69950 Perho - T: (06) 631231
Local Museum 08766

Pernaa

Iisakin Jussin Tupa, Kosolanmäki, Kauhava, 62220 Pernaa - T: (06) 80573, 352067
Local Museum 08767

Kalan Torppa, Hahtomaa, 62220 Pernaa - T: (06) 80573, 352067
Local Museum 08768

Perniö

Perniön Museo (Local Museum of Perniö), Museotie 9, 25500 Perniö - T: (02) 7759383, Fax: 7759301, E-mail: arja.niinistoalanne@pernio.fi, Internet: http://www.pernio.fi. Head: Arja Niinistö-Alanne
Local Museum / Ethnology Museum - 1930
Ethnography, culture, church, history, weapons, tin coll, old coins, textiles, furniture 08769

Pertteli

Pellonpään Talonpoikaistalo, 25360 Pertteli - T: (02) 86281
Local Museum 08770

Perttelin Kotiseutumuseo, 25360 Pertteli - T: (02) 86281
Local Museum 08771

Pertunmaa

Vanha-Rantalan Talomuseo, 2 km Kirkonkylästä, Toimisto Kulttuuritoimisto, 19430 Pertunmaa - T: (015) 71301
Local Museum 08772

Petalax

Petalax Hembygdsmuseum, 66240 Petalax - T: (06) 370256, 370448
Local Museum 08773

Pieksämäki

Pieksämäen Museo, Tasakatu 4 -6, 76100 Pieksämäki
Local Museum 08774

Savon Radan Museo (Railway Museum), Ratakatu 8, 76120 Pieksämäki - T: (015) 13838
Science&Tech Museum 08775

Pielavesi

Lepikon Torppa, Säviälle Vievän Tien Varrella, 72400 Pielavesi - T: (017) 22210, 21171
Local Museum 08776

Pielaveden Kotiseutumuseo (Pielavesi Local History Museum), 72400 Pielavesi - T: (017) 97811/261
Local Museum - 1958
Photographs, musical instruments, peasant culture, fishing and hunting, mansions, servant's quarters and various outbuildings (17th-20th c) 08777

Pihlajavesi

Pihlajaveden Kotiseutumuseo, Posti Pihlajaveden Kotiseutuyhdistys, 41770 Pihlajavesi - T: (014) 62051
Local Museum 08778

Pihtipudas

Pihtiputaan Kotiseutumuseo, Pl 16, 44800 Pihtipudas - T: (014) 61861
Local Museum 08779

Piikkiö

Pukkilan Kartano-ja Ajokalumuseo (Pukkila Manor and Vehicle Museum), Littoistentie 114, 21500 Piikkiö - T: (02) 4795320, Fax: 40509579, Internet: http://www.nba.fi. Head: Lea Värtinen
Historical Museum
Pukkila Manor and outbuildings (1762), 18th c. manor furnishings, 18th c. style garden 08780

Piippola

Viitainahon Kotiseutumuseo, Posti Kulttuurilautakunta, 92620 Piippola - T: (08) 71341, 71291
Local Museum 08781

Pirkkala

Reipin Museo, Museotie, 33960 Pirkkala - T: (03) 31342460, Fax: 31342465, E-mail: jouni.salonen@pirkkala.fi, Internet: http://www.pirkkala.fi. Head: Jouni Salonen
Local Museum / Agriculture Museum 08782

Pöljä

Pöljän Kotiseutumuseo (Pöljä Local History Museum), Museontie 58, 71820 Pöljä - T: (017) 401364/4618032, Fax: 401132, E-mail: anu.risssanen@siilinjarvi.fi, Internet: http://www.siilinjarvi.fi
Agriculture Museum / Open Air Museum / Archaeological Museum - 1933
Stones and ceramics (3,5000-1,500 B.C), farmhouse of 10 different buildings from the end of 19th c - library 08783

Pörtom

Pörtom Hembygdsmuseum, Dahlbacken, 66270 Pörtom - T: (06) 661143, 661189
Local Museum 08784

Pöytyä

Pöytyän Kotiseutumuseo (Local History Museum in Pöytyä), 21880 Pöytyä - T: (02) 4867111, Fax: 4867002, E-mail: antti.juva@kolumbus.fi. Head: Antti Juva
Local Museum 08785

Reppuniemen Ulkomuseo, 21880 Pöytyä - T: (02) 4867111, Fax: 4867002, E-mail: antti.juva@kolumbus.fi. Head: Antti Juva
Agriculture Museum 08786

Pohja

Billnäsin Kirvesmuseo, 36840 Pohja - T: (019) 377408, 3771
Local Museum 08787

Gillesgården, Skarpkulla, 36840 Pohja - T: (019) 56112, 56046
Local Museum 08788

Pohjaslahti

Heikintupa, 42850 Pohjaslahti - T: (03) 77113
Local Museum 08789

Polvijärvi

Makasiinimuseo, Talomuseo, Koulumuseo, 83700 Polvijärvi - T: (013) 631089
Historical Museum 08790

Pomarkku

Pomarkun Kotiseutumuseo, Posti Kunnanvirasto, 29630 Pomarkku - T: (03) 311666
Local Museum 08791

Pori

Luontotalo Arkki, Satakunnan Museo (Natural Museum Arkki), Pohjoispuisto 7, 28100 Pori - Internet: http://www.pori.fi/smu/arkki.htm
Natural History Museum 08792

Porin Taidemuseo (Pori Art Museum), Eteläranta, 28100 Pori - T: (02) 6211081, Fax: 6211091, E-mail: taidemuseo@pori.fi, Internet: http://www.pori.fi/art/satakunta/pori. Head: Esko Nummelin
Fine Arts Museum - 1981
Coll of Maire Gullichsen Art Foundation 08793

Satakunnan Museo, Hallituskatu 11, 28100 Pori 10 - T: (02) 6211078, Fax: 6211078, E-mail: satakunnenmuseo@pori.fi, Internet: http://www.pori.fi/smu. Head: Leena Sammallahti
Local Museum - 1888
Archaeology, hunting and fishing, furniture, rugs, silver, tin, weapons, glass, traditional Finnish paintings - library, archive, Toivo renovation centre 08794

Porvoo

Albert Edelfeltin Ateljeemuseo, Haikkoo, Posti Raili Björninen, 06400 Porvoo - T: (019) 17781
Fine Arts Museum 08795

Edelfelt-Vallgren Museo, Porvoon Museo (Edelfelt-Vallgren Museum), Välikatu 11, 06100 Porvoo 10, mail addr: Raatihuoneenkatu 21, 06100 Porvoo - T: (019) 580589, Fax: 582283, E-mail: info@porvoonmuseo.fi, Internet: http://www.porvoonmuseo.fi. Head: Marketta Tamminen
Fine Arts Museum - 1925
Paintings, sculpture, prints, drawings, especially works by A. Edelfelt, V. Vallgren, J. Knutson, L. Sparre, A.W. Finch, Art Nouveau ceramics and furniture by the Iris Factory 08796

J.L. Runebergin Koti (J.L. Runeberg's Home), Runeberginkatu 20, 06100 Porvoo - T: (019) 581330. Head: Marketta Tamminen
Special Museum - 1880
House of the Finnish national poet Johan Ludvig Runeberg (1804-1877), articles of the 1860's and 1870's 08797

Luonnonhistoriallinen Museo (Natural History Museum), Kaivokatu 40, 06100 Porvoo - T: (019) 5231700, Fax: 585591, E-mail: -borga.naturhistoriska@co.inet.fi. Head: Eirik Granqvist
Natural History Museum - 1957 08798

Maria de Lisitzin Fine Art and Historical Museum, Sibeliusbul 15, 06100 Porvoo - T: (019) 582111. Head: Jorma A. Aunela
Fine Arts Museum / Historical Museum 08799

Porvoon Museo, Välikatu 11, 06100 Porvoo, mail addr: Raatihuoneenkatu 21 - T: (019) 5747500, Fax: 582283, E-mail: info@porvoonmuseo.fi, Internet: http://www.porvoonmuseo.fi. Head: Marketta Tamminen
Local Museum / Decorative Arts Museum - 1896
Furniture, textiles, glass, porcelain, pewter, weapons, handicraft, photographs 08800

Walter Runebergin Veistoskokoelma (Walter Runeberg Sculpture Collection), Aleksanterinkatu 5, 06100 Porvoo - T: (019) 582186. Head: Marketta Tamminen
Fine Arts Museum - 1921
Works of sculptor Walter Runeberg (1838-1920), son of the poet J.L. Runeberg 08801

Yrjö A. Jäntin Taidekokoelma, Papinkatu 19, 06100 Porvoo - T: (019) 145990
Fine Arts Museum 08802

Posio

Kansainvälinen Kahvikuppimuseo (International Coffee Cup Museum), Pentik-Mäki, PB 32, 97901 Posio - T: (016) 3721412, Fax: 3722034, E-mail: matkailu@neuvonta@posio.fi, Internet: http://www.posio.fi. Head: Veijo Nykänen
Special Museum 08803

Pudasjarvi

Pudasjärven Kotiseutumuseo, Kirkon Seutu, 93100 Pudasjarvi - T: (08) 21200
Local Museum 08804

Pukkila

Pukkilan Kotiseutumuseo, 07560 Pukkila - T: (019) 76305, 75052
Local Museum 08805

Pulkkila

Pulkkilan Kotiseutumuseo, 92600 Pulkkila - T: (08) 21292, 24182
Local Museum 08806

Punkaharju

Lusto-Suomen-metsämuseo ja metsätietokeskus (Lusto - The Finnish Forest Museum), 58450 Punkaharju - T: (015) 34510100, Fax: 3451050, E-mail: lusto@lusto.fi, Internet: http://www.lusto.fi. Head: Timo Kukko
Natural History Museum - 1988
Photographs, films and tapes, books, forest working tools, equipment and machinery, wooden arts and handicrafts, forest and wood products, objects related to forest culture and recreation - archive 08807

Punkaharjun Kotiseutumuseo, Hälvänmäentie 71, Hiukkajoki, 58520 Punkaharju - T: (015) 7341256, Fax: 7341299, E-mail: elina.kosonen@punkaharju.fi, Internet: http://www.punkaharju.fi. Head: Elina Kosonen
Local Museum / Fine Arts Museum 08808

Punkalaidum

Talonpoikaismuseo Yli-Kirra (Yli-Kirra Museum), 31900 Punkalaidum - T: (02) 7674111, 7674256, Fax: 7674225. Head: Osmo Suvitie
Open Air Museum - 1947
Yli-Kirra farmhouse and outbuildings (17th-19th c), cotter's dwelling (18th c), furnishings and household objects, hunting equipment 08809

Purmo

Ålidens Hembygdsgård, 68930 Purmo - T: (06) 72532
Local Museum 08810

Pusula

Pusulan Museo, Pusula kk, 03850 Pusula - T: 66198
Local Museum 08811

Puumala

Sahan Museo, Sahanlahti, Matkailutoimisto, 52201 Puumala - T: (05) 801250
Local Museum 08812

Pyhäjärvi

Pyhäjärven Kotiseutumuseo, 86810 Pyhäjärvi - T: (08) 40135
Local Museum 08813

Pyhäjoki

Pyhäjoen Kotiseutumuseo (Pyhäjoki Local History Museum), Annalantie 20, 86100 Pyhäjoki - T: (08) 4390246, Fax: 4390266. Head: Eila Anttila
Open Air Museum - 1957
Annala farmhouse and outbuildings, windmill, smokehouse, smithy (18th-19th c), furnishings 08814

Pyhämaa

Pyhämaan Kotiseutumuseo, 23920 Pyhämaa - T: (02) 21010
Local Museum 08815

Pyhäntä

Pyhännän Kotiseutumuseo, Posti Kunnantoimisto, 92930 Pyhäntä - T: (08) 41351
Local Museum 08816

Pyhtää

Pyhtään Kotiseutumuseo, Kakaan Koulu, 49270 Pyhtää - T: (05) 31531
Local Museum 08817

Raahe

Raahen Museo (Raahe Museum), Rantakatu 36, 92100 Raahe - T: (08) 2992445, Fax: 2992205. Head: Eija Turunen
Local Museum / Natural History Museum - 1862
Articles connected with shipping and trade, furniture and textiles from middle class and artisan homes, ecclesiastical artifacts (17th c), numismatics, customs warehouse (1850), natural hist coll, botanical, zoological, and mineralogical objects - photo and research archives 08818

Rääkkylä

Rääkkylän Kotiseutumuseo, 82300 Rääkkylä - T: (013) 661411
Local Museum 08819

Raisio

Krookilan Kotiseutualue, 21200 Raisio - T: (02) 790111
Open Air Museum 08820

Rajamäki

Primalco Oy, Rajamäen Tehdasmuseo (Rajamäki Works Museum), 05200 Rajamäki - T: (09) 13311, Fax: 1331311
Science&Tech Museum - 1963
Alcohol making in pre- and early manufacturing stages, building of the former yeast works (1895) 08821

Rantasalmi

Rantasalmen Museo, Ohitustie 9, 58900 Rantasalmi - T: (015) 7371363, Fax: 7371510
Local Museum 08822

Rantsila

Rantsilan Kotiseutumuseo, Posti Rantsila-Seura, 92500 Rantsila - T: (08) 50177
Local Museum 08823

Ranua

Ranuan Pappila- ja Pitäjämuseo, Pappilantie, 97700 Ranua - T: (016) 51401, 51804
Religious Arts Museum 08824

Saukkojärven Kotiseutu- ja Koulumuseo (Saukkojärvi Local and School Museum), Saukkojärvi, 97700 Ranua - T: (016) 354764
Local Museum / Historical Museum 08825

Rauma

Kirsti Rauman Museo (Kirsti, Home of a Seaman Museum), Pohjakatu 3, 26130 Rauma - T: (02) 8343527, Fax: 8343524
Local Museum 08826

Lönnströmin Taidemuseo (The Lönnström Art Museum), Valtakatu 7, 26100 Rauma - T: (02) 83874722, Fax: 83874742, E-mail: kati.kivimaki@lonnstromintaidemuseo.fi, Internet: http://www.lonnstromintaidemuseo.fi. Head: Kati Kivimäki
Fine Arts Museum
Contemporary art, mainly Finnish, social art, enviromental art, art education 08827

Rauman Museo, Kauppakatu 24, 26100 Rauma 10 - T: (02) 8343525, Fax: 8343524, E-mail: rauman.museo@rauma.fi, Internet: http://www.rauma.fi. Head: Anna Nurmi-Nielsen
Local Museum - 1891
Articles from sailing vessels, fishing equipment, bobbin laces, religious and peasant artifacts 08828

Rauman Taidemuseo (Rauma Art Museum), Kuninkaankatu 37, 26100 Rauma - T: (02) 8224346, Fax: 8222183, E-mail: rtm@raumantaide-museo.inet.fi, Internet: http://www.pori.fi/art/satakunta. Head: Janne Koski
Fine Arts Museum - 1970
Local art 08829

Teresia ja Rafael Lönnströmin kotimuseo (The Teresia and Rafael Lönnström Home Museum), Syväraumankatu 41, 26100 Rauma - T: (02) 83874700, Fax: 83874742, E-mail: kati.kivimaki@lonnstromintaidemuseo.fi, Internet: http://www.lonnstromintaidemuseo.fi. Head: Kati Kivimäki
Fine Arts Museum
Older Finnish art, Finnish and international contemporary art 08830

Rautalampi

Kerkonkosken Myllymuseo (Mill-Museum), 77700 Rautalampi - T: (017) 38114, 38028
Science&Tech Museum 08831

Peuran Museo, 77700 Rautalampi - T: (017) 30014
Local Museum 08832

Rautalammin Museo (Rautalampi Museum), 77700 Rautalampi - T: (017) 12690. Head: Sanna Koponen
Local Museum / Ethnology Museum - 1938
Ethnography and cultural history, furniture, costumes, household articles, ecclesiastical artifacts, Finnish art collection, chimneyless dwelling, stores, church stable, 'church boat' 08833

Rautio

Raution Kotiseutumuseo, 85160 Rautio - T: (08) 465885. Head: Siiri Niskz
Local Museum 08834

Reisjärvi

Reisjärven Kotiseutumuseo, 85900 Reisjärvi - T: (08) 71433
Local Museum 08835

Renko

Härkätien Museo (Granary Museum), Muurila, 14300 Renko - T: (03) 769612
Agriculture Museum 08836

Replot

Replot Hembygdsmuseum, 65800 Replot - T: (06) 520291
Local Museum 08837

Riihimäki

Riihimäen Kaupunginmuseo (Riihimäki City Museum), Öllerinkatu 3, 11130 Riihimäki 13 - T: (019) 7417202, Fax: 7417854, E-mail: helena.lindsten@riihimaki.fi, Internet: http://www.riihimaki.fi/kaupmuseo. Head: Dr. Heikki Matiskainen
Local Museum - 1961
Local hist, home furnishings, handicrafts, trade, railway collection, hist of teaching, photograph and document archives, Carelian collection (small number of artifacts from 1800 to 1940) - library 08838

Riihimäen Taidemuseo (Riihimäki Art Museum), Temppelikatu 8, 11100 Riihimäki - T: (019) 7417333, Fax: 7417655, Internet: http://www.riihimaki.fi/taidemus
Fine Arts Museum
Finnish paintings and sculptures from 20th c, inernational art and antique coll 08839

Suomen Lasimuseo (Finnish Glass Museum), Tehtaankatu 23, 11910 Riihimäki 10 - T: (019) 7417494, Fax: 7417555, E-mail: -heikki.matiskainen@riihimaki.fi, Internet: http://www.riihimaki.fi/lasimus. Head: Dr. Heikki Matiskainen
Decorative Arts Museum / Science&Tech Museum - 1961
Tools for making Finnish glass, Finnish glass design from 1920 to the present - library 08840

Suomen Metsästymuseo (Hunting Museum of Finland), Tehtaankatu 23a, 11910 Riihimäki - T: (019) 722293, Fax: 719378, E-mail: metsastysmuseo@kolumbus.fi, Internet: http://www.kolumbus.fi/metsastysmuseo. Head: Lauri Haataja
Special Museum 08841

Valtakunnallinen Työväentalomuseo (National Museum of Workers' Halls), Peltosaari, 11130 Riihimäki - T: (019) 34753
Historical Museum 08842

Viestimuseo (Signal Museum), Varuskunta, 11311 Riihimäki 31 - T: (019) 35071
Military Museum - 1960
Objects and equipment connected with signal operations in the Finnish military forces, former officer's club (1913) 08843

Rovaniemi

Ethnographisches Museum Pöykkölä, Ranuantie, 96100 Rovaniemi 4 - T: (016) 3481095
Ethnology Museum 08844

Lapin Maakuntamuseo (Provincial Museum of Lapland), Pohjoisranta 4, 96200 Rovaniemi 10 - T: (016) 3222482, Fax: 3223091, E-mail: raili.huopainen@rovaniemi.fi, Internet: http://www.rovaniemi.fi/taide/maakmus/lamu.htm. Head: Raili Huopainen
Natural History Museum / Ethnology Museum - 1975
Artifacts, photographs, and samples describing conditions in Laplans and its natural history 08845

Lapin Metsämuseo (Lapland Forestry Museum), Metsämuseontie 7, 96400 Rovaniemi 40 - T: (016) 182083
Special Museum - 1962
Logging equipment, the first steam tug (1898) an locomotive used in Lappish lumbering, photograph collection, logger's buildings from different lumbering areas in Lapland 08846

Rovaniemen Kotiseutumuseo (Rovaniemi Museum), Pöykköläntie 4, 96400 Rovaniemi 40 - T: (016) 3481095. Head: Esko Pernu
Ethnology Museum - 1957
Peasant life in Southern Lapland, furnishings, photograph collection, local farm buildings (19th c) 08847

Rovaniemen Taidemuseo (Rovaniemi Art Museum), Lapinkävijäntie 4, 96100 Rovaniemi - T: (016) 3322821, Fax: 3223052, E-mail: hilkka.liikkanen@rovaniemi.fi, Internet: http://www.rovaniemi.fi/taide/taidemus/index.htm. Head: Hilkka Liikkanen
Fine Arts Museum - 1986
Finnish Contemporary art (paintings, graphics, sculpture) from Jenny and Antti Wihuri foundation coll 08848

Ruokolahti

Ruokolahden Kotiseutumuseo (Ruokolahti Local History Museum), 56100 Ruokolahti - T: (05) 4341728, Internet: http://www.otela.karjala.fi/yhdistykset/ruokolas. Head: Elina Hupponen
Local Museum / Ethnology Museum - 1954
Ethnolographical and ecclesiastical material, objects connected with the painter Albert Edelfelt, public granary (1861) and open-air museum - research archives 08849

Ruotsinpyhtää

Strömforsin Teollisuusmuseo (Strömforsin Works Museum), 07970 Ruotsinpyhtää - T: (019) 618474, Fax: 618475, E-mail: ruotsinpyhtaan.ruukkialue@co.inet.fi. Head: Annika Malms-Tepponen
Historic Site / Science&Tech Museum - 1962
Industry, iron work, log-floating and sylvicultural equipment, original waterwheel-operated hammers 08850

Ruovesi

Ruoveden Kotiseutumuseo (Ruovesi Local History Museum), 34600 Ruovesi - T: (03) 486111, Fax: 4861430. Head: Anja Latvala
Open Air Museum - 1932
17th-18th c farm buildings, 16th c storehouse - library 08851

Rusko

Ruskon Kotiseutumuseo ja Rindellin Mäkitupalaismuseo, Kirkonmäki, 21290 Rusko - T: (02) 788108
Local Museum 08852

Rymättylä

Rymättylän Kotiseutumuseo (Rymättylä Local History Museum), 21140 Rymättylä
Local Museum - 1964
Objects connected with agriculture, fishing and navigation, shoemaker's tools, household articles, farmhouse and outbuildings (17th-19th c) 08853

Saarijärvi

Kivikauden Kylä, Summassaari, 43101 Saarijärvi - T: (014) 422873, 4291411, Fax: 455117, E-mail: museo@saarijarvi.fi
Archaeological Museum 08854

Saarijärven Museo, Herajärventie 2, 43101 Saarijärvi - T: (014) 4291411, Fax: 455117, E-mail: museo@saarijarvi.fi. Head: Kari Kotilainen
Local Museum
Stone age relics, local cultural hist 08855

Sääksmäki

Voipaalas Taidekeskus, Sääksmäkitie 772, 37700 Sääksmäki - T: (03) 5881046, Fax: 5881176, E-mail: voipaala@vlk.fi. Head: Marja-Liisa Järvinen
Fine Arts Museum 08856

Säkylä

Säkylän Kotiseutumuseo, 27800 Säkylä - T: (02) 704400
Local Museum 08857

Säyneinen

Säyneisten Kotiseutumuseo, 73770 Säyneinen - T: (017) 761015
Local Museum 08858

Salla

Sallan Kotiseutumuseo, Museotie, 98900 Salla - T: (016) 879228, Fax: 832021, E-mail: - liisa.brandenstein@salla.fi
Local Museum 08859

Salo

Meritalon Museo (Meritalo Museum), Moisionkatu 18, 24100 Salo - T: (02) 7784886, Fax: 7784810, E-mail: maku@salo.fi, Internet: http://www.salo.fi
Local Museum 08860

Sammatti

Lammintalo, Elias Lönnrotin Vanhuudenkotitalo, Haarjärven Kylä, 09220 Sammatti - T: (09) 643165
Local Museum 08861

Lohilammen Museo, Lohilampi, 09220 Sammatti - T: (019) 56233
Local Museum 08862

Paikkarin Torppa (Paikkari Cottage), Torpantie 20, 09220 Sammatti - T: (019) 356659, Fax: 40509579, Internet: http://www.nba.fi. Head: Lea Värtinen
Special Museum - 1895
Personal accessories and home of Elias Lönnroth, the collector of the Finnish national epic, the Kalevala 08863

Sappee

Vihavuoden Myllymuseo (Mill Museum), Vihavuosi, 14930 Sappee - T: (03) 6547408. Head: Vesa Leppala
Folklore Museum
Water mill, miller's house and other buildings from 18th c 08864

Saukkola

Meijerimuseo (Dairy-Museum), 09430 Saukkola - T: (019) 371176, Fax: 50662385
Science&Tech Museum
Hist of dairy technology 08865

Sauvo

Sauvon Kotiseutumuseo, Vahtinen, 21570 Sauvo - T: (02) 730432
Local Museum 08866

Savonlinna

Nukkemuseo Suruton (Doll Museum), Kylpylaitoksentie 2, 57130 Savonlinna - T: (015) 273960, 5714666, Fax: 5714467, E-mail: Leila.Taupila@savonlinna.fi, Internet: http://www.savonlinna.fi/kulttuuri. Head: Käpy Tarus
Decorative Arts Museum 08867

Putkinotko, Lehtiniemi, 57130 Savonlinna - T: (015) 5714712, Fax: 5714717, E-mail: museo@savonlinna.fi, Internet: http://www.savonlinna.fi/sivistys/museo. Head: Mirja Kosunen
Special Museum / Open Air Museum
Local Finnish author Joel Lehtonen 08868

Savonlinnan Maakuntamuseo (Savonlinna Provincial Museum), Riihisaari, 57130 Savonlinna - T: (015) 5714712, Fax: 5714717, E-mail: museo@savonlinna.fi, Internet: http://www.savonlinna.fi/sivistys/museo. Head: Mirja Kosunen
Local Museum
Regional hist, hist of navigation in lake Saimaa, 3 hist steamships, prehist, logging 08869

Savonlinnan Taidemuseo (Savonlinna Art Gallery), Olavinkatu 40, 57130 Savonlinna - T: (015) 5714712, Fax: 5714717, E-mail: museo@savonlinna.fi, Internet: http://www.savonlinna.fi/sivistys/museo. Head: Mirja Kosunen
Fine Arts Museum / Public Gallery 08870

Savonranta

Säimenen Mylly, Kirkolta 10 km Joensuun Suuntaan, 58300 Savonranta - T: (015) 321539
Local Museum 08871

Seinäjoki

Etelä-Pohjanmaan Maakuntamuseo (Southern Ostrobothnia Museum), Törnävä, 60200 Seinäjoki 20 - T: (06) 4162642, Fax: 4162646, E-mail: - e_pohj.maakuntamuseo@seinajoki.fi. Head: Marja-Liisa Haveri-Nieminen
Open Air Museum - 1962
Furnished farm buildings typical of the area (17th-19th c), agriculture, Törnävä Manor, windmill, powder laboratory, pharmacy, country stores 08872

Seinäjoen Luonto-Museo (Seinäjoki Natural History Museum), Upankatu 3, 60100 Seinäjoki 10 - T: (06) 14162390
Natural History Museum
Natural history, especially concerning the marshes of Southern Ostrobothnia 08873

Suojeluskuntamuseo (Civil Guard Museum), Kauppakatu 17, 60100 Seinäjoki - T: (06) 162111
Military Museum 08874

Sideby

Kilens Hembygdsgård, 64490 Sideby - T: (06) 25611
Local Museum 08875

Sieppijärvi

Kolarin Kunnan Kotiseutumuseo, 95800 Sieppijärvi - T: (016) 61471/122
Local Museum 08876

Sievi

Sievin Kotiseutumuseo, Kunnantoimisto, 85410 Sievi - T: (08) 8443111, Fax: 8443100, Internet: http://www.sievi.fi 08877

Siikainen

Siikaisten Kotiseutumuseo, Kotiseutu- ja Museoyhdistys, 29810 Siikainen - T: (03) 521068
Local Museum 08878

Siilinjärvi

Harjamäen Sairaalamuseo (Museum of Harjamäki Mental Hospital), Harjamäen Sairaala, 71800 Siilinjärvi - T: (017) 401364, 401363, Fax: 401132, E-mail: anu.rissanen@siilinjarvi.fi, Internet: http://www.siilinjarvi.fi
Special Museum 08879

Siivikkala

Museo Villa Urpo, 33450 Siivikkala - T: (03) 31424100, Fax: 31424122, E-mail: villaurpo@yritys.tpo.fi, Internet: http://yritys.tpo.fi/villaurpo. Head: Maija Lahtinen
Fine Arts Museum 08880

Simonniemi

Simon Kotiseutumuseo, Simon Kirkon Läheisyydessä, 95220 Simonniemi - T: (016) 76001
Local Museum 08881

Simuna

Töllinmäen Museo, 39110 Simuna - T: (03) 716811
Local Museum 08882

Sipoo

Nikkilän Sairaalan Museo (Hospital Museum), Pyhän Sigfridintie 1, 04130 Sipoo - T: (09) 2351287, 231437
Special Museum 08883

Sippola

Sippolan Kotiseutumuseo (Sippola Museum), Sippolantie 18, 46710 Sippola - T: (05) 3666076, 7841640, Fax: 7841604, E-mail: jaana.vuorio-palmumaa@anjalankoski.fi
Local Museum
Local museum in a former parsonage from 1843 08884

Siuntio

Siuntion Kotiseutumuseo, Siuntio kk, 02570 Siuntio - T: (09) 261113
Local Museum 08885

Snappertuna

Snappertunan Talomuseo, 10710 Snappertuna - T: (019) 234033, 2633161, Fax: 2633150. Head: Ivar Nordlund
Local Museum 08886

Sodankylä

Sodankylän Kotiseutumuseo, Hampputörmäntie, 99600 Sodankylä - T: (016) 28218, 28645
Local Museum 08887

Södra Vallgrund

Granösunds Fiskeläge, Bulleråsvägen 322, 65930 Södra Vallgrund - T: (06) 3527823
Open Air Museum 08888

Soini

Soinin Museo, 63800 Soini - T: (06) 81297
Local Museum 08889

Somero

Pajulan Koulumuseo (School Museum), 31400 Somero - T: (02) 43338
Special Museum 08890

Peltotyökalumuseo (Agricultural Implements Museum), 31400 Somero - T: (02) 46005
Agriculture Museum 08891

Savenvalajamuseo (Potter's Museum), Kultelan Kylä, 31400 Somero - T: (02) 485367
Decorative Arts Museum 08892

Someron Museo (Somero Museum), 31400 Somero - T: (02) 46105. Head: Ritva Helminen
Open Air Museum - 1956
Croft buildings (18th-19th c), furnishings 08893

Someron Torppamuseo (Croft Museum), Museotie 1, 31400 Somero - T: (02) 748801
Agriculture Museum 08894

Sonera

Telegalleria, Elimäenkatu 9a, 00051 Sonera - T: 0204060027, Fax: 0204060034, E-mail: telegalleria@sonera.fi, Internet: http://www.telegalleria.fi. Head: Maija Elo
Science&Tech Museum - 1987
Historical colls concerning Telecommunication Services 08895

Sonkajärvi

Kansainvälinen Pullomuseo (International Bottle Museum), Rutakontie 18, 74300 Sonkajärvi - T: (017) 761470, 769611, Internet: http://www.sonkajarvi.fi
Special Museum 08896

Sonkajärven Kotiseutumuseo, Rutakontie 18, 74301 Sonkajärvi - T: (017) 761470, 769611, Internet: http://www.sonkajarvi.fi
Local Museum 08897

Sotkamo

Sotkamon Kotiseutumuseo, Sopalantie 1, 88600 Sotkamo - T: (08) 61351/232
Local Museum 08898

Tervajärven Talomuseo, Kaukola, Tervajärvi, 88600 Sotkamo - T: (08) 66366
Local Museum 08899

Storby

Ålands Jakt och Fiskemuseum (Aland Hunting and Fishing Museum), Fiskeläge 37, Storby, 22270 Storby - T: (018) 38299, Fax: 38299. Head: Maria Nummelin
Special Museum - 1995
Fishing and hunting objects (guns, stuffed animals, photographs) 08900

Hembygdsgården Labbas, 22270 Storby - T: (018) 38489
Folklore Museum 08901

Postrotemuseet (Postal Museum), 22270 Storby - T: (018) 39000. Head: E. Tudeer
Local Museum 08902

Sulkava

Rauhaniemen Kotiseutumuseo, Rauhaniemi, 58700 Sulkava - T: (015) 71121
Local Museum 08903

Sund

Bomarsundmuseet i Prästö Lotsstuga, Bomarsund, Prästö, 22530 Sund - T: (018) 43820, 43822
Local Museum 08904

Jan Karlsgarden, Kastelholm, 22530 Sund - T: (018) 43812, Fax: 43887. Head: Elisabeth Palamarz
Open Air Museum - 1930
Typical Åland farmstead from second half of the 19th c 08905

Kastleholm Castle, Kastelholm, 22520 Sund - T: (018) 43820, Fax: 43887. Head: Elisabeth Palamarz
Historical Museum - 1991
History of the castle 08906

Sundom

Sundomin Kotiseutumuseo, 65410 Sundom - T: (06) 112139
Local Museum 08907

Suodenniemi

Kirkonkylän Museo, Kunnantoimisto, 38510 Suodenniemi - T: (02) 7155
Open Air Museum 08908

Suolahti

Keitele-Museo, Suolahden Satama, 44201 Suolahti - T: (014) 52845, 494214
Local Museum 08909

Suolahden Museo, Posti Vanhan Äänekosken Kotiseutuyhdistys, 44200 Suolahti - T: (014) 41312, 42337
Local Museum 08910

Suomusjärvi

Suomusjärven Kotiseutumuseo, Kirkonkylä, 25410 Suomusjärvi - T: (02) 885552
Local Museum 08911

Suonenjoki

Suonenjoen Kotiseutumuseo, 77600 Suonenjoki - T: (017) 133605
Local Museum 08912

Sysmä

Sysmäen Kotiseutumuseo, Väihkyläntie 10, 19700 Sysmä - T: (014) 71355, 71088
Local Museum 08913

Taavetti

Svinhufvud- ja Kotiseutumuseo, Linnalantie 33, 54500 Taavetti - T: (05) 7281
Local Museum 08914

Taivalkoski

Kallioniemi, Jokijärvi, 93401 Taivalkoski - T: (08) 51611
Local Museum 08915

Taivalkosken Kotiseutumuseo, Rantatie 1, 93401 Taivalkoski - T: (08) 51611
Local Museum 08916

Taivassalo

Taivassalon Museo, Viianen, 23310 Taivassalo - T: (02) 878486. Head: Rauni Nummelin
Local Museum - 1961
Manorial furnishings, agricultural equipment, fishing equipment, handicrafts 08917

Tammela

Vekkilän Kotiseutumuseo, Vekkilä, 31300 Tammela - T: (03) 60007
Local Museum 08918

Tammijärvi

Peltolan Mäkitupalaismuseo (Peltola Cotters Museum), Tammijärventie 164, 19910 Tammijärvi - T: (014) 877108. Head: Arto Huuskola
Local Museum - 1959
Peltola cotters village, furnishings, displays depicting the life of the cotters 08919

Tammio

Tammio Museo, Mäntlahti, 49840 Tammio - T: (05) 51873, 40877
Local Museum 08920

Tampere

Amurin Työläismuseokortteli, Tampereen Museot (Amuri Museum of Workers' Housing), Makasiininkatu 12, 33101 Tampere, mail addr: PL 487, 33101 Tampere - T: (03) 31466690, 31466771, Fax: 31466808, E-mail: paula.leinonen@tt.tampere.fi. Head: Toimi Jaatinen
Open Air Museum - 1974
Development of workers' housing 1880-1970, with authentic buildings 08921

Hämeen Museo, Tampereen Museot (Häme Museum), Näsinpuisto, 33211 Tampere, mail addr: PL 487, 33101 Tampere - T: (03) 31466966, Fax: 31466808, Internet: http://www.tampere.fi/culture. Head: Toimi Jaatinen
Historical Museum - 1904
Ethnography and the cultural history of the Tampere and Häme province, folk art, rugs, ecclesiastical coll, archeology 08922

Hiekan Taidemuseo (Hiekka Art Museum), Pirkankatu 6, 33210 Tampere - T: (03) 2123973, Fax: 2123973, E-mail: hiekantm@vip.fi, Internet: http://www.vip.fi/~hiekantm. Head: Liisa Rintala
Fine Arts Museum - 1931
Interiors, applied art objects, gold and silver work, 18th-20th c Finnish art, works by Albert Edelfelt, Eero Järnefelt, Akseli Gallen-Kallela, Pekka Halonen and Wäinö Aaltonen 08923

Kivimuseo, Tampereen Museot (Tampere Mineral Museum), Hämeenpuisto 20, 33210 Tampere - T: (03) 31466046, Fax: 31466567, Internet: http://www.tampere.fi/kivimuseo. Head: Paavo Korhonen
Natural History Museum
Stones, minerals, fossils, etc. 08924

Lauri Viidan Museo, Portaanpää 8, 33250 Tampere - T: (03) 2233596
Local Museum
Childhood home of the Finnish writer Lauri Viita 08925

Lenin-Museo (Lenin Museum), Hämeenpuisto 28, 33200 Tampere - T: (03) 2768100, Fax: 2768121, E-mail: lenin@sci.fi, Internet: http://www.tampere.fi/culture/lenin. Head: Aimo Minkkinen
Special Museum - 1946
Photographic material and personal mementos of Vladimir Ilich Uljanov Lenin's life, work and connections to Finland, Soviet design - library, archive 08926

Museokeskus Vapriikki (Museum Centre Vapriikki), Veturiaukio 4, 33100 Tampere, mail addr: PL 487, 33101 Tampere - T: (03) 31466966, Fax: 31466839, E-mail: vapriikki@tampere.fi, Internet: http://www.tampere.fi/vapriikki. Head: Toimi Jaatinen
Local Museum - 1996
History of Tampere and Pirkanmaa Province, archaeology, technology, contemporary art - Photo archive 08927

Nukke- ja Pukumuseo (Museum of Dolls and Costumes), Hatanpään puistokuja 1, 33900 Tampere - T: (03) 2226261, Fax: 2226201, E-mail: haihara@sgic.fi, Internet: http://www.sgic.fi/haihara/
Special Museum 08928

Pyynikinlinna, Mariankatu 40, 33200 Tampere - T: (03) 2124551, Fax: 2126025, E-mail: pyynikinlinna@indigo.pp.fi. Head: Onerva Utriainen
Decorative Arts Museum / Fine Arts Museum 08929

Sara Hildénin Taidemuseo (Sara Hildén Art Museum), Särkänniemi, 33230 Tampere - T: (03) 2143134, Fax: 2229971, E-mail: sara.hilden@tampere.fi, Internet: http://www.tampere.fi/hilden. Head: Timo Vuorikoski
Fine Arts Museum - 1979
20th c Finnish and international art, especially post-war painting, sculpture and graphics 08930

Suomen Jääkiekko-Museo (Finnish Ice Hockey Museum), Veturiaukio 4, 33110 Tampere - T: (03) 31465303, Fax: 31466839, E-mail: vapriikki@tampere.fi, Internet: http://www.tampere.fi/vapri
Special Museum 08931

Suomen Koulumuseo, temporary closed (Finnish School Museum), Museum Centre Vapriikki, Veturiaukis 4, 33100 Tampere, mail addr: PL 487, 33101 Tampere - T: (03) 31466966, Fax: 31466808, E-mail: vapriikki@tampere.fi, Internet: http://www.tampere.fi/vapriikki. Head: Ritva Palo-oja
Special Museum
Material connected with the Finnish elementary school system, classroom interiors with small scale models and teaching material 08932

Taidekeskus Mältinranta (Artcentre Mältinranta), Kuninkaankatu 2, 33210 Tampere - T: (03) 2149214, Fax: 2149214, E-mail: maltti@sci.fi, Internet: http://www.sci.fi/~maltti. Head: Lars Holmström, Arja Moilanen
Public Gallery 08933

Tampereen Luonnontieteelinen Museo (Tampere Natural History Museum), Hämeenpuisto 20, 33210 Tampere. Head: Toimi Jaatinen
Natural History Museum - 1961
Flora and fauna of northern Satakunta and northern Häme provinces 08934

Tampereen Nykytaiteen Museo (Tampere Museum of Contemporary Art), Hatanpään Puistokuja 4, 33900 Tampere 10 - T: (03) 31465341, Fax: 31466808, E-mail: nykytaiteen.museo@tt.tampere.fi, Internet: http://www.tampere.fi/nymu. Head: Sirpa Joenniemi
Fine Arts Museum - 1966
Paintings, sculpture, graphics, mainly Finnish art since 1916 - library 08935

Tampereen Taidemuseo - Pirkanmaan Aluetaidemuseo (Tampere Art Museum - Regional Art Museum of Pirkanmaa), Puutarhakatu 34, 33230 Tampere - T: (03) 31466574, Fax: 31466584, E-mail: tamu@tampere.fi, Internet: http://www.tampere.fi/tamu. Head: Anneli Ilmonen
Fine Arts Museum - 1931
Paintings, sculptures, drawings, graphics, native art since the early 18th c, Tampere art coll, medal coll of the Finnish Medal Art Guild 08936

Tampereen Taidemuseon Muumilaakso (Moominvallay Collection of Tampere Art Museum), Hämeenpuisto 20, 33101 Tampere, mail addr: PL 487, 33101 Tampere - T: (03) 31466578, Fax: 31466567, E-mail: muumi@tampere.fi, Internet: http://www.tampere.fi/muumi. Head: Anneli Ilmonen
Fine Arts Museum - 1987
Original Moomin illustrations made by Tove Jansson, tableuax, moomin house 08937

Työväen Keskusmuseo (Central Museum of Labour in Finland), Väinö Linnan aukio 5, 33210 Tampere - T: (03) 2110404, Fax: 2110402, E-mail: info@tkm.fi, Internet: http://www.tkm.fi. Head: Pontus Blomster
Historical Museum 08938

Tankavaara

Kultamuseo Tankavaara (Gold Prospector Museum), Kultakylä, 99695 Tankavaara - T: (016) 626171, Fax: 626271, E-mail: inkeri.syrjanen@kultamuseo.inet.fi, Internet: http://www.tankavaara.fi. Head: Inkeri Syrjänen
Special Museum - 1973
Stone and mineral collections, gold prospecting equipment, buildings relocated from a gold prospectors' community in Lapland, photograph and tape collections, Golden World Exhibition with its outdoor museum area showing the global hist of gold - library 08939

Tarvasjoki

Tarvasjoen Kotiseutumuseo, Tarvasjoki kk, Tarvasj Kunta, Kuusikuja 5, 21450 Tarvasjoki - T: (02) 767371
Local Museum 08940

Teerijärvi

Terjärvs Hembygdsgård, 68700 Teerijärvi - T: (06) 75043
Local Museum 08941

Temmes

Temmeksen Kotiseutumuseo, Posti Temmeksen, 91950 Temmes - T: (08) 447197, 391950
Local Museum 08942

Tenala

Tenala Hembyggds Museum, Tenala K.B., 10520 Tenala - T: (019) 2451340
Agriculture Museum 08943

Tenholan Kotiseutumuseo → Tenala Hembyggds Museum

Teuva

Teuvan Museo, 64700 Teuva - T: (06) 71119
Local Museum 08944

Tikkakoski

Keski-Suomen Ilmailumuseo (Central Finland Aviation Museum), Tikkakoskentie 125, 41160 Tikkakoski - T: (014) 3752125, Fax: 3753620, E-mail: keski-suomen.ilmailumuseo@kolumbus.fi, Internet: http://www.jiop.fi/ksimuseo.htm. Head: Hannu Valtonen
Historical Museum / Military Museum - 1979
Scientific instruments, curiosity, photos, drawings 08945

Töysä

Töysän Museo, 63600 Töysä - T: (06) 48501
Local Museum 08946

Tohmajärvi

Kaurilan Koulumuseo (School Museum), 13 km Kirkonkylästä, Kaurila, 82600 Tohmajärvi - T: (013) 628252
Special Museum 08947

Pitäjämuseo ja Nymanin Talo, Maiju Lassilantie, Kirkkotie, 82600 Tohmajärvi - T: (013) 621711
Local Museum 08948

Toholampi

Häkkilän Museo, 4 km Toholammin Keskustasta, 69300 Toholampi - T: (06) 85056
Local Museum 08949

Toijala

Veturimuseo, Locomotive Museum, Ryödintie, 37801 Toijala, mail addr: PL 64, 37801 Toijala - T: (03) 5420308, 54201, E-mail: tt52301@uta.fi, Internet: http://www.toijala.fi/vapaa-aika/veturi. Head: Terni Tasanen
Science&Tech Museum
Finnish steam and diesel locomotives - archive, library 08950

Tokrajärvi

Aaronpiha (Aaronpiha Farmhouse), Kakonaho, 81350 Tokrajärvi - T: (013) 21707
Agriculture Museum - 1975
19th c farmhouse 08951

Tolosenmäki

Suorlahden Vanhahovi, Suoparsaari, 82380 Tolosenmäki - T: 426429
Local Museum 08952

Torittu

Padasjoen Kotiseutumuseo, 17710 Torittu - T: (03) 12141
Local Museum 08953

Tornio

Aineen Taidemuseo (Aine Art Museum), Torikatu 2, 95400 Tornio - T: (016) 43211, Fax: 432586. Head: Yrjö Nurkkala
Fine Arts Museum - 1985 08954

Alatornion Pitäjämuseo, Kirkonmäki, 94520 Tornio - T: (016) 41787
Local Museum 08955

Tornionlaakson Maakuntamuseo, Keskikatu 22, 95400 Tornio - T: (016) 432452, Fax: 432453. Head: Henri Nordberg
Ethnology Museum / Decorative Arts Museum - 1914
Ethnographical material from Tornionlaakso and Lapp territory, furniture, costumes, handicraft, silver work 08956

Tuiskula

Köyliön Torpparimuseo (Croft-Museum), Köyliö, 27730 Tuiskula - T: (03) 546230
Agriculture Museum 08957

Turku

Aboa Vetus - Arkeologis-historiallinen Museo (Museum of Archeology and History), Itäinen Rantakatu 4-6, 20700 Turku - T: (02) 2500552, Fax: 2794909, E-mail: info@aboavetusarsnova.fi, Internet: http://www.aboavetusarsnova.fi. Head: Minna Sartes
Archaeological Museum / Historical Museum 08958

Ars Nova - Nykytaiteen Museo (Museum of Contemporary Art), Itäinen Rantakatu 4-6, 20700 Turku - T: (02) 2500552, Fax: 2794909, E-mail: info@aboavetusarsnova.fi, Internet: http://www.aboavetusarsnova.fi. Head: Minna Sartes
Fine Arts Museum 08959

Forum Marinum, Linnankatu 72, 20100 Turku - T: (02) 2829511, Fax: 2829515, Internet: http://www.forum-marinum.fi. Head: Seppo Sarelius
Science&Tech Museum / Natural History Museum - 1998
Maritime hist coll (Åbo Akademi University, Turku Provincial Museum), ship model coll (Oy Rettig Ab Bore), museum ships, boats, ship models, navigation instruments, ship portraits, charts, drawings, logbooks, photographs - archives, library 08960

Kasvimuseo, Turun yliopisto (Museum of Plants, University of Turku), Turun Yliopisto, 20014 Turku - T: (02) 3335558, Fax: 3335564, E-mail: seppo.huhtinen@utu.fi, Internet: http://www.utu.fi/ml/biologia/kasvimuseo. Head: Prof. J. Salo
Natural History Museum / University Museum - 1919
Herbarium Vainio, worldwide lichen coll, 35,000 specimens, holarctic flora of the northern hemisphere - library 08961

Kuralan Kylämäki (The Village of Living History), Jaanintie 45, 20540 Turku - T: (02) 2620420, Fax: 2620429, E-mail: maakuntamuseo@turku.fi, Internet: http://www.turku.fi/museo. Head: Juhani Kostet
Agriculture Museum / Archaeological Museum / Open Air Museum
Ethnological coll from 1950 08962

Lasarettimuseo (Hospital Museum), Kiinamyllynkatu 4-8, 20520 Turku - T: (02) 3131231, Fax: 3132284, E-mail: maija.jansen@utu.fi
Special Museum 08963

Luostarinmäen Käsityöläismuseo (Luostarinmäki Handicraft Museum), Luostarinmäki, 20700 Turku 10 - T: (02) 2620350, Fax: 2620352, Internet: http://www.turku.fi/museo/luost.htm. Head: Solveig Sjöberg-Pietarinen
Open Air Museum / Ethnology Museum - 1940
Craftsmens' workshops and home interiors including those of a goldsmith, coppersmith, potter, bookbinder, rope maker, saddler, wig maker, glove maker, comb maker, violin maker, printing shop, tobacco house, in 17 wooden buildings 08964

Museet Ett Hem, Biskopsg 14, 20500 Turku 50 - T: (02) 2154396, Fax: 2752427, E-mail: John.Hackman@abo.fi, Internet: http://www.abo.fi/stiftelsen/ett_hem. Head: John Hackman
Decorative Arts Museum / Fine Arts Museum - 1925
Previous patrician home of consul Alfred Jacobsson and Mrs Helene Jacobsson. Furniture, furnishing textiles, silver, tin, porcelain, glass, Finnish art 08965

Museoalus Sigyn (Museum Ship Sigyn), c/o c/o Jarmo Koskinen, Harbour of Turku, Linnankatu 58-60, 20100 Turku - T: (02) 2534781, 2674102
Special Museum
Three masted barque, mariner's live and shipbuilding technique of the turn of the 19th c 08966

Qwensel ja Apteekkimuseo (Qwensel House and Pharmacy Museum), Läntinen Rantakatu 13b, 20100 Turku 10 - T: (02) 2620280, Fax: 2620444, E-mail: maakuntamuseo@turku.fi, Internet: http://www.turku.fi/museo/apteek. Head: Juhani Kostet
Historical Museum - 1958
Qwensel, middle class residence (18th c), pharmacy, pharmacist's home, fully equipped laboratory 08967

Sibelius Museum, c/o Åbo Akademi University, Biskopsgatan 17, 20500 Turku - T: (02) 2154494, 2154388, Fax: 2518528, E-mail: sibeliusmuseum@abo.fi, Internet: http://www.sibeliusmuseum.abo.fi. Head: Prof. Pirkko Moisala
Music Museum - 1926
Manuscripts of Jean Sibelius (1865-1957) and other Finnish composers, native and foreign sheet music coll, European and non-European art and folk music instruments - music library of the Turku Music Society (founded 1790) 08968

Sjöhistoriska Institutet vid Åbo Akademi (Maritime Institute of the Åbo Akademy), Slottsg 72, 20100 Turku - T: (02) 2153430, Fax: 2153431, E-mail: kim.montin@abo.fi. Head: Kim Montin
Historical Museum - 1936
Maritime history and ethnology 08969

Suomen Partiomuseo (Scout Museum of Finland), Virusmäentie 65 B 1, 20300 Turku - T: (02) 2377692, E-mail: partiomuseo@sp.partio.fi. Head: Kalevi Kuusinen
Special Museum 08970

Turun Biologinen Museo (Turku Biological Museum), Neitsytpolku 1, 20800 Turku 10 - T: (02) 2620340, Fax: 2620444, E-mail: maakuntamuseo@turku.fi, Internet: http://www.turku.fi/museo/biolm. Head: Juhani Kostet
Natural History Museum - 1907
Most mammals and half of species of birds nesting in Finland shown in 13 dioramas in museum building designed by A. Nyström 08971

Turun Kaupungin Historiallinen Museo, Turun Linna (Turku Historical Museum, Turku Castle), Linnankatu 80, 20100 Turku 10 - T: (02) 2620300, Fax: 2620314, E-mail: maakuntamuseo@turku.fi, Internet: http://www.turku.fi/museo. Head: Juhani Kostet
Historical Museum - 1881
Cultural history since the 13th c, costumes and other textiles, weapons, silver, tin, glass, porcelain, numismatics, restored Turku castle dating back to 1280 08972

Turun Maakuntamuseo (Turku Provincial Museum), Kalastajankatu 4, 20100 Turku - T: (02) 2620111, Fax: 2620444, E-mail: maakuntamuseo@turku.fi, Internet: http://www.turku.fi/museo. Head: Juhani Kostet
Local Museum 08973

Turun Taidemuseo (Turku Art Museum), Vartiovuorenmäki, 20700 Turku 10 - T: (02) 2747570, Fax: 2747599, E-mail: info@turuntaidemuseo.fi, Internet: http://www.turuntaidemuseo.fi. Head: Maija Koskinen
Fine Arts Museum - 1891
Finnish art from the end of 18th c until today, international print coll, animal sculptures by Jussi Mäntynen (1886-1978), surrealistic art of the Turku area, 08974

Turun Tuomiokirkkomuseo (Turku Cathedral Museum), Turun Tuomiokirkko, 20500 Turku - T: (02) 2510651, Fax: 2617318
Religious Arts Museum 08975

Wäinö Aaltosen Museo (Wäinö Aaltonen Museum of Art), Itäinen Rantakatu 38, 20810 Turku 81 - T: (02) 2620850, Fax: 2620862, E-mail: wam@turku.fi, Internet: http://www.wam.fi. Head: Päivi Kiiski-Finel
Fine Arts Museum - 1967
Coll of Wäinö Aaltonen's (1894-1966) work, Finnish modern art collection, photograph collection, Turku city art coll - library 08976

Turtola

Turtolan Kylämuseo, Turtolan Kirkon Vieressä, 95645 Turtola - T: (016) 84115
Local Museum 08977

Tuulos

Museo-Eerola, Sydänmaantie, 14820 Tuulos - T: (03) 6379101
Ethnology Museum / Open Air Museum 08978

Tuusniemi

Tuusniemen Kotiseutumuseo, 71200 Tuusniemi - T: (017) 741566/245
Local Museum 08979

Tuusula

Halosenniemi Museo, Halosenniemi, Rantatie, 04310 Tuusula - T: (09) 87183461, Fax: 87183463, E-mail: halosenniemi@tuusula.fi, Internet: http://www.tuusula.fi/english/thingstosee.htm. Head: Marke Naski-Multanen
Local Museum 08980

Ilmatorjuntamuseo (Anti-Aircraft Defence Museum), Klaavolantie 2, 04301 Tuusula - T: (09) 18162371, Internet: http://www.tuusulanrantatie.com/ilmatorjuntamuseo. Head: Matti Kulmala
Military Museum - 1968
Equipment for anti-aircraft defence and fire control, weapons, photograph and drawing collection, AA-guns and missiles - library 08981

Klaavola Museo, Kaavolantie, 04300 Tuusula - T: (09) 87183459/460, Fax: 87183458
Local Museum 08982

Tuusulan Museo, Klaavolantie 1, 04301 Tuusula - T: (09) 87181, 87183459, Fax: 87183458
Local Museum 08983

Tyrnävä

Tyrnävän Kotiseutumuseo, 91800 Tyrnävä - T: (08) 451330
Local Museum 08984

Urjalankylä

Urjalan Museo (Urjala Museum), 31720 Urjalankylä - T: (03) 5414261, Fax: 5414300, E-mail: aulis.ruuska@urjala.fi, Internet: http://www.urjala.fi. Head: Aulis Ruuska
Open Air Museum - 1950
Farm buildings (18th-20th c), furnishings 08985

Uusikaarlepyy

Kuddnäs Z. Topeliusksen Lapsuudenkoti, Z. Topelius Barndomshem (Childhome of Z. Topelius), 66900 Uusikaarlepyy - T: (06) 7856111. Head: Bo Kronquist
Special Museum - 1934 08986

Nykarleby Museum, Itäpuistikko 35, 66900 Uusikaarlepyy - T: (06) 21188, 21403
Local Museum 08987

Soldattorpet i Ytterjeppo, Löv, Ytterjeppo, 66900 Uusikaarlepyy - T: (06) 20337
Local Museum 08988

Uusikaupunki

Luotsitupa (Pilot Station), Vallimäki, 23500 Uusikaupunki - T: (02) 84515450, Fax: 84515457. Head: Mari Jalava
Science&Tech Museum 08989

Merimiehen Koti (Sailor's House), Myllykatu 18, 23500 Uusikaupunki - T: (02) 155413, 155447. Head: Mari Jalava
Historical Museum 08990

Uudenkaupungin Kultuurihistoriallinen Museo (Uusikaupunki Cultural History Museum), Ylinenkatu 11, 23500 Uusikaupunki - T: (02) 84515399, Fax: 84515457. Head: Mari Jalava
Local Museum - 1895
Shipping, wooden vessels, shipbuilding equipment, furniture, ceramics, costumes, numismatics 08991

Vaala

Säräisniemen Kotiseutumuseo, Säräisniemi, Kiertotie 15, 91700 Vaala - T: (08) 461394
Local Museum 08992

Vaasa

Bragegården (Museum Bragegården), Sandviken, 65350 Vaasa - T: (06) 3172271, 3127166, Fax: 3127166, E-mail: vasa.brage@kolumbus.fi, Internet: http://www.kulturfonden.fi/brage. Head: Inga Skott
Open Air Museum - 1933
Furnishings, bridal chamber, seal hunting equipment, peasant buildings from Southern Ostrobothnia: windmill, storehouse, smithy, treshing-building, smoke sauna 08993

Kuntsin Taidekokoelma (Kuntsi Art Collection), Hovioikeudenpuistikko 4, 65100 Vaasa 10 - T: (06) 3253915, Fax: 128862. Head: Anne-Maj Salin
Fine Arts Museum - 1970
Modern Finnish art 08994

Mejerimuseet vid Korsholms Lantbruksskolor (Dairy Museum), 6 km Vaasan Keskustasta itään, 63580 Vaasa - T: (06) 3567211, Fax: 3567506. Head: Ralf Nordstrom
Science&Tech Museum 08995

Ostrobothnia Australis, Biological Museum, Hovioikeudenpuistikko 9, 65100 Vaasa 10 - T: (06) 3178607. Head: Hans-Olof Lithén
Natural History Museum - 1924
Zoological, botanical and mineral collections, animals and specimens mainly from the Southern Ostrobothnia region and Scandinavia 08996

Pohjanmaan Museo (Ostrobothnian Museum), Museokatu 3, 65100 Vaasa 10 - T: (06) 3253800, Fax: 3253784, E-mail: pohjanmaan.museo@vaasa.fi, Internet: http://www.vaasa.fi/pohjanmaanmuseo. Head: Marianne Koshimies-Envall
Fine Arts Museum / Local Museum / Natural History Museum - 1895
Local history collection, peasant culture, folk art, crafts, art collection, 16th-17th c Italian, Dutch, Flemish and German art, 20th c native art - library 08997

Tikanojan Taidekoti (Tikanoja Art Museum), Hovioikeudenpuistikko 4, 65100 Vaasa - T: (06) 3253916, Fax: 3253918, E-mail: tikanojan.taidekoti@vaasa.fi, Internet: http://www.vaasa.fi/kulttuurijavapaa. Head: Anne-Maj Salin
Fine Arts Museum - 1951
Coll of Frithjof Tikanoja, French masters of the turn of the 20th c, Finnish art of the 19th and 29th cc 08998

Vaasan Auto- ja Moottorimuseo (Vaasa Car- and Motormuseum), Varastokatu 8, 65100 Vaasa - T: (06) 3176271
Science&Tech Museum 08999

Vaasan Merimuseo (Maritime Museum), Palosaaren Salmen Rannalla, 65200 Vaasa - T: (06) 3120511
Historical Museum 09000

Vääksy

Danielson-Kalmarin Huvila (Danielson-Kalmari Villa), 17201 Vääksy - T: (03) 8886234, 6256, Fax: 8886268, E-mail: asikkala.kunta@asikkala.fi, Internet: http://www.asikkala.fi/matkailu
Special Museum
Life and work of the Finnish author Danielson-Kalmari (1853 - 1933), presented in his villa 09001

Vääksyn Vesimylly- ja piensähkölaitosmuseo (Watermill Museum), 17201 Vääksy - T: (03) 7660860, 8886256, Fax: 8886268, E-mail: asikkala.kunta@asikkala.fi, Internet: http://www.asikkala.fi/matkailu
Science&Tech Museum 09002

Vähäkyrö

Vähänkyrön Museo, 66500 Vähäkyrö - T: (06) 784265
Local Museum 09003

Värtsilä

Värtsilän Myllymuseo (Mill Museum), 82655 Värtsilä - T: (013) 629487
Science&Tech Museum 09004

Västanfjärd

Skeppsvarvet sjöfartsutställning, Sagalund Museum (Exhibition at the Shipyard), 25830 Västanfjärd - T: (02) 421751, 421738, Fax: 421751, E-mail: skeppsvarvet@eugenia.pp.fi, Internet: http://www.eugenia.pp.fi
Special Museum 09005

Vakkola

Johannes Linnankosken Nuoruudenkoti (Johannes Linnankoski's Childhood Home), Niemenpellontie, 07510 Vakkola - T: (019) 5291231, Fax: 5291209, E-mail: askola@askola.fi, Internet: http://www.askola.fi. Head: Pia Keltti
Local Museum
Childhood home of the writer Johannes Linnankoski, alias Vihtori Peltonen (1869 - 1913) 09006

Valkeakoski

Emil Wikström Museo, Visavuori 80 Tarttila, 37700 Valkeakoski - T: (03) 5436528, Fax: 5436528, Internet: http://www.visavuori.com. Head: Pälvi Myllylä
Fine Arts Museum - 1966
Emil Wikström's sculptures home and studio with outbuildings of the sculptor (1864-1942), authentic interiors 09007

Kauppilanmäen Museo, Kauppilankatu 11-13, 37600 Valkeakoski - T: (03) 5844014, Fax: 5718138, E-mail: myllysaaren.museo@vlk.fi, Internet: http://www.vlk.fi/museot. Head: Rauni Laukkanen
Open Air Museum - 1960 09008

Myllysaaren Museo, Kanavanranta 3, 37600 Valkeakoski - T: (03) 5718100, Fax: 5718138, E-mail: myllysaaren.museo@vlk.fi, Internet: http://www.vlk.fi/museot. Head: Rauni Laukkanen
Science&Tech Museum - 1981
Paper converting in Finland, local hist - art exhibition 09009

Valkeala

Hirsmäen Museoalue, Hirsmäki, 45370 Valkeala - T: (05) 863283
Open Air Museum 09010

Valtimo

Murtovaaran Talomuseo (Murtovaara Farmhouse), Murtovaara, 75700 Valtimo - T: (013) 51009. Head: Kari Sallinen
Open Air Museum / Agriculture Museum - 1972
Murtovaara farmhouse and outbuildings, two chimneyless dwellings (18th-19th c), furnishings 09011

Vammala

Tyrvään Seudun Museo (Tyrvää Regional Museum), Jaatsinkatu 2, 38210 Vammala 2 - T: (03) 5198267, Fax: 5115467, E-mail: pekka.koskinen@vammala.fi, Internet: http://www.vammala.fi. Head: Pekka Koskinen
Local Museum - 1932
Hunting and agricultural equipment, household objects, handicrafts, furniture, glass, weapons, coins - library 09012

Vampula

Vampulan Museo, 32610 Vampula - T: (02) 7651142
Open Air Museum 09013

Vanhalinna

Liedon Vanhalinna (Vanhalinna Museum), Vanha Härkätie 111, 21410 Vanhalinna - T: (02) 4896700, Fax: 4896711, E-mail: tuula.leimu@utu.fi, Internet: http://www.liedonvanhalinna.fi. Head: Tuula Leimu
Archaeological Museum / Ethnology Museum - 1956
Archaeological finds from the Iron Age and the early Middle Ages on Vanhalinna castle hill, ethnographical material (1850-1940), furniture, Vanhalinna Manor and outbuildings (1927), crofter's cottage (1920) 09014

Vantaa

Helsinge Hembygdsmuseum (Helsinki Parish Museum), Helsingin pitäjän kirkonkylä, Kirkkotie, 01510 Vantaa - T: (09) 893219, 822330, E-mail: gunnar.weckstrom@suomi24.fi. Head: Gunnar Weckström
Decorative Arts Museum
Rural objects, handicraft products 09015

Heureka - The Finnish Science Centre, Tiedepuisto 1, 01301 Vantaa - T: (09) 85799, Fax: 8734142, E-mail: info@heureka.fi, Internet: http://www.heureka.fi. Head: Dr. Per-Edvin Persson
Natural History Museum / Science&Tech Museum - 1989
Interactive science exhibitions - planetarium, hemispheric cinema 09016

Rikosmuseo (Crime Museum), Jokiniemenkuja 4, Tikkurila, 01300 Vantaa - T: (09) 8388661, Fax: 83886509
Historical Museum 09017

Suomen Ilmailumuseo (Finnish Aviation Museum), Tietotie 3, 01531 Vantaa - T: (09) 8700870, Fax: 87008720, E-mail: info@suomenilmailumuseo.fi, Internet: http://www.suomenilmailumuseo.fi. Head: Yrjö Toivanen
Science&Tech Museum - 1972
History of civil aviation in Finland, aircrafts, uniforms, scale models; IVL A22 Hansa, Messerschmitt BF 109 G-2 - library 09018

Vantaan Kaupunginmuseo (Vantaa City Museum), Tikkurilan Vanha Asema, Hertaksentie 1, 01300 Vantaa - T: (09) 83924007, Fax: 83923638, E-mail: kaupunginmuseo@vantaa.fi, Internet: http://www.vantaa.fi/kaupunginmuseo. Head: Jorma Vimonen
Local Museum 09019

Vantaan Kaupunginmuseo - Kuvataideasiat (Vantaa City Museum - Visual Arts), Myyrmäkitalo, Kilterinraitti 6, 01600 Vantaa - T: (09) 83935570, Fax: 83935470, Internet: http://www.vantaa.fi/kaupunginmuseo/kuvataide
Fine Arts Museum 09020

Varkaus

Mekaanisen Musiikin Museo (Museum of Mechanical Music), Pelimanninkatu 8, 78850 Varkaus - T: (017) 5580643, Fax: 5566566, E-mail: pawel.kempf@pp.inet.fi. Head: Jürgen Kempf
Music Museum 09021

Savon Museo ja Taidemuseo → Varkauden Taidemuseo

Varkauden Museo (Varkaus Museum), Wredenkatu 5a, 78250 Varkaus - T: (017) 5794437, Fax: 5794441, E-mail: museo@vrk.varkauf.fi, Internet: http://www.varkaus.fi/sivistystoimi/museo. Head: Anja Ollikainen
Local Museum
Ethnography, houshold articles, textile-making equipment, numismatic, stamps 09022

Varkauden Taidemuseo (Varkaus Art Museum), Ahlströminkatu 17, 78250 Varkaus - T: (017) 5794538, Fax: 5794679, E-mail: taidemuseo@vrk.varkaus.fi, Internet: http://www.varkaus.fi/sivistystoimi/taidemuseo
Fine Arts Museum - 1956
Finnish Modernism, contemporary art 09023

Varpaisjärvi

Varpaisjärven Kotiseutumuseo, 73200 Varpaisjärvi - T: (017) 71331
Local Museum 09024

Vasarainen

Vasaraisten Museo, Kotiseutumuseo Muina, Rauma, 26740 Vasarainen - T: (02) 8236412, Internet: http://www.saunalahti.fi/khannula. Head: Eeva Yrjänen
Open Air Museum / Agriculture Museum 09025

Vasikka-Aho

Väinö Tuomaalan Museosäätiö, Väinöntalo-Evijärvi, 62540 Vasikka-Aho. Head: Juhani Tuomaala
Local Museum - 1960
Exhibits illustrating the rural life of the Järviseutu district - library 09026

Väinontalo - Järviseudun Museo (Lake District Museum of Southern Ostrobothnia - Väinö's House), Latukantie 99, 62540 Vasikka-Aho - T: (06) 7653160, 7699111, Fax: 7651682, E-mail: kulttuuri@evijarvi.fi. Head: Tuija Ahola
Open Air Museum - 1955
Household articles, agricultural implements, folk art and rural handicraft, 17th-19th c buildings from parishes in the Lake District of Southern Ostrobothnia 09027

Vehmaa

Vehmaan Kivityömuseo ja Huolilan Kotiseutumuseo, Lahdinka, 23210 Vehmaa - T: (02) 821290
Local Museum 09028

Vehmersalmi

Vehmersalmen Kotiseutumuseo, 71310 Vehmersalmi - T: (017) 551120/23
Local Museum 09029

Verla

Verlan Tehdasmuseo (Verla Mill Museum), 47850 Verla - T: (020) 4152170, Fax: 4152168, E-mail: helena.mauno@upm-kymmene.com, Internet: http://store.upm-kymmene.com/verla
Science&Tech Museum - 1882
Complete paper board mill from the beginning of the c 09030

Veteli

Vetelin Museo, 69700 Veteli - T: (06) 621611
Local Museum 09031

Vieremä

Hevosajoneuvomuseo Ameriikka (Cart and Sleigh Museum), 74200 Vieremä - T: (017) 84133
Special Museum 09032

Vihanti

Vihannin Kotiseutumuseo (Vihanti Local History Museum), 86400 Vihanti. Head: Matti A. Junttila
Local Museum - 1947
Peasant articles, furniture, dairy equipment objects, blacksmith's tools, public granary 09033

Vihti

Vihdin Museo, Kirkkoniementie 1, 03400 Vihti - T: (09) 22423811, E-mail: museo@vihti.fi, Internet: http://www.ekenas.fi/museum/vihti.htm. Head: Pirkko Aurell
Local Museum 09034

Viljamakasiinimuseo (Grain Store Museum), 03400 Vihti - T: (09) 2248211
Agriculture Museum 09035

Viinijärvi

Komperon Kotiseutumuseo, Liperin Siikakoski, Kompero, 83400 Viinijärvi - T: (013) 647129
Local Museum 09036

Viitasaari

Viitasaaren Metsätyömuseo (Forestry Museum), 44500 Viitasaari - T: (014) 29354
Agriculture Museum 09037

Vilppula

Vilppulan Museo, 35700 Vilppula - T: (03) 43259
Local Museum 09038

Vimpeli

Suksimuseo (Ski Museum), 62800 Vimpeli - T: (06) 51129
Special Museum 09039

Virolahti

Virolahden Kotiseutumuseo, Pyterlahti, 49900 Virolahti - T: (05) 3573545, Fax: 3471867, E-mail: anu.haapala@miehikkala.fi, Internet: http://www.virolahti.fi. Head: Anu Haapala
Local Museum 09040

Virrat

Halin Metsäkämppämuseo (Hali Logging Camp Museum), Herranen, 34800 Virrat - T: (03) 55121, 55075, 56509
Open Air Museum 09041

Mittamuseo (Measuring Museum), Herranen, 34800 Virrat - T: (03) 5121, 55075, 56509
Science&Tech Museum 09042

Rajalahden Talomuseo, Herranen, 34800 Virrat - T: (03) 5121, 55075, 56509
Open Air Museum 09043

Virtain Perinnekylä (Traditional Village), 34800 Virrat - T: (03) 512276, 55075
Historical Museum 09044

Virtasalmi

Virtasalmen Kotiseutumuseo, 77330 Virtasalmi - T: (015) 70202
Local Museum 09045

Vöyri

Fädernegården i Rejpelt, 66600 Vöyri - T: (06) 338514, 338508
Local Museum 09046

Myrbergsgården, Myrbergsby, 66600 Vöyri - T: (06) 330381, 330562
Local Museum 09047

Vöyrin Kotiseutumuseo (Vöyri Museum), 66600 Vöyri - T: (06) 330033
Local Museum - 1959
Farmhouse (18th c), furnishings, folk costumes 09048

Vuolijoki

Vuolijoen Kotiseutumuseo, Vuolijoki kk, Kuusirannantie, 88270 Vuolijoki - T: (08) 6895511, Fax: 6895700. Head: Olavi Rintala
Local Museum / Folklore Museum 09049

Ylämaa

Ylämaan Jalokivimuseo, Jalokivikylä, 54410 Ylämaa - T: (05) 77332
Local Museum 09050

Yläne

Yläneen Kotiseutumuseo (Yläne Local Histoy Museum), 21900 Yläne - T: (02) 563415. Head: V. Oivanen
Local Museum / Open Air Museum - 1964
Farm buildings (18th-19th c), smithy (1883), windmill (1763), agricultural objects, handicrafts, furnishings 09051

Ylihärmä

Ylihärmän Kotiseutumuseo, 62375 Ylihärmä - T: (06) 4846322
Local Museum 09052

Ylijärvi

Pätärin Talomuseo (Farmhouse Museum), 54460 Ylijärvi - T: (05) 77170
Agriculture Museum 09053

Ylikiiminki

Ylikiimingin Kotiseututalo ja Museo, 91300 Ylikiiminki - T: (08) 77110
Local Museum 09054

Ylistaro

Ylistaron Kotiseutumuseo, Kaskiontie, 61400 Ylistaro - T: (06) 700255, 740341
Local Museum 09055

Ylivieska

Puuhkalan Talomuseo, Museotie, 84100 Ylivieska - T: (08) 2941
Local Museum 09056

Ypäjä

Ypäjän Kotiseutumuseo, Saakkolantie 4, 32100 Ypäjä - T: (02) 76265203, Fax: 7677214, E-mail: paivi.klemela@yapja.fi, Internet: http://www.yapja.fi
Open Air Museum 09057

Yttilä

Yttilän Museokoulu (School Museum), 27740 Yttilä - T: (03) 541122, 541203
Special Museum 09058

France

Abbeville

Musée Boucher-de-Perthes, 24 Rue Gontier-Patin, 80100 Abbeville - T: 0322240849, Fax: 0322203503. Head: Pantxika De Paepe
Local Museum - 1837
Prehist of the Somme valley, esp prehistoric industrial finds, 15th-16th century wood carvings, French and Flemish paintings from the 15th-18th century, ceramics, 18th century furnishings, 17th century wall hangings, natural sciences exhibits, specimen of alca impennis - library 09059

Abilly

Atelier de Taille du Silex, Le Petit Paulmy, 37160 Abilly - T: 0247597801
Archaeological Museum 09060

Ablain-Saint-Nazaire

Musée du Souvenir 1914-1918, Tour-Lanterne, Cimetière National, 62153 Ablain-Saint-Nazaire - T: 0321451580, Fax: 0321591776
Military Museum 09061

Abries

Écomusée de la Vie Montagnarde, 05460 Abries - T: 0492467226
Folklore Museum 09062

Agde

Musée Agathois, 5 Rue de la Fraternité, 34300 Agde - T: 0467948251, Fax: 0467262913, E-mail: dau.sarret@libertysurf.fr
Local Museum - 1941
Local hist, religious and folk art, costumes, porcelain, glass, model ships, wine, Greek finds 09063

Musée de l'Ephèbe, Cap d'Agde, 34300 Agde - T: 0467946960, Fax: 0467946969, E-mail: musee@ville-agde.fr, Internet: http://www.ville-agde.fr. Head: Odile Bérard-Azzouz
Archaeological Museum / Local Museum / Museum of Classical Antiquities 09064

Agen

Musée de la Résistance et de la Déportation, 40 Rue Montesquieu, 47015 Agen - T: 0553660426
Historical Museum 09065

Musée des Beaux-Arts, Pl du Dr. Pierre Esquirol, 47916 Agen Cedex 9 - T: 0553694723, Fax: 0553694777, E-mail: musee@ville-agen.fr. Head: Marie-Dominique Nivière
Local Museum - 1876
Greek, Gallo-Roman, Merovingian, Celtic archaeological findings, faience and ceramics, paintings, 16th-19th c Spanish tableware, Spanish painting (Francisco de Goya) 09066

Aguessac

Musée Paléontologique, Av des Causses, 12520 Aguessac - T: 0565598399/598015
Archaeological Museum 09067

Ahun

Château-Musée de Villemonteix, 23150 Ahun - T: 0555623392/4024
Decorative Arts Museum 09068

Aigueperse

Exposition Permanente, Château de la Roche, 63260 Aigueperse - T: 0473636581
Decorative Arts Museum 09069

Aigues-Mortes

Exposition Artistique et Viticole, Domaine de Jarras, Listel, 30220 Aigues-Mortes - T: 0466511700, Fax: 0466511729, E-mail: tourisme@listel.fr, Internet: http://www.listel.fr. Head: Martial Pélatan
Decorative Arts Museum / Agriculture Museum 09070

Musée Archéologique, Porte Saint-Antoine, 30220 Aigues-Mortes - T: 0466537300
Archaeological Museum 09071

Tour de Constance, 30220 Aigues-Mortes - T: 0466536155/7998
Historical Museum 09072

Aigues-Vives

Écomusée de l'Agriculture, 09600 Aigues-Vives - T: 0561017004/030619
Agriculture Museum 09073

Maison Natale-Bibliothèque du Président Gaston-Doumergue, 52 Pl G.-Doumergue, 30670 Aigues-Vives - T: 0466353363
Special Museum / Library with Exhibitions 09074

Aiguillon

Hôtel Raoul Dastrac, Collection d'Arts et de Traditions Populaires, 47190 Aiguillon - T: 0553796258
Folklore Museum 09075

Aiguines

Musée des Tourneurs, Rue Haute, 83630 Aiguines - T: 0494702129/2193
Local Museum 09076

Aimargues

Château-Musée de Teillan, 30470 Aimargues - T: 0466880238
Archaeological Museum / Decorative Arts Museum 09077

Aime

Musée Archéologique et Minéralogique Pierre Borrione, Chapelle Saint-Sigismond, 73210 Aime - T: 0479097979/7357
Archaeological Museum / Natural History Museum 09078

Ainvelle

Exposition Permanente d'Archéologie, Mairie, 88320 Ainvelle - T: 0329079276
Archaeological Museum 09079

Aire-sur-Adour

Musée d'Art et d'Archéologie, Mairie, 40800 Aire-sur-Adour - T: 0558718204
Fine Arts Museum / Archaeological Museum 09080

Airvault

Abbaye-Musée, Rue de la Gendarmerie, Centre-Ville, 79600 Airvault - T: 0549647142/7013
Folklore Museum - 1975
Folk art and traditions - archives 09081

Aix-en-Provence

Archéosite de l'Oppidum Celto-Ligure d'Entremont, 13100 Aix-en-Provence - T: 0442233373/161900
Archaeological Museum 09082

Art Sacré, Église Sainte-Marie-Madeleine, 13100 Aix-en-Provence - T: 0442161161
Religious Arts Museum 09083

Atelier Paul Cézanne, 9 Av Paul-Cézanne, 13090 Aix-en-Provence - T: 0442210653, Fax: 0442219034, E-mail: atelier.cezanne@wanadoo.fr. Head: M.M. Fraisset
Fine Arts Museum
Former studio of the artist Paul Cézanne (1839-1906), memorabilia of Cézanne 09084

Espace Historique du Camp d'Internement, Les Milles, 13090 Aix-en-Provence - T: 0491549144/42161161
Historical Museum 09085

Fondation Vasarely, 1 Av Marcel-Pagnol, 13090 Aix-en-Provence - T: 0442200009, Fax: 0442591465, E-mail: fondation.vasarely@wanadoo.fr, Internet: http://fondationvasarely.com. Head: Christian Kert
Fine Arts Museum 09086

Musée-Château de la Pioline, 13090 Aix-en-Provence - T: 0442200781/161161
Fine Arts Museum / Decorative Arts Museum 09087

Musée des Tapisseries, 28 Pl des Martyrs de la Résistance, 13100 Aix-en-Provence - T: 0442230991, Fax: 0442235775. Head: Bruno Ely
Decorative Arts Museum - 1910
Ancient wall hangings from around the world, textiles, furnishings, 17th-18th century paintings - library, documentation center 09088

Musée d'Histoire Naturelle, Hôtel Boyer-d'Éguilles, 6 Rue Espariat, 13100 Aix-en-Provence - T: 0442262367
Natural History Museum - 1838
Ornithology, paleontology, botany, entomology, mineralogy 09089

Musée du Vieil Aix, 17 Rue de Saporta, 13100 Aix-en-Provence - T: 0442214355, Fax: 0442965276. Head: Nicole Martin-Vignes
Local Museum - 1936
Local hist, folklore, puppets, clay manger figures, ceramics, documents of the history of Aix, scale models, furniture, works of art 09090

Musée Granet, Pl Saint-Jean-de-Malte, 13100 Aix-en-Provence - T: 0442381470. Head: Denis Coutagne
Fine Arts Museum - 1765
European painting, sculpture beginning with Roman times, archaeology of Greece, Egypt, Rome, and ancient Gaul, applied arts from medieval times to the 17th c, furnishings, wall hangings, rugs, decorative arts, ceramics, armaments, prints, numismatics 09091

Musée Paul-Arbaud, 2a Rue du 4-Septembre, 13100 Aix-en-Provence - T: 0442383895
Fine Arts Museum - 1911
Painting, drawings, faience, archives on 19th-20th c Provencal writers, manuscripts, books 09092

Pavillon de Lenfant, 13090 Aix-en-Provence - T: 0442234880
Fine Arts Museum 09093

Pavillon de Vendôme, 34 Rue Célony, 13100 Aix-en-Provence - T: 0442210578, Fax: 0442235775. Head: Bruno Ely
Historic Site - 1954
17th century historic pavillon, furnishings and paintings from the 17th-18th century - audiovisual room, park 09094

Aix-les-Bains

Musée Archéologique et Lapidaire, Pl Maurice Mollard, 73100 Aix-les-Bains - T: 0479350592. Head: Françoise Guichon
Archaeological Museum - 1872
Gallo-Roman sculpture, pottery, inscriptions, temple ruins, local prehist 09095

Musée du Docteur Faure, Musée Municipal, 10 Blvd des Côtes, 73100 Aix-les-Bains - T: 0479610657, Fax: 0479882748. Head: Françoise Guichon
Fine Arts Museum - 1949
Impressionist paintings, sculpture and watercolours by Rodin, furnishings, memorabilia of the poet Alphonse de Lamartine 09096

Musée in Situ des Bains Romains, Pl Maurice Mollard - Thermes Nationaux, 73100 Aix-les-Bains - T: 0479353850, Fax: 0479340399
Archaeological Museum 09097

Ajaccio

Maison Nationale Bonaparte, 3 Rue Saint-Charles, 20000 Ajaccio - T: 0495214389
Historical Museum
House of Napoleon's birth, historic rooms with furnishings, farming tools, memorabilia, portraits and documents of the Bonaparte family 09098

Musée d'Histoire Militaire à Bandera, 1 Rue Levie, 20000 Ajaccio - T: 0495510734
Military Museum 09099

Musée du Capitellu, 18 Blvd Danielle-Casanova, 20000 Ajaccio - T: 0495215057
Local Museum / Decorative Arts Museum / Fine Arts Museum 09100

Musée Fesch, 50 Rue Fesch, 20000 Ajaccio - T: 0495214817
Fine Arts Museum - 1852
14th-18th century Italian paintings, 17th-18th century still life paintings, Spanish paintings - library, research and study section, documentation 09101

Musée-Maison des Milelli, Propriété des Bonaparte, Rte d'Alata, 20000 Ajaccio - T: 0495222213
Folklore Museum 09102

Musée Napoléonien, Hôtel de Ville, Pl Foch, 20000 Ajaccio - T: 0495219015
Historical Museum 09103

Alba-la-Romaine

Espace Muséal Archéologique, Rue de Chabrol, 07400 Alba-la-Romaine - T: 0475524642
Archaeological Museum 09104

Site Archéologique, Village Mediéval, Centre de Documentation, 07400 Alba-la-Romaine - T: 0472524642
Archaeological Museum 09105

Albaret-Sainte-Marie

Musée de la Nature, La Roche, 48200 Albaret-Sainte-Marie - T: 0466319283
Natural History Museum 09106

Albé

Maison du Val de Villé, 4 Pl du Tilleul, 67220 Albé - T: 0388570842, Fax: 0388571684, E-mail: tourisme@cc-canton-de-ville.fr
Local Museum 09107

Albertville

Musée des XVIes Jeux Olympiques d'Hiver (Museum of the 16th Winter Olympic Games), 11 Rue Pargoud, 73200 Albertville - T: 0479377571, Fax: 0479323875, E-mail: maisonjeuxolympiques@wanadoo.fr. Head: Auguste Picollet
Special Museum 09108

Albi

Musée Toulouse-Lautrec, Pl de la Berbie, 81000 Albi, mail addr: BP 100, 81003 Albi - T: 0563494870, Fax: 0563494888, E-mail: mairie.albi@inlink.fr. Head: Danièle Devynck
Fine Arts Museum - 1922
Paintings, drawings, lithographs, posters, and illustrated books be H. de Toulouse-Lautrec, works of his contemporaries 09109

Albon

Musée Aérorétro, Aérodrome du Creux de la Thine, 26140 Albon - T: 0475030358, Fax: 0475030358, E-mail: aero.retro3@freesbee.fr. Head: Christian Mafre
Science&Tech Museum 09110

Alby-sur-Chéran

Musée de la Cordonnerie, Mairie, Le Bourg, 74540 Alby-sur-Chéran - T: 0450681010
Special Museum 09111

Alençon

Musée de la Dentelle au Point d'Alençon, 31 Rue du Pont Neuf, 61000 Alençon - T: 0233262726
Special Museum 09112

Musée des Beaux-Arts et de la Dentelle, Cour Carré de la Dentelle, 61000 Alençon - T: 0233324007, Fax: 0233265166. Head: Aude Pessey-Lux
Fine Arts Museum 09113

Aléria

Musée Départemental d'Archéologie Jérôme-Carcopino, Fort-Matra, Rte Nationale 198, 20270 Aléria - T: 0495570092
Archaeological Museum 09114

Alès

Dépôt Archéologique du Fort Vauban, 30107 Alès - T: 0466863040
Archaeological Museum 09115

Mine Témoin d'Alès, Chemin de la Cité Sainte-Marie, Rochebelle, 30100 Alès - T: 0466304515, Fax: 0466784900, E-mail: dg@ales.cci.fr
Science&Tech Museum 09116

Musée-Bibliothèque Pierre-André Benoît, 52 Montée des Lauriers, Rochebelle, 30107 Alès - T: 0466869869, Fax: 0466342051. Head: Aleth Jourdan
Fine Arts Museum 09117

Musée du Colombier, Rue Jean-Mayodon, 30107 Alès - T: 0466863040. Head: Marc Bordreuil
Archaeological Museum / Fine Arts Museum - 1889
Prehistoric and medieval archaeological finds, 17th-18th century Flemish, Dutch, Italian, and Spanish paintings, 17th-20th century French paintings 09118

Musée Minéralogique de l'École des Mines d'Alès (Mineralogical Museum of Ecole des Mines d'Alès), c/o Ecole des Mines d'Alès, Centre de Recherche Matériaux de Grande Diffusion, 6 Av de Clavières, 30319 Alès Cedex - T: 0466785000, Fax: 0466785092, E-mail: jprolley@ema.fr, Internet: http://www.ema.fr/CMGD/musee.html. Head: Jean-Pierre Rolley
Natural History Museum 09119

Alfortville

Palais des Expositions Chinagora, 1 Pl du Confluent France Chine, 94140 Alfortville - T: 0143535818
Ethnology Museum 09120

Alise-Sainte-Reine

Musée Alésia, Rue de l'Hôpital, 21150 Alise-Sainte-Reine - T: 0380961095, 0380968590, Fax: 0380968103, E-mail: pouralesia@wanadoo.fr. Head: Claude Grapin
Archaeological Museum - 1906
Local Gallo-Roman and medieval finds, stone and bronze statues, ceramics, numismatics, siege 52 BC 09121

Allauch

Musée d'Allauch, Pl du Docteur Chevillon, 13718 Allauch - T: 0491104900, Fax: 0491104823, E-mail: info@allauch.com. Head: Nicolas Bousquet
Religious Arts Museum / Historical Museum
Religious costums, statues, religious items, goldery, paintings, pre 17th c pottery and ceramics, archaeological and historical items 09122

Allenc

Musée Local, Donjon du Villaret, 48190 Allenc - T: 0466476479
Local Museum 09123

Allevard-les-Bains

Musée Jadis Allevard, Maison des Forges, 38580 Allevard-les-Bains - T: 0476450362
Local Museum 09124

Alliat

Musée Cavernicole de la Grotte de la Vache, 09400 Alliat - T: 0561059506
Natural History Museum 09125

Allouville-Bellefosse

Musée de la Nature, Centre d'Hébergement, d'Étude sur la nature et l'environnement, 76190 Allouville-Bellefosse - T: 0235960654
Natural History Museum 09126

Ally

Salon de l'Automobile Miniature, Château de la Vigne du XVe s, 15700 Ally - T: 0471690020
Special Museum 09127

Aloxe-Corton

Musée de la Tonnellerie et du Vin, Château de Corton-André, 21420 Aloxe-Corton - T: 0380264425, Fax: 0380264357, E-mail: pandre@axnet.fr, Internet: http://www.pierre-andre.com. Head: Christian Ciamos
Special Museum
Wine, barrels 09128

Altkirch

Musée Sundgauvien, 1 Rue de l'Hôtel de Ville, 68130 Altkirch - T: 0389400004, Fax: 0389402180, E-mail: edith.knittel@wanadoo.fr. Head: Christiane Straehly
Archaeological Museum / Local Museum
Pre- and ancient hist, engravings, armaments, regional hist and customs, works of local painters 09129

Amancey-Cléron

Musée du Vieux Tacot, Cléron, 25330 Amancey-Cléron - T: 0381621331/0544
Science&Tech Museum 09130

Ambazac

Château de Montméry et son Parc, 87240 Ambazac - T: 0555567319, Fax: 0145028098. Head: Laure de Pourtalès
Decorative Arts Museum
Arboretum, the only American castle built in France 09131

Ambérieu-en-Bugey

Le Château des Allymes, 01500 Ambérieu-en-Bugey - T: 0474380607
Archaeological Museum / Local Museum 09132

Musée du Cheminot, 46 Rue Aristide-Briand, 01500 Ambérieu-en-Bugey - T: 0474383175/1002
Science&Tech Museum 09133

Ambert

Musée de la Fourme et des Fromages, 29 Rue des Chazaux, 63600 Ambert - T: 0473824923
Special Museum 09134

Musée de la Machine Agricole et à Vapeur, Rue de l'Industrie, 63600 Ambert - T: 0473826042, Fax: 0473829123, E-mail: Agrivap.musee@wanadoo.fr, Internet: http://www.agrivap.free.fr. Head: Jean-Paul Beal
Agriculture Museum / Science&Tech Museum 09135

Musée Historique du Papier, Moulin Richard de Bas, 63600 Ambert - T: 0473820311, Fax: 0473822541, E-mail: rdb@wanadoo.fr. Head: François Banière
Science&Tech Museum - 1943
Paper mill, paper production, hand-made paper fabrication, hist of paper and watermarks - library 09136

Ambierle

Musée Alice Taverne, 42820 Ambierle - T: 0477656099, Fax: 0477656099. Head: Henri Bertaud
Ethnology Museum - 1951
Exhibits on the life of regional peasants and craftsmen, reconstructed home interiors 09137

Ambleteuse

Musée du Fort Vauban, 62164 Ambleteuse - T: 0320546154/21326190
Local Museum 09138

Musée Historique de la Seconde Guerre Mondiale, Rte CD 940, 62164 Ambleteuse - T: 0321873301, Fax: 0321873501
Military Museum 09139

Ambleville

Musée du Bouton, Château d'Ambleville, 95710 Ambleville - T: 0134677176
Special Museum 09140

Amboise

Château Royal d'Amboise, 37400 Amboise - T: 0247570098, Fax: 0247575223, E-mail: chateau.amboise@wanadoo.fr
Decorative Arts Museum 09141

La Maison Enchantée - Le Monde Magique des Automates, 7 Rue du Général Foy, 37400 Amboise - T: 0247232450, Fax: 0247232450
Decorative Arts Museum / Fine Arts Museum 09142

Mini-Château, Rte de Chenonceaux, 37400 Amboise - T: 0247236563, Fax: 0247236564, Internet: http://www.alize-parc.fr. Head: J.L. Gallois
Special Museum 09143

Musée de la Poste et des Voyages, 6 Rue Joyeuse, 37400 Amboise - T: 0247570011, Fax: 0247231980. Head: Anne Debal-Morche
Special Museum / Historical Museum - 1971
Documents from the times of the pony express, models and originals of mail coaches, equipment of mail drivers 09144

Musée du Clos-Lucé, Demeure de Léonard de Vinci, 2 Rue du Clos-Lucé, 37400 Amboise - T: 0247576288/0073/0145743098. Head: Jean Saint-Bris
Special Museum / Historical Museum - 1954
Memorabilia of the artist Leonardo da Vinci, of the 16th century house where he died, models of his inventions (the first car, plane, parachute etc), furniture, tapestry 09145

Musée le Fou de l'Âne, La Ménaudière, 37400 Amboise - T: 0247234444
Natural History Museum / Agriculture Museum 09146

Musée Municipal, Hôtel de Ville, Rue François I, 37400 Amboise - T: 0247234723, Fax: 0247231980. Head: Anne Debal-Morche
Historical Museum - 1890
Religious art, stone carvings, Aubusson tapestries, Royal autographs, local hist 09147

Pagode de Chanteloup, Rte de Bléré, 37400 Amboise - T: 0247572097/6597
Fine Arts Museum 09148

Ambrière-les-Vallées

Musée des Tisserands Mayennais, Pl du Château, 53300 Ambrière-les-Vallées - T: 0243049619
Special Museum 09149

Amélie-les-Bains-Palalda

Musée d'Arts et de Traditions Populaires, Palalda, 66110 Amélie-les-Bains-Palalda - T: 0468393490
Folklore Museum 09150

Musée de la Poste, Parvis de l'Eglise de Palalda, 66110 Amélie-les-Bains-Palalda - T: 0468393490
Special Museum / Science&Tech Museum 09151

Amfreville-les-Champs

La Ferme au Fil des Saisons, Hameau de Yemauville, 76560 Amfreville-les-Champs - T: 0235564146
Folklore Museum 09152

Amiens

Collection Charles de l'Escalopier, 50 Rue de la République, 80000 Amiens, mail addr: c/o Bibliothèque Municipale, BP 0542, 80005 Amiens Cedex 1 - T: 0322971010, Fax: 0322971070. Head: Christine Carrier
Decorative Arts Museum - 1866
Ancient bronze objects, goldsmith's work, ivory, enamel, wood carvings, weaving, memorabilia of Monsignore Affre 09153

Musée de l'Hôtel de Berny, 36 Rue Victor-Hugo, 80000 Amiens - T: 0322971400, Fax: 0322971427. Head: Matthiew Pinette
Local Museum / Decorative Arts Museum - 1966
Furnishings and interiors, memorabilia of Laclos, Gresset, Jules Verne, Voiture, 18th century French decorative arts 09154

Musée de Picardie, 48 Rue de la République, 80000 Amiens - T: 0322971400, Fax: 0322971427. Head: Matthiew Pinette
Local Museum - 1854
Painting, sculpture, drawings, prints, tapestry, ceramics, art objects from ancient Egypt to Louis XII - library 09155

Musée d'Histoire Naturelle, 41 Rue de la République, 80000 Amiens - T: 0322917928
Natural History Museum 09156

Amilly

Musée de la Pailletterie, Domaine de la Pailletterie, Av d'Antibes, 45200 Amilly - T: 0238936413
Folklore Museum 09157

Amnéville-les-Thermes

Musée d'Histoire Naturelle, Aquarium, Bois de Coulange, 57360 Amnéville-les-Thermes - T: 0387703661
Natural History Museum 09158

Musée Historique des Incorporés de Force et de Tambow, Ecole du Parc, 57360 Amnéville-les-Thermes - T: 0387588333/712229
Military Museum 09159

Amou

Mosaïque Gallo-Romaine, Château, 40330 Amou - T: 0558890008, Fax: 0558890008, E-mail: asd.amon@wanadoo.fr
Historic Site 09160

Amplepuis

Musée Barthélemy-Thimonnier de la Machine à Coudre et du Cycle, Pl de l'Hôtel-de-Ville, 69550 Amplepuis - T: 0474890890
Science&Tech Museum / Historical Museum 09161

Ampus

Musée Municipal, Pl Neuve, 83111 Ampus - T: 0494709711
Agriculture Museum 09162

Ancenis

Musée sur l'Archéologie et l'Histoire du Pays d'Ancenis (closed) 09163

Ancy-le-Franc

Château du XVIe s, Château, 89160 Ancy-le-Franc - T: 0386751463
Decorative Arts Museum
Renaissance manor, interior decorations by Primatice and Niccolo dell'Abbate, Aubusson tapestries 09164

Andernos-les-Bains

Maison Municipale Louis-David, 14 Av Pasteur, 33510 Andernos-les-Bains - T: 0556820295
Local Museum 09165

Andillac

Musée Maurice et Eugénie de Guérin, Château du Cayla, 81140 Andillac - T: 0563339030. Head: Alain Soriano
Special Museum - 1936
Original interiors, letters and manuscripts of the poet M. de Guérin (1810-1839), housed in former home 09166

Andilly-en-Bassigny

Musée Archéologique, 52360 Andilly-en-Bassigny - T: 0325844133/0219
Archaeological Museum 09167

Andlau

Collections Historiques, Hôtel Zinck, 11 Rue de la Marne, 67140 Andlau - T: 0388082730
Historical Museum 09168

Anduze

La Chapeauthèque, 30140 Anduze - T: 0466617534
Special Museum 09169

Musée d'Instruments de Musique, Fg du Pont, 30140 Anduze - T: 0466618680
Music Museum 09170

Anet

Château-Musée d'Anet, 28260 Anet - T: 0237419007, Fax: 0237419645
Decorative Arts Museum 09171

Angers

Château d'Angers, Promenade du Bout du Monde, 49100 Angers - T: 0241874347/868194, Fax: 0241871750, Internet: http://www.monum.fr. Head: Laurent Heulot
Decorative Arts Museum - 1954
12th-18th century historic monument, French and Flemish tapestries from 14th-17th century, the 'Apocalypse' Tapestries (14th century) 09172

Collections du Conseil Général, Hôtel du Département, Mail de la Préfecture, 49000 Angers
Archaeological Museum / Decorative Arts Museum 09173

Du Tam-Tam au Satellite, Château de Pignerolle, 49124 Angers - T: 0241933838, Fax: 0241938934, Internet: http://www.museecommunication.org. Head: Guy Biraud
Science&Tech Museum 09174

Musée de la Tapisserie Contemporaine, 4 Blvd Arago, 49100 Angers - T: 0241241848, E-mail: patricklenouene@ville-angers.fr. Head: Patrick Le Nouëne
Decorative Arts Museum - 1841
Tapestry - Library, laboratory 09175

Musée de l'Étain, Le Logis de l'Estaignier, Rue Saint-Aignan, 49100 Angers - T: 0241886741
Special Museum 09176

Musée de l'Evolution du Style Plantagenêt, Cathédrale Saint-Maurice, 49000 Angers - T: 0241875845
Religious Arts Museum 09177

Musée des Beaux-Arts (reopening in 2004), 10 Rue du Musée, 49100 Angers - T: 0241886465, Fax: 0241860638, E-mail: patricklenouene@ville-angers.fr. Head: Patrick Le Nouëne
Fine Arts Museum - 1797
Early Italian sculpture, 16th-17th century Spanish, Flemish, Dutch sculptures, 18th-19th century French sculptures, Italian and French primitive paintings, 18th-19th century French paintings, 17th century European paintings, 15th century house 09178

Musée d'Histoire Naturelle, 43 Rue Jules Guitton, 49100 Angers - T: 0241860584, Fax: 0241247561, E-mail: museum.histnat@ville-anger.fr, Internet: http://www.ville-angers.fr/museum. Head: Vincent Dennys
Natural History Museum - 1798
Paleontology, geology, mineralogy, zoology, prehist 09179

Musée du Souvenir du Génie, 106 Rue Eblé, 49000 Angers - T: 0241248240
Military Museum
Hist of the Corps of Military Engineers from 1445 to present 09180

Musée Jean-Lurçat, Ancien Hôpital Saint-Jean, 4 Blvd Arago, 49100 Angers - T: 0241241845, Fax: 0241182441, E-mail: patricklenouene@ville-angers.fr. Head: Patrick Le Nouëne
Decorative Arts Museum 09181

Musée Pincé, 32bis Rue Lenepveu, 49100 Angers - T: 0241889427, Fax: 0241182441, E-mail: patrick.lenouene@ville-angers.fr. Head: Patrick Le Nouëne
Archaeological Museum / Decorative Arts Museum - 1849-1889
Egyptian antiquities, Greek, and Roman antiquities, Japanese woodcuts, Oriental art 09182

Anglards-de-Salers

Château-Musée de la Trémolière, 15380 Anglards-de-Salers - T: 0471400002
Local Museum 09183

Angoulême

Collections du Château d'Epernon, 61 Rue du Minage, 16000 Angoulême - T: 0545924835
Decorative Arts Museum 09184

Musée de la Société Archéologique et Historique de la Charente, 44 Rue Montmoreau, 16000 Angoulême - T: 0545384517/949075
Archaeological Museum - 1844
Prehistoric to early Christian finds, bronzes, Romanesque to Renaissance sculpture, 12th century sculptures of the cathedral, Limoges enamels, pottery, porcelain, folk art, engravings 09185

Musée des Beaux-Arts (closed between September 2002 until end of 2004), 1 Rue Friedland, 16000 Angoulême - T: 0545950769
Local Museum - 1838
Pre- and early hist, African and Oceanic anthropology, Italian, Dutch, Flemish, and French painting, 18th-19th c faience 09186

Musée du Papier Le Nil, 134 Rue de Bordeaux, 16000 Angoulême - T: 0545927343, Fax: 0545921599, E-mail: - musee.papier.angouleme.alienor@wanadoo.fr. Head: Denis Peaucelle
Science&Tech Museum 09187

Musée Georgette-Lemaire, 59 Rue Waldeck-Rousseau, 16000 Angoulême - T: 0545951107
Special Museum 09188

Angoustrine

Musée de la Filature, 66760 Angoustrine - T: 0468302289
Special Museum / Folklore Museum 09189

Angrie

Musée de la Meunerie et de la Boulangerie, Moulin Neuf La Marmite, 49440 Angrie - T: 0241920428
Science&Tech Museum 09190

Annecy

Musée Château d'Annecy et Observatoire Régional des Lacs Alpins, Pl du Château, 74000 Annecy - T: 0450338730. Head: William Saadé
Ethnology Museum / Archaeological Museum / Fine Arts Museum / Decorative Arts Museum - 1842
Ethnology, archaeology, fine arts, modern and regional art, observatory of Alpine lakes, traditional Alpine furniture 09191

Musée Salésien, 11 Av de la Visitation, 74000 Annecy - T: 0450452030
Religious Arts Museum 09192

Palais de l'Isle, Centre d'Interprétation Urbain, Vieilles Prisons, 74000 Annecy - T: 0450338731, Fax: 0450330084, E-mail: musees@ville-annecy.fr. Head: William Saadé
Historical Museum / Archaeological Museum 09193

Anneyron

Musée Saint-Jean, 18 Rue Aristide Briand, 26140 Anneyron - T: 0475315414
Science&Tech Museum / Natural History Museum 09194

Annoisin-Châtelans

Musée de la Lauze, Auberge de Larina-Châtelans, 38460 Annoisin-Châtelans - T: 0474951390/838060
Natural History Museum 09195

Annonay

Musée César-Filhol, 15 Rue Jean-Baptiste-Bechetoille, 07100 Annonay - T: 0475332451
Science&Tech Museum 09196

Ansouis

Château-Musée d'Ansouis, 84240 Ansouis - T: 0490098270
Fine Arts Museum / Decorative Arts Museum 09197

Musée de la Vigne et du Vin, Château Turcan, 84240 Ansouis - T: 0490098333
Special Museum 09198

Musée Extraordinaire Georges-Mazoyer, Rue du Vieux-Moulin, 84240 Ansouis - T: 0490098264
Fine Arts Museum / Decorative Arts Museum 09199

Antibes

Galerie du Bastion, Bastion Saint-André sur les Remparts, 06600 Antibes - T: 0492905435
Fine Arts Museum / Decorative Arts Museum
Fine and Decorative Arts 09200

Musée Bastion Saint-André, Bastion Saint-André, Av Maizière, 06600 Antibes - T: 0492905435, Fax: 0492905435, E-mail: musee.archeologie@antibes-juanlespins.com. Head: Karine Viatgé
Archaeological Museum
Archeology 09201

Musée de la Tour, Histoire et Traditions Locales, 1 Rue de l'Orme, 06600 Antibes - T: 0493345091
Local Museum 09202

Musée du Marineland, Rte de Biot, 06600 Antibes - T: 0493334949
Natural History Museum 09203

Musée Jungle des Papillons Vivants, 309 Av Mozart, 06600 Antibes - T: 0493335577
Natural History Museum 09204

Musée Naval et Napoléonien, Batterie du Graillon, Av John-Kennedy, 06600 Antibes - T: 0493614532
Historical Museum
Hist of the navy, coll on Napoleon I, hist of the Imperial epoch 09205

Musée Peynet, Pl Nationale, 06600 Antibes - T: 0492905430
Special Museum 09206

Musée Picasso, Château Grimaldi, 06600 Antibes - T: 0492905420, Fax: 0492905421, E-mail: musee.picasso@antibes-juanlespins.com
Fine Arts Museum - 1928
Classical Roman art, paintings, ceramics, drawings, gouaches, tapestry, sculpture, and lithographs by Pablo Picasso, modern painting, woodcuts, bronze sculptures 09207

Muséoparc La Petite Ferme Provençale, 309 Av Mozart près Marineland, 06600 Antibes - T: 0393335577
Natural History Museum 09208

Antignac

Exposition d'Archéologie Médiévale, 15240 Antignac - T: 0471402315/2126/2376
Archaeological Museum 09209

Antonne-et-Trigonant

Château Les Bories, 24420 Antonne-et-Trigonant - T: 0553060001
Decorative Arts Museum 09210

Anzin

Musée Théophile Jouglet, 215 Rue Anatole France, 59410 Anzin - T: 0327290045
Historical Museum
Life of the coal-miners, hist of coal-mining and Anzin, fossils 09211

Aoste

Musée Gallo-Romain d'Aoste, BP 17, 38490 Aoste - T: 0476325827, Fax: 0476325735, E-mail: musee.gallo-romain.aoste@wanadoo.fr. Head: Jean Guibal
Archaeological Museum - 1856
Gallo-Roman finds, ceramics, glass, numismatics 09212

Apremont-la-Forêt

Musée du Chemin de Fer, 55300 Apremont-la-Forêt - T: 0329904401
Science&Tech Museum 09213

Apremont-sur-Allier

Musée des Calèches, Château d'Apremont, 18150 Apremont-sur-Allier - T: 0248804141
Science&Tech Museum 09214

Apt

Maison du Parc Naturel Régional du Luberon, Musée de Paléontologie, 60 Pl Jean-Jaurès, 84400 Apt - T: 0490044200
Natural History Museum 09215

Musée Municipal Apt, 27 Rue de l'Amphithéâtre, 84400 Apt - T: 0490747845, Fax: 0490742813. Head: André Kauffmann
Decorative Arts Museum / Archaeological Museum - 1952
Faience, archaeology, prehist and Gallo-Roman hist, earthenware 18th to 20th c, Thanksgiving pictures (17th-19th c) 09216

Araches-les-Carroz

Musée des Traditions Populaires de la Frasse, 74300 Araches-les-Carroz - T: 0450900590
Folklore Museum 09217

Arbois

Maison de Louis Pasteur, 83 Rue de Courcelles, 39600 Arbois - T: 0384661172, Fax: 0384661285. Head: Hélène Gouinguenet
Historical Museum - 1935
Memorabilia of the scientist Louis Pasteur (1822-1895) in his former home 09218

Musée Cavernicole de la Grotte des Planches, 39600 Arbois - T: 0384660793/1374
Archaeological Museum 09219

Musée de la Vigne et du Vin de Franche-Comté, Château Pécauld, 39600 Arbois - T: 0384662614/24, Fax: 0384661029. Head: Didier Gagneur
Agriculture Museum 09220

Musée Saret de Grozon, 9 Grande Rue, 39600 Arbois - T: 0384722772, Fax: 0384728946. Head: Anne Dary
Fine Arts Museum / Decorative Arts Museum - 1821
19th century paintings, silverwork, porcelain 09221

Arc-en-Barrois

Musée de la Machine à Vapeur, Ancienne Scierie, 52210 Arc-en-Barrois - T: 0325025217, Fax: 0325025217. Head: Bérangère Goujat
Science&Tech Museum 09222

Arc-et-Senans

Institut Claude-Nicolas Ledoux, Anciennes Salines Royales, 25610 Arc-et-Senans - T: 0381544545
Science&Tech Museum 09223

Arcachon

Musée Océanographique, 2 Rue du Professeur Jolyet, 33120 Arcachon - T: 0556833332, Fax: 05568351043. Head: D.J. Dentraygues
Local Museum - 1865
Zoology, archeology, navigation, ostreiculture 09224

Arceau

Château d'Arcelot, 2 Rue de Champ Rosé, 21310 Arceau - T: 0380370232, Fax: 0380370091, E-mail: chateauarcelot@wanadoo.fr, Internet: http://www.arcelot.com
Decorative Arts Museum 09225

Arcizans-Avant

Musée du Château du Prince Noir, 65400 Arcizans-Avant - T: 0562970279
Natural History Museum 09226

Arcueil

Galerie Municipale d'Art Contemporain Julio-Gonzalez, 21 Av Paul-Doumer, 94110 Arcueil - T: 0146150978
Fine Arts Museum 09227

Arcy-sur-Cure

Musée Archéologique Parat, Mairie, 89270 Arcy-sur-Cure - T: 0386819169, Fax: 0386819169, E-mail: arcy@compuserve.com
Archaeological Museum 09228

Ardes-sur-Couze

Musée des Vieux Métiers, Pl du Foirail, 63420 Ardes-sur-Couze - T: 0473718141
Historical Museum 09229

Aren

Château-Musée, 64400 Aren - T: 0559880191
Decorative Arts Museum 09230

Argelès-Gazost

Musée de la Faune Sauvage, 65400 Argelès-Gazost - T: 0562979107/9158
Natural History Museum 09231

Argelès-sur-Mer

Musée Casa De Les Alberes, 4 Pl Castelans, 66700 Argelès-sur-Mer - T: 0468814274
Folklore Museum 09232

Argence

Musée du Jouet Automobile, La Tuilerie, 14370 Argence - T: 0231238585/7100
Science&Tech Museum 09233

Argent-sur-Sauldre

Musée des Métiers de France, Château, 18410 Argent-sur-Sauldre - T: 0248733310
Special Museum 09234

Argentan

Musée Dentelle Point d'Argentan, 2 Rue de l'Abbaye, 61200 Argentan - T: 0233671201, Fax: 0233356755
Special Museum 09235

Argenteuil

Musée du Vieil Argenteuil, 5 Rue Pierre-Guienne, 95100 Argenteuil - T: 0139476497
Local Museum
Prehist, medieval art, local hist, folklore, memorabilia of Héloise, hist of Jansenism and Mirabeau 09236

Argol

Musée des Vieux Métiers Vivants, Bourg, 29127 Argol - T: 0298277530
Special Museum 09237

Musée du Cidre Breton, Kermarzin, Rte de Brest, 29127 Argol - T: 0298277326/3413
Special Museum 09238

Argy

Musée des Métiers et Traditions Paysannes, 36500 Argy - T: 0254840498. Head: Daniel Guillemin
Folklore Museum 09239

Arlanc-en-Livradois

Musée de la Dentelle à la Main, 53 Rte Nationale, Hôtel de Ville, 63220 Arlanc-en-Livradois - T: 0473950003
Special Museum
Old lace samples, lace production 09240

Arlay

Château, 39140 Arlay - T: 0384444194, Fax: 0384481796, E-mail: chateau@arlay.com
Historic Site 09241

Arles

Fondation Van-Gogh Arles, 24bis Rond-Point des Arènes, 13200 Arles - T: 0490499404, 0490930808, Fax: 0490496132, E-mail: fondwga@wanadoo.fr, Internet: http://www.tourismeplus.com/fonf. Head: Yolande Clergue
Fine Arts Museum 09242

Musée Arlaten, Hôtel Laval-Castellane, Rue de la République, 13200 Arles - T: 0490960823
Local Museum - 1899
16th century house, life and customs of the Provence 09243

Musée Camarguais, Parc Naturel Régional de Camargue, Mas du Pont de Rousty, 13200 Arles - T: 0490971082
Ethnology Museum 09244

Musée de l'Arles Antique, Presqu'Ile du Cirque Romain, 13635 Arles - T: 0490188888, Fax: 0490188893, E-mail: info@arles-antique.org, Internet: http://www.arles-antique.org. Head: Claude Sintes
Museum of Classical Antiquities 09245

Musée de Site de l'Esplanade, Blvd des Lices, 13200 Arles
Archaeological Museum 09246

Musée Réattu, Rue du Grand Prieuré, 13200 Arles - T: 0490493758, Fax: 0490493697, E-mail: - musee.realtu.arles@provnet.fr. Head: Michèle Moutashar
Fine Arts Museum - 1868
16th century Arras tapestries, 18th century local painting, memorabilia of the painter Réattu, sculpture, photo coll, drawings and paintings by Picasso, sculptures by Zadkine, contemporary art in 16th-17th century seat of the Maltese Order 09247

Arles-sur-Tech

Musée Animé du Tissage, Tissages Catalans, 66150 Arles-sur-Tech - T: 0468391007/1199
Folklore Museum 09248

Armentières

Musée de la Bière, Brasserie Sébastien Artois, 75 Av Roger Salengro, 59280 Armentières - T: 0320483030
Special Museum 09249

Arnay-le-Duc

Musée Archéologique, Tour de la Motte-Forte, Rue de l'Église, 21230 Arnay-le-Duc - T: 0380901159
Archaeological Museum 09250

Musée Régional des Arts de la Table, Ancien Hospice Saint-Pierre du XVIIe s, 21230 Arnay-le-Duc - T: 0380901159
Special Museum 09251

Arpaillargues-et-Aureillac

Musée Animé 1900, Moulin de Chalier, 30700 Arpaillargues-et-Aureillac - T: 0466225864
Science&Tech Museum 09252

Musée du Train et du Jouet, Moulin de Chalier, 30700 Arpaillargues-et-Aureillac - T: 0466225864
Special Museum 09253

Arpajon-sur-Cère

Musée des Arts et Traditions Populaires de la Vallée de la Cère, Château Conros, 15130 Arpajon-sur-Cère - T: 0471635027, Fax: 0471645678, E-mail: conros@amisa.fr, Internet: http://www.conros.fr
Folklore Museum 09254

Arques (Aude)

Musée Déodat Roché, 11190 Arques (Aude) - T: 0468698562
Special Museum 09255

Arques (Pas-de-Calais)

Musée de la Navigation Fluviale/ Ascenseur à Bateaux, Rue Denis Papin, 62510 Arques (Pas-de-Calais) - T: 0321984301/126230
Science&Tech Museum / Special Museum 09256

Arras

Circuit Géologique des Boves, Hôtel de Ville, 62000 Arras - T: 0321512695
Natural History Museum / Archaeological Museum 09257

Musée des Beaux-Arts, Ancienne Abbaye Saint-Vaast, 22 Rue Paul Doumer, 62000 Arras - T: 0321712643, Fax: 0321231926, E-mail: musee.arras@wanadoo.fr, Internet: http://www.musenor.com/gm/Guide01-f.html. Head: Annick Notter
Fine Arts Museum - 1825
12th-16th century French sculptures, 17th-19th century French paintings, Dutch and Flemish paintings, 18th century porcelain from Tournai and Arras, religious objects - library 09258

Arreau

Musée des Petits Hommes en Pyrénées, Château des Nestes, 65240 Arreau - T: 0562401152
Science&Tech Museum 09259

Arrens-Marsous

Musée-Maison du Parc National et du Val d'Azun, 65400 Arrens-Marsous - T: 0562974313
Natural History Museum 09260

Arromanches-les-Bains

Musée d'Arromanches, Pl du 6 Juin 1944, 14117 Arromanches-les-Bains - T: 0231223431, Fax: 0231926883, Internet: http://www.normandy1944.com. Head: Gérard Legout
Historical Museum - 1954
Documents, dioramas, and films on the Allied landing in 1944, site of the landing 09261

Ars-sur-Formans

Maison du Saint-Curé, Presbytère, 01480 Ars-sur-Formans - T: 0474081717, Fax: 0474007550, E-mail: info@arsnet.org, Internet: http://www.arsnet.org
Religious Arts Museum 09262

Arsonval

Musée d'Art Sacré de Loukine, Mairie, 10200 Arsonval - T: 0325279254
Religious Arts Museum 09263

Artenay

Musée Archéologique, Quartier du Paradis, Mail Est, 45410 Artenay - T: 0238800973
Archaeological Museum 09264

Musée du Théâtre Forain, Quartier du Paradis, 45410 Artenay - T: 0238800973
Performing Arts Museum 09265

Musée-Moulin de Pierre, Rte Nationale 20, 45410 Artenay - T: 0238800461
Science&Tech Museum 09266

Arudy

Musée Municipal d'Ossau, Rue de l'Eglise, 64260 Arudy - T: 0559056171/058044
Local Museum 09267

Arvieux

Ecomusée de l'Agriculture Queyrassine, Hameau des Moulins, 05350 Arvieux - T: 0492450623, Fax: 0492452720
Agriculture Museum 09268

Musée du Tour de France, Sommet du Col de l'Izoard, 05350 Arvieux - T: 0492450623, Fax: 0492452720
Special Museum 09269

Arvieux-en-Queyras

Exposition du Jouet en Bois, Hameau de La Chalp, 05350 Arvieux-en-Queyras - T: 0492467386, Fax: 0492468215, E-mail: alpin.chez.lui@online.fr, Internet: http://www.alpinchezlui.com. Head: Jean-Paul Blanc
Special Museum 09270

Arvillard

Petit Musée de la Chartreuse Saint-Hugon, Karma-Ling, Hameau de Saint-Hugon, 73110 Arvillard - T: 0479257800, Fax: 0479257808, E-mail: karmaling@karmaling.org, Internet: http://www.karmaling.org. Head: Lama Denys
Religious Arts Museum 09271

Arville

Diaporama sur les Templiers, Commanderie des Templiers, 41170 Arville - T: 0254809073
Historical Museum 09272

Arzacq-Arraziguet

Musée de la Faune et Traditions du Béarn, Myocastor, 64410 Arzacq-Arraziguet - T: 0559045403
Natural History Museum 09273

Asco

Musée d'Arts Populaires, Hôtel du Cinto, 20276 Asco - T: 0495478207/8101
Folklore Museum 09274

Aspres-sur-Buech

Écomusée, 05140 Aspres-sur-Buech - T: 0492586034
Local Museum 09275

Assas

Collection Historique, Château, 34160 Assas - T: 0467596279/45
Historical Museum / Music Museum 09276

Assier

Château, 46320 Assier - T: 0565404099/109800
Decorative Arts Museum / Fine Arts Museum 09277

Asson

Collections d'Histoire Naturelle, Parc Zoologique et Botanique, 64800 Asson - T: 0559710334
Natural History Museum 09278

Athis-Mons

Musée Delta, 40 Av Jean-Pierre-Bénard, 91200 Athis-Mons - T: 0160481811
Science&Tech Museum 09279

Attigny

Musée André-Dhôtel, 08130 Attigny - T: 0324712129
Special Museum 09280

Aubagne

Exposition du Petit Monde de Pagnol, Esplanade Charles-de-Gaulle, 13400 Aubagne - T: 0442034998
Local Museum 09281

Maison de l'Argile, Ateliers Thérèse Neveu, Cour de Clastre, 13400 Aubagne - T: 0442034310
Decorative Arts Museum 09282

Musée de la Légion Étrangère, Caserne Quartier Vienot, 13400 Aubagne - T: 0442188299
Military Museum 09283

Musée du Pastis, Av du Pastre, 13400 Aubagne - T: 0442822957
Special Museum 09284

Aube

Musée de la Comtesse de Ségur, Ancien Presbytère, 3 Rue de l'Abbé Roger Derry, 61270 Aube - T: 0233246009, Fax: 0233246009, Internet: http://www.musee-comtessedesegur.com. Head: Nicole Thouret
Local Museum 09285

Musée de la Grosse Forge, 61270 Aube - T: 0233341493, Fax: 0233246009, E-mail: forgeaube@libertysurf.fr, Internet: http://www.forgeaube.fr.st/. Head: Nicole Thouret
Science&Tech Museum 09286

Aubenas

Musée du Château, 07200 Aubenas - T: 0475878100/880079
Fine Arts Museum / Local Museum 09287

Aubenton

Musée Jean-Mermoz, Mairie, 02500 Aubenton - T: 0323977517/7039
Special Museum 09288

Aubière

Musée de la Vigne et du Vin, 63170 Aubière - T: 0473440101, 0472276004
Special Museum 09289

Aubigné-Racan

Musée du Poète Racan, Mairie, 72620 Aubigné-Racan - T: 0243462070
Special Museum 09290

Aubigny-sur-Nère

Musée de l'Auld Alliance Franco-Écossaise, Château des Stuarts, 18700 Aubigny-sur-Nère - T: 0248815050, Fax: 0248583830
Fine Arts Museum / Decorative Arts Museum 09291

Musée Marguerite-Audoux, Château des Stuarts, 18700 Aubigny-sur-Nère - T: 0248815050, Fax: 0248583830
Special Museum 09292

Aubin

Musée de la Mine Lucien-Mazars, Maison du Peuple, 12110 Aubin - T: 0565631411/1916
Science&Tech Museum 09293

Aubusson

Musée de l'École Nationale d'Art Décoratif, Pl Villeneuve, 23200 Aubusson - T: 0555661428
Decorative Arts Museum 09294

Musée Départemental de la Tapisserie, Av des Lissiers, 23200 Aubusson, mail addr: BP 89, 23200 Aubusson - T: 0555663306, Fax: 0555838987, E-mail: giffault@musée-tap.cg23.fr, Internet: http://www.cg23.fr. Head: Michèle Giffault
Decorative Arts Museum - 1981
library, archive 09295

Auch

Château de Saint-Cricq, Direction de Gimont, 32000 Auch - T: 0562631017
Folklore Museum 09296

Collection Historique, Archives Départementales, Rue Edgar Quinet, 32000 Auch - T: 0562050318
Historical Museum 09297

Exposition de l'Habitat Gallo-Romain, C.E.S. Mathalin, 32000 Auch - T: 0562052853
Archaeological Museum 09298

Musée de la Résistance, Rue Pagodéoutès, 32000 Auch - T: 0562057125
Historical Museum 09299

Musée des Jacobins, 4 Pl Louis-Blanc, 32000 Auch - T: 0562057479, Fax: 0562619095
Fine Arts Museum / Ethnology Museum / Archaeological Museum / Museum of Classical Antiquities - 1979
Paintings, sculpture, crafts, 8th-18th c pre-Columbian, American, and colonial art of the southern states, busts, folklore and folk art of the Gascogne, Gallo-Roman and medieval archeology 09300

Salle des Illustres, Hôtel de Ville, 32000 Auch - T: 0562057124
Local Museum 09301

Auchel

Musée Vivant de la Mine, Blvd de la Paix, 62260 Auchel - T: 0321526610
Science&Tech Museum 09302

Auchy-la-Montagne

Ecomusée de la Forge, 60360 Auchy-la-Montagne - T: 0344469773
Science&Tech Museum 09303

Aucun

Musée Montagnard du Lavedan, Près de l'Eglise, 65400 Aucun - T: 0562971203. Head: Eric Delgado
Agriculture Museum / Ethnology Museum 09304

Audes-Reugny

Musée du Canal de Berry, 03190 Audes-Reugny - T: 0470067092. Head: René Chambareau
Science&Tech Museum 09305

Audierne

Musée de la Chaumière, Rte de la Plage, 29113 Audierne - T: 0298701220
Folklore Museum 09306

Musée Flottant-Architecture Navale, Sloop-Langoustier "Cap Sizun", 29113 Audierne - T: 0699323122. Head: Alain Daniel
Special Museum 09307

Audinghen

Musée du Mur de l'Atlantique, Blockhaus de la Batterie Todt, between Calais and Boulogne-sur-Mer, 62179 Audinghen - T: 0321329733, 0321826201, 0321821742, Fax: 0321320067. Head: Pascal Davies
Military Museum 09308

Audun-le-Tiche

Musée Archéologique, 1 Rue de l'Alzette, 57390 Audun-le-Tiche - T: 0382521303
Archaeological Museum 09309

Augirein

Musée d'Arts et de Traditions Populaires, 09800 Augirein - T: 0561967722
Folklore Museum 09310

Aulan

Château-Musée, 26570 Aulan - T: 0475288000. Head: Comte d' Aulan
Decorative Arts Museum / Fine Arts Museum 09311

Aulnay (Charente-Maritime)

Château-Musée de Dampierre-sur-Boutonne, 17470 Aulnay (Charente-Maritime) - T: 0546240224, Fax: 0146518715, E-mail: dampierre@netlink.fr, Internet: http://www.chateau-dampierre.com. Head: Jean-Louis Hedelin
Fine Arts Museum / Decorative Arts Museum / Historic Site 09312

Aumont-Aubrac

Musée Local, 48130 Aumont-Aubrac - T: 0466428870
Local Museum 09313

Aups

Musée Simon-Segal, Ancienne Chapelle du Couvent des Ursulines, Av Albert-Ier, 83630 Aups - T: 0494701298
Fine Arts Museum 09314

Aurec-sur-Loire

Musée-Château du Moine Sacristain, 43110 Aurec-sur-Loire - T: 0477352655
Special Museum / Historical Museum 09315

Auriac-du-Périgord

Ecomusée de l'Abeille, 24290 Auriac-du-Périgord - T: 0553518634
Special Museum 09316

Aurice

Musée d'Arts et de Traditions Populaires, Château d'Estignols, 40500 Aurice - T: 0558760160
Folklore Museum 09317

Aurignac

Musée de Préhistoire, Rue Fernand Lacorre, 31420 Aurignac - T: 0561989008/7006, Fax: 0561987133, Internet: http://www.aurignacien.com. Head: N. Rouquereol
Archaeological Museum
Prehistorical finds 09318

Aurillac

Musée d'Art et d'Archéologie, Centre Culturel Pierre Mendès-France, 37 Rue des Carmes, 15012 Aurillac Cedex - T: 0471454610, Fax: 0471454692, E-mail: musee-art@mairie-aurillac.fr. Head: Brigitte Lepine
Fine Arts Museum / Archaeological Museum - 1853
Painting, sculpture, archaeology, ethnography
Ancient and contemporary art, photography, archeology 09319

Musée de Cire-Historial de la Haute-Auvergne, Pl Gerbert, 15000 Aurillac - T: 0571484658/6438
Local Museum 09320

Muséum des Volcans, Château Saint-Etienne, 15000 Aurillac - T: 0471480700, Fax: 0471489740, E-mail: museum.volcans@wanadoo.fr. Head: Jean-François Heil
Natural History Museum - 1903
Volcanic rocks, local tertiary fossils, iconography of volcanism - library 09321

Auriol

Musée Martin Duby, Rue Augustin-Dupuy, 13390 Auriol - T: 0442728429
Ethnology Museum 09322

Auris-en-Oisans

Musée Rural, 38142 Auris-en-Oisans - T: 0476801352
Folklore Museum 09323

Auron

Musée de l'École, Maison du Tourisme, 06660 Auron - T: 0493024196, Fax: 0493024850, E-mail: auron@wanadoo.fr, Internet: http://www.auron.fr.st
Special Museum 09324

Aussois

Musée Local, 13 Rue de l'Artisanat, 73500 Aussois - T: 0479203040/80
Local Museum 09325

Auterive

Fondation René Pous, Les Escloupies, Rte de Crépiac, 31190 Auterive - T: 0561083403
Fine Arts Museum 09326

Autrans

Maison du Parc et des 4 Montagnes, 38880 Autrans - T: 0476953501, E-mail: maison4m@wanadoo.fr. Head: Patrice Quetard
Natural History Museum 09327

Autun

Musée National des Ecoles Préparatoires de l'Armée de Terre, Rue G. Joliet, 71400 Autun - T: 0385865599
Military Museum 09328

Musée Rolin, Musées Municipaux, 3 Rue des Bancs, 71400 Autun - T: 0385520976, Fax: 0385524741. Head: Brigitte Maurice-Chabard
Archaeological Museum / Fine Arts Museum /

Decorative Arts Museum - 1837
Prehistorical items, Gallo-Roman finds and Roman
sculptures, Gothic primitive paintings and statues,
16th-20th century paintings, sculptures,
furnishings 09329

Muséum d'Histoire Naturelle, 14 Rue Saint-Antoine,
71400 Autun - T: 0385520915, Fax: 0385863878,
E-mail: museum.autun@wanadoo.fr. Head:
Dominique Chabard
Natural History Museum 09330

Auvers (Haute-Loire)

Musée de la Résistance du Mont Mouchet, Maison
Forestière, Le Bourg, 43300 Auvers (Haute-Loire) -
T: 0471741128/91
Historical Museum 09331

Auvers-sur-Oise

Atelier-Maison Peinte de Daubigny, 61 Rue
Daubigny, 95430 Auvers-sur-Oise - T: 0134480303/
30367942
Decorative Arts Museum / Fine Arts Museum 09332

Château d'Auvers, Voyage au Temps des
Impressionnistes, Rue de Léry, 95430 Auvers-sur-
Oise - T: 0134484848, Fax: 0134484851,
E-mail: info@chateau-auvers.fr, Internet: http://
www.chateau-auvers.fr. Head: Axel Poniatowski
Historical Museum / Special Museum 09333

La Maison de Van Gogh, Pl de la Mairie, 95430
Auvers-sur-Oise - T: 0130366070,
Fax: 0130366071, E-mail: reservation@maison-de-
van-gogh.com. Head: Dominique-Charles Janssens
Special Museum / Library with Exhibitions / Historic
Site 09334

Musée Daubigny, Manoir des Colombières, Rue de la
Sansonne, 95430 Auvers-sur-Oise -
T: 0130368020, Fax: 0130368020. Head: Jacques
Leroy
Special Museum / Fine Arts Museum 09335

Musée de l'Absinthe, 44 Rue Alphonse-Callé, 95430
Auvers-sur-Oise - T: 0130368326
Ethnology Museum / Special Museum 09336

Auvillar

Musée du Vieil Auvillar, Pl de la Halle, 82340
Auvillar - T: 0563395733/6099
Decorative Arts Museum / Archaeological Museum
Prehistory, history, folklore, local faience, 18th-19th
century wrought iron, arms, topography,
paintings 09337

Auxerre

Collections de la Bibliothèque Municipale, Rue
d'Ardillière, 89000 Auxerre - T: 0386511755
Library with Exhibitions 09338

Fondation François-Brochet, 100 Rue de Paris,
89000 Auxerre - T: 0386510974/523396
Fine Arts Museum
18th century chapel, contemporary
sculptures 09339

Musée-Abbaye Saint-Germain, Pl Saint-Germain,
89000 Auxerre - T: 0386180550, Fax: 0386180554,
E-mail: musees.auxerre@wanadoo.fr. Head:
Micheline Durand
Archaeological Museum / Historical Museum /
Historic Site - 1848
Carolingian crypt, medieval collections, Gallo-
Roman coll, prehistoric and protohistoric coll -
library, lending gallery 09340

Musée-Conservatoire de la Nature Paul-Bert, 5
Blvd Vauban, 89000 Auxerre - T: 0386515164
Natural History Museum 09341

Musée Leblanc-Duvernoy, 9bis Rue d'Egleny, 89000
Auxerre - T: 0386524463, Fax: 0386180554,
E-mail: musees.auxerre@wanadoo.fr. Head:
Micheline Durand
Decorative Arts Museum
XVIIIth c private house of M. Leblanc-Duvernoy,
important collection of ceramics: greek
earthenware, 230 pieces of faïence dating from the
Revolution, stoneware of the Puisaye region, some
furniture and paintings, Beauvais tapestries from
XVIIIth century representing the chinese emperor
Kang-Xi 09342

Auxi-le-Château

Musée des Arts et Traditions Populaires, Rue du
Presbytère, 62390 Auxi-le-Château -
T: 0321040203, Fax: 0321041022
Folklore Museum 09343

Auxonne

Musée Bonaparte, Château Prost, 21130 Auxonne -
T: 0380311065/374252, Fax: 0380374252
Historical Museum
Prehistoric and Gallo-Roman finds, local history,
customs, memorabilia of Napoleon I (1769-1821),
folklore 09344

Musée de la Fortification, Tour Belvoir, 21130
Auxonne - T: 0380374252
Military Museum 09345

Auzances

Musée Archéologique, Chapelle Sainte-Marguerite,
Pl du Champ de Foire, 23700 Auzances -
T: 0555670017
Archaeological Museum 09346

Auzers

Château d'Auzers, 15240 Auzers - T: 0471786259/
6343
Decorative Arts Museum 09347

Auzon

Écomusée Sauvegarde du Vieil Auzon, 43390
Auzon - T: 0471761480
Local Museum 09348

Avallon

Centre d'Art Contemporain, Salle Saint-Pierre,
89200 Avallon - T: 0386341419/466889
Fine Arts Museum 09349

Maison des Traditions Agricoles et Artisanales,
L'Abattoir, 66 Rue de Lyon, 89200 Avallon -
T: 0386345350
Agriculture Museum 09350

Musée de la Mode, 6 Rue Belgrand, 89200 Avallon -
T: 0386340319/1995
Special Museum 09351

Musée de l'Avallonnais, Pl de la Collégiale, 89200
Avallon - T: 0386340319, Fax: 0386316367,
E-mail: avallon.mairie@wanadoo.fr
Local Museum - 1862
Pre- and early hist, Gallo-Roman finds, 2nd century
statues of Montmartre, sculptures, excavation finds
from Arcy-sur-Cure, religious folk art, arms, jewels,
19th-20th century paintings, numismatics 09352

Avensan

Musée de la Tour Carelot, Cave Braquessac, Le
Bourg, 33480 Avensan - T: 0556581707
Agriculture Museum 09353

Aventignan

Musée des Grottes Préhistoriques de Gargas,
65660 Aventignan - T: 0562397239,
Fax: 0562397618
Archaeological Museum / Fine Arts Museum 09354

Avesnes-sur-Helpe

Musée de l'Institut Villien, 16 Rue Villien, 59440
Avesnes-sur-Helpe - T: 0327613279/579240
Archaeological Museum
Gallo-Roman archeology, coins, jewelry, pottery
statuettes, 15th-17th century sculptures, local hist,
book illustrations, folk art, faience 09355

Avignon

Maison Jean-Vilar, Bibliothèque Nationale de France,
8 Rue de Mons, 84000 Avignon - T: 0490865964,
Fax: 0490860007. Head: Marie Claude Billard
Performing Arts Museum / Library with
Exhibitions 09356

Musée Angladon, 5 Rue Laboureur, 84000 Avignon -
T: 0490822903, Fax: 0490857807,
E-mail: angladon@angladon.com, Internet: http://
www.angladon.com. Head: Anne-Marie Peylhard
Decorative Arts Museum / Fine Arts Museum 09357

Musée Calvet, 65 Rue Joseph Vernet, 84000 Avignon
- T: 0490863384, Fax: 0490146245,
E-mail: musee.calvet@wanadoo.fr. Head: M. Pierre
Provoyeur
Fine Arts Museum / Archaeological Museum - 1810
Egyptian, Greek, Gallo-Roman archeology, 15th-
19th century smith work, 15th-20th century
paintings - library 09358

**Musée du Mont-de-Piété et de la Condition des
Soies**, 6 Rue Saluces, 84000 Avignon -
T: 0490808000, Fax: 0490279838,
E-mail: archives.avignon@wanadoo.fr. Head:
Sylvestre Clap
Special Museum 09359

Musée du Petit-Palais, Palais des Archevêques, Pl
du Palais des Papes, 84000 Avignon -
T: 0490864458, Fax: 0490821872, E-mail: -
musee.petitpalais@wanadoo.fr. Head: Esther
Moench
Fine Arts Museum - 1976
Italian paintings of the 13th-15th century, local
paintings from 14th-15th century, sculptures from
Avignon (12th-15th century), 7th-14th century
tombs - library, research and study center of
medieval art 09360

Musée-Hôtel d'Adhemar de Cransac, 11 Rue de
Taulignan, 84000 Avignon - T: 0490861328
Decorative Arts Museum 09361

Musée Lapidaire, 27 Rue de la République, 84000
Avignon - T: 0490863384/857538
Archaeological Museum - 1935
17th century chapel, Celtic sculptures, Roman
sculptures and inscriptions, Renaissance
sculptures 09362

Musée Louis-Vouland, 17 Rue Victor-Hugo, 84000
Avignon - T: 0490860379, Fax: 0490851204. Head:
Eliane Aujard-Catot
Decorative Arts Museum 09363

Musée Requien, 67 Rue Joseph-Vernet, 84000
Avignon - T: 0490824351, 0490146856,
Fax: 0490850899, E-mail: musee.requien@
wanadoo.fr. Head: Dr. Evelyne Crégut
Natural History Museum 09364

Musée Théodore-Aubanel, 7 Pl Saint-Pierre, 84000
Avignon - T: 0490829554
Special Museum / Historical Museum 09365

Palais des Papes et Musée du Vieil Avignon, Pl du
Palais, 84000 Avignon - T: 0490275074,
Fax: 0490863612, E-mail: rmg@palais-des-
papes.com. Head: Didier Auzet
Fine Arts Museum 09366

Palais du Roure, Bibliothèque et Collections, Pl Le
Cardonnel, 3 Rue Collège-du-Roure, 84000 Avignon
- T: 0490808088
Ethnology Museum / Library with Exhibitions 09367

Avignonet-Lauragais

Musée Mondial du Rugby, L'Ovalie, Aire Lauragais
A-61, 31290 Avignonet-Lauragais
Special Museum 09368

Musée Riquet et du Canal du Midi, Centre Pierre-
Paul Riquet, Aire Lauragais, A 61, 31290 Avignonet-
Lauragais - T: 0561271463
Special Museum 09369

Aviré

Collections de la Ferme d'Hier et d'Aujourd'hui,
49500 Aviré - T: 0241613120
Agriculture Museum 09370

Avranches

Musée d'Art et d'Histoire de l'Avranchin, Pl Jean de
Saint-Avit, 50300 Avranches - T: 0233582515.
Head: Hugues de la Touche
Local Museum - 1963
Manuscripts of Mont Saint Michel 8th-15th c 09371

Musée de la Percée d'Avranches, Le Moulinet,
50300 Avranches - T: 0233683583
Military Museum 09372

Avressieux

Château-Musée de Montfleury, 73240 Avressieux -
T: 0476329271
Military Museum 09373

Avrillé

Collections du Château de la Guignardière, 85440
Avrillé - T: 0251223306/0143593987
Decorative Arts Museum 09374

Musée de Préhistoire, 85440 Avrillé -
T: 0251223306
Archaeological Museum 09375

Aydat

Musée de Rouillas-Aydat et des Vallées, Rouillas-
Bas, 63970 Aydat - T: 0473793024
Natural History Museum / Historical Museum 09376

Ayssenes

Musée de l'Archerie Traditionnelle, Moulin de
Vabrette, 12430 Ayssenes - T: 0565460267,
Fax: 0565460514, Internet: http://
www.multimania.com/parthes. Head: Georges
Merlin
Special Museum 09377

Azannes-et-Soumazannes

Musée des Vieux Métiers Vivants, Domaine des
Roises, 55150 Azannes-et-Soumazannes -
T: 0329856062
Folklore Museum 09378

Azay-le-Ferron

Château d'Azay-le-Ferron, 36290 Azay-le-Ferron -
T: 0254392006, Fax: 0247216936
Decorative Arts Museum - 1952
15th-19th century architecture, regional and
international paintings, furnishings, tapestry,
enamel, porcelain, hunting 09379

Azay-le-Rideau

Château-Musée Renaissance, Château d'Azay-le-
Rideau, 37190 Azay-le-Rideau - T: 0247454204.
Head: Florence de la Roncière
Decorative Arts Museum - 1905
Original furnishings, art objects, 16th century
Flemish tapestries 09380

Musée Maurice-Dufresne, Le Moulin de Marnay,
37190 Azay-le-Rideau - T: 0247453618/2892
Science&Tech Museum 09381

Azé

Grottes d'Azé, 71260 Azé - T: 0385333223/4140
Natural History Museum 09382

Azincourt

Musée d'Histoire et de Traditions Populaires,
Mairie, 62310 Azincourt - T: 0321044112
Historical Museum / Folklore Museum 09383

Baccarat

Musée Baccarat, 20 Rue des Cristalleries, 54120
Baccarat - T: 0383766137
Decorative Arts Museum 09384

Baden

Musée Jean Farkas, Le Parun, 56870 Baden -
T: 0297570242
Music Museum / Special Museum 09385

Badonviller

Maison de la Faïence, 13 Ave Division Leclerc,
54540 Badonviller - T: 0383421957
Decorative Arts Museum / Science&Tech
Museum 09386

Bage-le-Chatel

Maison de Pays, 1 Rue Marsale, 01380 Bage-le-
Chatel - T: 0385305666
Local Museum 09387

Bages (Pyrénées-Orientales)

Le Palais des Naïfs, 9 Av de la Méditerranée, 66670
Bages (Pyrénées-Orientales) - T: 0468217133.
Head: Françoise Cauk
Fine Arts Museum 09388

Bagnères-de-Bigorre

Musée Bigourdan du Vieux Moulin, Rue Hount
Blanque, 65200 Bagnères-de-Bigorre -
T: 0562910733. Head: Alain Mousseigne
Folklore Museum - 1852
Regional ethnography, agriculture, clothes,
furniture 09389

Musée Historique de l'Observatoire du Pic du Midi,
Rte à Péage au Col du Tourmalet, 65200 Bagnères-
de-Bigorre
Natural History Museum / Science&Tech
Museum 09390

Musée Salies, Musée des Beaux-Arts, Blvd de
l'Hypéron, 65200 Bagnères-de-Bigorre -
T: 0562910726, Fax: 0562910293
Decorative Arts Museum / Natural History
Museum 09391

Muséum d'Histoire Naturelle, Blvd de l'Hypéron,
65200 Bagnères-de-Bigorre
Natural History Museum 09392

Bagnères-de-Luchon

Musée du Pays de Luchon, 18 Allée d'Etigny, 31110
Bagnères-de-Luchon - T: 0561792987,
Fax: 0561791123
Local Museum
Antiquities, anthropology, portraits, historial
monuments in the Eastern Pyrenees, Gallo-Roman
finds 09393

Bagnoles-de-l'Orne

Musée des Sapeurs-Pompiers de l'Orne, 16 Blvd A.
Christophle, 61140 Bagnoles-de-l'Orne -
T: 0233381034
Science&Tech Museum 09394

Bagnols-en-Forêt

Musée Archéologique, Pl de la Mairie, 83600
Bagnols-en-Forêt - T: 0494406468,
Fax: 0498113068, E-mail: bagnols-en-
foret.tourisme@wanadoo.fr
Archaeological Museum 09395

Bagnols-sur-Cèze

Musée Albert André, Hôtel de Ville, 30200 Bagnols-
sur-Cèze - T: 0466505056, 0466907580,
Fax: 0466907427, E-mail: girard_a@cg30.fr. Head:
Alain Girard
Fine Arts Museum - 1854
19th century Lyon paintings, Besson coll of
paintings, contemporary figurative paintings 09396

Musée Archéologique Léon Alègre, 24 Av Paul
Langevin, 30200 Bagnols-sur-Cèze -
T: 0466897400, 0466907580, Fax: 0466907427,
E-mail: girard_a@cg30.fr. Head: Alain Girard
Archaeological Museum - 1854 09397

Baguer-Morvan

Musée de la Paysannerie, Cours Paris, 35120
Baguer-Morvan - T: 0299480404
Local Museum 09398

Bailleul

Ecole Dentellière, Rue du Collège, 59270 Bailleul -
T: 0328412572
Special Museum 09399

Musée Benoît de Puydt, 24 Rue du Musée, 59270
Bailleul - T: 0328411613/491270,
Fax: 0328422932. Head: Laurent Guillaut
Decorative Arts Museum - 1859
Ceramics, lace, tapestries, paintings, wood
carvings, medals, Chinese and Japanese
porcelain 09400

Baixas

Galerie d'Art Municipale, Mairie, 66390 Baixas - T: 0468642212
Public Gallery 09401

Balizac

Maison de la Haute Lande, 33730 Balizac - T: 0556253473
Folklore Museum 09402

Ballancourt-sur-Essonne

Château-Musée du Grand-Saussay, Le Saussay, A6, Sortie Chevannes, Auvernaux, 91610 Ballancourt-sur-Essonne - T: 0164932010, Fax: 0164932902. Head: Jean-Louis de Bourbon Busset
Decorative Arts Museum 09403

Balleroy

Musée des Ballons, Château, 14490 Balleroy - T: 0231216061
Science&Tech Museum 09404

Ballon

Musée Donjon, 72290 Ballon - T: 0243273829
Decorative Arts Museum 09405

Bambiderstroff

Musée de la Ligne Maginot, Ouvrage, 57220 Bambiderstroff - T: 0387903011/3195
Military Museum 09406

Banassac

Musée Archéologique, 48500 Banassac - T: 0466328210
Archaeological Museum 09407

Bandol

Collections de la Fondation Roger-van-Rogger, Rte du Beausset, 83150 Bandol - T: 0494296977, Fax: 0559327190, E-mail: christine.andreucci@univ-pau.fr. Head: Daniel Kastler
Fine Arts Museum 09408

Espace Culturel Paul-Ricard, Ile de Bendor, 83150 Bandol - T: 0494044837
Fine Arts Museum 09409

Bannegon

Musée de la Meunerie, Auberge du Moulin de Chameron, 18210 Bannegon - T: 0248618380
Science&Tech Museum 09410

Banyuls-sur-Mer

Collection Viti-Vinicole, Coopérative de l'Étoile, Av du Puig-del-Mas, 66650 Banyuls-sur-Mer - T: 0468880010
Special Museum 09411

Musée-Aquarium du Laboratoire Arago, Au port, 66650 Banyuls-sur-Mer - T: 0468887339
Natural History Museum 09412

Musée Aristide-Maillon, Métairie Maillol, Fondation Dina-Vierny, 66650 Banyuls-sur-Mer - T: 0468881077
Special Museum / Fine Arts Museum 09413

Bapaume

Musée Historique, Rue J.-B. Lequette, 62450 Bapaume - T: 0321071487
Local Museum 09414

Bar-le-Duc

Musée Barrois, Esplanade du Château, 55000 Bar-le-Duc - T: 0329761467, Fax: 0329771638
Archaeological Museum / Decorative Arts Museum - 1841
Gallo-Roman hist, paintings, ceramics, sculptures 09415

Bar-sur-Seine

Musée Municipal Bar-sur-Seine, Mairie, 10110 Bar-sur-Seine - T: 0325388035
Local Museum 09416

Barbizon

Maison et Atelier de Jean-François Millet, 27 Grande-Rue, 77630 Barbizon - T: 0160662155
Fine Arts Museum 09417

Musée de l'École de Barbizon - Auberge Ganne, 92 Grande-Rue, 77630 Barbizon - T: 0160662227, Fax: 0160662296
Fine Arts Museum 09418

Barcelonnette

Musée de la Vallée de l'Ubaye, 10 Av de la Libération, 04400 Barcelonnette - T: 0492812715. Head: Pierre Coste
Local Museum - 1988
Archaeology, zoology, ornithology, fine art, ethnography, photography, Mexican folk art 09419

Barentin

Musée d'Arts et d'Histoire, Hôtel de Ville, Pl de la Libération, 76360 Barentin - T: 0232949020
Fine Arts Museum / Historical Museum 09420

Barenton

Maison de la Pomme et de la Poire, La Logeraie, 50720 Barenton - T: 0233595622
Agriculture Museum 09421

Barfleur

Maison Natale de Sainte Marie-Madeleine-Postel, Rue Julie-Postel, 50760 Barfleur - T: 0233540217
Local Museum 09422

Bargemon

Musée Camos, Pl Saint-Étienne, 83830 Bargemon - T: 0494767288
Historical Museum / Fine Arts Museum 09423

Barizey

Musée de la Viticulture, 71640 Barizey - T: 0385443313
Agriculture Museum 09424

Barr

Musée de la Folie Marco, 30 Rue du Docteur Sultzer, 67140 Barr - T: 0388089106. Head: M. Krieg
Decorative Arts Museum - 1963
17th-19th century furniture, 18th century porcelain and faience, manor (18th century), pewter 09425

Musée de la Schlitte, 30 Rue du Docteur Sultzer, 67140 Barr - T: 0388089472/6665
Local Museum 09426

Musée Vini-Viticole, 6 Av de la Gare, 67140 Barr - T: 0388585900
Special Museum 09427

Bartres

Musée de la Petite Bergère, Rue de l'Église, 65100 Bartres - T: 0562940818
Special Museum / Historical Museum 09428

Barzan

Musée Archéologique du Moulin-du-Fâ, 17120 Barzan - T: 0546904366
Archaeological Museum 09429

Bascons

Village et Musée de la Course Landaise, Quartier de Bostens, 40090 Bascons - T: 0558440031/429176
Folklore Museum 09430

Basse-Rentgen

Musée Historique, Château de la Preische, 57570 Basse-Rentgen - T: 0382834781/4408
Local Museum 09431

Bassoues

Musée de l'Histoire des Bastides et de l'Evolution de l'Habitat, Donjon, 32320 Bassoues - T: 0562709047/9734
Folklore Museum 09432

Bastia

Musée de la Confrérie de l'Immaculée-Conception, Rue Napoléon, 20200 Bastia - T: 0495316307
Religious Arts Museum 09433

Musée d'Ethnographie Corse, Palais des Gouverneurs, Citadelle, 20200 Bastia - T: 0495310912/321690
Ethnology Museum / Archaeological Museum - 1922
Greco-Roman archeology, local historical artifacts, natural history exhibits, ethnography, folk art, Cardinal Fesch coll of paintings - library 09434

Batz-sur-Mer

Musée des Marais Salants, 29bis Rue Pasteur, 44740 Batz-sur-Mer - T: 0240238279/95, Fax: 0240237151. Head: Gildas Buron
Special Museum - 1887
Hist and technology of salt extraction 09435

Baugé

Apothicairerie, Hôpital Local de Baugé, Rue Anne-de-Melun, 49150 Baugé - T: 0241891025, Fax: 0241890543
Decorative Arts Museum 09436

Baume-les-Messieurs

Collection d'Histoire Naturelle, Grottes de Baume, 39210 Baume-les-Messieurs - T: 0384446158/242705
Natural History Museum 09437

Musée des Arts et Traditions Populaires, Abbaye, 39210 Baume-les-Messieurs - T: 0384472693
Folklore Museum 09438

Musée Lapidaire, Abbaye, 39210 Baume-les-Messieurs - T: 0384446141
Archaeological Museum 09439

Bavay

Musée de la Bataille de Malplaquet, 6 Rue des Juifs, 59570 Bavay - T: 0327398895
Historical Museum 09440

Musée Site Départemental d'Archéologie de Bavay, 2 Rue de Gommeries, 59570 Bavay - T: 0327631395/0674, Fax: 0327395077, E-mail: museebavay@cg59.fr. Head: Véronique Deloffre
Archaeological Museum / Historic Site 09441

Bavinchove

Musée des Transports, 1521 Rue de Bourbourg, 59670 Bavinchove - T: 0328424458, Fax: 0328405899, E-mail: amitram@nordnet.fr, Internet: http://amitram.free.fr. Head: Marc Breuze
Science&Tech Museum 09442

Bax

Insectarium Collections d'Histoire Naturelle, Moulibeaux, 31310 Bax - T: 0561871702
Natural History Museum 09443

Bayel

Musée du Cristal, 2 Rue Belle Verrière, 10310 Bayel - T: 0325924268, Fax: 0325923434, E-mail: o.t.bayel@bayel_cristal.com, Internet: http://www.bayel_cristal.com. Head: Michel Lecuillier
Decorative Arts Museum / Ethnology Museum 09444

Bayeux

Centre Catherine-de-Saint-Augustin, Musée des Augustines, Allée des Augustines, 14400 Bayeux - T: 0231515151
Local Museum 09445

Musée Baron Gérard, Pl de la Liberté, 14400 Bayeux - T: 0231921421, Fax: 0231516051. Head: Antoine Verney
Local Museum - 1793
Paintings, decorative arts, porcelain and ceramics, tapestries, archaeology 09446

Musée de la Tapisserie de Bayeux, Centre Guillaume-le-Conquérant, Rue de Nesmond, 14400 Bayeux - T: 0231920548, Fax: 0231920341
Decorative Arts Museum
Tapestries of the 11th c 09447

Musée Diocésain d'Art Religieux, Hôtel du Doyen, 6 Rue Lambert-Leforestier, 14400 Bayeux - T: 0231921421
Religious Arts Museum 09448

Musée Mémorial de la Bataille de Normandie, Blvd Fabian Ware, 14400 Bayeux - T: 0231514690, Fax: 0231514691, E-mail: museedelabataille@free.fr. Head: Philippe Chapron
Military Museum 09449

Musée Mémorial du Général de Gaulle, 10 Rue Bourbesneur, 14400 Bayeux - T: 0231924555
Military Museum 09450

Bayonne

Galerie Le Carré, Musée Bonnat, 9 Rue Frédéric-Bastiat, 64100 Bayonne - T: 0559590852, Fax: 0559595326. Head: Vincent Ducourau
Fine Arts Museum 09451

Musée Basque et de l'Histoire de Bayonne, 37 Quai des Corsaires, 64100 Bayonne - T: 0559590898, Fax: 0559590371, E-mail: info@musee-basque.com, Internet: http://www.musee-basque.com. Head: Olivier Ribeton
Ethnology Museum - 1922
Hist and folklore of Bayonne, the French Basque country, the Spanish Basque country, and the Basques in the New World - library 09452

Musée Bonnat, 5 Rue Jacques Laffitte, 64100 Bayonne - T: 0559590852, Fax: 0559595326. Head: Vincent Ducourau
Fine Arts Museum - 1899
Greek and Roman sculptures, European schools of painting since 15th century (Rubens, Goya, Ingres, Bonnat), 15th century Italian medals, decorative arts, calligraphy, miniatures - library 09453

Muséum d'Histoire Naturelle de la Ville de Bayonne, Château Lauga, Av Jean Rostand, 64100 Bayonne - T: 0559571510, Fax: 0559571512. Head: Beate Cousino
Natural History Museum 09454

Bazas

Musée de l'Apothicairerie, Rue Saint-Antoine, 33430 Bazas - T: 0556252584
Special Museum 09455

Bazeilles

Musée de la Dernière Cartouche, Av de la Dernière-Cartouche, 08140 Bazeilles - T: 0324571147
Military Museum 09456

Bazens

Exposition Permanente d'Art, Galerie de la Tour, 47130 Bazens - T: 0553674977
Fine Arts Museum 09457

Bazincourt-sur-Saulx

Maison-Forte Musée, Au Sud de l'Eglise, 55000 Bazincourt-sur-Saulx - T: 0387981544
Decorative Arts Museum 09458

Bazoges-en-Pareds

Collections du Donjon, Cour du Donjon, 85390 Bazoges-en-Pareds - T: 0251512310, Fax: 0251512160, E-mail: donjonbazoges@compaqnet.fr. Head: Anne Loyau
Historical Museum 09459

Musée d'Art et de Tradition Populaire, Cour du Donjon, 85390 Bazoges-en-Pareds - T: 0251512310, Fax: 0251512160, E-mail: donjonbazoges@compaqnet.fr. Head: Anne Loyau
Folklore Museum 09460

Beanvezer

Maison de Pays du Haut Verdon, 04440 Beanvezer - T: 0492834784
Local Museum / Natural History Museum 09461

Beaucaire

Musée Auguste Jacquet, Château, 30300 Beaucaire - T: 0466594761. Head: Yves Gasco
Archaeological Museum - 1979
Local archeological finds 09462

Musée Vini-Viticole Gallo-Romain, Mas des Tourelles, 30300 Beaucaire - T: 0466591972
Archaeological Museum 09463

Beauchastel

Musée d'Art Brut, Maison du Patrimoine, 07800 Beauchastel - T: 0475853072
Fine Arts Museum 09464

Musée de la Pêche, Maison du Patrimoine, 07800 Beauchastel - T: 0475622372
Special Museum 09465

Musée Historique de la Médecine Scientifique et des Pratiques Populaires, Maison du Patrimoine, 07800 Beauchastel
Natural History Museum 09466

Beaucourt

Musée de l'Industrie Horlogère et Mécanique "Frédéric-Japy", 16 Rue Frédéric-Japy, 90500 Beaucourt - T: 0384565752
Science&Tech Museum 09467

Beaufort-en-Vallée

Musée Joseph Denais, 5 Pl Notre-Dame, 49250 Beaufort-en-Vallée - T: 0241574050
Local Museum - 1905
Natural sciences, painting, sculpture, ceramics, egypt, local hist, prehistory 09468

Beaugency

Musée Régional Arts et Traditions de l'Orléanais, Château Dunois, 45190 Beaugency - T: 0238445523, Fax: 0238464037. Head: Chantal Fromont
Fine Arts Museum / Historical Museum / Ethnology Museum 09469

Beaujeu

Musée des Traditions Populaires Marius Audin, Pl de l'Hôtel de Ville, 69430 Beaujeu - T: 0474692288, Fax: 0474692288, E-mail: beaujeu.beaujolais@wanadoo.fr, Internet: http://www.worldnet.net/~dmege. Head: Marise Durhône
Folklore Museum - 1942
Dolls with their furniture and accessories (19th to early 20 th c) 09470

Beaulieu-sur-Mer

Fondation Théodore Reinach, Villa Kérylos, Av Gustave Eiffel, 06310 Beaulieu-sur-Mer - T: 0493010144, 0493764409, Fax: 0493013110, E-mail: message@villa-kerylos.com
Archaeological Museum - 1908
Greek art, reconstructed Greek architecture, interiors, art objects, bronze objects, mosaics 09471

Beaulon

Musée Rural de la Sologne Bourbonnaise, Pl de la Mairie, 03230 Beaulon - T: 0470427089. Head: Bernard Larpent
Historical Museum 09472

Beaumes-de-Venise

Musée-Académie, Pl du Marché, 84190 Beaumes-de-Venise - T: 0490629439
Historical Museum 09473

Beaumesnil

Musée de la Reliure, Château de Beaumesnil, 27410 Beaumesnil - T: 0232444009, Fax: 0232444009
Historic Site 09474

Beaumont-du-Lac

Centre d'Art Contemporain de Vassivière en Limousin, Ile de Vassivière, 87120 Beaumont-du-Lac - T: 0555692727, Fax: 0555692931, E-mail: centre.d-art.vassiviere@wanadoo.fr. Head: Dominique Marchés
Fine Arts Museum - 1991
library 09475

Beaumont-en-Auge

Musée Laplace, Mairie, 14950 Beaumont-en-Auge - T: 0231648541
Fine Arts Museum 09476

Beaumont-sur-Sarthe

Musée de la Meunerie, Moulin du Bois-Landon, 72170 Beaumont-sur-Sarthe - T: 0243970086
Science&Tech Museum 09477

Beaune

Athénaeum de la Vigne et du Vin, 7 Rue de l'Hôtel-Dieu, 21200 Beaune - T: 0380221200
Special Museum 09478

Musée de l'Hôtel-Dieu, 2 Rue de l'Hôtel-Dieu, 21200 Beaune - T: 0380247575 poste 3500/4500
Decorative Arts Museum - 1443
15th century hospital, original interiors and equipment, paintings, including Rogier van der Weyden's 'Last Judgement', tapestries, furnishings, statuettes, pewter, 15th-16th century ivory, wood sculptures 09479

Musée des Beaux-Arts et Musée Marey, Hôtel de Ville, 21200 Beaune - T: 0380245692, Fax: 0380245620. Head: Daniel Rouvier
Fine Arts Museum / Science&Tech Museum - 1853/1955
17th century convent, Gallo-Roman finds, temporary exhibitions of art, chronophotography of Etienne-Jules Marey, technical history of the cinema, films - library 09480

Musée du Vin de Bourgogne, Ancien Palais des Ducs de Bourgogne, Rue d'Enfer, 21200 Beaune - T: 0380220819, Fax: 0380245620
Ethnology Museum / Decorative Arts Museum - 1947
History of wine production, viticulture traditions, coopery, tapestry of Jean Lurçat and Michel Tourlière - library 09481

Musée Étienne-Jules-Marey, Hôtel de Ville, 21200 Beaune - T: 0380245692/98, Fax: 0380245620. Head: Daniel Rouvier
Science&Tech Museum 09482

Beauvais

Galerie Nationale de la Tapisserie et de l'Art Textile, 22 Rue Saint-Pierre, 60000 Beauvais - T: 0344051428
Decorative Arts Museum 09483

Musée Départemental de l'Oise, Ancien Palais Episcopal, 1 Rue du Musée, 60000 Beauvais, mail addr: BP 618, 60006 Beauvais Cedex - T: 0344114383, Fax: 0344484945
Archaeological Museum / Decorative Arts Museum / Fine Arts Museum - 1908
Local archeological findings, regional ceramics from the 16th-18th century, faience, 12th-16th century sculptures, 16th-19th century French and Italian paintings, Art Deco, furnishings 09484

Beauvezer

Maison de Pays du Haut-Verdon, 04370 Beauvezer - T: 0492834784
Local Museum 09485

Beauvoir-en-Royans

Musée Delphinal, Pl de l'Eglise, 38160 Beauvoir-en-Royans - T: 0476640255
Folklore Museum / Local Museum 09486

Beblenheim

La Grange Béranger, Musée d'Arts Populaires, 26 Rue Jean-Macé, 68980 Beblenheim - T: 0389479454
Folklore Museum 09487

Musée Jean Macé, Mairie, 68980 Beblenheim - T: 0389479013
Special Museum 09488

Bécon-les-Granits

Musée du Granit, 22 Rue de Candé, 49370 Bécon-les-Granits - T: 0241770407
Science&Tech Museum 09489

Bédarieux

Musée-Maison des Arts des Hauts-Cantons, Av Abbé Tarroux, 34600 Bédarieux - T: 0467951662. Head: P. Maraval
Local Museum 09490

Phoros-Éco Parc, 34600 Bédarieux
Music Museum 09491

Bedeilhac

Musée de Préhistoire, Nord de Tarascon, 09400 Bedeilhac - T: 0561059506
Archaeological Museum 09492

Bedoues

Musée de l'Abeille, 48400 Bedoues - T: 0466450100
Natural History Museum 09493

Bégadan

Collection d'Outillage Vini-Viticole, Château La Tour de By, 33340 Bégadan - T: 0556415003
Special Museum 09494

Béganne

Château de Léhélec, 56350 Béganne - T: 0299360593
Local Museum 09495

Begard

Exposition sur la Vie Rurale d'Autrefois, Armoripark, 22140 Begard - T: 0296453636
Folklore Museum 09496

Bègles

Musée d'Art Brut, Création Franche, 58 Av du Maréchal de Lattre, 33130 Bègles - T: 0556858173/493472
Fine Arts Museum 09497

Belesta-de-la-Frontière

Château-Musée de Préhistoire, 66720 Belesta-de-la-Frontière - T: 0468845555, Fax: 0468845106, E-mail: office-tourisme.ille@wanadoo.fr. Head: Valérie Porra-Kuteni
Archaeological Museum 09498

Belfort

Musée d'Art et d'Histoire, Château de Belfort, 90000 Belfort - T: 0384542551, Fax: 0384285296. Head: M. Cousin
Fine Arts Museum / Historical Museum - 1872
Fine arts, local history, numismatics, antiquities, Merovingian goldsmith work, contemporary sculpture 09499

Bellac

Maison Natale de Jean Giraudoux (Jean Giraudoux' Birthplace), 4 Av Jean-Jaurès, 87300 Bellac - T: 0555680377, Fax: 0555680377, E-mail: body@univ-tours.fr. Head: Jean-Bernard Raimond
Special Museum
Furniture, objects and books belonging to Giraudoux - documentation centre of Giraudoux 09500

Belle-Ile-en-Mer

Musée Historique de la Citadelle, Citadelle Vauban, Palais, 56360 Belle-Ile-en-Mer - T: 0297318417, Fax: 0297314583
Historical Museum / Fine Arts Museum / Military Museum 09501

Bellefontaine (Manche)

Collection d'Automates, Le Village Enchanté, 50520 Bellefontaine (Manche) - T: 0233590193
Science&Tech Museum 09502

Bellerive-sur-Allier

Musée Bourbonnais de Vesse à Bellerive, Centre Communal d'Animation, Av de Russie, 03700 Bellerive-sur-Allier - T: 0470588700/2846
Local Museum 09503

Bellignies

Musée du Marbre et de la Pierre Bleue, Rue Cautipont, 59570 Bellignies - T: 0327668990/631601
Special Museum / Science&Tech Museum 09504

Belmont

Musée Louis Pergaud, 25530 Belmont - T: 0381604415
Special Museum 09505

Belmont-Luthézieu

Collection d'Archéologie, Château d'Hostel, 01260 Belmont-Luthézieu - T: 0479873357
Archaeological Museum 09506

Belvès

Musée Organistrum et des Vielles à Roues du Périgord Noir, 11 Rue Jacques Manchotte, 24170 Belvès - T: 0553201093/576950
Music Museum 09507

Belvoir

Château, 25430 Belvoir - T: 0381910602
Fine Arts Museum / Decorative Arts Museum 09508

Bendol

Musée des Vins et Spiritueux, Ile de Bendor, 83150 Bendol - T: 0494294434
Special Museum 09509

Bénévent-et-Charbillac

Écomusée de la Vie en Altitude, Pisançon, 05500 Bénévent-et-Charbillac - T: 0492500171
Ethnology Museum / Folklore Museum 09510

Bénouville

Exposition Nicolas-Ledoux, Château de Bénouville, Av de Caen, 14970 Bénouville - T: 0231955323
Special Museum 09511

Musée de l'Invasion Aéroportée, 1944 Pegasus-Bridge, 10 Rue du Commandant-Kieffer, 14970 Bénouville - T: 0231446254
Military Museum - 1974
Equipment, photographs, vehicles, models, documents of the British and Canadian Airborne Forces during the WW II 09512

Musée du Café Gondrée, 14970 Bénouville - T: 0231446225
Historical Museum 09513

Berck-sur-Mer

Musée Municipal Berck-sur-Mer, 60 Rue de l'Impératrice, 62600 Berck-sur-Mer - T: 0321840780, Fax: 0321849629, E-mail: musee@berck-sur-mer.fr. Head: Georges Dilly
Archaeological Museum / Decorative Arts Museum - 1979
Archeology, furniture 09514

Bergerac

Musée d'Art Sacré, Rue de la Mission, 24100 Bergerac - T: 0553573321
Religious Arts Museum 09515

Musée d'Histoire Urbaine de Bergerac, Pl du Feu, 24100 Bergerac - T: 0553630413, Fax: 0553619002
Historical Museum 09516

Musée d'Intérêt National du Tabac, Maison Peyrarède, Pl du Feu, 24100 Bergerac - T: 0553630413, Fax: 0553619002
Special Museum - 1950
Pipes, snuff boxes, tobacco, lithographs, books, a tobacco stand, paintings with tobacco as the subject 09517

Musée du Vin de la Batellerie et de la Tonnellerie, 5 Rue des Conférences, 24100 Bergerac - T: 0553578092
Special Museum 09518

Bergues

Musée d'Art et d'Histoire, 1 Rue du Mont de Piété, 59380 Bergues - T: 0328686044/1330. Head: Jean-Claude Guillemin
Local Museum
European paintings, drawings, manuscripts of Lamartine, Flemish folklore, natural science and hist coll, ornithology, butterfly coll 09519

Berlise

Musée de la Forge, 02340 Berlise - T: 0324723324
Science&Tech Museum 09520

Bernay

Musée des Beaux-Arts, Ancien Palais Abbatial, Pl Guillaume de Volpiano, 27300 Bernay - T: 0232466323, Fax: 0232441399
Fine Arts Museum / Decorative Arts Museum
Flemish and Spanish paintings, exhibits on Rouen ceramic works, arms, archeology, all in a 17th century abbot's home 09521

Bernières-sur-Mer

Exposition du Mémorial Capétien, Orangerie du Château de la Luzerne, 49 Rue Maréchal-Montgomery, 14990 Bernières-sur-Mer - T: 0231964475
Historical Museum 09522

Berrien

Maison des Sports Bretons, 29218 Berrien - T: 0298990380
Folklore Museum 09523

Berry-au-Bac

Musée du Souvenir Général Estienne, 23 Av du Général de Gaulle, 02190 Berry-au-Bac - T: 0323799525
Military Museum 09524

Besançon

Centre d'Art Contemporain, Hôtel de Ville, Pl du 8 Septembre, 25000 Besançon - T: 0381615109
Fine Arts Museum 09525

Musée Comtois, Citadelle, 25000 Besançon - T: 0381878316, Fax: 0381878306, E-mail: marie.spinelli@besancon.com. Head: Marie Spinelli-Flesch
Ethnology Museum - 1960
Provincial crafts, local folklore, popular theater, traditional farming 09526

Musée d'Art Populaire Africain, Citadelle, Rue des Fusillés, 25000 Besançon - T: 0381821622
Ethnology Museum 09527

Musée de la Résistance et de la Déportation, Citadelle, 25000 Besançon - T: 0381878312, Fax: 0381878314, E-mail: elizabeth.pastwa@besancon.com, Internet: http://www.besancon.com. Head: François Margot
Historical Museum - 1971
Nazism in Germany and Europe, France (1939-1945) 09528

Musée des Beaux-Arts et d'Archéologie, 1 Pl de la Révolution, 25000 Besançon - T: 0381878049, Fax: 0381878064, E-mail: musees@besancon.com. Head: Marie-Hélène Lavallée
Fine Arts Museum / Archaeological Museum - 1843
15th-20th century paintings, French and foreign drawings, ceramics, clocks and watches, Egyptian, Greek, and Gallo-Roman archeology 09529

Musée d'Histoire → Musée du Temps

Musée d'Histoire Naturelle, Citadelle, Rue des Fusillés, 25000 Besançon - T: 0381821622. Head: Gérard Galliot
Natural History Museum 09530

Musée du Temps, Palais Granvelle, 96 Grande Rue, 25000 Besançon - T: 0381814514, Fax: 0381814391. Head: Joëlle Mauerhan
Special Museum / Local Museum / Science&Tech Museum
Clocks, measurement of time, town hist 09531

Bessay

Collections de la Tour de Bessay, 85320 Bessay - T: 0251275138
Historical Museum 09532

Besse-en-Chandesse

Musée de la Pêche et de l'Eau, La Villetour, 63610 Besse-en-Chandesse - T: 0473795552/38
Natural History Museum 09533

Musée du Ski, Maison de la Reine Margot, Rue de la Boucherie, 63610 Besse-en-Chandesse - T: 0473795730/74670050
Special Museum 09534

Bessé-sur-Braye

Musée Historique, Château de Courtanvaux, 72310 Bessé-sur-Braye - T: 0243353443
Historical Museum 09535

Bétête

Exposition sur l'Art Cistercien, Les Abbayes Cisterciennes en Limousin, Abbaye de Prébenoit, 23270 Bétête - T: 0555807891, Fax: 0555808680, E-mail: abbaye@prebenoit.com, Internet: http://www.prebenoit.com. Head: Benoît Christen
Religious Arts Museum / Historic Site 09536

Béthune

Musée Régional d'Ethnologie du Nord/Pas-de-Calais, 637 Av du Pont-des-Dames, 62400 Béthune - T: 0321684074, Fax: 0321653435, E-mail: ethnologie@musee-bethune.com. Head: Vincent Maliet
Ethnology Museum 09537

Betschdorf

Musée de la Poterie de Grès, 2 Rue de Kuhlendorf, 67660 Betschdorf - T: 0388544807/00, Fax: 0388544970, E-mail: si.betschdorf@wanadoo.fr. Head: Gabriel Acker
Decorative Arts Museum 09538

Betton

Ec'Art, Ecole-Galerie, 3 Rue des Marronniers, 35830 Betton - T: 0299558475/8101
Fine Arts Museum 09539

Beure

Musée des Armées Lucien Roy, 1bis Chemin Maillot, 25720 Beure - T: 0381526030/6130
Military Museum 09540

Beurières

Exposition Apicole Péricard, Le Béal, 63220 Beurières - T: 0473950228
Agriculture Museum 09541

Beynac et Cazenac

Château Féodal de Beynac, 24220 Beynac et Cazenac - T: 0553295040, Fax: 0553298938
Historic Site 09542

Collection d'Étendards, Château, 24220 Beynac et Cazenac - T: 0553295040
Military Museum 09543

Musée de la Protohistoire, Parque Archéologique, Tour du Couvent, 24220 Beynac et Cazenac - T: 0553295128
Archaeological Museum   09544

Bèze

Maison de l'Éventail, 21310 Bèze
Special Museum   09545

Béziers

Musée des Beaux-Arts, Pl de la Révolution, 34500 Béziers - T: 0467283878, Fax: 0467629193. Head: Nicole Riche
Fine Arts Museum
French and foreign paintings (15th-20th c); sculptures by Injalbert (1845-1933)   09546

Musée des Beaux-Arts Hôtel Fayet, 9 Rue du Capus, 34500 Béziers - T: 0467283878, Fax: 0467629193. Head: Nicole Riche
Fine Arts Museum
Paintings 15th-20th c, sculptures 19th c   09547

Musée du Biterrois, Rampe du 96e, Caserne Saint-Jacques, 34500 Béziers - T: 0467367101, 0467367281, Fax: 0467367676, E-mail: gerard.collin@ville-beziers.fr. Head: Dr. Gérard Collin
Local Museum   09548

Musée du Trompe L'Oeil, Château de Raissac, Rte de Murviel, 34500 Béziers - T: 0467491760, Fax: 0467285182
Decorative Arts Museum   09549

Bezouce

Musée Archéologique, Salle des Fêtes, 30320 Bezouce - T: 0466752423
Archaeological Museum   09550

Bézu-la-Forêt

Musée à la Ferme de Rome, Rte de Lyons-la-Forêt, 27480 Bézu-la-Forêt - T: 0232496622
Agriculture Museum   09551

Biarritz

Musée de la Mer, Esplanade du Rocher de la Vierge, 14 Plateau Atalaye, 64200 Biarritz - T: 0559223334, 0559227540, Fax: 0559227530, E-mail: musee.mer@wanadoo.fr, Internet: http://www.museedelamer.com. Head: Françoise Pautrizel
Natural History Museum - 1933
Ethnography, local fauna, regional marine amimals and birds, exhibit on deep sea fishing - library, aquarium   09552

Musée du Vieux Biarritz, Ancienne Chapelle Anglicane, Rue Broquedis, 64200 Biarritz - T: 0559242024
Local Museum   09553

Bierre-les-Semur

Ferme-Conservatoire du Hameau, 21390 Bierre-les-Semur - T: 0380644668
Agriculture Museum   09554

Biesheim

Musée de l'Optique, Le Capitole, Pl de la Mairie, 68600 Biesheim - T: 0389720159, Fax: 0389721449. Head: Dr. Antoine Hirth
Science&Tech Museum   09555

Musée Gallo-Romain, Le Capitole, 68600 Biesheim - T: 0389720158, Fax: 0389720167. Head: Suzanne Plouin
Archaeological Museum   09556

Bièvres

Maison Littéraire de Victor Hugo, Château des Roches, 45 Rue de Vauboyen, 91570 Bièvres - T: 0169418284
Special Museum   09557

Moulin-Musée de Vauboyen, Rte de Vauboyen, 91570 Bièvres - T: 0169410125
Fine Arts Museum / Special Museum   09558

Musée Français de la Photographie, 78 Rue de Paris, 91570 Bièvres, mail addr: BP 3, 91570 Bièvres - T: 0169351650, Fax: 0160192111. Head: Eric Bourgougnon
Fine Arts Museum / Science&Tech Museum - 1960
History, technology, and art of photography, contemporary photos   09559

Musée Les Amis de l'Outil, Lado, 21 Pl de l'Église, 91570 Bièvres - T: 0169853126
Local Museum   09560

Bignan

Centre d'Art Contemporain, Domaine de Kerguehennec, 56500 Bignan - T: 0297604444, Fax: 0297604400, E-mail: info@art-kerguehennec.com. Head: Frédéric Paul
Fine Arts Museum   09561

Billom

Musée de l'Imprimerie, 20 Rue des Boucheries, 63160 Billom - T: 0473917675. Head: Paul-Henry Couty
Science&Tech Museum   09562

Binic

Musée d'Art et Traditions Populaires, Sq Fichet des Grèves, 22520 Binic - T: 0296733795. Head: Jeannine Kervern
Local Museum
Local hist, archeology, handicraft, furniture, 09563

Biot

Écomusée du Verre de Biot, Chemin des Combes, 06410 Biot - T: 0493650300
Science&Tech Museum   09564

Musée de Biot, Musée d'Histoire et de Céramique Biotoises, 9 Rue Saint-Sébastien, 06410 Biot - T: 0493655454, Fax: 0493655173
Local Museum   09565

Musée National Fernand Léger, Chemin du Val de Pôme, 06410 Biot - T: 0492915030, Fax: 0492915031, E-mail: nelly.maillard@culture.gouv.fr. Head: J.-M. Foray
Fine Arts Museum - 1960
Works of the artist F. Léger (1881-1955)   09566

Biscarrosse

Musée Historique de l'Hydraviation, 332 Av Louis Bréguet, 40600 Biscarrosse - T: 0558780065, Fax: 0558788197, E-mail: musee.hydraviation@wanadoo.fr. Head: Sylvie Berges
Science&Tech Museum   09567

Bischheim

Musée du Bain Rituel Juif, 17 Rue Nationale, 67800 Bischheim - T: 0388814947, Fax: 0388816153
Religious Arts Museum   09568

Bischwiller

Musée du Centenaire (closed)   09569

Musée Historique de la Laub, Ancienne Mairie, 67240 Bischwiller - T: 0388539953
Historical Museum   09570

Bisping

Maison du Parc Naturel Régional de Lorraine, Maison du Clément, 57930 Bisping - T: 0387865676/5510
Natural History Museum / Folklore Museum   09571

Bissey-la-Pierre

Musée du Machinisme Agricole, Ferme Voinchet, 21330 Bissey-la-Pierre - T: 0380814159
Science&Tech Museum   09572

Bitche

Musée de la Citadelle, Citadelle, 57230 Bitche - T: 0387961882/061616, Fax: 0387061617, E-mail: office-tour@ville-bitche.fr. Head: A. Botzong
Historical Museum   09573

Musée du Second-Empire, Ancienne Boulangerie, Citadelle, 57230 Bitche - T: 0387961882, Fax: 0387061617, E-mail: office-tour@ville-bitche.fr. Head: A. Botzong
Historical Museum   09574

Musée-Jardin d'Art Contemporain, Rue de la Paix, 57230 Bitche - T: 0387960013, Fax: 0387961023, E-mail: office-tour@ville-bitche.fr, Internet: http://www.ville-bitche.fr
Fine Arts Museum   09575

Muséosite de la Citadelle Vivante de Bitche, 57230 Bitche - T: 0387061616/961882
Historical Museum   09576

Bize-Minervois

Musée Ferroviaire, Gare, 11120 Bize-Minervois - T: 0468270594
Science&Tech Museum   09577

Blain

Musée-Atelier de Fresques, Château de la Groulais, 44130 Blain - T: 0240798951/871511
Religious Arts Museum / Fine Arts Museum   09578

Musée des Arts et Traditions Populaires, 2 Pl Jean Guihard, 44130 Blain - T: 0240871511. Head: Jean Doucet
Folklore Museum - 1968
Furniture, costumes, crafts, archeology   09579

Blangy-sur-Bresle

Éco-Musée du Matériel de la Ferme, 76340 Blangy-sur-Bresle
Historical Museum   09580

Musée de la Géologie, 76340 Blangy-sur-Bresle
Natural History Museum   09581

Musée de la Verrerie, 76340 Blangy-sur-Bresle
Decorative Arts Museum / Science&Tech Museum   09582

Musée du Centre Culturel, Manoir de Fontaine, 76340 Blangy-sur-Bresle - T: 0235944479
Local Museum   09583

Paroles d'Objets Africains du Togo, 76340 Blangy-sur-Bresle
Ethnology Museum   09584

Blanot

Musée Cavernicole, Aux Grottes, 71250 Blanot - T: 0385500359/58
Natural History Museum / Archaeological Museum   09585

Blanquefort

Château-Musée Dillon, Les Chais, 33290 Blanquefort - T: 0556355610
Decorative Arts Museum / Fine Arts Museum 09586

Collection Archéologique, Maison du Patrimoine, Allées de Carpinet, 33290 Blanquefort - T: 0556571942, Fax: 0556571942. Head: Dominique Jay
Archaeological Museum   09587

Blanzy

Musée de la Mine et les Hommes, Ancien Puits de Mine Saint-Claude, Rue du Bois Clair, 71450 Blanzy - T: 0385682285
Science&Tech Museum / Historical Museum 09588

Blasimon

Musée d'Art et d'Histoire, Mairie, 33540 Blasimon - T: 0556715217/12
Fine Arts Museum / Historical Museum / Archaeological Museum   09589

Blaye

Conservatoire de l'Estuaire de la Gironde, Pl d'Armes, 33390 Blaye - T: 0557428096, E-mail: conservatoire@estuairegironde.net, Internet: http://www.estuairegironde.net. Head: Daniel Binaud
Special Museum   09590

Blérancourt

Musée National de la Coopération Franco-Américaine, Château, 02300 Blérancourt - T: 0323396016, Fax: 0323396285, E-mail: - musee.blerancourt@culture.gouv.fr
Historical Museum / Fine Arts Museum - 1924
Memorabilia and documents on the War of Independence, items dealing with American humanitarian help during WW I and WW II, relations between America and France, paintings and sculpture of American artists in France and of French artists in America - library   09591

Blesle

Musée de la Coiffe, Vieil Hôpital, 43450 Blesle - T: 0471762690
Folklore Museum   09592

Bliesbruck

Parc Archéologique Européen de Bliesbruck-Reinheim, 1 Rue Robert Schuman, 57200 Bliesbruck - T: 0387022579/2232, Fax: 0387022480
Archaeological Museum   09593

Blois

Aître Saint-Saturnin, Rue Munier, 41000 Blois - T: 0254903333, Fax: 0254903330, E-mail: chateau@ville-blois.fr, Internet: http://www.ville-blois.fr. Head: Thierry Crépin-Leblond
Archaeological Museum   09594

Maison de la Magie, 1 Pl du Château, 41000 Blois - T: 0254552626, Fax: 0254552628, E-mail: magie-admin@ville-blois.fr, Internet: http://www.ville-blois.fr. Head: Francis Chevrier
Special Museum
Robert Houdin's coll of magic art, personal items, performances   09595

Musée Archéologique et Lapidaire, Château de Blois, 41000 Blois - T: 0254903333, Fax: 0254903330, E-mail: chateau@ville-blois.fr, Internet: http://www.ville-blois.fr. Head: Thierry Crépin-Leblond
Archaeological Museum   09596

Musée d'Art Religieux, Cloître des Jacobins, Rue Anne de Bretagne, 41000 Blois - T: 0254781714
Religious Arts Museum - 1930   09597

Musée de la Résistance et de la Libération en Loir-et-Cher, 1 Pl de Grève, 41000 Blois - T: 0254560702
Historical Museum   09598

Musée des Beaux-Arts, Château, 41000 Blois - T: 0254903333, Fax: 0254903330, E-mail: chateau@ville-blois.fr, Internet: http://www.ville-blois.fr. Head: Thierry Crépin-Leblond
Fine Arts Museum / Archaeological Museum / Decorative Arts Museum - 1843
Div of art: paintings, art objects, 15th-20th c tapestries, faience, costumes, local religious art, Div of archeology: prehistoric findings, Gallo-Roman antiquities, medieval findings, sculptures   09599

Museum d'Histoire Naturelle, Les Jacobins, Rue Anne de Bretagne, 41000 Blois - T: 0254902100, Fax: 0254902101. Head: Jean-Louis Pointal
Natural History Museum - 1883   09600

Blosseville

Collection de Voitures Hippomobiles, 76460 Blosseville - T: 0235976462
Science&Tech Museum   09601

Boën-sur-Lignon

Château-Musée, Pl de la République, 42130 Boën-sur-Lignon - T: 0477240910/07
Fine Arts Museum   09602

Exposition Permanente sur le Pisé, Château de Boën, Pl de la République, 42130 Boën-sur-Lignon - T: 0477240907/0910
Special Museum   09603

Musée du Vigneronnage, Pl de la République, 42130 Boën-sur-Lignon - T: 0477240907/0910
Special Museum   09604

Boersch

Collection de Tonnellerie, Domaine Schaetzel, 41 Rue Monseigneur Barth, 67530 Boersch - T: 0388958333, Fax: 0388958063, E-mail: - domaine.schaetzel@le-chatelain.com. Head: Désiré Schaetzel
Special Museum   09605

Collection Historique de la Marqueterie d'Art Spindler, 3 Cour du Chapitre, Saint-Léonard, 67530 Boersch - T: 0388958017, Fax: 0388959831, E-mail: marqueterie@spindler.tm.fr, Internet: http://www.spindler.tm.fr. Head: Jean-Charles Spindler
Decorative Arts Museum   09606

Boeschepe

Moulin à Vent de 1802, Ondank-Meulen, 59299 Boeschepe - T: 0328425024
Science&Tech Museum   09607

Bogny-sur-Meuse

Centre de Culture Technique "La Métallurgie au Pays des 4 Fils Aymon", Le Vrezy, 08120 Bogny-sur-Meuse - T: 0324321316/1199
Science&Tech Museum   09608

Centre d'Exposition de Minéralogie, 32 Rue Louis, 08120 Bogny-sur-Meuse - T: 0324320502
Natural History Museum   09609

Boigneville

Écomusée, Pl de l'Église, 91720 Boigneville - T: 0164994007
Local Museum   09610

Bois-d'Amont

Musée de la Boissellerie, 12 Rue du Petit Pont, 39220 Bois-d'Amont - T: 0384609054, Fax: 0384609522
Science&Tech Museum   09611

Bois-de-Céné

Collection de l'Abbaye de l'Ile Chauvet, Ile Chauvet, 85710 Bois-de-Céné - T: 0251681319
Religious Arts Museum   09612

Boissy-Saint-Léger

Musée Napoléonien du Château de Grosbois, Av du Maréchal-de-Lattre-de-Tassigny, 94470 Boissy-Saint-Léger - T: 0145102424, Fax: 0145102425
Decorative Arts Museum   09613

Bollène

Musée des Flûtes du Monde, Château la Croix-Chabrière, Rte de Sainte-Restitut, 84500 Bollène - T: 0490309060
Special Museum   09614

Bondues

Château du Vert-Bois, 59910 Bondues - T: 0320463032
Fine Arts Museum / Decorative Arts Museum 09615

Bonifacio

Musée d'Arts et de Traditions Populaires, Près Église Saint-François, 20169 Bonifacio - T: 0495731188
Folklore Museum   09616

Musée Océanographique, 71 Quai Comparetti, 20169 Bonifacio - T: 0495730369
Natural History Museum   09617

Bonnebosq

Collections du Manoir du Champ-Versant, 14340 Bonnebosq - T: 0231651107
Historical Museum / Decorative Arts Museum 09618

Bonnefamille

Château-Musée de la Nature, Château de Moidière, 38290 Bonnefamille - T: 0474964463
Natural History Museum   09619

Bonnemazon

Exposition Permanente d'Art Contemporain, Abbaye de l'Escaladieu, 65130 Bonnemazon - T: 0562391313
Fine Arts Museum 09620

Bonneval

Musée Bonnevallais, 19 Rue Saint-Roch, 28800 Bonneval - T: 0237472193
Fine Arts Museum / Local Museum 09621

Bonneville

Musée Haut Savoyard de la Résistance, 74 Rue Sainte-Catherine, 74130 Bonneville - T: 0450973842/0207
Historical Museum 09622

Bonnieux

Musée de la Boulangerie, 12 Rue de la République, 84480 Bonnieux - T: 0490758834/9028, Fax: 0490202244. Head: Eve Duperray
Special Museum - 1983
Bakery 09623

Bonnut

Musée Célestin-Freinet, École Quartier Saint-Martin, 64300 Bonnut - T: 0559679051
Special Museum 09624

Bordeaux

Art Cru Muséum, 34 Rue Chantecrit, 33300 Bordeaux - T: 0556690663, Fax: 0557106080, E-mail: art.cru@wanadoo.fr, Internet: http://www.art.cru.com. Head: Guy Lafargue
Special Museum 09625

CAPC Musée d'Art Contemporain, Entrepôt Lainé, Rue Ferrère, 33000 Bordeaux - T: 0556008150, Fax: 0556441207, E-mail: capc@mairie-bordeaux.fr, Internet: http://www.mairie-bordeaux.fr. Head: Maurice Frechuret
Fine Arts Museum 09626

Centre d'Art Contemporain, 7 Rue Ferrère, 33000 Bordeaux - T: 0556527836, Fax: 0556815149
Fine Arts Museum 09627

Galerie des Beaux-Arts, Pl du Colonel Raynal, 33000 Bordeaux - T: 0556101613/1749. Head: Philippe Le Leyzour
Fine Arts Museum 09628

Médaillier Municipal, Bibliothèque Municipal, 85 Cours Maréchal-Juin, 33000 Bordeaux - T: 0556103000, Fax: 0556103090, E-mail: bibli@mairie-bordeaux.fr. Head: Pierre Botineau
Decorative Arts Museum 09629

Musée à Flot, Croiseur C.A.A. Colbert, Quai des Chartrons, 33000 Bordeaux - T: 0556449611
Science&Tech Museum 09630

Musée Centre National Jean Moulin, Pl Jean Moulin, 33000 Bordeaux - T: 0556101580, Fax: 0556796604, E-mail: cnjm@mairie-bordeaux-fr.. Head: Marie-Anne Pommies
Local Museum 09631

Musée-Conservatoire International de la Plaisance, Ancienne BSM, Blvd Alfred-Daney, 33000 Bordeaux - T: 0556111150
Science&Tech Museum 09632

Musée d'Aquitaine, 20 Cours Pasteur, 33000 Bordeaux - T: 0556015100, Fax: 0556442436. Head: Hélène Lafont-Couturier
Ethnology Museum - 1960
Prehist, antiques, hist of Bordeaux from 1715 to the present, Africa, Oceania - library 09633

Musée de l'Imprimerie, 8-10 Rue du Fort Louis, 33800 Bordeaux - T: 0556926117, E-mail: - museeimprim.aquitaine@wanadoo.fr, Internet: http://perso.wanadoo.fr/musee.imprim.aquitaine. Head: Claude Chauffeteau
Science&Tech Museum / Association with Coll 09634

Musée des Arts Décoratifs, 39 Rue Bouffard, 33000 Bordeaux - T: 0556007252, Fax: 0556816967, E-mail: musad@mairie-bordeaux.fr. Head: Bernadette de Boysson
Decorative Arts Museum
European ceramics (12th-18th c), silver and furnishings, local hist 09635

Musée des Beaux-Arts de Bordeaux, 20 Cours d'Albret, 33000 Bordeaux - T: 0556102056, Fax: 0556102513, E-mail: bcaux-arts@atlantel.fr. Head: Françoise Garcia
Fine Arts Museum - 1801
17th-20th century European paintings, sculptures, drawings from the 16th-20th century - library 09636

Musée des Chartrons, 41 Rue de Borie, 33000 Bordeaux - T: 0556442777
Special Museum 09637

Musée des Télécommunications et de la Poste, 3bis Cours Saint-Louis, 33000 Bordeaux - T: 0557871317
Science&Tech Museum 09638

Musée d'Ethnographie de l'Université de Bordeaux II, 3 Pl de la Victoire, 33076 Bordeaux Cedex - T: 0556318314, Fax: 0556314694, E-mail: musee.ethnologie@musettinou-bordeaux2.fr. Head: Christian Mèriot
Ethnology Museum / University Museum - 1894 09639

Musée du Compagnonnage, 112 Rue Malbec, 33000 Bordeaux - T: 0556422201
Special Museum 09640

Musée Militaire, 192 Rue de Pessac, 33000 Bordeaux - T: 0556581945
Military Museum 09641

Musée National des Douanes, 1 Pl de la Bourse, 33000 Bordeaux - T: 0556488282, Fax: 0556488288. Head: Michèle Périssère
Historical Museum - 1983
Uniforms, arms 09642

Musée Paléochrétien de Saint-Seurin, Pl des Martyrs de la Résistance, 33000 Bordeaux - T: 0556442841
Religious Arts Museum / Archaeological Museum 09643

Muséum d'Histoire Naturelle de Bordeaux, Hôtel de Lisleferme, Jardin Public, 33000 Bordeaux - T: 0556482986, Fax: 0556012859. Head: Natalie Memoire
Natural History Museum - 1791 09644

Vinorama, 12 Cours du Médoc, 33300 Bordeaux - T: 0556393920
Local Museum 09645

Bordeaux-Saint-Clair

Collections des Ruchers d'Étretat, Ferme des Platanes, 76790 Bordeaux-Saint-Clair - T: 0235288236/9569
Special Museum / Natural History Museum 09646

Bormes-les-Mimosas

Musée Arts et Histoire, 103 Rue Carnot, 83230 Bormes-les-Mimosas - T: 0494715660
Fine Arts Museum / Historical Museum 09647

Bort-les-Orgues

Musée Historique, Halle aux Blés, Pl de l'Hôtel-de-Ville, 19110 Bort-les-Orgues - T: 0555960249
Local Museum 09648

Bosquentin

Musée de la Ferme et des Vieux Métiers, 27480 Bosquentin - T: 0232480722/493525
Agriculture Museum 09649

Botans

Musée Agricole Départemental Marcel-Mouilleseaux, 5 Rue de Dorans, 90400 Botans - T: 0384560808/0790/0791
Agriculture Museum 09650

Bouchain

Musée d'Ostrévant, Rue d'Ostrévant, 59111 Bouchain - T: 0327357397
Archaeological Museum / Historical Museum 09651

Boucieu-le-Roi

Musée Pierre-Vigne, Maison Pierre-Vigne, 07270 Boucieu-le-Roi - T: 0475067674
Religious Arts Museum 09652

Bouconville-Vauclair

Musée de l'Histoire de la Poterie, Vieille Abbaye, 02000 Bouconville-Vauclair - T: 0323224269
Decorative Arts Museum 09653

Boue

Musée de la Bataille de Leipzig, Mairie, 02450 Boue - T: 0323600068
Historical Museum 09654

Bouges-le-Château

Château de Bouges, 15 Rue du Château, 36110 Bouges-le-Château - T: 0254358826, Fax: 0254351696, E-mail: maldent@monuments-france.fr, Internet: http://www.monum.fr. Head: Dominique Maldent
Decorative Arts Museum
18thc furniture, saddlery, stables, carriages museum 09655

Bougival

Musée Ivan-Tourgueniev, 16 Rue Ivan-Tourgueniev, 78380 Bougival - T: 0145778712, Fax: 0145778712. Head: Dr. Alexandre Zviguilsky
Special Museum 09656

Bouillé-Courdault

Musée Maurice-Sabourin, 85420 Bouillé-Courdault - T: 0251524189
Special Museum 09657

Boulogne-Billancourt

Bibliothèque Marmottan, 7 Pl Denfert-Rochereau, 92100 Boulogne-Billancourt - T: 0141102470, Fax: 0141102479, E-mail: Nicole.Ambourg@mairie-boulogne-billancourt.fr, Internet: http://www.academie-des-beaux-arts.fr. Head: Bruno Foucart
Library with Exhibitions 09658

Expo-Musée Renault, 27 Rue des Abondances, 92100 Boulogne-Billancourt - T: 0146052158, Fax: 0146840233
Science&Tech Museum 09659

Musée Départemental Albert-Kahn, 14 Rue du Port, 92100 Boulogne-Billancourt - T: 0146045280, Fax: 0145038659, E-mail: museeakahn@cg92.fr. Head: Jeanne Beausoleil
Historical Museum - 1986
Gardens, photos, films covering life in France and abroad from 1910 to 1931 09660

Musée des Années 30 (Museum of the Thirties), 28 Av André-Morizet, 92100 Boulogne-Billancourt - T: 0155184642, Fax: 0155185158, E-mail: musee.annees30@mairie-boulogne-billancourt.fr, Internet: http://www.boulognebillancourt.com. Head: Emmanuel Bréon
Fine Arts Museum / Decorative Arts Museum
Sculptures, paintings, furniture, decorative art, colonial and sacred art 09661

Musée-Jardin Paul-Landowski, 14 Rue Max-Blondat, 92100 Boulogne-Billancourt - T: 0146058269, 0155184642, Fax: 0155185158, Internet: http://www.boulognebillancourt.com. Head: Michéle Lefrancois
Fine Arts Museum - 1963
Bronze, marble sculptures, ivories, and drawings by Paul Landowsky, housed in sculptor's former home 09662

Boulogne-sur-Mer

Castle-Museum, Rue de Bernet, 62200 Boulogne-sur-Mer - T: 0321100220, Fax: 0321100223
Local Museum 09663

Musée du Général San Martin, 113 Grand-Rue, 62200 Boulogne-sur-Mer - T: 0321315465
Military Museum 09664

Nausicaa, Centre National de la Mer, Blvd Sainte-Beuve, 62200 Boulogne-sur-Mer - T: 0321309999, Fax: 0321309394, E-mail: info@nausicaa.fr, Internet: http://www.nausicaa.fr
Natural History Museum 09665

Bouray-sur-Juine

Musée Á la Rencontre des Vieux Métiers, 55 Rue Haute, 91850 Bouray-sur-Juine - T: 0160822325/69274208
Science&Tech Museum / Folklore Museum 09666

Bourbon-Lancy

Musée de l'Uniforme Militaire Français et du Vieux Bourbon, 3 Rue de la Collégiale, 71140 Bourbon-Lancy - T: 0385891221
Military Museum / Local Museum 09667

Musée du Machinisme Agricole, 4 Rue du Docteur Pain, 71140 Bourbon-Lancy - T: 0385892323, Fax: 0385893020, E-mail: mairie.bourbon-lancy@wanadoo.fr
Science&Tech Museum 09668

Musée Municipal Bourbon-Lancy, Eglise Saint-Nazaire, 71140 Bourbon-Lancy - T: 0385892323, Fax: 0385893020, E-mail: mairie.bourbon-lancy@wanadoo.fr. Head: Hubert Louis
Local Museum / Fine Arts Museum 09669

Bourbon-l'Archambault

Musée Augustin-Bernard, Pl des Thermes, 03160 Bourbon-l'Archambault - T: 0470670179/0008
Local Museum 09670

Musée d'Art Sacré, Église Saint-Georges, 03160 Bourbon-l'Archambault - T: 0470670344/0979
Religious Arts Museum 09671

Bourbonne-les-Bains

Musée Municipal, Parc de l'Hôtel de Ville, 52400 Bourbonne-les-Bains - T: 0325901480, Fax: 0325906940, E-mail: mairie-de.bourbonne@wanadoo.fr, Internet: http://www.bourbonne.com. Head: André Noirot
Fine Arts Museum / Archaeological Museum 09672

Bourcefranc-le-Chapus

Musée Ostréicole, Fort du Chapus, 17560 Bourcefranc-le-Chapus - T: 0546850202/0759
Natural History Museum 09673

Bourdeilles

Musée-Château de Bourdeilles, 24310 Bourdeilles - T: 0553534435/037336
Decorative Arts Museum 09674

Bourg-en-Bresse

Musée de Brou, 63 Blvd de Brou, 01000 Bourg-en-Bresse - T: 0474228383, Fax: 0474247670, E-mail: monastere.de.brou@monuments-france.fr. Head: Marie Françoise Poiret
Decorative Arts Museum / Fine Arts Museum - 1854
Sculptures (15th-20th c), painting: Flemish (15th-17th c), Italian (17th-18th c), French (17th-19th c: 'Troubadour', G. Doré, Lyon School), abstract art and furniture (16th, 18th-19th c), faiences and local archaeology 09675

Musée des Pays de l'Ain, 34 Rue Général-Delestraint, 01000 Bourg-en-Bresse - T: 0474211520
Special Museum 09676

Musée Hospitalier - Apothicairerie, Hôtel-Dieu, 01000 Bourg-en-Bresse - T: 0474224940, Fax: 0474230628, E-mail: - bourgenbresse.officedetourisme@wanadoo.fr. Head: Martine Desbenoit
Special Museum 09677

Bourg-Saint-Maurice

Musée du Costume Savoyard, Pl de l'Eglise, 73700 Bourg-Saint-Maurice - T: 0479070901, Fax: 0479072729, E-mail: lesarcs@lesarcs.com
Folklore Museum 09678

Petit Musée Minéraux et Faune de l'Alpe, 82 Av du Maréchal Leclerc, 73700 Bourg-Saint-Maurice - T: 0479071274
Natural History Museum 09679

Bourg-sur-Gironde

Musée de la Voiture Hippomobile et de la Citadelle de Bourg, Parc de la Citadelle, 33710 Bourg-sur-Gironde - T: 0557682357, Fax: 0557683984. Head: N. Mayor
Science&Tech Museum / Historic Site 09680

Musée Maurice Poignant, Rue des Religieuses, 33710 Bourg-sur-Gironde - T: 0557684248
Local Museum 09681

Bourganeuf

Collections d'Histoire Locale, Tour Zizim, Pl du Mail, 23400 Bourganeuf - T: 0555640624/2054
Historical Museum 09682

Bourges

La Box, c/o Ecole Nationale des Beaux-Arts de Bourges, 9 Rue Edouard-Branly, 18006 Bourges Cedex - T: 0248247870, Fax: 0248247870, E-mail: la.box@enba-borges.org, Internet: http://www.enba-bourges.org. Head: Corinne Le Néün
Public Gallery 09683

Musée de l'École, 2 Rue de la Thaumassière, 18000 Bourges - T: 0248243103/704192. Head: Béatrice de Chancel-Bardelot
Special Museum 09684

Musée de l'Hôtel Lallemant, 6 Rue Bourbonnoux, 18014 Bourges - T: 0248578117, Fax: 0248704192. Head: Béatrice de Chancel-Baudelot
Decorative Arts Museum - 1951
Furnishings, tapestries, objects d'art clocks, etc, displayed in a Renaissance townhouse 09685

Musée d'Histoire Naturelle Gabriel-Foucher, Parc Saint-Paul, 4 Allée René-Ménard, 18000 Bourges - T: 0248653734/578244, Fax: 0248698998, E-mail: museum-bourges.net
Natural History Museum 09686

Musée du Berry, Hôtel Cujas, 4-6 Rue des Arènes, 18000 Bourges - T: 0248704192, Fax: 0248704192. Head: Béatrice de Chancel-Bardelot
Archaeological Museum / Decorative Arts Museum / Folklore Museum
Pre- and Romanesque archeology, ceramics, bronzes, sculpture, provincial folklore and folk art, household objects, costumes, paintings, in Renaissance house 09687

Musée Estève, Hôtel des Échevins, 13 Rue Edouard-Branly, 18000 Bourges - T: 0248247538
Fine Arts Museum 09688

Palais Jacques Coeur, Rue Jacques Coeur, 18000 Bourges - T: 0248240687, Fax: 0248705040. Head: Denis Pilven
Historic Site 09689

Bourgneuf-en-Retz

Musée d'Art Populaire du Pays de Retz, 6 Rue des Moines, 44580 Bourgneuf-en-Retz - T: 0240214083. Head: Roland de Moigne
Local Museum
Local hist, archeology, geology, handicraft, agriculture - library 09690

Bourgoin-Jallieu

Musée Bourgeon-Jallieu, 17 Rue Victor Hugo, 38300 Bourgoin-Jallieu - T: 0474281974, Fax: 0474939358. Head: Brigitte Riboreau
Decorative Arts Museum / Fine Arts Museum / Science&Tech Museum / Ethnology Museum 09691

Musée Victor Charreton → Musée Bourgeon-Jallieu

Bourgueil

Collections de la Cave de la Dive Bouteille, Chevrette, 37140 Bourgueil - T: 0247977201
Special Museum 09692

Musée de l'Abbaye de Bourgueil, 52 Av Le Jouteux, 37140 Bourgueil - T: 0247977204/7050
Religious Arts Museum 09693

Musée Van Œveren, Château des Sablons, 37140 Bourgueil - T: 0247979899
Special Museum 09694

Musée Viticole, 57 Rue de Lossay, 37140 Bourgueil - T: 0247973260
Special Museum 09695

Boury-en-Vexin

Château de Boury-en-Vexin, 60240 Boury-en-Vexin - T: 0332551510
Decorative Arts Museum / Fine Arts Museum 09696

Bousies

Musée des Evolutions, 19 Rue René Ruelle, 59222 Bousies - T: 0327773140/3046
Local Museum 09697

Boussac

Musée-Château de Boussac, 23600 Boussac - T: 0555650762, Fax: 0555658756
Decorative Arts Museum 09698

Musée de la Tapisserie, Hôtel de Ville, 23600 Boussac - T: 0555650109
Decorative Arts Museum 09699

Boussy-Saint-Antoine

Musée André Dunoyer-de-Ségonzac, Hôtel de Ville, Pl des Droits de l'Homme, 91800 Boussy-Saint-Antoine - T: 0169001317, Fax: 0169003227
Local Museum 09700

Bouvignies

Musée Colombophile, Château, 59870 Bouvignies - T: 0327912013/278827
Special Museum 09701

Bouxwiller

Collection de Peintures, Hôtel de Ville, 67330 Bouxwiller - T: 0388707016
Fine Arts Museum 09702

Musée de Bouxwiller et du Pays de Hanau, Hôtel de Ville, 67330 Bouxwiller - T: 0388707016, Fax: 0388713034
Local Museum / Folklore Museum - 1934
Hist of Hanau-Lichtenberg and Hessen-Darmstadt, local ethnography, furniture, fossils 09703

Musée Judéo-Alsacien, Ancienne Synagogue, Grand-Rue, 67330 Bouxwiller - T: 0388709717, Fax: 0388709717, Internet: http://www.sdv.fr/judaisme. Head: Gilbert Weil
Ethnology Museum 09704

Bouzigues

Musée de l'Etang de Thau, Quai du Port de Pêche, 34140 Bouzigues - T: 0467783357/3012. Head: Louis Higounet
Local Museum 09705

Musée du Sapeur-Pompier, Centre d'Intervention, près de la Gare, 34140 Bouzigues - T: 0467783257
Special Museum 09706

Boynes

Musée-Maison du Safran et de la Vigne, 45300 Boynes - T: 0238331305/1009
Special Museum / Agriculture Museum 09707

Brain-sur-Allonnes

Musée des Patenôtriers, Allée des Caves, 49650 Brain-sur-Allonnes - T: 0241520339, Fax: 0241520643, E-mail: info@mayand.fr. Head: Bernard Lissague
Religious Arts Museum 09708

Musée Médiéval, 12 Pl du Commerce, 49650 Brain-sur-Allonnes - T: 0241528740, Fax: 0241528740, E-mail: off.de.tourisme.nord.saumurois@wanadoo.fr. Head: Michel Boucher
Historical Museum / Archaeological Museum 09709

Site Archéologique La Cave Peinte, La Cave Peinte, 49650 Brain-sur-Allonnes - T: 0241528740, Fax: 0241528740, E-mail: -off.de.tourisme.nord.saumurois@wanadoo.fr. Head: Michel Boucher
Archaeological Museum 09710

Bram-le-Lauragais

Collection Archéologique, Mairie, 11150 Bram-le-Lauragais - T: 0468761075
Archaeological Museum 09711

Brantôme

Musée Médiumnique Fernand Desmoulin, Abbaye, 24310 Brantôme - T: 0553058063, Fax: 0553354518
Special Museum 09712

Brasparts

Exposition Permanente d'Art, Ferme Saint-Michel, 29190 Brasparts - T: 0298814669, Fax: 0298213742. Head: Patrick Leclerc
Fine Arts Museum 09713

Brassac-les-Mines

Musée de la Mine, Rte Nationale 9, 63570 Brassac-les-Mines - T: 0473543088
Science&Tech Museum 09714

Brassempouy

Musée de la Femme Préhistorique, 40330 Brassempouy - T: 0558890247
Archaeological Museum 09715

Braux-Sainte-Cohière

Musée d'Arts Populaires de l'Argonne, A 4 km de la Sortie de l'Autoroute A 6 vers Sainte-Menehould, 51800 Braux-Sainte-Cohière - T: 0326608351, Fax: 0326609830, E-mail: a.cazeaux@wanadoo.fr. Head: André Bussinger
Folklore Museum 09716

Bray-sur-Seine

Musée Archéologique, Pl du Tapis-Vert, 77480 Bray-sur-Seine. Head: M. Scherrer
Archaeological Museum 09717

Brebotte

Musée de l'Artisanat et des Traditions Rurales, Maison à Pans de Bois, 90140 Brebotte - T: 0384234237, Fax: 0384234238
Ethnology Museum 09718

Brecy-Brières

Musée-Conservatoire de l'Outil, 08400 Brecy-Brières - T: 0324711191
Agriculture Museum 09719

Breil-sur-Roya

Écomusée du Haut Pays de la Roya et de la Bevera, Gare, 06540 Breil-sur-Roya - T: 0493044691
Local Museum 09720

Espace Électricité de France, Gare SNCF, 06540 Breil-sur-Roya
Science&Tech Museum 09721

Espace Muséal Transport, Gare SNCF, 06540 Breil-sur-Roya
Science&Tech Museum 09722

Brem-sur-Mer

Musée du Vin, Moulin de Bellevue, Rte d'Ile d'Olonne, 85470 Brem-sur-Mer - T: 0251905628
Special Museum / Historical Museum 09723

Brennilis

Musée des Maisons d'Autrefois, Youdig-Kerveguenet, 29218 Brennilis - T: 0298996236
Local Museum 09724

Bressieux

Musée Archéologique du Château Féodal, Mairie, 38870 Bressieux - T: 0474200734, 0474200238, Fax: 0474201545, E-mail: rmoyroud@club-internet.fr. Head: Raymond Moyroud
Archaeological Museum 09725

Bressuire

Musée des Arts et Traditions Populaires, Pl de l'Hôtel-de-Ville, 79300 Bressuire - T: 0549652679
Local Museum 09726

Brest

Collection Historique Maritime, c/o Cercle des Officiers Mariniers, Rue Yves Collet, 29200 Brest - T: 0298807548
Special Museum / Science&Tech Museum 09727

Collections du Centre d'Instruction Navale de Brest, c/o Commandant du CIN, Ancienne Ecole Navale, 29200 Brest
Local Museum 09728

Conservatoire Botanique National de Brest, 52 Allée Bot-Stangalard, 29200 Brest - T: 0298418895
Natural History Museum 09729

Goclette La Recouvrance, Quai Malbert, 29275 Brest - T: 0298339540, Fax: 0298339550, E-mail: contact@larecouvrance.com. Head: Jacques Sevellec
Special Museum 09730

Musée des Beaux-Arts, 24 Rue Traverse, 29200 Brest - T: 0298008796, Fax: 0298008770
Fine Arts Museum - 1875/1968
Italian painting (17th-18th c), French painting 09731

Musée du Vieux Brest, Tour Tanguy, 29200 Brest - T: 0298450531/008860
Historical Museum
Local hist, diorama 09732

Musée Historique et Militaire, Mémorial du Finistère, Fort Montbarey, Allée Bir-Hackeim, 29200 Brest - T: 0298443946
Historical Museum / Military Museum 09733

Musée National de la Marine, Château de Brest, 29200 Brest - T: 0298221309, Fax: 0298433054, E-mail: g.prudhomme@musee_marine.fr, Internet: http://www.musee-marine.fr. Head: Georges Prudhomme
Historical Museum
Model ships (navy, merchant navy, fishing navy), paintings, figureheads, local maritime history 09734

Musées Historiques de l'Arsenal de la Marine Nationale, 29200 Brest - T: 0298221198
Special Museum 09735

Océanopolis, Port de Plaisance du Moulin Blanc, 29200 Brest - T: 0298344040, Fax: 0298344069, E-mail: oceanopolis@oceanopolis.com, Internet: http://www.oceanopolis.com. Head: Eric Hosseloot
Natural History Museum - 1990
Oceanography, marine biology 09736

Breteuil

Musée Archéologique de la Région de Breteuil, 5 Rue de l'Eglise, 60121 Breteuil Cedex - T: 0344071512, Fax: 0344781391. Head: Vincent Pomarede
Archaeological Museum - 1985 09737

Briançon

Collection Ski-Montagne, 37 Grande Gargouille, 05100 Briançon - T: 0492210083
Special Museum 09738

Exposition Minéralogique, 33 Grande Gargouille, 05100 Briançon - T: 0492203757
Natural History Museum 09739

Briançon

Musée-Bibliothèque A.-Albert (closed) 09740

Musée de la Mine, Ancienne Poudrière, 05100 Briançon - T: 0492211319/202949
Science&Tech Museum 09741

Musée des Cordeliers, Ancienne Église des Cordeliers, 05100 Briançon - T: 0492211319/202949
Archaeological Museum 09742

Briançon

Musée du Ski, Exposition Parc des Ecrins, Pl Médecin Général Blanchard, 05100 Briançon - T: 0492214215, Fax: 0492201834, E-mail: -ecrins.brianconnais@espaces_naturels.fr
Special Museum 09743

Briançonnet

Musée d'Arts Populaires, 06850 Briançonnet - T: 0493604271
Folklore Museum 09744

Briare

Musée de la Mosaïque et des Émaux, 1 Blvd Loreau, 45250 Briare - T: 0238312051
Decorative Arts Museum 09745

Bricquebec

Musée d'Archéologie et d'Art Populaire, Château, 50260 Bricquebec - T: 0233522113/65
Local Museum 09746

Briec-de-l'Odet

Musée de la Ferme Miniature, 29112 Briec-de-l'Odet - T: 0298945210
Local Museum 09747

Brienne-la-Vieille

Écomusée de la Forêt d'Orient, 10500 Brienne-la-Vieille - T: 0325929585/8883
Agriculture Museum 09748

Musée de la Charronnerie, 10500 Brienne-la-Vieille - T: 0325929584/8883
Science&Tech Museum 09749

Brienne-le-Château

Musée Napoléonien, 34 Rue de l'École Militaire, 10500 Brienne-le-Château - T: 0325928241
Historical Museum
Memorabilia of Napoleon I (1769-1821), Napoleonic military history 09750

Brignon

Musée Archéologique, Mairie, 30190 Brignon - T: 0466832172
Archaeological Museum 09751

Briord

Musée Archéologique, 01470 Briord - T: 0474367206
Historical Museum / Archaeological Museum 09752

Brioude

Exposition Permanente d'Arts Plastiques, Maison de Mandrin, Rue du 4-Septembre, 43100 Brioude - T: 0171749459
Fine Arts Museum 09753

Maison-Musée du Saumon et de la Rivière, Pl de la Résistance, 43100 Brioude - T: 0471749143, Fax: 0471749787
Natural History Museum 09754

Musée Hôtel de la Dentelle, 29 Rue du 4 Septembre, 43100 Brioude - T: 0471748002, Fax: 0471748762, E-mail: hoteldeladentelle@wanadoo.fr. Head: Odette Arpin
Decorative Arts Museum 09755

Brissac-Quincé

Château-Musée, 49320 Brissac-Quincé - T: 0241912221
Decorative Arts Museum 09756

Brive-la-Gaillarde

Musée d'Art et d'Histoire Labenche, 26bis Blvd Jules-Ferry, 19100 Brive-la-Gaillarde - T: 0555923939/241905, Fax: 0555245754, E-mail: FrederiqueBrengues@wanadoo.fr
Local Museum / Archaeological Museum / Fine Arts Museum / Decorative Arts Museum / Folklore Museum - 1883
Tapisserie coll, rigional history, archaeology, traditions 09757

Musée Denoix, Maîtres Liquoristes à Brive depuis 1839, 9 Blvd du Maréchal-Lyautey, 19100 Brive-la-Gaillarde - T: 0555743427
Science&Tech Museum 09758

Brouains

Écomusée de la Vallée de Brouains, Le Moulin, 50150 Brouains
Local Museum 09759

Brousses-et-Villaret

Le Moulin à Papier de Brousses, 11390 Brousses-et-Villaret - T: 0468266743, Fax: 0468266743, E-mail: moulin_a_papier@libertysurf.fr, Internet: http://perso.libertysurf.fr/moulin_a_papier/moulin_a_papier. Head: André Durand
Science&Tech Museum 09760

Brugnac

Le Chaudron Magique, RD 314, 47260 Brugnac - T: 0553888077, Fax: 0553889163, E-mail: chaudronmagique@wanadoo.fr, Internet: http://www.chavdronmagique.fr. Head: Martin Lavoyer
Agriculture Museum 09761

Bruley

Musée du Vin et de la Mirabelle, G.I.E., 54200 Bruley - T: 0383645509
Special Museum 09762

Brullioles

Écomusée Agricole de la Cadole, À Montizuel, 69690 Brullioles - T: 0474705295
Agriculture Museum 09763

Brûlon

Musée Claude Chappe, Maison de la Culture, Rue Pavée, 72350 Brûlon - T: 0243956100
Special Museum 09764

Brumath

Musée Archéologique, Pl du Château, Eglise Protestante, 67170 Brumath - T: 0388511030. Head: J.J. Kientz
Archaeological Museum 09765

Musée de l'Hôpital Psychiatrique, Etablissement Public de Santé Alsace Nord, 67170 Brumath - T: 0388646100, Fax: 0388646168
Special Museum 09766

Musée du Peintre Gustave Stoskopf, 1 Rue Gustave Stoskopf, 67170 Brumath - T: 0388601184
Fine Arts Museum 09767

Brunoy

Musée Municipal Robert Dubois-Corneau, 16 Rue de Réveillon, 91800 Brunoy - T: 0160463360, Fax: 0160463089. Head: Raphaël Gérard
Local Museum - 1951
Hist of bankers during the reign of Louis XV, hist of theater (18th and 19th c), local hist - library, archive 09768

Brunstatt

Espace d'Art Brut, Ferme Schultz, 15 Rue de l'Église, 68200 Brunstatt - T: 0389061096
Fine Arts Museum 09769

Bruyères

Musée Henri-Mathieu, Ancienne Synagogue, 88600 Bruyères - T: 0329502087
Decorative Arts Museum / Folklore Museum 09770

Bry-sur-Marne

Musée Adrien-Mentienne, Mairie, 1 Grande-Rue Charles-de-Gaulle, 94360 Bry-sur-Marne - T: 0145166800, Fax: 0145166838, E-mail: mairie-bry@ville-de-bry-sur-marne.fr, Internet: http://www.ville-de-bry-sur-marne.fr. Head: Margaret Calvarin
Local Museum 09771

Buffon

Musée de la Grande Forge, 21500 Buffon - T: 0380894030/921035
Science&Tech Museum 09772

Buironfosse

Musée du Sabot, Mairie, 02620 Buironfosse - T: 0323972428
Science&Tech Museum 09773

Buis-sur-Damville

Musée de l'Automobile Ancienne, Château du Gérier, 27240 Buis-sur-Damville - T: 0232345747
Science&Tech Museum 09774

Bulgnéville

Musée d'Art et d'Histoire, Mairie, 88140 Bulgnéville - T: 0329091073/1467
Folklore Museum / Historical Museum 09775

Bure-Tressange

Musée Militaire de Bure, 6 Rue des Castors, 57710 Bure-Tressange - T: 0382910123
Military Museum 09776

Bures-sur-Yvette

Musée de l'Optométrie, Institut et Centre d'Optométrie, 134 Rte de Chartres, 91440 Bures-sur-Yvette - T: 0164861213, Fax: 0169284999, E-mail: ico.direction@wanadoo.fr. Head: Jean-Paul Roosen
Special Museum 09777

Burnhaupt-le-Haut

Collection de Matériel Ferroviaire, 68520 Burnhaupt-le-Haut - T: 0389828848
Science&Tech Museum 09778

Bussières

Musée du Tissage et de la Soierie (Weaving and Silk Museum), Pl Vaucanson, 42510 Bussières - T: 0477273395, Fax: 0477273395, 0477273505, E-mail: musee-du-tissage-et-de-la-soierie@wanadoo.fr. Head: Pierre Berchoux
Science&Tech Museum 09779

Bussy-le-Grand

Château-Musée de Bussy-Rabutin, 21150 Bussy-le-Grand - T: 0380960003
Decorative Arts Museum 09780

Musée Gorsline, Rue des Connets, 21150 Bussy-le-Grand - T: 0380960329, Fax: 0380960084, E-mail: musee.gorsline@wanadoo.fr. Head: Marie Gorsline
Fine Arts Museum
Permanent collection of oils, watercolours and graphic works by Douglas Gorsline, temporary exhibitions of works related to those of Gorsline 09781

Butry-sur-Oise

Musée des Tramways à Vapeur et des Chemins de Fer Secondaires Français, Gare SNCF de Valmondois, 95430 Butry-sur-Oise - T: 0134730440, E-mail: mtvs@voila.fr, Internet: http://www.trains-fr.org/mtvs/. Head: O. Janneau
Science&Tech Museum 09782

Buzet-sur-Baise

Musée de la Vigne et du Vin, Les Vignerons de Buzet, 47160 Buzet-sur-Baise - T: 0553847430
Special Museum 09783

Cabanès (Aveyron)

Musée de la Résistance, Chapelle de Villelongue, 12800 Cabanès (Aveyron) - T: 0565470041/0776
Historical Museum 09784

Cabourg

Micromusée de Marcel Proust, Grand-Hôtel, Pl Marcel-Proust, 14390 Cabourg - T: 0231910179
Special Museum 09785

Cabrerets

Musée de l'Insolite, 46330 Cabrerets - T: 0565302101
Fine Arts Museum 09786

Musée de Préhistoire, Grotte de Pech-Merle, 46330 Cabrerets - T: 0565312333, Fax: 0565302126, E-mail: muspech@crdi.fr, Internet: http://www.quercy.net/pechmerle. Head: H. Nouyrit
Archaeological Museum - 1981
Quercy's prehistory, palaeolithic cave art in Quercy - library 09787

Cabrières

Caveau Muséalisé, Cave Coopérative, Rte de Fontès, 34800 Cabrières - T: 0467889160, Fax: 0467880015, E-mail: sca.cabrieres@wanadoo.fr
Archaeological Museum
Oldest copper mines in Europe 09788

Cabrières-d'Avignon

Musée de la Lavande, Coustellet, Rte de Gordes, 84220 Cabrières-d'Avignon - T: 0490769123
Special Museum / Natural History Museum 09789

Cabriès

Musée Edgar Melik, Château, 13480 Cabriès - T: 0442224281
Fine Arts Museum 09790

Caden

Musée d'Outillage Agricole Miniature, Pont Main, 56220 Caden - T: 0297678044
Agriculture Museum 09791

Cadenet

Musée de la Vannerie, La Glaneuse, 84160 Cadenet - T: 0490682444/3954
Special Museum / Historical Museum 09792

Cadillac

Château des Ducs d'Epernon, 33410 Cadillac - T: 0556626958
Fine Arts Museum / Decorative Arts Museum 09793

Cadouin

Musée du Suaire et du Pèlerinage, 24480 Cadouin - T: 0553633628
Religious Arts Museum 09794

Caen

Abbaye aux Hommes, Hôtel de Ville, Esplanade J.-M. Louvel, 14000 Caen - T: 0231304280
Local Museum 09795

Mémorial Caen-Normandie, Esplanade Eisenhower, 14000 Caen, mail addr: BP 6261, 14066 Caen - T: 0231060644, Fax: 0231060670, E-mail: contact@memorial-caen.fr, Internet: http://www.memorial-caen.fr. Head: Jacques Belin
Historical Museum - 1988
WWII and cold war 09796

Musée de la Poste et des Techniques de Communication de Basse-Normandie, 52 Rue Saint-Pierre, 14000 Caen - T: 0231501220, Fax: 0231863338, E-mail: muse.poste.caen@wanadoo.fr. Head: Yves Lecouturier
Science&Tech Museum 09797

Musée de Normandie, Château de Caen, 14000 Caen - T: 0231304760, Fax: 0231304769, E-mail: mdn@ville-caen.fr, Internet: http://www.ville-caen.fr/mdn. Head: Jean-Yves Marin
Local Museum - 1946
Medieval history and archeology of Normandy, folklore, farm implements, ceramics, costumes 09798

Musée de Rome, Université, Esplanade de la Paix, 14000 Caen - T: 0231466289/88
University Museum 09799

Musée des Beaux-Arts, Château, 14000 Caen - T: 0231852863
Fine Arts Museum - 1802
Italian, French, Flemish, Dutch paintings from the Middle Ages to the 20th c, drawings, ceramics, art objects, engravings, prints 09800

Musée d'Initiation à la Nature de Normandie, Enceinte de l'Abbaye aux Hommes, Hôtel de Ville, 14000 Caen - T: 0231304327
Natural History Museum 09801

Cagnes-sur-Mer

Musée d'Art Moderne Méditerranéen, Haut-de-Cagnes, 06800 Cagnes-sur-Mer - T: 0493208557. Head: Georges Dussaule
Fine Arts Museum 09802

Musée d'Histoire Locale, Haut-de-Cagnes, 06800 Cagnes-sur-Mer - T: 0493208557
Special Museum 09803

Musée Donation Suzy-Solidor, Haut-de-Cagnes, 06800 Cagnes-sur-Mer - T: 0493208557
Fine Arts Museum 09804

Musée Ethnographique de l'Olivier, Haut-de-Cagnes, 06800 Cagnes-sur-Mer - T: 0493208557
Ethnology Museum 09805

Musée Renoir, Domaine des Collettes, 06800 Cagnes-sur-Mer - T: 0493206107. Head: Georges Dussaule
Fine Arts Museum - 1960
House where the French painter Renoir spent his last 12 years, several of his paintings, his sculpture, original furnishings, important mural, photos, personal effects - garden 09806

Musées du Château Grimaldi, Haut-de-Cagnes, 06800 Cagnes-sur-Mer - T: 0493208557/729, Fax: 0493730920
Decorative Arts Museum / Fine Arts Museum
Castle fortress (14th-17th c), Renaissance interiors and furnishings, tapestries, coll of Suzy Solidor's portraits by Dufy, Cocteau and others, modern Mediterranean art 09807

Cahors

Château-Musée du Roussillon, Saint-Pierre la Feuille, 46000 Cahors - T: 0565368705
Folklore Museum 09808

Exposition Historique, Tour Centrale du Pont Valentré, 46000 Cahors - T: 0565350956
Historical Museum 09809

Galerie de l'Office du Tourisme, Pl Aristide Briand, 46000 Cahors - T: 0565350956
Fine Arts Museum / Historical Museum 09810

Maison Henri IV, Quai Champollion, 46000 Cahors - T: 0565350435/318007
Decorative Arts Museum 09811

Moulin-Bateau La Sainte-Catherine, Au Pied du Pont-Valentré, 46000 Cahors - T: 0565221400/60
Special Museum 09812

Musée du Vin de Cahors et de la Table Lotoise, Ancien Cuvier, 35 Rue de la Chantrerie, 46000 Cahors - T: 0565350956
Special Museum / Science&Tech Museum 09813

Musée Henri Martin, 792 Rue Emile Zola, 46000 Cahors - T: 0565239452, Fax: 0565239296, E-mail: museehenrimartin@free.fr. Head: Laurent Guillaut
Historical Museum
Portrait-paintings, memorabilia of the statesman Léon Gambetta, Henri Martin, Clément Marot 09814

Caissargues

Exposition Archéologique, Aire de Caissargues, A 54, 30132 Caissargues
Archaeological Museum 09815

Cajarc

Centre d'Art Contemporain Georges Pompidou, 46160 Cajarc - T: 0565407819/6397, Fax: 0565407716, E-mail: magp@mageos.com. Head: Jean-Paul Loussy
Fine Arts Museum 09816

Musée du Rail, Halle à Marchandises, Gare de Cajarc, 46160 Cajarc - T: 0565302166, 0565407204. Head: Pierre Bregeaut
Science&Tech Museum
Telephone, signalization, tools, lights, documents 09817

Calacuccia

Musée François-Flori "Ricordi Vividi Antichi Niulinchi", Couvent Saint-François, 20224 Calacuccia - T: 0495480011
Folklore Museum 09818

Calais

Musée de la Guerre, Parc Saint-Pierre, 62100 Calais - T: 0321342157/966240
Military Museum 09819

Musée des Beaux-Arts et de la Dentelle, 25 Rue Richelieu, 62100 Calais - T: 0321464840, Fax: 0321464847. Head: Annette Haudiquet
Fine Arts Museum / Decorative Arts Museum - 1837
15th-20th century paintings and watercolours, 19th-20th century sculptures, 15th-18th century Flemish and Dutch paintings, 17th-20th century French and Italian paintings, 19th-20th century English paintings and watercolours, local hist, local lace production, studies and sketches of the monument 'The Calais Citizens' by Rodin 09820

Cales

Musée Vivant de la Meunerie, Moulin Fortifié Le Cougnaguet, 46350 Cales - T: 0565387356
Science&Tech Museum 09821

Camares

Château de Montaigut, 12360 Camares - T: 0565998150, Fax: 0565998341, E-mail: chateau-montaigut@wanadoo.fr
Ethnology Museum / Archaeological Museum / Historic Site 09822

Musée d'Art et d'Histoire → Château de Montaigut

Camaret-sur-Mer

Exposition de la Mer, des Arts et de la Culture → Maison du Patrimoine Maritime

Maison du Patrimoine Maritime, Salle de Venise, Quai Kléber, 29570 Camaret-sur-Mer - T: 0298278260/8487, E-mail: nautisme-arts-culture@oreka.com, Internet: http://www.chez.com/nautismeartsculture. Head: Jean-Yves Pesqueur
Historical Museum 09823

Musée Maritime, Tour Vauban, 29129 Camaret-sur-Mer - T: 0298279112/9422, E-mail: nautisme-arts-culture@oreka.com, Internet: http://www.chez.com/nautismeartsculture. Head: Jean-Yves Pesqueur
Military Museum
17th century tower, maritime hist, military hist 09824

Musée-Mémorial de la Bataille de l'Atlantique, 29129 Camaret-sur-Mer - T: 0298279258
Military Museum 09825

Cambo-les-Bains

Musée Edmond Rostand, Villa Arnaga, Rte de Bayonne, 64250 Cambo-les-Bains - T: 0559297057, Fax: 0559293380. Head: Henry Courtelarre
Special Museum - 1961 09826

Cambrai

Château-Musée de Selles, 59400 Cambrai - T: 0327783675
Fine Arts Museum 09827

Musée d'Art et d'Histoire, 15 Rue de l'Epée, 59400 Cambrai - T: 0327822797/90. Head: Michel Bouvy
Local Museum 09828

Musée des Bêtises de Cambrai, Confiserie Afchain, 59400 Cambrai - T: 0327812549, Fax: 0327812040, E-mail: betises-de-camrai@wanadoo.fr, Internet: http://www.betises-de-cambrai.tm.fr. Head: Jean Pierre Nause
Special Museum 09829

Musée Militaire, Cour de la Manutention, 59400 Cambrai - T: 0327783675/3615
Military Museum 09830

Camembert

Musée du Camembert ou Tyrosémiophilique - Exposition d'Etiquettes de Camembert, Ferme de la Rivière, 61120 Camembert - T: 0233390890
Special Museum 09831

Camprieu

Archéosite de la Préhistoire, Abîme de Bramabiau, 30750 Camprieu - T: 0467826078
Archaeological Museum 09832

Canapville

Musée-Manoir des Évêques de Lisieux, 14800 Canapville - T: 0231652475
Ethnology Museum / Decorative Arts Museum 09833

Cancale

La Ferme Marine-Musée de l'Huître et du Coquillage, L'Aurore, 35260 Cancale - T: 0291896999, Fax: 0291898274
Special Museum 09834

Maison-Musée de Jeanne Jugan, Petit Croix, 35260 Cancale - T: 0299896273
Religious Arts Museum 09835

Musée d'Arts et Traditions Populaires, Ancienne Eglise de Saint-Méen, Pl Saint-Méen, 35260 Cancale - T: 0299897932/7126
Folklore Museum / Historical Museum 09836

Musée de la Sculpture sur Bois, Près de l'Eglise, 35260 Cancale - T: 0299896372/402321
Fine Arts Museum 09837

Canet-en-Roussillon

Musée des Vieilles Automobiles, Parking-Balcon Front de Mer, 66140 Canet-en-Roussillon - T: 0468732256, Fax: 0468738078
Science&Tech Museum 09838

Musée du Jouet, Résidence Casino, Pl de la Méditerranée, 66140 Canet-en-Roussillon - T: 0468732029
Special Museum 09839

Musée du Petit Bateau et des Aventures de la Mer, Parking-Balcon Front de Mer, 66140 Canet-en-Roussillon - T: 0468731248, Fax: 0468738078
Special Museum 09840

Le Village des Pêcheurs, Rte de Saint-Cyprien, 66140 Canet-en-Roussillon - T: 0468736060
Special Museum / Natural History Museum 09841

Cannes

La Malmaison, 47 La Croisette, 06400 Cannes - T: 0493990404, Fax: 0493384576. Head: René Corbier
Local Museum 09842

Musée-Chapelle Bellini, 67bis Av de Vallauris, 06400 Cannes - T: 0493386180, Fax: 0493386180. Head: Lucette Bellini
Fine Arts Museum 09843

Musée de la Castre, Le Suquet, 06400 Cannes - T: 0493385526, Fax: 0493388150
Ethnology Museum
Art and archeology of the Mediterranean, Near East, and Oceania, pre-Columbian and Iranian art and folklore 09844

Musée de la Mer, Fort Royal, Ile Sainte-Marguerite, 06400 Cannes - T: 0493431817, Fax: 0493388150. Head: Marie Wallet
Archaeological Museum / Historic Site 09845

Canteleu

Collection du Château de Canteleu, Rte de Sahurs, 76380 Canteleu - T: 0235360096
Natural History Museum / Decorative Arts Museum 09846

Cantenac

Château-Musée Prieuré Lichine, 33460 Cantenac - T: 0557883628
Decorative Arts Museum 09847

Canville-les-Deux-Églises

Exposition d'Œuvres de Sculptures, Fondation Roger-Douville, Le Campan'art, 76560 Canville-les-Deux-Églises - T: 0235965312
Fine Arts Museum 09848

Cany-Barville

Château-Musée de Cany, 76450 Cany-Barville - T: 0235977032
Decorative Arts Museum 09849

Écomusée du Moulin Saint-Martin, 3 Rue de l'Abreuvoir, 76450 Cany-Barville - T: 0235975971/7406
Historical Museum / Science&Tech Museum 09850

Capbreton

Ecomusée de la Mer, Pl de la Liberté, 40130 Capbreton - T: 0558724050
Special Museum / Natural History Museum 09851

Capdenac

Musée d'Archéologie, Donjon, 46100 Capdenac - T: 0565341723
Archaeological Museum 09852

Capendu

Exposition Permanente sur l'Histoire du Rugby, Maison de l'Aude, A 61, Aire des Corbières, 11700 Capendu - T: 0468790084
Special Museum 09853

Capoulet-Junac

Musée Paul Voivenel, 09400 Capoulet-Junac - T: 0561051257/6979
Special Museum 09854

Caramany

Exposition d'Art Populaire et Caveau, Ancien Presbytère, 66720 Caramany - T: 0468845185/80
Folklore Museum 09855

Carantec

Musée Maritime, 8 Rue Albert Louppe, 29226 Carantec - T: 0298670030/43
Science&Tech Museum / Natural History Museum 09856

Carbonne

Musée André Abbal, Rue du Sculpteur Abbal, 31390 Carbonne - T: 0561878267/66/5903
Fine Arts Museum 09857

Carcans

Maison des Arts et Traditions Populaires de la Lande Médocaine, Maubuisson, 33121 Carcans - T: 0556033665/3369
Folklore Museum 09858

Musée des Anciens Combattants, Rue de la Gare, 33121 Carcans - T: 0556033688
Historical Museum 09859

Carcassonne

Mémoires du Moyen Âge, Pont-Levis Pautard, 11000 Carcassonne - T: 0468710865
Historical Museum 09860

Musée de l'École, 3 Rue du Plo, 11000 Carcassonne - T: 0468470502/259514
Special Museum 09861

Musée des Beaux-Arts, 1 Rue de Verdun, 11000 Carcassonne - T: 0468777371, Fax: 0468102438. Head: Marie-Noëlle Maynard
Fine Arts Museum - 1836
17th-20th century French paintings, Dutch paintings, modern paintings, memorabilia of the poet André de Chéniers, faience 09862

Musée des Costumes, 6 Rue Viollet-Le-Duc, 11000 Carcassonne - T: 0468473506
Special Museum 09863

Musée Lapidaire de la Cité, Château Comtal, 11000 Carcassonne - T: 0468250166
Archaeological Museum
Sculptures from the Roman conquest to the 16th c, displayed in the palace of the Vicomtes de Carcassonne 09864

Cardaillac

Musée Eclaté d'Arts et de Traditions Populaires, Pl de la Tour, 46100 Cardaillac - T: 0565401063/1565/1284
Folklore Museum / Agriculture Museum 09865

Carennac

La Maison de la Dordogne, Château, 46110 Carennac - T: 0565109156, Fax: 0565386545
Decorative Arts Museum 09866

Musée du Lavandin, 46110 Carennac - T: 0565109116
Special Museum 09867

Carhaix-Plouguer

Maison du Patrimoine, Centre Culturel Ti Ar Vro, 29270 Carhaix-Plouguer - T: 0298933740
Folklore Museum 09868

Musée Historique, Maison du Sénéchal, Office du Tourisme, 29270 Carhaix-Plouguer - T: 0298930442
Folklore Museum / Historical Museum 09869

Carignan

Musée d'Archéologie, Centre d'Animation, 08110 Carignan - T: 0324222412/0889
Archaeological Museum 09870

Carla-Bayle

Musée Pierre-Bayle, 09130 Carla-Bayle - T: 0561685132
Special Museum 09871

Carnac

Musée de Préhistoire James Miln-Zacharie le Rouzic, 10 Pl de la Chapelle, 56340 Carnac - T: 0297522204, Fax: 0297526404, E-mail: musee.carnac@wanadoo.fr, Internet: http://www.museedecarnac.com
Archaeological Museum - 1882/1985
Ceramics, stone tools, jewelry from magalithic monuments of Carnac, neolithic coll - library 09872

Caromb

Musée des Vieux Outils Noël-Morard, Caves Saint-Marc, 84330 Caromb - T: 0490624024/4028
Folklore Museum 09873

Carpentras

Musée-Bibliothèque Inguimbertine, 234 Blvd Albin-Durand, 84200 Carpentras - T: 0490630492, Fax: 0490602871, E-mail: bib.inguimbertine@ville-carpentras.fr. Head: Christiane Imbert
Library with Exhibitions / Historical Museum / Music Museum 09874

Musée Comtadin, 234 Blvd Albin-Durand, 84200 Carpentras - T: 0490630492, Fax: 0490602871, E-mail: bib.inguimbertine@ville-carpentras.fr. Head: Christiane Imbert
Folklore Museum - 1888
Folklore, works of local painters 09875

Musée d'Art Sacré de la Cathédrale Saint-Siffrein, Cathédrale Saint-Siffrein, 84200 Carpentras - T: 0490630492
Religious Arts Museum
Sculpture and various religious objects from the 14th-18th c 09876

Musée de la Poésie, Rte des Perneps, 84200 Carpentras - T: 0490631949
Special Museum 09877

Musée Duplessis, 234 Blvd Albin-Durand, 84200 Carpentras - T: 0490630492, Fax: 0490602871, E-mail: bib.inguimbertine@ville-carpentras.fr. Head: Christiane Imbert
Fine Arts Museum - 1888
Paintings, folk art, paintings by Duplessis and Vernet, portrait of abbot de Rance by Rigaud, ancient bronze pieces 09878

Musée Lapidaire, Rue des Saintes-Maries, A la Chapelle de Visitandines, 84200 Carpentras - T: 0490630492/02, Fax: 0490602871. Head: Isabelle Battez
Archaeological Museum - 1936
Latin, Greek, and Hebrew inscriptions, Gallo-Roman pottery and glass, minerals 09879

Musée Sobirats, 112 Rue du Collège, 84200 Carpentras - T: 0490630492, Fax: 0490602871. Head: Isabelle Battez
Decorative Arts Museum - 1946
Aubusson tapestries from the 17th-18th c, regional furniture, faience, silver 09880

Carpiquet

Musée du Vélo, Parc de Festyland, Rte de Carpiquet, 14650 Carpiquet - T: 0231750404
Science&Tech Museum 09881

Carquefou

Musée du Temps qui Passe, 18 Pl Aristide Briand, 44470 Carquefou - T: 0240527930. Head: D. Jolivel
Historical Museum - 1980
Local hist, furniture and interior, traditional music 09882

Carrouges

Château-Musée, 61320 Carrouges - T: 0233272032. Head: Claude-Cathérine Terrier
Decorative Arts Museum / Fine Arts Museum 09883

Maison du Parc Naturel Régional de Maine-Normandie, Ancien Chapitre, 61320 Carrouges - T: 0233272115
Natural History Museum / Folklore Museum 09884

Carry-le-Rouet

Musée Fernandèl, 13620 Carry-le-Rouet - T: 0442449356
Special Museum 09885

Cases-de-Pène

Fondation de Jau, Château, 66600 Cases-de-Pène - T: 0468389138, Fax: 0468383133/9825, E-mail: daure@wanadoo.fr. Head: Regine Daure
Fine Arts Museum 09886

Cassaigne

Musée du Château de Cassaigne, 32100 Cassaigne - T: 0562280402, Fax: 0562284143, E-mail: - chateaudecassaigne@telepare.net. Head: Thierry Roques
Special Museum 09887

Cassel

Musée d'Art, d'Histoire et de Folklore, 12 Grand Pl, 59670 Cassel - T: 0328405285/55/424013, Fax: 0328405720. Head: Laurent Guillant
Fine Arts Museum / Historical Museum / Folklore Museum 09888

Cassis

Musée Municipal Méditeranéen de Cassis, Rue Xavier d'Authier, 13260 Cassis - T: 0442018866, Fax: 0442012831
Fine Arts Museum / Folklore Museum - 1910
Archaeology, fine arts, costumes, ship models 09889

Casteil

Maison de la Montagne et du Canigou, 66820 Casteil - T: 0468055139/67780291
Historical Museum / Natural History Museum 09890

Castella

Parc Préhistorique des Grottes de Fontirou, Grottes de Fontirou, Rte Nationale 21, 47340 Castella - T: 0553401529/1552
Archaeological Museum 09891

Castellane

La Maison des Sirènes et des Siréniens, Réserve Géologique de Haute-Provence, Pl Marcel Sauvaire, 04120 Castellane - T: 0492831923, Fax: 0492831927, E-mail: sirenes@club-internet.fr
Natural History Museum 09892

Musée d'Arts et Traditions Populaires de Castellane et du Moyen Verdon, 34 Rue Nationale, 04120 Castellane - T: 0492837180
Folklore Museum 09893

Castelnau-le-Lez

Centre Régional d'Histoire de la Résistance et de la Déportation, Ancienne Mairie, Pl de la Liberté, 34170 Castelnau-le-Lez - T: 0467482827
Historical Museum 09894

Collection Départementale L'Épicerie Ancienne, M.J.C. André-Malraux, 34170 Castelnau-le-Lez - T: 0467793111
Special Museum 09895

Castelnaud-la-Chapelle

Eco-Musée de la Noix, 24250 Castelnaud-la-Chapelle - T: 0553596963, Fax: 0553285934
Local Museum 09896

Musée de la Guerre au Moyen Age, Château de Castelnaud, 24250 Castelnaud-la-Chapelle - T: 0553313000, Fax: 0553289494, E-mail: - chateau.de.castelnaud@wanadoo.fr, Internet: http://www.castelnaud.com
Military Museum
Arms and weapons - Library 09897

Museum Josephine Baker, Château des Milandes, 24250 Castelnaud-la-Chapelle - T: 0553593121, Fax: 0553291733, E-mail: josephine-les-milandes@wanadoo.fr, Internet: http://www.milandes.com. Head: Angélique de Labarre
Local Museum 09898

Castelnou

Château de Castelnou, Pl du Château, 66300 Castelnou - T: 0468532291, Fax: 0468533381
Fine Arts Museum 09899

Castet-Arrouy

Musée du Machinisme Agricole, La Tardanne, 32340 Castet-Arrouy - T: 0562286179
Science&Tech Museum / Agriculture Museum 09900

Castillonnès

Galerie de Carbonnier, Mairie, 47330 Castillonnès - T: 0553368308
Public Gallery 09901

Castres

Centre d'Art Contemporain de Castres, 35 Rue Chambre-de-l'Édit, 81100 Castres - T: 0563593020, Fax: 0563725094
Fine Arts Museum 09902

Centre National et Musée Jean-Jaurès, Hôtel de Ville, 81100 Castres - T: 0563720101
Historical Museum
Memorabilia of the socialist Jean Jaurès (1859-1914), documents, photographs, portraits 09903

Musée Goya, Hôtel de Ville, 81108 Castres Cedex - T: 0563715927, Fax: 0563715926, E-mail: goya@ville-castres.fr, Internet: http://www.amis-musees-castres.asso.fr. Head: Jean-Louis Augé
Fine Arts Museum - 1840
Paintings by Goya (1746-1828), early Spanish art, paintings of Spain's Golden Age, including works by Murillo and Velazquez, contemporary Spanish art, Picasso 09904

Castries

Château, 34160 Castries - T: 0467706866, Fax: 0467701183
Decorative Arts Museum / Fine Arts Museum 09905

Cattenom

Ouvrage de la Ligne Maginot, Sentzich, Au Nord-Est du Village, 57570 Cattenom - T: 0382554071
Military Museum 09906

Caudebec-en-Caux

Musée Biochet-Brechot, Rue de la Boucherie, 76490 Caudebec-en-Caux - T: 0235969591/2065
Local Museum
Architecture, sculpture, engravings, local history, stone work, archives 711) E. Gremillet 09907

Musée de la Marine de la Seine, Rte de Villequier, 76490 Caudebec-en-Caux - T: 0235951013
Science&Tech Museum 09908

Caudeval

Musée d'Artillerie, Château, 11230 Caudeval - T: 0561254028
Military Museum 09909

Musée Romain, Château, Rte de Mirepoix à Limoux, 11230 Caudeval - T: 0561254028
Museum of Classical Antiquities 09910

Caudry

Musée de la Dentelle, Place des Mantilles, 59540 Caudry - T: 0327762977, Fax: 0327766201
Special Museum 09911

Caugé

Musée des Outils du Terroir Normand, 24 Rte de Ferrières, 27930 Caugé - T: 0232371300
Science&Tech Museum / Agriculture Museum 09912

Caumont-l'Event

Southerroscope des Ardoisières, ZA des Ardoisières, 14240 Caumont-l'Event - T: 0231711515/01
Natural History Museum 09913

Cavaillon

Collection de Peintures, Cathédrale Saint-Véran, Pl Joseph d'Arband, 84300 Cavaillon - T: 0490713201
Religious Arts Museum 09914

Musée Hôtel Dieu, Porte d'Avignon, 84300 Cavaillon - T: 0490760034, Fax: 0490714706. Head: Sylvie Grange
Local Museum - 1946
Prehistory, mainly of the Neolithic period, Gallo-Greek, Roman and medieval archaeology 09915

Musée Juif Comtadin, Synagogue, Rue Hébraïque, 84300 Cavaillon - T: 0490760034, Fax: 0490714706, E-mail: s.grange@libertysurf.fr. Head: Sylvie Grange
Religious Arts Museum / Historic Site - 1963
Old bakery of the former ghetto, ornaments, praying books, vestures used in the first synagogue (1792-1794) 09916

Cazaux-Saves

Collection d'Arts Décoratifs, Château de Caumont, 32130 Cazaux-Saves - T: 0562079420, Fax: 0562079507, Internet: http://www.caumont.org
Decorative Arts Museum 09917

Cazedarnes

Ancienne Abbaye de Fontcaude, Musée de Site, L'Est du Village, 34460 Cazedarnes - T: 0467382385
Religious Arts Museum 09918

Ceillac

Musée du Temps et de l'Art Religieux, Chapelle des Pénitents, 05600 Ceillac - T: 0492451517/0574
Religious Arts Museum   09919

Cellettes

Musée Historique, Château de Beauregard, 41120 Cellettes - T: 0254704005/4664
Fine Arts Museum / Decorative Arts Museum 09920

Cendras

Ecomusée de la Vallée du Galeizon, Mairie, 30480 Cendras - T: 0466302183
Local Museum   09921

Cénévières

Château de Cénévières, 46330 Cénévières - T: 0565312733
Fine Arts Museum / Decorative Arts Museum 09922

Cerdon

Musée du Cuivre, 01450 Cerdon - T: 0474399644/9686
Special Museum   09923

Musée Viticole, Caveau de Marcheroux, 01450 Cerdon - T: 0474399430/9895
Special Museum   09924

Céré-la-Ronde

Musée du Veneur, Château-Musée de Montpoupon, 37460 Céré-la-Ronde - T: 0247942115, Fax: 0247943084, E-mail: montpoupon@louvencourt.com, Internet: http://www.montpoupon.com. Head: Amaury de Louvencourt
Special Museum   09925

Céret

Maison de l'Archéologie, Pl Picasso, 66400 Céret
Archaeological Museum   09926

Musée Casa Catalana de la Cultura, Pl Pablo Picasso, 66400 Céret - T: 0468870036/3583/0887
Music Museum / Natural History Museum / Archaeological Museum   09927

Musée Municipal d'Art Moderne, Blvd Maréchal Joffre, 66400 Céret - T: 0468872776, Fax: 0468873192, E-mail: contact@musee-ceret.com, Internet: http://www.musee-ceret.com. Head: Josephine Matamoros
Fine Arts Museum - 1950
Picasso, Gris, Chagall, Masson, Kisling, Krémègne, Herbin, Manolo, Brune, Maillol, Matisse, Miró, Dali, Tàpies, Viallat, Capdeville   09928

Cérilly

Musée Charles-Louis-Philippe, 5 Rue Charles-Louis-Philippe, 03350 Cérilly - T: 0470675200/5162
Historical Museum   09929

Cérisy-la-Forêt

Musée Historique, Salle de Justice, 50680 Cérisy-la-Forêt - T: 0233573463/561215
Historical Museum   09930

Musée Lapidaire de l'Abbaye Saint-Vigor, 50680 Cérisy-la-Forêt - T: 0233573463/561215
Religious Arts Museum   09931

Cernay

Musée d'Art et d'Histoire, Porte de Thann, 68700 Cernay - T: 0389755410/5035
Military Museum / Folklore Museum   09932

Cerny

Musée Vivant de l'Aviation, Sur l'Aérodrome de Cerny, 91590 Cerny - T: 0164575585/7373
Science&Tech Museum   09933

Cérons

Musée de la Vigne et du Vin, Le Grillobois, Rte Nationale 113, 33720 Cérons - T: 0556271150
Special Museum   09934

Cervières

Musée de Cervières, Mairie, 42440 Cervières - T: 0477247679, Fax: 0477249358
Local Museum   09935

Cervione

Musée d'Arts et de Traditions Populaires, Ancien Séminaire, 20221 Cervione - T: 0495381283
Folklore Museum   09936

Cervon

Collections du Château de Lantilly, 58800 Cervon - T: 0368200122
Decorative Arts Museum   09937

Chacé

Musée Souterrain de l'Outillage Ancien, 62 Pl du Collier, 49400 Chacé - T: 0141529466
Science&Tech Museum   09938

Chaillé-les-Marais

Musée-Maison du Petit Poitou, 85450 Chaillé-les-Marais - T: 0251567730
Local Museum   09939

Chaille-sous-les-Ormeaux

Écomusée l'Aubonnière, L'Aubonnière, Rte de Champ-Saint-Père, 85310 Chaille-sous-les-Ormeaux - T: 0251349066/9907
Local Museum   09940

Chalençon

Musée Historique, Mairie, 07240 Chalençon - T: 0475581441
Historical Museum   09941

Challain-la-Potherie

Musée de la Meunerie, Moulin du Rat, 49880 Challain-la-Potherie - T: 0241941264/1483
Science&Tech Museum   09942

Chalon-sur-Saône

Musée de la Photographie Nicéphore Niépce, 28 Quai des Messageries, 71100 Chalon-sur-Saône - T: 0385484198, Fax: 0385486320, E-mail: contact@museeniepce.com, Internet: http://www.museeniepce.com
Fine Arts Museum / Special Museum   09943

Musée Denon, Pl de l'Hôtel de Ville, 71100 Chalon-sur-Saône - T: 0385480170 poste 4237/39. Head: André Laurencin
Local Museum - 16th c
Archeology, furniture, fine art   09944

Châlons-en-Champagne

Musée du Feu Adjudant-Chef Gérard, 50 Rue du Docteur-Maillot, 51000 Châlons-en-Champagne - T: 0326681770
Special Museum / Historical Museum   09945

Musée Garinet, 13 Rue Pasteur, 51000 Châlons-en-Champagne - T: 0326693853, Fax: 0326693801. Head: J.-P. Ravaux
Fine Arts Museum - 1899
Pictures, sculpture, furniture, art objects   09946

Musée Municipal, Pl Godart, 51000 Châlons-en-Champagne - T: 0326693853, Fax: 0326693801. Head: J.-P. Ravaux
Local Museum - 1794
Indian deities, items from the Stone Age to Gallo-Roman times, Romanesque and Gothic sculptures, paintings, Rodin's bronze sculptures, ethnography of Champagne   09947

Musée Notre-Dame en Vaux, 3 Pl Notre-Dame, 51000 Châlons-en-Champagne - T: 0326640387
Religious Arts Museum   09948

Chalus

Musée des Feuillardiers, Château de Châlus-Chabrol, 87230 Chalus - T: 0555785661
Ethnology Museum   09949

Chamagne

Maison Natale de Claude Gellée, 88130 Chamagne - T: 0329388607, Fax: 0329389943, E-mail: devallois@cg88.fr
Fine Arts Museum   09950

Chamalières

Galerie d'Art Contemporain, 3 Av de Fontmaure, 63400 Chamalières - T: 0473309722, Fax: 0473195760, E-mail: ville.chamalieres@wanadoo.fr
Public Gallery / Association with Coll   09951

Grotte du Chien, 19 Av de la Gare, 63400 Chamalières - T: 0473100550
Natural History Museum / Archaeological Museum   09952

Musée de la Résistance, de l'Internement et de la Déportation, 7 Pl Beaulieu, 63400 Chamalières - T: 0473312842
Historical Museum   09953

Chamalières-sur-Loire

Musée de la Dentelle, 43800 Chamalières-sur-Loire - T: 0471034467
Special Museum   09954

Chambéry

Musée des Beaux-Arts, Bibliothèque, 73000 Chambéry - T: 0479337503. Head: Henry Amann
Fine Arts Museum - 1783
Flemish and Dutch paintings (16th-17th c), Italian painting from the 16th to the 18th c, French painting (17th-19th c), Italian Renaissance painting and Italian faience   09955

Musée des Charmettes, Vallon des Charmettes, 73000 Chambéry - T: 0479333944. Head: Mireille Védrine
Special Museum - 1905
Farmer home of the philosopher and writer Jean-Jacques Rousseau from 1735 to 1740, furniture, engravings, documents, garden   09956

Musée d'Histoire Naturelle, 2 Av de Lyon, 73000 Chambéry - T: 0479621868. Head: Paul Pavlides
Natural History Museum - 1845   09957

Musée Savoisien, Sq de Lannoy de Bissy, 73000 Chambéry - T: 0479334448, Fax: 0479703088. Head: Chantal Fernex de Mongex
Local Museum - 1864
Classical archaeology, prehistoric objects, folklore, local hist, hist of the House of Savoy, prints, medals - library, documentation center   09958

Chamblac

Château-Musée de Bonneville, 27270 Chamblac - T: 0232446356, E-mail: cebroglie@aol.com. Head: Charles Edouard Prince de Broglie
Decorative Arts Museum   09959

Chamblanc

Musée La Voiture à Travers les Ages, Rue Verte, 21250 Chamblanc - T: 0380204875
Science&Tech Museum   09960

Chambolle-Musigny

Musée Vini-Viticole, Château A.-Ziltener, 21220 Chambolle-Musigny - T: 0380628137
Special Museum   09961

Chambord

Domaine National de Chambord, 41250 Chambord - T: 0254504000, Fax: 0254203469, Internet: http://www.chambord.org. Head: Xavier Patier
Local Museum   09962

Musée de la Chasse, Château, 41250 Chambord - T: 0254504000, Fax: 0254203469, Internet: http://www.chambord.org. Head: Isabelle de Gourcuff
Special Museum   09963

Chamonix-Mont-Blanc

Musée Alpin, 89 Av Michel Croz, 74400 Chamonix-Mont-Blanc - T: 0450532593, E-mail: chamonix.musee_alpin@chamonix.com, Internet: http://www.chamonix.com. Head: Catherine Poletti
Special Museum - 1969
Alpinism, ethnology, crystals, paintings by Gabriel Loppé   09964

Chamoux

Parc Préhistorique Imaginaire, Écomusée, 89660 Chamoux - T: 0386332833
Historical Museum / Open Air Museum / Archaeological Museum   09965

Champagnac-la-Rivière

Château-Musée de Brie, 87150 Champagnac-la-Rivière - T: 0555781752
Decorative Arts Museum   09966

Champagnac-les-Mines

Musée de la Mine, 15350 Champagnac-les-Mines - T: 0471696026/6155
Science&Tech Museum   09967

Champagney

Maison de la Négritude et des Droits de l'Homme, 70290 Champagney - T: 0384232545/1998
Ethnology Museum   09968

Champagnole

Musée Archéologique, 26 Rue Baronne Delors, 39300 Champagnole - T: 0384530129, 0384471213, Fax: 0384524932, E-mail: info@tourisme.champagnole.com. Head: Marie-Jeanne Lambert
Archaeological Museum   09969

Champagny

Ecole-Musée de Champagny, 21440 Champagny - T: 0380412382/350138/350164/350706
Special Museum   09970

Champclause

Maison du Lauzeron, Lac Bleu, 43260 Champclause - T: 0471596106
Special Museum   09971

Champeaux

Musée d'Histoire Naturelle, Au Sommet des Falaises, D 911, 50530 Champeaux - T: 0233618335/480556
Natural History Museum   09972

Champigny-sur-Marne

Musée de la Résistance Nationale, 88 Av Marx-Dormoy, 94500 Champigny-sur-Marne - T: 0148810080, Fax: 0148813336, Internet: http://www.musee-resistance.com. Head: André Tollet
Historical Museum   09973

Champlitte

Musée Départemental d'Histoire et de Folklore, Pl de l'Eglise, 70600 Champlitte - T: 0384678200, Fax: 0384678209. Head: Jean-Christophe Demard
Historical Museum / Folklore Museum - 1957   09974

Champoulet

Musée d'Outil, Ferme du Château, 45420 Champoulet - T: 0238319444
Science&Tech Museum   09975

Champvoux

Musée de Tigran, Le Grand Sourcy, 58400 Champvoux - T: 0386378543
Fine Arts Museum   09976

Chanas

Musée Minéralogique du Dolon, 44 Rte de Marseille, 38150 Chanas - T: 0475310560
Natural History Museum   09977

Chanonat

Château-Musée de la Batisse, 63450 Chanonat - T: 0473794104
Decorative Arts Museum   09978

Chantilly

Musée Condé, Château de Chantilly, 60500 Chantilly, mail addr: BP 70243, 60631 Chantilly Cedex - T: 0344626262, Fax: 0344626261. Head: Nicole Garnier
Fine Arts Museum / Decorative Arts Museum - 1897
Early French, Flemish, and Italian paintings, drawings by Raffael, Poussin, Watteau, Ingres, Delacroix, miniatures by Fouquet, furniture, manuscripts, engravings, money and medals, objects d'art, 14th-19th century paintings - library   09979

Musée du Patrimoine, 1 Pl Omer-Vallon, 60500 Chantilly - T: 0344574448
Local Museum   09980

Musée Vivant du Cheval, Grandes Ecuries du Prince de Condé, 60500 Chantilly, mail addr: BP 242, 60500 Chantilly - T: 0344571313/4040
Special Museum   09981

Chapelle-des-Bois

Musée Vivant de la Maison Michaud, La Combe des Cives, 25240 Chapelle-des-Bois - T: 0381692742
Folklore Museum   09982

Chapelon

Moulin à Vent Gaillardin, 45270 Chapelon - T: 0238955162
Science&Tech Museum   09983

Chaptuzat

Château-Musée de la Roche, 63260 Chaptuzat - T: 0473636581
Decorative Arts Museum   09984

Charavines

Maison d'Art et d'Histoire des Trois Vals, Maison de Pays, 38850 Charavines - T: 0476557747/066009, Fax: 0476556313, E-mail: info@museelacdepaladru.com, Internet: http://www.museelacdepaladru.com. Head: Jean Papait
Archaeological Museum   09985

Site-Chantier de Fouilles Archéologiques, Maison de Colletière, 38850 Charavines - T: 0476066468/557747
Archaeological Museum   09986

Charbonnières-les-Sapins

Parc Préhistorique Animalier Dino-Zoo, Château, 25660 Charbonnières-les-Sapins - T: 0381592705/2257
Natural History Museum / Open Air Museum   09987

Charbonnières-les-Varennes

Manoir de Veygoux, Scénomusée des Combrailles, 63410 Charbonnières-les-Varennes - T: 0473338300, Fax: 0473338576, E-mail: manoirdeveygoux@wanadoo.fr, Internet: http://www.manoir-de-veygoux.com. Head: Hervé Baulard
Special Museum / Historical Museum   09988

Chargé

Musée de la Résistance et de la Bataille du 19 Juin 1940, Ancienne Ecole, 37530 Chargé - T: 0247570401/0524
Military Museum   09989

Charleville-Mézières

Collections Internationales de Marionnettes, 7 Pl Winston-Churchill, 08000 Charleville-Mézières - T: 0324337250/564455
Special Museum 09990

Musée Arthur-Rimbaud, Quai A.-Rimbaud, 08000 Charleville-Mézières - T: 0324324465
Special Museum 09991

Musée de la T.S.F., 184 Av Charles-de-Gaulle, 08100 Charleville-Mézières - T: 0324561241
Science&Tech Museum 09992

Musée de l'Ardenne, Pl Ducale, 08109 Charleville-Mézières - T: 0324324464
Local Museum - 1912
Archeology, fine arts, numismatics, regional folklore 09993

Charlieu

Musée Armand Charnay, Abbaye Bénédictine, 42190 Charlieu - T: 0477600817
Religious Arts Museum 09994

Musée de la Soierie, Ancien Hôtel Dieu, 9 Blvd du Général Leclerc, 42190 Charlieu - T: 0477602884, Fax: 0477601416
Science&Tech Museum 09995

Musée Hospitalier, 9 Blvd du Général-Leclerc, 42190 Charlieu - T: 0477602884, Fax: 0477601416
Historical Museum / Science&Tech Museum 09996

Charmeil

Musée de la Cristallière, Rte de Vichy, 03110 Charmeil - T: 0470320148, Fax: 0470323207
Natural History Museum 09997

Charmes

Exposition Permanente sur la Déportation, Mairie, 88130 Charmes - T: 0329381709
Historical Museum 09998

Charmoille-Provenchère

Ecomusée de l'Agriculture, Ancienne Fruitière de Provenchère, 25380 Charmoille-Provenchère - T: 0381443029
Agriculture Museum 09999

Charnat

Musée Architectural, Parc Floral, 63290 Charnat - T: 0473948153
Special Museum 10000

Charolles

Musée René Davoine, 32 Rue René Davoine, 71190 Charolles - T: 0385883601. Head: Félix Davoine
Fine Arts Museum 10001

Charre

Musée de la Figurine Historique, Château de Mongaston, 64190 Charre - T: 0559386592
Historical Museum 10002

Charroux

Musée-Trésor d'Église - Art Sacré, Ancienne Abbaye Saint-Sauveur, 86250 Charroux - T: 0549876243/6012
Religious Arts Museum 10003

Charroux-d'Allier

Musée de Charroux et de son Canton, Rue de la Poulaillerie, 03140 Charroux-d'Allier - T: 0470568018, 0470568165, E-mail: - charroux.tourisme@vanadoo.fr, Internet: http://www.charroux.com
Local Museum
Hist of the town since its gallo-romic foundation, coll of fireplaces since 13th c, tools, sculptures, musical instruments, trade and agriculture since 17th c 10004

Chartres

Musée de l'Ecole, 1 Rue du 14 Juillet, 28000 Chartres - T: 0237300769
Special Museum 10005

Musée Municipal, 29 Cloître Notre-Dame, 28000 Chartres - T: 0237364139, Fax: 0237361469. Head: Hervé Joubeaux
Fine Arts Museum - 1834
Medieval sculptures, 16th to 19th Italian, Flemish, German and French paintings, tapestries, enamels, folklore, harpsichords and spinet, earthenware 10006

Muséum des Sciences Naturelles et de Préhistoire, 5bis Blvd de la Courtille, 28000 Chartres - T: 0237283609, Fax: 0237234199, E-mail: museum.chartres@wanadoo.fr, Internet: http://www.perso.wanadoo.fr/samnel.museum. Head: Pierre Boudier
Natural History Museum
Fossils 10007

Charvieu-Chavagneux

Exposition Permanente d'Histoire Naturelle, La Chaumière du Lac, Rte de Lyon, 38230 Charvieu-Chavagneux - T: 0478321152/75320808
Natural History Museum 10008

Chassagnes

Écomusée, Jardin Archéologique, 07140 Chassagnes - T: 0475372660
Archaeological Museum / Natural History Museum 10009

Chasselay

Musée de la Famille, Rue de la Chambre-du-Roy, 69380 Chasselay - T: 0478476243
Local Museum 10010

Chasteix

Musée de la Vie Rurale Locale et de l'Outil, 63680 Chasteix - T: 0473215534
Historical Museum 10011

Château-Chinon

Musée du Costume, Rue du Château, 58120 Château-Chinon - T: 0386851855
Special Museum / Folklore Museum 10012

Musée du Septennat de François Mitterrand, 6 Rue du Château, 58120 Château-Chinon - T: 0386851923/606762, Fax: 0386606753, E-mail: service@cg58.fr. Head: François Martin
Special Museum / Historical Museum / Decorative Arts Museum 10013

Château-du-Loir

Musée Heurteloup-Chevalier, 72500 Château-du-Loir - T: 0243440038
Local Museum 10014

Château-Gombert

Musée des Arts et Traditions Populaires du Terroir Marseillais, 5 Pl des Héros, 13013 Château-Gombert - T: 0491681438
Folklore Museum - 1928
Costumes, pewter, ceramics, furniture, manger figures 10015

Château-Gontier

Musée Municipal, Rue Jean Bourré, 53200 Château-Gontier - T: 0243072642/703407
Archaeological Museum / Fine Arts Museum
Greek and Roman archeology, wall paintings, drawings, wood sculpture, paintings 10016

Château-Meillant

Musée E. Chenon, Rue de la Victoire, 18370 Château-Meillant. Head: Jacques Gourvest
Archaeological Museum - 1961
Local archeology, Gallo-Roman remains, folklore 10017

Château-Queyras

Espace Géologique "Les Frissons de la Terre", Crypte, 05350 Château-Queyras - T: 0492468046/450623
Natural History Museum 10018

Château-Renault

Musée du Cuir et de la Tannerie, 105 Rue de la République, 37110 Château-Renault - T: 0247560359, 0247562222, Fax: 0247562222, E-mail: office-tourisme-castel.rena@wanadoo.fr. Head: Gérard Laballe
Special Museum 10019

Château-sur-Allier

Musée d'Art et d'Histoire, Château Saint-Augustin, 03320 Château-sur-Allier - T: 0470664201
Fine Arts Museum / Historical Museum 10020

Château-Thierry

Collection de Manuscrits Anciens, 14 Rue Racine, 02400 Château-Thierry - T: 0323691511
Special Museum / Historical Museum 10021

Musée Jean de la Fontaine, 12 Rue de la Fontaine, 02400 Château-Thierry - T: 0323690560, Fax: 0323848699, E-mail: lafontaine@casynet.fr
Special Museum - 1876
16th century house where the fabulist and poet Jean de la Fontaine was born, exhibits on his life and work - library 10022

Châteaubriant

Collections du Château, Château, 44110 Châteaubriant - T: 0240282352
Decorative Arts Museum 10023

Musée Municipal Châteaubriant, 44110 Châteaubriant - T: 0240810232
Local Museum 10024

Châteaudun

Château-Musée, Pl du Château, 28200 Châteaudun - T: 0237452270
Decorative Arts Museum
12th-16th century palace, 16th-17th century tapestries, 15th century sculptures 10025

Musée Municipal des Beaux Arts et d'Histoire Naturelle, 3 Rue Toufaire, 28200 Châteaudun - T: 0237455536, Fax: 0237455446. Head: Sandra-Diana Pellard
Fine Arts Museum / Natural History Museum / Local Museum - 1864
Prehist, egyptology, 19th century paintings, asiatic arts, 1870 war, African items, natural hist (2,500 and mammals) 10026

Châteaumeillant

Musée Archéologique Emile-Chenon, Hôtel de Marcillac, Rue de la Victoire, 18370 Châteaumeillant - T: 0248613317/3989
Archaeological Museum 10027

Châteauneuf (Côte-d'Or)

Musée Rural, 21320 Châteauneuf (Côte-d'Or) - T: 0380492164
Local Museum 10028

Châteauneuf-de-Randon

Musée du Guesclin, Hôtel du Guesclin, 48170 Châteauneuf-de-Randon - T: 0466479143
Special Museum 10029

Châteauneuf-d'Entraunes

Écomusée Le Grain de Sel, 06470 Châteauneuf-d'Entraunes - T: 0493055866
Folklore Museum / Historical Museum 10030

Châteauneuf-du-Pape

Musée des Outils de Vigneron, Père Anselme, 84230 Châteauneuf-du-Pape - T: 0490837007
Special Museum 10031

Châteauneuf-les-Martigues

Musée de Castrum Vetus, 4 Montée des Ruines, 13220 Châteauneuf-les-Martigues - T: 0442798483/8088
Archaeological Museum 10032

Châteauneuf-sur-Cher

Château-Musée, 18190 Châteauneuf-sur-Cher - T: 0248606421, Fax: 0248605157
Decorative Arts Museum 10033

Châteauneuf-sur-Loire

Musée de la Marine de Loire, Ecuries du Château, 1 Pl Aristide Briand, 45110 Châteauneuf-sur-Loire - T: 0238478446, Fax: 0238464101. Head: Cathérine Dupraz
Local Museum - 1962
Exhibits on Loire shipping, local hist, objects of art, archeology, folklore - library 10034

Châteauneuf-sur-Sarthe

Maison de la Rivière, Rue des Moulins, 49330 Châteauneuf-sur-Sarthe - T: 0241339164
Special Museum 10035

Châteauponsac

Maison du Terroir, 87290 Châteauponsac - T: 0555763952/5672
Ethnology Museum 10036

Musée d'Archéologie et d'Art Populaire René-Bauberot, Pl Saint-Thyrse, Ancien Prieuré, 87290 Châteauponsac - T: 0555763155/5672
Local Museum
Archeology exhibits, local history, folk art and folk traditions 10037

Châteaurenard (Loiret)

Musée Archéologique, Maison Jeanne d'Arc, 45220 Châteaurenard (Loiret) - T: 0238952184/3004
Archaeological Museum 10038

Musée Vivant de l'Apiculture Gâtinaise, La Cassine, Rte de Chuelles, 45220 Châteaurenard (Loiret) - T: 0238953556, Fax: 0238952045, E-mail: jacques.gant@wanadoo.fr, Internet: http://www.museevivant.com. Head: Jacques Gout
Natural History Museum 10039

Châteauroux (Indre)

Musée Bertrand, 2 Rue Descente des Cordeliers, 36000 Châteauroux (Indre) - T: 0254083349
Local Museum
18th century home of General Bertrand, his memorabilia, history of Napoleonic times, prehistory, Celtic sculpture, Gallo-Roman stelae, folklore, 13th-20th century art objects, ceramics, Renaissance furniture, 14th-20th century paintings, drawings 10040

Châtel-sur-Moselle

Musée d'Histoire Médiévale, Ancien Château, 8 Rue des Capucins, 88330 Châtel-sur-Moselle - T: 0329671418, Fax: 0329676492, E-mail: chatelmedieval@wanadoo.fr, Internet: http://assoc.wanadoo.fr/philippe.guiot. Head: Jacques Debry
Historical Museum 10041

Châtelais

Musée Archéologique, Presbytère, 5 Rue du Musée, 49960 Châtelais - T: 0241616868
Archaeological Museum 10042

Châtelguyon

Musée du Pays Brayaud, 17 Rue du Nord, 63140 Châtelguyon - T: 0473861239
Folklore Museum 10043

Musée National des Chantiers de Jeunesse, Rue du Commerce, 63140 Châtelguyon - T: 0473860188
Special Museum 10044

Châtellerault

Musée Auto Moto Vélo, La Manu, 86100 Châtellerault - T: 0549210346, Fax: 0549852588, E-mail: musées.chatellerault.alienor@wanadoo.fr. Head: Dominique Vila
Science&Tech Museum - 1991 10045

Musée Municipal, Hôtel Sully, 14 Rue Sully, 86100 Châtellerault - T: 0549210127, Fax: 0549197202, E-mail: musees.chatellerault.alienor@wanadoo.fr, Internet: http://www.alienor.org. Head: Dominique Vila
Local Museum - 1891 10046

Châtelus (Allier)

Musée de l'École, Le Bourg, 03640 Châtelus (Allier) - T: 0470550179
Special Museum 10047

Châtenay-Malabry

Musée du Bonsaï, 25 Rue de Châteaubriand, 92290 Châtenay-Malabry - T: 0147029199, Fax: 0147026176, E-mail: remy.samson@free.fr, Internet: http://www.lebonsai.com. Head: Rémy Samson
Natural History Museum 10048

Musée-Maison de Chateaubriand, 87 Rue de Chateaubriand, 92290 Châtenay-Malabry - T: 0147020862/5861
Special Museum 10049

Châtillon-Coligny

Musée de Châtillon-Coligny, Ancien Hôtel Dieu, Faubourg Puyrault, 45230 Châtillon-Coligny - T: 0238925544, Fax: 0238960944. Head: M. Zurfluh
Local Museum 10050

Châtillon-en-Dunois

Ecomusée Vivant de la Haie, 28290 Châtillon-en-Dunois - T: 0237970303
Local Museum 10051

Chatillon-sur-Chalaronne

Musée Traditions et Vie, Impasse des Remparts, 01400 Chatillon-sur-Chalaronne - T: 0474550227
Folklore Museum 10052

Châtillon-sur-Saône

Espace Muséal de la Maison du Berger, 88410 Châtillon-sur-Saône - T: 0329079178
Special Museum 10053

Espace Muséal de la Maison du Cordonnier, 88410 Châtillon-sur-Saône - T: 0329079178
Special Museum 10054

Musée Historique, Grosse Tour, 88410 Châtillon-sur-Saône - T: 0329079178
Historical Museum 10055

Châtillon-sur-Seine

Musée du Châtillonnais, Rue du Bourg, 21400 Châtillon-sur-Seine - T: 0380912467. Head: Jean-Louis Coudrot
Archaeological Museum / Local Museum
Excavation finds from Celtic, Greek, Gallic, and Frankian times, treasure of Vix (6th century B.), sculpture 10056

Chatte

Le Jardin Ferroviaire, 2 Rte de Lyon, 38160 Chatte - T: 0476385455, Fax: 0476640209, E-mail: - jardin.ferroviaire@wanadoo.fr. Head: Christian Abric
Science&Tech Museum 10057

Chauffailles

Musée de Tissage, Rue du 8 Mai, 71170 Chauffailles - T: 0385846516
Science&Tech Museum 10058

Musée et Salon Permanent de l'Automobile, 35 Rue du 8-Mai, 71170 Chauffailles - T: 0385846030
Science&Tech Museum
10059

Chaumont-en-Vexin

Musée Pillon, Mairie, 60240 Chaumont-en-Vexin - T: 0344490046
Local Museum
10060

Chaumont (Haute-Marne)

Musée d'Art et d'Histoire, Pl du Palais, 52000 Chaumont (Haute-Marne) - T: 0325306051, 0325030199, Fax: 0325012637. Head: Maud Grillet
Local Museum
13th and 16th century sections of former palace, Gallo-Roman and Merovingian finds, 15th-18th century sculptures, 17th-19th century paintings
10061

Musée de la Crèche, Annexe Rue des Frères Mistaret, 52000 Chaumont (Haute-Marne) - T: 0325323985, 0325030199, Fax: 0325012637. Head: Maud Grillet
Decorative Arts Museum
10062

Chaumont-sur-Loire

Château-Musée et Ecuries de Chaumont-sur-Loire, Château Ecuries, 41150 Chaumont-sur-Loire - T: 0254209803. Head: Martine Tissier de Mallerais
Decorative Arts Museum
Furniture, tapestry
10063

Chaumont (Yonne)

Musée d'Art Contemporain et d'Histoire Locale, Rue de l'Église, 89370 Chaumont (Yonne) - T: 0386961110
Fine Arts Museum / Historical Museum
10064

Chauny

Musée d'Arts et d'Histoire, Mairie, 02300 Chauny - T: 0323387070
Fine Arts Museum / Historical Museum
10065

Chauvigny

Musée de Traditions Populaires et d'Archéologie, Pl du Vieux-Marché, Ville Haute, 86300 Chauvigny - T: 0549464031/9156, Fax: 0549463545, E-mail: musee.chauvigny.alienor@wanadoo.fr. Head: Max Aubrun
Archaeological Museum / Historical Museum / Folklore Museum - 1960
10066

Chavaniac-Lafayette

Muse-Mémorial la Fayette, Château de Chavaniac-Lafayette, 43230 Chavaniac-Lafayette - T: 0471775032
Local Museum
10067

Chaveyriat

Collection Entomologique, Les Granges Noires, 01660 Chaveyriat - T: 0474519101
Natural History Museum
10068

Chavignon

Ateliers de l'Abeille, Rte Nationale 2, 02000 Chavignon - T: 0323216162, Fax: 0323216809
Special Museum
10069

Chazay-d'Azergues

Musée des Vieilles Pierres, Allée des Remparts, 69380 Chazay-d'Azergues - T: 0478436001/6819
Archaeological Museum / Historical Museum
10070

Chazé-sur-Argos

Musée-Château de Raguin, 49114 Chazé-sur-Argos - T: 0241614020
Fine Arts Museum
10071

Chazelles-sur-Lyon

Atelier-Musée du Chapeau, 16 Rte de Saint-Galmier, 42140 Chazelles-sur-Lyon - T: 0477942329, Fax: 0477542775, E-mail: mchapeau@museeduchapeau.com, Internet: http://www.museeduchapeau.com. Head: Gilles Rose
Special Museum
Hat industry and fashion from the end of 18th to 21st c - library, archive, training center, hatshop
10072

Chécy

Musée de la Tonnellerie, Musée Municipal, Pl du Cloître, 45430 Chécy - T: 0238869593
Special Museum
10073

Chef-du-Pont

Musée d'Art Contemporain, Hameau des Gardes, 50480 Chef-du-Pont - T: 0233413819
Fine Arts Museum
10074

Cheignieu-la-Balme

Musée du Vin, Château des Eclaz, 01510 Cheignieu-la-Balme - T: 0479818620
Special Museum
10075

Chelles

Musée Alfred-Bonno, Pl de la République, 77500 Chelles - T: 0164212785
Local Museum - 1947
Local prehistoric finds, Gallo-Roman, Merovingian, and medieval artifacts, historic documents, works of local artists
10076

Chémery

Château-Musée de Chémery, Château, 41700 Chémery - T: 0254718277, Fax: 0254717134, E-mail: axel.fontaine@libertysurf.fr. Head: Axel Fontaine
Local Museum
10077

Cheminon

Musée du Souvenir-Arts et Traditions Mullem-William, Café de la Place, Pl de la Mairie, 51250 Cheminon - T: 0326731189
Local Museum
10078

Chênehutte-Trêves-Cunault

Musée-Village Gallo-Romain de Chênehutte-les-Tuffeaux, 10 Rue des Ducs d'Anjou, 49350 Chênehutte-Trêves-Cunault - T: 0241518334
Museum of Classical Antiquities
10079

Chenillé-Changé

Musée-Moulin à Eau, Le Moulin, 49220 Chenillé-Changé - T: 0241951083/1098, Fax: 0241951083/1052
Special Museum / Science&Tech Museum
10080

Chenonceaux

Château-Musée de Chenonceau, Château de Chenonceau, 37150 Chenonceaux - T: 0247239007, Fax: 0247238088, E-mail: chateau.de.chenonceau@wanadoo.fr, Internet: http://www.chenonceau.com
Decorative Arts Museum / Fine Arts Museum
10081

Musée de Cires, Château de Chenonceau, 37150 Chenonceaux - T: 0247239007, Fax: 0247238088, E-mail: chateau.de.chenonceau@wanadoo.fr, Internet: http://www.chenonceau.com
Special Museum
10082

Chenôve

Collection des Pressoirs des Ducs de Bourgogne, 8 Rue Roger-Salengro, 21300 Chenôve - T: 0380528283
Science&Tech Museum
10083

Chens-sur-Léman

Musée de la Grange aux Outils, Association Art et Culture de Douvaine et du Chablais, Grange de Servette, 74140 Chens-sur-Léman - T: 0450940149/1055
Science&Tech Museum
10084

Cherbourg

Musée à Flot, A Chantereyne, Au Port des Flamands, Quai Pierre-le-Conte, 50100 Cherbourg - T: 0233430974
Special Museum
10085

Musée de la Libération, Fort du Roule, 50100 Cherbourg - T: 0233201412
Military Museum - 1954
Local military items from WW II and the liberation
10086

Musée Maritime, Port des Flamands, Quai Pierre le Conte, 50100 Cherbourg - T: 0233200471/432700
Special Museum / Historical Museum
10087

Musée Thomas Henry, Rue Vastel, 50100 Cherbourg - T: 0233444111. Head: Blanche Grinbaum
Fine Arts Museum
Italian, Flemish, Spanish, Dutch, German, and French paintings
10088

Muséum d'Histoire Naturelle, d'Ethnographie et d'Archéologie, 1 Rue de l'Abbaye, Parc Emmanuel Liais, 50100 Cherbourg - T: 0233535161
Natural History Museum / Archaeological Museum
10089

Cherves-Mirebeau

Musée de Cherves en Mirebalais, Pl de l'Eglise, 86170 Cherves-Mirebeau - T: 0549510287
Folklore Museum
10090

Musée des Arts et Traditions Populaires, 86170 Cherves-Mirebeau - T: 0549540033
Folklore Museum
10091

Cheverny

Château-Musée, 41700 Cheverny - T: 0254799602, Fax: 0254792538
Decorative Arts Museum
10092

Musée de Sologne, Château de Troussay, 41700 Cheverny - T: 0254442907, 0145040434
Fine Arts Museum / Historical Museum
10093

Chevregny

Musée Départemental de l'École Publique, Ancienne École, 02000 Chevregny - T: 0323216679, Fax: 0323216203
Special Museum
10094

Chichilianne

Maison du Parc Naturel du Vercors, 38930 Chichilianne - T: 0476344495
Natural History Museum / Historical Museum / Folklore Museum
10095

Chilhac

Musée Paléontologique Christian Guth, 43380 Chilhac - T: 0471774726/4171
Archaeological Museum
10096

Chilleurs-aux-Bois

Château-Promenade des Parfums, Château de Chamerolles, Rte de Gallerand, 45170 Chilleurs-aux-Bois - T: 0238398466, Fax: 0238329091, E-mail: chateau.chamerolles@cg45.fr, Internet: http://www.loiret.com. Head: Sandrine Joseph-Debaque
Special Museum
Hist of scents and hygiene since 16th c, home-, pleasure- and ceremonial garden created by Lancelot II in 16th c
10097

Chinon

Musée Animé du Vin et de la Tonnellerie, 12 Rue Voltaire, 37500 Chinon - T: 0247932563, Fax: 0247984444
Special Museum
10098

Musée d'Art et d'Histoire du Chinonais, Chapelle Sainte-Radegonde, Coteau Sainte-Radegonde, 37500 Chinon - T: 0247931785/1280
Folklore Museum
10099

Musée de la Batellerie et du Vieux Chinon, 44 Rue Haute Saint-Maurice, 37500 Chinon - T: 0247391812
Fine Arts Museum / Decorative Arts Museum
10100

Musée Jeanne d'Arc, Château, Tour de l'Horloge, 37500 Chinon - T: 0247931345. Head: Jean-Louis Sureau
Local Museum
10101

Chirac

Musée Archéologique, 48100 Chirac - T: 0466327006
Archaeological Museum
10102

Chirols

Musée Vivant du Textile - Écomusée du Moulinage, 07380 Chirols - T: 0475945407
Science&Tech Museum
10103

Chitry-les-Mines

Château-Musée, 58800 Chitry-les-Mines - T: 0386201148
Fine Arts Museum / Decorative Arts Museum
10104

Cholet

Maison-Musée des Sciences, Lettres et Arts, 27 Rue du Devau, 49300 Cholet - T: 0241624036, Fax: 0241719461, E-mail: sla.cholet@wanadoo.fr. Head: Edmond Rubion
Natural History Museum / Science&Tech Museum / Fine Arts Museum
10105

Musée d'Art et d'Histoire, 27 Av de l'Abreuvoir, 49300 Cholet - T: 0241492900, Fax: 0241492622. Head: Alain Katz
Fine Arts Museum / Historical Museum - 1993
Historical coll about the Vendée Wars (1793-1796, 1815, 1832), arts of 18th and 19th century esp Abstract Geometric Art (20th century)
10106

Musée de la Goubaudière, Base de Loisirs de Ribou, 49300 Cholet - T: 0241290907, Fax: 0241702625. Head: Alain Katz
Local Museum
10107

Musée de la Paysannerie → Musée de la Goubaudière

Musée du Textile, Rte de Beaupréau, 49300 Cholet - T: 0241752540, Fax: 0241752549
Decorative Arts Museum
10108

Choranche

Exposition Préhistorique, Grottes de Choranche, 38680 Choranche - T: 0476360988, Fax: 0476361191, E-mail: grottes.de.choanche@wanadoo.fr, Internet: http://www.grottes_de_-choranche.com. Head: Laurent Garnier
Natural History Museum
10109

Chouday

Maison de la Lentille du Berry, Le Bourg, 36100 Chouday - T: 0254211813
Special Museum
10110

Chouzé-sur-Loire

Musée des Mariniers, Batellerie et Folklore Touraine-Anjou, 4 Rue Saint-Pierre, 37140 Chouzé-sur-Loire - T: 0247951131/1010
Special Museum / Folklore Museum
10111

Ciboure

Conservatoire Maritime Basque, 2 Av J. Pouou, 64500 Ciboure - T: 0559478002, E-mail: itsas.begia@wanadoo.fr, Internet: http://assor.wanadoo.fr/itsas.begia. Head: Pierre Aguirre
Archaeological Museum
10112

Ciry-le-Noble

Ecomusée Eclaté du Creusot-Montceau-les-Mines, Rue Ph. Martin, 71420 Ciry-le-Noble - T: 0385791661
Fine Arts Museum
10113

Civray

Musée du Civraisien, Pl Leclerc, 86400 Civray - T: 0549870049/4773
Archaeological Museum
10114

Clairac

Musée du Train, 47320 Clairac - T: 0553880430, Fax: 0553880431
Science&Tech Museum
10115

Musée du Vieux Clairac, Rue Broustet, 47320 Clairac - T: 0553842221/2023
Local Museum
10116

Clamart

Musée-Centre d'Arts Plastiques Chanot, 33 Rue Brissart, 92140 Clamart - T: 0147360589, Fax: 0147360589, E-mail: centreartchanot@ville-clamart.fr. Head: Danielle Wallers-Bulot
Fine Arts Museum
10117

Musée-Fondation Arp, 21 Rue des Châtaigniers, 92140 Clamart - T: 0145342263/6218, Fax: 0146238030, Internet: http://www.fondationarp.org. Head: Claude Weil-Seigeot
Fine Arts Museum
10118

Clamecy

Musée d'Art et d'Histoire Romain Rolland, Hôtel de Bellegarde, Av de la République, 58500 Clamecy - T: 0386271799
Fine Arts Museum / Historical Museum
17th century Flemish painting, 18th-19th century French paintings, folklore, Nevers faience, archeology, ethnology, numismatics
10119

Claret

Verrerie d'Art, Av du Nouveau-Monde, 34270 Claret - T: 0467590639
Science&Tech Museum / Decorative Arts Museum
10120

Clécy

Musée du Chemin de Fer Miniature, Centre de Loisirs, 14570 Clécy - T: 0231690713, Fax: 0231679810, E-mail: cheminfer@clecy.com, Internet: http://www.cleacy.com. Head: Emmanuel Crué
Science&Tech Museum
10121

Musée Hardy, Pl de l'Église, 14570 Clécy - T: 0231697995, Fax: 0231697650, E-mail: dsi.clecy@libertysurf.fr
Fine Arts Museum
10122

Cleden-Poher

Musée du Canal, Maison Éclusière de Pont-Triffen, 29270 Cleden-Poher - T: 0298817645/268202
Special Museum
10123

Clérac

Musée des Métiers d'Autrefois, 17270 Clérac - T: 0546041885/1312
Local Museum
10124

Cléré-les-Pins

Château de Champchevrier, 37340 Cléré-les-Pins - T: 0247249393, Fax: 0247246263
Decorative Arts Museum
10125

Clères

Musée Militaire, Devant la Halle du Marché, 76690 Clères - T: 0235332302
Science&Tech Museum - 1958
Antique automobiles
10126

Clermont-Ferrand

Maison Départementale de l'Innovation, 23 Pl Delille, 63000 Clermont-Ferrand - T: 0473910040
Science&Tech Museum
10127

Musée Bargoin, 45 Rue Ballainvilliers, 63000 Clermont-Ferrand - T: 0473913731. Head: Gérard Tisserand
Local Museum
10128

Musée-Conservatoire du Pneu, Centre Michelin, 43 Rue Montlosier, 63000 Clermont-Ferrand - T: 0473302303/2554
Special Museum 10129

Musée d'Art Roger Quilliot, Pl Louis Deteix, 63100 Clermont-Ferrand - T: 0473161130, Fax: 0473161131, E-mail: musee.art@ville-clermont-ferrand.fr, Internet: http://www.clermont-ferrand.fr. Head: Nathalie Roux
Fine Arts Museum
Paintings, sculpture 10130

Musée du Ranquet, 34 Rue des Gras, 63000 Clermont-Ferrand - T: 0473373863, Fax: 0473426398. Head: Gérard Tisserand
Local Museum 10131

Musée du Tapis d'Art, Musée Bargoin, 45 Rue de Ballainvilliers, 63000 Clermont-Ferrand - T: 0473905748
Decorative Arts Museum 10132

Musée Lecoq, Museum d'Histoire Naturelle, 15 Rue Bardoux, 63000 Clermont-Ferrand - T: 0473919378, Fax: 0473144625, E-mail: musee.lecoq@nat.fr, Internet: http://www.ville.clermont.fr/aimer/musees/lecoq.htm. Head: Pierre Penicaud
Natural History Museum - 1873
Works by Lavoisier, Teilhard de Chardin, Pasteur and Henri Lecoq - library 10133

Clermont (Haute-Savoie)

Château-Musée d'Art Populaire et Religieux, 74270 Clermont (Haute-Savoie) - T: 0450696315. Head: Marie Noëlle Tétaz
Historical Museum / Fine Arts Museum 10134

Clermont-l'Hérault

Musée de l'Olive, Huilerie, Av Wilson, 34800 Clermont-l'Hérault - T: 0467961036
Special Museum 10135

Clermont (Oise)

Collections d'Art et d'Histoire, Ancien Hôtel de Ville, 60600 Clermont (Oise) - T: 0344508484/4025
Local Museum 10136

Clermont-Soubiran

Musée du Vin et de la Tonnellerie, Château de la Bastide, 47270 Clermont-Soubiran - T: 0553874102
Special Museum 10137

Clerval

Musée des Armées et du Souvenir, Château, 25340 Clerval - T: 0381978180
Military Museum 10138

Clichy

Musée Archéologique et Historique, Centre Culturel du Landy, 80 Blvd du Général-Leclerc, 92110 Clichy - T: 0147376705
Historical Museum / Archaeological Museum 10139

Clion-sur-Seugne

Musée Paysan, Ancien Presbytère, 17240 Clion-sur-Seugne - T: 0546704703
Folklore Museum 10140

Clohars-Carnoët

Maison Marie Henry, Le Pouldu, 10 Rue des Grands Sables, 29121 Clohars-Carnoët - T: 0298399851
Fine Arts Museum 10141

Cluny

Musée d'Art et d'Archéologie de Cluny, Palais Jean de Bourbon, 71250 Cluny - T: 0385592397, Fax: 0385591634. Head: Anne de Thoisy
Fine Arts Museum / Archaeological Museum - 1864
Paintings and drawings by Prud'hon, religious objects, documents on the influence of Benedictine order on the Middle Ages, medieval sculpture, models of the town through its historical development, furnishings, faience 10142

Musée du Farinier, Ancienne Abbaye, 71250 Cluny - T: 0385591279
Religious Arts Museum 10143

Cluses

Musée de l'Horlogerie et du Décolletage, Pl du 11 Novembre, 74300 Cluses - T: 0450891302
Science&Tech Museum - 1929
Sciences and technology, horology, fine mechanics, electrical mechanics 10144

Coarraze

Château de Dufau, 64800 Coarraze - T: 0559611027
Decorative Arts Museum / Fine Arts Museum 10145

Cocheren

Maison d'Histoire Locale, 57800 Cocheren - T: 0387814412
Historical Museum 10146

Coëx

Olfactorium de Coëx, Parc Floral, 85220 Coëx - T: 0251546118/2618
Special Museum 10147

Cognac

Espace Hennessy, Musée de la Tonnellerie, Hennessy et Cie., 1 Rue de la Richonne, 16100 Cognac - T: 0545357258/72
Special Museum 10148

Musée de Cognac, 48 Blvd Denfert-Rochereau, 16100 Cognac - T: 0545320725, Fax: 0545828641
Local Museum - 1892
Local archeology, ethnology, and history, European art and applied art, natural history, viticulture, distillation, coopery, glass, 16th-17th century German, Flemish and Dutch paintings 10149

Cogolin

Collection de Pipes de Bruyère, Ets Charles Courrieu, 58 Av Clemenceau, 83310 Cogolin - T: 0494546382
Special Museum 10150

Musée des Empreintes et Traditions (Templar and Medieval Museum), 46 Rue Nationale, 83310 Cogolin - T: 0494540842, Fax: 0494977018. Head: Pierre-Raymond Gay
Historical Museum 10151

Musée Raimu, 18 Av Georges-Clemenceau, 83310 Cogolin - T: 0494541800/4324
Special Museum 10152

Cohennoz

Musée de l'Outillage Miniature, Mairie, 73400 Cohennoz - T: 0479373382
Special Museum 10153

Colleville-Montgomery

Site Fortifié Hillmann, Rue du Suffolk Régiment, 14880 Colleville-Montgomery - T: 0231971261
Military Museum 10154

Collioure

Château Royal, Musée de la Côte Catalane, 66190 Collioure - T: 0468820643
Folklore Museum 10155

Le Chemin du Fauvisme, 66190 Collioure - T: 0468821547
Fine Arts Museum 10156

Musée d'Art Moderne des Templiers, Hôtel des Templiers, Rue Camille Pelletan, 66190 Collioure - T: 0468820558
Fine Arts Museum 10157

Musée Jean Peské, 6 Rte de Port-Vendres, 66190 Collioure - T: 0468821019. Head: Joséphine Matamoros
Fine Arts Museum
Contemporary and historic art - ateliers 10158

Collobrières

Musée de l'Ancienne Chartreuse de la Verne, 83610 Collobrières - T: 0494434541
Special Museum / Historical Museum 10159

Collonges-la-Rouge

Musée des Traditions Populaires, Maison de la Sirène, 19500 Collonges-la-Rouge - T: 0555840803
Folklore Museum 10160

Musée Vivant de l'Oie, Ferme Veyrie, 19500 Collonges-la-Rouge - T: 0555840240, Fax: 0555840240
Science&Tech Museum 10161

Collonges-lès-Bévy

Château-Musée, 21220 Collonges-lès-Bévy - T: 0380614005
Local Museum 10162

Colmar

Collection Maritime, Maison du Marin, 2 Rue de Thann, 68000 Colmar - T: 0389237252
Special Museum 10163

Musée Bartholdi, 30 Rue des Marchands, 68000 Colmar - T: 0389419060, Fax: 0389235077. Head: Régis Hueber
Fine Arts Museum - 1922
Memorabilia of the sculptor Bartholdi (1834-1904) in his birthhouse, original models of the Statue of Liberty 10164

Musée d'Art Juif J.C.-Katz, 30 Rue des Marchands, 68000 Colmar - T: 0389419060
Religious Arts Museum 10165

Musée d'Histoire Naturelle et d'Ethnographie, 11 Rue Turenne, 68000 Colmar - T: 0389238415, Fax: 0389412962, E-mail: shne.colmar@calixo.net
Natural History Museum / Ethnology Museum
Archaeology, geology, fauna and flora - Library 10166

Musée du Jouet et des Petits Trains, Animé, 40 Rue Vauban, 68000 Colmar - T: 0389419060
Special Museum / Science&Tech Museum 10167

Musée d'Unterlinden, 1 Rue d'Unterlinden, 68000 Colmar - T: 0389201550, Fax: 0389412622, E-mail: info@musee-unterlinden.com, Internet: http://www.musee-unterlinden.com. Head: Sylvie Lecoq-Ramond
Fine Arts Museum / Local Museum - 1852
Former Dominican convent, Isenheimer Altar by Matthias Grünewald, early Alsatian painting, medieval and Renaissance paintings, local hist, costumes, furniture, modern art, archeology 10168

Colombes

Musée d'Art et d'Histoire, 2 Rue Gabriel-Péri, 92700 Colombes - T: 0147863885
Historical Museum / Fine Arts Museum 10169

Musée des Transports Urbains (Museum is closed until 2006), 163 Blvd Charles de Gaulle, 92700 Colombes - T: 0142424396, Fax: 0146521681, E-mail: jlr.larosa@wanadoo.fr, Internet: http://www.cnam.fr/hebergement/amtuir. Head: Jean-Louis La Rosa
Science&Tech Museum - 1957
library, archives 10170

Colombey-les-Deux-Eglises

Exposition Charles de Gaulle, Pied du Mémorial, 52330 Colombey-les-Deux-Eglises - T: 0325015050
Special Museum 10171

Colomiers

Centre d'Art Contemporain, Espace des Arts, 31770 Colomiers - T: 0561781541, Fax: 0561781541, E-mail: culture@mairie-colomiers.fr. Head: Gève Tissier
Public Gallery 10172

Combourg

Château-Musée de Combourg, 23 Rue des Princes, 35270 Combourg - T: 0299732295, Fax: 0299732295, Internet: http://www.combourg.net
Local Museum 10173

Combrit

Ecomusée de la Ferme de Roscanvel, 29120 Combrit - T: 0298584571/564690
Folklore Museum 10174

Musée du Cidre Cloarec, 29120 Combrit - T: 0298570579/519084
Special Museum 10175

Commana

Ecomusée des Monts d'Arrée, Moulins de Kerouat, 29450 Commana - T: 0298688776, Fax: 0298688551. Head: Bertrand Roux
Open Air Museum
Breton furniture, 2 water mills, 2 bread ovens, exhibition about slate extraction, tannery, traditional house of the 19th century 10176

Musée d'Art et de Nature, Village de Kervelly, 29237 Commana - T: 0298780343
Natural History Museum 10177

Musée des Poupées Pascalines, 3 Pl de l'Église, 29237 Commana - T: 0298780013
Special Museum / Folklore Museum 10178

Commarin

Château-Musée du XVe et XVIIIe Siècle, 21320 Commarin - T: 0380492367, Fax: 0380492243, E-mail: commarin.rhdb@wanadoo.fr, Internet: http://www.commarin.com. Head: Louis de Vogue
Decorative Arts Museum 10179

Commeny

Musée-Maison du Pain, Grande-Rue, 95450 Commeny - T: 0130272178
Special Museum 10180

Commercy

Musée des Beaux-Arts, 55200 Commercy - T: 0329910218
Fine Arts Museum / Decorative Arts Museum 10181

Compiègne

Musée Antoine Vivenel, Hôtel de Songeons, 2 Rue d'Austerlitz, 60200 Compiègne - T: 0344202604, Fax: 0344202309. Head: Eric Blanchegorge
Archaeological Museum / Fine Arts Museum - 1839
European, Classican and Near Eastern archeology, Oriental and European arms, furnishings, Limoges enamels, Medieval and modern painting, drawing, sculpture 10182

Musée de la Figurine Historique, 28 Pl de l'Hôtel de Ville, 60200 Compiègne - T: 0344407255, Fax: 0344202309. Head: Eric Blanchegorge
Special Museum - 1948 10183

Musée National de la Voiture et du Tourisme, Palais de Compiègne, 60200 Compiègne, mail addr: BP 549, 60200 Compiègne - T: 0344384700, Fax: 0344384701, E-mail: chateau.compiegne@culture.gour.fr. Head: Jacques Perot
Science&Tech Museum - 1927
Old carriages, sedan chairs, survey of the development of the bicycle and the automobile, vehicles 10184

Musée National du Château de Compiègne et Musée du Second Empire, Musée de la Voiture et du Tourisme, Pl du Général de Gaulle, 60200 Compiègne - T: 0344384700, Fax: 0344384701, E-mail: chateau.compiegne@culture.gouv.fr. Head: Jacques Perot
Historical Museum
Reconstructed palace rooms of 18th-19th c, special section of 2nd Empire furnishings and fine arts 10185

Musée Wagon de l'Armistice, Clairière de l'Armistice, Rte de Soissons, 60200 Compiègne - T: 0344851418, Fax: 0344851418
Military Museum 10186

Concarneau

Musée de la Pêche, Rue Vauban, 29110 Concarneau - T: 0298971020, Fax: 0298507978, E-mail: museedelapeche@wanadoo.fr. Head: Henry Depoid
Special Museum - 1961
Fishing boats models from all over the world, preserved ships at float, aquariums - library, archive 10187

Conches-en-Ouche

Musée du Livre, de la Pierre et du Verre, Rte de Sainte-Marguerite, 27190 Conches-en-Ouche - T: 0232307642
Special Museum 10188

Concoret

Musée-Centre de l'Imaginaire Arthurien, Château de Comper, 56430 Concoret - T: 0297227996, Fax: 0297227996, E-mail: glot@club-internet.fr. Head: Claudine Glot
Association with Coll 10189

Concremiers

Musée d'Art Contemporain de la Brenne, Espace Art Brenne, Prigny, 36300 Concremiers - T: 0254374016
Fine Arts Museum 10190

Condé-en-Brie

Château-Musée de Condé, Rue du Château, 02330 Condé-en-Brie - T: 0323824225, Fax: 0323828666, E-mail: contact@chateaudeconde.com, Internet: http://www.chateaudeconde.com
Fine Arts Museum / Decorative Arts Museum 10191

Condé-sur-l'Escaut

Château de l'Hermitage, 59163 Condé-sur-l'Escaut - T: 0327402189
Decorative Arts Museum 10192

Collections Municipales d'Art et d'Histoire, Hôtel de Ville, 1 Pl Delcourt, 59163 Condé-sur-l'Escaut - T: 0327400162
Fine Arts Museum / Historical Museum 10193

Condé-sur-Seulles

Espace Croquet, Association Le Douet, Rte de Bayeux, 14400 Condé-sur-Seulles - T: 0231925844
Special Museum 10194

Condom

Exposition Historique de l'Armagnac, Maison Ryst-Dypeyron, 36 Rue Jean Jaurès, 32100 Condom - T: 0562280808
Local Museum 10195

Musée de l'Armagnac, 2 Rue Jules Ferry, 32100 Condom - T: 0562284717, Fax: 0562284705. Head: Michel Hue
Special Museum - 1848
Fabrication of Armagnac, production and exportation, local economy (19th-20th c) 10196

Conflans-en-Jarnisy

Musée de l'Art Forain et de la Musique Mécanique, Raymond D'Ys, 6 Pl Aristide Briand, 54800 Conflans-en-Jarnisy - T: 0382335730/2767
Music Museum 10197

Conflans-Sainte-Honorine

Musée de la Batellerie, Château du Prieuré, Pl Gévelot, 78700 Conflans-Sainte-Honorine - T: 0134903950, Fax: 0134903965. Head: Laurent Roblin
Science&Tech Museum - 1967
History of local navigation, shipping lore, shipping technology 10198

Connerré

Musée Ferroviaire, Chemin de Fer de Transvap, 72160 Connerré - T: 0243286503/890617
Science&Tech Museum 10199

Conques

Centre de Documentation Historique, 12320 Conques - T: 0565698511
Historical Museum   10200

Musée du Docteur Joseph Fau, 12320 Conques - T: 0565728500/8703
Decorative Arts Museum   10201

Cons-la-Grandville

Château-Musée, 54870 Cons-la-Grandville - T: 0382449041
Decorative Arts Museum   10202

Consolation-Maisonettes

Musée du Séminaire, 25390 Consolation-Maisonettes - T: 0381435471
Natural History Museum   10203

Contes

Écomusée des Vallées du Paillon, 06390 Contes - T: 0493791917, 0493790001, Fax: 0493790667. Head: Georges Tabaraud
Ethnology Museum   10204

Contz-les-Bains

Musée de la Viticulture et Renaissance du Vignoble, Rue de la Treille, 57480 Contz-les-Bains - T: 0382838026
Special Museum / Agriculture Museum   10205

Corbelin

Musée François Guiguet, Ancien Couvent, 38630 Corbelin - T: 0474889951
Fine Arts Museum   10206

Corbeny

Musée Vivant de l'Abeille, 19 Rte de Laon, 02820 Corbeny - T: 0323224014, Fax: 0323224199
Special Museum   10207

Cordemais

Musée du Temps des Baigneurs, 8 Rue de la Gorge Sèche, 44360 Cordemais - T: 0240578589
Special Museum   10208

Cordes

Musée Charles-Portal, Le Portail Peint, 81170 Cordes - T: 0563560040
Local Museum / Archaeological Museum
Prehistoric finds, Gallo-Roman archeology, the local law codification, 'Le Livre Ferrat' from the 13th-14th c, old textile mill   10209

Musée Yves-Brayer, Maison du Grand-Fauconnier, 81170 Cordes - T: 0563560040
Fine Arts Museum - 1960
Paintings by Yves Brayer   10210

Coren-les-Eaux

Collection d'Arts Populaires, Annexe du Musée de Saint-Flour, 15100 Coren-les-Eaux - T: 0471602232
Folklore Museum   10211

Corlay

Maison du Cheval, Château, 22320 Corlay - T: 0296294041
Special Museum   10212

Cormatin

Château-Musée, 71460 Cormatin - T: 0385501655
Fine Arts Museum / Decorative Arts Museum   10213

Cornimont

Exposition Permanente de Racines, 4 Chermenil, D 486, 88310 Cornimont - T: 0329241190
Special Museum / Decorative Arts Museum   10214

Corsavy

Musée d'Art et d'Artisanat, Rue Barry-d'Amont, 66150 Corsavy - T: 0468392651
Fine Arts Museum / Folklore Museum   10215

Musée des Traditions et des Arts Catalans, Mas de l'Aloy, 66150 Corsavy - T: 0468501052/398445
Folklore Museum   10216

Corseul

Musée Archéologique, Mairie, 22130 Corseul - T: 0296297617. Head: Suzanne Guidon
Archaeological Museum - 1977
Prehist, Gallo-Roman archeology   10217

Corte

Musée Régional d'Anthropologie, Citadelle, 20250 Corte - T: 0495610162
Ethnology Museum   10218

Cosne-Cours-sur-Loire

Musée de Cosne, Pl de la Résistance, 58200 Cosne-Cours-sur-Loire - T: 0386267102. Head: François Martin
Fine Arts Museum / Ethnology Museum   10219

Cossé-le-Vivien

Musée Robert Tatin, La Frénouse, 53230 Cossé-le-Vivien - T: 0243988089, Fax: 0243987889. Head: Elisabeth Henriot
Special Museum   10220

Couches

Château-Musée Marguerite de Burgogne, 71490 Couches - T: 0385455799, Fax: 0385496930
Decorative Arts Museum / Historic Site   10221

Coucouron

Musée de l'Outillage et des Techniques Traditionnelles de la Taille de Pierre, 07470 Coucouron - T: 0466461217
Science&Tech Museum   10222

Coucy-le-Château-Auffrique

Musée de la Tour, 8 Rue des Vivants, 02380 Coucy-le-Château-Auffrique - T: 0323524455, Fax: 0323524954
Local Museum   10223

Musée Salle Documentaire, Château de Coucy, 02400 Coucy-le-Château-Auffrique - T: 0323522128
Special Museum / Historical Museum   10224

Couffy

Musée Archéologique, 41110 Couffy - T: 0254753649
Archaeological Museum   10225

Couilly-Pont-aux-Dames

Musée de la Maison de Retraite, 77740 Couilly-Pont-aux-Dames
Local Museum   10226

Musée du Théâtre, Maison des Artistes, 77740 Couilly-Pont-aux-Dames - T: 0160040002. Head: André Burgère
Performing Arts Museum   10227

Coulanges-la-Vineuse

Musée du Vieux Pressoir et de la Vigne, 46bis Rue André Vildieu, 89580 Coulanges-la-Vineuse - T: 0386422059, Fax: 0386425177
Special Museum   10228

Coulmiers

Musée de Préhistoire, Mairie, 45130 Coulmiers - T: 0238742208
Archaeological Museum   10229

Coulommiers

Musée Municipal des Capucins, Hôtel de Ville, 77120 Coulommiers Cedex, mail addr: BP 171, 77527 Coulommiers - T: 0164651131, Fax: 0164751053. Head: Alexandrine Figueiredo
Local Museum - 1808
Church built in the beginning of XVIIth c   10230

Coupiac

Musée Rural du Bois, 12550 Coupiac - T: 0565997722
Special Museum   10231

Coupvray

Musée Louis-Braille, Rue Louis-Braille, 77450 Coupvray - T: 0160048280, Fax: 0164308651, E-mail: musee.braille@wanadoo.fr. Head: Margaret Calvarin
Special Museum   10232

Courances

Collections du Château de Courances, Rue du Château, 91490 Courances - T: 0164984118
Decorative Arts Museum / Fine Arts Museum   10233

Courbevoie

Musée Roybet Fould, 178 Blvd Saint-Denis, 92400 Courbevoie - T: 0143333073, Fax: 0141169156. Head: Georges Barbier-Ludwig
Local Museum - 1927   10234

Courniou-les-Grottes

Musée Français de la Spéléologie, Grottes de la Deveze, 34220 Courniou-les-Grottes - T: 0467970324, Fax: 0467973348
Natural History Museum   10235

Cournonterral

Collection de Parchemins Médiévaux, Mairie, 34660 Cournonterral - T: 0467850011/0364
Special Museum   10236

Courseulles-sur-Mer

Maison de la Mer, Pl du 6-Juin, 14470 Courseulles-sur-Mer - T: 0231379258/34
Natural History Museum   10237

Musée de la Corvette La Combattante, Centre Culturel, 17 Rue Amiral-Robert, 14470 Courseulles-sur-Mer - T: 0231377000
Historical Museum   10238

Musée des Médailles et Décorations, Centre Culturel, 14470 Courseulles-sur-Mer - T: 0231377000
Decorative Arts Museum   10239

Musée du Vieux Courseulles, Centre Culturel, 14470 Courseulles-sur-Mer - T: 0231377000
Special Museum / Historical Museum   10240

Courson-Monteloup

Château-Musée de Courson, 91680 Courson-Monteloup - T: 0164589012
Fine Arts Museum   10241

Courtelevant

Musée de la Meunerie, Moulin à Eau, 90100 Courtelevant - T: 0384296166/6234
Science&Tech Museum   10242

Courtillers

Musée d'Automates, 2 Allée du Petit-Village, 72300 Courtillers - T: 0243955560
Science&Tech Museum   10243

Courtils

Maison de la Baie, Relais de Courtils, 50220 Courtils - T: 0233896600, Fax: 0233896609, E-mail: musee.courtils@wanadoo.fr
Local Museum   10244

Coussac-Bonneval

Château de Bonneval, 87500 Coussac-Bonneval - T: 0555752011
Decorative Arts Museum   10245

Musée de l'Outillage, Moulin Authier, 87500 Coussac-Bonneval - T: 0555752286
Agriculture Museum   10246

Coustouge

Exposition Permanente, Mairie, 11220 Coustouge
Archaeological Museum   10247

Coutances

Musée Municipal, 2 Rue Quesnel-Morinière, 50200 Coutances - T: 0233451192, Fax: 0233765576. Head: Y. Papin-Drastik
Fine Arts Museum - 1868
17th-19th century paintings, works by Rubens, Le Sueur, and Stella Norman pottery   10248

Couture-sur-Loir

Château-Musée de la Possonnière, 41800 Couture-sur-Loir - T: 0254724005
Special Museum   10249

Coutures

Atelier Galerie du Manoir de la Caillère, Manoir de la Caillère, 49260 Coutures - T: 0241579797
Fine Arts Museum   10250

Coux-et-Bigaroque

Musée de la Préhistoire, Centre Culturel, 24220 Coux-et-Bigaroque - T: 0553316107
Archaeological Museum   10251

Couze-et-Saint-Front

Musée Historique du Papier, Moulin de la Rouzique, 24150 Couze-et-Saint-Front - T: 0553243616
Special Museum   10252

Cox

Maison du Potier, Ancienne Poterie, 31480 Cox - T: 0561856048/5971
Science&Tech Museum   10253

Craon

Le Château de Craon - 53400 Craon - T: 0243061102, Fax: 0243060518, E-mail: guebrian@club-internet.fr
Historic Site   10254

Château Musée → Le Château de Craon

Craponne (Rhône)

Musée de la Blanchisserie Artisanale Joseph-Gladel, 6 Rue Bergeron, 69290 Craponne (Rhône) - T: 0478571540, Fax: 0478571540, Internet: http://www.chez.com.grehc. Head: Henri Robert
Association with Coll   10255

Cravant-les-Côteaux

Musée du Vieux Cravant, Vieille Eglise, Vieux Bourg, 37500 Cravant-les-Côteaux - T: 0247931240/1359, Fax: 0247984190, E-mail: f2f@club-internet.fr. Head: Frédéric de Foucaud
Religious Arts Museum / Decorative Arts Museum   10256

Crazannes

Château de Crazannes, 17350 Crazannes - T: 0680654096, Fax: 0546913446, E-mail: crazannes@worldonline.fr. Head: Hervé de Rochefort
Historic Site   10257

Crécy-la-Chapelle

Musée de la Mairie de Crécy, Mairie, 77580 Crécy-la-Chapelle - T: 0164638346
Local Museum   10258

Creil

Musée Gallé-Juillet, 6 Allée du Musée, 60100 Creil - T: 0344295150
Decorative Arts Museum / Fine Arts Museum - 1931
Creil ceramics and pottery, furniture, paintings   10259

Crémeaux

Musée du Moulin de la Roue, 42260 Crémeaux - T: 0477625318/652105
Science&Tech Museum   10260

Crémieu

Collections Historiques, 38460 Crémieu - T: 0474904513
Religious Arts Museum   10261

Crépy-en-Valois

Musée du Valois et de l'Archerie, Vieux Château, 60800 Crépy-en-Valois - T: 0344592197. Head: Philippe Gouble
Local Museum
Etchings, standards of guilds, coll of archery and crossbows   10262

Crestet

Centre d'Art du Crestet, Chemin de la Verrière, 84110 Crestet - T: 0890363500, Fax: 0490363620
Fine Arts Museum   10263

Crévecœur-en-Auge

Espace Architectural Normand, Château, 14340 Crévecœur-en-Auge - T: 0231630245, Fax: 0231630596, E-mail: musee.schlumberger@wanadoo.fr. Head: Christoph de Ceunynck
Historic Site   10264

Musée Conrad-et-Marcel-Schlumberger, Château, 14340 Crévecœur-en-Auge - T: 0231630245, Fax: 0231630596, E-mail: musee.schlumberger@wanadoo.fr. Head: Christoph de Ceunynck
Science&Tech Museum   10265

Crillon-le-Brave

Musée de la Musique Mécanique, 84410 Crillon-le-Brave - T: 0490656159, Fax: 0490128228, E-mail: musique.mecanique@wanadoo.fr, Internet: http://perso.wanadoo.fr/misique.mecanique. Head: Thorsten Brix
Music Museum / Science&Tech Museum   10266

Croisset

Musée et Pavillon Flaubert, 18 Quai Gustave-Flaubert, 76000 Croisset - T: 0235364391
Special Museum   10267

Crozon

Maison des Minéraux, Rte du Cap de la Chèvre, Saint-Hernot, 29160 Crozon - T: 0298271973
Natural History Museum   10268

Cruas

Exposition Archéologique, Église, 07350 Cruas - T: 0475514088
Archaeological Museum   10269

Exposition de Beaux-Arts, Centre Auclair, 07350 Cruas - T: 0475514088
Fine Arts Museum   10270

Musée des Sports, Centre Auclair, 07350 Cruas - T: 0475514088
Special Museum   10271

Musée Historique de la Chaux, Centre Auclair, 07350 Cruas - T: 0475514088
Local Museum   10272

Cruzille-en-Mâconnais

Musée de l'Outillage Rural et Bourguignon, Domaine des Vignes de Maynes, 71260 Cruzille-en-Mâconnais - T: 0385332015
Science&Tech Museum   10273

Cruzy

Musée d'Art et d'Archéologie, Rue Roger-Salengro, 34310 Cruzy - T: 0467894146
Archaeological Museum / Fine Arts Museum 10274

Cucuron

Musée Marc-Deydier, Rue de l'Église, 84160 Cucuron - T: 0490772502
Archaeological Museum - 1968
Prehistorical local finds, archeological roman finds, ethnology, photography 10275

Cuiseaux

Ecomusée de la Bresse Bourguignonne, Château du Prince d'Orange, 71480 Cuiseaux - T: 0385762716
Special Museum 10276

Culan

Château-Musée de Culan, 18270 Culan - T: 0248566418
Decorative Arts Museum 10277

Curtil-Vergy

Musée de la Vigne et du Vin, Domaine Chaley, 21220 Curtil-Vergy - T: 0380614381
Special Museum / Folklore Museum 10278

Cussac-Fort-Médoc

Collection de Vieilles Étiquettes de Grands Crus, Château Fort de Vauban, Cussac-le-Vieux, 33460 Cussac-Fort-Médoc - T: 0556589338
Special Museum 10279

Collection d'Outillage Ancien de Tonnellerie, Château du Moulin Rouge, 33460 Cussac-Fort-Médoc - T: 0556589113
Science&Tech Museum 10280

Musée Communal des Traditions Populaires Locales, Fort Médoc, 33460 Cussac-Fort-Médoc - T: 0556589840
Folklore Museum 10281

Musée de l'Outillage Agricole et Viticole du Château Aney, Château Aney, 33460 Cussac-Fort-Médoc - T: 0556589489
Science&Tech Museum 10282

Musée du Cheval en 1900, Château de Lanessan, 33460 Cussac-Fort-Médoc - T: 0556589480, Fax: 0557888992, E-mail: bouteiller@bouteiller.com. Head: Hubert Bouteiller
Special Museum 10283

Cusset

Musée Municipal, Tour Prisonnière, 03300 Cusset - T: 0470308945/0470962917, Fax: 04703009559, E-mail: culture@ville-cusset.fr. Head: Marie-Anne Caradec
Fine Arts Museum / Historical Museum
Lapidarium, paintings, sculptures 10284

Cutry

Musée Archéologique, Vieux Château, 2 Rue de Longwy, 54720 Cutry - T: 0382243036
Archaeological Museum 10285

Dabo

Musée des Vieux Métiers et des Eaux-de-vie, 3 Pl de l'Église, 57850 Dabo - T: 0387074997/4815
Local Museum 10286

Rocher Saint-Léon, 57850 Dabo - T: 0387074751
Historical Museum 10287

Dambach-la-Ville

Collection de Tonnellerie, 92 Rue du Maréchal Foch, 67650 Dambach-la-Ville - T: 0388924119/4105
Special Museum 10288

Damery

Musée de la Cave, Collection Jeeper, 8 Rue Clemenceau, 51200 Damery - T: 0326584123, Fax: 0326586567, E-mail: info@champagne-jeeper.com, Internet: http://www.champagne-jeeper.com. Head: Christian Goutorche
Special Museum 10289

Dardilly

Musée du Curé d'Ars, 69570 Dardilly - T: 0478661906
Religious Arts Museum 10290

Darney

Musée Franco-Tchécolosvaque, Mairie, 88260 Darney - T: 0329093345
Historical Museum / Fine Arts Museum 10291

Davayat

Château-Musée, 63200 Davayat - T: 0473633027
Decorative Arts Museum / Fine Arts Museum 10292

Davézieux

Musée de la Papeterie Canson et Montgolfier, Maison Natale Montgolfier, 07100 Davézieux - T: 0475698800
Science&Tech Museum 10293

Dax

Musée de Borda, 27 Rue Cazade, 40100 Dax - T: 0558741291, Fax: 0558744522. Head: Elisabeth Campredon
Local Museum / Fine Arts Museum
Local hist, fine arts (19th-20th c) 10294

Musée de l'Aviation Légère de l'Armée de Terre, 58 Av de l'Aerodrome, 40100 Dax - T: 0558746619, Fax: 0558746619, E-mail: aamalat@wanadoo.fr, Internet: http://assoc.wanadoo.fr/aamalat/. Head: François Masuyer
Military Museum
Light-weight airplanes and helicopters 10295

Deauville

Villa Strassburger, 14800 Deauville - T: 0231882044
Decorative Arts Museum / Fine Arts Museum 10296

Decazeville

Musée Régional de Géologie Pierre Vetter, Av Paul Ramadier, 12300 Decazeville - T: 0565433008, Fax: 0565433008, E-mail: - museevetter.decazeville@wanadoo.fr, Internet: http://www.museevetter.multimania.com. Head: Dr. Frédéric Christophoul
Natural History Museum
Collection of palacobotanical fossiles from the Upper Carboniferous (Stephanian). Fossiles from France, Germany, Spain and Colombia 10297

Delme

Centre d'Art Contemporain, 33 Rue Poincaré, 57590 Delme - T: 0387014342, Fax: 0387014314
Fine Arts Museum 10298

Musée Archéologique, Mairie, 57590 Delme - T: 0387013719
Archaeological Museum 10299

Denain

Moulin Doisy, Rue du Moulin, 59220 Denain - T: 0327442851
Science&Tech Museum / Historical Museum 10300

Musée de la Résistance en Zone Interdite, 9 Pl Wilson, 59220 Denain - T: 0327446212
Historical Museum 10301

Musée Municipal d'Histoire et d'Archéologie, Pl Wilson, 59220 Denain - T: 0327446212
Historical Museum / Archaeological Museum 10302

Musée Régional du Chemin de Fer Nord-Pas-de-Calais, Rue du Turenne, 59220 Denain - T: 0327497852, E-mail: cefnord@aol.com, Internet: http://www.cefnord.fr.st. Head: Daniel Grépier
Science&Tech Museum 10303

Denazé

Musée de la Vieille Forge, Bourg, 53400 Denazé - T: 0243988427
Science&Tech Museum 10304

Deneuvre

Les Sources d'Hercule, Musée Archéologique de Site Gallo-Romain, Rue de la Porte Saint-Nicolas, 54120 Deneuvre - T: 0383754523
Archaeological Museum 10305

Dénezé-sous-Doué

Ecomusée de la Vie Troglodytique en Anjou, La Caverne, 49700 Dénezé-sous-Doué - T: 0241591540
Folklore Museum / Fine Arts Museum 10306

Musée Troglodytique de la Fosse, 49700 Dénezé-sous-Doué - T: 0241590032, Fax: 0241599468
Folklore Museum 10307

Desaignes

Musée Municipal de la Vie Rurale, Château, 07570 Desaignes - T: 0475066300
Agriculture Museum 10308

Desvres

Exposition de Faïences, 39 Rue Minguet, 62240 Desvres - T: 0321916399
Decorative Arts Museum 10309

Maison de la Faïence, Rue Jean Macé, 62240 Desvres - T: 0321832323
Decorative Arts Museum 10310

Deuil-la-Barre

Musée d'Histoire, La Chevrette, Rue Jean-Bouin et Rue du Château, 95170 Deuil-la-Barre - T: 0139840363
Historical Museum 10311

Dicy

Musée de la Fabuloserie, Rte Nationale 943, 89120 Dicy - T: 0386636421
Fine Arts Museum 10312

Die

Musée Municipal, Musée d'Art et d'Histoire Reynaud, 11 Rue Camille Buffardel, 26150 Die - T: 0475220069/0303. Head: Henri Desaye
Historical Museum - 1949
Pre- and ancient hist, Roman inscriptions, sculpture, bronzes, ceramics, Roman glass, early Christian, Carolingian, and Romanesque sculpture, documents on local 15th-20th century hist - Library 10313

Dieppe

Château-Musée de Dieppe, Rue de Chastes, 76200 Dieppe - T: 0235841976, Fax: 0232901279, E-mail: musee-dieppe@wanadoo.fr, Internet: http://www.mairie-dieppe.fr. Head: Pierre Ickowicz
Fine Arts Museum / Decorative Arts Museum - 1876
Paintings inspired by local area, especially Impressionists, pre-Columbian pottery, memorabilia of the composer C. Saint-Saëns, marine coll of maps, log books, compasses, and 18th century ship models, 16th-20th century ivory figurines, modern local sculptures, Georges Braque engravings 10314

Cité de la Mer ESTRAN, 37 Rue de l'Asile-Thomas, 76200 Dieppe - T: 0235069320/846850
Special Museum / Science&Tech Museum / Natural History Museum 10315

Dieue-sur-Meuse

Musée d'Arts Populaires, Près de l'Eglise, 55320 Dieue-sur-Meuse - T: 0329876168
Folklore Museum 10316

Dieulouard

Musée du Vieux Pays, Ancien Château, 54380 Dieulouard - T: 0383237813/5876. Head: Michel Tête
Archaeological Museum / Folklore Museum 10317

Digne

Musée de la Guerre 1939-1945, Pl Paradis, 04000 Digne - T: 0492305200
Military Museum 10318

Musée de Site, La Robine, 04000 Digne - T: 0492315131
Natural History Museum 10319

Musée-Fondation Alexandra David-Néel, 27 Av Maréchal Juin, 04000 Digne - T: 0492313238, Fax: 0492312808, E-mail: neel@alexandra-david-neel.org, Internet: http://www.alexandra-david-neel.org. Head: Frank Tréguier
Ethnology Museum 10320

Musée Municipal, Blvd Gassendi, 04000 Digne - T: 0492314529, Fax: 0492323864, E-mail: musdigne@imaginet.fr. Head: Nadine Gomez
Archaeological Museum / Fine Arts Museum / Science&Tech Museum - 1889
Prehistory, Gallo-Roman antiquities, 16th-17th c painting (Italian School), visual art 20th c, history of science coll 10321

Musée-Promenade, Réserve Géologique de Haute-Provence, Parc Saint-Benoît, 04000 Digne Cedex, mail addr: BP 156, 04005 Digne-les-Bains Cedex - T: 0492367070, Fax: 0492367071, E-mail: resgeol@calvanet.calvacom.fr, Internet: http://www.newsup.univ-mrs.fr/~wresgeol/index.html
Natural History Museum 10322

Digoin

Musée de la Céramique, Office du Tourisme, 71160 Digoin - T: 0385530081
Decorative Arts Museum 10323

Dijon

Centre d'Art Contemporain, 16 Rue Quentin, 21000 Dijon - T: 0380307523, Fax: 0380305974, E-mail: leconsortium@wanadoo.fr, Internet: http://www.leconsortium.com. Head: Xavier Douroux
Fine Arts Museum 10324

Historial de Bourgogne, 18 Rue Sainte-Anne, 21000 Dijon - T: 0380307352
Historical Museum 10325

Musée Archéologique, 5 Rue du Docteur-Maret, 21000 Dijon - T: 0380308854, 0380308623, Fax: 0380307157
Archaeological Museum - 1955
Protohistoric and prehistoric findings, golden bracelet of the 6th c, Gallo-Roman and Merovingian items, medieval art, bust of Christ by Claus Sluter - library 10326

Musée d'Art Sacré, Chapelle, 15 Rue Sainte-Anne, 21000 Dijon - T: 0380300644, Fax: 0380441278, E-mail: mvbppmas@ville-dijon.fr. Head: Madeleine Blondel
Religious Arts Museum 10327

Musée de la Cigarette, Seita, Usine de Dijon, 1 Rue de Cracovie, 21000 Dijon - T: 0380716634
Special Museum 10328

Musée de la Moutarde Amora, 48 Quai Nicolas-Rolin, 21000 Dijon - T: 0380444452
Special Museum 10329

Musée de la Vie Bourguignonne Perrin-de-Puycousin, 17 Rue Sainte-Anne, 21000 Dijon - T: 0380441269, Fax: 0380441278, E-mail: mvbppmas@ville-dijon.fr. Head: Madeleine Blondel
Ethnology Museum 10330

Musée des Beaux-Arts, Palais des Etats de Bourgogne, 21000 Dijon, mail addr: BP 1510, 21033 Dijon Cedex - T: 0380745270, Fax: 0380745344, E-mail: museedesbeauxarts@ville-dijon.fr, Internet: http://www.ville-dijon.fr. Head: Emmanuel Starcky
Fine Arts Museum - 1787
Gravestones, altar art, Egyptian items, 15th-18th century tapestries, early Flemish, Swiss, German, Italian and 16th-20th century French paintings, decorative objects of enamel, ivory, gold, medieval sculpture, French Renaissance furnishings, wood carving, armaments, stained-glass windows, 15th-16th century Burgundian sculpture, Oriental textiles, modern works 10331

Musée des Hospices Civils, 3 Rue du Faubourg Raines, 21000 Dijon - T: 0380293765
Historical Museum 10332

Musée d'Histoire Naturelle, Vivarium, 1 Av Albert-1er, 21000 Dijon - T: 0380416108/2625
Natural History Museum - 1836
Local geology, fauna of the area, exotic and French insects, shells of the world, mammals of Madagascar 10333

Musée Grévin, Historial des Ducs de Bourgogne, 13 Av Albert-1er, 21000 Dijon - T: 0380420303
Fine Arts Museum 10334

Musée Magnin, 4 Rue des Bons Enfants, 21000 Dijon - T: 0380671110, Fax: 0380664375, E-mail: musee.magnin@culture.fr. Head: Emmanuel Starcky
Fine Arts Museum - 1938
16th-19th century French, Italian and Northern paintings (Bourdon, Le Sueur, Vignon, Allori, Strozzi, Lairesse, Bylert), furnished house of the collector 10335

Musée Rude, 8 Rue Vaillant, Église Saint-Étienne, 21000 Dijon - T: 0380745270, Fax: 0380745344, E-mail: museedesbeauxarts@ville-dijon.fr, Internet: http://www.ville-dijon.fr. Head: Emmanuel Starcky
Fine Arts Museum 10336

Petit Musée de la Poupée, 23 Rue Condorcet, 21000 Dijon - T: 0380418871
Special Museum 10337

Dinan

Musée du Château, Rue du Château, 22100 Dinan - T: 0296394520. Head: Véronique Burnod
Archaeological Museum / Fine Arts Museum - 1850
Prehist, Roman and medieval findings, paintings, sculpture, 14th century military architecture, folklore 10338

Musée du Rail, Gare de Dinan, 22100 Dinan - T: 0296398233, Internet: http://www.museedurail-dinan.com. Head: Jacky Hamoniaux
Science&Tech Museum 10339

Dinard

Laboratoire Maritime de Dinard, Muséum National d'Histoire Naturelle, 17 Av George V, 35800 Dinard - T: 0299461390, Fax: 0299882942. Head: Ch. Retière
Natural History Museum
Aquarium - Library 10340

Musée du Site Balnéaire, Villa Eugénie, 12 Rue des Français Libres, 35800 Dinard - T: 0299468105, 0299163123, Fax: 0299164872, E-mail: musee@vilk-dinard.fr. Head: Florence Rionnet
Local Museum 10341

Dions

Collection d'Objets, Miniatures, M. Lucien Racanière, 30190 Dions - T: 0466810993
Agriculture Museum 10342

Dirinon

Musée des Traditions du Vieux Dirinon, Chapelle Sainte-Nonne, 29460 Dirinon - T: 0298070133
Folklore Museum 10343

Dol-de-Bretagne

Musée de Dol, 4 Pl de la Cathédrale, 35120 Dol-de-Bretagne - T: 0299480938, Fax: 0299483261
Historical Museum / Folklore Museum - 1977
Local hist, folk art, prehistory 10344

Dole

Musée des Beaux-Arts, 85 Rue des Arènes, 39100 Dole - T: 0384792585, Fax: 0384728946. Head: Anne Dary
Fine Arts Museum - 1821
Pre- and protohistoric archeological findings, Gallo-Roman items, local historical paintings from the 17th century, contemporary art, painting from the 15th century to 19th century, sculpture from the 13th century to the 16th century 10345

Musée Pasteur, 43 Rue Pasteur, 39100 Dole - T: 0384722061
Special Museum 10346

Domérat

Musée du Vignoble Montluçonnais, Parc de la Pérelle, 03410 Domérat - T: 0470642001/2369
Special Museum 10347

Domfront

Musée d'Art et d'Histoire, Mairie, 61700 Domfront - T: 0233386536
Local Museum 10348

Domjean

Château de l'Angotière, Château, 50420 Domjean - T: 0233563291
Decorative Arts Museum 10349

Domme

Musée d'Arts et Traditions Populaires Paul Reclus, Pl de la Halle, 24250 Domme - T: 0553283709, Fax: 0553293462
Local Museum 10350

Dompierre (Orne)

Musée du Fer et du Fil, Le Bourg., 61700 Dompierre (Orne) - T: 0233380325. Head: Josiane Collas
Association with Coll 10351

Dompierre-sur-Mer

Musée Militaire du Souvenir, 21 Rue du Moulin-Chagnolet, 17139 Dompierre-sur-Mer - T: 0546452208
Military Museum 10352

Domrémy-la-Pucelle

Maison Natale de Jeanne d'Arc et Centre Johannique, Rue de la Basilique, 88630 Domrémy-la-Pucelle - T: 0329069586, Fax: 0329068250, E-mail: site.de.domremy@wanadoo.fr
Historical Museum 10353

Musée Jehanne d'Hier et d'Aujourd'hui, Rue de l'Isle, 88630 Domrémy-la-Pucelle - T: 0329069602
Special Museum 10354

Donzère

Musée des Amis du Vieux Donzère, 30 Grand Rue, 26290 Donzère - T: 0475516116/6133
Historical Museum / Archaeological Museum 10355

Donzy

Musée de la Meunerie, Rue André Audinet, APSMM, 58220 Donzy - T: 0386393946
Science&Tech Museum 10356

Dormans-en-Champagne

Musée de l'Outil Champenois, 51700 Dormans-en-Champagne - T: 0326588030
Agriculture Museum 10357

Dossenheim-sur-Zinsel

Refuge Fortifié Muséalisé, Près de l'Eglise, 67330 Dossenheim-sur-Zinsel - T: 0388700004
Historical Museum 10358

Douai

Collection de Peintures, Collégiale Saint-Pierre, 59500 Douai - T: 0327882679
Fine Arts Museum 10359

Mesuroscope, 59500 Douai - T: 0327882679
Special Museum 10360

Musée d'Archéologie et de Sciences Naturelles, 191 Rue Saint-Albin, 59500 Douai - T: 0327713890, Fax: 0327713893, E-mail: arkeos@wanadoo.fr
Archaeological Museum / Natural History Museum 10361

Musée Municipal de la Chartreuse, 130 Rue des Chartreux, 59500 Douai - T: 0327713880, Fax: 0327713884, E-mail: musee@douai-ville.fr. Head: Françoise Baligand
Fine Arts Museum - 1792
Flemish, Dutch, Italian, and French painting (Bellegambe, Veronese, Carracci), Gallo-Roman and medieval antiquities 10362

Douarnenez

Musée du Bateau, Pl de l'Enfer, 29100 Douarnenez - T: 0298926520, Fax: 0298920541. Head: Denez L'Hostis
Science&Tech Museum - 1993
Historic ships and boats, maritime communities - Library, workshops, shipyards 10363

Port Muséalisé, 29100 Douarnenez - T: 0298926635/6520
Special Museum / Natural History Museum 10364

Douaumont

Collection Historique, Ossuaire Tour, 55100 Douaumont - T: 0329845481, Fax: 0329865654, E-mail: infos@verdun-douaumont.com, Internet: http://www.verdun-douaumont.com. Head: J.C. Minmeister
Historical Museum 10365

Musée Militaire du Fort, 55100 Douaumont - T: 0329861418
Military Museum 10366

Douchy-les-Mines

Centre Régional de la Photographie Nord-Pas-de-Calais, Pl des Nations, 59282 Douchy-les-Mines - T: 0327435650, Fax: 0327313193, E-mail: CRP.59.62@wanadoo.fr. Head: Pierre Devin
Fine Arts Museum 10367

Doué-la-Fontaine

Musée de la Mer des Faluns, Parc Zoologique, Rue de Cholet, 49700 Doué-la-Fontaine - T: 0241591858
Natural History Museum 10368

Musée des Commerces Anciens, Jardin des Roses, Ecuries du Foullon, 49700 Doué-la-Fontaine - T: 0241592823
Local Museum 10369

Doullens

Musée Lombard, 7 Rue du Musée, 80600 Doullens - T: 0322770007
Fine Arts Museum 10370

Dourdan

Musée-Château de Dourdan, Au Château, Pl du Général-de-Gaulle, 91410 Dourdan - T: 0164596683. Head: Elisabeth Mytton-Famié
Local Museum - 1977
archives 10371

Douvres-la-Délivrande

Musée du Radar, 14440 Douvres-la-Délivrande - T: 0231060645/377443
Science&Tech Museum 10372

Douzens

Musée Ornithologique et de la Faune, Moulin, 11700 Douzens - T: 0468790927/1006
Natural History Museum 10373

Douzillac

Micromusée de la Légion Etrangère, Mairie, 24190 Douzillac - T: 0553800314
Military Museum 10374

Douzy

Musée des Débuts de l'Aviation, Aérodrome de Sedan-Douzy, 08140 Douzy - T: 0324263870. Head: P. Germain
Special Museum 10375

Doyet

Musée Rural, Château de la Souche, 03170 Doyet - T: 0470077641
Agriculture Museum 10376

Draguignan

Musée de l'Artillerie, Ecole d'Application de l'Artillerie, Quartier Bonaparte, 83300 Draguignan - T: 0498108385, Fax: 0498108386, E-mail: musee.artillerie@worldonline.fr, Internet: http://perso.worldonline.fr/musee-artillerie. Head: Pierre P. Saint-Pol
Military Museum 10377

Musée des Arts et Traditions Populaires de Moyenne Provence, Rue Joseph Roumanille, 83300 Draguignan - T: 0494470572
Folklore Museum 10378

Musée Municipal de Draguignan, 9 Rue de la République, 83300 Draguignan - T: 0494472880
Archaeological Museum / Decorative Arts Museum / Fine Arts Museum 10379

Dreux

Collection de la Chapelle Royale Saint-Louis, 2 Sq d'Aumale, 28100 Dreux - T: 0237460706
Decorative Arts Museum / Local Museum 10380

Musée d'Art et d'Histoire, 7 Pl du Musée, 28100 Dreux - T: 0237501861, Fax: 0237467207. Head: Stéphanie Sobezyk
Fine Arts Museum / Historical Museum
Louis XV furniture, Romanesque chapel, modern paintings including Monet and Vlaminck, local history, documents on the Orléans family 10381

Musée du Beffroi, Grande Rue Maurice Viollette, 28100 Dreux - T: 0237501861
Folklore Museum 10382

Musée Rétromobile Drouais, Domaine de Comteville, 4 Rue Kennedy, 28100 Dreux - T: 0237422583
Science&Tech Museum 10383

Droyes

Musée Conservatoire du Matériel Agricole, Ferme de Berzillière, 52220 Droyes - T: 0325042252
Agriculture Museum 10384

Duilhac-sous-Peyrepertuse

Archéosite Cathare, 11350 Duilhac-sous-Peyrepertuse - T: 0468454055
Archaeological Museum 10385

Dun-sur-Auron

Musée du Canal du Duc de Berry, Pl du Chatelet, 18130 Dun-sur-Auron - T: 0248598526
Science&Tech Museum 10386

Dunkerque

Musée-Aquariophile, Av du Casino, Parc Malo, 59140 Dunkerque - T: 0328591918
Natural History Museum / Science&Tech Museum 10387

Musée des Beaux-Arts de Dunkerque, Pl du Général de Gaulle, 59140 Dunkerque - T: 0328592165, Fax: 0328664673, E-mail: musee@ville-dunkerque.fr. Head: Aude Cordonnier
Fine Arts Museum - 1841
Local hist, French, Flemish, Dutch and Italian painting from the 17th-19th c, natural hist - library 10388

Musée Portuaire, 9 Quai de la Citadelle, 59140 Dunkerque - T: 0328633339, Fax: 0328650662, E-mail: museeportuaire@nordnet.fr. Head: Jean Deweerdt
Historical Museum / Ethnology Museum 10389

Duras

Château-Musée des Ducs, 47120 Duras - T: 0553837732
Local Museum 10390

Durban-Corbières

Musée de la Viticulture, Auberge du Vieux Puits, Fontjoncouse, 11360 Durban-Corbières - T: 0468440434
Agriculture Museum 10391

Durenque

Musée du Moulin Roupeyrac, 12170 Durenque - T: 0565464139
Science&Tech Museum 10392

Durtal

Cachots et Oubliettes au Château, 49430 Durtal - T: 0241760344
Historical Museum 10393

Eaux-Puiseaux

Musée du Cidre du Pays d'Othe, La Ferme d'Othe, 10130 Eaux-Puiseaux - T: 0325421513/0165
Special Museum / Science&Tech Museum 10394

Eauze

Musée Archéologique, Le Trésor, Pl de la Rèpublique, 32800 Eauze - T: 0562097138, Fax: 0562097920. Head: Michel Hue
Archaeological Museum - 1995
Antiquities, archeology, ceramics, architecture, prehistory, numismatics, jewellery 10395

Ébreuil

Château-Musée de Veauce, 03450 Ébreuil - T: 0470585327
Fine Arts Museum 10396

Echery

Musée de l'Ecole, Ecole, 68160 Echery - T: 0389588050
Special Museum 10397

Échirolles

Musée de la Viscose, 27 Chemin du Tramblay, 38130 Échirolles - T: 0476330828, Fax: 0476330788, E-mail: musee-viscose@ville-echirolles.fr, Internet: http://www.ville-echirolles.fr
Science&Tech Museum 10398

Musée Géo Charles, 1 Rue Géo Charles, 38130 Échirolles - T: 0476225863
Fine Arts Museum / Decorative Arts Museum 10399

Éclaibes

Collection Archéologique, Communs du Château, 59330 Éclaibes - T: 0327688294
Archaeological Museum 10400

Écouen

Musée National de la Renaissance, Château, 95440 Écouen - T: 0134383851, Fax: 0139335107, E-mail: alain-erlande-brandenburg@culture.gouv.fr. Head: Alain Erlande-Brandenbourg
Decorative Arts Museum / Fine Arts Museum - 1977
Decorative arts of the Renaissance, tapestry, Iznik ceramics, French and Italian ceramics, Limoges enamels, furniture, interior decor - library 10401

Ecuillé

Château-Musée du Plessis-Bouré, 49460 Ecuillé - T: 0241320601/72, E-mail: scipb@hotmail.com. Head: B. de Sauvebeuf
Decorative Arts Museum 10402

Ecuisses

Maison-Musée du Canal, Ecomusée du Creusot, Neuvième Ecluse, 71210 Ecuisses - T: 0385789222
Local Museum 10403

Effiat

Château-Musée des Effiat, 63260 Effiat - T: 0473636401
Fine Arts Museum / Decorative Arts Museum 10404

Egliseneuve-d'Entraigues

Maison des Fromages d'Auvergne, Pl du Foirail, 63850 Egliseneuve-d'Entraigues - T: 0473719013/9369
Special Museum 10405

Éguilly

Exposition Permanente d'Art, Château, 21320 Éguilly - T: 0380907290
Fine Arts Museum 10406

Eguzon

Maison de l'Energie, Barrage d'Eguzon, 36270 Eguzon - T: 0254474775, Fax: 0254472038
Science&Tech Museum
Hist of electricity and Europe's biggest dam construction 10407

Musée de la Vallée de la Creuse, Château, 36270 Eguzon - T: 0254474775, Fax: 0254472038
Folklore Museum / Ethnology Museum / Science&Tech Museum 10408

Elbeuf

Musée d'Histoire Naturelle et d'Histoire Locale, Hôtel de Ville, 76500 Elbeuf - T: 0232969015, Fax: 0235817794. Head: Sylviane Lierville
Natural History Museum / Local Museum 10409

Elne

Musée Archéologique Le Cloitre, 66200 Elne - T: 0468227090
Archaeological Museum 10410

Musée Historique, Cloître, 66200 Elne - T: 0468227090
Historical Museum 10411

Musée Terrus, Rue Porte-Balaguer, 66200 Elne - T: 0468228888
Fine Arts Museum 10412

Eloyes

Musée Archéologique, 1 Rue de l'Église, 88510 Eloyes - T: 0329324194
Archaeological Museum 10413

Musée d'Histoire Naturelle, 1 Rue de l'Église, 88510 Eloyes - T: 0329324194
Natural History Museum 10414

Embermenil

Maison de l'Abbé Grégoire, Grande Rue, 54370 Embermenil - T: 0383712056, Fax: 0383712057. Head: F. Bier
Religious Arts Museum / Historical Museum 10415

Embrun

Musée d'Art Sacré de l'Ancienne Cathédrale Notre-Dame- du-Réal, Pl Général Dosse, 05200 Embrun - T: 0492437272, Fax: 0492435406
Religious Arts Museum 10416

Ensisheim

Musée Archéologique, Dans l'Ancien Palais de la Régence Autrichienne, 68190 Ensisheim - T: 0389264954
Archaeological Museum 10417

Musée de la Régence, Palais de la Régence, 68190 Ensisheim - T: 0389264954
Local Museum 10418

Musée du Mineur, Palais de la Régence, 68190 Ensisheim - T: 0389264954
Science&Tech Museum 10419

Entrains-sur-Nohain

Musée Archéologique, Maison des Fouilles, 58410 Entrains-sur-Nohain - T: 0386292206. Head: J. Neissonnier
Archaeological Museum 10420

France: Eze

Entrange

Musée de la Ligne Maginot, Zeiterholz, 57330 Entrange - T: 0382851143
Military Museum 10421

Entrecasteaux

Château-Musée d'Entrecasteaux, 83570 Entrecasteaux - T: 0494044395/4286
Fine Arts Museum / Decorative Arts Museum 10422

Entrevaux

Musée d'Art Sacré, Ancienne Cathédrale, 04320 Entrevaux - T: 0493054116
Religious Arts Museum 10423

Musée de la Meunerie, Gorge de la Chalvagne, 04320 Entrevaux - T: 0493054004
Science&Tech Museum 10424

Musée de la Motocyclette, Rue Haute, 04320 Entrevaux - T: 0493054004
Science&Tech Museum 10425

Eperlecques

Musée de la Base Secrète de V 2, 62910 Eperlecques - T: 0321884422
Military Museum 10426

Épernay

Exposition de la Tour de Castellane, 57 Rue de Verdun, 51200 Épernay - T: 0326551533/542481
Historical Museum 10427

Les Métiers du Champagne, 57 Rue de Verdun, 51200 Épernay - T: 0326551533
Local Museum 10428

Musée Champenois de l'Imprimerie, 57 Rue de Verdun, 51200 Épernay - T: 0326551533
Science&Tech Museum 10429

Musée de la Cave des Champagnes de Castellane, 57 Rue de Verdun, 51200 Épernay - T: 0326551533
Special Museum 10430

Musée de la Tradition Champenoise, 57 Rue de Verdun, 51200 Épernay - T: 0326551533
Special Museum 10431

Musée des Affiches Léonetto-Cappiello, Tour de Castellane, 51200 Épernay
Special Museum 10432

Musée Municipal d'Archéologie et du Vin de Champagne, 13 Av de Champagne, 51200 Épernay - T: 0326550356, Fax: 0326547734, E-mail: musee.epernay@libertysurf.fr. Head: Jean-Jacques Charpy
Archaeological Museum 10433

La Salle des Étiquettes, 57 Rue de Verdun, 51200 Épernay - T: 0326551533
Special Museum 10434

Épinal

Musée Départemental d'Art Ancien et Contemporain, 1 Pl Lagarde, 88000 Épinal - T: 0329822033
Archaeological Museum / Folklore Museum / Local Museum / Fine Arts Museum
Gallo-Roman medieval sculpture, antiquities, numismatics, regional folklore, 16th-20th century paintings, 18th century drawings 10435

Musée-Imprimerie d'Images, Pellerin, 42 Quai Dogneville, 88000 Épinal - T: 0329342187
Special Museum / Science&Tech Museum 10436

Musée International de l'Imagerie, 1 Pl Lagarde, 88000 Épinal - T: 0329822033
Fine Arts Museum 10437

Épineuil-le-Fleuriel

Musée-École du Grand Meaulnes, 18360 Épineuil-le-Fleuriel - T: 0248630482, Fax: 0248630482
Local Museum
Maison de écrivain Henri Alain-Fournier 10438

Époisses

Château des XIVe-XVIIe s, 21460 Époisses - T: 0380964056, Fax: 0380964056
Historic Site 10439

Équeurdreville-Hainneville

Espace Culturel Hippolite-Mars, Pl de l'Hôtel-de-Ville, 50120 Équeurdreville-Hainneville - T: 0233539600
Fine Arts Museum 10440

Ergué-Gabéric

Musée Océanographique de l'Odet, 29000 Ergué-Gabéric - T: 0298596385
Natural History Museum 10441

Ermont

Musée Archéologique, Bibliothèque Municipale, 95120 Ermont - T: 0134153902/130525
Archaeological Museum / Historical Museum / Ethnology Museum 10442

Ernée

Musée Archéologique, Ancienne Mairie, 53500 Ernée - T: 0243052110
Archaeological Museum 10443

Escalles

Musée International du Trans-Manche, Mont d'Hubert, 62179 Escalles - T: 0321855742
Science&Tech Museum / Local Museum 10444

Escaudain

Musée de la Vie en Bassin Minier, Rue Paul Bert, 59124 Escaudain - T: 0327440704/319448
Local Museum 10445

Eschau

Collections d'Arts Populaires, 2 Rue du 27-Novembre, 67114 Eschau - T: 0388642553
Science&Tech Museum 10446

Eschviller

Musée du Moulin à Eau, Moulin, 57320 Eschviller - T: 0387967583/7416
Science&Tech Museum 10447

Escolives-Sainte-Camille

Musée Archéologique, 9 Rue Raymond-Kapps, 89290 Escolives-Sainte-Camille - T: 0386533903/3479, Fax: 0386533909, E-mail: archeo.escolives@wanadoo.fr, Internet: http://www.archeoescolives.-multimania.com. Head: Pascale Laurent
Archaeological Museum 10448

Esnandes

Musée de la Mytiliculture, 17137 Esnandes - T: 0546013464
Special Museum 10449

Espalion

Musée de la Machine de Guerre, Château de Calmont, 12500 Espalion - T: 0565441589/1063, Fax: 0565480851, E-mail: calmontdolt@free.fr. Head: Thierry Plume
Historic Site 10450

Musée de la Plongée, Pl du Marché, 12500 Espalion - T: 0565440918
Decorative Arts Museum 10451

Musée du Rouergue, Ancienne Maison d'Arrêt Rénovée, Pl P. Frontin, 12500 Espalion
Folklore Museum 10452

Musée Joseph-Vaylet, Pl du Marché, 12500 Espalion - T: 0565440918
Ethnology Museum 10453

Espaly-Saint-Marcel

Musée-Diorama du Pèlerinage du 19 Mars, 43000 Espaly-Saint-Marcel - T: 0471091671
Religious Arts Museum 10454

Espaon

Musée Paysan de la Save, 32220 Espaon - T: 0562625495
Local Museum 10455

Esperaza

Dinosauria, Musée des Dinosaures, Av de la Gare, 11260 Esperaza - T: 0468740208/2688
Archaeological Museum / Natural History Museum 10456

Musée de la Chapellerie, Av de la Gare, 11260 Esperaza - T: 0468740075, Fax: 0468740075. Head: M. Boulbes
Fine Arts Museum
Arts, traditions 10457

Espezel

Musée de l'Outil, 11340 Espezel - T: 0468741644/203770
Science&Tech Museum 10458

Esse

Ecomusée des Traditions et Arts Populaires, Pays d'Accueil de la Roche aux Fées, 35150 Esse - T: 0299471036. Head: Alain Durand
Folklore Museum - 1988
Prehist, crafts, household articles, costume, tools 10459

Essigny-le-Grand

Mémorial Musée Privé de Souvenirs de la Grande Guerre 14-18, 1 Rue des Marronniers, 02690 Essigny-le-Grand - T: 0323633816
Military Museum 10460

Essises

Musée Historique 1814, Rue d'En-Haut, 02570 Essises - T: 0323698809/521304
Military Museum 10461

Essoyes

Maison de la Vigne, 10360 Essoyes - T: 0325296464/6047
Special Museum 10462

Estagel

Espace Muséal Arago, 66310 Estagel - T: 0468290032
Special Museum 10463

Expo Rétro Catalane, Cellier Dona, 66310 Estagel - T: 0468290032
Folklore Museum 10464

Estissac

Musée de la Mémoire Paysanne, Grande-Rue, Hameau de Thuisy, 10190 Estissac - T: 0325404581
Agriculture Museum 10465

Estivareilles

Musée de l'Armée Secrète dans la Loire → Musée d'Histoire du 20e Siècle

Musée d'Histoire du 20e Siècle, Rue du Couvent, 42380 Estivareilles - T: 0477502920, Fax: 0477508050. Head: Henri Pailler
Historical Museum 10466

Etagnac

Musée-Château de Rochebrune, 16150 Etagnac - T: 0545890042/2065, Fax: 0545893170
Military Museum / Decorative Arts Museum 10467

Etampes

Musée d'Étampes → Musée Municipal d'Étampes

Musée Municipal d'Étampes, Hôtel de Ville, 91150 Etampes - T: 0169926912, Fax: 0169926903, E-mail: musee@mairie-etampes.fr, Internet: http://www.mairie-etampes.fr.
Local Museum - 1875
Prehistoric Celtic finds, Gallo-Roman and medieval items, paintings, sculpture, natural history 10468

Etaples

Musée de la Marine, Ancienne Halle La Criée, Blvd de Impératrice, 62630 Etaples - T: 0321097721
Science&Tech Museum 10469

Musée Quentovic, 8 Pl du Général de Gaulle, 62630 Etaples - T: 0321940247. Head: Lionel François
Archaeological Museum - 1967
Archeology, mineralogy, geology, local hist 10470

Étaules

Musée Ostréicole, 17750 Étaules - T: 0546364278
Special Museum 10471

Etel

Ecomusée, Maison de Pays, 56410 Etel - T: 0277553519
Local Museum 10472

Eternoz

Musée des Métiers Ruraux, Ancienne Forge, 25330 Eternoz - T: 0381866508
Local Museum 10473

Étiolles

Centre d'Exposition Archéologique d'Étiolles, Orangerie du Domaine des Hauldres, Rue du Général-de-Gaulle, 91450 Étiolles - T: 0169891075
Archaeological Museum 10474

Musée en Plein Air de Sculptures Contemporaines, Office National des Forêts, Centre d'Information, Faisanderie de la Forêt de Sénart, 91450 Étiolles - T: 0160755417, Fax: 0160751364, Internet: http://www.onf.fr
Fine Arts Museum 10475

Etival-Clairefontaine

Ferme-Musée 1900, 11 Rue Sainte-Odile, 88480 Etival-Clairefontaine - T: 0325418935
Folklore Museum 10476

Etretat

Collection du Château Les Aygues, 76790 Etretat - T: 0235289277
Fine Arts Museum / Decorative Arts Museum 10477

Musée Nungesser-et-Coli, Sur la Falaise d'Amont, 76790 Etretat - T: 0235270747/0521
Science&Tech Museum 10478

Etueffont

Forge-Musée, 2 Rue de Lamadeleine, 90170 Etueffont - T: 0384546041/6040
Science&Tech Museum 10479

Eu

Musée Louis-Philippe, Château, 76260 Eu - T: 0235864400, Fax: 0235502779. Head: Martine Bailleux-Delbecq
Decorative Arts Museum - 1973
Furniture of King Louis-Philippe, 19th century wood floors, art objects and furniture designed by Viollet-le-Duc, glass, local folklore - library 10480

Évigny

Écomusée de la Vie Rurale, Ancienne Ferme, 08090 Évigny - T: 0324582141
Folklore Museum 10481

Evol

Exposition d'Art et d'Histoire, 66360 Evol - T: 0468970972/555993
Historical Museum / Fine Arts Museum 10482

Evreux

Musée d'Evreux, Ancien Evêché, 6 Rue Charles Corbeau, 27000 Evreux - T: 0232315229. Head: G. Guillot-Chene
Archaeological Museum / Decorative Arts Museum - 1833
Prehistoric and Gallo-Roman finds, bronze Jupiter statue, medieval art and enamel, art objects, 18th c furnishings, inlays, painting, ceramics 10483

Evry

Les Trains de Saint-Eutrope, Musée Vivant, Ville-Nouvelle, 91000 Evry - T: 0160781864
Science&Tech Museum 10484

Excideuil

Musée Ferroviaire La Lorraine en Périgord, 24160 Excideuil - T: 0553624649/9556
Science&Tech Museum 10485

Eygalières

Musée du Vieil Eygalières, Ancienne Chapelle du XVIIe s, 13810 Eygalières - T: 0490959152
Local Museum / Archaeological Museum 10486

Eyguières

Musée d'Art et d'Histoire, Rue de l'Hôpital, 13430 Eyguières - T: 0490598244
Fine Arts Museum / Historical Museum 10487

Eymet

Musée d'Art et d'Histoire, Château, 24500 Eymet - T: 0553237495/830276
Fine Arts Museum / Historical Museum 10488

Eymoutiers

Collection de Véhicules de Collection, Rempnat, 87120 Eymoutiers - T: 0555699894
Science&Tech Museum 10489

Espace Minéralogique Minéraux Couleur Nature, Rte de Nedde, 87120 Eymoutiers - T: 0555692774. Head: Marcel Tabeaud
Natural History Museum 10490

Exposition d'Art Contemporain, Mairie, 87120 Eymoutiers - T: 0555691021
Fine Arts Museum 10491

Musée des Trains-Jouets, Fougerolles (Haute-Vienne), 87120 Eymoutiers - T: 0555691144
Science&Tech Museum 10492

Musée Rebeyrolle, Espace Paul-Rebeyrolle, Rte de Nedde, 87120 Eymoutiers - T: 0555695888/96, Fax: 0555695893, E-mail: espace.rebeyrolle@wanadoo.fr
Fine Arts Museum 10493

Eyne

Circuits-Exposition de Musée de Cerdagne, 66800 Eyne - T: 0468047866
Natural History Museum / Archaeological Museum 10494

Eze

Art Sacré, Chapelle des Pénitentsblancs, 06360 Eze - T: 0492106060/93412600
Religious Arts Museum 10495

Exposition sur la Parfumerie, Galimard, Pl Général-de-Gaulle, 06360 Eze - T: 0493411070, Fax: 0493412761, E-mail: galimard@galimard.com, Internet: http://www.galimard.com. Head: Jean-Pierre Roux
Special Museum 10496

Maison de la Nature, Parc de la Grande-Corniche, 06360 Eze - T: 0493411587
Natural History Museum 10497

Musée Local d'Art, Rue de la Paix, 06360 Eze - T: 0492106060
Fine Arts Museum 10498

Ezy-sur-Eure

Musée du Peigne, Art et Traditions, 71 Rue Pasteur, Jardin de Brensbach, 27530 Ezy-sur-Eure - T: 0237646469
Special Museum   10499

Fabrezan

Musée Charles-Cros, Mairie, 11200 Fabrezan - T: 0468436111
Special Museum   10500

Fain-les-Moutiers

Musée Sainte-Catherine-Laboure, 21500 Fain-les-Moutiers - T: 0380967065
Ethnology Museum   10501

Falaise

Automates Avenue, Blvd de la Libération, 14700 Falaise - T: 0231900243, Fax: 0231900726, E-mail: automates@mail.cpod.fr, Internet: http://www.cpod.com/monoweb/automates-avenue/. Head: Céline Letourneur
Special Museum   10502

Musée Août-1944, La Bataille de la Poche de Falaise, Rte de Bretagne, Chemin des Roches, 14700 Falaise - T: 0231903719, Fax: 0233243699. Head: Michel Leloup
Military Museum / Local Museum / Historical Museum   10503

Falicon

Collection Jules-Romains, Auberge Bellevue, 06550 Falicon
Special Museum   10504

Fanjeaux

Maison Saint-Dominique, 11270 Fanjeaux - T: 0468247164
Decorative Arts Museum   10505

Fargniers

Musée Départemental de la Résistance et de la Déportation en Picardie, Pl Carnegie, 02700 Fargniers - T: 0323579377
Military Museum   10506

Fargues-sur-Ourbise

Ecomusée de Saint-Joseph, Forêt Domaniale de Campet, 47700 Fargues-sur-Ourbise - T: 0553930452
Folklore Museum / Natural History Museum   10507

Faugères

L'Oustal des Abeilles, La Falette Soumartre, 34600 Faugères - T: 0467230594
Natural History Museum   10508

Faverges

Musée Archéologique de Viuz-Faverges, Rte de Viuz, 74210 Faverges - T: 0450324599, Fax: 0450324599, E-mail: musee-de-viuz@wanadoo.fr, Internet: http://www.sav.org/fviuz.html. Head: Michel Duret
Archaeological Museum   10509

Faverolles (Cantal)

Château du Chassan, 15390 Faverolles (Cantal) - T: 0471234391
Local Museum   10510

Faymoreau

Musée de la Mine, Maison de la Mine, La Verrerie, Haute-Terrasse, 85240 Faymoreau - T: 0251004376
Science&Tech Museum   10511

Fécamp

Musée des Arts et de l'Enfance, 21 Rue Alexandre Legros, 76400 Fécamp - T: 0235283199, Fax: 0235290655. Head: Marie-Hélène Desjardins-Ménégalli
Ethnology Museum / Fine Arts Museum - 1879 Earthenware, baby bottles, furniture, painting 10512

Musée des Terre-Neuvas et de la Pêche, 27 Blvd Albert 1er, 76400 Fécamp - T: 0235283199, Fax: 0235290655. Head: Marie-Hélène Desjardins-Ménégalli
Science&Tech Museum / Ethnology Museum - 1988 Old model boats, traditional equipment and ex-voto, naval techniques, fishing, paintings 10513

Palais Bénédictine, 110 Rue Alexandre-Le-Grand, 76400 Fécamp - T: 0235102610, Fax: 0235285081, E-mail: palais.benedictine@bacardi.com, Internet: http://www.benedictine.fr. Head: Gérard Mathias
Special Museum - 1863 Statues, sculptures, paintings 10514

Fegreac

Musée-Maison du Canal, 1 Rue du Canal, 44460 Fegreac - T: 0240912496
Special Museum   10515

Felleries

Musée-Moulin des Bois Jolis, Musée Vivant, Ancien Moulin à Eau, 59740 Felleries - T: 0327590064/606611
Science&Tech Museum   10516

Felletin

Exposition de Tapisseries, Église du Château, 23500 Felletin - T: 0555665460, Fax: 0555675712, E-mail: ot.felletin@wanadoo.fr
Decorative Arts Museum   10517

Fénetrange

Musée Historique, Château, 57930 Fénetrange - T: 0387075378
Historical Museum   10518

Fenneviller

Musée du Vélo, 54540 Fenneviller - T: 0383422596/1379/1080
Science&Tech Museum   10519

Ferney-Voltaire

Château de Voltaire/L'Auberge de l'Europe, Allée du Château, 01210 Ferney-Voltaire - T: 0450400540, Fax: 0450400546, E-mail: contact@auberge-europe.org, Internet: http://www.auberge-europe.org. Head: Hervé Loichemol
Historic Site   10520

Ferrette

Musée Municipal (closed)   10521

Ferrière-Poussarou

Musée Archéologique, Maison du Parc Natural Régional du Haut-Languedoc, 34360 Ferrière-Poussarou - T: 0467380281
Archaeological Museum   10522

Ferrières-les-Verreries

Verrerie de Coulonbrines, Archéosite de la Renaissance, 34190 Ferrières-les-Verreries - T: 0467590507
Decorative Arts Museum / Historical Museum 10523

Ferrières (Seine-et-Marne)

Château-Musée, Château de Ferrières, 77164 Ferrières (Seine-et-Marne) - T: 0164663125
Decorative Arts Museum   10524

Ferrières-sur-Sichon

Musée de Glozel, Ferme de la Famille Fradin, 03250 Ferrières-sur-Sichon - T: 0470411296
Archaeological Museum   10525

Ferrières (Tarn)

Musée du Protestantisme en Haut Languedoc, Société de l'Histoire du Protestantisme Français, Maison du Luthier, 81260 Ferrières (Tarn) - T: 0563504793/740549. Head: Hélène Balfet
Historical Museum - 1967 Liturgical objects (17-20th c) - archives, library 10526

Musée Jacquaire, Château, 81260 Ferrières (Tarn) - T: 0563740353
Religious Arts Museum   10527

Fessenheim

Musée de la Hardt, Maison Schoelcher, 13 Rue des Seigneurs, 68740 Fessenheim - T: 0389486099, 0608998157, Fax: 0389485907. Head: Emile Beringer
Local Museum   10528

Fessy

Musée d'Art et de Folklore Régional, N 203, 74890 Fessy - T: 0450363193
Folklore Museum   10529

Feurs

Musée d'Assier, 3 Rue Victor de Laprade, Parc de Fleurs, 42110 Feurs - T: 0477260527. Head: Daniel Pouget
Local Museum   10530

Feytiat

Musée-Maison des Vanniers, Mas Gauthier, 87220 Feytiat - T: 0555484300
Ethnology Museum   10531

Figeac

Musée Champollion, 4 Rue Champollion, 46100 Figeac - T: 0565503108, Fax: 0565501679. Head: Marie Hélène Pottier
Archaeological Museum - 1986 Memorabilia of the archeologist J.-Fr. Champollion, the decipherer of the Rosetta Stone, egyptian coll 10532

Musée du Moyen Âge et de la Chevalerie, Commanderie Templière, 41 Rue Gambetta, 46100 Figeac
Historical Museum / Military Museum   10533

Musée du Vieux Figeac, Hôtel de la Monnaie, Pl Vival, 46100 Figeac - T: 0565340625, Fax: 0565500458, E-mail: figeac@wanadoo.fr., Internet: http://www.quercy.net/frgeac. Head: Marie Hélène Pottier
Local Museum
Ethnology, archeology   10534

Filain

Maison-Forte Musée, 70230 Filain - T: 0384783066/976006
Natural History Museum / Fine Arts Museum 10535

Fillières

Musée Campagnard Agricole, 45 Grande Rue, 54560 Fillières - T: 0382250072
Agriculture Museum   10536

Firmi

Musée d'Art et d'Histoire, 12300 Firmi - T: 0565634302/4194
Fine Arts Museum / Historical Museum   10537

Firminy

Ecomusée des Bruneaux, Château des Bruneaux, 3 Rue de Chanzy, 42700 Firminy - T: 0477893846, Fax: 0477892788
Local Museum   10538

Musée du Jouet, 3 Rue de Chanzy, 42700 Firminy - T: 0477893846, Fax: 0477892788
Special Museum   10539

Fismes

Musée Municipal de Préhistoire, 26 Rue René Latillay, 51170 Fismes - T: 0326488128, Fax: 0326481209
Archaeological Museum / Local Museum   10540

Fixin

Musée du Premier Empire, Musée Noisot, 21220 Fixin - T: 0380524562, Fax: 0380510964
Local Museum   10541

Musée Viticole Charles-Bernard, 10 Rue Abbé Chevallier, 21220 Fixin - T: 0380524551, Fax: 0380588076, E-mail: closstlouis@yahoo.fr. Head: Charles Bernard
Agriculture Museum
Viticulture   10542

Flamarens

Ecomusée de la Lomagne, Ferme de la Hitte, 32340 Flamarens - T: 0562286295/7698
Local Museum   10543

Flavigny-sur-Ozerain

Musée Archéologique de l'Ancienne Abbaye, 21150 Flavigny-sur-Ozerain - T: 0380962088, Fax: 0380962143. Head: Catherine Troubat
Archaeological Museum   10544

Flers

Musée de la Blanchardière (closed)   10545

Musée du Château, Château, 61100 Flers, mail addr: BP 229, 61104 Flers - T: 0233646649, Fax: 0233646633, E-mail: musee.flers@worldonline.fr. Head: Laurence Chesneau-Dupin
Fine Arts Museum / Decorative Arts Museum - 1874 17th-20th century paintings, regional hist, folk art and local traditions, decorative art and furniture 10546

Fleury-devant-Douaumont

Musée Mémorial de la Bataille de Verdun, 55100 Fleury-devant-Douaumont - T: 0329843534
Military Museum   10547

Fleury-la-Forêt

Centre Permanent d'Exposition de Poupées Anciennes, Château, 27480 Fleury-la-Forêt - T: 0232495434
Special Museum   10548

Fléville-devant-Nancy

Château de la Renaissance et Donjon de 1320, 54710 Fléville-devant-Nancy - T: 0383256471, Fax: 0383258493. Head: T. de Lambel
Local Museum / Decorative Arts Museum   10549

Floing

Musée de la Résistance et des Anciens Combattants, Cour de la Grotte-à-Gaulier, 08200 Floing - T: 0324292235/1742
Historical Museum   10550

Florange

Salle Gallo-Romaine, Complexe de Betange, 57190 Florange - T: 0382593260/573603
Archaeological Museum   10551

Foissac

Grotte et Parc Préhistorique, Musée Cavernicole, 12260 Foissac - T: 0565647704
Natural History Museum   10552

Foix

Musée de la Chasse et de la Nature, 09000 Foix - T: 0561650402
Special Museum / Natural History Museum   10553

Musée de l'Ariège, Château, 09000 Foix - T: 0561655605, Fax: 0561655605. Head: Anne-Marie Albertin
Local Museum - 1882 Prehistory, antiquity, exhibits on the Middle Ages, folklore, folk art, and customs 10554

Fondremand

Musée Historique, Donjon Roman, 70190 Fondremand - T: 0384782305
Local Museum   10555

Font-Romeu-Odeillo-Via

Musée de l'Insolite, Av E.-Brousse, 66120 Font-Romeu-Odeillo-Via - T: 0468300781
Historical Museum   10556

Fontaine-Chaalis

Musée Jacquemart-André, Abbaye de Chaalis, 60300 Fontaine-Chaalis - T: 0344540402, Fax: 0344540790, E-mail: chaalis@aol.com. Head: A. de Virieu
Fine Arts Museum / Decorative Arts Museum Colls of the castle (paintings, furniture, sculpture), Jean-Jacques Rousseau coll, 13th century monastery, chapel with Renaissance frescoes 10557

Fontaine-de-Vaucluse

Le Monde Souterrain, Norbert-Casteret, Chemin de la Fontaine, 84800 Fontaine-de-Vaucluse - T: 0490203413
Natural History Museum   10558

Moulin à Papier Vallis-Clausa, Chemin du Gouffre, 84800 Fontaine-de-Vaucluse - T: 0490203414, Fax: 0490202340. Head: P.M. Micol
Science&Tech Museum
Paper mill   10559

Musée-Bibliothèque F. Petrarque, Rive Gauche de la Sorgue, 84800 Fontaine-de-Vaucluse - T: 0490203720, Fax: 0490205345. Head: Eve Duperray
Library with Exhibitions - 1986
library   10560

Musée d'Histoire 1939-1945 L'Appel de la Liberté, Chemin du Gouffre, 84800 Fontaine-de-Vaucluse - T: 0490202400, Fax: 0490205345, E-mail: musee.dhistoire_39-45@libertysurf.fr, Internet: http://www.perso.libertysurf.fr/musee.dhistoire_39-45. Head: Eve Duperray
Historical Museum - 1990 Daily life and commitment (1940-1945) - library 10561

Musée du Santon et des Traditions de Provence, Galerie Vallis-Clausa, Chemin de la Fontaine, 84800 Fontaine-de-Vaucluse - T: 0490202083
Folklore Museum   10562

Musée Historique de la Justice et des Châtiments, 84800 Fontaine-de-Vaucluse - T: 0490202458
Special Museum / Historical Museum   10563

Fontaine-Française

Château-Musée du XVIIe Siècle, 21610 Fontaine-Française - T: 0380758040
Decorative Arts Museum   10564

Musée Archéologique, Mairie, 21610 Fontaine-Française - T: 0380758121/8016
Archaeological Museum   10565

Fontaine-Henry

Musée-Château de Fontaine-Henry, 14610 Fontaine-Henry - T: 0231800042, Fax: 0231081905, E-mail: fonthenry@aol.com. Head: Comtesse d' Oilliamson
Fine Arts Museum   10566

Fontaine-les-Coteaux

Musée Vivant de l'Arbre, Rte de Montoire à Troo, Parc Botanique de la Fosse, 41800 Fontaine-les-Coteaux - T: 0254853863, Fax: 0254852039
Natural History Museum   10567

Fontainebleau

Musée des Pompiers, Caserne des Sapeurs-Pompiers, 2 Pl Orloff, 77300 Fontainebleau - T: 0164224935/36
Science&Tech Museum   10568

Musée Napoléonien d'Art et d'Histoire Militaires, 88 Rue Saint-Honoré, 77300 Fontainebleau - T: 0164224980, poste 424 (mairie)
Military Museum 10569

Musée National du Château de Fontainebleau, 77300 Fontainebleau - T: 0160715070, Fax: 0160715071. Head: Amaury Lefébure
Fine Arts Museum / Decorative Arts Museum / Historic Site
4 Div: Great Apartments, Napoleon I Museum, Chinese Museum, Private Apartments; architecture, decoration, paintings, objects 10570

Fontenay-le-Comte

Château-Musée de Terre-Neuve, Château, 85200 Fontenay-le-Comte - T: 0251691775/500083, Fax: 0251500083. Head: Henri de Fontenivre
Decorative Arts Museum 10571

Musée Vendéen, Pl du 137e R.I., 85200 Fontenay-le-Comte - T: 0251693131. Head: M. Vital
Local Museum 10572

Fontenay-les-Briis

Musée Le Libertaire, 20 Rue du Bon Puits, 91640 Fontenay-les-Briis - T: 0164908018
Fine Arts Museum 10573

Fontenay-sur-Mer

Musée de l'Automobile Miniature, Château de Courcy, 50310 Fontenay-sur-Mer - T: 0233214110, Fax: 0233214110
Science&Tech Museum / Special Museum
About 7,200 small motorcars (1:43) 10574

Fontenoy-en-Puisaye

Centre Régional d'Art Contemporain, Château du Tremblay, 89520 Fontenoy-en-Puisaye - T: 0386440218
Fine Arts Museum 10575

Musée M'Am Jeanne, Château du Tremblay, 89520 Fontenoy-en-Puisaye - T: 0386440218
Fine Arts Museum 10576

Fontenoy-le-Château

Musée de la Broderie, 3 Pl Gilbert, 88240 Fontenoy-le-Château - T: 0329304048/363309
Folklore Museum 10577

Fontet

Musée des Monuments d'Allumettes, Couture, 33190 Fontet - T: 0556712045/612583
Special Museum 10578

Fontvieille

Archéosites Gallo-Romains, 13990 Fontvieille - T: 0490546749
Archaeological Museum 10579

Château Montauban, 13990 Fontvieille - T: 0490546749
Special Museum 10580

Espace Muséal de Beaux-Arts, Parc des Cordes, 13990 Fontvieille - T: 0490546944
Archaeological Museum / Fine Arts Museum 10581

Musée du Vieux Moulin de Daudet, Moulin Saint-Pierre, Av des Moulins, 13990 Fontvieille - T: 0490546749
Historic Site 10582

Forcalquier

Couvent des Cordeliers, Blvd des Martyrs, 04300 Forcalquier - T: 0492750238
Religious Arts Museum 10583

Musée Municipal, 1 Pl du Bourguet, 04300 Forcalquier - T: 0492752002/14
Local Museum - 1912
Archeology, furniture and items of daily life (XVIIth XVIIth and XVIIIth c, faiences 10584

Forges-les-Eaux

Musée de la Faïence, Rue Maréchal-Leclerc, 76440 Forges-les-Eaux - T: 0235905210, Fax: 0235903580
Decorative Arts Museum 10585

Musée de la Résistance et de la Déportation, Rue du Maréchal-Leclerc, 76440 Forges-les-Eaux - T: 0235905210/5390/3480
Historical Museum 10586

Fos-sur-Mer

Village-Musée, Pl de l'Hôtel de Ville, 13270 Fos-sur-Mer - T: 0442052757, Fax: 0442055942, E-mail: bienvenue@fos.tourisme.com, Internet: http://www.fos.tourisme.com. Head: Christine Gonzalez
Local Museum 10587

Foucherans

Musée Rural, 25660 Foucherans - T: 0381867320
Local Museum 10588

Fouesnant

Patrimoine Populaire, Axone Musique, 29170 Fouesnant - T: 0298949495
Music Museum 10589

Fougax-et-Barrineuf

Collections de Molinologie, Moulin de l'Espine, 09300 Fougax-et-Barrineuf - T: 0561018193, 0561675418
Science&Tech Museum 10590

Musée du Cochon et du Sanglier, 09300 Fougax-et-Barrineuf - T: 0561016408
Special Museum 10591

Fougères (Ille-et-Vilaine)

Musée de la Chaussure, Château, Pl Pierre Simon, 35300 Fougères (Ille-et-Vilaine) - T: 0299991898
Special Museum 10592

Musée Emmanuel de la Villéon, 51 Rue Nationale, 35300 Fougères (Ille-et-Vilaine) - T: 0299948800. Head: M. Durnoff
Fine Arts Museum - 1980
Works of the impressionist painter Emmanuel de la Villéon (1858-1944) 10593

Fougères-sur-Bièvre

Château de Fougères-sur-Bièvre, 41120 Fougères-sur-Bièvre - T: 0254202718
Decorative Arts Museum 10594

Fougerolles-du-Plessis

Château-Musée de Goué, 53190 Fougerolles-du-Plessis - T: 0243055860
Decorative Arts Museum / Fine Arts Museum 10595

Fougerolles (Haute-Saône)

Ecomusée de la Distillerie et du Pays Fougerollais, Petit Fahy, 70220 Fougerolles (Haute-Saône) - T: 0384491253. Head: Marcel Saire
Special Museum / Historical Museum 10596

Musée des Eaux de Vie, Ferme de Beaumont, Rte Nationale 57, 70220 Fougerolles (Haute-Saône) - T: 0384491066, Fax: 0384495856, E-mail: - hugues.de.miscault@wanadoo.fr
Special Museum 10597

Fouras

Musée d'Art et d'Histoire, Au Donjon, 17450 Fouras - T: 0546846296/6069
Local Museum 10598

Fources

Musée d'Arts Populaires, Village, 32250 Fources - T: 0562280080
Folklore Museum / Agriculture Museum 10599

Fourmies

Ecomusée de la Région Fourmies-Trélon, Pl Maria Blondeau, 59612 Fourmies Cedex - T: 0327606611/574472, Fax: 0327602388, E-mail: mgoujard@nordnet.fr
Local Museum
Regional hist, agriculture, industry 10600

Fournets-Luisans

Musée de la Ferme à Tué du Montagnon, Hameau de Grandfontaine, 25390 Fournets-Luisans - T: 0381676869/435786, Fax: 0381676868
Folklore Museum 10601

Fourquevaux

Château, 31450 Fourquevaux - T: 0562717103
Decorative Arts Museum 10602

Fraisse-sur-Agout

Ecomusée de la Ferme de l'Espinousse Prat Alaric, Maison du Parc Naturel Régional du Haut-Languedoc, 34330 Fraisse-sur-Agout - T: 0467976446/6114
Folklore Museum / Science&Tech Museum 10603

Francheville

Musée de la Ferronnerie et des Métiers Annexes, Pl du Village, 27160 Francheville - T: 0232326987/6171
Science&Tech Museum 10604

Fransèches

Musée-Hameau de Sculptures XIXe s, Masgot, 23480 Fransèches - T: 0555669888
Fine Arts Museum 10605

Fréhel

Château-Musée du Fort La Latte, 22240 Fréhel - T: 0296414031
Military Museum 10606

Freissinières

Espace Musée, Moulin des Ribes, 05310 Freissinières - T: 0492209460
Local Museum 10607

Fréjus

Collections du Site Préhistorique, Parc Aquatica, 93 Le Capou, 83600 Fréjus - T: 0494535858/512436
Science&Tech Museum 10608

Mémorial des Guerres en Indochine, Rte Nationale 7, Av du Général Cailliès, 83600 Fréjus - T: 0494444290
Historical Museum 10609

Musée Archéologique Municipal de Fréjus, Pl Calvini, 83600 Fréjus - T: 0494521578, Fax: 0494538501, E-mail: musee.frejus@wanadoo.fr, Internet: http://www.ville-frejus.fr. Head: Isabelle Béraud
Archaeological Museum 10610

Musée des Troupes de Marine, Quartier Lecocq, Rte de Bagnols-en-Forêt, 83600 Fréjus - T: 0494408175
Military Museum 10611

Musée la Villa Aurélienne, Parc Aurélien, Av J.-Cailliès, 83600 Fréjus - T: 0494531130
Fine Arts Museum 10612

Fréland

Maison du Pays Welche, 2 Rue de la Rochette, 68240 Fréland - T: 0389475713/719052
Folklore Museum 10613

Fresnay-sur-Sarthe

Musée des Coiffes, Tour de l'Ancien Château, Pl Bassum, 72130 Fresnay-sur-Sarthe - T: 0243972220/2375
Special Museum 10614

Fresneaux-Montchevreuil

Musée de la Boutique des Boutons de Nacre Lormeteau, 59 Rue de la Patte d'Oie, 60240 Fresneaux-Montchevreuil - T: 0344844599
Special Museum 10615

Fresnes (Val-de-Marne)

Écomusée de Fresnes, Ferme de Cottinville, 41 Rue Maurice Ténine, 94260 Fresnes (Val-de-Marne) - T: 0149845737/5735, Fax: 0146681033, E-mail: fresnes94.ecomusee@free.fr. Head: Alexandre Delarge
Local Museum / Ethnology Museum 10616

Musée-Maison d'Art Contemporain Chaillioux, 5 Rue Julien-Chaillioux, 94260 Fresnes (Val-de-Marne) - T: 0146685831, Fax: 0146684528. Head: Marcel Lubac
Fine Arts Museum 10617

Frespech

Musée du Foie Gras, Souleilles, 47140 Frespech - T: 0553412324, Fax: 0553413190, E-mail: souleill@terre-net.fr
Special Museum 10618

Freyming-Merlebach

Ecomusée des Houillères de Lorraine, Mine-Image Cuvelette, 57800 Freyming-Merlebach - T: 0387870854
Science&Tech Museum 10619

Musée Historique et Militaire, Pl de l'Hôtel de Ville, 57800 Freyming-Merlebach - T: 0387816575/15. Head: Eliane Olszak
Historical Museum / Military Museum 10620

Freyssenet

Musée Agricole du Verdus, À 6 km au Sud-Ouest de Privas, 07000 Freyssenet - T: 0475642740
Agriculture Museum 10621

Frizon

Maison de la Vie Rurale, Rue de la Croix, 88440 Frizon - T: 0329679090/1730
Agriculture Museum 10622

Frolois

Château de Frolois, 21150 Frolois - T: 0380962292
Decorative Arts Museum 10623

Frontignan

Musée d'Art et d'Histoire, 4bis Rue Lucien Salette, 34110 Frontignan - T: 0467463119/482669. Head: Jean Valette
Local Museum - 1973 10624

Fruges

Musée Abbé Deletoille, Fondation Boudenoot, 1 Rue du Général Leclerc, 62310 Fruges - T: 0321044076
Local Museum 10625

Frugières-le-Pin

Musée Joseph Lhoménède, 43230 Frugières-le-Pin - T: 0471764215/4237
Historical Museum 10626

Fumay

Musée de l'Ardoise, Rue des Fusillés, 08170 Fumay - T: 0324412755/420526
Science&Tech Museum 10627

Fumel

Musée du Compagnonnage du Tour de France, 10 Rue Waldeck-Rousseau, 47500 Fumel - T: 0553711552
Special Museum 10628

Gabarret

Maison du Gabardan, Demeure de 1456, 40310 Gabarret - T: 0558443495
Local Museum 10629

Gabian

Dépôt Archéologique, 34320 Gabian - T: 0467246518
Archaeological Museum 10630

Gacé

Musée de la Dame aux Camélias, Château, 61230 Gacé - T: 0233355024
Special Museum 10631

Gagny

Musée Français de Spéléologie, 20 Rue Contant, 93220 Gagny - T: 0143024435
Natural History Museum 10632

Gaillac

Musée des Arts et Traditions Populaires, Abbaye Saint-Michel, 81600 Gaillac - T: 0563410381, Fax: 0563573345. Head: Bertrand de Vivies
Folklore Museum - 1934 10633

Musée des Beaux-Arts, Château de Foucaud-d'Alzon, Av Dom-Vaysette, 81600 Gaillac - T: 0563571825, Fax: 0563575683
Fine Arts Museum 10634

Musée d'Histoire Naturelle Philadelphe Thomas, 2 Pl Philadelphe Thomas, 81600 Gaillac - T: 0563573631, Fax: 0563575683. Head: Bertrand de Vivies
Natural History Museum - 1912
Fossil coll, paleontology, mineralogy, ornithology - library 10635

Gallician

Exposition d'Histoire Naturelle, 30600 Gallician - T: 0466733450
Natural History Museum 10636

Ganges

Musée Fabrier de l'Industrie de la Soie, 34190 Ganges - T: 0467739287
Science&Tech Museum 10637

Gannat

Musée Municipal du Château, Pl Rantian, Château, 03800 Gannat - T: 0470900050/2378
Local Museum 10638

Gap

Musée Départemental des Hautes-Alpes, 6 Av Maréchal Foch, 05000 Gap - T: 0492510158, Fax: 0492526430, E-mail: musee.gap05@wanadoo.fr. Head: Christine Cordina-Baixe
Local Museum / Natural History Museum - 1906
Ornithology, paintings, prehistoric and Stone Age items, coins, ethnology, ceramics 10639

Gardanne

Musée Gardanne Autrefois, 21 Rue Courbet, 13120 Gardanne - T: 0442510273
Historical Museum / Folklore Museum 10640

Gargilesse-Dampierre

Maison-Musée de George Sand, Villa Algira, 36190 Gargilesse-Dampierre - T: 0254478414/8311
Special Museum 10641

Garin

Collection Archéologique, 31110 Garin
Archaeological Museum 10642

Gaujacq

Château de Sourdis, 40330 Gaujacq - T: 0558890101
Local Museum 10643

Gavaudun

Musée de la Préhistoire Pierre Blot, Communs du Château Fort, 47150 Gavaudun - T: 0553408229
Archaeological Museum 10644

Gelos

Haras National, Av Général Leclerc, 64110 Gelos - T: 0559066057
Historical Museum 10645

Genas

Centre d'Art Contemporain, Pl de la Libération, 69740 Genas - T: 0478901305
Fine Arts Museum 10646

Genay

Musée Montenot, 21140 Genay - T: 0380970034
Archaeological Museum 10647

Generac

Musée de la Tonnellerie, Château, 30510 Generac - T: 0466013114
Special Museum 10648

Generagues

Musée du Santon Animé, Pl du Tilleul, 30140 Generagues - T: 0466616674
Special Museum 10649

Genneteil

Collections du Château du Breil de Foin, 49490 Genneteil - T: 0241822513, Fax: 0241890036, E-mail: breildefoin@libertysurf.fr. Head: Jerome de Boissard
Decorative Arts Museum / Archaeological Museum 10650

Ger

Musée Régional de la Poterie, 50850 Ger - T: 0233059880
Decorative Arts Museum 10651

Gérardmer

Musée de la Guerre 1914-1918, 11 Rue de l'Église, 88400 Gérardmer - T: 0329608028
Historical Museum 10652

Gerberoy

Musée Municipal, Mairie, 60380 Gerberoy - T: 0344823158/3363, Fax: 0344825090, E-mail: mairie.gerberoy@wanadoo.fr
Local Museum / Archaeological Museum 10653

Germaine

Musée du Bûcheron, 51160 Germaine - T: 0326594444. Head: Sylviane Jonet
Ethnology Museum 10654

Germigny-des-Prés

Musée de Germigny et Grange Germignonne, 45110 Germigny-des-Prés - T: 0238582797
Religious Arts Museum 10655

Gertwiller

Musée du Pain d'Épices d'Alsace et des Douceurs d'Autrefois, 110 Rue Principale, 67140 Gertwiller - T: 0388089352
Special Museum / Folklore Museum 10656

Musée Vini-Viticole, 14-15 Rue Principale, 67140 Gertwiller - T: 0388080754
Special Museum 10657

Gétigné

Musée-Maison du Jardinier, Domaine de la Garenne-Lemot, 44190 Gétigné - T: 0240547585
Special Museum 10658

Ghyvelde

Écomusée de la Flandre Maritime Bommelaers Wall, Rte de Furnes, 59254 Ghyvelde - T: 0328201103
Local Museum 10659

Gien

Musée de la Faïencerie de Gien, 78 Pl de la Victoire, 45500 Gien - T: 0238670005, Fax: 0238674492. Head: Pierre Jeufroy
Decorative Arts Museum 10660

Musée International de la Chasse, Château, 45500 Gien - T: 0238676969, 0238050399, Fax: 0238380732, E-mail: museedelachasse@wanadoo.fr
Decorative Arts Museum / Special Museum / Fine Arts Museum - 1952
Tapestries, paintings, hunting weapons, screens by the animal painter Desportes, etchings and documents on hunting, trophies, horns, falconry, venery 10661

Giffaumont-Champaubert

Musée-Expo de la Grange des Abeilles, 51290 Giffaumont-Champaubert - T: 0326726197/739202
Special Museum 10662

Gignac (Hérault)

Maison du Fleuve Hérault, Barrage de la Meuse, 34150 Gignac (Hérault) - T: 0467579900, Fax: 0467579890, E-mail: maison_fleuvre@cg34.fr
Science&Tech Museum / Natural History Museum 10663

Gigondas

Musée de la Civilisation de la Vigne et du Vin, Château de Saint-Cosme, 84190 Gigondas - T: 0490658697
Special Museum 10664

Gilley

Collection d'Automates, Les Coteys Tuyé du Papy Gaby, 25650 Gilley - T: 0381143303
Historical Museum 10665

Gimont

Collection Lapidaire, Abbaye Cistérienne de Planselve, 32200 Gimont - T: 0562677787
Archaeological Museum 10666

Musée Archéologique et Historique Cantonal de Gimont, Pl de la Vieille Halle, 32200 Gimont - T: 0562677166/7699
Archaeological Museum / Historical Museum 10667

Ginals

Centre d'Art Contemporain, Ancienne Abbaye de Beaulieu-Rouergue, 82330 Ginals - T: 0563670684, Fax: 0563240163. Head: Jean-Pierre Colle, Geneviève Bonnefoi
Fine Arts Museum - 1970
Painters like Dubuffet, Michaux, Bissiere, Vieira da Silva, Lyric abstraction: Hantaï, Degottex, Benrath, K.O. Götz, Lerin, Cl. Georges Mathieu, J. Reigl, Olson, Serpan, Szénes, Saignes, Sonderborg, Viseux, Magnelli, F. Deux, Dahmen - documentation center 10668

Ginestas

Musée de la Chapellerie, Le Somail, 11120 Ginestas - T: 0468461926
Special Museum / Folklore Museum 10669

Giromagny

Fort Dorsner, 90200 Giromagny - T: 0384290900
Military Museum 10670

Musée de la Mine et des Techniques Minières, Pl des Commandos d'Afrique, 90200 Giromagny - T: 0384290900/0390
Science&Tech Museum 10671

Giverny

Musée Claude Monet, Rue Claude Monet, 27620 Giverny - T: 0232512821, Fax: 0232515418. Head: Gerald Van der Kemp
Fine Arts Museum - 1980
House, atelier and gardens of Claude Monet, his furniture, familiar objects, his coll of Japanese prints 10672

Givet

Centre Européen des Métiers d'Art, Quai des Fours, 08600 Givet - T: 0324427326. Head: Roger-Pierre Durracq
Special Museum 10673

Toussaint Forge, Ancien Corps de Garde, 08600 Givet - T: 0324420354
Archaeological Museum 10674

Givors

Maison du Rh"ne, Pl de la Liberté, 69130 Givors - T: 0478737037/079300
Historical Museum 10675

Givrand

Relais Archéologique de la Maison de la Cour, Aranov, Maison de la Cour, Mairie de Givrand, Rue du Bourg, 85800 Givrand - T: 0251551331
Archaeological Museum 10676

Gizeux

Collections du Château de Gizeux, 37340 Gizeux - T: 0247965092/5097
Decorative Arts Museum / Fine Arts Museum 10677

Gleize

Château de Vaurenard, 69400 Gleize - T: 0474682165
Decorative Arts Museum 10678

Musée de la Vigne, Cave Coopérative, 69400 Gleize - T: 0474683949
Special Museum 10679

Gomelange

Écomusée du Pays de Nied, Maison, 57220 Gomelange
Folklore Museum 10680

Gommerville

Château-Musée de Filières, Château de Filières, 76430 Gommerville - T: 0235205330. Head: Marquis de Persan
Fine Arts Museum / Local Museum / Historical Museum 10681

Gondrecourt-le-Château

Musée du Cheval, Château, 55130 Gondrecourt-le-Château - T: 0329897235/6338
Special Museum 10682

Gonesse

Apothicairerie, Centre Hospitalier de Gonesse, 25 Rue Pierre-de-Theilley, 95500 Gonesse - T: 0134532052
Decorative Arts Museum 10683

Gonfaron

Écomusée du Liège, Blvd de la République, 83590 Gonfaron - T: 0494782565
Special Museum / Science&Tech Museum 10684

Gordes

Moulins à Huile, Moulin des Bouillons, Rte de Saint-Pantaléon, 84220 Gordes - T: 0490722211/2048
Special Museum / Science&Tech Museum 10685

Musée des Bories, Rte de Cavaillon, 84220 Gordes - T: 0490720348, Fax: 0490720439
Historical Museum 10686

Musée du Vitrail, Rte de Saint-Pantaléon, 84220 Gordes - T: 0490722211/2048
Decorative Arts Museum 10687

Gornac

Musée de la Vigne, Moulin du Haut-Benauge, 33540 Gornac - T: 0556619615, Fax: 0556619680, E-mail: gornac.mairie@wanadoo.fr
Agriculture Museum 10688

Gorze

Maison de l'Histoire de la Terre de Gorze, 22 Rue de l'Eglise, 57680 Gorze - T: 0387520457, Fax: 0387520457, E-mail: musee.gorze@free.fr. Head: Etienne Manson
Archaeological Museum / Historical Museum 10689

Goult

Musée Missionaire, Maison des Oblats, 84220 Goult - T: 0490722218
Special Museum 10690

Gourdon (Alpes-Maritimes)

Musée des Arts Décoratifs et de la Modernité, Château de Gourdon, 06620 Gourdon (Alpes-Maritimes) - T: 0493096802, Fax: 0493096897, E-mail: chateaudegourdon@hotmail.com
Decorative Arts Museum
Art Deco masterpieces by famous designers of the 1920's-1930's (Ruhlmann, Chareau, Mallet-Stevens, Gray, Le Chevallier) and modern works (Dali, Tapiès) displayed in a medieval citadel surrounded with remarkable box tree gardens 10691

Musée Historique, Château de Gourdon, 06620 Gourdon (Alpes-Maritimes) - T: 0493096802, Fax: 0493096897, E-mail: chateaudegourdon@hotmail.com, Internet: http://www.provenceweb.fr/06/chateau-gourdon/
Historical Museum
Weapons, armors, antiques and paintings from 16th-17th c displayed in a medieval citadel surounded with remarkable box tree gardens 10692

Gouts

Musée de la Faune, 40400 Gouts - T: 0558734418
Natural History Museum 10693

Gouzeaucourt

Musée Archéologique, Syndicat d'Initiative, 59231 Gouzeaucourt - T: 0327821241
Archaeological Museum 10694

Gramat

Exposition de Beaux-Arts, 6 Av Louis Conte, 46500 Gramat - T: 0565331434
Fine Arts Museum 10695

Exposition d'Etains Anciens Arsène Maigne, Faubourg Saint-Pierre, 46500 Gramat - T: 0565387494
Decorative Arts Museum 10696

Musée d'Art Sacré, Pélerinage Notre-Dame de Rocamadour, 46500 Gramat - T: 0565336329. Head: P. Pourtalet
Religious Arts Museum
Virgin in majesty (12th c), shrine reliquaries 10697

Musée d'Arts Populaires, Office du Tourisme, Pl de la République, 46500 Gramat - T: 0565387360
Folklore Museum 10698

Gramont

Château-Musée, 82120 Gramont - T: 0563940526
Decorative Arts Museum 10699

Grand

Site de Grand, 4 Rue de la Mosaïque, 88350 Grand - T: 0329067737, Fax: 0329066989, E-mail: cdevallois@cg88.fr, Internet: site.de.-grand@wanadoo.fr
Historic Site / Archaeological Museum 10700

Grand-Combe-Châteleu

Fermes-Musée du Pays Horloger, Les Cordiers, 25570 Grand-Combe-Châteleu - T: 0381688690, Fax: 0381688766, E-mail: atp.beugnon@wanadoo.fr, Internet: http://www.morteau.org/fermes-musee
Agriculture Museum / Ethnology Museum / Science&Tech Museum 10701

Grand-Failly

Grange-Conservatoire de l'Othain, 1 Rue Catinat, 54260 Grand-Failly - T: 0382265502
Agriculture Museum / Local Museum 10702

Grand-Fort-Philippe

Maison du Sauvetage, Blvd de la République, 59153 Grand-Fort-Philippe - T: 0328239839, Fax: 0328239839, E-mail: gravelines@tourisme.norsys.fr. Head: Christine Beccart
Special Museum 10703

Grandcamp-Maisy

Musée des Rangers, Quai Crampon, 14450 Grandcamp-Maisy - T: 0231923351, Fax: 0231929995
Military Museum 10704

Grande-Synthe

Centre d'Exposition Langevin, Rue Cortot, 59760 Grande-Synthe - T: 0328279918/9141
Natural History Museum / Archaeological Museum 10705

Mémoires de Grande-Synthe, Maison du Patrimoine, 6 Av de l'Ancien-Village, 59760 Grande-Synthe - T: 0328219516
Science&Tech Museum / Historical Museum 10706

Grandfontaine (Bas-Rhin)

Musée-Galerie de la Mine de Fer de Framont, Les Minières, 67130 Grandfontaine (Bas-Rhin) - T: 0388972009/0002
Science&Tech Museum 10707

Granville

Musée-Aquarium Marin du Roc, Blvd Vaulfleury, 50400 Granville - T: 0233500313/1983/1910
Natural History Museum / Fine Arts Museum 10708

Musée Christian-Dior, Villa les Rhumbs, 50400 Granville - T: 0233614821
Special Museum 10709

Musée d'Art Moderne Richard Anacreon, Pl de l'Isthme, 50400 Granville - T: 0233510294
Fine Arts Museum 10710

Musée du Vieux Granville, Rue Lecarpentier, 50400 Granville - T: 0233504410, Fax: 0233503633. Head: Michèle Chartrain
Historical Museum
Local hist, (regional) costumes, documents on Newfoundlanders 10711

Musée Féerie des Coquillages, 50400 Granville - T: 0233500313
Special Museum 10712

Musée-Jardin, Papillons et Insectes, Le Roc, 50400 Granville - T: 0233500313
Natural History Museum 10713

Palais Minéral, Composition avec des Minéraux, 50400 Granville - T: 0233500113
Natural History Museum 10714

Gras

Museum d'Histoire Naturelle, Fauniscope, la Dent de Rez, 07700 Gras - T: 0475042264/3931
Natural History Museum 10715

Grasse

Musée d'Art et d'Histoire de Provence, 2 Rue Mirabeau, 06130 Grasse - T: 0493360161, Fax: 0493366487, E-mail: info@museesdegrasse.com, Internet: http://www.musees.de.grasse.com. Head: Marie-Christine Grasse
Fine Arts Museum / Decorative Arts Museum / Historical Museum / Archaeological Museum
17th-19th century furnishings, household objects, costumes, ceramics, antiques, customs, paintings, etchings, 18th century palace 10716

Musée de la Parfumerie Fragonard, 20 Blvd Fragonard, 06130 Grasse - T: 0493364465, Fax: 0493365732, E-mail: tourisme@fragonard.com, Internet: http://www.fragonard.com. Head: Eric Fabre
Special Museum 10717

Musée de la Parfumerie Galimard, 73 Rte de Cannes, 06130 Grasse - T: 0493092000, Fax: 0493703622, E-mail: galimard@galimard.com, Internet: http://www.galimard.com. Head: Jean-Pierre Roux
Special Museum
Perfumes 10718

Musée de la Parfumerie Molinard, 60 Blvd Victor-Hugo, 06130 Grasse - T: 0493360162
Special Museum 10719

Musée International de la Parfumerie, 8 Pl du Cours, 06130 Grasse - T: 0493360161, E-mail: info@museesdegrasse.com, Internet: http://www.museesdegrasse.com. Head: Marie-Christine Grasse
Special Museum 10720

Musée Jean-Honoré Fragonard, 23 Blvd Fragonard, 06130 Grasse - T: 0493360161, Fax: 0493366487, E-mail: info@museesdegrasse.com, Internet: http://www.museesdegrasse.com. Head: Marie-Christine Grasse
Local Museum / Fine Arts Museum 10721

Musée Mémorial de la Marine Amiral-de-Grasse, 2 Blvd du Jeu-du-Ballon, 06130 Grasse - T: 0493091071
Science&Tech Museum 10722

Grateloup

Écomusée de l'Abeille, 47400 Grateloup - T: 0553888023, Fax: 0553888023. Head: Joseph Barale
Natural History Museum 10723

Gratot

Exposition Permanente Historique, Huit Siècles de Vie, Château, 50200 Gratot - T: 0233451849/31852593
Historical Museum 10724

Graufthal

Musée de l'Habitat Troglodytique, Maison des Rochers, 67320 Graufthal - T: 0388701562
Historical Museum 10725

Gravelines

Exposition Historique, Fortification, Citadelle de Vauban, 59820 Gravelines - T: 0328233916
Historical Museum 10726

Musée du Dessin et de l'Estampe Originale, Château, 59820 Gravelines - T: 0328518100, Fax: 0328518101, E-mail: musee.de.gravelines@wanadoo.fr
Fine Arts Museum - 1982
Engravings, works by E. Leroy, W. Lam, G. Doré, Arman, Léger, Picasso, Dürer 10727

Gravelotte

Musée de la Guerre de 1870, 27 Rue de Metz, 57130 Gravelotte - T: 0387609256
Military Museum 10728

Graveson

Musée Auguste Chabaud, Cours National, 13690 Graveson - T: 0490905302
Fine Arts Museum 10729

Musée des Arômes et du Parfum, La Chevêche, Petite Rte du Grès, 13690 Graveson - T: 0490958172
Special Museum 10730

Gray

Musée Baron Martin, Rue Pigalle, 70100 Gray - T: 0384648346, Fax: 0384651375. Head: Viviane Ivol
Fine Arts Museum
Paintings of the 16th to 19th c 10731

Musée d'Histoire Naturelle, Ecuries du Château, 70100 Gray - T: 0384650015
Natural History Museum 10732

Musée National Espéranto, 19 Rue Victor Hugo, 70100 Gray - T: 0384651173/648192
Special Museum 10733

Greasque

Musée de la Mine, CCST du Bassin Minier de Provence, 13850 Greasque - T: 0442697216
Science&Tech Museum 10734

Grenoble

Collections Universitaires, Université Pierre-Mendès-France, 38000 Grenoble - T: 0476635930
Archaeological Museum 10735

Magasin - Centre National d'Art Contemporain, 155 Cours Berriat, 38000 Grenoble - T: 0476219584, Fax: 0476212422, E-mail: communication@magasin-cnac.org, Internet: http://www.magasin-cnac.org. Head: Yves Aupetitallot
Fine Arts Museum 10736

Maison Stendhal, 20 Grande-Rue, 38000 Grenoble - T: 0476420262, 0476862100, Fax: 0476862119. Head: Sylvie Truc
Special Museum 10737

Musée Archéologique - Eglise Saint-Laurent, Pl Saint-Laurent, 38000 Grenoble - T: 0476447868, Fax: 0476513559, E-mail: infos@musee-archeologique.grenoble.com, Internet: http://www.musee-archeologique.grenoble.com. Head: Renée Colardelle
Archaeological Museum 10738

Musée Dauphinois, 30 Rue Maurice Gignoux, 38031 Grenoble Cedex 1 - T: 0476851901, Fax: 0476876022, E-mail: dauphin@musee-dauphinois.fr, Internet: http://www.musee-dauphinois.fr. Head: Jean-Claude Duclos
Archaeological Museum / Folklore Museum - 1906
Archeological finds, regional hist, folklore in documents, early historical finds, wood carvings, local porcelain, folk pottery, 17th century former convent, "The Glorious history of skiing" (from prehistoric times to present day) 10739

Musée de Grenoble, 5 Pl de Lavalette, 38000 Grenoble - T: 0476634444, Fax: 0476634410, E-mail: olivier.tomasini@ville-grenoble.fr, Internet: http://www.ville-grenoble.fr/musee-de-grenoble. Head: Prof. Serge Lemoine
Fine Arts Museum - 1994
Impressionists, Cubism, art brût, abstract art, 15th-16th century Italian paintings, 17th-19th century European masters, sculptures, cabinet of drawing coll, coll of Egyptian, Greek and Roman antiquities 10740

Musée de la Résistance et de la Déportation, 14 Rue Hébert, 38000 Grenoble - T: 0476423853, Fax: 0476425589, E-mail: info@resistance_en_isere.com, Internet: http://www.resistance_en_isere.com. Head: Jean-Claude Duclos
Historical Museum 10741

Musée de l'Automobile, Fort de la Bastille, 38000 Grenoble - T: 0476545069/465927. Head: Michel Astier
Science&Tech Museum 10742

Musée des Troupes de Montagne, 19 Rue Hébert, 38000 Grenoble - T: 0476762011 poste 2311
Military Museum / Special Museum
Library 10743

Musée Stendhal, 1 Rue Hector Berlioz, 38000 Grenoble - T: 0476544414, 0476862100, Fax: 0476862119. Head: Sylvie Truc
Special Museum - 1931
Memorabilia of the writer Stendhal, pictures, engravings, manuscripts, drawings 10744

Muséum d'Histoire Naturelle, 1 Rue Dolomieu, 38000 Grenoble - T: 0476440535, Fax: 0476446599, Internet: http://www.ville-grenoble.fr. Head: Armand Fayard
Natural History Museum - 1851
Birds, insects of France and all over the world, minerals, ethnographical coll, aquariums 10745

Gréoux-les-Bains

Musée des Traditions et Arts Populaires, Maison de Pauline, 04800 Gréoux-les-Bains - T: 0492780108
Folklore Museum 10746

Musée du Santon, 36 Av des Alpes, 04800 Gréoux-les-Bains - T: 0492776108
Special Museum 10747

Musée Vivant du Vitrail et des Métiers d'Art du Verre, 3-7 Grand'Rue, 04800 Gréoux-les-Bains - T: 0492742785/875705
Decorative Arts Museum 10748

Grezels

Collection sur le Vin et la Gastronomie, Université du Goût, Château de la Coste, 46700 Grezels - T: 0565213418/3828
Special Museum 10749

Grezieu-la-Varenne

Musée de la Blanchisserie, Mairie, 69290 Grezieu-la-Varenne - T: 0478541605
Special Museum 10750

Grézolles

Musée d'Art et d'Histoire, Mairie, 42260 Grézolles - T: 0477625700
Local Museum
Local hist, customs, traditional families, geology, memorabilia of Father de la Chaise, the Father Confessor to Louis XIV 10751

Grignan

Atelier-Musée de la Typographie et du Livre, Maison du Bailli, 26230 Grignan - T: 0475465716
Science&Tech Museum / Special Museum 10752

Musée-Château, Château, 26230 Grignan - T: 0475465156, Fax: 0475469405
Historic Site / Decorative Arts Museum - 1942
Faience, tapestry, furnishings 10753

Grimaud

Musée Régional d'Arts et de Traditions Populaires, 558 Rte Nationale, 83310 Grimaud - T: 0494433929/2698
Folklore Museum 10754

Grisolles

Musée Calbet, 15 Rue Jean de Comère, 82170 Grisolles - T: 0563028306, Fax: 0563641786
Local Museum / Ethnology Museum - 1938
Fashion (1830-1930), fossils, Gallo Roman finds, old measures, reconstruction of a 19th century Kitchen, weapons 10755

Gruissan

Musée de la Vigne et du Vin, Château Lebouis, 11430 Gruissan - T: 0468490018/2154
Special Museum 10756

Guebwiller

Conservatoire Alsacien des Instruments de Musique, Salle des Dominicains, 68500 Guebwiller - T: 0389761063/3266
Music Museum 10757

Espace de la Route Romane d'Alsace, Hôtel de Ville, 68500 Guebwiller - T: 0389768061
Religious Arts Museum 10758

Musée Archéologique et Historique de la Vigne, Lieu-dit Kitterlé, Domaine Schlumberger, 68500 Guebwiller - T: 0389742700
Archaeological Museum / Historical Museum 10759

Musée du Florival, 1 Rue du 4 Février, 68500 Guebwiller - T: 0389742289
Local Museum 10760

Guer

Musée du Souvenir, Ecole de Coëtquidan, Cour Rivoli, 56380 Guer - T: 0297735692, Fax: 0297735295
Military Museum
Military hist, hist of the military school 10761

Guérande

Musée de la Poupée et des Jouets Anciens, Rue de Saillé, 44350 Guérande - T: 0240156913. Head: Lucien Mahé
Special Museum
Puppets and toys illustrating daily life between 1830 and 1930 10762

Musée Régional d'Art Populaire, Porte Saint-Michel, Pl du Marché au Bois, 44350 Guérande - T: 0240429652. Head: Pierre Chicoineau
Folklore Museum / Archaeological Museum - 1928
Local ethnology and hist, Gallo-Roman archeology, faience 10763

Guéret

Musée d'Art et d'Histoire, Centre du Jardin Public, 22 Av de la Sénatorerie, 23000 Guéret - T: 0555520720
Fine Arts Museum / Archaeological Museum / Historical Museum 10764

Musée Louis-Lacrocq, Ancien Présidial, 8 Pl du Marché, 23000 Guéret - T: 0555521044
Folklore Museum 10765

Guérigny

Musée des Amis du Vieux Guérigny, Av A. Delange, 58130 Guérigny - T: 0386370108
Local Museum 10766

Guerlesquin

Musée de Machines Agricoles Miniatures, 29248 Guerlesquin - T: 0298728179
Special Museum 10767

Guéthary

Musée des Beaux-Arts Saraleguinea, Parc Municipal, 64210 Guéthary - T: 0559265785/548637
Local Museum 10768

Guiclan

Exposition de Coiffes et Dentelles de Bretagne, Moulin de Trévilis, 29223 Guiclan - T: 0298794081
Special Museum 10769

Guimaec

Musée Rural de l'Outil, Beg Ar Fri, 29227 Guimaec - T: 0298676477
Local Museum 10770

Guines

Musée Emile Villez, 13 Rue du Bassin, 62340 Guines - T: 0321415835/352113
Archaeological Museum / Fine Arts Museum / Local Museum 10771

Guiry-en-Vexin

Château de Guiry-en-Vexin, 95450 Guiry-en-Vexin - T: 0134674031
Fine Arts Museum 10772

Musée Archéologique Départemental du Val-d'Oise, Pl du Château, 95450 Guiry-en-Vexin - T: 0134674507
Archaeological Museum 10773

Guise

Collection du Musée Archéologique, Château Fort, 02120 Guise - T: 0323611176, E-mail: chateaudeguise@free.fr, Internet: http://www.chateaudeguise.free.fr. Head: Daniel Guillemin
Archaeological Museum 10774

Musée Municipal Marcel Migrenne, Pl du Familistère, 02120 Guise - T: 0323618080, Fax: 0323611767. Head: Estienne Blecon
Local Museum 10775

Guîtres

Musée Ferroviaire et des Vieilles Gares, Ancienne Gare, 33230 Guîtres - T: 0557691069/245878
Science&Tech Museum 10776

Gujan-Mestras

Maison de l'Huître, Port de Larros, 33470 Gujan-Mestras - T: 0556662371/1265
Special Museum 10777

Gunsbach

Musée d'Art Africain, Mairie, 68140 Gunsbach - T: 0389773142
Ethnology Museum 10778

Musée-Maison Albert Schweitzer, 8 Rue Munster, 68140 Gunsbach - T: 0389773142, Fax: 0389773142
Special Museum 10779

Guyonvelle

Musée-Atelier de Maréchal Ferrant, 52400 Guyonvelle - T: 0325888500
Science&Tech Museum 10780

Gy-en-Sologne

Musée Locature de la Straize, 41230 Gy-en-Sologne - T: 0254838289
Decorative Arts Museum 10781

Habsheim

Collection de Vieux Avions, Aéro-Club de Mulhouse, Aérodrome, 68440 Habsheim - T: 0389642637
Science&Tech Museum 10782

Hagondange

Musée de la Planète Métal, Parc de Loisirs Walibi, 57300 Hagondange - T: 0387517390/05454647
Special Museum 10783

Haguenau

Musée Alsacien, 1 Pl Joseph Thierry, 67500 Haguenau - T: 0388733041, Fax: 0388934812, E-mail: musees-archives@ville-haguenau.fr. Head: Pia Wendling
Ethnology Museum - 1972 10784

Musée Historique, 9 Rue du Maréchal Foch, 67500 Haguenau, mail addr: BP 261, 67504 Haguenau - T: 0388937922, Fax: 0388934812, E-mail: musees-archives@ville-haguenau.fr. Head: Pia Wendling
Historical Museum - 1905
Bronze Age finds, Roman sculpture, Alsatian numismatics, local incunabula, furnishings, armaments, tools 10785

Hambye

Musée d'Art Sacré, Abbaye, Rte de Villedieu, 50650 Hambye - T: 0233617692
Religious Arts Museum 10786

Hannonville-sous-les-Côtes

Ecomusée de la Vie Rurale, Maison du P.N.R. de Lorraine, 55210 Hannonville-sous-les-Côtes - T: 0329873294
Folklore Museum 10787

Harfleur

Musée du Prieuré, 50 Rue de la République, 76700 Harfleur - T: 0235454062/133050, Fax: 0235133019. Head: Bruno Duvernois
Archaeological Museum 10788

Harnes

Musée d'Art et d'Histoire, 50 Rue André Deprez, 62440 Harnes - T: 0321201326/750301. Head: René Debarge
Local Museum - 1970 10789

Musée de l'Ecole et de la Mine, 20 Rue de Montceau, 62440 Harnes - T: 0321204670
Special Museum / Science&Tech Museum 10790

Haroué

Château-Musée de Craon, 54740 Haroué - T: 0383534014
Decorative Arts Museum
10791

Hartzviller

Exposition du Cristal, Cristallerie, 57870 Hartzviller - T: 0387251055
Decorative Arts Museum
10792

Hasparren

Musée Francis Jammes, Maison Francis Jammes, 64240 Hasparren - T: 0559294336
Special Museum
10793

Hatten

Musée de la Ligne Maginot, Casemate Esch, Rte de Seltz, 67690 Hatten - T: 0388800507
Military Museum
10794

Musée de l'Abri, Ligne Maginot, 67690 Hatten - T: 0388801490
Military Museum
10795

Haut-Clocher

Musée Lapidaire de la Grande Villa Gallo-Romaine de Saint-Ulrich, Au Nord de Sarrebourg, 57400 Haut-Clocher - T: 0387032786
Archaeological Museum
10796

Haute-Goulaine

Musée-Château de Haute-Goulaine, 44115 Haute-Goulaine - T: 0240549142, Fax: 0240549023, E-mail: chateau.goulaine@online.fr. Head: Marquis de Goulaine
Decorative Arts Museum
10797

Haute-Rivoire

Musée du Clocher, 69610 Haute-Rivoire - T: 0474263833
Local Museum
10798

Hautefort

Château de Hautefort, 24390 Hautefort - T: 0553505123, Fax: 0553516737
Historical Museum
10799

Hauteluce

Ecomusée de Beaufortain, Chef Lieu, 73620 Hauteluce - T: 0479388031
Historical Museum
10800

Hauteville-la-Guicharde

Exposition Historique, 50570 Hauteville-la-Guicharde - T: 0233458616
Historical Museum
10801

Hautvillers

Collection Viticole, Champagne G. Tribaut, Pl de la République, 51160 Hautvillers - T: 0326594057/4374
Science&Tech Museum / Historical Museum
10802

Musée, Champagne J.M. Gobillard, 38 Rue de l'Eglise, 51160 Hautvillers - T: 0326594420, Fax: 0326594420
Special Museum / Agriculture Museum
10803

Hauville

Musée du Vieux Moulin de Pierre, 27350 Hauville - T: 0232563732
Science&Tech Museum
10804

Hazebrouck

Musée Municipal, Pl Georges Degroote, 59190 Hazebrouck - T: 0328434446, Fax: 0328407866. Head: Patrick Descamps
Local Museum
Paintings, drawings, prints, ceramics, costumes
10805

Heiltz-le-Maurupt

Musée de Folklore de la Chée, Pl du Village, 51250 Heiltz-le-Maurupt - T: 0326731516
Folklore Museum
10806

Hendaye

Château d'Antoine d'Abbadie, Rte de la Corniche, 64700 Hendaye - T: 0559200451, Fax: 0559209051, E-mail: chateau-abbadie@wanadoo.fr. Head: J. Dercourt
Decorative Arts Museum / Science&Tech Museum
Castle (19th c) with neo-gothic interior, astronomical observatory
10807

Hennezel-Clairey

Musée de la Résistance, Résidence, 88260 Hennezel-Clairey - T: 0329070080
Historical Museum
10808

Musée de l'Industrie du Verre, du Fer et du Bois, Résidence, 88260 Hennezel-Clairey - T: 0329070080
Decorative Arts Museum
10809

Hérépian

Exposition Permanente de Grelots, Cloches et Sonnailles, Bruneau-Granier, 25 Av de l'Espinousse, 34600 Hérépian - T: 0497950796
Special Museum
10810

Héricourt

Musée Minal, Ancien Château, Sq Minal, 70400 Héricourt - T: 0384460205
Fine Arts Museum
19th century paintings, modern jewelry - library
10811

Hérisson

Musée du Terroir Hérissonnais, Pl Joseph-Lesage, 03190 Hérisson - T: 0470068940
Archaeological Museum
10812

Hermanville-sur-Mer

Exposition Historique Sword Beach, Pl Amiral-Courbet, 14880 Hermanville-sur-Mer - T: 0231972817
Historical Museum
10813

Hérouville-Saint-Clair

Centre d'Art Contemporain de Basse-Normandie, 7 Passage de la Poste, 14200 Hérouville-Saint-Clair - T: 0231955087, Fax: 0231953760, E-mail: wharf@cybercable.tm.fr. Head: Gilles Forest
Fine Arts Museum
10814

Herserange

Musée Privé Saint-Jean l'Aigle, Château de la Faïencerie, 54440 Herserange - T: 0382245820, Fax: 0382244376. Head: Jacques Peiffer
Decorative Arts Museum
10815

Herzeele

Collection d'Orgues Mécaniques, Palais des Orgues Mortier, 59470 Herzeele - T: 0328276302
Music Museum
10816

Hesdin

Musée d'Arts et d'Histoire, Hôtel de Ville, 62140 Hesdin - T: 0321868476
Local Museum
18th century Flemish tapestries, fine art, local history, arms
10817

Hestrud

Musée de la Douane et des Frontières, 59740 Hestrud - T: 0327616145
Special Museum
10818

Hétomesnil

Musée Conservatoire de la Vie Agricole et Rurale, Ecomusée des Pays de l'Oise, RD 151, 60360 Hétomesnil - T: 0344458810/463220
Special Museum / Agriculture Museum
10819

Hettange-Grande

Musée de la Ligne Maginot, Immerhof, 57330 Hettange-Grande - T: 0382531002
Military Museum
10820

Heudicourt

Château-Musée, 1 Grand-Rue, 27860 Heudicourt - T: 0232558606, Fax: 0232273846, E-mail: chateau-heudicourt@wanadoo.fr
Decorative Arts Museum
10821

Heugleville-sur-Scie

Arboretum d'Heugleville-sur-Scie, Mairie, 76720 Heugleville-sur-Scie - T: 0235328222
Natural History Museum
10822

Hières-sur-Amby

Musée du Patrimoine de l'Isle Crémieu, Maison du Patrimoine, Pl de l'Eglise, 38118 Hières-sur-Amby - T: 0474951390
Local Museum / Folklore Museum
10823

Parc Archéologique de Larina, 38118 Hières-sur-Amby - T: 0474951390
Archaeological Museum
10824

Hiers-Brouage

Brouage Citadelle du XVIIe s, 17320 Hiers-Brouage - T: 0546851916/417377
Military Museum
10825

Hirson

Musée-Centre de Documentation Alfred Desmasures, Impasse du Château, 02500 Hirson - T: 0323987742. Head: Ginette Day
Local Museum / Decorative Arts Museum - 1932
Stained glass of Auguste Labouret
10826

Hondschoote

Musée de l'Hôtel de Ville, Pl du Général de Gaulle, 59122 Hondschoote - T: 0328625300, 0328683155
Local Museum
10827

Honfleur

Musée du Vieux Honfleur, 8 Rue de la Prison, 14600 Honfleur - T: 0231891412. Head: Anne-Marie Bergeret
Local Museum - 1896
Norman furnishings, costumes, history of pirates and slave traders
10828

Musée Eugène Boudin, Pl Erik Satie, 14600 Honfleur - T: 0231895400, Fax: 0231895406. Head: Anne-Marie Bergeret
Fine Arts Museum - 1868
Pre-Impressionist, Impressionist, and modern painting, costumes, engravings, drawings, ethnography coll
10829

Musée Saint-Étienne, 8 Rue de la Prison, Annexe Saint-Étienne, 14600 Honfleur - T: 0231891412. Head: Anne-Marie Bergeret
Special Museum
Maritime museum, collection of model ships, maritime objets, engravings and other objects which bear witness to seafarers of past centuries
10830

Hotonnes

Musée de la Flore et de la Faune du Haut Bugey, Les Narcisses, 01260 Hotonnes - T: 0479876820
Natural History Museum
10831

Hourtin

Musée Regards sur le Passé, Rue des Écoles, 33990 Hourtin - T: 0556091900
Historical Museum
10832

Huisseau-sur-Mauves

Musée de la Meunerie, Moulin de Flia, 45130 Huisseau-sur-Mauves - T: 0238807377
Science&Tech Museum
10833

Hunawihr

Maison-Musée Vivant des Papillons Exotiques, Parc de Loisirs, 68150 Hunawihr - T: 0389736958
Natural History Museum
10834

Huningue

Musée Historique et Militaire, Rue des Boulangers, 68330 Huningue - T: 0389673674/446547. Head: Georges Baud
Historical Museum / Military Museum
10835

Hunspach

Musée de la Ligne Maginot, Fort de Schoenenbourg, Rue du Commandant Reynier, 67250 Hunspach - T: 0388805939, Fax: 0388804146, E-mail: maison-ungerer@wanadoo.fr, Internet: http://www.lignemaginot.com. Head: Marc Halter
Military Museum
10836

Hures-la-Parade

Ferme Caussenarde, À Hyelzas, 48150 Hures-la-Parade - T: 0466456525
Local Museum
10837

Huriel

Musée de la Vie Rurale Locale, Donjon de la Toque, 03380 Huriel - T: 0470286008
Folklore Museum
10838

Husseren-Wesserling

Musée Textile de Haute-Alsace, Parc de Wesserling, 68470 Husseren-Wesserling - T: 0389382808, Fax: 0389826832, E-mail: wesserling@hrmet.fr
Special Museum
10839

Hyères

Musée d'Art et d'Archéologie, Pl Théodore-Lefèvre, 83400 Hyères - T: 0494653967/359000
Fine Arts Museum / Archaeological Museum
10840

Musée des Ordres Religieux et Militaires, Commanderie Saint-Blaise, Pl Massillon, 83400 Hyères - T: 0494352236
Religious Arts Museum / Military Museum
10841

Ibarolle-Ibarla

Exposition Permanente de Bâtons Traditionnels Basques, Makhilas, Etxebestia, M. Harispuru, 64120 Ibarolle-Ibarla - T: 0559378231
Special Museum
10842

Igé

Musée de la Vigne et du Vin, Chapelle Romane, 71960 Igé - T: 0385333356
Special Museum
10843

Ile-d'Aix

Musée Africain, 17123 Ile-d'Aix - T: 0546846640
Ethnology Museum
10844

Musée Napoléonien, Rue Napoléon, 17123 Ile-d'Aix - T: 0546886640, Fax: 0546846967. Head: Bernard Chevallier
Special Museum
African museum: ethnology, natural hist, Napoleonic Museum: memorabilia, hist and legend of Napoleon
10845

Ile-de-Groix

Ecomusée de l'Ile de Groix, Port-Tudy, 56590 Ile-de-Groix - T: 0297868460, Fax: 0297865651, E-mail: ecomusee.groise@free.fr. Head: Sylvie San Quirce
Ethnology Museum - 1984
Local hist, archaeology, ethnology, marine biology, maritime heritage, agriculture, fish canning factories, works of the Breton poet Jean-Pierre Calloch (1888-1917), lifeboat annexe
10846

Maison-Musée de Kerland, Hameau de Kerland, 56590 Ile-de-Groix - T: 0297868460, Fax: 0297865651. Head: Sylvie Quirce
Open Air Museum
10847

Ile-de-Molène

Exposition sur le Sauvetage en Mer au Sémaphore, 29259 Ile-de-Molène - T: 0298073905
Special Museum
10848

Musée Communal des Naufragés, 29259 Ile-de-Molène - T: 0298073905
Local Museum
10849

Ile-de-Sein

Musée Historique de l'Ile-de-Sein, Abri du Marin, Quai des Painpolais, 29990 Ile-de-Sein
Local Museum
10850

Ile-d'Ouessant

Écomusée des Techniques et Traditions Ouessantines, Village de Niou-Huella, 29242 Ile-d'Ouessant - T: 0298488637/219069
Local Museum
10851

Musée Français des Phares et Balises, Phare de Créac'h, 29242 Ile-d'Ouessant - T: 0298488070
Science&Tech Museum - 1988
Light towers, nautical signs
10852

Ile-Tudy

Écomusée de l'Ile-Tudy, 29157 Ile-Tudy - T: 0298564257
Local Museum
10853

Ille-sur-Têt

Centre d'Art Sacré, Patrimoine Intercommunal, Hospices, 66130 Ille-sur-Têt - T: 0468848396
Religious Arts Museum
10854

Musée Départemental des Sapeurs-Pompiers, Caserne, 66130 Ille-sur-Têt - T: 0468840354
Science&Tech Museum
10855

Illiers-Combray

Musée-Maison Marcel Proust, Maison de Tante Léonie, 4 Rue du Docteur Proust, 28120 Illiers-Combray - T: 0237243097. Head: Maurice Schumann
Special Museum
Memorabilia of the writer Marcel Proust (1871-1922)
10856

Illkirch-Graffenstaden

Musée de Pharmacie Dusquenoy, Faculté de Pharmacie ULP, 74 Rte du Rhin, 67400 Illkirch-Graffenstaden - T: 0388676900
Special Museum
10857

Ingrandes (Indre)

Musée Henry de Monfreid, 1 Rue Henry de Monfreid, 36300 Ingrandes (Indre)
Special Museum
10858

Isle-Aumont

Musée Historique et Lapidaire, Église, 10800 Isle-Aumont - T: 0325418233/8681/8187, E-mail: troyes@club-internet.fr, Internet: http://www.pem.net/isle-aumont
Local Museum / Archaeological Museum
Carved stone and wooden statues, a polychrome stone alterpiece, Merovingian vertical tombstones
10859

Issac

Collection de Peintures, Château de Montréal, 24400 Issac - T: 0553811103
Fine Arts Museum
10860

Issoire

Musée de la Pierre Philosophale, 17 Sq René-Cassin, 63500 Issoire - T: 0473715370
Natural History Museum
10861

Issoudun

Musée de l'Hospice Saint-Roch, Rue Hospice Saint-Roch, 36100 Issoudun - T: 0254210176. Head:
Sophie Cazé
Religious Arts Museum - 1968
Reliefs, stained-glass windows, archeology 10862

Issy-les-Moulineaux

Collections du Groupe de Conservation de Vehicules Militaires, MVCG Ile-de-France, 224-226 Quai de Stalingrad, 92130 Issy-les-Moulineaux - T: 0140930033, 0148481944. Head: Guy Jolly
Military Museum
Military vehicles (1944) 10863

Istres

Centre d'Art Contemporain, 1 Blvd Peinlevé, 13800 Istres - T: 0442551710
Fine Arts Museum 10864

Musée d'Istres, Pl du Puits Neuf, 13800 Istres - T: 0442555008, Fax: 0442559015. Head: Martine Sciallano
Archaeological Museum - 1989
Paleontology, zoology, prehistory underwater Archeology, industrial archeology (XIX c) 10865

Isturitz

Exposition Ethnographique du Peuple Basque, Maison Xanxotea, Pl du Village, 64240 Isturitz - T: 0559291443
Ethnology Museum 10866

Ivry-sur-Seine

Galerie Fernand Léger, Centre d'Art d'Ivry, 93 Av Georges-Gosnat, 94200 Ivry-sur-Seine - T: 0149602506, Fax: 0149602507, E-mail: leger@worldnet.fr, Internet: http://www.tran-art.org. Head: Madeleine Van Doren, Thierry Sigg
Fine Arts Museum 10867

Izernore

Musée d'Archéologie, 01580 Izernore - T: 0474769676
Archaeological Museum 10868

Izieu

Musée Mémorial des Enfants d'Izieu, 01300 Izieu - T: 0479872000/2008
Historical Museum 10869

Jard-sur-Mer

Musée d'Arts Régionaux, Abbaye Royale Notre-Dame-du-Lieu-Dieu, Rte de Payré, 85520 Jard-sur-Mer - T: 0251334006
Decorative Arts Museum 10870

Jargeau

Musée du Graveur Oscar Roty, 3 Pl du Petit Cloître, 45150 Jargeau - T: 0238598013
Decorative Arts Museum 10871

Jarrie

Exposition Historique, Château Médiéval de Bon Repos, 38560 Jarrie - T: 0476720116/688111
Fine Arts Museum 10872

Musée de la Chimie, Le clos Jouvin, 100 Montée de la Creuse, 38560 Jarrie - T: 0476685218, Fax: 0476586218, E-mail: museechimie@wanadoo.fr. Head: M. Hauss
Historical Museum / Science&Tech Museum 10873

Jarville

Musée de l'Histoire du Fer, Av du Général de Gaulle, 54140 Jarville, mail addr: BP 15, 54140 Jarville-la-Malgrange - T: 0383152770, Fax: 0383531607. Head: Magdeleine Clermont-Joly
Science&Tech Museum / Historical Museum - 1966
Iron ore mining, history of metallurgy, iron and steel production technologies - library 10874

Jaulny

Musée Mistorique, Place-Forte, 54470 Jaulny - T: 0383819304
Historical Museum / Archaeological Museum 10875

Javols

Musée Archéologique, 48130 Javols - T: 0466428406
Archaeological Museum 10876

Jeansagnière

Musée Parc de la Droséra, 42920 Jeansagnière - T: 0477248144/8380
Special Museum 10877

Jenzat

La Maison du Luthier de Jenzat, Rue des Luthiers, 03800 Jenzat - T: 0470568178, E-mail: jean-francois.chassaing@wanadoo.fr. Head: Jean-François Chassaing
Music Museum 10878

Job

Musée Rural des Crêtes de Forez, Hôtel des Voyageurs, 63990 Job - T: 0473822606
Folklore Museum 10879

Joigny (Yonne)

Espace Jean-de-Joigny, Pl J.-de-Joigny, 89300 Joigny (Yonne) - T: 0386914961
Fine Arts Museum / Decorative Arts Museum 10880

Maison Natale de la Religieuse Sophie Barat, 11 Rue Davier, 89300 Joigny (Yonne) - T: 0386621393
Religious Arts Museum 10881

Musée-Bibliothèque de l'Histoire du Protestantisme, Ancienne Mairie, Pl Valet, 89300 Joigny (Yonne) - T: 0386914146
Religious Arts Museum - 1972
Protestantism 10882

Musée de la Résistance et de la Déportation, 5 Rue Boffrand, 89300 Joigny (Yonne) - T: 0386621357/2096
Historical Museum 10883

Joinville (Haute-Marne)

Musée de l'Auditoire, Rue Marcand, 52300 Joinville (Haute-Marne) - T: 0325941790
Local Museum 10884

Joncels

Musée-Trésor d'Église, Art Sacré de l'Ancienne Abbatiale, 34260 Joncels - T: 0467238060
Religious Arts Museum 10885

Jonvelle

Musée Archéologique Gallo-Romain, Foyer, 70500 Jonvelle - T: 0384925513/88
Archaeological Museum 10886

Musée d'Outillage Paysan, Foyer, 70500 Jonvelle - T: 0384925513/88
Science&Tech Museum 10887

Jonzac

Musée Archéologique, Rue des Carmes, 17500 Jonzac - T: 0546484929
Archaeological Museum 10888

Jonzieux

Musée de la Passementerie, Rue des Passementiers, 42660 Jonzieux - T: 0477399338. Head: Roger Boudarel
Special Museum / Decorative Arts Museum - 1973 10889

Josselin

Musée des Poupées, Collection Rohan, 3 Rue des Trente, 56120 Josselin - T: 0297223645, Fax: 0297756816. Head: Antoinette Duchesse de Rohan
Decorative Arts Museum - 1984
Doll furniture (19th-20th c), toys and games 10890

Jouarre

Musée Briard et de la Crypte Mérovingienne, Crypte de l'Abbaye, Pl Saint-Paul, 77640 Jouarre - T: 0160226454
Folklore Museum 10891

Musée de la Tour de l'Abbaye, 6 Rue Montmorin, 77640 Jouarre - T: 0160220611, Fax: 0160223125
Local Museum 10892

Jougne

Musée d'Histoire et de la Nature, 25370 Jougne - T: 0381491175/1050
Historical Museum / Natural History Museum 10893

Jouques

Musée d'Art et d'Histoire, Chapelle Saint-Jean, 74 Rue Grande, 13490 Jouques - T: 0442637297
Fine Arts Museum / Historical Museum 10894

Jouy-en-Josas

Musée Municipal de la Toile de Jouy, Château de l'Églantine, 54 Rue Charles-de-Gaulle, 78350 Jouy-en-Josas - T: 0139564864, Fax: 0139561798, E-mail: mairie-de-Jouy-en-Josas@wanadoo.fr
Decorative Arts Museum - 1977
18th-19th century printed textiles of Oberkampf, provincial and foreign manufactures: polychromatic floral designs and monochromatic figured subjects, costumes, archives and old printing material, scale model of the manufacture 10895

Jouy (Eure-et-Loir)

Musée du Patrimoine et des Pratiques Locales, Mairie, 28470 Jouy (Eure-et-Loir) - T: 0237222032
Folklore Museum 10896

Joyeuse

Musée de la Châtaigneraie, Parvis de l'Eglise, 07260 Joyeuse - T: 0475399066, Fax: 0475391398, E-mail: beaumedrobie.musee@wanadoo.fr. Head: Ulla Falke
Folklore Museum 10897

Jublains

Musée Archéologique Départemental, 13 Rue de la Libération, 53160 Jublains - T: 0243043016, Fax: 0243045534, E-mail: musee.jublains@cg53.fr, Internet: http://www.cg53.fr. Head: Jaques Naveau
Archaeological Museum 10898

Jugon-lès-Lacs

Musée de la Ferme d'Antan, Saint-Esprit des Bois, Plédéliac, 22270 Jugon-lès-Lacs - T: 0296341467. Head: Joël Hamelin
Agriculture Museum - 1974
Peasant life 10899

Juigné-Béné

Collections du Château de la Thibaudière, 49460 Juigné-Béné - T: 0241423514
Decorative Arts Museum 10900

Jujurieux

Musée Archéologique, Château de Chenavel, 01640 Jujurieux
Archaeological Museum 10901

Musée de la Soie, Tissages CJ Bonnet, 01640 Jujurieux - T: 0474368222
Special Museum / Decorative Arts Museum 10902

Jumilhac-le-Grand

Musée de l'Or, Château, 24630 Jumilhac-le-Grand - T: 0553525543
Special Museum 10903

Juniville

Musée-Café Verlaine, 08310 Juniville - T: 0324544684
Special Museum 10904

Jupilles

Musée du Bois et de l'Artisanat, Foyer Rural, Le Bourg, 72500 Jupilles - T: 0243794869/446417
Special Museum / Science&Tech Museum 10905

Jussy-Champagne

Château-Musée de Jussy, N 76, 18130 Jussy-Champagne - T: 0248250061, Fax: 0248250484. Head: Jean de Ponton d'Amecourt
Decorative Arts Museum 10906

Juvigné

Musée de l'Outil à la Ferme, Le Bourg, 53380 Juvigné - T: 0243685245
Agriculture Museum 10907

Juvigny-sous-Andaine

Musée du Machinisme Agricole et du Cheval de Trait de 1830 à nos Jours, Ferme de la Michaudière, 61440 Juvigny-sous-Andaine - T: 0233382778
Science&Tech Museum / Agriculture Museum 10908

Juvisy-sur-Orge

Espace d'Art Contemporain Camille-Lambert, 35 Av de la Terrasse, 91260 Juvisy-sur-Orge - T: 0169213289
Fine Arts Museum 10909

Kaysersberg

Musée Albert Schweitzer, 126 Rue du Général de Gaulle, 68240 Kaysersberg - T: 0389473655, Fax: 0389471474. Head: Joseph Braun
Special Museum - 1981
Memorabilia of A. Schweitzer 10910

Musée d'Art et d'Histoire, 62 Rue du Général de Gaulle, 68240 Kaysersberg - T: 0389781111, Fax: 0389781112. Head: Louis Zuger
Local Museum - 1973 10911

Kientzheim

Musée du Vignoble et des Vins d'Alsace, Château de la Confrérie Saint-Etienne, 68240 Kientzheim - T: 0389782136. Head: Francis Lichtlé, André Hugel
Agriculture Museum / Special Museum - 1980
Viticulture, wine cellar materials, cooper's workshop 10912

Kingersheim

Musée Océanographique, 9 Rue du Hagelbach, 68260 Kingersheim - T: 0389537272
Natural History Museum 10913

Klinglenthal

Maison de la Manufacture, 2 Rue de l'École, 67530 Klinglenthal - T: 0388959528
Special Museum / Science&Tech Museum 10914

Kolbsheim

Collections Littéraires, Cercle d'Études Jacques et Raissa Maritain, 21 Rue de la Division-Leclerc, 67120 Kolbsheim - T: 0388961790, Fax: 0388960459, E-mail: meritainkolbsheim@compuserve.com. Head: René Mougel
Special Museum 10915

Kutzenhausen

Maison Rurale de l'Outre-Forêt, 67250 Kutzenhausen - T: 0388804929
Folklore Museum 10916

La Balme-les-Grottes

Musée Cavernicole de la Grotte de Balme, 38390 La Balme-les-Grottes - T: 0474906376/946049
Natural History Museum / Historical Museum / Fine Arts Museum 10917

La Barben

Château-Musée, Rte Nationale 572, 13330 La Barben - T: 0490551912
Decorative Arts Museum / Fine Arts Museum 10918

La Barque

Musée Provençal des Transports Urbains et Régionaux, Gare, La Barque-Fuveau, 13710 La Barque - T: 0491981591
Science&Tech Museum 10919

La Bastide-de-Virac

Musée Historique et du Ver à Soie, Château des Roures, 07150 La Bastide-de-Virac - T: 0475386113
Historical Museum / Natural History Museum 10920

La Batie-Montgascon

Le Musée du Tisserand Dauphinois, Le Village, 38110 La Batie-Montgascon - T: 0474830899, Fax: 0474830899, E-mail: musee@batie-montgascon.com, Internet: http://www.batie-montgascon.com. Head: Marcel Jambon
Special Museum / Science&Tech Museum 10921

La Baule-Escoublac

Château de Careil, 44500 La Baule-Escoublac - T: 0240111947
Decorative Arts Museum 10922

La Bernerie-en-Retz

Collections de la Bibliothèque, Maison de l'Histoire, 25 Rue Jean Duplessis, 44760 La Bernerie-en-Retz - T: 0240821709
Historical Museum 10923

La Bourboule

Musée de Géologie Botanique, Quai Féron, 63150 La Bourboule - T: 0473811125
Natural History Museum 10924

Muséum du Conte de Fées, 63150 La Bourboule - T: 0473650666
Special Museum 10925

La Brède

Château de la Brède, Montesquieu, 33650 La Brède - T: 0556202049
Local Museum 10926

La Bussière

Château des Pêcheurs, 45230 La Bussière - T: 0238359335, Fax: 0238359413, E-mail: jouannet@coeur-de-france.com. Head: Geneviève de Chasseval
Special Museum - 1962
Art on theme of freshwater fish, 18th century English and German engravings, faience 10927

La Cadière-d'Azur

Exposition du Moulin à Huile, Saint-Côme, La Cadière, 83740 La Cadière-d'Azur - T: 0494901151
Special Museum / Science&Tech Museum 10928

La Canourgue

Centre Archéologique Charles-Morel, Rue de Maillan, 48500 La Canourgue - T: 0466329134
Archaeological Museum 10929

La Cassagne

Musée de la Caricature, Grange Dimière, 24120 La Cassagne - T: 0553516643
Fine Arts Museum 10930

La Celle-Guenand

Musée de l'Outil et des Vieux Métiers, Ancienne Ecole, 37350 La Celle-Guenand - T: 0247949307/4527
Science&Tech Museum 10931

La Celle-sur-Loire

Musée Paysan de Bourgogne Nivernaise, Domaine de Cadoux, N 7, 58440 La Celle-sur-Loire - T: 0386392284
Folklore Museum 10932

La Chaise-Dieu

Historial/Musée de Cire, Pl de l'Echo, 43160 La Chaise-Dieu - T: 0471000188, Fax: 0471000345, Internet: http://www.parc-livradois-forez.org/museedecire.htm. Head: Marie Claire Chauvel
Historical Museum 10933

Musée de la Collection, Rue Saint-Martin, 43160 La Chaise-Dieu
Decorative Arts Museum 10934

Musée du Bois et de la Forêt, Rue Saint-Martin, 43160 La Chaise-Dieu
Natural History Museum 10935

La Chaize-le-Vicomte

Musée Ornithologique Charles Payraudeau, Mairie, 85310 La Chaize-le-Vicomte - T: 0251058784, Fax: 0251057681. Head: Jean Vimpère
Natural History Museum 10936

La Chapelle-aux-Saints

Musée de l'Homme de Neandertal, 19120 La Chapelle-aux-Saints - T: 0555911800, Fax: 0555911800, E-mail: casap@club-internet.fr
Archaeological Museum 10937

La Chapelle-Caro

Musée du Costume, Château de Crévy, 56460 La Chapelle-Caro - T: 0297749195
Special Museum 10938

La Chapelle-d'Abondance

Musée de la Faune, Hôtel des Cornettes, 74360 La Chapelle-d'Abondance - T: 0450735024
Natural History Museum 10939

La Chapelle-d'Angillon

Musée Alain-Fournier et Jacques-Rivière, Château de Béthune, 18380 La Chapelle-d'Angillon - T: 0248739477
Local Museum / Decorative Arts Museum 10940

Musée Fondation Royale d'Albanie, Château de Béthune, 18380 La Chapelle-d'Angillon - T: 0248739477
Local Museum 10941

La Chapelle-des-Marais

Maison des Traditions, Mairie, 44410 La Chapelle-des-Marais - T: 44410
Folklore Museum 10942

Maison-Musée du Sabotier, Ecomusée de la Brière, 2 Rue des Ecluses, 44410 La Chapelle-des-Marais - T: 0240668501
Folklore Museum 10943

La Chapelle-des-Pots

Musée de l'Histoire de la Poterie, Le Bourg, 17100 La Chapelle-des-Pots - T: 0546915104
Decorative Arts Museum 10944

La Chapelle-Glain

Musée des Trophées de Chasse, Château de la Motte-Glain, 44670 La Chapelle-Glain - T: 0240555201
Special Museum 10945

La Chapelle-sous-Chaux

Musée Gantner, Le Genechey, 90300 La Chapelle-sous-Chaux - T: 0384292073, Fax: 0384291418, E-mail: contact@musee-gantner.com
Archaeological Museum / Fine Arts Museum / Open Air Museum 10946

La Chapelle-Thouarault

Atelier d'Art Animalier, La Basse Vallée, 35590 La Chapelle-Thouarault - T: 0299076190. Head: Pierre Roussia
Fine Arts Museum
Paintings, lithographies, dioramas on 250 animals by Pierre Roussia - Atelier de lithographie 10947

La Charité-sur-Loire

Musée Municipal, Hôtel Adam, 33 Rue des Chapelains, 58400 La Charité-sur-Loire - T: 0386703483, Fax: 0386703483, E-mail: si.lacharité@wanadoo.fr. Head: Marie José Garniche
Archaeological Museum - 1953
Medieval archeology, local ethnography, decorative art - library 10948

La Châtre

Musée George Sand et de la Vallée Noire, 71 Rue Venose, 36400 La Châtre - T: 0254483679. Head: Christiane Sand
Special Museum - 1937
Memorabilia of the writer George Sand, ethnography, local painters, coll of birds, Roman coins 10949

La Chevrolière

Musée-Maison du Pêcheur, Village de Passay, 16 Rue Yves Brisson, 44118 La Chevrolière - T: 0240313646, Fax: 0240313646. Head: Y. Thomas
Special Museum / Natural History Museum 10950

La Ciotat

Musée Ciotaden, 1 Quai Ganteaume, 13600 La Ciotat, mail addr: BP 110, 13702 La Ciotat Cedex - T: 0442714099, Fax: 0442082596. Head: Jean-Pierre Jouen
Local Museum 10951

La Cluse-et-Mijoux

Musée d'Histoire Militaire, Fort de Joux, 25300 La Cluse-et-Mijoux - T: 0381694795
Military Museum
Armaments, furnishings from the First Empire, Restoration and Second Empire in palace 10952

La Combe-de-Lancey

Musée Rural d'Arts et Traditions Populaires, Annexes du Château, 38190 La Combe-de-Lancey - T: 0476714809. Head: Paul Perroud
Folklore Museum 10953

La Côte-Saint-André

Collection d'Art, Château Louis XI, 38260 La Côte-Saint-André - T: 0474202700
Fine Arts Museum 10954

Musée des Liqueurs Cherry-Rocher, Av Cherry-Rocher, 38260 La Côte-Saint-André - T: 0474933810, Fax: 0474284673, E-mail: info@cherryrocher@com
Special Museum
Collection of old advertisement 10955

Musée Hector Berlioz, 69 Rue de la République, 38260 La Côte-Saint-André - T: 0474202488, Fax: 0474208333, E-mail: c.spillemaecker@cg38.fr. Head: Chantal Spillemaecker
Special Museum
Exhibits on the life of the composer Hector Berlioz (1803-1869), in the house of his birth 10956

Le Palais du Chocolat, Château Louis XI, 38260 La Côte-Saint-André - T: 0474203177/3589
Special Museum 10957

La Courneuve

Écomusée des Cultures Légumières, Banlieue Nord, 11 Rue de l'Abreuvoir, 93120 La Courneuve - T: 0148363960
Local Museum 10958

Réserves du Musée des Cultures Légumières, 93120 La Courneuve - T: 0148383393
Agriculture Museum 10959

La Couture-Boussey

Musée des Instruments de Musique à Vent, 2 Rue d'Ezy, 27750 La Couture-Boussey - T: 0232362880, Fax: 0232362880, E-mail: musee.couture.boussey@wanadoo.fr, Internet: http://www.perso.wanadoo.fr/musee.instrumental/. Head: Katherine Cros-Verlhac
Music Museum
Antique instruments and equipment, documents and archives 10960

La Couvertoirade

Musée Historique, Château Templier, Enceinte Hospitalière, 12230 La Couvertoirade - T: 0565622581/1162
Historical Museum 10961

La Croix-Barrez

Musée du Cardinal-Verdier, Sous l'Église, 12600 La Croix-Barrez - T: 0565660327/2063
Special Museum 10962

La Croix-Valmer

Musée Scout Varois, HLM Le Goubenet BT B3, Av Frédéric-Mistral, 83420 La Croix-Valmer - T: 0494546443
Special Museum 10963

La Fère

Musée Jeanne d'Aboville, 5 Rue du Général de Gaulle, 02800 La Fère - T: 0323567191, Fax: 0323564004. Head: Hervé Cabezas
Fine Arts Museum - 1860
Painting: German, Dutch and Flemish 15th-19th c, Italian 16th-18th c, French 17th-19th c, archeology 10964

La Ferrière-de-Flée

Musée Lilliput, Dépendance du Château, 49500 La Ferrière-de-Flée - T: 0241922176
Special Museum 10965

La Ferté-Macé

Musée des Beaux-Arts, Hôtel de Ville, Pl de la République, 61600 La Ferté-Macé - T: 0233374700
Fine Arts Museum 10966

La Ferté-Milon

Musée Jean-Racine, 2 Rue des Bouchers, 02460 La Ferté-Milon - T: 0323967777, Fax: 0323964844. Head: Claude Royer
Special Museum / Historical Museum 10967

Musée Régional du Machinisme Agricole, 68bis Rue de la Chaussée, 02460 La Ferté-Milon - T: 0323962985
Agriculture Museum / Science&Tech Museum 10968

La Ferté-Saint-Aubin

Musée-Château, 45240 La Ferté-Saint-Aubin - T: 0238765272
Decorative Arts Museum 10969

Musée du Cheval, Château, 45240 La Ferté-Saint-Aubin - T: 0238765272, Fax: 0238646743
Special Museum 10970

La Ferté-Saint-Cyr

Maison Natale du Père Brothier, 5 Rue de l'Église, 41220 La Ferté-Saint-Cyr - T: 0254879034
Special Museum 10971

La Ferté-sur-Chiers

Musée de la Ligne Maginot, 08370 La Ferté-sur-Chiers - T: 0324226083/6149
Military Museum 10972

La Ferté-Vidame

Musée Saint-Simon, Pavillon Saint-Dominique, 28340 La Ferté-Vidame - T: 0237376409
Local Museum 10973

La Ferté-Villeneuil

Ecomusée de la Vallée de l'Aigre, Ancien Presbytère, 28220 La Ferté-Villeneuil - T: 0237441810
Folklore Museum 10974

La Flèche

Musée du Souvenir du Prytanée Militaire, Rue du Collège, 72200 La Flèche - T: 0243940396
Military Museum 10975

Musée Jacques Bouillault, Faune Régionale, Parc Zoologique du Tertre Rouge, 72200 La Flèche - T: 0243940455/1398
Natural History Museum 10976

La Flocellière

Musée-Maison de la Vie Rurale en Pays de Pouzauges, Ferme de la Bernardière, 85700 La Flocellière - T: 0251577714
Agriculture Museum 10977

La Flotte-en-Ré

Flottille en Pertuis, Vieux Gréements des Pertuis Rénovés en État d'Origine, Basés à Marennes, Charron, Boyardville, 17630 La Flotte-en-Ré - T: 0546096139
Special Museum 10978

Maison du Platin, Av du Front-de-Mer, 17630 La Flotte-en-Ré - T: 0546096139
Folklore Museum 10979

La Garde

Maison du Patrimoine, Maison Communale Gérard-Philippe, Av Charles-Sandro, 83130 La Garde - T: 0494089934
Local Museum 10980

Musée Jean-Aicard, Les Lauriers-Roses, 83130 La Garde - T: 0494215966
Fine Arts Museum - 1980
Paintings and portraits, objects d'Art, porcelain, and furnishings from 1830-1930 10981

La Garde-Freinet

Musée du Pigeon "Le Mouron Rouge", Rte du Luc, Rte Nationale 558, 83310 La Garde-Freinet - T: 0494346532/6922
Special Museum 10982

La Garnache

Musée-Château de la Garnache, 85710 La Garnache - T: 0251491265
Historical Museum 10983

Musée de l'Habitat Rural Passé et des Traditions, La Borderie, Rte de Saint-Christophe-du-Lignon, 85710 La Garnache - T: 0251681281
Folklore Museum 10984

La Gaude

Écomusée Vivant, La Coupole, 06610 La Gaude - T: 0493249747
Natural History Museum 10985

La Glacerie

Musée d'Ethnographie Régionale, Hameau Luce, 50470 La Glacerie - T: 0233441367/203333
Ethnology Museum / Local Museum 10986

La Grand-Combe

Musée du Mineur, Vallée de Ricard, 30110 La Grand-Combe - T: 0466342893
Science&Tech Museum 10987

La Grande-Fosse

Musée de la Figurine Historique, Mairie, 88490 La Grande-Fosse - T: 0329512129/1165/589738
Special Museum 10988

La Grande-Verrière

Musée Minéralogique du Morvan, Les Vernottes, 71990 La Grande-Verrière - T: 0385825101
Natural History Museum 10989

La Grave

Musée Sous-Glaciaire, 05320 La Grave - T: 0476799207, Fax: 0476799533, E-mail: Bgardent@aol.com. Head: Bruno Gardent
Natural History Museum / Fine Arts Museum 10990

La Guerche

Château de la Guerche, 37350 La Guerche - T: 0247910239, Fax: 0146514773. Head: Bernard de Crouy-Chanel
Historic Site 10991

La Guérinière

Musée d'Arts et Traditions Populaires, Pl de l'Eglise, 85680 La Guérinière - T: 0251394139, Fax: 0251399836. Head: Vincent Cristofoli
Ethnology Museum 10992

La Guillaume

Exposition Apicole, 63250 La Guillaume - T: 0473519113
Natural History Museum 10993

La Haut-du-Them

Musée de la Montagne et de la Forêt, 70480 La Haut-du-Them - T: 0384204309
Natural History Museum 10994

La Haye-de-Routot

Musée de la Boulangerie Rurale, Antenne de l'Ecomusée de la Basse-Seine, 27350 La Haye-de-Routot - T: 0232573574, Fax: 0232573574, E-mail: orfol@aol.com. Head: Alain Joubert
Science&Tech Museum 10995

Musée du Sabot, Antenne de l'Ecomusée de la Basse-Seine, 27350 La Haye-de-Routot - T: 0232575967, Fax: 0232573574, E-mail: orfol@aol.com. Head: Alain Joubert
Science&Tech Museum 10996

La Horgne

Musée des Spahis, 08430 La Horgne - T: 0324356444
Military Museum 10997

La Jarne

Château-Musée de Buzay, 17220 La Jarne - T: 0546566321
Decorative Arts Museum / Fine Arts Museum 10998

La Louvesc

Musée Saint-François-Régis, Près de la Chapelle, 07520 La Louvesc - T: 0475678200, Fax: 0475678123, E-mail: sjlalouvesc@post.club-internet.fr. Head: Bernard Faivre
Religious Arts Museum 10999

La Lucerne-d'Outremer

Collection d'Art et d'Histoire Religieuse, Abbaye, 50320 La Lucerne-d'Outremer - T: 0233488356
Religious Arts Museum 11000

La Machine

Musée de la Mine, 1 Av de la République, 58260 La Machine - T: 0386509108. Head: François Martin
Ethnology Museum / Science&Tech Museum 11001

La Ménitré

Musée Marc Leclerc, Gare, 49250 La Ménitré - T: 0241456751
Special Museum 11002

La Motte-d'Aveillans

La Mine-Image, Musée de la Mine, Les Quatre-Galeries, 38770 La Motte-d'Aveillans - T: 0476306874
Historical Museum / Science&Tech Museum 11003

La Mure

Expositions du Chemin de Fer de Montagne, Gare de La Mure, 38350 La Mure - T: 0476813775/725711
Science&Tech Museum / Historical Museum 11004

Musée E.-Villard, Blvd Auguste-Vial, 38350 La Mure - T: 0476811103
Science&Tech Museum / Military Museum 11005

Musée Matheysin, Maison Caral, Rue Colonel-Escallon, 38350 La Mure - T: 0476309815, Fax: 0476309815. Head: Frédéric Lafond
Local Museum 11006

La Pacaudière

Musée Le Petit Louvre, Pl du Petit Louvre, 42310 La Pacaudière - T: 0477643018
Fine Arts Museum 11007

La Pesse

Maison-Musée de la Vie d'Autrefois et des Métiers, Syndicat d'Initiative, 39370 La Pesse - T: 0384427285
Folklore Museum 11008

La Petite-Pierre

Maison du Parc Naturel Régional des Vosges du Nord, Château, 67290 La Petite-Pierre - T: 0388014959, Fax: 0388014960, E-mail: contact@parc-vosges-nord.fr. Head: Jean Westphal
Natural History Museum 11009

Musée des Arts et Traditions Populaires, Positifs de Moules à Gâteaux, Magasin, 67290 La Petite-Pierre - T: 0388704865/301164. Head: Charles Haudot
Local Museum 11010

Musée du Sceau Alsacien, Chapelle Saint-Louis, 17 Rue du Château, 67290 La Petite-Pierre - T: 0388704865/301164. Head: Charles Haudot
Local Museum 11011

La Possonnière

Moulin-Musée de La Roche, 49170 La Possonnière - T: 0241391440
Science&Tech Museum 11012

La Réole

Maison des Arts et du Vin, 33190 La Réole - T: 0556611011/1088
Fine Arts Museum 11013

Musée d'Art et d'Histoire, Monastère des Bénédictins, 33190 La Réole - T: 0556611011
Fine Arts Museum / Archaeological Museum
Religious art, archeology, sculpture 11014

Musée d'Arts Populaires, Monastère des Bénédictins, 33190 La Réole - T: 0556611011
Folklore Museum 11015

Musée de l'Automobile et Militaires, 19 Rue Gabriel Chaigne, 33190 La Réole - T: 0556612925/2666
Science&Tech Museum 11016

Musée de Monuments d'Allumettes et d'Artisanat, La Fontine, 33190 La Réole - T: 0556612583
Special Museum 11017

La Riche

Château-Musée du Plessis-lès-Tours, Château, 37000 La Riche - T: 0247372280
Local Museum 11018

Musée Ronsard, Prieuré de Saint-Cosme, 37520 La Riche - T: 0247373270/314798
Archaeological Museum 11019

La Roche-Bernard

Musée de la Vilaine Maritime, Château des Basses Fosses, 56130 La Roche-Bernard - T: 0299908347, Fax: 0299908811. Head: Pierre Brat
Local Museum
Fishing, shipping, local ethnology 11020

La Roche-Blanche

Maison de Gergovie, 63670 La Roche-Blanche - T: 0473794009/4298
Archaeological Museum / Natural History Museum 11021

La Roche-Guyon

Château de la Roche-Guyon, 1 Rue de l'Audience, 95780 La Roche-Guyon - T: 0134797442
Historical Museum / Fine Arts Museum 11022

La Roche-Maurice

Exposition Historique du Château, Ossuaire, 29220 La Roche-Maurice - T: 0298204357
Historical Museum 11023

La Roche-sur-le-Buis

Musée J.-F. Leyraud, Chapelle, 26170 La Roche-sur-le-Buis - T: 0475281291
Folklore Museum / Agriculture Museum 11024

La Roche-sur-Yon

Collections du Haras, Haras National, Rue du Maréchal Galliéni, 85000 La Roche-sur-Yon - T: 0251069400, Fax: 0251378603, E-mail: haras.laroche@haras-nationaux.fr. Head: Philippe Gaubert
Historical Museum 11025

Musée Municipal, Rue Jean-Jaurès, 85000 La Roche-sur-Yon - T: 0251474850/374271, Fax: 0251374871. Head: Laurence Imbernon
Fine Arts Museum - 1880
Contemporary photographs, 19th and 20th century paintings 11026

La Rochefoucauld

Musée de la Préhistoire Charentaise, Cloître, 16110 La Rochefoucauld - T: 0545630745/0261
Archaeological Museum 11027

Musée de la Vieille Pharmacie, Hôpital, Pl du Château, 16110 La Rochefoucauld - T: 0545675400
Special Museum 11028

La Rochelle

Collection de l'Hôtel de Ville, 17000 La Rochelle - T: 0546515151/411468
Decorative Arts Museum 11029

Maison Henri-II, Musée de la Société d'Archéologie et d'Histoire de l'Aunis, 11bis Rue des Augustins, 17000 La Rochelle - T: 0546348859
Local Museum 11030

Musée-Cabinet Lafaille, 28 Rue Albert 1er, 17000 La Rochelle - T: 0546411825
Natural History Museum 11031

Musée de la Grosse Horloge, Tour de la Grosse-Horloge, 17000 La Rochelle - T: 0546515151
Science&Tech Museum 11032

Musée de Modèles Réduits, La Ville-en-Bois, Rue de la Désirée, 17000 La Rochelle - T: 0546416451
Special Museum 11033

Musée des Automates, Rue de la Désirée, 17000 La Rochelle - T: 0546416808/38
Special Museum 11034

Musée des Beaux-Arts, 28 Rue Gargoulleau, 17000 La Rochelle - T: 0546411883/6465, Fax: 0546292260, E-mail: musee-art-la-rochelle@wanadoo.fr. Head: Thierry Lefrançois
Fine Arts Museum
Extensive French paintings up to the 20th c, glass, drawings, castings of sculpture by Charles Depiau 11035

Musée d'Histoire Naturelle et d'Ethnographie, 28 Rue Albert 1er, 17000 La Rochelle - T: 0546411825, Fax: 0546506365. Head: Michele Dunand
Natural History Museum / Ethnology Museum - 1782
Natural science exhibits, prehistory, primitive art from Oceania and the Pacific - library 11036

Musée d'Orbigny-Bernon, 2 Rue Saint-Côme, 17000 La Rochelle - T: 0546411883, Fax: 0546292260, E-mail: Musee-Art-La-Rochelle@wanadoo.fr. Head: Thierry Lefrançois
Local Museum
Local and regional history, 18th century porcelain, pharmacy, archeology, castings of French monuments 11037

Musée du Flacon à Parfum, La Saponaire, 33 Rue du Temple, 17000 La Rochelle - T: 0546413240, Fax: 0546419234, Internet: http://www.museedu-flaconparfum.com. Head: Anne-Jean Séris
Special Museum 11038

Musée du Nouveau Monde, 10 Rue Fleuriau, 17000 La Rochelle - T: 0546414650, Fax: 0546419579, E-mail: Musee-Art-La-Rochelle@wanadoo.fr. Head: Thierry Lefrançois
Historical Museum 11039

Musée-Galerie Numismatique, 18 Rue Chef de Ville, 17000 La Rochelle - T: 0546416150
Special Museum 11040

Musée Historique de la Tour de la Chaîne, 17000 La Rochelle - T: 0546505236
Local Museum 11041

Musée Historique du Port, Tour Saint-Nicolas, 17000 La Rochelle - T: 0546417413
Local Museum 11042

Musée Maritime à Flot France I, Bassin des Chalutiers, Quai Ouest, 17000 La Rochelle - T: 0546505888/280300
Science&Tech Museum 11043

Musée Rochelais d'Histoire Protestante, 2 Rue Saint-Michel, 17000 La Rochelle - T: 0546508803. Head: Olga de Saint-Affrique
Religious Arts Museum - 1931
History of regional Protestantism 11044

Musée Tour de la Lanterne, 17000 La Rochelle - T: 0546415604
Special Museum 11045

Neptunea, Musée Maritime, Bassin des Chalutiers, Quai Prunier, 17000 La Rochelle - T: 0546280300
Special Museum 11046

La Rochette (Savoie)

Musée Savoyard, Pl Saint-Jean, 73110 La Rochette (Savoie) - T: 0479255032, Fax: 0479257825
Decorative Arts Museum / Historical Museum 11047

La Roque-d'Anthéron

Abbaye de Silvacane, 13640 La Roque-d'Anthéron - T: 0442504169
Archaeological Museum 11048

Museum de Géologie Provençale, Pl Paul Cézanne, 13640 La Roque-d'Anthéron - T: 0442504787
Natural History Museum 11049

La Roquebrussanne

Collection Gallo-Romaine, Domaine du Grand Laou, 83136 La Roquebrussanne - T: 0494869497
Archaeological Museum 11050

La Salle-et-Chapelle-Aubry

Musée Chaussures Humeau, 4 Rue Notre-Dame, 49110 La Salle-et-Chapelle-Aubry - T: 0241751422
Special Museum 11051

La Sauve-Majeure

Musée de l'Abbaye Romane, 2 Rue de la Abbaye, 33670 La Sauve-Majeure - T: 0556230155, Fax: 0556233859
Religious Arts Museum / Library with Exhibitions 11052

La Séauve-sur-Semène

Musée des Traditions Religieuses de la Haute-Loire, Musée de Saint-Didier, Chapelle Sainte-Marguerite, 43470 La Séauve-sur-Semène - T: 0477356210/71611593
Religious Arts Museum 11053

La Seyne-sur-Mer

Galerie d'Art Contemporain, La Tête d'Obsidienne, Fort Napoléon, Chemin Marc-Sangnier, 83500 La Seyne-sur-Mer - T: 0494872518/8343. Head: R. Bonaccorsi, C. Baudisson
Fine Arts Museum 11054

Mini-Musée Ferroviaire, Allée des Cyprès Mar-Vivo, 83500 La Seyne-sur-Mer - T: 0494062250
Science&Tech Museum 11055

Musée Naval Fort Balaguier, 924 Corniche Bonaparte, 83500 La Seyne-sur-Mer - T: 0494948472, Fax: 0494109044. Head: Françoise Santinacci-Boitelle
Science&Tech Museum - 1971
Ancient fortress, model ships - garden 11056

Musée Villa Tamaris Pacha, Grande-Maison de Tamaris, 5 Rue de la Grande-Maison, 83500 La Seyne-sur-Mer - T: 0494068400
Fine Arts Museum 11057

La Terrasse-sur-Dorlay

Musée-Maison des Tresses et des Lacets, Moulin Pinte, 42320 La Terrasse-sur-Dorlay - T: 0477209106/9521
Special Museum 11058

La Teste

Collection d'Histoire Naturelle, Parc Zoologique la Bécassière, 33260 La Teste - T: 0556547144
Natural History Museum 11059

La Tour-Blanche

Musée des Records, Salle Polyvalente, 24320 La Tour-Blanche - T: 0553911198
Special Museum 11060

La Tour-d'Aigues

Musée des Faïences Anciennes de la Tour d'Aigues, Château, 84240 La Tour-d'Aigues - T: 0490075029
Decorative Arts Museum 11061

Musée Historique du Pays d'Aigues, Caves du Château, 84240 La Tour-d'Aigues - T: 0490075029
Historical Museum 11062

La Tremblade

Musée Maritime et Ostréicole, 17 Blvd Roger Letelié, 17390 La Tremblade - T: 0546363011, Fax: 0546363730, E-mail: ot@la_tremblade.com, Internet: http://www.la_tremblade.com
Special Museum / Historical Museum 11063

La Tronche

Musée Départemental Hébert, Chemin Hébert, 38700 La Tronche - T: 0476429735, Fax: 0476429737, E-mail: mus.mhe@cg38.fr. Head: H. Nesme
Fine Arts Museum - 1979
Drawings and paintings of E. Hébert (1817-1908) 11064

La Turbie

Musée du Trophée des Alpes, 9 Pl Théodore de Bauville, 06630 La Turbie - T: 0493411011, Fax: 0493412689
Archaeological Museum 11065

La Varenne-Saint-Hilaire

Musée Municipal de Saint-Maur, 5 Rue Saint-Hilaire, 94210 La Varenne-Saint-Hilaire - T: 0148863328
Local Museum 11066

La Villeneuve-au-Châtelot

Musée Archéologique, La Poterie, 10400 La Villeneuve-au-Châtelot - T: 0325214167/4466
Archaeological Museum 11067

La Villeneuve-les-Convers

Exposition 1914-1918, 21450 La Villeneuve-les-Convers - T: 0380962345
Historical Museum 11068

Musée du Chien, 21450 La Villeneuve-les-Convers - T: 0380962132
Special Museum 11069

Musée du Machinisme Agricole, Guy Languereau, 21450 La Villeneuve-les-Convers - T: 0380962108
Science&Tech Museum / Agriculture Museum 11070

La Voulte-sur-Rhône

Musée de Paléontologie, 4 Quai Anatole-France, 07800 La Voulte-sur-Rhône - T: 0475624494
Natural History Museum 11071

Laas

Musée du Château, 64390 Laas - T: 0559389153
Decorative Arts Museum 11072

Musée du Maïs, Château, 64390 Laas - T: 0559389153
Special Museum / Historical Museum 11073

Labarde

Cabinet d'Art Asiatique, Château Siran, 33460 Labarde - T: 0557883404
Decorative Arts Museum 11074

Labastide-d'Armagnac

Ecomusée de l'Armagnac, Château Garreau, 40240 Labastide-d'Armagnac - T: 0558448435
Special Museum / Natural History Museum 11075

Labastide-Murat

Musée du Maréchal Murat, Pl de l'Eglise, 46240 Labastide-Murat - T: 0565311050, 0145275039
Special Museum / Historical Museum 11076

Labecede-Lauragais

Exposition des Vieux Métiers et Coutumes d'Antan, 11400 Labecede-Lauragais - T: 0468604642
Local Museum 11077

Labergement-Sainte-Marie

Maison de la Réserve Naturelle du Lac de Remoray, 28 Av de la Gare, 25160 Labergement-Sainte-Marie - T: 0381693599
Natural History Museum 11078

Musée de l'Art Campanaire, Fonderie C. Obertino, 25160 Labergement-Sainte-Marie - T: 0381693072
Folklore Museum 11079

Labourse

Musée de la Déportation, Rue Achille-Larue, 62113 Labourse - T: 0321659315/9507
Historical Museum 11080

Labrède

Château de Labrède, 33650 Labrède - T: 0556202049
Local Museum 11081

Lacapelle-Biron

Musée Bernard Palissy, Saint-Avit, 47150 Lacapelle-Biron - T: 0553409822/8498
Decorative Arts Museum 11082

Lacave

Château, Château de la Treyne, 46200 Lacave - T: 0565276060
Fine Arts Museum / Decorative Arts Museum 11083

Lachaux

Musée de l'Uranium, Mairie, 63290 Lachaux - T: 0473946141
Natural History Museum 11084

Lacoux-Hauteville-Lompnes

Musée d'Art Contemporain, A Lacoux, 01110 Lacoux-Hauteville-Lompnes - T: 0474353378/2561
Fine Arts Museum 11085

Laduz

Musée Rural des Art Populaires, 22 Rue de Montceau, 89110 Laduz - T: 0386737008, Fax: 0386737008, E-mail: musee.laduz@ wanadoo.fr. Head: Vincent Humbert
Folklore Museum / Historical Museum 11086

Lafitte-sur-Lot

Musée de la Prune et du Pruneau, Domaine du Gabach, 47320 Lafitte-sur-Lot - T: 0553840069, Fax: 0553840383
Special Museum 11087

Lafox

Château de Prades, 47270 Lafox - T: 0553685402
Special Museum 11088

Lagny-sur-Marne

Musée Gatien-Bonnet, 8 Cour Pierre-Herbin, 77400 Lagny-sur-Marne - T: 0164330078, E-mail: lagny77_musee@libertysurf.fr. Head: Céline Cotty
Local Museum 11089

Lagrasse

Collection Lapidaire et Historique sur l'Histoire de l'Abbaye de la Grasse, 11220 Lagrasse - T: 0468431397/1166
Historical Museum 11090

Laguiole

Magasin-Musée de la Coutellerie Traditionnelle, Calmels, 3 Allée de l'Amicale, 12210 Laguiole - T: 0565443003
Local Museum 11091

Musée du Haut-Rouergue, Pl du Forail, 12210 Laguiole - T: 0565443448/3594
Special Museum 11092

L'Aigle

Musée Archéologique, Pl Fulbert de Beina, 61300 L'Aigle - T: 0233241240
Archaeological Museum 11093

Musée de la Musique, Mairie, 61300 L'Aigle - T: 0233244499
Music Museum 11094

Musée Parlant de Juin 1944, Château, 61300 L'Aigle - T: 0233241944
Historical Museum 11095

Laissac

Musée Archéologique, 12310 Laissac - T: 0565707145, Fax: 0565707145. Head: Philippe Gruat
Archaeological Museum 11096

Musée des Arts et des Traditions Populaires, Pl Abbé-Bessou, 12310 Laissac - T: 0565696045/ 6787
Folklore Museum 11097

Lajoux

Maison-Musée du Parc Naturel Régional du Haut-Jura, Grenier Fort, 39310 Lajoux - T: 0384341230, Fax: 0384412401, E-mail: parc@parc-haut-jura.fr
Natural History Museum 11098

Lalouret-Laffiteau

Musée Lapidaire, Mairie, 31800 Lalouret-Laffiteau - T: 0561952048
Archaeological Museum 11099

L'Alpe-d'Huez

Maison du Patrimoine, Rue de la Poste, 38750 L'Alpe-d'Huez - T: 0476803297
Archaeological Museum / Ethnology Museum 11100

Lamballe

Musée du Vieux-Lamballe et du Penthièvre, 1 Pl du Martray, 22400 Lamballe - T: 0296347763. Head: Michel Souplet
Folklore Museum 11101

Musée Mathurin Méheut, Pl du Martray, 22400 Lamballe - T: 0296311999, Fax: 0296501979. Head: Henri Fromant Meurice
Fine Arts Museum - 1972
Works by the painter Mathurin Méheut (1882-1958) 11102

Lambesc

Musée du Vieux Lambesc, 1 Rue du Jas, 13410 Lambesc - T: 0442170050
Local Museum - 1936
Agriculture, ethnology, prehistory, religious art 11103

Lamoura

Maison du Lapidaire, Mairie, 39310 Lamoura - T: 0384412217
Special Museum 11104

Lampaul-Guimiliau

Maison du Patrimoine, 29230 Lampaul-Guimiliau - T: 0298687667
Folklore Museum 11105

Lancey

Musée de la Houille Blanche et de ses Industries, Maison Berges, 38190 Lancey - T: 0476456681, Fax: 0476456681. Head: Cécile Gouy-Gilbert
Special Museum 11106

Landerneau

Centre d'Exposition de Keraudan, Rue Jehan-Bazin, 29220 Landerneau - T: 0298216150
Local Museum 11107

Landévennec

Musée de l'Ancienne Abbaye de Landévennec, 29560 Landévennec - T: 0298273590, Fax: 0298273591. Head: Roger Lars
Archaeological Museum
Archeological finds of the region, local hist 11108

Landivisiau

Musée des Véhicules Anciens et Moros du Finistère, 67 Av Foch, 29230 Landivisiau - T: 0298684203
Science&Tech Museum 11109

Landrethun-le-Nord

Musée-Base V 3 de Mimoyecques, Le Canon de Londres, 62250 Landrethun-le-Nord - T: 0321871034, Fax: 0321833310, E-mail: mimoyecaves@wanadoo.fr. Head: Marie-Madeleine Vasseur
Military Museum 11110

Laneuveville-devant-Nancy

Château-Musée de Montaigu, 54410 Laneuveville-devant-Nancy - T: 0383531696
Archaeological Museum / Decorative Arts Museum 11111

Langé

Musée Géologique et Paléontologique, 36600 Langé - T: 0254408637/8221
Natural History Museum 11112

Langeac

Musée d'Arts Populaires, Maison du Jacquemart, Pl de la Liberté, 43300 Langeac - T: 0471764237/ 0212
Folklore Museum 11113

Langeais

Château de Langeais, 37130 Langeais - T: 0247967260, Fax: 0247965444. Head: Marie-France Camus
Decorative Arts Museum - 1467
Furniture and tapestries of the 13th-15th c, 15th c architecture 11114

Langoiran

Musée Historique du Château, Château de Langoiran, 33550 Langoiran - T: 0556671200, Fax: 0556671200. Head: Dominique de Tinguy de la Giroulière
Historical Museum 11115

Langonnet

Musée d'Arts Africains, Abbaye Notre-Dame, 56630 Langonnet - T: 0297239308. Head: Joël Lauens
Fine Arts Museum
African art, folk art, religious art, decorative arts 11116

Langres

Musée de Langres, Pl du Centenaire, 52200 Langres - T: 0325870805/882623, Fax: 0325888159, E-mail: museedelangres@worldonline.com. Head: Sophie Serra
Fine Arts Museum / Archaeological Museum - 1846
Archaeology, prehistory, Gallo-Roman, and medieval artefacts and sculpture, paintings (16th-19th c), engravings, earthenware from Aprey and Cutlery 11117

Musée du Breuil de Saint-Germain, 2 Rue Chambrulard, 52200 Langres - T: 0325870805. Head: Benoît Decron
Fine Arts Museum / Decorative Arts Museum - 1923
Faience and porcelain, pewter, locks and armor, paintings and engravings by Claude Gillot, memorabilia of the writer Diderot, incunabula and book bindings, furniture from medieval times to the 18th century, 15th-19th century paintings 11118

Musée du Livre, Bibliothèque Municipale, Rue Cardinal De La Luzesne, 52208 Langres - T: 0325876300, Fax: 0325844504, E-mail: bibli.arland@wanadoo.fr
Library with Exhibitions 11119

Lanhélin

Musée de la Faune, Cobac-Parc, 35720 Lanhélin - T: 0299738016, Fax: 0299737356, E-mail: cobac.parc@wanadoo.fr, Internet: http:// www.cobac-parc.fr
Natural History Museum 11120

Lanildut

Collection de Peintures, Rumorvan, 29236 Lanildut - T: 0298043205
Fine Arts Museum 11121

Lanobre

Château-Musée du Val, 15270 Lanobre - T: 0555960249/0471403020
Local Museum 11122

Lans-en-Vercors

Musée du Père Noël, Rte de Villard-de-Lans, Hameau du Père Noël, 38250 Lans-en-Vercors - T: 0476954014
Special Museum 11123

Musée la Magie des Automates, Rte de Villard-de-Lans, Hameau du Père Noël, 38250 Lans-en-Vercors - T: 0476954014
Special Museum 11124

Lansargues

Musée Local, Les Plantades, La Balestrière, 34130 Lansargues - T: 0467867211
Local Museum 11125

Lantheuil

Château-Musée de Lantheuil, 14480 Lantheuil - T: 0231801400, Fax: 0231801400, E-mail: - chateaudelantheuil@netcourier.com
Fine Arts Museum / Historical Museum 11126

Lanvellec

Château de Rosanbo, 22420 Lanvellec - T: 0296351877, Fax: 0296351030, E-mail: - chateauderosanbo@yahoo.fr. Head: Richard de Rosanbo
Decorative Arts Museum 11127

Lanvéoc-Poulmic

Musée de l'Ecole Navale, 29160 Lanvéoc-Poulmic - T: 0298275220, Fax: 0298234009, E-mail: musee@ecole_navale.fr
Science&Tech Museum / Historical Museum 11128

Laon

Musée d'Art et d'Archéologie, 32 Rue Georges Ermant, 02000 Laon - T: 0323201987, Fax: 0323202497, E-mail: Musee.Laon@ wanadoo.fr, Internet: http://perso.wanadoo.fr/ musee.laon. Head: C. Jorrand
Archaeological Museum / Fine Arts Museum - 1850
Egyptian, Greek, and Roman antiquities, prehistory, Gallo-Roman, Merovingian, and medieval regional archeology, paintings, sculpture, faience - library 11129

Lapalisse

Musée L'Art en Marche Lapalisse Art Brut, 9 Av du 8 Mai 1945, 03120 Lapalisse - T: 0470992178, Fax: 0475689617, E-mail: Luis.Marcel@ wanadoo.fr, Internet: http://www.art-en-marche.com. Head: Louis Marcel
Fine Arts Museum 11130

Lapoutroie

Musée des Eaux de Vie, Ancien Relais de Poste, 85 Rue du Général Dufieux, 68650 Lapoutroie - T: 0389475026, Fax: 0389472224, E-mail: rene.de.miscault@wanadoo.fr, Internet: http://www.musee-eaux-de-vie.com. Head: René de Miscault
Special Museum 11131

L'Arbresle

Musée du Vieux L'Arbresle, 20 Pl Sapion, 69210 L'Arbresle - T: 0474014887
Local Museum 11132

Larche

Musée Paléontologique du Gouffre de la Face, Fage de Noailles, A 20, 19600 Larche - T: 0555858062
Archaeological Museum 11133

L'Argentière-la-Bessée

Musée des Mines d'Argent des Gorges du Fournel (Silver Mines Museum), Château Saint-Jean, 05120 L'Argentière-la-Bessée - T: 0492232090, Fax: 0492230299. Head: Ian Cowburn
Science&Tech Museum / Local Museum / Historic Site
History, tools, machinery and finds of the mine, local hist, origin hydro-electric and aluminium works, Fournel slate quarries, flora and fauna - Research and Documentation Centre 11134

Laroque-des-Albères

Musée d'Arts Populaires, Casa del Castell, Rue de la Tour, 66740 Laroque-des-Albères - T: 0468892113/ 2169
Folklore Museum 11135

Laroquebrou

Musée Historique, Mairie, 15150 Laroquebrou - T: 0471460048
Historical Museum 11136

Larra

Château, 31330 Larra - T: 0561826251
Fine Arts Museum / Decorative Arts Museum 11137

Larressingle

Musée de la Halte du Pèlerin, 32100 Larressingle - T: 0562280808/1158
Historical Museum 11138

Larressore

Atelier-Musée du Bâton Basque, Maison Ainciart-Bergara, 64480 Larressore - T: 0559930305
Special Museum 11139

Larroque-Toirac

Château, 46160 Larroque-Toirac - T: 0565347812
Decorative Arts Museum 11140

Laruns

Maison de la Vallée d'Ossau, 64440 Laruns - T: 0559053141
Local Museum 11141

Lassay-sur-Croisne

Château-Musée du Moulin, 41230 Lassay-sur-Croisne - T: 0254838351
Decorative Arts Museum 11142

Lattes

Musée Archéologique Municipal Henri-Prades, 390 Av de Pérols, 34972 Lattes - T: 0467997720, Fax: 0467997721, E-mail: musee.lattes@free.fr, Internet: http://musee.lattes.free.fr/. Head: Christian Landes
Archaeological Museum - 1986
Nécropole Gallo-Romaine (Ier siècle av. n. ère, Ier siècle ap. n. ère), remarquables séries de verres soufflés et de stèles funéraires inscrites, vestiges importants du commerce Etrusque et Grec en Gaule méridionale - Library, Cinema, Educational Service, Temporary Exhibitions of Classical Archaeology 11143

Launstroff

Musée Européen de Sculptures Contemporaines en Plein Air, Chemin des Menhirs, 57480 Launstroff
Open Air Museum 11144

Laure-Minervois

Collection Archéologique, 11800 Laure-Minervois - T: 04687181245
Archaeological Museum 11145

Laurède

Musée de Peyne, 40250 Laurède - T: 0558979533
Local Museum 11146

Lautenbach-Zell

Vivarium, Musée de la Nature, 6 Rue du Moulin, 68610 Lautenbach-Zell - T: 0389740248
Natural History Museum 11147

Laval (Mayenne)

Musée des Sciences, Pl de Hercé, 53000 Laval (Mayenne) - T: 0243494781, Fax: 0243494573. Head: Labbé
Science&Tech Museum / Natural History Museum
Technology, mineralogy, zoological and scientific exhibits 11148

Musée du Bateau-Lavoir Le Saint-Julien, Quai Paul Boudet, 53000 Laval (Mayenne) - T: 0243533989
Science&Tech Museum 11149

Musée du Vieux-Château, Collections d'Art Naïf, Vieux-Château, Pl de la Trémoille, 53000 Laval (Mayenne) - T: 0243533989. Head: Marie-Colette Depierre
Fine Arts Museum - 1966
11th-15th century medieval castle, exhibition of international naive art, medieval items - library 11150

Musée-Ecole de Laval, 10 Rue du Douanier Rousseau, 53000 Laval (Mayenne) - T: 0243533574, Fax: 0243566322. Head: Bernard Le Gendre
Local Museum - 1936
Decorative arts, paintings by regional artists, cinema, the navigator Alain Gerbault 11151

Laval-Roquecezière

Musée des Arts et Traditions Populaires, Ancien Prieuré, 12380 Laval-Roquecezière - T: 0565996866/6143
Folklore Museum 11152

Lavardens

Château-Musée, 32360 Lavardens - T: 0562645120/5070
Folklore Museum 11153

Lavardin

Musée de la Seconde Guerre Mondiale, Etangs Neufs, Rte de Sillé-le-Guillaume, 72240 Lavardin - T: 0243277132
Military Museum 11154

Lavaudieu

Carrefour du Vitrail, Le Bourg, 43100 Lavaudieu - T: 0471764611
Decorative Arts Museum 11155

Musée d'Art et d'Histoire, 43100 Lavaudieu - T: 0471764589
Folklore Museum / Historical Museum 11156

Lavaufranche

Musée d'Arts et de Traditions Populaires, Commanderie des Ordres des Templiers et des Hospitaliers, 23600 Lavaufranche - T: 0555650762, Fax: 0555658756
Folklore Museum 11157

Lavaur

Musée du Pays Vaurais, Ancienne Chapelle, Rue de la Vraie, 81500 Lavaur - T: 0563831220/0031/580342
Local Museum
Local history, prehistory, Gallo-Roman finds, numismatics, sundials 11158

Laveissière

Maison du Buronnier, Fraisse-Haut, Rte du Lioran, 15300 Laveissière - T: 0471201900/04486868
Special Museum 11159

Lavelanet

Musée de la Laine Cardée, 65 Rue Jean-Jaurès, 09300 Lavelanet - T: 0561012220
Science&Tech Museum 11160

Musée du Peigne en Corne, 65 Rue Jean-Jaurès, 09300 Lavelanet - T: 0561012220
Science&Tech Museum 11161

Lavérune

Musée Hofer-Bury, Château, 34880 Lavérune - T: 0467275954
Fine Arts Museum 11162

Lavilledieu

Musée du Bizarre, Hameau de Bayssac, Rte Nationale 102, 07170 Lavilledieu - T: 0475948328
Fine Arts Museum - 1968 11163

Lavoûte-sur-Loire

Château-Musée, Château de Lavoûte-Polignac, 43800 Lavoûte-sur-Loire - T: 0471085002
Local Museum 11164

Lay-Saint-Christophe

Musée d'Art et d'Histoire, Hôtel de Ville, 54690 Lay-Saint-Christophe - T: 0383228047
Fine Arts Museum / Historical Museum 11165

Laye

Musée du Fromage, Col Bayard, 05500 Laye - T: 0492505006
Special Museum 11166

Le Bar-sur-Loup

Exposition Permanente d'Art et d'Artisanat, Château, 06620 Le Bar-sur-Loup - T: 0493427221
Fine Arts Museum 11167

Musée Provençal, 06620 Le Bar-sur-Loup - T: 0493427221
Local Museum 11168

Le Barroux

Centre d'Études Historiques et Archéologiques, Château, 84330 Le Barroux - T: 0490624311/4106
Historical Museum 11169

Le Beausset

Musée de la Poupée, 46 Rue de la République, 83330 Le Beausset - T: 0494986337
Special Museum 11170

Le Bersac

Musée du Machinisme Agricole, Rte Nationale 75, Plateau des Crès, 05700 Le Bersac
Agriculture Museum 11171

Le Blanc

Ecomusée de la Brenne, Château Naillac, 36300 Le Blanc - T: 0254372520, Fax: 0254286949, E-mail: ecomusee.brenne@wanadoo.fr. Head: Hélène Guillemot
Local Museum - 1986
Birds, anthropology and hist of the region 11172

Maison des Amis du Blanc, 11 Grande Rue, 36300 Le Blanc - T: 0254375875/0513
Local Museum 11173

Le Bocasse

Musée de la Machine Agricole, Établissements Ducastel, Val-Saint-Martin, 76690 Le Bocasse - T: 0232508080
Agriculture Museum 11174

Le Bouchon-sur-Saulx

Musée Archéologique, Mairie, 55500 Le Bouchon-sur-Saulx - T: 0329780615
Archaeological Museum 11175

Le Boulaye-Blaige

Musée Tibétain, Château de Blaige, 71320 Le Boulaye-Blaige - T: 0385794341
Ethnology Museum 11176

Le Bourg-d'Oisans

Musée des Minéraux et de la Faune des Alpes, Mairie, 38520 Le Bourg-d'Oisans - T: 0476802754/1211, Fax: 0476802674, E-mail: musee.bo@magic.fr, Internet: http://www.oisans.com/musee.bo. Head: Veronique Cardone
Natural History Museum 11177

Le Bourg-Saint-Léonard

Château-Musée, 61310 Le Bourg-Saint-Léonard - T: 0233671040
Decorative Arts Museum 11178

Le Bourget (Seine-Saint-Denis)

Collection de la Guerre de 1870, Mairie du Bourget, 65 Av de la Division-Leclerc, 93350 Le Bourget (Seine-Saint-Denis) - T: 0148389296/49967129/7095
Military Museum 11179

Musée de l'Air et de l'Espace, Aéroport du Bourget, 93350 Le Bourget (Seine-Saint-Denis) - T: 0149927199/7171/7022, Fax: 0149927141, E-mail: musee.air@wanadoo.fr, Internet: http://www.mae.org. Head: Jean-Paul Siffre
Science&Tech Museum / Historical Museum 11180

Le Breil-sur-Merize

Château-Musée de Pescheray, Centre Rural d'Entraide Professionnelle, 72370 Le Breil-sur-Merize - T: 0243898362
Science&Tech Museum / Special Museum 11181

Le Breuil

Musée de la Meunerie, Moulin de Montcient, 03120 Le Breuil - T: 0470550168
Science&Tech Museum 11182

Le Brugeron

Musée du Sabotier, Parc Naturel Régional du Livradois-Forez, 63880 Le Brugeron - T: 0473955431
Science&Tech Museum 11183

Le Brusc

Musée de Peintures de Monsieur Paul Ricard, 83140 Le Brusc
Special Museum 11184

Le Bugue

Exposition Géologique du Gouffre de Proumeyssac, 24260 Le Bugue - T: 0553072747
Archaeological Museum 11185

Maison de la Vie Sauvage, Rue de la République, 24260 Le Bugue - T: 0553082810
Local Museum 11186

Le Buisson-de-Cadouin

Cloître de Cadouin, 24480 Le Buisson-de-Cadouin - T: 0553633628/354040, Fax: 0553063094
Historic Site 11187

Le Cannet

Collection Apicole Les Ruchers des Dieux, Chemin de l'Aubarède, Rochville, 06110 Le Cannet - T: 0493450068
Natural History Museum 11188

Le Cateau-Cambrésis

Musée Matisse, Palais Fénelon, 13 Pl du Commandant Richez, 59360 Le Cateau-Cambrésis - T: 0327841315, Fax: 0327840878, E-mail: museematisse@cg59.fr, Internet: http://www.cg59.fr/matisse. Head: Dominique Szymusiak
Fine Arts Museum
Works of Henri Matisse and Auguste Herbin 11189

Le Chambon-sur-Lignon

Musée Historique, Groupe Scolaire, 43400 Le Chambon-sur-Lignon - T: 0471597156
Local Museum 11190

Le Château-d'Oléron

Musée Ostréicole, Sur le Port, 17480 Le Château-d'Oléron - T: 0546475334/56475631
Natural History Museum 11191

Le Château-d'Olonne

Musée Mondial du Sable, Collège Jean-Monnet, Rue des Plasses, 85100 Le Château-d'Olonne - T: 0251210224
Special Museum / Natural History Museum 11192

Le Cloître-Saint-Thégonnec

Musée du Loup, 29223 Le Cloître-Saint-Thégonnec - T: 0298797036
Natural History Museum 11193

Le Conquet

Musée d'Histoire Maritime, Parc Beauséjour, 29217 Le Conquet - T: 0298890427/0007
Historical Museum 11194

Le Coudray-Macquard

Exposition de la Girouette, Rue du Puits Venier, 49260 Le Coudray-Macquard - T: 0241679830
Science&Tech Museum 11195

La Magnanerie du Coudray, Maison de la Soie d'Anjou, Impasse Bel Air, 49260 Le Coudray-Macquard - T: 0241679124. Head: Marle Foyer
Science&Tech Museum 11196

Le Crès

Maison du Patrimoine, Rue de la Monnaie, 34920 Le Crès - T: 0467708737
Local Museum 11197

Le Crestet

Crestet-Centre d'Art, Chemin de la Verrière, 84110 Le Crestet - 0490363500, Fax: 0490363620, E-mail: crestet.centre.art@wanadoo.fr. Head: Cati Chambon
Fine Arts Museum 11198

Le Creusot

Ecomusée de la Communauté Le Creusot Montceau-les-Mines, Château de la Verrerie, 71200 Le Creusot, mail addr: BP 53, 71202 Le Creusot - T: 0385739200, Fax: 0385739209, E-mail: ecomusee@netmuseum.tm.fr, Internet: http://www.netmuseum.tm.fr. Head: Patrice Notteghem
Local Museum 11199

Le Croisic

Océarium du Croisic, Av de Saint-Goustan, 44490 Le Croisic, mail addr: BP 44, 44490 Le Croisic - T: 0240230244, Fax: 0240232293, E-mail: ocearium@aol.fr, Internet: http://www.ocearium-croisic.fr. Head: M.J. Auffret
Natural History Museum - 1992
Marine biology 11200

Le Crozet

Musée des Amis du Vieux Crozet, 42310 Le Crozet - T: 0477643079
Local Museum 11201

Le Douhet

Musée des Traditions Saintongeaises, Château, 17100 Le Douhet - T: 0546977814
Folklore Museum 11202

Le Faouët

Musée du Faouët, 1 Rue de Quimper, 56230 Le Faouët - T: 0297232323, Fax: 0297233674, E-mail: musee.du.faouet@wanadoo.fr. Head: Jean-Marc Michaud
Fine Arts Museum - 1987
Painting, folk art 11203

Musée l'Abeille Vivante, Kercadoret, 56320 Le Faouët - T: 0297230805, Fax: 0297231134, E-mail: info@abeilles-et-fourmis.com. Head: José Nadan
Natural History Museum 11204

Le Folgoët

Musée d'Art Religieux et des Traditions Locales, Pl de la Basilique, 29260 Le Folgoët - T: 0298830192
Local Museum
Local hist, religious art, sculpture 11205

Le Fuilet

Musée Maison du Potier, 2 Rue des Recoins, 49270 Le Fuilet - T: 0241709021, Fax: 0241702622. Head: Gérard Grellier
Decorative Arts Museum / Science&Tech Museum 11206

Le Gavre

Musée Benoist, Grande Rue, 44130 Le Gavre - T: 0240512718
Local Museum 11207

Le Grand-Pressigny

Musée Départemental de la Préhistoire, Château, 37350 Le Grand-Pressigny - T: 0247949020. Head: Jean-Claude Marquet
Archaeological Museum
12th-17th century palace, neolithic and paleolitic finds, fossils 11208

Le Grand-Village-Plage

La Maison Oléronaise, Ferme, Blvd de la Plage, 17370 Le Grand-Village-Plage - T: 0546474344
Folklore Museum 11209

Musée de la Coiffe et du Costume Oléronais, Blvd de la Plage, 17370 Le Grand-Village-Plage - T: 0546474344
Folklore Museum 11210

Le Grau-du-Roi

Musée de la Mer, Aquarium, Rive Gauche, Palais de la Mer, 30240 Le Grau-du-Roi - T: 0466515757
Natural History Museum 11211

Le Havre

Espace Maritime et Portuaire des Docks Vauban, Quai Frissard, 76620 Le Havre - T: 0235245100, Fax: 0235267669, E-mail: musees.histoire@ville-lehavre.fr
Science&Tech Museum 11212

Maison de l'Armateur, 3 Quai de l'Ile, 76600 Le Havre - T: 0235245100
Historical Museum 11213

Musée de l'Ancien Havre, 1 Rue Jérôme Bellarmato, 76600 Le Havre - T: 0235422790, Fax: 0235267669, E-mail: musees.historie@ville-lehavre.fr. Head: M. Maubano
Local Museum - 1955
Drawings and documents related to the founding of Le Havre by François I to contemporary periods 11214

Musée du Prieuré de Graville, 1 Rue Elisée Reclus, 76600 Le Havre - T: 0235471401, 0235245100, Fax: 0235267669, E-mail: musees.histoire@ville.lehavre.fr
Religious Arts Museum - 1926
Sculpture from the 12th to 18th c, religious art 11215

Musée Malraux, 2 Blvd Clémenceau, 76600 Le Havre - T: 0235196262, Fax: 0235199301, E-mail: Marie-Claude.Bourienne@ville-lehavre.fr. Head: Annette Haudiquet
Fine Arts Museum - 1961
16th-19th century French, Dutch, Flemish, and Italian paintings, 18th century modern paintings, modern art 11216

Muséum d'Histoire Naturelle, Pl du Vieux Marché, 76600 Le Havre - T: 0235413728, Fax: 0235421240, E-mail: museum@ville-lehavre.fr, Internet: http://www.ville-lehavre.fr/museum.htm. Head: Gérard Breton
Natural History Museum - 1845
Local and general paleontology, geology, mineralogy, prehistoric archaeology, ornithology, general zoology, botany, prehistory, drawings and paintings by Ch.A. Lesueur - library, research laboratory 11217

Le Hohwald

Musée du Schlittage et de la Forêt, 28 Rue du Herrenhaus, 67140 Le Hohwald - T: 0388083090
Science&Tech Museum 11218

Le Longeron

Exposition sur l'Histoire du Textile Choletais, Ets Mulliez, Usine de Gallard, 49710 Le Longeron - T: 0241637810
Special Museum 11219

181

Le Luc

Musée Historique du Centre-Var, Ancienne Chapelle Sainte-Anne, 24 Rue Victor-Hugo, 83340 Le Luc - T: 0494607012/7020
Local Museum 11220

Musée Régional du Timbre et de la Philatélie, Le Château, Pl de la Convention, 83340 Le Luc - T: 0494479616
Historical Museum / Science&Tech Museum 11221

Le Lude

Château du Lude, 72800 Le Lude - T: 0243946009, Fax: 0243452753, Internet: http://www.chateau-xandcountry.com/chateaux/lude
Decorative Arts Museum 11222

Le Mans

Musée de la Reine Bérengère, 7 à 11 Rue de la Reine Bérengère, 72000 Le Mans - T: 0243473851. Head: Serge Nikitine
Decorative Arts Museum - 1923
Regional ceramics from the Middle Ages to the 20th c, regional hist, pottery from Ligron and Prevelles, furniture, paintings, stain vessel 11223

Musée de l'Automobile du Mans, Circuit des 24 Heures, 72009 Le Mans - T: 0243727224, Fax: 0243853896, E-mail: -musee.automobile.lemans@wanadoo.fr. Head: F. Piquera
Science&Tech Museum - 1961/1991
Motocycles, automobiles, bicycles, etc. 11224

Musée de Tessé, 2 Av de Paderborn, 72000 Le Mans - T: 0243473851, Fax: 0243474993. Head: Françoise Chaserant
Fine Arts Museum / Religious Arts Museum / Ethnology Museum / Decorative Arts Museum / Archaeological Museum 11225

Musée d'Ethnographie, 9 Rue de la Reine Bérengère, 72000 Le Mans - T: 0243473851, Fax: 0243474993. Head: Françoise Chaserant
Ethnology Museum 11226

Musée d'Histoire Naturelle, 204 Av Jean Jaurès, 72100 Le Mans - T: 0243473994. Head: Françoise Chaserant
Natural History Museum 11227

Le Mas-d'Agenais

Collections de la Collégiale Saint-Vincent, 47430 Le Mas-d'Agenais
Historical Museum / Fine Arts Museum 11228

Musée-Palombière, Près de l'Aire de Repos de l'Autoroute, 47430 Le Mas-d'Agenais - T: 0553794714
Special Museum 11229

Le Mas-d'Azil

Musée Préhistorique, Mairie, 09290 Le Mas-d'Azil - T: 0561699018/9722
Archaeological Museum - 1981 11230

Le Mayet-en-Montagne

Musée de la Vannerie L'Osarium, près de l'Eglise, 03250 Le Mayet-en-Montagne - T: 0470597524. Head: Christiane Bonsonnard
Special Museum 11231

Musée des Miniatures Pompiers-Cirque, Rte de Laprugne, Sennepin, 03250 Le Mayet-en-Montagne - T: 0470597460
Science&Tech Museum 11232

Le Mée-sur-Seine

Musée Henri Chapu, 937 Rue Chapu, 77350 Le Mée-sur-Seine - T: 0164395273, Fax: 0164875559
Fine Arts Museum
Originals and castings by sculptor Henri Chapu 11233

Le Mesnil-Durdent

Écovillage, Documentation en Salle d'Exposition, 76460 Le Mesnil-Durdent - T: 0235571420
Local Museum 11234

Le Mesnil-sous-Jumièges

Musée Apicole, Le Monde Merveilleux des Abeilles, Le Halage, 76480 Le Mesnil-sous-Jumièges - T: 0235913676/373244/922367
Special Museum / Natural History Museum 11235

Le Mesnil-sur-Oger

Musée du Champagne, 7 Rte d'Oger, 51190 Le Mesnil-sur-Oger - T: 0326575015
Special Museum 11236

Le Molay-Littry

Musée de la Meunerie, Moulin de Marcy, 14330 Le Molay-Littry - T: 0231225514
Science&Tech Museum
History of mining, 18th century fire-extinguishers, fire-fighting equipment, mining utensils, 1893 plan of coal-pit - library 11237

Le Monastier-sur-Gazeille

Musée Municipal, Château Abbatiale, 43150 Le Monastier-sur-Gazeille - T: 0471039408/8001
Local Museum 11238

Le Mont-Saint-Michel

Archéoscope, Rue Principale, 50116 Le Mont-Saint-Michel - T: 0233601436/09/480937
Historical Museum 11239

Musée Le Mont-Saint-Michel, Pied de l'Abbaye, 50116 Le Mont-Saint-Michel - T: 0233601409
Local Museum 11240

Musée-Logis Thiphaine, 50116 Le Mont-Saint-Michel - T: 0233602334
Local Museum / Decorative Arts Museum 11241

Musée Maritime, Rue Principale, 50116 Le Mont-Saint-Michel - T: 0233602390/1409
Science&Tech Museum 11242

Le Moustier

Collection Préhistorique Pagès, Gisement Le Ruth, 24620 Le Moustier - T: 0553507402. Head: Solange Pagès
Archaeological Museum 11243

Le Muy

Musée de la Libération 15 Août 1944, Ancien Moulin à Huile, Rte Nationale 7, 83490 Le Muy - T: 0494451231
Military Museum 11244

Le Pallet

Musée du Vignoble Nantais, 82 Rue Pierre Abélard, 44330 Le Pallet - T: 0240809013, Fax: 0240804981. Head: Sophie Manceau
Agriculture Museum - 1980
Viticulture, Pierre Abélard and his time 11245

Le Passage

Musée d'Arts et de Traditions Populaires, Restaurant Le Campagnard, 38490 Le Passage - T: 0474881451
Fine Arts Museum / Folklore Museum 11246

Le Pègue

Musée d'Archéologie, 26770 Le Pègue - T: 0475536037, 0475465675, Fax: 0475535863, E-mail: museedupegue@yahoo.fr, Internet: http://museearcheolepegue.com. Head: Henri Veyradier
Archaeological Museum 11247

Le Petit-Couronne

Musée de Pierre-Corneille, 502 Rue Pierre-Corneille, 76650 Le Petit-Couronne - T: 0235681389, Fax: 0235702516. Head: Patrick Perin
Special Museum - 1879
Home of the dramatist Pierre Corneille, exhibits on his life and work, 17th century furniture 11248

Le Pin-au-Haras

Salle d'Exposition sur la Sellerie, Haras du Pin, 61310 Le Pin-au-Haras - T: 0233366868
Special Museum 11249

Le Pin-en-Mauges

Musée des Guerres de Vendée, 49110 Le Pin-en-Mauges - T: 0241700025
Historical Museum 11250

Le Plessis-Brion

Château-Musée, Rue de l'Eglise, 60150 Le Plessis-Brion - T: 0344760907
Decorative Arts Museum 11251

Le Plessis-Macé

Musée-Château, 49220 Le Plessis-Macé - T: 0241326793
Decorative Arts Museum 11252

Le Poët-Laval

Musée du Protestantisme Dauphinois, Vieux Village, 26160 Le Poët-Laval - T: 0475464633. Head: Prof. Pierre Bolle
Religious Arts Museum 11253

Le Pont-de-Beauvoisin

Musée Pontois, Rue Vaucanson, 38480 Le Pont-de-Beauvoisin - T: 0476370337
Local Museum / Fine Arts Museum 11254

Le Pont-de-Montvert

Ecomusée du Mont Lozère, 48220 Le Pont-de-Montvert - T: 0466458073/495300
Local Museum / Folklore Museum / Archaeological Museum 11255

Le Portel

Musée du Costume, Hôtel de Ville, 62480 Le Portel - T: 0321313890
Special Museum 11256

Le Pradet

Musée de la Mine de Cap Garonne, 1000 Chemin du Bau Rouge, 83220 Le Pradet - T: 0494083246, Fax: 0494219585, E-mail: mcg@fr.fm, Internet: http://www.mcg.fr.fm. Head: Roland Joffre
Natural History Museum / Science&Tech Museum 11257

Le Puy-en-Velay

Musée-Atelier Chaleyé, 6 Rue Jules Valette, 43000 Le Puy-en-Velay - T: 0471093138
Fine Arts Museum 11258

Musée Crozatier, Jardin Henri Vinay, 43000 Le Puy-en-Velay - T: 0471093890, Fax: 0471021809. Head: François Xavier Amprimoz
Local Museum
Mineralogy, paleontology, prehistoric finds, Roman remains, Carolingian, Romanesque, and Gotic art, crafts and laces, goldsmith art, paintings, sculpture, mechanics, natural sciences engineering, folk traditions 11259

Musée de la Dentelle du Puy-la-Galerie, 38-40 Rue Raphaël, 43000 Le Puy-en-Velay - T: 0471020168, Fax: 0471029256
Special Museum 11260

Trésor d'Art Regligieux, Cloître du Puy-en-Velay, 12 Blvd Philippe Jourde, 43000 Le Puy-en-Velay - T: 0471054552. Head: Benoît Chabanon
Religious Arts Museum 11261

Le Quiou-Évran

Collection de Vieux Coffres, Château du Hac, 22630 Le Quiou-Évran - T: 0296834306
Decorative Arts Museum 11262

Le Relecq-Kerhuon

Maison du Patrimoine, Pl de la Résistance, 29219 Le Relecq-Kerhuon - T: 0298281414/3698
Local Museum 11263

Le Revest-les-Eaux

Cabinet des Monnais et Médailles du Revest-les-Eaux, 83200 Le Revest-les-Eaux - T: 0494989015
Special Museum / Historical Museum 11264

Musée d'Art Sacré Copte et Byzantin Scete, 5 Rue Carnot, 83200 Le Revest-les-Eaux - T: 0494989059
Religious Arts Museum 11265

Musée d'Art Sacré Occidental, Mairie, 83200 Le Revest-les-Eaux - T: 0494989015
Religious Arts Museum 11266

Le Rozier

Musée de l'Architecture Locale, 48150 Le Rozier - T: 0466456525
Special Museum 11267

Le Sel-de-Bretagne

Musée des Arts et Traditions Populaires, Mairie, 35320 Le Sel-de-Bretagne - T: 0299446740
Folklore Museum / Open Air Museum 11268

Le Teil

Musée Départemental de la Résistance, 13 Rue de la République, 07400 Le Teil - T: 0475491046
Historical Museum 11269

Le Thoureil

Musée Archéologique, Mairie, 49350 Le Thoureil - T: 0241579391/9400
Archaeological Museum 11270

Le Touquet-Paris-Plage

Musée Municipal du Touquet, Av du Golf, 62520 Le Touquet-Paris-Plage - T: 0321056262, Fax: 0321067250. Head: Patrice Deparpe
Fine Arts Museum - 1989
Ecole d'Etaples (1880 to 1914), paintings, contemporary art, sculpture, ceramics, photography - Archives 11271

Le Touvet

Château-Musée du Touvet, Château, 38660 Le Touvet - T: 0476084227
Local Museum 11272

Le Tréport

Musée des Enfants du Vieux-Tréport, 1 Rue de l'Anguainerie "Ancienne Prison", 76470 Le Tréport - T: 0235861336
Special Museum 11273

Le Val

Maison de l'Olivier, Pl du Moulin, 83143 Le Val - T: 0494863469
Special Museum 11274

Musée de la Figurine Historique, Les Tanneries, 83143 Le Val - T: 0494863001
Historical Museum 11275

Musée du Santon, 2 Rue des Fours, 83143 Le Val - T: 0494864878/3469
Special Museum 11276

Le Village du Val au Siècle Dernier, 2 Rue des Fours, 83143 Le Val - T: 0494864878
Historical Museum 11277

Le Val-Saint-Germain

Musée du Château du Marais, 91530 Le Val-Saint-Germain - T: 0164589601
Decorative Arts Museum / Fine Arts Museum 11278

Le Verdon-sur-Mer

Musée du Phare de Cordouan, Phare de Grave, à la Pointe de Grave, 33123 Le Verdon-sur-Mer - T: 0556096178, Fax: 0556096132, Internet: http://www.littoral33.com
Natural History Museum 11279

Le Vernet

Musée du Camp d'Internement, Mairie, 09700 Le Vernet - T: 0561683643, E-mail: LeVernet@netcourrier.com, Internet: http://www.cc_pays_saverdun.fr/saverdun/pages/vernet/accueil.htm. Head: Louis Menendez
Historical Museum 11280

Le Vey

Écomusée de l'Abeille, Les Ruchers de la Suisse Normande, 14570 Le Vey - T: 0231694627
Natural History Museum 11281

Le Vigan (Gard)

Musée Cévenol, 1 Rue des Calquières, 30120 Le Vigan (Gard) - T: 0467810686, Fax: 0467819937, E-mail: museecevenol@hotmail.com. Head: Laurent Puech
Ethnology Museum / Archaeological Museum / Historical Museum - 1963
Folk art, tools, crafts, hist, silk, literature, 18th-19th century costumes 11282

Le Vigan (Lot)

Musée Henri-Giron, Les Prades, 46300 Le Vigan (Lot) - T: 0565413378
Fine Arts Museum 11283

Le Wast

Manoir du Huis Bois-Maison P.N.R. du Boulonnais, 21 Rue Principale, 62142 Le Wast - T: 0321833879
Local Museum 11284

Leaz

Fort l'Ecluse, Archéosite Militaire, 01200 Leaz - T: 0450595845/74321060
Military Museum 11285

Lectoure

Centre de Photographie de Lectoure, Rue Sainte-Claire, 32700 Lectoure - T: 0562688372, Fax: 0562688303, E-mail: photoalectoure@club-internet.fr. Head: François Saint-Pierre
Special Museum 11286

Exposition Permanente Souvenir du Maréchal Lannes, Hôtel de Ville, 32700 Lectoure - T: 0562687698
Military Museum / Decorative Arts Museum - 1975
Memorabilia of Marshal Lannes, items pertaining to the turn of the 19th c 11287

Musée Archéologique, Hôtel de Ville, Pl du Général de Gaulle, 32700 Lectoure - T: 0562687022, Fax: 0562689160. Head: Michel Hue
Archaeological Museum - 19th century
Antiquities, archaeology, ceramics, numismatics, sculptures, religion, oriental cults, taurobolic altars 11288

Musée des Illustres, Hôtel de Ville, 32700 Lectoure - T: 0562687698/7022
Fine Arts Museum 11289

Leers

Musée du Souvenir Leersois, 49 Rue Maréchal-Leclerc, 59115 Leers - T: 0320753206
Historical Museum 11290

Legé

Château-Musée de Bois-Chevalier, 44650 Legé - T: 0240266218
Decorative Arts Museum / Historical Museum 11291

Léhon

Musée Lapidaire, Abbaye Saint-Magloire, 22100 Léhon - T: 0296851475
Archaeological Museum 11292

Lembach

Exposition du Château Fort du Fleckenstein, Nord-Ouest de Lembach, 67510 Lembach - T: 0388944107/4316, Fax: 0388842004, E-mail: info@ot-lembach.com, Internet: http://www.ot-lembach.com. Head: Jacques Gunder
Archaeological Museum 11293

Musée de la Ligne Maginot, Ouvrage du Four à Chaux, 67510 Lembach - T: 0388944316, Fax: 0388942004, E-mail: info@ot-lembach.com, Internet: http://www.ot-lembach.com. Head: Jacques Gunder
Military Museum 11294

Lemberg

Exposition de Cristal Berg, Cristal-Hôtel, 57620 Lemberg - T: 0387064017
Decorative Arts Museum 11295

Lemere

Château du Rivau, 37120 Lemere - T: 0247957747, Fax: 0247957846
Decorative Arts Museum 11296

Lenoncourt

Château-Musée, 54110 Lenoncourt - T: 0383486029
Decorative Arts Museum 11297

Lepuix

Musée des Demineurs, Ballon d'Alsace, 90200 Lepuix - T: 0384290900
Military Museum 11298

Les Adrets-de-l'Estérel

Musée de l'Estérel, Quartier le Mourisque, 83600 Les Adrets-de-l'Estérel - T: 0494409211
Local Museum 11299

Les Andelys

Musée Municipal Nicolas Poussin, Rue Sainte-Clotilde, 27700 Les Andelys - T: 0232540416, Fax: 0232545811
Decorative Arts Museum / Fine Arts Museum - 1971
18th century furniture, 14th-16th century sculpture, local prehistoric and Gallo-Roman findings, contemporary art, memorabilia of the painter Nicolas Poussin (1593-1665) 11300

Les Angles

Muséoparc du Soleil et du Cosmos, 30133 Les Angles - T: 0490256682
Natural History Museum 11301

Les Arcs

Musée Provençal et Folklorique Taradeau, 83460 Les Arcs
Folklore Museum
Household objects, farm and craftsmen's tools, folklore, Roman finds 11302

Les Arques

Musée Zadkine, Mairie, 46250 Les Arques - T: 0565228337, Fax: 0565228755, E-mail: musee.zadkine@wanad00.fr, Internet: http://www.zadkine.org
Fine Arts Museum 11303

Les Barils

Musée Impérial de la Miniature, Musée Atelier de Soldats de Plomb, 14 Rue de Pontgouin, 27130 Les Barils - T: 0232376470. Head: Claude Alexandre
Special Museum 11304

Les Baux-de-Provence

Art Sacré, Chapelle des Pénitents Blancs, 13520 Les Baux-de-Provence - T: 0490543439
Religious Arts Museum 11305

Cathédrale d'Images, D 27, Val d'Enfer, 13520 Les Baux-de-Provence - T: 0490543865
Fine Arts Museum 11306

Château des Baux, 13520 Les Baux-de-Provence - T: 0490545556, Fax: 0490545500. Head: P. de Galliffet
Local Museum 11307

Musée d'Art Contemporain, 13520 Les Baux-de-Provence - T: 0490543403
Fine Arts Museum 11308

Musée de l'Olivier, Chapelle Saint-Blaise, 13520 Les Baux-de-Provence - T: 0490555656
Special Museum 11309

Musée des Santons, Rue de la Calade, 13520 Les Baux-de-Provence - T: 0490543403, Fax: 0490544923. Head: Marie-Christine Roquette-Gept
Special Museum 11310

Musée-Fondation Louis-Jou, Hôtel de Brion, 13520 Les Baux-de-Provence - T: 0490543411, Fax: 0490543417, E-mail: morvan@wanadoo.fr, Internet: http://www.perso.wanadoo.fr/fondationlouisjou/index.html. Head: Héléne Jeanbrau
Fine Arts Museum
library 11311

Musée Historique des Baux, 13520 Les Baux-de-Provence - T: 0490545556
Archaeological Museum 11312

Musée Iconographique et Historique, Hôtel de Manville, Impasse du Château, 13520 Les Baux-de-Provence - T: 0490543403, Fax: 0490544923. Head: Marie-Christine Roquette-Gept
Fine Arts Museum / Historical Museum 11313

Musée Yves Brayer, Hôtel des Porcelet, 13520 Les Baux-de-Provence - T: 0490543699, Internet: http://www.yvesbrayer.com. Head: Hermione Brayer
Fine Arts Museum 11314

Les Brouzils

Le Refuge de Grasla, Mairie des Brouzils, 85260 Les Brouzils - T: 0251422775
Historical Museum 11315

Les Cars

Collections du Château Médiéval des Cars, 87230 Les Cars - T: 0555369022
Decorative Arts Museum 11316

Les Cerqueux-sous-Passavent

Maison-Musée Ted Jacobs, 5 Rue du Petit-Anjou, 49310 Les Cerqueux-sous-Passavent - T: 0241595755, Fax: 0241598093, E-mail: tedart66@aol.com, Internet: http://www.bwwsociety.org/gallery/tedsethjacobs.htm, http://www.musexpo.com/france/jacobs. Head: Ted Seth Jacobs
Fine Arts Museum
Paintings, drawings, murals 11317

Les Épesses

Ecomusée Départemental de la Vendée, Château du Puy du Fou, 85590 Les Épesses - T: 0251576060, Fax: 0251461552. Head: Christophe Vital
Local Museum - 1978
Geology, archeology, medieval, renaissance hist 11318

Écomusée du Chemin de Fer en Vendée, Gare des Épesses, 85590 Les Épesses - T: 0251641111
Science&Tech Museum 11319

Écovillage de Vendée, Grand Parcours du Puy-du-Fou, 85590 Les Épesses - T: 0251641111, Fax: 0251573547, E-mail: info@puydufou.tn.fr. Head: Emmanuel de Villiers
Local Museum 11320

Les Eyzies-de-Tayac-Sireuil

Abri Pataud, Gisement préhistorique et Musée, Rue de la Clape, 24620 Les Eyzies-de-Tayac-Sireuil - T: 0553069246/355040, Fax: 0553063094
Historic Site 11321

Habitat de Laugerie Basse, Gisement Préhistorique, 24620 Les Eyzies-de-Tayac-Sireuil - T: 0553069270, Fax: 0553351755, E-mail: grandroc@perigord.com, Internet: http://www.grandroc.com. Head: A. Moltori
Archaeological Museum 11322

Musée National de Préhistoire, 24620 Les Eyzies-de-Tayac-Sireuil - T: 0553064545, Fax: 0553064555, E-mail: mnp.eyzies@culture.gouv.fr. Head: J.J. Cleyet-Merle
Archaeological Museum - 1921
Palaeolithic artefacts, flint and bone industries, engravings on stone blocks, Neanderthal and Cro-Magnon remains - library 11323

Les Gets

Musée de la Musique Mécanique, Pl de l'Eglise, 74260 Les Gets - T: 0450798575, Fax: 0450798567, E-mail: lesgets@lesgets.com, Internet: http://www.lesgets.com/musee. Head: Denis Bouchet
Music Museum 11324

Les Houches

Musée Montagnard, Pl de l'Eglise 2, 74310 Les Houches - T: 0450545474, E-mail: ot.les.houches@wanadoo.fr, Internet: http://www.montblanconline.fr
Folklore Museum 11325

Les Iffs

Château de Montmuran, 35630 Les Iffs - T: 0299458888/8369, Fax: 0299458490, E-mail: chateau.montmuran@wanadoo.fr, Internet: http://www.montmuran.com. Head: H. de la Villeon
Local Museum 11326

Les Loges-Marchis

Musée Artisanal Animé, Rte de Fougères, 50600 Les Loges-Marchis - T: 0233492767
Special Museum 11327

Les Mages

Collection Historique du Café, Le Pérou, Quartier des Tronquises, 30960 Les Mages - T: 0466256611
Special Museum 11328

Musée de Statues d'Enfants, Lamac, Villaret, 30960 Les Mages - T: 0466257308
Fine Arts Museum 11329

Les Matelles

Musée de la Préhistoire, Rue du Musée, 34270 Les Matelles - T: 0467841868/3023. Head: Laure Gigou
Archaeological Museum 11330

Les Ponts-de-Cé

Musée des Coiffes d'Anjou, Château, 4 Rue Charles de Gaulle, 49130 Les Ponts-de-Cé - T: 0241446864/797575
Folklore Museum 11331

Les Rairies

Maison de la Terre Cuite, Rte de Fougeré, 49430 Les Rairies - T: 0241763312, Fax: 0241691765, Internet: http://perso.wanadoo.fr/maison-terre-cuite. Head: Pascal Villoutreix
Science&Tech Museum 11332

Les Riceys

Musée des Vieux Tacots, Garage Christian Fournier, Les Riceys-Bas, 10340 Les Riceys - T: 0325293153/337238, Fax: 0325295977
Science&Tech Museum 11333

Les Rosiers-sur-Loire

Moulin à Farine et Musée de l'Outillage, Moulin des Basses-Terres, 49350 Les Rosiers-sur-Loire - T: 0241518293
Science&Tech Museum 11334

Les Rousses

Musée des Traditions Rousselandes, 39220 Les Rousses - T: 0384605113
Folklore Museum 11335

Musée du Ski et du Bobsleigh, Centre d'Accueil, 39220 Les Rousses - T: 0384605113
Special Museum 11336

Les Sables-d'Olonne

Musée-Chalutier Le Kifanlo, OCEAM, BP 190, 85100 Les Sables-d'Olonne - T: 0251320328
Special Museum 11337

Musée de la Guerre de Vendée, 72 Rue Napoléon, 85100 Les Sables-d'Olonne - T: 0251210327
Historical Museum 11338

Musée de la Mer OCEAM, Château Saint-Clair, La Chaume, 85100 Les Sables-d'Olonne - T: 0251320328
Science&Tech Museum 11339

Musée de l'Abbaye Sainte-Croix, Rue de Verdun, 85100 Les Sables-d'Olonne - T: 0251320116, Fax: 0251320117, E-mail: musee-lessables@wanadoo.fr. Head: Benoît Decron
Local Museum / Ethnology Museum / Fine Arts Museum
Local prehistoric finds, ethnography, navigation, contemporary art 11340

Les Salles-sur-Verdon

La Maison du Lac, 83630 Les Salles-sur-Verdon - T: 0494702184/2001
Local Museum 11341

Les Ternes

Château, 15100 Les Ternes - T: 0471730139
Decorative Arts Museum 11342

Les Vans

Exposition Permanente d'Art Paysan, Pl du Marché, 07140 Les Vans - T: 0475372182
Folklore Museum 11343

Musée d'Archéologie et d'Histoire, Centre d'Accueil, 07140 Les Vans - T: 0475373290
Local Museum 11344

Lescar

Musée Art et Culture, Rue de la Cité, 64230 Lescar - T: 0559810618/0559813191, Fax: 0559811871, E-mail: a.loustau@mairie-lescar.fr. Head: Alain Loustau
Folklore Museum / Archaeological Museum 11345

Musée Bérnais d'Art Populaire → Musée Art et Culture

Lesneven

Musée du Léon, 12 Rue de la Marne, 29260 Lesneven - T: 0298211718, Fax: 0298833019/0993/3357. Head: François Barjou
Local Museum - 1985
Prehist, religious art, furniture, costume - library 11346

Lesparre-Médoc

Musée de la Tour d'Honneur, Château, 33340 Lesparre-Médoc - T: 0556410675/2196
Local Museum 11347

Lesparrou

Musée des Vieux Métiers, 09300 Lesparrou - T: 0561591435
Local Museum 11348

Lespugue

Dépôt Archéologique, Mairie, 31350 Lespugue - T: 0561882495/7884/891247
Archaeological Museum 11349

Lestelle-Bétharram

Musée de la Congrégation des Pères de Bétharram, 64800 Lestelle-Bétharram - T: 0559719230
Religious Arts Museum / Local Museum 11350

Leutenheim

Ouvrage de la Ligne Maginot, Abri du Heidenbuckel, 67480 Leutenheim - T: 0388564039, Fax: 0388530375. Head: Gérard Lehmann
Military Museum 11351

Levallois-Perret

Musée de la Pêche et da la Nature, APNLE, 22 Allée Claude-Monet, 92300 Levallois-Perret - T: 0147517732, Fax: 0147580396, E-mail: mpnl@pechemedia.com, Internet: http://www.pechemedia.com/MPNL. Head: Sandrine Armirail
Special Museum / Natural History Museum 11352

Levens

Maison du Portal, 1 Pl Victor Masseglia, 06670 Levens - T: 0493798584. Head: Jean-Pierre Augier
Fine Arts Museum 11353

Musée Éducatif d'Entomologie de Levens, Les Traverses, 06670 Levens - T: 0493797012, Internet: http://www2.ac-nice.fr/svt/instituts/levens. Head: Guy Hug
Natural History Museum 11354

Lèves

Musée "Le Grenier de l'Histoire", 11bis Rue des Grands Prés, 28300 Lèves - T: 0237217777/1310
Local Museum 11355

Levie

Musée de l'Alta Rocca, Quartier Sorba, 20170 Levie - T: 0495784634/4798
Archaeological Museum - 1963
Archeological coll 11356

Levroux

Musée du Cuir et du Parchemin, Rue Gambetta, 36110 Levroux - T: 0254358358. Head: Pierre Lavie
Special Museum 11357

Lewarde

Centre Historique Minier, Fosse Delloye, 59287 Lewarde - T: 0327958282, Fax: 0327958283, E-mail: contact@chm-lewarde.com, Internet: http://www.chm-lewarde.com. Head: André Dubuc
Science&Tech Museum 11358

Lézignan-Corbières

Musée de la Vigne et du Vin, 3 Rue Turgot, 11200 Lézignan-Corbières - T: 0468270757, Fax: 0468273702, E-mail: asfodel@wanadoo.fr. Head: Claudine Saury-Serres
Agriculture Museum - 1973
Implements, documents, and machinery used by wine growers over the past two c 11359

Lezoux

Musée de la Poterie Gallo-Romaine, 1 Impasse Pasteur, 63190 Lezoux - T: 0473730100/0313. Head: Hugues Vertet
Decorative Arts Museum 11360

Lherm

Musée des Traditions Populaires Cap Al Campestre, 31 Chemin Français, 31600 Lherm - T: 0561511456, Fax: 0561511456, E-mail: renard.ferasin@worldonline.fr. Head: Luigi Ferasin
Folklore Museum 11361

Lhomme

Musée de la Viticulture, Rue du Val de Loire, 72340 Lhomme - T: 0243444362
Agriculture Museum 11362

L'Hôpital

Maison d'Histoire Locale, 57490 L'Hôpital - T: 0387932933
Historical Museum 11363

Lhuis

Conservatoire d'Outils, Maison Forte de Vareppe à Groslée, 01680 Lhuis - T: 0474398296/7284
Local Museum 11364

Liart

Maison de la Thiérache, 08290 Liart - T: 0324544833
Local Museum 11365

Libourne

Domaine de Galet, Collection Archéologique, 33500 Libourne - T: 0557414186
Archaeological Museum 11366

Musée des Beaux-Arts et d'Archéologie, 42 Pl Abel Surchamp, 33500 Libourne - T: 0557553344, Fax: 0557553376, E-mail: contact@musees-libourne.org. Head: Bernard Bégouin
Fine Arts Museum / Archaeological Museum / Decorative Arts Museum
16th-20th century paintings, sculptures, decorative arts 11367

Lichtenberg

Château de Lichtenberg, 67340 Lichtenberg - T: 0388899872, Fax: 0388899900, Internet: http://www.lichtenberg-alsace.com. Head: Gaston Dann
Historic Site 11368

Liessies

Conservatoire du Patrimoine Religieux, Presbytère, Rue Foch, 59740 Liessies - T: 0327606611
Religious Arts Museum 11369

Liffol-le-Grand

Musée Archéologique, 22 Rue Neuve, 88350 Liffol-le-Grand - T: 0329066025/6223
Archaeological Museum 11370

Lignac

Musée de Château Guillaume, Village de Château Guillaume, 36370 Lignac - T: 0254256281, Fax: 0254257202
Historic Site 11371

Lignan-de-Bordeaux

Musée de Lignan et du Canton de Créon, Ancien Presbytère, 33360 Lignan-de-Bordeaux - T: 0556212353
Local Museum 11372

Lignerolles

Musée de l'Epicerie d'Autrefois, Rte de Mortagne à l'Aigle, 61190 Lignerolles - T: 0233257355
Special Museum 11373

Ligny-en-Barrois

Musée d'Art et d'Histoire, Tour du Luxembourg, 55500 Ligny-en-Barrois - T: 0329780222
Fine Arts Museum / Historical Museum 11374

Ligny-le-Ribault

Ecomusée d'Arts et Traditions Populaires, 45240 Ligny-le-Ribault - T: 0238454319
Folklore Museum 11375

La Maison du Cerf, Rue du Général Leclerc, 45240 Ligny-le-Ribault - T: 0238454544, Fax: 0238454544. Head: Michele Lombardi
Special Museum / Natural History Museum 11376

L'Ile-Bouchard

Musée du Bouchardais, Ancienne Gare, 37220 L'Ile-Bouchard - T: 0247585015
Folklore Museum 11377

L'Ile-Rousse

Musée Océanographique, 20220 L'Ile-Rousse - T: 0495602781, Fax: 0495604420
Natural History Museum
Live animals (fishs, invertebrates) 11378

Lille

Collections Linières, 12 Rue des Weppes, 59000 Lille - T: 0320550263
Special Museum / Historical Museum 11379

Musée Charles de Gaulle, 9 Rue Princesse, 59000 Lille - T: 0328381205, Fax: 0328381209, E-mail: maisonnatale@charles-de-gaulle.org, Internet: http://www.charles-de-gaulle.org. Head: Marie-Cornélie Lenglet
Special Museum 11380

Musée d'Arts Populaires de Lille-Sud, 12 Rue Balzac, 59000 Lille - T: 0320537431. Head: J.-P. Parmentier
Folklore Museum 11381

Musée de Géologie, 19 Rue de Bruxelles, 59000 Lille - T: 0320533846
Natural History Museum 11382

Musée de l'Hospice Comtesse, 32 Rue de la Monnaie, 59800 Lille - T: 0320495090, Fax: 0320495490. Head: A. Cordonnier
Local Museum - 1963
13th century former hospital, Lille tiles, Dutch and Flemish furnishings, sculpture, flemish and Dutch paintings, ceramics, regional history, customs, musical instruments, regional and Dutch decorative arts 11383

Musée des Beaux-Arts, Pl de la République, 59000 Lille - T: 0320067800, Fax: 0320067815, E-mail: consvmba.lille@wanadoo.fr. Head: Arnauld Brejon de Lavergnée
Fine Arts Museum - 1801
Flemish, French, Dutch, Spanish, Italian, and German paintings, Italian and French drawings - library 11384

Musée des Canonniers Sédentaires de Lille, 44 Rue des Canonniers, 59800 Lille - T: 0320555890. Head: Jean-Marie Lesaffre
Military Museum / Historical Museum
Local and military history 11385

Musée d'Histoire Naturelle, 19 Rue de Bruxelles, 59000 Lille - T: 0328553080, Fax: 0320861482, E-mail: mh.n.l@wanadoo.fr, Internet: museumde-lille@com.fr. Head: Bertrand Radigois
Natural History Museum 11386

Musée Diocésan d'Art Religieux, 68 Rue Royale, 59000 Lille - T: 0320725361. Head: L.-E. Ghesquières
Religious Arts Museum - 1930
Romanesque statues, goldsmith work, wood sculptures, paintings 11387

Musée Houiller, 19 Rue de Bruxelles, 59000 Lille - T: 0320533846
Natural History Museum 11388

Musée Industriel et d'Ethnologie, 19 Rue de Bruxelles, 59000 Lille - T: 0328553080, Fax: 0320861482, E-mail: m.h.n.l@wanadoo.fr, Internet: museumdelille.com.fr. Head: Bertrand Radigois
Ethnology Museum 11389

Musée Pasteur, Calmette et Guérin, 1 Rue du Professeur Calmette, 59800 Lille - T: 0320877800
Special Museum 11390

Palais Rihour, Pl Rihour, 59002 Lille - T: 0320219421, Fax: 0320219420, E-mail: b.goval@lilletourism.com, Internet: http://www.lilletourism.com. Head: Jean Delannoy
Local Museum 11391

Lillebonne

Musée Municipal, 7 Rue Victor Hugo, 76170 Lillebonne - T: 0235385373, Fax: 0235385373. Head: Hebert Didier
Ethnology Museum / Archaeological Museum / Natural History Museum
Local history, Gallo-Roman finds, porcelain, decorative arts, furnishings, ornithology, folk art and customs 11392

Muséosite de l'Amphithéâtre Gallo-Romain, 76170 Lillebonne - T: 0235985510, Fax: 0235702516
Historic Site 11393

Limoges

FRAC Limousin, Impasse des Charentes, 87100 Limoges - T: 0555770898, Fax: 0555779070, E-mail: frac.limousin@wanadoo.fr. Head: Yannick Miloux
Fine Arts Museum 11394

Haviland, Pavillon de la Porcelaine, Zone Industrielle de Magré, Rte de Toulouse, 87000 Limoges - T: 0555302186, Fax: 0555301950. Head: Patrick Roure
Decorative Arts Museum 11395

Maison Traditionnelle de la Boucherie, 36 Rue de la Boucherie, 87000 Limoges - T: 0555344687
Special Museum 11396

Musée de la Résistance, Pl de la Cathédrale, 87000 Limoges - T: 0555456341, Fax: 0555456570. Head: Stéphane Capot
Historical Museum 11397

Musée de l'Automobile de Limoges, Centre Commercial la Coupole, 87000 Limoges - T: 0555354383
Science&Tech Museum 11398

Musée des Distilleries Limougeaudes, 52 Rue de Belfort, 87100 Limoges - T: 0555774659
Special Museum 11399

Musée du Phonographe et de Musique Mécanique, Hôtel de la Paix, 25 Pl Jourdan, 87000 Limoges - T: 0555343600/323706
Music Museum 11400

Musée-Maison Natale du Maréchal Jourdan, 37 Rue Pont Saint-Étienne, 87000 Limoges - T: 0555337010/343615
Military Museum 11401

Musée Municipal de l'Évêché, Pl de la Cathédrale, 87000 Limoges - T: 0555459810, Fax: 0555344414. Head: Véronique Notin
Local Museum / Decorative Arts Museum / Fine Arts Museum - 1912
18th century palace, Egyptian and Gallo-Roman antiquities and frescoes, enamel from the 12th century to the present, metalwork, paintings, sculptures, drawings and prints (16th-20th century) - Documentation and research center of invaluable resource with an unique collection of records, documentary photograph library 11402

Musée National Adrien Dubouché, Pl Winston Churchill, 87000 Limoges - T: 0555330850, Fax: 0555330855. Head: Chantal Meslin-Perrier
Decorative Arts Museum - 1900
Ceramics, pottery, faience, stoneware, porcelain, glasses 11403

Limousis

Musée Cabernicole, Grotte de Limousis, Près Hameau de Mormorières, 11600 Limousis - T: 0468775026
Archaeological Museum 11404

Limoux

Musée Petiet, Promenade du Tivoli, 11300 Limoux - T: 0468318503
Fine Arts Museum 11405

Liré

Musée Joachim du Belley, Le Grand Logis, 1 Rue Pierre de Rossard, 49530 Liré - T: 0240090413, Fax: 0240090087, E-mail: musee-du-bellay@wanadoo.fr, Internet: http://www.musee-du-bellay.fr.st. Head: Chloé Bernaudeau
Local Museum - 1958
Documents on the poet Joachim du Bellay (1522-1560) 11406

Lisieux

Musée d'Art et d'Histoire de Lisieux, 38 Blvd Pasteur, 14100 Lisieux - T: 0231620770, Fax: 0231624285. Head: Jean Bergeret
Local Museum - 1834/1968
19th century paintings, pottery, Gallo-Roman art - library 11407

Musée-Maison de Sainte-Thérèse, 22 Chemin des Buissonnets, 14100 Lisieux - T: 0231620870
Religious Arts Museum 11408

Salle des Souvenirs, Carmel de Lisieux, 37 Rue du Carmel, 14100 Lisieux - T: 0231629046, Fax: 0231622735, E-mail: accueil-information@therese-de-lisieux.com
Special Museum 11409

Salle Dorée du Palais Episcopal, Pl Thiers, 14100 Lisieux - T: 0231620841
Decorative Arts Museum / Fine Arts Museum 11410

L'Isle-Adam

Musée d'Art et d'Histoire Louis Senlecq, 46 Grande Rue, 95290 L'Isle-Adam - T: 0134694544, Fax: 0134082340, Internet: http://www.ville-isle-adam.fr. Head: Frédéric Chappey
Fine Arts Museum / Historical Museum - 1939
Local hist, works of artists who lived here, paintings by Vlaminck, Dupré, Joyant, etc, etchings, historical documents, ceramic dept, terracotta (19th c) - library, archives 11411

L'Isle-Jourdain

Musée Campanaire, Pl de l'Hôtel de Ville, 32600 L'Isle-Jourdain - T: 0562073001, Fax: 0562071222. Head: Michel Hue
Historical Museum - 1994
Bells from various periods and countries, archaeology, industrial heritage 11412

Lisle-sur-Tarn

Musée Raimond-Lafage, Rue Victor Maziès, 81310 Lisle-sur-Tarn - T: 0563404545/333518
Fine Arts Museum 11413

Listrac-Médoc

Collections d'Anciens Outils de Tonnellerie, Château Peyredon-Lagravette, 33480 Listrac-Médoc - T: 0556580555
Science&Tech Museum 11414

Collections d'Objets de Chais et Tonnellerie, Château Cap Léon-Vevrin, 33480 Listrac-Médoc - T: 0556580728
Science&Tech Museum 11415

Collections d'Outils de Tonnellerie et d'Appareils Viticoles Anciens, Château Fonréaud-Lestage, 33480 Listrac-Médoc - T: 0556580243
Science&Tech Museum 11416

Lit-et-Mixe

Musée des Vieilles Landes, 40170 Lit-et-Mixe - T: 0558428577
Folklore Museum 11417

Livarot

Musée sur le Fromage de Livarot, Manoir de l'Isle, 68 Rue Marcel-Gambier, 14140 Livarot - T: 0231634313
Special Museum 11418

Livry-Gargan

Musée d'Art et d'Histoire, Château de la Forêt, Av du Consul-Général-Nordling, 93190 Livry-Gargan - T: 0143887146
Local Museum / Fine Arts Museum 11419

Lizio

Ecomusée de la Ferme et des Vieux Métiers, 56460 Lizio - T: 0297749301, Fax: 0297747084, E-mail: guillardc@minitel.net. Head: Alain Guillard
Folklore Museum - 1985
Reconstructed old-fashioned (work)shops, farm houses; a 1900 schoolroom; old furniture, tools, clothing 11420

Loches (Indre-et-Loire)

Collections du Château, Château de Loches, 37600 Loches (Indre-et-Loire) - T: 0247590132
Fine Arts Museum / Decorative Arts Museum 11421

Maison Lansyer, 1 Rue Lansyer, 37600 Loches (Indre-et-Loire) - T: 0547590545, Fax: 0247940758, E-mail: lochesentouraine@wanadoo.fr
Fine Arts Museum 11422

Lochieu

Musée Rural du Valmorey, Maison Renaissance, 01260 Lochieu - T: 0479875223/74211520
Folklore Museum 11423

Lochrist-Inzinzac

Ecomusée Industriel de Lochrist-Inzinzac, Zone Industrielle, 56650 Lochrist-Inzinzac - T: 0297369821, Fax: 0297369821. Head: Gisèle Le Rouzic-Giovanneli
Science&Tech Museum
Metallurgy, forging (Musée des Metallurgistes des Forges d'Hennebont), hydraulic engineering (La Maison de l'Eau et de l'Hydraulique) 11424

Locronan

Conservatoire Régional de l'Affiche, Château de Kerguénolé, 29136 Locronan - T: 0298518059
Special Museum 11425

Musée des Arts et Traditions Populaires, Pl de la Mairie, 29136 Locronan - T: 0298917005/14
Fine Arts Museum / Decorative Arts Museum - 1934
Painting, religious art, handicraft 11426

Loctudy

Manoir de Kerazan, 29750 Loctudy - T: 0298874040, Fax: 0298874383. Head: Christoph de Calbiac
Fine Arts Museum
Castle (end of 16th c) with coll of european painting (16th-20th c), contemporary art 11427

Musée de la Conserverie Le Gall, Rue de la Grandière, 29750 Loctudy - T: 0298874008, 0130303537. Head: Jean-Philippe Chapalain
Science&Tech Museum
Industrial heritage, fish cannery 19th c 11428

Lodève

Musée de Lodève, Hôtel du Cardinal de Fleury, Sq Georges Auric, 34700 Lodève - T: 0467888610, Fax: 0467444833, E-mail: museelodeve@lodeve.com. Head: M. Valles-Bled
Fine Arts Museum / Local Museum 11429

Musée Fleury → Musée de Lodève

Lods

Musée de la Vigne et du Vin, Rte d'Athose, 25930 Lods - T: 0381609354
Agriculture Museum 11430

Lohéac

Manoir Automobile, La Cour Neuve, 35990 Lohéac - T: 0299340232, Fax: 0299340501. Head: Michel Hommell
Science&Tech Museum 11431

Loigny-la-Bataille

Musée de Sonis, Bataille du 2 Décembre 1870, Attenant à l'Eglise, 28140 Loigny-la-Bataille - T: 0237997496/901259, Fax: 0237997496
Military Museum 11432

Loix-en-Ré

Ecomusée du Marais Salant, Rte de la Passe, 17111 Loix-en-Ré - T: 0546290383, Fax: 0546290677, E-mail: ecomuseemarais@aol.com, Internet: http://www.marais-salant.com. Head: B. Poitevin
Open Air Museum / Ethnology Museum 11433

Lombez

Exposition Permanente, Mairie, 32220 Lombez - T: 0562623920
Special Museum 11434

Longfosse

Collection d'Art Céramique, Atelier Delarue, 25 Rue de la Brasserie, 62240 Longfosse - T: 0321830010/11
Decorative Arts Museum 11435

Musée de la Faïence, Géo Martel, Chaussée Brunehaut, 62240 Longfosse - T: 0321916828
Decorative Arts Museum 11436

Longueville

Musée Ferroviaire, 77650 Longueville - T: 0164602626, Fax: 0142931857
Science&Tech Museum 11437

Longuyon

Musée de la Ligne Maginot, Ouvrage du Fermont, 54260 Longuyon - T: 0382393534/896651
Military Museum 11438

Longwy

Faïences et Emaux, Porte de France, Rue de la Manutention, 54400 Longwy - T: 0382238519, Fax: 0382445437. Head: Dominique Dreycus
Local Museum - 1977
Historic finds, local hist, ornamental cast iron plates, 19th century faience, 19th century sculpture 11439

Musée de la Céramique Saint-Jean-l'Aigle, Château de la Faïencerie, Rue de la Chiers, 54400 Longwy - T: 0382245820, Fax: 0382245820
Decorative Arts Museum 11440

Musée du Fer à Repasser, Rue de la Manutention, 54400 Longwy - T: 0382238519, Fax: 0382445437. Head: Jean-Pierre Zuccali
Science&Tech Museum 11441

Lons-le-Saunier

Musée d'Archéologie, 25 Rue Richebourg, 39000 Lons-le-Saunier - T: 0384471213, Fax: 0384243034, E-mail: - musee.archeologie.lons@wanadoo.fr. Head: Marie-Jeanne Lambert
Archaeological Museum - 1812
Paleontology, archaeology from the West Jura areal incl Plateosaurus, the oldest dinosaur found in France, Jurassic fossils, prehist industry from Arlay and Gigny, neolithic lake sites as Chalain and Clairvaux, Bronze Age finds, Iron Age tumulus, Gallo-roman sites, Merovingian cemeteries and medieval castle - library, archives 11442

Musée Municipal, Pl Philibert de Chalon, 39000 Lons-le-Saunier, mail addr: 39000 Lons-le-Saunier - T: 0384476430, Fax: 0384478896. Head: Anne Dary
Fine Arts Museum
19th century French paintings and sculptures, 17th-18th century Flemish, Italian and French paintings 11443

Loqueffret

Maison des Pilhaoueriens, Ancien Presbytère, 29126 Loqueffret - T: 0298264450/219090
Ethnology Museum 11444

Maison du Recteur et de la Paroisse, Ancien Presbytère, 29530 Loqueffret - T: 0298264450/219090
Local Museum 11445

Lorgues

Musée Pictural Architectural Bob-Julien, Moulin Tré-Barry, Rue Barry, 83510 Lorgues - T: 0494737435
Special Museum 11446

Lorient

Musée de Tradition des Fusiliers Marins, 56100 Lorient, mail addr: c/o Commandant de l'Ecole des Fusiliers Marins, 56998 Lorient - T: 0297125352
Military Museum 11447

Loriol-sur-Drôme

Musée de l'Insolite, Manent Max, 28 Grand Rue, 26270 Loriol-sur-Drôme - T: 0475616388
Special Museum 11448

Lormont

Musée des Amis du Vieux Lormont, 1 Rue de la République, 33310 Lormont - T: 0556063560
Local Museum 11449

Lorris

Musée de l'Église de Lorris, Église Notre-Dame, 45260 Lorris - T: 0238948419/5324
Music Museum 11450

Musée Départemental de la Résistance et de la Déportation, Esplanade Charles de Gaulle, 45260 Lorris - T: 0238948419
Historical Museum 11451

Loubaresse

Écomusée de la Margeride, Ferme de Pierre Allègre, 15390 Loubaresse - T: 0471234296, Fax: 0471234296, E-mail: ecomusee-margeride@wanadoo.fr. Head: Colette Meindre
Ethnology Museum 11452

Loubens-Lauragais

Musée de Jules Gounon-Loubens, Château, 31460 Loubens-Lauragais - T: 0561831208, Fax: 0561831208, E-mail: chateaudeloubens@wanadoo.fr, Internet: http://www.chateaude-loubens.com. Head: Charles-Louis d' Orgeix
Historical Museum / Historic Site / Special Museum 11453

L'Oudon-Notre-Dame-de-Fresnay

Musée d'Histoire et Traditions Populaires, Foyer Rural du Billot, 14170 L'Oudon-Notre-Dame-de-Fresnay - T: 0231206272
Local Museum 11454

Loudun

Musée Charbonneau-Lassay, 24 Rue de Martray, 86200 Loudun - T: 0549980848/1596
Archaeological Museum / Folklore Museum - 1947
Celtic, Egyptian, and Gallo-Roman antiquities, armaments, African art, local art, paintings (19th c) 11455

Musée Renaudot, Rue Renaudot, 86200 Loudun - T: 0549982733/1596
Special Museum - 1981
Birthplace of Théophraste Renoudot the founder of the French press, furniture, documents, stamps, art, household articles 11456

Louhans

Ecomusée de la Presse Bourguignonne, 29 Rue des Dodânes, 71500 Louhans - T: 0385762716
Special Museum / Science&Tech Museum 11457

Musée Hospitalier et Apothicairerie, 3 Rue du Capitaine Vic, 71500 Louhans - T: 0385755432
Decorative Arts Museum 11458

Louhossoa

Musée Créatif du Tissage, Rte de Cambo, 64250 Louhossoa - T: 0559933207
Special Museum 11459

Louisfert

Musée René Louis Cadou, 3 Rue René Louis Cadou, 44110 Louisfert - T: 0240812264/2045
Special Museum 11460

Loupiac

Musée Archéologique, 33410 Loupiac - T: 0556629382/9962
Archaeological Museum 11461

Musée de la Vigne et du Vin, Château Mazarin, 33410 Loupiac - T: 0556629923
Special Museum 11462

Loupian

Musée Archéologique et Historique, Chapelle Saint-Hippolyte, 34140 Loupian - T: 0467438207
Archaeological Museum / Historical Museum 11463

Lourdes

Collections de la Chapelle du Château-Fort, Rue Le Bondidier, 65100 Lourdes
Decorative Arts Museum 11464

Historial de la Médaille Miraculeuse, La Vie de Sainte Catherine Labouré, 3 Rue du Porche, 65100 Lourdes - T: 0562944221
Historical Museum 11465

Musée Bernadette, Pavillon Notre-Dame, Blvd de la Grotte, 65100 Lourdes - T: 0562427878, Fax: 0562427938
Religious Arts Museum 11466

Musée Cachot, 15 Rue des Petits Fossés, 65100 Lourdes - T: 0562945130
Historical Museum 11467

Musée de la Nativité La Crèche Animée, 21 Quai Saint-Jean, 65100 Lourdes - T: 0562947100, Fax: 0562421717. Head: Pierre Sarie
Religious Arts Museum 11468

Musée de Lourdes, 11 Rue de l'Egalité, 65100 Lourdes - T: 0562942800
Local Museum 11469

Musée du Gemmail, 72 Rue de la Grotte, Pavillon Notre-Dame, 65100 Lourdes - T: 0562941315
Fine Arts Museum 11470

Musée du Moulin de Boly, 12 Rue Bernadette Soubirous, 65100 Lourdes - T: 0562427878, Fax: 0562427938
Religious Arts Museum 11471

Musée du Panorama de la Vie de Sainte-Bernadette, 38 Rue de la Grotte, 65100 Lourdes - T: 0562944384
Religious Arts Museum 11472

Musée du Petit Lourdes, 68 Av Peyramale, 65100 Lourdes - T: 0562942436
Historical Museum 11473

Musée Funéraire du Château, Rue du Fort, 65100 Lourdes - T: 0562940204
Special Museum 11474

Musée Grévin de Lourdes, 87 Rue de la Grotte, 65100 Lourdes - T: 0562943374, Fax: 0562420384
Special Museum 11475

Musée-Maison Paternelle de Bernadette, Moulin Lacadé, 2 Rue Bernadette, 65100 Lourdes - T: 0562942251
Religious Arts Museum 11476

Musée Notre-Dame, Musée du Gemmail, Pavillon Notre-Dame, Blvd Rémy-Sempé, 65100 Lourdes - T: 0562427878, Fax: 0562427938
Religious Arts Museum 11477

Musée Pyrénéen, Château Fort, 65100 Lourdes - T: 0562423737, Fax: 0562945523. Head: Geneviève Marsan
Local Museum - 1920
Costumes, ceramics, musical instruments, furniture, ethnography and local hist - library 11478

Lourdios-Ichère

Espace Muséal Un Village se Raconte, 64570 Lourdios-Ichère - T: 0559344484/4158
Historical Museum 11479

Louresse

Musée Troglodytique, Rochemenier, 49700 Louresse - T: 0241591815, Fax: 0241593513, E-mail: troglody@club-internet.fr, Internet: http://perso.club-internet.fr/troglody. Head: Victor Leray
Agriculture Museum - 1967
Countryside furniture, farming implements 11480

Lourmarin

Château de Lourmarin, 84160 Lourmarin - T: 0490681523, Fax: 0490682519. Head: Maurice Flory
Fine Arts Museum / Decorative Arts Museum / Historic Site
Furnished Renaissance palace, collection of engravings by Piranesi - Library 11481

Loury

Musée d'Archéologie et d'Histoire Locale, Société Archéologique et Historique, Mairie, Parc du Château, 45470 Loury - T: 0238656011
Archaeological Museum / Historical Museum 11482

Louviers

Maison Naïve, 80 Rue du Bal Champêtre, 27400 Louviers - T: 0232402271
Fine Arts Museum 11483

Musée Municipal, Pl Ernest Thorel, 27400 Louviers - T: 0232095854, Fax: 0232095813. Head: Michel Natier
Decorative Arts Museum / Fine Arts Museum - 1872
Ceramics, local and regional history, antiquities, furnishings, paintings, sculpture, contemporary art 11484

Louvres

Musée Intercommunal d'Histoire et d'Archéologie, Rue des Deux-Églises, 95380 Louvres - T: 0134685922, Fax: 0134685922, E-mail: asigaud@roissy.online.fr, Internet: http://roissy.online.com. Head: Anne Sigaud
Archaeological Museum / Historical Museum 11485

Musée Municipal d'Histoire et d'Archéologie → Musée Intercommunal d'Histoire et d'Archéologie

Lovagny

Musée Léon Marès, Château de Montrottier, 74330 Lovagny - T: 0450462302, Fax: 0450461148, E-mail: montiottier@aol.com. Head: M.C. Courtial
Military Museum / Decorative Arts Museum - 1919
Faience, ivories, weapons, rare objects from Africa and the Far East, 16th century bronze reliefs, furnitures 11486

Lozanne

Musée de Géologie, Usine Ciment Lafarge, 69380 Lozanne - T: 0478437060
Natural History Museum 11487

Luc-sur-Mer

Musée Maison de la Baleine, Parc Municipal, 14530 Luc-sur-Mer - T: 0231975593, Fax: 0231968182, E-mail: mairie-luc-sur-mer@wanadoo.fr
Natural History Museum 11488

Luçay-le-Male

Musée de la Pierre à Fusil, 4 Rue Roger Ménars, 36600 Luçay-le-Male - T: 0254404331
Military Museum 11489

Lucey

Musée Vivant de la Polyculture, 94 Grande Rue, 54200 Lucey - T: 0383438521
Special Museum 11490

Lunel

Archéosite de l'Oppidum d'Ambrussum, 34400 Lunel - T: 0467710137
Archaeological Museum 11491

Lunel-Vieil

Archéosite Gallo-Romain, Centre Archéologique, 34400 Lunel-Vieil - T: 0467711280/3118
Archaeological Museum 11492

Lunéville

Musée d'Art et d'Histoire, Château, 54300 Lunéville - T: 0383762357. Head: Pierre Chanel
Decorative Arts Museum / Military Museum - 1860
18th century faiences of the area, military artifacts 11493

Lusigny-sur-Barse

Musée Atelier d'Automates, 19 Rte Nationale, 10270 Lusigny-sur-Barse - T: 0325415551
Science&Tech Museum 11494

Lutterbach

Musée Brassicole, Mairie, 68460 Lutterbach - T: 0389507100
Special Museum 11495

Luxeuil-les-Bains

Musée-Conservatoire de la Dentelle, 1 Rue des Thermes, 70300 Luxeuil-les-Bains - T: 0384400641/1051
Special Museum 11496

Musée Maurice Beaumont, Bibliothèque Municipale, 2 Pl de la Baille, 70300 Luxeuil-les-Bains - T: 0384404660
Special Museum 11497

Musée Municipal, Tour des Echevins, 70300 Luxeuil-les-Bains - T: 0384400007
Local Museum 11498

Luxey

Ecomusée de la Grande Lande, 40430 Luxey - T: 0558080139/075270
Science&Tech Museum 11499

Luynes

Château de Luynes, 37230 Luynes - T: 0247555020/5096
Decorative Arts Museum 11500

Luz-Saint-Sauveur

Musée d'Art et d'Histoire de la Chapelle Notre-Dame, Ancienne Chapelle de l'Ordre des Hospitaliers, 65120 Luz-Saint-Sauveur - T: 0562928175
Religious Arts Museum 11501

Musée-Maison du Parc National et de la Vallée, Maison de la Vallée, Pl Saint-Clément, 65120 Luz-Saint-Sauveur - T: 0562923838
Local Museum / Folklore Museum 11502

Luzech

Musée Armand Viré, Maisons des Consuls, 46140 Luzech - T: 0565201727. Head: Robert Tardiem
Archaeological Museum 11503

Luzy

Musée et Exposition Archéologiques, Vieille Tour, 58170 Luzy - T: 0386300234
Archaeological Museum / Historical Museum 11504

Lyon

Atelier de Tissage, 10 Rue Richan, 69004 Lyon - T: 0478271713/296442
Special Museum 11505

Atelier Municipal de Passementerie, 21 Rue Richan, 69004 Lyon - T: 0478271713
Historical Museum 11506

Collections Historique du Guignol lyonnais, Théâtre, 2 Rue Louis-Carrand, 69004 Lyon
Special Museum / Folklore Museum 11507

Exposition des Compagnons du Devoir, 9 Rue Nérard, 69009 Lyon - T: 0478837603/7920
Fine Arts Museum 11508

Fondation de l'Automobile Marius-Berliet, 39 Av Esquirol, 69003 Lyon - T: 0478541534, Fax: 0472332025, Internet: http://www.fondation-berliet.org. Head: Dominique Brun, Paul Berliet
Association with Coll 11509

Musée Africain, 150 Cours Gambetta, 69361 Lyon Cedex 07 - T: 0478616098, Fax: 0478617197, E-mail: musaf@missions-africaines.org, Internet: http://www.perso.wanadoo.fr/missions.africaines. Head: Pierre Boutin
Ethnology Museum - 1926
Western African art, crafts, masks, sculpture, brass objects, folk art from Benin, Ivory Coast, Ghana, Togo, West Nigeria - library 11510

Musée Archéologique Mariste de Puylata, 4 Montée Saint-Barthélemy, 69000 Lyon - T: 0478283834
Archaeological Museum 11511

Musée d'Art Contemporain de Lyon, 81 Cité Internationale, Quai Charles de Gaulle, 69006 Lyon - T: 0472691718, Fax: 0472691700, E-mail: mac@mairie-lyon.fr, Internet: http://www.moca-lyon.org. Head: Thierry Raspail
Fine Arts Museum 11512

Musée d'Art Sacré de Fourvière, 8 Pl de Fourvière, 69005 Lyon - T: 0478251301, Fax: 0472382835, E-mail: info@lyon-fourviere.com, Internet: http://www.lyon-fourviere.com. Head: Dr. Bernard Berthod
Religious Arts Museum 11513

Musée de Gadagne, Musée Historique de Lyon, 14 Rue de Gadagne, 69005 Lyon - T: 0478420361, Fax: 0478427971, E-mail: blazy@lyon.asi.fr. Head: Simone Blazy
Historical Museum - 1921
Local hist, French and foreign puppets, ethnology 11514

Musée de la Civilisation Gallo-Romaine, 17 Rue Cléberg, 69005 Lyon - T: 0472388190, Fax: 0472387742, E-mail: fourviere@cg69.fr, Internet: http://www.cg69.fr/galloromain.htlm. Head: Jacques Lasfargues
Archaeological Museum - 1975
Gallo-Roman finds, mosaics, epigraphs - library 11515

Musée de la Compagnie Nationale du Rhône, 2 Rue de Bonin, 69000 Lyon - T: 0472006896/6969
Science&Tech Museum 11516

Musée de la Résistance et de la Déportation, Centre d'Histoire de la Résistance et de la Déportation, 14 Av Berthelot, 69007 Lyon - T: 0478722311, Fax: 0472733298, E-mail: chrd@mairie.lyon.fr. Head: Cathérine Zoldan
Historical Museum 11517

Musée de l'Imprimerie de Lyon, 13 Rue de la Poulaillerie, 69002 Lyon - T: 0478376598, Fax: 0478382595, E-mail: mil@mairie-lyon-fr, Internet: http://www.bm-lyon.fr/musee/imprimerie.htm
Science&Tech Museum 11518

Musée Dentaire de Lyon, c/o Faculté d'Odontologie, Rue Guillaume Paradin, 69372 Lyon - T: 0478778600, Fax: 0478778696
Special Museum 11519

Musée des Arts décoratifs, 34 Rue de la Charité, 69002 Lyon - T: 0478384200, Fax: 0472402512, E-mail: musees@lyon.cci.fr, Internet: http://www.lyon.cci.fr/musee-des-arts-decos/. Head: Guy Blazy
Decorative Arts Museum - 1925
16th-19th century French decorative art, French and Flemish tapestries from the 16th-18th century, 15th-17th century Italian majolicas - library 11520

Musée des Beaux-Arts, Palais Saint-Pierre, 20 Pl des Terreaux, 69001 Lyon - T: 0472101740, Fax: 0478281245. Head: Vincent Pomarede
Fine Arts Museum - 1803
17th century abbey, sculpture, paintings by European masters of all periods from the 15th century to the present, incl Perugino, Tintoretto, Veronese, Delacroix, Géricault, Degas, Picasso etc, drawings, decorative arts, Oriental and Moslem art, local school of painting, medals, numismatics, antiques from Egypt, Greece and Rome - library, documentation center 11521

Musée des Hospices Civils de Lyon, Hôtel Dieu, 1 Rue de l'Hôpital, 69002 Lyon - T: 0472413042, Fax: 0472413142. Head: Ph. Paillard
Local Museum - 1935
17th century building, art coll, 16th-18th century furnishings, busts, tapestries, 16th-19th century apothecary jars and other memorabilia of local history of medicine 11522

Musée des Moulages, c/o Université Lumière Lyon 2, 3 Rue Rachais, 69003 Lyon - T: 0472848112, Fax: 0472848570, E-mail: musee.des.moulages@univ-lyon2.fr. Head: O. Balandraud
University Museum / Fine Arts Museum - 1893
Castings of Greek, Roman, Medieval and Modern art 11523

Musée des Sapeurs-Pompiers du Grand Lyon, Caserne Sapeurs-Pompiers, 350 Av de Champagne, 69000 Lyon, mail addr: 17 Rue Rabelais, 69003 Lyon - T: 0478351242
Science&Tech Museum 11524

Musée des Télécommunications Rhône-Alpes, 12bis Rue Burdeau, 69001 Lyon - T: 0478398889
Science&Tech Museum 11525

Musée des Tissus, 34 Rue de la Charité, 69002 Lyon - T: 0478384200, Fax: 0472402512, E-mail: musees@lyon.cci.fr, Internet: http://www.lyon.cci.fr/musee-des-tissus. Head: Guy Blazy
Decorative Arts Museum - 1864
Textiles from the Mediterranean area dating from 300 BC to the 19th c, important French silk coll from the 17th-20th c, esp Art Deco silks, Oriental silks, Persian and Near Eastern rugs from the 16th-17th c - library 11526

Musée des Trains Miniatures, 4 Pl Jules-Ferry, 69006 Lyon - T: 0472750035
Science&Tech Museum 11527

Musée d'Histoire de la Médecine et de la Pharmacie, 8 Av Rockefeller, 69000 Lyon - T: 0478777000/7141
Special Museum 11528

Musée du Président Herriot, Pl du Petit Collège, 69000 Lyon - T: 0478420361
Special Museum 11529

Musée du Souvenir Militaire de Lyon, Cercle Mixte, Quartier Général Frère, 69998 Lyon - T: 0437272197
Military Museum 11530

Musée en Plein Air d'Art Naïf, 83 Grande Rue de la Croix Rousse, 69000 Lyon - T: 0478305223
Open Air Museum / Fine Arts Museum 11531

Musée Fantastique de Guignol, Boutique Cardelli, 6 Rue Saint-Jean, 69005 Lyon - T: 0478370167, Fax: 0478370167, E-mail: patrice.cardelli@free.fr. Head: Patrice Cardelli
Special Museum / Folklore Museum 11532

Musée Henri Ughetto, 49 Rue des Tables Claudiennes, 69000 Lyon - T: 0478427160
Fine Arts Museum 11533

Musée-Maison des Canuts, 10-12 Rue d'Ivry, 69004 Lyon - T: 0478286204, Fax: 0478281693
Local Museum 11534

Musée Urbain Tony Garnier, 4 Rue des Serpollières, 69008 Lyon - T: 0478751675, Fax: 0472787637, E-mail: museetonygarnier@club-internet.fr, Internet: http://www.museeurbaintonygarnier.com. Head: Danielle Rivière
Open Air Museum 11535

Musée Vivant du Cinéma, Institut Lumière, 25 Rue du Premier Film, 69008 Lyon - T: 0478781895, Fax: 0478013662, E-mail: contact@institut-lumiere.org, Internet: http://www.institut-lumiere.org. Head: Bertrand Tavernier, Thierry Frémaux
Science&Tech Museum / Historical Museum 11536

Muséum d'Histoire Naturelle, 28 Blvd des Belges, 69006 Lyon - T: 0472690500, Fax: 0478946225, E-mail: museum@cg69.fr, Internet: http://www.museum-lyon.org. Head: Michel Coté
Natural History Museum / Ethnology Museum - 1772
Egyptian art, natural hist - library 11537

Muséum Testut, Laterjet de Médicine et d'Anatomie de Lyon, 8 Av Rockefeller-Faculté, 69003 Lyon - T: 0478774143
Special Museum / Natural History Museum 11538

Palais de la Miniature, 2 Rue de la Juiverie, 69005 Lyon - T: 0472002477
Fine Arts Museum 11539

Renaissance des Automates, 100 Rue Saint-Georges, 69005 Lyon - T: 0472777520, 0472777528, Fax: 0472777521, E-mail: asg@automates-ema.com, Internet: http://www.automates-ema.com. Head: Robert Ema
Special Museum 11540

Lys-Saint-Georges

Musée de Tourisme et d'Artisanat, Le Bourg, 36230 Lys-Saint-Georges - T: 0254308155
Decorative Arts Museum / Historical Museum 11541

Mâcon

Musée des Ursulines, 5 Rue des Ursulines, 71000 Mâcon - T: 0385399038, Fax: 0385382060, E-mail: musees@ville-macon.fr, Internet: http://www.macon-en.ligne.net. Head: Marie Lapalus
Local Museum / Fine Arts Museum - 1968
17th century convent, pre- and early hist, antiquities, medieval European paintings (16th-20th century), regional ethnography, contemporary art, rowning 11542

Musée Lamartine, 41 Rue Sigorgne, 71000 Mâcon - T: 0385399038, Fax: 0385382060, E-mail: musees@ville-macon.fr, Internet: http://www.macon-en-ligne.net. Head: Marie Lapalus
Special Museum - 1969
Furnishings, tapestries, ceramics, painting, literature, memorabilia of the poet and politician Alphonse de Lamartine 11543

Madré

Ecomusée de la Ferme du Chemin, Parc Naturel Régional de Maine-Normandie, 53250 Madré - T: 0243085703
Special Museum / Agriculture Museum 11544

Magalas

Collections de Sonnailles, Fonderie du Libron-ZAE l'Audacieuse, 34480 Magalas - T: 0467366713
Special Museum 11545

Musée Archéologique, Mairie, 34480 Magalas - T: 0467362019
Archaeological Museum 11546

Magnac-Laval

Musée Archéologique en Plein Air, Cour de l'Hôpital Beauséjour, Parc de l'Hôpital, 87190 Magnac-Laval - T: 0555685254
Archaeological Museum 11547

Magny-Cours

Ecovillage Centre Africain Reconstitué, Les Pitiaux, 58470 Magny-Cours - T: 0386581073/212159
Open Air Museum / Ethnology Museum 11548

Magny-en-Vexin

Musée Pigeard, Mairie, 95420 Magny-en-Vexin
Local Museum 11549

Magny-lès-Hameaux

Musée de l'Abbaye de Port-Royal, 78114 Magny-lès-Hameaux - T: 0130437493
Religious Arts Museum 11550

Musée National des Granges de Port Royal, 78114 Magny-lès-Hameaux - T: 0139307272, Fax: 0130647955, E-mail: musee.port-royal@culture.gouv.fr. Head: Véronique Alemany
Religious Arts Museum - 1952
History of Port-Royal and Jansenism, in the of 'Petites Ecoles' where Racine studied 11551

Mailhac

Dépôt de Fouilles Archéologiques, Rte de Bize, 11120 Mailhac - T: 0468461405
Archaeological Museum 11552

Maillane

Musée Frédéric-Mistral, 11 Rue Lamartine, 13910 Maillane - T: 0490957406
Special Museum 11553

Maillebois

Château-Musée, 28170 Maillebois - T: 0237481701
Fine Arts Museum / Decorative Arts Museum 11554

Maillezais

La Maison des Vieux Métiers, 22 Chemin du Port-d'Anchais, 85420 Maillezais - T: 0251007385
Local Museum 11555

Musée Lapidaire de l'Abbaye Saint-Pierre, Abbaye Saint-Pierre de Maillezais, 85420 Maillezais - T: 0251007011/872879
Archaeological Museum 11556

Maincy

Musée des Équipages, Domaine de Vaux-le-Vicomte, 77950 Maincy - T: 0164414190, Fax: 0160699085, E-mail: chateau@vaux-le-vicomte.com, Internet: http://www.vaux-le-vicomte.com. Head: Patrice de Vogüé
Science&Tech Museum 11557

Maintenon

Fondation du Château de Maintenon, Pl Aristide Briand, 28130 Maintenon - T: 0237230009, Fax: 0237230079
Decorative Arts Museum 11558

Maisons-Alfort

Musée d'Histoire Locale et de la Coiffure, 9 Rue Victor-Hugo, 94700 Maisons-Alfort - T: 0143967799
Historical Museum 11559

Musée Fragonard de l'Ecole Nationale Vétérinaire d'Alfort, 7 Av du Général-de-Gaulle, 94700 Maisons-Alfort - T: 0143967172, Fax: 0143963162, E-mail: degueurc@vet_alfort.fr, Internet: http://www.vet_alfort.fr/FR/musee/musee.htm
Historical Museum / Natural History Museum
Fragonard, anatomy coll 11560

Maisons-Laffitte

Château de Maisons-Laffitte, Centre des Monuments Nationaux, 2 Av Carnot, 78600 Maisons-Laffitte - T: 0139620149, Fax: 0139123437. Head: Florence de la Roncière
Fine Arts Museum / Decorative Arts Museum - 1642
Paintings, sculptures, tapestries, furniture, François Mansart (1598-1666) 11561

Maisons-lès-Chaource

Musée des Poupées d'Antan, 10210 Maisons-lès-Chaource - T: 0325700746
Special Museum 11562

Malain

Collection Archéologique de la Maison des Fouilles et Maison du Memontois, Rue Gaudot, 21410 Malain - T: 0380236608, Fax: 0360751348, E-mail: malain_gam@hotmail.com. Head: Louis Roussel
Archaeological Museum / Ethnology Museum 11563

Malansac

Parc de Préhistoire de Bretagne, 56220 Malansac - T: 0297433417, Fax: 0297433424, E-mail: contact@prehistoire.com
Archaeological Museum 11564

Malbrans

Musée de la Tuilerie, Aux Combes du Punay, 25660 Malbrans - T: 0381557150
Science&Tech Museum 11565

Malesherbes

Musée-Château, 45330 Malesherbes - T: 0238348018
Decorative Arts Museum 11566

Malicorne-sur-Sarthe

Musée des Faïences E. Tessier et de Faïencerie d'Art de Malicorne (closed) 11567

Mallemort

Musée des Engins de Travaux Publics, Centre E. Pico, Pont Royal, 13370 Mallemort - T: 0490594205
Science&Tech Museum 11568

Mallièvre

La Maison de l'Eau, 7 Rue de la Poterie, 85590 Mallièvre - T: 0251653399
Special Museum / Natural History Museum 11569

Mandelieu

Musée Henry Clews, Château de la Napoule, Blvd Henry Clews, 06210 Mandelieu - T: 0493499505, Fax: 0492976271. Head: Patricia Corbett
Fine Arts Museum 11570

Mandeure

Exposition Archéologique Gallo-Romaine, Théâtre, 25350 Mandeure - T: 0381352008
Archaeological Museum 11571

Mane

Musée Conservatoire Ethnologique de Haute-Provence, Prieuré de Salagnon, Rte d'Apt, 04300 Mane - T: 0492751993
Ethnology Museum 11572

Maniquerville

L'Agriculture au Fil du Temps, 76400 Maniquerville - T: 0235293128/273032
Agriculture Museum 11573

Manneville-sur-Risle

Musée Départemental de la Résistance et de la Déportation, Hameau Bonnebos, 27500 Manneville-sur-Risle - T: 0232569486, Fax: 0232579147
Historical Museum 11574

Manom

Château-Musée de la Grange, Rte Nationale 53, 57100 Manom - T: 0382538503, Fax: 0382538892
Decorative Arts Museum 11575

Manosque

Centre Jean-Giono, 1 Blvd E.-Bourges, 04100 Manosque - T: 0492727610
Special Museum 11576

Ecomusée du Savon, ZI Saint-Maurice, 04100 Manosque - T: 0492701950, Fax: 0492701951, E-mail: accueil@loccitane.fr. Head: Patulia Montesinos
Special Museum / Decorative Arts Museum 11577

Fondation Carzou, 9 Blvd Élémir-Bourges, 04100 Manosque - T: 0492874049, Fax: 0492870521. Head: Jean-Marie Carzou
Fine Arts Museum 11578

Maison Jean-Giono, Le Paraïs, Montée des Vraies Richesses, 04100 Manosque - T: 0492877303
Special Museum 11579

Mansencôme

Château de Busca-Naniban, 32310 Mansencôme - T: 0562284038
Decorative Arts Museum / Fine Arts Museum 11580

Mantes-la-Jolie

Musée Maximilien-Luce, Mairie, 31 Rue Gambetta, 78200 Mantes-la-Jolie - T: 0134788100
Local Museum 11581

Marans

Musée Cappon, 62 Rue d'Aligre, 17230 Marans - T: 0546011287
Archaeological Museum 11582

Marcé

Musée Régional de l'Air, Groupement Préservation Patrimoine Aéronautique, Aérodrome d'Angers, 49140 Marcé - T: 0241330410, Fax: 0241775950, E-mail: gpparavel@wanadoo.fr. Head: Christian Ravel
Science&Tech Museum 11583

Marcellaz-Albanais

Art de l'Enfance, 74150 Marcellaz-Albanais - T: 0450697374. Head: Yves Rifaux
Special Museum / Ethnology Museum 11584

Marchamp

Musée Paléo-Écologique, Cerin, 01680 Marchamp - T: 0474398575. Head: Yvette Weber
Natural History Museum 11585

Marchenoir

Château de Talcy, 41370 Marchenoir - T: 0254810301. Head: Martine Tissier de Mallerais
Decorative Arts Museum
Furniture, tapestry 11586

Marchesieux

Maison des Marais, 50190 Marchesieux - T: 0233071520/467251
Local Museum 11587

Village Miniature, Rte de Periers, 50190 Marchesieux - T: 0233467498
Local Museum 11588

Marchiennes

Musée Historique Loseleur, Pl Gambetta, 59870 Marchiennes - T: 0327905795/4477
Local Museum 11589

Marciac

Musée Doubrère, Hôtel de Ville, 32230 Marciac - T: 0562090355
Fine Arts Museum 11590

Musée Joseph Abeilhe, Mairie, 32230 Marciac - T: 0562093803
Natural History Museum
Zoology (birds), geology and mineralogy, paleontology, prehistory, ethnography 11591

Territoires du Jazz, Pl Chevalier-d'Antras, 32230 Marciac - T: 0562093018, Fax: 0562093188, E-mail: ot.marciac@wanadoo.fr. Head: Jean-Louis Guichaumon
Music Museum 11592

Marcigny

Musée de la Tour du Moulin, 7 Rue de la Tour, 71110 Marcigny - T: 0385253705. Head: Guy Tixier
Local Museum - 1913
Folklore, faiences and ceramics, statues, woodwork, tower from the 15th c, Burgundy prehist, archaeology, wallpapers (Dufour-Zuber), local hist - library 11593

Marcillac-Vallon

Musée de Site du Gouffre de Barriac, 12330 Marcillac-Vallon
Natural History Museum / Archaeological Museum 11594

Marcillé-Robert

Maison-Musée de la Nature, Villa Bedon, Rte de Retiers, 35240 Marcillé-Robert - T: 0299465024, Fax: 0299465024
Natural History Museum 11595

Marcilly-sur-Maulne

Musée Vivant et Historique du Chemin de Fer à Voie Etroite, Lac de Rillé, 37330 Marcilly-sur-Maulne - T: 0547246019
Science&Tech Museum 11596

Marckolsheim

Musée Mémorial de la Ligne Maginot du Rhin, Rte du Rhin, 67390 Marckolsheim - T: 0388925779/5170. Head: Ernest Bertout
Military Museum 11597

Marcq-en-Barœul

Fondation Prouvost, Septentrion, Chemin des Coulons, 59700 Marcq-en-Barœul - T: 0320462637
Fine Arts Museum / Natural History Museum 11598

Musée Régional des Télécommunications en Flandres, 12 Av Foch, 59700 Marcq-en-Barœul - T: 0320723028, Fax: 0320412112
Science&Tech Museum
Two centuries of telecommunication hist: from telegraph, over Morse, manual, automatic, electronic telephone to French telematic network 11599

Marcy-l'Étoile

Château-Musée, Domaine de Lacroix-Laval, 69280 Marcy-l'Étoile - T: 0478878700, Fax: 0478442928, E-mail: museepoupee@cg69.fr. Head: Olivier Desmules
Special Museum 11600

Musée d'Anatomie Lesbres-Tagand de l'Ecole Vétérinaire de Lyon, 1 Av Bourgelat, 69280 Marcy-l'Étoile - T: 0478872530, Fax: 0478872517, E-mail: e.chatelain@vet-lyon.fr. Head: Prof. E. Chatelain
Special Museum / Natural History Museum / University Museum 11601

Mardeuil

Collection Viticole, Champagne Beaumont des Crayères, 64 Rue de la Liberté, 51530 Mardeuil - T: 0326552940, Fax: 0326542630, E-mail: champagne-beuamont@wanadoo.fr. Head: Jean-Paul Bertus
Special Museum 11602

Mareau-aux-Prés

Musée de la Vigne et du Vin, 560 Rue Saint-Fiacre, 45370 Mareau-aux-Près - T: 0238456155, Fax: 0238456658
Special Museum 11603

Marennes

Château-Musée de la Gataudière, D 728, 17320 Marennes - T: 0546850107
Local Museum / Decorative Arts Museum 11604

Musée de l'Huître, La Cayenne, 17320 Marennes - T: 0546850106
Special Museum 11605

Musée du Jouet Ancien "Atlantrain", Saint-Just-Luzac, 17320 Marennes - T: 0546853335, Fax: 0546853335. Head: André Flon
Special Museum 11606

Mareuil-sur-Belle

Musée du Maréchal Lannes, Château, 24340 Mareuil-sur-Belle - T: 0553607413
Military Museum / Historical Museum 11607

Margaux

Collection de Matériel Ancien de Cuvier, Château d'Alesme-Becker, 33460 Margaux - T: 0556887027
Science&Tech Museum 11608

Collection de Vieilles Bouteilles, Château Margaux, 33460 Margaux - T: 0556887028
Special Museum 11609

Marignane

Musée des Arts et Traditions Populaires, Cour d'Honneur du Château, Rue de Covet, 13700 Marignane - T: 0442097883
Folklore Museum 11610

Maringues

Musée des Tanneurs et des Ciriers, 3 Rue Saint-Maurice, 63350 Maringues - T: 0473687042/6384
Special Museum 11611

Marle

Musée des Temps Barbares, Moulin de Marle, 02250 Marle - T: 0323240133
Historical Museum 11612

Marles-sur-Canche

Musée Paysan du Bras de Brosne, Marant, 62170 Marles-sur-Canche - T: 0321061050/0427/818513
Science&Tech Museum / Folklore Museum 11613

Marlhes

Musée de la Beate, Hameau de l'Allier, 42660 Marlhes - T: 0477512470/2033
Local Museum 11614

Marly-le-Roi

Musée-Promenade intercommunal Marly-le-Roi/Louveciennes, La Grille Royale, Parc de Marly, 78160 Marly-le-Roi - T: 0139690626
Fine Arts Museum 11615

Marmande

Musée Albert Marzelles, 15 Rue Abel Boyé, 47200 Marmande - T: 0553644204. Head: M. Clemens
Local Museum 11616

Marmoutier

Centre Européen de l'Orgue, Ancienne Abbaye, 67440 Marmoutier - T: 0388564767, Fax: 0388564767, E-mail: ceorgue@wanadoo.fr, Internet: http://www.perso.wanadoo.fr/ceorgue. Head: Marcel Thomann
Music Museum 11617

Collection Archéologique, Crypte de l'Abbatiale, 67440 Marmoutier - T: 0388706008, 0388714684, Fax: 0388714407, E-mail: Tourisme.Marmoutier@wanadoo.fr
Archaeological Museum 11618

Musée d'Arts et Traditions Populaires, 6 Rue du Général Leclerc, 67440 Marmoutier - T: 0388714684, Fax: 0388714407
Folklore Museum
Alsactian earthenware and stoneware pottery, rural judaism 11619

Marquay

Château de Puymartin, 24200 Marquay - T: 0553592997, Fax: 0553298752
Local Museum 11620

Musée Cavernicole de Marquay, Cap Blanc, 24620 Marquay - T: 0553592174
Natural History Museum 11621

Marquillies

Musée de l'Attelage, 344 Rte de Sainghin, 59274 Marquillies - T: 0320290799
Science&Tech Museum 11622

Mars-la-Tour

Musée Militaire Faller, Pl Jeanne d'Arc, 54800 Mars-la-Tour - T: 0382339212
Military Museum 11623

Marsac-en-Livradois

Musée des Pénitents Blancs, Pl de l'Eglise, 63940 Marsac-en-Livradois - T: 0473956008/67/6503. Head: Luc Duchamp
Religious Arts Museum - 1958 11624

Marsais

Musée Jean-Philippe-Marchand, 17700 Marsais - T: 0546510108
Archaeological Museum / Folklore Museum 11625

Marsal

Musée du Sel, Porte de France, 57630 Marsal - T: 0387011675, Fax: 0387011675. Head: Michel Remillon
Special Museum - 1973
Technique of salt evaporation from the prehistoric period widely used in Marsal 11626

Marsannay-la-Côte

Maison du Patrimoine, Rue de Mazy, 21160 Marsannay-la-Côte - T: 0380522773/1270, Fax: 0380523023, E-mail: ot_marsannay@wanadoo.fr, Internet: http://www.ot_marsannay.com
Local Museum 11627

Marseillan

Collections Historiques, Mairie, 34340 Marseillan - T: 0467362019
Historical Museum 11628

La Halle aux Oiseaux, Pl du 14 Juillet, 34340 Marseillan - T: 0467017420
Natural History Museum 11629

Musée de l'Apéritif Noilly-Prat, 34340 Marseillan - T: 0467772015
Special Museum 11630

Marseille

Cabinet des Médailles, Palais des Beaux-Arts, Pl A.-Carli, 13001 Marseille - T: 0491420569
Historical Museum 11631

Centre de la Vieille Charité, 2 Rue de la Charité, 13002 Marseille - T: 0491145880, Fax: 0491145881, Internet: http://www.mairie-marseille.fr. Head: Daniele Giraudy
Special Museum 11632

Château d'If, Musée Carcéral, 13001 Marseille - T: 0491590230/555009
Special Museum / Archaeological Museum 11633

Espace d'Art Contemporain, 1 Pl Chirat, 13002 Marseille - T: 0491912755, Fax: 0491902850, E-mail: fnacpaca@free.fr. Head: Eric Mangion
Fine Arts Museum 11634

Exposition Préhistorique, Grotte Sous-Marine Cosquer, 13002 Marseille - T: 0491138900
Archaeological Museum 11635

Galerie d'Art/Artothèque Antonin-Artaud, 9 Chemin Notre-Dame de la Consolation, 13000 Marseille - T: 0491667817/063805
Fine Arts Museum 11636

Galerie de l'École d'Art, 41 Rue Montgrand, 13006 Marseille - T: 0491331199
Fine Arts Museum 11637

Galerie des Transports, Métro Noailles, Pl du Marché-des-Capucins, 13001 Marseille - T: 0491541515
Science&Tech Museum 11638

Musée Cantini, 19 Rue Grignan, 13006 Marseille - T: 0491547775, Fax: 0491550361. Head: Nicolas Cendo
Fine Arts Museum / Decorative Arts Museum - 1936
17th century palace, 17th-18th century Provencal porcelain, decorative arts, contemporary paintings and sculptures - library, museobus 11639

Musée d'Archéologie Méditerranéenne, Centre de la Vieille Charité, Rue de Charité, 13002 Marseille - T: 0491145880, Fax: 0491145876, E-mail: adurand@mairie_marseille.fr. Head: Agnes Durand
Archaeological Museum - 1863
Egyptian finds, a sacrifical altar, Mediterranean antiquities, sarcophagi, terracotta statues, Greek vases, glass, bronzes, Celtic-Ligurian finds 11640

Musée d'Art Contemporain, 69 Blvd de Haïfa, 13008 Marseille - T: 0491250107, Fax: 0491721727. Head: Nathalie Ergino
Fine Arts Museum 11641

Musée de la Faïence, Château Pastre, 157 Av de Montredon, 13008 Marseille - T: 0491724347
Decorative Arts Museum 11642

Musée de la Marine et de l'Économie de Marseille, Palais de la Bourse, 13001 Marseille - T: 0491393333, Fax: 0491395615, E-mail: patrick.boulanger@marseille-provence.cci.fr, Internet: http://www.marseille-provence.cci.fr/patrimoine. Head: Patrick Boulanger
Special Museum - 1933
Maritime and economic hist, with emphasis on the development of the harbour of Marseille from antiquity to the present, etchings, paintings, drawings on naval themes, ship models, maps, photographs, hist of Marseille and the Provence - library 11643

Musée de la Mode, 11 La Canebière, 13001 Marseille - T: 0491149200
Special Museum 11644

Musée de la Moto, Quartier du Merlan, Traverse Saint-Paul, 13013 Marseille - T: 0491022955
Science&Tech Museum 11645

Musée de la Réparation Navale, Port Autonome, 7 Blvd des Bassins de Radoub Porte 3A, 13002 Marseille - T: 0491988167
Special Museum / Science&Tech Museum 11646

Musée des Arts Africains, Océaniens et Amérindiens, 2 Rue de la Charité, 13002 Marseille - T: 0491145838, Fax: 0491145882, E-mail: anicolas@mairie-marseille.fr, Internet: http://www.mairie-marseille.fr. Head: Alain Nicolas
Ethnology Museum 11647

Musée des Arts Décoratifs, Château Borely, Av Clot-Bey, 13008 Marseille - T: 0491562838
Decorative Arts Museum 11648

Musée des Beaux-Arts, Palais Longchamp, Pl Bernex, 13004 Marseille - T: 0491145930, Fax: 0491145931. Head: Marie-Paule Vial
Fine Arts Museum - 1801
Sculpture, paintings, drawings, watercolours by Puget, 17th-19th century Provence paintings, Daumiers's busts and lithographs, European paintings, French paintings from 15th-19th century 11649

Musée des Docks Romains, 28 Pl Vivaux, 13001 Marseille - T: 0491912462, Fax: 0491145876. Head: Agnes Durand
Archaeological Museum - 1963
Roman warehouse, hist of the Roman port at Marseille, documentation on commerce during antiquity, models and charts, marine archaeology finds 11650

Musée d'Histoire de Marseille, Centre Bourse, Sq Belsunce, 13001 Marseille - T: 0491904222, Fax: 0491904378. Head: Myriame Morel-Deledalle
Historical Museum - 1983
History of Marseille from the 6th century BC - 18th century AD, archaeology, engravings, models, naval archaeology - library, video section 11651

Musée d'Histoire Naturelle, Palais Longchamp, 13004 Marseille - T: 0491623078
Natural History Museum - 1869
Natural hist of the Provence, paleontology, botany, zoology, mineralogy, anthropology, ethnography, prehist, 19th century frescos 11652

Musée du Santon, Maison Marcel Carbonnel, 47 Rue Neuve Sainte-Catherine, 13007 Marseille - T: 0491542658
Special Museum 11653

Musée du Vieux Marseille, Maison Diamantée, 2 Rue de la Prison, 13002 Marseille - T: 0491551019. Head: Anne Sportiello
Local Museum - 1911
Religious figurines and manger scenes, playing cards, traditional costumes from Marseille, painting, drawings, engravings, maps, Provence furniture, household objects - audio-visual room 11654

Musée Grobet-Labadié, 140 Blvd Longchamp, 13001 Marseille - T: 0491622182, Fax: 0491956031. Head: Danielle Maternati-Baldouy
Fine Arts Museum - 1926
Early Flemish, German, and Italian paintings, French paintings and drawings, sculpture from the medieval times to the Renaissance, 16th-18th century tapestries, Oriental rugs, decorative arts, musical instruments 11655

Musée-Préau des Accoules, 29 Montée des Accoules, 13002 Marseille - T: 0491915206, Fax: 0491915206. Head: Laurence Rossellini
Special Museum 11656

Tour du Roy Rene, Fort Saint-Jean, 13002 Marseille - T: 0491911707/541539/42961229
Fine Arts Museum / Historical Museum 11657

Trésor d'Église, Art Sacré, Basilique Saint-Victor, 13007 Marseille - T: 0491549111
Religious Arts Museum 11658

Marsillargues

Musée du Château Paul Pastre, Château, 34590 Marsillargues - T: 0467835210/716265
Local Museum 11659

Marsilly

Musée Historique de Graffiti, Église Salle du Clocher-Porche, 17137 Marsilly - T: 0546013464/ 3010/3770
Historical Museum 11660

Marsoulas

Musée Préhistorique, Grotte, 31260 Marsoulas - T: 0561906402
Archaeological Museum 11661

Martainville-Epreville

Musée des Traditions et Arts Normands, Château de Martainville, 76116 Martainville-Epreville - T: 0235234470, Fax: 0235231684, E-mail: alain.joubert@cg76.fr. Head: Alain Joubert
Folklore Museum - 1963
Stylistic evolution of regional furniture (Haute-Normandie) from 15-19th c, farm house decor, 19th c household utensils, history of Norman clothing during 18-19th c 11662

Martel

Collection de Peintures de Van Loo, Eglise, 46600 Martel
Fine Arts Museum / Religious Arts Museum 11663

Musée d'Uxellodunum, Palais la Raymondie, 46600 Martel - T: 0565373003
Historical Museum / Archaeological Museum 11664

Martigny

Musée du Souvenir Militaire de Thiérache, 02500 Martigny - T: 0323580254
Military Museum 11665

Martigues

Archéosite de la Chapelle Saint-Julien, Saint-Julien-les-Martigues, 13500 Martigues
Archaeological Museum 11666

Maison-Musée de Charles Maurras, 22 Chemin du Paradis, 13500 Martigues
Special Museum 11667

Musée-Jardin Lapidaire, 13500 Martigues
Archaeological Museum 11668

Musée Ziem, Blvd du 14 Juillet, 13500 Martigues - T: 0442806606, Fax: 0442803326. Head: Sophie Biass-Fabiani
Fine Arts Museum - 1908
Local archaeology, ethnology, 19th century Provencal paintings, contemporary art (Ziem, Dufy, Derain, Mangui, Picabia, Signac) 11669

Martizay

Musée Archéologique, 1 Rue du Musée, 36220 Martizay - T: 0254280196. Head: Jean-Claude Marquet
Archaeological Museum
Prehist, Gallo-Roman hist, Merovingian hist 11670

Martres-Tolosane

Musée d'Archéologie, Donjon, 31220 Martres-Tolosane - T: 0561988002
Local Museum 11671

Marvejols

Musée Archéologique, Mairie, 48100 Marvejols - T: 0466320045
Archaeological Museum 11672

Marzy

Musée Municipal Gautron du Coudray, 22 Pl de l'Eglise, 58180 Marzy - T: 0386592847, Fax: 0386365962
Local Museum 11673

Massangis

Musée-Maison des Pierreux, Mairie, 89440 Massangis - T: 0386338568/8425
Science&Tech Museum 11674

Muséotrain Animé, Gare, 89440 Massangis - T: 0386338120/8044
Special Museum 11675

Matour

Musée de Matour, Maison du Patrimoine, 71520 Matour - T: 0385597156/7037
Archaeological Museum / Natural History Museum 11676

Maubeuge

Maison des Fortifications, Porte de Mons, 59600 Maubeuge
Historical Museum / Fine Arts Museum 11677

Musée Henri Boez, Hôtel de Ville, 59607 Maubeuge, mail addr: BP 269, 59607 Maubeuge - T: 0327649799, Fax: 0327580836. Head: Laurence Hardy-Marais
Local Museum - 1878
Gallo-Roman finds, local hist, 17th-20th century paintings, 19th-20th century graphic arts, porcelain 11678

Maubourguet

Musée d'Histoire et d'Archéologie, Rue Michelet, 65700 Maubourguet - T: 0562963233
Historical Museum / Archaeological Museum 11679

Maule

Musée Victor Aubert, Rue Quincampoix, 78580 Maule - T: 0130908049
Local Museum 11680

Mauléon-Licharre

Château-Musée d'Andurain, 64130 Mauléon-Licharre - T: 0559280418, Fax: 0559281967
Decorative Arts Museum 11681

Maureillas-las-Illas

Musée du Liège, Av Maréchal Joffre, 66480 Maureillas-las-Illas - T: 0468831541/4800, Fax: 0468831466. Head: Bruno Goumand, Roger Figueres
Special Museum 11682

Mauriac

Musée d'Arts Appliqués et d'Histoire, Rue du Président-Émile-Delalo, 15200 Mauriac - T: 0471680724/673026
Decorative Arts Museum / Historical Museum 11683

Mauroux

La Ferme des Étoiles, 32380 Mauroux - T: 0562060976, Fax: 0562062499, E-mail: etoiles.fleurance@mipnet.fr, Internet: http:// www.gascogne.fr/ferme. Head: Christian de Lary
Science&Tech Museum 11684

Maussane-les-Alpilles

Musée des Santons Animés, Rte de Saint-Rémy, 13520 Maussane-les-Alpilles - T: 0490543900
Special Museum 11685

Mauvezin (Gers)

Exposition Arts et Histoire, Mairie, 32120 Mauvezin (Gers) - T: 0562068145/8264
Archaeological Museum / Historical Museum 11686

Mauvezin (Hautes-Pyrénées)

Musée Gaston Phoebus, Associaton Escole Gastou Fébus, Château, 65130 Mauvezin (Hautes-Pyrénées) - T: 0562391027
Local Museum / Folklore Museum 11687

Maves

Musée du Vieux Moulin à Vent, Cidex 419, Pontitou, 41500 Maves - T: 0254873135
Science&Tech Museum 11688

Mazan

Musée Municipal, Rue Saint-Nazaire, 84380 Mazan - T: 0490697019. Head: C. Pautet
Local Museum - 1971
Agricultural tools, costumes, lighting, paintings, documents (13th-15th c) - library, archive 11689

Mazé

Château-Musée de Montgeoffroy, 49250 Mazé - T: 0241806002
Decorative Arts Museum 11690

Mazeray

Château Beaufief, Impasse du Château, 17400 Mazeray - T: 0546323593. Head: Louis-Georges Bonvalet
Historic Site 11691

Mazères (Ariège)

Musée du Vieux Mazeres, Hôtel Pastelier-Ardoyn, 16 Rue de la République, 09270 Mazères (Ariège) - T: 0561694204
Historical Museum 11692

Mazères (Gironde)

Musée Historial, Château de Roquetaillade, 33210 Mazères (Gironde) - T: 0556761461, Fax: 0556761461, E-mail: roquetaillade@ hotmail.com. Head: M. de Baritault du Carpia
Historical Museum / Decorative Arts Museum 11693

Musée Vivant de la Métairie de Crampet, 33210 Mazères (Gironde) - T: 0556761416, Fax: 0556761461, E-mail: roquetaillade@ hotmail.com. Head: M. de Baritault du Carpia
Folklore Museum 11694

Mazet-Saint-Voy

Exposition des Éditions Tarmeye, Rte du Chambon, 43520 Mazet-Saint-Voy - T: 0471650153, 0477435814, Fax: 0471650154
Special Museum 11695

Mazières-en-Mauges

Exposition de la Préhistoire, Mairie, 49280 Mazières-en-Mauges - T: 0241623512, Fax: 0241623512. Head: Gérard Berthaud
Archaeological Museum 11696

Meaux

Musée Bossuet, Ancien Palais Episcopal, 5 Pl Charles de Gaulle, 77100 Meaux - T: 0164348445, Fax: 0160239752. Head: Anne Maillard
Fine Arts Museum - 1900
16th-19th century paintings, 18th-19th century sculptures 11697

Megève

Musée de Megève, Ancien Hospice, 66 Rue Comte de Capré, 74120 Megève - T: 0450212101
Local Museum 11698

Musée du Haut-Val-d'Arly, 88 Ruelle du Vieux Marché, 74120 Megève - T: 0450918100
Folklore Museum 11699

Mehun-sur-Yèvre

Musée Charles-VII, Collections Médiévales et Archéologiques, Château Jean de Berry, 18500 Mehun-sur-Yèvre - T: 0248573025/0071/3551
Decorative Arts Museum
Antiquities, porcelain 11700

Meillant

Château de Meillant, Château, 18200 Meillant - T: 0248633058/3105, E-mail: chateau.de.meillant@ frn.fr
Decorative Arts Museum 11701

Meisenthal

Musée-Maison du Verre, Pl Robert Schumann, 57960 Meisenthal - T: 0387969151/8395
Decorative Arts Museum 11702

Melgven

Musée des Vieux Métiers, Chapelle de la Trinité, 29140 Melgven - T: 0298592726
Local Museum 11703

Mellac

Manoir de Kernault, 29130 Mellac - T: 0298719060
Local Museum 11704

Mellecey

Château de Germolles, 71640 Mellecey - T: 0385451055
Fine Arts Museum 11705

Melleray-la-Vallée

Musée Historique du Cidre, La Duretière, Rte de Chantrigné-Melleray, 53110 Melleray-la-Vallée - T: 0243047148, Fax: 0243040326
Special Museum 11706

Melun

Musée de la Gendarmerie, Ecole des Officiers de la Gendarmerie Nationale, Quartier Augereau, 77010 Melun Cedex - T: 0164143317, Fax: 0164090215. Head: Raymond Duplan
Special Museum - 1946
Uniforms, badges, folk art, head-dress, decorations, docs, arms, flags, paintings, figurines, faiences 11707

Musée de Melun, Maison de la Vicomté, 5 Rue du Franc Mûrier, 77008 Melun Cedex - T: 0164797770, Fax: 0164797771, E-mail: musee.melun@ wanadoo.fr. Head: Annie-Claire Lussiez
Local Museum - 1860
Gallo-Roman finds, medieval sculpture, decorative arts, paintings, furnishings, works by sculptor Henri Chapu, faience from Rubelles, paintings by Jacob van Hulsdonck 11708

Menat

Musée de Paléontologie, Le Gîte à Fossiles, Le Bourg, 63560 Menat - T: 0473855029
Archaeological Museum 11709

Mende

Musée d'Art et d'Histoire Ignon-Fabre, 3 Rue de l'Epine, 48000 Mende - T: 0466496666. Head: P. Peyre
Local Museum 11710

Ménerbes

Musée du Tire-Bouchon, Domaine de la Citadelle, 84560 Ménerbes - T: 0490724158, Fax: 0490724159, E-mail: citadelle@pac.wan.fr. Head: Yves Rousset-Rouard
Special Museum 11711

Menessaire

Maison du Seigle, 21430 Menessaire - T: 0380642865/0778
Ethnology Museum 11712

Ménestreau-en-Villette

Conservatoire de la Faune Sauvage de Sologne, Domaine de Ciran, 45240 Ménestreau-en-Villette - T: 0238769093, Fax: 0238694430
Natural History Museum 11713

Menetou-Salon

Musée de Voitures Anciennes et Sellerie, Château, 18510 Menetou-Salon - T: 0248640861, Fax: 0248640861, E-mail: chateau.menetou@ wanadoo.fr
Historic Site 11714

Menétrux-en-Joux

Muséoparc de la Ferme de l'Aurochs, Vallée du Hérisson, 39130 Menétrux-en-Joux - T: 0382257295
Open Air Museum / Natural History Museum 11715

Menou

Collections Historiques, Château, 58210 Menou - T: 0386398430
Decorative Arts Museum / Historical Museum 11716

Mens

Musée du Trièves, Pl de la Halle, 38710 Mens - T: 0476348828
Local Museum 11717

Menthon-Saint-Bernard

Château-Musée, 74290 Menthon-Saint-Bernard - T: 0450601205
Local Museum 11718

Menton

Écomusée de la Forge, 2 Rue des Grenadiers, 06500 Menton - T: 0493577278
Folklore Museum 11719

Galerie d'Art Contemporain, Palais de l'Europe, Av Boyer, 06500 Menton - T: 0493354971, Fax: 0492100540, E-mail: musees@ villedementon.com. Head: Hugues de la Touche
Fine Arts Museum - 1950
Modern and contemporary art 11720

Jardin de Sculptures et d'Agrumes du Palais, 3 Av de la Madone, 06500 Menton - T: 0493354971, Fax: 0492100540, E-mail: musees@ villedementon.com. Head: Hugues de la Touche
Fine Arts Museum / Natural History Museum 11721

Musée de Préhistoire Régionale, Rue Lorédan Larchey, 06500 Menton - T: 0493358464, Fax: 0492100540, E-mail: cremli2@ac-nice.fr, Internet: http://www.ac-nice.fr. Head: Hugues de la Touche
Archaeological Museum - 1909
Prehistoric excavation finds, regional hist, folklore, art 11722

Musée des Beaux-Arts, Palais Carnolès, 3 Av de la Madone, 06500 Menton - T: 0493354971, Fax: 0492100540, E-mail: musees@ villedementon.com. Head: Hugues de la Touche
Fine Arts Museum - 1977
Italian, Flemish primitive, 13th-18th century schools, contemporary paintings and sculptures 11723

Musée Jean Cocteau, Le Bastion, Port de Menton, 06500 Menton - T: 0493354971, Fax: 0492100540, E-mail: musees@villedementon.com. Head: Hugues de la Touche
Fine Arts Museum - 1966
Jean Cocteau's drawings, tapestries, ceramics, works of Picasso 11724

Muséum National d'Histoire Naturelle du Val Rameh, Av Saint-Jacques, 06500 Menton - T: 0493358672
Natural History Museum 11725

Mer

Musée de la Corbillière, Parc de la Corbillière, 41500 Mer - T: 0254810203
Local Museum 11726

Musée Militaire, 4 Rue Simon Heime, 41500 Mer - T: 0254813511
Military Museum 11727

Mercues

Le Prieuré des Arts, Château Les Bouysses, 46090 Mercues - T: 0565309185
Fine Arts Museum / Agriculture Museum 11728

Mériel

Musée Jean-Gabin, Pl Jean-Gabin, 95630 Mériel - T: 0130364255
Special Museum 11729

Mérignac (Gironde)

Conservatoire Air et Espace, 9 Rue Masséna, 33700 Mérignac (Gironde) - T: 0556470326
Science&Tech Museum 11730

Mérindol

Exposition Historique des Vaudois du Luberon, La Muse, 84360 Mérindol - T: 0490729164
Historical Museum 11731

Merkwiller-Pechelbronn

Exposition Muséale A l'Ancienne forge, 51 Rue Principale, 67250 Merkwiller-Pechelbronn - T: 0388080189
Historical Museum 11732

Musée du Pétrole, 4 Rue des Ecoles, 67250 Merkwiller-Pechelbronn - T: 0388809108, Fax: 0388809108. Head: Troger Guy
Science&Tech Museum 11733

Mervent

Musée-Maison des Amis de la Forêt, La Jamonière, D 65 entre les Oullins et la Croix-Méraud, 85200 Mervent - T: 0251000087
Natural History Museum 11734

Merville

Musée de la Batterie de Merville, Mairie de Merville, 14810 Merville - T: 0231914753, Fax: 0231914753, E-mail: museebatterie@compagnet.fr, Internet: http://www.mairie-mervillefranceville.fr
Military Museum 11735

Musée du Vieux Merville, Rue Général-de-Gaulle, 59660 Merville - T: 0328483427/428399
Historical Museum 11736

Mesnières-en-Bray

Collections du Château de Misnières-en-Bray, Institution Saint-Joseph, 76270 Mesnières-en-Bray - T: 0235931004
Fine Arts Museum / Decorative Arts Museum 11737

Messeix

Musée de l'École Rurale d'Auvergne, 63750 Messeix - T: 0473214506
Special Museum 11738

Mettray

Micro-Musée de l'Ex-Colonie Pénitentiaire, Les Bourgetteries, 37390 Mettray - T: 0247624242, Fax: 0247548605. Head: Alain Bidault
Local Museum 11739

Metz

Dépôt-Musée Diocésain, 15 Pl Sainte-Glossinde, 57019 Metz Cedex 1 - T: 0387745420, Fax: 0387370062, E-mail: eveche.metz@wanadoo.fr
Religious Arts Museum 11740

Musée-Mémorial de la Résistance et de la Déportation, Fort de Queuleu, 57000 Metz - T: 0387754509
Historical Museum 11741

Musée Trésor d'Église, Art Sacré de la Cathédrale Saint-Étienne, Pl d'Armes, 57000 Metz - T: 0387855461/5376
Religious Arts Museum 11742

Musées de la Cour d'Or, 2 Rue du Haut-Poirier, 57000 Metz - T: 0387682500, Fax: 0387365114, Internet: http://www.mairie-metz.fr. Head: Claude Valentin
Historical Museum / Archaeological Museum / Fine Arts Museum / Military Museum - 1839
Gallo-Roman objects, Merovingian and Carolingian sculpture, architectural Fragments, medieval art, European painting 15-19th c, contemporary art, military history 11743

Meudon

Musée d'Art et d'Histoire, 11 Rue des Pierres, 92190 Meudon - T: 0146238713, Fax: 0146230631. Head: Francis Villadier
Fine Arts Museum / Historical Museum - 1943
50s to 60s sculptures, 16th to 20th century paintings, local history (documents, engravings, tools, topographical models) - park with sculptures 11744

Musée National Auguste Rodin, Villa des Brillants, 19 Av Auguste Rodin, 92190 Meudon - T: 0145341309, Fax: 0145343654, E-mail: penseur@musee-rodin.fr. Head: Jacques Vilain
Fine Arts Museum - 1919
Former dwelling of A. Rodin (1840-1917), housing sketches, castings, and original private coll of the sculptor 11745

Meung-sur-Loire

Château-Musée, 16 Pl du Martroi, 45130 Meung-sur-Loire - T: 0238443647, Fax: 0238442737, E-mail: jouannet@hol.fr
Decorative Arts Museum 11746

Meursault

L'Archéodrome de Bourgogne, Aire de Beaune Tailly, Autoroute A6, 21190 Meursault - T: 0380268700, Fax: 0380214095, E-mail: info@archeodrome-bourgogne.fr, Internet: http://www.archeodrome-bourgogne.com. Head: Josiane David
Archaeological Museum / Open Air Museum - 1978
Reconstructions of archaeological sites 11747

Exposition de Peintures sur le Thème du Vin, Château, 21190 Meursault - T: 0380212298
Special Museum 11748

Meusnes

Musée de la Pierre à Fusil, Mairie, 41130 Meusnes - T: 0254710023/0731
Historical Museum 11749

Meux

Château de Meux, 17500 Meux - T: 0546481661
Historical Museum 11750

Meximieux

Musée du Vieux Pérouges, Pl du Tilleul, Pérouges, 01800 Meximieux
Local Museum 11751

Meylan

Musée des Traditions et Arts Populaires, Domaine des Capucins, 38240 Meylan - T: 0476908050 poste 295/410405
Folklore Museum 11752

Meymac

Centre d'Art Contemporain, Abbaye Saint-André, Pl du Bûcher, 19250 Meymac, mail addr: BP 26, 19250 Meymac - T: 0555952330, Fax: 0555956995, E-mail: cac.meymac@club-internet.fr. Head: Caroline Bissière
Fine Arts Museum 11753

Collections de la Fondation Marius-Vazelles, Abbaye Saint-André, Pl du Bûcher, 19250 Meymac - T: 0555951705
Archaeological Museum / Museum of Classical Antiquities 11754

Meyrueis

Château de Roquedols, Exposition du Parc National des Cévennes, 48150 Meyrueis - T: 0466456281
Decorative Arts Museum 11755

Mèze

Mini-Musée de l'Aviation, Lotissement l'Embatut No. 6, 34140 Mèze - T: 0467436810
Special Museum 11756

Mezin

Musée du Liège et du Bouchon, Rue Puits-Saint-Côme, 47170 Mezin - T: 0553656816, Fax: 0553653303
Science&Tech Museum 11757

Mialet

Médiathèque du Protestantisme, Maison d'Abraham Mazel à Falguières, 30140 Mialet
Special Museum 11758

Musée du Désert, Le Mas-Soubeyran, 30140 Mialet - T: 0466850272, Fax: 0466850002, E-mail: musee@museedudesert.com, Internet: http://www.museedudesert.com
Historical Museum - 1911
Documents, memorials, historical objects relating to the period of the 'Désert' (1685-1787), a time of persecution of Protestant churches in France, coll of bibles - Library 11759

Miers

Grotte Préhistorique Ornée, Les Fieux, 46500 Miers - T: 0565336150
Archaeological Museum 11760

Migron

Écomusée du Cognac, Logis des Bessons, 17770 Migron - T: 0546499116
Special Museum 11761

Millau

Écomusée du Larzac, Rte Nationale 9, 12100 Millau - T: 0565604358
Folklore Museum 11762

Musée de la Ganterie et de la Peau, Pl Foch, 12100 Millau - T: 0565590108
Science&Tech Museum / Special Museum 11763

Musée Municipal de Millau, Hôtel de Pegayrolles, Pl Foch, 12100 Millau - T: 0565590108, Fax: 0565612691
Archaeological Museum - 1904
Prehistoric finds, Gallo-Roman pottery from la Graufesenque, regional paleontology, The Leather and the Glove - library on leather working and on regional Archaeology 11764

Milly-la-Forêt

Musée-Chapelle Saint-Blaise-des-Simples, Rte de l'Amiral-de-Graville, 91490 Milly-la-Forêt - T: 0164988494
Fine Arts Museum
Chapel decorated with drawings by Cocteau, busts of Cocteau, the poet's grave 11765

Musée d'Art Contemporain en Plein Air le Cyclop, 91490 Milly-la-Forêt - T: 0164988317
Fine Arts Museum 11766

Mimizan

Musée d'Arts et de Traditions Populaires, 40200 Mimizan - T: 0558090061
Folklore Museum 11767

Minerve

Musée Archéologique et de Paléontologie, Pl du Monument, 34210 Minerve - T: 0468912292/894798
Archaeological Museum / Natural History Museum 11768

Musée Huperel de l'Histoire Cathare, Rue des Martyrs, 34210 Minerve - T: 0468911226, Fax: 0468911226. Head: Michel Gasc
Historical Museum 11769

Mirabel (Ardèche)

Musée Olivier-de-Serres, Le Pradel, 07170 Mirabel (Ardèche) - T: 0475367656, Fax: 0475367685, E-mail: alain.juton@educagri.fr. Head: Alain Juton
Agriculture Museum 11770

Miradoux

Ecomusée de la Lomagne, Ferme de la Hitte, Flamarens, 32340 Miradoux - T: 0562687698, Fax: 0562286295. Head: Michel Hue
Ethnology Museum 11771

Miramas

Musée Ferroviaire, 7 Av Maréchal-Juin, 13140 Miramas - T: 0490580824
Science&Tech Museum 11772

Miramont-de-Guyenne

Musée Vivant du Parchemin et de l'Enluminure, 47800 Miramont-de-Guyenne - T: 0553207555
Science&Tech Museum 11773

Mirande

Musée des Beaux-Arts, 13 Rue de l'Evêché, 32300 Mirande - T: 0562666810, Fax: 0562667889. Head: Michel Hue
Fine Arts Museum - 1971
15th-19th century paintings, faience, 19th century sculptures 11774

Musée d'Histoire et d'Art, 13 Rue de l'Evêché, 32300 Mirande - T: 0562666810, Fax: 0562668709, E-mail: bienvenue@ot_mirande.com
Fine Arts Museum / Historical Museum - 1930
Works of regional artists, items of local historical interest 11775

Mirebeau-sur-Bèze

Archéosite et Exposition de la Cité Militaire Romain de la VIII Légion, Rue des Moulins, 21310 Mirebeau-sur-Bèze - T: 0380367190
Archaeological Museum 11776

Mirecourt

Maison de la Musique Mécanique, 24 Rue Chanzy, 88500 Mirecourt - T: 029375113, Fax: 029375105
Music Museum - 1985 11777

Musée de la Dentelle, Mairie, 88500 Mirecourt - T: 0329370522
Folklore Museum 11778

Musée de la Lutherie et de l'Archèterie Françaises, 32 Rue du Général Leclerc, 88500 Mirecourt - T: 0329370522, Fax: 0329370646, E-mail: mirecourt.patrimoine@wanadoo.fr
Music Museum 11779

Mirepeisset

Musée de la Viticulture, Ancienne Gare, 11120 Mirepeisset - T: 0468334142
Agriculture Museum 11780

Mizerieux

Collection Minéralogique, Lycée Agricole Édouard-Herriot, 01600 Mizerieux - T: 0474001180
Natural History Museum 11781

Mizoën-en-Oisans

Musée du Terroir des Clots, GR 54/ Refuge, 38142 Mizoën-en-Oisans - T: 0476800310
Historical Museum 11782

Moirans-en-Montagne

Musée du Jouet (Toy Museum), 5 Rue du Murgin, 39260 Moirans-en-Montagne - T: 0384423864, Fax: 0384423897, E-mail: info@musee-du-jouet.com, Internet: http://www.musee-du-jouet.com
Special Museum
Toys 11783

Moisdon-la-Rivière

Musée Maison du Pays, La Forge, 44520 Moisdon-la-Rivière - T: 0240072244
Science&Tech Museum 11784

Moissac

Musée Claustral, Art Sacré, Cloître de l'Ancienne Abbaye Saint-Pierre du XIe s, 82200 Moissac - T: 0563040185
Religious Arts Museum 11785

Musée des Arts et Traditions Populaires et des Arts Appliqués, 4 Rue de l'Abbaye, 82200 Moissac - T: 0563040308/61042023
Folklore Museum 11786

Molezon

Magnanerie Muséalisée de la Roque, Mairie, 48110 Molezon - T: 0466451177, Fax: 0466452879, E-mail: mairie.molezon@voila.fr. Head: Frédéric Monod
Special Museum 11787

Molière-Cavaillac

Chemin de la Soie, Maison des Magnans, 30120 Molière-Cavaillac - T: 0467810506/66852444
Decorative Arts Museum 11788

Molsheim

Mémorial Bugatti, Cours des Chartreux, 67120 Molsheim - T: 0388382510, Fax: 0388386742
Historical Museum / Science&Tech Museum 11789

Musée de la Ville de Molsheim, Cours des Chartreux, 67120 Molsheim - T: 0388382510
Local Museum 11790

Monbazillac

Château de Monbazillac, Rte de Mont de Marsan, 24240 Monbazillac - T: 0553636500/615252, Fax: 0553636509
Local Museum 11791

Musée des Arts et Traditions Populaires, 24240 Monbazillac
Folklore Museum 11792

Moncley-Recologne

Château, 25170 Moncley-Recologne - T: 0381809255
Fine Arts Museum / Decorative Arts Museum 11793

Mondoubleau

Musée du Poids Lourd et des Véhicules Anciens, Cormenon, 41170 Mondoubleau - T: 0254807708/7314/8685
Science&Tech Museum 11794

Monêtier-les-Bains

Les Métiers d'Antan, Musée d'Art et de Traditions Populaires (closed) 11795

Musée d'Art Sacré, Chapelle Saint-Pierre, 05220 Monêtier-les-Bains - T: 0492245714, Fax: 0492245218, E-mail: monetier@monetier.com, Internet: http://www.monetier.com. Head: Joelle Finat
Religious Arts Museum 11796

Monflanquin

Musée-Maison de la Vie Rurale, Marsal, Rte de Villeneuve, 47150 Monflanquin - T: 0553419019
Folklore Museum 11797

Monistrol-sur-Loire

Musée-Château des Evêques de Monistrol, 4bis Rue du Château, 43120 Monistrol-sur-Loire - T: 0471616366
Fine Arts Museum / Historical Museum 11798

Musée de l'Arme Blanche et Conservatoire de l'Épée, France-Lames, La Borie, 43120 Monistrol-sur-Loire - T: 0471756060, Fax: 0471756061, E-mail: info@france-lames.fr, Internet: http://www.france-lames.fr
Science&Tech Museum 11799

Monoblet

Chemin de la Soie, Filature de Gréfeuilh, 30170 Monoblet - T: 0466776647
Decorative Arts Museum 11800

Monpazier

Atelier des Bastides, 24540 Monpazier - T: 0553226038/6572/6301
Archaeological Museum 11801

Château de Biron, 24540 Monpazier -
T: 0553631339/355040, Fax: 0553063094
Historic Site 11802

Mons (Var)

Musée Marine-et-Montagne, Rue Pierre-Porré,
83440 Mons (Var) - T: 0494763834
Folklore Museum 11803

Monségur

Musée Archéologique, Maison du Paysan, Mairie,
33580 Monségur - T: 0556616012/37
Archaeological Museum / Agriculture
Museum 11804

Monsireigne

Musée de la France Protestante de l'Ouest, Le
Bois-Tiffrais, 85110 Monsireigne - T: 0251664103.
Head: François Loyau
Religious Arts Museum - 1946
History of French Protestantism, etchings, pictures,
manuscripts, books, memorabilia 11805

Mont-Dauphin

**Musée Vauban et de la Fortification dans les
Alpes**, 05600 Mont-Dauphin - T: 0492454240
Military Museum 11806

Mont-de-Lans

Maison des Traditions et des Arts, 38860 Mont-de-
Lans - T: 0476802397
Folklore Museum 11807

Mont-de-Marsan

Centre d'Art Contemporain, 11 Rue Saint-Vincent de
Paul, 40000 Mont-de-Marsan - T: 0558755584
Fine Arts Museum 11808

Musée Despiau Wlerick, 6 Pl Marguerite de Navarre,
40000 Mont-de-Marsan - T: 0558750045,
Fax: 0558859002. Head: Philippe Camin
Fine Arts Museum - 1886
Sculpture, faience 11809

Mont-Louis

Four Solaire, Blvd Vauban, 66210 Mont-Louis -
T: 0468041489
Special Museum / Science&Tech Museum 11810

Musée du Roy Soleil, Blvd Vauban, 66210 Mont-
Louis - T: 0468041489
Special Museum / Historical Museum 11811

Musée du Vitrail, 66210 Mont-Louis
Science&Tech Museum / Historical Museum 11812

Mont-Saint-Michel

Musée Historique, Vannier, 50116 Mont-Saint-Michel
Historical Museum
Copper painting (15th-17th c), bas-reliefs,
armaments, wax museum, periscope coll 11813

Mont-Saint-Vincent

Musée Archéologique Jean Régnier, Grenier à Sel,
71690 Mont-Saint-Vincent - T: 0385573851
Archaeological Museum 11814

Montagnac-la-Crempse

Habitat Ancien, Patrimoine Architectural Rural,
Hameau de la Grange, 24140 Montagnac-la-
Crempse - T: 0553819319
Folklore Museum / Fine Arts Museum 11815

Montagnac-sur-Lède

Collection du Moulin du Cros, 47150 Montagnac-
sur-Lède - T: 0553364478
Local Museum 11816

Montagne

Ecomusée du Libournais, Le Bourg, 33570
Montagne - T: 0557745689, Fax: 0557552101,
E-mail: ecomusee.libournais@educagri.fr
Special Museum 11817

Montaigu (Vendée)

Musée du Nord de la Vendée, Château, 85600
Montaigu (Vendée) - T: 0251940271. Head: M. Vital
Local Museum
Prehistory, Gallo-Roman, medieval finds, painting,
sculpture, folklore 11818

Montalba-le-Château

Exposition Permanente de la Viticulture, Cave
Coopérative, 66130 Montalba-le-Château -
T: 0468847653
Agriculture Museum 11819

Montalieu-Vercieu

Maison de la Pierre et du Ciment, 1 Rue du Rhône,
38390 Montalieu-Vercieu - T: 0474886795,
Fax: 0474886796, E-mail: mpc.montalieu@
wanadoo.fr
Special Museum 11820

Montaner

Château de Montaner, 64460 Montaner -
T: 0559819829
Historical Museum 11821

Montarcher

Musée de l'Audiovisuel, Ancienne Ecole, Le Bourg,
42380 Montarcher - T: 0477502697
Special Museum 11822

Montargis

Écomusée de l'Apiculture, Rte Nationale 7,
Montargis Sud, 45207 Montargis - T: 0238853202,
Fax: 0238984760
Natural History Museum 11823

Musée Archéologique du Gatinais, 7 Rue du
Château, 45207 Montargis - T: 0238980781,
Fax: 0238932684
Archaeological Museum 11824

Musée des Tanneurs, Rue du Château, 45207
Montargis - T: 0238980087, Fax: 0238893234.
Head: Michel Métais
Folklore Museum 11825

Musée Girodet, 2 Rue de la Chaussée, 45200
Montargis - T: 0238980781, Fax: 0238932684
Fine Arts Museum
Classical art, 13th-19th century sculpture, 16th-
19th century paintings, decorative arts 11826

Montauban

Musée de la Résistance et de la Déportation, 33
Grand-Rue, Villenouvelle, 82000 Montauban -
T: 0563660311. Head: Edmée Ladier
Historical Museum 11827

Musée d'Histore Naturelle Victor-Brun, 2 Pl
Antoine-Bourdelle, 82000 Montauban -
T: 0563221385. Head: E. Ladier
Natural History Museum - 1854
3,000 species of birds, paleontology, fossils,
prehistorical skeletons and petrified items,
meteorites, mineralogy - library 11828

Musée Ingres, Palais des Evêques, 19 Rue de la
Mairie, 82000 Montauban - T: 0563221291,
Fax: 0563921699. Head: Georges Vigne
Fine Arts Museum - 1843
Fine arts, archeology, ceramics, folk art, 4000
drawings and 37 paintings by J.A.D. Ingres,
sculptures by Bourdelle, contemporary art 11829

Montaure

Musée du Cidre, Château, 27400 Montaure -
T: 0232506499, E-mail: www.montaure@
cybercable.fr. Head: Philippot
Special Museum 11830

Montaut

Musée Préhistorique et de Peinture, Pl des Tilleuls,
40500 Montaut - T: 0558760513
Archaeological Museum / Fine Arts Museum 11831

Montazels

Collection de Moules de Chapeaux, Chapellerie,
11190 Montazels - T: 0468740393
Fine Arts Museum 11832

Montbard

Musée Archéologique, Tour de l'Aubépin, Parc
Buffon, 21500 Montbard - T: 0380920134
Archaeological Museum 11833

Musée Buffon, Rue du Parc Buffon, 21500 Montbard
- T: 0380920134, Fax: 0380891199. Head: Pierre
Ickowicz
Science&Tech Museum / Natural History Museum /
Local Museum / Decorative Arts Museum 11834

Musée des Beaux-Arts, Rue Piron, Ancienne
Chapelle, 21500 Montbard - T: 0380920134,
Fax: 0380891199
Fine Arts Museum - 1911/1930
Painting, drawing, sculpture 11835

Musée du Château et des Anciennes Écuries, Parc
Buffon, 21500 Montbard - T: 0380925042,
Fax: 0386891199. Head: Sandrine Balan
Military Museum / Science&Tech Museum - 1988
Weapons and cycles 11836

Salon de Peinture Permanent, Mairie, 21500
Montbard - T: 0380920134. Head: Louis Arnoux
Fine Arts Museum 11837

Montbazin

Collections Historiques, 34140 Montbazin -
T: 0467787202
Historical Museum 11838

Montbéliard

Centre d'Art et de Plaisanterie, Scène Nationale, 54
Rue Clemenceau, 25200 Montbéliard -
T: 0381913711
Fine Arts Museum 11839

Centre Régional d'Art Contemporain, 19 Av des
Alliés, 25200 Montbéliard Cedex - T: 0381321232,
Fax: 0381955275, E-mail: dix.nlerf.crac@
wanadoo.fr
Fine Arts Museum 11840

Musée d'Art et Historique, Hôtel Beurnier, Pl Saint-
Martin, 25200 Montbéliard - T: 0381992493,
Fax: 0381913983. Head: Goetz Bernard
Fine Arts Museum / Historical Museum 11841

Musée du Château des Ducs de Wurtemberg,
25200 Montbéliard - T: 0381992261,
Fax: 0381913983, E-mail: bernard.goetz@
montbeliard.com. Head: Bernard Fauchille
Local Museum
Natural hist, archeology, Gallo-Roman finds, fine
arts, hist, science, contemporary art 11842

Montblanc

Musée Edouard Barthe, Hôtel de Ville, 34290
Montblanc - T: 0467985077
Fine Arts Museum 11843

Montboucher-sur-Jabron

Atelier-Musée de la Soie, Rte de Dieulefit, 26740
Montboucher-sur-Jabron - T: 0475014740
Special Museum / Science&Tech Museum 11844

Montbrison

Musée d'Allard, Blvd de la Préfecture, 42600
Montbrison - T: 0477583307, Fax: 0477588334,
E-mail: museeallard@ville-montbrison.fr. Head:
Henri Pailler
Local Museum
Numismatics, mineralogy, ornithology, toys 11845

Musée de la Poupée, Blvd de la Préfecture, 42600
Montbrison - T: 0477583307
Special Museum 11846

Musée La Diana, Rue du Cloître Notre-Dame, 42600
Montbrison - T: 0477960110, Fax: 0477588990,
E-mail: mathevot@ladiana.com, Internet: http://
www.ladiana.com. Head: Vincent Guichard
Archaeological Museum - 1862
Neolithicum, Second Iron Age - Library 11847

Montcaret

Musée Pierre Tauziac, 24230 Montcaret -
T: 0553585018, Fax: 0553732650
Archaeological Museum - 1946
Gallo-roman house from the 4th century, open air
remains, 11th century church 11848

Montceau-les-Mines

Musée des Fossiles, 76 Quai Jules Chagot, 71300
Montceau-les-Mines - T: 0385573851
Archaeological Museum 11849

Montchal

Collections Archéologiques et du Tissage, Pl de
l'Église, 42360 Montchal - T: 0477287436/6499
Archaeological Museum / Local Museum 11850

Montcornet-en-Ardenne

**Collections Historiques du Château Fort des XIe-
XVe s**, 08090 Montcornet-en-Ardenne -
T: 0324549348/8098
Historical Museum 11851

Montcy-Notre-Dame

Écomusée du Linge, École Maternelle, 08090
Montcy-Notre-Dame - T: 0324330889/2752
Special Museum 11852

Montebourg

Musée du Lait, Rue des Perruquettes, 50310
Montebourg - T: 0233411348
Special Museum 11853

Montecheroux

Musée de la Pince, Rue de la Pommeraie, 25190
Montecheroux - T: 0381925065/00/5118
Science&Tech Museum 11854

Montélimar

Musée d'Art et d'Histoire, Château des Adhémar,
26200 Montélimar - T: 0475010785
Archaeological Museum / Historical Museum 11855

Musée-Usine de Nougats, Escobar, Pl Léopold Blanc,
26200 Montélimar - T: 0475012553
Special Museum 11856

Montendre-les-Pins

Musée des Arts et Traditions Populaires, Tour
Carrée, 17130 Montendre-les-Pins -
T: 0546492632/4144
Folklore Museum 11857

Montereau-Fault-Yonne

Musée de la Faïence, 2 Pl René Cassin, 77130
Montereau-Fault-Yonne - T: 0164329564. Head:
Cendrine Nougué
Decorative Arts Museum - 1985
Faiences from Creil and Montereau 11858

Montesquieu-des-Albères

Musée des Batailles, Mairie, 66740 Montesquieu-
des-Albères - T: 0468896049
Military Museum 11859

Musée du Cinéma Amateur, Mairie, 66740
Montesquieu-des-Albères - T: 0468896049
Special Museum 11860

Montet et Bouxal

**Musée de l'Histoire de France à travers son
Armée**, 46210 Montet et Bouxal - T: 0565402976
Military Museum 11861

Montfermeil

Collections du Moulin, 138 Rue des Moulins, 93370
Montfermeil - T: 0143301711
Science&Tech Museum 11862

Musée du Travail Charles-Peyre, 1 Rue de l'Église,
93370 Montfermeil - T: 0145092856/43304381
Historical Museum 11863

Montferrat

Musée Adolphe-Pégoud, Mairie, 38620 Montferrat -
T: 0476323002/3028
Special Museum 11864

Montferrer

Musée d'Art et d'Histoire, Mairie, 66150 Montferrer
- T: 0468391244
Fine Arts Museum / Historical Museum 11865

Montferrier

Musée Patrimoine et Traditions, 09300 Montferrier -
T: 0561019147. Head: Arlette Homs-Chabbert
Historical Museum 11866

Montfort-en-Chalosse

Musée de la Chalosse, Domaine Carcher, 40380
Montfort-en-Chalosse - T: 0558986927
Folklore Museum 11867

Montfort-l'Amaury

Musée Maurice Ravel, 5 Rue Maurice Ravel, 78490
Montfort-l'Amaury - T: 0134860089,
Fax: 0134868796, E-mail: tourisme@
ville_montfort_l_amaury.fr
Special Museum
Memorabilia of the composer Maurice Ravel,
original family furnishings 11868

Montfort-sur-Meu

Ecomusée du Pays de Montfort, 2 Rue du Château,
35160 Montfort-sur-Meu - T: 0299093181. Head:
Gaby Marcon
Local Museum
Costume, prehist, local hist 11869

Montgeron

Musée Municipal Joseph-Jacquiot, 64 Av de la
République, 91230 Montgeron - T: 0169520030/
030734
Special Museum / Historical Museum 11870

Montgesoye

Musée du Costume Franc-Comtois, 14 Rue de
Besançon, 25111 Montgesoye - T: 0381621848
Folklore Museum 11871

Montgobert

Musée du Bois et de l'Outil, Château de Montgobert,
47 Allée du Château, 02600 Montgobert -
T: 0323963669, Fax: 0323961902,
E-mail: montgobert@chateaux-france.com. Head: E.
d' Albufera
Special Museum 11872

Montguers

Maison-Musée des Arômes, 26170 Montguers -
T: 0475280867
Special Museum 11873

Musée de la Lavande, 26170 Montguers -
T: 0475286271
Special Museum 11874

Montguillon

Musée du Costume, Château de Bouillé-Thévalle,
49500 Montguillon - T: 0241610905
Decorative Arts Museum 11875

Monthermé

Collection de 2000 ex-voto, Église des Hauts-Buttés,
08800 Monthermé - T: 0324530274
Religious Arts Museum 11876

Montignac

Lascaux II, Fac-similé de Lascaux, 24290 Montignac
- T: 0553519503/355040, Fax: 0553063094
Fine Arts Museum
Beautiful copies (paintings) of "Lascaux" 11877

Musée d'Arts Populaires du Périgord Eugène Leroy, Pl Bertrand de Born, 24290 Montignac - T: 0553518260
Local Museum 11878

Musée du Regourdou, 24290 Montignac - T: 0553518123
Archaeological Museum 11879

Montigny-le-Gannelon

Musée des Machines Agricoles Anciennes, Château, 28220 Montigny-le-Gannelon - T: 0237983003, Fax: 0237984591, E-mail: delamot@club-internet.fr, Internet: http://www.chateauxandcountry.com/-montigny. Head: Marquise de la Motte Saint-Pierre
Science&Tech Museum 11880

Montjean-sur-Loire

Ecomusée de Montjean, La Forge, Pl du Vallon, 49570 Montjean-sur-Loire - T: 0241390848
Science&Tech Museum / Folklore Museum 11881

Montlieu-la-Garde

Maison du Patrimoine, 17210 Montlieu-la-Garde - T: 0546046117
Local Museum 11882

Montlouis-sur-Loire

Maison de la Loire, 60 Quai Albert Baillet, 37270 Montlouis-sur-Loire - T: 0247509752/450046
Natural History Museum 11883

Musée de la Viticulture, Cave Touristique, 37270 Montlouis-sur-Loire - T: 0247451819
Special Museum 11884

Montluçon

Musée des Musiques Populaires, Château des Ducs de Bourbon, 03100 Montluçon - T: 0470025656, Fax: 0470280410, E-mail: c.baldoni@mairie-montlucon.fr
Music Museum - 1959
History and manufacture of string and various popmusic instruments, bagpipes, electric guitars, drums, 17th-19th century French porcelain 11885

Musée du Château de la Louviere, Av du Cimetière de l'Est, 03100 Montluçon - T: 0470025656/050491
Local Museum / Decorative Arts Museum / Fine Arts Museum 11886

Montmaur

Musée d'Arts et Traditions Populaires, Château, 05400 Montmaur - T: 0492581142
Folklore Museum 11887

Montmaurin

Dépôt de Fouilles Gallo-Romaines et Préhistoriques de Montmaurin, 31350 Montmaurin - T: 0561881084, Fax: 0561881084, E-mail: mairie.montmaurin@wanadoo.fr
Archaeological Museum 11888

Montmédy

Musée Bastien Lepage, Citadelle, 55600 Montmédy - T: 0329801590/1189, Fax: 0329800579, E-mail: montmedy@wanadoo.fr. Head: Claude Leonard
Fine Arts Museum / Archaeological Museum - 1904/1988 11889

Montmélian

Musée des Amis de Montmélian, Hôtel Nicolle de Laplace, Ancienne Mairie, Rue F. Dumas, 73800 Montmélian - T: 0479842573
Local Museum / Archaeological Museum 11890

Montmirail

Château-Musée, 72320 Montmirail - T: 0243936501/7271, E-mail: bertrand.de-buffevent@wanadoo.fr
Fine Arts Museum / Historic Site 11891

Montmorency

Musée Jean-Jacques Rousseau, 4 Rue du Mont Louis, 95160 Montmorency - T: 0139648013, Fax: 0139899123. Head: Robert Thiery
Historical Museum - 1951
Home of Rousseau from 1757 to 1762 where he wrote his main works, showrooms with etchings, manuscripts, original editions - library 11892

Montmorillon

Musée Municipal de Montmorillon, 6 Rue des Augustins, 86500 Montmorillon - T: 0549910232
Local Museum 11893

Montmorin

Musée des Arts et Traditions Populaires, Château, 63160 Montmorin - T: 0473683094
Folklore Museum 11894

Montmort-Lucy

Musée-Château, 51270 Montmort-Lucy - T: 0326591004, Fax: 0326523573
Decorative Arts Museum 11895

Montoire-sur-le-Loir

Musée du Vélo, 55 Rue du Général Leclerc, 41800 Montoire-sur-le-Loir - T: 0254852501
Science&Tech Museum 11896

Montolieu

Musée des Métiers et Arts Graphiques, Manufacture Royale, 11170 Montolieu
Special Museum / Science&Tech Museum 11897

Montpellier

Agropolis Muséum, 951 Av Agropolis, 34000 Montpellier - T: 0467047500/7504
Historical Museum 11898

Centre de Documentation du Patrimoine, D.R.A.C., 5 Rue Salle l'Evêque, 34000 Montpellier - T: 0467023200. Head: Chantal Creste
Historical Museum / Archaeological Museum / Ethnology Museum 11899

Château de Mogère, 2235 Rte de Vauguières, 34000 Montpellier - T: 0467657201/7751
Decorative Arts Museum / Fine Arts Museum 11900

Mikve, Bain Rituel Juif, 1 Rue Barralerie, 34000 Montpellier - T: 0467586758
Archaeological Museum 11901

Musée Atger, 2 Rue de l'Ecole de Médecine, 34000 Montpellier - T: 0467662777, Fax: 0467661924, E-mail: direction.bumed@sc.univ-montp1.fr. Head: Hélène Lorblanchet
Fine Arts Museum - 1813
16th-18th century French, Italian, Flemish drawings 11902

Musée d'Anatomie, 2 Rue de l'Ecole de Médecine, 34000 Montpellier - T: 0467607371
Special Museum 11903

Musée de la Pharmacie Albert Ciurana, c/o Faculté de Pharmacie, 15 Av Charles Flahault, 34093 Montpellier Cedex 5 - T: 0467566552004, 0467548062, Fax: 0467548062, E-mail: ccharlot@pharm.univ-montp1.fr. Head: Colette Charlot
Special Museum / University Museum 11904

Musée de la Pharmacie Populaire, Couvent de la Miséricorde, 1 Rue de la Monnaie, 34080 Montpellier - T: 0467792346
Decorative Arts Museum 11905

Musée de l'Infanterie, Caserne Guillaut, Av Lepic, 34057 Montpellier Cedex 1 - T: 0467072023/2139
Military Museum 11906

Musée des Arts Décoratifs Sabatier d'Espeyran, 6 Rue Montpelliéret, 34000 Montpellier - T: 0467661346, Fax: 0467660920, E-mail: musee.fabre@ville-montpellier.fr, Internet: http://www.ville-montpellier/fr/clr/0705-musee-fr.htm. Head: Michel Hilaire
Decorative Arts Museum 11907

Musée des Moulages, Université Paul Valéry, Rte de Mende, 34199 Montpellier Cedex 5 - T: 0467142377, Fax: 0467142452, E-mail: mdm@univ-montp3.fr. Head: Chr. Llinas
Museum of Classical Antiquities / Fine Arts Museum - 1890
Classical antiquities, sculpture, medieval art 11908

Musée du Château de Flaugergues, 1744 Av Albert Einstein, 34000 Montpellier - T: 0467655172/7964, Fax: 0467652185. Head: Brigitte de Colbert
Local Museum 11909

Musée du Commissariat de l'Armée de Terre, 4 Rue du 81e R.I., 34000 Montpellier - T: 0467072375
Military Museum 11910

Musée du Vieux Montpellier, Pl Pétrarque, Hôtel de Varennes, 34000 Montpellier - T: 0467660294, Fax: 0467348751
Local Museum 11911

Musée du Zinc, 68 Rue de Lunaret, 34000 Montpellier - T: 0467796222, 0467723141, Fax: 0467021209. Head: D. Michel
Decorative Arts Museum 11912

Musée Fabre, 13 Rue Montpelliéret, 34000 Montpellier - T: 0467148300, Fax: 0467660920, E-mail: musee.fabre@ville_montpellier.fr, Internet: http://www.ville_montpellier.fr/cultur. Head: Michel Hilaire
Fine Arts Museum - 1825
Italian, Spanish, Flemish, Dutch, English, and French paintings, sculpture, drawings 11913

Musée Historique de la Médecine, Faculté de Médecine, 2 Rue de l'École-de-Médecine, 34000 Montpellier - T: 0467607371
Special Museum / Science&Tech Museum 11914

Musée Languédocien, 7 Rue Jacques Coeur, 34000 Montpellier - T: 0467529303, Fax: 0467660208
Archaeological Museum / Decorative Arts Museum / Fine Arts Museum / Association with Coll 11915

Musée Lou Fougou Montpelierenc, 2 Pl Pétrarque, 34000 Montpellier - T: 0467660294
Local Museum 11916

Montpeyroux

Musée d'Art Ancien, Château du Bousquet, 12210 Montpeyroux - T: 0565484113, Fax: 0565484754, E-mail: chateau.du.bousquet@wanadoo.fr. Head: Pierre Dijols
Decorative Arts Museum 11917

Montpont

Musée du Terroir Bressan, Romenay, 71470 Montpont - T: 0385409111
Local Museum 11918

Montréal-du-Gers

Musée Archéologique, A l'OT, 32250 Montréal-du-Gers - T: 0562294285, Fax: 0562294246, E-mail: -otsi.montrealdugers@wanadoo.fr. Head: Jane Massartic
Archaeological Museum 11919

Muséosite de la Villa Gallo-Romaine de Séviac, 32250 Montréal-du-Gers - T: 0562294857, Fax: 0562294843, E-mail: seviac.villa@wanadoo.fr, Internet: http://www.seviac-villa.fr.gt. Head: Jean Gugole
Archaeological Museum 11920

Montréjeau

Musée d'Histoire Militaire, Hôtel de Lassus, Rue du Barry, 31210 Montréjeau - T: 0561958022
Military Museum 11921

Montrésor

Musée d'Art Polonais, Château, 37460 Montrésor - T: 0247926019
Fine Arts Museum 11922

Montreuil-Bellay

Musée-Château, Château, 49260 Montreuil-Bellay - T: 0241523306, Fax: 0241523770. Head: X. de Thuy
Decorative Arts Museum / Open Air Museum 11923

Musée du Ver à Soie, La Soie Vivante, Les Petits Augustins, Pl des Augustins, 49260 Montreuil-Bellay - T: 0241387258, Fax: 0241388698. Head: Claude Bernay
Science&Tech Museum 11924

Montreuil (Pas-de-Calais)

Musée d'Art et d'Histoire Roger Rodière, 8 Rue du Paon, 62170 Montreuil (Pas-de-Calais) - T: 0321060133/0427, Internet: http://www.montreuil62.net
Local Museum / Historical Museum / Religious Arts Museum 11925

Montreuil (Seine-Saint-Denis)

Musée de l'Histoire Vivante Parc Montreau, 31 Blvd Théophile Sueur, 93100 Montreuil (Seine-Saint-Denis) - T: 0148706162, Fax: 0148551634, E-mail: mhv@wanadoo.fr. Head: Gérard Lefevre
Historical Museum - 1939 11926

Montrevel-en-Bresse

Ferme-Musée à Pans de Bois de Sougey, 01340 Montrevel-en-Bresse - T: 0474524712/308694/7189
Agriculture Museum 11927

Musée Océanien de Cuet, Cure, 01340 Montrevel-en-Bresse - T: 0474254684/308694
Ethnology Museum 11928

Montrichard

Musée des Amis du Vieux Montrichard, Tivoli, Entrée du Donjon, 41400 Montrichard - T: 0254320510/0490
Historical Museum 11929

Petit Musée du Vin, Rue Porte-au-Roi, 41400 Montrichard - T: 0254325107
Special Museum 11930

Montricoux

Musée Marcel-Lenoir, Château, 82800 Montricoux - T: 0563672648
Special Museum 11931

Montrozier

Musée Départemental d'Archéologie, 12630 Montrozier - T: 0565707145, Fax: 0565707775. Head: Philippe Gruat
Archaeological Museum 11932

Montségur-le-Château

Archéosite du Château et Village Médiéval, 32 Village, 09300 Montségur-le-Château - T: 05610694/1027, Fax: 0561031127, E-mail: mairie.montsegur@wanadoo.fr. Head: Fabrice Chambon
Archaeological Museum 11933

Musée Archéologique Municipal, Mairie, 09300 Montségur-le-Château - T: 0561011027, Fax: 0561031127, E-mail: mairie.montsegur@wanadoo.fr, Internet: http://www.citaenet.com/montsegur. Head: Philippe Walter
Archaeological Museum 11934

Montseret

Musée Archéologique, Ancien Lavoir, 11200 Montseret - T: 0468433282/75
Archaeological Museum 11935

Montsoreau

Champignonnière-Musée du Saut aux Loups, Rte de Saumur à Chinon, 49730 Montsoreau - T: 0241517030, Fax: 0241381530, E-mail: SautAuxLoups@fr.st. Head: Yannick Neveux
Special Museum / Agriculture Museum 11936

Montville

Musée des Sapeurs-Pompiers de France, Rue Baron Bigot, 76710 Montville - T: 0235331351, Fax: 0235331351, E-mail: info@mairie-montville.fr, Internet: http://www.mairie-montville.fr. Head: Pascal Martin
Science&Tech Museum 11937

Morestel

Maison A.-Ravier, Centre Culturel, 38510 Morestel - T: 0474800680
Fine Arts Museum 11938

Moret-sur-Loing

Musée d'Art et d'Histoire, Pl de Samois, 77250 Moret-sur-Loing - T: 0160703230
Fine Arts Museum / Local Museum 11939

Morez

Musée de la Lunetterie, 5 Rue Lamartine, 39400 Morez - T: 0384330873
Special Museum 11940

Musée Jourdain, 5 Rue Lamartine, 39400 Morez - T: 0384330873. Head: M. Bourgeois-Lechartier
Fine Arts Museum 11941

Morlaas

Musée du Maïs, Pl de la Mairie, 64160 Morlaas - T: 0559334041
Special Museum / Historical Museum 11942

Musée Historique et Lapidaire, Pl de la Mairie, 64160 Morlaas - T: 0559334041
Local Museum 11943

Morlaix

Musée des Jacobins, Pl des Jacobins, 29600 Morlaix - T: 0298886888, Fax: 0298880892, E-mail: museedemorlaix@wanadoo.fr. Head: Patrick Jourdan
Local Museum - 1887
Art, archeology, hist, ethnology 11944

Morlanne

Musée des Beaux-Arts et Arts Décoratifs Raymond Ritter, Château, 64370 Morlanne - T: 0559816027
Fine Arts Museum / Decorative Arts Museum 11945

Mormoiron

Musée Archéologique, 84570 Mormoiron - T: 0490619635
Archaeological Museum 11946

Mornant

Maison de Pays, 6 Rue Joseph-Venet, 69440 Mornant - T: 0478440376, Fax: 0478449170, E-mail: alain.meyer@free.fr, Internet: http://www.maison.pays.mornant.free.fr. Head: Alain Meyer
Special Museum 11947

Mornas

Forteresse de Mornas, 84550 Mornas - T: 0490370126
Historical Museum 11948

Morogues

Château-Musée de Maupas, 18220 Morogues - T: 0248644171, Fax: 0248641982
Decorative Arts Museum
Unique coll of 887 faience dishes 11949

Mortagne-au-Perche

Musée Percheron, 8 Rue du Portail Saint-Denis, 61400 Mortagne-au-Perche
Local Museum 11950

Morteau

Collection de Cloches, 44 Rue Loubière, 25500 Morteau - T: 0381670408
Special Museum 11951

Horlogerie Automates Yves Cupillard, 14 Rue des Moulinots, 25500 Morteau - T: 0381671001
Science&Tech Museum 11952

Musée de l'Horlogerie du Haut-Doubs, Château Pertusier, 25500 Morteau - T: 0381674088, Fax: 0381675042, E-mail: pertusie@fc-net.fr. Head: Gregory Maugain
Science&Tech Museum 11953

Mortrée

Château-Musée, Château, 61500 Mortrée - T: 0233353469
Decorative Arts Museum 11954

Mouans-Sartoux

Espace de l'Art Concret, Château de Mouans-Sartoux, 06370 Mouans-Sartoux - T: 0493757150, Fax: 0493758888, E-mail: d.boudou.eac@wanadoo.fr. Head: Dominique Boudou
Fine Arts Museum 11955

Musée d'Histoire Locale, Château, 06370 Mouans-Sartoux - T: 0492924724
Historical Museum 11956

Moudeyres

Musée des Frères Perrel, 43150 Moudeyres - T: 0471051213
Folklore Museum 11957

Mougins

Exposition Permanente d'Art Le Lavoir, 06250 Mougins - T: 0493758767
Fine Arts Museum 11958

Musée de la Photographie, Porte Sarrazine, 06250 Mougins - T: 0493758567, Fax: 0493758567, E-mail: dircom@mougins-coteazur.org. Head: Roger Duhalde
Science&Tech Museum - 1986
Antique cameras 11959

Musée de l'Automobiliste, Autoroute A8, 06250 Mougins - T: 0493692780, Fax: 0493460136, E-mail: musauto@club-internet.fr. Head: Adrien Maeght
Science&Tech Museum 11960

Musée Municipal, Pl du Commandant Lamy, 06250 Mougins - T: 0493925042, Fax: 0493901515, E-mail: dircom@mougins-coteazur.org. Head: Joëlle Dalmasso
Fine Arts Museum 11961

Mouilleron-en-Pareds

Musée des Deux-Victoires Clemenceau-de Lattre, Mairie, 85390 Mouilleron-en-Pareds - T: 0251003149, Fax: 0251003431
Military Museum 11962

Musée-Maison Natale de Jean de Lattre de Tassigny, Rue Jean-de-Lattre-de-Tassigny, 85390 Mouilleron-en-Pareds - T: 0251003149/3431
Special Museum 11963

Moulineaux

Musée des Vikings, Château-Fort de Robert-le-Diable, 76530 Moulineaux - T: 0235180236/238110
Historical Museum 11964

Moulins (Allier)

Musée Anne de Beaujeu, Pl du Colonel Laussedat, 03000 Moulins (Allier) - T: 0470204847, Fax: 0470208931, E-mail: a.beaujeu@musee-moulins.fr, Internet: http://www.musee-moulins.fr. Head: Nadine Berthelier
Fine Arts Museum
16th century pavillon, ancient pottery, bronzes, statuettes, early German paintings and 19th century French paintings, sculpture, decorative arts, porcelain, archaeology 11965

Musée Diocésain d'Art Sacré, 43-45 Rue de Paris, 03000 Moulins (Allier) - T: 0470468226, Fax: 0470469858, E-mail: cperrot@cs3i.fr. Head: C. Perrot
Religious Arts Museum 11966

Musée du Folklore et du Vieux Moulin, 6 Pl de l'Ancien-Palais, 03000 Moulins (Allier) - T: 0470443903
Local Museum - 1934
Traditional costumes, 150 flat irons, dolls from all over the world, objects and tools dealing with mills, reconstructed interior of peasant home, engravings and photographs - library 11967

Musée Historique du Bourbonnais, Archives Départementales de l'Allier, 03000 Moulins (Allier) - T: 0470200140
Historical Museum 11968

Trésor de la Cathédrale Notre-Dame, Pl des Vosges, 03000 Moulins (Allier) - T: 0470208965
Religious Arts Museum 11969

Moulis-en-Médoc

Musée de la Barrique (closed) 11970

Musée des Arts et Métiers de la Vigne et du Vin, Château Maucaillou, 33480 Moulis-en-Médoc - T: 0556580123
Special Museum 11971

Moureze

Espace Muséal Les Courtinals, 34800 Moureze - T: 0467960842
Archaeological Museum 11972

Moussy

Galerie-Musée de l'Auberge Champenoise, 6 RD 51, 51200 Moussy - T: 0326540348
Local Museum 11973

Moustey

Musée des Croyances Populaires et du Patrimoine Religieux, Eglise Notre-Dame, 40410 Moustey - T: 0558075270/7126
Religious Arts Museum 11974

Moustiers-Sainte-Marie

Musée Historique de la Faïence, 04360 Moustiers-Sainte-Marie - T: 0492746164, Fax: 0492746223. Head: Bernadette de Rességuier
Decorative Arts Museum - 1929
Local ceramics (17th-20th c) 11975

Mouthier-Haute-Pierre

Musée Phisalix, Mairie, 25920 Mouthier-Haute-Pierre - T: 0381609110
Special Museum 11976

Mouthiers-sur-Boême

Musée d'Art et d'Histoire du 3ème Âge, Maison des Jeunes et de la Culture, Pl de la Gare, 16440 Mouthiers-sur-Boême - T: 0545679232
Folklore Museum / Local Museum 11977

Moutiers-Saint-Jean

Musée de la Vieille Pharmacie, Hôpital Saint-Sauveur XVIIe s, 21500 Moutiers-Saint-Jean - T: 0380967337
Special Museum 11978

Moutiers (Savoie)

Musée de l'Academie de la Val d'Isère, 23 Pl Saint-Pierre, 73600 Moutiers (Savoie) - T: 0479240423, Fax: 0479245605, Internet: http://assoc.wanadoo.fr/academie.moutiers
Historical Museum - 1865 11979

Mouzon

Archéosite Gallo-Romain des Flaviers, 08210 Mouzon - T: 0324261063, Fax: 0324262773, E-mail: mairie.mouzon@wanadoo.fr
Historic Site 11980

Musée de la Porte de Bourgogne, Rue Porte de Bourgogne, 08210 Mouzon - T: 0324261063, Fax: 0324262773, E-mail: mairie.mouzon@wanadoo.fr
Archaeological Museum / Local Museum / Historical Museum / Historic Site 11981

Musée du Feutre, Centre de Culture Technique, Pl du Colombier, 08210 Mouzon - T: 0324265076, Fax: 0324262773, E-mail: musee-atelier.du.feutre@wanadoo.fr
Science&Tech Museum
Hist of felt industry 11982

Moyen

Musée, Château, 54118 Moyen - T: 0383427126
Special Museum 11983

Mozac

Musée Lapidaire, Pl de l'Abbaye, 63200 Mozac - T: 0473386547/337171
Fine Arts Museum / Archaeological Museum 11984

Muhlbach-sur-Munster

Musée de la Schlitte et des Métiers du Bois, 11 Rue de la Gare, 68380 Muhlbach-sur-Munster - T: 0389776108, Fax: 0389776946, E-mail: mairie-de-muhlbach-munster@wanadoo.fr. Head: J.-M. Sengele
Special Museum / Ethnology Museum / Historical Museum 11985

Mulhouse

Centre d'Art International, Maison de la Céramique, 25 Rue Josué-Hofer, 68200 Mulhouse - T: 0389433255
Decorative Arts Museum 11986

Collection Schlumpf, Musée National de l'Automobile, 192 Av de Colmar, 68100 Mulhouse - T: 0389332323, Fax: 0389320809, E-mail: message@collection-schlumpf.com, Internet: http://www.collection-schlumpf.com. Head: Emmanuel Bacquet
Science&Tech Museum 11987

Collections Lapidaires, Chapelle Saint-Jean, Grand'Rue/Rue Saint-Jean, 68100 Mulhouse - T: 0389456831. Head: Benoît Bruant
Religious Arts Museum 11988

Musée de l'Impression sur Etoffes, 14 Rue Jean-Jacques Henner, 68072 Mulhouse, mail addr: BP 1468, 68072 Mulhouse - T: 0389468300, Fax: 0389468310, E-mail: conservation@musee-impression.com, Internet: http://www.musee-impression.com. Head: Martine Feigel
Decorative Arts Museum - 1858
Archives 11989

Musée des Beaux-Arts, Villa Steinbach, 4 Pl Guillaume-Tell, 68100 Mulhouse - T: 0389454320/6831. Head: Benoît Bruant
Fine Arts Museum - 1884/1983
Paintings from Middle Ages to 20th c, drawings, coll of lithographs 11990

Musée du Fil D.M.C., 13 Rue de Pfastatt, 68200 Mulhouse - T: 0389324444
Decorative Arts Museum 11991

Musée du Sapeur-Pompier, 2 Rue Alfred Glehn, 68100 Mulhouse - T: 0389422567
Science&Tech Museum - 1978
Exhibits on fire fighting, fire-fighting technology, uniforms and helmets, documents, fire engines 11992

Musée EDF Electropolis, L'Aventure de l'Electricité, 55 Rue du Pâturage, 68200 Mulhouse - T: 0389324850, E-mail: electropolis@electropolis.tm.fr, Internet: http://www.electropolis.tm.fr. Head: Claude Welty
Science&Tech Museum 11993

Musée Français du Chemin de Fer, 2 Rue Alfred Glehn, 68100 Mulhouse - T: 0389422567. Head: Jean-Paul Muller
Science&Tech Museum - 1971
Hist of train transportation and technology, models, photographs 11994

Musée Historique, Pl de la Réunion, 68100 Mulhouse - T: 0389454320. Head: Benoît Bruant
Historical Museum - 1853
Regional archeological finds, items from Stone Age, Hallstatt period, and Roman times, costumes, history from Middle Ages to 19th c, fine and decorative art - Educational services 11995

Musée Minéralogique de la Société Industrielle, Ecole Nationale Superieure de Chimie, 3 Rue Alfred Werner, 68100 Mulhouse - T: 0389336888, Fax: 0389336885, E-mail: Muse-Miner.enscmu@uha.fr. Head: Dr. Jacques Baron
Natural History Museum 11996

Temple Réformé Mulhouse, Paroisse Saint-Etienne, Pl de la Réunion, 68100 Mulhouse - T: 0389465825, Fax: 0389663019. Head: Sibylle Klumpp
Religious Arts Museum 11997

Traversothèque, Musée du Chemin de Fer, 2 Rue Alfred-Glehn, 68100 Mulhouse - T: 0389422567
Science&Tech Museum 11998

Munster

Maison du Parc Naturel Régional des Ballons des Vosges, 1 Cour de l'Abbaye, 68140 Munster - T: 0389779034, Fax: 0389779030, E-mail: info@parc-ballons-vosges.fr, Internet: http://www.parc-ballons-vosges.fr. Head: Damien Parmentier
Natural History Museum 11999

Musée Hartmann, 68140 Munster - T: 0389773180
Special Museum / Fine Arts Museum 12000

Murat (Cantal)

Maison de la Faune, Mairie, 15300 Murat (Cantal) - T: 0471200947/0052
Natural History Museum 12001

Murat-le-Quaire

Musée de la Toinette, 63150 Murat-le-Quaire - T: 0473811228
Folklore Museum 12002

Muret

Collection de Vieux Avions, Aérodrome Jean-Mermoz, 31600 Muret - T: 0561510385/1839
Science&Tech Museum 12003

Musée Clément Ader, Hôtel de Ville, 27 Rue Castelvielh, 31600 Muret - T: 0561569696
Military Museum / Historical Museum 12004

Murol

Musée Archéologique, Mairie, 63790 Murol - T: 0473886067
Archaeological Museum 12005

Musée Vivant Médiéval, Château, 63790 Murol - T: 0473886894/6711
Historical Museum 12006

Murs

Maison Natale du Brave Crillon, Fidèle Compagnon d'Henri IV, 84220 Murs - T: 0490720001
Archaeological Museum / Folklore Museum 12007

Murviel-les-Montpellier

Musée Archéologique, Mairie, 34570 Murviel-les-Montpellier - T: 0467477972
Archaeological Museum 12008

Mussidan

Musée d'Arts et de Traditions Populaires, Musée André Voulgre, 1 Rue Raoul Grassin, 24400 Mussidan - T: 0553812355
Folklore Museum 12009

Mussy-sur-Seine

Musée de la Résistance, Rue Boursault, 10250 Mussy-sur-Seine - T: 0325384010/4205
Historical Museum 12010

Mutzig

Musée Régional des Armes, Château des Rohan, 67190 Mutzig - T: 0388383198
Historical Museum / Local Museum 12011

Salle d'Honneur du 44e, Quartier Moussy, 67190 Mutzig - T: 0389497899
Military Museum 12012

Muzillac

Musée du Papier Chiffon, Site de Pen-Mur, 56190 Muzillac - T: 0297414379, Fax: 0297456078
Science&Tech Museum 12013

Nages-et-Solorgues

Musée Archéologique, Mairie, 30114 Nages-et-Solorgues - T: 0466350526
Archaeological Museum 12014

Nançay

Galerie Capazza, Musée Imaginaire du Grand Meaulnes, Grenier de Villâtre, 18330 Nançay - T: 0248518022, Fax: 0248518327, E-mail: capazza-galerie@aol.com, Internet: http://www.capazza.galerie.com. Head: Gérard Capazza
Fine Arts Museum / Decorative Arts Museum 12015

Nances

Musée-Atelier de Poupées Francépoque, 73470 Nances - T: 0479287490
Special Museum 12016

Nancray

Musée de Plein Air des Maisons Comtoises, 25360 Nancray - T: 0381552977
Open Air Museum / Agriculture Museum 12017

Nancy

Galerie de l'École Nationale des Beaux-Arts, 1 Av Boffrand, 54000 Nancy - T: 0383401625
Fine Arts Museum 12018

Maison de l'Espace Vert, Parc Sainte-Marie, 54000 Nancy - T: 0383286045
Natural History Museum 12019

Musée d'Art et Traditions Populaires, Musée Lorrain, Couvent des Cordeliers, 66 Grand Rue, 54000 Nancy - T: 0383321874, Fax: 0383379915. Head: Prof. François Streiff
Folklore Museum - 1981
Lorraine folk art, ceramics 12020

Musée de la Porte de la Craffe, Rue de la Craffe, 54000 Nancy - T: 0383321874
Religious Arts Museum 12021

Musée de l'Ecole de Nancy, 36-38 Rue du Sergent Blandan, 54000 Nancy - T: 0383401486, Fax: 0383408331, E-mail: menancy@mairie-nancy.fr
Decorative Arts Museum - 1901
Glass designed by Gallé, ceramics, wall hangings, Art Nouveau posters, paintings, furniture 12022

Musée des Beaux-Arts, 3 Pl Stanislas, 54000 Nancy - T: 0383853072, Fax: 0383853076, E-mail: mbanancy@mairie-nancy.fr. Head: Beatrice Salmon
Fine Arts Museum / Decorative Arts Museum - 1793
European paintings from 14th-20th century (Perugino, Tintoretto, Caravaggio, Rubens, Claude Lorrain, Delacroix, Monet, Manet, Modigliani, Picasso, prints and drawings, complete etchings and engravings of Jacques Callot, coll of satirical drawings of Grandville, important glass coll 12023

Musée du Téléphone, Maison de la Communication, 11 Rue Maurice Barrès, 54039 Nancy - T: 0383348589, Fax: 0383327072
Special Museum / Science&Tech Museum 12024

Musée Lorrain, 64 Grande Rue, 54000 Nancy - T: 0383321874, Fax: 0383379915. Head: Prof. François Streiff
Historical Museum - 1849
Early hist, Gallo-Roman, Merovingian objects, medieval hist, Thirty Years' War, 17th century Lorraine masters, 18th-19th century iron, glass, furnishings, ceramics, fortress fragments, religious sculpture, works by Georges de la Tour and Jacques Callot 12025

Musée Vivant d'Histoire Naturelle, 100 Rue du Jardin Botanique, 54000 Nancy - T: 0383414747
Natural History Museum 12026

Museum-Aquarium de Nancy, 34 Rue Sainte-Catherine, 54000 Nancy - T: 0383329997, Fax: 0383323016, E-mail: all-man@uhp.u-nancy.fr, Internet: http://www.uhp-nancy.fr/. Head:
Natural History Museum 12027

Villa Art Noveau Majorelle, Rue Majorelle, 54000 Nancy - T: 0383413535
Decorative Arts Museum 12028

Nangy

Musée du Vin, Boringes, 74380 Nangy - T: 0450362542
Special Museum 12029

Nans-sous-Sainte-Anne

Musée de la Taillanderie, 25330 Nans-sous-Sainte-Anne - T: 0381866418, Fax: 0381865470. Head: J.-Claude Freyburger
Science&Tech Museum / Agriculture Museum 12030

Nanterre

Musée Édouard-Pinaud, France Parfums, 44 Rue de la Coix, 92000 Nanterre - T: 0147191143/8744
Special Museum 12031

Nantes

Galerie de l'École Régionale des Beaux-Arts, 5 Rue Fénelon, 44000 Nantes - T: 0240359020, Fax: 0240359069, E-mail: secretariat.erban@mairie-nantes.fr. Head: Robert Fleck
Fine Arts Museum 12032

Musée à Flot de l'Escorteur d'Escadre, Musée Naval Maillé Brézé, Quai de la Fosse, 44000 Nantes Cedex 04 - T: 0240695682, Fax: 0240697515. Head: Jean-Marie Poiret
Military Museum - 1988
Two warships (17th century and 1930) 12033

Musée Archéologique, 18 Rue Voltaire, 44000 Nantes - T: 0240710350
Archaeological Museum 12034

Musée d'Art Populaire Régional, Château des Ducs de Bretagne, 4 Pl Marc Elder, 44000 Nantes - T: 0240415656. Head: Marie-Hélène Jouzeau
Decorative Arts Museum - 1928
Shipping, crafts, furniture, costumes 12035

Musée de la Poste des Pays de Loire, 10 Blvd A. Pageot, 44038 Nantes - T: 0240299308. Head: Régine Le Gall
Historical Museum
Postal hist 12036

Musée de l'Imprimerie, Association Pro Arte Graphica, 24 Quai de la Fosse, 44000 Nantes - T: 0240732655, E-mail: musee.imprimerie@free.fr, Internet: http://www.mairie.fr. Head: Jacques Noël
Science&Tech Museum
Hist of printing 12037

Musée de l'Union Compagnonnique des Devoirs Unis, Compagnons du Tour de France, 14 Rue Guillon Verne, 44100 Nantes - T: 0240693055/437904/6905
Science&Tech Museum / Historical Museum 12038

Musée des Beaux-Arts, 10 Rue Georges Clémenceau, 44000 Nantes - T: 0240416565, Fax: 0240416790, E-mail: musees-beaux-arts@mairie-nantes.fr. Head: Guy Tosatto
Fine Arts Museum - 1801
Paintings by Perugino, Gentileschi, Tintoretto, G. de La Tour, Rubens, Watteau, Greuze, Gros, Delacroix, Ingres, Courbet, Monet, Max Ernst, Picasso - library 12039

Musée d'Histoire Naturelle, 12 Rue Voltaire, 44000 Nantes - T: 0240992620, Fax: 0251840191, E-mail: museum.sciences@mairie-nantes.fr, Internet: http://www.museum.nantes.fr. Head: Pierre Watelet
Natural History Museum
Prehistory, zoology, mineralogy, paleontology, botany - students and adults scientific library, youth scientific library, department of photos 12040

Musée Dobrée, 18 Rue Voltaire, 44000 Nantes - T: 0240710350, Fax: 0240732940, E-mail: musee.dobree@cg44.fr, Internet: http://www.cg44.fr. Head: Jacques Santrot
Archaeological Museum / Decorative Arts Museum / Fine Arts Museum - 1897
Prehistory, Gallo-Roman, Merovingian, Egyptian archeology, Greek, Etruscan ceramics, ethnography, medieval art, ivory, enamels, book illumination, 16th-17th c armaments, engravings, militaria - Library 12041

Musée Jules Verne, 3 Rue de l'Ermitage, 44100 Nantes - T: 0240697252
Special Museum 12042

Musée Laennec, Bibliothèque Universitaire, Chemin de la Sensive, 44322 Nantes - T: 0240141230, E-mail: musee-laennec@bu.univ-nantes.fr, Internet: http://www.bu.univ-nantes.fr. Head: Claire Voisin-Thiberge
Library with Exhibitions / University Museum 12043

Musée-Maison de l'Erdre, Ile de Versailles, 44000 Nantes - T: 0240294111
Natural History Museum / Science&Tech Museum 12044

Musée-Manoir de la Touche, 18 Rue Voltaire, 44000 Nantes - T: 0240710350
Historical Museum / Folklore Museum 12045

Nantillé

Musée Municipal d'Art Naïf, Chez Audebert, 17770 Nantillé - T: 0546959212
Fine Arts Museum / Open Air Museum 12046

Nantua

Musée Départemental de la Résistance et de la Déportation, 3 Montée de l'Abbaye, 01130 Nantua - T: 0474750750, Fax: 0474752758, E-mail: museenantua@minitel.net
Historical Museum 12047

Narbonne

Domaine de l'Hospitalet, Ensemble Muséographique du Vignoble, Rte du Narbonne Plage, 11100 Narbonne - T: 0468453447, Fax: 0468452349, E-mail: info@domaine-hospitalet.com, Internet: http://www.domaine-hospitalet.com
Local Museum 12048

Horreum, Musée Archéologique, Rue Rouget-de-Lisle, 11100 Narbonne - T: 0468903066
Archaeological Museum - 1976
Stones from destroyed Roman monuments, ancient ruins of Roman warehouse 12049

Musée Conservatoire Maritime et Rural, Le Grand Caste'lon, 11100 Narbonne - T: 0468491240, Fax: 0468491299, E-mail: serge.pagot@wanadoo.fr. Head: Serge Pagot
Natural History Museum / Agriculture Museum / Ethnology Museum 12050

Musée d'Art et d'Histoire, Palais des Archevêques, 11100 Narbonne - T: 0468903054, Fax: 0468903059, E-mail: Lepage@mairie-narbonne.fr, Internet: http://www.mairie-narbonne.fr. Head: Jean Lepage
Fine Arts Museum / Decorative Arts Museum - 1833
Ceramics, European paintings, 90 Oriental paintings, busts, 17th century palace and furnishings 12051

Musée de la Tonnellerie, 22 Quai de Lorraine, 11100 Narbonne - T: 0468425210
Special Museum 12052

Musée Lapidaire, Palais des Archevêques, 11100 Narbonne, mail addr: BP 823, 11108 Narbonne Cedex - T: 0468903054, Fax: 0468903059, Internet: http://www.mairie-narbonne.fr. Head: Jean Lepage
Archaeological Museum - 1850
1300 stone remains of Roman monuments 12053

Musée-Maison Vigneron dans l'Ancienne Poudrière, 8 Rue Ancienne-Porte-Neuve, 11100 Narbonne - T: 0468651560/326482
Special Museum 12054

Trésor d'Église, Art Sacré, Ancienne Cathédrale Saint-Just-et-Saint-Pasteur, Rue A.-Gauthier, 11100 Narbonne - T: 0468323160
Religious Arts Museum 12055

Natzwiller

Musée du Mémorial National de la Déportation, Camp du Struthof, 67130 Natzwiller - T: 0388767899
Historical Museum 12056

Naucelle

Musée Toulouse-Lautrec, Château du Bosc, 12800 Naucelle - T: 0565692083, Fax: 0565720019
Fine Arts Museum 12057

Navarrenx

Musée Historique, Porte Saint-Antoine, 64190 Navarrenx - T: 0559661022
Historical Museum 12058

Naveil

Musée de Sculptures Louis Leygue, Rue des Venages, 41100 Naveil - T: 0254772613/0861
Fine Arts Museum 12059

Nay

Musée du Béret, 64800 Nay - T: 0559610132
Special Museum 12060

Nébias

Musée de la Chasse et de la Faune du Languedoc et des Pyrénées, 11500 Nébias - T: 0468200613/8016
Natural History Museum 12061

Nedde

Musée Apicole, Centre Agricole "L'Abeille" de Vassivière, 87120 Nedde - T: 0555699522
Natural History Museum 12062

Nemours

Château-Musée, Rue Gautier-1er, 77140 Nemours - T: 0164282742
Historical Museum 12063

Musée de Préhistoire d'Île-de-France, 48 Av de Stalingrad, 77140 Nemours - T: 0164284037
Archaeological Museum 12064

Nérac

Musée du Château d'Henri IV, Rue Henri IV, 47600 Nérac - T: 0553652111, Fax: 0553973374, E-mail: chateau.nerac@ville_Nerac.fr
Local Museum / Archaeological Museum 12065

Néris-les-Bains

Musée du Patrimoine, Rue de Montluçon, 03310 Néris-les-Bains - T: 0470034211
Archaeological Museum 12066

Nernier

Musée du Lac Léman, Maison du Lac, 74140 Nernier - T: 0450728588
Fine Arts Museum 12067

Neuf-Brisach

Musée Vauban, Porte de Belfort, 68600 Neuf-Brisach - T: 0389725666/5168. Head: Jules Roth
Military Museum
Local historical items, military hist, historical drawings of the local fortress, historical models 12068

Neufchâtel-en-Bray

Musée J.B. Mathon et André Durand, Grande Rue Saint-Pierre, 76270 Neufchâtel-en-Bray - T: 0235930655. Head: Wendy David
Local Museum 12069

Neufchâtel-en-Saosnois

Maison du Sabot Neufchâtelois, Pl de l'Eglise, 72600 Neufchâtel-en-Saosnois - T: 0243977415
Science&Tech Museum 12070

Neufchef

Musée des Mines de Fer de Lorraine, Vallée de Sainte-Neige, 57700 Neufchef - T: 0382857655
Science&Tech Museum / Historical Museum 12071

Neuil

Musée Géologique Fossiles Préhistoire, 15 Rue du Marron, 37190 Neuil - T: 0247658771
Natural History Museum 12072

Neuilly-sous-Clermont

Collections de la Commanderie, 231 Rue de la Commanderie, 60290 Neuilly-sous-Clermont - T: 0344730053
Local Museum 12073

Neuilly-sur-Seine

Maison-Musée des Charcot, 29 Rue Saint-James, 92200 Neuilly-sur-Seine - T: 0147476025
Special Museum 12074

Musée Arturo-Lopez → Musée des Automates

Musée des Automates (closed until 2003), 12 Rue du Centre, 92200 Neuilly-sur-Seine - T: 0147452940, Fax: 0147225842, E-mail: museeautomates-neuilly@wanadoo.fr
Special Museum 12075

Neuvic (Corrèze)

Musée de la Résistance Henri-Queuille, Rue du Commerce, 19160 Neuvic (Corrèze) - T: 0555959687
Historical Museum 12076

Musée du Machinisme Agricole, Lycée Professionnel, Rue de l'Artisanat, 19160 Neuvic (Corrèze) - T: 0555958280
Science&Tech Museum 12077

Neuvic-sur-l'Isle

Musée-Atelier de Poterie, Château de Fratteau, 24190 Neuvic-sur-l'Isle - T: 0553816193/52
Decorative Arts Museum 12078

Neuville-aux-Bois

Collections Archéologiques, Pl de l'Église, 45170 Neuville-aux-Bois - T: 0238910484
Archaeological Museum 12079

Neuville-Saint-Vaast

Musée de la Targette, Rte Nationale 48, 62580 Neuville-Saint-Vaast - T: 0321591776, Fax: 0321591776
Military Museum 12080

Neuville-sur-Ailette

Musée Ornithologique Henri-Boileau, Maison de la Nature, 6 Rue de la Vallée, 02860 Neuville-sur-Ailette - T: 0323247341/7264
Natural History Museum 12081

Neuviller-la-Roche

Musée des Traditions du Ban-de-la-Roche, 19 Rue Principale, 67130 Neuviller-la-Roche - T: 0388978756/1334/0575
Local Museum 12082

Neuwiller-les-Saverne

Espace Muséal de la Route Romane d'Alsace, Salle du Chapitre, 67330 Neuwiller-les-Saverne - T: 0388700018
Fine Arts Museum 12083

Nevers

Châsse Sainte-Bernadette et Musée, 34 Rue Saint-Gildard, 58000 Nevers - T: 0386577999, Fax: 0386215681
Religious Arts Museum 12084

Collection de Faïences, Atelier Montagnon, 10 Rue de la Porte du Croux, 58000 Nevers - T: 0386572716
Decorative Arts Museum 12085

Musée Archéologique de la Porte du Croux, Rue de la Porte du Croux, 58000 Nevers - T: 0386591785. Head: X. Macquart-Moulin
Archaeological Museum 12086

Musée Municipal Frédéric Blandin, Promenade des Remparts, Jardins du Musée, 58000 Nevers - T: 0386684646 poste 4542
Local Museum 12087

Niaux

Musée Cavernicole d'Art Magdalénien, 09400 Niaux - T: 0561058837
Archaeological Museum 12088

Musée Pyrénéen, 09400 Niaux - T: 0561058836
Folklore Museum 12089

Nibelle

Musée Le Masque en Liberté, 4 Rte de Chemault, 45340 Nibelle - T: 0238322396
Special Museum 12090

Musée Saint-Sauveur Nibelle Autrefois, 42 Rue Saint-Sauveur, 45340 Nibelle - T: 0238322366/2705
Local Museum 12091

Nice

Galerie du Château, Espace Graphique, 14 Rue Droite, 06300 Nice - T: 0493859436
Fine Arts Museum 12092

Galerie Municipale Renoir, 8 Rue de la Loge, 06000 Nice - T: 0493134046
Fine Arts Museum 12093

Jazzothèque, 49 Av de la Marne, 06100 Nice - T: 0493535202
Music Museum 12094

Musée d'Art et d'Histoire, Palais Masséna, 35 Promenade des Anglais, 06000 Nice Cedex 1 - T: 0493881134/0622, Fax: 0493823979, Internet: http://www.ville-nice.fr/francais/culture/musee/arthistoire. Head: Paul-Louis Malausssena
Fine Arts Museum / Decorative Arts Museum / Historical Museum - 1921
Empire decoration and furnishings, local and regional history from the 7th-19th c, Italian, Spanish, Flemish, and French painting, Provencal and Mediterranean earthenware, arms and armor, popular jewelry - library, restoration workshop 12095

Musée d'Art Moderne et d'Art Contemporain, Promenade des Arts, 06300 Nice - T: 0493626162, Fax: 0493130901. Head: Gilbert Perlein
Fine Arts Museum - 1990
Coll are based on avant-garde French and American painters from the 1960s to the present day - video dep, documentation centre 12096

Musée d'Art Naif, Av Val Marie, 06200 Nice - T: 0493717833, Fax: 0493723410. Head: Anne Devroye-Stilz
Fine Arts Museum - 1982
Naive painting (18th-20th c) by Bauchant, Bombois, Vivin, Rimbert, Lefranc and Seraphine 12097

Musée d'Art Sacré à la Cathédrale Russe de 1912, Av Nicolas-II, 06000 Nice - T: 0493968802
Religious Arts Museum 12098

Musée de Paléontologie Humaine de Terra Amata, 25 Blvd Carnot, 06300 Nice - T: 0493555993, Fax: 0493899131
Archaeological Museum / Historic Site - 1976
Prehistoric finds, exhibits on the environment and way of life of the archanthropine - library 12099

Musée des Beaux-Arts Jules Chéret, 33 Av des Baumettes, 06000 Nice - T: 0492152828, Fax: 0493976707
Fine Arts Museum - 1928
400 years European art, neo-classic and impressionistic paintings from Vanloo, Boudin, Sisley, Monet, Degas, Cheret, Caepeaux, Rodin, Signac, Kisling, Buegel to Fragnard, Dufy, Van dongen, Alexis and G. Mossa - library, educational center 12100

Musée et Site Archéologiques de Cimiez, 1 Av Montecroce, 06000 Nice - T: 0493815957, Fax: 0493810800, Internet: http://www.nice-coteazur.org. Head: Monique Jannet
Archaeological Museum / Historic Site - 1963
Ceramics, glass, tools, sculpture, inscriptions, jewelry from 1st-3rd century A.D., Roman town Cemenelum, 5th-2nd century B.C. Greek ceramics, archeological site 6 thermal baths 12101

Musée-Galerie Alexis et Gustave-Adolf Mossa, 59 Quai des États-Unis, 06300 Nice - T: 0493623711
Local Museum 12102

Musée-Galerie Raoul-Dufy, 77 Quai des États-Unis, 06300 Nice - T: 0493623124. Head: Claude Fournet
Local Museum 12103

Musée Matisse, 164 Av des Arènes, 06000 Nice - T: 0493534053, Fax: 0493530022, E-mail: matisse@nice-coteazur.org, Internet: http://www.nice-coteazur.org. Head: Marie-Thérèse Pulvenis de Séligny
Fine Arts Museum - 1963
Paintings, drawings, etchings, sculpture, sketches, and gouaches by the artist Henri Matisse (1869-1954), furnishings and memorabilia of the painter 12104

Musée National Message Biblique Marc Chagall, Av du Docteur Ménard, 06000 Nice - T: 0493538720, Fax: 0493538739, E-mail: francaise.paquet-rossini@culture.gouv.fr. Head: Jean-Michel Foray
Fine Arts Museum - 1973
'Message Biblique' by Marc Chagall, a cyclus of paintings of scenes from the Bible, sketches, gouaches, copper plates, mosaics, tapestry, stained glass windows, sculptures - library 12105

Musée Naval de Nice, Galerie de la Marine, Quai des Etats-Unis, 06300 Nice - E-mail: g.prudhomme@musee_marine.fr, Internet: http://www.musee-marine.fr. Head: Georges Prudhomme
Historical Museum
Model ships (navy, merchant navy, fishing navy), paintings, figureheads, local maritime history 12106

Musée Palais Lascaris, 15 Rue Droite, 06300 Nice - T: 0493620534/54, Fax: 0493920419. Head: C. Astro
Decorative Arts Museum - 1964
17th and 18th century frescoes and furniture 12107

Musée Religieux d'Art Franciscain, Pl du Monastère, 06000 Nice - T: 0493810004, Fax: 0493813804. Head: Roland Marghieri
Religious Arts Museum 12108

Muséum d'Histoire Naturelle, 60bis Blvd Risso, 06300 Nice - T: 0497134680, Fax: 0497134685, E-mail: denicemuseum@minitel.net, Internet: http://www.mhnnice.org. Head: A. Bidar
Natural History Museum - 1846
Exhibits on natural sciene, mushrooms mouldings, coll J.B. Barla, birds, invertebrates fossils, malacology - library 12109

Parc Floral Phœnix, 405 Promenade des Anglais, 06200 Nice - T: 0493180333
Natural History Museum 12110

Prieuré du Vieux Logis, 59 Av Saint-Barthélémy, 06100 Nice - T: 0493844474
Decorative Arts Museum
Decorative arts, 15th-16th century interiors, sculpture, objects of wood, stone, and iron, window art 12111

Villa Arson/Centre National d'Art Contemporain, 20 Av Stephen Liégeard, 06105 Nice Cedex 2 - T: 0492077373, Fax: 0493844155, E-mail: biblio@cnap-villa-arson.fr, Internet: http://www.cnap-villa-arson.fr. Head: Alain Lombard
Fine Arts Museum
school of arts, art library 12112

Niderviller

Collections d'Arts de la Table, 57116 Niderviller - T: 0387238004
Decorative Arts Museum 12113

Niederbronn-les-Bains

Maison de l'Archéologie des Vosges du Nord, 44 Av Foch, 67110 Niederbronn-les-Bains - T: 0388803637
Archaeological Museum 12114

Nieul-sur-l'Autise

Maison de la Meunerie, 16 Rue du Moulin, 85240 Nieul-sur-l'Autise - T: 0251524743/4383
Historical Museum 12115

Nîmes

Artothèque-Sud, 9 Rue Emile Jamais, 30900 Nîmes - T: 0466760201. Head: Serge de Albertis
Association with Coll 12116

Carré d'Art, Musée d'Art Contemporain, Pl de la Maison Carrée, 30031 Nîmes Cedex 1 - T: 0466673570, Fax: 0466763585, E-mail: carreart@mnet.fr. Head: Françoise Cohen
Fine Arts Museum 12117

Exposition d'Art, Pl de la Comédie, Maison Carrée, 30000 Nîmes - T: 0466672557
Fine Arts Museum 12118

Galerie Taurine, 13bis Blvd Amiral Courbet, 30000 Nîmes - T: 0466673914
Special Museum 12119

Maison du Protestantisme, 3 Rue Claude-Brousson, 30000 Nîmes - T: 0466679740
Religious Arts Museum 12120

Maison-Expo de Compagnonnage, Maison des Compagnons, Blvd Boegner, 30900 Nîmes - T: 0466642367
Special Museum 12121

Musée Archéologique, 13bis Blvd Amiral Courbet, 30000 Nîmes - T: 0466672557, Fax: 0466213323. Head: Dominique Darde
Archaeological Museum - 1823
Protohistoric and gallic and Roman archeology, medieval archeology, numismatics, Greek ceramics 12122

Musée des Beaux-Arts, Rue Cité Foulc, 30000 Nîmes - T: 0466673821, Fax: 0466212997, E-mail: musee.beauxarts@ville-nimes.fr. Head: Françoise Cohen
Fine Arts Museum 12123

Musée d'Histoire Naturelle et de la Préhistoire, 13bis Blvd Amiral Courbet, 30000 Nîmes - T: 0466767345, Fax: 0466767346. Head: Luc Gomel
Natural History Museum
Prehist, natural hist, zoology 12124

Musée du Vieux Nîmes, Pl de la Cathédrale, 30000 Nîmes - T: 0466360064, Fax: 0466212997. Head: Martine Nougarède
Local Museum - 1921
Local history, folklore and popular culture 12125

Musée Espace du Cheminot, 97 Rue Pierre-Semard, 30000 Nîmes - T: 0466753403/360251
Science&Tech Museum 12126

Musée Minéralogique, Taillerie de Nîmes, 212 Impasse Vincent d'Indy, 30000 Nîmes - T: 0466270074, Fax: 0466271112, E-mail: opale212@aol.com, Internet: http://sites.netscape.net/opale212lee/homepage. Head: Lee N. Brown
Natural History Museum 12127

Niort

Musée Bernard d'Agesci, 28 Av de Limoges, 79000 Niort - T: 0549787200, Fax: 0549787219, E-mail: musees@agglo-niort.fr. Head: Christian Gendron
Fine Arts Museum 12128

Musée d'Arts et d'Histoire du Donjon, Pl du Donjon, 79000 Niort - T: 0549787200, Fax: 0549787219, E-mail: musees@agglo-niort.fr
Fine Arts Museum / Historical Museum 12129

Musée du Pilori, Pl du Pilori, 79000 Niort - T: 0549787200, Fax: 0549787219, E-mail: musees@agglo-niort.fr. Head: Christian Gendron
Local Museum 12130

Musée Ethnographique du Donjon, Pl du Donjon, 79000 Niort - T: 0549787200, Fax: 0549787219, E-mail: musees@agglo-niort.fr. Head: Christian Gendron
Ethnology Museum - 1896 12131

Nissan-lez-Enserune

Espace Vini-Viticole, Château Péries, Rte de Narbonne, 34440 Nissan-lez-Enserune - T: 0467370134
Special Museum 12132

Musée National Archéologique et Site, 34440 Nissan-lez-Enserune - T: 0467370123. Head: M. Schwaller
Local Museum 12133

Nœux-les-Mines

Musée de la Mine, Av P.-M. Guillon, 62290 Nœux-les-Mines - T: 0321263464/3555
Science&Tech Museum 12134

Nogent-en-Bassigny

Musée de la Coutellerie, BP 1, 52800 Nogent-en-Bassigny - T: 0325318577, Fax: 0325318013
Science&Tech Museum
Local cutlery industry 12135

Nogent-le-Rotrou

Musée du Château Saint-Jean, Rue du Château, 28400 Nogent-le-Rotrou - T: 0237521802, Fax: 0237296869. Head: Françoise Lecuyer
Local Museum - 1959
Prehistory, paintings, costumes, ceramics, sculpture, ethnography 12136

Nogent-sur-Marne

Musée de Nogent, 36 Blvd Gallieni, 94130 Nogent-sur-Marne - T: 0148755125. Head: Olivier Maitre-Allain
Historical Museum - 1962
Engravings by Watteau, local hist, everyday life, Belle Epoque 12137

Nogent-sur-Seine

Château de la Motte-Tilly, CNMHS, 10400 Nogent-sur-Seine - T: 0325399967/8454/0254
Decorative Arts Museum 12138

Musée P. Dubois-A. Boucher, Rue A. Boucher, 10400 Nogent-sur-Seine - T: 0325397179/4200, Fax: 0325399874. Head: Jacques Piette
Fine Arts Museum - 1902
Castings of sculptures by Paul Dubois and Alfred Boucher, regional archeology 12139

Nohant-Vic

Maison-Souvenir de George Sand, Château, 36100 Nohant-Vic - T: 0254310604/349785
Special Museum - 1763
Memorabilia of George Sand and her circle 12140

Nointel (Oise)

Musée de l'Automobile Miniature et des Poupées Anciennes, Château, 60840 Nointel (Oise) - T: 0344784848, Fax: 0344783636
Special Museum 12141

Musée International du Menu Gastronomique, Château, 60840 Nointel (Oise) - T: 0344784848, Fax: 0344783636
Special Museum 12142

Noirmoutier-en-l'Ile

Maison-Musée du Sel, 12 Rue de l'Écluse, 85330 Noirmoutier-en-l'Ile - T: 0251390830
Special Museum 12143

Musée de la Construction Navale, Rue de l'Ecluse, 85330 Noirmoutier-en-l'Ile - T: 0251392400. Head: Vincent Cristofoli
Science&Tech Museum - 1986 12144

Musée du Château, Pl d'Armes, 85330 Noirmoutier-en-l'Ile - T: 0251391042. Head: Vincent Cristofoli
Historical Museum - 1884 12145

Noisiel

Centre d'Art Contemporain, Allée de la Ferme, 77437 Noisiel - T: 0164627700, Fax: 0164627799
Fine Arts Museum 12146

Nolay

Micromusée de la Maison de Retraite, Rue du Docteur-Lavirotte, 21340 Nolay - T: 0380217064
Decorative Arts Museum 12147

Musée du Vieux Nolay, Rue du Docteur-Lavirotte, 21340 Nolay - T: 0380217300
Local Museum 12148

Nontron

Musée de la Poupée et des Jeux de Jadis Marie-Camille de Monneron, Château, Av du Général Leclerc, 24300 Nontron - T: 0553562080, Fax: 0553732072. Head: Françoise Magnan
Special Museum 12149

Notre-Dame-de-Bondeville

Musée Industriel Corderie Vallois, 76960 Notre-Dame-de-Bondeville - T: 0235743535, Fax: 0235745845. Head: Alain Joubert
Science&Tech Museum - 1994
Late 19th century floodgates, paddle wheel, transmission system, steam regulator, French and English machines for the production of braided and twisted cotton ropes 12150

Notre-Dame-de-Londres

Château-Musée Médiéval, 34380 Notre-Dame-de-Londres - T: 0467550212/589731
Decorative Arts Museum / Fine Arts Museum 12151

Notre-Dame-de-Monts

Salle Panoramique de Notre-Dame-de-Monts, Château d'Eau, Rte de Perrier, 85690 Notre-Dame-de-Monts - T: 0251588609/0789
Special Museum 12152

Nouvron-Vingre

Le Soldat Artiste, Association du Soissonnais 14-18, Ferme de Confrecourt, 02290 Nouvron-Vingre - T: 0323742590, Internet: http://perso.wanadoo.fr/patrick.laffe. Head: Jean-Luc Pamart
Military Museum / Historic Site 12153

Novion-Porcien

Musée de la Bataille des Ardennes, 08270 Novion-Porcien
Military Museum 12154

Noyant

Musée Populaire des Arts et Métiers, Le Mortier aux Loups, 49490 Noyant - T: 0241895740
Folklore Museum 12155

Noyers (Yonne)

Centre d'Art Contemporain, La Croix Blanche, Pl Marché au Blé, 89310 Noyers (Yonne) - T: 0386826303
Fine Arts Museum 12156

Musée d'Art Naïf, Rue de l'Église, 89310 Noyers (Yonne) - T: 0386558372/828909
Local Museum 12157

Noyon

Musée Calvin, 6 Pl Aristide Briand, 60400 Noyon - T: 0344440359, Fax: 0344933639, E-mail: musees.noyon@wanadoo.fr. Head: Sibille Barbara
Religious Arts Museum - 1927
Paintings and engravings (portraits and scenes of Calvin's life), furniture (Renaissance Chest, Portable chair), coll of books and printed documents of the 16th c (sedition hanbill against mass 1534, the Olivetan Bible 1535, the first edition of the Christian Institution in 1536) 12158

Musée de l'Ancienne Cathédrale (closed) 12159

Musée du Noyonnais, 7 Rue de l'Evêché, 60400 Noyon - T: 0344094341, Fax: 0344933639, E-mail: musees.noyon@wanadoo.fr. Head: Sibille Barbara
Fine Arts Museum / Decorative Arts Museum - 1931
Medieval furniture, lapidary coll, coll of oriental painting by Joseph-Felix Bouchor, archeology 12160

Nuits-Saint-Georges

Musée Municipal, 12 Rue Camille Rodier, 21700 Nuits-Saint-Georges - T: 0380620137, 0380620134, Fax: 0380620137. Head: Marie-Noëlle Retière
Archaeological Museum - 1975
Gallo-Roman and Merovingian finds, paintings 12161

Nyoiseau

Écomusée du Domaine de la Petite Couère, Rte de Renazé, 49500 Nyoiseau - T: 0241947373, Fax: 0241947371
Historical Museum 12162

Nyons

Musée de l'Olivier, Pl des Tilleuls, 26110 Nyons - T: 0475261212
Special Museum 12163

Oberdorff

Collection d'Arts Populaires, 8 Pl de la Fontaine, 57320 Oberdorff - T: 0387784367
Folklore Museum 12164

Obermodern

Collection de Locomotives à Vapeur, 119 Rue de la Moder, 67330 Obermodern - T: 0388908041
Science&Tech Museum 12165

Obernai

Collections Historiques, Hôtel de Ville, 67210 Obernai - T: 0388956413
Fine Arts Museum / Decorative Arts Museum 12166

Musée du Cheval et de l'Attelage, Domaine de la Leonardsau, 67210 Obernai - T: 0388956131/6413
Special Museum 12167

Obersoultzbach

Les Mémoires d'Obersoultzach, Pl de la Mairie, 67330 Obersoultzbach - T: 0388895939
Historical Museum 12168

Obersteinbach

Maison des Châteaux Forts, 42 Rue Principale, 67510 Obersteinbach - T: 0388095065/5634/5569
Local Museum 12169

Odenas

Exposition Historique, Château de la Chaize, 69460 Odenas - T: 0474034105
Historical Museum 12170

Offendorf

Musée de la Batellerie, Quai des Bateliers, 67850 Offendorf - T: 0388968002
Special Museum 12171

Offranville

Musée J.-E.-Blanche, Étage de la Maison du Parc du Colombier, 76550 Offranville - T: 0235854042, Fax: 0235042454
Fine Arts Museum 12172

Offwiller

Maison d'Offwiller, 42 Rue de la Libération, 67340 Offwiller - T: 0388899098/3656. Head: Jean-Paul Oertlin
Folklore Museum 12173

Oger

Musée du Mariage et de ses Traditions, Champagne Henry de Vaugency, 1 Rue d'Avize, 51190 Oger - T: 0326575089/515771
Special Museum 12174

Oherville

Musées des Colombiers Cauchois, Association du Manoir d'Auffray, 76560 Oherville - T: 0235966969
Special Museum 12175

Oignies

Centre Historique de la Mine, de la Machine à Vapeur et du Chemin de Fer, Rue Emile Zola, 62590 Oignies - T: 0321373259
Science&Tech Museum 12176

Oigny-en-Valois

Musée du Château d'Oigny-en-Valois, 02600 Oigny-en-Valois - T: 0323960111/3818
Local Museum   12177

Oiron

Château d'Oiron, 79100 Oiron - T: 0549965742, Fax: 0549965256, Internet: http://www.monum.fr. Head: Paul-Hervé Parsy
Fine Arts Museum
Renaissance paintings and contemporary art collections   12178

Oisly

Musée d'Arts et de Traditions Populaires, Presle, 41700 Oisly - T: 0254795269
Folklore Museum   12179

Oisy-le-Verger

Musée d'Art et d'Histoire, Mairie, 62860 Oisy-le-Verger - T: 0321595118
Fine Arts Museum / Historical Museum   12180

Oizon

Musée-Château de La Verrerie, 18700 Oizon - T: 0248815160, Fax: 0248582125, E-mail: laverrerie@wanadoo.fr, Internet: http://www.chateauxcountry.com/chateaux/verrerie. Head: Comte B. de Vogüé
Decorative Arts Museum / Historic Site   12181

Olargues

Musée d'Histoire Locale, Patrimoine Historique, Arts et Traditions Populaires, Escalier de la Commanderie, 34390 Olargues - T: 0467977079
Local Museum   12182

Musée Géologique, Escalier de la Commanderie, 34390 Olargues - T: 0467977079
Natural History Museum   12183

Olliergues

Musée d'Art et des Métiers, 5 Av de Lattre, 63880 Olliergues - T: 0473955490
Local Museum   12184

Olonne-sur-Mer

Musée des Traditions Populaires, Mémoire des Olonnes, 30 Rue Marechal Foch, 85340 Olonne-sur-Mer - T: 0251907585, Fax: 0251969553. Head: Colette Renou
Folklore Museum   12185

Olonzac

Exposition d'Armes Anciennes, 34210 Olonzac - T: 0468912108
Military Museum   12186

Musée Archéologique et Minéralogique, Mairie, 34210 Olonzac - T: 0468912011
Archaeological Museum / Natural History Museum   12187

Oloron-Sainte-Marie

Maison du Patrimoine d'Oloron et du Haut Béarn, 52 Rue Dalmais, 64400 Oloron-Sainte-Marie - T: 0559391063
Archaeological Museum   12188

Oltingue

Musée Paysan du Sundgau, 10 Rue Principale, 68480 Oltingue - T: 0389407924, Fax: 0389073098. Head: Théo Tschamber
Local Museum   12189

Omonville-la-Petite

Maison Jacques Prévert, 50440 Omonville-la-Petite - T: 0233527238
Special Museum   12190

Onzain

Musée de la Vigne et du Vin, Maison du Tourisme, 3 Rue Gustave Marc, 41150 Onzain - T: 0254208155
Special Museum   12191

Opio

Moulin à Huile, 2 Rte de Châteauneuf, 06650 Opio - T: 0493772303
Science&Tech Museum   12192

Oradour-sur-Glane

Centre de la Mémoire d'Oradour, 87520 Oradour-sur-Glane - T: 0555430430, Fax: 0555430431, E-mail: oradour@wanadoo.fr
Special Museum / Historical Museum   12193

Orainville

Musée des Machines Agricoles Anciennes, A la Ferme, 02190 Orainville - T: 0323238023
Agriculture Museum   12194

Musée d'Histoire d'Orainville, 02190 Orainville - T: 0323238023
Historical Museum   12195

Orbais-l'Abbaye

Musée d'Art Populaire, Mairie, 51270 Orbais-l'Abbaye - T: 0326592023
Folklore Museum   12196

Orbec

Musée Municipal d'Orbec, Le Vieux Manoir, 107 Rue Grande, 14290 Orbec - T: 0231328202/5889, Fax: 0231322048, E-mail: mairie-orbec@wanadoo.fr, Internet: http://www.mairie-orbec.fr. Head: Elizabeth Lescroat-Cazenave
Local Museum - 1873
Local hist in Renaissance building   12197

Orbey

Musée d'Arts et Traditions Populaires, 97 Rue Charles de Gaulle, 68370 Orbey - T: 0389712765
Folklore Museum   12198

Musée-Mémorial du Linge, Site du Linge, 68370 Orbey - T: 0389712354/410327
Military Museum   12199

Orcet

Espace Muséal, Maison des Comtes, 63670 Orcet - T: 0473847317
Local Museum   12200

Orchies

La Maison de la Chicorée, 25 Rue Jules Roch, 59310 Orchies - T: 0320648370, Fax: 0320717789. Head: Michel Hermand
Special Museum   12201

Orcières

Exposition d'Arts Populaires, Forest des Estavis, Bergerie, 05170 Orcières - T: 0492556126
Folklore Museum   12202

Musée Rural et d'Arts Populaires, La Casse Prapic, 05170 Orcières - T: 0492557089
Folklore Museum   12203

Ordan-Larroque

Dépôt de Fouilles Archéologiques, 32350 Ordan-Larroque - T: 0562646009
Archaeological Museum   12204

Ordonnac

Exposition Viticole, Moulin de Hontemieux, 33340 Ordonnac - T: 0556090347
Special Museum   12205

Orgerus

Musée du Papillon, 28 Rue du Clos-des-Bourgognes, 78910 Orgerus - T: 0134872289
Natural History Museum   12206

Orgnac-l'Aven

Musée Régional de Préhistoire, 07150 Orgnac-l'Aven - T: 0475386510
Archaeological Museum   12207

Orgon

Musée Automobile de Provence, 13660 Orgon - T: 0490730137
Science&Tech Museum   12208

Le Passé du Canton, Près Notre-Dame-de-Beauregard, 13660 Orgon - T: 0490730452
Historical Museum / Folklore Museum   12209

Origny-en-Thiérache

Musée Monseigneur-Pigneau-de-Behaine, Rue du Musée, 02550 Origny-en-Thiérache - T: 0323984177
Special Museum   12210

Orist

Musée de l'Ecologie des Rives de l'Adour, 40300 Orist - T: 0558573161
Natural History Museum   12211

Orléans

Centre Jeanne d'Arc, 24 Rue Jeanne-d'Arc, 45000 Orléans - T: 0238624779, Fax: 0238792082, E-mail: ya@ville-orleans.ft, Internet: http://www.ville-orleans.fr
Special Museum   12212

Hôtel-Musée Groslot, Hôtel de Ville, Pl de l'Etape, 45000 Orléans - T: 0238792230, Fax: 0238792113
Local Museum   12213

Maison Jeanne d'Arc, 3 Pl Général de Gaulle, 45000 Orléans - T: 0238529989, Fax: 0238792082, E-mail: ya@ville-orleans.fr, Internet: http://www.ville-orleans.fr
Historical Museum   12214

Musée-Centre Charles-Péguy, 11 Rue du Tabour, 45000 Orléans - T: 0238532023, Fax: 0238625924. Head: Julie Bertrand-Sabiani
Special Museum   12215

Musée des Beaux-Arts, 1 Rue Fernand Rabier, 45000 Orléans - T: 0238792155, Fax: 0238792008, E-mail: musée-ba-doc@ville-orleans.fr, Internet: http://www.ville-orleans.fr. Head: Annick Notter
Fine Arts Museum - 1823
Sculpture, European painting, 17th-20th century drawings, etchings, pastels, French painting (16th-20th century) - library   12216

Musée du Para, 27 Rue de la Bienvenue, 45000 Orléans - T: 0238881214
Military Museum   12217

Musée Historique et Archéologique de l'Orléanais, Sq Abbé Desnoyers, Rue Sainte-Catherine, 45000 Orléans - T: 0238792155, Fax: 0238792008, E-mail: musee-ba-doc@ville-orleans.fr, Internet: http://www.ville-orleans.fr. Head: Annick Notter
Historical Museum - 1855
16th century building, Gallo-Roman finds, bronze Gallic treasure from Neuvy-en-Sullias, decorative arts, medieval objects   12218

Musée-Trésor d'Eglise de la Cathédrale Sainte-Croix, Presbytère Sainte-Croix, Pl Sainte-Croix, 45000 Orléans - T: 0238534723
Religious Arts Museum   12219

Muséum des Sciences Naturelles, 6 Rue Marcel Proust, 45000 Orléans - T: 0238546105, Fax: 0238531967. Head: Dr. Dominique Jammot
Natural History Museum - 1823
Coll of preserved ancient plants, mammals from the Miocene period, dioramas of mammals, preditors and their prey - library   12220

Ornans

Maison Nationale de la Pêche et de l'Eau, 36 Rue Saint-Laurent, 25290 Ornans - T: 0381571449
Special Museum   12221

Musée-Maison Natale Gustave Courbet, Pl Robert Fernier, 25290 Ornans - T: 0381622330, Fax: 0345244700. Head: Jean-Jaques Fernier
Special Museum - 1947
Paintings and memorabilia of Gustave Courbet - library   12222

Orschwiller

Château du Haut-Koenigsbourg, 67600 Orschwiller - T: 0388825060, Fax: 0388825061, E-mail: haut-koenigsbourg@monum.fr, Internet: http://www.monum.fr. Head: Monique Fuchs
Historic Site   12223

Musée d'Histoire Locale, Rue des Prélats, 67600 Orschwiller - T: 0388920655
Historical Museum   12224

Musée Vigneron, 3 Pl de la Mairie, 67600 Orschwiller - T: 0388928657
Special Museum   12225

Orthez

Maison Francis Jammes, Maison Chrestia, 7 Av Francis Jammes, 64300 Orthez - T: 0559691124, Fax: 0559690834, E-mail: ass.jammes@wanadoo.fr, Internet: http://www.francis-jammes.com. Head: Michel Haurie
Special Museum   12226

Osny

Musée Départemental des Sapeurs-Pompiers, Caserne Beaux-Soleils, Rue du Général-de-Gaulle, 95520 Osny - T: 0130312200
Science&Tech Museum   12227

Ostheim

Maison Berckheim du Parc Anglais de Schoppenwihr, 68150 Ostheim - T: 0389412237
Local Museum / Natural History Museum   12228

Ouistreham

Musée du Mur de l'Atlantique Riva-Bella, Observatoire d'Artillerie, Av du 6-Juin, 14150 Ouistreham - T: 0231972869
Military Museum   12229

Musée No.4 Commando, Pl Alfred-Thomas, 14150 Ouistreham - T: 0231966310/970039
Military Museum - 1965
No. 4 Commando coll   12230

Oulches-la-Vallée-Foulon

Musée Caverne du Dragon, RD 18, 02160 Oulches-la-Vallée-Foulon - T: 0323251418, Fax: 0223251411, E-mail: caverne@CG02.fr
Historical Museum   12231

Ouzouer-sur-Trézée

Château-Musée de Pont-Chevron, 45250 Ouzouer-sur-Trézée - T: 0238319202
Fine Arts Museum / Decorative Arts Museum   12232

Oyonnax

Musée du Peigne et de la Plasturgie, Centre Culturel Aragon, Pl Georges Pompidou, 01100 Oyonnax - T: 0474819682, Fax: 0474738768, E-mail: museepeigne.plasturgie@wanadoo.fr. Head: Cathérine Blanchard
Decorative Arts Museum - 1977
Marie-Léon Arbez-Carme: Celluloid Art objects 1880-1928, Clément Joyard: Celluloid combs, 1900-1920, Auguste Bonaz: Celluloid combs, 1880-1950   12233

Padirac

Micromusée Archéologique, 46500 Padirac - T: 0565336456
Archaeological Museum   12234

Pailhares

Micromusée du Village Ardéchois, Col du Buisson, 07410 Pailhares - T: 0475066747/0065/232395
Folklore Museum   12235

Paimpol

Musée de la Mer, Rue Labenne, 22500 Paimpol - T: 0296220219, Fax: 0296553189
Special Museum - 1960
Shipping, fisheries   12236

Musée du Costume Trégor-Goëlo, Rue Pellier, 22500 Paimpol - T: 0296553170
Ethnology Museum
19th century local costume, furniture, household articles   12237

Palaiseau

Musée Palaisien du Hurepoix, Hôtel Brière, 5 Pl de la Victoire, 91120 Palaiseau - T: 0160108070
Local Museum   12238

Palaja

Musée Archéologique, Mairie, 11570 Palaja - T: 0468796215
Archaeological Museum   12239

Palau-del-Vidre

Musée-Écurie de l'Insolite, Le Haras, 66690 Palau-del-Vidre - T: 0468223984/1561
Folklore Museum   12240

Palavas-les-Flots

Musée de l'Humour, A. Dubout, Redoute de Ballestras, 34250 Palavas-les-Flots - T: 0467685641
Special Museum   12241

Palinges

Musée d'Arts et de Traditions Populaires, Rue de l'Eglise, 71430 Palinges - T: 0385702082/881188
Folklore Museum / Archaeological Museum   12242

Pandrignes

Petit Écomusée de Cinve, Le Mas, 19150 Pandrignes - T: 0555291509/1138
Special Museum   12243

Pange

Château-Musée, 57530 Pange - T: 0387640184/0441
Decorative Arts Museum / Fine Arts Museum   12244

Pannes

Musée La Main et l'Outil, Ancienne Gare, Rue de la Gare, 45700 Pannes - T: 0238878463
Science&Tech Museum   12245

Panossas

Musée Archéologique, Mairie, 38460 Panossas - T: 0474902008
Archaeological Museum   12246

Pantin

Centre International de l'Automobile, 25 Rue d'Éstienne-d'Orves, 93500 Pantin - T: 0148108000/8001
Science&Tech Museum / Special Museum   12247

Paradou

La Petite Provence du Paradou, Av Vallée des Baux, 13520 Paradou - T: 0490543265
Ethnology Museum   12248

Paray-le-Monial

Musée de la Faïence, Prieuré, Av Jean-Paul II, 71600 Paray-le-Monial - T: 0385888307
Decorative Arts Museum   12249

Parçay-les-Pins

Musée des Sculptures Jules Desbois, 49390 Parçay-les-Pins - T: 0241826174
Fine Arts Museum   12250

Parentignat

Château Petit Versailles, 63500 Parentignat - T: 0473893300/5110
Decorative Arts Museum / Fine Arts Museum 12251

Parentis-en-Born

Musée du Pétrole, Rte du Lac, 40160 Parentis-en-Born - T: 0558784103
Science&Tech Museum 12252

Paris

L'Argonaute, Cité des Sciences et de l'Industrie, 30 Av Corentin Cariou, 75930 Paris Cedex 19 - T: 0136682930, Fax: 0140058190
Military Museum / Science&Tech Museum
1950s submarine, disarmed in 1982 12253

L'Atelier de Nicolas Schöffer á la Villa des Arts, 15 Rue Hégésippe-Moreau, 75018 Paris - T: 0142942654, Fax: 0145226792, E-mail: schoffer@club-internet.fr, Internet: http://www.olats.org/schoffer
Association with Coll 12254

L'Auberge Verte, Centre de Documentation Rimbaldienne, 128 Rue Lamarck, 75018 Paris - T: 0142296349
Library with Exhibitions 12255

Biblioludothèque, Maison de la Nature, Parc Floral de Paris, Rte de la Pyramide, 75011 Paris - T: 0143284763
Library with Exhibitions 12256

Bibliothèque d'Art et d'Archéologie Jacques Doucet, 2-4 Rue Vivienne, 75083 Paris Cedex 02 - T: 0147037623, Fax: 0147038925, E-mail: Baa.Doucet@paris4.sorbonne.fr. Head: François Lemelle
Library with Exhibitions / Fine Arts Museum 12257

Bibliothèque de l'Arsenal, 1 Rue Sully, 75004 Paris - T: 0153012509, Fax: 0142770163
Library with Exhibitions 12258

Bibliothèque Mazarine, 23 Quai Conti, 75006 Paris - T: 0144414406, Fax: 0144414407, E-mail: webmaster@bibliotheque-mazarine.fr, Internet: http://www.bibliotheque-mazarine.fr. Head: Christian Péligry
Library with Exhibitions 12259

Bibliothèque-Musée de la Comédie-Française, Pl Colette, 75001 Paris - T: 0144581317, Fax: 0144581359, E-mail: joel.huthwohl@comedie-francaise.fr, Internet: http://www.comedie-francaise.fr. Head: Joël Huthwohl
Performing Arts Museum
library, archives 12260

Bibliothèque-Musée Forney, 1 Rue du Figuier, 75004 Paris - T: 0142781460, Fax: 0142782259
Library with Exhibitions 12261

Cabinet des Medailles et Antiques, c/o Bibliothèque Nationale de France, 58 Rue de Richelieu, 75084 Paris Cedex 02 - T: 0147038340, Fax: 0147038330 0147037529, E-mail: cabmed@bnf.fr. Head: Jean-Pierre Angremy, Philippe Belaval, Jean-Pierre Angremy
Fine Arts Museum - 1981
Coins and medals from Antiquity to the present - Numismatic documentation centre, library 12262

Catacombes, 1 Pl Denfert-Rochereau, 75014 Paris - T: 0143224763. Head: Jean-Pierre Willesme
Historic Site
The underground world of Paris 12263

CEDIAS Musée Social, 5 Rue Las Cases, 75007 Paris - T: 0145516610, Fax: 0144180181, E-mail: biblio.cedias@wanadoo.fr. Head: B. Bouquet
Historical Museum - 1894
Social hist - library 12264

Centre de la Mer, 195 Rue Saint-Jacques, 75005 Paris - T: 0144321070, Fax: 0140517316, E-mail: cme@oceano.org, Internet: http://www.oceano.org/. Head: Lucien Laubier
Natural History Museum - 1978
Models, reconstruction of marine landscapes, interactive elements, audio-visual material 12265

Centre de Recherches Historiques sur les Maîtres Ebénistes, 92 Rue La Fayette, 75009 Paris - T: 0147701902, Fax: 0147701317. Head: Louis Faton, J.N. Ronfort
Library with Exhibitions
French furniture hist (1600-1850) - Extensive photo library and data base on French furniture and decorative arts artists. The most extensive existing archives on the subject 12266

Centre National de la Photographie, 11 Rue Berryer, 75008 Paris - T: 0153761232, Fax: 0153761233, E-mail: centre.national.de.la.photographie@wanadoo.fr, Internet: http://www.cnp-photographie.com. Head: Régis Durand
Fine Arts Museum / Public Gallery 12267

Cité des Sciences et de l'Industrie, Parc de la Villette, 30 Av Corentin-Cariou, 75930 Paris 75019 - T: 0136682930, Fax: 0140057222
Science&Tech Museum
Collections of history, industry, medicine, photography, sciences, technology and scale models 12268

Collection de Dessins de Soieries, La Manach, 31 Rue du 4 Septembre, 75002 Paris - T: 0147425294
Special Museum 12269

Collection de Minéraux de l'Université Paris VI Pierre et Marie Curie, 34 Rue Jussieu, 75005 Paris - T: 0144275288, Fax: 0144273785, E-mail: boulliar@lmcp.jussieu.fr, Internet: http://www.lmcp.jussieu.fr
University Museum / Natural History Museum 12270

Collection des Cristalleries de Saint-Louis, 13 Rue Royale, 75008 Paris - T: 0140170174, Fax: 0140170387
Decorative Arts Museum 12271

Collection des Serrures Fontaine, 190 Rue de Rivoli, 75001 Paris - T: 0142615153
Decorative Arts Museum 12272

Collection Deyrolle, 46 Rue du Bac, 75007 Paris - T: 0142223007/3202
Natural History Museum 12273

Collection Frits Lugt, c/o Institut Néerlandais, 121 Rue de Lille, 75007 Paris - T: 0147057519, Fax: 0145556535, E-mail: coll.lugt@fondationcustodia.fr, Internet: http://www.fondation-custodia.fr. Head: M. Van Berge-Gerbaud
Fine Arts Museum 12274

Collection Historial Cognacq-Jay, La Samaritaine, 19 Rue de la Monnaie, 75001 Paris - T: 0140412020
Historical Museum 12275

Collections de la Bibliothèque Sainte-Geneviève, 10 Pl du Panthéon, 75005 Paris - T: 0144419797, Fax: 0144419796, E-mail: bsgmail@univ-paris1.fr, Internet: http://www.panoramix-univ-paris1.fr/bsg/. Head: Nathalie Jullian
Library with Exhibitions 12276

Collections de la Maison de la R.A.T.P., 189 Rue de Bercy, 75012 Paris - T: 0144682020
Science&Tech Museum 12277

Collections de la Salle des Martyrs, 128 Rue du Bac, 75007 Paris - T: 0144391040
Religious Arts Museum 12278

Collections de la Serrurerie Dantin, 87 Blvd Richard Lenoir, 75011 Paris - T: 0148057350
Special Museum 12279

Collections de la Tour Eiffel, Champ-de-Mars, 75007 Paris - T: 0144112323
Science&Tech Museum 12280

Collections de l'Ecole Nationale Supérieure des Beaux-Arts, 13 Quai Malaquais, 75272 Paris - T: 0147035082, Fax: 0147035298, Internet: http://www.ensba.fr. Head: Annie Jacques
Fine Arts Museum - 1648
Architectural drawings, drawings by the Old Masters incl Raffael and Michelangelo, miniatures, manuscrips, stamps, photographs, paintings, sculptures - library 12281

Collections de l'Hôtel Relais-Christine, 3 Rue Christine, 75006 Paris - T: 0143267180
Decorative Arts Museum 12282

Collections du Relais Louis XIII, 8 Rue des Grands-Augustins, 75006 Paris - T: 0143267596
Decorative Arts Museum / Fine Arts Museum 12283

Collections du Restaurant Procope, 13 Rue de l'Ancienne-Comédie, 75006 Paris - T: 0143269920
Special Museum 12284

Collections in Situ de l'Unesco, 7 Pl de Fontenoy, 75007 Paris - T: 0145681000/0359
Fine Arts Museum 12285

Écomusée des Anciennes Carrières de Pierre "Les Capucins", 27 Rue du Faubourg-Saint-Jacques, 75014 Paris - T: 0146331635
Science&Tech Museum 12286

Espace Salvador Dalí, 11 Rue Poulbot, 75018 Paris - T: 0142644010, Fax: 0142649317, E-mail: dali.montmartre@libertysurf.fr. Head: G. Ionesco
Fine Arts Museum
Sculptures, illustrations, lithographs 12287

Fondation Cartier pour l'Art Contemporain, 261 Blvd Raspail, 75014 Paris - T: 0142185650, Fax: 0142185652, E-mail: herve.chandes@vendome.com, Internet: http://www.fondation.cartier.fr. Head: Hervé Chandès
Fine Arts Museum
Contemporary art, furniture and interior, design, painting, photography, sculpture, video, installation, new technology 12288

Fondation Dosne-Thiers, Bibliothèque Thiers, 27 Pl Saint-Georges, 75009 Paris - T: 0148781433, Fax: 0148789292, E-mail: bibliotheque.thiers@free.fr. Head: Danuta Monachon
Library with Exhibitions
Library specialised in the history of France in the 19th century, Napoleonic memorabilia 12289

Fondation Dubuffet, 137 Rue de Sèvres, 75006 Paris - T: 0147341263, Fax: 0147341951, Internet: http://www.dubuffetfondation.com. Head: Isalmina Dubuffet
Fine Arts Museum 12290

Fondation Le Corbusier, Villa La Roche, 10 Sq du Docteur Blanche, 75016 Paris - T: 0142884153, Fax: 0142883317, Internet: http://www.fondationle-corbusier.asso.fr. Head: E. Trehin
Special Museum / Fine Arts Museum - 1923
Largest collection of Le Corbusier drawings, studies and plans, paintings, sculptures, art drawings 12291

Galerie Daguerre, Photo-Club du Val de Bièvre, 28ter Rue Gassendi, 75014 Paris - T: 0169411060, Fax: 0143221112, E-mail: secretariat@photo-bievre.org, Internet: http://www.photo-bievre.org. Head: André Fage
Public Gallery - 1949
Photographic activities, exhibitions and lessons 12292

Galerie de Minéralogie, 36 Rue Geoffroy-Saint-Hilaire, 75005 Paris - T: 0140793446, Fax: 0140793860, E-mail: chiapper@mnhn.fr
Natural History Museum 12293

Galerie de Paléobotanique, 18 Rue Buffon, 75005 Paris - T: 0140793003
Natural History Museum 12294

Galerie de Paléontologie, 2 Rue Buffon, 75005 Paris - T: 0140793003
Natural History Museum 12295

Galerie d'Exposition sur la Bourse, Palais Brongniart, Rue Notre-Dame-des-Victoires, 75002 Paris - T: 0140416220/6223
Special Museum 12296

Galerie Dorée du Comte de Toulouse, Banque de France, 48 Rue Croix des Petits Champs, 75001 Paris - T: 0145262677
Fine Arts Museum / Decorative Arts Museum 12297

Galerie du Panthéon Bouddhique du Japon et de la Chine, 19 Av d'Iéna, 75116 Paris - T: 0147236165, Fax: 0147205750
Religious Arts Museum
Located in a superb neo-baroque mansion with a Japanese garden, 300 works from Japan and China 12298

Galerie Nationale du Jeu de Paume, 1 Pl de la Concorde, 75008 Paris - T: 0147031250, Fax: 0147031251, Internet: http://www.jeudepaume.org. Head: Daniel Abadie
Fine Arts Museum / Public Gallery
Contemporary art, painings, sculptures, photography 12299

Galeries Nationales du Grand Palais, 3 Av du Général Eisenhower, 75008 Paris - T: 0144131717, Fax: 0145635433
Fine Arts Museum
Built for the Universal Exhibition of 1900, major national temporary exhibitions organised by the Réunion des Musées Nationaux, Association Française d'Action Artistique and the Délégation des Arts Plastiques 12300

Imprimerie Nationale - Musée-Conservatoire Nationale de la Typographie, 27 Rue de la Convention, 75015 Paris - T: 0140583000 poste 3472
Special Museum 12301

Institut Français d'Architecture, 6 Rue de Tournon, 75006 Paris - T: 0146339036
Special Museum 12302

Le Jardin des Papillons, Parc Floral de Paris, Bois de Vincennes, 75012 Paris - T: 0143284763
Natural History Museum 12303

Maison d'Auguste Comte, 10 Rue Monsieur-le-Prince, 75005 Paris - T: 0143260856
Special Museum 12304

Maison de Balzac, 47 Rue Raynouard, 75016 Paris - T: 0155744180, Fax: 0145251922, Internet: http://www.paris-france.org/musees/balzac. Head: Yves Gagneux
Special Museum - 1960
House where Balzac lived from 1840 to 1847, portraits, caricatures, engraving manuscripts and documents dealing with Balzac, his work, his contemporaries, and his times - library 12305

Maison de la Nature, Parc Floral de Paris, Rte de la Pyramide, 75012 Paris - T: 0143284763
Natural History Museum 12306

Maison de l'Air, 27 Rue Piat, 75020 Paris - T: 0143284763
Special Museum 12307

Maison de Victor Hugo, 6 Pl des Vosges, 75004 Paris - T: 0142721016, Fax: 0142720664, E-mail: constance.allard@mairie-paris.fr, Internet: http://www.paris-france.org/MUSEES/Maison_de_Victor_Hugo/. Head: Danielle Molinari
Special Museum - 1903
Portraits and memorabilia of Victor Hugo and his family, drawings by Hugo, first editions of his works and manuscripts 12308

Maison des Cinq Sens, 28 Rue Pierre-Gourdault, 75013 Paris - T: 0143284763
Special Museum 12309

Maison Européenne de la Photo, 5-7 Rue de Fourcy, 75004 Paris - T: 0144787800/0434
Special Museum / Science&Tech Museum 12310

Mémorial du Maréchal Leclerc au Musée Jean Moulin, 23 Dalle-Jardin Atlantique, Allée de la 2e D.B., 75015 Paris - T: 0140643944
Historical Museum
History of French resistance and liberation through Field Marshal Leclerc and Jean Moulin 12311

Mini Musée Militaria, 27 Rue Montgallet, 75011 Paris - T: 0143420448
Military Museum 12312

Musée Adam Mickiewicz, 6 Quai d'Orléans, 75004 Paris - T: 0155428383, Fax: 0146333631. Head: Pierre Zaleski
Special Museum - 1903
Life and work of the Polish poet Adam Mickiewicz (1798-1855), portraits, sculptures, manuscripts, and documents on his circle 12313

Musée Adzak, 3 Rue Jonquoy, 75014 Paris - T: 0145430698
Fine Arts Museum
Workshop of photographer-sculptor Roy Adzak 12314

Musée Arménien de France, 59 Av Foch, 75016 Paris - T: 0145561588
Historical Museum
From the vestiges of Ourartou (800 BC) to contemporary creation, material and spiritual life of the Armenian people 12315

Musée-Atelier du Cuivre et de l'Argent, 113 Av Daumesnil, 75012 Paris - T: 0143402020/6060
Special Museum 12316

Musée Auguste Rodin, 77 Rue de Varenne, 75007 Paris - T: 0144186110, Fax: 0145515538. Head: Jacques Vilain
Fine Arts Museum - 1916
Works of Rodin incl sculptures, drawings, paintings, engravings, his personal coll of art from antiquity, the Middle Ages, the 19th c, and the Orient - library, archive 12317

Musée Baccarat, 30bis Rue de Paradis, 75010 Paris - T: 0147706430, Fax: 0148242901
Decorative Arts Museum
Masterpieces created for the universal exhibitions for which Baccarat obtained gold medals or Grand Prix 12318

Musée Boleslaw Biegas (Museum is closed until 2003), c/o Bibliothèque Polonaise de Paris, 6 Quai d'Orléans, 75004 Paris - T: 0155428383, Fax: 0146333631. Head: Pierre Zaleski
Fine Arts Museum
Paintings and sculptures by Polish artists from the end of the 19th century to the beginning of the 20th century 12319

Musée Bouchard, 25 Rue de l'Yvette, 75016 Paris - T: 0146476346, Fax: 0146477050, E-mail: musee@musee-bouchard.com, Internet: http://www.musee-bouchard.com. Head: Marie Bouchard
Fine Arts Museum
Studio of the sculptor Henri Bouchard. Works in bronze, stone, marble, original plasters, tools and moulds 12320

Musée Bouilhet-Christofle, 9 Rue Royale, 75009 Paris - T: 0149334300, Fax: 0149334339
Decorative Arts Museum
Plate and cutlery of the house of Christofle through 150 years 12321

Musée Bourdelle, 16-18 Rue Antoine Bourdelle, 75015 Paris - T: 0149547373, Fax: 0142228502. Head: Rhodia Dufet-Bourdelle
Fine Arts Museum - 1949
Sculptures, paintings, drawings by Emile-Antoine Bourdelle (1861-1929), the artist's studio and appartment - library 12322

Musée Bricard, 1 Rue de la Perle, 75003 Paris - T: 0142777962
Decorative Arts Museum 12323

Musée Carnavalet - Histoire de Paris, 23 Rue de Sévigné, 75003 Paris - T: 0144595858, Fax: 0144595810, Internet: http://www.paris-france/musees/musee-carnavalet/. Head: Jean-Marc Leri
Historical Museum - 1880
Hist of Paris in paintings, sculptures, drawings, sign posts etc, period rooms from Parisian hotels, literary recoll of Madame de Sévigné 12324

Musée Cernuschi, Musée des Arts de l'Asie de la Ville de Paris, 7 Av Velasquez, 75008 Paris - T: 0145635075, Fax: 0145637816. Head: Gilles Béguin
Fine Arts Museum
Chinese Art from its origins to the 14th century, traditional contemporary paintings in ink on paper 12325

Musée Cognacq-Jay, 8 Rue Elzévir, 75003 Paris - T: 0140270721, Fax: 0140278944. Head: Georges Brunel
Fine Arts Museum / Decorative Arts Museum - 1929
18th century arts, paintings, pastels, Meissen porcelain, snuff boxes, miniatures, furniture 12326

Musée Curie, 11 Rue Pierre-et-Marie-Curie, 75005 Paris - T: 0142346749, Fax: 0142346749, E-mail: musee@curie.fr, Internet: http://www.curie.fr/musee. Head: Soraya Boudia
Historic Site / Science&Tech Museum 12327

Musée d'Anatomie Delmas-Orfila-Rouvière, c/o Université Paris V, Institut d'Anatomie, 45 Rue des Saints-Pères, 75006 Paris - T: 0142862047, Fax: 0142860402
Special Museum
Presentation of 5800 anatomical items, largest museum of Anatomy in France 12328

Musée Dapper, 35 Rue Paul Valery, 75116 Paris - T: 0145000150, Fax: 0145002716, E-mail: dapper@club-internet.fr. Head: Christiane Falgayrettes
Special Museum
Primitive and pre-colonial African art 12329

Musée d'Art et d'Histoire du Judaïsme, 71 Rue du Temple, 75003 Paris - Fax: 0142729747. Head: Laurence Sigal
Ethnology Museum / Religious Arts Museum 12330

Musée d'Art Juif, 42 Rue des Saules, 75018 Paris - T: 0142578415, Fax: 0142572630
Religious Arts Museum
Religious and popular art objects, paintings, sculptures, models of synagogues, tomb stones - Specialised book shop 12331

Musée d'Art Moderne de la Ville de Paris, 11 Av du Président Wilson, 75116 Paris - T: 0153674000, Fax: 0147233598, E-mail: veronique.prest@mairie-paris.fr. Head: Suzanne Pagé
Fine Arts Museum - 1961
20th century art, animation and research, children's section - library 12332

Musée d'Art Naïf Max-Fourny, Halle Saint-Pierre, 2 Rue Ronsard, 75018 Paris - T: 0142587289, Fax: 0142643978. Head: Sylvie Girardet
Fine Arts Museum
Permanent collections of naive art from all over the world 12333

Musée d'Art Sacré, Trésor de la Cathédrale Notre-Dame, Pl du Parvis Notre-Dame, Sacristie du Chapitre, 75004 Paris - T: 0142345610
Religious Arts Museum 12334

Musée de Bible et Terre Sainte, c/o Institut Catholique de Paris, 21 Rue d'Assas, 75270 Paris - T: 0145480915. Head: J. Briend
Archaeological Museum / Religious Arts Museum - 1962
Ceramics and other objects from Palestine from 5000 BC to 600 AD 12335

Musée de Chaussures de Di Mauro-Bottier, 14 Rue du Faubourg-Saint-Honoré, 75008 Paris - T: 0142653552
Special Museum 12336

Musée de la Chasse et de la Nature, 60 Rue des Archives, 75003 Paris - T: 0153019240, Fax: 0142774570, E-mail: fmcn@wanadoo.fr. Head: Claude d' Anthenaise
Special Museum / Natural History Museum - 1967
17th century house, arts décoratifs, mobilier, peintures, sculptures, textile, manuscrits, tapisseries, armes, trophées d'animaux 12337

Musée de la Conciergerie, 1 Quai de l'Horloge, 75001 Paris - T: 0153737850, Fax: 0140517036
Local Museum 12338

Musée de la Contrefaçon, 16 Rue de la Faisanderie, 75116 Paris - T: 0156261400, Fax: 0156261401, E-mail: info@unifab.com, Internet: http://www.unifab.com
Historical Museum
Originals and imitations of products 12339

Musée de la Curiosité et de la Magie, c/o Ecole de Magie, 11 Rue Saint-Paul, 75004 Paris - T: 0142721326, Fax: 0145360148
Special Museum
Antiques linked to magic, optical illusions, automatons, interactive games for chilren, demonstration of magic tricks 12340

Musée de la Marine, Palais de Chaillot, 17 Pl du Trocadéro, 75116 Paris - T: 0145533170, Fax: 0147274967
Historical Museum
One of the largest maritime museums in the world, ship models, exotic vehicles 12341

Musée de la Mode et du Costume → Musée Galliéra

Musée de la Mode et du Textile, Union Centrale des Arts Décoratifs, 107 Rue de Rivoli, 75001 Paris - T: 0144555750, Fax: 0144555784, Internet: http://www.ucad.fr. Head: Hélène David-Weill, Sophie Durrleman, Béatrice Salmon
Special Museum - 1986
Textiles, clothing, dresses, accessories, shoes, stockings, fans, gloves, jewels - archives 12342

Musée de la Monnaie, 11 Quai de Conti, 75006 Paris - T: 0140465533, Fax: 0140465709. Head: Evelyne Cohen
Special Museum - 1988
Coins and medals from antiquity to modern times 12343

Musée de la Musique, Cité de la Musique, 221 Av Jean Jaurès, 75019 Paris - T: 0144844484, Fax: 0144844601, E-mail: musee@cite-musique.fr, Internet: http://www.cite-musique.fr. Head: Frédéric Dassas
Music Museum - 1862
More than 900 musical instruments from the last four centuries, sound samples - documentation centre, research and restoration, laboratory 12344

Musée de la Parfumerie, 9 Rue Scribe, 75009 Paris - T: 0147420456, Fax: 0147421745, E-mail: tourisme@fragonard.com, Internet: http://www.fragonard.com. Head: Eric Fabre
Special Museum 12345

Musée de la Parfumerie Fragonard, 39 Blvd des Capucines, 75002 Paris - T: 0142603714, Fax: 0142603229, E-mail: tourisme@fragonard.com, Internet: http://www.fragonard.com. Head: Eric Fabre
Special Museum
Perfume bottles from the Egyptians to 19th century, pot-pourris, incense burners, paintings, test tubes, plant and animal raw materials used in making fragrances, extraction techniques 12346

Musée de la Poste, 34 Blvd de Vaugirard, 75015 Paris - T: 0142792424, Fax: 0142792400
Special Museum - 1946
History of the post, stamps - library 12347

Musée de la Poupée, Impasse Berthaud, au Niveau du 22 Rue Rambuteau, 75003 Paris - T: 0142727311, Fax: 0142727311. Head: Samy Odin
Special Museum / Decorative Arts Museum / Ethnology Museum
French dolls and babies from 1860-1960, lecturers on the history of dolls 12348

Musée de la Publicité, 107 Rue de Rivoli, 75001 Paris - T: 0144555750, Fax: 0144555784, E-mail: rejane.bargiel@ucad.fr, Internet: http://www.museedelapub.org. Head: Hélène David-Weill, Sophie Durrleman, Béatrice Salmon
Special Museum
80.000 old and contemporary posters presented by thematics, artists or brands retrospectives - Interactive multimedia library 12349

Musée de la Sculpture en Plein Air, Jardin du Port Saint-Bernard, Quai Saint-Bernard, 75005 Paris - T: 0143269190
Open Air Museum - 1980
Sculptures from the second half of the 20th century: Brancusi, Gilioli, César 12350

Musée de la Serrure-Bricard, 1 Rue de la Perle, 75003 Paris - T: 0142777962, Fax: 0142776106
Science&Tech Museum
History of locks since Roman times to the present 12351

Musée de la Société de l'Histoire du Protestantisme Français, 54 Rue des Saints-Pères, 75007 Paris - T: 0145486207
Religious Arts Museum 12352

Musée de la Tradition de la Brigade des Sapeurs-Pompiers de Paris, 1 Pl Jules-Renard, 75017 Paris - T: 0147546818
Science&Tech Museum 12353

Musée de la Vie Romantique, Maison Renan-Scheffer, 16 Rue Chapt, 75009 Paris - T: 0148749538, Fax: 0148742842
Local Museum / Historical Museum
Former studio of the painter Ary Scheffer, memorabilia of George Sand 12354

Musée de l'Arc de Triomphe, Pl de l'Etoile, 75008 Paris - T: 0155377377, Fax: 0143806412, E-mail: jeannot@monuments-france.fr
Historical Museum 12355

Musée de l'Armée, Hôtel National des Invalides, 6 Pl Vauban, 75700 Paris - T: 0144423772, Fax: 0144423764, E-mail: bdevaux-ma@invalides-org, Internet: http://www.invalides.org. Head: Bernard Devaux
Military Museum - 1905
Artillery, armour, uniforms, banners, history of the French Army from its origin to present times, photographs, prints, tomb of Napoleon 1st in the Dome church - library 12356

Musée de l'Armée Russe, 87 Blvd Exelmans, 75016 Paris - T: 0145246434
Military Museum 12357

Musée de l'Assistance Publique-Hôpitaux de Paris, 47 Quai de la Tournelle, 75005 Paris - T: 0140275005, Fax: 0140274648, E-mail: musee-aphp@teaser.fr. Head: A. Nardin
Historical Museum
Hospital history, history of medicine and their professions 12358

Musée de l'Éclairage au Gaz, Ets Lumière de l'Œil, 4 Rue Flatters, 75005 Paris - T: 0147076347
Science&Tech Museum 12359

Musée de l'Eventail, Atelier Hoguet, 2 Blvd de Strasbourg, 75010 Paris - T: 0142089020, Fax: 0142083091, E-mail: eventail@cyberbrain.com, Internet: http://www.village.cy-berbrain.com/musee/eventail. Head: Anne Hoguet
Special Museum
Fans from 18th century to the present day 12360

Musée de l'Histoire de France, 60 Rue des Francs-Bourgeois, 75141 Paris Cedex 03 - T: 0140276096, Fax: 0140276645, E-mail: ariane.james-sarazin@culture.gouv.fr. Head: Ariane James-Sarazin
Historical Museum - 1867
Original documents of French history, former royal chambers with paintings 12361

Musée de l'Histoire de l'Eau et des Egouts, Angle Quai d'Orsay et Pont de l'Alma, 75007 Paris - T: 0147051029
Historical Museum 12362

Musée de l'Holographie, Les Halles, Niveau 1, Portes Berger-Rambuteau, 15-21 Grand Balcon, 75001 Paris - T: 0140399683, Fax: 0142743357
Special Museum
3D laser pictures, sciences, technology, holograms 12363

Musée de l'Homme, Palais de Chaillot, 17 Pl du Trocadéro, 75116 Paris - T: 0144057272, Fax: 0144057292, E-mail: presscomm@mnhn.fr, Internet: http://www.mnhn.fr. Head: Prof. Henry de Lumley, Lionel Gauthier
Ethnology Museum
Ethnography, anthropology, prehistory - library 12364

Musée de l'Institut du Monde Arabe, 1 Rue des Fossés-Saint-Bernard, 75005 Paris - T: 0140513838, Fax: 0143547645, E-mail: ima@imaarabe.org, Internet: http://www.imarabe.org. Head: Brahim Alaoui
Archaeological Museum / Special Museum / Fine Arts Museum 12365

Musée de l'Observatoire, 61 Av de l'Observatoire, 75014 Paris - T: 0140512221, Fax: 0143541804, E-mail: pa.presidence@obspm.fr, Internet: http://www.obspm.fr. Head: Pierre Couturier
Science&Tech Museum - 1878
16th-20th scientific and astronomical instruments, statues, pictures of astronomers 12366

Musée de l'Opéra National de Paris, 8 Rue Scribe, 75009 Paris - T: 0147420702, Fax: 0142651016, E-mail: bib.opera@bnf.fr, Internet: http://www.bnf.fr. Head: Pierre Vidal
Performing Arts Museum - 1881
Hist of lyric theatre, dance, music, memorabilia of composers, drawings, costums, decorations 12367

Musée de l'Ordre de la Libération, Hôtel National des Invalides, 51bis Blvd de Latour-Maubourg, 75007 Paris - T: 0147050410, Fax: 0147050410, E-mail: musee@ordredelaliberation.fr, Internet: http://www.ordredelaliberation.fr. Head: Vladimir Trouplin
Military Museum - 1971
3 galleries and 6 rooms, manuscripts of General de Gaulle, actions of resistance 12368

Musée de Matière Médicale, c/o Université Paris-V, Faculté de Pharmacie, Av de l'Observatoire 4, 75006 Paris - T: 0153739810/803, Fax: 0140469658, E-mail: tillequin@pharmacie.univ-paris5.fr. Head: Prof. François Tillequin
Special Museum
Medical plants, drugs 12369

Musée de Minéralogie de l'Ecole des Mines de Paris, 60 Blvd Saint-Michel, 75272 Paris Cedex 06 - T: 0140519139, Fax: 0146342596, E-mail: touret@musee.ensmp.fr, Internet: http://www.ensmp.fr/Fr/Services/Musee/musee.html. Head: Lydie Touret
Natural History Museum - 1783
One of the top ten largest collections in the world, 100.000 samples including 80.000 minerals, 15.000 rocks, 4.000 ores, 400 meteorites, 700 gems and 300 artificial minerals 12370

Musée de Montmartre, 12 Rue Cortot, 75018 Paris - T: 0146066111, Fax: 0146063075
Historical Museum
Paintings, graphics, posters, 18th century porcelains, a refurnisheld old 'bistro', history of Montmartre district 12371

Musée de Notre-Dame-de-Paris, 10 Rue du Cloître Notre-Dame, 75004 Paris - T: 0143254292
Religious Arts Museum
History of the cathedral, of Paris and of France 12372

Musée de Pharmacie, 4 Av de l'Observatoire, 75006 Paris - T: 0143291208
Natural History Museum 12373

Musée de Radio France, 116 Av du Président Kennedy, 75016 Paris - T: 0156401576, Fax: 0156404282, Internet: http://www.radiofrance.fr
Historical Museum / Science&Tech Museum - 1963
Replicas of studios and laboratories illustrating the history of technology over the century - sound and image archives, photographs, manuscripts 12374

Musée de Tradition de la Brigade des Sapeurs-Pompiers de Paris, 37 Blvd Masséna, 75013 Paris - T: 0145826818
Science&Tech Museum 12375

Musée d'Ennery, 59 Av Foch, 75116 Paris - T: 0147236165, Fax: 0147205750
Decorative Arts Museum - 1903
Chinese and Japanese art, ceramics, furnishings, Namban chests, wood and ivory carvings, enamel, inlays - library 12376

Musée Dermatologique, 2 Pl Alfred-Fournier, 75010 Paris - T: 0142499915
Special Museum 12377

Musée des Arts Décoratifs (museum is closed until the end of 2004), 107 Rue de Rivoli, 75001 Paris - T: 0144555750, Fax: 0144555784, Internet: http://www.ucad.fr. Head: Hélène David-Weill, Sophie Durrleman
Decorative Arts Museum - 1863
Medieval to modern decorative arts, drawings, tapestries, furniture, porcelain, enamels, documents on textiles and wallpapers, toys, glass, 220.000 items - library 12378

Musée des Arts et Metiers, 292 Rue Saint-Martin, 75003 Paris - T: 0153018200, Fax: 0153018201, Internet: http://www.cnam.fr/museum/. Head: Daniel Thoulouze
Science&Tech Museum - 1794
Old planes, automobiles since 1769, bicycles, train models, hist of photography, film, radio, and television, radar, astronomy, industrial life 12379

Musée des Collections Historiques de la Préfecture de Police, 1bis Rue des Carmes, 75005 Paris - T: 0144415250
Historical Museum
History of Paris police from the 16th century to the present - library 12380

Musée des Collections Historiques de la Préfecture de Police, 1bis Rue des Carmes, 75005 Paris - T: 0144415100
Special Museum 12381

Musée des Egouts de Paris, Pont de l'Alma, opposite 93 Quai d'Orsay, 75007 Paris - T: 0153682781, Fax: 0153682789
Special Museum
500 metres into the sewers of Paris to trace their history and that of Lutecia to the present day, models and machinery used yesterday and today, exhibition room on the techniques of the future 12382

Musée des Materiaux du Centre de Recherche sur les Monuments Historiques, Palais de Chaillot, 9 Av Albert de Mun, 75116 Paris - T: 0147278464, Fax: 0147045583
Historical Museum
Presentation of materials and building materials used in historical monuments, scale models of buildings and framework 12383

Musée des Plans et Reliefs, Hôtel National des Invalides, Cour d'Honneur, 75007 Paris - T: 0145519505, Fax: 0147051107
Historical Museum - 1668
Models of 63 fortified towns in France and 23 in other countries constructed 1668-1670, drafts of plans constructed in the 19th century, 18th century manuscripts of plans 12384

Musée des Sous-Stations R.A.T.P., 45 Rue de Toul, 75012 Paris - T: 0140487207
Science&Tech Museum 12385

Musée d'Histoire Contemporaine, Bibliothèque de Documentation Internationale Contemporaine, Hôtel National des Invalides, Cour d'Honneur, 75007 Paris - T: 0144425491, Fax: 0144189384. Head: Laurent Gervereau
Historical Museum - 1914
1,5 million documents, paintings, engravings, photographs, posters, cartoons dealing with the history of the 20th century 12386

Musée d'Histoire de la Médecine, 12 Rue de l'École-de-Médecine, 75270 Paris - T: 0140461693, Fax: 0140461892, E-mail: clin@univ-paris5.fr, Internet: http://www.univ-paris5.fr. Head: Marie-Véronique Clin
Historical Museum / University Museum
Surgical instruments 12387

Musée d'Orsay, 62 Rue de Lille, 75343 Paris Cedex 07 - T: 0140494814, Fax: 0145485660
Fine Arts Museum - 1986
19th and early 20th century art (paintings, sculptures, architecture, decorative arts, photography) 12388

Musée du Barreau de Paris, 25 Rue du Jour, 75001 Paris - T: 0147835003, Fax: 0147836248
Special Museum 12389

Musée du Centre de Recherches sur les Monuments Historiques, Palais de Chaillot, Pl du Trocadéro, 75116 Paris - T: 0147278464, Fax: 0147045583. Head: Jean-Daniel Pariset
Special Museum
Castings of Romanesque, Gothic, Renaissance and Classic monuments reproductions of nearly all French Frescos, art from the Carolingian-Gothic periods 12390

Musée du Cinéma Henri Langlois, Palais de Chaillot, 1 Pl du Trocadéro, 75016 Paris - T: 0153647440, Fax: 0153647497, E-mail: museeducinema@free.fr. Head: Laurent Gervereau
Special Museum - 1972
Collections of history, photography, posters and documents, costumes, paintings, drawings 12391

Musée du Compagnonnage, 10 Rue Mabillon, 75006 Paris - T: 0143262503
Special Museum
History, scale Models 12392

Musée du Football en France, 60bis Av d'Iéna, 75016 Paris - T: 0144317300
Special Museum 12393

Musée du Grand Orient de France et de la Franc-Maçonnerie Européenne, 16 Rue Cadet, 75009 Paris - T: 0145232092, Fax: 0142471287
Historical Museum - 1972
Freemasonry 12394

Musée du Hard Rock Café, 14 Blvd Montmartre, 75009 Paris - T: 0142461000/4970
Special Museum 12395

Musée du Louvre, 34-36 Quai du Louvre, 75058 Paris Cedex 01 - T: 0140205050, Fax: 0140205442, Internet: http://www.louvre.fr. Head: Henri Loyrette
Fine Arts Museum / Decorative Arts Museum / Archaeological Museum - 1793
Oriental antiquities, Egyptian antiquities, Greek, Roman, Etruscan art, Christian and Moslem archaeology, medieval and Renaissance sculpture, decorative arts, jewellery, tapestries, 17th-18th century French furnishings, paintings of Italian, Dutch, French, Flemish, German, Spanish schools, drawings, pastels, and etchings 12396

Musée du Luxembourg, 19 Rue de Vaugirard, 75006 Paris - T: 0142342595
Fine Arts Museum
Paintings, sculptures 12397

Musée du Mémorial du Martyr Juif Inconnu, 37 Rue de Turenne, 75003 Paris - T: 0142774472, Fax: 0144598262, E-mail: contact@memorial-cdjc.org, Internet: http://www.memorial-cdjc.org. Head: Eric de Rothschild, Jacques Fredj
Historical Museum 12398

Musée du Thé, Mariage Frères, 30 Rue de Bourg-Tibourg, 75004 Paris - T: 0142722811, Fax: 0142745168, E-mail: info@mariagefreres.com, Internet: http://www.mariagefreres.com. Head: Kitti Cha Sangmanée
Special Museum 12399

Musée du Val-de-Grâce, 1 Pl Alphonse-Lavéran, 75005 Paris
Local Museum 12400

Musée du Vin, 5 Sq Charles Dickens, 75016 Paris - T: 0145256326, Fax: 0140509122
Special Museum
Installed in the old cellars of the Abbey of Passy, history of wine in France and the main wine-producing areas, tools, wax models, wine tasting 12401

Musée Dupuytren, 15 Rue de l'Ecole de Médecine, 75006 Paris - T: 0143292860. Head: P. de Saint-Maur
Special Museum - 1832
Wax mouldings of pathological specimens, bones and skeletons, hist of pathology 12402

Musée Edith Piaf, 5 Rue Crespin du Gast, 75011 Paris - T: 0143555272, Fax: 0143555272. Head: Bernard Marchois
Special Museum / Music Museum
Private museum in an apartment, memorabilia of Edith Piaf, china collection 12403

Musée Edouard Branly, c/o Institut Catholique de Paris, 21 Rue d'Assas, 75006 Paris - T: 0149545220
Science&Tech Museum
Instruments used in the experiments of Edouard Branly, the inventor of the cordless telegraph 12404

Musée en Herbe, Jardin d'Acclimatation, Bois de Boulogne, 75116 Paris - T: 0140679766, Fax: 0140679213
Fine Arts Museum
Temporary exhibitions and workshops for children 12405

Musée Ernest Hébert, 85 Rue du Cherche-Midi, 75006 Paris - T: 0142222382, Fax: 0145484239. Head: I. Julia
Fine Arts Museum
Paintings of Ernest Hébert, Italian landscapes 12406

Musée-Ferme Georges-Ville, Ferme de la Route du Pesage, Bois de Vincennes, 75011 Paris - T: 0143284763
Special Museum 12407

Musée-Galerie de la Seita, 12 Rue Surcouf, 75007 Paris - T: 0145566017, Fax: 0145566667, E-mail: marie-claire.ades@seita.fr, Internet: http://www.seita.fr/musee. Head: Marie-Claire Ades
Special Museum - 1979
Hist of tobacco and its use - library; fine arts gallery 12408

Musée Galliéra, Musée de la Mode de la Ville de Paris, 10 Av Pierre 1er de Serbie, 75116 Paris - T: 0156528600, Fax: 0147233837, E-mail: - bibliothequegalliera@free.fr, Internet: http://paris_france.org/MUSEES/default.htm. Head: Catherine Join-Diéterle
Special Museum - 1978
French fashion from 1735 to the present 12409

Musée Georges Clemenceau, 8 Rue Benjamin Franklin, 75116 Paris - T: 0145205341
Special Museum
Documents on the life and work of Georges Clemenceau, statesman's former home 12410

Musée Grévin, 10 Blvd Montmartre, 75009 Paris - T: 0147708505, Fax: 0147700653, E-mail: veronique.berecz@revin.com, http://www.grevin.com. Head: Béatrice de Roynìès
Special Museum
Wax museum with approx. 280 characters on international actuality and the French history, Palais des Mirages 12411

Musée Hermès, 24 Rue du Faubourg-Saint-Honoré, 75008 Paris - T: 0140174717
Special Museum 12412

Musée Historique, Inja, 56 Blvd des Invalides, 75015 Paris - T: 0144491535
Special Museum 12413

Musée Institut Tessin, c/o Centre Culturel Suédois, 11 Rue Payenne, 75003 Paris - T: 0144788020, Fax: 0144788027, E-mail: c.c.s@wanadoo.fr, Internet: http://www.amb-suede.fr. Head: Annika Levin
Fine Arts Museum
History of Franco-Swedish artistic exchanges 12414

Musée Jacquemart-André, 158 Blvd Haussman, 75008 Paris - T: 0142890491, Fax: 0145621636, E-mail: givaudan@musee-jacquemart-andre.com
Fine Arts Museum - 1913
French, Italian, Flemish, English painting (Rembrandt, Botticelli, Uccello, Boucher, van Dyck) tapestries, furnishings, art objects, Italian and French sculptures 12415

Musée Jean-Moulin, Bâtiment Nord, Parc Dalle, Jardin Atlantique, 75015 Paris - T: 0147537138
Special Museum 12416

Musée Kwok-On, 41 Rue des Francs-Bourgeois, 75015 Paris - T: 0142729942
Performing Arts Museum
Theatre in Asia, masks, puppets, instruments, costume 12417

Musée Lénine, 4 Rue Marie-Rose, 75014 Paris - T: 0142799958
Historical Museum
Reconstructed apartment where Lenin lived from July 1909 to June 1912 12418

Musée Maçonnique de la Grande Loge de France, 8 Rue de Puteaux, 75017 Paris - T: 0153424141, Fax: 0145221152. Head: Philippe Morbach
Local Museum / Fine Arts Museum
Library, archives 12419

Musée Maillol, Fondation Dina Vierny, 59-61 Rue de Grenelle, 75007 Paris - T: 0142225958, Fax: 0142841444
Fine Arts Museum - 1995
Drawings, engravings, paintings, sculptures, decorative arts, original plaster and terracotta works of Maillol, Dina Vierny collection: masters of French naive art, drawings by Matisse, Degas, Picasso, Ingres, Cézanne, Suzanne Valadon, Foujita, drawings and watercolours by Raoul Dufy, paintings by Bonnard, lithographs by Odile Redon, wood and watercolours by Gauguin, sculptures by Rodin, paintings by Serge Poliakoff, Kandinsky, Marcel Duchamp, Duchamp-Villon, Jacques Villon, Gilioli, Couturier, Zitman and Russian artist 12420

Musée Marmottan Claude Monet, c/o Académie des Beaux Arts, Institut de France, 2 Rue Louis Boilly, 75016 Paris - T: 0144965033, Fax: 0140506584, E-mail: marmottan@marmottan.com, Internet: http://www.marmottan.com. Head: Jean-Marie Granier
Decorative Arts Museum / Fine Arts Museum - 1932
Primitives, Renaissance, Empire, and Impressionists, exhibit on Monet and his friends - Library 12421

Musée Mobile de l'Escadron de l'Histoire, 35 Av des Gobelins, 75013 Paris - T: 0143314762
Military Museum 12422

Musée Moissan, c/o Université Paris V René Descartes, Faculté de Pharmacie, 4 Av de l'Observatoire, 75006 Paris - T: 0153739668, Fax: 0153739668, E-mail: dugue@pharmacie.univ-paris5.fr. Head: Prof. J. Dugué
University Museum 12423

Musée National d'Art Moderne, Centre Pompidou, 19 Rue du Renard, 75191 Paris Cedex 04 - T: 0144781233/1463/4625, Fax: 0144781203, Internet: http://www.cnac-gp.fr. Head: Jean-Jacques Aillagon, Werner Spies
Public Gallery - 1975
20th century coll: visual arts (paintings, sculptures, films, photographs), architecture and design (designer originals, models, furniture); works from Fauvism (1905) and from after the 1914-18 war up to the 1960's, Modern and Contemporary art (Surrealism, Pop Art, New Realism) - media dept, archives, cinema, documentation centre, library 12424

Musée National de la Légion d'Honneur et des Ordres de Chevalerie, 2 Rue de la Légion d'Honneur, 75007 Paris - T: 0140628425, Fax: 0147537950. Head: Anne de Chefdebien
Historical Museum - 1925
Hist of orders of all countries since the Middle Ages, costumes, paintings, fine arts, Memorabilia of Napoleon - library, documentation center 12425

Musée National de la Marine, Palais de Chaillot, 17 Pl du Trocadéro, 75116 Paris - T: 0153656969, Fax: 0153658103, E-mail: g.prudhomme@musee_marine.fr, Internet: http://www.musee-marine.fr. Head: Georges Prud'homme
Historical Museum - 1827
17th-20th century ship models, paintings, weapons, 20 maritime objects from the 16th century to the present - library 12426

Musée National de l'Orangerie (closed until end of 2002), Jardin des Tuileries, Pl de la Concorde, 75001 Paris - T: 0142974816, Fax: 0142613082. Head: Pierre Georgel
Fine Arts Museum - 1927
Paintings by Claude Monet, Jean Walter and Paul Guillaume collection 12427

Musée National des Arts Asiatiques Guimet, 19 Av d'Iéna, 75116 Paris - T: 0147236165, Fax: 0147205750, Internet: http://www.museeguimet.fr. Head: Jean-François Jarrige
Fine Arts Museum
Largest museum of Buddhist art in Europe; one of the twelve major museums in France. Art and archaeology from the 17 countries of antiquity, from Afghanistan to Japan. Leading collection in the West for art from Afghanistan, Cambodia, Tibet and Buddhist Japan. Rare porcelain from China - Public library 12428

Musée National des Arts d'Afrique et d'Océanie, 293 Av Daumesnil, 75012 Paris - T: 0144748480, Fax: 0143432753, Internet: http://www.musee-afriqueoceanie.fr. Head: Germain Viatte
Fine Arts Museum - 1960
North African, African and Oceanian art - library, tropical aquarium 12429

Musée National des Arts et Traditions Populaires, 6 Av du Mahatma-Gandhi, 75116 Paris - T: 0144176000, Fax: 0144176060, Internet: http://www.culture.fr. Head: Michel Colardelle
Ethnology Museum - 1937
Anthropology, ethnology, ethnography, customs, folk art, costumes - library, research laboratory 12430

Musée National des Monuments Français, Palais de Chaillot, 1 Pl du Trocadéro, 75116 Paris - T: 0144053910, Fax: 0147554013. Head: Guy Cogeval
Fine Arts Museum / Special Museum
Buildings and monumental sculptures from the Middle Ages to the 19th century in 6000 moulds and life-size reproductions, models, old photographs 12431

Musée National du Moyen Age, 6 Pl Paul Painlevé, 75005 Paris - T: 0153737800, Fax: 0146345175, E-mail: cluny@culture.fr, Internet: http://www.musee-moyenage.fr. Head: Viviane Huchard
Fine Arts Museum - 1844
Gallo-Roman and medieval art, chapel in the Flamboyant style, tapestries, art objects, sculpture, enamel, religious art, altar from Basel, ancient palace with 15th-16th century furniture - library 12432

Musée National du Sport, 24 Rue du Commandant Guilbaud, 75016 Paris - T: 0140459912, Fax: 0146516554, E-mail: musee.nat.sport@jeunesse-sports.gouv.fr. Head: Patrick Porte
Special Museum
History and evolution of physical and sports activities in France from their origins 12433

Musée National Eugène Delacroix, 6 Rue de Furstenberg, 75006 Paris - T: 0144418650, Fax: 0146345573, Internet: http://www.musee-delacroix.fr. Head: Arlette Sérullaz
Fine Arts Museum - 1971
Life and work of the painter Eugène Delacroix (1798-1863), exhibits displayed in artist's former home and studio 12434

Musée National Gustave Moreau, 14 Rue de la Rochefoucauld, 75009 Paris - T: 0148743850, Fax: 0148741871. Head: Geneviève Lacambre
Fine Arts Museum - 1902
Works by the artist Gustave Moreau, paintings, sketches, drawings, watercolours, apartment of the artist, works by Chassériau, Degas, Delaunay 12435

Musée National Jean-Jacques Henner, 43 Av de Villiers, 75017 Paris - T: 0147634273, Fax: 0143800082. Head: Rodolphe Rapetti
Fine Arts Museum - 1920
Paintings by Jean-Jacques Henner 12436

Musée Nissim de Camondo, Union Centrale des Arts Décoratifs, 63 Rue de Monceau, 75008 Paris - T: 0153890640/0650, Fax: 0153890642, Internet: http://www.ucad.fr. Head: Hélène David Weill, Sophie Durrleman, Béatrice Salmon
Decorative Arts Museum - 1935
Reconstructed 18th century aristocratic house, furniture, paintings, rugs, porcelain, goldplate 12437

Musée Pasteur, Institut Pasteur, 25 Rue du Docteur Roux, 75015 Paris - T: 0145688282/83, Fax: 0145688972, E-mail: musee@pasteur.fr. Head: Annick Perrot
Special Museum - 1936
Memorabilia, works of art, original publications, furniture of the scientist Louis Pasteur housed in his former apartment, scientific instruments including microscopes, sterilizers, cultures illustrating Pasteur's scientific research - library, scientific archives, phototheque 12438

Musée Picasso, Hôtel Salé, 5 Rue de Thorigny, 75003 Paris - T: 0142712521, Fax: 0148047546. Head: Gérard Regnier
Fine Arts Museum
Works of Picasso, received by the State after the death of the artist and the artist's personal, paintings, sculptures collection 12439

Musée Pierre Fauchard, Musée d'Art Dentaire, 22 Rue Emile Ménier, 75116 Paris - T: 0145534005, Fax: 0147043655
Special Museum
Dental art, 17th century Dutch paintings, furniture, instruments, antique books 12440

Musée Pierre Marly, 380 Rue Saint-Honoré, 75001 Paris - T: 0140200698
Special Museum
3.000 eyeglasses and lorgnettes from the 13th century to the present 12441

Musée-Placard d'Erik Satie, 6 Rue Cortot, 75018 Paris - T: 0142781518
Special Museum
Smallest museum in the world, former home of composer Erik Satie 12442

Musée-Restaurant Planet Hollywood, 78 Av des Champs-Élysées, 75008 Paris - T: 0145613525/53837827
Special Museum 12443

Musée Valentin Haüy, 5 Rue Duroc, 75007 Paris - T: 0144492727, Fax: 0144492710, E-mail: avh@avh.asso.fr. Head: Noëlle Roy
Special Museum - 1886
Education for blind people since 1771, old books and documents, specialized equipment for blind people from the end of the 18th century to present, history of education 12444

Musée Zadkine, 100bis Rue d'Assas, 75006 Paris - T: 0143269190, Fax: 0140468427
Fine Arts Museum - 1982
About 100 sculptures by Ossip Zadkine exhibited 12445

Muséosite de la Crypte, Archéologique de Notre-Dame, Pl du Parvis Notre-Dame, 75004 Paris - T: 0143298351
Archaeological Museum 12446

Muséum National d'Histoire Naturelle, 57 Rue Cuvier, 75005 Paris - T: 0140793000, Fax: 0140793484
Natural History Museum - 1635
Botany, zoology, paleontology, mineralogy - library 12447

Notre-Dame-de-Paris, Crypte Archéologique, Pl du Parvis de Notre-Dame, 75004 Paris - T: 0143298351
Religious Arts Museum
Largest archaeological crypt in Europe, life and scenes of the Ile-de-la-Cité from the 3rd to the 19th century 12448

Palais de la Découverte, Av Franklin D. Roosevelt, 75008 Paris - T: 0140748000, Fax: 0140748181. Head: Michel Demazure
Science&Tech Museum - 1937
Demonstrations of experiments in all scientific fields, photos, models - planetarium, library, cinema room 12449

Palais de Tokyo, Site de Création Contemporaine, 13 Av du Président Wilson, 75116 Paris - T: 0147235401, Fax: 0147201531, E-mail: contact@palaisdetokyo.com, Internet: http://www.palaisdetokyo.com. Head: Nicolas Bourriaud, Jérôme Sans
Fine Arts Museum - 1937/2002
Photographie, contemporary art 12450

Panthéon, Pl du Panthéon, 75005 Paris - T: 0144321800, Fax: 0144073223
Historical Museum 12451

Pavillon de l'Arsenal, 21 Blvd Morland, 75004 Paris - T: 0142763397, Fax: 0142762632
Local Museum
Architecture, town planning and documentation centre of the City of Paris, large scale models - Photo library 12452

Pavillon des Arts, Les Halles, Terrasse Lautréamont, 101 Rue Rambuteau, 75001 Paris - T: 0142338250, Fax: 0140289322
Fine Arts Museum
Temporary exhibitions open to all forms of art, all cultures and all eras 12453

Petit Musée de la Table, La Tour d'Argent, 15 Quai de la Tournelle, 75005 Paris - T: 0143542331, Fax: 0144071204. Head: Claude Terrail
Special Museum 12454

Petit Musée de l'Argenterie, Ateliers du Cuivre et de l'Argent, Viaduc des Arts, 109-113 Av Daumesnil, 75012 Paris - T: 0143402020, Fax: 0140406060
Special Museum
Objects linked to tableware, wine, tea, tobacco or fashion 12455

Petit-Palais, Musée des Beaux Arts de la Ville de Paris (closed until 2003), 1 Av Dutuit, 75008 Paris - T: 0142651273, Fax: 0142652460, E-mail: gilles.chazal@mairie-paris.fr. Head: Gilles Chazal
Fine Arts Museum / Decorative Arts Museum / Religious Arts Museum / Museum of Classical Antiquities - 1902
Antiques, Middle Age and Renaissance, 17th-20th c sculptures, porcelains, furniture, etchings, drawings and paintings 12456

Pharmacie Musée, 3 Rue Soufflot, 75005 Paris
Science&Tech Museum 12457

Salle des Traditions de la Garde Républicaine, 12 Blvd Henri IV, 75004 Paris - T: 0142761323/24, Fax: 0142761333
Military Museum
Models, men and horses, documents, hairstyles, uniforms, equipment, harnessing, musical instruments, arms 12458

Saon-Musée Maître-Alain, 8 Rue Saint-Claude, 75003 Paris - T: 0142775580
Special Museum 12459

Parly

Centre International d'Art Graphique, Hameau Petit Arran, La Métairie-Bruyères, 89240 Parly - T: 0386442135
Fine Arts Museum 12460

Parmain

Collections Archéologiques, Hôtel de Ville, Pl Georges-Clemenceau, 95620 Parmain - T: 0134089595
Archaeological Museum 12461

Parthenay

Musée Municipal Georges Turpin, 1 Rue Vau Saint-Jacques, 79200 Parthenay, mail addr: BP 3, 79200 Parthenay - T: 0549645373, E-mail: musee@district-parthenay.fr, Internet: http://www.district-parthenay.fr/sommaire/patrimoine.htm. Head: Maria Cavaillès
Local Museum - 1934
Medieval archeology, ethnology, faiences 12462

Passavant-la-Rochère

Galerie d'Art Moderne, Verrerie, 70210 Passavant-la-Rochère - T: 0384786100
Fine Arts Museum 12463

Pau

Centre d'Art Contemporain, Centre Leclerc, Av Louis Sallenave, 64000 Pau - T: 0559808093, Fax: 0559808007
Fine Arts Museum 12464

Musée Béarnais, Château de Pau, 64000 Pau - T: 0559270736
Ethnology Museum - 1923
Ethnography, literature, art, fauna, flora 12465

Musée Bernadotte, 8 Rue Tran, 64000 Pau - T: 0559274842. Head: Philippe Comte
Historical Museum - 1952
Memorabilia of Jean-Baptiste Bernadotte, Marshal under Napoleon, house where he was born 12466

Musée de la Confiture, Maison Miot, 48 Rue Joffre, 64000 Pau - T: 0559276951/7765
Special Museum / Historical Museum 12467

Musée des Beaux-Arts, Rue Mathieu Lalanne, 64000 Pau - T: 0559273302, Fax: 0559980963. Head: Guillaume Ambroise
Fine Arts Museum - 1864
Spanish, Italian, Flemish, Dutch, English, and French painting, sculpture, contemporary art 12468

Musée des Parachutistes, Av des Martyrs du Pont Long, 64082 Pau - T: 0559725218, Fax: 0559725218
Special Museum / Military Museum 12469

Musée National du Château de Pau, Musée Henri IV, Château, 64000 Pau - T: 0559823800, Fax: 0559823818. Head: Paul Mironneau
Historical Museum
Historical building, once seat of the Kings of Navarre (15th-16th c), portraits and documents relating to the 16th c, cradle of King Henry IV who was born in castle, 16th-17th century Flanders and Gobelin tapestries - library 12470

Pauillac

Collection d'Art, Château Pichon-Longueville Comtesse de Lalande, 33250 Pauillac - T: 0556591940, Fax: 0556592656, E-mail: pichon@pichon-lalande.com, Internet: http://www.pichon-lalande.com. Head: May-Eliane de Lencquesaing
Fine Arts Museum 12471

Collection de l'Outillage de Tonnellerie, Château du Colombier-Monpelou, 33250 Pauillac - T: 0556590148, Fax: 0556591201
Science&Tech Museum 12472

Maison du Tourisme et du Vin de Pauillac, 33250 Pauillac - T: 0556590308
Special Museum 12473

Musée d'Art du Château Mouton-Rothschild → Musée du Vin dans l'Art

Musée du Vin dans l'Art, Château Mouton-Rothschild, 33250 Pauillac - T: 0556592222, Fax: 0556732044, E-mail: webmaster@bpdr.com, Internet: http://www.mouton-rothschild.com. Head: Philippine Baronesse de Rothschild
Fine Arts Museum 12474

Paulx

Collection de Vieux Pressoirs, Cave du Moulin La Minoterie, 44270 Paulx - T: 0240260691
Science&Tech Museum 12475

Payrac

Musée Roger Thières, 46350 Payrac
Fine Arts Museum 12476

Payrignac

Musée de la Grotte de Cougnac, 46300 Payrignac - T: 0565414754/2225/2203/376413
Natural History Museum / Fine Arts Museum 12477

Peaugres

Musée de l'Outil à Bois, 07340 Peaugres - T: 0475348128
Special Museum 12478

Peille

Musée du Terroir de Peille, Pl de l'Arma, 06440 Peille - T: 0493799032
Local Museum 12479

Peillon

Collection de Sculptures, Le Vieux Logis, 2 Carriera Centrala, 06440 Peillon - T: 0493799137, Fax: 0017079248778, E-mail: -gabriel.mariani.sculpteur@wanadoo.fr, Internet: http://www.perso.wanadoo.fr/gabriel.mariani.sculpteur/. Head: Gabriel Mariani
Fine Arts Museum
Bronze sculptures 12480

Pelissanne

Musée Archéologique Municipal, Pl Cabardel, 13330 Pelissanne - T: 0490551187
Archaeological Museum 12481

Pellafol

Musée d'Histoire et d'Arts Populaires, Hameau des Payas, 38350 Pellafol - T: 0476300162/0447
Historical Museum / Folklore Museum 12482

Pellevoisin

Musée de l'Archiconfrérie Notre-Dame de la Miséricorde, Musée Jean Giraudoux, 25 Rue Jean Giraudoux, 36180 Pellevoisin - T: 0254390068
Religious Arts Museum / Historical Museum 12483

Pénestin

Musée de la Mytiliculture, 15 Rue du Port, 56760 Pénestin - T: 0299903002
Special Museum 12484

Penmarch

Musée de la Préhistoire à Saint-Guenole, Rue du Musée Préhistorique, Pors Carn, 29132 Penmarch - T: 0298586035. Head: Jean-Laurent Monnier
Archaeological Museum - 1921
Prehistory, anthropology 12485

Phare-Musée de Penmarch, 29132 Penmarch - T: 0298585730/6117
Special Museum 12486

Pennautier

Collection Historique (closed) 12487

Penne-d'Agenais

Musée Historique, Rue du 14 Juillet, 47140 Penne-d'Agenais - T: 0553412153/3780
Historical Museum / Archaeological Museum 12488

Père

Musée-Ferme Conservatoire Bigourdane, Les Coustalats N 117, 65130 Père - T: 0562391643, 056239205, Fax: 0562391643. Head: Milou Giraud
Agriculture Museum 12489

Periers

Musée Vivant de la Bicyclette, Rte Nationale 175, l'Épine, 50190 Periers - T: 0233467318
Science&Tech Museum 12490

Périgny-sur-Yerres

Musée de la Fondation Jean-Dubuffet, Ruelle aux Chevaux, 94520 Périgny-sur-Yerres - T: 0147341263
Fine Arts Museum 12491

Périgueux

Musée du Perigord, 22 Cours Tourny, 24000 Périgueux - T: 0553064070, Fax: 0553064071, E-mail: musee-perigord@wanadoo.fr. Head: Véronique Merlin-Anglade
Archaeological Museum - 1836
Prehist, Gallo-Roman and medieval finds, ethnography, 17th-18th century French, Italian, Flemish, Dutch painting and art objects, history, skeleton of 'man from Chancelade', painting on natural bones, wood, horns 12492

Musée Militaire des Gloires et Souvenirs du Périgord, 26-32 Rue des Farges, 24000 Périgueux - T: 0553534736
Military Museum 12493

Péronne

Musée Danicourt, Mairie, 80200 Péronne - T: 0322840116 poste 353
Archaeological Museum 12494

Pérouges

Musée d'Art et d'Histoire du Vieux Pérouges, Pl du Tilleul, 01800 Pérouges - T: 0474610088
Archaeological Museum / Decorative Arts Museum
Archeology, porcelain, furnishings, armaments, local historical artifacts 12495

Perpignan

Archéosite Gallo-Romain Ruscino, Château Roussillon, 66000 Perpignan - T: 0468674717. Head: Rémy Marichal
Archaeological Museum / Museum of Classical Antiquities 12496

Centre de Culture Catalane, C.D.A.C.C., 42 Av de Grande-Bretagne, 66000 Perpignan - T: 0468356630/341170, Fax: 0468347655
Folklore Museum 12497

Centre de Documentation Archéologique du Roussillon, Palais des Rois de Majorque, Rue des Archers, 66000 Perpignan - T: 0468344829
Archaeological Museum / Historical Museum 12498

Musée Catalan des Arts et Traditions Populaires, Casa Pairal Joseph Deloncle, Le Castillet, Pl de Verdun, 66000 Perpignan - T: 0468354205, Fax: 0468663280. Head: Jacques-Gaspard Deloncle
Folklore Museum - 1963 12499

Musée de l'Algérie Française, 52 Rue Maréchal-Foch, 66000 Perpignan - T: 0468804154
Historical Museum / Fine Arts Museum 12500

Musée d'Histoire Naturelle, 12 Rue Fontaine Neuve, 66000 Perpignan - T: 0468663368, Fax: 0468663687, E-mail: museum-histnat@mairie-perpignan.com. Head: Robert Bourgat
Natural History Museum - 1841
Paleontology, ornithology, entomology, ichtyology 12501

Musée Hyacinthe Rigaud, 16 Rue de l'Ange, 66000 Perpignan - T: 0438354340, Fax: 0468347347, E-mail: museerigaud@caramail.com. Head: Marie-Claude Valaison
Fine Arts Museum - 1830
Works by H. Rigaud, A. Maillol, P. Picasso, R. Dufy, P. Daura, peinture gothique Catalan, ceramics, contemporary art - library, documentation 12502

Musée Numismatique J. Puig, 42 Av de Grande-Bretagne, 66000 Perpignan, mail addr: BP 931, 66931 Perpignan Cedex - T: 0468341170, Fax: 0468347655, E-mail: musee-puig@mairie-perpignan.com. Head: A. Castor
Special Museum - 1983
Catalan numismatic coll - numismatic library 12503

Perquie

Château-Musée de Ravignan, 40190 Perquie - T: 0558452204/2644, Fax: 0558458085
Decorative Arts Museum 12504

Perrecy-les-Forges

Musée du Prieuré, Ecomusée du Creusot-Montceau, Eglise, 71420 Perrecy-les-Forges - T: 0385793294/550111
Local Museum 12505

Perros-Guirec

Musée de Cire et Salle de Documents Historiques, Le Linkin Port, 22700 Perros-Guirec - T: 0296912345/232264
Local Museum 12506

Pessac

Musée Historial du Vieux Pessac, Château de Camponac, 33600 Pessac - T: 0556554949/452486
Historical Museum / Archaeological Museum 12507

Musée Le Corbusier, 4 Rue Le Corbusier, 33600 Pessac - T: 0556365046/7656
Special Museum 12508

Petit-Bersac

Musée Archéologique, 24600 Petit-Bersac - T: 0553900861
Archaeological Museum 12509

Petite-Rossele

Musée du Bassin Houiller Lorrain, Carreau Wendel, C.C.S.T.I., 57540 Petite-Rosselle - T: 0387870854
Science&Tech Museum 12510

Peyriac-de-Mer

Musée Archéologique, Rue de l'Étang, 11440 Peyriac-de-Mer - T: 0468414990
Archaeological Museum 12511

Peyrilles

Musée Postal du Lot, 46310 Peyrilles - T: 0565310613
Special Museum / Historical Museum 12512

Peyrusse-le-Roc

Musée Historique, 12220 Peyrusse-le-Roc - T: 0565806089
Historical Museum 12513

Peyzac-le-Moustier

Musée de la Préhistoire/Paléontologie, 24620 Peyzac-le-Moustier - T: 0553508102
Archaeological Museum / Natural History Museum 12514

Pézenas

Musée de Vulliod Saint-Germain, 3 Rue Albert Alliès, 34120 Pézenas - T: 0467989059. Head: Laure Gigou
Fine Arts Museum / Decorative Arts Museum
16th-19th century painting, 17th-18th century furnishings, tapestries, memorabilia of J.-B. Molière (1622-1673), folklore, porcelain, customs 12515

Pezens

Musée d'Art et d'Histoire, 11170 Pezens - T: 0468249153
Fine Arts Museum / Historical Museum 12516

Pfaffenhoffen

Musée de l'Imagerie Populaire, 38 Rue du Docteur Schweitzer, 67350 Pfaffenhoffen - T: 0388077023. Head: François Lotz
Folklore Museum 12517

Pfastatt-Château

Tissuthèque D.M.C, Texunion, Chemin de Dornach, 68120 Pfastatt-Château - T: 0389513001
Special Museum 12518

Phalsbourg

Musée Militaire et d'Erckmann-Chatrian, Hôtel de Ville, Pl d'Armes, 57370 Phalsbourg - T: 0387244120, Fax: 0387241000. Head: A. Schrub
Military Museum 12519

Pied-de-Borne

Musée de la Châtaigne, Maison de la Châtaigne, 48800 Pied-de-Borne - T: 0466698223
Special Museum 12520

Pierre-de-Bresse

Ecomusée de la Bresse Bourguignonne, Château, 71270 Pierre-de-Bresse - T: 0385762716, Fax: 0385728433, E-mail: ecomusee.de.la.bresse@wanadoo.fr, Internet: http://www.ecomusee-de-la-bresse.com. Head: Dominique Rivière
Local Museum / Archaeological Museum 12521

Pierreclos

Musée de la Vigne, du Vin et de la Tonnellerie, Château, 71960 Pierreclos - T: 0385357373
Special Museum 12522

Musée du Blé au Pain, Château, 71960 Pierreclos - T: 0385357373
Special Museum 12523

Pierrefeu (Alpes-Maritimes)

Musée de Peintures Contemporaines Hors du Temps, 06910 Pierrefeu (Alpes-Maritimes) - T: 0493085818, Fax: 0493085129. Head: Marie-Chantal Castel
Fine Arts Museum / Local Museum 12524

Pierrefeu-du-Var

Musée du Santon, Domaine de l'Aumérade, 83390 Pierrefeu-du-Var - T: 0494282031
Religious Arts Museum 12525

Pierrefitte-Nestalas

Musée-Marinarium du Haut Lavédan, 2 Rue Jean Moulin, 65260 Pierrefitte-Nestalas - T: 0562927956
Natural History Museum 12526

Pierrefonds

Expositions du Château, Château, 60350 Pierrefonds - T: 0344428077/3723, Fax: 0344423659
Archaeological Museum / Historical Museum 12527

Pierrelatte

Musée Municipal, Rue Bermine, 26700 Pierrelatte - T: 0475040300/963112
Archaeological Museum / Local Museum 12528

Pignans

L'Atelier, Centre d'Art et d'Echanges Culturels, Rte de Flassans, 83790 Pignans - T: 0494332321, Fax: 0494332321
Fine Arts Museum 12529

Pineuilh

Ferme-Musée Barret, Goubières, 33220 Pineuilh - T: 0557462618/412177
Special Museum 12530

Piolenc

Musée Vivant Européen du Cirque, Cirque National Alexis-Gruss, 84420 Piolenc - T: 049090296481
Performing Arts Museum 12531

Pionsat

Exposition d'Art et d'Histoire, Château, 63330 Pionsat - T: 0473856156
Fine Arts Museum / Historical Museum 12532

Pirou

Château-Musée, Château-Fort, 50770 Pirou - T: 0233488356/463471
Decorative Arts Museum 12533

Pithiviers-le-Vieil

Musée Archéologique, Pl de l'Église, 45300 Pithiviers-le-Vieil - T: 0238302512
Archaeological Museum 12534

Muséosite Gallo-Romain, Rue Laumonet, Le Bourg, 45300 Pithiviers-le-Vieil
Archaeological Museum 12535

Pithiviers (Loiret)

Musée d'Art et d'Histoire, 17 Rue de la Couronne, 45300 Pithiviers (Loiret) - T: 0238301072. Head: Claude Peron
Historical Museum / Fine Arts Museum
Paleontology, prehistory, religious art, ceramics, arms 12536

Musée des Transports, Rue Carnot, 45300 Pithiviers (Loiret) - T: 0146282347, Fax: 0146282347. Head: Maurice Geiger
Science&Tech Museum - 1966
Steam locomotives, railcar, railway line, medals, watches, and other objects relating to railways 12537

Musée Duhamel du Monceau, 1 Rue Duhamel du Monceau, Dadonville, 45300 Pithiviers (Loiret) - T: 0238306833/1038
Science&Tech Museum 12538

Plan-d'Aups

Écomusée de la Sainte-Baume, Hostellerie de la Sainte-Baume, 83640 Plan-d'Aups - T: 0442625646
Local Museum 12539

Plancoët

Musée de la Société Archéologique de Corseul, Mairie, 22130 Plancoët - T: 0296279617
Archaeological Museum 12540

Plassac

Conservatoire Vinicole, Le Rey, 33390 Plassac - T: 0557421663, Fax: 0557423122. Head: Jean-Michel Baudet
Special Museum 12541

Musée Archéologique et Site Gallo-Romain, Rue Chardonnet, 33390 Plassac - T: 0557420342/8480
Archaeological Museum / Museum of Classical Antiquities 12542

Plauzat

Musée de la Vigne et de la Vie Rurale, 10 Rue Mégemont, 63730 Plauzat - T: 0473395421, Fax: 0473395866, Internet: http://www.nat.fr/nat/hompages/lpinchem/avp/avp.html. Head: Danièle Chaumet
Agriculture Museum 12543

Pleaux

Maison de la Forêt de Miers, M.F. du Pestre, 15700 Pleaux - T: 0471673593
Natural History Museum 12544

Plélo

Musée Agricole-Ferme des Aïeux, Famille Lamour, 22170 Plélo - T: 0296741363
Agriculture Museum 12545

Pleudaniel

Moulin à Mer de Traou-Meur-Écomusée, Le Passage, 22740 Pleudaniel - T: 0296201732
Science&Tech Museum 12546

Pleudihen-sur-Rance

Musée de la Pomme et du Cidre, La Ville Hervy, 22690 Pleudihen-sur-Rance - T: 0296832078. Head: Jean-Yves Prie
Agriculture Museum
Cultivation of apples, cider production 12547

Pleumeur-Bodou

Écovillage Gaulois, 22560 Pleumeur-Bodou - T: 0296918395/239689
Open Air Museum 12548

Pleyben

Mini-Musée de l'Ossuaire, 29190 Pleyben - T: 0298267105
Religious Arts Museum 12549

Ploërmel

Musée du Père Jean-Marie de la Mennais, 1 Blvd Foch, 56800 Ploërmel - T: 0297740667
Religious Arts Museum 12550

Plombières-les-Bains

Musée de Peinture Louis-Français, 30 Av Louis-Français, 88370 Plombières-les-Bains - T: 0329660130/0024
Fine Arts Museum 12551

Pavillon des Princes, 88370 Plombières-les-Bains - T: 0329660024
Historical Museum 12552

Plomelin

Musée Historique, Château du Perennou, 29700 Plomelin - T: 0298942272
Historical Museum 12553

Plomodiern

Musée Rural du Porzay, Auberge Ti Glaz, Saint-Nic, 29127 Plomodiern - T: 0298260190. Head: Patrick Fontaine
Agriculture Museum - 1991
Peasant life, agricultural machinery 12554

Plouarzel

Écomusée du Phare de Trezien, 29229 Plouarzel - T: 0298896016/6725
Special Museum 12555

Ploubezre

Château de Kergrist, 22300 Ploubezre - T: 0296389144
Local Museum 12556

Ploudalmézeau

Exposition Permanente de Peintures, 18 Rue Jules Fortin, 29262 Ploudalmézeau - T: 0298481412
Fine Arts Museum 12557

Ploudiry

Musée de la Ferme d'Antan, 29220 Ploudiry - T: 0298251121
Agriculture Museum 12558

Plouezoch

Musée Préhistorique du Tumulus de Barnenez, 29252 Plouezoch - T: 0298672473
Archaeological Museum 12559

Plougastel-Daoulas

Maison du Patrimoine et de la Fraise, Rue Louis Nicolle, 29213 Plougastel-Daoulas - T: 0298402118
Local Museum 12560

Plougonvelin

Musée de la Pointe Saint-Mathieu, 29217 Plougonvelin - T: 0298483573
Historical Museum 12561

Musée du Vieux Fort de Bertheaume, 29217 Plougonvelin - T: 0298483018
Historical Museum 12562

Plouguenast

Château de Pongamp, 22150 Plouguenast - T: 0296287199
Special Museum 12563

Plouguerneau

Maison de nos Ancêtres, 22 Rue de Lannilis, 29232 Plouguerneau - T: 0298047244
Historical Museum 12564

Musée des Goémoniers, Karrezhir, Rte de Saint-Michel, 29880 Plouguerneau - T: 0298046030
Local Museum 12565

Musée des Missions, Rte de Lesneven-Le Grouaneg, 29232 Plouguerneau - T: 0298047093/5031
Special Museum / Historical Museum 12566

Plouharnel

Musée à Flot du Galion, Anse du Bégo, Rte de Quiberon, 56720 Plouharnel - T: 0297523956
Special Museum 12567

Musée de la Chouannerie et des Guerres de l'Ouest, Bois du Bégo, 56720 Plouharnel - T: 0297523131
Military Museum 12568

Plounéour-Trez

Musée des Traditions Locales, Ossuaire, 29238 Plounéour-Trez - T: 0298834120/03
Folklore Museum 12569

Plouvien

Musée d'Arts Populaires, Skolig al Louarn, 75 Rue Laennec, 29860 Plouvien - T: 0298400064, Fax: 0298400064, E-mail: skolig-al-louarn@wanadoo.fr, Internet: http://perso.wanadoo.fr/skolig-al-louarn/. Head: Anna-Vari Arzur
Folklore Museum 12570

Plozevet

Musée des Petits Meubles Bretons, 1 Impasse de la Poste, 29143 Plozevet - T: 0298914204/3073
Decorative Arts Museum 12571

Podensac

Musée Lillet, Rte Nationale 113, 33720 Podensac - T: 0556270811
Special Museum 12572

Poissy

Musée d'Art et d'Histoire, 12 Rue Saint-Louis, 78300 Poissy - T: 0139650606, Fax: 0139650314, E-mail: jdamamme@ville-poissy.fr. Head: Jeanne Damamme
Fine Arts Museum / Historical Museum - 1980
Local hist items, ethnography 12573

Musée du Jouet, 1 Enclos de l'Abbaye, 78300 Poissy - T: 0139650606, Fax: 0139650314, E-mail: jdamamme@ville-poissy.fr, Internet: http://www.ville-poissy-fr. Head: Jeanne Damamme
Special Museum - 1976
Toys and games (19th century-1950), dolls and accessories - Documentation centre 12574

Poitiers

Musée Rupert-de-Chièvres, 9 Rue Victor-Hugo, 86000 Poitiers - T: 0549414221
Fine Arts Museum / Decorative Arts Museum - 1889
Painting (16th-18th c), enamel (16th-17th c), furniture (16th-19th c) 12575

Musée Sainte-Croix, 61 Rue Saint-Simplicien, 86000 Poitiers - T: 0549410753
Local Museum - 1974
Local history, fine arts 12576

Poleymieux-au-Mont-d'Or

Musée André-Marie-Ampère, Maison d'Ampère, 69250 Poleymieux-au-Mont-d'Or - T: 0478919077, E-mail: georges.asch@wanadoo.fr, Internet: http://musee-ampere.univ-lyon1.fr. Head: Georges Asch
Special Museum / Science&Tech Museum 12577

Poligny

Maison du Comté, Av de la Résistance, 39800 Poligny - T: 0384372351, Fax: 0384370785, E-mail: cigc@comte.com, Internet: http://www.comte.com
Folklore Museum 12578

Pomarez

Musée de la Course Landaise, Café Laborde, 40360 Pomarez - T: 0558898742
Special Museum 12579

Pomerol

Musée du Vin et du Pèlerinage de Saint-Jacques de Compostelle, Château La Croix, 33500 Pomerol - T: 0557514186
Special Museum 12580

Pommard

Exposition d'Arts Populaires, Domaine R. Launay, Rue des Charmots, 21630 Pommard - T: 0380240803
Folklore Museum 12581

Pommiers (Loire)

Musée du Vieux Pommiers, Sur les Remparts, 42260 Pommiers (Loire) - T: 0477654702
Agriculture Museum / Historical Museum 12582

Pompey

Centre d'Histoire Locale du Canton de Pompey, 7 Rue de Lattre de Tassigny, 54340 Pompey - T: 0383490149
Historical Museum 12583

Poncé-sur-le-Loir

Musée d'Arts et de Traditions Populaires, Château, 72340 Poncé-sur-le-Loir - T: 0243444539
Folklore Museum 12584

Pons

Archéosite de l'Hospice des Pèlerins de St.-Jacques-de-Compostelle, 17800 Pons
Archaeological Museum 12585

Musée Archéologique, Chapelle St Gilles, 17800 Pons - T: 0546961331/912009
Archaeological Museum / Historical Museum 12586

Musée du Patrimoine Pontois, Annexe de la Mairie, 17800 Pons
Local Museum 12587

Pont-à-Mousson

Centre Européen d'Art, Abbaye des Prémontrés, Rue Saint-Martin, 54700 Pont-à-Mousson - T: 0383811032
Fine Arts Museum / Decorative Arts Museum 12588

Pont-Audemer

Cloches de Corneville, Rte de Rouen, Corneville-sur-Risle, 27500 Pont-Audemer - T: 0232570104, Fax: 0232571096. Head: J.M. Tixier
Special Museum 12589

Pont-Aven

Centre Paul Gauguin, Chemin Kerempерhec, 29123 Pont-Aven - T: 0298060844
Fine Arts Museum 12590

Ecomusée de Keranpercheg, Ville Haute de Pont-Aven, 29123 Pont-Aven - T: 0298061650
Local Museum / Fine Arts Museum 12591

Musée de Pont-Aven, Pl de l'Hôtel de Ville, 29930 Pont-Aven - T: 0298061443, Fax: 0298060126/0339, Internet: http://www.musee.pont-aven@wanadoo.fr. Head: Catherine Puget
Fine Arts Museum - 1985
19th and 20th century French paintings 12592

Pont-Croix

Marquisat de Pont-Croix, Musée du Patrimoine, Rue de la Prison, 29790 Pont-Croix - T: 0298705343/5186. Head: Claude Trividic
Folklore Museum 12593

Pont-de-Vaux

Musée Chintreuil, Hôtel de Ville, 01190 Pont-de-Vaux - T: 0385514565, Fax: 0385303489, E-mail: mairie.pont-de-vaux@wanadoo.fr, Internet: http://www.almac.co.uk/pdv. Head: Catherin Nelly
Fine Arts Museum / Natural History Museum - 1866
Fine arts 12594

Petit Musée d'Art, Hôtel-Dieu, 01190 Pont-de-Vaux - T: 0385303002
Decorative Arts Museum / Fine Arts Museum 12595

Pont-de-Veyle

Exposition du Compagnonnage, Château Prévôté, 01290 Pont-de-Veyle - T: 0385315687
Special Museum 12596

Pont-du-Château

Musée Pierre Mondanel, Mairie, 63430 Pont-du-Château - T: 0473830376/2000
Science&Tech Museum / Historical Museum 12597

Pont-en-Royans

Collections d'Histoire Locale, OTSI des Gorges de la Bourne, 38680 Pont-en-Royans - T: 0476360910
Local Museum 12598

Pont-l'Abbé

Ecomusée de la Ferme de Kervazegan, Rte de Loctudy, 29120 Pont-l'Abbé - T: 0298872444/3563
Local Museum 12599

Musée Bigouden, Château, 29120 Pont-l'Abbé - T: 0298872444
Local Museum
Local hist, folk art, costumes 12600

Pont-l'Abbé-d'Arnoult

Musée de l'Atelier de Saintonge, Rue de la Lirette, 17250 Pont-l'Abbé-d'Arnoult - T: 0546970037
Local Museum 12601

Pont-l'Évêque

Musée aux Dominicaines, Pl du Tribunal, 14130 Pont-l'Évêque
Local Museum 12602

Musée de l'Automobile La Belle Époque, Château de Betteville, 14130 Pont-l'Évêque - T: 0231650502
Science&Tech Museum 12603

Musée du Calvados et des Métiers Anciens de Pont-l'Évêque, Ets Debrise-Dulac, Le Lieu-des-Champs, Rte de Trouville, 14130 Pont-l'Évêque - T: 0231543031
Special Museum / Local Museum 12604

Pont-Saint-Esprit

Musée d'Art Sacré du Gard, Maison des Chevaliers, 2 Rue Saint-Jacques, 30130 Pont-Saint-Esprit - T: 0466391761, 0466907580, Fax: 0466907427, E-mail: girard_a@cg30.fr. Head: Alain Girard
Religious Arts Museum - 1995
Religious art, historic monument with 14th and 15th c ceiling fresco 12605

Musée Paul Raymond, Pl de l'Ancienne Mairie, 30130 Pont-Saint-Esprit - T: 0466390998, 0466907580, Fax: 0466907427, E-mail: girard_a@cg30.fr. Head: Alain Girard
Fine Arts Museum
Paintings, drawings of Benn (1905–1989) 12606

Pont-sur-Sambre

Maison de Pays, 113 Grand-Rue, 59138 Pont-sur-Sambre - T: 0327674019/666293/390437
Historical Museum / Folklore Museum 12607

Pontarlier

Musée d'Art et d'Histoire, 2 Pl d'Arçon, 25300 Pontarlier - T: 0381467368
Fine Arts Museum / Historical Museum / Decorative Arts Museum 12608

Musée de la Distillerie, Pierre Guy, 49 Rue des Lavaux, 25300 Pontarlier - T: 0381390470
Special Museum 12609

Pontault-Combault

Centre Photographique d'Ile-de-France, 107 Av de la Republique, 77340 Pontault-Combault - T: 0170024980, Fax: 0170054984, E-mail: cpif@chello.fr, Internet: http://www.tram-art.org. Head: Sylvian Lizon
Fine Arts Museum 12610

Pontcharra

Musée Bayard et de la Chevalerie, Château, 38530 Pontcharra - T: 0476971165
Military Museum 12611

Pontchâteau

Musée du Calvaire de Pontchateau, Le Calvaire, 44160 Pontchâteau - T: 0240881144, Fax: 0240456494. Head: Bernard Burel
Local Museum 12612

Pontécoulant

Musée Départemental → Musée du Château de Pontécoulant

Musée du Château de Pontécoulant, Château, 14110 Pontécoulant - T: 0231696254, Fax: 0231696254, E-mail: patrimoine@cg14.fr
Decorative Arts Museum / Fine Arts Museum 12613

Pontgibaud

Château-Musée de Château Dauphin, Château Dauphin, 63230 Pontgibaud - T: 0473887339, Fax: 0473885665, E-mail: chateau/dauphin@chateauxandcountry.com, Internet: http://www.chateauxandcountry.com/chateaux/dauphin. Head: Comte Gabriel de Germiny
Historic Site 12614

Pontis

Musée de l'École en Montagne, Ancienne École, 05160 Pontis - T: 0492442694/812715
Special Museum 12615

Pontivy

Collections du Château des Rohan, 56300 Pontivy - T: 0297250033
Local Museum 12616

Pontlevoy

Musée de l'Imagerie Publicitaire sur le Chocolat, 35 Rue du Colonel Filloux, 41400 Pontlevoy - T: 0254326080
Special Museum 12617

Pontmain

Musée Missionnaire, Maison des Pères Oblats, Rue de Mausson, 53220 Pontmain - T: 0243050759
Religious Arts Museum 12618

Pontoise

Musée Pissarro, 17 Rue du Château, 95300 Pontoise - T: 0130380240, Fax: 0130323294, E-mail: museetavet@aol.com, Internet: http://www.ville-pontoise.com. Head: Christophe Duvivier
Fine Arts Museum - 1980
Works and archives of the painter Camille Pissarro, 19th century regional artists 12619

Musée Tavet-Delacour, 4 Rue Lemercier, 95300 Pontoise - T: 0130380240, Fax: 0130323294, E-mail: museetavet@aol.com, Internet: httptp://www.ville-pontoise.fr. Head: Christophe Duvivier
Fine Arts Museum - 1892
Sculpture, painting 15th-20th century drawings, mosaics, glass, ancient and contemporary engravings, documents, contemporary art, regional history, religious sculpture - library 12620

Porquerolles

Exposition du Fort Sainte-Agathe, Ile de Porquerolles, 83400 Porquerolles - T: 0494583116
Archaeological Museum 12621

Port-Barcarès

Musée du Lydia, Paquebot Échoué, Plage de Port-Barcarès, 66420 Port-Barcarès - T: 0468863265
Natural History Museum 12622

Port-Cros

Exposition du Fort de l'Estissac, Parc National de Port-Cros, Ile de Port-Cros, 83400 Port-Cros - T: 0494058017
Special Museum 12623

Port-de-Bouc

Musée Morales, Av des Pins, 13110 Port-de-Bouc - T: 0442064901/2629
Fine Arts Museum 12624

Port-d'Envaux

Château-Musée de Panloy, 17350 Port-d'Envaux - T: 0546917323, Fax: 0546917323
Decorative Arts Museum 12625

Port-des-Barques

Musée Archéologique, 17730 Port-des-Barques - T: 0546848730
Archaeological Museum 12626

Port-en-Bessin-Huppain

Musée des Épaves Sous-Marines du Débarquement, Rte de Bayeux-Commes, 14520 Port-en-Bessin-Huppain - T: 0231211706
Military Museum 12627

Port-Joinville

Musée Historial, 11 Rue de la République, 85350 Port-Joinville - T: 0251583688
Historical Museum 12628

Musée Maritime Islais, Abri du Marin, 7 Quai de la Chapelle, 85350 Port-Joinville - T: 0251593100/583787
Special Museum / Science&Tech Museum 12629

Port-Louis

Musée de la Compagnie des Indes, Citadelle, 56290 Port-Louis - T: 0297821913, Fax: 0297824288, E-mail: museeindes@mairie-loirent.fr
Decorative Arts Museum / Local Museum 12630

Musée National de la Marine, Av du Fort de l'Aigle, Cittadelle de Port-Louis, 56290 Port-Louis - T: 0297825672, Fax: 0297821728, E-mail: g.prudhomme@musee_marine.fr, Internet: http://www.musee-marine.fr. Head: Georges Prudhomme
Local Museum
Model ships (navy, merchant navy, fishing navy), paintings, figureheads, local maritime history 12631

Port-Navalo

Musée Marin, Criée de Port-Navalo, Av du Général de Gaulle, 56640 Port-Navalo - T: 0297534460
Natural History Museum 12632

Port-Sainte-Foy

Musée Fluvial, Quai de la Batellerie, 33220 Port-Sainte-Foy - T: 0553247208
Local Museum 12633

Port-Vendres

Mémorial de l'Algérie Française, Monument de Sidi Ferruch, Redoute Bear, 66660 Port-Vendres
Historical Museum 12634

Portel-des-Corbières

Musée de la Viticulture et des Arts Populaires, 11490 Portel-des-Corbières - T: 0468482800
Agriculture Museum / Folklore Museum 12635

Terra-Vinea, Les Caves Rocbère, 11490 Portel-des-Corbières - T: 0468486490
Special Museum 12636

Portets

Musée Historique Valdec-de Lessart, Château de Mongenan, 33640 Portets - T: 0556671811, Fax: 0556672388, E-mail: info@chateau-de-mongenan.tm.fr. Head: Florence Mothe
Decorative Arts Museum / Historical Museum / Natural History Museum / Historic Site
XVIII century, French revolution, porcelain, period costumes 12637

Poudenas

Château-Musée, Haut du Village, 47170 Poudenas - T: 0553657053, Fax: 0553658737, E-mail: j2nad@terre-net.fr
Local Museum 12638

Pougues-les-Eaux

Centre d'Art Contemporain, Parc Saint-Léger, Mairie, 58320 Pougues-les-Eaux - T: 0386688606, Fax: 0386688683
Fine Arts Museum 12639

Pourcy

Musée-Maison du Parc Naturel Régional de la Montagne de Reims, 51160 Pourcy - T: 0326594444
Natural History Museum 12640

Pourrain

Musée de la Seconde Guerre Mondiale, Maison Sontrop les Vernes, 89240 Pourrain - T: 0386411327
Military Museum 12641

Pouydesseaux

Musée Centre Jean Rostand, 40120 Pouydesseaux - T: 0558939243
Natural History Museum 12642

Pouzauges

Musée de la Meunerie, 85700 Pouzauges - T: 0251575283
Agriculture Museum 12643

Pouzols-Minérvois

Musée des Contenants Vinaires, Cave des Producteurs, 11120 Pouzols-Minérvois - T: 0468461376
Special Museum 12644

Pradelles

Musée Vivant du Cheval de Trait et de l'Attelage, Rue du Breuil, 43420 Pradelles - T: 0471008787/90910770, Fax: 0490435650
Science&Tech Museum / Historical Museum 12645

Prades

Exposition Philosophique, Rue Victor-Hugo, 66500 Prades - T: 0468962758
Special Museum 12646

Musée Archéologique, Rue Victor Hugo, 66500 Prades - T: 0468054102, Fax: 0468052179, E-mail: prades-conflent@little-france.com, Internet: http://www.prades.com
Archaeological Museum 12647

Musée du Fer et des Traditions Catalanes, Rue Victor Hugo, 66500 Prades - T: 0468054102, Fax: 0468052179, E-mail: prades-conflent@little-france.com, Internet: http://www.prades.com
Folklore Museum 12648

Musée Pablo Casals, Rue Victor Hugo, 66500 Prades - T: 0468054102, Fax: 0468052179, E-mail: infos@prades-tourisme.com, Internet: http://www.prades.com. Head: Christine Hicks
Special Museum / Music Museum 12649

Pradinas

Musée des Traditions Agricoles du Ségala, Mairie, 12240 Pradinas - T: 0565699452/9284
Agriculture Museum 12650

Pranles

Musée du Vivarais Protestant, Le Bouschet, 07000 Pranles - T: 0475642274, E-mail: lblache@wanadoo.fr. Head: Gérard Cadier
Religious Arts Museum - 1932
Old bibles, letters, registers for marriages (18th c), birthplace of Pierre and Marie Durand 12651

Prats-de-Mollo-la-Preste

Musée Vauban, Vieux Fort Lagarde, 66230 Prats-de-Mollo-la-Preste - T: 0468397490/7083
Military Museum / Historical Museum 12652

Prayssas

Musée de la Vigne et du Vin (closed) 12653

Préchac

Château de Cazeneuve, 33730 Préchac - T: 0556254816, Fax: 0556254816, E-mail: cazeneuve@chateaudecazeneuve.com, Internet: http://www.chateaudecazeneuve.com. Head: Comte E. de Sabran-Ponteves
Decorative Arts Museum / Historic Site 12654

Preignac

Musée de la Comédie, Château de Malle, 33210 Preignac - T: 0556623686, Fax: 0556768240, E-mail: chateaudemalle@wanadoo.fr, Internet: http://www.chateau-de-malle.fr. Head: Comtesse de Bournazel
Performing Arts Museum 12655

Prémanon

Centre Polaire Paul-Emile Victor, 1 Rue de la Sambine, 39220 Prémanon - T: 0384607771, Fax: 0384607772
Ethnology Museum / Historical Museum / Science&Tech Museum 12656

Pressagny-l'Orgueilleux

Musée Casimir Delavigne, Château de la Madeleine, 27510 Pressagny-l'Orgueilleux - T: 0232213598
Special Museum 12657

Preuilly-sur-Claise

Musée d'Arts et d'Histoire de la Poterne, Carroir des Anciennes Prisons, 37290 Preuilly-sur-Claise - T: 0247945004/6100
Folklore Museum 12658

Prignac-et-Marcamps

Musée Cavernicole, Grotte Pair non Pair, 33710 Prignac-et-Marcamps - T: 0557683176
Archaeological Museum 12659

Pringy

Collection Archéologique, Mairie, 74370 Pringy - T: 0450272912
Archaeological Museum 12660

Prinsuéjols-Marvejols

Château de la Baume, 48100 Prinsuéjols-Marvejols - T: 0466325159
Local Museum / Decorative Arts Museum 12661

Prissac

Musée du Machinisme Agricole, Rte de Bélâbre, 36370 Prissac - T: 0254250151
Science&Tech Museum 12662

Privas

Exposition de Peinture Contemporaine, 1 Rue de Bir-Hakeim, 07000 Privas - T: 0475650161
Fine Arts Museum 12663

Musée de la Terre Ardèchoise, 2 Pl des Récollets, 07000 Privas - T: 0475644369
Natural History Museum / Archaeological Museum 12664

Proupiary

Musée Archéologique et Historique, Ancienne Abbaye de Bonnefont, 31360 Proupiary - T: 0561975901
Archaeological Museum / Local Museum 12665

Provins

Musée de Provins et du Provinois, 7 Rue du Palais, 77160 Provins - T: 0164014019, Fax: 0160676461. Head: Annick Michelet
Local Museum - 1974
Prehist, Gallo-Roman finds, sculptures from medieval times to the Renaissance, medieval pottery, medieval pavements, free masoury objects, antique and medieval coins, medieval keys 12666

Prudhomat

Château, 46130 Prudhomat - T: 0565109800
Decorative Arts Museum 12667

Prunay-en-Yvelines

Musée d'Art Religieux Ancien du Dimanche, Église de Craches, 78660 Prunay-en-Yvelines - T: 0134844118
Religious Arts Museum 12668

Prunoy

Musée Archéologique, Mairie, 89120 Prunoy - T: 0386918716
Archaeological Museum 12669

Puget-Rostang

Écomusée du Pays de la Roudoule, Pl des Tilleuls, 06260 Puget-Rostang - T: 0493050738. Head: Ange Maurin
Local Museum 12670

Puivert

Musée du Quercorb, 16 Rue Barry du Lion, 11230 Puivert - T: 0468208098, Fax: 0468208098, E-mail: musee.quercorb@wanadoo.fr, Internet: http://www.quercorb.com
Ethnology Museum / Music Museum 12671

Puteaux

Espace Histoire, Espace Point Info, Esplanade de la Défense, 92800 Puteaux - T: 0147763713
Historical Museum 12672

Musée de l'Automobile, Colline de la Défense, 1 Pl du Dôme, 92800 Puteaux - T: 0146924545/46924600
Science&Tech Museum 12673

Musée Pierre-Gaudin, 31 Rue Cartault, 92800 Puteaux - T: 0146929353
Local Museum 12674

Puyloubier

Musée de l'Uniforme Legionnaire, L'Institution des Invalides, Château du Général, 13114 Puyloubier - T: 0442663820
Military Museum 12675

Puymoyen

Musée de la Papeterie, Moulin du Verger, 16400 Puymoyen - T: 0545611038/54
Special Museum 12676

Quarante

Caveau-Musée Les Vignerons de Rouèire, Domaine de Rouèire, 34310 Quarante - T: 0467894010, Fax: 0467893220, Internet: http://www.roueire.com
Special Museum 12677

Musée Archéologique, Près de l'Eglise, 34310 Quarante - T: 0467894491
Archaeological Museum 12678

Québriac

Musée International de la Faune, Les Brulons, Rte de Tinténiac à Combourg, 35190 Québriac - T: 0299681022, Fax: 0299680572, E-mail: laurent.liliane@libertysurf.fr, Internet: http://www.zooloisirs/asteria.fr. Head: Gérard Vialla
Natural History Museum 12679

Quiberon

Musée, Rue du Port Haliguen, 56170 Quiberon - T: 0297500784. Head: Alain Didier
Local Museum - 1986
Local hist, ethnography, costume, furniture and interior 12680

Quimper

Centre d'Art Contemporain, 10 Esplanade François Mitterand, 29000 Quimper Cedex - T: 0298555577, Fax: 0298558714, E-mail: le.quartier@wanadoo.fr, Internet: http://www.le.quartier.net. Head: Dominique Abensour
Fine Arts Museum 12681

Exposition d'Art Celte, Magasin Ar Bed Keltick, 2 Rue du Roi Gradlon, 29000 Quimper - T: 0298954282
Folklore Museum 12682

Lapidaire Gallo-Romain, Château de Perennou, 29000 Quimper - T: 0298942272
Archaeological Museum 12683

Musée de la Crêpe Dentelle des Crêpes Bretonnes (closed) 12684

Musée de la Faïence Jules Verlingue, 14 Rue Jean-Baptiste Bousquet à Locmaria, 29000 Quimper - T: 0298901272, Internet: http://www.quimper-faiences.com
Decorative Arts Museum 12685

Musée de la Faïencerie de Quimper H.-B. Henriot, Rue Haute-Locmaria, 29102 Quimper Cedex, mail addr: BP 1219, 29102 Quimper Cedex - T: 0298900936, Fax: 0298901602, E-mail: hb.henriot@wanadoo.fr
Decorative Arts Museum 12686

Musée de l'Alambic, Ergué Armel, 29000 Quimper - T: 0298903830
Science&Tech Museum 12687

Musée Départemental Breton, 1 Rue du Roi Gradlon, 29000 Quimper - T: 0298952160, Fax: 0298958969, E-mail: musee.breton@cg29.fr. Head: Philippe Le Stum
Local Museum - 1846
Prehist, costumes, ceramics, hist, sculpture, furniture, Gallo-Roman finds and goldsmith's work 12688

Musée des Beaux-Arts, 40 Pl Saint-Corentin, 29000 Quimper - T: 0298954520, Fax: 0298901342. Head: André Cariou
Fine Arts Museum - 1872
Paintings by masters of various schools 12689

Quimperlé

Musée de la Villemarque et des Traditions Bretonnes, 7 Rue Dom Morice, 29130 Quimperlé - T: 0298869632/960141. Head: Evelyne Leproust
Historical Museum / Folklore Museum
Folklore, local hist 12690

Quineville

Musée de la Liberté, Rue de la Plage, 50310 Quineville - T: 0233214044
Historical Museum 12691

Quintin

Château de Beaumanoir, Le Leslay, 22800 Quintin - T: 0296749082
Fine Arts Museum 12692

Musée d'Art et d'Industrie, Château, 22800 Quintin - T: 0296749479/0463
Fine Arts Museum / Science&Tech Museum 12693

Quistinic

Ecomusée du Village Breton de Poul-Fetan, 56310 Quistinic - T: 0297397282, Fax: 0297397366
Folklore Museum 12694

Rablay-sur-Layon

Maison des Beaux-Arts, 49190 Rablay-sur-Layon - T: 0241783274
Fine Arts Museum 12695

Rambervillers

Musée de la Terre, Rue de la Faïence, 88700 Rambervillers - T: 0329651229/1207
Decorative Arts Museum / Agriculture Museum / Fine Arts Museum 12696

Rambouillet

Château-Musée de Rambouillet, 78120 Rambouillet - T: 0134830025
Fine Arts Museum 12697

Musée du Mouton et de la Bergerie Nationale, Parc du Château, 78120 Rambouillet - T: 0161086800, Fax: 0134830754, E-mail: animation.bn@educagri.fr, Internet: http://www.educagri.fr/bergerie.nationale. Head: Jean-François Ayats
Agriculture Museum - 1792 12698

Musée Rambolitrain, 4 Pl Jeanne-d'Arc, 78120 Rambouillet - T: 0134831593
Historical Museum 12699

Rarecourt

Musée de la Vallée et de la Faïencerie, Maison Forte, 55120 Rarecourt - T: 0382461554
Decorative Arts Museum / Local Museum 12700

Rasteau

Musée du Vigneron Paul Coulon et Fils, Domaine de Beaurenard, Rte de Vaison-la-Romaine, 84110 Rasteau - T: 0490461175, Fax: 0490837806, E-mail: paul.coulon@beaurenard.fr, Internet: http://www.beaurenard.fr
Special Museum 12701

Raulhac

Château de Messilhac, 15800 Raulhac - T: 0471495555, Fax: 0471495823, E-mail: massilhac@geocities.com, Internet: http://www.geocieties.com/~messilhac. Head: Oliver Dubois
Historic Site 12702

Ravel

Musée d'Art et d'Histoire, Château, 63190 Ravel - T: 0473684463
Fine Arts Museum / Historical Museum 12703

Réaumur

Musée-Manoir de Réaumur, Cercle des Amis de Réaumur, 85700 Réaumur - T: 0251664096
Special Museum 12704

Recey-sur-Ource

Musée Lacordaire, Prieuré, 21290 Recey-sur-Ource - T: 0380810210
Religious Arts Museum 12705

Redon

Musée de la Batellerie de l'Ouest, Quai Jean Bart, Ancienne Corderie, 35600 Redon - T: 0299723095/710527/0604. Head: Charlie Bayou
Science&Tech Museum
Ships and shipping, maritime life 12706

Regnéville-sur-Mer

Musée du Littoral et de la Construction Navale, 50590 Regnéville-sur-Mer - T: 0233078046/059889
Historical Museum 12707

Musée Maritime de Regnéville, Les Fours à Chaux, 50590 Regnéville-sur-Mer - T: 0233468218, Fax: 0233453474
Science&Tech Museum 12708

Regniowez

Musée Bonaventure Fieullien, Ancien Presbytère, 08230 Regniowez - T: 0324541478
Special Museum 12709

Reichshoffen

Musée du Fer, 7 Rue Jeanne d'Arc, 67110 Reichshoffen - T: 0388803449/096700
Science&Tech Museum 12710

Reillanne

Musée des Arts Populaires, Blvd Long-Barn, 04110 Reillanne - T: 0492764625/4246
Folklore Museum 12711

Reims

Musée de l'Ancien Collège des Jésuites, 1 Pl Museux, 51100 Reims - T: 0326855150
Religious Arts Museum / Special Museum
16th century library 12712

Musée de l'Automobile Française, Collection Philippe Charbonneaux, 84 Av Georges Clemenceau, 51100 Reims - T: 0326828384
Science&Tech Museum 12713

Musée des Beaux-Arts, 8 Rue Chanzy, 51100 Reims - T: 0326472844, Fax: 0326868775. Head: David Liot
Fine Arts Museum - 1795
Painting, tapestries, sculpture, ceramics, 16th-20th c furniture 12714

Musée du Vin de Champagne Piper-Heidsieck, 51 Blvd Henry Vasnier, 51100 Reims - T: 0326844300/44, Fax: 0326844384. Head: Jean-Pierre Giraud
Special Museum 12715

Musée Historique du Fort de la Pompelle, Rte Nationale 44, 51100 Reims - T: 0326491185
Historical Museum / Military Museum 12716

Musée Historique du Groupe Lorraine, Base Aérienne 112, 51100 Reims, mail addr: c/o Colonel Commandant la BA 112, 51090 Reims
Military Museum 12717

Musée-Hôtel Le Vergeur, 36 Pl du Forum, 51100 Reims - T: 0326472075, Fax: 0326477953
Local Museum / Historic Site - 1909
Local history in portraits and etchings, engravings by Albrecht Dürer and Robert Nanteuil - library, archives 12718

Musée Saint-Remi, 53 Rue Simon, 51100 Reims - T: 0326852336, Fax: 0326820799. Head: Marc Bouxin
Local Museum - 1978
Prehistory, Gallic, Gallo-Roman, and Merovingian periods, medieval sculpture, 16th-19th century weapons, tapestry, numismatics - library, conference room 12719

Musée Salle de Reddition, Lycée Technique de Garçons, 12 Rue Franklin-Roosevelt, 51100 Reims - T: 0326478419, Fax: 0326777533
Historical Museum 12720

Palais du Tau, Centre des Monuments Nationaux, 2 Pl Cardinal Luçon, 51072 Reims Cedex - T: 0326478179, Fax: 0326478565, E-mail: lacomblez@monuments-france.fr, Internet: http://www.monum.fr. Head: Thierry Dumanoir
Religious Arts Museum - 1972
Tapestries of the 16th, 17th and 18th c, original sculptures of the Cathedral 12721

Remilly-sur-Lozon

Musée de la Vannerie Normande, Le Hodey, 50570 Remilly-sur-Lozon - T: 0233562101
Folklore Museum 12722

Remiremont

Musée Charles-de-Bruyères, 70 Rue Charles-de-Gaulle, 88200 Remiremont - T: 0329624217
Local Museum 12723

Musée Friry, 12 Rue Général-Humbert, 88200 Remiremont - T: 0329624217
Local Museum 12724

Renazé

Musée de l'Ardoise, Les Perreyeurs Mayennais, Longchamp, 53800 Renazé - T: 0243064174, Fax: 0243068250. Head: Etienne Noël
Special Museum / Science&Tech Museum 12725

Rennes (Ille-et-Vilaine)

Ecomusée du Pays de Rennes, Ferme de la Bintinais, Rte de Châtillon-sur-Seiche, 35200 Rennes (Ille-et-Vilaine) - T: 0299513815, Fax: 0299506835, E-mail: ecomusee.rennes@agglo-rennesmetropole.fr. Head: François Hubert
Agriculture Museum - 1987
Agricultural hist, peasant life, rural architecture, rare breeds (plants and farm animals) 12726

Espace des Sciences, Centre d'Affaires Hermès, 6 Pl des Colombes, 35000 Rennes (Ille-et-Vilaine) - T: 0299352820, Fax: 0299352821, E-mail: magali.colin@espace-sciences.org, Internet: http://www.espace-sciences.org. Head: Michel Cabaret
Science&Tech Museum 12727

Musée de Bretagne, 20 Quai Emile Zola, 35000 Rennes (Ille-et-Vilaine) - T: 0299285584, Fax: 0299284017, E-mail: museebzk.rennes@wanadoo.fr. Head: Jean-Yves Veillard
Local Museum - 1960
Pre- and early hist, Gallo-Roman and medieval hist, historical documents, geology, furnishings, jewelry, costumes, Breton, popular and contemporary regional art 12728

Musée de l'Institut de Géologie et de Géoscience de Rennes, Campus Scientifique, 263 Av du Général-Leclerc, 35042 Rennes (Ille-et-Vilaine) Cedex - T: 0299286074. Head: Jean Plaine
Natural History Museum / University Museum - 1972
Paleontology, mineralogy 12729

Musée des Beaux-Arts et d'Archéologie, 20 Quai Emile Zola, 35000 Rennes (Ille-et-Vilaine) - T: 0299285871, Fax: 0299285599, E-mail: musee@mbar.org, Internet: http://www.mbar.org
Fine Arts Museum - 1799
15th-20th century paintings and drawings of all schools, sculptures, engravings from ancient to modern times, Egyptian, Greek, Etruscan and Roman archeology - library 12730

Rennes-le-Château

Domaine de l'Abbé Saunière, Villa Bethania, 11190 Rennes-le-Château - T: 0468743116
Religious Arts Museum 12731

Musée de l'Abbé Saunière, Ancien Presbytère, 11190 Rennes-le-Château - T: 0468741456
Historical Museum 12732

Renwez

Musée de la Forêt Ardennaise, Près du Lac des Vieilles-Forges, 08150 Renwez - T: 0324548266
Natural History Museum 12733

Retiers

Musée Edouard Mahé, Hôtel de Ville, 35240 Retiers - T: 0299435141/471036
Fine Arts Museum 12734

Retournac

Collection de Préhistoire, Office du Tourisme, Pl Boncompain, 43130 Retournac - T: 0471652050
Archaeological Museum 12735

Rettel

Musée du Monde Rural, Maison de la Dîme, 57480 Rettel - T: 0382837209, Fax: 0382832595, E-mail: rettel.maire@wanadoo.fr
Historical Museum 12736

Reuilly (Indre)

Musée du Pays et du Vignoble de Reuilly, Pl de la Mairie, 36260 Reuilly (Indre) - T: 0254492494
Special Museum 12737

Reulle-Vergy

Musée des Arts et des Traditions Populaires des Hautes-Côtes, Pl de la Fontaine, 21220 Reulle-Vergy - T: 0380614293/4095
Folklore Museum
Regional folk art and folklore 12738

Revel

Musée de la Fédération Nationale de Spéléologie, Blvd Carnot, 31250 Revel - T: 0561835006
Natural History Museum / Archaeological Museum 12739

Musée du Canal du Midi, 31250 Revel - T: 0561275567
Special Museum 12740

Revel-Tourdan

Musée Archéologique Gallo-Romain, Tourdan, 38270 Revel-Tourdan - T: 0474845703/17
Archaeological Museum 12741

Musée des Arts et Traditions Populaires, Revel, 38270 Revel-Tourdan - T: 0474845703/17
Folklore Museum 12742

Revest-Saint-Martin

Musée du Machinisme Agricole, 220 Rocade, 04230 Revest-Saint-Martin - T: 0492751873
Science&Tech Museum 12743

Revin

Centre d'Art Contemporain, Parc Rocheteau, 08500 Revin - T: 0324401072/1295
Fine Arts Museum 12744

Musée Raguet, 183 Rue Jean-Jacques-Rousseau, 08500 Revin - T: 0324401041
Science&Tech Museum 12745

Ribeauvillé

Musée Municipal (closed) 12746

Musée Vivant de l'Impression, Manufacture Beauvillé, 19 Rte de Sainte-Marie Aux Mines, 68150 Ribeauvillé - T: 0389737474
Special Museum 12747

Richelieu

Musée Agricole et Viticole, Domaine de Richelieu, Caves du Parc du Château, 37120 Richelieu - T: 0247581009
Agriculture Museum 12748

Musée du Parc, Domaine du Parc, 37120 Richelieu - T: 0247581009
Historical Museum 12749

Musée Municipal, Hôtel de Ville, 37120 Richelieu - T: 0247581013
Historical Museum - 1961
17th century objects, memorabilia of Cardinal Richelieu (1585-1642), tapestries, memorabilia of J.M. de Heredia 12750

Riez

Maison de l'Abeille et du Miel, Rte de Puimoisson, 04500 Riez - T: 0492745715
Special Museum 12751

Musée Lapidaire, Baptistère, Rte de Marseille, 04500 Riez - T: 0492778280
Archaeological Museum 12752

Nature en Provence, 4 Allées Louis-Gardiol, 04500 Riez - T: 0492778280
Natural History Museum
Natural hist of the region 12753

Rigny-Ussé

Château d'Ussé, 37420 Rigny-Ussé - T: 0247955405, Fax: 0247955405
Decorative Arts Museum 12754

Rillé

Musée Vivant et Historique du Train Historique du Lac de Rillé, 37340 Rillé - T: 0247246019/0795
Science&Tech Museum 12755

Rilly-la-Montagne

Ferme-Musée des Bernant, 51500 Rilly-la-Montagne - T: 0326976650
Historical Museum 12756

Riom

Musée Francisque Mandet, 14 Rue de l'Hôtel de Ville, 63200 Riom - T: 0473381853. Head: Marie-Josée Linou
Fine Arts Museum - 1866
16th-18th century Flemish and Dutch paintings, 18th-19th century French paintings, art objects, sculptures and furniture from antiquity to the 18th c 12757

Musée Régional d'Auvergne, 10bis Rue Delille, 63200 Riom - T: 0473381731. Head: Marie-Josée Linou
Folklore Museum - 1969
18th century palace, regional art, customs and ethnography of the Auvergne 12758

Riorges

Musée de la Maille, Château de Beaulieu, Rue Saint-André, 42300 Riorges - T: 0477700242
Special Museum 12759

Riquewihr

Maison Hansi, 16 Rue Général-de-Gaulle, 68340 Riquewihr - T: 0389479700
Special Museum 12760

Musée de la Diligence, Ecuries Seigneuriales, 68340 Riquewihr - T: 0389479380, Fax: 0389478471, E-mail: musee@shpta.com, Internet: http://www.shpta.com. Head: Astrid Mull
Historical Museum - 1993
Collection of mail-coaches from the 18th to the early 20th century (unique in France) - Library, archive 12761

Musée d'Histoire des PTT d'Alsace, Château, 68340 Riquewihr - T: 0389479380, Fax: 0389478471, E-mail: musee@shpta.com, Internet: http://www.shpta.com. Head: Astrid Mull
Historical Museum - 1971
2000 years of posts and telecommunications particularly in Alsace - library, archive 12762

Musée du Dolder, Rue du Général de Gaulle, 68340 Riquewihr - T: 0389490840, Fax: 0389490849, E-mail: info@ribeauvillé-riquewihr.com, Internet: http://www.ribeauville-riquewihr.com. Head: André Hugel
Archaeological Museum / Historical Museum - 1902
Alsatian history, customs, armaments, 13th century tower 12763

Tour des Voleurs, Rue des Juifs, 68340 Riquewihr - T: 0389490840, Fax: 0389490849, E-mail: info@ribeauville-riquewihr.com, Internet: http://www.ribeauville-riquewihr.com. Head: André Hugel
Historical Museum - 1902
Medieval torture chamber with pit, dungeons, guard rooms 12764

Rittershoffen

Musée Scolaire, École Primaire, 174 Rue de l'École, 67690 Rittershoffen - T: 0388801552
Special Museum 12765

Rivarennes

Musée de la Poire Tapée, Chemin de la Buronnière, 37190 Rivarennes - T: 0247954778
Special Museum 12766

Rivesaltes

Musée Maréchal Joffre, Rue Maréchal Joffre, 66600 Rivesaltes - T: 0468642498
Military Museum 12767

Rixheim

Musée du Papier Peint, La Commanderie, 68171 Rixheim - T: 0389642456, Fax: 0389543306, E-mail: musee.papier.peint@wanadoo.fr. Head: B. Jacqué
Special Museum - 1982 12768

Roanne

Ecomusée du Roannais, Passage du Général Giraud, 42300 Roanne - T: 0477713188, Fax: 0477707856. Head: Yves Delorme
Special Museum 12769

Musée des Beaux-Arts et d'Archeologie Joseph Déchelette, 22 Rue Anatole France, 42300 Roanne - T: 0477236877, Fax: 0477236878, E-mail: musee@mairie-roanne.fr. Head: Brigitte Bouret
Archaeological Museum / Fine Arts Museum / Decorative Arts Museum
Roman and Egyptian archeology, fine arts 15th-20th c, ceramics 15th-20th c 12770

Robecourt

Fonderie de Cloches, Ancienne Fonderie, 88320 Robecourt - T: 0329073423/3311
Ethnology Museum 12771

Robiac-Rochessadoule

Musée Minéralogique et Paléontologique, 30160 Robiac-Rochessadoule - T: 0466250081
Natural History Museum 12772

Rocamadour

Musée de Cire Roland Le Preux, 46500 Rocamadour - T: 0565336683
Special Museum 12773

Musée du Jouet Ancien Automobile, Pl Ventadour, 46500 Rocamadour - T: 0565336075
Special Museum / Science&Tech Museum 12774

Musée Historique et du Pèlerinage Francis Poulenc, Art Sacré, Parvis du Sanctuaire, 46500 Rocamadour - T: 0565332323
Religious Arts Museum 12775

Tapisseries Jean-Lurçat, Mairie, 46500 Rocamadour - T: 0565336259
Decorative Arts Museum 12776

Roche-la-Molière

Château-Musée, Pl Victor Hugo, 42230 Roche-la-Molière - T: 0471656415
Decorative Arts Museum / Fine Arts Museum 12777

Miellerie des Gorges de la Loire, Rte de Saint-Victor-sur-Loire, 42230 Roche-la-Molière - T: 0477906182, Fax: 0477504592
Natural History Museum / Special Museum 12778

Rochechinard

Musée de la Mémoire du Royans, Ancien Presbytère, 26190 Rochechinard - T: 0475486253, 0475477423, E-mail: Musee.du.Royans@wanadoo.fr. Head: Josselin Derbier
Ethnology Museum 12779

Rochechouart

Musée Départemental d'Art Contemporain de Rochechouart, Pl du Château, 87600 Rochechouart Cedex - T: 0555037777, Fax: 0555037240, E-mail: sec-musee@cg87.fr. Head: Jean-Marc Prévost
Fine Arts Museum - 1985
Contemporary art 12780

Rochecorbon

Les Caves Rupestres, Rue de Vaufoynard, 37210 Rochecorbon - T: 0247525175
Fine Arts Museum 12781

Musée de la Coiffe et Broderies de Touraine, 68 Quai de la Loire, 37210 Rochecorbon - T: 0247528016
Folklore Museum 12782

Rochefort (Charente-Maritime)

Ancienne École de Médecine Navale, 25 Rue Amiral Meyer, 17300 Rochefort (Charente-Maritime) - T: 0546995957, Fax: 0546880973, E-mail: g.prudhomme@musee_marine.fr, Internet: http://www.musee-marine.fr. Head: Georges Prudhomme
Historical Museum
Naval medicine instruments, books and pharmacopoeia (17th-20th c) 12783

Ecomusée du Commerce et de l'Artisanat, 12 Rue Lesson, 17300 Rochefort (Charente-Maritime) - T: 0546839150, Fax: 0546839150
Special Museum 12784

Musée Archéologique, La Vieilleparoisse, Av Rochambeau, 17300 Rochefort (Charente-Maritime)
Archaeological Museum 12785

Musée d'Art et d'Histoire, 63 Av du Général-de-Gaulle, 17300 Rochefort (Charente-Maritime) - T: 0546998399
Fine Arts Museum / Historical Museum - 1860
Fine arts, paintings, asiatic art, african art, local history 12786

Musée de Tradition de l'Aéronautique Navale, Hangar de la Base-École, Blvd Pouzet, 17300 Rochefort (Charente-Maritime) - T: 0546843497/3301 poste 2280
Science&Tech Museum 12787

Musée National de la Marine, 1 Pl de la Galissonnière, 17300 Rochefort (Charente-Maritime) - T: 0546998657, Fax: 0546875327, E-mail: g.prudhomme@musee_marine.fr, Internet: http://www.musee-marine.fr. Head: Georges Prud'homme
Historical Museum
Ship models (navy, merchant navy, fishing navy), paintings, figureheads, local maritime history 12788

Musée Pierre-Loti, 141 Rue Pierre-Loti, 17300 Rochefort (Charente-Maritime) - T: 0546991688
Special Museum - 1969
Birthplace of the writer Pierre Loti 12789

Rochefort-en-Terre

Château de Rochefort-en-Terre, Le Bourg, 56220 Rochefort-en-Terre - T: 0297433156. Head: Jean-Marc Michaud
Historical Museum - 1978
Hist of the fortress, painting, furniture 12790

Rochetaillée-sur-Saône

Musée Henri Malartre, 645 Chemin du Musée, 69270 Rochetaillée-sur-Saône - T: 0478221880, Fax: 0478226960. Head: Bernard Vaireaux
Science&Tech Museum - 1960
Cars, motorcycles, cycles 12791

Rocroi

Musée de la Bataille, Pl du Luxembourg, 08230 Rocroi - T: 0324542006, Fax: 0324542006, E-mail: ot.rocroi@wanadoo.fr, Internet: http://www.otrocroi.com. Head: Sylviane Bentz
Historical Museum 12792

Rodemack

Mini-Musée Historique, 57570 Rodemack - T: 0382512550
Historical Museum / Archaeological Museum 12793

Rodez

Musée des Archives Départementales de l'Aveyron, Conseil Général de l'Aveyron, 25 Av Victor-Hugo, 12000 Rodez - T: 0565738070, Fax: 0565738071. Head: Jean Delmas
Historical Museum 12794

Musée des Beaux-Arts Denys-Puech, Pl G.-Clemenceau, 12000 Rodez - T: 0565427064/6328
Fine Arts Museum
17th century Italian paintings, contemporary paintings, sculpture 12795

Musée Fenaille, Pl Eugène Raynaldy, 12000 Rodez - T: 0565738430, Fax: 0565738431, E-mail: musee-fenaille@wanadoo.fr. Head: Annie Philippon
Archaeological Museum / Historical Museum 12796

Rodilhan

Musée de Peinture, Centre Culturel, Av Mistral, 30230 Rodilhan - T: 0466200891/16
Fine Arts Museum 12797

Rogliano

Musée Archéologique, Maison du Port de Macinaggio, 20247 Rogliano - T: 0495354257/99
Archaeological Museum 12798

Rohrbach-les-Bitche

Ouvrage Maginot de Rohrbach, Fort Casso, RD 84, 57410 Rohrbach-les-Bitche - T: 0387097095
Military Museum 12799

Romanèche-Thorins

Musée de la Vigne Benoit-Raclet, La Pierre, 71570 Romanèche-Thorins - T: 0385355026
Special Museum 12800

Musée Guillon du Compagnonnage, 71570 Romanèche-Thorins - T: 0385355026/2202
Local Museum 12801

Romans-sur-Isère

Centre Historique de la Résistance en Drôme et de la Déportation, 6 Rue Saint-Just, 26100 Romans-sur-Isère - T: 0475055190, Fax: 0475029726, E-mail: cmagnat@ville-romans26.fr. Head: Chantal Magnat
Historical Museum 12802

Musée de la Chaussure et d'Ethnographie Régionale, 2 Rue Sainte-Marie, 26100 Romans-sur-Isère, mail addr: BP 12, 26100 Romans-sur-Isère - T: 0475058130. Head: Marie-Josèphe Bossan
Historical Museum / Folklore Museum - 1954
Hist, local customs, folklore, 4000 years of shoemaking craft 12803

Romenay

Musée de la Volaille de Bresse, 71470 Romenay - T: 0385403090
Special Museum 12804

Musée du Terroir Bressan, Pl de l'Eglise, 71470 Romenay - T: 0385403090
Local Museum 12805

Romorantin-Lanthenay

Espace Automobiles Matra, 17 Rue des Capucins, 41200 Romorantin-Lanthenay - T: 0254945555, Fax: 0254945556. Head: Marc Tavernier
Science&Tech Museum 12806

Musée de la Course Automobile → Espace Automobiles Matra

Musée de Sologne, Moulin du Chapitre, 41206 Romorantin-Lanthenay - T: 0254953366, Fax: 0254950360
Folklore Museum
Regional folklore 12807

Musée Marcel de Marcheville, Carroir Doré, Rue de la Pierre, 41200 Romorantin-Lanthenay - T: 0254762206. Head: Hélène Leclert
Archaeological Museum 12808

Ronchamp

Musée de la Mine, Marcel Maulini, Pl de la Mairie, 70250 Ronchamp - T: 0384207050
Science&Tech Museum 12809

Roquebrun

Maison du Parc Naturel Régional du Haut-Languedoc, Les Moulins, 34460 Roquebrun - T: 0467973822
Local Museum 12810

Roquebrune-Cap-Martin

Cabanon de Le Corbusier, 06190 Roquebrune-Cap-Martin - T: 0493356287, Fax: 0493285700, E-mail: office.du.tourisme.rcm@wanadoo.fr. Head: Anne-Hélène Mazzoni
Special Museum 12811

Musée du Château, Vieux Village, 06190 Roquebrune-Cap-Martin - T: 0493350722
Decorative Arts Museum 12812

Roquefort-sur-Soulzon

Centre d'Exposition Fromager, 5 Rue Saint-Pierre, 12250 Roquefort-sur-Soulzon - T: 0565585008
Special Museum 12813

Musée Municipal de Préhistoire, Rue Saint-Pierre, 12250 Roquefort-sur-Soulzon - T: 0565609195
Archaeological Museum
Prehistory, archaeology 12814

Roquettes

Musée Historique du Foie Gras, Ferme Beaucru, 31120 Roquettes - T: 0561763898
Special Museum 12815

Roquevaire

La Maison de celle qui peint, Pont de l'Étoile, 13360 Roquevaire - T: 0442042532
Fine Arts Museum 12816

Rosans

Musée de la Tour Carrée, 05150 Rosans
Local Museum 12817

Rosay

Musée de la Pomme et du Cidre et des Métiers Traditionnels, 76680 Rosay - T: 0235943166
Special Museum / Science&Tech Museum 12818

Roscoff

Musée de la Station Biologique, Pl Georges Teissier, 29682 Roscoff Cedex, mail addr: BP 74, 29682 Roscoff Cedex - T: 0298292323, Fax: 0298292380, E-mail: aquarium@sb-roscoff.fr, Internet: http://www.sb-roscoff.fr. Head: Dr. André Toulmond
Natural History Museum 12819

Musée du Johnnie, 29211 Roscoff - T: 0298611213
Historical Museum 12820

Musée Historique de la Seconde Guerre Mondiale, Le Rhun, Rte du Car-Ferry, 29211 Roscoff - T: 0298697147/7673
Military Museum 12821

Rosenwiller

Musée Scolaire, École Élémentaire de Rosenwiller, 67560 Rosenwiller - T: 0388719190
Special Museum 12822

Roset-Fluans

Musée Cavernicole de la Grotte d'Osselle, 25410 Roset-Fluans - T: 0381636209
Natural History Museum 12823

Rosey

Musée Morice Lipsi, Rte de Mailley, 70000 Rosey - T: 0384788222, Fax: 0384788744, E-mail: info@musee-lipsi.com, Internet: http://www.musee-lipsi.com. Head: Gabrielle Beck-Lipsi
Fine Arts Museum - 1990
Work of the sculptor Morice Lipsi (1898-1986) in stone, wood, bronze, drawings, work of Hildegard Weber-Lipsi (1901-2000), oil paintings, water colours and drawings 12824

Rosheim

Espace Muséal, Maison Romane, 67560 Rosheim - T: 0388492760
Local Museum 12825

Rosières-aux-Salines

Collection de Voitures Hippomobiles, Haras National, 54110 Rosières-aux-Salines - T: 0383481418
Science&Tech Museum 12826

Rosnay

Collections du Château du Bouchet, Château du Bouchet, 36300 Rosnay - T: 0254378289
Decorative Arts Museum / Fine Arts Museum 12827

Rosny-sous-Bois

Musée Historique, 7 Rue Saint-Claude, 93110 Rosny-sous-Bois - T: 0145284317
Historical Museum / Military Museum / Folklore Museum 12828

Musée Régional Ferroviaire, Gare de Rosny-sous-Bois, Pl de Martyrs de la Résistance, 93110 Rosny-sous-Bois - T: 0140182000
Science&Tech Museum 12829

Rothéneuf

Musée de Plein Air de Rothéneuf, 35400 Rothéneuf - T: 0299569764
Open Air Museum / Fine Arts Museum 12830

Roubaix

Musée d'Art et d'Industrie de Roubaix, Hôtel de Ville, 59100 Roubaix, mail addr: BP 737, 59066 Roubaix Cedex 1 - T: 0320664693, Fax: 0320664688. Head: Bruno Gaudichon
Fine Arts Museum / Special Museum - 1844
Textiles, sculptures and painting 19th and 20th c, decorative art 12831

Rouen

Galerie des Estampes, Bibliothèque Municipale, 3 Rue Jacques-Villon, 76000 Rouen - T: 0235712882/1310
Historical Museum / Folklore Museum 12832

Musée Corneille, 4 Rue de la Pie, 76000 Rouen - T: 0235716392, Fax: 0235700156, E-mail: bm.villon@rouen.fr. Head: Françoise Legendre
Historic Site 12833

Musée de la Céramique, Hôtel d'Hocqueville, 1 Rue Faucon, 76000 Rouen - T: 0235073174, Fax: 0235154323, E-mail: musees@rouen.fr, Internet: http://www.musees-rouen.com. Head: Laurent Salomé
Decorative Arts Museum - 1864 12834

Musée Départemental des Antiquités de la Seine-Maritime, 198 Rue Beauvoisine, 76000 Rouen - T: 0235985510, Fax: 0235702516. Head: Geneviève Sennequier
Local Museum / Archaeological Museum - 1831
Celtic, Gallo-Roman, Merovingian, Viking, and medieval archeology, Renaissance objects and art, Egyptian, Oriental, Greek, and Etruscan art, Italian and Moor ceramics, mosaic of Lillebonne, tapestries ! 12835

Musée des Beaux-Arts, Sq Verdrel, 76000 Rouen - T: 0235712840, Fax: 0235154323, E-mail: musees@rouen.fr, Internet: http://www.musees-rouen.com. Head: Laurent Salomé
Fine Arts Museum / Decorative Arts Museum - 1809
Dutch, Flemish, Spanish, and French paintings from various periods, sculpture 12836

Musée d'Histoire Naturelle, 198 Rue Beauvoisine, 76000 Rouen - T: 0235714150, Fax: 0235154564, E-mail: museum@rouen.fr. Head: Monique Fouray
Natural History Museum / Ethnology Museum / Archaeological Museum - 1828 12837

Musée du Donjon, Rue du Donjon, 76000 Rouen - T: 0232083240
Local Museum 12838

Musée Flaubert et d'Histoire de la Médecine, 51 Rue Lecat, 76000 Rouen - T: 0235155995, Fax: 0232030496, E-mail: gustave.flaubert@libertysurf.fr, Internet: http://www-chu-rouen.fr. Head: Arlette Dubois
Special Museum / Science&Tech Museum / Fine Arts Museum 12839

Musée Jeanne-d'Arc, 33 Pl du Vieux Marché, 76000 Rouen - T: 0235880270, Fax: 0235985325, E-mail: musee.jeannedarc@wanadoo.fr, Internet: http://www.pro.wanadoo.fr/musee.jeannedarc. Head: Alain Préaux
Historical Museum 12840

Musée Le Secq des Tournelles - Musée de la Ferronnerie, Église Saint-Laurent, Rue J.-Villon, 76000 Rouen - T: 0235884292, Fax: 0235754323, E-mail: musees@rouen.fr, Internet: http://www.musees-rouen.com. Head: Laurent Salomé
Science&Tech Museum - 1921
Wrought-iron objects, keys, locks, tools, gates, household items 12841

Musée Maritime, Fluvial et Portuaire, Hangar Portaire 13, Quai Émile Duchemin, 76000 Rouen - T: 0232101551, Fax: 0232084230, Internet: http://www.musee-maritime-rouen.asso.fr. Head: Pierre Degon
Special Museum 12842

Musée National de l'Éducation, 185 Rue Eau-de-RobecVaubois, 76000 Rouen - T: 0232829595, Fax: 0232829596, E-mail: museenat@inrp.fr, Internet: http://www.inrp.fr
Historical Museum - 1879
School furniture, exercise books, toys, drawings and prints of children, photographs, autographs - library 12843

Musée National d'Histoire de l'Éducation de Rouen
→ Musée National de l'Éducation

Rouffach

Musée Historique du Bailliage de Rouffach, Pl de la République, 68250 Rouffach - T: 0389496527/785315. Head: Pierre-Paul Faust
Local Museum 12844

Rouffignac-Saint-Cernin

Château de Fleurac, 24580 Rouffignac-Saint-Cernin - T: 0553059501, Fax: 0553059847
Historic Site 12845

Grotte de Rouffignac, 24580 Rouffignac-Saint-Cernin - T: 0553054171, Fax: 0553354471
Archaeological Museum
Paintings and engravings 12846

Rougemont

Musée d'Archéologie et de Géologie, Mairie, 25680 Rougemont - T: 0381869006
Archaeological Museum / Natural History Museum 12847

Rougiers

Un Village Provençal dans l'Histoire, 83170 Rougiers - T: 0494804010
Archaeological Museum 12848

Roujan

Musée de Noé, 34320 Roujan - T: 0467984053
Special Museum / Historical Museum 12849

Roulans

Musée Saint-Michel, 25640 Roulans - T: 0381555458
Military Museum 12850

Roussillon (Isère)

Salle de l'Edit de Roussillon, Mairie, 38150 Roussillon (Isère) - T: 0474297425
Local Museum 12851

Rousson

Château, 30340 Rousson - T: 0466856031
Decorative Arts Museum 12852

Le Préhistorama, 30340 Rousson - T: 0466858696, Fax: 0466858693, Internet: http://www.provence.-guideweb.com/prehistorama. Head: Eirik Granqvist
Natural History Museum / Ethnology Museum / Archaeological Museum 12853

Routot

Maison du Lin, Pl du Général Leclerc, 27350 Routot - T: 0232562176, Fax: 0232424426. Head: Eric Dezellus
Special Museum 12854

Rouvray

Ferme Apicole du Morvan, 21530 Rouvray - T: 0380647061
Natural History Museum 12855

Rouziers-de-Touraine

Ecomusée de la Gâtine Tourangelle, Ancienne Ecole, 37360 Rouziers-de-Touraine - T: 0246566426/6013
Folklore Museum 12856

Royan

Musée d'Art et d'Histoire, Jardin de l'Hôtel-de-Ville, 17200 Royan - T: 0546053005/395656
Fine Arts Museum / Historical Museum 12857

Royat-les-Bains

Musée La Maison du Passé, 8 Rue Docteur Pegnoux, 63130 Royat-les-Bains - T: 0473588018/8001
Local Museum 12858

Royol-Canadel-sur-Mer

Musée d'Histoire Naturelle, Domaine du Rayol, Av du Commandant-Rigaud, 83820 Royol-Canadel-sur-Mer - T: 0494053250
Natural History Museum 12859

Rubrouck

Maison Guillaume de Rubroek, 59285 Rubrouck - T: 0328430383
Special Museum 12860

Rueil-Malmaison

Musée d'Art et d'Histoire, 6 Rue Paul-Vaillant-Couturier, 92500 Rueil-Malmaison - T: 0147326650, Fax: 0147321258. Head: Liliane Kalenitchenko
Local Museum 12861

Musée National des Châteaux de Malmaison et de Bois-Préau, Av du Château de Malmaison, 92500 Rueil-Malmaison - T: 0141290555, Fax: 0141290556. Head: Bernard Chevallier
Historical Museum / Fine Arts Museum - 1906/1958
Napoleonic hist, souvenirs of the empress Joséphine, souvenirs of St. Helena, Napoleonic legend 12862

Ruelle

Musée de l'Établissement des Constructions Navales de Ruelle, 1 Av Jean-Jaurès, 16600 Ruelle - T: 0545243015
Science&Tech Museum 12863

Rumilly

Musée de l'Albanais, 23 Av Gantin, 74150 Rumilly - T: 0450011953/645832, Fax: 0450646921, Internet: http://www.culture.fr. Head: Jeanne Marin
Local Museum 12864

Ruynes-en-Margeride

Écomusée de la Margeride, La Tour, Le Jardin de Saint-Martin, 15320 Ruynes-en-Margeride - T: 0471234296, Fax: 0471234296, E-mail: ecomusee-margeride@wanadoo.fr. Head: Colette Meindre
Ethnology Museum 12865

Ry

Galerie Bovary, Musée d'Automates, Pl Gustave-Flaubert, 76116 Ry - T: 0235236144
Science&Tech Museum 12866

Saales

Musée Scolaire Freinet, École Élémentaire de Bourg-Bruche, 67420 Saales - T: 0388977292
Special Museum 12867

Sabres

Ecomusée de la Grande Lande, Marquèze, 40630 Sabres - T: 0558075270
Open Air Museum / Folklore Museum 12868

Saché

Musée Balzac, Château Saché, 37190 Saché - T: 0247268650, Fax: 0247268028. Head: Gérard Coulon
Historical Museum
Residence of the writer Honoré de Balzac, memorabilia, portraits, letters and manuscripts, first editions of his works 12869

Sadirac

Musée de la Poterie et de la Céramique Sadicaise, 33670 Sadirac - T: 0556306003
Decorative Arts Museum 12870

Sagonne

Château-Musée Mansart, Rte National 76, 18600 Sagonne - T: 0248800127, Fax: 0147335925
Decorative Arts Museum / Historical Museum / Special Museum / Historic Site 12871

Sagy

Ecomusée de la Bresse Bourguignonne, Maison Communale, 71580 Sagy - T: 0385762716
Science&Tech Museum 12872

Sailhan

La Maison d'Aure, Musée Paysan - Arts et Traditions Populaires, 65170 Sailhan - T: 0562395807
Folklore Museum 12873

Saille

Maison des Paludiers, 18 Rue des Prés-Garnier, 44350 Saille - T: 0240622196, Fax: 0240150346
Folklore Museum 12874

Sailly

Musée de l'Art Africain (closed) 12875

Sainghin-en-Weppes

Écomusée du Cuir de la Tannerie Nory, 789 Rue Gambetta, 59184 Sainghin-en-Weppes - T: 0320584059, Fax: 0320582260, E-mail: priory@nordnet.fr. Head: Jean-Marc Nory
Special Museum 12876

Sains-du-Nord

Ecomusée du Bocage, 35 Rue J.-B. Lebas, 59177 Sains-du-Nord - T: 0327618524/606611
Agriculture Museum 12877

Saint-Aignan (Loir-et-Cher)

Musée Viticole, Maison Eclusière, Quai du Cher, 41110 Saint-Aignan (Loir-et-Cher) - T: 0254751256
Special Museum 12878

Saint-Alban-Auriolles

Musée Alphonse-Daudet, Mas de la Vignasse, 07120 Saint-Alban-Auriolles - T: 0475396507
Local Museum 12879

Musée d'Arts et Traditions Rurales, 07120 Saint-Alban-Auriolles - T: 0475396507
Folklore Museum 12880

Musée de la Soie de l'Ardesco, 07120 Saint-Alban-Auriolles - T: 0475396507
Special Museum 12881

Saint-Alyre-ès-Montagne

Muséoparc de Découverte des Tourbières et du Cezallier, Près La Godivelle, 63420 Saint-Alyre-ès-Montagne - T: 0473658936
Open Air Museum 12882

Saint-Amand-de-Coly

Abbaye de Saint-Amand de Coly, 24290 Saint-Amand-de-Coly - T: 0553516750, Fax: 0553508314
Historic Site 12883

Saint-Amand-en-Puisaye

Musée du Grès, Château, 58310 Saint-Amand-en-Puisaye - T: 0386397497, Fax: 0386396372. Head: François Martin
Decorative Arts Museum 12884

Saint-Amand-les-Eaux

Musée Municipal, Tour Abbatiale, Grand Pl, 59230 Saint-Amand-les-Eaux - T: 0327222455
Local Museum / Religious Arts Museum / Fine Arts Museum / Decorative Arts Museum - 1950
17th century abbey with antique carillon, local history, faïence and contemp ceramics, 17th-18th century religious art 12885

Saint-Amand-Montrond

Musée Saint-Vic, Cours Manuel, 18200 Saint-Amand-Montrond - T: 0248965520, Fax: 0248821091, E-mail: musee.saint.vic@libertysurf.fr. Head: Ch. Planchard
Local Museum - 1922
16th-18th century paintings, prehistoric archeology, folk art and customs, céramics of la Borne - library, photo library 12886

Saint-Amans

Musée du Machinisme Agricole, Ferme de Fiougoge, 48700 Saint-Amans - T: 0466473465
Agriculture Museum 12887

Saint-Amant-Roche-Savine-Fournols

Musée du Bois, 63890 Saint-Amant-Roche-Savine-Fournols - T: 0473957022
Natural History Museum 12888

Saint-Amarin

Musée Serret et de la Vallée, 3 Rue Clemenceau, 68550 Saint-Amarin - T: 0389387588/826001. Head: Dr. R. Horber
Local Museum 12889

Saint-Ambroix

Musée de Préhistoire, de Spéléologie et de Géologie, 30500 Saint-Ambroix - T: 0466240157
Archaeological Museum / Natural History Museum 12890

Saint-Ame

Musée des Trois-Guerres, 25 Rue de la Moselotte, 88120 Saint-Ame - T: 0329612018/2203
Military Museum 12891

Parc Miniature Alsace-Lorraine, Rte de Cleurie, 88120 Saint-Ame - T: 0329612082/2138
Special Museum 12892

Saint-Andiol

Musée du Jus de Fruit, Pressoir de Provence, 13670 Saint-Andiol - T: 0442954956/90050202
Special Museum 12893

Saint-André-de-la-Marche

Musée de l'Industrie Régionale de la Chaussure, 3 Rue des Bordages, 49450 Saint-André-de-la-Marche - T: 0241463565
Local Museum / Science&Tech Museum 12894

Saint-André-d'Embrun

Musée Rural, 05200 Saint-André-d'Embrun - T: 0492433414, Fax: 0492433414, E-mail: lancelot.a@ifrance.com. Head: Antoine Lancelot
Folklore Museum 12895

Saint-André-du-Bois

Château Malromé, 33490 Saint-André-du-Bois - T: 0556764492, Fax: 0556764618, E-mail: malrome@malrome.com, Internet: http://www.malrome.com. Head: Philippe Decroix
Historic Site 12896

Saint-Anthème

Musée des Jasseries des Monts du Forez, Jasserie du Coq Noir, Village du Grand-Genévrier, 63660 Saint-Anthème - T: 0473820311
Local Museum 12897

Saint-Antoine-l'Abbaye

Musée de la Taille de Pierre, Atelier des Bons Ouvriers, 38160 Saint-Antoine-l'Abbaye - T: 0476364412
Special Museum 12898

Musée Départemental Jean Vinay, Monastère, 38160 Saint-Antoine-l'Abbaye - T: 0476364068
Fine Arts Museum 12899

Trésor d'Église, Art Sacré, Montée des Anges, 38160 Saint-Antoine-l'Abbaye - T: 0476364446
Religious Arts Museum 12900

Saint-Antonin-Noble-Val

Musée Archéologique et Minéralogique, Grotte du Bosc, 82140 Saint-Antonin-Noble-Val - T: 0563560312/306003/6291
Archaeological Museum / Natural History Museum 12901

Musée d'Art et d'Histoire, Maison Romane, Pl de la Halle, 82140 Saint-Antonin-Noble-Val - T: 0563306347/6023
Archaeological Museum / Folklore Museum 12902

Musée du Machinisme Agricole, Le Bosc, 82140 Saint-Antonin-Noble-Val - T: 0563306283
Agriculture Museum 12903

Saint-Antonin-sur-Bayon

Maison de la Sainte-Victoire, 13100 Saint-Antonin-sur-Bayon - T: 0442669151
Local Museum 12904

Saint-Arcons-d'Allier

Musée National de la Ferblanterie, 43300 Saint-Arcons-d'Allier - T: 0471741014/0204
Science&Tech Museum 12905

Saint-Arnoult-en-Yvelines

Maison d'Elsa Triolet et Louis Aragon, Moulin de Villeneuve, 78730 Saint-Arnoult-en-Yvelines - T: 0130412015, Fax: 0130414392
Special Museum 12906

Saint-Aubin-sur-Loire

Château de Saint-Aubin-sur-Loire, 71140 Saint-Aubin-sur-Loire - T: 0385539196
Decorative Arts Museum
17th century manor, period furniture, tapestries 12907

Saint-Avit-Frandat

Château-Musée de Lacassagne, RN 21, 32700 Saint-Avit-Frandat - T: 0562688324
Fine Arts Museum 12908

Saint-Avit-Senieur

Musée de Géologie, Abbaye, 24440 Saint-Avit-Senieur - T: 0553223227
Natural History Museum 12909

Saint-Barthélemy-d'Anjou

Musée Cointreau, Rue de la Croix Blanche, ZI Saint-Barthélemy, 49124 Saint-Barthélemy-d'Anjou - T: 0241315050, Fax: 0241315032, E-mail: reservationmusee@remy-cointreau.com, Internet: http://www.cointreau.com
Special Museum 12910

Saint-Beauzely

Musée Mémoire de la Vie Rurale, Château, 12620 Saint-Beauzely - T: 0565620390
Local Museum 12911

Saint-Berthevin

Maison de l'Industrie - Exposition Permanente, Parc des Expositions, Blvd des Loges, 53940 Saint-Berthevin - T: 0243690945
Science&Tech Museum 12912

Saint-Bertrand-de-Comminges

Musée Archéologique Départemental, 31510 Saint-Bertrand-de-Comminges - T: 0561883179, Fax: 0561883179. Head: Jean-Luc Schenck
Archaeological Museum 12913

Saint-Bonnet-de-Joux

Musée Archéologique, Pl de la Poste, 71220 Saint-Bonnet-de-Joux - T: 0385247387
Archaeological Museum 12914

Saint-Bonnet-le-Château

Musée International Pétanque et Boules, Esplanade de la Boule, 42380 Saint-Bonnet-le-Château
Special Museum 12915

Saint-Bonnet-le-Troncy

Musée Jean-Claude Colin, Association Art Culture Amitié, 69870 Saint-Bonnet-le-Troncy - T: 0474020472
Historical Museum 12916

Saint-Bonnet-les-Oules

Musée La Ferme Forézienne, Mairie, 42330 Saint-Bonnet-les-Oules - T: 0477540582
Agriculture Museum 12917

Saint-Brévin-les-Pins

Ferme aux Abeilles, Rte de Paimbœuf, 44250 Saint-Brévin-les-Pins - T: 0240273367
Natural History Museum 12918

Musée de la Marine, Pl de la Marine, 44250 Saint-Brévin-les-Pins - T: 0240270064/0618
Science&Tech Museum - 1983
Ships, hist of the fortress 12919

Saint-Brieuc

Musée Anatole-Le-Braz, Collège, Rue du 71e R.I., 22000 Saint-Brieuc - T: 0296331267
Special Museum 12920

Musée d'Art et d'Histoire, Cour Francis Renaud, Rue des Lycéens Martyrs, 22000 Saint-Brieuc - T: 0296625520/611465, Fax: 0296611465
Historical Museum - 1986
Local hist 12921

Saint-Bris-le-Vineux

Chapelle de Bailly, Centre d'Art Georges-Hosotte, 89530 Saint-Bris-le-Vineux - T: 0386533055
Fine Arts Museum 12922

Espace Muséal, Carrières de Bailly, 89530 Saint-Bris-le-Vineux
Fine Arts Museum 12923

Saint-Brisson (Nièvre)

Musée de la Résistance en Morvan, Maison du Parc, 58230 Saint-Brisson (Nièvre) - T: 0386787299, 0386787906, Fax: 0386787422, Internet: http://www.parcdumorvan.org/musres/index.htm. Head: Jean Longhi
Historical Museum 12924

Saint-Brisson-sur-Loire

Château-Musée, 9 Rue du Château, 45500 Saint-Brisson-sur-Loire - T: 0238367129
Decorative Arts Museum 12925

Saint-Calais

Musée Municipal, Rue Charles Garnier, 72120 Saint-Calais - T: 0243631515
Local Museum 12926

Saint-Cannat

Musée Suffren et du Vieux Saint-Cannat, Espace Suffren, Pl Jean Jaurès, 13760 Saint-Cannat - T: 0442508200, Fax: 0442508201. Head: Jean-Claude Klein
Local Museum - 1949
Sailor and Bailli de Suffren, born in Saint-Cannat and his family, Lords (Marquis) of Saint-Cannat, hist (and ethnology) of Saint-Cannat, tools (agriculture), paintings 12927

Musée-Village des Automates, Rte Nationale 7, 13760 Saint-Cannat - T: 0442573030
Science&Tech Museum 12928

Saint-Céré

Exposition d'Art, Casino, 46400 Saint-Céré - T: 0565381960, Fax: 0565381754. Head: Andrée Delbos
Fine Arts Museum 12929

Saint-Cezaire

Musée de la Préhistoire, Les Bujotiers, 17770 Saint-Cezaire - T: 0546915689
Archaeological Museum 12930

Saint-Chamant

Collection de Tapisseries d'Aubusson et des Flandres, Château, 15140 Saint-Chamant - T: 0471692201/2667
Decorative Arts Museum 12931

Saint-Chamas

Musée du Vieux Saint-Chamas → Musée Municipal Paul Lafran

Musée Municipal Paul Lafran, Ancien Hôtel de Ville, Pl des Pénitents, 13250 Saint-Chamas - T: 0490508561/33, E-mail: musee.paullafran@free.fr
Local Museum / Archaeological Museum / Folklore Museum 12932

Saint-Chef

Exposition des Fresques Romanes, Pl de l'Église, 38890 Saint-Chef - T: 0474951390/924248
Fine Arts Museum 12933

Saint-Chély-d'Apcher

Musée des Papillons, 15 Rue des Pénitents, 48200 Saint-Chély-d'Apcher - T: 0466311795
Natural History Museum 12934

Saint-Chiron

Musée Talleyrand, Château du Marais, 91530 Saint-Chiron - T: 0164589601
Special Museum 12935

Saint-Christol-lès-Alès

Musée du Scribe, 42 Rue du Clocher, 30380 Saint-Christol-lès-Alès - T: 0466608810, Fax: 0466608685. Head: J. Lovis Bonnefille
Special Museum 12936

Saint-Christophe-des-Bardes

Collection de Tire-Bouchons, Château Haut-Sarpe, 33330 Saint-Christophe-des-Bardes - T: 0557247098/514186
Special Museum 12937

Musée de Bouteilles Anciennes et Originales, Château Haut-Badette, 33330 Saint-Christophe-des-Bardes - T: 0557247098/514186
Special Museum 12938

Saint-Christophe-en-Oisans

Écomusée du Haut-Vénéon, 38143 Saint-Christophe-en-Oisans - T: 0476795350/592079
Folklore Museum 12939

Saint-Christophe-la-Montagne

Musée Campagnard du Haut-Beaujolais, M. Carrette, 69860 Saint-Christophe-la-Montagne - T: 0474047606
Folklore Museum 12940

Saint-Ciers-sur-Gironde

Musée d'Art et d'Histoire, Mairie, 33820 Saint-Ciers-sur-Gironde - T: 0557326413/6045
Decorative Arts Museum / Historical Museum 12941

Saint-Cirq-Lapopie

Château, Près de l'Eglise, 46330 Saint-Cirq-Lapopie - T: 0565312748
Decorative Arts Museum 12942

Musée Rignault, La Gardette, 46330 Saint-Cirq-Lapopie - T: 0565312322
Fine Arts Museum / Ethnology Museum 12943

Saint-Clar-de-Lomagne

Musée Départemental de l'École Publique, 32380 Saint-Clar-de-Lomagne - T: 0562664045/4169/4328
Special Museum 12944

Saint-Claude

Musée de la Pipe, du Diamant et du Lapidaire, 1 Pl Jacques Faizant, 39200 Saint-Claude - T: 0384451700
Special Museum 12945

Saint-Clément-des-Baleines

Complexe Muséographique Arche de Noé, 17590 Saint-Clément-des-Baleines - T: 0546292323/2727
Natural History Museum 12946

Musée de la Mer du Phare des Baleines, 17590 Saint-Clément-des-Baleines - T: 0546294448
Natural History Museum 12947

Saint-Cloud

Musée Historique du Domaine National, Cour d'Honneur, Av du Palais, 92210 Saint-Cloud - T: 0141120290, Fax: 0147713820. Head: Gilles Bonnevialle
Historical Museum
History of the palace and garden of Saint-Cloud 12948

Musée Municipal, 60 Rue Gounod, 92210 Saint-Cloud - T: 0146026718, Fax: 0147712700
Fine Arts Museum / Decorative Arts Museum / Historical Museum 12949

Saint-Connan

Musée de la Résistance, Mairie, 22840 Saint-Connan - T: 0296214357
Historical Museum 12950

Saint-Crépin-Carlucet

Château de Lacypierre, 24590 Saint-Crépin-Carlucet - T: 0553293928
Historic Site 12951

Saint-Crépin-de-Richemont

Musée du Souvenir Pierre de Bourdeille, Château, 24310 Saint-Crépin-de-Richemont - T: 0553057281
Special Museum 12952

Saint-Cyprien

Centre d'Art Contemporain, Pl de la République, 66750 Saint-Cyprien - T: 0468213207
Fine Arts Museum 12953

Musée Desnoyer, 4 Rue Emile Zola, 66750 Saint-Cyprien - T: 0468210696
Fine Arts Museum 12954

Saint-Cyr-en-Talmondais

Château-Musée de la Court d'Aron, Château, 85540 Saint-Cyr-en-Talmondais - T: 0251308182
Decorative Arts Museum / Religious Arts Museum / Archaeological Museum 12955

Saint-Cyr-la-Rosière

Musée Départemental des Arts et Traditions Populaires du Perche, Sainte-Gauburge, 61130 Saint-Cyr-la-Rosière - T: 0233734806, Fax: 0233731894, E-mail: ecomusee.du.perche@wanadoo.fr., Internet: http://ecomusee-du-perche.free.fr. Head: Evelyne Wander
Folklore Museum - 1972 12956

Saint-Cyr-l'École

Musée du Lycée Militaire de Saint-Cyr, Av Jean Jaurès, 78210 Saint-Cyr-l'École - T: 0134606190, Fax: 0139506807, E-mail: versailles.tourisme@wanadoo.fr
Military Museum 12957

Saint-Cyr-les-Lecques

Musée de Tauroentum, Rte de La Madrague, 83270 Saint-Cyr-les-Lecques - T: 0494263046. Head: Jacques Guion
Archaeological Museum 12958

Saint-Cyr-sur-Menthon

Musée de la Vieille Ferme Bressane à Pans de Bois, Domaine des Planons, La Mulatière, 01380 Saint-Cyr-sur-Menthon - T: 0385363122
Local Museum 12959

Saint-Cyr-sur-Mer

Centre d'Art Sébastien, Blvd Jean-Jaurès, 83270 Saint-Cyr-sur-Mer - T: 0494261920
Fine Arts Museum 12960

Musée Gallo-Romain de Tauroentum, 7 Rte de la Madrague, 83270 Saint-Cyr-sur-Mer - T: 0494263046
Archaeological Museum 12961

Saint-Denis-de-l'Hôtel

Musée Maurice Genevoix, Pl du Cloître, 45550 Saint-Denis-de-l'Hôtel - T: 0238590224/1280
Special Museum 12962

Saint-Denis-de-Pile

Exposition L'Eau dans tous ses États, Mairie, 33910 Saint-Denis-de-Pile - T: 0557742963/554430
Natural History Museum 12963

Saint-Denis (Seine-Saint-Denis)

Collection de la Nécropole Royale, Cathédrale-Basilique Saint-Denis, Chapelle, 93200 Saint-Denis (Seine-Saint-Denis) - T: 0148098354
Religious Arts Museum 12964

Musée d'Art et d'Histoire, 22bis Rue Gabrièl Péri, 93200 Saint-Denis (Seine-Saint-Denis) - T: 0142430510, Fax: 0148200760, E-mail: musee.saint-denis@wanadoo.fr. Head: Sylvie Gonzalez
Religious Arts Museum / Historical Museum / Archaeological Museum / Decorative Arts Museum - 1905
Finds of Merovingian, and medieval periods, coll on the poet Paul Eluard, paintings and drawings 20th c, Paris Commune, furniture and architectural drawings by Francis Jourdain, lithogr by Honoré Daumier, religious art 12965

Saint-Desirat

Musée de l'Alambic, Distillerie Jean Gauthier, 07340 Saint-Desirat - T: 0475342311
Special Museum 12966

Saint-Didier-en-Velay

Musée Départemental des Arts et Traditions Populaires de la Haute-Loire et du Massif Central, Pl de la Halle, 43140 Saint-Didier-en-Velay - T: 0471662261, 0471611593
Folklore Museum 12967

Saint-Dié-des-Vosges

Musée Bijoux de Braque, Tour de la Liberté, Parc Jean Mansuy, 88107 Saint-Dié-des-Vosges - T: 0329551762, Fax: 0329567230, Internet: http://www.ville-saintdie.fr. Head: Pascal Morel
Decorative Arts Museum 12968

Musée de la Bibliothèque-Médiatèque, 11 Rue Saint-Charles, 88100 Saint-Dié-des-Vosges - T: 0329516040
Special Museum 12969

Musée Pierre Noël, Pl Georges Trimouille, 88107 Saint-Dié-des-Vosges - T: 0329516035, Fax: 0329516041, Internet: http://www.ville-saintdie.fr. Head: Daniel Grandidier
Local Museum - 1875
German and French military items, memorabilia of the political figure Jules Ferry, archaeological finds, local art, ornithology, folk art and customs, national and international art of the 20th c, work of the writers Claire and Ivan Goll, works by Le Corbusier 12970

Saint-Dier-d'Auvergne

Château-Musée Les Martinanches, 63520 Saint-Dier-d'Auvergne - T: 0473708002
Decorative Arts Museum / Fine Arts Museum 12971

Saint-Diéry

Musée Paysan du Moulin Neuf, Près Saurier, 63320 Saint-Diéry - T: 0473963009/7779
Folklore Museum 12972

Saint-Dizier

Musée de la Brasserie, 510 Av de la République, 52100 Saint-Dizier - T: 0325055306
Special Museum 12973

Musée Municipal, Hôtel de Ville, 52100 Saint-Dizier - T: 0325073150. Head: M.-B. Herbage
Local Museum - 1881
Mineralogy, archaeology, ornithology, sculptures from ancient Carthage, 19th-10th century local paintings - library 12974

Saint-Emilion

Musée Archéologique et d'Histoire Locale, Logis Malet, Rue des Anciennes Ecoles, 33330 Saint-Emilion - T: 0557247203/52
Historical Museum / Archaeological Museum 12975

Saint-Estèphe

Collection de Tonnellerie, Château Haut-Coteau, 33250 Saint-Estèphe - T: 0556593984
Special Museum 12976

Collection d'Outillage Viticole, Maison du Vin, Pl de l'Église, 33250 Saint-Estèphe - T: 0556593059
Special Museum 12977

Saint-Étienne

Musée Archéologique Forez-Jarez, Maison des Associations, 4ter Rue André-Malraux, 42000 Saint-Étienne - T: 0477472314
Archaeological Museum 12978

Musée d'Art et d'Industrie, 2 Pl Louis Comte, 42000 Saint-Étienne - T: 0477397300, Fax: 0477497305, E-mail: museemai@mairie-st-etienne.fr, Internet: http://www.mairie-st-etienne.fr. Head: Nadine Besse
Special Museum - 1833
Armaments, weaving, ceramics, ribbons, ribbons looms, bicycles 12979

Musée d'Art Moderne, La Terrasse, 42000 Saint-Étienne - T: 0477795252, Fax: 0477795250, E-mail: mam@agglo-st-etienne.fr. Head: Jacques Beauffet
Fine Arts Museum - 1987
French coll of modern and contemporary art: Claude Monet, Auguste Rodin, Henri Matisse, Alberto Magnelli, Pablo Picasso, Fernand Léger, Vassily Kandinsky, surrealist art (Marcel Duchamp, Kurt Schwitters, Max Ernst, Joan Miró, Hans Arp, Yves Tanguy), Pop Art, New Realism (Andy Warhol, Roy Lichtenstein, Tom Wesselmann) - library 12980

Musée de la Mine, 3 Blvd Franchet-d'Esperey, 42000 Saint-Étienne - T: 0477438323, Fax: 0477438329
Science&Tech Museum 12981

Musée de l'École des Mines, 158 Cours Fauriel, 42100 Saint-Étienne - T: 0477420265
Natural History Museum 12982

Musée des Amis du Vieux Saint-Etienne, 13bis Rue Gambetta, 42000 Saint-Étienne - T: 0477257432, Fax: 0477381728, E-mail: amisvse42@aol.com, Internet: http://www.emse.fr/AVSE. Head: Bernard Rivatton
Historical Museum - 1932
Local historical items, paintings, furniture, items of local production from wood and iron, textiles, mining - library, archive 12983

Saint-Étienne-de-Baigorry

Musée de la Pelote Basque, Pl de l'Eglise, 64430 Saint-Étienne-de-Baigorry - T: 0559374728
Special Museum 12984

Saint-Étienne-de-Tinée

Musée des Traditions Stéphanoises, Four Communal, 06660 Saint-Étienne-de-Tinée - T: 0493024441. Head: Marie-Madeleine Fulconis
Ethnology Museum 12985

Musée du Lait et des Traditions, Rue de l'École, 06660 Saint-Étienne-de-Tinée - T: 0493024196
Special Museum / Local Museum 12986

Saint-Étienne-du-Bois

Musée d'Art Populaire des Mangettes, 01370 Saint-Étienne-du-Bois - T: 0474305245/5096/5254
Folklore Museum 12987

Musée de la Ferme de la Claison, 01370 Saint-Étienne-du-Bois - T: 0474305245/5096/5254
Agriculture Museum 12988

Saint-Étienne-le-Mollard

Château de la Bastie d'Urfé, 42130 Saint-Étienne-le-Mollard - T: 0477975468/961490
Decorative Arts Museum 12989

Saint-Fargeau

Musée de la Reproduction du Son, Pl de l'Hôtel de Ville, 89170 Saint-Fargeau - T: 0386741306, Fax: 0386741518, E-mail: musee.sonq@wanadoo.fr, Internet: http://perso, wanadoo.fr/museedelareproductionduson/
Special Museum / Music Museum / Science&Tech Museum 12990

Musée-Ferme d'Antan, Ferme du Château-Le Ferrier, 89170 Saint-Fargeau - T: 0386740376
Folklore Museum 12991

Saint-Faust

Musée-Cité des Abeilles, Chemin des Crêtes, 64110 Saint-Faust - T: 0559831031
Special Museum 12992

Saint-Fiacre-sur-Maine

Musée des Caves de la Cantrie, La Cantrie, 44690 Saint-Fiacre-sur-Maine - T: 0240548226
Fine Arts Museum / Natural History Museum 12993

Saint-Florent (Gard)

Maison des Liqueurs de l'Auzonnet, 30960 Saint-Florent (Gard) - T: 0466256439
Special Museum / Science&Tech Museum 12994

Saint-Florent-le-Vieil

Musée Archéologique, Abbatiale, 49410 Saint-Florent-le-Vieil - T: 0241725237
Archaeological Museum 12995

Musée des Guerres de Vendée, Chapelle du Sacré Cœur, 49410 Saint-Florent-le-Vieil - T: 0241725020
Historical Museum / Folklore Museum
History of the "Loire" region, the Vikings, the war of the "Vendée" region, local history of the 19th c: traditional bonnets, handicraft, paintings, fauna 12996

Saint-Flour (Cantal)

Musée Alfred-Douët, Maison Consulaire, 17 Pl d'Armes, 15100 Saint-Flour (Cantal) - T: 0471604499, Fax: 0471609256. Head: Benoît-Henry Papounaud
Decorative Arts Museum - 1952
Limoges enamels, Aubusson Tapestries, arms, pewters, Italian Renaissance furniture 12997

Musée de la Haute-Auvergne, 1 Pl d'Armes, 15100 Saint-Flour (Cantal) - T: 0471602232, Fax: 0471606847, E-mail: musee_haute_auvergne@yahoo.fr. Head: Laurent Védrine
Ethnology Museum - 1967
Ethnographie, archeology, religious art 12998

Musée Postal d'Auvergne, Marché des Jacobins, 15100 Saint-Flour (Cantal) - T: 0471603803/0855
Special Museum 12999

Saint-Flovier

Musée de la Préhistoire, Mairie, 37600 Saint-Flovier - T: 0247947224
Archaeological Museum 13000

Saint-Front-sur-Lemance

Château de Bonaguil, 47500 Saint-Front-sur-Lemance - T: 0553713975
Decorative Arts Museum 13001

Saint-Galmier

Maison de la Miniature, Pl Vieille-Grenette, 42330 Saint-Galmier - T: 0477540608/1296
Special Museum 13002

Musée de la Verrerie, Atelier du Souffleur de Verre, Office du Tourisme, Blvd du Sud, 42320 Saint-Galmier - T: 0477540608
Science&Tech Museum 13003

La Provence Miniature, Rte de Cuzieu, 42330 Saint-Galmier - T: 0477540608/525004
Special Museum 13004

Saint-Gaudens

Musée Municipal de Saint-Gaudens, Blvd Bepmale, Pl Mas Saint-Pierre, 31806 Saint-Gaudens Cedex - T: 0561890542, Fax: 0561947878, E-mail: stgaudens@stgaudens.com, Internet: http://www.stgaudens.com
Decorative Arts Museum / Local Museum
Local history, porcelain and faiences of Valentine 13005

Saint-Gelven

Musée Minéralogique et Paléontologique de Guerledan, Abbaye du Bon-Repos, 22570 Saint-Gelven - T: 0296369358
Natural History Museum / Archaeological Museum 13006

Saint-Gengoux-le-National

Musée de Saint-Gengoux-le-Royal, Impasse de la Rue du Commerce, 71460 Saint-Gengoux-le-National - T: 0385925205
Local Museum 13007

Saint-Géoire-en-Valdaine

Collections d'Arts Décoratifs du Château de Longpra, Château, 38620 Saint-Géoire-en-Valdaine - T: 0476075724
Decorative Arts Museum 13008

Saint-Georges-de-Commiers

Musée de la Voie Étroite et des Chemins de Fer de Montagne, Dépôt de Matériel, 38450 Saint-Georges-de-Commiers - T: 0476725711
Science&Tech Museum 13009

Saint-Georges-de-Reneins

Musée Archéologique Ludna, Château de Montchervet, 69830 Saint-Georges-de-Reneins - T: 0474676145
Archaeological Museum 13010

Saint-Georges-des-Sept-Voies

Musée Jacques Warminski, L'Orbière, 49350 Saint-Georges-des-Sept-Voies - T: 0241579592
Special Museum 13011

Saint-Georges-sur-Loire

Château-Musée de Serrant, 49170 Saint-Georges-sur-Loire - T: 0241391301
Decorative Arts Museum 13012

Saint-Germain-au-Mont-d'Or

Musée Thimonnier-Doyen, 11 Av de la Paix, 69650 Saint-Germain-au-Mont-d'Or - T: 0472081919
Science&Tech Museum 13013

Saint-Germain-de-Calberte

Château, 48370 Saint-Germain-de-Calberte - T: 0466459030
Fine Arts Museum / Historical Museum 13014

Saint-Germain-de-Livet

Musée-Château de Saint-Germain-de-Livet, 14100 Saint-Germain-de-Livet - T: 0231310003, Fax: 0231311230. Head: Jean Bergeret
Decorative Arts Museum - 1977
18th century furniture, works by Henri and Léon Riesener 13015

Saint-Germain-de-Marencennes

Maison des Arts Ruraux, 17700 Saint-Germain-de-Marencennes - T: 0546688112
Local Museum 13016

Saint-Germain-du-Bois

Ecomusée de la Bresse Bourguignonne, Maison Collinet, 71330 Saint-Germain-du-Bois - T: 0385762716
Special Museum / Science&Tech Museum 13017

Saint-Germain-du-Teil

Musée du Buron, 48340 Saint-Germain-du-Teil - T: 0466326380
Local Museum 13018

Saint-Germain-en-Laye

Musée Claude Debussy, 38 Rue Au Pain, 78100 Saint-Germain-en-Laye - T: 0134510512, 0139730264, Fax: 0134513601, E-mail: -Saint.Germain.en.Laye.Tourisme@wanadoo.fr, Internet: http://www.ville-st-germain-en-laye.fr
Music Museum 13019

Musée de l'Apothicairerie des Hôpitaux Généraux Royaux, 3 Rue Henri-IV, 78100 Saint-Germain-en-Laye - T: 0139739292, 0134510512
Decorative Arts Museum 13020

Musée Départemental Maurice-Denis, Le Prieuré, 2bis Rue Maurice-Denis, 78100 Saint-Germain-en-Laye - T: 0139737787, Fax: 0139737529, E-mail: -museemauricedenis@cg78.fr, Internet: http://www.musee-mauricedenis.fr. Head: Agnès Delannoy
Fine Arts Museum
Symbolism and Nabis, Groupe de Pont-Aven - documentation centre, library 13021

Musée des Antiquités Nationales, Château, 78100 Saint-Germain-en-Laye - T: 0139101300, Fax: 0134517393. Head: Dr. Patrick Perin
Archaeological Museum - 1862
Antiquities of prehistoric times, the Bronze age, and Celtic, Gallo-Roman, and Merovingian periods 13022

Saint-Germain-Laval

Automusée du Forez, Zone d'Activités de Saint-Germain-Laval, Rte Départementale 8, 42260 Saint-Germain-Laval - T: 0477655347, Fax: 0477655408
Science&Tech Museum 13023

Musée Lapidaire, 42260 Saint-Germain-Laval - T: 0477654130
Archaeological Museum 13024

Musée Municipal, Pl de l'Hôtel de Ville, 42260 Saint-Germain-Laval - T: 0477654130
Local Museum / Decorative Arts Museum 13025

Saint-Germain-Lembron

Château de Villeneuve, 63340 Saint-Germain-Lembron - T: 0473964164
Decorative Arts Museum 13026

Saint-Germain-l'Herm

Musée de la Forge et des Sapeurs-Pompiers, 63630 Saint-Germain-l'Herm - T: 0473720050
Science&Tech Museum / Historical Museum 13027

Saint-Gervais-sur-Mare

Écomusée Castaret-le-Haut, 34610 Saint-Gervais-sur-Mare - T: 0467236672
Folklore Museum 13028

Musée de la Châtaigneraie, Rue du Pont, 34610 Saint-Gervais-sur-Mare - T: 0467236888, 0467236926 (evening). Head: Martine Lebé
Historical Museum / Folklore Museum 13029

Saint-Géry

Musée du Rail, 46330 Saint-Géry - T: 0565314008/354691
Science&Tech Museum 13030

Saint-Gilles-Croix-de-Vie

Musée la Maison du Pêcheur, 22 Rue du Maroc, 85800 Saint-Gilles-Croix-de-Vie - T: 0251540809
Special Museum 13031

Saint-Gilles-du-Gard

Musée Archéologique, Maison Romane, 30800 Saint-Gilles-du-Gard - T: 0466874042/3375, Fax: 0466877819. Head: Marie-Françoise Griffeuille
Archaeological Museum / Ethnology Museum / Natural History Museum - 1950
Archeology, ethnography, ornithology - Library 13032

Musée-Château d'Espéran, 30800 Saint-Gilles-du-Gard - T: 0466873375
Decorative Arts Museum / Fine Arts Museum 13033

Musée des Traditions Populaires, Maison Romane, 30800 Saint-Gilles-du-Gard - T: 0466874042/3375, Fax: 0466877819. Head: Marie F. Griffeuille
Folklore Museum / Archaeological Museum / Natural History Museum 13034

Saint-Goazec

Espace Muséographique, Château de Trevarez, 29520 Saint-Goazec - T: 0298268279, Fax: 0298268677
Fine Arts Museum 13035

Saint-Goussaud

Musée Archéologique et d'Art Populaire, Mairie École, 23430 Saint-Goussaud - T: 0555643140
Archaeological Museum / Folklore Museum 13036

Saint-Guilhem-le-Désert

Musée Lapidaire, Ancien Réfectoire, 34150 Saint-Guilhem-le-Désert - T: 0467577145/7580, Fax: 0467573356
Archaeological Museum 13037

Saint-Hernin

Musée de la Laine, Ferme de la Bruyère, 29270 Saint-Hernin - T: 0298995352
Special Museum 13038

Saint-Hilaire-de-Chaléons

Musée Vivant de la Gare Rurale d'Autrefois, 25 Rue de la Mairie, 44680 Saint-Hilaire-de-Chaléons - T: 0240317042
Special Museum / Science&Tech Museum 13039

Saint-Hilaire-de-Loulay

Musée du Vin, Château de La Preuille, 85600 Saint-Hilaire-de-Loulay - T: 0251463232, Fax: 0251464898. Head: Philippe Dumortier, Christian Dumortier
Special Museum 13040

Saint-Hilaire-de-Riez

Musée Maraîchin de la Bourrine du Bois Juquaud, Écomusée Départemental, Rte de Challans, D 69, 85270 Saint-Hilaire-de-Riez - T: 0251492737/9403
Historical Museum 13041

Saint-Hilaire-d'Ozilhan

Collection Viticole, Cave Coopérative, 30210 Saint-Hilaire-d'Ozilhan - T: 0466372825
Special Museum 13042

Saint-Hilaire-en-Lignière

Musée des Traditions Populaires, Château du Plaix, Rte de Saint-Hilaire, 18160 Saint-Hilaire-en-Lignière - T: 0248602214
Folklore Museum 13043

Saint-Hilaire-la-Forêt

Centre Archéologique d'Initiation et de Recherche sur le Néolithique, 85440 Saint-Hilaire-la-Forêt - T: 0251333838
Archaeological Museum 13044

Saint-Hilaire-Saint-Florent

Collections du Masque César, 1 Rue de l'Abbaye, 49400 Saint-Hilaire-Saint-Florent - T: 0241507526
Special Museum 13045

Musée du Champignon, Rte de Gennes, 49400 Saint-Hilaire-Saint-Florent - T: 0241503155, Fax: 0241506194
Special Museum 13046

Saint-Hippolyte-du-Fort

Musée Archéologique, 30170 Saint-Hippolyte-du-Fort - T: 0466779165
Archaeological Museum 13047

Musée de la Soie, Pl du 8 Mai, 30170 Saint-Hippolyte-du-Fort - T: 0466776647/852909
Special Museum 13048

Saint-Imoges

Maison-Musée du Vigneron de Champagne, 51160 Saint-Imoges - T: 0326528800
Special Museum 13049

Saint-Jans-Cappel

Musée Marguerite-Yourcenar, 59270 Saint-Jans-Cappel - T: 0328490803, Fax: 0328422702. Head: Jean-André Vandelannoote
Local Museum 13050

Saint-Jean-Cap-Ferrat

Maison Papillorama au Jardin Zoologique, 06230 Saint-Jean-Cap-Ferrat - T: 0493760498
Natural History Museum 13051

Villa et Jardins Ephrussi de Rothschild, 06230 Saint-Jean-Cap-Ferrat - T: 0493013309/4590, Fax: 0493013110, E-mail: message@villa-ephrussi.com, Internet: http://www.villa-ephrussi.com. Head: Alexis Vrousos
Fine Arts Museum / Decorative Arts Museum - 1934
Tapestries and rugs, 18th century furnishings, paintings and porcelain of the 18th c, Oriental art objects, folk arts, wrought-iron items - library 13052

Saint-Jean-d'Angély

Musée d'Art et d'Histoire, 17 Rue de Verdun, 17400 Saint-Jean-d'Angély - T: 0546322654
Fine Arts Museum / Historical Museum 13053

Saint-Jean-d'Arvey

Musée-Conservatoire des Productions Fruitières, Derrière le Château de Chaffardon, 73230 Saint-Jean-d'Arvey - T: 0479284061
Special Museum 13054

Saint-Jean-de-Beauregard

Château de Saint-Jean-de-Beauregard, 91940 Saint-Jean-de-Beauregard - T: 0160120001
Decorative Arts Museum 13055

Saint-Jean-de-Bournay

Musée de Peinture J. Drevon, Château Picard, 38440 Saint-Jean-de-Bournay - T: 0474587040
Fine Arts Museum 13056

Saint-Jean-de-Braye

Musée Campanaire Bollée, 156 Faubourg de Bourgogne, 45800 Saint-Jean-de-Braye - T: 0238862947
Special Museum 13057

Saint-Jean-de-Côle

Musée Historique du Papier, Château de la Marthonie, 24800 Saint-Jean-de-Côle - T: 0553623025
Historical Museum 13058

Saint-Jean-de-Fos

Musée de la Poterie, Mairie, 34150 Saint-Jean-de-Fos - T: 0467575383/7297
Decorative Arts Museum 13059

Saint-Jean-de-Luz

Ecomusée de la Toile Basque Jean Vier, Ferme Berraïn, Rte Nationale 10, 64500 Saint-Jean-de-Luz - T: 0559510606
Special Museum 13060

Musée Grévin, 3 Rue Mazarine, 64500 Saint-Jean-de-Luz - T: 0559512488
Local Museum 13061

Musée-Maison Lohobiague dite Maison Louis XIV, Pl Louis XIV, 64500 Saint-Jean-de-Luz - T: 0559260156
Decorative Arts Museum 13062

Saint-Jean-de-Maurienne

Musée d'Archéologie, du Costume, d'Art et Traditions Populaires, Ancien Evêché, Pl de la Cathédrale, 73300 Saint-Jean-de-Maurienne - T: 0479640312
Archaeological Museum / Folklore Museum 13063

Musée Opinel, Galerie Artisanale, Av Henri Falcoz, 73300 Saint-Jean-de-Maurienne - T: 0479640478
Science&Tech Museum 13064

Saint-Jean-de-Védas

Exposition sur la Presse Ecrite, Midi Libre, Le Mas de Grille, 34430 Saint-Jean-de-Védas - T: 0467076717
Special Museum 13065

Saint-Jean-des-Champs

Musée du Cidre, Ferme de l'Hermitière, 50320 Saint-Jean-des-Champs - T: 0233613151, Fax: 0233618727, E-mail: infos@ferme-hermitiere.com, Internet: http://www.ferme-hermitiere.com. Head: Jean-Luc Coulombier
Special Museum / Agriculture Museum 13066

Saint-Jean-des-Vignes

Espace Pierres-Folles, 69380 Saint-Jean-des-Vignes - T: 0478436920, Fax: 0478436920, E-mail: epf@espace-pierres-folles.asso.fr, Internet: http://www.espace-pierres-folles.asso.fr. Head: René Nespoulet
Natural History Museum 13067

Saint-Jean-du-Gard

Atlandide, Muséoparc, Av de la Résistance, 30270 Saint-Jean-du-Gard - T: 0466750666/853232
Natural History Museum 13068

Collection de Téléphones Anciens, Gare de Saint-Jean, 30270 Saint-Jean-du-Gard - T: 0466851317
Science&Tech Museum 13069

Musée des Vallées Cévenoles, Acropolis Museum Montpellier, 95 Grand Rue, 30270 Saint-Jean-du-Gard - T: 0466851048, Fax: 0466851361, E-mail: valceven@aol.com, Internet: http://www.members.aol.com/valceven
Ethnology Museum 13070

Saint-Jean-Lespinasse

Château-Musée de Montal, près Saint-Céré, 46400 Saint-Jean-Lespinasse - T: 0565381372, Fax: 0146561890, E-mail: bruno@panafieu.com. Head: Bruno de Panafieu
Fine Arts Museum 13071

Saint-Jean-Saint-Nicolas

Maison de la Vallée, Pont du Fossé, 05260 Saint-Jean-Saint-Nicolas - T: 0492559544
Natural History Museum / Folklore Museum 13072

Musée du Moulin, Pont du Fossé, 05260 Saint-Jean-Saint-Nicolas - T: 0492559104/9646
Folklore Museum 13073

Saint-Joachim

Maison de la Mariée, 130 Ile de Fédrun, 44720 Saint-Joachim - T: 0240916591/884204, E-mail: info@parc-naturel-briere.fr
Folklore Museum 13074

Saint-Julien-Chapteuil

Bourgeneuf 1900, Office du Tourisme, 43260 Saint-Julien-Chapteuil - T: 0471087770
Special Museum 13075

Musée Jules Romains, 43260 Saint-Julien-Chapteuil - T: 0471087770
Special Museum 13076

Musée-Moulin de Guerin, 43260 Saint-Julien-Chapteuil - T: 0471087949/7770
Science&Tech Museum 13077

Saint-Julien-du-Sault

Musée d'Art et d'Histoire, 10 Rue de l'Hôtel de Ville, 89330 Saint-Julien-du-Sault - T: 0386632295
Historical Museum / Fine Arts Museum 13078

Saint-Julien-en-Beauchene

Exposition Permanente, 05140 Saint-Julien-en-Beauchene - T: 0492581698
Local Museum 13079

Saint-Julien-en-Beaujolais

Musée Claude Bernard, Fondation Marcel Merieux, Hameau de Châtenay, 69640 Saint-Julien-en-Beaujolais - T: 0474675144, Fax: 0474675942, E-mail: annick.opinel@fond-merieux.org, Internet: http://www.fond-merieux.org. Head: Annick Opinel
Science&Tech Museum - 1965
Instruments, experimental physiology 13080

Saint-Julien-Mont-Denis

Musée Ardoisien, Rue de la Rochette, 73870 Saint-Julien-Mont-Denis - T: 0479596085
Local Museum 13081

Saint-Just-Saint-Rambert

Musée du Prieuré, Pl Madeleine Rousseau, 42170 Saint-Just-Saint-Rambert - T: 0477520311, Fax: 0477520915. Head: Daniel Pouget
Local Museum 13082

Saint-Lambert-du-Lattay

Musée de la Vigne et du Vin d'Anjou, Pl des Vignerons, 49750 Saint-Lambert-du-Lattay - T: 0241784275, Fax: 0241785964, Internet: http://www.mvvanjou.com. Head: Pierre Cesbron
Special Museum
Wine museum 13083

Saint-Lary-Soulan

La Maison de l'Ours, Pl du Téléphérique, 65170 Saint-Lary-Soulan - T: 0562395083/4029
Special Museum 13084

Saint-Laurent-de-Cerdans

Musée d'Art et de Traditions Populaires André Abet, Rue Joseph Nivel, 66260 Saint-Laurent-de-Cerdans - T: 0468395575
Historical Museum 13085

Usine-Musée de l'Espadrille, Rue Joseph-Nivel, 66260 Saint-Laurent-de-Cerdans - T: 0468395006
Science&Tech Museum 13086

Saint-Laurent-de-la-Plaine

Cité des Métiers de Tradition, 7 Pl Abbé-Moreau, 49290 Saint-Laurent-de-la-Plaine - T: 0241782408, Fax: 0241785687. Head: Joseph Grelier
Local Museum 13087

Saint-Laurent-de-la-Salanque

Musée de la Marine, 11 Av Joffre, 66250 Saint-Laurent-de-la-Salanque - T: 0468596542
Science&Tech Museum / Historical Museum 13088

Saint-Laurent-de-Trèves

Écomusée de la Cévenne, Ancienne Église, 48400 Saint-Laurent-de-Trèves - T: 0466495301, Fax: 0466495302, E-mail: pnc@bsi.fr, Internet: http://www.bsi.fr/pnc. Head: Daniel Travier
Natural History Museum
Dinosaurs, paleontology 13089

Saint-Laurent-des-Autels

Musée de Matériel Agricole, Ferme La Coulée du Cerf, La Michelière, 49270 Saint-Laurent-des-Autels - T: 0240837325/7825
Agriculture Museum 13090

Musée de Matériel Viticole, Ferme La Coulée du Cerf, La Michelière, 49270 Saint-Laurent-des-Autels - T: 0240837325/7825
Special Museum 13091

Saint-Laurent-d'Olt

Musée Jean-Boudou et Lucien-Girma, 12560 Saint-Laurent-d'Olt - T: 0565474526
Special Museum 13092

Saint-Laurent-du-Pont

Musée d'Archéologie Imaginaire, Centre de Recherche des Charbinières, 38380 Saint-Laurent-du-Pont - T: 0476552214
Archaeological Museum 13093

Le Petit Musée Maison de Mariette, 38380 Saint-Laurent-du-Pont - T: 0476551773
Religious Arts Museum 13094

Saint-Laurent-les-Tours

Musée Jean Lurçat, Château, 46400 Saint-Laurent-les-Tours - T: 0565382821. Head: Monique Escat
Special Museum / Fine Arts Museum 13095

Saint-Laurent-sur-Mer

Musée Omaha Beach, Rue de la Mer, 14710 Saint-Laurent-sur-Mer - T: 0231219744/927280
Military Museum 13096

Saint-Laurent-sur-Sèvre

Musée Religieux Saint-Louis Marie Grignion-de-Montfort, Rue des Couvents, 85290 Saint-Laurent-sur-Sèvre - T: 0251643700/678734
Historical Museum 13097

Saint-Léger-les-Mélèzes

Musée d'Histoire Naturelle, Les Forests, 05260 Saint-Léger-les-Mélèzes - T: 0492504052
Natural History Museum 13098

Saint-Léger-près-Troyes

Ferme Musée Rustique, 3 Rue de la Joncière, Rte Nationale 171, 10800 Saint-Léger-près-Troyes - T: 0325417252
Agriculture Museum 13099

Saint-Léger-sous-Beuvray

Salle Bibracte, Mairie, 71990 Saint-Léger-sous-Beuvray - T: 0385825300
Archaeological Museum 13100

Saint-Léger-Vauban

Musée du Maréchal de Vauban, Maison Vauban, 89830 Saint-Léger-Vauban - T: 0386322630
Military Museum 13101

Salle Marc-Hénard, Maison Vauban, 89830 Saint-Léger-Vauban - T: 0386322630
Special Museum 13102

Saint-Léonard-de-Noblat

HistoRail Limousin du Chemin de Fer, 18 Rue de Beaufort, 87400 Saint-Léonard-de-Noblat - T: 0555561112, Fax: 0685664176, E-mail: historail@historail.com, Internet: http://www.historail.com/. Head: Jacques Ragon
Science&Tech Museum 13103

Musée Gay-Lussac, Rue Roger-Salengro, 87400 Saint-Léonard-de-Noblat - T: 0555560013
Special Museum / Science&Tech Museum 13104

Saint-Léons

Musée Jean-Henri Fabre, Le Bourg, 12780 Saint-Léons - T: 0565588054, Fax: 0565588054, E-mail: jeanhenri.fabre@wanadoo.fr, Internet: http://www.musee-jeanhenrifabre.com
Special Museum / Natural History Museum 13105

Saint-Lizier

Musée Départemental, Palais des Évêques, 09190 Saint-Lizier - T: 0561048186
Historical Museum / Archaeological Museum / Natural History Museum 13106

Saint-Lô

Musée des Beaux-Arts, Pl du Champ de Mars, 50000 Saint-Lô - T: 0233725255, Fax: 0233578249. Head: Michel Carduner
Fine Arts Museum
Tapestries, paintings, drawings, miniatures, Roman sculpture 13107

Musée du Bocage Normand, Ferme de Boisjugan, 50000 Saint-Lô - T: 0233562698, Fax: 0233560912. Head: Hubert Godefroy
Agriculture Museum / Ethnology Museum - 1986
Breeding, milk and dairy of Normandy 13108

Saint-Louis-Arzviller

Musée de la Batellerie et du Plan Incliné, Au Plan Incliné, 57820 Saint-Louis-Arzviller - T: 0387253069, Fax: 0387254182, E-mail: asso@plan-incline.com.fr, Internet: http://www.plan-incline.com.fr. Head: Marcel Lantz
Special Museum 13109

Saint-Louis-la-Chaussée

Mémoire du Rhin, Petite Camargue Alsacienne, Rue de la Pisciculture, 68300 Saint-Louis-la-Chaussée - T: 0389897859, 0389897850, Fax: 0389897858, E-mail: petitecamarguealsacienne@wanadoo.fr, Internet: http://www.perso.wanadoo.fr/petite.camargue.alsacienne. Head: Philippe Knibiely
Special Museum / Natural History Museum 13110

Saint-Louis-les-Bitche

Musée de la Cristallerie, 57620 Saint-Louis-les-Bitche - T: 0387064004/1616
Decorative Arts Museum 13111

Saint-Loup

Musée de la Machine Agricole Ancienne, Foyer Rural, 58200 Saint-Loup - T: 0386262748/399141
Science&Tech Museum 13112

Saint-Lyphard

Musée de Kerhinet, Village de Kerhinet, 44410 Saint-Lyphard - T: 0240619524, E-mail: info@parc.naturel.briere.fr
Open Air Museum
Peasant life (19th c), folk art 13113

Saint-Macaire

Musée Archéologique, Prieuré, 33490 Saint-Macaire - T: 0556633452
Archaeological Museum 13114

Musée Océanographique/Aquariophilie, Pl de l'Horloge, 33490 Saint-Macaire - T: 0556630562
Natural History Museum 13115

Musée Postal du Relais Henri IV, Musée Postal d'Aquitaine, Pl du Mercandieu, 33490 Saint-Macaire - T: 0556630881
Science&Tech Museum / Special Museum 13116

Saint-Maixant (Gironde)

Musée François Mauriac, Château de Malagar, Rte de Sore, 33490 Saint-Maixant (Gironde) - T: 0556170059
Special Museum 13117

Saint-Malo-de-Guersac

Maison de l'Eclusier, Maison de l'Eclusier à Rozé, 44550 Saint-Malo-de-Guersac - T: 0240911780, E-mail: info@parc-naturel-briere.fr
Folklore Museum
Furniture and interior, peasant life, costume 13118

Saint-Malo (Ille-et-Vilaine)

Malouinière-Musée, Le Bos, Rte de la Passagère-Quelmer, 35400 Saint-Malo (Ille-et-Vilaine) - T: 0299814011, Fax: 0299314216
Local Museum 13119

Musée d'Histoire de la Ville et d'Ethnographie du Pays Malouin, Grand-Donjon du Château, Esplanade Felicité Lamennais, 35400 Saint-Malo (Ille-et-Vilaine), mail addr: BP 147, 35408 Saint-Malo (Ille-et-Vilaine) Cedex - T: 0299407157, Fax: 0299407156, E-mail: musee@ville-saint-malo.fr. Head: Philippe Petout
Historical Museum - 1950
Hist of the corsars, hist of the town, regional ethnography 13120

Musée International du Long Cours Cap Hornier, Tour Solidor, 35400 Saint-Malo (Ille-et-Vilaine) - T: 0299407158, Fax: 0299407156, E-mail: musee@ville-saint-malo.fr. Head: Philippe Petout
Historical Museum - 1969
Hist of sea voyages, sailing, Cape Horn sailors, maps and prints 13121

Musée Océanographique Aquarium, Pl Vauban (dans les Remparts), 35400 Saint-Malo (Ille-et-Vilaine) - T: 0299569477, Fax: 0299241901, E-mail: contact@aquarium-st.malo.com. Head: M. Charlot
Natural History Museum 13122

Saint-Marcan

Musée in Situ du Mont Saint-Michel, 35120 Saint-Marcan - T: 0299802215
Local Museum 13123

Saint-Marcel-de-Félines

Château de Saint-Marcel, 42122 Saint-Marcel-de-Félines - T: 0477632308
Decorative Arts Museum 13124

Saint-Marcel (Indre)

Musée Archéologique d'Argentomagus, Les Mersans, 36200 Saint-Marcel (Indre) - T: 0254244731, Fax: 0254241170. Head: Patrick Paillet
Archaeological Museum - 1990 13125

Saint-Marcel (Morbihan)

Musée de la Résistance Bretonne, Les Hardys Behelec, 56140 Saint-Marcel (Morbihan) - T: 0297751690, Fax: 0297751692. Head: Denise Andersen
Historical Museum - 1978
Hist of French Resistance 13126

Saint-Marcellin

Musée du Fromage, 2 Av du Collège, 38160 Saint-Marcellin - T: 0476385385
Special Museum 13127

Saint-Martin-d'Aubigny

Musée de la Brique de Basse-Normandie, Ancienne Briqueterie, 50190 Saint-Martin-d'Aubigny - T: 0233077392
Special Museum 13128

Saint-Martin-de-Bromes

Musée Archéologique, Tour des Templiers, 04800 Saint-Martin-de-Bromes - T: 0492780202, Fax: 0492780706, E-mail: mairie-smdb@wanadoo.fr
Archaeological Museum 13129

Saint-Martin-de-Crau

Ecomusée de la Crau, Ancienne Bergerie, Blvd de Provence, 13310 Saint-Martin-de-Crau - T: 0490470201
Natural History Museum / Local Museum 13130

Saint-Martin-de-Fressengeas

Musée de la Protohistoire, Grotte des Fraux, 24800 Saint-Martin-de-Fressengeas - T: 0553625131
Archaeological Museum 13131

Saint-Martin-de-la-Place

Musée-Château de Boumois, 49160 Saint-Martin-de-la-Place - T: 0241384316
Decorative Arts Museum / Fine Arts Museum 13132

Saint-Martin-de-Ré

Musée Cognacq, Av Victor Bouthillier, 17410 Saint-Martin-de-Ré - T: 0546092122. Head: Jeanne Bernard-Grit
Historical Museum - 1905
15th-16th century hotel, figureheads, ancient weapons, ship models, illustrating local history 13133

Saint-Martin-de-Villenglose

Village Miniature avec Jardins et Plan d'Eau in Situ, 53290 Saint-Martin-de-Villenglose - T: 0243706248
Fine Arts Museum 13134

Saint-Martin-des-Besaces

La Percée du Bocage 1944, N 175, 14350 Saint-Martin-des-Besaces - T: 0231675278. Head: Jean Ménard
Military Museum 13135

Saint-Martin-des-Olmes

Musée de l'Ecole 1900, 63600 Saint-Martin-des-Olmes - T: 0473826680
Special Museum 13136

Saint-Martin-du-Lac

Musée des Attelages de la Belle Epoque, Château Lagarde, 71110 Saint-Martin-du-Lac - T: 0385250372
Science&Tech Museum 13137

Saint-Martin-en-Bresse

Ecomusée de la Bresse Bourguignonne, Ecole de Perrigny, 71620 Saint-Martin-en-Bresse - T: 0385762716
Natural History Museum / Fine Arts Museum 13138

Saint-Martin-la-Sauveté

Maison des Traditions Rurales, Le Bourg, 42260 Saint-Martin-la-Sauveté - T: 0477622146
Local Museum 13139

Saint-Martin-Lacaussade

Maison du Terroir, Mairie, 33390 Saint-Martin-Lacaussade - T: 0557420206
Agriculture Museum 13140

Saint-Martin-le-Vinoux

La Casamaures, 13bis Rue de la Résistance, 38950 Saint-Martin-le-Vinoux - T: 0476471350, Fax: 0476471353, E-mail: casamaures@free.fr, Internet: http://www.casamaures.free.fr. Head: Christiane Guichard
Archaeological Museum / Historical Museum 13141

Saint-Martin-Vésubie

Musée des Traditions Vésubiennes, Quartier des Moulins, 06450 Saint-Martin-Vésubie - T: 0493033272, E-mail: isnartc@club-internet.fr, Internet: http://www.perso.club-internet.fr/alchemy
Ethnology Museum 13142

Saint-Mathurin-sur-Loire

Musée-Observatoire de la Vallée d'Anjou, Ancienne Gare S.N.C.F., 49250 Saint-Mathurin-sur-Loire - T: 0241570818
Natural History Museum 13143

Saint-Maurice-de-Rotherens

Musée Galletti, 73240 Saint-Maurice-de-Rotherens - T: 0476317638
Science&Tech Museum 13144

Saint-Maurice-d'Ételan

Château d'Ételan, 76330 Saint-Maurice-d'Ételan - T: 0235399127
Fine Arts Museum / Decorative Arts Museum 13145

Saint-Maurice-sur-Moselle

Musée des Démineurs, Situé au Ballon d'Alsace, près du Café "Sevrin", 88560 Saint-Maurice-sur-Moselle - T: 0384290900/29251226
Special Museum / Military Museum 13146

Saint-Maurin

Musée de la Vie Rurale Régionale, Abbaye, 47270 Saint-Maurin - T: 0553953125
Folklore Museum / Agriculture Museum 13147

Saint-Méard

Musée Gallo-Romain, Mairie, Le Bourg, 87130 Saint-Méard - T: 0555717058
Archaeological Museum 13148

Saint-Mesmin

Exposition La Guerre de 100 Ans, Achasme, Mairie, 85700 Saint-Mesmin - T: 0251664096
Historical Museum 13149

Saint-Michel-de-Llotes

Musée de l'Agriculture Catalane, 66130 Saint-Michel-de-Llotes - T: 0468847640
Agriculture Museum 13150

Saint-Michel-de-Montjoie

Musée du Granit, Le Haut du Bourg, 50670 Saint-Michel-de-Montjoie - T: 0233598494/80. Head: Marcel Cathrin
Open Air Museum 13151

Saint-Michel-en-l'Herm

Musée Le Temple du Soleil, 4 Rue de l'Étendard, 85580 Saint-Michel-en-l'Herm - T: 0251302515
Fine Arts Museum 13152

Saint-Michel-en-Thierache

Musée de la Vie Rurale et Forestière, Abbaye Saint-Michel, 34 Blvd Savart, 02830 Saint-Michel-en-Thierache - T: 0323582777
Local Museum 13153

Saint-Michel (Gers)

Musée d'Histoire Naturelle, Château, 32300 Saint-Michel (Gers) - T: 0562670106
Natural History Museum 13154

Saint-Michel-l'Observatoire

Musée d'Art Sacré, Presbytère, 04870 Saint-Michel-l'Observatoire - T: 0492766004/6411
Religious Arts Museum 13155

Saint-Michel-Mont-Mercure

Musée de la Meunerie, Moulin des Justices, 85700 Saint-Michel-Mont-Mercure - T: 0251577909
Science&Tech Museum 13156

Saint-Michel-sur-Loire

Musée de la Cadillac, Château de Planchoury, 37130 Saint-Michel-sur-Loire - T: 0247968152, Fax: 0247965198, Internet: http://www.musee.cadillac.com. Head: Genenièe Keyaerts, Magali Keyaerts
Science&Tech Museum 13157

Saint-Mihiel

Musée Départemental d'Art Sacré, Rue du Palais de Justice, 55300 Saint-Mihiel - T: 0329890647
Religious Arts Museum 13158

Saint-Mitre-les-Remparts

Site Archéologique de Saint-Blaise, 13920 Saint-Mitre-les-Remparts - T: 0442809855/440168
Archaeological Museum 13159

Saint-Nazaire-en-Royans

Musée Cavernicole de la Grotte de Thais, 26190 Saint-Nazaire-en-Royans - T: 0475484576
Natural History Museum 13160

Saint-Nazaire (Loire-Atlantique)

Ecomusée de Saint-Nazaire, Av de Saint-Hubert, 44600 Saint-Nazaire (Loire-Atlantique) - T: 0251100303, Fax: 0251101203, E-mail: ecomusee@mairie-saintnazaire.fr. Head: D. Sicard
Science&Tech Museum - 1988
Ships, hist of the harbour, industrial hist, hist of the city, liners 13161

Saint-Nectaire

Maison du Saint-Nectaire, Rte de Murol, 63710 Saint-Nectaire - T: 0473885166
Historical Museum 13162

Saint-Nic-Pontrez

Musée Rural du Porzay, 29127 Saint-Nic-Pontrez - T: 0298265036/849686/260190
Local Museum 13163

Saint-Nicolas-d'Aliermont

Musée de l'Horlogerie, Château Communal, Parking de la Poste, 76510 Saint-Nicolas-d'Aliermont - T: 0235858187/8011
Special Museum 13164

Saint-Nicolas-de-la-Grave

Musée Lamothe-Cadillac, Maison Natale, 82210 Saint-Nicolas-de-la-Grave - T: 0563959255
Special Museum 13165

Saint-Nicolas-de-Port

Musée Français de la Brasserie, 62 Rue Charles Courtois, 54210 Saint-Nicolas-de-Port - T: 0383469552, Fax: 0383469552, E-mail: mfb@passionbrasserie.com, Internet: http://www.passionbrasserie.com. Head: Benoît Taveneaux
Science&Tech Museum 13166

Saint-Omer

Musée de l'Hôtel Sandelin, 14 Rue Carnot, 62500 Saint-Omer - T: 0321380094, Fax: 0321985574, E-mail: musee.sandelin@free.fr, Internet: http://m3.dnsalias.com/sandelin/. Head: Yves Bourel
Fine Arts Museum / Decorative Arts Museum - 1829
Furnishings, Flemish, German, and French painting, ceramics, 12th-16th century art objects, Greek and Roman art, Gallo-Roman medieval items 13167

Musée du Parchemin et du Sceau, Bibliothèque, 40 Rue Gambetta, 62500 Saint-Omer - T: 0321383508
Library with Exhibitions 13168

Musée Henri Dupuis, 11 Rue Henri Dupuis, 62500 Saint-Omer - T: 0321382413. Head: Guy Blazy
Natural History Museum / Folklore Museum - 1889
Natural hist (birds, minerals), Flemish kitchen, popular art 13169

Saint-Ouen-des-Toits

Musée de Jean Cottereau, La Closerie des Poiriers, 53410 Saint-Ouen-des-Toits - T: 0243377331
Folklore Museum / Local Museum 13170

Saint-Ouen-l'Aumône

Musée Départemental de l'Éducation, 2 Pl des Écoles, 95310 Saint-Ouen-l'Aumône - T: 0134640874, Fax: 0134645208, E-mail: - francoise.saghaar@ac.versailles-fr, Internet: http://www.ac.versailles-fr/pedagogi/musee-education. Head: Francoise Saghaar-Bessière
Special Museum 13171

Saint-Ouen-le-Pin

Château du Val Richer, Val Richer, 14340 Saint-Ouen-le-Pin
Decorative Arts Museum 13172

Saint-Ouen (Seine-Saint-Denis)

Musée des Beaux-Arts, Château, 12 Rue Albert-Dhalenne, 93400 Saint-Ouen (Seine-Saint-Denis) - T: 0149489520
Local Museum / Fine Arts Museum 13173

Saint-Ours-les-Roches

Muséosite du Volcan à Ciel Ouvert, Carrière de Lemptegy, D 941B, Rte de Limoges, 63230 Saint-Ours-les-Roches - T: 0473622325, Fax: 0473622381, E-mail: info@auvergne-volcan.com, Internet: http://www.auvergne-volcan.com
Natural History Museum 13174

Saint-Pal-de-Mons

Musée Archéologique, Mairie, 43620 Saint-Pal-de-Mons - T: 0471610151, Fax: 0471661740
Archaeological Museum 13175

Saint-Palais (Pyrénées-Atlantiques)

Musée de Basse-Navarre et des Chemins de Saint-Jacques, Institut Culturel Basque, Pl de l'Hôtel de Ville, 64120 Saint-Palais (Pyrénées-Atlantiques) - T: 0559657178, Fax: 0559657940. Head: Clement Urruti Bemety
Historical Museum 13176

Saint-Pandelon

Collections de Papier Peint, Château des Evêques, 40180 Saint-Pandelon - T: 0558987219
Decorative Arts Museum 13177

Saint-Paterne-Racan

Château-Musée de la Roche-Racan, 37410 Saint-Paterne-Racan - T: 0247292003/2002
Special Museum 13178

Saint-Paul (Alpes-Maritimes)

Fondation Maeght, 623 Chemin des Gardettes, 06570 Saint-Paul (Alpes-Maritimes) - T: 0493328163, Fax: 0493325322, E-mail: contact@fondation-maeght, Internet: http://www.fondation-maeght.com. Head: Jean-Louis Prat
Fine Arts Museum - 1964
Architecture, mosaics, sculpture, ceramics, 20th c paintings, modern and contemporary art - library 13179

Musée de Saint-Paul, 2 Rue Grande, 06570 Saint-Paul (Alpes-Maritimes) - T: 0493328695, Fax: 0493326027, E-mail: artdevivre@wanadoo.fr. Head: René Buron, Phillippe Mosica
Fine Arts Museum - 1964
Contemporary art 13180

Musée d'Histoire Locale, Pl de l'Eglise, 06570 Saint-Paul (Alpes-Maritimes) - T: 0493324113
Historical Museum 13181

Saint-Paul-de-Fenouillet

Musée d'Arts et de Traditions Populaires, F. Arnaudies, Chapitre, 66220 Saint-Paul-de-Fenouillet - T: 0468590026/0757
Local Museum 13182

Saint-Paul-de-Varax

Musée Louis-Jourdan, Pl Louis-Jourdan, 01240 Saint-Paul-de-Varax - T: 0474425013
Local Museum 13183

Saint-Paul-sur-Ubaye

Exposition sur l'Alpinisme d'Hier, 04530 Saint-Paul-sur-Ubaye - T: 0492843109/812715
Special Museum 13184

Musée de l'Agriculture de Montagne, Maison Amaud, 04530 Saint-Paul-sur-Ubaye - T: 0492843236
Agriculture Museum 13185

Saint-Paul-Trois-Châteaux

Maison-Musée de la Truffe et du Tricastin, 26130 Saint-Paul-Trois-Châteaux - T: 0475966129
Special Museum 13186

Saint-Paulet-de-Caisson

Exposition Monastique, Chartreuse, 30130 Saint-Paulet-de-Caisson - T: 0466827932
Special Museum 13187

Saint-Paulien

Château-Musée de la Rochelambert, La Rochelambert, 43350 Saint-Paulien - T: 0471004899
Decorative Arts Museum / Fine Arts Museum 13188

Musée Archéologique, Chapelle des Pénitents, 43350 Saint-Paulien - T: 0471005001
Archaeological Museum 13189

Saint-Pé-de-Bigorre

Musée du Monde Paysan d'Autrefois, 28 Rue du Général de Gaulle, 65270 Saint-Pé-de-Bigorre - T: 0562418235/8007
Folklore Museum 13190

Saint-Père-sous-Vezelay

Musée Archéologique Régional, Pl de l'Église, 89450 Saint-Père-sous-Vezelay - T: 0386332662/2314
Archaeological Museum 13191

Musée Lapidaire des Fontaines Salées, Site Archéologique, 89450 Saint-Père-sous-Vezelay - T: 0386332662
Archaeological Museum 13192

Saint-Philbert-de-Grand-Lieu

Maison du Lac, Musée Avifaune du Lac de Grandlieu, Rue de l'Abreuvoir, 44310 Saint-Philbert-de-Grand-Lieu - T: 0240787388, Fax: 0240788342
Natural History Museum 13193

Saint-Pierre-de-Chartreuse

Musée de la Correrie, La Correrie, 38380 Saint-Pierre-de-Chartreuse - T: 0476886045
Local Museum - 1957 13194

Musée Départemental d'Art Religieux Contemporain, Eglise Saint-Hugues, 38380 Saint-Pierre-de-Chartreuse - T: 0476886501
Religious Arts Museum 13195

Saint-Pierre-de-la-Palud

Musée de la Mine de Cuivre et de Soufre, 69210 Saint-Pierre-de-la-Palud - T: 0474703966, Fax: 0474703966. Head: Jean-Claude Beuf
Special Museum / Science&Tech Museum 13196

Musée Minéralogique et Paléontologique, 69210 Saint-Pierre-de-la-Palud - T: 0474703966, Fax: 0474703966. Head: Jean-Claude Beuf
Natural History Museum 13197

Saint-Pierre-de-Manneville

Manoir-Musée de Villers, Manoir, 76113 Saint-Pierre-de-Manneville - T: 0235320702
Decorative Arts Museum 13198

Saint-Pierre-d'Irube

Musée de la Spéléologie, des Mines et Ecologie des Sols, Ancienne Mairie, 64990 Saint-Pierre-d'Irube - T: 0559642779
Natural History Museum / Science&Tech Museum 13199

Saint-Pierre-d'Oléron

Musée de l'Ile d'Oleron Aliénor d'Aquitaine, 31 Rue Pierre-Loti, 17310 Saint-Pierre-d'Oléron - T: 0546750277, Fax: 0546720277, E-mail: musee.oleron@wanadoo.fr
Ethnology Museum - 1963
Headgear, viticulture, prehist, ethnology, agriculture, forts and citadels, life and work of Pierre Loti, salt, life of Aliénor d'Aquitaine 13200

Saint-Pierre-le-Vigier

Exposition Permanente du Lin, Kiosque, 76740 Saint-Pierre-le-Vigier - T: 0235974251/4133
Historical Museum / Science&Tech Museum 13201

Saint-Pierre-sur-Dives

Musée des Techniques Fromagères, 23 Rue Saint-Benoist, 14170 Saint-Pierre-sur-Dives - T: 0231209790
Special Museum 13202

Saint-Pierreville

Musée d'Histoire Locale, 07190 Saint-Pierreville - T: 0475666014
Historical Museum 13203

Saint-Point

Château-Musée de Lamartine, 71520 Saint-Point - T: 0385505030
Special Museum 13204

Saint-Pol-sur-Ternoise

Musée d'Art et d'Histoire, Chapelle de l'Ancien Couvent des Sœurs Noires, Rue Oscar Ricque, 62166 Saint-Pol-sur-Ternoise Cedex - T: 0321034270/470010, Fax: 0321475033
Fine Arts Museum / Historical Museum 13205

Saint-Pons-de-Thomières

Musée de la Préhistoire, 6 Rue Barry, 34220 Saint-Pons-de-Thomières - T: 0467972261/0234
Archaeological Museum 13206

Saint-Porchaire

Musée de la Préhistoire, Château de la Roche-Courbon, 17250 Saint-Porchaire - T: 0546956010, Fax: 0546956522, E-mail: larochecourbon@t3a.com
Archaeological Museum 13207

Saint-Pourçain-sur-Besbre

Château de Thoury, 03290 Saint-Pourçain-sur-Besbre - T: 0470420041
Decorative Arts Museum 13208

Musée des Automates, Parc d'Attraction et Animalier du PAL, 03290 Saint-Pourçain-sur-Besbre - T: 0470420360, Fax: 0470420152, E-mail: parc_lepal@wanadoo.fr
Science&Tech Museum 13209

Saint-Pourçain-sur-Sioule

Musée de la Vigne et du Terroir, 1 Cour des Bénédictins, 03500 Saint-Pourçain-sur-Sioule - T: 0470456207/3273
Special Museum 13210

Saint-Priest (Rhône)

Centre d'Art Contemporain Théo Argence, Pl F. Buisson, 69800 Saint-Priest (Rhône) - T: 0478200250/0366
Fine Arts Museum 13211

Saint-Privat-des-Près

Musée de l'Outil et de la Vie au Village, 24410 Saint-Privat-des-Près - T: 0553912287
Science&Tech Museum / Folklore Museum 13212

Musée des Maquettes, 24410 Saint-Privat-des-Près - T: 0553912287, Fax: 0553912287
Special Museum 13213

Saint-Prix

Musée Archéologique et d'Histoire Locale, Salle des Fêtes, 45 Rue d'Ermont, 95390 Saint-Prix - T: 0134274444
Archaeological Museum / Local Museum 13214

Saint-Puy

Musée du Pousse-Rapière, Château de Monluc, 32310 Saint-Puy - T: 0562285502/5833
Special Museum 13215

Saint-Quentin (Aisne)

Musée Antoine Lécuyer, 28 Rue Antoine Lécuyer, 02100 Saint-Quentin (Aisne) - T: 0323069398, Fax: 0323050508. Head: Hervé Cabezas
Fine Arts Museum / Decorative Arts Museum - 1856
17th-20th century pastels and paintings (Maurice-Quentin de la Tour 1704-88), portraits, 18th century ceramics, ivory, enamel, porcelain, tapestry, furniture, sculptures 13216

Musée Entomologique, 14 Rue de la Sellerie, 02100 Saint-Quentin (Aisne) - T: 0323063000
Natural History Museum 13217

Saint-Quentin-en-Yvelines

Écomusée de Saint-Quentin-en-Yvelines, 3 Pl Robert-Schumann, 78182 Saint-Quentin-en-Yvelines - T: 0134522880, Fax: 0134522741
Local Museum 13218

Saint-Quentin-Fallavier

Musée des Majorettes, 20 Rue des Cerisiers, 38290 Saint-Quentin-Fallavier - T: 0474942863
Special Museum 13219

Saint-Quentin-la-Poterie

Terra Viva, Rue de la Fontaine, 30700 Saint-Quentin-la-Poterie - T: 0466224878, Fax: 0466224878, E-mail: serge.brigitte@galerie-teraviva.com, Internet: http://www.galerie-terraviva.com. Head: Serge Tribouillois
Decorative Arts Museum
European and French ceramics 13220

Saint-Quintin-sur-Soule

Château, 63440 Saint-Quintin-sur-Soule
Decorative Arts Museum / Fine Arts Museum 13221

Saint-Racho

Exposition d'Arts, Château de Chevannes, 71800 Saint-Racho - T: 0385281774
Fine Arts Museum / Historical Museum 13222

Saint-Rambert-en-Bugey

Collections d'Arts Populaires, Maison de Pays, Av de l'Europe, 01230 Saint-Rambert-en-Bugey - T: 0474363286
Folklore Museum / Agriculture Museum 13223

Saint-Raphaël

Musée d'Archéologie Sous-Marine, Pl de la Vieille Église, 83700 Saint-Raphaël - T: 0494192575
Archaeological Museum 13224

Saint-Remèze

Musée du Monde Souterrain et Historique de la Spéléologie Française, Av Marzal, 07700 Saint-Remèze - T: 0475041245/551482
Natural History Museum 13225

Muséosite Cavernicole de la Grotte de la Madeleine, 07700 Saint-Remèze - T: 0475042220
Natural History Museum 13226

Saint-Rémy-de-Provence

Archéosite de Glanum/Les Antiques, 13210 Saint-Rémy-de-Provence - T: 0466673750/90922379
Archaeological Museum 13227

Centre d'Art Présence Van Gogh, 8 Rue Estrine, 13210 Saint-Rémy-de-Provence - T: 0490923472, Fax: 0490920484. Head: Philippe Latourelle
Fine Arts Museum 13228

Maison de l'Amandier, 11 Blvd Marceau, 13210 Saint-Rémy-de-Provence - T: 0490920228
Fine Arts Museum 13229

Musée Archéologique, Hôtel de Sade, 1 Rue du Parage, 13210 Saint-Rémy-de-Provence - T: 0490926404, Fax: 0490926402
Archaeological Museum 13230

Musée de Peinture Mario-Prassinos, Chapelle Notre-Dame-de-Pitié, Av Durand-Maillane, 13210 Saint-Rémy-de-Provence - T: 0490923513
Fine Arts Museum 13231

Musée des Alpilles, Pl Favier, 13210 Saint-Rémy-de-Provence - T: 0490926824, 0490927014, Fax: 0490922863, E-mail: musee.alpilles@wanadoo.fr. Head: Evelyne Duret
Local Museum - 1919
Portraits, sculpture, geology 13232

Musée des Arômes de Provence, 34 Blvd Mirabeau, 13210 Saint-Rémy-de-Provence - T: 0490924870, Fax: 0490924880, E-mail: florame@wanadoo.fr. Head: M. Sommerard
Special Museum 13233

Musée du Mas de la Pyramide, Glanum, 13210 Saint-Rémy-de-Provence - T: 0490920081
Archaeological Museum 13234

Saint-Rémy-sur-Orne

Les Fosses d'Enfer, Maison des Ressources Géologiques de Normandie, Rte de Caen, 14570 Saint-Rémy-sur-Orne - T: 0231696777, Fax: 0231697039. Head: Jacqueline Leblanc
Natural History Museum / Science&Tech Museum 13235

Saint-Renan

Musée d'Histoire Locale, 16 Rue Saint-Mathieu, 29290 Saint-Renan - T: 0298324494, E-mail: mus.saint-renan@wanadoo.fr. Head: Mauricette Guermont
Historical Museum
Local hist, prehist, costume, furniture 13236

Saint-Restitut

Exposition sur la Pierre et la Civilisation du Vin, Cave-Cellier des Dauphins, 26130 Saint-Restitut - T: 0475049587
Special Museum 13237

Saint-Riquier

Musée Départemental de l'Abbaye de Saint-Riquier, BP 3, 80135 Saint-Riquier - T: 0322282020, Fax: 0322289018, E-mail: museestriquier@cg80.fr
Folklore Museum 13238

Réserves Nationales des Arts et Traditions Populaires Picardie, Annexe du Musée National des A.T.P., 80135 Saint-Riquier - T: 0322282020
Fine Arts Museum 13239

Saint-Rivoal

Ecomusée des Monts d'Arrée, Maison Cornec, 29190 Saint-Rivoal - T: 0298688776/814099, Fax: 0298688551. Head: Bertrand Roux
Local Museum 13240

Saint-Romain-de-Benet

Musée des Alambics, Distillerie Brillouet, 17600 Saint-Romain-de-Benet - T: 0546020014. Head: Jean-Marc Brillonet
Special Museum 13241

Saint-Romain-en-Gal

Musée et Sites Archéologiques de Saint-Romain-en-Gal-Vienne, Rte Départementale 502, 69560 Saint-Romain-en-Gal - T: 0474537401, Fax: 0474537419, E-mail: saintromain@cg69.fr, Internet: http://www.cg69.fr/saintromain.htlm. Head: Jacques Lasfargues
Archaeological Museum - 1996
Gallo-Roman finds, mosaics, paintings 13242

Saint-Romain-Lachalm

Musée d'Arts et Traditions Populaires, 43600 Saint-Romain-Lachalm - T: 0471610008
Folklore Museum 13243

Saint-Rome

Écovillage, Maison du Monde, 31290 Saint-Rome
Special Museum 13244

Saint-Saturnin-de-Lenne

Micro-Musée du Château-Fort, La Roque Valzerque, 12560 Saint-Saturnin-de-Lenne - T: 0565704470
Local Museum 13245

Saint-Sauves-d'Auvergne

Musée du Train et de la Miniature, Le Corneloux, 63950 Saint-Sauves-d'Auvergne - T: 0473655461
Special Museum 13246

Saint-Sauveur-en-Puisaye

Musée Colette, Château, 89520 Saint-Sauveur-en-Puisaye - T: 0386456195
Special Museum 13247

Saint-Sauveur-le-Vicomte

Exposition Permanente sur l'Histoire de l'Abbaye, Abbaye, 50390 Saint-Sauveur-le-Vicomte - T: 0233416037
Historical Museum / Religious Arts Museum 13248

Musée Barbey d'Aurevilly, 66 Rue Bottin-Desylles, 50390 Saint-Sauveur-le-Vicomte - T: 0233416317, Fax: 0233414912, E-mail: dupontjo@minitel.net. Head: Joel Dupont
Special Museum - 1925
Letters and manuscripts of the writer Barbey d'Aurevilly, house where he lived, his bust by Rodin - library 13249

Saint-Sauveur-Lendelin

Château-Musée du Grand Taute, 50490 Saint-Sauveur-Lendelin - T: 0233451801
Decorative Arts Museum 13250

Saint-Ségal

Musée des Champs, 15 Rue Menez-Boss, 29550 Saint-Ségal - T: 0298730107. Head: Jean-Pierre Gestin
Agriculture Museum
Agricultural machinery 13251

Saint-Sernin-du-Bois

Musée d'Art et d'Histoire, Château, 71200 Saint-Sernin-du-Bois - T: 0385553508
Fine Arts Museum / Historical Museum 13252

Saint-Servais

Musée Yan' d'Argent, Ossuaire de l'Enclos Paroissial, 29230 Saint-Servais - T: 0298681521
Fine Arts Museum 13253

Saint-Seurin-de-Cadourne

Château-Musée Verdus et Bardis, Château, 33250 Saint-Seurin-de-Cadourne - T: 0556593159
Special Museum 13254

Saint-Sever (Landes)

Musée d'Archéologie, Couvent des Jacobins, 40500 Saint-Sever (Landes) - T: 0558760002/3464
Archaeological Museum 13255

Musée Lapidaire Municipal, Rue Lamarque, 40500 Saint-Sever (Landes) - T: 0558760138. Head: Paul Dubedat
Archaeological Museum - 1940
Gallo-Roman capitals, ancient stone relics, miniatures by Beatus of St Sever (11th c) 13256

Saint-Siffret

Collection de Peintures, Exposition Ven Hard, 15 Les Lembertes, 30700 Saint-Siffret - T: 0466226160
Fine Arts Museum 13257

Saint-Simon (Charente)

Musée du Gabarier, Maison du Gabarier, Le Bourg, 16120 Saint-Simon (Charente) - T: 0545973224
Special Museum 13258

Saint-Sorlin-d'Arves

Musée de Saint-Sorlin-d'Arves, Vie de la Montagne, Presbytère, 73530 Saint-Sorlin-d'Arves - T: 0479597060
Local Museum 13259

Saint-Sulpice-de-Faleyrens

Ecomusée Les Outils de la Vigne et du Vin, Château Le Castelot, 33330 Saint-Sulpice-de-Faleyrens - T: 0557514186
Science&Tech Museum 13260

Musée Henri IV, Château Le Castelot, 33330 Saint-Sulpice-de-Faleyrens - T: 0557514186
Local Museum 13261

Saint-Sulpice-le-Verdon

Mémorial de Vendée, Musée du Logis de la Chabotterie, 85260 Saint-Sulpice-le-Verdon - T: 0251465565
Local Museum 13262

Tract'Expo, 85260 Saint-Sulpice-le-Verdon - T: 0251428475/8081
Agriculture Museum 13263

Saint-Sulpice (Loir-et-Cher)

Musée Ferroviaire, Mairie, 41000 Saint-Sulpice (Loir-et-Cher) - T: 0254431820/0001
Science&Tech Museum 13264

Saint-Sylvain-d'Anjou

Écomusée du Château-Fort, Motte Féodale de la Haie Joulan, 49480 Saint-Sylvain-d'Anjou - T: 0241764580
Local Museum 13265

Saint-Symphorien-sous-Chomerac

Relais de la Muse du Van les Bayles, 07210 Saint-Symphorien-sous-Chomerac - T: 0475659196
Local Museum 13266

Saint-Symphorien-sur-Coise

Musée de l'Océanie, Maison des Pères Maristes, La Neylière-Pomeys, 69590 Saint-Symphorien-sur-Coise - T: 0478484033
Ethnology Museum 13267

Saint-Thibéry

Dépôt Archéologique, 34630 Saint-Thibéry - T: 0467778057, Fax: 0467770660, E-mail: -mairie_de_saint_thibery@wanadoo.fr
Archaeological Museum 13268

Saint-Thomas-de-Conac

Musée Vivant de la Meunerie, Vieux Moulin, 17150 Saint-Thomas-de-Conac - T: 0546860340
Science&Tech Museum 13269

Saint-Thurien

Ecomusée du Moulin de Kerchuz, 29114 Saint-Thurien - T: 0298398371
Science&Tech Museum 13270

Saint-Trivier-de-Courtes

Écomusée de la Ferme de la Forêt, Courtes, 01560 Saint-Trivier-de-Courtes - T: 0474307189/7345
Agriculture Museum 13271

Saint-Trojan-les-Bains

Musée Ostréicole, Sur le Port, 17370 Saint-Trojan-les-Bains - T: 0546760816/0086
Special Museum 13272

Saint-Tropez

L'Annonciade, Musée de Saint-Tropez, Pl Georges Grammont, 83990 Saint-Tropez - T: 0494970401, Fax: 0494978724. Head: Jean-Paul Monery
Fine Arts Museum - 1955
Modern paintings, sculpture, French art (1890-1940), Neo-Impressionists, Fauves, Nabis artists 13273

Collection Lartigue, 9 Rue Étienne-Berny, 83990 Saint-Tropez - T: 0494976345/2460
Fine Arts Museum 13274

Musée National de la Marine, Citadelle de Saint-Tropez, 83990 Saint-Tropez - T: 0494975943, Fax: 0494972440, E-mail: g.prudhomme@musee_marine.fr, Internet: http://www.musee-marine.fr. Head: Georges Prudhomme
Historical Museum
Model ships (navy, merchants navy, fishing navy), paintings, figureheads, local maritime history 13275

Saint-Vaast-la-Hougue

Musée de l'Épicerie Gosselin, 23 Rue de Verrue, 50550 Saint-Vaast-la-Hougue - T: 0233544006
Fine Arts Museum / Folklore Museum 13276

Musée Gosselin, 1 Rue des Thins, 50550 Saint-Vaast-la-Hougue - T: 0233544522
Fine Arts Museum 13277

Musée Maritime de l'Ile de Tatihou, BP 3, 50550 Saint-Vaast-la-Hougue - T: 0233231992, 0233543333, Fax: 0233543347, E-mail: ile.tatihou@cg50.fr, Internet: http://www.tatihou.com. Head: Jean-François Detrée
Ethnology Museum / Local Museum / Historical Museum 13278

Saint-Valery-en-Caux

Collections de la Maison Henri-IV, Quai de la Batellerie, 76460 Saint-Valery-en-Caux - T: 0235970063
Local Museum 13279

Saint-Vallier-de-Thiey

Musée de Plein Air, Parc Préhistorique, Grottes des Audides, Rte de Cabris, 06460 Saint-Vallier-de-Thiey - T: 0493426415, E-mail: -grottesdesaudides@free.fr, Internet: http://www.grottedesaudides.free.fr. Head: Jacqueline Reich
Archaeological Museum / Natural History Museum / Open Air Museum 13280

Saint-Véran

Musée de la Maison d'Autrefois, Centre du Village Ancien, Quartier Foranes, 05490 Saint-Véran - T: 0492458642
Folklore Museum 13281

Musée de la Maison Traditionelle du Queyras, Centre du Village Ancien, Quartier Pierre-Belle, 05490 Saint-Véran - T: 0492458477
Local Museum 13282

Saint-Viatre

Maison-Musée de la Vie des Etangs, 41210 Saint-Viatre - T: 0254889320
Natural History Museum 13283

Saint-Victor-sur-Arlanc

Musée de la Radio Les Années 30, Le Bourg, 43500 Saint-Victor-sur-Arlanc - T: 0471033425, Fax: 0471033677
Science&Tech Museum 13284

Saint-Vidal

Château-Musée, N 102 et D 112, D 590, 43320 Saint-Vidal
Military Museum 13285

Saint-Vincent-de-Paul

Maison Natale de Saint-Vincent-de-Paul, Ferme Ranquines, 40180 Saint-Vincent-de-Paul - T: 0558559311, Fax: 0558559798
Religious Arts Museum 13286

Saint-Vincent-sur-Jabron

Musée du Casque de Combat, Restaurant de la Vallée, 04200 Saint-Vincent-sur-Jabron - T: 0492620825
Military Museum 13287

Saint-Vincent-sur-Jard

Musée Clemenceau, Maison de Belesbat, 85520 Saint-Vincent-sur-Jard - T: 0251334032
Special Museum 13288

Saint-Vivien-de-Médoc

Château-Musée Listran, 33590 Saint-Vivien-de-Médoc - T: 0556094859/5483
Special Museum 13289

Saint-Vougay

Musée de Mobilier Breton, Château de Kerjean, 29225 Saint-Vougay - T: 0298699369
Folklore Museum / Decorative Arts Museum 13290

Saint-Vrain

Muséoparc de la Préhistoire, Parc de Saint-Vrain, 91770 Saint-Vrain - T: 0164561080
Archaeological Museum 13291

Saint-Yrieix-la-Perche

Musée de la Porcelaine, Les Palloux, 87500 Saint-Yrieix-la-Perche - T: 0555751038
Decorative Arts Museum 13292

Saint-Yzans-de-Médoc

Musée Viticole, Château Loudenne, 33340 Saint-Yzans-de-Médoc - T: 0556731780
Special Museum 13293

Petit Musée du Métier de Tonnelier, Château Les Tuileries, 33340 Saint-Yzans-de-Médoc - T: 0556090531
Folklore Museum 13294

Sainte-Agathe-en-Donzy

Moulin Maître Marcel, 42510 Sainte-Agathe-en-Donzy - T: 0477286336
Science&Tech Museum 13295

Sainte-Agnès

Musée Archéologique, 06500 Sainte-Agnès - T: 0493571460
Archaeological Museum 13296

Musée de la Ligne Maginot Alpine, Ouvrage de Sainte-Agnès, 06500 Sainte-Agnès - T: 0493571460
Military Museum 13297

Musée du Temps Passé, Pl de l'Église, 06500 Sainte-Agnès - T: 0493571460
Historical Museum 13298

Sainte-Anne-d'Auray

Musée du Costume Breton, Esplanade, 56400 Sainte-Anne-d'Auray - T: 0297576880
Folklore Museum 13299

Musée Historial de Sainte-Anne, 6 Rue de Vannes, 56400 Sainte-Anne-d'Auray - T: 0297576405
Local Museum 13300

Sainte-Bazeille

Musée Archéologique, Rte de Couture-sur-Garonne, 47200 Sainte-Bazeille - T: 0553944028/4892
Archaeological Museum 13301

Sainte-Cathérine-de-Fierbois

Musée d'Arts et Traditions Populaires, Rue de Boucicault, 37800 Sainte-Cathérine-de-Fierbois - T: 0247656911
Folklore Museum 13302

Musée Jeanne d'Arc, Pl Jeanne d'Arc, 37800 Sainte-Cathérine-de-Fierbois - T: 0247654346
Religious Arts Museum 13303

Sainte-Colombe-sur-Seine

Musée des Canadiens Nord-Bourguignons, Pl de l'Eglise, 21400 Sainte-Colombe-sur-Seine - T: 0380910846, Fax: 0380914299. Head: Annie Hernandez
Ethnology Museum 13304

Musée Éclaté de la Sidérurgie en Bourgogne du Nord (closed) 13305

Sainte-Consorce

Musée Antoine Brun, Pl de l'Eglise, 69280 Sainte-Consorce - T: 0478870112
Fine Arts Museum 13306

Sainte-Croix-aux-Mines

Musée de la Scierie Ariel-Vincent, 1A Rue Maurice Burrus, 68160 Sainte-Croix-aux-Mines - T: 0389587818. Head: Ariel Vincent
Science&Tech Museum 13307

Sainte-Croix-Vallée-Française

Musée de l'Homme et de sa Montagne, Pont-Ravagers, 48110 Sainte-Croix-Vallée-Française - T: 0466447102
Archaeological Museum / Local Museum / Folklore Museum 13308

Sainte-Croix-Volvestre

Musée des Vieux Métiers et des Traditions Populaires, Ancienne Gendarmerie, Rte de Cazères, 09230 Sainte-Croix-Volvestre - T: 0561667383
Folklore Museum 13309

Sainte-Enimie

Musée du Folklore, Vieux Logis, 48210 Sainte-Enimie - T: 0466485009/5344
Folklore Museum 13310

Sainte-Eulalie

Ferme-Musée des Sources de la Loire, Café Ceyte, 07510 Sainte-Eulalie
Local Museum 13311

Maison du Bison d'Europe, 48120 Sainte-Eulalie - T: 0466314040
Natural History Museum 13312

Sainte-Foy-la-Grande

Centre d'Etude et de Recherches Préhistoriques Charles Nardin, 102 Rue de la République, 33220 Sainte-Foy-la-Grande - T: 0557460300
Archaeological Museum 13313

Sainte-Foy-l'Argentière

Musée du Train à Vapeur, Gare, 69610 Sainte-Foy-l'Argentière - T: 0474709064/79694923
Special Museum / Science&Tech Museum 13314

Sainte-Geneviève (Meurthe-et-Moselle)

Musée des Vieux Tracteurs, 6 Rte de Bezaumont, 54700 Sainte-Geneviève (Meurthe-et-Moselle) - T: 0383821460
Science&Tech Museum 13315

Sainte-Julie

Collection de Peintures Héraldiques, Château, 01150 Sainte-Julie - T: 0474619586
Special Museum 13316

Sainte-Léocadie

Musée de Cerdagne, Ferme Cal Mateu, 66800 Sainte-Léocadie - T: 0468040805, Fax: 0468040714, E-mail: musee.cerdagne@netcarrier.com. Head: Dominique Pilato
Ethnology Museum 13317

Sainte-Lucie

Muscole de Gévaudan, 20144 Sainte-Lucie - T: 0466471948
Local Museum 13318

Sainte-Marguerite

Ferme-Musée lé Moho dé Soyotte, Musée Arts et Traditions Populaires, 684 Chemin du Greffier, 88100 Sainte-Marguerite - T: 0329566889, Fax: 0329562842, E-mail: soyotte@yahoo.fr. Head: Marie-Thérèse Bernard
Agriculture Museum / Ethnology Museum / Folklore Museum 13319

Sainte-Marie-au-Bosc

Exposition Permanente d'Attelages de Collection, Ferme Masson, 76280 Sainte-Marie-au-Bosc - T: 0235282726/2495
Special Museum 13320

Sainte-Marie-aux-Mines

Collections de la Mine d'Argent Saint-Barthélemy, Rue Saint-Louis, 68160 Sainte-Marie-aux-Mines - T: 0389587228
Natural History Museum 13321

Collections de la Mine Saint-Louis, Asepam, 68160 Sainte-Marie-aux-Mines - T: 0389586211/8050
Historical Museum / Natural History Museum 13322

Maison de Pays, Pl du Prensureux, 68160 Sainte-Marie-aux-Mines - T: 0389585667. Head: Dr. Philippe Gasperment
Science&Tech Museum - 1989
Textile mining 13323

Musée Minéralogique et du Patrimoine Minier, Maison de Pays, 68160 Sainte-Marie-aux-Mines - T: 0389585657/8050
Special Museum / Natural History Museum 13324

Musée Technique des Tissus, Maison de Pays, 68160 Sainte-Marie-aux-Mines - T: 0389585657/8050
Science&Tech Museum 13325

Sainte-Marie-du-Lac-Nuisement

Ecomusée du Village Champenois, 51290 Sainte-Marie-du-Lac-Nuisement - T: 0326726325/6280/3633
Folklore Museum 13326

Sainte-Marie-du-Mont

Musée du Débarquement à Utah Beach, Plage, 50480 Sainte-Marie-du-Mont - T: 0233715335/5800. Head: Michel de Vallvieille
Military Museum 13327

Sainte-Maure-de-Peyriac

La Ruche Gasconne, Le Peyré, 47170 Sainte-Maure-de-Peyriac - T: 0553656101
Natural History Museum 13328

Sainte-Maure-de-Touraine

Musée d'Arts et d'Histoire, Château des Rohan, Rue du Château, 37800 Sainte-Maure-de-Touraine - T: 0247656620, Fax: 0247340428
Fine Arts Museum / Historical Museum / Decorative Arts Museum 13329

Sainte-Maxime

Musée de la Tour Carrée, Pl Aliziers, 83120 Sainte-Maxime - T: 0494967030
Local Museum 13330

Musée du Phonographe et de la Musique Mécanique, Parc Saint-Donat, Rte du Muy, 83120 Sainte-Maxime - T: 0494965052
Music Museum 13331

Sainte-Menehould

Musée de l'Argonne, Pl du Général Leclerc, 51800 Sainte-Menehould - T: 0326608021, Fax: 0326607254, Internet: http://www.ville.ste-menehould.fr. Head: Gérard Mourlet
Local Museum 13332

Sainte-Mère-Eglise

Musée de la Ferme du Contentin, Ferme de Beauvais, 50480 Sainte-Mère-Eglise - T: 0233413025
Agriculture Museum - 1979 13333

Musée des Troupes Aéroportées, Airborn Museum, Pl du 6 Juin 1944, 50480 Sainte-Mère-Eglise - T: 0233414135. Head: Ph. Jutras
Military Museum 13334

Sainte-Mondane

Château de Fénelon, 24370 Sainte-Mondane - T: 0553298145, Fax: 0553298899
Historical Museum
Arms and weapons 13335

Sainte-Sigolène

Écomusée La Fabrique, Rue des Riouze, 43600 Sainte-Sigolène - T: 0471666434
Local Museum / Decorative Arts Museum 13336

Sainte-Suzanne

Forteresse-Château, 53270 Sainte-Suzanne - T: 0243014077/10
Fine Arts Museum 13337

Musée de l'Auditoire, Grande Rue, 53270 Sainte-Suzanne - T: 0243014265, Fax: 0243014265, E-mail: musee.auditoire@wanadoo.fr, Internet: http://www.sainte-suzanne.com. Head: Gérard Morteveille
Historical Museum - 1972
Weapons of the Middle Ages 13338

Saintes

Maison du Folklore de Saintonge, 89 Rue Saint-Pallais, 17100 Saintes - T: 0546936709
Folklore Museum 13339

Musée Archéologique, Esplanade André-Malraux, 17100 Saintes - T: 0546742097, Fax: 0546976233, E-mail: musees.saintes.alienor@wanadoo.fr
Archaeological Museum
Prehistoric items, Gallo-Roman finds - library 13340

Musée de l'Échevinage, Rue Alsace-Lorraine, 17100 Saintes - T: 0546935239
Fine Arts Museum / Decorative Arts Museum 13341

Musée des Beaux-Arts, Le Présidial et l'Echevinage, Rue Victor-Hugo, 17100 Saintes - T: 0546930394/5239, E-mail: musees.saintes.alienor@wanadoo.fr
Fine Arts Museum - 1967/1977
16th-20th century paintings of French, Italian, Dutch and Flemish schools, screens, portraits, 16th-20th century ceramics, Sèvres porcelain 13342

Musée Éducatif de la Préhistoire, 140 Av Gambetta, 17100 Saintes - T: 0546934327
Historical Museum 13343

Musée Régional Dupuy-Méstreau, 4 Rue Monconseil, 17100 Saintes - T: 0546933671, Fax: 0546976233, E-mail: musees.saintes.alienor@wanadoo.fr
Local Museum 13344

Saintes-Maries-de-la-Mer

Château d'Avignon, RD 570, 13460 Saintes-Maries-de-la-Mer - T: 0490978632
Decorative Arts Museum 13345

Écomusée-Panorama des Gens du Voyage, Rte de Cacharel, 13460 Saintes-Maries-de-la-Mer - T: 0490975285
Ethnology Museum 13346

Maison du Parc Naturel Régional de Camargue, Pont de Gau, 13460 Saintes-Maries-de-la-Mer - T: 0490978632, Fax: 0490977082, E-mail: centre-information.pnrc@wanadoo.fr
Natural History Museum 13347

Musée Baroncelli, Ancien Hôtel de la Ville, Rue Victor-Hugo, 13460 Saintes-Maries-de-la-Mer - T: 0490978760
Local Museum - 1942
Archaeology, natural hist, ornithology of Camargue, folk art, agricultural equipment 13348

Musée de Cire, RD 570, Rte d'Arles, 13460 Saintes-Maries-de-la-Mer - T: 0490978265
Folklore Museum 13349

Saints-en-Puisaye

Écomusée de la Ferme du Moulin Vanneau, RD 211, 89520 Saints-en-Puisaye - T: 0386455980, Fax: 0386455980, E-mail: contact@moulinvanneau.org
Agriculture Museum 13350

Sainville

Musée Eugène Farcot, Pl du Carrefour, 28700 Sainville - T: 0237246006
Special Museum 13351

Saissac

Musée des Vieux Métiers, D 629, Tour, 11310 Saissac - T: 0468244780/4655
Local Museum 13352

Salbris

Musée de l'Abeille et du Braconnage, La Ruche, Rte Nationale 20 Sud, 41300 Salbris - T: 0254972928, Fax: 0254972928
Special Museum 13353

Salers

Collection d'Arts Décoratifs, Maison de Bargues, 15410 Salers - T: 0471404342
Decorative Arts Museum 13354

Maison des Templiers, Musée Art et Tradition du Pays de Salers, Rue des Templiers, 15410 Salers - T: 0471407597, Fax: 0471407240. Head: Philippe Garrigue
Folklore Museum - 1988
Pharmacy, cheese production, cattle breed, history of town, folklore 13355

Salies-de-Béarn

Musée des Traditions Béarnaises, Pl du Bayaa, 64270 Salies-de-Béarn - T: 0559380033
Folklore Museum 13356

Musée du Sel, Rue des Puits-Salants, 64270 Salies-de-Béarn - T: 0559380033
Special Museum 13357

Salins-les-Bains

Musée de la Faïencerie, Av Aristide Briand, 39110 Salins-les-Bains - T: 0384730145
Decorative Arts Museum 13358

Musée Municipal Max Claudet, Pl des Salines, 39110 Salins-les-Bains - T: 0384730134, Fax: 0384379285, E-mail: contact@salins-les-bains.com
Local Museum 13359

Sallanches

Musée des Réserves Naturelles de la Haute-Savoie, Château des Rubins, 74700 Sallanches - T: 0450583213
Natural History Museum 13360

Sallèles-d'Aude

Musée des Potiers Gallo-Romains, Amphoralis, Allée des Potiers, 11590 Sallèles-d'Aude - T: 0468468948
Archaeological Museum 13361

Sallenelles

Musée-Maison de la Nature et de l'Estuaire de l'Orne, Blvd Maritime, 14121 Sallenelles - T: 0231787106
Natural History Museum 13362

Sallertaine

La Bourine à Rosalie, VC 119, 85300 Sallertaine - T: 0251494360/51617361
Decorative Arts Museum / Folklore Museum 13363

Musée Maraîchin, Église Romane, 85300 Sallertaine - T: 0251355181
Folklore Museum 13364

Musée-Moulin à Vent de Rairé, 85300 Sallertaine - T: 0251355182
Science&Tech Museum 13365

Salles-Arbuissonnas-en-Beaujolais

Musée de la Vigne, La Péreuse, 69460 Salles-Arbuissonnas-en-Beaujolais - T: 0474675267
Special Museum 13366

Musée Historique du Cloître, Salle Capitulaire, 69460 Salles-Arbuissonnas-en-Beaujolais - T: 0474675181
Historical Museum 13367

Salles-d'Angles

Musée d'Arts et d'Histoire, Presbytère, 16130 Salles-d'Angles - T: 0545837113
Fine Arts Museum / Historical Museum 13368

Salles-la-Source

Musée des Arts et Métiers, Ancienne Filature, 12330 Salles-la-Source - T: 0565672896
Ethnology Museum 13369

Salmiech

Musée du Charroi Rural, Ancienne Église, 12120 Salmiech - T: 0563742355. Head: Georges Désirat
Science&Tech Museum / Agriculture Museum / Ethnology Museum - 1980
Vehicles used in farms before motorisation 13370

Salon-de-Provence

Maison de Nostradamus, 11 Rue de Nostradamus, 13300 Salon-de-Provence - T: 0490566431. Head: Jacqueline Allemand
Special Museum 13371

Musée-Conservatoire de la Savonnerie Marius-Fabre, 148 Av Paul Bourret, 13300 Salon-de-Provence - T: 0490532477
Special Museum 13372

Musée de l'Empéri, Château de l'Empéri, 13300 Salon-de-Provence - T: 0490562236, Fax: 0490560812. Head: Marie-Christine Braillard
Military Museum - 1967
French military hist and art: armament, uniforms and equipment, flags, harnesses, painting, drawings, etchings, iconography, documents, etc since the 17th c - library 13373

Musée de Salon et de la Crau, Av Roger Donnadieu, 13300 Salon-de-Provence - T: 0490562837, Fax: 0490560812. Head: Marie-Christine Roquette-Gept
Special Museum - 1975
Histoire de la technique de fabrication du Savon de Marseille, culture de l'olivier et hegou de l'huile d'o line, ornithologie regionale, histoire du pastoralisme transhumant de la Crau 13374

Musée Grévin de la Provence, Pl des Centuries, 13300 Salon-de-Provence - T: 0490563630, Fax: 0490560812. Head: Corinne Lambon
Historical Museum 13375

Salses-le-Château

Musée Catalan d'Histoire, 14 Av de Gaulle, 66600 Salses-le-Château - T: 0468366613
Local Museum / Decorative Arts Museum 13376

Musée de la Forteresse, 66600 Salses-le-Château - T: 0468386013
Military Museum 13377

Samadet

Musée de la Faïence → Musée de la Faïence et des Arts de la Table

Musée de la Faïence et des Arts de la Table, 2378 Rte de Hagetmau, 40320 Samadet - T: 0558791300, Fax: 0558460835, E-mail: musees@cg40.fr
Decorative Arts Museum - 1969
Faïence, life in Chalosse during the 18th c - library 13378

Samatan

Musée du Foie Gras et des Traditions Populaires, 3 Rue du Chanoine Dieuzaide, 32130 Samatan - T: 0562625540
Special Museum / Folklore Museum 13379

Samer

Musée de la Nature, A.-Caron, 20 Pl de l'Abbaye, 62830 Samer - T: 0321335866
Natural History Museum 13380

Musée de Peintures Cazin, Hôtel de Ville, 62830 Samer - T: 0321335064. Head: Jean Basilien
Fine Arts Museum 13381

Sampigny

Musée Raymond Poincaré, Le Clos, 55300 Sampigny - T: 0329907050, Fax: 0329907514, E-mail: cdmm@cg55.fr. Head: Philippe Pagnotta
Historical Museum 13382

Sanary-sur-Mer

Musée de l'Automobile Sportive, 4303 Ancien Chemin de Toulon, 83110 Sanary-sur-Mer - T: 04946363/0002
Science&Tech Museum 13383

Sancey-le-Long

Musée Sainte-Jeanne-Antide-Thouret, 25430 Sancey-le-Long - T: 0381868241, Fax: 0381868879
Religious Arts Museum 13384

Sancoins

Centre Artistique Jean-Baffier, 18600 Sancoins - T: 0248745081/5888
Fine Arts Museum 13385

Sanguinet

Musée d'Archéologie Sublacustre, Pl de la Mairie, 40460 Sanguinet - T: 0558785420/6084. Head: Bernard Maurin
Archaeological Museum 13386

Sannois

Musée Utrillo-Valadon, Pl du Général Leclerc, 95110 Sannois - T: 0139982113, Fax: 0139982011, E-mail: culture@sannois.org, Internet: http://www.ville-sannois.fr. Head: Jean Fabris
Fine Arts Museum 13387

Santenay

Caveau-Musée des Jacobines, 21590 Santenay - T: 0380206009
Special Museum 13388

Musée de la Viticulture, Château Philippe-Le-Hardi, 21590 Santenay - T: 0380206187, Fax: 0380206366
Special Museum 13389

Sapois-Menaurupt

Collection Internationale d'Épinettes, Rte du Col, 88120 Sapois-Menaurupt - T: 0329248518, Fax: 0329232938, E-mail: toussaint.christophe@free.fr, Internet: http://epinette.free.fr. Head: Christophe Toussaint
Music Museum 13390

Sarcelles

Musée Naval de Sarcelles, 27 Blvd du Général-de-Gaulle, 95200 Sarcelles - T: 0139868850/34191182
Special Museum / Military Museum 13391

Sare

Grottes Préhistoriques de Sare-Lezea, 64310 Sare - T: 0559542188
Fine Arts Museum 13392

Musée de la Pelote Basque, 64310 Sare - T: 0559542014
Special Museum 13393

Musée Ethnographique de Site, José-Miguel de Barandiarau, 64310 Sare
Ethnology Museum / Archaeological Museum 13394

Sarge-sur-Braye

Musée du Roussard, Église Saint-Martin, 41170 Sarge-sur-Braye - T: 0254801105
Special Museum 13395

Sarlat-la-Canéda

Château de Temniac, 24200 Sarlat-la-Canéda - T: 0553302526, E-mail: temniac@ifrance.com/temniac. Head: M. Desvigne
Historic Site
Historic monument, ruins of the former bishops' residence of Sarlat 13396

Distillerie du Périgord, Parc de Madrazès, 24200 Sarlat-la-Canéda - T: 0553593110, Fax: 0553311874, E-mail: distillerie.perigord@perigord.com, Internet: http://www.perigord.com/distillerie_perigord
Special Museum 13397

Galerie d'Art Contemporain, Gorodka, 24200 Sarlat-la-Canéda - T: 0553320200, 0553291893
Public Gallery 13398

Sarniguet

Ferme-Musée, 65390 Sarniguet - T: 0562365577/346437
Agriculture Museum 13399

Sarralbe

Musée du Pays d'Albe, 40 Rue Clemenceau, 57430 Sarralbe - T: 0387978017/9090. Head: Louis Serpe
Folklore Museum / Historical Museum 13400

Musée Historique de la Ligne Maginot Aquatique, Maison des Têtes, 40 Rue Clemenceau, 57430 Sarralbe - T: 0387979090/8017. Head: Louis Serpe
Military Museum / Historical Museum 13401

Souvenirs de Temps Passé, 25 Rue de l'Étang, 57430 Sarralbe - T: 0387978145
Historical Museum 13402

Sarrance

Ecomusée des Pratiques Religieuses, Chemin de Saint-Jacques-de-Compostelle, 64490 Sarrance - T: 0559347369/5496
Religious Arts Museum 13403

Sarre-Union

Musée Pédagogique de Circonscription, Inspection E.N., 67260 Sarre-Union - T: 0388001251
Special Museum 13404

Musée Régional de l'Alsace Bossue, Ancien Collège des Jésuites, 67260 Sarre-Union - T: 0388002808
Science&Tech Museum 13405

Sarrebourg

Musée du Pays de Sarrebourg, 13 Av de France, 57400 Sarrebourg - T: 0387032786, Fax: 0387030519. Head: Dominique Heckenbenner
Archaeological Museum - 1905
Pre- and protohist, Gallo- Roman and Merovingian items, medieval and modern sculpture - library 13406

Sarreguemines

Musée de la Faïence, 15-17 Rue Poincaré, 57322 Sarreguemines - T: 0387989350, Fax: 0387983728, E-mail: curator@sarreguemines-museum.com, Internet: http://www.sarreguemines-museum.com. Head: E. Decker
Decorative Arts Museum - 1972 13407

Musée des Techniques Faïencières, 125 Av de la Blies, 57200 Sarreguemines - T: 0387989350, Fax: 0387983728, E-mail: curator@sarreguemines-museum.com, Internet: http://www.sarreguemines-museum.com. Head: E. Decker
Science&Tech Museum - 1998 13408

Sars-Poteries

Musée du Verre, 1 Rue du Général de Gaulle, 59216 Sars-Poteries - T: 0327616144, Fax: 0327616564, E-mail: museeduverre@cg59.fr. Head: Anne Vanlatum
Decorative Arts Museum - 1967
19th century glasswork and contemporary glass sculpture 13409

Sartène

Musée Départemental de Pré et Protohistoire Corse, Rue Croce, 20100 Sartène - T: 0495771009
Archaeological Museum
Regional prehistory 13410

Sarzay

Musée des Vieux Métiers et du Travail, Château de Sarzay, 36230 Sarzay - T: 0254313225
Folklore Museum 13411

Sarzeau

Château-Musée du Suscinio, Suscinio, 56370 Sarzeau - T: 0297419191. Head: Jean-Marc Michaud
Historical Museum - 1987
Hist of the castle, painting, Breton hist, medevial paving tiles 13412

Sauclières

Musée des Automates, 12230 Sauclières - T: 0565621181
Special Museum 13413

Saugues

Collections François-Fabre, Rue du Prieuré, 43170 Saugues - T: 0471778253
Natural History Museum 13414

Diorama Saint-Bénilde, Maison Saint-Bénilde, Rue du Prieuré, 43170 Saugues - T: 0471778253
Special Museum 13415

Musée de la Forêt, Tour des Anglais, Rue de la Tour, 43170 Saugues - T: 0471778122
Natural History Museum 13416

Muséosite de Montchauvet, Rte de Malzieu, 43170 Saugues - T: 0471776171
Local Museum 13417

Sauliac-sur-Célé

Ecomusée de Plein Air du Quercy, Domaine de Cuzals, 46330 Sauliac-sur-Célé - T: 0565225863, E-mail: MuseedePleinAirduQuercy@wanadoo.fr. Head: J.-L. Obereiner
Open Air Museum / Agriculture Museum - 1985
Local architecture, rural life - documentation centre, library 13418

Musée Vivant de l'Enfance, Domaine de Cuzals, 46330 Sauliac-sur-Célé - T: 0565225863
Special Museum 13419

Saulieu

Musée François-Pompon, Pl Docteur-Roclore, 21210 Saulieu - T: 0380641951/0021
Local Museum
Religious art, 12th-18th century sculptures, crafts, archeology, reional and local history, Gallo-Roman stelae of the antique necropolis of Saulieu, original works of the sculptor François Pompon 13420

Sault-lès-Rethel

Musée de la Bécane à Grand-Père, 22 Av Bourgoin, 08300 Sault-lès-Rethel - T: 0324384627
Science&Tech Museum 13421

Sault (Vaucluse)

Musée Archéologique et d'Histoire Naturelle, 84390 Sault (Vaucluse) - T: 0490640230/0301
Local Museum 13422

Musée de la Chasse et de l'Environnement, Av de l'Oratoire, 84390 Sault (Vaucluse) - T: 0490641396
Natural History Museum 13423

Saulty

Salle-Musée du Spitfire, 62158 Saulty - T: 0321714625
Special Museum 13424

Saumane-de-Vaucluse

Musée Archéologique, Mas de la Crémade, 84800 Saumane-de-Vaucluse - T: 0490616474
Archaeological Museum 13425

Saumur

Centre d'Art Contemporain Bouvet-Ladubay, Rue Ackermann, 49400 Saumur - T: 0241838382, Fax: 0241502432, E-mail: bouvet-ladubay@saumur.net, Internet: http://www.bouvet-ladubay.fr. Head: Patrice Monmousseau
Public Gallery 13426

Musée de la Cavalerie, 49400 Saumur - T: 0241839306
Military Museum 13427

Musée de la Distillerie Combier, Rue Beaurepaire, 49415 Saumur - T: 0241402300, Fax: 0241402309, E-mail: f-choisne@combier.fr. Head: Franck Choisne
Special Museum 13428

Musée de la Figurine - Jouets, Rue des Remparts, 49400 Saumur - T: 0241673923/520281
Special Museum 13429

Musée des Arts Décoratifs, Château, 49400 Saumur - T: 0241402440, Fax: 0241402449. Head: Jacqueline Mongellaz
Decorative Arts Museum - 1829
Local prehistoric and Gallo-Roman finds, 13th-18th century wood sculptures, Limoges enamels, 15th-18th century tapestries and furniture, 16th-18th century French faience and porcelain 13430

Musée des Blindés, 1043 Rte de Fontevraud, 49400 Saumur - T: 0241530699, Fax: 0241530690, E-mail: museedesblindes@wanadoo.fr, Internet: http://www.musee-des-blindes.asso.fr
Military Museum 13431

Musée du Cheval, Château, 49400 Saumur - T: 0241402440, Fax: 0241402449. Head: Jacqueline Mongellaz
Special Museum - 1829
Hist of horse and horse breeding, horse equipment of all times and all countries, 18th-19th century English engravings of horses and races - library 13432

Musée du Moteur, 18 Rue Alphonse-Cailleau, 49400 Saumur - T: 0241502610, E-mail: musee.moteur@worldonline.fr, Internet: http://perso.worldonline.fr/museemoteur. Head: Philippe Billier
Science&Tech Museum 13433

Musée Maxime Mabilleau des Vins Effervescents, Caves Gratien et Meyer, Rte de Montsoreau, 49400 Saumur - T: 0241510154
Science&Tech Museum / Special Museum 13434

Saussey

Musée du Verre et de la Crèche, Manoir, 50200 Saussey - T: 0233451965
Decorative Arts Museum 13435

Sauvain

Musée de la Maison Sauvagnarde, 42990 Sauvain - T: 0477768378
Special Museum / Folklore Museum 13436

Sauveterre-de-Béarn

Musée d'Histoire Paul Mirat, Mairie, 64390 Sauveterre-de-Béarn - T: 0559385017
Historical Museum 13437

Sauveterre-de-Guyenne

Exposition Permanente, 2 Rue Saint-Romain, 33540 Sauveterre-de-Guyenne - T: 0556715345
Local Museum 13438

Sauveterre-de-Rouergue

Centre d'Études et d'Exposition des Bastides du Rouergue, Rue Notre-Dame, 12800 Sauveterre-de-Rouergue - T: 0565720252
Historical Museum 13439

Musée d'Art Populaire, L'Oustal Rouergat, Pl des Arcades, 12800 Sauveterre-de-Rouergue - T: 0565470532
Folklore Museum 13440

Sauveterre-la-Lémance

Château des Rois Ducs, Château, 47500 Sauveterre-la-Lémance - T: 0553406717
Archaeological Museum 13441

Musée de Préhistoire Mésolitique L. Coulonges, Mairie, 47500 Sauveterre-la-Lémance - T: 0553407303, Fax: 0553406386, E-mail: musee.sauveterre-la-lemance@wanadoo.fr
Archaeological Museum 13442

Sauvigny-Le-Bois

Musée des Voitures Présidentielles, RD 957, 89200 Sauvigny-Le-Bois - T: 0386344642, Fax: 0386316683, E-mail: odelafon@aol.com
Special Museum 13443

Sauxillanges

Exposition Historique du Monastère, Maison du Patrimoine, 63490 Sauxillanges - T: 0473968025
Religious Arts Museum 13444

Saverne

Musée Archéologique, Château des Rohan, 67700 Saverne - T: 0388910628, Fax: 0388910583. Head: Gabrielle Feyler
Archaeological Museum 13445

Musée de la Tour Chappe, Au Haut-Barr, 67700 Saverne - T: 0388529899, Fax: 0388521811, E-mail: contactst@shpta.com, Internet: http://www.shpta.com. Head: Harry Franz
Science&Tech Museum 13446

Musée de la Vache, 18 Rue du Serpent, 67700 Saverne - T: 0388912387
Special Museum 13447

Musée de la Ville de Saverne, Château des Rohan, 67700 Saverne - T: 0388910628, Fax: 0388910583. Head: Gabrielle Feyler
Local Museum / Fine Arts Museum / Historical Museum - 1858
Archaeological colls, Donation Louise Weiss 13448

Musée des Sapeurs-Pompiers, Caserne, 67700 Saverne - T: 0388912722
Science&Tech Museum / Historical Museum 13449

Musée Louise Weiss, Château des Rohan, 67700 Saverne - T: 0388910628, Fax: 0388910583. Head: Gabrielle Feyler
Historical Museum 13450

Savigné-sur-Lathan

Musée des Trains et des Transports Miniatures, Chemin du Pont-de-la-Forge, 37340 Savigné-sur-Lathan - T: 0247246019
Science&Tech Museum 13451

Musée du Savignéen, Faubourg de la Rüe, 37340 Savigné-sur-Lathan - T: 0247249514
Local Museum 13452

Savigny-les-Beaune

Collection Rare de Tracteurs Viticoles, Château, 21420 Savigny-les-Beaune - T: 0380215503
Science&Tech Museum 13453

Musée de la Moto, Château, 21420 Savigny-les-Beaune - T: 0380215503
Science&Tech Museum 13454

Musée de la Voiture de Course, Château, 21420 Savigny-les-Beaune - T: 0380215503
Science&Tech Museum 13455

Musée de l'Aviation, Château, 21420 Savigny-les-Beaune - T: 0380215503
Science&Tech Museum 13456

Musée de Modélisme, Château, 21420 Savigny-les-Beaune
Science&Tech Museum 13457

Savigny (Rhône)

Musée Lapidaire de l'Abbaye, Ancien Cuvier, 69210 Savigny (Rhône) - T: 0474014887/70011141
Archaeological Museum 13458

Savigny-sous-Mâlain

Musée d'Histoire Locale, 21540 Savigny-sous-Mâlain - T: 0380236608/6073
Archaeological Museum 13459

Savonnières

Musée de la Pétrification, Grottes Pétrifiantes, 37510 Savonnières - T: 0247500009
Special Museum 13460

Saxon-Sion

Musée Archéologique et Missionnaire, Rue Notre-Dame, 54330 Saxon-Sion - T: 0387251222
Archaeological Museum / Religious Arts Museum 13461

Sceaux

Musée de l'Ile de France, Château, 92330 Sceaux - T: 0146610671, Fax: 0146610088, E-mail: museeid@cg92.fr. Head: Cécile Dupont-Logié
Fine Arts Museum / Decorative Arts Museum - 1937
Art, hist, ceramics, paintings, drawings, etchings, tapestries - library, documentation center, park, auditorium, children's museum 13462

Sceaux-du-Gatinais

Musée Archéologique, Sacristie de l'Eglise, 45490 Sceaux-du-Gatinais - T: 0238874027
Archaeological Museum 13463

Scey-sur-Saône-et-Saint-Albin

Musée de l'Histoire du Costume, 1 Chemin des Vignes, 70360 Scey-sur-Saône-et-Saint-Albin - T: 0384688177
Special Museum 13464

Scherwiller

Épicerie-Musée Klein, 50 Rue de l'Ortenbourg, 67750 Scherwiller - T: 0388821202
Special Museum 13465

Musée des Châteaux Forts, Ancien Corps de Garde, 67750 Scherwiller - T: 0388922562
Historical Museum 13466

Schirmeck

Musée d'Art et d'Histoire, Château, 67130 Schirmeck - T: 0388496380/970310
Local Museum 13467

Schoeneck

Maison d'Histoire Locale, 4 Rue Pasteur, 57600 Schoeneck - T: 0387876048
Historical Museum 13468

Scy-Chazelles

Maison de Robert Schuman, 57160 Scy-Chazelles - T: 0387601990, Fax: 0387602974
Local Museum 13469

Musée Robert Schuman → Maison de Robert Schuman

Sebourg

Patrimoine Historique et Études du Repassage, 8 Rue des Censes d'en Haut, 59990 Sebourg - T: 0327265409
Science&Tech Museum / Folklore Museum 13470

Seclin

Musée d'Histoire et d'Archéologie, Salle de Justice, Clocher Collégiale Saint-Piat, 59113 Seclin - T: 0320900002
Historical Museum / Archaeological Museum 13471

Sedan

Historium de Sedan, Château Fort, 08200 Sedan - T: 0324277373, Fax: 0324290328, E-mail: ot.sedan@wanadoo.fr, Internet: http://www.sedan-bouillon.org
Historical Museum 13472

Musée des Anciennes Industries, Dijonval, Av Marguerite, 08200 Sedan - T: 0324270467
Science&Tech Museum 13473

Sées

Musée Départemental d'Art Religieux, Pl du Général de Gaulle, 61500 Sées, mail addr: Archives Départementales, 6-10 Av de Basingstoke, 61017 Alençon - T: 0233812302, Fax: 0233812301, E-mail: archives@cg61.fr. Head: Jean-Pascal Foucher
Religious Arts Museum - 1967 13474

Seguret

Musée-Chapelle Sainte-Thècle, 84110 Seguret - T: 0490469108/9134
Folklore Museum 13475

Musée G.-Delage, 84110 Seguret - T: 0490469108/9134
Folklore Museum 13476

Seix

Fromagerie Coumes, La Tuilerie, 09140 Seix - T: 0561965406
Special Museum 13477

Musée de Géologie et du Marbre, 09140 Seix - T: 056195290
Natural History Museum 13478

Sélestat

Maison du Pain d'Alsace, 7 Rue du Sel, 67600 Sélestat - T: 0388584590, Fax: 0388584595, E-mail: maison.du.pain.d.alsace@wanadoo.fr
Special Museum / Association with Coll 13479

Musée-Bibliothèque Humaniste, 1 Rue de la Bibliothèque, 67600 Sélestat - T: 0388580720, Fax: 0388828064, E-mail: -bibliotheque.humaniste@ville-selestat. Head: Hubert Meyer
Library with Exhibitions 13480

Selles-sur-Cher

Musée du Val-de-Cher, Cloître de l'Abbaye, Pl Charles de Gaulle, 41130 Selles-sur-Cher - T: 0254952540, Fax: 0254952550
Historical Museum 13481

Seltz

Musée Celte, 67470 Seltz - T: 0388055979,
Fax: 0388055977, E-mail: otsi.seltz@voila.fr,
Internet: http://www.seltz.com. Head: Suzanne
Knobloch
Historical Museum 13482

Semur-en-Auxois

Musée de la Tour de l'Orle d'Or, 21140 Semur-en-
Auxois - T: 0380970731/2425
Science&Tech Museum 13483

Musée Municipal, Rue Jean-Jacques-Collenot,
21140 Semur-en-Auxois - T: 0380972425. Head:
Matthieu Pinette
Local Museum - 1834
Roman archeology, medieval sculpture, painting and
sculpture of the 19th c 13484

Semur-en-Brionnais

Collection d'Affiches de la Période
Révolutionnaire, Château Saint-Hugues, Maison du
Geôlier, 71110 Semur-en-Brionnais -
T: 0385250294/3906
Fine Arts Museum 13485

Semussac

Musée Agricole, Château de Didonne, 17120
Semussac - T: 0546058226, E-mail: jacky.herbert@
wanadoo.fr, Internet: http://www.didonne.com.
Head: Jacky Herbert
Agriculture Museum 13486

Semuy

Musée Mai-Juin 1940, Moulin de Waroux, 08130
Semuy - T: 0324714109
Military Museum 13487

Sénas

Collection Singulière d'Art Contemporain Insolite,
Quartier de la Peyronnette, 13560 Sénas -
T: 0490572318
Fine Arts Museum 13488

Senez

Musée d'Art Sacré, Ancienne Cathédrale, 04330
Senez - T: 0492342104, Fax: 0492342717. Head:
G. Hermellin
Religious Arts Museum 13489

Senlis

Fondation Cziffra, Chapelle Royale-Saint-Frambourg,
60300 Senlis - T: 0344533999, Fax: 0344534452,
E-mail: fondation.cziffra@wanadoo.fr
Music Museum / Historic Site 13490

Musée d'Art, Pl Notre-Dame, 60300 Senlis -
T: 0344320083, Fax: 0344531199,
E-mail: senlisart@aol.com. Head: Bénédicte
Ottinger
Fine Arts Museum / Archaeological Museum 13491

Musée de la Vénerie et des Spahis, Château Royal,
Pl du Parvis Notre Dame, 60300 Senlis -
T: 0344530080 poste 1315, Fax: 0344531199,
E-mail: senlisart@aol.com. Head: Bénédicte
Ottinger
Special Museum - 1935
Hunting trophies, painting and sculpture on the
theme of hunting, costumes, hunting bugles -
library 13492

Musée de l'Hôtel de Vermandois, Pl du Parvis Notre-
Dame, 60300 Senlis - T: 0344320082,
Fax: 0344531199, E-mail: senlisart@aol.com.
Head: Bénédicte Ottinger
Local Museum 13493

Senonches

Musée Atelier de Soldats de Plomb, 14 Rue de
Pontgouin, 28250 Senonches - T: 0237378458/
9174
Military Museum 13494

Musée d'Art et d'Histoire, Château, Rue du Château,
28250 Senonches - T: 0237378427
Local Museum 13495

Senones

Exposition sur l'Histoire de la Principauté de Salm,
Bibliothèque, 6 Pl Clémenceau, 88210 Senones -
T: 0329576767
Fine Arts Museum / Historical Museum 13496

Sens

Musées de Sens, Pl de la Cathédrale, 89100 Sens -
T: 0386641527, Fax: 0386953195. Head: Lydwine
Saulnier
Local Museum / Religious Arts Museum 13497

Sentheim

Maison de Géologie de Haute-Alsace, Pl de l'Eglise,
68780 Sentheim - T: 0389825555
Natural History Museum 13498

Sergeac

Site Préhistorique de Castel Merle, 24290 Sergeac
- T: 0553507970
Archaeological Museum
Excavations, sculptures 13499

Sérignan-du-Comtat

Musée-Atelier Werner-Lichtner-Aix, 84830
Sérignan-du-Comtat - T: 0490700140
Fine Arts Museum 13500

Sérignan (Hérault)

Musée de l'Attelage et du Cheval, 146 Av de la
Plage, 34410 Sérignan (Hérault) - T: 0467325757
Science&Tech Museum 13501

Sermentizon

Château-Musée d'Aulteribe, 63120 Sermentizon -
T: 0473531455
Fine Arts Museum / Decorative Arts Museum 13502

Serralongue

Musée Animé des Arts et Traditions Populaires, Pl
du Village, 66230 Serralongue - T: 0468396214/
6083
Folklore Museum 13503

Serrières

Musée des Mariniers et de la Batellerie du Rhône,
Église Saint-Sornin, 07340 Serrières -
T: 0475640126/340046
Historical Museum 13504

Servian

Exposition Archéologique, Maison des Jeunes et de
la Culture, Blvd de la Lène, 34290 Servian -
T: 0467391010
Archaeological Museum 13505

Servoz

Musée de la Faune Alpine, Plaine Saint-Jean, 74310
Servoz - T: 0450472110
Natural History Museum 13506

Sessenheim

Memorial Goethe, Rue Frédérique Brion, 67770
Sessenheim - T: 0388869725. Head: Yves Kéler
Special Museum
Memorabilia of Goethe and his stay in Alsace 13507

Micromusée Goethe, Dans la Vieille Auberge au
Bœuf, 67770 Sessenheim - T: 0388869714
Special Museum 13508

Sète

Centre Régional d'Art Contemporain, Quai Aspirant-
Herber, 34200 Sète - T: 0467741704
Fine Arts Museum 13509

Espace Georges-Brassens, 67 Blvd Camille-Blanc,
34200 Sète - T: 0467533277
Special Museum 13510

Musée Paul Valéry, Rue François Desnoyer, 34200
Sète - T: 0467462098/2121 poste 343. Head: M.
Freises
Special Museum
Memorabilia of the writer P. Valéry, 19th-10th
century works of art 13511

Seuilly

Maison de Pays, 37500 Seuilly - T: 0247958328
Folklore Museum 13512

Musée Rabelais, La Devinière, 37500 Seuilly -
T: 0247959118. Head: Jean-Louis Sureau
Special Museum 13513

Seurre

Écomusée du Val de Saône, Rue Bossuet, 21250
Seurre - T: 0380210902, E-mail: louisroussel@
hotmail.com. Head: Louis Roussel
Local Museum 13514

Maison Familiale de Bossuet, Rue Bossuet, 21250
Seurre
Special Museum 13515

Musée de Plein Air, L'Étang Rouge, 21250 Seurre -
T: 0380300520, E-mail: louisroussel@hotmail.com.
Head: Louis Roussel
Open Air Museum / Agriculture Museum / Ethnology
Museum 13516

Séverac-le-Château

Musée d'Archéologie, 12150 Séverac-le-Château -
T: 0565476731
Archaeological Museum 13517

Sèvres

Maison des Jardies/Musée Léon Gambetta, Centre
des Momuments Nationaux, 14 Av Gambetta, 92310
Sèvres - T: 0145346122, Fax: 0145346122,
E-mail: boyer@monuments-france.fr,
Internet: http://www.monum.fr. Head: Jean-Marc
Boyer
Historical Museum / Historic Site - 1887 13518

Musée National de Céramique, Pl de la
Manufacture, 92310 Sèvres - T: 0141140420
Decorative Arts Museum 13519

Sévrier

Musée de la Cloche, N 508, 74320 Sévrier -
T: 0450524711
Special Museum 13520

Seyne-les-Alpes

Fort de Seyne, 04140 Seyne-les-Alpes -
T: 0492350011/00
Military Museum 13521

Micro-Musée de la Lessive, Rue Haute, 04140
Seyne-les-Alpes - T: 0492350051/2329
Special Museum / Folklore Museum 13522

Micro-Musée de l'École, Rue Basse, 04140 Seyne-
les-Alpes - T: 0492350051/2329
Special Museum 13523

Micro-Musée du Tailleur, Rue Basse, 04140 Seyne-
les-Alpes - T: 0492350051/2329
Special Museum 13524

Musée Vivant de la Forge, 04140 Seyne-les-Alpes -
T: 0492351100
Special Museum 13525

Seynod

Musée des Trois Guerres, 7 Av Zanaroli, 74600
Seynod - T: 0450453291/527889
Military Museum 13526

Seyssel

Collections du Patrimoine, Office du Tourisme,
01420 Seyssel - T: 0450592018
Local Museum 13527

Musée du Bois, Pl de la République, 01420 Seyssel -
T: 0450592155/2656
Fine Arts Museum 13528

Siersthal

Musée National de la Fortification Maginot, 57230
Siersthal - T: 0387061616, Fax: 0387061617,
E-mail: office-tour@ville-bitche.fr, Internet: http://
www.ville-bitche.fr
Military Museum 13529

Sigean

L.A.C. Lieu d'Art Contemporain, Hameau du Lac,
11130 Sigean - T: 0468488362, Fax: 0468488362,
E-mail: lac@narbonne.com, Internet: http://
www.lac.narbonne.com. Head: Layla Moget
Fine Arts Museum 13530

Musée d'Arts et d'Histoire des Corbières, Pl de la
Libération, 11130 Sigean - T: 0468402424
Local Museum 13531

Siorac-en-Périgord

Musée du Château, Château, 24170 Siorac-en-
Périgord - T: 0553316369, Fax: 0553594027,
E-mail: jacoupy.charles@wanadoo.fr. Head: Charles
Jacoupy
Decorative Arts Museum / Special Museum
Decorative art 13532

Sisteron

Musée d'Art et d'Histoire du Vieux Sisteron, Av des
Arcades, 04200 Sisteron - T: 0492611227
Local Museum 13533

Musée de la Citadelle, Corps de Garde, 04200
Sisteron - T: 0492612757
Military Museum 13534

Musée Scout Baden-Powell, 6 Rue de la Mission,
04200 Sisteron - T: 0492610316/626790
Special Museum 13535

Six-Fours-les-Plages

Musée du Patrimoine, Maison du Patrimoine,
Comiche des Iles, Le Brusc, 83140 Six-Fours-les-
Plages - T: 0494749643
Fine Arts Museum 13536

Sizun

Maison de la Pisciculture, Barrage du Drennec,
29237 Sizun - T: 0298688633
Natural History Museum 13537

Maison de la Rivière, de l'Eau et de la Pêche,
Moulin de Vergraon, 29237 Sizun - T: 0298688633
Natural History Museum 13538

Musée d'Art et des Traditions Populaires, Ossuaire,
Enclos Paroissial, 29237 Sizun - T: 0298688760
Folklore Museum 13539

Sochaux

Musée Peugeot, Carrefour Europe, 25600 Sochaux -
T: 0381994203, Fax: 0381994206, E-mail: musee-
peugeot@wanadoo.fr. Head: M. Macchi
Science&Tech Museum 13540

Soissons

Musée Municipal Ancienne Abbaye Saint-Léger, 2
Rue de la Congrégation, 02200 Soissons -
T: 0323933050, Fax: 0323933051,
E-mail: musee@ville-soissons.fr. Head: Dominique
Roussel
Archaeological Museum / Fine Arts Museum - 1857
Prehist, antiquities, paintings, medieval
sculpture 13541

Solesmes

Musée de la Préhistoire, Hôtel de Ville, Grand Pl,
59730 Solesmes - T: 0327373111,
Fax: 0327721779
Archaeological Museum 13542

Sollières-Sardières

Musée Archéologique, Sollières Envers, 73500
Sollières-Sardières - T: 0429205933,
Fax: 0429205359
Archaeological Museum 13543

Solliès-Ville

Musée du Vêtement Provençal, Rue de la
Marseillaise, 83210 Solliès-Ville - T: 0494333322/
3323
Folklore Museum 13544

Musée Jean Aicard, Pl E.-Silvain, 83210 Solliès-Ville
- T: 0494337202
Local Museum 13545

Solutré-Pouilly

Musée Départemental de Préhistoire, Site
Souterrain, Rte de Mâcon, 71960 Solutré-Pouilly -
T: 0385358524. Head: Geneviève Lagardere
Archaeological Museum 13546

Sommepy-Tahure

Musée Franco-Américain, Mairie, Pl de la Mairie,
51600 Sommepy-Tahure - T: 0326668004/07
Local Museum 13547

Sommery

Ferme-Musée, Hameau de Bray, 76440 Sommery -
T: 0235905727
Agriculture Museum 13548

Sorde-l'Abbaye

Musée Lapidaire Gallo-Romain, 40300 Sorde-
l'Abbaye - T: 0558730728
Archaeological Museum 13549

Sorede

Collection Historique de Fouets, C.A.T. 4 Rue des
Fabriques, 66690 Sorede - T: 0468890450
Science&Tech Museum / Historical Museum 13550

Sorges

Ecomusée de la Truffe, 24420 Sorges -
T: 0553059011/9518
Special Museum 13551

Sospel

Collection Ferroviaire, Gare de Sospel, 06380 Sospel
- T: 0493040017
Science&Tech Museum 13552

Musée de la 1re Division Française Libre, Ouvrage
Saint-Roch, 06380 Sospel
Military Museum 13553

Musée de la Ligne Maginot des Alpes, Ouvrage
Saint-Roch, 06380 Sospel - T: 0493040070/1580
Military Museum 13554

Musée de la Résistance, Ouvrage Saint-Roch, 06380
Sospel
Historical Museum 13555

Musée de l'Armée des Alpes, Fort Suchet dit du
Barbonnet, Col Saint-Jean, 06380 Sospel -
T: 0493041580
Military Museum / Historic Site 13556

Souchez

Centre Européen de la Paix, RD 937, 62153 Souchez
- T: 0321726655
Special Museum 13557

Musée Historique et Diorama 1914-1918, Notre-
Dame de Lorette, 62153 Souchez - T: 0321451580,
Fax: 0321591776. Head: David Bardiaux
Historical Museum / Military Museum 13558

Soucht

Ecomusée du Sabotier (Wooden Shoes Museum),
Rue des Sabotiers, 57960 Soucht - T: 0387968697/
651, Fax: 0387969946
Science&Tech Museum 13559

Souffrignac

Conservatoire Rural, 16380 Souffrignac - T: 0545702703
Agriculture Museum 13560

Souillac

Exposition Mexico d'Hier et d'Aujourd'hui, L'Ajoupa, Rte Nationale 20, 46200 Souillac - T: 0565370734
Local Museum / Archaeological Museum 13561

Musée de l'Alambic Louis Roque, Av de la Gare, 46200 Souillac - T: 0565327816
Special Museum 13562

Musée des Attelages de la Belle Epoque, Rue P. Chambert, 46200 Souillac - T: 0565370775
Special Museum / Historical Museum 13563

Musée National de l'Automate et de la Robotique, Pl de l'Abbaye, 46200 Souillac - T: 0565370707. Head: Monique Escat
Science&Tech Museum 13564

Souilly

Musée de la Voie Sacrée, Mairie, 55220 Souilly - T: 0329805276
Military Museum 13565

Soulac-sur-Mer

Musée Archéologique, 23 Rue Victor Hugo, 33780 Soulac-sur-Mer - T: 0556099050
Archaeological Museum 13566

Musée d'Art Moderne, Fondation Aquitaine, Av El Burzo de Osmo, 33780 Soulac-sur-Mer - T: 0556098399/732937
Fine Arts Museum 13567

Soulages-Bonneval

Exposition Vie du Bois, Ferme Pédagogique, 12210 Soulages-Bonneval - T: 0565443163
Special Museum / Natural History Museum 13568

Soullans

Musée Milcendeau-Jean Yole, Le Bois-Durand, 85300 Soullans - T: 0251350384, Fax: 0251461552. Head: Christophe Vital
Fine Arts Museum - 1982
Coll of the painter Charles Milcendeau and the writer Jean Yole 13569

Soulosse-sous-Saint-Élophe

Musée Archéologique, Près de l'Église Gothique de Soulosse, 88630 Soulosse-sous-Saint-Élophe - T: 0329069794, Fax: 0329069661. Head: Jocelyne Valentin
Archaeological Museum 13570

Soultz-Haut-Rhin

Musée Château du Bucheneck, Rue Kageneck, 68360 Soultz-Haut-Rhin - T: 0389760222, Fax: 0389830663
Local Museum
Archaeology, portrait gallery, famous families from Soultz, illustrations by Robert Belk, religious art, Jewish worship articles, handicraft, costumes and tradition 13571

Nef des Jouets, Commanderie Saint-Jean, 12 Rue Jean Jaurès, 68360 Soultz-Haut-Rhin - T: 0389743092, Fax: 0389764805, E-mail: lanefdesjouets@free.fr. Head: Catherine Galliath
Special Museum 13572

Souvigny

Musée de Souvigny, Mairie, Pl Aristide-Briand, 03210 Souvigny - T: 0470436038
Local Museum 13573

Soyons

Archéosite de la Bregoule, 07130 Soyons - T: 0475608886/9212
Archaeological Museum 13574

Grottes Préhistoriques, 07130 Soyons - T: 0475608886
Archaeological Museum 13575

Musée Archéologique, 07130 Soyons - T: 0475608886/9312
Archaeological Museum - 1987
Local history, prehistorical and touristic caves, archeological excavations 13576

Parc Ardèche Miniature, Rte Nationale 86, 07130 Soyons - T: 0475609658
Natural History Museum 13577

Spezet

Collection de Sous-Bock de Bière, Rte de Châteauneuf, 29135 Spezet - T: 0298938482
Special Museum 13578

Steenwerck

Musée de la Vie Rurale (Rural Life Museum), Rue du Musée, 59181 Steenwerck - T: 0328499478, Fax: 0328404617. Head: Jean-Pierre Renaux
Agriculture Museum 13579

Stenay

Musée de la Bière, Rue de la Citadelle, 55700 Stenay - T: 0329806878, Fax: 0329803111, E-mail: stenay.stenay@wanadoo.fr. Head: Pierre de Martin
Special Museum - 1986
library, archives 13580

Strasbourg

Ancienne Douane, 1a Rue du Vieux-Marché-aux-Poissons, 67000 Strasbourg - T: 0388525000
Local Museum 13581

Cabinet des Estampes et des Dessins, 5 Pl du Château, 67000 Strasbourg - T: 0388525000, Fax: 0388525009. Head: Anny-Claire Haus
Fine Arts Museum - 1898
Engravings, lithographs, drawings (15th-20th c), posters, photogr 13582

Cabinet Numismatique de la Bibliothèque Nationale et Universitaire de Strasbourg, 5 Rue Maréchal-Joffre, 67070 Strasbourg Cedex - T: 0388252800, Fax: 0388252803, E-mail: bnus@bnus.u-strasbg.fr, Internet: http://www.-bnus.u-strasbg.fr
Historical Museum 13583

Centre Européen d'Actions Artistiques Contemporaines, 7 Rue de l'Abreuvoir, 67000 Strasbourg - T: 0388256970, Fax: 0388355977, E-mail: info@ceaac.org, Internet: http://www.ceaac.org. Head: Robert Grossmann
Fine Arts Museum 13584

Centre Tomi Ungerer, Musées de Strasbourg, 4 Rue de la Haute-Montée, 67000 Strasbourg - T: 0388323154, Fax: 0388525009, E-mail: twiller@cus-strasbourg.net. Head: Thérèse Willer
Special Museum
Original drawings, posters, sculptures, toys, games, family archives, press articles, photos of the artist 13585

Collection d'Antiquites Nationales, Université S.H. 9 Pl de l'Université, 67000 Strasbourg - T: 0388259778
Archaeological Museum 13586

Collection d'Archéologie Biblique USH, 9 Pl de l'Université, Institut de Théologie Protestante, 67000 Strasbourg - T: 0388259735
Archaeological Museum 13587

Collection de Costumes Alsaciens J. Bossert, 11bis Quai Turckheim, 67000 Strasbourg - T: 0388322847
Folklore Museum 13588

Collection Historique du Gymnasium Protestant, École Jean-Sturm, 8 Pl des Étudiants, 67000 Strasbourg - T: 0388323868
Historical Museum 13589

Collections Brassicoles, Brasserie Kronenbourg, 68 Rte d'Oberhausbergen, 67200 Strasbourg - T: 0388274488
Special Museum 13590

Collections Hospitalières, H"pitaux Universitaires de Strasbourg, 67000 Strasbourg - T: 0388116768
Special Museum 13591

Espace Arts Déco La Chaufferie, 5 Rue de la Manufacture de Tabac, 67000 Strasbourg - T: 0388353858
Decorative Arts Museum 13592

Galerie du Conseil Général du Bas-Rhin, Pl du Quartier Blanc, 67000 Strasbourg - T: 0388706767
Fine Arts Museum 13593

Haras National, 1 Rue Sainte-Élisabeth, 67000 Strasbourg - T: 0388256030
Special Museum 13594

Maison des Compagnons du Devoir du Tour de France, 2 Rue de Wasselonne, 67000 Strasbourg - T: 0388323085
Fine Arts Museum 13595

Musée Alsacien, 23 Quai Saint-Nicolas, 67000 Strasbourg - T: 0388525001, Fax: 0388436418. Head: Malou Schneider
Folklore Museum - 1902
Folk art, costumes, religious painting, peasant life 13596

Musée Archéologique, Palais Rohan, 2 Pl du Château, 67000 Strasbourg - T: 0388525000, Fax: 0388525009. Head: Bernadette Schnitzler
Archaeological Museum
Prehistoric building fragments, ceramics, sculpture, various finds, hist of the Alsace from 600 BC to 800 AC 13597

Musée d'Anatomie Normale, c/o Faculté de Médecine, 4 Rue Kirschleger, 67085 Strasbourg - T: 0390243930. Head: J.-M. Le Minor
Special Museum 13598

Musée d'Anatomie Pathologique, Hospices Civils, 67000 Strasbourg - T: 0388116768/361805
Special Museum 13599

Musée d'Art Moderne et Contemporain, 1 Pl Hans-Jean Arp, 67000 Strasbourg - T: 0388233131, Fax: 0388233132. Head: Roland Recht
Fine Arts Museum - 1973
Painting and sculpture from Impressionism to modern times, decorative art since 1870, church windows from 1870 to the present - library, children's atelier 13600

Musée de la Conscription Militaire, Caserne Turenne, 42 Rue Lauth, 67000 Strasbourg - T: 0388565804
Military Museum 13601

Musée de la Faculté de Médecine, 4 Rue Kirschlager, 67000 Strasbourg - T: 0388358700
Special Museum 13602

Musée de la Médecine Légale, 11 Rue Humann, 67085 Strasbourg - T: 0390243363, Fax: 0390243362, E-mail: institut-iml@iml-ulp.u-strasbg.fr
Special Museum 13603

Musée de la Ville de Strasbourg, 2 Pl du Château, 67070 Strasbourg - T: 0388525000, Fax: 0388525009, E-mail: fpayn@cus.sdv.fr
Local Museum 13604

Musée de l'Institut d'Égyptologie, Palais Universitaire, 67000 Strasbourg - T: 0388259779
Archaeological Museum 13605

Musée de l'Oeuvre Notre-Dame, 3 Pl du Château, 67000 Strasbourg - T: 0388525000, Fax: 0388525009, E-mail: musees@cus.sdv.fr, Internet: http://www.musees-strasbourg.org. Head: Cécile Dupeux
Religious Arts Museum / Fine Arts Museum - 1931
Medieval sculpture, stained-glass windows, statuettes, paintings, early Alsacian and Renaissance art, furnishings, still-life paintings, art objects 13606

Musée de Minéralogie, c/o Ecole et Observatoire des Sciences de la Terre, Université Louis Pasteur, 1 Rue Blessig, 67084 Strasbourg - T: 0390240452, Fax: 0388367235, E-mail: leypold@illite.u-strasbg.fr, Internet: http://www.science-ouverte.u-strasbg.fr
University Museum 13607

Musée de Moulages, c/o Université Marc Bloch de Strasbourg, Pl de l'Université, 67084 Strasbourg - T: 0388259777, Fax: 0388356523, E-mail: tpetit@umb.u.strasbg.fr. Head: Prof. Th. Petit
Fine Arts Museum / University Museum / Archaeological Museum / Museum of Classical Antiquities 13608

Musée de Sismologie et Magnétisme Terrestre, 7-9 Rue de l'Université, 67000 Strasbourg - T: 0388416492, Fax: 0388616747, E-mail: musee@eost.u-strasbg.fr, Internet: http://eost.u-strasbg.fr/musee/Accueil.html. Head: Dr. Valerie Ansel
Science&Tech Museum 13609

Musée des Arts Décoratifs, Château des Rohan, 2 Pl du Château, 67000 Strasbourg - T: 0388525000, Fax: 0388525009, E-mail: musees@ms.strasbourg.net. Head: Etienne Martin
Decorative Arts Museum
Complete hist of ceramics (1681-19th c), porcelain of famous European manufacture, pewter, wrought-iron objects, furniture, sculpture, clocks, toys by Tomi Ungerer 13610

Musée des Beaux-Arts, Palais Rohan, 2 Pl du Château, 67000 Strasbourg - T: 0388525000, Fax: 0388525009. Head: Dominique Jacquot
Fine Arts Museum - 1801
14th-19th century Italian, Spanish, Dutch, Flemish and French paintings, paintings of the Alsatian school - library, educational service, documentation 13611

Musée des Glacières, Hôtel Le Régent, 5 Rue des Moulins, 67000 Strasbourg - T: 0388764343
Science&Tech Museum 13612

Musée Géologique ULP, Institut de Géologie, 1 Rue Blessig, 67000 Strasbourg - T: 0388358568
Natural History Museum 13613

Musée Historique, 3 Pl de la Grande-Boucherie, 67000 Strasbourg - T: 0388322563/525007. Head: Jean-Pierre Klein
Historical Museum
Topographical, political, economic, and military hist of Strasbourg, 16th-17th century firearms, 19th century arms and uniforms, 19th century collection of painted toy soldiers, mechanical toys from 1850-1914, paintings, lithographs, furniture 13614

Musée Louis Pasteur, Institut de Bactériologie, 3 Rue Kœberlé, 67000 Strasbourg - T: 0388211970 poste 902
Special Museum 13615

Musée Scolaire de Hautepierre, 12 Pl A. de Musset, 67000 Strasbourg - T: 0388270149
Special Museum 13616

Musée Zoologique de l'Université Louis Pasteur et de la Ville de Strasbourg, 29 Blvd de la Victoire, 67000 Strasbourg - T: 0390240489, Fax: 0390240558. Head: Elisabeth Lang
Natural History Museum / University Museum - 1804
Sponges, crustaceous, entomology, ornithology - library 13617

Naviscope Alsace, A Bord du Poisseur "Strasbourg", à Quai Rue du Général Picquart, 67000 Strasbourg - T: 0388602223, Fax: 0388619611. Head: Gerard Criqui
Natural History Museum 13618

Sucy-en-Brie

Fort Muséalisé de Sucy, Allée des Douves, 94370 Sucy-en-Brie - T: 0145902648
Historical Museum 13619

Musée de Sucy, Pl du Château, Rue du Temple, 94370 Sucy-en-Brie - T: 0145901537, Fax: 0145901537. Head: Prof. Michel Balard
Local Museum 13620

Suippes

Musée Archéologique, Mairie, 51600 Suippes - T: 0326700855
Archaeological Museum 13621

Sully-sur-Loire

Château de Sully-sur-Loire, 45600 Sully-sur-Loire - T: 0238363686, Fax: 0238364502, E-mail: chateau.sully@cg45.fr, Internet: http://www.coeur.de.france.com
Fine Arts Museum / Decorative Arts Museum 13622

Suresnes

Musée Colombophile du Mont-Valérien, Fort du Mont-Valérien, 92150 Suresnes - T: 0141185213
Special Museum 13623

Musée de Suresnes René-Sordes, Passerelle Musée-Av du Général-de-Gaulle, 92150 Suresnes - T: 0141181875, Fax: 0141181676, E-mail: musee@ville-suresnes.fr. Head: Marie-Pierre Deguillaume
Historical Museum 13624

Surgères

Musée d'Histoire Naturelle, Donation Fournier-Collection Personnelle, 4bis Av Saint-Pierre, 17700 Surgères - T: 0546070084
Natural History Museum 13625

Surrain

Musée de la Libération de la Normandie, Rte Nationale 13, 14710 Surrain - T: 0231225756
Military Museum 13626

Survilliers

Musée François Mauriac, Mairie de Vémars, 95470 Survilliers - T: 0134683340
Special Museum 13627

Sury-le-Comtal

Collections du Château de Sury-le-Comtal, 42450 Sury-le-Comtal - T: 0477308158
Decorative Arts Museum / Fine Arts Museum 13628

Suze-la-Rousse

Université du Vin, Château, 26130 Suze-la-Rousse - T: 0475048609
Special Museum 13629

Taingy

Carrière Souterraine d'Aubigny, 89560 Taingy - T: 0386523879, Fax: 0386523879, E-mail: carriereaubigny@multimania.com, Internet: http://www.multimania.com/carriereaubigny. Head: J.B. Letertre
Special Museum 13630

Talmont-Saint-Hilaire

Musée de l'Automobile de Vendée, La Vieille-Biée, Rte de Talmont, 85440 Talmont-Saint-Hilaire - T: 0251220581/0620
Science&Tech Museum 13631

Musée-Maison Natale de Saint-Henri-Dorie, Port de la Guittière, 85440 Talmont-Saint-Hilaire - T: 0251339487
Special Museum 13632

Talmont-sur-Gironde

Musée Historique et de la Pêche, Ancienne École, Rue de l'Église, 17120 Talmont-sur-Gironde - T: 0546904387
Historical Museum 13633

Tamnies

Musée d'Initiation à la Préhistoire, Mairie, 24620 Tamnies - T: 0553296895
Archaeological Museum 13634

Tancarville

Château Médiéval de Tancarville, Pont de Tancarville, 76430 Tancarville - T: 0235960021/564182, Fax: 0235564182. Head: E. Gremillet
Decorative Arts Museum / Folklore Museum / Open Air Museum / Historic Site 13635

Tanlay

Centre d'Art Contemporain, Château de Tanlay, 89430 Tanlay - T: 0386757633, E-mail: centredart@cg89.fr, Internet: http://www.amis-musees.fr. Head: Jacques Py
Fine Arts Museum 13636

Château-Musée des XVIe-XVIIe s, 89430 Tanlay - T: 0386757061/7748
Fine Arts Museum / Decorative Arts Museum - 16th-17th c
17th century wood panels, period furniture, portraits, frescoes, paintings 13637

Taradeau

Musée Provençal et Folklorique, Domaine Saint-Martin, 83460 Taradeau - T: 0494730201. Head: Comtesse de Gasquet
Historical Museum / Folklore Museum 13638

Tarare

Musée Archéologique, Rue du Château, 69170 Tarare - T: 0474054929/634328
Archaeological Museum 13639

Tarascon (Bouches-du-Rhône)

Exposition du Cloître des Cordeliers, Pl F.-Mistral, 13150 Tarascon (Bouches-du-Rhône) - T: 0490910352, 0490913871, Fax: 0490915160, E-mail: tourisme@tarascon.org, Internet: http://www.tarascon.org
Fine Arts Museum
Local art 13640

Musée de la Maison de Tartarin, 55bis Blvd d'Ittam, 13150 Tarascon (Bouches-du-Rhône) - T: 0490910508, Fax: 0490915160, E-mail: mairie@tarascon/org, Internet: http://www.tarascon.org
Special Museum 13641

Musée du Château du Roy René, Blvd du Roi-René, 13150 Tarascon (Bouches-du-Rhône) - T: 0490910193/0352
Decorative Arts Museum 13642

Musée du Tissu Provençal, 39 Rue Proudhon, 13150 Tarascon (Bouches-du-Rhône) - T: 0490910880
Folklore Museum 13643

Musée Souleiado Charles Demery, 39 Rue Proudhon, 13150 Tarascon (Bouches-du-Rhône) - T: 0490910880, Fax: 0490910108
Special Museum / Historical Museum
Printing blocks of the 18th century, late 19th century Provence home 13644

Tarascon-sur-Ariège

Exposition Gadal de Préhistoire et d'Archéologie, Porte d'Espagne, 09400 Tarascon-sur-Ariège - T: 0561059494/8157
Archaeological Museum 13645

Parc Pyrénéen de l'Art Préhistorique, Rte Bonat-Lacombe, 09400 Tarascon-sur-Ariège - T: 0561059494/1010
Fine Arts Museum 13646

Tarbes

Musée de la Déportation et de la Résistance, 63 Rue Georges Lassalle, 65000 Tarbes - T: 0562511160
Historical Museum 13647

Musée de Tarbes, Musée Mixte, Jardin Massey, 65000 Tarbes - T: 0562363149
Local Museum 13648

Musée des Beaux-Arts, 65000 Tarbes
Fine Arts Museum 13649

Musée du Maréchal Foch, Maison Natale, 2 Rue de la Victoire, 65000 Tarbes - T: 0562931002. Head: Mariano Marcos
Military Museum - 1951
Paintings, statues of Marshal Foch, WW I memorabilia, books and manuscripts 13650

Musée International des Hussards, 65000 Tarbes
Military Museum - 1955
15th-20th century arms, 130 complete uniforms, equipment, iconography of hussars of 34 countries - library 13651

Tarquimpol

Maison du Pays des Étangs, Rue du Théâtre, 57260 Tarquimpol - T: 0387868810
Special Museum / Natural History Museum 13652

Tautavel

Musée Centre Européen de Préhistoire, Av Léon Jean Gregory, 66720 Tautavel - T: 0468290776/1208. Head: Jean Abelanet
Archaeological Museum - 1979
Stone tools, fossils, paleolithic pottery, bronzes, metal tools of neolithic times 13653

Tence

Musée d'Art Religieux, Ancienne Chapelle des Pénitents, Pl du Chatiague, 43190 Tence - T: 0471598199
Religious Arts Museum 13654

Tende

Archéosite de la Vallée des Merveilles, 06430 Tende - T: 0493046264/6866
Archaeological Museum 13655

Musée des Merveilles, 06430 Tende - T: 0493047910/6113
Fine Arts Museum 13656

Termes-d'Armagnac

Musée du Panaché Gascon, Tour des Termes, 32400 Termes-d'Armagnac - T: 0562692512
Folklore Museum 13657

Terraube

Château de Galard, Château, 32700 Terraube - T: 0562689385
Local Museum 13658

Thann

Espace Muséal, Porte Sud de la Rte des Vins d'Alsace, 68800 Thann - T: 0389379620
Natural History Museum / Special Museum 13659

Musée de la Cabane des Bangards, Rue des Bangards, 68800 Thann - T: 0389379620
Fine Arts Museum 13660

Musée des Amis de Thann, 24 Rue Saint-Thiébaut, 68800 Thann - T: 0389379620/700393. Head: Yves Boeglin
Local Museum - 1918
14th-18th century sculptures, Alsacian life, local hist, crafts, mineralogy, World War I and II 13661

Thanvillé

Exposition Permanente, Château de Thanvillé, 67220 Thanvillé - T: 0388856995
Historical Museum 13662

Therouanne

Musée Archéologique, 62129 Therouanne - T: 0321955425
Archaeological Museum 13663

Thésée-la-Romaine

Musée Archéologique de Thésée-la-Romaine, Le Vaux Saint-Georges, Mairie, 41140 Thésée-la-Romaine - T: 0254710088, Fax: 0254713728, E-mail: jean.epron@wanadoo.fr
Archaeological Museum 13664

Thiaucourt

Musée Militaire de Thiaucourt, Rue Neuve, 54470 Thiaucourt - T: 0383819836, Fax: 0387365087, E-mail: huret.j@infonie.fr. Head: J. Huret
Military Museum 13665

Thiers

Centre d'Art Contemporain, Vallée des Usines, 63300 Thiers - T: 0473802656, Fax: 0473802808. Head: Frédéric Bouglé
Fine Arts Museum 13666

Musée de la Coutellerie, 58 Rue de la Coutellerie, 63300 Thiers - T: 0473805886, Fax: 0473802939. Head: Brigitte Liabeuf
Special Museum - 1982
International cutler's craft 13667

Thionville

Collection d'Archives et de Peintures sur Jacques Brel, Centre Culturel Jacques Brel, 7 Sq Jean-Moulin, 57311 Thionville - T: 0382519495/538238/511326
Special Museum / Fine Arts Museum 13668

Musée de la Résistance et de la Déportation, Centre Culturel, Sq Jean Moulin, 57100 Thionville - T: 0382519495
Historical Museum 13669

Musée de la Tour aux Puces, Mairie, Cour du Château, 57311 Thionville - T: 0382533536, Fax: 0382542381. Head: Sylvain Chimello
Local Museum - 1966 13670

Thiviers

Musée National du Foie Gras, Maison de l'Oie et du Canard, 24800 Thiviers - T: 0553622800/551250. Head: Robert Cruège
Special Museum 13671

Thomery

Musée de l'Atelier de Rosa-Bonheur, 12 Rue Rosa-Bonheur, 77810 Thomery - T: 0164705165
Fine Arts Museum 13672

Thonac

Château de Losse, 24290 Thonac - T: 0553508008, Fax: 0553508008. Head: Amélie Morteyrol
Historic Site 13673

Espace Cro-Magnon-Musée et Parc, 24290 Thonac - T: 0553355010/507044
Archaeological Museum / Folklore Museum / Natural History Museum 13674

Thônes

Musée du Pays de Thônes, Rue Blanche, 74230 Thônes - T: 0450029776. Head: L. Cochat
Local Museum 13675

Thonon-les-Bains

Château-Musée de Ripaille, 74200 Thonon-les-Bains - T: 0450266444, Fax: 0450265474, Internet: http://www.ripaille.fr
Special Museum 13676

Ecomusée de la Pêche, Port des Pêcheurs de Rives, 74200 Thonon-les-Bains - T: 0450702696. Head: Gilles Bondaz
Special Museum - 1987
Boats and ships 13677

Musée du Chablais, Château de Sonnaz, Pl de l'Hôtel de Ville, 74200 Thonon-les-Bains - T: 0450715634, Fax: 0450706954. Head: Philippe Petey-Hache
Folklore Museum / Fine Arts Museum / Historical Museum - 1863
Folklore of the Chablais region, regional hist, prehist, Gallo-Roman archeology 13678

Thoré-la-Rochette

Château de Rochambeau, Sur D 917, 41100 Thoré-la-Rochette - T: 0254728043, Fax: 0254728043. Head: M. De Rochambeau
Historical Museum 13679

Thorens-Glières

Musée d'Art et d'Histoire, Château, 74570 Thorens-Glières - T: 0450224202
Fine Arts Museum / Historical Museum / Decorative Arts Museum 13680

Thorey-Lyautey

Château-Musée du Maréchal Lyautey, Château, 54115 Thorey-Lyautey - T: 0383562000/251721
Military Museum 13681

Musée Général du Scoutisme en France, Château, 54115 Thorey-Lyautey - T: 0383562000
Special Museum 13682

Thorigny-sur-Oreuse

Château de Fleurigny, Grande Rue, 89260 Thorigny-sur-Oreuse - T: 0386976538. Head: Comtesse F. de Limburg-Stirum
Local Museum
13th-16th century chapel, sculpture by Jean Cousin, wood panels, monumental Renaissance chimney 13683

Thouars

Musée Henri-Barre, 7 Rue Marie-de-la-Tour, 79100 Thouars - T: 0549663697/2424
Local Museum 13684

Thourie

Musée Ferme d'Autrefois et Matériel Artisanal, Le Grand Beaumont, 35240 Thourie - T: 0299431155/41
Agriculture Museum / Science&Tech Museum 13685

Thueyts

Musée Ardeche d'Autrefois, Pl du Champ-de-Mars, 07330 Thueyts - T: 0475364238/4627
Local Museum 13686

Thuillières

Musée Eve-Lavallière, 88260 Thuillières - T: 0329082548
Special Museum 13687

Thuir

Caves Muséalisées Byrrh, Cusenier, 6 Blvd Violet, 66300 Thuir - T: 0468530542, Fax: 0468533100, Internet: http://www.byrrh.com. Head: A. Palisse
Special Museum 13688

Musée de la Nature et de la Chasse, Blvd Violet, 66300 Thuir - T: 0468533629/846767
Natural History Museum 13689

Musée-Maison de l'Aspre, Arts et Traditions Populaires, Blvd Violet, 66300 Thuir - T: 0468533629/846767
Folklore Museum 13690

Tieffenbach

Collection de Sculptures sur Bois, Mille Club, 67290 Tieffenbach - T: 0388015673
Fine Arts Museum 13691

Tiffauges

Conservatoire des Machines de Guerre Médiévales, Château, 85130 Tiffauges - T: 0251657501, Fax: 0251657567, Internet: http://www.chateau-bleue.com
Military Museum 13692

Musée Centre de l'Alchimie, Château de Tiffauges, RD 753, 85130 Tiffauges - T: 0251657051, Fax: 0251657567, Internet: http://www.chateau-barbe-bleue.com
Special Museum 13693

Tigy

Musée de l'Artisanat Rural Ancien, 60 Rue de Sully, 45510 Tigy - T: 0238580042
Special Museum / Agriculture Museum 13694

Tillay-le-Péneux

Château-Musée de Villeprévost, Château, 28140 Tillay-le-Péneux - T: 0237994517
Decorative Arts Museum / Historic Site 13695

Tilly-sur-Seulles

Musée de la Bataille de Tilly et de la Région, Chapelle Notre-Dame-du-Val, Rue du 18-Juin-1944, 14250 Tilly-sur-Seulles - T: 0231808026/3846
Historical Museum 13696

Tinchebray

Musée du Tribunal Révolutionnaire, Rue de la Prison, 61800 Tinchebray - T: 0233666013/7800
Special Museum / Historical Museum 13697

Tinténiac

Musée de l'Outil et des Métiers, 5 Quai de la Donac, 35190 Tinténiac - T: 0299680203
Science&Tech Museum 13698

Tivernon

Musée Beauceron du Grand Breau, 45170 Tivernon - T: 0238394146
Folklore Museum 13699

Tonnerre

Musée Marguerite-de-Bourgogne, Hôtel-Dieu, 89700 Tonnerre - T: 0386543300 poste 9142
Special Museum 13700

Torigni-sur-Vire

Musée du Château, 50160 Torigni-sur-Vire - T: 0233567144
Decorative Arts Museum 13701

Tornac

Musée-Moulin du Pape Malaval, 30140 Tornac - T: 0466617742
Science&Tech Museum 13702

Tôtes

Collections de l'Auberge du Cygne, 3 Rue Guy-de-Maupassant, 76890 Tôtes - T: 0235329203
Decorative Arts Museum 13703

Toucy

Musée de la Gare SNCF, 89130 Toucy
Special Museum 13704

Toudon

Musée du Ferronnier, Villa La Forge à Vescons, 06830 Toudon - T: 0493085986
Fine Arts Museum / Science&Tech Museum 13705

Touet-sur-Var

Musée Républicain, Mairie, 06710 Touet-sur-Var - T: 0493057557
Special Museum 13706

Toujouse

Écomusée du Paysan Gascon, 32240 Toujouse - T: 0562096733/6250. Head: Jean Capin
Agriculture Museum 13707

Toul

Musée d'Art et d'Histoire de Toul, 25 Rue Gouvion Saint-Cyr, 54200 Toul - T: 0383641338, Fax: 0383637001. Head: Michel Hachet
Local Museum / Decorative Arts Museum - 1872
Popular arts and traditions, tapestries, icons, ornamentel arts, porcelain, ceramics from Toul, archaeology 13708

Musée Municipal → Musée d'Art et d'Histoire de Toul

Salle d'Honneur du 516e Régiment du Train, Quartier Fabvier, 54200 Toul - T: 0383430131 postes 210-223
Military Museum 13709

Toulon (Var)

Musée d'Art, 113 Blvd Maréchal Leclerc, 83000 Toulon (Var) - T: 0494368100, Fax: 0494368221. Head: M.F.X. Amprimoz
Decorative Arts Museum / Fine Arts Museum - 1887
Painting (16th-20th c), contemporary art, photographs, sculptures 13710

Musée de la Figurine, Rue Nicolas Augier, Pl du Globe, 83000 Toulon (Var) - T: 0494930759
Military Museum
Coll of uniforms 13711

Musée d'Histoire Naturelle, 113 Blvd du Maréchal Leclerc, 83000 Toulon (Var) - T: 0494368221, Fax: 0494895721. Head: Ph. Orsini
Natural History Museum - 1888
Ornithology, mammalogy, geology, paleontology 13712

Musée du Débarquement en Provence, Plateau du Mont Faron, 83000 Toulon (Var) - T: 0494880809
Military Museum 13713

Musée du Vieux Toulon, 69 Cours Lafayette, 83100 Toulon (Var) - T: 0494922923
Local Museum 13714

Musée-Mémorial National du Débarquement en Provence (1944), Ancien Fort de la Tour Beaumont, Mont Faron, 83100 Toulon (Var) - T: 0494880809
Military Museum 13715

Musée Municipal d'Arts Asiatiques, 106 Blvd Eugène Pelletan, 83000 Toulon (Var) - T: 0494319170
Fine Arts Museum 13716

Musée National de la Marine, Pl Monsenergue, Quai de Norfolk, 83100 Toulon (Var) - T: 0494020799, Fax: 0494021588, E-mail: g.prudhomme@musee_marine.fr, Internet: http://www.musee-marine.fr. Head: Georges Prud'homme
Historical Museum - 1981
Ship models, figureheads, portraits and busts of seamen 13717

La Tour Royale, Av de la Tour Royale, Le Mourillon, 83000 Toulon (Var) - T: 0494021799, Fax: 0494021588, E-mail: g.prudhomme@musee_marine.fr, Internet: http://www.musee-marine.fr. Head: Georges Prudhomme
Historical Museum
Maritime heritage monument 13718

Toulouse

Aérospatiale, 316 Rte de Bayonne, 31000 Toulouse - T: 0561935555/8831/154400
Science&Tech Museum 13719

Bibliothèque-Musée, 1 Rue du Périgord, 31000 Toulouse - T: 0561222178. Head: Pierre Jullien
Library with Exhibitions 13720

La Cinémathèque de Toulouse, 69 Rue du Tour, 31080 Toulouse - T: 0562303010, Fax: 0562303012, E-mail: cinetls@club-internet.fr. Head: Daniel Toscan du Plantier
Special Museum / Performing Arts Museum 13721

Cinémathèque Historique → La Cinémathèque de Toulouse

Galerie Municipale du Château d'Eau, 1 Pl Laganne, 31300 Toulouse - T: 0561770940, Fax: 0561420270, E-mail: chateau@galeriechateaudeau.com, Internet: http://www.galeriechateaudeau.com. Head: Jean-Marc Lacabe
Fine Arts Museum 13722

Monument à la Gloire de la Résistance, Av Frédéric Mistral, 31400 Toulouse - T: 0561550384, Fax: 0561146559, E-mail: courrier.pauldupuy@mairie-toulouse.de. Head: Jean Penent
Historical Museum 13723

Musée Archéologique de l'Institut Catholique, 31 Rue de la Fonderie, 31068 Toulouse Cedex 7 - T: 0561368100, Fax: 0561368108. Head: G. Baccrabere
Archaeological Museum / Military Museum / Folklore Museum - 1974
Roman sculptures 13724

Musée d'Art Moderne et Contemporain, Les Abattoirs, 76 Allées Charles de Fitte, 31300 Toulouse - T: 0562485800, Fax: 0562485801, E-mail: lesabattoirs@lesabattoirs.org, Internet: http://www.lesabattoirs.org. Head: Alain Mousseigne
Fine Arts Museum 13725

Musée de l'Abeille et de la Cire, Chemin de Pechbusque, 31000 Toulouse - T: 0561767004
Natural History Museum 13726

Musée de l'Affiche de la Carte Postale et de l'Art Graphique, 58 Allée Charles de Fitte, 31300 Toulouse - T: 0561592464/222464. Head: François-Régis Gastou
Special Museum 13727

Musée de l'Histoire de la Médecine de Toulouse, Hôtel Dieu, 2 Rue Viguerie, 31000 Toulouse - T: 0561778425, E-mail: museemedecine@free.fr, Internet: http://www.museemedecine.free.fr. Head: Dr. Arielle Auvergnat
Special Museum
Medical history in Toulouse during 7 centuries 13728

Musée de Site Le Bazacle, 11 Quai Saint-Pierre, 31000 Toulouse - T: 0561232381
Science&Tech Museum 13729

Musée Départemental de la Résistance et de la Déportation Jean Philippe, 52 Allées des Demoiselles, 31000 Toulouse - T: 0561148040/110222
Historical Museum
Library 13730

Musée des Augustins, 21 Rue de Metz, 31000 Toulouse - T: 0561222182, Fax: 0561223469, E-mail: courrier@augustins.org, Internet: http://www.augustins.org. Head: Alain Daguerre de Hureaux
Fine Arts Museum - 1795
Paintings of the Italian, Dutch, French and Toulouse schools, Romanesque and Gothic sculptures, 14th-19th century paintings, 16th-19th century sculptures 13731

Musée des Transports, du Tourisme et des Communications, 93 Av Jules Julien, 31400 Toulouse - T: 0561550210. Head: Georges Chatenet
Science&Tech Museum / Special Museum 13732

Musée du Tri Postal Ambulant, Gare Raynal, Chemin du Raisin, 31200 Toulouse - T: 0561134446
Special Museum 13733

Musée du Vieux Toulouse, 7 Rue du May, 31000 Toulouse - T: 0562271150, Fax: 0562275088, E-mail: toulousains.de.toulouse@wanadoo.fr. Head: Jean Penent
Local Museum 13734

Musée-Fondation Bemberg, Hôtel d'Assezat, Pl d'Assezat, 31000 Toulouse - T: 0561120689
Fine Arts Museum 13735

Musée George Labit, 43 Rue des Martyrs de la Libération, 31400 Toulouse - T: 0561539825, Fax: 0561146559, E-mail: courrier.pauldupuy@mairie-toulouse.fr. Head: Jean Penent
Fine Arts Museum - 1893
Oriental art, decorative arts, sculpture, Japanese prints, Egyptian archeology 13736

Musée Paul Dupuy, 13 Rue de la Pleau, 31000 Toulouse - T: 0561146550, Fax: 0561146559, E-mail: courrier.pauldupuy@mairie-toulouse.fr. Head: Jean Penent
Decorative Arts Museum - 1944
Crafts, regional decorative arts from the 11th century to the present, drawings, etchings, regional hist, clocks and watches - library 13737

Musée Saint-Raymond, Musée des Antiques de Toulouse, Pl Saint-Sernin, 31000 Toulouse - T: 0561222185, Fax: 0561113125. Head: Daniel Cazes
Archaeological Museum - 1892
Greek vases, bronzes, numismatics, Roman and Gallo-Roman sculpture, mosaics, epigraphs - library 13738

Muséum d'Histoire Naturelle de Toulouse, 35 Allée Jules-Guesde, 31000 Toulouse - T: 0561520014, Fax: 0561554275, E-mail: mhn@mairie-toulouse.fr. Head: J.-F. Lapeyre
Natural History Museum / Archaeological Museum / Ethnology Museum 13739

Toulx-Sainte-Croix

Musée Lapidaire Paléochrétien, Clocher de l'Église du XIe s, 23600 Toulx-Sainte-Croix - T: 0555651548
Archaeological Museum 13740

Tour-en-Bessin

Château-Musée de Vaulaville, 14400 Tour-en-Bessin - T: 0231925262
Decorative Arts Museum 13741

Tour-en-Sologne

Château-Musée de Villesavin, 41250 Tour-en-Sologne - T: 0254464288
Decorative Arts Museum 13742

Musée de Voitures Hippomobiles Anciennes, 41250 Tour-en-Sologne - T: 0254464288
Special Museum 13743

Tourcoing

Centre d'Art et d'Industrie, 11 Pl Charles Roussel, 59200 Tourcoing - T: 0320244610
Fine Arts Museum / Science&Tech Museum 13744

Centre d'Histoire Locale, 11bis Pl Charles Roussel, 59200 Tourcoing - T: 0320248918/275524, Fax: 0320249918, E-mail: jbarbieux@ville-tourcoing.fr. Head: José Barbieux
Historical Museum 13745

Musée de la Guerre des Ondes, Message Verlaine, Blockhaus QG/15e Armée, 4bis Av de la Marne, 59200 Tourcoing - T: 0320242500/3409
Military Museum / Science&Tech Museum 13746

Musée des Beaux-Arts, 2 Rue Paul Doumer, 59200 Tourcoing - T: 0320253892, Fax: 0320766157, E-mail: museebeauxarts@ville-tourcoing.fr. Head: Evelyne-Dorothée Allemand
Fine Arts Museum
17th century Flemish and Dutch paintings, 17th-20th century engravings, contemporary paintings, ancient pottery, sculptures 13747

Tournemire

Château-Musée Anjony, 15310 Tournemire - T: 0471476167
Decorative Arts Museum 13748

Tournon-sur-Rhône

Château-Musée du Rhône, Château, 6 Pl Auguste Fauré, 07300 Tournon-sur-Rhône - T: 0475081030/10-23, Fax: 0475078389, E-mail: info@ville.tournon.com
Local Museum 13749

Tournus

Hôtel-Dieu, Musée Greuze, 21 Rue de l'Hôpital, 71700 Tournus - T: 0385512350, Fax: 0385270339. Head: Christelle Rochette
Fine Arts Museum / Historical Museum
Paintings, drawings, archeology, hospital objects and site 13750

Musée Bourguignon Perrin de Puycousin, 8 Pl de l'Abbaye, 71700 Tournus - T: 0385511310/2968. Head: Hubert Miot-Putigny
Local Museum 13751

Tourouvre

Musée de l'Histoire de l'Emigration Percheronne au Canada, Pl Saint-Laurent, 61190 Tourouvre - T: 0233257455
Historical Museum 13752

Tourrette-Levens

Château-Musée, Château, 06690 Tourrette-Levens - T: 0493910320/0016
Decorative Arts Museum 13753

Tours

Atelier Histoire de Tours, Logis des Gouverneurs, 25 Quai d'Orléans, 37000 Tours - T: 0247649052
Historical Museum 13754

Historial de Touraine, Musée Grévin, Château Royal, Quai d'Orléans, 37000 Tours - T: 0247610295, Fax: 0247669404. Head: Eliane Courrand
Local Museum 13755

Musée Archéologique, Hôtel Gouin, 25 Rue du Commerce, 37000 Tours - T: 0247662232. Head: Jacques Dubois
Archaeological Museum - 1851
Art from the Middle Ages to the Renaissance, crafts, regional antiquities, prehistoric finds, Gallo-Roman objects, sculpture, numismatics 13756

Musée des Beaux-Arts, 18 Pl François Sicard, 37000 Tours - T: 0247056873, 0247216811, Fax: 0247053891, E-mail: mbatours@yahoo.fr. Head: Philippe Le Leyzour
Fine Arts Museum - 1793
14th-20th century Italian, Dutch and French paintings, sculptures, furnishings, decorative arts - library 13757

Musée des Equipages Militaires et du Train, Quartier Beaumont, Rue du Plat d'Etain, 37000 Tours - T: 0247773307, Fax: 0247773475
Military Museum / Science&Tech Museum 13758

Musée des Vins de Touraine, Celliers Saint-Julien, 16 Rue Nationale, 37000 Tours - T: 0247610793, Fax: 0247216890. Head: Laurent Bastard
Ethnology Museum - 1975
Costumes of wine confraternities, silverware, ceramics, tools, pictures 13759

Musée du Compagnonnage, 8 Rue Nationale, 37000 Tours - T: 0247610793, Fax: 0247216890. Head: Laurent Bastard
Ethnology Museum - 1968
Handicraft from Antiquity to the present, tools, engravings, flags, archives on history and rites 13760

Musée du Gemmail, Art de Lumière, Hôtel Raimbault, 7 Rue du Mûrier, 37000 Tours - T: 0247610119
Decorative Arts Museum 13761

Musée Religieux Franco-Canadien, Chapelle Saint-Michel, 2 Rue du Petit Pré, 37000 Tours - T: 0247666595
Religious Arts Museum 13762

Musée Saint-Martin, Chapelle Saint-Jean, 3 Rue Rapin, 37000 Tours - T: 0247644887
Religious Arts Museum 13763

Muséum d'Histoire Naturelle, 3 Rue du Président Merville, 37000 Tours - T: 0247641331
Natural History Museum 13764

Tourtour

Musée Géologique, Rue du Moulin à Huile, 83690 Tourtour - T: 0494705474
Natural History Museum 13765

Tourville-sur-Arques

Château-Musée de Miromesnil, 76550 Tourville-sur-Arques - T: 0235850280, Fax: 0235855505. Head: T. Comtesse de Vogüé
Decorative Arts Museum 13766

Tourzel-Ronzieres

Maison de Pays, 63320 Tourzel-Ronzieres - T: 0473714301, Fax: 0473714127, E-mail: - dauphine.auvergne@micro-assist.fr
Agriculture Museum 13767

Musée de la Cochonnaille, 63320 Tourzel-Ronzieres - T: 0473714301, Fax: 0473714127, E-mail: dauphine-auvergne@nicio-assest.fr
Special Museum 13768

Touvois

Maison-Musée du Paysan, 44650 Touvois - T: 0240316286
Folklore Museum 13769

Trambly

Musée Curiosités de la Pierre, 71520 Trambly - T: 0385504698
Natural History Museum 13770

Tramont-Emy

Collection Archéologique, 54115 Tramont-Emy - T: 0383523346
Archaeological Museum 13771

Treffort-Cuisiat

Musée du Revermont, Ancienne École du Cuisiat, 01370 Treffort-Cuisiat - T: 0474513242/211520
Special Museum 13772

Tréflaouenan

Ferme-Musée du Léon, Lanqueran, 29440 Tréflaouenan - T: 0298295307. Head: Marie-José Néar
Local Museum 13773

Trégarvan

Musée de l'Ecole Rurale, Ecole, 29560 Trégarvan - T: 0298260472, Fax: 0298260646, E-mail: - musee.ecole.bretagne@wanadoo.fr. Head: Monique Rogé
Special Museum - 1977
History of schools in the rural region 13774

Trégastel

Musée du Moulin à Marée, Chaussée du Port, 22730 Trégastel - T: 0296234748, Fax: 0296153805
Science&Tech Museum 13775

Tréguier

Musée Renan, 20 Rue Ernest Renan, 22220 Tréguier - T: 0296924563
Historical Museum - 1946
Birthplace of the writer Ernest Renan (1823-1892), religious studies, 13776

Treignac

Musée des Arts et Traditions de la Haute-Vézère, 5 Rue Docteur-Albert-Flayssac, 19260 Treignac - T: 0555980156
Folklore Museum 13777

Treigny

Château de Ratilly, 89520 Treigny - T: 0386747006/7954
Decorative Arts Museum / Fine Arts Museum 13778

Maison du Chanoine, Le Chêneau, 89520 Treigny - T: 0386747299
Decorative Arts Museum 13779

Trélazé

Musée de l'Ardoise, 32 Chemin de la Maraîchère, 49800 Trélazé - T: 0241690471
Science&Tech Museum 13780

Trélon

Atelier Musée du Verre, Ancienne Verrerie Parant, Rue Clavon, 59132 Trélon - T: 0327597102/606611
Science&Tech Museum 13781

Trois-Fontaines

Musée du Vieux Vélo, Abbaye, 51250 Trois-Fontaines - T: 0326730394
Science&Tech Museum 13782

Troissereux

Musée du Commerce International et de la Vie Quotidienne des Armateurs, Négociants et Corsaires, 1 Rue du Château, 60112 Troissereux - T: 0344790000
Special Museum / Military Museum 13783

Troo

Musée d'Arts et Traditions Populaires, Rue Haute, 41800 Troo - T: 0254725335
Fine Arts Museum 13784

Trouville-sur-Mer

Galerie du Musée Montebello, 32 Blvd F.-Moureaux, 14360 Trouville-sur-Mer - T: 0231883619
Fine Arts Museum / Historical Museum 13785

Musée Montebello, Villa Montebello, 64 Rue du Général-Leclerc, 14360 Trouville-sur-Mer - T: 0231881626
Local Museum 13786

Troyes

Centre Culturel Marguerite-Bourgeois, 38 Rue Georges-Clemenceau, 10000 Troyes - T: 0325733730
Religious Arts Museum 13787

Maison de l'Outil et de la Pensée Ouvrière, Hôtel de Mauroy, 7 Rue de la Trinité, 10000 Troyes - T: 0325732826, Fax: 0325739047, E-mail: maison.de.l.outil@wanadoo.fr, Internet: http://www.maison-de-l-outil.com. Head: Pascal Serge
Historical Museum - 1974 13788

Musée Aubois d'Histoire de l'Éducation, IUFM, 6 Av de Lombards, 10000 Troyes - T: 0325820134, Fax: 0325824295
Historical Museum / Special Museum 13789

Musée d'Art Moderne, Donation Pierre et Denise Levy, Pl Saint-Pierre, 10000 Troyes - T: 0325762680
Fine Arts Museum - 1982
Fauvism (Derain, Braque, Vlaminck, Friesz), French art (1850-1950) 13790

Musée de la Bonneterie, Hôtel de Vauluisant, 4 Rue de Vauluisant, 10000 Troyes - T: 0325423333 poste 3692, Fax: 0325801800, E-mail: musart@ville-troyes.fr/musees, Internet: http://www.ville-troyes.fr/musees. Head: Chantal Rouquet
Historical Museum - 1934
Knitting machines (18th-20th c), crafts, bonnets 13791

Musée des Beaux-Arts et d'Archéologie, Musée d'Histoire Naturelle, Ancienne Abbaye Saint-Loup, 1 Rue Chrestien-de-Troyes, 10000 Troyes - T: 0325762160, Fax: 0325801800, E-mail: musart@ville-troyes.fr, Internet: http://www.ville-troyes.fr/musees. Head: Chantal Rouquet
Fine Arts Museum / Archaeological Museum / Natural History Museum - 1792
Classical and Egyptian archeology, prehistory to Merovingian times, jewelry, 15th-20th century French and foreign paintings and sculptures, glass, enamel, furnishings 13792

Musée d'Histoire Naturelle, 1 Rue Chrestien de Troyes, 10000 Troyes - T: 0325762167, Fax: 0325801800. Head: Chantal Rouquet
Natural History Museum - 1964
Natural history, birds, butterflies, fossils 13793

Musée Historique de Troyes et de la Champagne, 4 Rue de Vauluisant, 10000 Troyes - T: 0325423333 poste 3692, Fax: 0325801800, E-mail: musart@ville-troyes.fr/musees, Internet: http://www.ville-troyes.fr/musees. Head: Chantal Rouquet
Historical Museum - 1934
Local 16th century art and history, paintings, sculpture, portraits, decorative arts, ceramics, 16th century church windows of the school of Troyes 13794

Passages Centre d'Art Contemporain, 9 Rue Jeanne d'Arc, 10000 Troyes - T: 0325732827, Fax: 0325732595, E-mail: cac.passages@wanadoo.fr. Head: Françoise Gibert-Balboni
Fine Arts Museum 13795

Pharmacie-Musée de l'Hôtel Dieu le Comte, Quai des Comtes de Champagne, 10000 Troyes - T: 0325809897, Fax: 0325801800, E-mail: musart@ville-troyes.fr/musees, Internet: http://www.ville-troyes.fr/musees. Head: Chantal Rouquet
Special Museum - 1979
Pharmacy from the 18th c, history of hospitals during the Ancient Regime 13796

Trésor de la Cathédrale de Troyes, Pl Saint-Pierre, 10000 Troyes - T: 0325805846
Religious Arts Museum - 1200
Cathedral treasure, religious objects, robes, enamel, ivory, 9th-12th century codexes - library 13797

Truchtersheim

Maison du Kochersberg, 4 Pl du Marché, 67370 Truchtersheim - T: 0388696260
Fine Arts Museum 13798

Tulle

Musée Départemental de la Résistance et de la Déportation, 2 Quai Edmond-Perrier, 19000 Tulle - T: 0555262436
Historical Museum 13799

Musée des Armes Anciennes, 1 Pl Albert-Faucher, 19000 Tulle - T: 0555201009 poste 346
Military Museum 13800

Musée du Cloître, Pl de la Cathédrale, 19012 Tulle - T: 0555262205
Local Museum - 1928
Paleontology, prehistory, Gallo-Roman antiquities, medieval architecture, numismatics, local artifacts, iconography, porcelain, armaments, regional religious art 13801

Tullins-Fures

Musée du Machinisme Agricole, À Corcelles, 38210 Tullins-Fures - T: 0476070198
Agriculture Museum / Science&Tech Museum 13802

Turckheim

Musée de la Poche de Colmar, 25 Rue du Conseil, 68230 Turckheim - T: 0389271808
Military Museum 13803

Turquant

Écomusée de la Conservation du Fruit, Le Val-Hulin, 49730 Turquant - T: 0241514830
Special Museum 13804

Habitation Troglodytique Seigneuriale, La Grande Vignolle, Rte de Chinon, 49730 Turquant - T: 0241529084
Special Museum 13805

Musée de l'Outil, Moulin de la Herpinière, 49730 Turquant - T: 0241517522
Science&Tech Museum / Folklore Museum 13806

Tursac

La Madeleine, Abri sous Roche Archéosite d'un Village Troglodytique, 24620 Tursac - T: 0553069249/355040
Archaeological Museum 13807

Préhisto-Parc, 24620 Tursac - T: 0553507319
Archaeological Museum 13808

Tusson

Maison du Patrimoine, Club Marpen, 16140 Tusson - T: 0545311732, Fax: 0545314580, E-mail: anim-patri@wanadoo.fr. Head: Jackie Flaud
Local Museum 13809

Musée de la Vie Rurale, Maison du Patrimoine, 16140 Tusson - T: 0545311732, Fax: 0545303464, E-mail: anim-patri@wanadoo.fr, Internet: http://www.perso.wanadoo.fr/tusson. Head: Jackie Flaud
Ethnology Museum 13810

Uffheim

Casemate, Mémorial de Haute-Alsace, Aschenbach, 68510 Uffheim - T: 0389815142/5629/5162
Military Museum 13811

Ugine

Musée d'Arts et Traditions Populaires du Val d'Arly, Château Crest-Cherel, 73400 Ugine - T: 0479375633, Fax: 0479890169, E-mail: soffice@ugine.com. Head: Hervé Nozet
Folklore Museum 13812

Uhlwiller

Musée du Pain, 54 Rue des Perches, 67350 Uhlwiller - T: 0388727705/077029/077492
Special Museum 13813

Ungersheim

Ecomusée d'Alsace, BP 71, 68190 Ungersheim - T: 0389744474, Fax: 0389481530, E-mail: contact@ecopares.com, Internet: http://www.ecomusee-alsace.com. Head: Marc Grodwohl
Open Air Museum - 1984
An open-air museum comprising a reconstituted village of 65 cottages, showing life in olden days with a baker, an oil-mill, a blacksmith, a clog-maker, a sawmill working on site, nature walks, seminars - library 13814

Urçay

Maison de la Dentelle, Le Bourg, 03660 Urçay - T: 0470069269
Special Museum 13815

Urimenil

Collection Républicaine, Mairie, 88220 Urimenil - T: 0329308156, Fax: 0329307470
Special Museum 13816

Urrugne

Château-Musée d'Urrugne, Château d'Uturbie, Rte Nationale 10, 64122 Urrugne - T: 0559543115
Decorative Arts Museum 13817

Ussat-les-Bains

Collection Antonin-Gadal, Maison Peyce-Bousse, 09400 Ussat-les-Bains - T: 0561058157
Archaeological Museum 13818

Usson-en-Forez

Musée Rural, Écomusée des Monts du Forez, Quartier Saint-Joseph, Rue Poncetom, 42550 Usson-en-Forez - T: 0477506797, Fax: 0477506489
Local Museum 13819

Uxegney

Fort Muséalisé d'Uxegney, Rue des Forts, 88390 Uxegney - T: 0329383209, E-mail: fort-uxegney@wanadoo.fr. Head: Patrick Visini
Historical Museum 13820

Uzès

Duché d'Uzès, Pl du Duché, 30700 Uzès - T: 0466221896, Internet: http://www.duche-uzes.fr
Decorative Arts Museum 13821

Musée d'Arts et de Traditions de l'Uzège Georges Borias, Ancien Evêché, 30700 Uzès - T: 0466224023
Local Museum - 1907
Local hist, folklore, regional prehistory, Gallo-Roman finds, ceramics, paintings, memorabilia of André Gide (1869-1951) 13822

Musée du Bonbon Haribo, Pont des Charettes, 30700 Uzès - T: 0466032200
Special Museum 13823

Vaas

Moulin-Musée Le Rotrou, 72420 Vaas - T: 0243467022
Science&Tech Museum 13824

Vachères

Musée Archéologique, École Publique, 04110 Vachères - T: 0492764215/6116
Archaeological Museum 13825

Vacheresse-les-Basses

Musée des Couronnes de Mariées, Manoir de Vacheresse-les-Basses, 28210 Vacheresse-les-Basses - T: 0237827146, Fax: 0143201004, E-mail: vacheresses@chateaux-france.com
Special Museum 13826

Vadencourt

Musée Les Ateliers du Bois, 02120 Vadencourt - T: 0323611096
Ethnology Museum 13827

Vaiges

Musée Gletton, Mairie, 53480 Vaiges
Local Museum 13828

Vains

Maison de la Pêche à Pied et Anciennes Salines, La Chaussée, Saint-Léonard, 50300 Vains - T: 0233708142
Special Museum 13829

Manoir-Musée, 50300 Vains - T: 0233582446
Decorative Arts Museum 13830

Vaison-la-Romaine

Musée Archéologique, Fouilles de Puymin, 84110 Vaison-la-Romaine - T: 0490365005, Fax: 0490365029, E-mail: vaison@wanadoo.fr. Head: Patrick Fabre
Archaeological Museum - 1974
Roman archaeology, stone coll, statues, mural painting, mosaics, daily life 13831

Musée Lapidaire du Cloître de l'Ancienne Cathédrale, Cathédrale Notre-Dame-de-Nazareth, 84110 Vaison-la-Romaine - T: 0490360211, Fax: 0490365029, E-mail: patrimoine@vaison.la.romaine.com. Head: C. Bezin
Archaeological Museum 13832

Valbonne

Musée des Arts et Traditions Populaires, Pl de l'Église, 06560 Valbonne - T: 0493123456
Folklore Museum 13833

Valdeblore

Musée du Terroir Saint-Dalmas, 06420 Valdeblore - T: 0493028229
Folklore Museum 13834

Valençay

Musée de l'Automobile, 12 Av de la Résistance, 36600 Valençay - T: 0254000774, Fax: 0254003239, E-mail: pays.de.valencay@wanadoo.fr, Internet: http://www.cc-valencay.fr
Science&Tech Museum 13835

Parc et Château de Valencay, 36600 Valençay - T: 0254001066, Fax: 0254000237, E-mail: message@chateau_valencay.com, Internet: http://www.chateau-valencay.com. Head: C. Doucet, E. Barheret-Girardin
Fine Arts Museum / Local Museum 13836

Valence-d'Agen-Golfech

Exposition sur l'Énergie Nucléaire, Centrale de Golfech, 82400 Valence-d'Agen-Golfech - T: 0563293906
Science&Tech Museum 13837

Valence (Drôme)

Exposition Permanente Valence Ville d'Art et d'Histoire, 57 Grande Rue, 26000 Valence (Drôme) - T: 0475792086, Fax: 0475828342
Historical Museum 13838

Musée Municipal des Beaux-Arts, 4 Pl des Ormeaux, 26000 Valence (Drôme) - T: 0475792080, Fax: 0475792084, E-mail: musee-valence@wanadoo.fr. Head: Hélène Moulin
Fine Arts Museum - 1850
Paintings of French and foreign schools, contemporary art, prehistory, 15th and 17th century wall paintings, historic house, coll of drawings by Hubert Robert 13839

Valence-sur-Baise

Abbaye de Flaran (Abbey of Flaran), 32310 Valence-sur-Baise - T: 0562285019, Fax: 0562289776, E-mail: mhue@cg32.fr, Internet: http://www.gers-gascogne.com. Head: Michel Hue
Religious Arts Museum - 1151
Cisterian abbay (12th-18th c) 13840

Valenciennes

Galerie L'Aquarium, 8 Rue Ferrand, 59300 Valenciennes - T: 0327225763, Fax: 0327225760, E-mail: eba@ville-valenciennes.fr, Internet: http://www.ville-valenciennes.fr/rubrique.culture
Public Gallery 13841

Musée des Beaux-Arts, Blvd Watteau, 59300 Valenciennes - T: 0327225720, Fax: 0327225722, Internet: http:/www.valenciennes.fr. Head: P. Ramade
Fine Arts Museum
Flemish and French paintings, sculpture, archaeology 13842

Valensole

Musée Vivant de l'Abeille, Rte de Manosque, 04210 Valensole - T: 0492748528
Special Museum 13843

Valeyrac

Château Le Temple, 33340 Valeyrac - T: 0556415362
Special Museum 13844

Valignat

Musée de La Source, 03330 Valignat - T: 0470583344, 0470583288, Fax: 0470583344. Head: Jean-Charles Baudet
Agriculture Museum 13845

Vallabrègues

Musée de la Vannerie, 5 Rue Carnot, 30300 Vallabrègues - T: 0466592341/4814
Special Museum 13846

Vallauris

Musée de la Poterie, Rue Sicard, Céramique, 06220 Vallauris - T: 0493646651, Fax: 0493649346
Decorative Arts Museum / Ethnology Museum 13847

Musée Magnelli, Musée de la Céramique, Pl de la Libération, 06220 Vallauris - T: 0493641605, Fax: 0493645032, E-mail: musee.vallauris@free.fr. Head: Sandra Benachetti
Fine Arts Museum
Ceramics, works by Picasso and Alberto Magnelli 13848

Musée National Picasso La Guerre et la Paix, Pl de la Libération, 06220 Vallauris - T: 0493649805, Fax: 0493645032. Head: Jean-Michel Foray
Fine Arts Museum - 1959
Wood mural by Pablo Picasso, 'La Guerre et la Paix' 13849

Valleraugues

Musée de la Météorologie, Observatoire du Mont Aigoual, 30570 Valleraugues - T: 0467826001
Special Museum / Science&Tech Museum 13850

Musée de la Soil, Filature du Mazal, 30570 Valleraugues - T: 0467822278
Decorative Arts Museum 13851

Vallerysthal-Troisfontaines

Musée du Cristal, Cristallerie, 57870 Vallerysthal-Troisfontaines - T: 0387251133
Decorative Arts Museum 13852

Vallon-en-Sully

Musée de Maquettes Animées sur les Ateliers, Métiers et Scènes de Jadis, Rte de Chazemais, 03190 Vallon-en-Sully - T: 0470065075/5722
Local Museum 13853

Vallon-Pont-d'Arc

Archeosite de la Préhistoire, Grotte Chauvet, 68 Rue du Miarou, 07150 Vallon-Pont-d'Arc - T: 0475371768
Fine Arts Museum 13854

La Bouteillerie, Rue du Barry, 07150 Vallon-Pont-d'Arc - T: 0475880826
Special Museum 13855

Musée Agricole Paysan, Hameau de Saint-Martin, 07150 Vallon-Pont-d'Arc - T: 0475880346
Special Museum 13856

Musée de la Grotte des Huguenots, Rte des Gorges, 07150 Vallon-Pont-d'Arc - T: 0475880671/1163. Head: Erwin Tscherter
Archaeological Museum / Historical Museum 13857

Musée Ma Magnanerie, Les Mazes, 07150 Vallon-Pont-d'Arc - T: 0475880127, Fax: 0475881334. Head: Sylvette Cauvin
Special Museum / Folklore Museum / Natural History Museum 13858

Vallouise

Maison du Parc National des Ecrins, 05290 Vallouise - T: 0492233231
Local Museum 13859

Valognes

Musée-Hôtel de Beaumont, Rue Barbey d'Aurevilly, 50700 Valognes - T: 0233401230
Decorative Arts Museum 13860

Musée-Hôtel Granval-Caligny, 32 Rue des Religieuses, 50700 Valognes - T: 0233400175
Decorative Arts Museum 13861

Musée Régional du Cidre et du Calvados, Rue du Petit Versailles, 50700 Valognes - T: 0233402273, Fax: 0233952323, E-mail: maire.officetourisme.valognes@wanadoo.fr
Agriculture Museum / Folklore Museum / Ethnology Museum
Cider hist of 5 c, grinders and presses, pottery works, transportation, costumes, furniture, tools, materials, machines, trade, stone, iron and leather works 13862

Valprivas

Château-Musée, Centre Culturel, 43210 Valprivas - T: 0471667133
Fine Arts Museum 13863

Valréas

Château de Simiane, Hôtel de Ville, 84600 Valréas - T: 0490350045
Fine Arts Museum / Decorative Arts Museum / Historical Museum 13864

Musée du Cartonnage et de l'Imprimerie, 3 Av Foch, 84600 Valréas - T: 0490355875, Fax: 0490353251. Head: Magali Baussan
Science&Tech Museum 13865

Vals-les-Bains

Collections d'Histoire Naturelle d'Océanie, 10 Av Paul-Ribeyre, 07600 Vals-les-Bains - T: 0475374446
Natural History Museum 13866

Vandœuvre-les-Nancy

Musée de l'Histoire de la Médecine, c/o Faculté de Médecine, 9 Av de la Forêt de Haye, 54505 Vandœuvre-les-Nancy - T: 0383592833, Fax: 0383446065, E-mail: grignon@facmed.u-nancy.fr. Head: Prof. Georges Grignon
Historical Museum / University Museum 13867

Vandré

Musée de la Vie d'Autrefois, Rue de la Boulangerie, 17700 Vandré - T: 0546070507
Folklore Museum 13868

Vannes-le-Châtel

Espace Verre, 54112 Vannes-le-Châtel - T: 0383254744, Fax: 0383254999, E-mail: garcia@idverre.net. Head: Denis Garcia
Decorative Arts Museum 13869

Vannes (Morbihan)

La Cohue, Musée de Vannes, 9 Pl Saint-Pierre, 56000 Vannes (Morbihan) - T: 0297473586, Fax: 0297492234. Head: Marie-Françoise Le Saux
Fine Arts Museum - 1885
Painting, sculpture, archeology - libraries 13870

Musée de la Société Polymathique du Morbihan, Château Gaillard, 2 Rue Noé, 56000 Vannes (Morbihan) - T: 0297425980. Head: Joël Lecornec
Archaeological Museum - 1912
Megalithic, Bronze Age, Iron Age periods in Britanny, Roman and historical periods, religious art - library 13871

La Papillonneraie, Musée Vivant, Parc du Golfe, 56000 Vannes (Morbihan) - T: 0297460102
Natural History Museum 13872

Varages

Musée des Faïences de Varages, Maison Gassendi, Pl de la Libération, 83670 Varages - T: 0494798318/8138
Decorative Arts Museum 13873

Varaignes

Atelier-Musée des Tisserands et de la Charentaise, Château, 24360 Varaignes - T: 0553563576
Folklore Museum / Historical Museum 13874

Varaire

Musée de la Meunerie, Moulin de Fontvieille, 46260 Varaire - T: 0565315234
Science&Tech Museum 13875

Varces

Musée du Modèle Réduit, Z.A.C. Saint-Ange, 38760 Varces - T: 0476728927, Fax: 0476725566, E-mail: eurorail@wanadoo.fr. Head: M. Laubie
Science&Tech Museum
Coll of 6,000 toys 13876

Varennes-en-Argonne

Musée d'Argonne, 55270 Varennes-en-Argonne - T: 0329807114, Fax: 0329807143
Historical Museum - 1973
Exhibits on Louis XVI during his arrest in 1791, World War I, art and local traditions 13877

Musées d'Art et d'Histoire, Rue de Boureuilles, 55270 Varennes-en-Argonne - T: 0329807101
Folklore Museum / Local Museum / Archaeological Museum 13878

Varennes-Vauzelles

Musée de la Résistance, 4bis Rue André Malraux, 58640 Varennes-Vauzelles - T: 0386573166
Historical Museum 13879

Vars

Musée de Peinture Contemporaine, Mairie, 05560 Vars - T: 0492465009
Fine Arts Museum 13880

Varzy

Musée Municipal Auguste Grasset, Pl de la Mairie, 58210 Varzy - T: 0386297203. Head: François Martin
Local Museum / Fine Arts Museum 13881

Vascœuil

Château de Vascœuil, Rue Jules Michelet, 27910 Vascœuil - T: 0235236235, Fax: 0235230290. Head: Marie Laure Papillard
Historical Museum / Fine Arts Museum / Historic Site / Open Air Museum 13882

Vassieux-en-Vercors

Mémorial de la Résistance en Vercors, 26420 Vassieux-en-Vercors - T: 0475482600
Historic Site 13883

Vatan

Musée du Cirque, 1 Pl de la Liberté, 36150 Vatan - T: 0254497778, Fax: 0254497778, E-mail: info@musee-du-cirque.com, Internet: http://www.musee-du-cirque.com. Head: Michel Caudoux
Special Museum / Association with Coll 13884

Vaucouleurs

Musée Johannique, 55140 Vaucouleurs - T: 0329895182. Head: Simonne Poette
Local Museum 13885

Vaudeurs

Musée de la Pomme et du Cidre, Hameau Brissot, 89320 Vaudeurs - T: 0386962537
Special Museum 13886

Vauhallan

Collections de l'Abbaye Bénédictine de Saint-Louis-du-Temple, Limon, 91430 Vauhallan - T: 0169852100, Fax: 0169852898, E-mail: limon@wanadoo.fr
Special Museum / Decorative Arts Museum
Memorabilia of Louis XVI and Marie Antoinette, drawings by Genevieve Gallois 13887

Vaujours

Musée Technique des Poudres, DGA, Association des Amis du Parc Forestier National de Sevran, Allée Eugène Burlot, 93410 Vaujours - T: 0148601258/43835301
Science&Tech Museum 13888

Vauvert

Musée Historique de la Vigne, Château Boissy-d'Anglas, Gallician, 30600 Vauvert - T: 0466733085/3268
Special Museum 13889

Vaux-devant-Damloup

Musée du Fort de Vaux, Fort, 55400 Vaux-devant-Damloup - T: 0329841885/861418
Military Museum 13890

Vaux-en-Beaujolais

Musée de la Vigne et du Vin, Le Bourg, 69460 Vaux-en-Beaujolais - T: 0474032658
Special Museum 13891

Vaux-le-Pénil

Musée de Surréalisme, Château, 77000 Vaux-le-Pénil - T: 0160680095
Fine Arts Museum 13892

Vayrac

Musée Archéologique d'Uxellodunun, Pl Luctérius, 46110 Vayrac - T: 0565325250, 0565324026, Fax: 0565324130
Archaeological Museum 13893

Veauce

Musée d'Art Contemporain du Château de Veauce, 03450 Veauce - T: 0470585327
Fine Arts Museum 13894

Veauche

Musée de la Verrerie, Usine B.S.N., Rue Abbé Delorme, 42340 Veauche - T: 0477361400
Science&Tech Museum 13895

Veckring

Musée de la Ligne Maginot, Hackenberg, 57920 Veckring - T: 0382823008
Military Museum 13896

Velaine-en-Haye

Musée de l'Automobile, Zone de Loisirs, Parc de Haye, 54840 Velaine-en-Haye - T: 0383232838, Fax: 0383367576, E-mail: alaacl@en-lorraine.com, Internet: http://www.en-lorraine.com/alaacl
Science&Tech Museum 13897

Velaux

Tour-Musée de Velaux, 13880 Velaux - T: 0442874444
Historical Museum / Folklore Museum 13898

Vemars

Musée François-Mauriac, Château de la Motte, 5 Rue Léon-Bouchard, 95470 Vemars - T: 0134683410
Special Museum 13899

Venas

La Maison Couleur du Temps, Hameau de Clemagnet, 03190 Venas - T: 0470068483
Special Museum 13900

Vence

Chapelle Matisse, 468 Av Henri-Matisse, 06140 Vence - T: 0493580326
Fine Arts Museum 13901

Château de Villeneuve, 2 Pl du Frène, 06140 Vence - T: 0493581578, 0493242423, Fax: 0493246852. Head: Zia Mirabdolbaghi
Fine Arts Museum
Modern and contemporary art 13902

Galerie Beaubourg, Château Notre-Dame des Fleurs, 2618 Rte de Grasse, 06140 Vence - T: 0493245200, Fax: 0493245219, E-mail: info@galeriebeaubourg.com, Internet: http://www.galerie-beaubourg.com. Head: Pierre Nahon
Special Museum / Fine Arts Museum / Open Air Museum 13903

Vendeuvre

Château-Musée, Château, 14170 Vendeuvre - T: 0231409383, Fax: 0231401111, E-mail: chateau@vendeuvre.com, Internet: http://www.vendeuvre.com. Head: Elyane de Vendeuvre
Decorative Arts Museum 13904

Musée International de Mobilier Miniature, Château, 14170 Vendeuvre - T: 0231409383, Fax: 0231401111, E-mail: chateau@vendeuvre.com, Internet: http://www.vendeuvre.com. Head: Elyane de Vendeuvre
Decorative Arts Museum 13905

Vendôme

Musée de Vendôme d'Art et d'Histoire, Abbaye, Cloître de la Trinité, 41100 Vendôme - T: 0254772613/0507. Head: Laurence Guilbaud
Fine Arts Museum / Archaeological Museum / Decorative Arts Museum - 1862
Prehistoric finds, sculptures from medieval times to the Renaissance, 17th century French and Dutch paintings, ceramics, regional lore 13906

Vendres

Exposition Permanente Archéologique, Rue de la Commune, 34350 Vendres - T: 0467396339
Archaeological Museum 13907

Vénissieux

Maison du Peuple, 8 Blvd Laurent-Gerin, 69200 Vénissieux - T: 0472788888
Fine Arts Museum 13908

Musée Communal de la Résistance et de la Déportation, Pl Léon Sublet, 69200 Vénissieux - T: 0472500767
Historical Museum 13909

Venosc

Exposition Permanente d'Art et d'Histoire, OTSI près de Télécabine, 38143 Venosc - T: 0476800682
Natural History Museum / Historical Museum 13910

Vensac

Musée du Vieux Moulin à Vent, Moulin, 33590 Vensac - T: 0556094500
Science&Tech Museum 13911

Ventabren

Musée Archéologique La Calade, 13122 Ventabren - T: 0442234744/288481
Archaeological Museum 13912

Ventron

Musée du Textile des Vosges, 88310 Ventron - T: 0329242306
Decorative Arts Museum / Science&Tech Museum 13913

Ver-sur-Mer

Musée America-Gold Beach, 2 Pl Amiral Byrd, 14114 Ver-sur-Mer - T: 0231225858, Fax: 0231225858. Head: Jean-Pierre Dupont
Historical Museum 13914

Verdelais

Musée d'Art Sacré, Pl des Allées, 33490 Verdelais - T: 0556620206/04
Religious Arts Museum 13915

Verdigny

Musée Viticole, Mairie, 18300 Verdigny - T: 0248793501/3103
Agriculture Museum 13916

Verdun (Meuse)

Musée de la Citadelle Militaire, Citadelle, 55100 Verdun (Meuse) - T: 0329861418
Historical Museum / Military Museum - 1929 13917

Musée de la Princerie, 16 Rue de la Belle Vierge, 55100 Verdun (Meuse) - T: 0329861062, Fax: 0329834423. Head: Marie-Emmanuelle Meyer
Archaeological Museum / Fine Arts Museum / Decorative Arts Museum - 1823
Archaeology, painting, ceramics 13918

Musée de l'Evêché, Pl Monseigneur Ginesty, 55100 Verdun (Meuse) - T: 0329860240/0172/1839
Religious Arts Museum 13919

Verdun-sur-le-Doubs

Musée du Blé et du Pain, Ecomusée de la Bresse Bourguignonne, Rue Pont Saint-Jean, 71350 Verdun-sur-le-Doubs - T: 0385762716. Head: Dominique Rivière
Special Museum 13920

Véretz

Musée Paul-Louis Courier, Mairie, 37270 Véretz - T: 0247503012
Special Museum 13921

Verfeil

Musée Historique et Littéraire, Mairie, 31590 Verfeil - T: 0561356105
Historical Museum / Special Museum 13922

Vergèze

Musée de la Tonnellerie, Pl de la Mairie, 30310 Vergèze - T: 0466354592
Special Museum 13923

Vermand

Musée d'Art Religieux, Pl de l'Hôtel-de-Ville, Mairie, 02490 Vermand - T: 0323641146
Religious Arts Museum 13924

Musée des Sapeurs-Pompiers, Pl de l'Hôtel-de-Ville, Mairie, 02490 Vermand - T: 0323641146
Science&Tech Museum 13925

Musée d'Uniformologie, Mairie, 02490 Vermand - T: 0323641146
Military Museum / Archaeological Museum 13926

Musée Ethnologique Intercommunal du Vermandois, Mairie, 02490 Vermand - T: 0323641146
Archaeological Museum / Ethnology Museum 13927

Verneuil-en-Bourbonnais

Musée du Lavage et du Repassage, Pl de La Fontaine, 03500 Verneuil-en-Bourbonnais - T: 0470459153/4734, Fax: 0470454734, E-mail: eurofer@wanadoo.fr, Internet: http://www.eurofer.wanadoo.fr. Head: Jacques Lebrun
Special Museum / Science&Tech Museum 13928

Verneuil-en-Halatte

Musée de la Mémoire des Murs et d'Archéologie Locale, Allée Jules Ferry, 60550 Verneuil-en-Halatte - T: 0344245481, Fax: 0344253902. Head: Serge Ramond
Archaeological Museum / Fine Arts Museum / Folklore Museum / Ethnology Museum - 1987 13929

Vernon

Musée Municipal A.G. Poulain, 12 Rue du Pont, 27200 Vernon - T: 0232212809, Fax: 0232511117, Internet: http://www.ville-vernon27.fr/musee. Head: Sophie Fourny-Dargère

Fine Arts Museum - 1862
School of animalier artists (19th-20th c): sculptors and painters, American and French Impressionist painters in Giverny 13930

Verny

Archeosite Militaire, Groupe Fortifié l'Aisne, 57420 Verny - T: 0387527691, E-mail: adfm.secretaire@voila.fr, http://www.geocities.com/pentagon/bunker/3752/. Head: Raymond Decker
Military Museum 13931

Verrières-le-Buisson

Musée de Verrières-le-Buisson, Centre André Malraux, 13 Rue d'Antony, 91370 Verrières-le-Buisson - T: 0169206893/94. Head: Michel Colonna Ceccaldi
Local Museum 13932

Versailles

Musée des Carrosses, 1 Av de Paris, 78000 Versailles - T: 0130837800. Head: Pierre Azizzoli-Clémentel
Science&Tech Museum
Coaches, carriages, and litters from the 18th-19th c 13933

Musée Lambinet, 54 Blvd de la Reine, 78000 Versailles - T: 0139503032, Fax: 0139519088. Head: Cathérine Gendre
Fine Arts Museum - 1932
Medieval religious art, liturgical objects, local documents, local history, sculptures, 18th century furnishings 13934

Musée National des Châteaux de Versailles et de Trianon, Château, 78000 Versailles - T: 0130837800, Fax: 0130837790, Internet: http://www.chateauversailles.fr. Head: Pierre Arizzoli-Clémentel
Decorative Arts Museum / Fine Arts Museum / Historical Museum / Historic Site - 1834
Furniture, interiors, objects d'art, sculptures, 16th-19th century paintings - library 13935

Vervins

Exposition Permanente sur les Églises Fortifiées de la Thiérache, OTSI, Pl du Général-de-Gaulle, 02140 Vervins - T: 0323981198/0247
Local Museum 13936

Musée de la Thiérache, Pl du Général-de-Gaulle, 02140 Vervins - T: 0323980030/1368
Archaeological Museum / Historical Museum - 1873
Paleontology, prehistory, antiquities, geology, ethnography, regional objects, archives 13937

Vesoul

Musée Garret, 1 Rue des Ursulines, 70000 Vesoul - T: 0384765154. Head: Sabine Gangi
Fine Arts Museum - 1882
19th century academic paintings 13938

Veynes

Écomusée du Cheminot Veynois, 3 Rue du Jeu-de-Paume, 05400 Veynes - T: 0492580049, Fax: 0492581971, E-mail: ecomusee.cheminot@wanadoo.fr. Head: Martine Meissimilly-Rosin
Science&Tech Museum 13939

Vez

Musée du Valois, Donjon de Vez, 60117 Vez - T: 0344885518, Fax: 0344883970. Head: Francis Briest
Local Museum / Open Air Museum / Historic Site
Local hist, modern and contemporary art - sculpture garden 13940

Vézelay

Musée d'Art Contemporain, Préfiguration de la Fondation Zervos, Pl de la Basilique, 89450 Vézelay - T: 0386332462
Fine Arts Museum 13941

Musée de la Pierre, La Goulotte, 89450 Vézelay - T: 0386332136/2369
Natural History Museum 13942

Musée de l'Œuvre de la Madeleine, Ancien Dortoir des Moines, Pl de la Basilique, 89450 Vézelay - T: 0386332462
Fine Arts Museum 13943

Viaprès-le-Petit

Musée de la Commanderie, SVLP, Old Cars Expo 10, 10380 Viaprès-le-Petit - T: 0325377030
Science&Tech Museum 13944

Viarmes

Musée d'Histoire Locale, Château de la Mairie, Pl Pierre-Salvi, 95270 Viarmes - T: 0130354020
Historical Museum 13945

Vic-de-Chassenay

Château de Bourbilly, 21140 Vic-de-Chassenay - T: 0380970502, Fax: 0380972540, E-mail: bourbilly@wanadoo.fr
Decorative Arts Museum / Religious Arts Museum / Historic Site 13946

Vic-sur-Seille

Musée Historique, Hôtel de la Monnaie, 57170 Vic-sur-Seille - T: 0387011626
Historical Museum 13947

Vichy

Bibliothèque-Musée Valéry-Larbaud, 106 Rue Maréchal-Lyautey, 03200 Vichy - T: 0470584250, Fax: 0470584251, E-mail: mediatheque@ville-vichy.fr
Library with Exhibitions 13948

Centre de Recherches Archéologiques et Historiques de Vichy et sa Région, 2 Rue de la Porte-de-France, 03200 Vichy - T: 0470326725
Archaeological Museum / Historical Museum 13949

Musée Arts d'Afrique et d'Asie, 18 Av Thermale, 03200 Vichy - T: 0470977640, Fax: 0470960134, E-mail: mus-missionaire@wanadoo.fr. Head: Marie-Line Therre
Religious Arts Museum / Ethnology Museum
Religious history of the missions, African and Asiatic art, music room 13950

Musée Municipal, 15 Rue du Maréchal-Foch, 03200 Vichy - T: 0470321533
Local Museum 13951

Vienne-en-Val

Musée Archéologique, Rte de Tigy, 45510 Vienne-en-Val - T: 0238588472
Archaeological Museum 13952

Vienne (Isère)

Musée des Beaux-Arts et d'Archéologie, Pl de Miremont, 38200 Vienne (Isère) - T: 0474855042. Head: Roger Lauxerois
Fine Arts Museum / Archaeological Museum - 1895
Prehistoric finds, Gallo-Roman archeology, decorative arts, paintings, numismatics 13953

Vierville-sur-Mer

D-Day Omaha Musée, Mairie, 14710 Vierville-sur-Mer - T: 0231217180. Head: Michel Brissard
Military Museum 13954

Vierzon

Musée Municipal Les Fours Banaux, 7 Rue du Château, 18100 Vierzon - T: 0248526515, Fax: 0248719806, E-mail: office-tourisme@ville-vierzon.fr, Internet: http://www.ville-vierzon.fr
Local Museum 13955

Vieux

Salle d'Exposition Archéologique, Le Bas de Vieux, 14930 Vieux - T: 0231848170
Archaeological Museum 13956

Vieux-Berquin

Musée Abbé-Jules-Lemire, Grand-Pl, 59232 Vieux-Berquin - T: 0328427007
Special Museum / Religious Arts Museum 13957

Vigneulles-lès-Hattonchâtel

Musée Louise Cottin, Ancienne Ecole, 55210 Vigneulles-lès-Hattonchâtel - T: 0329893073
Fine Arts Museum 13958

Villaines-la-Juhel

Musée Lapidaire, 53700 Villaines-la-Juhel - T: 0243304550, Fax: 0243304550
Archaeological Museum 13959

Villaines-les-Rochers

Musée de la Vannerie, 22 Rue des Caves Fortes, 37190 Villaines-les-Rochers - T: 0247452319
Folklore Museum 13960

Villandraut

Musée Municipal, Rue Lapeyre, 33730 Villandraut - T: 0556253762
Local Museum 13961

Musée Vinicole, Syndicat d'Initiative, 33730 Villandraut - T: 0556715345
Special Museum 13962

Villandry

Château-Musée, Château, 37510 Villandry - T: 0247500209, Fax: 0247501285, E-mail: villandry@wanadoo.fr
Local Museum 13963

Villar-d'Arène

Exposition Botanique, Maison du Parc National des Ecrins, 05480 Villar-d'Arène - T: 0492210849/244162
Natural History Museum 13964

Musée du Pain Bouilli et du Four Communal, 05480 Villar-d'Arène - T: 0476799055, Fax: 0476799143
Special Museum 13965

Villar-Loubière

Musée du Vieux Moulin, 05800 Villar-Loubière - T: 0492552519/3247
Science&Tech Museum 13966

Villar-Saint-Pancrace

Musée de la Mine, 05100 Villar-Saint-Pancrace - T: 0492210527
Science&Tech Museum 13967

Musée des Pénitents, Chapelle, 05100 Villar-Saint-Pancrace - T: 0492210705
Religious Arts Museum 13968

Villard-de-Lans

Maison du Patrimoine, Pl de la Libération, 38250 Villard-de-Lans - T: 0476951731, Fax: 0476951731. Head: Karen Faure-Comte
Ethnology Museum 13969

Villaries

Galerie d'Exposition d'Art et d'Histoire, Près de l'Eglise, 31380 Villaries - T: 0561842482, Fax: 0561849317, E-mail: musee.villaries@wanadoo.fr. Head: Joseph Falco
Historical Museum / Archaeological Museum / Religious Arts Museum 13970

Villars (Dordogne)

Château-Musée de Puyguilhem, 24530 Villars (Dordogne) - T: 0553355010/548218
Decorative Arts Museum 13971

Villars-les-Blamont

Micromusée Républicain, Mairie, 25310 Villars-les-Blamont - T: 0381351079
Local Museum 13972

Villars-les-Dombes

Collection de Véhicules Anciens, Parc Départemental des Oiseaux, Rte Nationale 83, 01330 Villars-les-Dombes - T: 0474980554
Science&Tech Museum 13973

Villars (Loire)

Musée de la Mine - Tissage, Histoires Jean-Marie Somet, Rue du Puits Gallois, 42390 Villars (Loire) - T: 0477792617
Science&Tech Museum / Historical Museum 13974

Villarzel-Cabardes

Collection Archéologique, 11600 Villarzel-Cabardes - T: 0468770211
Archaeological Museum 13975

Ville-d'Avray

Musée Municipal, Château de Ville-d'Avray, 8 Rue de Marnes, 92410 Ville-d'Avray - T: 0147504402
Local Museum 13976

Ville-sous-Anjou

Musée Animalier, Grange Neuve, 38150 Ville-sous-Anjou - T: 0474844939
Natural History Museum 13977

Ville-sous-la-Ferté

Musée de l'Abbaye de Clairvaux, Abbaye de Clairvaux, 10310 Ville-sous-la-Ferté
Religious Arts Museum 13978

Ville-sur-Illon

Musée Vosgien de la Brasserie, 88270 Ville-sur-Illon - T: 0329365318/6311
Local Museum 13979

Ville-sur-Yron

Écovillage de Lorraine, 54800 Ville-sur-Yron - T: 0382339170/9316
Local Museum 13980

Villebadin

Musée du Manoir d'Argentelles, Prés Le Haras du Pin, 61310 Villebadin - T: 0233365952. Head: Laurent du Mesnil du Buisson
Historical Museum 13981

Villechauve

Musée Magie des Abeilles, Rte Nationale 10, 41310 Villechauve - T: 0254803339
Natural History Museum 13982

Villecroze

Collection d'Icônes, Rte de Salernes, 83690 Villecroze - T: 0494707064
Fine Arts Museum 13983

Villedieu-les-Poêles

Maison de l'Etain, 15 Rue du Général Huart, 50800 Villedieu-les-Poêles - T: 0233510508/3185
Science&Tech Museum 13984

Musée-Atelier du Cuivre, 54 Rue du Général Huard, 50800 Villedieu-les-Poêles - T: 0233513185, Fax: 0233510496, E-mail: acuivre@artisansfrancais.com, Internet: http://www.artisans-francais.com/atcuivre/index.htm. Head: Etienne Dulin
Science&Tech Museum 13985

Musée de l'Horlogerie, 50 Rue Carnot, 50800 Villedieu-les-Poêles - T: 0233909538
Science&Tech Museum 13986

Musée du Cuivre et de la Dentelle, 25 Rue du Général Huart, 50800 Villedieu-les-Poêles - T: 0233902092
Special Museum 13987

Musée du Meuble Normand, Rue du Reculé, 50800 Villedieu-les-Poêles - T: 0233611178
Decorative Arts Museum 13988

Villefagnan

Musée-Conservatoire d'Arts et Traditions Populaires, Grenier des Halles, 16240 Villefagnan - T: 0545317073
Folklore Museum 13989

Villefranche-de-Conflent

Exposition Permanente Cavernicole Les Grandes Canalettes, Rte de Vernet-les-Bains, 66500 Villefranche-de-Conflent - T: 0468962311/802589
Natural History Museum 13990

Exposition Permanente du Fort Vauban, Grotte Fortifiée de Cova-Bastera, Rte de Montlouis, 66500 Villefranche-de-Conflent - T: 0468052075/965454
Historical Museum 13991

Musée Archéologique, 66500 Villefranche-de-Conflent
Archaeological Museum 13992

Musée Carcéral Souterrain, 66500 Villefranche-de-Conflent
Historical Museum 13993

Musée de Spéléologie, 66500 Villefranche-de-Conflent
Archaeological Museum 13994

Musée du Château Fort-Liberia, 66500 Villefranche-de-Conflent - T: 0468963401
Decorative Arts Museum 13995

Villefranche-de-Lonchat

Musée Historique, Mairie, Pl de la Liberté, 24610 Villefranche-de-Lonchat - T: 0553807725
Historical Museum / Decorative Arts Museum 13996

Villefranche-de-Rouergue

Collection Discographique et Bibliographique du Jazz, Maison de la Musique Discographique/Bibliothèque, 12220 Villefranche-de-Rouergue - T: 0565812736
Music Museum 13997

Musée Urbain-Cabrol, Pl de la Fontaine, 12200 Villefranche-de-Rouergue - T: 0565454437
Local Museum 13998

Villefranche-du-Périgord

Musée du Châtaignier, Marrons et Champignons, Rue Notre-Dame, 24550 Villefranche-du-Périgord - T: 0553299837, Fax: 0553304012
Agriculture Museum 13999

Villefranche-sur-Mer

Musée d'Archéologie Sous-Marine, Citadelle, 06230 Villefranche-sur-Mer - T: 0493766546/3333
Archaeological Museum 14000

Musée des Chasseurs Alpins, Citadelle, 06230 Villefranche-sur-Mer - T: 0493763333
Military Museum 14001

Musée Fondation Musée Volti, Citadelle, 06230 Villefranche-sur-Mer - T: 0493763327
Decorative Arts Museum 14002

Musée Goetz-Boumeester, Citadelle, 06230 Villefranche-sur-Mer - T: 0493763344
Fine Arts Museum 14003

Musée Roux, Citadelle, 06230 Villefranche-sur-Mer - T: 0493763333
Decorative Arts Museum 14004

Villefranche-sur-Saône

Espace d'Arts Plastique → Musée Paul Dini

Musée Paul Dini, Pl Faubert, 69400 Villefranche-sur-Saône - T: 0474683370/0518, Fax: 0474623513. Head: Brigitte Laurençon
Fine Arts Museum
Regional paintings from 1875 to actually, important particuliar donation 14005

Villegongis

Château de Villegongis, 36110 Villegongis - T: 0254366051
Decorative Arts Museum 14006

Villemagne-l'Argentière

Salle d'Exposition du Centre Archéologique des Hauts Cantons, Église Saint Grégoire, 34600 Villemagne-l'Argentière - T: 0467230679/0889
Archaeological Museum 14007

Villemur-sur-Tarn

Musée du Grenier du Roy Louis XIII, Ancien Appartement de Gestion, 31340 Villemur-sur-Tarn - T: 0561090335
Fine Arts Museum / Local Museum 14008

Villeneuve (Alpes-de-Haute-Provence)

Musée d'Histoire et d'Archéologie, Pl de la Fontaine-Ronde, 04130 Villeneuve (Alpes-de-Haute-Provence) - T: 0492784231
Historical Museum / Archaeological Museum 14009

Villeneuve-d'Ascq

Musée Archéologique, Château de Flers, Chemin du Chat Botté, 59650 Villeneuve-d'Ascq - T: 0320435571, Fax: 0320912828, E-mail: archeo@mairie-villeneuvedascq.fr
Archaeological Museum 14010

Musée d'Art Moderne, 1 Allée du Musée, 59650 Villeneuve-d'Ascq - T: 0320196868, Fax: 0320196899, E-mail: mam@nordnet.fr. Head: Joëlle Pijaudier-Cabot
Fine Arts Museum - 1983
Georges Braque, Fernand Léger, Joan Miro, Pablo Picasso, Amedeo Modigliani, Henri Laurens - library, bookshop 14011

Musée de l'Ecole d'Autrefois, 107 Rue de Babylone, Flers, 59650 Villeneuve-d'Ascq - T: 0320721666/1731
Special Museum 14012

Musée d'Egyptologie, Université Charles de Gaulle, Rue du Barreau, 59650 Villeneuve-d'Ascq - T: 0320096162/919202, Fax: 0320416306
Archaeological Museum / University Museum - 1970 14013

Musée du Terroir, 12 Carriere Delporte, Rue Pasteur, 59650 Villeneuve-d'Ascq - T: 0320918757, Fax: 0320342407, E-mail: shvam@shvam.asso.fr, Internet: http://www.shvam.asso.fr. Head: Sylvain Calonne
Agriculture Museum / Ethnology Museum - 1972
Agricultural and ethnological coll of Lille area, ceramics from the Quiquempois moated-site (XIII-XVIIth c) and from Flers castle (XVIIth c) 14014

Musée Régional des Moulins, Aram, Rue Albert-Samain, 59650 Villeneuve-d'Ascq - T: 0320054934, Fax: 0320051106. Head: Jean Bruggeman
Science&Tech Museum 14015

Parc Archéologique/Ecovillage Historique, Rue du 8 Mai 1945, 59650 Villeneuve-d'Ascq - T: 0320055556
Archaeological Museum / Open Air Museum 14016

Villeneuve-de-Berg

Le Monde des Abeilles, L'Enclos de la Plaine, 07170 Villeneuve-de-Berg - T: 0475947137
Natural History Museum 14017

Villeneuve-de-la-Raho

Musée de l'Aviation Charles-Noetinger, 66200 Villeneuve-de-la-Raho - T: 0468540879
Science&Tech Museum 14018

Villeneuve-la-Comptal

Musée des Archives, Mairie, 11400 Villeneuve-la-Comptal - T: 0468230911
Local Museum 14019

Villeneuve-la-Comtesse

Musée Éducatif de Préhistoire et de Géologie, 17330 Villeneuve-la-Comtesse - T: 0546246706
Archaeological Museum / Natural History Museum 14020

Villeneuve-la-Garenne

Petit Musée Ambulant de la Musique Mécanique, Une Journée au Cirque, Parc des Chanteraines, 115 Blvd Charles de Gaulle, 92390 Villeneuve-la-Garenne - T: 0147994040, 0147994340, Fax: 0147990222, Internet: http://www.journeeocirque.com. Head: Danielle Schoeller
Music Museum 14021

Villeneuve-lès-Avignon

Abbaye Saint-André, Fort Saint-André, 30400 Villeneuve-lès-Avignon - T: 0490255595
Decorative Arts Museum / Fine Arts Museum 14022

Musée Pierre de Luxembourg, 3 Rue de la République, 30400 Villeneuve-lès-Avignon - T: 0490274966, 0466907580, Fax: 0466907427, E-mail: Girard_a@cg30.fr. Head: Alain Girard
Religious Arts Museum - 1868
15th-17th century paintings of the Provencal school, 14th ivory 'Virgin and child' 14023

Villeneuve-Loubet

Musée de l'Art Culinaire, Fondation Auguste-Escoffier, 3 Rue Escoffier, 06270 Villeneuve-Loubet - T: 0493208051, Fax: 0493739379, E-mail: contact@fondation-escoffier.org, Internet: http://www.fondation-escoffier.org. Head: Pierre Gouirand
Fine Arts Museum 14024

Musée Militaire, Pl de Verdun, 06270 Villeneuve-Loubet - T: 0493220156
Military Museum 14025

Villeneuve-sur-Allier

Musée-Château du Riau, Le Riau, 03460 Villeneuve-sur-Allier - T: 0470433447/3074. Head: Joseph Durye
Fine Arts Museum 14026

Villeneuve-sur-Lot

Musée d'Eysses, Pl Saint-Sernin, 47303 Villeneuve-sur-Lot - T: 0553706519
Archaeological Museum / Historic Site 14027

Villeneuve-sur-Yonne

Musée des Beaux-Arts, 2 Rue Carnot, 89500 Villeneuve-sur-Yonne - T: 0386457037
Fine Arts Museum 14028

Musée Villeneuvien, Porte de Joigny, 89500 Villeneuve-sur-Yonne - T: 0386870745
Local Museum 14029

Villequier

Musée Victor-Hugo, Rue Ernest-Binet, 76490 Villequier - T: 0235567831
Special Museum - 1959
Memorabilia of the writer Victor Hugo and his family, letters, drawings, and portraits 14030

Villeréal

Collections du Château de Born, 47210 Villeréal - T: 0553360303
Decorative Arts Museum / Historical Museum 14031

Villerest

Musée de l'Heure et du Feu, Pl Jean Baudinat, 42300 Villerest - T: 0477696666
Special Museum / Science&Tech Museum 14032

Villerouge-Termenès

Le Monde de Belibaste, Épopée Cathare, Château, 11330 Villerouge-Termenès - T: 0468700911, 0468700489, Fax: 0468700437, E-mail: chateau-villerouge@wanadoo.fr
Historical Museum 14033

Villers-Cotterêts

Musée Alexandre Dumas, 24 Rue Demoustier, 02600 Villers-Cotterêts - T: 0323962330. Head: Dominique Roussel
Special Museum - 1905
Memorabilia of Général Dumas, A. Dumas père, and A. Dumas fils, letters, autographs, manuscripts, portraits 14034

Villers-Outréaux

Maison de la Broderie, 20 Rue Victor-Hugo, 59142 Villers-Outréaux - T: 0327820508
Special Museum 14035

Villers-sur-Mer

Musée Paléontologique, Pl Jean-Mermoz, 14640 Villers-sur-Mer - T: 0231870118
Natural History Museum 14036

Villersexel

Château-Musée de Villersexel, 63 Rue François de Grammont, 70110 Villersexel - T: 0384205153, Fax: 0384205036, E-mail: chateau@villersexel.com, Internet: http://www.villersexel.com. Head: Jean-Pierre Potet
Historic Site 14037

Villerville

Musée Mer et Désert, 10 Rue du Général Leclerc, 14113 Villerville - T: 0231811381/2070
Natural History Museum 14038

Villespassans

Musée d'Art et d'Histoire, Mairie, 34360 Villespassans - T: 0467380453
Fine Arts Museum / Historical Museum 14039

Villeurbanne

Exposition d'Architecture et de Design, 247 Cours Émile-Zola, 69100 Villeurbanne - T: 0478680404
Special Museum 14040

Institut d'Art Contemporain, 11 Rue Docteur Dolard, 69605 Villeurbanne Cedex, mail addr: BP 3077, 69605 Villeurbanne Cedex - T: 0478034700, Fax: 0478034709, E-mail: jlm@i-art-c.org, odonat@i-art-c.org, Internet: http://www.i-art-c.org. Head: Jean-Louis Maubant, Olivier Donat
Fine Arts Museum 14041

Maison du Livre, de l'Image et du Son, Arthothèque, 247 Cours Emile Zola, 69100 Villeurbanne - T: 0478680404
Special Museum / Fine Arts Museum 14042

Musée de Paléontologie, Sciences de la Terre; Centre de Paléontologie Stratigraphique et Paléoécologie, c/o Université Cl. Bernard, 2 Rue Raphaël Dubois, 69622 Villeurbanne Cedex - T: 0472448488, Fax: 0472448382, E-mail: abel.prieur@univ-lyon1.fr, Internet: http://www.univ-lyon1.fr/colpaleo. Head: Abel Prieur
University Museum / Natural History Museum
Fossils coll - Geological library 14043

Villeveyrac

Musée Lapidaire, Abbaye de Valmagne, 34140 Villeveyrac - T: 0467780609/981182
Archaeological Museum 14044

Villevielle

Collection d'Arts Décoratifs, Château, 30250 Villevielle - T: 0466800162
Decorative Arts Museum 14045

Villey-le-Sec

Musée de la Fortification Cuirassée, Fort de Villey-le-Sec, 2 Pl de l'Eglise, 54840 Villey-le-Sec - T: 0383639009, E-mail: fort@villey-le-sec.com, Internet: http://www.villey-le-sec.com. Head: Régis Mercer
Military Museum / Historical Museum 14046

Villiers-le-Bacle

Maison-Atelier Foujita, Rte de Gif, 91190 Villiers-le-Bacle - T: 0160919191
Special Museum 14047

Villiers-le-Duc

Musée de la Chasse et de la Venerie, Abbaye du Val des Choues, 21400 Villiers-le-Duc - T: 0380810109, Fax: 0380810191. Head: Michel Monot
Special Museum 14048

Villiers-Saint-Benoit

Musée d'Art Régional, Rue de la Gare, 89130 Villiers-Saint-Benoit - T: 0386457305
Decorative Arts Museum 14049

Villiers-sur-Marne

Musée Émile-Jean, 31 Rue Louis-Lenoir, 94350 Villiers-sur-Marne - T: 0149302191
Local Museum / Folklore Museum 14050

Villieurs-le-Bel

Musée du Pays de France, 2bis, Rue Jules-Ferry, 95400 Villieurs-le-Bel - T: 0139906382
Archaeological Museum / Ethnology Museum 14051

Villy-le-Maréchal

Musée Agricole, 2 Rue aux Courbes, 10800 Villy-le-Maréchal - T: 0325418444, E-mail: michel.penard@wanadoo.fr, Internet: http://www.wanadoo.fr/villytourismeaube. Head: Michel Penard
Agriculture Museum 14052

Vimoutiers

Musée du Camembert, 10 Av du Général de Gaulle, 61120 Vimoutiers - T: 0233393029/2010, Fax: 0233676611, E-mail: ot.vimoutiers@wanadoo.fr
Special Museum 14053

Vincennes

Collections du Service Historique de l'Armée de l'Air, SHAA, Av de Paris, 94300 Vincennes - T: 0149573200
Science&Tech Museum / Military Museum 14054

Musée de l'Insigne et de la Symbolique Militaire, Château de Vincennes, Pavillon du Roi, 94300 Vincennes - T: 0149573285
Special Museum / Military Museum 14055

Musée des Chasseurs à Pied, Tombeau de Braves, Château de Vincennes, Av de Paris, 94300 Vincennes - T: 0149573200
Military Museum 14056

Musée du Château de Vincennes, Av de Paris, 94300 Vincennes - T: 0148083120, 0143652919, Fax: 0158642395, E-mail: bordaz@monuments-france.fr. Head: Odile Bordaz
Historical Museum 14057

Vincey

Musée d'Art Militaire, 13 Rue d'Alsace, 88450 Vincey - T: 0329389937
Military Museum 14058

Violay

Musée de Préhistoire et d'Art Populaire, Rue du 8 Mai, 42780 Violay - T: 0477639092
Archaeological Museum / Folklore Museum 14059

Viols-en-Laval

Archéosite Préhistorique de Cambous, Pl de la Mairie, 34380 Viols-en-Laval - T: 0467557145/7057
Archaeological Museum 14060

Viols-le-Fort

Musée de la Préhistoire L'Age des Garrigues, Centre du Village, 34380 Viols-le-Fort - T: 0467550186
Archaeological Museum 14061

Vire

Musée Municipal, 2 Pl Sainte-Anne, 14500 Vire, mail addr: BP 62, 14502 Vire Cedex - T: 0231681049, Fax: 0231673005
Local Museum - 1866
Paintings, furnishings, local folklore - workshops 14062

Virieu-sur-Bourbre

Château-Musée, 38730 Virieu-sur-Bourbre - T: 0474882732/2010
Decorative Arts Museum 14063

Viry-Noureuil

Collection de Sculptures, 15 Rue Jean-Jaurès, 02300 Viry-Noureuil - T: 0323393517
Fine Arts Museum 14064

Vitré

Musée de la Chapelle Saint-Nicolas, Rue Pasteur, 35500 Vitré - T: 0299750454, Fax: 0299740826, E-mail: musees@mairie-vitre.fr, Internet: http://www.ot-vitre.fr. Head: Patrice Forget
Religious Arts Museum 14065

Musée de la Faucillonnais, Manoir de la Faucillonnais, 3 km au N-O de Vitré, sur la Route Départementale 178, Taillis, 35500 Vitré - T: 0299750454, Fax: 0299740826, E-mail: musees@mairie-vitre.fr, Internet: http://www.ot-vitre.fr. Head: Patrice Forget
Decorative Arts Museum - 1993
Furniture of rich peasants, rural architecture 14066

Musée du Château de Vitré, Pl du Château, 35500 Vitré - T: 0299750454, Fax: 0299740826, E-mail: musees@mairie-vitre.fr, Internet: http://www.ot-vitre.fr. Head: Patrice Forget
Fine Arts Museum / Decorative Arts Museum / Local Museum 14067

Viverols

Musée Terrasse, Mairie, 63840 Viverols - T: 0473959690/3133
Local Museum 14068

Vives

Institut Méditerranéen du Liège, 66400 Vives - T: 0468833983
Local Museum 14069

Viviers (Ardèche)

Musée d'Art Sacré, Cathédrale de Saint-Vincent, 07220 Viviers (Ardèche) - T: 0475527700
Decorative Arts Museum / Archaeological Museum 14070

Vivoin

Musée de la Vie d'Autrefois, Prieuré, 72170 Vivoin - T: 0243970483/48
Historical Museum 14071

Vizille

Musée de la Révolution Française, Château, 38220 Vizille, mail addr: BP 1753, 38220 Vizille - T: 0476680735, Fax: 0476680853, E-mail: musee.revolution@cg38.fr. Head: Alain Chevalier
Historical Museum - 1984
library 14072

Vogue

Château, 07200 Vogue - T: 0475370195, Fax: 0475377748, Internet: http://www.chateau-devogue.com
Local Museum 14073

Voingt

Musée du Patrimoine du Canton de Giat, 63620 Voingt - T: 0473217199
Archaeological Museum 14074

Voiron

Cave des Chartreux, 10 Blvd Edouard Kofler, 38500 Voiron - T: 0476058177
Special Museum 14075

Musée Mainssieux, Hôtel de Ville, 38507 Voiron, mail addr: BP 262, 38507 Voiron - T: 0476656717. Head: François Roussier
Fine Arts Museum 14076

Vollore-Ville

Château-Musée de Vollore, 63120 Vollore-Ville - T: 0473537106, Fax: 0473537244, E-mail: chateau-vollore@wanadoo.fr. Head: Aubert la Fayette
Historical Museum / Decorative Arts Museum 14077

Volnay

Musée Vini-Viticole, Domaine Vaudoisey-Mutin, 21190 Volnay - T: 0380216244
Special Museum 14078

Volvic

Maison de la Pierre de Volvic, 63530 Volvic - T: 0473335692, Fax: 0473335692. Head: Patrick Delmont
Natural History Museum 14079

Maison du Miel, Les Goulots, 63530 Volvic - T: 0473335038
Natural History Museum 14080

Musée Marcel Sahut, Château de Bosredon, 63530 Volvic - T: 0473335733, Fax: 0473338574, E-mail: mairie-de-volvic@wanadoo.fr, Internet: http://www.volvic-tourisme.com. Head: Claire Lebouteiller
Special Museum / Fine Arts Museum 14081

Vongnes

Musée des Traditions Vigneronnes, Le Caveau Bugiste, 01350 Vongnes - T: 0479879232, Fax: 0479879111
Agriculture Museum 14082

Vonnas

Musée des Attelages, de la Carrosserie et du Charronnage, Rue du Moulin, 01540 Vonnas - T: 0474500974/0248
Science&Tech Museum 14083

Vougeot

Château du Clos de Vougeot, 21640 Vougeot - T: 0380628609, Fax: 0380628275, E-mail: tastevin@axnet.fr
Historical Museum
12th century wine cellar, four colossal wine presses, wine taster's coll (Tastevins), seat of the brotherhood of knights "du Tastevin" 14084

Vouvray

Ecomusée du Canton de Vouvray, Espace Vigne et Vin, 30 Rue Victor Hérault, 37210 Vouvray - T: 0247526604
Special Museum 14085

Vraux

Musée du Terrain d'Aviation de Vraux Aasf 1939/1940 et des Opérations Aériennes 1939-1945, 23 Rue Basse, 51800 Vraux - T: 0326661210
Science&Tech Museum 14086

Vrigne-aux-Bois

Maison de la Fonderie, 405 Rue de la Roche, 08330 Vrigne-aux-Bois - T: 0324522062
Science&Tech Museum 14087

Vrigny

La Maison du Père Mousset, 17 Rue de Foncemagne, 45300 Vrigny - T: 0238341816
Historical Museum 14088

Vroncourt

Musée de la Machine Agricole, Grande-Rue, 54330 Vroncourt - T: 0383262551
Agriculture Museum / Science&Tech Museum 14089

Vulaines-sur-Seine

Musée Départemental Stéphane Mallarmé, Pont de Valvins, 4 Quai Stéphane Mallarmé, 77870 Vulaines-sur-Seine - T: 0164237327, Fax: 0164237830, E-mail: mallarme@cg77.fr
Local Museum
Museum takes place in the poet Mallarmé's home 14090

Waldersbach

Musée Oberlin, 25 Montée Oberlin, 67130 Waldersbach - T: 0388973027, Fax: 0388973221, E-mail: oberlin@club-internet.fr. Head: Edmond Stussi
Local Museum 14091

Musée Vivant de l'Apiculture du Ban-de-la-Roche, 9 Rue de la Suisse, 67130 Waldersbach - T: 0388973133
Natural History Museum 14092

Wambrechies

Collections Claeyssens, Distillerie, Av des Châteaux, 59118 Wambrechies - T: 0320396425
Special Museum 14093

Warcq

Musée du Vieux Warcq, 08000 Warcq - T: 0324560162/590966
Local Museum 14094

Wasigny

Espace Muséal du Four à Pain, Halle, 08270 Wasigny - T: 0324722747
Special Museum 14095

Wasquehal

Musée des Pompiers, 31 Rue Jacques-Brel, 59290 Wasquehal - T: 0320459090
Military Museum 14096

Wassigny

Musée Louis-Cornu, 5 Pl de l'Église, 02630 Wassigny - T: 0323607626/6213
Special Museum 14097

Wassy

Musée Protestant de la Grange de Wassy, Rue du Temple, 52130 Wassy - T: 0325557225
Religious Arts Museum / Historical Museum 14098

Wattrelos

Musée des Arts et Traditions Populaires, 96 Rue François-Mériaux, 59150 Wattrelos - T: 0320451909
Folklore Museum 14099

Wattwiller

Musée Mémorial 1914-1918, Vieil Armand, Rte des Crêtes, 68700 Wattwiller - T: 0389755035/231203
Military Museum 14100

Werentzhouse

Musée des Amoureux, 68480 Werentzhouse - T: 0389404234
Special Museum 14101

Wervicq-Sud

Musée des Petits Métiers de la Ferme, Parc Château Dalle-Dumont, 59117 Wervicq-Sud - T: 0320390571
Folklore Museum 14102

Weyersheim

Musée de la Maison du Petit Village, 67720 Weyersheim - T: 0388517391
Historical Museum 14103

Wimille

Château-Musée le Denacre, 62126 Wimille - T: 0321832260
Decorative Arts Museum 14104

Musée Vivant de la Meunerie, Moulin de Grisendal, 62126 Wimille - T: 0321320743
Science&Tech Museum 14105

Wimmenau

Maison du Patrimoine, Rue Principale, 67290 Wimmenau - T: 0388897116
Local Museum 14106

Wintzenheim

Musée Castral, Château du Hohlandsberg, 68000 Wintzenheim - T: 0389226685
Historical Museum 14107

Wismes

Musée Historique de la Poterie, Mairie, 62380 Wismes - T: 0321396351
Decorative Arts Museum 14108

Wissant

Musée du Moulin, Rue A. Davids, 62179 Wissant - T: 0321359187, Fax: 0321854810, E-mail: moulin.wissant@wanadoo.fr, Internet: http://www.lemoulin-wissant.com. Head: Michel Coënen
Science&Tech Museum 14109

Wissembourg

Musée Westercamp, Rue du Musée, 67160 Wissembourg - T: 0388542814, Fax: 0388941882, E-mail: tourisme.wissembourg@wanadoo.fr
Local Museum
Antiques, costumes, furnishings, sarcophagi, sculpture, armaments, hist of 1870-1871 war 14110

Wittelsheim

Ecomusée et Maison du Mineur de Potasse, 212 Rue de Reiningue, 68310 Wittelsheim - T: 0389554780/2010
Science&Tech Museum 14111

Wittenheim

Collection de Machinisme Agricole Fischesser, 1 Rue du Bourg, Wittenheim - T: 0389500476
Agriculture Museum 14112

Woerth

Musée de la Bataille du 6 Août 1870, Château, 2 Rue du Moulin, 67360 Woerth - T: 0388093021, Fax: 0388094707, E-mail: musbaout@woerth-en-alsace.com, Internet: http://www.woerth-en-alsace.com. Head: Hubert Walther
Military Museum 14113

Wormhout

Musée de Folklore Flamand Jeanne-Devos, 17 Rue de l'Église, 59470 Wormhout - T: 0328628123/656257
Folklore Museum 14114

Wuenheim

Musée du Vigneron, Cave coopérative, Rte de Cernay, 68500 Wuenheim - T: 0389767375
Special Museum 14115

Wy-Dit-Joli-Village

Musée de l'Outil et du Balnéaire Romain, La Forge Médiévale, 95420 Wy-Dit-Joli-Village - T: 0134674179
Local Museum 14116

Xaintrailles

Collections du Château, 47230 Xaintrailles - T: 0553655149
Decorative Arts Museum 14117

Xonrupt-Longemer

Musée de la Moineaudière, Rte du Valtin, 88400 Xonrupt-Longemer - T: 0329633711/0724
Natural History Museum 14118

Yerres

Exposition Caillebotte, 91330 Yerres - T: 0169493410
Local Museum 14119

Ygrande

Musée Émile-Guillaumin, Les Vignes, 03160 Ygrande - T: 0470663066
Special Museum 14120

Yssingeaux

Musée de l'Hôpital, 43200 Yssingeaux - T: 0471657700, Fax: 0471657791
Local Museum 14121

Yvetot

Musée Bourvil, Le Fay, 76190 Yvetot - T: 0235950369
Special Museum 14122

Musée des Ivoires, 76190 Yvetot - T: 0235950840, Fax: 0235956502, E-mail: mairie-yvetot@wanadoo.fr
Decorative Arts Museum 14123

Musée des Vieux-Commerces, Le Fay, 76190 Yvetot - T: 0235950369
Special Museum 14124

Musée du Pays de Caux, Hameau du Fay, 76190 Yvetot - T: 0235950369
Agriculture Museum 14125

Yviers

Musée de la Bohème, Hameau de Lavaure, 16210 Yviers - T: 0545980265
Fine Arts Museum 14126

Yzeron

Maison de l'Araire, 23 Rte de la Cascade, 69510 Yzeron - T: 0478453909
Local Museum 14127

Yzeures-sur-Creuse

Musée Archéologique de Minerve, Pl du Musée, 37290 Yzeures-sur-Creuse - T: 0247945501
Archaeological Museum 14128

Musée Mado Robin, Centre Médico-Social, Pl Mado Robin, 37290 Yzeures-sur-Creuse - T: 0247945501
Special Museum 14129

Zellenberg

Collection Vini-Viticole et de Tonnellerie, Caveau J. Becker, 4 Rte d'Ostheim, Zellenberg - T: 0389479016
Agriculture Museum 14130

French Guiana

Cayenne

Musée Départemental, 1 Av du Général-de-Gaulle, 97300 Cayenne - T: 308931
Local Museum
Flora and fauna, historical documents, archeology, fine art 14131

Musée Local, 2 Av du Général-de-Gaulle, 97300 Cayenne
Local Museum
Flora and fauna, historical documents 14132

Kourou

Musée de l'Espace, 97310 Kourou - T: 334812
Special Museum / Science&Tech Museum 14133

French Polynesia

Faranui

Musée de Marine, Faranui, Bora Bora - T: 677524
Historical Museum 14134

Papara

Musée du Coquillage, PK 35,9, Papara - T: 574522, Fax: 573778
Natural History Museum 14135

Papeete

Musée de la Perle, Centre Vaima Papeete, 98713 Papeete - T: 452122, Fax: 454892, E-mail: museeperle@tahitiperles.pf, Internet: http://www.tahitiperles.com. Head: Robert Wan
Natural History Museum 14136

Musée Paul Gauguin, BP 16019-98727, Papeete - T: 571058, Fax: 571042. Head: Brenda Chin Foo
Fine Arts Museum - 1965
Documents on Gauguin's (1848-1903) life and work, 20 original works by Gauguin (paintings, sculptures, watercolours) - library 14137

Punaauia

Musée de Tahiti et des Iles, Pointe des Pêcheurs, Punaauia, mail addr: BP 380354, Tamanu - T: 583476, Fax: 584300. Head: Manouche Lehartel
Historical Museum / Ethnology Museum / Archaeological Museum / Music Museum / Military Museum - 1974
Polynesian hist, ethnography, archeology, musical instruments, weapons, oral tradition - library, archives, oral tradition dep, archeology dep 14138

Uahuka

Musée de Uahuka, Uahuka - T: 927415
Local Museum 14139

Uturoa

Na Te Ara Museum, Uturoa, Raiatea - T: 662700
Local Museum 14140

Gabon

Libreville

Musée des Arts et Traditions du Gabon, Av du Général de Gaulle, Libreville, mail addr: BP 3115, Libreville
Folklore Museum
Ethnography, prehistory, musical instruments, jewelry, masks, statues, handicrafts, art 14141

Musée National du Gabon, BP 4018, Libreville - T: 761456
Local Museum 14142

Gambia

Banjul

Gambia National Museum, Independence Dr, Banjul - T: 226244, Fax: 227461, E-mail: musmon@qanet.gm. Head: B.A. Ceesay
Archaeological Museum / Historical Museum - 1982 14143

Georgia

Batumi

State Museum of Adjar, Dzhincharadze 4, Batumi
Natural History Museum / Historical Museum / Folklore Museum - 1910
Natural history, history, economics, culture - library 14144

Chinvali

State Museum of the South-Ossetian Autonomous District, Ul 13 Kommunarov 7, Chinvali
Natural History Museum / Historical Museum / Folklore Museum - 1941
Natural history, history, economics, culture - library 14145

Gori

The State House-Museum of I.V. Stalin, ul Stalina 32, Gori - T: (0270) 25215
Special Museum
Stalin's carriage, his personal things, Stalin's family, historical photographs, oil paintings, water-colours and pencil drawings about Stalin's life, various presents from foreign countries given to Stalin (porcelain and glass vases, pieces of woodcuts, portraits made of colour sand, carpets etc.) 14146

Kutaisi

Kutaisskij Gosudarstvennyj Muzej Istorii i Etnografii (Kutaisi State Museum of History and Ethnography), ul Tbilisi 1, Kutaisi - T: 55676. Head: M.V. Nikoleišvili
Historical Museum / Ethnology Museum - 1912
10th-13th c icons, 11th-19th c religious manuscripts, armour, anthropological material on Georgia native peoples - library 14147

Suchumi

State Museum of Abkhasia, ul Lenina 22, Suchumi. Head: A.A. Argun
Local Museum / Natural History Museum - 1915
Regional hist, natural hist, memorabilia of the Abchazian poet Dmitri Gulia - library 14148

Tbilisi

David Kakabadze Doma, Leonidze ul 11a, 380008 Tbilisi - T: (08832) 934372
Special Museum 14149

Georgian State Art Museum, ul Kecchoveli 1, Tbilisi. Head: S.J. Amiranišvili
Fine Arts Museum
library 14150

Georgian State Museum of Oriental Art, ul Azizbekova 3, Tbilisi. Head: G.M. Gvišiani
Fine Arts Museum
Georgian oriental art, carpets 14151

Georgian State Picture Gallery, pr Rustaveli 11, Tbilisi. Head: M.A. Kipiani
Fine Arts Museum
Paintings, contemporary art 14152

Gosudarstvennyj Muzej Narodnogo Obrazovanija Gruzii, Ul Čičnadze 1, Tbilisi
Historical Museum 14153

Ilja Čavčavadze Memorial Museum, Ordžonikidze 22, Tbilisi
Special Museum - 1957
Memorabilia of the writer Ilya Chavchavadze, literary history - library 14154

Museum of Fine Arts, Pushkin 4, Tbilisi
Fine Arts Museum 14155

State Literature Museum of Georgia, Džordžiašvili 8, 380004 Tbilisi - T: (08832) 998667. Head: I. Orgonikidze
Special Museum - 1928
Georgian literary hist since the 19th c - library, manuscript dep 14156

State Museum of Georgia, pr Rustaveli 3, Tbilisi - T: (08832) 998022. Head: L.A. Čilašvili
Historical Museum / Archaeological Museum / Ethnology Museum - 1852
Archeology, Georgian hist and ethnography from ancient times to the present - library 14157

State Theatrical Museum, Kecchoveli 1, Tbilisi
Performing Arts Museum - 1927
Performing arts, documents, photographs - library 14158

Tbilisi State Museum of Anthropology and Ethnography, Komsomolskij pr 11, Tbilisi. Head: A.V. Tkešelašvili
Historical Museum / Ethnology Museum
Archeology, history, ethnography - library 14159

Germany

Aachen

Auto-Sammlung Gut-Hand, Handerweg 71, 52072 Aachen - T: (0241) 34832, 14237, Fax: 405801. Head: Heinz Vogel
Science&Tech Museum - 1960
Ca. 70 German motor cars (1911-1950) - repair workshop, archives 14160

Computermuseum Aachen, Sommerfeldstr 32, 52074 Aachen - T: (0241) 807607
Science&Tech Museum 14161

Couven Museum, Hühnermarkt 17, 52062 Aachen - T: (0241) 4324421, Fax: 37075, E-mail: info@suermont-ludwig-museum.de, Internet: http://www.couven-museum.de. Head: Prof. Dr. Ulrich Schneider
Decorative Arts Museum - 1928
18th-19th c furnishings and interiors from the Aachen-Lüttich area, Baroque furniture, tapestry, tiles 14162

Domschatzkammer, Klosterpl 2, 52062 Aachen - T: (0241) 47709127, Fax: 47709150, E-mail: info@aachendom.de, Internet: http://www.aachendom.de. Head: Dr. Georg Minkenberg
Religious Arts Museum - 1931
Religious art from the Carolingian and Ottonian epochs, the Gothic and baroque periods, and the 19th c 14163

Internationales Zeitungsmuseum der Stadt Aachen, Pontstr 13, 52062 Aachen - T: (0241) 4324508, Fax: 4090656, E-mail: info@izm.de, Internet: http://www.izm.de. Head: Dr. Christof Spuler
Historical Museum - 1886
165,000 newspapers and journals from throughout the world, incl in particular first, last, anniversary, and special issues, overview of the hist of the newspaper since the 16th c, Oscar von Forckenbeck (1822-1898) - library 14164

Kunst aus Nordrhein-Westfalen, Ministerium für Städtebau und Wohnen, Kultur und Sport des Landes Nordrhein-Westfalen, Abteigarten 6, 52076 Aachen - T: (02408) 6492, Fax: 959415. Head: Maria Engels
Fine Arts Museum 14165

Ludwig-Forum für Internationale Kunst, Jülicher Str 97-109, 52070 Aachen - T: (0241) 18070, Fax: 1807101, E-mail: ludwigforum@aachen.heimat.de, Internet: http://www.heimat.de/ludwigforum. Head: Dr. Annette Lagler
Fine Arts Museum - 1991
Pop art, photo realism, conceptual art, new expressionism, art in the 80s conceptual art, new expressionism, contemporary art from (China, Russia, Cuba) - library 14166

Missionsmuseum des päpstlichen Missionswerks der Kinder in Deutschland, Stephanstr 35, 52064 Aachen - T: (0241) 21067, 44610, Fax: 446140, E-mail: kontakt@kindermissionswerk.de, Internet: http://www.kindermissionswerk.de. Head: Winfried Pilz
Decorative Arts Museum
Handicrafts with religious background from Africa, Asia, South America and Oceania 14167

Museum Burg Frankenberg, Bismarckstr 68, 52066 Aachen - T: (0241) 4324410, Fax: 37075, E-mail: Adam.C.Oellers@mail.aachen.de, Internet: http://www.burgfrankenberg.de. Head: Prof. Dr. Ulrich Schneider
Local Museum - 1910/1961
Local history, handicrafts, in 13th c castle - mint cabinet 14168

Suermondt-Ludwig-Museum, Wilhelmstr 18, 52070 Aachen - T: (0241) 479800, Fax: 37075, E-mail: info@suermont-ludwig.museum.de, Internet: http://www.suermondt-ludwig-museum.de. Head: Prof. Dr. Ulrich Schneider
Fine Arts Museum - 1878
Medieval sculpture, 15-17th c painting, glass windows, goldsmith work 14169

Zollmuseum Friedrichs, Horbacher Str 497, 52072 Aachen - T: (0241) 9970615. Head: Prof. Dr. Ulrich Schneider
Historical Museum 14170

Aalen

Bergbaumuseum im Besucherbergwerk Tiefer Stollen, Erzhäusle 1, 73433 Aalen - T: (07361) 970249, Fax: 970259, E-mail: tiefer-stollen@aalen.de, Internet: http://www.bergwerk-aalen.de. Head: F. Rosenstock
Science&Tech Museum - 1987
Mining equipment, geological exhibition 14171

Limesmuseum Aalen, Zweigmuseum des Württembergischen Landesmuseums Stuttgart, Sankt-Johann-Str 5, 73430 Aalen - T: (07361) 961819, Fax: 961839, E-mail: - limesmuseum.aalen@t-online.de, Internet: http://www.aalen.de/aalen/inhalt/kultur/m_lim.htm. Head: Martin Kemkes
Archaeological Museum - 1964
Site of largest Roman castellum north of Alps, maps, and models of original castellum, excavation finds including armaments, coins, utensils, and sculpture, gravestones and altar stones, diorama - library 14172

Museum am Markt / Schubarts Museum, Marktpl 4, 73430 Aalen - T: (07361) 522219, Fax: 523921, E-mail: museen@aalen.de, Internet: http://www.aalen.de. Head: Dr. Roland Schurig
Historical Museum - 1907
Life and works of Christian Friedrich Daniel Schubart, town culture, prehistory and local early hist, industrial development, hist of crafts, handicraft, linguistic island of Wischau 14173

Museum Wasseralfingen, Stefanspl 5, Wasseralfinger Bürgerhaus, 73433 Aalen - T: (07361) 73594. Head: Werner Bieg, Dr. Roland Schurig
Local Museum - 1957
Paleontology, local history, industrial development, local ironwork - library 14174

Ofenplattensammlung der Schwäbische Hüttenwerke GmbH, Wilhelmstr 67, Wasseralfingen, 73433 Aalen - T: (07361) 502286, Fax: 502666, E-mail: Annette.Seisser@shw.de, Internet: http://www.shw.de
Special Museum 14175

Römisches Parkmuseum (closed) 14176

Urweltmuseum Aalen, Reichsstädter Str 1, 73430 Aalen - T: (07361) 6556, Fax: 961839, E-mail: - limesmuseum.aalen@t-online.de, Internet: http://www.urweltmuseum-aalen.de. Head: Ulrich Sauerborn
Natural History Museum - 1977
Fossils, stones and minerals from the Jura formations in the Swabian Alps, in 19th c town hall 14177

Abenberg

Burg Abenberg, Burgstr 16, 91183 Abenberg - T: (09178) 90618, Fax: 905185, E-mail: info@museen-abenberg.de, Internet: http://www.museen-abenberg.de. Head: Brigitte Korn
Historical Museum / Fine Arts Museum
History of Franken, modern art 14178

Klöppelmuseum und Heimatkundliche Sammlung, Rathaus, Stillapl 1, 91183 Abenberg - T: (09178) 1233, 98800, Fax: 988080
Decorative Arts Museum / Local Museum
Lace coll 14179

Abensberg

Aventinus-Museum, Karmelitenpl 5, 93326 Abensberg - T: (09443) 5921, 6672
Local Museum - 1926
Ethnology, pre- and early hist, local hist, coins and weapons, in former 15th c cloister 14180

Achberg

Schloß Achberg, Schloß, 88147 Achberg - T: (0751) 85373
Public Gallery 14181

Achern

Sensen- und Heimatmuseum, Berliner Str 31, 77855 Achern - T: (07841) 9045, Fax: 280949
Local Museum / Science&Tech Museum - 1963
Scythes, tools and machines for the production of scythes, history of scythe production, local history - library 14182

Achstetten

Wieland-Gedenkzimmer, Kirchstr 7, 88480 Achstetten - T: (07392) 2364. Head: Walter Müller
Special Museum - 1975
Birth place of the writer Christoph Martin Wieland, documents, busts and paintings, his literary works 14183

Adelschlag

Römische Villa Rustica Möckenlohe, Tauberfelder Weg 1, 85111 Adelschlag - T: (08424) 277, Fax: 3877. Head: J. Heigl
Historical Museum - 1993
Reconstruction of a Roman villa 14184

Adelsdorf

Heimatmuseum, Hauptstr 16, 91325 Adelsdorf - T: (09195) 94320
Local Museum - 1996 14185

Jagd- und Fischereimuseum, Neuhaus, Adelsdorfer Str, 91325 Adelsdorf - T: (09195) 94320
Special Museum - 1999 14186

Adelsheim

Gedenkstätte Ehemalige Synagoge, Dorfmuseum Sennfeld, Hauptstr 43, 74740 Adelsheim - T: (06291) 1408, Fax: 646757, E-mail: heidelochmann@gmx.de. Head: Reinhart Lochmann
Local Museum / Folklore Museum - 1970
Local crafts, agriculture, domestic utensils, in former 19th c synagogue 14187

Städtische Sammlungen, Bauländer Heimatmuseum, Schloßgasse 14, 74740 Adelsheim - T: (06291) 62000, Fax: 620035. Head: Hans Rückert
Local Museum - 1908
Agricultural implements, 19th c town and farm furniture, local history 14188

Adlkofen

Erstes Niederbayerisches Automobil- und Motorrad-Museum, Frauenbergstr 14, 84166 Adlkofen - T: (08707) 464, Fax: 464. Head: Walter Proebst
Science&Tech Museum 14189

Adorf, Vogtland

Museum Adorf, Freiberger Str 8, 08626 Adorf, Vogtland - T: (037423) 2247, Fax: 2247
Local Museum - 1955
Local hist (17th-20th c), economic hist, mother-of-pearl objects, models of sights of Vogtland 14190

Agathenburg

Schloss Agathenburg, Hauptstr, 21684 Agathenburg - T: (04141) 64011, Fax: 64861, E-mail: info@schlossagathenburg.de, Internet: http://www.schlossagathenburg.de. Head: Bettina Roggmann
Historical Museum / Fine Arts Museum - 1991
17th c castle, furniture, social hist, exhibitions on contemporary art 14191

Ahlen

Fritz-Winter-Haus, Galerie für moderne Kunst, Südberg 72-74, 59229 Ahlen - T: (02382) 61582, Fax: 65528. Head: Helga Gausling
Fine Arts Museum 14192

Heimatmuseum Ahlen, Wilhelmstr 12, 59227 Ahlen - T: (02382) 59476, 805869, Fax: 59558
Local Museum 14193

Kunst-Museum Ahlen in der Theodor F. Leifeld-Stiftung, Weststr 98, 59227 Ahlen - T: (02382) 91830, Fax: 918383, E-mail: kunstmuseum@ahlen.de, Internet: http://www.ahlen.de/kunstmuseum. Head: Burkhard Leismann
Fine Arts Museum - 1993/96
Art of the 20th c 14194

Museum im Goldschmiedehaus, Oststr 69, 59227 Ahlen - T: (02382) 2914. Head:
Decorative Arts Museum 14195

Ahorn, Kreis Coburg

Gerätemuseum des Coburger Landes, Alte Schäferei 2, 96482 Ahorn, Kreis Coburg - T: (09561) 1304, Fax: 1364, Internet: http://www.mon.de/ofr/geraetemuseum
Agriculture Museum / Science&Tech Museum / Folklore Museum / Open Air Museum - 1970
Public relations in agriculture 14196

Ahrensburg

Museum Schloß Ahrensburg, Lübecker Str 1, 22926 Ahrensburg - T: (04102) 42510, Fax: 678831. Head: Silke Geppert
Decorative Arts Museum / Fine Arts Museum - 1932
18th-19th c furnishings and interiors, porcelain (Meissen), paintings and portraits, in 18th c moated castle built in the late Renaissance style - Porcelain 14197

Aichach

Heimatmuseum Aichach, Schulstr 2, 86551 Aichach - T: (08251) 9020
Local Museum - 1972
Local history, romanic baptismal font, coll of rosaries 14198

Wittelsbachermuseum Aichach, Archäologische Staatssammlung München, Unteres Stadttor, 86551 Aichach - T: (08251) 827471, Internet: http://www.stmukwk.bayern.de/kunst/zwmuseen/aichach.html. Head: P. Haller
Archaeological Museum - 1989
Archeological and finds of the castle Oberwittelsbach 14199

Aichtal

Heimatmuseum Grötzingen, Hindenburgstr 18,
Helenenheim, 72631 Aichtal - T: (07127) 51662
Local Museum - 1980
Handicraft, early hist, local hist   14200

Aidhausen

Schlepper-, Auto- und Gerätemuseum Hesse,
Obere Gasse 9, 97491 Aidhausen - T: (09523) 894
Science&Tech Museum - 1970   14201

Aidlingen

**Baudenkmal Hopfenhaus - Landwirtschaftliche
Gerätesammlung - Alt-Seilerei - Ostdeutsche
Heimatstube**, Brettergäßle 6, 71134 Aidlingen -
T: (07034) 12525, Fax: 12550
Local Museum / Science&Tech Museum -
1987   14202

Heimatmuseum, Deufringer Str 16, 71134 Aidlingen
- T: (07056) 2606, Fax: 96269
Local Museum - 1983
Rural life   14203

Ainring

Eisenmuseum, Werk 9, Hammerau, 83404 Ainring -
T: (08654) 8001
Science&Tech Museum   14204

Aken

Heimatmuseum, Köthener Str 15, 06385 Aken -
T: (034909) 82308
Local Museum - 1926
Pre- and early history, local history, crafts and
shipping, biology - archives   14205

Albstadt

Galerie Albstadt, Kirchengraben 11, 72458 Albstadt -
T: (07431) 1601491, Fax: 1601497,
E-mail: galerie.albstadt@t-online.de,
Internet: http://www.albstadt.de. Head: Dr. Marina
Sauer
Fine Arts Museum - 1975
20th c graphics and prints incl Expressionism and
art from 1920 to 1945, paintings, drawings -
workshops   14206

Maschenmuseum, Stadtverwaltung Albstadt,
Museumsamt, Wasenstr 10, 72461 Albstadt -
T: (07431) 1601465, Fax: 1601497,
E-mail: galerie.albstadt@t-online.de,
Internet: http://www.albstadt.de. Head: Susanne
Goebel
Science&Tech Museum - 1987
Knitwear, textile machinery   14207

Museum im Kräuterkasten, Im Hof 19, 72458
Albstadt - T: (07431) 1601465, Fax: 1601497,
E-mail: galerie.albstadt@t-online.de,
Internet: http://www.albstadt.de. Head: Susanne
Goebel
Natural History Museum - 1986
Pre and early hist, local fauna, fossils   14208

Musikhistorische Sammlung Jehle, Stauffenberg-
Schloß, Lautlingen, 72459 Albstadt - T: (07431)
1601465, 6041, Fax: 74306. Head: Ursula Eppler-
Jehle
Music Museum   14209

Nähmaschinen-Museum Gebr. Mey, Auf Steingen 6,
72459 Albstadt - T: (07431) 1601465
Science&Tech Museum   14210

Philipp-Matthäus-Hahn-Museum, Albert-Sauter-Str
15, 72461 Albstadt - T: (07432) 1601465. Head: S.
Goebel
Science&Tech Museum - 1989
Clocks, scales   14211

**Stauffenberg-Schloß und Stauffenbergge-
dächtniszimmer**, Lautlingen, 72459 Albstadt -
T: (07431) 1601465, 6041, Fax: 74306. Head:
Ursula Eppler-Jehle
Historical Museum   14212

Aldersbach

Brauereimuseum, Freiherr-von-Aretin-Pl 1, 94501
Aldersbach - T: (08543) 96040, Fax: 96044,
E-mail: info@aldersbacher.de, Internet: http://
www.aldersbacher.de
Science&Tech Museum - 1979
Brewery   14213

Alfeld, Leine

Fagus-Gropius-Ausstellung, Hannoversche Str 58,
31061 Alfeld, Leine - T: (05181) 790, Fax: 79225,
E-mail: expo2000@fagus.de, Internet: http://
www.fagus.de. Head: Karl Schünemann
Historical Museum
Fagus industrial site built by Walter Gropius from
1911-24   14214

Heimatstube Alfeld, Auf dem Gutshof, Brunkensen,
31061 Alfeld, Leine - T: (05181) 1563
Local Museum
Domestic everyday life, trade workshops, local hist,
mineralogy, fossils   14215

Hirschberger Heimatstuben, Ständehausstr 1-2,
31061 Alfeld, Leine - T: (05181) 704254,
Fax: 704235
Local Museum - 1959
Geological, political, geographical and cultural
aspects of the Hirschberg Valley   14216

Museum der Stadt Alfeld (Leine), Am Kirchhof 4-5,
31061 Alfeld, Leine - T: (05181) 703181,
Fax: 703216, E-mail: museum.alfeld@t-online.de,
Internet: http://www.alfeld.de. Head: Gerhard Kraus
Local Museum - 1928
Pre- and early hist, local hist, local economic
development, 17th c woodcarving, zoology,
conservation, archives - library   14217

Schnarch-Museum Alfeld, Wilhelm-Knigge-Str 20,
Langenholzen, 31061 Alfeld, Leine - T: (05181)
829187, Internet: http://www.schnarchmuseum.de
Special Museum
Snoring   14218

Algermissen

Heimatmuseum Algermissen, Neue Str 10, 31191
Algermissen - T: (05126) 488
Local Museum - 1981
Village school, pharmacy, trade workshops, hist of
clubs, organisations and societies   14219

Allendorf, Lumda

Heimatmuseum, Kirchstr 42, 35469 Allendorf,
Lumda - T: (06407) 6376
Local Museum - 1978
Growing and processing of flax, folk costumes for
various occasions   14220

Allensbach

Bodanrück-Bauernmuseum, Dorfpl 2, 78476
Allensbach - T: (07533) 6535
Agriculture Museum - 1990
Agricultural tools, handicraft   14221

Heimatmuseum, Rathauspl, 78476 Allensbach -
T: (07533) 6535
Local Museum - 1962
Pre- and early history, local history, folklore 14222

Allstedt

Burg- und Schloßmuseum Allstedt, Schloß, 06542
Allstedt - T: (034652) 519, Fax: 519. Head: Rainer
Böge
Local Museum - 1975
Memorabilia of the theologist Thomas Müntzer
(1489-1525) and history of the Peasant Wars, local,
pre- and early history, Goethe exhibition -
archive   14223

Alpirsbach

Museum für Stadtgeschichte, Ambrosius-Blarer-Pl
10, 72275 Alpirsbach - T: (07444) 9516281,
Fax: 9516283, E-mail: tourist-info@alpirsbach.de,
Internet: http://www.alpirsbach.de
Local Museum - 1982
Local hist, crafts   14224

Alsbach-Hähnlein

Heimatmuseum Hähnlein, Gernsheimer Str 36,
64665 Alsbach-Hähnlein - T: (06257) 50080
Local Museum - 1983
Pre-historic animal bones, stone axes, trade and
agricultural implements   14225

Alsfeld

Regionalmuseum Alsfeld, Rittergasse 3-5, 36304
Alsfeld - T: (06631) 4300, E-mail:
regmuseumalsfeld@aol.com. Head: Dr. Monika
Hoelscher, Günther Schulz
Local Museum - 1897
Early hist, crafts and industrial development, local
hist, traditional costumes, 16th-18th c furnishings
and interiors, religious art, paintings of local artists,
manuscripts, in two 17th c half-timbered buildings -
library, archive   14226

Alt Schwerin

Freilichtmuseum Alt Schwerin, Agrarhistorisches
Museum, Dorfstr 21, 17214 Alt Schwerin -
T: (039932) 49918, Fax: 49917, E-mail:
museumaltschwerin@t-online.de;, Internet: http://
home.t-online.de/museumaltschwerin. Head: Claus
Ludwig
Open Air Museum / Agriculture Museum - 1962
Regional agricultural history and folklore, more than
24 buildings including huts, old schoolhouse,
blacksmith, farm-house, Dutch mill, history of
milling, 17th-20th c peasant work tools and
machines, field railway 600mm, steam tractor MAN
1918 - library   14227

Altdorf bei Nürnberg

Altdorfer Universitäts-Museum, Neubaugasse 5,
90518 Altdorf bei Nürnberg - T: (09187) 8070,
Fax: 807290
Historical Museum
Museum of the University of Altdorf (1623) - open
1998   14228

Altdorf, Niederbayern

Heimatmuseum Adlhoch-Haus, Weinbergstr 1,
84032 Altdorf, Niederbayern - T: (0871) 30333
Local Museum
Archaeological finds   14229

Altena

Deutsches Drahtmuseum, Fritz-Thomée-Str 12,
58762 Altena - T: (02352) 9667034, 9275911,
Fax: 9275921, E-mail: museen.mk@t-online.de.
Head: Stephan Sensen
Science&Tech Museum - 1965/1994
Hist and production of wire   14230

Museum der Grafschaft Mark, Fritz-Thomée-Str 80,
58762 Altena - T: (02352) 9667033/34, Fax: 25316,
E-mail: museen.mk@t-online.de. Head: Stephan
Sensen
Local Museum - 1875
Art and art hist, geology, pre- and early hist,
weapons, hist of smithwork, technology, rooms of
the first youth hostel in the world   14231

Stadtgalerie Altena, Lennestr 93, 58762 Altena -
T: (02352) 209346/47, Fax: 209308, E-mail: post@
altena.de, Internet: http://www.altena.de. Head:
Barbara Langos
Public Gallery   14232

Altenau, Harz

Heimatstube Altenau, Hüttenstr 5, 38707 Altenau,
Harz - T: (05328) 461
Local Museum - 1958/95
Hist of mining, iron and steel industry, forestry,
charcoal burning, cartage business, works by the
artist Karl Reinecke   14233

Altenbeken

Egge-Museum Altenbeken, Alter Kirchweg, 33184
Altenbeken - T: (05255) 12000
Science&Tech Museum - 1976
16th-17th c stoves and stove plates, history of local
iron ore mining and iron production, train
production, minerals and fossils   14234

Altenberg, Erzgebirge

Bergbaumuseum, Mühlenstr 2, 01773 Altenberg,
Erzgebirge - T: (035056) 31703, Fax: 32542,
Internet: http://www.altenberg-online.de. Head:
Christoph Schröder
Science&Tech Museum - 1957
Tin processing plantwith mine, stamping machinery,
washing wheel and dressing-floor, tools, pewter -
Schaustollen "Neubeschert-Glück-Stollen"   14235

Museum Huthaus Zinnwald, Galerie Ewald
Schönberg, Zinnwald-Georgenfeld, Am Huthaus 1,
01773 Altenberg, Erzgebirge - T: (035056) 31630,
Fax: 31631. Head: Christoph Schröder
Local Museum / Public Gallery   14236

Altenbrak

Heimatstube Altenbrak, Bergstr 1, 38889 Altenbrak
- T: (039456) 205
Local Museum   14237

Altenburg, Thüringen

Lindenau-Museum, Gabelentzstr 5, 04600 Altenburg,
Thüringen - T: (03447) 2510, Fax: 895544,
E-mail: lindenau-museum@gmx.de. Head: Jutta
Penndorf
Fine Arts Museum - 1848
The holdings are based on a donation by scholar
Bernhard von Lindenau (1779-1854). Italian panel
painting (13th-16th c), antique vases (17th-2nd c
b.c.), plaster casts after Antique and Rennaissance
sculptures, sculptures and paintings 17th-20th c,
graphic department 20th c photo coll -
library   14238

Mauritianum, Naturkundliches Museum, Parkstr 1,
04600 Altenburg, Thüringen - T: (03447) 2589,
Fax: 2589, E-mail: direktion.mauritianum@
freenet.de, Internet: http://www.mauritianum.htm.
Head: Dr. Norbert Höser
Natural History Museum - 1817
Comparative natural history, ornithology, geology,
memorabilia of the Africa expedition of A.E. Brehm
(1829-1884) - library   14239

Schloß- und Spielkartenmuseum, Schloß 2-4,
04600 Altenburg, Thüringen - T: (03447) 315193,
Fax: 502661. Head: Perdita Schachtschneider
Local Museum / Decorative Arts Museum / Special
Museum - 1919
Local, pre- and early hist, arms and armory, peasant
life, tools, costumes, arts and crafts like furniture
and porcelain, sacral plastics, playing cards (1475
to present time) - library, restoration of
furniture   14240

Altenhof

Herrenhaus Altenhof, Schlossstr 1, 24340 Altenhof -
T: (04351) 41334, 41428, Fax: 751012,
E-mail: gut-altenhof@t-online.de. Head: C. von
Bethmann-Hollweg
Decorative Arts Museum - 1954
Furnishings and interiors in Louis XV and Louis XVI
styles, paintings, porcelain - library   14241

JERUSALEM
PAN RAMA
KREUZIGUNG CHRISTI
ALTÖTTING OBERBAYERN

Gebhard-Fugel-Weg 10
Durchgang vom Kapellplatz: Gasthof Scharnagl
Busparkplatz: Zufahrt Innerer
Ring/Kreszentiaheimstraße

Denkmalschutzmedaille Bayern
Einziges historisches Panorama
Deutschlands

Kulturgutschutz der UNESCO Paris
Eine Weltberühmtheit Europas

Geöffnet: März – Okt. tägl. 9 – 17 Uhr,
Nov. – Febr. Sa./So. 11 – 14 Uhr
Telefon + Fax 0 86 71-69 34 (Besucherdienst)

SPA Stiftung Panorama Altötting

Altenstadt an der Waldnaab

Heimatstube, Hauptstr 21, 92665 Altenstadt an der
Waldnaab - T: (09602) 4713, Fax: 4713,
Internet: http://www.new-wen.net/homepages/
nw1938/heim.htm
Local Museum - 1996   14242

Altensteig

Museum im Alten Schloß, Kirchstr 11, 72213
Altensteig - T: (07453) 1360, Fax: 946150,
E-mail: info@altensteig.de, Internet: http://
www.altensteig.de. Head: M. Schullerus
Historical Museum / Folklore Museum - 1985
Interior design (early renaissance period), local
hist   14243

Altenthann

Heimatmuseum des Landkreises Regensburg,
Vorwaldstr 22, 93177 Altenthann - T: (09408) 912,
283, Fax: 4009292
Local Museum - 1989
Local history   14244

Altheim bei Riedlingen

Oberschwäbische Galerie Kloster Heiligkreuztal,
Äbtissingebäude, OEW-Saal, 88499 Altheim bei
Riedlingen - T: (07371) 1860, Fax: 18643,
E-mail: Kloster-Heiligkreuztal@t-online.de
Fine Arts Museum
Contemporary art   14245

Altkirchen

Dorfmuseum Altkirchen, Am Freibad 7, 04626
Altkirchen - T: (034491) 22233, Fax: 80081
Local Museum - 1982
Peasant life and traditions, natural history   14246

Altmannstein

**Hammer- und Waffenschmiede-Museum
Hexenagger**, Schambachweg 3, Hexenagger, 93336
Altmannstein - T: (09446) 1386
Local Museum
Old iron-forge   14247

Heimatmuseum Altmannstein, Rathaus, 93336
Altmannstein - T: (09446) 90210, Fax: 2102,
E-mail: altmannstein@altmuehlnet.baynet.de,
Internet: http://www.altmuehlnet.baynet.de/
gemeinden/altmannstein
Local Museum - 1950
Prehistoric and ancient items, 19th c articles from
peasant culture, documents on the 18th c sculptor
Ignaz Günther   14248

Hopfen-Erlebnis-Hof, Schulstr 9, 93336 Altmannstein - T: (09446) 1285, Fax: 2803, E-mail: michael.forster@altmuehlnet.de, Internet: http://hopfenerlebnishof.de
Agriculture Museum 14249

Altötting

Bruder-Konrad-Museum, Kapuzinerstr 1, 84503 Altötting - T: (08671) 9830
Religious Arts Museum - 1930
Work of the holy brethren Konrad von Parzham (1818-1894) 14250

Dioramenschau Altötting, Kapellpl 18, 84503 Altötting - T: (08671) 6827, Fax: 881532
Religious Arts Museum 14251

Museum Jerusalem Panorama Kreuzigung Christi, Gebhard-Fugel-Weg 10, 84503 Altötting - T: (08671) 6934, Fax: 6934. Head: Dr. Gebhard Streicher
Religious Arts Museum - 1903
Painted panorama of Jerusalem 14252

Schatzkammer, Kapellpl 21, 84503 Altötting - T: (08671) 5166, Fax: 12947, E-mail: Stadt-Altoetting@t-online.de, Internet: http://www.altoetting.de. Head: Alois Furtner
Religious Arts Museum - 1960
Votive offerings, cult articles, rosaries, 16th c sculpture 14253

Stadtgalerie Altötting, Kapellpl 9, 84503 Altötting - T: (08671) 8068/69, Fax: 85858, E-mail: info@altoetting-touristinfo.de, Internet: http://www.altoetting-touristinfo.de. Head: Herbert Bauer
Public Gallery 14254

Wallfahrts- und Heimatmuseum, Kapellpl 4b, 84503 Altötting - T: (08671) 5166, Fax: 12947, E-mail: Stadt-Altoetting@t-online.de, Internet: http://www.altoetting.de. Head: Alois Furtner
Local Museum - 1912
Pre- and early history, local flora and fauna, town culture, local history, history of pilgrimage center, graphics, paintings, sculpture, devotional paintings 14255

Altomünster

Brauereimuseum, Am Vogelgarten 2, 85250 Altomünster - T: (08254) 1222, Fax: 9234
Science&Tech Museum - 1985 14256

Gaudnek-Museum, Sandizeller Gasse, 85250 Altomünster - T: (08254) 439, 9543, Fax: 439, E-mail: wgaudnek@mail.ucf.edu, Internet: http://www.oir.ucf.edu/gaudnek
Fine Arts Museum - 1999 14257

Heimatmuseum Altomünster, Sankt Birgittenhof 4-6, 85250 Altomünster - T: (08254) 1519, 99780, Fax: 997811, E-mail: museum@altomuenster.de, Internet: http://www.altomuenster.de
Local Museum
History of the Birgittenorder 14258

Museumsgalerie, Sankt Birgittenhof 5, 85250 Altomünster - T: (08254) 1519, 99780, Fax: 997811, E-mail: museum@altomuenster.de, Internet: http://www.altomuenster.de. Head: Peter Schultes
Public Gallery 14259

Altranft

Brandenburgisches Freilichtmuseum Altranft, Dorfstr 27, 16259 Altranft - T: (03344) 414300, Fax: 414325, E-mail: Freilichtmuseum-Altranft@t-online.de, Internet: http://www.freilichtmuseum-altranft.de. Head: Peter Natuschke
Open Air Museum
Reconstructed farm village envolving castle, church, forge, house of a fisherman (18th c school, windmill) 14260

Altranstädt

Friedenszimmer im Schloß Altranstädt, Lindenstr 2, 04420 Altranstädt - T: (034205) 58469
Historic Site 14261

Altusried

Historisches Käsemuseum, Haus des Gastes, Hauptstr 18, 87452 Altusried - T: (08373) 7051, Fax: 7054, E-mail: verkehrsamt.altusried@allgaeu.org, Internet: http://www.altusried.de
Special Museum - 1986
Cheese-dairy (19th and 20th c) 14262

Naturkundliche Sammlung, Schulstr 1, 87452 Altusried - T: (08373) 662
Natural History Museum - 1980
Preparations of animals and plants 14263

Alzenau

Heimatmuseum Michelbacher Schlößchen (closed until 2003), Schloßstr, 63755 Alzenau - T: (06023) 7987
Local Museum - 1984
Local history 14264

Alzey

Museum Alzey, Antoniterstr 41, 55232 Alzey - T: (06731) 495240, Fax: 495555, E-mail: information@alzey.de, Internet: http://www.alzey.de. Head: Dr. Eva Heller-Karneth, Dr. Rainer Karneth
Local Museum - 1906
Geology, paleontology, findings from the Neolithic, Hallstatt, and Latène periods, Roman finds, articles from the Merovingian period, folkore - library, archive 14265

Amberg, Oberpfalz

Stadtmuseum Amberg, Zeughausstr 18, 92224 Amberg, Oberpfalz - T: (09621) 10283, Fax: 10855. Head: Judith von Rauchbauer
Local Museum - 1902
Local hist (15th-19th c), religious folk art, faience, items from the local 19th c arms factory 14266

Vorgeschichtsmuseum der Oberpfalz, Archäologische Staatssammlung München, Klösterl, Eichenforstgasse 12, 92224 Amberg, Oberpfalz - T: (09621) 10247, Fax: 10203, Internet: http://www.stmukwk.bayern.de/kunst/zwmuseen/amberg.html. Head: D. van Endert
Archaeological Museum - 1991
Early hist of Upper Palatinate 14267

Amelinghausen

Museum Amelinghausen, Marktstr 1, 21385 Amelinghausen - T: (04132) 910450
Local Museum
Early and prehist, agricultural implements 14268

Amerang

Bauernhausmuseum Amerang des Bezirks Oberbayern, Im Hopfgarten 2, 83123 Amerang - T: (08075) 915090, Fax: 9150930, E-mail: verwaltung@bhm-amerang.de, Internet: http://www.bhm-amerang.de. Head: Dr. Helmut Keim
Open Air Museum - 1977
Different types of farmsteads (16th-mid of 20th c), smithy, bakery, sawmill, ropery, grain mill 14269

EFA Museum für Deutsche Automobilgeschichte, Wasserburger Str 38, 83123 Amerang - T: (08075) 8141, Fax: 1549, E-mail: info@efa-automuseum.de, Internet: http://www.efa-automuseum.de. Head: Jakob Maier
Science&Tech Museum - 1990
Hist of German automobiles, model railway 14270

Schloßmuseum Amerang, Schloß 1, 83123 Amerang - T: (08075) 91920, Fax: 919233, E-mail: info@schlossamerang.de, Internet: http://www.schlossamerang.de. Head: Ortholf Freiherr von Crailsheim
Local Museum - 1971
16th c Renaissance castle, hall with hunting trophies, period furnishings and interiors, Gothic chapel 14271

Amöneburg

Heimatmuseum Amöneburg, Schulstr 2, 35287 Amöneburg - T: (06422) 92950, 2474, Fax: 8500022
Local Museum - 1984
Early and prehistory of the region, geology, agriculture 14272

Amorbach

Fürstlich Leiningensche Sammlungen - Heimatmuseum, Kellereigasse 4, 63916 Amorbach - T: (09373) 97150, Fax: 971550
Local Museum - 1932 14273

Sammlung Berger, Wolkmannstr 2, 63916 Amorbach - T: (09373) 99081, 20940, Fax: 902515. Head: Eva-Marie Berger
Fine Arts Museum
Coll of teapots and puppets, Pepsi Cola design and modern art 14274

Templerhaus, Bädersweg, 63916 Amorbach - T: (09373) 20940, Fax: 20933, E-mail: touristinfo@amorbach.de, Internet: http://www.amorbach.de
Historic Site
Oldest framework house of Bavaria 14275

Andechs

Heilige Kapelle und Schatzkammer, Kloster- und Wallfahrtskirche, Bergstr 2, 82346 Andechs - T: (08152) 3760, Fax: 376267
Religious Arts Museum
Pilgrimage-church (1755) with a coll of relics 14276

Andernach

Stadtmuseum Andernach, Hochstr 99, 56626 Andernach - T: (02632) 922218, Fax: 922242, E-mail: kultur-vhs@andernach.de, Internet: http://www.andernach.de. Head: Dr. Klaus Schäfer
Local Museum - 1936 14277

Angelburg

Angelburger Kunst- und Kulturhaus, Schelde-Lahn-Str 39, 35719 Angelburg - T: (06464) 7066, Fax: 7066
Public Gallery / Association with Coll
Bert Hubl "Hub-Art" 14278

Heimatmuseum Altes Rathaus, Lindenstr 7, Frechenhausen, 35719 Angelburg - T: (06464) 5860
Local Museum - 1988
Implements for flax processing, agricultural tools and machines, native birds, shoemaker's workshop, mining 14279

Angermünde

Ehm-Welk-Literaturmuseum, Puschkinallee 10, 16278 Angermünde - T: (03331) 33381, Fax: 33381. Head: Felicitas Borchardt
Special Museum - 1974
Memorabilia and works of writer Ehm Welk - library 14280

Heimatmuseum, Schwedter Str 14, 16278 Angermünde - T: (03331) 32249, Fax: 32249
Local Museum - 1913
Pre- and early hist, local modern hist, crafts, geology, gun powder tower, monastery church - archive 14281

Ankershagen

Heinrich-Schliemann-Museum, Lindenallee 1, 17219 Ankershagen - T: (039921) 3252, Fax: 3212, E-mail: info@schliemann-museum.de, Internet: http://www.schliemann-museum.de. Head: Dr. Wilfried Bölke
Historic Site - 1980
Publications and autographies of Heinrich Schliemann - reference library, archiv 14282

Anklam

Museum im Steintor, Schulstr 1, 17389 Anklam - T: (03971) 245503, Fax: 245500. Head: Waltraud Gleffe
Local Museum - 1927
Early and prehistory, regional history, town history 14283

Otto-Lilienthal-Museum, Ellbogenstr 1, 17389 Anklam - T: (03971) 245500, Fax: 245580, E-mail: LilienthalMuseum@t-online.de, Internet: http://www.lilienthal-museum.de. Head: Dr. Bernd Lukasch
Science&Tech Museum - 1991
Memorabilia of the glider constructor Otto Lilienthal, prehistory of aircraft - room for aerodynamical experiments 14284

Annaberg-Buchholz

Adam-Ries-Museum, Johannisgasse 23, 09456 Annaberg-Buchholz - T: (03733) 22186, Fax: 429087, E-mail: museum@adam-ries-bund.de, Internet: http://www.adam-ries-bund.de. Head: Dr. Rainer Gebhardt
Special Museum / Natural History Museum - 1984
Memorabilia of Adam Ries, old weights and measures 14285

Erzgebirgsmuseum mit Besucherbergwerk, Große Kirchgasse 16, 09456 Annaberg-Buchholz - T: (03733) 23497, Fax: 23497. Head: Jörg Nicklaus
Local Museum - 1887
Town hist, mining, numismatics, late Gothic art, Reformation and peasant war, crafts, folkart, lace-bobbin, 19th c industrial development, folklore, mineralogy, geology - library, mine 14286

Kunstkeller Annaberg, Wilischstr 11, 09456 Annaberg-Buchholz - T: (03733) 42001, Fax: 42001, E-mail: kunstkeller@web.de, Internet: http://www.kunstkeller.purespace.de. Head: Jörg Seifert
Public Gallery / Association with Coll
library 14287

Technisches Museum Frohnauer Hammer, Sehmatalstr 3, 09456 Annaberg-Buchholz - T: (03733) 22000, Fax: 671277, Internet: http://www.annaberg-buchholz.de. Head: Jörg Bräuer
Science&Tech Museum - 1951
Former forge, historic furnishing and equipment, folk art, soft steel hammer 14288

Annweiler

Burg Trifels, 76855 Annweiler - T: (06346) 8470
Local Museum 14289

Ansbach

Infozentrum und Elektromuseum, c/o Fränkisches Überlandwerk AG, Eyber Str 89, 91522 Ansbach - T: (0981) 9695495240, Fax: 9695495205, E-mail: klaus.ehrlich@fuew.de, Internet: http://www.fuew.de
Science&Tech Museum - 1988
Old techniques of power supply, development of use of electricity in private households 14290

Jägerndorfer Heimatstuben, Martin-Luther-Pl 1, 91522 Ansbach - T: (0981) 51248, 51249, Fax: (0911) 5430976
Local Museum
History of the duchy of Jägerndorf 14291

Markgrafenmuseum Ansbach, Kaspar-Hauser-Pl 1, 91522 Ansbach - T: (0981) 9775056, 51248, Fax: 15501. Head: Werner Bürger
Local Museum - 1830
Kaspar Hauser 14292

Residenz Ansbach, Promenade 27, 91522 Ansbach - T: (0981) 9538390, Fax: 95383940
Historic Site
14th-18th c royal residence, interiors with original Baroque and Rococo furnishings, faience and porcelain, gallery with European Baroque paintings 14293

Staatsgalerie in der Residenz, Bayerische Staatsgemäldesammlungen, Promenade 27, 91522 Ansbach - T: (0981) 9538390, Fax: 95383940
Fine Arts Museum
Paintings of Johann Christian Sperling, Friedrich Gotthard Naumann, Anthony van Dyk, Jan Fyt, Cornelis Janssens van Ceulen, Ludolf Backhuysen, Jan van Ravesteyn, Jean-Baptiste Le Prince and Joseph Vernet 14294

Antonsthal

Technisches Museum Silberwäsche, Jägerhäuser Str 17, 08359 Antonsthal - T: (03774) 25222, Fax: 20243
Science&Tech Museum - 1969
Technology of silver mining 14295

Apfeltrach

Mühlenmuseum Katzbrui, Köngetried, 87742 Apfeltrach - T: (08269) 575, Fax: 576
Science&Tech Museum 14296

Apolda

Glockenmuseum, Bahnhofstr 41, 99510 Apolda - T: (03644) 650331, Fax: 650331, E-mail: -glockenmuseum.apolda@t-online.de, Internet: http://www.Apolda.de. Head: Heike Schlichting
Special Museum - 1952
Bells from the 1st c b.c., bell decoration (12th to 20th c), bell foundry 14297

Kunsthaus Apolda Avantgarde, Bahnhofstr 42, 99510 Apolda - T: (03644) 562480, Fax: 562480
Public Gallery 14298

Wirker- und Strickermuseum, Bahnhofstr 41, 99510 Apolda - T: (03644) 650331, Fax: 650331. Head: Heike Schlichting
Special Museum - 1979
Knit- and weaving machines 14299

Arendsee, Altmark

Heimatmuseum und Klosterruine, Am See 3, 39619 Arendsee, Altmark - T: (039384) 479
Local Museum - 1959
Prehistoric finds, botany, fishing, local and modern history relating to the area and monastery Arendsee 14300

Arneburg

Heimatmuseum, Breite Str 16, 39596 Arneburg - T: (039321) 51817, Fax: 51818, E-mail: VGArneburg-Krusemark@t-online.de, Internet: http://www.arneburg-krusemark.de
Local Museum - 1934
Pre- and early hist, animals and plants, local hist, crafts and trades, shipping, ceramics, traditional costume of the oldmark, combat by Altenzaun 1806 14301

Arnsberg

Sauerland-Museum, Alter Markt 24-26, 59821 Arnsberg - T: (02931) 4098, Fax: 4114, E-mail: sauerland-museum@t-online.de, Internet: http://www.sauerland-museum.de. Head: Dr. Jürgen Schulte-Hobein
Local Museum - 1925
Local cultural history, 16th-19th c religious art, prehistory - library 14302

Arnstadt

Schloßmuseum, Schloßpl 1, 99310 Arnstadt - T: (03628) 602932, Fax: 48264, E-mail: -Schlossmuseum.Arnstadt@t-online.de. Head: Matthias Klein
Fine Arts Museum - 1919
Historic inventory (18th c), ceremony hall, porcelain and ceramics, doll houses, tapestry, arts and crafts, paintings (16th-20th c) 14303

Stadtgeschichtsmuseum Arnstadt "Haus zum Palmbaum" mit Bachgedenkstätte und Literatenkabinett, Markt 3, 99310 Arnstadt - T: (03628) 602978, Fax: 602978, E-mail: Haus.zum.Palmbaum@t-online.de. Head: Ina-Maria Dressel
Local Museum / Historic Site - 1935
Memorabilia to Johann Sebastian Bach and his family 14304

Arnstorf

Alt-Arnstorf-Haus, Vorderer Berg 2, 94424 Arnstorf - T: (08723) 2234, 1262, Fax: 3365
Local Museum - 1980
Local history and shoemaker's workshop 14305

Arzberg, Oberfranken

Sandauer Heimatstube, Friedhofstr 2, 95659 Arzberg, Oberfranken - T: (09233) 8263
Local Museum - 1965
Local hist 14306

Volkskundliches Gerätemuseum, Wunsiedler Str 12-14, 95659 Arzberg, Oberfranken - T: (09233) 5225, Fax: 78933. Head: Wilhelm Siemen
Open Air Museum / Folklore Museum / Agriculture Museum - 1993
Farmhouses and agricultural tools, rustic culture 14307

Asbach-Bäumenheim

Schulheimatmuseum, Josef-Dunau-Ring 4, 86663 Asbach-Bäumenheim - T: (0906) 9317, Fax: 91803, E-mail: vs.baeumenh@dw.donau-ries.de
Local Museum - 1980
Old school and a coll of agricultural tools 14308

Asbach bei Schmalkalden

Besucherbergwerk Finstertal, 98574 Asbach bei Schmalkalden - T: (03683) 488037, Fax: 488037
Science&Tech Museum - 1959
Hist of mining, mining technology 14309

Asbach-Sickenberg

Grenzmuseum Schifflersgrund, 37318 Asbach-Sickenberg - T: (036087) 98409, Fax: 98414, E-mail: GreMu1991@aol.com, Internet: http://www.grenzmuseum.de. Head: Wolfgang Ruske
Historical Museum
Two log cabins, boundary tower, former border protection between East- and West-Germany, original vehicles 14310

Aschaffenburg

Erstes Deutsches Motorroller-Museum, Obernauer Str 125, 63743 Aschaffenburg - T: (06722) 4696, Fax: 9115900, E-mail: motorrollermuseum@web.de, Internet: http://www.motorrollermuseum.de. Head: Hans Krüger
Science&Tech Museum
Vespa's hist 14311

Gentilhaus, Grünewaldstr 20, 63739 Aschaffenburg - T: (06021) 3867414, Fax: 3867430. Head: Dr. Ingrid Jenderko-Sichelschmidt
Decorative Arts Museum
Art coll of Anton Gentil (1867-1951) 14312

Graslitzer Gedenk- und Informationsraum, Schönborner Hof, Wermbachstr 15, 63739 Aschaffenburg - T: (06188) 5141, Fax: 77425, E-mail: info@druckerei-kolb.de. Head: Klaus Hoyer, Rainer Kolb
Historical Museum - 1976
Wood carvings (Johannes Nepomuk), music instruments and work of local artists 14313

Künstlerhaus Walter Helm, Pompepejanumstr 1, 63739 Aschaffenburg - T: (06021) 246616, Fax: 442528, Internet: http://www.walter-helm.de
Fine Arts Museum
Life and works of Walter Helm 14314

Naturwissenschaftliches Museum, Schönborner Hof, Wermbachstr 15, 63739 Aschaffenburg - T: (06021) 386740, 3306220, 3306223, Fax: 3867430. Head: Dr. Ingrid Jenderko-Sichelschmidt
Natural History Museum - 1970
Zoology, entomology, botany, mineralogy 14315

Pompejanum, Pompejanumsstr 5, 63739 Aschaffenburg
Decorative Arts Museum 14316

Rosso Bianco-Auto Museum, Obernauer Str 125, 63743 Aschaffenburg - T: (06021) 21358, Fax: 20636, E-mail: hhfrenzel@rosso-bianco.de, Internet: http://www.rosso-bianco.de. Head: Peter Kaus, Hans-Holger Frenzel
Science&Tech Museum - 1987
Coll of old automobiles: Bugatti, Ferrari, Maserati, Porsche and Jaguar, largest sports car collection of the world 14317

Schloß und Park Schönbusch, Schloß- und Gartenverwaltung Aschaffenburg, Kleine Schönbuschallee 1, 63741 Aschaffenburg - T: (06021) 386570, Fax: 3865716, E-mail: info@bs.bayern.net
Local Museum / Decorative Arts Museum
Castle (1782) and landscape garden 14318

Schloßmuseum der Stadt Aschaffenburg, Schloßpl 4, 63739 Aschaffenburg - T: (06021) 386740, Fax: 3867430, E-mail: Stadt-AB.Museum@t-online.de. Head: Dr. Ingrid Jenderko-Sichelschmidt
Local Museum / Decorative Arts Museum - 1972
Local history, pewter, silver, and earthenware, Baroque faience, porcelain, German glassware from late Gothic to the Biedermeier period, 17th-19th c furniture, ceramics, local art from 19th-20th c 14319

Staatsgalerie im Schloß Johannisburg, Bayerische Staatsgemäldesammlungen, Schloßpl 4, 63739 Aschaffenburg - T: (06021) 22417
Fine Arts Museum - 19645
Paintings of Lucas Cranach the Elder, Pieter Paul Rubens, Aert de Gelder, Ferdinand Kobell and Christian Georg Schütz 14320

Städtische Dauerausstellung zur Geschichte der Aschaffenburger Juden, Treibgasse 20, 63739 Aschaffenburg - T: (06021) 29087, Fax: 29087, E-mail: ssa@info-aschaffenburg.de. Head: Elisabeth Gehrig
Ethnology Museum - 1984
Jewish hist of Aschaffenburg 14321

Städtische Galerie Jesuitenkirche, Pfaffengasse 26, 63739 Aschaffenburg - T: (06021) 218698, Fax: 581146, E-mail: galerie-jesuitenkirche@aschaffenburg.de, Internet: http://www.galerie-aschaffenburg.de/jesuitenkirche. Head: Dr. Brigitte Schad
Public Gallery 14322

Stiftsmuseum der Stadt Aschaffenburg, Stiftspl 1a, 63739 Aschaffenburg - T: (06021) 4447950, Fax: 3867430. Head: Dr. Ingrid Jenderko-Sichelschmidt
Fine Arts Museum / Archaeological Museum / Religious Arts Museum - 1854
12th-17th c architectural sculpture, wood sculpture (13th-18th c), religious handicrafts, 16th c paintings, prehist 14323

Aschau im Chiemgau

Priental-Museum, Schloß Hohenaschau, 83229 Aschau im Chiemgau - T: (08052) 904937, Fax: 904945, E-mail: info@aschau.de, Internet: http://www.aschau.de
Local Museum - 1988
History of ironindustry 14324

Ascheberg, Westfalen

Burgturm Davert, Mühlendamm, 59387 Ascheberg, Westfalen - T: (02593) 1241, E-mail: webmaster@davensberg.de, Internet: http://www.davensberg.de
Local Museum 14325

Aschersleben

Städtisches Museum, Markt 21, 06449 Aschersleben - T: (03473) 810056, Fax: 958920. Head: Udo Schulz
Local Museum - 1908
Geology, paleontology, mining, local hist, arms and armory, numismatics, photo coll - library 14326

Aschheim

Geschichtlich-heimatkundliche Sammlung, Münchner Str 8, 85609 Aschheim - T: (089) 9033588, Fax: 9291208, Internet: http://www.aschheim.de
Local Museum / Archaeological Museum
Local early hist 14327

Asendorf bei Bruchhausen-Vilsen

Automobil-Museum, Essener Str 5, 27330 Asendorf bei Bruchhausen-Vilsen - T: (04253) 714. Head: Joachim Pett
Science&Tech Museum
Hist of the motorbikes, bicycles and children vehicles 14328

Aßlar

Heimatmuseum im Schloß zu Werdorf, Bachstr 78, 35614 Aßlar - T: (06443) 3588
Local Museum
Town and castle hist, trades, industrial hist 14329

Attendorn

Südsauerlandmuseum, Alter Markt 1, 57439 Attendorn - T: (02722) 3711. Head: Otto Höffer
Local Museum - 1967
Art and culture of the region, geology 14330

Aub

Spitalmuseum, Hauptstr 29-33, 97239 Aub - T: (09335) 97100
Special Museum - 2001 14331

Aue, Sachsen

Museum der Stadt Aue, Bergfreiheit 1, 08280 Aue, Sachsen - T: (03771) 23654, Internet: http://www.de.Aue. Head: Ralf Petermann
Local Museum - 1973
Local history, mineralogy, mining history and technology - library 14332

Auerbach, Oberpfalz

Maffeischächte der Grube Auerbach-Nitzlbuch, 91275 Auerbach, Oberpfalz - T: (09624) 832
Science&Tech Museum 14333

Auerbach, Vogtland

Göltzschtalgalerie-Nicolaikirche, Rodewischer Str 2, 08209 Auerbach, Vogtland - T: (03744) 211815, Fax: 213903, E-mail: göltzschtalgalerie@t-online.de, Internet: http://www.göltzschtalgalerie-nicolaikirche.de
Public Gallery 14334

Museum Auerbach, Schloßstr 11, 08209 Auerbach, Vogtland - T: (03744) 835513/14, Fax: 835519
Local Museum - 1968
Local history, excavations, minerals, butterflies 14335

Auetal

Heimatmuseum Auetal, Langenfelder Str 47, 31749 Auetal - T: (05752) 595, Fax: 1549, E-mail: auetalermuseum@aol.com, Internet: http://www.heimatmuseum-auetal.de
Local Museum - 1984
Flax processing, linen weaving, trade and post hist, peasant school, craft, photographies 14336

Aufseß

Schloß Unteraufseß, Schloß, 91347 Aufseß - T: (09198) 656, Fax: 656
Local Museum
Private castle (12th c) with chapel (1840) 14337

Augsburg

Architekturmuseum Schwaben, Thelottstr 11, 86150 Augsburg - T: (0821) 2281830, Fax: 22818333, E-mail: ams@lrz.tum.de, Internet: http://www.architekturmuseum.de. Head: Prof. Dr. W. Nerdinger
Fine Arts Museum
History of architecture in Swabia (Bavaria), industrial architecture - library, archive 14338

Augsburger Puppentheatermuseum Die Kiste, Spitalgasse 15, 86150 Augsburg - T: (0821) 4503450, Fax: 45034533, E-mail: info@diekiste.net, Internet: http://www.diekiste.de. Head: Erik Raskopf
Performing Arts Museum - 2001 14339

Brechthaus, Auf dem Rain 7, 86150 Augsburg - T: (0821) 3242779, Fax: 3242127. Head: Dr. Helmut Gier, Dr. Jürgen Hillesheim
Special Museum - 1985
Birthplace of Bertolt Brecht (1898-1956), life and work of the author 14340

Deutsche Barockgalerie, Städtische Kunstsammlungen, Maximilianstr 46, Schaezlerpalais, 86150 Augsburg - T: (0821) 3244102, 3244109, Fax: 3244105, E-mail: -kunstsammlungen.stadt@augsburg.de, Internet: http://www.augsburg.de. Head: Dr. Björn R. Kommer, Dr. Gode Krämer
Fine Arts Museum - 1970
German paintings from the Baroque and Rococo periods, in Rococo palace - library, workshops 14341

Diözesanmuseum Sankt Afra, Kornhausgasse 3-5, 86152 Augsburg - T: (0821) 3166333, Fax: 3166339, E-mail: museum.st.afra@t-online.de, Internet: http://www.bistum-augsburg.de. Head: Melanie Thierbach
Religious Arts Museum - 2000 14342

Fuggerei-Museum, Mittlere Gasse 13, 86152 Augsburg - T: (0821) 3198810, Fax: 31988112, E-mail: info@fugger.de, Internet: http://www.fugger.de. Head: W.-D. Graf von Hundt
Historical Museum
The first social housing estate (16th c) 14343

Graphische Sammlung, Städtische Kunstsammlungen, Maximilianstr 46, Schaezler-Palais, 86150 Augsburg - T: (0821) 3244109, Fax: 3244105, E-mail: kunstsammlungen.stadt@augsburg.de. Head: Dr. Gode Krämer, Dr. Björn R. Kommer
Fine Arts Museum - 1970
Drawings and prints, especially of the Baroque and Rococo period 14344

Heimatmuseum Stadt und Landkreis Neudek im Erzgebirge, Von-Cobres-Str 5, 86199 Augsburg - T: (0821) 84683, 880555
Local Museum / Folklore Museum - 1984
Local hist - library 14345

Jüdisches Kulturmuseum, Synagoge, Halderstr 8, 86150 Augsburg - T: (0821) 513658, Fax: 513626, E-mail: jkm-as@t-online.de. Head: Dr. Benigna Schönhagen
Historical Museum / Historic Site - 1985
Jewish hist 14346

Lettl-Atrium, Museum für surreale Kunst, Stettenstr 1-3, 86150 Augsburg - T: (0821) 551642, Fax: 3162385, E-mail: info@lettl.de, Internet: http://www.lettl.de. Head: F. Lorian
Fine Arts Museum - 1993 14347

MAN Museum, Heinrich-von-Buz-Str 28, 86153 Augsburg - T: (0821) 3223791, Fax: 3223291, E-mail: Gerlinde_Simon@mra.man.de, Internet: http://www.man.de. Head: Gerlinde Simon
Science&Tech Museum - 1953
MAN products, especially Diesel engines (first of the world) beginning in 1893, printing presses since 1845 and documents on the company's hist, commercial vehicles - Historical Archives 14348

Maximilianmuseum, Städtische Kunstsammlungen, Philippine-Welser-Str 24, 86150 Augsburg - T: (0821) 3244111/12, Fax: 3244105, E-mail: -kunstsammlungen.stadt@augsburg.de, Internet: http://www.augsburg.de. Head: Dr. Björn R. Kommer, Dr. Christoph Emmendörffer
Fine Arts Museum / Decorative Arts Museum - 1855
Handicrafts, goldsmith work, local history, sculpture 14349

Mozarthaus, Frauentorstr 30, 86152 Augsburg - T: (0821) 3243894, Fax: 3243883, E-mail: -stadtarchiv.stadt@augsburg.de. Head: Dr. Josef Mančal
Music Museum - 1937
17th c building in which Leopold Mozart, the father of Wolfgang Amadeus Mozart, was born, graphics, printed music, and other memorabilia of the Mozarts, both father and son 14350

Naturmuseum der Stadt Augsburg, Im Thäle 3, 86152 Augsburg - T: (0821) 3246740/30, Fax: 3246741, E-mail: naturmuseum.stadt@augsburg.de, Internet: http://www.augsburg.de. Head: Dr. M. Achtelig
Natural History Museum - 1854
Palaebotany 14351

Neue Galerie im Höhmann-Haus, Städtische Kunstsammlungen, Maximilianstr 48, 86150 Augsburg - T: (0821) 3244107, 3244102, Fax: 3244105, E-mail: kunstsammlungen.stadt@augsburg.de. Head: Dr. Thomas Elsen
Public Gallery - 1996
Contemporary artists 14352

Reichenberger Heimatstube und Archiv, Konrad-Adenauer-Allee 55 I, 86150 Augsburg - T: (0821) 312707, Fax: 155103, E-mail: hreichenberg@xoommail.com. Head: Hannelore Pieke
Local Museum - 1953
Local history of Reichenberg 14353

Römisches Museum, Städtische Kunstsammlungen, Dominikanergasse 15, 86150 Augsburg - T: (0821) 3244131, Fax: 3244133. Head: Dr. Lothar Bakker
Archaeological Museum - 1966
Prehistoric and Roman finds in Augsburg and Bavarian Swabia, finds from recent excavations, coll of finds from Greece, Italy and Egypt - workshop 14354

Schwäbisches Handwerkermuseum, Beim Rabenbad 6, 86150 Augsburg - T: (0821) 3259270, Fax: 3259207, E-mail: pkuehnl@hwk-schwaben.de, Internet: http://www.hwk-schwaben.de. Head: Sandra Peters
Special Museum / Folklore Museum - 1985
Crafts 14355

Staats- und Stadtbibliothek, Schaezlerstr 25, 86152 Augsburg - T: (0821) 3242739, Fax: 3242732, E-mail: bibliothek.stadt@augsburg.de, Internet: http://www.augsburg.de/Seiten/augsburg_d/bildung/staatsbibliothek/staatsbibliothek_u/stbibliothek.shtml. Head: Dr. Helmut Gier
Library with Exhibitions 14356

Staatsgalerie am Schaezler-Palais, Bayerische Staatsgemäldesammlungen, Maximilianstr 46, 86150 Augsburg - T: (0821) 510350, E-mail: -kunstsammlungen.stadt@augsburg.de
Fine Arts Museum - 1835
Swabian painting 15th-16th c 14357

Staatsgalerie in der Kunsthalle, Bayerische Staatsgemäldesammlungen, Imhofstr 7-13, 86159 Augsburg - T: (0821) 3242178, Fax: 3242771
Fine Arts Museum - 1985
German paintings and sculptures from the 19th and 20th c: Max Liebermann, Lovis Corinth, Franz Marc, Paul Klee, Emil Nolde and Hans Arp 14358

Augustusburg

Kutschenmuseum, Schloß Augustusburg, 09573 Augustusburg - T: (037291) 3800, Fax: 38024, E-mail: 0372577133-1@t-online.de, Internet: http://www.augustusburg-schloss.de. Head: W. Sieber
Decorative Arts Museum
Renaissance castle 14359

Motorrad-Museum, Schloß Augustusburg, 09573 Augustusburg - T: (037291) 3800, Fax: 38024, E-mail: 0372577133-1@t-online.de, Internet: http://www.augustusburg-schloss.de. Head: U. Meinig
Science&Tech Museum - 1961
Two-stroke motorcycles, history of racing, carriages and coaches (18th-19th c) 14360

Museum für Jagdtier- und Vogelkunde des Erzgebirges, Schloß Augustusburg, 09573 Augustusburg - T: (037291) 38012, Fax: 38024, E-mail: 0372577133-1@t-online.de, Internet: http://www.augustusburg-schloss.de. Head: U. Meinig
Natural History Museum - 1969
Birds, mammals, eggs 14361

Aukrug

Dat ole Hus, Na't ole Hus 1, 24613 Aukrug - T: (04873) 603
Open Air Museum / Folklore Museum 14362

Aulendorf

Schloßmuseum Aulendorf-Kunst des Klassizismus-Altes Spielzeug, Zweigmuseum des Württembergischen Landesmuseums Stuttgart, Hauptstr 35, 88326 Aulendorf - T: (07525) 934203, Fax: 934103, E-mail: info@aulendorf.de, Internet: http://www.schloss-museum.de. Head: Susanne Biegel
Fine Arts Museum / Special Museum 14363

Aumühle bei Hamburg

Eisenbahn-Museum Lokschuppen Aumühle, Am Geleise 6, 21521 Aumühle bei Hamburg - T: (040) 6531875, Fax: 6531875, E-mail: info@vvm-museumsbahn.de, Internet: http://www.vvm-museumsbahn.de. Head: Claus-Jürgen Wincke
Science&Tech Museum
Railway 14364

Aurach

Vogteimuseum mit Blumenauer Heimatstube, Am Rathauspl, Im Mooshof 4, 91589 Aurach - T: (09804) 1245
Local Museum / Science&Tech Museum 14365

Aurich

Historisches Museum Aurich, Burgstr 25, 26603 Aurich - T: (04941) 18311, Fax: 66285. Head: Brigitte Junge
Local Museum / Historic Site / Historical Museum - 1985
History and culture of the East-Frisian region 14366

Mühlenfachmuseum, Oldersumer Str 28, 26603 Aurich - T: (04941) 18989, Fax: 3986
Science&Tech Museum
Five-storey mill from 1858, implements and machinery 14367

Autenried

Ikonenmuseum, Schloß Autenried, 89335 Autenried - T: (08223) 862, Fax: 910065, E-mail: schloss-hofberg@t-online.de, Internet: http://www.ikonen.org. Head: James Puckett
Fine Arts Museum / Religious Arts Museum - 1959
Icons from Russia, Byzantium, Crete, Greece, Rumania, and the Balkan countries, goldsmith work, bronzes, vestiments, embroidery, manuscripts and incunabula from the eastern orthodox area (3rd-19th c) - library 14368

Aying

Heimathaus Aying, Münchner Str 4, 85653 Aying - T: (08095) 880
Local Museum - 1978 14369

Babenhausen, Schwaben

Fugger-Museum, Schloß, 87727 Babenhausen, Schwaben - T: (08333) 2931, 920927, Fax: 920929. Head: Markus Graf Fugger-Babenhausen
Decorative Arts Museum - 1885
Decorative art from the 16th-19th c including goldsmith work, glass, porcelain, bronzes, ivory, religious art, and miniatures, weapons, folk art, books, portraits, hist of the Fugger family 14370

Bach an der Donau

Baierweinmuseum, 93090 Bach an der Donau - T: (09403) 95020
Agriculture Museum - 1998 14371

Historisches Schmucksteinbergwerk Silberschacht, Am Kittenrain, 93090 Bach an der Donau - T: (09403) 961073, Fax: (0921) 61233
Science&Tech Museum 14372

Backnang

Galerie der Stadt Backnang, Stiftshof 2, Turmschulhaus, 71522 Backnang - T: (07191) 72186, Fax: 340757, E-mail: kulturamt@backnang.de, Internet: http://www.backnang.de. Head: Martin Schick
Public Gallery 14373

Museum Helferhaus, Heimat- und Kunstverein, Stiftshof 8, 71522 Backnang - T: (07191) 72186
Local Museum 14374

Ungarndeutsches Heimatmuseum Backnang, Talstr 1-5, 71522 Backnang - T: (07191) 894213, Fax: 894140, E-mail: klaus.loderer@t-online.de. Head: Klaus J. Loderer
Folklore Museum - 1977
Hist and tradition of Germans in Hungary - archive 14375

Bad Abbach

Heimatmuseum → Museum Bad Abbach

Museum Bad Abbach, Rathaus, Raiffeisenstr 72, 93077 Bad Abbach - T: (09453) 95900, Fax: 959050, E-mail: markt@bad-abbach.de, Internet: http://www.bad-abbach.de
Local Museum / Archaeological Museum
Archeological finds, local and hist of sulphur bathing 14376

Bad Aibling

Heimatmuseum Bad Aibling, Wilhelm-Leibl-Pl 2, 83043 Bad Aibling - T: (08061) 7283, 8724
Local Museum - 1908
Rustic culture, work of Wilhelm Leibl (1844-1900) 14377

Bad Alexandersbad

Dorfmuseum, Kleinwendern 5, 95680 Bad Alexandersbad - T: (09232) 99250, 2559, Fax: 992525
Local Museum - 1965
Farmhouse 14378

Bad Arolsen

Museum Bad Arolsen, Große Allee 26, 34454 Bad Arolsen - T: (05691) 801194, 1727, Fax: 801189. Head: Dr. Birgit Kümmel
Local Museum / Fine Arts Museum - 1951/1973/1986
Paintings, drawings, and sketches by Wilhelm von Kaulbach, Friedrich Kaulbach, Friedrich August von Kaulbach, and Hermann Kaulbach, memorabilia, furniture, carpenter's workshop, Christian Daniel Rauch memorial in his birth house - Schreibersches Haus, Schloßstr 24, Kaulbach-Haus, Kaulbachstr 3, Ch.D. Rauch-Haus, Rauchstr 6, Ausstellungen im Schloß 14379

Schloß Arolsen, Stiftung des Fürstlichen Hauses Waldeck und Pyrmont, Schloßstr 27, 34454 Bad Arolsen - T: (05691) 895526, Fax: 3046, E-mail: information@schloss-arolsen.de, Internet: http://www.schloss-arolsen.de. Head:
Fine Arts Museum / Decorative Arts Museum
18th c castle, furniture by Kaulbach, paintings by Tischbein 14380

Wasserkunst von 1535, Im Burggrund, Landau, 34454 Bad Arolsen, mail addr: Amselweg 66, 34454 Bad Arolsen - T: (05691) 4961, E-mail: wasserkunst-landau@gmx.de. Head: Heinz-Willi Müller
Science&Tech Museum - 1981
Water mills 14381

Bad Bayersoien

Museum im Bierlinghaus, Dorfstr 46, 82435 Bad Bayersoien - T: (08845) 1854, Fax: 9000
Folklore Museum - 2000 14382

Bad Bederkesa

Museum Burg Bederkesa, Amtsstr 17, 27624 Bad Bederkesa - T: (04745) 94390, Fax: 5146, E-mail: info@burg-bederkesa.de, Internet: http://www.burg-bederkesa.de. Head: Matthias D. Schön
Archaeological Museum
Hist of the fortress, excavations, archaeology 14383

Museum des Handwerks Bremerhaven-Wesermünde in Bederkesa, Heubruchsweg 8, 27624 Bad Bederkesa - T: (04745) 1819. Head: Egon Wehmeyer
Special Museum 14384

Bad Bellingen

Oberrheinisches Bäder- und Heimatmuseum Bad Bellingen, Alte Weinstr 25, Bamlach, 79415 Bad Bellingen - T: (07635) 822160, Fax: 811939, Internet: http://www.bad-bellingen.de
Local Museum - 1991
Cultural hist of the spa in the Roman regio since the Middle Ages 14385

Bad Bentheim

Brasilienmuseum im Kloster Bardel, Klosterstr 11, 48455 Bad Bentheim - T: (05924) 787248, Fax: 787250. Head: Pater Klemens Diekmann
Religious Arts Museum / Ethnology Museum
Franciscan missionaries' souvenirs and exhibits from Brasil 14386

Briefmarkenmuseum im Kloster Bardel, Klosterstr 11, 48455 Bad Bentheim - T: (05924) 787248, Fax: 787250. Head: Pater Klemens Diekmann
Religious Arts Museum / Special Museum
Religious motives on stamps 14387

Radiomuseum, Schloßstr 18, 48455 Bad Bentheim - T: (05922) 5098, Fax: 7354
Science&Tech Museum
Hist of the radio and radio technique 14388

Schloßmuseum, Burg Bentheim, 48455 Bad Bentheim - T: (05922) 939128, Fax: 939155. Head: Oskar Prinz zu Bentheim
Historical Museum
Neo-Gothic castle 14389

Bad Bergzabern

Gedächtnisstätte von Scheidt-Saalfeld, Renaissancehaus Zum Engel, Königstr 45, 76887 Bad Bergzabern - T: (06343) 70114. Head: Dr. Berthold Roland
Local Museum / Historical Museum 14390

Stadtmuseum Bad Bergzabern, Königstr 45, 76887 Bad Bergzabern - T: (06343) 7010. Head: Günther Volz
Local Museum 14391

Zinnfiguren-Museum, Marktstr 14, 76887 Bad Bergzabern - T: (06343) 939172. Head: Kurt Wilms
Historical Museum 14392

Bad Berka

Goethe-Stube, Parkstr, 99438 Bad Berka - T: (036458) 22012, Fax: 21010
Special Museum 14393

Bad Berleburg

Alexander-Mack-Museum, Oberes Hüttental, Schwarzenau, 57319 Bad Berleburg - T: (02755) 725, Fax: (02751) 923288, E-mail: b_julius@bad-berleburg.de
Local Museum 14394

Landwirtschaftsmuseum Hof Espe, 57319 Bad Berleburg - T: (02751) 3862, 3153, Fax: 2672
Agriculture Museum 14395

Museum der Stadt Bad Berleburg, Goethepl 3, 57319 Bad Berleburg - T: (02751) 923232, 923283, Fax: 923288, E-mail: r_riedesel@bad-berleburg.de, Internet: http://www.bad-berleburg.de. Head: Rikarde Riedesel
Local Museum - 1966
Iron casting, printing, childhood in Wittgenstein, pietism in Wittgenstein, architectural hist, hist of fire fighting 14396

Schloß Berleburg, Altstadt, 57319 Bad Berleburg - T: (02751) 421
Historic Site 14397

Schmiedemuseum Arfeld, Arfetalstr 13, 57319 Bad Berleburg - T: (02755) 250
Science&Tech Museum
Historical smith's workshop 14398

Bad Berneck

Stadtmuseum Bad Berneck, Marktpl 44, 95460 Bad Berneck - T: (09273) 890, Fax: 8936
Local Museum - 1951
Local archaeological finds, herbarium 14399

Bad Bevensen

Kloster Medingen, Klosterweg 1, 29549 Bad Bevensen - T: (05821) 2286. Head: Monika von Kleist
Religious Arts Museum
Cistercian nunnery, medieval furniture, art treasures 14400

Schliekau-Museum, Kurze Str 4, 29549 Bad Bevensen - T: (05821) 1384, Fax: 43804. Head: Jürgen Schliekau
Local Museum - 1958
Prehist, natural history, craft, lights and fire, glass, porcellain, bonnets, household effects mineralogy, folk costumes 14401

Bad Bocklet

Graf-Luxburg-Museum, Museen Schloss Aschach, Schloßstr 24, 97708 Bad Bocklet - T: (09708) 6142, 358, Fax: 6104, E-mail: schloss-aschach@bezirk-unterfranken.de, Internet: http://www.bezirk-unterfranken.de. Head: Annette Späth
Decorative Arts Museum / Fine Arts Museum - 1957
Chinese coll, oriental carpets 14402

Schulmuseum des Bezirks Unterfranken, Schloß Aschach, Schloßstr 24, 97708 Bad Bocklet - T: (09708) 6142, 358, Fax: 6104
Special Museum - 1982
Hist of basic education 14403

Volkskundemuseum des Bezirks Unterfranken, Museen Schloss Aschach, Schloßstr 24, 97708 Bad Bocklet - T: (09708) 6142, 358, Fax: 6104, E-mail: schloss-aschach@bezirk-unterfranken.de, Internet: http://www.bezirk-unterfranken.de. Head: Annette Späth
Folklore Museum / Agriculture Museum - 1984
Agricultural tools and rural life in Lower Franconia (1850-1950) 14404

Bad Bodenteich

Burgmuseum Bad Bodenteich, Burgstr 8, 29389 Bad Bodenteich - T: (05824) 1320, Fax: 3308
Local Museum - 1988
Hist of the fortress 14405

Bad Brambach

Heimatstube Bad Brambach, Karl-Liebknecht-Pl 7, 08648 Bad Brambach - T: (037438) 328
Local Museum 14406

Bad Brückenau

Museum im Alten Rathaus, Alter Rathauspl 1, 97769 Bad Brückenau - T: (09741) 80455, Fax: 6904, E-mail: kultur@bad-brueckenau.de, Internet: http://www.bad-brueckenau.de. Head: Dieter Sternecker
Local Museum - 1961
Local history, balneology, geology, mineralogy, traditional peasant furniture, handicrafts, tools for processing flax - archives 14407

Bad Buchau

Federseemuseum Bad Buchau, Zweigmuseum des Württembergischen Landesmuseums und Staatlichen Museums für Naturkunde Stuttgart, August-Gröber-Pl 2, 88422 Bad Buchau - T: (07582) 8350, Fax: 933810, E-mail: info@federseemuseum.de, Internet: http://www.federseemuseum.de. Head: Dr. Ralf Baumeister
Archaeological Museum / Open Air Museum / Natural History Museum - 1919
Archeology, natural history 14408

Stiftsmuseum, Schloßpl, Oggelshauser Str 13, 88422 Bad Buchau - T: (07582) 91200, Fax: 91201
Religious Arts Museum - 1983
Religions art, sculpture, liturgical implements, cribs 14409

Bad Camberg

Stadt- und Turmmuseum, Am Amthof, 65520 Bad Camberg - T: (06434) 6174. Head: H. Angst, W. Lottermann
Local Museum - 1981
Geology, paleontology, early and pre-hist, trades, agriculture, forestry 14410

Bad Doberan

Ehm Welk-Haus, Dammchaussee 23, 18209 Bad Doberan - T: (038203) 62325, Fax: 62325. Head: Silvana Rieck
Special Museum 14411

Stadt- und Bädermuseum Bad Doberan, Beethovenstr 8, 18209 Bad Doberan - T: (038203) 2026. Head: Silvana Rieck
Local Museum 14412

Bad Driburg

Friedrich-Wilhelm-Weber-Museum, Weberpl, 33014 Bad Driburg - T: (05253) 2572. Head: Johannes Heinemann
Special Museum - 1953
Birth place of the 19th c poet Friedrich Wilhelm Weber, original furnishings, memorabilia, 19th c household utensils and tools, 18th c half-timbered house - archive 14413

Völkerkundliches exotisches, zoologisches und heimatkundliches Missionsmuseum, Dringenberger Str 32, 33014 Bad Driburg - T: (05253) 4021
Ethnology Museum 14414

Bad Driburg-Dringenberg

Museum in der Burg, Burg Dringenberg, 33014 Bad Driburg-Dringenberg - T: (05259) 932040
Special Museum 14415

Bad Düben

Landschaftsmuseum der Dübener Heide, Burg, Neuhofstr 3, 04849 Bad Düben - T: (034243) 23691, Fax: 23612, E-mail: ladschaftsmuseum.baddueben@t-online.de
Local Museum - 1953
Geology, ancient history, local and castle history (10th-19th c), crafts, documentation on Michael Kohlhaas and Hans Kohlhase, 16th c political figure 14416

Bad Dürkheim

Pfalzmuseum für Naturkunde - POLLICHIA-Museum, Hermann-Schäfer-Str 17, 67098 Bad Dürkheim - T: (06322) 94130, Fax: 941311, E-mail: pfalzmuseum@t-online.de, Internet: http://www.pfalzmuseum.de, http://www.naturale.de. Head: Dr. Reinhard Flößer
Natural History Museum - 1981
Zoology, botany, paleontology, geology, mineralogy, 14417

Bad Dürrenberg

Borlach-Museum, Borlach-Pl, 06231 Bad Dürrenberg - T: (03462) 19433, Fax: 83992, E-mail: BorlachTourist@aol.com, Internet: http://www.stadt-bad-duerrenberg.de
Science&Tech Museum - 1956
History of local salt source, models, plans, tools, geology, local balneology 14418

Bad Dürrheim

Narrenschopf, Fasnachtsmuseum, Im Kurpark, 78073 Bad Dürrheim, mail addr: Postfach 1416, 78068 Bad Dürrheim - T: (07726) 6492, Fax: 977602, Internet: http://www.narrenschopf.de. Head: Arnulf Oesterlein
Folklore Museum - 1973
Swabian and Alemannic masks and carnival costumes from the 18th c to the present 14419

Prof.-Fritz-Behn-Museum, Luisenstr 7, 78073 Bad Dürrheim - T: (07726) 666266, Fax: 666301, E-mail: info@badduerrheim.de, Internet: http://www.badduerrheim.de
Fine Arts Museum - 1973
Sculpture and statuettes, busts, paintings, drawings, and sketches by the sculptor and painter Fritz Behn 14420

Tier- und Jagdmuseum, Luisenstr 7, 78073 Bad Dürrheim - T: (07726) 666281, Fax: 666301
Natural History Museum 14421

Bad Eilsen

Heimatmuseum Bad Eilsen, Bückeburger Str 2, 31707 Bad Eilsen - T: (05722) 85372, Fax: 88651, Internet: http://www.shg-web.de/bad-eilsen
Local Museum
Folk costumes and culture 14422

Bad Ems

Künstlerhaus Schloß Balmoral, Villenpromenade 11, 56130 Bad Ems - T: (02603) 94190, Fax: 941916, E-mail: info@balmoral.de, Internet: http://www.balmoral.de. Head: Dr. Danièle Perrier
Public Gallery 14423

Kur- und Stadtmuseum, Römerstr 97, 56130 Bad Ems - T: (02603) 3572, Fax: 79375, E-mail: sbems@rz-online.de. Head: Dr. Hans-Jürgen Sarholz
Local Museum - 1906
Balneology 14424

Bad Endbach

Heimatmuseum Wommelshausen, Rathausstr, 35080 Bad Endbach - T: (02776) 1408
Local Museum - 1986
Costumes, sacral objects, land registers and account books 14425

Bad Essen

Mus'ign, Schloß Hünnefeld, 49152 Bad Essen - T: (05472) 94090, Fax: 940940, E-mail: info@musign-designmuseum.de, Internet: http://www.musign-designmuseum.de
Special Museum 14426

Bad Frankenhausen

Kreis-Heimatmuseum, Schloß, 06567 Bad Frankenhausen - T: (034671) 62086, Fax: 62086. Head: Renate Weinert
Local Museum - 1921/1922
Geology, paleontology, local history, flora and fauna of the area, medieval ceramics, numismatics, diorama of the theologist Thomas Müntzer and the battle at Frankenhausen (1525), hist of button making, hist of balneology, cultural hist of the Kyffhäuser region - library, auditorium 14427

Kyffhäuser-Denkmal, 06567 Bad Frankenhausen - T: (034651) 2780, Fax: 2308. Head: Ralf Rödger
Historic Site - 1896 14428

Panorama Museum, Am Schlachtberg 9, 06567 Bad Frankenhausen - T: (034671) 6190, Fax: 62050, E-mail: info@panorama-museum.de, Internet: http://www.panorama-museum.de. Head: Gerd Lindner
Fine Arts Museum - 1989
Contemporary realistic painting esp the complete work of Werner Tübke 14429

Bad Freienwalde

Oderlandmuseum, Uchtenhagenstr 2, 16259 Bad Freienwalde - T: (03344) 2056, Fax: 32724, E-mail: oderlandmuseum-frw@kultur-in-mol.de, Internet: http://www.kultur-in-mol.de. Head: Dr. R. Schmook
Local Museum - 1889
Pre and early hist, local hist, peasant folk art (18th-19th c) Over river gap - library 14430

Bad Füssing

Bauernhausmuseum, Im Kurpark, 94072 Bad Füssing - T: (08531) 981326
Folklore Museum - 1959 14431

Bernstein Museum (Amber Museum), Heilig-Geist-Str 2, 94072 Bad Füssing - T: (08531) 981034, Fax: (08506) 762, E-mail: bernstein-museum@form-und-farbe.com, Internet: http://www.bernsteinmuseum.com. Head: Emma Maria Kuster
Natural History Museum
Coll of amber (insects, sculpture, chessboard and men, Chinese carvings from Emperors Age, Indian jewellry, geology, biology, hist of the Bernsteinzimmer) 14432

Leonhardi-Museum Aigen, Penningerweg 7, 94072 Bad Füssing - T: (08537) 91089
Religious Arts Museum - 1996 14433

Museum Bad Füssing, Bruckmann-Haus, Illyrerweg 3, 94072 Bad Füssing - T: (08531) 21424, Fax: (08504) 4926. Head: Georg Höltl
Local Museum - 1980
Rustic coll 14434

Bad Gandersheim

Museum der Stadt Bad Gandersheim, Markt 10, 37581 Bad Gandersheim - T: (05382) 73413, Fax: 73440, E-mail: stadt@bad-gandersheim.de, Internet: http://www.bad-gandersheim.de. Head: Anne Katrin Race
Local Museum - 1926
History of the chapter Gandersheim, lamps and lighting, militaria - library, archive 14435

Bad Gottleuba

Heimatmuseum, Nothelferweg, 01816 Bad Gottleuba - T: (035023) 66841, Fax: 62390
Local Museum - 1957
Local hist 14436

Bad Grund

Bergbaumuseum Schachtanlage Knesebeck, Knesebeck 1, 37539 Bad Grund - T: (05327) 8298012, Fax: 8298010, E-mail: knesebeckschacht@t-online.de, Internet: http://www.knesebeckschacht.de
Science&Tech Museum - 1986
Hist of mining, vehicles, conveyors 14437

Uhrenmuseum, Elisabethstr 14, 37539 Bad Grund - T: (05327) 1020, Fax: 829342, E-mail: torge.berger@t-online.de, Internet: http://www.uhrenmuseum-badgrund.de. Head: Karin Berger, Erwin Berger
Science&Tech Museum - 1984/94
Wall and grandfather clocks, pocket watches, clocks with musical mechanisms, chimes, Rolling-Ball-Clock 14438

Bad Harzburg

Haus der Geschichte, Bad Harzburger und Scheibenhauer Heimatstube, Burgbergmuseum, Forstwiese 3, 38667 Bad Harzburg - T: (05322) 74120, Fax: 74278, E-mail: stadt@bad-harzburg.gs.shuttle.de, Internet: http://www.stadt-bad-harzburg.de. Head: Günter Bothe
Local Museum
Archaeological finds, historical everydays items 14439

Rathausgalerie, Forstwiese 5, 38667 Bad Harzburg - T: (05322) 74120, Fax: 74278, E-mail: stadt@bad-harzburg.gs.shuttle.de, Internet: http://www.stadt-bad-harzburg.de. Head: Dieter Lipka
Public Gallery 14440

Bad Herrenalb

Spielzeug-Museum Bad Herrenalb, Klosterstr 2, 76332 Bad Herrenalb - T: (07083) 4144. Head: Marusia Furtwengler
Decorative Arts Museum - 1982
Passed lifestyles shown by dollhouses, toys from Biedermeier period until 1920 14441

Bad Hersfeld

Haus Mährisch-Schönberg, Neumarkt 38, 36251 Bad Hersfeld - T: (06621) 201266
Historical Museum
Hist of exiles from the Sudentenland, everyday life objects, costumes, minerals - Library 14442

Museum Stadt Bad Hersfeld, Im Stift 6a, 36251 Bad Hersfeld - T: (06621) 75774, Fax: 201285
Local Museum - 1919/80
Hist of the abbey under imperial protection and its economic, religious and cultural significance, murals, historic finds, industrialisation, ethnology 14443

Bad Homburg

Fossilienmuseum, Neue Mauerstr 4, 61348 Bad Homburg - T: (06172) 6522
Natural History Museum 14444

Museum im Gotischen Haus, Tannenwaldweg 102, 61350 Bad Homburg - T: (06172) 37618, Fax: 937216. Head: Dr. Roswitha Mattausch-Schirmbeck, Ursula Stiehler
Local Museum - 1916/1985
Town history, regional history, Hölderlin - head museum, Marienbad coll, coin coll 14445

Saalburgmuseum, Saalburg-Kastell, 61350 Bad Homburg - T: (06175) 93740, Fax: 937411, E-mail: info.Saalburg@Saalburgmuseum.de, Internet: http://www.saalburgmuseum.de. Head: Prof. Dr. Egon Schallmayer
Archaeological Museum / Open Air Museum - 1873
Reconstructed Roman fort on the limes, Roman finds, weapons, tools, domestic items, leather articles 14446

Schloß und Schloßpark Bad Homburg, c/o Verwaltung der Staatl. Schlösser & Gärten Hessen, 61348 Bad Homburg - T: (06172) 926200, Fax: 9262190. Head: Dr. Kai R. Mathieu
Decorative Arts Museum
17-19th c Baroque castle, summer residence of the Prussian kings, interiors, Baroque mirror-lined room, furnishings of the 19th c, 17th-18th c objects of art 14447

Sinclair-Haus der Altana AG, Ecke Löwengasse/Dorotheenstr, 61348 Bad Homburg - T: (06172) 182931/32, Fax: 182933, Internet: http://www.altana.de/de/kultur. Head: Andrea Firmenich
Fine Arts Museum
Art of the 20th c and 21th c 14448

Bad Honnef

Stiftung Bundeskanzler-Adenauer-Haus, Konrad-Adenauer-Str 8c, 53604 Bad Honnef - T: (02224) 921234, Fax: 921111, E-mail: stiftung@adenauerhaus.de, Internet: http://www.adenauerhaus.de. Head: Dr. Michael Krekel
Special Museum - 1967
Original house and gardens of Konrad Adenauer, documents on German history (1876-1967), archives, photos and documentary films on Adenauer Era 14449

Bad Iburg

Münzmuseum, Schloß, 49186 Bad Iburg - T: (05403) 401612, Fax: 6025, E-mail: tourist_info@badiburg.de, Internet: http://www.badiburg.de
Special Museum
Coin coll, numismatics 14450

Uhrenmuseum, Am Gografenhof 5, 49186 Bad Iburg - T: (05403) 2888. Head: Peter Taschenmacher
Science&Tech Museum
Cross-section through the hist of clocks and watches 14451

Bad Karlshafen

Deutsches Hugenotten-Museum, Hafenpl 9a, 34385 Bad Karlshafen - T: (05672) 1410, Fax: 925072, Internet: http://www.hugenotten.de. Head: Andrea Emmel
Ethnology Museum - 1980
History of the Huguenots (graphic coll, workshops, customs) - genealogical advisory board, library, archive 14452

Museum an der Krukenburg, Krukenberg 1, 34385 Bad Karlshafen - T: (05672) 755. Head: Heinrich Arnemann
Religious Arts Museum - 1985
Book illumination, lives of the Benedictine monks, glass painting, murals 14453

Bad Kissingen

Bismarck-Museum, Museum Obere Saline, Obere Saline 20, 97688 Bad Kissingen - T: (0971) 7851241, Fax: 7851243, E-mail: bismarckmuseum@stadt.badkissingen.de, Internet: http://www.badkissingen.de. Head: Peter Weidisch
Local Museum - 1998 14454

Schulmuseum, Museen Schloss Aschach, Schloßstr 24, 97708 Bad Kissingen - T: (09708) 6142, Fax: 6104, E-mail: schloss.aschach@bezirk-unterfranken.de, Internet: http://www.bezirk-unterfranken.de. Head: Annette Späth
Decorative Arts Museum / Fine Arts Museum / Folklore Museum 14455

Bad König

Heimatmuseum Bad König, Schloßpl 3, 64732 Bad König - T: (06063) 50090, Fax: 500954, E-mail: info@badkoenig.de, Internet: http://www.badkoenig.de
Local Museum - 1993
Hist of farm life, trade workshops 14456

Bad Königshofen

Grenzmuseum, Am Kurzentrum 1, 97631 Bad Königshofen - T: (09761) 91200, Fax: 912040, E-mail: tourismus@bad-koenigshofen.btl.de, Internet: http://www.btl.de/bad-konigshofen
Historical Museum - 1993
Local history of the German-German border (BRD and DDR) till 1989, photographs, orginal border material and documents 14457

Vorgeschichtsmuseum im Grabfeldgau, Archäologische Staatssammlung München, Martin-Reinhard-Str 9, 97631 Bad Königshofen - T: (09761) 40934
Historical Museum - 1988
Early hist of East Low Franconia 14458

Bad Kösen

Museen der Stadt Bad Kösen, Romanisches Haus, Kunsthalle, Käthe-Kruse-Puppenmuseum, Am Kunstgestänge, 06628 Bad Kösen - T: (034463) 27668, Fax: 27668. Head: Lutz Toepfer
Local Museum - 1955
Architectural hist of monastery and castle, Roman tombstones, fragments, hist of baths, salt source, dolls of Käthe Kruse 14459

Bad Köstritz

Forschungs- und Gedenkstätte im Geburtshaus des Komponisten Heinrich-Schütz-Haus, Heinrich-Schütz-Str 1, 07586 Bad Köstritz - T: (036605) 2405, 36198, Fax: 36199, E-mail: Heinrich-Schuetz-Haus@t-online.de, Internet: http://www.heinrich-schuetz-haus.de. Head: Friederike Böcher
Music Museum - 1985
Memorabilia of composer H. Schütz (1585-1672) in his birthplace, musical life (17th c) - library 14460

Bad Kreuznach

Römerhalle, Hüffelsheimer Str 11, 55545 Bad Kreuznach - T: (0671) 800248, Fax: 800248, Internet: http://www.stadt-bad-kreuznach.de/kultur-freizeit/museen-index.htm. Head: Dr. Angela Nestler-Zapp
Archaeological Museum
Roman mosaics, 3rd c Roman villa 14461

Schloßparkmuseum, Dessauer Str 49, 55545 Bad Kreuznach - T: (0671) 800248, Fax: 800248, Internet: http://www.stadt-bad-kreuznach.de/kultur-freizeit/museen-index.htm. Head: Dr. Angela Nestler-Zapp
Fine Arts Museum / Decorative Arts Museum - 1986
Cauer dynasty of sculpturers, paleontology - archive 14462

Bad Krozingen

Kunst in der Klinik, Südring 15, 79189 Bad Krozingen - T: (07633) 4020
Public Gallery 14463

Sammlung historischer Tasteninstrumente Neumeyer-Junghanns-Tracey, Am Schloßpark 7, 79189 Bad Krozingen - T: (07633) 3700, Fax: 407157, E-mail: kulturamt@bad-krozingen.de, Internet: http://www.bad-krozingen.de. Head: Sally Fortino
Music Museum - ca. 1930
Original keyboard instruments from 1580 to 1880, reconstructions, concert series, early music 14464

Bad Laasphe

Internationales Radiomuseum, Bahnhofstr 33, 57334 Bad Laasphe - T: (02752) 9798. Head: Hans Necker
Science&Tech Museum
Historical audio systems, "Radio Kurios" 14465

Bad Laer

Heimatmuseum Bad Laer, Kesselstr 4, 49196 Bad Laer - T: (05424) 291112
Local Museum
Linen processing, loom, geology 14466

Bad Langensalza

Heimatmuseum, Wiebeckpl 7, 99947 Bad Langensalza - T: (03603) 813002, Fax: 859100, E-mail: Stadt.Bad-Langensalza@t-online.de, Internet: http://www.badlangensalza.de
Local Museum - 1900
Monastery (restored in 18th c), militaria, battle of 1866, local history and crafts, historic printing, geology 14467

Bad Lauchstädt

Historische Kuranlagen und Goethe-Theater Bad Lauchstädt, Parkstr 18, 06246 Bad Lauchstädt - T: (034635) 7820, Fax: 20083, E-mail: info@goethe-theater-bad-lauchstaedt.de, Internet: http://www.goethe-theater-bad-lauchstaedt.de. Head: Bernd Heimühle
Performing Arts Museum / Historic Site - 1968
Goethe theatre, hist of town, balneology, hist of local theatre 14468

Bad Lauterberg

Heimatmuseum Bad Lauterberg, Ritscherstr 13, 37431 Bad Lauterberg - T: (05524) 5722
Local Museum - 1969/89
Local hist, historical costumes and uniforms, trade workshops 14469

Kinderland- und Spielzeugmuseum, Ritscherstr 4, 37431 Bad Lauterberg - T: (05524) 92040, Fax: 5506, E-mail: kurverwbl@badlauterberg.de, Internet: http://www.badlauterberg.de
Special Museum 14470

Bad Liebenwerda

Kreismuseum Bad Liebenwerda, Dresdener Str 15, 04924 Bad Liebenwerda - T: (035341) 12455. Head: Ralf Uschner
Local Museum - 1953
Geology, ancient and early history, local history, crafts, farming, photo coll, 16th c palace - library 14471

Bad Mergentheim

Deutschordensmuseum Bad Mergentheim, Schloß 16, 97980 Bad Mergentheim - T: (07931) 52212, Fax: 52669, E-mail: info@deutschordensmuseum.de, Internet: http://www.deutschordensmuseum.de. Head: Maike Trentin-Meyer
Historical Museum - 1864
Baroque, Rococo, and Classical interiors, hist of the Teutonic Order, local hist, doll houses, Adelsheim-coll, Eduard Mörike (1804-1875), Carl Joseph von Adelsheim (1790-1864) - library 14472

Ottmar-Mergenthaler-Museum, Ottmar-Mergenthaler-Str, Hachtel, 97980 Bad Mergentheim - T: (07931) 2242, Fax: 2365. Head: Paul Brunner
Local Museum / Science&Tech Museum - 1924
Birth house of Ottmar Mergenthaler, the inventor of Linotype, exhibits on the history of printing machines, their influence on book and newspaper production 14473

Bad Münder

Heimatmuseum Bad Münder, Kellerstr 13, 31848 Bad Münder - T: (05042) 52276
Local Museum
Town hist, salt and coal mining, pottery, brick making, glassworks 14474

Bad Münster

Künstlerbahnhof Ebernburg, Berliner Str 77, 55583 Bad Münster - T: (06708) 2762, Fax: 3475
Association with Coll 14475

Bad Münstereifel

Hürten-Heimatmuseum, Langenhecke 6, Romanisches Haus, 53902 Bad Münstereifel - T: (02253) 8027, Fax: 505114
Local Museum - 1912
Finds from the Stone Age to the Middle Ages, local history, sacred art, bourgeois and peasant cultural implements 14476

Bad Muskau

Stadt- und Parkmuseum, Altes Schloß, 02953 Bad Muskau - T: (035771) 60352, Fax: 60352. Head: Regina Barufke
Local Museum / Historic Site - 1965
Local hist, hist of mud bath, park, pottery, crafts - library, archive 14477

Bad Nauheim

Rosenmuseum Steinfurth, Alte Schulstr 1, 61231 Bad Nauheim Steinfurth - T: (06032) 86001, Fax: 87915, E-mail: rosenmuseum@bad-nauheim.de, Internet: http://www.bad-nauheim.de. Head: Sabine Kübler
Special Museum - 1974/90
Hist of local rose cultivation, cultural hist of the rose 14478

Bad Nenndorf

Agnes-Miegel-Haus, Agnes-Miegel-Pl 3, 31542 Bad Nenndorf - T: (05723) 917317, Fax: 914967
Special Museum - 1974
Works and personal belongings of the writer Agnes Miegel 14479

Bad Neuenahr-Ahrweiler

Museum der Stadt Bad Neuenahr-Ahrweiler, Altenbaustr 5, 53474 Bad Neuenahr-Ahrweiler - T: (02641) 31516, Fax: 31516. Head: Heike Wernz-Kaiser
Local Museum - 1907 14480

Museum Roemervilla, Am Silberberg 1, 53474 Bad Neuenahr-Ahrweiler - T: (02641) 5311, Fax: 87180. Head: Karin Joachim
Archaeological Museum - 1993
Roman excavation: Roman villa of the 2nd c with well-preserved wall paintings, floor heating systems and other architectural details 14481

Bad Neustadt an der Saale

Heimatmuseum, Rathausgasse 2, 97616 Bad Neustadt an der Saale
Local Museum - 1906
Bourgeois and peasant folk art, wood carvings 14482

Kaiserpfalz Salzburg, 97616 Bad Neustadt an der Saale
Local Museum 14483

Wagstädter Heimatstube, Hohntorturm in der Hohnstr, 97616 Bad Neustadt an der Saale - T: (09771) 3987, 97786
Local Museum - 1578
Hist of Wagstadt in Sudeten-Silesia 14484

Bad Oeynhausen

Deutsches Märchen- und Wesersagenmuseum, Am Kurpark 3, 32545 Bad Oeynhausen - T: (05731) 22428, Fax: 22048, E-mail: Info@badoeynhausen.de, Internet: http://www.badoeynhausen.de. Head: Dr. Hanna Dose
Special Museum - 1973
Fairy tales and legends, graphic presentations of narrators (of folktales) - library 14485

Museumshof, Schützenstr 35a, 32545 Bad Oeynhausen - T: (05731) 91488, Fax: 22048, E-mail: Info@badoeynhausen.de, Internet: http://www.badoeynhausen.de. Head: Dr. Hanna Dose
Open Air Museum - 1969
Peasant culture (18th and 19th c), domestic crafts 14486

Norddeutsches Auto- und Motorrad-Museum, Weserstr 225, 32547 Bad Oeynhausen - T: (05731) 9960. Head: Willy Helmerding
Science&Tech Museum - 1973
Automobiles, motorcycles and bicycles 14487

Bad Oldesloe

Heimatmuseum Bad Oldesloe, Königstr 32, 23843 Bad Oldesloe - T: (04531) 2143, Fax: 5322, Internet: http://www.Badoldesloe.de/heimatmuseum. Head: Dr. K. Baumgarten
Local Museum - 1931
Local history (prehistoric to present), municipal history 14488

Bad Orb

Heimatmuseum, Burgring 14, 63619 Bad Orb - T: (06052) 860
Local Museum - 1916
History of the spa, minicipal history, folklore 14489

Bad Pyrmont

Museum im Schloß Bad Pyrmont, Schloßstr 13, 31812 Bad Pyrmont - T: (05281) 949248, Fax: 969126, E-mail: museum-pyrmont@t-online.de, Internet: http://www.museum-pyrmont.de. Head: Dr. Dieter Alfter
Local Museum - 1987
Glass, porcelain, 18th and 19th c painting, early history, prehistory 14490

Bad Rappenau

Bad Rappenauer Museum, Heinsheimer Str 16, 74906 Bad Rappenau - T: (07264) 86129
Local Museum - 1930
Hist of salt mine, balneology 14491

Bad Reichenhall

Bad Reichenhaller Salzmuseum, c/o Südsalz GmbH Saline Bad Reichenhall, Alte Saline 9, 83435 Bad Reichenhall - T: (08651) 7002146, Fax: 7002196, E-mail: info@suedsalz.de, Internet: http://www.suedsalz.de. Head: Elisabeth Hiltermann
Science&Tech Museum
History of salt mining 14492

Georg Papendicks Faschings- und Karnevalsordenmuseum, Heilingbrunner Str 3, 83435 Bad Reichenhall - T: (08651) 1346
Special Museum - 1984 14493

Glashütte, In der alten Saline, 83435 Bad Reichenhall - T: (08651) 69738, Fax: 69739, E-mail: info@viedl-glaskunst.de, Internet: http://www.viedl-glaskunst.de. Head: Monika Riedl
Decorative Arts Museum 14494

Städtisches Museum, Getreidegasse 4, 83435 Bad Reichenhall - T: (08651) 5324, Fax: 775200, E-mail: stadt_bad_reichenhall@t-online.de. Head: Fritz Hofmann
Local Museum
Local early hist of Bad Reichenhall 14495

Bad Rodach

Heimatmuseum, Jagdschloß, Schloßpl, 96476 Bad Rodach - T: (09564) 1550, 3117, Fax: 4169
Local Museum - 1982
Earthenware 14496

Bad Rothenfelde

Dr.-Bauer-Heimatmuseum, Wellengartenstr 10, 49214 Bad Rothenfelde - T: (05424) 223160, Fax: 223197
Local Museum
Hist of the spa, salt mining, Dutch ceramics, early and prehistory 14497

Bad Sachsa

Glasmuseum Steina, Mitteldorf, 37441 Bad Sachsa - T: (05523) 441. Head: Jörge Schiers
Decorative Arts Museum - 1994
Historic forest glassworks 14498

Grenzland-Museum Bad Sachsa, Dorfgemeinschaftshaus Tettenborn, Hinterstr 1a, 37441 Bad Sachsa - T: (05523) 999773, Fax: 999773, Internet: http://www.bad-sachsa.de/grenzlandmuseum. Head: Rainer Böhle
Historical Museum - 1992
Former East/West German border protection area, barracks 14499

Bad Säckingen

Hochrheinmuseum, Schloß, 79713 Bad Säckingen - T: (07761) 51311. Head: Dr. Ludwig Schnitzler
Local Museum 14500

Kirchenschatz im Sankt Fridolinsmünster, Münsterpl 8, 79713 Bad Säckingen - T: (07761) 568190, Fax: 568199. Head: Peter Berg
Religious Arts Museum 14501

Trompetenmuseum, Schloß, 79713 Bad Säckingen - T: (07761) 2217, Fax: 51321. Head: Dr. Edward H. Tarr
Music Museum - 1985
Old records, instruments of famous trumpeters, trompets 17th-20th c - phono archive 14502

Bad Salzdetfurth

Heimatstube Wehrstedt, Am Sportpl 8, 31162 Bad Salzdetfurth - T: (05063) 627
Local Museum
Trade and agricultural implements, smithy - archive 14503

Kunstverein Bad Salzdetfurth e.V., Schlosshof Bodenburg, Teichstr 15a, 31162 Bad Salzdetfurth - T: (05060) 961201, Fax: 961202, E-mail: Kunstverein.Bad-Salzdetfurth@t-online.de. Head: Hans-Werner Kalkmann
Association with Coll 14504

Stadthistorisches Museum, SK-Bergbaumuseum, Sankt Georgspl 1, 31162 Bad Salzdetfurth - T: (05063) 960267, Fax: 960267. Head: Ernst Mundel
Historical Museum / Science&Tech Museum
Hist of the salt spa, potash and salt mining, mineralogy, portrait paintings by Carl Huter 14505

Bad Salzuflen

Das Fachwerk, Pfarrkamp 8, 32108 Bad Salzuflen - T: (05222) 85308
Public Gallery 14506

Stadt- und Bädermuseum, Lange Str 41, 32105 Bad Salzuflen - T: (05222) 59766, Fax: 960607. Head: Franz Meyer
Local Museum / Special Museum - 1969
Spa-glasses and Spa-souvenirs 14507

Bad Saulgau

Galerie Am Markt, Marktpl 3, 88348 Bad Saulgau - T: (07581) 207161, Fax: 207863. Head: Andreas Ruess
Fine Arts Museum - 1986
20th c painting 14508

Städtische Galerie Die Fähre, Schulstr 6, 88348 Bad Saulgau - T: (07581) 207161, Fax: 207863
Public Gallery 14509

Bad Schandau

Heimatmuseum, Badallee 10-11, 01814 Bad Schandau - T: (035022) 42173
Local Museum - 1940
Geology, old mines and sandstone quarry (since 1600), nature, local history, crafts, shipping, cultural history, tourism, sports 14510

Kellergedenkstätte Krippen, Stadtverwaltung Bad Schandau, Dresdner Str 3, 01814 Bad Schandau - T: (035022) 42357, Fax: 42539. Head: Gerd Englick
Science&Tech Museum - 1972
Memorabilia on Friedrich Gottlob Keller, inventor of mechanical pulp 14511

Bad Schussenried

Klostermuseum in der Pfarrkirche Sankt Magnus, Klosterhof 7, 88427 Bad Schussenried - T: (07583) 2240. Head: A. Schmid
Religious Arts Museum - 1983
Hist of the "White Monks" (premonstratensians), paintings, furniture 14512

Oberschwäbisches Museumsdorf Kreisfreilichtmuseum Kürnbach, Griesweg 30, 88427 Bad Schussenried - T: (07351) 52204, Fax: 52405, E-mail: kreisarchiv@biberach.de, Internet: http://www.biberach.de. Head: Dr. Kurt Diemer
Open Air Museum - 1969
Old farm buildings, incl four thatched-roof buildings, from 1499-1945 14513

Bad Schwalbach

Apothekenmuseum Bad Schwalbach → Bad Schwalbacher Kur-, Stadt- und Apothekenmuseum

Bad Schwalbacher Kur-, Stadt- und Apothekenmuseum, Adolfstr 38, 65307 Bad Schwalbach - T: (06124) 500102, Fax: 500199, E-mail: stadt.bad.schwalbach@t-online.de, Internet: http://www.bad-schwalbach.de
Local Museum / Special Museum - 1970/2002
Hist of 17th c pharmacy, original interior, local history 14514

Heimatmuseum Langenseifen, Lorcher Str 41, Langenseifen, 65307 Bad Schwalbach - T: (06124) 9470
Local Museum - 1993
Village school, farm kitchen, agricultural implements and machines, herbarium of indigenous plants, dresses and clothing of former times 14515

Bad Schwartau

Museum der Stadt Schwartau, Schillerstr 8-10, 23611 Bad Schwartau - T: (0451) 2000103
Local Museum 14516

Bad Segeberg

Alt-Segeberger Bürgerhaus, Lübecker Str 15, 23795 Bad Segeberg - T: (04551) 964203/04, Fax: 964111, E-mail: a2000@badsegeberg.de, Internet: http://www.badsegeberg.de. Head: Erwin Rohdt
Local Museum - 1963/64
Furniture and furnishings, 17th to 19th c, and tools of local craftsmen, housed in 16th c half-timber house 14517

Otto-Flath-Kunsthalle, Bismarckallee 5, 23795 Bad Segeberg - T: (04551) 879900, 995749, Fax: 964915, E-mail: TOURIST-INFO@badsegeberg.de, Internet: http://www.badsegeberg.de. Head: Ursula Ludwig
Fine Arts Museum - 1978
Watercolours, sculptures and drawings by Otto Flath - Archive Otto Flath 14518

Bad Sobernheim

Rheinland-Pfälzisches Freilichtmuseum Bad Sobernheim, 55566 Bad Sobernheim - T: (06751) 3840, Fax: 1207
Open Air Museum 14519

Bad Soden am Taunus

Photomuseum CAMERAMA, Sodener Weg 24, 65812 Bad Soden am Taunus - T: (06196) 3915. Head: Rolf Oberländer
Fine Arts Museum 14520

Stadtmuseum Bad Soden, Königsteiner Str 86, 65812 Bad Soden am Taunus - T: (06196) 208253, 208254, Fax: 208888, E-mail: info@bad-soden.de, Internet: http://www.bad-soden.de. Head: Simone Reuter
Local Museum - 1910
Town and spa hist, medieval finds 14521

Bad Sooden-Allendorf

Heimatmuseum Luditzer Kreis, Haus des Gastes, Brunnenpl 5, 37242 Bad Sooden-Allendorf - T: (0561) 522656
Local Museum - 1961
Costumes, porcelain, coats of arms, flags, folklore 14522

Salzmuseum, Söder Tor, Rosenstr 1-3, 37242 Bad Sooden-Allendorf - T: (05652) 50166
Science&Tech Museum - 1913/79
Hist of salt mining 14523

Bad Steben

Grafik Museum Stiftung Schreiner, c/o Staatliche Kurverwaltung, Badstr 31, 95138 Bad Steben - T: (09288) 9600, Fax: 96010
Fine Arts Museum - 1994
East European contemporary graphic art 14524

Bad Sülze

Salzmuseum, Saline 8, 18334 Bad Sülze - T: (038229) 80680, Fax: 80677
Natural History Museum - 1953
Hist of baths, salt source development 14525

Bad Sulza

Saline- und Heimatmuseum, Naumburger Str 2, 99518 Bad Sulza - T: (036461) 82110, Fax: 82111, E-mail: kurgesellschaft@bad-sulza.de
Science&Tech Museum / Historical Museum - 1953
Hist of salt mine, prehistoric finds 14526

Bad Tölz

Heimatmuseum der Stadt Bad Tölz, Marktstr 48, 83646 Bad Tölz - T: (08041) 504688, Fax: 72266, E-mail: stadtverwaltung@bad-toelz.de, Internet: http://www.bad-toelz.de
Local Museum - 1886
Local history, timber industry, furniture and furnishings, esp. Empire and Biedermeier, folk costumes, religious folk art, local rocks, sculpture 14527

Bad Urach

Grammophonmuseum, Friedhofstr 7, 72574 Bad Urach - T: (07125) 3241. Head: R. Geigle
Science&Tech Museum - 1989
Hist of sound recording 14528

Historisches Museum Schloß Bad Urach, Bismarckstr 16, 72574 Bad Urach - T: (07125) 158490, Fax: 158499, Internet: http://www.schloesser-und-gaerten.de
Historical Museum
Courtly pomp sledges 14529

Stadtmuseum Klostermühle, Hermann-Prey-Pl 3, 72574 Bad Urach - T: (07125) 40600, Fax: 946080. Head: Thomas Braun
Local Museum - 1990
Local hist 14530

Bad Vilbel

Brunnenmuseum, Klaus-Havenstein-Weg 2, Wasserburg, 61118 Bad Vilbel - T: (06101) 559310, Fax: 559330, E-mail: AlteMuehle@t-online.de, Internet: http://www.bad-vilbel.de
Local Museum 14531

Bad Waldsee

Städtisches Museum im Kornhaus Bad Waldsee, Rathauspl, 88339 Bad Waldsee - T: (07524) 48228, 97950, Fax: 979512. Head: Rupert Leser
Local Museum 14532

Bad Wiessee

Töpferstube mit Keramikmuseum, Anton-v.-Rieppel-Str 21, 83707 Bad Wiessee - T: (08022) 8267
Decorative Arts Museum 14533

Bad Wildbad

Heimat- und Flößermuseum Calmbach, Bergstr 1, 75323 Bad Wildbad - T: (07081) 930111
Local Museum / Ethnology Museum - 1991
Rafting from 1880-1920 14534

Bad Wildungen

Heimatmuseum Bad Wildungen, Lindenstr 9, 34537 Bad Wildungen - T: (05621) 73666, Fax: 701461
Local Museum - 1907 14535

Historisches Bergamt Bad Wildungen-Bergfreiheit, Kellerwaldstr 12, 34537 Bad Wildungen - T: (05621) 1736, Fax: 701461, Internet: http://www.bad-wildungen.de
Science&Tech Museum
Geology, hist of mining, metal extraction, smelting, old smithery 14536

Kurmuseum Bad Wildungen, Brunnenallee 1, 34537 Bad Wildungen - T: (05621) 72942, Fax: 701461, E-mail: kurmuseum@t-online.de, Internet: http://www.bad-wildungen.de. Head: Dr. Volker Brendow
Special Museum - 1985
Balneological culture, hist of health cures, tourism and the fashionable luxury and life-style of the spa 14537

Titanicmuseum, Bierweg 9, 34537 Bad Wildungen - T: (05621) 71767
Special Museum 14538

Uhr-, Militär- und Jagdgeschichtliche Sammlung, Staatliche Museen Kassel, Schloß Friedrichstein, 34537 Bad Wildungen - T: (05621) 6577, Fax: (0561) 7846222, E-mail: info@museum-kassel.de, Internet: http://www.museum-kassel.de. Head: Dr. Michael Eissenhauer
Military Museum - 1980
Hessian military hist from the middle ages to 1866 hunting weapons and tropheies 14539

Bad Wimpfen

Galerie der Stadt, Hauptstr 45, 74206 Bad Wimpfen - T: (07063) 950314, Fax: 1352, E-mail: kulturamt@badwimpfen.org, Internet: http://www.badwimpfen.de. Head: Gereon Schatten
Public Gallery 14540

Kirchengeschichtliches Museum in der Pfalzkapelle, Burgviertel, 74206 Bad Wimpfen - T: (07063) 8779. Head: Günther Haberhauer
Religious Arts Museum 14541

Museum im Steinhaus, Burgviertel 15, 74206 Bad Wimpfen - T: (07063) 8779. Head: Günther Haberhauer
Local Museum - 1952
Prehist, early hist and local hist, medieval art, weapons and coins, peasant culture 14542

Ödenburger Heimatmuseum, Langgasse 2, 74206 Bad Wimpfen - T: (07063) 8103
Local Museum
Cultural life of the German from Ödenburg (now Sopron/Hungary) and surroundings 14543

Puppen-, Bären- und Spielzeugmuseum, Salzgasse 6, 74206 Bad Wimpfen - T: (07063) 950073, 200
Decorative Arts Museum - 1980
Dolls and puppets (1860 until today), Käthe Kruse, Sasha Morgenthaler 14544

Reichstädtisches Museum, Hauptstr 45, 74206 Bad Wimpfen - T: (07063) 53151. Head: Günther Haberhauer
Local Museum 14545

Schweine-Museum, Kronengäßchen 2, 74206 Bad Wimpfen - T: (07063) 6689, Fax: (0711) 613535, E-mail: info@schweinemuseum.de, Internet: http://www.schweinemuseum.de
Decorative Arts Museum - 1988
Portrayals of pigs, piggy banks, travelling exhibitions "Pigs on the Road", hist of pigs 14546

Bad Windsheim

Archäologiemuseum im Fränkischen Freilandmuseum, Archäologische Staatssammlung München, Eisweiherweg 1, 91438 Bad Windsheim - T: (09841) 66800, Fax: 668099, E-mail: info@freilandmuseum.de, Internet: http://www.freilandmuseum.de. Head: Prof. Dr. Konrad Bedal
Archaeological Museum - 2001
Early local hist 14547

Fränkisches Freilandmuseum, Eisweiherweg 1, 91438 Bad Windsheim - T: (09841) 66800, Fax: 668099, E-mail: info@freilandmuseum.de, Internet: http://www.freilandmuseum.de. Head: Prof. Dr. Konrad Bedal
Open Air Museum - 1979
Rural buildings, architecture, framework, agriculture, furniture, handicraft, textiles, religious folk art - library, archive 14548

Reichsstadtmuseum im Ochsenhof, Seegasse 27, 91438 Bad Windsheim - T: (09841) 1073. Head: Jan K. Kube
Local Museum - 1981
Rustic furniture, glass and porcelain coll, national costumes 14549

Bad Wörishofen

Sebastian-Kneipp-Museum, c/o Kurdirektion, Klosterhof 1, 86825 Bad Wörishofen - T: (08247) 969039/50, Fax: 32323, E-mail: info@bad-woerishofen.de, Internet: http://www.bad-woerishofen.de. Head: Bernarda Schädle
Special Museum - 1986
Memorabilia of Sebastian Kneipp, originator of the so-called 'Kneipp cure' 14550

Bad Wurzach

Galerie im Amtshaus, Schloßstr 19, 88410 Bad Wurzach - T: (07564) 302112, Fax: 302170, E-mail: menig@bad-wurzach.de. Head: Irene Menig
Public Gallery 14551

Museum für klösterliche Kultur, Pfarrhof Eggmannsried, 88410 Bad Wurzach - T: (07564) 2753, Fax: 935013. Head: J. Hohl
Religious Arts Museum - 1986
Religious folk art, cribs, order costumes 14552

Bad Zwischenahn

Freilandmuseum Ammerländer Bauernhaus, Auf dem Winkel 26, 26160 Bad Zwischenahn - T: (04403) 2071, Fax: 1876
Open Air Museum - 1910
Farm houses and buildings, peasant culture 14553

Museum Specken, Speckener Weg 34, 26160 Bad Zwischenahn
Local Museum 14554

Ostdeutsche Heimatstube, Auf dem Winkel 8, 26160 Bad Zwischenahn - T: (04403) 4130
Local Museum
Exhibits by expellees from the former German provinces in East-Europe 14555

Baden-Baden

Brahmshaus, Maximilianstr 85, 76534 Baden-Baden - T: (07221) 99872, Fax: 71104, E-mail: brahms.baden-baden@t-online.de. Head: Dr. Werner Hoppe
Music Museum - 1968
Memorabilia of Johannes Brahms, housed in rooms in which Brahms vacationed, Brahms library including scores and phonograph records 14556

Heimatmuseum Steinbach, Steinbacher Str 62, 76534 Baden-Baden - T: (07223) 57055
Local Museum 14557

Das kleine Spielzeugmuseum, Gernsbacher Str 48, 76534 Baden-Baden - T: (07221) 32511. Head: U. Furtwengler
Decorative Arts Museum - 1983
Toys from last two centuries 14558

Museum der Cistercienserinnen-Abtei Lichtenthal, Hauptstr 40, 76534 Baden-Baden - T: (07221) 504910, Fax: 5049166. Head: Hildegard Bung
Religious Arts Museum / Fine Arts Museum / Decorative Arts Museum / Historic Site - 1912
Sacred art, handicrafts, embroidery, glass, manuscripts, furniture, tin, porcelain, paintings, history, Lucas Cranach (the Elder), "Lichtenthaler Meister" 14559

Reblandmuseum, Steinbacher Str 62, 76534 Baden-Baden - T: (07223) 57055. Head: K. Schwab
Local Museum - 1976
Agricultural and viticultural implements, local hist, paintings 14560

Staatliche Kunsthalle Baden-Baden, Lichtentaler Allee 8a, 76530 Baden-Baden - T: (07221) 300763, Fax: 38590, E-mail: info@kunsthalle-baden-baden.de, Internet: http://www.kunsthalle-baden-baden.de. Head: Dr. Matthias Winzen
Public Gallery - 1909 14561

Stadtmuseum Baden-Baden, Küferstr 3, 76530 Baden-Baden - T: (07221) 932272, Fax: 932066, E-mail: stadtmuseum@baden-baden.de, Internet: http://www.baden-baden.de/tourismus/baden-baden_erleben/sehenswuerdigkeiten. Head: Heike Kronenwett
Local Museum - 1892
archive 14562

Stadtmuseum Baden-Baden, Zweigstelle im Neuen Schloss, Schloßstr 22, 76530 Baden-Baden - T: (07221) 22180, Fax: 932066, E-mail: stadtmuseum@baden-baden.de, Internet: http://www.baden-baden.de/tourismus/baden-baden_erleben/sehenswuerdigkeiten. Head: Heike Kronenwett
Special Museum - 1892
Toys, dolls 14563

Badenhausen

Heimatstube Badenhausen, Thüringer Str 254, 37534 Badenhausen - T: (05522) 8860
Local Museum 14564

Bärnau

Deutsches Knopfmuseum, Tachauer Str 2, 95671 Bärnau - T: (09635) 920217, 1830, Fax: 920399, E-mail: stbaerna@tirnet.de
Decorative Arts Museum - 1983
Coll of buttons 14565

Baiersdorf

Meerrettichmuseum, Judengasse 11, 91083 Baiersdorf - T: (09133) 603040
Special Museum - 1997 14566

Balingen

Bauernmuseum Ostdorf, Rathaus, 72336 Balingen - T: (07433) 170216, Fax: 170222
Agriculture Museum - 1981
Agricultural implements, furniture 14567

Friedrich-Eckenfelder-Galerie, Neue Str 59, Zehntscheuer, 72336 Balingen - T: (07433) 170261, Fax: 170222, E-mail: stadtarchiv@balingen.de. Head: Dr. Hans Schimpf-Reinhardt
Fine Arts Museum
Paintings by Friedrich Eckenfelder 14568

Heimatmuseum Balingen, Neue Str 59, Zehntscheuer, 72336 Balingen - T: (07433) 170216, Fax: 170222, E-mail: stadtarchiv@balingen.de
Local Museum
Geology, pre and early history, local history, handicraft 14569

Museum für Waage und Gewicht, Bizerba Waagenmuseum, Zollernschloß, 72336 Balingen - T: (07433) 170216, Fax: 170222, E-mail: stadtarchiv@balingen.de. Head: Dr. Hans Schimpf-Reinhardt
Science&Tech Museum - 1943
History of weights and scales, scales from around the world 14570

Städtische Galerie im Rathaus, Färberstr 2, 72336 Balingen - T: (07433) 170261, Fax: 2701004, E-mail: stadt@balingen.de, Internet: http://www.balingen.de
Public Gallery 14571

Balje

Natureum Niederelbe, Ostemündung, 21730 Balje - T: (04753) 842110, Fax: 8193, E-mail: natureum-niederelbe@t-online.de, Internet: http://www.natureum-niederelbe.de. Head: Dr. Reinhard Kölmel
Natural History Museum / Open Air Museum - 1990
Ornithology, fish tanks, ecology, landscape, Elbe-Estuary 14572

Ballenstedt

Städtisches Heimatmuseum, Allee 37, 06493 Ballenstedt - T: (039483) 8866. Head: Eberhard Nier
Local Museum - 1910
Geology, pre- and early history, local history (since 11th c), crafts, costumes, farm tools, living style, photo coll 14573

Balve

Luisenhütte, 58802 Balve
Local Museum 14574

Bamberg

Diözesanmuseum, Dompl 5, 96049 Bamberg - T: (0951) 502325/329, Fax: 502320, E-mail: diozesanmuseum-bamberg@t-online.de, Internet: http://www.erzbistum-bamberg.de
Religious Arts Museum - 1966
Sacred art from the 11th c onward, medieval textiles, Cathedral treasure 14575

E.T.A. Hoffmann-Haus mit Sammlung, Schillerpl 26, 96047 Bamberg - E-mail: dr.heimritz@bnv-bamberg.de, Internet: http./www.etahg.de. Head: Dr. Reinhard Heinritz
Special Museum - 1930
Memorabilia from the period of Hoffmann's residence in Bamberg, first editions of Hoffmann's works 14576

Fränkisches Brauereimuseum, Michaelsberg 10f, 96049 Bamberg - T: (0951) 53016, Fax: 52540. Head: Johannes Schulters
Science&Tech Museum - 1979
Brewing, malting, coopering 14577

Gärtner- und Häckermuseum, Mittelstr 34, 96052 Bamberg - T: (0951) 201618
Agriculture Museum - 1979
Tools and implements, costumes, and furnishings illustrating history of gardening 14578

Historisches Museum Bamberg, Museen der Stadt Bamberg, Dompl 7, 96049 Bamberg - T: (0951) 871142, 5190746, Fax: 871464, E-mail: museum@bamberg.de, Internet: http://www.bamberg.de/museum. Head: Dr. Regina Hanemann
Local Museum - 1838
Handicrafts and guilds, municipal history, clocks and astronomical instruments, painting and sculpture 14579

Holowood - Holographiemuseum Bamberg, Willy-Lessing-Str 10, 96047 Bamberg - T: (0951) 2080814, Fax: 2028817, E-mail: info@holowood.de, Internet: http://www.holographie.de. Head: M.T. Frieb
Science&Tech Museum / Decorative Arts Museum / Special Museum - 1999
Holographic art, physics experiments, laser technic 14580

Missionsmuseum Bug, Schloßstr 30, 96049 Bamberg - T: (0951) 56214, Fax: 55245. Head: Arnold Peine
Religious Arts Museum - 1965
Religious folklore 14581

Museum der Kommunikations- und Bürogeschichte, Am Kranen 12a, 96047 Bamberg - T: (0951) 201782, Fax: 9230099, E-mail: A.Kutz@bnv-bamberg.de, Internet: http://www.stadtplan-bamberg.de/museum/kutz
Special Museum 14582

Museum für Frühislamische Kunst, Austr 29, 96047 Bamberg - T: (0951) 871142, Fax: 871464. Head: Manfred Bumiller
Decorative Arts Museum - 1995
Early islamic decorative art, Iran bronces, ceramic, silver, glass, bones, stone, metal, wood 14583

Naturkunde-Museum Bamberg, Fleischstr 2, 96047 Bamberg - T: (0951) 8631249, Fax: 8631250, E-mail: matthias.maeuser@en.uni-bamberg.de, Internet: http://www.uni-bamberg.de/NatMus/. Head: Dr. Matthias Mäuser
Natural History Museum - 1793
Zoology, palaeontology, mineralogy and geology 14584

Neue Residenz, Dompl 8, 96049 Bamberg - T: (0951) 519390, 51939113, Fax: 51939129, E-mail: info@bsv.bayern.de. Head: Dr. Werner Helmberger
Fine Arts Museum - 1613
Late Baroque, Rococo and Classicist furnishings, paintings 14585

Sammlung Ludwig in Bamberg, Museen der Stadt Bamberg, Altes Rathaus, Obere Brücke 1, 96047 Bamberg - T: (0951) 871142, 871871, Fax: 871464, E-mail: museum@bamberg.de, Internet: http://www.bamberg.de/museum. Head: Dr. Regina Hanemann
Decorative Arts Museum - 1995
Coll of porcelain 18th c 14586

Staatsarchiv Bamberg, Hainstr 39, 96047 Bamberg - T: (0951) 986220, Fax: 9862250. Head: Dr. Rainer Hambrecht
Library with Exhibitions 14587

Staatsbibliothek Bamberg, Dompl 8, 96049 Bamberg - T: (0951) 955030, Fax: 9550329, E-mail: info@staatsbibliothek-bamberg.de, Internet: http://www.staatsbibliothek-bamberg.de. Head: Prof. Dr. Bernhard Schemmel
Library with Exhibitions 14588

Staatsgalerie in der Neuen Residenz, Bayerische Staatsgemäldesammlungen, Dompl 8, 96049 Bamberg - T: (0951) 519390, Fax: 51939129, Internet: http://www.stuwfk.bayern.de/kunst/zweigmuseen/bamberg.html
Fine Arts Museum - 1817
Masterworks of Cologne and Franconian schools (late Gothic painting), European baroque 14589

Stadtgalerie Bamberg - Villa Dessauer, Museen der Stadt Bamberg, Hainstr 4a, 96047 Bamberg - T: (0951) 871142, 871861, Fax: 871464, E-mail: museum@bamberg.de, Internet: http://www.bamberg.de/museum. Head: Dr. Regina Hanemann
Public Gallery 14590

Bammental

Heimatmuseum Bammental, Bahnhofstr 11, 69245 Bammental - T: (06223) 953030, Fax: 953088, E-mail: rathaus@bammental.de, Internet: http://www.bammental.de
Local Museum - 1982
Agriculture, crafts, wallpaper production, printing hist (from Gutenberg to Offset) 14591

Makonde Art Museum, Hermann-Löns-Weg 11-13, 69245 Bammental, mail addr: Postfach 82, 69245 Bammental - T: (06223) 5243, Fax: 49696, E-mail: imohl@hotmail.com, Internet: http://www.makonde-art-museum.de. Head: Dr. Max Mohl
Ethnology Museum / Fine Arts Museum - 1965
Makonde sculptures of East Africa, contemporary paintings (Ivory-Coast) 14592

Bardowick

Gildehaus Bardowick, St.-Johannis-Str 3, 21357 Bardowick - T: (04131) 128319
Historical Museum
Former medieval centre of trade 14593

Bargteheide

Ortskundliche Sammlung Bargteheide, Hamburger Str 3, 22941 Bargteheide - T: (04532) 7603
Local Museum - 1970 14594

Barmstedt

Museum der Grafschaft, Rantzau 8, 25355 Barmstedt - T: (04123) 68101
Local Museum 14595

Barsinghausen

Museum Barsinghausen, Deisterstr 10, 30890 Barsinghausen - T: (05105) 774372, Fax: 774398
Local Museum
Town hist, agricultural tools and implements, sandstone and coal mining, minerals, uniforms 14596

Barßel

Moor- und Fehnmuseum, Oldenburger Str 1, Elisabethfehn, 26676 Barßel - T: (04499) 2222, Fax: 74477
Natural History Museum
Moor colonisation, implements 14597

Battenberg, Eder

Heimatmuseum Battenberg-Laisa, Kirchstr, 35088 Battenberg, Eder - T: (06452) 3817
Local Museum - 1982
Exhibits from rural and domestic life from around 1900 14598

Bauerbach

Schiller-Museum, Stiftung Weimarer Klassik, Hauptstr 3, 98617 Bauerbach - T: (036945) 50301, Fax: (03643) 545303, E-mail: museen@weimar-klassik.de, Internet: http://www.weimar-klassik.de. Head: Dr. Renate Müller-Krumbach
Special Museum - 1953
Memorabilia on Friedrich Schiller's stay and his dramas written here (1782/83) 14599

Baunach

Heimatmuseum Baunach, Burgstr 2, 96148 Baunach - T: (09544) 2990, Fax: 29920, E-mail: vg.baunach@bnv-bamberg.de, Internet: http://www.stadt-baunach.de
Local Museum - 1983
Local history 14600

Baunatal

Museum Hessenstube, Ritterstr, 34225 Baunatal - T: (0561) 49920, Fax: 4992300, E-mail: magistrat@baunatal.de, Internet: http://www.baunatal.de. Head: Lisa Funke
Local Museum - 1983
Village life between 1850 and 1900, typical rooms, costumes and implements 14601

Bautzen

Domschatzkammer Sankt Petri, An der Petrikirche 6, 02625 Bautzen - T: (03591) 44102, Fax: 44124. Head: Birgit Mitzscherlich
Religious Arts Museum 14602

Serbski muzej - Sorbisches Museum (closed until October 2002), Ortenburg 3, 02625 Bautzen, mail addr: Postfach 1346, 02603 Bautzen - T: (03591) 42403, Fax: 42425, Internet: http://www.sorben-wenden.de. Head: Tomasz Nawka
Historical Museum / Folklore Museum / Local Museum - 1904
History, traditional way of life, art, music, literature of the Sorbians - library 14603

Stadtmuseum Bautzen, Regionalmuseum der sächsischen Oberlausitz, Kornmarkt 1, 02625 Bautzen - T: (03591) 49850, Fax: 498540, E-mail: stadtmuseum@bautzen.de, Internet: http://www.bautzen.de. Head: Ophelia Rehor
Local Museum - 1869
Paintings (16th-20th c), sculpture, carvings, drawings, graphics, furniture and crafts (17th-20th c), pre- and early hist, geology, porcelain, costumes - library, archives, graphical cabinet 14604

Technisches Museum Alte Wasserkunst, Wendischer Kirchhof 7, 02625 Bautzen - T: (03591) 41588, Fax: 44071. Head: Dr. Erika Rosjat
Science&Tech Museum - 1957
Old guard rooms, artificial fountain and a significant modern waterwork 14605

Bayerisch Eisenstein

Localbahnmuseum Bayerisch Eisenstein, c/o Localbahnverein e.V., Bahnhofstr 44, 94252 Bayerisch Eisenstein - T: (09925) 1376, Fax: 1376, E-mail: karl.niederwieser@t-online.de, Internet: http://www.tegernsee.de/blv. Head: Dr. Reinhard Müller
Science&Tech Museum - 1975
Bavarian branch lines, Bavarian States Railway, local Bavarian railways, years 1840-1960 14606

Bayreuth

Altes und Neues Schloß Eremitage, Eremitage 1, 95448 Bayreuth - T: (0921) 7596937, Fax: 7596915, E-mail: info@bsv.bayern.de, Internet: http://www.schloesser.bayern.de. Head: Josef Öttl
Decorative Arts Museum
Period rooms, grotto with late Gothic fountain, garden architecture 14607

Archäologisches Museum des Historischen Vereins für Oberfranken, Ludwigstr 25b, 95444 Bayreuth - T: (0921) 65307, Fax: 65307, E-mail: - historisch.verein.oberfranken@t-online.de, Internet: http://www.hvo.franken.org. Head: Norbert Hübsch
Archaeological Museum - 1827
Archeological finds 14608

CampusGalerie, der British American Tobacco, Universitätsstr, Foyer des Audimax der Universität Bayreuth, 95440 Bayreuth - T: (0921) 61090, Fax: 61095, E-mail: info@campusgalerie.de, Internet: http://www.campusgalerie.de
Public Gallery 14609

Deutsches Freimaurermuseum, Im Hofgarten 1, 95444 Bayreuth - T: (0921) 69824, Fax: 512850, E-mail: Deutsches_Freimaurermuseum@t-online.de, Internet: http://www.freimaurer.org/museum. Head: Hans-Georg Lesser van Waveren
Historical Museum - 1902
Freemasonry - archive, library 14610

Deutsches Schreibmaschinenmuseum, Bernecker Str 11, 95448 Bayreuth - T: (0921) 23445, Fax: 7857475. Head: Hans Gebhardt
Science&Tech Museum - 1985
Coll of typewriters 14611

Feuerwehrmuseum, An der Feuerwache 4, 95445 Bayreuth - T: (0921) 251299
Science&Tech Museum 14612

Franz-Liszt-Museum der Stadt Bayreuth, Wahnfriedstr 9, 95444 Bayreuth - T: (0921) 5166488, Fax: 7572822, E-mail: info@wagnermuseum.de, Internet: http://www.bayreuth.de/deutsch/rathaus/broschueren/museumswegweiser/frame6.htm. Head: Dr. Sven Friedrich
Music Museum - 1993
House where Franz Liszt in 1886 died, memorabilia of the composer, documents and portraits 14613

Historisches Museum Bayreuth, Kirchpl 4, 95444 Bayreuth - T: (0921) 764010, Fax: 7640123. Head: Dr. Sylvia Habermann
Local Museum - 1894
Local cultural hist, incl specimens of peasant and bourgeois furnishings, fayence, glass, works of Bayreuth painters 14614

Iwalewa Haus, Münzgasse 9, 95444 Bayreuth - T: (0921) 553681, Fax: 553684, E-mail: iwalewa@uni-bayreuth.de, Internet: http://www.uni-bayreuth.de/Afrikanologie/iwalewa. Head: Dr. Till Förster
Ethnology Museum 14615

Jean-Paul-Museum der Stadt Bayreuth, Wahnfriedstr 1, 95444 Bayreuth - T: (0921) 5071444, Fax: 7572822, E-mail: info@wagnermuseum.de, Internet: http://www.bayreuth.de/deutsch/rathaus/broschueren/museumswegweiser/frame6.htm. Head: Dr. Sven Friedrich
Special Museum - 1980
Memorabilia of the poet Jean Paul, portraits, autographs, first editions, Philipp Hausser coll 14616

Jean-Paul-Zimmer in der Rollwenzelei, Königsallee 84, 95448 Bayreuth - T: (0921) 92413. Head: Wilhelm Mädl, Else Mädl
Special Museum
Memorabilia of the poet Jean Paul in his former study, orginal furniture and documents 14617

Johann-Baptist-Graser-Schulmuseum, Schulstr 4, 95444 Bayreuth - T: (0921) 251333, Fax: 251563
Special Museum - 2000 14618

Kleines Plakatmuseum, Friedrich-Puchta-Str 12, 95444 Bayreuth - T: (0921) 82458, Fax: 84879. Head: Dr. Franz Joachim Schultz
Fine Arts Museum - 1986
Coll of European literature-, theater-, film- and artposters 14619

Kunstmuseum Bayreuth mit Tabakhistorischer Sammlung, Maximilianstr 33, 95444 Bayreuth - T: (0921) 7645310, Fax: 7645320, E-mail: info@kunstmuseum-bayreuth.de, Internet: http://www.kunstmuseum.bayreuth.de. Head: Dr. Marina von Assel
Fine Arts Museum 14620

Maisel's Brauerei- und Büttnerei-Museum, Privatbrauerei Gebr. Maisel, Kulmbacher Str 40, 95445 Bayreuth - T: (0921) 401234, Fax: 401233, E-mail: brauereimuseum@maisel.com, Internet: http://www.maisel.com. Head: Oscar Maisel
Science&Tech Museum - 1981
400 enamel signs and 4,000 drinking glasses, vessels and jars 14621

Museum für bäuerliche Arbeitsgeräte des Bezirks Oberfranken, Adolf-Wächter-Str 17, 95447 Bayreuth - T: (0921) 57515. Head: Günter Schmidt
Agriculture Museum / Science&Tech Museum - 1975
Agricultural tools and implements, housed in 1734 barn 14622

Museum im Umweltschutz-Informationszentrum Oberfranken mit Kinder-Erlebnis-Museum, Lindenhof, Karolinenreuther Str 58, 95448 Bayreuth - T: (0921) 759420, Fax: 7594222, E-mail: lindenhof@lbv.de, Internet: http://www.lbv.de/lindenhof. Head: Heike Wofing
Natural History Museum - 1996
Flora and fauna of Franconia 14623

Neues Schloß Bayreuth, Ludwigstr 21, 95444 Bayreuth - T: (0921) 759690, Fax: 7596915, E-mail: info@bsv.bayern.de, Internet: http://www.schloesser.bayern.de. Head: Josef Öttl
Decorative Arts Museum / Archaeological Museum - 1918
Period rooms (Bayreuth Rococo), Hohenzollern family portraits, tapestries, faience, paintings by Pesne and Mengs 14624

Richard-Wagner-Museum, Haus Wahnfried, Richard-Wagner-Str 48, 95444 Bayreuth - T: (0921) 757280, Fax: 7572822, E-mail: info@wagnermuseum.de, Internet: http://www.wagnermuseum.de. Head: Dr. Sven Friedrich
Music Museum - 1976
Documents from the life and works of Richard Wagner; history of the Bayreuth Festival - Recording studio, archive - library, archive, research dept. 14625

Spielzeugmuseum/Kellerkunstmuseum im Auktionshaus Boltz, Brandenburger Str 36, 95448 Bayreuth - T: (0921) 20616
Decorative Arts Museum / Fine Arts Museum 14626

Urwelt-Museum Oberfranken, Kanzleistr 1, 95444 Bayreuth - T: (0921) 511211, Fax: 511212, E-mail: Urwelt-Museum-Oberfranken@t-online.de, Internet: http://www.urwelt-museum.de. Head: Dr. Joachim Martin Rabold
Natural History Museum - 1833
Geology, palaeontology and mineralogy 14627

Bayrischzell

Atelierhaus Philipp Harth, Tannerhofstr 44, 83735 Bayrischzell - T: (08023) 429, Fax: 911896, E-mail: philipp.harth@tierplastik.de, Internet: http://www.tierplastik.de. Head: Krista Ibing
Fine Arts Museum - 1990
Sculptures by Philipp Harth, drawings and photographs 14628

Bebra

Eisenbahnmuseum Historischer Wasserturm, Am Wasserturm 1, 36179 Bebra - T: (06623) 7964, Fax: (06621) 71870, E-mail: m-schreiner@t-online.de, Internet: http://www.ef-bebra.de. Head: Manfred Reyer
Science&Tech Museum - 1985
Hist of the railway, ticket office, telephone system 14629

Spielzeugmuseum Solz, Burgring, 36179 Bebra Solz - T: (06627) 776. Head: Sibylle Kopf
Decorative Arts Museum - 1989
Coll of Antje Kind-Hasenclever, toys from East-German and East-European areas 14630

Bechhofen

Deutsches Pinsel- und Bürstenmuseum, Dinkelsbühler Str 21, 91572 Bechhofen - T: (09822) 87105, Fax: 87119
Special Museum - 1995
Coll of paintbrushes and other brushware 14631

Beckum

Stadtmuseum Beckum, Markt 1, 59269 Beckum - T: (02521) 29266, Fax: 29264, E-mail: stadt@beckum.de, Internet: http://www.beckum.de. Head: Dr. Martin Gesing
Local Museum / Fine Arts Museum - 1986 14632

Bedburg-Hau

Museum Schloss Moyland, Sammlung van der Grinten, Joseph Beuys Archiv des Landes Nordrhein-Westfalen, Am Schloss 4, 47551 Bedburg-Hau - T: (02824) 95100, 951060, Fax: 951099, E-mail: info@moyland.de, Internet: http://www.moyland.de. Head: Franz Joseph van der Grinten, Johannes Look
Fine Arts Museum
Art 19th/20th c (sculpture, painting, printing, drawing, crafts, object art, photography), over 4000 works of Joseph Beuys - library, archive 14633

Beeskow

Burg Beeskow, Frankfurter Str 23, 15848 Beeskow - T: (03366) 352701, Fax: 21117. Head: Tilman Schladebach
Local Museum - 1906
Geology, local history, pre- and early history of the area - auditorium, library, gallery 14634

Beierfeld

Heimatecke am Seifenbach, Talstr 28, Waschleithe, 08358 Beierfeld - T: (03774) 22901, Fax: 22905
Local Museum / Open Air Museum
Farmyards, half-timbered houses, castles and transport on a scale of 1:40, geology 14635

Beilngries

Felsenkeller-Labyrinth im Hirschberg - Brauereimuseum, Bräuhausstr 36, 92339 Beilngries - T: (08461) 1033, Fax: 7606, E-mail: Prinstner@t-online.de, Internet: http://www.altmuehltal.de. Head: Wilhelm Rose
Science&Tech Museum - 1982
Brewery in a cellar cut out of the rock 14636

Spielzeug anno dazumal - Museum Beilngries, Hauptstr 49, 92339 Beilngries - T: (08461) 601176, 8318, Fax: 9188. Head: Dr. Helge Vergho
Special Museum
Toys and model railways from Arnold, tin figures 14637

Belzig

Museum Burg Eisenhardt, Wittenberger Str 14, 14806 Belzig - T: (033841) 42461, Fax: 42461. Head: Thomas Schmöhl
Local Museum - 1956
Pre- and early history, local history, tools and handicrafts (19th c), peasant living style 14638

Bendestorf

Filmmuseum Bendestorf, Poststr 4, 21227 Bendestorf - T: (04183) 6154. Head: Kurt Kaumanns
Performing Arts Museum
Film studio for more than 35 post-war films 14639

Bendorf, Rhein

Rheinisches Eisenkunstguss Museum, Abteistr 1, 56170 Bendorf, Rhein - T: (02622) 902913, Fax: 902917, E-mail: museum@bendorf.de, Internet: http://www.bendorf.de. Head: Barbara Friedhofen
Fine Arts Museum / Science&Tech Museum - 1972
Hist of iron industry 14640

Sayner Gießhalle, c/o Heinrich Strüder GmbH, Koblenz-Olper-Str 184-188, 56170 Bendorf, Rhein - T: (02622) 12232. Head:
Science&Tech Museum
Foundry since the 19th c 14641

Stadtmuseum Bendorf im Schloss Sayn → Rheinisches Eisenkunstguss Museum

Benediktbeuern

Historische Fraunhofer-Glashütte, Don-Bosco-Str 1, 83671 Benediktbeuern - T: (08857) 880, Fax: 88376, E-mail: kloster-benediktbeuern@t-online.de, Internet: http://www.kloster-benediktbeuern.de
Science&Tech Museum - 1963
Workroom and glass manufacturing tools of J. von Fraunhofer (1787-1926), glass samples 14642

Benndorf

Mansfelder Bergwerksbahn e.V., Bahnhof Klostermannsfeld, Hauptstr 15, 06308 Benndorf, mail addr: Postfach 1240, 06284 Lutherstadt Eisleben - T: (03475) 648427, Fax: (034772) 27640, E-mail: mansfelder@bergwerksbahn.de, Internet: http://www.bergwerksbahn.de. Head: Thomas Fischer
Science&Tech Museum
Historic steam mine train 14643

Benningen

Museum im Adler, Ludwigsburger Str 9, 71726 Benningen - T: (07144) 13329, 12508, Fax: 13329, E-mail: musiad1@aol.com. Head: I. Rietzke
Folklore Museum / Archaeological Museum - 1989
Peasant life and traditions, Roman ceramics 14644

Bensheim

Museum der Stadt Bensheim, Marktpl 13, 64625 Bensheim - T: (06251) 103801, Fax: 103802, E-mail: info@bensheim.de, Internet: http://www.bensheim.de. Head: Manfred Berg
Local Museum - 1909
19th c everyday life, town hist, Baroque and Rococo furniture, early and pre-history, agricultural implements, viticulture, geology 14645

Benz

Kunst-Kabinett Usedom, Kirchstr 14a, 17429 Benz - T: (038379) 20184
Public Gallery 14646

Beratzhausen

Heimatmuseum Beratzhausen, Bischof-Weig-Str 49, 93176 Beratzhausen
Local Museum 14647

Berching

Heimatmuseum Berching mit Ritter-v.-Gluck-Archiv, An der Johannesbrücke 2, 92334 Berching - T: (08462) 952790, Fax: 20590, E-mail: info@berching.de, Internet: http://www.berching.de
Local Museum / Library with Exhibitions - 1979
Country style wardrobes 14648

Berchtesgaden

Dokumentation Obersalzberg - Orts- und Zeitgeschichte, Salzbergstr 41, 83471 Berchtesgaden - T: (08652) 947960, Fax: 947969, E-mail: info@obersalzberg.de, Internet: http://www.obersalzberg.de
Historical Museum
History of Obergalzberg and the NS-dictatorship 14649

Heimatmuseum Schloß Adelsheim, Schroffenbergallee 6, 83471 Berchtesgaden - T: (08652) 4410, Fax: 948660. Head: Bärbel Sigl
Local Museum - 1907
Folk art of the Berchtesgaden area, including costumes, furniture and sculptures, splint boxes, filigree turnery, bone turnery, straw inlaid work, wood toy 14650

Nationalparkhaus, Franziskanerpl 7, 83471 Berchtesgaden - T: (08652) 64343, Fax: 69434, E-mail: poststelle@nationalpark-berchtesgaden.de, Internet: http://www.nationalpark-berchtesgaden.de. Head: Hubert Zierl
Natural History Museum 14651

Salzbergwerk mit Salzmuseum, Bergwerkstr 83, 83471 Berchtesgaden - T: (08652) 600213, Fax: 600260, E-mail: info@suedsalz.de, Internet: http://www.salzbergwerk.berchtesgaden.de. Head: Elisabeth Hiltermann
Science&Tech Museum - 1840
Displays of ancient salt routes and salt mining towns, history of salt trade and industry, geology, miners life and traditions 14652

Schloßmuseum und Königliches Schloss, Schlosspl 2, 83471 Berchtesgaden - T: (08652) 947980, Fax: 9479812, E-mail: bgd.waf@t-online.de, Internet: http://www.haus-bayern.com. Head: Guido Burkhardt
Decorative Arts Museum - 1923
Furniture, tapestries, porcelain, glass and weapons 14653

Berge bei Quakenbrück

Museum Stift Börstel, 49626 Berge bei Quakenbrück - T: (05435) 898, 822, Fax: 955378
Religious Arts Museum 14654

Bergen, Chiemgau

Maxhütten-Museum, Maxhüttenstr 10, 83346 Bergen, Chiemgau - T: (08662) 48850, 8255, Fax: 488511
Science&Tech Museum - 2000 14655

Museum Blauer Anger, Hochfellnstr 42, 83346 Bergen, Chiemgau - T: (08662) 3209, Fax: 488511
Local Museum
Local hist, rustic culture and costumes 14656

Bergen, Kreis Celle

Afrika-Museum, Buhrnstr 9, Sülze, 29303 Bergen, Kreis Celle - T: (05054) 604. Head: Ulrich Lotze
Ethnology Museum - 1966 14657

Heimatmuseum Römstedthaus, Am Friedenspl 7, 29303 Bergen, Kreis Celle - T: (05051) 6612, Fax: 47936, E-mail: Hans-Hermann.Schmitz@bergen-online.de
Local Museum - 1913
Archaeology, agricultural and trade implements, furniture, beekeeping 14658

Bergheim, Erft

Informationszentrum Schloß Paffendorf, Rheinbraun AG, Burggasse, 50126 Bergheim, Erft - T: (02271) 75120043
Science&Tech Museum - 1967
History of brown coal mining 14659

Bergisch Gladbach

Bergisches Museum für Bergbau, Handwerk und Gewerbe, Burggraben 9-21, 51429 Bergisch Gladbach - T: (02204) 55559, Fax: (02202) 142340. Head: Dr. Wolfgang Vomm
Science&Tech Museum - 1928 14660

Krypta 182, Kunstverein Bergisch Gladbach, Hauptstr 182, 51465 Bergisch Gladbach - T: (02202) 52319, Fax: 52319, E-mail: g.kraemer@krypta182.de, Internet: http://www.krypta182.de. Head: Gerd Krämer
Public Gallery 14661

Papiergeschichtliche Sammlung, Stiftung Zanders, Hauptstr 267, 51465 Bergisch Gladbach - T: (02202) 152060, Fax: 31794, E-mail: info@stiftung-sanders.de, Internet: http://www.stiftung-zanders.de. Head:
Special Museum - 1977
History of paper production, coll of watermarks 14662

Rheinisches Industriemuseum Bergisch Gladbach, Papiermühle Alte Dombach, Kürtener Str, 51465 Bergisch Gladbach - T: (02202) 9366823, Fax: 9366821, E-mail: s.herz@lvr.mail.de, Internet: http://www.lvr.de. Head: Dr. Sabine Schachtner
Historical Museum - 1987 14663

Schulmuseum Bergisch Gladbach, Kempener Str 187, 51467 Bergisch Gladbach - T: (02202) 84247
Special Museum - 2000
School hist 14664

Städtische Galerie Villa Zanders, Konrad-Adenauer-Pl 8, 51465 Bergisch Gladbach - T: (02202) 142334, Fax: 142340. Head: Dr. Wolfgang Vomm
Fine Arts Museum - 1974
Works on and with paper 14665

Bergkamen

Stadtmuseum Bergkamen, Jahnstr 31, Museumspl, 59192 Bergkamen - T: (02306) 8676, Fax: 84701, E-mail: stadtmuseum@helimail.de, Internet: http://beam.to/stadtmuseum. Head: Barbara Strobel
Local Museum / Archaeological Museum - 1965
Roman and Germanic archeology (Roman camp Oberaden), housing, local hist 14666

Städtische Galerie sohle 1, Stadtmuseum Bergkamen, Jahnstr 31, Museumspl, 59192 Bergkamen - T: (02307) 965460, Fax: (02306) 84701, E-mail: info@bergkamen.de, Internet: http://www.bergkamen.de. Head: Tanja Muschwitz
Fine Arts Museum
Contemporary art, East European and Turkish artists, prints 14667

Berkatal

Heimatmuseum Berkatal, Berkastr 54, 37297 Berkatal - T: (05657) 98910, Fax: 989121
Local Museum
Ceramic dishes, bottles, jars, pots and baking tins, implements for flax and wool manufacture, for agriculture and wood production 14668

Berkenbrück bei Fürstenwalde

Hans-Fallada-Gedenkstätte, Am Roten Krug 12, 15518 Berkenbrück bei Fürstenwalde - T: (033634) 281
Special Museum 14669

Berlin

Abgußsammlung antiker Plastik, Schloßstr 69b, 14059 Berlin - T: (030) 83853712, 3424054, Fax: 83856578, E-mail: stemmerk@zedat.fu-berlin.de, Internet: http://www.fu-berlin.de/klassarch. Head: Dr. Klaus Stemmer
Archaeological Museum / Fine Arts Museum / Museum of Classical Antiquities / University Museum - 1695/1988
Plaster Casts of Ancient Sculptures 14670

Ägyptisches Museum und Papyrussammlung, Staatliche Museen zu Berlin - Preußischer Kulturbesitz, Schloßstr 70, 14059 Berlin - T: (030) 34357311, Fax: 34357312, E-mail: aemp@smb.spk-berlin.de, Internet: http://www.smb.spk-berlin.de/amp. Head: Prof. Dr. Dietrich Wildung
Archaeological Museum - 1823
Egyptian art and culture, papyrology 14671

Akademie der Künste, Hanseatenweg 10, 10557 Berlin - T: (030) 390760, Fax: 39076175, E-mail: info@adk.de, Internet: http://www.adk.de. Head: György Konrád, Matthias Flügge
Public Gallery / Library with Exhibitions
Bildende Kunst, Baukunst, Musik, Literatur, Darst.Kunst, Film- und Medienkunst 14672

Akademie der Künste, Kunstsammlung der Stiftung Archiv, Luisenstr 60, 10117 Berlin - T: (030) 28538532, Fax: 28538533, E-mail: kunstsammlung@adk.de, Internet: http://www.adk.de. Head: Dr. Wolfgang Trautwein, Gudrun Schmidt
Fine Arts Museum 14673

Alliierten-Museum Berlin, Clayallee 135, 14195 Berlin - T: (030) 8181990, Fax: 81819991, E-mail: info@alliiertenmuseum.de, Internet: http://www.alliiertenmuseum.de. Head: Dr. Helmut Trotnow
Historical Museum - 1994 14674

Alte Nationalgalerie, Staatliche Museen zu Berlin - Preußischer Kulturbesitz, Bodestr 1-3, 10178 Berlin - T: (030) 20905801, Fax: 20905802, Internet: http://www.smb.spk-berlin.de. Head: Prof. Dr. Peter-Klaus Schuster
Fine Arts Museum 14675

Altes Postfuhramt Berlin → Ehemaliges Postfuhramt

Anti-Kriegs-Museum, Brüsseler Str 21, 13353 Berlin - T: (030) 45490110, Fax: 41729868, E-mail: Anti-Kriegs-Museum@gmx.de, Internet: http://www.anti-kriegs-museum.de. Head: Tommy Spree
Historical Museum 14676

Antikensammlung, Staatliche Museen zu Berlin - Preußischer Kulturbesitz, Bodestr 1-3, 10178 Berlin - T: (030) 20905201, Fax: 20905202, E-mail: ant@smb.spk-berlin.de, Internet: http://www.smb.spk-berlin.de. Head: Prof. Dr. Wolf-Dieter Heilmeyer
Museum of Classical Antiquities / Archaeological Museum / Special Museum - 1830
Greek and Roman architecture, sculpture, vases, bronzes, treasures 14677

Artothek der Zentral- und Landesbibliothek Berlin, c/o Amerika-Gedenkbibliothek, Blücherpl 1, 10961 Berlin - T: (030) 90226104, Fax: 90226262, E-mail: artothek@zlb.de, Internet: http://www.zlb.de/bibliothek/fachbereiche/artothek.htm. Head: Christian Wollert
Public Gallery
Contemporary art since 1945 14678

Bauhaus-Archiv, Museum für Gestaltung, Klingelhöferstr 14, 10785 Berlin - T: (030) 2540020, Fax: 25400210, E-mail: bauhaus@bauhaus.de, Internet: http://www.bauhaus.de. Head: Dr. Peter Hahn
Fine Arts Museum - 1960
Architectural sketches and models by Walter Gropius, Ludwig Mies van der Rohe, Georg Muche, Ludwig Hilberseimer, drawings and paintings by H. Beyer, Lyonel Feininger, Wassily Kandinsky, Paul Klee, furniture, ceramics, metal work and weaving, photography 14679

Berliner Kinomuseum, Großbeerenstr 57, 10965 Berlin. Head: Max Cichocki
Performing Arts Museum 14680

Berliner Medizinhistorisches Museum der Charité, Schumannstr 20-21, 10117 Berlin - T: (030) 450536156/122, Fax: 450536905, E-mail: bmm@charite.de, Internet: http://www.bmm.charite.de. Head: Prof. Dr. Thomas Schalke
Historical Museum / Public Gallery - 1899/1998
Pathology, medical history, Virchow coll, modern art 14681

Berlinische Galerie, Landesmuseum für Moderne Kunst Photographie und Architektur (closed now - during building new home for this museum), Methfesselstr 28-48, 10965 Berlin - T: (030) 78902600/02, Fax: 78902701, E-mail: info@berlinischegalerie.de, Internet: http://www.BerlinischeGalerie.de. Head: Prof. Jörn Merkert
Fine Arts Museum - 1975
Art from 1850 to the present, photogr of the 20's, architecture - Archive 14682

Besucherdienste, Staatliche Museen zu Berlin - Preußischer Kulturbesitz, Stauffenbergstr 41, 10785 Berlin - T: (030) 2662987, Fax: 2662161, E-mail: aussenamt@smb.spk-berlin.de, Internet: http://www.smpk.de. Head: Christoffer Richartz 14683

Bezirksmuseum Marzahn-Hellersdorf, Alt-Marzahn 51, 12685 Berlin - T: (030) 54790921, Fax: 54790920, E-mail: museum.marzahn-hellersdorf@t-online.de, Internet: http://www.marzahn-hellersdorf.de. Head: Dorothee Ifland
Local Museum 14684

Blinden-Museum, c/o Johann-August-Zeune-Schule für Blinde, Rothenburgstr 14, 12165 Berlin - T: (030) 63212390, Fax: 63212013, E-mail: info@blindenschule-berlin.de, Internet: http://www.blindenschule-berlin.de. Head: Uwe Benke
Special Museum - 1891
Exhibits on the development of the Braille script and Braille typewriters, Braille educational material (maps, atlases) - library 14685

Botanisches Museum Berlin-Dahlem, Königin-Luise-Str 6-8, 14191 Berlin - T: (030) 83850100, Fax: 83850186, E-mail: zebgbm@org.bgbm, Internet: http://www.bgbm.org/bgbm. Head: Prof. W. Greuter
Natural History Museum - 1679/1815
Botanical findings from all over the world, hist of systematic botany in Berlin - herbarium, library 14686

Brecht-Haus Weißensee, Kommunale Galerie Weißensee, Berliner Allee 185, 13088 Berlin - T: (030) 9268044, Fax: 9252820. Head: Annette Tietz
Public Gallery 14687

Brecht-Weigel-Gedenkstätte, Chausseestr 125, 10115 Berlin - T: (030) 283057044, Fax: 283057033, E-mail: pfeil@adk.de, Internet: http://www.adk.de. Head: Elke Pfeil
Performing Arts Museum / Special Museum - 1978
Literature and theater 14688

Bröhan-Museum, Landesmuseum für Jugendstil, Art Deco und Funktionalismus (1889-1939), Schloßstr 1a, 14059 Berlin - T: (030) 32690600, Fax: 32690626, E-mail: info@broehan-museum.de, Internet: http://www.broehan-museum.de. Head: Dr. Margrit Bröhan
Decorative Arts Museum - 1983
Art of the turn of the century and the twenties, painting of the Berlin Secessionists, decorative art, Art Nouveau and Art Deco 14689

Brücke Museum, Bussardsteig 9, 14195 Berlin - T: (030) 8312029, Fax: 8315961, E-mail: bruecke-museum@t-online.de, Internet: http://www.bruecke-museum.de. Head: Prof. Magdalena Moeller
Fine Arts Museum - 1967
Drawings, paintings, graphics, sculpture of members of the Brücke Group, bequests of Karl Schmidt-Rottluff and Erich Heckel 14690

Bürgerhaus Grünau, Kommunale Galerie Treptow-Köpenick, Regattastr 141, 12527 Berlin - T: (030) 6744371, Fax: 67821794, E-mail: -buergerhausgruenau@freenet.de. Head: Constanze Albrecht
Public Gallery 14691

Büro Friedrich, Holzmarktstr 15-18, S-Bahnbogen 49, 10179 Berlin - T: (030) 20165115, Fax: 20166118, E-mail: office@buerofriedrich.org, Internet: http://www.buerofriedrich.org. Head: Waling Boers
Public Gallery
Contemporary art 14692

daadgalerie, Kurfürstenstr 58, 10785 Berlin - T: (030) 2613640, Fax: 2041267, E-mail: seitz.berlin@daad.de. Head: Dr. Friedrich Meschede
Public Gallery 14693

DaimlerChrysler Contemporary, Alte Potsdamer Str 5, 10785 Berlin - T: (030) 25941420, Fax: 25941429, E-mail: kunst.sammlung@daimlerchrysler.com, Internet: http://www.sammlung.daimlerchrysler.com. Head: Dr. Renate Wiehager
Public Gallery 14694

Deutsche Guggenheim Berlin, Unter den Linden 13-15, 10117 Berlin - T: (030) 2020930, Fax: 20209320, E-mail: berlin.guggenheim@db.com, Internet: http://www.deutsche-guggenheim-berlin.de. Head: Svenja Simon
Fine Arts Museum - 1997 14695

Deutsche Mediathek im Filmhaus, Potsdamer Str 2, 10785 Berlin - T: (030) 25751133/34, Fax: 25751132, E-mail: info@deutsche-mediathek.de, Internet: http://www.deutsche-mediathek.de
Special Museum 14696

Deutsches Historisches Museum (only administration, exhibition closed until 2004), Unter den Linden 2, 10117 Berlin - T: (030) 203040, Fax: 20304543, E-mail: webadmin@dhm.de, Internet: http://www.dhm.de. Head: Dr. Hans Ottomeyer
Historical Museum - 1987
library 14697

Deutsches Historisches Museum im Kronprinzenpalais (until April 2003, from May 2003 new: Pei-Bau, Hinter dem Gießhaus 3), Unter den Linden 3, 10117 Berlin - T: (030) 203040, Fax: 20304543, E-mail: webadmin@dhm.de, Internet: http://www.dhm.de. Head: Dr. Hans Ottomeyer
Historical Museum - 1987
library 14698

Deutsches Technikmuseum Berlin, Trebbiner Str 9, 10963 Berlin - T: (030) 254840, Fax: 25484175, Internet: http://www.dtmb.de. Head: Dr. Lieselotte Kugler
Science&Tech Museum - 1982
Historical development of transportation, street and rail, navigation, aviation, automobile coll, typewriter and computer coll, standardization, phonographs, telecommunication, textile work, scientific

instruments, stereo photography, wind- and watermills, power engineering, manufacturing technics, science center "SPECTRUM" - scientific archives 14699

DOMizil im Berliner Dom, Am Lustgarten, Spreeseite, 10178 Berlin - T: (030) 20269114, Fax: 20269115, E-mail: berlin@kunstdienst.de
Public Gallery 14700

Ehemaliges Postfuhramt, Tucholskystr 19-27, 10117 Berlin - T: (030) 4858899, Fax: 4858899
Public Gallery 14701

Erotik-Museum, Joachimstaler Str 4, 10623 Berlin - T: (030) 8860666, Fax: 8860646
Special Museum - 1989
Shunga, bronces 14702

Ethnologisches Museum, Staatliche Museen zu Berlin - Preußischer Kulturbesitz, Lansstr 8, 14195 Berlin - T: (030) 83010, 8301438 (Information), Fax: 8301506, E-mail: mv@smb.spk-berlin.de, Internet: http://www.smb.spk-berlin.de. Head: Dr. Viola König
Ethnology Museum - 1873
Div: folk art from South Sea, American archeology, American Indian tribes, West Asia, South Asia, East Asia, non- German Europe, music ethnology, junior and Braille museum - library, workshop, photo laboratory, auditorium 14703

Filmmuseum Berlin - Deutsche Kinemathek, Stiftung Deutsche Kinemathek, Potsdamer Str 2, 10785 Berlin - T: (030) 3009030, Fax: 30090313, E-mail: info@filmmuseum-berlin.de, Internet: http://www.filmmuseum-berlin.de. Head: Hans Helmut Prinzler
Special Museum - 2000 14704

FlurGalerie, Kommunale Galerie Köpenick, Freiheit 15, 12555 Berlin - T: (030) 65844396, Fax: 65844388
Public Gallery 14705

Forschungs- und Gedenkstätte Normannenstrasse - Stasi Museum, Ruschestr 103, Haus 1, 10365 Berlin - T: (030) 5536854, Fax: 5536853, E-mail: mfsmuseum@aol.com, Internet: http://www.stasimuseum.de. Head: Jörg Drieselmann
Historical Museum 14706

Fotogalerie, Helsingforser Pl 1, 10243 Berlin - T: (030) 2961684, Fax: 2961684
Public Gallery 14707

Freilichtmuseum Domäne Dahlem, Stiftung Stadtmuseum Berlin, Königin-Luise-Str 49, 14195 Berlin - T: (030) 8325000, Fax: 8316382, E-mail: kontakt@domaene-dahlem.de, Internet: http://www.domaene-dahlem.de. Head: Dr. Peter Lummel
Agriculture Museum / Open Air Museum - 1976
Agriculture, apiculture, children's toys, food 14708

Freimaurer-Museum, Emser Str 12-13, 10719 Berlin - T: (030) 3735901. Head: Herbert Klemstein
Historical Museum 14709

Galerie 100, Konrad-Wolf-Str 99, 13055 Berlin - T: (030) 9711103
Public Gallery 14710

Galerie am Prater, Kastanienallee 100, 10435 Berlin - T: (030) 4484549, Fax: 42402514
Public Gallery 14711

Galerie Arcus, Kommunale Galerie Hohenschönhausen, Warnitzer Str 18, 13057 Berlin - T: (030) 9281006, Fax: 9281006. Head: Soult
Public Gallery 14712

Galerie Bezirksamt Mitte, Singerstr 1, 10179 Berlin - T: (030) 2493390
Public Gallery 14713

Galerie Grünstraße, Grünstr 16, 12555 Berlin - T: (030) 6557201, 650156009, Fax: 6557201, E-mail: galerie-gruenstrasse@t-online.de, Internet: http://galerie-gruenstrasse.bei.t-online.de. Head: Kornelia Münch-Severin
Public Gallery 14714

Galerie im Einstein, Unter den Linden 42, 10117 Berlin - T: (030) 2043632, Fax: 2043635, E-mail: g.uhlig.newscafe@t-online.de
Public Gallery 14715

Galerie im Fontanehaus, Wilhelmsruher Damm 142c, 13439 Berlin - T: (030) 4166099, Fax: 41924715. Head: Michael Bitomsky
Public Gallery 14716

Galerie im Gemeinschaftshaus, Bat-Yam-Pl 1, 12353 Berlin - T: (030) 68091413, Fax: 68091420, E-mail: gemeinschftshaus.gropinstadt@ba-nkn.verwalt-berlin.de, Internet: http://www.kultur-neukoelln.de
Public Gallery 14717

Galerie im Körnerpark, Kommunale Galerie Neukölln, Schierker Str 8, 12051 Berlin - T: (030) 68092876, Fax: 68093775
Public Gallery 14718

Galerie im Körnerpark, Kommunale Galerie Neukölln, Karl-Marx-Str 141, 12043 Berlin - T: (030) 68093772, Fax: 68093775, E-mail: karin.grunz@ba-nku.verwalt-berlin.de. Head: Karin Grunz
Public Gallery 14719

Galerie im Kulturhaus Spandau, Mauerstr 6, 13597 Berlin - T: (030) 3334022, Fax: 3338514, Internet: http://www.kulturhaus-spandau.de
Public Gallery
Paintings 14720

Galerie im Parkhaus, Puschkinallee 5, 12435 Berlin - T: (030) 5337952, Fax: 5337953
Public Gallery 14721

Galerie im Rathaus Köpenick, Alt Köpenick 21, 12555 Berlin - T: (030) 6557201, Fax: 6557201
Public Gallery 14722

Galerie im Saalbau → Galerie im Körnerpark

Galerie im Turm, Frankfurter Tor, 10243 Berlin - T: (030) 4229426, Fax: 2960366
Public Gallery 14723

Galerie im Willy-Brandt-Haus, Stresemannstr 28, 10963 Berlin - T: (030) 25993785, Fax: 25993788, E-mail: Freundeskreis-WBH@t-online.de
Public Gallery 14724

Galerie in der Alten Schule, Kommunale Galerie Treptow, Dörpfeldstr 56, 12489 Berlin - T: (030) 67776811, Fax: 67776812, E-mail: galerie@kmza.de, Internet: http://www.kmza.de. Head: F. Stein
Public Gallery 14725

Galerie K & S, Linienstr 156-157, 10115 Berlin - T: (030) 28385096, Fax: 28385098, E-mail: k.s.@p-soft.de, Internet: http://www.art-exchange-berlin.de/ks. Head: Miriam Bers
Public Gallery
Contemporary art 14726

Galerie M, Marzahner Promenade 13, 12679 Berlin - T: (030) 5450294, Fax: 9311060, Internet: http://www.berlin.de/marzahn-hellersdorf. Head: Dr. Gunter Nimmich
Public Gallery 14727

Galerie Parterre, Kommunale Galerie Prenzlauer Berg, Danziger Str 101, 10405 Berlin - T: (030) 42401084, 42401267, Fax: 42402514, E-mail: info@kulturamt.prenzlberg.de, Internet: http://www.kulturamt.prenzlberg.de/programm/parterre.htm. Head: Kathleen Krenzlin
Public Gallery
Graphics, esp by Berlin artists, and works on paper 14728

Gedenkstätte Deutscher Widerstand, Stauffenbergstr 13-14, 10785 Berlin - T: (030) 26995000, Fax: 26995010, E-mail: info@gdw-berlin.de, Internet: http://www.gdw-berlin.de. Head: Dr. Johannes Tuchel
Historical Museum / Historic Site 14729

Gedenkstätte Plötzensee für die Opfer des Nationalsozialismus, Hüttigpfad, 13627 Berlin - T: (030) 3443226, 26995000, Fax: 26995010, E-mail: info@gdw-berlin.de, Internet: http://www.gdw-berlin.de. Head: Dr. Johannes Tuchel
Historic Site - 1952
Memorial centre to the victims of Hitler's dictatorship during the years 1933-45, former executions place 14730

Gemäldegalerie, Staatliche Museen zu Berlin - Preußischer Kulturbesitz, Kulturforum im Tiergarten, Matthäikirchpl, 10785 Berlin - T: (030) 2662101, Fax: 2662103, E-mail: gg@smb.spk-berlin.de, Internet: http://www.smb.spk-berlin.de. Head: Prof. Dr. Jan Kelch
Fine Arts Museum - 1830
Italian, Spanish, English, Dutch, Flemish, French and German paintings (13th-18th c), miniatures, photo coll 14731

Georg-Kolbe-Museum, Sensburger Allee 25, 14055 Berlin - T: (030) 3042144, Fax: 3047041, E-mail: Kolbe.Museum@t-online.de, Internet: http://www.georg-kolbe-museum.de. Head: Dr. Ursel Berger
Fine Arts Museum - 1950
Drawing, graphics and sculpture of Georg Kolbe, Impressionist and Expressionist works from the estate of Kolbe, 20th c sculpture from Berlin - Kolbe archives 14732

Gipsformerei, Staatliche Museen zu Berlin - Preußischer Kulturbesitz, Sophie-Charlotten-Str 17-18, 14059 Berlin - T: (030) 3267690, Fax: 32676912, Internet: http://www.smb.spk-berlin.de. Head: Axel Möller
Special Museum - 1819
6600 plaster casts 14733

Gotisches Haus, Breite Str 32, 13597 Berlin - T: (030) 3339388
Public Gallery 14734

Graphothek Berlin, Buddestr 21, 13507 Berlin - T: (030) 41778018, Fax: 41778019. Head: N.N.
Library with Exhibitions 14735

Grünauer Wassersportmuseum, Stiftung Stadtmuseum Berlin, Regattastr 191, 12527 Berlin - T: (030) 6744002, Fax: 6744687, E-mail: wassersportmuseum@gmx.de, Internet: http://www.stadtmuseum.de. Head: Werner Philipp
Special Museum - 1990 14736

Gutshaus Steglitz, Schloßstr 48, 12165 Berlin - T: (030) 63213924, Fax: 63213382, E-mail: presse@ba-steglitz.verwalt-berlin.de, Internet: http://www.steglitz-zehlendorf.de
Public Gallery 14737

Hamburger Bahnhof - Museum für Gegenwart Berlin, Staatliche Museen zu Berlin - Preußischer Kulturbesitz, Invalidenstr 50-51, 10557 Berlin - T: (030) 3978340, Fax: 39783413, E-mail: hbf@smb.spk-berlin.de, Internet: http://www.smb.spk-berlin.de. Head: Prof. Dr. Peter-Klaus Schuster
Fine Arts Museum - 1996
Coll Erich Marx; painting, sculpture, video since 1960: works by Beuys, Warhol, Rauschenberg, Twombly, Kiefer, Long, Merz - Medienarchiv Joseph Beuys 14738

Handwerksmuseum und Friseurmuseum, Stiftung Stadtmuseum Berlin, Alt-Marzahn 31, 12685 Berlin - T: (030) 5410231, Fax: 5436900, E-mail: info@stadtmuseum.de, Internet: http://www.stadtmuseum.de. Head: Prof. Reiner Güntzer
Historical Museum - 1988
Craft and hairdresser coll 14739

Hanf-Museum, Mühlendamm 5, 10178 Berlin - T: (030) 2424827, Fax: 24720234, E-mail: hanfmuseum@hanflobby.de, Internet: http://www.hanflobby.de/hanfmuseum
Special Museum - 1994
Hist of hemp growing and its social impact, use of cannabis and different cultures, the (il)legal situation of cannabis in Germany 14740

Haus am Kleistpark, Kunstamt Schöneberg, Grunewaldstr 6-7, 10823 Berlin - T: (030) 75606964, Fax: 75604613
Public Gallery 14741

Haus am Lützowplatz, Lützowpl 9, 10785 Berlin - T: (030) 2613805, 2614303, Fax: 2644713, E-mail: office@hausamluetzowplatz-berlin.de, Internet: http://www.hausamluetzowplatz-berlin.de. Head: Karin Pott
Association with Coll 14742

Haus am Waldsee, Argentinische Allee 30, 14163 Berlin - T: (030) 8018935, 63215234, Fax: 8022028, E-mail: info@hausamwaldsee-berlin.de, Internet: http://www.hausamwaldsee-berlin.de. Head: Barbara Straka
Fine Arts Museum 14743

Haus der Kulturen der Welt, John-Foster-Dulles-Allee 10, 10557 Berlin - T: (030) 397870, Fax: 3948679, E-mail: info@hkw.de, Internet: http://www.hkw.de. Head: Dr. Hans-Georg Knopp
Public Gallery 14744

Heimatmuseum Charlottenburg-Wilmersdorf, Schloßstr 69, 14059 Berlin - T: (030) 902913201, Fax: 9029132017
Local Museum 14745

Heimatmuseum Friedrichshain, Marchlewskistr 6, 10243 Berlin - T: (030) 2496875, Fax: 293479431. Head: Heike Naumann
Local Museum 14746

Heimatmuseum Hohenschönhausen, Lindenweg 7, 13053 Berlin - T: (030) 9827378, Fax: 9827379. Head: Bärbel Ruben
Local Museum 14747

Heimatmuseum Köpenick, Alter Markt 1, 12555 Berlin - T: (030) 65843351, Fax: 65843352, E-mail: info@heimatmuseum-koepenick.de, Internet: http://www.heimatmuseum-koepenick.de. Head: Claus-Dieter Sprink
Local Museum 14748

Heimatmuseum Lichtenberg, Parkaue 4, 10367 Berlin - T: (030) 55042721/22
Local Museum 14749

Heimatmuseum Neukölln, Museum für Stadtkultur und Regionalgeschichte, Ganghoferstr 3-5, 12040 Berlin - T: (030) 68092535, Fax: 68093811, E-mail: museum-neukoelln@ipn.de, Internet: http://www.dhm.de/museen/neukoelln
Local Museum - 1897
Everyday life and culture in Berlin from 1880-1970, hist of reform pedagogics Jewish life and resistance 14750

Heimatmuseum Pankow, Heynstr 8, 13187 Berlin - T: (030) 4814047, Fax: 4814047
Local Museum 14751

Heimatmuseum Reinickendorf, Alt-Hermsdorf 35, 13467 Berlin - T: (030) 4044062, 40009270, Fax: 41778019. Head: Dr. Cornelia Gerner
Local Museum - 1980
Local hist (literature, photos) - archive 14752

Heimatmuseum Tempelhof, Alt-Mariendorf 43, 12107 Berlin - T: (030) 75607465, Fax: 75607415
Local Museum - 1962
Local history 14753

Heimatmuseum Tiergarten, Zwinglistr 2, 10555 Berlin - T: (030) 39052728, Fax: 39053457. Head: Bernd Hildebrandt
Local Museum 14754

Heimatmuseum Treptow, Sterndamm 102, 12487 Berlin - T: (030) 53315629, Fax: 53315630, Internet: http://www.heimatmuseum-treptow.de. Head: Barbara Zibler
Local Museum 14755

Heimatmuseum und Archiv des Heimatvereins für den Bezirk Steglitz, Drakestr 64a, 12205 Berlin - T: (030) 8332109, Fax: 84306309. Head: Wolfgang Holtz
Local Museum 14756

Heimatmuseum Wedding, Pankstr 47, 13357 Berlin - T: (030) 45754158, Fax: 45754159. Head: Gabriele Lang
Local Museum
Archives, library 14757

Heimatmuseum Zehlendorf, Clayallee 355, 14169 Berlin - T: (030) 8022441, Fax: 80903291, E-mail: heimatverein.zehlendorf@t-online.de, Internet: http://heimatmuseum-zehlendorf.de/. Head: Joachim Scharnowski
Local Museum
archive 14758

Historische Ausstellung "Fragen an die deutsche Geschichte" → Parlamentsausstellung des Deutschen Bundestages "Wege, Irrwege, Umwege"

Historischer Ausstellungsraum im Heizkraftwerk Moabit, c/o Bewag AG, Friedrich Krause Ufer 10-15, 13353 Berlin - T: (030) 26718432, Fax: 26718282, E-mail: huebner.horst@bewag.com, Internet: http://bewag.de
Science&Tech Museum
History of thermal power station 14759

Hugenotten-Museum, Gendarmenmarkt, 10117 Berlin - T: (030) 2291760, Fax: 2041505
Religious Arts Museum
History of reformed church and French Huguenots in Germany, documents 14760

Humboldt-Museum Schloß Tegel, Adelheidallee 19-21, 13507 Berlin - T: (030) 4343156, Fax: 4337017. Head: Ulrich von Heinz
Special Museum / Historic Site - 1824
Residence of Wilhelm von Humboldt, coll of classical art, art of classicism - library, archives incl Humboldt archive 14761

Hundemuseum (closed) 14762

ifa-Galerie Berlin, Institut für Auslandsbeziehungen, Linienstr 139-140, 10115 Berlin - T: (030) 22679616, Fax: 22679618, E-mail: barsch@ifa.de, Internet: http://www.ifa.de. Head: Dr. Barbara Barsch
Public Gallery 14763

Institut für Museumskunde, Staatliche Museen zu Berlin - Preußischer Kulturbesitz, In der Halde 1, 14195 Berlin - T: (030) 8301460, Fax: 8301504, E-mail: ifm@smb.spk-berlin.de, Internet: http://www.smb.spk-berlin.de/ifm. Head: Prof. Dr. Bernhard Graf
Library with Exhibitions 14764

Jüdische Galerie Berlin, Oranienburger Str 31, 10117 Berlin - T: (030) 2828623, Fax: 2828529, E-mail: kontakt@juedische-galerie.de, Internet: http://www.juedische-galerie.de. Head: Dmitri Jurchuk
Public Gallery 14765

Jüdisches Museum Berlin, Lindenstr 9-14, 10969 Berlin - T: (030) 25993300, Fax: 25993409, E-mail: info@jmberlin.de, Internet: http://www.jmberlin.de. Head: Prof. Dr. W. Michael Blumenthal
Historical Museum / Fine Arts Museum - 1999
Geman-Jewish history, culture and art 14766

Jugendmuseum Schöneberg, Hauptstr 40-42, 10827 Berlin - T: (030) 75606163, Fax: 75606329. Head: Petra Zwaka
Local Museum / Historical Museum 14767

JuniorMuseum im Ethnologischen Museum, Staatliche Museen zu Berlin - Preußischer Kulturbesitz, Arnimallee 23, 14195 Berlin - T: (030) 8301255, 8301455, Fax: 8301506, E-mail: md@smb.spk-berlin.de, Internet: http://www.juniormuseum.de
Ethnology Museum 14768

Käthe-Kollwitz-Museum Berlin, Fasanenstr 24, 10719 Berlin - T: (030) 8825210, Fax: 8811901, E-mail: info@kaethe-kollwitz.de, Internet: http://www.kaethe-kollwitz.de. Head: Martin Fritsch
Fine Arts Museum - 1986
Drawings, prints, posters, sculptures 14769

Keramik-Museum Berlin, Neufertstr 6, 14059 Berlin - T: (030) 3212322, Fax: 32102007, E-mail: kmb.keramik-theis@snafu.de, Internet: http://www.keramik-museum-berlin.de. Head: Heinz-Joachim Theis
Decorative Arts Museum - 1990
German Ceramics from the middle of the 19th c to the present - library, archive (museum still in the process of being set up) 14770

Kinder- und Jugendmuseum im Prenzlauer Berg, Senefelder Str 6, 10437 Berlin - T: (030) 74778200, Fax: 74778205, E-mail: ki.jumus.pb@museum.b.shuttle.de, Internet: http://www.b.shuttle.de/museum/index.htm. Head: Marie Lorbeer, Karen Hoffmann
Special Museum 14771

Kleine Humboldt-Galerie, Unter den Linden 6, 10117 Berlin - T: (030) 6153031
Public Gallery 14772

Kleine Humboldt-Galerie in der Humboldt-Universität, Unter den Linden 631, 10117 Berlin - T: (030) 20932959, Fax: 20932959
Public Gallery 14773

Kommunale Galerie, Kunstamt Wilmersdorf, Hohenzollerndamm 176, 10713 Berlin - T: (030) 902916700, Fax: 902916705. Head: Udo Christoffel
Public Gallery - 1974 14774

Kreuzberg Museum, Adalbertstr 95A, 10999 Berlin - T: (030) 50585231/33, Fax: 50585258, E-mail: info@kunstamtkreuzberg.de, Internet: http://www.kunstamtkreuzberg.de. Head: Martin Düspohl
Historical Museum 14775

Künstlerhaus Bethanien, Mariannenpl 2, 10997 Berlin - T: (030) 6169030, Fax: 61690330, E-mail: kb@bethanien.de, Internet: http://www.bethanien.de. Head: Christoph Tannert
Fine Arts Museum 14776

Kulturamt Neukölln, Karl-Marx-Str 141, 12043 Berlin - T: (030) 68092431, E-mail: kulturneuk@aol.com. Head: Dr. Dorothea Kolland
Public Gallery 14777

Kulturamt Tiergarten, Turmstr 75, 10551 Berlin - T: (030) 39053452, Fax: 39053457. Head: Dr. Marlise Hoff
Public Gallery 14778

Kunst-Werke Berlin, Auguststr 69, 10117 Berlin - T: (030) 2434590, Fax: 24345999, E-mail: info@kw-berlin.de, Internet: http://www.kw-berlin.de. Head: Judith Becker
Fine Arts Museum
Contemporary art 14779

Kunstamt Tempelhof-Schöneberg, Alt-Mariendorf 43, 12107 Berlin - T: (030) 75607465, Fax: 75607415. Head: Wilfried Postier
Public Gallery 14780

Kunstbank, Galerie der Senatsverwaltung für Wissenschaft, Forschung und Kultur, Brunnenstr 188-190, 10119 Berlin - T: (030) 90228870, Fax: 90228457, E-mail: kunstbank@senwfk.verwalt-berlin.de, Internet: http://www.berlin.de/home/land/senwisskult/kult/kunstbank/kunstbank.html
Public Gallery 14781

Kunstbibliothek, Staatliche Museen zu Berlin - Preußischer Kulturbesitz, Matthäikirchpl 6, 10785 Berlin - T: (030) 2662029, Fax: 2662958, E-mail: kb@smb.spk-berlin.de, Internet: http://www.smb.spk-berlin.de. Head: Prof. Dr. Bernd Evers
Library with Exhibitions - 1867
Graphics on the history of costumes (Lipperheidesche Kostümbibliothek), engraving series on architecture and European handicrafts, illustrated books, artist's books 15th-20th c (Grisebach coll) prints and posters, photography - library 14782

Kunstgewerbemuseum, Staatliche Museen zu Berlin - Preußischer Kulturbesitz, Tiergartenstr 6, 10785 Berlin - T: (030) 2662902, Fax: 2662947, E-mail: kgm@smb.spk-berlin.de, Internet: http://www.smb.spk-berlin.de. Head: Dr. Angela Schönberger
Decorative Arts Museum - 1867
Medieval goldsmith work, silver, faience and porcelain, glass, 16th-19th-c and 20th/21th c furniture, textiles, modern arts and crafts, contemporary design - library, photo laboratory, workshop 14783

Kunstgewerbemuseum im Schloß Köpenick, Staatliche Museen zu Berlin - Preußischer Kulturbesitz (closed until 2002), Schloß Köpenick, 12557 Berlin, mail addr: Tiergartenstr 6, 10785 Berlin. Head: Dr. Angela Schönberger
Decorative Arts Museum 14784

KunstRaum Berlin, Lindower Str 18, 13347 Berlin - T: (030) 4658013, Fax: 4658013, E-mail: office@kunstraum-berlin.de, Internet: http://www.kunsraum-berlin.de. Head: E. Lina Schneider
Public Gallery 14785

Kunstraum Kreuzberg/Bethanien, Mariannenpl 2, 10997 Berlin - T: (030) 25884151, Fax: 25884153, E-mail: mail@kunstamtkreuzberg.de, Internet: http://www.kunstamtkreuzberg.de
Public Gallery 14786

Kunststiftung Poll, Gipsstr 3, 10119 Berlin - T: (030) 28496250, Fax: 28496211, E-mail: kunst@poll-berlin.de, Internet: http://www.poll-berlin.de. Head: Lothar C. Poll
Fine Arts Museum / Public Gallery 14787

Kupferstichkabinett - Sammlung der Zeichnungen und Druckgraphik, Staatliche Museen zu Berlin - Preußischer Kulturbesitz, Matthäikirchpl 4, 10785 Berlin - T: (030) 2662023, 2662002, Fax: 2662959, E-mail: kk@smb.spk-berlin.de, Internet: http://www.smb.spk-berlin.de. Head: Prof. Dr. Alexander Dückers
Fine Arts Museum - 1831
14th-21th c drawings, prints, illuminated manuscripts, illustrated books, topographic coll, collection of wood blocks and copper plates - library, phototheque 14788

Labyrinth Kindermuseum Berlin, Osloer Str 12, 13359 Berlin - T: (030) 49308901, 4945348, Fax: 4948097, E-mail: kontakt@labyrinth-kindermuseum.de, Internet: http://www.kindermuseum-labyrinth.de. Head: R. von der Goltz, S. Lembke, K. Tobis
Special Museum 14789

Lapidarium, Berlinische Galerie, Hallesches Ufer 78, 10963 Berlin - T: (030) 43095333, Fax: 43095338, E-mail: BerlinischeGalerie@t-online.de, Internet: http://www.BerlinischeGalerie.de
Public Gallery 14790

Luftwaffenmuseum der Bundeswehr, Kladower Damm 182, 14089 Berlin - T: (030) 36872601/04, Fax: 36872610, E-mail: LwMuseumBw@snafu.de. Head: Dr. Harald Potempa
Military Museum 14791

Märkisches Museum, Stiftung Stadtmuseum Berlin, Am Köllnischen Park 5, 10179 Berlin - T: (030) 308660, 30866249, Fax: 24002150, E-mail: info@stadtmuseum.de, Internet: http://www.stadtmuseum.de. Head: Prof. Reiner Güntzer
Historical Museum - 1874
Pre- and early history, local history, religious sculpture, numismatics, memorabilia of Theodor Fontane, Gerhart Hauptmann and Heinrich Zille 14792

Martin-Gropius-Bau, Niederkirchnerstr 7, 10963 Berlin - T: (030) 254860, Fax: 25486107, E-mail: post@gropiusbau.berlinerfestspiele.de, Internet: http://www.gropiusbau.de. Head: Gereon Sievernich
Fine Arts Museum / Local Museum - 1973 14793

Mauermuseum, Haus am Checkpoint Charlie, Friedrichstr 43-45, 10969 Berlin - T: (030) 2537250, Fax: 2512075, E-mail: info@mauer-museum.com, Internet: http://museum-haus-am.checkpointcharlie.org. Head: Dr. Rainer Hildebrandt
Historical Museum - 1963
Hist of the Berlin Wall, fight for human rights, Wolf Vostell, Hanah Höch, Keith Haring, Max Bill - archive, publishing house, film studio 14794

Mies van der Rohe Haus, Oberseestr 60, 13053 Berlin - T: (030) 9824192
Fine Arts Museum
Architectural monument 14795

Münzkabinett, Staatliche Museen zu Berlin - Preußischer Kulturbesitz (closed until 2004), Bodestr 1-3, 10178 Berlin - T: (030) 20905701, Fax: 20905702, E-mail: mk@smb.spk-berlin.de, Internet: http://www.smb.spk-berlin.de. Head: Prof. Dr. Bernd Kluge
Decorative Arts Museum - 1868
Coins from modern to ancient times (since 6th c BC), 16th-19th c medals, seals, photo coll, literature 14796

Museum Berlin-Karlshorst, Zwieseler Str 4, 10318 Berlin - T: (030) 50150810, Fax: 50150840, E-mail: kontakt@museum-karlshorst.de, Internet: http://www.museum-karlshorst.de. Head: Dr. Peter Jahn
Historical Museum
German-Soviet relations 1917-1990, the war against the Soviet Union 14797

Museum Berliner Arbeiterleben (closed) 14798

Museum Blindenwerkstatt Otto Weidt, Jüdisches Museum Berlin, Rosenthaler Str 39, 10178 Berlin - T: (030) 28599407, Fax: 25762614, E-mail: ausstellung@blindes-vertrauen.de, Internet: http://www.blindes-vertrauen.de
Historical Museum - 2001
Shelter of blind Jewish worker (1941-1943) 14799

Museum der Dinge-Werkbundarchiv, Niederkirchnerstr 7, 10963 Berlin - T: (030) 25486900, Fax: 25486901, E-mail: ifo@museumderdinge.de, Internet: http://www.museumderdinge.de. Head: Anna Maigler
Decorative Arts Museum - 1973
Hist of the "Werkbund", 20th c everyday culture 14800

Museum Ephraim-Palais, Stiftung Stadtmuseum Berlin, Poststr 16, 10178 Berlin - T: (030) 24002121, Fax: 24002187, E-mail: info@stadtmuseum.de, Internet: http://www.stadtmuseum.de. Head: Prof. Reiner Güntzer
Fine Arts Museum / Historical Museum 14801

Museum Europäischer Kulturen, Staatliche Museen zu Berlin - Preußischer Kulturbesitz, Im Winkel 6-8, 14195 Berlin - T: (030) 8390101, Fax: 83901283, E-mail: mek@smb-berlin.de, Internet: http://www.smb.spk-berlin.de. Head: Prof. Dr. Konrad Vanja
Folklore Museum - 1889
Comparative European material goods of middle and lower social levels, popular prints, posters, traditional and modern costumes, reading materials, textiles, furniture, glass, ceramics, tools, amateur paintings, devotional items - library, workshop 14802

Museum für Indische Kunst, Staatliche Museen zu Berlin - Preußischer Kulturbesitz, Lansstr 8, 14195 Berlin - T: (030) 8301361/62, Fax: 8301502, E-mail: mik@smb.spk-berlin.de, Internet: http://www.smb.spk-berlin.de. Head: Prof. Dr. Marianne Yaldiz
Fine Arts Museum - 1963
Indian art, sculpture, arts and crafts, miniatures, bronzes; paintings sculpture, bronzes, painting from Tibet and Nepal, brick reliefs from Southeast Asia, wallpaintings clay sculptures, bronzes and manuscripts from Central Asia - library, study coll, archives 14803

Museum für Islamische Kunst, Staatliche Museen zu Berlin - Preußischer Kulturbesitz, Bodestr 1-3, 10178 Berlin - T: (030) 20905401, Fax: 20905402, E-mail: isl@smb.spk-berlin.de, Internet: http://www.smb.spk-berlin.de/isl. Head: Prof. Dr. Claus-Peter Haase
Fine Arts Museum - 1904
Islamic art and handicrafts from all epochs incl metalwork, ivory, ceramics, glass, faience, rugs, miniatures and Koran manuscripts 14804

Museum für Kommunikation Berlin, Leipziger Str 16, 10117 Berlin - T: (030) 202940, Fax: 20294111, E-mail: mkb.berlin@t-online.de, Internet: http://www.museumsstiftung.de. Head: Dr. Joachim Kallinich
Science&Tech Museum - 1872
History and development of post, telephone and telegraph, archives, philatelic coll - library 14805

Museum für Naturkunde der Humboldt-Universität zu Berlin, Invalidenstr 43, 10115 Berlin - T: (030) 20938591, Fax: 20938814, E-mail: gesine.steiner@rz.hu-berlin.de, Internet: http://www.museum.hu-berlin.de. Head: Prof. Dr. H.-P. Schultze
Natural History Museum - 1810
Mineralogy, palaeontology, zoology 14806

Museum für Ostasiatische Kunst, Staatliche Museen zu Berlin - Preußischer Kulturbesitz, Lansstr 8, 14195 Berlin - T: (030) 8301381, Fax: 8301501, E-mail: oak@smb.spk-berlin.de, Internet: http://www.smb.spk-berlin.de. Head: Prof. Dr. Willibald Veit
Fine Arts Museum / Decorative Arts Museum - 1906
Fine arts from China, Korea, and Japan including painting, woodcuts, ceramics, lacquer items, statuettes, bronze articles, study coll, archives 14807

Museum für Verkehr und Technik, Trebbiner Str 9, 10963 Berlin - T: (030) 254840
Science&Tech Museum 14808

Museum für Vor- und Frühgeschichte, Staatliche Museen zu Berlin - Preußischer Kulturbesitz, Schloß Charlottenburg, Langhansbau, 14059 Berlin - T: (030) 32674811, Fax: 32674812, E-mail: mvf@smb.spk-berlin.de, Internet: http://www.smb.spk-berlin.de. Head: Prof. Dr. Wilfried Menghin
Archaeological Museum - 1829
Late Stone Age, early Stone Age, Bronze Age, Iron Age to the early Middle Ages, Near Eastern archeology - library 14809

Museum Galgenhaus, Stiftung Stadtmuseum Berlin, Brüderstr 10, 10178 Berlin - T: (030) 2011208, Fax: 2011367, E-mail: info@stadtmuseum.de, Internet: http://www.stadtmuseum.de. Head: Prof. Reiner Gützner
Historical Museum 14810

Museum im Wasserwerk, Berliner Wasserbetriebe, Müggelseedamm 307, 12587 Berlin - T: (030) 86447695, Fax: 86447746, E-mail: museum@bwb.de, Internet: http://www.bwb.de. Head: Jelena Butter
Science&Tech Museum / Historical Museum - 1987
Documentation on water production, processing of drinking water, sewage purification, social hist and hygiene of Berlin - historical archive 14811

Museum Kindheit und Jugend, Stiftung Stadtmuseum Berlin, Wallstr 32, 10179 Berlin - T: (030) 2750383, Fax: 2792979, E-mail: mukiju@web.de, Internet: http://www.berlin-kindheitundjugend.de. Head: Dr. Martina Weinland
Historical Museum 14812

Museum Knoblauchhaus, Stiftung Stadtmuseum Berlin, Poststr 23, 10178 Berlin - T: (030) 24002171, Fax: 24002187, E-mail: info@stadtmuseum.de, Internet: http://www.stadtmuseum.de. Head: Prof. Reiner Güntzer
Local Museum
Biedermeier interior, hist of the family Knoblauch 14813

Museum Nicolaihaus, Stiftung Stadtmuseum Berlin, Brüderstr 13, 10178 Berlin - T: (030) 20458164, Fax: 24002187, E-mail: info@stadtmuseum.de, Internet: http://www.stadtmuseum.de. Head: Prof. Reiner Gützner
Historical Museum 14814

Museum Nikolaikirche, Stiftung Stadtmuseum Berlin, Nikolaikirchpl, 10178 Berlin - T: (030) 24002182, Fax: 24002187, E-mail: info@stadtmuseum.de, Internet: http://www.stadtmuseum.de. Head: Prof. Reiner Güntzer
Local Museum / Religious Arts Museum / Music Museum
Local history, history of the church, sacred music 14815

Museum Plagiarius, Kulturbrauerei 4.3W, Schönhauser Allee 37, 10435 Berlin - T: (030) 53212944, Internet: http://www.plagiarius.com. Head: Christel Kluge
Special Museum
Copies of industrial design 14816

Museumsdorf Düppel, Stiftung Stadtmuseum Berlin, Clauertstr 11, 14163 Berlin - T: (030) 8026671, 8023310, Fax: 8026699, E-mail: info@stadtmuseum.de, Internet: http://www.dueppel.de. Head: Prof. Reiner Güntzer
Archaeological Museum / Historical Museum - 1975
Excavation of 12th c village site, demonstration of prehistoric handicrafts 14817

Musikinstrumenten-Museum, Staatliches Institut für Musikforschung Preußischer Kulturbesitz, Tiergartenstr 1, 10785 Berlin - T: (030) 254810, Fax: 25481172, E-mail: mim@sim.spk-berlin.de, Internet: http://www.sim.spk-berlin.de. Head: Prof. Dr. Conny Restle
Music Museum - 1888
archives 14818

Nationalgalerie Friedrichswerdersche Kirche - Schinkelmuseum, Staatliche Museen zu Berlin - Preußischer Kulturbesitz, Werderscher Markt, 10117 Berlin - T: (030) 2081323, Fax: 20905802, E-mail: g.boesel@smb.spk-berlin.de, Internet: http://www.smb.spk-berlin.de/fwk. Head: Prof. Dr. Peter-Klaus Schuster
Fine Arts Museum
Life and works of the architect Karl Friedrich Schinkel, sculptures (19th c) 14819

Naturwissenschaftliche Sammlungen, Stiftung Stadtmuseum Berlin, Schloßstr 69a, 14059 Berlin - T: (030) 3425030, Fax: 3424597, E-mail: info@stadtmuseum.de, Internet: http://www.stadtmuseum.de. Head: Prof. Reiner Güntzer
Natural History Museum 14820

Neue Galerie Oberschöneweide der Karl-Hofer-Gesellschaft, Wilhelminenhofstr 83-85, 12459 Berlin - T: (030) 31852349, Fax: 31852349, E-mail: khghe@udk-berlin.de. Head: Dr. Utha Herzbruch-Rueß
Public Gallery
Students works, international artists 14821

Neue Gesellschaft für bildende Kunst e.V., Oranienstr 25, 10999 Berlin - T: (030) 6153031, Fax: 6152290, E-mail: ngbk@ngbk.de, Internet: http://www.ngbk.de. Head: Leonie Baumann
Public Gallery 14822

Neue Nationalgalerie, Staatliche Museen zu Berlin - Preußischer Kulturbesitz, Potsdamer Str 50, 10785 Berlin - T: (030) 2662651, Fax: 2662654, E-mail: nng@smb.spk-berlin.de, Internet: http://www.smb.spk-berlin.de. Head: Prof. Dr. Peter-Klaus Schuster
Fine Arts Museum - 1861
Painting, sculpture, 19th-20th c - library, workshop 14823

Neuer Berliner Kunstverein, Chausseestr 128-129, 10115 Berlin - T: (030) 2807020/22, Fax: 2807019, E-mail: nbk@nbk.org, Internet: http://www.nbk.org. Head: Dr. Alexander Tolnay
Association with Coll 14824

Neues Kunstquartier Berlin, Gustav-Meyer-Allee 25, 13355 Berlin - T: (030) 21252900, Fax: 21252905, E-mail: Karla.Hendler@investitionsbank.de, Internet: http://www.investitionsbank.de. Head: Karla Hendler
Public Gallery 14825

Parlamentsausstellung des Deutschen Bundestages "Wege, Irrwege, Umwege", Gendarmenmarkt 1, 10117 Berlin - T: (030) 22730431, Fax: 22730438, E-mail: -ausstellungsbuero.pi5@bundestag.de, Internet: http://www.bundestag.de. Head: Andrea Kerstges
Historical Museum - 1971/2002 14826

Parochialkirche, Klosterstr 67, 10179 Berlin - T: (030) 28386281, Fax: 28599738
Public Gallery 14827

Polizeihistorische Sammlung Berlin, Pl der Luftbrücke 6, 12101 Berlin - T: (030) 69935050, Fax: 69935013, E-mail: ppr.phs@snafu.de, Internet: http://www.polizei.berlin.de. Head: Dr. Bärbel Schönefeld
Historical Museum - 1987
History of the Berlin police, documents, pictures, uniforms, technical equipment - library, archive 14828

Rathaus-Galerie, Kunstamt Reinickendorf, Eichborndamm 215, 13437 Berlin - T: (030) 4177800, Fax: 41778019. Head: Werner Kopp
Public Gallery 14829

Rathgen-Forschungslabor, Staatliche Museen zu Berlin - Preußischer Kulturbesitz, Schloßstr 1a, 14059 Berlin - T: (030) 32674910, Fax: 32674912, E-mail: rf@smb.spk-berlin.de, Internet: http://www.smb.spk-berlin.de. Head: Prof. Dr. Josef Riederer 14830

Robert-Koch-Museum, Dorotheenstr 96, 10117 Berlin - T: (030) 450524010, Fax: 450524902, E-mail: ulf.goebel@charite.de, Internet: http://www.charite.de/imh. Head: Prof. Dr. Dr. Ulf Göbel
Special Museum - 1960
Memorabilia of scientist Robert Koch (1843-1910), historic building (1874) 14831

Rotkreuz-Museum Berlin, Bundesallee 73, 12161 Berlin - T: (030) 85005255
Historical Museum 14832

Royal Art Museum, Holbeinstr 11, 12205 Berlin - T: (030) 8332570
Fine Arts Museum 14833

Sammlung Berggruen, Staatliche Museen zu Berlin - Preußischer Kulturbesitz, Schloßstr 1, 14059 Berlin - T: (030) 3269580, Fax: 32695819, E-mail: g.boesel@smb.spk-berlin.de, Internet: http://www.smb.spk-berlin.de. Head: Prof. Dr. Peter-Klaus Schuster
Fine Arts Museum
Picasso, Klee, Matisse, Bracque, Giacometti 14834

Sammlung Hoffmann, Sophienstr 21, 10178 Berlin - T: (030) 28499121, Fax: 28499112, E-mail: sammlung@sophie-gips.de, Internet: http://www.sophie-gips.de. Head: Elke Ahrens
Fine Arts Museum
Private art collection 14835

Sammlung industrielle Gestaltung, Stiftung Stadtmuseum Berlin, Knaackstr 97, 10435 Berlin - T: (030) 4439382, Fax: 4439382, E-mail: info@stadtmuseum.de, Internet: http://www.stadtmuseum.de. Head: Hein Köster
Special Museum - 1950
Product design in the SBZ (the Russian zone) of the DDR (GDR), industrial design in East-Germany before 1945 14836

Schloß Friedrichsfelde, Stiftung Stadtmuseum Berlin, Am Tierpark 125, 10319 Berlin - T: (030) 5138141, Fax: 5138142, E-mail: info@stadtmuseum.de, Internet: http://www.stadtmuseum.de. Head: Prof. Reiner Güntzer
Fine Arts Museum / Decorative Arts Museum / Historical Museum
Art and culture of 17th - 19th c 14837

Schwartzsche Villa, Grunewaldstr 55, 12165 Berlin - T: (030) 6321-2302, 6321-2210, Fax: 6321-2213, E-mail: kultur.steglitz@zehlendorf@berlin.de
Public Gallery 14838

Schwules Museum, Mehringdamm 61, 10961 Berlin - T: (030) 6931172, 69599050, Fax: 6934037, E-mail: schwulesmuseumev@aol.com, Internet: http://www.schwulesmuseum.de. Head: Dr. A. Sternweiler
Special Museum / Historical Museum
History, art, costumes, private photographies - archive, library 14839

Siemens-Forum in Berlin, Nonnendammallee 101, 10629 Berlin - T: (030) 38625673, Fax: 38629510
Science&Tech Museum
Hist and development of Siemens 14840

Skulpturensammlung und Museum für Byzantinische Kunst, Staatliche Museen zu Berlin - Preußischer Kulturbesitz (closed until end of 2004), Bodestr 1-3, 10178 Berlin - T: (030) 20616811, Fax: 20616812, E-mail: a.effenberger@smb.spk-berlin.de, Internet: http://www.smb.spk-berlin.de. Head: Prof. Dr. Arne Effenberger
Fine Arts Museum / Museum of Classical Antiquities / Archaeological Museum / Special Museum - 1904
Most important coll of late antique and Byzantine art (sacophagi, sculpture, mosaics, icons), Italian sculpture (medieval, Renaissance, Baroque) in Germany - rich coll of North European medieval sculpture especially of the later Gothic periods as well as of the German Renaissance, Baroque and Rococo including parts of the former Kunstkammer in Berlin - library 14841

Sportmuseum Berlin, Stiftung Stadtmuseum Berlin, Deutsches Sportforum, Hanns-Braun-Str, 14053 Berlin - T: (030) 3058300, Fax: 3058340, E-mail: - sportmuseum.Berlin@t-online.de, Internet: http://www.stadtmuseum.de. Head: Martina Behrendt
Special Museum - 1970
AIMS-Marathon Museum of Runnig, Olympic Games of 1936, sport hist in the GDR, german gym-history, German labour sport movement - library, archives 14842

Staatliche Museen zu Berlin - Preußischer Kulturbesitz, Generaldirektion, Stauffenbergstr 41, 10785 Berlin - T: (030) 2660, Fax: 2662992, E-mail: generaldirektion@smb.spk-berlin.de, Internet: http://www.smb.spk-berlin.de. Head: Prof. Dr. Peter-Klaus Schuster 14843

Staatsbibliothek zu Berlin, Preußischer Kulturbesitz, Unter den Linden 8, 10117 Berlin - T: (030) 2660, Fax: 2661751, E-mail: generaldir@sbb.spk-berlin.de, Internet: http://www.sbb.spk-berlin.de. Head: Graham Jefcoate
Library with Exhibitions
Historical books, Occidental and Oriental manuscripts, notes, maps, colls for East European, Oriental and East Asian studies 14844

Staatsbibliothek zu Berlin, Preußischer Kulturbesitz, Potsdamer Str 33, 10785 Berlin - T: (030) 2660, Fax: 2661751, E-mail: generaldir@sbb.spk-berlin.de, Internet: http://www.sbb.spk-berlin.de. Head: Graham Jefcoate
Library with Exhibitions
Historical books, Occidental and Oriental manuscripts, notes, maps, colls for East European, Oriental and East Asian studies 14845

Stadtgeschichtliches Museum Spandau, Zitadelle, Am Juliusturm, 13599 Berlin - T: (030) 354944297, Fax: 354944296. Head: A. Theissen
Local Museum
department in Gotisches Haus, Breite Str 32, 13597 Berlin 14846

Stadtgeschichtliches Museum Weißensee, Pistoriusstr 8, 13086 Berlin - T: (030) 9250549
Local Museum 14847

Ständige Ausstellung Umweltschutz, Umweltbundesamt, Bismarckpl 1, 14193 Berlin - T: (030) 89032180, Fax: 89032910
Natural History Museum - 1976
Exhibits on the environment, information about the tasks of the environmental protection agency - library 14848

Statthaus Böcklerpark, Prinzenstr 1, 10969 Berlin - T: (030) 6158787, Fax: 6158787
Local Museum 14849

Stiftung Preussische Schlösser und Gärten Berlin-Brandenburg, Jagdschloß Grunewald, Hüttenweg, 14193 Berlin - T: (030) 8133597, Fax: 81497348. Head: Dr. Burkhardt Göres
Fine Arts Museum - 1927
15th-19th c German and Dutch paintings, contemporary furniture, hunting trophies, in Renaissance residence 14850

Stiftung Preussische Schlösser und Gärten Berlin-Brandenburg, Schloß auf der Pfaueninsel, Pfaueninsel, 14109 Berlin - T: (030) 80586832/31, Fax: 80586841/38, Internet: http://www.spsg.de. Head: Dr. Burkhardt Göres
Fine Arts Museum - 1926
18th c castle with other buildings from the 17th-19th c, historical interiors 14851

Stiftung Preussische Schlösser und Gärten Berlin-Brandenburg, Schloß Charlottenburg, im Schloßpark Neuer Pavillon (Schinkel-Pavillon), Belvedere (KPM-Porzellan-Sammlung), Mausoleum, Luisenpl, 14059 Berlin - T: (030) 320911, Fax: 32091200, Internet: http://www.spsg.de. Head: Dr. Burkhardt Göres
Fine Arts Museum - 1927
18th-19th c painting, French painting from the 18th c, German Romantic painting, furniture, porcelain, silver, chinese and japanese porcelain - Library, KPM-archive (Royal Porcelain Manufactory) 14852

Stiftung Preussische Schlösser und Gärten Berlin-Brandenburg, Schloß Glienicke, Königstr 36, 14109 Berlin - T: (030) 8053041, Fax: 80109744, Internet: http://www.spsg.de. Head: Dr. Burkhardt Göres
Fine Arts Museum
19th c castle with other buildings from the 19th c, 14853

Stiftung Stadtmuseum Berlin, Landesmuseum für Kultur und Geschichte Berlins, Generaldirektion und Verwaltung, Poststr 13-14, 10178 Berlin - T: (030) 24002150, Fax: 24002187, E-mail: gendir@stadtmuseum.de, Internet: http://www.stadtmuseum.de. Head: Prof. Reiner Güntzer
Historical Museum - 1874 14854

Stiftung Starke, Löwenpalais, Königsallee 30-32, 14193 Berlin - T: (030) 8257685, Fax: 8258734, E-mail: info@stiftungstarke.de, Internet: http://www.stiftungstarke.de. Head: Jörg Starke
Public Gallery 14855

Stiftung Topographie des Terrors, Niederkirchnerstr 8, 10963 Berlin - T: (030) 25486703, 2545090, Fax: 2627156, E-mail: info@topograhie.de, Internet: http://www.topographie.de. Head: Prof. Dr. Reinhard Rürup
Historical Museum
library 14856

Tschechisches Zentrum-ChechPoint, Friedrichstr 206, 10969 Berlin - T: (030) 2082592, Fax: 2044415, E-mail: ccberlin@czech.cz, Internet: http://www.czech-berlin.de. Head: Jan Bondy
Public Gallery 14857

Universität der Künste Berlin, Einsteinufer 43-53, 10587 Berlin - T: (030) 31852450, Fax: 31852635, E-mail: presse@udk-berlin.de, Internet: http://www.udk-berlin.de. Head: Prof. Lothar Romain
Fine Arts Museum / Library with Exhibitions 14858

Universitätsbibliothek der Humboldt-Universität zu Berlin, Dorotheenstr 27, 10117 Berlin - T: (030) 20933212, Fax: 20933207, E-mail: info@ub.hu-berlin.de, Internet: http://ub.hu-berlin.de. Head: Dr. Milan Bulaty
Library with Exhibitions 14859

Das Verborgene Museum, Dokumentation der Kunst von Frauen e.V., Schlüterstr 70, 10625 Berlin - T: (030) 3133656, Fax: 8613464. Head: Marion Beckers
Public Gallery 14860

Villa Oppenheim, Forum für Kunst, Kultur und Medien, Schlossstr 55, 14059 Berlin - T: (030) 902924151/50, Fax: 902924160, E-mail: villa_oppenheim@t-online.de, Internet: http://www.villaoppenheim.de. Head: Ulrike Blome
Public Gallery - 1987
Contemporary art - Graphothek City 14861

Vitra Design Museum Berlin, Kopenhagener Str 58, 10437 Berlin - T: (030) 4737770, Fax: 47377720, E-mail: info@design-museum.de, Internet: http://www.design-museum-berlin.de. Head: Alexander von Vegesack
Decorative Arts Museum - 2000 14862

Vorderasiatisches Museum, Staatliche Museen zu Berlin - Preußischer Kulturbesitz, Bodestr 1-3, 10178 Berlin - T: (030) 20905301, Fax: 20905302, E-mail: vam@smb.spk-berlin.de, Internet: http://www.smb.spk-berlin.de/vam. Head: Prof. Dr. Beate Salje
Museum of Classical Antiquities / Fine Arts Museum / Archaeological Museum / Special Museum / Historical Museum - 1899
Art and culture of the Ancient Near East, Mesopotamia, Syria, Anatolia, stamp and cylinder seals, architecture, cuneiform documents - Archives 14863

Wäscherei-Museum Omas Waschküche, Luisenstr 23, 12557 Berlin - T: (030) 6516424, Fax: 65494298, E-mail: mk2174@aol.com, Internet: http://www.omas-waschkueche.de. Head: Lothar Amlow
Science&Tech Museum - 1990 14864

Wilmersdorf Archiv, Hohenzollerndamm 177, 10713 Berlin - T: (030) 8641-3080, Fax: 8641-3995. Head: Udo Christoffel, Elke-Luise von der Lieth
Local Museum - 1981
Postcards, photos, newspaper 14865

Zentralarchiv, Staatliche Museen zu Berlin - Preußischer Kulturbesitz, Bodestr 1-3, 10178 Berlin - T: (030) 20906201, Fax: 20906002, E-mail: za@smb.spk-berlin.de, Internet: http://www.smb.spk-berlin.de. Head: Dr. Jörn Grabowski 14866

Zucker-Museum, Amrumer Str 32, 13353 Berlin - T: (030) 31427574, Fax: 31427586, E-mail: zuckermuseum@berlin.de, Internet: http://www.dtmb.de/Zucker-Museum. Head: Dr. B.E. Nickl
Science&Tech Museum / Natural History Museum - 1904
History and technology of sugar production, synthetic production of sugar, by-products, model of the oldest beet-sugar factory, sugar advertisement over 100 years, sugar bowls from the 17th c on, archives - library 14867

Bermsgrün

Erzgebirgische Volkskunststube, Ernst-Schneller-Str, 08340 Bermsgrün - T: (03774) 2240
Decorative Arts Museum
Folk art from the Erzgebirge 14868

Bernau, Baden

Hans-Thoma-Museum, Rathaus, 79872 Bernau, Baden - T: (07675) 160040, Fax: 160090. Head: Heinz-Walter Kistler
Fine Arts Museum - 1949
Paintings, drawings, graphics, glass painting, carvings by Hans Thoma, furniture designed by Thoma, documents on his life and works, works of the winners of the Hans Thoma prize 14869

Resenhof, Bürgermeisteramt, 79872 Bernau, Baden - T: (07675) 160040, Fax: 160090. Head: Heinz-Walter Kistler
Local Museum - 1977
Tools, exhibits on the different processes of making wooden items, domestic utensils from wood, including wooden spoons, mouse traps, wooden boxes, minerals, original interiors, in 18th c farmstead 14870

Bernau bei Berlin

Heimatmuseum, Hohe Steinstr 26, 16321 Bernau bei Berlin - T: (03338) 5614
Local Museum - 1882
Battlements, hist prison cells, hist of local judiciary, dungeon, arms and armoury (15th-16th c) - Henkerhaus, Museum Steintor, library 14871

Bernbeuren

Molkerei-Museum, c/o H. Bauer, Füssener Str 24, 86975 Bernbeuren - T: (08860) 8480, Fax: 8480, Internet: http://www.SIGRUDBAUER.de. Head: Sigrud Bauer, Hans Bauer
Science&Tech Museum / Agriculture Museum - 1990
Equipment and machinery for cheese and butter production 14872

Bernburg

Museum Schloß Bernburg, Schloßstr 24, 06406 Bernburg - T: (03471) 625007, Fax: 623074, E-mail: museumschlossbernburg@t-online.de, Internet: http://www.museumschlossbernburg.de. Head: Jürgen Weigelt
Local Museum
Geology, mining, mineralogy, entomology, ornithology, numismatics, architectural sculpture (16th-18th c), local history and crafts - library 14873

Bernkastel-Kues

Cusanus-Geburtshaus, Nikolausufer 49, 54470 Bernkastel-Kues - T: (06531) 2831
Historical Museum 14874

Bernried, Niederbayern

Museumsstadl, Pitzen 2a, 94505 Bernried, Niederbayern - T: (09905) 935, 999, Fax: 8138
Science&Tech Museum - 1998 14875

Schloß Egg, 94505 Bernried, Niederbayern - T: (09905) 8001, Fax: 8262. Head: Georg L. Hartl
Historic Site - 1989
Castle in Neo-Gothic style 14876

Bernried, Starnberger See

Sammlung Buchheim - Museum der Phantasie, Am Hirschgarten 1, 82347 Bernried, Starnberger See - T: (08158) 997020, Fax: 997061, E-mail: info@buchheimmuseum.de, Internet: http://www.buchheimmuseum.de. Head: Prof. Dr. Lothar-Günther Buchheim
Fine Arts Museum / Folklore Museum - 2001
German expressionism, ethnology, folklore 14877

Bernstadt auf dem Eigen

Heimatmuseum Stadt Bernstadt an der Eigen, Kirchpl 2, 02748 Bernstadt auf dem Eigen - T: (035874) 2850, Fax: 28540, E-mail: stv-bernstadt.a.d.Eigen@t-online.de, Internet: http://www.bernstadt.de.vu
Local Museum
Local hist, spinning, organizations and societies, handicrafts, domestic implements, local tests of liquid-fuel rockets, beginnings of rocket research 14878

Bersenbrück

Museum im Kloster - Museum des Landkreises Osnabrück, Stiftshof 4, 49593 Bersenbrück - T: (05439) 441
Local Museum - 1912
Folk art and culture 14879

Betzenstein

Heimatmuseum Betzenstein, Bayreuther Str 1, 91282 Betzenstein - T: (09244) 477
Local Museum - 1938
Geological and mineralogical coll, local history 14880

Beuren bei Nürtingen

Freilichtmuseum Beuren, Museum des Landkreises Esslingen für ländliche Kultur, In den Herbstwiesen, 72660 Beuren bei Nürtingen - T: (07025) 911900, Fax: 9119010, E-mail: info@freilichtmuseum-beuren.de, Internet: http://www.freilichtmuseum-beuren.de. Head: Steffi Cornelius
Open Air Museum - 1995
Peasant life and traditions 14881

Beuron

Bibelmuseum, Abteistr 2, 88631 Beuron - T: (07466) 17190, Fax: 17107, E-mail: benediktschwank@t-online.de, Internet: http://www.erzabtei-beuron.de. Head: Prof. Dr. Benedikt Schwank
Religious Arts Museum - 1863
Original biblical manuscripts, archeological finds 14882

Bevern, Kreis Holzminden

Heimatmuseum im Weserrenaissance Schloß, Rathaus, Angerstr 13a, 37639 Bevern, Kreis Holzminden - T: (05531) 994419, Fax: 994450
Local Museum - 1978
Agricultural and domestic implements, trade workshops 14883

Beverungen

Stuhlmuseum Burg Beverungen, An der Weserbrücke, 37688 Beverungen - T: (05273) 37890, Fax: 378933, E-mail: museum@tecta.de, Internet: http://www.tecta.de. Head: A. Bruchhäuser
Decorative Arts Museum - 1982/85
Coll of chairs, reconstructions, Walter Gropius, Ludwig Mies van der Rohe, Marcel Breuer - Jean Prouvé Archive 14884

Bexbach

Saarländisches Bergbaumuseum, Niederbexbacher Str, 66450 Bexbach - T: (06826) 4887, Fax: 510884, E-mail: saarl.bergbaumuseum@t-online.de, Internet: http://home.t-online.de/home/saarl.bergbaumuseum/berg1.htm. Head: Rolf B. Bongard
Science&Tech Museum - 1934
Geology, mining, metallurgy, mine safety 14885

Biberach an der Riß

Braith-Mali-Museum, Museumstr 6, 88400 Biberach an der Riß - T: (07351) 51331, Fax: 51314, E-mail: braith-mali-museum@biberach-riss.de, Internet: http://www.biberach-riss.de/kultur/. Head: Frank Brunecker
Fine Arts Museum / Local Museum / Archaeological Museum / Natural History Museum / Folklore Museum - 1902
Art of the late Gothic, prehist, local hist, 17th-20th c painting, original atelier and estate of the animal painters A. Braith and Chr. Mali, works by Ernst Ludwig Kirchner, natural science, sculpture, archives - library, classroom 14886

Wieland-Archiv, Zeppelinring 56, 88400 Biberach an der Riß - T: (07351) 51458, Fax: 51459, E-mail: biberach.kultur@t-online.de, Internet: http://www.biberach-riss.de. Head: V. Ottenbacher
Library with Exhibitions - 1905
Works by and memorabilia of Wieland 14887

Wieland-Gartenhaus, Saudengasse 10, 88400 Biberach an der Riß - T: (07351) 51458, Fax: 51459, E-mail: wieland-museum@biberach-riss.de, Internet: http://www.biberach-riss.de. Head: V. Ottenbacher
Historic Site - 1905
Portrayal of "literary" gardens, Christoph Martin Wieland's connection to garden life 14888

Wieland-Schauraum, Zeughausgasse 4, 88400 Biberach an der Riß - T: (07351) 51458, Fax: 51459, E-mail: wieland-museum@biberach-riss.de, Internet: http://www.biberach-riss.de. Head: V. Ottenbacher
Special Museum
Literature of and about C.M. Wieland 14889

Biberach, Baden

Ketterer-Haus-Museum, Hauptstr 27, Rathaus, 77781 Biberach, Baden - T: (07835) 63650, Fax: 636520, E-mail: tourist-info@biberach-baden.de, Internet: http://www.biberach-baden.de
Local Museum 14890

Bickenbach, Bergstraße

Kommunales Museum der Gemeinde Bickenbach, Darmstädter Str 35, 64404 Bickenbach, Bergstraße - T: (06257) 3031, Fax: 5647
Local Museum - 1989
Town hist, tobacco production, industrial development 14891

Biebelnheim

Little Cavern, Beatles-Museum, 55234 Biebelnheim - T: (06733) 7204. Head: Mathias Spang, Michael Wahle
Music Museum 14892

Biebertal

Hof Haina mit Heimatmuseum, 35444 Biebertal - T: (06409) 51487
Local Museum
Portrayal of farm life, weaver's workshop, embroidery, knitwear, agricultural implements 14893

Biebesheim

Heimatmuseum Biebesheim, Rheinstr 44, 64584 Biebesheim - T: (06258) 81599, Fax: 971048
Local Museum - 1963/81
Grave finds, helmets from the Bronze Age, fossils, trade tools and implements, farm life utensiles, furniture and clothes, Roman Toga statue (20-10 BC) 14894

Biedenkopf

Hinterlandmuseum Schloss Biedenkopf, im Schloss 1, 35216 Biedenkopf - T: (06461) 924652, Fax: 924653, Internet: http://www.biedenkopf.de/kultur/museum.htm
Local Museum - 1908
Hist of the casle, fire protection, iron industry, border walking, costume, every-day life, building crafts 14895

Photographisch-optisches Museum, Dexbacher Str 60, 35216 Biedenkopf - T: (06461) 3541. Head: Günther Hinz
Science&Tech Museum
Contemporary documents from 1845 to present: cameras, microscopes, photocopier, laternae magicae, film and television cameras 14896

Bielefeld

Bauernhaus-Museum, Dornberger Str 82, 33619 Bielefeld - T: (0521) 5218550, Fax: 5218552, E-mail: bauernhausmuseum@owl-online.de, Internet: http://www.bielefelder-bauernhausmuseum.de. Head: Dr. Rosa Rosinski
Open Air Museum - 1917
Folk art from the 16th to the 19th c, in 16th c half-timbered hall farm house, 17th-18th c mill and silo, furniture, costume, jewellery, household articles 14897

Fächerkabinett, Barisch Stiftung, Am Bach 19, 33602 Bielefeld - T: (0521) 64186, Fax: 64187. Head: M. Barisch, G. Barisch
Decorative Arts Museum - 1995
Fans from the 17th-20th c from various countries 14898

Historische Sammlung Bethel, Kantensiek 9, 33617 Bielefeld - T: (0521) 1442024
Local Museum 14899

Historisches Museum Bielefeld, Ravensberger Park 2, 33607 Bielefeld - T: (0521) 513630, Fax: 516745, E-mail: historisches.museum@bielefeld.de, Internet: http://www.historisches-museum-bielefeld.de. Head: Dr. Cornelia Foerster
Historical Museum - 1978
Archaeological finds, everyday life in the age of industrialization, bicycles, sewing-machines 14900

Kunsthalle Bielefeld, Artur-Ladebeck-Str 5, 33602 Bielefeld - T: (0521) 32999500, 329995010, Fax: 329995050, E-mail: info@kunsthalle-bielefeld.de, Internet: http://www.kunsthalle-bielefeld.de. Head: Dr. Thomas Kellein
Fine Arts Museum - 1968
Expressionist painting, American painting after 1945, Cubistic sculpture, graphics, German figurative art - library, children's atelier 14901

Museum Huelsmann, Kunstgewerbesammlung der Stadt Bielefeld/ Stiftung Huelsmann, Ravensberger Park 3, 33607 Bielefeld - T: (0521) 513767, Fax: 513768, E-mail: info@museumhuelsmann.de, Internet: http://www.museumhuelsmann.de. Head: Dr. Hildegard Wiewelhove
Decorative Arts Museum - 1995 14902

Museum Waldhof, Bielefelder Kunstverein e.V., Welle 61, 33602 Bielefeld - T: (0521) 178806, Fax: 178810, E-mail: kontakt@bielefelder-kunstverein.de, Internet: http://www.bielefelder-kunstverein.de. Head: Prof. Dr. Andreas Beaugrand
Fine Arts Museum - 1964/1984 14903

Naturkunde-Museum, Kreuzstr 20, 33602 Bielefeld - T: (0521) 516734, Fax: 512481, E-mail: isolde.wrazidlo@bielefeld.de. Head: Dr. Isolde Wrazidlo
Natural History Museum - 1906
Mineralogy, geology, geobotany, entomology, ornithology, stratigraphy, paleontology - library 14904

Bietigheim-Bissingen

Stadtmuseum Hornmoldhaus, Hauptstr 61-63, 74321 Bietigheim-Bissingen - T: (07142) 74352, 74373, Fax: 74353, E-mail: stadt@bietigheim-bissingen.de, Internet: http://www.bietigheim-bissingen.de. Head: Regina Ille-Kopp
Local Museum - 1983
Town hist 14905

Städtische Galerie, Hauptstr 60-64, 74321 Bietigheim-Bissingen - T: (07142) 74483, Fax: 74446, E-mail: stadt@bietigheim-bissingen.de, Internet: http://www.bietigheim-bissingen.de. Head: Herbert Eichhorn
Public Gallery - 1989
Linocut, 20th c graphics 14906

Zuckmantler Heimatstube, Schieringer Str 20, 74321 Bietigheim-Bissingen. Head: Walter Zwiener
Local Museum 14907

Billerbeck

Kulturzentrum Kolvenburg, An der Kolvenburg 3, 48727 Billerbeck - T: (02543) 1540, Fax: 8211, Internet: http://www.kreis-coesfeld.de. Head: Dr. J. Sarrazin
Fine Arts Museum 14908

Bingen am Rhein

Historisches Museum am Strom - Hildegard von Bingen, Museumstr 3, 55411 Bingen am Rhein - T: (06721) 990654, Fax: 990653, E-mail: historisches-museum@bingen.de, Internet: http://www.bingen.de. Head: Dr. Matthias Schmandt
Local Museum
Romantic at Rhine, local hist, Hildegard von Bingen, photography 14909

Stefan-George-Museum im Stefan-George-Haus, Freidhof 9, 55411 Bingen am Rhein, mail addr: In den Rödern 46, 64297 Darmstadt - T: (06721) 991094. Head: Gisela Eidemüller
Special Museum / Library with Exhibitions - 1968
Life and work of the poet Stefan George, his library, portrayal of the poet by means of sculptures, paintings and photographs, secondary lit on George's work, library of his great uncle - library 14910

Birkenfeld, Nahe

Museum des Vereins für Heimatkunde im Landkreis Birkenfeld, Friedr.-August-Str, 55765 Birkenfeld, Nahe - T: (06782) 6382, Fax: 989589, Internet: http://www.landkreis-birkenfeld.de/museum
Local Museum / Archaeological Museum - 1910
Celts and Romans in the Birkenfeld area, 18th-19th c industry, school system, from flax to linen system - archive 14911

Birkenwerder

Clara-Zetkin-Museum, Summter Str 4, 16547 Birkenwerder - T: (03303) 402709, Fax: 402709. Head: Manuela Dörnenburg
Special Museum - 1957
Memorabilia of women's rights fighter Clara Zetkin (1857-1933), pictures, documents, writings, historic furnishings - library 14912

Bischofsheim an der Rhön

Osterburgsammlung, 97653 Bischofsheim an der Rhön
Archaeological Museum 14913

Bischofsheim bei Rüsselsheim

Museum Bischofsheim, Darmstädter Str 2, 65474 Bischofsheim bei Rüsselsheim - T: (06144) 94282, Fax: 94282, E-mail: hgr.bischofsheim@gmx.de. Head: Ulrich Thon
Local Museum - 1950
Exhibits from pre-history, finds from the Ice and Bronze Age, domestic objects, history of the local railway station 14914

Bisingen

Burg Hohenzollern, 72379 Bisingen - T: (07471) 2428, Fax: 6812, E-mail: verwaltung@burg-hohenzollern.com, Internet: http://www.burg-hohenzollern.de. Head: Joachim Alisch
Historical Museum / Historic Site - 1867
Edwin v. Campe coll of engraved portraits of Friedrich the Great, Hohenzollern family portraits, stained glass windows 14915

Bispingen

Heidemuseum Dat ole Huus, Wilsede 3a, 29646 Bispingen - T: (04175) 445
Local Museum - 1907
Farm life implements, objects, furniture, finds from the Stone Age to the Middle Ages 14916

Bissingen an der Teck

Mörikehaus, Eduard-Mörike-Str 15, 73266 Bissingen an der Teck - T: (07023) 2304. Head: G. König
Special Museum - 1981
Memorabilia of the poet Eduard Mörike in the place where he lived 1832/33 14917

Bitterfeld

Kreismuseum Bitterfeld, Kirchpl 3, 06749 Bitterfeld - T: (03493) 23295, Fax: 23295, E-mail: Kreismuseum-Bitterfeld@gmx.de. Head: Uwe Holz
Local Museum - 1892
Prehistory and early hist, geology, pleistocene, fauna, ornithology, local history, amber, mining, ballooning - library, archive 14918

Blankenburg, Harz

Historische Gesellenherberge, Herbergsmuseum, Bergstr 15, 38889 Blankenburg, Harz - T: (03944) 5007
Historical Museum
Traditional journeyman's inn 14919

Museum Kleines Schloß, Schnappelberg 6, 38889 Blankenburg, Harz - T: (03944) 2658, Fax: 2658. Head: Hartmut Wegner
Local Museum - 1896
Local history, historic findings, esp ceramics and religious applied arts, Baroque living style, photo coll, coins, oven plates 17th-19th c - library 14920

Stiftung Kloster Michaelstein/Museum, Michaelstein 3, 38889 Blankenburg, Harz, mail addr: PF 24, 38881 Blankenburg, Harz - T: (03944) 90300, Fax: 903030, E-mail: rezeption@kloster-michaelstein.de, Internet: http://www.kloster-michaelstein.de. Head: Andreas Walter
Music Museum / Open Air Museum - 1988
Former Cistercian monastery, coll of historical musical instruments - herb garden 14921

Blankenheim, Ahr

Eifelmuseum Blankenheim, Ahrstr 55-57, 53945 Blankenheim, Ahr - T: (02449) 95150, Fax: 951520, E-mail: eifelmuseum-blankenheim@t-online.de, Internet: http://www.kreis-euskirchen.de/bildung/abt105/museum.htm. Head: Klaus Ring
Local Museum - 1954
Local and regional hist, fossils - library 14922

Kreismuseum → Eifelmuseum Blankenheim

Blankensee bei Luckenwalde

Bauernmuseum Blankensee, Dorfstr 4, 14959 Blankensee bei Luckenwalde - T: (033731) 80011, Fax: 80011
Local Museum - 1958 14923

Blaubeuren

Heimatmuseum Blaubeuren, Klosterhof, 89143 Blaubeuren - T: (07344) 921026, Fax: 966936
Folklore Museum / Historic Site - 1947
Local history 14924

Historische Hammerschmiede, Blautopfstr 9, 89143 Blaubeuren - T: (07344) 921027, Fax: 8646
Historical Museum 14925

Klosterkirche Blaubeuren, Klosterhof 3, 89143 Blaubeuren - T: (07344) 96260, Fax: 962696, E-mail: evsem.blb@t-online.de, Internet: http://www.evseminar.ul.bw.schule.de. Head: Gerhard Klein
Religious Arts Museum 14926

Urgeschichtliches Museum, Karlstr 21, 89143 Blaubeuren - T: (07344) 921030, Fax: 921052, E-mail: urmu.blb@web.de, Internet: http://www.blaubeuren.de/museen/urgeschichte. Head: S. Kölbl
Archaeological Museum - 1965
Local Ice Age finds, late Stone Age items demonstrating primitive technology and life in Africa and the American Arctic 14927

Bleckede

Elbtal-Haus Bleckede, Lauenburger Str 15, 21354 Bleckede - T: (05852) 2899, Fax: 3303, E-mail: Elbtalhaus@uni-lueneburg.de, Internet: http://www.uni-lueneburg.de
Natural History Museum 14928

Bleicherode

Heimatmuseum Bleicherode, Hauptstr 56, 99752 Bleicherode - T: (036338) 43535, Fax: 43536, E-mail: tourismus@bleicherode.de, Internet: http://www.bleicherode.de
Local Museum 14929

Bliedersdorf

Heimatstube Bliedersdorf, Hauptstr 49, 21640 Bliedersdorf - T: (04163) 2180
Local Museum
Folk art, agricultural implements 14930

Blindheim

Heimatmuseum, Weiherbrunnenstr 9, 89434 Blindheim - T: (09074) 3239
Local Museum - 1998 14931

Bocholt

Kunsthaus Stadt Bocholt, Osterstr 69, 46397 Bocholt - T: (02871) 953337, Fax: 953342, E-mail: stadtverwaltung@mail.bocholt.de, Internet: http://www.bocholt.de. Head: Georg Ketteler
Fine Arts Museum 14932

Kunstkammer der Pfarrkirche Sankt Georg, Sankt-Georg-Pl 11-13, 46399 Bocholt - T: (02871) 25440, Fax: 12322, E-mail: rudi-gehrmann@freenet.de, Internet: http://www.bocholt.de/museen.html. Head: Rudi Gehrmann
Religious Arts Museum / Fine Arts Museum - 1980
archive 14933

Stadtmuseum Bocholt, Osterstr 66, 46397 Bocholt - T: (02871) 184579, Fax: 953342, E-mail: stadtverwaltung@mail.bocholt.de, Internet: http://www.bocholt.de. Head: Georg Ketteler
Local Museum / Fine Arts Museum - 1992
Engravings by Israhel van Meckenem, bequest of the set-designer Josef Fenneker 14934

Westfälisches Industriemuseum, Textilmuseum, Uhlandstr 50, 46397 Bocholt - T: (02871) 216110, Fax: 2161133, E-mail: textilmuseum@lwl.org, Internet: http://www.textilmuseum-bocholt.de. Head: Dr. Hermann-Josef Stenkamp
Science&Tech Museum 14935

Bochum

Brauerei-Kontor, Kleines Museum der Privatbrauerei Moritz Fliege, Scharnhorststr 19-25, 44787 Bochum - T: (0234) 6898111
Science&Tech Museum 14936

Deutsches Bergbau-Museum, Am Bergbaumuseum 28, 44791 Bochum - T: (0234) 58770, Fax: 5877111, E-mail: info@bergbaumuseum.de, Internet: http://www.bergbaumuseum.de. Head: Prof. Dr. Rainer Slotta
Science&Tech Museum - 1930
Technology of mining, science of geological deposits and raw materials, economics and technology of mining, historic mining equipment and plants, mining and archaeology, cultural influence of mining - Mining archive, library, workshops 14937

Deutsches Forum für Figurentheater und Puppenspielkunst (closed) 14938

Eisenbahnmuseum Bochum-Dahlhausen, Dr.-C.-Otto-Str 191, 44879 Bochum - T: (0234) 492516, Fax: (0201) 540699, E-mail: info@eisenbahnmuseum-bochum.de, Internet: http://www.eisenbahnmuseum-bochum.de. Head: Harald Vogelsang
Science&Tech Museum - 1977
Steam, electric, and diesel locomotives, motor railcar, coaches - library, workshop 14939

Kunstsammlungen der Ruhr-Universität Bochum, Universitätsstr 150, 44780 Bochum - T: (0234) 3224738, Fax: 3214234, E-mail: cornelia.weber-lehmann@ruhr-uni-bochum.de. Head: Dr. Cornelia Weber-Lehmann, Prof. Dr. Monika Steinhauser
Fine Arts Museum / Museum of Classical Antiquities / University Museum - 1975
Greek and Roman antiquities, modern European and American art 14940

Medizinhistorische Sammlung der Ruhr-Universität Bochum, Institut für Geschichte der Medizin, Markstr 258a, 44799 Bochum - T: (0234) 3223394, Fax: 3214205, E-mail: Geschichte.MedizinAnfrage@ruhr-uni-bochum.de, Internet: http://www.ruhr-uni-bochum.de/malakow/home.htm. Head: Prof. Dr. Irmgard Müller
Special Museum - 1990
Medical technique, medical instruments, Winterstein archive - library 14941

Museum Bochum, Kunstsammlung, Kortumstr 147, 44777 Bochum - T: (0234) 5160030, Fax: 5160010, E-mail: museum@bochum.de, Internet: http://www.bochum.de/museum. Head: Dr. Hans Günter Golinski
Fine Arts Museum - 1960
Art after 1945, painting, graphics, sculpture, in 19th c Villa Marckhoff - library 14942

Rittergut Haus Laer, Höfestr 45, Wasserburg Haus Laer, 44803 Bochum - T: (0234) 383044, Fax: 385375, Internet: http://www.rittergut-haus-laer.de. Head: Volker Frielinghaus
Local Museum / Historic Site 14943

Schulhistorische Sammlung Cruismannschule, Cruismannstr 2, 44807 Bochum - T: (0234) 6213880
Special Museum 14944

Situation Kunst, c/o Kunstsammlungen der Ruhr-Universität Bochum, Im Schloßpark Weitmar, Schloßstr 1a, 44795 Bochum - T: (0234) 452194, Fax: 3214450, E-mail: Kai-Uwe.Hemken@Ruhr-Uni-Bochum.de, Internet: http://www.kgi.ruhr-uni-bochum.de/index1.htm. Head: Prof. Dr. Monika Steinhauser
Fine Arts Museum - 1990
Contemporary paintings, drawings and environments by Kricke, Rainer, Graubner, Serra, Nordman, Rabinowitsch 14945

Bockenem

Automuseum Störy, Sankt-Adrians-Pl 5, 31167 Bockenem - T: (05067) 759, Fax: 69296. Head: Otto Künnecke
Science&Tech Museum - 1972
Cars and motor bikes from various countries 14946

Turmuhren- und Heimatmuseum Bockenem, Buchholzmarkt 21, 31167 Bockenem - T: (05067) 2420, E-mail: Info@Bockenem.de. Head: Heinrich Bothe
Local Museum / Science&Tech Museum - 1970
Tower clocks, hist of the town of Bockenem 14947

Bodenfelde

Heimatmuseum Bodenfelde, Amelither Str, 37194 Bodenfelde - T: (05572) 893, 1280
Local Museum 14948

Jagdschloß Nienover, 37194 Bodenfelde - T: (05572) 893
Decorative Arts Museum 14949

Bodenheim

Bodenheimer Heimatmuseum, Dolleshaus, 55294 Bodenheim - T: (06135) 2780
Local Museum 14950

Bodenmais

Historisches Erzbergwerk im Silberbergwerk Bodenmais, Marktpl 3, 94249 Bodenmais - T: (09924) 304
Science&Tech Museum - 1962
History of iron and silver ore mining, galleries, underground lake 14951

Bodenwerder

Münchhausen-Erinnerungszimmer und Heimatmuseum, Münchhausenpl 1, 37619 Bodenwerder - T: (05533) 40541, Fax: 40540, E-mail: museum@bodenwerder.de, Internet: http://www.bodenwerder.de. Head: Thekla Gehrmann
Local Museum / Special Museum / Historic Site - 1937/67
Memorabilia of Hieronymus Karl Friedrich Freiherr von Münchhausen, translations, town and trade hist 14952

Böblingen

Deutsches Bauernkriegsmuseum, Pfarrgasse 2, Zehntscheuer, 71032 Böblingen - T: (07031) 669475, Fax: 669688, E-mail: g.scholz_g@boeblingen.de, Internet: http://www.boeblingen.de. Head: Dr. G. Scholz
Historical Museum - 1988
Hist of the Peasant War, diorama of the battle which took place around Böblingen in May 1525 (1 200 pewter figures) 14953

Deutsches Fleischermuseum, Marktpl 27, 71032 Böblingen - T: (07031) 669473, Fax: 669688, E-mail: g.scholz@boeblingen.de, Internet: http://www.boeblingen.de. Head: Dr. G. Scholz
Special Museum - 1984 14954

Galerie Contact, Marktgässle 4, 71032 Böblingen - T: (07031) 669476, Fax: 669688, Internet: http://www.boeblingen.de
Local Museum / Public Gallery 14955

Heimatmuseum des Nordböhmischen Niederlandes, Marktpl 27, 71032 Böblingen - T: (07031) 669473, Fax: 669688, E-mail: g.scholz@boeblingen.de. Head: Dr. G. Scholz
Local Museum - 1987 14956

Städtische Galerie, Zehntscheuer, Pfarrgasse 2, 71032 Böblingen - T: (07031) 669475, Fax: 669688, E-mail: Froitzheim@Boeblingen.de, Internet: http://www.boeblingen.de. Head: Dr. Eva-Marina Froitzheim
Fine Arts Museum - 1986
Art in South West Germany (1913-1963) 14957

Böhl-Iggelheim

Museum Böhl-Iggelheim, Weinbietstr 15, 67459 Böhl-Iggelheim - T: (06324) 76353, Fax: 963170
Local Museum 14958

Bönnigheim

Museum Charlotte Zander, Schloß, Hauptstr 15, 74357 Bönnigheim - T: (07143) 4226, Fax: 4220, E-mail: charlotte@sammlung-zander.de, Internet: http://www.sammlung-zander.de. Head: Charlotte Zander
Fine Arts Museum - 1996
Naive art, Art brut 14959

Schwäbisches Schnapsmuseum, Meiereihof 7, 74357 Bönnigheim - T: (07143) 22563, Fax: 22563. Head: K. Sartorius
Special Museum - 1993
Cultural hist of alcohol, afterbirth burials 14960

Börgerende

Heimatmuseum Börgerende-Rethwisch, Seestr 14, 18211 Börgerende - T: (038203) 81245
Local Museum 14961

Bösingen

Bauernmuseum Pfarrscheuer, Kirchwiesen 14, 78662 Bösingen - T: (07404) 1806
Agriculture Museum / Ethnology Museum - 1979
Agricultural machinery and implements, crafts, peasant life 14962

Boffzen

Glasmuseum Boffzen, Bahnhofstr 9c, 37691 Boffzen - T: (05271) 49909, 956024, Fax: 5521, E-mail: sg@boffzen.de, Internet: http://www.boffzen.de
Decorative Arts Museum / Local Museum
Glas manufacture 14963

Bogen

Kreis- und Heimatmuseum, Auf dem Bogenberg, 94327 Bogen - T: (09422) 5786
Local Museum - 1962
Local history, furniture, costumes, weapons and religious objects 14964

Boitzenburg

Produktionsmuseum Klostermühle, Mühlenstr 5, 17268 Boitzenburg - T: (039889) 236. Head: Science&Tech Museum 14965

Boizenburg

Heimatmuseum Boizenburg, Kirchpl 13, 19258 Boizenburg - T: (038847) 52074, Fax: 52074
Local Museum - 1935 14966

Bonn

Akademisches Kunstmuseum der Universität, Antikensammlung, Am Hofgarten 21, 53113 Bonn - T: (0228) 735011, Fax: 737282, E-mail: ai.museum@uni-bonn.de, Internet: http://www.antikensammlung.uni-bonn.de. Head: Prof. Dr. Harald Mielsch
Museum of Classical Antiquities - 1818
Casts of Greek and Roman sculptures, objects from the early Bronze Age to late Antiquity: vases, bronzes, terracotta figurines, marble sculpture, coins, coptic textiles, glasses - library, workshops 14967

Archäologisch-Ethnographische Lehr- und Studiensammlung des Instituts für Altamerikanistik und Ethnologie der Universität Bonn, Regina-Pacis-Weg 7, 53113 Bonn - T: (0228) 735737, Fax: 734385, E-mail: sammlung@voelk.uni-bonn.de. Head: Prof. Dr. Hanns J. Prem
Archaeological Museum / Ethnology Museum 14968

Archiv für Philatelie der Museumsstiftung Post und Telekommunikation, Heinrich-von-Stephan-Str 1, 53175 Bonn - T: (0228) 1850, Fax: 185192, E-mail: mspt.hahn@t-online.de, Internet: http://www.museumsstiftung.de. Head: Dr. Andreas Hahn
Library with Exhibitions
Stamps - archives 14969

Arithmeum, rechnen einst und jetzt, Lennéstr 2, 53113 Bonn - T: (0228) 738790, Fax: 738771, E-mail: arithmeum@or.uni-bonn.de, Internet: http://arithmeum.uni-bonn.de. Head: Ina Prinz
Science&Tech Museum
Historical calculating machines 14970

Artothek im Bonner Kunstverein, Hochstadenring 22, 53119 Bonn - T: (0228) 693936, Fax: 695589, E-mail: artothek@bonner-kunstverein.de, Internet: http://www.bonner-kunstverein.de/artothek.htm. Head: Dr. Johannes Stahl
Association with Coll 14971

August Macke Haus, Bornheimer Str 96, 53119 Bonn - T: (0228) 655531, Fax: 691550, E-mail: buero@august-macke-haus.de, Internet: http://www.august-macke-haus.de. Head: Dr. Margarethe Jochimsen
Fine Arts Museum / Public Gallery
Expressionism 14972

Beethoven-Haus, Bonngasse 20, 53111 Bonn - T: (0228) 981750, Fax: 9817526, E-mail: beethov@issay-com, Internet: http://www.beethoven-haus-bonn.de. Head: Prof. Dr. Andreas Eckhardt
Music Museum / Fine Arts Museum / Association with Coll - 1889
Music instruments, autographs, prints, paintings collected by the composer, in 17th c house in which Beethoven was born - library 14973

Beethovenhalle, Wachsbleiche 17, 53111 Bonn - T: (0228) 630031
Public Gallery 14974

Cassius Forum Bonn, Forum für religiöse Kunst und Begegnung, Irmintrudisstr 1, 53111 Bonn - T: (0228) 639475. Head: Volker Engel
Association with Coll / Religious Arts Museum 14975

Deutsches Museum Bonn, Forschung und Technik in Deutschland nach 1945, Im Wissenschaftszentrum, Ahrstr 45, 53175 Bonn - T: (0228) 302252, 302255, Fax: 302254, E-mail: eule.dmb@real-net.de, Internet: http://www.deutsches-museum-bonn.de. Head: Dr. Peter Frieß
Science&Tech Museum - 1995
100 outstanding examples of research and technology in Germany since 1945 incl many discoveries which were awarded a Nobel Prize 14976

Ernst-Moritz-Arndt-Haus, Stadt Museum Bonn, Adenauerallee 79, 53113 Bonn - T: (0228) 772094, 241435, Fax: 774298, E-mail: stadtmuseum@bonn.de, Internet: http://www.bonn.de/stadtmuseum. Head: Dr. Ingrid Bodsch
Special Museum - 1956
19th c house of the writer Ernst Moritz Arndt, memorabilia of Arndt, interiors, local history (16th-19th c) 14977

Frauen Museum, Szenarien aus Kunst und Geschichte e.V., Im Krausfeld 10, 53111 Bonn - T: (0228) 691344, Fax: 696144, E-mail: frauenmuseum@bonn-online.com, Internet: http://frauenmuseum.textur.com. Head: Marianne Pitzen
Fine Arts Museum / Historical Museum - 1981
Fine arts, history 14978

Galerie-Rotunde, Ev. Trinitatiskirche Bonn, Brahmstr 14, 53121 Bonn - T: (0228) 9784011
Public Gallery 14979

Haus der Geschichte der Bundesrepublik Deutschland, Willy-Brandt-Allee 14, 53113 Bonn - T: (0228) 91650, Fax: 9165302, E-mail: post@hdg.de, Internet: http://www.hdg.de. Head: Prof. Dr. Hermann Schäfer
Historical Museum - 1994
Contemporary German history, history of the GDR - library, mediathek 14980

Heimatmuseum Beuel, Steinerstr 34-36, 53225 Bonn - T: (0228) 463074
Local Museum 14981

Heimatmuseum Lengsdorf, Lengsdorfer Hauptstr 16, 53127 Bonn - T: (0228) 259337
Local Museum 14982

ifa-Galerie Bonn, Institut für Auslandsbeziehungen, Willy-Brandt-Allee 9, 53113 Bonn - T: (0228) 224450, Fax: 212251, E-mail: eckstein@ifa.de, Internet: http://www.ifa.de. Head: Beate Eckstein
Public Gallery 14983

Kunst- und Ausstellungshalle der Bundesrepublik Deutschland Bonn, Friedrich-Ebert-Allee 4, 53113 Bonn - T: (0228) 9171200, Fax: 9171209, E-mail: info@kah-bonn.de, Internet: http://www.bundeskunsthalle.de. Head: Dr. Wenzel Jacob
Fine Arts Museum / Historical Museum / Museum of Classical Antiquities / Archaeological Museum 14984

Kunstmuseum Bonn, Friedrich-Ebert-Allee 2, 53113 Bonn - T: (0228) 776260, Fax: 776220, E-mail: Kunstmuseum@bonn.de, Internet: http://www.bonn.de/kunstmuseum. Head: Prof. Dr. Dieter Ronte
Fine Arts Museum - 1882
20th c art, August Macke and Rhein Expressionism, international graphics after 1945, German art since 1945, Joseph Beuys - library 14985

Kurfürstliches Gärtnerhaus, Beethovenpl, 53115 Bonn - T: (0228) 221865
Public Gallery 14986

Mineralogisches Museum der Universität Bonn, Poppeldorfer Schloß, 53115 Bonn - T: (0228) 739047, 732764, Fax: 732763, E-mail: R.Schumacher@uni-bonn.de, Internet: http://www.min.uni-bonn.de/german/museum. Head: Dr. Renate Schumacher
Natural History Museum - 1818
Systematic mineralogy, petrology, economic mineral deposits, meteorites, gems, minerals and rocks from the local vulcanic area - library, workshop 14987

Museumsstiftung Post und Telekommunikation, Heinrich-von-Stephan-Str 1, 53175 Bonn - T: (0228) 1850, Fax: 185190, E-mail: museumsstiftung@t-online.de, Internet: http://www.museumsstiftung.de. Head: Dr. Hartwig Lüdtke
Science&Tech Museum 14988

Rheinisches Landesmuseum Bonn (closed until end of 2003), Fraunhoferstr 8 (während Umbau), 53121 Bonn - T: (0228) 98810, Fax: 9881299, E-mail: RLMB@lvr.de, Internet: http://www.lvr.de. Head: Prof. Dr. Frank Günter Zehnder
Local Museum / Archaeological Museum / Fine Arts Museum / Historical Museum - 1820
Prehistory, Roman epoch, early Christianity, Franks, medieval archeology, art and handicrafts of medieval and modern times, coins, archives - library, workshops, photo laboratory 14989

Rheinisches Landesmuseum Bonn, Alte Rotation des Generalanzeigers, Justus-von-Liebig-Str 15, 53121 Bonn - T: (0228) 6688580, Fax: 9881299, E-mail: RLMB@lvr.de, Internet: http://www.lvr.de. Head: Prof. Dr. Frank Günter Zehnder
Public Gallery - 1820 14990

Stadtmuseum Bonn, Franziskanerstr 9, 53113 Bonn - T: (0228) 772094, 772877, Fax: 774298, E-mail: stadtmuseum@bonn.de, Internet: http://www.bonn.de/stadtmuseum. Head: Dr. Ingrid Bodsch
Local Museum 14991

Universitäts- und Landesbibliothek Bonn, Adenauerallee 39-41, 53113 Bonn - T: (0228) 737350, Fax: 737546, E-mail: ulb@ulb.uni-bonn.de, Internet: http://www.ulb.uni-bonn.de. Head: Dr. Renate Vogt
Library with Exhibitions 14992

Zoologisches Forschungsinstitut und Museum Alexander Koenig, Adenauerallee 160, 53113 Bonn - T: (0228) 91220, Fax: 9122212, E-mail: secretary.zfmk@uni-bonn.de, Internet: http://www.museum-koenig.de. Head: Prof. Dr. Clas M. Naumann
Natural History Museum - 1912 14993

Bonndorf im Schwarzwald

Kulturzentrum Schloß Bonndorf, Schloß, 79848 Bonndorf im Schwarzwald - T: (07703) 7978, Fax: (07751) 86373, E-mail: kultur@landkreis-waldshut.de, Internet: http://www.landkreis-waldshut.de. Head: Dr. Jürgen Glocker
Local Museum - 1978
Contemporary and classical modernist art 14994

Bopfingen

Heimatstube Trochtelfingen, Ostalbstr, 73441 Bopfingen - T: (07362) 7353
Local Museum 14995

Museum im Seelhaus, Spitalpl 1, 73441 Bopfingen - T: (07362) 3855, Fax: 80150, E-mail: info@bopfingen.de, Internet: http://www.bopfingen.de. Head: Felix Sutschek
Local Museum - 1987
Geology, archeological finds, town hist, peasant life 14996

Schloß Baldern, 73441 Bopfingen - T: (07362) 96880, 968850, Fax: 968860, E-mail: schloesser@fuerst-wallerstein.de, Internet: http://www.fuerst-wallerstein.de. Head: Dr. Volker von Volckamer
Fine Arts Museum 14997

Boppard

Museum der Stadt Boppard, Kurfürstliche Burg, Burgstr, 56154 Boppard - T: (06742) 10369, Fax: 10330, E-mail: stadt@boppard.de, Internet: http://www.boppard.de
Local Museum 14998

Borgentreich

Orgelmuseum Borgentreich, Marktstr 6, 34434 Borgentreich - T: (05643) 8090, Fax: 80990, E-mail: info@borgentreich.de, Internet: http://www.borgentreich.de. Head: Jörg Kraemer
Music Museum - 1980
History, technology, building of organs 14999

Borken, Hessen

Nordhessisches Braunkohle-Bergbaumuseum, Am Amtsgericht 2, 34582 Borken, Hessen - T: (05682) 5738, Fax: 808165, E-mail: bergbaumuseum@borken-hessen.de, Internet: http://www.borken-hessen.de. Head: Gerhard Lenz
Science&Tech Museum - 1992
Hist of brown coal mining 15000

Borken, Westfalen

Stadtmuseum Borken, Westfalen, Marktpassage 6, 46322 Borken, Westfalen - T: (02861) 939221, Fax: 939253, E-mail: uta.gerissen@borken.de
Local Museum - 1964
Puppets 15001

Borkheide

Hans-Grade-Museum, Flugplatz Borkheide, 14822 Borkheide - T: (033845) 40210, 40369, Fax: (033841) 8447, E-mail: -Hans.Grade.Borkheide@web.de, Internet: http://www.hansgrade.foru.de. Head: H. Müller
Science&Tech Museum 15002

Borkum

Heimatmuseum Dykhus, Roeloff-Gerritz-Meyer-Str, 26757 Borkum - T: (04922) 4860
Local Museum - 1958
Island hist, ornithology 15003

Borna bei Leipzig

Museum der Stadt Borna, An der Mauer 2-4, 04552 Borna bei Leipzig - T: (03433) 27860, Fax: 278640, E-mail: 0343327860-0001@t-online.de. Head: Gabriele Kämpfner
Local Museum / Public Gallery - 1935
Local and crafts hist, industrial development, coal mining, military history, coll of music instruments - library, gallery of modern art 15004

Bottrop

Das Junge Museum, Blumenstr 12-14, 46236 Bottrop - T: (02041) 703836, Fax: 703833, E-mail: kulturwerkstatt@bottrop.de, Internet: http://www.bottrop.de. Head: Katrin Reck
Special Museum 15005

Quadrat Bottrop, Josef-Albers-Museum, Moderne Galerie, Studio Galerie, Museum für Ur-und Ortsgeschichte, Im Stadtgarten 20, 46236 Bottrop - T: (02041) 29716, Fax: 22578, E-mail: quadrat@bottrop.de, Internet: http://www.quadrat-bottrop.de. Head: Dr. Ulrich Schumacher
Fine Arts Museum / Natural History Museum / Public Gallery - 1976 15006

Bovenden

Ortsgeschichtliche Sammlung, Rathauspl 1, 37120 Bovenden - T: (0551) 8201171, Fax: 83691, E-mail: archiv@bovenden.de, Internet: http://www.bovenden.de
Local Museum - 1967 15007

Boxberg, Baden

Heimatmuseum Boxberg, Altes Rathaus, 97944 Boxberg, Baden
Local Museum 15008

Brachttal

Werksmuseum der Waechtersbacher Keramik, Fabrikstr, 63636 Brachttal - T: (06053) 8010, E-mail: service@waechtersbach.com
Decorative Arts Museum
Stoneware development 15009

Brackenheim

Heimatmuseum Brackenheim, Gülthausstr, altes Rathaus, 74336 Brackenheim - T: (07135) 7849
Local Museum - 1987
Crafts, agricultural implements, household articles 15010

Bräunlingen

Kelnhof-Museum, Zwingelgasse 1, 78199 Bräunlingen - T: (0771) 603132, Fax: 603169, E-mail: JSchweitzer@Braeunlingen.de, Internet: http://www.braeunlingen.de
Local Museum - 1923 15011

Brake, Unterweser

Schiffahrtsmuseum der Oldenburgischen Weserhäfen, Breite Str 9, 26919 Brake, Unterweser - T: (04401) 6791, 4383, Fax: 5266. Head: Klaus Müller
Science&Tech Museum - 1960
History of navigation, wood ship building in the 19th c, development of the Oldenburg harbours, seamen's folk art, Dutch tiles with depictions of ships 15012

Brakel

Stadtmuseum Brakel, Am Markt 5, 33034 Brakel - T: (05272) 360269, Fax: 360360, E-mail: brassel@brakel.de, Internet: http://www.info@brakel.de. Head: Dirk Brassel
Local Museum 15013

Bramsche

Tuchmacher-Museum Bramsche, Mühlenort 6, 49565 Bramsche - T: (05461) 94510, Fax: 945115, E-mail: Tuchmachermuseum@bramsche.de, Internet: http://www.bramsche.de. Head: Dr. Susanne Meyer
Science&Tech Museum - 1995
Hist of textile industry 15014

Varusschlacht im Osnabrücker Land, Museum und Park Kalkriese, Venner Str 69, 49565 Bramsche - T: (05468) 92040, Fax: 920445, E-mail: kontakt@mupk.de, Internet: http://www.mupk.de. Head: Christian Jaletzke
Archaeological Museum
Antique battlefield, Roman excavation finds from 9 AD BC 15015

Brand-Erbisdorf

Museum Huthaus Einigkeit, Jahnstr 14, 09618 Brand-Erbisdorf - T: (037322) 41666, 50699, Fax: 32341, E-mail: info@brand-erbisdorf.de, Internet: http://www.brand-erbisdorf.de
Science&Tech Museum - 1931
Local hist, silver and lead mining (17th-20th c), models, tools, ore coll of the area 15016

Brand, Oberpfalz

Max-Reger-Gedächtniszimmer, Max-Reger-Str 7, Rathaus, 95682 Brand, Oberpfalz - T: (09236) 230, Fax: 6151, E-mail: Gemeinde.Brand@t-online.de
Music Museum
Memorabilia of composer Max Reger (1873-1916) 15017

Brandenburg an der Havel

Dommuseum, Burghof 9, 14776 Brandenburg an der Havel - T: (03381) 200325, Fax: 224394, E-mail: -dommuseum.brandenburg@t-online.de, Internet: http://www.brandenburg.deu.net/deutsch/dom/default.htm. Head: Gerda Arndt
Religious Arts Museum - 1979
Sacral sculptures, manuscripts, incunabula, book art (16th c), medieval paraments, furniture - library, archive 15018

Industriemuseum Brandenburg, August-Sonntag-Str 5, 14770 Brandenburg an der Havel - T: (03381) 304646, Fax: 304648, E-mail: stahlmuseum@aol.com. Head: Dr. Sieglinde von Treskow
Science&Tech Museum
History of steel production in Brandenburg, metallurgical development 15019

Kinder-und Jugend-Kunst-Galerie Sonnensegel, Gotthardtkirchpl 4-5, 14770 Brandenburg an der Havel - T: (03381) 522837, Fax: 522837, E-mail: sonnensegel@arcormail.de, Internet: http://www.sonnensegel.de. Head: Armin Schubert
Public Gallery 15020

Museum im Frey-Haus, Ritterstr 96, 14770 Brandenburg an der Havel - T: (03381) 522048, Fax: 223987. Head: Dr. Hans-Georg Kohnke
Local Museum - 1887
Geology, history, furnishing (17th-19th c), European graphics (since 16th c), ornamental engraving coll, photo coll - library 15021

Museum im Steintorturm, Steinstr, 14776 Brandenburg an der Havel - T: (03381) 200265. Head: Dr. Hans-Georg Kohnke
Local Museum 15022

Braubach

Burgmuseum Marksburg, Marksburg, 56338 Braubach - T: (02627) 206, Fax: 8866, E-mail: marksburg@deutsche-burgen.org, Internet: http://www.marksburg.de. Head: Gerhard A. Wagner
Historical Museum - 1900
Local hist, folk art and folklore, hist of the Rheinland, medieval interiors, Gimbel coll of weapons, in a medieval fortress on the Rhein - library, archives 15023

Braunfels

Schloss Braunfels, Schloß, 35619 Braunfels - T: (06442) 5002, Fax: 5306, E-mail: schloss@braunfels.de, Internet: http://www.braunfels.de/schloss. Head: Fürst zu Solms
Fine Arts Museum / Historical Museum - ca 1887
Sacral art from the Cloister Altenberg, picture gallery, coll of coins, medals, arms and porcelain, prehistoric finds, period rooms (Renaissance to Empire), coaches, hunting equipment, stove plates (16th-18th c) uniforms, costumes (17th-19th c) 15024

Stadtmuseum Obermühle, Tiefenbacher Str, 35619 Braunfels - T: (06442) 5694. Head: Rudolf Linnertz
Local Museum - 1972
Fully furnished living, bed and children's room from the 19th c, smithery, coach building tools 15025

Waldmuseum Dr. Kanngiesser, Hecksbergstr 21, 35619 Braunfels
Local Museum - 1916
Exhibits from 1871, picture gallery, herbary - Library, archive 15026

Braunlage

Heimat- und Ski-Museum, Am Graben 4, 38700 Braunlage - T: (05520) 1646
Local Museum - 1916
Geology, agriculture, forestry, hist of skiing since 1883 15027

Braunschweig

Altstadtrathaus, Städtisches Museum Braunschweig, Altstadtmarkt, 38100 Braunschweig - T: (0531) 4704551, Fax: 4704555, E-mail: -staedtisches.museum@braunschweig.de, Internet: http://www.braunschweig.de/staedtisches_museum. Head: Dr. Gerd Spies
Local Museum 15028

Braunschweigisches Landesmuseum, Burgpl 1, 38100 Braunschweig - T: (0531) 12150, Fax: 12152607, E-mail: info@landesmuseum-bs.de, Internet: http://www.landesmuseum-bs.de. Head: Dr. Gerd Biegel, Dr. Angela Klein
Local Museum - 1891
Regional hist incl prehist, folk art and culture, including jewellery, furniture, textiles, and agricultural implements, Jewish culture and art 15029

Die Brücke, Steintorwall 3, 38100 Braunschweig - T: (0531) 4704801, Fax: 4704809, E-mail: kulturinstitut@braunschweig.de, Internet: http://www.braunschweig.de. Head: Dr. Anja Hesse
Public Gallery 15030

Formsammlung der Stadt Braunschweig, Städtisches Museum Braunschweig, Löwenwall 16, 38100 Braunschweig - T: (0531) 4704540, 4704505, Fax: 4704555, E-mail: -staedtisches.museum@braunschweig.de, Internet: http://www.braunschweig.de/staedtisches_museum. Head: Dr. Gerd Spies
Special Museum - 1942
Vessels and containers of various materials and from various periods illustrating the development of industrial form 15031

Herzog Anton Ulrich-Museum, Kunstmuseum des Landes Niedersachsen, Museumstr 1, 38100 Braunschweig - T: (0531) 12250, Fax: 12252408, E-mail: info@museum-braunschweig.de, Internet: http://www.museum-braunschweig.de. Head: Prof. Dr. Jochen Luckhardt
Fine Arts Museum - 1754
European painting (15th-18th c), decorative arts, religious art from local churches and monasteries, prints and drawings 15032

Kunstverein Braunschweig e.V., Lessingpl 12, 38100 Braunschweig - T: (0531) 49556, Fax: 124737, E-mail: info@kunstverein-bs.de, Internet: http://www.kunstverein-bs.de. Head: Karola Grässlin
Association with Coll 15033

Landtechnik-Museum Gut Steinhof, Celler Heerstr 336, 38112 Braunschweig - T: (0531) 513370, Fax: 513770. Head: Heinrich Peters
Science&Tech Museum - 1984
Agricultural machines and implements, vehicles, domestic utensils 15034

Mineralien-Kabinett der TU Braunschweig, Gaußstr 28, 38106 Braunschweig - T: (0531) 3913655, Fax: 3918131. Head: Prof. Dietmar Reinsch
Natural History Museum - 1980
Mineralogy 15035

Museum Camera, Hagenbrücke 5, 38100 Braunschweig - T: (0531) 2403663
Fine Arts Museum 15036

Museum für Photographie, Helmstedter Str 1, 38102 Braunschweig - T: (0531) 75000, Fax: 75036, E-mail: info@photomuseum.de, Internet: http://www.photomuseum.de. Head: Klaus G. Kohn, Wiebke Ratzeburg
Special Museum - 1984
Early photographs (1840-1870), 20s to 30s photographs, contemporary photographs 15037

Raabe-Haus, Leonhardstr 29a, 38102 Braunschweig - T: (0531) 4704841, Fax: 4704844, E-mail: raabe-haus@braunschweig.de, Internet: http://www.braunschweig.de. Head: Andreas Böttcher
Special Museum - 1948
Library, drawings, water colors, and manuscripts of Wilhelm Raabe, housed in the writer's last dwelling 15038

Staatliches Naturhistorisches Museum, Pockelsstr 10, 38106 Braunschweig - T: (0531) 3914351, Fax: 3914370, E-mail: museum@snhm.niedersachsen.de, Internet: http://www.naturhistorisches-museum.de. Head: N.N.
Natural History Museum - 1754
Zoology and ornithology, entomology, living fishes and reptiles - library 15039

Städtisches Museum Braunschweig, Am Löwenwall, 38100 Braunschweig, mail addr: Postfach 3309, 38023 Braunschweig - T: (0531) 4704505, Fax: 4704555, E-mail: -staedtisches.museum@braunschweig.de, Internet: http://www.braunschweig.de/staedtisches_museum. Head: Dr. Gerd Spies
Local Museum - 1861
Coins and money, preindustrial production methods, guilds and handicrafts, religious articles, iron work, municipal history 15040

Zisterziensermuseum Riddagshausen, Klostergang, 38104 Braunschweig - T: (0531) 372253, Fax: 2858255
Religious Arts Museum
Cistercian cloister, sacral objects, illustrations 15041

Breckerfeld

Heimatmuseum Breckerfeld, Ostring 19, 58339 Breckerfeld - T: (02338) 80932, Fax: 80967
Local Museum - 1985 15042

Bredstedt

Naturzentrum Nordfriesland, Bahnhofstr 23, 25821 Bredstedt - T: (04671) 4555, Fax: 933516, E-mail: naturzentrum@bredstedt.de, Internet: http://www.naturzentrum-nf.de. Head: Johann-Georg Carstensen
Natural History Museum 15043

Brehna

Bockwindmühle Brehna, Quetzer Weg 9, 06796 Brehna - T: (034954) 43025, E-mail: gelei@t-online.de
Science&Tech Museum
19th c windmill 15044

Breisach am Rhein

Galerie Schloß Rimsingen, 79206 Breisach am Rhein
Public Gallery 15045

Museum für Stadtgeschichte, Rheintorpl 1, 79206 Breisach am Rhein - T: (07667) 83265, 7089, Fax: 83247, Internet: http://www.breisach.de. Head: Uwe Fahrer
Local Museum - 1991 15046

Breitenberg, Niederbayern

Webereimuseum, Gegenbachstr 50, 94139 Breitenberg, Niederbayern - T: (08584) 1490, 961816, Fax: 961826, E-mail: info@breitenberg.de, Internet: http://www.breitenberg.de. Head: Helmut Rührl
Open Air Museum - 1973
Weavingmuseum with a coll of rustic 'Seidl'-furniture 15047

Breitenbrunn, Erzgebirge

Bergmännisches Traditionskabinett mit Besucherbergwerk, Sankt Christoph 12, Schachtstr, 08359 Breitenbrunn, Erzgebirge - T: (037756) 1324. Head: Horst Peter
Folklore Museum / Science&Tech Museum 15048

Breitscheid, Hessen

Austellung zur Erd- und Vorgeschichte, Mühlweg 4, 35767 Breitscheid, Hessen - T: (02777) 1312
Natural History Museum - 1972
Finds and fossils, tools and clay fragments 15049

Bremen

Azaleen-Museum, Rhododendronpark, Marcusallee 60, 28359 Bremen - T: (0421) 3613025, Fax: 3613610, E-mail: JWesthoff@Stadtgruen.Bremen.de, Internet: http://www.bremen.de/info/stadtgruen/Azaleen.htm. Head: Julia Westhoff
Natural History Museum 15050

Bleikeller, Sankt Petri Domgemeinde, Am Dom 1, 28195 Bremen - T: (0421) 365040, Fax: 3650425. Head: Bernd Krause
Religious Arts Museum - 1823
Coffins with mummified bodies, Evangelist figures 20th.c 15051

Bremer Rundfunkmuseum, Findorffstr 22-24, 28215 Bremen - T: (0421) 357406, Fax: 357406. Head: Bernhard Budde
Science&Tech Museum
Radios, tape and record players 15052

Dom-Museum Bremen, Sankt Petri-Dom, 28195 Bremen, mail addr: Sandstr 10-12, 28195 Bremen - T: (0421) 3650475, 3650441, Fax: 3650425. Head: Dr. Ingrid Weibezahn
Religious Arts Museum - 1987
Religious art, 11th15th c textiles out of tombs of the Bremen bishops 15053

Focke-Museum, Bremer Landesmuseum, Schwachhauser Heerstr 240, 28213 Bremen - T: (0421) 3613575, Fax: 3613903, E-mail: post@focke-museum.bremen.de, Internet: http://www.bremen.de/info/focke. Head: Prof. Dr. Jörn Christiansen
Local Museum / Decorative Arts Museum / Archaeological Museum / Folklore Museum - 1900
18th and 19th c culture, city and state hist of Bremen, craft 15054

Galerie Inkatt, Theodor-Billroth-Str 5, 28277 Bremen - T: (0421) 8729133, Fax: 8729133, E-mail: info@inkatt.de, Internet: http://www.inkatt.de. Head: Rainer Bommert
Public Gallery 15055

Gerhard-Marcks-Haus, Am Wall 208, 28195 Bremen - T: (0421) 327200, Fax: 3378675, E-mail: info@marcks.de, Internet: http://www.marcks.de. Head: Dr. Jürgen Fitschen
Fine Arts Museum - 1971
Drawings, graphics and sculpture of Gerhard Marcks (1889-1981), housed in Classicist building 15056

Gesellschaft für Aktuelle Kunst, Teerhof 21, Weserburg, 28199 Bremen - T: (0421) 500897, Fax: 593337, E-mail: GAK-Bremen@t-online.de, Internet: http://www.gak-bremen.de. Head: Dr. Eva Schmidt
Association with Coll 15057

Grüttert Uhrenmuseum Bremen, Galerie Juwelier Grüttert, Sögestr 70, 28195 Bremen - T: (0421) 309050. Head: Volker Schmidt
Science&Tech Museum - 1994
History of horology, navy and tidal clocks, rare exhibits 15058

Heimatmuseum Schloß Schönebeck, Im Dorfe 3-5, 28757 Bremen - T: (0421) 623432, Fax: 623432, E-mail: museum.schloss.schoenebeck@nwn.de. Head: Holger Schleider
Local Museum - 1911
Whaling, stoneware factory Witteburg, herring fishery Africa explorer Gerhard Rohlfs 15059

Krankenhausmuseum am Zentralkrankenhaus Bremen-Ost, Züricher Str 40, 28325 Bremen - T: (0421) 4081781, Fax: 4082898, E-mail: achimtischer@yahoo.de, Internet: http://www.is-bremen.de/is-bremen/Bremen/Museen/Krankenhausmuseum/IS.html. Head: Achim Tischer
Historical Museum / Special Museum
Social hist of psychiatric patients, development of diagnosis and treatments 15060

Kunsthalle Bremen, Am Wall 207, 28195 Bremen - T: (0421) 329080, Fax: 3290847, E-mail: office@kunsthalle-bremen.de, Internet: http://www.kunsthalle-bremen.de. Head: Prof. Dr. Wulf Herzogenrath
Fine Arts Museum - 1849
Painting (Middle Ages to present), with emphasis on 19th and 20th c French and German works, 18th-20th c sculpture, graphic art of all European schools and periods (15th-20th c), 15th-20th c European drawings, illustrated manuscripts and books, 19th and 20th c European posters, 20th c international media art 15061

Mühle Oberneuland, Bremer Landesmuseum für Kunst-und Kulturgeschichte, Mühlenweg 34, 28355 Bremen - T: (0421) 259214, Fax: 3613903, E-mail: post@focke-museum.bremen.de, Internet: http://bremen.de/info/focke/home1.html. Head: Prof. Dr. Jörn Christiansen
Science&Tech Museum 15062

Neues Museum Weserburg Bremen, Teerhof 20, 28199 Bremen - T: (0421) 598390, Fax: 505247, E-mail: nmwb@gegenwartskunst.de, Internet: http://www.nmwb.de. Head: Prof. Dr. Thomas Deecke
Fine Arts Museum - 1991
Contemporary international art since 1960, artist books 15063

Paula Modersohn-Becker Museum. Museum im Roselius-Haus. Bernhard Hoetger Sammlung, Kunstsammlungen Böttcherstraße, Böttcherstr 6-10, 28195 Bremen - T: (0421) 3365077, Fax: 3398295,

E-mail: paula@zfn.uni-bremen.de, Internet: http://www.uni-bremen.de/~paula. Head: Rainer Stamm
Fine Arts Museum - 1927/28
Furnishings of Bremen patrician families with their art coll, silver coll, paintings and drawings by Paula Modersohn-Becker, sculptures, paintings, drawings, arts and crafts by Bernhard Hoetger 15064

Paula Modersohn-Becker-Stiftung (die Sammlung der Stiftung befindet sich in der Kunsthalle Bremen und im Paula Modersohn-Becker Museum (Böttcherstr)), Rembertistr 1a, 28203 Bremen - T: (0421) 327478, Fax: 325949. Head: Dr. Gisela Götte
Fine Arts Museum 15065

Schulgeschichtliche Sammlung, Auf der Hohwisch 61-63, 28207 Bremen - T: (0421) 3613030, Fax: 36159264, E-mail: irohleder@schulmuseum.bremen.de, Internet: http://schulmuseum.bremen.de. Head: Ulla M. Nitsch
Historical Museum - 1983
Hist of the institution of school 15066

Städtische Galerie im Buntentor und Graphothek, Buntentorsteinweg 112, 28201 Bremen - T: (0421) 3616920, 3616567, Fax: 3615745, E-mail: RPfister@kunst.bremen.de. Head: Dr. Hans-Joachim Manske
Public Gallery 15067

Stiftung Fritz und Hermine Overbeck, Alte Hafenstr 30, 28757 Bremen - T: (0421) 663665, Fax: 663665. Head: Gertrud Overbeck
Fine Arts Museum
Works by the painters 15068

Übersee-Museum, Bahnhofspl 13, 28195 Bremen - T: (0421) 16038101, Fax: 1603899, E-mail: uem1@uni-bremen.de, Internet: http://www.uebersee-museum.de. Head: Dr. Andreas Lüderwald
Ethnology Museum / Natural History Museum - 1896
Ethnology, natural sciences, trade hist of Bremen 15069

Universum Science Center Bremen, Fahrenheitsstr 6, 28359 Bremen - T: (0421) 33460, Fax: 3346109, E-mail: info@universum-sc.de, Internet: http://www.usc-bremen.de. Head: Gotthilf Stan Dyck
Science&Tech Museum - 2000
Human, earth, cosmos 15070

Bremerhaven

Bremerhavener Versorgungs- und Verkehrsmuseum, Hansastr 17, 27568 Bremerhaven - T: (0471) 4771329, Fax: 4771109. Head: Jörn Hoffmann
Science&Tech Museum - 1977
Hist of public transport, coll of domestic appliances 15071

Deutsches Schiffahrtsmuseum, Hans-Scharoun-Pl 1, 27568 Bremerhaven - T: (0471) 482070, Fax: 4820755, E-mail: postmaster@dsm.de, Internet: http://www.dsm.de. Head: Prof. Dr. Detlev Ellmers, Hans-Walter Keweloh
Historical Museum / Science&Tech Museum / Open Air Museum - 1971
German ships, shipping and seamanship from prehistoric times to present, German navy from 1848 to present, water sports in Germany, German fishing and whaling, German maritime and polar research - library, archive, photo archive, chemical laboratory 15072

Historisches Museum Bremerhaven, Morgenstern-Museum, An der Geeste, 27570 Bremerhaven - T: (0471) 20138, Fax: 5902700, E-mail: - historischesmuseum@bremerhaven.de, Internet: http://www.historisches-museum-bremerhaven.de. Head: Dr. Alfred Kube, Dr. Anja Benscheidt
Local Museum - 1896
Fishing, harbours, shipbuilding, art, pre- and early history, 15073

Kunsthalle Bremerhaven, Karlsburg 4, 27568 Bremerhaven - T: (0471) 46838, Fax: 417550, E-mail: kunstverein@nord.com.net. Head: Jürgen Wesseler
Association with Coll - 1886
Art of the 20th c, Classic modern art 15074

Museumsschiff FMS Gera, Fischkai, 27572 Bremerhaven - T: (0471) 308160, Fax: 5902700, E-mail: historischesmuseum@bremerhaven.de, Internet: http://www.historisches-museum-bremerhaven.de. Head: Dr. Alfred Kube
Science&Tech Museum 15075

Nordseemuseum, Wissenschaftliche Sammlung des Alfred-Wegener-Instituts für Polar- und Meeresforschung, Am Handelshafen 12, 27570 Bremerhaven - T: (0471) 4831402, Fax: 4831425
Natural History Museum - 1921
Marine flora and fauna, palaeontology, tides 15076

Technikmuseum U-Boot "Wilhelm Bauer", Hans-Scharoun-Pl 1, 27568 Bremerhaven - T: (0471) 482070, Fax: 48207055, E-mail: postmaster@dsm.de, Internet: http://www.dsm.de. Head: Joachim Massalsky
Science&Tech Museum - 1983
Submarine technology 15077

Volkskundliches Freilichtmuseum im Stadtpark Speckenbüttel, Marschenhausweg 2, 27580 Bremerhaven - T: (0471) 85039. Head: Karl Willms
Open Air Museum - 1910
Fenland house, mill 15078

Bremervörde

Bachmann-Museum, Vorwerkstr 19, 27432 Bremervörde - T: (04761) 814603, Internet: http://www.bremervoerde.de/kut/sehen/se04.htm. Head: Ulrich Schliemann
Historical Museum / Folklore Museum - 1909
Geology, palaeontology 15079

Bäckerei- und Dorfgeschichtliches Museum, Talstr 1, Elm, 27432 Bremervörde - T: (04761) 4130
Special Museum
Bakery history, village life 15080

Ehemalige Erzbischöfliche Kanzlei, Bachmann-Museum, Amtsallee 8, 27432 Bremervörde - T: (04761) 814603, Internet: http://www.bremervoerde.de/kut/sehen/se04.htm. Head: Ulrich Schliemann
Historical Museum - 1909
Early and Prehistory, history of moor 15081

Heimathaus Mehedorf, An der Mehe 20, 27432 Bremervörde - T: (04769) 1044
Local Museum
Local history and life 15082

Heimathausanlage Schafstall, Beverwehr, Plönjeshausen, 27432 Bremervörde - T: (04767) 920000
Local Museum
Local history and life 15083

Historische Apothekenausstellung, Bachmann-Museum, Vorwerkstr 21, 27432 Bremervörde - T: (04761) 814603, Internet: http://www.bremervoerde.de/kut/sehen/se04.htm. Head: Ulrich Schliemann
Historical Museum
Medical service and history, destillery 15084

Museum des ehemaligen Kreises Stuhm, Vorwerkstr 17, 27432 Bremervörde - T: (04761) 8170073
Local Museum
Local history 15085

Museumsscheune, Amtsallee 8, 27432 Bremervörde - T: (04761) 8170073
Agriculture Museum
Agricultural implements and machinery, potato steamer 15086

Brensbach

Brensbach Museum und Galerie im alten Rathaus, Höchster Str 3, 64395 Brensbach - T: (06061) 449
Local Museum 15087

Bretten

Melanchthonhaus Bretten, Melanchthonstr 1, 75015 Bretten - T: (07252) 94410, Fax: 944116, E-mail: info@melanchthon.com, Internet: http://www.melanchthon.com. Head: Dr. Günter Frank
Special Museum - 1897
Writings of Philipp Melanchthon and documents on his life and work, works on the history of the Humanist movement and the Reformation - library 15088

Stadtmuseum Bretten, Marktpl 1, 75015 Bretten - T: (07252) 957621, Fax: 2628, E-mail: stadt@bretten.de, Internet: http://www.bretten.de. Head: Dr. W.D. Albert
Local Museum - 1990
Geology, ancient and early hist, industrial hist, Georg Wörner cabinet 15089

Breuberg

Breuberg-Museum, Burg Breuberg, 64747 Breuberg, mail addr: Wertheimer Str 19a, 64747 Breuberg - T: (06165) 530, Fax: 70955, E-mail: info@breuberg.de. Head: Ludwig Funck
Local Museum - 1963
Examples of various building styles from the Romanesque period to Gothic and late Renaissance, decorative art, trade, handicraft 15090

Brigachtal

Heimatmuseum Brigachtal, Bondelstr 25, 78086 Brigachtal - T: (07721) 90090, Fax: 90091, E-mail: reimond.kammerer@t-online.de, Internet: http://www.brigachtal.de
Local Museum 15091

Brome

Museum Burg Brome, Junkerende, 38465 Brome - T: (05833) 1820, E-mail: - Kreisarchaeologie.Gifhorn@web.de, Internet: http://www.Gifhorn.de. Head: Dr. Andreas Wallbrecht
Special Museum - 1974
Textile industry, regional hist, especially crafts 15092

Bruchhausen-Vilsen

Niedersächsisches Kleinbahn-Museum Bruchhausen-Vilsen, Bahnhof, 27305 Bruchhausen-Vilsen - T: (04252) 93000, Fax: 930012, E-mail: info@museumseisenbahn.de, Internet: http://www.museumseisenbahn.de. Head: Insa Konukiewitz
Science&Tech Museum
Hist of the narrow-gauge railway, economic significance 15093

Bruchköbel

Heimatmuseum im Alten Rathaus, Hauptstr 52, 63486 Bruchköbel - T: (06181) 76244
Local Museum - 1978
Village hist, documents, porcelain, Roman finds - Library, archive 15094

Heimatmuseum im Neuen Spielhaus, Spielhausgasse 1, 63486 Bruchköbel - T: (06181) 72800
Local Museum - 1987
Agricultural, trade and craft implements - Library, archive 15095

Bruchsal

Heimatmuseum Heidelsheim, Merianstr 16, 76646 Bruchsal - T: (07251) 55720
Local Museum 15096

Heimatmuseum Untergrombach, Obergrombacher Str 32, 76646 Bruchsal - T: (07257) 1502
Local Museum - 1983
Peasant life, cigar industry 15097

Kindergartenmuseum, c/o Caritasverband für die Erzdiözese Freiburg e.V., Friedhofstr 11, 76646 Bruchsal - T: (06221) 410233, Fax: 410251, E-mail: herta.pelz@caritas-dicv-fr.de. Head: H. Pelz
Special Museum - 1988
Religious education, educational theory, textbooks, exercise books, revues, material, diaries, Fröbel and Montessori material, documents 15098

Museum Mechanischer Musikinstrumente, Sammlung Jan Brauers (Zweigmuseum des Badischen Landesmuseums), Schloß Bruchsal, 76646 Bruchsal - T: (07251) 742661, Fax: 742675. Head: Dr. Wolfram Metzger
Music Museum - 1984
Instruments from the Black Forest 15099

Schloß Bruchsal, 76646 Bruchsal - T: (07251) 742661, Fax: 742675. Head: Prof. Dr. Harald Siebenmorgen
Decorative Arts Museum - 1975
Flemish and French tapestries (17th and 18th c), religious articles, sculpture, ceramics and textiles, 18th c hunting weapons 15100

Städtisches Museum, Schloß, 76646 Bruchsal - T: (07251) 79253, Fax: 79455. Head: E. Reinig
Local Museum - 1902
Ancient and early hist, local hist, medals 15101

Bruck, Oberpfalz

Heimat- und Bauernmuseum, Hintere Marktstr 13, 92436 Bruck, Oberpfalz - T: (09434) 3068, Fax: 1368
Local Museum - 1975
Local history and flora and fauna of Upper Palatinate 15102

Bruckmühl

Wallfahrtsmuseum, Katholische Kirchenstiftung Weihenlinden-Högling, Wallfahrtskirche, 83052 Bruckmühl - T: (08062) 1281, Fax: 806661. Head: Gregor Bartkowski
Religious Arts Museum
Pilgrimage museum with religious objects, sculptures and paintings 15103

Brüggen, Niederrhein

Jagd- und Naturkundemuseum, Burg Brüggen, 41379 Brüggen, Niederrhein - T: (02163) 5270
Natural History Museum - 1979
History of hunting 15104

Brühl, Baden

Jugendstilmuseum Reissenweber, Schwetzinger Str 24, 68782 Brühl, Baden - T: (06202) 77762. Head: E. Reissenweber
Decorative Arts Museum - 1988
Art Nouveau ceramics, furniture and other items 15105

Brühl, Rheinland

Finanzgeschichtliche Sammlung der Bundesfinanzakademie, Willy-Brandt-Str 10, 50321 Brühl, Rheinland - T: (0228) 6825103, Fax: 6825185, E-mail: poststelle@bfabm.bfinv.bund400.de, Internet: http://www.bundesfinanzakademie.de. Head: Hanns U. Hundt-Esswein
Special Museum 15106

Max-Ernst-Kabinett, Bahnhofstr 21, 50321 Brühl, Rheinland - T: (02232) 792700, Fax: 792720, E-mail: stadtverwaltung@bruehl.de, Internet: http://www.bruehl.de. Head: Dr. Jürgen Pech
Fine Arts Museum - 1980
Works and graphics by Max Ernst, catalogues, books, posters, articles, newspaper clippings, videos, photos by famous photographers, Max Ernst portraits 15107

Rathausgalerie der Stadt Brühl, Uhlstr 2, 50321 Brühl, Rheinland - T: (02232) 792710, Fax: 792720, E-mail: stadtverwaltung@bruehl.de, Internet: http://www.bruehl.de. Head: Dr. Nicole Ritter
Public Gallery 15108

Schloß Augustusburg, Schloßstr 6, 50321 Brühl, Rheinland - T: (02232) 44000, 9443117, Fax: 9443127, E-mail: info@schlossbruehl.de, Internet: http://www.schlossbruehl.de. Head: Ingo Hebler
Historical Museum
Archbishop and electorate prince Clemens August (1700-1761) 15109

Schloß Falkenlust, An der Otto-Wels-Str, 50321 Brühl, Rheinland - T: (02232) 44000, 12111, Fax: 43254, E-mail: info@schlossbruehl.de, Internet: http://www.schlossbruehl.de. Head: Ingo Hebler
Historical Museum 15110

Brüssow

Heimatmuseum Brüssow, Karl-Marx-Str 16a, 17326 Brüssow - T: (039742) 80034, 80360, Fax: 80320
Local Museum
Tools 15111

Brunsbüttel

Atrium an der Schleuse, Gustav-Meyer-Pl, 25541 Brunsbüttel - T: (04852) 8850, Fax: 885408, E-mail: atrium@nok-wsa.de. Head: D. Goos
Historical Museum
Buildung, operation and importence of the Nord-Ostsee-Kanal 15112

Heimatmuseum Brunsbüttel, Markt 4, 25541 Brunsbüttel - T: (04852) 7212, Fax: 7212, E-mail: museum.brunsb@t-online.de, Internet: http://www.brunsbuettel.de/museum/home.htm
Local Museum - 1990 15113

Stadtgalerie im Elbeforum, Von-Humboldt-Pl 5, 25541 Brunsbüttel - T: (04852) 540017/21, Fax: 540044
Public Gallery 15114

Bubenreuth

Geigenbau-Museum, Rathaus, Birkenallee, 91088 Bubenreuth - T: (09131) 23028, 21382
Music Museum - 1979
Coll of violins and other music instruments 15115

Buchen

Bezirksmuseum, Kellereistr 25-29, 74722 Buchen - T: (06281) 8898, Fax: 556898, E-mail: info@bezirksmuseum.de, Internet: http://www.bezirksmuseum.de. Head: Dr. Heinrich Laier
Local Museum - 1911
Painting and graphic: painter colony of Hollerbach, Wilhelm Emelé, Wilhelm Schnarrenberger, Anselm Kiefer, Ludwig Schwerin, folk song coll Albert Brosch, religious folk art, furniture, agricultural machinery, glass, ceramics, trades and guilds, textiles, arms, prehist, music, historical photography - library 15116

Buchenberg bei Kempten

Heimatmuseum Buchenberg, Eschacher Str 35b, 87474 Buchenberg bei Kempten - T: (08378) 573, Fax: 573
Local Museum - 1993
Rustic furniture, tools and a shoemaker's workshop 15117

Buchhofen

Bauernhofmuseum, Untere Dorfstr 6, Nindorf, 94533 Buchhofen - T: (09938) 496, Fax: 903927
Agriculture Museum
Agricultural tools, farming machines and handicrafts 15118

Buchholz in der Nordheide

Buchholzer Heimatmuseum, Zum Mühlenteich 3, 21244 Buchholz in der Nordheide - T: (04181) 7396
Local Museum
Local hist, mill 15119

Buchloe

Heimatmuseum Buchloe, Rathauspl 9, 86807 Buchloe - T: (08241) 4551
Local Museum
Printing-office, coll of clocks and work of the painters Eduard Bechteler (1890-1983) and Joseph Schwarz (1709-1766) 15120

Buckow, Märkische Schweiz

Literaturmuseum Brecht-Weigel-Haus, Bertolt-Brecht-Str 30, 15377 Buckow, Märkische Schweiz - T: (033433) 467, Fax: 56215, E-mail: brecht-weigel-haus@kultur-in-mol.de, Internet: http://www.kultur-in-mol.de. Head: Margret Brademann
Special Museum - 1977
Memorabilia of Bertolt Brecht and Helene Weigel in the house where they lived since 1952 15121

Bückeburg

Fürstliches Schloß mit Gemäldegalerie, Mausoleum, Schloßpl 1, 31675 Bückeburg - T: (05722) 5039, Fax: 955858, E-mail: info@schloss-bueckeburg.de, Internet: http://www.schloss-bueckeburg.de. Head: Alexander Perl
Fine Arts Museum 15122

Hubschraubermuseum, Hubschrauberzentrum Bückeburg, Sablé-Pl 6, 31675 Bückeburg - T: (05722) 5533, Fax: 71539, E-mail: hubmus@t-online.de, Internet: http://www.hubschraubermuseum.de. Head: Dr. Siegfried Sobotta
Science&Tech Museum - 1963/1971
Development of verticle takeoff aircraft, model and test helicopters - Archive 15123

Landesmuseum für schaumburg-lippische Geschichte, Landes- und Volkskunde, Lange Str 22, 31675 Bückeburg - T: (05722) 4868, Fax: 4841, E-mail: mail@schaumburg-lippischer-heimatverein.de, Internet: http://www.schaumburg-lippischer-heimatverein.de. Head: Dr. Roswitha Sommer
Local Museum / Folklore Museum / Archaeological Museum - 1905
Early hist, paleontology, folk costumes, various trade workshops 15124

Büddenstedt

Heimatmuseum Büddenstedt, Rathauspl 1, 38372 Büddenstedt - T: (05352) 7207, Fax: 7137
Local Museum - 1989
Half-timbered house from 1811 with bakery, kitchen and other rooms, ceramics 15125

Büdelsdorf

Eisenkunstgußmuseum, Stiftung Schleswig-Holsteinische Landesmuseen Schloß Gottorf, Glück-Auf-Allee 4, 24782 Büdelsdorf - T: (04331) 38711, (04621) 8130, E-mail: info@schloss-gottorf.de, Internet: http://www.schloss-gottorf.de. Head: Dr. Herwig Guratzsch
Decorative Arts Museum - 1963
Iron stoves, fireplaces and related ornamental ironwork 15126

Büdingen

Fürstlich Ysenburg- und Büdingensches Schloßmuseum, Schloßgasse 2, 63654 Büdingen - T: (06042) 8890, 889212, Fax: 3274, E-mail: ysenburg.sekretariat@t-online.de, Internet: http://www.buedingen.de. Head: Gustav-A. Ortel, Dr. K.P. Decker
Historical Museum / Local Museum - 1951
Romanesque and Gothic interiors, frescoes from the 14th to the 16th c, alchemist's and apothecary's workroom and equipment, weapons, furnishings, glass, ceramics, tapestries, iron implements, etc. - library, Ysenburgisches Archiv 15127

Heuson-Museum im Rathaus, Rathausgasse 6, 63654 Büdingen - T: (06042) 950032, 2853, Fax: 2853, E-mail: heusonmuseum@stadt-buedingen.de, Internet: http://www.buedingen.net/heusonmuseum. Head: Willi Luh
Local Museum / Historical Museum - 1938/1971
Local and regional hist, cultural hist, folklore, hist smithy 15128

Bühl, Baden

Heimatmuseum Bühl, Baden, Luisenstr 2, 77815 Bühl, Baden - T: (07223) 940876, Fax: 9408777, E-mail: stgi-buehl@t-online.de
Local Museum - 1910 15129

Heimatmuseum Weitenung, Weitenunger Str 16, 77815 Bühl, Baden - T: (07223) 57253
Local Museum 15130

Bühlau

Heimatstube Bühlau, Hauptstr 19, 01909 Bühlau - T: 3204, Fax: 3228
Local Museum 15131

Bünde

Deutsches Tabak- und Zigarrenmuseum, Fünfhausenstr 12, 32257 Bünde - T: (05223) 161325. Head: Michael Strauß
Special Museum - 1937
Historical pipes, history of tobacco culture and cultivation, historical furniture and cigar manufacturing equipment 15132

Dobergmuseum/Geologisches Museum Ostwestfalen-Lippe, Fünfhausenstr 8-12, 32257 Bünde - T: (05223) 793300, Fax: 793301, E-mail: infoservice@museum-buende.de, Internet: http://www.Museum-Buende.de. Head: Michael Strauß
Natural History Museum
Geology, palaeontology, pre- and early hist 15133

Kreisheimatmuseum Striediecks Hof, Fünfhausenstr 8-12, 32257 Bünde - T: (05223) 161325. Head: Michael Strauß
Local Museum - 1937
Local hist 15134

Büren

Kreismuseum Wewelsburg, Burgwall 19, 33142 Büren - T: (02955) 6108, 7120, Fax: 7117
Historical Museum - 1925
Contemporary hist (Nationalsocialism) 15135

Bürgel

Keramik-Museum, Eisenberger Str 23, 07616 Bürgel - T: (036692) 22250, Fax: 22253, Internet: http://home.t-online.de/kommunales/Stadt-Buergel. Head: Antje Kaden
Decorative Arts Museum - 1880 15136

Bürgstadt

Museum Bürgstadt, Am Mühlgraben 1, 63927 Bürgstadt - T: (09371) 99560, 93830, Fax: 69200
Local Museum - 1995
Winemuseum and memorabilia of composer Johann Michael Breunig (1699-1755), sandstone production, tabac 15137

Büsum

Zwischen den Deichen, Alte Hafeninsel, 25761 Büsum - T: (04834) 1282
Public Gallery 15138

Bützow

Gedenkstätte Zuchthaus Dreibergen, Heimatmuseum Bützow, Schloßpl 2, 18246 Bützow - T: (038461) 66915, Fax: 66924
Local Museum - 1929 15139

Heimatmuseum Bützow, Schloßpl 2, 18246 Bützow - T: (038461) 66915, Fax: 66924
Local Museum - 1929 15140

Burg auf Fehmarn

Mühlen- und Landschaftsmuseum, Bahnhofstr 56, 23769 Burg auf Fehmarn - T: (04372) 1894, 1818
Agriculture Museum / Science&Tech Museum 15141

Peter-Wiepert-Museum, Bahnhofstr 56, 23769 Burg auf Fehmarn - T: (04371) 9627, Fax: 9532. Head: Hans Wilhelm Maas
Local Museum - 1897
Geology and prehist, local hist, weapons, money coll, domestic implements, crafts and folklore 15142

Burg, Dithmarschen

Waldmuseum, Obere Waldstr, 25712 Burg, Dithmarschen - T: (04825) 2985, Fax: 358, Internet: http://www.schleswig-holstein.de/nat_wis/waldmuseum_burg.html
Natural History Museum - 1968
Native animal and plant life, amber, hunting trophies, glacial debris, local hist 15143

Burg Schlitz

Schmiede Burg Schlitz, 17166 Burg Schlitz - T: (039975) 212
Historical Museum - 1982
Hist of the castle, smithy 15144

Burg Stargard

Heimatmuseum Burg Stargard, Burg 1, 17094 Burg Stargard - T: (039603) 22852
Local Museum 15145

Burgau, Schwaben

Heimatmuseum Burgau, c/o N. Kastner, Norbert-Schuster-Str 11, 89331 Burgau, Schwaben - T: (08222) 40060, Fax: 400650, E-mail: rathaus@burgau.de, Internet: http://www.burgau.de/rathaus
Local Museum - 1986
Implements, handicrafts and a coin coll 15146

Tiermuseum, Haldenwanger Str 1, 89331 Burgau, Schwaben - T: (08222) 2794
Natural History Museum 15147

Burgdorf, Kreis Hannover

Stadtmuseum Burgdorf, Schmiedestr 6, 31303 Burgdorf, Kreis Hannover - T: (05136) 1862, Fax: 873744, E-mail: vvvburgdorf@aol.com, Internet: http://www.vvvburgdorf.de. Head: Gerhard Bleich
Local Museum - 1983
Tin figure coll, local hist, prehist 15148

Burghausen, Salzach

Burg zu Burghausen, Burg 48, 84489 Burghausen, Salzach - T: (08677) 4659, Fax: 65674, E-mail: info@bsv.bayern.de. Head: Dr. Brigitte Langer
Fine Arts Museum
15th and 16th c interiors, Gothic paintings, sculpture, Renaissance tapestries 15149

Foltermuseum, Burg 48, 84489 Burghausen, Salzach - T: (08677) 64190, 62900, Fax: 65674
Special Museum 15150

Haus der Fotografie - Dr. Robert-Gerlich-Museum, Burg 1, 84489 Burghausen, Salzach - T: (08677) 4734, Fax: 911127, E-mail: hausderfotografie@burghausen.de, Internet: http://www.burghausen.de/fotografie. Head: Hildegard Fickert
Science&Tech Museum / Fine Arts Museum - 1983
Technical development of photography, cameras, works of german photographers 15151

Historisches Stadtmuseum, Burg 48, 84489 Burghausen, Salzach - T: (08677) 65198, Fax: 878828, 887222, E-mail: stadtmuseum@burghausen.de, Internet: http://www.burghausen.de/stadtmuseum. Head: Josef Schneider
Local Museum - 1899
Early and prehistory, municipal history, handicrafts, painting and sculpture from 13th to 20th c, religious folk art, costumes, furniture, weapons, bird coll 15152

Museum für Brauereigeschichte, Kloster Raitenhaslach, 84489 Burghausen, Salzach - T: (08677) 3075
Special Museum 15153

Staatsgalerie in der Burg, Bayerische Staatsgemäldesammlungen, Burg Nr 48, 84489 Burghausen, Salzach - T: (08677) 4659, Fax: 65674
Fine Arts Museum - 1897
Austrian and Bavarian late Gothic painting 15154

Burgheim

Archäologisches Museum, Marktpl 13, 86666 Burgheim - T: (08432) 94120, Fax: 941222
Archaeological Museum - 1996
Late roman archeological finds 15155

Burgk

Museum Schloß Burgk, 07907 Burgk - T: (03663) 400119, 402821, Fax: 402821, E-mail: Museum_Burgk@t-online.de. Head: Ina Scheffler
Local Museum - 1952
Historic furnishing, local hist, armaments, in 15th c place, 60000 exlibris, book art - library, archive 15156

Burgkunstadt

Deutsches Schustermuseum, Marktpl 1, 96224 Burgkunstadt - T: (09572) 38834, Fax: 38835, E-mail: rathaus@burgkunstadt.de, Internet: http://www.burgkunstadt.de
Special Museum - 1990
History of shoemaking 15157

Burglengenfeld

Oberpfälzer Volkskundemuseum, Berggasse 3, 93133 Burglengenfeld - T: (09471) 701842, Fax: 701845, E-mail: Stadt_Burglengenfeld@t-online.de, Internet: http://www.burglengenfeld.de
Folklore Museum / Local Museum - 1987
Local history, implements and the history of industrialization in Upper Palatinate 15158

Burgpreppach

Museum Nostalgie der 50er Jahre, Rathaus, Schulgasse 53, 97469 Burgpreppach - T: (09536) 272
Decorative Arts Museum - 1999 15159

Burgrieden

Museum Villa Rot - Kunstsammlung Hoenes-Stiftung, Schloßweg 2, 88483 Burgrieden - T: (07392) 8335, Fax: 17190, E-mail: info@villa-rot.de, Internet: http://www.villa-rot.de. Head: Dr. Norbert Deuchert
Fine Arts Museum - 1992
European and asean art and handicraft, china, sculpture 15160

Burgstädt

Historische Arztpraxis, Rochlitzer Str 2, 09217 Burgstädt - T: (03724) 7461
Science&Tech Museum
Original physician's surgery from 1927, historic x-ray 15161

Buschow

Jagdmuseum, Waldkolonie 15, 14715 Buschow - T: (03876) 233
Natural History Museum
3600 trophies collected since 1768, 130 preserved animals 15162

Busdorf

Wikinger Museum Haithabu, Stiftung Schleswig-Holsteinische Landesmuseen Schloß Gottorf, Am Haddebyer Noor, 24688 Busdorf, mail addr: Schloß Gottorf, 24837 Schleswig - T: (04621) 8130, Fax: 813535, E-mail: info@schloss-gottorf.de, Internet: http://www.schloss-gottorf.de. Head: Prof. Dr. C. von Carnap-Bornheim
Archaeological Museum - 1985
Archaeology and history of Haithabu (700-1100 A.D.) 15163

Butjadingen

Nationalpark-Haus, Museum Butjadingen, Am Hafen 4, 26969 Butjadingen - T: (04733) 8517, Fax: 8550, E-mail: nlph.museum.fed-siel@nwn.de. Head: Ewald Deharde
Natural History Museum / Archaeological Museum / Folklore Museum - 1994
Mud-flats of Lower Saxony, tides model, archaeology, fishing 15164

Buttenheim

Geburtshaus Levi Strauss Museum Jeans und Kult, Marktstr 33, 96155 Buttenheim - T: (09545) 442602, Fax: 1878, E-mail: levi-strauss-museum@web.de, Internet: http://www.levi-strauss-museum.de. Head: Tanja Rappelt
Special Museum - 2000
Hist of the Jeans, emigration hist, biography, coll of vintage jeans of Europe 15165

Buttstädt

Heimatmuseum, Freiheitstr, 99628 Buttstädt - T: (036373) 333, 334
Local Museum - 1907
Ancient history, local history, local crafts, burgher and peasant household objects, costumes, history of firefighting 15166

Butzbach

Museum der Stadt Butzbach im Solms-Braunfelser Hof, Färbgasse 16, 35510 Butzbach - T: (06033) 65005, Fax: 65005. Head: Dieter Wolf
Local Museum
Archaeological finds, folk costumes, agricultural implements, trade objects, machines for industrial shoe-making 15167

Buxheim bei Memmingen

Deutsches Kartausen-Museum, c/o Gemeindeverwaltung, Kartause, 87740 Buxheim bei Memmingen - T: (08331) 97700, 61804, Fax: 963429, Internet: http://www.heimatdienst-buxheim.de. Head: Hans Haugg
Religious Arts Museum - 1975
Ignaz Waibl - library 15168

Buxtehude

Buxtehude Museum für Regionalgeschichte und Kunst, Stavenort 2, 21614 Buxtehude - T: (04161) 4021, 501241, Fax: 501298. Head: Dr. Klaus Frerichs
Local Museum / Fine Arts Museum / Historical Museum - 1913 15169

Cadolzburg

Rangau-Heimathaus, Pisendelpl 1, 90556 Cadolzburg - T: (09103) 7886, Fax: 50910
Local Museum
Local crafts and history, geological coll 15170

Calau

Heimatmuseum Calau, Kirchstr 33, 03205 Calau - T: (03541) 8910, Fax: 89153
Local Museum - 1961
Ancient and early hist, local hist, hist of crafts and guilds 15171

Sammlung historischer Maschinen und Geräte, Altnauer Str 71, 03205 Calau - T: (03541) 2002, Fax: 808963, E-mail: frank.bareinz@t-online.de. Head: Reinhard Bareinz
Science&Tech Museum
Stationary engines, steam engines, tractors, 150-years-old working mechanical workshop 15172

Calbe

Heimatstube Calbe, Markt 13, 39240 Calbe - T: (039291) 2727
Local Museum 15173

Calden

Museumsstube Obermeiser, Kirchweg, 34379 Calden - T: (05677) 221
Local Museum - 1990
Regional art and implements, working loom, authentic rooms portraying farmer's life 15174

Schloß und Schloßpark Wilhelmsthal, 34379 Calden - T: (05674) 6898, Fax: 4053. Head: Dr. Kai R. Mathieu
Historic Site
18th c castle with main bldg and working areas, furniture and art objects 15175

Calw

Bauernhausmuseum Altburg, Theodor-Dierlamm-Str 16, 75365 Calw - T: (07051) 50187
Agriculture Museum - 1989
Peasant life, household articles, agricultural implements 15176

Hermann-Hesse-Museum, Marktpl 30, 75365 Calw - T: (07051) 7522, 167260, Fax: 9352210, 930835, E-mail: stadtarchiv@calw.de, Internet: http://www.hermann-hesse.com. Head: Paul Rathgeber
Special Museum - 1990
Life and work of Hermann Hesse 15177

Klostermuseum Hirsau, Calwer Str 6, 75365 Calw - T: (07051) 59015. Head: Prof. Dr. Harald Siebenmorgen
Religious Arts Museum - 1991 15178

Museum der Stadt Calw, Palais Vischer, Bischofstr 48, 75365 Calw - T: (07051) 167260, Fax: 930835, E-mail: stadtarchiv@calw.de, Internet: http://www.calw.de. Head: Paul Rathgeber
Local Museum - 1965/1991
Town hist 15179

Camburg

Heimatmuseum, Amtshof 1-2, 07774 Camburg - T: (036421) 22188
Local Museum - 1910
Geology, ancient and early hist, local hist, 17th-20th c, crafts, folk art, ceramics 15180

Castrop-Rauxel

Rathausgalerie, Europapl 1, 44575 Castrop-Rauxel - T: (02305) 1062423, Fax: 1062421, E-mail: kulturbuero@castrop-rauxel.de
Public Gallery 15181

Celle

Bomann-Museum Celle, Schloßpl 7, 29221 Celle - T: (05141) 12372, Fax: 12535, E-mail: bomann-museum@celle.de, Internet: http://www.bomann-museum.de
Local Museum
Uniforms of the Hanoverian army, silver of Celle, furniture, town history, regional craftsmenship, historical toys, interiors around 1800-1850 - historic rooms in the palace 15182

Das Deutsche Stickmuster-Museum Celle, Palais im Prinzengarten, 29223 Celle - T: (05141) 382626, Fax: 382638. Head: Elfi Connemann, Hans-Joachim Connemann
Decorative Arts Museum / Folklore Museum - 1986
Social hist, sampler embroidered trosseau pieces (17th-20th c), 4 centuries women's hist 15183

Herzogschloss, Schlosspl 1, 29221 Celle - T: (05141) 12373, 550714, Fax: 550715, E-mail: touristinfo@celle.de, Internet: http://www.celle.de
Historic Site
Paintings (eg Jacob Jordaens, Marten de Vos), 17th c theatre, state hist, baroque furniture, renaissance chapel 15184

Kunstmuseum Celle mit Sammlung Robert Simon, Schloßpl 7, 29221 Celle - T: (05141) 12355, Fax: 12495, E-mail: susanne.mcdowell@celle.de, Internet: http://www.celle.de/kunst/24stunden.htm. Head: Susanne McDowell
Fine Arts Museum 15185

Max-Böcker-Museum, Imkereigeschichtliche und bienenkundliche Sammlungen, Wehlstr 4a, 29221 Celle - T: (05141) 9050340, Fax: 9050344, E-mail: info@bieneninstitut.de, Internet: http://www.bieneninstitut.de. Head: Dr. Werner von der Ohe
Agriculture Museum
History, theory and practice of beekeeping 15186

Cham

Galerie Profil, Probsteistr 10, 93413 Cham - T: (09971) 4542
Public Gallery 15187

Museum SPUR Cham, Schützenstr 7, 93413 Cham - T: (09971) 40790
Fine Arts Museum
Modern Art 15188

Sakrale Kunst in der Sankt-Anna-Kapelle, Kirchpl, Chammünster, 93413 Cham - T: (09971) 30288
Religious Arts Museum - 1989
Gothic chapel 15189

Städtische Galerie im Cordonhaus, Propsteistr 46, 93413 Cham - T: (09971) 803496, Fax: 79842, E-mail: tourismus@ti-cham.btl.de, Internet: http://www.cham.de. Head: Brigitte Weiss
Fine Arts Museum - 1982
Local contemporary art 15190

Chemnitz

Deutsches Spielemuseum e.V., Neefestr 78a, 09119 Chemnitz - T: (0371) 306565, Fax: 306565, Internet: http://www.musehen.de
Science&Tech Museum - 1995 15191

Felsendome Rabenstein, Nach dem Kalkwerk 4, 09117 Chemnitz - T: (0371) 8080037, Fax: 8080038, Internet: http://www.felsendome.de
Natural History Museum - 1936
Historic limestone quarry, processing exhibit 15192

Industriemuseum Chemnitz, Annaberger Str 114, 09120 Chemnitz - T: (0371) 539220, Fax: 5392233, E-mail: chemnitz@saechsisches-industriemuseum.de, Internet: http://www.saechsisches-industriemuseum.de. Head: Dr. Jörg Feldkamp
Science&Tech Museum - 1991
Textile machinery, machine tools, office machinery, economic and social history, industrial history of Saxony 15193

Kunstsammlungen Chemnitz, Theaterpl 1, 09111 Chemnitz - T: (0371) 4884424, Fax: 4884499, E-mail: kunstsammlungen@Stadt-Chemnitz.de, Internet: http://www.chemnitz.de/kustsammlungen. Head: Ingrid Mössinger
Fine Arts Museum - 1920
Arts and crafts, textile coll, 19th c German painting, German Impressionism and Expressionism, 20th c art, 19th - 20th c French and German sculpture, drawings and graphic arts (15th - 20th c) - textile coll 15194

Museum für Naturkunde, Theaterpl 1, 09111 Chemnitz - T: (0371) 4884551, Fax: 4884597, E-mail: naturkundemuseum@stadt-chemnitz.de, Internet: http://www.stadt-chemnitz.de/naturkundemuseum. Head: Dr. R. Rössler
Natural History Museum - 1868
'Sterzeleanum', mollusks, entomology, Petrified Forest of Chemnitz, palaeontology - library 15195

Museum für Sächsische Fahrzeuge, Wasserschloßweg 6, Klaffenbach, 09221 Chemnitz - T: (0371) 266350, Internet: http://www.musehen.de
Science&Tech Museum - 1995 15196

Neue Sächsische Galerie, Str der Nationen 33, 09111 Chemnitz - T: (0371) 305879, Fax: 305880. Head: Dr. Werner Ballarin
Fine Arts Museum
Saxonian fine and applied art since 1945 15197

Schloßbergmuseum, Schloßberg 12, 09113 Chemnitz - T: (0371) 4884500/01, Fax: 4884599, E-mail: schlossbergmuseum@stadt-chemnitz.de, Internet: http://www.schlossbergmuseum.de. Head: Dr. Thomas Schuler
Local Museum - 1931
Local hist, development of handicrafts, 13th-18th c sculpture, 18th-19th c local painting, 13th-17th c architecture, 13th-20th c furniture, works of Hans Witten, labour movement 15198

Chieming

Pferde- und Kutschenmuseum, Kirchberg 3, Ising, 83339 Chieming - T: (08667) 790
Natural History Museum / Science&Tech Museum - 1986
Coaches, sleighs, agricultural tools 15199

Chiemsee

Torhalle Frauenchiemsee und Vikarhaus, Frauenchiemsee 41, 83256 Chiemsee - T: (08054) 7256. Head: Eva Posch
Historical Museum
Medieval architecture and fresco paintings 15200

Clausthal-Zellerfeld

Geosammlung der Technischen Universität Clausthal, Adolph-Roemer-Str 2a, 38678 Clausthal-Zellerfeld - T: (05323) 722586, Fax: 722810, E-mail: karl.strauss@tu-clausthal.de, Internet: http://www.tu-clausthal.de/geosammlung. Head: Dr. Karl W. Strauss
Natural History Museum
Ore deposits, minerals 15201

Oberharzer Bergwerksmuseum, Museum für Technik-und Kulturgeschichte, Bornhardtstr 16, 38678 Clausthal-Zellerfeld - T: (05323) 98950, Fax: 989569, E-mail: info@OberharzerBerg-werksmuseum.de, Internet: http://www.Oberharzer-Bergwerksmuseum.de. Head: Helmut Radday, Wilhelm Marbach
Science&Tech Museum / Historical Museum / Open Air Museum - 1892
Hist models of mines, iron and steel works, mineralogy, housing in the 18th and 19th c 15202

Cleebronn

Trillarium, Waffensammlung und Heimatmuseum, Altweibermühle Tripsdrill, 74389 Cleebronn - T: (07135) 9999, Fax: 9996666, E-mail: info@tripsdrill.de, Internet: http://www.tripsdrill.de. Head: Kurt Fischer
Local Museum - 1960
Household articles, arms 15203

Vinarium, Weinbaumuseum und Weinbaufrei-lichtmuseum, Altweibermühle Tripsdrill, 74389 Cleebronn - T: (07135) 9999, Fax: 999666, E-mail: info@tripsdrill.de, Internet: http://www.tripsdrill.de. Head: Kurt Fischer
Agriculture Museum - 1976 15204

Cloppenburg

Museumsdorf Cloppenburg, Niedersächsisches Freilichtmuseum, Bether Str 6, 49661 Cloppenburg - T: (04471) 94840, Fax: 948474, E-mail: museumsdorf@nwn.de, Internet: http://www.museumsdorf.de. Head: Dr. Uwe Meiners
Local Museum / Open Air Museum - 1922/1934
Original buildings (16th-20th c), former trades and crafts, folklore, local art history, peasant history of Lower Saxony, clothing and dress, farming, horticulture, machinery 15205

Coburg

Coburger Puppen-Museum, Rückertstr 2-3, 96450 Coburg - T: (09561) 74047, Fax: 27116. Head: Carin Lossnitzer, Dr. Hans Lossnitzer
Decorative Arts Museum - 1987
Dolls and doll's houses, furniture, porcelain 15206

Friedrich-Rückert-Gedächtnisstätte, Friedrich-Rückert-Str 13, Neuses, 96450 Coburg - T: (09561) 66308, Fax: 66428
Special Museum
House of the professor of oriental studies Friedrich Rückert (1788-1866) 15207

Grabungsmuseum Kirchhof, Steingasse 18, 96450 Coburg - T: (09561) 74180, Fax: 741829
Archaeological Museum - 1994 15208

Kunstsammlungen der Veste Coburg, Veste Coburg, 96450 Coburg - T: (09561) 8790, 87979, Fax: 87966, E-mail: sekretariat@kunstsammlungen-coburg.de, Internet: http://www.kunstsammlungen-coburg.de. Head: Dr. Klaus Weschenfelder
Decorative Arts Museum / Fine Arts Museum - 1838
Print-room, glasses, arms and armor, paintings, sculptures, coins, autographs 15209

Naturkunde-Museum, Park 6, 96450 Coburg - T: (09561) 808120, Fax: 808140, E-mail: info@naturkunde-museum-coburg.de, Internet: http://www.naturkunde-museum-coburg.de. Head: Dr. Werner Korn
Natural History Museum - 1844
Zoology, botany, mineralogy, palaeontology, prehistory and ethnology 15210

Sammlung Herzoglicher Kunstbesitz, Stiftung der Herzog von Sachsen-Coburg und Gotha'schen Familie, Schloß Callenberg, 96450 Coburg - T: (09561) 551510, Fax: 551555, E-mail: schloss-callenberg@t-online.de, Internet: http://www.schloss-callenberg.de. Head: Dr. Ewald Jeutter
Fine Arts Museum - 1998 15211

Schloß Ehrenburg, Schloßpl 1, 96450 Coburg - T: (09561) 80880, Fax: 808840, E-mail: info@bsv.bayern.de
Local Museum - 1919
Municipal hist, 17th c interiors, 19th c furnishings, Baroque carpets and paintings 15212

Zahnhistorische Sammlung, Julius-Popp-Str 20, 96450 Coburg - T: (09561) 15910, Fax: 237919, E-mail: peter-bodirsky@t-online.de, Internet: http://www.zahntechnik-coburg.de. Head: Peter Bodirsky
Science&Tech Museum
Coll of dentist instruments 15213

Cölbe

Heimatmuseum Bürgeln, Baumgartenstr 18, 35091 Cölbe - T: (06427) 8398
Local Museum - 1987
Agricultural implements, dairy farming exhibits, furniture from 1919, trade workshops, medical equipment, coll of old radios 15214

Coesfeld

Glasmuseum Alter Hof Herding, Letter Berg 38, 48653 Coesfeld - T: (02546) 93050
Fine Arts Museum 15215

Heimatmuseum Lette, Bahnhofsallee 10, 48653 Coesfeld - T: (02546) 234, Fax: 760447, E-mail: heimatverein-lette@coesfeld.de
Local Museum 15216

Stadtmuseum Coesfeld und Städtische Turmgalerie, Mühlenpl 3, 48653 Coesfeld - T: (02541) 4723, 880018, Fax: 880020
Local Museum 15217

Colditz

Johann-David-Köhler-Haus, Zweigstelle des Museums der Stadt Colditz, An der Kirche 1, 04680 Colditz - T: (034381) 43519, 44987, Fax: 43404, 44987, Internet: http://www.colditz.de
Special Museum / Decorative Arts Museum
Numismatics 15218

Museum der Stadt Colditz, Tiergartenstr 1, 04680 Colditz - T: (034381) 44987, Fax: 44987, Internet: http://www.colditz.de. Head:
Local Museum / Military Museum - 1874
Ancient hist, local hist, justice, local crafts, pottery and porcelain, numismatics, WW II 15219

Coppenbrügge

Museum in der Burg, Schloßstr 1, 31863 Coppenbrügge - T: (05156) 8623, Fax: 7027, Internet: http://members.aol.com/muscop. Head: Gernot Hüsam
Historical Museum - 1986
Trade workshops, castle hist, county Spiegelbergm pilgrimage country at Ith, Tsar Peter I in Coppenbrügge, historical Coppenbrügge, nature and landscape, from flax to linen, pottery, shoemaker's workshop 15220

Cornberg

Cornberger Sandsteinmuseum, Kloster Cornberg, 36219 Cornberg - T: (05650) 969715, Fax: 969716. Head: Heinz Moch
Natural History Museum - 1994
Hist of sandstone quarry, historic finds, fossils 15221

Cospeda

Museum 1806, Jenaer Str 12, 07751 Cospeda - T: (03641) 820925, Fax: 508861, E-mail: info@jena1806.de, Internet: http://www.jena1806.de. Head: Holger Nowak
Historical Museum / Military Museum / Historic Site - 1956
Graphics, dioramas and historic weapons of the Battle of Jena-Auerstädt in 1806 15222

Coswig, Anhalt

Museum, Schloßstr 57, 06869 Coswig, Anhalt - T: (034903) 61052, Fax: 61057, E-mail: stadt-coswig-anhalt@t-online.de, Internet: http://www.coswig-anhalt.de. Head: Karl Schmidt
Science&Tech Museum / Local Museum - 1950
Development of pottery since early history, machines, models, technical ceramics for chemistry and construction, rivers of Anhalt 15223

Coswig bei Dresden

Karrasburg Museum Coswig, Karrasstr 4, 01640 Coswig bei Dresden - T: (03523) 66450, Fax: 75506, E-mail: stadt@coswig.de, Internet: http://www.coswig.de/museum. Head: Evelies Baumann
Local Museum - 1957
Local, regional hist, pre-historic finds 15224

Cottbus

Brandenburgische Kunstsammlungen Cottbus, Museum für zeitgenössische Kunst, Fotografie und Plakat, Spremberger Str 1, 03046 Cottbus - T: (0355) 22042, 794051, Fax: 22043, E-mail: kunstmuseum-cottbus@t-online.de, Internet: http://www.kunstmuseum-cottbus.de. Head: Dr. Perdita von Kraft
Fine Arts Museum - 1977
Painting, sculpture, objects, graphic, drawings, photogr and posters 15225

Fürst Pückler Museum - Park und Schloß Branitz, Kastanienallee 11, 03042 Cottbus - T: (0355) 7515221, Fax: 7515230, E-mail: pueckler-museum.info@t-online.de, Internet: http://www.pueckler-museum.de. Head: Berthold Ettrich
Local Museum - 1995
Located in a late baroque castle (built 1772), paintings of Carl Blechen (1798-1840), memorabilia of Hermann Fürst von Pückler-Muskau (1785-1871) 15226

Galerie Haus 23, Marienstr 23, 03046 Cottbus - T: (0355) 702357, Fax: 702357, Internet: http://www.cottbus.de/kultur/haus23
Public Gallery 15227

Museum der Natur und Umwelt Cottbus, Am Amtsteich 17-18, 03046 Cottbus - T: (0355) 797818, 797935, Fax: 24282, Internet: http://www.dhm.de/museen/mnu_cottbus/. Head: Sigrid Robel
Natural History Museum - 1887
Geological and palaeontologic finds, coal-mining, entomological coll 15228

Niederlausitzer Apothekenmuseum, Löwen-Apotheke, Altmarkt 24, 03046 Cottbus - T: (0355) 23997, Fax: 3831848, E-mail: info@niederlausitzer-apothekenmuseum.de, Internet: http://www.niederlausitzer-apothekenmuseum.de
Special Museum
Pharmacy opened 1573, complete interior design from 1830 and early 20th c, historic coll of pharmaceuticals 15229

Serbski muzej/ Wendisches Museum, Stadtgeschichtliche Sammlungen Cottbus, Mühlenstr 12, 03046 Cottbus - T: (0355) 794930, Fax: 701275. Head: Steffen Krestin
Local Museum / Folklore Museum - 1994
Local hist, peasant life, folk art, literature, music of the Sorbians/Wends 15230

Stadtmuseum Cottbus, Bahnhofstr 52, 03046 Cottbus - T: (0355) 380770, Fax: 3807799, Internet: http://www.cottbus.de. Head: Steffen Krestin
Local Museum - 1887/1990
Local hist, ceramic, carpet and glas industry - library 15231

Crailsheim

Stadtmuseum im Spital, Spitalstr 2, 74564 Crailsheim - T: (07951) 94640, Fax: 946419, Internet: http://www.crailsheim.de/stadtmuseum.htm. Head: Susanna Sackstetter
Local Museum
Faience, local history, musical instruments 15232

Creglingen

Feuerwehr-Museum Schloß Waldmannshofen, Schloß Waldmannshofen, 97993 Creglingen - T: (07931) 2677, Fax: 46534
Science&Tech Museum - 1967 15233

Fingerhutmuseum, Kohlesmühle 6, 97993 Creglingen - T: (07933) 370, Fax: 443. Head: B. Greif
Decorative Arts Museum - 1982
Thimbles from Roman times until today, Helmut Greif (thimble maker) 15234

Vom Kloster zum Dorf, Klosterkirche Frauental, 97993 Creglingen - T: (07933) 7128, Fax: 20015
Local Museum - 1990
Hist of the monastery and town liturgical items 15235

Cremlingen

Museum für moderne Kunst, Nordstr 31, 38162 Cremlingen - T: (05306) 4363. Head: Prof. Bernd Löbach
Fine Arts Museum 15236

Creußen

Krüge-Museum, Hinteres Tor, Am Rennsteig 8, 95473 Creußen - T: (09270) 9890, Fax: 98977, E-mail: stadt@creussen.de, Internet: http://www.creussen.de
Special Museum - 1950
Crockery called "Creußener Steinzeug, 17th c and 18th c 15237

Crimmitschau

Agrar- und Freilichtmuseum, Schloß Blankenhain, 08451 Crimmitschau - T: (036608) 2321, Fax: 2332, E-mail: Agrarmuseum@compuserve.de, Internet: http://www.freilichtmuseum-blankenhain.de. Head: Jürgen Knauss
Agriculture Museum / Open Air Museum - 1981
Apiculture, agriculture, brewery, ethnography, architecture 15238

Westsächsisches Textilmuseum Crimmitschau, Leipziger Str 125, 08451 Crimmitschau - T: (03762) 931939, Fax: 931938, E-mail: crimmitschau@saechsisches-industriemuseum.de, Internet: http://www.saechsisches-industriemuseum.de. Head: Andrea Bergler
Historical Museum / Science&Tech Museum / Local Museum 15239

Crostau

Heimatstube Crostau, Kirschauer Str 5, 02681 Crostau
Local Museum - 1954
Local history, weaving, castle ruins 15240

Cumlosen

Heimatstube Cumlosen, 19322 Cumlosen - T: (038794) 211
Local Museum - 1955
Native bird fauna, local history 15241

Cunewalde

Polenz-Museum, Gänseberg 7, 02733 Cunewalde - T: (035877) 80888, Fax: 23030, E-mail: touristinfo@cunewalde.de, Internet: http://www.cunewalde.de
Special Museum - 1992
Memorabilia of writer Wilhelm von Polenz 15242

Cuxhaven

Stadtmuseum Cuxhaven, Südersteinstr 38, 27472 Cuxhaven - T: (04721) 62213, 399670, Fax: 399671
Local Museum
Early hist of the Elbe-Weser triangle, local harbour and shipping, local culture 15243

Uns lütt Schiffsmuseum, Wehrbergsweg 7, 27476 Cuxhaven - T: (04721) 48158
Science&Tech Museum 15244

Wrackmuseum, Dorfstr 80, 27476 Cuxhaven - T: (04721) 23341, Fax: 690876 23341. Head: Peter Baltes
Science&Tech Museum - 1980
Salvage work, diving 15245

Dachau

Bezirksmuseum Dachau, Augsburger Str 3, 85221 Dachau - T: (08131) 56750, Fax: 78305, E-mail: info@dachauer-galerien-museen.de, Internet: http://www.dachauer-galerien-museen.de. Head: Ursula Katharina Nauderer
Local Museum - 1905
Local history 15246

Gemäldegalerie Dachau, Konrad-Adenauer-Str 3, 85221 Dachau - T: (08131) 567516, Fax: 78305, E-mail: DachauerGalerienundMuseen@t-online.de. Head: Dr. Elisabeth Boser
Fine Arts Museum
Landscape painting 19th/20th c, artists' colony Dachau 15247

KZ-Gedenkstätte mit Museum, Alte Römerstr 75, 85221 Dachau - T: (08131) 669970, Fax: 2235, E-mail: info@cc-memorial-site-dachau.org, Internet: http://www.cc-memorial-site-dachau.org. Head: Dr. Barbara Distel
Historical Museum - 1965
History of the Dachau and other concentration camps from 1933 to 1945 - library and archives 15248

Neue Galerie, Brunngartenstr 5, 85221 Dachau - T: (08131) 56750, 567517, Fax: 78305, E-mail: info@dachauer-galerien-museen.de, Internet: http://www.dachauer-galerien-museen.de. Head: Dr. Elisabeth Boser
Public Gallery 15249

Schloß Dachau, Schloßstr 7, 85221 Dachau - T: (08131) 87923, Fax: 78573, E-mail: info@bsv.bayern.de
Local Museum - 1980
Former country-seat of the Wittelsbach family 15250

Dachwig

Heimatmuseum Dachwig, Lange Str 27, 99100 Dachwig - T: (036206) 23205, Fax: 20433
Local Museum 15251

Dahlen, Sachsen

Heimatmuseum, Wurzener Str 1, 04774 Dahlen, Sachsen - T: (034361) 53401
Local Museum - 1955
Local and regional history, geology of the Dahlener Heide including samples of boulders 15252

Dahlenburg

Heimatmuseum Sankt Laurentius, Am Markt 17, 21368 Dahlenburg - T: (05851) 860, Fax: 8640, E-mail: museum@dahlenburg-net.de, Internet: http://www.dahlenburg-net.de
Local Museum - 1928
Town hist 15253

Dahme, Mark

Heimatmuseum Dahme, Mark, Töpferstr 16, 15936 Dahme, Mark - T: (035451) 493, Fax: 493, Internet: http://www.dahme.de
Local Museum - 1905
Furniture of the 18th and 20th c, household articles, costumes, 700 years old treasure box, coins and medals by F.W. Kullrich, blue print of the Lower Fläming 15254

Dahn

Galerie N, Marktstr, Altes Rathaus, 66994 Dahn - T: (06391) 2811, E-mail: galerie-N@kunst-Wasgau.de, Internet: http://www.kunst-wasgau.de. Head: Christine Bernauer-Keller
Public Gallery 15255

Kreisgalerie, Schulstr 14, 66994 Dahn - T: (06331) 809165, Fax: 809373, E-mail: e.huber@lksuedwestpfalz.de, Internet: http://www.lksuedwestpfalz.de. Head: Hans Jörg Duppré
Public Gallery 15256

Damme, Dümmer

Stadtmuseum Damme, Lindenstr 20, 49401 Damme, Dümmer - T: (05491) 4622. Head: Wolfgang Friemerding
Local Museum / Natural History Museum
Town hist, hist of carnival since 1614, Damme iron mining (palaeontology, mineralogy) 15257

Dannenberg, Elbe

Historisches Feuerwehrmuseum Lüchow-Dannenberg, Neu Tramm, 29451 Dannenberg, Elbe - T: (05861) 2242
Science&Tech Museum
Hist of fire fighting 15258

Städtisches Heimatmuseum im Waldemarturm, Am Amtsberg, 29451 Dannenberg, Elbe - T: (05861) 808196, Fax: 808100, E-mail: dannenberg@dannenberg.de, Internet: http://www.dannenberg.de. Head: Undine Stiwich
Local Museum 15259

Dannewerk

Museum am Dannewerk, Ochsenweg 5, 24867 Dannewerk - T: (04621) 37814, Fax: 31025. Head: Nis Hardt
Historical Museum / Historic Site 15260

Darmstadt

Eisenbahnmuseum Darmstadt-Kranichstein, Steinstr 7, 64291 Darmstadt - T: (06151) 376401, Fax: 377600, E-mail: museumsbahn@t-online.de, Internet: http://home.t-online.de/home/museumsbahn. Head: Uwe Breitmeier
Science&Tech Museum - 1976
Locomotives from 1887 to 1965, railroad equipment and techniques, working railways on museum's railway line 15261

Großherzoglich-Hessische Porzellansammlung, Schloßgartenstr 10, 64289 Darmstadt - T: (06151) 713233, Fax: 712920, E-mail: -porzellanmuseum.darmstadt@t-online.de, Internet: http://www.porzellanmuseum-darmstadt.de. Head: Bettina John-Willeke
Decorative Arts Museum - 1907
18th and 19th c European porcelain and faience - library 15262

Hessische Landes- und Hochschulbibliothek, Schloß, 64283 Darmstadt - T: (06151) 165800, Fax: 165897, E-mail: auskunft@lhb.tu-darmstadt.de, Internet: http://elib.tu-darmstadt.de/lhb. Head: Dr. Hans-Georg Nolte-Fischer
Library with Exhibitions 15263

Hessisches Landesmuseum, Friedenspl 1, 64283 Darmstadt - T: (06151) 165703, Fax: 28942, E-mail: info@hlmd.de, Internet: http://www.hlmd.de. Head: Dr. Ina Busch
Historical Museum / Fine Arts Museum / Natural History Museum - 1787/1820
European painting from the Middle Ages to the present, graphic art, art nouveau crafts, archaeology, geology and mineralogy, zoology 15264

Institut für Neue Technische Form, Eugen-Bracht-Weg 6, 64287 Darmstadt - T: (06151) 48008, Fax: 46553, E-mail: info@intef.de, Internet: http://www.intef.de. Head: Michael Schneider
Science&Tech Museum 15265

Kommunale Galerie, Justus-Liebig-Haus, Große Bachgasse 2, 64283 Darmstadt - T: (06151) 133021, Fax: 133398
Public Gallery 15266

Kunst Archiv Darmstadt, Kasinostr 3, 64293 Darmstadt - T: (06151) 291619, Fax: 291683, E-mail: kunstarchivdarmstadt@t-online.de, Internet: http://www.kunstarchivdarmstadt.de. Head: C.K. Netuschil
Fine Arts Museum 15267

Kunsthalle Darmstadt, Steubenpl 1, 64293 Darmstadt - T: (06151) 891184, Fax: 897797, E-mail: kunsthalle-darmstadt@web.de, Internet: http://www.kunsthalledarmstadt.de. Head: Peter Joch
Fine Arts Museum - 1837
Contemporary art 15268

Museum Jagdschloß Kranichstein, Stiftung Hessischer Jägerhof, Kranichsteiner Str 261, 64289 Darmstadt - T: (06151) 718613, 717032, Fax: 732332, Internet: http://www.jagdschloss-kranichstein.de. Head: Monika Kessler
Historical Museum / Special Museum / Historic Site - 1917
Hunting weapons and equipment from the 16th to the 19th c, 18th and 19th c interiors, trophies and paintings 15269

Museum Künstlerkolonie, Institut Mathildenhöhe, Alexandraweg, 64287 Darmstadt - T: (06151) 133385, Fax: 133739, E-mail: instmath@stadt.darmstadt.de, Internet: http://www.darmstadt.de. Head: Dr. Klaus Wolbert
Decorative Arts Museum - 1899
New prototypes of furniture, interiors, houses by the colony of artists, development of the Art Nouveau style ("Jugendstil") 15270

Schloßmuseum Darmstadt, Residenzschloß, Glockenbau, 64283 Darmstadt - T: (06151) 24035, Fax: 997457. Head: Dr. Volker Illgen
Museum of Classical Antiquities - 1924
Hessian history and cultural life (17th to 20th c), European painting carriages and court uniforms 15271

Städtische Kunstsammlungen und Direktion, Institut Mathildenhöhe, Olbrichweg 13, 64287 Darmstadt - T: (06151) 132778, Fax: 133739, E-mail: instmath@stadt.darmstadt.de, Internet: http://www.darmstadt.de. Head: Dr. Klaus Wolbert
Fine Arts Museum 15272

Wella Museum, c/o Wella AG, Berliner Allee 65, 64295 Darmstadt - T: (06151) 342459, Fax: 342748, E-mail: sschwab@wella.de, Internet: http://www.wella.com. Head: Sigrid Schwab
Special Museum - 1952
History of cosmetics and beauty care from antiquity to the present, temporarily closed 15273

Wixhäuser Dorfmuseum, Römergasse 17, 64291 Darmstadt - T: (06150) 7731, Fax: 990802, Internet: http://www.darmstadt.de/kultur/dorfmuseum.html. Head: Hans-Eberhard Ruhl
Local Museum - 1980
Cultural and social hist of the village 15274

Dassel

Blankschmiede Neimke, Teichpl 2, 37586 Dassel - T: (05564) 2721
Science&Tech Museum
Smithy 15275

Datteln

Hermann-Grochtmann-Museum Datteln, Genthiner Str 7, 45711 Datteln - T: (02363) 107362, Fax: 107446, E-mail: kultur@datteln.de, Internet: http://www.datteln.de. Head: Rosemarie Schloßer
Local Museum - 1927/88
Prehist, early hist, religious hist, hist of industry 15276

Dautphetal

Alte Kirche Friedensdorf, Kirchweg 4, Friedensdorf, 35232 Dautphetal - T: (06466) 361. Head: Walter Gerlach
Religious Arts Museum
Church with 13th c chorus, pointed arches, flat, half-timbered nave 15277

Heimatmuseum Buchenau, Alte Landstr, 35232 Dautphetal - T: (06466) 380
Local Museum - 1983
Folk costumes, various trade implements, agricultural machines and tools, toys, kitchen utensils and appliances 15278

Deckenpfronn

Dorfmuseum Deckenpfronn, Zehntscheuer, Marktpl 1, 75392 Deckenpfronn - T: (07056) 92790, Fax: 927950, E-mail: Gemeinde@deckenpfronn.de, Internet: http://www.deckenpfronn.de
Local Museum - 1987
Peasant life, social conditions 15279

Museum Kalt-Heiß, Pfarrscheuer, Marktpl 1, 75392 Deckenpfronn - T: (07056) 92790, Fax: 927950, E-mail: Gemeinde@deckenpfronn.de, Internet: http://www.deckenpfronn.de
Local Museum - 1987 15280

Dedelstorf

Jagdmuseum Wulff, Hässelmühler Weg, 29386 Dedelstorf - T: (05832) 2233
Special Museum 15281

Deggendorf

Handwerksmuseum, Maria-Ward-Pl 1, 94469 Deggendorf - T: (0991) 4084, Fax: 340321, E-mail: museen@deggendorf.de, Internet: http://www.deggendorf.de
Special Museum - 1991
Tools, machines, handicraft 15282

Stadtmuseum Deggendorf, Östlicher Stadtgraben 28, 94469 Deggendorf - T: (0991) 2960555, Fax: 2960559, E-mail: museen@deggendorf.de, Internet: http://www.deggendorf.de. Head: Birgitta Petschek-Sommer
Local Museum - 1954
Furniture, tin, glass, ceramics, textiles, pharmacy equipment 15283

Deidesheim

Deutsches Film- und Fototechnik Museum, Weinstr 33, 67146 Deidesheim - T: (06326) 6568, 981068, Fax: 981069, E-mail: immel@film-fotomuseum.de, Internet: http://www.dftm.de. Head: Dr. Wolfgang Immel
Science&Tech Museum
Photography, film, television, video recording, video projection, magnetic and optical sound, LCD-technique, HS-film, stereoscopy, laterna magica 15284

Museum für Film- und Fototechnik → Deutsches Film- und Fototechnik Museum

Museum für Weinkultur, Weinstr, 67146 Deidesheim - T: (06326) 6140, 70214
Agriculture Museum 15285

Deinste

Deutsches Feld- und Kleinbahnmuseum, Kleinbahnhof, 21715 Deinste - T: (0449) 931565, Fax: 931567, E-mail: VHollander@t-online.de. Head: Rainer Uhlig, Volker Hollander
Science&Tech Museum / Agriculture Museum / Open Air Museum - 1967 15286

Delitzsch

Museum Schloß Delitzsch, Schloßstr 31, 04509 Delitzsch - T: (034202) 3399900, Fax: 3399911, E-mail: Stadt-Delitzsch@t-online.de, Internet: http://www.Stadt-Delitzsch.de. Head: Dr. Manfred Wilde
Local Museum - 1900
Ancient and early history, documents of nature researcher C.G. Ehrenberg, local history (11th-17th c), historic furniture, clock and watches, farming and crafts equipment - library 15287

Schulze-Delitzsch-Haus, Außenstelle des Museums Schloß Delitzsch, Kreuzgasse 10, 04509 Delitzsch - T: (034202) 3399900, 63864, Fax: 3399911, 63864, E-mail: stadt-delitzsch@t-online.de, Internet: http://www.stadt-delitzsch.de. Head: Dr. Manfred Wilde
Historical Museum / Special Museum - 1992
Bookbinding, memorabilia of Hermann Schulze-Delitzsch and development of co-operative system 15288

Delligsen

Dorfmuseum Delligsen, Rote Str 1, 31073 Delligsen - T: (05187) 1424, E-mail: gemeinde@delligsen.de
Local Museum 15289

Delmenhorst

Fabrikmuseum Nordwolle, Am Turbinenhaus 12, 27749 Delmenhorst - T: (04221) 992477, Fax: 992943, E-mail: info@museen.delmenhorst.de. Head: Dr. Gerhard Kaldewei
Science&Tech Museum / Historical Museum - 1997
Modern industry, hist of industrialization 15290

Museumsmühle Hasbergen, Hasberger Dorfstr 1, 27751 Delmenhorst - T: (04221) 41803, Fax: 120953
Science&Tech Museum - 1991
Historic mill, various objects 15291

Stadtmuseum Delmenhorst, Am Turbinenhaus 10, 27749 Delmenhorst - T: (04221) 992425, Fax: 992943, E-mail: info@museen.delmenhorst.de. Head: Dr. Gerhard Kaldewei
Local Museum - 1997
Town hist, modern industry, migration 15292

Städtische Galerie Haus Coburg, Fischstr 30, 27749 Delmenhorst - T: (04221) 14132, Fax: 14192, E-mail: info@staedtische-galerie-delmenhorst.de, Internet: http://www.staedtische-galerie-delmenhorst.de. Head: Barbara Alms
Fine Arts Museum - 1974
Fritz Stuckenberg (1881-1944) 15293

Demmin

Kreisheimatmuseum, Am Hanseufer, Speicher, 17109 Demmin - T: (03998) 222152. Head: Regine Köhn
Local Museum - 1914
Ancient and early hist, local hist, 13th-18th c art and crafts, smithwork and tin, porcelain, rococo and Biedermeier furnishings, coin and writing coll - library 15294

Demnitz bei Fürstenwalde

Heimatstube Demnitz, Dorfstr 47, 15518 Demnitz bei Fürstenwalde - T: (033636) 5121
Local Museum 15295

Denklingen

Museum Abodiacum, Altes Feuerwehrhaus Epfach, Schongauer Str 27, 86920 Denklingen - T: (08243) 2066
Local Museum - 1991
Finds and documents of Roman Epfach (Abodiacum) 15296

Denzlingen

Altdenzlinger Heimethüs mit Otto-Raupp-Stube, Hauptstr 76, 79211 Denzlingen - T: (07666) 3797
Local Museum - 1982
Agricultural implements 15297

Dermbach

Museum Dermbach, Kirchberg 5, 36466 Dermbach - T: (036964) 8760, Fax: 8764, E-mail: Hartmut.Westphal@t-online.de, Internet: http://www.Museum-Dermbach.de
Local Museum - 1959
Geology, ancient and early hist, agriculture, crafts and industry, glass, porcelain, carvings - library 15298

Dessau

Anhaltische Gemäldegalerie, Schloß Georgium, Puschkinallee 100, 06846 Dessau - T: (0340) 66126000, 613874, Fax: 66126017. Head: Dr. Norbert Michels
Public Gallery - 1927
Old German and Netherlandsh paintings, paintings of the 16th-18th c, Classicism, Romanticism and the period of Biedermeier 16th - 20th c paintings - print room 15299

Büro Otto Koch, c/o K.I.E.Z. e.V., Bertolt-Brecht-Str 29, 06844 Dessau - T: (0340) 212032, Fax: 212038. Head: Johanna Bartl
Public Gallery
Contemporain installations 15300

Heimatstube Alten, Kastanienhof 31, 06847 Dessau
Local Museum 15301

Museum für Naturkunde und Vorgeschichte, Askanische Str 32, 06842 Dessau - T: (0340) 214824, Fax: 2303465. Head: Ernst Görgner
Natural History Museum / Archaeological Museum / Local Museum - 1927
Ancient and early history, local history, entomology, ceramics 13th-16th c, geology, mineralogy, ornithology, botany - library 15302

Museum für Stadtgeschichte Dessau, Johannbau-Gewölbe, Schloßpl 3a, 06844 Dessau - T: (0340) 2209612, Fax: 8003795. Head: Dr. Barbara Czerannowski
Historical Museum 15303

Museum Schloss Luisium, Kulturstiftung DessauWörlitz, 06844 Dessau - T: (0340) 2183711, Fax: 6461510, E-mail: ksdw@ksdw.de, Internet: http://www.ksdw.de. Head: Dr. Thomas Weiss
Fine Arts Museum
Paintings (17th-18th c), furniture, decorative objects, porcelain 15304

Schloss Großkühnau - Verwaltung, Kulturstiftung DessauWörlitz, 06846 Dessau - T: (0340) 646150, Fax: 6461510, E-mail: ksdw@ksdw.de, Internet: http://www.ksdw.de. Head: Dr. Thomas Weiss
1918 15305

Schloss Mosigkau, Kulturstiftung DessauWörlitz, Erdmannsdorffallee 2-3, 06847 Dessau - T: (0340) 521139, Fax: 521181, E-mail: ksdw@ksdw.de, Internet: http://www.ksdw.de. Head: Dr. Thomas Weiss
Fine Arts Museum - 1951
17th-18th c paintings, furniture, decorative objects, porcelain 15306

Stiftung Bauhaus Dessau, Gropiusallee 38, 06846 Dessau - T: (0340) 65080, Fax: 6508226, E-mail: besuch@bauhaus-dessau.de, Internet: http://www.bauhaus-dessau.de. Head: Prof. Dr. Omar Akbar
Historic Site / Fine Arts Museum
Bauhaus hist 1919-1933: Walter Gropius, Hannes Meyer, Marcel Breuer, Ludwig Mies van der Rohe, the painters Wassily Kandinsky, Lyonel Feininger, Paul Klee, Oskar Schlemmer, the sculptors Gerhard Marcks and László Moholy-Nagy and others 15307

Detern

Museum Burg Stickhausen, Burgstr 3, 26847 Detern - T: (04957) 707, Fax: 912179. Head: H. Ukena, A. Lübbers-Ukena
Historical Museum - 1969
Domestic objects, ornithology 15308

Detmold

Art Kite Museum, Charles-Lindbergh-Ring 10, 32756 Detmold - T: (05231) 309930, Fax: 309933, E-mail: artkite@detmold.de, Internet: http://www.artkite.de. Head: Inga Hagen, Inga Beyer
Fine Arts Museum - 2000
Coll of 156 art kites in Japanese tradition, designed by contemporary artists 15309

Fürstliches Residenzschloß, Schloß, 32756 Detmold - T: (05231) 70020, Fax: 700249, E-mail: Verwaltung@Schloss-Detmold.de, Internet: http://www.Schloss-Detmold.de. Head: Hans-Theo Böhle
Fine Arts Museum / Decorative Arts Museum
Period rooms (Baroque, Empire, eclectic), Amsterdam and Brussels tapestries, glass, weapons, trophies and furniture, painting 15310

Lippische Landesbibliothek, Hornsche Str 41, 32756 Detmold - T: (05231) 926600, Fax: 9266055, E-mail: llbmail@llb-detmold.de, Internet: http://www.llb-detmold.de. Head: Detlev Hellfaier
Library with Exhibitions 15311

Lippisches Landesmuseum, Ameide 4, 32756 Detmold - T: (05231) 99250, Fax: 992525, E-mail: mail@lippisches-landesmuseum.de, Internet: http://www.lippisches-landesmuseum.de. Head: Prof. Dr. Rainer Springhorn
Local Museum - 1835
Peru Coll Dr. Eduard Gaffron, coins, costumes, furniture and design, period rooms (Renaissance, Baroque, Empire, Biedermeier), painting, weapons - library 15312

Westfälisches Freilichtmuseum Detmold, Landesmuseum für Volkskunde, Krummes Haus, 32760 Detmold - T: (05231) 7060, Fax: 706106, E-mail: wfm-detmold@lwl.org, Internet: http://www.freilichtmuseum-detmold.de. Head: Prof. Dr. Stefan Baumeier
Open Air Museum / Folklore Museum - 1960
Historical buildings and farmsteads from 16th-20th c, furnishings, domestic utensils, agricultural tools and machines, folk art, exhibit on the mechanization of agriculture in the 19th-20th c, photo and blueprint archives - library, workshops 15313

Dettelbach

Kolpings- und Handwerksmuseum im Faltertor, Faltertor, 97337 Dettelbach - T: (09324) 1305, 30441
Decorative Arts Museum / Religious Arts Museum - 1968
Religious objects, handicrafts 15314

Dettenhausen

Kathree Häusle, Kirchstr, 72135 Dettenhausen - T: (07157) 1260
Historic Site - 1988
Tiny half-timbered house built 1839, furnishings 15315

Schönbuch Museum, Ringstr 3, 72135 Dettenhausen - T: (07157) 1260, Fax: 12615. Head: U. Hägele
Local Museum - 1989
Sandstone working, forestry 15316

Dettingen an der Iller

Dorfmuseum Dettingen/Iller, Kirchdorfer Str 7, 88451 Dettingen an der Iller - T: (07354) 1077, Fax: 2195
Local Museum - 1976
Peasant life, agricultural implements 15317

Dieburg

Kreis- und Stadtmuseum, Schloß Fechenbach, 64807 Dieburg - T: (06071) 23365, Fax: 2002100. Head: Maria Porzenheim
Local Museum - 1926
Early and pre-history, grave finds, town hist, pottery 15318

Diepholz

Heimatmuseum Aschen, Aschen 168, 49356 Diepholz - T: (05441) 2234
Local Museum
Agricultural machinery, implements, domestic utensils, trade workshops 15319

Diesdorf, Altmark

Freilichtmuseum, Molmker Str 23, 29413 Diesdorf, Altmark - T: (03902) 450, Fax: 450
Open Air Museum - 1911
Low German farmhouse, bakery, loft, storeroom, 17th-19th c historic furniture 15320

Dießen am Ammersee

Carl Orff Museum, Hofmark 3, 86911 Dießen am Ammersee - T: (08807) 91981, Fax: 91981
Music Museum - 1991
Life and work of composer Carl Orff (1895-1982) 15321

Kreisheimatstuben Riederau, Neuwiese 2, 86911 Dießen am Ammersee Riederau - T: (08807) 1501
Local Museum - 1975
Rustic culture and work of local artists: Thomas Th. Heine, Wilhelm Leibl, Eduard Thöny 15322

Pfarrmuseum, Klosterhof 10, 86911 Dießen am Ammersee - T: (08807) 948940, Fax: 9489420. Head: Manfred Mayr
Religious Arts Museum - 1989
Religious art and objects 15323

Dietenhofen

Heimatmuseum, Schloßstr 5, Altes Schloß, 90599 Dietenhofen - T: (09824) 422, E-mail: info@markt-dietenhofen.de, Internet: http://www.dietenhofen.de
Local Museum
Local history, implements 15324

Dietfurt

Altmühltaler Mühlenmuseum, Rengnathmühle, Hauptstr 51, 92345 Dietfurt - T: (08464) 209, Fax: 9206
Science&Tech Museum 15325

Museum im Hollerhaus, Pfarrgasse 6, 92345 Dietfurt - T: (08464) 9145, Fax: 640035, E-mail: touristik@dietfurt.de, Internet: http://www.dietfurt.de
Archaeological Museum - 1993
History and coll of finds of the Rhine-Main-Danube canal 15326

Dietzenbach

Feuerwehrmuseum, Rathenaustr 16, 63128 Dietzenbach - T: (06074) 33311
Science&Tech Museum - 1981
Fire brigade implements and machines, fire extinguishing since the 19th c 15327

Heimatmuseum Dietzenbach, Darmstädter Str 11, 63128 Dietzenbach - T: (06074) 41742
Local Museum - 1976
Furniture, early and pre-history, stone-age artefacts, mineralogy, toys, trade workshops, agricultural machines 15328

Diez

Oranien-Nassau-Museum Oranienstein, Parkstr 35a, 65582 Diez - T: (06432) 2661, 4961. Head: Fred Storto
Local Museum 15329

Dillenburg

EAM-live-Museum Wasserkraftwerk Merkenbach, c/o Energie-AG Mitteldeutschland, Bahnhofspl 1, 35683 Dillenburg - T: (02771) 873165
Science&Tech Museum
Hist of hydroelectric power station 15330

Kutschenmuseum Hessisches Landgestüt, Wilhelmstr 24, 35683 Dillenburg - T: (02771) 89830, Fax: 898320, E-mail: hlg.dillenburg@t-online.de, Internet: http://www.landgestuet-dillenburg.de. Head: Bert Petersen
Science&Tech Museum
One and more-in-hand coaches 15331

Wilhelmsturm Dillenburg Museum, Am Schloßberg, 35683 Dillenburg - T: (02771) 800065, Fax: 800067. Head: Thomas Schmidt
Historical Museum - 1875
Hist of House Nassau and Oranien-Nassau 15332

Wirtschaftsgeschichtliches Museum Villa Grün, Schloßberg 3, 35683 Dillenburg - T: (02771) 266160, Fax: 800067. Head: Thomas Schmidt
Historical Museum - 1983
Geology, mining, metalwork, kitchen hist, stoves and cookers 15333

Dillingen an der Donau

Stadt- und Hochstiftmuseum, Am Hafenmarkt 11, 89407 Dillingen an der Donau - T: (09071) 4400, Fax: 54199, E-mail: gutmair@dillingen-donau.de, Internet: http://www.dilingen-donau.de. Head: Dr. Rudolf Poppa
Local Museum - 1888
Roman times, migration of the peoples, folklore, crafts, Wilhelm Bauer (inventor of the first submarine) - printery 15334

Dillingen, Saar

Heimatmuseum Pachten, Fischerstr 2, 66763 Dillingen, Saar - T: (06831) 78907
Local Museum 15335

Dingolfing

Museum Dingolfing, Obere Stadt 15, 84130 Dingolfing - T: (08731) 312228, Fax: 501166, E-mail: stadt@dingolfing.de, Internet: http://www.dingolfing.de. Head: Dr. Fritz Markmiller
Local Museum - 1905
Local hist 15336

Dinkelsbühl

Historisches Museum im Spital, Dr.-Martin-Luther-Str 6, 91550 Dinkelsbühl - T: (09851) 3293. Head: Christopher Glenk
Local Museum - 1893
Ocal history, handicrafts, 17th-20th c painting, traditional costumes, farm and town interiors and furnishings, ceramics, weapons, toys, agricultural tools 15337

Mies-Pilsner-Heimatmuseum, Bauhofstr 41, 91550 Dinkelsbühl - T: (09851) 53003, Fax: 53004, E-mail: Dolleisch@t-online.de, Internet: http://www.dingolfing.org/members/mies-pilsen
Local Museum 15338

Museum 3. Dimension, Nördlinger Tor, 91550 Dinkelsbühl - T: (09851) 6336, Fax: 2882, E-mail: gohame@aol.com, Internet: http://www.3d-museum.de. Head: Gerhard Stief
Fine Arts Museum - 1987
3-D, optical illusions, stereoscopic art, holographic art, pop-up books, light and laser 15339

Dinkelscherben

Heimatmuseum Reischenau, Augsburger Str 27, 86424 Dinkelscherben - T: (08292) 3422, Fax: 34533, E-mail: nieko@t-online.de, Internet: http://www.heimatverein.reischenau.de
Local Museum
Early local finds, religious folklore and a coll (glass)paintings by Joseph Scherer 15340

Dinslaken

Museum Voswinckelshof, Brückstr 31, 46535 Dinslaken - T: (02064) 2449, Fax: 777169, E-mail: Museum-Voswinckelshof@gmx.de, Internet: http://www.dinslaken.de. Head: Dr. Peter Theißen
Local Museum 15341

Dippoldiswalde

Lohgerber-, Stadt- und Kreismuseum, Freiberger Str 18, 01744 Dippoldiswalde - T: (03504) 612418, Fax: 612418, Internet: http://www.lohgerbermuseum.de. Head: Dr. Günter Groß
Local Museum / Science&Tech Museum - 1975
Tannery, folk art 15342

Museum Osterzgebirgsgalerie im Schloß, Kirchpl 8, 01744 Dippoldiswalde, mail addr: Freiberger Str 18, 01744 Dippoldiswalde - T: (03504) 612418, Fax: 612418, Internet: http://www.lohgerbermuseum.de. Head: Dr. Günter Groß
Public Gallery / Fine Arts Museum - 1999 15343

Dirlewang

Heimatmuseum Dirlewang, Tavernenstr 4, 87742 Dirlewang - T: (08267) 387
Local Museum - 1930
Local history, religious folkore and rustic culture 15344

Dischingen

Dischinger Heimatmuseum, Hauptstr 5, 89561 Dischingen - T: (07327) 6358. Head: Dr. Horst Moeferdt
Local Museum - 1959/1965
Prehistory, geology, household utensils 15345

Jagdkundemuseum, Schloß Taxis, 89561 Dischingen
Natural History Museum - 1978
Hist of hunting 15346

Dissen, Niederlausitz

Domowniski muzej Dešno, Heimatmuseum Dissen, Hauptstr 32, 03096 Dissen, Niederlausitz - T: (035606) 256, Fax: 237, Internet: http://www.disseu-spreewald.de. Head:
Local Museum / Folklore Museum - 1984
Local hist, Sorbian culture and folk art 15347

Ditzingen

Stadtmuseum Ditzingen, Am Laien 5, 71254 Ditzingen - T: (07156) 164308, Fax: 164301, E-mail: museum@ditzingen.de, Internet: http://www.ditzingen.de. Head: Dr. H. Hoffmann
Local Museum - 1935/1992
Town hist, pre and early hist 15348

Doberlug-Kirchhain

Weißgerbermuseum, Potsdamer Str 18, 03253 Doberlug-Kirchhain - T: (035322) 2293, Fax: 2271, E-mail: Stadt-Doberlug-Kirchhain@t-online.de, Internet: http://www.Doberlug-Kirchhain.de. Head: Andreas Hanslok
Science&Tech Museum - 1963
Development of tannery and leather production 15349

Döbeln

Stadtmuseum Döbeln/Kleine Galerie, Obermarkt 1, 04720 Döbeln - T: (03431) 579138, Fax: 579291, E-mail: sschirm2@ntwm.de. Head: A. Petzold
Local Museum - 1981
Local hist and culture 15350

Dömitz

Heimatmuseum, Auf der Festung, 19303 Dömitz - T: (038758) 22401. Head: Karl Schwarnweber
Local Museum - 1953
Local history, shipping, 19th-20th c household objects, memorabilia on Fritz Reuter (1810-1874) - library 15351

Dörfles-Esbach

Schiefer- und Ziegelmuseum Dörfles-Esbach, Oberer Kirchweg 9, 96487 Dörfles-Esbach - T: (09561) 66301, 62149, Fax: 68116
Special Museum
Coll of tiles and bricks 15352

Dohna

Heimatmuseum Dohna, Am Markt 2, 01809 Dohna - T: (03529) 512628, Fax: 563699
Local Museum - 1906
Local history and geology, paleontology, early and prehistory, handicraft, mineralogy, butchery painting/graphic arts, straw weaving, straw hat making 15353

Donaueschingen

Donauhalle, Donauhalle AB, 78166 Donaueschingen - T: (0771) 857221
Public Gallery 15354

Fürstlich Fürstenbergisches Schloßmuseum (closed) 15355

Donaustauf

Walhalla, Walhallastr 48, 93093 Donaustauf - T: (09403) 961680, Fax: 961682, Internet: http://www.stmukwk.bayern.de/kunst/museen/walhalla. Head: Robert Raith
Historical Museum - 1842
125 busts, 64 plaques from German-speaking personalities 15356

Donauwörth

Archäologisches Museum, Reichsstr 34, Im Tanzhaus, 86609 Donauwörth - T: (0906) 789185, Fax: 789159, E-mail: museen@donauwoerth.de, Internet: http://www.donauwoerth.de. Head: Erich Bäcker, Gudrun Reißer
Archaeological Museum - 1980
Local archeological finds 15357

Haus der Stadtgeschichte, Städtische Museen, Spitalgasse 11, Rieder Tor, 86609 Donauwörth - T: (0906) 789185, Fax: 789159, E-mail: museen@donauwoerth.de, Internet: http://www.donauwoerth.de. Head: Gudrun Reißer
Local Museum - 1986
Local history 15358

Heimatmuseum im Hintermeierhaus, Hindenburgstr 15, 86609 Donauwörth - T: (0906) 789185, Fax: 789159, E-mail: museen@donauwoerth.de, Internet: http://www.donauwoerth.de
Local Museum - 1929
Handicrafts, implements, rustic furniture and religious folklore 15359

Käthe-Kruse-Puppen-Museum, Städtische Museen, Pflegstr 21a, 86609 Donauwörth - T: (0906) 789185, Fax: 789159, E-mail: museen@donauwoerth.de, Internet: http://www.donauwoerth.de. Head: Gudrun Reißer
Decorative Arts Museum - 1993
Museum of Käthe Kruse (1883-1968) dolls 15360

Lovriner Stube, Museumsgasse 15, 86609 Donauwörth - T: (0906) 789185, Fax: 789159, E-mail: museen@donauwoerth.de, Internet: http://www.donauwoerth.de. Head: Gudrun Reißer
Local Museum - 1989
Local history 15361

Städtische Kunstgalerie im Deutschordenshaus, Kapellstr 3, 86609 Donauwörth - T: (0906) 789180, Fax: 789329, E-mail: stadt@donauwoerth.de. Head: Dr. Ottmar Seuffert
Public Gallery - 1993
Coll of local artists: Stephan Kessler (1622-1700) and Johann Baptist Enderle (1725-1798) 15362

Werner-Egk-Begegnungsstätte, Pflegstr 21a, 86609 Donauwörth - T: (0906) 789151, 789185, Fax: 789159, E-mail: stadt@donauwoerth.de, Internet: http://www.donauwoerth.de. Head: Karl Batz, Gudrun Reißer
Music Museum - 1982/1993
Life and work of composer Werner Egk (1901-1983) - library, archives 15363

Dorf Mecklenburg

Kreisagrarmuseum, Rambower Weg, 23972 Dorf Mecklenburg - T: (03841) 790020, Fax: 790114, E-mail: poststelle@nordwestmecklenburg.de, Internet: http://www.nordwestmecklenburg.de
Agriculture Museum / Local Museum - 1978
Development of agriculture, agricultural and domestic implements 15364

Dorfchemnitz bei Sayda

Eisenhammer Dorfchemnitz, Hauptstr 11, 09619 Dorfchemnitz bei Sayda - T: (037320) 1777
Science&Tech Museum
18th-19th c iron forge 15365

Dormagen

Haus Tannenbusch, Stadtverwaltung, Postfach, 41539 Dormagen - T: (02133) 257870, Fax: 257898. Head: Brunhilde Willenbrink
Natural History Museum 15366

Kreismuseum Zons, Schloßstr 1, 41541 Dormagen - T: (02133) 46715, 44001, Fax: 46715. Head: Helene Blum-Spicker
Fine Arts Museum / Decorative Arts Museum - 1972
Art Noveau pewter 15367

Missionsmuseum der Spiritaner Knechtsteden, 41540 Dormagen - T: (02133) 86953
Ethnology Museum / Religious Arts Museum - 1927
Ethnography (Africa, Brasilia, Indians) 15368

Dornburg, Saale

Dornburger Schlösser, Stiftung Weimarer Klassik, 07778 Dornburg, Saale - T: (036427) 22291, Fax: 20153, E-mail: gnm@weimar-klassik.de, Internet: http://www.weimar-klassik.de
Historical Museum - 1922
Castle from renaissance and rococo period, historical rooms, decorative objects, J.W. Goethe memorabilia, furniture 15369

Dornburg, Westerwald

Dorfmuseum Wilsenroth, Bahnhofsstr 2, 65599 Dornburg, Westerwald - T: (06436) 2308
Local Museum - 1989
Village hist, trades 15370

Dornstetten

Heimatmuseum Dornstetten, Das lebendige Volkskundemuseum, Marktpl, 72280 Dornstetten - T: (07443) 5163, Fax: 962096
Local Museum - 1956
Brewery, local hist, agriculture 15371

Dornum

Gedenkstätte Synagoge, Kirchstr 6, 26553 Dornum - T: (04933) 342. Head: Georg Murra-Regner
Historical Museum - 1991
Hist of the Jewish community, Jewish hist, religion, tradition 15372

Oma-Freese-Huus, Gartenstr 1, 26553 Dornum - T: (04933) 1343
Local Museum - 1987 15373

Dorsten

Museum der Stadt Dorsten, Am Markt 1, 46282 Dorsten - T: (02362) 25725. Head: Wolfgang Müller
Local Museum - 1935/1957
Early and prehist, town hist 15374

Museum Schloss Lembeck, Schloss 1, 46286 Dorsten - T: (02362) 7167, Fax: 77391. Head: Catherine Gräfin von Merveldt
Local Museum / Decorative Arts Museum - 1954
Baroque and Biedermeier interiors, 17th c Flemish gobelins, East Asian porcelain, local history, prehistoric finds, agricultural tools 15375

Tüshaus-Mühle, Weseler Str 433, 46286 Dorsten - T: (02362) 664050, Fax: 665743
Science&Tech Museum 15376

Dortmund

Altes Hafenamt, Ständige Ausstellung für Hafen und Schiffahrt, Sunderweg 130, 44147 Dortmund - T: (0231) 98395, Fax: 9839699, E-mail: info@dortmunder-hafen.de, Internet: http://www.dortmunder-hafen.de. Head: Hubert Collas
Historical Museum - 1970
Shipping 15377

Deutsche Arbeitsschutzausstellung der Bundesanstalt für Arbeitsschutz und Arbeitsmedizin, Friedrich-Henkel-Weg 1-25, 44149 Dortmund - T: (0231) 9071645, Fax: 9071267, E-mail: dasa@baua.de, Internet: http://www.dasa-dortmund.de. Head: Prof. Dr. Gerhard Kilger
Science&Tech Museum / Special Museum 15378

Deutsches Kochbuchmuseum, An der Buschmühle, 44139 Dortmund - T: (0231) 5025741, Fax: 5025511, E-mail: Kochbuchmuseum@stadtdo.de, Internet: http://www.museendortmund.de. Head: Wolfgang E. Weick, Dr. Gisela Framke
Special Museum - 1988
Famous cookbooks by Henriette Davidis 15379

Galerie Torhaus Rombergpark, Am Rombergpark, 44225 Dortmund - T: (0231) 5025177, Fax: 5022497, E-mail: mhoppe@stadtdo.de, Internet: http://www.dortmund.de/kulturbuero. Head: Michael Hoppe
Public Gallery 15380

Heimatmuseum Lütgendortmund, Dellwiger Str 13, 44379 Dortmund - T: (0231) 631349
Local Museum 15381

Mahn- und Gedenkstätte Steinwache, Stadtarchiv Dortmund, Steinstr 50, 44147 Dortmund - T: (0231) 5025002, Fax: 5026011, E-mail: epeters@stadtdo.de, Internet: http://www.ns-gedenkstaetten.de/nrw. Head: Dr. Günther Högl
Historic Site - 1992
Resistance against Nazism, Holocaust 15382

Museum am Ostwall, Ostwall 7, 44135 Dortmund - T: (0231) 5023247/48, Fax: 5025244, E-mail: mo@stadtdo.de, Internet: http://www.museendortmund.de/museumamostwall. Head: Dr. Ingo Bartsch
Fine Arts Museum - 1949
Expressionism, post-War painting ('Informel'), modern graphics and sculpture, art of the 60s, 70s ('Zero', 'Fluxus') and 80s, works by Max Beckmann, Joseph Beuys, Alexej von Jawlensky, August Macke, Emil Schumacher - library, children's studio 15383

Museum für Kunst und Kulturgeschichte der Stadt Dortmund, Hansastr 3, 44137 Dortmund - T: (0231) 5025515, 5026028, Fax: 5025511, E-mail: mkk@stadtdo.de, Internet: http://www.museendortmund.de/mkk. Head: Wolfgang E. Weick
Fine Arts Museum - 1883
Furniture from the Gothic to Art Deco period, tiles, wall hangings, porcelain, local history, prehistoric archaelogy, Roman and medieval antiquities, Westfalian folk art, painting and sculpture up to 1900, designs, photography, textiles - library, workshops 15384

Museum für Naturkunde, Münsterstr 271, 44145 Dortmund - T: (0231) 5024856/50, Fax: 5024852, E-mail: naturkundemuseum@stadtdo.de, Internet: http://www.museendortmund.de. Head: Dr. Walter Tanke
Natural History Museum - 1910
Geological and biological sciences incl geology, paleontology, mineralogy, zoology, botany - course rooms, geological garden, demonstrational aquarium and mine 15385

Stadt- und Landesbibliothek Dortmund, Artothek, Königswall 18, 44122 Dortmund - T: (0231) 5024970, E-mail: stlb@stadtdo.de, Internet: http://www.dortmund.de/bibliotheken. Head: Ulrich Moeske
Library with Exhibitions 15386

Westfälisches Industriemuseum, Grubenweg 5, 44388 Dortmund - T: (0231) 69610, Fax: 6961114, E-mail: industriemuseum@lwl.org, Internet: http://www.industriemuseum.de. Head: Helmut Bönnighausen
Science&Tech Museum
Hist of mining and textile industry, inland navigation, glass, industry, brickworks, iron and steel industry 15387

Westfälisches Schulmuseum, An der Wasserburg 1, 44379 Dortmund - T: (0231) 613095, Fax: 7261802, E-mail: schulmuseum@stadtdo.de. Head: Jochen Löher
Special Museum 15388

Dorum

Niedersächsisches Deichmuseum, Poststr 16, 27632 Dorum - T: (04742) 1020, 474. Head: Eibe Seebeck
Natural History Museum - 1985
Dyke building, storm tides, coast protection, the Southern North sea during the millenia 15389

Dossenheim

Heimatmuseum der Gemeinde Dossenheim, Rathausstr 47, Altes Rathaus, 69221 Dossenheim - T: (06221) 86510, Fax: 865138, E-mail: -gemeinde.dossenheim@t-online.de
Local Museum - 1976/78
Local hist, crafts, household articles, tools, castles, quarry industry, expellees 15390

Dotternhausen

Fossilienmuseum im Werkforum Rohrbach Zement, Dormettinger Str 25, 72359 Dotternhausen - T: (07427) 79211, Fax: 79201, E-mail: info@rohrbach-zement.de, Internet: http://www.rohrbach-zement.de. Head: Dr. M. Jäger
Natural History Museum - 1989
Fossils of the Jurassic oil shale and of the whole Jurassic of the Swabian Alb 15391

Drakenburg

Heimatmuseum Ole Schüne, Alter Postweg 5, 31623 Drakenburg - T: (05024) 394, 8645, Fax: 8645
Local Museum 15392

Dreetz bei Neustadt, Dosse

Heimatstube Dreetz, Wilhelm-Pieck-Str 57, 16845 Dreetz bei Neustadt, Dosse - T: (033970) 86140, Fax: 86140
Local Museum 15393

Dreieich

Dreieich-Museum, Fahrgasse 52, 63303 Dreieich - T: (06103) 84914, Fax: 88506. Head: Ingeborg Dittler
Local Museum - 1910
9th c historical ruins, prehist, geology, local history, medieval archeological finds, peasant interiors, handicrafts, dolls, archives, minerals - library 15394

Städtische Galerie, Fichtestr 50, 63303 Dreieich - T: (06103) 60000, Fax: 600077, E-mail: buergerhaus@buergerhaeuser-dreieich.de, Internet: http://www.buergerhaeuser-dreieich.de. Head: Till Friedrich
Public Gallery 15395

Dresden

Buchmuseum der Sächsische Landesbibliothek - Staats- und Universitätsbibliothek Dresden, Marienallee 12, 01099 Dresden - T: (0351) 8130162, Fax: 8130200, E-mail: museum@slub-dresden.de, Internet: http://www.tu-dresden.de/slub. Head: Katrin Nitzschke
Library with Exhibitions - 1952
Rare books, manuscripts, incunabula 15396

Carl-Maria-von-Weber-Museum, Dresdner Str 44, 01326 Dresden - T: (0351) 2618234, Fax: 2618234, E-mail: weber@stmd.de, Internet: http://www.stmd.de. Head: Adelheid von Lüder-Zschiesche
Music Museum - 1948
Memorabilia on composer Carl Maria von Weber (1786-1826) and the time he served as local music master, pictures, instruments, letters 15397

Deutsches Hygiene-Museum, Das Museum vom Menschen, Lingnerpl 1, 01069 Dresden - T: (0351) 48460, Fax: 4955162, E-mail: museum@dhmd.de, Internet: http://www.dhmd.de. Head: Klaus Vogel
Special Museum - 1912
Medicine and hygiene, health education - medical library, Forum Science, Health and Environment, Congress Center 15398

Erich Kästner Museum Dresden, Antonstr 1, 01097 Dresden - T: (0351) 8045086, Fax: 8045087, E-mail: info@erich-kaestner-museum.de, Internet: http://www.erich-kaestner-museum.de. Head: Andrea O'Brien
Special Museum
Literature, communication 15399

Fahrradmuseum der Fahrrad-Veteranen-Freunde-Dresden 1990 (Bicycle Museum), Schützengasse 16-18, 01067 Dresden - T: (03501) 445657, Fax: 445657, E-mail: museum@fahrradsammler.de, Internet: http://www.fahrradsammler.de. Head: Dr. Matthias Kielwein
Special Museum 15400

Gedenkstätte Münchner Platz Dresden, George-Bähr-Str 7, 01069 Dresden - T: (0351) 4636466, 4631990, Fax: 46331991, E-mail: Gedenkstaette@mailbox.tu-dresden.de, Internet: http://www.stsg.de. Head: Dr. Birgit Sack
Historical Museum - 1959 15401

Gemäldegalerie Alte Meister, Staatliche Kunstsammlungen Dresden, Theaterpl 1, 01067 Dresden - T: (0351) 4914619, Fax: 4914616, E-mail: info@staatl-kunstsammlungen-dresden.de, Internet: http://www.staatl-kunstsammlungen-dresden.de. Head: Prof. Dr. Harald Marx
Fine Arts Museum - 1722
15th-18th c European painting 15402

Gemäldegalerie Neue Meister, Staatliche Kunstsammlungen Dresden, Albertinum, Georg-Treu-Pl 2, 01067 Dresden - T: (0351) 4914731, Fax: 4914732, E-mail: info@staatl-kunstsammlungen-dresden.de, Internet: http://www.staatl-kunstsammlungen-dresden.de. Head: Dr. Ulrich Bischoff
Fine Arts Museum - 1931/1959
19th-20th c paintings (German Romantic, French Impressionism, German Expressionism), sculptures - library 15403

Grünes Gewölbe, Staatliche Kunstsammlungen Dresden, Schloßstr 25, 01067 Dresden - T: (0351) 4914590, Fax: 4914599. Head: Dr. Dirk Syndram
Decorative Arts Museum - 1724
15th-18th c European gold and jewellery, 16th-18th c glass, enamel, ivory, and amber, bronze sculptures 15404

Heimat- und Palitzsch-Museum Prohlis, Gamigstr 24, 01239 Dresden - T: (0351) 2840730, Fax: 2812948, E-mail: palitzschhof@prohlis-online.de, Internet: http://www.palitzschhof.de
Local Museum - 1988
Life and work of astronomer Johann Georg Palitzsch, local hist, historical hand weaving conducted by Webmeisterin Marianna Kay-Gatsch 15405

Historisches Museum Dresden → Rüstkammer

Kraszewski-Museum, Stadtmuseum Dresden, Nordstr 28, 01099 Dresden - T: (0351) 8044450, Fax: 8044450, E-mail: kraszewski@stmd.de, Internet: http://www.stmd.de. Head: Joanna Magacz
Fine Arts Museum - 1960
Memorabilia on artist Josef I. Kraszewski (1812-1887) in his former house - polish library 15406

Kunstgewerbemuseum, Staatliche Kunstsammlungen Dresden, Schloß Pillnitz, 01326 Dresden - T: (0351) 2613201, Fax: 2613222, E-mail: info@staatl-kunstsammlungen-dresden.de. Head: Dr. Igor A. Jenzen
Decorative Arts Museum - 1876
Handicraft from the Middle Ages to the present: furniture, textiles, glass, pottery, metal, stonework, bookbindings, leather, tapestries, Middle and East Asia, jewellery, music instruments, design - library 15407

Kunsthalle Dresden, Maxstr 2, 01067 Dresden - T: (0351) 49220, Fax: 4922776, E-mail: dresden@artotel.de, Internet: http://www.artotel.de. Head: Christian Kübler
Public Gallery 15408

Kunsthaus Dresden, Städtische Galerie für Gegenwartskunst, Rähnitzgasse 8, 01097 Dresden - T: (0351) 8041456, Fax: 8041582. Head: Harald Kunde
Public Gallery 15409

Kupferstich-Kabinett, Staatliche Kunstsammlungen Dresden (closed until spring 2003), Güntzstr 34, 01307 Dresden - T: (0351) 4914211, Fax: 4914222, E-mail: k-k@sk-dresden.de, Internet: http://www.staatl-kunstsammlungen-dresden.de. Head: Dr. Wolfgang Holler, Dr. Hans-Ulrich Lehmann
Fine Arts Museum - 1720
Sheets of European graphics (450 000), 15th-20th c Japanese woodcuts, photographic art, illustrated books, posters - library, Josef-Hegenbarth-Archiv (Calberlastraße 2) 15410

Landesmuseum für Vorgeschichte, Landesamt für Archäologie, Palaispl 11, Japanisches Palais, 01097 Dresden, mail addr: Zur Wetterwarte 7, 01109 Dresden - T: (0351) 89260, Fax: 8926666, E-mail: Presse@archsax.smwk.sachsen.de, Internet: http://www.archsax.sachsen.de. Head: Dr. Judith Oexle
Archaeological Museum - 1874
Ancient and early hist of Saxony, medieval and modern times 15411

Leonhardi-Museum, Grundstr 26, 01326 Dresden - T: (0351) 2683513, Fax: 2683513, Internet: http://www.leonhardi-museum.de. Head: Ulrike Haßler-Schobbert
Fine Arts Museum / Public Gallery - 1884
Memorabilia of painter E. Leonhardi (1828-1905) in his former home 15412

Lichtdruck-Werkstatt-Museum, Bärensteiner Str 30, 01277 Dresden - T: (0351) 3187028, Fax: 3187038, E-mail: lichtdruck@druckhaus-dresden.de, Internet: http://www.druckhaus-dresden.de/lichtdruck. Head: Karl Nolle
Science&Tech Museum 15413

Mathematisch-Physikalischer Salon, Staatliche Kunstsammlungen Dresden, Zwinger, 01067 Dresden - T: (0351) 4914661, Fax: 4914666. Head: Dr. Peter Plaßmeyer
Science&Tech Museum - 1560/1728
Historic scientific instruments, clocks and watches from 16th to 19th c, globes - library 15414

Militärhistorisches Museum der Bundeswehr, Olbrichtpl 2, 01099 Dresden - T: (0351) 8232800, Fax: 8232805, E-mail: MilHistMuseumBW@bwb.org, Internet: http://www.milhistmuseum-dresden.via.t-online.de. Head: Dr. Thomas Scheerer
Military Museum - 1897
Arms, flags, uniforms, documents, National People's Army - library 15415

Münzkabinett, Staatliche Kunstsammlungen Dresden (closed until summer 2003), Georgenbau, Schloss, Schlosspl, 01067 Dresden - T: (0351) 4914231, Fax: 4914233, E-mail: info@staatl-kunstsammlungen-dresden.de, Internet: http://www.staatl-kunstsammlungen-dresden.de. Head: Dr. Paul Arnold
Special Museum - 16th c
History of minting and economics, coins and medals, decorations, banknotes - library 15416

Museum für Mineralogie und Geologie, Staatliche Naturhistorische Sammlungen Dresden, Königsbrücker Landstr 159, 01109 Dresden - T: (0351) 8926403, Fax: 8926404, Internet: http://www.snsd.de. Head: Dr. Ulf Linnemann
Natural History Museum - 2000
Mineralogy, geology, paleontology, petrograpgy 15417

Museum für Sächsische Volkskunst, Staatliche Kunstsammlungen Dresden, Köpckestr 1, Jägerhof, 01097 Dresden - T: (0351) 8030817, Fax: 8044963, E-mail: info@staatl-kunstsammlungen-dresden.de, Internet: http://www.staatl-kunstsammlungen-dresden.de. Head: Dr. Johannes Just
Decorative Arts Museum / Folklore Museum / Performing Arts Museum - 1897
Folk art from Saxony, furniture, ceramics, smithwork, toys, costumes, pewter figures - puppet theatre collection 15418

Museum für Tierkunde, Staatliche Naturhistorische Sammlungen Dresden, Königsbrücker Landstr 159, 01109 Dresden - T: (0351) 8926326, Fax: 8926327, Internet: http://www.snsd.de. Head: Dr. U. Fritz
Natural History Museum
Variability, adaption and development of fauna of the world - library 15419

Museum zur Dresdner Frühromantik im Kügelgen-Haus, Hauptstr 13, 01097 Dresden - T: (0351) 8044760, Fax: 4951288, E-mail: mdf@stmd.de, Internet: http://www.stmd.de. Head: Michaela Hausding
Special Museum - 1981
Memorabilia of Ludwig Tieck, Christian Gottfried und Theodor Körner, Heinrich von Kleist, Caspar David Friedrich, Carl Gustav Carus, Carl Maria von Weber, Gerhard von Kügelgen Wilhelm von Kügelgen 15420

Neuer Sächsischer Kunstverein, Sankt-Petersburger-Str 2, 01069 Dresden - T: (0351) 43822310, Fax: 43822310, E-mail: kv@saechsischer-kunstverein.de, Internet: http://www.saechsischer-kunstverein.de
Public Gallery / Association with Coll 15421

Porzellansammlung, Staatliche Kunstsammlungen Dresden, Zwinger, Sophienstr, 01067 Dresden - T: (0351) 4914612, Fax: 4914629, E-mail: info@staatl-kunstsammlungen-dresden.de, Internet: http://www.staatl-kunstsammlungen-dresden.de. Head: Dr. Ulrich Pietsch
Decorative Arts Museum - 1717
Chinese, Japanese and Meißen porcelain 15422

Rüstkammer, Staatliche Kunstsammlungen Dresden, Georgenbau, Schloß, Schloßstr 25, 01067 Dresden - T: (0351) 4914626, Fax: 4914690, E-mail: info@staatl-kunstsammlungen-dresden.de, Internet: http://www.staatl-kunstsammlungen-dresden.de. Head: Dr. Heinz-Werner Lewerken
Fine Arts Museum - 1567
European and Oriental Weapons of the 15th-18th c, armoury, riding equipment, saddles, fire arms, hunting weapons, orientalica, noble costumes 15423

Sammlungen der Technischen Universität Dresden, Mommsenstr 13, 01062 Dresden - T: (0351) 4632180, Fax: 4637229. Head: Dr. Klaus Mauersberger
Science&Tech Museum - 1979
Technical hist 15424

Schillerhäuschen, Stadtmuseum Dresden, Schillerstr 19, 01326 Dresden - T: (0351) 656480, Fax: 4951288, E-mail: schiller@stmd.de, Internet: http://www.stmd.de. Head: Matthias Griebel
Special Museum - 1955
Memorabilia on Friedrich Schiller (1759-1805) in house where he completed 'Don Carlos' 15425

Schloßausstellung, Staatliche Kunstsammlungen Dresden, Schloßstr 25, 01067 Dresden - T: (0351) 4914590, Fax: 4914599, E-mail: grg@sk-dresden.de. Head: Dr. Dirk Syndram
Historic Site
Renaissance castle 15426

Skulpturensammlung, Staatliche Kunstsammlungen Dresden, Albertinum, Georg-Treu-Pl 2, 01067 Dresden - T: (0351) 4914740, Fax: 4914350. Head: Dr. Moritz Woelk
Fine Arts Museum - 1728
German, French and Italian sculpture from the 15th-20th c, Renaissance bronzes, Baroque sculpture, original models by Ernst Rietschel and Ernst Julius Hähnel, sculpture of the 20th c, Mengs cast coll, Rodin, Meunier - library, restoration workshop 15427

Staatliche Kunstsammlungen Dresden, Generaldirektion, Georg-Treu-Pl 2, 01067 Dresden - T: (0351) 4914700, Fax: 4914777, E-mail: martin.roth@sk-dresden.de, Internet: http://www.staatl-kunstsammlungen-dresden.de. Head: Dr. Martin Roth
Fine Arts Museum - 1560 15428

Staatliches Museum für Völkerkunde Dresden, Palaispl 11, Japanisches Palais, 01097 Dresden - T: (0351) 8144841, Fax: 8144888. Head: Dr. Annegret Nippa
Ethnology Museum - 1875
Ethnography, anthropology of all continents, non European skull coll - library 15429

Staatliches Museum für Völkerkunde Dresden, Sammlungen, Königsbrücker Landstr 159, 01109 Dresden - T: (0351) 8926202, Fax: 8926203. Head: Dr. Annegret Nippa
Ethnology Museum - 1875
Ethnography, anthropology of all continents, non European skull coll - library 15430

Stadtmuseum Dresden, Wilsdruffer Str 2, 01067 Dresden - T: (0351) 656480, Fax: 4951288, E-mail: landhaus@stmd.de, Internet: http://www.stmd.de. Head: Matthias Griebel
Local Museum / Historical Museum - 1891
Local hist, hist of the labour-movement in Dresden, paintings 18th-20th c, graphics, 16th-20th c, sculptures, furniture, arms, numismatics, hist of fire fighting 15431

Technische Sammlungen der Stadt Dresden, Junghansstr 1-3, 01277 Dresden - T: (0351) 3144150, Fax: 3144151, E-mail: service@tsd.de, Internet: http://www.tsd.de. Head: Dr. Helmut Lindner
Science&Tech Museum
Photography, kinematography, technic of entertainment, office, household, scientific instruments building, computer 15432

Verkehrsmuseum Dresden, Augustusstr 1, 01067 Dresden - T: (0351) 86440, Fax: 8644110, E-mail: verkehrsmuseum@verkehrsmuseum.sachsen.de, Internet: http://www.verkehrsmuseum.sachsen.de. Head: Dr. Michael Dünnebier
Science&Tech Museum - 1952
Development of railroad, telecommunication, shipping and motorcars, postage stamps, coins, uniforms - library, archives 15433

Duderstadt

Heimatmuseum Duderstadt, Bei der Oberkirche 3, 37115 Duderstadt - T: (05527) 2539. Head: Dieter Wagner
Local Museum - 1931
Prehistory and early history, ecclestical art and hist, folklore, local crafts, tobacco growing and manufacturing, itinerant work and trade, rural and urban life in the 19th/20th c, archaeology 15434

Düren

Leopold-Hoesch-Museum Düren, Hoeschpl 1, 52349 Düren - T: (02421) 252561, Fax: 252560, E-mail: museum.dueren@t-online.de, Internet: http://www.artcontent.de/dueren. Head: Dr. Dorothea Eimert
Fine Arts Museum - 1905
Modern art with emphasis on German Expressionism, painting, sculpture, graphics, and drawings, paper art - library 15435

Papiermuseum, Wallstr 2-8, 52349 Düren - T: (02421) 252561, 252313, Fax: 252560, E-mail: museum.dueren@t-online.de, Internet: http://www.artcontent.de/dueren. Head: Dr. Dorothea Eimert
Science&Tech Museum - 1990
Watermarks, dip sieves 15436

Düsseldorf

Conzen-Sammlung, Bilker Str 5, 40213 Düsseldorf - T: (0211) 133066, Fax: 325427. Head: Dr. Fritz Conzen
Fine Arts Museum - 1961
Engravings, paintings, and drawings of the city Düsseldorf from the 17th c to 1900, picture and mirror frames from the Gothic through Art Nouveau periods 15437

Deutsches Kunststoff Museum, Ehrenhof 2, 40479 Düsseldorf - T: (0211) 4560413, Fax: 45608537, E-mail: kvm@kunststoff-museums-verein.de, Internet: http://www.deutsches-kunststoff-museum.de. Head: Ellen Kreutz
Special Museum 15438

Galerie des Polnischen Instituts Düsseldorf, Citadellstr 7, 40213 Düsseldorf - T: (0211) 866960, Fax: 8669620, E-mail: info@pol-institut.de, Internet: http://www.pol-institut.de. Head: M. Grudzinska
Public Gallery 15439

Gerhart-Hauptmann-Haus, Bismarckstr 90, 40210 Düsseldorf - T: (0211) 169910, Fax: 353118, E-mail: gerhart-hauptmann-haus@t-online.de. Head: Dr. Walter Engel
Historical Museum - 1957
Customs, traditional living style, and history of the Eastern German settlements, charter of displaced persons, graphics of central and East German artists, traditional costumes, engravings of historical events - library, conference and lecture rooms 15440

Goethe-Museum Düsseldorf, Anton-und-Katharina-Kippenberg-Stiftung, Schloß Jägerhof, Jacobistr 2, 40211 Düsseldorf - T: (0211) 8996262, Fax: 8929144, E-mail: goethemuseum@duesseldorf.de, Internet: http://www.goethe-museum.com. Head: Prof. Dr. Dr. Volkmar Hansen
Special Museum - 1956
18th c Rococo castle, exhibits on the life and works of Goethe, autographs, paintings, busts, graphics, first editions, coins, medaillons, coll of Faust motifs, technique and history of the silhouette, archives - library 15441

Heinrich-Heine-Institut-Museum, Bilker Str 12-14, 40213 Düsseldorf - T: (0211) 8992902, 8995574, Fax: 8929044, E-mail: heineinstitut@duesseldorf.de, Internet: http://www.duesseldorf.de/kultur/heineinstitut. Head: Prof. Dr. Joseph A. Kruse
Special Museum / Library with Exhibitions - 1970
Archives of the poet Heinrich Heine, Heine and his contemporaries, autographs and literature, art, music, exhibit on the local region from the 16th c to the present - library 15442

Hetjens-Museum, Deutsches Keramikmuseum, Schulstr 4, 40213 Düsseldorf - T: (0211) 8994201, 8994210, Fax: 8929166, E-mail: hetjensmuseum@stadt.duesseldorf.de. Head: Dr. Bernd Hakenjos
Decorative Arts Museum - 1909
Prehistoric ceramics, Greek and Roman pottery, medieval and German stoneware, lead-glazed earthenware, ceramics from South and Central America, the Middle East, and the Far East, European faience and porcelain, international contemporary ceramics - library 15443

K20 Kunstsammlung am Grabbeplatz, K20K21 Kunstsammlung Nordrhein-Westfalen, Grabbepl 5, 40213 Düsseldorf - T: (0211) 8381130, Fax: 8381201/02, E-mail: info@kunstsammlung.de, Internet: http://www.kunstsammlung.de. Head: Prof. Dr. Armin Zweite, Dr. Pia Müller-Tamm
Fine Arts Museum - 1961
International art of the 20th c from Fauvism and Expressionsm to the present (Paul Klee, Joseph Beuys, Pablo Picasso, Wassily Kandinski) - library 15444

K21 Kunstsammlung im Ständehaus, K20K21 Kunstsammlung Nordrhein-Westfalen, Ständehausstr 1, 40217 Düsseldorf - T: (0211) 8381600, Fax: 8381601/02, E-mail: info@kunstsammlung.de, Internet: http://www.kunstsammlung.de. Head: Prof. Dr. Armin Zweite, Dr. Julian Heynen
Fine Arts Museum - 2002
International art of the 21th c from 1980 to the present, installation, sculpture, film, video, painting, photography 15445

Kultur Bahnhof Eller, Vennhauser Allee 89, 40229 Düsseldorf - T: (0211) 2108488, Fax: 216163
Public Gallery 15446

Kunsthalle Düsseldorf, Grabbepl 4, 40213 Düsseldorf - T: (0211) 8996240, Fax: 8929168, E-mail: kunsthalle@duesseldorf.de, Internet: http://www.kunsthalle-duesseldorf.de. Head: Ulrike Groos
Fine Arts Museum - 1967 15447

Kunstmuseum Düsseldorf im Ehrenhof → Museum Kunst Palast mit Sammlung Kunstakademie und Glasmuseum Hentrich

Kunstraum Düsseldorf, Himmelgeister Str 107e, 40200 Düsseldorf - T: (0211) 8996148, Fax: 8929043, E-mail: ulla.lux@stadt.duesseldorf.de, Internet: http://www.duesseldorf.de/kultur/kunstraum. Head: Ulla Lux
Public Gallery 15448

Kunstverein für die Rheinlande und Westfalen, Grabbepl 4, 40213 Düsseldorf - T: (0211) 327023, Fax: 329070, E-mail: kunstverein.duesseldorf@rp-online.de, Internet: http://www.kunstverein-duesseldorf.de. Head: Rita Kersting
Association with Coll 15449

Mahn- und Gedenkstätte Düsseldorf, Mühlenstr 29, 40200 Düsseldorf - T: (0211) 8996205, Fax: 8929137, E-mail: gedenkstaette@duesseldorf.de, Internet: http://www.ns-gedenkstaetten.de/nrw/duesseldorf. Head: Angela Genger
Historic Site / Historical Museum 15450

Museum Kunst Palast mit Sammlung Kunstakademie und Glasmuseum Hentrich, Ehrenhof 4-5, 40479 Düsseldorf - T: (0211) 8994242, Fax: 8929504, Internet: http://www.museum-kunst-palast.de. Head: Jean-Hubert Martin
Fine Arts Museum - 2001
Paintings, drawings and sculpture from Middle Ages untill today, applied art, glass, Islamic art, design 15451

Naturkundliches Heimatmuseum Benrath, Benrather Schloßallee 102, 40597 Düsseldorf - T: (0211) 8997219, Fax: 8997216. Head: Dr. Wolfgang W. Gettmann, Dr. Hubert Heuwinkel
Natural History Museum 15452

NRW-Forum Kultur und Wirtschaft, Ehrenhof 2, 40479 Düsseldorf - T: (0211) 8926690, Fax: 8926682, E-mail: bützer@NRW-Forum.de, Internet: http://www.nrw-forum.de. Head: Michael Bützer
Public Gallery - 1926/1998 15453

Orangerie Benrath, Urdenbacher Allee 6, 40593 Düsseldorf - T: (0211) 8996175. Head: Manfred Scherer
Fine Arts Museum 15454

Sammlung Ernst Schneider, Hetjens Museum, Jacobistr 2, 40211 Düsseldorf - T: (0211) 8994210, Fax: 8929166, E-mail: hetjensmuseum@stadt.duesseldorf.de. Head: Dr. Bernd Hakenjos
Decorative Arts Museum - 1954
German porcelain, esp from Meißen, Far Eastern porcelain, European silver, furniture, archives - library 15455

SchifffahrtMuseum, Stadtmuseum Düsseldorf, Burgpl 30, 40213 Düsseldorf - T: (0211) 8996165, Fax: 8936165, E-mail: annette.fimpeler@stadt.duesseldorf.de. Head: Dr. Wieland Koenig
Science&Tech Museum - 1930
Ship models, tools, paintings, documents on Rhine navigation, river construction and loading cranes, fishing ships - Multi Media Show 15456

Schloß Benrath, Stadtmuseum Düsseldorf, Benrather Schloßallee 104, 40597 Düsseldorf - T: (0211) 8997271/73, Fax: 8929253, E-mail: claudia.bender@stadt.duesseldorf.de, Internet: http://www.duesseldorf.de/kultur. Head: Dr. Wieland Koenig
Decorative Arts Museum
Porcelain of Frankenthal 15457

Stadtmuseum Düsseldorf, Berger Allee 2, 40213 Düsseldorf - T: (0211) 8996170, Fax: 8994019, E-mail: claudia.bender@stadt.duesseldorf.de, Internet: http://www.duesseldorf.de/stadtmuseum. Head: Dr. Wieland Koenig
Local Museum - 1874 15458

Stiftung Ernst Schneider → Sammlung Ernst Schneider

Theatermuseum der Landeshauptstadt, Dumont-Lindemann-Archiv, Jägerhofstr 1, 40479 Düsseldorf - T: (0211) 8994660, Fax: 8929045, E-mail: winrich.meiszies@stadt.duesseldorf.de. Head: Dr. Winrich Meiszies
Performing Arts Museum
Hist of Düsseldorf theatre, puppet theatre, costumes, posters, photographs - archive (photographs, AV, clippings, programmes) 15459

Duingen

Töpfermuseum, Töpferstr 9, 31089 Duingen - T: (05185) 6090
Decorative Arts Museum
Duinger Earthenware from 9 centuries 15460

Duisburg

Cubus Kunsthalle, Friedrich-Wilhelm-Str 64, 47051 Duisburg - T: (0203) 26236, Fax: 21792, E-mail: info-cubus-kunsthalle.de, Internet: http://www.cubus-kunsthalle.de. Head: Dr. Claudia Schaefer
Fine Arts Museum 15461

Erstes Niederrheinisches Karneval-Museum, Wehofer Str 45, 47169 Duisburg - T: (0203) 5030640. Head: Werner J. Beckmann
Special Museum - 1973
Decorations, caps, uniforms, keys, flags - archive 15462

Galerie der Bezirksbibliothek Rheinhausen, Händelstr 6, 47226 Duisburg - T: (02065) 9058463
Public Gallery 15463

Haniel Museum, Franz-Haniel-Pl 3, 47119 Duisburg - T: (0203) 806231, Fax: 806738, E-mail: - bweberbrosamer.FHC@haniel.de, Internet: http://www.haniel.de. Head: Dr. Bernhard Weber-Brosamer
Local Museum - 1968
Mining, metallurgy, industrialization, local and harbor hist, shipping on Rhine 15464

Haus der Naturfreunde, Düsseldorfer Str 565, 47055 Duisburg - T: (0203) 735133. Head: Friedrich Elsposch
Natural History Museum 15465

Kultur- und Stadthistorisches Museum Duisburg, Johannes-Corputius-Pl 1, 47049 Duisburg - T: (0203) 2832640, 2832656, Fax: 2834352, E-mail: KSM@stadt-duisburg.de, Internet: http://www.stadtmuseum-duisburg.de. Head: Dr. Susanne Sommer
Historical Museum - 1902
Cartographical coll, coin coll, archaeology, Gerhard Mercator (1512-1594) 15466

Museum der Deutschen Binnenschifffahrt Duisburg-Ruhrort, Apostelstr 84, 47119 Duisburg - T: (0203) 808890, Fax: 8088922, E-mail: info@binnenschifffahrtsmuseum.de, Internet: http://www.binnenschifffahrtsmuseum.de. Head: Dr. Gernot Tromnau
Science&Tech Museum / Special Museum - 1979
Hist of inland navigation in central Europe, local hist of Duisburg, early 20th c steamboat on view - library 15467

Museum Küppersmühle, Philosophenweg 55, 47051 Duisburg - T: (0203) 30194811. Head: Hans Grothe
Fine Arts Museum
Coll of works by German artists 15468

Museum Stadt Königsberg, Karmelpl 5, 47049 Duisburg - T: (0203) 2832151. Head: Ute Saalmann
Historical Museum - 1968
Hist of Königsberg before 1945, memorial site of Kant, amber room - archive, library 15469

Naturwissenschaftliches Museum Duisburg, Am See 22, 47279 Duisburg - T: (0203) 2837365. Head: Karl-Heinz Dietz
Natural History Museum 15470

Stiftung DKM, Philosophenweg 17a, 47051 Duisburg - T: (0203) 2981438
Fine Arts Museum 15471

Stiftung Wilhelm Lehmbruck Museum, Zentrum Internationaler Skulptur, Friedrich-Wilhelm-Str 40, 47049 Duisburg - T: (0203) 2832630, 2833294, Fax: 2833892, E-mail: info@lehmbruckmuseum.de, Internet: http://www.lehmbruckmuseum.de. Head: Dr. Christoph Brockhaus
Fine Arts Museum - 1902
Complete works of the sculptor Wilhelm Lehmbruck, 20th c sculpture, painting, drawings, prints, photographs - library, archives, arthothek, children museum 15472

Durbach

Wein- und Heimatmuseum, Tal 36, 77770 Durbach - T: (0781) 48321, Fax: 41590, E-mail: josef_werner@gmx.de. Head: Dr. Herbert Gruber
Local Museum / Agriculture Museum - 1993
Viticulture, peasant life, local hist 15473

Durmersheim

Heimatmuseum Durmersheim, Ritterstr 16, 76448 Durmersheim - T: (07245) 2529
Local Museum 15474

Eberdingen

Keltenmuseum Hochdorf/Enz, Keltenstr 2, 71735 Eberdingen - T: (07042) 78911, Fax: 799466, E-mail: buergermeisteramt@eberdingen.de, Internet: http://www.keltenmuseum.de. Head: Dr. T. Bader
Archaeological Museum - 1991
Celtic grave finds from 6th c BC 15475

Schloßgalerie Kastenscheuer, Hemminger Str, Hochdorf/Enz, 71735 Eberdingen - T: (07042) 98679
Public Gallery - 1976
Contemporary art 15476

Ebergötzen

Europäisches Brotmuseum e.V., Göttinger Str 7, 37136 Ebergötzen - T: (05507) 999498, Fax: 999594. Head: Prof. Dr. Wilfried Seibel, Wilhelm Bruinjes
Special Museum - 1970
Bread baking, Cultural history of 6000 years of Bread 15477

Wilhelm-Busch-Mühle, Mühlengasse 8, 37136 Ebergötzen - T: (05507) 7181, Fax: 7181, Internet: http://www.wilhelm-busch-muehle.de. Head: Kurt Grohs, Susanne Simon
Science&Tech Museum - 1972
Working water mill, life and work of Wilhelm Busch 15478

Ebermannstadt

Heimatmuseum Ebermannstadt, c/o Stadtverwaltung, Bahnhofstr 5, 91320 Ebermannstadt - T: (09194) 1571, 5060, Fax: 50650, E-mail: Heimatmuseum@ebermannstadt.de, Internet: http://www.ebermannstadt.de. Head: Dr. Manfred Franze
Local Museum - 1923
Local history 15479

Ebern

Heimatmuseum Ebern, Marktpl 42, 96106 Ebern - T: (09531) 62914, Fax: 62956, E-mail: info@ebern.de, Internet: http://www.ebern.de
Local Museum - 1974
Genre painter Willi Schütz (hunting scenes) 15480

Ebersbach an der Fils

Jakob-Grünenwald-Gedächtnisstätte, Ortsstr 49, 73061 Ebersbach an der Fils - T: (07163) 161101, Fax: 161244. Head: Klaus Schneider
Fine Arts Museum - 1984
Works and memorabilia of the painter Jakob Grünenwald (1821-1896) - archive 15481

Stadtmuseum Alte Post, Martinstr 10, 73061 Ebersbach an der Fils - T: (07163) 6026, Fax: 161244. Head: Dr. Eberhard Haußmann
Local Museum - 1996
Local hist 15482

Ebersbach, Sachsen

Heimatmuseum Ebersbach in der Humboldt-Baude, Schlechteberg 1, 02730 Ebersbach, Sachsen - T: (03586) 365504
Local Museum / Natural History Museum - 1862
Geology, ancient and early history, local and settlement history, furniture, ceramics, glass, costumes, blueprinting 15483

Ebersberg

Museum Wald und Umwelt (reopening in 2002), Ludwigshöhe, 85560 Ebersberg - T: (08092) 825560, Fax: 825599. Head: Winfried Freitag
Natural History Museum - 1987
Forestry 15484

Eberswalde

Museum in der Adler-Apotheke, Steinstr 3, 16225 Eberswalde - T: (03334) 64520, Fax: 64521, E-mail: stadtverwaltung@eberswalde.de, Internet: http://www.eberswalde.de. Head: Ingrid Fischer
Local Museum - 1905
Ancient and early historic finds, local and regional history 15485

Ebstorf

Kloster Ebstorf, Kirchpl 10, 29574 Ebstorf - T: (05822) 2304
Religious Arts Museum
Benedictine nunnery from the 12th c, stained glas paintings, sculptures, illustrations, world map from the 13th c 15486

Echzell

Heimatmuseum Echzell, Lindenstr 3, 61209 Echzell - T: (06008) 405
Local Museum - 1987
Prehist, early hist, Roman times, modern times 15487

Eckartsberga

Historisches Kabinett Burgruine Eckartsburg, Burgweg 13b, 06648 Eckartsberga - T: (034467) 20415, Fax: 61017, E-mail: eckartsburg@t-online.de
Historical Museum 15488

Eckernförde

Museum Eckernförde, Rathausmarkt 8, 24340 Eckernförde - T: (04351) 712547, Fax: 712549, E-mail: museum-eckernfoerde@gmx.de, Internet: http://www.eckernfoerde.net/museum. Head: Dr. Uwe Beitz
Local Museum - 1975
Town hist, cultural hist, art, local workers' movement and National Socialism, resistance and prosecution - Carl-Bössenroth-Archives 15489

Eckersdorf

Gartenkunst-Museum Schloß Fantasie, Bamberger Str 3, Donndorf, 95488 Eckersdorf - T: (0921) 7314000
Local Museum - 2000 15490

Edenkoben

Museum für Weinbau und Stadtgeschichte, Weinstr 107, 67480 Edenkoben - T: (06323) 81514, 595222, Fax: 959288, E-mail: Anfrage@museum-edenkoben.de, Internet: http://www.museum-edenkoben.de. Head: Herbert Hartkopf
Agriculture Museum / Local Museum / Folklore Museum 15491

Schloß Villa Ludwigshöhe mit Max-Slevogt-Galerie, Villastr, 67480 Edenkoben - T: (06323) 3148. Head: Dr. Berthold Roland
Public Gallery / Decorative Arts Museum - 1980
Furniture 15492

Edewecht

Literaturium / Micro Hall Art Center, Heidedamm 6, Klein Scharrel, 26188 Edewecht - T: (04486) 2697, Fax: 6485, E-mail: kgroh@bigfoot.com, Internet: http://www.kulturserver.de/literaturium.htm. Head: Dr. Klaus Groh
Special Museum - 1990
Literature of the twenties (Kästner, Ringelnatz, Roda Roda, Tucholsky, Valentin, von Ossietzky), Avantgarde literature, experimental theatre, mail art, poesie 15493

Wittenberger Freilichtmuseum, Tollhus up'n Wurnbarg, Wittenberger Str 14, 26188 Edewecht - T: (04405) 6965. Head: Jan-Dirk Meirose
Open Air Museum - 1958
Carriage shed, barn, bakehouse, domestic and agricultural implements and machines 15494

Efringen-Kirchen

Museum in der Alten Schule, Nikolaus-Däublin-Weg 2, 79588 Efringen-Kirchen - T: (07628) 8205, Fax: 80611, E-mail: museum@efringen-kirchen.de, Internet: http://www.efringen-kirchen.de. Head: Dr. V. Alborino
Local Museum - 1990
Geology, local hist 15495

Egeln

Museum für Vor- und Frühgeschichte, Wasserburg 6, 39435 Egeln - T: (039268) 32194, Fax: 2213, E-mail: rathaus-egeln@t-online.de, Internet: http://www.egeln.via.t-online.de
Local Museum
Pre- and early history 15496

Egelsbach

Fahrzeugmuseum, Bahnhof, 63329 Egelsbach - T: (06103) 44248
Science&Tech Museum 15497

Egenhofen

Furthmühle, 82281 Egenhofen - T: (08134) 99191/93, Fax: 519205
Science&Tech Museum
Old Mill 15498

Eggenfelden

Hofmarkmuseum, Gotisches Steildachstadel, Hofmark Gern, 84307 Eggenfelden - T: (08721) 77521, Fax: 70810, E-mail: stadt@eggenfelden.de, Internet: http://www.eggenfelden.de
Historical Museum - 2002 15499

Niederbayerisches Feuerwehrmuseum, Feuerwehrhaus, Hofmark Gern, 84307 Eggenfelden - T: (08721) 70835, 4855, Fax: 70810, E-mail: stadt@eggenfelden.de, Internet: http://www.eggenfelden.de
Historical Museum - 1979/2001 15500

Schauraum, Haus der Begegnung Gern, 84307 Eggenfelden - T: (08721) 911439, Fax: 911439, E-mail: stadt@eggenfelden.de, Internet: http://www.eggenfelden.de. Head: Dr. Petra Noll
Public Gallery
Contemporain Art 15501

Eggenstein-Leopoldshafen

Heimatmuseum Leopoldshafen, Leopoldstr 12, 76344 Eggenstein-Leopoldshafen - T: (0721) 9788613, Fax: (0721) 9788623, E-mail: info@egg-leo.de, Internet: http://www.egg-leo.de
Local Museum - 1980
Local hist, prehistoric finds, tools 15502

Egloffstein

Museum Schloß Hundshaupten, Schloß Hundshaupten, 1349 Egloffstein - T: (09191) 860, Fax: 154
Fine Arts Museum / Decorative Arts Museum 15503

Ehingen, Donau

Besenmuseum, Schloß Mochental, 89584 Ehingen, Donau - T: (07375) 418, Fax: 467, E-mail: Galerie.Schrade@t-online.de, Internet: http://www.schrade-mochental.de
Special Museum
Brooms from all over the world 15504

Museum der Stadt Ehingen, Kasernengasse 6, 89584 Ehingen, Donau - T: (07391) 503531, Fax: 503555, E-mail: l.ohngemach@ehingen.de, Internet: http://www.Ehingen.de. Head: Dr. Ludwig Ohngemach
Local Museum - 1985
Folk art, trades and guilds from the 19th-20th c 15505

Römermuseum in der Grundschule Rißtissen, Römerweg 38, 89584 Ehingen, Donau - T: (07392) 4740, Fax: 968696. Head: Franz Wilhelm
Archaeological Museum 15506

Ehrenfriedersdorf

Bergbau- und Greifenstein-Museum, Greifensteinstr 44, 09427 Ehrenfriedersdorf - T: (037346) 6870, Fax: 68720
Local Museum - 1921
Local history, 16th-19th c native pewter mining, carvings, furniture 15507

Zinngrube Ehrenfriedersdorf, Besucherbergwerk - Mineralogisches Museum, Am Sauberg 1, 09427 Ehrenfriedersdorf - T: (037341) 2557, Fax: 50159, E-mail: zinngrube-ehrenfriedersdorf@t-online.de, Internet: http://www.zinngrube.de. Head: Matthias Kreibich
Science&Tech Museum
One of the oldest pewter mines in Europe, mineralogy 15508

Eibau

Heimat- und Humboldtmuseum, Beckenbergstr 12, 02739 Eibau - T: (03586) 387073, Fax: 780439, E-mail: christfried.heinrich@t-online.de, Internet: http://www.eibau-oberlausitz.de
Local Museum - 1864
Local and regional history, ceramics, glass, peasant furniture, carvings 15509

Eibelstadt

Heimatmuseum, Hauptstr 12, 97246 Eibelstadt - T: (09303) 90610
Local Museum - 1987
Local history and handicrafts 15510

Eibenstock

Stickereimuseum Eibenstock, Bürgermeister-Hesse-Str 7-9, 08309 Eibenstock - T: (037752) 2141, Fax: 2141
Local Museum / Science&Tech Museum - 1955
Local and regional history, geology, technology 15511

Eichenau

Pfefferminzmuseum, Parkstr 43, 82223 Eichenau - T: (08141) 7646, Fax: 500833, Internet: http://members.aol.com/minzmuseum. Head: Hans Kugler
Natural History Museum - 1986
History of peppermint 15512

Eichendorf

Haus der Natur, Eichenberg 1, 94428 Eichendorf - T: (09952) 477, Fax: 897
Natural History Museum - 1988 15513

Vilstaler Bauernmuseum, 94428 Eichendorf - T: (09952) 477, Fax: 897
Folklore Museum - 1998 15514

Eichenzell

Museum Schloss Fasanerie, Hessische Hausstiftung, 36124 Eichenzell - T: (0661) 94860, Fax: 43795, E-mail: schloss-fasanerie@t-online.de, Internet: http://www.schloss-fasanerie.de. Head: Dr. Markus Miller
Decorative Arts Museum
Porcelain, antiques, furniture, silver, paintings - archive, library 15515

Eichstätt

C.O. Müller-Galerie, Residenzpl 1, Landratsamt, 85072 Eichstätt - T: (08421) 70220, Fax: 70222, E-mail: adam.wahler@landkreis-eichstaett.de, Internet: http://www.landkreis-eichstaett.de
Public Gallery - 1977
Work of the painter Carl Otto Müller (1901-1970) 15516

Domschatz- und Diözesan-Museum Eichstätt, Residenzpl 7, 85072 Eichstätt - T: (08421) 50740, 50266, Fax: 50269, E-mail: d.ablassmeier.ba@bfk.ku-eichstaett.de, Internet: http://www.ku-eichstaett.de/Bistum/Museum. Head: Dr. Emanuel Braun
Religious Arts Museum / Fine Arts Museum - 1901
History of the diocese, late Gothic and Baroque sculpture, religious folk art, archaeological finds in the cathedral - workshop 15517

Jura-Museum, Willibaldsburg, Burgstr 19, 85072 Eichstätt - T: (08421) 2956, Fax: 89609, E-mail: Jura-MuseumVF@altmuehlnet.de, Internet: http://www.altmuehlnet.de. Head: Dr. Viohl
Natural History Museum - 1976
Solnhofen limestone slabs, natural hist, mineralogy, zoology, hist of the Altmühlalb - library, specimen workshop 15518

Museum Bergér, Harthof 1, Schernfeld, 85072 Eichstätt - T: (08421) 4663, Fax: 905591, E-mail: g.h.berger@t-online.de. Head: Georg Berger
Natural History Museum - 1968
Fossils from nearby Blumenberg and twenty foreign countries, minerals, shells, specimen sea animals, tools - workshop, stone quarry 15519

Museum für Ur- und Frühgeschichte, Willibaldsburg, Burgstr 19, 85072 Eichstätt - T: (08421) 89450, Fax: 80926, E-mail: webmaster@histver.de, Internet: http://www.histver.de. Head: Albert J. Günther
Historical Museum - 1886
Roman provincial archaeology, Merowinger 15520

Willibaldsburg, Burgstr 19, 85072 Eichstätt - T: (08421) 4730, Fax: 8194, E-mail: info@bsv.bayern.de, Internet: http://www.schloesser.bayern.de. Head: B. Ringholz
Natural History Museum / Local Museum / Archaeological Museum - 1355
Fortified castle of Eichstätt, Jura-museum, bastions garden 15521

Eigeltingen

Kutschensammlung, Lochmühle, 78253 Eigeltingen - T: (07774) 93930, Fax: 939393, E-mail: lochmuehle-eigeltingen@t-online.de, Internet: http://www.lochmuehle-eigeltingen.de. Head: A. Bihler
Science&Tech Museum - 1967
Carriages, vehicles of all kinds 15522

Eilenburg

Stadtmuseum Eilenburg, Dr.-Belian-Str 3, 04838 Eilenburg - T: (03423) 750641, Fax: 750642. Head: Andreas Flegel
Local Museum - 1900
Ancient and early history, local history 15523

Eime

Heimatstube Eime, Hauptstr 8, 31036 Eime - T: (05182) 6258
Local Museum - 1983
Local hist, fossils, mineralogy, early hist, coins, trade workshops 15524

Einbeck

Einbecker Schreibmaschinenmuseum, Maschenstr 47, 37574 Einbeck - T: (05561) 4540, Fax: 7926464. Head: Fritz Nepputh
Science&Tech Museum - 1957
Coll of typewriters 15525

Städtisches Museum Einbeck, Steinweg 11, 37574 Einbeck - T: (05561) 971710, Fax: 971711, E-mail: museum@einbeck.de, Internet: http://www.einbeck-online.de. Head: Dr. Elke Heege
Local Museum - 1894
Pre and early hist, hist of bicycle, craft, coin hist, ceramics, F.W. Sertürner (discovered morphium), S. Stukenbrok (bicycle manufacturer) - archive, library, Fahrrad u Stukenbrok-Museum 15526

Eisenach

Bachhaus Eisenach, Frauenplan 21, 99817 Eisenach - T: (03691) 79340, Fax: 793424, E-mail: info@bachhaus.de, Internet: http://www.bachhaus.de. Head: Dr. Franziska Nentwig
Music Museum - 1907
In former Bach home, historic household objects, memorabilia on Johann Sebastian Bach's (1685-1750) works, 16th-19th c musical instruments 15527

Gedenkstätte Goldener Löwe, Marienstr 57, 99817 Eisenach - T: (03691) 75434, Fax: 75434, E-mail: august-bebel-gesellschaft@t-online.de, Internet: http://www.august-bebel-gesellschaft.de. Head: Sabine Doht
Historical Museum - 1992
Memorabilia of August Bebel, hist of Eisenach (1869) 15528

Lutherhaus, Lutherpl 8, 99817 Eisenach - T: (03691) 29830, Fax: 298331, E-mail: lutherhaus@t-online.de, Internet: http://www.lutherhaus-eisenach.de. Head: Dr. Hagen Jäger
Religious Arts Museum - 1956
Memorabilia on Reformation, portraits, writings, medals, books, Martin Luther (1483-1546) rooms, history of the German Protestant Vicarage 15529

Reuterhaus mit Richard-Wagner-Sammlung, Thüringer Museum Eisenach, Reuterweg 2, 99817 Eisenach - T: (03691) 743293, Fax: 743294. Head: Hanna-Sabine Hummel
Special Museum / Historic Site - 1896/97
Memorabilia on composer Richard Wagner (1813-1883), Fritz Reuter - library 15530

Sammlung Mittelalterliche Kunst in Thüringen, Thüringer Museum Eisenach, Predigerpl 2, 99817 Eisenach - T: (03691) 784678, Fax: 670945, E-mail: info@eisenach.de, Internet: http://www.eisenach.de. Head: Hanna-Sabine Hummel
Fine Arts Museum - 1899
Medieval Thüringen, religious sculpture 12th - 16th c 15531

Thüringer Museum Eisenach, Schloss, Markt 24, 99817 Eisenach - T: (03691) 670450, Fax: 670945, E-mail: info@eisenach.de, Internet: http://www.eisenach.de. Head: Hanna-Sabine Hummel
Decorative Arts Museum / Fine Arts Museum - 1899
Thuringian porcelain, glass, ceramics, German painting 19th-20th c - library, auditorium 15532

Wartburg, Auf der Wartburg, 99817 Eisenach - T: (03691) 2500, Fax: 203342, E-mail: info@wartburg-eisenach.de, Internet: http://www.wartburg-eisenach.de. Head: Günter Schuchardt
Historic Site / Fine Arts Museum - 1922
Historic rooms, Gothic furnishings, 15th-18th c crafts, 16th c paintings, Gothic sculpture, M. Luther (1483-1546) library - library 15533

Eisenberg, Allgäu

Burgenmuseum Eisenberg, Dorfstr 12, 87637 Eisenberg, Allgäu - T: (08363) 94430, Fax: 94430, E-mail: poelcher@online-service.de. Head: Bertold Pölcher
Local Museum - 1984
Ruin with a coll implements 15534

Eisenberg, Thüringen

Stadtmuseum Eisenberg, Markt 26, 07607 Eisenberg, Thüringen - T: (036691) 733, Fax: 73460, Internet: http://www.stadteisenberg.de. Head: Jörg Petermann
Local Museum 15535

Eisenhüttenstadt

Dokumentationszentrum Alltagskultur der DDR, Erich-Weinert-Allee 3, 15890 Eisenhüttenstadt - T: (03364) 417355, Fax: 418947, E-mail: info@alltagskultur-ddr.de, Internet: http://www.alltagskultur-ddr.de. Head: Andreas Ludwig
Historical Museum - 1993
Everydays objects from the GDR - archive "Verlag Volk und Welt" 15536

Städtische Galerie, Oderstr 5, 15890 Eisenhüttenstadt - T: (03364) 2146, Fax: 2366. Head: Michael Tillmann
Fine Arts Museum - 1994
Art of GDR 15537

Städtisches Feuerwehr-Museum, Heinrich-Pritzsche-Str 26, 15890 Eisenhüttenstadt - T: (03364) 28243, Fax: 2366. Head: Jürgen Preuß
Science&Tech Museum - 1992 15538

Städtisches Museum, Löwenstr 4, 15890 Eisenhüttenstadt - T: (03364) 2146, Fax: 2366. Head: Michael Tillmann
Local Museum - 1980
Ancient and early hist, local industrial hist, brown coal mining 15539

Eisfeld

Museum Otto Ludwig, Schloß Eisfeld, Markt 2, 98673 Eisfeld - T: (03686) 300308, Fax: 301859, E-mail: museum@stadt-eisfeld.de. Head: Heiko Haine
Local Museum / Folklore Museum - 1949
Ancient and early history finds, local history, crafts, 17th-19th c peasant living style, tools and costumes, modern applied arts, history of Thuringian porcelain industry, memorabilia on writer Otto Ludwig (1813-1865) 15540

Elbingerode, Harz

Schaubergwerk Büchenberg, An der B244, 38875 Elbingerode, Harz - T: (039454) 42200, Fax: 42200
Science&Tech Museum 15541

Ellingen, Bayern

Kulturzentrum Ostpreußen, Schloßstr 9, 91792 Ellingen, Bayern - T: (09141) 86440, Fax: 864414, E-mail: kulturz.ostpreussen@wugnet.de, Internet: http://www.wugnet.de/kulturz-ostpreussen. Head: Wolfgang Freyberg
Local Museum
History of East Prussia - Library, archive 15542

Residenz Ellingen, Schloßstr 9, 91792 Ellingen, Bayern - T: (09141) 3327, Fax: 72953, E-mail: info@bsv.bayern.de. Head: Dr. Albrecht Miller
Historical Museum - 1954
History of the German order, furnishings from the classical French Empire style, coins, mirrors, coats of arms 15543

Ellrich

Heimatmuseum Ellrich, Hospitalstr 40, 99755 Ellrich - T: (036332) 250, 260, Fax: 20395, 2623
Local Museum 15544

Heimatstuben, Goeckingstr 31, 99755 Ellrich
Local Museum - 1967
Local history, history of labour-movement 15545

Ellwangen

Schloßmuseum, Schloß 12, 73479 Ellwangen - T: (07961) 54380, Fax: 54380
Local Museum - 1908
Prehistory, local history, church history, religious art, especially Baroque manger scenes, faience, metalwork, historical prints, Baroque drawings, works of the painter Karl Stirner 15546

Ellzee

Kreisheimatstube, Schwaninger Str 18, Stoffenried, 89352 Ellzee - T: (08283) 2131, Fax: (08221) 95440, E-mail: info@landkreis-guenzburg.de, Internet: http://www.landkreis-guenzburg.de
Local Museum - 1984
Local history, agricultural tools 15547

Elmshorn

Industriemuseum Elmshorn, Catharinenstr 1, 25335 Elmshorn - T: (04121) 268870, Fax: 268872, E-mail: industriemuseum@t-online.de, Internet: http://www.industriemuseum-sh.de. Head: Bärbel Böhnke
Local Museum - 1991 15548

Elsenfeld

Heimatmuseum, Hauptstr 21, 63820 Elsenfeld - T: (06022) 50070, 9200, Fax: 500766, E-mail: wiffhamann@main-echo.net, Internet: http://www.home.main-echo.net/~geschumuseum
Local Museum - 1980
Local history, rustic culture 15549

Eltmann

Heimatmuseum, c/o Schloßsteige 17, Brunnenstr 4, 97483 Eltmann - T: (09522) 7944
Local Museum - 1985
Agricultural tools, shoemaker's workshop and local history 15550

Eltville

Erbacher Heimatzimmer, Erbach, Markt 1, 65346 Eltville - T: (06123) 62160
Local Museum - 1985
Domestic objects, documents, wine bottles 15551

Gutenberg-Gedenkstätte, Burgstr 1, 65343 Eltville - T: (06123) 2718. Head: Dr. Hermann Peters
Historical Museum
Documents and publications on Gutenberg and the hist of printing and printing techniques 15552

Historische Sammlung Eltville, Burgstr 1, 65343 Eltville - T: (06123) 697155. Head: Ulrike Bergmann
Historical Museum
Early historic finds, coins, documents, etchings 15553

Elzach

Heimatkundliche Sammlung, Hauptstr 39, 79215 Elzach - T: (07682) 8040, Fax: 80455, E-mail: stadt@elzach.de, Internet: http://www.elzach.de
Local Museum - 1967 15554

Elze

Heimatmuseum Elze, Mühlenstr 14, 31008 Elze - T: (05068) 46456
Local Museum - 1987
Water mill, agriculture, domestic work, trades 15555

Elztal

Museum am Odenwaldlimes, Mosbacher Str 7, Neckarburken, 74834 Elztal - T: (06261) 5706, Fax: 5706, E-mail: Manfred.Waltereit@t-online.de. Head: Manfred Waltereit
Archaeological Museum 15556

Emden

Kunsthalle in Emden, Stiftung Henri und Else Nannen & Schenkung Otto van de Loo, Hinter dem Rahmen 13, 26721 Emden - T: (04921) 975050, Fax: 975055, E-mail: kunsthalle@kunsthalle-emden.de, Internet: http://www.kunsthalle-emden.de. Head: Dr. Achim Sommer
Fine Arts Museum - 1986
German Expressionism, Russian Avantgarde of the Eighties, Neue Sachlichkeit, CoBra, SPUR and Informel 15557

Museumsfeuerschiff Amrumbank/Deutsche Bucht, Georg-Breusing-Promenade, 26725 Emden - T: (04921) 23285, 33236, Fax: 33203, E-mail: info@amrumbank.de, Internet: http://www.amrumbank.de
Science&Tech Museum / Special Museum - 1984
Former lightship, exhibition on pilots 15558

Museumslogger AE7 Stadt Emden, Im Ratsdelft, 26721 Emden, mail addr: Petkumer Str 220, 26725 Emden - T: (04921) 51212, E-mail: info@heringslogger.de, Internet: http://www.heringslogger.de. Head: Johannes Sonntag
Science&Tech Museum - 1986
Emden trawler and fishing ship, herring fishery 15559

Ostfriesisches Landesmuseum und Emder Rüstkammer, Rathaus am Delft, Neutorstr, 26721 Emden - T: (04921) 872058, Fax: 872063, E-mail: landesmuseum@emden.de, Internet: http://www.landesmuseum-emden.de. Head: Dr. F. Scheele
Local Museum - 1833
Pre- and early hist, local hist, paintings, arms and armour, archives - library 15560

Pelzerhaus, Pelzerstr 2, 26721 Emden - T: (04921) 25335. Head: Dr. Helmut Eichhorn
Historical Museum
Preserved Renaissance town house in Flemish-Netherlandish style from 1585 15561

Emmendingen

Museum im Markgrafen-Schloß, Schlosspl 1, 79312 Emmendingen - T: (07641) 452221, 452325, Fax: 452237, E-mail: emmuseum1@aol.com, Internet: http://www.emmendingen.de. Head: Hans-Jörg Jenne
Local Museum - 1901
Prehistory, local history, handicrafts and the guilds, peasant life, works of the painter and graphic artist Fritz Boehle, memorabilia of Goethe and his sister Cornelia Schlosser 15562

Emmerich

Museum für Kaffeetechnik, c/o Probat-Werke von Gimborn Maschinenfabrik GmbH, Reeser Str 94, 46446 Emmerich - T: (02822) 9120, Fax: 912444, E-mail: info@probat.com, Internet: http://www.probat.com/de/museum. Head: C.H. von Gimborn
Science&Tech Museum
History of coffee roasting techniques, coffee grinders 15563

Plakatmuseum am Niederrhein, Grollscher Weg 1, 46446 Emmerich - T: (02822) 939921, Fax: 939922. Head: Dr. Martin Müller
Decorative Arts Museum - 1968
Olympic games, theatre, art exhibitions (Josef Beuys, HAP Grieshaber) music, posters, graphic design 15564

Rheinmuseum, Martinikirchgang 2, 46446 Emmerich - T: (02822) 75400, Fax: 75417, E-mail: Rheinmuseum-Emmerich@t-online.de, Internet: http://www.emmerich.de. Head: Dr. Herbert Kleipaß
Science&Tech Museum / Special Museum - 1964
Hist of navigation on the Rhine, models of ships and dockyards - library 15565

Schlösschen Borghees, Hüthumer Str 80, 46446 Emmerich - T: (02822) 939913
Fine Arts Museum 15566

Emmerthal

Museum für Landtechnik und Landarbeit, Frenker Str 22, Börry, 31860 Emmerthal - T: (05157) 209. Head: Martin Delker
Science&Tech Museum - 1990
Agricultural implements, original rooms, trades 15567

Schloß Hämelschenburg, Schloßstr 2, 31860 Emmerthal - T: (05155) 951690, Fax: 951691, E-mail: vklencke@aol.com, Internet: http://www.haemelschenburg.de. Head: Lippold von Klencke
Local Museum - 1973
Weser-Renaissance, paintings, furniture, ceramics, arms 15568

Emsbüren

Heimathof Emsbüren, Luidgeristr 2, 48488 Emsbüren - T: (05903) 1969, 566, Fax: 932180
Agriculture Museum 15569

Emsdetten

August-Holländer-Museum, Mühlenstr 28, 48282 Emsdetten - T: (02572) 120, Fax: 12209. Head: Heinz Ibeler
Local Museum - 1993
Weaving, industrialization, daily life, local hist 15570

Galerie Münsterland, Friedrichstr 3, 48282 Emsdetten - T: (02572) 89007, Fax: 920686, E-mail: galerie-muensterland@t-online.de, Internet: http://www.galerie-muensterland.de. Head: Ulrike Wachsmund
Public Gallery 15571

Wannenmachermuseum, Mühlenstr 30, 48282 Emsdetten - T: (02572) 120, Fax: 12209. Head: Karl Finke
Historical Museum - 1985 15572

Emskirchen

Heimatmuseum Emskirchen, Hindenburgstr 32, 91448 Emskirchen - T: (09104) 3874, 1033
Local Museum - 1989
Agricultural tools, forge and shoemaker's workshop 15573

Rundfunkmuseum Schloß Brunn, Am Schloß 2, 91448 Emskirchen - T: (09104) 2482, Fax: 2482, Internet: http://www.rundfunkmuseum.nea-online.de. Head: Ludwig Schroll
Science&Tech Museum - 1992
Hist of broadcasting, consumer electronics 15574

Endingen

Kaiserstühler Heimatmuseum, Marktpl 1, 79346 Endingen - T: (07642) 689990, Fax: 689999. Head: Gerda Kauschat
Local Museum - 1972 15575

Engelsbrand

Waldhufen-Heimatmuseum Salmbach, Pforzheimer Str 15, 75331 Engelsbrand - T: (07235) 661
Local Museum - 1978
Peasant life 15576

Engelskirchen

Rheinisches Industriemuseum, Außenstelle Engelskirchen, Engelspl 2, 51766 Engelskirchen - T: (02263) 20114, Fax: 47395, E-mail: t.schleper@lvr.de, Internet: http://www.unter-spannung.de. Head: Dr. Thomas Schleper
Historical Museum
Electrical appliances and equipment 15577

Engen

Städtisches Museum Engen und Galerie, Klostergasse 19, 78234 Engen - T: (07733) 502257, Fax: 502299, E-mail: rathaus@engen.de, Internet: http://www.engen.de. Head: Dr. Ulf Wendler
Local Museum / Fine Arts Museum / Archaeological Museum - 1937/1988
Religious art, archaeology 15578

Enger

Widukind-Museum (closed until 2003), Kirchpl 10, 32130 Enger - T: (05224) 1752, Fax: 690366. Head: Regine Krull
Special Museum - 1939/1983
Life and work of Saxonian noble man Widukind 15579

Engstingen

Automuseum Engstingen, Kleinengstinger Str 2, 72829 Engstingen - T: (07129) 7387. Head: K. Bilharz
Science&Tech Museum - 1987
Automobiles from 1888 until 1975 15580

Epfenbach

Heimatmuseum Epfenbach, Kreisental 4, 74925 Epfenbach - T: (07263) 749, 5389
Local Museum - 1968 15581

Eppingen

Elsenzer Heimatstuben, Sinsheimer Str 8, 75031 Eppingen - T: (07260) 255
Local Museum - 1950/1988 15582

Heimatstube Mühlbach mit Philipp-Neubrand-Gedächtnisstube, Hauptstr 9, 75031 Eppingen - T: (07262) 8552
Local Museum 15583

Heimatstube Rohrbach, Bruchsaler Str 68, 75031 Eppingen - T: (07262) 6040
Local Museum - 1981 15584

Museum Jordanbad, Küfergasse 2, 75031 Eppingen - T: (07262) 920118, Fax: 920177, E-mail: p.riek@eppingen.de, Internet: http://www.eppingen.de. Head: Peter Riek
Historical Museum 15585

Stadt- und Fachwerkmuseum Alte Universität, Fleischgasse 2, 75031 Eppingen - T: (07262) 920118, Fax: 920177, E-mail: p.riek@eppingen.de, Internet: http://www.eppingen.de. Head: Peter Riek
Local Museum - 1988 15586

Steinhauermuseum Mühlbach, Hauptstr, 75031 Eppingen - T: (07262) 920118, Fax: 920177, E-mail: p.riek@eppingen.de, Internet: http://www.eppingen.de. Head: Peter Riek
Special Museum 15587

Eppstein

Stadt- und Burgmuseum, Hauptstr 99, 65817 Eppstein - T: (06198) 305110, Fax: 305109, E-mail: info@eppstein.de, Internet: http://www.eppstein.de. Head: Dr. Bertold Picard
Local Museum / Historical Museum - 1908
Town and castle hist, hist of the Lord of Eppstein 15588

Erbach, Donau

Museum der deutschen Sprachinselorte bei Brünn, Schloß Erbach, 89155 Erbach, Donau - T: (07305) 5200. Head: I. Biefel, H. Biefel
Ethnology Museum - 1971
Local hist 15589

Schloßmuseum, Schloß, 89155 Erbach, Donau - T: (07305) 4646. Head: Franz Freiherr von Ulm zu Erbach
Historic Site 15590

Erbach, Odenwald

Deutsches Elfenbeinmuseum Erbach, Otto-Glenz-Str 1, 64711 Erbach, Odenwald - T: (06062) 919990, Fax: 9199921, E-mail: elfenbeinmuseum@t-online.de, Internet: http://www.hessennet.de/erbach. Head: Brigitte Dinger
Decorative Arts Museum - 1966
Ivories from around the world, ivory-carving - library, workshop 15591

Gräfliche Sammlungen und Afrikanisches Jagdmuseum, Marktpl 11, 64711 Erbach, Odenwald - T: (06062) 95920, Fax: 959230, E-mail: heim-rentkammer@t-online.de. Head: Franz Graf zu Erbach-Erbach
Local Museum - Late 18th c
Hunting trophies, hunting equipment, 16th-19th c small arms, Roman sculpture, coins, prehist, local archaeological finds, trophies from various African countries 15592

Erbendorf

Heimatmuseum im Alten Kloster, Kirchgasse 4, 92681 Erbendorf - T: (09682) 921022, 1484, Fax: 921092
Local Museum
Coll of minerals and stones, local history 15593

Erding

Bauernhausmuseum des Landkreises Erding, Taufkirchener Str 24, 85435 Erding - T: (08122) 58251, 93320, Fax: 58279
Ethnology Museum - 1986
Farmhouses 15594

Städtisches Heimatmuseum Erding, Prielmayerstr 1, 85435 Erding - T: (08122) 187533, Fax: 408250, E-mail: kulturamt@erding.de, Internet: http://www.museum.erding.de. Head: Paul Adelsberger
Local Museum - 1856
Religious folklore, local history 15595

Erdweg

Huttermuseum, Walkertshofener Str 14, 85253 Erdweg - T: (08138) 931710, Fax: 9317020
Local Museum - 1997
Rustic culture 15596

Erfurt

Angermuseum, Anger 18, 99084 Erfurt - T: (0361) 5623311, Fax: 5626645, E-mail: angermuseum@t-online.de, Internet: http://www.angermuseum.de. Head: Dr. Wolfram Morath
Fine Arts Museum - 1886
14th-16th c German paintings and sculpture, medieval glasspainting, 18th-20th c landscape paintings by German artists, German impressionism, 20th c art, medieval Renaissance crafts, Gothic-Rococo furnishing, 14th-20th c wrought iron, decorative objects - library 15597

Artothek der Stadt und Regionalbibliothek Erfurt, Dompl 1, 99084 Erfurt - T: (0361) 6551576, Fax: 6551599, E-mail: bibliothek@erfurt.de, Internet: http://www.erfurt.de. Head: Heidemarie Trenkmann
Library with Exhibitions 15598

Brückenhausmuseum, Krämerbrücke 20-21, 99084 Erfurt - T: (0361) 5626771
Historic Site
14th c stone bridge and its hist, dolls and embroidery 15599

Deutsches Gartenbaumuseum Erfurt, Cyriaksburg, Gothaer Str 50, 99094 Erfurt - T: (0361) 223990, Fax: 2239913, E-mail: deutsches-gartenbaumuseum@t-online.de, Internet: http://www.gartenbaumuseum.de. Head: Dr. Harald Bischoff
Agriculture Museum - 1961
History and development of horticulture, art of gardening 15600

Ehemalige Barfüßerkirche, Außenstelle des Angermuseums, Barfüßerstr 20, 99084 Erfurt - T: (0361) 5623311, Fax: 5626645, E-mail: angermuseum@t-online.de, Internet: http://www.angermuseum.de. Head: Dr. Wolfram Morath
Religious Arts Museum 15601

Forum Konkrete Kunst Erfurt, Michaelisstr 10, 99084 Erfurt - T: (0361) 6551960
Public Gallery 15602

Forum Konkrete Kunst - Peterskirche, Lowetscher Str 42c, 99089 Erfurt - T: (0361) 735742, Fax: 735742, Internet: http://www.erfurt.de. Head: Heidi Bierwisch
Fine Arts Museum
Modern and contemporary constructive/concrete art, art objects, panel paintings, graphics, installations - colloquiums 15603

Galerie Haus Dacheröden, Anger 37-38, 99084 Erfurt - T: (0361) 5624182, Fax: 6551613, Internet: http://www.erfurt.de. Head: Steffi Gorka
Public Gallery 15604

Gedenkstätte Erfurter Parteitag 1891, Futterstr 15-16, 99084 Erfurt. Head: Angela Röscher
Historical Museum - 1964
History of the German labour movement at scene of local Party Day 1891 15605

Haus zum Stockfisch - Stadtmuseum, Johannesstr 169, 99084 Erfurt - T: (0361) 6555644, Fax: 6555659, E-mail: stadtmuseum@erfurt.de, Internet: http://www.erfurt.de. Head: Hardy Eidam
Local Museum 15606

Kunsthalle Erfurt im Haus zum Roten Ochsen, Fischmarkt 7, 99084 Erfurt - T: (0361) 6422188, 5626210, Fax: 6463092, E-mail: kunsthalle.erfurt@t-online.de, Internet: http://www.kunsthalle-erfurt.de. Head: Dr. Kai Uwe Schierz
Public Gallery 15607

Museum für Thüringer Volkskunde Erfurt, Juri-Gagarin-Ring 140a, 99084 Erfurt - T: (0361) 6555607, Fax: 6555609, E-mail: volkskundemuseum@erfurt.de, Internet: http://www.volkskundemuseum-erfurt.de. Head: Dr. Marina Moritz
Folklore Museum - 1955
Local antiquities, peasant folk culture of Thuringia, costumes, crafts, decorative objects, toys, glass, porcelain 15608

Museum Neue Mühle, Schlösserstr 25a, 99084 Erfurt - T: (0361) 6461059
Historic Site
Historical watermill, machinery 15609

Naturkundemuseum Erfurt, Große Arche 14, 99084 Erfurt - T: (0361) 6422085, Fax: 6422086, E-mail: NMEm.hartmann@t-online.de, Internet: http://www.erfurt.de/naturkundemuseum. Head: Gerd-Rainer Riedel
Natural History Museum - 1922
Geology, biology, zoology, entomology, ornithology, herpetology - library 15610

Ergoldsbach

Heimatmuseum, Rathaus, Hauptstr 29, 84061 Ergoldsbach - T: (08771) 300, Fax: 3041
Local Museum - 1978
Early and local history, costumes, agricultural tools 15611

Eriskirch

Heimatmuseum Eriskirch, Kirchpl 3, 88097 Eriskirch - T: (07541) 97080
Local Museum 15612

Erkelenz

Feuerwehrmuseum Lövenich, An der Vogelstange 15, 41812 Erkelenz - T: (02435) 531
Science&Tech Museum 15613

Erkheim

Erstes Allgäu-Schwäbisches Dorfschulmuseum, Altes Schulhaus Daxberg, 87746 Erkheim - T: (08336) 7760
Special Museum - 1988
Old school house 15614

Erkner

Gerhart-Hauptmann-Museum, Gerhart-Hauptmann-Str 1-2, 15537 Erkner - T: (03362) 3663, Fax: 3663, E-mail: G.H.M.Erkner@gmx.de, Internet: http://www.Gerhart-Hauptmann-Museum.de. Head: Stefan Rohlfs
Special Museum - 1987
Memorabilia on writer Gerhart Hauptmann (1862-1946), photo coll, newspaper clippings, artistic portrayals - research, library 15615

Museumshof am Sonnenlück, Heimatmuseum Erkner, Heinrich-Heine-Str 17-18, 15537 Erkner - T: (03362) 22452
Local Museum 15616

Erlangen

Anatomische Sammlung, Friedrich-Alexander-Universität Erlangen-Nürnberg, Krankenhausstr 9, 91054 Erlangen - T: (09131) 8522269, Fax: 8522863. Head: Prof. Dr. W.L. Neuhuber
Natural History Museum 15617

Antikensammlung der Friedrich-Alexander-Universität Erlangen-Nürnberg, Kochstr 4/19, 91054 Erlangen - T: (09131) 8522391, 8526336, Fax: 8522313, E-mail: prkranz@phil.uni-erlangen.de, Internet: http://www.phil.uni-erlangen.de/~p1altar/home.html. Head: Prof. Dr. P. Kranz
Museum of Classical Antiquities - 1857
Coll of plaster-figures and orginal ceramics 15618

Brüxer und Komotauer Heimatstuben, Palais Stutterheim, Marktpl 1, 91054 Erlangen - T: (09131) 301490, 208898
Local Museum - 1972
Local history 15619

Gemäldesammlung, Friedrich-Alexander-Universität Erlangen-Nürnberg, Schloßgarten 1, 91054 Erlangen - T: (09131) 859260
Fine Arts Museum 15620

Graphische Sammlung der Universität, Universitätsstr 4, 91054 Erlangen - T: (09131) 8522158, Fax: 8529309, E-mail: handschriften@bib.uni-erlangen.de. Head: Hans-Otto Keunecke
Fine Arts Museum 15621

Mineralogische Sammlung, Friedrich-Alexander-Universität Erlangen-Nürnberg, Schloßgarten 5, 91054 Erlangen - T: (09131) 853982. Head: Prof. Hans-Jürgen Kuzel
Natural History Museum 15622

Museum im Amtshausschlüpfla, Brauhofgasse 2b, 91056 Erlangen - T: (09131) 992171, Fax: 992171, E-mail: triantafyllidis@web.de, Internet: http://www.museum-schuepfla.de. Head: Jutta Triantafyllidis
Historical Museum / Folklore Museum / Agriculture Museum - 1987
Rustic culture 15623

Musikinstrumentensammlung, Friedrich-Alexander-Universität Erlangen-Nürnberg, Bismarckstr 1, 91054 Erlangen - T: (09131) 8522398, Fax: 8522403, E-mail: tsroeder@phil.uni-erlangen.de, Internet: http://www.phil.uni-erlangen.de/~p1musik/. Head: Prof. Dr. Andreas Haug
Music Museum - 1922
Pianos 15624

Platenhäuschen, Burgbergstr 92a, 91054 Erlangen - T: (09131) 862219, Fax: 862876
Special Museum - 1925/1977 15625

Stadtmuseum Erlangen, Martin-Luther-Pl 8-9, 91054 Erlangen - T: (09131) 862408, Fax: 862876, E-mail: stadtmuseum@stadt.erlangen.de, Internet: http://www.stadt.erlangen.de/kultur/bildung/stadtmuseum. Head: Dr. Christoph Friederich
Local Museum - 1964
Prehist, local hist, development of handicrafts, folk art, local artists, toys, industrial culture 15626

Städtische Galerie Erlangen, Palais Stutterheim, Marktpl 1, 91054 Erlangen - T: (09131) 862839, 862533, Fax: 862117, E-mail: kulturamt@stadt.erlangen.de, Internet: http://www.kubiss.de/erlangen. Head: Karl Manfred Fischer
Fine Arts Museum - 1967
Contemporary arts and photography 15627

Ur- und Frühgeschichtliche Sammlung, Friedrich-Alexander-Universität Erlangen-Nürnberg, Kochstr 4/18, 91054 Erlangen - T: (09131) 8522794, Fax: 8526394, E-mail: p1altuf@phil.uni-erlangen.de, Internet: http://www.uf.uni-erlangen.de/sammlung/sammlung.html. Head: Prof. Dr. Ludwig Reisch
Archaeological Museum - 1914
Central and Western European prehistory, Roman times, early Middle Ages, finds from pre-Columbian America and the Far East - workshop, laboratory 15628

Erlenbach, Kreis Heilbronn

Weinbaumuseum Alte Kelter, Bei der Kelter 1, 74235 Erlenbach, Kreis Heilbronn - T: (07132) 933531, Fax: 933514
Agriculture Museum - 1987
Viticulture 15629

Ermsleben

Konradsburg Ermsleben, Auf der Konradsburg, 06463 Ermsleben - T: (034743) 92565, Fax: 92563
Historical Museum - 1990
Former castle and Benedictine monastery 15630

Eschach

Schwäbisches Bauern- und Technikmuseum, Seifertshofen, Marktstr 5, 73569 Eschach - T: (07175) 360, Fax: 7369. Head: E. Kiemele
Science&Tech Museum / Agriculture Museum - 1984
Peasant life, agricultural implements 15631

Eschborn

Museum der Stadt Eschborn, Eschenpl 1, 65760 Eschborn - T: (06196) 490232, 484670, Fax: 484671, E-mail: museum@eschborn.de, Internet: http://www.eschborn.de. Head: Gerhard Raiss
Local Museum - 1989
Bequest of the painter Hanny Franke, grave finds from 5th c AC 15632

Eschenburg

Heimatmuseum Eschenburg, Marktstr 1a, 35713 Eschenburg - T: (02774) 912908, Fax: 912909, E-mail: winfriedk1@aol.com, Internet: http://www.heimatmuseum.foerdervereine.de
Local Museum - 1987
Half-timbered house with changing exhibitions on painting, photography, mining and agriculture, living, bed rooms and kitchen from 19th c, spinning 15633

Eschershausen

Museum Raabe-Haus, Raabestr 5, 37632 Eschershausen - T: (05534) 3969, Fax: 999768
Special Museum - 1999
Furniture, pictures and paintings, letters and first editions of Raabe housed in the writer's birthplace 15634

Eschlkam

Waldschmidt-Ausstellung, Waldschmidtpl 14, 93458 Eschlkam - T: (09948) 751, 446
Special Museum - 1987
Life and work of the author Maximilian Schmidt (1832-1919) 15635

Eschwege

Eisenbahnmuseum, Pommertor 3, 37269 Eschwege - T: (05651) 21301
Science&Tech Museum 15636

Heimatmuseum Eschwege, Vor dem Berge 14a, 37269 Eschwege - T: (05651) 5284. Head:
Local Museum - 1913/64
Representative artefacts from prehist to the time of the Franks, vessels and tools, fossilized bones, studio of the photographer Oscar Tellgmann 15637

Kleines Museum der Sparkasse Werra-Meißner, Friedrich-Wilhelm-Str 40-42, 37269 Eschwege - T: (05651) 306671, Fax: 306785, E-mail: marketing@sparkasse-werra-meissner.de
Special Museum 15638

Eschweiler

Städtische Kunstsammlung, Kulturzentrum Talbahnhof, Bismarckstr 25-27, 52249 Eschweiler - T: (02403) 71219, Fax: 71519. Head:
Fine Arts Museum - 1980 15639

Esens

August-Gottschalk-Haus, Gedenkstätte und Ausstellung zur neueren Geschichte der ostfriesischen Juden, Burgstr 8, 26427 Esens - T: (04971) 2306, Fax: 2306. Head: Wolfgang Ritter
Special Museum / Historical Museum / Historic Site - 1990
Former Jewish parish house, school room, bath, persecution and extermination of East Frisian Jews in the Third Reich 15640

Heimatmuseum in der Peldemühle → Museum Leben am Meer

Museum für Holographie, Am Kirchpl, 26427 Esens - T: (04489) 5198, Fax: 6391, E-mail: elmar@digi-art.de, Internet: http://www.holarium.de. Head: Elmar Spreer
Decorative Arts Museum 15641

Museum Leben am Meer, Beusersieler Str 1, 26427 Esens - T: (04971) 5332
Local Museum - 1989
Town hist, mill, grave finds 15642

Turmmuseum Sankt Magnus, Am Kirchpl 5-7, 26427 Esens - T: (04971) 919712, Fax: 919723
Religious Arts Museum - 1982
Architectural hist of the church, various church objects 15643

Espelkamp

Museum Gauselmann, Merkur-Allee 1-15, 32339 Espelkamp - T: (05772) 49486, Fax: 49488, E-mail: Mkokoska@gauselmann.de, Internet: http://www.gauselmann.de. Head: Monika Kokoska
Science&Tech Museum - 1995
Historical slot machines, fruit machines, jukeboxes, vending machines, service machines, pinball machines, amusement machines, games of skill, music boxes, amusement machines with prize 15644

Essen

Alte Cuesterey, Weidkamp 10, 45355 Essen - T: (0201) 3643528, Fax: 3643528. Head: Jürgen Becker
Historical Museum 15645

Alte Synagoge, Museen der Stadt Essen, Steeler Str 29, 45127 Essen - T: (0201) 8845218, Fax: 8845225, E-mail: info@alte-synagoge.essen.de, Internet: http://www.essen.de/kultur/synagoge. Head: Dr. Edna Brocke
Local Museum / Historic Site - 1980
Jewish history (history of the Jews in Essen), National Socialism in Essen - library, archives 15646

Archäologische Sammlung, Ruhrlandmuseum, Goethestr 41, 45128 Essen - T: (0201) 8845200, Fax: 8845138, E-mail: info@ruhrlandmuseum.de, Internet: http://www.ruhrlandmuseum.de. Head: Dr. Charlotte Trümpler
Archaeological Museum 15647

Bergbau- und Heimatmuseum Paulushof, Stemmering 20, 45259 Essen - T: (0201) 466471. Head: Werner Hamacher
Local Museum 15648

Deutsches Plakat Museum, Rathenaustr 2, 45127 Essen - T: (0201) 8845108, Fax: 8845122, E-mail: contact@plakatmuseum.de, Internet: http://www.plakatmuseum.de. Head: Dr. Frieder Mellinghoff
Decorative Arts Museum 15649

Domschatzkammer, Burgpl 2, 45127 Essen - T: (0201) 2204206, Fax: 2204507, E-mail: Domkapitel-Essen@t-online.de, Internet: http://www.bistum-essen.de/dom/schatz.htm. Head: Alfred Pothmann
Religious Arts Museum
Sacred art from the Middle Age to the 16th c 15650

Foto-Museum, Burg Horst, Haus Horst 1, 45279 Essen - T: (0201) 538590, Fax: (02325) 75049. Head: Hans-Dieter Abring
Decorative Arts Museum 15651

Gaseum, Huttropstr 60, 45138 Essen - T: (0201) 1842029, Fax: 1844393, E-mail: info@ruhrgas.com, Internet: http://www.ruhrgas.de. Head: Frank Stahn
Science&Tech Museum 15652

Historische Ausstellung Krupp, Villa Hügel, Hügel 1, 45133 Essen - T: (0201) 1884821, Fax: 1884859, E-mail: Archiv@hak.krupp-stiftung.de. Head: Dr. Renate Köhne-Lindenlaub
Historical Museum - 1961
Documents, paintings, models and other items illustrating the hist of the Krupp family and firm 15653

Kunsthaus Essen, Rübezahlstr 33, 45134 Essen - T: (0201) 443313, Fax: 472241, E-mail: khe@kunsthaus-essen.de, Internet: http://www.kunsthaus-essen.de. Head: Dr. Carola Schneider
Public Gallery 15654

Kunstraum Notkirche, An der Apostelkirche 8, 45145 Essen - T: (0201) 740788, Fax: 7490312, E-mail: werner.sonnenberg@t-online.de, Internet: http://www.apostelkirche-essen.de
Public Gallery 15655

Kunstschacht Katernberg, Bullmannaue 11, 45327 Essen - T: (0201) 370045
Public Gallery 15656

Markt- und Schaustellermuseum, Hachestr 68, 45127 Essen - T: (0201) 228749, 340001, Fax: 350434, Internet: http://www.divio.de/Schaustellermuseum.html. Head: Erich Knocke
Historical Museum - 1978 15657

Mineralienmuseum Essen, Museen der Stadt Essen, Kupferdreher Str 141-143, 45257 Essen - T: (0201) 8845200, 8845230, Fax: 8845138, E-mail: info@ruhrlandmuseum.de, Internet: http://www.ruhrlandmuseum.de. Head: Ulrike Stottrop
Natural History Museum - 1984 15658

Museum Folkwang Essen, Goethestr 41, 45128 Essen - T: (0201) 8845301, Fax: 8845325, Internet: http://www.museum-folkwang.de. Head: Dr. Georg-W. Költzsch
Fine Arts Museum - 1901/22
19th and 20th c painting and sculpture, post-1950 American painting, 19th and 20th c graphics, photogr, posters, classical art of the Mediterranean area, East Asian art, African art 15659

Museumslandschaft Deilbachtal, Nierenhofer Str 8-10, 45257 Essen - T: (0201) 8845200, Fax: 8845138, E-mail: info@ruhrlandmuseum.de, Internet: http://www.ruhrlandmuseum.de. Head: Prof. Dr. Ulrich Borsdorf
Open Air Museum 15660

Red Dot Design Museum im Design Zentrum Nordrhein Westfalen, Gelsenkirchener Str 181, 45309 Essen - T: (0201) 301040, Fax: 3010440, E-mail: info@dzurw.com, Internet: http://www.design-germany.de. Head: Prof. Dr. Peter Zec
Decorative Arts Museum 15661

Ruhrlandmuseum Essen, Goethestr 41, 45128 Essen - T: (0201) 8845200, Fax: 8845138, E-mail: info@ruhrlandmuseum.de, Internet: http://www.essen.de. Head: Prof. Dr. Ulrich Borsdorf
Local Museum / Natural History Museum - 1904
Natural hist, social hist, archaeology, photography - archives and library 15662

Schatzkammer der Basilika Sankt Ludgerus, Brückstr 54, 45239 Essen - T: (0201) 491801, Fax: 4900526, E-mail: h.klein@cneweb.de, Internet: http://www.essen-werden.de. Head: Johannes Kronenbers
Religious Arts Museum - 1975
Romanesque and Baroque art and liturgical items 15663

Städtische Galerie im Museum Folkwang, Goethestr 41, 45128 Essen - T: (0201) 8845103, Fax: http://www.kommunikation-staedtische-galerie.de, E-mail: necmi.soenmez@museum-folkwang.essen.de. Head: Dr. Necmi Sönmez
Public Gallery 15664

Zollverein Ausstellungen, Gesellschaft für zeitgenössische Kunst, Gelsenkirchener Str 181, Halle 6, 45309 Essen - T: (0201) 303011, Fax: 371297, Internet: http://www.zollverein.de. Head: Jochen Krüper
Fine Arts Museum / Public Gallery 15665

Essenbach

Archäologisches Museum Essenbach, Rathauspl 14, 84051 Essenbach - T: (08703) 8080, Fax: 80838
Archaeological Museum - 1996
Local early history and archeological finds 15666

Esslingen

Ausgrabungsmuseum Esslinger Stadtkirche, Marktpl 17, 73728 Esslingen - T: (0711) 357129. Head: J. Lienerth
Archaeological Museum - 1964 15667

Bahnwärterhaus, Galerien der Stadt Esslingen, Pulverwiesen 25, 73728 Esslingen - T: (0711) 35122640, Fax: 35122903, E-mail: andreas.baur@esslingen.de, Internet: http://www.esslingen.de. Head: Andreas Baur
Public Gallery 15668

Heinrich-Mayer-Haus Elektromuseum, c/o Neckarwerke Elektrizitätsversorgungs-AG, Rennstr 16, 73728 Esslingen - T: (0711) 31904122, Fax: 31903438. Head: R. Föller
Science&Tech Museum
Electrical appliances, hist of electricity 15669

J. F. Schreiber-Museum, Untere Beutau 8-10, 73728 Esslingen - T: (0711) 35123240, Fax: 35123229, E-mail: museen@esslingen.de, Internet: http://www.esslingen.de. Head: Dr. Kirsten Fast
Local Museum - 1999
Books, picture 15670

Schwörhaus, Galerien der Stadt Esslingen, Beim Münster Sankt Paul, 73728 Esslingen - T: (0711) 35122991, 35122950, Fax: 35122903, E-mail: abaur@esslingen.de. Head: Andreas Baur
Public Gallery 15671

Stadtmuseum Esslingen, Hafenmarkt 7, 73728 Esslingen - T: (0711) 35123240, Fax: 35123229, E-mail: museen@esslingen.de, Internet: http://www.esslingen.de. Head: Dr. Kirsten Fast
Local Museum - 1908
Local hist, crafts 15672

Villa Merkel, Galerien der Stadt Esslingen, Pulverwiesen 25, 73728 Esslingen - T: (0711) 35122640, Fax: 35122903, E-mail: andeasbaur@esslingen.de, Internet: http://www.villa-merkel. Head: Andreas Baur
Public Gallery - 1973
Art of the 20th c, graphics 15673

Ettal

Schloß Linderhof, Linderhof 12, 82488 Ettal - T: (08822) 92030, Fax: 920311, E-mail: info@bsv.bayern.de
Local Museum - 1878
Ornamental residence of King Ludwig II of Bavaria (1869-1878), grotto of Venus (Tannhäuser), cottage of Hunding (Die Walküre), Moorish kiosk, Maroccan house, Gurnemanz hermitage 15674

Ettersburg

Schloß Ettersburg, 99439 Ettersburg - T: (03643) 545300, Fax: 545303
Historic Site 15675

Ettlingen

Museum der Stadt Ettlingen, Schloßpl 3, 76275 Ettlingen - T: (07243) 101273, Fax: 101532, E-mail: museum@ettlingen.de, Internet: http://www.ettlingen.de
Fine Arts Museum / Local Museum / Ethnology Museum / Folklore Museum - 1924
Local history, archaeology, Badenish artists - Archaeological Department, Albgaumuseum, Städtische Galerie, East Asian Department 15676

Museum der Stadt Ettlingen, Albgaumuseum, Schloßpl 3, 76275 Ettlingen - T: (07243) 101273, Fax: 101532, E-mail: museum@ettlingen.de, Internet: http://www.ettlingen.de
Folklore Museum / Local Museum - 1924 15677

Museum der Stadt Ettlingen, Städtische Galerie, Schloßpl 3, 76275 Ettlingen - T: (07243) 101273, Fax: 101532, E-mail: museum@ettlingen.de, Internet: http://www.ettlingen.de
Fine Arts Museum - 1995
Badenish artists 15678

Euskirchen

Rheinisches Industriemuseum Euskirchen, Tuchfabrik Müller, Carl-Koenen-Str, 53881 Euskirchen - T: (02251) 14880, Fax: 1488120, E-mail: d.stender@mail.lvr.de, Internet: http://www.lvr.de/kultur/rim/euskirchen. Head: D. Stender
Historical Museum - 1988
History of textile industry, textile factory Müller with complete machinery and equipment, clothing since 1850 15679

Stadtmuseum Euskirchen, Kirchstr 12, 53879 Euskirchen - T: (02251) 970386
Local Museum 15680

Eutin

Ostholstein-Museum, Schlosspl 1, 23701 Eutin - T: (04521) 70180, Fax: 701818, E-mail: oh-museum.eutin@t-online.de, Internet: http://www.oh-museum.de. Head: Dr. Klaus-Dieter Hahn
Local Museum - 1889
Silver from Eutin, faiences from Stockelsdorf 15681

Produzentengalerie - OHa Kunst im Wasserturm, Bismarckstr, 23701 Eutin - T: (04521) 766027
Public Gallery 15682

Stiftung Schloß Eutin, Schloß Eutin, 23701 Eutin - T: (04521) 70950, Fax: 709530, E-mail: julianemoser@t-online.de, Internet: http://www.schlosseutin.de. Head: Dr. Juliane Moser
Historic Site
Portraits of former European sovereigns (16th-19th c), 19th c portraits, 18th and 19th c furniture and furnishings, early 18th c model ships from the coll of Czar Peter III 15683

Falkenberg, Elster

Eisenbahnmuseum, Bahnhofstr 8, 04895 Falkenberg, Elster - T: (035365) 450
Science&Tech Museum 15684

Falkenberg, Oberpfalz

Burg Falkenberg, Burg, 95685 Falkenberg, Oberpfalz - T: (09637) 270, Fax: 529. Head: Sonnhild Gräfin von der Schulenburg
Historical Museum - 1952
Antique furniture, paintings, weapons, books, glass, Friedrich Werner Graf von der Schulenburg (German diplomat in Moscow 1934-41, executed on 10th Nov 1944 in Berlin-Plötzensee) 15685

Falkensee

Heimatmuseum, Falkenhagener Str 77, 14612 Falkensee - T: (03322) 22288, Fax: 22288, Internet: http://www.falkensee.net/heimatmuseum
Local Museum - 1968
Local hist - gallery 15686

Falkenstein, Oberpfalz

Museum Jagd und Wild auf Burg Falkenstein, Burgstr 10, 93167 Falkenstein, Oberpfalz - T: (09462) 244, 784, Fax: 5310, E-mail: tourist@falkenstein.landkreis-cham.de, Internet: http://www.markt-falkenstein.de. Head: F.J. Brey
Natural History Museum - 1982
Stuffed animals, hunting weapons, falconry equipment 15687

Falkenstein, Vogtland

Heimatmuseum, Schloßpl 1, 08223 Falkenstein, Vogtland - T: (03745) 6076, Fax: 6076
Local Museum - 1930
13th-19th c local history, crafts, jurisdiction, pewter and iron mining, costumes, wood carving 15688

Feldberg, Mecklenburg

Hans-Fallada-Haus, Carwitz, Zum Bohnenwerder 2, 17258 Feldberg, Mecklenburg - T: (039831) 20359, Fax: 20359, E-mail: hfg@fallada.de, Internet: http://www.fallada.de. Head: Manfred Kuhnke
Special Museum
Home and study of the writer ("Kleiner Mann, was nun?") from 1933 to 1944 15689

Heimatstube Feldberg, Amtspl 13, 17258 Feldberg, Mecklenburg - T: (039831) 20676
Local Museum 15690

Feldkirchen-Westerham

Wasserkraftmuseum Leitzachwerk, c/o Stadtwerke München, Hauptabt. Elektrotechnik, Leitzachwerkstr 50, 83620 Feldkirchen-Westerham - T: (08062) 1061, Fax: 1061
Science&Tech Museum - 1984
Hist of use of water power, water power technology 15691

Fellbach

Galerie der Stadt Fellbach, Marktpl 4, 70734 Fellbach - T: (0711) 5851417, Fax: 5851119, E-mail: rathaus@fellbach.de, Internet: http://www.fellbach.de. Head: Dr. Heribert Sautter
Public Gallery 15692

Ostdeutsche Heimatstube, Friedensstr 11, 70734 Fellbach - T: (0711) 512624. Head: Dr. H. Noske
Historical Museum - 1986
Hist of Germans in Eastern Europe 15693

Stadtmuseum Fellbach, Hintere Str 26, 70734 Fellbach - T: (0711) 5851391, Fax: 5851397. Head: Dr. Ralf Beckmann
Local Museum - 1977
Pietism, viniculture, handicrafts 15694

Felsberg

Heimatmuseum Gensungen, Elbinger Str 5, 34587 Felsberg - T: (05662) 1573
Local Museum - 1973
Early and prehistoric finds, farm and domestic implements 15695

Feucht

Hermann-Oberth-Raumfahrt-Museum, Pfinzingstr 12-14, 90537 Feucht - T: (09128) 3502, Fax: 14920, E-mail: oberth@compuserve.com, Internet: http://www.oberth-museum.org. Head: Dr. Harry O. Ruppe
Science&Tech Museum - 1971
Hermann Oberth, father of space travel 15696

Zeidel-Museum, Pfinzingstr 6, 90537 Feucht - T: (09128) 12184, Fax: 726644. Head: Wolfgang Mittwoch
Agriculture Museum / Natural History Museum - 1986
Bee-farming - Library 15697

Feuchtwangen

Fahrradmuseum Zumhaus, Zumhaus 4, 91555 Feuchtwangen - T: (09852) 549
Science&Tech Museum 15698

Fränkisches Museum, Museumsstr 19, 91555 Feuchtwangen - T: (09852) 2575, 615224, E-mail: info@fraenkisches-museum.de, Internet: http://www.fraenkisches-museum.de. Head: Susanne Klemm
Local Museum / Folklore Museum - 1902
Typical work rooms of former trades, glass, tin, faience, costumes, farm implements, smithy 15699

Handwerkerstuben, Marktpl 3, 91555 Feuchtwangen - T: (09852) 90455
Science&Tech Museum
Local crafts 15700

Sängermuseum, Am Spittel 4-6, 91555 Feuchtwangen - T: (09852) 4833, Fax: 3961, E-mail: info@chorwesen.de, Internet: http://www.saengermuseum.de. Head: Helena Karz
Music Museum - 1989
Singer and chorus museum, music instruments and documents - archive 15701

Fichtelberg

Silbereisenbergwerk Gleißinger Fels, Panoramastr, 95686 Fichtelberg - T: (09272) 848, Fax: (0921) 61233, E-mail: bergwerk@firemail.de. Head: Joseph Hartmann
Science&Tech Museum 15702

Filderstadt

Gottlieb-Häußler-Heimatmuseum, Klingenst 19, 70794 Filderstadt - T: (0711) 7003235, Fax: 7003330
Local Museum - 1985
Agricultural equipment, handicraft 15703

Städtische Galerie Filderstadt, Bernhäuser Hauptstr 2, 70794 Filderstadt - T: (0711) 702663, Fax: (07158) 934024, E-mail: rektorazi@web.de, Internet: http://www.staedtische-galerie-filderstadt.de
Fine Arts Museum / Association with Coll 15704

Finsing

Schwemmgut-Museum, Seestr 3, 85464 Finsing - T: (08121) 709211
Special Museum - 1999 15705

Finsterbergen

Heimatmuseum Finsterbergen, Hauptstr 28, 99898 Finsterbergen - T: (03623) 306143, Fax: 306396
Local Museum - 1913 15706

Finsterwalde

Kreismuseum, Lange Str 6-8, 03238 Finsterwalde - T: (03531) 501989, Fax: 501988, E-mail: LK-EF.Museum-Finsterwalde@t-online.de. Head: Dr. Rainer Ernst, Olaf Weber
Local Museum - 1981
Ancient historic finds, stones, old shop and office, local history 15707

Fischbachau

Historische Gebirgsmühle mit Bastelkunstwerken, Kirchpl 10, 83730 Fischbachau
Science&Tech Museum 15708

Fischbachtal

Museum Schloss Lichtenberg, Schloss Lichtenberg, 64405 Fischbachtal - T: (06166) 404. Head: Winfried Wackerfuß
Local Museum - 1951
History and geography, agricultural implements and other artefacts illustrating social history of the farmer class, works of the Odenwald painter J. Lippmann, 19th c pharmacy, lead and tin soldier coll 15709

Fischen im Allgäu

Fischinger Heimathaus mit Schimuseum, Gschwenderhaus, Hauptstr 3, 87538 Fischen im Allgäu - T: (08326) 36460, Fax: 364656, E-mail: touristikinfo@fischen.de, Internet: http://www.fischen.de
Special Museum - 1994
Ski museum 15710

Fladungen

Fränkisches Freilandmuseum Fladungen, Bahnhofstr 19, 97650 Fladungen - T: (09778) 91230, Fax: 912345, E-mail: orf.FLM-Fladungen@t-online.de, Internet: http://www.freilandmuseum-fladungen.de. Head: Albrecht Wald
Open Air Museum - 1990
Rural architecture (17th-20th c) 15711

Rhön-Museum, Am Marktpl 2, 97650 Fladungen - T: (09778) 1575, 1597. Head: Albrecht Wald
Natural History Museum - 1920
Natural history, country furniture, costumes, agricultural and domestic tools and utensils, liturgical art, pottery, regional history 15712

Flensburg

Flensburger Schiffahrtsmuseum und Rum-Museum, Schiffbrücke 39, 24939 Flensburg - T: (0461) 852970, Fax: 851665, E-mail: schiffahrtsmuseum@flensburg.de, Internet: http://www.flensburg.de/kultur/museen/schiffahrtsmuseum. Head: Dr. Jutta Glüsing
Special Museum / Science&Tech Museum - 1984
Hist of regional shipping, whaling, passage to the West Indies, ship building, social hist of the sailors, navigation - Rum museum 15713

Museumsberg Flensburg, Städtische Museen und Sammlungen für den Landesteil Schleswig, Museumsberg 1, 24937 Flensburg - T: (0461) 852956, Fax: 852993, E-mail: museumsberg.flensburg@foni.net. Head: Dr. Ulrich Schulte-Wülwer
Local Museum - 1876
Schleswig painting, sculpture, furniture, crafts, porcelain and faience (Gothic to Art Nouveau), local hist, postage stamp coll 15714

Naturwissenschaftliches Museum der Stadt Flensburg, Museumsberg 1, 24937 Flensburg - T: (0461) 852504, Fax: 852993, E-mail: Barkemeyer.Stadt.Flensburg@t-online.de. Head: Dr. Werner Barkemeyer
Natural History Museum 15715

Flintsbach

Pfarrmuseum, Kirchpl 5, 83126 Flintsbach - T: (08034) 644
Religious Arts Museum - 1985
Religious folklore, archeological finds 15716

Flörsheim am Main

Heimatmuseum und Stadtarchiv, Hauptstr 43, 65439 Flörsheim am Main - T: (06145) 6649, Fax: 502995, E-mail: Diether.Klockner@t-online.de
Local Museum / Library with Exhibitions - 1978
Law books, faience, 18th c painting, etchings and sketches, early history 15717

Flörsheim-Dalsheim

Weinbaumuseum, c/o Weingut Schales, Alzeyer Str 160, 67592 Flörsheim-Dalsheim - T: (06243) 7045, Fax: 6142, E-mail: weingutschales@t-online.de
Agriculture Museum - 1976
Glass, old wines 15718

Flossenbürg

KZ-Grab- und Gedenkstätte Flossenbürg, Gedächtnisallee 5-7, 92696 Flossenbürg - T: (09603) 921980, Fax: 921990, E-mail: information@gedenkstaette-flossenbuerg.de, Internet: http://www.gedenkstaette-flossenbuerg.de. Head: Jörg Skriebeleit
Historical Museum
History of the Flossenbürg concentration camp from 1938-1945, memorial site, anti-fascist resistance 15719

Forbach

Murgtäler Dorfmuseum → Murgtal-Museum

Murgtal-Museum, Kirchstr 15, 76596 Forbach - T: (07228) 2428. Head: G. Wunsch
Local Museum - 1986
Crafts, agriculture 15720

Forchheim, Oberfranken

Braunauer Heimatmuseum, Paradepl 2, 91301 Forchheim, Oberfranken - T: (09191) 64563. Head: Wolfgang Meier
Local Museum / Folklore Museum - 1959
Costume, writer Hugo Scholz, painter, Ernst Birke and Fritz Stonner - library, archive 15721

Pfalzmuseum, Pfalzgebäude, Kapellenstr 16, 91301 Forchheim, Oberfranken - T: (09191) 67812, 714327, Fax: 714206, E-mail: tourist@forchheim.de, Internet: http://www.forchheim.de. Head: Susanne Fischer
Local Museum - 1911
Prehist, early hist, local hist and culture, frescoes, folklore 15722

Forchtenberg

Heimat und Bildhauer Kern Museum, Hafenmarktgasse 29, 74670 Forchtenberg - T: (07947) 91110, Fax: 911135, E-mail: stadt@forchtenberg.de, Internet: http://www.forchtenberg.de
Historical Museum - 1989
Hans and Sophie Scholl memorial 15723

Sindringer Heimatmuseum, Rathaus, Sindringen, 74670 Forchtenberg - T: (07948) 2215
Local Museum - 1987
Local hist, fossils, hist of local nobility, "Sindringer Kalenderstreit" 15724

Forst, Lausitz

Brandenburgisches Textilmuseum, Sorauer Str 37, 03149 Forst, Lausitz - T: (03562) 97356, Fax: 973579, E-mail: info@textilmuseum-forst.de, Internet: http://www.textilmuseum-forst.de
Science&Tech Museum - 1995
Regional cloth and linen industry, regional hist - clothworker's show factory 15725

Fränkisch-Crumbach

Heimatmuseum Rodenstein, Darmstädter Str 3, 64407 Fränkisch-Crumbach - T: (06164) 718
Local Museum - 1978
Knights of Rodenstein, trade and agricultural implements 15726

Frankenberg, Eder

Kreisheimatmuseum, Bahnhofstr 8-10, 35066 Frankenberg, Eder - T: (06451) 743672, Fax: 743600. Head: Doris Reinius
Local Museum - 1952
Farming implements and tools, costumes, arms 15727

Museum Thonet, Stuhlmuseum, Michael-Thonet-Str 1, 35066 Frankenberg, Eder - T: (06451) 5080, Fax: 508108, E-mail: info@thonet.de, Internet: http://www.thonet.de. Head: Anke Thonet
Decorative Arts Museum
450 exhibits (chairs, tables, beds, dolls and other items of furniture from various materials) 15728

Frankenberg, Sachsen

Heimatmuseum, Hainicher Str 5a, 09669 Frankenberg, Sachsen - T: (037206) 2579, Fax: 64180, Internet: http://www.Frankenberg.de
Local Museum - 1909
Furniture, glass, toys, painting, handicraft, dungeon 15729

Frankenthal, Pfalz

Erkenbert-Museum, Rathauspl, 67227 Frankenthal, Pfalz - T: (06233) 89495, Fax: 89553, E-mail: erkenbert-museum@stadt-frankenthal.ft.eunet.de, Internet: http://www.frankenthal.de. Head: Dr. Edgar J. Hürkey
Local Museum - 1893
Frankenthal painters (around 1600), 18th c porcelain 15730

Frankfurt am Main

Airport Gallery 1 & 2, Flughafen, Terminal 1-2, 60547 Frankfurt am Main - T: (069) 69066076, Fax: 69044261, E-mail: m.wustrack@frnport.de, Internet: http://www.frnport.de. Head: Dr. Michael K. Wustrack
Fine Arts Museum - 1973 15731

Chaplin-Archiv Wilhelm Staudinger, Klarastr 5, 60433 Frankfurt am Main - T: (069) 95294477, Fax: 95294479, E-mail: chaplin-archiv@t-online.de, Internet: http://www.chaplin-archiv.bei.t-online.de. Head: Wilhelm Staudinger
Special Museum
Portrayal of the artist, actor, director and composer Charles Spencer Chaplin (1889-1977) 15732

Deutsches Albert-Schweitzer-Zentrum, Archiv, Museum und Forschungsstätte, Neue Schlesingergasse 22-24, 60311 Frankfurt am Main - T: (069) 284951, Fax: 2978525, E-mail: albert-schweitzer-zentrum@t-online.de, Internet: http://www.albert-schweitzer-zentrum.de. Head: Marlies Böhnert
Ethnology Museum - 1969
Exhibits from West-Central-Africa - library, archive 15733

Deutsches Architektur Museum, Schaumainkai 43, 60596 Frankfurt am Main - T: (069) 21238844, Fax: 21236386, E-mail: info.dam@stadt-frankfurt.de, Internet: http://www.dam-online.de. Head: Prof. Dr. Ingeborg Flagge
Fine Arts Museum - 1979
Sketches, plans, drawings, models illustrating the history of architecture in the 20th c - library 15734

Deutsches Filmmuseum, Schaumainkai 41, 60596 Frankfurt am Main - T: (069) 21238830, Fax: 21237881, E-mail: info@deutsches-filmmuseum.de, Internet: http://www.deutsches-filmmuseum.de. Head: Prof. Walter Schobert
Special Museum / Performing Arts Museum - 1980
Film hist, films, posters, photos, architecture, equipment - library, archive, cinema, video library 15735

Deutsches Werbemuseum, Löwengasse 27, 60385 Frankfurt am Main - T: (069) 96860152, Fax: 96860153, E-mail: nmk-r.scholze@t-online.de. Head: Rainer Scholze
Decorative Arts Museum
Advertising 15736

Dommuseum, Dompl 14, 60311 Frankfurt am Main - T: (069) 13376184/86, Fax: 29703249, E-mail: Dommuseum-Ffm@t-online.de. Head: Dr. August Heuser
Religious Arts Museum - 1987 15737

Fotografie Forum international, Weckmarkt 17, 60311 Frankfurt am Main - T: (069) 291726, Fax: 28639, E-mail: Fotografie_Forum@web.de. Head: P. Celina Lunsford
Public Gallery 15738

Frankfurter Äpfelwein-Museum, c/o Historix, Historisches Museum, Saalgasse 19, 60311 Frankfurt am Main - T: (069) 764899, Fax: 557644. Head: Helmut Lenz
Agriculture Museum - 1991
Cider processing and utensiles (glasses, presses) 15739

Frankfurter Feldbahnmuseum, Am Römerhof 15a, 60486 Frankfurt am Main - T: (069) 709292. Head: Udo Przygoda
Science&Tech Museum - 1987
Industrial narrow gauge railway - library, archive, photo archive 15740

Frankfurter Goethe-Museum mit Goethe-Haus → Freies Deutsches Hochstift/ Frankfurter Goethe-Museum mit Goethe-Haus

Frankfurter Kunstverein e.V., Markt 44, 60311 Frankfurt am Main - T: (069) 2193140, Fax: 21931411, E-mail: post@fkv.de, Internet: http://www.fkv.de. Head: Nicolaus Schafhausen
Association with Coll 15741

Frankfurter Sportmuseum, Mörfelder Landstr 362, 60528 Frankfurt am Main - T: (069) 678040, Fax: 676860. Head: Wolfgang Klameth
Special Museum - 1990 15742

Freies Deutsches Hochstift/ Frankfurter Goethe-Museum mit Goethe-Haus, Großer Hirschgraben 23-25, 60311 Frankfurt am Main - T: (069) 138800, Fax: 13880222, Internet: http://www.goethehaus-frankfurt.de. Head: Prof. Dr. Christoph Perels
Historic Site / Public Gallery - 1859
Paintings, manuscripts and books of German writers 1750-1850, 1890-1930, period furnishings - library, graphic coll, archive of manuscripts 15743

Galerie 37. Kunst im Museum für Völkerkunde, Schaumainkai 37, 60594 Frankfurt am Main - T: (069) 21235391, Fax: 21230704, E-mail: voelkerkunde.museum@stadt-frankfurt.de. Head: Fine Arts Museum - 1997
Contemporary art from all continents 15744

Geldmuseum der Deutschen Bundesbank, Wilhelm-Epstein-Str 14, 60431 Frankfurt am Main - T: (069) 95663073, Fax: 95664059, E-mail: geldmuseum@bundesbank.de, Internet: http://www.bundesbank.de. Head: Prof. Dr. Dieter Lindenlaub, Dr. Ursula Hagen-Jahnke
Special Museum - 1999
History of money from antiquity to modern times, monetary and foreign exchange policy 15745

Haus Giersch - Museum Regionaler Kunst, Schaumainkai 83, 60596 Frankfurt am Main - T: (069) 63304128, 63148724, Fax: 63304144, E-mail: haus-giersch@schaumainkai.de, Internet: http://www.haus-giersch.de. Head: Dr. Manfred Großkinsky
Fine Arts Museum
Regional art 15746

Heimatmuseum Frankfurt-Bergen-Enkheim, Marktstr, Altes Rathaus, 60388 Frankfurt am Main - T: (06109) 32609, (069) 21241255. Head: Horst R. Becker
Local Museum - 1957
Memorabilia of the Battle of Bergen in 1759, town hist 15747

Heimatmuseum Frankfurt-Nied, Beunestr 9a, 65934 Frankfurt am Main Nied - T: (069) 394539. Head: Adalbert Vollert
Local Museum - 1986
Town hist, early and prehist 15748

Heimatmuseum Schwanheim, Alt Schwanheim 6, 60529 Frankfurt am Main - T: (069) 356007. Head: Lilo Günzler
Local Museum - 1973
Early and prehist, grave finds 15749

Heinrich-Hoffmann-Museum, Schubertstr 20, 60325 Frankfurt am Main - T: (069) 747969, Fax: 742581, E-mail: HoffmannMu@aol.com, Internet: http://www.heinrich-hoffmann-museum.de. Head: Beate Zekorn
Special Museum - 1977
Books, pictures, letters, drawings, photos, and memorabilia illustrating the life and work of H. Hoffmann, author of Struwwelpeter 15750

Heussenstamm Stiftung, Berliner Str 27, 60311 Frankfurt am Main - T: (069) 1310016, Fax: 90028492, E-mail: info@heussenstamm-stiftung.de, Internet: http://www.heussenstamm-stiftung.de
Fine Arts Museum / Public Gallery 15751

Historisches Museum Frankfurt am Main, Saalgasse 19, 60311 Frankfurt am Main - T: (069) 21235599, Fax: 21230702, E-mail: info.historisches-museum@stadt-frankfurt.de, Internet: http://www.historisches-museum.frankfurt.de. Head: Prof. Dr. Rainer Koch
Historical Museum - 1878
Local hist, painting and sculpture, numismatics, graphics, textiles, weapons, tools, glass, porcelain, faiences, furniture, photogr, toys, technical instruments - children's museum, museum of cartoons, Kronberger Haus (dependance for Höchst porcelain) 15752

Ikonen-Museum der Stadt Frankfurt am Main, Stiftung Dr. Schmidt-Voigt, Brückenstr 3-7, 60594 Frankfurt am Main - T: (069) 21236262, Fax: 21239968, E-mail: info.ikonen-museum@stadt-frankfurt.de, Internet: http://www.ikonen-museum.frankfurt.de. Head: Dr. Richard Zacharuk
Fine Arts Museum
Russian icons 15753

Jüdisches Museum, Untermainkai 14-15, 60311 Frankfurt am Main - T: (069) 21238805, Fax: 21230705, E-mail: info.jmf@stadt-frankfurt.de, Internet: http://www.juedischesmuseum.de. Head: Georg Heuberger
Historical Museum / Ethnology Museum / Fine Arts Museum - 1988
Jewish history in Frankfurt 15754

Kindermuseum, c/o Historisches Museum, Saalgasse 19, 60311 Frankfurt am Main - T: (069) 21235154, Fax: 21242078, E-mail: info.kindermuseum@stadt-frankfurt.de, Internet: http://www.kindermuseum.-frankfurt.de. Head: Susanne Gesser
Historical Museum - 1972
Hands-on exhibitions for children 15755

Kommunale Galerie im Leinwandhaus, Weckmarkt 17, 60311 Frankfurt am Main - T: (069) 21235435, Fax: 2124768, E-mail: klaus.klemp@stadt-frankfurt.de, Internet: http://www.kultur-frankfurt.de. Head: Dr. Klaus Klemp
Fine Arts Museum - 1973 15756

Kronberger Haus, Historisches Museum, Bolongarostr 152, 65929 Frankfurt am Main - T: (069) 21237773, Fax: 21230702, E-mail: patricia.stahl@stadt-frankfurt.de. Head: Patricia Stahl
Decorative Arts Museum
Faience, porcellain 15757

Museum für Angewandte Kunst, Schaumainkai 17, 60594 Frankfurt am Main - T: (069) 21238522, Fax: 21230703, E-mail: info@mak.frankfurt.de, Internet: http://www.mak.frankfurt.de. Head: Dr. James Bradburne
Decorative Arts Museum - 1877
European, Islamic, Chinese and Japanese crafts from all periods, book art and graphics, design 15758

Museum für Höchster Geschichte, Höchster Schloßpl 16, 65929 Frankfurt am Main - T: (069) 3056988, 30581063, Fax: 30516829, E-mail: service@histocom.de. Head: Wolfgang Metternich
Local Museum - 1976
Artefacts from prehist to Roman times, faience, porcelain and ceramics from Höchst manufacturers, furniture, municipal hist 15759

Museum für Industrie- und Technikgeschichte, Straßenbahndepot Eckenheim, 60435 Frankfurt am Main - T: (069) 2126199
Science&Tech Museum 15760

Museum für Kommunikation Frankfurt, Schaumainkai 53, 60596 Frankfurt am Main - T: (069) 60600, Fax: 6060666, E-mail: mk.frankfurt@t-online.de, Internet: http://www.museumsstiftung.de. Head: Dr. Helmut Gold
Science&Tech Museum - 1872
Hist of post and telecommunications - library 15761

Museum für Kunst in Steatit, Hynspergstr 4, 60322 Frankfurt am Main - T: (069) 556716, Fax: 5964295. Head: Karl Heinz Arnold
Fine Arts Museum - 1980
Steatite objects from all periods and cultures, with emphasis on China 15762

Museum für Moderne Kunst Frankfurt am Main, Domstr 10, 60311 Frankfurt am Main - T: (069) 21230447, Fax: 21237882, E-mail: mmk@stadt-frankfurt.de, Internet: http://www.mmk-frankfurt.de. Head: Udo Kittelmann
Fine Arts Museum - 1991
Contemporary art of the 1960s until today 15763

Museum für Uhren, Schmuck und Kunst, Hostatostr 3, Glockenspielhaus, 65929 Frankfurt am Main - T: (069) 303030, Fax: 319013. Head: Jürgen Hösch, Dr. Rudolf Hartleib
Decorative Arts Museum - 1987 15764

Museum für Völkerkunde, Schaumainkai 29-37, 60594 Frankfurt am Main - T: (069) 21235391, Fax: 21230704, E-mail: voelkerkunde.museum@stadt-frankfurt.de. Head:
Ethnology Museum - 1904
Cultural artefacts from all continents 15765

Museum für Vor- und Frühgeschichte - Archäologisches Museum, Karmelitergasse 1, 60311 Frankfurt am Main - T: (069) 21235896, Fax: 21230700, E-mail: info.archaeolmus@stadt-frankfurt.de, Internet: http://www.frankfurt.de. Head: Dr. Egon Warmers
Archaeological Museum - 1937
Local prehist and medieval, antique handicrafts and objects d'art, Oriental artifacts, Greek and Roman archaeology 15766

Museum Judengasse mit Börnegalerie, Börnepl, Kurt-Schumacher-Str 10, 60311 Frankfurt am Main - T: (069) 2977419, Fax: 21230705, E-mail: info.jmf@stadt-frankfurt.de, Internet: http://www.juedischesmuseum.de. Head: Georg Heuberger
Historical Museum / Fine Arts Museum / Historic Site - 1992
Jewish history in Frankfurt 15767

Naturmuseum und Forschungsinstitut Senckenberg, Senckenberganlage 25, 60325 Frankfurt am Main - T: (069) 75420, Fax: 746238, E-mail: fsteinin@sng.uni-frankfurt.de, Internet: http://www.senckenberg.uni-frankfurt.de. Head: Prof. Dr. Fritz F. Steininger
Natural History Museum - 1817
Comprehensive coll in all fields of natural hist 15768

Orthopädisches Geschichts- und Forschungsmuseum, Marienburgstr 2, 60528 Frankfurt am Main - T: (069) 6705377, Fax: 6705367, E-mail: DGOT-Frankfurt@t-online.de. Head: Prof. Dr. L. Zichner
Historical Museum / Special Museum 15769

Portikus, Schöne Aussicht 2, 60311 Frankfurt am Main - T: (069) 21998760/59, Fax: 21998761, E-mail: portikus@pop.stadt-frankfurt.de, Internet: http://www.portikus.de. Head: Dr. Daniel Birnbaum
Fine Arts Museum / Public Gallery 15770

Schirn Kunsthalle Frankfurt, Römerberg, 60311 Frankfurt am Main - T: (069) 2998820, Fax: 29988240, E-mail: welcome@schirn.de, Internet: http://www.schirn.de. Head: Max Hollein
Public Gallery - 1986 15771

Stadt- und Universitätsbibliothek, Bockenheimer Landstr 134-138, 60325 Frankfurt am Main - T: (069) 21239230, Fax: 21239062, E-mail: direktion@stub.uni-frankfurt.de, Internet: http://www.stub.uni-frankfurt.de. Head: Berndt Dugall
Library with Exhibitions 15772

Das Städel, Städelsches Kunstinstitut und Städtische Galerie, Schaumainkai 63, 60596 Frankfurt am Main - T: (069) 6050980, Fax: 610163, E-mail: staedel@t-online.de, Internet: http://www.staedelmuseum.de. Head: Prof. Dr. Herbert Beck
Fine Arts Museum - 1816
European painting (14th-20th c), European sculpture (19th-20th c), Graphic arts (14th-20th c) 15773

Städtische Galerie Liebieghaus, Museum Alter Plastik, Schaumainkai 71, 60596 Frankfurt am Main - T: (069) 21238617, Fax: 21230701, E-mail: liebieghaus.amt45D@stadt-frankfurt.de, Internet: http://www.liebieghaus.de. Head: Prof. Dr. Herbert Beck, Prof. Dr. Peter C. Bol
Fine Arts Museum - 1907
European sculpture from Egyptian antiquity to Classicism, Oriental sculpture 15774

Steinhausen-Museum, c/o Steinhausen-Stiftung, Wolfsgangstr 152, 60322 Frankfurt am Main - T: (069) 5972326. Head: Wilhelm Dieter Vogel
Fine Arts Museum - 1978
Paintings, sketches, drawings, etchings, lithographies 15775

Stoltze-Turm und Stoltze-Museum der Frankfurter Sparkasse, Töngesgasse 34-36, 60311 Frankfurt am Main - T: (069) 26414006, Fax: 26414026, E-mail: petra.breitkreuz@fraspa1822.de, Internet: http://www.fraspa1822.de. Head: Petra Breitkreuz
Local Museum
Town hist, satirical writings by Friedrich Stoltze 15776

Struwwelpeter-Museum, Sammlung der Originale Dr. Heinrich Hoffmanns (Nachlaß), Römerberg, Bendergasse 1, 60311 Frankfurt am Main - T: (069) 281333, Fax: 554577. Head: G.H. Herzog
Special Museum - 1982
Coll of originals by Heinrich Hoffmann, bequest of Hoffmann 15777

Teplitz-Schönauer Heimatmuseum, Adolf-Haeuser Str 14, 65929 Frankfurt am Main - T: (069) 313625. Head: Siegfried Gabriel
Local Museum
Hist of the oldest spa of North-Bohemia Teplitz-Schönau, glass, ceramics 15778

Verkehrsmuseum Schwanheim der Verkehrsgesellschaft Frankfurt am Main, Rheinlandstr 133, 60529 Frankfurt am Main - T: (069) 21326251, Fax: 21322965, E-mail: Presse@VGF-FFM.de, Internet: http://www.vgf-ffm.de
Science&Tech Museum - 1984
Hist of Frankfurt public transport, original vehicles of various periods 15779

Frankfurt/Oder

Gedenk- und Dokumentationsstätte Opfer politischer Gewaltherrschaft, Collegienstr 10, 15230 Frankfurt/Oder - T: (0335) 401560, Fax: 5004383, E-mail: verwaltung@museum-viadrina.ff.shuttle.de, Internet: http://www.ff.shuttle.de/museum-viadrina. Head: Prof. Dr. Brigitte Rieger-Jähner
Historical Museum 15780

Kleines Museum - Kinder der Welt, c/o RAA Frankfurt/O., Große Oderstr 26-27, 15230 Frankfurt/Oder - T: (0335) 5524066, Fax: 5524066. Head: Jürgen Maerz
Special Museum 15781

Kleist-Museum, Kleist Gedenk- und Forschungsstätte, Faberstr 7, 15230 Frankfurt/Oder - T: (0335) 531155, Fax: 5004945, E-mail: kleist-museum@t-online.de, Internet: http://www.kleist-museum.de. Head: Prof. Dr. Lothar Jordan
Special Museum - 1969
Memorabilia on poets Heinrich von Kleist (1777-1811), Ewald Christian von Kleist (1715-59), Franz Alexander von Kleist (1769-97), Friedrich de la Motte Fouqué (1777-1843), and their time, graphics, sculptures, painting, exhibits, research - library 15782

Museum Viadrina; Museum Junge Kunst → Städtische Museen Junge Kunst und Viadrina

Schulmuseum, Museum Viadrina, Potsdamer Str 4, 15234 Frankfurt/Oder - T: (0335) 22315
Historical Museum - 1992
Hist of school system in Frankfurt/Oder since 15th c until now, school utensils 15783

Städtische Museen Junge Kunst und Viadrina, Carl-Philipp-Emanuel-Bach-Str 11, 15230 Frankfurt/Oder - T: (0335) 401560, Fax: 4015611, E-mail: verwaltung@museum-viadrina.ff.shuttle.de, Internet: http://www.ff.shuttle.de/museum-viadrina. Head: Prof. Dr. Brigitte Rieger-Jähner
Historical Museum / Fine Arts Museum - 1957
Prehist, hist of the city, the inner city research (13th-20th c) 15784

Franzburg

Smiterlöwsche Sammlung, Ernst-Thälmann-Str 85-86, 18461 Franzburg
Local Museum
Coll of Swedish-Westpommeranian seals, preparations (beetles, butterflies) 15785

Frasdorf

Höhlenmuseum, Schulstr 7, 83112 Frasdorf - T: (08052) 179625, Fax: 179628
Natural History Museum 15786

Frauenau

Glasmuseum, Am Museumspark 1, 94258 Frauenau - T: (09926) 940035, Fax: 940036, E-mail: info@glasmuseum-frauenau.de, Internet: http://www.glasmuseum-frauenau.de. Head: Karin Rühl
Decorative Arts Museum - 1970
History of glass, with specimens from antiquity to the present, 600 years of glass manufacturing in the Bavarian Forest 15787

Frauenchiemsee

Torhalle, 83256 Frauenchiemsee - T: (08054) 603
Decorative Arts Museum 15788

Frauenstein

Museum Gottfried Silbermann, Am Schloß 3, 09623 Frauenstein - T: (037326) 1224, Fax: 83819, E-mail: fra-frauenstein@freuenstein-erzgebirge.de, Internet: http://www.islandnet.com/~arton/silbdeu.html. Head: Gisela Müller
Special Museum - 1983
Memorabilia of the organ-builder Gottfried Silbermann, local history 15789

Frauenwald

Heimatstube Frauenwald, Promenade, 98711 Frauenwald - T: (036782) 925, Fax: 239
Local Museum 15790

Frechen

Keramikmuseum, Hauptstr 110-112, 50226 Frechen - T: (02234) 501421, Fax: 52031, Internet: http://www.stadt-frechen.de. Head: Dorette Kleine
Decorative Arts Museum / Folklore Museum - 1985
Local pottery and ceramics, local 'Bartmannkrüge', faience 15791

Keramion, Museum für zeitgenössische keramische Kunst, Bonnstr 12, 50226 Frechen - T: (02234) 22891, Fax: 24199. Head: Peter-Winfried Bürkner
Decorative Arts Museum - 1971
Contemporary ceramics of the German speaking countries from the sixties onwards - library, sculpture garden 15792

Kunstverein zu Frechen, Kolpingpl 1, 50226 Frechen - T: (02234) 16967, Fax: 16967. Head: Eva Middelhoff
Association with Coll 15793

Museum für Holographie und neue visuelle Medien, Augustinusstr 9a, 50226 Frechen - T: (02234) 963220, Fax: 9632267. Head: Matthias Lauk
Performing Arts Museum
Holography 15794

Freden

Alt-Freden-Sammlung, Bergstr 5, 31084 Freden - T: (05184) 1288
Local Museum - 1958
Daily life objects within the house, in agriculture and trade workshops, prehistoric finds 15795

Freest

Heimatstube Freest, Dorfstr 67, 17440 Freest - T: (038370) 20339
Local Museum - 1957
Folk art, local crafts, knotting "Freester Fischerteppiche" live 15796

Freiberg am Neckar

Museum im Schlößle, Unterer Schloßhof 3, 71691 Freiberg am Neckar - T: (07141) 72617, Fax: 72617, E-mail: museum@freiberg-an.de, Internet: http://www.freiberg-an.de. Head: Irene Ott
Agriculture Museum / Ethnology Museum / Archaeological Museum / Fine Arts Museum - 1987
Agricultural hist in Freiberg, household articles 15797

Freiberg, Sachsen

Freiberger Silberbergwerke - Himmelfahrt-Fundgrube, TU Bergakademie Freiberg, Fuchsmühlenweg 9, 09596 Freiberg, Sachsen - T: (03731) 394570, Fax: 22195
Science&Tech Museum
Ore mining, water-wheel from 1857 15798

Geowissenschaftliche Sammlungen, TU Bergakademie Freiberg, Brennhausgasse 14, 09599 Freiberg, Sachsen - T: (03731) 392264, Fax: 392122, E-mail: karin.rank@mineral.tu-freiberg.de, Internet: http://www.tu-freiberg.de/~geowsam. Head: Karin Rank
Natural History Museum - 1765
Mineralogy, petrology, paleontology, stratigraphy, geology, Abraham Gottlob Werner 15799

Historisches Kabinett - Sammlung für Bergbaukunde, Modellsammlung, Winkler-Gedenkstätte und Karzer, TU Bergakademie Freiberg, Nonnengasse 22, 09599 Freiberg, Sachsen - T: (03731) 392653, Fax: 392832. Head: Dr. S. Richter, Dr. F. Jentsch
Science&Tech Museum / University Museum - 1980
Clemens Winkler memorial, model coll esp mining technology, detention cell, hist of mining, hist of Bergakademie Freiberg 15800

Institut für Wissenschafts- und Technikgeschichte, Kustodie, TU Bergakademie Freiberg, Nonnengasse 22, 09596 Freiberg, Sachsen - T: (03731) 513476, Fax: 22195
Science&Tech Museum
Early hist, hist of mining, historic mining machinery 15801

Naturkundemuseum Freiberg, Waisenhausstr 10, 09599 Freiberg, Sachsen - T: (03731) 32014. Head: Dr. Ulrich Thiel
Natural History Museum - 1864
Mineralogy, botany, zoology, atomic physics 15802

Stadt- und Bergbaumuseum Freiberg, Am Dom 1, 09599 Freiberg, Sachsen - T: (03731) 20250, Fax: 23197, E-mail: info@museum-freiberg.de, Internet: http://www.museum-freiberg.de. Head: Dr. Ulrich Thiel
Local Museum / Decorative Arts Museum / Science&Tech Museum - 1861
Town history and crafts, labour-movement, painting, sculpture, furnishings, musical instruments, 16th-19th c weapons, decorative objects, smithwork, glass 15803

Freiburg im Breisgau

Adelhausermuseum, Natur- und Völkerkunde, Gerberau 32, 79098 Freiburg im Breisgau - T: (0761) 2012566, Fax: 2012563, E-mail: Adelhausermuseum@Stadt.Freiburg.de. Head: Dr. Eva Gerhards
Ethnology Museum / Natural History Museum - 1895
Art and cultural artifacts from Africa, Asia, Australia and the South Seas with emphasis on former German colonies, local and exotic animals, local rocks and minerals, precious stones, local varieties of wood - library 15804

Archäologische Sammlung der Universität, Werthmannpl 3, 79085 Freiburg im Breisgau - T: (0761) 2033081, Fax: 2033103, E-mail: archinst@uni-freiburg.de, Internet: http://www.uni-freiburg.de/Archaeologie/Frames.html. Head: Prof. Dr. V.M. Strocka
Archaeological Museum - 1988
Greek and Roman archaeology 15805

Augustinermuseum, Augustinerpl 1-3, 79098 Freiburg im Breisgau - T: (0761) 2012531, Fax: 2012597, E-mail: augustinermuseum@stadt.freiburg.de, Internet: http://www.augustinermuseum.de. Head: Dr. Saskia Durian-Ress
Fine Arts Museum - 1861
Medieval and Baroque art of the Upper Rhein, sculpture and treasure from the Freiburg cathedral, 19th and 20th c art from Baden, European glass, staines glass, paintings (middle ages) 15806

E-Werk Freiburg, Hallen für Kunst, Eschholzstr 77, 79106 Freiburg im Breisgau - T: (0761) 280322, Fax: 287053, E-mail: hallenfuerkunst@t-online.de, Internet: http://www.hallenfuerkunst.de. Head: Dr. Christoph Schneider
Public Gallery 15807

Freiburger Fasnetmuseum, Turmstr 14, 79098 Freiburg im Breisgau - T: (0761) 22611
Local Museum
Carnival, masques 15808

Kleines Stuck-Museum, Liebigstr 11, 79108 Freiburg im Breisgau - T: (0761) 500555, Fax: 502525. Head: Hans Rich
Decorative Arts Museum - 1979
19th and 20th c stucco - workshop 15809

Kunstraum Alter Wiehrebahnhof, Urachstr 40, 79102 Freiburg im Breisgau - T: (0761) 709595, Fax: 709595. Head: Nicole Mittas
Public Gallery 15810

Kunstverein Freiburg im Marienbad, Dreisamstr 21, 79098 Freiburg im Breisgau - T: (0761) 34944, Fax: 34914, E-mail: kunstverein-freiburg@t-online.de. Head: Dorothea Strauss
Association with Coll 15811

Museum für Neue Kunst, Städtische Museen, Marienstr 10a, 79098 Freiburg im Breisgau - T: (0761) 2012581, Fax: 2012589. Head: Dr. Jochen Ludwig
Fine Arts Museum - 1985 15812

Museum für Stadtgeschichte, Augustinermuseum, Münsterpl 30, Wentzigerhaus, 79098 Freiburg im Breisgau - T: (0761) 2012515, 2012101, Fax: 2012598. Head: Dr. Saskia Durian-Rees
Local Museum 15813

Museum für Ur- und Frühgeschichte, Rotteckring 5, Colombischlößle, 79098 Freiburg im Breisgau - T: (0761) 2012571, Fax: 2012579, E-mail: museumuf@stadt.freiburg.de. Head: Dr.

Hilde Hiller
Archaeological Museum - 1983
Prehistoric, Roman and early medieval finds from Southwest Germany 15814

Städtische Galerie Schwarzes Kloster, Rathausgasse 48, 79098 Freiburg im Breisgau - T: (0761) 2012101, Fax: 2012199, E-mail: kulturamt@stadt.freiburg.de, Internet: http://www.freiburg-galerien.de. Head: Dr. Ludwig Krapf
Public Gallery
Documentary photography 15815

Städtisches Turmmuseum Freiburg, Zinnfigurenklause im Schwabentor, Hermannstr 8, 79098 Freiburg im Breisgau - T: (0761) 383315, 24321. Head: Andreas Müller
Decorative Arts Museum - 1969
Diorama displays of tin figures in typical period settings - archive, library 15816

Stiftung für Konkrete Kunst Roland Phleps, Pochgasse 71-73, 79104 Freiburg im Breisgau - T: (0761) 54161, Fax: 54161, Internet: http://www.stiftung-konkrete-kunst.de. Head: Dr. Roland Phleps
Fine Arts Museum 15817

Freilassing

Stadtmuseum, Lindenstr 5, 83395 Freilassing - T: (08654) 67439
Local Museum - 1998
Postcards 15818

Freising

Barockgalerie im Diözesanmuseum, Domberg 21, 85354 Freising - T: (08161) 48790, Fax: 181205, E-mail: dioezesanmuseum.freising@weihenstephan.org, Internet: http://www.weihenstephan.org/~dioemuse. Head: Dr. Peter B. Steiner
Fine Arts Museum - 1998
Baroque paintings, sculptures and furniture 15819

Diözesanmuseum, Domberg 21, 85354 Freising - T: (08161) 48790, Fax: 487925, E-mail: - dioezesanmuseum.freising@weihenstephan.org, Internet: http://www.weihenstephan.org/~dioemuse. Head: Dr. P. Steiner, Dr. Sylvia Hahn
Religious Arts Museum / Fine Arts Museum / Decorative Arts Museum - 1974
Medieval and Baroque altar paintings, sculpture, religious folk arts, Upper Bavarian handicrafts, icons, Christmas cribs, coins 15820

Museum des Historischen Vereins Freising, Marienpl 7, 85354 Freising - T: (08161) 54222, Fax: 54231, E-mail: museum@freising.de. Head: Dr. Ulrike Götz
Local Museum - 1890
Town hist 15821

Museum im Schafhof Bayerns Landwirtschaft seit 1800, Zweigmuseum des Bayerischen Nationalmuseum, Plantagenweg 63, 85354 Freising - T: (08161) 21272, Fax: 21272, Internet: http://www.bayerisches-nationalmuseum.de
Agriculture Museum
Bavarian agriculture museum 15822

Freital

Haus der Heimat Freital, Burgker Str 61, 01705 Freital - T: (0351) 6491562
Local Museum 15823

Städtische Sammlungen Freital, Altburgk 61, 01705 Freital - T: (0351) 6491562, Fax: 6491562. Head: Rolf Günther
Local Museum / Fine Arts Museum / Science&Tech Museum - 1923
Mining, 20th c art coll (Otto Dix) 15824

Frelsdorf

Freilichtmuseum "Frelsdorfer Brink", Brinkstr, 27616 Frelsdorf - T: (04749) 684. Head: Günter Lührs
Open Air Museum
Barns, farm and baking house 15825

Frensdorf

Bauernmuseum Landkreis Bamberg, c/o Landratsamt Bamberg, Hauptstr 5, 96158 Frensdorf - T: (09502) 8308, Fax: 921866, E-mail: iraba@bamberg.baynet.de, Internet: http://www.mon.de/ofr./bauermuseum.314538
Agriculture Museum 15826

Freudenstadt

Dorfmuseum Dietersweiler, Fruchtspeicher, 72250 Freudenstadt - T: (07441) 7106
Local Museum - 1977
Crafts, agricultural implements, household articles 15827

Heimatmuseum Freudenstadt, Marktpl, 72250 Freudenstadt - T: (07441) 6177
Local Museum - 1912/1974
Local hist, mineralogy, trades and guilds, zoology 15828

Freyburg

Friedrich-Ludwig-Jahn-Museum, Schloßstr 11, 06632 Freyburg - T: (034464) 27426, Fax: 66560, E-mail: jahn-museum@gmx.de, Internet: http://www.jahn-museum.de. Head: Dr. Hans-Joachim Bartmuß, Ilona Kohlberg
Special Museum - 1952
Memorabilia on sports promoter Friedrich Ludwig Jahn (1778-1852) in his former home 15829

Museum Schloss Neuenburg, Schloß 1, 06632 Freyburg - T: (034464) 35530, Fax: 35555, E-mail: Neuenburg@t-online.de, Internet: http://www.schloss-neuenburg.de. Head: Kristine Glatzel
Local Museum - 1934
Historic furnishings, geology, ancient and early history, local history 15830

Freyenstein

Museum Burg Freyenstein, Schloßpark, 16918 Freyenstein - T: (033967) 60372
Historical Museum
Castle built 1556, furniture of the 16th and 18th c 15831

Freyung

Heimatmuseum Winterberg im Böhmerwald, Am Markt 2, 94078 Freyung - T: (08551) 58850, 7086
Local Museum - 1990
Local history 15832

Schloß Wolfstein mit Jagd- und Fischereimuseum und Galerie Wolfstein, Wolfkerstr 3, 94078 Freyung - T: (08551) 57109/246, Fax: 57252, E-mail: museum@lra.landkreis-frg.de. Head: Christian Binder
Natural History Museum / Fine Arts Museum 15833

Wolfsteiner Heimatmuseum im Schramlhaus, Abteistr 8, 94078 Freyung - T: (08551) 1276, Fax: 58855, E-mail: touristinfo@freyung.de, Internet: http://www.freyung.de
Local Museum - 1981
Verre églomisé picture, folk art, handicraft, tools 15834

Fridingen

Museum Oberes Donautal, Heimatmuseum Fridingen, ehem. Ifflinger Schloß, Schloßgasse 20, 78567 Fridingen - T: (07463) 8474, 8370, Fax: 83750, E-mail: museum@fridingen.de, Internet: http://www.fridingen.de. Head: Hans Bucher
Local Museum - 1974
Town history, early history, prehistory, fossils, folklore 15835

Friedberg, Bayern

Museum der Stadt Friedberg, Schloßstr 21, 86316 Friedberg, Bayern - T: (0821) 605651, Fax: 607875, E-mail: museum@friedberg.de, Internet: http://www.heimatmuseum-friedberg.de. Head: Dr. Adelheid Riolini-Unger
Local Museum - 1886
Local history, handicrafts, coll of clocks and watches (17.-19. c.), fayence-manufacture of Friedberg chemist's shop 15836

Friedberg, Hessen

Wetterau-Museum, Haagstr 16, 61169 Friedberg, Hessen - T: (06031) 88215/18, Fax: 18396. Head: Johannes Kögler
Local Museum - 1913
Early and pre-history, domestic and agricultural implements, stone memorials, altars, coins, amphoras 15837

Friedeburg, Ostfriesland

Heimatkundliches Museum, Hauptstr 60, 26446 Friedeburg, Ostfriesland - T: (04465) 219, Fax: 942919
Local Museum - 1983
Town hist, archaeological finds 15838

Friedewald, Hessen

Heimatmuseum Friedewald, Schloßpl 2, 36289 Friedewald, Hessen - T: (06674) 8459
Local Museum - 1968
Industrial hist (mining), trades, mining and agricultural implements 15839

Friedland bei Neubrandenburg

Heimatmuseum, Mühlenstr 1, 17098 Friedland bei Neubrandenburg - T: (039601) 26779, Fax: 26779
Local Museum - 1928
Local and regional hist, hist of local labour movement, militaria, narrow gange railway 15840

Friedrichroda

Marienglashöhle Friedrichroda, 99894 Friedrichroda - T: (03623) 304953, Fax: 304953, E-mail: friedrichroda.kur@t-online.de, Internet: http://www.friedrichroda.de. Head: Bernd Scharfenberg
Natural History Museum 15841

Friedrichsdorf, Taunus

Heimatmuseum Friedrichsdorf-Seulberg, Alt Seulberg 46, 61381 Friedrichsdorf, Taunus - T: (06172) 71811, Fax: 763861, E-mail: hansjue@t-online.de
Local Museum - 1972
Trade workshops, agricultural implements, furnished rooms 15842

Philipp-Reis-Gedächtnisstätte, Museum für Post und Kommunikation Frankfurt am Main, Hugenottenstr 93, 61381 Friedrichsdorf, Taunus - T: (06172) 731289, Fax: 731282, E-mail: stadtverwaltung@friedrichsdorf.de, Internet: http://www.friedrichsdorf.de. Head: Dr. Erika Dittrich
Science&Tech Museum - 1952/84
Original and model telephones, books, pictures, and documents illustrating the invention of the telephone by Philipp Reis (1834-74) 15843

Philipp-Reis-Haus Friedrichsdorf, Hugenottenstr 93, 61381 Friedrichsdorf, Taunus - T: (06172) 731289, Fax: 731282, E-mail: stadtverwaltung@friedrichsdorf.de, Internet: http://www.friedrichsdorf.de. Head: Dr. Erika Dittrich
Historical Museum
Hist of the Huguenot colony founded in 1687, marriage contracts, official correspondence 15844

Friedrichshafen

Galerie Bodenseekreis im Landratsamt, Albrechtstr 75, 88045 Friedrichshafen - T: (07541) 204872, Fax: 204875, E-mail: info@Bodenseekreis.de, Internet: http://www.bodenseekreis.de/bodenseekreis/Landratsamt/Kreisarchiv/Galerie-1.htm. Head: Eva Moser
Fine Arts Museum - 1979
20th c paintings and sculpture, photogr, small sculpture 15845

Schulmuseum Friedrichshafen am Bodensee, Friedrichstr 14, 88045 Friedrichshafen - T: (07541) 32622, Fax: 370335, Internet: http://www.friedrichshafen.de/kultur/museen/schulmuseum. Head: Norbert Steinhauser, Erich H. Müller-Gaebele
Historical Museum - 1979
School affairs, prints, photos, books, picture book for children 15846

Zeppelin Museum Friedrichshafen, Seestr 22, 88045 Friedrichshafen - T: (07541) 38010, Fax: 380181, E-mail: zeppelin@zeppelin-museum.de, Internet: http://www.zeppelin-museum.de. Head: Dr. Wolfgang Meighörner
Science&Tech Museum / Fine Arts Museum - 1869
History of zeppelin flight, painting and sculpture of the Upper Swabian region (Middle Ages to present) - library (literature on zeppelins) 15847

Friedrichsruh bei Hamburg

Bismarck-Museum, Am Museum 2, 21521 Friedrichsruh bei Hamburg - T: (04104) 2419, Fax: 960327. Head: Ingeborg Köpke
Historical Museum - 1927
Manuscripts, medals and awards, paintings (13 Lenbach originals) and other memorabilia of Otto von Bismarck 15848

Friedrichstadt

Fünf-Giebel-Haus & Alte Münze, Am Fürstenburg-Wall 12, 25840 Friedrichstadt - T: (04881) 7985
Local Museum 15849

Fritzlar

Domschatz und Museum des Sankt Petri-Domes, Dr.-Jestädt-Pl 11, 34560 Fritzlar - T: (05622) 99990, Fax: 999919. Head: Conrad Müller
Religious Arts Museum - 1874
Liturgical art incl Gothic sculpture and altar pieces, Romanesque goldwork, medieval crafts and precious liturgical items 15850

Regionalmuseum Fritzlar, Am Hochzeitshaus 6, 34560 Fritzlar - T: (05622) 988628. Head: Karl Wilhelm Lange
Local Museum - 1956
Early and prehistoric finds, ceramics, agricultural implements, spinning mill 15851

Fröndenberg

Heimatstube Fröndenberg, Kirchpl 2, 58730 Fröndenberg - T: (02378) 752232
Local Museum 15852

Frohburg

Museum im Schloß, Florian-Geyer-Str 1, 04654 Frohburg - T: (034348) 51563
Local Museum - 1917
Local history, peasant crafts and tools, ceramics, historical toys 15853

Frohnau

Frohnauer Hammer, Sehmatalstr 3, 09456 Frohnau - T: (03733) 22000
Science&Tech Museum 15854

Fürstenberg, Havel

Heimatmuseum Fürstenberg/Havel, Brandenburgerstr 60, 16798 Fürstenberg, Havel - T: (033093) 37224
Local Museum - 1979
Town hist, glassworks, shipping, domestic utensils 15855

Mahn- und Gedenkstätte Ravensbrück, Stiftung Brandenburgische Gedenkstätten, Str der Nationen, 16798 Fürstenberg, Havel - T: (033093) 6080, Fax: 60829, E-mail: mgr@brandenburg.de, Internet: http://www.ravensbrueck.de. Head: Dr. Sigrid Jacobeit
Historical Museum - 1959
Different museums on the hist of the Nazi concentration camp (1939-1945) - Reference library, archive 15856

Fürstenberg, Weser

Museum im Schloss, Porzellanmanufaktur Fürstenberg, Meinbrexener Str 2, 37699 Fürstenberg, Weser - T: (05271) 401163, Fax: 401100, E-mail: museum@fuerstenberg-porzellan.com, Internet: http://www.fuerstenberg-porzellan.com. Head: Thomas Krüger
Decorative Arts Museum - 1747
Hand-painted porcelain (18th- 20th c) illustrating the history of the former Ducal Braunschweig Porcelain Manufactory 15857

Fürstenfeldbruck

Energiemuseum, Bullachstr 27, 82256 Fürstenfeldbruck - T: (08141) 401241
Science&Tech Museum 15858

Stadtmuseum Fürstenfeldbruck, Fürstenfeld 1, 82256 Fürstenfeldbruck - T: (08141) 61130, 44046, Fax: 611333, E-mail: stadtmuseumffb@yahoo.de, Internet: http://www.stadtmuseumffb.de. Head: Angelika Mundorff
Local Museum / Archaeological Museum - 1991
Local history 15859

Fürstenwalde, Spree

Städtische Galerie im Alten Rathaus, Am Markt 1, 15517 Fürstenwalde, Spree - T: (03361) 775310
Public Gallery 15860

Städtisches Museum Fürstenwalde, Domstr 1, 15517 Fürstenwalde, Spree - T: (03361) 2130, Fax: 2130. Head: Florian Wilke
Local Museum - 1915/1980
Local hist, historic tools, household articles, ancient and early hist, geology, fine arts, painter Gerhard Goßmann - library 15861

Fürstenwerder

Uckermärkische Heimatstuben, Ernst-Thälmann-Str 17, 17291 Fürstenwerder - T: (039859) 202. Head: Günther Markert
Local Museum
Household articles and tools needed in farming around 1900, mineralogic and ceramic findings from stone and bronze age 15862

Fürth, Bayern

Jüdisches Museum Franken in Fürth, Königstr 89, 90762 Fürth, Bayern - T: (0911) 770577, Fax: 7417896, E-mail: info@juedisches-museum.org, Internet: http://www.juedisches-museum.org. Head: Bernhard Purin
Historical Museum - 1999
Hist of the Jews in Fürth - library (Nürnberger Str 3) 15863

Rundfunkmuseum der Stadt Fürth, Kurgartenstr 37, 90762 Fürth, Bayern - T: (0911) 7568110, Fax: 7567110, E-mail: rundfunkmuseum@fuerth.de, Internet: http://www.rundfunkmuseum.fuerth.de. Head: Gerd Walther
Science&Tech Museum - 1993
Hist of broadcasting, consumer electronics 15864

Stadtmuseum Fürth, Schloßhof 12, 90768 Fürth, Bayern - T: (0911) 975343, Fax: 97534511, E-mail: stadtarchiv.fuerth@odn.de. Head: Dr. Helmut Richter
Local Museum - 1937
Prehistory and early history, geology and local natural history, folk art and folklore, painting and graphics (16th-19th c) - library, archive 15865

Füssen

Museum der Stadt Füssen, Lechhalde 3, 87629 Füssen - T: (08362) 903146, Fax: 903201, E-mail: kultur@fuessen.de, Internet: http://www.fuessen.de. Head: Thomas Riedmiller
Local Museum / Music Museum - 1913
Instruments of lute and violin makers from Füssen 15866

Staatsgalerie im Hohen Schloß, Bayerische Staatsgemäldesammlungen, Magnuspl 10, 87629 Füssen - T: (08362) 903164, 903145, Fax: 903201, E-mail: kultur@fuessen.de, Internet: http://www.fuessen.de
Fine Arts Museum - 1931
Painting and sculpture from Swabia and the Allgäu (15th-16th c) 15867

Städtische Gemäldegalerie, Magnuspl 10, 87629 Füssen - T: (08362) 903164, 903145, Fax: 903201, E-mail: kultur@fuessen.de, Internet: http://www.fuessen.de. Head: Thomas Riedmiller
Fine Arts Museum - 1931
19th c art 15868

Fulda

Archiv und Museum des Heimatkreises Leitmeritz, Schloßstr 12, 36037 Fulda - T: (0661) 78952, Fax: 22179. Head: Wendeline Weinelt
Library with Exhibitions / Historical Museum - 1975
Portrayal of the daily life of refugees in 1946 15869

Deutsches Feuerwehrmuseum, St.-Laurentius-Str 3, 36041 Fulda - T: (0661) 75017, Fax: 241757, E-mail: DeutschesFeuerwehr-Museum@t-online.de, Internet: http://www.dfv.org/feuerwehrmuseum. Head: Rolf Schamberger
Science&Tech Museum - 1963
Model and original fire engines from earliest hand-pumped types to modern systems, rescue equipment, alarms, uniforms and fire protection devices 15870

Dom-Museum, Dompl, 36037 Fulda - T: (0661) 87207, Fax: 87535, E-mail: presse.bgv-fulda@t-online.de, Internet: http://www.bistumfulda.net. Head: Johannes Kapp
Religious Arts Museum - 1965
Carolingian and Romanesque architectural fragments, reliquaries and liturgical items, paintings and altar pieces, cathedral treasure 15871

Hessische Landesbibliothek Fulda → Hochschul-und Landesbibliothek

Historische Räume des Stadtschlosses, Schloßstr 1, 36037 Fulda - T: (0661) 928350, Fax: 9283513, E-mail: museum@fulda.de, Internet: http://www.fulda.de. Head: Dr. Gregor Stasch
Historic Site - 1960
Coll of Fulda and Thuringia porcelain 15872

Hochschul-und Landesbibliothek, Heinrich-von-Bibra-Pl 12, 36037 Fulda - T: (0661) 97490, Fax: 974925, E-mail: hlb@hlb.fh-fulda.de, Internet: http://www.fh-fulda.de/hlb. Head: Dr. Marianne Riethmüller
Library with Exhibitions
Prints, manuscripts, incunabuli 15873

Jüdisches Kulturzentrum, Von-Schildeck-Str 13, 36043 Fulda - T: (0661) 70252, Fax: 47465, E-mail: jgfulda@nexgo.de. Head: Linde Weiland
Ethnology Museum - 1987
Hist of Jewish community in Fulda - Library 15874

Kinder-Akademie Fulda Werkraummuseum, Mehlerstr 4, 36043 Fulda - T: (0661) 902730, Fax: 9027323, E-mail: kaf@rhoen.de, Internet: http://www.kaf.de. Head: Helen Bonzel, Dr. Gabriele König
Special Museum
Esp for children on the subjects of natural sciences, technology and art 15875

Vonderau-Museum, Jesuitenpl 2, 36037 Fulda - T: (0661) 928350, Fax: 9283513, E-mail: museum@fulda.de, Internet: http://www.fulda.de. Head: Dr. Gregor Stasch
Local Museum - 1875
Town hist, natural hist, pre and early hist, cultural hist, regional painting and sculpture - planetarium 15876

Fuldatal

Währungsreform von 1948 und Konklave in Rothwesten, Fritz-Erler-Kaserne, 34233 Fuldatal - T: (05607) 6085139, Fax: 6085139. Head: Alfons Kössinger
Historical Museum - 1993
Economic miracle as a result of the monetary reform in 1948, photographs, video 15877

Furth im Wald

Deutsches Drachenmuseum und Stadtmuseum, Museum des Heimatkreises Bischofteinitz/ Sudetenland, Schloßpl 4, 93437 Furth im Wald - T: (09973) 50970, Fax: 50985, E-mail: stadt@furth.de, Internet: http://www.furth.de. Head: Peter Ochsenmeier
Special Museum / Historical Museum / Folklore Museum - 1922
Arts and crafts, local hist, folk art and folklore, articles from local manufacturers, country furniture, art and culture of the Sudetenland 15878

Museum Flederwisch, Am Lagerpl 5, 93437 Furth im Wald - T: (09973) 1229, Fax: 9233, E-mail: Schueler.Furth@gmx.de, Internet: http://www.landkreis-cham.de/lk_kul/nus_fled.htm
Local Museum - 1995 15879

Voithenberghammer, Hammerschmiede von 1823, Voithenberghütte 26, 93437 Furth im Wald - T: (09973) 50970, Fax: 50985, E-mail: stadt@furth.de
Science&Tech Museum - 1981
Old forge 15880

Waldmuseum, Sengenbühl, Steinbruchweg 9, 93437 Furth im Wald - T: (09973) 4476
Natural History Museum - 1976
Local natural hist 15881

Furtwangen

Deutsches Uhrenmuseum, Robert-Gerwig-Pl 1, 78120 Furtwangen - T: (07723) 920117, Fax: 920120, E-mail: museum-info@deutsches-uhrenmuseum.de, Internet: http://www.deutsches-uhrenmuseum.de. Head: Prof. Dr. Jakob Messerli
Science&Tech Museum / Decorative Arts Museum - 1852
Clocks and watches from Renaissance on, Black forest clocks, history of time-measuring 15882

Fußgönheim

Deutsches Kartoffelmuseum Fußgönheim, Hauptstr 62, 67136 Fußgönheim - T: (06237) 929266, Fax: 3288, E-mail: dkm.hkk@t-online.de, Internet: http://www.kendzia.de/kartoffelmuseum
Agriculture Museum
Potatos 15883

Gablingen

Archäologisches Museum Gablingen, Grünholdstr 7, 86456 Gablingen - T: (08230) 701349, 9943
Archaeological Museum - 1999 15884

Gadebusch

Gadebuscher Galerie am Schlossberg, Am Schlossberg, 19205 Gadebusch - T: (03886) 2221. Head: Ulrich Rudolph
Fine Arts Museum 15885

Heimatmuseum Gadebusch, Am Renaissance-Schloß, 19205 Gadebusch - T: (03886) 711864, Fax: 712025
Local Museum - 1957
Local and regional hist 15886

Gaggenau

Städtische Galerie Haus am Markt, Hauptstr 71, 76571 Gaggenau - T: (07225) 62211, Fax: 62377
Public Gallery 15887

Gaienhofen

Hermann-Hesse-Höri-Museum, Kapellenstr 8, 78343 Gaienhofen - T: (07735) 81837, Fax: 81832, E-mail: info@gaienhofen.de, Internet: http://www.gaienhofen.de. Head: Dr. Ute Hübner
Local Museum - 1988/1993
20th c paintings, local hist, H. Hesse as painter and writer, Ludwig Finckh as writer, peasant life 15888

Otto-Dix-Haus Hemmenhofen, Otto-Dix-Weg 6, 78343 Gaienhofen - T: (07735) 3151, Fax: 8918, E-mail: otto-dix-haus@t-online.de, Internet: http://www.seeseiten.de/user/dixhaus. Head: Doris Blübaum
Fine Arts Museum - 1991
House where the painter Otto Dix lived and worked from 1936 until 1969 15889

Gaildorf

Gaildorfer Stadtmuseum im Alten Schloß, Schloßstr 12, 74405 Gaildorf - T: (07971) 6718. Head: S. Hinderer
Local Museum - 1988
Local hist 15890

Kutschenmuseum, Karlstr 61, 74405 Gaildorf - T: (07971) 7024. Head: R. Geiger
Science&Tech Museum - 1986
Carriages from 1800 onwards 15891

Gantikow

Lügenmuseum Schloß Gantikow, Am Anger 1, 16866 Gantikow - T: (033971) 54782, Fax: 30084, E-mail: info@luegenmuseum.de, Internet: http://www.luegenmuseum.de
Special Museum 15892

Garbsen

Heimatmuseum Garbsen, Hannoversche Str 134, 30823 Garbsen - T: (05137) 76300
Local Museum
1890-kitchen of brickworks factory "hands", early and prehist, brickworks industry 15893

Garching an der Alz

Museum Garching an der Alz, Rathauspl, 84518 Garching an der Alz - T: (08634) 8434
Local Museum
Early local history, archeological finds 15894

Gardelegen

Mahn- und Gedenkstätte Isenschnibber-Feldscheune, Rathauspl 10, 39638 Gardelegen - T: (03907) 6519, Fax: 716220. Head: Dr. H. Becker
Historic Site - 1963
Hist of Nazi-atrocity 15895

Stadtmuseum Gardelegen, Rathauspl 10, 39638 Gardelegen - T: (03907) 6519, Fax: 716220. Head: Dr. H. Becker
Local Museum / Public Gallery - 1963
Local and crafts history, peasant tools and costumes 15896

Garding

Theodor-Mommsen-Gedächtnisstätte, Norderring 15, 25836 Garding - T: (04862) 17267, Fax: 100312
Special Museum - 1934
Documents on the life and work of historian T. Mommsen, housed in the scholar's birthplace 15897

Garmisch-Partenkirchen

Königshaus am Schachen und Alpengarten, 82467 Garmisch-Partenkirchen - T: (08821) 2996, 92030, Fax: 920311
Decorative Arts Museum - ca 1870 15898

Kunst auf der Zugspitze, c/o Bayrische Zugspitzbahn AG, Olympiastr 27, 82467 Garmisch-Partenkirchen - T: (08821) 7970, Fax: 797901, Internet: http://www.zugspitze.de. Head: Lucius Grisebach
Public Gallery 15899

Stiftung Aschenbrenner, Kurhaus, 82467 Garmisch-Partenkirchen - T: (08821) 1800
Decorative Arts Museum 15900

Werdenfelser Museum, Ludwigstr 47, 82467 Garmisch-Partenkirchen - T: (08821) 6212, Fax: 9378266
Decorative Arts Museum - 1925
Arts and crafts of the area, including carnival costumes and customs, graphics and sculptures (16th-19th c) - library 15901

Garz, Rügen

Ernst-Moritz-Arndt-Museum, An den Anlagen 1, 18574 Garz, Rügen - T: (038304) 12212, E-mail: Arndt-Museum-Garz@gmx.de. Head: Sylvia Knöpfel
Special Museum - 1929
Local, regional history, memorabilia of the writer Ernst M. Arndt (1769-1860), pictures, writings, first editions 15902

Gaste

Werksmuseum der Amazonen-Werke, c/o H. Dreyer GmbH & Co. KG, 49202 Gaste - T: (05405) 5010. Head: K. Dreyer
Science&Tech Museum
Agricultural machines 15903

Gaukönigshofen

Museum Klingelbeutel, Rittershausen, Otto-Menth-Str 11, 97253 Gaukönigshofen - T: (09337) 996889
Decorative Arts Museum / Folklore Museum / Religious Arts Museum
Religous folk art, custumes of order before 15904

Geeste

Emsland-Moormuseum, Geestmoor 6, 49744 Geeste - T: (05937) 1866, Fax: 2358, E-mail: emsland-moormuseum@t-online.de, Internet: http://www.moormuseum.de
Natural History Museum
Hist of peat cutting, natural and social hist 15905

Geesthacht

Krügersches Haus, Bergedorfer Str 28, 21502 Geesthacht - T: (04152) 835979, Fax: 78967, E-mail: MUSGEEST@aol.com, Internet: http://www.geesthacht.de
Local Museum 15906

Gehrden, Hannover

Heimatmuseum → Stadtmuseum Gehrden

Stadtmuseum Gehrden, Dammstr 15, 30989 Gehrden, Hannover - T: (05108) 927159, Fax: 927179, Internet: http://www.gehrden.de
Local Museum - 1973
Archaeological finds from the Stone, Bronze and Ice Age, earth hist, prehistory, graves from about 7th c, coins, crafts adn agriculture (1740-1900) 15907

Geiersthal

Burgmuseum Altnußberg, c/o Gemeindeverwaltung, Schloßberg, 94244 Geiersthal - T: (09923) 841511, Fax: 841520, E-mail: gemeinde@geiersthal.de, Internet: http://www.geiersthal.de
Archaeological Museum - 1996
Finds from excavations at the former castle Altnußberg (1125-1469) 15908

Geilenkirchen

Kreismuseum Geilenkirchen, Vogteistr 2, 52511 Geilenkirchen - T: (02452) 134027, Fax: 134095, E-mail: Museum@Kreis-Heinsberg.de. Head: Dr. Rita Müllejans-Dickmann
Local Museum 15909

Geiselhöring

Bäuerliches Heimatmuseum der Landtechnik, Industriestr 5a, 94333 Geiselhöring - T: (09423) 940016, Internet: http://www.geiselhoering.de
Agriculture Museum - 1998 15910

Museum der Seefahrt, Stadtpl 7, 94333 Geiselhöring - T: (09423) 1570, 3105
Science&Tech Museum
Coll of maritime instruments 15911

Geisenfeld

Hallertauer Hopfen- und Heimatmuseum, Rathausstr 11, 85290 Geisenfeld - T: (08452) 9824
Local Museum / Agriculture Museum - 1985
Local and early history, religious folklore, history of making beer and local crafts 15912

Geising

Silberstollen Geising, Im Erdbachtal, 01778 Geising - T: (035056) 4291
Science&Tech Museum 15913

Geislingen an der Steige

Heimatmuseum Geislingen, Moltkestr 11, 73312 Geislingen an der Steige - T: (07331) 24347
Local Museum 15914

Südmährisches Landschaftsmuseum, Hauptstr 19, 73312 Geislingen an der Steige - T: (07331) 43893, Fax: 40933, E-mail: slr@suedmaehren.de, Internet: http://www.suedmaehren.de
Local Museum - 1962
Geology, archeology, costumes 15915

Geithain

Stadtmuseum Geithain, Chemnitzer Str 20-22, 04643 Geithain - T: (034341) 44403, Fax: 45995, E-mail: stadt@geithain.de, Internet: http://www.geithain.de. Head: Reinhild Mitschke
Local Museum - 1986/95
Local hist, handicraft, agriculture, industry, pharmacy, enamel production 15916

Geldern

Kunstverein Gelderland e.V., Utrechter Str 19, 47608 Geldern - T: (02831) 88202, Fax: 992279, E-mail: inge-giesen@t-online.de
Public Gallery 15917

Gelenau, Erzgebirge

Deutsches Strumpfmuseum, Rathauspl 1, 09423 Gelenau, Erzgebirge - T: (037297) 849614, Fax: 849640, E-mail: Gemeinde-Gelenau@t-online.de, Internet: http://www.gelenau.de
Science&Tech Museum - 1992
Hosiery factory engines 15918

Gelnhausen

Heimatmuseum Meerholz, Rathausstr, 63571 Gelnhausen - T: (06051) 66688
Local Museum - 1965
Reconstructed farm parlour, domestic utensils 15919

Kaiserpfalzruine, Verwaltung der Staatlichen Schlösser und Gärten Außenstelle Steinau/ Gelnhausen, Burgstr 14, 63571 Gelnhausen - T: (06051) 3805, Fax: 16787. Head: Dr. Kai R. Mathieu
Historic Site - 1987 15920

Museum der Barbarossastadt Gelnhausen, Augusta Schule am Obermarkt, 63571 Gelnhausen - T: (06051) 830255, Fax: 830303. Head: Gerda Jost
Local Museum - 1909
Municipal hist, prehist, memorial rooms from H.J.Chr. von Grimmelshausen (ca 1622-1676) and Philipp Reis (1834-1874) 15921

Gelsenkirchen

Horster Motorrad-Museum, Wallstr 52, 45899 Gelsenkirchen - T: (0209) 56014. Head: Karlheinz Rebuschat
Science&Tech Museum 15922

Jazz & Art Galerie, Florastr 28, 45879 Gelsenkirchen - T: (0209) 145730, Fax: 145730
Public Gallery 15923

Kommunale Galerie Gelsenkirchen, Ebertstr, Hans-Sachs-Haus, 45875 Gelsenkirchen - T: (0209) 1694179, Fax: 1694801, E-mail: museum@gelsen-net.de. Head: Reinhard Hellrung
Public Gallery 15924

Städtisches Museum Gelsenkirchen, Horster Str 5-7, 45897 Gelsenkirchen - T: (0209) 1694377, 1694133, Fax: 1694801, E-mail: museum@gelsen-net.de, Internet: http://www.gelsenkirchen.de. Head: Dr. Doris Edler, Reinhard Hellrung, Leane Schäfer
Fine Arts Museum - 1950
Kinetics 15925

Geltow

Handweberei Henni Jaensch-Zeymer, Am Wasser 19, 14542 Geltow - T: (03327) 55272, Fax: 56289. Head: Ulla Schünemann
Decorative Arts Museum / Science&Tech Museum / Special Museum 15926

Gemünden am Main

Unterfränkisches Verkehrsmuseum, Huttenschloß, Frankfurter Str 2, 97737 Gemünden am Main - T: (09351) 800150, 800126, Fax: 800160. Head: Prof. Dr. H.-P. Schäfer
Science&Tech Museum - 1988
Local transport 15927

Gengenbach

Flößerei- und Verkehrsmuseum, Grünstr 1, 77723 Gengenbach - T: (07803) 1767, 3764, Fax: 7473, E-mail: info@floesserei.museum.de, Internet: http://www.floesserei-museum.de. Head: K. Schilli
Science&Tech Museum - 1991
Rafting, forestry 15928

Kirchenmuseum in der Pfarrei, 77723 Gengenbach
Religious Arts Museum 15929

Museum Haus Löwenberg, Binzmattstr 28, 77723 Gengenbach - T: (07803) 4229, Fax: 930147, E-mail: ev.end@t-online.de. Head: Reinhard End
Local Museum
Religious art, sculpture, local hist 15930

Genthin

Kreismuseum Jerichower Land, Mützelstr 22, 39307 Genthin - T: (03933) 803521, Fax: 803521. Head: Antonia Beran
Local Museum - 1886
Ancient and early history, numismatics, peasant tools and objects, book, maps, photo coll - library 15931

Georgensgmünd

Heimatstube Stadt und Landkreis Saaz, Im Schlösslein, 91166 Georgensgmünd - T: (09172) 1734, Fax: 1734
Local Museum 15932

Jüdisches Museum Georgensgmünd, Ehemalige Synagoge Am Anger, 91166 Georgensgmünd - T: (09172) 7030, Fax: 70350, E-mail: rathaus@georgensmuend.de, Internet: http://www.georgensmuend.de
Historical Museum / Ethnology Museum - 1996
History of the Jews in Georgensgmünd 15933

Georgenthal

Kornhaus Georgenthal-Klosterruinen, Finkenberg, 99887 Georgenthal - T: (036253) 380, 38108, Fax: 38102
Religious Arts Museum / Historic Site - 1966
History of local cloister, medieval painting 15934

Georgsmarienhütte

Museum Villa Stahmer, Carl-Stahmer-Weg 13, 49124 Georgsmarienhütte - T: (05401) 40755. Head: Inge Becher
Local Museum
Agricultural implements, exhibits on bourgeois style of living, musical instruments 15935

Gera

Historische Höhler, Stadtmuseum Gera, Geithes Passage, 07545 Gera, mail addr: Heinrichstr 2, 07545 Gera - T: (0365) 8381470, Fax: 8381475. Head: Dr. Martin Müller
Historical Museum 15936

Museum für Angewandte Kunst, Greizer Str 37, 07545 Gera - T: (0365) 8381430, Fax: 8381432. Head: Hans-Peter Jakobson
Decorative Arts Museum - 1984
Bauhaus ceramic coll, GDR applied graphics 15937

Museum für Naturkunde der Stadt Gera, Nicolaiberg 3, 07545 Gera - T: (0365) 52003, Fax: 52025. Head: Christel Russe
Natural History Museum - 1878
Geology, mineralogy, botany, zoology - library, botanical garden, mining dept. 15938

Orangerie, Kunstsammlung Gera, Küchengartenallee 4, 07548 Gera - T: (0365) 8322147, Fax: 8322112. Head: Ulrike Lorenz
Fine Arts Museum - 1972/1991
20th c art, paintings, graphics (16th c until today), drawings - library, cabinet for art education 15939

Otto-Dix-Haus, Kunstsammlung Gera, Mohrenpl 4, 07548 Gera - T: (0365) 8324927, Fax: 8324927. Head: Dr. Ulrike Lorenz
Fine Arts Museum 15940

Stadtmuseum Gera, Heinrichstr 2, 07545 Gera - T: (0365) 8381470, Fax: 8381475. Head: Dr. Martin Müller
Historical Museum - 1878 15941

Gerabronn

Alte Oberamtei, Hauptstr 17, 74582 Gerabronn - T: (07952) 5777. Head: R. Hohbaum
Local Museum
Local hist 15942

Geretsried

Heimatmuseum Geretsried, Karl-Lederer-Pl 1, 82538 Geretsried - T: (08171) 649237, Fax: 649238, E-mail: Museum-Geretsried@gmx.de
Local Museum - 1946
Museum of exiled East Germans who founded Geretsried 15943

Kolbenheyer-Archiv und Gedenkstätte, c/o Kolbenheyer-Gesellschaft e.V., Graslitzer Str 28, 82538 Geretsried - T: (08171) 6829, Fax: 6829, E-mail: dr.walter.hawelka@t-online.de. Head: Dr. Walter Hawelka
Special Museum
Life and work of author Erwin Guido Kolbenheyer (1878-1962) - library 15944

Gerlingen

Stadtmuseum Gerlingen - Gerlinger Heimatmuseum - Museum der Deutschen aus Ungarn, Weilimdorfer Str 9-11, 70839 Gerlingen - T: (07156) 205366. Head: Heidrun Rothe-Wörner
Local Museum 15945

Germersheim

Deutsches Straßenmuseum, Im Zeughaus, 76726 Germersheim - T: (07274) 500500, Fax: 500505, E-mail: info@deutsches-strassenmuseum.de, Internet: http://www.deutsches-strassenmuseum.de. Head: Dr. Albrecht Gill
Special Museum / Science&Tech Museum - 1989
Hist of street, material of construction, archeology, planning, measuring, constr of bridges, tunnels 15946

Stadt- und Festungsmuseum im Ludwigstor, 76726 Germersheim - T: (07274) 960220, Fax: 960247, E-mail: info@germersheim.de, Internet: http://www.germersheim.de
Historical Museum / Military Museum
Military history 19th-20th c, enamel label production, printing, tiles production, distilling, cigars 15947

Gernsbach

Amtshofmuseum, Schloßstr 37-39, 76593 Gernsbach - T: (07224) 64443
Local Museum 15948

Handwerker- und Heimatstube, Staufenberger Str 90, 76593 Gernsbach - T: (07224) 40992, 4574
Local Museum 15949

Gernsheim

Heimatmuseum der Stadt Gernsheim, Schöfferpl 1, 64579 Gernsheim - T: (06258) 3605, Fax: 3027
Local Museum - 1978
Relics of animals from the Ice Age, Roman finds, town hist, sacral objects 15950

Gerolstein

Museum Villa Sarabodis, Sarresdorfer Str 19, 54568 Gerolstein - T: (06591) 3362, Fax: 81224. Head: Archaeological Museum 15951

Gerolzhofen

Museum Altes Rathaus, Marktpl 20, 97447 Gerolzhofen - T: (09382) 6105, 60735, Fax: 6105
Local Museum - 1978
Local history 15952

Gersfeld

Deutsches Segelflugmuseum mit Modellflug, Wasserkuppe, 36129 Gersfeld - T: (06654) 7737, Fax: 7736, E-mail: info@segelflugmuseum.de, Internet: http://www.segelflugmuseum.de. Head: Theo Rack
Science&Tech Museum - 1987
Development of gliding, techniques, historical objects 15953

Gerstetten

Ortsmuseum Ursulastift, Marktstr 2, 89547 Gerstetten - T: (07323) 6121
Local Museum - 1973
Household articles 15954

Gersthofen

Ballonmuseum, Alter Wasserturm, Bahnhofstr 12, 86368 Gersthofen - T: (0821) 2993362, Fax: 2993364, E-mail: stadtbibliothek-gersthofen@gmx.de, Internet: http://www.stadt-gersthofen.de. Head: Ingrid Gölitz
Science&Tech Museum - 1985
Hist of ballooning 15955

Gerstungen

Heimatmuseum, Sophienstr 2, 99834 Gerstungen - T: (036922) 20327
Local Museum - 1932
Ancient and early hist, local hist, 18th-19th c peasant living style and tools, peasant crafts, industry, pottery ("Werrakeramik") 15956

Gescher

Museum Kutschen-Wagen-Karren, Museen der Stadt Gescher, Armlandstr 18, 48712 Gescher - T: (02542) 7144, Fax: 98012, E-mail: sonntag@gescher.de, Internet: http://www.gescher.de. Head: Dr. Johannes-Hendrik Sonntag
Agriculture Museum / Science&Tech Museum - 1988
Carriages - library 15957

Museumshof auf dem Braem, Museen der Stadt Gescher, Armlandstr 20-21, 48712 Gescher - T: (02542) 7144, Fax: 98012, E-mail: sonntag@gescher.de, Internet: http://www.gescher.de. Head: Dr. Johannes-Hendrik Sonntag
Open Air Museum - 1967
Peasant life, furniture, carpentry, framework - library 15958

Westfälisch-niederländisches Imkereimuseum, Museen der Stadt Gescher, Lindenstr 2, 48712 Gescher - T: (02542) 7144, Fax: 98012, E-mail: sonntag@gescher.de, Internet: http://www.gescher.de. Head: Dr. Johannes-Hendrik Sonntag
Special Museum / Agriculture Museum - 1995
Beekeeping and honey making 15959

Westfälisches Glockenmuseum, Museen der Stadt Gescher, Lindenstr 4, 48712 Gescher - T: (02542) 7144, Fax: 98012, E-mail: sonntag@gescher.de, Internet: http://www.gescher.de. Head: Dr. Johannes-Hendrik Sonntag
Special Museum / Music Museum - 1980
Hist of bells, bell-making, church bells, carillons, bell foundry - library 15960

Geseke

Städtisches Hellweg-Museum, Hellweg 13, 59590 Geseke, mail addr: Postfach 1425, 59585 Geseke - T: (02942) 78141, Fax: 2379, E-mail: VFHGeseke@aol.com, Internet: http://members.aol.com/vfhgeseke/. Head: A. Arens
Local Museum - 1926
Ethnology, tin, lamps, coins, housing, local hist 15961

Gessertshausen

Schwäbisches Volkskundemuseum und Bauernhofmuseum Staudenhaus, Oberschönenfeld, 86459 Gessertshausen - T: (08238) 30010, Fax: 300110, E-mail: svo1@s-planet.de, Internet: http://www.schwaebisches-volkskundemuseum.de. Head: Prof. Dr. Hans Frei
Agriculture Museum - 1984
Agricultural implements, housing, religious ethnography, piety, rural crafts 15962

Gettorf

Heimatmuseum in der Windmühle Gettorf, An der Mühle, 24214 Gettorf - T: (04346) 91112
Local Museum 15963

Geversdorf

Heimatmuseum Greversdorf, Hauptstr 5, 21784 Geversdorf - T: (04752) 327
Local Museum
Town hist 15964

Geyer

Heimatmuseum im Wachtturm, Am Lotterhof, 09468 Geyer - T: (037346) 1244, Fax: 10562
Local Museum - 1952
14th-19th c pewter mining hist, minerals, pewter coll, local hist, lace products, Evan Evans, Hieronymus Lotter 15965

Giengen

Margarete-Steiff-Museum, Alleenstr 2, 89537 Giengen - T: (07322) 131204, Fax: 131221, E-mail: manuela.fustig@steiff.de, Internet: http://www.steiff.de. Head: Manuela Fustig
Special Museum - 1980
Steiff Toys from 1880 onwards 15966

Stadtmuseum Giengen, Dettinger Str 3, Hürben, 89537 Giengen - T: (07322) 4803, Fax: 952264, E-mail: stadtverwaltung@giengen.de, Internet: http://www.giengen.de. Head: Dr. Alexander Usler
Local Museum - 1977
Anthropology, archaeology, local hist 15967

Giesen

Heimatmuseum Ahrbergen, Krugstr 4, 31180 Giesen - T: (05066) 4389
Local Museum
Domestic life and implements of the past two centuries 15968

Heimatmuseum Giesen, Rathausstr 42, 31180 Giesen - T: (05121) 770215
Local Museum - 1989
Various objects (clothes, bonnets, shoes) portraying the life around the turn of the century 15969

Gießen

Forum Gießen, Berliner Pl 1, 35398 Gießen - T: (0641) 3062532, Fax: 3062474, E-mail: gkarl@giessen.de, Internet: http://www.forum-giessen.de
Public Gallery 15970

Kunst- und Kunsthandwerk-Sammlung, Oberhessisches Museum, Brandpl 2, 35390 Gießen - T: (0641) 3062477. Head: Dr. Friedhelm Häring
Fine Arts Museum - 1879
Painting, drawing and graphics, sculpture (ca. 1500 and Baroque), faience (18th, 19th c), ceramics and coins 15971

Kunsthalle Gießen, Berliner Pl 2, 35390 Gießen - T: (0641) 3062532, Fax: 3062474, E-mail: gkarl@giessen.de, Internet: http://www.hessennet.de/giessen/kultur/kunsthalle
Public Gallery 15972

Liebig-Museum, Liebigstr 12, 35390 Gießen - T: (0641) 76392, Fax: 9934149, E-mail: wolfgang.laqua@anorg.chemie.uni-giessen.de, Internet: http://www.uni-giessen.de/~gi04/. Head: Prof. Dr. Wolfgang Laqua
Natural History Museum - 1920
Laboratory equipment and documents on the life and work of Justus von Liebig (1803-1873), housed in the chemist's former laboratory, plant nutrition 15973

Oberhessisches Museum und Gail'sche Sammlungen, Brandpl 2, 35390 Gießen - T: (0641) 3062477. Head: Dr. Friedhelm Häring
Local Museum - 1879
Reconstructed old castle, houses Leib and Wallenfels with trade hist and geological finds 15974

Sammlung Vor- und Frühgeschichte und Völkerkunde, Oberhessisches Museum, Brandpl 2, 35390 Gießen - T: (0641) 3062477. Head: Friedrich Häring
Ethnology Museum - 1879
Local prehistory and early history, ethnology (Ceylon, Java, East and West Africa, New Guinea and Australia) 15975

Gifhorn

Historisches Museum Schloß Gifhorn, Museen des Landkreises Gifhorn, Schloßpl 1, 38518 Gifhorn - T: (05371) 82422-5, Fax: 82413, Internet: http://www.gifhorn.de. Head: Dr. J. Conrad
Local Museum - 1914
Early and prehist, nobility and farmers, natural hist 15976

Internationales Wind- und Wassermühlenmuseum, Bromer Str 2, 38518 Gifhorn - T: (05371) 55466, Fax: 55640, Internet: http://www.mühlenmuseum.de. Head: Horst Wrobel
Science&Tech Museum - 1980
Nine mills from various countries 15977

Kavalierhaus Gifhorn- Museum für bürgerliche Wohnkultur, Museen des Landkreises Gifhorn, Steinweg 3, 38518 Gifhorn - T: (05371) 82417, Fax: 82421, E-mail: kavalierhaus@gifhorn.de, Internet: http://www.gifhorn.de/Museen/Kavalier_A.htm. Head: Wolfgang Böser
Historical Museum
Living culture in Gifhorn (1st half of 20th c) 15978

Gingen

Heimatstube Untere Baranya, Bahnhofsgebäude, 73333 Gingen - T: (0721) 709720
Local Museum - 1983
Life of Swabian settlers on the Danube in Hungary 15979

Gingst

Historische Handwerkerstuben, Dammstr 19-20, 18569 Gingst - T: (038305) 304
Science&Tech Museum / Decorative Arts Museum - 1971
History of labour-movement, native history, crafts 15980

Gladbeck

Museum der Stadt Gladbeck, Wasserschloß Wittringen, Burgstr 64, 45964 Gladbeck - T: (02043) 23029, Fax: 928325, E-mail: museum@stadt-gladbeck.de. Head: Dr. Wolfgang Schneider
Local Museum - 1928
Computer art, local and natural history, mining 15981

Städtische Galerie im Rathauspark, Willy-Brandt-Pl 2g, 45964 Gladbeck - T: (02043) 928324, Fax: 991410, E-mail: stadt@Gladbeck.de. Head: Georg Schmidt
Public Gallery - 1984 15982

Gladenbach

Heimatmuseum Amt Blankenstein, Haus des Gastes, Karl-Waldschmidt-Str, 35075 Gladenbach - T: (06462) 7163
Local Museum - 1954
Excavation finds of the fortress Blankenstein, hist of local Jewish population, trade workshops, costumes, furniture 15983

Künstlerhaus Lenz, 35075 Gladenbach - T: (06462) 8484. Head: Berta Lenz
Fine Arts Museum 15984

Glashütte, Sachsen

Uhrenmuseum Glashütte, Altenberger Str 1, 01768 Glashütte, Sachsen - T: (035053) 46281, Fax: 46205. Head: Reinhard Reichel
Science&Tech Museum - 1984
Hist of local watch industry - archive of the company A. Lange & Söhne 15985

Glattbach

Krippenmuseum, Hauptstr 114, 63864 Glattbach - T: (06021) 34910, Fax: 349144, E-mail: poststelle@glattbach.bayern.de, Internet: http://www.glattbach.de. Head: Friedolin Bernhard
Decorative Arts Museum - 1988
Cribs 15986

Glauburg

Glauberg-Museum, Hauptstr 17, Glauberg, 63695 Glauburg - T: (06041) 8813, Fax: 800316, Internet: http://www.keltenfuerst.de. Head: Werner Erk
Archaeological Museum
Finds from the Neolithic Age to the Middle Ages, esp Celtic age, agricultural implements 15987

Heimatmuseum, Glauburg-Sammlung, Alte Schule, 63695 Glauburg - T: (06041) 727
Local Museum 15988

Glauchau

Museum und Kunstsammlung Schloß Hinterglauchau, Schloß Hinterglauchau, 08371 Glauchau - T: (03763) 2931, Fax: 2931. Head: Steffen Winkler
Local Museum / Fine Arts Museum - 1884
Renaissance - historicism furnishings and paintings, Gothic sculpture and drawings, ancient and early history, geology, mineralogy, crafts, decorative objects, Georgius Agricola memorabilia, books (15-19th c) 15989

Gleichen

Historische Spinnerei Gartetal, Steinsmühle 3, Klein Lengden, 37130 Gleichen - T: (05508) 1218, Fax: 999730, E-mail: info@historische-spinnerei.de, Internet: http://www.historische-spinnerei.de. Head: Jürgen Haese
Science&Tech Museum - 1982
Spinning mill, various machines, techniques and objects connected 15990

Glindow

Märkisches Ziegelei-Museum Glindow, Alpenstr 47, 14542 Glindow - T: (03327) 669395, Fax: 669395, E-mail: info@glindower-ziegelei.de, Internet: http://www.afg-teltow.de/glindow. Head: Wolfgang Firl
Science&Tech Museum - 1993
Hist of regional tile-making industry, bricks, terracottas 15991

Glonn

Heimatmuseum Glonn, Klosterweg 7, 85625 Glonn - T: (08093) 4949, 691
Local Museum - 1995
Local history, coll of photographs 15992

Glücksburg, Ostsee

Stiftung Schloß Glücksburg, Schloss, 24960 Glücksburg, Ostsee - T: (04631) 2213, 2243, Fax: 2450, E-mail: info@schloss-gluecksburg.de, Internet: http://www.schloss-gluecksburg.de. Head: Dr. Peter Otzen
Decorative Arts Museum 15993

Glückstadt

Detlefsen-Museum, Am Fleth 43, Brockdorff-Palais, 25348 Glückstadt - T: (04124) 937630, Fax: 930111. Head: Tatjana Ceynowa-Barth
Agriculture Museum / Military Museum / Local Museum / Folklore Museum - 1894 15994

Palais für Aktuelle Kunst, Am Hafen 46, 25348 Glückstadt - T: (04124) 604776, Fax: 604778, E-mail: monsluce@t-online.de. Head: Cordula Lichtenberg
Association with Coll 15995

Gnandstein

Museum Burg Gnandstein, Dorfstr 1, 04655 Gnandstein - T: (034344) 61309, Fax: 61383, E-mail: Burg.Gnandstein@t-online.de. Head: Simona Schellenberger
Local Museum / Fine Arts Museum / Historical Museum - 1932
Local and castle hist, crafts, costumes, paintings, late Gothic chapel, memorabilia on poet Theodor Körner's (1791-1813) stay here, peasant living culture, hist of labour-movement 15996

Gnarrenburg

Glas-Museum Marienhütte und Teufelsmoor-Museum und Teufelsmoor-Galerie, Augustendorf Nr. 1, 27442 Gnarrenburg - T: (04763) 7487. Head: Hans-Werner Beissert
Science&Tech Museum / Special Museum / Folklore Museum / Public Gallery
Glass from Gnarrenburg, Teufelsmoor coll, regional art and culture, paintings antiques 15997

Museumshof Historischer Moorhof Augustendorf, Augustendorf 11, 27442 Gnarrenburg - T: (04285) 513, Fax: 639, E-mail: gieschen-glinstedt@t-online.de
Open Air Museum - 1985
Smoke house, stables, barns, fountains, peat cutting 15998

Gneisenaustadt Schildau

Gneisenau-Gedenkstätte, Gneisenaustr 2, 04889 Gneisenaustadt Schildau - T: (034221) 54710, Fax: 54726, E-mail: fremdenverkehrsamt@stadt-schildau.de
Military Museum - 1979 15999

Goch

Museum Goch, Museum für Kunst und Kulturgeschichte, Kastellstr 9, 47574 Goch - T: (02823) 970811, Fax: 970825, E-mail: museum.goch@t-online.de, Internet: http://www.goch.de/museum. Head: Dr. Stephan Mann
Fine Arts Museum / Local Museum - 1991
Contemporary art, Town history, bequest of Ferdinand Langenberg, 19th c: paintings, glass, bronzes - library, sculpture garden 16000

Gochsheim

Reichsdorf-Museum Gochsheim, Am Plan 2, 97469 Gochsheim - T: (09721) 630323, Fax: 630323, E-mail: Jaeger-Leo@t-online.de. Head: Leo Jäger
Local Museum / Folklore Museum - 1982
Local crafts, rustic culture, toys and a coll of porcelain, bicycle coll - bookbinding 16001

Göhrde

Waldmuseum Göhrde, König-Georg-Allee 5, 29473 Göhrde - T: (05855) 675
Natural History Museum
Geology, forestry, zoology 16002

Göhren, Rügen

Mönchguter Museum, Strandstr, 18586 Göhren, Rügen - T: (038308) 2175, Fax: 2175
Local Museum - 1960
Peasant living style, fishing, crafts, geography, geology, ancient and early hist, costumes, folk art 16003

Göldenitz bei Rostock

Landschulmuseum Göldenitz, Am See 7, 18196 Göldenitz bei Rostock - T: (038208) 264, Fax: 13096, E-mail: goeldenitz-landschulmuseum@t-online.de, Internet: http://www.aufdertenne.de
Historical Museum - 1976
School history from the beginning to the present - library, archive 16004

Göppingen

Dokumentationsraum für staufische Geschichte, Kaiserbergsteige 22, 73037 Göppingen - T: (07161) 979522, Fax: 979521, E-mail: -archiv.museen.stadt.goeppingen@t-online.de. Head: Dr. Karl-Heinz Rueß
Library with Exhibitions - 1977
Hist of mountain and castle Hohenstaufen 16005

Jüdisches Museum, Jebenhausen, Boller Str 82, 73035 Göppingen - T: (07161) 44600, Fax: 979521, E-mail: archiv.museen.Stadt.goeppingen@t-online.de. Head: Dr. Karl-Heinz Rueß
Ethnology Museum - 1992
Hist of Jews in Göppingen from 1777 until 1945 16006

Kunsthalle Göppingen, Marstallstr 55, 73033 Göppingen - T: (07161) 650777, Fax: 27672, E-mail: kunsthalle-gp@fto.de, Internet: http://www.goeppingen.de/kunsthalle. Head: Werner Meyer
Fine Arts Museum - 1989
International and contemporary art 16007

Landschaftsmuseum Schönhengstgau, Schloßstr 14, 73033 Göppingen - T: (07161) 69922, Fax: 14640. Head: Richard Schönich
Natural History Museum / Folklore Museum - 1988 16008

Märklin-Museum, Holzheimer Str 8, 73037 Göppingen - T: (07161) 608289, Fax: 608151, E-mail: museum@maerklin.de, Internet: http://www.maerklin.de. Head: Roland Gaugele
Science&Tech Museum - 1859
Model train sets from 1891 until today 16009

Mooreichensammlung Johann Weber, Heininger Str 20, 73037 Göppingen - T: (07161) 60020, Fax: 78593. Head: Gerd Wölz
Natural History Museum - 1967
Oak tree-trunks and roots from 6000 BC until 500 AC 16010

Städtisches Museum Göppingen im Storchen, Wühlestr 36, 73033 Göppingen - T: (07161) 979522, Fax: 979521, E-mail: -archiv.museen.Stadt.goeppingen@t-online.de. Head: Dr. Karl-Heinz Rueß
Local Museum - 1949
Toys, folklore, faience, tin 16011

Städtisches Naturkundliches Museum, Boller Str 102, 73035 Göppingen - T: (07161) 979522, Fax: 979521, E-mail: archiv-museen.stadt.-goeppingen@t-online.de. Head: Dr. Karl-Heinz Rueß
Natural History Museum - 1970
Fossils, birds, early and prehistory 16012

Görlitz

Kulturhistorisches Museum Barockhaus, Städtische Sammlungen für Geschichte und Kultur Görlitz, Neißstr 30, 02826 Görlitz - T: (03581) 671354, Fax: 671704, E-mail: kaisertrutz@goerlitz.de. Head: Dr. Jasper von Richthofen
Local Museum - 1873
Ancient and early history of region, local and economic history, cultural life, crafts, drawings - library 16013

Kulturhistorisches Museum Kaisertrutz/ Reichenbacher Turm, Städtische Sammlungen für Geschichte und Kultur Görlitz, Demianipl 1, 02826 Görlitz - T: (03581) 671351, Fax: 671704, E-mail: kaisertrutz@goerlitz.de, Internet: http://www.goerlitz.de. Head: Annerose Klammt
Local Museum - 1873
Local and economic history: historic weapons of the 18th c, archaeological objects from Stone Age to Middle Ages, history of the arts: 18th-19th c German painting 14th-15th c watchtower 16014

Schlesisches Museum zu Görlitz, Untermarkt 4, 02826 Görlitz - T: (03581) 87910, Fax: 8791200, E-mail: schlesisches.museum.goerlitz@t-online.de, Internet: http://www.schlesisches-museum.de. Head: Dr. Markus Bauer
Local Museum
Silesian hist 16015

Staatliches Museum für Naturkunde, Am Museum 1, 02826 Görlitz - T: (03581) 4760100, Fax: 4760101, E-mail: naturmuseum.gr@t-online.de, Internet: http://www.inf-gr.htw-zittau.de/nkmgr/. Head: Prof. Dr. Willi Xylander
Natural History Museum - 1811
Soil arthropods, entomology, zoology, botany, geology - library 16016

Görwihl

Heimatmuseum Görwihl, Am Marktpl, 79733 Görwihl - T: (07754) 203, E-mail: touristinfo@goerwihl.de
Local Museum - 1975
Costumes, salpetre extraction, spinning and weaving, looms, "The old school" 16017

Gößnitz, Thüringen

Heimatmuseum Gößnitz, Kauritzer Str 8, 04639 Gößnitz, Thüringen - T: (034493) 31859, Fax: 21473, Internet: http://www.abinsmuseum.de
Local Museum 16018

Gößweinstein

Haus des Gastes mit heimatkundlicher Sammlung, Burgstr 6, 91326 Gößweinstein - T: (09242) 456, Fax: 1863
Local Museum - 1990
Local history and geological coll 16019

Göttingen

Anthropologische Sammlung der Universität Göttingen, Bürgerstr 50, 37073 Göttingen - T: (0551) 393642, Fax: 393645
Ethnology Museum 16020

Künstlerhaus mit Galerie, Gotmarstr 1, 37073 Göttingen - T: (0551) 46890, Fax: 541348
Public Gallery 16021

Kunstsammlung der Universität Göttingen, Nikolausberger Weg 15, 37073 Göttingen - T: (0551) 395092, Fax: 392069. Head: Dr. Gerd Unverfehrt
Fine Arts Museum - 1770
Netherlandish painting, late medieval Italian painting, Renaissance and Baroque graphic arts, 19th and 20th c art 16022

Museum am Thie, Am Geismar Thie 2, 37083 Göttingen - T: (0551) 793389. Head: Reinhard Lindert
Folklore Museum - 1971 16023

Museum der Göttinger Chemie, Tammannstr 4, 37077 Göttingen - T: (0551) 393024, Fax: 393373, E-mail: gbeer@gwdg.de, Internet: http://www.museum.chemie.uni-goettingen.de. Head: Dr. Günther Beer
Natural History Museum - 1979
Lab objects, documents, historical slide preparations 16024

Museum für Geologie und Paläontologie am Geowissenschaftlichen Zentrum der Universität Göttingen, Goldschmidtstr 3, 37077 Göttingen - T: (0551) 397900, Fax: 397918, E-mail: uggp@gwdg.de, Internet: http://www.imgp.gwdg.de. Head: Prof. Dr. J. Reitner
Natural History Museum
Geology, mineralogy, fossils 16025

Musikinstrumentensammlung der Universität, Kurze Geismarstr 1, 37073 Göttingen - T: (0551) 395075, Fax: 399353, E-mail: k.p.brenner@phil.uni-goettingen.de, Internet: http://www.gwdg.de/~musik/mumuseum.htm. Head: Dr. Klaus-Peter Brenner
Music Museum - 1964
1802 musical instruments of Europe, Africa (incl. Ancient Egypt) and Asia 16026

Rechnermuseum der Gesellschaft für wissenschaftliche Datenverarbeitung, Am Faßberg, 37077 Göttingen - T: (0551) 2011539, Fax: 21119, E-mail: meyssel@gwdg.de, Internet: http://www.gwdg.de/museum. Head: Science&Tech Museum - 1980
Hist of Computer Technology 16027

Sammlungen des Archäologischen Instituts der Universität, Nikolausberger Weg 15, 37073 Göttingen - T: (0551) 397502, Fax: 392060, E-mail: sekretariat.archinst@phil.uni-goettingen.de, Internet: http://www.gwdg.de/~archaeo. Head: Prof. Marianne Bergmann
Archaeological Museum - 1767
Greek and Roman sculpture, coins, gems, ceramics, bronzes and terracotta, plaster copies of antique sculpture 16028

Städtisches Museum Göttingen, Ritterplan 7-8, 37073 Göttingen - T: (0551) 4002843, Fax: 4002059, E-mail: museum@goettingen.de, Internet: http://www.phil.uni-erlangen.de/~p1ges/goettingen/st_mus.html. Head: Dr. Jens-Uwe Brinkmann
Local Museum - 1889
Local hist and hist of the university, medieval and Baroque art, Jewish ceremonial instruments (17th-19th c), Fürstenberg porcelain, Münden faience, Göttingen tin and painted porcelain, modern studio glass 16029

Völkerkundliche Sammlung der Universität, Institut für Ethnologie, Theaterpl 15, 37073 Göttingen - T: (0551) 397892, Fax: 397359, E-mail: ethno@gwdg.de, Internet: http://www.gwdg.de/~ethno/voehome.htm. Head: Prof. Dr. Brigitta Hauser-Schäublin
Ethnology Museum - 1773
Comprehensive coll from around the world, incl Cook and Forster South Seas coll and von Asch coll of Northern Asian and Northwestern American cultures 16030

Zoologisches Museum der Universität, Institut für Zoologie und Anthropologie, Berliner Str 28, 37073 Göttingen - T: (0551) 395442, Fax: 395579, E-mail: gtroest@gwdg.de, Internet: http://www.gwdg.de/~gtroest/abteilung/morph/hallo.html. Head: Prof. Dr. R. Willmann, Dr. G. Tröster
Natural History Museum - 1778
Tropical butterflies, molluscs, tropical birds 16031

Goldberg, Mecklenburg

Natur-Museum mit Bauerngarten, Müllerweg 2, 19399 Goldberg, Mecklenburg - T: (038736) 41416
Natural History Museum - 1927
Geology, ancient and early history, crafts and industrial history - library 16032

Goldkronach

Bergbau- und Heimatmuseum, Marktpl 16, 95497 Goldkronach - T: (09273) 98413, Fax: 96380
Local Museum
Local and history of the local gold mine 16033

Gomadingen

Gestütsmuseum Offenhausen, Klosterhof, 72532 Gomadingen - T: (07385) 969633, Fax: 969622, E-mail: info@gomadingen.de, Internet: http://www.gomadingen.de. Head: Dr. Harald Lorenz
Agriculture Museum - 1980
Hist of horse breeding in Baden-Württemberg 16034

Goslar

Brunnenmuseum, Grauhof Brunnen, 38644 Goslar - T: (05321) 81081
Science&Tech Museum 16035

Domvorhalle, Kaiserbleek 10, 38640 Goslar - T: (05321) 704358, 75780, Fax: 757875, E-mail: kulturressort@goslar.de, Internet: http://www.goslar.de. Head: Dr. Heidi Roch-Stübler
Religious Arts Museum 16036

Goslarer Museum, Königstr 1, 38640 Goslar - T: (05321) 43394, Fax: 757875, E-mail: kulturressort@goslar.de, Internet: http://www.goslar.de. Head: Dr. Heidi Roch-Stübler
Local Museum - 1922
Art and cultural hist, natural hist, municipal and local hist, pre- and early hist, economic hist, religious objects 16037

Goslarer Zinnfiguren-Museum, Münzstr 11, 38640 Goslar - T: (05321) 25889. Head: Joachim Baensch
Decorative Arts Museum / Historical Museum - 1985
Reconstruction of historical scenes with pewter figures 16038

Huldigungssaal und Rathaus, Markt 1, 38640 Goslar - T: (05321) 704241, 75780, Fax: 757875, E-mail: kulturressort@goslar.de, Internet: http://www.goslar.de. Head: Dr. Heidi Roch-Stübler
Local Museum
Goslar hist, 16th c mural paintings 16039

Kaiserpfalz mit Sankt Ulrichskapelle, Kaiserbleek 6, 38640 Goslar - T: (05321) 704358, 75780, Fax: 757875, E-mail: kulturressort@goslar.de, Internet: http://www.goslar.de. Head: Dr. Heidi Roch-Stübler
Historical Museum / Historic Site
Local hist, hist painter Hermann Wislicenus 16040

Mönchehaus-Museum für moderne Kunst, Mönchestr 1-3, 38640 Goslar - T: (05321) 29570, 4948, Fax: 42199, E-mail: MoenchehausMuseum@t-online.de, Internet: http://www.stadtsparkasse-goslar.de. Head: Th. K.P. Schenning
Fine Arts Museum - 1978
Contemporary art, incl international graphic coll 16041

Museum im Zwinger, Thomasstr 2, 38640 Goslar - T: (05321) 43140, E-mail: info@goslarer-zwinger.de, Internet: http://www.zwinger.de. Head: Andreas Kuboschek
Historical Museum / Museum of Classical Antiquities
Siege machines and objects, arms and armour, torture instruments 16042

Museum und Besucherbergwerk Rammelsberg, Bergtal 19, 38640 Goslar - T: (05321) 7500, Fax: 750130, E-mail: info@rammelsberg.de, Internet: http://www.rammelsberg.de. Head: Prof. Dr. Reinhard Roseneck, Jürgen Meier
Science&Tech Museum
Industrial culture, history of work, social history, mining, engineering, mineralogy 16043

Musikinstrumenten- und Puppenmuseum, Hoher Weg 5, 38640 Goslar - T: (05321) 26945. Head: Walter Johannes Erdmann
Music Museum / Decorative Arts Museum / Historic Site - 1975
17th-20th c musical instruments, toys and puppets and a figurative collection " magic of grace" 16044

Gotha

Ekhof-Theater, Schloß Friedenstein, Westturm, 99853 Gotha, mail addr: Postfach 100319, 99867 Gotha - T: (03621) 823415, Fax: 823419, E-mail: -museum.regionalgeschichte@gmx.de. Head: Elisabeth Dobritzsch
Performing Arts Museum - 1683
Hist of theatre, music instruments 16045

Gustav-Freytag-Gedenkstätte, Weimarer Str 145, 99867 Gotha
Historical Museum - 1960
Memorabilia on writer and art historian Gustav Freytag (1816-1895) in his former home 16046

Museum der Natur, Parkallee 15, 99867 Gotha, mail addr: Postfach 100319, 99853 Gotha - T: (03621) 823010, Fax: 823020. Head: Rainer Samietz
Natural History Museum - 1640
Geology, paleontology, mineralogy, zoology, entomology, ornithology, malacology - library 16047

Museum für Regionalgeschichte und Volkskunde, Schloß Friedenstein, Westturm, 99853 Gotha, mail addr: Postfach 100319, 99867 Gotha - T: (03621) 823415, Fax: 823419, E-mail: -museum.regionalgeschichte@gmx.de. Head: Elisabeth Dobritzsch
Local Museum / Folklore Museum / Archaeological Museum - 1928
Early and prehist, textiles, handicraft, posters, maps - photo library, cartographical museum, Ekhof-theatre 16048

Schloßmuseum, Schloß Friedenstein, 99853 Gotha, mail addr: Postfach 217, 99867 Gotha - T: (03621) 82340, Fax: 852669. Head: Bernd Schäfer
Fine Arts Museum - 1656
Historic rooms 17-19th c, medieval-Renaissance painting and sculpture, engravings, numismatics, 17th-19th c crafts, decorative objects, netherland paintings, classicistic sculptures by Houdon, coll of modern art 16049

Schloßmuseum und Galerie für moderne Kunst → Schloßmuseum

Graben-Neudorf

Heimatmuseum Graben-Neudorf, Karlsruher Str 47, 76676 Graben-Neudorf - T: (07251) 4870, 4334
Local Museum 16050

Grabenstätt

Römermuseum Multerer, Erlstätter Str 1, 83355 Grabenstätt - T: (08661) 242, Fax: 1472
Archaeological Museum
Archeological finds and a partial reconstruction of a Roman villa 16051

Grabow, Mecklenburg

Heimatmuseum, Marktstr 19, 19300 Grabow, Mecklenburg - T: (038756) 70054, Fax: 50347
Local Museum - 1934
Ancient, early hist, local hist, crafts, furniture, household articles 16052

Grafenau, Niederbayern

Bauernmöbelmuseum, Im Kurpark, 94481 Grafenau, Niederbayern - T: (08552) 3318
Decorative Arts Museum - 1978
Cabinets, chests and other rustical furniture from the Bavarian Forest, loom and weaver's workroom 16053

Schnupftabakmuseum, Spitalstr, 94481 Grafenau, Niederbayern - T: (0175) 2138409
Special Museum - 1979
Manufacture and use of snuff, snuff boxes, liturature on snuff 16054

Stadtmuseum Grafenau, Spitalstr, 94481 Grafenau, Niederbayern - T: (0175) 2138409. Head: Ariane Strößenreuther
Local Museum
Town history 16055

Grafenau, Württemberg

Heimatmuseum Grafenau Schloß Dätzingen, 71120 Grafenau, Württemberg - T: (07033) 40300, 43926, Fax: 43926
Agriculture Museum / Local Museum / Historical Museum - 1986
Agricultural implements, household articles, local hist 16056

Grafenhausen

Museum Hüsli- Sammlung Schwarzwälder Volkskunst, Rothaus, 79865 Grafenhausen - T: (07748) 212, Fax: (07751) 86373, E-mail: kultur@landkreis-waldshut.de, Internet: http://www.landkreis-waldshut.de. Head: Dr. Jürgen Glocker
Local Museum / Folklore Museum - 1966
Black Forest folk art housed in reconstructed typical farmhouse 16057

Schwarzwälder Mühlenmuseum, Tannenmühlenweg 5, 79865 Grafenhausen - T: (07748) 215. Head:
Science&Tech Museum - 1988
Agricultural implements 16058

Grafenrheinfeld

Schatzkammer Grafenrheinfeld, c/o Gemeinde Grafenrheinfeld, Marktpl 1, 97506 Grafenrheinfeld - T: (09723) 91330, Fax: 913325, E-mail: gemeinde@grafenrheinfeld.de, Internet: http://www.grafenrheinfeld.de
Religious Arts Museum
Religious objects 16059

Grafenwöhr

Kultur- und Militärmuseum, Martin-Posser-Str 14, 92655 Grafenwöhr - T: (09641) 8501, Fax: 8501, E-mail: museum@grafenwoehr.de, Internet: http://www.grafenwoehr.de/museum
Local Museum / Military Museum - 1932
History of Grafenwöhr, military history 16060

Grafing bei München

Heimatmuseum Grafing, Bahnhofstr 10, 85567 Grafing bei München - T: (08092) 32105, Fax: 70337, Internet: http://www.ebe-online.de/home/sgrafing
Local Museum - 1965
Domestic utensils, folk costumes, religious objects, furniture, agricultural and trade implements, painters Max Joseph Wagenbauer and Baron Ernst von Maydell 16061

Grafling

Heimatmuseum Grafling, Bahnhofstr 25, 94539 Grafling - T: (0991) 290360, Fax: 27824
Local Museum - 1987
Local history 16062

Gransee

Heimatmuseum Gransee, Rudolf-Breitscheid-Str 44, 16775 Gransee - T: (03306) 21606, Fax: 2467
Local Museum
Early and prehist, agriculture, Gothic cupboard 16063

Grassau, Chiemgau

Bayerisches Moor- und Torfmuseum, Torfbahnhof, Samerweg 8, 83224 Grassau, Chiemgau - T: (08641) 2126, Fax: 2126, E-mail: @torfbahnhof-rottau.de, Internet: http://www.torfbahnhof-rottau.de. Head: Klaus-Dieter Hortz
Science&Tech Museum / Natural History Museum - 1989
Old turfstation 16064

Soleleitungsmuseum Brunnhaus Klaushäusl, 83224 Grassau, Chiemgau - T: (08641) 5467, 400818, Fax: 400831
Science&Tech Museum - 1995
Saltwater spa 16065

Grebenstein

Ackerbürgermuseum Haus Leck, Schachtener Str 11, 34393 Grebenstein - T: (05674) 1354. Head: Wolfgang Toelle
Local Museum - 1984
Three-storey half-timbered house with various rooms and stables, implements, linen weavery 16066

Greding

Museum Natur und Mensch, Marktpl 8, 91171 Greding - T: (08463) 1731, 605371
Natural History Museum - 1976
Geology, fossils from the Jura mountains, local customs, hunting weapons 16067

Sparkassen-Museum, Marktpl 6, 91171 Greding - T: (08463) 64030, Fax: 64032589, E-mail: sparkasse-roth-schwabach@t-online.de, Internet: http://www.sparkasse.roth-schwabach.de
Special Museum - 1989
History of banking 16068

Grefrath

Niederrheinisches Freilichtmuseum, An der Dorenburg 28, 47929 Grefrath - T: (02158) 91730, Fax: 917316, E-mail: pressestelle@kreisviersen.de, Internet: http://www.kreisviersen.de. Head: Dr. Heinz-Peter Mielke
Open Air Museum - 1973
Country culture, customs, manners, old fashioned posthouse, tannery, toys 16069

Greifenstein

Altes Haus, An der Kirche, 35753 Greifenstein - T: (06478) 2152. Head: Heinrich Jung
Historic Site - 1960
Half-timbered farm house with agricultural and domestic implements, appliances and tools, bible (1665) 16070

Deutsches Glockenmuseum, Talstr 19, 35753 Greifenstein - T: (06449) 921132, Fax: 6073, E-mail: dgm.gr@t-online.de. Head: Dr. Konrad Bund
Special Museum - 1984
50 historic bells and equipment such as bell cages, bays and tongues 16071

Greifensteiner Burgmuseum, Talstr 17, 35753 Greifenstein - T: (06449) 6460, Fax: 6073. Head: Klaus Baumann
Local Museum - 1972
Local hist, mineralogy and geology, peasant culture, iron casting 16072

Greifswald

Anatomisches Museum, Friedrich-Loeffler-Str 23c, 17489 Greifswald - T: (03834) 865300, Fax: 865302, E-mail: faghe@rz.uni-greifswald.de
Natural History Museum
250 skulls of anthropoid apes and other rare animals 16073

Geologische Landessammlung von Vorpommern, Institut für Geologische Wissenschaften, Friedrich-Ludwig-Jahn-Str 17a, 17489 Greifswald - T: (03834) 864580, 864570, Fax: 864572, E-mail: dietrih@uni-greifswald.de, Internet: http://www.uni-greifswald.de/~geo/sammlung/sammlung.htm. Head: Prof. Dr. Maria-Theresia Schafmeister
Natural History Museum - 1908
Scandinavian fossils, erratic boulders, upper cretaceous from Rügen - archive for erratic boulders 16074

Gustaf-Dalman-Institut für biblische Landes- und Altertumskunde, Am Rubenowpl 2/3, 17489 Greifswald - T: (03834) 862516, 862517, Fax: 862502, E-mail: jmaennch@mail.uni-greifswald.de. Head: Prof. Dr. Christof Hardmeier
Library with Exhibitions - 1920
Palestine studies - Library 16075

Pommersches Landesmuseum, Mühlenstr 15, 17489 Greifswald - T: (03834) 894357, Fax: 894358, E-mail: info@pommersches-landesmuseum.de, Internet: http://www.pommersches-landesmuseum.de. Head: Dr. U. Schröder
Public Gallery - 1996
Painting 19th c 16076

Victor-Schultze-Institut für christliche Archäologie und Geschichte der kirchlichen Kunst, Rübenowpl 2-3, 17487 Greifswald - T: (03834) 862503, 862501, Fax: 862502, E-mail: christku@uni-greifswald.de, Internet: http://www.greifswald.de/~theol/institute/victor.htm. Head: Prof. Dr. Dr. Claudia Nauert
Archaeological Museum 16077

Greiz

Heimatmuseum und Textil-Schauwerkstatt, Unteres Schloß, Burgpl 12, 07973 Greiz - T: (03661) 3666, Fax: 3666
Local Museum / Science&Tech Museum - 1912
Local hist, folk culture, numismatics, costume, furniture, paintings, graphics, sculpture, weapons, toy 16078

Satiricum, Staatliche Bücher und Kupferstichsammlung Greiz, Sommerpalais, 07973 Greiz - T: (03661) 70580, Fax: 705825, E-mail: sommerpalais@greiz.encotel.de. Head: Gotthard Brandler
Fine Arts Museum 16079

Staatliche Bücher- und Kupferstichsammlung Greiz, Stiftung der Älteren Linie des Hauses Reuß, Sommerpalais, 07973 Greiz - T: (03661) 70580, Fax: 705825, E-mail: sommerpalais@greiz.encotel.de. Head: Gotthard Brandler
Fine Arts Museum - 1922
Hist of illustrated books since 1500, drawings, mezzotints, caricatures, maps - satiricum 16080

Grenzach-Wyhlen

Museum Römervilla, Ecke Steingasse/Hauptstr, 79639 Grenzach-Wyhlen - T: (07624) 5898. Head: Dr. Erhard Richter
Archaeological Museum - 1986
Roman finds 16081

Greußen

Agrarmuseum, Grüninger Str, 99718 Greußen - T: (03636) 446
Agriculture Museum
Agricultural life, implements 16082

Heimatmuseum, Lindenstr 14, 99718 Greußen - T: (03636) 701028, Fax: 701033, Internet: http://www.greussen.de
Local Museum - 1936
Geology, local and regional history, crafts 16083

Grevenbroich

Museum im Stadtpark, Am Stadtpark 1, 41515 Grevenbroich - T: (02181) 659696, Fax: 608202, E-mail: helma.rose@grevenbroich.de. Head: Dr. Bodo Schwalm
Ethnology Museum - 1989
Ethnology, archaeology, geology, Islamic calligraphic coll 16084

Griesbach im Rottal

Geburtshaus des heiligen Konrad von Parzham, Parzham 4, 94086 Griesbach im Rottal - T: (08532) 2311, 920114, Fax: 920214
Religious Arts Museum - 1971 16085

Sammlung Irmgard Friedl, Thalhamer Str 9, 94086 Griesbach im Rottal - T: (08532) 8195. Head: Gerlinde Friedl
Archaeological Museum
Archeological finds 16086

Grillenburg

Forstliche und Jagdkundliche Lehrschau Grillenburg, Technische Universität Dresden, Hauptstr 7, 01737 Grillenburg - T: (035202) 2027, Fax: 381218, E-mail: fachri@forst.tu-dresden.de, Internet: http://www.tu-dresden.de/forst.html. Head: Prof. Ernst Ulrich Köpf
Natural History Museum - 1966
Hunting trophies, game birds, hunting equipment, forest technology, weapons 16087

Grimma

Göschenhaus / Seume-Gedankstätte, Schillerstr 25, 04668 Grimma - T: (03437) 911118, Fax: 911118, E-mail: seumearchivsa@web.de, Internet: http://www.seume.de. Head: Annett Höhne
Special Museum - 1954
Memorabilia on publisher Göschen (1752-1805) in his former house and on his visitors Schiller, Seume and Körner, steel engravings, pictures, furniture, household utensils of tin, porcelain and glass in Empire and Biedermeier style - library 16088

Kreisheimatmuseum, Paul-Gerhard-Str 43, 04668 Grimma - T: (03437) 911132, Fax: 911132. Head: Marita Pesenecker
Local Museum - 1901
Geology, ancient and early historic finds, local history, peasant crafts, tools and living style, history of local Hussar Regiment, toys, ethnography, basket coll - library 16089

Rathausgalerie Grimma, Markt 27, 04668 Grimma - T: (03437) 9858290
Local Museum 16090

Schiffmühle Höfgen, Höfgen, 04668 Grimma - T: (03437) 987713, Fax: 987715, E-mail: landschaftspark@hoefgen.de, Internet: http://www.hoefgen.de. Head: Dr. Uwe Andrich
Science&Tech Museum
Hist of Central European river-shipmills 16091

Studiogalerie Kaditzsch, Denkmalschmiede Höfgen, Teichstr 12, Kaditzsch, 04668 Grimma - T: (03437) 98770, Fax: 987710, E-mail: galerie@hoefgen.de, Internet: http://www.hoefgen.de. Head: Dr. Uwe Andrich
Fine Arts Museum / Public Gallery 16092

Grimmen

Heimatmuseum Grimmen "Im Mühlentor", Mühlenstr 9a, 18501 Grimmen - T: (038326) 2261, 470, Fax: 47255, Internet: http://www.grimmen.de
Historical Museum / Local Museum
Early and prehistoric settling, town hist, agricultural and domestic implements 16093

Gröbenzell

Galerie im Bürgerhaus, Rathausstr 1, 82194 Gröbenzell - T: (08142) 50546
Public Gallery 16094

Heimat- und Torfmuseum, Rathausstr 3, 82194 Gröbenzell - T: (08142) 50549, Fax: 50559, E-mail: Gemeinde@grobenzell.de, Internet: http://www.groebenzell.de
Local Museum
Local and early hist 16095

Gröbzig

Museum Synagoge Gröbzig, Langestr 8-10, 06388 Gröbzig - T: (034976) 22209, Fax: 22209. Head: Dr. Marion Méndez
Religious Arts Museum - 1934
Regional culture and history of Jewish community 18th-19th c in the context of general developments 16096

Grömitz

Austellungszentrum Kloster Cismar, Stiftung Schleswig-Holsteinische Landesmuseen Schloß Gottorf, Bäderstr 42, 23743 Grömitz - T: (04621) 1080, Fax: 813555, E-mail: info@schloss-gottorf.de, Internet: http://www.schloss-gottorf.de. Head: Dr. Herwig Guratzsch
Fine Arts Museum 16097

Groitzsch bei Pegau

Heimatmuseum, Markt, 04539 Groitzsch bei Pegau - T: (034296) 3222
Local Museum - 1990
Pre and early hist, printing, handicrafts 16098

Gronau, Leine

Museum und Archiv der Stadt Gronau (Leine), Junkernstr 16, 31028 Gronau, Leine - T: (05182) 1800, Fax: 947049, E-mail: info@Gronau-Leine.de, Internet: http://www.Gronau-Leine.de. Head: Friedesine Balden
Local Museum
Town hist, documents on the linguist, literary figure and humanist Dr. Georg Sauerwein, Breiner estate with photographies 16099

Gronau, Westfalen

Drilandmuseum Gronau, Bahnhofstr 8, 48599 Gronau, Westfalen - T: (02562) 4419. Head: Heinz Cierpka, Dr. Lennart Schleicher
Local Museum 16100

Groß-Gerau

Stadtmuseum Groß-Gerau, Am Marktpl 3, 64521 Groß-Gerau - T: (06152) 716295, Fax: 938495. Head: Jürgen Volkmann
Local Museum - 1929
Archaeology, town hist, ceramics 16101

Groß Leuthen

Schloß Groß Leuthen, Dorfstr 21, 15913 Groß Leuthen - T: (030) 3447779
Local Museum 16102

Groß Nemerow

Heimatstube Groß Nemerow, 17094 Groß Nemerow - T: (039605) 206
Local Museum 16103

Groß Raden

Archäologisches Landesmuseum Mecklenburg-Vorpommern, Freilichtmuseum Groß Raden, Kastanienallee, 19406 Groß Raden - T: (03847) 2252, Fax: 451624, E-mail: archaeomuseum.m-v@t-online.de. Head: Dr. Friedrich Lüth
Open Air Museum / Archaeological Museum - 1987
Culture of the North West Slavs 16104

Groß Schönebeck

Museum für Forst- und Jagdwirtschaft, Schloßstr 6, 16348 Groß Schönebeck - T: (033393) 65272
Agriculture Museum 16105

Groß-Umstadt

Kunstraum, Hanauer Gasse 311, 64823 Groß-Umstadt - T: (06078) 2878. Head: Annemarie Kapp de Thouzellier, Jochen Wierich
Fine Arts Museum 16106

MAK - Museum für Aktuelle Kunst, Im Pfarrhof 6, 64823 Groß-Umstadt - T: (06078) 75522, Fax: 75522. Head: Annemarie Kapp de Thouzellier
Fine Arts Museum - 1995
Art since 1945 esp in view of regional aspects 16107

Großalmerode

Glas- und Keramikmuseum, Kleiner Kirchrain 3, 37247 Großalmerode - T: (05604) 1362. Head: D. Bernhardt
Decorative Arts Museum
Ceramics, earthenware, water pipes, ointment stone jars and other vessels 16108

Großbeeren

Gedenkstätte Großbeeren 1813, Dorfaue, Gedenkturm, 14979 Großbeeren - T: (033701) 328861, Fax: 328844
Historical Museum 16109

Großbodungen

Heimatstube Großbodungen, 37345 Großbodungen - T: (036077) 223, Fax: 20223
Local Museum 16110

Großbothen

Wilhelm-Ostwald-Gedenkstätte, Haus Energie, 04668 Großbothen - T: (034384) 71429, Fax: 72691, E-mail: ostwald.energie@t-online.de, Internet: http://www.wilhelm-ostwald.de. Head: Anna-Elisabeth Hansel
Natural History Museum - 1974
Physical chemistry, philosophy of nature, theory of colour, scientific bequest of Prof. Wilhelm Ostwald, 3 000 paintings and sketches by Wilhelm Ostwald - library, archive 16111

Großefehn

Fehnmusuem Eiland, Leerer Landstr 59, 26629 Großefehn - T: (04945) 1333, Fax: 912906, E-mail: info@fehntouristik-eiland.de, Internet: http://www.fehntouristik-eiland.de
Local Museum - 1991
Peat cutting, hist of settling, shipping 16112

Großengottern

Heimatmuseum, Langensalzaer Str 11, 99991 Großengottern - T: (036022) 96385, Fax: 94231
Local Museum - 1956
Ancient historic finds, local history, peasant equipment, household objects, costumes, nature 16113

Großenhain, Sachsen

Museum Alte Lateinschule Großenhain, Kirchpl 4, 01558 Großenhain, Sachsen - T: (03522) 502086, Fax: 527456, E-mail: museum@grossenhain.de, Internet: http://museum.grossenhain.de
Local Museum - 1907
History of military, textile industry, - Library 16114

Großheide

Wald- und Moormuseum Berumerfehn, Kirchweg 1a, 26532 Großheide - T: (04936) 526
Natural History Museum - 1964
Native woodland creatures, ornithology, wood 16115

Großkochberg

Schloß Kochberg mit Liebhabertheater, Stiftung Weimarer Klassik, Schloß, 07407 Großkochberg - T: (036743) 22532, Fax: 22532, E-mail: gnm@weimar-klassik.de, Internet: http://www.weimar-klassik.de
Historical Museum - 1949
Memorabilia on J.W. Goethe (1749-1832) and Charlotte von Stein (1742-1827) 16116

Großkrotzenburg

Museum Großkrotzenburg, Breitestr 20, 63538 Großkrotzenburg - T: (06186) 8922, Fax: 7156. Head: Hannelore Kreß
Local Museum - 1966
Site of a former Roman fort, early and pre-hist, regional hist 16117

Großostheim

Bachgau-Museum, Nöthigs-Gut, 63762 Großostheim - T: (06026) 1226. Head: Ewald Lang
Local Museum - 1975
Agricultural tools, religious folklore and local crafts 16118

Großpösna

Sanitätsmuseum, Pfarrgasse 3, Seifertshain, 04463 Großpösna - T: (034297) 42161, Fax: 42161, Internet: http://www.grosspoesna.de
Historical Museum / Military Museum 16119

Großröhrsdorf, Oberlausitz

Heimatmuseum, Mühlstr 5, 01900 Großröhrsdorf, Oberlausitz - T: (035952) 30000
Local Museum - 1899
Local, regional history, 19th c suspenders, peasant crafts and objects, 19th c hunting equipment, ceramics, jewelry 16120

Technisches Museum, Schulstr 2, 01900 Großröhrsdorf, Oberlausitz - T: (035952) 48247, Fax: 28350, E-mail: info@grossroehrsdorf.de, Internet: http://www.grossroehrsdorf.de. Head: Eckhard Hennig
Science&Tech Museum - 1998
Development of the band-weaving technique from the 17th c to the present time 16121

Großschönau, Sachsen

Deutsches Damast- und Frottiermuseum Großschönau, Schenaustr 3, 02779 Großschönau, Sachsen - T: (035841) 35469, Fax: 2553, Internet: http://www.grossschoenau.de. Head: Peter Becker
Science&Tech Museum - 1905
Historic objects, damask coll, local crafts, religious art, native birds, looms and different textile machines 16122

Motorrad-Veteranen- und Technik-Museum, David-Goldberg-Str 7, 02779 Großschönau, Sachsen - T: (035841) 2708
Science&Tech Museum 16123

Großwallstadt

Heimschneidermuseum, Hauptstr 3, 63868 Großwallstadt - T: (06022) 22070, Fax: 220777, E-mail: gemeinde@grosswallstadt.de, Internet: http://www.grosswallstadt.de. Head: Leo Markert
Local Museum - 1987
Local crafts at home 16124

Großweil

Freilichtmuseum Glentleiten, An der Glentleiten 4, 82439 Großweil - T: (08851) 1850, 18510, Fax: 18511, E-mail: freilichtmuseum@glentleiten.de, Internet: http://www.glentleiten.de. Head: Dr. Helmut Keim
Open Air Museum - 1971
Tools, handicrafts, dwellings, etc. illustrating country culture through five c - library 16125

Großzschepa

Heimatmuseum, Karl-Marx-Str 18, 04808 Großzschepa - T: (034263) 41037
Local Museum - 1989
Local hist, pre and early hist 16126

Grube, Holstein

Dorfmuseum, Hauptstr 18, 23749 Grube, Holstein - T: (04364) 8379
Local Museum 16127

Grünenplan

Erich Mäder-Glasmuseum, c/o Schott DESAG AG, Am Park 1, 31073 Grünenplan - T: (05187) 771229, Fax: 771551, E-mail: bernd.vache@schott.com, Internet: http://www.desag.de. Head: Bernd Vache
Science&Tech Museum - 1969
Hist of glassworks since the Middle Ages 16128

Glasmuseum Grünenplan, Kirchtalstr 13, 31073 Grünenplan - T: (05187) 771229, Fax: 771551, E-mail: bernd.vache@schott.com, Internet: http://www.schott.com/desag. Head: Bernd Vache
Science&Tech Museum - 1966
Models of glass-manufacturing equipment, glass from various periods 16129

Grünwald

Burgmuseum Grünwald, Archäologische Staatssammlung München, Zeillerstr 3, 82031 Grünwald - T: (089) 6413218, Internet: http://www.wissenschaftsministerium.bayern.de. Head: Prof. Dr. Ludwig Wamser
Archaeological Museum - 1979
Early hist of the Munich aera 16130

Gruibingen

Heimatmuseum Straub, Boller Sattel, 73344 Gruibingen
Local Museum 16131

Guben

Städtisches Museum Sprucker Mühle, Mühlenstr 5, 03172 Guben - T: (03561) 52038, Fax: 52038. Head: Bernd Pilz
Local Museum / Science&Tech Museum 16132

Güglingen

Bürgerstiftung Kunst für Güglingen, Rathaus, 74363 Güglingen - T: (07135) 7792, Fax: 16170
Public Gallery 16133

Güntersberge

Mausefallen- und Galerie der Stillen Örtchen, Klausstr 138, 06507 Güntersberge - T: (039488) 430, Fax: 430
Special Museum 16134

Günzach

Dorfmuseum Günzach, Kirchpl, 87634 Günzach - T: (08372) 345
Local Museum - 1981
Town hist 16135

Günzburg

Heimatmuseum Günzburg, Rathausgasse 2, 89312 Günzburg - T: (08221) 38828, Fax: 903117, E-mail: Grabert@rathaus.guenzburg.de, Internet: http://www.guenzburg.de. Head: Walter Grabert
Local Museum / Archaeological Museum - 1904
Geology, paleontology, Roman sepulchral relics and hist of exiled East Germ ans 16136

Güstrow

Ernst Barlach Stiftung Güstrow, Gertrudenkapelle, Atelierhaus, Ausstellungsforum, Heidberg 15, 18273 Güstrow - T: (03843) 82299, Fax: 82487, E-mail: Barlach-Stiftung@t-online.de, Internet: http://www.Ernst-Barlach-Stiftung.de. Head: Dr. Volker Probst
Fine Arts Museum - 1994
Works of artist Ernst Barlach (1870-1938), bequest, literary manuscripts - archives, library 16137

Museum der Stadt Güstrow, Franz-Parr-Pl 7, 18273 Güstrow - T: (03843) 681144. Head: Ira Koch
Local Museum - 1892
Ancient and early history, local history, burgher living style, playbills since 1740 - library 16138

Schloss Güstrow, Staatliches Museum Schwerin, Franz-Parr-Pl 1, 18273 Güstrow - T: (03843) 7520, Fax: 682251, E-mail: otto@museum-schwerin.de, Internet: http://www.museum-schwerin.de. Head: Dr. Regina Erbentraut
Fine Arts Museum / Decorative Arts Museum - 1972
Antique ceramics, maiolicas, glass, hunting weapons, medieval art from Mecklenburg, painting from the Renaissance and the GDR 16139

Gütersloh

Miele-Museum, Carl-Miele-Str 29, 33332 Gütersloh - T: (05241) 892500, Fax: 892090, E-mail: info@miele.de, Internet: http://www.miele.de. Head: Science&Tech Museum
Development of the washing machine, ironing machines, vacuum cleaners, motor bikes and bicycles 16140

Stadtmuseum Gütersloh, Kökerstr 7-11a, 33330 Gütersloh - T: (05241) 26685, Fax: 29072. Head: Heinrich Lakämper-Lührs
Local Museum
Local hist, medical care 16141

Gundelfingen an der Donau

Automobil-Veteranen-Salon, Bächingerstr 68, 89423 Gundelfingen an der Donau - T: (09073) 2575, Internet: http://www.fia.com. Head: Jürgen Mayr
Science&Tech Museum - 1972
Private coll of rare antique automobiles, automobile motors and parts 16142

Gundelsheim, Württemberg

Siebenbürgisches Museum Gundelsheim, Dauerausstellung, Schloss Horneck, 74831 Gundelsheim, Württemberg - T: (06269) 90621, Fax: 422323, E-mail: - siebenbuerg.museum.gundelsheim@t-online.de, Internet: http://www.siebenbuergisches-museum.de
Local Museum - 1968
Paintings, graphic arts, textiles, handicraft 16143

Siebenbürgisches Museum Gundelsheim, Sonderausstellungen, Heilbronner Str 13, 74831 Gundelsheim, Württemberg - T: (06269) 42230, Fax: 422323, E-mail: - siebenbuerg.museum.gundelsheim@t-online.de
Local Museum - 1968
Traditional costumes and textiles, painting, graphics and veduta prints, goldsmith's art, pewter vessel, furniture, pottery and glass 16144

Gunzenhausen

Heimatstuben Weipert und Erzgebirgsschau, Zum Schießwasen 1, 91710 Gunzenhausen - T: (09831) 508109, Fax: 508179
Local Museum
Local hist, handicrafts and folklore 16145

Museum für Vor- und Frühgeschichte, Brunnenstr 1, 91710 Gunzenhausen - T: (09831) 508306, Fax: 508179, E-mail: stadt.gunzenhausen@gunnet.de, Internet: http://www.gunzenhausen.de. Head: Werner Mühlhäußer
Archaeological Museum - 1998 16146

Stadtmuseum Gunzenhausen, Rathausstr 12, 91710 Gunzenhausen - T: (09831) 508306, Fax: 508179, E-mail: stadt.gunzenhausen@gunnet.de. Head: Werner Mühlhäußer
Local Museum - 1921
Paving tiles 16147

Gusow

Museum zur brandenburg-preußischen Geschichte/ Zinnfigurenmuseum, Schloßstr 7, 15306 Gusow - T: (03346) 8725, Fax: 845542, Internet: http://www.schloss-gusow.de
Decorative Arts Museum / Historical Museum
Hist of Brandenburg and Prussia 16148

Zinnfigurenmuseum → Museum zur brandenburg-preußischen Geschichte/ Zinnfigurenmuseum

Gutach, Schwarzwaldbahn

Schwarzwälder Freilichtmuseum Vogtsbauernhof, 77793 Gutach, Schwarzwaldbahn - T: (07831) 93560, Fax: 935629, E-mail: info@vogtsbauernhof.org, Internet: http://www.vogtsbauernhof.org. Head: Dr. Dieter Kauß
Open Air Museum - 1964
Six furnished farmhouses with outbuildings typical of the Black Forest style in the 16th,17th and 18th c - library, archive 16149

Guxhagen

Gedenkstätte Breitenau, Archiv und Ausstellung der Gesamthochschule/Universität Kassel, Brückenstr 12, 34302 Guxhagen - T: (05665) 3533, Fax: 1727. Head: Prof. Dr. Dietfrid Krause-Vilmar
Historic Site / Historical Museum - 1984
Memorial to the victims and persecuted of the concentration camp Breitenau (1940-45), early concentration camp (1933-34), educational Gestapo work camp (1940-45) 16150

Haag, Oberbayern

Museum des Haager Landes, c/o Geschichtsverein Reichsgrafschaft Haag, Im Schloßturm, 83527 Haag, Oberbayern - T: (08072) 8937, 8858, Fax: 373621, E-mail: info@museum-haag.de, Internet: http://www.museum-haag.de
Local Museum - 1986
Local hist, ceramics and folklore 16151

Habichtswald

Original-Dorfschmiede Ehlen, Kohlenstr, 34317 Habichtswald - T: (05606) 9527. Head: Kurt Jordan
Science&Tech Museum - 1993
Complete blacksmith's workshop from 1883 16152

Hachenburg

Landschaftsmuseum Westerwald, Im Burggarten, 57627 Hachenburg - T: (02662) 7456, Fax: 4654, E-mail: info@landschaftsmuseum-ww.de, Internet: http://www.landschaftsmuseum-westerwald.de. Head: Dr. Juliana Köhler
Open Air Museum 16153

Hadamar

Gedenkstätte Hadamar, Mönchberg 8, 65589 Hadamar - T: (06433) 917172, Fax: 917175, E-mail: gedenkstaette-hadamar@LWV-hessen.de. Head: Dr. Georg Lilienthal
Historical Museum / Historic Site - 1983
Memorial site for victims of euthanasia during the NS-regime in WWII - Library, archive 16154

Glasmuseum Hadamar, Gymnasiumstr 4, 65589 Hadamar - T: (06433) 91290, Fax: 912930, E-mail: glasfachschule@region-online.de, Internet: http://www.region-online.de/bildung/glasfach. Head: Hartmut Lieb
Decorative Arts Museum - 1989
Different kinds of glass 16155

Stadtmuseum Hadamar, Schloßpl 2-8, 65589 Hadamar - T: (06433) 890, Fax: 89155. Head: Heinz Will
Fine Arts Museum - 1988
Portraits by Ernst Moritz Engert, paintings and children's books' illustrations by Karl-Wilhelm Diefenbach, paintings and graphic art by Alois Koch 16156

Häuslingen

Asyl der Kunst, Hauptstr 3, 27336 Häuslingen - T: (05165) 2436
Public Gallery
Exhibitions of died artists of the 20th c 16157

Hagen am Teutoburger Wald

Heimatmuseum im Alten Pfarrhaus, Rathaus, 49170 Hagen am Teutoburger Wald - T: (05401) 97744
Local Museum 16158

Hagen bei Bremerhaven

Burg Hagen, Burgallee 1, 27628 Hagen bei Bremerhaven - T: (04746) 6043. Head: Matthias D. Schön
Local Museum
13th c castle, murals, archaeological finds 16159

Hagen, Westfalen

Deutsches Kaltwalzmuseum, Alter Schloßweg 30, 58119 Hagen, Westfalen - T: (02334) 2527, Fax: (02331) 364307, E-mail: kmarsteller@cdw.de
Science&Tech Museum 16160

Deutsches Museum für Schulkunst, Wichernstr 9, 58099 Hagen, Westfalen - T: (02331) 67222, Fax: 963523, E-mail: herhack@aol.com, Internet: http://www.museum-fuer-schulkunst.de. Head: Hermann Hackstein
Fine Arts Museum - 1986 16161

Hohenhof, Museum des Hagener Impulses, Stirnband 10, 58093 Hagen, Westfalen - T: (02331) 55990, Fax: 207402, E-mail: keom@hagen.de, Internet: http://www.keom.de. Head: Dr. Michael Fehr
Fine Arts Museum / Historic Site 16162

Karl Ernst Osthaus-Museum der Stadt Hagen, Hochstr 73, 58095 Hagen, Westfalen - T: (02331) 2073138, Fax: 207402, E-mail: keom@hagen.de, Internet: http://www.keom.de. Head: Dr. Michael Fehr
Fine Arts Museum - 1902
German art from Expressionism to the present: Henry van de Velde, Christian Rohlfs, Emil Schumacher, International contemporary art - archives 16163

Museum Schloß Hohenlimburg, Alter Schloßweg 30, 58119 Hagen, Westfalen - T: (02331) 2072740, Fax: 2072447, E-mail: Historisches.Centrum@stadt-hagen.de, Internet: http://www.hco.hagen.de. Head: Beate Hobein
Local Museum - 1927
Local hist, early and prehist 16164

Stadtmuseum Hagen, Eilper Str 71-75, 58091 Hagen, Westfalen - T: (02331) 2072740, Fax: 2072447, E-mail: Historisches.Centrum@stadt-hagen.de, Internet: http://www.hco.hagen.de. Head: Beate Hobein
Local Museum - 1984
Local history, early and prehistory 16165

Westfälisches Freilichtmuseum Hagen, Landesmuseum für Handwerk und Technik, Mäckingerbach, 58091 Hagen, Westfalen - T: (02331) 78070, Fax: 780720, E-mail: freilichtmuseum-hagen@lwl.org, Internet: http://www.freilichtmuseum-hagen.de. Head: Dr. Michael Dauskardt
Open Air Museum - 1960
60 workshops and factories, many in working condition, illustrating crafts, trades and early industrial techniques from 800 to the Industrial Revolution - library 16166

Hagenow

Museum der Stadt Hagenow, Lange Str 79, 19230 Hagenow - T: (03883) 722042, Fax: 21087
Local Museum - 1974
History of the jews in Hagenow, local history, handicraft 16167

Haidmühle

Bauern- und Waldmuseum, Schwarzenthaler Str 60, Bischofsreuth, 94145 Haidmühle - T: (08550) 241
Agriculture Museum / Natural History Museum - 1975
Agricultural tools 16168

Haiger

Heimatmuseum Haiger, Marktpl 2, 35708 Haiger - T: (02773) 5685
Local Museum - 1978
Geology, early and prehist, town and church hist, trades 16169

Heimatstube Haiger, Ehemalige Dorfschmiede, Dillstr 39, 35708 Haiger Sechshelden - T: (02771) 36216, E-mail: museum@cks-online.de, Internet: http://www.cks-online.de/museum.html
Local Museum - 1978
Objects from village life, trade implements, loom (1755), furniture 16170

Heimatstube Langenaubach, Lähbachstr 1, 35708 Haiger Langenaubach - T: (02773) 5249
Local Museum - 1981
Original furniture, domestic and agricultural implements, clothes and tools, minerals 16171

Leinen- und Spitzenmuseum, Seelbach, Seelbachstr 9, 35708 Haiger - T: (02773) 1789, Fax: 1789, Internet: http://www.haigerseelbach.de. Head: Jan Janzweert
Special Museum - 1983 16172

Haigerloch

Atom Museum, Pfluggasse, 72401 Haigerloch - T: (07474) 69726, Fax: 6068, Internet: http://www.haigerloch.de. Head: E. Fechter
Science&Tech Museum - 1980
Nuclear energy 16173

Galerie im Bürgerhaus, Oberstadtstr 9, 72401 Haigerloch - T: (07474) 69726, Fax: 6068, E-mail: fechter@haigerloch.de, Internet: http://www.haigerloch.de. Head: E. Fechter
Public Gallery 16174

Haimhausen

Heimatmuseum, Rathaus, Hauptstr 15, 85778 Haimhausen - T: (08133) 93030, Fax: 930330, E-mail: gemeinde.haimhausen@haimhausen.de
Local Museum - 1986
Agricultural tools, rustic furniture 16175

Haina, Kloster

Psychiatriemuseum Haina, Kloster, Zentrum für Psychatrie, 35114 Haina, Kloster - T: (0561) 10042277, Fax: 10041277, E-mail: vanja@lwv-hessen.de, Internet: http://www.lwv-hessen.de. Head: Dr. Christina Vanja
Historical Museum - 1992
Hist of the psychiatric hospital from the 16th c and euthanasia during National Socialism to modern therapy, Tischbein family of painters 16176

Hainichen, Sachsen

Gellert-Museum, Oederaner Str 10, 09661 Hainichen, Sachsen - T: (037207) 2498, Fax: 2498, E-mail: admin@hainichen.de, Internet: http://www.hainichen.de. Head: Angelika Fischer
Special Museum - 1985
Writings and memorabilia of Gellert, coll of art of fable - library 16177

Haiterbach

Heimatmuseum Haiterbach, Hohenrainstr 39-41, 72221 Haiterbach - T: (07456) 6960, Fax: 69639
Local Museum - 1969
Handicraft, local hist, agricultural machinery 16178

Halberstadt

Dom und Domschatz Halberstadt, Dompl 16a, 38820 Halberstadt - T: (03941) 24237, Fax: 24237. Head: Dr. Petra Sevrugian
Religious Arts Museum - 1936
Religious art 5th-18th c: treasury, reliquaries, liturgical implements, robes, tapestries, Gothic paintings and sculpture, Carolingian-Gothic manuscripts 16179

Das Gleimhaus, Dompl 31, 38820 Halberstadt - T: (03941) 68710, Fax: 687140, E-mail: gleimhaus@t-online.de, Internet: http://www.gleimhaus.de. Head: Dr. Ute Pott
Special Museum - 1862
Memorabilia on poet J.W.L. Gleim (1719-1803), 18th c intellectual life, portraits, writings, letters, books - library 16180

Museum Heineanum, Museum für Vogelkunde, Dompl 37, 38820 Halberstadt - T: (03941) 551461, Fax: 551469, E-mail: heineanum-hbs@t-online.de. Head: Dr. B. Nicolai
Natural History Museum - 1850
Ornithology, pre-historic saurian - library 16181

Städtisches Museum, Dompl 36, 38820 Halberstadt - T: (03941) 551471/74, Fax: 551048, E-mail: museum.halberstadt@t-online.de, Internet: http://www.halberstadt.de. Head: G. Maseberg
Historical Museum - 1905
Ancient and early finds, natural science coll, local history, Renaissance-baroque culture, paintings, military 16182

Haldensleben

Museum Haldensleben, Breiter Gang, 39340 Haldensleben - T: (03904) 2710, Fax: 2710. Head: Ulrich Hauer
Local Museum - 1910
Geology, ancient and early historic finds, local history, industry, ceramics, household objects and costumes, armaments, paintings, graphics, zoology - library 16183

Halle, Saale

Beatles Museum, Alter Markt 12, 06108 Halle, Saale - T: (0345) 2903900, Fax: 2903908, E-mail: BeatlesMuseum@t-online.de, Internet: http://www.BeatlesMuseum.Halle.de. Head: Rainer Moers
Special Museum - 1989 16184

Christian-Wolff-Haus, Stadtmuseum Halle, Große Märkerstr 10, 06108 Halle, Saale - T: (0345) 2213030, Fax: 2926289, E-mail: Stadtmuseum.halle@t-online.de, Internet: http://www.Stadtmuseum-halle.de. Head: Dr. Michael Platen
Historical Museum - 1954
Local history - library 16185

Die Franckeschen Stiftungen zu Halle, Franckepl 1, Haus 37, 06110 Halle, Saale - T: (0345) 2127400/450, Fax: 2127433, E-mail: leitung@francke-halle.de, Internet: http://www.francke-halle.de. Head: Prof. Dr. Jan-Hendrik Olbertz
Historical Museum / Library with Exhibitions / Natural History Museum
historical library, cabinet of curiosities (Baroque) 16186

Galerie im Volkspark, Burgstr 27, 06114 Halle, Saale - T: (0345) 5238699
Public Gallery 16187

Galerie Marktschlößchen, Marktpl 13, 06108 Halle, Saale - T: (0345) 2029141, Fax: 2032691, E-mail: galerie-marktschloesschen@t-online.de. Head: Ulrich Zeiner
Public Gallery 16188

Galerie Talstrasse, Talstr 23, 06120 Halle, Saale - T: (0345) 5507510, Fax: 5507674, E-mail: talstrasse@t-online.de, Internet: http://www.kunstverein-talstrasse.de. Head: Matthias Rataiczyk
Public Gallery 16189

Geiseltalmuseum der Martin-Luther-Universität, Institut für Geologische Wissenschaften, Domstr 5, 06108 Halle, Saale - T: (0345) 5526100, Fax: 5527179, E-mail: institut@geologie.uni-halle.de, Internet: http://www.geologie.uni-halle.de/gm. Head: Prof. Dr. H. Haubold
Natural History Museum / University Museum - 1934
Fossils, hist, prehist of Geiseltal, brown coal fauna and flora - library 16190

Händel-Haus, Musikmuseum der Stadt Halle, Große Nikolai-Str 5, 06108 Halle, Saale - T: (0345) 500900, Fax: 50090411, E-mail: haendel@halle.de, Internet: http://www.haendelhaus.de. Head: Dr. Edwin Werner
Music Museum - 1948
Birthplace of G.F. Händel (1685-1759) with coll of 700 musical instruments, Samuel Scheidt, Wilhelm Friedemann Bach, Daniel Gottlob Türk, Johann Friedrich Reichardt, Carl Loewe, Robert Franz - library, restauration of historical musical instruments 16191

Landesmuseum für Vorgeschichte Sachsen-Anhalt, Richard-Wagner-Str 9-10, 06114 Halle, Saale - T: (0345) 524730, Fax: 5247351, E-mail: poststelle@lfa.mk.lsa-net.de, Internet: http://www.archlsa.de. Head: Dr. Harald Meller
Archaeological Museum - 1882
Palaeolithic Age, Stone Age, Bronze Age, Iron Age to Early hist of Saxony-Anhalt, anthropology human evolution, medieval town archaeology, archaeozoology - library, archives 16192

Museum für Haustierkunde Julius Kühn, c/o Institut für Tierzucht und Tierhaltung, Adam-Kuckhoff-Str 35, 06108 Halle, Saale - T: (0345) 5522322, Fax: 5527291, E-mail: wussow@landw.uni-halle.de, Internet: http://www.landw.uni-halle.de/lfak/museum/. Head: Prof. Dr. Dr. von Lengerken
Natural History Museum / University Museum / Agriculture Museum
3,000 complete skeletons, 4,000 skulls of domestic animals (old landraces) 16193

Musikinstrumenten-Ausstellung des Händel-Hauses, Am Marktpl, 06108 Halle, Saale - T: (0345) 2025977, Fax: 50090411, E-mail: haendel@halle.de, Internet: http://www.halle.de. Head: Dr. Edwin Werner
Music Museum
Musical instruments, beginning of industrial piano building 16194

Oberburg Giebichenstein, Seebener Str 1, 06114 Halle, Saale - T: (0345) 2025103. Head: Bernd Werner
Historic Site - 1964 16195

Robertinum, Archäologisches Museum der Martin-Luther-Universität, Universitätspl 12, 06099 Halle, Saale - T: (0345) 5524018/024, Fax: 5527069, E-mail: loehr@altertum.uni-halle.de, Internet: http://www.altertum.uni-halle.de. Head: Prof. M. Oppermann
Archaeological Museum - 1845
Ancient art objects, ancient greek vases, cast coll 16196

Schützenhaus Glaucha, Stadtmuseum Halle, Lerchenfeldstr 14, 06110 Halle, Saale - T: (0345) 2926260, Fax: 2926289, E-mail: Stadtmuseum.halle@t-online.de, Internet: http://www.Stadtmuseum-halle.de. Head: Bernd Werner
Local Museum
Town history 16197

Staatliche Galerie Moritzburg Halle, Landeskunstmuseum Sachsen-Anhalt, Friedemann-Bach-Pl 5, 06108 Halle, Saale - T: (0345) 212590, Fax: 2029990, E-mail: poststelle@moritzburg.mk.lsa-net.de, Internet: http://www.moritzburg.halle.de. Head: Dr. Katja Schneider
Fine Arts Museum - 1885
Decorative objects, German painting, 19th-20th c sculpture, 12th-17th c local architectural sculpture, drawings since 15th c, numismatics, 20th c photogr 16198

Technisches Halloren- und Salinenmuseum, Mansfelder Str 52, 06108 Halle, Saale - T: (0345) 2025034, Fax: 2021488. Head: Rüdiger Just
Science&Tech Museum - 1967
Hist of salt, hist of salt workers of Halle 16199

Zoologische Sammlungen des Institutes für Zoologie, Martin-Luther-Universität Halle-Wittenberg, Dompl 4, 06108 Halle, Saale - T: (0345) 5526455, 5526444, Fax: 5527152, E-mail: heidecke@zoologie.uni-halle.de, Internet: http://www.zoologische-sammlungen.uni-halle.de
Natural History Museum - 1769
Mollusks, anthropoda, vertebrata, birds and mammals worldwide 16200

Halle, Westfalen

Museum Halle, Kirchpl 3, 33790 Halle, Westfalen
Local Museum 16201

Hallstadt

Heimatmuseum Hallstadt, Fischergasse 4, 96103 Hallstadt - T: (0951) 7500, 43774, Fax: 75039
Local Museum - 1989
Early and local hist, geological coll, religious folklore and a coll of pencils 16202

Hamburg

Alstertalmuseum, Wellingsbüttler Weg 75a, 22391 Hamburg - T: (040) 5366679
Local Museum 16203

Altonaer Museum in Hamburg, Norddeutsches Landesmuseum, Museumstr 23, 22765 Hamburg, mail addr: Postfach 500125, 22701 Hamburg - T: (040) 428113582, Fax: 428112122, 428112143, E-mail: am@kulturbehoerde.hamburg.de, Internet: http://www.hamburg.de/Altonaer-Museum/. Head: Prof. Dr. Axel Feuß
Local Museum - 1863
Cultural hist, fine arts, crafts and decorative arts, shipping and fishing, geology of North Germany 16204

Botanisches Museum, Martin-Luther-King-Pl 3, 20146 Hamburg - T: (040) 428382378, Fax: 428383335, E-mail: Bfrauendorfe@botanica.iangbot.uni-hamburg.de, Internet: http://www.physnet.uni-hamburg.de/botany/museum_dt.html. Head: Dr. Bernd Frauendorfer
Natural History Museum - 1883
Useful plants, Collectio Fructuum Hamburgense (carpological coll) 16205

Deichtorhallen Hamburg, Deichtorstr 1-2, 20095 Hamburg - T: (040) 321030, Fax: 32103230, E-mail: info@deichtorhallen.de, Internet: http://www.deichtorhallen.de. Head: Zdenek Felix
Fine Arts Museum
International contemporary art 16206

Deutsches Maler- und Lackierer-Museum, Billwerder Billdeich 72, 22113 Hamburg - T: (040) 343887, Fax: 3480625. Head: Joachim Germann
Special Museum - 1984
Stencils and pattern books - library 16207

Deutsches Zollmuseum, Alter Wandrahm 16, 20457 Hamburg - T: (040) 30087611, Fax: 30087620, E-mail: zollmuseum@gmx.de, Internet: http://www.deutsches-zollmuseum.de. Head: Klaus Bente
Special Museum - 1992
History of German customs authority, smuggling and crime prevention in customs work 16208

Eduard Bargheer-Haus, Rutsch 2, 22587 Hamburg - T: (040) 865007, Fax: 86663048, E-mail: nachlass@eduard-bargheer-haus.de, Internet: http://www.eduard-bargheer-haus.de. Head: Dirk Justus, Peter Silze
Public Gallery 16209

Eidelstedter Heimatmuseum, Alte Elbgaustr 12, 22523 Hamburg - T: (040) 5709599, Fax: 5708363
Local Museum 16210

Ernst Barlach Haus, Stiftung Hermann F. Reemtsma, Baron-Voght-Str 50a, Jenischpark, 22609 Hamburg - T: (040) 826085, Fax: 826415, E-mail: info@barlach-haus.de, Internet: http://www.barlach-haus.de. Head: Sebastian Giesen
Fine Arts Museum - 1962
Manuscripts, drawings, graphics, ceramics and sculpture documenting the life and work of Ernst Barlach - library, archive 16211

Erotic Art Museum Hamburg, Nobistor 10a, 22767 Hamburg - T: (040) 31784126, Fax: 31784110, E-mail: eam@erotic-art-museum.hamburg.de, Internet: http://www.erotic-art-museum.hamburg.de. Head: Gisela Schädel
Fine Arts Museum
Erotic art (16th-20th c), Asian art 16212

Flughafen Modellraum, Paul-Bäumer-Pl 3, 22335 Hamburg - T: (040) 50752643, Fax: 50751234
Science&Tech Museum - 1954
1500 models 16213

Fotogalerie Landesbildstelle, Kieler Str 171, 22525 Hamburg - T: (040) 5499306
Fine Arts Museum 16214

Geologisch-Paläontologisches Museum der Universität Hamburg, Bundesstr 55, 20146 Hamburg - T: (040) 41234999
Natural History Museum 16215

Hamburger Kunsthalle, Glockengießerwall, 20095 Hamburg - T: (040) 428545765, Fax: 428542482, E-mail: info@hamburger-kunsthalle.de, Internet: http://www.hamburger-kunsthalle.de. Head: Prof. Dr. Uwe M. Schneede
Fine Arts Museum - 1869
Painting (14th-20th c), 19th and 20th c sculpture, coins, medaillons, graphic arts (14th c to present); Galerie der Gegenwart: modern art from 1960 (Warhol, Nauman and others) - library, print and drawing coll 16216

Hamburger Schulmuseum, Seilerstr 42, 20359 Hamburg - T: (040) 352946, Fax: 31795107, E-mail: hsm@public.uni-hamburg.de, Internet: http://www.hamburgerschulmuseum.de. Head: Prof. Dr. Reiner Lehberger
Historical Museum 16217

Heimatmuseum Wandsbek, Böhmestr 20, 22041 Hamburg - T: (040) 684786, Fax: 68913268. Head: Ilse Fischer
Local Museum
archive 16218

Heine-Haus, Altonaer Museum in Hamburg, Elbchaussee 31, 22765 Hamburg - T: (040) 428112152, Fax: 428112143, E-mail: am@kulturbehoerde.hamburg.de, Internet: http://www.hamburg.de/altonaer-museum. Head: Torkild Hinrichsen
Special Museum / Historic Site 16219

Helms-Museum, Hamburger Museum für Archäologie und die Geschichte Harburgs, Museumspl 2, 21073 Hamburg - T: (040) 428713693, Fax: 428712684, E-mail: hma@kulturbehoerde.hamburg.de, Internet: http://www.hamburg.de/helms-museum. Head: Prof. Dr. Ralf Busch
Local Museum / Museum of Classical Antiquities / Archaeological Museum - 1898
Coll in the areas of prehistory and early history, anthropology, and municipal history - library and archive, education center 16220

Hot Spice Gewürzmuseum, Am Sandtorkai 32, 20457 Hamburg - T: (040) 367989, Fax: 367992, E-mail: mail@hotspice.de, Internet: http://www.hotspice.de. Head: Viola Vierk, Uwe Paap
Special Museum - 1991
60 original spices to be touched, smelt and tasted, herbs 16221

Jenisch-Haus, Museum Großbürgerlicher Wohnkultur, Baron-Voght-Str 50, 22609 Hamburg - T: (040) 828790
Decorative Arts Museum - 1927
Furniture and furnishings illustrating 19th c upper middle class taste (Classicism and Biedermeier), furniture and furnishings from the late Renaissance to the turn of the c (Art Nouveau) 16222

Kindermuseum Hamburg, Achtern Born 127, 22549 Hamburg - T: (040) 41099777, Fax: 41099165, Internet: http://www.Kindermuseum-Hamburg.de. Head: Margot Reinig
Special Museum 16223

Kunsthaus, Klosterwall 15, 20095 Hamburg - T: (040) 335803, Fax: 321732. Head: Claus Mewes
Public Gallery 16224

Kunstraum Farmsen, Berner Heerweg 183, 22159 Hamburg - T: (040) 64558411
Public Gallery 16225

Kunstverein in Hamburg e.V, Klosterwall 23, 20095 Hamburg - T: (040) 322157, Fax: 322159, E-mail: hamburg@kunstverein.de, Internet: http://www.kunstverein.de. Head: Yilmaz Dziewior
Association with Coll 16226

KX., Jarrestr 20, 22303 Hamburg - T: (040) 2792394, Fax: 2792394, E-mail: kx@kx-kampnagel.de, Internet: http://www.kx-kampnagel.de
Public Gallery - 1987 16227

KZ-Gedenkstätte Neuengamme, Jean-Doldier-Weg 39, 21039 Hamburg - T: (040) 4289603, Fax: 42896525, E-mail: info@kz-gedenkstaette-neuengamme.de, Internet: http://www.kz-gedenkstaette-neuengamme.de. Head: Dr. Detlef Garbe
Historic Site / Historical Museum - 1981
Memorial site to the former concentration camp Neuengamme 16228

Mineralogisches Museum der Universität Hamburg, Grindelallee 48, 20146 Hamburg - T: (040) 428382051/58, Fax: 428382422, E-mail: minmushh@public.uni-hamburg.de, Internet: http://www.rrz.uni-hamburg.de/mpi/museum. Head: Dr. J. Schlüter
Natural History Museum - 1843/1969
Meteorites, gems, rocks, minerals 16229

Museum der Arbeit, Wiesendamm 3, 22305 Hamburg - T: (040) 428322364, Fax: 428323179, E-mail: info@museum-der-arbeit.de, Internet: http://www.museum-der-arbeit.de. Head: Prof. Gernot Krankenhagen
Local Museum / Science&Tech Museum - 1990
Labour and culture in the age of industrialization - library, archives 16230

Museum der Elbinsel Wilhelmsburg, Kirchdorfer Str 163, 21109 Hamburg - T: (040) 7540491, Internet: http://www.museum-wilhelmsburg.de. Head: Wolfram Rettig
Local Museum / Agriculture Museum
Agriculture, local history, ship building 16231

Museum für Bergedorf und die Vierlande, Museum für Hamburgische Geschichte, Bergedorfer Schloß, 21029 Hamburg - T: (040) 428912509, Fax: 428912974, E-mail: museum@bergedorf.de, Internet: http://www.schloss-bergedorf.de. Head: Olaf Matthes
Local Museum - 1955
Regional hist - library, archive 16232

Museum für Hamburgische Geschichte, Holstenwall 24, 20355 Hamburg - T: (040) 428412380, Fax: 428433103, E-mail: info@HamburgMuseum.de, Internet: http://www.HamburgMuseum.de. Head: Prof. Dr. Gisela Jaacks
Historical Museum - 1908
Comprehensive coll illustrating all aspects of the social, cultural, political and economic history of Hamburg - library, archive 16233

Museum für Kommunikation Hamburg, Gorch-Fock-Wall 1, 20354 Hamburg - T: (040) 3576360, Fax: 35763620, E-mail: mk.hamburg@t-online.de, Internet: http://www.museumsstiftung.de. Head: Dr. Oliver Rump
Historical Museum / Science&Tech Museum - 1937
Historical telegraph and telephone equipment, cable technology, maritime radio service, postage stamps and postal marks, rubber stamp coll 16234

Museum für Kunst und Gewerbe Hamburg, Steintorpl, 20099 Hamburg - T: (040) 428542732, Fax: 428542834, E-mail: service@mkg-hamburg.de, Internet: http://www.mkg-hamburg.de. Head: Prof. Dr. Wilhelm Hornbostel, Helmut Sander, Dr. Johanna Lessmann
Decorative Arts Museum - 1877
Arts, crafts and design from Antiquity to the 20th c, modern and contemporary art, Asiatic coll, photography coll, textile coll, graphic-design coll, coll of historical Keyboards instruments - education program, library, design labor 16235

Museum für Völkerkunde Hamburg, Rothenbaumchaussee 64, 20148 Hamburg - T: (01805) 308888, Fax: 428482242, E-mail: marketing@voelkerkundemuseum.com, Internet: http://www.voelkerkundemuseum.com. Head: Prof. Dr. Wulf Köpke, Rüdiger Röhricht
Ethnology Museum - 1879
Extensive coll from Middle East and South and East Asia Permanent exhibitions on Europe, Africa, Indonesia, South Seas and America - library, photo archive, witch archive 16236

Museum Mana Kumaka, Kramerkoppel 24, 22041 Hamburg - T: (040) 6560657
Local Museum 16237

Museumsdorf Volksdorf mit Spiekerhus, Im alten Dorfe 46-48, 22359 Hamburg - T: (040) 6039098, Fax: 6039098, E-mail: despieker@volksdorf.net, Internet: http://www.volksdorf.net. Head: Egbert Läufer
Open Air Museum - 1962
Farmhouses from the 17th to the 19th c, 1831 smithy, mid-17th c barn, farm implements and peasant crafts 16238

Museumsgalerie Krokodil, Palmerstr 30, 20535 Hamburg - T: (040) 2508954, Fax: 2503961. Head: Wolf Anschütz
Fine Arts Museum - 1969
20th c art, Neue Sachlichkeit, Bauhaus - archive 16239

Puppenmuseum Falkenstein, Sammlung Elke Dröscher, Grotiusweg 79, 22587 Hamburg - T: (040) 810582, Fax: 818166, E-mail: elke.droescher@t-online.de, Internet: http://www.elke-droescher.de/museu1.html. Head: Elke Dröscher
Decorative Arts Museum - 1986
Dollhauses 16240

Rieck-Haus / Vierländer Freilichtmuseum, Curslacker Deich 284, 21039 Hamburg - T: (040) 7231223
Open Air Museum 16241

Sammlung Warburg im Planetarium, Hindenburgstr 1b, 22303 Hamburg - T: (040) 5149850, Fax: 51498510, E-mail: verwaltung@planetarium-hamburg.de, Internet: http://www.planetarium-hamburg.de. Head: Thomas W. Kraupe
Science&Tech Museum / Historic Site / Natural History Museum - 1930
Pictorial exhibits illustrating the history of astronomy, space travel, and astrology 16242

Sielemuseum der Hamburger Stadtentwässerung, Bei den Sankt Pauli Landungsbrücken 49, 20359 Hamburg - T: (040) 34985055, E-mail: info@hhse.de
Special Museum 16243

Speicherstadtmuseum, Sankt-Annen-Ufer 2, 20457 Hamburg - T: (040) 321191, Fax: 321350, E-mail: -SpeicherstMuseum@aol.com, Internet: http://www.speicherstadtmuseum.de. Head: Henning Rademacher
Science&Tech Museum / Historical Museum 16244

Staats- und Universitätsbibliothek Hamburg Carl von Ossietzky, Von-Melle-Park 3, 20146 Hamburg - T: (040) 428382213, Fax: 428383352, E-mail: auskunft@sub.uni-hamburg.de, Internet: http://www.sub.uni-hamburg.de. Head: Prof. Dr. Peter Rau
Library with Exhibitions 16245

Tabakhistorische Sammlung Reemtsma, Parkstr 51, 22605 Hamburg - T: (040) 82201597, Fax: 82201831, E-mail: claudia.wagner@reemtsma.de, Internet: http://www.reemtsma.com. Head: Prof. Hans Weckerle
Special Museum - 1928
Pipes, paintings, cartoons, smoking utensils, etc. illustrating the history and habit of smoking 16246

Taxameter-Museum, Rothenbaumchaussee 79, 20148 Hamburg - T: (040) 448643, Fax: 453551
Science&Tech Museum 16247

Zirkus und Varieté Archivsammlung Reinhard Tetzlaff, Nienkamp 25, 22453 Hamburg - T: (040) 5523132
Performing Arts Museum 16248

Zoologisches Museum der Universität Hamburg, Martin-Luther-King-Pl 3, 20146 Hamburg - T: (040) 41233880, Fax: 41233937
Natural History Museum 16249

Hameln

Dorfmuseum Tündern, Lange Str 29, 31789 Hameln - T: (05151) 21444
Local Museum - 1909
Domestic and agricultural implements, trades, early and prehist 16250

Museum Hameln, Osterstr 8-9, 31785 Hameln - T: (05151) 202215, Fax: 202815, E-mail: museum@hameln.de, Internet: http://www.hameln.de/museum. Head: Dr. Gesa Snell
Local Museum - 1898
Prehist and early hist, regional and military hist, municipal hist, folklore incl Pied Piper coll, products of historical glass manufactory Lauenstein (18th c) - library, slide coll 16251

Hamm, Westfalen

Gustav-Lübcke Museum, Neue Bahnhofstr 9, 59065 Hamm, Westfalen - T: (02381) 175701, 175714, Fax: 172989, E-mail: gustav-luebcke-museum@stadt.hamm.de, Internet: http://www.hamm.de/gustav-luebcke-museum. Head: Dr. Ellen Schwinzer
Local Museum / Fine Arts Museum / Decorative Arts Museum - 1886
Prehistory and early history, Egyptian, Greek, and Roman art and culture, decorative arts (Gothic to 20th c), European domestic furnishings, Medieval miniatures and sculpture, 17th c Netherlandish painting, graphic arts, numismatics, contemporary art - art library 16252

Naturkundemuseum im Tierpark, Grünstr, Im Tierpark, 59063 Hamm, Westfalen - T: (02381) 57966, 53132, Fax: 580031, E-mail: Tierpark-Hamm@gmx.net. Head: Dr. Hans-Henning Berding
Natural History Museum 16253

Regionales Eisenbahnmuseum der Museumseisenbahn Hamm im Maximilianpark, Grenzweg 76, 59071 Hamm, Westfalen - T: (02381) 102381, Fax: 102405. Head: Karl-Heinz Silber
Science&Tech Museum 16254

Hammelburg

Stadtmuseum Herrenmühle, Turnhouter Str 15, 97762 Hammelburg - T: (09732) 902176, Fax: 902184, E-mail: touristik@hammelburg.de, Internet: http://www.hammelburg.de. Head: Elfriede Böck
Special Museum - 1991
Local agricultural hist, viticulture, cooper's workshop, distillery, mill hist, bread baking, bread and wine in religion and tradition 16255

Hamminkeln

Heimathaus Dingden, Hohe Str 1, 46499 Hamminkeln - T: (02852) 4316. Head: Johannes Vehns
Local Museum 16256

Hanau

Deutsches Goldschmiedehaus, Altstädter Markt 6, 63450 Hanau - T: (06181) 295430, Fax: 20291
Decorative Arts Museum - 1942
Jewellery and gold ornaments, housed in a 16th c half timbered house 16257

Hessisches Puppenmuseum, Parkpromenade 4, Wilhelmsbad, 63454 Hanau - T: (06181) 86212, Fax: 840076, E-mail: hesspuppenmuseum@aol.com, Internet: http://www.hessisches-puppenmuseum.de. Head: Martin Hoppe
Decorative Arts Museum - 1983
European puppets from 500 BC to the present, doll houses and miniature furniture and utensils, puppets from around the world, ancient toys with stress on Japan 16258

Museum Großauheim, Pfortenwingert 4, 63457 Hanau - T: (06181) 573763, 20209, Fax: 257939, E-mail: info@museen-hanau.de, Internet: http://www.museen-hanau.de. Head: Richard Schaffer-Hartmann
Agriculture Museum / Local Museum / Science&Tech Museum / Fine Arts Museum - 1983
Agriculture, industrial hist, steam engines, animal sculptures by August Gaul, paintings by August Penkert 16259

Museum Hanau, Schloß Philippsruhe, 63454 Hanau - T: (06181) 20209, Fax: 257939, E-mail: info@museen-hanau.de, Internet: http://www.museen-hanau.de. Head: Dr. Anton Merk
Decorative Arts Museum - 1967
Faience, silver regional art from the 17th c to the 20th c, town history, paintings 16th-20th c - Paper theatre museum 16260

Museum Schloß Steinheim, Schloßstr 9, 63456 Hanau - T: (06181) 659701, 20209, Fax: 659701, 257939, E-mail: info@museen-hanau.de, Internet: http://www.museen-hanau.de. Head: Sabine Hengster
Local Museum / Archaeological Museum - 1986
Prehistory, early history, town history 16261

Handeloh

Naturkundliches Museum und Schulungsstätte "Alte Schmiede", Hauptstr 42, 21256 Handeloh - T: (04188) 7413. Head: Dr. Klaus Hamann
Natural History Museum - 1994
Landscape formations, animals and plants of Northern Germany 16262

Hanerau-Hademarschen

Heimatmuseum mit ostdeutscher Heimatstube, Im Kloster, 25557 Hanerau-Hademarschen - T: (04872) 2020
Local Museum 16263

Hankensbüttel

Kloster Isenhagen, Klosterstr 2, 29386 Hankensbüttel - T: (05832) 313, Fax: 979408. Head: Barbara Möhring
Religious Arts Museum
13th c Cistercian cloister, medieval chests and wardrobes, embroideries, coll of Bibles and theological works 16264

Hann Münden

Städtisches Museum Hann Münden, Schloßpl 5, 34346 Hann Münden - T: (05541) 75348, Fax: 75402, E-mail: museum@hann.muenden.de, Internet: http://www.hann.muenden/kultur/museum. Head: Martina Krug
Local Museum - 1898
Münden faience (1753-1854), municipal hist, tin foundry and other local trades 16265

Hannover

Blindenmuseum, Landesbildungszentrum für Blinde, Bleekstr 22, 30559 Hannover - T: (0511) 52470, Fax: 5247349, E-mail: webkontakt@lbzs.de, Internet: http://www.lbzs.de. Head: Günter Mosel
Historical Museum - 1995
Education of the blind since 1843, learning materials in braille 16266

Feuerwehrmuseum Hannover, Feuerwehrstr 1, 30169 Hannover - T: (0511) 9121714. Head: Horst Knigge
Science&Tech Museum 16267

Haus der Fotografie, Klewergarten 4, 30449 Hannover - T: (0511) 3535969, Fax: 3535970, E-mail: hausfoto@yahoo.de, Internet: http://www.nananet.de/hausfoto. Head: Wolfgang Bartels
Public Gallery 16268

Heimatmuseum Ahlem, Krugstr 17, 30453 Hannover - T: (0511) 481097
Local Museum - 1982
Furnished rooms and various objects, fossils, grave finds 16269

Herrenhausen-Museum, Alte Herrenhäuser Str 14, 30419 Hannover - T: (0511) 750947, Fax: (05069) 7852. Head: Karl-Ludwig Riechert
Local Museum
Period rooms and paintings from the house of Braunschweig-Lüneburg (late 17th-20th c) 16270

Historisches Museum am Hohen Ufer, Pferdestr 6, 30159 Hannover - T: (0511) 16842352, Fax: 16845003, E-mail: historisches.museum@hannover-stadt.de, Internet: http://www.hannover.de. Head: Dr. Thomas Schwark
Historical Museum - 1903
Local and municipal history, folklore 16271

Kestner Gesellschaft, Goseriede 11, 30159 Hannover - T: (0511) 701200, Fax: 7012020, E-mail: kestner@real-net.de, Internet: http://www.kestner.org. Head: Dr. Carl Haenlein
Public Gallery 16272

Kestner-Museum, Trammpl 3, 30159 Hannover - T: (0511) 16842120, Fax: 16846530, E-mail: kestner-museum@hannover-stadt.de, Internet: http://www.hannover.de. Head: Dr. Wolfgang Schepers
Decorative Arts Museum - 1889
Egyptian art and art of classical antiquity, European applied arts from the Middle Ages to modern times, design, numismatics 16273

Kubus Hannover, Theodor-Lessing-Pl 2, 30159 Hannover - T: (0511) 16845790, Fax: 16845073, E-mail: kubus@hannover-stadt.de, Internet: http://www.hannover.de. Head: Gabriele Ciecior
Public Gallery 16274

Kunsthalle Faust, Zur Bettfedernfabrik 3, 30451 Hannover - T: (0511) 2134860
Public Gallery 16275

Kunstverein Hannover, Sophienstr 2, 30159 Hannover - T: (0511) 324594, Fax: 3632247, E-mail: mail@kunstverein-hannover.de, Internet: http://www.kunstverein-hannover.kulturserver.de. Head: Dr. Stephan Berg
Association with Coll 16276

Mobiles Kindermuseum im Freizeitheim Vahrenwald, Vahrenwalder Str 92, 30165 Hannover - T: (0511) 1683862, Fax: 16843865, E-mail: - Franziska.Schmidt@Hannover-stadt.de, Internet: http://www.hannover.de. Head: Franziska Schmidt
Special Museum 16277

Münzkabinett der Preussag AG, Karl-Wiechert-Allee 4, 30625 Hannover - T: (0511) 56600, Fax: 5661150. Head: Karl Müseler, Ingo Busch
Special Museum
Coll of coins, banknotes concerning mines and mining 16278

Museum für Energiegeschichte(n), Avacon AG, Humboldtstr 32, 30169 Hannover - T: (0511) 9161878, Fax: 9161357, E-mail: museum@avacon.de, Internet: http://www.energiegeschichte.de. Head: Ulrike Nevermann
Science&Tech Museum - 1979
Energy 16279

Niedersächsisches Landesmuseum Hannover, Willy-Brandt-Allee 5, 30169 Hannover - T: (0511) 98075, Fax: 9807640, E-mail: NLMHLG@compuserve.com, Internet: http://www.nlmh.de. Head: Dr. Heide Grape-Albers
Archaeological Museum / Natural History Museum / Fine Arts Museum / Ethnology Museum - 1852
Art, natural hist, prehist, ethnology 16280

Niedersächsisches Münzkabinett der Deutschen Bank, Georgspl 20, 30159 Hannover - T: (0511) 3652577, 3652578, Fax: 3652359, E-mail: 0511365-0033@t-online.de. Head: Dr. Reiner Cunz
Special Museum
Numismatic literature (all topics), coins and medals
Northern Germany and british Empire 16281

Orientteppich-Museum, Georgstr 54, 30159 Hannover - T: (0511) 327566. Head: Dr. Amir Pakzad
Special Museum
Carpets from the Middle East 16282

Sammlung Dr. Berkowitz, Münzkabinett der Stadt Hannover, Raschpl 4, 30161 Hannover - T: (0511) 3462580, Fax: 3462583, E-mail: ssk-hannover@t-online.de, Internet: http://www.stadtsparkasse-hannover.de. Head: R. Kalmus
Special Museum 16283

Sprengel Museum Hannover, Kurt-Schwitters-Pl, 30169 Hannover - T: (0511) 16843875, Fax: 16845093, E-mail: sprengel-museum@hannover-stadt.de, Internet: http://www.sprengel-museum.de. Head: Prof. Dr. Ulrich Krempel
Fine Arts Museum - 1979
20th c sculpture, painting and graphic art (Picasso, Niki de Saint Phalle, Léger, Klee, Beckmann, Nolde, Schwitters) nouveaux realisme minimal art, new figuratives and photographie - library, photo gallery 16284

Theatermuseum Hannover, Prinzenstr 9, 30159 Hannover - T: (0511) 99992040, Fax: 99992940. Head: Dr. Carsten Niemann
Performing Arts Museum 16285

Veterinärmedizinhistorisches Museum der Tierärztlichen Hochschule Hannover, Bischofsholer Damm 15, 30173 Hannover - T: (0511) 8567503, Fax: 8567676, Internet: http://www.tiho-hannover.de/einricht/geschich/index.htm, http://www.vethis.de. Head: Prof. Dr. Dr. Johann Schäffer
Special Museum - 1973
History of veterinary medicine in Germany, history of the Hannover Veterinary College, military veterinary medicine - library 16286

Wilhelm-Busch-Museum Hannover, Deutsches Museum für Karikatur und kritische Grafik, Georgengarten 1, 30167 Hannover - T: (0511) 16999916, Fax: 7011222, E-mail: information@wilhelm-busch.museum.de, Internet: http://www.wilhelm-busch-museum.de. Head: Dr. Hans Joachim Neyer
Fine Arts Museum - 1937
Paintings, drawings, original wood blocks, first editions and memorabilia of Wilhelm Busch, caricature and critical graphics coll of national and international architects - library, archive 16287

Harburg

Schloss Harburg, Burgstr 1, 86655 Harburg - T: (09080) 96860, Fax: 968666, E-mail: burg-harburg@fuerst-wallerstein.de, Internet: http://www.fuerst-wallerstein.de. Head: Fürst zu Oettingen-Wallerstein
Historical Museum / Historic Site 16288

Hardegsen

Ellermeiers Burgmannshof, Baudenkmal und Geigenmuseum, Burgstr 4, 37181 Hardegsen - T: (05505) 5413, E-mail: ellermeier@debitel.net, Internet: http://www.sumerisches-glossar.de. Head: Dr. Friedrich Ellermeier
Library with Exhibitions / Music Museum / Historic Site
Hist of the castle, violin-making - theologic and old orintal research centre 16289

Hardheim

Erfatal-Museum Hardheim, Schloßpl 5, 74736 Hardheim - T: (06283) 5847, 5832, Fax: 5855, E-mail: museum@erfatal-museum.de, Internet: http://www.erfatal-museum.de. Head: Peter Wanner
Local Museum - 1922
Local hist, aeronautics, Walter Hohmann 16290

Haren

Mühlenmuseum Haren (Ems), Landegger Str, 49733 Haren - T: (05932) 2858, 6196, Fax: (05931) 44446, E-mail: wilhmenke@aol.com, Internet: http://www.haren.de/heimat.htm. Head: Wilhelm Menke
Science&Tech Museum - 1980
Mill hist, grinding techniques 16291

Schiffahrtsmuseum Haren (Ems), Kanalstr, 49733 Haren - T: (05932) 5843. Head: Reinhard Wessels
Science&Tech Museum
Shipbuilding techniques 16292

Harsefeld

Museum für Kloster- und Heimatgeschichte, Am Amtshof 3, 21698 Harsefeld - T: (04164) 6910, E-mail: touristinfo@harsefeld.de, Internet: http://www.harsefeld.de
Local Museum / Archaeological Museum / Religious Arts Museum
Grave finds, architectural fragments, hist of the cloister 16293

Harsum

Gemeinde-Heimatmuseum Harsum, Opfergasse 3, Borsum, 31177 Harsum - T: (05127) 4302
Local Museum - 1994
Historical development and topography, folk art, trade workshops 16294

Hartenstein bei Zwickau

Museum Burg Stein, Stein 1, 08118 Hartenstein bei Zwickau - T: (037605) 6296, Fax: 76420. Head: Gerd Eigler
Historical Museum - 1954
Castle and regime history since 12th c, armaments, local and crafts history, medieval law, Paul Fleming memorabilia 16295

Haselünne

Brennereimuseum Haselünne, c/o Der Berentzen-Hof GmbH, Ritterstr 7, 49740 Haselünne - T: (05961) 502556, Fax: 502558, E-mail: berentzenhof@berentzen.de, Internet: http://www.berentzen.de
Science&Tech Museum - 1982
Corn schnaps distillery, cellars 16296

Haselünner Heimathäuser, Lingener Str, 49740 Haselünne - T: (05961) 502214
Open Air Museum - 1932
Stone Age finds, farm and domestic implements, coins from the Ems region, workrooms of early craftsmen (blacksmith, barrel maker, shoemaker) - library 16297

Haslach

Hansjakobmuseum im Freihof, Hansjakobstr 17, 77716 Haslach - T: (07832) 4715. Head: Manfred Hildenbrand
Special Museum - 1960
Memorabilia of the writer politician and priest Heinrich Hansjakob (1837-1916) 16298

Schwarzwälder Trachtenmuseum, Klosterstr 1, 77716 Haslach - T: (07832) 706172, Fax: 706179, E-mail: info@haslach.de. Head: Alois Krafczyk
Folklore Museum - 1980
Original peasant costumes from the Black Forest and Upper Rhein region, costume accessories 16299

Haßfurt

Brauerei-Museum, Unterer Stadtturm, Hauptstr 77, 97437 Haßfurt - T: (09521) 3031
Science&Tech Museum 16300

Haßmersheim

Burgmuseum Burg Guttenberg, Burgstr 1, 74855 Haßmersheim - T: (06266) 91020, Fax: 91021, E-mail: info@burg-guttenberg.de, Internet: http://www.burg-guttenberg.de. Head: Freiherr von Gemmingen
Local Museum - 1949
History of the fortress and environs, tin figures, weapons and armory, hunting trophies, porcelain, documents (14th-19th c) - library 16301

Hatten

Druckereimuseum, Sandkrug, Astruper Str 42, 26209 Hatten - T: (04481) 6903, Fax: 6538. Head: Horst Kolter
Science&Tech Museum - 1989
Printing workshop with various machines and objects 16302

Schmiedemuseum, Sandweg 23, 26209 Hatten - T: (04481) 7606, Fax: 7734
Science&Tech Museum 16303

Hattingen

Bauernhausmuseum Hattingen, An der Kemnade 10, 45527 Hattingen - T: (02324) 30268, Fax: (0234) 5160010, E-mail: museum@bochum.de, Internet: http://www.bochum.de/museum. Head: Dr. Hans Günter Golinski
Local Museum 16304

Kulturgeschichtliches Museum Bügeleisenhaus, Haldenpl 1, 45525 Hattingen - T: (02324) 54318, Fax: 570477, Internet: http://vereine.freepage.de/heimatverein.hattingen. Head: Petra Kamburg
Local Museum - 1962 16305

Ostasiatika-Sammlung Ehrich, Museum Bochum, An der Kemnade 10, 45527 Hattingen - T: (02324) 30268, Fax: (0234) 5160010, E-mail: museum@bochum.de, Internet: http://www.bochum.de/museum. Head: Dr. Hans Günter Golinski
Fine Arts Museum 16306

Regionalgeschichtliche Sammlung mit Musikinstrumentensammlung Hans und Hede Grumbt Wasserburg Haus Kemnade, An der Kemnade 10, 45527 Hattingen - T: (02324) 30268, Fax: (0234) 5160010, E-mail: museum@bochum.de, Internet: http://www.bochum.de/museum. Head: Dr. Hans Günter Golinski
Local Museum / Music Museum
Musical instruments 16307

Stadtmuseum Hattingen, Marktpl 1-3, 45527 Hattingen - T: (02324) 681610, Fax: 204681629, E-mail: stadtmuseum@hattingen.de, Internet: http://www.stadtmuseum.hattingen.de. Head: Petra Kamburg
Local Museum - 2001 16308

Wasserburg Haus Kemnade, Museum Bochum, An der Kemnade 10, 45527 Hattingen - T: (02324) 30268, Fax: (0234) 5160010, E-mail: museum@bochum.de, Internet: http://www.bochum.de/museum. Head: Dr. Hans Günter Golinski
Historical Museum 16309

Hausach

Moler hiisli, Breitenbachstr 36, 77756 Hausach - T: (07831) 7970, Fax: 7957, E-mail: verkersamt@hausach.de
Local Museum - 1985
Memorabilia of the painter and dialect poet Eugen Falk-Breitenbach (1903-1979) 16310

Museum im Herrenhaus, Hauptstr 1, 77756 Hausach - T: (07831) 1483, Fax: 7956, E-mail: spinnerh@t-online.de. Head: Helmut Spinner
Local Museum - 1985
Local hist 16311

Hausen im Wiesental

Dorfmuseum Hausen im Wiesental, Heimathaus des alemannischen Dichters J. P. Hebel, Bahnhofstr 1, 79688 Hausen im Wiesental - T: (07622) 68730, Fax: 687399
Local Museum - 1960
Documents, manuscripts, letters, contracts, original furnishings and other memorabilia of J.P. Hebel, housed in the poet's home (built 1562) 16312

Hausen ob Verena

Kunstmuseum Hohenkarpfen, Hofgut Hohenkarpfen, 78595 Hausen ob Verena - T: (07424) 4017, Fax: 504425, E-mail: info@kunststiftung-hohenkarpfen.de, Internet: http://www.kunststiftung-hohenkarpfen.de. Head: Prof. Dr. Friedemann Maurer
Fine Arts Museum - 1986
Landscape painting (19th-20th c) 16313

Hausen, Oberfranken

Dorfmuseum im Greifenhaus, Dr.-Kupfer-Str 4, 91353 Hausen, Oberfranken - T: (09191) 73720, Fax: 737221, E-mail: gemeinde@hausen.de, Internet: http://www.hausen.de
Local Museum - 1969
Town hist, religious folklore and rustic furniture 16314

Hausham

Bergbaumuseum, Rathausstr 2, 83734 Hausham - T: (08026) 39090, Fax: 390924, Internet: http://www.hausham.de
Science&Tech Museum - 1977
Hist of mining 16315

Hauzenberg

Museum und Besucherbergwerk der Graphit Kropfmühl AG, Langheinrichstr 1, 94051 Hauzenberg - T: (08586) 6090, Fax: 609111
Science&Tech Museum - 1982
Black-lead mining 16316

Havelberg

Heimat-Naturmuseum Untere Havel, Sandauer Str 1, 39539 Havelberg - T: (039387) 88266
Natural History Museum 16317

Prignitz-Museum Havelberg, Am Dom, 39539 Havelberg - T: (039387) 21422, Fax: 88778, Internet: http://www.Prignitz-Museum.de. Head: Frank Hoche
Local Museum - 1904
Ancient and early hist, hist of the city, Cathedral hist, religious arts, Roman Gothic cathedral and monastery complex 16318

Havixbeck

Droste-Museum, Burg Hülshoff, Schonebeck 6, 48329 Havixbeck - T: (02507) 1052, E-mail: vvh@havixbeck.de, Internet: http://www.havixbeck.de/vvh/
Special Museum 16319

Haynrode

Dorfmuseum Haynrode, Hagenstr 1, 37339 Haynrode - T: (036077) 21056
Local Museum 16320

Hebertsfelden

Heimatmuseum Hebertsfelden, Bahnhofstr 3, 84332 Hebertsfelden - T: (08721) 96360
Local Museum - 1988 16321

Hechingen

Alte Synagoge, Goldschmiedstr 20, 72379 Hechingen - T: (07471) 6628, Fax: 933232. Head: L. Vees, K.H. Buckle
Religious Arts Museum / Local Museum - 1991
Jewish hist in Hechingen 16322

Römisches Freilichtmuseum, Stein, 72379 Hechingen - T: (07471) 6400, 3614, Fax: 14805, E-mail: GerdSchollian@swol.de, Internet: http://www.villa-rustica.de. Head: Gerd Schollian
Open Air Museum - 1991
Roman Portikusvilla 16323

Städtisches Museum, Schloßpl 5, 72379 Hechingen - T: (07471) 621847, Fax: 940108. Head: Helga Ciriello
Local Museum
Hohenzollerische coll, town history, Steuben exhibition, room of partnertown Oels 16324

Heeslingen

Bördenheimatmuseum Heeslingen, Bremer Str 2, 27404 Heeslingen - T: (04281) 7795
Local Museum
Folk life and costumes, hist of trade and crafts 16325

Heide, Holstein

Klaus-Groth-Museum, Lüttenheid 48, 25746 Heide, Holstein - T: (0481) 63742, Fax: 65211, E-mail: stadtarchiv@stadt-heide.de, Internet: http://www.heide-nordsee.de. Head: Dr. Telse Lubitz

Special Museum - 1914
Music coll of Doris and Klaus Groth, Biedermeier furniture, memorabilia of the poet Klaus Groth - archive, library 16326

Museum für Dithmarscher Vorgeschichte, Heider Heimatmuseum, Brahmsstr 8, 25746 Heide, Holstein - T: (0481) 2183, Fax: 2183, E-mail: museum-heide@dithmarschen.de, Internet: http://www.dithmarschen.de. Head: Dr. Volker Arnold
Archaeological Museum / Local Museum - 1904
Ceramics 16327

Heideck

Heimatkundliche Sammlung, Rathaus, Marktpl 24, 91180 Heideck - T: (09177) 49400, Fax: 494040
Local Museum
Local hist 16328

Heidelberg

Antikenmuseum und Abgußsammlung des Archäologischen Instituts der Universität Heidelberg, Marstallhof 4, 69117 Heidelberg - T: (06221) 542512, 542515, Fax: 543385, E-mail: antikenmuseum@urz.uni-heidelberg.de, Internet: http://www.uni-heidelberg.de/institute/fak8/arch/institut/sammlung.htm. Head: Prof. Tonio Hölscher
Archaeological Museum - 1848
Decorative arts from classical Greece, Italy and Cyprus (4th mill BC to 3rd c AD), painted Greek vases, terracottas and bronzes, casts of monumental antique sculpture, Greek coins - library, slide coll 16329

Bonsai Museum Heidelberg, Mannheimer Str 401, 69123 Heidelberg - T: (06221) 84910, Fax: 849130, E-mail: Info@bonsai-centrum.de. Head: Paul Lesniewicz
Natural History Museum - 1986
Bonsai forests from Japan, China, Taiwan, the USA and Europe 16330

Deutsches Apotheken-Museum im Heidelberger Schloß, Schloßhof 1, 69117 Heidelberg - T: (06221) 25880, Fax: 181762, E-mail: - deutsches_apotheken_museum@t-online.de, Internet: http://www.deutsches-apotheken-museum.de. Head: Elisabeth Huwer
Special Museum - 1937
Documents, cabinets, instruments and equipment illustrating the history of drugs and apothecaries - library, picture archive 16331

Deutsches Verpackungs-Museum, Hauptstr 22, 69117 Heidelberg - T: (06221) 21361, Fax: (0611) 8410766, E-mail: info@verpackungsmuseum.de, Internet: http://www.verpackungsmuseum.de. Head: Hans-Georg Böcher
Special Museum 16332

Heidelberger Kunstverein, Hauptstr 97, 69117 Heidelberg - T: (06221) 184086, Fax: 164162, E-mail: hdkv@hdkv.de, Internet: http://www.hdkv.de. Head: Hans Gercke
Public Gallery 16333

Heimatmuseum Kirchheim, Schäfergasse 58, 69124 Heidelberg - T: (06221) 781840. Head: D. Neuer
Local Museum - 1982
Local hist, tools, agricultural implements 16334

Kurpfälzisches Museum der Stadt Heidelberg, Hauptstr 97, 69117 Heidelberg - T: (06221) 583400/02, Fax: 583490, E-mail: - kurpfaelzischesmuseum@heidelberg.de. Head: Dr. Frieder Hepp
Fine Arts Museum / Local Museum - 1879
European painting, sculpture and graphic arts, archaeology of the Rhein-Neckar region, art and history of the former Palatinat, Frankenthal porcelain - library 16335

Museum für Sakrale Kunst und Liturgie, Jesuitenkirche, Richard-Hauser-Pl, 69117 Heidelberg - T: (06221) 166391, Fax: 475622. Head: Beatrice Fritz
Religious Arts Museum 16336

Museum Geologie/Paläontologie, Im Neuenheimer Feld 234, 69120 Heidelberg - T: (06221) 546047, Fax: 545503, E-mail: noor.farsan@urz.uni-heidelberg.de. Head: Dr. N.M. Farsan
Natural History Museum - 1970 16337

Museum Haus Cajeth, Haspelgasse 12, 69117 Heidelberg - T: (06221) 24466, Fax: 24460. Head: Egon Hassbecker
Fine Arts Museum - 1982
Primitive painting of the 20th c, art brut, art of mentally ill persons, art of 'outsiders' 16338

Reichspräsident-Friedrich-Ebert-Gedenkstätte, Untere Str 27, 69117 Heidelberg - T: (06221) 91070, Fax: 910710, E-mail: friedrich@ebert-gedenkstaette.de, Internet: http://www.ebert-gedenkstaette.de. Head: Ulrich Graf
Historical Museum / Historic Site - 1989
Memorabilia of the politician Friedrich Ebert (1871-1925) in his birthplace - library, archive 16339

Sammlung des Ägyptologischen Instituts, Universität Heidelberg, Marstallhof 4, 69117 Heidelberg - T: (06221) 542536, Fax: 542551, E-mail: Erika.Feucht@urz.uni-heidelberg.de, Internet: http://www.uni-heidelberg.de/institute/fak8/aegy. Head: Prof. Dr. E. Feucht
Fine Arts Museum - 1914
Egyptian arts and crafts from prehistoric to Coptic period - library, slide coll 16340

Sammlung Prinzhorn, Psychiatrische Universitätsklinik Heidelberg, Voßstr 2, 69115 Heidelberg - T: (06221) 564492, Fax: 561723, E-mail: Bettina_Brand@med.uni-heidelberg.de, Internet: http://www.prinzhorn.uni-hd.de. Head: Dr. Bettina Brand-Claussen
Fine Arts Museum / Special Museum - 1919
Art made in psychiatric institutions from 1880-1930 16341

Schloß Heidelberg, Schloßhof 1, 69117 Heidelberg - T: (06221) 53840, Fax: 167702. Head: Kendel
Decorative Arts Museum
Furniture, tapestries, tin and ceramics (16th-18th c), gigantic wine barrel from 1751 16342

Textilmuseum Max Berk, Brahmsstr 8, 69118 Heidelberg - T: (06221) 800317, Fax: 809657, E-mail: textilmuseum.mb@t-online.de. Head: Jürgen H. Winter
Special Museum - 1978
Historical garments, textile art, tools, antique quilts - library 16343

Völkerkundemuseum der von Portheim-Stiftung, Hauptstr 235, 69117 Heidelberg - T: (06221) 22067, Fax: 914370. Head: Dr. Margareta Pavaloi
Ethnology Museum - 1919
Art and culture of non-European societies 16344

Zoologisches Museum der Universität Heidelberg, Im Neuenheimer Feld 230, 69120 Heidelberg - T: (06221) 545656, Fax: 544913, E-mail: volker.storch@urz.uni-heidelberg.de, Internet: http://www.zoo.uni-heidelberg.de. Head: Prof. Dr. Volker Storch
Natural History Museum - 1819
Comparative anatomy of vertebrates, Middle European birds, Australian mammals and birds, insect coll 16345

Heidenheim an der Brenz

Kunstmuseum Heidenheim, Marienstr 4, 89518 Heidenheim an der Brenz - T: (07321) 327392, Fax: 327689, E-mail: kunstmuseum@heidenheim.com, Internet: http://www.kunstmuseum.heidenheim.com. Head: Dr. René Hirner
Fine Arts Museum - 1989
Poster and Print Coll of Picasso 16346

Museum für Kutschen, Chaisen, Karren, Zweigmuseum des Württembergischen Landesmuseums Stuttgart, Schloß Hellenstein, Fruchtkasten, 89522 Heidenheim an der Brenz - T: (07321) 327394, E-mail: heike.schmid@heidenheim.de. Head: Thomas Brune
Science&Tech Museum - 1987
Carriages and vehicles (1720-1940), social hist of transportation 16347

Museum im Römerbad, Theodor-Heuss-Str 3, 89518 Heidenheim an der Brenz - T: (07321) 327397, Fax: 327696. Head: P. Heinzelmann
Archaeological Museum - 1984
Roman finds 16348

Museum Schloss Hellenstein, Schloss Hellenstein, 89522 Heidenheim an der Brenz, mail addr: Postfach 1146, 89501 Heidenheim an der Brenz - T: (07321) 43381, Fax: 327505, E-mail: helmut.weimert@heidenheim.de. Head: Dr. Helmut Weimert
Local Museum - 1901
Local prehist and ancient hist, development of local industry and trades, folklore and country culture, Indian coll, beetle coll, Southern German and alpine sculpture (Gothic and Baroque) 16349

Heidenheim, Mittelfranken

Heimat- und Hafnermuseum, Ringstr 8a, 91719 Heidenheim, Mittelfranken - T: (09833) 241, 209, Fax: 1780, 5634
Local Museum - 1985
Pottery, agricultural tools 16350

Heilbad Heiligenstadt

Eichsfelder Heimatmuseum, Kollegiengasse 10, 37308 Heilbad Heiligenstadt - T: (03606) 612618, Fax: 4004
Local Museum - 1932
Geology, ancient hist, local and regional hist, peasant crafts and living style, costumes, native birds, religious sculpture - library 16351

Literaturmuseum Theodor Storm, Am Berg, Mainzer Haus, 37308 Heilbad Heiligenstadt - T: (03606) 613794, Fax: 613794. Head: Antonia Günther
Special Museum - 1988
Memorabilia of Storm, his works, portraits, book illustrations, films, memorial room for Heine's baptism in 1825 at St Martin's 16352

Heilbronn

Archäologie-Museum, Städtische Museen Heilbronn, Deutschhofstr 6, 74072 Heilbronn - T: (07131) 562295, 563144, Fax: 563194, E-mail: - staedtischemuseenheilbronn@hst.net, Internet: http://web.museen.de/heilbronn/staedtische.museen. Head: Dr. Andreas Pfeiffer
Local Museum - 1878
Prehistory and ancient history 16353

Besucherbergwerk Bad Friedrichshall-Kochendorf, Salzgrund 67, 74076 Heilbronn, mail addr: c/o Südwestdeutsche Salzwerke AG, Postfach 3161, 74021 Heilbronn - T: (07136) 271303, Fax: 271200, E-mail: info@salzwerke.de, Internet: http://www.salzwerke.de. Head:
Science&Tech Museum
History of salt mining 16354

Kunstverein Heilbronn, Allee 28, Harmonie, 74072 Heilbronn - T: (07131) 83970, Fax: 83972, E-mail: - kunstverein.heilbronn@t-online.de. Head: Dr. Matthia Löbke
Public Gallery 16355

Naturhistorisches Museum, Städtische Museen Heilbronn, Kramstr 1, 74072 Heilbronn - T: (07131) 562302, Fax: 562859, E-mail: - staedtischemuseenheilbronn@hst.net, Internet: http://web.museen.de/heilbronn/staedtische.museen. Head: Dr. Andreas Pfeiffer
Natural History Museum
Natural siences, flora and fauna since Trias era 16356

Neckarschiffahrts-Museum und Weinbau, Städtische Museen Heilbronn, Frankfurter Str 75, 74072 Heilbronn - T: (07131) 562295, Fax: 563194, E-mail: staedtischemuseenheilbronn@hst.net, Internet: http://web.museen.de/heilbronn/staedtische.museen. Head: Dr. Andreas Pfeiffer
Historical Museum
2000 years of water transportation at river Neckar 16357

Skulpturenmuseum, Städtische Museen Heilbronn, Deutschhofstr 6, 74072 Heilbronn - T: (07131) 562295, 563144, Fax: 563194, E-mail: - staedtischemuseenheilbronn@hst.net, Internet: http://web.museen.de/heilbronn/staedtische.museen. Head: Dr. Andreas Pfeiffer
Fine Arts Museum
19th-20th c art, mainly Franconian artists 16358

Städtische Museen Heilbronn, Deutschhofstr 6, 74072 Heilbronn - T: (07131) 562295, 563141, Fax: 563194, E-mail: - staedtischemuseenheilbronn@hst.net, Internet: http://web.museen.de/heilbronn/staedtische.museen. Head: Dr. Andreas Pfeiffer
Local Museum - 1878
Natural sciences, prehist and ancient hist, municipal hist, 19th and 20th c art, mainly Franconian artists, Neckar water transportation 16359

Heiligenberg

Schloß Heiligenberg, 88633 Heiligenberg - T: (07554) 242. Head: Norbert Wittke
Local Museum 16360

Heiligenhafen

Heimatmuseum Heiligenhafen, Thulboden 11a, 23774 Heiligenhafen - T: (04362) 3876, Fax: 3876, Internet: http://www.schleswig-holstein.de/museen/reg_hei/heimu_heiligenhafen.html. Head: Petra Mischke
Local Museum - 1954/1992
Carl Bütje Coll (stone age), tools, fossils, models of sailing ships 16361

Heinade

Wald- und Lönsmuseum, Sollingstr, 37627 Heinade - T: (05564) 8672
Natural History Museum 16362

Heinersbrück

Sorbische Bauernstube, Hauptstr 2, 03185 Heinersbrück - T: (035601) 82663
Folklore Museum 16363

Heinsberg

Kreismuseum Heinsberg, Hochstr 21, 52525 Heinsberg - T: (02452) 134027, Fax: 134095, E-mail: museum@kreis-heinsberg.de. Head: Dr. Rita Müllejans-Dickmann
Local Museum - 1927 16364

Heinsen

Heimat- und Schiffahrtsmuseum, Weserstr 21, 37649 Heinsen - T: (05535) 604
Local Museum / Science&Tech Museum - 1982
Shipping on the river Weser, rafting 16365

Heitersheim

Johanniter- und Maltesermuseum, Malteserschloß, 79423 Heitersheim - T: (07634) 4020. Head: F. Fünfgeld
Religious Arts Museum - 1984
Hist of the Order of the Knights of Malta, uniforms, paintings, coins - Library 16366

Heldrungen

Thomas-Müntzer-Gedenkstätte, Wasserburg, 06577 Heldrungen - T: (034673) 91224. Head: Frank Krüger
Historical Museum - 1955
Local and regional history, the German Peasant War 1524-25 16367

Helmbrechts

Oberfränkisches Textilmuseum, Münchberger Str 17, 95233 Helmbrechts - T: (09252) 92430, Fax: 70111. Head: Heinz König
Science&Tech Museum - 1923/1992
Pre-WWI textiles, documentation on crafts and guilds, stone coll, pattern books, clothes, scarfs - archive 16368

Helmstedt

Helmstedter Freundeskreis für Paramentik und christliche Kunst, Gustav-Steinbrecher-Str 11, 38350 Helmstedt - T: (05351) 8031, Fax: 542160, E-mail: Haus-Kloth@t-online.de. Head: Kloth Ernst-Adolf
Association with Coll 16369

Kloster Sankt Marienberg, Klosterstr 14, 38350 Helmstedt - T: (05351) 6769, Fax: 6781, E-mail: - klostermarienberg@gmx.de. Head: M. von Veltheim
Religious Arts Museum - 1984
In 12th c Sankt Marienberg monastery, medieval religious ornaments, 20th c religious art 16370

Kreis- und Universitätsmuseum Helmstedt, Alte Universität, Collegienpl 1, 38350 Helmstedt - T: (05351) 120461, Fax: 1211627, E-mail: - Landkreis.Helmstedt@t-online.de, Internet: http://www.helmstedt.de. Head: Marita Sterly
Local Museum
Hist of the University 16371

Kreisheimatmuseum → Kreis- und Universitätsmuseum Helmstedt

Museumshof Emmerstedt, Leineweberstr 3, 38350 Helmstedt - T: (05351) 34843, Fax: 31206
Ethnology Museum / Folklore Museum - 1991
Originally equipped and furnished rooms, folk costumes, native birds, toys, beekeeping, agricultural machines and implements, trade workshops 16372

Zonengrenz-Museum Helmstedt, Südertor 6, 38350 Helmstedt - T: (05351) 1211133, Fax: 1211627, E-mail: landkreis.helmstedt@t-online.de. Head: Marita Sterly
Local Museum - 1994
Former East-West German border, its development and fall in 1989, various objects (uniforms, certificates, newspaper clippings) 16373

Hemau

Spielzeugmuseum, Altes Rathaus, Stadtpl 4, 93155 Hemau - T: (09491) 94000, 774, 1300
Decorative Arts Museum - 1995 16374

Hemer

Felsenmeer-Museum, Hönnetalstr 21, 58675 Hemer - T: (02372) 10719
Local Museum
Local hist, geology, natural hist 16375

Hengersberg

Spital Hengersberg, Passauer Str 38, 94491 Hengersberg - T: (09901) 2809, Fax: 930740, E-mail: markt@hengersberg.de, Internet: http://www.hengersberg.de
Fine Arts Museum - 1997
Contemporary art of Bavaria 16376

Hennef

Harmonium-Museum, Sammlung Thein, Mechthildisstr 12, 53773 Hennef - T: (02248) 445533. Head: Udo Thein
Music Museum - 1999
47 Harmoniums - library, archive 16377

Turmmuseum Stadt Blankenberg, 53773 Hennef - T: (02248) 2511
Local Museum 16378

Heppenheim

Museum für Stadtgeschichte und Volkskunde, Amtsgasse 5, 64646 Heppenheim - T: (06252) 13285. Head: Ulrich Lange
Local Museum / Ethnology Museum
Town hist, ethnology 16379

Ostdeutsche Kultur- und Heimatstuben mit Schönbacher Stube, Amtsgasse 5, 64646 Heppenheim - T: (06252) 2226. Head: Alfred Gafert
Local Museum - 1976
Hist and culture of east Germany and other regions of expulsion of Germans - Library 16380

Herbertingen

Heuneburgmuseum, Binzwanger Str 14, 88518 Herbertingen - T: (07586) 1679, Fax: 1679, Internet: http://www.dhm.de/museen/heuneburg
Archaeological Museum - 1985
Archeological finds 16381

Herborn, Hessen

Herborner Heimatmuseum, Schulhofstr, 35745 Herborn, Hessen - T: (02772) 708216. Head: Joachim Wienecke
Local Museum
Memorabilia of the "Hohe Schule" (Protestant academy for priests and civil servants, 1584-1817), Jan Amos Comenius 16382

Naturkunde-Museum K.-W. Donsbach, Alte Hauptstr 13, 35745 Herborn, Hessen - T: (02772) 2241
Natural History Museum 16383

Herbrechtingen

Heimatmuseum, Eselsburger Str 26, 89542 Herbrechtingen - T: (07324) 6710
Local Museum - 1984
Living and working conditions in 19th c 16384

Museum der Donauschwaben, Elsterweg 5, 89542 Herbrechtingen - T: (07324) 3090, Fax: 3090
Local Museum 16385

Herbstein

Fastnachtsmuseum, Manggasse 5, 36358 Herbstein - T: (06643) 221. Head: Erwin Ruhl
Folklore Museum - 1983
Carnival costumes and customs 16386

Herford

Daniel-Pöppelmann-Haus, Museum der Stadt Herford, Deichtorwall 2, 32052 Herford - T: (05221) 189689, 132213, Fax: 132252, E-mail: - kommunalarchiv.herford@t-online.de. Head: Christoph Laue
Local Museum / Public Gallery - 1882
Local hist, crafts and trades, architectural fragments from local monuments, military hist 16387

Hergensweiler

Heimatmuseum, Kirchweg 2, 88138 Hergensweiler - T: (08388) 217, 273, Fax: 724, E-mail: heimatmuseum@hergensweiler.de, Internet: http://www.hergensweiler.de/allgemeines/heimatmuseum.htm
Local Museum / Folklore Museum - 1989
Religious folklore 16388

Heringen, Werra

Waldmuseum Herfa, Siebertsberger Weg 16, 36266 Heringen, Werra - T: (06674) 241
Natural History Museum
All existing types of wood in Germany, the most important types of foreign wood, forest pests, skulls of all native hoofed and predatory game, bird's nests and their clutch of eggs, feathers and antlers 16389

Werra-Kalibergbau-Museum, Dickesstr 1, 36266 Heringen, Werra - T: (06624) 5127, 919413, Fax: 919414, E-mail: kalimuseum@heringen.de, Internet: http://www.heringen.de/kalimuseum. Head: H.-J. Hohmann
Science&Tech Museum - 1994
Hist of potash mining - library, archive 16390

Heringsdorf

Museum Villa Irmgard, Maxim-Gorki-Str 13, 17424 Heringsdorf - T: (038378) 22361, Fax: 22964. Head: Dr. Karin Lehmann
Special Museum 16391

Hermannsburg

Heimatkundliche Sammlung und Ausstellung, Harmsstr 3a, 29320 Hermannsburg - T: (05052) 3874
Local Museum 16392

Ludwig-Harms-Haus, Ausstellung und Veranstaltungshaus des Ev.-luth. Missionswerkes in Niedersachsen, Harmsstr 2, 29320 Hermannsburg - T: (05052) 69274, Fax: 69222, E-mail: LHH-Hermannsburg@gmx.de, Internet: http://www.candace.de
Religious Arts Museum / Special Museum
Masks, costumes, jewellery, musical instruments from South Africa, South America, India, Ethiopia 16393

Hermeskeil

Dampflok-Museum, Bahnbetriebswerk, 54411 Hermeskeil - T: (06503) 1204, Fax: 1204. Head: Bernd Falz
Science&Tech Museum - 1986
50 locomotives 16394

Herne

Emschertal-Museum der Stadt Herne, Unser-Fritz-Str 108, 44653 Herne - T: (02325) 75255, Fax: 162660. Head: Dr. Alexander von Knorre
Local Museum - 1926
International drawings since 1945 16395

Flottmann-Hallen, Flottmannstr 94, 44625 Herne - T: (02323) 162956, Fax: 132292, E-mail: flottmann-hallen@freenet.de, Internet: http://www.flottmann-hallen.de
Public Gallery
Current fine arts 16396

Heimat- und Naturkunde Museum Wanne-Eickel, Emschertal-Museum der Stadt Herne, Unser Fritz Str 108, 44653 Herne - T: (02325) 75255, 162611
Science&Tech Museum / Natural History Museum 16397

Schloß Strünkede, Karl-Brandt-Weg 5, 44629 Herne - T: (02323) 162611, 161072, Fax: 162660, Internet: http://www.herne.de/kultur/emschertal.html-ssi.. Head: Dr. Alexander von Knorre
Local Museum 16398

Städtische Galerie im Schloßpark Strünkede, Karl-Brandt-Weg 2, 44629 Herne - T: (02323) 162659, 162611, Fax: 162660, Internet: http://www.herne.de/kultur/emschertal.html-ssi.. Head: Dr. Alexander von Knorre
Public Gallery 16399

Heroldsbach

Heimatkundliche Sammlung, Hauptstr 9, 91336 Heroldsbach - T: (09190) 929212, Fax: 1407, E-mail: gemeinde@heroldsbach.de, Internet: http://www.heroldsbach.de
Local Museum - 1990
Agricultural tools and handicrafts 16400

Herrenchiemsee

König Ludwig II.-Museum, Altes Schloß 3, 83209 Herrenchiemsee - T: (08051) 68870, Fax: 688799, E-mail: info@bsv.bayern.de. Head:
Decorative Arts Museum - 1987
Historic furnishings from the time of King Ludwig II of Bavaria (1845-1886), memorabilia of King Ludwig II of Bavaria, stage sets of Richard Wagner's operas, in a residence built in 1876/86 16401

Museum im ehemaligen Augustiner-Chorherrenstift, Altes Schloß 3, 83209 Herrenchiemsee - T: (08051) 68870, Fax: 688799, E-mail: info@herren-chiemsee.de, Internet: http://www.herren-chiemsee.de
Local Museum 16402

Neues Schloß Herrenchiemsee, Altes Schloß 3, 83209 Herrenchiemsee - T: (08051) 68870, Fax: 688799, E-mail: info@herren-chiemsee.de, Internet: http://www.herren-chiemsee.de
Fine Arts Museum
Residence built for King Ludwig II of Bavaria, with eclectic interiors 16403

Herrischried

Freilichtmuseum Klausenhof, Gerhard-Jung-Pl, 79737 Herrischried - T: (07764) 6162, Fax: 920049, Internet: http://www.hotzenwald.de/herrischried. Head: Oskar Sandmann
Open Air Museum / Folklore Museum - 1981
Farmhouse 15th c, sawmill 16th c, old equipment 16404

Herrnhut

Heimatmuseum der Stadt Herrnhut, Comeniusstr 6, 02747 Herrnhut - T: (035873) 2288, 30733, Fax: 30734, E-mail: Herrnhut-Stadt@t-online.de, Internet: http://www.herrnhut-lol.de
Local Museum - 1878/1962
18th c house with complete Biedermeier interiors, hist of brothership, craft and trade, folklore 16405

Völkerkundemuseum Herrnhut, Außenstelle des Staatlichen Museums für Völkerkunde Dresden, Goethestr 1, 02747 Herrnhut - T: (035873) 2403, Fax: 2403. Head: Dr. Annegret Nippa
Ethnology Museum - 1878
Ethnology 16406

Hersbruck

Deutsches Hirtenmuseum, Eisenhüttlein 7, 91217 Hersbruck - T: (09151) 2161, Fax: 823753, E-mail: hirtenmuseum@hersbruck.de, Internet: http://www.hersbruck.de. Head: Barbara Hörmann
Agriculture Museum / Special Museum - 1925
Documents, implements and specimens from the hist of sheep and cows raising around the world, peasant cultural artifacts, farm implements, toys, crafts, hist of herdsmen 16407

Herten

Heimatkabinett Westerholt, Freiheit 1, 45701 Herten, mail addr: Heidgarten 9, 45701 Herten - T: (0209) 358744
Local Museum - 1954
Pictures of the Madonna 16408

Puppenmuseum im Kunsthof, Am Bungert 19, 45701 Herten - T: (0209) 620106, Fax: 62807, E-mail: info@kunsthof.de, Internet: http://www.kunsthof.de. Head: Ulrich Knoop
Decorative Arts Museum 16409

Herzberg am Harz

Schloß-Museum Welfenschloß Herzberg, Welfenschloß, Postfach 1340, 37412 Herzberg am Harz - T: (05521) 4799, Fax: 852120, E-mail: touristinfo@herzberg.de, Internet: http://www.herzberg.de. Head:
Historical Museum - 1985
Guelph castle from the 16th c, forestry, pewter figures 16410

Zinnfigurenmuseum, Welfenschloß, 37412 Herzberg am Harz - T: (05521) 4799, Fax: 852120, E-mail: touristinfo@herzberg.de, Internet: http://www.herzberg.de. Head:
Local Museum - 1985
Pewter figures 16411

Herzogenaurach

Stadtmuseum Herzogenaurach, Kirchenpl 2, 91074 Herzogenaurach - T: (09132) 735120, Fax: 735122, E-mail: rathaus@herzogenaurach.de. Head: Irene Lederer
Local Museum - 1908
Town hist and crafts 16412

Hessisch Oldendorf

Stift Fischbeck, 31840 Hessisch Oldendorf - T: (05152) 8603, Fax: 962489
Religious Arts Museum
Romanesque elements from the 12th c, sculptures, tapestry 16413

Hettstedt, Sachsen-Anhalt

Mansfeld-Museum Hettstedt, Schloßstr 7, 06333 Hettstedt, Sachsen-Anhalt - T: (03476) 200809, 200753, Fax: 200753. Head: Dr. Ludwig Rommel
Science&Tech Museum
Copper-shale mining, metallurgy, machinery, minerals and fossils of the coppershale, art and culture of mining 16414

Heubach, Württemberg

Heimat- und Miedermuseum Heubach, Hauptstr 53, 73540 Heubach, Württemberg - T: (07173) 1810, Fax: 18149, E-mail: info@heubach.de, Internet: http://www.heubach.de
Local Museum - 1970/71
Undergarments documenting the history of the J.G. Weber corset factory and the local undergarment industry, local prehistory and ancient history 16415

Schloß Heubach, Schloßstr 9, 73540 Heubach, Württemberg - T: (07173) 3637
Local Museum 16416

Heuchelheim, Kreis Gießen

Heimatmuseum Heuchelheim-Kinzenbach, Bahnhofsstr 30, 35452 Heuchelheim, Kreis Gießen - T: (0641) 61429
Local Museum - 1989
Development from rural to industrial village, trade workshops 16417

Heusenstamm

Heimatmuseum Heusenstamm, Historischer Torbau, Haus Winter, Kirchstr 43, 63150 Heusenstamm - T: (06104) 5035
Local Museum
Old trade workshops 16418

Heynitz

Heimatstube Heynitz, Schloß, 01683 Heynitz - T: (035244) 296, Fax: 41041, E-mail: Gemeinde-Heynitz@t-online.de
Local Museum 16419

Hildburghausen

Stadtmuseum Hildburghausen, Apothekergasse 11, 98646 Hildburghausen - T: (03685) 403689, Fax: 403689. Head: Michael Römhild
Local Museum - 1904
Local, regional hist, crafts, 19th c living style, publisher Joseph Meyer (1796-1856) and foundation of Bibliographical Institute 16420

Trützschler's Milch- und Reklamemuseum, Am Bertholdstor, 98646 Hildburghausen - T: (03685) 700510
Special Museum
Dairy farming and processing, butter churns, centrifuges, enamel signs 16421

Hilden

Elektro-Museum, Am Jägersteig 7, 40724 Hilden - T: (02103) 334400. Head: Günter Rateike
Science&Tech Museum - 1991
Electronic appliances such as telephones, radios, televisions, vacuum cleaners, coffee machines 16422

Hildesheim

Dom-Museum Hildesheim, Domhof 4, 31134 Hildesheim - T: (05121) 1791640, Fax: 1791644, E-mail: dommuseum@bistum-hildesheim.de, Internet: http://www.dommuseum-hildesheim.de. Head: Dr. Michael Brandt
Religious Arts Museum - 1978
Liturgical implements, sculpture, manuscripts, paintings, documents, cathedral treasure 16423

Galerie im Kehrwiederturm, Kehrwieder 2, 31134 Hildesheim - T: (05121) 301270, Internet: http://www.kunstverein-hildesheim.de
Public Gallery 16424

Neisser Haus - Heimathaus und Archiv, Gelber Stern 21, 31134 Hildesheim - T: (05121) 46431, Fax: 41416, E-mail: trouw@t-online.de. Head: Bernward Trouw
Local Museum - 1974
Folk art, memorabilia on Joseph von Eichendorff and Max Hermann-Neisse - Archive 16425

Roemer- und Pelizaeus-Museum, Am Steine 1-2, 31134 Hildesheim - T: (05121) 93690, Fax: 35283, E-mail: info@rpmuseum.de, Internet: http://www.rpmuseum.de. Head: Dr. Eleni Vassilika, Prof. Manfred Boetzkes
Local Museum / Archaeological Museum / Natural History Museum / Ethnology Museum / Museum of Classical Antiquities - 1911
Geology, paleontology and prehistory, mineralogy, botany and zoology, ethnology, art works, Egyptian antiquities 16426

Stadtmuseum im Knochenhauer-Amtshaus, Roemer-Museum, Markt 7, 31134 Hildesheim - T: (05121) 301163/64, Fax: 301162, E-mail: sk.rpm@t-online.de
Local Museum 16427

Hilpoltstein

Museum Schwarzes Ross, Markstr. 10, 91116 Hilpoltstein - T: (09174) 48476, Fax: 48477
Special Museum
Town hist and archeological finds, building trade, building trade, hist house building 16428

Stadtgeschichtliches Museum → Museum Schwarzes Ross

Hilter

Heimatmuseum Borgloh, Kirchstr 5, 49176 Hilter - T: (05409) 742
Local Museum 16429

Hilzingen

Bürger- und Bauernmuseum, Hauptstr, 78247 Hilzingen - T: (07731) 63732
Ethnology Museum - 1977
Peasant life (18th-19th c), tools 16430

Himmelkron

Stiftskirchenmuseum, Klosterberg 9, 95502 Himmelkron - T: (09227) 9310, Fax: 93131, E-mail: gemeinde@himmelkron.de, Internet: http://www.himmelkron.de
Religious Arts Museum - 1975/87
Church und local hist 16431

Hindelang

Friedenshistorisches Museum, Hindelangerstr 20, 87541 Hindelang - T: (08324) 379, (0821) 517830, Fax: (0821) 517830, E-mail: info@friedensmuseum.de, Internet: http://www.friedensmuseum.de. Head: Thomas Wechs
Historical Museum 16432

Heimatkundliche Sammlung des Heimatdienstes Hindelang, Rathaus, 87541 Hindelang - T: (08324) 1470
Local Museum 16433

Hinternah

Heimatstube Hinternah, Alte Hauptstr 18, 98553 Hinternah - T: (036841) 41082, Fax: 47838
Local Museum 16434

Hirschhorn, Neckar

Langbeinmuseum, Alleeweg 2, 69434 Hirschhorn, Neckar - T: (06272) 9230. Head: Dr. U. Spiegelberg
Local Museum - 1980
Various collector's items such as buttons, paintings, roof tiles, furniture, coins and books 16435

Hirzenhain

Museum für Eisenkunstguß, Nidderstr 10, 63697 Hirzenhain - T: (06045) 68235, Fax: 68101, E-mail: kunstguss@guss.buderus.de. Head: Jörg Firnges
Decorative Arts Museum - 1967
Decorative iron panels, stoves and ovens (16th-19th c), early 19th c decorative iron work 16436

Hitzacker

Archäologisches Zentrum Hitzacker, Hitzacker-See, 29456 Hitzacker - T: (05862) 6794, Fax: 985988, E-mail: azh@archaeo-centrum.de, Internet: http://www.archaeo-centrum.de. Head: Dr. Arne Lucke
Archaeological Museum / Open Air Museum - 1990
Reconstruction of 3 Bronze Age longhouses, pit house, early and prehist excavation site with finds from the Neolithic age, bronze age up to the Middle Ages, nature trail 16437

Walter-Honig-Heimatmuseum, Zollstr 1, 29456 Hitzacker - T: (05862) 8838, Fax: 7501
Local Museum
Hist of settling, town hist, guild of hunters, agricultural implements 16438

Hitzhofen

Jura-Bauernhof-Museum, Hofstetten, Schloßstr 19, 85122 Hitzhofen - T: (08406) 1200
Agriculture Museum - 1986
Old farm 16439

Hochheim am Main

Otto-Schwabe-Museum, Mainzer Str 22-24, 65239 Hochheim am Main - T: (06146) 900142, Fax: 900199, E-mail: info@hochheim.de, Internet: http://www.hochheim.de
Local Museum - 1969
Geology, archaeology, regional and folk art 16440

Hockenheim

Motor-Sport-Museum Hockenheimring, Am Motodrom, 68766 Hockenheim - T: (06205) 6005, Fax: 950299, E-mail: info@hockenheimring.de, Internet: http://www.hockenheimring.de. Head: Hartmut Tesseraux
Science&Tech Museum - 1986
Historical racing cars 16441

Tabak-Museum der Stadt Hockenheim, Obere Hauptstr 8, 68766 Hockenheim - T: (06205) 21524, 210, Fax: 21260, E-mail: info@hockenheim.de, Internet: http://www.hockenheim.de
Agriculture Museum - 1984
Tobacco cultivation, tobacco industry pipes and pipe coll 16442

Höchberg

Museum in der Präparandenschule, Sonnemannstr 15, 97204 Höchberg - T: (0931) 497070
Local Museum - 1997 16443

Höchstadt an der Aisch

Städtisches Heimatmuseum, Altes Rathaus, Hauptstr 5, 91315 Höchstadt an der Aisch - T: (09193) 6260, 3462, Fax: 3462, 626183. Head: Sebastian Schmidt
Local Museum / Folklore Museum - 1926
Guilds, carp breeding, local early history, old craftsman' stores 16444

Höchstädt an der Donau

Heimatmuseum Höchstädt an der Donau, Marktpl 7, 89420 Höchstädt an der Donau - T: (09074) 4956, Fax: 4455, E-mail: museum@hoechstaedt.de, Internet: http://www.hoechstaedt.de/museum.html
Local Museum - 1986
Tin figure diorama 16445

Schloß Höchstädt, Herzogin-Anna-Str, 89420 Höchstädt an der Donau - T: (08431) 8897, Fax: 42689, E-mail: poststelle@bsv.bayern.de. Head: Dr. Horst Stierhof
Decorative Arts Museum / Religious Arts Museum - 1995
Ceramics, religious art 16446

Höchstädt, Oberfranken

Schloßmuseum, Schloßpl 19, 95186 Höchstädt, Oberfranken - T: (09235) 1464, Fax: 96501
Local Museum - 1464
Agricultural tools, rustic furniture 16447

Höhbeck

Heimatmuseum Vietze, Hauptstr 1, 29478 Höhbeck - T: (05846) 532, 407. Head: Reiner Purwing
Local Museum - 1935
Grave finds from the Stone Age to the Middle Ages, native animals, agricultural implements, forestry, fishing, shipping, old fire hose 16448

Höhr-Grenzhausen

Burgmuseum, Burg Grenzau, 56203 Höhr-Grenzhausen - T: (02624) 5651. Head: Reinhard Stauber
Historical Museum 16449

Keramikmuseum Westerwald, Deutsche Sammlung für Historische und Zeitgenössische Keramik, Lindenstr, 56203 Höhr-Grenzhausen - T: (02624) 946010, Fax: 9460120, E-mail: info@keramikmuseum.de, Internet: http://www.keramikmuseum.de. Head: Monika Gass
Decorative Arts Museum - 1976
Historical specimens of Westerwald crockery, all media of contemporary ceramic art 16450

Merkelbach-Museum, c/o Merkelbach Manufaktur GmbH, Brunnenstr 13, 56203 Höhr-Grenzhausen - T: (02624) 3021, Fax: 3023, E-mail: merkelbach@t-online.de, Internet: http://www.keramik.de/merkelbach. Head: Judith Engelmann
Decorative Arts Museum
Ceramics, earthenware 16451

Töpferei und Museum im Kannenofen, Kleine Emserstr 4-6, 56203 Höhr-Grenzhausen - T: (02624) 7251
Decorative Arts Museum - 1962
Silesian ceramics, stoneware, Silesiaca 16452

Höpfingen

Heimatmuseum, Am Plan 1, 74746 Höpfingen - T: (06283) 6388, 1252
Local Museum - 1965
Peasant life, crafts 16453

Hörstel

Heimathaus Bevergern, Kirchstr 4, 48477 Hörstel - T: (05459) 1058
Local Museum 16454

Höxter

Museum Höxter-Corvey, Schloß Corvey, 37671 Höxter - T: (05271) 68139, 68132, Fax: 68140. Head: Dr. Werner Altmeier
Local Museum - 1948
History of the local monastery and documentation on period of secularization, town history, archeological finds 16455

Hof, Saale

Brauerei Museum Bürger-Bräu Hof, Ascher Str 3-5, 95028 Hof, Saale - T: (09281) 73660, Fax: 736619
Science&Tech Museum - 1994
Brewery 16456

Museum Bayerisches Vogtland, Unteres Tor 5a-b, 95028 Hof, Saale - T: (09281) 815622, Fax: 815621, E-mail: archiv-museum@stadt-hof.de, Internet: http://www.hof.de. Head: Dr. Arnd Kluge
Local Museum - 1908
Regional hist, folklore, natural hist 16457

Teddy Museum Berlin in Hof/Bayern (Teddy Bear Museum), Ludwigstr 6, 95028 Hof, Saale - T: (09281) 820802, Fax: 820803, E-mail: info@stadtmarketingbuero-hof.de, Internet: http://www.hof.de. Head: Florentine C. Bredow
Special Museum - 1986
Teddybears 16458

Hofgeismar

Apothekenmuseum, Apothekenstr 5, 34369 Hofgeismar - T: (05671) 737, Fax: 993530. Head: Harald Friedrich-Sander
Historical Museum - 1989
Development from the alchemist's kitchen to the modern pharmacy 16459

Forst- und Jagdmuseum, Tierpark Sababurg, Kasinoweg 22, 34369 Hofgeismar - T: (05671) 8001251, Fax: 8001250, E-mail: - strukturfoerderung@landkreiskassel.de, Internet: http://www.tierpark-sababurg.de. Head: Gerhard Briel
Natural History Museum - 1973
Forestry, geology, botany, zoology, hunting department, charcoal burning 16460

Galerie am Markt, Markt 4, 34369 Hofgeismar. Head: Armin Lörper
Fine Arts Museum 16461

Stadtmuseum Hofgeismar, Petripl 2, 34369 Hofgeismar - T: (05671) 4791, 3476, Fax: 40861, 999200, E-mail: Stadt-Hofgeismar-@t-online.de, Internet: http://www.museum-hofgeismar.de. Head: Helmut Burmeister
Local Museum / Fine Arts Museum / Archaeological Museum - 1938
Bibles, work of Theodor Rocholl, prints, local artists, Jewish hist and culture, hist of Huguenots and Waldenses, Chinese textiles 16462

Hofheim am Taunus

Stadtmuseum Hofheim am Taunus, Burgstr 11, 65719 Hofheim am Taunus - T: (06192) 900305, Fax: 902838, E-mail: stadtmuseum@hofheim.de, Internet: http://www.hofheim.de. Head: Dr. Eva Scheid
Local Museum / Fine Arts Museum - 1993
Modern art, town hist, Roman archaeology - library, archive 16463

Hofheim, Unterfranken

Eisenbahnmuseum Lehmann, Bahnhof, 97461 Hofheim, Unterfranken - T: (09523) 1305
Science&Tech Museum - 1976
Hist of a local trainstation 16464

Rotkreuzmuseum, Großmannsdorfer Tor, 97461 Hofheim, Unterfranken - T: (09521) 95500
Special Museum - 1999 16465

Hohberg

Hohberger Bienenmuseum, Rathaus Diersburg, Talstr 7, 77749 Hohberg - T: (07808) 3999, Fax: 3911, E-mail: info@bienenmuseum.de, Internet: http://www.bienenmuseum.de. Head: Paul Zimmermann
Agriculture Museum - 1982
Old honey extractors, equipment 16466

Hohburg

Museum Steinarbeiterhaus, Martin-Luther-Str 5, 04808 Hohburg - T: (034263) 41344, Fax: 78399. Head: Matthias Müller
Local Museum / Open Air Museum - 1980
Local hist, stone industry 16467

Hohen Demzin

Schmiedemuseum, Burg Schlitz, 17166 Hohen Demzin - T: (03996) 173564, Fax: (039933) 70450
Science&Tech Museum 16468

Hohenberg an der Eger

Deutsches Porzellanmuseum, Freundschaft 2, 95691 Hohenberg an der Eger - T: (09233) 77220, Fax: 772230, E-mail: dt.porzellanmuseum@t-online.de, Internet: http://www.dt-porzellanmuseum.de. Head: Wilhelm Siemen
Decorative Arts Museum / Science&Tech Museum - 1982
19th and 20th c porcelain, machines 16469

Hohenfelden

Thüringer Freilichtmuseum Hohenfelden, Im Dorfe 63, 99448 Hohenfelden - T: (036450) 43918, 30285, Fax: 43917, E-mail: tfmhohenfelden@compuserve.com, Internet: http://www.thueringer-freilichtmuseum-hohenfelden.de. Head: Michael Happe
Open Air Museum 16470

Hohenhameln

Heimatstube Hohenhameln, Elbinger Weg 3, 31249 Hohenhameln - T: (05128) 5652
Local Museum / Historical Museum
Domestic and agricultural implements and objects, sugar refinery, local organizations and societies 16471

Hohenkirchen

Künstlerhaus Hooksiel, Helmsteder Str 1, Hooksiel, 26434 Hohenkirchen - T: (04425) 81408, 1278, Fax: (04463) 989150, E-mail: - gemeinde.wangerland@kdo.de
Public Gallery 16472

Hohenleuben

Museum Reichenfels, Reichenfels 1a, 07958 Hohenleuben - T: (036622) 7102, Fax: 83350, E-mail: museum-reichenfels@t-online.de, Internet: http://www.leubatal.de
Local Museum - 1825
Ancient and early hist, stones, minerals, fauna, crafts hist, 16th c armaments - library 16473

Hohenlockstedt

Kunsthaus Boskamp, Breite Str 18, 25551 Hohenlockstedt - T: (04826) 59170, Fax: 5172, E-mail: kunsthaus.boskamp@t-online.de, Internet: http://www.pohl-boskamp.de/kunsthaus
Fine Arts Museum 16474

Hohenpeißenberg

Schatzkammer der Wallfahrtskirche, Matthäus-Günther-Pl 6, 82383 Hohenpeißenberg - T: (08805) 200, Fax: 955044. Head: Georg Jocher
Religious Arts Museum - 1990
Pilgrimage church 16475

Hohenschäftlarn

Heimathaus Neuchl-Anwesen, Oberdorf 6, 82061 Hohenschäftlarn - T: (08178) 93030
Local Museum - 1998 16476

Hohenstein-Ernstthal

Karl-May-Haus, Karl-May-Str 54, 09337 Hohenstein-Ernstthal - T: (03723) 42159, Fax: 42159, Internet: http://www.karl-may-gesellschaft.de/krug/kmh/index.htm. Head: André Neubert
Special Museum - 1985
Life and work of Karl May in his birthplace 16477

Museum Buntes Holz im Postgut am Altmarkt → Museum Erzgebirgische Volkskunst "Buntes Holz" im Postgut am Altmarkt

Museum Erzgebirgische Volkskunst "Buntes Holz" im Postgut am Altmarkt, Friedrich-Engels-Str 1, 09337 Hohenstein-Ernstthal - T: (03723) 42236, Fax: 42147, E-mail: info@hohenstein-ernstthal.de, Internet: http://www.hohenstein-ernstthal.de
Decorative Arts Museum 16478

Textil- und Heimatmuseum, Antonstr 6, 09337 Hohenstein-Ernstthal - T: (03723) 47711
Local Museum 16479

Hohenstein, Württemberg

Bauernhausmuseum Hohenstein, Württemberg, Jahnweg 1-3, 72531 Hohenstein, Württemberg - T: (07387) 98700, Fax: 987029, E-mail: rathaus@gemeinde-hohenstein.de
Agriculture Museum / Historical Museum / Open Air Museum / Historic Site - 1978
Peasant life 16480

Hohenwarth

Mineralien-Sammlung, Hauptstr, Kindergartengeb., 93480 Hohenwarth - T: (09946) 229
Natural History Museum 16481

Hohenwestedt

Heimatmuseum Hohenwestedt, Friedrichstr 11, 24594 Hohenwestedt - T: (04871) 2229, Fax: 3636, E-mail: rathaus@hohenwestedt.de, Internet: http://www.hohenwestedt.de. Head: Dr. Michael Junge
Local Museum - 1986
Lithographs, handicraft 16482

Hohenzieritz

Heimatstube Hohenzieritz, In der alten Schmiede, 17237 Hohenzieritz - T: (039824) 20020
Local Museum 16483

Hohnstein

Museum Burg Hohnstein, Am Markt 1, 01848 Hohnstein - T: (035975) 81202, Fax: 81203, E-mail: Burg.Hohnstein@nfh.de, Internet: http://www.nfh.de. Head: Winfried Pätzold
Historical Museum - 1988
Memorial to concentration camp victims 16484

Hoisdorf

Stormarnsches Dorfmuseum, Altes Bauernhaus am Thie, Sprenger Weg 1, 22955 Hoisdorf - T: (04107) 4556, E-mail: Museum-Hoisdorf-Moeller@t-online.de, Internet: http://www.museum-hoisdorf.de
Local Museum - 1974
Ornithology, measures and weights, village school, rural crafts, Hermann Claudius memorial 16485

Holle

Glashaus-Derneburg, Schloßstr 16, 31188 Holle - T: (05062) 2665, Fax: 2635, E-mail: gemeinde@holle.de, Internet: http://www.holle.de/glashaus.htm
Public Gallery / Local Museum 16486

Holler Heimatmuseum, Bertholdstr 16, 31188 Holle - T: (05062) 8393, Fax: 29929
Local Museum - 1981
Trade workshops (blacksmith's, shoemaker's, saddler's), grocery store, natural hist, geology 16487

Hollfeld

Kunst und Museum, Eiergasse 13, 96142 Hollfeld - T: (09274) 947595, Fax: 947595, E-mail: info@kunst-museum-hollfeld.de, Internet: http://www.kunst-museum-hollfeld.de. Head: Wolfgang Pietschmann
Fine Arts Museum / Public Gallery 16488

Museumsscheune Fränkische Schweiz, Judengasse 10, 96142 Hollfeld - T: (09274) 9800, 947595, Fax: 98029, E-mail: stadt@hollfeld.baynet.de, Internet: http://www.hollfeld.de. Head: Wolfgang Pietschmann
Agriculture Museum - 1993
Agricultural tools and crafts 16489

Hollingstedt bei Schleswig

Heimatkundliche Schulsammlung, Klues, 24876 Hollingstedt bei Schleswig - T: (04627) 212
Local Museum 16490

Holzgerlingen

Heimatmuseum Holzgerlingen, Friedhofstr 6, 71088 Holzgerlingen - T: (07031) 602107
Local Museum - 1957
Agricultural machinery, handicraft 16491

Holzhausen

Museum Gasteiger-Haus, Eduard-Thöny-Str 43, 86919 Holzhausen - T: (08806) 2682, 2091, Fax: (08143) 930430
Fine Arts Museum - 1994
Work of the sculptor Mathias Gasteiger and painter Anna Sophie Gasteiger 16492

Holzheim

Heimatkundliche Sammlung Bergendorf, Dorfstr, 86684 Holzheim - T: (08276) 1704, 232
Local Museum - 1984
Rustic furniture, old classroom and handicrafts 16493

Holzmaden

Urwelt-Museum Hauff, Aichelberger Str 90, 73271 Holzmaden - T: (07023) 2873, Fax: 4618, E-mail: hauff@urweltmuseum.de, Internet: http://www.urweltmuseum.de. Head: Rolf Bernhard Hauff
Natural History Museum - 1936/37
Fossils 16494

Holzminden

Museumsschiff STÖR, Neue Str 12, 37603 Holzminden - T: (05531) 959203, Fax: 9595203, E-mail: stadt@holzminden.de. Head: Michael Berinskat
Science&Tech Museum - 1985 16495

Puppen- und Spielzeugmuseum, Oberbachstr 45, 37603 Holzminden - T: (05532) 948187, Fax: 948186
Decorative Arts Museum - 1990
Dolls, puppets, doll's houses, games, children's books, toys 16496

Stadtmuseum Holzminden, Bahnhofstr 31, 37603 Holzminden - T: (05531) 6202, Fax: 6202. Head: Dr. Matthias Seeliger
Local Museum - 1926
Town hist, local archaeology, guilds, local organizations and societies 16497

Waldmuseum im Wildpark Neuhaus, Eichenallee 21, 37603 Holzminden - T: (05536) 95020, Fax: 950255
Natural History Museum - 1972
Forestry, conservation, damages to the wood 16498

Holzwickede

Haus Opherdicke, Dorfstr 29, 59439 Holzwickede - T: (02303) 271241
Public Gallery 16499

Homberg, Efze

Heimatmuseum Hochzeitshaus, Pfarrstr 26, 34576 Homberg, Efze - T: (05681) 2640
Local Museum - 1974
Regional folk art, domestic implements, trade products 16500

Homberg, Ohm

Museum im alten Brauhaus, Marktstr 26, 35315 Homberg, Ohm - T: (06633) 1840. Head: Walter Seitz
Local Museum - 1994
Medieval trades and implements 16501

Homburg

Stiftung Römermuseum Homburg-Schwarzenacker, Homburger Str 38, 66424 Homburg - T: (06848) 875, Fax: 730774, E-mail: - touristikinformation@homburg.de, Internet: http://www.homburg.de. Head: Dr. Klaus Kell
Archaeological Museum - 1966
Gallo-Roman finds from site excavations, domestic items from the Roman period 16502

Hooge

Königspesel, Hanswarft, 25859 Hooge - T: (04849) 219, 259, Fax: 337. Head: Uwe Bendixen, Maren Bendixen
Local Museum 16503

Horb

Berthold-Auerbach-Museum, Ritterschaftsstr 4, 72160 Horb - T: (07451) 2274, Fax: 51379, E-mail: stadtinfo@Horb.de, Internet: http://www.Horb.de. Head: Klaus Bok
Special Museum - 1986
Memorabilia of the Jewish writer Berthold Auerbach (1812-1882) 16504

Heimatmuseum Horb, Neckarstr 74, 72160 Horb - T: (07451) 3611, Fax: 901290
Local Museum - 1966 16505

Horn-Bad Meinberg

Traktoren-Museum Kempen, Kempener Str 33, 32805 Horn-Bad Meinberg - T: (05255) 236, E-mail: j.glitz@traktoren-museum.de
Science&Tech Museum 16506

Hornburg, Kreis Wolfenbüttel

Heimatmuseum Hornburg, Montelabbatepl 1, 38315 Hornburg, Kreis Wolfenbüttel - T: (05334) 1507
Local Museum - 1972
Town and castle hist, trades, folk costumes, agricultural implements and vehicles 16507

Hosenfeld

Heimatmuseum Blankenau, Propsteipl 1, 36154 Hosenfeld - T: (06650) 1212
Local Museum - 1985
Trade and agricultural implements, geology, sacral art 16508

Hoya

Heimatmuseum Grafschaft Hoya, Im Park 1, 27318 Hoya - T: (04251) 7689
Local Museum - 1995
Town and social hist, trades 16509

Hoyerswerda

Feuerstätten-Ausstellung im Lausitzer Bergbaumuseum, Ernst-Thälmann-Str 8, Knappenrode, 02977 Hoyerswerda - T: (03571) 604267, 604268, Fax: 604275, E-mail: knappenrode@saechsisches-industriemuseum.de. Head: Wilfrid Sauer
Special Museum
Fireplaces, pokers, coal-boxes, irons, various kinds of coals, chimneys, wash-boards, wooden wash-boilers, rotary irons 16510

Lausitzer Bergbaumuseum Knappenrode, Ernst-Thälmann-Str 8, Knappenrode, 02977 Hoyerswerda - T: (03571) 604267/68, Fax: 604275, E-mail: knappenrode@saechsisches-industriemuseum.de, Internet: http://www.saechsisches-industriemuseum.de. Head: Wilfrid Sauer
Science&Tech Museum / Open Air Museum - 1994
History of brown coal mining, mineralogy, geology, survey, fire sites and fire departments, refinement of brown coal, railroads, enviroment, technology, art - technical/enviromental library 16511

Stadtmuseum Schloß Hoyerswerda, Schloßpl 1, 02977 Hoyerswerda - T: (03571) 456490, Fax: 456495. Head: Karl-Heinz Hempel
Historical Museum - 1932
Geology, ancient hist, local hist, pewter, costumes, Sorbian folk art, natural hist 16512

Hude, Oldenburg

Museum Kloster Hude, Sammlung zur Klostergeschichte, Von-Witzleben-Allee 1, 27798 Hude, Oldenburg - T: (04408) 1716, Fax: 808710, E-mail: krimhild.stoever@t-online.de, Internet: http://www.klosterhude.de. Head: Hartmut Stöver
Historic Site
Grave finds, models and maps on the hist of the Cistercian cloister, building techniques 16513

Hückeswagen

Heimatmuseum der Stadt Hückeswagen, Schloß, 42499 Hückeswagen - T: (02192) 82087
Local Museum 16514

Hüfingen

Römerbadmuseum, Schosenweg, 78183 Hüfingen - T: (0771) 600924, Fax: 600922. Head: Beatrice Scherzer
Archaeological Museum - 1821
Roman heating technology and bathing culture 16515

Stadtmuseum Hüfingen, Hauptstr 6, 78183 Hüfingen
Local Museum - 1988
19th c painting 16516

Hüllhorst

Heimatmuseum in der ehemaligen Schule Hüllhorst, Schnathorster Str 3, 32609 Hüllhorst - T: (05744) 1500, 931515
Local Museum 16517

Hünfeld

Friedlandstube Hünfeld, Am Anger 4, 36088 Hünfeld - T: (06652) 18114
Historical Museum - 1966
16th c hist, costumes 16518

Museum Modern Art, Hersfelder Str 25, 36088 Hünfeld - T: (06652) 72433. Head: Prof. Jürgen Blum
Fine Arts Museum - 1990
Avantgarde, Constructivists, Pop-Art, East-European art 16519

Stadt- und Kreisgeschichtliches Museum, Kirchpl 4-6, 36088 Hünfeld - T: (06652) 919884, Fax: 180194. Head: Berthold Baier
Local Museum / Science&Tech Museum - 1977
Early and pre-hist, town hist, sacral art, hunting, economic hist - Archive 16520

Hünfelden

Heimatmuseum Kirberg, Burgstr 38, 65597 Hünfelden Kirberg - T: (06438) 83843
Local Museum - 1991
Pre-historic finds, town hist, agriculture, forestry 16521

Steinscher Hof Kirberg, Freiherr-vom-Stein-Gedenkstätte, Bubenheimer Str 3, 65597 Hünfelden - T: (06438) 920505, Fax: 920506. Head: Prof. Gerhard Eimer
Historic Site - 1974
gallery 16522

Hünxe

Otto-Pankok-Museum, Otto-Pankok-Weg 4, 46569 Hünxe - T: (02856) 754
Fine Arts Museum 16523

Otto Pankok Museum, Haus Esselt, Otto-Pankok-Weg 4, 46569 Hünxe - T: (02856) 754. Head: Eva Pankok
Fine Arts Museum - 1968
Works by the painter Otto Pankok 16524

Hüttenberg

Heimatmuseum Hüttenberg, Goethehaus Volpertshausen, Rheinfelser Str 65, 35625 Hüttenberg - T: (06441) 74037
Local Museum - 1992
Agricultural implements, cheese production and processing, flax processing, ball room (Goethe was guest in 1772) 16525

Hüttlingen

Heimatmuseum im Vogteigebäude, Fuggerstr 3, 73460 Hüttlingen - T: (07361) 73423
Local Museum - 1974
Peasant life, fossils, mineralogy, Roman coins, prehistory 16526

Hundisburg

Schulmuseum, Dönstedter Str, 39343 Hundisburg - T: (03904) 241113
Local Museum 16527

Technisches Denkmal Ziegelei Hundisburg, Süplinger Str 2, 39343 Hundisburg - T: (03904) 42835, Fax: 464530, E-mail: verwaltung@ziegelei-hundisburg.de, Internet: http://www.ziegelei-hundisburg.de
Science&Tech Museum 16528

Hungen

Heimatmuseum Obbornhofen, Oberhofstr 2-4, 35410 Hungen - T: (06036) 2160
Local Museum - 1967
Portrayal of former village life: furnished rooms, agricultural and handworker implements, tools 16529

Husum, Nordsee

Freilichtmuseum Ostenfelder Bauernhaus, Zweckverband Museumsverbund Nordfriesland, Nordhusumer Str 13, 25813 Husum, Nordsee - T: (04841) 2545, Fax: 63280, E-mail: nf-museum.nissenhaus@gmx.de, Internet: http://www.nissenhaus.de. Head: Dr. Klaus Lengsfeld
Open Air Museum - 1899
Farm implements and machinery, peasant furniture, 17th c buildings 16530

Nordfriesisches Museum Ludwig-Nissen-Haus, Zweckverband Museumsverbund Nordfriesland, Herzog-Adolf-Str 25, 25813 Husum, Nordsee - T: (04841) 2545, Fax: 63280, E-mail: nf-museum.nissenhaus@gmx.de, Internet: http://www.nissenhaus.de. Head: Dr. Klaus Lengsfeld
Local Museum / Archaeological Museum / Fine Arts Museum / Natural History Museum - 1928
Local natural history, documentation on local dikes and floods, folklore and cultural history of Husum and North Friesland, works of North Friesland artists - Ludwig Nissen Foundation: Works of US-American artists 1880-1920 16531

Schiffahrtsmuseum Nordfriesland, Zingel 15, 25813 Husum, Nordsee - T: (04841) 5257, Fax: 880198, E-mail: schiffahrtsmuseum-nf@t-online.de, Internet: http://www.schiffahrtsmuseum-nf.de. Head: Dr. Klaus Lengsfeld
Historical Museum 16532

Schloß vor Husum, Zweckverband Museumsverbund Nordfriesland, Herzog-Adolf-Str 25, 25813 Husum, Nordsee - T: (04841) 2545, 8973130, Fax: 63280, E-mail: nf-museum.nissenhaus@gmx.de, Internet: http://www.nissenhaus.de. Head: Dr. Klaus Lengsfeld
Historic Site - 1978/79 16533

Theodor-Storm-Haus, Wasserreihe 31, 25813 Husum, Nordsee - T: (04841) 666270, Fax: 666270, E-mail: info@storm-gesellschaft.de, Internet: http://www.storm-gesellschaft.de. Head: Dr. Gerd Eversberg
Special Museum - 1972
Books, furniture, documents and memorabilia of writer Theodor Storm, in original setting - library 16534

Ibbenbüren

Motorrad Museum, Markweg 26, 49479 Ibbenbüren - T: (05451) 6454. Head: Robert Stockmann
Science&Tech Museum - 1978
Development of the motorbike, 150 exhibits (scooters, motor-assisted bicycles) 16535

Sammlungen des Kunstvereins, Oststr 28, 49477 Ibbenbüren - T: (05451) 931750, Internet: http://www.bnet-ibb.de/webtest/Kunstverein. Head: Dr. Annette Kleinert
Association with Coll 16536

Ichenhausen

Bayerisches Schulmuseum, Unteres Schloß, Schloßpl 3, 89335 Ichenhausen - T: (08223) 6189, Fax: 408642, E-mail: hsichenhausen@bnv-gz.de, Internet: http://www.bayerisches-nationalmuseum.de. Head: Dr. Eickelmann
Special Museum - 1984
Historical class rooms 16537

Ehemalige Synagoge mit Ausstellung Juden auf dem Lande- Beispiel Ichenhausen, Haus der Begegnung, Vordere Ostergasse 22, 89335 Ichenhausen - T: (08221) 95157, Fax: 95440, E-mail: info@landkreis-guenzburg.de, Internet: http://www.landkreis-guenzburg.de
Religious Arts Museum - 1987
Jewish hist 16538

Ikonenmuseum Schloß Autenried, Schloß Autenried, 89335 Ichenhausen - T: (08223) 862, Fax: (08774) 910065, E-mail: schloss-hofberg@t-online.de, Internet: http://www.ikonen.org. Head: Jakobus Puckett
Decorative Arts Museum
Icons from Russia, Byzaninic area, Greece, Balkan countries, metal and goldsmith's works, wood-carvings, graphics, manuscripts, embroideries, ivory 16539

Idar-Oberstein

Deutsches Edelsteinmuseum, Hauptstr 118, 55743 Idar-Oberstein - T: (06781) 944280, 900980, Fax: 944266, E-mail: info@edelsteinmuseum.de, Internet: http://www.edelsteinmuseum.de. Head: Dr. Joachim Zang
Decorative Arts Museum - 1973
System and structure of precious stones, "Glyptothek", a coll of the 6 000 years old hist of gemstone engraving art, gem materials used in the technical world 16540

Museum Idar-Oberstein, Hauptstr 436, 55743 Idar-Oberstein - T: (06781) 24619, Fax: 28303
Decorative Arts Museum - 1932
Minerals and gemstones, jewelry 16541

Idstedt

Idstedt-Gedächtnishalle, Idstedtkirche Nr 1, 24879 Idstedt - T: (04625) 402, Fax: (04621) 87203, E-mail: kreis@schleswig-flensburg.de. Head: Herbert Jensen
Historical Museum / Military Museum
Schleswig-Holstein uprising 1848-51, battle of Idstedt 1950 16542

Idstein

Stadtmuseum Killingerhaus, König-Adolf-Pl 2, 65510 Idstein - T: (06126) 78215/19, Fax: 78280, E-mail: info@idstein.de, Internet: http://www.idstein.de
Local Museum - 1987
Town hist 16543

Ihringen

Heimatmuseum Ihringen, Bachenstr 42, 79241 Ihringen - T: (07668) 71080, Fax: 710850, E-mail: gemeinde@ihringen.de
Local Museum - 1984
Peasant life, crafts 16544

Ilfeld

Steinkohlen-Besucherbergwerk Rabensteiner Stollen, Netzkater 8, 99768 Ilfeld - T: (036331) 48153, Fax: 49802, Internet: http://www.rabensteiner-stollen.de. Head: Science&Tech Museum
History of hard coal mining 16545

Illertissen

Egerländer-Elbogner Heimatstuben, Hauptstr 2, 89257 Illertissen - T: (07303) 17211, Fax: 17228, E-mail: heinrich@illertissen.de
Local Museum - 1984 16546

Heimatmuseum und Karl-August-Forster-Bienenmuseum, Vöhlinschloß, 89257 Illertissen - T: (07303) 17211, 6965, Fax: (0731) 7040666, E-mail: lra-nu@neu-ulm.de, Internet: http://www.landkreis.neu-ulm.de
Local Museum / Special Museum - 1983
Local and the hist of bee-farming 16547

Illesheim

Kleines Kirchengeschichtsmuseum Sankt Gumbertus, Evang.-Luth. Pfarramt Illesheim, Kirchstr 6, 91471 Illesheim - T: (09841) 8468, Fax: 8468. Head: Jürgen Hofmann
Religious Arts Museum - 1987
Church hist 16548

Illingen

Museum Illingen, Kirchstr 12, 66557 Illingen - T: (06825) 4060290
Local Museum 16549

VSE Elektro-Museum, Gymnasialstr 72a, 66557 Illingen - T: (06825) 2313, 2316, Fax: 4022300. Head: Alfred Putze
Science&Tech Museum - 1981 16550

Ilmenau

Goethe-Gedenkstätte im Amtshaus, Museum der Stadt Ilmenau, Am Markt 1, 98681 Ilmenau - T: (03677) 202667, 600106, Fax: 600200, E-mail: rathaus@ilmenau.de, Internet: http://www.ilmenau.de. Head: Claudia Fiala
Special Museum - 1910
Memorabilia on J.W. Goethe (1749-1832), glass, porcelain, regional hist 16551

Jagdhaus Gabelbach, Stiftung Weimarer Klassik, Waldstr 24, 98693 Ilmenau - T: (03677) 202626, Fax: (03643) 545303, E-mail: museen@weimar-klassik.de, Internet: http://www.weimar-klassik.de. Head: Prof. Dr. Gerhard Schuster
Special Museum - 1949
Memorabilia on poet J.W. Goethe (1749-1832) and his stay here, ducal hunting area and facilities, unique historical hunting lodge near Ilmenau 16552

Ilsenburg

Hütten- und Technikmuseum Ilsenburg, Marienhöfer Str 9b, 38871 Ilsenburg - T: (039452) 2222. Head: W. Burger
Science&Tech Museum - 1954
Ancient and early hist, geology, use of granite and quartz, paintings, drawings, watercolours, artistic casting 16553

Immenhausen

Glasmuseum, Am Bahnhof 3, 34376 Immenhausen - T: (05673) 2060, Fax: 911430, E-mail: glasmuseum@immenhausen.de,

Internet: http://www.immenhausen.de. Head: F.K. Baas
Decorative Arts Museum - 1987
Glassworks in Immenhausen, glass design of the 20th c, modern glass art 16554

Immenstaad

Café-Museum Zum Puppenhaus, Kirchberger Str 15, 88090 Immenstaad - T: (07545) 6510
Decorative Arts Museum - 1989
Puppets, toys 16555

Heimatmuseum, Montfortstr 13, 88090 Immenstaad - T: (07545) 6537
Local Museum - 1992
Crafts, agriculture, furnishings 16556

Immenstadt

Museum Hofmühle, An der Aach 14, 87509 Immenstadt - T: (08323) 3663, 914112, Fax: 91428112, E-mail: m.kamp@immenstadt.de, Internet: http://www.immenstadt.com/hofmuehle
Local Museum 16557

Inchenhofen

Wallfahrtsmuseum Inchenhofen, Klosterberg 3, 86570 Inchenhofen - T: (08257) 1220
Religious Arts Museum - 1993
Place of pilgrimage 16558

Ingelheim

Museum bei der Kaiserpfalz, François-Lachenal-Pl 5, 55218 Ingelheim - T: (06132) 1374, Fax: 432908, E-mail: museum@ingelheim.de, Internet: http://www.ingelheim.de. Head: Dr. Gabriele Mendelssohn
Historical Museum - 1917
Charlemagne and his Imperial Palais in Ingelheim, memorabilia of Sebastian Münster, local hist of Ingelheim 16559

Ingersleben

Heimatmuseum Ingersleben/Neudietendorf, Karl-Marx-Str 40, 99192 Ingersleben - T: (036202) 82211
Local Museum - 1979
Coll of seal stamps and prints, manuscripts; on the writer, politician and scientist Herman Anders Krüger (1871-1945), the writers Margarethe and Frieda von Bülow and the painter Arthur Rose 16560

Ingolstadt

Alf Lechner Museum, Esplanade 9, 85049 Ingolstadt - T: (0941) 3052250, Fax: 3052251
Fine Arts Museum - 2000 16561

Bauerngerätemuseum des Stadtmuseums, Probststr 13, 85051 Ingolstadt - T: (0841) 3051881, Fax: 3051888, E-mail: stadtmuseum@ ingolstadt.de, Internet: http://www.ingolstadt.de/ stadtmuseum/. Head: Dr. Beatrix Schönewald
Agriculture Museum - 1995
Agricultural implements 16562

Bayerisches Armeemuseum, Neues Schloß, Paradepl 4, 85049 Ingolstadt - T: (0841) 93770, Fax: 9377200, E-mail: sekretariat@bayerisches-armeemuseum.de, Internet: http:// www.bayerisches-armeemuseum.de. Head: Dr. Ernst Aichner
Military Museum - 1879
Pre-19th c weapons and equipment, art, military music, arms and equipment of the Bavarian army from medieval times up to 1918, military equipment from 1918 to the present - library, workshops, photo laboratory 16563

Deutsches Medizinhistorisches Museum, Anatomiestr 18-20, 85049 Ingolstadt - T: (0841) 3051860, Fax: 910844, E-mail: - deutschesmedizinhistorischesmuseum@ ingolstadt.de. Head: Prof. Dr. Dr. Christa Habrich
Science&Tech Museum / Special Museum - 1973
Medical tools, instruments, and equipment, anatomic specimens, objects documenting the development of medicine in the early advanced civilizations in Egypt, Greece, Rome, and pre-Columbian America, the art of healing in Africa and Asia (China, Japan, and Ceylon), European medicine from the Middle Ages to the present, graphic portraits of physicians, exhibit on the hist of dentistry, ophthalmology, and homeopathy - garden with curative plants 16564

Heimatmuseum Niemes und Prachatitz, Hohe-Schul-Str 2, 85049 Ingolstadt - T: (0841) 38311
Local Museum
Hist of exiled East Germans, documents, photographs 16565

Historische Sammlung Auto Union → Museum Mobile

Kunstverein Ingolstadt, Ludwigstr 28, 85049 Ingolstadt - T: (0841) 33621, Fax: 35874, E-mail: peter.volkwein@ingolstadt.de. Head: Dr. Isabella Kreim, Karl-Manfred Fischer, Peter Volkwein
Association with Coll 16566

Museum für konkrete Kunst, Tränktorstr 6-8, 85049 Ingolstadt - T: (0841) 3051871, Fax: 3051877, E-mail: mkk@ingolstadt.de. Head: Peter Volkwein
Fine Arts Museum
Concrete/Constructive art 16567

Museum Mobile, Audi Forum Ingolstadt, 85045 Ingolstadt - T: (0841) 8937575, Fax: 8936167, Internet: http://www.museummobile.de
Science&Tech Museum - 2000
History of the car manufacturer Audi, development of the first steam power car 16568

Spielzeugmuseum, Stadtmuseum Ingolstadt, Auf der Schanz 45, 85049 Ingolstadt, mail addr: Postfach 210964, 85024 Ingolstadt - T: (0841) 3051880/85, Fax: 3051888, E-mail: Stadtmuseum@ ingolstadt.de, Internet: http://www.ingolstadt.de/ kultur/stadtmus. Head: Dr. Beatrix Schönewald
Decorative Arts Museum - 1989
Coll of toys 16569

Stadtmuseum Ingolstadt im Kavalier Hepp, Auf der Schanz 45, 85049 Ingolstadt - T: (0841) 3051880, Fax: 3051888, E-mail: Stadtmuseum@ ingolstadt.de, Internet: http://www.ingolstadt.de/ kultur/stadtmus. Head: Dr. Beatrix Schönewald
Local Museum - 1905
Prehistory, local history from the Middle Ages to the present, history of the university at Ingolstadt, crafts - Stadtarchiv, Wiss. Bibl. 16570

Städtische Galerie im Theater Ingolstadt, Museum für konkrete Kunst, Schloßlände 1, 85049 Ingolstadt - T: (0841) 3051871, Fax: 3051877, E-mail: mkk@ ingolstadt.de. Head: Peter Volkwein
Public Gallery 16571

Inzigkofen

Bauernmuseum Inzigkofen, Parkweg 7, 72514 Inzigkofen - T: (07571) 51167
Agriculture Museum / Ethnology Museum - 1983
Peasant life 16572

Iphofen

Fränkisches Bauern- und Handwerkermuseum Kirchenburg Mönchsondheim, Kirchstr 7, 97346 Iphofen - T: (09326) 1224, Fax: (09321) 928381, E-mail: lra@kitzingen.de, Internet: http:// www.kitzingen.de. Head: Reinhard Hüßner
Local Museum / Open Air Museum - 1975
Town hist 16573

Knauf-Museum, Maxstr, 97343 Iphofen - T: (09323) 31528, 31625, Fax: 5022
Fine Arts Museum
Plaster casts 16574

Kulturhistorische Sammlung, Rathaus, Marktpl 1, 97346 Iphofen - T: (09323) 871554, Fax: 871555. Head: Andreas Brombierstäudl
Local Museum
Local hist 16575

Irsee

Kloster Irsee, Klosterring 14, 87660 Irsee - T: (08341) 90600, Fax: 74278, E-mail: hotel@ kloster-irsee.de, Internet: http://www.kloster-irsee.ch. Head: Dr. Rainer Jehl
Religious Arts Museum
Coll of documents, music and scientific instruments, hist of the cloister 16576

Klosterbräu Brauereimuseum, Klosterring 1-3, 87660 Irsee - T: (08341) 432260, Fax: 432269, E-mail: irseerklosterbraeu@t-online.de, Internet: http://www.irseerklosterbraeu.de
Science&Tech Museum 16577

Isen

Heimatkundliche Sammlung, Altes Rathaus, Am Marktpl 3, 84424 Isen - T: (08083) 53010, Fax: 530120, E-mail: poststelle@isen.de
Local Museum - 1969
Local hist 16578

Iserlohn

Gelbgießerei und Nadelmuseum in der Historischen Fabrikanlage Barendorf, Baarstr 222-224, 58636 Iserlohn - T: (02371) 14237, 44448
Science&Tech Museum / Special Museum 16579

Höhlenkundemuseum Dechenhöhle, Dechenhöhle 5, 58644 Iserlohn - T: (02374) 71421, Fax: 750100, E-mail: Dechenhoehle@t-online.de, Internet: http:// www.dechenhoehle.de. Head: Dr. Stefan Niggemann, Elmar Hammerschmidt
Historical Museum / Natural History Museum / Archaeological Museum 16580

Stadtmuseum Iserlohn, Fritz-Kühn-Pl 1, 58636 Iserlohn - T: (02371) 2171960, Fax: 2171960, E-mail: museum@iserlohn.de, Internet: http:// www.iserlohn.de. Head: Gerd Schäfer
Local Museum - 1987 16581

Städtische Galerie Iserlohn, Theodor-Heuss-Ring 24, 58636 Iserlohn - T: (02371) 2171970, Fax: 2171971, E-mail: galerie@iserlohn.de, Internet: http://www.iserlohn.de. Head: Rainer Danne
Public Gallery - 1991 16582

Städtisches Museum, Hagener Str 62, Haus Letmathe, 58642 Iserlohn - T: (02371) 2171960, Fax: 2171960. Head: Gerd Schäfer
Local Museum 16583

Villa Wessel, Gartenstr 31, 58636 Iserlohn - T: (02371) 14238, Fax: 14238, E-mail: info@villa-wessel.de, Internet: http://www.villa-wessel.de. Head: Dr. T. Bergenthal
Association with Coll 16584

Isernhagen

Nordhannoversches Bauernhaus-Museum, Wöhler-Dusche-Hof, Am Ortfelde 40, 30916 Isernhagen - T: (0511) 731620
Open Air Museum - 1994
Architectural memorial from the 16th c, farmhouse, barn, garden, meadow, bakehouse 16585

Ismaning

Kallmann-Museum, Orangerie, Schloßstr 3b, 85737 Ismaning - T: (089) 9612948, Fax: 963812. Head: Gisela Hesse
Fine Arts Museum - 1992
Paintings and drawings by Hans Jürgen Kattmann 16586

Schloßmuseum Ismaning, Schloßstr 4, 85737 Ismaning - T: (089) 9609000, Fax: 963468
Local Museum - 1986
Town hist 16587

Isny

Museum am Mühlturm, Fabrikstr 21, 88316 Isny - T: (07562) 70168, Fax: 70167. Head: Martin Kratzert
Local Museum - 1989
Local hist, coins, medieval mint 16588

Praedicantenbibliothek der Nikolaikirche, Kirchpl 1, 88316 Isny - T: (07562) 2314, Fax: 93112, E-mail: EvangPfarramt-Isny@web.de
Religious Arts Museum / Library with Exhibitions 16589

Wassertor-Museum, Städt. Museen Isny, Fabrikstr 21, 88316 Isny - T: (07562) 70168. Head: Martin Kratzert
Local Museum
Hist of the tower formerly used as prison, fire fighting 16590

Isselburg

Museum Wasserburg Anholt, Wasserburg Anholt, 46419 Isselburg - T: (02874) 45353, Fax: 45356, E-mail: museum@fuerst-salm.de, Internet: http:// www.fuerst-salm.de. Head: Dr. D. Van Krugten
Local Museum - 1966
Paintings, porcelain, furniture, tapestries, medieval kitchen coins, armory - library, archive 16591

Itzehoe

Kreismuseum Prinzeßhof, Kirchenstr 20, 25524 Itzehoe - T: (04821) 64068, Fax: 747012, E-mail: princesshof@freenet.de. Head: Dr. Anita Chmielewski-Hagius
Local Museum / Folklore Museum - 1938
Silver, glasses 16592

Wenzel-Hablik-Museum, Reichenstr 21, 25524 Itzehoe - T: (04821) 603377, Fax: 603294, E-mail: museum@wenzel-hablik.de, Internet: http:// www.wenzel-hablik.de. Head: Dr. Elisabeth Fuchs-Belhamri
Fine Arts Museum - 1995
Works by Wenzel Hablik (paintings, drawings, prints, handicraft), crystal coll of the artist - archive 16593

Jagsthausen

Schloßmuseum Jagsthausen, Götzenburg, 74249 Jagsthausen - T: (07943) 2335, Fax: 8157. Head: Hans Reinhard Freiherr von Berlichingen
Local Museum - 1924
Local history, Roman Finds, weapons, the iron hand of Götz von Berlichingen 16594

Jena

Akademisches Münzkabinett, Institut für Altertumswissenschaften der Friedrich-Schiller-Universität Jena, Kahlaische Str 1, 07745 Jena - T: (03641) 944825, Fax: 944802, E-mail: x7scgu@ rz.uni-jena.de, Internet: http://www.uni-jena.de/ philosophie/altertum/klassarch. Head: Prof. A. Geyer
Archaeological Museum - 1846
Greek and Roman coins 16595

Ernst-Haeckel-Haus, Berggasse 7, 07745 Jena - T: (03641) 949500, Fax: 949502, E-mail: b6brol@ nds.rz.uni-jena.de, Internet: http://www.uni-jena.de/ biologie/ehh/haeckel.htm. Head: Prof. Dr. Dr. O. Breidbach
Natural History Museum / University Museum - 1920
Memorabilia on zoologist Ernst Haeckel, hist of Darwinism (1834-1919), bequest, letters, manuscripts, pictures, historic furnishings, coll of hist of medicine - archive 16596

Galerie der JENOPTIK AG, Carl-Zeiss-Str 1, 07743 Jena - T: (03641) 652358, Fax: 652484, E-mail: PR@jenoptik.com
Fine Arts Museum 16597

Galerie des Jenaer Kunstvereins, Zwätzengasse 16, 07743 Jena - T: (03641) 449722, Fax: 449722
Association with Coll / Public Gallery 16598

Goethe-Gedenkstätte, Friedrich-Schiller-Universität Jena, Fürstengraben 26, 07743 Jena - T: (03641) 931188, Fax: 931187. Head: Dr. Michael Platen
Special Museum - 1921/53
Memorabilia on J.W. Goethe (1749-1832) in his former Jena home 16599

Hilprecht-Sammlung Vorderasiatischer Altertümer der Friedrich-Schiller-Universität Jena, Kahlaische Str 1, 07745 Jena - T: (03641) 944870, Fax: 944802, Internet: http://www.uni-jena.de/ philosophie/iskvo. Head: Prof. Dr. Manfred Krebernik
Archaeological Museum - 1925
3,000-7th c Cuneiform writing, Aramaic writings 16600

Optisches Museum der Ernst-Abbe-Stiftung Jena, Carl-Zeiss-Pl 12, 07743 Jena - T: (03641) 443165, Fax: 443224, Internet: http:// www.optischesmuseum.de. Head: R.F. Schmalbrock
Science&Tech Museum - 1922
Microsope, glasses, telescopes, cameras - reconstruction of the Zeiss factory of 1866 16601

Phyletisches Museum, Friedrich-Schiller-Universität, Vor dem Neutor 1, 07743 Jena - T: (03641) 949140, Fax: 949142, E-mail: b6suel@pan.zoo.uni-jena.de, Internet: http://www.zoo.uni-jena.de. Head: Prof. Dr. Martin S. Fischer
Natural History Museum - 1908
Phyletic systematics, genetics, comparative anatomy and embryology, paleontology, zoogeography, anatomical specimens, anthropology, entomology 16602

Romantikerhaus, Unterm Markt 12a, 07743 Jena - T: (03641) 443263, Fax: 228829, E-mail: ks@ romantikerhaus.jetzweb.de, Internet: http:// www.jena.de. Head: Klaus Schwarz
Fine Arts Museum - 1981
Memorial of August Wilhelm and Friedrich Schlegel, Ludwig Tieck, Novalis, German early romantic period 16603

Sammlung Antiker Kleinkunst, Institut für Altertumswissenschaften der Friedrich-Schiller-Universität Jena, Kahlaische Str 1, 07745 Jena - T: (03641) 944820, Fax: 944802, E-mail: - guenther.schoerner@rz.uni-jena.de, Internet: http:// www.uni-jena.de/philosophie/altertum/klassarch. Head: Prof. Dr. A. Geyer
Archaeological Museum - 1846
Ancient vases, terracottas, glasses 16604

Schillers Gartenhaus der Friedrich-Schiller-Universität, Schillergäßchen 2, 07745 Jena - T: (03641) 931188, Fax: 931187, Internet: http:// www.Verwaltung.uni-jena.de/uni/ Schillersghaus.html
Special Museum / University Museum - 1924/90
Memorabilia on Friedrich Schiller (1759-1805) in his former Jena home, historic furnishings 16605

Städtische Museen Jena - Historische Schlosserei Pelzer, Fischergasse 1, 07743 Jena - T: (03641) 443275, 826867, Fax: 443245. Head: Holger Nowak
Science&Tech Museum
Historical metalworking shop 16606

Städtische Museen Jena - Stadtmuseum Göhre, Markt 7, 07743 Jena - T: (03641) 35980, Fax: 359820, E-mail: galerie@stadtmuseum.- jellonet.de, Internet: http://www.thueringen.de/de/ museen/jena/stadtmuseum/index.html. Head: Holger Nowak
Local Museum / Public Gallery - 1903
Hist of city and university, crafts, industry, sculpture, drawings, pewter, porcelain, textiles 16607

Thüringer Universitäts- und Landesbibliothek Jena, Bibliothekspl 2, 07743 Jena - T: (03641) 940000, Fax: 490002, E-mail: thulb@thulb.uni-jena.de, Internet: http://www.thulb03.biblio.uni-jena.de. Head: Dr. Sabine Wefers
Library with Exhibitions 16608

Jerichow

Klostermuseum Jerichow, Am Gut 1, 39319 Jerichow - T: (039343) 285, Fax: 285. Head: Rolf Naumann
Religious Arts Museum
Medieval dishes 16609

Jesteburg

Kunststätte Bossard, Bossardweg 95, Lüllau, 21266 Jesteburg - T: (04183) 5112, Fax: (040) 7926464, E-mail: info@bossard.de, Internet: http:// www.bossard.de. Head: Oliver Fok
Decorative Arts Museum / Fine Arts Museum 16610

Jever

Mühlen- und Landwirtschaftsmuseum, Hooksweg, 26441 Jever - T: (04461) 2106, E-mail: - schlossmuseum.jever@ewetel.net, Internet: http:// www.schlossmusem.de. Head: Dr. Antje Sander
Science&Tech Museum / Agriculture Museum
Mill from the 18th/19th c, farmyard, agriculture 16611

Schloßmuseum Jever, Schloßpl, 26441 Jever - T: (04461) 2106, E-mail: schlossmuseum.jever@ ewetel.net, Internet: http:// www.schlossmuseum.de. Head: Dr. Antje Sander
Decorative Arts Museum - 1921
Faience, tin, silver, furniture, 16th-19th c style of home décor, folk art and archaeology of Jever country - library, archive 16612

Jockgrim

Zehnthaus, Ludwigstr 26, 76751 Jockgrim - T: (07271) 52818, 52138, Fax: 5739, Internet: http://www.zehnthaus.de
Association with Coll / Fine Arts Museum 16613

**Städtische Galerie Karlsruhe
Lichthof 10 beim ZKM,
Lorenzstraße 27
76135 Karlsruhe**

Telefon +49-(0)721 133-4444/4401
Telefax +49-(0)721 133-4409

Internet
www.staedtische.galerie.de
E-mail
staedtische-galerie@karlsruhe.de

Öffnungszeiten:
Mittwoch 10–20 Uhr
Donnerstag bis Samstag 10–18 Uhr
Montag und Dienstag geschlossen

Ziegeleimuseum, Untere Buchstr 26, 76751
Jockgrim - T: (07271) 981393, 52895, Fax: 981707
Special Museum　　16614

Johanngeorgenstadt

Lehr- und Schaubergwerk Frisch Glück,
Wittigsthalstr 13-15, 08349 Johanngeorgenstadt -
T: (03773) 882140, Fax: 882140, Internet: http://
www.johanngeorgenstadt.de. Head: M. Krauß
Science&Tech Museum / Natural History Museum -
1974
Tools and equipment from the time of mining silver
ore, bismuth and uranium, Henry Becquerel, Martin
Heinrich Klaproth, radiation protection　　16615

Jork

Heimatmuseum und Galerie neue diele,
Mittelnkirchen-Hinterdeich 176, 21635 Jork -
T: (04162) 5364, Fax: 1316
Local Museum / Public Gallery　　16616

Museum Altes Land, Westerjork 49, 21635 Jork -
T: (04162) 5715, Fax: 5715, E-mail: gemeinde@
jork.de, Internet: http://www.jork.de. Head: Dieter-
Theodor Bohlmann
Local Museum
Half-timbered house from the 18th c, architecture
and building techniques, fruit-growing,
orchards　　16617

Jühnde

Heinrich-Sohnrey-Archiv und Gedächtnisstätte,
Mautturm, Jühnder Schloß, Dorfstr 13, 37127
Jühnde - T: (05502) 2798, Fax: 2746. Head:
Hubertus Menke
Special Museum　　16618

Jülich

Museum Brückenkopf, Stadtgeschichtliches
Museum Jülich, Brückenkopf -Park, Rurauenstr 11,
52428 Jülich - T: (02461) 97950, Fax: 63354,
979522, E-mail: brueckenkopf-park@t-online.de,
Internet: http://www.brueckenkopf-park.de. Head:
Andreas Kupka, Marcel Perse
Local Museum / Archaeological Museum - 1998
Hist of the building, hist of the French period in the
Rhineland 1794-1814　　16619

Museum Zitadelle, Stadtgeschichtliches Museum
Jülich, Zitadelle, Schloßstr, 52428 Jülich -
T: (02461) 63228, 63353, Fax: 63354,
E-mail: museum@juelich.de, Internet: http://
www.juelich.de/museum. Head: Marcell Perse
Military Museum / Historical Museum / Decorative
Arts Museum - 1993
Printed writings about architecture and military hist
(16th-19th c), fortification history　　16620

Stadtgeschichtliches Museum Jülich, Kleine Rurstr
20, 52428 Jülich - T: (02461) 63228, Fax: 63354,
E-mail: museum@juelich.de, Internet: http://
www.juelich.de/museum. Head: Marcell Perse
Local Museum / Archaeological Museum - 1902
Local archaeological finds from prehistoric, Roman,
Frankish and medieval times, landscape painting
19th c by J.W. Schirmer　　16621

Jüterbog

Städtisches Museum Abtshof, Regionalmuseum des
Niederen Flämings, Planeberg 9, 14913 Jüterbog -
T: (03372) 401531, Fax: 401531, Internet: http://
www.jueterbog.de. Head: Norbert Jannek
Historical Museum / Military Museum / Folklore
Museum - 1954
Local arts, crafts, costumes, ancient and early hist,
German hist garrison (1746-1945), Russian hist
garrison (1945-94), painter Erich Sturtevant, Fritz
Bilkenroth - library, archive　　16622

Juist

Küstenmuseum, Loogster Pad, 26571 Juist -
T: (04935) 1488, 990077, Fax: 990077. Head: H.
Kolde
Natural History Museum - 1956
Hist of sea cartography, seamarks and nautical
science, marine biology, natural gas from the North
Sea, 3 500-metre core sample, sea rescue service,
marine life - library, archives　　16623

Kaarst

Städtische Galerie Kaarst, Am Rathauspl 23,
Büttgen, 41564 Kaarst - T: (02131) 987417,
Fax: 987121, E-mail: info@kaarst.de
Public Gallery　　16624

Kaiserslautern

Pfalzgalerie Kaiserslautern, Museumspl 1, 67657
Kaiserslautern - T: (0631) 3647201, Fax: 3647202,
E-mail: info@pfalzgalerie.de, Internet: http://
www.pfalzgalerie.de. Head: Dr. Britta E. Buhlmann
Public Gallery / Fine Arts Museum - 1875
Glass painting, wall hangings, ceramics and
handicrafts from the 15th-18th c, 19th-20th c
graphics, paintings and sculpture, Peter Behrens
plan coll　　16625

Theodor-Zink-Museum und Wadgasserhof, Steinstr
48/55, 67657 Kaiserslautern - T: (0631) 3652327,
Fax: 3652322. Head: Dr. Peter Dunkel
Local Museum - 1925
Folk customs and art, archeological finds,
handicrafts, local history　　16626

Kaisheim

Bayerisches Strafvollzugsmuseum, Abteistr 4,
86687 Kaisheim - T: (09099) 9990, Fax: 999300
Historical Museum
Hist of corporal punishment and
imprisonment　　16627

Leitheimer Schloß-Museum, Schloß Leitheim,
86687 Kaisheim - T: (09097) 1016, Fax: 1019,
E-mail: schlosskonzerte@tucher-leitheim.de,
Internet: http://www.tucher-leitheim.de. Head:
Bernhard Freiherr von Tucher
Fine Arts Museum - 1960
Frescos by Godefried Bernhard Göz　　16628

Kalkar

Kunstsammlung Sankt Nicolai-Kirche, Sankt
Nicolai, 47546 Kalkar - T: (02824) 2380
Religious Arts Museum - 1445
Medieval altars, religious panel paintings　　16629

Städtisches Museum, Grabenstr 66, 47546 Kalkar -
T: (0281) 13118. Head: Gabriela Mander
Fine Arts Museum　　16630

Kallmünz

Gummeum im Raitenbucher Schloß, Raitenbucher
Schloß, Vilsgasse 10, 93183 Kallmünz - T: (09621)
33316
Fine Arts Museum - 1999　　16631

Kamen

Kostede Museum für Überlebenskunst, Im Winkel
1, 59174 Kamen - T: (02307) 39560
Fine Arts Museum　　16632

Städtisches Museum Kamen, Bahnhofstr 21, 59174
Kamen - T: (02307) 553412/13, Fax: 553414,
E-mail: museum@stadt-kamen.de, Internet: http://
www.stadt-kamen.de. Head: Hans-Jürgen Kistner
Local Museum　　16633

Kamenz

Lessing-Museum, Lessingpl 1-3, 01917 Kamenz -
T: (03578) 38050, Fax: 380525, E-mail: kontakt@
lessingmuseum.de, Internet: http://
www.lessingmuseum.de. Head: Dieter Fratzke
Special Museum - 1931
Memorabilia on poet Gotthold E. Lessing (1729-
1781), theater history - library　　16634

Museum der Westlausitz Kamenz, Macherstr 140,
01917 Kamenz - T: (03578) 3746710,
Fax: 3746799, E-mail: post@lra-kamenz.de,
Internet: http://www.kamenz.de. Head: Friederike
Koch
Local Museum / Natural History Museum - 1954
Hist of Westlausitz, zoology, botany, culture, pewter,
crafts - auditorium, library　　16635

Kamp-Bornhofen

Flößer- und Schiffermuseum, Rathaus, 56341
Kamp-Bornhofen - T: (06773) 360
Special Museum　　16636

Kamp-Lintfort

Ordensmuseum Abtei Kamp, Abteipl 24, 47475
Kamp-Lintfort - T: (02842) 4062, Fax: 4063,
E-mail: reinecke.k@t-online.de, Internet: http://
www.kloster-kamp.de. Head: Klaus Reinecke
Religious Arts Museum - 1987
Orders, graphics coll - library　　16637

Kandern

Heimat- und Keramikmuseum, Ziegelstr 21, 79400
Kandern - T: (07626) 7622
Local Museum - 1976
Local ceramics, history of iron production　　16638

Kapellendorf

Burgmuseum der Wasserburg Kapellendorf, Am
Burgpl 1, 99510 Kapellendorf - T: (036425) 22485,
Fax: 22485
Local Museum - 1950
Geology, ancient and early history, castle and local
history, peasant folklore, farm tools　　16639

Kappeln

Schleimuseum, Mittelstr 8, 24376 Kappeln -
T: (04642) 1428
Local Museum　　16640

Karben

Landwirtschafts- und Heimatmuseum,
Degenfeld'sches Schloß, Rathauspl 1, 61184 Karben
- T: (06039) 48115, Fax: 48130,
E-mail: stadtkarben@aol.com. Head: Herbert
Schuch
Agriculture Museum / Local Museum
Agricultural implements, tools and machines　16641

Karlsbad

Heimatmuseum Ittersbach, Friedrich-Dietz-Str 2,
76307 Karlsbad - T: (07248) 391
Local Museum - 1985
Agriculture, household items　　16642

Karlsdorf-Neuthard

Heimatmuseum Karlsdorf, Amalienstr, 76689
Karlsdorf-Neuthard - T: (07251) 40599, 41936
Local Museum
Local hist　　16643

Karlshuld

Freilicht- und Heimatmuseum Donaumoos, Haus
im Moos, Kleinhohenried 108, 86668 Karlshuld -
T: (08454) 95205, Fax: 95207, E-mail: info@haus-
im-moos.de, Internet: http://www.haus-im-moos.de
Local Museum / Open Air Museum - 1984
Local crafts　　16644

Karlsruhe

Badische Landesbibliothek, Erbprinzenstr 15, 76133
Karlsruhe - T: (0721) 1752222, Fax: 1752333,
E-mail: sekretariat@blb-karlsruhe.de,
Internet: http://www.blb-karlsruhe.de. Head: Dr.
Peter Michael Ehrle
Library with Exhibitions　　16645

Badischer Kunstverein, Waldstr 3, 76133 Karlsruhe
- T: (0721) 28226, Fax: 29773, E-mail: info@
badischer-kunstverein.de, Internet: http://
www.badischer-kunstverein.de. Head: Angelika
Stepken
Association with Coll　　16646

Badisches Landesmuseum Karlsruhe, Schloss,
76131 Karlsruhe - T: (0721) 9266514,
Fax: 9266537, E-mail: info@landesmuseum.de,
Internet: http://www.landesmuseum.de. Head: Prof.
Dr. Harald Siebenmorgen
Historical Museum - 1919
Egyptian art, classical archeology, provincial Roman
art, local prehistory, folk customs and art, textiles,
ceramics, arms and armor, furniture, glass painting,
numismatics, ethnography, furniture - library,
workshops, photo laboratory　　16647

GEDOK Künstlerinnenforum, Markgrafenstr 14,
76131 Karlsruhe - T: (0721) 374137, Fax: 374137
Fine Arts Museum　　16648

Karl-Seckinger-Ausstellung, Rathauspl, 76229
Karlsruhe - T: (0721) 48518. Head: A. Ruf
Fine Arts Museum - 1985
Works of sculptor Karl Seckinger (1897-
1978)　　16649

Karpatendeutsches Museum, Schloß Karlsburg
Durlach, Pfinztalstr 9, 76227 Karlsruhe - T: (0721)
1334204, 133428, Fax: 1334209, E-mail:
karpatendeutsches-museum@kultur-karlsruhe.de,
Internet: http://www.karpatendeutsche.de. Head:
Ernst Hochberger
Local Museum - 1969
Cultural items of the German settlers in Slovakia -
library, archiv　　16650

Kindermuseum, Staatliche Kunsthalle Karlsruhe,
Hans-Thoma-Str 2-6, 76133 Karlsruhe - T: (0721)
9263370, Fax: 9262573, E-mail: muse@kunsthalle-
karlsruhe.de, Internet: http://www.kunsthalle-
karlsruhe.de. Head: Dr. Sibylle Brosi
Special Museum / Fine Arts Museum　　16651

Medienmuseum → ZKM Medienmuseum

**Museum beim Markt - Angewandte Kunst seit
1900**, Badisches Landesmuseum Karlsruhe, Karl-
Friedrich-Str 6, 76133 Karlsruhe - T: (0721)
9266578, Fax: 9266537, E-mail: info@
landesmuseum.de, Internet: http://
www.landesmuseum.de. Head: Prof. Dr. Harald
Siebenmorgen
Decorative Arts Museum - 1992
Decorative and applied art since 1900 (Art Nouveau,
Art Déco, Funktionalismus, Industrial Design,
Contemporary Crafts)　　16652

Museum für Literatur am Oberrhein, Karlstr 10,
76133 Karlsruhe - T: (0721) 1334087,
Fax: 1334089, E-mail: mlo@karlsruhe.de,
Internet: http://www.karlsruhe.de/Kultur/MLO. Head:
Prof. Dr. Hansgeorg Schmidt-Bergmann
Special Museum - 1965
Manuscripts, first editions, reprints, paintings,
illustrations, portraits of writers of the Upper Rhein
area (from Middle Ages to the present), archives -
library　　16653

Museum für Neue Kunst, ZKM Zentrum für Kunst- und Medientechnologie, Lorenzstr 9, 76135 Karlsruhe - T: (0721) 81001300/1325, Fax: 81001309, E-mail: mnk@zkm.de, Internet: http://www.mnk.zkm.de. Head: Prof. Dr. Götz Adriani
Fine Arts Museum - 1997
Coll of media art (painting, sculpture, graphics) by Bill Viola, Nam June Paik, Bruce Nauman and works of 4 private colls (Froehlich, FER, Grässlin, S. Weishaupt) 16654

Museum in der Majolika-Manufaktur, Badisches Landesmuseum Karlsruhe, Ahaweg 6, 76131 Karlsruhe - T: (0721) 9266583, Fax: 9266537, E-mail: info@landesmuseum.de, Internet: http://www.landesmuseum.de. Head: Prof. Dr. Harald Siebenmorgen
Decorative Arts Museum - 1988
Products of the 'Grossherzogliche/Staatliche Majolika-Manufaktur Karlsruhe' from its beginnings in 1901 to the present 16655

Pfinzgaumuseum, Schloß Karlsburg, Durlach, 76227 Karlsruhe - T: (0721) 1334228, Fax: 1334299. Head: Dr. Susanne Asche
Historical Museum - 1922
Local history, documents of the revolution of 1848/49 in Baden, Durlach faience, samples of 16th c bookprinting, paintings and drawings of the Durlach painter Karl Weysser, agricultural implements - archives 16656

Rechtshistorisches Museum, Stephanienstr 19, 76133 Karlsruhe - T: (0721) 29353, Fax: 29353. Head: Dr. K. Zippelius
Historical Museum - 1979
Legal hist 16657

Staatliche Kunsthalle Karlsruhe, Hans-Thoma-Str 2-6, 76133 Karlsruhe - T: (0721) 9263355, Fax: 9266788, E-mail: info@kunsthalle-karlsruhe.de, Internet: http://www.kunsthalle-karlsruhe.de. Head: Prof. Dr. Klaus Schrenk
Fine Arts Museum - 1845
German painting 14th-20th c, Dutch and Flemish painting 16th-18th c, French painting 17th-20th c, German and French sculpture 19th-20th c, prints and drawings 15th-20th c, Hans Thoma, Children's museum - library, conservation dept., workshops, education dept., ateliers 16658

Staatliches Museum für Naturkunde, Erbprinzenstr 13, 76133 Karlsruhe, mail addr: Postfach 111364, 76063 Karlsruhe - T: (0721) 1752161, Fax: 1752111, E-mail: museum@naturkundeka-bw.de, Internet: http://www.naturkundemuseum-bw.de. Head: Prof. Dr. Volkmar Wirth
Natural History Museum - 1785
Botany, geological sciences, entomology, zoology - library, photo laboratory, specimen workshop, vivarium 16659

Stadtmuseum im Prinz-Max-Palais, Karlstr 10, 76124 Karlsruhe - T: (0721) 1334230, Fax: 1334239, E-mail: stadtmuseum@karlsruhe.de, Internet: http://www.karlsruhe.de/kultur/stadtmuseum. Head: Dr. Peter Pretsch
Local Museum - 1885
Architectural drafts to local and regional 19th c buildings, portraits of princes, graphic prints, paintings of battles, caricatures, photo documentation of WWII, coins, medallions 16660

Städtische Galerie Karlsruhe, Lorenzstr 27, Hallenbau A, Lichthof 10, 76135 Karlsruhe - T: (0721) 1334401, 1334444, Fax: 1334409, E-mail: staedtische-galerie@karlsruhe.de, Internet: http://www.staedtische-galerie.de. Head: Prof. Dr. Erika Rödiger-Diruf
Fine Arts Museum - 1981
German art from romantic to now, paintings, sculptures, objects, works of paper, photography, Garnatz coll 16661

Verkehrsmuseum Karlsruhe, Werderstr 63, 76137 Karlsruhe - T: (0721) 374435, Fax: 563276. Head: Dr. H. Dittrich
Science&Tech Museum - 1969
History of transportation and motor vehicles, coaches, sleds, four-, three-, and two-wheeled vehicles, automobiles from 1885 to 1960, model trains, archives 16662

ZKM Medienmuseum, ZKM Zentrum für Kunst- und Medientechnologie Karlsruhe, Lorenzstr 19, 76135 Karlsruhe - T: (0721) 81001100, Fax: 81001139, E-mail: info@zkm.de, Internet: http://www.zkm.de. Head: Prof. Peter Weibel
Fine Arts Museum - 1997
New art, picturial media, music and acustic - Mediathek 16663

Karlstadt

Europäisches Klempner- und Kupferschmiede-Museum, Ringstr 47c, 97753 Karlstadt - T: (09353) 996330, Fax: 996331, E-mail: klempnermuseum@hotmail.de. Head: Ulrike Börtlein
Science&Tech Museum - 1997
Plumber and coppersmith's crafts 16664

Stadtgeschichtliches Museum im Landrichterhaus, Hauptstr 11, 97753 Karlstadt - T: (09353) 3536, 79020, Fax: 790299, E-mail: info@Karlstadt.de, Internet: http://www.Karlstadt.de. Head: Dr. Axel von Erffa
Local Museum - 1985
Town hist 16665

Karlstein am Main

Heimatmuseum, Schulstr 2, 63791 Karlstein am Main - T: (06188) 78410, Fax: 78450, Internet: http://www.karlstein.de
Local Museum - 1975
Local and military hist, archaeological finds 16666

Kassel

Antikensammlung, Staatliche Museen Kassel, Schloß Wilhelmshöhe, 34131 Kassel - T: (0561) 93777, Fax: 9377666, E-mail: info@museum-kassel.de, Internet: http://www.museum-kassel.de. Head: Dr. Michael Eissenhauer
Fine Arts Museum - End of 18th c/1974
Antique art from Egypt, Greece, Rome, and the Roman provinces - library, workshops, photo laboratory, archives 16667

Brüder Grimm-Museum Kassel, Brüder-Grimm-Pl 4a, 34117 Kassel - T: (0561) 103235, Fax: 713299, E-mail: grimm-museum@t-online.de. Head: Dr. Bernhard Lauer
Special Museum / Fine Arts Museum / Historical Museum - 1959
Manuscripts and original documents on the life and works of the brothers Jacob and Wilhelm Grimm, first editions und reprints of their works, secondary literature, translations, documents on their political and scientific work, 19th c art - library, archive 16668

Deutsches Tapetenmuseum, Staatliche Museen Kassel, Brüder-Grimm-Pl 5, 34117 Kassel - T: (0561) 78460, Fax: 7846222, E-mail: info@museum-kassel.de, Internet: http://www.museum-kassel.de. Head: Dr. Michael Eissenhauer
Decorative Arts Museum - 1923
Leather-hanging and historical wallpapers of all epochs and from all countries, ancient tools used to produce wallpaper, modern equipment, documents on the history of wallpapers 16669

documenta Archiv für die Kunst des 20. und 21 Jahrhunderts, Untere Karlsstr 4, 34117 Kassel - T: (0561) 7874022, Fax: 7874028, E-mail: info@documentaArchiv.de, Internet: http://www.documenta.Archiv.de. Head: Karin Stengel
Library with Exhibitions 16670

EAM-live-Museum Wasserkraftwerk Wülmersen, c/o Energie-AG Mitteldeutschland, Monteverdistr 2, 34131 Kassel - T: (0561) 9331056, Fax: 9332507, E-mail: info@eam.de, Internet: http://www.eam.de
Science&Tech Museum - 1990
Hist of the hydroelectric power station 16671

Gemäldegalerie Alte Meister, Staatliche Museen Kassel, Schloß Wilhelmshöhe, 34131 Kassel - T: (0561) 93777, Fax: 9377666, E-mail: info@museum-kassel.de, Internet: http://www.museum-kassel.de. Head: Dr. Michael Eissenhauer
Fine Arts Museum - End of 18th c/1974
Paintings by Old Masters department - library, workshops, photo laboratory, archives 16672

Graphische Sammlung, Staatliche Museen Kassel, Schloß Wilhelmshöhe, 34131 Kassel - T: (0561) 93777, Fax: 9377666, E-mail: info@museum-kassel.de, Internet: http://www.museum-kassel.de. Head: Dr. Michael Eissenhauer
Fine Arts Museum - End of 18th c/1974
Prints and drawings - library, workshops, photo laboratory, archives 16673

Handschriftenabteilung der Universitätsbibliothek, Handschriftenabteilung, Brüder-Grimm-Pl 4a, 34117 Kassel - T: (0561) 8047315, Fax: 8047301, E-mail: kowi@bibliothek.uni-kassel.de, Internet: http://www.uni-kassel.de/bib/murhardsche/. Head: Dr. Konrad Wiedemann
Library with Exhibitions - 1580
Manuscripts, rare prints 16674

Johannes-Molzahn-Centrum für Documentation und Publication, Rheinweg 8-10, 34131 Kassel - T: (0561) 33704, Fax: 3164897, E-mail: Reisse@molzahn-centrum.de, Internet: http://www.molzahn-centrum.de. Head: Hans Peter Reisse
Fine Arts Museum 16675

Kunsthalle Fridericianum, Friedrichspl 18, 34117 Kassel - T: (0561) 7072720, Fax: 774578, E-mail: office@fridericianum-kassel.de, Internet: http://www.fridericanum-kassel.de. Head: René Block
Fine Arts Museum 16676

Kunsthandwerk und Plastik Sammlung, Staatliche Museen Kassel, Brüder-Grimm-Pl 5, 34117 Kassel - T: (0561) 78460, Fax: 7846222, E-mail: info@museum-kassel.de, Internet: http://www.museum-kassel.de. Head: Dr. Michael Eissenhauer
Decorative Arts Museum - 1913
Folk art 16677

Landes-, Universitäts und Murhardsche Bibliothek
→ Handschriftenabteilung der Universitätsbibliothek

Louis Spohr-Gedenk- und Forschungsstätte, Museum der Geschichte des Violinspiels, Schöne Aussicht 2, Palais Bellevue, 34117 Kassel - T: (0561) 15209. Head: Maurice F. Powell
Music Museum 16678

Museum für Astronomie und Technikgeschichte, Staatliche Museen Kassel, An der Karlsaue 20c, 34121 Kassel - T: (0561) 701320, Fax: 7013211, E-mail: info@museum-kassel.de, Internet: http://www.museum-kassel.de. Head: Dr. Michael Eissenhauer
Science&Tech Museum - 1992
Astronomical instruments, scientific instruments, clocks and the first computer 16679

Museum für Sepulkralkultur, Weinbergstr 25-27, 34117 Kassel - T: (0561) 918930, Fax: 9189310, E-mail: sekretariat@sepulkralmuseum.de, Internet: http://www.sepulkralmuseum.de. Head: Prof. Dr. Reiner Sörries
Special Museum - 1992
Funeral, cementary, mourning culture - library, archive (prints, music and photo) 16680

Museumspädagogische Beratung, Staatliche Museen Kassel, Wilhelmshöher Allee 380, 34131 Kassel - T: (0561) 312828, Fax: 312828, E-mail: info@museum-kassel.de, Internet: http://www.museum-kassel.de. Head: Dr. Michael Eissenhauer 16681

Naturkundemuseum im Ottoneum, Steinweg 2, 34117 Kassel - T: (0561) 7874014, Fax: 7874058. Head: Dr. Franz Malec
Natural History Museum - 1888
Botany, geology and paleontology, zoology, - library, specimen workshop, geological laboratory, archive 16682

Neue Galerie, Staatliche und Städtische Kunstsammlungen, Staatliche Museen Kassel, Schöne Aussicht 1, 34117 Kassel - T: (0561) 709630, Fax: 7096345, E-mail: info@museum-kassel.de, Internet: http://www.museum-kassel.de. Head: Dr. Michael Eissenhauer
Fine Arts Museum - 1976
German and European painting and sculpture from 1750 to the present, art of the sixties and seventies - Dep: 19th c painting 16683

Staatliche Museen Kassel, Direktion und Verwaltung, Schloß Wilhelmshöhe, 34131 Kassel, mail addr: Postfach 410420, 34066 Kassel - T: (0561) 93777, Fax: 9377666, E-mail: info@museum-kassel.de, Internet: http://www.museum-kassel.de. Head: Dr. Michael Eissenhauer
18th c
library 16684

Staatliche Museumsberatung für Nordhessen, Staatliche Museen Kassel, Kölnische Str 44-46, 34117 Kassel - T: (0561) 7889305, Fax: 7889594, E-mail: info@museum-kassel.de, Internet: http://www.museum-kassel.de. Head: Dr. Uwe Reher
Local Museum 16685

Stadtmuseum Kassel, Ständepl 16, 34117 Kassel - T: (0561) 7871400, Fax: 7874102, Internet: http://www.kassel.de. Head: Karl-Hermann Wegner
Local Museum - 1979
Townscape and town development in models, paintings, photos - Judaica div, Huguenot div 16686

Volkskunde Sammlung, Staatliche Museen Kassel, Brüder-Grimm-Pl 5, 34117 Kassel - T: (0561) 78460, Fax: 7846222, E-mail: info@museum-kassel.de, Internet: http://www.museum-kassel.de. Head: Dr. Michael Eissenhauer
Folklore Museum - 1913
Folk art 16687

Vor- und Frühgeschichte Sammlung, Staatliche Museen Kassel, Brüder-Grimm-Pl 5, 34117 Kassel - T: (0561) 78460, Fax: 7846222, E-mail: info@museum-kassel.de, Internet: http://www.museum-kassel.de. Head: Dr. Michael Eissenhauer
Archaeological Museum - 1913
Prehistorical finds - workshops 16688

Kastl bei Amberg

Heimatmuseum Kastl, Hohenburger Str 44, 92280 Kastl bei Amberg - T: (09625) 91173, 1742
Local Museum
Clocks, scales and religious folklore 16689

Kaub

Blüchermuseum, Metzgergasse, 56349 Kaub - T: (06774) 400, Internet: http://www.rhein-lahn-info.de/kaub/museum/bluechermuseum.htm. Head: Bruno Dreier
Military Museum - 1913
Memorabilia of Field Marshal Blücher, his furnishings, uniforms, weapons, army equipment of the War of 1812-1815, paintings of Blücher's crossing of the Rhine 16690

Kaufbeuren

Crescentia-Gedenkstätte, Obstmarkt 5, 87600 Kaufbeuren - T: (08341) 9070, Fax: 907102
Religious Arts Museum - 1975
Memorial place of the blessed Crescentia Höß (1682-1744) 16691

Feuerwehrmuseum, Neugablonzer Str 10, 87600 Kaufbeuren - T: (08341) 8727, Internet: http://www.kaufbeuren.de
Science&Tech Museum 16692

Gablonzer Archiv Museum, Postfach 749, 87585 Kaufbeuren Neugablonz - T: (08341) 61910, 64362, Fax: 635292, 68146. Head: Dr. Martin Posselt
Decorative Arts Museum / Library with Exhibitions - 1952
Hist of exiled Germans, paintings and sculptures - Archive, library, collection of cribs 16693

Gablonzer Haus mit Isergebirgsmuseum, Marktgasse 8, 87600 Kaufbeuren - T: (08341) 64362, 67848, Fax: 68146, 61091
Local Museum - 2001 16694

Heimatstube Schlesien, Müllergäßchen 4, 87600 Kaufbeuren - T: (08341) 18956
Local Museum - 1991 16695

Kunsthaus Kaufbeuren, Spitaltor 2, 87600 Kaufbeuren - T: (08341) 8644, Fax: 8655, E-mail: mail@kunsthaus-kaufbeuren.de, Internet: http://www.kunsthaus-kaufbeuren.de. Head: Hilke Gesine Möller
Fine Arts Museum - 1996
Art 16696

Neugablonzer Industrie- und Schmuckmuseum (closed until 2002), Marktgasse 8, 87584 Kaufbeuren, mail addr: Postfach 623, 87584 Kaufbeuren - Fax: 61091. Head: Gertrud Hofmann
Science&Tech Museum / Decorative Arts Museum / Historical Museum - 1976
Hist of Neugablonz - jewellery museum 16697

Puppentheatermuseum, Ludwigstr 41a, 87600 Kaufbeuren - T: (08341) 14121, 14329, 2555
Performing Arts Museum - 1987
Coll of puppets, posters and music instruments 16698

Stadtmuseum Kaufbeuren, Kaisergäßchen 12-14, 87600 Kaufbeuren - T: (08341) 100232, 4566, Fax: 9558797. Head: Dr. Astrid Pellengahr
Local Museum - 1879
Prehist, local hist, town and peasant furnishings, folk art, paintings, sculpture, ceramics, guilds, crucifixes, coins and medaillons, memorial to the writer Ludwig Ganghofer including his work room with memorabilia and manuscripts 16699

Kaufungen, Hessen

Regionalmuseum Alte Schule, Schulstr 33, 34260 Kaufungen, Hessen - T: (05605) 7307, Fax: 802104, E-mail: gemeinde-kaufungen.hess@t-online.de. Head: Winfried Wroz
Local Museum / Folklore Museum - 1986
Village life (school, farm and bourgeois houses, trade workshops) 16700

Kefenrod

Heimatmuseum Kefenrod, Hitzkirchener Str 17, 63699 Kefenrod - T: (06049) 96060, Fax: 960617
Local Museum - 1977
Hist of village and farm life 16701

Kehl

Hanauer Museum, c/o Kultur- und Verkehrsamt, Großherzog-Friedrich-Str 19, 77694 Kehl - T: (07851) 78783, Fax: 78783, E-mail: kulturamt@kehl.de, Internet: http://www.kehl.de. Head: Hartmut Stüwe
Local Museum - 1956
Town history 16702

Keilhau

Fröbelmuseum, c/o Sprachheilschule Friedrich Fröbel, 07407 Keilhau - T: (03672) 413382, Fax: 413382. Head: Gabriele Wächter
Historical Museum 16703

Kelheim

Archäologisches Museum der Stadt Kelheim, Ledergasse 11, 93309 Kelheim - T: (09441) 10492, 10409, Fax: 701229, Internet: http://www.altmuehltal.de. Head: Petra Neumann-Eisele
Archaeological Museum - 1908/1981
Early history, prehistory 16704

Befreiungshalle Kelheim, Befreiungshallestr 3, 93309 Kelheim - T: (09441) 682070, Fax: 682077, E-mail: info@bsv.bayern.de. Head: Dr. Brigitte Langer
Historic Site - 1863
Memorial site 16705

Orgelmuseum Kelheim, Am Kirchensteig 4, 93309 Kelheim, mail addr: Am Waldrand 10, 93346 Ihrlerstein - T: (09441) 5508, Fax: 5508
Music Museum 16706

Kellinghusen

Museum Kellinghusen, Hauptstr 18, 25548 Kellinghusen - T: (04822) 376210, Fax: 376215, Internet: http://www.kellinghusen.de. Head: Hans-Georg Bluhm
Local Museum / Decorative Arts Museum - 1953
Faience 16707

Kellmünz

Archäologischer Park mit Museums-Turm, Rechbergring, 89293 Kellmünz - T: (0731) 7040118, Fax: 7040666, E-mail: lra-nu@neu-ulm.de, Internet: http://www.landkreis.neu-ulm.de. Head: Walter Wörtz
Archaeological Museum - 1995
Roman finds 16708

Keltern

Heimatmuseum Keltern, Ettlinger Str 15, 75210 Keltern - T: (07236) 6878
Local Museum - 1988
Crafts, watches, viticulture, jewellery 16709

Kemnath

Heimat- und Handfeuerwaffenmuseum, Trautenbergstr 36, 95478 Kemnath - T: (09642) 7070, Fax: 914060, E-mail: hakkem@bigfoot.com, Internet: http://home.t-online.de/home/hakkem/museum.htm
Military Museum - 1984
Rustic culture, weapons and prehistorical objects passionplay 1988 16710

Kempen

Museum für Niederrheinische Sakralkunst, Burgstr 19, 47906 Kempen - T: (02152) 917384. Head: Elisabeth Friese
Religious Arts Museum 16711

Städtisches Kramer-Museum und Museum für Niederrheinische Sakralkunst im Kulturforum Franziskanerkloster, Burgstr 19, 47906 Kempen - T: (02152) 917271, 917264, Fax: 917384, E-mail: museum@kempen.de, Internet: http://www.kempen.de. Head: Dr. Elisabeth Friese
Religious Arts Museum / Decorative Arts Museum - 1912/1979
Coll of chests 16712

Kempten

Allgäu-Museum, Großer Kornhauspl 1, 87439 Kempten - T: (0831) 5402120, Fax: 2525463, E-mail: museen@kempten.de, Internet: http://www.allgaeu-museum.de. Head: Dr. Rainhard Riepertinger
Local Museum - 1883
Folk art objects, art, clocks, coins 16713

Allgäuer Burgenmuseum, Westendstr 21, 87439 Kempten - T: (08378) 1354, E-mail: stadtarchaeologie@allgaeu.org
Historical Museum
Medieval fortresses 16714

Alpenländische Galerie, Zweigmuseum des Bayerischen Nationalmuseums, Landwehrstr 4, 87439 Kempten - T: (0831) 540180, Internet: http://www.kempten.de/touristen/museen.html. Head: Dr. Reinhold Baumstark
Fine Arts Museum - 1991
Work of local artists (15th and 16th c) 16715

Alpinmuseum, Zweigmuseum des Bayerischen Nationalmuseums, Landwehrstr 4, 87439 Kempten, Allgäu - T: (0831) 540180, Internet: http://www.kempten.de/touristen/museen.html. Head: Dr. Reinhold Baumstark
Local Museum - 1990
Alpine hist 16716

Archäologischer Park Cambodunum - APC, Cambodunumweg 3, 87437 Kempten - T: (0831) 574250, Fax: 5742522, E-mail: stadtarchaeologie@allgaeu.org, Internet: http://www.kempten.de. Head: Dr. Gerhard Weber
Archaeological Museum / Open Air Museum - 1987
Roman finds excavated in the ancient ruins of Cambodunum, Gallo-Roman temple area, bath of the praetorium, forum area 16717

Prunkräume in der Residenz, Residenzpl 4-6, 87435 Kempten - T: (0831) 256251, Fax: 256260
Decorative Arts Museum
Baroque cloister (1732-1742) 16718

Zumsteinhaus mit Römischem Museum und Naturkunde-Museum, Residenzpl 31, 87435 Kempten - T: (0831) 12367, Fax: 2525463, E-mail: museen@kempten.de, Internet: http://www.kempten.de/touristen/museen.html
Archaeological Museum / Natural History Museum 16719

Kenzingen

Oberrheinische Narrenschau, Alte Schulstr 20, 79341 Kenzingen - T: (07644) 900113, Fax: 900160, E-mail: stadt-info@kenzingen.de, Internet: http://www.kenzingen.de. Head: Wolfram Stippich
Folklore Museum - 1976
200 life-size carnival dolls with wooden masks, photos and writings of the carnival celebration in the upper Rhein area 16720

Ketzin

Heimatmuseum der Stadt Ketzin, Rathausstr 32, 14669 Ketzin - T: (033233) 72012, Fax: 72099
Local Museum - 1982
Trades and guilds, tile-making industry, local hist 16721

Kevelaer

Niederrheinisches Museum für Volkskunde und Kulturgeschichte, Hauptstr 18, 47623 Kevelaer - T: (02832) 95410, Fax: 970962, E-mail: museum-kevelaer@t-online.de, Internet: http://www.kevelaer.de/museum. Head: Dr. Robert Plötz
Historical Museum / Folklore Museum - 1910
Prehist, local and regional hist, folk customs and art, hist of economics, religious art, regional sculpture, glass, textiles, ironwork, minerals, furnishings, toys, ceramics, graphics of the 18/19th c emergency currency, model coll, devotionalia, historical Leuker crib - library, workshops 16722

Kiedrich

Sammlung handgeschriebener Choralbücher, Suttonstr 1, 65399 Kiedrich - T: (06123) 2810. Head: Rainer Hilkenbach
Religious Arts Museum - 1965
Old choir books and manuscripts 16723

Kiefersfelden

Museum im Blaahaus am Unteren Römerweg, Innstr 52, 83088 Kiefersfelden - T: (08033) 609854, Fax: 609854
Local Museum - 2000 16724

Kiel

Antikensammlung, Kunsthalle zu Kiel, Düsternbrooker Weg 1-7, 24105 Kiel - T: (0431) 8802053, Fax: 8807309, E-mail: antikenslg@klassarch.uni-kiel.de, Internet: http://www.uni-kiel.de/klassarch/antisa.htm. Head: Prof. Bernhard Schmaltz
Museum of Classical Antiquities - 1843
Casts of Greek and Roman art, original antique vases, bronzes, sculpture, ceramics, and coins 16725

Geologisches und Mineralogisches Museum der Christian-Albrechts-Universität, Institut für Geowissenschaften, Ludewig-Meyn-Str 10, 24118 Kiel - T: (0431) 8802851, Fax: 8804457, 8804376, E-mail: kw@gpi.uni-kiel.de, Internet: http://www.ifg.uni-kiel.de/museum. Head: Prof. W. Depmeier
Natural History Museum 16726

Gut Seekamp der Hans Kock-Stiftung, Seekamper Weg 10, 24159 Kiel - T: (0431) 372322, 371837
Fine Arts Museum 16727

Kieler Stadt- und Schiffahrtsmuseum, Dänische Str 19, 24103 Kiel - T: (0431) 9013425, Fax: 9709728. Head: Dr. Jürgen Jensen
Historical Museum / Science&Tech Museum - 1970
Town hist, art and art hist, industrial hist, photography, boats and shipping 16728

Kunsthalle zu Kiel der Christian-Albrechts-Universität, Gemäldegalerie und Graphische Sammlung, Düsternbrooker Weg 1, 24105 Kiel - T: (0431) 8805751/56, Fax: 8805754, E-mail: buero@kunsthalle.uni-kiel.de, Internet: http://www.kunsthalle.uni-kiel.de. Head: Dr. Beate Ermacora
Fine Arts Museum / University Museum - 1855
German and Dutch masters of the 17th c, 18th c painting, 18th-21th c painting from Schleswig-Holstein and scandinavia, international contemporary art, graphics from 16th to 21th c - library 16729

Landesgeschichtliche Sammlung der Schleswig-Holsteinischen Landesbibliothek, Schloß, 24103 Kiel - T: (0431) 9067160/65, Fax: 9067167, E-mail: landesbibliothek@shlb.ki.shuttle.de, Internet: http://www.ki.shuttle.de/shlb. Head: Prof. Dr. Dieter Lohmeier, Dr. Renate Paczkowski
Local Museum / Library with Exhibitions 16730

Medizin- und Pharmaziehistorische Sammlung Kiel, Brunswiker Str 2, 24105 Kiel - T: (0431) 8805720/21, Fax: 8805727, E-mail: medmuseum@med-hist.uni-kiel.de, Internet: http://www.med-hist.uni-kiel.de. Head: Prof. Dr. Jörn Henning Wolf
Special Museum / Science&Tech Museum / University Museum 16731

Museum für Völkerkunde der Universität Kiel, Hegewischstr 3, 24105 Kiel - T: (0431) 5974000. Head: Prof. Katesa Schlosser
Ethnology Museum - 1884
South Sea weapons, clothing, shell ornaments, wood carving, masks, boat models, - library 16732

Stadtgalerie Kiel, Heinrich-Ehmsen-Stiftung, Andreas-Gayk-Str 31, 24103 Kiel - T: (0431) 9013410/11, Fax: 90163475, E-mail: stadtgalerie@LHStadt.Kiel.de. Head: Wolfgang Zeigerer
Public Gallery - 1988
Contemporary art, expressionism 16733

Theatergeschichtliche Sammlung und Hebbel-Sammlung, Olshausenstr 40-60, 24118 Kiel - T: (0431) 8803409
Performing Arts Museum - 1924
Documents on the hist of the European, esp the German language, theatre, books, manuscripts, pictures, records, scenery designs, portraits of actors, memorabilia of the playwright and poet Friedrich Hebbel and his circle, theatrical hist of Hebbel's dramas, archives 16734

Zoologisches Museum, Christian-Albrechts-Universität, Hegewischstr 3, 24105 Kiel - T: (0431) 8805180, Fax: 8805177, E-mail: zoolmuseum@email.uni-kiel.de, Internet: http://www.uni-kiel.de. Head: Dr. Wolfgang Dreyer
Natural History Museum - 18th c
Invertebrate marine animals, insects, comparative coll of fauna from northern Central Europe, the North Sea, and the Baltic Sea, animals of the Ice Age from Schleswig-Holstein, extinct birds - library 16735

Kienberg, Oberbayern

Dorfmuseum, Schulhaus, 83361 Kienberg, Oberbayern - T: (08628) 752, E-mail: herbert.schiebl@t-online.de
Folklore Museum - 1989
Local hist and crafts 16736

Kinding

Technik anno dazumal - Museum Kratzmühle, Mühlweg 1, 85125 Kinding - T: (08461) 9682, 8318, Fax: 9188, Internet: http://www.altmuehltal.de/kinding/technikmuseum.htm. Head: Dr. Helge Vergho
Science&Tech Museum
Old crafts and technology 16737

Kipfenberg

Fastnachtsmuseum Fasenickl, Torbäckgasse 1, 85110 Kipfenberg - T: (08465) 3232, Fax: 941043, E-mail: Tourist-Info@Kipfenberg.de, Internet: http://www.Kipfenberg.de
Folklore Museum - 1985
Hist of the carnival, masks, costumes, folklore 16738

Römer und Bajuwaren Museum Burg Kipfenberg, Burg, 85110 Kipfenberg - T: (08465) 905707, Fax: 905708, E-mail: bajuwarenmuseum@altmuehlnet.de, Internet: http://www.bajuwaren-kipfenberg.de. Head: Christian Weiss
Archaeological Museum / Local Museum - 1997
Roman and old Bavarian hist, archeological finds, local hist 16739

Kirchanschöring

Bauernhofmuseum Hof, Hof 1, 83417 Kirchanschöring - T: (08685) 469
Agriculture Museum - 1975
Agricultural implements and tools, rustic culture 16740

Kirchberg an der Jagst

Sandelsches Museum (closed until end of 2002), Kirchstr 17, 74592 Kirchberg an der Jagst - T: (07954) 98010, Fax: 980119, E-mail: info@kirchberg-jagst.de, Internet: http://www.kirchberg-jagst.de
Local Museum - 1930
Local hist 16741

Schloßmuseum, Schloßstr 16, 74592 Kirchberg an der Jagst - T: (07954) 8020, Fax: 80210. Head: S. Benzel
Historic Site 16742

Kirchdorf an der Amper

Bavaria Airways-Museum, Obere Dorfstr 15, 85414 Kirchdorf an der Amper - T: (08166) 7920
Science&Tech Museum
Aircraft models, uniforms 16743

Kirchdorf auf Poel

Heimatmuseum, Möwenweg 4, 23999 Kirchdorf auf Poel - T: (038425) 20732
Local Museum - 1958
Hist of the Poel isle, folk hist 16744

Kirchentellinsfurt

Schlossmuseum, Schlosshof 9, 72138 Kirchentellinsfurt - T: (07121) 90050, Fax: 900550, E-mail: info@kirchentellinsfurt.de, Internet: http://www.kirchentellinsfurt.de. Head:
Folklore Museum - 1977
Furniture, decorative art, militaria, religious art, peasant life 16745

Kirchhain

Heimatmuseum Großseelheim, Marburger Ring 31, 35274 Kirchhain - T: (06422) 3339, 3980, E-mail: boethgue@aol.com
Local Museum - 1984
Historical farm house and smithery 16746

Kirchheim, Schwaben

Heimatmuseum Kirchheim, Schwaben, Rathaus, Marktpl, 87757 Kirchheim, Schwaben - T: (08266) 86080
Local Museum - 1961
Local hist and crafts 16747

Kirchheim unter Teck

Fürstenzimmer im Schloß Kirchheim, Alleenstr, 73230 Kirchheim unter Teck - T: (07021) 974553/54, Fax: 974588, E-mail: info@schloss-ludwigsburg.de, Internet: http://www.schloesser-magazin.de. Head: Ulrich Krüger
Decorative Arts Museum / Local Museum - 1985
Furniture and paintings from the late 18th c and first half of 19th c, 18th/19th c hist of Württemberg 16748

Heimatstube Freiwaldau-Bieletal, Kornstr 4, 73230 Kirchheim unter Teck - T: (07021) 3059
Local Museum - 1953
Customs, costumes, crafts - archive, library 16749

Städtische Galerie im Kornhaus, Max-Eyth-Str 19, 73230 Kirchheim unter Teck - T: (07021) 973032, Fax: 973060, E-mail: info@kirchheim.vhs.org, Internet: http://www.kirchheim.vhs.org
Public Gallery - 1922
Regional art 16750

Kirchheimbolanden

Heimatmuseum für Stadt- und Landkreis, Amtsstr 14, 67292 Kirchheimbolanden - T: (06352) 400415
Local Museum 16751

Kirchlauter

Schmiedemuseum Kirchlauter, Kirchenstr 6, 96166 Kirchlauter - T: (09536) 352, Fax: 1512, Internet: http://www.Kirchlauter-Neubrunn.de
Science&Tech Museum - 1996
Forge 16752

Kirchzell

Waldmuseum Watterbacher Haus, Preunschen 1, 63931 Kirchzell - T: (09373) 97430, Fax: 974324, E-mail: gemeinde@kirchzell.de, Internet: http://www.kirchzell.de
Local Museum
Hist of forestry 16753

Kirschau

Burgmuseum, Am Schloßberg 25, 02681 Kirschau - T: (03592) 38780, Fax: 387899, E-mail: carmen.wendler@kirschau.de, Internet: http://www.kirschau.de
Historical Museum - 1927
Castle ruins, armaments, ceramics, textiles 16754

Kißlegg

Museum Expressiver Realismus, Neues Schloß, 88353 Kißlegg - T: (07563) 936142, Fax: 936199, E-mail: tourist@kisslegg.de, Internet: http://www.kisslegg.de
Fine Arts Museum 16755

Neues Schloß und Instrumentenmuseum, Schloßstr, 88353 Kißlegg - T: (07563) 18131, Fax: 2382. Head:
Decorative Arts Museum / Music Museum - 1960
18th c castle built by Johann Georg Fischer, interiors, staircase, frescoes, sculpture, furniture, painting, porcelain, Chinese paintings, musical instruments 16756

Kitzingen

Deutsches Fastnachtmuseum, Falterturm, 97318 Kitzingen - T: (09321) 23355, Fax: 23355. Head: Hans-Joachim Schumacher
Folklore Museum - 1967
History of local carnival customs, masks and costumes, writings and documents - archive 16757

Städtisches Museum (closed until 2003), Landwehrstr 23, 97318 Kitzingen - T: (09321) 927063, Fax: 20320, E-mail: museum@stadt.kitzingen.de, Internet: http://www.stadt.kitzingen.de. Head: Doris Badel
Local Museum - 1895
Local hist and crafts 16758

Klasdorf

Museumsdorf und Technisches Denkmal, c/o Verein Glashütte e.V., Hüttenweg 20, 15837 Klasdorf - T: (033704) 98090, 980914/19, Fax: 980922, E-mail: info@museumsdorf-glashuette.de, Internet: http://www.museumsdorf-glashuette.de. Head: Christoph Schulze
Science&Tech Museum / Open Air Museum / Historical Museum - 1991
History of glass works, the thermos flask and its inventor Reinhold Burger 16759

Kleve

Museum Kurhaus Kleve, Ewald Mataré-Sammlung, Tiergartenstr 41, 47533 Kleve - T: (02821) 75010, Fax: 750111, E-mail: info@museumkurhaus.de, Internet: http://www.museumkurhaus.de. Head: Drs. Guido de Werd
Fine Arts Museum - 1997
Painting and sculpture of the Middle Ages, Dutch Baroque painting of the 17th c, art of the 19th c, local hist, modern art, work of the sculptor Ewald Mataré (1887-1965), special focus on photography Andreas Gursky and Thomas Struth, contemporary - library 16760

Stiftung B.C. Koekkoek-Haus, Kavarinerstr 33, 47533 Kleve - T: (02821) 768833, Fax: 768834, E-mail: museum.kurhaus@t-online.de. Head: Dr. Guido de Werd
Fine Arts Museum
Art of the 19th c 16761

Klingenberg am Main

Teddymuseum, In der Altstadt 7, 63911 Klingenberg am Main - T: (09372) 921167, Fax: 921199
Decorative Arts Museum - 1994
Hist of the teddy bear 16762

Weinbau- und Heimatmuseum, Wilhelmstr 13, 63911 Klingenberg am Main - T: (09372) 921259, Fax: 12354, E-mail: verkehrsamt@klingenberg-main.de, Internet: http://www.klingenberg-main.de
Local Museum / Agriculture Museum
Wine-growing and local hist 16763

Klockenhagen

Freilichtmuseum Klockenhagen, Mecklenburger Str 57, 18311 Klockenhagen - T: (03821) 2775, Fax: 2775. Head: Heiner Morgenroth
Open Air Museum 16764

Kloster, Hiddensee

Gerhart-Hauptmann-Haus, Kirchweg 13, 18565 Kloster, Hiddensee - T: (038300) 397, Fax: 397, Internet: http://www.gerhart-hauptmann-museen.de. Head: Dr. Sonja Kühne
Special Museum - 1956
Memorabilia on poet Gerhart Hauptmann (1862-1946) - library 16765

Heimatmuseum der Insel Hiddensee, Kirchweg 1, 18565 Kloster, Hiddensee - T: (038300) 363, Fax: 64225
Local Museum - 1954
Geology, natural history, culture and history of the isle - library 16766

Kloster Veßra

Hennebergisches Museum, Kloster Veßra, Anger, 98660 Kloster Veßra - T: (036873) 69030, Fax: 69049, E-mail: info@museumklostervessra.de, Internet: http:www.museumklostervessra.de. Head: Dr. Günther Wölfing
Historical Museum / Folklore Museum / Open Air Museum - 1975
History of the former Veßra and the country of the Earls of Henneberg (region in the South Thuringia), ethnography, development of agriculture technologies, animals husbandry - library 16767

Kloster Zinna

Museum Kloster Zinna, Am Kloster 6, 14913 Kloster Zinna - T: (03372) 439505, Fax: 439505. Head: Historic Site - 1956
Cloister hist, weaving, brewery - library 16768

Knetzgau

Maintal-Steigerwald-Museum, Schloß Oberschwappach, Schloßstr 6, 97478 Knetzgau - T: (09527) 790, Fax: 7923
Local Museum 16769

Knittlingen

Faust-Museum, Kirchpl 2, 75438 Knittlingen - T: (07043) 37370, Fax: 37371. Head: Dr. Günther Mahal
Special Museum / Library with Exhibitions - 1980
Items dealing with the historical person Faust and his times, the mythological and literary figure Faust, Faust in the arts, manuscripts and books, documents - archive 16770

Koblenz

Kunsthalle Koblenz, Gymnasialstr 9-11, 56068 Koblenz - T: (0261) 3002899, Fax: 12143, E-mail: kunsthalle-koblenz@t-online.de, Internet: http://www.kunsthalle-koblenz.de. Head: Oliver L. Zimmermann
Public Gallery 16771

Landesmuseum Koblenz, Staatliche Sammlung technischer Kulturdenkmäler, Festung Ehrenbreitstein, 56077 Koblenz - T: (0261) 97030, Fax: 701989, E-mail: lmuseum@abo.rhein-zeitung-de, Internet: http://homes.rhein-zeitung.de/~lmuseum. Head: Thomas Metz
Science&Tech Museum / Archaeological Museum - 1956
Tools and machines oft the past used in mining, winegrowing implements, brandy brewery, water supply equipment, machinery for processing tobacco, ceramics, machinery for processing pumice-stones, famous designers and engineers of Rhineland-Palatinate (Otto, Thonet, Horch, Pfaff, Wagner, Bücker) - library, workshops, photo laboratory 16772

Ludwig Museum im Deutschherrenhaus, Danziger Freiheit 1, 56068 Koblenz, mail addr: Postfach 2080, 56020 Koblenz - T: (0261) 304040, Fax: 3040413, E-mail: sludwigm@abo.rhein-zeitung.de. Head: Dr. Beate Reifenscheid-Ronnisch
Fine Arts Museum - 1992
Contemporary French art, modern art since 1950 16773

Mittelrhein-Museum, Florinsmarkt 15-17, 56068 Koblenz - T: (0261) 1292520, Fax: 1292500, E-mail: info@mittelrhein-museum.de, Internet: http://www.mittelrhein-museum.de. Head: Dr. Mario Kramp
Fine Arts Museum - 1835
Prehist, medieval paintings and sculpture, Baroque sculpture and painting, Dutch paintings, local Romantic landscape paintings from the 19th-20th c, Januarius Zick (1730-97) 16774

Rhein-Museum Koblenz, Charlottenstr 53a, 56077 Koblenz - T: (0261) 703450, Fax: 703450, E-mail: info@rhein-museum.de, Internet: http://www.rhein-museum.de. Head: Dr. Rainer Doetsch
Science&Tech Museum / Local Museum - 1912
Navigation of the Rhein, ship models, construction of the current, seamarks, hydrology, hydrological instruments, steam engines, fish and fisheries, preparations of biology, hist of the river Rhine, anthropology, hist of the Neanderthal men 16775

Kochel am See

Franz-Marc-Museum, Herzogstandweg 43, 82431 Kochel am See - T: (08851) 7114, Fax: 615021, E-mail: info@kochel.de, Internet: http://www.franz-marc-museum.de. Head: Dr. Wolfgang Eberl
Fine Arts Museum - 1986
Paintings, graphics, sculpture by Franz Marc and other members of the "Der Blaue Reiter"-group, memorabilia of Franz Marc 16776

Ködnitz

Dorfschulmuseum, Ködnitz 6, 95361 Ködnitz - T: (09221) 1529
Local Museum / Special Museum - 1993
Local school 16777

Kölleda

Heimatmuseum, Roßpl 39, 99625 Kölleda - T: (03635) 482887, Fax: 450125
Local Museum - 1929
Geology, ancient and early history, fauna, local history, crafts, numismatics - library 16778

Köln

4711-Museum, Schwertnergasse 1 und Glockengasse 4711, 50667 Köln - T: (0221) 2573911
Special Museum - 1980
Perfume 16779

Agfa Photo-Historama, Museum Ludwig, Bischofsgartenstr 1, 50667 Köln - T: (0221) 22122411, 22123948, Fax: 22124114, E-mail: Dewitz@ml.museenkoeln.de, Internet: http://www.museenkoeln.de. Head: Dr. Bodo von Dewitz
Science&Tech Museum - 1974/1986
Cameras and photo studios illustrating the history of photography, Hugo Erfurth portrait coll 16780

artothek, Am Hof 50, 50667 Köln - T: (0221) 22122332, Fax: 22123265, Internet: http://www.museenkoeln.de. Head: Christiane Dinges
Fine Arts Museum 16781

Deutsches Sport- und Olympia-Museum, Rheinauhafen 1, 50678 Köln - T: (0221) 336090, Fax: 3360999, E-mail: sportmuseum@sportmuseum-koeln.de, Internet: http://www.sportmuseum-koeln.de. Head: Dr. Karlheinz Wiegmann
Special Museum - 1999 16782

Deutsches Tanzarchiv Köln, Im Mediapark 7, 50670 Köln - T: (0221) 2265757, Fax: 2265758, E-mail: tanzarchiv@aol.com, Internet: http://www.sk-kultur.de. Head: Frank-Manuel Peter
Performing Arts Museum - 1948/1997 16783

Domschatzkammer, Roncallipl 2, 50667 Köln - T: (0221) 27280130, Fax: 27280150, E-mail: dombauarchiv-koeln@arcormail.de
Religious Arts Museum 16784

DuMont Kunsthalle, Boltensternstr 173, 50735 Köln
Public Gallery 16785

Erzbischöfliches Diözesanmuseum Köln, Roncallipl 2, 50667 Köln - T: (0221) 2577672, Fax: 254828, E-mail: Kolumba@t-online.de, Internet: http://www.kolumba.de. Head: Dr. Joachim M. Plotzek
Fine Arts Museum / Religious Arts Museum - 1854
Religious art dating from Merovingian times to the 19th c, Christian archeological finds, arts and crafts, pious folk art, grave monuments, illuminated manuscripts (9th-16th c), coins and medaillons, 20th-c art, early Gothic, contemporary art (Kounellis, Beuys, Thek, Tollens, Saura, Wahrhol and others) - library 16786

Forschungsarchiv für römische Plastik, Universität zu Köln, Albertus-Magnus-Pl, 50931 Köln - T: (0221) 4702946
Library with Exhibitions 16787

Galeria Erotica-Museum für erotische Kunst, Heinsbergstr 16, 50674 Köln - T: (0221) 237079
Fine Arts Museum 16788

Geldgeschichtliches Museum, Kreissparkasse Köln, Neumarkt 18-24, 50667 Köln - T: (0221) 2272370, Fax: 2273761, E-mail: geldgeschichte@KSK-Koeln.de, Internet: http://www.geldgeschichte.de. Head: Thomas Lautz
Historical Museum - 1953
Coins, scales, bank notes, savings account books, purses, safes, money boxes, "primitive" and traditional money 16789

GeoMuseum der Universität, Mineralogische, Zülpicher Str 49b, 50674 Köln - T: (0221) 4703368, Fax: 4705199, E-mail: r.hollerbach@min.uni-koeln.de, Internet: http://www.geomuseum.uni-koeln.de. Head: Dr. R. Hollerbach, Dr. M. Grigo, Geolog.-Paläontologische Abteilung
Natural History Museum / University Museum - 1969
Mineralogy, geology, paleonthology 16790

Gothaer Kunstforum, Alteburger Wall 1, 50878 Köln - T: (0221) 30901029
Fine Arts Museum 16791

Haus des Waldes, Gut Leidenhausen, 51147 Köln - T: (02203) 39987, Fax: 39987
Natural History Museum - 1982
Development of natural forests, forest soils, physiology of trees, fungi, animals and the ecological chain, forests as protective elements for water resources, dendrochronology 16792

Historische Braustätte der Küppers Brauerei, Alteburger Str 155, 50968 Köln - T: (0221) 37790, Fax: 3779320. Head: Christian Bügel
Science&Tech Museum - 1982
Beer advertising (poster) - Brewery of 1880 16793

Historische Lehrsammlung der Feuerwehr Köln, Feuer- und Rettungswache 3, Gleueler Str 223-225, 50935 Köln - T: (0221) 9748431, Fax: 9748434. Head: Stephan Neuhoff
Science&Tech Museum - 1997 16794

Historisches Archiv der Stadt Köln, Severinstr 222-228, 50676 Köln - T: (0221) 2212327. Head: Dr. Everhard Kleinertz
Library with Exhibitions 16795

Imhoff-Stollwerck-Museum, Museum für Geschichte und Gegenwart der Schokolade, Rheinauhafen 1a, 50678 Köln - T: (0221) 9318880, Fax: 93188814, Internet: http://www.koeln.org/imhoff-stollwerck-museum.de. Head: Maria Mrachacz
Special Museum - 1993
Porcelain, pre-Columbian art, posters, enamel signs, chocolate fountain - archive, library, indoor tropical forest 16796

Japanisches Kulturinstitut, Universitätsstr 98, 50674 Köln - T: (0221) 9405580, Fax: 9405589, E-mail: jfco@jki.de, Internet: http://www.jki.de
Fine Arts Museum
Japanese art 16797

Josef-Haubrich-Kunsthalle, Museen der Stadt Köln, Josef-Haubrich-Hof 1, 50676 Köln - T: (0221) 22122335, Fax: 22124552, E-mail: kunsthalle@netcologne.de, Internet: http://www.museenkoeln.de
Fine Arts Museum - 1967 16798

Käthe Kollwitz Museum Köln, Neumarkt 18-24, 50667 Köln - T: (0221) 2272899, 2272602, Fax: 2273762, E-mail: kollwitz@ksk-koeln.de, Internet: http://www.kollwitz.de. Head: Hannelore Fischer
Fine Arts Museum - 1985 16799

Kölnischer Kunstverein, Cäcilienstr 33, 50667 Köln - T: (0221) 217021, Fax: 210651, E-mail: koelnkv@netcologne.de, Internet: http://www.isp.de/koelnischerkunstverein. Head: Kathrin Rhomberg
Public Gallery 16800

Kölnisches Stadtmuseum, Museen der Stadt Köln, Zeughausstr 1-3, 50667 Köln - T: (0221) 22125789, Fax: 22124154, E-mail: ksm@museenkoeln.de, Internet: http://www.museenkoeln.de. Head: Dr. Werner Schäfke
Local Museum - 1888
Local history and local art, Judaica, textiles, graphic arts, musical instruments, Rhine illustrations from 16-19th c - Library, graphic coll, arthothek, Kölnische Galerie 16801

Kulturbunker Mülheim, Berliner Str 70, 51063 Köln
Public Gallery 16802

Kunst- und Museumsbibliothek, Museen der Stadt Köln, Kattenbug 18-24, 50667 Köln - T: (0221) 22122388, Fax: 22122210, E-mail: kmb@stadt-koeln.de, Internet: http://www.museenkoeln.de/kmb. Head: Dr. Karl Stamm
Library with Exhibitions - 1957 16803

Kunstraum Fuhrwerkswaage, Bergstr 79, 50999 Köln - T: (02236) 61049, Fax: 967339. Head: Jochen Heufelder
Public Gallery
Modern art 16804

Kunstverein Köln rechtsrheinisch e.V., Regentenstr 82, 51063 Köln - T: (0221) 625040, Fax: 625040, Internet: http://www.kunstverein-koeln.de. Head: Irmgard Mantzke
Public Gallery 16805

Museum für Angewandte Kunst, Museen der Stadt Köln, An der Rechtschule, 50667 Köln - T: (0221) 22123860, Fax: 22123885, E-mail: -museumfuerangewandtekunst@stadt-koeln.de, Internet: http://www.museenkoeln.de. Head: Dr. Susanne Anna
Decorative Arts Museum - 1888
Applied art from the Middle Ages to the present day, design, fashion coll 16806

Museum für Ostasiatische Kunst, Museen der Stadt Köln, Universitätsstr 100, 50674 Köln - T: (0221) 9405180, Fax: 407290, E-mail: mok@mok.museenkoeln.de, Internet: http://www.museenkoeln.de/mok. Head: Dr. Adele Schlombs
Fine Arts Museum - 1909
Chinese, Korean, and Japanese art from prehistoric period to present - library 16807

Museum für visuelle Kommunikation, Postfach 501119, 50971 Köln - T: (0221) 387048, Fax: 374878, E-mail: Auction@Breker.com. Head: Uwe H. Breker
Science&Tech Museum - 1978
Printing presses, typewriters, duplicating machines and copying apparatus, optical illusions, cameras, projectors, beginnings of television (1926-46), magic lanterns 16808

Museum Kölner Karnevalsorden, Unter Käster 12, 50667 Köln - T: (0221) 252981
Folklore Museum 16809

Museum Ludwig, Museen der Stadt Köln, Bischofsgartenstr 1, 50667 Köln - T: (0221) 22122370, Fax: 2214114, E-mail: ml@ml.museenkoeln.de, Internet: http://www.museenkoeln.de. Head: Prof. Kasper König
Fine Arts Museum - 1976
20th c art (German Expressionism, Russian Avantgarde, Picasso, Pop-Art), International contemporary artists - photography, video dep, library, Agfa-Photo-Historama 16810

Museum Ludwig in der Halle Kalk, Neuerburgstr, 51103 Köln - T: (0221) 22122382
Fine Arts Museum 16811

Museum Schnütgen, Museen der Stadt Köln, Cäcilienstr 29, 50667 Köln - T: (0221) 22122310, Fax: 22128489, E-mail: schnuetgen@netcologne.de, Internet: http://www.museenkoeln.de. Head: Dr. Hiltrud Westermann-Angerhausen
Religious Arts Museum - 1910
Art from the early Middle Ages to the Baroque period, including sculpture, ivories, enamel, bronze and gold, illuminated manuscripts, stained glass, textiles - library 16812

Rautenstrauch-Joest-Museum, Museum für Völkerkunde, Ubierring 45, 50678 Köln - T: (0221) 336940, 3369413, Fax: 3369410, E-mail: rjm@rjm.museenkoeln.de, Internet: http://www.museenkoeln.de. Head: Dr. Klaus Schneider
Ethnology Museum - 1901
Ethnographic coll from America, Africa, Near East, South East Asia and Oceania - library, coll of historical photogr 16813

Rheinisches Bildarchiv, Museen der Stadt Köln, Kattenbug 18-24, 50667 Köln - T: (0221) 22122354, Fax: 22122296, E-mail: rba@rbakoeln.de, Internet: http://www.museenkoeln.de/rba. Head: Dr. Roswitha Neu-Kock
Library with Exhibitions - 1936 16814

Römisch-Germanisches Museum, Museen der Stadt Köln, Roncallipl 4, 50667 Köln - T: (0221) 22124438, Fax: 22124030, E-mail: roemisch-germanisches-museum@stadt-koeln.de, Internet: http://www.museenkoeln.de. Head: Prof. Dr. Hansgerd Hellenkemper
Archaeological Museum - 1946
Prehistoric finds from the Cologne and Rhein regions, monuments from the local Roman period, glass, lamps, coins, jewelry and other decorative and applied arts - library 16815

Theaterwissenschaftliche Sammlung, Universität zu Köln, Burgallee 2, Schloß Wahn, 51127 Köln - T: (02203) 600920, Fax: 6009230, E-mail: tws@uni-koeln.de, Internet: http://www.uni-koeln.de/phil-fak/thefife/home/wahn_hp.html. Head: Prof. Dr. Elmar Buck
Performing Arts Museum / Ethnology Museum
European theater since the 16th c, ostasiatica - film archive 16816

Wallraf-Richartz-Museum - Fondation Corboud, Museen der Stadt Köln, Martinstr 39, 50667 Köln - T: (0221) 22122372, Fax: 22122629, E-mail: wrm@wrm.museenkoeln.de, Internet: http://www.museenkoeln.de/wrm/. Head: Dr. Rainer Budde
Fine Arts Museum - 1824
Painting from the Cologne school (1300-1550), German and Netherlandish painting to 1550, Netherlandish painting from 1550-1800, painting from the Latin countries, contemporary painting and sculpture, graphic coll (1900) 16817

Königsberg in Bayern

Gerätesammlung Koch, Haus Nr 80, 97486 Königsberg in Bayern - T: (09525) 1555, Fax: 1842
Science&Tech Museum - 1981
Agricultural implements and tools, local crafts and rustic culture 16818

Königsbronn

Torbogenmuseum, Im Klosterhof 1, 89551 Königsbronn - T: (07328) 96250, Fax: 962527, Internet: http://www.gemeinde@koenigsbronn.de. Head: Michael Stütz
Local Museum - 1971
History of the local Cistercian monestary, iron ore mining and smelting, archaelogical finds, domestic and farming implements - Landesfischereimuseum 16819

Königsbrunn

Archäologische Sammlung mit Heimatvertriebenenstube und Kruk-Sammlung, Marktpl 7 (Rathaus), 86343 Königsbrunn - T: (08231) 916487
Local Museum / Archaeological Museum 16820

Lechfeldmuseum, Schwabenstr 36, 86343 Königsbrunn - T: (08231) 916487, Fax: 916488, E-mail: kulturbuero@koenigsbrunn.de, Internet: http://www.koenigsbrunn.de/kult_bild/museen/lerchfeldmuseum.htm. Head: Franz Moritz
Folklore Museum - 1974
Local hist and crafts, religious folkore 16821

Naturkundliche Sammlung, Bürgermeister-Wohlfarth-Str 54, 86343 Königsbrunn - T: (08231) 916487, Fax: 916488, E-mail: kulturbuero@koenigsbrunn.de, Internet: http://www.koenigsbrunn.de
Natural History Museum
Geology and paleontology - library 16822

Königsdorf

Heimatmuseum Königsdorf, Beuerberger Str 6, 82549 Königsdorf - T: (08197) 931212
Local Museum - 1985
Agricultural tools, rustic furniture and local hist 16823

Königsfeld im Schwarzwald

Dorfmuseum Buchenberg, Dörfle 24, 78126 Königsfeld im Schwarzwald - T: (07725) 7500
Local Museum - 1987
Local hist, peasant life, crafts, ceramics, paintings 16824

Königshain-Wiederau

Alte Schule mit Clara-Zetkin-Gedächtnisstätte, Rochlitzer Str 14, 09306 Königshain-Wiederau - T: (037202) 8040, Fax: 80418, E-mail: gem.koewie@t-online.de, Internet: http://www.wiederau.de
Historical Museum - 1952
Memorabilia of political figure Clara Zetkin (1857-1933) and her circle in house of her birth, school system history 16825

Königslutter

Kaiserdom-Museum, Vor dem Kaiserdom 3-4, 38154 Königslutter - T: (05353) 2729, Fax: 501155. Head: Wolfgang Itter
Religious Arts Museum - 1986
Town, cathedral, chapter and Benedictine cloister hist, stonemasonry 16826

Museum mechanischer Musikinstrumente, Am Plan 2, 38154 Königslutter - T: (05353) 4005. Head: Jens Carlson
Music Museum
Mechanical musical instruments, musical boxes, barrels 16827

Königstein im Taunus

Burg- und Stadtmuseum Königstein, Altes Rathaus, Kugelherrnstr 1, 61462 Königstein im Taunus - T: (06174) 21455, Fax: 21455, E-mail: klaus.bordes@t-online.de, Internet: http://home.t-online.de/home/klaus.bordes/museum.htm. Head: Rudolf Krönke
Local Museum
Town hist, coins, ceramics 16828

Königstein, Sächsische Schweiz

Festung Königstein, 01824 Königstein, Sächsische Schweiz - T: (035021) 64601, Fax: 64602, E-mail: festung-koenigstein@t-online.de, Internet: http://www.festung-koenigstein.de. Head: Dr. Angelika Taube
Historical Museum / Military Museum - 1955
Military hist coll, graphics, portraits, postcards, hist of the fortress (1241-1589) - library 16829

Königswinter

Museum für schlesische Landeskunde im Haus Schlesien, Dollendorfer Str 412, Heisterbacherrott, 53639 Königswinter - T: (02244) 8860, Fax: 886200, E-mail: museum@haus-schlesien.de, Internet: http://www.schlesisches.museum.com. Head: Dr. Stephan Kaiser
Historical Museum / Decorative Arts Museum
Hist of Silesia, glass, tin, silver, fayence, porcelain, Bunzlau ceramics, sculptures and furniture from five centuries 16830

Siebengebirgsmuseum, Kellerstr 16, 53639 Königswinter - T: (02223) 3703, Fax: 909272, E-mail: info@siebengebirgsmuseum.de, Internet: http://www.siebengebirgsmuseum.de. Head: Elmar Scheuren
Local Museum / Historical Museum - 1927
Prints (18th-19th c), local history, economic history, Rhine Romanticism and tourism, geology 16831

Körle

Margret-Knoop-Schellbach-Museum, Im Mülmischtal 2, 34327 Körle - T: (05665) 94980, Fax: 949813, E-mail: meldeamt@koerle.de, Internet: http://www.koerle.net
Fine Arts Museum
Oil and watercolour painting, sketches, copper and silver works, sculptures, glas mosaics and verre églomisé picture 16832

Kösching

Heimatmuseum Kösching, Am Stadtweg 2, 85092 Kösching - T: (08456) 98910, Fax: 989124
Local Museum - 1957
Roman finds 16833

Museum für Archäologie und Volkskunde, Klosterstr 3, 85092 Kösching - T: (08456) 963009, Fax: 989124, E-mail: info@markt-koesching.de
Archaeological Museum / Agriculture Museum / Local Museum
Geology and finds 16834

Köthen, Anhalt

Bach-Gedenkstätte im Schloß Köthen, Schloßpl 4, 06366 Köthen, Anhalt - T: (03496) 212546, Fax: 214068. Head: Günther Hoppe
Music Museum - 1912
J.S. Bach and his life in Köthen 16835

Kulturhistorisches Museum Schloss Köthen, Schlosspl 4, 06366 Köthen, Anhalt - T: (03496) 212546, Fax: 214068, Internet: http://www.kulturserver.de/home/ssbg/koethen.htm
Historic Site / Historical Museum
Prehistory, homoeopathy, local and crafts hist, religious art, Anhaltinian coins and medals 16836

Naumann-Museum, Schloßpl 4, 06366 Köthen, Anhalt - T: (03496) 212074, Fax: 303868. Head: Dr. Wolf-Dieter Busching
Special Museum / Natural History Museum / Historical Museum - 1915
Memorabilia on science researcher J.F. Naumann, ornithology coll 16837

Kötzting

Pfingstritt-Museum Kötzting, Kirchenburg, Herrenstr 11, 93444 Kötzting - T: (09941) 6020, 602134, Fax: 602130, E-mail: poststelle@koetzting.de
Folklore Museum - 1996
Annual village festival 16838

Schnapsmuseum, Pfingstreiterstr 44, 93444 Kötzting - T: (09941) 3251
Special Museum 16839

Waldschmidthaus Waldfrieden, Regenstein 12, 93444 Kötzting - T: (09941) 4695, Fax: 4695, Internet: http://www.ug.btl.de
Public Gallery / Local Museum 16840

Kohren-Sahlis

Lindigtmühle am Lindenvorwerk, Lindenvorwerk, 04655 Kohren-Sahlis - T: (034344) 61285, Fax: 62592, E-mail: info@lindigtmuehle.de, Internet: http://www.lindigtmuehle.de. Head: Günter Barthel
Science&Tech Museum
Watermill built 1524 16841

Töpfermuseum, Baumgartenstr 18, 04655 Kohren-Sahlis - T: (034344) 61547
Decorative Arts Museum - 1961
18th c potter's workshop, workers equipment - Schwind pavilion Rudigsdorf 16842

Kolbermoor

Heimat- und Industriemuseum, Bahnhofstr 12, 83059 Kolbermoor - T: (08031) 920485, Fax: 920486, E-mail: Heimatmuseum.Kolbermoor@t-online.de, Internet: http://www.Kolbermoor.de
Local Museum - 1993 16843

Kolitzheim

Museum für Militär- und Zeitgeschichte, Stammheim, Waldweg 5, 97509 Kolitzheim - T: (09381) 9255, Fax: 9850, E-mail: info@g-weissenseel.de, Internet: http://www.militaer-museum.de
Military Museum 16844

Konstanz

Archäologisches Landesmuseum Baden-Württemberg, Benediktinerpl 5, 78467 Konstanz - T: (07531) 98040, Fax: 68452, E-mail: info@konstanz.alm-bw.de, Internet: http://www.konstanz.alm-bw.de. Head: Prof. Dr. Dieter Planck
Archaeological Museum - 1992
Archaeological finds from all periods 16845

Bodensee-Naturmuseum, Wallgutstr 14, 78462 Konstanz - T: (07531) 12873900, Fax: 128739017. Head: Dr. Ingo Schulz-Weddigen
Natural History Museum - 1969
Geology, paleontology, zoology, botany 16846

Hus-Museum, Hussenstr 64, 78462 Konstanz - T: (07531) 29042. Head: Michael Müller
Special Museum - 1965
Documents on the life and work of Johannes Hus, Hieronymus of Prague, and John Wycliff, housed in dwelling used by Hus during the Council of Constance (1414) 16847

Kunstverein Konstanz e.V., Wessenbergstr 39-41, 78462 Konstanz - T: (07531) 22351, Fax: 22358, E-mail: kunstverein.konstanz@uni-konstanz.de, Internet: http://www.kunstverein-konstanz.uni-konstanz.de. Head: Michael Günther
Association with Coll 16848

Neuwerk Kunsthalle, Reichenauerstr 186, 78467 Konstanz - T: (07531) 4549406
Public Gallery 16849

Rosgartenmuseum, Rosgartenstr 3-5, 78459 Konstanz - T: (07531) 900246, Fax: 900608, E-mail: gleichensteine@stadt.konstanz.de, Internet: http://home.konstanz.de. Head: Elisabeth von Gleichenstein
Local Museum / Fine Arts Museum - 1870/71
Art and cultural history of the Lake Constance region (painting and sculpture, 14th/15th and 17th/18th/19th c), coins, folk art, handicrafts, chronic of the Council of Constance, archaeology of the Lake of Constance area - library 16850

Städtische Wessenberg-Galerie, Wessenbergstr 43, 78462 Konstanz, mail addr: Rosgartenstr 3-5, 78459 Konstanz - T: (07531) 900246, Fax: 900608, E-mail: starkb@stadt.konstanz.de, Internet: http://www.stadt.konstanz.de. Head: Dr. Barbara Stark
Fine Arts Museum - 1860/1970
Painting (16th-20th c), drawings (15th-19th c), with emphasis on Italian and Netherlandish masters, graphics (15th-16th and 19th-20th c) 16851

Konz

Volkskunde- und Freilichtmuseum, Roscheider Hof, 54329 Konz - T: (06501) 92710, Fax: 927111, E-mail: info@roscheiderhof.de, Internet: http://www.roscheiderhof.de. Head: Dr. U. Haas
Folklore Museum / Open Air Museum / Agriculture Museum
Agricultural implements, viticulture, old crafts, cast-iron stoves, reconstructed buildings 16852

Korb

Steinzeitmuseum, Sammlung Reinhard, Schulstr 22, 71404 Korb - T: (07151) 606532. Head: Rolf Reinhard, Erika Reinhard
Archaeological Museum - 1928/74 16853

Korbach

Städtisches Museum, Kirchpl, 34497 Korbach - T: (05631) 53289, Fax: 53200, E-mail: info@korbach.de, Internet: http://www.korbach.de/museum.htm. Head: Dr. Wilhelm Völcker-Janssen
Local Museum - 1924/1994
Prehistory, mining and geology, folklore, peasant costumes and household utensils, weapons, minerals, regional history, Palaeontology, baroque and contemporary art 16854

Korntal-Münchingen

Heimatmuseum Münchingen, Kirchgasse 1, 70825 Korntal-Münchingen - T: (07150) 920725, Fax: 920740
Local Museum - 1986 16855

Kornwestheim

Schulmuseum Nordwürttemberg in Kornwestheim, Schillerstr 13, 70806 Kornwestheim - T: (07154) 202373, 16100, Fax: 202202, E-mail: office@kornwestheim.de, Internet: http://www.kornwestheim.de
Historical Museum - 1983
School hist, hist of the cultural techniques reading and writing, primers, writing and teaching implements, historic ABC-books and reader, wall pics - education library 16856

Koserow

Atelier Otto Niemeyer-Holstein, Die Neue Galerie, Lüttenort, 17459 Koserow - T: (038375) 20213, 22004, Fax: 22005, E-mail: atelier-onh@t-online.de, Internet: http://www.atelier-otto-niemeyer-holstein.de. Head: Franka Keil
Fine Arts Museum
Paintings, watercolour and hand drawings, printings by the artist (1896-1984) 16857

Kraiburg am Inn

Heimatmuseum Kraiburg am Inn, Jettenbacher Str 5, 84559 Kraiburg am Inn - T: (08638) 98380, Fax: 983829
Local Museum - 1935
Early and local hist, crafts and rustic furniture 16858

Kraichtal

Badisches Bäckereimuseum und Erstes Deutsches Zuckerbäckermuseum, Hintere Gasse 2, 76703 Kraichtal - T: (07250) 7744, Fax: 7775, E-mail: kultur@kraichtal.de, Internet: http://www.kraichtal.de
Special Museum - 1978
Old fashioned tools and equipment of the bakers' trade, old recipe books, documents and certificates illustrating the history of the bakers' trade, agricultural tools and machinery 16859

Museum der Stadt Kraichtal, Hauptstr, Schloß Gochsheim, 76703 Kraichtal - T: (07250) 7744, Fax: 7775, E-mail: kultur@kraichtal.de, Internet: http://www.kraichtal.de
Local Museum - 1989
Viticulture, local hist, art, folklore 16860

Ursula Blickle Stiftung, Mühlweg 18, 76703 Kraichtal - T: (07251) 60919, Fax: 68687, E-mail: ursula-blickle-stiftung@t-online.de, Internet: http://www.ursula-blickle-stiftung.de. Head: Ursula Blickle
Public Gallery
International Art 16861

Kranenburg, Niederrhein

Museum Katharinenhof, Mühlenstr 9, 47559 Kranenburg, Niederrhein - T: (02826) 623, Fax: 8138. Head: Gerhard Rozyn
Fine Arts Museum - 1922
19th c painting, folk art 16862

Krautheim, Jagst

Johanniter-Museum, Burgweg 3, 74238 Krautheim, Jagst - T: (06294) 9812, Fax: 9848, E-mail: stadt@krautheim.de. Head: Dieter Hirschbiegel
Religious Arts Museum - 1978 16863

Krefeld

Deutsches Textilmuseum Krefeld, Andreasmarkt 8, 47809 Krefeld - T: (02151) 9469450, Fax: 9469455, E-mail: textilmuseum@krefeld.de. Head: Prof. Dr. Brigitte Tietzel
Decorative Arts Museum - 1880
Textiles from Europe, Orient, India, Peru, West Africa - library 16864

Haus Esters, Wilhelmshofallee 97, 47800 Krefeld - T: (02151) 770044, Fax: 770368, E-mail: kunstmuseen@krefeld.de, Internet: http://www.krefeld.de. Head: Dr. Martin Hentschel
Fine Arts Museum 16865

Haus Lange, Wilhelmshofallee 91, 47800 Krefeld - T: (02151) 770044, Fax: 770368, E-mail: kunstmuseen@krefeld.de, Internet: http://www.krefeld.de. Head: Dr. Martin Hentschel
Fine Arts Museum - 1955 16866

Hülser Heimatstuben, Konventstr 13, 47839 Krefeld - T: (02151) 733313
Local Museum 16867

Kaiser Wilhelm Museum, Karlspl 35, 47798 Krefeld - T: (02151) 770044, Fax: 770368, E-mail: kunstmuseen@krefeld.de, Internet: http://www.krefeld.de. Head: Dr. Martin Hentschel
Fine Arts Museum 16868

Museumszentrum Burg Linn, Rheinbabenstr 85, 47809 Krefeld - T: (02151) 570036, Fax: 571972, E-mail: dr.ch.reichmann@krefeld.de. Head: Dr. Christoph Reichmann
Local Museum - 1926
Finds from the Krefeld-Gellep Roman-Frankish burial grounds, culture of the Lower Rhein region, fortress with 16th and 17th c furnishings 16869

Kreiensen

Heimatmuseum Greene, c/o Hermann Regenhardt, Steinweg 24, 37547 Kreiensen - T: (05563) 6370, Fax: 6370
Local Museum - 1989 16870

Krempe

Historisches Rathaus, Am Markt 1, 25361 Krempe - T: (04824) 816. Head: Harald Bolten
Local Museum
Silver from local medieval guild, weapons, and domestic utensils, housed in 1570 hall 16871

Kressbronn am Bodensee

Lände, Seestr 24, 88079 Kressbronn am Bodensee - T: (07543) 60246
Fine Arts Museum - 1980
Regional modern art 16872

Kreuth

Erstes Ethnisches Puppenmuseum der Welt, Zentrum für Außergewöhnliche Museen, Tegernseerstr 32, 83708 Kreuth - T: (08022) 95300, Fax: 95683. Head: Manfred Klauda
Ethnology Museum / Decorative Arts Museum - 1996
Dolls out of 170 countries 16873

Erstes Korkenziehermuseum der Welt, Zentrum für Außergewöhnliche Museen, Tegernseerstr 32, 83708 Kreuth - T: (08022) 95300, Fax: 95683. Head: Manfred Klauda
Science&Tech Museum - 1990
300 years of corkscrews 16874

Erstes Schutzengel-Museum der Welt, Zentrum für Außergewöhnliche Museen, Tegernseerstr 32, 83708 Kreuth - T: (08022) 95300, Fax: 95683. Head: Manfred Klauda
Religious Arts Museum
Guardian angels, holy water fonts, house altars and epitaphs 16875

Nachttopf-Museum, Zentrum für Außergewöhnliche Museen, Tegernseer Str 32, 83708 Kreuth - T: (08022) 93500, Fax: 95683. Head: Manfred Klauda
Special Museum - 1996
Hist of the chamber pot since BC 16876

Ur-Wolpertinger-Museum, Zentrum für Außergewöhnliche Museen, Tegernseerstr 32, 83708 Kreuth - T: (08022) 95300, Fax: 95683. Head: Manfred Klauda
Folklore Museum
Hist and various appearances of the Bavarian phenomenon "Wolpertinger", a phantasy creature in the shape of various native animals 16877

Zentrum für Außergewöhnliche Museen, Tegernseerstr 32, 83708 Kreuth - T: (08022) 95300, Fax: 95683, E-mail: zam-museum@zam-museum.de. Head: Manfred Klauda
Special Museum 16878

Kriebstein

Museum Burg Kriebstein, Kriebsteiner Str 7, 09648 Kriebstein - T: (034327) 9520, Fax: 95222, E-mail: burg-kriebstein@t-online.de, Internet: http://www.burg-kriebstein.de. Head: Bernd Wippert
Local Museum - 1947
Historic rooms, Gothic chapel, frescos, religious sculptures 15th-17th c, painting, ceramics 16879

Kriftel

Schulgeschichtliche Sammlung im Main-Taunus-Kreis, Staufenstr 14-20, 65830 Kriftel - T: (06192) 99700, Fax: (06196) 61187, E-mail: info@schulmuseumkriftel.de, Internet: http://www.schulmuseumkriftel.de
Historical Museum - 1980
School hist of Nassau 16880

Kröpelin

Kröpeliner Heimatstube, Am Markt 1, 18236 Kröpelin - T: (038292) 682, 85120, Fax: 85110
Local Museum 16881

Kronach

Die Festung Rosenberg - Deutsches Festungsmuseum, Festung 1, 96317 Kronach - T: (09261) 60410, Fax: 604118, E-mail: ti-kronach@gmx.de, Internet: http://www.kronach.de. Head: H. Geiger
Historical Museum
Late medieval castle 16882

Fränkische Galerie, Zweigmuseum des Bayerischen Nationalmuseums, Festung Rosenberg, 96317 Kronach - T: (09261) 60410, Fax: 604118, E-mail: ti-kronach@gmx.de, Internet: http://www.kronach.de. Head: H. Geiger
Fine Arts Museum
Medieval and Renaissance religious art (sculpture, panel paintings), works in wood and stone by Tilman Riemenschneider, panels by Hans von Kulmbach and Wolf Traut, paintings by Lucas Cranach the Elder 16883

Frankenwaldmuseum, Festung Rosenberg, 96317 Kronach - T: (09261) 60410, Fax: 604118, E-mail: ti-kronach@gmx.de, Internet: http://www.kronach.de. Head: H. Geiger
Local Museum - 1890
Finds from a 8th/9th c rampart, arms from the 16th-19th c, crafts by Gottfried Neukams (1892-1959), drawings and paintings by Lorenz Kaim (1813-1885) 16884

Heimatstube Podersam-Jechnitz, Lucas-Cranach-Str 27, 96317 Kronach
Local Museum - 1986
Sudetenland memorabilia 16885

Kronberg

Burgmuseum Kronberg, Schloßstr 10, 61476 Kronberg - T: (06173) 79956
Decorative Arts Museum
Furniture and furnishings (17th and 18th c), housed in fortress dating from 1225 16886

Fritz-Best-Museum, Talweg 41, 61476 Kronberg - T: (06173) 5263. Head: Hermann zur Strassen
Fine Arts Museum - 1984
Paintings and sculptures of the artist (1894-1980) 16887

Kronburg

Schloßmuseum, Burgstr 1, 87758 Kronburg - T: (08394) 271, Fax: 1671, Internet: http://www.schloss-kronburg.de
Local Museum
13th c castle 16888

Schwäbisches Bauernhofmuseum Illerbeuren, Museumsstr 8, Illerbeuren, 87758 Kronburg - T: (08394) 1455, Fax: 1454, E-mail: sekretariat@bauernhofmuseum.de, Internet: http://www.bauernhofmuseum.de. Head: Dr. Otto Kettemann
Open Air Museum - 1954
Peasant life, furnishings and tools from 18th and 19th c, equipment for processing flax, loom and weaving implements, traditional costumes, crafts, carriages, sledges 16889

Schwäbisches Schützenmuseum, Museumsstr 8, Illerbeuren, 87758 Kronburg - T: (08394) 1455, Fax: 1454, E-mail: sekretariat@bauernhofmuseum.de, Internet: http://www.bauernhofmuseum.de. Head: Dr. Otto Kettemann
Special Museum - 1982
Targets since 1508, documents, flags, brushes 16890

Krumbach, Schwaben

Mittelschwäbisches Heimatmuseum Krumbach, Heinrich-Sinz-Str 3-5, 86381 Krumbach, Schwaben - T: (08282) 3740, Fax: 3730
Local Museum - 1932
Town hist, trades and guilds, religious objects, folk costumes, uniforms, arms 16891

Krummennaab

Schloßmuseum, 92703 Krummennaab - T: (09682) 247
Local Museum 16892

Krummhörn

Bäckereimuseum, Sielstr 21, 26736 Krummhörn - T: (04926) 1393, 1331
Special Museum 16893

Ostfriesisches Freilichtmuseum Pewsum, Burg- und Mühlenmuseum, Rathausstr 14, 26736 Krummhörn - T: (04923) 7106, Fax: 8965. Head: Alfred Fröhlich
Open Air Museum - 1968
Agricultural implements and trade displays illustrating the history of East Fresian culture, tombstone coll (12th-19th c), folklore 16894

Ostfriesisches Landwirtschaftsmuseum, Krummhörner Str, 26736 Krummhörn - T: (04926) 1282, Fax: 8965
Agriculture Museum - 1991
Historical agricultural implements 16895

Kuchelmiß

Wassermühle Kuchelmiß, Mühlenweg 5, 18292 Kuchelmiß - T: (038456) 60666, Fax: 60153
Science&Tech Museum
13th c mill, local hist, agriculture 16896

Kümmersbruck

Bergbau- und Industriemuseum Ostbayern, Schloß Theuern, Portnerstr 1, 92245 Kümmersbruck - T: (09624) 832, Fax: 2498, E-mail: MuseumTheuern@t-online.de, Internet: http://www.museumtheuern.de. Head: Dr. Helmut Wolf
Science&Tech Museum - 1972
Historical industrial and technical facilities illustrating the history of mining and industry in Upper Bavaria 16897

Künzelsau

Hirschwirtscheuer-Museum für die Künstlerfamilie Sommer, Scharfengasse 12, 74653 Künzelsau - T: (07940) 57155, Fax: 154200, E-mail: museum@wuerth.com, Internet: http://www.wuerth.com. Head: C.S. Weber
Fine Arts Museum - 1989
Main works (paintings, sculptures) of the Sommer family who lived in Künzelsau from 1642 until 1785 16898

Museum Würth, Reinhold-Würth-Str 15, 74653 Künzelsau - T: (07940) 152200, Fax: 154200, E-mail: museum@wuerth.com, Internet: http://www.wuerth.com. Head: C. Sylvia Weber
Fine Arts Museum - 1992
Tools, hist of the development of screws and threads, 20th c sculpture, Austrian art (Rudolf Hausner), painting after 1945 Robert Jacobsen, Hans Arp) 16899

Künzing

Archäologiemuseum, Osterhofener Str 2, 94550 Künzing - T: (08549) 973112, Fax: 973111, E-mail: museum@kuenzing.de, Internet: http://www.museum-quintana.de. Head: Dr. Eva Bayer-Niemeier
Archaeological Museum 16900

Kürnbach

Erstes Deutsches Historic-Actien-Museum, Sternenfelser Str 1, 75057 Kürnbach - T: (07258) 1230, Fax: 92398, E-mail: info@edham-edhac.de, Internet: http://www.edham-edhac.de. Head: Thomas H. Frank, Prof. Dr. E. Wanner
Special Museum - 1975
Stocks and bonds from around the world, 19th and early 20th c German stocks, historic typewriter coll 16901

Museum für Blasmusikinstrumente, Musikakademie, 75057 Kürnbach - T: (07258) 91220, Fax: 912220, E-mail: -musikakademie.kuernbach@t-online.de. Head: H. Lernbaß
Music Museum
Wind instruments, percussion and drums 16902

Küsten

Freilichtmuseum Wendlandhof → Rundlingmuseum Wendlandhof-Lübeln

Heimathaus des Vereins zur Erhaltung der Rundlinge im Hannoverischen Wendland, 29482 Küsten
Local Museum 16903

Rundlingmuseum Wendlandhof-Lübeln, OT Lübeln, 29482 Küsten - T: (05841) 3675, Fax: 120278, E-mail: info@luechow-dannenberg.de, Internet: http://www.rundlingmuseum.com. Head: Wolfgang Jürries
Open Air Museum - 1972
Farmyard with various buildings, fashion 19th-20th c, settlement, German-Slavic culture 16904

Kulmbach

Armeemuseum 'Friedrich der Große', Plassenburg, 95326 Kulmbach - T: (08542) 860, Fax: 91576, E-mail: info@bsv.bayern.de
Military Museum 16905

Badhaus Museum und Galerie, Oberhacken 34, 95326 Kulmbach - T: (09221) 95880, Fax: 958844
Local Museum / Fine Arts Museum - 1999 16906

Bayerisches Brauereimuseum Kulmbach, Hofer Str 20, 95326 Kulmbach - T: (09221) 80510, Fax: 80515, E-mail: kulmbacher-moenchshof@kulmbacher.de. Head: Bernhard Sauermann
Science&Tech Museum / Special Museum - 1994
Hist of beer brewing 16907

Deutsches Zinnfigurenmuseum, Plassenburg, 95326 Kulmbach - T: (09221) 804571, Fax: 804576. Head: Dr. Wolfgang Mössner
Special Museum - 1929
European made tin figures and related objects illustrating the history of tin figures, largest coll of tin figures in the world 16908

Landschaftsmuseum Obermain, Plassenburg, 95326 Kulmbach - T: (09221) 804571, Fax: 804579. Head: Dr. Wolfgang Mössner
Local Museum / Natural History Museum - 1979
Natural history and paleontology, local history, furniture, crafts, coins, items related to local culture 16909

Museum Hohenzollern in Franken, Plassenburg, 95326 Kulmbach - T: (09221) 822011, Fax: 822026, E-mail: info@bsv.bayern.de
Local Museum / Decorative Arts Museum 16910

Plassenburg, Plassenburg, 95326 Kulmbach - T: (09221) 822011, Fax: 822026, E-mail: info@bsv.bayern.de
Decorative Arts Museum 16911

Sammlung historischer Jagdwaffen, Zweigmuseum des Bayerischen Nationalmuseums, Plassenburg, 95326 Kulmbach - T: (09221) 4116
Special Museum - 1982
Arms, hunting weapons from the 15th-19th c and accessoires 16912

Staatsgalerie in der Plassenburg, Bayerische Staatsgemäldesammlungen, Plassenburg, 95326 Kulmbach - T: (09221) 4116
Public Gallery - 1961
Baroque history paintings (famous battles and hunting scenes) 16913

Kurort Jonsdorf

Weberstube Jonsdorf, Große Seite 4, 02796 Kurort Jonsdorf - T: (035844) 70935
Science&Tech Museum / Folklore Museum 16914

Kurort Oberwiesenthal

Ski- und Heimatmuseum, Karlsbader Str 3, 09484 Kurort Oberwiesenthal - T: (037348) 614
Local Museum - 1983
Hist of winter sports 16915

Kurort Oybin

Burg- und Klosteranlage Oybin, Hauptstr 16, 02797 Kurort Oybin - T: (035844) 7340, Fax: 73427. Head: Elke Manke
Historical Museum / Open Air Museum - 1879
History of castle and cloister 16916

Kurort Seiffen

Erzgebirgisches Freilichtmuseum, Hauptstr 203, 09548 Kurort Seiffen - T: (037362) 8388, E-mail: info@spielzeugmuseum-seiffen.de, Internet: http://www.spielzeugmuseum-seiffen.de. Head: Dr. Konrad Auerbach
Open Air Museum
Local culture and architecture, wood-processing 16917

Erzgebirgisches Spielzeugmuseum, Hauptstr 73, 09548 Kurort Seiffen - T: (037362) 8239, Fax: 8239, E-mail: info@spielzeugmuseum-seiffen.de, Internet: http://www.spielzeugmuseum-seiffen.de. Head: Dr. Konrad Auerbach
Decorative Arts Museum - 1953
Development of toy production - library 16918

Kusel

Stadt- und Heimatmuseum, Marktstr 27, 66869 Kusel - T: (06381) 8222
Local Museum 16919

Kutenholz

Heimatdiele Kutenholz, Schulstr 10, 27449 Kutenholz - T: (04762) 1276
Local Museum - 1996
Folk art, domestic implements and utensils, agricultural machinery 16920

Laatzen

Luftfahrt-Museum Laatzen-Hannover, Ulmer Str 2, 30880 Laatzen - T: (0511) 8791791/92, Fax: 8791793, E-mail: ursula.leonhardt@t-online.de, Internet: http://www.luftfahrtmuseum-hannover.de. Head: Günter Leonhardt
Science&Tech Museum / Historical Museum - 1992
30 historical aircrafts, aviation 16921

Laboe

Marine-Ehrenmal und Technisches Museum U 995, Strandstr 92, 24235 Laboe - T: (04343) 42700, Fax: 427070, E-mail: vz@deutscher-marinebund.de, Internet: http://www.deutscher-marinebund.de
Military Museum 16922

Ladbergen

Heimatmuseum Ladbergen, In der Hermann-Löns-Heide, 49549 Ladbergen - T: (05485) 8101465
Local Museum 16923

Ladelund

KZ-Gedenk- und Begegnungsstätte, Ehemalige Außenstelle des Konzentrationslagers Neuengamme, Raiffeisenstr 3, 25926 Ladelund - T: (04666) 449, Fax: 449. Head: Karin Penno
Historic Site / Historical Museum 16924

Ladenburg

Auto Museum Dr. Carl Benz, Am Sägewerk 6-8, 68526 Ladenburg - T: (06203) 181786, Fax: 2503, Internet: http://www.automuseum-dr-carl-benz.de. Head: W.A. Seidel
Science&Tech Museum - 1984/96
Vehicles, hist of mobility 16925

Lobdengau-Museum, Bischofshof, 68526 Ladenburg - T: (06203) 700, Fax: 70250, E-mail: post@ladenburg.de, Internet: http://www.ladenburg.de. Head: Dr. Berndmark Heukemes
Archaeological Museum / Museum of Classical Antiquities / Folklore Museum / Open Air Museum / Historic Site - 1992
Excavations of the Roman city Lopodunum (Ladenburg), coll of Odenwald cabinet painting (18th/19th c), local hist 16926

Lage, Lippe

Museum Ziegelei Lage, Westfälisches Industriemuseum, Sprickernheide 77, 32791 Lage, Lippe - T: (05232) 94900, Fax: 949038, E-mail: ziegelei-lage@lwl.org, Internet: http:www.ziegelei-lage.de. Head: Willi Kulke
Local Museum / Open Air Museum / Science&Tech Museum 16927

Lahnau

Heimatmuseum Lahnau-Waldgirmes, Friedenstr 20, 35633 Lahnau - T: (06441) 64260
Local Museum - 1971
100 complete folk costumes, trade techniques, early and pre-history, fossils, anthropology 16928

Lahnstein

Museum der Stadt Lahnstein im Hexenturm, Salhofpl, 56112 Lahnstein - T: (02621) 914296, Fax: 914330, E-mail: Hauptamt@Stadt-Lahnstein.de, Internet: http://www.lahnstein.de. Head: Willi Eisenbarth
Local Museum - 1880 16929

Lahntal

Ländliches Heimatmuseum, Zum Feiselberg 4, 35094 Lahntal - T: (06420) 238
Local Museum 16930

Lahr, Schwarzwald

Geroldsecker-Museum im Storchenturm, Marktstr/Kreuzstr, 77933 Lahr, Schwarzwald - T: (07821) 9100416, Fax: 9100222, E-mail: museum@lahr.de, Internet: http://www.lahr.de. Head: G. Bohnert
Local Museum - 1966
Local hist 16931

Museum der Stadt Lahr, Villa Jamm im Stadtpark, Kaiserstr 101, 77933 Lahr, Schwarzwald - T: (07821) 22730, 9100416, Fax: 9100222, E-mail: museum@lahr.de, Internet: http://www.lahr.de. Head: G. Bohnert
Local Museum
Local hist, mineralogy, prehist, Roman times 16932

Lahstedt

Heimatstube Münstedt, Schulstr 2, 31246 Lahstedt - T: (05172) 2198
Local Museum
Early and prehist, agricultural, domestic and trade implements, clothes 16933

Laichingen

Museum für Höhlenkunde, Schallenlau 1, 89150 Laichingen - T: (07333) 4414
Natural History Museum
Cave finds, models, plans and pictures relating to speleology 16934

Weberei- und Heimatmuseum, Weitestr, 89150 Laichingen - T: (07333) 7177. Head: Rolf Riek
Local Museum - 1950
Weaving, local hist, folk art 16935

Lam

Mineralien-Museum Andreas Gabrys, Daxenhöhe 1, 93462 Lam - T: (09943) 557
Natural History Museum - 1969
Minerals from Europe and the colliery Buchet 16936

Lambrecht

Deutsches Schaustellermuseum, Vereinsstr 8, 67466 Lambrecht - T: (06325) 8873
Folklore Museum   16937

Lampertheim

Heimatmuseum Lampertheim, Römerstr 21, 68623 Lampertheim - T: (06206) 910539
Local Museum - 1978
Primeval finds, farming implements   16938

Lamspringe

Heimatmuseum Lamspringe, Kloster 3, 31195 Lamspringe - T: (05183) 5000, Fax: 50010, E-mail: samtgemeinde-lamspringe@t-online.de, Internet: http://www.lamspringe.de
Local Museum - 1979
History of the Benedictine cloister, jurisdiction, weaving school, interior of a 19th-c chemist's, milliner's   16939

Lamstedt

Börde-Heimatmuseum, Hinter den Höfen 11, 21769 Lamstedt - T: (04773) 1210
Local Museum
Folk art, furniture, costumes, migration 16940

Landau an der Isar

Heimatmuseum Landau, Höckinger Str 9, 94405 Landau an der Isar - T: (09951) 59737, Fax: 59737
Local Museum - 1958
Farm life, furniture, textiles, ceramics, pewter, domestic implements   16941

Niederbayerisches Vorgeschichtsmuseum, Archäologische Staatssammlung München, Kastenhof, Oberer Stadtpl 20, 94405 Landau an der Isar - T: (09951) 2385, Fax: 1701, Internet: http://www.stmukwk.bayern.de/kunst/zwmuseen/landau.html
Archaeological Museum - 1995   16942

Landau in der Pfalz

Städtische Galerie Villa Streccius, Südring 20, 76829 Landau in der Pfalz - T: (06341) 898472, Fax: 13294, E-mail: sabine.haas@landau.de, Internet: http://www.landau.de. Head: Sabine Haas
Public Gallery   16943

Städtisches Heimatmuseum, Marienring 8, 76829 Landau in der Pfalz - T: (06341) 13155, Fax: 13154, E-mail: michael.martin@landau.de. Head: Dr. Michael Martin
Local Museum - 1895
Town history, history of the fortress Landau - archive   16944

Landsberg am Lech

Herkomer-Museum am Mutterturm, Von-Kühlmann-Str 2, 86899 Landsberg am Lech - T: (08191) 942328, Fax: 942327, E-mail: neues_stadtmuseum@landsberg.de. Head: Hartfrid Neunzert
Fine Arts Museum - 1990
Paintings by Sir Hubert von Herkomer (1849-1914): socialcritical and realistic portraits   16945

Historisches Schuhmuseum, Am Vorderen Anger 271, 86899 Landsberg am Lech - T: (08191) 42296
Special Museum   16946

Neues Stadtmuseum Landsberg am Lech, Von-Helfensteingasse 426, 86899 Landsberg am Lech - T: (08191) 942326, Fax: 942327, E-mail: neues_stadtmuseum@landsberg.de, Internet: http://www.landsberg.de. Head: Hartfrid Neunzert
Local Museum - 1987
Tile coll, paintings by Walter Georgi (1871-1924) and Hubert von Herkomer   16947

Landsberg bei Halle, Saale

Doppelkapelle Sankt Crucis, c/o Museum Bernhard Brühl, 06188 Landsberg bei Halle, Saale - T: (034602) 20690, Fax: 20690, Internet: http://www.stadt-landsberg.de. Head: Inge Fricke
Religious Arts Museum - 1961
Hist of Doppelkapelle St. Crucis, hist of settlement, fortress hist 12th-16th c   16948

Museum Bernhard Brühl, Hillerstr 8, 06188 Landsberg bei Halle, Saale - T: (034602) 20690, Fax: 20690, E-mail: info@stadt-landsberg.de, Internet: http://www.stadt-landsberg.de. Head: Inge Fricke
Local Museum - 1916
Local hist, pre and early hist, nature study, guilds, agriculture, pharmacy ca. 1900   16949

Landshut

Burg Trausnitz, Burg Trausnitz 168, 84036 Landshut - T: (0871) 924110, 9241144, Fax: 9241140, E-mail: info@bsv.bayern.de. Head: Dr. Brigitte Langer
Fine Arts Museum
Gothic and Renaissance cultural artefacts, religious art, tapestries, 13th c castle   16950

Heiliggeistkirche, Museen der Stadt Landshut, Heiliggeistgasse 394, 84028 Landshut, mail addr: Altstadt 300, 84028 Landshut - T: (0871) 9223890, Fax: 9223899, E-mail: museen@landshut.de. Head: Dr. Franz Niehoff
Public Gallery   16951

Museum im Kreuzgang, Museen der Stadt Landshut, Alter Franziskanerpl 1, 84028 Landshut, mail addr: Altstadt 300, 84028 Landshut - T: (0871) 9223890, Fax: 9223899, E-mail: museen@landshut.de. Head: Dr. Franz Niehoff
Public Gallery   16952

Sammlungen im Adelmannschloß, Museen der Stadt Landshut (temporary closed), Adelmannstr 2, 84036 Landshut, mail addr: Altstadt 300, 84028 Landshut - T: (0871) 9223890, Fax: 9223899, E-mail: museen@landshut.de. Head: Dr. Franz Niehoff
Fine Arts Museum
Baroque castle from 1680, paintings by Max Slevogt, Rudolf Petuel, Adam Kunz, Willi Geiger and Paul Weiß, Baroque works by Jusepe Ribera and Carlo Maratti, mineralogy and military hist   16953

Skulpturenmuseum im Hofberg, Stiftung Koenig, Am Prantlgarten 1, 84028 Landshut - T: (0871) 89021, Fax: 89023, Internet: http://www.stadt.landshut.de. Head: Stefanje Weinmayr
Fine Arts Museum - 1998
20th c sculpture, Œvre Fritz Koenig, Africa coll of Koenig   16954

Stadt- und Regionalmuseum Landshut, Museen der Stadt Landshut (temporary closed), Altstadt 79, 84028 Landshut, mail addr: Altstadt 300, 84028 Landshut - T: (0871) 9223890, Fax: 9223899, E-mail: museen@landshut.de. Head: Dr. Franz Niehoff
Local Museum - 1935
Early and prehist, town hist, art hist, paintings, pewter figures, weapons, ethnography, military hist   16955

Stadtresidenz, Altstadt 79, 84028 Landshut - T: (0871) 924110, Fax: 9241140, Internet: http://www.schloesser.bayern.de
Fine Arts Museum - 1931   16956

Landwüst

Vogtländisches Freilichtmuseum Landwüst/Eubabrunn, Rohrbacher Str 4, 08258 Landwüst - T: (037422) 2136, Fax: 6836, E-mail: - Vogtl.Freilichtmuseum@t-online.de, Internet: http://www.vogtland-kultur.de. Head: Gabriele Maiwald
Open Air Museum - 1968
Folklore, medieval to present-day peasant culture, carved butter forms, beekeeping   16957

Langballig

Landschaftsmuseum Angeln, Unewatterstr 1a, 24977 Langballig - T: (04636) 1021, Fax: 8226. Head: Jochen Clausen
Folklore Museum
Everyday life and culture, agri-technic, animal breeding, architecture, mills   16958

Langelsheim

Heimatmuseum Langelsheim, Mühlenstr 10, 38685 Langelsheim - T: (05326) 50480, 50463, Fax: 50444
Local Museum - 1979
Regional cultural objects, furnished and equipped rooms, trade workshops   16959

Heimatstuben, Hüttenweg 12, 38685 Langelsheim - T: (05326) 5040
Local Museum   16960

Niedersächsisches Bergbaumuseum, Wildemanner Str 11-21, Lautenthal, 38685 Langelsheim - T: (05325) 4490, Fax: 6979. Head: Wolfgang Borges
Science&Tech Museum - 1974
Mining and smelting technology, mineralogy of the Upper Harz region, multivision show - historical silver mine   16961

Langen bei Bremerhaven

Heimatmuseum Debstedt, Kirchenstr 6, 27607 Langen bei Bremerhaven - T: (04743) 2225, Fax: 7064
Local Museum - 1984
Farming and agricultural implements, beekeeping   16962

Heimatmuseum Neuenwalde, Bederkesaer Str 19, 27607 Langen bei Bremerhaven - T: (04707) 320
Local Museum - 1993
Agricultural implements and machinery, prehistoric finds, animal preparations, costumes, furniture, tools   16963

John-Wagener-Haus Sievern, Lange Str 11, 27607 Langen bei Bremerhaven - T: (04743) 4087, Fax: 7064. Head: Artur Burmeister
Local Museum
Hist of John Wagener who migrated to the USA in the early 19th c, family farmhouse, general store   16964

Langen in Hessen

Museum der Stadt Langen, Wilhelm-Leuschner-Pl 3, 63225 Langen in Hessen - T: (06103) 52283, Fax: 26302. Head: Joachim Kolbe
Local Museum   16965

Museum für Zeitgenössische Glasmalerei, 40 Rathaus, Südliche Ringstr 80, 63225 Langen in Hessen - T: (06103) 203120, Fax: 26302, E-mail: JKolbe@langen.de, Internet: http://www.langen.de. Head: Joachim Kolbe
Fine Arts Museum - 1983
Town hist, contemporary glass painting   16966

Langenargen

Museum Langenargen/ Bodensee, Marktpl 20, 88085 Langenargen - T: (07543) 2200, 3410, Fax: 2250. Head: Eduard Hindelang
Fine Arts Museum - 1976
Painting and sculpture (Romanesque to present), coll of Hans Purrmann paintings   16967

Langenau, Württemberg

Heimatmuseum Langenau, Kirchgasse 4, 89129 Langenau, Württemberg - T: (07345) 7453
Local Museum   16968

Museum für Vor- und Frühgeschichte, Kirchgasse 9, 89129 Langenau, Württemberg - T: (07345) 7453. Head: E. Junginger
Archaeological Museum - 1932
Prehistoric finds   16969

Ungarn-deutsche Heimatstuben, Kirchgasse 9, 89129 Langenau, Württemberg - T: (07345) 962433. Head: W. Rittlinger
Ethnology Museum - 1980
Hist of the Swabian settlements in Hungary, peasant life and traditions   16970

Langenburg

Deutsches Automuseum Schloss Langenburg, Schloss 1, 74595 Langenburg - T: (07905) 264, Fax: 1040, E-mail: Schloss-Langenburg@t-online.de, Internet: http://www.schloss-langenburg.de. Head: Fürst zu Hohenlohe-Langenburg
Science&Tech Museum - 1970
Automobiles from 1893 to 1939, historic and contemporary sport and racing cars from various countries   16971

Grabungsmuseum, Unterregenbach, 74595 Langenburg - T: (07905) 91020, 332, Fax: 491, E-mail: post@langenburg.de, Internet: http://www.langenburg.de. Head: G. Stachel, M. Stachel
Archaeological Museum - 1979
Findings from 1th c church   16972

Hohenloher Kunstverein e.V., Hofratshaus, 74595 Langenburg - T: (07905) 711, Fax: 1240. Head: Ursula Schaeff
Association with Coll   16973

Schlossmuseum, Schloss Langenburg, 74595 Langenburg - T: (07905) 264, Fax: 1040, E-mail: - Schloss.Langenburg@t-online.de, Internet: http://www.schlosslangenburg.de. Head: Fürst zu Hohenlohe-Langenburg
Decorative Arts Museum - 1960
Tapestries, weapons, armor, porcelain and other artifacts from the Renaissance to the 19th c 16974

Langenenslingen

Schloß Wilflingen, Stauffenbergstr 12, 88515 Langenenslingen - T: (07376) 381, Fax: 1540, E-mail: forstamt-stauffenberg@t-online.de. Head: Franz Schenk Freiherr von Stauffenberg
Historic Site
Furniture and furnishings (16th-18th c), family portraits - library   16975

Langeneß

Friesenstube Honkenswarf, Honkenswarf, 25863 Langeneß - T: (04684) 260. Head: Hermann Johannsen
Decorative Arts Museum - 1965
Typical Friesland furniture and furnishings, family documents, manuscripts   16976

Kapitän Tadsen Museum, Ketelswarft, 25863 Langeneß - T: (04684) 217, Fax: 289, E-mail: info@langeness.de, Internet: http://www.langeness.de. Head: Renate Boysen
Special Museum   16977

Langenfeld

Kulturelles Forum im Freiherr-vom-Stein-Haus, Hauptstr 83, 40764 Langenfeld - T: (02173) 9193960, Fax: 9193977, E-mail: archiv.museum@langenfeld.de
Local Museum   16978

Langenselbold

Heimatmuseum Langenselbold, Braugasse 1, 63505 Langenselbold - T: (06184) 61336
Local Museum - 1975
Agricultural implements, trade workshops, archaeologial finds   16979

Langenzenn

Heimatmuseum Langenzenn, Martin-Luther-Pl 4, 90579 Langenzenn - T: (09101) 8140
Local Museum - 1957
Agricultural and domestic implements, furniture   16980

Langeoog

Schiffahrtsmuseum mit Nordseeaquarium Nordseeheilbad Langeoog, Kurzentrum, Haus der Insel, 26465 Langeoog - T: (04972) 693211, Fax: 693116, E-mail: Kurverwaltung@Langeoog.de, Internet: http://www.langeoog.de. Head: Hans-Uwe Paap
Science&Tech Museum - 1981
Sea and coast shipping, models, implements and objects connected   16981

Langerwehe

Töpfereimuseum, Pastoratsweg 1, 52379 Langerwehe - T: (02423) 4446, Fax: 5990
Decorative Arts Museum - 1939
Development of local pottery craft - library 16982

Langgöns

Bärner Heimatstube, 35428 Langgöns - T: (06407) 6395
Local Museum   16983

Lanz

Friedrich-Ludwig-Jahn-Gedenkstätte, Am Ring 21, 19309 Lanz - T: (038780) 7221
Special Museum   16984

Lassan

Lassaner Mühle, Mühlenstr 2, 17440 Lassan - T: (038374) 80233/34
Local Museum
Town hist, early archaeological finds   16985

Laubach, Hessen

Heimatmuseum Laubach, Fridericianum, Friedrichstr 11, 35321 Laubach, Hessen - T: (06405) 1503
Local Museum - 1981
Industrial and cultural development of the town and its surrounding areas, trades   16986

Laucha, Unstrut

Glockenmuseum, Glockenmuseumstr 1, 06636 Laucha, Unstrut - T: (034464) 20509, Fax: 3745492202. Head: Klaus Pfeifer
Science&Tech Museum - 1932
18th c bell casting, workshop, tools, 15th-19th c bell coll   16987

Lauchhammer

Kunstgußmuseum Lauchhammer, Grünhauser Str 19, 01979 Lauchhammer - T: (03574) 892667, Fax: 892667. Head:
Decorative Arts Museum - 1993
Art foundry, sculptures, reliefs, furniture, bells, ornaments, medallions   16988

Lauchheim

Heimatmuseum im Oberen Torturm, Hauptstr 1, 73466 Lauchheim - T: (07363) 850, Fax: 8516
Local Museum - 1903
Local hist, prehistory, crafts   16989

Lauda-Königshofen

Heimatmuseum Lauda-Königshofen, c/o Stadt Lauda-Königshofen, Lauda, Rathausstr 25, 97922 Lauda-Königshofen - T: (09343) 4517, Fax: 501100
Local Museum - 1965
Wine-grower's apartment, town hist, crafts, farming, railroad hist   16990

Lauenau

Heimatmuseum Lauenau, Rodenberger Str 7, 31867 Lauenau - T: (05043) 2633, Fax: 1328
Local Museum - 1978
Local hist, coal mining, guild and trade workshops   16991

Lauenburg

Elbschiffahrtsmuseum mit stadtgeschichtlicher Sammlung, Elbstr 59, 21481 Lauenburg - T: (04153) 51251, Fax: 550754. Head: Werner Hinsch
Science&Tech Museum / Local Museum - 1927
History of inland shipping, original steam-engines - archive   16992

Lauenstein

Osterzgebirgsmuseum, Schloß Lauenstein, 01778 Lauenstein - T: (035054) 25402, Fax: 25402. Head: Jürgen Albertus
Local Museum
Local hitory, handicraft, agricultural tools, George Bährs builder of the Frauenkirche Dresden, natural history, mailing-miles column of the electorate of Saxony - gallery 16993

Lauf an der Pegnitz

Industrie Museum Lauf, Sichartstr 5-25, 91207 Lauf an der Pegnitz - T: (09123) 99030, Fax: 990313, E-mail: industriemuseum@lauf.de, Internet: http://www.industriemuseum.lauf.de. Head: Dr. Renate Kubli
Science&Tech Museum - 1992
Water powered trades, trade life of the 1950s and 60s, urban living and working conditions 16994

Stadtarchiv mit städtischen Sammlungen, Spitalstr 5, 91207 Lauf an der Pegnitz - T: (09123) 184166, Fax: 988542, E-mail: info@stadt.lauf.de. Head: Ewald Glückert
Local Museum / Library with Exhibitions - 1934
Graphic coll, calendar - town archive 16995

Laufen, Salzach

Laufener Stiftsschatz, Pfarramt Laufen - Mariä Himmelfahrt, Spannbruckerpl 6, 83410 Laufen, Salzach - T: (08682) 89610, Fax: 216, E-mail: kath.pfarramtlaufen@t-online.de. Head: Simon Eibl
Religious Arts Museum - 2000 16996

Lauffen am Neckar

Erdgeschichtliches Werksmuseum der ZEAG, c/o Zementwerk Lauffen - Elektrizitätswerk Heilbronn AG, Oskar-von-Miller-Str 48, 74348 Lauffen am Neckar - T: (07133) 1020, Fax: 1023040, E-mail: Uwe.Fabich@zeag-zement.de. Head: Uwe Fabich
Natural History Museum - 1957
Fossils, skeletons 16997

Museum der Stadt Lauffen am Neckar, Klosterhof 6, 74348 Lauffen am Neckar - T: (07133) 12222, 5865. Head: V. Friebel
Local Museum - 1984
Prehist and early hist of Lauffen, Hölderlin 16998

Lauingen

Heimathaus der Stadt Lauingen, Herzog-Georg-Str 57, 89415 Lauingen - T: (09072) 998113, Fax: 998192, E-mail: stadt@lauingen.de, Internet: http://www.lauingen.de. Head: Bernhard Ehrhart
Local Museum / Archaeological Museum / Fine Arts Museum - 1792/1961
Albertus medals, holy pictures, crib moulds, Mathis Gerung (ca 1500-1570), religious graphic, prints 16999

Mineraliensammlung, Donaustr 28, 89415 Lauingen - T: (09072) 4122. Head: Reinhard Kochendörfer
Natural History Museum 17000

Laupheim

Museum zur Geschichte von Christen und Juden, Schloss Großlaupheim, Kirchberg 11, 88471 Laupheim - T: (07392) 968000, Fax: 9680018, E-mail: museum.laupheim@t-online.de, Internet: http://www.laupheim.de. Head: Alfred Jerg
Historical Museum - 1998
Judaica of Southern Germany (co-existence of Jews and non-Jews, Holocaust) 17001

Lauscha

Museum für Glaskunst, Oberlandstr 10, 98724 Lauscha - T: (036702) 20724, Fax: 30836, E-mail: Glasmuseum.Lauscha@t-online.de, Internet: http://www.glasmuseum.lauscha.de. Head: Uwe Claassen
Decorative Arts Museum - 1897
Glass industry of Thüringen, glass art and technology, optical use, glass eyes, christmas tree decorations 17002

Lauterbach, Hessen

Hohhaus-Museum, Berliner Pl 1, 36341 Lauterbach, Hessen - T: (06641) 2402. Head: Horst Reuter
Local Museum - 1935/83
Prehistoric and neolithic finds, fully furnished rooms, trades, arms 17003

Lauterstein

Institut für wissenschaftliche Fotografie- Manfred und Christina Kage, Schloss Weissenstein, 73111 Lauterstein - T: (07332) 6358, Fax: 3330, E-mail: institut.kage@t-online.de, Internet: http://www.jourfix.de/potfolio/f-wissen.htm. Head: Prof. Manfred Kage
Special Museum 17004

Lautertal, Odenwald

Felsberg-Museum, Reichenbacher Str 42, 64686 Lautertal, Odenwald - T: (06254) 7178
Local Museum 17005

Heimatmuseum Gadernheim, Nibelungenstr, 64686 Lautertal, Odenwald - T: (06254) 1808
Local Museum - 1975
Farmhouse parlour with Odenwald folk costumes, furniture, agricultural implements, mineralogy 17006

Lebusa

Heimatmuseum Bockwindmühle, Vorwerk 29a, 04936 Lebusa - T: (035364) 232, 79669, Fax: 232
Local Museum / Science&Tech Museum 17007

Lechbruck

Lechflößermuseum (open probability 2002), Weidach 10, 86983 Lechbruck - T: (08862) 7113, 7114, Fax: 7516
Special Museum - 2002 17008

Leer

Heimatmuseum Leer, Neue Str 12-14, 26789 Leer - T: (0491) 2019, Fax: 2019
Folklore Museum - 1912 17009

Samson-Haus, Rathausstr 16-18, 26789 Leer. Head: W. Wolff
Historical Museum
Merchant house in Netherlandish style, East Frisian culture of living 17010

Legau

Wallfahrtsmuseum, Pfarrheim Maria Steinbach, 87764 Legau - T: (08394) 9240, Fax: 92429, E-mail: KircheMSt@aol.com, Internet: http://aol.com/KircheMSt. Head: Heinrich Mühlbauer
Religious Arts Museum - 1984
Votive tablets, liturgical objects 17011

Lehde bei Lübbenau

Freilichtmuseum Lehde, An der Giglitza, 03222 Lehde bei Lübbenau - T: (03542) 2682. Head: Christel Lehmann-Enders
Open Air Museum - 1957
Farm 18th c with historic buildings, furnishings, equipment, costumes 17012

Lehesten, Thüringer Wald

Historischer Schieferbergbau Lehesten, Obere Marktstr 1, 07349 Lehesten, Thüringer Wald - T: (036653) 22212, Fax: 22518
Science&Tech Museum - 1993
History of slate quarrying 17013

Leimen, Baden

Eleker Heimatmuseum, Weberstr 5, 69181 Leimen, Baden - T: (06224) 55219
Local Museum 17014

Kunewälder Heimatstube, Weberstr 4, 69181 Leimen, Baden - T: (06224) 704237
Local Museum 17015

Stadtmuseum Leimen - Sankt Ilgen, Weberstr 4, 69181 Leimen, Baden - T: (06224) 71828. Head: O. Kothe
Local Museum - 1984
Early hist, tools, local industry, agricultural implements, local hist 17016

Leinfelden-Echterdingen

Deutsches Spielkartenmuseum, Ein Zweigmuseum des Württembergischen Landesmuseums Stuttgart, Schönbuchstr 32, 70771 Leinfelden-Echterdingen, mail addr: Postfach 100351, 70747 Leinfelden-Echterdingen - T: (0711) 7560120, Fax: 7560121, E-mail: spielkartenmuseum@le-mail.de, Internet: http://www.spielkartenmuseum.de. Head: Dr. Annette Köger-Kaufmann
Special Museum - 1923
Playing cards from all periods and cultures - library 17017

Feuerwehrmuseum Musberg, Ludwigstr 9, 70771 Leinfelden-Echterdingen - T: (0711) 7542971. Head: R. Metzger
Science&Tech Museum - 1987
Fire fighting 17018

Städtische Galerie Filderhalle, Bahnhofstr 61, 70771 Leinfelden-Echterdingen - T: (0711) 1600244, Fax: 1600350, E-mail: julia.oelgemoeller@leinfelden-echterdingen.de, Internet: http://www.leinfelden-echterdingen.de
Public Gallery 17019

Leingarten

Heimatmuseum Leingarten Altes Rathaus Schluchtern, Eppinger Str 150, 74211 Leingarten - T: (07131) 900173, Fax: 406138
Local Museum - 1972
Rural crafts, archeological finds 17020

Leinsweiler

Slevogthof Neukastel, Sitz des Malers Prof. Max Slevogt mit Gemäldegalerie, Slevogthof, 76829 Leinsweiler - T: (06345) 3685, Fax: 918042, E-mail: info@slevogthof.de, Internet: http://www.slevogt.de. Head: Nina Emanuel
Fine Arts Museum 17021

Leipheim

Christophs Friseur-Museum, Günzburger Str 21, 89340 Leipheim - T: (08221) 7853
Special Museum - 1999 17022

Heimatmuseum Leipheim, Kirchpl 8, 89340 Leipheim - T: (08221) 72044, Fax: 70790
Local Museum - 1986
Peat cutting, weaving, culture of living in the 19th c 17023

Leipzig

Ägyptisches Museum der Universität Leipzig, Schillerstr 6, 04109 Leipzig - T: (0341) 9737010, Fax: 9737029, E-mail: aegmus@rz.uni-leipzig.de, Internet: http://www.uni-leipzig.de/~egypt. Head: Prof. Dr. Hans-W. Fischer-Elfert
Archaeological Museum - 1842/1976
Nubian antiquities 17024

Alte Börse, Stadtgeschichtliches Museum Leipzig, Naschmarkt, 04109 Leipzig - T: (0341) 9651322, Fax: 9651322, E-mail: Stadtmuseum.Leipzig@t-online.de, Internet: http://www.t-online.de/home/Stadtmuseum.Leipzig. Head: Dr. Volker Rodekamp, Kathleen Schönfelder
Local Museum 17025

Antikenmuseum der Universität Leipzig, Alte Nikolaischule, Nikolaikirchof 2, 04109 Leipzig - T: (0341) 9730700, Fax: 9730709, E-mail: klarch@rz.uni-leipzig.de, Internet: http://www.uni-leipzig.de/antik. Head: Prof. Dr. Hans-Ulrich Cain
Museum of Classical Antiquities - 1840 17026

Archiv Bürgerbewegung Leipzig, Stadtgeschichtliches Museum der Stadt Leipzig, Katharinenstr 11, 04109 Leipzig - T: (0341) 8611626, Fax: 8611626
Historical Museum
Documents (files, photographs, video and audio tapes) about civil movement and opposition in the GDR 17027

Automatik-Museum, Alte Nikolaischule, Nikolaikirchof 2, 04109 Leipzig - T: (0341) 30761199, 30766219, Fax: 30766456, E-mail: niemitz@r.htwk-leipzig.de, Internet: http://www.et.htwk-leipzig.de/museum. Head: Prof. Dr. Hans-Ulrich Niemitz
Science&Tech Museum 17028

Deutsches Buch- und Schriftmuseum der Deutschen Bücherei Leipzig, Deutscher Pl 1, 04103 Leipzig - T: (0341) 2271250, 2271324, Fax: 2271240, E-mail: dbsm@dbl.ddb.de, Internet: http://www.ddb.de. Head: Lothar Poethe
Special Museum / Library with Exhibitions - 1884
Manuscripts, incunabula, old books (16th-19th c), book plates, book art, script art, graphic, watermarks, paper samples, coloured papers, archival materials, instruments and machines for book- and papermaking - library, special collections 17029

Deutsches Kleingärtnermuseum, Aachener Str 7, 04109 Leipzig - T: (0341) 2111194, Fax: 2618697, E-mail: kleingaertnermuseum@t-online.de. Head: Dr. Brigitte Düsterwald
Special Museum 17030

Dresdner Bank am Dittrichring, Dittrichring 5-9, 04109 Leipzig - T: (0341) 1241626
Public Gallery 17031

Eisenbahnmuseum Bayerischer Bahnhof zu Leipzig, Museumsbetriebswerk Bahnhof Plagwitz, 04179 Leipzig, mail addr: Schönauer Str 113, 04207 Leipzig - T: (0341) 6883678, 9682687, Fax: 9682514, Internet: http://www.eisenbahnmuseum-leipzig.com. Head: Thilo Gruber
Science&Tech Museum 17032

Galerie der Hochschule für Graphik und Buchkunst, Wächterstr 11, 04107 Leipzig - T: (0341) 2135149, Fax: 2135166. Head: Christine Rink
Fine Arts Museum 17033

Galerie für Zeitgenössische Kunst Leipzig, Karl-Tauchnitz-Str 11, 04107 Leipzig - T: (0341) 140810, Fax: 1408111, E-mail: office@gfzk.de, Internet: http://www.gfzk.de. Head: Barbara Steiner
Fine Arts Museum 17034

Galerie im Hörsaalbau, Kustodie der Universität Leipzig, Universitätsstr, 04109 Leipzig - T: (0341) 9730170/72, Fax: 9730179, E-mail: behrends@rz.uni-leipzig.de, Internet: http://www.uni-leipzig.de. Head: Rainer Behrends
Public Gallery / University Museum 17035

Gedenkstätte Museum in der Runden Ecke, STASI-Macht und Banalität, Dittrichring 24, 04109 Leipzig, mail addr: PF 100345, 04003 Leipzig - T: (0341) 9612443, Fax: 9612499, E-mail: mail@runde-ecke-leipzig.de, Internet: http://www.runde-ecke-leipzig.de. Head: Dr. Konrad Taut
Historical Museum
Former administrative building of the STASI, the state security service of the GDR, documents, original objects, e.g. bugs, fake passports and mail which has never reached their addressees 17036

Grassimuseum Leipzig, Museum für Kunsthandwerk (Interim), Neumarkt 20, 04109 Leipzig - T: (0341) 2133719, Fax: 2133715, E-mail: grassimuseum@leipzig.de, Internet: http://www.grassimuseum.de. Head: Dr. Eva Maria Hoyer
Decorative Arts Museum - 1874
Ancient art objects, furnishing, 16th c religious sculpture, decorative objects, medals since 16th c, textiles, rugs, pewter, ceramics, glass, graphic coll relating to ornament, ancient asiatica and other noneuropean art - library with graphic and photographic colls 17037

Haus der Geschichte der Bundesrepublik Deutschland, Zeitgeschichtliches Forum Leipzig, Grimmaische Str 6, 04109 Leipzig - T: (0341) 22200, Fax: 2220500, E-mail: zfl@hdg.de, Internet: http://www.hdg.de/zfl. Head: Dr. Rainer Eckert
Historical Museum - 1999 17038

Historischer Straßenbahnhof Leipzig-Möckern, Georg-Schumann-Str 244, 04159 Leipzig - T: (0341) 4921818, Fax: 4921814, E-mail: info@strassenbahnmuseum.de, Internet: http://www.strassenbahnmuseum.de
Science&Tech Museum
Historic Trams 17039

Johann-Sebastian-Bach-Museum, Bach-Archiv Leipzig, Thomaskirchhof 15-16, 04109 Leipzig - T: (0341) 9644135, Fax: 9644122, E-mail: info@bach-leipzig.de, Internet: http://www.bach-leipzig.de. Head: Cornelia Krumbiegel
Music Museum - 1985
Autographs, prints, 18th c furniture, literature, music related to Bach 17040

Kamera- und Fotomuseum Leipzig, Gottschalkstr 9, 04316 Leipzig - T: (0341) 6515711, Fax: 6513924, E-mail: langner@fotomuseum-leipzig.de, Internet: http://www.fotomuseum-leipzig.de. Head: Kerstin Langner
Science&Tech Museum / Fine Arts Museum
Technical development of photography since 1880, photographic art - gallery 17041

Kunsthalle Sparkasse Leipzig, Otto-Schill-Str 4a, 04109 Leipzig - T: (0341) 9869898, Fax: 9869899, E-mail: kunsthalle@sparkasse-leipzig.de. Head: Peter Krakow
Fine Arts Museum - 2001 17042

Kunstsammlung der Universität Leipzig, Kroch-Haus, Goethestr 2, 04109 Leipzig - T: (0341) 9730170/72, Fax: 9730179, E-mail: behrends@rz.uni-leipzig.de, Internet: http://www.uni-leipzig.de. Head: Rainer Behrends
Fine Arts Museum / Public Gallery / University Museum 17043

Lichtdruck-Kunst Leipzig e.V., Nonnenstr 38, 04229 Leipzig - T: (0341) 4796401, Fax: 4956749, E-mail: info@lichtdruck.de, Internet: http://www.lichtdruck.de
Association with Coll 17044

Mendelssohn-Haus, Goldschmidtstr 12, 04103 Leipzig - T: (0341) 1270294, Fax: 2115288, E-mail: IMS@mendelssohn-stiftung.de, Internet: http://www.mendelssohn-stiftung.de. Head: Jürgen Ernst
Special Museum / Historic Site
Flat of Felix Mendelssohn Bartholdy 17045

Mineralogisch-petrographische Sammlung der Universität Leipzig, c/o Institut für Mineralogie, Kristallographie und Materialwissenschaft, Scharnhorststr 20, 04275 Leipzig - T: (0341) 9736250, Fax: 9736299, E-mail: hoebler@rz.uni-leipzig.de, Internet: http://www.uni-leipzig.de/~minkrist/. Head: Prof. Dr. Klaus Bente
Natural History Museum / University Museum - 1809 17046

Museum der bildenden Künste, Grimmaische Str 1-7, 04109 Leipzig - T: (0341) 216990, 2169914, Fax: 9609925, E-mail: Museum.d.bild.Kuenste.Leipzig@t-online.de, Internet: http://www.leipzig.de/museum_d_bild_kuenste.htm. Head: Dr. Hans-Werner Schmidt
Fine Arts Museum - 1837 17047

Museum für Druckkunst, Nonnenstr 38, 04229 Leipzig - T: (0341) 490490, Fax: 4904949, E-mail: info@druckkunst-museum.de, Internet: http://www.druckkunst-museum.de
Decorative Arts Museum / Science&Tech Museum - 1995
Printing machines, machines for bookbinding, type patterns and steel stamps 17048

Museum für Industrie und Arbeit Leipzig-Plagwitz, Zschortauer Str, Halle 4, 04129 Leipzig - T: (0341) 9081074/76, Fax: 5646444, E-mail: tcl@www.uni-leipzig.de. Head: Dr. Angelika Träger-Nestler
Historical Museum
History of industry in Leipzig 17049

Museum für Völkerkunde zu Leipzig, Grimmaische Str 2-4, Interim Mädler-Passage, 04109 Leipzig, mail addr: Postfach 955, 04009 Leipzig - T: (0341) 5958218, Fax: 5958262, E-mail: mvl-grassimuseum@mvl.smwk.sachsen.de, Internet: http://www.mvl-grassimuseum.de. Head: Dr. Claus Deimel
Ethnology Museum - 1869
Cultures of Asia, America, Africa, Australia, Oceania - library 17050

Museum in der Runden Ecke → Gedenkstätte Museum in der Runden Ecke

Museum Zum Arabischen Coffe Baum, Stadtgeschichtliches Museum Leipzig, Kleine Fleischergasse 4, 04109 Leipzig - T: (0341) 9602632, 965130, Fax: 9602632, 9651352, E-mail: Stadtmuseum.Leipzig@t-online.de, Internet: http://www.t-online.de/home/Stadtmuseum.Leipzig. Head: Dr. Volker Rodekamp
Special Museum 17051

Musikinstrumenten-Museum der Universität Leipzig (Interim), Thomaskirchhof 20, 04109 Leipzig - T: (0341) 2142120/25, Fax: 2142135, E-mail: musik.museum@uni-leipzig.de, Internet: http://www.uni-leipzig.de/museum/musik/. Head: Dr. Eszter Fontana
Music Museum / University Museum - 1929
Musical instruments from the 16th c to the present, mechanical instruments, European and non-European folk instruments - library, archives 17052

Naturkundemuseum Leipzig, Lortzingstr 3, 04105 Leipzig - T: (0341) 982210, Fax: 9822122. Head: Dr. Rudolf Schlatter
Natural History Museum - 1906
Geology, zoology, botany, archaeology - library, photographic archives 17053

Rübesams Da Capo Oldtimermuseum, Karl-Heine-Str 105, 04229 Leipzig - T: (0341) 4830501, 4830360, Internet: http://www.ruebesam-dacapo.de. Head: Manfred Rübesam
Science&Tech Museum - 2001 17054

Sächsisches Apothekenmuseum Leipzig, Thomaskirchhof 12, 04109 Leipzig - T: (0341) 336520, Fax: 3365210
Special Museum - 1999 17055

Sächsisches Psychiatriemuseum, Mainzer Str 7, 04109 Leipzig - T: (0341) 14061413, Fax: 14061419, E-mail: museum@durchblick-ev.de, Internet: http://www.durchblick-ev.de. Head: Thomas Müller
Historical Museum
History of saxonian psychiatry 17056

Schillerhaus, Stadtgeschichtliches Museum Leipzig, Menckestr 42, 04155 Leipzig - T: (0341) 5662170, Fax: 5662170, E-mail: Stadtmuseum.Leipzig@t-online.de, Internet: http://www.t-online.de/home/Stadtmuseum.Leipzig. Head: Dr. Volker Rodekamp, Dietmar Schulze
Historic Site - 1842
Memorabilia on Friedrich Schiller's (1759-1805) stay in Leipzig 1785 17057

Schulmuseum - Werkstatt für Schulgeschichte Leipzig, Goerdelerring 20, 04109 Leipzig - T: (0341) 2130568, Fax: 2130568, E-mail: eurban@freenet.de. Head: Elke Urban
Historical Museum - 1984
Local and regional school hist since 1212, audio visual teaching aids 17058

Schumann-Haus, Inselstr 18, 04103 Leipzig - T: (0341) 3939620, E-mail: info@schumann-verein.de, Internet: http://www.schumann-verein.de. Head: Dr. Petra Dießner
Music Museum 17059

Sportmuseum Leipzig, Stadtgeschichtliches Museum Leipzig, Friedrich-Ebert-Str 130, 04105 Leipzig - T: (0341) 9806491, 9805112, Fax: 9806491, E-mail: sportmuseum.leipzig@t-online.de, Internet: http://www.t-online.de/home/stadtmuseum.leipzig. Head: Dr. Volker Rodekamp
Special Museum - 1977
Hist of sport in Saxony, hist of German workers'sport, gym festival movement in Germany, gym and sport equipment, sportswear, posters, certificates, photos, documents, literature, sport prizes, inheritances, personal effects 17060

Stadtgeschichtliches Museum Leipzig, Altes Rathaus, Markt 1, 04109 Leipzig - T: (0341) 965130, Fax: 9651352, E-mail: - Stadtmuseum.Leipzig@t-online.de, Internet: http://www.t-online.de/home/Stadtmuseum.Leipzig. Head: Dr. Volker Rodekamp, Doris Mundus
Local Museum - 1909
Historical rooms, portraits, medieval ceramics and pottery, numismatics, 13th-18th c armaments, 15th-16th c printing crafts, Baroque furnishings, sculpture, prints, paintings, pewter, weights and measures, costumes - library 17061

Studiensammlung, Kustodie der Universität Leipzig, Ritterstr 26, 04109 Leipzig - T: (0341) 9730170/72, Fax: 9730179, E-mail: behrends@rz.uni-leipzig.de, Internet: http://www.uni-leipzig.de. Head: Rainer Behrends
Fine Arts Museum / University Museum 17062

Torhaus Dölitz, Helenenstr 24, 04279 Leipzig - T: (0341) 3389107
Historical Museum
Pewter figures portraying town, regional, cultural and military hist 17063

Universitätsbibliothek der Universität Leipzig, Beethovenstr 6, 04107 Leipzig - T: (0341) 9730577, Fax: 2132168, E-mail: auskunft@ub.uni-leipzig.de, Internet: http://www.ub.uni-leipzig.de. Head: Dr. Ekkehard Henschke
Library with Exhibitions 17064

Völkerschlachtdenkmal und Forum 1813, Museum zur Geschichte der Völkerschlacht, Stadtgeschichtliches Museum Leipzig, Prager Str, 04299 Leipzig - T: (0341) 8780471, Fax: 8780471, E-mail: Stadtmuseum.Leipzig@t-online.de, Internet: http://home.t-online.de/home/stadtmuseum.leipzig. Head: Dr. Volker Rodekamp
Military Museum
Political and military situation of Saxony, Prussia and Leipzig during the Napoleonic Wars, arms, pewter figures 17065

Zwangsarbeiter Gedenkstätte, Permoserstr 15, 04315 Leipzig - T: (0341) 2352075
Historical Museum
Forced labour while WWII in Leipzigian armamental industry 17066

Leisnig

Burg Mildenstein, Burglehn 6, 04703 Leisnig - T: (034321) 12652, Fax: 51537, E-mail: info@burg-mildenstein.de, Internet: http://www.burg-mildenstein.de. Head: Dr. Brigitte Riese
Historical Museum - 1890
Medievial history, jail and administration history, chapel with religious sculpture - library 17067

Leitzkau

Stiftung Schlösser, Burgen und Gärten LSA, Schloß Leitzkau, 39279 Leitzkau - T: (039241) 93430
Historic Site 17068

Lembruch

Dümmer-Museum, 49459 Lembruch - T: (05447) 341, Fax: 921797. Head: H. Dannhus
Natural History Museum
Hist of settling, natural hist, fauna and flora of the lake 17069

Lemgo

Hexenbürgermeisterhaus, Städtisches Museum, Breite Str 17-19, 32657 Lemgo - T: (05261) 213276, Fax: 213346, E-mail: - hexenbuergermeisterhaus@t-online.de, Internet: http://www.lemgo.de. Head: Jürgen Scheffler
Local Museum - 1926
Hist of craft and trade, witch-hunt in Lemgo, Engelbert Kämpfer (1651-1712), physician and traveller, jews in Lemgo - Frenkel-Haus 17070

Junkerhaus, Hamelner Str 36, 32657 Lemgo - T: (05261) 213276, Fax: 213346, E-mail: - hexenbuergermeisterhaus@t-online.de, Internet: http://www.junkerhaus.de. Head: Jürgen Scheffler
Local Museum 17071

Schloß Brake - Das Weserrenaissance-Museum, Schloßstr 18, 32657 Lemgo - T: (05261) 94500, Fax: 945050, E-mail: Weserrenaissance-Museum@t-online.de, Internet: http://www.wrm.lemgo.de. Head: Dr. Vera Lüpkes
Fine Arts Museum / Decorative Arts Museum / Historic Site - 1986
Art and art hist 16th-early 17th c, Renaissance, hist of architecture, 16th c prints, cultural hist 17072

Städtische Galerie Eichenmüllerhaus, Braker Mitte 39, 32657 Lemgo - T: (05261) 213273, Fax: 213453, E-mail: a.bleibaum@lemgo.de, Internet: http://www.lemgo.de
Public Gallery 17073

Lengefeld, Erzgebirge

Museum Kalkwerk Lengefeld, Sächsisches Industriemuseum, Kalkwerk 4a, 09514 Lengefeld, Erzgebirge - T: (037367) 2274, Fax: 82692, E-mail: lengefeld@saechsisches-industriemuseum.de, Internet: http://www.saechsisches-industriemuseum.de. Head: Jutta Sachse
Science&Tech Museum
Lime works and mining, further processing and machinery 17074

Lengenfeld, Vogtland

Feuerwehrmuseum, Poststr 39, 08485 Lengenfeld, Vogtland - T: (037606) 2610, 34334, Fax: 2610
Special Museum / Science&Tech Museum 17075

Heimatmuseum, Hauptstr 57, 08485 Lengenfeld, Vogtland - T: (037606) 32178, Fax: 30546
Local Museum - 1955
Geology, local history, history of local crafts, costumes 17076

Klopfermühle mit Mühlenmuseum, Zwickauer Str 29, 08485 Lengenfeld, Vogtland - T: (037606) 2622, Fax: 2622
Science&Tech Museum 17077

Lengerich, Westfalen

Westfälisches Feldbahnmuseum der Eisenbahnfreunde Lengerich, Lienener Str, 49525 Lengerich, Westfalen - T: uwe.Steinek-ker@freenet.de. Head: Uwe Stieneker
Science&Tech Museum 17078

Lenggries

Heimatmuseum Lenggries, Rathauspl 1, 83661 Lenggries - T: (08042) 2071
Local Museum 17079

Tiermuseum, Bergweg 12, 83661 Lenggries - T: (08042) 2510, Fax: 4702. Head: Kaspar Waldherr
Natural History Museum - 1971
2,000 preserved birds and mammals from Central Europe 17080

Lennestadt

Museum der Stadt Lennestadt, Kölner Str 57, 57368 Lennestadt - T: (02721) 1404
Local Museum 17081

Lenzen, Elbe

Burgmuseum, Burghof, 19309 Lenzen, Elbe - T: (038792) 7291
Local Museum - 1954
Ancient and early hist finds, stone coll, local hist and crafts 17082

Leonberg, Württemberg

Galerieverein Leonberg e.V., Im Zwinger 7, 71229 Leonberg, Württemberg - T: (07152) 399182, Fax: 399182, E-mail: info@galerieverein-leonberg.de, Internet: http://www.galerieverein-leonberg.de. Head: Prof. Dr. Axel Kuhn
Association with Coll 17083

Stadtmuseum Leonberg, Pfarrstr 1, 71229 Leonberg, Württemberg - T: (07152) 9901422, Fax: 9901490, E-mail: kon@leonberg.de, Internet: http://www.leonberg.de. Head: Klaus Konz
Local Museum - 1979/1983 17084

Leun

Stadtmuseum Leun, Limburger Str 3, 35638 Leun - T: (06473) 8994. Head: Waldemar Becker
Local Museum - 1984
Porcelain, original folk costumes, needlework, trade and domestic implements 17085

Leutershausen

Flugpionier-Gustav-Weißkopf-Museum, Altes Stadtschloß, Plan 6, 91578 Leutershausen - T: (09823) 9510, Fax: 95150, E-mail: - stadt.leutershausen@an-netz.de, Internet: http://www.weisskopf.de. Head: Hermann Betscher
Local Museum - 1970
Aeronautics, Gustav Weißkopf (pioneer in flying) 17086

Heimat-und Handwerkermuseum, Altes Stadtschloß, Plan 6, 91578 Leutershausen - T: (09823) 9510, Fax: 95150, E-mail: - stadt.Leutershausen@an-netz.de, Internet: http://www.leutershausen.de. Head: Hermann Betscher
Local Museum 17087

Heimatmuseum im Unteren Turm, Unterer Torturm, Am Markt 22, 91578 Leutershausen - T: (09823) 9510, Fax: 95150, E-mail: 101505.314@compuserve.com
Local Museum - 1908
Agricultural implements, folk art and costumes, furniture 17088

Heimatmuseum Leutershausen, Altes Stadtschloß, Plan 6, 91578 Leutershausen - T: (09823) 9510, Fax: 95150
Local Museum
Local hist 17089

Leutkirch im Allgäu

Museum im Bock, Am Gansbühl 9, 88299 Leutkirch im Allgäu - T: (07561) 87149. Head: Prof. Dr. Manfred Thierer
Local Museum
Cheese-making, fossils, local hist 17090

Leverkusen

Schloß Morsbroich, Städtisches Museum Leverkusen, Gustav-Heinemann-Str 80, 51377 Leverkusen - T: (0214) 855560, Fax: 8555644, E-mail: 412@stadt.leverkusen.de, Internet: http://www.leverkusen.de. Head: Dr. Gerhard Finckh
Fine Arts Museum
Painting, graphic arts and sculpture since 1945 17091

Lich

Heimatkundliche Sammlung, Kirchenpl 4-6, 35423 Lich - T: (06404) 8060, Fax: 806224
Local Museum - 1963
Town hist, kitchen utensils, agricultural implements - Library 17092

Langsdorfer Heimatmuseum, Birklarer Weg, 35423 Lich Langsdorf - T: (06404) 7771
Local Museum - 1980
Agricultural implements, domestic appliances, loom, flax processing, 17093

Lichtenfels, Bayern

Heimatmuseum Klosterlangheim, Abt-Mösinger-Str 4, 96215 Lichtenfels, Bayern - T: (09571) 795134, Fax: 795190, E-mail: stadt-lichtenfels@t-online.de, Internet: http://www.lichtenfels-city.de
Local Museum 17094

Sammlung Fossilien des Jura, Historisches Rathaus, Marktpl 1, 96215 Lichtenfels, Bayern - T: (09571) 795134
Natural History Museum - 1997 17095

Stadtmuseum Lichtenfels, Bamberger Str 3a, 96215 Lichtenfels, Bayern - T: (09571) 739422, Fax: 795190, E-mail: stadt-lichtenfels@t-online.de, Internet: http://www.lichtenfels-city.de. Head: Christine Wittenbauer
Local Museum - 1907/97
Town hist, trades and guilds, agricultural implements, basket-making 17096

Lichtenstein

Schloß Lichtenstein, 72805 Lichtenstein - T: (07129) 4102, Fax: 5259. Head: Manfred Wälder
Decorative Arts Museum
Weapons, glass painting, altar panel paintings from the 14th and 15th c, glass 17097

Liebenau bei Dippoldiswalde

Bauernmuseum Liebenau, Hauptstr 4, 01778 Liebenau bei Dippoldiswalde - T: (035054) 25619
Agriculture Museum / Ethnology Museum - 1975
Agricultural tools, household items, furniture, machines, woodcarving, smithy, carriages, tractors 17098

Lieberose

Antifaschistische Mahn- und Gedenkstätte, Bahnhofstr, 15868 Lieberose - T: (033671) 2511, Fax: 2511, E-mail: pkotzan36@aol.com. Head: Peter Kotzan
Historical Museum
Hist of the concentration camp Lieberose 17099

Liebstadt

Museum Schloß Kuckuckstein, Am Schloßberg 1, 01825 Liebstadt - T: (035025) 50283, Fax: 56117. Head: Regine Hengelhaupt
Historical Museum - 1952
Freemasonry - library 17100

Lilienthal

Heimatmuseum Lilienthal, Klosterstr 16b, 28865 Lilienthal - T: (04298) 6011, 1044, 4744, Fax: 4744
Local Museum - 1966
Early hist, Cistercian cloister, observatory from 1782 17101

Lilienhof, Worphauser Landstr 26a, 28865 Lilienthal - T: (04792) 7679, Fax: 7679
Agriculture Museum
Cultural and farming objects 17102

Niedersächsisches Kutschenmuseum, Trupe 10, 28865 Lilienthal - T: (0421) 271521. Head: Heinrich Klüver
Science&Tech Museum - 1973
Historical carriages and coaches 17103

Schulmuseum Lilienthal, Falkenberger Landstr 67, 28865 Lilienthal - T: (04298) 1044, 4744, 2816, Fax: 4744
Historical Museum - 1985
Historical school room - Library 17104

Limbach-Oberfrohna

Heimatmuseum Fronfeste, Rathausstr, 09212 Limbach-Oberfrohna - T: (03722) 780
Local Museum - 1992
Development of hosiery industry 17105

Industriemuseum, Sachsenstr 3, 09212 Limbach-Oberfrohna - T: (03722) 93039
Science&Tech Museum 17106

Limburg an der Lahn

Kunstsammlungen der Stadt Limburg, Fischmarkt 21, 65549 Limburg an der Lahn - T: (06431) 212912, Fax: 212918, E-mail: Stadt-Limburg@region-online.de, Internet: http://www.limburg.de. Head: Maria Lamard
Fine Arts Museum - 1985
Portraits by Ernst Moritz Engert, Expressionists paintings by Josef Eberz 17107

Missions-Museum der Pallottiner Limburg, Wiesbadener Str 1, 65549 Limburg an der Lahn - T: (06431) 4011, Fax: 401266, E-mail: schroeers@pallot.oms.de, Internet: http://www.pallotiner.org. Head: August Grezinger
Religious Arts Museum / Ethnology Museum
Souvenirs by missionaries brought back from West-Australia and Kamerun 17108

Staurothek, Domschatz und Diözesanmuseum, Domstr 12, 65549 Limburg an der Lahn - T: (06431) 295443, 295482, 295327, Fax: 295471, E-mail: dioezesanmuseum@bistumlimburg.de. Head: Georg Freiherr von Boeselager
Religious Arts Museum - 1903
Religious art since the 10th c, goldsmith work from the early Middle Ages and Baroque period - photo archive 17109

Lindau, Bodensee

Friedensräume, Museum in Bewegung der Pax Christi, Bad Schachen, Lindenhofweg 25, 88131 Lindau, Bodensee - T: (0821) 517751, Fax: 150325, E-mail: pc.augsburg@gmx.de
Religious Arts Museum
On both famous and unknown people having paved the way for peace 17110

Stadtarchiv und Stadtbibliothek, Altes Rathaus, 88131 Lindau, Bodensee - T: (08382) 944653, Fax: 944654, E-mail: StadtarchivLindau@web.de, Internet: http://www.lindau.de. Head: Heiner Stauder
Library with Exhibitions 17111

Stadtmuseum Haus zum Cavazzen, Marktpl 6, 88131 Lindau, Bodensee - T: (08382) 918400, Fax: 918298, E-mail: stadt.lindau@allgaeu.org. Head: Dr. Angela Heilmann

Music Museum / Fine Arts Museum / Decorative Arts Museum - 1889
Graphics and paintings from the 15th-20th c, sculpture, handicrafts, furniture, pewter, glass, weapons, textiles - library, archives 17112

Lindberg

Bauernhaus-Museum, Kramerstr 4, 94227 Lindberg - T: (09922) 9346, Fax: (09921) 4152. Head: Helga Handlos
Agriculture Museum / Folklore Museum - 1975
Folk costumes, agricultural implements 17113

Linden, Hessen

Hüttenberger Heimatmuseum, Am Heimatmuseum, 35440 Linden, Hessen - T: (06403) 6050, Fax: 60525. Head: Dr. Heinz-Lothar Worm
Local Museum - 1952
Costumes for various occasions, agricultural and domestic implements 17114

Lindenberg im Allgäu

Städtisches Hutmuseum, Im Brennterwinkel 4, 88161 Lindenberg im Allgäu - T: (08381) 5138
Decorative Arts Museum - 1981
Hatmaking industry, various exhibits, materials, and machines 17115

Lindenfels

Lindenfelser Museum, Burgstr 39, 64678 Lindenfels - T: (06255) 2425, Fax: 30645, E-mail: - lindenfels.touristik@hessenet.de, Internet: http://www.lindenfels.de. Head: Peter Bauer
Local Museum - 1979
Town hist, trade workshops, farmhouse parlour, domestic and agricultural implements 17116

Lindlar

Bergisches Freilichtmuseum für Ökologie und bäuerlich-handwerkliche Kultur, Schloss Heiligenhoven, 51789 Lindlar - T: (02266) 90100, Fax: 9010200, E-mail: bergisches-freilichtmuseum@lvr.de, Internet: http://www.bergisches-freilandmuseum.lvr.de. Head: Hans Haas
Open Air Museum / Agriculture Museum 17117

Lingen

Emslandmuseum Lingen, Burgstr 28 a/b, 49808 Lingen - T: (0591) 47601, Fax: 7106824, E-mail: museum.lingen@t-online.de, Internet: http://www.lingen.de. Head: Dr. A. Eiynck
Historical Museum - 1927
Tin, Dutch tiles and faience, Jewish community life 17118

Kunstverein Lingen e.V., c/o Kunsthalle, Kaiserstr, 49809 Lingen - T: (0591) 59995, Fax: 59905, E-mail: KVLingen@t-online.de, Internet: http://www.kunstvereine.de/lingen
Association with Coll 17119

Kunstverein Lingen Kunsthalle, Kaiserstr, 49809 Lingen - T: (0591) 59995, Fax: 59905, E-mail: kvlingen@t-online.de, Internet: http://www.kunstvereine.de. Head: Heiner Schepers
Association with Coll 17120

Linnich

Deutsches Glasmalerei-Museum Linnich, Rurstr 9-11, 52441 Linnich - T: (02462) 99170, Fax: 991725, E-mail: info@glasmalerei-museum.de, Internet: http://www.glasmalerei-museum.de. Head: Dr. Iris Nestler
Fine Arts Museum
Painted and stained glass, drawings, oils, sculpture 19th/ 20th c and contemporary 17121

Lippstadt

Städtisches Heimatmuseum, Rathausstr 13, 59555 Lippstadt - T: (02941) 720891, Fax: 720893, E-mail: wfl.lippstadt@t-online.de, Internet: http://www.lippstadt.de. Head: Ulrich Becker
Local Museum - 1927
Fan coll, old toys, school affairs 17122

Lisberg

Burgmuseum, Burg 1, 96170 Lisberg - T: (09549) 207
Historical Museum
One of the oldest fortresses of Franconia, furniture, objects of art 17123

Lobenstein

Regionalmuseum der Stadt Lobenstein, Schloßberg 20, 07356 Lobenstein - T: (036651) 2492, Fax: 77100
Local Museum 17124

Löbau

Oberlausitzer Sechsstädtebund- und Handwerksmuseum Löbau, Johannisstr 5, 02708 Löbau - T: (03585) 404116, Fax: 404116, E-mail: svloebau_tour@t-online.de, Internet: http://www.loebau.de
Local Museum - 1894
Ancient and early hist, local hist, geology, crafts, religious sculpture, toys, paintings, folk art, 'Sechsstädtebund' (six cities alliance) 17125

Löffingen

Museum Löffingen, Rathauspl 14, 79843 Löffingen - T: (07654) 400, Fax: 77250, E-mail: Kurverwaltung@loeffingen.de, Internet: http://www.loeffingen.de. Head:
Local Museum - 1959/1990 17126

Lörrach

Museum am Burghof, Basler Str 143, 79540 Lörrach - T: (07621) 919370, Fax: 9193720, E-mail: museum@loerrach.de, Internet: http://www.loerrach.de. Head: Markus Moehring
Local Museum - 1932
17th-20th c painting, religious sculpture from the upper Rhein area (13th-18th c), prehist, local and regional hist, folk customs and art, geology, mineralogy - library 17127

Villa Aichele, Städtische Galerie der Stadt Lörrach, Basler Str 122, 79540 Lörrach - T: (07621) 8191, E-mail: kultur@loerrach.de, Internet: http://www.loerrach.de. Head: Dr. Ulrike Hoppe-Oehl
Public Gallery 17128

Löwenstein

Stadt- und Manfred-Kyber-Museum, Freihaus, 74245 Löwenstein - T: (07131) 70601, 6125, Fax: 2250, 6125. Head: Günther Rosemann
Local Museum - 1968
Archeological finds, local history, estate of the writer Manfred Kyber 17129

Lohberg

Sellner Glashütte, Brennerstr 1, 93470 Lohberg - T: (09943) 902831
Special Museum 17130

Lohfelden

Hessisches Kutschen- und Wagenmuseum, Friedrich-Ebert-Ring 14, 34253 Lohfelden - T: (0561) 516894, Fax: 5102200, E-mail: info@kutschenmuseum.de, Internet: http://www.kutschenmuseum.de. Head: Horst Fehr
Science&Tech Museum - 1982
Horsedrawn Carriages and sledges, coll of lithographies and prints - library 17131

Lohheide

Gedenkstätte Bergen-Belsen, 29303 Lohheide - T: (05051) 6011, Fax: 7396, E-mail: Bergen-Belsen@t-online.de, Internet: http://www.nlpb.de. Head: Wilfried Wiedemann
Historical Museum
Former concentration camp, mass and single graves, exhibition, persecution and resistance between 1933 and 45 17132

Lohmen, Sachsen

Felsenburg Neurathen, Basteistr 79, 01847 Lohmen, Sachsen - T: (03501) 581024, Fax: 581025, E-mail: touristinformation@lohmen-sachsen.de, Internet: http://www.lohmen-sachsen.de
Open Air Museum
13th c castle, catapult, rock gate 17133

Lohne, Oldenburg

Industriemuseum, Gertrudenstr 11, 49393 Lohne, Oldenburg - T: (04442) 886104, Fax: 886245
Science&Tech Museum
Industrial hist of the town, cork processing, brush production 17134

Lohr am Main

Spessartmuseum, Schloßpl 1, 97816 Lohr am Main - T: (09352) 2061, Fax: 1409. Head: H. Bald
Local Museum - 1936
Ceramics, glass, mirrors, ironware, wood manufacture, wood carving, domestic utensils, painting 17135

Städtisches Schulmuseum, Sendelbacher Str 21, 97816 Lohr am Main - T: (09352) 4960
Special Museum - 1989
Fully furnished class rooms and teacher's flat 17136

Lollar

Heizungsmuseum im Kundeninformationszentrum Lollar der Buderus Heiztechnik, Justus-Kilian-Str 1, 35457 Lollar - T: (06441) 4182338, Fax: 4182553, E-mail: Informationszentrum.Lollar@Heiztechnik.buderus.de. Head: Dr. Frank Döring
Science&Tech Museum - 1973
Technology of central heating from the 18th-20th c 17137

Lommatzsch

Heimatmuseum, Am Markt 1, 01623 Lommatzsch - T: (035241) 5400, Fax: 54017, 54019
Local Museum 17138

Lorch, Rheingau

Kunst- und Heimatmuseum, Große Au 18, 65391 Lorch, Rheingau - T: (06726) 528, Fax: 528
Local Museum
Medieval sculpture, sacral objects, Roman ceramics finds 17139

Lorch, Württemberg

Heimatmuseum Lorch, Kloster Lorch, 73547 Lorch, Württemberg - T: (07172) 927170, Fax: 9271719, E-mail: kloster-lorch@staufer-strasse.de, Internet: http://www.staufer-strasse.de
Local Museum - 1933
Roman finds in Lorch, local hist, memorabilia of the poets Friedrich Schiller and Eduard Mörike 17140

Lorsch

Museumszentrum Lorsch, Nibelungenstr 32, 64653 Lorsch - T: (06251) 1038211, Fax: 587140, E-mail: info@kloster-lorsch.de, Internet: http://www.kloster-lorsch.de. Head: Dr. Hermann Schefers
Local Museum / Religious Arts Museum / Historic Site - 1995
Hist of the Benedictine monastery in terms of religion, culture, politics, book illustrations, ivory carving, sculpture, ceramics, earthenware, furniture 17141

Tabakmuseum, Museumszentrum, 64653 Lorsch - T: (06251) 5967410/11, Fax: 596760. Head: Reinhard Diehl
Agriculture Museum - 1982
Hist of 300 yrs of tobacco growing in Hesse 17142

Loßburg

Heimatmuseum Obere Mühle, Brunnenweg 3, 72290 Loßburg - T: (07446) 41919, Fax: 950410, E-mail: wernerJoppek@swol.de, Internet: http://vereine.swol.de/lossburg/schwarzwaldverein
Local Museum - 1969
Peasant life, work and domestic tools, traditional costumes, religious art 17143

Luckau, Niederlausitz

Heimatmuseum und Karl-Liebknecht-Gedenkstätte, Lange Str 71, 15926 Luckau, Niederlausitz - T: (03544) 2293, Fax: 2948, E-mail: AmtLuckau@t-online.de, Internet: http://www.brandenburg.de/kommunen/luckau
Local Museum - 1912
Ancient and early history, native animals, peasant culture and tools, crafts history, numismatics - Karl Liebknecht memorial 17144

Luckenwalde

Kreisheimatmuseum, Markt 11, 14943 Luckenwalde - T: (03371) 611359. Head: Roman Schmidt
Local Museum - 1906
Ancient and early history, local history, development of local industry 17145

Kunsthalle Vierseithof, Am Herrenhaus 2, 14943 Luckenwalde - T: (03371) 626885
Fine Arts Museum 17146

Ludwigsburg, Württemberg

Schloss Ludwigsburg, Schlossstr 30, 71634 Ludwigsburg, Württemberg - T: (07141) 186440, Fax: 186434, E-mail: info@schloss-ludwigsburg.de, Internet: http://www.schloess-ludwigsburg.de. Head: U. Krüger
Decorative Arts Museum - 1704
18th c Baroque castle, Rococo and Classical furnishings, painting, sculpture, tapestry 17147

Städtisches Museum Ludwigsburg, Wilhelmstr 9, 71638 Ludwigsburg, Württemberg - T: (07141) 9102290, Fax: 9102605, E-mail: museum@stadt.ludwigsburg.de, Internet: http://www.ludwigsburg.de. Head: Dr. Andrea Fix
Local Museum
Prehist, town hist, crafts, famous local writers, graphic coll 'Württembergica' 17148

Strafvollzugsmuseum, Schorndorfer Str 38, 71638 Ludwigsburg, Württemberg - T: (07141) 186265, Fax: 901695. Head: Dr. E. Viehöfer
Historical Museum - 1986
Hist of penal system 17149

Ludwigsfelde

Museum der Stadt Ludwigsfelde, Str der Jugend/ Brandenburgische Str, 14974 Ludwigsfelde - T: (03378) 804620, Fax: 827124, Internet: http://www.ludwigsfelde.de
Science&Tech Museum 17150

Ludwigshafen am Rhein

Ernst-Bloch-Zentrum, Walzmühlstr 63, 67061 Ludwigshafen am Rhein - T: (0621) 5042041, 5043041, Fax: 5042450, E-mail: klaus.kufeld@ludwigshafen.de, Internet: http://www.bloch.de. Head: Klaus Kufeld
Special Museum
Scientific heritage of Ernst Bloch, principle hope, going upright - library, research 17151

K.O. Braun Museum, Rathauspl 2, 67059 Ludwigshafen am Rhein - T: (0621) 5042573, Fax: 5043784. Head: Peter Ruf
Local Museum
Local hist, rural culture 17152

Museum Friesenheim, Luitpoldstr 48, 67063 Ludwigshafen am Rhein - T: (0621) 5042169, 692306, Fax: 50430806, 692306
Local Museum 17153

Schillerhaus, Schillerstr 6, 67071 Ludwigshafen am Rhein
Special Museum - 1959
House in which Schiller lived as a fugitive in 1782, documents, letters, paintings, graphics, first editions of Schiller, local hist 17154

Schulmuseum Mozartschule Rheingönheim, Hilgundstr 21, 67067 Ludwigshafen am Rhein - T: (0621) 504423110, Fax: 504423198, E-mail: mozartschule-gs-lu@t-online.de, Internet: http://www.mozartschule-rheingoenheim.de. Head: Theodor Berger
Historical Museum 17155

Stadtmuseum Ludwigshafen, Rathaus-Center, 67059 Ludwigshafen am Rhein - T: (0621) 5042574, Fax: 5042450, E-mail: stadtmuseum@ludwigshafen.she.de, Internet: http://www.ludwigshafen.de. Head: Peter Ruf
Local Museum - 1907 17156

Wilhelm-Hack-Museum Ludwigshafen am Rhein, Berliner Str 23, 67059 Ludwigshafen am Rhein - T: (0621) 5043411, 5043045, Fax: 5043780, Internet: http://www.wilhelm-hach-museum.de. Head: Dr. Richard W. Gassen
Fine Arts Museum - 1979
Frankish grave finds, medieval altar panel paintings, sculpture, liturgical items, paintings of the 20th c, russian suprematism (Malewitsch, El Lissitzky), dutch de stijl (Mondrian, Doesburg), german expressionists (Beckmann, Kirchner) etc., specialization on constructivist-concrete art (Bill, Lohse, Morellet, L.P. Smith, etc.) - workshops, audiovisual center 17157

Ludwigslust

Schloß Ludwigslust, Schloßfreiheit, 19288 Ludwigslust - T: (03874) 28114, Fax: 28114, E-mail: otto@museum-schwerin.de, Internet: http://www.museum-schwerin.de. Head: Prof. Dr. Kornelia von Berswordt
Historical Museum
Baroque castle, hunting weapons, art objects 17158

Ludwigsstadt

Burg Lauenstein, Burgstr 3, 96337 Ludwigsstadt - T: (09263) 400, Fax: 974422, E-mail: info@bsv.bayern.de. Head: Dr. Werner Helmberger
Decorative Arts Museum / Folklore Museum / Fine Arts Museum - 12th c
In 12th c fortress: 13th-19th c furniture, paintings, tile ovens, weapons, ironwork, musical instruments, lamps, historic keys and locks 17159

Profanierte Marienkapelle, Lauensteiner Str 1, 96337 Ludwigsstadt - T: (09263) 9490, Fax: 94940, E-mail: info@.ludwigsstadt.de, Internet: http://www.ludwigsstadt.de
Special Museum - 1995
Local poets and archeological finds 17160

Schiefermuseum, Lauensteiner Str 44, 96337 Ludwigsstadt - T: (09263) 974541, Fax: 974542, E-mail: schiefermuseum@gmx.de, Internet: http://www.ludwigstadt.de/
Science&Tech Museum
Slate mining and manufacturing, school slate tables 17161

Lübbecke

Heimatmuseum Lübbecke, Burgmannshof am Markt 19, 32312 Lübbecke - T: (05741) 2760, Fax: 90561
Local Museum 17162

Lübbenau

Spreewald-Museum Lübbenau/Lehde, Topfmarkt 12, 03222 Lübbenau - T: (03542) 2472, Fax: 403425. Head: Christel Lehmann-Enders
Local Museum - 1899
Ancient and early history, Sorabian history, Luther prints, Reformation pamphlets, crafts, costumes, 17th-19th c painting and prints, decorative objects, porcelain, glass, graphic 17163

Lübeck

Behnhaus/Drägerhaus, Museum für Kunst und Kulturgeschichte der Hansestadt Lübeck, Königstr 9-11, 23552 Lübeck, mail addr: Düvekenstr 21, 23552 Lübeck - T: (0451) 1224148, Fax: 1224183, Internet: http://www.luebeckmuseen.de. Head: Dr. Thorsten Rodiek
Fine Arts Museum - 1923
19th c German painting, 20th c paintings and sculpture, interiors from the 18th and 19th c, arts and crafts 17164

Buddenbrookhaus, Heinrich-und-Thomas-Mann-Zentrum, Mengstr 4, 23552 Lübeck - T: (0451) 1224142, Fax: 1224140, E-mail: info@buddenbrookhaus.de, Internet: http://

www.buddenbrookhaus.de. Head: Dr. Hans Wißkirchen
Special Museum - 1993
Memorabilia of Thomas and Heinrich Mann, coll of the "Buddenbrooks" - Photo-archive 17165

Holstentor, Museum für Kunst und Kulturgeschichte der Hansestadt Lübeck, Holstentorpl, 23552 Lübeck, mail addr: Düvekenstr 21, 23552 Lübeck - T: (0451) 1224129, Fax: 1224183, Internet: http://www.luebeckmuseen.de. Head: Dr. Thorsten Rodiek
Local Museum - 1934
Local archaeological finds, town hist, models, documents, paintings, medieval torture, ship models, weapons 17166

Kulturforum Burgkloster, Hinter der Burg 2-4, 23552 Lübeck - T: (0451) 1224195, 1221184, Fax: 1224198, E-mail: kulturforum-burgkloster@luebeck.de, Internet: http://www.luebeck.de. Head: Dr. Ingaburgh Klatt
Local Museum / Historic Site 17167

Museum für Kunst und Kulturgeschichte der Hansestadt Lübeck, Düvekenstr 21, 23552 Lübeck - T: (0451) 1224134, Fax: 1224183, E-mail: mkk@luebeck.de, Internet: http://www.luebeckmuseen.de. Head: Dr. Thorsten Rodiek
Fine Arts Museum - 1915 17168

Museum für Natur und Umwelt, Mühlendamm 1-3, 23552 Lübeck - T: (0451) 1224122, Fax: 1224199, E-mail: naturmuseum@luebeck.de, Internet: http://www.luebeck.de. Head: Dr. Wolfram Eckloff
Natural History Museum - 1799
Paleontology, geology and mineralogy, botany and zoology of Schleswig-Holstein, environmental groups 17169

Museum für Puppentheater, Sammlung Fritz Fey jun., Kolk 16, 23552 Lübeck - T: (0451) 78626, Fax: 78436
Performing Arts Museum - 1982
Puppets and marionettes from India, China, Africa, Germany and other countries and continents, masks, posters 17170

Museumskirche St. Katharinen, Museum für Kunst und Kulturgeschichte der Hansestadt Lübeck, Königstr, Ecke Glockengießerstr, 23552 Lübeck, mail addr: Düvekenstr 21, 23552 Lübeck - T: (0451) 1224134, Fax: 1224183, E-mail: mkk@luebeck.de, Internet: http://www.luebeckmuseen.de. Head: Dr. Thorsten Rodiek
Religious Arts Museum / Fine Arts Museum - 1920 17171

Sankt-Annen-Museum, Museum für Kunst und Kulturgeschichte der Hansestadt Lübeck, Sankt-Annen-Str 15, 23552 Lübeck, mail addr: Düvekenstr 21, 23552 Lübeck - T: (0451) 1224137, Fax: 1224183, Internet: http://www.luebeckmuseen.de. Head: Dr. Thorsten Rodiek
Religious Arts Museum / Museum of Classical Antiquities / Local Museum - 1934
16th c cloister, medieval religious art, interiors, china, ceramics, glass, silver, furniture 16th-18th c, toys, Dutch and German paintings 15th-18th c, graphics 17th-20th c 19th c 17172

Städtische Münzsammlung im Archiv der Hansestadt Lübeck, Mühlendamm 1-3, 23552 Lübeck - T: (0451) 1224152, Fax: 1221517. Head: Dr. A. Graßmann
Decorative Arts Museum 17173

Studiensammlung der Lübecker Bodenfunde, c/o Amt für Archäologische Denkmalpflege, Meesenring 8, 23566 Lübeck - T: (0451) 6206150, Fax: 6206190. Head: Dr. Manfred Gläser
Archaeological Museum 17174

Völkerkundesammlung, Museum für Kunst und Kulturgeschichte der Hansestadt Lübeck, Zeughaus am Dom, Parade 10, 23552 Lübeck, mail addr: Großer Bauhof 14, 23552 Lübeck - T: (0451) 1224342, Fax: 1224348, E-mail: vks@luebeck.de, Internet: http://www.luebeckmuseen.de. Head: Dr. Thorsten Rodiek
Ethnology Museum - 1893
Folk customs and art from America, Africa, Oceania, Australia, East and Southeast Asia, and Europe, Pangwe-Sammlung Günther Tessmann, Orient-Sammlung Richard Karutz 17175

Lübz

Stadtmuseum Amtsturm, Am Markt 25, 19386 Lübz - T: (038731) 23475, Fax: 22234, E-mail: stadtluebz@aol.com, Internet: http://www.luebz.de. Head: Ilona Paschke
Local Museum - 1976
Town hist, brewery Lübz GmbH 17176

Lüchow, Wendland

Amtsturm-Museum, Wendländischer Altertumsverein, Amtsgarten, 29439 Lüchow, Wendland - T: (05841) 6375, 126249. Head: Martin Krüger
Historic Site - 1930
Hist of the tower and castle 17177

Lüdenscheid

Sammlung der Städtischen Galerie, Museen der Stadt Lüdenscheid, Sauerfelder Str 14, 58511 Lüdenscheid - T: (02351) 171496, Fax: 171709, E-mail: post@luedenscheid.de, Internet: http://www.luedenscheid.de. Head: Uwe Obier
Fine Arts Museum - 1988
library 17178

Schmiedemuseum Bremecker Hammer, c/o Stadtverwaltung Lüdenscheid, Brüninghauser Str 95, 58513 Lüdenscheid - T: (02351) 42400, Fax: 171709
Science&Tech Museum - 1980
History of local iron industry 17179

Stadtmuseum Lüdenscheid, Museen der Stadt Lüdenscheid, Sauerfelder Str 14-20, 58511 Lüdenscheid - T: (02351) 171496, Fax: 171709, E-mail: post@luedenscheid.de, Internet: http://www.luedenscheid.de. Head: Dr. Eckhard Trox
Local Museum / Military Museum - 1937
History of local iron industry, button production, buttons from throughout the world, orders and medaillons, town history, numismatics, fire fighting, airship coll 17180

Städtische Galerie Lüdenscheid, Museen der Stadt Lüdenscheid, Alte Rathausstr 1, 58511 Lüdenscheid - T: (02351) 171583, 171492, Fax: 171703/09, E-mail: museon@luedenscheid.de, Internet: http://www.luedenscheid.de. Head: Uwe Obier
Public Gallery - 1980
German art since 1945, artistic buttons 17181

Lüdinghausen

Burg Vischering, Münsterlandmuseum, Berenbrock 1, 59348 Lüdinghausen - T: (02591) 79900, Fax: 799029, E-mail: kultur@kreis-coesfeld.de, Internet: http://www.kreis-coesfeld.de. Head: Dr. Jenny Sarrazin
Historical Museum / Fine Arts Museum - 1972
Documentation of the castle hist, exhibition for children "knights and hoses" 17182

Lügde

Heimatmuseum Lügde, Hintere Str 86, 32676 Lügde - T: (05281) 7151
Local Museum 17183

Lüneburg

Altes Rathaus, Am Ochsenmarkt, 21335 Lüneburg - T: (04131) 309230, Fax: 309188. Head: Gerhard Eiselt
Local Museum
Town hall from the 13th c 17184

Brauereimuseum im historischen Kronen-Brauhaus zu Lüneburg, c/o Holsten-Brauerei AG, Heiligengeiststr 39, 21335 Lüneburg - T: (04131) 41021, Fax: 401402. Head:
Science&Tech Museum - 1985
History of beer brewing, coll of drinking vessels 17185

Deutsches Salzmuseum - Industriedenkmal Saline Lüneburg, Sülfmeisterstr 1, 21335 Lüneburg - T: (04131) 45065, Fax: 45069, E-mail: salzmuseum@aol.com, Internet: http://www.salzmuseum.de. Head: Dr. Christian Lamschus
Science&Tech Museum - 1989
Salt mining and processing, saltworks 17186

Halle für Kunst e.V., Feldstr 1c, 21335 Lüneburg - T: (04131) 402001, Fax: 402001, E-mail: hfk@lueneburg.de, Internet: http://www.halle-fuer-kunst.de
Public Gallery 17187

Kloster Lüne, 21337 Lüneburg - T: (04131) 52318, Fax: 56052, E-mail: kloster-luene@gmx.de. Head: Barbara-Ulrike Taglang
Religious Arts Museum
Sacral art objects, embroideries, tapestries 17188

Museum für das Fürstentum Lüneburg, Wandrahmstr 10, 21335 Lüneburg - T: (04131) 43891, Fax: 405497. Head: Dr. Eckhard Michael
Local Museum - 1878
Prehistory, local town history, peasant life, religious art, globes and maps - library, archives 17189

Naturmuseum Lüneburg, Haus für Natur und Umwelt, Salzstr 25-26, 21335 Lüneburg - T: (04131) 403883, Fax: 244757. Head: Prof. Dr. Kurt Horst
Natural History Museum - 1891
Local and regional rock coll, Glacial pebbles coll, regional herbarium 17190

Ostpreußisches Landesmuseum, Ritterstr 10, 21335 Lüneburg - T: (04131) 759950, Fax: 7599511, E-mail: Ostpreuss.Land.-museum@t-online.de, Internet: http://ostpreuss.landes-museum.luene-info.de. Head: Dr. Ronny Kabus
Local Museum - 1987
Natural hist, hunting, forestry, native and extinct animals, amber 17191

Lünen

Museum der Stadt Lünen, Gesindehaus Schloß Schwansbell, Schwansbeller Weg 32-34, 44532 Lünen - T: (02306) 1041649. Head: Dr. Wingolf Lehnemann
Local Museum - 1937
Housing 1840-1930, dolls and toys, cast iron and stoves 17192

Stadtgalerie Lünen, Kurt-Schumacher-Str 42, 44532 Lünen - T: (02306) 104579, Fax: 25286, E-mail: Kulturbuero@luenen.de, Internet: http://www.luenen.de
Public Gallery 17193

Lützen

Gustav-Adolf-Gedenkstätte, Gustav-Adolf-Str 42, 06686 Lützen - T: (034444) 20317, Fax: 20317, E-mail: stadt.luetzen@t-online.de, Internet: http://www.luetzen-info.de. Head: Maik Reichel
Historical Museum / Historic Site - 1932
Monument to Swedish king Gustav-Adolf, Swedish house with Gustav-Adolf room, battle relief, battle-field finds at scene of battle here 1632 17194

Museum im Schloß Lützen, Schloßstr 4, 06686 Lützen - T: (034444) 20228, Fax: 90693, E-mail: museum@luetzen-info.de, Internet: http://www.luetzen-info.de. Head: Maik Reichel
Local Museum - 1928
History of Thirty Years' War, local history, autographs, graphics - library, archive 17195

Lugau, Erzgebirge

Heimat- und Bergbaumuseum, Obere Hauptstr 26, 09385 Lugau, Erzgebirge - T: (037295) 5264, Fax: 5243
Local Museum - 1958
History of mining, local history 17196

Lunzenau

Museum Schloß Rochsburg, Schloßstr 1, 09328 Lunzenau - T: (037383) 6703, Fax: 6703. Head: Sylvia Karsch
Decorative Arts Museum - 1911
Historic rooms, furnishings, Baroque, Rococo and Biedermeier interior 17197

Lutherstadt Eisleben

Mansfeld-Galerie, Friedensstr 12, 06295 Lutherstadt Eisleben - T: (03475) 602926, Fax: 602926
Fine Arts Museum
Contemporary art, "cosmos-painting" by Andrej Sokolow 17198

Martin Luthers Geburtshaus, Lutherstr 15, 06295 Lutherstadt Eisleben - T: (03475) 602775, Fax: 602775, E-mail: regio.knape@martinluther.de, Internet: http://www.martinluther.de. Head: Dr. Stefan Rhein
Special Museum
Documents on Luther's childhood and youth before entering the monastery 17199

Martin Luthers Sterbehaus, Andreaskirchpl 7, 06295 Lutherstadt Eisleben - T: (03475) 602885, Fax: 602885, E-mail: regio.knape@martinluther.de, Internet: http://www.martinluther.de. Head: Dr. Stefan Rhein
Local Museum 17200

Museen in der Lutherstadt Eisleben, Petristr 9, 06295 Lutherstadt Eisleben. Head: Heinz Frühling
Local Museum - 1913
Ancient and early history, local history, mining of Mansfeld since 1200, labour-movement of Mansfeld 1891-1945, crafts, textiles, numismatic, medals, natural history, minerals, bird and beetle coll - library 17201

Museumsbibliothek, Stiftung Luthergedenkstätten in Sachsen-Anhalt, Andreaskirchpl 10, 06295 Lutherstadt Eisleben - T: (03475) 602139, Fax: 602775. Head: Dr. Stefan Rhein
Library with Exhibitions 17202

Lutherstadt Wittenberg

Galerie ART der Cranach-Stiftung Wittenberg, Collegienstr 32, 06886 Lutherstadt Wittenberg - T: (03491) 400381. Head: Eva Löber
Public Gallery 17203

Galerie im Cranach-Haus, Markt 4, 06886 Lutherstadt Wittenberg - T: (03491) 4201911, Fax: 4201919, E-mail: cranach-hoefe@t-online.de, Internet: http://www.cranach.de/cranach-hoefe/. Head: Eva Löber
Association with Coll / Fine Arts Museum 17204

Lutherhalle Wittenberg, Collegienstr 54, 06886 Lutherstadt Wittenberg - T: (03491) 42030, Fax: 420327, E-mail: lutherhalle@martinluther.de, Internet: http://www.martinluther.de. Head: Dr. Stefan Rhein
Historical Museum 17205

Melanchthonhaus Wittenberg, Collegienstr 60, 06886 Lutherstadt Wittenberg - T: (03491) 403279, Fax: 420327, E-mail: lutherhalle@martinluther.de, Internet: http://www.martinluther.de. Head: Dr. Stefan Rhein
Historic Site / Special Museum - 1967
Memorabilia of Philipp Melanchthon in his former home, medals, frescos, armaments, local hist, hist of the University of Wittenberg (1502-1817) 17206

Museum für Naturkunde und Völkerkunde Julius Riemer, Schloß, 06886 Lutherstadt Wittenberg - T: (03491) 4334920. Head: Charlotte Riemer
Natural History Museum / Ethnology Museum - 1949
Zoological evolution, human evolution, anthropology, historical finds from the area, ethnology (Africa, Australia, Pacific, Japan - library 17207

Stadtgeschichtliches Museum, Schloß, 06886 Lutherstadt Wittenberg - T: (03491) 2046. Head: Karin Binder
Local Museum - 1969
Ancient and early history, history of city, documents, pictures 17208

Machern

Museum im Stasi-Bunker, Museum in der Runden Ecke, Alfred-Frank-Siedlung 439, 04827 Machern, mail addr: c/o Bürgerkommitee Leipzig e.V., PF 100345, 04003 Leipzig - T: (0341) 9612443, Fax: 9612499, E-mail: mail@runde-ecke-leipzig.de, Internet: http://www.runde-ecke-leipzig.de. Head: Dr. Konrad Taut
Historical Museum
Former bunker of the state security of the GDR, original objects 17209

Magdeburg

Gedenkstätte für die Opfer politischer Gewalt in Sachsen-Anhalt 1945-1989, Umfassungsstr 76, 39124 Magdeburg - T: (0391) 2445590
Historical Museum 17210

Kulturhistorisches Museum Magdeburg, Otto-von-Guericke-Str 68-73, 39104 Magdeburg - T: (0391) 5403501/08, Fax: 5403510, E-mail: museen@magdeburg.de, Internet: http://www.magdeburg.de/kultur/museen.html. Head: Dr. Matthias Puhle
Historical Museum - 1906
Ancient and early hist, town hist, furniture, handicraft, Der Magdeburger Reiter (13th c) - library 17211

Kunstmuseum Kloster Unser Lieben Frauen, Regierungsstr 4-6, 39104 Magdeburg - T: (0391) 565020, Fax: 5650255, E-mail: presse@kunstmuseum-magdeburg.de, Internet: http://www.kunstmuseum-magdeburg.de. Head: Dr. Annegret Laabs
Fine Arts Museum - 1974
20th c sculpture, medieval crafts - library 17212

Literaturhaus, Thiemstr 7, 39104 Magdeburg - T: (0391) 4044995, Fax: 4044995. Head: Dr. Gisela Zander
Special Museum / Library with Exhibitions
Local literature and writers, graphics and painting 17213

Magdeburger Museen, Direktion, Otto-von-Guericke-Str 68-73, 39104 Magdeburg - T: (0391) 5403501, Fax: 5403510, E-mail: museen@magdeburg.de, Internet: http://www.magdeburg.de/kultur/museen.html. Head: Dr. Matthias Puhle
Local Museum - 1906 17214

Museum für Naturkunde, Otto-von-Guericke-Str 68-73, 39104 Magdeburg - T: (0391) 5403535, Fax: 5403510, E-mail: museen@magdeburg.de, Internet: http://www.magdeburg.de/kultur/museen.html. Head: Dr. Hans Pellmann
Natural History Museum - 1875
Mineralogy, geology, zoology 17215

Otto-von-Guericke-Museum in der Lukasklause, Schleinufer 1, 39104 Magdeburg - T: (0391) 5410616, 6716986, Fax: 6716529, E-mail: webmaster-OvGG@uni-magdeburg.de, Internet: http://www.uni-magdeburg.de/org/ovgg. Head: Prof. Dr. Siegfried Kattanek
Natural History Museum / Local Museum / Science&Tech Museum / Historic Site / Historical Museum
Vaccum pumps till 1750, electricity machines till 1750 (spherical), printings and documents about vaccum technique, electrical statics and about the town hist of Magdeburg 1550-1750 - Otto von Guericke archive 17216

Schiffsmuseum Seitenradschleppdampfer "Württemberg", Heinrich-Heine-Pl, 39114 Magdeburg - T: (0391) 5411283, E-mail: museen@magdeburg.de, Internet: http://www.magdeburg.de/kultur/museen.html
Science&Tech Museum 17217

Schulgeschichtliche Sammlung, Kulturhistorisches Museum, Max-Josef-Metzger-Str 8, 39104 Magdeburg - T: (0391) 5439836, 5403507, Fax: 5403510, E-mail: museen@magdeburg.de, Internet: http://www.magdeburg.de/kultur/museen.html
Historical Museum
School history 1945-1990, educational material 17218

Technikmuseum Magdeburg, Dodendorfer Str 65, 39112 Magdeburg - T: (0391) 6223906, Fax: 6223907, E-mail: info@technikmuseum-magdeburg.de, Internet: http://www.technikmuseum-magdeburg.de. Head: Dr. Karin Kanter
Science&Tech Museum 17219

Magstadt

Heimatmuseum Magstadt, Marktpl 6, 71106 Magstadt - T: (07159) 41563
Local Museum - 1984
Local hist, crafts 17220

Mahlberg

Oberrheinisches Tabakmuseum, Kirchstr 2, 77972 Mahlberg - T: (07825) 843813, Fax: 1234, E-mail: stadt@mahlberg.de, Internet: http://www.mahlberg.de. Head: Josef Naudascher
Historical Museum - 1981
Hist of tobacco cultivation 17221

Maihingen

Rieser Bauernmuseum, Klosterhof 8, 86747 Maihingen - T: (09087) 778, 1041, Fax: 711, Internet: http://www.rieser-bauernmuseum.de. Head: Prof. Dr. Hans Frei
Folklore Museum - 1973
Agricultural implements, peasant life, handicrafts, folk art 17222

Mainbernheim

Schützenscheibensammlung, An der Schießstelle 6, 97350 Mainbernheim - T: (09323) 871133
Special Museum
Coll of a rifleclub 17223

Mainburg

Hallertauer Heimat- und Hopfenmuseum, Abensberger Str 15, 84048 Mainburg - T: (08751) 4027, Fax: 70456, E-mail: mai@hallertau.net, Internet: http://www.mainburg.de
Local Museum - 1912
Hop dept 17224

Mainhardt

Museum für römische Funde → Römermuseum

Pahl Museum, Hauptstr 1, 74535 Mainhardt - T: (07903) 91500, Fax: 915050, E-mail: rathaus@mainhardt.de. Head: Adam Matheis
Fine Arts Museum - 1975
Paintings and graphics by the painter Manfred Pahl 17225

Römermuseum, Hauptstr 6, 74535 Mainhardt - T: (07903) 2759, 2308, Fax: 915050. Head: Horst Clauß, Hermann Pasler
Archaeological Museum - 1987
Roman findings 17226

Maintal

Heimat-Museum Maintal, Hauptstr 9, 63477 Maintal - T: (06181) 46695
Local Museum / Folklore Museum - 1985
Viticulture, cidre production, pressing equipment 17227

Mainz

Bischöfliches Dom- und Diözesanmuseum Mainz, Domstr 3, 55116 Mainz - T: (06131) 253344, Fax: 253349. Head: Dr. H.J. Kotzur
Religious Arts Museum - 1925
Religious art, paraments, manuscripts, prints, cathedral treasures, sculptures, archives - library, workshop 17228

Deutsches Buchbindermuseum, Liebfrauenpl 5, 55116 Mainz. Head: Erhart Köhler
Science&Tech Museum - 1962
History of bookbinding, tools, customs, tools used for gold illumination, steps in production of a hand-bound and machine-bound book 17229

Gutenberg-Museum, Liebfrauenpl 5, 55116 Mainz - T: (06131) 122640, 122644, Fax: 123488, E-mail: gutenberg-museum@stadt.mainz.de, Internet: http://www.gutenberg.de. Head: Dr. Eva-Maria Hanebutt-Benz
Science&Tech Museum / Special Museum - 1900
History of book production from the 15th to the 20th c, development of writing, book bindings, history of printing in Far East, ex libris, history of typefaces and printing machines, history of paper, posters and graphics - library, audiovisual room, printing workshop, bookshop 17230

Kupferberg-Museum, Kupferbergterrasse 17-19, 55116 Mainz - T: (06131) 9230, Fax: 923222, E-mail: info@kupferberg.de, Internet: http://www.kupferberg.de. Head: Dr. Ingrid Faust
Special Museum - 1960
History of the champagne firm Kupferberg, history of champagne, advertising graphics since 1880, engravings, historical sparkling wine receptacles, Roman finds - Archives 17231

Landesmuseum Mainz, Große Bleiche 49-51, 55116 Mainz - T: (06131) 28570, Fax: 285757. Head: Dr. Isabella Fehle
Archaeological Museum / Decorative Arts Museum / Fine Arts Museum / Historical Museum - 1803
Prehist, roman times, period of folk migration (franconian time), medieval paintings and sculpture, 16th c painting, Baroque sculpture, Dutch and German painting of the 17th c, Höchster porcelain, local 18th c art, 19th c German painting, 20th c painting and sculpture, prints, drawings, Prinz Johann-Georg coll, local hist, judaica 17232

Münzkabinett im Stadtarchiv Mainz, Rheinallee 3b, 55116 Mainz - T: (06131) 122178, Fax: 123569, E-mail: stadtarchiv@stadt.mainz.de, Internet: http://www.mainz.de/archiv.htm. Head: Friedrich Schütz
Decorative Arts Museum - 1784 17233

Museum für Antike Schiffahrt des Römisch-Germanischen Zentralmuseums, Neutorstr 2b, 55116 Mainz - T: (06131) 286630, Fax: 2866324, E-mail: rzentral@mainz-online.de, Internet: http://index.waterland.net/navis/Musea/Mainz/Navismus.htm. Head: Dr. Barbara Pferdehirt
Archaeological Museum - 1989 17234

Naturhistorisches Museum, Landessammlung für Naturkunde Rheinland-Pfalz, Reichklarastr 1, 55116 Mainz - T: (06131) 122646, Fax: 122975, E-mail: lsnhmmz@mail.uni-mainz.de, Internet: http://www.uni-mainz.de/~lsnhmmz. Head: Dr. Fr. O. Neuffer
Natural History Museum - 1910
Exhibits on geological periods of importance for region, esp the Pleistocene and the Tertiary periods, fauna and flora, fossils, mollusks - library, specimen room 17235

Römisch-Germanisches Zentralmuseum, Forschungsinstitut für Vor- und Frühgeschichte, Ernst-Ludwig-Pl 2, 55116 Mainz - T: (06131) 91240, Fax: 9124199. Head: Dr. Konrad Weidemann
Archaeological Museum - 1852
Div: prehistory, Roman times, early Middle Ages, archives - library, workshops, photo laboratory, research laboratories 17236

Städtische Galerie Brückenturm, gegenüber Rathaus, 55116 Mainz - T: (06131) 122522
Public Gallery 17237

Malgersdorf

Bauern- und Handwerker-Museum, Haberskirchner Str, Heilmfurt 6, 84333 Malgersdorf - T: (09954) 7309, Internet: http://home.t-online.de/home/310084090167-0001/charly.htm
Folklore Museum - 1998 17238

Malsfeld

Korbmacher-Museum, Mühlenstr 18, Beiseförth, 34323 Malsfeld - T: (05661) 50027
Special Museum - 1993
Hist of basket making 17239

Manching

Keltisch-Römisches Museum, Ingolstädter Str 2, 85077 Manching - T: (08459) 850, 2215, Fax: 7267, E-mail: mayr-manching@t-online.de. Head: Herbert Mayr
Archaeological Museum - 1988
Celtic and Roman archaeology 17240

Mannheim

Curt-Engelhorn-Zentrum, Reiss-Engelhorn-Museen, B 4, 10a, 68159 Mannheim - T: (0621) 2933150/51, Fax: 2933099, E-mail: reiss-engelhorn-museen@mannheim.de, Internet: http://www.reiss-engelhorn-museen.mannheim.de. Head: Prof. Dr. Alfried Wieczorek
Fine Arts Museum / Local Museum / Performing Arts Museum - 1957
Art, town hist, theater, books printed in Mannheim - library, workshops, photo laboratory 17241

Fotogalerie Alte Feuerwache, Brückenstr 2, 68167 Mannheim - T: (0621) 2939283, Fax: 2939293, E-mail: thomas.schirmboeck@mannheim.de, Internet: http://www.altefeuerwache.com. Head: Thomas Schirmböck
Public Gallery 17242

Heart Gallery Projekt, G 7, 20, 68159 Mannheim - T: (0621) 20265, Fax: 20265, Internet: http://www.heart-gallery.projekt.de
Public Gallery 17243

Landesmuseum für Technik und Arbeit in Mannheim, Museumsstr 1, 68165 Mannheim - T: (0621) 42989, Fax: 4298754, E-mail: direktion@lta.mannheim.de, Internet: http://www.landesmuseum-mannheim.de. Head: Prof. Dr. Jakob Messerli
Science&Tech Museum - 1990
Technical, social and political hist of Southwest Germany, hist workshops, industrial plants, offices, private and public transport, Carl Benz - library, research institute 17244

Museum für Archäologie, Völkerkunde und Naturkunde, Reiss-Engelhorn-Museen, D 5, 68159 Mannheim - T: (0621) 2933150/51, Fax: 2933099, E-mail: reiss-engelhorn-museen@mannheim.de, Internet: http://www.reiss-engelhorn-museen.mannheim.de. Head: Prof. Dr. Alfried Wieczorek
Archaeological Museum / Ethnology Museum / Natural History Museum - 1988
Archeological finds from stone Age until Middle Age, ethnological coll, natural hist 17245

Museum für Kunst-, Stadt-, Theater- und Musikgeschichte, Reiss-Engelhorn-Museen, Zeughaus, C 5, 68159 Mannheim - T: (0621) 2933150/51, Fax: 2933099, E-mail: reiss-engelhorn-museen@mannheim.de, Internet: http://www.reiss-engelhorn-museen.mannheim.de. Head: Prof. Dr. Alfried Wieczorek
Fine Arts Museum / Local Museum / Performing Arts Museum - 1957
Art, town hist, theater, books printed in Mannheim - library, workshops, photo laboratory 17246

Museumsschiff Mannheim des Landesmuseums für Technik und Arbeit, Am Museumsufer, 68165 Mannheim - T: (0621) 1565756, Fax: 4298754, E-mail: direktion@lta.mannheim.de, Internet: http://www.landesmuseum-mannheim.de. Head: Prof. Dr. Jakob Messerli
Science&Tech Museum - 1986/90
Hist of shipping on the river Rhine 17247

Reiss-Engelhorn-Museen, Zeughaus, C 5, 68159 Mannheim - T: (0621) 2933150/51, Fax: 2933099, E-mail: reiss-engelhorn-museum@mannheim.de, Internet: http://www.reiss-engelhorn-museum.mannheim.de. Head: Prof. Dr. Alfried Wieczorek
Archaeological Museum / Historical Museum / Fine Arts Museum / Ethnology Museum - 1763 17248

Schloß Mannheim, Bismarckstr, 68159 Mannheim - T: (0621) 2922890, Fax: 2922893, E-mail: info@schloss-schwetzingen.de, Internet: http://www.schloesser-und-gaerten.de. Head: Andreas Falz
Historical Museum 17249

Städtische Kunsthalle Mannheim, Moltkestr 9, 68165 Mannheim - T: (0621) 2936411/30, Fax: 2936412, E-mail: kunsthalle@mannheim.de, Internet: http://www.kunsthalle-mannheim.de. Head: Prof. Dr. Manfred Fath
Fine Arts Museum - 1907
German painting of the 19th c, German Impressionism, French and German Expressionism, 20th c painting, painting of the 50s and 60s, 19th-20th c sculpture, master graphics of the 19th-20th c - library, workshops, photo laboratory 17250

Mansfeld, Südharz

Luther-Stube Mansfeld, Lutherstr 26, 06343 Mansfeld, Südharz - T: (034782) 20210, Fax: 20210
Religious Arts Museum
Home of Luther's parents, portrayal of the childhood and youth of the reformator, regional hist, mining 17251

Marbach am Neckar

Heimatmuseum Rielingshausen, Paul-Gerhardt-Str 15, 71672 Marbach am Neckar - T: (07144) 3134
Local Museum 17252

Schiller-Nationalmuseum und Deutsches Literaturarchiv, Schillerhöhe 8-10, 71672 Marbach am Neckar - T: (07144) 848601, Fax: 848690, E-mail: museum@dla.marbach.de, Internet: http://www.dla-marbach.de. Head: Prof. Dr. Ulrich Ott, Dr. Jochen Meyer
Special Museum - 1903
German literature from 1750 to present, mss, autographs, tapes, 1100 bequests of writers, archives, library, doc on grey literature, theatre, radio and television, picture dept 17253

Schillers Geburtshaus, Niklastorstr 31, 71672 Marbach am Neckar - T: (07144) 17567, Fax: 102300, E-mail: touristik@schillerstadt-marbach.de. Head: Herbert Pötzsch
Special Museum / Historic Site - 1859
House where the dramatist and poet Friedrich von Schiller was born, exhibits on his life and works 17254

Marburg

Antiken- und Abgußsammlung des Archäologischen Seminars, Biegenstr 11, 35037 Marburg - T: (06421) 2822353, Fax: 2828977, E-mail: froning@mailer.uni-marburg.de, Internet: http://www.uni-marburg.de/geschichte. Head: Prof. Dr. H. Froning, Dr. T. Mattern, Prof. Dr. H. Lauter
Archaeological Museum - 1875
Study coll of 600 casts of Greek and Roman sculpture, antique objects of art, ceramics and terracottas - library 17255

Bildarchiv Foto Marburg, Ernst-von-Hülsen-Haus, Wolffstr, 35037 Marburg - T: (06421) 2823600, Fax: 2828931, E-mail: bildarchiv@fotomr.uni-marburg.de, Internet: http://fotomr.uni-marburg.de. Head: Dr. Brigitte Walbe
Library with Exhibitions 17256

Circus-, Varieté- und Artistenarchive, c/o Kulturhistorische Gesellschaft für Circus- und Varietékunst e.V., Ketzerbach 21 1/2, 35037 Marburg - T: (06421) 42346
Performing Arts Museum / Library with Exhibitions - 1987
Costumes, requisites, art exhibits made by circus performers 17257

Deutsches Spiele-Archiv, Barfüsserstr 2a, 35037 Marburg - T: (06421) 62728, Fax: 62720, E-mail: Spiele-Archiv@t-online.de, Internet: http://www.uni-marburg.de/spiele-archiv/. Head: Dr. Bernward Thole
Special Museum 17258

Kindheitsmuseum, Barfüßer Tor 5, 35037 Marburg - T: (06421) 24424. Head: Prof. Dr. Helge Hyamus-Peter
Historical Museum - 1979
First German childhood museum, old children's books, school books, lithographies, toys, authentic sceneries, fairy tale room 17259

Marburger Universitätsmuseum für Kunst und Kulturgeschichte, Biegenstr 11, 35032 Marburg - T: (06421) 2822355, Fax: 2822166, E-mail: fischerr@verwaltung.uni-marburg.de. Head: Dr. Jürgen Wittstock, Dr. Günther Junghans
Fine Arts Museum / Historical Museum / University Museum - 1875
Painting, sculpture, graphics, arts and crafts, folk art, pre- and ancient history - library, workshops 17260

Mineralogisches Museum der Philipps-Universität Marburg, Firmaneipl, 35032 Marburg - T: (06421) 2822257, Fax: 2827077, E-mail: schuerma@mailer.uni-marburg.de, Internet: http://www.uni-marburg.de/geowissenschaften/minmus.htm. Head: Dr. Kay U. Schürmann
Natural History Museum / University Museum - 1790/1977
Herz mineral coll (1853), Prüm mineral coll (1879), Brøgger rock coll Norway, Stürtz rock coll 17261

Museum Anatomicum, Robert-Koch-Str 5, 35033 Marburg - T: (06421) 2864078, 2867011, Fax: 2867090, E-mail: gruendenau@mailer.uni-marburg.de, Internet: http://www.uni-marburg.de/anatomie/geschichtedermedizin. Head: Prof. Aumüller
Historical Museum - 1991
Hist of anatomy since the Enlightenment in 3 000 exhibits, obstetrice 17262

Religionskundliche Sammlung der Philipps-Universität, Landgraf-Philipp-Str 4, 35032 Marburg - T: (06421) 2822480, Fax: 2822399, E-mail: relsamm@mailer.uni-marburg.de, Internet: http://www.uni-marburg.de/relsamm/. Head: Dr. Peter J. Bräunlein
Religious Arts Museum / University Museum - 1927
Tribal religions of Africa and the South Sea, shamanism, extinct religions, Christianity, Judaism, Islam, Parseeism, Hinduism, Taoism and Confucianism, Shinto, Buddhism, new religions, archives - library 17263

Völkerkundliche Sammlung der Philipps-Universität, Kugelgasse 10, 35032 Marburg - T: (06421) 2823749, Fax: 2822140, E-mail: ethno@mailer.uni-marburg.de, Internet: http://www.uni-marburg.de/fb03/neu/vk/welcome.html. Head: Prof. Dr. Mark Münzel
Ethnology Museum / University Museum - 1929
Study coll of ethnographic objects from around the world 17264

Marienberg

Stadt- und Heimatmuseum, Im Zschopauer Torturm, 09496 Marienberg - T: (03735) 23506, Fax: 22307, E-mail: marienberg.erzgebirge@abo.freiepresse.de, Internet: http://www.freiepresse.de/ORTE/Marienberg. Head: Gabriele Harbort
Local Museum - 1966
Local history, pewter and silver mining 17265

Marienhafe

Kirchenmuseum, Am Markt, 26529 Marienhafe - T: (04934) 6285. Head:
Religious Arts Museum
13th c East Frisian church, sculptures, friezes 17266

Markersdorf bei Görlitz

Schlesisch-Oberlausitzer Dorfmuseum, Kirchstr 2, 02829 Markersdorf bei Görlitz - T: (035829) 60329, Fax: 60408
Local Museum - 1992
Agriculture, crafts in a 200 years old farmhouse 17267

Markkleeberg

Deutsches Landwirtschaftsmuseum Markkleeberg (closed) 17268

Westphalsches Haus, Dölitzer Str 12, 04416 Markkleeberg - T: (0341) 3911117
Public Gallery 17269

Markneukirchen

Musikinstrumenten-Museum, Bienengarten 2, 08258 Markneukirchen - T: (037422) 2018, Fax: 6023, E-mail: museum.mkn@t-online.de, Internet: http://www.markneukirchen.de. Head: Heidrun Eichler
Music Museum - 1883
Local history, musical instruments of all cultures, mechanical instruments 17270

Markranstädt

Heimatmuseum, Markt 5, 04420 Markranstädt - T: (034205) 61105, Fax: 88246
Local Museum - 1925
Structure and economical development of the township and the landscape (nature, handicraft, industry a.s.o), landscape painter and graphic artist Kurt Schiering (1886-1918) 17271

Markt Einersheim

Markt Einersheimer Heimatstuben, Würzburger Torturm, 97348 Markt Einersheim - T: (09161) 7973
Local Museum 17272

Markt Erlbach

Rangau-Handwerkermuseum, Hauptstr 2, 91459 Markt Erlbach - T: (09106) 326, 92930
Local Museum - 1978
Local handicrafts and history 17273

Marktbreit

Museum Malerwinkelhaus, Bachgasse 2, 97340 Marktbreit - T: (09332) 40546, Fax: 40542, 40544, E-mail: touristinfo@marktbreit.de, Internet: http://www.marktbreit.de
Local Museum - 1991
Town hist, social hist of woman 17274

Marktheidenfeld

Galerie im Franck-Haus, Untertorstr 6, 97828 Marktheidenfeld - T: (09391) 50040, Fax: 7940, E-mail: maron@marktheidenfeld.de, Internet: http://www.marktheidenfeld.de
Fine Arts Museum - 2000
Work of the painter Hermann Gradl (1883-1964) 17275

Museum im Franck-Haus, Untertorstr 6, 97828 Marktheidenfeld - T: (09391) 50040, Fax: 7940, E-mail: maron@marktheidenfeld.de, Internet: http://www.marktheidenfeld.de
Local Museum - 1998
Local hist 17276

Marktl, Inn

Heimatmuseum Marktl, Marktpl 1, 84533 Marktl, Inn - T: (08678) 1594, 1068
Local Museum - 1925
Local hist, rustic culture and religious folklore 17277

Marktoberdorf

Heimatmuseum im Hartmannhaus, Meichelbeckstr 16, 87616 Marktoberdorf - T: (08342) 95463, 1501, 7211
Local Museum - 1985
Winter sports coll, rural craft and housing 17278

Paul-Röder-Museum, Eberle-Kögl-Str 11, 87616 Marktoberdorf - T: (08342) 5168, Fax: 400875. Head: Alfred Schauerte
Fine Arts Museum - 1978
Life and work of the painter Paul Röder (1896-1962) 17279

Riesengebirgsmuseum, Eberle-Kögl-Str 11, 87616 Marktoberdorf - T: (08342) 95545, Fax: 95545, Internet: http://www.marktoberdorf. Head: Gottlieb Fischer
Local Museum / Folklore Museum - 1955
Town hist and hist of German expellees 17280

Stadtmuseum und Riesengebirgsmuseum → Riesengebirgsmuseum

Städtische Galerie, Kunst- und Kulturstiftung Dr. Geiger-Haus, Jahnstr 1, 87616 Marktoberdorf - T: (08342) 2978, Fax: 2123. Head: Franz Schmid
Public Gallery 17281

Marktredwitz

Egerland-Museum, Fikentscherstr 24, 95615 Marktredwitz - T: (09231) 3907, Fax: 5264, E-mail: egerlandmuseum@egerlaender.de
Local Museum - 1973
Rustic culture and local crafts, religious folklore, manufacturing of porcelain, decorated glass and music instruments, spa culture - library, art gallery 17282

Marktrodach

Flößermuseum Unterrodach, Kirchpl 3, 96364 Marktrodach - T: (09261) 20511, 60310, Fax: 603150
Special Museum - 1968
History of raft transportation, tools, equipment, models of rafts - library, video library, photo archive 17283

Marktschellenberg

Gerbereimuseum, Alpenstr 62-66, 83487 Marktschellenberg - T: (08650) 402, (08652) 5153
Special Museum 17284

Marl, Westfalen

Skulpturenmuseum Glaskasten Marl, Creiler Pl 1, 45768 Marl, Westfalen - T: (02365) 992257, Fax: 992603, E-mail: skulpturenmuseum@stadt.marl.de, Internet: http://www.marl.de. Head: Dr. Uwe Rüth
Fine Arts Museum - 1982
Sculpture of the 20th c, art of video and new media 17285

Stadt- und Heimatmuseum der Stadt Marl, Am Volkspark 6, 45768 Marl, Westfalen - T: (02365) 56919. Head: Dr. Uwe Rüth
Local Museum - 1927
Peasant life, geology, paleontology, crafts, town hist 17286

Marne

Heimatmuseum Marner Skatklub von 1873, Museumstr 2, 25709 Marne - T: (04851) 3518
Local Museum - 1928 17287

Marsberg

Heimatmuseum der Stadt Marsberg, Bahnhofstr 11, 34431 Marsberg - T: (02992) 3077
Local Museum 17288

Marxen

Feuerwehrmuseum des Landkreises Harburg, Außenstelle des Freilichtmuseums am Kiekeberg, Hauptstr 20, 21439 Marxen - T: (04105) 76822, Fax: 7926464
Science&Tech Museum
Regional hist of fire fighting 17289

Marxzell

Fahrzeugmuseum Marxzell, Albtalstr 2, 76359 Marxzell - T: (07248) 6262, Fax: 9249901. Head: Klara Reichert
Science&Tech Museum - 1968
Automobiles, motorcycles, bicycles, motors, models, locomotives, trollies, horse-drawn streetcars, coaches, tractors, tools, threshing machines, fire engines, telephones, record players, office machines, sewing machines, radios, cameras and projectors, handicraft tools, musical instruments - film room 17290

Maselheim

Klostermuseum Heggbach, Heggbach 1, 88437 Maselheim - T: (07353) 81101, Fax: 81116, E-mail: info@heggbach.de, Internet: http://www.heggbach.de. Head: Olafa Mayer
Religious Arts Museum - 1981
Hist of the monastery, religions art 17291

Maßbach

Heimatmuseum Maßbach, Kirchgasse, 97711 Maßbach - T: (09733) 4172
Local Museum - 1988
Early and local hist, handicrafts 17292

Massing

Das Berta-Hummel-Museum im Hummelhaus, Berta-Hummel-Str 2, 84323 Massing - T: (08724) 960250, Fax: 960299, E-mail: info@hummelmuseum.de, Internet: http://www.hummelmuseum.de. Head: Alfred Hummel
Fine Arts Museum - 1994
Life and work of the artist Berta Hummel and M.I. Hummel 17293

Freilichtmuseum Massing, Steinbüchl 5, 84323 Massing - T: (08724) 96030, Fax: 960366, E-mail: massing@freilichtmuseum.de, Internet: http://www.freilichtmuseum.de. Head: Dr. Martin Ortmeier
Open Air Museum - 1969 17294

Mauersberg

Mauersberger-Museum, Hauptstr 22, 09518 Mauersberg - T: (03735) 90888, Fax: 64257. Head: Gerlinde Siegel
Special Museum
Life and work of the church musicians Rudolf and Erhard Mauersberger 17295

Maulbronn

Klosteranlage mit Klostermuseum, Klosterhof 5, 75433 Maulbronn - T: (07043) 926610, Fax: 926611, E-mail: info@kloster-maulbronn.de, Internet: http://www.schloesser-und-gaerten.de
Religious Arts Museum
Documentation on the hist of the Cistercian order, the cloister, and the seminar, town hist, architectural remains of the original 13th c cloister, UNESCO-memorial of world culture (since 12/93) 17296

Mauth

Freilichtmuseum Finsterau, Museumsstr 51, Finsterau, 94151 Mauth - T: (08557) 96060, Fax: 960666, E-mail: finsterau@freilichtmuseum.de, Internet: http://www.freilichtmuseum.de. Head: Dr. Martin Ortmeier
Open Air Museum 17297

Maxberg

Museum beim Solenhofer Aktien-Verein, Maxberg, Mörnsheim, 91807 Maxberg - T: (09145) 411, 601315. Head: Dr. Theo Kress
Natural History Museum / Fine Arts Museum - 1929
Fossils from Solnhofen, development of lithography 17298

Mayen

Eifelmuseum, Eifelvereinsmuseum, Genovevaburg, 56727 Mayen - T: (02651) 903558, 903561, Fax: 903557. Head: Dr. Bernd C. Oesterwind
Local Museum - 1904
Geology of Eifel region, volcanism, basalt-lava industry, slade-mining history, pre- and ancient history, local history, folk customs, regional sculpture and painting, material on the legend of Genovefa - workshops, laboratory 17299

Mechernich

Rheinisches Freilichtmuseum und Landesmuseum für Volkskunde Kommern, Auf dem Kahlenbusch, 53894 Mechernich - T: (02443) 99800, Fax: 9980133, E-mail: kommern@Lvr.de, Internet: http://www.kommern.lvr.de. Head: Dr. Dieter Pesch
Open Air Museum / Folklore Museum / Agriculture Museum - 1958
Peasant life, historic buildings, folk art, ceramics, doll houses, architectural achives, toys - library, photo laboratory, workshops 17300

Meeder

Friedensmuseum, Schloßhof 2, 96484 Meeder - T: (09566) 80188, Fax: 80190, E-mail: friedensmuseum.meeder@t-online.de, Internet: http://www.friedensdank.de. Head: Karl Eberhard Sperl
Historical Museum - 1982
Peace memorial 17301

Meerane

Heimatmuseum Meerane, Markt 3, 08393 Meerane - T: (03764) 2027, Fax: 56261, Internet: http://www.westsachsen.de/meerane/heimatmuseum
Local Museum - 1888
Geology, ancient and early hist, local hist, textile industry and crafts - library 17302

Meersburg

Bibelgalerie Meersburg, Kirchstr 4, 88709 Meersburg - T: (07532) 5300, Fax: 7322, E-mail: bibelgalerie-lbg@t-online.de, Internet: http://www.bibelgalerie.de. Head: Thea Groß
Religious Arts Museum - 1988
Hist of the Bible 17303

Burg Meersburg, Schloßpl 10, 88709 Meersburg - T: (07532) 80000, Fax: 800088, E-mail: burg.meersburg@t-online.de, Internet: http://www.burg-meersburg.de. Head: Vinzenz Naeßl-Doms
Historical Museum / Museum of Classical Antiquities / Historic Site - 1879
Historical interiors from different c, domestic utensils, weapons, weapon smithy, memorabilia of the poetess Annette von Droste-Hülshoff, 17th c chapel 17304

Dorniermuseum im Neuen Schloß, Schloßpl 1, 88709 Meersburg - T: (07532) 414071
Science&Tech Museum - 1970
Models of seaplanes, modern airplanes, aerospace research 17305

Droste-Museum im Fürstenhäusle, Stettener Str 9, 88709 Meersburg - T: (07532) 6088. Head: Gerlinde Schmid-Nafz
Special Museum - 1915
House in which the poetess Annette von Droste-Hülshoff lived, manuscripts, furnishings, memorabilia of the poetess and her family, archives, first editions of her work - library 17306

Fürstbischöfliches Museum, Neues Schloß, 88709 Meersburg - T: (07532) 440265, Fax: 431120, E-mail: info@meersburg.de, Internet: http://www.meersburg.de. Head: Dr. Franz Schwartzbauer
Historic Site - 1960
18th c Baroque residence, stairway designed by Balthasar Neumann, frescoes, 18th c furnishings 17307

Galerie Bodenseekreis im Roten Haus, Schlosspl 13, 88709 Meersburg - T: (07532) 494129, Fax: 494133, E-mail: info@bodenseekreis.de, Internet: http://www.bodenseekreis.de/bodenseekreis/Landratsamt/Kreisarchiv/GalMeers.htm. Head: Eva Moser
Fine Arts Museum - 2001
20th c paintings and sculpture, photogr, small sculpture 17308

Stadtmuseum Meersburg, Kirchstr 4, 88709 Meersburg - T: (07532) 440260, Fax: 440264, E-mail: kulturamt@meersburg.de, Internet: http://www.meersburg.de. Head: Dr. Franz Schwarzbauer
Local Museum - 1989
Town hist 17309

Städtische Galerie, Neues Schloß Meersburg, Schloßpl 12, 88701 Meersburg - T: (07532) 414071, Fax: 440264, E-mail: kulturamt@meersburg.de, Internet: http://www.meersburg.de. Head: Dr. Franz Schwarzbauer
Fine Arts Museum - 1990
20th c painting 17310

Städtische Galerie Meersburg, Neues Schloß Meersburg, 88709 Meersburg - T: (07532) 440260
Public Gallery 17311

Weinbaumuseum Meersburg, Vorburggasse 11, 88709 Meersburg - T: (07532) 431180, Fax: 431120, E-mail: info@meersburg.de, Internet: http://www.meersburg.de. Head: Bernhard Joachim
Agriculture Museum - 1969
Equipment and items from a 17th c winery, wine press, 50,160-liter wine container, documents on wine growing in Meersburg 17312

Zeppelin-Museum Meersburg, Schloßgasse 8, 88709 Meersburg - T: (07532) 7909, Fax: 7909. Head: Heinz Urban
Science&Tech Museum - 1989
Hist of air shipping, memorabilia of Graf von Zeppelin 17313

Mehlmeisel

Waldmuseum, Rathauspl, 95694 Mehlmeisel - T: (09272) 9790, Fax: 97924, E-mail: information-mehlmeisel@fichtelgebirge.de, Internet: http://www.fichtelgebirge.de/mehlmeisel
Local Museum - 1982
Mineralogy, preparations of birds, implements 17314

Mehrstetten

Heimatmuseum Mehrstetten, Krautgasse 17, 72537 Mehrstetten - T: (07381) 93830
Local Museum - 1991
Local hist, peasant life 17315

Meinhard

Heimatmuseum Meinhard, Am Lindenanger, 37276 Meinhard - T: (05651) 50659
Local Museum - 1989
Various trade workshops, school, kitchen and living-room from 19th c, historical telephones 17316

Meiningen

Literaturmuseum im Baumbachhaus, Meininger Museen, Burggasse 22, 98617 Meiningen - T: (03693) 502848, Fax: 503644, E-mail: service@meiningermuseen.de, Internet: http://www.meiningermuseen.de. Head: Winfried Wiegand
Special Museum
Memorabilia on Rudolf Baumbach 17317

Schloss Elisabethenburg, Meininger Museen, Schlosspl 1, 98617 Meiningen - T: (03693) 503641, Fax: 503644, E-mail: service@meiningermuseen.de, Internet: http://www.meiningermuseen.de. Head: Winfried Wiegand
Fine Arts Museum / Local Museum - 1947
17th-19th c European paintings, religious sculpture, 20th c furnishings, prints, paintings, 19th-20th c theater hist, 17th-19th c musical instruments, 18th c Italian operas, memorabilia on Max Reger, hist of saxe-meiningen - library 17318

Städtische Galerie ada Meiningen, Wintergasse 8, 98617 Meiningen - T: (03693) 502004, Fax: 471686, Internet: http://www.meiningen.de/ada. Head: Ralf-Michael Seele
Public Gallery 17319

Theatermuseum in der Reithalle, Meininger Museen, Schlosspl 2, 98617 Meiningen - T: (03693) 471290, Fax: 9300035, E-mail: service@meiningermuseen.de, Internet: http://www.meiningermuseen.de. Head: Winfried Wiegand
Performing Arts Museum - 2000 17320

Meißen

Albrechtsburg, Dompl 1, 01662 Meißen - T: (03521) 47070, Fax: 470711, E-mail: albrechtsburg@aol.com, Internet: http://www.albrechtsburg-meissen.de. Head: Dr. Angelika Lasius
Fine Arts Museum / Historical Museum - 1881
Historic rooms, 15th-16th c religious sculpture, Meissen porcelain production in 18/19th c, 15th c castle, wall paintings 17321

Museum der Staatlichen Porzellan-Manufaktur Meissen, Talstr 9, 01662 Meißen - T: (03521) 468208, Fax: 468804, E-mail: tp@meissen.de, Internet: http://www.meissen.de. Head: Dr. Hans Sonntag
Special Museum - 1916
Meissen Porcelain 18th-20th c - workshop 17322

Stadtmuseum Meißen, Dompl 4, 01662 Meißen - T: (03521) 453312, Fax: 453312. Head: Hans-Jörg Neumann
Local Museum - 1901
Ancient and early hist, local medieval hist, wine production, rooms in Baroque, Rococo, Empire, Biedermeier styles, clocks, pottery, 18th-19th c Meissen porcelain 17323

Meißner

Besucherbergwerk Grube Gustav, Hinterweg 4, 37290 Meißner - T: (05657) 7500, Fax: 91260, E-mail: gemeinde.meissner@kgrz-kassel.de
Science&Tech Museum - 1968
Hist of copper slate mining 17324

Meldorf

Dithmarscher Landesmuseum, Bütjestr 2-4, 25704 Meldorf - T: (04832) 600060, Fax: 6000617. Head: Dr. Wolf Könenkamp
Local Museum - 1872
Hist of everyday life, handicrafts, folk art, navigation, toys, land reclamation, schools, merchants' shops, home economics in the 16th to 20th c, Carsten Niebuhr - library 17325

Schleswig-Holsteinisches Landwirtschaftsmuseum und Dithmarscher Bauernhaus, Jungfernstieg 4, 25704 Meldorf - T: (04832) 979390, Fax: 6000617. Head: Dr. Wolf Könenkamp
Agriculture Museum - 1986
Agricultural machinery and tools of the last 100 years, rural life, workshops, merchants' shops - archive 17326

Melle

Geschichte auf Rädern, Automuseum Melle, Pestelstr 38-40, 49324 Melle - T: (05422) 965312, Fax: 965320, E-mail: tourist@stadt-melle.de, Internet: http://www.stadt-melle.de. Head: Heiner Rössler
Science&Tech Museum / Special Museum 17327

Grönegau-Museum, Friedrich-Ludwig-Jahn-Str 8-12, 49324 Melle - T: (05422) 5425, Fax: 5425. Head: Hartmut Wippermann
Local Museum - 1960
Peasant life, historical handicrafts including flax processing, shoemaking, and wooden shoemaking, traditional costumes, porcelain, silver, jewellery, religious items and writings, archives - library 17328

Mellrichstadt

Heimatmuseum Mellrichstadt, Fronhof 9, 97638 Mellrichstadt - T: (09776) 1484, 9241, Fax: 7342
Local Museum - 1983
Local hist and handicrafts 17329

Kreisgalerie, Hauptstr 5, 97638 Mellrichstadt - T: (09776) 6080, Fax: (09771) 94300, E-mail: lra@rhoen-grabfeld.de
Fine Arts Museum
Work of local artists 17330

Melsungen

Heimatmuseum Melsungen, Brückenstr 30, 34212 Melsungen - T: (05661) 2378, Fax: 2378
Local Museum - 1986
Hist of half-timber building, trade, agriculture, textile manufacture 17331

Memmelsdorf

Schloß Seehof mit Ferdinand Tietz-Sammlung, 96117 Memmelsdorf - T: (0951) 40950
Fine Arts Museum 17332

Memmingen

Stadtmuseum im Hermansbau und Heimatmuseum Freundenthal, Zangmeisterstr 8, 87700 Memmingen - T: (08331) 850131, Fax: 850149. Head: Dr. Hans-Wolfgang Bayer, U. Braun
Local Museum - 1880
Pre- and ancient hist, hist of the local guilds, local hist, faience from Künersberg, local jewish hist., Rococo interiors, in 18th c patrician residence 17333

Strigel-Museum und Antoniter-Museum, Martin-Luther-Pl 1, 87700 Memmingen - T: (08331) 850245, Fax: 850246. Head: Prof. Dr. Joseph Kiermeier-Debre
Special Museum / Fine Arts Museum / Historic Site - 1996
Hist of a religious order and work of the painter Bernhard Strigel 17334

Menden

Städtisches Museum, Marktpl 3, 58706 Menden - T: (02373) 903451. Head: Jutta Törnig-Struck
Local Museum - 1912
Local history, folk customs, pre- and ancient history of region, weapons, local, paleontology - library 17335

Mengen

Städtisches Museum, Hauptstr 96, 88512 Mengen - T: (07572) 607105, Fax: 607710, E-mail: info@mengen.de, Internet: http://www.mengen.de. Head: Christian Lange
Local Museum - 1968
Paintings, local history, fossils, agricultural machinery, Celts 17336

Mengerskirchen

Turmmuseum Schloß Mengerskirchen, Schloßstr 3, 35794 Mengerskirchen - T: (06476) 91360, Fax: 4190098
Local Museum - 1984
Hist or trade, flax processing 17337

Meppen

Stadtmuseum Meppen, Obergerichtsstr 7, 49716 Meppen - T: (05931) 1086, Fax: 153379. Head: Friedrich Hoegen
Local Museum - 1990
Town hist, hist of settling 17338

Mering

Heimatmuseum, Bürgerzentrum Schloßmühle, 86415 Mering - T: (08233) 92023
Local Museum - 1997 17339

Merkendorf, Mittelfranken

Heimatmuseum Merkendorf, Marktpl 4, 91732 Merkendorf, Mittelfranken - T: (09826) 6500, Fax: 65051, E-mail: stadt.merkendorf@gunnet.de, Internet: http://www.merkendorf.de
Local Museum - 1987
Local hist and handicrafts, religious folklore 17340

Merseburg

Kulturhistorisches Museum Schloß Merseburg, Dompl 9, 06217 Merseburg - T: (03461) 401318/08, Fax: 401302, E-mail: MQ.Kultur.Krehan@t-online.de, Internet: http://www.merseburg-querfurt.de. Head: Dr. Peter Ramm
Local Museum / Historic Site - 1906
Renaissance and barogue culture, early middle ages, late Gothic, lighters and igniters, glass bead works, Makonde (ebony sculptures from Tansania) - library 17341

Mertingen

Dorfmuseum Mertingen, Riedstr 28, 86690 Mertingen - T: (09078) 434
Local Museum - 1975
Local hist 17342

Meschede

Heimatmuseum Eversberg e.V., Mittelstr 12, 59872 Meschede - T: (0291) 50674, Fax: 50674
Local Museum 17343

Mespelbrunn

Schloßmuseum Mespelbrunn, Schloß, 63875 Mespelbrunn - T: (06092) 269. Head: Graf zu Ingelheim, gen. Echter von Mespelbrunn
Decorative Arts Museum
Weapons, hunting trophies, coll of porcelain 17344

Messel

Fossilien- und Heimatmuseum, Langgasse 2, 64409 Messel - T: (06159) 256
Local Museum
Hist of oil shale open-cast mining, geology, regional hist 17345

Meßkirch

Städtisches Heimatmuseum, Schloßstr 1, 88605 Meßkirch - T: (07575) 20646, Fax: 4732. Head: Dr. Werner Fischer
Local Museum - 1934 17346

Meßstetten

Heimatmuseum Hossingen, Dorfstr 13, 72469 Meßstetten - T: (07436) 1304
Local Museum - 1969
Tools, crafts 17347

Museum für Volkskunst, Sammlung Hagenlocher, Hangergasse 16, 72469 Meßstetten - T: (07431) 634958
Folklore Museum / Decorative Arts Museum - 1988
Folk art, ceramics, jewellery 17348

Mettingen

Tüötten-Museum, Markt 6-8, 49497 Mettingen - T: (05452) 3011, Fax: 911121, E-mail: telsemeyer@romantikhotels.com
Local Museum
Hist of linen dealer (Tüötten) 17349

Mettlach

Keramik Museum Mettlach e.V., Schloß Ziegelberg, 66688 Mettlach - T: (06864) 811496, Fax: 1478, E-mail: schneider.esther@villeroy-boch.de. Head: Ester Schneider
Decorative Arts Museum - 1979
Ceramics from Lothringen, Luxembourg, Belgium, Germany (16th c - beginning of the 20th c) 17350

Mettmann

Neanderthal Museum, Talstr 300, 40822 Mettmann - T: (02104) 979797, Fax: 979796, E-mail: museum@neanderthal.de, Internet: http://www.neanderthal.de. Head: Prof. Dr. Gerd-C. Weniger
Archaeological Museum / Natural History Museum - 1996
Human evolution from the beginnings (4 mio yrs) to the present, skeleton finds, tools, weapons, stone age animal 17351

Metzingen

Sieben-Keltern-Museum, Kelternpl, 72555 Metzingen - T: (07123) 166147. Head: Dr. H. Ostarhild
Historical Museum - 1978
Viticulture 17352

Michelau

Deutsches Korbmuseum, Bismarckstr 4, 96247 Michelau - T: (09571) 83548, Fax: 970727, E-mail: info@korbmuseum.de, Internet: http://www.korbmuseum.de
Decorative Arts Museum - 1929
Domestic and foreign basketry 17353

Michelstadt

Elfenbein-Museum, Am Kirchpl 7, 64720 Michelstadt - T: (06061) 3157, Fax: 3157. Head: Ulrich Seidenberg
Decorative Arts Museum - 1976
European and Asian ivory work, erotic art 17354

Landesrabbiner Dr. I.E. Lichtigfeld-Museum, Mauerstr 19, ehem. Synagoge, 64720 Michelstadt - T: (06061) 74146, Fax: 74174. Head: Martin Schmall
Religious Arts Museum - 1979
Memorabilia of the former regional rabbi Lichtigfeld 17355

Motorradmuseum, Walter-Rathenau-Allee 17, 64720 Michelstadt - T: (06061) 73707
Science&Tech Museum 17356

Nikolaus Matz Bibliothek (Kirchenbibliothek), Marktpl 1, 64720 Michelstadt - T: (06061) 740. Head: Erwin Müller
Library with Exhibitions / Religious Arts Museum 17357

Odenwaldmuseum, Kellerei, Einhardspforte 3, 64720 Michelstadt - T: (06061) 74139, Fax: 74174, E-mail: michel.stadt@t-online.de. Head: Herbert Hartung
Local Museum - 1910
Fossils, Roman finds, domestic utensils, interiors, guildhall, seal and coin coll, in a 15th c frame-work house 17358

Spielzeugmuseum, Amtshaus in der Kellerei, 64720 Michelstadt - T: (06061) 74139, Fax: 74174. Head: Prof. Helmut Anthes, Hedi Anthes
Decorative Arts Museum - 1982
Wooden toys from the Erzgebirge, dolls and doll's houses 17359

Middelhagen, Rügen

Schulmuseum und Hallenhaus, Mönchguter Museum, 18586 Middelhagen, Rügen - T: (038308) 2476
Historical Museum
School hist 17360

Miesbach

Heimatmuseum Miesbach, Waagstr 2, 83714 Miesbach - T: (08025) 70000, Fax: 700011, E-mail: info@waizinger-keller.de, Internet: http://www.waizinger-keller.de
Local Museum - 1907
Local hist 17361

Mietingen

Bauernkriegsstube Baltringen → Erinnerungsstätte Baltringer Haufen Bauernkrieg in Oberschwaben

Erinnerungsstätte Baltringer Haufen Bauernkrieg in Oberschwaben, Hauptstr 19, Baltringen, 88487 Mietingen - T: (07356) 2321, Fax: 928488, E-mail: info@mietingen.de, Internet: http://www.baltringer-haufen.de. Head: F. Liesch
Historical Museum - 1984/2000
Hist of German peasant war (early 16th c) 17362

Mildenberg

Ziegeleipark Mildenberg, Ziegeleiweg 10, 16775 Mildenberg - T: (03307) 310410, Fax: 310411, E-mail: info@ziegeleipark.de, Internet: http://www.ziegeleipark.de. Head: Frank Stege
Science&Tech Museum
Hist of brick works since the industrialisation, development of the steam power engine, historical workshops 17363

Miltach

Replikate der Welt-Kunst im Schloss, Schlossweg 1, Altrandsberg, 93468 Miltach - T: (09944) 341523, Fax: 341522, E-mail: poststelle@miltach.de
Fine Arts Museum 17364

Schloß Miltach, Chamer Str 9, 93468 Miltach - T: (09944) 305044, Fax: 305045, E-mail: schloss-miltach@t-online.de, Internet: http://www.schloss-miltach.de
Fine Arts Museum 17365

Miltenberg

Museum der Stadt Miltenberg und Porzellansammlung Kreis Dux, Hauptstr 169-175, 63897 Miltenberg - T: (09371) 404153, Fax: 404153, E-mail: museum@miltenberg.de, Internet: http://www.miltenberg.de. Head: Hermann Neubert
Local Museum - 1903
Roman finds, local history, ethnography, 13th-19th c ceramics, works by the painter Philipp Wirth, religious art, glass, lapidarium, in a frame-work house built 1541, musical instruments, judaica 17366

Mindelheim

Heimatmuseum Mindelheim, Hauberstr 2, 87719 Mindelheim - T: (08261) 6964, Fax: 6405, E-mail: museen@mindelheim.de, Internet: http://www.mindelheim.de
Local Museum - 1903
Local history, religious art, folk art, graphics, in an 18th c baroque cloister 17367

Jesuitenkolleg, Hermelestr 4, 87719 Mindelheim - T: (08261) 6964, Fax: 6405, E-mail: museen@mindelheim.de, Internet: http://www.mindelheim.de
Religious Arts Museum / Archaeological Museum / Folklore Museum
Cribs, textile and early hist 17368

Schwäbisches Krippenmuseum im Jesuitenkolleg, Hermelestr 4, 87719 Mindelheim - T: (08261) 6964, Fax: 6405, E-mail: museen@mindelheim.de, Internet: http://www.mindelheim.de. Head: Christian Schedler
Religious Arts Museum - 1989
Figurative christmas and easter display - library 17369

Schwäbisches Turmuhrenmuseum, Hungerbachgasse 9, 87719 Mindelheim - T: (08261) 6964, 8339, Fax: 6405, E-mail: mindelhm@primus.baynet.de, Internet: http://www.mindelheim.de. Head: Christian Schedler, Wolfgang Vogt
Science&Tech Museum - 1979
Clocks on a tower from 16th - 20th c 17370

Südschwäbisches Vorgeschichtsmuseum im Jesuitenkolleg, Hermelestr 4, 87719 Mindelheim - T: (08261) 6964, Fax: 6405, E-mail: museen@mindelheim.de, Internet: http://www.mindelheim.de. Head: Dr. Dorothea Van Endert
Archaeological Museum - 1994
Finds of Stone Age, Celthic, Roman, Alemannic culture, Roman carriage, Roman bath 17371

Textilmuseum im Jesuitenkolleg, Hermelestr 4, 87719 Mindelheim - T: (08261) 6371, Fax: 6405, E-mail: museen@mindelheim.de, Internet: http://www.mindelheim.de. Head: Christian Schedler, Prof. Hilda Sandtner
Decorative Arts Museum - 1986
Textiles and fashion, paintings - library, textile design workshop 17372

Minden, Westfalen

Domschatzkammer, Kleiner Domhof 30, 32423 Minden, Westfalen - T: (0571) 83764100, Fax: 83764111, E-mail: dom-minden@t-online.de, Internet: http://www.dom-minden.de. Head: Paul Jakobi
Religious Arts Museum 17373

Informationszentrum am Wasserstraßenkreuz Minden, Am Hohen Ufer 1-3, 32425 Minden, Westfalen - T: (0571) 64581115, Fax: 64581200, E-mail: reg@wsa-mi.wsv.de, Internet: http://www.wsa-minden.de
Science&Tech Museum - 1990
Boats and shipping on the Weser River, inland navigation and shipping traffic 17374

Mindener Museum für Geschichte, Landes- und Volkskunde, Ritterstr 23-33, 32423 Minden, Westfalen - T: (0571) 89316, 89331, Fax: 89681, E-mail: museum@minden.de, Internet: http://www.minden.de. Head: Martin Beutelspacher
Local Museum
Paleontology, prehistory, ethnology, local hist, coins, culture of coffee, historical fashion, military hist, handicrafts 17375

Missen-Wilhams

Carl-Hirnbein-Museum, Hauptstr 45, 87547 Missen-Wilhams - T: (08320) 456, 228, Fax: 268, E-mail: gemeinde@missen-wilhams.de, Internet: http://www.missen-wilhams.de. Head: Josef Bettendorf
Agriculture Museum - 1991
Hist of dairy farming 17376

Mistelbach

Fränkisches Turmuhrenmuseum, Zeckenmühle 1, 95511 Mistelbach - T: (09201) 261, (0921) 13560, Fax: (0921) 853677
Science&Tech Museum - 1980
Horology, history of watchmaking, in an old mill granary - watchmaker's workshop 17377

Mittenaar

Heimatstube Offenbach, Am Kirchberg 1, 35756 Mittenaar - T: (02778) 2994
Local Museum - 1982
Hist of mininig, minerals, migration to the USA, old school, trade and agricultural implements 17378

Mittenwald

Erstes Internationales Wolpertingermuseum, Innsbrucker Str 40, 82481 Mittenwald - T: (08823) 1240
Folklore Museum 17379

Geigenbau- und Heimatmuseum, Ballenhausgasse 3, 82481 Mittenwald - T: (08823) 2511, Fax: 5871, E-mail: kurverwaltung@mittenwald.de, Internet: http://www.mittenwald.de. Head: Anton Maller
Local Museum / Music Museum - 1930
Stringed instruments, violinmaking, peasant life and traditions, in the house of the violinmaker Mathias Klotz built in 1684 17380

Mitterfels

Heimatmuseum Mitterfels, Burgstr 2, 94360 Mitterfels - T: (09961) 940025, Fax: 940020, E-mail: info@mitterfels.de, Internet: http://www.mitterfels.de. Head: Josef Brembeck
Local Museum - 1984
Handicrafts and implements, prison objects 17381

Mitterteich

Molwitz-Stube, Kirchpl 2, 95666 Mitterteich - T: (09633) 89132, Fax: 89299, E-mail: tourismus@mitterteich.btl.de, Internet: http://www.mitterteich.de
Fine Arts Museum
Life and work of graphic artist Herbert Molwitz (1901-1970) 17382

Mittweida

Grube Alte Hoffnung Erbstolln, Feldstr 15, Schönborn-Dreiwerden-Seifersbach, 09648 Mittweida - T: (03727) 91845, E-mail: gri@ifu.de, Internet: http://www.schaubergwerk.de
Science&Tech Museum
Mining hist 17383

Museum der Stadt Mittweida "Alte Pfarrhäuser", Kirchberg 3-7, 09648 Mittweida - T: (03727) 3450, Fax: (03724) 979616. Head: Heiko Weber
Local Museum - 1899
History, city architecture, crafts, guilds, paintings, drawings, 10th-17th c religious sculpture 17384

Mitwitz

Wasserschloß Mitwitz, Unteres Schloß 4, 96268 Mitwitz - T: (09266) 9833
Open Air Museum 17385

Modautal

Heimatgeschichtliches Museum, Schulstr 6, 64397 Modautal
Local Museum - 1976
Village hist, crafts, trades 17386

Möckmühl

Heimatmuseum, Kirchpl 7, 74219 Möckmühl - T: (06298) 7606
Local Museum - 1985
Prehist, household articles, costumes 17387

Möhra

Lutherstube, Lutherpl 2, 36433 Möhra - T: (03695) 84273, Fax: 840218, E-mail: pfarramtmoehra@t-online.de, Internet: http://www.luthersammort-moehra.de. Head: Christoph Neumann
Religious Arts Museum
Dr. Martin Luther and Möhra 17388

Möllin

Denkmalhof Rauchhaus Möllin, Möllin 12, 19205 Möllin - T: (03886) 711196, Fax: 40081
Agriculture Museum / Ethnology Museum
Farm life and culture, original farmer's kitchen 17389

Mölln

Eulenspiegel Museum, Am Markt 12, 23879 Mölln - T: (04542) 835462, Fax: 836503, E-mail: stadt_moelln@t-online.de, Internet: http://www.moelln.de. Head: Michael Packheiser
Special Museum 17390

Möllner Museum Historisches Rathaus, Am Markt 12, 23879 Mölln - T: (04542) 835462, Fax: 836503, E-mail: Stadt_Moelln@t-online.de, Internet: http://www.moelln.de. Head: Michael Packheiser
Local Museum - 1889
Till Eulenspiegel 17391

Mömbris

Strötzbacher Mühle, Doppelmühle, Mühlweg 23, 63776 Mömbris - T: (06029) 995378, 7896
Science&Tech Museum
Old mill 17392

Volkskundliche Sammlung, Große Wiese 16, 63776 Mömbris - T: (06029) 8474, 7731
Local Museum - 1977
Local hist, tools and implements 17393

Mönchberg

Museum im Alten Rathaus, Hauptstr 42, 63933 Mönchberg - T: (09374) 7000, Fax: 7640. Head: Monika Grimm
Historical Museum - 1994
Man and authority in a franconian rural community, daily life 17394

Mönchengladbach

Haus Westland, Hindenburgstr 201, 41061 Mönchengladbach - T: (02161) 253951, Fax: 253969, E-mail: kulturamt@moenchengladbach.de, Internet: http://www.moenchengladbach.de
Public Gallery 17395

Karnevalmuseum, Weiherstr 2, 41061 Mönchengladbach - T: (02161) 391119
Folklore Museum 17396

Städtisches Museum Abteiberg, Abteistr 27, 41061 Mönchengladbach - T: (02161) 252631, Fax: 252659, E-mail: administration@museumabteiberg.de, Internet: http://www.museumabteiberg.de. Head: Dr. Veit Loers
Fine Arts Museum - 1982
20th c art - library, restoration workshop 17397

Städtisches Museum Schloß Rheydt, Schloßstr 508, 41238 Mönchengladbach - T: (02166) 928900, Fax: 9289049, E-mail: wilhelm.stratmann@moenchengladbach.de. Head: Dr. Carsten Sternberg
Fine Arts Museum / Local Museum - 1953
Fine arts (Renaissance, baroque), local history, weaving, decorative arts 17398

Mörfelden-Walldorf

Heimatmuseum Walldorf, Langstr 96, 64546 Mörfelden-Walldorf - T: (06105) 938274, Fax: 938222
Local Museum - 1968
Town hist, Roman grave finds, hist of Waldenser and Huguenots - Library 17399

Mörfelden Museum, Langgasse 45, 64546 Mörfelden-Walldorf - T: (06105) 938875, Fax: 938901. Head: Cornelia Rühlig
Local Museum
Everyday objects and implements, early and pre-history, impact of industrialisation 17400

Moers

Grafschafter Museum im Moerser Schloß, Kastell 9, 47441 Moers - T: (02841) 28094, Fax: 28095. Head: Christine Knupp-Uhlenhaut
Local Museum - 1908
Archeology, decorative arts, toys, mining 17401

Niederrheinisches Motorradmuseum, Friemersheimer Str 106, 47441 Moers - T: (02841) 508522. Head: Anton Schuth
Science&Tech Museum 17402

Städtische Galerie Peschkenhaus, Meerstr 1, 47441 Moers - T: (02841) 201738, Fax: 201888. Head: Christine Knupp-Uhlenhaut
Public Gallery 17403

Mörsbach

Mörsbacher Museum, Zur Lichterbach 4, 57629 Mörsbach - T: (02688) 593
Local Museum 17404

Mössingen

Heimatmuseum, Sulzgasse 35, 72116 Mössingen - T: (07473) 370243, Fax: 370163, Internet: http://www.onlinemuseum.moessingen.de
Local Museum / Folklore Museum
Crafts, tools 17405

Holzschnitt-Museum Klaus Herzer, Obergasse 1, Öschingen, 72116 Mössingen - T: (07473) 274301, Fax: 3671, Internet: http://www.moessingen.de/aktuelles
Fine Arts Museum - 2001
Woodcuts by Klaus Herzer 17406

Moisburg

Moisburger Mühlenmuseum, Außenstelle des Freilichtmuseums am Kiekeberg, Auf dem Damm 12, 21647 Moisburg - T: (040) 7906357, Fax: 7926464, E-mail: info@kiekeberg-museum.de, Internet: http://www.kiekeberg-museum.de. Head: Prof. Dr. Rolf Wiese
Science&Tech Museum
Techniques and functions of a mill 17407

Molfsee

Schleswig-Holsteinisches Freilichtmuseum e.V., Hamburger Chaussee 97, 24113 Molfsee - T: (0431) 659660, Fax: 6596625, E-mail: zentrale@freilichtmuseum-sh.de, Internet: http://www.freilichtmuseum-sh.de. Head: Dr. Hermann Heidrich
Open Air Museum - 1961
57 buildings in 18 farmyard complexes characteristic of the different areas, utensils, tools, crafts, mills - library, workshops 17408

Molmerswende

Gottfried-August-Bürger-Museum, Hauptstr 14, 06543 Molmerswende - T: (034779) 20580, Fax: 20580, Internet: http://www.mansfelder-Land.futurnet.de
Special Museum - 1972
Memorabilia of the poet Gottfried-August Bürger 17409

Molsdorf

Museum Schloß Molsdorf, Schlosspl 6, 99192 Molsdorf - T: (036202) 90505, Fax: 22084. Head: Rolf Ehrenberg
Historical Museum / Decorative Arts Museum - 1966
Historic rooms, 18th century furniture, paintings 17410

Monheim am Rhein

Schelmenturm, Grabenstr 30, 40789 Monheim am Rhein - T: (02173) 953351, Fax: 953349, E-mail: RBugey@monheim.de
Fine Arts Museum 17411

Monschau

Stiftung Scheibler-Museum Rotes Haus, Laufenstr 10, 52156 Monschau - T: (02472) 5071, E-mail: Rotes-Haus@t-online.de, Internet: http://www.lvr.de/kultur/monschau/scheibl.htm. Head: Horst Melcher
Local Museum - 1963 17412

Moosburg an der Isar

Heimatmuseum, Kastuluspl 3, 85368 Moosburg an der Isar - T: (08761) 68420, Fax: 68477
Local Museum - 1934
Early and local hist 17413

Morgenröthe-Rautenkranz

Deutsche Raumfahrtausstellung, Bahnhofstr 8, 08262 Morgenröthe-Rautenkranz - T: (037465) 2538, Fax: 2549, E-mail: raumfahrt@t-online.de, Internet: http://www.morgenroethe-rautenkranz.de. Head: Konrad Stahl
Science&Tech Museum - 1979
Hist of space technology, advantage of the space flights 17414

Moringen

Heimatmuseum Moringen, Amtsfreiheit 10, 37186 Moringen - T: (05554) 8160
Local Museum 17415

Moritzburg

Museum Schloss Moritzburg, Schloss, 01468 Moritzburg - T: (035207) 8730, Fax: 87311. Head: Ingrid Möbius
Decorative Arts Museum - 1947
17th-18th c furniture, paintings, porcelain, glass, leather wall coverings, sets of antlers, 18th c handicraft 17416

Mosbach, Baden

Haus Kickelhain, Stadtmuseum im Alten Hospital, Harnischgasse, 74821 Mosbach, Baden - T: (06261) 899240, Fax: 899241, E-mail: museum@mosbach.de, Internet: http://www.mosbach.de/kuf. Head: Jan Merk
Local Museum / Historical Museum / Folklore Museum - 1972 17417

Lohrbacher Heimatstuben, Tannenhof, 74821 Mosbach, Baden - T: (06261) 14357
Local Museum 17418

Museum für Druck, Odenwaldstr 19, 74821 Mosbach, Baden - T: (06261) 14805, Fax: 18471, E-mail: info@kremo.de, Internet: http://www.kremo.de. Head: Karl Kretschmer
Science&Tech Museum
Printing history 17419

Stadtmuseum im Alten Hospital, Hospitalgasse 4, 74821 Mosbach, Baden - T: (06261) 899240, Fax: 899241, E-mail: museum@mosbach.de, Internet: http://www.mosbach.de/kuf. Head: Jan Merk
Local Museum / Historical Museum / Folklore Museum - 1902
Faïence coll, Odenwald Cultural History collection, Judaica collection 17420

Motten

Werberger Stuben, Alte Schule in Kothen, 97786 Motten - T: (09748) 1080, 449
Local Museum - 1987 17421

Mücke

Rathausmuseum Nieder-Ohmen, Rathausgasse, 35325 Mücke - T: (06400) 8001
Local Museum - 1982
Domestic village life, early and pre-history 17422

Mügeln bei Oschatz

Heimatmuseum, Schulpl 4, 04769 Mügeln bei Oschatz - T: (03462) 41016
Local Museum - 1925
Geology, ancient and early history, local history 17423

Müglitztal

Museum Schloß Weesenstein, Am Schloßberg 1, 01809 Müglitztal - T: (035027) 6260, Fax: 5552, E-mail: weesenstein@t-online.de, Internet: http://www.schloss-weesenstein.de. Head: Hendrik Börnighausen
Local Museum - 1933
Empire and Biedermeier rooms, hunting hall, French, Chinese and leather wall hangings, paintings, architecture 17424

Mühlacker

Museum, Kelterpl 5, 75417 Mühlacker - T: (07041) 876325, Fax: 876321, E-mail: ateschner@stadt-muehlacker.de, Internet: http://www.muehlacker.de. Head: Adelheid Teschner
Local Museum - 1935
Prehistory, peasant life, decorative arts, history of the Waldensians, romains, middleage, furniture, handcrafts 17425

Mühlberg, Elbe

Stadtmuseum Mühlberg, Elbe, Klosterstr 9, 04931 Mühlberg, Elbe - T: (035342) 70687, Fax: 70687, E-mail: stadt-muehlberg@t-online.de, Internet: http://www.muehlberg-elbe.de. Head: Martina Hofmann
Local Museum - 1926
Ancient and early hist, local hist, religious sculpture, shipping and fishing, war prison camp 1939-1945, "Speziallager Nr. 1" 1945-1948 - library 17426

Mühldorf am Inn

Kreismuseum im Lodronhaus, Tuchmacherstr 7, 84453 Mühldorf am Inn - T: (08631) 2351, 2610, 5155, Fax: 987643. Head: Ernst Eicher
Local Museum
Town and early hist, religious folkore, handicrafts 17427

Mühlhausen, Oberpfalz

Landlmuseum Sulzbürg, Marktpl 5, 92360 Mühlhausen, Oberpfalz - T: (09181) 407300
Local Museum - 1954
Geology, prehist, local hist, religious hist, crafts, housing 17428

Mühlhausen, Thüringen

Bauernkriegsmuseum Kornmarktkirche, Mühlhäuser Museen, 99974 Mühlhausen, Thüringen, mail addr: Kristanpl 7, 99974 Mühlhausen, Thüringen - T: (03601) 816066, Fax: 816066. Head: Dr. Gerhard Seib
Historical Museum / Historic Site
Hist of German peasant awr 1525 17429

Brunnenhaus Popperode, Mühlhäuser Museen, 99974 Mühlhausen, Thüringen, mail addr: Kristanpl 7, 99974 Mühlhausen, Thüringen - T: (03601) 816066, Fax: 816066. Head: Dr. Gerhard Seib
Local Museum / Folklore Museum - 1976 17430

Historische Wehranlage, Mühlhäuser Museen, Am Frauentor, 99974 Mühlhausen, Thüringen, mail addr: Kristanpl 7, 99974 Mühlhausen, Thüringen - T: (03601) 816066, Fax: 816066. Head: Dr. Gerhard Seib
Historical Museum / Historic Site
Seven towers with furnishing and local history - library 17431

Museum am Lindenbühl, Mühlhäuser Museen, Kristanpl 7, 99974 Mühlhausen, Thüringen - T: (03601) 816066, Fax: 816066. Head: Dr. Gerhard Seib
Natural History Museum / Archaeological Museum / Local Museum - 1879
Geology, paleontology, mineralogy, zoology, city and crafts history, costumes, decorative objects, numismatics - library 17432

Museumsgalerie Allerheiligenkirche, Mühlhäuser Museen, Unterer Steinweg, 99974 Mühlhausen, Thüringen, mail addr: Kristanpl 7, 99974 Mühlhausen, Thüringen - T: (03601) 870021, Fax: 816904. Head: Dr. Gerhard Seib
Public Gallery / Historic Site 17433

Reichsstädtisches Archiv, Rathaushalle und Ratsstube, Ratsstr 19, 99974 Mühlhausen, Thüringen - T: (03601) 452142, Fax: 452137, E-mail: info@muehlhausen.de, Internet: http://www.muehlhausen.de
Local Museum 17434

Sankt Marien, Müntzergedenkstätte, Mühlhäuser Museen, 99974 Mühlhausen, Thüringen, mail addr: Kristanpl 7, 99974 Mühlhausen, Thüringen - T: (03601) 870023, 816066, Fax: 816066. Head: Dr. Gerhard Seib
Historical Museum / Historic Site
Thomas-Müntzer-Exposition 17435

Mühlheim am Main

Stadtmuseum Mühlheim, Marktstr 2, 63165 Mühlheim am Main - T: (06108) 6010, Fax: 601611, E-mail: stadt@muehlheim.de, Internet: http://www.muehlheim.de. Head: Klaus Schäfer
Local Museum - 1985
Early and pre-history, ceramics, weapons, jewellery 17436

Mühlheim an der Donau

Museum im Vorderen Schloss, Schlossstr 1, 78570 Mühlheim an der Donau - T: (07463) 1870, Fax: 994020, E-mail: museum@muelheim-donau.de. Head: Silvia Schaible
Local Museum - 1991
Pre and early hist, town hist, pilgrimage, church hist, bequest of Josef Alfons Wirth 17437

Mülheim an der Ruhr

Aquarius Wassermuseum, c/o RWW Rheinisch-Westfälische Wasserwerksgesellschaft mbH, Burgstr 70, 45476 Mülheim an der Ruhr - T: (0208) 4433390, Fax: 4433391, E-mail: aquarius@rww.de, Internet: http://www.aquarius-wassermuseum.de. Head: Gerd Müller
Natural History Museum - 1992
Everything on the element of water 17438

Büromuseum, Friedrich-Ebert-Str 43, 45468 Mülheim an der Ruhr - T: (0208) 4554137, Fax: 4554134, E-mail: kunstmuseum@stadt-mh.de, Internet: http://www.muelheim-ruhr.de. Head: Dr. Gabriele Uelsberg
Science&Tech Museum - 1977 17439

Heimatmuseum, Städtisches Museum, Teinerstr 1, Tersteegenhaus, 45468 Mülheim an der Ruhr - T: (0208) 383945, Fax: 4554134, Internet: http://www.muelheim-ruhr.de. Head: Dr. Gabriele Uelsberg
Local Museum - 1909
Gerhard Tersteegen (1697-1769) 17440

Kunstmuseum, Städtisches Museum, Viktoriapl 1, 45468 Mülheim an der Ruhr - T: (0208) 4554171, Fax: 4554134, E-mail: Kunstmuseum@stadt-mh.de, Internet: http://www.muelheim-ruhr.de. Head: Dr. Gabriele Uelsberg
Fine Arts Museum
20th c German painting, graphics, local artists 17441

Museum für Fotokopie, Kettwiger Str 33, 45468 Mülheim an der Ruhr - T: (0208) 34461. Head: Klaus Urbons
Science&Tech Museum - 1985
Copy, computer and fax art, hist of foto copy 17442

Städtisches Museum, Viktorispl 1, 45468 Mülheim an der Ruhr - T: (0208) 4554171
Local Museum 17443

Müllheim

Markgräfler Museum Müllheim, Wilhelmstr 7, 79379 Müllheim - T: (07631) 15446, Internet: http://www.muellheim.de/berges.html. Head: Dr. Antje M. Lechleiter
Local Museum - 1979/1991
Geology, pre and early hist, Roman archaeology, town hist, local industry, viticulture, furnishings, regional fine art, folklore 17444

Müllrose

Heimatmuseum, Kietz 5, 15299 Müllrose - T: (033606) 4967, Fax: 667, Internet: http://www.schlaubetal-online.de
Local Museum - 1955
Ancient and early history, local crafts and guilds, peasant folk art and culture 17445

München

Aktionsforum Praterinsel, Praterinsel 3-4, 80538 München - T: (089) 2123830, Fax: 29160876, E-mail: info@praterinsel.org, Internet: http://www.praterinsel.org
Fine Arts Museum 17446

Alpines Museum des Deutschen Alpenvereins, Praterinsel 5, 80538 München - T: (089) 2112240, Fax: 21122440, E-mail: alpines-museum@alpenverein.de, Internet: http://www.alpenverein.de. Head: Friederike Kaiser
Historical Museum - 1996
Paintings, postcards, reports on the alps, clothes, tools, hooks, carabiners and ropes 17447

Alte Pinakothek, Bayerische Staatsgemäldesammlungen, Barer Str 27, 80333 München - T: (089) 23805216, Fax: 23805221, Internet: http://www.alte-pinakothek.de. Head: Prof. Dr. Reinhold Baumstark
Fine Arts Museum - 1836
Various coll of 14th-18th c European painting (approx 850 paintings) 17448

Altes Residenztheater, Residenzstr 1, 80333 München - T: (089) 290671, Fax: 29067225
Decorative Arts Museum - 1958 17449

Anthropologische Staatssammlung, Karolinenpl 2a, 80333 München - T: (089) 595251, 1782066, Fax: 5501924, E-mail: asm.grupe@extern.lrz-muenchen.de, Internet: http://www.lrz-muenchen.de/~NatSamm/Anthropologie. Head: Prof. Dr. Gisela Grupe
Natural History Museum - 1902
Anthropology, evolution of man 17450

Archäologische Staatssammlung München, Museum für Vor- und Frühgeschichte, Lerchenfeldstr 2, 80538 München - T: (089) 2112402, Fax: 21124401, E-mail: archaeologische.staatssammlung@extern.lrz-muenchen.de, Internet: http://www.stmukwk.bayern.de/kunst/museen/praehist.html. Head: Prof. Dr. Ludwig Wamser
Archaeological Museum - 1885
Prehistory of Bavaria, the Mediterranean and the Near East, archeology from former Roman provincial sites, history of the early Middle Ages - library, archives 17451

Architekturmuseum der Technischen Universität München, Arcisstr 21, 80333 München - T: (089) 28922493, Fax: 28928333, E-mail: archmus@lrz.tu-muenchen.de, Internet: http://www.architekturmuseum.de. Head: Prof. Dr. Winfried Nerdinger
Historical Museum - 1868
Sketches, drawings, models and photographs of 18th-20th c architecture (Carl von Fischer, Friedrich Gärtner, Theodor Fischer, Richard Riemerschmid, Friedrich Thiersch, Günter Behnisch) - archives 17452

Ausstellungsforum FOE 156, Oberföhringer Str 156, 81925 München - T: (089) 62489844, 9579506, Fax: 62489844, E-mail: info@foe156.de, Internet: http://www.foe156.de. Head: Christopher Kramatschek
Public Gallery 17453

Bayerische Staatsbibliothek, Ludwigstr 16, 80539 München - T: (089) 286380, Fax: 286382200, E-mail: direktion@bsb-muenchen.de, Internet: http://www.bsb-muenchen.de. Head: Dr. Hermann Leskien
Library with Exhibitions 17454

Bayerische Staatsgemäldesammlungen, Direktion, Barer Str 29, 80799 München - T: (089) 238050, Fax: 23805221, Internet: http://www.pinakotheken-muenchen.de. Head: Prof. Dr. Reinhold Baumstark
Fine Arts Museum - 1759
library, archives 17455

Bayerisches Nationalmuseum, Prinzregentenstr 3, 80538 München - T: (089) 2112401, Fax: 21124201, E-mail: bay.nationalmuseum@extern.lrz-muenchen.de, Internet: http://www.bayerisches-nationalmuseum.de. Head: Dr. Renate Eikelmann
Decorative Arts Museum / Fine Arts Museum / Folklore Museum - 1855
Nativity scenes, clocks, Baroque sketches, Meißen porcelain, painting, sculpture, crafts, religious folk art, fine and decorative art - library 17456

Billardmuseum, Schellingstr 54, 80799 München - T: (089) 2720788
Special Museum 17457

BMW Museum, Petuelring 130, 80788 München - T: (089) 38223307, 38225652, Fax: 38227500, E-mail: bmw.callcenter@bmw.de, Internet: http://www.bmw-mobiletradition.com. Head: Holger Lapp
Science&Tech Museum - 1973
Development of BMW AG by means of aeroengines, motorcycles and automobiles, slide shows, video programmes and films inform about social, political, and future developments 17458

Botanische Staatssammlung München, Menzinger Str 67, 80638 München - T: (089) 17861265/66, Fax: 17861193, E-mail: bsm@botanik.biologie.uni-muenchen.de, Internet: http://www.botanik.-biologie.uni-muenchen.de/botsamml/. Head: Prof. Dr. Jürke Grau
Natural History Museum - 1914
Botany 17459

Deutsches Jagd- und Fischereimuseum, Neuhauser Str 2, 80331 München - T: (089) 220522, Fax: 2904037. Head: Bernd E. Ergert
Historical Museum - 1938
Fossils, trophies, paintings and graphic art with hunting themes, hunting artifacts, fishing implements from stone age to present - library, archives 17460

Deutsches Museum, Museumsinsel 1, 80538 München - T: (089) 21791, Fax: 2179324, E-mail: info@deutsches-museum.de, Internet: http://www.deutsches-museum.de. Head: Prof. Dr. Dr. Wolf Peter Fehlhammer
Science&Tech Museum - 1903
Coll of most disciplines of science and technology (e.g. chemistry, physics, electronics, navigation, aviation, astronomy), crafts and trades - library, archives, research institute, Kerschensteiner College 17461

Deutsches Theatermuseum, formerly Clara-Ziegler-Stiftung, Galeriestr 4a6, 80539 München - T: (089) 2106910, Fax: 21069191, E-mail: deutsches-theatermuseum@extern.lrz-muenchen.de, Internet: http://www.stmwfk.bayern.de/kunst/museen/theatmus.html. Head: Dr. Eckehart Nölle
Performing Arts Museum - 1910
Stage sets, costumes, masks, theatrical requisites, portraits, scenic photographs, architecture, stage techniques, Quaglios, Littmann, Semper, L. Erler, Ch. Flemming, S. Busse, C. Neher, H.-U. Schmückle - archives, photo archive, library 17462

Doerner-Institut, Bayerische Staatsgemäldesammlungen, Barer Str 29, 80799 München - T: (089) 23805155, Fax: 23805156, E-mail: doerner.institut@doerner-institut.de, Internet: http://www.pinakothek-der-moderne.de
Fine Arts Museum 17463

Erstes Nachttopf-Museum der Welt, Westenriederstr 41, 80331 München - T: (089) 2904121, Fax: 22802773, E-mail: zam-museum@web.de, Internet: http://www.zam-museum.de. Head: Manfred Klauda
Special Museum - 1980
First chamberpot museum of the world 17464

Erwin von Kreibig-Museum, Südliches Schloßrondell 1, 80638 München - T: (089) 1781169, Fax: 175292. Head: Hildegard Merzenich
Fine Arts Museum
Work of the graphic artist Erwin von Kreibig (1904-1961) and work of other contemporary artists 17465

Filmmuseum, Münchner Stadtmuseum, Sankt-Jakobs-Pl 1, 80331 München - T: (089) 23322348, Fax: 23323931, E-mail: filmmuseum@muenchen.de, Internet: http://www.stadtmuseum-online.de. Head: Stefan Drössler
Performing Arts Museum - 1962 17466

Forum der Technik, Museumsinsel 1, 80538 München - T: (089) 21125180/83, Internet: http://www.fdt.de
Science&Tech Museum 17467

Fotomuseum im Münchner Stadtmuseum, Sankt-Jakobs-Pl 1, 80331 München - T: (089) 23322948, Fax: 23327967, E-mail: stadtmuseum@compuserve.com, Internet: http://www.stadtmuseum-online.de. Head: Dr. Ulrich Pohlmann
Decorative Arts Museum - 1961
19th c photography 17468

Galerie Goethe 53, Goethestr 53, 80336 München - T: (089) 23323536, Fax: 23328645
Public Gallery 17469

Galerie Handwerk, Max-Joseph-Str 4, 80333 München - T: (089) 595584, Fax: 595544, Internet: http://www.hwk-muenchen.de/galerie
Public Gallery
Arts and crafts 17470

Geologisches Museum München, Luisenstr 37, 80333 München - T: (089) 21806513, Fax: 21806514, E-mail: geol.sammlung@iaag.geo.uni-muenchen.de, Internet: http://www.iaag.geo.uni-muenchen.de/sammlung/. Head: Prof. Dr. H. Miller
Natural History Museum - 1920
Geology, mineral deposits of the world - library, laboratory 17471

Haidhausen-Museum, Kirchenstr 24, 81675 München - T: (089) 4485292
Local Museum 17472

Haus der Kunst, Prinzregentenstr 1, 80538 München - T: (089) 21127115, Fax: 21127157, E-mail: mail@hausderkunst.de, Internet: http://www.hausderkunst.de. Head: Dr. Christoph Vitali
Fine Arts Museum 17473

James-Krüss-Turm, Schloss Blutenburg, Obermenzing, 81247 München - T: (089) 8912110, Fax: 8117553, E-mail: bib@ijb.de, Internet: http://www.ijb.de. Head: Dr. Barbara Scharioth
Special Museum - 2001 17474

Jüdisches Museum, Reichenbachstr 27, 80469 München - T: (089) 20009693, Fax: 2024438. Head: Richard Grimm
Historical Museum - 1989
Hist of the Jews in Munich 17475

Das Kartoffelmuseum, Grafinger Str 2, 81671 München - T: (089) 404050, Fax: 4081886. Head: Barbara Kosler
Fine Arts Museum / Special Museum
International hist of the potato - library 17476

Kinder- und Jugendmuseum, Arnulfstr 3, 80335 München - T: (089) 54540880, Fax: 54540990, E-mail: kindermuseum@web.de, Internet: http://www.kindermuseum-muenchen.de. Head: Dr. Haimo Liebich
Special Museum 17477

Kulturzentrum der Aktion Lebensqualität, Augustenstr 43, 80333 München - T: (089) 522065/66, Fax: 54212534
Fine Arts Museum 17478

Kunstbunker Tumulka, Prinzregentenstr 97a, 81677 München - T: (089) 45555541, Fax: 45555533, E-mail: heufelder@internatsberatung.com, Internet: http://www.kunstbunker-tumulka.de. Head: Michael Heufelder
Public Gallery - 1993 17479

Kunstforum Arabellapark, Rosenkavalierpl 16, 81925 München - T: (089) 9287810, 62082014, Fax: 9103736, E-mail: stb.bogenhausen.kul@muenchen.de. Head: Hagen Meyer-Kröger, Birgit Möller-Arnsberg
Public Gallery 17480

Kunsthalle der Hypo-Kulturstiftung, Theatinerstr 8, 80333 München - T: (089) 224412, Fax: 29160981, E-mail: kontakt@hypo-kunsthalle.de, Internet: http://www.hypo-kunsthalle.de. Head: Dr. Johann Georg Prinz von Hohenzollern
Public Gallery 17481

Kunstpavillon, Alter Botanischer Garten, Sophienstr 7a, 80333 München - T: (089) 597359, Fax: 54506770
Association with Coll 17482

Kunstraum München e.V., Goethestr 34, 80336 München - T: (089) 54379900, Fax: 54379902. Head: Dr. Luise Horn
Association with Coll 17483

Kunstsammlung des Herzoglichen Georgianums, Prof.-Huber-Pl 1, 80539 München - T: (089) 286201, Fax: 28620210. Head: Prof. Dr. R. Kaczynski
Fine Arts Museum
Religious art coll 17484

Lithographiesteinarchiv und druckhistorische Werkstätte, c/o Bayerisches Landesvermessungsamt, Alexandrastr 4, 80538 München - T: (089) 21291000, Fax: 21291324, E-mail: Andreas.Feigel@blva.bayern.de, Internet: http://www.geodatm.bayern.de. Head: Prof. Günter Nagel
Science&Tech Museum - 1999 17485

Marstallmuseum, Schloß Nymphenburg, 80638 München - T: (089) 179080, Fax: 17908627, E-mail: info@bsv.bayern.de. Head: Dr. Elmar D. Schmid
Fine Arts Museum - 1923
Housed in the building of the royal stables in Nymphenburg Castle (1740), carriages, sleighs, riding equipage and paintings from 1680-1918 17486

Michael-Ende-Museum, Schloss Blutenburg, Obermenzing, 81247 München - T: (089) 8912110, Fax: 8117553, E-mail: bib@ijb.de, Internet: http://www.ijb.de. Head: Dr. Barbara Scharioth
Special Museum 17487

Modemuseum, Münchner Stadtmuseum, Sankt-Jakobs-Pl 1, 80331 München - T: (089) 2337370, Fax: 23325033, E-mail: stadtmuseum@compuserve.com, Internet: http://www.muenchen.de/stadtmuseum. Head: Dr. Andreas Ley
Decorative Arts Museum
Hist of fashion 17488

Die Möbelsammlung, Münchner Stadtmuseum, Sankt-Jakobs-Pl 1, 80331 München - T: (089) 23322370, Fax: 23325033, E-mail: gabriele.meise@muenchen.de, Internet: http://www.stadtmuseum-online.de. Head: Dr. Helmut Bauer
Decorative Arts Museum
3,000 pieces of furniture 17489

Monacensia-Literaturarchiv und Bibliothek, Maria-Theresia-Str 23, 81675 München - T: (089) 4194720, Fax: 4709619, E-mail: monacensia@web.de. Head: Dr. Elisabeth Tworek
Library with Exhibitions 17490

Münchner Feuerwehrmuseum, An der Hauptfeuerwache 8, 80331 München - T: (089) 23534150, Fax: 23533182, E-mail: bfm.direktion@ems.muenchen.de, Internet: http://www.museen-in-bayern.de/muenchen-feuerwehrmuseum.htm
Historical Museum 17491

Münchner Puppenmuseum, Gondershauser Str 37, 80939 München - T: (089) 3228950, Fax: 32369291, E-mail: vonmassenbach@gmx.de. Head: Elisabeth von Massenbach
Special Museum
Dolls and toys from 1780 to 1930 17492

Münchner Stadtmuseum, Sankt-Jakobs-Pl 1, 80331 München - T: (089) 23322370, Fax: 23325033, E-mail: stadtmuseum@muenchen.de, Internet: http://www.stadtmuseum-online.de. Head: Dr. Wolfgang Till
Local Museum / Decorative Arts Museum - 1854
Graphic art, posters and paintings, costumes, musical instruments, puppets, fairground art, photography, interior design, furniture, arms and armour, films, arts and crafts, folk art, local hist, hist of civilization, hist of design, hist of photography and film 17493

Münchner Tiermuseum, Truderinger Str 219, 81825 München - T: (089) 43690728
Natural History Museum
About 1000 animal and bird species from all over the world 17494

Museum für Abgüsse Klassischer Bildwerke, Meiserstr 10, 80333 München - T: (089) 28927690, Fax: 28927680, E-mail: mfa@lrz.uni-muenchen.de, Internet: http://www.abgussmuseum.de. Head: Prof. Dr. Paul Zanker
Archaeological Museum - 1869
Replicas of Greek and Roman statues and busts - library 17495

Museum Mensch und Natur, Schloss Nymphenburg, 80638 München - T: (089) 171382, Fax: 1784380, E-mail: museum@musmn.de, Internet: http://www.musmn.de. Head: Dr. Hans-Albert Treff
Natural History Museum - 1990
Natural history 17496

Museum Reich der Kristalle, Theresienstr 41, 80333 München - T: (089) 23944312, Fax: 23944334, E-mail: mineralogische.staatssammung@lrz.uni-muenchen.de, Internet: http://www.lrz-muenchen.de/~Mineralogische.Staatssammlung. Head: Prof. Dr. P. Gille
Natural History Museum - 1797
Bavarian, Alpine and Russian minerals, gemstones, meteorites 17497

Museum Synthese, Theresienstr 56, 80333 München - T: (089) 2800412, Fax: 28659880, E-mail: museum@addcom.de, Internet: http://www.museum-synthese.com. Head: Gaston Bischler
Association with Coll
Modern graphic, paintings, sculptures 17498

Museum 'Vermessen in Bayern - von der Messlatte zur Antenne', Bayerisches Landesvermessungsamt, Alexandrastr 4, 80538 München - T: (089) 21291558, Fax: 21291558, E-mail: Klaus.Zaglmann@blva.bayern.de, Internet: http://www.geodatm.bayern.de. Head: Prof. Günter Nagel
Science&Tech Museum - 1999 17499

Musikinstrumentenmuseum, Münchner Stadtmuseum, Sankt-Jakobs-Pl 1, 80331 München - T: (089) 23322367, Fax: 23323650, E-mail: stadtmuseum@muenchen.de, Internet: http://www.stadtmuseum-online.de. Head: Dr. Gunther Joppig
Music Museum
Non-European and European musical instruments 17500

Neue Pinakothek, Bayerische Staatsgemäldesammlungen, Barer Str 29, 80799 München - T: (089) 23805195, Fax: 23805185, Internet: http://www.neue-pinakothek.de. Head: Prof. Dr. Reinhold Baumstark
Fine Arts Museum - 1853
19th-20th c painting and sculpture, esp of romantic, French impressionist, Jugendstil and symbolistic schools - archives, library 17501

Die Neue Sammlung, Staatliches Museum für angewandte Kunst, Prinzregentenstr 3, 80538 München - T: (089) 227844, Fax: 220282, E-mail: info@die-neue-sammlung.de, Internet: http://www.die-neue-sammlung.de. Head: Prof. Dr. Florian Hufnagl
Decorative Arts Museum - 1925
Industrial design, graphic design, arts and crafts from ca 1900 to the present 17502

Nymphenburger Porzellan-Sammlung Bäuml, Schloß Nymphenburg, 80638 München - T: (089) 179080, Fax: 17908627. Head: Dr. Elmar D. Schmid
Decorative Arts Museum - 1918
Bäuml coll of Nympphenburg porcelain 17503

Orangerie im Englischen Garten, Englischer Garten 1a, 80538 München - T: (089) 386663914, Fax: 386663923
Public Gallery 17504

Paläontologisches Museum München, Richard-Wagner-Str 10, 80333 München - T: (089) 21806630, Fax: 21806601, E-mail: pal.sammlung@lrz.uni-muenchen.de, Internet: http://www.palaeo.de/museum-muenchen. Head: Prof. Dr. R. Leinfelder
Natural History Museum - 1843
Micropaleontology, fossil invertebrates, fossil vertebrates, paleobotany - library, laboratories 17505

Parfum-Flacon-Museum, Westenriederstr 41, 80331 München - T: (089) 2904121, Fax: 2904121, E-mail: info@flacon-collectors-club.de, Internet: http://www.flacon-collectors-club.de. Head: Beatrice Frankl
Special Museum
Hist and coll of perfume bottles 17506

von Parish-Kostümbibliothek, Münchner Stadtmuseum, Kemnatenstr 50, 80639 München - T: (089) 177717, Fax: 1781068. Head: Dr. Elisabeth Heller-Winter
Special Museum 17507

Pinakothek der Moderne, Bayerische Staatsgemäldesammlungen (open 2002), Barer Str 40, 80333 München - T: (089) 238050, Fax: 23805125, Internet: http://www.pinakothek-der-moderne.de. Head: Prof. Dr. Reinhold Baumstark
Fine Arts Museum - 2002
20th c European painting and sculpture 17508

Prähistorische Staatssammlung München → Archäologische Staatssammlung München

Privatmuseum Sammlung Holzinger, Kunst der Autodidakten, Galeriestr 2, 80539 München - T: (089) 292487, Fax: 8116388. Head: Hans Holzinger
Fine Arts Museum 17509

Puppentheatermuseum mit Abteilung Schaustellerei, Münchner Stadtmuseum, Sankt-Jakobs-Pl 1, 80331 München - T: (089) 23322347, Fax: 23324124, E-mail: stadtmuseum@compuserve.com, Internet: http://www.stadtmuseum-online.de. Head: Dr. Florian Dering
Performing Arts Museum - 1940
Theatre Puppets, fairground amusement 17510

Rathausgalerie München, Marienpl 8, 80313 München - T: (089) 23321194
Public Gallery 17511

Residenzmuseum, Residenzstr 1, 80333 München - T: (089) 290671, Fax: 29067225, E-mail: info@bsv.bayern.de, Internet: http://www.schloesser.bayern.de. Head: Dr. Sabine Heym
Decorative Arts Museum / Local Museum - 1385/1920
Period rooms (16th-19th c), porcelain, silver, bronze, carpets, majolica, paintings, furniture 17512

Ruhmeshalle und Bavaria, Theresienhöhe 16, 80339 München - T: (089) 290671, Fax: 29067225, E-mail: info@bsv.bayern.de, Internet: http://www.schloesser.bayern.de. Head: Dr. Heym
Historical Museum - 1853
Bavarian hall of fame 17513

Sammlung Goetz, Oberföhringer Str 103, 81925 München - T: (089) 95939690, Fax: 959396969, E-mail: sammlunggoetz@t-online.de, Internet: http://germangalleries.com/Sammlung_Goetz. Head: Rainald Schumacher
Fine Arts Museum - 1993 17514

Schack-Galerie, Bayerische Staatsgemäldesammlungen, Prinzregentenstr 27, 80538 München - T: (089) 23805224, Fax: 23805251, Internet: http://www.schack-galerie.de. Head: Prof. Dr. Reinhold Baumstark
Fine Arts Museum - 1909
19th c German painting 17515

Schatzkammer der Residenz München, Residenzstr 1, 80333 München - T: (089) 290671, Fax: 29067225, E-mail: info@bsv.bayern.de, Internet: http://www.schloesser.bayern.de. Head: Dr. Sabine Heym
Decorative Arts Museum - 1565/1958
10th-19th c European goldsmith work, gemstones, jewellery, ivory carvings, religious art, carvings, amber, clocks 17516

SiemensForum, Oskar-von-Miller-Ring 20, 80333 München - T: (089) 63632660, Fax: 63632616, E-mail: siemensforum@mchw.siemens.de, Internet: http://www.siemensforum.de. Head: Dr. Walter Conradi
Science&Tech Museum - 1916
Hist and modern electrical engineering - archive 17517

Spielzeugmuseum im Alten Rathausturm, Marienpl 15, 80331 München - T: (089) 294001, Fax: 2717014. Head: Ivan Steiger
Decorative Arts Museum
Coll of toys 17518

Staatliche Antikensammlungen und Glyptothek, Königspl 13, 80333 München, mail addr: Meiserstr 10, 80333 München - T: (089) 28927502/03, Fax: 28927516, E-mail: info@antike-am-koenigsplatz.mwn.de, Internet: http://www.stmwfk.bayern.de/kunst/museen/glypto.html. Head: Prof. Dr. Raimund Wünsche
Museum of Classical Antiquities - 1816
Coll of antiquities, Greek and Roman terracotta and bronze, antique jewellery, Etruscan art; Glyptothek: Greek and Roman sculpture - library 17519

Staatliche Graphische Sammlung, Meiserstr 10, 80333 München - T: (089) 28927650, Fax: 28927653, Internet: http://www.stmukwk.bayern.de/kunst/museen/graphik.html. Head: Dr. Michael Semff
Fine Arts Museum - 1758
European graphic art and drawings (15th-20th c) 17520

Staatliche Münzsammlung, Residenzstr 1, 80333 München - T: (089) 227221, Fax: 299859, E-mail: smm.muenchen@t-online.de, Internet: http://www.stmukwk.bayern.de/kunst/museen/muenz.html. Head: Prof. Dr. Bernhard Overbeck
Library with Exhibitions / Historical Museum / Fine Arts Museum - 1565
Coins, medals and monetary tokens, paper money from all over the world, gemstones and cameos 17521

Staatliche Porzellan-Manufaktur Nymphenburg, Nördliches Schloßrondell 6-8, 80638 München - T: (089) 17919710
Decorative Arts Museum 17522

Staatliches Museum Ägyptischer Kunst, Residenz, Hofgartenstr 1, 80539 München - T: (089) 28927630, Fax: 28927638, E-mail: info@aegyptisches-museum-muenchen.de, Internet: http://www.aegyptisches-museum-muenchen.de. Head: Dr. Sylvia Schoske
Fine Arts Museum / Archaeological Museum / Museum of Classical Antiquities - 18th c
Egyptian artifacts of prehistoric, classical and Hellenistic periods, early Christian art of the Nile Valley, Nubian hist - library, archives 17523

Staatliches Museum für Völkerkunde München, Maximilianstr 42, 80538 München - T: (089) 210136100, Fax: 210136247, Internet: http://www.kunstministerium.bayern.de. Head: Dr. Claudius C. Müller
Ethnology Museum - 1868
Coll from Asia, Africa, Americas, Oceania (art and cultural hist) - archives, library 17524

Staatsgalerie moderner Kunst → Pinakothek der Moderne

Städtische Galerie im Lenbachhaus, Luisenstr 33, 80333 München - T: (089) 23332000, Fax: 23332003/04, E-mail: lenbachhaus@muenchen.de, Internet: http://www.lenbachhaus.de. Head: Prof. Dr. Helmut Friedel
Fine Arts Museum - 1929
19th c painting by Munich artists, the Lenbach Coll, contemporary art, graphic art, works by artists of 'Der Blaue Reiter' group, housed in the former villa (1891) of Franz von Lenbach 17525

Sudetendeutsches Archiv, Hochstr 8, 81669 München - T: (089) 48000330, Fax: 48000338, E-mail: sudetendeutschesarchiv-km@t-online.de
Library with Exhibitions / Historical Museum - 1955
Documents and hist of exiled Germans 17526

Trambahn-Museum, Westendstr 200, 80672 München - T: (089) 6256716, Fax: 6256716, E-mail: fmtm@tram.org, Internet: http://www.trambahn.de. Head: Markus Trommer
Science&Tech Museum
archive 17527

Universitätsbibliothek, Geschwister-Scholl-Pl 1, 80539 München - T: (089) 21802429, Fax: 21803836, E-mail: Direktion@ub.uni-muenchen.de, Internet: http://www.ub.uni-muenchen.de. Head: Dr. Günter Heischmann
Library with Exhibitions 17528

Valentin-Karlstadt Musäum, Tal 50, 80331 München - T: (089) 223266, Fax: 294672. Head: Gudrun Köhl
Performing Arts Museum - 1959
Memorabilia and works of Karl Valentin (1882-1948) and Liesl Karlstadt (1892-1960), housed in a tower of the city gate (1337) - library, archives 17529

Villa Stuck Museum, Prinzregentenstr 60, 81675 München - T: (089) 45555125, Fax: 45555124, E-mail: villastuck@compuserve.com, Internet: http://www.muenchen.de/villastuck. Head: Jo-Anne Birnie Danzker
Fine Arts Museum - 1968
Housed in the villa (1898) belonging to painter Franz v. Stuck (1863-1928), paintings, sculpture and furniture, Jugendstil glass and ceramics, porcelain - library 17530

Werksmuseum der MTU, Dachauer Str 665, 80995 München - T: (089) 14892698, Fax: 14898757, Internet: http://www.mtu.de
Science&Tech Museum 17531

Zählermuseum, Franzstr 9, 80802 München - T: (089) 38101361, Fax: 38101376. Head: Klaus Köhler
Science&Tech Museum
Coll of about 700 electricity meters 17532

Zentrum für Außergewöhnliche Museen, Westenriederstr 41, 80331 München - T: (089) 2904121, Fax: 22802773, E-mail: zam-museum@web.de, Internet: http://www.zam-museum.de. Head: Manfred Klauda
Special Museum - 1991
Coll of chamber pots, corkscrews, memorabilia of empress Sissi and pedal cars, Easter bunnies 17533

Zoologische Staatssammlung, Münchhausenstr 21, 81247 München - T: (089) 81070, Fax: 8107300, E-mail: zsm@zsm.mwn.de, Internet: http://www.zsm.mwn.de. Head: Prof. Dr. Gerhard Haszprunar
Natural History Museum - 1807
Entomology, mollusca, mammalia, herpetology, crustacea 17534

Münnerstadt

Henneberg-Museum, Deutschordenschloß, 97702 Münnerstadt - T: (09733) 810529, Fax: 810565, E-mail: hauptamt@muennerstadt.de. Head: Dr. Kai Uwe Tapken
Local Museum - 1923
Religious art, peasant life, ceramics 17535

Münsingen

Ausstellung Juden in Buttenhausen, Zwiefalter Str 30, 72525 Münsingen - T: (07381) 182115, Fax: 182101, E-mail: roland.deigendesch@muensingen.de, Internet: http://www.muensingen.de/museum. Head: Roland Deigendesch
Local Museum - 1994 17536

Heimatmuseum Münsingen, Schloßhof 2, 72525 Münsingen - T: (07381) 182115, Fax: 182101, E-mail: stadtverw.archiv.museum@muensingen.de
Local Museum - 1913 17537

Max-Kommerell-Gedenkstätte, Bürgerhaus Zehntscheuer, 72525 Münsingen - T: (07381) 182115, Fax: 182101, E-mail: - roland.deigendesch@muensingen.de. Head: Roland Deigendesch
Special Museum - 1986 17538

Museum und Stiftung Anton Geiselhart, Am Bürzel 1, Gundelfingen, 72525 Münsingen - T: (07383) 515, Fax: (07121) 923444, E-mail: malerundmehr@topmail.de. Head: Sabine Lang
Fine Arts Museum / Public Gallery 17539

Münster

Archäologisches Museum der Universität Münster, Dompl 20-22, 48143 Münster - T: (0251) 8324581, Fax: 8325422, E-mail: archmus@uni-muenster.de, Internet: http://www.uni-muenster.de/Rektorat/museum/d2museam.htm. Head: Prof. Dr. Dieter Salzmann
Archaeological Museum - 1883
Greek and Roman art (original finds and plaster casts) and architectural models of ancient monument and ancient sites 17540

Bibelmuseum, c/o Institut für neutestamentliche Textforschung, Georgskommende 7, 48143 Münster - T: (0251) 8325216, Fax: 8322582, E-mail: weltem@uni-muenster.de. Head: Prof. Dr. Barbara Aland
Religious Arts Museum - 1979
History of the bible, translation of the bible in German and other languages, biblical research, Greek New Testament manuscript collection 17541

Bischöfliches Diözesanmuseum für christliche Kunst, Spiekerhof 29-30, 48143 Münster - T: (0251) 495274, Fax: 4956196. Head: Dr. Udo Grote
Religious Arts Museum - 1864
Sculptures, handicraft, paintings, coins 17542

Domkammer der Kathedralkirche Sankt Paulus zu Münster, Dompl 28, 48143 Münster - T: (0251) 495333, Fax: 519796. Head: Dr. Udo Grote
Religious Arts Museum 17543

Droste-Museum, Am Rüschhaus 81, 48161 Münster - T: (02533) 1317, Fax: 3109. Head: Annemarie Lucas
Special Museum
Memorabilia of Annette von Droste-Hülshoff, in the Baroque countryseat Rüschhaus where the poetess lived from 1826 to 1848, original 19th c interiors 17544

Geologisch-Paläontologisches Museum, Pferdegasse 3, 48143 Münster - T: (0251) 8323942, Fax: 8324891, E-mail: bertlin@uni-muenster.de, Internet: http://www.uni-muenster.de/Geomuseum. Head: Dr. Markus Bertling
Natural History Museum - 1824
Pleistocene skeletons of mammals, Upper Cretaceous fishes of Westphalia, regional geology and palaeontology of Westfalen-Lippe (Westphalia) 17545

Graphikmuseum Pablo Picasso Münster, Königsstr 5, 48143 Münster - T: (0251) 414470, Fax: 4144777, E-mail: info@graphikmuseum.de, Internet: http://www.graphikmuseum.de. Head: Dr. Markus Müller
Fine Arts Museum - 2000
900 graphic works of Picasso 17546

Humbert Collection, Ermlandweg 14, 48159 Münster - T: (0251) 212146, Fax: 217099, E-mail: wjk@kors.net. Head: Helga Korsmeier-Humbert
Fine Arts Museum - 1970
Sculpture, paintings, carpets 17547

Kunsthaus Kannen, Alexianerweg 9, 48163 Münster - T: (02501) 966560
Public Gallery 17548

Mineralogisches Museum (Kristalle und Gesteine), Universität Münster, Hüfferstr 1, 48149 Münster - T: (0251) 8333404, Fax: 8338397, E-mail: riegraf@nwz.uni-muenster.de, Internet: http://www.uni-muenster.de/MineralogieMuseum. Head: Dr. Cornelia Schmitt-Riegraf
Natural History Museum / University Museum - 1824
Mineralogy, precious stones, ores, rocks, meteorites, products of metal and mining, porcelain, glass and chemical industries, biomineralogy - library, archives 17549

Mühlenhof-Freilichtmuseum Münster, c/o Verein De Bockwindmüel e.V., Theo-Breider-Weg 1, 48149 Münster - T: (0251) 98120, Fax: 98129040, E-mail: info@muehlenhof-muenster.de, Internet: http://www.muehlenhof-muenster.de. Head: Willi Niemann
Open Air Museum - 1965
Needlework, "Hauben"-coll - folklore dep 17550

Museum für Lackkunst, Windthorststr 26, 48143 Münster - T: (0251) 418510, Fax: 4185120, Internet: http://www.muenster.de/lackkunst. Head: Dr. Monika Kopplin
Fine Arts Museum - 1993 17551

Pängelanton-Eisenbahnmuseum, Albersloher Weg 419, 48167 Münster - T: (0251) 615742
Science&Tech Museum 17552

Stadthaus-Galerie, Pl des Westfälischen Friedens, 48143 Münster - T: (0251) 4924103, Fax: 4927752, E-mail: ermelina@stadt-muenster.de. Head: Andreas Ermeling
Public Gallery 17553

Stadtmuseum Münster, Salzstr 28, 48143 Münster - T: (0251) 4924501/03, Fax: 4927726, E-mail: museum@stadt-muenster.de, Internet: http://www.muenster.de/stadt/museum. Head: Dr. Barbara Rommé
Local Museum / Fine Arts Museum - 1989
Numismatics, pictures of pilgrimage, historical photogr 17554

Städtische Ausstellungshalle, Am Hawerkamp 22, 48155 Münster - T: (0251)4924191
Public Gallery 17555

Universitäts- und Landesbibliothek Münster, Krummer Timpen 3-5, 48143 Münster - T: (0251) 8324021, Fax: 8328398, E-mail: ULBmail@uni-muenster.de, Internet: http://www.uni-muenster.de/ULB. Head: Dr. Roswitha Poll
Library with Exhibitions 17556

Westfälischer Kunstverein e.V., Dompl 10, 48143 Münster - T: (0251) 46157, Fax: 45479, E-mail: wkv@muenster.de, Internet: http://www.westfaelischer-kunstverein.de. Head: Dr. Carina Plath
Association with Coll - 1831 17557

Westfälisches Landesmuseum für Kunst und Kulturgeschichte Münster, Dompl 10, 48143 Münster - T: (0251) 590701, Fax: 5907210, E-mail: landesmuseum@lwl.org, Internet: http://www.landesmuseum-muenster.de. Head: Prof. Dr. Klaus Bußmann
Fine Arts Museum - 1908
Regional 8th to 20th c art, regional history, painting, graphic arts, sculpture, applied art, textiles, numismatics, coll of portrait prints - library 17558

Westfälisches Museum für Naturkunde, Landesmuseum und Planetarium, Sentruper Str 285, 48161 Münster - T: (0251) 59105, Fax: 5916098, E-mail: naturkundemuseum@lwl.org, Internet: http://www.naturkundemuseum-muenster.de. Head: Dr. Alfred Hendricks
Natural History Museum - 1892
Astronomy, botany, geology, palaeontology, zoology, hist of the human evolution, mineralogy, prairie and plainsindians - library, technical workshop 17559

Westpreussisches Landesmuseum, Am Steintor 5, 48167 Münster - T: (02506) 2550, Fax: 6782, E-mail: westpreussisches-museum@t-online.de, Internet: http://www.westpreussisches-landesmuseum.de. Head: Dr. Lothar Hyss
Historical Museum - 1975
Majolica, church hist, Danzig room 17560

Münstertal

Bienenkundemuseum, Spielweg 55, 79244 Münstertal - T: (07636) 1457
Natural History Museum
Apiculture 17561

Schaubergwerk Teufelsgrund, Muldenstr, 79244 Münstertal - T: (07636) 70730, Fax: 70748, E-mail: touristinfo@muenstertal.de, Internet: http://www.muenstertal.de
Science&Tech Museum / Local Museum 17562

Waldmuseum, Rathaus, 79244 Münstertal - T: (07636) 70730, Fax: 70748, E-mail: touristinfo@muenstertal.de, Internet: http://www.muenstertal.de
Local Museum - 1979 17563

Münzenberg

Burgruine Münzenberg, Badgasse 11, 35516 Münzenberg - T: (06004) 2928, Fax: 2928
Historic Site 17564

Munderkingen

Städtisches Museum im ehemaligen Heiliggeistspital, Donaustr, 89597 Munderkingen - T: (07393) 598100, Fax: 598130, E-mail: rathaus@munderkingen.de, Internet: http://www.munderkingen.de. Head: Dr. W. Nuber
Local Museum - 1986
Roman and Aleman finds, local industry, guilds, local hist, local church 17565

Munster

Heimathaus Ollershof, Kirchgarten 2, 29633 Munster - T: (05192) 2810, 130240, Fax: 130215, E-mail: stadtverwaltung@munster.de, Internet: http://www.munster.de
Local Museum 17566

Panzermuseum, Hans-Krüger-Str 33, 29633 Munster - T: (05192) 2552, Fax: 130215, E-mail: kulturamt@munster.de, Internet: http://www.panzermuseum.de
Military Museum / Science&Tech Museum
Tanks, armoured vehicles, hand weapons, uniforms 17567

Rathausgalerie Munster, Wilhelm-Bockelmann-Str 32, 29633 Munster - T: (05192) 130240, Fax: 130215, E-mail: stadtverwaltung@munster.de, Internet: http://www.munster.de
Public Gallery 17568

Murnau

Münter-Haus, Kottmüllerallee 6, 82418 Murnau - T: (08841) 628880, Fax: 628881
Fine Arts Museum - 1984
Russenhaus, House and work of Gabriele Münter (1877-1962) and Wassily Kandinsky (1866-1944) 17569

Schloßmuseum Murnau, Schloßhof 4-5, 82418 Murnau - T: (08841) 476201/07, Fax: 476277, E-mail: schlossmuseum@murnau.de, Internet: http://www.schlossmuseum-murnau.de. Head: Brigitte Salmen
Fine Arts Museum - 1993
Verre églomisé picture, Gabriele Münter and the 'Blauen Reiter' 17570

Murrhardt

Carl-Schweizer-Museum, Seegasse 27, 71540 Murrhardt - T: (07192) 5402, Fax: 900188, E-mail: info@carl-schweizer-museum.de, Internet: http://www.carl-schweizer-museum.de. Head: Dr. Rolf Schweizer
Natural History Museum / Local Museum / Special Museum / Historical Museum - 1931
Natural history, history, geology 17571

Städtische Kunstsammlung, Oetinger Str 1, 71540 Murrhardt - T: (07192) 2130, Fax: 213150, E-mail: touristik@murrhardt.de, Internet: http://www.murrhardt.de. Head: Heinrich Dyckmans
Fine Arts Museum - 1969
20th c painting 17572

Mutzschen

Stadtmuseum Mutzschen, Schloß Mutzschen, 04688 Mutzschen - T: (034385) 80711, Fax: 80722. Head: J. Barthel
Local Museum - 1999
Local and regional hist, native stove industry, ancient and early hist 17573

Mylau

Museum Burg Mylau, Burg 1, 08499 Mylau - T: (03765) 34247, Fax: 385124, 392806, E-mail: stadt-mylau@t-online.de. Head: Andreas Raithel
Local Museum - 1883
Geology, zoology, local history, textiles, history of bridge construction (Göltzschtal and Elstertal bridges) - library 17574

Nabburg

Museum der heimischen Tierwelt, Feuerwehrhaus, Brunnanger 15, 92507 Nabburg - T: (09433) 6204, 6249, Fax: 6204
Natural History Museum
Preparations of local and extincted animals 17575

Museum im SchmidtHaus, Oberer Markt 4, 92507 Nabburg - T: (09433) 202965, Fax: 1833, E-mail: touristik@nabburg.de, Internet: http://www.nabburg.de. Head: Christa Schlosser
Fine Arts Museum 17576

Oberpfälzer Freilandmuseum Neusath-Perschen, Neusath 200, 92507 Nabburg - T: (09433) 24420, Fax: 2442222, E-mail: Freilandmuseum@bezirk-oberpfalz.de, Internet: http://www.bezirk-oberpfalz.de. Head: Dr. Ralf Heimrath
Open Air Museum - 1964
Furniture, agriculture, crafts, trade 17577

Vorgeschichtliche Sammlung, Am Oberen Markt, 92507 Nabburg - T: (09433) 6191
Archaeological Museum 17578

Nagold

Heimatmuseum Stadt Nagold-Steinhaus, Badgasse 3, 72202 Nagold - T: (07452) 681282, Fax: 681122, E-mail: herma.klar@nagold.de. Head: Herma Klar
Local Museum - 1989 17579

Naila

Städtisches Heimatmuseum, Peunthgasse 5, 95119 Naila - T: (09282) 6826, Fax: 6837. Head: Dr. Marion Soganci
Local Museum - 1986
Town hist, religious folklore, handicrafts and coll of embroidery 17580

Weberhaus Marlesreuth, Marlesreuth, 95119 Naila - T: (09282) 6829, Fax: 6837
Science&Tech Museum - 1984
Home of weaver 17581

Nassenfels

Archäologische Ausstellung in der Schule, Weingartenweg 1, 85128 Nassenfels - T: (08424) 3340, Fax: 3806, E-mail: volksschule.nassenfels@t-online.de. Head: Wunibald Iser
Archaeological Museum - 1990
Fossils and Roman finds 17582

Nattheim

Korallen- und Heimatmuseum, Neresheimer Str 9, 89564 Nattheim - T: (07321) 97840, Fax: 978432, E-mail: info@nattheim.de
Natural History Museum / Local Museum - 1990
Corals, local hist 17583

Nauen

Museum der Stadt Nauen, Rathauspl 2, 14641 Nauen - T: (03321) 446840/41, Fax: 446828, E-mail: Stadtnauen@t-online.de, Internet: http://www.stadt-nauen.de. Head: Martina Al-Diban
Local Museum - 1901
Local agricultural and industrial history 17584

Nauheim

Heimatmuseum Nauheim, Schulstr 6, 64569 Nauheim - T: (06152) 63223, 639219, Fax: 6510, E-mail: gemeindenauheim@t-online.de, Internet: http://www.heimatmuseum-nauheim.de. Head: Werner Dammel
Local Museum - 1962/87
Musical instruments, wood-carving, trades, farm life 17585

Naumburg, Hessen

Heimatmuseum Naumburg, Kronbergweg 30, 34311 Naumburg, Hessen - T: (05625) 1632
Local Museum - 1983
Agricultural and domestic implements, trade workshops, sacral art 17586

Naumburg, Saale

Haus zur Hohen Lilie, Stadtmuseum Naumburg, Markt 18, 06618 Naumburg, Saale, mail addr: Grochlitzer Str 49, 06618 Naumburg, Saale - T: (03445) 703503, 200648, Fax: 703503, E-mail: Post@museumnaumburg.de, Internet: http://www.museumnaumburg.de. Head: Dr. Siegfried Wagner
Historical Museum
Town hist, guilds and trade 17587

Max-Klinger-Gedenkstätte, Blütengrund 1, 06618 Naumburg, Saale - T: (03445) 202693
Fine Arts Museum - 1957
Works and life of painter Max Klinger (1857-1920) in his former home 17588

Nietzsche-Haus, Weingarten 18, 06618 Naumburg, Saale - T: (03445) 703503, 201638, Fax: 703503, E-mail: Post@museumnaumburg.de, Internet: http://www.museumnaumburg.de. Head: Dr. Siegfried Wagner
Special Museum
Portrayal of Nietzsche's life 17589

Nebel

Amrumer Heimatmuseum, 25946 Nebel - T: (04682) 872, Fax: 96274, E-mail: harkthomsen@t-online.de
Local Museum 17590

Neckarbischofsheim

Heimatmuseum im Fünfeckigen Turm, Bergstr, 74924 Neckarbischofsheim - T: (06222) 770126, Fax: 770126
Local Museum - 1964
Crafts, agriculture, local hist, uniforms 17591

Museum im Alten Schloß, Kernerstr 11, 74924 Neckarbischofsheim - T: (07263) 6971, Fax: 604428. Head: P. Beisel
Local Museum - 1985
Local hist 17592

Neckargemünd

Museum im Alten Rathaus, Hauptstr 25, 69151 Neckargemünd - T: (06223) 804186, Fax: 804280, E-mail: stadtverwaltung@neckargemuend.de. Head: Doris Meyer zu Schwabedissen
Local Museum / Fine Arts Museum - 1988
Local hist, geology 17593

Waltscher Heimatstube, Stadttor, 69151 Neckargemünd - T: (06223) 71932
Local Museum 17594

Neckargerach

Heimatmuseum, Bahnhofstr, 69437 Neckargerach - T: (06263) 1739
Local Museum - 1978
Peasant life, furnishings, crafts 17595

Neckarsulm

Deutsches Zweirad- und NSU-Museum, Urbanstr 11, 74172 Neckarsulm - T: (07132) 35271, Fax: 35402, E-mail: info@zweirad-museum.de, Internet: http://www.zweirad-museum.de. Head: Dr. Klaus-Dieter Roos
Science&Tech Museum - 1956
Historical and technical development of the bicycle and the motorcycle 17596

Neckartenzlingen

Mineralien-Fossilien-Museum, Metzinger Str 10, Melchior-Festhalle, 72654 Neckartenzlingen - T: (07127) 18010, Fax: 180173, E-mail: Rathaus_@_neckartenzlingen.KDRS.de, Internet: http://www.neckartenzlingen.de
Natural History Museum - 1988
Minerals, fossils 17597

Nellingen

Heimatmuseum, Schulpl 4, 89188 Nellingen - T: (07337) 6775
Local Museum - 1972
Peasant life, tools 17598

Nentershausen, Hessen

Heimat- und Bergbaumuseum, Altes Amtsgericht, Ruhl 2, 36214 Nentershausen, Hessen - T: (06627) 274
Local Museum / Science&Tech Museum - 1983
Hist of mining, agricultural implements 17599

Neresheim

Härtsfeld-Museum, Hauptstr 22, 73450 Neresheim - T: (07326) 8149, Fax: 8146, E-mail: tourist@neresheim.de, Internet: http://www.neresheim.de. Head: Holger Fedyna
Local Museum - 1986
Local hist, weapons, furniture, agricultural implements, household articles 17600

Härtsfeldbahn-Museum, Dischinger Str 11, 73450 Neresheim - T: (07326) 5755, Fax: (07631) 87587, E-mail: gerald.stempel@t-online.de, Internet: http://home.t-online.de/home/gerald.stempel/hmb.htm. Head: Werner Kuhn
Science&Tech Museum / Open Air Museum 17601

Neroth

Mausefallen-Museum, Mühlenweg 1, 54570 Neroth - T: (06591) 5822, 3544, Fax: 4783, Internet: http://www.gerolstein.de/vg/tourist/ne_mau.htm
Special Museum 17602

Nersingen

Museum für bildende Kunst im Landkreis Neu-Ulm, Alte Landstr 1a, Oberfahlheim, 89278 Nersingen - T: (0731) 7040118, Fax: 7040666, E-mail: lra-nu@neu-ulm.de, Internet: http://www.landkreis.neu-ulm.de. Head: Walter Wörtz
Fine Arts Museum - 1999 17603

Neschwitz

Naturschutzausstellung der Naturschutzstation, Altes Schloß, Park 1, 02699 Neschwitz - T: (035933) 30077, Fax: 30078, E-mail: Naturschutzstation-Neschwitz@t-online.de, Internet: http://www.naturschutz-neschwitz.de
Natural History Museum 17604

Nesselwang

Brauerei-Museum, c/o Post-Brauerei, Hauptstr 25, 87484 Nesselwang - T: (08361) 30910, Fax: 30973, E-mail: info@post-brauerei.nesselwang.de, Internet: http://www.post-brauerei-nesselwang.de. Head: Karl Meyer
Science&Tech Museum - 1650/1983
History of beer brewing 17605

Heimathaus, Füssener Str 13, 87484 Nesselwang - T: (08361) 923040, Fax: 923044
Local Museum 17606

Nettetal

Die Scheune Alt Kämpken, Spinnen/Weben Kunst, Hinsbeck-Hombergen, Krickenbecker Allee, 41334 Nettetal - T: (02162) 13524, (02153) 60851. Head: Walter Tillmann
Special Museum / Science&Tech Museum / Decorative Arts Museum / Fine Arts Museum - 1967
Hist of Lower Rhine textile industry, weaving, spinning, textile art - library 17607

Neu-Anspach

Freilichtmuseum Hessenpark, Laubweg, 61267 Neu-Anspach - T: (06081) 5880, Fax: 588160, E-mail: info@hessenpark.de, Internet: http://www.hessenpark.de. Head: Joachim Renz
Open Air Museum - 1974
Farm houses and working quarters, historical grocery store and workshops 17608

Neu-Isenburg

Museum der Stadt Neu-Isenburg Haus zum Löwen, Löwengasse 24, 63263 Neu-Isenburg - T: (06102) 33251, Fax: 38177, E-mail: bettina.stuckard@stadt-neu-isenburg, Internet: http://www.hugenottenhalle.de
Local Museum - 1963
Town hist and hist of the Huguenots, handicraft, domestic utensils, trades 17609

Zeppelin-Museum, Kapitän-Lehmann-Str 2, 63263 Neu-Isenburg - T: (069) 694390, Fax: 692016, E-mail: zeppelin-museum@t-online.de, Internet: http://www.zeppelin-museum-zeppelinheim.de. Head: Margot Chelius
Science&Tech Museum - 1977/88
History of the Zeppelin airship (1900-1939), Zeppelin models, aviation, uniforms, medals, photographs, documents 17610

Neu-Ulm

Abteilung Handwerk und dörfliches Leben des Heimatmuseums Neu-Ulm, Altes Rathaus, 89231 Neu-Ulm Pfuhl - T: (0731) 7050400, Fax: 7050191
Ethnology Museum / Decorative Arts Museum - 1986
Local hist and crafts, rustic culture 17611

Archäologisches Museum Neu-Ulm, Archäologische Staatssammlung München, Petruspl 4, 89231 Neu-Ulm - T: (0731) 9726180, Fax: 9709527. Head: Prof. Dr. Ludwig Wamser
Archaeological Museum
Early hist 17612

Edwin-Scharff-Museum, Petruspl 4, 89231 Neu-Ulm - T: (0731) 9726318, 9709526, Fax: 9709527, E-mail: edwin.scharff.museum@stadt.neu-ulm.de, Internet: http://www.neu-ulm.de. Head: Dr. Helga Gutbrod
Fine Arts Museum - 1977
Works by the sculptor Edwin Scharff (1887-1955) 17613

Heimatmuseum Neu-Ulm-Pfuhl, Hauptstr 73, 89233 Neu-Ulm - T: (0731) 9726318, Fax: 9709527
Local Museum - 1966 17614

Märchenofen, Fachmuseum Gußeiserne Öfen/Feuerstättenmuseum, Stauffenbergstr 5, 89233 Neu-Ulm - T: (0731) 713792, Fax: 714103, E-mail: maerchenofen.neu-ulm@web.de, Internet: http://www.maerchenofen.de. Head: Wilfried Schrem
Science&Tech Museum - 1977
Technical history, history of heating engineering 17615

Neualbenreuth

Grenzlandheimatstuben des Heimatkreises Marienbad, Marktpl 10, 95698 Neualbenreuth - T: (09638) 933250, Fax: 91133, E-mail: info@neualbenreuth.deth.btl.de, Internet: http://www.neualbenreuth.de. Head: Franz Norbert Pany
Local Museum
Local hist of the region Marienbad 17616

Neubrandenburg

Kunstsammlung Neubrandenburg, Am Pferdemarkt 1, 17033 Neubrandenburg - T: (0395) 5826229, Fax: 5826245. Head: Dr. Merete Cobarg
Fine Arts Museum - 1982 17617

Regionalmuseum Neubrandenburg, Treptower Str 38, 17033 Neubrandenburg - T: (0395) 5551271, Fax: 5552936, E-mail: museum@neubrandenburg.de, Internet: http://www.neubrandenburg.de. Head: Dr. Rolf Voß
Local Museum - 1872
Ancient and early history, 13th-20th c local history, medieval armaments, 13th-15th c ceramics, crafts, religious arts and crafts 17618

Neubukow

Heinrich-Schliemann-Gedenkstätte, Mühlenstr 7, 18233 Neubukow - T: (038294) 78523, Fax: 78522, E-mail: stadt@neubukow.de, Internet: http://www.neubukow.de
Historical Museum / Public Gallery - 1974
Memorabilia on archaeologist Heinrich Schliemann, his life and expeditions 17619

Neubulach

Historisches Silberbergwerk "Hella-Glücksstollen", 75387 Neubulach - T: (07053) 969510, 7899, Fax: 6416, E-mail: info@neubulach.de. Head: Dietmar Nittel
Science&Tech Museum - 1969
Silver mining, tools 17620

Schwarzwälder Mineralienmuseum, Marktpl 1, 75387 Neubulach - T: (07053) 969512, Fax: 6416. Head: Karlheinz Dümmel
Science&Tech Museum / Natural History Museum - 1976
Mining, mineralogy 17621

Neuburg an der Donau

Biohistoricum, Museum und Forschungsarchiv für die Geschichte der Biologie, Amalienstr A33, 86633 Neuburg an der Donau - T: (08431) 605430/31, Fax: 605432. Head: Prof. Dr. Armin Geus
Natural History Museum - 1998
Hist of biology 17622

Schloßmuseum Neuburg, Archäologische Staatssammlung, Residenzstr 2, 86633 Neuburg an der Donau - T: (08431) 8897, Fax: 42689, E-mail: info@bsv.bayern.de. Head: Dr. Brigitte Langer
Fine Arts Museum / Archaeological Museum
Renaissance/Baroque castle, early and local hist, religious textiles and folklore 17623

Stadtmuseum im Weveldhaus (temporary closed), Amalienstr 19, 86633 Neuburg an der Donau - T: (08431) 49334, Fax: 49334, E-mail: - historischer.verein@neusob.de, Internet: http://www.neusob.de/historischervereinneuburg. Head: Matthias Schieber
Local Museum - 1873
Town hist 17624

Neuburg an der Kammel

Hammerschmiede und Stockerhof, Naichen, 86476 Neuburg an der Kammel - T: (08283) 928606, Fax: 928608. Head: Dr. Hans Frei
Science&Tech Museum - 1990
Smithcraft 17625

Neudenau

Josefine-Weihrauch-Heimatmuseum, Billigheimer Str 3, 74861 Neudenau - T: (06264) 6133, 1014, Fax: 920511, E-mail: Zentrale@neudenau.bw-online.de. Head: Dr. Margarete Hendel, Wilfried Straßer
Local Museum - 1933
Household articles, local hist, religions images, artisans and gilds 17626

Neuenburg am Rhein

Museum für Stadtgeschichte, Franziskanerpl 4, 79395 Neuenburg am Rhein - T: (07631) 7910, Fax: 791222, E-mail: stadtverwaltung@neuenburg.de, Internet: http://www.neuenburg.de. Head: Winfried Studer
Local Museum 17627

Neuendettelsau

Dauerausstellung des Missionswerkes, Hauptstr 2, 91564 Neuendettelsau - T: (09874) 91530, Fax: 9330, E-mail: Ausstellung@missionswerk-bayern.de, Internet: http://www.missionswerk-bayern.de. Head: Dr. Hermann Vorländer
Religious Arts Museum / Ethnology Museum
Hist of missionary, ethnological coll from Papua-Neuguinea 17628

Löhe-Zeit-Museum, Bahnhofsgebäude, Bahnhofstr 38, 91564 Neuendettelsau - T: (09874) 686868, Internet: http://www.gemeinde-neuendettelsau.de. Head: Dr. Hans Rößler
Historical Museum / Folklore Museum - 1998
Social history, emigration to North-America, Wilhelm Löhe (1808-1872) 17629

Neuenhaus

Heimatmuseum Schulte-Wessels, Hauptstr 45, 49828 Neuenhaus - T: (05941) 6010
Local Museum 17630

Kunstverein Grafschaft Bentheim, Hauptstr 37, 49828 Neuenhaus - T: (05941) 98019, Fax: 98065, E-mail: kunstverein.neuenhaus@t-online.de. Head: Gudrun Thiessen-Schneider
Public Gallery 17631

Neuenkirchen, Lüneburger Heide

Kunstverein Springhornhof e.V., Tiefe Str 4, 29643 Neuenkirchen, Lüneburger Heide - T: (05195) 933963, Fax: 933962, E-mail: springhornhof@aol.com, Internet: http://www.springhornhof.de. Head: Bettina von Dziembowski
Association with Coll - 1977
Landscape art, sculpture 17632

Neuenmarkt

Deutsches Dampflokomotiv-Museum, Birkenstr 5, 95339 Neuenmarkt - T: (09227) 5700, Fax: 5703, E-mail: ddm@dampflokmuseum.de, Internet: http://www.dampflokmuseum.de. Head: Volker Dietel
Science&Tech Museum - 1977
Steam locomotives 17633

Neuenstein, Württemberg

Hohenlohe-Museum, Schloß Neuenstein, 74632 Neuenstein, Württemberg - T: (07942) 2209, Fax: (07941) 609920. Head: Katharina Fürstin zu Hohenlohe-Oehringen
Local Museum - 1952 17634

Neuffen

Ordenmuseum, Unterer Graben 26, 72639 Neuffen - T: (07025) 3965. Head: H. Seewöster
Local Museum / Decorative Arts Museum - 1982
Local hist, Decorations and medals 17635

Neuharlingersiel

Buddelschiff-Museum, Am Hafen, Westseite 7, 26427 Neuharlingersiel - T: (04974) 224. Head: Jürgen Landmann
Decorative Arts Museum - 1971
Miniature bottle ships and boats 17636

Museum für Seenotrettungsgeräte, Am Hafen, Westseite, 26427 Neuharlingersiel - T: (04974) 430
Science&Tech Museum 17637

Neuhaus-Schierschnitz

Heimatstube Neuhaus-Schiernitz, Schloßbergring 3, 96524 Neuhaus-Schierschnitz - T: (036764) 72416
Local Museum - 1954
18th-20th c mining history, 19th c peasant culture, furniture, costumes, household objects, porcelain industry, bird types 17638

Neuhausen ob Eck

Freilichtmuseum Neuhausen ob Eck, Museumsdorf, 78579 Neuhausen ob Eck - T: (07461) 926141/142, Fax: 926622, E-mail: flm.neuhausen@t-online.de, Internet: http://www.freilichtmuseum-neuhausen.de. Head: W. Knittel
Open Air Museum - 1988
Peasant life, farm houses and yards, agricultural machinery and implements, peasant furniture from the SW of Germany 17639

Neukirch, Lausitz

Heimatmuseum, Hauptstr 24, 01904 Neukirch, Lausitz - T: (035951) 32134, Fax: 25114, E-mail: fremdenverkehr@neukirch-lausitz.de, Internet: http://www.Neukirch-Lausitz.de
Local Museum - 1916
Ancient history, local and provincial history, crafts, 18th-19th c peasant living styles, costumes 17640

Neukirchen bei Niebüll

Nolde-Museum, Stiftung Seebüll Ada und Emil Nolde, Seebüll, 25927 Neukirchen bei Niebüll - T: (04664) 364, Fax: 1475, Internet: http://www.nolde-stiftung.de. Head: Dr. Manfred Reuther
Fine Arts Museum - 1957
Paintings, watercolors, drawings and graphics of Emil Nolde (1867-1956), in the artist's house, built in 1927 at Seebüll 17641

Neukirchen beim Heiligen Blut

Wallfahrtsmuseum, Marktpl 10, 93453 Neukirchen beim Heiligen Blut - T: (09947) 940822, Fax: 940844, E-mail: tourist@neukirchen.landkreis-cham.de, Internet: http://www.landkreis-cham.de/ServiceNetz/museen/wallfahrtsmuseum.htm. Head: Günther Bauernfeind
Religious Arts Museum - 1987
Hist of pilgrimage and religious folklore 17642

Neukirchen, Knüllgebirge

Heimatmuseum Neukirchen, Marktpl 5-6, 34626 Neukirchen, Knüllgebirge - T: (06694) 440, 8080, Fax: 80840, E-mail: kurverwaltung@neukirchen.com
Local Museum - 1977
Town history, old school, medieval finds, cultural items from former German areas 17643

Neukirchen-Vluyn

Museum Neukirchen-Vluyn, Von-der-Leyen-Pl 1, 47506 Neukirchen-Vluyn - T: (02845) 20657, Fax: 20657, Internet: http://www.neukirchen-vluyn.de. Head: Wilhelm Maas
Local Museum / Folklore Museum 17644

Neulingen, Enzkreis

Landesschau Äthiopien, Schloß Bauschlott, 75245 Neulingen, Enzkreis - T: (07237) 286. Head: Prof. Dr. St. Sandkühler
Ethnology Museum - 1976 17645

Neumarkt

Brauereimuseum in der Brauerei Franz Xaver Glossner, Schwesterhausgasse 8-16, 92318 Neumarkt - T: (09181) 2340, Fax: 23460, E-mail: brauerei-franz-xaver-glossner@glossner.de, Internet: http://www.glossner.de. Head: F.X. Gloßner
Special Museum
Brewery 17646

Kunsthalle Neumarkt, Residenzpl, 92318 Neumarkt
Fine Arts Museum 17647

Stadtmuseum Neumarkt, Adolf-Kolping-Str 4, 92318 Neumarkt - T: (09181) 2401, Fax: 255198, E-mail: stadtmuseum@stadt.neumarkt.de, Internet: http://www.stadt.neumarkt.de. Head: Petra Henseler
Local Museum - 1989
Town history, company history, cycles (1884-1959) 17648

Neumünster

Textilmuseum (temporary closed), Parkstr 17, 24534 Neumünster - T: (04321) 9422316, Fax: 9423422. Head: Klaus Tidow
Science&Tech Museum - 1914
History of textile manufacture, tools, textile machines, weaving, clothing and dress 17649

Neunburg vorm Wald

Schwarzachtaler Heimatmuseum, Im Berg 12, 92431 Neunburg vorm Wald - T: (09672) 4183, 91180, Fax: 91182, E-mail: rathaus.stadt@neunburg.de, Internet: http://www.neunburg.de
Local Museum - 1912
Militaria, folk religiousness (verre églomisé pictures) 17650

Neunheilingen

Heimatstube Neunheilingen, Feldstr 1, 99947 Neunheilingen - T: 279
Local Museum 17651

Neunkirchen am Brand

Felix-Müller-Museum im Zehntspeicher, Zehntpl, 91077 Neunkirchen am Brand - T: (09134) 70542, Fax: 70580, E-mail: info@markt-neunkirchen.de
Religious Arts Museum / Fine Arts Museum - 2000 17652

Synagoge und Jüdisches Museum Ermreuth, Wagnergasse 8, 91077 Neunkirchen am Brand - T: (09134) 70557, Fax: 70580, E-mail: info@markt-neunkirchen.de. Head: Dr. Rajaa Nadler
Religious Arts Museum / Ethnology Museum - 1994
Hist of Jewish life 17653

Neunkirchen am Sand

Fränkische Hopfenscheune mit heimatkundlicher Sammlung, Speikern, Kersbacher Str 18, 91233 Neunkirchen am Sand - T: (09123) 75640, Fax: 75687
Agriculture Museum / Folklore Museum - 1993 17654

Neunkirchen bei Mosbach

Heimatmuseum Neunkirchen, Luisenstr 25, 74867 Neunkirchen bei Mosbach - T: (06262) 6846
Local Museum - 1975
Crafts, local hist 17655

Neunkirchen, Saar

Galerie im Bürgerhaus, Marienstr 2, 66538 Neunkirchen, Saar - T: (06821) 2900621, Fax: 17580, E-mail: galerie-im-buergerhaus@web.de. Head: Nicole Nix
Public Gallery 17656

Neuötting

Stadtmuseum Neuötting, Ludwigstr 12, 84524 Neuötting - T: (08671) 2130, Fax: 882670, E-mail: museum@neuoetting.de, Internet: http://www.neuoetting.de/museum. Head: Christoph Obermeier
Local Museum - 1996
Graphic depictions showing the town - library 17657

Neureichenau

Brauereikulturmuseum Gut Riedelsbach, Gut Riedelsbach, 94089 Neureichenau - T: (08583) 96040, Fax: 960413, E-mail: gut-riedelsbach@t-online.de, Internet: http://www.gut-riedelsbach.de
Science&Tech Museum - 1999 17658

Heimatmuseum Neureichenau, Lackenhäuser Str 92, 94089 Neureichenau - T: (08583) 96010, Fax: 960110
Local Museum
Agricultural tools, rustic furniture 17659

Neuried, Ortenaukreis

Heimatmuseum Neuried, Kirchstr, 77743 Neuried, Ortenaukreis - T: (07807) 970, 3537
Local Museum - 1977
Agriculture, fisheries, tabac and hemp grow, extinct craft 17660

Neuruppin

Kunstraum Neuruppin, Schinkelstr 9, 16816 Neuruppin
Public Gallery 17661

Museum Neuruppin, August-Bebel-Str 14-15, 16816 Neuruppin - T: (03391) 458060, Fax: 4580628. Head: Dr. Irina Rockel
Local Museum / Public Gallery - 1865
Ancient and early hist, cultural hist, artists of Neuruppin (Karl Friedrich Schinkel, Theodor Fontane, Wilhelm Gentz), contemporary hist - Neuruppiner Bilderbogen 17662

Neusalza-Spremberg

Heimatmuseum Reiterhaus, Zittauer Str 37, 02742 Neusalza-Spremberg - T: (035872) 32957
Local Museum - 1966
Local and regional history, linen weavery 17663

Neuss

Clemens-Sels-Museum, Am Obertor, 41460 Neuss - T: (02131) 904141, Fax: 902472, E-mail: museum@stadt.neuss.de, Internet: http://www.clemens-sels-museum.de. Head: Dr. Christiane Zangs
Fine Arts Museum / Archaeological Museum / Local Museum - 1845
Archaeology (Roman and Middle Ages), Symbolists, 19th-21th c art, local hist, art brût - library 17664

Haus Rottels, Oberstr 58-60, 41460 Neuss - T: (02131) 904144, Fax: 902472, E-mail: info@clemens-sels-museum.de, Internet: http://www.clemens-sels-museum.de. Head: Dr. Christiane Zangs
Local Museum / Historical Museum - 1989 17665

Kulturforum Alte Post, Neustr 28, 41456 Neuss - T: (02131) 904122, Fax: 902494, E-mail: info@altepost.de, Internet: http://www.altepost.de. Head: Thomas Brandt
Public Gallery 17666

Museum Insel Hombroich, Holzheim, 41464 Neuss - T: (02182) 2094, Fax: 1229, E-mail: stiftung@inselhombroich.de, Internet: http://www.inselhombroich.de. Head: Karl Müller, Karl-Heinrich Müller
Fine Arts Museum
Fine arts 17667

Neustadt am Main

Lapidarium, Megingaudstr 1, 97845 Neustadt am Main - T: (09393) 530, Fax: 997836
Archaeological Museum / Religious Arts Museum 17668

Neustadt am Rübenberge

Hufschmiede Museum Frehrking, Alte Heerstr 21, 31535 Neustadt am Rübenberge - T: (05072) 1575, Fax: 770105, E-mail: Hensel-Helstorf@t-online.de, Internet: http://www.hufschmiedemuseum-helstorf.de. Head: Diethardt Hensel
Local Museum / Science&Tech Museum - 1989
Historic blacksmith's workshop, agricultural equipment 17669

Kloster Mariensee, Hölty-Str 1, 31535 Neustadt am Rübenberge - T: (05034) 4777, Fax: 926734, Internet: http://www.kloster-mariensee.city-map.de. Head: Ingmar-Elisabeth Hornschuh
Religious Arts Museum
Hist of the Cistercian cloister and church, tapestries, bibles, prayer-books, Erich Klahn coll 17670

Torfmuseum, Schloß Landestrost, Schloß-Str 1, 31535 Neustadt am Rübenberge - T: (05032) 899156, 899158, Fax: 899156, E-mail: - Christine.Engelmann@region-hannover.de. Head: Christine Engelmann
Special Museum - 1980
Hist of the utilization of peatbogs and nature conservancy 17671

Neustadt an der Aisch

Heimatmuseum Neustadt an der Aisch, Untere Schloßgasse 8, 91413 Neustadt an der Aisch - T: (09161) 66611, 66670, Fax: 60793
Local Museum - 1960
Town hist, rustic culture and agricultural implements 17672

Neustadt an der Donau

Römisches Museum für Kur- und Badewesen, Bad Gögging, Trajansstr 8, 93333 Neustadt an der Donau - T: (09445) 95750, Fax: 957533
Archaeological Museum - 1997 17673

Neustadt an der Waldnaab

Stadtmuseum Neustadt an der Waldnaab, Stadtpl 10, 92660 Neustadt an der Waldnaab - T: (09602) 8929
Local Museum - 1916
Town hist, religious folklore, glass dept (lead crystall production) 17674

Neustadt an der Weinstraße

Eisenbahnmuseum Neustadt an der Weinstraße, Schillerstr, 67434 Neustadt an der Weinstraße - T: (06321) 32572, Fax: 398162, E-mail: info@eisenbahnmuseum-neustadt.de. Head: Horst Kayser
Science&Tech Museum - 1981 17675

Galerie des Kunstvereins Neustadt an der Weinstraße, Ägyptenpfad 26, 67433 Neustadt an der Weinstraße - T: (06321) 855447, E-mail: wolfgang.glass@arcormail.de
Public Gallery
Contemporary paintings 17676

Hambacher Schloß, 67434 Neustadt an der Weinstraße - T: (06321) 30881, Fax: 482672, E-mail: info@hambacher-schloss.de, Internet: http://www.hambacher-schloss.de. Head: Susanne Walter
Historic Site 17677

Museum der Stadt Neustadt an der Weinstraße, Maximilianstr 25, 67433 Neustadt an der Weinstraße - T: (06321) 855450, Fax: 855402, E-mail: rolf.schaedler@stadt-nw.de. Head: Helmut W. Hoffmann
Local Museum - 1914 17678

Otto-Dill Museum, Rathausstr 12, 67433 Neustadt an der Weinstraße - E-mail: info@otto-dill-museum.de, Internet: http://www.otto-dill-museum.de
Fine Arts Museum - 2002
Paintings, drawings and memorabilia by Otto Dill (1884-1957) 17679

Weinbaumuseum im Herrenhof, An der Eselshaut 18, Mussbach, 67433 Neustadt an der Weinstraße - T: (06321) 9639990, Fax: 96399913, E-mail: herrenhof@mussbach.de
Agriculture Museum 17680

Neustadt bei Coburg

Museum der Deutschen Spielzeugindustrie, Hindenburgpl 1, 96465 Neustadt bei Coburg - T: (09568) 5600, Fax: 89490. Head: Udo Leidner
Science&Tech Museum / Decorative Arts Museum - 1930
Hist of toy industry, folk costumes, dolls 17681

Neustadt in Holstein

Ostholstein-Museum Neustadt, Krempertor, 23730 Neustadt in Holstein - T: (04561) 558424, Fax: 558428. Head: Johannes Hugo Koch
Local Museum - 1908 17682

Neustrelitz

Museum der Stadt Neustrelitz, Schloßstr 3, 17235 Neustrelitz - T: (03981) 205874, Fax: 203126. Head: Gerlinde Kienitz
Local Museum 17683

Neutraubling

Museum der Stadt Neutraubling - Ortsgeschichtliche Dokumentation, Adalbert-Stifter-Str 10, 93073 Neutraubling - T: (09401) 8000, Fax: 80066, E-mail: info@stadt-neutraubling.de, Internet: http://www.neustraubling.de. Head: Cäcilie Vilsmeier
Local Museum 17684

Neuwied

Kreismuseum, Raiffeisenpl 1a, 56564 Neuwied - T: (02631) 803379, Fax: 359869. Head: Bernd Willscheid
Local Museum - 1928
Prehist, early hist, folklore, ironwork, Roentgen furniture - library 17685

Museum für die Archäologie des Eiszeitalters, Schloß Monrepos, 56567 Neuwied - T: (02631) 97720, Fax: 76357, E-mail: museum.monrepos@rz-online.de, Internet: http://rz-home.de/~rgzm.neuwied/. Head: Prof. Dr. Gerhard Bosinski
Archaeological Museum - 1988
Palaeolithic archeology 17686

Städtische Galerie Mennonitenkirche, Schloßstr 2, 56564 Neuwied - T: (02631) 802468, Fax: 802801, E-mail: pmagnus@neuwied.de, Internet: http://www.neuwied.de
Public Gallery 17687

Neuzelle

Stiftung Stift Neuzelle, Stiftspl 7, 15898 Neuzelle - T: (033652) 8140, Fax: 81419, E-mail: stift_neuzelle@t-online.de, Internet: http://www.stift-neuzelle.de. Head: Walter Ederer
Religious Arts Museum / Historic Site 17688

Nidda

Heimatmuseum Nidda, Raun 1, 63667 Nidda - T: (06043) 4139, Fax: 950311
Local Museum - 1983
Johannes Pistorius Niddanus (father: 1502-1583; son: 1546-1608), Roland Krug von Nidda - Printery, town hist, early and pre-history, trades 17689

Nidderau

Dorfmuseum Ostheim, Limesstr 12, 61130 Nidderau - T: (06187) 3743
Local Museum - 1988
Village hist, agriculture, trade 17690

Städtisches Museum im Hospital, Hospitalgasse 1, 61130 Nidderau - T: (06187) 201124
Local Museum - 1993
Regional hist, Roman finds, Jewish life 17691

Niebüll

Friesisches Heimatmuseum, Freilichtmuseum, Osterweg 76, 25899 Niebüll - T: (04661) 4590
Local Museum / Open Air Museum 17692

Naturkundemuseum Niebüll, Hauptstr 108, 25899 Niebüll - T: (04661) 5691, Fax: 5691, E-mail: info@nkm-niebuell.de, Internet: http://www.nkm-niebuell.de. Head: Peter Lorenz Hartwigsen
Natural History Museum - 1979
Dioramas, fossils, living bees, aquariums, mushroom, minerals 17693

Richard-Haizmann-Museum, Rathauspl, 25899 Niebüll - T: (04661) 1010, Fax: 60166, Internet: http://www.shinfo.de/haizmann-museum. Head: Dr. Uwe Haupenthal
Fine Arts Museum - 1986
Memorabilia of Richard Haizmann (1895-1963) 17694

Niederaichbach

Heimatmuseum Niederaichbach, Isarstr 3, 84100 Niederaichbach - T: (08702) 94040, Fax: 940440
Local Museum
Local hist 17695

Niedercunnersdorf

Heimatmuseum Alte Weberstube, Niedere Haupstr 37, 02708 Niedercunnersdorf - T: (035875) 60200, 60936, Fax: 60950, E-mail: Weidemann-NC@t-online.de
Local Museum - 1930
Weaving, local and regional history 17696

Niedereschach

Heimatstube Fischbach, Sinkinger Str 2, 78078 Niedereschach - T: (07725) 7720
Local Museum - 1986
Roman finds, peasant life 17697

Niederstetten

Jagd- und Naturkunde Museum, Schloß, 97996 Niederstetten - T: (07932) 205
Natural History Museum - 1976
Trophies, preserved animals 17698

Kelter- und Weinbaumuseum, Kelterhaus 11, 97996 Niederstetten - T: (07932) 8344. Head: F. Habel
Agriculture Museum / Science&Tech Museum - 1987
Viticulture 17699

Lapidarium - Historische Grenzsteinsammlung, Am Schloßberg, 97996 Niederstetten - T: (07932) 910238, Fax: 910239
Historical Museum - 1983
Boundary stones 17700

Nienburg, Weser

Museum Nienburg, Leinstr 48, 31582 Nienburg, Weser - T: (05021) 12461, Fax: 62377, E-mail: info@museum-nienburg.de, Internet: http://www.museum-nienburg.de. Head: Dr. Eilert Ommen
Local Museum - 1908
Prehist, old saxons, local/ regional hist, farm implements, Weserregion, lace, glass, Biedermeier, Rococo tapestry, coins, tiles, costum, iron stove plates, limestones, glass beds - library, education 17701

Nierstein

Paläontologisches Museum Nierstein, Marktpl 1, 55283 Nierstein - T: (06133) 58312, E-mail: museum.nierstein@t-online.de, Internet: http://www.museum-nierstein.de. Head: Arnulf Stapf
Natural History Museum 17702

Niesky

Museum Niesky, Zinzendorfpl 8, 02906 Niesky - T: (03588) 25600, Fax: 255815, E-mail: touristinfo@niesky.de, Internet: http://www.niesky.de. Head: Eva-Maria Bergmann
Local Museum - 1986
Local hist, handicraft, industry, furniture 17703

Nitschareuth

Bauernmuseum mit Kräutergarten, Nr. 13, 07980 Nitschareuth
Agriculture Museum / Ethnology Museum 17704

Nittenau

Stadtmuseum Nittenau, Kirchpl 2, 93149 Nittenau - T: (09436) 9027/29, Fax: 9032, E-mail: stadt.nittenau@sadnet.de, Internet: http://www.nittenau.de/museum.htm. Head: Rudolf Heininger
Local Museum - 1979
Stoneware, local crafts and minerals 17705

Nördlingen

Bayerisches Eisenbahnmuseum, Am Hohenweg 6a, 86720 Nördlingen - T: (09081) 9808, Fax: (09083) 388, E-mail: info@bayerisches-eisenbahnmuseum.de, Internet: http://www.bayerisches-eisenbahnmuseum.de. Head: E. Böhnlein
Science&Tech Museum - 1969
Locomotives and trainwagons 17706

Rieskrater-Museum, Eugene-Shoemaker-Pl 1, 86720 Nördlingen - T: (09081) 2738220, Fax: 27382220, E-mail: rieskratermuseum@noerdlingen.de, Internet: http://www.iaag.geo.uni-muenchen.de/sammlung/rieskrater/rieskrater-museum.html. Head: Dr. Michael Schieber
Natural History Museum - 1990
Geology, meteorites, planetology, impact cratering 17707

Stadtmauermuseum Nördlingen, Löpsinger Torturm, 86720 Nördlingen - T: (09081) 9180, Fax: 84102, E-mail: stadtverwaltung@noerdlingen.de, Internet: http://www.noerdlingen.de. Head: Aksel Rinck
Military Museum - 1987
Citywall of Nördlingen 17708

Stadtmuseum Nördlingen, Vordere Gerbergasse 1, 86720 Nördlingen - T: (09081) 2738230, Fax: 84102, E-mail: stadtmuseum@noerdlingen.de, Internet: http://www.noerdlingen.de. Head: Andrea Kugler
Local Museum / Fine Arts Museum - 1867
Archeology, local hist, painting 17709

Nörvenich

Kunstmuseum Nörvenich, Museum Arno Breker, Sammlung Europäische Kunst, Schloß, 52388 Nörvenich - T: (02426) 4632, Fax: 1311, E-mail: JohnG.Bodenstein@gmx.net. Head: John Gilbert Bodenstein
Fine Arts Museum - 1980 17710

Norden

Heimatmuseum Norden und Ostfriesisches Teemuseum → Das Ostfriesische Teemuseum und Norder Heimatmuseum

Muschel- und Schneckenmuseum, In der Gnurre 40, 26506 Norden - T: (04931) 12615, Internet: http://www.muschel-und-schneckenmuseum.de. Head: Helga Wiltfang
Natural History Museum - 1994
Privat coll of mussels, shells and sea snails from the seven seas 17711

Das Ostfriesische Teemuseum und Norder Heimatmuseum, Am Markt 36, 26506 Norden - T: (04931) 12100, Fax: 12100, E-mail: -heimatmuseum.norden@ewetel.net, Internet: http://www.teemuseum.de. Head: Dr. Marion Roehmer
Local Museum / Special Museum - 1920/1989
Early and prehist, town hist, trades, tea (origin, plant, trade object, sale, international tea culture) 17712

Nordenham

Museum Moorseer Mühle, Abbehausen, Butjadinger Str 132, 26954 Nordenham - T: (04731) 88983, Fax: (04401) 9273473
Science&Tech Museum
Three-storey mill and its hist, agricultural implements 17713

Museum Nordenham, Hansingstr 18, 26954 Nordenham - T: (04731) 88831, Fax: 923904, E-mail: museum.nordenham@nwn.de, Internet: http://www.nordenham.de/kultur/musnord.htm. Head: Dr. Timothy Saunders
Historical Museum - 1978
Early and prehist, furniture, Netherlandish tiles, town history, industry 17714

Norderney

Norderneyer Fischerhausmuseum, Weststrandstr 1, 26548 Norderney - T: (04932) 1791, Fax: 1791. Head: Johann Visser
Local Museum - 1937
Hist of the island with the oldest German seaside resort from 1797, fishing and shipping 17715

Norderstedt

Feuerwehrmuseum Schleswig-Holstein, Friedrichsgaber Weg 290, 22846 Norderstedt - T: (040) 5256742, Fax: 5256540. Head: Rosmarie Tarnow
Science&Tech Museum 17716

Stadtgeschichtliche Sammlung → Stadtmuseum Norderstedt

Stadtmuseum Norderstedt, Friedrichsgaber Weg 290, 22846 Norderstedt - T: (040) 53595959/56, Fax: 53595957. Head: Dr. Manfred von Essen
Local Museum 17717

Nordhalben

Internationale Spitzensammlung, Klöppelschule 4, 96365 Nordhalben - T: (09267) 375, Fax: 1751, E-mail: kloeppelschule@kloeppelschule.de, Internet: http://www.kloeppelschule.de. Head: Beate Agten
Decorative Arts Museum - 1986
Lace coll 17718

Nordhausen

KZ-Gedenkstätte Mittelbau-Dora, Kohnsteinweg 20, 99734 Nordhausen, mail addr: Postfach 100751, 99727 Nordhausen - T: (03631) 49580, Fax: 495813, E-mail: gedenkstaette.mittelbau-dora@t-online.de, Internet: http://www.dora.de. Head: Dr. Jens-Christian Wagner
Historical Museum - 1964
Crimes of German imperialism, the system of concentration camps, anti-fascist resistance - documentation 17719

Meyenburg-Museum, Alexander-Puschkin-Str 31, 99734 Nordhausen - T: (03631) 881091, Fax: 898011, E-mail: cehser@t-online.de. Head: Claudia Ehser
Decorative Arts Museum / Fine Arts Museum / Historical Museum - 1876
Furniture, numismatics, ceramics, glass, works in graphic art and paintings from the region 17720

Tabakspeicher, Museum für Nordhäuser Handwerks- und Industriegeschichte, Bäckerstr 20, 99734 Nordhausen - T: (03631) 982737, Fax: 898011, Internet: http://www.nordhausen.de. Head: Claudia Ehser
Science&Tech Museum / Archaeological Museum - 1995
Hist of chewing tobacco industry and distilling, crafts, archaeology 17721

Nordholz

Aeronauticum - Deutsches Luftschiff- und Marinefliegermuseum Nordholz, Peter-Strasser-Pl 3, 27637 Nordholz - T: (04741) 18190, Fax: 181915, E-mail: aeronauticum@t-online.de, Internet: http://www.aeronauticum.de. Head: Alf-Rico Denck, Dr. Anja Dörfer
Military Museum / Science&Tech Museum
Hist of the German naval aviation since 1913, German airships, helicopters 17722

Nordhorn

Stadtmuseum Povelturm, Vechteaue 2, 48529 Nordhorn - T: (05921) 721500, Fax: 990802. Head: Werner Straukamp
Historical Museum - 1996
Town hist and textile industry, social topography, industrialists' and labourers' CVs, fashion photography 1950-1980, industry photography 1942-1996, textile machinery (1940-1990) with spinning and weaving 17723

Städtische Galerie Nordhorn - Kunstwegen, Vechteaue 2, 48529 Nordhorn - T: (05921) 971100, Fax: 971105, E-mail: kunstinfo@kunstwegen.-nordhorn.de, Internet: http://www.kunstwegen.-nordhorn.de. Head: Martin Köttering
Fine Arts Museum 17724

Nordwalde

Georg-Kramann-Heimatmuseum, Hermann-Stehr-Str 14, 48356 Nordwalde - T: (02573) 3767
Local Museum 17725

Northeim

Heimatmuseum der Stadt Northeim, Am Münster 32-33, 37154 Northeim - T: (05551) 65060, Fax: 65060, Internet: http://www.northeim.de
Local Museum
Early and prehist, medieval sacral art, town hist, trades and guilds, railway system, graphic art, political hist 1848-1948 17726

Nossen

Staatlicher Schloßbetrieb Schloß Nossen / Kloster Altzella, Am Schloß 3, 01683 Nossen - T: (035242) 68700, Fax: 68700. Head: Ingrid Welzig
Local Museum - 1915
Ancient hist, stones, zoology, local hist, 18th-19th c peasant and court living style 17727

Nüdlingen

Heimatmuseum Nüdlingen, Münnerstädter Str 4-6, 97720 Nüdlingen - T: (0971) 2631, 65506
Local Museum - 1964
Local hist, fire brigade 17728

Nümbrecht

Haus der Kunst, Jacob-Engels-Str 2, 51588 Nümbrecht - T: (02293) 30229
Fine Arts Museum 17729

Museum des Oberbergischen Kreises, Schloß Homburg, 51588 Nümbrecht - T: (02293) 91010, Fax: 910140, E-mail: schloss-homburg@oberbergischer-kreis.de, Internet: http://www.oberbergischer-kreis.de. Head: Dr. Gudrun Sievers-Flägel
Local Museum - 1926
History of hunting (17th-18th c) 17730

Nürnberg

Albrecht-Dürer-Gesellschaft, Kunstverein Nürnberg, Füll 12, 90403 Nürnberg - T: (0911) 241562, Fax: 241563, E-mail: webmaster@kunstverein-nbg.de, Internet: http://www.kunstverein-nbg.de. Head: Stefanie-Vera Kockot, Anton-Wolfgang Graf von Faber-Castell
Association with Coll 17731

Albrecht-Dürer-Haus, Museen der Stadt Nürnberg, Albrecht-Dürer-Str 39, 90403 Nürnberg - T: (0911) 2312568, Fax: 2315422, E-mail: museen@stadt.nuernberg.de, Internet: http://www.museen.nuernberg.de. Head: Dr. Jutta Tschoeke
Special Museum / Historic Site - 1828
Memorabilia on Albrecht Dürer, graphic art, located in the house in which Dürer lived from 1509-1528, film "Albertus Durer Noricus" - painting/printing-workshop 17732

Ausstellung Faszination und Gewalt - Dokumentationszentrum Reichsparteitagsgelände, Museen der Stadt Nürnberg, Bayernstr 110, 90478 Nürnberg - T: (0911) 2315666, 2318409, Fax: 2318412, E-mail: -dokumentationszentrum@ref4.stadt.nuernberg.de, Internet: http://museen.nuernberg.de. Head: Hans-Christian Täubrich
Historical Museum - 2001 17733

DB Museum im Verkehrsmuseum Nürnberg, c/o Deutsche Bahn AG, Lessingstr 6, 90443 Nürnberg - T: (0911) 2192424, Fax: 2193740, E-mail: dbnostalgie@dbmuseum.de, Internet: http://www.dbmuseum.de. Head: Dr. Jürgen Franzke
Science&Tech Museum - 1899
Original vehicles of the Deutsche Bahn, locomotive and train models 1:10, railroad technique, shipping - library, archives, photoarchive 17734

Ehemaliges Reichsparteitagsgelände, Museen der Stadt Nürnberg, Bayernstr, 90317 Nürnberg - T: (0911) 869897, Fax: 2315422, E-mail: museen@stadt.nuernberg.de, Internet: http://www.nuernberg.de/ver/him/index. Head: Dr. Franz Sonnenberger
Historical Museum - 1985
Hist of National Socialism and the site of the Nuremberg party conference during the Third Reich 17735

Forum für Angewandte Kunst im Bayerischen Kunstgewerbeverein e.V., Wilhelm-Marx-Str 9, 90419 Nürnberg - T: (0911) 3938055/56, Fax: 3786635, E-mail: forum-ak@kubiss.de, Internet: http://www.kubiss.de/forum-ak
Fine Arts Museum 17736

Garnisonmuseum Nürnberg, Hochbunker Hohe Marter, Zweibrückener Str 54, 90441 Nürnberg - T: (0911) 6491159, Fax: 6491162, E-mail: kaiser@garnisonmuseum.de, Internet: http://www.garnisonmuseum.de. Head: Michael Kaiser
Military Museum / Historical Museum - 1992 17737

Germanisches Nationalmuseum, Kartäusergasse 1, 90402 Nürnberg - T: (0911) 13310, Fax: 1331200, E-mail: info@gnm.de, Internet: http://www.gnm.de. Head: Prof. Dr. G. Ulrich Großmann
Historical Museum - 1852
Art and culture from prehistoric times to contemporary, folk art, painting, medieval art, art (15th-20th c), prints and drawings, coins and medals, history musical instruments, weapons, huntiny gear, paleolithic hand-axes, portraits of Albrecht Dürer to Joseph Beuys, art and social hist of the German-speaking world - research library, archives, institute of art technology and conservation 17738

Gewerbemuseum der LGA im Germanischen Nationalmuseum, Kartäusergasse 1, 90402 Nürnberg, mail addr: Postfach 119580, 90105 Nürnberg - T: (0911) 13310, Fax: 1331200, E-mail: s.glaser@gnm.de, Internet: http://www.gnm.de. Head: Dr. G. Ulrich Großmann
Decorative Arts Museum - 1869
Objects made of glass, ceramics and metal, clocks, textiles, toys, ivory, furniture, East-Asiatica 17739

Graphische Sammlung, Museen der Stadt Nürnberg, Äußere Sulzbacher Str 60, 90491 Nürnberg - T: (0911) 2312271, Fax: 2314971, E-mail: museen@stadt.nuernberg.de, Internet: http://www.nuernberg.de/ver/him/index. Head: Mathias Mende
Fine Arts Museum - 1970
Graphic art, especially depicting the cultural history of the city, portraits - library 17740

Heimatmuseum Kornburg, Kornburger Hauptstr 31, 90455 Nürnberg - T: (09129) 8222
Local Museum 17741

Heimatmuseum Nürnberg, Neunhofer Schloßpl 6, 90427 Nürnberg - T: (0911) 305685
Local Museum - 1935
Local hist 17742

Historische Lochgefängnisse im Alten Rathaus, Museen der Stadt Nürnberg, Altes Rathaus, Rathauspl, 90403 Nürnberg - T: (0911) 2312690, Fax: 2315422, 2314144, E-mail: museen@stadt.nuernberg.de, Internet: http://www.nuernberg.de/ver/him/index. Head: Dr. Franz Sonnenberger
Historic Site - 1925
Authentic medieval jail (14th c) with the original prisoners' cells, torture chambers, instruments of torture, smithy, kitchen 17743

Historisches Straßenbahn-Depot Sankt Peter, Schloßstr 1, 90478 Nürnberg - T: (0911) 2834665, Fax: 2834623
Science&Tech Museum - 1985
Local trams, conductor uniforms 17744

Institut für moderne Kunst, Luitpoldstr 5, 90402 Nürnberg - T: (0911) 2402120, Fax: 2402119, E-mail: info@moderne-kunst.org, Internet: http://www.moderne-kunst.org. Head: Manfred Rothenberger
Library with Exhibitions 17745

Kaiserburg Nürnberg, Germanisches Nationalmuseum, Auf der Burg 13, 90403 Nürnberg - T: (0911) 225726, Fax: 2059117, E-mail: info@bsv.bayern.de, Internet: http://www.schloesser.bayern.de. Head: Dr. Albrecht Miller
Local Museum
Fortress built in 1050 including the knights' and the emperor's hall, rooms of the guards, wells, the emperor's living room with period furnishings 17746

Krankenhausmuseum, Klinikum Nürnberg-Nord, Haus 1 Altbau, Prof.-Ernst- Nathan-Str 1, 90340 Nürnberg - T: (0911) 3982303, Fax: 3983288, E-mail: korn@klinikum-nuernberg.de, Internet: http://www.klinikum.nuernberg.de/1_08_01_museum.html
Special Museum 17747

Kunsthalle Nürnberg, Lorenzer Str 32, 90402 Nürnberg - T: (0911) 2312853, Fax: 2313721, E-mail: kunsthalle@stadt.nuernberg.de, Internet: http://www.kunsthalle.nuernberg.de. Head: Ellen Seifermann
Fine Arts Museum - 1967 17748

Kunsthaus Nürnberg, Königstr 93, 90402 Nürnberg - T: (0911) 203110, Fax: 2418106, E-mail: info@kunsthaus-nuernberg.de, Internet: http://www.kunsthaus-nuernberg.de. Head: Joachim Bleistein, Hans-Peter Miksch
Public Gallery
Painting, sculpture, installations etc. 17749

Museum für Kommunikation Nürnberg, Lessingstr 6, 90443 Nürnberg - T: (0911) 230880, Fax: 2308896, E-mail: mk.nuernberg@t-online.de, Internet: http://www.museumsstiftung.de. Head: Dr. Stefan Kley
Science&Tech Museum
Hist of postalservices (especially in bavaria) and telecommunications - library, archive 17750

Museum im Koffer - Kindermuseum Nürnberg, Michael-Ende-Str 17, 90439 Nürnberg - T: (0911) 600040, Fax: 6000459, E-mail: info@museum-im-koffer.de, Internet: http://www.kindermuseum-nuernberg.de
Special Museum 17751

Museum Industriekultur mit Motorradmuseum, Schulmuseum und Kinderabteilung, Museen der Stadt Nürnberg, Äußere Sulzbacher Str 62, 90491 Nürnberg - T: (0911) 2313875, Fax: 2313470, E-mail: museen@stadt.nuernberg.de, Internet: http://www.nuernberg.de/ver/him/index. Head: Matthias Murko
Science&Tech Museum / Special Museum - 1988
Machinery, traffic 17752

Naturhistorisches Museum, Marientorgraben 8, 90402 Nürnberg - T: (0911) 227970, Fax: 2447441, E-mail: info@nhg-nuernberg.de, Internet: http://www.nhg-nuernberg.de. Head: Rainer Ott
Natural History Museum - 1884
Geology, paleontology, speleology, botany, prehistory, Jordanian and Costa Rican archeology, anthropology (Africa, Sibiria, New Guinea) - library, archives 17753

Neues Museum, Staatliches Museum für Kunst und Design in Nürnberg, Klarissenpl, 90402 Nürnberg, mail addr: Luitpoldstr 5, 90402 Nürnberg - T: (0911) 240200, Fax: 2402029, E-mail: info@nmn.de, Internet: http://www.nmn.de. Head: Dr. Lucius Grisebach
Fine Arts Museum 17754

Rotkreuz-Museum, Sulzbacher Str 42, 90489 Nürnberg - T: (0911) 5301211, Fax: 5301298, E-mail: info@kvnuernberg-stadt.drk.de, Internet: http://www.kvnuernberg.stadt.drk.de. Head: G. Herold
Historical Museum - 1984
Hist of the Red Cross 17755

Schloß Neunhof, Germanisches Nationalmuseum, Schloßpl 2, 90427 Nürnberg - T: (0911) 13310, Fax: 1331200, Internet: http://www.gnm.de. Head: Dr. G. Ulrich Großmann
Local Museum - 1963
16th c castle, 16th-18th c domestic utensils, hunting artifacts and antiques, period furnishings 17756

Schulmuseum Nürnberg, Museen der Stadt Nürnberg, Äußere Sulzbacher Str 60-62, 90491 Nürnberg - T: (0911) 2313875, Fax: 5302588, E-mail: mlschnei@ewf.uni-erlangen.de, Internet: http://www.paed1.ewf.uni-erlangen.de/schulm.htm. Head: M. Schneider
Historical Museum - 1985
Schoolbook coll, school hist coll 17757

Spielzeugmuseum, Museen der Stadt Nürnberg, Karlstr 13-15, 90403 Nürnberg - T: (0911) 2313164, Fax: 2315495, E-mail: spielzeugmuseum@stadt.nuernberg.de, Internet: http://www.spielzeugmuseum-nuernberg.de. Head: Dr. Helmut Schwarz
Decorative Arts Museum - 1966
Toys from all over the world and made of various materials, toy manufacture, children's books, paintings depicting toys and games 17758

Stadtmuseum Fembohaus, Museen der Stadt Nürnberg, Burgstr 15, 90317 Nürnberg - T: (0911) 2312595, Fax: 2315422, E-mail: museen@stadt.nuernberg.de, Internet: http://www.nuernberg.de/ver/him/index. Head: Dr. Franz Sonnenberger
Historical Museum - 1953
Renaissance, Baroque furnishings, models of the city, paintings, graphic art, works in bronze, ceramic by Nuremberg artists - Noricama multimedia show 17759

Tucherschloss mit Hirsvogelsaal, Museen der Stadt Nürnberg, Hirschelgasse 9-11, 90317 Nürnberg - T: (0911) 2315421, Fax: 2315422, E-mail: museen@stadt.nuernberg.de, Internet: http://www.museen.nuernberg.de. Head: Dr. Franz Sonnenberger
Fine Arts Museum / Decorative Arts Museum / Historic Site - 1973
Completely furnished summer residence of the Tucher family, built in 1533, painting, glass painting, Gobelins, renaissance Hirsvogel-hall from 1535 17760

Nürtingen

Sammlung Domnick, Oberensinger Höhe 4, 72622 Nürtingen - T: (07022) 51414, Fax: 51616, E-mail: stiftung@domnick.de, Internet: http://www.domnick.de. Head: Dr. Werner Esser
Fine Arts Museum
Abstract Art 17761

Stadtmuseum Nürtingen, Wöhrtstr 1, 72622 Nürtingen - T: (07022) 36334, Fax: 36334. Head: Angela Wagner-Gnam
Local Museum
Literature dept 17762

Ober-Mörlen

Heimatmuseum Langenhain-Ziegenberg, Im Lettig 2, 61239 Ober-Mörlen - T: (06002) 50234
Local Museum - 1985
Village life, agricultural implements, early and prehist, coins - temporarily closed 17763

Ober-Ramstadt

Museum Ober-Ramstadt, Grafengasse, 64372 Ober-Ramstadt - T: (06154) 1797. Head: Otto Weber
Local Museum - 1965
School room, smithy, combs, hist of the car industry (Röhr, Falcon), coll of G.Chr. Lichtenberg (1742-1799) 17764

Oberammergau

Heimatmuseum Oberammergau, Dorfstr 8, 82487 Oberammergau - T: (08822) 94136, Fax: 32233. Head: Florian Lang
Local Museum - 1905
Toys, cribs, carvings, verre églomisé pictures 17765

Oberaudorf

Audorfer Museum im Burgtor, c/o Gemeindeverwaltung, Im Burgtor 2, 83080 Oberaudorf - T: (08033) 30120
Archaeological Museum - 1991
Early local hist, geology 17766

Galerie der Sammlung Berthold-Sames, Sudelfeldstr 31, 83080 Oberaudorf - T: (08033) 1319/14, Fax: 1319
Fine Arts Museum - 1970
Work of the sculptor Joachim Berthold (1917-1990) 17767

Oberderdingen

Heimatmuseum Oberderdingen, Im Flehinger Wasserschloß, 75038 Oberderdingen - T: (07258) 7583
Local Museum 17768

Obereisenheim

Erzgebirgischer Spielzeugwinkel, Wipfelder Str 16, 97247 Obereisenheim - T: (09386) 90159, Fax: 90154, E-mail: hohnchris@aol.com, Internet: http://www.spielzeugwinkel.dewinkel. Head: A. Walter
Fine Arts Museum / Decorative Arts Museum - 1997
Folk art from the Erzgebirge (12,000 items) 17769

Oberelsbach

Deutsches Tabakpfeifenmuseum, Marktpl 3, 97656 Oberelsbach - T: (09774) 9240, Fax: 9241, E-mail: rathaus@oberelsbach.de
Special Museum - 1996
Tobacco pipes and birthplace of the composer Valentin Rathgeber (1682-1750) 17770

Obergünzburg

Heimatmuseum Obergünzburg mit Südseesammlung, Unterer Markt 2-4, 87634 Obergünzburg - T: (08372) 92000, 1819, Fax: 920040, E-mail: kfburg@t-online.de, Internet: http://www.oberguenzburg.de
Local Museum / Ethnology Museum - 1910
Works by the painter Johann Kaspar (1822-1885), South Seas coll, Roman excavations 17771

Oberhausen-Rheinhausen

Postmuseum Rheinhausen, Hauptstr 3, 68794 Oberhausen-Rheinhausen - T: (07254) 71365, Fax: 71365. Head: Hans-Walter Reinert
Historical Museum - 1990
Postal services 17772

Oberhausen, Rheinland

Ludwig Galerie Schloß Oberhausen, Konrad-Adenauer-Allee 46, 46042 Oberhausen, Rheinland - T: (0208) 8253811, Fax: 8253813, E-mail: -sekretariat.ludwig-galerie@oberhausen.de, Internet: http://www.ludwiggalerie.de. Head: Bernhard Mensch
Fine Arts Museum - 1947/98
International contemporary art, classical art, Ludwig-Coll East German Art of 70s and 80s, worldwide Ludwig coll - education dept 17773

Rheinisches Industriemuseum, Das Museum für Industrie- und Sozialgeschichte im Rheinland/Zentrale, Hansastr 18, 46049 Oberhausen, Rheinland - T: (0208) 8579281, Fax: 8579101, E-mail: rim-service@lvr.de, Internet: http://www.lvr.de/kultur/rheinischesindustriemuseum. Head: Milena Karabaic
Historical Museum / Historic Site - 1984
Zinc factory Altenberg, living and working conditions in the heavy industry 17774

Tennismuseum Gasber, Nohlstr 82, 46045 Oberhausen, Rheinland - T: (0208) 802983
Special Museum 17775

Oberkirch

Heimat- und Grimmelshausenmuseum, Hauptstr 32, 77704 Oberkirch - T: (07802) 82246, Fax: 82179
Local Museum - 1991
Local hist, trades and guilds, Grimmelshausen memorial 17776

Oberkochen

Optisches Museum, Carl Zeiss Ausstellungszentrum, Carl-Zeiss-Str 1, 73446 Oberkochen - T: (07364) 203408, Fax: 203370, E-mail: brocksch@zeiss.de, Internet: http://www.zeiss.de. Head: Dr. Dieter Brocksch
Science&Tech Museum - 1971
Development of optical instruments 17777

Obernburg

Heimatmuseum Eisenbach, Brückenstr 4, 63785 Obernburg - T: (06022) 6910
Local Museum - 1989
Local hist 17778

Römermuseum, Untere Wallstr 29a, 63785 Obernburg - T: (06022) 619136, Fax: 619139, E-mail: stadtverwaltung@obernburg.de, Internet: http://www.obernburg.de. Head: L. Wefner
Archaeological Museum - 1996
Roman hist and finds 17779

Oberndorf am Lech

Heimatmuseum Oberndorf am Lech, Rainerstr 7, 86698 Oberndorf am Lech - T: (09002) 2685
Local Museum
Agricultural tools, local crafts 17780

Oberndorf am Neckar

Heimat- und Waffenmuseum, Klosterstr 14, 78727 Oberndorf am Neckar - T: (07423) 77126, Fax: 77111, E-mail: obd5101@oberndorf.de
Local Museum / Science&Tech Museum - 1939
Weapons, early hist, local hist 17781

Obernfeld

Heimatmuseum Obernfeld, Kirchgasse 8, 37434 Obernfeld - T: (05527) 2919, 941310, Fax: 999393, Internet: http://home.t-online.de/home/museum-obernfeld
Local Museum - 1985/92
House and farmkeeping, dairy farming 17782

Obernkirchen

Berg- und Stadtmuseum, Am Kirchpl 5, 31683 Obernkirchen - T: (05724) 39559. Head: Rolf de Groot
Local Museum
Browncoal mining, pharmacy, glassworks 17783

Stift Obernkirchen, Bergamtsstr 12, 31683 Obernkirchen - T: (05724) 8450
Religious Arts Museum 17784

Obernzell

Keramikmuseum Schloss Obernzell, Zweigmuseum des Bayerischen Nationalmuseums, Schlosspl 1, 94130 Obernzell - T: (08591) 1066, Fax: 9116150, E-mail: bay.nationalmuseum@extern.lrz.muenchen.de, Internet: http://

www.bayerisches-nationalmuseum.de. Head: Prof. Dr. Ingolf Bauer
Decorative Arts Museum - 1982
Ceramics since Neolithic period to this days 17785

Obernzenn

Blaues Schloß, Blaues Schloß Obernzenn, 91619 Obernzenn - T: (09844) 979923, Fax: 979979, E-mail: mpw@obernzenn.de. Head: Edith Schoeneck
Local Museum 17786

Uhrenmuseum Matthäus, Am Plärrer 18, 91619 Obernzenn - T: (09844) 266
Science&Tech Museum 17787

Oberostendorf

Heimatstube Gutenberg, c/o Gemeindeverwaltung, Schulstr 2, 86869 Oberostendorf - T: (08344) 597, 685, Fax: 8356
Local Museum
Town hist 17788

Oberreute

Skimuseum, Hauptstr 34, 88179 Oberreute - T: (08387) 1233, Fax: 8707, E-mail: info@oberreute.de, Internet: http://www.oberreute.de
Special Museum - 1995
Hist of skiing 17789

Oberried

Bauernhausmuseum Schniderlihof, Hofsgrund, 79254 Oberried - T: (07601) 444
Local Museum - 1972
Peasant life 17790

Oberriexingen

Römischer Weinkeller Oberriexingen, Zweigmuseum des Württembergischen Landesmuseums Stuttgart, Weilerstr 14, 71739 Oberriexingen - T: (07042) 4570, 9090. Head: Geiger
Archaeological Museum - 1962 17791

Oberrot

Sägmühlmuseum Marhördt, Wiesengrundstr 8, 74420 Oberrot - T: (07977) 740, Fax: 7444, E-mail: buergermeisteramt@oberrot.de, Internet: http://www.oberrot.de
Science&Tech Museum - 1983
Timber processing, tools 17792

Oberschleißheim

Altes Schloß Schleißheim, Oekumenische Sammlung Gertrud Weinhold "Das Gottesjahr und seine Feste", Bayrisches Nationalmuseum, Maximilianshof 1, 85764 Oberschleißheim - T: (089) 3155272, Fax: 31597403, E-mail: - stoessl.schleissheim@extern.lrz-muenchen.de, Internet: http://www.bayerisches-nationalmuseum.de. Head: Dr. Renate Eikelmann
Religious Arts Museum / Ethnology Museum / Folklore Museum
Celebration of the church around the year, religious art, icons, folk art (Eastern Europe, South America), cribs, Easter eggs worldwide 17793

Altes Schloß Schleißheim, Sammlung zur Landeskunde Ost- und Westpreußens, Bayerisches Nationalmuseum, Maximilianshof 1, 85764 Oberschleißheim - T: (089) 3155272, Fax: 31597403, E-mail: stoessl.schleissheim@extern.lrz-muenchen.de, Internet: http://www.bayerisches-nationalmuseum.de. Head: Dr. Renate Eikelmann
Historical Museum
Castle built from 1598 to 1623 with furnishings from Peter Candid, ethnology, pre-industrial implements, hist and culture of Prussia 17794

Deutsches Museum - Flugwerft Schleißheim, Museum für Luft- und Raumfahrt, Effnerstr 18, 85764 Oberschleißheim - T: (089) 3157140, Fax: 31571450, E-mail: fws@deutsches-museum.de, Internet: http://www.deutsches-museum.de/zweig/werft/fws.htm. Head: Prof. Dr. Wolf Peter Fehlhammer
Science&Tech Museum - 1992
Hist of aviation 17795

Haus der Ost- und Westpreußen, Ferdinand-Schulz-Allee 3, 85764 Oberschleißheim - T: (089) 3152513, Fax: 3153009. Head: Dr. Hannes Kaschkat
Local Museum - 1982
Hist culture and decline of Prussia 17796

Kostüm-Museum im neuen Schloß Schleißheim, Bayerisches Nationalmuseum, 85764 Oberschleißheim
Local Museum - 1999
Costumes 17797

Meißener Porzellan-Sammlung der Stiftung Ernst Schneider, Zweigmuseum des Bayerischen Nationalmuseums, Schloß Lustheim, 85764 Oberschleißheim - T: (089) 31587242, Internet: http://www.bayerisches-nationalmuseum.de. Head: Dr. Renate Hanemann
Decorative Arts Museum - 1968
One of the largest coll of Meißener porcelain in the world, china and ceramic animals dating from 1710 to the 2nd half of the 18th c 17798

Neues Schloß Schleißheim, c/o Schloß- und Gartenverwaltung Schleißheim, Max-Emanuel-Pl 1, 85764 Oberschleißheim - T: (089) 3158720, Fax: 31587250
Decorative Arts Museum
Baroque castle completed in 1720 for Prince Elector Max Emanuel, baroque furnishings, period rooms with stuccowork, 18th c gobelins - picture gallery 17799

Schloß Lustheim, c/o Schloß- und Gartenverwaltung Schleißheim, Max-Emanuel-Pl 1, 85764 Oberschleißheim - T: (089) 3158720, Fax: 31587250. Head: Max Kirmeß
Decorative Arts Museum - 1971
Baroque furnishings, paintings, frescoes, the castle was built for Prince Elector Max Emanuel in 1684 - dep of Meissen porcelain 17800

Staatsgalerie im Neuen Schloß, Bayerische Staatsgemäldesammlungen, 85764 Oberschleißheim - T: (089) 3158720, Fax: 31587250
Public Gallery - 1978
Masterpieces of European baroque painting, housed in the new Schleißheim Castle 17801

Oberstaufen

Bauernhausmuseum Knechtenhofen, Knechtenhofen 7, 87534 Oberstaufen - T: (08325) 9510
Agriculture Museum - 1979
Rustic culture and agricultural tools 17802

Färberhaus, Färberweg 1, 87534 Oberstaufen - T: (08386) 7998, 93000, Fax: 930020, E-mail: oberstaufen@t-online.de, Internet: http://www.oberstaufen.de
Special Museum 17803

Museum im Strumpferhaus, Jugetweg 10, 87534 Oberstaufen - T: (08386) 1300, 4242, 93000
Local Museum
Local hist 17804

Oberstdorf

Heimatmuseum Oberstdorf, Oststr 13, 87561 Oberstdorf - T: (08322) 5470, 2370, 5679, E-mail: info@oberstdorf-heimatmuseum.de, Internet: http://www.oberstdorf-heimatmuseum.de
Local Museum - 1932
Local crafts and hist, rustic furniture 17805

Obersulm

Museum zur Geschichte der Juden in Kreis und Stadt Heilbronn, Untere Gasse 6, 74182 Obersulm - T: (07130) 6478. Head: Dr. W. Angerbauer, Martin Ritter
Historical Museum - 1989
Judaica, hist of the Jewish community in Obersulm and Heilbronn 17806

Oberursel

Hans-Thoma-Gedächtnisstätte und Vortaunusmuseum, Marktpl 1, 61440 Oberursel - T: (06171) 502389. Head: Renate Messer
Local Museum / Fine Arts Museum - 1976
Early and pre-hist, town hist, trade workshops 17807

Oberviechtach

Dr. Eisenbarth- und Heimatmuseum, Marktpl 13, 92526 Oberviechtach - T: (09671) 30716
Local Museum - 1967 17808

Oberweißbach

Memorialmuseum Friedrich Fröbel, Markt 10, 98744 Oberweißbach - T: (036705) 62123, Fax: 62249, E-mail: Froebelstadt@t-online.de, Internet: http://www.oberweissbach.de
Special Museum - 1982 17809

Oberweißbacher Bergbahn Maschinenhalle, c/o Deutsche Bahn AG, Lichtenhain Bergbahn, 98744 Oberweißbach - T: (036705) 62038
Science&Tech Museum
Historical mountain railway 17810

Oberweser

Heimatstube Arenborn, Torweg, 34399 Oberweser - T: (05574) 1241
Local Museum
Domestic implements, trade workshops 17811

Oberwolfach

Bergbau- und Mineralienmuseum, Schulstr 5, 77709 Oberwolfach - T: (07834) 9420, Fax: 859362, E-mail: mineralienmuseum@t-online.de, Internet: http://www.mineralienmuseum.de
Natural History Museum / Science&Tech Museum - 1986
Minerals, mining 17812

Ochsenfurt

Heimatmuseum Ochsenfurt, Im Schlösschen, Brückenstr 26, 97199 Ochsenfurt - T: (09331) 9711, 5855, Fax: 9752
Local Museum - 1905
Viticulture, town hist 17813

Kartäusermuseum Tückelhausen, Konventstr 3, 97199 Ochsenfurt - T: (09331) 1451, Fax: 89584
Religious Arts Museum - 1991
Hist of Carthusian monastery 17814

Trachtenmuseum, Greisinghaus, Spitalgasse 12, 97199 Ochsenfurt - T: (09331) 9711, 5855, Fax: 9752
Folklore Museum
Costumes 17815

Trias-Museum, Judengasse 3, 97199 Ochsenfurt - T: (09331) 2873, Fax: 7385
Natural History Museum - 1981
Fossils 17816

Oderberg, Mark

Binnenschifffahrts-Museum Oderberg, Hermann-Seidel-Str 44, 16248 Oderberg, Mark - T: (033369) 470. Head: Ute Weber
Science&Tech Museum / Local Museum / Open Air Museum - 1954
Archeology, geology, local and crafts hist, shipping, shipmodels, shipbuilding, fishery, open air exposition: original boats and ships, motorboats, steamships, steam-engines, shipmotors, shipmodels 17817

Oederan

Heimatmuseum, Pfarrgasse 5, 09569 Oederan - T: (037292) 22323, Fax: 27270, E-mail: stadt.oederan@t-online.de, Internet: http://www.oederan.de
Local Museum - 1909
Local crafts, history, folk art, history of labour-movement - archive, hand weaving mill 17818

Schauwerkstatt Historische Handweberei, Richard-Wagner-Str 1, 09569 Oederan - T: (037292) 4961, Fax: 27270, E-mail: stadt.oederan@t-online.de
Science&Tech Museum 17819

Öhringen

Auto- und Motorrad-Museum, Stettiner Str 22, 74613 Öhringen - T: (07941) 8027, Fax: 608539, E-mail: oehringen@heyd.de, Internet: http://www.heyd.de. Head: Paul Heyd
Decorative Arts Museum / Science&Tech Museum - 1980
Design and artwork of the 50s and 60s, handicraft, enamel signs 17820

Weygang-Museum, Karlsvorstadt 38, 74613 Öhringen - T: (07941) 35394, Fax: 960910, Internet: http://www.oehringen.de/wegangmuseum.htm. Head: Karin Bertalan
Decorative Arts Museum - 1952
Pewterware and factory 17821

Oelsnitz, Erzgebirge

Bergbaumuseum, Pflockenstr, 09376 Oelsnitz, Erzgebirge - T: (037298) 12612, Fax: 2414, E-mail: info@bergbaumuseum.org. Head: Andrea Riedel
Science&Tech Museum - 1986
Mining, geology 17822

Museum Schloß Voigtsberg, Schloßstr 32, 09376 Oelsnitz, Erzgebirge - T: (037421) 22977
Local Museum - 1957
Local and regional history, history of carpet production 17823

Oelsnitz, Vogtland

Löwen-Drogerie und Museum, Untere Kirchstr 5, 08606 Oelsnitz, Vogtland - T: (037421) 22235, Fax: 22291, Internet: http://www.loewen-drogerie.de
Special Museum
Drugstore items 17824

Oerlenbach

Heimatmuseum Ebenhausen, Ebenhausen, Hennbergstr 6, 97714 Oerlenbach - T: (09725) 203, 71010, Fax: 710127
Local Museum - 1990 17825

Oerlinghausen

Archäologisches Freilichtmuseum Oerlinghausen, Am Barkhauser Berg 2-6, 33813 Oerlinghausen - T: (05202) 2220, Fax: 2388, E-mail: info@afm-oerlinghausen.de, Internet: http://www.afm-oerlinghausen.de. Head: M. Schmidt
Open Air Museum / Archaeological Museum - 1979
Experimental archaeology 17826

Oestrich-Winkel

Rothmühler Heimatmuseum und Archiv, Zanger Str 3, 65375 Oestrich-Winkel Hallgarten - T: (06723) 4911, Fax: 4911
Local Museum / Library with Exhibitions - 1988
Documents, manuscripts, maps, pictures, kitchen utensils, agricultural implements 17827

Östringen

Gustav-Wolf-Kunstgalerie, Am Leiberg 6, 76684 Östringen - T: (07253) 20717, Fax: 21558, E-mail: - buergermeisteramt@oestringen.de, Internet: http://www.oestringen.de
Fine Arts Museum - 1994
Prints and paintings by Gustav Wolf (1887-1947), exhibitions of modern art 17828

Historisches Heimatmuseum, Hauptstr 100, 76684 Östringen - T: (07253) 22417, Fax: 21558
Local Museum 17829

Ötisheim

Henri-Arnaud-Haus - Waldensermuseum, Henri-Arnaud-Str 27, 75443 Ötisheim - T: (07041) 7436, Fax: 863677, E-mail: Henri-Arnaud-Haus@t-online.de, Internet: http://www.waldenser.de. Head: Dr. Albert de Lange
Historical Museum - 1939
Waldenser library 17830

Oettingen

Heimatmuseum Oettingen, Hofgasse 14, 86732 Oettingen - T: (09082) 2315, Fax: 2316, E-mail: heimatmuseum@oettingen.de, Internet: http://www.heimatmuseum-oettingen.de
Local Museum - 1908
Ceramics 17831

Residenzschloß Oettingen, Schlossstr 1, 86732 Oettingen - T: (09082) 969424, Fax: 969451, E-mail: kanzlei@oettingen-spielberg.de, Internet: http://www.oettingen-spielberg.de. Head: Dr. E. Lasson
Historic Site / Decorative Arts Museum
Early baroque stucco 17832

Zweigmuseum des Staatlichen Museum für Völkerkunde, Residenzschloß Oettingen, Schlossstr 1, 86732 Oettingen - T: (09082) 3910
Ethnology Museum - 1988
Non-European ethnology 17833

Offenbach am Main

Deutsches Ledermuseum/ Schuhmuseum Offenbach - DLM, Frankfurter Str 86, 63067 Offenbach am Main - T: (069) 8297980, Fax: 810900, E-mail: info@ledermuseum.de, Internet: http://www.ledermuseum.de. Head: Dr. Christian Rathke
Decorative Arts Museum / Ethnology Museum - 1917
Leather crafts, furniture, ethnology and folk costumes, 19th c leather articles, contemporary leather art and craft, history of footwear from all over the world 17834

Klingspor-Museum, Herrnstr 80, 63065 Offenbach am Main - T: (069) 80652954, Fax: 80652669, E-mail: klingspormuseum@offenbach.de, Internet: http://www.klingspor-museum.de. Head: Dr. Stefan Soltek
Fine Arts Museum - 1953
Bookmaking arts and crafts, bookbindings, typography, posters, ex libris, carpets, callygraphy - library, archives 17835

Stadtmuseum Offenbach am Main, Parkstr 60, 63067 Offenbach am Main - T: (069) 80652446, 2646, Fax: 80652469. Head: Gerd Vollmer
Local Museum - 1917
Prehist, hist of the town, Senefelder coll dealing with the invention of lithography, ivory, fayence, paintings from local artists 17836

Offenburg

Museum im Ritterhaus, Ritterstr 10, 77652 Offenburg - T: (0781) 824255, Fax: 827521, E-mail: museum@offenburg.de, Internet: http://www.museum-offenburg.de. Head: Michael Friedmann
Local Museum - 1900
Early history, regional and town history, geology, religious art, folk art and costumes, hunting trophies, 18th-20th c paintings by local artists 17837

Städtische Galerie im Kulturforum, Amand-Goegg-Str 2, 77654 Offenburg - T: (0781) 824255, Fax: 827521, E-mail: museum@offenburg.de, Internet: http://www.offenburg.de. Head: Dr. Gerlinde Brandenburger-Eisele
Public Gallery 17838

Oftersheim

Gemeinde- und Forstmuseum, Mannheimer Str 59-61, 68723 Oftersheim - T: (06202) 5970, Fax: 55051, E-mail: rathaus@gemeinde.oftersheim.de, Internet: http://www.oftersheim.de
Local Museum - 1977
Forestry, local hist, agriculture, crafts 17839

Ohlstadt

Kaulbachatelier, Kaulbachstr 22, 82441 Ohlstadt - T: (08841) 6010, Fax: 601700, E-mail: lva-ufr@t-online.de, Internet: http://www.kaulbachvilla.de
Fine Arts Museum 17840

Ohrdruf

Museum Schloß Ehrenstein, Schloß Ehrenstein, 99885 Ohrdruf - T: (03624) 402329. Head: Peter Cramer
Local Museum - 1935
Geology, wooden toys, town hist, Johann Sebastian Bach in Ohrdruf, military training area
Ohrdruf 17841

Technisches Denkmal Tobiashammer, Suhler Str 34, 99885 Ohrdruf - T: (03624) 402792, Fax: 402792
Science&Tech Museum
Pile-drivers, steam engine 17842

Olbernhau

Denkmalkomplex Saigerhütte Olbernhau-Grünthal mit Technischem Museum und Kupferhammer → Museum Saigerhütte Olbernhau- Kupferhammer

Haus der Heimat, Markt 7, 09526 Olbernhau - T: (037360) 72180, Fax: 72180
Local Museum - 1957
Folk art, mechanical local mountains, household equipment, natural hist, crafts, toys 17843

Museum Saigerhütte Olbernhau- Kupferhammer, In der Hütte 10, 09526 Olbernhau - T: (037360) 73367, Fax: 73367, Internet: http://www.saigerhütte-olbernhau.de. Head: Peter Getter
Science&Tech Museum - 1961
Forge of 16th c, copper mine, workshops 17844

Oldenburg in Holstein

Gilde-Museum, Museumshof, Prof.-Struve-Weg 1, 23758 Oldenburg in Holstein - T: (04361) 2674, 4980, Fax: 498200, E-mail: tourist-buero@old.de, Internet: http://www.old.de. Head: Heike Müller
Historical Museum 17845

Museumshof-Galerie, Prof.-Struve-Weg 1, 23758 Oldenburg in Holstein - T: (04361) 2674, 4980, Fax: 498200, E-mail: tourist-buero@old.de, Internet: http://www.old.de. Head: Heike Müller
Public Gallery 17846

Wall-Museum, Museumshof, Prof.-Struve-Weg 1, 23758 Oldenburg in Holstein - T: (04361) 2674, 4980, Fax: 498200, E-mail: tourist-buero@old.de, Internet: http://www.old.de. Head: Heike Müller
Archaeological Museum 17847

Oldenburg, Oldenburg

Horst-Janssen-Museum, Am Stadtmuseum 4-8, 26121 Oldenburg, Oldenburg - T: (0441) 2352891, Fax: 2353350, E-mail: info@horst-janssen-museum.de, Internet: http://www.horst-janssen-museum.de. Head: Prof. Dr. Ewald Gäßler
Fine Arts Museum 17848

Landesbibliothek Oldenburg, Pferdemarkt 15, 26121 Oldenburg, Oldenburg - T: (0441) 7992800, Fax: 7992865, E-mail: lbo@lb-oldenburg.de, Internet: http://www.lb-oldenburg.de. Head: Dr. Egbert Koolman
Library with Exhibitions 17849

Landesmuseum für Natur und Mensch, Damm 38-44, 26135 Oldenburg, Oldenburg - T: (0441) 9244300, Fax: 9244399, E-mail: museum@naturundmensch.de, Internet: http://www.naturundmensch.de. Head: Prof. Dr. Mamoun Fansa
Natural History Museum / Archaeological Museum - 1836
Natural hist, minerals, flora and fauna of the region, prehist - library 17850

Landesmuseum Oldenburg, Schloß und Augusteum, Schloßpl 26, 26122 Oldenburg, Oldenburg - T: (0441) 2207300, Fax: 2207309, E-mail: info@landesmuseum-oldenburg.de, Internet: http://www.landesmuseum-oldenburg.de. Head: Dr. Bernd Küster
Local Museum / Fine Arts Museum - 1919
Modern art, gallery of old masters, medieval art, history of County and Dukedom of Oldenburg - library 17851

Oldenburger Fahrradmuseum, Donnerschweer Str 45, 26123 Oldenburg, Oldenburg - T: (0441) 8850387, Fax: 8850388. Head: Gabriele Kalkhoff
Science&Tech Museum - 1995
Historical bicycles 17852

Staatliches Museum für Naturkunde und Vorgeschichte → Landesmuseum für Natur und Mensch

Stadtmuseum Oldenburg, Am Stadtmuseum 4-8, 26121 Oldenburg, Oldenburg - T: (0441) 2352881, Fax: 2353145, E-mail: stadtmuseum@stadt-oldenburg.de, Internet: http://www.oldenburg.de. Head: Prof. Dr. Ewald Gäßler
Local Museum - 1915
Local art, cultural history and painting (17th to 19th c), graphics, classical vases and terracotta, local history - library 17853

Oppenau

Regionales Heimatmuseum für das Renchtal, Rathaus, 77728 Oppenau - T: (07804) 910830, Fax: 910832, E-mail: info@oppenau.de, Internet: http://www.badenpage.de/oppenau
Local Museum - 1938
Costumes, rural tools 17854

Oppenheim

Deutsches Weinbaumuseum, Wormser Str 49, 55276 Oppenheim - T: (06133) 2544, Fax: 70727, Internet: http://ewr.de/region/wbm/deutsche.htm. Head: Hugo Bindereif
Agriculture Museum - 1978
History of viticulture - library 17855

Oranienbaum

Kreismuseum Gräfenhainichen, Schloß, 06785 Oranienbaum - T: (034904) 259
Local Museum - 1969
Technology, crafts, regional history 17856

Schloss Oranienbaum, Kulturstiftung DessauWörlitz, 06785 Oranienbaum - T: (034904) 20259, Fax: 6461510, E-mail: ksdw@ksdw.de, Internet: http://www.ksdw.de. Head: Dr. Thomas Weiss
Fine Arts Museum
Paintings (18th-19th c) 17857

Oranienburg

Gedenkstätte und Museum Sachsenhausen, Str der Nationen 22, 16515 Oranienburg - T: (03301) 2000, Fax: 810928, E-mail: GuMS@brandenburg.de, Internet: http://www.sachsenhausen.-brandenburg.de. Head: Dr. Günter Morsch
Historical Museum - 1961
Different museums on the hist of the Nazi concentration camp (1936-45), the Soviet special camp (1945-50), history of the memorial (1950-1989), Jewish prisoners - Reference library, archive 17858

Kreismuseum Oranienburg, Breitestr 1, 16515 Oranienburg - T: (03301) 3863, Fax: 3863. Head: M. Vehma-Çiftçi
Local Museum - 1932
Ancient and early history, local history and crafts, shipping, birds, memorabilia of the chemist F.F. Runge (1795-1867), fayence 17859

Schlossmuseum Oranienburg, Stiftung Preußische Schlösser und Gärten Berlin-Brandenburg, Sclosspl 2, 16515 Oranienburg - T: (03301) 537437, Fax: 537439, Internet: htpp://www.spsg.de. Head: Dr. Burkhardt Göres
Fine Arts Museum - 2001
Art in relation to Preussen and the Netherlands, paintings by van Dyck, Thomas Willeboirts, Jan Lievens, Govert Flinck and Jan Mijtens, sculptures by François Dieussart and Gabriel Grupello, rare ivory furniture 17860

Orsingen-Nenzingen

Fastnachtmuseum Schloß Langenstein, Schwarzwaldstr 10, 78359 Orsingen-Nenzingen - T: (07771) 2175, Fax: 62280. Head: Dr. Heinrich Rehm
Folklore Museum - 1969
The celebration of carnival in the Linzgau, Bodensee, Hegau, Heuberg and Baar regions, original costumes and masks, the history of carnival - archives 17861

Ortenberg, Baden

Weinbaumuseum der Winzergenossenschaft, Winzerkellerweg 1, 77799 Ortenberg, Baden - T: (0781) 31282
Agriculture Museum 17862

Ortenberg, Hessen

Burgmuseum, Schloßpl 11, 63683 Ortenberg, Hessen - T: (06046) 1328, Fax: 7149. Head: Alexander Graf zu Stolberg-Wernigerode
Local Museum - 1956
Weapons, weights and measures, agricultural implements 17863

Musikinstrumentenmuseum Lißberg, Schloßgasse, 63683 Ortenberg, Hessen - T: (06046) 467, Fax: 941889, E-mail: kurt.racky@t-online.de, Internet: http://www.lissberg.de. Head: Kurt Reichmann
Music Museum - 1990
Hurdy-gurdies, bagpipes, coll of ethnological wind instruments, Louvet, Chedeville, Caron (famous builders of musical instruments) 17864

Ortenburg

Schloßmuseum, Vorderschloß 1, 94496 Ortenburg - T: (08542) 2174
Local Museum - 1979
Local hist 17865

Ortrand

Stadtgeschichts- und Schradenmuseum, Bahnhofstr 43, 01990 Ortrand - T: (035755) 53940, Fax: 605230, E-mail: amt-ortrand@t-online.de. Head: Reinhard Kißro
Local Museum
Early and prehist, town hist, trade and industry - Library 17866

Oschatz

Stadtmuseum Oschatz, Frongasse 1, 04758 Oschatz - T: (03435) 920285, Fax: 970277. Head: Dagmar Grundmann
Local Museum - 1897
Ancient historic finds, local hist, peasant living style, development of local scales production, scales 17867

Oschersleben

Kreismuseum, Halberstädter Str 72, 39387 Oschersleben - T: (03949) 3055, Fax: 3055. Head: Dr. Thomas Ruppel
Local Museum 17868

Osnabrück

Domschatzkammer und Diözesanmuseum, Kleine Domsfreiheit 24, 49074 Osnabrück - T: (0541) 318480/81, Fax: 318482. Head: Dr. M.-L. Schnackenburg
Religious Arts Museum / Fine Arts Museum - 1918
Sacral art objects (reliquaries, chapter crucifix, sculptures, paintings, textiles) 17869

Dreikronenhaus, Kulturgeschichtliches Museum Osnabrück, Marienstr 5, 49074 Osnabrück - T: (0541) 3232207, Fax: 3232739, E-mail: o.huesemann@osnabrueck.de, Internet: http://www.osnabrueck.de. Head: Dr. Eva Berger
Decorative Arts Museum - 2001
Decorative art and design 17870

Erich Maria Remarque-Friedenszentrum, Markt 6, 49074 Osnabrück - T: (0541) 3232109, Fax: 9692431, E-mail: remarque-zentrum@uos.de, Internet: http://www.remarque.uos.de. Head: Dr. Thomas Schneider
Historical Museum 17871

Felix-Nussbaum-Haus, Kulturgeschichtliches Museum Osnabrück, Lotter Str 2, 49078 Osnabrück - T: (0541) 3232207, Fax: 3232739, E-mail: huesemann@osnabrueck.de, Internet: http://www.osnabrueck.de. Head: Inge Jaehner
Local Museum - 1998
Felix Nussbaum coll, condemned artists - library, archives 17872

Kultur- und Kommunikationszentrum Lagerhalle Osnabrück, Rolandsmauer 26, 49074 Osnabrück
Public Gallery 17873

Kulturgeschichtliches Museum Osnabrück, Lotter Str 2, 49078 Osnabrück - T: (0541) 3232207, Fax: 3232739, E-mail: o.huesemann@osnabrueck.de, Internet: http://www.osnabrueck.de. Head: Dr. Eva Berger
Local Museum - 1879
Art and science - library, archives 17874

Kunsthalle Dominikanerkirche, Rißmüllerpl, 49074 Osnabrück - T: (0541) 3232405, Fax: 3232705, E-mail: kunsthalle@osnabrueck.de, Internet: http://www.osnabrueck.de. Head: André Lindhorst
Fine Arts Museum 17875

Museum am Schölerberg, Natur und Umwelt-Planetarium, Am Schölerberg 8, 49082 Osnabrück - T: (0541) 560030, Fax: 5600337, E-mail: ahaenel@nos.de, Internet: http://www.nostromo.physik.uni-osnabrueck.de/astro/. Head: Dr. Dietmar Grote
Natural History Museum - 1988
Regional mineralogy, geology, soil, fauna, flora, moor and biotopes 17876

Museum Industriekultur, Süberweg 50a, 49090 Osnabrück - T: (0541) 9127845, Fax: 9127847, E-mail: Museum.Industriekultur.Os@t-online.de. Head: Rolf Spilker
Historical Museum / Science&Tech Museum
Quarry and waste disposal site, exploitation of mineral resources in the 19th c 17877

Schatz von Sankt Johann, Johannisstr, 49074 Osnabrück - T: (0541) 23370
Religious Arts Museum 17878

Stadtgalerie Osnabrück, Große Gildewart 14, 49074 Osnabrück - T: (0541) 25151, Fax: 3232707
Public Gallery 17879

Ossmannstedt

Wielandgut Ossmannstedt mit Wieland-Gedenkstätte, Stiftung Weimarer Klassik, 99510 Ossmannstedt - T: (036462) 32375, E-mail: museen@weimar-klassik.de, Internet: http://www.weimar-klassik.de. Head: Erika Senf
Special Museum - 1956
Memorabilia on poet Christoph M. Wieland (1733-1813) in his former house, memorial rooms 17880

Ostbevern

Museum der historischen Waschtechnik, Schmedehausener Str 4-6, 48346 Ostbevern - T: (02532) 1400, 8217
Science&Tech Museum / Local Museum 17881

Osten

Heimat- und Buddelmuseum, Am Markt 5, 21756 Osten - T: (04771) 3682, 5254, Fax: 2725
Local Museum - 1989
Schnapps bottles, trade and industry, fishing 17882

Osterburg

Kreismuseum, Str des Friedens 21, 39606 Osterburg - T: (03937) 83730, Fax: 83730. Head: Frank Hoche
Local Museum
Geology, ancient and early history, fauna, local and industrial history, excavation finds - library 17883

Osterburken

Römermuseum, Zweigmuseum des Badischen Landesmuseums Karlsruhe, Römerstr 8, 74706 Osterburken - T: (06291) 4010, Fax: 40130. Head: Prof. Dr. Harald Siebenmorgen
Archaeological Museum - 1983
Roman finds 17884

Ostercappeln

Linnenschmidt'sche Vormals Landesherrliche Mühle zu Venne, Osnabrücker Str 4, Venne, 49179 Ostercappeln - T: (05476) 462, Fax: (05495) 1532, E-mail: Udo.Thoerner@t-online.de, Internet: http://www.os-regio.net/os/muehlen/muehlen_venne1.htm. Head: Erich Möhlmeyer
Science&Tech Museum 17885

Osterhofen

Heimatmuseum Osterhofen, Stadtpl 15, 94486 Osterhofen - T: (09932) 4030, 403115, Fax: 403175, E-mail: stadtverwaltung@osterhofen.de, Internet: http://www.osterhofen.de
Local Museum - 1978
Early and local hist, local crafts 17886

Osterholz-Scharmbeck

Museumsanlage Kulturstiftung Landkreis Osterholz, Bördestr 42, 27711 Osterholz-Scharmbeck - T: (04791) 13105, Fax: 964114, E-mail: info@kulturstiftung-ohz.de, Internet: http://www.kulturstiftung-ohz.de. Head: Dr. Karen Elisabeth Hammer
Local Museum - 1929
Local trades (cigar making and clothworking), peat cutting, shipping, bird museum 17887

Norddeutsches Vogelmuseum, Sammlung Dr. Baumeister, Bördestr 42, 27711 Osterholz-Scharmbeck - T: (04791) 13105, Fax: 964114, E-mail: info@kulturstiftung-ohz.de, Internet: http://www.kulturstiftung-ohz.de. Head: Dr. Karen-Elisabeth Hammer
Natural History Museum
Ornithology (birds from Central Europe, moor- and seabirds) 17888

Osterode am Harz

Städtisches Heimatmuseum, Rollberg 32, 37520 Osterode am Harz - T: (05522) 318351, Fax: 318201
Local Museum - 1936
Town hist, guilds and trades, Tilman Riemenschneider (*1460 in Osterode), early and prehist, geology 17889

Osterwieck

Heimatmuseum, Markt 1, 38835 Osterwieck - T: (039421) 29441, Fax: 72263
Local Museum - 1930
Geology, ancient history, local history, crafts 17890

Ostfildern

Städtische Galerie im Rathaus Ruit, Otto-Vatter-Str 12, Ruit, 73760 Ostfildern - T: (0711) 3404236, Fax: 3404201, E-mail: Stadt.Ostfildern@t-online.de
Public Gallery 17891

Ostheim vor der Rhön

Orgelbaumuseum, Paulinenstr 20, 97645 Ostheim vor der Rhön - T: (09777) 1743, Fax: 1743. Head: Sigruth Strobel
Music Museum - 1994
Organ coll and organ workshop 17892

Ostseebad Ahrenshoop

Galerie Peters-Barenbrock im Haus Elisabeth von Eicken, Dorfstr 39, 18347 Ostseebad Ahrenshoop - T: (038220) 6990, Fax: 69924, E-mail: galerie@elisabethvoneicken.de, Internet: http://www.elisabethvoneicken.de. Head: Sabine Peters-Barenbrock
Public Gallery 17893

Kunstkaten Ahrenshoop, Strandweg 1, 18347 Ostseebad Ahrenshoop - T: (038220) 80308, Fax: 80307, E-mail: ahrenshoop@kunstkaten.de, Internet: http://www.kunstkaten.de. Head: Sabine Jastram-Porsche
Public Gallery 17894

Neues Kunsthaus Ahrenshoop, Bernhard-Seitz-Weg 3a, 18347 Ostseebad Ahrenshoop - T: (038220) 80726, Fax: 82495, E-mail: post@neues-kunsthaus-ahrenshoop.de, Internet: http://www.neues-kunsthaus-ahrenshoop.de. Head: Gerlinde Creutzburg
Public Gallery 17895

Strandhalle Ahrenshoop, Dorfstr 16b, 18347 Ostseebad Ahrenshoop - T: (038220) 82522, Fax: 82523
Public Gallery 17896

Ostseebad Binz

Berliner Hundemuseum, Villa Saxonia II, Wylichstr 8, 18609 Ostseebad Binz - T: (038393) 21559. Head: Klau-Dieter Moldenhauer
Special Museum - 1999 17897

Fälschermuseum, c/o Galerie Jahreszeiten, Margaretenstr 20, 18609 Ostseebad Binz - T: (038393) 13112
Special Museum 17898

Jagdschloß Granitz, 18609 Ostseebad Binz - T: (038393) 2263, Fax: 21283. Head: Klaus-Dieter Mickschat
Historical Museum - 1959
History of Rügen, cultural development, feudal epoch 17899

Museum zum Anfassen, Museumsmeile, Objektstr Prora, Block 4, 18609 Ostseebad Binz - T: (038393) 32640
Science&Tech Museum 17900

NVA-Museum, Objektstr Prora, Block 3, 18609 Ostseebad Binz - T: (038393) 32696, Fax: 32696
Military Museum 17901

Prora-Museum, Museumsmeile, Objektstr Prora, Block 3, 18609 Ostseebad Binz - T: (038393) 32640
Historical Museum 17902

Rügen-Museum, Objektstr Prora, Block 3, 18609 Ostseebad Binz - T: (038393) 32696, Fax: 32696
Local Museum 17903

Wasserwelt Erlebnismuseum, Museumsmeile, Objektstr Prora, Block 5, 18609 Ostseebad Binz - T: (038393) 32640
Science&Tech Museum / Natural History Museum 17904

Ostseebad Prerow

Darß-Museum, Waldstr 48, 18375 Ostseebad Prerow - T: (038233) 69750, Fax: 69750. Head: Antje Hückstädt
Natural History Museum / Folklore Museum - 1953
Geology, botany, marine algae, forestry, fishing, shipping, ethnography - National park Vorpommersche Boddenlandschaft 17905

Ostseebad Rerik

Heimatmuseum der Stadt Rerik, Dünenstr 4, 18230 Ostseebad Rerik - T: (038296) 78294, Fax: 78513, E-mail: Ostseebad-Rerikt-online.de, Internet: http://www.rerik.de
Local Museum - 1953
Ancient and early hist, local hist, fishing equipment 17906

Ostseebad Zingst

Heimatmuseum Haus Morgensonne, Strandstr 1, 18374 Ostseebad Zingst - T: (038232) 15561
Local Museum - 1953
Historic interior, ship model, sailors' memorabilia, local history 17907

Ottendorf bei Sebnitz

Technisches Denkmal Neumannmühle, Kirnitzschtalstr 3, 01855 Ottendorf bei Sebnitz - T: (035022) 40796
Science&Tech Museum
Sawmill 17908

Ottenhöfen

Das Mühlendorf, Mühlenrundweg, 77883 Ottenhöfen - T: (07842) 80444, Fax: 80445, E-mail: Tourist-Info@Ottenhoefen.de, Internet: http://www.ottenhoefen.de
Special Museum / Agriculture Museum / Science&Tech Museum - 1982
Different types of mills 17909

Otterndorf

Das Kranichhaus Museum, Museum des alten Landes Hadeln, Reichenstr 3, 21762 Otterndorf - T: (04751) 91480, Fax: 914891. Head: Dr. Axel Behne
Local Museum / Historical Museum - 1934 17910

Studio A Otterndorf, Museum gegenstandsfreier Kunst des Landkreises Cuxhaven, Sackstr 4, 21762 Otterndorf - T: (04751) 6309, Fax: 6377, E-mail: studio-a@otterndorf.de, Internet: http://www.studio-a.de. Head: Dr. Ulrike Schick
Fine Arts Museum - 1974
Concrete art, classics, gesticulary painting, zero, drawings, graphics, sculptures 17911

Torhaus Otterndorf, Sammlung Labiau/Ostpreußen, Am Großen Specken 6, 21762 Otterndorf - T: (04751) 3850. Head:
Local Museum - 1962
Regional hist 17912

Ottersberg

Museum Heimathaus Irmintraut, Kirchstr 2, Fischerhude, 28870 Ottersberg - T: (04293) 7186
Local Museum - 1934
Agricultural implements and tools 17913

Otto Modersohn Museum, Fischerhude, In der Bredenau 95, 28870 Ottersberg - T: (04293) 328, Fax: 1435, E-mail: info@modersohn-museum.de, Internet: http://www.modersohn-museum.de. Head: Christian Modersohn
Fine Arts Museum - 1974
Memorabilia of the painter Otto Modersohn (1865-1945), paintings, drawings, diaries, letters, documents 17914

Ottobeuren

Klostermuseum der Benediktiner-Abtei, Sebastian-Kneipp-Str 1, 87724 Ottobeuren - T: (08332) 7980, Fax: 798125, Internet: http://www.abtei-ottobeuren.de. Head: Rupert Prusinovsky
Religious Arts Museum / Fine Arts Museum / Historical Museum - 1881
library 17915

Staatsgalerie in der Benediktiner-Abtei, Bayerische Staatsgemäldesammlungen, Sebastian-Kneipp-Str 1, 87724 Ottobeuren - T: (08332) 7980, Fax: 798125. Head: Dr. Helge Siefert
Fine Arts Museum - 1966
Gothic, Renaissance, baroque and rococo paintings 17916

Ottobrunn

Otto-König von Griechenland-Museum, Rathausstr 3, 85521 Ottobrunn - T: (089) 60808104, Fax: 51604468. Head: Prof. Dr. Jan Murken
Historical Museum - 1976
Objects concerning the relation between Bavaria and Greece 17917

Otzberg

Museum Otzberg, Sammlung zur Volkskunst in Hessen, Veste Otzberg, 64853 Otzberg - T: (06162) 71114, Fax: 71114, Internet: http://www.otzberg.de/kultur/museum. Head: Gerd J. Grein
Ethnology Museum / Folklore Museum - 1974
Ethnography, folk art, costumes, ceramics, toys 17918

Ovelgönne

Norddeutsches Handwerkermuseum, Breite Str 27, 26939 Ovelgönne - T: (04401) 81955, Fax: 81955. Head: Gabriele Speckels
Historical Museum / Folklore Museum - 1981
Trades and shops 17919

Paderborn

Baugeschichte der ehemaligen Fürstbischöflichen Residenz Schloß Neuhaus, Ausstellung im Remter des Schlosses, Residenzstr 2, 33104 Paderborn - T: (05251) 881062, Fax: 881041, E-mail: staedtische-galerien@paderborn.de, Internet: http://www.paderborn.de/kunstundkultur/kunstundkultur-haupt.htm. Head: Dr. Andrea Wandschneider, Dr. Norbert Börste
Historical Museum 17920

Erzbischöfliches Diözesanmuseum und Domschatzkammer, Markt 17, 33098 Paderborn - T: (05251) 125400, Fax: 125495, E-mail: erzb.pb.mus@t-online.de, Internet: http://www.dioezesanmuseum.paderborn.de. Head: Prof. Dr. Christoph Stiegemann
Religious Arts Museum - 1853
9th-19th c sculpture, paintings, textiles, folk art, icons, bells, glass art, treasury - library, archives, restoration workshop 17921

Heinz Nixdorf MuseumsForum, Fürstenallee 7, 33102 Paderborn - T: (05251) 306600, Fax: 306609, E-mail: info@hnf.de, Internet: http://www.hnf.de. Head: Norbert Ryska, Dr. Kurt Beiersdörfer
Science&Tech Museum - 1996
Hist of information technology from 3000 BC to the 20th c, arithmetical instruments, calculating machines, desk and pocket calculators, writing instruments, typewriters, accounting machines, telephones, computers 17922

Historisches Museum im Marstall, Marstallstr 9, Schloß Neuhaus, 33104 Paderborn - T: (05254) 80152, Fax: 80141, E-mail: n.boerste@paderborn.de, Internet: http://www.paderborn.de/kultur.htm. Head: Dr. Norbert Börste
Historical Museum / Military Museum - 1994
Development of the Paderborn borough of Schloß Neuhaus from the Stone Age t o the present (finds, documents, art objects) 17923

Museum für Stadtgeschichte im Adam-und-Eva-Haus, Hathumarstr 7, 33098 Paderborn - T: (05251) 881350, Fax: 881350, Internet: http://www.paderborn.de. Head: Dr. Andrea Wandschneider, Christoph Gockel-Böhner
Local Museum
Town hist, finds, documents, art objects 17924

Museum in der Kaiserpfalz, Am Ikenberg, 33098 Paderborn - T: (05251) 10510, Fax: 281892, E-mail: kaiserpfalz@lwl.org, Internet: http://www.lwl.org/wmfa. Head: Prof. Dr. Matthias Wemhoff
Archaeological Museum 17925

Naturkundemuseum im Marstall, Marstallstr 9, Schloß Neuhaus, 33104 Paderborn - T: (05251) 881052, Fax: 881041, E-mail: k.wollmann@paderborn.de, Internet: http://www.paderborn.de/kunstundkultur/kunstundkultur-haupt/htm. Head: Dr. Andrea Wandschneider, Dr. Klaus Wollmann
Natural History Museum - 1994 17926

Städtische Galerie, Sammlung des 20. Jahrhunderts, Am Abdinghof 11, 33098 Paderborn - T: (05251) 881247, Fax: 882141, E-mail: staedtische-galerien@paderborn.de, Internet: http://www.paderborn.de/kultur.htm. Head: Dr. Andrea Wandschneider
Public Gallery 17927

Städtische Galerie in der Reithalle, Marstallstr 12, Schloß Neuhaus, 33104 Paderborn - T: (05251) 881076/77, Fax: 881061, E-mail: staedtische-galerien@paderborn.de, Internet: http://www.paderborn.de/kunstundkultur/kunstundkultur-haupt.htm. Head: Dr. Andrea Wandschneider
Public Gallery - 1994 17928

Panschwitz-Kuckau

Ćišinski-Gedenkstätte, Ćišinskistr 16, 01920 Panschwitz-Kuckau - T: (035796) 96091, E-mail: gku2243009@AOL.com. Head: Alfons Kuring, Gertrud Kuring
Special Museum 17929

Serbski muzej - Sorbisches Museum (open while reconstrucion until October 2002), Kloster Sankt Marienstein, 01920 Panschwitz-Kuckau, mail addr: Postfach 1346, 02603 Bautzen - T: (03591) 42403, Fax: 42425, Internet: http://www.sorben-wenden.de. Head: Tomasz Nawka
Historical Museum / Folklore Museum / Local Museum
History, traditional way of life, art, music, literature of the Sorbians - library 17930

Pansfelde

Museum Burg Falkenstein, Stiftung Schlösser, Burgen und Gärten des Landes Sachsen-Anhalt, 06543 Pansfelde - T: (034743) 8135, Fax: 61942, E-mail: museum-burg-falkenstein@t-online.de, Internet: http://www.kulturserver.de. Head: Joachim Schymalla
Local Museum / Historic Site - 1946
Furniture, paintings, hunting weapons 17931

Papenburg

Dokumentations- und Informationszentrum Emslandlager (DIZ), Wiek rechts 22, 26871 Papenburg - T: (04961) 916306, Fax: 916308, E-mail: mail@diz-emslandlager.de, Internet: http://www.diz-emslandlager.de. Head: Kurt Buck
Historical Museum
Hist of the concentration camps, prison camps, camps for prisoners of war in Emsland (1933-1945) - library, archive 17932

Emslandmuseum Papenburg, Museum für Industrie und Technik, Ölmühlenweg 21, 26871 Papenburg - T: (04961) 992266, Fax: 5840, E-mail: -emslandmuseum.papenburg@ewetel.net, Internet: http://www.ewetel.net/~emslandmuseum.papenburg. Head: Dr. Claus Veltmann
Science&Tech Museum - 1995
Hist of industry and transport 17933

Heimatmuseum Papenburg, Hauptkanal rechts 13, 26871 Papenburg - T: (04961) 916416, 916444
Local Museum
Town hist 17934

Pappenheim

Burg Pappenheim mit Naturmuseum und Historischen Museum, c/o Gräflich Pappenheim'sche Verwaltung, Burg, 91788 Pappenheim - T: (09143) 83890, Fax: 6445, E-mail: graefl.verw.pappenheim@t-online.de, Internet: http://www.burgpappenheim.de. Head: Dr. Albrecht Graf von und zu Egloffstein
Historical Museum / Natural History Museum
Gottfried Heinrich Graf zu Pappenheim, field marshal 30-yeary war - Botanical garden, herb garden 17935

Burgmuseum mit Folterkammer und Naturmuseum → Burg Pappenheim mit Naturmuseum und Historischen Museum

Parchim

Moltke-Gedächtnisstätte, Museum der Stadt Parchim, Lange Str 28, 19370 Parchim - T: (03871) 267748, E-mail: www.museum@parchim.de. Head: Wolfgang Kaelcke
Historical Museum - 1994
Memorabilia of the field marshal Helmuth Graf von Moltke in his birthplace 17936

Museum der Stadt Parchim, Lindenstr 38, 19370 Parchim - T: (03871) 213210, Fax: 212843, E-mail: www.museum@parchim.de. Head: Wolfgang Kaelcke
Local Museum - 1974
Ancient, early and local hist 17937

Parsberg

Burg-Museum, Untere Burg, 92331 Parsberg - T: (09492) 1505, Fax: 941830. Head: Theodor Döllinger
Historical Museum / Folklore Museum
Early and modern local hist, crafts, religious folklore, rustic furniture 17938

Partenstein

Ahler Kråm - Volkskundliche Sammlung, Am Herrenhof 8, 97846 Partenstein - T: (09355) 972120, Fax: 972122. Head: Dr. Wolfgang Nätscher
Folklore Museum / Local Museum
Local hist, crafts and agricultural tools 17939

Parthenstein

Feuerwehrmuseum Grethen, Steinberger Str 1, Grethen, 04668 Parthenstein - T: (03437) 763448, Fax: 913647
Science&Tech Museum
Hist of fire fighting 17940

Pasewalk

Museum der Stadt Pasewalk und Künstlergedenkstätte Paul Holz, Prenzlauer Str 23a, 17309 Pasewalk - T: (03973) 433182
Fine Arts Museum
Memorabilia of the West-Pommeranian painter Paul Holz 17941

Passau

Ausstellungsraum Sankt Anna-Kapelle, Heiliggeistgasse 4, 94032 Passau - T: (0851) 37659, 396506, Fax: 37641, E-mail: contact@kunstverein-passau.de, Internet: http://www.kunstverein-passau.de. Head: Franz X. Scheuerecker
Fine Arts Museum 17942

Domschatz- und Diözesanmuseum, Residenzpl 8, 94032 Passau - T: (0851) 393374, Fax: 393840. Head: Franz S. Gabriel
Religious Arts Museum - 1989
Religious objects and art 17943

Museum Moderner Kunst - Stiftung Wörlen, Bräugasse 17, 94032 Passau - T: (0851) 3838790, Fax: 38387979, E-mail: info@woerlen-mmk.de, Internet: http://www.mmk-passau.de. Head: Hanns Egon Wörlen
Fine Arts Museum - 1988 17944

Neue Sammlung, Rathauspl 2, 94032 Passau - T: (0851) 396224, Fax: 396481, E-mail: christa.hartl@passau.de. Head: Christa Hartl
Fine Arts Museum
Contemporary art 17945

Oberhausmuseum Passau, Oberhaus, Sankt Georgsberg 125, 94034 Passau - T: (0851) 493350, Fax: 4933510, E-mail: oberhausmuseum@passau.de, Internet: http://www.oberhausmuseum.de. Head: Dr. Richard Loibl
Local Museum / Fine Arts Museum - 1905
Local hist, folk art, religious items, weapons, development of fire fighting (17th-20th c), porcelain, shipping, sculptor Prof. Hans Wimmer 17946

Passauer Glasmuseum, Am Rathauspl, 94032 Passau - T: (0851) 35071, Fax: 31712, E-mail: info@rotel.de, Internet: http://www.glasmuseum.de. Head: Georg Höltl
Decorative Arts Museum - 1985
Bohemian glasses from 1700-1950, cookery book coll 17947

Römermuseum Kastell Boiotro, Archäologische Staatssammlung - Museum für Vor- und Frühgeschichte, Lederergasse 43, 94032 Passau - T: (0851) 34769, Fax: 32241, E-mail: joerg-peter.niemeier@passau.de, Internet: http://www.stadtarchaeologie.de. Head: Prof. Dr. Ludwig Wamser
Archaeological Museum - 1986
Roman archaeology 17948

Pattensen

Schloß Marienburg, Schulenburg, 30982 Pattensen - T: (05069) 407, Fax: 7852. Head: Karl-Ludwig Riechert
Historical Museum
Neo-Gothic castle and furniture, paintings, arms and armour, porcelain 17949

Paulinzella

Jagdschloß Paulinzella, Museum zur Geschichte des Klosters sowie zur Forst- und Jagdgeschichte (reopen October 2002), Nr 3, 07422 Paulinzella, mail addr: c/o Klosterruine und Museum im Jagdschloß, Postfach 142, 07393 Rudolstadt
Historical Museum
History of the cloiser, forrest and hunting history 17950

Peenemünde

Historisch-Technisches Informationszentrum, Im Kraftwerk, 17449 Peenemünde - T: (038371) 5050, Fax: 505111, E-mail: HTI@peenemuende.de, Internet: http://www.peenemuende.de. Head: D. Zache
Historical Museum / Science&Tech Museum / Open Air Museum / Historic Site
Local hist, place where the German physicist Wernher von Braun developed the rocket types V1 and V2 for Hitler's warfare in the early 1940s 17951

Pommersches Bettenmuseum, Flugplatzmuseum Peenemünde, Am Flugplatz 3, 17449 Peenemünde - T: (038371) 28295, Fax: 28295, Internet: http://www.pommerngreif.de/frei/einr/kultur/bettenmu/index.html. Head: Joachim Saathoff
Special Museum 17952

Peine

Kreismuseum Peine mit Kreisarchiv, Stederdorfer Str 17, 31224 Peine - T: (05171) 401500, Fax: 401608, E-mail: kreismuseum.peine@landkreis-peine.de, Internet: http://www.kreismuseum-peine.de. Head: Dr. Ulrika Evers
Local Museum - 1988
Economic, social, cultural and regional hist, early and prehist 17953

SchokoMuseum in SchokoLand, Wilhelm-Rausch-Str 4, 31228 Peine - T: (05171) 990120
Special Museum 17954

Peißenberg

Bergbaumuseum Peißenberg, Am Tiefenstollen 2, 82380 Peißenberg - T: (08803) 5102, Fax: 690150, Internet: http://www.museum-in-bayern.de/dfs/museum.php?820. Head: Konrad Fünfgelder
Science&Tech Museum - 1988
Hist of mining, geology 17955

Peiting

Museum im Klösterle, Kapellenstr 1, 86971 Peiting - T: (08861) 6535
Special Museum
History of skiing 17956

Peitz

Eisenhüttenmuseum, Schulstr 6, 03185 Peitz - T: (035601) 22080, Fax: 81515, E-mail: Peitz@Peitz.de, Internet: http://www.Peitz.de
Science&Tech Museum 17957

Pellworm

Inselmuseum, Uthlandstr 2, 25849 Pellworm - T: (04844) 189
Local Museum 17958

Penzberg

Bergwerksmuseum, Karlstr 36-38, 82377 Penzberg - T: (08856) 4722, Fax: 4722
Science&Tech Museum
Hist of mining 17959

Stadtmuseum, Karlstr 61, 82377 Penzberg - T: (08856) 933856, 813124
Local Museum 17960

Penzlin bei Waren

Johann-Heinrich-Voss-Gedenkstätte → Museum Alte Burg Penzlin

Museum Alte Burg Penzlin, Am Wall 15, 17217 Penzlin bei Waren - T: (03962) 210494, Fax: 210135. Head: Dr. Andrea Rudolp
Special Museum
Magic 17961

Perl

Museum Römische Villa Nennig, 66706 Perl. Head: Dr. Alfons Kolling
Archaeological Museum 17962

Perleberg

Heimatmuseum, Mönchort 7-11, 19348 Perleberg - T: (03876) 612964, Fax: 612259
Local Museum - 1905
Ancient and early hist, local hist, crafts, trades, photographer Max Zeisig (1867-1937), letters, photographs and records of opera singer Lotte Lehmann (1888-1976) - library, photo archive 17963

Petersberg bei Halle, Saale

Museum Petersberg, Hallesche Str 28, 06193 Petersberg bei Halle, Saale - T: (034606) 20229, Fax: 35778, E-mail: foerderverein-petersberg@t-online.de. Head: Bernd Hartwich
Local Museum
Regional hist, cultural and social hist of the farm population 17964

Petershagen, Weser

Heimat- und Heringsfängermuseum Heimsen, Am Mühlenbach 9, 32469 Petershagen, Weser - T: (05768) 479
Local Museum / Special Museum 17965

Pfaffenhausen

Heimatmuseum Pfaffenhausen, Hauptstr 30, 87772 Pfaffenhausen - T: (08265) 1389
Local Museum - 1987
Old shoemaker's workshop, forge and colonial store 17966

Pfaffenhofen an der Ilm

Dichtermuseum Joseph Maria Lutz, Platzl 2, 85276 Pfaffenhofen an der Ilm - T: (08441) 9605. Head: Franz Rutsch
Special Museum - 1987
Library and study of the poet Joseph Maria Lutz (1893-1972) 17967

Lebzelterei- und Wachsziehereimuseum, Hauptpl 6, 85276 Pfaffenhofen an der Ilm - T: (08441) 9787
Special Museum - 1986
Hist of gingerbread production, religious objects made out of wax 17968

Museum im Mesnerhaus, Scheyerer Str 5, 85276 Pfaffenhofen an der Ilm - T: (08441) 27442, 3722, Fax: 27443, E-mail: heimatmuseum.paf@landratsamt-paf.de, Internet: http://landkreis.pfaffenhofen.de. Head: Martin Sedlmeier
Local Museum / Folklore Museum - 1978
Religious art and folk art of the region 17969

Pfaffenhofen an der Roth

Hermann-Köhl-Museum, Kirchpl 6, 89284 Pfaffenhofen an der Roth - T: (07302) 96000, Fax: 960096, E-mail: vg-pfaffenhofen.a.d.Roth@online.de, Internet: http://www.markt-pfaffenhofen.de. Head: Bernd Weiß
Special Museum
Documents and photographs of Hermann Köhl (1888-1938). Köhl was amongst the first to cross the Atlantic Ocean by plane in 1928. 17970

Pfaffenweiler

Dorfmuseum, Rathausgasse 4, 79292 Pfaffenweiler - T: (07664) 7027, Fax: 6287
Local Museum - 1967/1983
Viticulture, quarry work 17971

Pfarrkirchen

Heimathaus Pfarrkirchen, Stadtpl 1, 84347 Pfarrkirchen - T: (08561) 30680, Fax: 30681, E-mail: info@Pfarrkirchen.de, Internet: http://www.pfarrkirchen.de
Local Museum - 1918
Early and town hist, crafts 17972

Kulturzentrum Hans-Reiffenstuel-Haus, Bahnhofspl, 84343 Pfarrkirchen - T: (08561) 970877-5428, Fax: 30681, E-mail: info@Pfarrkirchen.de. Head: Hans Kremsreiter
Special Museum - 1997
Estate of the artist Hans Reiffenstuel - Library, music school 17973

Pforzheim

Mineralienmuseum Pforzheim-Dillweißenstein, Hirsauer Str 224, 75180 Pforzheim - T: (07231) 391391. Head: M. Kramer
Natural History Museum - 1979
Mineralogy, hist of mining 17974

Schmuckmuseum Pforzheim im Reuchlinhaus, Jahnstr 42, 75173 Pforzheim - T: (07231) 392126, Fax: 391441, E-mail: schmuckmuseum@stadt-pforzheim.de, Internet: http://www.schmuckmuseum-pforzheim.de. Head: Dr. Fritz Falk
Decorative Arts Museum - 1961
Ancient and modern jewellery, coll of finger rings - library, archives 17975

Stadtmuseum Pforzheim, Westliche Karl-Friedrich-Str 243, 75172 Pforzheim - T: (07231) 392559, Fax: 392740. Head: Dr. A. Hübner
Local Museum
Trades and guilds 17976

Technisches Museum der Pforzheimer Schmuck- und Uhrenindustrie, Bleichstr 81, 75173 Pforzheim - T: (07231) 392869, Fax: 26249. Head: F. Wurster
Science&Tech Museum - 1983
Clocks and watches, jewelry 17977

Pfronten

Heimatkundliche Sammlung, Heimathaus, Kirchsteige 1, 87459 Pfronten - T: (08363) 6980, Fax: 69855, E-mail: info@pfronten.de, Internet: http://www.pfronten.de
Local Museum - 1995
Local crafts and rustic furniture 17978

Pfullingen

Mühlenmuseum, Josefstr 5, 72793 Pfullingen - T: (07121) 703208, Fax: 703213, E-mail: info@Pfullingen.de, Internet: http://www.Pfullingen.de. Head: Martin Fink
Science&Tech Museum 17979

Stadtgeschichtliches Museum, Griesstr 24, 72793 Pfullingen - T: (07121) 703208, Fax: 703213, E-mail: info@Pfullingen.de, Internet: http://www.Pfullingen.de. Head: Martin Fink
Local Museum - 1974 17980

Württembergisches Trachtenmuseum, Josefstr 5, 72793 Pfullingen - T: (07121) 703208, Fax: 703213, E-mail: info@Pfullingen.de, Internet: http://www.Pfullingen.de. Head: Martin Fink
Ethnology Museum - 1988
Costumes in Württemberg 17981

Pfungstadt

Städtisches Museum, Borngasse 7, 64319 Pfungstadt - T: (06157) 930495, Fax: 930494. Head: Helga Hake
Local Museum - 1973
Early and pre-history, agricultural implements, Roman objects 17982

Philippsburg

Festungs- und Waffengeschichtliches Museum, Schlachthausstr 2, Senator Dr.-Burda-Haus, 76661 Philippsburg - T: (07256) 87210, Fax: 87119, Internet: http://www.philippsburg.de. Head: Rainer Schröder
Historical Museum / Military Museum - 1978
Development of the construction of fortresses, coins, weapons 17983

Heimatmuseum Philippsburg, Hieronymus-Nopp-Schule, 76661 Philippsburg - T: (07256) 7443, Fax: 939496
Local Museum - 1924 17984

Pinneberg

Stadtmuseum Pinneberg, Dingstätte 25, Altes Amtsgericht, 25421 Pinneberg - T: (04101) 207465, Fax: 211566
Local Museum 17985

Pirna

Richard-Wagner-Museum Graupa, Richard-Wagner-Str 6, 01796 Pirna - T: (03501) 548229, Fax: 548206. Head: Dr. Christian Mühne, Annette Weirauch
Music Museum - 1907
Memorabilia of Richard Wagner, historical musical instruments 17986

Stadtmuseum Pirna, Klosterhof 2-3, 01796 Pirna - T: (03501) 527985, Fax: 556266, E-mail: info@pirna.de, Internet: http://www.pirna.de. Head: Manfred Hickmann
Local Museum - 1861
Graphics, coins, photos, local and regional culture 17987

Pittenhart

Herz'sche Heimatstiftung Hilgerhof, Hilgerhof, 83132 Pittenhart - T: (08624) 2143, 2172
Local Museum
Rustic furniture, crafts 17988

Planegg

Deutsches Skimuseum, Hubertusstr 1, 82152 Planegg - T: (089) 85790270, Fax: 85790294, E-mail: fds@ski-online.de, Internet: http://www.ski-online.de
Special Museum - 1985
Hist of skiing 17989

Plauen

Galerie im Malzhaus, Alter Teich 9, 08527 Plauen - T: (03741) 153232, Fax: 153231, E-mail: galerie@kunstverein-plauen.de, Internet: http://www.kunstverein-plauen.de
Public Gallery - 1995 17990

Plauener Spitzen Museum, Altes Rathaus, Altmarkt, 08523 Plauen - T: (03741) 222355, Fax: 281192, E-mail: bv.plauenerspitze@t-online.de, Internet: http://www.exclusives-ambiente.de. Head: Dietrich Wetzel
Decorative Arts Museum / Special Museum / Science&Tech Museum 17991

Vogtlandmuseum Plauen, Nobelstr 9-13, 08523 Plauen - T: (03741) 2912401, Fax: 2912409, E-mail: poststelle@plauen.de. Head: Anette Schwohl
Local Museum - 1923
Historic rooms, geology, personal colls Hermann Vogel, Julius Mosen - library 17992

Pleinfeld

Heimat- und Brauereimuseum, Kirchenpl 3, 91785 Pleinfeld - T: (09144) 92000, Fax: 920050, E-mail: pleinfeld@gmx.de, Internet: http://www.pleinfeld.de
Local Museum / Science&Tech Museum - 1984
Town hist, photographs, crafts and hist of brewing 17993

Pleystein

Katharinas Puppenhaus, Hagenmühle im Zotbachtal, 92714 Pleystein - T: (09658) 1260, 381
Decorative Arts Museum - 1998 17994

Mineralien- und Heimatmuseum, Marktpl 25, 92714 Pleystein - T: (09654) 1515
Natural History Museum / Local Museum - 1967 17995

Pliezhausen

Dorfmuseum Ahnenhaus, Entenhof 17, 72124 Pliezhausen - T: (07127) 9770, Fax: 977160, E-mail: markus.conzelmann@pliezhausen.de, Internet: http://www.pliezhausen.de
Local Museum - 1978
Peasant life, construction of heating systems and chimneys 17996

Plochingen

Galerie der Stadt Plochingen, Neues Rathaus, Schulstr 7, 73207 Plochingen - T: (07153) 7005204, Fax: 7005199, E-mail: rathaus@plochingen.de, Internet: http://www.plochingen.de
Public Gallery 17997

Plön

Museum des Kreises Plön mit norddeutscher Glassammlung, Johannisstr 1, 24306 Plön - T: (04522) 744391, Fax: 744393, E-mail: post@kreismuseum-ploen.de, Internet: http://www.kreismuseum-ploen.de. Head: Dr. Hans-Joachim Kruse
Local Museum / Decorative Arts Museum - 1955
Glass coll, pre and early hist, ceramics, handicraft, apothecary equipment, marksmanship 17998

Plößberg

Krippenstube-Heimatstube, Jahnstr 1, Rathaus, 95703 Plößberg - T: (09636) 92110, Fax: 921133, E-mail: maploess@tirnet.de, Internet: http://www.ploessberg.de
Local Museum / Religious Arts Museum - 1980
Cribs 17999

Pobershau

Schaubergwerk Zum Tiefen Molchner Stolln, Amtsseite Dorfstr 67, 09496 Pobershau - T: (03735) 62522, Fax: 62522
Science&Tech Museum - 1934
Tin and silver mining 18000

Pockau

Technisches Museum Ölmühle, Mühlenweg 8, 09509 Pockau - T: (037367) 31319, Fax: 31318, E-mail: Pockau.Erzgebirge@t-online.de
Science&Tech Museum - 1970
Oil-mill used for processing flax and rape 18001

Pocking

Rottauer Museum für Fahrzeuge, Wehrtechnik und Zeitgeschichte bis 1948, Rottau 11a, 94060 Pocking - T: (08531) 32900, 3510, Fax: 32900
Military Museum / Science&Tech Museum - 1994 18002

Polling, Kreis Weilheim

Heimatmuseum, Rathaus, Kirchpl 11, 82398 Polling, Kreis Weilheim - T: (0881) 5778
Local Museum - 1929
Early and local hist, religious handicrafts and agricultural tools 18003

Pommersfelden

Schloß Weissenstein, Schloß 1, 96178 Pommersfelden - T: (09548) 98180, Fax: 981818, E-mail: info@schoenborn.de, Internet: http://www.schoenborn.de. Head: Dorothee Feldmann
Fine Arts Museum / Historic Site
Dutch/ Flemish paintings (16th-18th c), Italian paintings 18004

Poppenhausen, Wasserkuppe

Sieblos-Museum Poppenhausen, Paläontologisch-geologisches Museum, Von-Steinrück-Pl 1, 36163 Poppenhausen, Wasserkuppe - T: (06658) 96000, Fax: 960022, E-mail: info@poppenhausen-wasserkuppe.de, Internet: http://www.poppenhausen-wasserkuppe.de. Head: Prof. Dr. Erlend Martini
Natural History Museum - 1994
Geology, paleontology 18005

Postbauer-Heng

Heimatmuseum Postbauer-Heng, Centrumstr 11, 92353 Postbauer-Heng - T: (09188) 94060, Fax: 1884
Local Museum - 1987
Local hist and peasant life 18006

Posterstein

Museum Burg Posterstein, Posterstein 83, 04626 Posterstein - T: (034496) 22595, Fax: 22595
Local Museum - 1953
Hist of city and castle, crafts, peasant household objects 18007

Potsdam

Altes Rathaus Kulturhaus Potsdam, Am Alten Markt 9, 14467 Potsdam - T: (0331) 293112
Public Gallery 18008

Berliner S-Bahn-Museum, Rudolf-Breitscheid-Str 203, 14482 Potsdam - T: (030) 78705511, Fax: 78705510, E-mail: igeb@igeb.org, Internet: http//www.igeb.org/seiten/sbmuseum.htm
Science&Tech Museum - 1997 18009

E. v. Kameke Museum, Persiusstr, 14469 Potsdam - T: (0331) 2705966
Fine Arts Museum 18010

Filmmuseum Potsdam, Marstall am Lustgarten, 14467 Potsdam - T: (0331) 271810, Fax: 2718126, E-mail: info@filmmuseum-potsdam.de, Internet: http://www.filmmuseum-potsdam.de. Head: Dr. Bärbel Dalichow
Performing Arts Museum - 1981
Film cameras, projectors, scripts, photographs, costumes, drawings 18011

Potsdam-Museum, Natur-Geschichte-Kunst, Breite Str 8-12, 14467 Potsdam - T: (0331) 2896600, Fax: 2896608. Head: Dr. Monika Bierschenk
Natural History Museum / Local Museum - 1909
Geology, native flora and fauna, glass, pewter, smithwork, numismatics, paintings, decorative arts, history of Potsdam 18012

Stiftung Preußische Schlösser und Gärten Berlin-Brandenburg, Park Sanssouci (Schloß Sanssouci, Neue Kammern, Chinesisches Haus, Neues Palais, Schloß Charlottenhof, Römische Bäder, Normannischer Turm, Orangerieschloß, Historische Mühle), Neuer Garten (Schloß Cecilienhof mit Historischer Stätte der Potsdamer Konferenz, Marmorpalais, Gotische Bibliothek), Park Babelsberg (Schloß Babelsberg, Flatowturm), Moschee (Dampfmaschinenhaus), Belvedere Pfingstberg, Pomonatempel, Jagdschloß Stern, Schloß und Park Caputh, Schloß und Park Rheinsberg, Schloß und Park Sacrow, Schloß und Park Königs Wusterhausen, Schloß Paretz, Schloß Oranienburg, Park Charlottenburg (Schloß Charlottenburg, Schinkelpavillon, Mausoleum, Belvedere), Park Glienicke (Schloß Glienicke, Casino), Jagdschloß Grunewald, Allee nach Sanssouci 5, 14471 Potsdam - T: (0331) 96940, Fax: 9694101, E-mail: Pressereferat@spsg.de, Internet: http://www.spsg.de. Head: Dr. Thomas Köstlin, Dr. Gabriele Horn, Dr. Burkhard Göres, Prof. Dr. Michael Seiler, Dr. Alfons Schmidt
Fine Arts Museum / Decorative Arts Museum - 1995
Painting collection, sculpture collection, furniture collection, graphic art collection, KPM (Berlin porcelain collection and archive), applied art collection, cast iron collection, historic libraries, collection of 19th century Raffael copies, Dohna-Schlobitten collection 18013

Pottenstein

Fränkische-Schweiz-Museum, Am Museum 5, 91278 Pottenstein - T: (09242) 1640, Fax: 1056, E-mail: info@fsmt.de, Internet: http://www.fsmt.de. Head: Rainer Hofmann
Local Museum - 1985
Paleontology, guilds, judaica, original synagogue of the 18th c, medieval excavations, handicraft, costume, furniture 18014

Museum Burg Pottenstein, 91278 Pottenstein - T: (09243) 7221, Fax: 7332, E-mail: burg.pottenstein@t-online.de, Internet: http://www.burgpottenstein.de. Head: Margit Freifrau von Winzingerode
Local Museum 18015

Preetz, Holstein

Erstes Circusmuseum in Deutschland, Mühlenstr 14, 24211 Preetz, Holstein - T: (04342) 1869, 81114, Fax: 84964, Internet: http://www.circus-museum.de. Head: Axel Peers-Gloyer
Performing Arts Museum - 1974
Ernst Jakob Renz, Circus Barum, Malmström 18016

Kloster-Kunstsammlung, 24211 Preetz, Holstein
Fine Arts Museum 18017

Prenzlau

Jakob-Philipp-Hackert Ausstellung, Uckerwiek 813, 17291 Prenzlau - T: (03984) 865100, Fax: 865169, E-mail: mailbox@dominikanerkloster-prenzlau.de, Internet: http://www.dominikanerkloster-prenzlau.de. Head: Dirk Keil
Fine Arts Museum
Paintings of landscapes 18018

Kulturhistorisches Museum Prenzlau, Uckerwiek 813, 17291 Prenzlau - T: (03984) 865130/132, Fax: 865169, E-mail: mailbox@dominikanerkloster-prenzlau.de, Internet: http://www.dominikanerkloster-prenzlau.de. Head: Cäcilia Genschow
Local Museum / Historical Museum - 1899/1957
Historic rooms, medieval cultural hist, ancient and early hist - library, photogr archive 18019

Pressath

Heimatmuseum Pressath, Kemnather Str 2, 92690 Pressath - T: (09644) 8695, 418
Local Museum - 1964
Local hist 18020

Prettin

Kreismuseum Wittenberg, Schloß Lichtenburg, 06922 Prettin - T: (035386) 22382, Fax: 22134. Head: Kerstin Drabow
Historical Museum / Historic Site - 1974 18021

Preußisch Oldendorf

Feuerwehrmuseum Schröttinghausen, Dahlinghauser Str 5, 32361 Preußisch Oldendorf - T: (05742) 2814, Fax: 5680, E-mail: pr.oldendorf@t-online.de, Internet: http://www.preussischoldendorf.de
Science&Tech Museum 18022

Prichsenstadt

Privatmuseum Hans Klein, Hauptstr 28, 97357 Prichsenstadt - T: (09383) 7008
Natural History Museum / Agriculture Museum - 1982
Mineralogy, fossils and agricultural tools 18023

Prien

Galerie im Alten Rathaus, Alte Rathausstr 22, 83209 Prien - T: (08051) 92928, Fax: 60669
Fine Arts Museum - 1985
Painter 19th-20th c, "Chiemseemaler" 18024

Heimatmuseum Prien, Friedhofweg 1, 83209 Prien - T: (08051) 690542, Fax: 690540, E-mail: info@prien.chiemsee.de, Internet: http://www.prien.chiemsee.de
Local Museum - 1913
Local crafts and hist 18025

Prieros

Heimatmuseum, Dorfaue 1, 15752 Prieros - T: (033768) 50144
Local Museum - 1955
Ancient and early history, local history 18026

Pritzwalk

Heimatmuseum, Magazinpl 8, 16928 Pritzwalk - T: (03395) 302802, Fax: 760814, Internet: http://www.staedtenetz.prignitz.de. Head: Dr. Rolf Rehberg
Local Museum - 1954
Local and regional hist, industrial history (brewery, clothing industry) 18027

Pulsnitz

Stadtmuseum Pulsnitz, Goethestr 20a, 01896 Pulsnitz - T: (035955) 44006. Head: C. Reppe
Local Museum - 1904
Local and regional history 18028

Putbus

Galerie des Landkreises Rügen, Circus 1, 18581 Putbus - T: (038306) 62958, Fax: 62958
Public Gallery
Contemporary art, installations, graphics, sculpture, photography 18029

Quakenbrück

Stadtmuseum Quakenbrück, Markt 7, 49610 Quakenbrück - T: (05431) 6777, Fax: 3183. Head: Heinrich Böning
Local Museum - 1978
Town hist, trade, school hist, scales - archive 18030

Quedlinburg

Domschatz der Sankt Servatius-Stiftskirche, Schloßberg 9, 06484 Quedlinburg - T: (03946) 3552, Fax: 3552. Head: Werner Bley
Religious Arts Museum 18031

Fachwerkbaumuseum im Ständerbau, Städtische Museen Quedlinburg, Wordgasse 3, 06472 Quedlinburg - T: (03946) 3828, Fax: 515975. Head: Christian Mühldorfer-Vogt
Fine Arts Museum - 1975
Framework 18032

Galerie Kunsthoken der Stadt Quedlinburg, Marktstr 2, 06484 Quedlinburg - T: (03946) 905666, Fax: 2119
Public Gallery 18033

Historische Bibliothek, Städtische Museen Quedlinburg, Schloßberg 1, 06472 Quedlinburg - T: (03946) 2730, Fax: 515975. Head: Christian Mühldorfer-Vogt
Library with Exhibitions 18034

Holzwurm-Museum, Halberstädter Str 47, 06484 Quedlinburg
Special Museum 18035

Klopstock Museum, Städtische Museen Quedlinburg, Schloßberg 12, 06472 Quedlinburg - T: (03946) 2610, Fax: 515975. Head: Christian Mühldorfer-Vogt
Special Museum - 1898
Memorabilia of Friedrich Klopstock (1724-1803) in house of his birth, memorabilia of physician Dorothea C. Erxleben (1715-1762), memorabilia of sports teacher J.C. GutsMuths (1759-1839), memorabilia of Carl Ritter (1779-1839), hist of culture, medicine and gender 18036

Lyonel-Feininger-Galerie, Finkenherd 5a, 06484 Quedlinburg - T: (03946) 2238, 2384, Fax: 2384, Internet: http://www.feininger-galerie.de. Head: Dr. Ingrid Wernecke
Fine Arts Museum
Graphic art coll of Lyonel Feininger 18037

Schloßmuseum, Städtische Museen Quedlinburg, Schloßberg 1, 06472 Quedlinburg - T: (03946) 2730, Fax: 515975. Head: Christian Mühldorfer-Vogt
Local Museum - 1929
Early German history, lapidarium, costumes, painting, coins, arms, hist of the city of Quedlinburg - historical library 18038

Querfurt

Museum Burg Querfurt, Burg, 06268 Querfurt - T: (034771) 52190, Fax: 521999. Head: Johanna Rudolph
Local Museum - 1910
Ancient history, castle and city history - farm museum 18039

Rabenau, Sachsen

Stuhlbau- und Heimatmuseum, Lindenstr 2, 01734 Rabenau, Sachsen - T: (0351) 6413611, Fax: 6413611, E-mail: museumrabenau@t-online.de
Local Museum / Special Museum - 1922
Chairs since the Renaissance, tools, local hist, technology of chair production 18040

Radeberg

Museum Schloß Klippenstein, Schloßstr 6, 01454 Radeberg - T: (03528) 442600, Fax: 455785, E-mail: stadtverwaltung@radeberg.de. Head: Katja Altmann
Local Museum - 1953
Geology, ancient hist, city views, pewter, locks 18041

Radebeul

Karl-May-Museum, Karl-May-Str 5, 01445 Radebeul - T: (0351) 8373010, Fax: 8373055, E-mail: kmay@karl-may-museum.de, Internet: http://www.karl-may-museum.de. Head: René Wagner
Historical Museum - 1928
Indians of North America, tools, weapons, costumes, jewelry, trophies and cult objekts, books from Karl May 18042

Puppentheatersammlung, Staatliche Kunstsammlungen Dresden, Barkengasse 6, 01445 Radebeul - T: (0351) 8387571, Fax: 8387571, Internet: http://www.staatl-kunstsammlungen-dresden.de. Head: Dr. Johannes Just
Performing Arts Museum - 1952 18043

Weingutmuseum Hoflößnitz, Knohllweg 37, 01445 Radebeul - T: (0351) 8398333, Fax: 8308356, E-mail: weinmuseumweinmuseum.de, Internet: http://www.weinmuseum.de. Head: Ingrid Zeidler
Agriculture Museum - 1924
Hist rooms, wine industry, painting, cooperage, basket-making 18044

Radeburg

Heimatmuseum, Heinrich-Zille-Str 9, 01471 Radeburg - T: (035208) 4341, Fax: 96125
Local Museum - 1928
Ancient history, local history, crafts, industry, drawings by local native artist Heinrich Zille (1858-1929) 18045

Radolfzell

Stadtmuseum Radolfzell, Tegginger Str 16, 78315 Radolfzell - T: (07732) 81390, Fax: 81411, E-mail: museum@radolfzell.de, Internet: http://www.radolfzell.de. Head: Achim Fenner
Local Museum - 1909
Joseph Victor von Scheffel 18046

Raesfeld

Museum Raesfeld, Schloßfreiheit 19, 46348 Raesfeld - T: (02865) 1667
Local Museum 18047

Rahden

Museumshof, Lange Str 9, 32369 Rahden - T: (05771) 2282, 7317, Fax: 7350, E-mail: info@rahden.de, Internet: http://www.rahden.de. Head: Magdalene Kottenbrink
Agriculture Museum / Open Air Museum - 1966
Linen production, costumes 18048

Rain am Lech

Gebrüder-Lachner-Museum, Kirchpl 7, 86641 Rain am Lech - T: (09090) 7030, Fax: 4529, E-mail: info@rain.de, Internet: http://www.rain.de. Head: Harald J. Mann
Special Museum - 1989
Documents and manuscripts by composer Franz Lachner (1803-1890) and his brothers 18049

Heimatmuseum Rain am Lech, Oberes Eck 3, 86641 Rain am Lech - T: (09090) 7030, Fax: 4529, E-mail: Stadt_Rain@t-online.de, Internet: http://www.rain.de
Local Museum - 1988
Town hist 18050

Rainau

Freilichtmuseum am Rätischen Limes, Schloßberg 12, 73492 Rainau - T: (07961) 90020, Fax: 900222, E-mail: info@rainau.de, Internet: http://www.rainau.de
Open Air Museum - 1969 18051

Raisting

Heimatmuseum Alter Pfarrhof, Herrenstr 3, 82399 Raisting - T: (08807) 6155, 91347, Fax: 91347
Local Museum - 1990 18052

Kulturhaus der Otto-Hellmeier-Stiftung, Wielenbacher Str, 82399 Raisting - T: (089) 165903, (08807) 7145
Fine Arts Museum - 2001 18053

Rammenau

Museum Barockschloß Rammenau, Schloß Rammenau, 01877 Rammenau - T: (03594) 703559, Fax: 705983, E-mail: info@barockschloss-rammenau.com, Internet: http://www.barockschloss-rammenau.com. Head: Roswitha Förster
Special Museum - 1967
Memorabilia on philosopher Johann G. Fichte (1762-1814), letters, pictures, literature 18054

Randersacker

Steinhauermuseum, Historischer Mönchshof, 97236 Randersacker - T: (0931) 705317, 706593
Special Museum 18055

Ranis

Museum Burg Ranis, Burg Ranis, 07389 Ranis - T: (03647) 413345, Fax: 423945, E-mail: rathaus@stadt-ranis.de, Internet: htpp://www.stadt-ranis.de. Head: Klaus Schache
Local Museum - 1957
Geology, ancient hist, Old- and new Stone Age finds, seismology 18056

Ransbach-Baumbach

Töpfermuseum Im alten Kannenofen, c/o Zöller GmbH Eulerhof, Töpferstr 1, 56235 Ransbach-Baumbach - T: (02623) 2316, Fax: 80216, Internet: http://www.keramik.de/eulerhof. Head: Michael Gerharz
Decorative Arts Museum - 1986
Hist of ceramics and earthenware, salt varnished earthenware, historical tools, earthenware kiln classified as an historical monument 18057

Rasdorf

Landschaftsinformationszentrum (LIZ) Hessisches Kegelspiel Rasdorf, Großentafter Str 10, 36169 Rasdorf - T: (06651) 96010, Fax: 960120, E-mail: info@rasdorf.de, Internet: http://www.rasdorf.de. Head: Kurt Schloßbauer
Natural History Museum - 1994
Geology, walking trails acc to various themes 18058

Rastatt

Erinnerungsstätte für die Freiheitsbewegungen in der deutschen Geschichte, Herrenstr 18, 76437 Rastatt - T: (07222) 771390, Fax: 771397, E-mail: -erinnerungsstaette@barch.ra.uunet.de, Internet: http://www.erinnerungsstaette-rastatt.de. Head: Prof. Dr. Wolfgang Michalka
Historical Museum - 1974
Documents on the revolution of 1848/49 - library 18059

Pagodenburg Rastatt, In der Pagodenburg, 76437 Rastatt - T: (07222) 22625
Historical Museum 18060

Riedmuseum, Stadtmuseum Rastatt, Kirchpl 6, 76437 Rastatt - T: (07222) 972440, Fax: 972128, E-mail: kultur@rastatt.de, Internet: http://www.rastatt.de. Head: I. Baumgärtner
Natural History Museum / Open Air Museum - 1994
Agriculture, peasant life, crafts, river-bett correction of the Rhine, typical farming house 18061

Schloß Favorite, Staatliche Schlösser und Gärten Baden-Württemberg, 76437 Rastatt - T: (07222) 41207, Fax: 41207, Internet: http://www.schloesser-magazin.de. Head: Dr. W. Wiese
Decorative Arts Museum - 1962
Furniture, ceramics 18062

Stadtmuseum Rastatt, Herrenstr 11, 76437 Rastatt - T: (07222) 972440, Fax: 972128, E-mail: kultur@rastatt.de, Internet: http://www.rastatt.de. Head: Iris Baumgärtner
Local Museum - 1895/1983
Early and ancient hist, local hist 18063

Städtische Galerie Fruchthalle Rastatt, Kaiserstr 48, 76437 Rastatt - T: (07222) 972441/43, Fax: 972466, E-mail: galerie@rastadt.de. Head: Dr. Ingeborg Ströle-Jegge
Fine Arts Museum - 1993
Contemporary art, art in Baden after 1945, foundation Lütze, coll Westermann 18064

Wehrgeschichtliches Museum Rastatt, Schloß, Herrenstr 18, 76437 Rastatt - T: (07222) 34244, 31958, Fax: 30712, E-mail: hermes@wgm-rastatt.de, Internet: http://www.wgm-rastatt.de. Head: Dr. Joachim Niemeyer

Military Museum - 1934
Documents on the German armed forces from the 18th c to present times, uniforms. medals, arms - library 18065

Rathenow

Kreismuseum, Rhinower Str 19d, 14712 Rathenow - T: (03385) 512681, Fax: 512681. Head: Dr. Bettina Götze
Local Museum - 1909
Optical instruments, memorabilia of Johann Heinrich August Duncker (1767-1843) in his birthplace, pre- and early hist, folklore 18066

Ratingen

Museum der Stadt Ratingen, Peter-Brüning-Pl 1, 40878 Ratingen - T: (02102) 982442, Fax: 98383, E-mail: stadt@ratingen.de, Internet: http://www.ratingen.de. Head: Dr. U. Mildner
Local Museum / Public Gallery
Local hist, dolls, toys, art, art hist 18067

Oberschlesisches Landesmuseum, Bahnhofstr 62, 40883 Ratingen - T: (02102) 9650, Fax: 965240, E-mail: osl@oberschlesisches-landesmuseum.de, Internet: http://www.hoesel-info.de/oberschlesisches-landesmuseum. Head: Dr. Nikolaus Gussone
Local Museum
Eichendorff Coll, cultural hist of Upper Silesia, esp historical topography, industrial hist, faience, cast iron works of art, traditional costumes 18068

Rheinisches Industriemuseum, Außenstelle Ratingen, Cromforder Allee 24, 40878 Ratingen - T: (02102) 870309, Fax: 849720, E-mail: ebolenz@mail.lvr.de, Internet: http://www.lvr.de. Head: Dr. Eckhard Bolenz
Historical Museum - 1984
Cotton spinning mill Brügelmann (oldest factory on the continent), fashion in the 18th c 18069

Rattenberg

Heimatmuseum, Hauptstr 12a, 94371 Rattenberg - T: (09963) 94100, Fax: 941033
Local Museum - 1992 18070

Ratzeburg

A. Paul Weber-Museum, Domhof 5, 23909 Ratzeburg - T: (04541) 860720, Fax: 860710, E-mail: kreismuseum-rz@t-online.de, Internet: http://www.weber-museum.de. Head: Dr. Klaus J. Dorsch
Fine Arts Museum - 1974
Graphic arts - lithographical workshop 18071

Ernst Barlach Museum Altes Vaterhaus, Barlachpl 3, 23909 Ratzeburg - T: (04541) 3789, Fax: 84722. Head: Klaus Tiedemann
Fine Arts Museum - 1956
Sculpture, drawings, lithographs, woodcuts by Ernst Barlach (1870-1938), memorabilia of the artist, letters, documents, in a house (built 1840) where E. Barlach lived from 1878 to 1884 - clipping archive 18072

Kreismuseum Herzogtum Lauenburg, Domhof 12, 23909 Ratzeburg - T: (04541) 86070, Fax: 860710, E-mail: kreismuseum-rz@t-online.de. Head: Dr. Klaus J. Dorsch
Local Museum 18073

Stiftung Mecklenburg, Domhof 41, 23909 Ratzeburg - T: (04541) 83668, Fax: 858379. Head: Dr. Klaus Lüders
Local Museum 18074

Rauenberg

Winzermuseum Rauenberg, Alte Kirchgasse 1a, 69231 Rauenberg - T: (06222) 61970. Head: G. Geißler
Agriculture Museum - 1970
Viticulture, crafts 18075

Raunheim

Heimatmuseum Raunheim, Mainstr 25, 65479 Raunheim - T: (06142) 402286
Local Museum - 1963
Sacral objects of art, town hist, - Library 18076

Rauschenberg

Dorfmuseum Daniel-Martin-Haus, Winterseite, 35282 Rauschenberg - T: (06425) 1517, Internet: http://welcome.to/schwabendorf
Local Museum / Folklore Museum
Hist of religious refugees from France who arrived in 1687, hosiery and cloth making, milliner's, genealogy 18077

Heimatmuseum Rauschenberg, Schloßstr 1, 35282 Rauschenberg - T: (06425) 6245, Fax: 6330
Local Museum - 1989
Town hist, trade and agricultural implements, furniture from the 19th c 18078

Ravensburg

Feuerwehrmuseum Ravensburg, Charlottenstr 40, 88212 Ravensburg - T: (0751) 24445. Head: S. Schmid
Science&Tech Museum - 1983
Fire fighting 18079

Städtische Galerie, Am Gespinstmarkt, 88212 Ravensburg - T: (0751) 82203, 82109, Fax: 82165, E-mail: kultur@ravensburg.de, Internet: http://www.ravensburg.de. Head: Dr. Thomas Knubben
Fine Arts Museum 18080

Städtisches Museum Vogthaus, Charlottenstr 36, 88212 Ravensburg - T: (0751) 82201, Fax: 82550, E-mail: andreas.schmauder@ravensburg.de. Head: Dr. Andreas Schmauder
Local Museum - 1955
Trades and guilds, local hist 18081

Verlagsmuseum der Unternehmensgruppe Ravensburger, Marktstr 26, 88212 Ravensburg - T: (0751) 860, Fax: 861657, Internet: http://www.ravensburger.de
Special Museum
Hist of the parlour game and toy factory since 1883 18082

Ravenstein

Jörg-Metzler-Stube, Baltenberg, 74747 Ravenstein - T: (06297) 219
Local Museum 18083

Reckahn

Gedenkstätte und Schulmuseum F.E. v. Rochow → Schlossmuseum Reckahn

Schlossmuseum Reckahn, Dorfstr 37, 14778 Reckahn - T: (033835) 60672, Fax: 60665, E-mail: schloss.reckahn@t-online.de, Internet: http://www.reckahn.de. Head: Silke Siebrecht
Historical Museum / Historic Site
Englightenment, reform of education and agriculture 18084

Recklinghausen

Ikonen-Museum, Museen der Stadt Recklinghausen, Kirchpl 2a, 45657 Recklinghausen - T: (02361) 501941, Fax: 501942, E-mail: haustein@ikonen-museum.com, Internet: http://www.kunst-in-recklinghausen.de. Head: Dr. Ferdinand Ullrich
Fine Arts Museum - 1956
13th-19th c Russian icons, Greek icons, Coptic coll, Romanian glass icons, religious cult objects and liturgical vestments of the Orthodox church, in an 18th c building 18085

Städtische Kunsthalle, Museen der Stadt Recklinghausen, Große-Perdekamp-Str 25-27, 45657 Recklinghausen - T: (02361) 501935, 501931, Fax: 501932, E-mail: kunst.re@t-online.de, Internet: http://www.kunst-in-recklinghausen.de. Head: Dr. Ferdinand Ullrich
Fine Arts Museum - 1950
International contemporary art, 'junger westen' group, kinetic art objects, 20th-c Westphalian art - library 18086

Vestisches Museum, Hohenzollernstr 12, 45659 Recklinghausen - T: (02361) 501946, Fax: 501932, E-mail: kunst.re@t-online.de, Internet: http://www.kunst-in-recklinghausen.de. Head: Dr. Ferdinand Ullrich
Local Museum / Fine Arts Museum - 1925/87
Regional and local hist, pre- and early hist, sculptures and paintings incl Flemish, Dutch and Westphalian objects, numismatics, geology, regional native art - library 18087

Regen

Museum im fressenden Haus - Burgkasten Weißenstein, Weißenstein, 94209 Regen - T: (09921) 5106. Head: Heinz Wölfl
Local Museum - 1984
Study of the poet Siegfried von Vegesack (1888-1974), coll of snuffboxes 18088

Niederbayerisches Landwirtschaftsmuseum, Schulgasse 2, 94209 Regen - T: (09921) 5710, Fax: 60433. Head: Dr. Helmut Bitsch
Agriculture Museum - 1988
Agricultural hist of Lower Bavaria 18089

Regensburg

Brückturm-Museum über der 'Steinernen Brücke', Arbeitskreis Schiffartsmuseum Regensburg e.V, Weiße-Lamm-Gasse 1, 93047 Regensburg - T: (09417) 52510, Fax: 9459118. Head: Dr. Horst Erbguth, Rosemarie Völkl
Historic Site - 2000 18090

Diözesanmuseum Sankt Ulrich, Dompl 2, 93047 Regensburg - T: (0941) 595322530, 51688, Fax: 595322531, E-mail: museum@bistum-regensburg.de, Internet: http://www.bistumsmuseen-regensburg.de. Head: Dr. Hermann Reidel
Religious Arts Museum - 1986
Religious graphic 16th-20th c 18091

Domschatzmuseum, Krauterermarkt 3, 93047 Regensburg - T: (0941) 595322530, Fax: 595322531, 57645, E-mail: museum@bistum-regensburg.de, Internet: http://www.bistumsmuseen-regensburg.de. Head: Dr. Hermann Reidel
Religious Arts Museum - 1974
Church treasury of the cathedral in the rooms of the former bishop's palace, including goldsmith work, reliquaries, vestments and religious arts and crafts - library 18092

Donau-Schiffahrts-Museum-Regensburg, Arbeitskreis Schiffartsmuseum Regensburg e.V, Liegeplatz Werftstr, 93059 Regensburg, mail addr: Postfach 110510, 93018 Regensburg - T: (0941) 52510, Fax: 9459118. Head: Dr. Horst Erbguth, Rainer Ehm
Science&Tech Museum / Open Air Museum - 1983
Shipping, inland water navigation - archiv, library 18093

Fürst Thurn und Taxis Marstallmuseum, Emmeramspl 6, 93047 Regensburg - T: (0941) 5048133, Fax: 5048140, E-mail: uweiss@thurnundtaxis.de, Internet: http://www.thurnundtaxis.de. Head: Dr. Martin Dallmeier
Historical Museum - 1927
Coaches, carriages and vehicles (18th-20th c), uniforms of the prince's servants, sleighs, litters, harnesses 18094

Fürst Thurn und Taxis Schloßmuseum - Museum Kreuzgang, Emmeramspl 5, 93047 Regensburg - T: (0941) 5048133, Fax: 5048140, E-mail: uweiss@thurnundtaxis.de, Internet: http://www.thurnundtaxis.de. Head: Dr. Martin Dallmeier
Historical Museum - ca 1930
Furnishings and furniture from the former princely residences at Brussels and Frankfurt, 17th-c tapestries from Brussels, paintings (18th-19th c), cloister with Romanic and Gothic architectural frames 18095

Fürst Thurn und Taxis Zentralarchiv und Hofbibliothek, Emmeramspl 5, 93047 Regensburg - T: (0941) 5048132, Fax: 5048140, E-mail: mdallmeier@thurnundtaxis.de, Internet: http://www.thurnundtaxis.de. Head: Dr. Martin Dallmeier
Library with Exhibitions 18096

Historisches Museum Regensburg, Museen der Stadt Regensburg, Dachaupl 2-4, 93047 Regensburg - T: (0941) 5071440, Fax: 5074449, E-mail: museen_der_stadt@regensburg.de, Internet: http://www.museen-regensburg.de. Head: Dr. Martin Angerer
Historical Museum 18097

Karthaus-Prüll Museen des Bezirksklinikums Regensburg, Ludwig-Thomas-Str 14, 93053 Regensburg - T: (0941) 9411947, E-mail: bruno.feldmann@bkr.regensburg.de
Special Museum - 1997 18098

Kepler-Gedächtnishaus, Museen der Stadt Regensburg, Keplerstr 5, 93047 Regensburg - T: (0941) 5071440/42, Fax: 5074449, E-mail: museen_der_stadt@regensburg.de, Internet: http://www.museen-regensburg.de. Head: Dr. Martin Angerer
Fine Arts Museum - 1962
House of Johannes Kepler, mathematician and astronomer, who died here in 1630, documents on Kepler's life and work 18099

Museum Ostdeutsche Galerie, Dr.-Johann-Maier-Str 5, 93049 Regensburg - T: (0941) 297140, Fax: 2971433, E-mail: mogregensburg@t-online.de, Internet: http://www.mog-regensburg.de. Head: Dr. Pavel Liška
Fine Arts Museum - 1970
Painting, graphics, sculpture, topographical coll of Eastern Germany (Lovis Corinth, Käthe Kollwitz, Max Pechstein, Emil Orlik) - library 18100

Naturkundemuseum Ostbayern, Am Prebrunntor 4, 93047 Regensburg - T: (0941) 5073446, Fax: 5073445, E-mail: fun@naturkundemuseum-regensburg.de. Head: Dr. Hansjörg Wunderer
Natural History Museum - 1961
Entomology, ornitholog, natural hist from the Eastern Bavarian region 18101

Reichstagsmuseum, Museen der Stadt Regensburg, Rathauspl 1, 93047 Regensburg - T: (0941) 5071442, Fax: 5074449, E-mail: museen_der_stadt@regensburg.de, Internet: http://www.museen-regensburg.de. Head: Dr. Martin Angerer
Historical Museum - 1910
Documentation on the hist of the 'Reichstag' in Regensburg, esp of the 'Immerwährender Reichstag' (1663-1803), and on jurisprudence - library, archives 18102

Staatsgalerie im Leeren Beutel, Bayerische Staatsgemäldesammlungen, Bertoldstr 9, 93047 Regensburg - T: (0941) 5072440
Fine Arts Museum
German paintings (19th c) 18103

Städtische Galerie Leerer Beutel, Museen der Stadt Regensburg, Bertoldstr 9, 93047 Regensburg - T: (0941) 5071440/42, Fax: 5074449, E-mail: museen_der_stadt@regensburg.de, Internet: http://www.museen-regensburg.de. Head: Dr. Martin Angerer
Fine Arts Museum - 1980
Works of the "Spur", art of Eastern Bavaria 18104

Thurn und Taxis Museum, Bayerisches Nationalmuseum, Emmeramspl 6, Schloß Sankt Emmeram, Marstallgebäude, 93047 Regensburg - T: (0941) 5048133, 5048242, Fax: 5048140, E-mail: bay.nationalmuseum@extern.lrz-muenchen.de, Internet: http://www.bayerisches-nationalmuseum.de. Head: Dr. Renate Eikelmann
Fine Arts Museum 18105

Uhrenmuseum, Ludwigstr 3, 93047 Regensburg - T: (0941) 5999595, Fax: 5999596, E-mail: uhrenmuseum@muehlbacher.de, Internet: http://www.muehlbacher.de. Head: Peter Mühlbacher
Science&Tech Museum - 1997 18106

Regenstauf

Rot-Kreuz-Museum, Marktpl 9a, 93128 Regenstauf - T: (09402) 4405, Fax: 4405
Special Museum - 1998 18107

Sangerberger Heimatstube, Bahnhofstr 13, 93128 Regenstauf - T: (09402) 5090
Local Museum - 1988
Hist of German expellees 18108

Rehau

Feuerwehrmuseum, Goethestr 12, 95111 Rehau - T: (09283) 9705, Fax: 9705
Historical Museum - 1983
Firebrigade 18109

Mechanische Schau-Werkstätte, Angergässchen 2, 95111 Rehau - T: (09283) 1647. Head: Dietrich Metzner
Science&Tech Museum 18110

Museumszentrum-Rehau, Rehauer,- Schlesicher,- Ascher Heimatstuben und Roßbacher Weberstuben, Maxpl 7, 95111 Rehau - T: (09283) 1647, 2027, Fax: 2060, E-mail: info@stadt-rehau.de, Internet: http://www.stadt-rehau.de. Head: Dietrich Metzner
Local Museum / Science&Tech Museum
Town hist, crafts and hist of German expellees 18111

Rehburg-Loccum

Dinosaurier-Freilichtmuseum Münchehagen, Alte Zollstr 5, 31547 Rehburg-Loccum - T: (05037) 2073, Fax: 5739, E-mail: dino-park@t-online.de, Internet: http://www.dinopark.de. Head: Bernd Wolter
Natural History Museum
Palaentology, Copies of life-size dinosaurs 18112

Reichelsheim, Odenwald

Regionalmuseum Reichelsheim Odenwald, Rathauspl 7, 64385 Reichelsheim, Odenwald - T: (06164) 2369, E-mail: Gemeinde@reichelsheim.de, Internet: http://www.reichels-heim.museum.com. Head: Wolfgang Schwinn
Local Museum - 1976
Equipped rooms, trade implements, mining, local railway organization, trad. schoolroom 18113

Reichenau an der Pulsnitz

Heimatmuseum, Königsbrücker Str 22, 01936 Reichenau an der Pulsnitz - T: (035795) 2588
Local Museum - 1930
Local and regional history 18114

Reichenau, Baden

Museum Reichenau, Ergat 1, 78479 Reichenau, Baden - T: (07534) 92070, Fax: 920777. Head: Karl Wehrle
Local Museum
Agriculture, carnival, local hist, viticulture, water-bird coll, faksimiles, rural life 18115

Schatzkammer des Münsters, Mittelzell, Burgstr, 78479 Reichenau, Baden - T: (07534) 249. Head: Josef Christ
Religious Arts Museum - 1443
Crosses, reliquaries, Gothic ciborium and late antique ivory vessel, book art, chalices, incense vessels, monstrances, liturgical vestments, stained glass windows, architectural fragments 18116

Reichenau bei Dippoldiswalde

Weicheltmühle, Gimmlitztal 42, 01762 Reichenau bei Dippoldiswalde - T: (037326) 1235, Fax: 1235. Head: Jürgen Bretschneider
Science&Tech Museum 18117

Reichenbach, Vogtland

Neuberin-Museum, Johannispl 3, 08468 Reichenbach, Vogtland - T: (03765) 21131, Fax: 21131. Head: Marion Schulz
Historical Museum / Science&Tech Museum - 1968
Memorabilia of actress Caroline Neuber (1697-1760) in the house of her birth, town hist - library, archive 18118

Reichenow

Albrecht-Daniel-Thaer-Gedenkstätte-Landesausstellung, Hauptstr, Möglin, 15345 Reichenow - T: (033456) 35164, Fax: 35164, Internet: http://www.albrecht-daniel-thaer.org. Head: Prof. Dr. Hans Rudolf Bork
Agriculture Museum - 1978
A.D. Thaer (born 1752), agricultural scientist, lived and tought here, memorabilia of A.D. Thaer, agricultural implements he developed - library, archive 18119

Reichmannsdorf

Porzellanmuseum Reichmannsdorf, c/o Porzellanfiguren Gräfenthal GmbH, Saalfelder Str 2, 98739 Reichmannsdorf - T: (036701) 31203, Fax: 80298. Head:
Decorative Arts Museum - 1992
Porcelain, porcelain miniatures, round kiln 18120

Reilingen

Heimatmuseum Reilingen, Hauptstr 1, 68799 Reilingen - T: (06205) 4707
Local Museum - 1986
Local hist, rural crafts, prehist 18121

Reinbek

Keramiksammlung Dr. Thiemann → Schloß Reinbek

Museum Rade am Schloß Reinbek, Sammlung Rolf Italiaander, Hans Spegg, Schloßstr 4, 21465 Reinbek - T: (040) 7229158, Fax: 72734620. Head: Bernd M. Kraske
Fine Arts Museum - 1970
Folk art from all over the world 18122

Schloß Reinbek, Schloßstr 5, 21465 Reinbek - T: (040) 7273460, 72734612, Fax: 72734620. Head: Bernd M. Kraske
Fine Arts Museum 18123

Reinfeld, Holstein

Städtisches Heimatmuseum, Neuer Garten 9, 23858 Reinfeld, Holstein - T: (04533) 4991, Fax: 200169, Internet: http://www.reinfeld.de. Head: Bodo Zunk
Local Museum - 1913
Prehistory, history and monuments of the Cistercian monastery, history of the dukes of Holstein-Plön, documents, autographs, first editions, pictures, letters related to Matthias Claudius (1740-1815) - library 18124

Reinheim

Heimatmuseum Reinheim, Kirchstr 41, 64354 Reinheim - T: (06162) 8050
Local Museum - 1911
Equipped kitchen, loom and flax processing, smithery 18125

Reit im Winkl

Hausenhäusl, Weitseestr 11, 83242 Reit im Winkl - T: (08640) 80020/21, Fax: 80029
Local Museum
Rustic culture and local crafts 18126

Reitzengeschwenda

Volkskundemuseum, Ortsstr 24, 07338 Reitzengeschwenda - T: (036737) 22294, Fax: 22299
Local Museum - 1969
Ancient and early hist, native, local and regional hist 18127

Reken

Heimatmuseum Windmühle Reken, Mühlenberg 5, 48734 Reken - T: (02864) 88801242
Local Museum 18128

Museum Alte Kirche, Dosstener Str, 48734 Reken - T: (02864) 2411
Religious Arts Museum 18129

Remagen

Europäisches Kulturzentrum Galerie Villa Rolandshof, Mainzer Str 14, 53424 Remagen - T: (02228) 7564, Fax: 7370. Head: Rosemarie Bassi
Fine Arts Museum 18130

Friedensmuseum, Alter Fuhrweg 39, 53424 Remagen - T: (02642) 2010, Fax: 20127, E-mail: k.kleemann@remagen.de, Internet: http://www.bruecke-remagen.de. Head: Hans Peter Kürten
Historical Museum 18131

Römisches Museum Remagen, Kirchstr 9, 53424 Remagen - T: (02642) 2010, Fax: 20127, E-mail: k.kleemann@remagen.de. Head: Kurt Kleemann
Archaeological Museum 18132

Stiftung Hans Arp und Sophie Taeuber-Arp e.V., Bonner Str 54, 53424 Remagen - T: (02228) 942516/18, Fax: 942522, E-mail: - Krupp.Stiftung.arp@t-online.de. Head: Dieter G. Lange
Fine Arts Museum - 1978
Dada, surrealism, art of the 20th c, sculptures 18133

Remscheid

Deutsches Röntgen-Museum, Schwelmer Str 41, Lennep, 42897 Remscheid - T: (02191) 62759, Fax: 446145. Head: Ulrich Henning
Science&Tech Museum - 1932
Memorabilia on W.C. Röntgen (1845-1923), his bequest, x-ray cabinet (1900), history of x-ray discovery, technique and physics of x-rays, x-ray diagnostics, biology and theraphy, protective screening - restoration laboratory, library 18134

Deutsches Werkzeugmuseum, Historisches Zentrum der Stadt Remscheid, Cleffstr 2-6, 42855 Remscheid - T: (02191) 162519, Fax: 163155, E-mail: werkzeugmuseum-hiz@str.de, Internet: http://www.werkzeugmuseum.org. Head: Dr. Urs Diederichs
Science&Tech Museum / Local Museum - 1927/67
Deutsches Werkzeugmuseum: development of tools from the palaeolithic period to the present, first electric arc furnace, development of the seamless tire, craft workshops, coll of European tools, catalogues, graphics, maps; Haus Cleff: 18th-19th c furnishings, tin figures, J.P. Hasenclever (1810-53) coll of landscape painting - library, archives 18135

Galerie der Stadt Remscheid, Scharffstr 7-9, 42853 Remscheid - T: (02191) 162798, Fax: 162912, Internet: http://remscheid.sds.de. Head: Helga Müller-Serre
Fine Arts Museum 18136

Tuchmuseum Lennep der Anna-Hardt-Stiftung, Hardtstr 2, 42897 Remscheid - T: (02191) 669264, Fax: 669264, Internet: http://www.bergisches-staedtedreieck.de/tuchmuseum_lennep. Head: Franz Werner von Wismar
Science&Tech Museum - 1986
Hist of clothworking 18137

Rendsburg

Elektro-Museum Schleswag, Stormstr 1, 24768 Rendsburg - T: (04331) 182465, Fax: 182685, Internet: http://www.schleswag.de. Head: Esther Seemann
Science&Tech Museum - 1972
Development of electrical appliances 18138

Jüdisches Museum Rendsburg und Dr.-Bamberger-Haus, Stiftung Schleswig-Holsteinische Landesmuseen Schloß Gottorf, Prinzessinstr 7-8, 24768 Rendsburg - T: (04331) 25262, Fax: 24714, E-mail: jmuseumrd@t-online.de, Internet: http://www.juedisches-museum-rendsburg.de. Head: Dr. Frauke Dettmer
Historical Museum / Fine Arts Museum - 1985/1988
Works by persecuted jewish artists, documents of jewish life in Schleswig-Holstein, and ritual objects - library, archive 18139

Museen im Kulturzentrum, Historisches Museum Rendsburg/ Druckmuseum, Arsenalstr 2-10, 24768 Rendsburg - T: (04331) 331336, Fax: 27687, E-mail: museumrendsburg@web.de, Internet: http://www.rendsburg.de. Head: Dr. Martin Westphal
Science&Tech Museum / Local Museum - 1906/91
Printing, local history, shipping 18140

Rennertshofen

Archäologisches Museum in der Feldmühle, Gutsverwaltung Feldmühle, 86643 Rennertshofen - T: (08427) 223
Archaeological Museum - 1997
Archeological finds, old wooden bridge 18141

Renthendorf

Brehm-Gedenkstätte, Dorfstr 22, 07646 Renthendorf - T: (036426) 22216, Fax: 22216, E-mail: BREHM_e.V@t-online.de, Internet: http://www.brehms-tierleben.de. Head: Jörg Hitzing
Natural History Museum - 1946
Memorabilia of animal scientists C.L. Brehm and A.E. Brehm, mss, specimen, ornithology - library 18142

Retschow

Denkmalhof Retschow, 18211 Retschow - T: (038292) 7208
Agriculture Museum 18143

Reuterstadt Stavenhagen

Fritz-Reuter-Literaturmuseum, Markt 1, 17153 Reuterstadt Stavenhagen - T: (039954) 21072, Fax: 21072, E-mail: cnenz@t-online.de, Internet: http://www.Fritz-Reuter-Literaturmuseum.de. Head: Cornelia Nenz
Special Museum - 1960
Memorabilia of poet Fritz Reuter (1810-1874) in house of his birth, writers from Mecklenburg - library 18144

Reutlingen

Firmenmusemum Novatech, Föhrstr 39, 72760 Reutlingen - T: (07121) 306251. Head:
Science&Tech Museum
Development of the loom for paper and textile manufacture 18145

Heimatmuseum Reutlingen, Oberamteistr 22-32, 72764 Reutlingen - T: (07121) 3032050, Fax: 3032768, E-mail: heimatmuseum@reutlingen.de, Internet: http://www.reutlingen.de/kultur. Head: Dr. Werner Ströbele
Local Museum - 1889
Industrial culture, Friedrich List, Hermann Kurz 18146

Museum Im Dorf, Außenstelle des Heimatmuseums Reutlingen, Im Dorf 16, 72770 Reutlingen - T: (07121) 579390, Fax: 3032768, E-mail: heimatmuseum@reutlingen.de, Internet: http://www.reutlingen.de/kultur. Head: Dr. Werner Ströbele
Folklore Museum - 1988
Peasant life and traditions 18147

Naturkundemuseum, Weibermarkt 4, 72764 Reutlingen - T: (07121) 3032022, Fax: 3032016, E-mail: naturkundemuseum@reutlingen.de, Internet: http://www.reutlingen.de. Head: Dr. Barbara Karwatzki
Natural History Museum - 1883
Geology, paleontology, mineralogy, zoology, botany 18148

Stadtbibliothek Reutlingen, Spendhausstr 2, 72764 Reutlingen - T: (07121) 3032859, Fax: 3032821, E-mail: post@stadtbibliothek-reutlingen.de, Internet: http://www.stadtbibliothek-reutlingen.de. Head: Christa Gmelch
Library with Exhibitions 18149

Städtische Galerie Reutlingen, Eberhardstr 14, 72762 Reutlingen - T: (07121) 3032322, Fax: 3032706, E-mail: kunstmuseum@reutlingen.de, Internet: http://www.reutlingen.de/kultur. Head: Dr. Beate Thurow
Public Gallery 18150

Städtisches Kunstmuseum Spendhaus Reutlingen, Spendhausstr 4, 72764 Reutlingen - T: (07121) 3032213, 3032322, Fax: 3032706, E-mail: kunstmuseum@reutlingen.de, Internet: http://www.reutlingen.de/kultur/. Head: Dr. Beate Thurow
Fine Arts Museum - 1989
Modern woodcut and contemporary art 18151

Stiftung für Konkrete Kunst, Eberhardstr 14, 72764 Reutlingen - T: (07121) 370328. Head: Dr. Gabriele Kübler
Fine Arts Museum - 1987
Modern poetry 18152

Rhauderfehn

Fehn- und Schiffahrtsmuseum, Rajen 5, 26817 Rhauderfehn - T: (04952) 903280, Fax: 903280, Internet: http://www.ourworldcompuservecom/homepages/amrumbank/ag-mus.htm
Historical Museum - 1949
Flora and fauna, moor cultivation, peat cutting, trades, shipping 18153

Rheda-Wiedenbrück

Heimatmuseum Wiedenbrück, Lange Str 50, 33378 Rheda-Wiedenbrück - T: (05242) 963522, 8799
Local Museum 18154

Leineweber-Museum, Kleine Str 11, 33378 Rheda-Wiedenbrück - T: (05242) 47335
Ethnology Museum 18155

Westfalia-Auto-Museum, Stromberger Str, 33378 Rheda-Wiedenbrück - T: (05242) 150, Fax: 15470
Science&Tech Museum - 1979 18156

Rhede, Ems

Landwirtschaftsmuseum, Emsstr 15, 26899 Rhede, Ems - T: (04964) 1800, Fax: 959110, E-mail: Museum@Rhede-Ems.de, Internet: http://www.rhede-ems.de/museum.htm. Head: Albert Vinke
Agriculture Museum - 1995
Hist and development of agriculture in Emsland 18157

Rheinau

Heimatmuseum der Stadt Rheinau in Freistett, Hauptstr 16, 77866 Rheinau - T: (07844) 4641. Head: Renate Demuth
Local Museum - 1954/1990
Shipping on canal and Rhine 18158

Rheinbach

Glasmuseum Rheinbach, Himmeroder Wall 6, 53359 Rheinbach - T: (02226) 927410, Fax: 927420, E-mail: glasmuseum.rheinbach@t-online.de, Internet: http://www.glasmuseum-rheinbach.de. Head: Dr. Ruth Fabritius
Decorative Arts Museum - 1968
Bohemian glass 18159

Rheine

Museum Kloster Bentlage, Städtische Museen Rheine, Bentlager Weg 130, 48432 Rheine - T: (05971) 920610, Fax: 920614, E-mail: falkenhofmuseum@rheine.kultur.de. Head: Dr. Mechthild Beilmann-Schöner
Historical Museum / Fine Arts Museum - 1996
Medieval art, painting of the classical Westfalian modernism - library 18160

Rheinsberg

Kurt-Tucholsky-Gedenkstätte, Schloß Rheinsberg, 16831 Rheinsberg - T: (033931) 39007, Fax: 39103, E-mail: kurttucho@aol.com, Internet: http://members.aol.com/kurttucho. Head: Dr. Peter Böthig
Special Museum 18161

Stiftung Preussische Schlösser und Gärten Berlin-Brandenburg, Schloß Rheinsberg, Postfach 1128, 16830 Rheinsberg - T: (033931) 7260, Fax: 72626. Head: Dr. Detlef Fuchs
Historic Site 18162

Ribnitz-Damgarten

Deutsches Bernsteinmuseum, Im Kloster 1-2, 18311 Ribnitz-Damgarten - T: (03821) 2931, Fax: 895140, E-mail: postmaster@german-amber-museum.de, Internet: http://www.german-amber-museum.de. Head: Ulf Erichson
Natural History Museum / Decorative Arts Museum - 1954
Natural and cultural hist of amber 18163

Riedbach

Feuerwehrmuseum Kalmbach, Schulhaus, 97519 Riedbach - T: (09526) 1654
Special Museum - 1987
Coll of firebrigade helmets 18164

Riedenburg

Burg Prunn, Schlossprunn 1, 93339 Riedenburg - T: (09442) 3323, Fax: 3335
Historic Site
Castle 18165

Hofmarkmuseum Schloß Eggersberg, Obereggersberg, 93339 Riedenburg - T: (09442) 1374, Fax: 34089996
Local Museum
Castle, exhibition "The horse in art" 18166

Jagd- und Falknereimuseum, Burg Rosenburg, 93339 Riedenburg - T: (09442) 2752, Fax: 3287
Natural History Museum - 1978
Hist of a falconry 18167

Kristallmuseum Riedenburg, Bergkristallstr 1, 93339 Riedenburg - T: (09442) 1811, 1447, Fax: 1861
Natural History Museum / Decorative Arts Museum - 1982
Coll of crystals and diamonds 18168

Riedenburger Bauernhofmuseum, Echendorf 11, 93339 Riedenburg - T: (09442) 20357, Fax: 3464, E-mail: Josef.Boehm@Keh.net.de, Internet: http://www.altmuehltal.de/riedenburg/muse-bau.htm
Agriculture Museum - 1988
Agricultural implements and machinery 18169

Riedlingen

Heimatmuseum Riedlingen, Am Wochenmarkt, 88499 Riedlingen - T: (07371) 7612, Fax: 18355
Local Museum - 1950
Prehistorical finds, Christian art, verre églomisé picture 18170

Riedstadt

Georg-Büchner-Museum Goddelau, Weidstr 9, 64560 Riedstadt - T: (06158) 1810. Head: Rotraud Pöllmann
Special Museum
All works by the writer Georg Büchner, early and pre-hist, ceramics 18171

Heimatmuseum Crumstadt, Alte Schule, Poppenheimer Str 3, 64560 Riedstadt - T: (06158) 83241
Local Museum 18172

Heimatmuseum Leeheim, Backhausstr 8, 64560 Riedstadt - T: (06158) 71822
Local Museum - 1984
Early and pre-history, furniture, agricultural and trade implements 18173

Philipp Schäfer II Museum, Wilhelm-Leuschner-Str 28, 64560 Riedstadt - T: (06158) 1810, Fax: 181100, E-mail: kultur_riedstadt@t-online.de, Internet: http://www.riedstadt.de. Head: Walter Glock
Local Museum - 1953
Agricultural implements, trade, geology - archiv 18174

Psychiatrie Museum im Philippshospital, Zentrum für soziale Psychatrie Phillipshospital, Riedstadt, 64560 Riedstadt - T: (06158) 1830, Fax: 183233
Historical Museum 18175

Rieneck

Heimatmuseum Rieneck, Hauptstr 5, 97794 Rieneck - T: (09354) 1318, 455
Local Museum - 1993
Local hist and coll of toys 18176

Riesa

Städtisches Zentrum für Geschichte und Kunst, Poppitzer Pl 3, 01589 Riesa - T: (03525) 659300, Fax: 659308, E-mail: museumriesa@t-online.de. Head: Maritta Prätzel
Local Museum / Fine Arts Museum - 1923
Ancient and early hist, local hist, industry, shipping, transportation, first railroad, stones, natural hist - library 18177

Riesbürg

Goldberg-Museum, Ostalbstr 31, 73469 Riesbürg - T: (09081) 79223, E-mail: klaus-m.gross. Head: Klaus M. Groß
Archaeological Museum - 1984
Prehistoric finds 18178

Rimbach bei Eggenfelden

Landmaschinenmuseum - Sammlung Speer, Rattenbacher Str 10, Mitterrohrbach, 84326 Rimbach bei Eggenfelden - T: (08727) 1203, Fax: (08561) 941009
Science&Tech Museum - 1990
Agricultural implements and machinery 18179

Rimpar

Archäologisches Museum, Am Schleifweg 4, 97222 Rimpar - T: (09365) 9245
Archaeological Museum 18180

Bäckereimuseum, Am Schleifweg 4, 97222 Rimpar - T: (09365) 9245
Special Museum 18181

Schloßmuseum Rimpar, Freundeskreis Schloß Grumbach e.V., Am Schleifweg 4, 97222 Rimpar - T: (09365) 9245
Local Museum 18182

Ringelai

Hexenmuseum, Hotel Groß, Dorfstr 22, 94160 Ringelai - T: (08555) 258, Fax: 1790, E-mail: mail@hotel-gross.de, Internet: http://www.hotel-gross.de
Historical Museum 18183

Rinteln

Die Eulenburg, Historisches Museum Rinteln, Klosterstr 21, 31737 Rinteln - T: (05751) 41197, Fax: 921464, E-mail: museum.eulenburg@t-online.de. Head: Stefan Meyer
Local Museum / Archaeological Museum - 1909
Archaeology of Schaumburg, History of university, town and witch-hunt 18184

Schaumburgisches Heimatmuseum "Eulenberg"
→ Die Eulenburg

Rittersgrün

Sächsisches Schmalspurbahn-Museum Rittersgrün, Kirchstr 4, 08355 Rittersgrün - T: (037757) 7440, Fax: 88196, Internet: http://www.schmalspurbahnmuseum.de. Head: Hans-Jürgen Knabe
Science&Tech Museum - 1977
Railroad history 18185

Rochlitz

Museum Schloß Rochlitz, Sörnziger Weg 1, 09306 Rochlitz - T: (03737) 492310, Fax: 492312, E-mail: info@schloss-rochlitz.de, Internet: http://www.schloss-rochlitz.de
Local Museum - 1892
Geology, ancient and early hist, local hist, flax processing, textile industry, ceramics - library 18186

Rockenhausen

Nordpfälzer Heimatmuseum, Bezirksamtsstr 8, 67806 Rockenhausen - T: (06361) 1089
Local Museum / Folklore Museum - 1930
Hist library, archive 18187

Rodenberg, Deister

Heimatmuseum Rodenberg, Burgstr, 31552 Rodenberg, Deister - T: (05723) 4313
Local Museum - 1981
Early and prehist, town hist, mining, agriculture, trades, folk costumes 18188

Rodewald

Heimatmuseum Rodewald, Dorfstr 3, 31637 Rodewald - T: (05074) 366
Local Museum
Furniture and equipment of country physician's surgery 18189

Rodewisch

Museum Göltzsch, Schloßstr 2, 08228 Rodewisch - T: (03744) 33186, Fax: 33186
Local Museum - 1951
Geology, archaeology, ceramics, tools, city and industrial history, spinning and embroidery 18190

Roding

Feuerwehrmuseum, Feuerwache, Ziehringer Weg 1, 93426 Roding - T: (09461) 941819, 941849
Science&Tech Museum - 1985
Firebrigade objects and uniforms 18191

Schulmuseum Fronau, Kirchpl, Fronau, 93426 Roding - T: (09465) 344, (09971) 78218
Local Museum - 1982
Old school 18192

Röckwitz

Heimatstube Röckwitz, Ringstr 3, 17091 Röckwitz - T: (039600) 465
Local Museum
Agricultural and domestic implements, furniture, dishes 18193

Rödental

Museum für Modernes Glas, Kunstsammlungen der Veste Coburg, Orangerie, Schloß Rosenau, 96472 Rödental - T: (09563) 1606, (09561) 8790, Fax: (09561) 87966, E-mail: sekretariat@kunstsammlungen-coburg.de, Internet: http://www.kunstsammlungen-coburg.de. Head: Klaus Weschenfelder
Decorative Arts Museum - 1989
Modern glass coll 18194

Porzellanmuseum, Coburger Str 7, 96472 Rödental - T: (09563) 920, Fax: 92590, E-mail: info@goebel.de, Internet: http://www.goebel.de. Head: D.E. Schneider
Decorative Arts Museum - 1973
Coll of porcelain 18195

Schloß Rosenau, Park Rosenau, 96472 Rödental - T: (09563) 308413, Fax: 308429, Internet: http://www.sgvcoburg.de
Local Museum
Birthplace of prince Albert of Saxonia-Coburg Gotha who married Queen Victoria in 1840 18196

Rödermark

Töpfermuseum, Bachgasse 28, 63322 Rödermark - T: (06074) 5920
Decorative Arts Museum - 1984
Hist of pottery trade 18197

Röhrnbach

Heimatstube Röhrnbach-Kaltenbach, Rathauspl 1, 94133 Röhrnbach - T: (08582) 96090, Fax: 960992, E-mail: markt.roehrnbach@frg.baynet.de, Internet: http://www.roehrnbach.de
Local Museum - 1976
Town and hist of German expellees 18198

Römerstein

Heimatmuseum Pfarrscheuer, Bei der Kirche, 72587 Römerstein - T: (07382) 384
Local Museum - 1982
Local hist, Roman finds 18199

Römhild

Museum Schloß Glücksburg, Griebelstr 28, 98631 Römhild - T: (036948) 80140, Fax: 20520. Head: Hans Joachim Gelszinnis
Local Museum / Fine Arts Museum - 1968 and 1984
Hönn Coll of peasant life and crafts, ceramics coll - Library, archive 18200

Steinsburg-Museum, Waldhaussiedlung 8, 98631 Römhild - T: (036948) 20561, Fax: 20561. Head: W. Büttner
Archaeological Museum - 1929
Ancient and early history, local history, celtic culture - library 18201

Röthenbach an der Pegnitz

Museum für historische Wehrtechnik, Heinrich-Diehl-Str, 90552 Röthenbach an der Pegnitz - T: (09120) 9168, Fax: 181472, E-mail: info@wehrtechnikmuseum.de, Internet: http://www.wehrtechnikmuseum.de. Head: Werner Sünkel
Military Museum - 1983
Ammunition, intelligence service gadgets, anti aircraft and artillery material, radio and telephone equipment, optics 18202

Rötz

Heimatmuseum Rötz, Böhmerstr 18, 92444 Rötz - T: (09976) 902073
Local Museum - 1997
Town hist 18203

Oberpfälzer Handwerksmuseum, Hillstr 52, Hillstett, 92444 Rötz - T: (09976) 1482, Fax: 941199
Special Museum - 1984
Crafts 18204

Roggenburg

Klostermuseum, Klosterstr 5, 89297 Roggenburg - T: (07300) 5223, Fax: (0731) 7040665, E-mail: Ira-nu@neu-ulm.de, Internet: http://www.landkreis.neu-ulm.de. Head: Walter Wörtz
Religious Arts Museum - 1991
Religious art 18205

Rohne

Sorbische Stube, Dorfstr 53, 02959 Rohne - T: (035773) 300, Fax: 300. Head:
Folklore Museum 18206

Rohr, Niederbayern

Sammlungen der Benediktiner-Abtei Braunau, Asamstr 7, 93352 Rohr, Niederbayern - T: (08783) 96000, Fax: 96022, Internet: http://www.kloster-rohr.de. Head: Dr. Johannes Zeschick
Religious Arts Museum - 1972
Monastery, religious folklore and music hist, Bohemian music 18207

Rohrdorf

Bäuerliches Museum im Achentaler Heimathaus, Falkensteinstr 14, 83101 Rohrdorf - T: (08032) 5337
Folklore Museum - 1988 18208

Rommerskirchen

Kulturzentrum Sinsteden des Kreises Neuss, Landwirtschaftsmuseum und Skulpturenhallen Ulrich Rückriem, Grevenbroicher Str 29, Sinsteden, 41569 Rommerskirchen - T: (02183) 7045, Fax: 440204, E-mail: kulturzentrumsinsteden@t-online.de. Head: Dr. Kathrin Wappenschmidt
Agriculture Museum / Fine Arts Museum - 1995 18209

Ronneburg, Hessen

Museum Burg Ronneburg, Auf der Ronneburg, 63549 Ronneburg, Hessen - T: (06048) 950905, Fax: 950906, Internet: http://www.burg-ronneburg.de. Head: Jean Eckel
Historical Museum - 1988
Hist of the castle 18210

Ronnenberg

Bergbaudokumentation Hansa Empelde, An der Halde 8, 30952 Ronnenberg
Science&Tech Museum - 1995
Potash mining 18211

Heimatmuseum Ronnenberg, Über den Beeken 13, 30952 Ronnenberg - T: (05109) 4218
Local Museum - 1975
Farmyard, potash mining, geology, town hist 18212

Rosenfeld

Heinrich-Blickle-Museum, Sammlung gußeiserner Ofenplatten, Frauenberggasse 8, 72348 Rosenfeld - T: (07428) 8678. Head: K. Hartmann
Science&Tech Museum - 1982
Top plates from different epochs 18213

Rosengarten, Kreis Harburg

Freilichtmuseum am Kiekeberg, Ehestorf, Am Kiekeberg 1, 21224 Rosengarten, Kreis Harburg - T: (040) 7901760, Fax: 7926464, E-mail: info@kiekberg-museum.de, Internet: http://www.kiekeberg-museum.de. Head: Prof. Dr. Rolf Wiese
Open Air Museum / Agriculture Museum / Folklore Museum - 1953
Agricultural implements, three farmyards from the 17th-19th c 18214

Rosenheim

Holztechnisches Museum, Max-Josefs-Pl 4, 83022 Rosenheim - T: (08031) 16900, Fax: 380864, E-mail: kulturamt@bnro.de, Internet: http://www.rosenheim.de. Head: Arno Kurz, Walter Leicht
Science&Tech Museum - 1990
Wood industry 18215

Inn-Museum, Wasserbau- und Schiffahrtstechnische Sammlung, Innstr 74, 83022 Rosenheim - T: (08031) 30501, Fax: 305179, E-mail: poststelle@wwa-ro.bayern.de, Internet: http://www.bayern.de/wwa-ro. Head: Werner Kraus
Science&Tech Museum - 1949
Shipping, shipbuilding, hydraulic engineering 18216

Klepper-Faltbootmuseum, Klepperstr 18, 83026 Rosenheim - T: (08031) 21670, Fax: 216777
Science&Tech Museum - 2000 18217

Städtische Galerie Rosenheim, Max-Bram-Pl 2, 83022 Rosenheim - T: (08031) 361447, Fax: 362063, E-mail: kulturamt@rosenheim.de, Internet: http://www.rosenheim.de. Head: Monika Wernick
Fine Arts Museum - 1937
Munich School 18218

Städtisches Museum Rosenheim, Mittertor, Ludwigspl 26, 83022 Rosenheim - T: (08031) 798994, Fax: 380864, E-mail: museum@bnro.de, Internet: http://www.rosenheim.de. Head: Walter Leicht
Local Museum - 1895
Early and prehist housing, Roman coll, ceramics from the 17th c, River Inn shipping, trades and guilds, verre églomisé picture, town hist till 1960, ancient kitchen 18219

Roßdorf bei Darmstadt

Südhessisches Handwerksmuseum, Holzgasse 7, 64380 Roßdorf bei Darmstadt - T: (06154) 9751, Fax: 9751, Internet: http://www.kulturhistorischer-verein-rossdorf.de. Head: Ursula Richter
Local Museum 18220

Roßtal

Museumshof, Schulstr 13, 90574 Roßtal - T: (09127) 8691, 579788
Local Museum - 1994
Granny's housekeeping 18221

Roßwein

Heimatmuseum Roßwein, Markt 4, 04741 Roßwein - T: (034322) 4660, Fax: 46619
Local Museum - 1924
Early hist, crafts and guilds, silver mining, hist of local handicraft 18222

Rostock

Forst- und Köhlerhof, Wiethagen, 18182 Rostock - T: (038202) 2533, 2035, Fax: 29437. Head: Gerd Heil
Science&Tech Museum / Natural History Museum
Tar ovens, charcoal burning, forestry 18223

Heimatmuseum Warnemünde, Alexandrinenstr 30-31, 18119 Rostock - T: (0381) 52667, Fax: 5486837, Internet: http://www.rostock.de. Head: Sigrun Horn
Local Museum
Folklore, fishery, shipping, ceramics, postcards, regional painters 18224

Kulturhistorisches Museum Rostock, Kloster Zum Heiligen Kreuz, Klosterhof, 18055 Rostock - T: (0381) 455913/14, Fax: 4934705, Internet: http://www.rostock.de. Head: Dr. Heidrun Lorenzen
Folklore Museum / Historical Museum / Fine Arts Museum - 1903
Ancient and early hist, hist of town and trade, crafts, industry, religious sculpture, paintings, prints, "colony of artists" 18225

Kulturhistorisches Museum Rostock, Kröpeliner Tor, Kröpeliner Str, 18055 Rostock - T: (0381) 454177, Fax: 4934705, Internet: http://www.rostock.de. Head: Dr. Heidrun Lorenzen
Local Museum / Historical Museum
Town hist 18226

Kunsthalle Rostock, Hamburger Str 40, 18069 Rostock - T: (0381) 82336/37, Fax: 8016288, Internet: http://www.rostock.de. Head: Katrin Arrieta
Fine Arts Museum - 1969
Paintings from former GDR and Mecklenburg-Vorpommern esp Otto Niemeyer-Holstein, changing exhibitions - library 18227

Münzkabinett und Archäologische Lehrsammlung der Universität Rostock, Institut für Altertumswissenschaften, Universitätspl 1, 18051 Rostock - T: (0381) 4982786, 4982783, Fax: 4982787, E-mail: lorenz.winkler-horacek@philfak.uni-rostock.de, Internet: http://www.phf.uni-rostock.de/fkw/iaw. Head: Prof. Dr. Konrad Zimmermann
Archaeological Museum / University Museum 18228

Schiffahrtsmuseum auf dem Traditionsschiff, Abteilung Schiffbaugeschichte des Schiffahrtsmuseum Rostock, Liegeplatz Schmarl, 18106 Rostock - T: (0381) 1211600, 1219726, Fax: 1219727, Internet: http://www.rostock.de. Head: Peter Danker-Carstensen
Science&Tech Museum
Compartment shipbuilding hist, technological equipment hist of navigation 18229

Schiffahrtsmuseum Rostock, August-Bebel-Str 1, 18055 Rostock - T: (0381) 252060, Fax: 27254, Internet: http://www.rostock.de. Head: Peter Danker-Carstensen
Science&Tech Museum - 1968
Navigation hist 18230

Rot

Reubacher Heimatmuseum, Zur Linde 9, 74585 Rot - T: (07958) 604
Local Museum - 1974
Peasant life 18231

Rotenburg an der Fulda

Kreisheimatmuseum Weißes Haus, Äußerer Schloßhof, 36199 Rotenburg an der Fulda - T: (06623) 81779/80, Fax: 81720. Head: Sabine Sindermann
Local Museum - 1931
Geological hist coll, prehist 18232

Rotenburg, Wümme

Heimatmuseum Rotenburg, Burgstr 2, 27356 Rotenburg, Wümme - T: (04261) 4520, Fax: 2411
Local Museum - 1953
Smokehouse, original furniture, agricultural implements 18233

Roth, Mittelfranken

Fabrikmuseum der Leonischen Industrie, Obere Mühle 4, 91154 Roth, Mittelfranken - T: (09171) 60564, 856661
Science&Tech Museum - 1988
Hist of metal-processing industry, wire pulling, wire mesh, jewellery for christmas tree - library 18234

Heimatstube der Stadt Saaz, Am Weinberg 37, 91154 Roth, Mittelfranken - T: (09172) 1734
Local Museum - 1987 18235

Historischer Eisenhammer, Eckersmühlen, 91154 Roth, Mittelfranken - T: (09171) 81331, Fax: 81399, E-mail: tourismus@landratsamt.roth.de, Internet: http://www.roth.de
Science&Tech Museum - 1986
Forge 18236

Museum Schloß Ratibor, Kirchpl 4, 91154 Roth, Mittelfranken - T: (09171) 848371, Fax: 848333, E-mail: schlossratibor@t-online.de. Head: G. Schmid
Local Museum - 1904
Ceramics, toys   18237

Rothenburg ob der Tauber

Alt-Rothenburger Handwerkerhaus, Alter Stadtgraben 26, 91541 Rothenburg ob der Tauber - T: (09861) 2098, Fax: 2692
Local Museum
Furniture and interiors, crafts, tools, implements, in a 13th c house   18238

Historiengewölbe, Rathaus, Herrengasse, 91541 Rothenburg ob der Tauber - T: (09861) 3240
Local Museum - 1966
Town hist and prison   18239

Kunstausstellung des Rothenburger Künstlerbundes, Marktpl 9, 91541 Rothenburg ob der Tauber - T: (09861) 6174-0
Public Gallery   18240

Mittelalterliches Kriminalmuseum, Burggasse 3-5, 91541 Rothenburg ob der Tauber - T: (09861) 5359, Fax: 8258, E-mail: info@kriminalmuseum.rothenburg.de, Internet: http://www.kriminalmuseum.-rothenburg.de. Head: Karl-Heinz Schneider
Historical Museum - 1890
13th-19th c administration of justice, medieval torture chamber, superstitions, in a 14th c building - library   18241

Puppen- und Spielzeugmuseum Sammlung Katharina Engels, Hofbronnengasse 11-13, 91541 Rothenburg ob der Tauber - T: (09861) 7330, Fax: 86748, E-mail: claudia.lingmann@gmx.de, Internet: http://www.spielzeugmuseum.rothenburg.de
Special Museum - 1984
Special exhibition of ancient Christmas cribs (1st advent-28th Febr)   18242

Reichsstadtmuseum, Klosterhof 5, 91541 Rothenburg ob der Tauber - T: (09861) 939043, Fax: 935206, E-mail: reichsstadtmuseum@ rothenburg.de, Internet: http://www.reichsstadtmuseum.rothenburg.de. Head: Dr. Helmut Möhring
Local Museum - 1936
Regional and local hist, furnishings, painting, sculpture, Jewish items, important coll of arms and weapons, crafts, farm implements, cloister interiors, in a 13th-16th c Dominican nunnery convent 18243

Schäfertanz-Kabinett, Beim Klingentor, 91541 Rothenburg ob der Tauber - T: (09861) 6295, 40492
Agriculture Museum - 1986   18244

Toppler-Schlößchen, Taubertalweg 98, 91541 Rothenburg ob der Tauber - T: (09861) 7358. Head: Heinz Boas
Historical Museum - 1925
Little castle   18245

Rothenburg, Oberlausitz

Heimatmuseum für Wild, Wald und Naturschutz, Marktpl 1, 02929 Rothenburg, Oberlausitz - T: (035891) 35134, Fax: 35163
Natural History Museum - 1931
Local and regional hist   18246

Rothenklempenow

Heimatstube Rothenklempenow, Schloßstr 2, 17321 Rothenklempenow - T: (039744) 219
Local Museum   18247

Rottach-Egern

Kutschen-, Schlitten- und Wagenmuseum Rottach-Egern, Feldstr 16, 83700 Rottach-Egern - T: (08022) 671341, Fax: 671347, E-mail: info@ rottach-egern.de, Internet: http://www.rottach-egern.de
Science&Tech Museum - 2001   18248

Rottenburg am Neckar

Diözesanmuseum Rottenburg, Karmeliterstr 9, 72108 Rottenburg am Neckar - T: (07472) 922180, Fax: 922189, E-mail: museum@bo.drs.de. Head: Wolfgang Urban
Religious Arts Museum - 1862
Late-Gothic votive painting and wooden sculptures, religious art, historical textiles, devotional objects and prints, coll of medieval glasses in a 18th c building   18249

Sülchgau-Museum, Bahnhofstr 16, 72108 Rottenburg am Neckar - T: (07472) 165351, Fax: 165392, E-mail: archiv@rottenburg.de, Internet: http://www.rottenburg.de. Head: K. Geppert
Local Museum - 1890   18250

Sumelocenna - Römisches Stadtmuseum, Am Stadtgraben, 72108 Rottenburg am Neckar - T: (07472) 165371, Fax: 165392, E-mail: archiv@ rottenburg.de, Internet: http://www.rottenburg.de. Head: K. Geppert
Archaeological Museum - 1992
Local and regional archeology   18251

Rottenburg an der Laaber

Radiomuseum, Neufahrner Str 3, 84056 Rottenburg an der Laaber - T: (08781) 2862, Fax: 8380, Internet: http://www.rolaa.de
Science&Tech Museum - 1997   18252

Rotthalmünster

Museum Kloster Asbach, Bayerisches Nationalmuseum München, 94094 Rotthalmünster - T: (08533) 2300
Religious Arts Museum - 1984
Plaster casts, gravestones, iron and cupper handicrafts   18253

Rottweil

Dominikanermuseum Rottweil, Zweigmuseum des Württembergischen Landesmuseums Stuttgart, Am Kriegsdamm 4, 78628 Rottweil - T: (0741) 494330, 7862, Fax: 494377, E-mail: stadtarchiv@ rottweil.de, Internet: http://www.dominikanermuseum-rottweil.de. Head: Dr. Winfried Hecht
Fine Arts Museum / Archaeological Museum - 1991
Medieval painting and sculpture, Roman finds, Roman mosaic   18254

Kunstsammlung Lorenzkapelle Rottweil, Lorenzgasse 17, 78628 Rottweil - T: (0741) 494330, 9429633, Fax: 494377, E-mail: stadtarchiv@rottweil.de, Internet: http://www.lorenzkapelle-rottweil.de. Head: Dr. Winfried Hecht
Fine Arts Museum - 1851
14th-17th c Gothic and Renaissance stone sculptures in a 16th c chapel   18255

Salinenmuseum Unteres Bohrhaus, Primtalstr 19, 78628 Rottweil - T: (0741) 43822, Fax: 494355, Internet: http://www.rottweil.de. Head: Wolfram Langbein, Dr. Winfried Hecht
Science&Tech Museum - 1979
Geology, cultural hist, tools   18256

Stadtmuseum Rottweil, Hauptstr 20, 78628 Rottweil - T: (0741) 494330, 9429634, Fax: 494377, E-mail: stadtarchiv@rottweil.de, Internet: http://www.rottweil.de. Head: Dr. Winfried Hecht
Local Museum - 1884
Carnival of Rottweil, cribs   18257

Rudersberg

Ölmühle, Weilerwiesen 1, 73635 Rudersberg - T: (07183) 2755. Head: A. Kurz
Science&Tech Museum - 1990
Oldest oil mill in Baden-Württemberg   18258

Rudolstadt

Thüringer Landesmuseum Heidecksburg Rudolstadt, Schloßbezirk 1-3, 07407 Rudolstadt - T: (03672) 42900, Fax: 429090, E-mail: museum@ heidecksburg.de, Internet: http://www.heidecksburg.de. Head: Horst Fleischer
Local Museum / Natural History Museum / Fine Arts Museum - 1950
Hist rooms, furnishings, paintings, archaeology, religious art, decorative archaeology, numismatics, prints, minerals, botany, zoology, armaments, uniforms, porcelain   18259

Volkskunde-Museum, Thüringer Bauernhäuser, Große Wiese 2, 07407 Rudolstadt - T: (03672) 422465, Fax: 429090, E-mail: museum@ heidecksburg.de, Internet: http://www.heidecksburg.de. Head: Doreen Winker
Open Air Museum / Folklore Museum - 1914/15
2 half-timbered houses, peasant furnishings, household objects, work tools, crafts, peasant life 17th-19th c   18260

Rübeland

Rübeländer Tropfsteinhöhlenmuseum, Blankenburger Str 35, 38889 Rübeland - T: (039454) 49132, Fax: 53475, E-mail: Frbetrieb@ aol.com, Internet: http://www.ruebeland.com. Head: A. Müller
Natural History Museum   18261

Rüdersdorf bei Berlin

Museumspark, c/o Gemeindeverwaltung, Heinitzstr 11, 15562 Rüdersdorf bei Berlin - T: (033638) 76510, Fax: 76511, E-mail: kontakt@ museumspark.de, Internet: http://www.museumspark.de. Head: Eva Köhler
Science&Tech Museum / Open Air Museum - 1994
Area and buildings related to limestone mining   18262

Rüdesheim am Rhein

Erstes Deutsches Museum für mechanische Musikinstrumente, Oberstr 27-29, 65385 Rüdesheim am Rhein - T: (06722) 49217, Fax: 4587, E-mail: mechanischesmusikkabinett@t-online.de, Internet: http://www.musicboxworld.de. Head: Siegfried Wendel
Music Museum - 1969
18th-20th c mechanical musical instruments, music boxes and clocks, pianolas, barrels - restoration workshop   18263

Freiligrath Museum, Krone Assmannshausen, Assmannshausen, Rheinuferstr 10, 65385 Rüdesheim am Rhein - T: (06722) 4030. Head: Special Museum
Hotel room in which the poet Ferdinand Freiligrath completed his "Glaubensbekenntniß"   18264

Mittelalterliches Foltermuseum, Grabenstr 13, 65385 Rüdesheim am Rhein - T: (06722) 47510
Historical Museum
Documentation from "amnesty international", photography   18265

Rheingauer Weinmuseum Brömserburg e.V., Rheinstr 2, 65385 Rüdesheim am Rhein - T: (06722) 2348, Fax: 2676, E-mail: info@rheingauer-weinmuseum.de, Internet: http://www.rheingauer-weinmuseum.de. Head: Marianne Berger
Special Museum / Agriculture Museum - 1948
Pre- and early hist, local hist, wine growing in Rheingau, glass, ceramics, bottles - library   18266

Rüsselsheim

Museum der Stadt Rüsselsheim, Hauptmann-Scheuermann-Weg 4, 65428 Rüsselsheim - T: (06142) 832950, Fax: 832965, Internet: http://www.stadt-ruesselsheim.de. Head: Dr. Peter Schirmbeck
Local Museum - 1976
Prehist, medieval to industrial age hist, development of the Opel works, historical machinery, Rüsselsheim working class movement (1863-1945), art and industrial revolution, man and nature (ecological department), industrial technology in social, cultural and natural context - library 18267

Ruhla

Heimatmuseum, Obere Lindenstr 29-31, 99842 Ruhla - T: (036929) 89014, Fax: 80365. Head: Heike Helbig
Local Museum - 1906
Geology, history of mining, iron crafts, knifesmith work, metal and clock industry, pipe coll, costumes, furnishings   18268

Uhren- und Pfeifenmuseum, Obere Lindenstr 29-31, 99842 Ruhla - T: (036929) 89014, Fax: 80365. Head: Heike Helbig
Folklore Museum - 1906
Geology, cutlery trade, tobacco pipe trade, clock and metal industry, instruments for children, furniture, traditional costumes, personalities   18269

Ruhland

Heimatstube Ruhland, Gutshof 2, 01945 Ruhland - T: (035752) 21872189, Fax: 2097
Local Museum   18270

Ruhmannsfelden

Bauernhaus-Museum, Haus Nr 6, 94239 Ruhmannsfelden - T: (09929) 1634
Agriculture Museum / Ethnology Museum - 1977
Agricultural tools   18271

Ruhpolding

Bartholomäus-Schmucker-Heimatmuseum, Schloßstr 2, 83324 Ruhpolding - T: (08663) 41230, Fax: 540177
Local Museum - 1922
Rustic culture, porcelain, religious objects, mineralogy and fossils, military and hunting weapons   18272

Glockenschmiede, Haßlberg 6, 83324 Ruhpolding - T: (08663) 2309, 1268, Fax: 2306, E-mail: glockenschmiede@t-online.de. Head: Tyrena Ullrich
Science&Tech Museum
Bell foundry   18273

Holzknechtmuseum Ruhpolding, Laubau 12, 83324 Ruhpolding - T: (08663) 639, Fax: 800829
Local Museum - 1988
Hist of forestry   18274

Museum für bäuerliche und sakrale Kunst, Roman-Friesinger-Str 1, 83324 Ruhpolding
Fine Arts Museum / Religious Arts Museum - 1971
Religious art, votive painting, stained glass, 17th-19th c sculpture and painting, folk art, costumes, implements, ceramics   18275

Schnauferlstall, Bacherwinkel 5, 83324 Ruhpolding - T: (08663) 9948
Science&Tech Museum
Coll of motorcycles (1924-1960)   18276

Runkel

Privatsammlung Burg Runkel, Schloßpl, 65594 Runkel - T: (06482) 4222, Fax: 2014, Internet: http://www.burg-runkel.de. Head: Fürst zu Wied, M. Prinz zu Wied
Local Museum   18277

Saalfeld, Saale

Saalfelder Feengrotten, Feengrottenweg 2, 07318 Saalfeld, Saale - T: (03671) 55040, Fax: 550440, E-mail: info@feengrotten.de, Internet: http://www.feengrotten.de. Head: Yvonne Habermann
Natural History Museum - 1914
Cave with stalactites and stalacmites   18278

Stadtmuseum Saalfeld, Münzpl 5, 07318 Saalfeld, Saale - T: (03671) 598471, Fax: 598470, E-mail: museum@stadt-saalfeld.de. Head: Dirk Henning
Local Museum - 1904
Regional history, medieval art, geology   18279

Saarbrücken

Abenteuermuseum Saarbrücken - Sammlung Heinz Rox-Schulz, Altes Rathaus, Schloßpl, 66119 Saarbrücken - T: (0681) 9054902, Fax: 9054956, E-mail: leonardy@abenteuermuseum.de, Internet: http://www.abenteuermuseum.de. Head: Heinz Rox-Schulz
Ethnology Museum
Ethnology from travelling to Africa, South America, Asia and New Guinea   18280

Geologisches Museum der DSK-Saar, c/o Deutsche Steinkohle AG, Trierer Str 4, 66111 Saarbrücken - T: (0681) 4054098. Head: Dr. Rudolf Becker
Natural History Museum - 1982
Saar geology, mineralogy, palaeontology   18281

Historisches Museum Saar, Schloßpl 15, 66119 Saarbrücken - T: (0681) 5064501, Fax: 5064590, E-mail: hms@hismus.de, Internet: http://www.historisches-museum-saar.de. Head: Gerhard Ames
Historical Museum   18282

Museum für Vor- und Frühgeschichte, Stiftung Saarländischer Kulturbesitz, Schloßpl 16, 66119 Saarbrücken - T: (0681) 9540511, Fax: 9540510. Head: Dr. Andrei Miron
Archaeological Museum - 1930
Prehist, Roman frescos and sculptures, early Middle Age, Celtic burial remains - restoration lab 18283

Saarland Museum, Stiftung Saarländischer Kulturbesitz, Bismarckstr 11-19, 66111 Saarbrücken - T: (0681) 99640, Fax: 9964248, E-mail: info@saarlandmuseum.de, Internet: http://www.saarlandmuseum.de
Fine Arts Museum - 1924/1952
Old coll of arts and crafts from Middle Ages till 19th c, impressionistic and comtemporary art, 20th c art, graphic arts coll, sculptures, art by Alexander Archipenko, Hans Purrmann, Max Slevogt and Albert Weisgerber - library   18284

Stadtgalerie Saarbrücken, Sankt Johanner Markt 24, 66111 Saarbrücken - T: (0681) 936830, Fax: 9368333, E-mail: info@stadtgalerie.de, Internet: http://www.stadtgalerie.de. Head: Prof. Bernd Schulz
Public Gallery   18285

Saarlouis

Museum Haus Ludwig für Kunstausstellungen, Kaiser-Wilhelm-Str 2, 66740 Saarlouis - T: (06831) 128540, Fax: 128547, E-mail: museumhausludwig@saarlouis.de, Internet: http://www.saarlouis.de. Head: Walter Birk
Fine Arts Museum   18286

Sachsenheim

Stadtmuseum Sachsenheim, Oberriexinger Str 29, 74343 Sachsenheim - T: (07147) 922394, Fax: 922392, E-mail: Stadtmuseum@ sachsenheim.de. Head: Diana Finkele
Local Museum - 1998
Local hist, agriculture, crafts, costumes   18287

Salem, Baden

Feuerwehrmuseum, 88682 Salem, Baden - T: (07553) 81438, Fax: 81440, E-mail: a.ziegler@ salem.de, Internet: http://www.salem.de
Science&Tech Museum - 1976
Development of firefighting (18th-20th c)   18288

Schloss Salem, 88682 Salem, Baden - T: (07553) 81438, Fax: 81440, E-mail: a.ziegler@salem.de, Internet: http://www.salem.de. Head: Annegret Ziegler
Religious Arts Museum
Hist of the monastery, baroque stucco   18289

Salzbergen

Feuerwehrmuseum Salzbergen, Overhuesweg 16, 48499 Salzbergen - T: (05976) 94393, Fax: 94465, E-mail: feuerwehrmuseum-salzbergen@gmx.de, Internet: http://www.salzbergen-online.de/fwms
Science&Tech Museum
Hist of the local fire brigade   18290

Salzgitter

Kunstverein Salzgitter e.V., Wehrstr 27, 38226 Salzgitter - T: (05341) 17161, 53340, Fax: 5519500. Head: Dr. Klaus Berner
Association with Coll   18291

Städtische Kunstsammlung Schloß Salder, Museumstr 34, 38229 Salzgitter - T: (05341) 8394611/13, Fax: 8394630, E-mail: kulturamt@ stadt.salzgitter.de. Head: Dr. Jörg Leuschner
Local Museum - 1962
Town hist, trades, furniture, art coll, toys, geology, early and prehist   18292

Werksmuseum der Firma Linke-Hofmann-Busch GmbH, Postfach 411160, 38233 Salzgitter - T: (05341) 211
Science&Tech Museum   18293

Salzhemmendorf

Besucher-Bergwerk Hüttenstollen, Orts- und Bergwerksmuseum Osterwald, 31020 Salzhemmendorf - T: (05153) 6816
Science&Tech Museum
Brown coal mining 18294

Salzwedel

Jenny-Marx-Haus, Jenny-Marx-Str 20, 29410 Salzwedel - T: (03901) 423081. Head: Christine Lehmann
Special Museum - 1969
Memorabilia on Marx family in house of Jenny Marx' birth, contemporary history, fine arts 18295

Johann-Friedrich-Danneil-Museum, An der Marienkirche 3, 29410 Salzwedel - T: (03901) 423380, Fax: 423380. Head: Christine Lehmann
Local Museum - 1836
History of the Altmark area, history of the shipping city, pewter, numismatics, religious sculpture, memorabilia on J.Fr. Danneil - library 18296

Sande, Kreis Friesland

Heimatmuseum Neustadtgödens, Brückstr 19, 26452 Sande, Kreis Friesland - T: (04422) 4199, 750, Fax: 958840, E-mail: gemeinde-sande@nwn.de, Internet: http://www.sande.de
Local Museum - 1986
Village hist, dyke building, coast development, religious hist, Frisian jurisdiction between 800 and 1809 18297

Sandhausen

Heimatmuseum, Am Lège-Cap-Ferret-Platz, 69207 Sandhausen - T: (06224) 2875
Local Museum - 1973
Local hist 18298

Sandstedt

Hermann-Allmers-Haus, Mittelstr 1, Rechtenfleth, 27628 Sandstedt - T: (04702) 810, Fax: 810, Internet: http://www.kulturlandschaft.de
Historical Museum
Home of the poet Hermann Allmers (1821-1902), co-founder of the German vernacular revival movement, fine arts, furnishings 18299

Sangerhausen

Spengler-Museum, Bahnhofstr 33, 06526 Sangerhausen - T: (03464) 573048, Fax: 565270, E-mail: bibliothek.sangerhausen@t-online.de, Internet: http://www.spengler-museum.de. Head: Veronika Otto
Local Museum - 1952
Old Pleistocene fauna, ancient and early history, regional history, mining, birds, butterflies and mollusk coll - library 18300

Sankt Andreasberg

Historisches Silbererzbergwerk Grube Samson und Heimatmuseum, Am Samson 2, 37444 Sankt Andreasberg - T: (05582) 1249, Fax: 923051, E-mail: grube_samson@t-online.de, Internet: http://www.sankt-andreasberg.de/samson.htm
Science&Tech Museum / Local Museum
Hist of mining 18301

Sankt Augustin

Haus Völker und Kulturen - Ethnologisches Museum, Arnold-Janssen-Str 26, 53757 Sankt Augustin - T: (02241) 237406, Fax: 237407, E-mail: hvk@steyler.de, Internet: http://www.steyler.de/stichworte/museen. Head: Gebard Rahe
Ethnology Museum - 1973
Ethnological collections from Africa, Papua New Guinea, Ethiopia, Christian China and Non European Christian Art 18302

Sankt Blasien

Museum des Landkreises Waldshut - Sankt Blasien, Haus des Gastes, 79837 Sankt Blasien - T: (07672) 41437, Fax: (07751) 86373, E-mail: kultur@landkreis-waldshut.de, Internet: http://www.landkreis-waldshut.de. Head: Dr. Jürgen Glocker
Local Museum - 1983
Hist of the monastery, geology 18303

Sankt Egidien

Heimatmuseum Sankt Egidien, Lungwitzer Str 77, 09356 Sankt Egidien - T: (037204) 5275, 7600
Local Museum 18304

Sankt Georgen im Schwarzwald

Deutsches Phonomuseum, Rathaus, Hauptstr 9, 78112 Sankt Georgen im Schwarzwald - T: (07724) 87187, Fax: 87128, E-mail: info@stadtverwaltung.st-georgen.de, Internet: http://www.st-georgen.de. Head: Paul Benz
Science&Tech Museum / Music Museum - 1972
Clocks, gramophones 18305

Phonomuseum → Deutsches Phonomuseum

Sankt Goar

Heimatkundliche Sammlung Burg Rheinfels, Burg Rheinfels, 56329 Sankt Goar - T: (06741) 383, Fax: 7209
Local Museum - 1965
Excavation finds, plans and drawings, etchings, documents, heraldry 18306

Sankt Ingbert

Museum Sankt Ingbert, Am Markt 7, 66386 Sankt Ingbert - T: (06894) 13358, 13352, Fax: 13530, E-mail: SFolz@st-ingbert.de, Internet: http://www.st-ingbert.de. Head: Dr. Winfried Brandenburg
Fine Arts Museum - 1988
Albert Weisgerber coll and archive, changing exhibitions 18307

Sankt Johann, Württemberg

Ski- und Heimatmuseum Upfingen, Kirchgasse 1, 72813 Sankt Johann, Württemberg - T: (07122) 1373
Local Museum - 1984
Hist of skiing 18308

Sankt Märgen

Heimatsammlung, Rathauspl 1, 79274 Sankt Märgen - T: (07669) 911817, Fax: 911840, E-mail: info-st.maergen@t-online.de, Internet: http://www.st-maergen.de
Local Museum - 1991
Clocks, folk art, religious art 18309

Sankt Michaelisdonn

Freimaurermuseum der Großen Landesloge der Freimaurer von Deutschland, Meldorfer Str 2, 25693 Sankt Michaelisdonn - T: (04853) 562, Fax: 701. Head: Günter Stramm
Historical Museum - 1979
Objects of Freemasonry 18310

Sankt Oswald

Waldgeschichtliches Museum Sankt Oswald, Klosterallee 4, 94568 Sankt Oswald - T: (08552) 961136, Fax: 961142
Natural History Museum - 1986
Hist of the Bavarian and Bohemian Forest 18311

Sankt Ottilien

Missionsmuseum, Erzabtei, 86941 Sankt Ottilien - T: (08193) 710, Fax: 71332. Head: Arnold Walloschek
Ethnology Museum - 1911
History of missions and ethnology in East Africa, South Africa, Korea, Manchuria, zoology of East Africa 18312

Sankt Peter-Ording

Eiderstedter Heimatmuseum, Olsdorfer Str 6, 25826 Sankt Peter-Ording - T: (04863) 1226, Fax: 703337, Internet: http://www.schleswig-holstein.de/museen/reg_hei/heimu_eiderstedt.htm
Local Museum 18313

Sankt Wendel

Museum Sankt Wendel, Mia-Münster-Haus, In der Mott, 66606 Sankt Wendel - T: (06851) 809183, Fax: 809184. Head: Drs. Cornelieke Lagerwaard
Local Museum / Fine Arts Museum
Regional art and hist 18314

Sasbach bei Achern, Baden

Toni-Merz-Museum, Schulstr 25, 77880 Sasbach bei Achern, Baden - T: (07841) 26079, Fax: 709452, E-mail: kurt.degen@gmx.de, Internet: http://www.sasbach-ortenau.de. Head: Kurt Degen
Fine Arts Museum - 1975
Paintings and other works of Toni Merz 18315

Sassen, Vorpommern

Schullandheim Sassen, Heimatkundliche Einrichtung, Nr 56, 17121 Sassen, Vorpommern - T: (039998) 10624
Local Museum
Agricultural implements and machinery, domestic utensils 18316

Saßnitz

Archäologisches Landesmuseum Mecklenburg-Vorpommern, Museum für Unterwasserarchäologie, Alter Fährhafen, 18546 Saßnitz - T: (038392) 32300, Fax: 32300, E-mail: archaeomuseum.m-v@t-online.de. Head: Dr. Friedrich Lüth
Archaeological Museum - 1998
Underwater archaeology, artifacts(stone age to modern times) and shipwrecks (Gellenkogge from 1939 and Ralswiekboat from 995) 18317

Sauerlach

Troadkasten, Holzkirchener Str 22, 82054 Sauerlach - T: (08104) 666111, Fax: 666111. Head: Dagmar Gräfin von Matuschka
Local Museum - 1989
Agricultural tools, handicrafts 18318

Scharfenberg bei Meißen

Heimatmuseum, OT Bergwerk 12, 01665 Scharfenberg bei Meißen - T: (03521) 457131, Fax: 457131
Local Museum - 1958
Geology, mining 18319

Schauenstein

Heimat- und Feuerwehrmuseum, Schloßpl 1, 95197 Schauenstein - T: (09252) 96600
Local Museum / Science&Tech Museum - 1988
Local crafts and fire brigade 18320

Weberhausmuseum, Neudorf 64, 95197 Schauenstein - T: (09252) 7954, 6899. Head: Christl Hanus-Möller
Science&Tech Museum - 1971
Weaving mill 18321

Scheeßel

Heimatmuseum Scheeßel, Zevener Str 18, 27383 Scheeßel - T: (04263) 8551, Fax: 8551. Head: Friedrich Behrens
Local Museum / Fine Arts Museum - 1908/13
Paintings by Ernst Müller-Scheeßel, advertising graphics by Heinz Fehling, printing and weaving workshops 18322

Schefflenz

Schefflenztal-Sammlungen, Dallauer Str 2, 74850 Schefflenz - T: (06293) 8880. Head: W. Weirether
Local Museum
Crafts, furnishings 18323

Scheidegg

Heimathaus-Handwerkermuseum, Schlosserweg 3, 88175 Scheidegg - T: (08381) 8950, 7812, Fax: 89543, 7812, E-mail: german.weh@t-online.de, Internet: http://www.scheidegg.de
Local Museum
Local crafts 18324

Scheinfeld

Heimatstuben im Oberen Tor, Haupstr 27, 91443 Scheinfeld - T: (09162) 7373, 929141
Local Museum - 1978
Geology, crafts and agricultural tools 18325

Schelklingen

Stadtmuseum Schelklingen, Spital zum heiligen Geist, Spitalgasse, 89601 Schelklingen - T: (07394) 2876, 2480, Fax: 24850, E-mail: info@schelklingen.de, Internet: http://www.schelcklingen.de. Head: R. Blumentritt
Local Museum - 1980
Geology, prehist 18326

Schellerten

Heimatstube Wendhausen, Schulstr, 31174 Schellerten - T: (05121) 37622
Local Museum
Village school with accessories 18327

Schermbeck

Heimatmuseum Schermbeck, Steinstorstr 17, 46514 Schermbeck - T: (02853) 9100, Fax: 910119
Local Museum - 1987 18328

Scheßlitz

Museum des Heimatkundlichen Vereins, 96110 Scheßlitz - T: (09542) 1216, 1505
Local Museum 18329

Schieder-Schwalenberg

Städtische Galerie, Museum alter lippischer Maler, Marktstr 5, 32816 Schieder-Schwalenberg - T: (05282) 6010, Fax: 60135
Public Gallery / Fine Arts Museum 18330

Schifferstadt

Heimatmuseum Schifferstadt, Kirchenstr 17, 67105 Schifferstadt - T: (06235) 6636
Local Museum - 1926 18331

Schillingsfürst

Historische Ochsentretanlage im Brunnenhausmuseum, Brunnenhausweg, 91583 Schillingsfürst - T: (09868) 5889, 222, Fax: 986233
Local Museum / Science&Tech Museum - 1970
Old pumping station, agricultural tools 18332

Ludwig-Doerfler-Galerie, Neue Gasse 1, 91583 Schillingsfürst - T: (09868) 986211, Fax: 986233, E-mail: vg.schillingsfuerst@t-online.de, Internet: http://www.schillingfuerst.de
Local Museum / Fine Arts Museum - 1995
Work of the painter Ludwig Doerfler 18333

Schloßmuseum Hohenlohe-Schillingsfürst, Am Wall 14, 91583 Schillingsfürst - T: (09868) 201, Fax: 7441
Local Museum
Castle and hist of falconry 18334

Schiltach

Apotheken-Museum, Marktpl 5, 77761 Schiltach - T: (07836) 360, Fax: 1222, E-mail: -stadtapotheke.schiltach@t-online.de, Internet: http://www.stadtapotheke.net. Head: H. Rath, I. Rath
Historical Museum - 1985
Furnishings drugs and implements of an early 19th c pharmacy 18335

Museum am Markt, Marktpl 13, 77761 Schiltach - T: (07836) 5875, Fax: 5858, E-mail: fuchs@stadt-schiltach.de, Internet: http://www.schiltach.de. Head: Dr. Felizitas Fuchs
Local Museum - 1989
Textiles, photography 18336

Schüttesägemuseum, Hauptstr 1, 77761 Schiltach - T: (07836) 5875, Fax: 5858, E-mail: fuchs@stadt-schiltach.de, Internet: http://www.schiltach.de. Head: Dr. Felizitas Fuchs
Science&Tech Museum - 1989
Rafting, forest economy, tannery 18337

Schirgiswalde

Heimatmuseum Carl Swoboda, Hauptstr 11a, 02681 Schirgiswalde - T: (03592) 38660, Fax: 386633, E-mail: stadt@schirgiswalde.de, Internet: http://www.schirgiswalde.de
Local Museum - 1924
Local hist 18338

Schkeuditz

Heimatmuseum Dölzig, OT Dölzig, Paul-Wäge-Str 15, 04435 Schkeuditz
Local Museum 18339

Museum der Stadt Schkeuditz, Mühlstr 50, 04435 Schkeuditz - T: (034204) 2092. Head: A. Fischer
Local Museum - 1926
Ancient and early history, city history 18340

Schladen

Heimathaus Alte Mühle, Mühlenstr 1, 38315 Schladen - T: (05335) 1683, 275
Local Museum - 1968
Regional hist, hist of Königspfalz Werla 18341

Schleiz

Johann-Friedrich-Böttger-Gedenkstätte, Neumarkt, 07907 Schleiz - T: (03663) 2438
Special Museum 18342

Schlepzig

Agrarhistorisches Museum, Dorfstr 26, 15910 Schlepzig - T: (035472) 225
Agriculture Museum - 1985
Agricultural hist, implements and machinery 18343

Schleswig

Archäologisches Landesmuseum, Stiftung Schleswig-Holsteinische Landesmuseen Schloß Gottorf, Schloß Gottorf, 24837 Schleswig - T: (04621) 8130, Fax: 813535, E-mail: bibliothek.alm@t-online.de, Internet: http://www.schloss-gottorf.de. Head: Prof. Dr. Claus von Carnap-Bornheim
Archaeological Museum - 1836
Prehistory (120,000 B.C.-500 A.D.) and medieval archaeology (500-1,500 A.D.) of Schleswig-Holstein - library, archives, restoration labs, model construction workshop 18344

Landesmuseum für Kunst und Kulturgeschichte, Stiftung Schleswig-Holsteinische Landesmuseen Schloß Gottorf, Schloß Gottorf, 24837 Schleswig - T: (04621) 8130, Fax: 813555, E-mail: info@schloss-gottorf.de, Internet: http://www.schloss-gottorf.de. Head: Dr. Herwig Guratzsch
Fine Arts Museum / Decorative Arts Museum / Folklore Museum / Historic Site - 1875
Painting and sculpture 15th-19th c, Klassische Moderne (Expressionismus), arts and crafts 15th-20th c - library, archives, restoration and photo labs, research center 18345

Museum für Outsiderkunst, Stadtweg 57, Präsidentenkloster, 24837 Schleswig - T: (04621) 850839, Fax: 936899, E-mail: kulturamt@schleswig.de, Internet: http://www.schleswig.de. Head: Dr. Holger Rüdel
Fine Arts Museum 18346

Städtisches Museum, Friedrichstr 9-11, 24837 Schleswig - T: (04621) 936820, Fax: 936899, E-mail: kulturamt@schleswig.de, Internet: http://www.schleswig.de. Head: Dr. Holger Rüdel
Local Museum - 1879
Local history, folk art, domestic utensils, toys, history of printing, documentation on excavations in ancient Schleswig - library, picture archives 18347

Völkerkundliche Sammlung, Stiftung Schleswig-Holsteinische Landesmuseen Schloß Gottorf, Schloß Gottorf, 24837 Schleswig - T: (04621) 8130, Fax: 813535, E-mail: info@schloss-gottorf.de, Internet: http://www.schloss-gottorf.de. Head: Dr. Herwig Guratzsch
Ethnology Museum - 1836 18348

Volkskundliche Sammlungen, Stiftung Schleswig-Holsteinische Landesmuseen Schloß Gottorf, Hesterberg, 24837 Schleswig - T: (04621) 96760, Fax: 96734, E-mail: shlm.hesterberg@t-inline.de, Internet: http://www.schloss-gottorf.de. Head: Dr. Herwig Guratzsch
Folklore Museum 18349

Schleusingen

Naturhistorisches Museum Schloß Bertholdsburg, Burgstr 6, 98553 Schleusingen - T: (036841) 5310, Fax: 531225
Natural History Museum / Local Museum - 1934/1984
Minerals, fossils, rocks, animals, plants, book hist, papermaking, school hist, art - library 18350

Schliengen

Schloß Bürgeln, 79418 Schliengen - T: (07626) 237, Fax: 8782. Head: F.D. Pfau
Local Museum 18351

Trottenmuseum, Am Sonnenstück, 79418 Schliengen - T: (07635) 1031
Special Museum 18352

Schliersee

Heimatmuseum Schliersee, Lautererstr 8, 83727 Schliersee - T: (08026) 2329, 4671
Local Museum - 1916
Rustic culture, religious folklore 18353

Schlitz

Heimatmuseum Schlitz, An der Vorderburg 1, 36110 Schlitz - T: (06642) 9700, Fax: 97055, E-mail: stadt.schlitz@t-online.de, Internet: http://www.schlitz.de
Local Museum - 1926
Local costumes, weapons, furniture, local hist, weaving, loom, linen, archaeological finds 18354

Schlüchtern

Bergwinkelmuseum, Lauterschlößchen, Schloßstr 15, 36381 Schlüchtern - T: (06661) 8567
Local Museum - 1948
Agricultural and trade implements 18355

Holzgerätemuseum, Burg Brandenstein, Elm, 36381 Schlüchtern - T: (06661) 2350, Fax: 72341. Head: Ameli von Brandenstein
Science&Tech Museum - 1970
Various items of folk art made from wood, trade implements 18356

Schlüsselfeld

Stadtmuseum Schlüsselfeld, Marktpl 25, 96132 Schlüsselfeld - T: (09552) 92220, Fax: 922230, Internet: http://www.abseits.de/smsf. Head: Wilfried Auer
Local Museum - 1993
Local hist, geology and ecology 18357

Schlunkendorf

Spargelmuseum, Kietz 36, 14547 Schlunkendorf - T: (033204) 42112
Special Museum - 1998 18358

Schmalkalden

Museum Schloß Wilhelmsburg, Schloßberg 9, 98574 Schmalkalden - T: (03683) 403186, Fax: 601682, E-mail: museum.sm@gmx.de, Internet: http://www.schmalkalden.de. Head: Bertin Gentges
Local Museum - 1878
Historical rooms, mining, iron industry, local hist, apothecary science, stoves, costumes, decorative objects, furnishings, numismatics 16th c, renaissance, reformation 18359

Technisches Denkmal Neue Hütte, Gothaer Str, 98574 Schmalkalden - T: (03683) 403018, Fax: 403018. Head: Monika Schwintek
Science&Tech Museum
Classicist blast furnace 18360

Schmallenberg

Museum im Kloster Grafschaft, Mutterhaus Kloster Grafschaft, 57392 Schmallenberg - T: (02972) 79100, Fax: 791245. Head: Dr. Otmar Plassmann
Fine Arts Museum / Religious Arts Museum 18361

Schmiedeberg, Osterzgebirge

Galerie Skell, Tal Naundorf 29d, 01762 Schmiedeberg, Osterzgebirge - T: (035052) 67789
Public Gallery 18362

Schmitten

Museum im Alten Rathaus, Rathauspl 1, 61389 Schmitten - T: (06084) 582. Head: Béatrice Träger
Local Museum - 1981
Pearl wreath industry 18363

Schnackenburg

Grenzlandmuseum, Am Markt, 29493 Schnackenburg - T: (05840) 210, Fax: 210. Head: Reinhard Kögl
Historical Museum - 1995
Hist of the former East/West-German border 18364

Schnaittach

Heimatmuseum Schnaittach, Museumsgasse 16, 91220 Schnaittach - T: (09153) 7434
Local Museum - 1923
Local hist 18365

Jüdisches Museum Franken in Schnaittach, Museumsgasse 12-16, 91220 Schnaittach - T: (09153) 7434, (0911) 770577, Fax: (0911) 7417896, E-mail: info@juedisches-museum.org, Internet: http://www.juedisches-museum.org. Head: Bernhard Purin
Historical Museum - 1996
History of the Jews in Franconia - library in Fürth, Nürnberger Str 3 18366

Schneeberg, Erzgebirge

Museum für bergmännische Volkskunst Schneeberg, Obere Zobelgasse 1, 08289 Schneeberg, Erzgebirge - T: (03772) 22446, Internet: http://www.schneeberg.de. Head: Regina Krippner
Folklore Museum - 1929
Folk art, ores of minerals of area mines, hist crafts, carving pewter casting, town hist, lace making 18367

Schnepfenthal

Gedenkstätte für C.G. Salzmann und J.C.F. GuthsMuths, Salzmannschule (temporary closed), Klostermühlenweg 2-8, 99880 Schnepfenthal - T: (03622) 9130, Fax: 913222, E-mail: salzmann.schule@t-online.de, Internet: http://www.salz.gth.schule.de. Head: A. Schreiner
Historical Museum - 1959
Memorabilia on the teacher J.C.E. GutsMuths (1759-1839) and the philanthrop C.G. Salzmann 18368

Schneverdingen

Heimathaus De Theeshof, Langelohsberg, Hansahlener Dorfstr, 29640 Schneverdingen - T: (05193) 2199
Local Museum - 1978
Farm life now and then, trades 18369

Schönau im Schwarzwald

Heimatmuseum Klösterle, Neustadtstr 21, 79677 Schönau im Schwarzwald - T: (07673) 82040, Fax: 820414
Local Museum - 1990
Local hist, silver mining, local industry 18370

Schönberg, Holstein

Kindheitsmuseum, Knüllgasse 16, 24217 Schönberg, Holstein - T: (04344) 6865, E-mail: - Schoenberg.Ostsee@t-online.de, Internet: http://www.kindheitsmuseum.de. Head: Marta Sakmirda
Folklore Museum 18371

Probsteier Heimatmuseum, Ostseestr 8, 24217 Schönberg, Holstein - T: (04344) 3174, Fax: 412834, E-mail: probsteierheimatmuseum@t-online.de, Internet: http://www.schleswig-holstein.de/Museen
Local Museum 18372

Schönberg, Mecklenburg

Bechelsdorfer Schulzenhaus, Johannes-Boye-Str, 23923 Schönberg, Mecklenburg - T: (038828) 21539
Local Museum 18373

Volkskundemuseum, An der Kirche 8-9, 23923 Schönberg, Mecklenburg - T: (038828) 21539. Head: Heidemarie Frimodig
Local Museum - 1903
Ancient and early historic finds, regional history, crafts, work tools, pewter, costumes, ethnology of former princedom Ratzeburg 18374

Schönebeck, Elbe

Kreismuseum Schönebeck, Pfännerstr 41, 39218 Schönebeck, Elbe - T: (03928) 69417, Fax: 845814, E-mail: landratsamt@schönebeck.de, Internet: http://www.landkreis.schoenebeck.de. Head: Rüdiger Radicke
Local Museum - 1924
Pre- and early hist, salt production, shipping on river Elbe, hist, regional hist, folklore, natural hist, art, geology, arms, coins, medals - library, archive 18375

Museum des Landkreises Schönebeck → Kreismuseum Schönebeck

Schöneck, Vogtland

Heimatstube Schöneck, Bauhofstr1, 08261 Schöneck, Vogtland - T: (037464) 88910, 82533, Fax: 80050
Local Museum - 1977
Local and regional history 18376

Schöneiche bei Berlin

Heimatmuseum, Dorfaue 8, 15566 Schöneiche bei Berlin - T: (030) 6491105, Fax: 6498875
Local Museum - 1935
Peasant life, local and regional history 18377

Schönfels

Burgmuseum Schönfels, Burgstr 34, 08115 Schönfels - T: (037600) 2327, Fax: 25777, Internet: http://www.westsachsen.de/lichtentanne/burg-schoenfels
Local Museum - 1975
Folklore, folk art, native crafts, natural hist, environment and hunting 18378

Schöngeising

Bauernhofmuseum Jexhof des Landkreises Fürstenfeldbruck, Jexhof 1, 82296 Schöngeising - T: (08153) 93250, Fax: 932525, E-mail: drexler@jexhof.de, Internet: http://www.jexhof.de
Open Air Museum
History of farming, agricultural implements, regional folklore 18379

Schöningen

Heimatmuseum Schöningen, Markt 33, 38364 Schöningen - T: (05352) 2214, Fax: 512199
Local Museum - 1927
Town hist, brown coal archaeology, textiles, club flags, postcards 18380

Schönsee

Dr.-Arthur-Lindgens-Jagdmuseum, Hotel St. Hubertus, 92539 Schönsee - T: (09674) 92290, Fax: 922929
Natural History Museum - 1977
African hunting trophies, animal preparations 18381

Schönwalde am Bungsberg

Dorfmuseum, Hörn 2, 23744 Schönwalde am Bungsberg - T: (04528) 737
Local Museum 18382

Schönwalde bei Tangerhütte

Heimatstube Schönwalde, Dorfstr 22, 39517 Schönwalde bei Tangerhütte - T: (03935) 212334
Local Museum 18383

Schöppenstedt

Till-Eulenspiegel-Museum, Nordstr 4a, 38170 Schöppenstedt - T: (05332) 6158, Fax: 938101, E-mail: info@schoeppenstedt.de, Internet: http://www.eulenspiegel-online.de. Head: Dorothee C. Papendorf
Historical Museum - 1940
Memorabilia and literature on Tijl Uilenspiegel (in German known as Till Eulenspiegel) - archive 18384

Schongau

Stadtmuseum Schongau, Christophstr 53-57, 86956 Schongau - T: (08861) 20602, Fax: 200625, E-mail: museum-archiv@schongau.de, Internet: http://www.schongau.de. Head: Richard Ide
Local Museum / Public Gallery - 1891
Numismatics, town hist, former hospitality church 18385

Schopfheim

Museum der Stadt Schopfheim, Wallstr 10, 79650 Schopfheim - T: (07622) 63750, Fax: 396201, E-mail: u.schmid@schopfheim.de. Head: Dr. Ulla K. Schmid
Local Museum - 1956
Roggenbach-Gayling Stiftung, Johann Peter Hebel, Max Picard, Fritz-Heeg-Erasmus, games and bags 18386

Schorndorf, Württemberg

Heimatmuseum Weiler, Schorndorfer Str 22, 73614 Schorndorf, Württemberg - T: (07181) 7866
Local Museum - 1964
Agricultural and domestic implements 18387

Stadtmuseum Schorndorf, Kirchpl 7-9, 73614 Schorndorf, Württemberg - T: (07181) 21351, Fax: 602190, E-mail: mail@stadtmuseum-schorndorf.de, Internet: http://www.stadtmuseum-schorndorf.de. Head: Dr. Wolfgang Morlok
Local Museum - 1929
Porcelain from Schorndorf, local hist, crafts, industry, archaeological finds from mesolithic to medieval times, hist of the ancient fortress (16th-19th c), panel paintings from the 16th, 18th-19th c furniture 18388

Schotten

Vogelsberger Heimatmuseum, Vogelsbergstr 95, 63679 Schotten - T: (06044) 2702
Local Museum - 1937
Neolithic finds, geology, furniture, ceramics, flax processing tools, embroidery 18389

Schramberg

Europäische Glasmalerei- und Krippenausstellung, Alte Sankt Laurentius-Kirche, 78713 Schramberg - T: (07422) 52294, Fax: 55128. Head: Lorenz Roming
Decorative Arts Museum / Religious Arts Museum - 1980
Hist of glass production, glass painting, cribs 18390

Podium Kunst, Schloß Schramberg, 78713 Schramberg - T: (07422) 29268, Fax: 29262, E-mail: museum@schramberg.de
Public Gallery 18391

Stadtmuseum Schramberg, Schloß, Bahnhofstr 1, 78713 Schramberg - T: (07422) 29266/68, Fax: 29262, E-mail: museum@schramberg.de, Internet: http://www.stadtschramberg.de. Head: Gisela Lixfeld
Local Museum - 1979 18392

Schrecksbach

Schwälmer Dorfmuseum, Pfarrhof, Brunnenstr 11, 34637 Schrecksbach - T: (06698) 1670
Local Museum - 1959
Furniture, costumes, domestic and agricultural implements and tools, needlework 18393

Schriesheim

Museum Theo Kerg, Talstr 52, 69198 Schriesheim - T: (06203) 6020, Fax: 602191, E-mail: zentrale@schriesheim.de. Head: Lynn Schoene
Fine Arts Museum - 1989
Paintings and other works of the artist Theo Kerg (1930-1988) 18394

Schrobenhausen

Europäisches Spargelmuseum, Am Hofgraben 1a, 86529 Schrobenhausen - T: (08252) 7013, Fax: 90225, E-mail: stadt@schrobenhausen.de, Internet: http://www.schrobenhausen.de. Head: Dr. Klaus Englert
Agriculture Museum - 1983
Asparagus 18395

Lenbachmuseum, Ulrich-Peißer-Gasse 1, 86529 Schrobenhausen - T: (08252) 90214, Fax: 90225, E-mail: stadt@schrobenhausen.de, Internet: http://www.schrobenhausen.de. Head: Dr. Sonja von Baranow
Fine Arts Museum - 1936/37
Birthplace of Franz von Lenbach (1836-1904), memorabilia of the painter, paintings by his friend Johann Baptist Hofner 18396

Zeiselmairhaus, In der Lachen 1, 86529 Schrobenhausen - T: (08252) 90214, Fax: 90225, E-mail: stadt@schrobenhausen.de, Internet: http://www.schrobenhausen.de. Head:
Local Museum - 1990
Local crafts, archeological finds 18397

Schrozberg

Schloßmuseum, Schloß Bartenstein, 74575 Schrozberg - T: (07936) 272, Fax: 765, E-mail: bartenstein1@t-online.de. Head: Ferdinand Fürst zu Hohenlohe-Bartenstein
Fine Arts Museum / Local Museum - 1971
Hist of the family, local and regional hist - art exhibition 18398

Schuttertal

s'Buchholze Hisli, Heimatmuseum, Laulisgraben, 77978 Schuttertal - T: (07826) 604
Local Museum 18399

Schwabach

Stadtmuseum Schwabach, Museumsstr/ Ansbacher Str, Geb. 1002 Kaserne, 91126 Schwabach - T: (09122) 833933, Fax: 833935, E-mail: stadtmuseum@schwabach.de, Internet: http://www.schwabach.de/stadtmuseum. Head: Jürgen Söllner
Local Museum - 1957
Local hist and crafts, Egg coll 18400

Schwabmünchen

Museum und Galerie der Stadt, Holzheystr 12, 86830 Schwabmünchen - T: (08232) 963378/54, Fax: 963323. Head: Sabine Sünwoldt
Local Museum - 1913
19th c painting (Nazarener), textiles, Roman settlement (Rapis and Schwabegg) - library, town archive 18401

Schwabstedt

Heimatgeschichtliche Sammlung des Kirchspiels, Haus des Kurgastes, 25876 Schwabstedt - T: (04884) 283
Local Museum 18402

Die große Sommerausstellung

Carl Spitzweg

Gemälde und Zeichnungen

im Museum Georg Schäfer

5. Mai bis 6. Oktober 2002

Museum Georg Schäfer
Schweinfurt

Brückenstrasse 20 · 97421 Schweinfurt am Main
Tel.: +49 97 21 5 1917 od. 51920 · www.museumgeorgschaefer.de

Schwäbisch Gmünd

Brünner Heimatmuseum, Johannis-Pl 3, 73525 Schwäbisch Gmünd - T: (0711) 366220. Head: Theo Ballak
Local Museum 18403

Galerie im Prediger, Johannispl 3, 73525 Schwäbisch Gmünd - T: (07171) 6034130, Fax: 6034129, E-mail: museum@schwaebisch-gmuend.de, Internet: http://www.schwaebisch-gmuend.de. Head: Dr. Gabriele Holthuis
Public Gallery - 1994 18404

Museum im Prediger, Johannispl 3, 73525 Schwäbisch Gmünd - T: (07171) 6034130, Fax: 6034129, E-mail: museum@schwaebisch-gmuend.de, Internet: http://www.schwaebisch-gmuend.de. Head: Dr. Gabriele Holthuis
Decorative Arts Museum / Fine Arts Museum - 1876
Geology, paleontology, handicraft, cultural hist of Schwäbisch Gmünd, local artists, 17th-20th c rosaries and jewellery, roman finds 18405

Silberwaren- und Bijouteriemuseum, Ott-Pausersche Fabrik, Milchgäßle 10, 73525 Schwäbisch Gmünd - T: (07171) 38910, Fax: 998785, E-mail: museum@schwaebisch-gmuend.de, Internet: http://www.schwaebisch-gmuend.de. Head: Dr. Gabriele Holthuis
Science&Tech Museum / Decorative Arts Museum - 1992
19th c fabric with machines and tools, jewelry 18406

Schwäbisch Hall

Hällisch-Fränkisches Museum, Keckenhof 6, 74523 Schwäbisch Hall - T: (0791) 751360, Fax: 751305, E-mail: hfm@schwaebischhall.de, Internet: http://www.schwaebischhall.de. Head: N.N.
Local Museum - 1847
Regional cultural hist, geology, prehistory, local hist, judaica, hist of performing art 18407

Haller Feuerwehrmuseum, Im Ripperg 3, 74523 Schwäbisch Hall - T: (0791) 751216/246, Fax: 9781608, E-mail: Eller.Quelle@t-online.de. Head: E. Eller
Science&Tech Museum - 1968
Fire fighting 18408

Haus der Ortsgeschichte, Hauptstr 35, 74523 Schwäbisch Hall - T: (07907) 2254
Local Museum - 1979
Local hist 18409

Hohenloher Freilandmuseum, Wackershofen, 74523 Schwäbisch Hall - T: (0791) 971010, Fax: 9710140, E-mail: info@wackershofen.de, Internet: http://www.wackershofen.de. Head: Albrecht Bedal
Open Air Museum - 1979
Peasant life, viticulture 18410

Kunsthalle Würth, Lange Str 35, 74532 Schwäbisch Hall - T: (0791) 946720, Fax: 9467250, Internet: http://www.wuerth.com. Head: C. Sylvia Weber
Fine Arts Museum - 2001
Modern and present time arts 18411

Ostdeutsche Heimatstube, Untere Herrengasse 6, 74523 Schwäbisch Hall - T: (0791) 7406. Head: Franz Skandera
Historical Museum - 1977
Hist of former German settlements in Eastern Europe 18412

Schwaigern

Karl-Wagenplast-Museum, Massenbacher Str, 74193 Schwaigern - T: (07138) 7748. Head: E. Steinle
Archaeological Museum - 1982
Prehistoric finds 18413

Schwalmstadt

Museum der Schwalm, Paradepl 1, 34613 Schwalmstadt - T: (06691) 3893. Head: Peter Müller
Local Museum / Association with Coll - 1938
Embroidery coll, earthenware and ceramics, trade workshops, costumes 18414

Schwalmtal, Niederrhein

Heimatmuseum Schwalmtal, Niederrhein, Niederstr 52, 41366 Schwalmtal, Niederrhein - T: (02163) 49667
Local Museum 18415

Schwandorf

Oberpfälzer Künstlerhaus-Kebbel-Villa, Fronberger Str 31, 92421 Schwandorf - T: (09431) 9716, Fax: 96311, E-mail: opf.kuenstlerhaus@schwandorf.de, Internet: http://www.schwandorf.de. Head: Heiner Riepl
Fine Arts Museum - 1988
Painting, sculpture and graphic art from the Upper Palatinate 18416

Stadtmuseum Schwandorf mit Falkenauer Heimatstube, Rathausstr 1, 92421 Schwandorf - T: (09431) 41553, Fax: 960948, E-mail: stadtmuseum@schwandorf.de, Internet: http://www.schwandorf.de/kultur/ulmus.htm
Local Museum 18417

Schwanfeld

Heimatmuseum Schwanfeld, Rathauspl, 97523 Schwanfeld - T: (09384) 97170, 1293, Fax: 971725, E-mail: info@schwanfeld.de, Internet: http://www.schwanfeld.de
Local Museum - 1978
Early and town hist, rustic culture and crafts 18418

Schwangau

Römerbad, Tegelbergbahn-Talstation, 87645 Schwangau - T: (08362) 819810, Fax: 819825
Local Museum - 1999 18419

Schloß Hohenschwangau, 87645 Schwangau - T: (08362) 81128, Fax: 887102. Head: G. Meyer
Decorative Arts Museum - 1913
12th c castle, 19th c interiors, frescos pertaining to German myths 18420

Schloß Neuschwanstein, c/o Staatl. Schloßverwaltung Neuschwanstein, Neuschwansteinstr 20, 87645 Schwangau - T: (08362) 81035, 81801, Fax: 8990
Decorative Arts Museum
Residence built for King Ludwig II of Bavaria, with original late romantic (eclectic) interiors designed by Julius Hofmann - unfinished 18421

Schwarza, Suhl

Heimatmuseum Schwarza, Hauptstr 52b, 98547 Schwarza, Suhl - T: (036843) 208, Fax: 208
Local Museum
Local history - 14th c castle built in water 18422

Schwarzach am Main

Missionsmuseum, Abtei, 97359 Schwarzach am Main Münsterschwarzach - T: (09324) 20275/79, Fax: 20270. Head: Dr. Basilius Doppelfeld
Religious Arts Museum
Hist of missionary 18423

Schwarzburg

Kaisersaal Schwarzburg, Thüringer Landesmuseum Heidecksburg Rudolstadt, Schloßstr 4, 07427 Schwarzburg - T: (036730) 22263, Fax: (03672) 429090. Head: Dr. Lutz Unbehaun
Fine Arts Museum 18424

Schwarzenbek

Amtsrichterhaus, Körnerpl 10, 21493 Schwarzenbek - T: (04153) 52220, Fax: 52240. Head: Hans-Jürgen Rupf
Public Gallery 18425

Schwarzenberg

Eisenbahnmuseum Schwarzenberg, Schneeberger Str 60, 08340 Schwarzenberg - T: (03774) 23212, Fax: 23212, E-mail: vse.eisenbahnmuseum@t-online.de, Internet: http://www.eisenbahnmuseum-schwarzenberg.de. Head: Thomas Strömsdörfer
Science&Tech Museum
Railways history of Saxony 18426

Museum Schloß Schwarzenberg, Obere Schloßstr 36, 08340 Schwarzenberg - T: (03774) 23389, Fax: 23389, E-mail: schwarzenberginfo@abo.freiepresse.de. Head: Marlies Steinau
Decorative Arts Museum - 1947
Iron, laces, mining, folk art, pewter-ware 18427

Schwarzenfeld

Mineralogisch-Geologische Gesteins-Sammlung, Viktor-Koch-Str 4, 92521 Schwarzenfeld - T: (09435) 3090, Fax: 309227, E-mail: schwarzenfeld@sadnet.de. Head: Michael Niederalt
Natural History Museum - 1958
Fluor spar, "Wölsendorfer Revier" 18428

Schwedt

Galerie im Ermelerspeicher, Städtische Museen Schwedt/Oder, Lindenallee 36, 16303 Schwedt - T: (03332) 23245, Fax: 838346, E-mail: galerie.stadt@schredt.de. Head: Claudia Riechert
Public Gallery - 1988
Coll of landsacpe paintings 18429

Stadtmuseum Schwedt, Städtische Museen Schwedt/Oder, Jüdenstr 17, 16303 Schwedt - T: (03332) 23460, Fax: 23460. Head: Claudia Riechert
Historical Museum - 1930
Ancient and early hist, hist of city, industrial hist, peasant traditions 18430

Schweinfurt

Bibliothek Otto Schäfer, Museum für Buchdruck, Graphik, Kunsthandwerk, Judithstr 16, 97422 Schweinfurt - T: (09721) 3985, Fax: 3984, E-mail: bibliothekos@aol.com, Internet: http://www.bibliothek-otto-schaefer.de. Head: Georg Drescher
Library with Exhibitions - 1995
German literature - Library 18431

Galerie Alte Reichsvogtei, Städtische Sammlungen Schweinfurt, Obere Str 11, 97421 Schweinfurt - T: (09721) 51479, Fax: 51320, E-mail: sammlungen@schweinfurt.de, Internet: http://www.sammlungen-schweinfurt.de. Head: Dr. Erich Schneider
Public Gallery - 1980
Contemporary arts of Franconia and germany since 1945 18432

Museum Altes Gymnasium, Städtische Sammlungen Schweinfurt, Martin-Luther-Pl 12, 97421 Schweinfurt - T: (09721) 51479, Fax: 51320, E-mail: sammlungen@schweinfurt.de, Internet: http://www.schweinfurt.de. Head: Dr. Erich Schneider
Local Museum - 1890
Prehist, town and local hist, scientific instruments, decorative and temporary art 18433

Museum Georg Schäfer, Brückenstr 20, 97421 Schweinfurt - T: (09721) 51920, Fax: 51371, E-mail: info@mgs-online.de, Internet: http://www.museumgeorgschaefer.de. Head: Dr. Sigrid Bertuleit
Fine Arts Museum - 2000 18434

Museum Gunnar-Wester-Haus, Städtische Sammlungen Schweinfurt, Martin-Luther-Pl 5, 97421 Schweinfurt - T: (09721) 51479, Fax: 51320, E-mail: sammlungen@schweinfurt.de, Internet: http://www.schweinfurt.de. Head: Dr. Erich Schneider
Decorative Arts Museum - 1986
Lamps and lighting 18435

Naturkundliches Museum in der Harmonie, Städtische Sammlungen Schweinfurt, Brückenstr 39, 97421 Schweinfurt - T: (09721) 51479, 51215, Fax: 51320, E-mail: sammlungen@schweinfurt.de, Internet: http://www.schweinfurt.de. Head: Dr. Erich Schneider
Natural History Museum - 1892
Coll of birds, herbarium 18436

Schwelm

Museum Haus Martfeld, Haus Martfeld 1, 58332 Schwelm - T: (02336) 914437, Fax: 914438, E-mail: info@Schwelm.de. Head: Cornelia Hackler
Historical Museum / Historic Site - 1890
Textiles (history and trade), ironwork - coins and medals cabinet, communal archives 18437

Schwerin

Kunstsammlungen, Staatliches Museum Schwerin, Alter Garten 3, 19055 Schwerin - T: (0385) 59580, Fax: 563090, E-mail: otto@museum-schwerin.de, Internet: http://www.musuem-schwerin.de. Head: Prof. Dr. Kornelia von Berswordt-Wallrabe
Fine Arts Museum / Decorative Arts Museum - 1882
17th c Dutch painting, 18th-20th c art, handicraft, tools, coins - library 18438

Mecklenburgisches Volkskundemuseum Schwerin, Freilichtmuseum Schwerin-Mueß, Alte Crivitzer Landstr 13, 19063 Schwerin - T: (0385) 208410, Fax: 2180074, E-mail: -volkskundemuseum.schwerin@web.de. Head: Dr. Gesine Kröhnert
Open Air Museum / Agriculture Museum / Local Museum / Folklore Museum 18439

Schleifmühle Schwerin, Stadtgeschichts- und Museumsverein Schwerin e.V., Schleifmühlenweg 1, 19061 Schwerin - T: (0385) 562751, Fax: 565617, E-mail: schleifmuehle@prohistoria.de, Internet: http://www.schleifmuehle-schwerin.de
Science&Tech Museum - 1985 18440

Schlossmuseum, Staatliches Museum Schwerin, Lennéstr 1, 19053 Schwerin - T: (0385) 565738, Fax: 563091, E-mail: otto@museum-schwerin.de, Internet: http://www.museum-schwerin.de. Head: Prof. Dr. Kornelia von Berswordt
Fine Arts Museum
Historic castle, seat of the state parliament, ancestral portrait gallery, state apartments, paintings Dresden china and other European porcelain from the 18th-20th c 18441

Stadtgeschichtsmuseum Schwerin, Museen der Landeshauptstadt Schwerin, Großer Moor 38, 19055 Schwerin - T: (0385) 560971, Fax: 565617, E-mail: stadtgeschichtsmuseum@prohistoria.de, Internet: http://www.stadtgeschichtsverein-schwerin.de/stadtgeschichtsmuseum. Head: Gesine Kröhnert
Local Museum - 1966
History of the town of Schwerin 18442

Technisches Landesmuseum, c/o IHK zu Schwerin, Schloßstr 17, 19053 Schwerin - T: (0385) 512925, Fax: 512926, E-mail: info@tlm-mv.de, Internet: http://www.tlm-mv.de. Head: Dr. Wolf Karge
Science&Tech Museum - 1961
Energy, traffic, informationstechnology, metallurgy, relationship man and technology, aero- and space industry 18443

Schwerte

Kunstverein Schwerte e.V., Kötterbachstr 2, 58239 Schwerte - T: (02304) 22175, Fax: 22175
Association with Coll 18444

Ruhrtalmuseum, Brückstr 14, 58239 Schwerte - T: (02304) 219950, Fax: 219902, E-mail: RTM@ruhrtalmuseum.de, Internet: http://www.ruhrtalmuseum.de. Head: John Loftus
Local Museum - 1933 18445

Schwesing

KZ-Gedenkstätte Husum-Schwesing, 25813 Schwesing - T: (04841) 89730, Fax: 8973111, E-mail: kulturamt@nordfriesland.de
Historic Site 18446

Schwetzingen

Schloß Schwetzingen, Schloß, Mittelbau, 68723 Schwetzingen - T: (06202) 81484, Fax: 81386, E-mail: info@schloss-schwetzingen.de, Internet: http://www.schloss-schwetzingen.de. Head: A. Falz
Historic Site / Decorative Arts Museum - 1918
Medieval castle with moat, 18th c Apollo temple, Rococo theatre (1752), 18th-19th c interiors and furnishings, paintings 18447

Xylon Museum, Schloßgarten 2, 68723 Schwetzingen - T: (06202) 17400
Fine Arts Museum 18448

Sebnitz

Sebnitzer Kunstblumen- und Heimatmuseum Prof. Alfred Meiche, Hertigswalder Str 12, 01855 Sebnitz - T: (035971) 52590, Fax: 53079
Local Museum / Special Museum - 1909
Regional hist, regional ethnography, regional art, hist of artificial flowers production 18449

Seebach, Baden

Erzstollen Silbergründle, Ruhesteinstr 21, 77889 Seebach, Baden - T: (07842) 948320, Fax: 948399, E-mail: tourist-info@seebach.de, Internet: http://www.seebach.de. Head: Reinhard Schmälzle
Science&Tech Museum 18450

Heimatmuseum Vollmers Mühle, Hilsenhof 1, 77889 Seebach, Baden - T: (07842) 948320, Fax: 948399, E-mail: tourist-info@seebach.de, Internet: http://www.seebach.de
Local Museum - 1979
Water mill from 18th c, household utensils 18451

Trachten- und Volkskunstmuseum, Ruhesteinstr 9, 77889 Seebach, Baden - T: (07842) 3188, Fax: 600002
Folklore Museum 18452

Seebad Bansin

Museum Rolf Werner, Seestr 60, 17429 Seebad Bansin - T: (038378) 29228. Head: Dr. Sigrid Werner
Fine Arts Museum
Life and works by the painter and graphic designer from 1930 to 1989 18453

Seebad Heringsdorf

Maxim-Gorki-Gedächtnisstätte, Maxim-Gorki-Str 13, 17424 Seebad Heringsdorf - T: (038378) 22770, Fax: 2964. Head: Dr. Karin Lehmann
Historical Museum - 1948
Memorabilia on poet Maksim Gorki former home 18454

Seebruck

Römermuseum Bedaium, Heimat-und Geschichtsverein Bedaium in Seebruck e.V, Römerstr 3, 83358 Seebruck - T: (08667) 7503, Fax: 809248, E-mail: info@roemermuseum-seebruck.de, Internet: http://www.roemermuseum-seebruck.de
Archaeological Museum
Celtic and Roman finds 18455

Seefeld, Oberbayern

Staatliches Museum für Ägyptische Kunst, Schloß Seefeld, 82229 Seefeld, Oberbayern - T: (08152) 70652, 79394, Fax: 79394, Internet: http://www.aegyptisches-museum-muenchen.de. Head: Dr. Sylvia Schoske
Museum of Classical Antiquities - 1994
Egyptian art 18456

Seeg

Heimatmuseum Seeg, Hauptstr 66, 87637 Seeg - T: (08364) 98300
Local Museum - 1986
Local crafts and hist, agricultural tools 18457

Seeheilbad Graal-Müritz

Heimatstube Seeheilbad Graal-Müritz, Parkstr 21, 18181 Seeheilbad Graal-Müritz - T: (038206) 77599
Local Museum 18458

Seeheim-Jugenheim

Gemeindemuseum im Historischen Rathaus, Ober-Beerbacher-Str 1, 64342 Seeheim-Jugenheim - T: (06257) 84750, Fax: 836352, E-mail: Juergen.Eck@telekom.de
Local Museum - 1981
Hist of the castle 18459

Seelow

Gedenkstätte/Museum Seelower Höhen, Küstriner Str 28a, 15306 Seelow - T: (03346) 597, Fax: 598, Internet: http://www.kultur-in-mol.de. Head: Heidemarie Daher
Historical Museum
Memorial site to the battles during WWII 18460

Seelze

Heimatmuseum Seelze, Im Sande 14, Letter, 30926 Seelze - T: (0511) 404555, 485704, Internet: http://www.heimatmuseum-seelze.de
Local Museum - 1991
Early hist, various trade workshops 18461

Seeon

Kloster Seeon, Klosterweg 1, 83370 Seeon - T: (08624) 8970, Fax: 897210, E-mail: kultur@kloster-seeon.de, Internet: http://www.kloster-seeon.de. Head: Wolfgang Stamm
Historic Site 18462

Seesen

Heimatmuseum Rhüden, An der Schule, 38723 Seesen - T: (05384) 318
Local Museum - 1963
Fossils, trade, agricultural implements, furniture and clothes 18463

Städtisches Heimatmuseum, Wilhelmspl 4, 38723 Seesen - T: (05381) 48891. Head:
Local Museum - 1964
William Steinway - Steinway and Sons, minerals, agricultural tools, tin industry - archive 18464

Wilhelm-Busch-Gedenkstätte, Wilhelm-Busch-Gesellschaft, Pastor-Nöldeke-Weg 7, 38723 Seesen - T: (05384) 90886
Special Museum - 1950
Coll of paintings, graphics and manuscripts by Wilhelm Busch, photographies, letters, parsonage where he lived (1898-1908) 18465

Seevetal

Telefonmuseum Hittfelder Bahnhof, Gustav-Becker-Str 9, 21218 Seevetal - T: (04105) 12676, Fax: 159976, E-mail: telefonmuseum.hittfeld@t-online.de, Internet: http://www.telefonmuseum-hittfeld.de. Head: Rainer Pfeiffer
Science&Tech Museum 18466

Sehnde

Hannoversches Straßenbahn-Museum, Hohenfelser Str 16, 31319 Sehnde - T: (0511) 6463312, Fax: 6463312, E-mail: hsminfo@gmx.de, Internet: http:/www.wehmingen.de. Head: Klaus Flegel-Wantier
Science&Tech Museum - 1987
Ancient tramways from all over the Federal Republic of Germany - archive 18467

Seifhennersdorf

Karasek-Museum, Nordstr 21a, 02782 Seifhennersdorf - T: (03586) 406757, Fax: 406758
Local Museum - 1977
Local hist, geology, paleontology, mining 18468

Seitenroda

Museum Leuchtenburg, Dorfstr 100, 07768 Seitenroda - T: (036424) 22258, Fax: 22258. Head: Kurt Haufschild
Local Museum - 1906
Thuringian porcelain 18469

Selb

Europäisches Industriemuseum für Porzellan und technische Keramik, Bahnhofstr 3, 95100 Selb - T: (09287) 918000, Fax: 9180030, E-mail: info@eimpk.de, Internet: http://www.eimpk.de. Head: Wilhelm Siemen
Science&Tech Museum - 1996
Hist of porcelain industry 18470

Selfkant

Kleines Guß-Museum, Neustr 25, 52538 Selfkant - T: (02456) 2207
Decorative Arts Museum 18471

Seligenstadt

Ehemalige Benediktinerabtei, Kloserhof 2, 63500 Seligenstadt - T: (06182) 22640, Fax: 28726. Head: Dr. Kai R. Mathieu
Religious Arts Museum
Baroque interior, furniture - Library 18472

Kreismuseum der Heimatvertriebenen, Klosterhof 2, 63500 Seligenstadt - T: (06182) 20455, Fax: 20455. Head: Achim Zöller
Historical Museum - 1988
Exhibits from former German provinces in Eastern Europe, hist of the expellees after WWII, crafts, lace making, domestic objects, annual Easter market 18473

Landschaftsmuseum, Klosterhof 2, 63500 Seligenstadt - T: (06182) 20455, Fax: 20455. Head: Achim Zöller
Local Museum - 1937/95
Beadwork, political documents, crafts 18474

Selm

Schloss Cappenberg, Schlossberg, 59379 Selm - T: (02303) 271041, Fax: 272096. Head: Thomas Hengstenberg
Public Gallery
Art and art history, regional history 18475

Selsingen

Heimathaus Greven Worth, Greven Worth 8, 27446 Selsingen - T: (04284) 326
Local Museum
Farmyard, agricultural implements 18476

Senden, Westfalen

Schiffs- und Marinemuseum, Kanalstr 24-30, 48308 Senden, Westfalen - T: (02597) 8320, Fax: 8320. Head: H.F. Klapp
Ethnology Museum / Historical Museum - 1983
Shipping instruments from four centuries, 'Buddelschiffe', hist sailing boats and passenger shipping, sea shells 18477

Senftenberg

Festungsanlage-Museum Senftenberg, Schloß, 01968 Senftenberg - T: (03573) 2628, Fax: 2628. Head: Christel Lehmann-Enders
Local Museum - 1907
Ancient and early history, city and castle history, mining, peasant crafts and domestic utensils, religious art 18478

Galerie am Schloß, Schloß, 01968 Senftenberg - T: (03573) 2628, Fax: 2628. Head: Christel Lehmann-Enders
Public Gallery 18479

Kreismuseum Senftenberg → Festungsanlage-Museum Senftenberg

Senheim

Weinmuseum Schlagkamp-Desoye Senheim, Zeller Str 11, 56820 Senheim - T: (02673) 4381, Fax: 4351, E-mail: schlagkamp@t-online.de, Internet: http://www.schlagkamp-desoye.de. Head: Dieter Schlagkamp
Agriculture Museum - 1969
Wine presses and other implements used in Mosel viticulture, cellars, destillery 18480

Seßlach

Heimatmuseum Seßlach, Rathaus, Marktpl 98, 96145 Seßlach - T: (09569) 922540, Fax: 922525, Internet: http://www.sesslach.de
Local Museum - 1985
Peasant life 18481

Siebenlehn

Heimatmuseum Siebenlehn, Otto-Altenkirch-Str 44, 09634 Siebenlehn - T: (035242) 68224
Local Museum 18482

Siegbach

Heimatmuseum Siegbach, Hohe Str 6, 35768 Siegbach - T: (02778) 2129
Local Museum - 1977
Hist of mining, trade 18483

Siegburg

Schatzkammer der katholischen Pfarrkirche Sankt Servatius, Mühlenstr 6, 53721 Siegburg - T: (02241) 63146
Religious Arts Museum
Religious shrines, altars, medieval textiles 18484

Stadtmuseum Siegburg, Markt 46, 53721 Siegburg - T: (02241) 9698510, Fax: 9698525, E-mail: stadtmuseum@siegburg.de, Internet: http://www.siegburg.de. Head: Dr. Gert Fischer
Local Museum / Public Gallery - 1990
Rhineland stone ware, fossils, geology 18485

Torhaus-Museum, Alfred-Keller-Str 55, 53721 Siegburg - T: (02241) 102325, E-mail: andrea.korte-boeger@siegburg.de. Head: Dr. Andrea Korte-Böger
Local Museum 18486

Siegen

Glocken-Museum Machinek, In der Hubach 50, Eiserfeld, 57080 Siegen - T: (0271) 387331. Head: Hubert Machinek
Special Museum - 1959
Bells, small rod and other sound inst 18487

Museum für Gegenwartskunst Siegen, Unteres Schloß 1, 57052 Siegen - T: (0271) 4057710, Fax: 4057732, E-mail: info@kunstmuseum-siegen.de, Internet: http://www.kunstmuseum-siegen.de. Head: N.N.
Fine Arts Museum - 2001
Development of art in photography, film and computer; present day art 18488

Siegerlandmuseum mit Ausstellungsforum Haus Oranienstraße, Oberes Schloß Burgstr/Oranienstr 9, 57072 Siegen - T: (0271) 230410, Fax: 2304120. Head: Prof. Dr. Ursula Blanchebarbe
Local Museum - 1905
Prehist, paintings, graphics, folk art - library 18489

Städtische Galerie Haus Seel, Kornmarkt 20, 57072 Siegen - T: (0271) 4041259, Fax: 4042745. Head: Gerhard Lange
Fine Arts Museum - 1962 18490

Siegenburg

Ortsgeschichtliches Museum, Hopfenstr 2, 93354 Siegenburg - T: (09444) 97840, Fax: 978424
Local Museum - 1987
Local hist and crafts 18491

Siegsdorf

Südostbayerisches Naturkunde- und Mammut-Museum, Auenstr 2, 83313 Siegsdorf - T: (08662) 13316, Fax: 13316, E-mail: mammut@museum-siegsdorf.de, Internet: http://www.museum-siegsdorf.de. Head: Dr. Robert Darga
Natural History Museum
Geology and fossils, Ice Age 18492

Wastlbauernhof, Mauer 5, 83313 Siegsdorf - T: (08662) 7841
Agriculture Museum 18493

Sierksdorf

Bananenmuseum, Prof.-Haas-Str 59, 23730 Sierksdorf - T: (04563) 8335, Fax: 8279, E-mail: paulstell@a.d.com, Internet: http://www.awgd.de/projekte/mm2424/pauli/banane/home.html
Natural History Museum 18494

Sigmaringen

Fürstlich Hohenzollernsche Sammlungen, Schloß, 72488 Sigmaringen - T: (07571) 729160, Fax: 729105, E-mail: kempf@hohenzollern.com, Internet: http://www.hohenzollern.com. Head: Peter Kempf
Historical Museum - 1867
Prehistory, 15th-16th c Alemannic art, 14th-20th c weapons - library, archives 18495

Heimatmuseum Runder Turm, Antonstr 22, 72488 Sigmaringen - T: (07571) 106223, Fax: 106166, E-mail: tourismus@sigmaringen.de, Internet: http://www.sigmaringen.de
Local Museum - 1987
Local hist, paintings, coins 18496

Städtische Galerie in der Alten Schule, Antonstr, 72488 Sigmaringen - T: (07571) 13081
Public Gallery 18497

Simbach am Inn

Heimatmuseum Simbach am Inn, Innstr 21, 84359 Simbach am Inn - T: (08571) 920605, Fax: 60662, E-mail: brigitte.schwarzbauer@simbach.de, Internet: http://simbach.de
Local Museum - 1912
Town hist 18498

Simmelsdorf

Historische Fahrzeugsammlung, Nürnberger Str 4, 91245 Simmelsdorf - T: (0911) 357575, Fax: 3609454. Head: Dr. Bernhard Knöchlein
Science&Tech Museum - 1984
Old automobiles 18499

Simmern, Hunsrück

Hunsrückmuseum, Schloßpl, 55469 Simmern, Hunsrück - T: (06761) 7009, Fax: 908044, E-mail: info@hunsrueck-museum.de, Internet: http://www.hunsrueck-museum.de. Head: Dr. Fritz Schellack
Local Museum 18500

Sindelfingen

Deutsches Fleischermuseum, Hohenstaufenstr 8, 71067 Sindelfingen
Special Museum 18501

Galerie der Stadt Sindelfingen, Marktpl 1, 71063 Sindelfingen - T: (07031) 94392, Fax: 94790, E-mail: Galerie@Sindelfingen.de, Internet: http://www.Sindelfingen.de/. Head: Otto Pannewitz
Fine Arts Museum - 1990
Art of South-Germany since 1870, Coll Lütze II 18502

Haus der Donauschwaben, Sammlungen heimatlichen Erbes, Goldmühlestr 30, 71065 Sindelfingen - T: (07031) 7937630, Fax: 3937640
Local Museum 18503

Stadtmuseum Sindelfingen, Lange Str 13, 71063 Sindelfingen - T: (07031) 94212, Fax: 94556, E-mail: museum@sindelfingen.de, Internet: http://www.@sindelfingen.de. Head: Horst Zecha

Local Museum - 1958
Hand-weaving in the 19th c, agricultural machinery, household articles, archeological finds, historical toys 18504

Singen, Hohentwiel

Hegau-Museum, Gräfl. Schloß, Am Schloßgarten 2, 78224 Singen, Hohentwiel - T: (07731) 85267, Fax: 85696, Internet: http://www.singen.de. Head: Ralph Stephan
Natural History Museum / Archaeological Museum - 1951
Mineralogy, geology, paleontology, butterflies, regional archaeological coll 18505

Städtisches Kunstmuseum Singen, Ekkehardstr 10, 78224 Singen, Hohentwiel - T: (07731) 85270, 85271, Fax: 85373. Head: Christoph Bauer
Fine Arts Museum - 1990
Regional modern and contemporary art 18506

Sinsheim

Auto & Technik Museum, Obere Au 2, 74889 Sinsheim - T: (07261) 92990, Fax: 13916, E-mail: info@technik-museum.de, Internet: http://www.technik-museum.de. Head: Hermann Layher
Science&Tech Museum - 1981
Cars, oldtimer, motorcycles, locomotives, military 18507

Museum der Stadt Sinsheim, Hauptstr 92, 74889 Sinsheim - T: (07261) 404950, Fax: 4044545, E-mail: museum@sinsheim.de, Internet: http://www.sinsheim.de. Head: Holger Friedrich
Local Museum / Historical Museum - 1946
Local hist, trades and guilds, monastery 11th c, General Franz Singel, archaeology, emigration to the USA, revolution 1848/49 18508

Museumshof Lerchennest - Friedrich-der-Große-Museum, Lerchennestsr 18, 74889 Sinsheim - T: (07261) 3934. Head: Hans Appenzeller
Historical Museum - 1974 18509

Pomázer Heimatstube, Eichelbergerstr 1, 74889 Sinsheim - T: (07265) 218
Folklore Museum 18510

Sinzig, Rhein

Museum für Holzhandwerke, Welfenstr 5, 53489 Sinzig, Rhein - T: (02642) 993394, Fax: 993395
Historical Museum
Wood, craft 18511

Sittensen

Heimathaus Sittensen, Breslauer Str 4, 27419 Sittensen - T: (04282) 5422
Local Museum
Beekeeping, folk costumes, domestic and trade implements 18512

Sögel

Emslandmuseum Schloß Clemenswerth, 49751 Sögel - T: (05952) 932325, Fax: 932330, E-mail: schloss@clemenswerth.de, Internet: http://www.clemenswerth.de. Head: Eckard Wagner
Local Museum - 1972
Life-hist of Clemens August (1700-1761) Duke of Bavaria, Prince-Elector and Archbishop of Cologne, his passions for hunting and collecting porcelain, faiences and engraved glass-goblets, the Teutonic Order under leadership of Clemens August, local history, contemporary ceramic art 18513

Söhlde

Heimatmuseum Hoheneggelsen, Hauptstr 28, 31185 Söhlde - T: (05129) 286
Local Museum
Local hist, agricultural folk art and implements 18514

Sömmerda

Ur- und Frühgeschichtliche Ausstellung, Stadtmauertürme, 99610 Sömmerda - T: (03634) 22112
Archaeological Museum 18515

Soest

Burghofmuseum, Stadtgeschichtliches Museum, Burghofstr 22, 59494 Soest - T: (02921) 1031020, Fax: 1039999, E-mail: reimer.moeller@t-online.de. Head: Dr. Reimer Möller
Local Museum
Town hist 18516

Osthofentor-Museum, Wehrkundliches Museum zur Stadtgeschichte, Osthofenstr, 59494 Soest - T: (02921) 1031020, Fax: 1031299, E-mail: touristinfo@soest.de, Internet: http://www.soest.de. Head: Dr. Reimer Möller
Historical Museum / Military Museum 18517

Sankt Patrokli-Dom-Museum Soest, Propst-Nübel-Str 2, 59494 Soest - T: (02921) 13302. Head: Karl-Josef zu Heiden
Religious Arts Museum - 1968
12th-19th c liturgical utensils, stone inscriptions, documentation on the architectural history of the dome, ecclesiastical art 18518

Wilhelm-Morgner-Haus, Thomästr 2, 59494 Soest - T: (02921) 13524, Fax: 1031299, E-mail: touristinfo@soest.de, Internet: http://www.soest.de. Head: Dr. Reimer Möller
Fine Arts Museum - 1962
Expressionism, paintings, drawings and prints by Wilhelm Morgner (1891-1917) - cultural center 18519

Sohland

Heimatmuseum, Hainspacher Str 19, 02689 Sohland - T: (035936) 37190
Local Museum - 1957
18th c weaver's house, historic weaving shops, local history 18520

Solingen

Bergisches Museum Schloß Burg, Schloßpl 2, 42659 Solingen - T: (0212) 242260, Fax: 2422640, E-mail: schloss.burg@t-online.de, Internet: http://www.schlossburg.de. Head: Dr. Dirk Soechting
Local Museum - 1894
13th c fortress, wallpaintings (1900), medieval to 18th c weapons, medieval, Renaissance and 18th-19th c local culture, furniture, domestic utensils, ceramics, glass, prehistory, numismatic cabinet, pharmaceutical history 18521

Deutsches Klingenmuseum Solingen, Klosterhof 4, 42653 Solingen - T: (0212) 258360, Fax: 2583630, E-mail: klingenmuseum@solingen.de, Internet: http://www.klingenmuseum.de. Head: Dr. Barbara Grotkamp-Schepers
Special Museum - 1904
Cutlery, art of the table, knives, edged weapons, 3,000 years of smithwork - library 18522

Museum Baden, Wuppertaler Str 160, 42653 Solingen - T: (0212) 258140, Fax: 2581444, E-mail: museum-baden@t-online.de, Internet: http://www.museum-baden.de. Head: Dr. Rolf Jessewitsch
Fine Arts Museum 18523

Rheinisches Industriemuseum, Außenstelle Solingen, Merscheider Str 289-297, 42699 Solingen - T: (0212) 232410, Fax: 320429, E-mail: d.langen@mail.lvr.de. Head: Dr. Jochem Putsch
Historical Museum
Cutler industry 18524

Solinger Fotoforum, Börsenstr 87, 42657 Solingen - T: (0212) 78261
Public Gallery 18525

Solms

Besucherbergwerk Grube Fortuna, Grube Fortuna 01, Oberbiel, 35606 Solms - T: (06443) 82460, Fax: 2043, E-mail: grube-fortuna@t-online.de, Internet: http://www.grube-fortuna.de
Science&Tech Museum - 1987
Hist of mining 18526

Feld- und Grubenbahnmuseum, Grube Fortuna, Oberbiel, 35606 Solms - T: (06441) 47772. Head: Rolf Georg
Science&Tech Museum
Narrow-gauge railway, carriages for mining 18527

Kloster Altenberg, Königsberger Diakonissen-Mutterhaus der Barmherzigkeit, 35606 Solms - T: (06441) 23014
Religious Arts Museum 18528

Leica Stammbaum und Museum, c/o Leica Camera AG, Oskar Barnack-Str 11, 35606 Solms - T: (06442) 208593, Fax: 208333, Internet: http://www.leica-camera.com. Head: Sigfried Brueck
Science&Tech Museum
History and development of the 35mm camera 18529

Solnhofen

Bürgermeister-Müller-Museum, Bahnhofstr 8, Rathaus, 91807 Solnhofen - T: (09145) 832020, Fax: 832050, E-mail: solnhofen@wugnet.de, Internet: http://www.solnhofen.de. Head: Dr. Martin Röper
Local Museum - 1969
Fossils, lithographs 18530

Soltau

Museum Soltau, Rühberg 3, 29614 Soltau - T: (05191) 4717, 14449. Head: Hans Schlieper
Local Museum - 1966
Ice Age geology, folk art by war prisoners 18531

Norddeutsches Spielzeugmuseum, Poststr 7, 29614 Soltau - T: (05191) 82182, Fax: 82181, E-mail: ernstsoltau@hotmail.com. Head: Hannelore Ernst, Mathias Ernst
Decorative Arts Museum - 1984
Dolls, doll's houses, railways, teddy bears, games, toy grocer's shop, toy animal department 18532

Sommerach

Theo-Steinbrenner-Turm-Museum, Maintorstr 25, 97334 Sommerach - T: (09381) 4143, (09324) 1054, Fax: 2709. Head: Theophil Steinbrenner
Fine Arts Museum - 1987
Work of the artist Theo Steinbrenner 18533

Sondershausen

Schlossmuseum Sondershausen, Schloss, 99706 Sondershausen - T: (03632) 663120, Fax: 663110, E-mail: schlossmuseum.sdh@t-online.de, Internet: http://schlossmuseum.sondershausen.de. Head: Christa Hirschler
Local Museum / Fine Arts Museum / Music Museum - 1901
Palace rooms, furnishings, Baroque-Biedermeier paintings and applied arts, geology, paleontology, ancient early and local history, music history, numismatics, decorative objects 18534

Sonneberg, Thüringen

Deutsches Spielzeugmuseum, Beethovenstr 10, 96515 Sonneberg, Thüringen - T: (03675) 702856, Fax: 742817, E-mail: -DeutschesSpielzeugmuseum@t-online.de, Internet: http://www.spielzeugmuseum-sonnenberg.de. Head: Dr. Ernst Hofmann
Decorative Arts Museum - 1901
Hist of area and industry, toys - library 18535

Sonnenbühl

Ostereimuseum, Steigstr 8, 72820 Sonnenbühl - T: (07128) 774, Fax: 92550, E-mail: info@sonnenbuehl.de, Internet: http://www.sonnenbuehl.de. Head: Anna Barkefeld
Folklore Museum 18536

Sontheim an der Brenz

Heimatmuseum Schloß Brenz, Schloß Benz, 89567 Sontheim an der Brenz - T: (07325) 4960, 1734, Fax: 1747
Local Museum - 1906
Geology, ceramics, weapons 18537

Sonthofen

Gebirgsjägermuseum, Traditionssammlung der Gebirgstruppe Sonthofen, Grünten Kaserne, Salzweg 24, 87527 Sonthofen - T: (08321) 724068, Fax: 2781064. Head: Dieter Bischoff
Military Museum
Hist of the German mountain troops 18538

Heimathaus Sonthofen, Sonnenstr 1, 87527 Sonthofen - T: (08321) 3300, Fax: 615294, E-mail: stadt@sonthofen.de, Internet: http://www.sonthofen.de. Head: Sonja Karnath
Local Museum - 1930
Local hist 18539

Sontra

Mühlenmuseum, Steinmühlenweg 5, 36205 Sontra - T: (05653) 5433
Science&Tech Museum - 1985
Hist of the mill, agricultural implements 18540

Museum im Boyneburgischen Schloß, Schloßpl 1, 36205 Sontra - T: (05658) 8294, Fax: 8490. Head: Dorette von Boyneburgh
Historical Museum 18541

Spaichingen

Gewerbe-Museum, Bahnhofstr 5, 78549 Spaichingen - T: (07424) 501445, Fax: 501445. Head: Angelika Feldes
Local Museum - 1991
Hist of crafts and industrialization, local hist, geology, archeology 18542

Spalt

Feuerwehrmuseum, Altes Rathaus, 91174 Spalt - T: (09175) 79650, Fax: 796580, E-mail: poststelle@spalt.de, Internet: http://www.spalt.de
Science&Tech Museum
Fire brigade 18543

Heimatstuben im Arrestturm, Turmgasse 1, 91174 Spalt - T: (09175) 79917
Local Museum - 1979 18544

Spangenberg

Heimatmuseum Spangenberg, Burgsitz 2-3, 34286 Spangenberg - T: (05663) 50900, Fax: 509026
Local Museum - 1972
Geology, trade workshops, furniture, town hist 18545

Jagd- und Schloßmuseum Spangenberg, Schloß, 34286 Spangenberg - T: (05663) 385, Fax: 509026
Historical Museum - 1985
Hunting trophies, antlers, boar weapons, genre paintings, furniture 18546

Sperenberg

Heimatstube Sperenberg, Hauptstr 1, 15838 Sperenberg - T: (033703) 7344
Local Museum - 1965
Local hist, native hist, folk art 18547

Speyer

Historisches Museum der Pfalz, Dompl, 67324 Speyer - T: (06232) 620222, Fax: 132540, E-mail: info@museum.speyer.de, Internet: http://www.museum.speyer.de. Head: Dr. Cornelia Ewigleben
Historical Museum / Decorative Arts Museum / Fine Arts Museum / Religious Arts Museum - 1869
Wine museum, hist from prehist to modern times, cathedral treasure chamber - children's museum 18548

Kunstverein Speyer, Kulturhof, Flachgasse 3, 67346 Speyer - T: (06232) 919858, Fax: 919858, Internet: http://www.speyer.de. Head: Franz Dudenhöffer
Association with Coll 18549

Technik Museum Speyer, Geibstr 2, 67346 Speyer - T: (06232) 67080, Fax: 670820, E-mail: speyer@technik-museum.de, Internet: http://www.technik-museum.de. Head: Hermann Layher
Science&Tech Museum - 1991
Oldtimer, locomotives, aeroplanes (eg AN-22), Submarine U9, mechanical music instruments, fire rescue vehicles, marine and models building, historical fashion - IMAX theatre 18550

Spiekeroog

Inselmuseum Spiekeroog, Noorderloog 1, 26474 Spiekeroog - T: (04976) 910120, Fax: 910128
Local Museum - 1995 18551

Museum der Hermann-Lietz-Schule, Hellerpad 2, 26474 Spiekeroog - T: (04976) 413, 414
Historical Museum 18552

Spremberg

Niederlausitzer Heidemuseum, Regionale Forschungs- und Bildungsstätte für Geschichte, Volks- und Landschaftskunde, Schloßbezirk 3, 03130 Spremberg - T: (03563) 602350, Fax: 602353, E-mail: kontakt@heidemuseum.de, Internet: http://www.heidemuseum.de. Head: Manfred Ihle
Local Museum - 1911
Peasant life, cloth making, furniture household articles ancient and early hist 18553

Sprendlingen

Heimatmuseum Sprendlingen, Sankt-Johanner-Str 14, 55576 Sprendlingen - T: (06701) 7197
Local Museum 18554

Springe

Jagdschau im Jagdschloss Springe, Jagdschloss, 31832 Springe - T: (05041) 94680, Fax: 946855, E-mail: Poststelle@nfa-saupark.niedersachsen.de. Head: Joachim Menzel
Historical Museum - 1967
Hist of hunting, hunting animals 18555

Museum auf dem Burghof, Auf dem Burghof 1a, 31832 Springe - T: (05041) 61705, Fax: 63536, E-mail: info@museum-springe.de/com, Internet: http://www.museum-springe.de/com. Head: Prof. Dr. H. Callies
Historical Museum - 1969
Textile techniques and fashion, Heinrich Goebel, inventor of the light bulp 18556

Sprockhövel

Heimatstube Am Grevendiek, Hauptstr 85, 45549 Sprockhövel - T: (02324) 71606
Local Museum / Folklore Museum / Science&Tech Museum - 1982/1997
Hist of mining, cultural life - archive 18557

Stade

Alt-Stade im Baumhaus (Privatmuseum), Wasser Ost 28, 21682 Stade - T: (04141) 45434, Fax: 45434
Local Museum 18558

Freilichtmuseum, Auf der Insel, 21680 Stade - T: (04141) 951821, Fax: 45751, E-mail: -schwedenspeicher@t-online.de, Internet: http://www.schwedenspeicher.de. Head: Dr. Gerd Mettjes
Open Air Museum - 1913
Altländer farmhouse of 1734 18559

Heimatmuseum Stade, Inselstr 12, 21682 Stade - T: (04141) 2332, Fax: 45751, E-mail: -schwedenspeicher@t-online.de, Internet: http://www.schwedenspeicher.de. Head: Dr. Gerd Mettjes
Local Museum / Folklore Museum - 1904
Bourgeois and farmers' culture of "Altes Land", traditional costumes 18560

Kulturgeschichtliches Museum im Elbe-Weser-Gebiet, Schwedenspeicher-Museum, Wasser West 39, 21682 Stade - T: (04141) 3222, Fax: 45751, E-mail: schwedenspeicher@t-online.de, Internet: http://www.Schwedenspeicher.de. Head: Dr. Gerd Mettjes
Historical Museum - 1977
20th c Art, archaeology, town hist, coins 18561

Kunsthaus in Stade, Wasser West 7, 21682 Stade - T: (04141) 44824, Fax: 45751, E-mail: -schwedenspeicher@t-online.de, Internet: http://www.Schwedenspeicher.de. Head: Dr. Gerd Mettjes
Fine Arts Museum - 1987
Paintings, Art colonies 18562

Patenschaftsmuseum Goldalp in Ostpreußen, Große Schmiedestr 5, 21682 Stade - T: (04141) 64011
Local Museum - 1970/87
Regional hist 18563

Technik- und Verkehrsmuseum, Freiburger Str 60, 21682 Stade - T: (04141) 2888, Fax: 43898, E-mail: technikmuseum.std@city-map.de, Internet: http://www.city-map.de/technikmuseum. Head: K. Heinz Pittner
Science&Tech Museum
Public transport, horse carriages, railway, bicycles, steam and diesel technic, railway, trades and crafts, energy, broadcast, printing, fire fighting 18564

Stadt Wehlen

Heimatmuseum Wehlen, Lohmener Str 18, 01829 Stadt Wehlen - T: (035024) 70413, Fax: 70434
Local Museum
Stone masonry, glass beehive, shipping on the river Elbe 18565

Stadthagen

Museum Amtspforte Stadthagen, Obernstr 32a, 31655 Stadthagen - T: (05721) 924900, Fax: 782110, E-mail: stadtverwaltung@stadthagen.de, Internet: http://www.stadthagen.de. Head: Susanne Slanina
Local Museum - 1992
Town hist, economic life and folk costumes 18566

Stadtilm

Heimatmuseum Stadtilm, Str der Einheit 1, 99326 Stadtilm - T: (03629) 668837, Fax: 668812, E-mail: stadtstadtilm@stadtilm.de, Internet: http://www.stadtilm.de
Local Museum - 1902
Geology, early hist, local crafts and industry, 17th-19th c peasant furnishings, hist of former nuclear laboratory of Dr. Diebner 18567

Stadtlauringen

Brauhausmuseum, Marktpl 1, 97488 Stadtlauringen - T: (09724) 91040, Fax: 910450
Science&Tech Museum 18568

Gerätesammlung Georg Bauer, Marktpl 16, 97488 Stadtlauringen - T: (09724) 2979
Agriculture Museum / Science&Tech Museum - 1975
Agricultural tools 18569

Stadtoldendorf

Stadtmuseum Stadtoldendorf, Amtsstr 8-10, 37627 Stadtoldendorf - T: (05532) 4255, Fax: 4255. Head: H. Walter
Local Museum - 1935
Local trade (pottery, glassworks), geology, mineralogy, paleontology 18570

Stadtprozelten

Feuerwehrmuseum, Hauptstr 131, 97909 Stadtprozelten - T: (09392) 97600, Fax: 976018
Science&Tech Museum
Hist of the local fire brigade 18571

Stadtsteinach

Heimatmuseum Stadtsteinach, Kulmbacher Str 11, 95346 Stadtsteinach - T: (09225) 95780, Fax: 957832, E-mail: tourismus@stadtsteinach.btl.de
Local Museum - 1989
Agricultural tools, religious folklore and town hist 18572

Staffelstein, Oberfranken

Museum der Stadt Staffelstein, Kirchgasse 13, 96231 Staffelstein, Oberfranken - T: (09573) 4160, Fax: 4170. Head: Alfred Meixner
Local Museum
Fossils, mineralogy and geology 18573

Petrefaktensammlung, Hanns-Seidel-Stiftung, Kloster Banz, 96231 Staffelstein, Oberfranken - T: (09573) 33744, Fax: 33733, E-mail: banz@HSS.de. Head: H. König
Natural History Museum - 1829
Paleontology, Egyptian souvenirs of Duke Max in Bavaria 18574

Starnberg

Heimatmuseum Stadt Starnberg, Possenhofener Str 5, 82319 Starnberg - T: (08151) 772132/105, Fax: 772142, E-mail: Gerhard.Dix@starnberg.de, Internet: http://www.stadt.starnberg.de
Local Museum - 1914
Town hist, sculptures and paintings 18575

Staufen

Keramikmuseum Staufen, Badisches Landesmuseum Karlsruhe, Wettelbrunner Str 3, 79219 Staufen - T: (07633) 6721, Fax: 50593. Head: Prof. Dr. Harald Siebenmorgen
Decorative Arts Museum - 1991 18576

Stadtmuseum Stubenhaus, Marktpl, 79219 Staufen - T: (07633) 80553, Fax: 50593, E-mail: info@staufen.de, Internet: http://www.staufen.de. Head: G. Seeliger
Local Museum - 1990
Local hist 18577

Staufenberg, Hessen

Heimatmuseum Staufenberg, Kornblumenstr 8, 35460 Staufenberg, Hessen - T: (06406) 3775
Local Museum - 1965
Photo historic coll esp Leicas 18578

Stein

Schloß Faber-Castell, Nürnberger Str 2, 90546 Stein - T: (0911) 99650
Local Museum 18579

Steinach, Thüringen

Deutsches Schiefermuseum Steinach/Thür., Dr.-Max-Volk-Str 21, 96523 Steinach, Thüringen - T: (036762) 30619, Fax: 34814, E-mail: webmaster@steinach-thueringen.de
Natural History Museum - 1990
Slate, slate pencils, geology 18580

Steinau an der Straße

Brüder Grimm-Haus Steinau, Brüder-Grimm-Str 80, 36396 Steinau an der Straße - T: (06663) 7605, Fax: 963133, E-mail: verkehrsbuero.steinau@t-online.de, Internet: http://www.steinau.de. Head: Burkhard Kling
Special Museum - 1982/94
Brothers Grimm memorial, life and work of the brothers Grimm 18581

Puppenausstellung des Steinauer Marionetten-Theaters, Am Kumpen 2-4, 36396 Steinau an der Straße - T: (06663) 245. Head: Karl Magersuppe
Decorative Arts Museum 18582

Schloßmuseum mit Brüder-Grimm-Gedenkstätte, 36396 Steinau an der Straße - T: (06663) 6843, Fax: 7518. Head: Dr. Mathieu
Historical Museum - 1963
Permanent exhibition "Contemporaries of the Brothers Grimm between the Revolution and Restoration" 18583

Steinbach, Taunus

Heimatmuseum Das Schaufenster, Gartenstr 10, 61449 Steinbach, Taunus - T: (06171) 73236, Fax: 73236
Local Museum - 1979
Flags and flagpoles, clothing, farmers' tools and small machines, household implements - library, archive 18584

Steinberg, Oberpfalz

Heimat- und Braunkohlemuseum, Pfarrer-Geschwendtner-Str 5, 92449 Steinberg, Oberpfalz - T: (09431) 64477, Fax: 64581
Local Museum / Science&Tech Museum - 1994
Town hist and hist of mining 18585

Steinfurt

Stadtmuseum Steinfurt, An der Hohen Schule 13, 48565 Steinfurt - T: (02551) 5987, Fax: 919743, E-mail: stadt-steinfurt@t-online.de, Internet: http://www.heimatverein-burgsteinfurt.de
Local Museum - 1910 18586

Steingaden

Wallfahrtsmuseum, Wies 12, 86989 Steingaden - T: (08862) 932930, Fax: 9329310, Internet: http://www.wieskirche.de. Head: Prof. Dr. Hans Pörnbacher
Religious Arts Museum - 1988
Place of pilgrimage 18587

Steinheim am Albuch

Meteorkrater-Museum, Hochfeldweg 4, Sontheim, 89555 Steinheim am Albuch - T: (07329) 7370, 96060, Fax: 960670, E-mail: info@steinheim-am-albuch.de, Internet: http://www.steinheim.com
Natural History Museum - 1978 18588

Steinheim an der Murr

Museum zur Kloster- und Stadtgeschichte, Friedrichstr 8, 71711 Steinheim an der Murr - T: (07144) 2630, 207958, Fax: 263100, E-mail: hans-dietl@t-online.de, Internet: http://www.stadt-steinheim.de
Local Museum - 1989
Hist of the monastery and town 18589

Urmensch-Museum, Kirchpl 4, 71711 Steinheim an der Murr - T: (07144) 21226, Fax: 263100, Internet: http://www.stadt-steinheim.de
Ethnology Museum 18590

Steinhorst, Niedersachsen

Schulmuseum Steinhorst, Museen des Landkreises Gifhorn, Marktstr 20, 29367 Steinhorst, Niedersachsen - T: (05148) 4015, Fax: 911105, E-mail: schulmuseum.steinhorst@t-online.de, Internet: http://www.gifhorn.de/Museen/Schulm_A.htm
Special Museum - 1992
Hist. of school and education 18591

Steinwiesen

Heimatmuseum Steinwiesen, Am Kirchpl 1, 96349 Steinwiesen - T: (09262) 99150, Fax: 991525
Local Museum - 1987
Town hist 18592

Teichmühle, nördlich von Steinwiesen an der Rodach, 96349 Steinwiesen - T: (09262) 297, 562
Science&Tech Museum 18593

Stendal

Altmärkisches Museum, Schadewachten 48, 39576 Stendal - T: (03931) 212415. Head: Dr. Stephanie-Gerrit Bruer
Local Museum - 1888
Prehistory, early history, medieval sculpture, costumes of the Altmark - library 18594

Landes-Feuerwehrmuseum, Arneburgerstr 146a, 39576 Stendal - T: (03931) 212575
Science&Tech Museum 18595

Winckelmann-Museum, Winckelmannstr 36-37, 39576 Stendal - T: (03931) 215226, Fax: 215227, E-mail: Winckelmann-Stendal@t-online.de, Internet: http://www.winckelmann-gesellschaft.de. Head: Dr. Max Kunze, Dr. Stephanie-Gerrit Bruer
Archaeological Museum / Museum of Classical Antiquities / Fine Arts Museum - 1955
Memorabilia of archaeologist J.J. Winckelmann, Greek and Roman archeology, fine arts 18596

Stendenitz

Waldmuseum Stendenitz (Forest Museum), 16827 Stendenitz - T: (03391) 7144
Natural History Museum 18597

Sternberg

Heimatmuseum, Mühlenstr 6, 19406 Sternberg - T: (03847) 2162
Local Museum - 1977
Geology, pre and early hist, crafts, interior 18598

Stockach

Heimatmuseum im Bürgerhaus Adler Post, Hauptstr 7, 78333 Stockach - T: (07771) 8020, Fax: 5788
Local Museum - 1930
Prehist finds, postal service, guilds, carnival 18599

Stockstadt am Main

Heimatmuseum Stockstadt am Main, Maingasse 1, 63811 Stockstadt am Main - T: (06027) 20050, Fax: 200588
Local Museum - 1995
Town hist 18600

Stockstadt am Rhein

Regionalmuseum, Oberstr 8, 64589 Stockstadt am Rhein - T: (06158) 84739
Local Museum 18601

Stölln

Gedenkstätte der Luftfahrt, Am Gollenberg, 14728 Stölln - T: (033875) 32020
Science&Tech Museum 18602

Stolberg, Harz

Heimatmuseum, Niedergasse 19, 06547 Stolberg, Harz - T: (034654) 85960, 454, Fax: 729, E-mail: info@stadt-stolberg-harz.de, Internet: http://www.stadt-stolberg-harz.de
Local Museum - 1951
Geology, mining history, city history, industrial processing, mint workshop, numismatics, local crafts, memorial to theologian Thomas Müntzer (1489-1525) 18603

Museum Altes Bürgerhaus, Rittergasse 14, 06547 Stolberg, Harz - T: (034654) 85955, 454, Fax: 729, E-mail: info@stadt-stolberg-harz.de, Internet: http://www.stadt-stolberg-harz.de
Local Museum - 1932
15th c frame house, 16th-18th c living style, furnishings 18604

Stolberg, Rheinland

Heimat- und Handwerks Museum Stolberg, Burg Stolberg, Torburg, Lucia Weg, 52222 Stolberg, Rheinland - T: (02402) 81720
Local Museum 18605

Stolpen

Burg Stolpen, Schloßstr 10, 01833 Stolpen - T: (035973) 23410, Fax: 23419, E-mail: burg.stolpen@t-online.de, Internet: http://www.burg-stolpen.de. Head: Jürgen Major
Historical Museum / Historic Site - 1874
15th-16th c armaments, instruments of torture, cannon models, firefighting tools, Baroque everyday objects 18606

Museum zur Stadtgeschichte, Am Markt 27, 01833 Stolpen - T: (035973) 6341
Local Museum 18607

Stove bei Wismar

Dorfmuseum Stove, Nr 24, 23974 Stove bei Wismar - T: (038427) 247, Fax: 247
Local Museum 18608

Holländer-Windmühle, 23974 Stove bei Wismar - T: (038427) 247
Science&Tech Museum 18609

Stralsund

Deutsches Meeresmuseum, Museum für Meereskunde und Fischerei, Katharinenberg 14-20, 18439 Stralsund - T: (03831) 265010, Fax: 265060, E-mail: info@meeresmuseum.de, Internet: http://www.meeresmuseum.de. Head: Dr. Harald Benke
Natural History Museum - 1951
Marine organisms: plants and animals from all areas of the world oceans, marine geology and paleontology, Baltic Sea flora and fauna, esp marine mammals, oceanography and seafishery - Sea aquarium, natureum, nautineum 18610

Kulturhistorisches Museum Stralsund, Mönchstr 25-27, 18439 Stralsund - T: (03831) 28790, Fax: 280060, E-mail: KHM@gmx.net, Internet: http://www.stralsund.de. Head: Dr. Andreas Grüger
Historical Museum - 1858
Archeology, religious sculpture, town hist, military hist, crafts, customs, shipping, fishing, metalwork, porcelain, playing card coll, peasant culture, tools, costumes, toys, numismatics, European painting and prints, Northeast German painting and drawings, textiles, furniture 18611

Strasburg

Heimatmuseum Strasburg, Pfarrstr 22a, 17335 Strasburg - T: (039753) 27223, Fax: 21837
Local Museum 18612

Straubing

Bilder und Zeichen der Frömmigkeit - Sammlung Rudolf Kriss, Zweigmuseum des Bayerischen Nationalmuseums, Schloßpl 2b, 94315 Straubing - T: (09421) 21114, Fax: 944113, E-mail: stadt@straubing.baynet.de, Internet: http://www.straubing.de. Head: Dr. Nina Gockerell
Religious Arts Museum - 1995
Religious objects and folklore 18613

Gäubodenmuseum, Fraunhoferstr 9, 94315 Straubing - T: (09421) 81811, Fax: 81811, E-mail: stadt@straubing.de, Internet: http://www.straubing.de. Head: Dr. Johannes Prammer
Local Museum - 1880
Prehistory, Roman times, Bajuwaren 18614

Strausberg

Heimatmuseum, August-Bebel-Str 33, 15344 Strausberg - T: (03341) 23655, Fax: 23655
Local Museum - 1908
Local and regional history 18615

Strodehne

Kunsthaus Strodehne, Am Gahlberg 1, 14467 Strodehne - T: (033875) 31472
Public Gallery 18616

Stromberg

Heimatmuseum Stromberg, 55442 Stromberg - T: (06724) 6447
Local Museum 18617

Struppen

Robert-Sterl-Haus, Robert-Sterl-Str 30, Naundorf, 01796 Struppen - T: (035020) 70216, Fax: 70218, E-mail: robert-sterl-haus@t-online.de. Head: Katja Margarethe Mieth
Fine Arts Museum 18618

Stützerbach

Goethe-Museum Stützerbach mit Museum zur Geschichte des technischen Glases, Stiftung Weimarer Klassik, Sebastian-Kneipp-Str 18, 98714 Stützerbach - T: (036784) 50277, Fax: 50277, E-mail: gnm@weimar-klassik.de, Internet: http://www.weimar-klassik.de
Special Museum - 1962
Memorabilia on J.W. Goethe's (1749-1832) stay here, glass technology - Glass museum 18619

Stulln

Oberpfälzer Flußspat-Besucherbergwerk Reichhart-Schacht, Freiung 2, 92551 Stulln - T: (09433) 1555
Science&Tech Museum - 1980 18620

Stutensee

Hugenotten-Museum und Heimatmuseum, Marktpl, 76297 Stutensee - T: (07249) 358
Local Museum 18621

Stuttgart

Ausstellungen im Bosch-Archiv, c/o Robert Bosch GmbH, Wernerstr 1, Tor 9, 70469 Stuttgart - T: (0711) 81145878, Fax: 8114504, E-mail: Bosch.Archiv@de.bosch.com,

NEED ART NEEDS VIEWERS

STAATSGALERIE STUTTGART

- Mediaeval German painting
- Italian painting
- Dutch painting
- Painting and sculpture of the 19th century

- Graphic arts collection
- Drawings and prints from the 15th to the 20th century
- Illustrated books, books as art objects
- Poster collection
- Fine-art photography
- Marcel Duchamp Room

- Sohm Archive
- Oskar Schlemmer Archive
- Will Grohmann Archive
- Adolf Hölzel's art-theoretical writings

Staatsgalerie Stuttgart
Konrad Adenauer Str. 30 – 32
Telephone: ++49-711-212 4050/4028
www.staatsgalerie.de

Opening times:
10.00 a.m. – 6.00 p.m.
Thursdays 10.00 a.m. – 9.00 p.m.
Closed Mondays

Art Night
Every first Saturday in the month
10.00 p.m. – midnight

Internet: http://www.Bosch.de. Head: Dr. Rolf Becker
Science&Tech Museum / Historical Museum - 1932
Hist of precision and electrical engineering, 19th c Bosch ignitions, first magneto ignition from 1887, first fridge from the 30s 18622

Auwärter-Museum, Vaihinger Str 122, 70567 Stuttgart - T: (0711) 7835264, Fax: 7801696. Head:
Science&Tech Museum - 1990
Hist of vehicle construction 18623

Bibelmuseum Stuttgart, Balinger Str 31, 70567 Stuttgart - T: (0711) 7181253, Fax: 7181250, E-mail: infoabt@dbg.de, Internet: http://www.bibelgesellschaft.de. Head: Dr. Jan-A. Bühner, Dr. Volkmar Loebel
Religious Arts Museum - 1982
History of the bible, first editions and early copies of the Luther bible, European and non-European editions 18624

Design Center Stuttgart des Landesgewerbeamtes Baden-Württemberg, Willi-Bleicher-Str 19, 70174 Stuttgart - T: (0711) 1232781, Fax: 1232577, E-mail: design@lgabw.de, Internet: http://www.design-center.de. Head: Henning Horn
Decorative Arts Museum 18625

Deutsches Landwirtschaftsmuseum, Garbenstr 9-9a, 70599 Stuttgart - T: (0711) 4592146, Fax: 4593404, E-mail: kh650@uni-hohenheim.de, Internet: http://www.uni-hohenheim.de. Head: Dr. Klaus Herrmann
Agriculture Museum / University Museum - 1972
Exhibits on agricultural hist from the early Stone Age to the present 18626

Exploratorium - Kindermuseum Stuttgart und Region, Lerchenstr 65, 70176 Stuttgart - T: (0711) 6364668, Fax: 6364675, E-mail: rau@s.netic.de. Head: Prof. Dr. Weinig
Special Museum 18627

Feuerwehrmuseum → Stuttgarter Feuerwehrmuseum

Galerie der Stadt Stuttgart, Schlosspl 2, 70173 Stuttgart - T: (0711) 2162188, Fax: 2167820, E-mail: galeriestuttgart@stuttgart.de, Internet: http://www.galerie-stuttgart.de. Head: Dr. Johann-Karl Schmidt
Public Gallery / Fine Arts Museum - 1925
19th and 20th c painting, realism, impressionism, contemporary art (Adolf Hölzel, Otto Dix, Willi Baumeister, Dieter Roth) 18628

Gottlieb Daimler-Gedächtnisstätte, Taubenheimstr, Kurpark Cannstadt, 70372 Stuttgart - T: (0711) 1722655, Fax: 1751173, E-mail: nb.museum@daimlerchrysler.com, Internet: http://www.mercedes-benz.com/classic. Head: Max Gerrit von Pein
Historic Site - 1992 18629

Grabkapelle Württemberg, Württembergstr 340, 70327 Stuttgart - T: (0711) 337149
Religious Arts Museum 18630

Hauptstaatsarchiv Stuttgart, Konrad-Adenauer-Str 4, 70173 Stuttgart - T: (0711) 2124335, Fax: 2124360, E-mail: Hauptstaatsarchiv@S.lad-bw.de, Internet: http://www.lad-bw.de. Head: Dr. R. Kretzschmar
Library with Exhibitions 18631

Hegelhaus, Eberhardstr 53, 70173 Stuttgart - T: (0711) 2166733, Fax: 2164456, Internet: http://www.stuttgart.de/stadtarchiv. Head: Dr. R. Müller
Historical Museum - 1991
Memorabilia of the philosopher G.W.F. Hegel (1770-1831) in his birthplace 18632

Heimatmuseum der Deutschen aus Bessarabien, Florianstr 17, 70188 Stuttgart - T: (0711) 2625481, Fax: 2628092, Internet: http://www.bessarabien.de. Head: Ingo Rüdiger Isert
Local Museum 18633

ifa-Galerie Stuttgart, Institut für Auslandsbeziehungen, Charlottenpl 17, 70173 Stuttgart - T: (0711) 2225173, Fax: 2225194, E-mail: lenz@ifa.de, Internet: http://www.ifa.de. Head: Iris Lenz
Public Gallery 18634

Kunststiftung Baden-Württemberg, Gerokstr 37, 70184 Stuttgart - T: (0711) 2364720, Fax: 2361049, E-mail: info@kunststiftung.de, Internet: http://www.kunststiftung.de. Head: Ingeborg Kimmig
Public Gallery
Young art 18635

Linden-Museum, Staatliches Museum für Völkerkunde, Hegelpl 1, 70174 Stuttgart - T: (0711) 20223, Fax: 2022590, E-mail: sekretariat@lindenmuseum.de, Internet: http://www.lindenmuseum.de. Head: Prof. Dr. Thomas Michel
Ethnology Museum - 1889
Folklore and anthropology of the Americas, Africa, the Orient, Oceania and Asia - library, workshops 18636

Mercedes-Benz Museum, Mercedesstr 137, Untertürkheim, 70327 Stuttgart - T: (0711) 1722578, Fax: 1751173, Internet: http://www.mercedes-benz.com/classic. Head: Wolfgang Rolli
Science&Tech Museum - 1961/1986
Originals and models of products made by the Daimler, Benz and Mercedes from 1883 to the present - workshops, library, archives 18637

Museum für Medizinische Endoskopie Max Nitze, Arminstr 10, 70178 Stuttgart - T: (0711) 6460283, Fax: 9604088, E-mail: reuter.hj@t-online.de. Head: Prof. H.J. Reuter
Historical Museum - 1984
Hist of medical endoscopy 18638

Oskar Schlemmer Archiv, Staatsgalerie Stuttgart, Urbanstr 35, 70182 Stuttgart - T: (0711) 2124073, 2124054, Fax: 2124068. Head: Dr. Karin von Maur
Fine Arts Museum 18639

Porsche Museum, Porschepl 1, 70435 Stuttgart - T: (0711) 9115685, Fax: 9117300, E-mail: Porschemuseum@porsche.de, Internet: http://www.porsche.com. Head: Klaus Bischof
Science&Tech Museum - 1976
25 Porsche automobiles and racing cars (40-1100 PS), the life and work of Professor Porsche 18640

Schloß Solitude, Solitude 1, 70197 Stuttgart - T: (0711) 696699, Fax: 696699, Internet: http://www.schloesser-und-gaerten.de
Decorative Arts Museum 18641

Staatliches Museum für Naturkunde Stuttgart, Museum am Löwentor und Museum Schloss Rosenstein, Rosensteinpark, Rosenstein 1, 70191 Stuttgart - T: (0711) 89360, Fax: 8936100, E-mail: museum.smns@naturkundemuseum-bw.de, Internet: http://www.naturkundemuseum-bw.de/stuttgart. Head: Dr. A. Schlüter
Natural History Museum - 1791
Zoology, entomology, botany, geology, paleontology - library, archives, workshops 18642

Staatsgalerie Stuttgart, Konrad-Adenauer-Str 30-32, 70173 Stuttgart, mail addr: Postfach 104342, 70038 Stuttgart - T: (0711) 2124050, 2124028, Fax: 2369983, E-mail: info@staatsgalerie.de, Internet: http://www.staatsgalerie.de. Head: Prof. Dr. Christian von Holst
Fine Arts Museum - 1843
19th-20th c art, paintings and sculptures (Oskar Schlemmer, Pablo Picasso, Willi Baumeister, Max Beckmann), photo coll, Oskar Schlemmer archive, Will Grohmann archive, Sohm archive - documentation centre, archives, library 18643

Stadtmuseum Bad Cannstatt, Marktstr 71, Klösterle, 70372 Stuttgart - T: (0711) 2166327, Fax: 2164456, Internet: http://www.stuttgart.de/stadtarchiv. Head: Dr. Roland Müller
Local Museum - 1988
Prehist, Roman hist, local hist, memorabilia of the poets and writers Berthold Auerbach (1812-1882), Ferdinand Freiligrath (1810-1876), Hermann Hesse (1877-1962), Thaddäus Troll (1914-1980) 18644

Städtisches Lapidarium, c/o Stadtarchiv, Mörikestr 24, 70178 Stuttgart - T: (0711) 2164448, Fax: 2164456, E-mail: stadtarchiv@stuttgart.de, Internet: http://www.stuttgart.de/stadtarchiv. Head: Dr. Roland Müller
Open Air Museum - 1950
Roman artifacts; inscriptions, sculpture, architecture, fragments of former buildings of Stuttgart 18645

Stuttgarter Feuerwehrmuseum, Feurwehrverein Stuttgart e.V, Katharinenstr 12, 70182 Stuttgart - T: (0711) 5066214, Fax: 5066311. Head: H. Mayer
Science&Tech Museum - 2001
Fire fighting 18646

Stuttgarter Gesellschaft für Kunst und Denkmalpflege, Studiensammlung Möbel, Lenbachstr 22, 70192 Stuttgart - T: (0711) 854641, Fax: 854641. Head: Astrid Debus-Steinberg, Franz J. Much
Decorative Arts Museum 18647

Stuttgarter Kunstverein e.V., Filderstr 34, 70180 Stuttgart - T: (0711) 606867, E-mail: info@stuttgarter-kunstverein.de, Internet: http://www.stuttgarter-kunstverein.de. Head: Hanns-Michael Rupprechter
Association with Coll
European and Asian contemporary art 18648

Universitätsmuseum Hohenheim, Exotischer Garten 1, 70599 Stuttgart - T: (0711) 4592114, Fax: 4593803, E-mail: uniarch@unihohenheim.de, Internet: http://www.uni-hohenheim.de/~uniarch/museum.html. Head: Dr. Ulrich Fellmeth
University Museum 18649

Weinbaumuseum Stuttgart-Uhlbach, Uhlbacher Pl 4, 70329 Stuttgart - T: (0711) 2162857, Fax: 2167683, E-mail: 230038@stuttgart.de. Head: Eberhard Maurer
Agriculture Museum - 1979
Viticulture 18650

Württembergische Landesbibliothek, Postfach 105441, 70047 Stuttgart - T: (0711) 2124424, Fax: 2124422, E-mail: direktion@wlb-stuttgart.de, Internet: http://www.wlb-stuttgart.de. Head: Dr. Hannsjörg Kowark
Library with Exhibitions 18651

Württembergischer Kunstverein Stuttgart, Am Schloßpl 2, 70173 Stuttgart - T: (0711) 223370, Fax: 293617, E-mail: info@wkv-stuttgart.de, Internet: http://www.wkv-stuttgart.de. Head: Dr. Andreas Jürgensen
Association with Coll 18652

Württembergisches Landesmuseum Stuttgart, Altes Schloß, Schillerpl 6, 70173 Stuttgart - T: (0711) 2790, 2793481, Fax: 2793499, E-mail: info@landesmuseum-stuttgart.de, Internet: http://www.landesmuseum-stuttgart.de. Head: Prof. Dr. Volker Himmelein
Archaeological Museum / Historic Site / Fine Arts Museum / Local Museum / Folklore Museum / Music Museum - 1862
Archeological finds from the Stone Age, Iron Age, Roman period and Middle Ages, medieval and 19th-20th c Swabian sculpture, crafts, clocks, weapons, musical instruments, textiles, coins, folklore - library, archives 18653

Zoologisches und Tiermedizinisches Museum der Universität Hohenheim, Schloß Hohenheim, 70599 Stuttgart, mail addr: Postfach 700562, 70574 Stuttgart - T: (0711) 4592255/2410, Internet: http://www.uni-hohenheim.de. Head: Prof. Dr. Rahmann, Prof. Dr. Amselgruber
Natural History Museum / University Museum
Veterinary instruments, horseshoes, skeletons, wood library, insects, anatomical preparations 18654

Suderburg

Landwirtschaftsmuseum Lüneburger Heide, Museumsdorf Hösseringen, Am Landtagspl, 29556 Suderburg - T: (05826) 1774, Fax: 8392, E-mail: museumsdorf-hoesseringen@freenet.de, Internet: http://www.museumsdorf-hoesseringen.de. Head: Dr. Horst W. Löbert
Open Air Museum - 1975
20 reconstructed buildings (farm houses, trade workshops, barns), fields, pastures, meadows, orchards, a pond 18655

Südbrookmerland

Dörpmuseum Münkeboe, Mühlenstr 3a, 26624 Südbrookmerland - T: (04942) 646, (04934) 1587
Local Museum - 1992
Village hist, windmill, trades 18656

Moormuseum Moordorf, Victorburer Moor 7a, 26624 Südbrookmerland - T: (04942) 2734, Fax: 5346
Open Air Museum - 1984
Portrayal of the life of people of fen communities and peat bogs 18657

Sugenheim

Spielzeugmuseum im Alten Schloß, Jan und Manuela Kube, Schloßstr 47, 91484 Sugenheim - T: (09165) 650, Fax: 1292, E-mail: info@kube-auktionen.de, Internet: http://www.museumsland-mittelfranken.de. Head: Jan K. Kube
Local Museum - 1988
Toy museum 18th-20th c, castle museum (period rooms) 18658

Suhl

Fahrzeugmuseum Suhl, Meininger Str 222, 98529 Suhl - T: (03681) 705004, Fax: 705004, Internet: http://www.thuringia-online.de/fahrzeugmuseum-suhl. Head: Dietmar Uhlig
Science&Tech Museum
100 years of motor manufacturing industry in Suhl, vehicles, bikes, bicycles 18659

Waffenmuseum Suhl, Friedrich-König-Str 19, 98527 Suhl - T: (03681) 720698, Fax: 721308, E-mail: info@waffenmuseumsuhl.de, Internet: http://www.waffenmuseumsuhl.de. Head: Dr. Thomas Müller
Science&Tech Museum - 1971
Ancient and early historic finds, weapons, weapon industry, hand weapons since 16th c, regional hist - library, historic half-timbered house, restoration workshop 18660

Suhlendorf

Handwerksmuseum am Mühlenberg, Mühlenweg 15, 29562 Suhlendorf - T: (05820) 370, Fax: 987929, E-mail: museum-suhlendorf@t-online.de, Internet: http://www.handwerksmuseum-suhlendorf.city-map.de
Local Museum / Open Air Museum - 1974
Miniature models of a number of wind and watermills, trades, craftmen's show, real working mill (Bockwindmühle) 18661

Sulzbach-Rosenberg

Erstes Bayerisches Schulmuseum, Schloßbergweg 10a, 92237 Sulzbach-Rosenberg - T: (09661) 7533, Fax: 7533
Special Museum - 1981
Hist of education - library 18662

Literaturarchiv Sulzbach-Rosenberg, Rosenberger Str 9, 92237 Sulzbach-Rosenberg - T: (09661) 2659, 810114, Fax: 3626, E-mail: literaturarchiv@asamnet.de, Internet: http://www.literaturarchiv.de. Head: Dr. Barbara Baumann-Eisenack
Library with Exhibitions - 1977
Letters, manuscripts and photographs of German authors 18663

Stadtmuseum Sulzbach-Rosenberg, Neustadt 14-16, 92237 Sulzbach-Rosenberg - T: (09661) 510131, Fax: 811000, E-mail: - Stadtmuseum.Sulzbach-Rosenberg@asamnet.de, Internet: http://www.sulzbach-rosenberg.de. Head: Elisabeth Vogl
Local Museum / Historic Site - 1907
Ceramics, medieval and further archaeology, mining, printing 18664

Sulzberg

Burgmuseum, Burgruine Sulzberg, 87477 Sulzberg - T: (08376) 92010, 920188
Historical Museum 18665

Sulzburg

Landesbergbaumuseum Baden-Württemberg, Hauptstr 56, 79295 Sulzburg - T: (07634) 560040, Fax: 560050, E-mail: stadt@sulzburg.de, Internet: http://www.sulzburg.de. Head: J. Grosspietsch
Science&Tech Museum - 1982
Mining tools, minerals, mining art objects, mining hist in Baden-Württemberg 18666

Sulzdorf

Stein- und Fossiliensammlung Albert, Am Hain 4, 97528 Sulzdorf - T: (09763) 1216, Fax: 1535
Archaeological Museum - 1970
Fossils and mineralogy 18667

Surwold

Waldmuseum, Waldstr, 26903 Surwold - T: (04965) 91310, Fax: 913199, E-mail: info@surwold.de, Internet: http://www.surwold.de
Natural History Museum - 1962
Animal kingdom and plant world in the moor, heath, hedge, forest 18668

Syke

Kreismuseum Syke, Herrlichkeit 65, 28857 Syke - T: (04242) 2527, Fax: 3118, E-mail: info@kreismuseumsyke.de. Head: Dr. Ralf Vogeding
Local Museum - 1938
Agriculture, crafts, farmyard, prehistory, nature 18669

Sylt-Ost

Altfriesisches Haus, Keitum, Am Kliff 13, 25980 Sylt-Ost - T: (04651) 31101, Fax: 32884, E-mail: - soelring.foriining@syltweb.de, Internet: http://www.syltweb.de. Head: Klaus Koehn
Historic Site - 1907
18th c farmhouse, interiors from past life on Sylt, furniture, domestic utensils, furnishings from the 18th and 19th c 18670

Sylter Heimatmuseum, Keitum, Am Kliff 19, 25980 Sylt-Ost - T: (04651) 31669, Fax: 32884, E-mail: - soelring.foriining@syltweb.de, Internet: http://www.syltweb.de
Local Museum - 1908 18671

Syrau

Drachenhöhle, Höhlenberg 10, 08548 Syrau - T: (037431) 3735, Fax: 80912, E-mail: syrau@t-online.de, Internet: http://www.drachenhoehle.de. Head: Heidrun Bauer
Open Air Museum 18672

Museum für Mühlenbautechnik, Windmühle Syrau Drachenburg, 08548 Syrau, mail addr: Höhlenberg 10, 08548 Syrau - T: (037431) 3735, Fax: 80912, E-mail: Syrau@t-online.de, Internet: http://www.syrau.de. Head: Heidrun Bauer
Science&Tech Museum - 1982 18673

Tambach-Dietharz

Heimatmuseum Tambach-Dietharz, Burgstallstr 31a, 99897 Tambach-Dietharz - T: (036252) 34428, Fax: 34429, E-mail: StadtverwaltungT.-D.@web.de, Internet: http://www.tambachdietharz.de
Local Museum 18674

Tangerhütte

Buddelschiff-Museum, Breite Str 33, 39517 Tangerhütte - T: (03935) 28567
Decorative Arts Museum 18675

Tangermünde

Heimatmuseum, Arneburger Str 94, 39590 Tangermünde - T: (039322) 42153
Local Museum - 1929
Historic finds, local history, industrial development, shipping, fishing, peasant crafts and living style, ship models 18676

Tann, Rhön

Freilichtmuseum Rhöner Museumsdorf, Schloßstr 3, 36142 Tann, Rhön - T: (06682) 1655, Fax: 8922. Head: Dr. Klaus-Dieter Koch
Open Air Museum - 1974
Farm houses with furniture and domestic utensils 18677

Rhöner Naturmuseum, Marktpl 6, 36142 Tann, Rhön - T: (06682) 1655, Fax: 8922. Head: Dr. Klaus-Dieter Koch
Natural History Museum - 1983
Native animals 18678

Tanna bei Schleiz

Nicolaus-Schmidt-Künzel-Gedenkstätte, c/o Detlev Hohenwald, Rothenacker 26a, 07922 Tanna bei Schleiz - T: (036646) 22697
Special Museum / Local Museum 18679

Tarmstedt

Heimatstube im "Spieker Anno 1754", Bremer Landstr 18, 27412 Tarmstedt - T: (04283) 1821
Local Museum
Farm life, mineralogy, archaeology, early and prehist 18680

Tauberbischofsheim

Tauberfränkisches Landschaftsmuseum, Schloßpl, 97941 Tauberbischofsheim - T: (09341) 3760. Head: G. Wamser
Local Museum - 1970
Stone age to franconian acquisition of land, furniture, costumes, crafts, religious art, clocks 18681

Taucha bei Leipzig

Städtisches Heimatmuseum, Brauhausstr 24, 04425 Taucha bei Leipzig - T: (034298) 68207, Fax: 70134
Local Museum - 1926
Geology, native fauna, ancient and early historic finds, city and crafts history 18682

Taufkirchen, Kreis München

Heimatmuseum im Wolfschneiderhof, Münchener Str 12, 82024 Taufkirchen, Kreis München - T: (089) 6127475/1273
Local Museum
Peasant life 18683

Keltenhaus, Am Köglweg, 82024 Taufkirchen, Kreis München - T: (089) 66672112
Archaeological Museum - 1997 18684

Tecklenburg

Kreismuseum Steinfurt in Tecklenburg, Wellenberg 1, 49545 Tecklenburg - T: (05482) 703739, Fax: 703777, E-mail: Kreis-Steinfurt@t-online.de. Head: Ulrich Harte
Local Museum - 1967 18685

Puppen- und Spielzeugmuseum, Kreismuseum Steinfurt in Tecklenburg, Wellenberg 1, 49545 Tecklenburg - T: (05482) 703739, Fax: 703777, E-mail: Kreis-Steinfurt@t-online.de. Head: Ulrich Harte
Decorative Arts Museum - 1973
17th c house, dolls from all over the world, costumes, materials, manufacture, dolls' houses, toys, history of the educational aspect of dolls and toys, puppets 18686

Tegernsee

Ludwig-Thoma-Haus, Auf der Tuften 12, 83684 Tegernsee - T: (08022) 5382
Special Museum
Home and study of the poet Ludwig Thoma (1867-1921) 18687

Museum für islamische Fliesen und Keramik, Westerhof-Klinik, Olaf-Gulbransson-Str 19, 83684 Tegernsee - T: (08022) 1810
Decorative Arts Museum - 1977
Muslim ceramics 18688

Museum Tegernseer Tal, Seestr 17, 83684 Tegernsee - T: (08022) 4978, Fax: 937380
Local Museum - 1904/1999
Local hist 18689

Olaf-Gulbransson-Museum, Bayerische Staatsgemäldesammlungen, Im Kurgarten 5, 83684 Tegernsee - T: (08022) 3338, Fax: 3338, E-mail: olaf.gulbransson@gmx.de, Internet: http://www.olaf-gulbransson-museum.de. Head: Dr. Ekkehard Storck
Fine Arts Museum - 1966
Simplicissimus documentation, exhibitions 18690

Teisendorf

Bergbaumuseum Achthal, Teisendorfer Str 63, Achthal, 83317 Teisendorf - T: (08666) 7149, 1029
Science&Tech Museum
Mining 18691

Telgte

Krippenmuseum, Herrenstr 1, 48291 Telgte - T: (02504) 93120, Fax: 7919, E-mail: museum@telgte.com, Internet: http://www.museum-telgte.de. Head: Dr. Thomas Ostendorf
Folklore Museum - 1994
Religious folk art, handicraft, cultural hist of Christmas, historical and international cribs 18692

Museum Heimathaus Münsterland, Herrenstr 2, 48291 Telgte - T: (02504) 93120, Fax: 7919, E-mail: museum@telgte.com, Internet: http://www.museum-telgte.de. Head: Dr. Thomas Ostendorf
Local Museum / Folklore Museum - 1934 18693

Teltow

Heimatmuseum Stadt Teltow, Hoher Steinweg 13, 14513 Teltow - T: (03328) 474120
Local Museum 18694

Templin

Uckermärkisches Volkskundemuseum Templin, Prenzlauer Tor, 17268 Templin - T: (03987) 2725, Fax: 2030104. Head: Konstanze Rätsch
Folklore Museum / Local Museum / Science&Tech Museum - 1957
Local and regional history - Library 18695

Teningen

Heimatmuseum-Menton, Kirchstr 2, 79331 Teningen - T: (07641) 580636, Fax: 580680, E-mail: info@teningen.de, Internet: http://www.teningen.de
Local Museum - 1990
Early and ancient hist, viticulture, handicraft 18696

Teterow

Stadtmuseum Teterow, Schulkamp 2, 17166 Teterow - T: (03996) 172827, 173095, Fax: 172827. Head: Meike Jezmann
Special Museum / Historical Museum
Hist of Bergring (motocross race), school, station 18697

Stadtmuseum Teterow, Südliche Ringstr 1, 17166 Teterow - T: (03996) 172827, Fax: 172827. Head: Meike Jezmann
Local Museum
Town hist, original prisoner's cells 18698

Tettenweis

Franz von Stuck Geburtshaus Tettenweis, Kirchpl 4, 94167 Tettenweis - T: (08534) 1299, Fax: (0851) 9293949, E-mail: a.messmer@woerlen.de, Internet: http://www.woerlen.de. Head: Alois Messmer
Fine Arts Museum
Birthplace of the painter and sculptor Franz von Stuck (1863-1928) 18699

Tettnang

Montfort-Museum, Montfortstr 43, Torschloß, 88069 Tettnang - T: (07542) 938850, Fax: 510275, E-mail: rathaus@tettnang.de, Internet: http://www.tettnang.de. Head: Dr. Angelika Barth
Local Museum - 1961
Local hist 18700

Neues Schloß, Scloßmuseum, Montfortpl 1, 88069 Tettnang - T: (07542) 939194, Fax: 939196, E-mail: tourist-info@tettnang.de
Decorative Arts Museum 18701

Thale

Walpurgishalle Thale, Auf dem Hexentanzpl über der Bode, 06502 Thale
Historical Museum - 1901
Hall in Old-Germanic style with ornaments, figuring in the Walpurgis legend of Goethes "Faust", geology, ancient history, botany, zoology 18702

Thalmässing

Vor- und Frühgeschichtliches Museum, Marktpl 1, 91177 Thalmässing - T: (09173) 9134
Archaeological Museum - 1988
Early hist 18703

Thammhausen

Museum im Tuchmacherhaus, Edmund-Zimmermann-Str 16, 86470 Thammhausen - T: (08281) 3772
Local Museum - 2000 18704

Tharandt

Stadtmuseum Tharandt, Dresdner Str 4, 01737 Tharandt - T: (035203) 8451. Head: Dr. B. Bélafi
Local Museum - 1992
Ancient and early history, city history, conservation, geology, mining, development of traffic, crafts and industry 18705

Thierhaupten

Klostermühlenmuseum, Franzengasse 21, 86672 Thierhaupten - T: (08271) 1769, Fax: 816777
Science&Tech Museum 18706

Trachten- und Heimatstuben, Herzog-Tassilo-Str 34, 86672 Thierhaupten - T: (08271) 3398
Local Museum / Folklore Museum - 1973 18707

Thießen bei Dessau

Technisches Denkmal Kupferhammer, Kupferhammer 43, 06862 Thießen bei Dessau - T: (034907) 20440, Fax: 20440. Head: Klaus Liensdorf
Science&Tech Museum 18708

Thurnau

Töpfermuseum Thurnau, Kirchpl 12, 95349 Thurnau - T: (09228) 5351, 971441, Fax: 95151, 971442, E-mail: toepfermuseum-thurnau@t-online.de, Internet: http://www.thurnau.de
Decorative Arts Museum
Crockery coll 18709

Tiefenbach, Oberpfalz

Ludwig-Gebhard-Museum, Hauptstr 23, 93464 Tiefenbach, Oberpfalz - T: (09673) 92210, Fax: 922130, E-mail: poststelle@tiefenbach-opf.de, Internet: http://www.tiefenbach-opf.de
Fine Arts Museum - 2000 18710

Museum ehemalige Klöppelschule Tiefenbach, Hauptstr 33, 93464 Tiefenbach, Oberpfalz - T: (09673) 92210, Fax: 922130, E-mail: poststelle@tiefenbach-opf.de, Internet: http://www.tiefenbach-opf.de
Folklore Museum - 2000 18711

Tilleda

Königspfalz Freilichtmuseum, 06537 Tilleda - T: (034651) 2923. Head: Jürgen Schröter
Open Air Museum
233 medieval houses, workshops, imperial lodgings 18712

Tirschenreuth

Oberpfälzer Fischereimuseum, Regensburger Str 6, 95643 Tirschenreuth - T: (09631) 6122
Natural History Museum - 1993
Hist of fishing 18713

Plan-Weseritzer Heimatstuben mit Archiv, Hochwartstr 1, Klostergebäude, 95643 Tirschenreuth - T: (09631) 1226
Local Museum - 1976
Hist of German expellees 18714

Titisee-Neustadt

Heimatstuben der Stadt, Scheuerlenstr 31, 79822 Titisee-Neustadt - T: (07651) 206124, Fax: 206290, E-mail: stadt@titisee.de, Internet: http://www.titisee-neustadt.de. Head: Martin Vogelbacher
Local Museum - 1968
Handicraft, watches made in the region 18715

Tittling

Museumsdorf Bayerischer Wald, Am Dreiburgensee, 94104 Tittling - T: (08504) 40461, Fax: 40496, E-mail: info@rotel.de, Internet: http://www.museumsdorf.com. Head: Georg Höltl
Open Air Museum - 1974
Religious folk art, wagons, forestry, peasant furniture, glas, textiles 18716

Tittmoning

Heimathaus des Rupertiwinkels und Heimatstube der Sudetendeutschen, Burg Tittmoning, 84529 Tittmoning, mail addr: Stadtpl 12 - T: (08683) 700710, Fax: 700730
Local Museum - 1889/1900
Targets, wrought-iron gravestones and crosses 18717

Todtmoos

Heimatmuseum Todtmoos, Murgtalstr 15, 79682 Todtmoos - T: (07674) 90600, Fax: 906025, E-mail: todtmoos-touri@rrz-freiburg.de, Internet: http://www.todtmoos.de/heimethuus
Local Museum 18718

Töpen

Deutsch-Deutsches Museum Mödlareuth, Museum zur Geschichte der deutschen Teilung, Mödlareuth 13, 95183 Töpen - T: (09295) 1334, Fax: 1319, E-mail: museum.moedlareuth@t-online.de, Internet: http://www.moedlareuth.de. Head: Arndt R. Schaffner, Robert Lebegern
Historical Museum - 1990
German-German hist - library and archive 18719

Torgau

Kreismuseum Torgau - Schloß Hartenfels, Schloßstr 27, 04860 Torgau - T: (03421) 739036, Fax: 739036. Head: Dr. Armin Schneiderheinze
Historical Museum - 1951
Ancient and early hist, local hist, hist of the castle, historic armaments, relief of battle 18720

Traben-Trarbach

Mittelmoselmuseum im Barockhaus Böcking, Casinostr 2, 56841 Traben-Trarbach - T: (06541) 9480
Local Museum - 1928
Prehistory, local history, weapons, coins, history of wine cultivation - library 18721

Traunstein

Katzenmuseum, Daxerau 7, 83278 Traunstein - T: (0861) 8983, Fax: 8983
Special Museum - 1997 18722

Kunstraum Klosterkirche, Ludwigstr 10, 83278 Traunstein - T: (0861) 2374
Public Gallery 18723

Museum im Heimathaus, Stadtpl 2-3, 83278 Traunstein - T: (0861) 164786, Fax: 65294. Head: Dr. Jürgen Eminger
Local Museum - 1882
Local hist, crafts and toys 18724

Städtische Galerie, Ludwigstr 12, 83278 Traunstein - T: (0861) 164319, Fax: 1665174, E-mail: galerie@traunstein.de, Internet: http://www.traunstein.de. Head:
Fine Arts Museum - 1986
Woodcarving and local contemporary art 18725

Trautskirchen

Hans-Böckler-Geburtshaus, Hans-Böckler-Str 15, 90619 Trautskirchen - T: (09107) 255
Special Museum
Documents and photographs of the trade unionist Hans Böckler (1875-1951) 18726

Trebbus

Bockwindmühlenmuseum, Dorfstr 3, 03253 Trebbus - T: (035322) 4966. Head: Klaus-J. Wilker
Science&Tech Museum 18727

Trebur

Heimatmuseum Trebur, Wilhelm-Leuschner-Pl, 65468 Trebur - T: (06147) 8417, Fax: 8051
Local Museum - 1980/94
Fossils, grave finds, jewellery, ceramics 18728

Trechtingshausen

Kunstsammlung im Schloß Rheinstein, Burg-Rheinstein-Weg, 55413 Trechtingshausen - T: (06721) 6348, Fax: 6659, E-mail: info@burg-rheinstein.de, Internet: http://www.burg-rheinstein.de. Head: Markus Hecher
Fine Arts Museum 18729

Treuchtlingen

Aurnhammer-Sammlung, Heinrich-Aurnhammer-Str 3, 91757 Treuchtlingen - T: (09142) 3840, Fax: 3120
Science&Tech Museum - 1987
Town and hist of metal industry 18730

Ortssammlung Wettelsheim, Pfarrgasse 5, 91757 Treuchtlingen - T: (09142) 8550, Fax: 8623, E-mail: pamatthi@aol.com
Local Museum - 1924
Local hist and ceramics 18731

Volkskundemuseum Treuchtlingen, Heinrich-Aurnhammer-Str 12, 91757 Treuchtlingen - T: (09142) 3840, Fax: 3120. Head: Johannes Dankbar
Local Museum - 1970
Crockery, costumes, furniture, tools, peasant furnishings, clocks, prehistoric findings, town hist, tin 18732

Treuenbrietzen

Heimatmuseum, Großstr 105, 14929 Treuenbrietzen - T: (033748) 70506
Local Museum - 1939
Local hist, early hist, botany 18733

Triberg

Schwarzwald-Museum, Wallfahrtstr 4, 78098 Triberg - T: (07722) 4434, Fax: 920110. Head: Adolf Hermann
Local Museum / Music Museum
Trades and guilds, Black Forest clocks, coll of mechanical music instruments, barrel-organs, Saba radios 18734

Tribsees

Heimatstube Tribsees, Steintor, 18465 Tribsees - T: (038320) 61783, Fax: 61784
Local Museum - 1976
Local and regional history 18735

Triefenstein

Museum Papiermühle Homburg, Gartenstr, 97855 Triefenstein - T: (09395) 99222, Fax: 99222, E-mail: papiermuehle-homburg@t-online.de, Internet: http://www.papiermuehle-homburg.de
Science&Tech Museum - 1997
Paper mill 18736

Privatsammlung Leo Gesell, Trennfeld, Blumenstr 18, 97855 Triefenstein - T: (09395) 1668
Local Museum - 1989
Rustic furniture and agricultural tools 18737

Trier

Bischöfliches Dom- und Diözesanmuseum, Windstr 6-8, 54290 Trier - T: (0651) 7105255, Fax: 7105348, E-mail: museum@bgv-trier.de, Internet: http://www.museum.bistum-trier.de. Head: Dr. Winfried Weber
Religious Arts Museum / Archaeological Museum / Fine Arts Museum - 1904
Early Christian archeology, history of art, religious art, 11th-19th c sculpture - library 18738

Domschatz, Hinter dem Dom 6, 54290 Trier - T: (0651) 7105332, Fax: 7105273, E-mail: Bistum-trier@bistum-trier.de. Head: Prof. Dr. Dr. Franz Ronig
Religious Arts Museum
Hivory carvings 5th-17th c, goldsmith work 6th-20th c, 10th c portable altar, medieval books 18739

Galerie Palais Walderdorff, Domfreihof 1b, 54290 Trier - T: (0651) 66671, Fax: 9961241, E-mail: info@gb-kunst.de, Internet: http://www.gb-kunst.de. Head: Horst Schmitt
Public Gallery / Association with Coll 18740

Karl-Marx-Haus, Brückenstr 10, 54290 Trier - T: (0651) 970680, Fax: 97068140, E-mail: koenigk@fes.de, Internet: http://www.libraray/kmhkat.html. Head: Dr. Hans Pelger
Special Museum - 1928
Birthplace and memorabilia of Karl Marx (1818-1883), documents concerning social history in 19th c Germany, history of the international proletarian movement - library 18741

Original- und Abgußsammlung der Universität Trier, Kohlenstr, 54286 Trier - T: (0651) 2012429, Fax: 2013926. Head: Prof. Dr. Günter Grimm
University Museum / Archaeological Museum 18742

Rheinisches Landesmuseum Trier, Weimarer Allee 1, 54290 Trier - T: (0651) 97740, Fax: 9774222, E-mail: RLMTrier@t-online.de, Internet: http://www.landesmuseum-trier.de. Head: Dr. Hans-Peter Kuhnen
Archaeological Museum / Museum of Classical Antiquities - 1877
Celtic archaeology, roman goldtreasure, roman mosaics, statues, ceramics, glass and Christian tombstones, Frankish cultural history, medieval and modern sculpture, glass and porcelain - library, archives, restoration workshops 18743

Spielzeugmuseum, Nagelstr 4-5, 54290 Trier - T: (0651) 75850, Fax: 9943875, E-mail: info@spielzeugmuseum-trier.de, Internet: http://www.spielzeugmuseum-trier.de. Head: Michael Berger
Special Museum - 1989 18744

Stadtbibliothek Trier - Schatzkammer und Ausstellung, Weberbach 25, 54290 Trier - T: (0651) 7182430, Fax: 7183432. Head: Dr. G. Franz
Library with Exhibitions 18745

Städtisches Museum Simeonstift, Simeonstiftpl, 54290 Trier - T: (0651) 7181450, Fax: 7181458, E-mail: stadtmuseum@trier.de, Internet: http://www.museum-trier.de. Head: Dr. Elisabeth Dühr
Local Museum - 1904
15th-19th c sculpture, painting, folklore and handicrafts of the Trier region, 16th and 17th c Dutch painting, graphic arts, furniture ceramics 18746

Troisdorf

Museum der Stadt Troisdorf, Burg Wissem, 53840 Troisdorf - T: (02241) 884111/17, Fax: 884120, E-mail: museum@troisdorf.de, Internet: http://www.troisdorf.de. Head: Dr. Maria Linsmann
Local Museum 18747

Trossingen

Auberlehaus, Trossinger Heimatmuseum, Marktpl 6, 78647 Trossingen - T: (07425) 27703, Fax: 8092. Head: Jörg Tisken
Local Museum - 1977
Geology, paleontology, rural tools, housing, Plateosaurus Trossingensis 18748

Deutsches Harmonikamuseum, Löwenstr 11, 78647 Trossingen - T: (07425) 21623, Fax: 8289, E-mail: HarmonikaM@aol.com, Internet: http://www.harmonika-museum.de. Head: Martin Häffner
Music Museum - 1991
Hist of harmonica instruments 18749

Trostberg

Stadtmuseum Trostberg, Schedling 7-11, 83308 Trostberg - T: (08621) 645261
Local Museum - 1939
Local history, natural history, crafts and guilds, furniture, folk art 18750

Tübingen

Ägyptische Sammlung der Universität/ Museum Schloß Hohentübingen, Schloß Hohentübingen, 72070 Tübingen - T: (07071) 2977384, Fax: 2975659, E-mail: museum@uni.tuebingen.de, Internet: http://www.uni-tuebingen.de/aegyptologie. Head: N.N.
Archaeological Museum / University Museum - 1959
Displays concerning Egypt from prehistoric times to the beginning of the Islamic period - library, archives 18751

Auto- und Spielzeugmuseum Boxenstop, Brunnenstr 18, 72074 Tübingen - T: (07071) 929020, 551122, Fax: 929099. Head: R. Klink
Science&Tech Museum / Special Museum - 1985
Vehicles, motorbikes, toys from all areas 18752

Ehemaliges Jagdschloß Bebenhausen, Staatliche Schlösser und Gärten Baden-Württemberg, Im Schloß 1, 72074 Tübingen - T: (07071) 602802, Fax: 602803, E-mail: info@kloster-bebenhausen.de, Internet: http://www.schloesser-magazin.de/beb
Decorative Arts Museum - 1986
Decorative art, furniture, paintings from 1600-1918 18753

Graphische Sammlung am Kunsthistorischen Institut der Universität Tübingen, Bursagasse 1, 72070 Tübingen - T: (07071) 2972382, 2977058, Fax: 295304, E-mail: anette.michels@uni-tuebingen.de, Internet: http://www.uni-tuebingen.de. Head: Dr. Anette Michels
Fine Arts Museum / University Museum 18754

Hölderlinhaus, Bursagasse 6, 72070 Tübingen - T: (07071) 22040, Fax: 22948, E-mail: info@hoelderlin-gesellschaft.de, Internet: http://www.hoelderlin-gesellschaft.de. Head: Valérie Lawitschka
Special Museum - 1922
Life and work of Friedrich Hölderlin (1770-1843), housed in the city tower where Hölderlin lived from 1807 on - library 18755

Institut und Museum für Geologie und Paläontologie, Sigwartstr 10, 72076 Tübingen - T: (07071) 292489, Fax: 296990. Head: Prof. Dr. Hans-Ulrich Pfretzschmer
Natural History Museum - 1904
Geology, paleontology, fossils, reptiles, ammonites - library 18756

Isinger Dorfmuseum - Alte Kelter, Kirchhalde 10, 72070 Tübingen - T: (07073) 7550. Head: H. Silber
Local Museum - 1986
Agriculture, viticulture, peasant life, prehist, Roman finds 18757

Kunsthalle Tübingen, Philosophenweg 76, 72076 Tübingen - T: (07071) 96910, Fax: 969133, E-mail: kunsthalle@tuebingen.de, Internet: http://www.kunsthalle-tuebingen.de. Head: Prof. Dr. Götz Adriani
Public Gallery - 1971 18758

Mineralogische Schau- und Lehrsammlung, Wilhelmstr 56, 72074 Tübingen - T: (07071) 2972600, Fax: 293060, E-mail: udo.neumann@uni-tuebingen.de, Internet: http://www.uni-tuebingen.de/uni/emi/sammlung.html. Head: Dr. U. Neumann
Natural History Museum / University Museum - 1918
Mineralogy, petrology, meteorites 18759

Stadtmuseum Tübingen, Kornhausstr 10, 72070 Tübingen - T: (07071) 2041711, 945460, Fax: 945489, E-mail: stadt@tuebingen.de, Internet: http://www.tuebingen.de/stadtmuseum. Head: Claudine Pachnicke
Local Museum - 1991
Town history, University history, commerce and trade 18760

Universitätssammlung antiker und nachantiker Münzen und Medaillen, Schloß Hohentübingen, 72070 Tübingen - T: (07071) 2972378, 2974369, Fax: 295778, E-mail: reinhard.wolters@uni-tuebingen.de. Head: Prof. Dr. Reinhard Wolters
University Museum / Museum of Classical Antiquities 18761

Zahnärztliches Museum, Osianderstr 2-8, 72076 Tübingen - T: (07071) 2982152, Fax: 295967, E-mail: wolfgang.lindemann@med.uni-tuebingen.de, Internet: http://www.zahnklinik.uni-tuebingen.de. Head: Prof. Dr. Lindemann
Science&Tech Museum - 1968
Instruments used in dental surgery, hist of dentistry 18762

Zisterzienserkloster Bebenhausen, Staatliche Schlösser und Gärten Baden-Württemberg, Kloster, 72074 Tübingen - T: (07071) 602802, Fax: 602803, E-mail: info@kloster-bebenhausen.de, Internet: http://www.schloesser-magazin.de/beb
Religious Arts Museum / Fine Arts Museum - 1961
Medieval sculpture, paintings, religious objects and triptychs 18763

Zoologische Schausammlung, Sigwartstr 3, 72076 Tübingen - T: (07071) 292668, Fax: 294634, E-mail: erich.weber@uni-tuebingen.de. Head: Dr. Erich Weber
Natural History Museum 18764

Türkheim

Sieben-Schwaben-Museum, Maximilian-Philipp-Str 32, 86842 Türkheim - T: (08245) 5312, 713, Fax: 5322
Local Museum - 1992
Local and town hist 18765

Tüßling

Brauereimuseum Bräu im Moos, Moos 21, 84577 Tüßling - T: (08633) 1041, Fax: 7941, E-mail: BraeuimMoos@t-online.de, Internet: http://www.braugasthoefe.com. Head: Eugen Münch
Science&Tech Museum - 1980
History of beer brewing 18766

Tuttlingen

Fruchtkasten, Museen der Stadt Tuttlingen, Donaustr 50, 78532 Tuttlingen - T: (07461) 15135, Fax: 164651, E-mail: info@museen-tuttlingen.de, Internet: http://www.tuttlingen.de. Head: Gunda Woll
Local Museum - 1997
Geology, environment, archaeology, local hist, industrial hist, medical instruments 18767

Galerie der Stadt Tuttlingen, Rathausstr 7, 78532 Tuttlingen - T: (07461) 99318, 15551, Fax: 99335, E-mail: info@galerie-tuttlingen.de, Internet: http://www.tuttlingen.de. Head: Marjatta Hölz
Public Gallery - 1969
Paintings 20th c, contemporary sculpture, graphic art, photography 18768

Museum im Rathaus Möhringen, Museen der Stadt Tuttlingen, Hermann-Leiber-Str 4, Möhringen, 78532 Tuttlingen - T: (07461) 15135, Fax: 164651, E-mail: info@museen.tuttlingen.de, Internet: http://www.tuttlingen.de. Head: Gunda Woll
Local Museum - 1997
Hist of the small town Möhringen 18769

Tuttlinger Haus, Museen der Stadt Tuttlingen, Donaustr 19, 78532 Tuttlingen - T: (07461) 15135, Fax: 164651, E-mail: info@museen-tuttlingen.de, Internet: http://www.tuttlingen.de. Head: Gunda Woll
Local Museum - 1997
Town hist 18770

Tutzing

Museum G. Frey des Entomologischen Instituts, Hofrat-Beisele-Str 8, 82327 Tutzing - T: (08158) 565. Head: Dr. Georg Frey
Natural History Museum 18771

Niederebersdorfer Heimat- und Archivstuben, Altes Feuerhaus, Oskar-Schüler-Str 2, 82327 Tutzing - T: (08158) 2755
Local Museum - 1964
Hist of German expellees 18772

Ubstadt-Weiher

Römermuseum Stettfeld, Lußhardtstr 14, 76698 Ubstadt-Weiher - T: (07253) 70298, Internet: http://www.roemermuseum-stettfeld.de. Head: Wolfgang Fischer
Archaeological Museum 18773

Überlingen

Historisches Waffenmuseum im Zeughaus, Zeughausgasse 2, 88662 Überlingen - T: (07551) 64417, Fax: 5209. Head: Friedrich Hebsacker
Historical Museum - 1975
4 centuries of arms development 18774

Städtische Galerie Fauler Pelz, Seepromenade, 88662 Überlingen - T: (07551) 991070/71, Fax: 991077, E-mail: g.mueller@ueberlingen.de, Internet: http://www.ueberlingen.de. Head: Guntram Brummer
Public Gallery 18775

Städtisches Museum, Krummebergstr 30, 88662 Überlingen - T: (07551) 991079, Fax: 991079, Internet: http://www.ueberlingen. Head: Guntram Brummer
Local Museum - 1913
Prehistory, local history, sculpture and painting, especially from the Bodensee area, furniture, folk art, weapons, historical doll houses dating from the Renaissance to Jugendstil periods 18776

Übersee

Künstlerhaus Exter, Blumenweg 5, Feldwies, 83236 Übersee - T: (08642) 895083, Fax: 895085, E-mail: info@bsv.bayern.de
Fine Arts Museum
Study and workshop of the painter Julius Exter (1863-1939) 18777

Ueckermünde

Haffmuseum Ueckermünde, Am Rathaus 3, 17373 Ueckermünde - T: (039771) 28442, Fax: 28444, E-mail: haffmuseum@ueckermuende.de, Internet: http://www.ueckermuende.de. Head: Hannelore Reinhardt
Local Museum / Historical Museum - 1950
Early and prehist, fishing, shipping, brick and tile - making works 18778

Uelzen

Heimatmuseum Uelzen mit Gläsersammlung Röver, Schloß Holdenstedt, Schloßstr 4, 29525 Uelzen - T: (0581) 3892482, 6037, Fax: 800100, Internet: http://www.kreis-uelzen.de/museum. Head: Dr. Reimer Egge
Local Museum / Decorative Arts Museum - 1911/66
Glasses, style of home décor (17th-20th c), silverwork, tin, prehist 18779

Kulturspeicher im Schamuhn Museum, An der Rosenmauer 13-17, 29525 Uelzen - T: (0581) 76535
Public Gallery 18780

Uetersen

Museum Langes Tannen, Heidgrabener Str, 25436 Uetersen - T: (04122) 714202, Fax: 714202
Local Museum / Historic Site / Fine Arts Museum 18781

Uetze

Heimatmuseum Uetze, Breslauer Str 20, 31311 Uetze - T: (05173) 6130
Local Museum 18782

Heimatstube Hänigsen, Haus am Pappaul, 31311 Uetze - T: (05147) 1263
Local Museum
Town hist, remnants of the oldest oil deposits in Northern Germany 18783

Uffenheim

Uffenheimer Gollachgaumuseum, Schloßpl 5, 97215 Uffenheim - T: (09842) 98700, Fax: 987090, E-mail: Raiffeisenbank.Uffenheim.eG@t-online.de. Head: Fritz Klaußecker
Local Museum - 1914
Prehist, paleontology 18784

Uftrungen

Karstmuseum Heimkehle, Postfach 61, 06548 Uftrungen - T: (034653) 305. Head: Reinhard Völker
Natural History Museum 18785

Uhingen

Heimatmuseum im Berchtoldshof, Bismarckstr 4, 73066 Uhingen - T: (07161) 9380103, Fax: 9380199
Local Museum - 1984
Prehist, early hist, archeological finds, local hist, crafts, glass industry 18786

Uhldingen-Mühlhofen

Pfahlbaumuseum Unteruhldingen, Strandpromenade 6, 88690 Uhldingen-Mühlhofen - T: (07556) 8543, Fax: 5886, E-mail: info@pfahlbauten.de, Internet: http://www.pfahlbauten.de. Head: Dr. G. Schöbel
Open Air Museum / Archaeological Museum
Archeological finds of the Bodensee-Oberschwaben region - library 18787

Ulm

Deutsches Brotmuseum, Salzstadelgasse 10, 89073 Ulm - T: (0731) 69955, Fax: 6021161, E-mail: info@brotmuseum-ulm.de, Internet: http://www.brotmuseum-ulm.de. Head: Monika Machnicki
Special Museum - 1955
Technical, cultural and social hist of bread and baking, gallery of agriculture, bread in religion and art, hunger documentation - library, archives 18788

HfG-Archiv, Ulmer Museum, Basteistr 46, 89070 Ulm - T: (0731) 1614370, Fax: 1614373, E-mail: hfg-archivulm.de. Head: Dr. Brigitte Reinhardt
Special Museum 18789

Naturkundliches Bildungszentrum, Kornhausgasse 3, 89073 Ulm - T: (0731) 1614742, Fax: 1611681, Internet: http://www.naturkunde-museum.ulm.de. Head: Dr. Peter Jankov
Natural History Museum - 1923
Geology, zoology, botany 18790

Stadthaus Ulm, Münsterpl 38, 89073 Ulm - T: (0731) 1617700, Fax: 1617701, E-mail: stadthaus@ulm.de, Internet: http://www.stadthaus.ulm.de. Head: Dr. Joachim Gerner
Fine Arts Museum
Contemporary art, photography, architecture 18791

Ulmer Museum, Marktpl 9, 89070 Ulm - T: (0731) 1614300, Fax: 1611626, E-mail: info.ulmer-museum@ulm.de, Internet: http://www.museum.ulm.de. Head: Dr. Brigitte Reinhardt
Local Museum / Fine Arts Museum - 1924
Regional medieval art (1300-1530), local hist, crafts and guilds, graphic arts, prehistoric finds, international contemporary art 18792

Ulrichstein

Museum für ländliches Kulturgut, Landwirtschaft, Forsten und Jagd, Hauptstr 33, 35327 Ulrichstein - T: (06645) 7267, Fax: 961022. Head: Peter Kraus
Agriculture Museum / Natural History Museum 18793

Ummendorf

Börde-Museum, Meaendorffstr 4, 39365 Ummendorf - T: (039409) 522, Fax: 93863
Local Museum - 1924/1953
Ancient and early history, geology, peasant living style, tools, costumes, jewelry, mushroom coll 18794

Unna

Hellweg-Museum der Stadt Unna, Burgstr 8, 59423 Unna - T: (02303) 103411, Fax: 103411. Head: Dieter Fölster
Local Museum / Historical Museum - 1928
Numismatics 18795

Oldenburg-Museum, Am Loerweg 1, 59427 Unna - T: (02303) 4592
Fine Arts Museum
Paintings, graphics and sculptures 18796

Zentrum für internationale Lichtkunst, Massener Str 31, 59423 Unna - T: (02303) 592319, Fax: 103475, Internet: http://www.unna.de/ankerpunkt/ankerpunkt.htm
Fine Arts Museum - 2001 18797

Unterdießen

Malura-Museum, Mühlweg 2, Oberdießen, 86944 Unterdießen - T: (08243) 3638
Fine Arts Museum - 1993
Work of the painter Oswald Malura 18798

Unterföhring

Feringa Sach - Ortsgeschichte und heimatkundliche Sammlung, Bahnhofstr 12, 85774 Unterföhring - T: (089) 95001306, 9504219
Local Museum - 2000 18799

Unterlüß

Albert-König-Museum, Albert-König-Str 10, 29345 Unterlüß - T: (05827) 369, Fax: 970213. Head: Dr. Klaus Homann
Fine Arts Museum - 1987
Paintings, drawings, wood engravings by Albert König 18800

Unterpleichfeld

Sammlung landwirtschaftlicher Geräte, Fischergasse 2, 97294 Unterpleichfeld - T: (09367) 2120
Science&Tech Museum / Agriculture Museum 18801

Unterwellenborn

Schaudenkmal Gaszentrale, c/o Förderverein, Thälmannstr 19, 07333 Unterwellenborn - T: (03671) 614936
Science&Tech Museum - 1992
Hist of iron and steel works, hist of large-scale gas machines (Thyssen, 1923, type DT 14) 18802

Urbach

Schloß Urbach, Schloßstr 26, 73660 Urbach
Local Museum 18803

Wittumsmuseum, Mühlstr 11, 73660 Urbach
Local Museum 18804

Ursberg

Klostermuseum der Sankt Josefskongregation, Klosterhof 7, 86513 Ursberg - T: (08281) 922121/24, Fax: 921000. Head: M. Ellensint Kremer
Religious Arts Museum / Fine Arts Museum - 1984
Cloister library (18th c) with frescos by Konrad Huber 18805

Urspringen

Synagogen-Museum, c/o Verwaltungsgemeinschaft Marktheidenfeld, Judengasse, 97857 Urspringen - T: (09396) 887, Fax: 993886
Religious Arts Museum - 1992
Jewish hist 18806

Usedom

Heimatstube Usedom, Anklamer Tor, 17406 Usedom - T: (038372) 7500, Fax: 70214
Local Museum 18807

Userin

Vylym-Hütte, Bauernende 18, 17237 Userin - T: (03981) 204395, Fax: 204395, Internet: http://www.userin.de. Head: B. Schmidt
Natural History Museum
Native animals and plants 18808

Usingen

Heimatmuseum Usingen, Untergasse 2, 61250 Usingen - T: (06081) 2071
Local Museum - 1977
Town hist, linen processing, early hist, toys 18809

Uslar

Kali-Bergbaumuseum Volpriehausen, Wahlbergstr 1, 37170 Uslar - T: (05573) 541, Fax: 541. Head: Detlev Herbst
Science&Tech Museum - 1985
Salt minerals 18810

Museum Uslar, Mühlentor 4, 37170 Uslar - T: (05571) 307142. Head: Dr. Wolfgang Schäfer
Local Museum - 1969
Town hist, rural crafts and industrial culture 18811

Vaihingen

Städtisches Museum Peterskirche, Stuttgarter Str 31, 71665 Vaihingen - T: (07042) 98100, Fax: 18200, E-mail: archiv@vaihingen.de, Internet: http://www.vaihingen.de. Head: Lothar Behr
Local Museum - 1958 18812

Weinmuseum, Alte Keltergasse 1, 71665 Vaihingen - T: (07042) 32852. Head: B. Ilshöfer
Agriculture Museum - 1974 18813

Valley

Orgelmuseum Altes Schloß, Graf-Arco-Str 30, 83626 Valley - T: (08024) 4144, Fax: 48135. Head: Dr. Sixtus Lampl
Music Museum
Organ coll 18814

Varel

Franz Radziwill Haus, Sielstr 3, Dangast, 26316 Varel - T: (04451) 2777, Fax: 2777. Head: Dr. Ekkehard Seeber
Public Gallery - 1987
Franz Radziwill 18815

Heimatmuseum Varel, Neumarktpl 3, 26316 Varel - T: (04451) 4936
Local Museum - 1953
Imperialist navy, photos, parts of uniforms, souvenirs from the colonies 18816

Museumsmühle mit heimatkundlicher Sammlung, Mühlenstr 52, 26316 Varel - T: (04451) 86081, 7688
Agriculture Museum / Science&Tech Museum
Five-storey Dutch windmill from 1847, agriculture, fishing, trades 18817

Vechelde

Schulmuseum Vechelde, Albert-Schweitzer-Str 2, 38159 Vechelde - T: (05302) 1751
Historical Museum
Hist of school and education 18818

Vechta

Museum im Zeughaus, An der Zitadelle, 49377 Vechta - T: (04441) 886450. Head: Axel Fahl-Dreger
Local Museum - 1995
Hist of the town and fortress, arsenal 18819

Veitshöchheim

Jüdisches Kulturmuseum und Synagoge, Thüngersheimer Str 17, 97209 Veitshöchheim - T: (0931) 9802764, 960851, Fax: 9802766, E-mail: museum@veitshoechheim.de, Internet: http://www.veitshoechheim.de. Head: Dr. Martina Edelmann, Karen Heußner
Historical Museum - 1994
Jewish hist - archive 18820

Schloß Veitshöchheim, Hofgarten 1, 97209 Veitshöchheim - T: (0931) 91582, E-mail: info@bsv.bayern.de, Internet: http://www.schloesser.bayern.de
Local Museum
Castle and Rococo garden 18821

Velbert

Deutsches Schloß- und Beschläge-Museum, Forum Niederberg, Oststr 20, 42551 Velbert - T: (02051) 262285, Fax: 262297, E-mail: museen@velbert.de, Internet: http://www.velbert.de. Head: Dr. Heiderose Langer
Science&Tech Museum - 1936 18822

Museum Schloß Hardenberg, Zum Hardenberger Schloß 4, 42553 Velbert - T: (02053) 912212, Fax: (02051) 262297, E-mail: museen@velbert.de, Internet: http://www.schloss-hardenberg.city-map.de. Head: Dr. Heiderose Langer
Fine Arts Museum 18823

Stadtgeschichtliche Sammlung, Zum Hardenberger Schloß 4, 42553 Velbert - T: (02051) 262264, Fax: 262112. Head: Christoph Schotten
Local Museum
Pilgrimage 18824

Velburg

Heimatmuseum Velburg, Hinterer Markt 1, 92355 Velburg - T: (09182) 93020, Fax: 930244
Local Museum 18825

Velen

Museum Burg Ramsdorf, Burgpl 4, 46342 Velen - T: (02863) 926215, 6820, Fax: 5376. Head: Michael Kleiner
Historical Museum - 1931 18826

Vellberg

Natur- und Heimatmuseum Vellberg, Eschenauer Str 7, 74541 Vellberg - T: (07907) 87730, Fax: 87712
Local Museum - 1984
Local hist, zoology, archeological finds 18827

Vellmar

Rathausgalerie Vellmar, Rathauspl 1, 34246 Vellmar - T: (0561) 8292118, Fax: 82979047, E-mail: info@vellmar.de, Internet: http://www.vellmar.de
Fine Arts Museum 18828

Velten

Ofen- und Keramikmuseum Velten, Wilhelmstr 32, 16727 Velten - T: (03304) 31760, Fax: 505887, E-mail: info@ofenmuseum-velten.de, Internet: http://www.ofenmuseum-velten.de. Head: Monika Dittmar
Science&Tech Museum / Decorative Arts Museum - 1905
Local and regional history, local stove industry, tools, stove coll, models, tiles 17th-20th c, clay processers - library 18829

Verden

Deutsches Pferdemuseum, Hippologisches Institut, Holzmarkt 9, 27283 Verden - T: (04231) 807140, Fax: 807160, E-mail: Pferdemuseum@t-online.de, Internet: http://www.dpm-verden.de. Head: Dietrich Fröba
Natural History Museum - 1965
Equestrian hist, equipment, paintings, prints and sculptures with equestrian subjects - library 18830

Historisches Museum Verden, Domherrenhaus, Untere Str 13, 27283 Verden - T: (04231) 2169, Fax: 930020. Head: Dr. Björn Emigholz
Local Museum / Folklore Museum
Town hist, trades, social hist 18831

Veringenstadt

Prähistorisches Heimatmuseum, Im Städtle 116, 72519 Veringenstadt - T: (07577) 9300, Fax: 1681, E-mail: poststelle@veringenstadt.ikdulm.bwl.de. Head: Prof. Dr. Erwin Zillenbiller
Local Museum - 1966
Prehistoric finds, town hist 18832

Strübhaus-Haus der Malkunst, Am Kirchberg 138, 72519 Veringenstadt - T: (07577) 3232. Head: Prof. Dr. Erwin Zillenbiller
Fine Arts Museum - 1974
Paintings (15th-16th c), works by Hans, Jakob and Peter Strüb jun 18833

Verl

Handwerksmuseum Dingwerth, Eichendorffstr 77, 33415 Verl - T: (05246) 4102, Fax: 8483. Head: L. Dingwerth
Historical Museum - 1986
Nine original workshops (smithy, saddlery, carpentry, shoemaker) 18834

Viechtach

Die Ägayrischen Gewölbe, Spitalgasse 5, 94234 Viechtach - T: (09942) 801638, Fax: 801639, E-mail: info@reinhardschmid.de, Internet: http://www.ge-woelbe.de. Head: Reinhard Schmid
Museum of Classical Antiquities / Fine Arts Museum 18835

Kristallmuseum, Linprunstr 4, 94234 Viechtach - T: (09942) 5497, Fax: 6065
Natural History Museum
Mineralogy 18836

Museum Viechtach, Regerstr 2, 94234 Viechtach - T: (09942) 442, Fax: 6709. Head: Helmut Grotz
Local Museum - 1997
Town hist, pictures and signs of folk devoutness, photogrpphies of Viechtach 18837

Wachsstöcklkabinett - Wachzieher- und Lebzelter-Museum, Ringstr 7, 94234 Viechtach - T: (09942) 8812, Fax: 7069
Local Museum
Local crafts, chandler and gingerbread prod 18838

Vielstedt

Vielstedter Bauernhaus, Heimatmuseum der Delmenhorster Geest, Am Bauernhaus 13, 27798 Vielstedt - T: (04408) 369, Fax: 60806, E-mail: info@vielstedter-bauernhaus.de, Internet: http://www.vielstedter-bauernhaus.de. Head: Wilfried Strackerjan
Local Museum - 1936
Local hist, forestry 18839

Vienenburg

Eisenbahnmuseum, Bahnhofsstr 8, 38690 Vienenburg - T: (05324) 1777, Fax: 8891, E-mail: StadtVienenburg@t-online.de, Internet: http://www.vienenburg.de. Head: Dieter Dombrowski
Science&Tech Museum - 1988
Hist of the local railway, track building 18840

Viernheim

Heimatmuseum Viernheim, Berliner Ring 28, 68519 Viernheim - T: (06204) 988315, Fax: 963611, E-mail: Gisela.Wittemann@viernheim.de, Internet: http://www.viernheim.de
Local Museum - 1934
Archaeological finds, agriculture, trades 18841

Viersen

Dülkener Narrenmuseum, Waldnielerstr 53c, 41751 Viersen - T: (02162) 24505, Fax: 13044. Head: Dr. Volker Müller
Folklore Museum 18842

Städtische Galerie im Park, Rathauspark 1, 41747 Viersen - T: (02162) 101160, Fax: 101476, E-mail: adelheid.limbach@viersen.de. Head: Dr. Adelheid Limbach
Public Gallery 18843

Villingen-Schwenningen

Bauernmuseum Mühlhausen, Tuninger Str 9, 78056 Villingen-Schwenningen - T: (07720) 4258
Ethnology Museum - 1973
Agricultural tools 18844

Franziskanermuseum, Rietgasse 2, 78050 Villingen-Schwenningen - T: (07721) 822351, Fax: 822357, Internet: http://www.villingen-schwenningen.de/kultur. Head: Dr. Heinrich Maulhardt
Local Museum - 1982
Local hist, religious hist and traditions, crafts and guilts, ethnology (Black Forest coll), Celtic Tomb, industrial hist 18845

Heimat- und Uhrenmuseum, Kronenstr 16, 78054 Villingen-Schwenningen - T: (07720) 822371, Fax: 822377, E-mail: heimatmuseum@villingen-schwenningen.de, Internet: http://www.villingen-schwenningen.de/kultur/heimatunduhren.html. Head: Ingeborg Kottmann
Local Museum - 1910
Prehist, local hist, horology, folk art, glass from the Black Forest glassmakers, Swabian furniture 18846

Heimatstube Mühlhausen, Tuninger Str 5, 78056 Villingen-Schwenningen - T: (07720) 61409, Fax: 822027
Local Museum - 1971
Furniture, peasant life, household articles 18847

Internationales Luftfahrtmuseum, Spittelbronner Weg 78, 78050 Villingen-Schwenningen - T: (07720) 66302, Fax: 66302. Head: Manfred Pflumm
Science&Tech Museum - 1988
Hist of aeronautics 18848

Städtische Galerie Lovis-Kabinett, Friedrich-Ebert-Str 35, 78054 Villingen-Schwenningen - T: (07720) 821098, Fax: 821097, E-mail: galerie@villingen-schwenningen.de, Internet: http://www.villingen-schwenningen.de. Head: Wendelin Renn
Fine Arts Museum - 1990
19th c painting, Lovis press, contemporary art 18849

Uhrenindustriemuseum, Bürkstr 39, 78054 Villingen-Schwenningen - T: (07720) 38044, Fax: 992925, E-mail: regina.helbig@villingen-schwenningen.de, Internet: http://www.uhrenindustriemuseum.de
Science&Tech Museum - 1994
Clocks, watches, watch- and clock making machines 18850

Vilsbiburg

Heimatmuseum Vilsbiburg, Stadtpl 39-40, 84137 Vilsbiburg - T: (08741) 7828, Fax: 30538, E-mail: peter.barteit@landshut.org, Internet: http://www.vilsbiburg.de/wappen6/heimat/heimat.htm. Head: Lambert Grasmann
Local Museum - 1909
Early hist, handicrafts and photographs 18851

Heimatstuben Schlesien, Frontenhausener Str 17, 84137 Vilsbiburg - T: (08741) 1304
Local Museum
Cultural hist of Silesia 18852

Vilseck

Erstes Deutsches Türmermuseum, Marktpl 23, 92249 Vilseck - T: (09662) 701811, Fax: 9919, E-mail: poststelle@vilseck.bayern.de, Internet: http://www.vilseck.de
Special Museum - 2000
Life and profession of watchmen in the Oberpfalz, fans, clock-room 18853

Vilshofen

Museum für Waffentechink, Ausrüstung, Auszeichnungswesen, Eben, 94474 Vilshofen - T: (08548) 565
Military Museum - 1993 18854

Schwarz-Afrika-Museum, Kloster Schweiklberg, 94474 Vilshofen - T: (08541) 2090, Fax: 209174, E-mail: bruder_ulrich@vilstal.net, Internet: http://www.vilstal.net/schweiklberg. Head: Dr. Christian Schütz
Ethnology Museum - 1990
Souvenirs from Africa 18855

Stadtraum Vilshofen, Altstadt, 94474 Vilshofen - T: (08541) 2080
Public Gallery 18856

Völklingen

Weltkulturerbe Völklinger Hütte, Europäisches Zentrum für Kunst und Industriekultur, Gebläsehaus, Schlachthofstr 1, 66302 Völklingen - T: (06898) 91000, Fax: 9100111, E-mail: mail@voelklinger-huette.org, Internet: http://www.voelklinger-huette.org. Head: Dr. Meinrad Maria Grewenig
Fine Arts Museum / Science&Tech Museum / Open Air Museum 18857

Vogtsburg

Kaiserstühler Weinbaumuseum, Schloßbergstr, 79235 Vogtsburg - T: (07662) 8120, Fax: 81246, E-mail: info@vogtsburg.de, Internet: http://www.vogtsburg.de. Head: G. Schweizer
Agriculture Museum - 1981 18858

Vohenstrauß

Heimatmuseum der Stadt Vohenstrauß, Sophienstr 9, 92648 Vohenstrauß - T: (09651) 4114
Local Museum - 1929
Town and industrial hist 18859

Mineralienschau, Amselweg 10, 92648 Vohenstrauß - T: (09651) 1413
Natural History Museum - 1981
Mineralogy 18860

Volkach

Heimatmuseum im Schelfenhaus, Schelfengasse 1, 97332 Volkach - T: (09381) 40112, Fax: 40116, E-mail: tourismus@volkach.de, Internet: http://www.volkach.de
Local Museum
Town hist, town palace 18861

Museum Kartause Astheim, Kartäuserstr, Astheim, 97332 Volkach - T: (0931) 386290, Fax: 386262, E-mail: museen@bistum-wuerzburg.de. Head: Dr. Jürgen Lenssen
Religious Arts Museum / Fine Arts Museum / Historic Site / Folklore Museum 18862

Volkmarsen

Heimatstuben, Kasseler Str 6, 34471 Volkmarsen - T: (05693) 1401
Local Museum - 1986
Ceramics and porcelain, coll of coins, agricultural tools and implements 18863

Vreden

Hamaland-Museum und Westmünsterliche Hofanlage, Kreismuseum Borken, Butenwall 4, 48691 Vreden - T: (02564) 39180, Fax: 391829, E-mail: hamaland-museum@t-online.de, Internet: http://www.kreis-borken.de. Head: Dr. Annette Menke
Local Museum / Folklore Museum
Regional pottery, textiles, stoves 18864

Wackersdorf

Heimat- und Industriemuseum, Ehemaliges BBI-Laborgebäude, Werk III, 92442 Wackersdorf - T: (09431) 755560
Local Museum - 1997 18865

Wadersloh

Museum Abtei Liesborn, Museum des Kreises Warendorf, Liesborn, Abteiring 8, 59329 Wadersloh - T: (02523) 98240, Fax: 982411, E-mail: museum.abteiliesborn@t-online.de. Head: Dr. Bennie Priddy
Fine Arts Museum / Local Museum - 1966
Art from the Middle Ages to the present, decorative arts, folklore and crafts, coll of crucifixes from 11th c to present, textiles, embroidery, Dutch paintings 17th c 18866

Wächtersbach

Heimatmuseum Wächtersbach, Marktpl 12, 63607 Wächtersbach - T: (06053) 3883
Local Museum - 1968
Farming implements, cast-iron stoves, trade workshops, earthenware, ceramics of Wächtersbach (1832-1960) 18867

Wäschenbeuren

Staufergedächtnisstätte und Museum Wäscherschloß, Schloß Wäscherburg, 73116 Wäschenbeuren - T: (07172) 6232, Fax: 22016, E-mail: info@waescherschloss.de, Internet: http://www.waesserschloss.de. Head: Paul Kaißer
Historical Museum - 1961
Hist of Staufer dynasty, peasant life and traditions 18868

Waffenbrunn

Babls Uhrensammlung, Angerweg 1, Rhanwalting, 93494 Waffenbrunn - T: (09971) 1570
Science&Tech Museum - 1986
Coll of clocks 18869

Waghäusel

Heimatstube Wiesental, Wagbachstr 48, 68753 Waghäusel - T: (07254) 2400
Local Museum 18870

Museum im Alten Rathaus, Kirchstr 6, 68753 Waghäusel - T: (07254) 1221
Local Museum 18871

Waging

Bajuwarenmuseum Waging am See, Salzburger Str 32, 83329 Waging - T: (08681) 45870, Fax: 45872
Archaeological Museum - 1997
Tombs 18872

Vogelmuseum, Graben 1, 83329 Waging - T: (08681) 4461
Natural History Museum - 1961
Coll of birds 18873

Wahlsburg

EAM-live-Museum Lippoldsberg, Mühlenstr 2, 37194 Wahlsburg - T: (05572) 708229. Head: Hans Kirchhoff
Science&Tech Museum
Hydroelectric power station 18874

Museum im Schäferhaus, Schäferhof 22, 37194 Wahlsburg - T: (05572) 921195, Fax: 921196. Head: Barbara Maier-Schöler
Local Museum - 1981
Daily working and living conditions of farm workers 18875

Wahrenbrück

Heimatstube Wahrenbrück, Graunpl 6, 04924 Wahrenbrück
Local Museum - 1953
Local hist, trades and guilds, botany, minerals 18876

Waiblingen

Galerie der Stadt Waiblingen Kameralamt, Lange Str 40, 71332 Waiblingen - T: (07151) 18037, Fax: 59345, E-mail: museum@waiblingen.de. Head: Dr. Helmut Herbst
Public Gallery 18877

Heimatstuben der Csávolyer im Beinsteiner Torturm, Lange Str 1, 71332 Waiblingen - T: (07151) 54919
Local Museum
Peasant life and traditions of the formerly German settlement in Csávoly (Southern Hungary) 18878

Museum der Stadt Waiblingen, Weingärtner Vorstadt 20, 71332 Waiblingen - T: (07151) 18037, Fax: 59345, E-mail: museum@waiblingen.de. Head: Dr. Helmut Herbst
Local Museum - 1991
Local hist, crafts, Roman ceramics, tiles, contemporary art, framework-architecture 18879

Waischenfeld

Stadt- und Heimatmuseum mit Galerie, Haus des Gastes, Burg Waischenfeld, Schloßberg 80, 91344 Waischenfeld - T: (09202) 960117, Fax: 960129, E-mail: tourist-info@waischenfeld.de, Internet: http://www.waischenfeld.de
Local Museum - 1984
Local hist 18880

Waldaschaff

Heimatmuseum Waldaschaff, Aschaffenburger Str 31, 63857 Waldaschaff - T: (06021) 52736
Local Museum - 1990
Agricultural tools 18881

Waldbronn

Heimatstuben, Stuttgarter Str 23, 76337 Waldbronn - T: (07243) 609220, Fax: 60988, E-mail: Gemeinde@Waldbronn.de, Internet: http://www.waldbronn.de
Local Museum - 1976
Peasant life 18882

Radiomuseum, Stuttgarter Str 25, 76337 Waldbronn - T: (07243) 609203, Fax: 60988, E-mail: Gemeinde@waldbronn.de, Internet: http://www.waldbronn.de. Head: H. Masino
Science&Tech Museum - 1989
Radio receivers since 1924 18883

Waldbrunn, Westerwald

Heimatmuseum Waldbrunn, Hintermeilinger Str 28, 65620 Waldbrunn, Westerwald - T: (06436) 4938
Local Museum - 1987
Geology, geography, trade hist, domestic implements and objects, costumes 18884

Waldbüttelbrunn

Straßenbau - einst und jetzt, Zeller Str 11, 97297 Waldbüttelbrunn - T: (0931) 39200, Fax: 392113, E-mail: poststelle@sbawue.bayern.de
Science&Tech Museum
Hist of road construction 18885

Waldeck, Hessen

Burgmuseum Waldeck, Schloß, 34513 Waldeck, Hessen - T: (05623) 5890, Fax: 589289, E-mail: schlosswa@aol.com, Internet: http://www.schloss-waldeck.de
Local Museum - 1950
Medieval stronghold with various rooms and interior 18886

Waldems

Heimatmuseum Steinfischbach, Usinger Str, 65529 Waldems - T: (06087) 2561
Local Museum
Bread baking, pre-history, church and farm life 18887

Waldenbuch

Museum für Volkskultur in Württemberg, Württembergisches Landesmuseum Stuttgart, Schloß, Kirchgasse 3, 71111 Waldenbuch - T: (07157) 8204, Fax: 520079. Head: Dr. Hans-Ulrich Roller
Folklore Museum - 1989/90
Furniture, costume, amateur art, religiousness, popular graphics 18888

Waldenburg, Sachsen

Heimatmuseum und Naturalienkabinett, Geschwister-Scholl-Pl 1, 08396 Waldenburg, Sachsen - T: (037608) 22519, Fax: 16060, E-mail: museum-waldenburg@t-online.de, Internet: http://www.waldenburg.de
Local Museum / Natural History Museum - 1840
Local hist, pottery, earthenware, pipe coll, zoology (mammals, insects, birds, fish, reptiles), botany (herbs, coll of wood and drugs), mineralogy, paleontology, physical and astronomical instruments, Linck coll (cabinet of curiosities, rare exhibits from the 17th/18th c) 18889

Waldenburg, Württemberg

Hohenloher Urweltmuseum, Hauptstr 13, 74638 Waldenburg, Württemberg - T: (07942) 1080, Fax: 10888, E-mail: stadt@waldenburg-hohenlohe.de, Internet: http://www.waldenburg-hohenlohe.de
Natural History Museum - 1987
Fossils 18890

Siegelmuseum Schloß Waldenburg, 74638 Waldenburg, Württemberg - T: (07942) 1040, Fax: 10477. Head: F.K. Fürst zu Hohenlohe-Waldenburg
Decorative Arts Museum 18891

Walderbach

Kreismuseum Walderbach, Kirchstr 4, 93194 Walderbach - T: (09971) 78220, Fax: 78399, E-mail: kultur@lra.landkreis-cham.de, Internet: http://www.kreismuseum-walderbach.de. Head: Dr. Bärbel Kleindorfer-Marx
Local Museum - 1969 18892

Waldkirch

Elztalmuseum - Regionalgeschichte und Orgelbau, Kirchpl 14, 79183 Waldkirch - T: (07681) 404104, Fax: 25562. Head: Dr. Evelyn Flögel
Local Museum / Music Museum - 1931/1985
Mechanical instruments, costumes, local history, Georg Scholz graphics 18893

Waldkirchen, Niederbayern

Museum Goldener Steig, Büchl 22, 94065 Waldkirchen, Niederbayern - T: (08581) 20216, Fax: 20213, E-mail: stadt.waldkirchen@t-online.de, Internet: http://www.waldkirchen.de. Head: Karl Saxinger
Local Museum - 1987
Town hist and cultural hist between Bavaria and Bohemia 18894

Waldkraiburg

Heimatstube Adlergebirge, Braunauer Str 10, 84478 Waldkraiburg - T: (08638) 67465
Local Museum 18895

Stadtmuseum Waldkraiburg, Braunauer Str 10, 84478 Waldkraiburg - T: (08638) 959335, Fax: 959316, E-mail: museum@kultur-waldkraiburg.de. Head: Elke Keiper
Special Museum / Local Museum
Glass coll, hist of German expellees, Waldkraiburg hist 18896

Städtische Galerie Waldkraiburg, Braunauer Str 10, 84478 Waldkraiburg - T: (08638) 959308, Fax: 959316, E-mail: galerie@kultur-waldkraiburg.de. Head: Elke Keiper
Public Gallery - 2000 18897

Waldmünchen

Grenzland- und Trenckmuseum, Schloßhof 4, 93449 Waldmünchen - T: (09972) 3070, 8298
Local Museum 18898

Waldsassen

Stiftlandmuseum, Museumsstr 1, 95652 Waldsassen - T: (09632) 91247, 91248, Fax: 91249, E-mail: stadt@waldsassen.de, Internet: http://www.waldsassen.de. Head: Adolf Gläßel, Robert Treml
Local Museum
Town hist, religious folklore, crafts and rustic culture 18899

Waldshut-Tiengen

Klettgau-Museum, Schloßpl 2, 79761 Waldshut-Tiengen - T: (07741) 4733
Local Museum - 1971
Local hist, archeological finds 18900

Waldthurn

Heimatmuseum Waldthurn, Am Rathaus 5, 92727 Waldthurn - T: (09657) 515, Fax: 1291
Local Museum - 1970
Town hist and flax processing 18901

Walheim

Römerhaus Walheim, Römerstr 16, 74399 Walheim - T: (07143) 80410, Fax: 804133, E-mail: epple@walheim.kdrs.de, Internet: http://www.walheim.de
Archaeological Museum - 1991
Roman business house 18902

Walldorf, Baden

Museum im Astorhaus, Johann-Jakob-Astor-Str, 69190 Walldorf, Baden - T: (06227) 2143. Head: Jürgen Herrmann
Local Museum
Agricultural machinery and tools, crafts, archeological finds 18903

Walldürn

Elfenbeinmuseum, Burgstr 24, 74731 Walldürn - T: (06282) 92030. Head: Oscar Stalf
Decorative Arts Museum - 1954
Ivory works (12th-20th c) 18904

Odenwälder Freilandmuseum, Weiherstr 12, 74731 Walldürn - T: (06286) 320, Fax: 1349, E-mail: Odenwaelder_Freilandmuseum@t-online.de, Internet: http://www.wallduern.de/Freizeit/museen.html. Head: Thomas Naumann
Open Air Museum - 1984
Apiculture 18905

Stadt- und Wallfahrtsmuseum, Hauptstr 39, 74731 Walldürn - T: (06282) 67107, 8764, Internet: http://www.wallduern.de. Head: Robert Hollerbach
Local Museum / Religious Arts Museum / Folklore Museum - 1965
Hist of pilgrimage 18906

Wallerstein

Neues Schloss Wallerstein, 86757 Wallerstein - T: (09081) 782285, 782300, Fax: 7028, E-mail: schloesser@fuerst-wallerstein.de, Internet: http://www.fuerst-wallerstein.de. Head: Fürst zu Oettingen-Wallerstein
Decorative Arts Museum - 1971
Porcelain, glass, furniture, uniforms, family history 18907

Wallhausen, Württemberg

Jüdische Gedenkstätte und ehemalige Synagoge, Judengasse 4, Michelbach an der Lücke, 74599 Wallhausen, Württemberg - T: (07955) 2155, 2239, Fax: 938126, E-mail: info@gemeinde-wallhausen.de, Internet: http://www.gemeinde-wallhausen.de
Historical Museum - 1984
Hist of the Jewish community in former synagogue 18908

Walsrode

Deutsches Vogelbauer-Museum, Vogelpark Walsrode, Am Rieselbach, 29664 Walsrode - T: (05161) 60440, Fax: 8210, E-mail: office@vogelpark-walsrode.de, Internet: http://www.vogelpark-walsrode.de. Head: Hans Geiger
Special Museum - 1962
Bird cages and houses 18909

Heidemuseum Rischmannshof Walsrode, Freilichtmuseum, Hermann-Löns-Str 8, 29664 Walsrode - T: (05161) 977270, Fax: 977262, E-mail: stadt@walsrode.de, Internet: http://www.walsrode.de. Head: Dr. Gunther Gerhardt
Open Air Museum / Local Museum - 1911/12
Rural tools, Löns coll and library, local hist, school, smithy, shoemaker's workshop, beekeeping 18910

Kloster Walsrode, Kirchpl 2, 29664 Walsrode - T: (05161) 5343
Religious Arts Museum
Benedictine nunnery, 18th-c art objects 18911

Waltersdorf bei Zittau

Volkskunde- und Mühlenmuseum, Dorfstr 89, 02799 Waltersdorf bei Zittau - T: (035841) 72872, Fax: 35477
Science&Tech Museum / Local Museum / Folklore Museum - 1956
Grist mill, development of miller's crafts, local hist, peasant household objects, composer Friedrich Schneider (1786-1853) 18912

Waltershausen

Heimatmuseum Schloß Tenneberg, Schloß Tenneberg, 99880 Waltershausen - T: (03622) 2929
Local Museum 18913

Waltrop

Heimatmuseum Waltrop, Riphausstr, 45731 Waltrop - T: (02309) 930208
Local Museum - 1971
Farm life, agriculture and trade, mining, sacral objects, town hist - archive 18914

Westfälisches Industriemuseum, Altes Schiffshebewerk Henrichenburg, Am Hebewerk 2, 45731 Waltrop - T: (02363) 97070, Fax: 970712, E-mail: schiffshebewerk@lwl-org, Internet: http://www.schiffshebewerk-henrichenburg.de. Head: Herbert Niewerth
Science&Tech Museum - 1992
Inland navigation, historic ships, tools 18915

Wandersleben

Burg Gleichen, 99869 Wandersleben - T: (036202) 82440. Head: Kristina Baum
Open Air Museum 18916

Wandlitz

Agrarmuseum Wandlitz, Breitscheidstr 22, 16348 Wandlitz - T: (033397) 21558, Fax: 60888, E-mail: papendieck@agrarmuseum-wandlitz.de, Internet: http://www.agrarmuseum-wandlitz.de. Head: Hans Papendieck
Agriculture Museum - 1955
Local history, peasant living style and work tools 18917

Wanfried

Heimatmuseum und Dokumentationszentrum zur Deutschen Nachkriegsgeschichte, Marktstr 2, 37281 Wanfried - T: (05655) 98940, Fax: 989430
Local Museum - 1924
Regional hist, archaeology, geology, early and prehistory, traditional furniture and costumes, ceramics, paintings 18918

Wangen im Allgäu

Deutsches Eichendorff-Museum, Lange Gasse 1, 88239 Wangen im Allgäu - T: (07522) 3840, 3704, Fax: 74199, Internet: http://wangen.de/eichendorff-museum/. Head: Sybille Heimann
Special Museum - 1936
Documents and memorabilia on the German author Joseph Freiherr von Eichendorff (1788-1857) - archive 18919

Gustav-Freytag-Archiv und Museum, Lange Gasse 1, 88239 Wangen im Allgäu - T: (07522) 4369, 3704, Fax: 74199, Internet: http://wangen.de/gustav-freytag-museum/. Head: Sybille Heimann
Special Museum - 1952 18920

Städtische Galerie In der Badstube, Lange Gasse 9, 88239 Wangen im Allgäu - T: (07522) 74246, Fax: 74243, Internet: http://www.galerie.wangen1.de
Public Gallery 18921

Städtische Museen Wangen im Allgäu, Eselberg 1, 88239 Wangen im Allgäu - T: (07522) 74211, Fax: 74111. Head: Dr. Rainer Jensch
Local Museum - 1885
Milling cheese making, works by the painter Joseph Anton von Gegenbaur (1800-1876), peasant life and traditions, coin coll, in a 16th c frame-work house mechanical music instruments, painting, historic bathroom 18922

Wangerland

Internationales Muschelmuseum, Lange Str 17, Hooksiel, 26434 Wangerland - T: (04461) 6579
Natural History Museum - 1994
Mussels, shells and sea snails mainly from around the North Sea coast, coral aquarium 18923

Wangerooge

Inselmuseum im Alten Leuchtturm, Zedeliusstr 3, 26486 Wangerooge - T: (04469) 8324
Local Museum - 1980
Lighthouse from 1856, hist of the island, shipping, ornithology, mussels, sea snails, amber 18924

Wanna

Heimatmuseum Wanna, Museumsweg 3, 21776 Wanna - T: (04757) 499, E-mail: wanna@online.de, Internet: http://www.wanna.de
Local Museum / Archaeological Museum - 1967
Domestic implements, moor cultivation, finds from the Stone and Iron Age, agricultural machinery, trade tools 18925

Waren

Müritz-Museum, Friedensstr 5, 17192 Waren - T: (03991) 667600, Fax: 667601, Internet: http://www.mueritz.de. Head: R. Seemann
Natural History Museum - 1866
Botany, entomology, malacology, ornithology, nature conservancy, natural hist coll of Mecklenburg-Vorpommern, geology - aquarium, garden, library 18926

Warendorf

Heimathaus der Stadt Warendorf, Rathaus, Markt 1, 48231 Warendorf - T: (02581) 54230, Fax: 54797, E-mail: kultur@warendorf.de, Internet: http://www.warendorf.de
Local Museum - 1976 18927

Warmensteinach

Freilandmuseum Grassemann Naturpark-Infostelle, Grassemann Haus, Nr. 3, 95485 Warmensteinach - T: (09277) 6105, Fax: (0921) 72888
Open Air Museum - 1992
Peasant life and exhibits on the topics of people and forest 18928

Glasmuseum, Oberwarmensteinacher Str 420, 95485 Warmensteinach - T: (09277) 1401, Fax: 1613, E-mail: verkehrsamt@warmensteinach.de, Internet: http://www.warmensteinach.de
Decorative Arts Museum
Coll of glass objects 18929

Warnkenhagen

Thünen-Museum-Tellow, Dorfstr 15, Tellow, 17168 Warnkenhagen - T: (039976) 5410, Fax: 54116, E-mail: Thünen-Museum-Tellow@t-online.de, Internet: http://www.thuenen.de. Head: Rolf-Peter Bartz
Open Air Museum 18930

Warstein

Städtisches Museum Haus Kupferhammer, Belecker Landstr 9, 59581 Warstein - T: (02902) 1078, Fax: 81216, E-mail: post@warstein.de, Internet: http://www.warstein.de. Head: Dietmar Lange
Local Museum 18931

Warthausen

Schloßmuseum Warthausen, Schloß, 88447 Warthausen - T: (07351) 14503, Fax: 6893. Head: Franz Freiherr von Ulm zu Erbach
Historical Museum
Furniture, faience, weapons, medieval paintings and scultpures, mss of Graf von Stadion, Christoph Martin Wieland (1733-1813), Sophie von la Roche 18932

Waschleithe

Lehr- und Schaubergwerk Herkules Frisch Glück, Fürstenbergstr, 08358 Waschleithe - T: (03774) 24252
Science&Tech Museum
Mining hist 18933

Wasserburg am Inn

Erstes Imaginäres Museum - Sammlung Günter Dietz, Bruckgasse 2, 83512 Wasserburg am Inn - T: (08071) 4358. Head: Günter Dietz
Fine Arts Museum - 1979
'Original' reproductions by the painter and illustrator Dietz, which can only be distinguished from the originals with the help of X-rays, coll includes early altar pieces, Dutch painting (17th-18th c), romanticism, impressionism, expressionism 18934

Feuerwehrmuseum, Im Hag 3, 83512 Wasserburg am Inn - T: (08071) 6400, Fax: 10570. Head: Heinrich Kurz
Special Museum - 1982
Old fire brigade 18935

Museum Wasserburg, Kunst- und kulturgeschichtliche Sammlungen der Stadt, Herrengasse 15-17, 83512 Wasserburg am Inn - T: (08071) 925290, Fax: 10570, E-mail: heimatmuseum@stadt.wasserburg.de, Internet: http://www.wasserburg.de. Head: Ferdinand Steffan
Local Museum - 1888
Religious art, furniture, musical instruments - archive, historical library 18936

Wegmachermuseum, Herderstr 5, 83512 Wasserburg am Inn - T: (08071) 91850, Fax: 918519, E-mail: smWasserburg@s.baro.bayern.de. Head: H. Grasberger-Lorenz
Science&Tech Museum - 1977
Hist of road construction 18937

Wasserburg, Bodensee

Museum im Malhaus, Halbinselstr 77, 88142 Wasserburg, Bodensee - T: (08382) 887197, Fax: 89369
Local Museum
Local hist and fishing 18938

Wassertrüdingen

Fischereimuseum, Im Törle, 91717 Wassertrüdingen - T: (09832) 68220, Fax: 682230
Local Museum
Fishing 18939

Imker- und Heimatmuseum, Am Ölgraben 12, 91717 Wassertrüdingen - T: (09832) 649
Local Museum 18940

Wedel

Buddelschiff-Museum, Schulauer Fährhaus, 22880 Wedel - T: (04103) 920016, Fax: 920050. Head: Binikowski
Decorative Arts Museum - 1984
Shells, corals, snails, 'Buddelschiff' coll 18941

Ernst Barlach Museum Wedel, Mühlenstr 1, 22880 Wedel - T: (04103) 918291, Fax: 97135, E-mail: kontakt@ernst-barlach.de, Internet: http://www.ernst-barlach.de. Head: Jürgen Doppelstein
Fine Arts Museum
Ernst Barlach exhibition, artists of classical modern art 18942

Heimatmuseum Wedel, Küsterstr 5, 22880 Wedel - T: (04103) 13202, Fax: 707300, E-mail: museum@unser-wedel.de, Internet: http://www.heimatmuseum.net/museum-wedel
Local Museum 18943

Wedemark

Richard-Brandt-Heimatmuseum Bissendorf, Gottfried-August-Bürger-Str, 30900 Wedemark - T: (05130) 581226, Fax: 581205, E-mail: -gemeinde.wedemark@t-online.de
Local Museum - 1973
Violin making, Gottfried August Bürger, Karl Montag 18944

Weener

Heimatmuseum Reiderland, Hütthausstr 2, 26826 Weener - T: (04951) 1828
Local Museum - 1919
Cultural hist, early and prehist, settling, brickworks, pottery, agricultural implements, dairy farming 18945

Heimatmuseum Weener, Neue Str 26, 26826 Weener - T: (04951) 1828
Local Museum 18946

Wegberg

Flachsmuseum Beeck, Holtumer Str 19a, Beeck, 41844 Wegberg - T: (02434) 927614, Fax: 3535, Internet: http://www.flachsmuseum.de. Head: Heinz Gerichhausen
Special Museum / Folklore Museum
Flax and linen, European traditional costumes 18947

Wegscheid

Zollmuseum, Ebenäckerring 1, 94110 Wegscheid - T: (08592) 477, 8880, Fax: 88840, E-mail: tourismus@wegscheid.btl.de, Internet: http://www.wegscheid.de
Historical Museum - 1987
Hist of local customs and smuggling between Bavaria, Austria and Czechoslovakia 18948

Wehrheim

Heimat- und Dorfmuseum Pfaffenwiesbach, Lindenstr, 61273 Wehrheim - T: (06081) 3271
Local Museum - 1984/91
Village chronicle and hist, coll of Bibles 18949

Stadttormuseum, Zum Stadttor, 61273 Wehrheim - T: (06081) 9384. Head: Helmut Michel
Local Museum - 1983 18950

Weichering

Archäologisches Museum im Rathaus (not yet open), Kapellenpl 3, 86706 Weichering - T: (08454) 94970, Fax: 949722, E-mail: -gemeinde.weichering@neusob.de
Archaeological Museum
Archeological finds and tombs 18951

Weida

Museum auf der Osterburg, Schloßberg 14, 07570 Weida - T: (036603) 62775, Fax: 62257, E-mail: info@weida.de, Internet: http://www.weida.de
Local Museum / Public Gallery - 1930
Local and regional history, development of crafts and guilds, leather industry - library 18952

Weiden, Oberpfalz

Galerie Spitalgasse, Kunstverein Weiden, Spitalgasse, 92637 Weiden, Oberpfalz - T: (0961) 46308, Fax: 4162173, E-mail: info@kunstvereinweiden.de, Internet: http://www.kunstvereinweiden.de
Association with Coll 18953

Internationales Keramik-Museum, Die Neue Sammlung München, Luitpoldstr 25, 92637 Weiden, Oberpfalz - T: (0961) 32030, Fax: 3810627, E-mail: keramikmuseum@weiden-oberpfalz.de, Internet: http://www.die-neue-sammlung.de. Head: Stefanie Dietz
Decorative Arts Museum - 1990
Chinaware and porcelain from China, ceramics from ancient Egypt and the Near East - reference library (on request) 18954

Weidenberg

Freilichtmuseum Scherzenmühle Weidenberg, In der Au, 95466 Weidenberg - T: (09278) 1301, Fax: 773094, Internet: http://www.fichtelgebirgsverein.de
Open Air Museum - 1991
Old mill 18955

Volkskundliche Sammlung des Fichtelgebirgsvereins, In der Verbandsschule, 95466 Weidenberg - T: (09278) 1339, 1301, Fax: 773094, Internet: http://www.weidenberg.fichtelgebirgsverein.de. Head: Adolf Schlegel
Local Museum / Folklore Museum - 1980
Local hist and shoemaker's workshop 18956

Zinnkeller, Alte Bayreuther Str 52, 95466 Weidenberg - T: (09278) 8430
Local Museum - 1985
Tin figures 18957

Weikersheim

Forstmuseum im Hochwildpark Karlsberg, Hochwildpark Karlsberg, 97990 Weikersheim - T: (07934) 1209, Fax: 992290
Natural History Museum - 1983
Hist of forestry 18958

Schloß Weikersheim, 97990 Weikersheim - T: (07934) 8364, Fax: 8364. Head: Dr. Klaus Merten
Fine Arts Museum 18959

Tauberländer Dorfmuseum, Marktpl, 97990 Weikersheim - T: (07934) 1209, Fax: 992290
Local Museum - 1965
Agriculture, agricultural implements, peasant life, viticulture 18960

Weil am Lech

Prähistorische Siedlung Pestenacker, An der Staatsstr, 86947 Weil am Lech - T: (08191) 70249, Fax: 70249
Historical Museum - 2001 18961

Weil am Rhein

Freilichtmuseum Dorfstube Ötlingen, Dorfstr 61, 79576 Weil am Rhein - T: (07621) 64433. Head: Peter Zuberer
Open Air Museum - 1990
Peasant life 18962

Landwirtschaftsmuseum, Bläsiring 23, 79576 Weil am Rhein - T: (07621) 704411, Fax: 704124, E-mail: kultur@weil-am-rhein.de. Head: Tonio Paßlick
Agriculture Museum - 1990
Coll of enamel plates and signs 18963

Museum am Lindenplatz, Lindenpl 1, 79576 Weil am Rhein - T: (07621) 792219, Fax: 704124, E-mail: museumamlindenplatz@gmx.de. Head: Tonio Paßlick
Local Museum
Architectural finds, town hist 18964

Städtische Galerie Stapflehus, Bläsiring 10, 79576 Weil am Rhein - T: (07621) 704411, 704416, Fax: 704124, E-mail: kultur@weil-am-rhein. Head: Tonio Paßlick
Public Gallery 18965

Vitra Design Museum, Charles-Eames-Str 1, 79576 Weil am Rhein - T: (07621) 7023200, Fax: 7023590, E-mail: info@design-museum.de, Internet: http://www.design-museum.de. Head: Alexander von Vegesack
Decorative Arts Museum - 1989 18966

Weil der Stadt

Keplermuseum, Keplergasse 2, 71263 Weil der Stadt - T: (07033) 301131. Head: Prof. A. Hermann
Special Museum - 1940
House where Johannes Kepler was born, furnishings in the style of the period, documents on the life and work of Kepler (1571-1630) - library, archives 18967

Stadt-Museum, Marktpl 12, 71263 Weil der Stadt - T: (07033) 301141
Local Museum 18968

Weilbach

Dorfmuseum Weckbach, Ohrnbachtalstr 23, 63937 Weilbach - T: (09373) 2741
Local Museum / Folklore Museum / Agriculture Museum - 1988
Town hist 18969

Weilburg

Bergbau- und Stadtmuseum Weilburg, Schloßpl 1, 35781 Weilburg - T: (06471) 379447, Fax: 379452, E-mail: museum@weilburg.de, Internet: http://www.weilburg.de. Head: Paul Wienand
Science&Tech Museum / Local Museum - 1911
Mining, mineralogy - show mine "Tiefer Stollen" 18970

Deutsches Baumaschinen-Modellmuseum, Brückenstr 46, 35781 Weilburg - T: (06471) 5020, Fax: 50270, E-mail: feickert.weilburg@t-online.de, Internet: http://www.feickert-bau.de. Head: Rudolf Feickert
Science&Tech Museum - 1989
Building machineries 18971

Dillhäuser Fachwerkhaus im Tiergarten Weilburg, Frankfurter Str 31, 35781 Weilburg - T: (06471) 39075, Fax: 1786, E-mail: faweilburg@forst.hessen.de. Head: Dr. Backhaus
Open Air Museum - 1969
Deer park 18972

Höhlenmuseum Kubacher Kristallhöhle und Freilicht-Steinemuseum, c/o Höhlenverein Kubach e. V., Kubach-Freienfels, K422, 35781 Weilburg - T: (06471) 94000, Fax: 94000, Internet: http://www.kubacherkristallhoehle.de. Head: Edmund Letschert
Natural History Museum / Open Air Museum - 1981
Geology, mineralogy, fossils 18973

Renaissance- und Barock-Schloß Weilburg, Schloßpl 3, 35781 Weilburg - T: (06471) 2236, Fax: 1806. Head: Dr. Kai R. Mathieu
Decorative Arts Museum - 1934
Interior of the castle 18974

Weiler-Simmerberg

Kornhaus-Museum, Hauptstr 11, 88171 Weiler-Simmerberg - T: (08387) 1654, Internet: http://www.westallgäuer-heimatmuseum.de. Head: Dr. Elmar Holzer
Local Museum - 1981
Local hist and agricultural tools 18975

Westallgäuer Heimatmuseum, Hauptstr 2, 88171 Weiler-Simmerberg - T: (08387) 650
Local Museum - 1924
Local hist, sculptures, old store (18th c.) and rustic furniture 18976

Weilheim, Oberbayern

Schützenmuseum der Königlich privilegierten Feuerschützengesellschaft Weilheim, Schützenstr 28, 82362 Weilheim, Oberbayern - T: (0881) 7549
Special Museum - 1995
Shooting club 18977

Stadtmuseum Weilheim, Marienpl 1, 82362 Weilheim, Oberbayern - T: (0881) 682100, Fax: 682123, E-mail: stadt.weilheim@weilheim.de, Internet: http://www.weilheim.de. Head: Dr. Reinhardt Helm
Fine Arts Museum - 1882
Local art (1590-1630), tin, prehist, early hist 18978

Weilmünster

Rohnstädter Heimatstube, Langenbacher Str 4, 35789 Weilmünster - T: (06472) 7921
Local Museum - 1985
Village life, agriculture, forestry, mining 18979

Weilrod

Heimatmuseum Gemünden, Emmershäuser Str, 61276 Weilrod - T: (06083) 1060
Local Museum / Historic Site
Regional and local hist 18980

Weiltingen

Trachten- und Heimatmuseum, c/o Gemeinde Weiltingen, Schloßweg 6, 91744 Weiltingen - T: (09853) 253, 1414, Fax: 389774
Local Museum
Local hist, costumes 18981

Weimar, Thüringen

Albert-Schweitzer-Gedenk- und Begegnungsstätte, Kegelpl 4, 99423 Weimar, Thüringen - T: (03643) 202739, Fax: 202775, E-mail: asgbweimar@t-online.de, Internet: http://www.01019.freenet.de/as-stiftung. Head: Beate Lepper
Special Museum 18982

Bauhaus-Museum, Kunstsammlungen zu Weimar, Theaterpl, 99423 Weimar, Thüringen, mail addr: Burgpl 4, 99423 Weimar, Thüringen - T: (03643) 5460, 546130, Fax: 546101, E-mail: kunstsammlungen-weimar@t-online.de, Internet: http://www.kunstsammlungen-weimar.de. Head: Prof. Rolf Bothe
Fine Arts Museum
19th Modern art, German avontgarde 1900-1930 18983

Deutsches Bienenmuseum, Ilmstr 3, 99425 Weimar, Thüringen - T: (03643) 901032, Fax: 901032, E-mail: stadt.weimar.stadtmuseum@t-online.de, Internet: http://www.stadtmuseum-weimar.de. Head: Reinhard Herb
Natural History Museum 18984

Fürstengruft mit russisch-orthodoxer Kirche, Am Poseckschen Garten, 99423 Weimar, Thüringen - T: (03643) 545380, Fax: 545356, E-mail: museen@weimar-klassik.de, Internet: http://www.weimar-klassik.de
Historical Museum 18985

Gedenkstätte Buchenwald, Buchenwald, 99427 Weimar, Thüringen - T: (03643) 4300, Fax: 430100, E-mail: buchenwald@buchenwald.de, Internet: http://www.buchenwald.de. Head: Dr. Volkhard Knigge
Historic Site / Historical Museum - 1958/95
Hist of concentration camp 1937/45, hist of the Soviet Special Camp no 2 1945/50 - archives, library 18986

Goethe- und Schiller-Archiv, Stiftung Weimarer Klassik, Hans-Wahl-Str 4, 99425 Weimar, Thüringen - T: (03643) 545240, Fax: 545241, E-mail: gsa@weimar-klassik.de, Internet: http://www.weimar-klassik.de. Head: Dr. Jochen Golz
Library with Exhibitions 18987

Goethes Gartenhaus - Goethe-Nationalmuseum, Stiftung Weimarer Klassik, Im Park an der Ilm, 99423 Weimar, Thüringen - T: (03643) 545375, Fax: 545356, E-mail: gnm@weimar-klassik.de, Internet: http://www.weimar-klassik.de
Historic Site - 1885
Historic interiors, memorabilia of J.W. Goethe (1749-1832) 18988

Goethes Wohnhaus mit Goethe-Nationalmuseum, Stiftung Weimarer Klassik, Frauenplan, 99423 Weimar, Thüringen - T: (03643) 545310, Fax: 545356, E-mail: museen@weimar-klassik.de, Internet: http://www.weimar-klassik.de
Special Museum - 1886
Memorabilia on J.W. v. Goethe (1749-1832), documents, furniture, manuscripts, history, portraits, pictures 18989

Kirms-Krackow-Haus, Stiftung Weimarer Klassik, Jakobstr 10, 99423 Weimar, Thüringen - T: (03643) 545383, Fax: 545365, E-mail: museen@weimar-klassik.de, Internet: http://www.weimar-klassik.de
Historic Site - 1916
Memorabilia of J.D. Falk (1768-1826), J.G. Herder (1744-1803) and J.K.A. Musäus (1735-1787), furniture 18990

Kunsthalle am Goetheplatz, Stadtmuseum Weimar, Goethepl 9b, 99423 Weimar, Thüringen - T: (03643) 502364, Fax: 8260110, E-mail: - stadt.weimar.stadtmuseum@t-online.de, Internet: http://www.stadtmuseum-weimar.de. Head: Dr. Rüdiger Wiese
Fine Arts Museum 18991

Liszthaus - Goethe-Nationalmuseum, Stiftung Weimarer Klassik, Marienstr 17, 99423 Weimar, Thüringen - T: (03643) 545388, Fax: 545356, E-mail: gnm@weimar-klassik.de, Internet: http://www.weimar-klassik.de
Special Museum / Historic Site - 1887
Memorabilia of composer Franz Liszt in his former home, portraits, sculpture, sheet music, first edition 18992

Museum für Ur- und Frühgeschichte Thüringens, Humboldtstr 11, 99423 Weimar, Thüringen - T: (03643) 818300, Fax: 818390, E-mail: posr@tlad.de. Head: Dr. Sigrid Dušek
Archaeological Museum - 1892
Evolution, anthropology, ancient and early hist of Thüringen - library, archive, restoration 18993

Neues Museum Weimar, Kunstsammlungen zu Weimar, Weimarpl 4, 99423 Weimar, Thüringen, mail addr: Burgpl 4, 99423 Weimar, Thüringen - T: (03643) 546163, 546130, Fax: 546101, E-mail: kunstsammlungen-weimar@t-online.de, Internet: http://www.kunstsammlungen-weimar.de. Head: Prof. Dr. Rolf Bothe
Fine Arts Museum 18994

Nietzsche-Archiv, Humboldstr 36, 99425 Weimar, Thüringen - T: (03643) 545159, Fax: 545356, E-mail: museen@weimar-klassik.de, Internet: http://www.weimar-klassik.de. Head: Prof. Dr. Gerhard Schuster
Special Museum
Home of Nietzsche during the last three years of his life, library, working room, furnishings by Henry van de Velde, portraits 18995

Orangerie und Schloßpark Belvedere, Stiftung Weimarer Klassik, Belvedere, 99425 Weimar, Thüringen, mail addr: Postfach 2012, 99401 Weimar, Thüringen - T: (03643) 5450, 545190, Fax: 545431, E-mail: garten@weimar-klassik.de, Internet: http://www.weimar-klassik.de. Head: Dorothee Ahrendt
Open Air Museum / Historic Site 18996

Römisches Haus - Goethe-Nationalmuseum, Stiftung Weimarer Klassik, Im Park an der Ilm, 99425 Weimar, Thüringen - T: (03643) 545382, Fax: 545356, E-mail: gnm@weimar-klassik.de, Internet: http://www.weimar-klassik.de
Historic Site - 1962
Summer home of Duke Karl-August of Sachsen-Weimar (1757-1828), historic furnishings 18997

Rokokomuseum Schloß Belvedere, Kunstsammlungen zu Weimar, Belvedere, 99425 Weimar, Thüringen, mail addr: Burgpl 4, 99423 Weimar, Thüringen - T: (03643) 5460, 546130, Fax: 564101, E-mail: kunstsammlungen-weimar@t-online.de, Internet: http://www.kunstsammlungen-weimar.de. Head: Prof. Rolf Bothe
Fine Arts Museum - 1923
18th c court art, painting, decorative objects, textiles, building plans, porcelain, faiences, glass ware from the 17-19th c 18998

Schillerhaus, Goethe-Nationalmuseum, Stiftung Weimarer Klassik, Schillerstr 12, 99423 Weimar, Thüringen - T: (03643) 545350, Fax: 545356, E-mail: gnm@weimar-klassik.de, Internet: http://www.weimar-klassik.de
Historic Site - 1847
Living quarters of Schiller and his family 18999

Schloßmuseum, Kunstsammlungen zu Weimar, Burgpl 4, 99423 Weimar, Thüringen - T: (03643) 5460, 546130, Fax: 546101, E-mail: info@kunstsammlungen-weimar.de, Internet: http://www.kunstsammlungen-weimar.de. Head: Prof. Rolf Bothe
Fine Arts Museum - 1922
Classical historic rooms, 16th-20th c decorative arts, Paul Maenz Coll, Weimarer Malerschule, Lucas-Cranach-Galerie - library 19000

Schloßpark Tiefurt, Stiftung Weimarer Klassik, Hauptstr 14, 99425 Weimar, Thüringen - T: (03643) 850666, Fax: 850668, E-mail: gnm@weimar-klassik.de, Internet: http://www.weimar-klassik.de
Historical Museum - 1885
Historic furniture and porcelain 19001

Stadtmuseum und Stadtarchiv Weimar, Karl-Liebknecht-Str 5-9, 99423 Weimar, Thüringen - T: (03643) 82600, Fax: 8260110, E-mail: - stadtweimar.stadtmuseum@t-online.de, Internet: http://www.stadtmuseum-weimar.de. Head: Dr. Rüdiger Wiese
Local Museum / Natural History Museum - 1903
City hist, peasant living style and costumes, beekeeping - apiculture coll 19002

Stiftung Weimarer Klassik, Burgpl 4, 99423 Weimar, Thüringen - T: (03643) 5450, Fax: 545454, E-mail: praesident@weimar-klassik.de, Internet: http://www.weimar-klassik.de. Head: Hellmut Seemann
Historical Museum 19003

Wittumspalais - Goethe-Nationalmuseum, Stiftung Weimarer Klassik, Theaterpl 1, 99423 Weimar, Thüringen - T: (03643) 545377, Fax: 545356, E-mail: gnm@weimar-klassik.de, Internet: http://www.weimar-klassik.de
Historic Site / Special Museum - 1953
18th c Baroque home, scene of meetings of literary circles, historic furnishings of Rococo, classic and Empire periods 19004

Weinbach

Kunstmuseum Dr. Krupp, Privatmuseum für moderne Kunst und Ausstellung zur Schloßgeschichte, Schloß Elkerhausen, Burgring 18, 35796 Weinbach - T: (06474) 8390. Head: Dr. Ingrid Krupp
Fine Arts Museum - 1980 19005

Weingarten, Württemberg

Alamannenmuseum, Karlstr 28, Kornhaus, 88250 Weingarten, Württemberg - T: (0751) 405125, Fax: 405268, E-mail: museen.weingarten@t-online.de, Internet: http://www.weingarten-online.de. Head: Uwe Lohmann
Archaeological Museum - 1976
Archeology 19006

Weinheim

Antikes Wohnmuseum, Münzgasse 13, 69469 Weinheim - T: (06201) 17726. Head: Peter Gérard
Decorative Arts Museum - 1984
Furniture and interior 19007

Museum der Stadt Weinheim, Amtsgasse 2, 69469 Weinheim - T: (06201) 82334, Fax: 962044, E-mail: museum_weinheim@t-online.de, Internet: http://www.weinheim.de. Head: Claudia Buggle
Local Museum - 1906
Archaeological finds, crafts, town history, Pre-Columbian ceramics, Heinrich Hübsch (1795-1862), August Wolf (1842-1915) 19008

Weinsberg

Justinus-Kerner-Haus, Oehringer Str 3, 74189 Weinsberg - T: (07134) 2553. Head: Emil Englert
Special Museum
Memorabilia of the poet Justinus Kerner (1786-1862) furniture, household articles 19009

Weinstadt

Bauernkriegsmuseum, Stiftstr 11, Altes Rathaus, 71384 Weinstadt - T: (07151) 693289, Fax: 693112, E-mail: stadtarchiv@weinstadt.de. Head: Dr. Thomas Holub
Historical Museum - 1989
Hist of Peasant War, weapons, peasant life 19010

Heimatmuseum Beutelsbach, Stiftstr 11, Altes Rathaus, 71304 Weinstadt - T: (07151) 693289, Fax: 693112, E-mail: stadtarchiv@weinstadt.de
Local Museum - 1965
Agricultural implements 19011

Heimatmuseum Strümpfelbach, Hauptstr 4, 71384 Weinstadt - T: (07151) 61241, Fax: 693112, E-mail: stadtarchiv@weinstadt.de
Local Museum
Household articles, painted furniture of late 19th c 19012

Heimatstube Endersbach, Schulstr 12, 71384 Weinstadt - T: (07151) 693289, Fax: 693112, E-mail: stadtarchiv@weinstadt.de
Local Museum
Agricultural implements, household articles 19013

Silcher-Museum Schnait, Silcherstr 49, 71384 Weinstadt - T: (07151) 65230, Fax: 65305, E-mail: museum@ssb1849.de, Internet: http://www.ssb1849.de. Head: Hannelore Rauscher
Special Museum - 1912
Memorabilia of the pedagogue and musician Friedrich Silcher (1789-1860) local hist - library, archive 19014

Städtische Galerie Weinstadt, Rathaus Beutelsbach, 71384 Weinstadt - T: (07151) 693284
Fine Arts Museum 19015

Weisbach

Ausstellung Haus Wysburg und Ruine Wysburg, 07356 Weisbach - T: (036643) 20000, Fax: (036640) 44925, E-mail: info@wysburg.de, Internet: http://www.wysburg.de
Historical Museum / Archaeological Museum / Local Museum / Open Air Museum / Historic Site
Documents on medieval siege techniques, stone catapult, archaeological finds 19016

Weisendorf

Heimatmuseum, Am Mühlberg, 91085 Weisendorf - T: (09135) 467
Local Museum - 1992 19017

Weismain

Museum NordJura, Kirchpl 7, 96260 Weismain - T: (09575) 921329, Fax: 921329, E-mail: info@stadt-weismain.de, Internet: http://www.stadt-weismain.de. Head: Andrea Göldner
Local Museum - 1907
Town hist, coll of weapons 19018

Weissach im Tal

Heimatmuseum, Brüdener Str 7, 71554 Weissach im Tal - T: (07191) 52941
Local Museum - 1975
Agricultural implements 19019

Weissach, Württemberg

Heimatmuseum Flacht, Leonberger Str 2, 71287 Weissach, Württemberg - T: (07044) 32109, E-mail: Hermann-Heimerdingen@t-online.de, Internet: http://www.weissach.de/allgemein/heimat1.htm
Local Museum - 1978
Peasant life, local hist 19020

Weißenberg

Museum Alte Pfefferküchlerei, Markt 3, 02627 Weißenberg - T: (035876) 40429, Fax: 40429, E-mail: museum.weissenberg@t-online.de. Head: Gundula Wenzel
Science&Tech Museum - 1941
Hist of gingerbread production, town hist 19021

Weißenburg in Bayern

Reichsstadtmuseum Weißenburg, Martin-Luther-Pl 3, 91781 Weißenburg in Bayern - T: (09141) 907124, Fax: 907121, E-mail: Stadt.Weissenburg@wugnet.baynet.de, Internet: http://www.stadt-weissenburg.de. Head: Helmut Richter
Local Museum - 1996
Town hist 19022

Römermuseum Weißenburg, Archäologische Staatssammlung München, Martin-Luther-Pl 3, 91781 Weißenburg in Bayern - T: (09141) 907124, Fax: 907121, E-mail: Stadt.Weissenburg@wugnet.baynet.de, Internet: http://www.stadt-weissenburg.de. Head: Prof. Dr. Ludwig Wamser
Archaeological Museum - 1983
Roman finds and early local hist 19023

Römische Thermenanlage, Am Römerbad 17a, 91781 Weißenburg in Bayern - T: (09141) 907124/126, Fax: 907121, E-mail: Stadt.Weissenburg@wugnet.baynet.de, Internet: http://www.stadt-weissenburg.de. Head: Helmut Richter
Archaeological Museum - 1985
Roman bath 19024

Schatzkammer der Evangelisch-Lutherischen Sankt Andreaskirche, Dr.-Martin-Luther-Pl 11, 91781 Weißenburg in Bayern - T: (09141) 97460, Fax: 974614, E-mail: pfarramt@st-andreaskirche.de, Internet: http://www.st-andreaskirche.de
Religious Arts Museum - 1995
Treasure room and religious objects 19025

Stiftung Kohl'sche Einhorn-Apotheke, Rosenstr 3, 91781 Weißenburg in Bayern - T: (09141) 2307, Fax: 73471
Special Museum
Pharmacy 19026

Weißenfels

Gustav-Adolf-Museum, Geleithaus, Große Burgstr 22, 06667 Weißenfels - T: (03443) 205031, Fax: 208137, E-mail: stadt-weissenfels@t-online.de, Internet: http://www.weissenfels.de. Head: Dr. Astrid Fick
Historical Museum - 1997
Hist of the war 1618-1648, battles near Weißenfels, death of the Swedish King Gustav Adolf in Weißenfels 1632 19027

Heinrich-Schütz-Haus, Nicolaistr 13, 06667 Weißenfels - T: (03443) 302835, Fax: 302835, E-mail: schuetz-weissenfels@t-online.de, Internet: http://www.weissenfels.de. Head: Dr. Astrid Fick
Music Museum - 1956
Memorabilia of musician Heinrich Schütz (1585-1672) 19028

Museum Schloß Neu-Augustusburg, Zeitzer Str 4, 06667 Weißenfels - T: (03443) 302552, Fax: 208137, E-mail: museum.weissenfels@t-online.de, Internet: http://www.weissenfels.de. Head: Dr. Astrid Fick
Local Museum - 1910
Ancient and early hist, local hist, crafts and guilds hist, shoe industry, glass and ironwork, music, musicians (Heinrich Schütz), literature (Novalis) - library, Gleitshaus 19029

Weißenhorn

Archäologische Sammlung der Stadt Weißenhorn, Schulstr 4, 89264 Weißenhorn - T: (07309) 8421, Internet: http://www.archaeologie-online.de/links. Head: Dr. Werner Durchschein
Archaeological Museum 19030

Weißenhorner Heimatmuseum, An der Mauer 2, 89264 Weißenhorn - T: (07309) 8453/54, Fax: 8459
Local Museum - 1908
Local artists, posters 19031

Weißenstadt

Drogerie-Museum, Kirchenlamitzer Str 12, 95163 Weißenstadt - T: (09253) 254
Special Museum - 1989
Pharmacy 19032

Weisswasser

Glasmuseum Weisswasser, Forster Str 12, 02943 Weisswasser - T: (03576) 204000, Fax: 216448, E-mail: kultur.stadt@weißwasser.de. Head: Helma Orosz
Local Museum / Special Museum - 1994
History of Weisswasser and glass-industry, glass of W. Wagenfeld and F. Bundtzen 19033

Weiterstadt

Stein- und Beinmuseum, Niederwiesenstr 13, 64331 Weiterstadt - T: (06150) 51107. Head: Siegfried Berndt
Natural History Museum
Minerals, fossils, ivory, mammoth teeth 19034

Weitramsdorf

Jagd- und Fischereimuseum Schloß Tambach, Tambach, Schloßallee 1a, 96479 Weitramsdorf - T: (09567) 1861, Fax: 1863
Agriculture Museum - 1995
Hunting and fishing 19035

Wellheim

Ur-Donautal-Museum, Torbogenhaus, Burgstr 7, 91809 Wellheim - T: (08427) 99110, Fax: 991120, E-mail: Markt.Wellheim@AltmuehlNet.de, Internet: http://www.altmuehlnet.de/gemeinden/wellheim
Local Museum - 1990
Town hist 19036

Welzheim

Städtisches Museum, Pfarrstr 8, 73642 Welzheim - T: (07182) 800815. Head: Jutta Halder
Local Museum - 1981
Geology, Roman finds, prehistory, household articles 19037

Wemding

Heimatmuseum Wemding, Haus des Gastes, Schlosshof, 86650 Wemding - T: (09092) 96900, Fax: 969050, E-mail: tourismus@wemding.btl.de
Local Museum - 1989
Town hist, crafts 19038

Wendeburg

BLM Bauernhaus-Museum Bortfeld, Braunschweigisches Landesmuseum, Katzhagen 7, 38176 Wendeburg - T: (05303) 2851, Fax: 1215, E-mail: info@landesmuseum-bs.de, Internet: http://www.landesmuseum-bs.de. Head: Gerd Biegel
Open Air Museum - 1968
Rooms, furniture, agricultural and domestic implements 19039

Wendelstein, Mittelfranken

Drechsler- und Metalldrücker-Museum, Schwabacher Str/Wasserhaus, 90530 Wendelstein, Mittelfranken - T: (09129) 4010
Special Museum - 1990 19040

Heimathaus Wendelstein, Untere Rathausgasse 24, 90530 Wendelstein, Mittelfranken - T: (09129) 4010
Local Museum - 1990
Crafts and local hist 19041

Wendlingen am Neckar

Galerie der Stadt Wendlingen am Neckar, Weberstr 2, 73240 Wendlingen am Neckar - T: (07024) 55458, Fax: 6520, E-mail: info@galerie-wendlingen.de, Internet: http://www.galerie-wendlingen.de. Head: Rainer Ihlau
Fine Arts Museum - 1982
Contemporary art 19042

Heimatmuseum Unterboihingen, Altes Rathaus, 73240 Wendlingen am Neckar - T: (07024) 3441
Local Museum - 1962 19043

Wennigsen

Heimatmuseum Wennigsen, Mühlenstr 6, 30974 Wennigsen - T: (05103) 7713
Local Museum - 1975
Historic watermill, coal mining, pharmacy, forestry, hunting, textile processing, trade objects and implements 19044

Heimatstube Bredenbeck, Wennigser Str 23, 30974 Wennigsen - T: (05109) 6165, Fax: 6165
Local Museum
Village hist, Stone Age objects, trade workshops, literature by the writer Adolf von Knigge 19045

Werben, Altmark

Heimatstube Werben, Langestr, 39615 Werben, Altmark - T: (039393) 219
Local Museum 19046

Werdau, Sachsen

Stadt- und Dampfmaschinenmuseum, Holzstr 2, 08412 Werdau, Sachsen - T: (03761) 594255, Fax: 594255, Internet: http://www.werdau.de. Head: Dr. H.-J. Beier
Local Museum / Science&Tech Museum - 1917
Local hist, steam engine, model railway, porcelain, industrial hist, painter Ernst Eichler 19047

Werder, Havel

Obstbaumuseum, Kirchstr 6-7, 14542 Werder, Havel - T: (03327) 783374, Fax: 783322, E-mail: werder-tourismus@t-online.de, Internet: http://www.werder-havel.com
Agriculture Museum - 1962
Fruit farming, natural conditions, geology, soil types, climate, social developments in fruit growing areas since the 17th c 19048

Werdum

Kleines Heimatmuseum Windmühle, Edenserlooger Str 13, 26427 Werdum - T: (04974) 363
Local Museum 19049

Werl

Museum Forum der Völker, Völkerkundemuseum der Franziskaner, Melsterstr 15, 59457 Werl - T: (02922) 2635, Fax: 85655, E-mail: - Franziskanermission@t-online.de, Internet: http://www.forum-der-voelker.de. Head: Reinhard Kellerhoff
Ethnology Museum - 1909
Chinese coin coll, Sumerian cuneiform script, coll from Tibet, China, Japan, Egypt, Brazil, Palastine, Africa, Papua-Neuguinea 19050

Städtisches Museum, Am Rykenberg 1, 59457 Werl - T: (02922) 861631, Fax: 800229. Head: Hartmut Platte
Local Museum - 1981
Educational program 19051

Wermsdorf

Schloßmuseum Hubertusburg, Schloß Hubertusburg, 04779 Wermsdorf - T: (034364) 52341. Head: Ursula Lehmann
Historical Museum - 1968 19052

Werne

Karl Pollender-Stadtmuseum, Altes Amtshaus, Kirchhof 13, 59368 Werne - T: (02389) 71537, Fax: 71537, E-mail: museum-werne@t-online.de, Internet: http://www.werne.de/kultur/museum. Head: Heidelore Fertig-Möller
Local Museum - 1962
library, archive 19053

Wernigerode

Harzmuseum, Klint 10, 38855 Wernigerode - T: (03943) 654454, Fax: 654497. Head: Silvia Lisowski
Local Museum - 1954
Paleontology, mineralogy 19054

Krell'sche Schmiede, Breite Str 95, 38855 Wernigerode - T: (03943) 601772, Fax: 601772, E-mail: kschmiede95@aol.com, Internet: http://www.schmiedemuseum-wernigerode.de. Head: Peter Nichterlein
Science&Tech Museum / Military Museum
Original smithy, yard, machinery and tools, allied time 1945 in Germany 19055

Mahn- und Gedenkstätte Wernigerode, Veckenstedter Weg 43, 38855 Wernigerode - T: (03943) 632109, Fax: 632109. Head: Rotraud Urbaneck
Historical Museum - 1974
History of labour movement, socialist documents, photos, graphics, paintings, history of KPD 19056

Schloß Wernigerode, Zentrum für Kunst- und Kulturgeschichte des 19. Jahrhunderts, Am Schloß 1, 38855 Wernigerode - T: (03943) 553030, Fax: 553055, E-mail: schlosswr@t-online.de, Internet: http://www.schloss-wernigerode.de. Head: Christian Juranek
Historical Museum / Historic Site - 1930
Historic interior, religious art, decorative objects, glass, goldsmith work, paintings, armaments, local and regional history, graphic art, special coll about the 19th c Europe - library 19057

Wertach

Heimatmuseum Wertach, Grüntenseestr 27, 87497 Wertach - T: (08365) 214, 266, Fax: 1538, E-mail: info@wertach.de, Internet: http://www.wertach.de
Local Museum - 1931
Agricultural tools, rustic furniture and religious folklore 19058

Wertheim

Glasmuseum Wertheim, Mühlenstr 24, 97877 Wertheim - T: (09342) 6866, Fax: 916711, E-mail: info@glasmuseum-wertheim.de, Internet: http://www.glasmuseum-wertheim.de. Head: Marianne Tazlari
Science&Tech Museum / Decorative Arts Museum - 1976
Technological development of the glass industry, antique, medieval and contemporary glasses, regional glass industry 19059

Grafschaftsmuseum, Rathausgasse 6-10, 97877 Wertheim - T: (09342) 301411/12, Fax: 301411, E-mail: grafschaftsmuseum@t-online.de, Internet: http://www.grafschaftsmuseum.de. Head: Dr. Jörg Paczkowski
Local Museum - 1878
Otto Modersohn coll, Franconian artists of the 19th c and 20th c, coin coll, Biedermeier, costumes, furniture, silhouettes, hist of clothing, porcelain 19060

Wertingen

Heimatmuseum Wertingen, Schulstr 12, Schloß, 86637 Wertingen - T: (08272) 8433, Fax: 8427
Local Museum - 1920s
Moulds for cloth printing from the 19th c 19061

Wesel

Galerie im Centrum → Städtisches Museum Wesel

Heimatmuseum Bislich, Dorfstr 24, 46487 Wesel - T: (02859) 1519, Fax: 1519
Local Museum - 1983
Ornithological coll, religious folk art 19062

Heimatmuseum Büderich, Marktpl, Altes Rathaus, 46487 Wesel - T: (02803) 4276
Local Museum 19063

Preußen-Museum Nordrhein-Westfalen, An der Zitadelle 14-20, 46483 Wesel - T: (0281) 339960, Fax: 33996330, E-mail: wesel@preussenmuseum.de, Internet: http://www.preussenmuseum.de. Head: Dr. Veit Veltzke
Historical Museum - 1998 19064

Städtisches Museum Wesel, Galerie im Centrum, Kornmarkt, Ritterstr 14, 46483 Wesel - T: (0281) 203350, Fax: 203617, E-mail: juergen.becks@wesel.de, Internet: http://www.wesel.de. Head: Jürgen Becks
Fine Arts Museum / Local Museum - 1975
15th-19th c Rhine art, silver and goldsmith work, hist of fortress Wesel - library 19065

Städtisches Museum Wesel, Schill-Kasematte und Festungsgeschichtliche Abteilung, An der Zitadelle, 46483 Wesel - T: (0281) 203350, Fax: 203617, E-mail: juergen.becks@wesel.de, Internet: http://www.wesel.de. Head: Jürgen Becks
Historical Museum - 1975 19066

Wesselburen

Hebbel-Museum, Österstr 6, 25764 Wesselburen - T: (04833) 4190, Fax: 4191, E-mail: Hebbel-Museum@t-online.de, Internet: http://www.Hebbel-Museum.de. Head: Volker Schulz
Special Museum - 1911
House of the poet Friedrich Hebbel (1813-1863), historic rooms, documents, manuscripts, first editions, photos, engravings and sculptures 19067

Wesseling

Städtische Galerie Wesseling, An Sankt Germanus 7, 50389 Wesseling - T: (02236) 1536, Fax: 701339, E-mail: stadt_wesseling@t-online.de
Public Gallery 19068

Westerhausen

Heimatmuseum Westerhausen, Oberndorf 7, 06484 Westerhausen - T: (03946) 6332
Local Museum
Early hist, local hist 19069

Westerkappeln

Traktorenmuseum, Lotter Str 20, 49492 Westerkappeln - T: (05404) 1785, Fax: 88777
Science&Tech Museum - 1986 19070

Westfehmarn

Mühlen- und Landwirtschaftsmuseum, Lemkenhafen, 23769 Westfehmarn - T: (04372) 9627, Fax: 9532. Head: Hans Wilhelm Maas
Agriculture Museum / Science&Tech Museum 19071

Westoverledingen

Mühlenmuseum Mitling-Mark mit Sammlung Omas Küche, Marker Mühlenweg 2, 26810 Westoverledingen - T: (04955) 8872, Fax: 933135, E-mail: Gemeinde@Westoverledingen.de. Head: Siegfried Brink
Science&Tech Museum / Special Museum - 1990
Mill, domestic objects with motives of mills 19072

Ostfriesisches Schulmuseum Folmhusen, Leerer Str 7-9, 26810 Westoverledingen - T: (04955) 4989, Fax: 4989, E-mail: schulmuseum@westoverledingen.de, Internet: http://www.ostfriesisches-schulmuseum.de
Historical Museum - 1987
School in the 18th and 19th cent - historical school library 19073

Wettenberg

Froaschgass-Museum, Krofdorf-Gleiberg, Rodheimer Str 34, 35435 Wettenberg - T: (0641) 82776
Local Museum - 1987
Hessian ceramics, tin objects, toys, agricultural and trade implements 19074

Heimatmuseum Wettenberg, Poststr 11, 35435 Wettenberg - T: (0641) 84184
Local Museum 19075

Heimatmuseum Wißmar, Schulstr 8, 35435 Wettenberg - T: (06406) 2484, Fax: 904515, E-mail: dehus.k.u.chr.wettenb.@t-online.de
Local Museum - 1958/1976
Agricultural implements, flax processing 19076

Wetter, Hessen

Dorfmuseum Alter Forsthof, Im Rosphetal 8, 35083 Wetter, Hessen - T: (06437) 7150
Local Museum - 1990
Village life of women, agricultural implements and machines 19077

Wetzlar

Dorfstube Münchholzhausen, Rechtenbacher Str 2, 35581 Wetzlar - T: (06441) 97143
Local Museum - 1946/86
Early and pre-history, domestic utensils and agricultural implements, costumes, flax processing, furniture 19078

Galerie am Dom, Krämerstr 1, 35578 Wetzlar - T: (06441) 46473, Fax: 46473, E-mail: info@galerie-am-dom.de, Internet: http://www.galerie-am-dom.de. Head: Jacqueline Marks, Michael Marks
Public Gallery 19079

Galerie im Kreishaus, Karl-Kellner-Ring 51, 35576 Wetzlar - T: (06441) 4071200, Fax: 4071060, E-mail: landrat@lahn-dill-kreis.de
Public Gallery 19080

Heimatmuseum Garbenheim, Untergasse 3, 35583 Wetzlar - T: (06441) 46256
Local Museum - 1985
Appearance of Garbenheim as Wahlheim in Goethe's "Die Leiden des jungen Werther", early and pre-history, town and church hist, trades, mining, costumes 19081

Jerusalemhaus mit Verwaltung der Städtischen Sammlungen Wetzlar, Schillerpl 5, 35578 Wetzlar - T: (06441) 99269, Fax: 99592, E-mail: museum@wetzlar.de, Internet: http://www.wetzlar.de. Head: Hartmut Schmidt
Historical Museum
Hist of town and industry, connections to Goethe's "Werther", paintings and graphics, furniture 19082

Landwirtschaftliches Museum Wetzlar, Frankfurter Str 113, 35578 Wetzlar - T: (06441) 782220. Head: Dieter Spieß
Agriculture Museum - 1985
Agricultural machines and implements, vehicles 19083

Palais Papius, Kornblumengasse 1, 35578 Wetzlar. Head: Rolf Beck
Decorative Arts Museum - 1967
Furniture, clocks, tapestries, faience, European arts and crafts (16th-18th c) 19084

Reichskammergerichtsmuseum, Hofstatt 19, 35578 Wetzlar - T: (06441) 99612, Fax: 99614, E-mail: museum@wetzlar.de, Internet: http://www.wetzlar.de. Head: Hartmut Schmidt
Historical Museum - 1987
Printed material, furniture 19085

Sammlung Dr. Irmgard von Lemmers-Danforth, Europäische Wohnkultur aus Renaissance und Barock, Kornblumengasse 1, 35578 Wetzlar - T: (06441) 99366, 99269, Fax: 99395, E-mail: museum@wetzlar.de, Internet: http://www.wetzlar.de. Head: Hartmut Schmidt
Decorative Arts Museum 19086

Sammlung historischer Mikroskope von Ernst Leitz, Neues Rathaus, Ernst-Leitz-Str, 35578 Wetzlar - T: (06441) 292343, Fax: 292599, E-mail: Rolf.Beck@lmw.leica.com. Head: Rolf Beck
Science&Tech Museum - 1890
History of microscopy, history of optical instruments 19087

Stadt- und Industriemuseum Lottehaus, Lottestr 8-10, 35578 Wetzlar - T: (06441) 99221, Fax: 99395, E-mail: museum@wetzlar.de, Internet: http://www.wetzlar.de. Head: Hartmut Schmidt
Local Museum / Science&Tech Museum - 1863

Stadtmuseum: Pre- and early hist, local hist, militaria, peasant life and traditions, paintings, Lottehaus: memorabilia on J.W. von Goethe's novel 'Die Leiden des jungen Werther', furniture, Zehntscheune: iron casting, optical instruments - library 19088

Stadthaus am Dom, Dompl 15, 35578 Wetzlar - T: (06441) 99380
Public Gallery 19089

Widdern

Heimat- und Schmiedemuseum, Talstr 49, 74259 Widdern - T: (07943) 2191
Local Museum / Science&Tech Museum - 1963
Still working forge, tools 19090

Wiedensahl

Heimatmuseum Wiedensahl, Kloses heimatgeschichtliche Sammlung, Hauptstr 89, 31719 Wiedensahl - T: (05726) 700, 449, Fax: 989685
Local Museum - 1969
Early and prehist, geology, coll of arms, trade workshops, agricultural implements, flax growing and linen weaving 19091

Wilhelm-Busch-Gedenkstätte, Hauptstr 68a, 31719 Wiedensahl - T: (05726) 388. Head: Dr. Hans Joachim Neyer
Special Museum - 1927
Original furniture and objects by the writer and his family 19092

Wiederstedt

Novalis-Museum, Schloß Oberwiedenstedt, Schäfergasse 6, 06333 Wiederstedt - T: (03476) 812359, Fax: 812359
Special Museum
Life and work of the poet, philosopher and jurist Philip Friedrich von Hardenberg (Novalis), Romantic period - Library 19093

Wiehl

Werksmuseum Achse, Rad und Wagen, Ohlerhammer, 51674 Wiehl, mail addr: Postfach 1280, 51656 Wiehl - T: (02262) 781280, Fax: 781738, E-mail: info@bpw.de, Internet: http://www.bpw.de. Head: Thomas Köppen
Science&Tech Museum - 1952
Cars, carriages, coaches, smithwork, ironwork, tools and implements 19094

Wienhausen

Kloster Wienhausen, An der Kirche 1, 29342 Wienhausen - T: (05149) 357, Fax: 92867, E-mail: kloster.wienhausen@arcormail.de. Head: Renate von Randow
Religious Arts Museum
Gothic architecture, medieval furniture and objects, frescos, murals, sculptures, tapestry 19095

Wiepersdorf bei Jüterbog

Bettina und Achim von Arnim Museum, Bettina-von-Arnim-Str 13, 14913 Wiepersdorf bei Jüterbog - T: (033746) 69915, Fax: 69919, E-mail: schloss.wiepersdorf@t-online.de, Internet: http://www.wiepersdorf.de. Head: Doris Sossenheimer
Fine Arts Museum / Special Museum 19096

Wiesbaden

Dotzheimer Museum, Römergasse 13, 65199 Wiesbaden - T: (0611) 420318. Head: Klaus Kopp
Local Museum - 1985
Trade workshops, early and pre-history, town hist 19097

ESWE-technicum an der Fasanerie, Fasanerie, 65195 Wiesbaden - T: (0611) 7802165, Fax: 7802340, E-mail: roland.kraemer@oswe.com, Internet: http://www.eswe.com
Science&Tech Museum - 1981
Hist of the pumping station, traffic, water, gas 19098

Frauen Museum Wiesbaden, Wörthstr 5, 65185 Wiesbaden - T: (0611) 3081763, Fax: 378660, E-mail: info@frauenmuseum-wiesbaden.de, Internet: http://www.frauenmuseum-wiesbaden.de. Head: Kim Engels, Beatrixe Klein, Eva Schuster
Local Museum - 1984
Hist of women in Wiesbaden, basic research concerning women as carriers of culture, portraits of female artists 19099

Harlekinäum-Lachmuseum, c/o Harlekin Geschenke GmbH, Wandersmannstr 39, 65205 Wiesbaden Erbenheim - T: (0611) 74001, Fax: 711406, Internet: http://www.lachmuseum.de. Head: Michael Berger
Decorative Arts Museum - 1990
Funny designer objects 19100

Heimatmuseum Biebrich, Rudolf-Dyckerhoff-Str 4, 65203 Wiesbaden - T: (0611) 67559
Local Museum - 1978
Town hist - Library 19101

Heimatmuseum Erbenheim, Wandersmannstr 25, 65205 Wiesbaden - T: (0611) 976160. Head: Dieter Breuer
Local Museum - 1983
Town hist in 19th-20th c 19102

Museum Wiesbaden, Friedrich-Ebert-Allee 2, 65185 Wiesbaden - T: (0611) 3352170, Fax: 3352192, E-mail: info@museum-wiesbaden.de, Internet: http://www.museum-wiesbaden.de. Head: Dr. Volker Rattemeyer
Fine Arts Museum / Natural History Museum / Archaeological Museum - 1825
Art coll, German Expressionism, Constructivism, American painting, archaeology, natural hist, antiquities of Nassau - library, restoration workshop 19103

Wiesenbach, Baden

Heimatmuseum, Hauptstr 26, 69257 Wiesenbach, Baden - T: (06223) 40114, Fax: 950218, Internet: http://www.wiesenbach.online.de
Local Museum - 1981
Local hist, peasant life 19104

Wiesenburg, Mark

Heimatstube Wiesenburg, Görzestr 38, 14827 Wiesenburg, Mark - T: (033849) 50445
Local Museum 19105

Wiesenfelden

Naturkundliches Museum, Schloß Wiesenfelden, 94344 Wiesenfelden - T: (09966) 1270, Fax: 490, E-mail: bw@bund-naturschutz.de, Internet: http://www.bn-bildungswerk.den. Head: Beate Seitz-Weinzierl
Natural History Museum - 1984
Animal preparations, photographs 19106

Wiesent

Hudetz-Turm, Bachgasse 4, 93109 Wiesent - T: (09482) 1386. Head: Peter Lutz
Fine Arts Museum - 1990
Home and workshop of the painter Karl Anton Hudetz (1890-1977) 19107

Wiesenttal

Modelleisenbahnmuseum Die Bahnschranke, Bayreuther Str 23, Muggendorf, 91346 Wiesenttal - T: (09196) 1630, Fax: 998973
Special Museum 19108

Wiesloch

Städtisches Museum, Marktstr 13, 69168 Wiesloch - T: (06222) 84305, Fax: 84478, E-mail: manfred.kurz@wiesloch.de, Internet: http://www.wiesloch.de. Head: Manfred Kurz
Local Museum - 1963
Mining, medieval weapons, prehistoric and Roman archaeology 19109

Wietze

Deutsches Erdölmuseum, Schwarzer Weg 7-9, 29323 Wietze - T: (05146) 92340, Fax: 92342, E-mail: erdoelmuseum@t-online.de, Internet: http://www.kulturserver.de/home/demw. Head: Dr. Susanne Abel
Science&Tech Museum - 1970
Geology, oil drilling and technology, prehist 19110

Wiggensbach

Heimatmuseum der Marktgemeinde Wiggensbach, Kempter Str 3, 87487 Wiggensbach - T: (08370) 8435, Fax: 379, E-mail: info@wiggensbach.de
Local Museum - 1930
Town hist, wood carving, religious folk art, Karl Krumbacher (linguist), Franz Xaver Knoll (painter and caricaturist) 19111

Historische Käsküche, Kempter Str 3, 87487 Wiggensbach - T: (08370) 8435, Fax: 379, E-mail: info@wiggensbach.de
Special Museum - 1994
Cheese dairy 19112

Wildberg, Württemberg

Museum Wildberg, Kloster Reuthin, 72218 Wildberg, Württemberg - T: (07054) 2010, Fax: 20126, E-mail: info@wildberg.de, Internet: http://www.wildberg.de
Local Museum - 1976
Local hist, agricultural implements, interior design 19113

Wildenhain bei Großenhain, Sachsen

Schulmuseum Wildenhain, Alte Schule, 01561 Wildenhain bei Großenhain, Sachsen - T: (03522) 310139
Historical Museum 19114

Wildeshausen

Dampfkornbranntweinbrennerei-Museum, Wittekindstr 2, 27793 Wildeshausen - T: (04431) 1744. Head: Klaus Viehmeier
Science&Tech Museum
Brandy distillery from 1857 19115

Druckereimuseum, Bahnhofsstr 13, 27793 Wildeshausen - T: (04431) 9891120, Fax: 71120
Science&Tech Museum
Hist and develoment of printing techniques since 1850 19116

Wilhelmsdorf, Mittelfranken

Zirkelmuseum, Hugenottenpl 8, 91489 Wilhelmsdorf, Mittelfranken - T: (09104) 829230, Fax: 897815, 897931, E-mail: kulturamt@rg-emskirchen.de
Science&Tech Museum - 1992
Coll of compasses 19117

Wilhelmsdorf, Württemberg

Benedikt-Nimser-Haus, Zußdorfer Str, 88271 Wilhelmsdorf, Württemberg - T: (07503) 9210. Head:
Religious Arts Museum
Interior design (early 19th c) in a house built by pietist settlers 19118

Museum für bäuerliches Handwerk und Kultur, Hoffmannstr 27, 88271 Wilhelmsdorf, Württemberg - T: (07503) 1716. Head: E. Schelshorn
Historical Museum - 1985
Rural crafts, agricultural implements 19119

Wilhelmshaven

Institut für Vogelforschung -Vogelwarte Helgoland, Heinrich-Gätke-Halle, An der Vogelwarte 21, 26386 Wilhelmshaven - T: (04421) 96890, Fax: 968955, E-mail: ifv@ifv.terramare.de, Internet: http://www.vogelwarte-helgoland.de. Head: Prof. Dr. Franz Bairlein
Natural History Museum - 1971
Ornithology in the mud-flats and at the North Sea coast 19120

Küsten-Museum der Stadt Wilhelmshaven (closed) 19121

Kunsthalle Wilhelmshaven, Adalbertstr 28, 26382 Wilhelmshaven - T: (04421) 41448, Fax: 43987, E-mail: kunsthalle.wilhelmshaven@t-online.de. Head: Dr. Ute Riese
Fine Arts Museum 19122

Willebadessen

Europäischer Skulpturenpark, Schloß, 34439 Willebadessen - T: (05646) 777, Fax: 942077, E-mail: euroskulpa@t-online.de, Internet: http://www.euroskulpa.de. Head: Berndt van Nüss
Open Air Museum / Fine Arts Museum - 1979
European sculpture 19123

Willich

Temporäre Galerie Schloß Neersen, Hauptstr 6, 47877 Willich - T: (02156) 949263, Fax: 949101. Head: Doris Thiel
Fine Arts Museum 19124

Willingen, Upland

Besucherbergwerk Schiefergrube Christine, Schwalefelder Str 28, 34508 Willingen, Upland - T: (05632) 6611, Fax: 401150, E-mail: willingen@willingen.de
Science&Tech Museum
Hist of slate quarry mining 19125

Haus der Natur, Briloner Str 62, 34508 Willingen, Upland - T: (05632) 401180, Fax: 401150, E-mail: willingen@willingen.de
Natural History Museum 19126

Heimatmuseum Usseln, Ringstr 52, 34508 Willingen, Upland - T: (05632) 7092
Local Museum - 1982
Restored farm house with coll of old domestic and agricultural tools and implements 19127

Willingshausen

Malerstübchen Willingshausen, Gerhardt-von-Reutern-Haus, Merzhäuser Str 2, 34628 Willingshausen - T: (06631) 4169. Head: Helmut Geißel
Fine Arts Museum - 1931/89
Artists of the painter colony Willingshausen 19128

Wilster

Altes Rathaus Wilster, Op de Göten 8, 25554 Wilster - T: (04823) 94040, Fax: 7152, E-mail: StadtWilster@t-online.de
Local Museum 19129

Wilthen

Heimatstube Wilthen, Bahnhofstr 8, 02681 Wilthen - T: (03592) 38540, Fax: 385499
Local Museum - 1952
Weaver's room, flax processing and linen weaving tools 19130

Windeck

Heimatmuseum Windeck, Im Thal Windeck, 51570 Windeck - T: (02292) 2071, 8942, 3888
Local Museum 19131

Windischeschenbach

Waldnaabtal-Museum in der Burg Neuhaus, Burgstr 13, 92670 Windischeschenbach - T: (09681) 534, 401240
Local Museum - 1985
Town hist, crafts, geology 19132

Wingst

Waldmuseum Wassermühle, Am Waldmuseum 9, 21789 Wingst - T: (04778) 490
Natural History Museum - 1966
Forestry, native animals and plants, protection of birds 19133

Winnenden

Dorfmuseum Hanweiler, Städtisches Museum, Silvanerstr 1, 71364 Winnenden - T: (07195) 13211
Local Museum - 1977
Vintage implements 19134

Feuerwehrmuseum Winnenden, Bahnhofstr 43, 71364 Winnenden - T: (07195) 103055, Fax: 103079, E-mail: fw-museum@feuerwehr.com, Internet: http://www.feuerwehr.winnenden.de
Science&Tech Museum - 1963
Fire fighting machinery 19135

Historische Turmstuben, Städtisches Museum, Marktstr, Torturm, 71364 Winnenden - T: (07195) 13211, Fax: 13400. Head: Dr. S. Reustle
Local Museum - 1938
Local hist 19136

Winsen, Aller

Winser Museumshof, Brauckmanns Kerkstieg, 29308 Winsen, Aller - T: (05143) 8140
Historical Museum - 1987
Farmyard portraying the life in the heathland of Lüneburg in the 18th and 19th c 19137

Winsen, Luhe

Museum im Marstall, Schloßpl 11, 21423 Winsen, Luhe - T: (04171) 3419, Fax: 3383, Internet: http://www.winsen.de. Head: Ilona Johannsen
Local Museum - 1966
Town hist, rebuilt trade workshops, printing machines, costume and embroidery of the region, Eckermann 19138

Winterbach bei Schorndorf

Dorf- und Heimatmuseum, Adlerstr 33, 73650 Winterbach bei Schorndorf - T: (07181) 72164
Local Museum - 1968 19139

Winzer

Ziegel- und Kalkmuseum, 94577 Winzer - T: (08545) 91041
Special Museum - 1996
Brickstone and lime works 19140

Wippra

Heimatmuseum Wippra, Anger 3, 06543 Wippra - T: (034775) 20016, 20097
Local Museum
300-year-old half-timbered house, furniture, domestic and trade implements, clothes, toys 19141

Wismar

Galerie Hinter dem Rathaus, Gemeinschaft Wismarer Künstler und Kunstfreunde e.V, Hinter dem Rathaus 8, 23966 Wismar - T: (03841) 213255
Public Gallery 19142

Stadtgeschichtliches Museum Schabbellhaus, Schweinsbrücke 8, 23966 Wismar - T: (03841) 282350, Fax: 210070, E-mail: mehr@schabbellhaus.de, Internet: http://www.schabbellhaus.de. Head: Béatrice Busjan
Local Museum - 1863
Ancient historic finds, local hist, paintings, costumes, medical and pharmaceutical hist 19143

Wittelshofen

Heimatmuseum Heinrich Zoller, Schloßstr 11, 91749 Wittelshofen - T: (09854) 425
Local Museum
Local hist 19144

Witten

Hebezeug-Museum, Windenstr 2-4, 58455 Witten - T: (02302) 2080, Fax: 208286, E-mail: info@jdn.de, Internet: http://www.jdn.de. Head: Johann Diederich Neuhaus
Science&Tech Museum 19145

Heimatmuseum Witten, Ruhrstr 69, 58452 Witten - T: (02302) 5812550
Local Museum - 1886 19146

Märkisches Museum, Kulturforum Witten, Husemannstr 12, 58452 Witten - T: (02302) 5812552, Fax: 5812569. Head: Dr. Wolfgang Zemter
Fine Arts Museum
20th c German art 19147

Das Kunstmuseum Wolfsburg, ein Bau aus Glas und Stahl mit seinem offenen, säulengestützten Eingangsbereich, liegt im Herzen Wolfsburgs. Das Haus versteht sich als ein Forum der Auseinandersetzung mit zeitgenössischer Kunst und bietet dem Besucher einen spannungsvollen Dialog von klassischer Moderne und Gegenwartskunst.

Vom 14.09.2002 bis zum 05.01.2003 wird die Ausstellung BLAST TO FREEZE: BRITISCHE KUNST IM ZEITALTER DER EXTREME 1914-1988 zu sehen sein.

Porschestraße 53 D-38440 Wolfsburg
Telefon (05361) 266 90
Telefax (05361) 266 966,
E-mail: info@kunstmuseum-wolfsburg.de
http://www.kunstmuseum-wolfsburg.de

ÖFFNUNGSZEITEN
Mittwoch bis Sonntag 11.00 - 18.00 Uhr,
Dienstag 11.00 - 20.00 Uhr,
Montag geschlossen.

Wittenberge

Galerie des Kultur- und Festspielhauses Wittenberge, Paul-Lincke-Pl, 19322 Wittenberge - T: (03877) 953961, Fax: 953969, E-mail: kfh-w@t-online.de, Internet: http://www.kfhw.de. Head: Hans-Joachim Böse
Public Gallery 19148

Stadtmuseum Alte Burg Wittenberge, Putlitzstr 2, 19322 Wittenberge - T: (03877) 405266/67, Fax: 405268, E-mail: stadtmuseum.wittenberge@t-online.de, Internet: http://www.wittenberg.de. Head: Dr. Oliver Hermann
Local Museum / Science&Tech Museum
Hist of sewing machine 19149

Wittenburg

Agrar- und Forstmuseum, Hagenower Chaussee, 19243 Wittenburg - T: (038852) 2740
Natural History Museum
Windmill, agricultural hist, forestry, hunting 19150

Wittingen

Museum im Dorf, Lüben, 29378 Wittingen - T: (05831) 7120
Local Museum 19151

Wittlich

Georg-Meistermann-Museum, Städtische Galerie für Moderne Kunst, Altes Rathaus am Markt, 54516 Wittlich - T: (06571) 14660, Fax: 146616, E-mail: - kulturamtwittlich@t-online.de, Internet: http://www.wittlich.de. Head: Dr. Justinus Maria Calleen
Fine Arts Museum - 1994 19152

Wittmund

Deutsches Sielhafenmuseum in Carolinensiel, Pumphusen 3, 26409 Wittmund - T: (04462) 456, Fax: 8433, E-mail: info@deutsches-sielhafenmuseum.de, Internet: http://www.deutsches-sielhafenmuseum.de. Head: Manfred Sell
Historical Museum / Folklore Museum
Sluice, hist of shipping, fishing, trades, sailor's pub and souvenirs, coastal culture 19153

Heimatmuseum Peldemühle, Esenser Str 14, 26409 Wittmund - T: (04462) 5279
Local Museum - 1977
Regional hist, wedding dresses from 1900, trade tools and implements, agriculture, vehicles, smithy and bakehouse, filling station from 1910 19154

Sielhafenmuseum der niedersächsischen Nordseeküste → Deutsches Sielhafenmuseum in Carolinensiel

Wittstock bei Prenzlau

Bauernmuseum Wittstock, Am Dorfpl, 17291 Wittstock bei Prenzlau - T: (039852) 560, 3422
Local Museum 19155

Wittstock, Dosse

Museen Alte Bischofsburg, Amtshof 1-5, 16909 Wittstock, Dosse - T: (03394) 433725, 449077, Fax: 449078. Head: Dr. Wolfgang Dost
Local Museum / Historical Museum - 1957
Ancient and early history, regional history, city as bishops' residence, peasant crafts, work tools, castle fragments, soldier's and civilian's life and suffering during the war - library 19156

Museum des Todesmarsches im Belower Wald, Belower Damm 1, 16909 Wittstock, Dosse - T: (039925) 2478, Fax: 2478
Historical Museum
Memorial site to the death march of the evacuated prisoners of the concentration camps Sachsenhausen, Ravensbrück and Heinkel 19157

Witzenhausen

Archiv der deutschen Jugendbewegung, Burg Ludwigstein, 37214 Witzenhausen - T: (05542) 501720, Fax: 501723. Head: Dr. Winfried Mogge
Library with Exhibitions 19158

Auto- und Motorradmuseum, Erlebnispark Ziegenhagen, Ziegenberg 3, 37217 Witzenhausen - T: (05545) 246, Fax: 6372, Internet: http://www.erlebnispark-ziegenhagen.de. Head: Axel Surup
Science&Tech Museum - 1975
300 vehicles, motorcycles, cars, old-timers, sleds, carriages, fire engines 19159

Eisenkunstgußmuseum, Erlebnispark Ziegenhagen, Ziegenberg 3, 37217 Witzenhausen - T: (05545) 246, Fax: 6372, Internet: http://www.erlebnispark-ziegenhagen.de. Head: Axel Surup
Science&Tech Museum - 1977
Old iron oven-plates 19160

Museum für Völkerkunde, Steinstr 19, 37213 Witzenhausen - T: (05542) 60721, Fax: 60739, E-mail: museum@ditsl.de, Internet: http://www.wiz.uni-kassel.de/ditsl/de/sammlung.html.

Head: Prof. Dr. E. Baum
Ethnology Museum - 1977
Exhibits from former German colonies in Africa and Oceania such as masks, sculptures, tools, domestic implements, costumes and jewellery 19161

Volkskundliche Sammlungen, Erlebnispark Ziegenhagen, Ziegenberg 3, 37217 Witzenhausen - T: (05545) 246, Fax: 6372, Internet: http://www.erlebnispark-ziegenhagen.de. Head: Axel Surup
Folklore Museum - 1970
Folklore, artistic puppets, radios, local dying out professions 19162

Witzwort

Roter Haubarg, 25889 Witzwort - T: (04864) 845, Fax: 67376
Local Museum - 1988
Farming 19163

Wöbbelin

Mahn- und Gedenkstätten Wöbbelin, Ludwigsluster Str 1a, 19288 Wöbbelin - T: (038753) 80792, Fax: 80792. Head: Edeltraut Schure
Historical Museum
Memorabilia of poet Theodor Körner, documents, etchings, grave site, National Socialism, concentration camp in Mecklenburg-Vorpommern 19164

Wörlitz

Gotisches Haus, Kulturstiftung DessauWörlitz, Wörlitzer Anlage, 06786 Wörlitz - T: (034905) 20302, Fax: 40930, E-mail: ksdw@ksdw.de, Internet: http://www.ksdw.de. Head: Dr. Thomas Weiss
Fine Arts Museum - 1918
Paintings (17th-18th c, furniture, decorative objects, porcelain 19165

Schloss Wörlitz und Englisches Landhaus, Kulturstiftung DessauWörlitz, 06786 Wörlitz - T: (034905) 40918, Fax: 40930, E-mail: ksdw@ksdw.de, Internet: http://www.ksdw.de. Head: Dr. Thomas Weiss
Fine Arts Museum - 1918
Paintings (17th-18th c, furniture, decorative objects, porcelain 19166

Wörth am Main

Schiffahrts- und Schiffbaumuseum, Rathausstr 72, 63939 Wörth am Main - T: (09372) 292599, Fax: 989340
Science&Tech Museum - 1980
Inland navigation and ship building esp. in the Main region - library 19167

Wörth an der Donau

Nostalgie-Museum, Zur Alten Donau 4, 93086 Wörth an der Donau - T: (09482) 90086, Fax: 90086, Internet: http://www.regensburgland.de. Head: Alexander Freiherr von Eyb, Silvia Freifrau von Eyb
Special Museum 19168

Wohlhausen

Private Sammlung Mechanischer Musikinstrumente, Hauptstr 10, 08258 Wohlhausen - T: (037422) 2069
Music Museum
Mechanical musical instruments 19169

Woldegk

Mühlenmuseum, Karl-Liebknecht-Pl 1, 17348 Woldegk - T: (03963) 211384, 256540, Fax: 256565. Head: R. Stapel
Science&Tech Museum / Local Museum - 1971
Milling and town history 19170

Wolfach

Flößer- und Heimatmuseum, Hauptstr 40, Schloß, 77709 Wolfach - T: (07834) 835353, Fax: 835359, E-mail: wolfach@wolfach.de, Internet: http://www.wolfach.de
Local Museum / Special Museum - 1938
Minerals (coll Armbruster), rafting, carnival 19171

Wolfegg

Auto-Museum Fritz B. Busch, Schloß Wolfegg, 88364 Wolfegg - T: (07527) 6294, Fax: (07532) 5142, Internet: http://www.automuseum-busch.de. Head: Fritz B. Busch
Science&Tech Museum - 1973 19172

Bauernhaus-Museum, Fischergasse 29, 88364 Wolfegg - T: (07527) 6300
Agriculture Museum - 1976
Peasant life, crafts 19173

Wolfen

Industrie- und Filmmuseum Wolfen, Bunsenstr 4, 06766 Wolfen - T: (03494) 636446, Fax: 636091, E-mail: ifm-wolfen@gmx.de, Internet: http://www.ifm-wolfen.de. Head: Uwe Holz
Science&Tech Museum
History of manufacturing of photographic film in original building 19174

Wolfenbüttel

Braunschweigisches Landesmuseum, Abteilung Ur- und Frühgeschichte, Kanzleistr 3, 38300 Wolfenbüttel - T: (05331) 27071, Fax: 29497. Head: Gerd Biegel
Archaeological Museum - 1937/1945
Early and prehist, archaeological finds (oldest human skull in Lower Saxony) 19175

Gedenkstätte in der JVA Wolfenbüttel, Ziegenmarkt 10, 38300 Wolfenbüttel - T: (05331) 807244, Fax: 881083, E-mail: gedenkstaette-jva-wf@freenet.de. Head: Wilfried Knauer
Historical Museum - 1990
NS-penal system between 1933 and 1945, former execution site, memorial for Resistance fighters from France, Belgium and the Netherlands 19176

Herzog August Bibliothek, Lessingpl 1, 38304 Wolfenbüttel - T: (05331) 808100, Fax: 808134, E-mail: direktor@hab.de, Internet: http://www.hab.de. Head: Prof. Dr. Helwig Schmidt-Glintzer
Library with Exhibitions - 1572
European book history esp of medieval manuscripts, 15th to 18th c printings and books depicting 20th-c painting, graphic art, maps, portrait engravings, Lessing house with documents on the poet and his time, printed books of the 17th c - library 19177

Museum im Schloß Wolfenbüttel, Stadt- und Kreisheimatmuseum, Schloßpl 13, 38304 Wolfenbüttel - T: (05331) 92460, Fax: 924618, E-mail: stadt@wolfenbuettel.de, Internet: http://www.wolfenbüttel.de/fmis. Head: Dr. Hans-Henning Grote
Local Museum - 1894
Baroque castle, former residence of the Dukes of Braunschweig-Wolfenbüttel (1432-1754), historic furniture and furnishings, paintings, tapestries, porcelain, bronzes, coins, medals and arms, local history - library 19178

Wolfhagen

Regionalmuseum Wolfhagen, Neues Museum im Alten Renthof und in der Zehntscheune, Ritterstr 1, 34466 Wolfhagen - T: (05692) 1808, 992431, Fax: 992434, E-mail: regionalmuseum.wolfhagen@tiscalinet.de. Head: Dr. Axel Lindloff
Local Museum - 1980
Hist of houses and framework architecture, geology, crafts 19179

Wolframs-Eschenbach

Museum Wolfram von Eschenbach, Wolfram-von-Eschenbach-Pl 9, 91639 Wolframs-Eschenbach - T: (09875) 975534, 97550, Fax: 9671, E-mail: rathaus@wolframs-eschenbach.de, Internet: http://www.wolframs-eschenbach.de. Head: Oskar Geidner
Special Museum - 1994
Work of the poet Wolfram von Eschenbach (before 1200-1217) 19180

Wolfratshausen

Heimatmuseum Wolfratshausen, Untermarkt 10, 82515 Wolfratshausen - T: (08171) 214412, Fax: 214112
Local Museum - 1977
Local hist 19181

Wolfsburg

AutoMuseum Volkswagen, Dieselstr 35, 38446 Wolfsburg - T: (05361) 52071, Fax: 52010, E-mail: ext.1automuse@vwmail.de. Head: Dr. Bernd Wiersch
Science&Tech Museum - 1985
Hist of the Volkswagen works since 1938, cars, motorbikes, engines, models 19182

Burg Neuhaus, 38446 Wolfsburg - T: (05363) 40017, Fax: (05361) 275757, E-mail: bettina.greffrath@stadt.wolfsburg.de, Internet: http://www.wolfsburg.de/wobline/kultur/museen/index.htm. Head: Dr. Bettina Greffrath
Historical Museum
Grave finds, coins, arms 19183

Heinrich-Büssing-Haus, c/o MAN Nutzfahrzeuge AG, Nordsteimke, Hehlinger Str 11, 38446 Wolfsburg - T: (05341) 281740, Fax: 281743, E-mail: Eckhard_Fischer@mn.man.de, Internet: http://www.man.de. Head: Dr. Eckhard Fischer
Science&Tech Museum - 1985
Old smithy, development of farm, commercial, public and other utility vehicles 19184

Hoffmann-von-Fallersleben-Museum, Museum zur Geschichte deutscher Dichtung und Demokratie im 19. Jh., Schloß Fallersleben, 38442 Wolfsburg - T: (05362) 52623, Fax: 665981, E-mail: -bettina.grefffrath@wolfsburg.de, Internet: http; //www.wolfsburg.de. Head: Dr. Bettina Greffrath
Special Museum - 1936
Manuscripts, first editions, prints, 19th c literature - library 19185

Kunstmuseum Wolfsburg, Porschestr 53, 38440 Wolfsburg - T: (05361) 26690, Fax: 266911, 266966, E-mail: info@kunstmuseum-wolfsburg.de, Internet: http://www.kunstmuseum-wolfsburg.de. Head: Dr. Gijs van Tuyl
Fine Arts Museum - 1994
Art under the headings of nature, hist, technology, classical modern and contemporary art (Andre, Artschwager, Cragg, Daniels, Dibbets, Gilbert & George, Kiefer, Koons, Warhol etc) 19186

Stadtmuseum Schloss Wolfsburg, Schlossstr 8, 38448 Wolfsburg - T: (05361) 828540, Fax: 828541, E-mail: bettina.greffrath@stadt.wolfsburg.de, Internet: http://www.wolfsburg.de/wobline/kultur/museen/index.htm. Head: Dr. Bettina Greffrath
Local Museum - 1951
Agricultural implements and machinery 19187

Städtische Galerie Wolfsburg, Schlossstr 8, 38448 Wolfsburg - T: (05361) 828510/17, Fax: 828525, E-mail: staedtische.galerie@stadt.wolfsburg.de, Internet: http://www.stadt.wolfsburg.de/galerie. Head: Dr. Susanne Pfleger
Fine Arts Museum / Public Gallery / Historic Site - 1974
Contemporary art esp painting and sculpture from the German-speaking countries and international graphic arts in a Renaissance castle 19188

Wolfsegg

Burgmuseum, Burg Wolfsegg, 93195 Wolfsegg - T: (09409) 1660, 478, E-mail: epost@regensburg-land.de, Internet: http://www.regensburg-land.de
Local Museum
Medieval life 19189

Wolgast

Museum der Stadt Wolgast, Rathauspl 6, 17438 Wolgast - T: (03836) 203041, Fax: 203041, Internet: http://www.stadt-wolgast.de. Head: B. Roggow
Local Museum - 1955
Ancient and early hist, city hist 19190

Rungehaus, Kronwiekstr 45, 17438 Wolgast - T: (03836) 202000, Fax: 202000, Internet: http://www.stadt-wolgast.de. Head: B. Roggow
Fine Arts Museum - 1997 19191

Wolkenstein

Heimatmuseum Schloß Wolkenstein, Schloßpl 1, 09429 Wolkenstein - T: (037369) 19898
Historical Museum - 1957
Native history, contemporary chronicle 19192

Wolmirstedt

Museum des Ohrekreises, Schloßdomäne, 39326 Wolmirstedt - T: (039201) 21363
Local Museum - 1927
Ancient and early historic finds, native birds, local history - library 19193

Wolnzach

Deutsches Hopfenmuseum, Hausnerstr 25, 85283 Wolnzach - T: (08442) 7574, 8213, Fax: 7115, E-mail: info@hopfenmuseum.de, Internet: http://www.hopfenmuseum.de. Head: Christoph Pinzl
Agriculture Museum
Processing of hop 19194

Museum Kulturgeschichte der Hand, Am Brunnen 1b, 85283 Wolnzach - T: (08442) 1456, 8213, Fax: 7026, E-mail: museen.wolnzach@-online.de, Internet: http://www.museum-der-hand.de. Head: Norbert Nemetz
Local Museum - 1996
Mosaics depicting the hand 19195

Wonsees

Burg Zwernitz, 96197 Wonsees - T: (09274) 330, 480
Local Museum
Medieval castle, coll of weapons, furniture 16-18th c 19196

Felsengarten Sanspareil und Morgenländischer Bau, 96197 Wonsees - T: (09274) 330
Local Museum
Castle and garden 19197

Worbis

Museum Gülden Creutz, Kirchstr 19, 37339 Worbis - T: (036074) 70228, Fax: 94858, E-mail: ibz-worbis@t-online.de, Internet: http://www.worbis-eichsfeld.de
Local Museum - 1956
Ancient and early history, agriculture, local history, textile crafts 19198

Worms

Jüdisches Museum im Raschi-Haus, Hintere Judengasse 6, 67547 Worms - T: (06241) 8534707, 8534701, Fax: 8534710, E-mail: stadtarchiv@worms.de. Head: Dr. Gerold Bönnen
Historical Museum - 1982
Jewish hist 19199

Museum der Stadt Worms, Weckerlingpl 7, 67547 Worms - T: (06241) 946390, 9463914, Fax: 24068. Head: Thomas Schiwek
Local Museum - 1881
Pre- and early history, archeological finds including curvilinearly ceramics, Hallstatt, La Tène and Roman finds, regional and local history, painting and graphic art 19200

Museum Heylshof, Stephansgasse 9, 67547 Worms - T: (06241) 22000, Internet: http://www.heylshof.de. Head: Cornelius A. von Heyl
Decorative Arts Museum / Fine Arts Museum - 1886
Historic glass from Venice, porcelain, hist ceramics 16th- 17th from Frankenthal, oil paintings (Rubens, Tintoretto, Guardi) 19201

Worpswede

Artothek Worpswede, Lindenallee 1-3, 27726 Worpswede - T: (04792) 1302, Fax: 310757, E-mail: info@kulturstiftung-ohz.de, Internet: http://www.kulturstiftung-ohz.de. Head: Dr. Karen Elisabeth Hammer
Fine Arts Museum 19202

Barkenhoff Stiftung, Ostendorfer Str 10, 27726 Worpswede - T: (04792) 3968, Fax: 310486, E-mail: museum@barkenhoff-stiftung.de, Internet: http://www.barkenhoff-stiftung.de. Head: Beate C. Arnold
Fine Arts Museum / Historic Site - 1981
Workplace and home of Heinrich Vogeler, five art studios for students holding a scholarship - Archiv 19203

Barkenhoff-Stiftung Worpswede, Osterdorfer Str 10, 27726 Worpswede - T: (04792) 3968, Fax: (04791) 90890203, E-mail: kulturamt@landkreis-osterholz.de. Head: Dr. H.J. Siewert
Fine Arts Museum - 1981
Heinrich Vogeler - archive 19204

Galerie Altes Rathaus, Bergstr 1, 27726 Worpswede - T: (04792) 3568, Fax: 2112
Fine Arts Museum 19205

Große Kunstschau, Lindenallee 3, 27726 Worpswede - T: (04792) 1302, Fax: 310757, E-mail: info@kulturstiftung-ohz.de, Internet: http://www.kulturstiftung-ohz.de. Head: Dr. Karen-Elisabeth Hammern
Fine Arts Museum - 1927
Works by Paula Modersohn-Becker, paintings by the artists from the 'Worpsweder Künstlerkolonie' (Otto Modersohn, Fritz Mackensen, Hans am Ende, Fritz Overbeck, Heinrich Vogeler), by Carl Vinnen, Karl Krummacher and further painter 19206

Heinrich-Vogeler-Sammlung, Haus im Schluh, Im Schluh 34-37, 27726 Worpswede - T: (04792) 950061, 522, Fax: 950063, 4321, E-mail: dpschluh@talknet.de, Internet: http://www.haus-im-schluh.de. Head: Berit Müller, Daniela Platz
Fine Arts Museum / Decorative Arts Museum - 1920
Vogeler coll incl paintings, drawings, graphic arts, furniture and Art Nouveau design, art nouveau - library 19207

Heinrich-Vogeler-Sammlung und Worpsweder Archiv → Heinrich-Vogeler-Sammlung

Ludwig-Roselius-Museum für Ur- und Frühgeschichte, Lindenallee 5, 27726 Worpswede - T: (04792) 1302, Fax: 310757, E-mail: info@kulturstiftung-ohz.de, Internet: http://www.kulturstiftung-ohz.de. Head: Dr. Karen Elisabeth Hammer
Archaeological Museum - 1971
European early hist 19208

Torfschiffwerftmuseum, Schlußdorfer Str 22, 27726 Worpswede - T: (04792) 2750, Fax: 2750, E-mail: d.hornig@t-online.de. Head: Dieter Hornig
Science&Tech Museum
Restored shipyard, peat cutting 19209

Wremen

Museum für Wattenfischerei, Wurster Landstr 118, 27638 Wremen - T: (04705) 1217. Head: Gerd Holst
Natural History Museum - 1992
Fishing (prawns) 19210

Wülfrath

Niederbergisches Museum Wülfrath, Bergstr 22, 42489 Wülfrath - T: (02058) 925880, Fax: 925885, E-mail: museum@stadt.wuelfrath.de, Internet: http://www.museum.wuelfrath.de. Head: Dr. Jutta de Jong
Local Museum - 1913 19211

Wünsdorf

Archäologisches Landesmuseum, Wünsdorfer Pl 4-5, 15838 Wünsdorf - T: (033702) 71400, Fax: 71401, E-mail: juergen.kunow@bldam.brandenburg.de. Head: Prof. Dr. Jürgen Kunow
Archaeological Museum - 1953
Ancient and early hist of the area, archaeological materials from recent excavations - library, archive 19212

Würzburg

Banater Schaufenster, Am Ostbahnhof 20, 97084 Würzburg - T: (0931) 661009
Local Museum 19213

Domschatz, Plattnerstr, 97070 Würzburg - T: (0931) 386290, 386414, Fax: 386262, E-mail: museen@bistum-wuerzburg.de, Internet: http://www.bistum-wuerzburg.de/domschatz. Head: Dr. Jürgen Lenssen
Religious Arts Museum 19214

Festung Marienberg mit Museum im Fürstenbau, Festung Marienberg, Nr 239, 97082 Würzburg - T: (0931) 43838, 43016, Fax: 43018, E-mail: info@bsv.bayern.de. Head: Gerhard Weiler
Decorative Arts Museum / Local Museum - 1937
Historical fortress dating back to the 13th c, Renaissance furniture, gobelins, religious artifacts, treasury, town history 19215

First Infantry Division Museum, Leighton Barracks, Geb. 66, Rottendorfer Str, 97074 Würzburg - T: (0931) 8897337, Fax: 8896966, E-mail: toronyg@hq.1id.army.mil
Military Museum - 1986
Uniforms, weapons 19216

Handschriftenabteilung der Universitätsbibliothek, Graphische Sammlung, Am Hubland, 97074 Würzburg - T: (0931) 8885964, Fax: 8885970, E-mail: handschriften@bibliothek.uni-wuerzburg.de, Internet: http://www.bibliothek.uni-wuerzburg.de. Head: Dr. Karl Südekum
Library with Exhibitions 19217

Historischer Saal der Fischerzunft, Saalgasse 6, 97082 Würzburg - T: (0931) 42338
Local Museum
Hist of guilds and fishing - archive, library 19218

Mainfränkisches Museum Würzburg, Festung Marienberg, 97082 Würzburg - T: (0931) 205940, Fax: 2059456, Internet: http://www.wuerzburg.de/mainfraenkisches-museum. Head: Dr. Hans-Peter Trenschel
Local Museum / Fine Arts Museum / Decorative Arts Museum / Historic Site - 1913
Frankish pre- and early hist, cultural hist, Gothic sculptures, garden statues, tombstones, Bozzetti coll, arts and crafts, ethnology, local hist, works by Tilman Riemenschneider, Balthasar Neumann, Ferdinand Tietz, Peter Wagner, Giovanni Battista Tiepolo 19219

Martin-von-Wagner-Museum der Universität Würzburg, Antikensammlung und Neuere Abteilung mit Graphischer Sammlung, Residenzpl 2, Tor A, 97070 Würzburg - T: (0931) 312866, 312283, 312288, Fax: 312507, 8887073, E-mail: museum.ant@mail.uni-wuerzburg.de, museum.na@mail.uni-wuerzburg.de, Internet: http://www.uni-wuerzburg.de/museum. Head: Prof. Dr. Ulrich Sinn, Prof. Dr. Stefan Kummer
Fine Arts Museum / Museum of Classical Antiquities / University Museum - 1832
Ancient Greek ceramics as amasis brygos and terracotta, European painting, German sculpture, sketches and graphic arts of the 15th-20th c (Tiepolo, C.A. Lünenschloß, J.W. v.d. Auwera, J.M. v. Wagner, F. Barrocci, C. Marchionni) - library, archive of J.M. von Wagner 19220

Mineralogisches Museum der Universität, Am Hubland, 97074 Würzburg - T: (0931) 8885421, 8885407, Fax: 8884620, E-mail: mineralogie@mail.uni-wuerzburg.de, Internet: http://www.uni-wuerzburg.de/mineralogie/museum.html. Head: Dr. Eckard Amelingmeier
Natural History Museum - 1972
Mineralogy, petrography, natural resources, meteorites, gemstones, minerals from Franconia 19221

Missionsmuseum der Mariannhiller Missionare, Mariannhillstr 1, 97074 Würzburg - T: (0931) 796990
Religious Arts Museum
Souvenirs from Africa 19222

Museum im Kulturspeicher, Veitshöchheimer Str 5, 97080 Würzburg - T: (0931) 322250, Fax: 3222518, Internet: http://www.wuerzburg.de/kulturspeicher. Head: Dr. Marlene Lauter
Fine Arts Museum - 1941
19th and 20th c painting, sculpture and graphic arts, beginning of a coll of constructivist art - library 19223

Otto-Richter-Kunsthalle der Freunde Mainfränkischer Kunst und Geschichte e.V., Hofstr 11, 97070 Würzburg - T: (0931) 51552. Head: H.H. Rummel
Fine Arts Museum 19224

Residenz Würzburg, Residenzpl 2, Tor B, 97070 Würzburg - T: (0931) 355170, Fax: 51925. Head: Gerhard Weiler
Decorative Arts Museum - 1920
Rooms with Baroque and Rococo furnishings, frescos by G.B. Tiepolo, located in the former residence of the Würzburg prince-bishops, Balthasar Neumann 19225

Riesengebirgsstube, Neubaustr 12, 97070 Würzburg - T: (0931) 12141, Fax: 571230. Head: Werner Haase
Local Museum - 1949
Hist of German expellees 19226

Röntgen-Gedächtnisstätte, Röntgenring 8, 97070 Würzburg - T: (0931) 3511102, Fax: 3511333, E-mail: p-amt@mail.fh-wuerzburg.de, Internet: http://www.fh-wuerzburg.de/roentgen. Head: Prof. Dr. Dietbert Hahn
Special Museum - 1985
Life and work of the scientist Wilhelm Conrad Röntgen 19227

Sammlungen des Instituts für Hochschulkunde der Deutschen Gesellschaft für Hochschulkunde, c/o Universitätsbibliothek, Am Hubland, 97074 Würzburg - T: (0931) 8885966, 8885982, Fax: 8885983, E-mail: dgfh@bibliothek.uni-wuerzburg.de, Internet: http://www.bibliothek.uni-wuerzburg.de/DGfH/dgfh.html
Historical Museum / University Museum
Student life 19228

Siebold-Museum, Frankfurter Str 87, 97082 Würzburg - T: (0931) 413541, Fax: 413541, E-mail: sieboldgesellschaft@web.de, Internet: http://www.wuerzburg.de/siebold-museum. Head: Wolfgang Klein-Langner
Special Museum - 1995
Life and work of the Japanese specialist, collector and doctor Philipp Franz von Siebold (1796-1866) - library and archive 19229

Staatsgalerie in der Residenz Würzburg, Bayerische Staatsgemäldesammlungen, Residenzpl 2, 97070 Würzburg - T: (0931) 355170, Fax: 51925
Fine Arts Museum - 1974
17th and 18th c Venetian painting (Giovanni Battista Tiepolo, Giovanni Domenico Tiepolo) 19230

Städtische Galerie → Museum im Kulturspeicher

Werksmuseum Koenig & Bauer AG, Friedrich-Koenig-Str 4, 97080 Würzburg - T: (0931) 9094567, Fax: 9096015, E-mail: marketing@kba-print.de, Internet: http://www.kba-print.de
Science&Tech Museum
History of printing machine manufacture, first mechanical printing press 19231

Wunsiedel

Fichtelgebirgsmuseum, Spitalhof, 95632 Wunsiedel - T: (09232) 2032, Fax: 4948, E-mail: info@fichtelgebirgsmuseum.de, Internet: http://www.fichtelgebirgsmuseum.de. Head: Dr. Karl-Heinz Plitek
Local Museum - 1907
Local history, minerals, folklore, crafts, folk costumes, mangers, weapons, furniture - library 19232

Wunstorf

Festung Wilhelmstein im Steinhuder Meer, 31515 Wunstorf - T: (05033) 1436. Head: Hermann Brand
Historic Site
Former military academy 19233

Fischer- und Webermuseum Steinhude, Neuer Winkel 8, 31515 Wunstorf - T: (05033) 5599, Fax: 3143. Head: Dieter Thiele
Local Museum
Fishing, weaving, farm life and work, trades 19234

Spielzeug- und Kinderwelt Museum, Unter den Hestern 3, Steinhude, 31515 Wunstorf - T: (05033) 2299. Head: Gudrun Scholtz-Knobloch
Decorative Arts Museum
Dolls, doll's houses, fortresses, railways, games, teddy bears, boxes of bricks and other toys 19235

Wuppertal

Friedrich-Engels-Haus, Engelsstr 10, 42283 Wuppertal - T: (0202) 5636498, Fax: 5638027, E-mail: engelshaus@t-online.de. Head: Dr. Michael Knieriem
Special Museum - 1970
Birthplace and memorabilia of Friedrich Engels (1820-1895), exhibits depicting the workers's movement and early socialism in Wuppertal 19236

Fuhlrott-Museum, Auer-Schulstr 20, 42103 Wuppertal - T: (0202) 5632618, Fax: 5638026, E-mail: fuhlrott-museum@t-online.de, Internet: http://www.fuhlrott-museum.de. Head: Prof. Dr. H. Hermann Schleich
Natural History Museum - 1967
Insects and funghi of the Rhineland, fossils, minerals 19237

Galerie Palette Röderhaus, Sedanstr 68, 42281 Wuppertal - T: (0202) 506281, Fax: 2505555. Head: Marcel Thomas
Fine Arts Museum - 1950 19238

Historisches Zentrum, Museum für Frühindustrialisierung, Engelsstr 10, 42283 Wuppertal - T: (0202) 5636498, Fax: 5638027, E-mail: engelshaus@t-online.de. Head: Dr. Michael Knieriem
Historical Museum - 1983
Early industrialization of the Wuppertal area 19239

Kindermuseum, Schaufenster, Schule und Kinderkunst e.V., Beyeröhde 1, 42389 Wuppertal - T: (0202) 605278, Fax: 6080070, E-mail: kindermuseum-wuppertal@t-online.de, Internet: http://www.bergisches-staedtedreieck.de/kindermuseum. Head: Klaus Alter
Special Museum 19240

Kunsthalle Barmen, Von der Heydt-Museum, Geschwister-Scholl-Pl 4-6, 42275 Wuppertal - T: (0202) 5636571, 5636231, Fax: 5638091, Internet: http://www.wuppertal.de/von-der-heydt-museum. Head: Dr. Sabine Fehlemann
Fine Arts Museum 19241

Völkerkundemuseum der Archiv- und Museumsstiftung Wuppertal, Missionsstr 9, 42285 Wuppertal - T: (0202) 89004210, Fax: 89004240, E-mail: museum@vemission.org. Head: Heidemarie Koch
Ethnology Museum - 1916
Nias, North-East Newguinea, Namibia, Sumatra, Tanzania 19242

Von der Heydt-Museum, Turmhof 8, 42103 Wuppertal - T: (0202) 5636231, Fax: 5638091, E-mail: von_der_heydt-museum@stadt.wuppertal.de, Internet: http://www.von-der-heydt-museum.de. Head: Dr. Sabine Fehlemann
Fine Arts Museum - 1902
17th c Dutch painting, 19th c German and French painting, art around 1900, works by expressionists, fauvists, impressionists, futurists, art of the 1920s, the post-war years, sculptures 19th and 20th c, graphics - library, copperplate engraving cabinet 19243

Wuppertaler Uhrenmuseum, Poststr 11, 42103 Wuppertal - T: (0202) 493990, Fax: 4939959, E-mail: info@abeler.de, Internet: http://www.abeler.de. Head: Jürgen Abeler
Science&Tech Museum - 1958
Development and history of time measuring - library, workshop 19244

Wurzbach

Technisches Schaudenkmal Gießerei Heinrichshütte, Leutenberger Str 44, 07343 Wurzbach - T: (036652) 22717, Fax: 22717
Science&Tech Museum 19245

Wurzen

Kulturgeschichtliches Museum Wurzen mit Ringelnatzsammlung, Domgasse 2, 04808 Wurzen - T: (03425) 926653, Fax: 926653. Head: Angelika Wilhelm
Local Museum / Public Gallery - 1927
Ancient and early history, local history, art coll, personalities, literature, archaeology, trade, playing cards, postcards, wallpapers and carpets, photos and maps, papers 19246

Ringelnatz-Museum (closed) 19247

Städtische Galerie am Markt Wurzen, Markt 1, 04808 Wurzen - T: (03425) 926653, Fax: 926653. Head: Angelika Wilhelm
Public Gallery 19248

Wusterhausen

Stadt- und Kreismuseum, Am Markt 3, 16868 Wusterhausen - T: (033979) 472
Local Museum - 1963
Local handicraft, flora and fauna of the region, room with paintings of Theophil Dombrowski (1880-1969) - library 19249

Wustrow, Niedersachsen

Museum Wustrow, Lange Str 9, 29462 Wustrow, Niedersachsen - T: (05843) 244
Local Museum
19th and 20th c regional hist, colonial produce store 19250

Wyhratal

Volkskundemuseum Wyhra, Benndorfer Weg 3, 04552 Wyhratal - T: (03433) 851071, Fax: 851071. Head: Prof. Rainer Arnold
Ethnology Museum / Folklore Museum - 1991
Agricultural tools and handicraft, costume, home décor 19251

Wyk auf Föhr

Dr.-Carl-Haeberlin-Friesen-Museum, Rebbelstieg 34, 25938 Wyk auf Föhr - T: (04681) 2571, Fax: 2571, E-mail: info@friesen-museum.de, Internet: http://www.friesen-museum.de. Head: Jutta Kollbaum-Weber
Local Museum - 1902
Prehist, geology, zoology, local hist, navigation, ethnology, folk costumes and architecture, furnished farmhouse (1617) - library 19252

Xanten

Archäologischer Park Xanten, Wardter Str, Am Amphitheater, 46509 Xanten - T: (02801) 7120, Fax: 712149, E-mail: g.precht@lvr.de, Internet: http://www.lvr.de. Head: Dr. Gundolf Precht
Open Air Museum - 1977
Roman archaeology, reconstructions 19253

Heimat- und Wallfahrtsmuseum, Emil-Underberg-Str 3, 46509 Xanten - T: (02801) 1452
Local Museum 19254

Regionalmuseum Xanten, Kapitel 18, 46509 Xanten - T: (02801) 7120, Fax: 712149, E-mail: hj.schalles@lvr.de, Internet: http://www.lvr.de. Head: Dr. Hans-Joachim Schalles
Archaeological Museum - 1974
Archaeology, paleontology, prehist - library 19255

Stiftsmuseum und Domschatzkammer, Kapitel 21, 46509 Xanten - T: (02801) 713136, Fax: 713137, E-mail: xanten-stiftsarchiv@t-online.de. Head: Dr. Udo Grote
Religious Arts Museum
Reliquaries, liturgical utensils, paraments, sculptures 19256

Zabeltitz

Bauernmuseum Zabeltitz, Hauptstr 54, 01561 Zabeltitz - T: (03522) 310930, Fax: 310920, E-mail: gemeinde@zabeltitz.de, Internet: http://www.zabeltitz.de
Agriculture Museum - 1982
Agricultural machines and tools, peasant life 19257

Zarrentin, Mecklenburg

Heimatmuseum Zarrentin, Klosterscheune, Kirchpl, 19246 Zarrentin, Mecklenburg - T: (038851) 25426
Local Museum
Town hist, fossils, prehistoric excavation finds, convent hist 19258

Zechlinerhütte

Alfred-Wegener-Gedenkstätte, Rheinsberger Str 14, 16831 Zechlinerhütte - T: (033921) 70217, Fax: 70217. Head: Detlef Kröplin
Historical Museum - 1969
Memorabilia on geophysician and meteorologist Prof. Alfred Wegener, objects he used during his scientific expeditions in Greenland 19259

Zeil am Main

Zeiler Foto- und Filmmuseum, Schulring 2, 97475 Zeil am Main - T: (09524) 7460, 9490, Fax: 302734, E-mail: fotomuseumzeil@onlinemed.de, Internet: http://www.zeiler-fotomuseum.de. Head: Gerhard Binder
Science&Tech Museum / Special Museum - 1993
Hist of photography, film history and cameras 19260

Zeißholz

Dorfmuseum Zeissholz, Dorfstr 1, 02994 Zeißholz
Local Museum 19261

Zeitz, Elster

Museum Schloß Moritzburg, Schloßstr 6, 06712 Zeitz, Elster - T: (03441) 212546, Fax: 214040, E-mail: moritzburg@zeitz.de, Internet: http://www.zeitz.de. Head: Kristin Otto
Local Museum / Fine Arts Museum / Special Museum - 1931
Perambulators, graphics, early and prehist, natural hist - archive, library, photoarchive 19262

Zell am Harmersbach

Fürstenbergerhof, Steinrücken 5, 77736 Zell am Harmersbach - T: (07835) 8051. Head:
Agriculture Museum - 1974
Peasant life 19263

Storchenturm-Museum, Kanzleipl 1, 77736 Zell am Harmersbach - T: (07835) 636947, Fax: 636950, E-mail: tourist-info@zell.de, Internet: http://www.zell.de. Head: Kurt Kussi
Local Museum - 1938 19264

Villa Haiss, Museum für Zeitgenössische Kunst, Am Park 1, 77736 Zell am Harmersbach - T: (07835) 549987, Fax: 549988, E-mail: villa-hais-museum@t-online.de, Internet: http://www.villa-haiss-museum.de. Head: Walter Bischoff
Fine Arts Museum 19265

Zell, Oberfranken

Informationszentrum und Heimatsammlung, Bahnhofstr 10, 95239 Zell, Oberfranken - T: (09257) 9420, Fax: 94292, E-mail: MARKT.ZELL@hochfranken.de, Internet: http://www.hochfranken.de/Zell
Local Museum - 1988
Natural and town hist, geology 19266

Oberfränkisches Bauernhofmuseum, Kleinlosnitz 5-6, 95239 Zell, Oberfranken - T: (09251) 3525
Open Air Museum / Agriculture Museum - 1983
Rural craft 19267

Zella-Mehlis

Gesenkschmiede Lubenbach, Lubenbach 4, 98544 Zella-Mehlis - T: (03682) 43345
Science&Tech Museum
Drop forge from 1918, tools 19268

Heimatmuseum, Hauptstr 2, 98544 Zella-Mehlis - T: (03682) 483471, Fax: 487143
Local Museum / Science&Tech Museum - 1909/1963
Geology, folklore, industrial hist, Mercedes office machines, production of arms, shepherding - mechanic workshop 19269

Zerbst

Museum der Stadt Zerbst mit Sammlung Katharina II., Schlossfreiheit 12, 39261 Zerbst - T: (03923) 4228. Head: Heinz-Jürgen Friedrich
Local Museum - 1952
Geology, ancient and early history, city history, pewter figures, numismatics, folk art 19270

Zetel

Heimatmuseum Rauchkate, Karl-Bunje-Str 3, 26340 Zetel - T: (04452) 7135, Fax: 7135
Local Museum
Town hist, domestic and agricultural implements, smokehouse 19271

Nordwestdeutsches Schulmuseum Friesland, Wehdestr 97, 26340 Zetel - T: (04453) 1381, Fax: 938275, E-mail: schulmuseum.zetel@t-online.de, Internet: http://www.schulmuseum.de. Head: Ursel Wacker
Historical Museum - 1978
Village school, teaching materials - Library 19272

Zeulenroda

Städtisches Museum, Aumaische Str 30, 07937 Zeulenroda - T: (036628) 64135, Fax: 82515, E-mail: Zeulenroda@t-online.de, Internet: http://www.zeulenroda.de. Head: Ute U. Arnold
Local Museum - 1903
Furniture 19273

Zeuthen

Ausstellung Fontane und Hankels Ablage, Platanenallee 6, 15738 Zeuthen - T: (033762) 770, Fax: 77413
Special Museum 19274

Zeven

Feuerwehrmuseum Zeven, Meyerhöfen 7, 27404 Zeven - T: (04281) 2376
Science&Tech Museum
Hist of regional fire fighting, fire engines, uniforms 19275

Museum Kloster Zeven, Klostergang 3, 27404 Zeven - T: (04281) 999800, Fax: 999803, E-mail: samtgemeinde@zeven.de, Internet: http://www.zeven.de. Head: Luise Del Testa
Local Museum
Hist of the nunnery, regional hist, costumes, porcelain 19276

Städtische Galerie im Königin-Christinen-Haus, Lindenstr 11, 27404 Zeven - T: (04281) 999801, Fax: 999803, E-mail: samtgemeinde@zeven.de, Internet: http://www.zeven.de. Head: Luise Del Testa
Public Gallery 19277

Ziegenrück

VEAG Wasserkraftmuseum, Lobensteiner Str 6, 07924 Ziegenrück - T: (036483) 7606, Fax: 76074. Head: Andreas Schmidt
Science&Tech Museum - 1966
Hist of use of water power, water power technology, crafts 19278

Zinnwald-Georgenfeld

Besucherbergwerk Vereinigt Zwitterfeld zu Zinnwald, Tiefer-Bünau-Stollen, Goetheweg 8, 01773 Zinnwald-Georgenfeld - T: (035056) 31344, Fax: 31344, E-mail: info@besucherbergwerk-zinnwald.de, Internet: http://www.besucherbergwerk-zinnwald.de. Head: Wolfgang Barsch
Local Museum / Science&Tech Museum - 1983
Local hist, hist of mining 19279

Zirndorf

Heimatstube Lichtenstadt, Fürther Str 8, 90513 Zirndorf - T: (0911) 69200
Local Museum - 1972
Hist of German expellees 19280

Städtisches Museum Zirndorf, Spitalstr 2, 90513 Zirndorf - T: (0911) 96060590, Fax: 960605920, E-mail: museum@zirndorf.de, Internet: http://www.Zirndorf.de/museum. Head: Sabine Finweg
Local Museum / Public Gallery - 1995
Town and hist of toy industry 19281

Zittau

Galerie Kunstlade, Lindenstr 15, 02763 Zittau - T: (03583) 700720
Public Gallery 19282

Kulturhistorisches Museum Franziskanerkloster, Städtische Museen Zittau, Klosterstr 3, 02763 Zittau - T: (03583) 554790, Fax: 510270, E-mail: museum@zittau.de, Internet: http://www.zittau.de. Head: Dr. Volker Dudeck

Local Museum
Paintings and prints, numismatics, arms, musical instruments, toys, glass paintings, peasant culture 19283

Museum für Naturkunde des Zittauer Landes, Städtische Museen Zittau, Kirchstr 13, 02763 Zittau - T: (03583) 510270, Fax: 510270. Head: Dr. Volker Dudeck
Natural History Museum - 1976
Geology and ancient hist, local prehist, geologist Dr. Curt Heinke 19284

Museum Kirche zum Heiligen Kreuz, Städtische Museen Zittau, Frauenstr 23, 02763 Zittau - T: (03583) 510270, 500890, Fax: 5008916, E-mail: museum@zittau.de, Internet: http://www.zittau.de. Head: Dr. Volker Dudeck
Religious Arts Museum - 1999
The large Lenten veil of Zittau from 1472 19285

Zöblitz

Heimatstube Ansprung, Rübenauer Str 1A, 09517 Zöblitz - T: (037363) 7243
Local Museum - 1972
Crafts and trades, minerals, stone coll 19286

Serpentinsteinmuseum Zöblitz, Bahnhofstr 1, 09517 Zöblitz - T: (037363) 7704, Fax: 45230
Local Museum / Science&Tech Museum 19287

Zörbig

Heimatmuseum im Schloß, Am Schloß 10, 06780 Zörbig - T: (034956) 25605
Local Museum - 1923
Ancient and early hist, hist of castle and city, peasant and burgher living style, crafts, the poet Victor Blüthgen (1844-1920) 19288

Zorge

Heimatmuseum Zorge, Am Kurpark 4, 37449 Zorge - T: (05586) 1590
Local Museum - 1978
Regional hist, iron works and foundry, cowbells tuned in F major 19289

Zülpich

Städtisches Propsteimuseum mit Römerthermen, Mühlenberg 7, 53909 Zülpich - T: (02252) 2770, Fax: 952877, E-mail: museum.zuelpich@t-online.de. Head: Hans-Gerd Dick
Local Museum / Archaeological Museum / Fine Arts Museum 19290

Zusmarshausen

50er Jahre Erlebnisswelt (closed until 2003), Augsburger Str 30, 86441 Zusmarshausen - T: (08291) 9130, Fax: 9130
Folklore Museum 19291

Heimatmuseum Zusmarshausen, Augsburger Str 11, 86441 Zusmarshausen - T: (08291) 870
Local Museum
Archeological finds, town hist 19292

Museum der 50er Jahre → 50er Jahre Erlebnisswelt

Zweibrücken

Stadtmuseum Zweibrücken, Herzogstr 8, 66482 Zweibrücken - T: (06332) 871380, Fax: 871462, E-mail: stadtmuseum@zweibruecken.de
Local Museum - 1926 19293

Zwickau

August Horch Museum Zwickau, Walter-Rathenau-Str 51, 08058 Zwickau - T: (0375) 3323854, E-mail: automobilmuseum@t-online.de, Internet: http://www.automobilmuseum-zwickau.de
Science&Tech Museum
Production of Audi, DKW, Horch, Wanderer and Trabant automobiles 19294

Galerie am Domhof, Domhof 2, 08056 Zwickau - T: (0375) 215687, Fax: 215687, Internet: http://www.zwickau.de/zw-6.htm. Head: Karla Schoppe
Public Gallery - 1977 19295

Robert-Schumann-Haus Zwickau, Hauptmarkt 5, 08056 Zwickau - T: (0375) 215269, Fax: 281101, E-mail: schumannhaus@zwickau.de, Internet: http://www.robert-schumann-haus.de. Head: Dr. Gerd Nauhaus
Historic Site / Music Museum - 1910/56
Memorabilia on composer Robert Schumann, original decorations of birthplace, manuscripts, pictures, sheet music, first prints, programme coll 19296

Städtische Galerie Peter Breuer, Hauptstr, 08056 Zwickau - T: (0375) 25992
Fine Arts Museum
Works and sculptures by the wood carver Peter Breuer (1470-1541), Netherlandish paintings, works of the 16th-20th c (Liebermann, Pechstein) 19297

Städtische Museen Zwickau, Lessingstr 1, 08058 Zwickau - T: (0375) 834510, Fax: 834545. Head: Wilfried Stoye
Decorative Arts Museum - 1914
Mineralogy, stones, mining, religious sculpture, painting, portraits, prints, Max Pechstein - library 19298

Zwiesel

Spielzeugmuseum, Stadtpl 35, 94227 Zwiesel - T: (09922) 5526
Decorative Arts Museum - 1988
Toys 19299

Theresienthaler Glasmuseum, Schlößchen Theresienthal 15, 94227 Zwiesel - T: (09922) 1030, 4920, Fax: 1621. Head: M. Gangkofner
Decorative Arts Museum - 1985
Royal glass coll 19300

Waldmuseum, Stadtpl 29, 94227 Zwiesel - T: (09922) 60888, Fax: 840545
Local Museum - 1966
Geology, biology, forestry and lumbering, local history, crafts and trades, glass dating back to the 15th c, musical instruments 19301

Zwingenberg, Bergstraße

Museum in der Scheuergasse, Scheuergasse 11, 64673 Zwingenberg, Bergstraße - T: (06251) 700328, Fax: 700333. Head: Werner Korschan
Local Museum - 1983
Domestic utensils, agricultural implements, trade workshops, doll's houses, old school, coll of arms 19302

Zwönitz

Museum Knochenstampfe, Dorfchemnitz, Am Anger 1, 08297 Zwönitz - T: (037754) 2866, Fax: 2837. Head: Jürgen Zabel
Folklore Museum / Science&Tech Museum - 1971
Folk art, hosiery, bone and hide stamping, entomology, ornithology, peasant tools 19303

Technisches Museum Papiermühle, Köhlerberg 1, 08297 Zwönitz - T: (037754) 2690. Head: Eckhard Stölzel
Science&Tech Museum 19304

Zwota

Heimatstube Zwota → Zungeninstrumenten-Sammlung Zwota

Zungeninstrumenten-Sammlung Zwota, Sammlung historischer und neuzeitlicher Zungeninstrumente, Kirchstr 2, 08267 Zwota - T: (037467) 22262, 64832, Fax: 64825, E-mail: -TouristInformationKlingenthal@t-online.de, Internet: http://www.vogtlandkreis.de/zwota/index.ht. Head: Elke Eßbach
Music Museum
Coll of harmonicas, mouth organs and accordeons since the middle of the 19th c 19305

Ghana

Accra

Ghana Museum of Science and Technology, Libera Rd, Accra, mail addr: POB 3343, Accra - T: (021) 673963. Head: K.A. Addison
Natural History Museum / Science&Tech Museum - 1965
Anatomy, physiology, automobiles, engines, local flora 19306

Ghana National Museum, Barnes Rd, Accra, mail addr: POB 3343, Accra - T: (021) 671633, 671635. Head: Dr. Issac N. Debrah
Local Museum - 1957
Archeology, Ghanian painting and art, gold and brass, ethnography - library 19307

Cape Coast

Cape Coast Castle Museum, Ghana Museums and Monuments Board, Castle St, Cape Coast, mail addr: POB 281, Cape Coast - T: (042) 32701, 32529, Fax: 3364, E-mail: ghct@ghana.com. Head: Raymond Agbo
Historical Museum - 1971
West African history, text/articles dealing with European colonialization of West Africa, documents on the Trans-Atlantic slave trade, African in the Diasopa in the Americas, family and social life organization of the region - library, youth art and craft studio 19308

Gramophone Records Museum, Cape Coast. Head: Kwame Sarpong
Music Museum 19309

Ho

Volta Regional Museum, POB 340, Ho - T: (091) 403. Head: Dr. Issac N. Debrah
Local Museum - 1973
Natural history, ethnographical and archeological materials of the Volta Region, traditional iron-smelting and weaving 19310

Kumasi

Ghana Armed Forces Museum, Fort, Steward Av, Kumasi, mail addr: Private Mail Bag, Kumasi - T: (051) 5331 ext 214. Head: Fred L. Ofuatey-Kodjoe
Military Museum
War trophies, weapons, historical photographs 19311

Prempeh II Jubilee Museum, Bantama St, Kumasi, mail addr: POB 3085, Kumasi
Decorative Arts Museum
Pottery, gold, silver, leather, and bronze work, baskets, clay sculpture 19312

Legon

Geology Museum, c/o University of Ghana, Dept. of Geology, POB 58, Legon - T: (021) 500300, Fax: 66770, E-mail: Deansci@Eug.gn.aps.org
Natural History Museum - 1951
Geology, fossils, rocks 19313

Institute of African Studies Teaching Museum, Maintenance Rd, Legon, mail addr: c/o University of Ghana, POB 73, Legon
Ethnology Museum / University Museum - 1963
Ethnology and ethnography, Coptic textiles, visual arts 19314

Museum of Archaeology, c/o University of Ghana, POB 3, Legon - T: (021) 502278, E-mail: archdept@ug.edu.gh. Head: Leonard B. Crossland
Archaeological Museum - 1951
Ghanaian archaeology, human paleontology, terracotta figurines, ethnographic coll - library, conservation lab 19315

Zoology Museum, c/o Zoology Department, University of Ghana, Legon - T: (021) 75381 ext 8446
Natural History Museum / University Museum
Vertebrates, invertebrates, insects, reptiles 19316

Gibraltar

Gibraltar

Gibraltar Museum, 18-20 Bomb House Ln, Gibraltar - T: 74289, Fax: 79158, E-mail: jcfinlay@gibnet.gi. Head: J.C. Finlayson
Archaeological Museum / Historical Museum - 1930
Archeological and palaeontological coll from Gibraltar's palaeolithic caves, Phoenician scarab coll - ecology research unit 19317

Greece

Agiassos

Collection of the Church of the Pangia, 811 01 Agiassos
Religious Arts Museum 19318

Agion Oros

Karyes-Protaton, Karyes, Agion Oros - T: (0377) 023712, 023314, Fax: 023315. Head: Ioannis Tavlakis
Religious Arts Museum 19319

Agios Andreas

Agios Andreas Monastery Museum, 281 00 Agios Andreas
Religious Arts Museum
Frescoes, icons, woodcarvings, vestments, religious embroidery 19320

Agios Georgios Nilias

Dimitrion Ikima, Museum of the Sculptor Nikolas, Community of Agios Georgios Nilias, 385 00 Agios Georgios Nilias - T: (0428) 093100, Fax: 093100. Head: Kostas Liapis
Fine Arts Museum - 1992
Paintings, woodcuts and sculptures by Nikolas in his house 19321

Agios Kirikos

Archeological Collection, Gymnasium and Secondary School, 220 06 Agios Kirikos
Archaeological Museum
Archaic Roman pottery 19322

Agios Nikolaos

Museum Agios Nikolaos, Konstantinou Palaiologou St 68, 721 00 Agios Nikolaos - T: (0841) 022462, Fax: 022462. Head: N. Papadakis, Dr. C. Davaras, Dr. M. Tsipopoulou
Archaeological Museum - 1969
Minoan pottery, clay coffins, seals, bronze weapons, archaic, classical, geometric, Hellenistic and Roman pottery, figurines, coins, finds from Myrtos, Agios Fotia, Petsophas, Prinias, Modi, Olous, Zakros, Agios Nikolaos, Siteia, Krya, Myrsini, Malia 19323

Agrinion

Archeological Museum of Agrinion, 301 00 Agrinion - T: (0641) 027377. Head: Lazaros Kolonas
Archaeological Museum / Decorative Arts Museum - 1968
Prehistoric weapons, sculpture, decorative objects, terra cotta, bronze, inscriptions, finds from Aetolia and Akamania 19324

Christos Capralos Museum, Papastratos Foundation, Papastratos St, 301 00 Agrinion - T: (0641) 022393
Fine Arts Museum - 1991
Early works by Capralos (1930-50) 19325

Aiani

Archeological Museum of Aiani, 500 04 Aiani - T: (0461) 098551, 098800, Fax: 098800. Head: Georgia Karamitrou-Mentesidi
Archaeological Museum - 1960
Prehistoric pottery, weapons, Greek and Roman decorative objects, numismatics 19326

Aigina

Archeological Museum of Aigina, Kolonna, 180 10 Aigina - T: (0297) 022248. Head: George Steinhauer
Archaeological Museum - 1829
Neolithic Greek pottery, sculpture, architectural fragments, terra cotta, decorative arts, early Christian and Byzantine sculpture, inscriptions 19327

Aigion

Monastery of the Taxiarchs, 251 00 Aigion
Religious Arts Museum
Vestments, post-Byzantine religious embroidery, manuscripts, documents 19328

Alexandroupolis

Archeological Collection, 681 00 Alexandroupolis - T: (0551) 026359
Archaeological Museum
Hellenistic and Roman sculpture, fragments of prehistoric, Hellenistic and Roman periods 19329

Almyros

Monastery of the Panagia Xenia, 371 00 Almyros - T: (0422) 031216
Religious Arts Museum 19330

Amfissa

Museum of Contemporary Greek Painters, Town Hall, 331 00 Amfissa
Fine Arts Museum
Paintings by local contemporary artists 19331

Amorgos

Museum Chora, Chora, 840 08 Amorgos. Head: Emmanouil Despotidis
Local Museum 19332

Anafi

Archeological Collection, Primary School, 840 09 Anafi
Archaeological Museum
Roman sculptures 19333

Ancient Corinth

Archaeological Museum of Ancient Corinth, 210 10 Ancient Corinth - T: (0741) 031207, Fax: 031207, E-mail: depka@culture.gr. Head: Elizabeth Spathari
Archaeological Museum - 1884
Prehistoric finds, items from the Geometric to the Hellenistic period, Roman and Byzantine finds, excavation finds from the Asklepieion of Corinth, coll of sculptures and inscriptions 19334

Andros

Archeological Museum, Primary School, 845 00 Andros - T: (0282) 023664, Fax: 023664
Archaeological Museum - 1981
Archaeological remains of pre-classical and classical periods, also some Byzantine and later exhibits 19335

Maritime Museum of Andros, 845 00 Andros - T: (0282) 022275, Fax: 024166
Special Museum - 1972
Ship models, old freight contracts lithographs 19336

Museum of Contemporary Art, Basil and Elise Goulandris Foundation, 845 00 Andros, mail addr: P. Aravantinou 6, 106 74 Athinai - T: (0282) 022444, Fax: 022490. Head: Kyriakos Koutsomallis, Fleurette Karadontis
Fine Arts Museum - 1979/1986
New and old wing, sculptures of Michael Tombros, Greek and international contemporary artists and sculptors - glyphothek 19337

Theophilos Kairis Museum, 845 00 Andros - T: (0282) 022275, Fax: 024166
Special Museum - 1980
Mementos of Theophilos Kaïris (1784-1853) 19338

Ano Kardamyla

Kardamyla Cultural Centre of Michael and Stamatia Xylas, 821 00 Ano Kardamyla
Decorative Arts Museum
Icons, woodcarving, weaving 19339

Ano Mera

Collection of the Panagia Tourliani, 846 00 Ano Mera
Religious Arts Museum 19340

Antissa

Collection of the Monastery of Saint John the Divine, Ypsilou, 811 03 Antissa
Religious Arts Museum
Icons, religious objects, embroidery, woodcarvings, manuscripts 19341

Apeirathos

Archeological Collection, Apeirathos
Archaeological Museum
Prehistoric stone and terra cotta objects, Cycladic plaques, daggers, Roman reliefs 19342

Apoaika

Collection of the Monastery of Agios Nikolaos, 845 00 Apoaika
Religious Arts Museum 19343

Apoikia

Agios Nikolaos Monastery, nr Apoikia, Apoikia
Religious Arts Museum
Religious objects, embroidery 19344

Archaia Nemea

Archaeological Museum of Nemea, 205 00 Archaia Nemea - T: (0746) 022739, Fax: (0752) 024690, E-mail: pepka@depka.culture.gr. Head: Elizabeth Spathari
Archaeological Museum
Coll and pictures of Nemea by travellers of the 18th - 20th cc., coins, prehistoric pottery, tools, weapons etc. from the Nemea district, pottery and jewellry from the Mycenaean cemetry at Aidonia and from Aghia Irini, parts of monuments at Nemea, coll of inscriptions 19345

Argos

Archaeological Museum of Argos, Vassilissis Olgas 1, 212 00 Argos - T: (0751) 068819, Fax: 068819, E-mail: protocol@depka.culture.gr. Head: Alexander Mandis
Archaeological Museum
Finds from the Neolithic to the Mycenaean period from Lerna, from the Middle Helladic to the late Roman period from Argos and surroundung areas, mostly from the Mycenaean cemetery of the Deiras and ancient Agora and the theatre of Argos 19346

Argostolion

Archeological Museum, 281 00 Argostolion. Head: Lazaros Kolonas
Archaeological Museum
Mycenaean and sub-Mycenaean pottery, bronze weapons, geometric and archaic pottery, Hellenistic sculpture and pottery, Roman bronze head 19347

Collection of the Metropolis of Kefallinia, Bishop's Palace, 281 00 Argostolion
Religious Arts Museum
Post-Byzantine icons and vestments 19348

Corgialenios Historical and Cultural Museum, Elia Zervou 12, 281 00 Argostolion - T: (0671) 028835, Fax: 028835, E-mail: corgmuse@hol.gr. Head: Helen Cosmetatos
Folklore Museum / Historical Museum - 1968
17th-19th c icons, weaving, woodcarvings, metalwork, lithographs, maps, textiles, portraits, furniture, docs 19349

Natural History Museum of Cephalonia, 3 Germeni St, 281 00 Argostolion - T: (0671) 022270, Fax: 024548
Natural History Museum - 1944
Rocks, fossils, shells, island flora, photo coll 19350

Arta

Archeological Collection, Trapeza tis Parigoritissas, 471 00 Arta - T: (0681) 022795
Archaeological Museum / Decorative Arts Museum - 1989
Classical and Hellenistic sculpture, decorative objects, Byzantine sculpture, icons, art objects 19351

Asklepieion

Mouseio Epidaurou (Epidavros Museum), P Epidavros, 210 52 Asklepieion - T: (0753) 022009
Local Museum
Local history 19352

Asklepieion Lygourio

Archaeological Museum of Epidaurus, 210 52 Asklepieion Lygourio - T: (0753) 022009, 022666, Fax: 023234, E-mail: protocol@depka.culture.gr. Head: Alexander Mandis
Archaeological Museum - 1884
Coll of inscriptions, bills of construction, votive and honorary incl hymns and descriptions of miraculous cures, Greek and Roman votive statues and pedimenta sculptures, Propylaia (temple of Asklepios), temples of Artemis and Apollo Maleatas, Tholos tiles, votive and medical instruments 19353

Astros

Archeological Museum of Astros, Arcadia Greete, 220 01 Astros - T: (0755) 022559. Head: Sakalis Ilias
Archaeological Museum 19354

Museum Astros, 220 01 Astros - T: (0755) 022201. Head: Prof. Dr. Theodoros Spyropoulos
Archaeological Museum - 1985
Finds, mostly sculpture, from the recent excavations, of the large Roman Villa of Herodes Atticus, situated of Loukou, a site identified with the ancient city of Eva 19355

Astypalaia

Archeological Collection, Chora, 859 00 Astypalaia
Archaeological Museum 19356

Atalante

Archeological Museum, Varonou Velliou 21, 352 00 Atalante - T: (0233) 023355, Fax: 023355, E-mail: protocol@idepka.culture.gr, Internet: http://www.culture.gr. Head: Dr. Fanouria Dakoronia
Archaeological Museum
Pottery, clay, metal, bone and stone artifacts, sculpture, inscriptions, coins from Neolithic to late Roman period 19357

Athinai

Agora Museum, Monastiraki, Stoa of Attalos, Athinai - T: (01) 03210185. Head: P. Kalligas
Museum of Classical Antiquities - 1956
Neolithic, Helladic and Mycenaean pottery, jewelry, ivory, geometric vases and statuettes, weapons, classical, archaic, Hellenistic and Roman sculpture, pottery, Hellenistic-Roman vases, bronze, terra cotta, household objects, lamps, 4th c mosaic floor, Byzantine pottery, reproduction of the original building of the 2nd c B.C. 19358

Alex Mylonas Museum, Aghion Assomaton 5, 105 53 Athinai - T: (01) 09215173, Fax: 09215173
Fine Arts Museum
Works by the sculptress Mylonas 19359

Andreadis Collection, Vas. Georgious II 11, Athinai 138
Archaeological Museum
Ancient pottery, icons 19360

Anoyanakis Collection, Sevastias 4, Athinai
Music Museum
Folk instruments (18th-21th c) 19361

Archipelagos Cultural Center, Iasiou 6, 115 21 Athinai - T: (01) 07227308. Head: Markos S. Botsaris
Folklore Museum - 1993
Greek folk art from 17th-20th c 19362

Artemis Collection, Panayi Kyriakou 42, Athinai
Archaeological Museum
Cycladic figurines, vases, ancient coins 19363

Athens University Museum, c/o University of Athens, Tholou 5, Plaka, 105 56 Athinai - T: (01) 03218420, Fax: 03218420, E-mail: museum@uoa.gr, Internet: http://museumsdi.uoa.gr. Head: Elena Yatras-Dehove
Historical Museum / University Museum - 1987
Athens university documents, paintings, charts, books, scientific instruments 19364

Averoff Gallery, c/o E. Averoff-Tossizza Foundation, Marathonodromou 59, 154 52 Athinai P.Phychiko - T: (010) 6778244, Fax: 6715543, E-mail: averoff@otenet.gr. Head: Tatiana Averoff-Ioannou
Fine Arts Museum - 1988
Modern Greek painting and sculpture 19365

Botanical Museum of the National Gardens, Vassilissis Amalias 1, 105 57 Athinai - T: (01) 07215019
Natural History Museum - 1980
Botany coll for specialists and amateurs 19366

Byzantine Christian Museum, Leoforos Vassilissis Sophias 22, 106 75 Athinai - T: (01) 07211027, 07232178, Fax: 07231883, E-mail: protocol@bma.culture.gr, Internet: http://www.culture.gr. Head: Dr. Dimitris Kontantios
Archaeological Museum / Fine Arts Museum - 1914
Early Christian, Byzantine and Frankish sculpture, architectural fragments, Byzantine and post-Byzantine icons, frescoes, manuscripts, embroidered vestments, works of Minor Arts, religious objects, woodcarvings, pottery, mosaic floors, ivory and bronzes, jewelry, some exhibits of enamel - library, archives (with documents and photographs) 19367

Centre for the Study of Greek Traditional Pottery, Melidoni 4-6, 105 53 Athinai - T: (01) 033184916, Fax: 03318490, E-mail: kmnk@ath.forthnet.gr. Head: Betty Psarapoulou, Mimika Griannopoullou
Ethnology Museum
Pottery 19368

Christos Capralos Museum, Tripou 7, Coucaki, 117 41 Athinai - T: (01) 09239041. Head: Souli Capralos
Fine Arts Museum - 1991
Sculptures by Capralos, 40m frieze, works in wood, marble, porous stone, painting, terracotta, pottery 19369

Cultural Center Hellenic Cosmos, Peiraios 254, 177 78 Athinai - T: (01) 04835300, Fax: 04834634, E-mail: helleniccosmos@fhw.gr, Internet: http://www.hellenic-cosmos.gr
Historical Museum / Science&Tech Museum 19370

Economopoulos Collection, Navarchou Nikodimou 27, Athinai
Religious Arts Museum / Archaeological Museum - 1960
Byzantine icons, pottery, seals, coins, Greek vases 19371

Eleftherios K. Venizelos Museum, Evzonon 10, Parko Eleftherias, 115 21 Athinai - T: (01) 07224238, Fax: 07248150. Head: Ourania Pyrrou-Drivalou
Special Museum - 1986
Memorabilia of statesman Venizelos - library 19372

Elliniko-Paidiko Mouseio, Dimos Athinaion Pneym., Kydathinaion 14, 105 58 Athinai - T: (01) 03312995/96/97
Historical Museum 19373

Epigraphical Museum, Tositsa 1, 106 82 Athinai - T: (01) 08217637, Fax: 08225733, E-mail: protocol@ema.culture.gr, Internet: http://www.culture.gr/2/21/214/21402m/e21402m.html. Head: Charalambos Kritzas
Archaeological Museum - 1885
Inscriptions from the 8th c B.C. to 300 A.D., incl decree of Themistocles, lists of tribute paid to the Athenian empire, accounts of Phidias' statue of Athena - library 19374

Ethniki Pinakothiki & Mouseio Alexander Soytzoy (National Picture Gallery and Alexander Soutzos Museum), Vass. Konstantinou 50, 116 01 Athinai - T: (01) 07235937, 07235857, Fax: 07224889. Head: Prof. Dr. Marina Lambraki-Plaka
Fine Arts Museum - 1900
Greek painting (17th-20th c), sculptures and prints, European painting (14th-20th c), including works by El Greco, Jan Brueghel, Giordano, Jordaens, Poussin, Tiepolo, Delacroix, Mondrian, Picasso, engravings, drawings - library, educational dept 19375

Evraiko Mouseio tis Ellados (Jewish Museum of Greece), 39 Nikis St, 105 58 Athinai - T: (01) 03225582, Fax: 03231577, E-mail: jmg@otenet.gr, Internet: http://www.jewishmuseum.gr. Head: Zanet Battinou
Historical Museum - 1977
Objects, photos, costumes and jewellery of the Jewish community in Greece - library, photographic archive 19376

Goulandris Collection, Veotypton Douka, Athinai - T: (01) 022444, Fax: 022490
Archaeological Museum
Cycladic figurines, vases, Greek sculpture, pottery 19377

Hadjidimou Collection, Vas Sofias 12, Athinai
Archaeological Museum
Vases, statuettes 19378

Hellenic Children's Museum, Kidathineou 14, 105 58 Athinai - T: (01) 03312995/96, Fax: 03312997, E-mail: hcm@compulink.gr
Special Museum - 1987
Installations for children to learn, to play, think and experiment - library 19379

Hellenic Folklore Research Centre, c/o Academy of Athens, Leoforos Sygrou 129 and B. Dipla 1, 117 45 Athinai - T: (01) 09344811, Fax: 9370030, E-mail: keel@academyofathens.gr, Internet: http://www.academyofathens.gr. Head: Dr. Aik. Polymerou-Kamilakis
Folklore Museum - 1918
Weaving, embroidery and lace, pottery, musical instruments, metal- and woodwork, dresses and suits, domestic utensils 19380

Hellenic Theatre Museum and Study Center, Akademias 50, 106 79 Athinai - T: (01) 03629430, Fax: 03637453. Head: Manolis Korres
Performing Arts Museum - 1938
Stage set models, costumes, production pictures, memorabilia of theatrical figures 19381

I. and D. Passas Museum of European and Oriental Art, Evelpidou 2, 113 62 Athinai - T: (01) 08212372
Fine Arts Museum
Paintings, Chinese art objects 19382

Ilias Lalaounis Jewelry Museum, Karyatidon 4-6 and Kallisperi 12 Sts, 117 42 Athinai - T: (01) 09221044, Fax: 09237358, E-mail: jewelrymuseum@ath.forthnet.gr, Internet: http://www.lalaounis.jewelrymuseum.gr. Head: Ioanna Lalaounis
Decorative Arts Museum - 1994
Ancient and modern jewellery - library, educational dept, jewellery workshop 19383

Jannis Spyropoulos Museum, Phaedras 5, Ekali, 145 78 Athinai - T: (01) 08134265, Fax: 08133420, E-mail: spyropf@hol.gr, Internet: http://www.spyropoulosfoundation.com. Head: Olga Daniylopoulou
Fine Arts Museum - 1990
Paintings by Spyropoulos, important coll of Greek modern sculpture 19384

Konstandoglou Collection, Xenokratous 13, Athinai
Religious Arts Museum / Decorative Arts Museum
Religious objects, decorative arts, woodcarvings 19385

Kyrou Collection, Yperidou 29, Athinai
Special Museum
Numismatics, coins 19386

Moschakeion, International Museum of Marine Research, Pindou 14, Moschato, 183 44 Athinai - T: (01) 09412393
Natural History Museum - 1944
Molluscs, marine fauna (500 kinds), 11.000 fossils 19387

Mouseio Akropoleos (Acropolis Museum), Makriyianni 2-4, 117 42 Athinai - T: (01) 03210219, 03236665, Fax: 09239023, E-mail: protocol@aepkaculture.gr. Head: Dr. Alkestis Choremi
Museum of Classical Antiquities / Archaeological Museum - 1878
Archaic and classical sculpture, pediments, friezes, statues of the Parthenon, Temple of Niké, Erechteion, terra cotta plaques and figures 19388

Mouseio Ellinikis Laïkis Technis (Museum of Greek Folk Art), Kidathineon 17, Plaka, 105 58 Athinai - T: (01) 03213018, 03229031, Fax: 03226979, E-mail: melt@culture.gr, Internet: http://www.culture.gr/4/42/421/42101/42101p/g42101a.html. Head: Helen Karastamati
Folklore Museum - 1916
Embroideries, woodcraft, traditional costumes, metalware, silverware, jewellery, pottery, weaving, shadow theatre, paintings, stone reliefs - library, educational dept, archives 19389

Mouseio Ethnikon Archaiologikon (National Archaeological Museum), Tositsa 1, 106 82 Athinai - T: (01) 08217724, Fax: 8213573, E-mail: protocol@eam.culture.gr, Internet: http://www.culture.gr. Head: Dr. Nikolaos Kaltsas
Archaeological Museum - 1874
Prehistoric coll, sculpture, vases, bronzes and jewelry from Greek and Roman periods, Egyptian coll 19390

Mouseio Geologiko & Palaiontologiko Ethnikou Panepi, Panepistimioupoli, 157 00 Athinai - T: (01) 07247322, 07247401
Natural History Museum
Geology, paleontology, ethnology 19391

Mouseio Isrorias tis Ellinikis Endymasias, Dimokritou 7, 106 71 Athinai - T: (01) 03616690, 03629513
Special Museum 19392

Mouseio Istorias Laografias Aharnon, Kentriki Plateia, 136 71 Athinai - T: (01) 02462701
Special Museum 19393

Mouseio Kerameikou, Ermoy 148, 118 54 Athinai - T: (01) 03463552
Archaeological Museum
Archaic-classical grave sculpture, sub-Mycenaean-Roman pottery, burial relics, statuettes, bronzes 19394

Mouseio Laikon Organon (Museum of Greek Popular Musical Instruments), Diogenous 1-3, 105 56 Athinai - T: (01) 03250198, Fax: 03254119. Head: L. Liavas
Music Museum - 1991 19395

Mouseio Mpenaki (Benaki Museum), Koumpari 1, 106 74 Athinai - T: (01) 03611619, Fax: 03622547. Head: Irini Kalliga, Prof. Dr. Angelos Delivorrias
Decorative Arts Museum / Historical Museum / Archaeological Museum - 1930
Ancient pottery and bronze, Byzantine and post-Byzantine icons, vestments, embroidery, woodcarvings, folk art, costumes, metalwork, Oriental armaments, memorabilia of the War of Independence (1821), memorabilia of the politician E. Venizelos, engravings, Islamic coll, Chinese pottery - library, historical archives, photographic archive, educational programmes, documentation dep 19396

Mouseio Trenon (Railway Museum), Liosion 301 and Siokou 4, 104 45 Athinai - T: (01) 05246580, 05297522
Science&Tech Museum - 1979
Steam locomotives from 1884, royal cars, 19th c technical equipment 19397

Municipal Gallery of Athens, Piraeos 51, 105 53 Athinai - T: (01) 03243023, Fax: 03243022, E-mail: grweboro@attglobal.net. Head: Nelli Kyriazi
Fine Arts Museum - 1914
Greek art from 1870 till today, engravings and paintings - art library 19398

Museum-Art Collection of the National Bank, Aeolou 86, 102 32 Athinai - T: (01) 03215606
Fine Arts Museum
Greek and foreign painting and sculpture 19th and 20th c 19399

Museum of Anatomy of the Department of Anatomy, Mikras Asias 75, Goudi, 115 27 Athinai - T: (01) 07771142, Fax: 07771203. Head: Prof. N. Papadopoulos
Special Museum - 1870
Bones and grass anatomy, anatomical preparations 19400

Museum of Atlantis, Praxagora 27, Neos Kosmos, 117 45 Athinai - T: (01) 09214982
Archaeological Museum - 1982
2500 objects in relation to the lost Kingdom of Atlantis 19401

Museum of Cycladic and Ancient Greek Art, c/o Nicholas P. Goulandris Foundation, Neophytou Douka 4, 106 74 Athinai - T: (01) 07228321/22/23, Fax: 07239382, E-mail: info@cycladic-m.gr, Internet: http://www.cycladic-m.gr
Museum of Classical Antiquities
Cycladic art, Ancient Greek art 19402

Museum of Decorative Arts, Mosquée de Monastiraki, Athinai
Decorative Arts Museum - 1916
Decorative and applied arts and crafts 19403

Museum of Mineralogy, Petrology and Geology, c/o Technical University of Athens, Heroon Polytechniou Zografou 9, 157 73 Athinai - T: (01) 07722086, Fax: 07722087, E-mail: mmgski@central.ntua.gr. Head: Prof. I. Koumantakis
Natural History Museum - 1875
Mineralogy, petrology, rocks 19404

Museum of Postindependence Athens, Aghiou Andreou 5, 105 56 Athinai - T: (01) 03250378
Historical Museum
Materials from Greek war of independence until 50s, stage reproduction Athens streets 19405

Museum of Sacred Icons, Archbishop's Palace, Ayias Filotheis 21, Athinai - T: (01) 0237654
Religious Arts Museum
Post-Byzantine icons, vestments, religious objects, ecclesiastical documents 19406

Museum of Sculpture and Figurines of Loukia Georganti, Anapafseos 20, 116 36 Athinai - T: (01) 09232568
Fine Arts Museum - 1922
Statues, figurines, molds and busts by Georganti 19407

Museum of the City of Athens, Vouros-Eutaxias Foundation, Paparrigopoulou 7, 105 61 Athinai - T: (01) 03231397, Fax: 03220765, E-mail: mveathen@otenet.gr. Head: Dr. Athos Tsoutsos
Historical Museum - 1980
18th to 20th c city hist, ottoman occupation paintings, personal belongings of Greece's first royal couple - historical dept, picture gallery 19408

Museum of the History of the University of Athens
→ Athens University Museum

Museum of the Statesman Eleftherios Venizelos and the Corresponding Historical Period, Leshi Fileleytheron, Chr. Lada 2, 105 61 Athinai - T: (01) 03221254, Fax: 03221756. Head: Stasinopoulos Michalis
Special Museum - 1986
Archive of publications 1900-1936, memorabilia of Venizelos - library, photo coll 19409

N. Hadjikyriakos-Ghikas Gallery, Benaki Museum, Kriezotou 3, 106 71 Athinai - T: (01) 03621225, Fax: 03626266, E-mail: ghika_gallery@benaki.gr, Internet: http://www.benaki.gr. Head: Dr. Ioanna Providi
Fine Arts Museum - 1991
Drawings, paintings and sculptures by the artist N. Hadjikyriakos-Ghikas (1906-1994) 19410

National Historical Museum, Old Parliament Bldg, Stadiou St, 105 61 Athinai - T: (01) 03237617/315, Fax: 03213786, E-mail: nhmuseum@tee.gr, Internet: http://www.culture.gr
Historical Museum - 1882
Hist of Greek Independence Wars, arms, local costumes, folk arts, flags, stamps, paintings, prints, photographs, personal mementos, medals, posters, maps - historical and photographic archives, library 19411

National Museum of Contemporary Art, Kallirois Av and Am. Frantzi St, 11743 Athinai - T: (01) 092421112, Fax: 09245200, E-mail: protocol@emst.culture.gr. Head: Anna Kafetsi
Fine Arts Museum - 2000 19412

Nikolaos Perantinos Museum of Sculpture, Euphorionos 14, Pangrati, 116 35 Athinai - T: (01) 07216149
Fine Arts Museum - 1991
Perantionos' workshop, 192 sculptures, reliefs, medals 19413

Numismatic Museum, Athens, El. Venizelou 12, 106 71 Athinai - T: (01) 08217769, 08226798, Fax: 08216926, E-mail: protocol@nm.culture.gr, Internet: http://www.nm.culture.gr. Head: Dr. Ioannis Touratsoglou
Special Museum - 1829
Currency from the 7th c BC up to the present, rare Greek, Roman, Byzantine, medieval, and modern European coins, lead seals, ancient copper and lead tokens, ancient and Byzantine weights, gems 19414

P. and Al. Canellopoulos Museum, Theorias St, 105 55 Athinai - T: (01) 03212313. Head: Alketis Choremis
Archaeological Museum / Religious Arts Museum - 1976
Greek sculpture, bronze vases, statuettes, jewelry, coins, Byzantine and post-Byzantine icons, religious objects, decorative objects 19415

Palamas Museum, Asklepiou 3, 106 79 Athinai - T: (01) 03603039, 03634811, Fax: 03603039. Head: Tasos Athanasiadis
Special Museum
Manuscripts, personal library and belongings of Poet Palamas 19416

Polemiko Mouseio (War Museum), Vassilissis Sophias Av, Rizari 2, 106 75 Athinai - T: (01) 07290543, 07252975, Fax: 07245838
Historical Museum - 1975
Greek struggle for freedom, prehistory until today 19417

Tactual Museum, Greek Lighthouse for the Blind, Doiranis 198, Kallithea, 176 73 Athinai - T: (01) 09415222, Fax: 09415271
Special Museum
Tactual experience of Greek culture for the blind 19418

Tahydromiko Moyseio (Philatelic Museum), Plateia Panathinaúkoy Stadiou 5, 116 35 Athinai - T: (01) 07519042/066, Fax: 07519279
Special Museum - 1978
Maquettes of stamps, medals, printing plates of stamps, postal uniforms, mailbags, trumpets, postboxes, scules, typewriters, calculators, postmarks - library 19419

Vaos Collection, Polymnias 27, Holargos, Athinai
Archaeological Museum - 1959
Neolithic objects, plowshares, cultivation tools, axes, drills, chisels for chipping wood, saws, knives, spearheads, arrowheads, needles 19420

Yiannis Tsarouchis Museum, Ploutarchou 28, Maroussi, 151 22 Athinai - T: (01) 08062636
Fine Arts Museum - 1981
Paintings, drawings, models by Tsarouchis 19421

Zoological Museum, c/o Department of Biology, University of Athens, Panepistimiopolis, 157 84 Athinai - T: (01) 07274372, Fax: 07274249, E-mail: alegakis@biol.uoa.gr, Internet: http://www.uoa.gr/biology/zoology/welcome.htm. Head: Dr. Maria Moraitou-Apostolopoulou
Natural History Museum / University Museum - 1858
Zoology - library 19422

Avlon

Folklore Museum of Avlon, Avlon
Decorative Arts Museum / Folklore Museum
Decorative and applied arts and crafts, embroidery, goldembroidery 19423

Batsi

Monastery of the Zoodochos Pigi or Agia, 845 03 Batsi
Religious Arts Museum
Icons, vestments, religious objects, codices 19424

Chaironeia

Archeological Museum, Chaironeia
Archaeological Museum
Neolithic, Helladic and Mycenaean pottery, classical and Roman vases, sculptures, inscriptions, armaments 19425

Chalkida

Archeological Museum, El Venizelou 21, 341 00 Chalkida
Archaeological Museum 19426

Byzantine Collection, Mosque, 341 00 Chalkida
Archaeological Museum
Mosaics, sculpture and pottery of early Christian and Byzantine periods, Venetian coats of arms, Turkish reliefs 19427

Chania

Archaeological Museums of Chania and Rethymnon, Chalidon 21, 731 31 Chania - T: (0821) 090334, 044418, Fax: 094487, E-mail: protocol@keepka.culture.gr. Head: Maria Andreadaki-Vlasaki
Archaeological Museum - 1963
Neolithic, Minoan, Geometric, Classical, Hellenistic and Roman pottery objects, sculpture, armor, numismatics, roman mosaics 19428

Historical Museum, I. Sfakianaki 20, 731 31 Chania - T: (0821) 028092
Historical Museum / Decorative Arts Museum
Cretan history, memorabilia of the literary figure E. Benizelos, folklore, weaving, embroidery, other crafts 19429

Nautical Museum of Crete, Akti Koundourioti, 731 36 Chania - T: (0821) 026437, Fax: 027936
Science&Tech Museum - 1973
Old and modern ships and equipment, Navy coll 19430

Chios

Archeological Museum, Michalon 10, 821 00 Chios - T: (0271) 026664, E-mail: protocol@kepka.culture.gr, Internet: http://www.culture.gr. Head: Aglaia Archontidou-Argyri
Archaeological Museum - 1977
Neolithic and early Helladic finds, archaic, classical, Hellenistic and Roman sculpture and pottery, Byzantine sculpture and vases, Frankish sculpture, numismatics 19431

Ethnological and Folklore Museum, Adamantios Korais Library, Korai St, 821 00 Chios
Ethnology Museum / Folklore Museum - 1937
Costumes, weaving, embroidery, carvings 19432

Chora

Archeological Collection, Village Hall, 246 00 Chora
Archaeological Museum
Archaic-Hellenistic sculpture, inscriptions 19433

Archeological Museum, Council Offices, Chora. Head: Angelos Liagouras
Archaeological Museum
Minoan vases from Kastri excavations, Mycenaean pottery, 4th c sculptural fragments 19434

Monastery of the Archangel Michael Panormitis, 246 00 Chora
Religious Arts Museum
Vestments, silver 19435

Delos

Archeological Museum, Delos - T: (0289) 022259, Fax: 023413
Archaeological Museum
Archaic, classical, Hellenistic sculpture, architectural fragments, pottery, terra cotta, bronze figurines, jewelry, 2nd-1st c B.C. frescoes, household objects 19436

Delphi

Archeological Museum of Delphi, National Rd Arachova-Delphi, 330 54 Delphi - T: (0265) 082313, Fax: 082966, E-mail: protocol@iepka.culture.gr. Head: Rozina Kolonia
Archaeological Museum - 1903
Findings from the Delphic excavations, archaic, classical, Hellenistic and Roman sculpture, inscriptions, pottery, Christian mosaic statuettes, bronze weapons, tools - library 19437

Didymoteichon

Archeological Collection, Secondary School, 683 00 Didymoteichon
Archaeological Museum 19438

Dimitsana

Archeological Collection, Library, 220 07 Dimitsana
Archaeological Museum 19439

Dion

Archeological Museum, 601 00 Dion - T: (0351) 053206. Head: Dr. Julia Vokotopoulou
Archaeological Museum 19440

Drama

Archeological Collection, Cathedral, 661 00 Drama
Archaeological Museum
Roman and early Christian sculpture 19441

Edessa

Archeological Collection, Mosque, 582 00 Edessa
Archaeological Museum 19442

Elasson

Archeological Collection, 402 00 Elasson - T: (0493) 023000
Archaeological Museum - 1987 19443

Elefsis

Archeological Museum, Iera 2, 192 00 Elefsis - T: (01) 05546019. Head: Kalliopi Papangeli
Archaeological Museum 19444

Eresos

Archeological Museum, Eresos
Archaeological Museum
Hellenistic and Roman sculpture, pottery, statuettes from the 4th c, early Christian sculpture and mosaic floors 19445

Eretria

Archeological Museum, 340 08 Eretria
Archaeological Museum
Prehistoric, archaic, classical and Hellenistic pottery, classical and Hellenistic sculpture, grave inscriptions 19446

Ermoupolis

Archeological Collection, Town Hall, 841 00 Ermoupolis
Archaeological Museum
Prehistoric marble and earthenware vases, Hellenistic and Roman sculpture and inscriptions 19447

Falika

Panachrantos Monastery, 845 00 Falika
Religious Arts Museum
Religious objects, liturgical vestments, wood carvings, embroidery 19448

Farsala

Archeological Collection, 403 00 Farsala - T: (0491) 023524. Head: Athanasios Tziafalias
Archaeological Museum
Hellenistic and Roman architectural fragments and inscriptions 19449

Feneos

Archeological Collection, Primary School, Feneos
Archaeological Museum 19450

Feres

Archeological Collection, Church of Pantanassa, 685 00 Feres
Archaeological Museum
Roman sarcophagus, Byzantine architectural fragments, 13th c Byzantine church of the Pantanassa 19451

Filiatra

Archeological Collection, Town Hall, 243 00 Filiatra
Archaeological Museum
Icons, early Christian sculpture 19452

Florina

Archeological Museum, Railway Station Sq, 531 00 Florina
Archaeological Museum - 1972
Prehistoric, Hellenistic and Roman pottery, Hellenistic and Roman reliefs, post-Byzantine icons, folklore 19453

Folklore Museum of Florina, Syllogos Aristotelis, 531 00 Florina
Folklore Museum
Ethnography 19454

Museum of Contemporary Art, 103 ElefTherias Av, 531 00 Florina - T: (0385) 029444, Fax: 029444, E-mail: alfo@compulink.gr. Head: Themis Milosis
Fine Arts Museum - 1977
Greek and foreign modern art (sculpture, engravings, paintings, installations, constructions) - Florina Artists Gallery 19455

Folegandros

Archeological Collection, Village Hall, 840 11 Folegandros
Archaeological Museum 19456

Galaxidi

Archeological Collection, Village Hall, 330 52 Galaxidi
Archaeological Museum 19457

Nautical Museum of Galaxidi, 330 52 Galaxidi - T: (0265) 041795, Fax: 041954
Special Museum
Paintings, ship logs, equipment 19458

Geraki

Archeological Collection, Ralleion Bldg, 230 58 Geraki
Archaeological Museum
Hellenistic and Roman architectural fragments 19459

Glyfada

Pierides Museum of Contemporary Art, Leof. Vas. Georgiou 29, 166 75 Glyfada - T: (01) 08980166, Fax: 08980603. Head: Takisis Maurotasonis
Fine Arts Museum - 1980
Modern Greek painting, sculpture and engraving - library, archives, press information office 19460

Grevena

Archeological Collection, Primary School, Spilation, 511 00 Grevena
Archaeological Museum 19461

Archeological Collection, Secondary School, 511 00 Grevena
Archaeological Museum 19462

Gythion

Archeological Collection, Town Hall, 232 00 Gythion. Head: Prof. Dr. Theodoros Spyropoulos
Archaeological Museum
Archaic Laconian reliefs, Greek, Roman and Byzantine sculpture, inscriptions 19463

Historical and Ethnological Museum of the Mani, Pyrgos Tzannetaki, Kranae, 232 00 Gythion - T: (0733) 022676
Historical Museum / Ethnology Museum - 1989
History and ethnology of the Mani 19464

Ioannina

Archeological Museum of Ioannina, 25th March Sq 6, 452 21 Ioannina, mail addr: POB 1135, 451 10 Ioannina - T: (0651) 025490, Fax: 022595, E-mail: protocol@ibepka.culture.gr. Head: Dr. K. Zachos
Archaeological Museum - 1963/66
Paleolithic tools and bones, neolithic and Bronze Age pottery, weapons, jewelry, geometric-Roman bronze objects from the Dodoni sanctuary, classical, Hellenistic and Roman sculpture, architectural fragment, inscriptions, coins - library 19465

Gallery of the Society for Epirot Studies, Paraskevopoulou 4, 454 44 Ioannina - T: (0651) 025233, Fax: 020980. Head: Costas Costoulas
Fine Arts Museum / Decorative Arts Museum / Folklore Museum - 1985
Modern Epirot painting, folklore, costumes, silver, gold, woodcarving, stonecarving, agricultural tools 19466

Municipal Ethnographic Museum, Aslan Pasha Mosque, 452 21 Ioannina - T: (0651) 026356, Fax: 026272
Folklore Museum / Ethnology Museum
Weaving, embroidery, silver, wood carvings, armaments 19467

Museum of Greek History, c/o Paul P. Vzellis, Roma 51, 450 01 Ioannina - T: (0651) 092128, Fax: 092128. Head: Paul P. Vrellis
Historical Museum - 1983
Historical displays on varoius levels, with houses, caves, churches, alleys 19468

Ios

Archeological Collection, Primary School, Ios
Archaeological Museum
Cycladic and Roman pottery, Roman reliefs and inscriptions, Egyptian statuettes 19469

Ipati

Natural History Museum of Oeta, Holy Monastery of Agathon, 350 16 Ipati - T: (0231) 022410
Natural History Museum
Manuals, birds, reptiles, insects, rocks 19470

Iráklion

Archeological Museum, Xanthoudidou 2, 712 02 Iráklion - T: (081) 0226092. Head: Al. Karetsou
Archaeological Museum - 1904
Minoan archeological finds, frescoes, vases of stone, earthenware and alabaster, terra cotta and bronze figurines, sarcophagi, weapons, jewelry, sealstone ivory, houshold objects, inscriptions, archaic, classical, Hellenistic and Roman sculpture, pottery - library 19471

Historical Museum of Crete, Lysimahou Kalokerinou 7, 712 02 Iráklion - T: (081) 0283219, 0288708, Fax: 0283754, E-mail: info@historical-museum.gr, Internet: http://www.historical-museum.gr. Head: Alexis Kalokerinos
Historical Museum - 1953
Early Christian, Byzantine, Venetian and Turkish sculpture, inscriptions, Byzantine-medieval frescoes, post-Byzantine icons, woodcarvings, vestments, 17th c pottery, folklore, folk arts, weaving, embroidery, lace, local costumes, jewelry, crafts, armaments, documents, militaria, memorabilia of the novelist and poet Nikos Kazantzakis (1883-1957) and the prime-minister of Greece (1941) Em. Tsouderos, early pointing of D. Theotocopoulos (El Greco) 19472

Kazantzakis Museum, Varvaroi, Myrtia, 701 00 Iráklion - T: (081) 0742451
Special Museum
Personal belongings of the Poet, first editions, translations photos, reviews 19473

Metaxas Collection, Plateia Analipseos 4, 713 06 Iráklion
Archaeological Museum
Stone and earthenware vases, figurines and statuettes, bronzes and sealstones of the Minoan period, Greek and Roman vases, statuettes, bronzes and jewelry, coins from the period of Arab occupation 19474

Municipal Museum of the Battle of Crete and the National Resistance, Doukos Beaufort, 715 00 Iráklion - T: (081) 0221227
Military Museum - 1991
Paintings, photos, documents about the battle of Crete (1941) 19475

Saint George Epanosifis Monastery, Iráklion
Religious Arts Museum
Religious objects, vestments, embroidery, bound gospels, illuminated manuscripts 19476

Isthmia

Archaeological Museum of Isthmia, 20010 Isthmia - T: (0741) 037244, Fax: (0752) 024690, E-mail: pepka@depka.culture.gr. Head: Elizabeth Spathari
Archaeological Museum
Finds fron the sanctuary of Poseidon, the sanctuary of Palaimon, the Hellenistic settlement at Rachi, from the area of Isthmia and from the ancient harbour of Cenchreai 19477

Istiaia

Archeological Collection, Town Hall, 200 10 Istiaia
Archaeological Museum
Hellenistic pottery, Roman sculpture, architectural fragments 19478

Kabos

Archeological Museum, 240 16 Kabos
Archaeological Museum 19479

Kalamata

Archeological Museum, Benakis Mansion, Benaki St, 241 00 Kalamata
Archaeological Museum
Meolithic pottery, stone tools from Malthi, Mycenaean, protogeometric and geometric finds from Karpophora, archaic and Hellenistic pottery, classical, Hellenistic and Roman sculpture, Roman mosaic, post-Byzantine icons, folk embroidery, memorabilia of the 1821 revolt 19480

Gallery of Modern Greek Art of Kalamata, Laiki Bibliothiki, 241 00 Kalamata - T: (0721) 022607. Head: Costas Yamako
Fine Arts Museum - 1962 19481

Historical and Folklore Museum, Kyriakou, 241 00 Kalamata
Historical Museum / Folklore Museum
Household objects, weapons, paintings on the 1821 revolt 19482

Museum of the Metropolis of Messinia, Frangolimnis, 241 00 Kalamata
Religious Arts Museum
Icons, religious objects, manuscripts, vestments 19483

Open Air Railway Museum, Aristomenous, 241 00 Kalamata - T: (07210) 095611, Fax: 095614, E-mail: info@depak.gr, Internet: http://www.depak.gr. Head: Dimitrios Giannimaras
Open Air Museum / Science&Tech Museum - 1985
Old station-master building with the airbridge and the water tower, old trains, railways in Greece 19484

Kalamos

Archeological Museum, Amphiareion, 310 81 Kalamos
Archaeological Museum 19485

Kalavryta

Agia Lovra Monastery, 250 01 Kalavryta
Religious Arts Museum
Icons, 11th-14th c Byzantine manuscripts, religious vestments, ecclesiastical gold embroidery, Venetian and Turkish documents 19486

Collection of the Mega Spileon Monastery, Mega Spileon, 250 01 Kalavryta - T: (0692) 022401
Religious Arts Museum
Icons, illuminated manuscripts, religious objects, vestments, carvings, embroidery, silverware 19487

Museum of the Sacrifice of the People of Kalavryta, 250 01 Kalavryta - T: (0692) 022380
Historical Museum - 1993
Holocaust of the people of Kalavryta 1943, centre for peace education 19488

Kallitheaathinas

Tactual Museum of the Lighthouse for the Blind in Greece, Athinas 17, 176 73 Kallitheaathinas - T: (01) 09415222
Special Museum 19489

Kalloni

Collection of the Monastery of Saint Ignatios, 811 07 Kalloni
Religious Arts Museum
Icons, religious objects, gold embroidery, folk art, carvings, manuscripts, Byzantine and Muslim art 19490

Kalymnos

Archeological Museum, Palio Tapitouryion, 852 00 Kalymnos
Archaeological Museum
Neolithic and classical pottery, classical and Roman sculpture, inscriptions, old carpet maker's workshop 19491

Vouvalina Museum, 852 00 Kalymnos
Decorative Arts Museum / Fine Arts Museum
Handicrafts, interiors, copies of 19th-20th c paintings 19492

Kardamyli

Archeological Collection, Mourdzinos Tower, 240 22 Kardamyli
Archaeological Museum
Archaic and classical sculpture, fragments, prehistoric and Hellenistic pottery, folk art, woodcarvings, 17th c tower 19493

Karditsa

Anthiros Monastery, Anthiros, 430 65 Karditsa - T: (0441) 092202
Religious Arts Museum - 1985
Post-Byzantine icons 19494

Collection of the Koroni Monastery, 431 00 Karditsa
Religious Arts Museum 19495

Collection of the Rendina Monastery, 431 00 Karditsa
Religious Arts Museum 19496

Folklore Museum, Town Hall, 431 00 Karditsa
Folklore Museum
Local costumes, weaving, embroidery, woodcarving, folk art 19497

Karpenission

Collection of the Proussou Monastery, 361 00 Karpenission
Religious Arts Museum
Icons, vestments, silver, crosses, bound gospels, manuscripts 19498

Collection of the Tatarna Monastery, 361 00 Karpenission
Religious Arts Museum
Icons, 13th c mosaic icon, gold embroidery, religious objects, carvings, manuscripts, documents 19499

Karystos

Archeological Museum, Yiokaleion Foundation, 340 01 Karystos
Archaeological Museum
Hellenistic and Roman reliefs, pottery 19500

Kastelli Kisamou

Archeological Museum, Main Sq, 734 00 Kastelli Kisamou
Archaeological Museum
Greek and Roman sculpture, fragments, pottery, spears, coins, early Christian inscriptions 19501

Kastellorizon

Archeological Museum, Mosque, 851 11 Kastellorizon
Archaeological Museum
Hellenistic and Roman sculpture, pottery, inscriptions, costumes, weaving, embroidery, Greek handicraft 19502

Kastro

Archeological Collection, 853 00 Kastro
Archaeological Museum 19503

Kastron Agiou Georgiou

Collection of the Church of the Evangelistria, 281 00 Kastron Agiou Georgiou
Religious Arts Museum 19504

Kavala

Archeological Museum, Erythrou Stavron 17, 651 10 Kavala - T: (051) 0222335, 0228660/690, Fax: 0224717, 0833366. Head: Zisis Bonias
Archaeological Museum - 1963
Late Neolithic and Bronze Age pottery and figurines, architectural fragments from the temple of the Parthenos at Neapolis (5th c B.C.), classical, Hellenistic and Roman sculpture, pottery, statuettes from the archaic to Roman periods, part of the 3rd c B.C. tomb from Amphipolis with wall paintings and painted stelae - library, archives 19505

Collection of the Kavala Metropolis, Bishop's Palace, Kavala
Religious Arts Museum 19506

Historical and Ethnological Museum of Cappadocia, N. Karvali, 640 06 Kavala - T: (051) 0316192
Historical Museum / Ethnology Museum - 1981
Costumes, documents, icons, ecclesiastical objects by refugees from Anatolia 19507

Municipal Museum of Kavala, Philippou 4, 654 03 Kavala - T: (051) 0227706
Fine Arts Museum - 1986
Works by Vagis, archive, international press reviews, photos, films 19508

Kea

Archeological Collection, Village Hall, 840 02 Kea
Archaeological Museum 19509

Kerkyra

Angelos and Angeliki Giallina Gallery, Capodistriou 16, 490 10 Kerkyra - T: (0661) 030108
Fine Arts Museum - 1992
Painting of Gallianas will 19510

Archeological Museum, Garitsa, Vraila 1, 491 00 Kerkyra - T: (0661) 030680, Fax: 043389. Head: Kalliopi Preka-Alexandri
Archaeological Museum - 1968
Historic relics, folk art, 17th-19th c painting, Gorgon pediment and lion from funerary mound of Menekrates, archaic terra cotta, architectural fragments, Corinthian vases, statuettes, bronzes, Roman sculpture, coins - library, dept of conservation 19511

Byzantine Collection, Royal Palace, 491 00 Kerkyra
Fine Arts Museum / Archaeological Museum
11th-13th c frescoes, icons, mosaics, sculpture 19512

Historical Museum, 491 00 Kerkyra
Local Museum 19513

Municipal Gallery of Corfu, Acadimias 1, 491 00 Kerkyra - T: (0661) 039553
Fine Arts Museum - 1978
Paintings by Samartzis, Papa, Makotsis, and 19th c 19514

National Gallery of Corfu, Castellino-Kato Korakiana, 490 83 Kerkyra - T: (0661) 093333, Fax: 07224889
Fine Arts Museum - 1992
Greek and foreign painting 19515

Sino-Japanese Museum, Royal Palace, 491 00 Kerkyra - T: (0661) 030443, Fax: 043389. Head: Kalliopi Preka-Alexandri
Fine Arts Museum / Decorative Arts Museum - 1927
Neolithic to 19th c Chinese and Japanese art, decorative objects, porcelain, paintings, theater, armaments, sculpture, miniature art 19516

Solomos Museum, 3rd Parodos of Arseniou, 491 00 Kerkyra - T: (0661) 030674
Special Museum - 1963
Memorabilia of the poet Dionysios Solomos (1789-1857) 19517

Kiato

Archeological Museum, 202 00 Kiato
Archaeological Museum 19518

Kifissia

Mouseion Goulandri Fysikis Istorias (Goulandris Natural History Museum), Levidou 13, 145 62 Kifissia - T: (01) 08015870, Fax: 08080674, E-mail: goul@gnhm.gr. Head: Niki Angelos Goulandris
Natural History Museum - 1963
Botany, entomology, geology, herpetology, marine zoology (mollusca), wetland ecology, soil biology - Biotope and wetland centre, environmental research centre 19519

Pinakothiki Kouvoutsaki, Levidou 11, 145 62 Kifissia - T: (01) 06233682, Fax: 06748175, E-mail: kouvinst@otenet.gr. Head: Panagiotis Kouvoutsakis
Fine Arts Museum 19520

Kilkis

Archeological Museum, Ouskouni-Regoukou 1, 611 00 Kilkis - T: (0341) 022477, Internet: http://alexander.macedonia.culture.gr. Head: Dr. D. Grammenos
Archaeological Museum
Archaic Kouros, reliefs, portraits, inscriptions, small finds, mainly Roman 19521

Techni Gallery of Kilkis, 20 Martiou 25 St, 611 00 Kilkis - T: (0341) 024217, Fax: 024217, E-mail: techni@iname.com, Internet: http://users.forthnet.gr/ath/hollamby/tehni.html. Head: K. Papadopoulou-Pangou
Fine Arts Museum - 1980
Post-war Greek painting and engraving - painting workshops 19522

Kimolos

Archeological Collection, 840 04 Kimolos
Archaeological Museum 19523

Kolonaki

Collections of Cypriot Painting, Sculpture and Graphics, Scoufa and Heracletou 10, 106 73 Kolonaki - T: (01) 03641217, 03641218, Fax: 03602894
Fine Arts Museum 19524

Kolymvari

Collection of the Monastery of Odigitria, 730 06 Kolymvari
Religious Arts Museum 19525

Gonias Monastery, 730 06 Kolymvari
Religious Arts Museum
Religious objects, vestments, post-Byzantine icons, documents, manuscripts 19526

Komotini

Archeological Museum of Komotini, Symeonidou 4, 691 00 Komotini - T: (0531) 022411
Archaeological Museum
Prehistoric vases and tools, sculpture from the archaic to early Christian periods, grave stelae, gold head of Septimius Severus, Klazomenian type sarcophagus - library 19527

Ecclesiastical Museum, Ioakeimideion Boy's Orphanage, Mitropolitou Anthimou, 691 00 Komotini - T: (0531) 03305. Head: S. Hanictakis
Religious Arts Museum
Icons, gold embroidery, woodcarvings, post-Byzantine pottery, silver 19528

Folklore Museum of Thrace, Kouloglou 8, 691 00 Komotini
Folklore Museum
Costumes, silver, woodcarvings, embroidery, bronze utensils, handicrafts 19529

Konitsa

Ethnological Museum of Pyrsogianni Stonemasons, 440 15 Konitsa - T: (0655) 031269
Ethnology Museum
Rare photographs from Sudan, Egypt, Persia, stonemasons' work contracts, tools, reliefs 19530

Kórinthos

Archeological Museum, Palaia Kórinthos, 200 07 Kórinthos - T: (0741) 031207, Fax: 031207. Head: Phani Pachiyanni
Archaeological Museum
Neolithic pottery, Helladic and Mycenaean objects, protogeometric, geometric, proto-Corinthian and Corinthian vases, figurines, classical, Hellenistic and Roman pottery, statuettes, lamps, gold jewelry, household articles, archaic and Roman sculpture, classical and Roman mosaics, early Christian and Byzantine sculpture, Byzantine pottery, small finds of metal, bronze and glass, coins, inscriptions, ruins of Corinth 19531

Kos

Archeological Collection, Platanos, 853 00 Kos
Archaeological Museum
Classical and early Christian sculptures, Hellenistic, Roman, early Christian and Byzantine inscriptions 19532

Archeological Museum, Eleutherias, 853 00 Kos
Archaeological Museum
Prehistoric pottery and figurines, classical, Hellenistic and Roman sculpture and pottery, Hellenistic mosaic floor, inscriptions 19533

Folk Art Museum of the Metropolis of Kos, Bishop's Palace, 853 00 Kos
Folklore Museum
Post-Byzantine icons, embroidery, weaving, woodcarvings, pottery 19534

International Hippocratic Foundation of Kos, Platani, 853 00 Kos - T: (0242) 0221301
Special Museum - 1992
Antique Greek medicine, writings, medals, stamps 19535

Kozani

Archeological Collection, Primary School, Mavropigi, 501 00 Kozani
Archaeological Museum
Hellenistic and Roman vases, coins 19536

Archeology Museum of Kozani, Dimokratras 8, 501 00 Kozani - T: (0461) 026210, Fax: 026210. Head: Karamitrou Georgia
Archaeological Museum - 1989 19537

Historical, Folk Art and Natural History Museum of Kozani, I. Dragoumi 9-11, 501 00 Kozani - T: (0461) 033978
Natural History Museum / Historical Museum / Folklore Museum - 1987
Herbs, minerals, fossils, cave, rural life, Greek hist 19538

Kythira

Archeological Museum, Council Office, 801 00 Kythira
Archaeological Museum 19539

Lamia

Archeological Museum, Kástro Lamias, 351 00 Lamia - T: (0231) 029992, Fax: 046106, E-mail: protocol@idepka.culture.gr, Internet: http://www.culture.gr. Head: Dr. Aikaterini Kyparissi-Apostolika
Archaeological Museum - 1994
Pottery, clay, metal, bone and stone artifacts, sculpture, inscriptions, coins from Neolithic to late Roman period 19540

Lárissa

Archeological Museum, Triakostis Protis Avgoustou 2, 412 21 Lárissa - T: (041) 0288515, Fax: 0289106, E-mail: ieepka.culture.gr@culture.gr. Head: Athanasios Tziafalias
Archaeological Museum - 1960
Paleolithic and Neolithic finds, menhir, archaic, classical and Hellenistic grave stelae, Roman grave stelae, archaic, classical and Hellenistic pottery, early Christian and Frankish reliefs, Byzantine plutenses 19541

Art Gallery of the Municipality of Larrisa, Museum G. Katsigra, Roosevelt 59, 412 22 Lárissa - T: (041) 0222379. Head: Irene Katsigra-Lytra
Fine Arts Museum - 1983
Greek paintings 19542

Ethnographical Historical Museum of Lárissa, Mandelara 74, 412 23 Lárissa - T: (041) 0239446, Fax: 0239446. Head: Lena Gouriotis
Folklore Museum - 1974
Ethnography, textiles, engravings 19543

Gouriotis Collection, Kouma 23, 412 23 Lárissa - T: (041) 0226469. Head: G. Gouriotis
Decorative Arts Museum - 1960
Mother-of-pearl objects, post-Byzantine jewelry, silver, icons 19544

Lavrion

Mineralogical Museum of Lavrion, Heroön Polytechneiou, 341 95 Lavrion - T: (0292) 025295
Natural History Museum - 1986
Minerals and metals, very rare exhibits 19545

Lemnos

Museum of the History of Children's Games and Books, Myrina, 814 00 Lemnos - T: (01) 03600040
Special Museum
Childrens' toys and books coll 19546

Levidion

Alexandros Papanastassiou Museum, 220 02 Levidion - T: (0796) 022211
Special Museum - 1976
Mementoes of Statesman Papanastassiou, library, manuscripts 19547

Liknades

Archeological Collection, Primary School, 501 00 Liknades
Archaeological Museum
Prehistoric tools, fragments, classical, Hellenistic and Roman pottery, coins 19548

Limenaria

Museum Papageorgiou, Thassos, 640 02 Limenaria - T: (0593) 051205, Fax: 051477. Head: Ioannis Papageorgiou
Archaeological Museum / Local Museum / Folklore Museum - 1962/94
Statuettes, vases, Greek and Roman metalwork, coins, weaving and embroidery 19549

Lindos

Archeological Collection, Papakonstandinou Mansion, 851 07 Lindos
Archaeological Museum
Classical and Hellenistic sculpture, inscriptions 19550

Georgiou Collection, 851 07 Lindos
Decorative Arts Museum
Traditional pottery 19551

Ioannidis Collection, 851 07 Lindos
Decorative Arts Museum
Ornamental plates 19552

Kaskines Collection, 851 07 Lindos
Decorative Arts Museum
Traditional pottery 19553

Livadia

Municipal Gallery of Livadia, Platia Ethnikis Antistassis, 321 00 Livadia - T: (0261) 025330, Fax: 026945
Fine Arts Museum - 1992
Contemporary Greek painting, 70 works by Lazaris 19554

Lixouri

Archeological Collection, Iakovateios Public Library, 282 00 Lixouri
Archaeological Museum
Classical and Hellenistic pottery, icons 19555

Loutra Aidipsou

Archeological Collection, Town Hall, 343 00 Loutra Aidipsou - T: (0226) 0235012. Head: Dr. Efi Sapouna-Sakellaraki
Archaeological Museum - 1987
Roman sculptures and inscriptions 19556

Maroneia

Archeological Collection, Primary School, 694 00 Maroneia - T: (0533) 041294
Archaeological Museum
Prehistoric cave finds, neolithic and early Helladic vases and tools, classical, Hellenistic and Roman sculpture and inscriptions 19557

Mavradzei

Timios Stavros Monastery, Mavradzei
Religious Arts Museum
Religious objects, manuscripts, books 19558

Megalopolis

Museum Megalopolis, 222 00 Megalopolis. Head: Prof. Dr. Theodoros Spyropoulos
Local Museum 19559

Mégara

Archeological Collection, M. Mpenardi 25, 191 00 Mégara - T: (0296) 026144. Head: Pandeli Zoridis
Archaeological Museum
Classical and Roman sculpture, pottery 19560

Scironian Museum of Costas Polychronopoulos, Old Athens-Corinth National Rd km 50, Mégara - T: (0296) 062170
Fine Arts Museum - 1976
Modern works by Polychronopoulos 19561

Mesolongion

Art Gallery of the Municipality and Town of Mesolongion, Town Hall, 302 00 Mesolongion
Fine Arts Museum
19th-20th c Greek and foreign paintings, lithographs 19562

Museum of the History and Art of the Holy City of Missolonghi, Botsaris 1, 302 00 Mesolongion - T: (0631) 022134, Fax: 028669
Historical Museum / Fine Arts Museum
Battle of Missolonghi memorabilia, Lord Byron's manuscripts 19563

Messinia

Archeological Collection, Kardamyli, 242 00 Messinia
Archaeological Museum 19564

Metéora

Agion Panton Church Museum, Varlaam Monastery, Metéora
Religious Arts Museum
Icons, manuscripts, religious objects, embroidery, woodcarvings, frescoes - library 19565

Agios Stephanos Monastery, Metéora
Religious Arts Museum
Icons, religious objects, embroidery, woodcarving 19566

Metamorphosis Church Museum, Meteoron Monastery, Metéora - T: (0654) 022278. Head: Alexios Archimanaritis
Religious Arts Museum - 1965
Byzantine and post-Byzantine art, manuscripts, letters of emperors (Chryssovula), icons, sacred vestments, utensils and covers, wood-carved crosses, frescoes 19567

Metsovon

Averoff Gallery, 442 00 Metsovon - T: (06560) 41210, Fax: 42397, E-mail: averoff@mail.otenet.gr. Head: Tatiana Averoff-Ioannou
Fine Arts Museum - 1988
Modern Greek painting and sculpture 19568

Museum of Epirot Folk Art, 442 00 Metsovon
Folklore Museum
Icons, furnishings, woodcarvings, houshold objects, armaments, Baron Tositsa foundation 19569

Mithymna

Archeological Collection, Mayor's Residence, Mithymna
Archaeological Museum 19570

Molyvos

Archeological Collection, Mayor's Residence, Molyvos
Archaeological Museum
Hellenistic and Roman sculpture and pottery, coins 19571

Monemvassia

Archeological Collection, Mosque, 230 70 Monemvassia
Archaeological Museum
Byzantine and Frankish sculptures 19572

Mykonos

Aegean Maritime Museum, Enoplon Dynameon 10, 846 00 Mykonos - T: (0289) 022700, (01) 08125547, Fax: (01) 08125580, E-mail: museum@emproslines.com, Internet: http://www.aegean-maritime-museum.gr
Historical Museum - 1985
Ship models, maps, equipment, indoor and outdoor coll, ancient artifacts, gravures, Armenistis lighthouse, Thalis o Milissios steamship, Evangelistria perama-type ship 19573

Archeological Museum, 846 00 Mykonos - T: (0289) 022325, Fax: 022325
Archaeological Museum
Protogeometric, geometric, archaic, classical pottery and statuettes, Hellenistic sculpture, bronze vessels, inscriptions 19574

Mykonos Folklore Museum, Kastro, 846 00 Mykonos - T: (0289) 022591. Head: Prof. Basil Kyriazopoulos
Folklore Museum - 1958
Folkloristic and historic items of the area of Mikonos and the sea, windmill in operation - library 19575

Myrina

Archeological Museum, 814 00 Myrina - T: (0254) 022990, Fax: 020745, E-mail: protocol@kepka.culture.gr, Internet: http://www.culture.gr. Head: Aglaia Archontidou-Argyri
Archaeological Museum
Prehistoric finds from Polyochni and Myrina excavations, figurines, vases, sculpture, bronzes, inscriptions from Archaic to Roman times 19576

Mystras

Museum Mistra, Mystras Archaeological Site, 231 00 Mystras - T: (07310) 083377, Fax: 025363, E-mail: protocol@5eba.culture.gr, Internet: http://www.culture.gr. Head: Emilia Bacourou
Archaeological Museum - 1951
'Byzantium and the West', sculptures, manuscripts, dress and garment 19577

Mytilini

Archeological Museum, Eftalioti, 811 00 Mytilini - T: (0251) 028032, Fax: 020745, E-mail: protocol@kepka.culture.gr, Internet: http://www.culture.gr. Head: Aglaia Archontidou-Argyri
Archaeological Museum - 1900/1965
Protohelladic, helladic, archaic classical Hellenic and Roman pottery, Aeolic capitals from the temple of Klopedi, Hellenistic and Roman sculpture, mosaic floors, inscriptions 19578

Binos Collection, Harilaou Trikoupi 2, 811 00 Mytilini
Decorative Arts Museum
Carved chests, embroideries 19579

National Folk Museum of Lesbos, 811 00 Mytilini - T: (0251) 041388, Fax: 029300. Head: Joanna Soloyeni
Folklore Museum - 1983
Pottery, embroidery and lace, woodcarvings, metalwork, Byzantine and post-Byzantine manuscripts and documents 19580

Nikou Collection, Vyronos 19, 811 00 Mytilini
Decorative Arts Museum
Carved chests 19581

Teriade Museum, Varia, 811 00 Mytilini - T: (0251) 023372. Head: Manolis Calliyannis
Decorative Arts Museum / Fine Arts Museum
Teriade's famous great books, modern 20th c art 19582

Vlachos Collection, Mitropoleos 6, 811 00 Mytilini
Decorative Arts Museum
Carved chests, weaving, embroidery, metalwork 19583

Nafplion

Archeological Museum of Nafplion, Syntagma Sq, 211 00 Nafplion - T: (0752) 027502, Fax: 024690, E-mail: protocol@depka.culture.gr. Head: Alexander Mandis
Archaeological Museum
Paleolithic to Neolithic finds from the caves of Franchthi and Kephalari, Dendra, Nauplia, finds from Asine, Berbati, Kazarma Tiryns from early, middle and late Hellenistic and Geometric periods 19584

Mouseio Kompologiou (Kombolois Museum), Staúkopoulou 25, 211 00 Nafplion - T: (0752) 021618, Fax: 021618, E-mail: arisevag@otenet.gr, Internet: http://www.komboloi.gr. Head: Evangelinos Aris
Special Museum 19585

Nafplion Folklore Museum, Vass. Alexandrou 1, 211 00 Nafplion - T: (0752) 028379, 028947, Fax: 027960, E-mail: pff@otenet.gr, Internet: http://www.pli.gr. Head: Ioanna Papantoniou
Folklore Museum - 1974
Ethnography, costumes, fashion, toys, shadow theater - library, children's museum 19586

Naoussa

Ecclesiastical Collection, Church of Saint Nicholas, Naoussa
Religious Arts Museum 19587

Navpaktos

Archeological Collection, Library, 843 00 Navpaktos
Archaeological Museum
Classical and Roman sculpture, inscriptions 19588

Naxos

Archeological Museum, Gymnasium, 843 00 Naxos
Archaeological Museum
Prehistoric finds, Mycenaean weapons, decorative objects, Roman sculpture, geometric and archaic pottery, Byzantine icons 19589

Néa Anchialos

Archeological Collection, 374 00 Néa Anchialos
Archaeological Museum
Architectural fragments, sculptures, early Christian pottery, Roman gold jewelry, ruins of Thebes 19590

Néa Kifissia

Foundation Skironio Museum Polychronopoulos, Skironio Centrum Kifissia, St. Georgiou Lyra 73, 145 64 Néa Kifissia - T: (01) 06206437. Head: Mari Elleneca Polychronopoulos
Open Air Museum / Fine Arts Museum - 1985
Open air centre for modern Greek and foreign sculpture, international biennial exhibitions - archive, library, educational programmes 19591

Museum of Telecommunications, 25 Proteos St, 145 64 Néa Kifissia - T: (01) 06201899, 06201999, Fax: 08078119, E-mail: ote-museum@ote.gr. Head: Savvas Stavropoulos

Science&Tech Museum - 1990
Communication technology from antiquity till today, visual and acoustic telegraphs, telephone services, 1st Greek TV studio 19592

Néa Moni

Collection of the Néa Moni Monastery, 821 00 Néa Moni
Religious Arts Museum
Religious objects, gold embroidery, mosaics, 11th c monastery 19593

Néa Moudiana

Museum of Shells of the Greek Seas, Kyprou 1, 632 00 Néa Moudiana - T: (0373) 023990, Fax: 023990. Head: Stavros Kovrakis
Natural History Museum - 1982
Important shell coll, sailors' gear 19594

Neos Skopos

Archeological Collection, Primary School, 620 44 Neos Skopos
Archaeological Museum
Hellenistic and Roman vases and statuettes 19595

Oia

Maritime Museum of Thera (Santorini), 847 02 Oia - T: (0286) 071156, Fax: 071271
Special Museum - 1981
Ship equipment, sailors' belongings, paintings 19596

Oinoussai

Oinoussian Maritime Museum, 821 01 Oinoussai - T: (0271) 051182. Head: Nikolas S. Lemos
Special Museum - 1965
Ships, paintings, mostly by A. Glykas, and a unique coll of French Prisoner of War ship models (33 pieces) 19597

Olympia

Archeological Collection, 270 65 Olympia
Archaeological Museum
Classical and early Christian sculpture, lamps 19598

Archeological Museum, Arhaia, 270 65 Olympia - T: (0624) 022529, Fax: 022529. Head: Xeni Arapoyanni
Archaeological Museum - 1886
Finds from the Bronze Age, reliefs, terra cotta, Greek and Roman sculpture, early classical bronze, mosaics, vases Mycenaean finds, geometric and archaic bronzes, statues from Zeus' temple, architectural fragments, pre-classical terra cottas 19599

Paiania

Mouseio Vorre (Vorres Museum of Contemporary Greek Art), Diad Konstantinou 4, 190 02 Paiania - T: (01) 06644771, 06642520, Fax: 06645775. Head: Ian Vorres, George Vones
Fine Arts Museum - 1983
Greek folk art and architecture, modern Greek paintings and sculpture 19600

Palaiochora

Archeological Museum of Somothraki, 730 01 Palaiochora
Archaeological Museum
Archaic, classical and Hellenistic sculpture, architectural fragments, reconstructed sanctuary (Bronze Age, 7th-6th c B.C.), classical and Hellenistic pottery, votive offerings, decorative and houshold objects relating to the workship of Cabires, Hellenistic and Roman grave finds, coins, inscriptions, Byzantine pottery, bronze 19601

Panagitsa Pellis

Collection of the Church of Koimissis tis Theotokou, Panagitsa Pellis
Religious Arts Museum 19602

Paramythia

Archeological Collection, 462 00 Paramythia
Archaeological Museum
Roman architectural fragments and inscriptions, small classical and Roman finds 19603

Parga

Church of the Holy Apostles Collection, 480 60 Parga
Religious Arts Museum
Local history relics, religious objects, 17th-18th c vestments, bound gospels, manuscripts 19604

Paros

Archeological Museum, Secondary School, 844 00 Paros - T: (0284) 021231, Fax: 021231
Archaeological Museum
Neolithic and Cycladic vases and figurines, archaic, classical and Roman sculpture, pottery, statuettes and inscriptions, Roman mosaic floors from Katapoliani 19605

Byzantine Museum of Katapoliani, 844 00 Paros
Religious Arts Museum / Archaeological Museum
Post-Byzantine icons, vestments and religious objects, Byzantine sculpture 19606

Patmos

Collection of the Saint John the Divine Monastery, 855 00 Patmos - T: (02470) 31223, 31017/18, Fax: 34098, E-mail: moni@12net.gr
Religious Arts Museum
Byzantine and post-Byzantine icons, vestments, embroidery, religious objects, Byzantine manuscripts, old books 19607

Patrai

Archeological Museum, Mezonos 42, 261 10 Patrai - T: (061) 0275408. Head: L. Kolonas
Archaeological Museum - 1936
Roman copies (gold ivory statue of Athena Panthenos of Pheidias), Mycenaean pottery, classical sculptures, decorative and household objects, weapons 19608

Gallery of the Municipality of Patras, Maisonos 110, 262 21 Patrai - T: (061) 0279008, Fax: 0226567
Fine Arts Museum - 1988
Contemporary Greek painters, photographs of old Patras 19609

Historical and Ethnological Museum of Patras, Megaron Logou kai Technis, King George 1st Sq, 262 21 Patrai - T: (061) 0274034. Head: Christos Moulias
Historical Museum - 1968
Independence fight coll, maps, albums, engravings, banknotes 19610

Pella

Archeological Museum of Pella, Pella
Archaeological Museum - 1973
Finds from Pella excavations, classical and Hellenistic bronze and marble sculpture, architectural fragments, pottery, jewelry, small finds, mosaic floors, inscriptions 19611

Perachora

Perachora Museum, Perachora
Archaeological Museum - 1962
Corinthian pottery and bronzes from the excavations of the Heraion sanctuary 19612

Peratata

Collection of the Monastery of Agios Andreas, Peratata
Religious Arts Museum 19613

Petra

Eleftheriadis Collection, 811 09 Petra
Fine Arts Museum / Folklore Museum
Paintings by the folk artist T. Hadjimichail, folk art pottery, metalwork 19614

Phocis

Historical and Folk Art Museum of Artotina, Artotina, Doris, 330 59 Phocis - T: (0266) 061210
Historical Museum / Folklore Museum - 1979
Icons and objects of Artotina chieftains 19615

Piraeus

Archaeological Museum of Piraeus, Char. Trikoupi 31, 185 36 Piraeus - T: (01) 04521598, Fax: 04518395. Head: Dr. Georg Steinhauer
Archaeological Museum
5th-4th c B.C. funerary and votive reliefs, Hellenistic and Roman sculpture, classical pottery, Mycenean pottery from Salamis, Attica, Methana, Geometric, black- and red-figure vases, funerary and votive reliefs, bronze statues, small finds, coins 19616

Maritime Tradition Museum, Acti Tzelepi 4, 185 31 Piraeus - T: (01) 04114096, Fax: 04123250. Head: Georgi Marloyannis
Special Museum - 1992
Memorabilia of Greek maritime tradition, evolution and function of the merchant ships from antiquity until today, ship models, ancient coins, old books, documents and manuscripts, nautical instruments, amphora, etc - library, research coll 19617

Municipal Gallery of Piraeus, Piraeus Municipal Theatre, Plateia Korai, 185 35 Piraeus - T: (01) 04120333
Fine Arts Museum - 1957
Sculptures by Kastriotis, modern Greek painting 19618

Museum of the Merchant Marine, Terma Ekonomou, Hadjikyriakeio, 185 38 Piraeus - T: (01) 04281665, Fax: 04178101
Special Museum - 1991
Merchant ship models, instruments, logs, lithographs 19619

Nautikon Mouseiontis Ellados (Hellenic Maritime Museum), Freattidos Bay, Akti Themistokleous, 185 37 Piraeus - T: (01) 04516264, 04286959, Fax: 04516822, E-mail: nme@internet.gr, Internet: http://www.hmm.eexi.gr. Head: Constantin Paizis-Paradelis
Special Museum - 1949
Ship models, battle relics, Greek maritime life, maps, documents, memorabilia, part of the ancient murals incorporated into the building - library, photographic archives 19620

Panos Aravantinos Theatrical Museum of Painting and Stage Design, Aghiou Constantinou 2, 185 31 Piraeus - T: (01) 04122339
Performing Arts Museum
Stage designs, paintings, portraits, posters 19621

Venetsanos Museum of Modern Art, Akti Miaouli 81, 185 38 Piraeus - T: (01) 04283315, Fax: 04283318
Fine Arts Museum - 1993
Greek and foreign modern art 19622

Plaka

Archeological Museum, 848 00 Plaka
Archaeological Museum
Cycladic vases, figurines and obsidian blades, Greek and Roman sculpture, pottery and inscriptions 19623

Platanos

Archeological Collection, Municipal Library, 854 00 Platanos
Archaeological Museum 19624

Pogoniani

Folklore Museum, 440 05 Pogoniani
Folklore Museum
Ethnography 19625

Polygyros

Archeological Museum, 631 00 Polygyros - T: (0371) 022148. Head: Dr. Julia Vokotopoulou
Archaeological Museum
Classical and Hellenistic sculpture and vases 19626

Lambropoulos Collection, 631 00 Polygyros - T: (0371) 022208. Head: Iraklis Lambropoulos
Archaeological Museum - 1932
Athenian black- and redfigured vases, golden ornaments, bronzes, Hellenistic and Byzantine pottery, terra cotta 19627

Museum of Natural History and Historical Photography, Polytechneiou 38, 631 00 Polygyros - T: (0371) 022313, Fax: 022266
Natural History Museum / Historical Museum - 1987
Walk-in laboratory, science photo coll, taxidermy 19628

Preveza

Archeological Collection, Nikopolis, Preveza
Archaeological Museum
Ruins of the Roman and early Christian city, Roman sculpture, architectural fragments, inscriptions 19629

Pylos

Antonopouleion Archeological Museum, Pylos. Head: Konstantinos Tsakos
Archaeological Museum
Mycenean pottery, bath made of earthenware, gold vases and jewelry, Hellenistic pottery and glassware form Tsopani Rakhi and Yalova excavations, Roman bronze statues, engravings collected by René Pyaux 19630

Pyrgos

Nomikos Collection, 847 01 Pyrgos
Decorative Arts Museum
19th c weavings, embroidery, metalwork, paintings, porcelain 19631

Profitis Ilias Monastery, Pyrgos
Religious Arts Museum
Post-Byzantine icons, religious objects, carved wooden crosses, vestments, books, firmans, bound gospels 19632

Pythagoreion

Archeological Collection, Village Hall, 831 03 Pythagoreion
Archaeological Museum
Archaic and Roman sculpture, architectural fragments, inscriptions 19633

Rethymnon

Archeological Museum, Fortetsa, 741 00 Rethymnon - T: (0831) 029975, Fax: 029975, E-mail: protocol@keepka.culture.gr. Head: Maria Andreadaki-Vlasaki
Archaeological Museum
Sub-neolithic and Mycenean vases, Minoan figurines, sarcophagi, sealstones, amulets, Egyptian scarabs and Minoan double-headed axes, Greek and Roman sculpture 19634

Arkadi Monastery Collection, 741 00 Rethymnon
Religious Arts Museum
Fragments, post-Byzantine icons, religious art objects, weapons, woodcarvings, gold embroidery, relics of revolts 19635

Likion Ton Ellinidon Collection, Prokymea El Venizelou, 741 00 Rethymnon
Decorative Arts Museum
Decorative arts, crafts, embroidery, folk art pottery 19636

Preveli Monastery, 741 00 Rethymnon
Religious Arts Museum - 15th c
Post-Byzantine icons, religious objects, vestments 19637

Rhodos

Archeological Museum, Hospital of the Knights, 851 00 Rhodos - T: (0241) 027674. Head: Dr. Joannis Papachristodoulou
Archaeological Museum - 1440
Ancient sculpture, pottery from Ialysos and Camiros from the geometric to late classical periods, votive and sepulchral altars, inscriptions, weapons, stelae, tombstones and other objects from the medieval Period of the Knights, prehistoric vases, early christian mosaics - library 19638

Decorative Arts Collection, Agyrokastrou Sq, Old Town, 851 00 Rhodos - T: (0241) 025500, Fax: 02555163. Head: Maria Michaelidon
Decorative Arts Museum - 1965
Handicrafts, carved chests, carvings, embroidery, pottery, glass 19639

Historical and Archaeological Institute of Dodecanese, Argyrokastrou Sq, 851 00 Rhodos - T: (0241) 027674. Head: Dr. Joannis Papachristodoulou
Historical Museum / Archaeological Museum 19640

Municipal Gallery of Rhodes, Symis Sq 2, 851 00 Rhodos - T: (0241) 023766, Fax: 036646, E-mail: mun-gallery@rho.forthnet.gr, Internet: http://www.helios.gr/rhodes/artgallery. Head: Manolis Antonoglou
Fine Arts Museum - 1962
20th c Greek painting 19641

Salamina

Archeological Museum, 189 00 Salamina
Archaeological Museum
Classical grave reliefs, Mycenaean pottery, statuettes, grave sculptures, inscriptions 19642

Samos

Archeological Museum, 831 00 Samos
Archaeological Museum
Finds from excavations at Heraion, archaic, classical and Roman sculpture, Cypriot statuettes and vases, Egyptian and Assyrian statuettes and utensils, geometric and archaic bronze, ivory and wooden figurines, utensils and pottery 19643

Byzantine Museum of the Metropolis of Samos and Ikaria, Bishop's Palace, 831 00 Samos
Religious Arts Museum
Post-Byzantine icons, vestments, religious objects, books 19644

Municipal Gallery of Samos, Municipality of Samos, 831 00 Samos - T: (0273) 027340
Fine Arts Museum 19645

Samothráki

Archeological Museum, Palaiopolis, 680 02 Samothráki
Archaeological Museum - 1939
Architecture, sculpture, pottery and glass from the Sanctuary of the Great Gods in Samothraki and from other sites on the island 19646

Serrai

Archeological Collection, Bezesteni, Primary School, 840 05 Serrai
Archaeological Museum
Hellenistic and Roman sculpture, in a 15th-16th c Turkish building 19647

Serres

Sarakatsani Folklore Museum, Konstantinoupoleos 57, 65 062 Serres - T: (0321) 025602, Fax: 056180. Head: Vassilis Tsaoussis
Folklore Museum - 1979
Costumes, weaving, dairying, customs 19648

Siatista

Archeological Collection, Gymnasium, 503 00 Siatista
Archaeological Museum
Pottery, stone tools, weapons, bronze and iron ornaments from prehistoric to Roman times 19649

Sicyon

Archeological Museum, Sicyon
Archaeological Museum
Archaic, Hellenistic and Roman sculpture, terra cotta, architectural fragments from Artemis' temple, pottery, statuettes, 4th c B.C. mosaic floor, early Christian and Byzantine sculpture, Roman bathhouse among ancient city ruins 19650

Sifnos

Archeological Collection, Church of Saint Antony at Kastro, 840 03 Sifnos
Archaeological Museum
Hellenistic and Roman sculpture, archaic statuettes and vases 19651

Sikinos

Archeological Collection, Primary School, 840 10 Sikinos
Archaeological Museum
Reliefs and inscriptions 19652

Siteia

Archaeological Museum of Siteia, Od Piskokephalou, 723 00 Siteia - T: (0843) 023917, Fax: 023917. Head: Dr. Nikos Papadakis
Archaeological Museum - 1984 19653

Skiathos

Collection of the Evangelismos tis Theotokou, Agallianos, Mount Karafildzanakas, 370 02 Skiathos
Religious Arts Museum
Post-Byzantine icons, religious objects, glassware, porcelain, books, documents, bulls, firmans 19654

Skopelos

Monastery of the Evangelistria, 370 03 Skopelos
Religious Arts Museum
Post-Byzantine icons, religious objects, embroidery 19655

Skyros

Folklore Museum of Skyros, 340 07 Skyros
Folklore Museum
Ethnography 19656

Manos Faltaitis Museum, 340 07 Skyros - T: (0222) 091232
Archaeological Museum
Helladic and Mycenaean pottery, protogeometric vases, sculpture, Roman and Byzantine reliefs and inscriptions, reconstructed local interior 19657

Spárti

Agei Saranda Monastery, 231 00 Spárti
Religious Arts Museum
Post-Byzantine icons, religious objects, vestments, bulls 19658

Archeological Museum, Dionysiou Dafnou, 231 00 Spárti - T: (0731) 028575. Head: Prof. Dr. Theodoros Spyropoulos
Archaeological Museum - 1906
Neolithic pottery, tools and jewelry from caves of Alepotrypa and Pyrgos tou Dirou, Menelaion and Mycenaean tomb finds, archaic, classical, Hellenistic and Roman sculpture, geometric and archaic pottery, terra cotta fragments, votive offerings and several mosaic pavements - library, archives 19659

Collection of the Metropolis of Monemvassia and Spárti, Bishop's Palace, 231 00 Spárti
Religious Arts Museum
Post-Byzantine icons, carved wooden crosses 19660

Collection of the Monastery of Agli Saranda, 231 00 Spárti
Religious Arts Museum 19661

Spetsai

Museum Spetsai, Hadjiyannis Mexis Mansion, 180 50 Spetsai
Local Museum
Maritime History, flag of the 1821 revolution, paintings on ships, memorabilia, documents on leading families, Roman, Christian sculpture, post-Byzantine icons, embroidery, costumes, folk art, pottery 19662

Stavros Ithakis

Archeological Museum, Aredatidos, 283 01 Stavros Ithakis - T: (06740) 031305, Fax: 031305, Internet: http://www.culture.gr/2/21/211/21106m/e211fm03.htm. Head: Fotini Kouvaras
Archaeological Museum
Helladic, Mycenaean, geometric and Corinthian pottery, bronze fragments, early Hellenic pottery 19663

Steiri

Monastery of Ossios Loukas, 321 00 Steiri
Religious Arts Museum
11th c mosaics and frescoes, icons, vestments, religious objects, Byzantine monastery 19664

Symi

Archeological Collection, 856 00 Symi
Archaeological Museum
Hellenistic and Roman sculpture and inscriptions, Byzantine and post-Byzantine sculpture and icons, folk art woodcarvings, weaving, silverware, metalwork, pottery 19665

Tanagra

Archeological Collection, Tanagra
Archaeological Museum
Archaic-Byzantine sculpture, terra cotta, architectural fragments, inscriptions, pottery 19666

Tegea

Archeological Museum, Alea Tegea, 220 12 Tegea - T: (071) 0556540. Head: Prof. Dr. Theodoros Spyropoulos
Archaeological Museum - 1910
Prehistoric pottery from Asea, Ayiorghitika, sculpture, mainly from Athena temple, classical pottery, Hellenistic statuettes and small bronze votive offerings 19667

Thassos

Archeological Museum, 640 04 Thassos - T: (0593) 022180
Archaeological Museum
Archaic, classical, Hellenistic and Roman sculpture, bronze and terra cotta statuettes, archaic and classical pottery and lamps, reliefs, jewelry, coins, inscriptions, ancient city ruins 19668

Polygnotos Vagis Museum, Potamia, 640 04 Thassos - T: (0593) 061182
Fine Arts Museum - 1981
Paintings and sculpture by Vagis 19669

Thebes

Archaeological Museum of Thebes, Threpsiadi 1, 322 00 Thebes - T: (0262) 027913, Fax: 023559, E-mail: protocol@thepka.culture.gr. Head: Dr. Vassilis Aravantinos
Archaeological Museum - 1962
Helladic pottery, clay sarcophagi, Mycenaean finds from Cadmeia, archaic, classical, Hellenistic, Roman, early Christian and Byzantine sculpture and mosaics, Roman pottery and sculpture, coins, inscriptions 19670

Thermo

Archeological Museum, 300 08 Thermo
Archaeological Museum
Painted terra cotta metopes from the Apollo temple, architectural fragments, tiles, Mycenaean, archaic, Hellenistic pottery, inscriptions 19671

Thessaloniki

Folklore and Ethnological Museum of Macedonia and Thrace, Vasilissis Olgas 68, 546 42 Thessaloniki - T: (031) 0830591, Fax: 0844848. Head: Dr. E. Miliadzidou-Ioannou
Folklore Museum / Ethnology Museum - 1970
Greek traditional costumes, embroidery, jewellery, copperware, woodcarvings, tools, housewares - library 19672

Folklore Museum, c/o University of Thessaloniki, 540 06 Thessaloniki - T: (031) 0997288, 0997227, Fax: 0997199, E-mail: areti@hist.auth.gr. Head: Prof. Ch. Hatzitaki-Kapsomenou
Folklore Museum - 1926
Woodcarvings, embroidery, weaving, metalwork, pottery 19673

Gallery of the Society for Macedonian Studies, Ethnikis Amynis 4, 546 21 Thessaloniki - T: (031) 0271195
Fine Arts Museum
Period and modern Macedonian paintings and engravings 19674

Jewish Museum of Thessaloniki, Agiou Mina 13, 546 24 Thessaloniki - T: (031) 02504067, Fax: 0250407, E-mail: jctmuseo@compulink.gr, Internet: http://www.jmth.gr. Head: Solita Saltiel
Historical Museum - 2001
Culture of Greek Jews, Jewish history in Thessaloniki - library, Simon Marks Museum 19675

Kyriazopoulos Collection, Vassileos Konstantinou 11, Thessaloniki
Decorative Arts Museum
Decorative arts and crafts, contemporary Greek folk pottery, mainly by M. Arramidis 19676

Mouseio Arhaion Vyzantinon & Matavyzantinon Mousik, Katouni 12-14, 546 25 Thessaloniki - T: (031) 0555263
Archaeological Museum
Archaeology, Byzantine mosaic 19677

Mouseion Arhaiologikon (Archaeological Museum), M. Andronikou 6, 546 21 Thessaloniki - T: (031) 0830538, 0831037, Fax: 0861306, E-mail: istepka@culture.gr, Internet: http://alexander.macedonia.culture.gr. Head: Dr. D. Grammenos
Archaeological Museum
Prehistoric coll, Sindos cemetery, Coins of Macedon, Gold of Macedon, archaic, classical, Hellenistic and Roman sculpture, Thessaloniki, 2300 years 19678

Municipal Art Gallery, Vassilissis Olgas 162, 546 46 Thessaloniki - T: (031) 0425531, Fax: 0411101. Head: Paraskevi Manakou
Fine Arts Museum - 1966
Thessalonian artists (1898-1967), engravings, icon coll (14th-19th c), coll of works illustrating the evolution of modern Greek art 19679

Museum of Byzantine Culture, Stratou 2, 546 40 Thessaloniki - T: (031) 0868570, Fax: 0838597, E-mail: protocol@mbp.culture.gr. Head: A. Tourta
Archaeological Museum - 1994
Byzantine culture and archaeology 19680

Museum of Casts and Archeological Collection, c/o Department of Archeology and Art History, University of Thessaloniki, Faculty of Philosophy, 540 06 Thessaloniki - T: (031) 0997279, Fax: 0997303, E-mail: hmdnak@hist.auth.gr, Internet: http://www.rotonda-hist.auth.gr/archaeology/substructure/ekmageig. Head: Prof. Dr. Th. Stefanidou-Tiveriou
Archaeological Museum / University Museum - 1930 19681

Musical Museum of Macedonia (closed) 19682

Technology Museum of Thessaloniki, Industrial Zone, 2nd St, Bldg 47, 541 10 Thessaloniki - T: (031) 0799773, Fax: 0796816, E-mail: info@tmth.edu.gr, Internet: http://www.tmth.edu.gr. Head: Prof. A. Goulas
Science&Tech Museum - 1978
Electricity, communication, computers, photography, space, meteorology, crafts, industry development, printing machines, holography, ancient Greek technology 19683

Thessaloniki Museum of the Macedonian Struggle, Proxenou Koromila 23, 546 22 Thessaloniki - T: (031) 0229778, Fax: 0233108, E-mail: museum@mma.the.forthnet.gr. Head: D.K. Zannas, Despina Syrri
Historical Museum - 1982
Weapons, uniforms, pictures and personalia of early 20th c chieftains - research center 19684

Vassiliou Collection, Paraskevopoulou 6, 546 40 Thessaloniki - T: (031) 054640
Archaeological Museum
Ancient pottery, bronze, coins, jewelry, icons 19685

Thira

Archeological Museum, 847 00 Thira
Archaeological Museum - 1962
Prehistoric pottery, archaic, classical, geometric, Hellenistic and Roman sculpture and pottery, Roman glass, lamps, inscriptions 19686

Thira Ecclesiastical Museum, Bishop's Palace, 847 00 Thira
Religious Arts Museum
Icons, carved wooden crosses 19687

Tilos

Archeological Collection, Village Hall, 850 02 Tilos
Archaeological Museum
Classical and Hellenistic sculpture, inscriptions 19688

Timbaki

Museum of Cretan Ethnology, Vory, 702 00 Timbaki - T: (08920) 091110/11, Fax: 091394, E-mail: crethno@germanosnet.gr, Internet: http://www.southerncrete.gr/euroheritagedays. Head: Dr. Christopher Vallianos
Ethnology Museum - 1988
Cretean objects of daily life use (18th-19th c), ethnology, nutrition, architecture, weaving, crafts and commerce, transport, customs, social organization - library, photographic and audio archives, research and congress centre 19689

Tinos

A. Sohos Museum, Church of the Panagia Evangelistria, 842 00 Tinos - T: (0283) 022256, Fax: 022196, E-mail: piiet@thn.fourthnet.gr. Head: Evaggelos Paraskevas-Gizis
Fine Arts Museum
Sculptures by A. Sohos 19690

Archeological Museum, Tinos
Archaeological Museum
Archaic and classical sculpture, geometric pottery, inscriptions 19691

Byzantine Museum, Church of the Panagia Evangelistria, 842 00 Tinos - T: (0283) 022256, Fax: 022196, E-mail: piiet@thn.fourthnet.gr. Head: Evaggelos Paraskevas-Gizis
Religious Arts Museum
Post-Byzantine icons 19692

Papadopoulos Picture Gallery, Evangelistria Holy Foundation, Church of the Panagia Evangelistria, 842 00 Tinos - T: (0283) 022256, Fax: 022196, E-mail: piiet@thn.fourtnet.gr. Head: Evaggelos Paraskevas-Gizis
Fine Arts Museum - 1961
Modern Greek paintings by K. Volanakis, K. Parthenis, copies of Renaissance paintings, 18th c interior 19693

Trikala

Agios Vissarion Monastery, 421 00 Trikala
Religious Arts Museum
Post-Byzantine icons, religious objects, embroidery, books, documents 19694

Ecclesiastical Museum of the Metropolis of Trikki and Stagoi, Bishop's Palace, 421 00 Trikala - T: (0431) 027365. Head: Lahurakis Konstantinus
Religious Arts Museum
16th-18th c icons, embroidery, religious objects, woodcarvings 19695

Tripoli

Archeological Museum of Arcadia, Evangelistrios 8, 221 00 Tripoli - T: (071) 0242148. Head: Prof. Dr. Theodoros Spyropoulos
Archaeological Museum - 1986
Neolithic pottery, Mycenaean pottery, bronze weapons 19696

Tsotili

Archeological Collection, Secondary School, 500 02 Tsotili
Archaeological Museum 19697

Varia Lesbos

Museum of Works by Theophilos, POB 49, 811 00 Varia Lesbos - T: (0251) 041644, Fax: 025555. Head: Vasiliki Damdoumi
Fine Arts Museum - 1965 19698

Vathy

Archeological Museum, 310 83 Vathy
Archaeological Museum
Proto-Corinthian and Corinthian pottery, small bronze articles from Mt Athos 19699

Veria

Archeological Museum of Veroia, Anixeos 47, 591 00 Veria - T: (0331) 024972, Fax: 022829. Head: L. Stefani
Archaeological Museum - 1971
Neolithic, Bronze Age and Iron Age finds, geometric, classical, Hellenistic, Roman and Byzantine pottery, Hellenistic and Roman sculpture, Greek and Roman inscriptions, coins, Byzantine and post-Byzantine icons, documents - library, archives 19700

Vitsa

Folklore Museum, Vitsa
Folklore Museum
Ethnography 19701

Volos

Athanassakeion Archeological Museum, Athanassaki 1, 380 01 Volos - T: (0421) 028563, 025285, Fax: 028563, E-mail: protocol@igepka.culture.gr. Head: Vassiliki Adrimi-Sismani
Archaeological Museum - 1909
Paleolithic, mesolithic and neolithic finds, neolithic and Bronze Age pottery, figurines, bone and stone tools, archaic, classical, Hellenistic and Roman sculpture, 3rd-2nd c B.C. Dimitrias stelae, geometrical and classical pottery, grave finds, glass, coins - library, conservation lab, archives 19702

Makris Collection, Afendouli 22, 382 22 Volos
Decorative Arts Museum / Fine Arts Museum
Folk murals, Greek paintings, carvings, weaving, jewelry, utensils, miniatures 19703

Sefel Collection, Pef Kakia, 382 22 Volos
Archaeological Museum
Geometric vases, bronze statuettes 19704

Vravrón

Archeological Museum, Vravrón - T: (0299) 027020, Fax: 027020
Archaeological Museum 19705

Xanthi

Collection of the Metropolis of Xanthi, Bishop's Palace, 671 00 Xanthi
Religious Arts Museum
Icons, manuscripts 19706

Folklore Museum, Philoproödos Enossis Xanthis, 7 Antika Od, 671 00 Xanthi - T: (0541) 078383, Fax: 078383, E-mail: www.syntherm@otenet.gr, Internet: http://www.fex.gr. Head: Ioannis Frangos
Folklore Museum
Costumes, embroidery, furniture, metal-, wooden- and porcelain-objects, photos - archives 19707

Municipal Art Gallery of Xanthi, Plateia Dioikitiriou, 671 00 Xanthi - T: (0541) 022415, Fax: 23525
Fine Arts Museum - 1974
Engravings, works by Sikeliotis, Kopsidis, Tsarouchis 19708

Ypati

Agathonos Monastery Collection, 350 16 Ypati
Religious Arts Museum
Post-Byzantine icons, vestments, religious objects, carved wooden crosses, 18th-19th c religious books 19709

Zakynthos

Byzantine Museum, Solomou Sq, 291 00 Zakynthos. Head: Nikolaos Zias
Religious Arts Museum / Fine Arts Museum
Frescoes, post-Byzantine icons, paintings of the Heptanesian School, woodcarvings, Hellenistic and Byzantine sculpture, coats of arms - library 19710

Solomos Museum, Plateia Agiou Markou 15, Eleftherias Sq, 291 00 Zakynthos - T: (0695) 048982, Fax: 048982, E-mail: museumsolomos@ aias.gr. Head: Ioanis Demetis
Special Museum
Memorabilia of D. Solomos, famous 19th c residents, costumes, armaments 19711

Zakynthos Museum of the Natural Heritage, Community of Agalas, 290 92 Zakynthos - T: (0695) 034234
Natural History Museum
WWF aided flora and fauna coll, famous Keri turtles 19712

Zerbitsa

Collection of the Koimissis tis Theotokou, Zerbitsa
Religious Arts Museum 19713

Zografou

Gounaropoulos Museum of Zografou, Gounaropoulou 6, 157 71 Zografou - T: (01) 07777601
Fine Arts Museum
Works and personal belongings of the artist 19714

Greenland

Aasiaat

Aasiaat Katersugaasiviat Museum, Aasiaat Museum, Otto Rosingsvej 6, 3950 Aasiaat - T: 892597, Fax: 892597, E-mail: aasmuseum@ greennet.gl, Internet: http://iserit.greennet.gl/ aasmuseum. Head: José D. Ruiz-Martinez
Local Museum - 1978
archive 19715

Ilulissat

Aalisarnermut Piniarnermullu Katersugaasivik (Museum of Catching and Fishing), Noah Møgård-Ip Aqq, Ilulissat, mail addr: Postboks 99, 3952 Ilulissat - T: 944489, Fax: 943643, E-mail: ilumus@ greennet.gl, Internet: http://www.ilumus.gl
Historical Museum 19716

Ilulissat Katersugaasiviat (Ilulissat Town Museum), Nuisaeiannouaq 9, Ilulissat, mail addr: Postboks 99, 3952 Ilulissat - T: 944330, Fax: 943643, E-mail: ilumus@greennet.gl, Internet: http:// www.ilumus.gl. Head: Kirsten Strandgaard
Local Museum 19717

Qalipakkanik Katersugaasivik (Art Museum), Aron Mathiassen-Ip Aqq 7, Ilulissat, mail addr: Postboks 99, 3952 Ilulissat - T: 944443, Fax: 944443, E-mail: ilumus@greennet.gl, Internet: http:// www.ilumus.gl
Fine Arts Museum 19718

Maniitsoq

Maniitsup Katersugaasivia, Sukkertoppen Museum, Postboks 145, 3912 Maniitsoq - T: 13100. Head: Thomas Petrussen
Local Museum 19719

Nanortalik

Nanortallip Katersugaasivia (Nanortalik Local Museum), Boks 90, 3922 Nanortalik - T: 613406, Fax: 613706, E-mail: nanortalik.museum@ greennet.gl. Head: Kristine Raahauge
Local Museum 19720

Narsaq

Narsaq Museum, Kikkevej B84, Narsaq, mail addr: Postboks 177, 3921 Narsaq - T: 661659, 572306, Fax: 661744, E-mail: narsaq.museum@greennet.gl, Internet: http://www.museum.gl. Head: Rie Oldenburg
Ethnology Museum / Archaeological Museum - 1985 19721

Nuuk

Nunatta Katersugaasivia Allagaateqarfialu (Greenland National Museum and Archives), Hans Egedesvej 8, 3900 Nuuk, mail addr: Postboks 145, 3900 Nuuk - T: 322611, Fax: 322622, E-mail: grnatmus@greenet.gl, Internet: http:// www.natmus.gl. Head: Emil Rosing
Local Museum - 1965
Prehist and hist of Greenland, greenlandic art - library, archives 19722

Paamiut

Paamiune Katersugausivik, Paamiut Museum, Postboks 99, 3940 Paamiut - T: 17673, Fax: 17854. Head: Søren T. Thuesen
Local Museum - 1981 19723

Qaanaaq

Avanersuup Katersugaasivia, Thule Museum, Postboks 82, 3971 Qaanaaq - T: 971126, Fax: 971126, E-mail: thulemuseum@greennet.gl. Head: Torben Diklev
Local Museum 19724

Qaqortoq

Qaqortup Katersugaasivia, Qaqortoq Museum, Postboks 154, 3920 Qaqortoq - T: 641080, Fax: 642833, E-mail: gn@qaqkom.ki.gl
Local Museum 19725

Qasigiannguit

Qasigiannguit Katersugaasiviat, Christianshåb Lokalmuseum, Poul Egedesvej 24, 3951 Qasigiannguit, mail addr: Postboks 130, 3951 Qasigiannguit - T: 911477, Fax: 911477, E-mail: lm@qaskom.ki.gl, Internet: http:// www.museum.gl/qasigiannguit. Head: Laila Mikaelsen
Local Museum - 1982
Local hist, Saqqaq culture (Stone Age, 4,000 years old) 19726

Qeqertasuaq

Qeqertarsuaq Museum, Postboks 113, 3953 Qeqertasuaq - T: 47153. Head: Johanne Olsen
Local Museum 19727

Sisimiut

Sisimiuni Katersugaasiviat (Sisimiut Museum), Jukkorsuup Aqq 9, 3911 Sisimiut, mail addr: Postboks 308, 3911 Sisimiut - T: 865087, Fax: 864475, E-mail: sismus@greennet.gl, Internet: http://www.museum.gl/sisimiut. Head: Klaus Georg Hansen
Local Museum - 1985
Saqqaq culture, whaling, shipping, fishing industry, industrial work, V.C. Frederiksen coll (early 20th c), colonial history, archaeology 19728

Tasiilaq

Tasiilap Katersugaasivia, Ammassalik Museum, Postboks 112, 3913 Tasiilaq - T: 981311, Fax: 981711, E-mail: tasiilaq.museum@ greennet.gl, Internet: http://www.ammassalik.gl/ mus_eng.html. Head: Ole G. Jensen
Ethnology Museum - 1990
East Greenlandic Inuit art coll 19729

Upernavik

Upernavik Museum, Niuertup Ottup Aqq, Upernavik, mail addr: Postboks 93, 3962 Upernavik - T: 961085, Fax: 961112, E-mail: upernavik.museum@greennet.gl, Internet: http://iserit.greennet.gl/inussuk. Head: Bo Albrechtsen
Local Museum - 1951 19730

Uummannaq

Uummannaq Katersugaasivia (Uummannaq Museum), Alfred Berthelsenip Aqqutaa B9, 3961 Uummannaq - T: 954461, Fax: 952104, E-mail: lulu@uummannaq.gl, Internet: http:// www.uummannaq.gl. Head: Lucia Ludvigsen
Local Museum - 1988 19731

Grenada

Saint George's

Grenada National Museum, Young St, Saint George's - T: (809) 440-3725. Head: Jeanne Fisher
Archaeological Museum / Historical Museum - 1976
Archaeology, history 19732

Guadeloupe

Grand Bourg

Ecomusée de Marie Galante, Musée Schœlcher, Habitation Murat, 97112 Grand Bourg - T: 979441. Head: C. Mombrun
Local Museum / Science&Tech Museum - 1980
Local hist, arts and traditions, hist of sugar cane - library 19733

Le Gosier

Fort Fleur d'Epée, Bas du Fort, 97160 Le Gosier
Military Museum - 1759
Military hist, art gallery 19734

Le Moule

Musée Edgard Clerc, Parc de la Rosette, 97160 Le Moule - T: 235757/43, Fax: 238967
Archaeological Museum 19735

Pointe-à-Pitre

Musée Municipal Saint-John-Perse, 9 Rue de Nozières, 97110 Pointe-à-Pitre - T: 0590900192, Fax: 0590839801, E-mail: musee.st-john-perse@ wanadoo.fr. Head: Sylvie Tersew
Special Museum - 1987
Ethnography, letters, original editions, photographies, postcards, souvenirs, objects, poet Alexis Leger (Nobel prize-winner of literature) 19736

Musée Schœlcher, 24 Rue Peynier, 97110 Pointe-à-Pitre - T: 820804, Fax: 837839
Local Museum 19737

Saint-Barthélemy

Collection Historique → Musée Municipal de Saint-Barthélemy

Musée International du Coquillage, Corrosl, 97133 Saint-Barthélemy - T: 276297
Natural History Museum 19738

Musée Municipal, Wall House, Gustavia, 97133 Saint-Barthélemy - T: 278907
Local Museum 19739

Musée Municipal de Saint-Barthélemy, Gustavia, Wall House, Rue de Piteå, 97133 Saint-Barthélemy - T: 0590297155, Fax: 0590277177, E-mail: mairie.stbarth@wanadoo.fr
Local Museum
Traditions, historical documents and objects, costumes, tools 19740

Saint-Martin

Musée de Saint-Martin, 97150 Saint-Martin - T: 875723
Local Museum 19741

Sainte-Rose

Musée du Rhum, Bellevue, 97115 Sainte-Rose - T: 287004, Fax: 288255, E-mail: museedurhum@ outremer.com. Head: H. Reimonenq
Special Museum 19742

Vieux-Habitants

Musée-Maison du Café, La Grivelière, 97119 Vieux-Habitants - T: 984842
Agriculture Museum 19743

Guam

Adelup

Faninadahen Kosas Guahan, Guam Museum, Ricardo J. Bordallo Govenors' Complex, Adelup, GU 96910 - T: (671) 475-4228, 475-4229, Fax: (671) 475-6727, E-mail: airamire@ns.gov.gu. Head: Antonio Palomo
Local Museum / Folklore Museum - 1932
General museum, in 1776 Garden house 19744

Agana

Guam Museum, 254 Martyr St, Agana, GU 96910 - T: 472-6417, Fax: 477-9777. Head: Christine Schott-Smith
Historical Museum - 1932
Artifacts from 1500 BC, Spanish Colonial period historical artifacts, 17th c to 1899 - library 19745

Asan

War in the Pacific National Historical Park, 115 Marine Dr, Haloda Bldg, Asan, GU 96922 - T: (671) 472-7240, 477-9362, Fax: (671) 472-7241, E-mail: wapa_administration@nps.gov, Internet: http://www.nps.gov/wapa. Head: Karen Gustin
Military Museum - 1982
World War II Military hist 19746

Mangilao

Isla Center for the Arts at the University of Guam, U.O.G. Station, 15 Dean's Circle, Mangilao, GU 96923 - T: 735-2965, Fax: 735-2967, E-mail: isla@ uog9.uog.edu, Internet: http://www.uog.edu/isla/ index.htm. Head: Carrie Brewster
Fine Arts Museum - 1980
Pacific artifacts, prints, paintings, sculpture 19747

Guatemala

Antigua

Museo Colonial, Calle 0. 5 No 5a, Antigua
Historical Museum - 1936
Period furniture, paintings, sculpture 19748

Museo de Santiago de los Caballeros, Palacio Ayuntamiento, Plaza Central, Antigua - T: 8322868, Fax: 8322868, E-mail: museosantiago@ enantigua.net. Head: Maria Antonieta Godoy Muñoz
Local Museum - 1956
History, furniture, armaments, colonial art, Pedro de Alvarado's sword, conqueror of Guatemala 1525, old jail of the poor's, torture and flagellation items 19749

Museo del Libro Antiguo, Portal Municipal, Plaza Mayor, Antigua. Head: Manuel Reyes
Historical Museum - 1956
History of Guatemala 19750

Chichicastenango

Museo Regional, Plaza Central, 14006 Chichicastenango. Head: Raúl Pérez Maldonado
Historical Museum / Folklore Museum - 1950
History, crafts of Maya-Quiché tribes 19751

Guatemala City

Centro de Estudios Conservacionistas, Av La Reforma 0-63, Zona 10, 01010 Guatemala City - T: (02) 310904, Fax: 347664
Natural History Museum - 1981
Woodland natural museum 19752

Museo Nacional de Arqueología y Etnología, Edificio 5, La Aurora, Zona 13, 01013 Guatemala City. Head: Dora Guerra de González
Archaeological Museum / Ethnology Museum - 1948
Mayan and other archeological finds, ethnography 19753

Museo Nacional de Arte Moderno, Edificio 6, La Aurora, Zona 13, 01013 Guatemala City - T: (02) 310403. Head: J. Oscar Barrientos
Fine Arts Museum - 1975
Art, history, furniture, numismatics 19754

Museo Nacional de Historia, Calle 9-70 No 9, Zona 1, 01001 Guatemala City - T: (02) 536149, Fax: 25956. Head: Miguel Alvárez Arévalo
Historical Museum - 1975
Antique photogr, 18th and 19th c paintings and furniture 19755

Museo Nacional de Historia Natural, Calle 7-30 No 6A, Zona 12, 01012 Guatemala City, mail addr: Apdo 987, Guatemala City. Head: Jorge A. Ibarra
Natural History Museum - 1950
Botany, zoology, geology - library 19756

Museo Nacional y Zoológico La Aurora, Blvd Juan Pablo II, La Aurora Zona 13, Guatemala City, mail addr: Apdo 1120, Guatemala City - T: 4750894, Fax: 4715286, E-mail: directorazoo@hotmail.com, Internet: http://www.laurorazoo.centroamenca.com. Head: Rosa María Pérez
Natural History Museum
Botany, zoology 19757

Museo Universitario de San Carlos, 9a Av 9-79, Zona 1, Guatemala City - T: 2327666, 2320721, Fax: 2320721, E-mail: amg@hotmail.com
University Museum / Historical Museum 19758

Guinea

Beyla

Musée Regional de Beyla, Beyla
Local Museum
Ethnology, prehistory, art 19759

Boké

Musée Préfectoral de Boké, BP 01, Boké
Local Museum 19760

Conakry

Musée Botanique, c/o Institut Polytechnique de Conakry, BP 1147, Conakry
Natural History Museum
Botany 19761

Musée Géologique, c/o Institut Polytechnique de Conakry, BP 1147, Conakry
Natural History Museum
Geology 19762

Musée National de Conakry, BP 561, Conakry - T: 445040. Head: Mamadou Sampil
Ethnology Museum - 1960
Prehist, ethnology, art, fetishes, masks of the 'Forêt Sacrée' 19763

Kissidougou

Musée Annexe de Kissidougou, Kissidougou
Ethnology Museum
Prehistory, ethnology, art, masks, fetishes 19764

Koundara

Musée Fédérale Annexe de Koundara, Koundara
Ethnology Museum
Ethnology, ethnography coll of the Coniagui and Bassare tribes 19765

N'Zerekore

Musée de Recherche et de Documentation, BP 114, N'Zerekore. Head: Mara Kanfela
Local Museum
Art, ethnography, botany, zoology, tattoo instruments, pipes carved out of stone 19766

Youkounkoun

Musée Annexe de Youkounkoun, Youkounkoun
Ethnology Museum
Prehistory, ethnology, art, ethnographical coll of the Koundara region 19767

Guinea-Bissau

Bissau

Musée da Guine Portugesa, Praça do Império, Bissau, mail addr: CP 37, Bissau
Ethnology Museum
Ethnographical exhibits 19768

Museu Etnografico Nacional, Complexo Escolar 14 de Novembro, Bissau, mail addr: CP 338, Bissau - T: 215600, Fax: 204400
Ethnology Museum 19769

Guyana

Georgetown

Guyana Museum, Company Path, North St, Georgetown, mail addr: POB 1026, Georgetown - T: (0223) 257191. Head: Clayton Rodney
Local Museum / Natural History Museum / Fine Arts Museum - 1853
Art, history, archaeology, anthropology, zoology, industry - library 19770

Haiti

Port-au-Prince

Centre d'Art, 58 Rue Roy, Port-au-Prince. Head: Francine Murat
Public Gallery - 1944 19771

Musée d'Art Haïtien, Collège Saint-Pierre, Port-au-Prince, mail addr: BP 1540, Port-au-Prince - T: 222510, Fax: 227272. Head: Gerald Alexis
Fine Arts Museum 19772

Musée du Panthéon National Haïtien, Pl des Héros de l'Indépendance, Champ de Mars, Port-au-Prince - T: 2223167, 2218838, 5109458, Fax: 2223167, 2223177, E-mail: mupanah@hainet.net. Head: Lionel Lerebours
Local Museum - 1983
Art, history 19773

Musée du Peuple Haïtien, Cité de l'Exposition, Port-au-Prince
Local Museum 19774

Musée Nader, 18 Rue Bouvrevil, Deprez, Port-au-Prince - T: 2454524, Fax: 2450565. Head: Georges S. Nader
Fine Arts Museum
Contemporary Haitian art, paintings, sculpture 19775

Unité Musée Numismatique, Banque de République d'Haïti, Angle des Rues du Quai et Pavée, Port-au-Prince, mail addr: BP 1570, Port-au-Prince - T: 2991162/67, Fax: 2991338, E-mail: musee@brh.net, Internet: http://www.brh.net
Special Museum
Money of Haiti, medals, notes, manuscripts 19776

Honduras

Ciudad de Copán

Museo Regional de Arqueología Maya, Ciudad de Copán. Head: Prof. Osmin Rivera
Archaeological Museum - 1939
Important relics of Mayan civilization, ceramics, stone sculptures, jade, obsidian, Mayan handicraft, human bones 19777

Comayagua

Museo Arqueológico de Comayagua, 0 Av N., 6a Calle N.E., Frente a Plaza San Franciso, Comayagua CM2100 - T: 7720386, Fax: 7722693, E-mail: pmch@hondutel.hn. Head: Marian Zapata
Archaeological Museum - 1946
Ceramics, jade, sculptures of Lenca's culture 19778

Comayagüela

Museo de Arte Religioso, Apdo 41, Comayagüela
Religious Arts Museum 19779

Omoa

Museo Nacional de Historia Colonial, Castillo de San Fernando de Omoa, Omoa. Head: Ramón Zúñiga Andrade
Historical Museum - 1959
Colonial and historical items, in former prison 19780

San Pedro Sula

Museo Antropologia e Historia Valle de Sula, San Pedro Sula - Internet: http://www.globalnet.hn/museo/museum01.htm
Historical Museum / Ethnology Museum - 1994 19781

Tegucigalpa

Galería Nacional de Arte, Contiguo a la Iglesia La Merced, bajos del Palacio Legislativo, Tegucigalpa - T: 379884
Fine Arts Museum 19782

Museo del Hombre, Banco del País, Tegucigalpa - T: 389198
Museum of Classical Antiquities / Fine Arts Museum 19783

Museo Nacional de Tegucigalpa, Villa Roy, Barrio Buenos Aires, Tegucigalpa 1518 AP - T: 221468. Head: Prof. José Luis N. López
Historical Museum / Archaeological Museum / Fine Arts Museum
Political and natural hist, archaeology, colonial art 19784

Hungary

Abony

Abony Lajos Falumúzeum (Abony Lajos Village Museum), Zalka Máté ú 17, 2740 Abony. Head: Pál Györe
Local Museum - 1959
Local hist, coll of bricks 19785

Aggetelek

Természettudományi Múzeum (Grotto Museum), 3759 Aggetelek
Natural History Museum - 1985
Within the biggest carst landscape of Hungary 19786

Aszód

Petőfi Múzeum, Szontágh Lépcső 2, 2170 Aszód - T: (028) 400014, Fax: 400014, E-mail: apm@axelero.hu. Head: Isrván Asztalos
Historical Museum - 1958
Literature, archaeology, ethnography, hist (local art), poet Sándor Petőfi - library 19787

Baja

Nagy István Képtár, Arany Jànos ú 1, 6500 Baja - T: (079) 325649
Fine Arts Museum 19788

Türr István Múzeum, Deák Ferenc ú 1, 6500 Baja, mail addr: POB 55, 6501 Baja - T: (079) 324173, Fax: 324173. Head: Zsuzsa Merk
Local Museum - 1937
Archeology, ethnography, modern Hungarian painting, local historical coll - library, archives 19789

Balassagyarmat

Palóc Múzeum (Museum of Nógrád County), Palóc Liget 1, 2660 Balassagyarmat, mail addr: POB 15, 2661 Balassagyarmat - T: (035) 300168. Head: Dr. Márta Kapros
Ethnology Museum / Open Air Museum - 1891
Local folk art, shepherd's art, costumes, religious folk art, folk musical instruments - library 19790

Balatonfüred

Jókai Mór Emlékmúzeum, Mór Jókai Memorial Museum, Honvéd ú 1, 8230 Balatonfüred - T: (086) 43426
Special Museum
Bequest of the writer Mór Jókai in his former summer residence 19791

Balatonszárszó

József Attila Emlékmúzeum, Attila József Memorial Museum, József Attila ú 7, 8624 Balatonszárszó
Special Museum - 1957
Life and work of the poet Attila József in his last home, manuscripts, books, works by modern painters 19792

Balatonszemes

Postamúzeum (Postmuseum), Bajcsy-Zsilinszky ú 46, 8636 Balatonszemes - T: (084) 45160
Special Museum - 1962
Research and documentation institute and permanent exhibition of the history of post and telecommunications - library 19793

Balatonszentgyörgy

Népmüvészeti Tájház (Folk Art Museum), Csillagvár ú 6, 8710 Balatonszentgyörgy
Folklore Museum 19794

Balmazujváros

Semsey Andor Múzeum, Debreceni ú 1, 4060 Balmazujváros - T: (052) 580640, E-mail: S.A.Mu@mail.datanet.hu, Internet: http://www.wywaras.hu. Head: József Pozsonyi
Local Museum - 1972
Local history, memorial exhibition on life and work of the Semsey family and of Péter Veres, famous Hungarian peasant writer - library 19795

Barcs

Dráva Múzeum, Széchenyi ú 22, 7570 Barcs - T: (082) 463207, Fax: 463207, E-mail: musdrava@c3.hu, Internet: http://www.c3.hu/~musdrava. Head: Zoltán Orzsi
Local Museum - 1979
Archaeology, ethnography, natural sciences, art hist 19796

Békés

Jantyik Mátyás Múzeum, Széchenyi tér 6, 5630 Békés - T: 341437. Head: B. Szücs-Irén
Local Museum - 1938
History, ethnography - library 19797

Békéscsaba

Gabonamúzeum (Cereal Museum), Gyulai u 65, 5600 Békéscsaba - T: (066) 441026, Fax: 323377. Head: Dr. Imre Szatmári
Agriculture Museum
Farm from Békéscsaba and wind mill from Csókás 19798

Munkácsy Mihály Múzeum, Széchenyi u 9, 5600 Békéscsaba, mail addr: POB 46, 5601 Békéscsaba - T: (066) 323377, Fax: 323377, E-mail: munkacsy_muzeum@bmmi.hu. Head: Dr. Imre Szatmári
Open Air Museum / Local Museum - 1899
Archaeology, regional ethnography, natural science, works by the painter Mihály Munkácsy, modern Hungarian paintings and graphics, Slovakian ethnographic coll, regional hist - library 19799

Szlovák Tájház (Slovakian Museum of Local History), 5600 Békéscsaba
Folklore Museum
History of the Slovakian people in Békés who were settled in 1718 after the Turkish Invasion, pieces of furniture, folk costumes, tools 19800

Berettyóujfalu

Bihari Múzeum, Kálvin tér 1, 4100 Berettyóujfalu - T: (054) 402390, 400938, E-mail: bihari.m1@axelero.hu. Head: Kállai Irén
Local Museum - 1974
Hist, ethnography, literature, archaeology, fine arts - library 19801

Budapest

Ady Endre Emlékmúzeum, Endre Ady Memorial Museum, Veres Pálné ú 4-6, 1053 Budapest - T: (01) 1378563
Special Museum - 1977
Life and work of the poet Endre Ady in his last home, manuscripts, books, pieces of furniture 19802

Aquincumi Múzeum, Budapesti Történeti Múzeum, Szentendrei u 139, 1031 Budapest - T: (01) 2404248, Fax: 4301083, E-mail: h74582szu@ella.hu, Internet: http://origo.hnm.hu/aquincum. Head: Dr. Paula Zsidi
Archaeological Museum - 1894
Finds from Roman Budapest (Aquincum and sourroundind area), stone, glass, mosaics, wallpainting, ceramics, jewellery, coins, epigraphic, hydra or water organ, enviroment - archives, Hercules-Villa, Thermae maiores (Roman baths) 19803

Arany Sas Patika, Pharmacy Museum, Tárnok ú 18, 1014 Budapest - T: (01) 1759772, Fax: 3753936, E-mail: s.museum@axelero.hu. Head: Dr. Károly Kapronczay
Historical Museum - 1966
Pharmacy building from the 18th c with original furnishings 19804

Attila József Memorial Room, Gát u 3, Budapest - T: (01) 2180183
Local Museum 19805

Bajor Gizi Emlékmúzeum, Szinháztörténeti Múzeum (Gizi Bajor Memorial and Theatre Museum), Stromfeld Aurél u 16, 1124 Budapest - T: (01) 1564294
Performing Arts Museum - 1952
Bequest of famous Hungarian actors, memorabilia, costumes, documents, posters 19806

Banknote and Coin Collection of the National Bank of Hungary, Szabadság tér 8-9, Budapest - T: (01) 3023000 ext 1352/2905, Fax: 3023000 ext 1362, E-mail: garamie@mnb.hu, Internet: http://www.mnb.hu. Head: Ákos Radó
Special Museum 19807

Bartók Béla Emlékház (Béla Bartók Memorial Museum), Csalán ú 29, 1025 Budapest - T: (01) 3942100, Fax: 3944472. Head: Zsuzsa Nyujtó
Music Museum - 1981
Life and work of the Hungarian composer Béla Bartók 19808

Bélyegmúzeum (Stamp Museum), Hársfa ú 47, 1074 Budapest, mail addr: POB 86, 1400 Budapest - T: (01) 3415526, Fax: 3423757. Head: Rosalia Solymosi
Special Museum - 1930
Hungarian and foreign postage stamps, Hungarian stamp designs, printing materials for Hungarian stamps, First Day Covers, pre-stamp mail, 69 special collections on different fields and topics of Hungarian philately - library 19809

Budapesti Történeti Múzeum, Vármúzeum (Budapest History Museum), Szent György tér 2, 1014 Budapest - T: (01) 2257809, Fax: 2257818, E-mail: btm@mail.btm.hu, Internet: http://www.btm.hu. Head: Dr. Sándor Bodó
Historical Museum - 1887
Gothic sculptures, remains of the medieval Royal Palace - library of medieval archaeology 19810

Budavári Mátyás Templom Egyházmüvészeti Gyüjteménye (Matthias Church of Buda Castle Ecclesiastical Art Collection), Szentháromság tér 2, 1014 Budapest - T: (01) 4890717, Fax: 4890717, E-mail: mateffyb@freemail.hu, Internet: http://www.matyas-templom.hu. Head: Dr. Balázs Mátéffy
Religious Arts Museum - 1964
Applied art, documents, religious art and symbolism hist of the Holy Crown of Hungury 19811

Dunamelléki Református Egyházkerület Biblia Muzeuma (Bible Museum of the Danubian District of the Hungarian Reformed Church), Ráday ú 28, 1092 Budapest - T: (01) 2176321, Fax: 2176321. Head: Pál Németh
Religious Arts Museum - 1988
Bibles, religious art - library 19812

Ernst Múzeum, Nagymező ú 8, 1065 Budapest - T: (01) 3414355, Fax: 3414355, E-mail: ernst@ernstmuzeum.hu. Head: Dr. Keserü Katalin
Public Gallery 19813

Evangélikus Országos Múzeum (Lutheran Church Museum), Deák F. tér 4, 1052 Budapest - T: (01) 3174173, Fax: 2350207. Head: Dr. Tibor Fabiny
Religious Arts Museum - 1973
Lutheranism in Hungarian culture 19814

Fővárosi Képtár (Municipal Picture Gallery), Kiscelli ú 108, 1037 Budapest - T: (01) 3888560, Fax: 3687917. Head: Péter Fitz
Fine Arts Museum
19th and 20th c fine arts 19815

Goethe Institut, Andrassy út 24, 1061 Budapest - T: (01) 3744070, Fax: (01) 3744080
Public Gallery 19816

Hadtörténeti Múzeum (Museum of War History), Tóth Árpád Sétány 40, 1014 Budapest, mail addr: POB 7, 1250 Budapest - T: (01) 3569522, Fax: 3561575. Head: Dr. József Lugosi
Military Museum - 1918
Hungary military hist, arms, documents, models, flags, uniforms, medals, weapons, military technic, arts, personal objects, photos - library, educational department 19817

Hopp Ferenc Kelet-Ázsiai Müvészeti Múzeum, Iparművészeti Múzeum (Ferenc Hopp Museum of Eastern Asiatic Arts), Andrássy ú 103, 1062 Budapest, mail addr: POB 3, 1450 Budapest - T: (01) 1228476, Fax: 1175838. Head: Dr. Mária Ferenczy
Decorative Arts Museum - 1919
East Asian coll of Ferenc Hopp - library 19818

Húsipari Múzeum (Museum of Meat Industry), Gubacsi ú 6b, 1097 Budapest - T: (01) 2157350, Fax: 2150626. Head: Dr. Kálmán Incze
Special Museum - 1974
Hist of the meat industry - library 19819

Iparművészeti Múzeum (Museum of Applied Arts), Üllőei ú 33-37, 1091 Budapest, mail addr: POB 3, 1450 Budapest - T: (01) 2175222, Fax: 2175838. Head: Dr. Zsuzsa Lovag
Decorative Arts Museum - 1872
Decorative arts and crafts, applied arts, ivory works, bookbinding, furnishings, textiles, metalworks, ceramics, jewelry - library, educational department 19820

Jókai Memorial Room, Koltoë u 21, Budapest - T: (01) 1173611
Special Museum 19821

Kassák Museum, Foë tér 1, Zichy-kastély, 1033 Budapest - T: (01) 3687021, Fax: 3687021. Head: Dr. Ferenc Csaplar
Fine Arts Museum - 1976
Live and work, memorabilia of the avant-garde artist, writer and painter Lajos Kassák (1887-1967), exhibition in the Zichy castle, paintings, graphics, photos - library 19822

Kiscelli Múzeum, Kiscelli ú 108, 1037 Budapest - T: (01) 3888560, Fax: 3687917. Head: Dr. Annamária Vígh
Local Museum - 1887
Local contemporary hist, fine art, crafts, industry, technique 19823

Kodály Zoltán Emlékmúzeum (Zoltán Kodály Memorial Museum), Kodály Körönd 1, 1062 Budapest - T: (01) 3428448, Fax: 3229647, E-mail: kodalyzm@axelero.hu, Internet: http://www.iks.hu/museum.htm. Head: Márta Vandulek
Music Museum - 1990
House of the composer,folksong collector and music educator Zoltán Kodály - Zoltán Kodály Archives 19824

Közlekedési Múzeum (Transport Museum), Városligeti krt 11, 1146 Budapest - T: (01) 3430565, Fax: 3440322, E-mail: km@ella.hu, Internet: http://www.km.iif.hu. Head: Dr. András Katona
Science&Tech Museum - 1896
Railway transportation, models, old vehicles, nautical and aeronautical transportation, roads and bridge construction, city transport, cars, and carriages - library, archives, coach museum, railway museum, underground museum, museum ship 19825

Kortárs Művészeti Múzeum - Ludwig Múzeum Budapest (Ludwig Museum Budapest - Museum of Contemporary Art), Royal Palace, Building A, Budapest, mail addr: POB 23, 1250 Budapest - T: (01) 3759175, 3560657, 3757848, Fax: 2122534, 3757048, E-mail: info@ludwigmuseum.hu, Internet: http://www.ludwigmuseum.hu. Head: Katalin Néray
Fine Arts Museum 19826

Liszt Ferenc Emlékmúzeum és Kutatóközpont (Liszt Ferenc Memorial Museum and Research Centre), Vörösmarty u 35, 1064 Budapest - T: (01) 4131526, Fax: 3427320, E-mail: eckhardt@lib.liszt.hu, Internet: http://www.lisztmuseum.hu. Head: Mária Eckhardt
Music Museum - 1986
Liszt's furniture, instruments, library and music library and personal things - chamber concert hall, research library 19827

Magyar Elektrotechnikai Múzeum (Hungarian Museum of Electrical Engineering), Kazinczy ú 21, 1075 Budapest - T: (01) 3220472, Fax: 3425750, E-mail: info@emuzeum.hu. Head: Dr. Sándor Jeszenszky
Science&Tech Museum - 1975
Hist of electrical engineering, electrical machines and equipment - library 19828

Magyar Építészeti Múzeum (Hungarian Museum of Architecture), Mókus u 20, 1036 Budapest - T: (01) 3886170/3672686, Fax: 3886170. Head: László Pusztai
Fine Arts Museum - 1968
Hist of the Hungarian architecture, bequest of famous Hungarian architects - library, photogr archive 19829

Magyar Képzömüvészek Ésiparmüvészek Szövetsége, Vörösmarty tér 1, 1051 Budapest, mail addr: POB 51, 1364 Budapest - T: (01) 1184074, 1186765, Fax: 1186765
Association with Coll 19830

Magyar Kereskedelmi és Vendéglátóipari Múzeum (Hungarian Museum of Commerce and Catering Trade), Fortuna ú 4, 1014 Budapest - T: (01) 3756249, Fax: 3756249, E-mail: mkvn@freestart.hu, Internet: http://www.topflopp.hu/muzeum. Head: Dr. Balázs Draveczky
Special Museum - 1966
Sales and services, particulary in tourism, hotels and hostelry, cuisine, coffee houses, confectionary, documents, photos, development from the Csárda to today's restaurants, advertisment, furniture of shops and stores - library, archives, data bank 19831

Magyar Mezőgazdasági Múzeum (Museum of Hungarian Agriculture), Városliget, Vajdahunyadvár, 1146 Budapest, mail addr: POB 129, 1367 Budapest - T: (01) 3631117, Fax: 3640076, E-mail: mmm@axelero.hu, Internet: http://www.dr-web.hu/mezogazdasagi. Head: Dr. György Fehér
Agriculture Museum - 1896
Hist of agriculture in Hungary, documents, objects, models, hunting, forestry - library 19832

Magyar Mezőgazdasági Múzeum (Museum of Hungarian Agriculture), Széchenyi-Sziget, Budapest, mail addr: POB 129, 1367 Budapest - T: (01) 3640071, Fax: 3640076, E-mail: mmm@axelero.hu, Internet: http://www.dr-web.hu/mezogazdasagi. Head: Dr. György Fehér
Agriculture Museum
Viticulture, oenology, forestry, stockbreeding, hunting, fishing, horticulture, archives 19833

Magyar Nemzeti Galéria (Hungarian National Gallery), Budavári Palota, Budapest, mail addr: POB 31, 1250 Budapest - T: (01) 3757533, Fax: 3758898, E-mail: mng@mng.hu, Internet: http://www.mng.hu. Head: Dr. Lóránd Bereczky
Fine Arts Museum - 1957
Hungarian paintings, sculptures, medals, drawings, engravings, panel paintings, (11th-20th c) - library, archives 19834

Magyar Nemzeti Múzeum (Hungarian National Museum), Múzeum krt 14-16, 1088 Budapest, mail addr: PF 364, 1370 Budapest - T: (01) 3382122, Fax: 3177806, E-mail: info@hnm.hu, Internet: http://www.hnm.hu. Head: Dr. Tibor Kovács
Historical Museum / Archaeological Museum - 1802
Archaeology, Roman finds, medieval, modern and contemporary hist, costumes, numismatics, arms, historical pictures and photos - library 19835

Magyar Nemzeti Múzeum Legújabbkori Történeti Múzeuma (Museum of Contemporary History), Budavári Palota, Budapest, mail addr: POB 23, 1250 Budapest - T: (01) 1757533, Fax: 1560657. Head: Dr. Ferenc Szikossy
Historical Museum - 1948
Hist of Hungary since the 1880s - historical photo archives, library 19836

Magyar Természettudományi Múzeum (Hungarian Natural History Museum), Baross ú 13, 1088 Budapest, mail addr: POB 137, 1431 Budapest - T: (01) 2677100, Fax: 3171669, E-mail: meszaros@zoo.zoo.nhmus.hu, Internet: http://www.nhmus.hu. Head: Dr. István Matskási
Natural History Museum - 1802
Mineralogy, petrography, geology, paleontology, botany, zoology, mammals, fossils, anthropology - library, educational department 19837

Millenniumi Földalatti Vasúti Múzeum, Budapesti Közlekedési Részvénytársaság (Millenium Underground Museum), Deák Téri Aluljáró, 1052 Budapest - T: (01) 3433216. Head: Dr. András Katona
Science&Tech Museum - 1975
Urban transport coll, underground building 19838

Molnár C. Pál Gyüjtemény, Ménesi ú 65, 1118 Budapest - T: (01) 3853637, Fax: 2090179. Head: Péter Csillag
Fine Arts Museum 19839

Műcsarnok (Hall of Art), Dózsa György ú 37, 1146 Budapest - T: (01) 3437401, Fax: 3435205, E-mail: info@mucsarnok.hu, Internet: http://www.mucsarnok.hu. Head: Dr. Júlia Fabényi
Fine Arts Museum - 1896
Temporary exhibition of Hungarian and foreign art 19840

Nagytétényi Kastélymúzeum, Iparművészeti Múzeum (Castle Museum of Nagytétény), Kastélypark u 9-11, 1225 Budapest - T: (01) 2070005, Fax: 2074680, Internet: http://www.museum.hu/nagytetenyikastelymuzeum. Head: Elvira Király
Decorative Arts Museum - 1948
14th-19th c European furniture, 14th-19th c Hungarian furniture 19841

Néprajzi Múzeum (Museum of Ethnography), Kossuth Lajos tér 12, 1055 Budapest - T: (01) 4732400, 4732411, Fax: 4732401, E-mail: info@ethno.hu, Internet: http://www.ethno.hu. Head: Dr. Zoltán Fejös
Ethnology Museum - 1872
Ethnography, peasant and tribal cultures, costumes, textiles, musical instruments, crafts - library, archives 19842

Obudai Helytörténeti Gyüjtemény (Obuda Local Museum), Foë tér 1, 1033 Budapest - T: (01) 803340. Head: Eva Janek
Local Museum - 1973
Local history, ethnography, history of the labour movement, toys 19843

Óbudai Pincegaléria, Fö ter 1, 1033 Budapest - T: (01) 2500288, Fax: 3878376, E-mail: gandrasi@c3.hu
Public Gallery 19844

Óbudai Társaskör Galéria, Kiskorona u 7, 1036 Budapest - T: (01) 2500288, Fax: 3878376, E-mail: gandrasi@c3.hu
Public Gallery 19845

Öntödei Múzeum (Foundry Museum), Bem József ú 20, 1027 Budapest - T: (01) 2014370, Fax: 2014370. Head: Katalin Lengyel-Kiss
Science&Tech Museum - 1969
19th c original foundry equipment, history of technological development of foundry trade, old mouldings Life of Á. Ganz and of A. Mechwar - library, archives 19846

Országos Geológia Múzeum, Stafánia ú 14, Budapest - T: (01) 2671427
Natural History Museum 19847

Országos Műszaki Múzeum (National Museum of Science and Technology), Kaposvár ú 13-15, 1117 Budapest - T: (01) 2044095, Fax: 2044088, E-mail: vam13378@helka.iif.hu. Head: Dr. Éva Vámos
Natural History Museum / Science&Tech Museum - 1973
Natural sciences and technology, historic exhibits from the early days of industry and its development to the present 19848

Országos Pedagógiai Múzeum és Könyvtár (Natioal Museum of Education and Library), Honvéd ú 15, 1055 Budapest - T: (01) 3020600/1379, Fax: 3126862, E-mail: h7243bal@ella.hu, Internet: http://www.opkm.iif.hu. Head: Mihály Balogh
Special Museum
Hist of pedagogy and education, documents, manuscripts, social sciences - library 19849

Országos Színháztörténeti Múzeum és Intézet (Hungarian Theatre Museum and Institute), Krisztina krt 57, 1013 Budapest - T: (01) 3751184, Fax: 3751184, E-mail: oszmi@ella.hu, Internet: http://www.oszmi.hu. Head: Dr. Peter Müller
Performing Arts Museum - 1952
Hist of Hungarian theatre and stage, scenery, costumes, videos, photos, manuscripts, sound record archive, puppet collection, dance archive, dep of contemporary theatre - library, archive 19850

Országos Zsidó Vallási és Történeti Gyüjtemény (Museum of Jewish Religion and History), Dohány ú 2, 1075 Budapest - T: (01) 3428949, E-mail: bpjewmus@visio.c3.hu. Head: Róbert B. Turán
Religious Arts Museum / Historical Museum - 1916
Jewish art, applied art, documents 19851

Pesterzsébeti Múzeum, Baross ú 53, 1203 Budapest - T: (01) 278502. Head: Enil Bogyirka
Local Museum - 1951
Local history - library 19852

Petoëfi Irodalmi Múzeum (Petőfi Museum of Hungarian Literature), Károlyi Mihály 16, 1053 Budapest - T: (01) 3173611, Fax: 3171722, E-mail: muzeum@pim.hu, Internet: http://www.pim.hu. Head: Dr. Rita Ratzky
Historical Museum - 1957
Hungarian literary history, paintings, portraits, manuscripts, photos - library, educational department, archive 19853

Postamúzeum (Postal Museum), Andrássy ú 3, 1061 Budapest - T: (01) 2681997, Fax: 2681958, E-mail: muzeum1@mail.matav.hu, Internet: http://www.ceg.matav.hu, http://www.muzeum.matav.hu. Head: Irén Kovács
Special Museum - 1896
History of post and telecommunication - library 19854

Ráth György Museum, Iparművészeti Múzeum, Városligeti fasor 12, 1068 Budapest, mail addr: POB 3, 1450 Budapest - T: (01) 3423916. Head: Gyula Rózsa
Decorative Arts Museum - 1906
Chinese and Japanese art 19855

Római Katonai Fürdö (Thermae Maiores), Flórián tér 4-6, 1033 Budapest
Archaeological Museum 19856

Semmelweis Orvostörténeti Múzeum (Semmelweis Museum of the History of Medicine), Apród ú 1-3, 1013 Budapest - T: (01) 3753533/2011577, Fax: 3753936, E-mail: s.museum@matarnet.hu. Head: Dr. Károly Kapronczay
Special Museum - 1965
Hist of medicine, pharmacology, birth place of the physician Semmelweis; anatomical wax models, 19857

Szépművészeti Múzeum (Museum of Fine Arts), Dózsa György út 41, 1146 Budapest, mail addr: POB 463, 1396 Budapest - T: (01) 3637655, 3637856, Fax: 3636398, E-mail: info@szepmuveszeti.hu, Internet: http://www.szepmuveszeti.hu. Head: Miklós Mojzer
Fine Arts Museum / Museum of Classical Antiquities / Archaeological Museum - 1896
Egyptian and Greco-Roman antiquities, foreign old masters, sculptures, drawings, engravings, modern art - library 19858

Szoborpark (Statue Park), Corner of Balatoni ú and Szabadkai ú, Budapest - T: (01) 4247500, Fax: 3375050, E-mail: office@szoborpark.hu, Internet: http://www.szoborpark.hu. Head: Akos Rethly
Fine Arts Museum
Statues of the leaders of the communist era, of Soviet Soldier, the Republic of Councils and others 19859

Testnevelési és Sportmúzeum (Museum of Physical Education and Sports), Dózsa György ú 13, 1143 Budapest - T: (01) 2521696, Fax: 2521696. Head: Lajos Szabó
Special Museum - 1955
Relics of sports and physical education - library, archives 19860

Textilmúzeum (Museum of Textile Industry), Lajos u 138, 1036 Budapest - T: (01) 3675910, Fax: 3675910. Head: Magdolna Bálint
Science&Tech Museum - 1972
Hist of the textile industry in Hungary and Middle-Europe, textile machinery 19861

Tüzoltó Múzeum (Fire Brigade Museum), Martinovics tér 12, 1105 Budapest - T: (01) 1572190. Head: Dr. Lászlóne Váry
Science&Tech Museum - 1955
Fire-fighting equipment, pumps and hoses, universal and Hungarian hist of fire protection, its means and organization - library 19862

Városi Tömegközlekedési Múzeum, Budapesti Közlekedési Részvénytársaság (Urban Public Transport Museum), Deák Téri Aluljáró, 1052 Budapest - T: (01) 3433216. Head: Dr. András Katona
Science&Tech Museum - 1975
Urban transport coll, underground building 19863

Vasarely Múzeum, Szépművészeti Múzeum, Szentélek tér 1, 1033 Budapest - T: (01) 1887551. Head: Maria Egri
Fine Arts Museum 19864

Zenetörténeti Múzeum (Museum of Music History), Táncsics u 7, 1014 Budapest - T: (01) 2146770, Fax: 2146670253, E-mail: zoltanf@zti.hu, Internet: http://www.zti.hu. Head: Dr. Zoltán Falvy
Music Museum - 1969
Music, musical instruments, life and work of Hungarian musicians, bequest of Béla Bartók 19865

Bugac

Pásztormúzeum (Shepherd's Museum), 6114 Bugac
Special Museum
Tools, clothing (shepherd's coats), musical instruments and the decorated wooden sticks of the shepherds 19866

Buzsák

Tájház (Local History Museum), Táncsics tér 6, 8695 Buzsák
Local Museum
Regional arts and crafts, embroidery 19867

Cegléd

Kossuth Múzeum, Múzeum ú 5, 2701 Cegléd, mail addr: POB 32, 2701 Cegléd - T: (053) 310637. Head: Dr. Gyula Kocsis
Local Museum - 1917
Ethnography, archaeology, art, memorabilia on the revolutionary leader Lajos Kossuth - library 19868

Csákvár

Vértes Múzeum, Kossuth Lajos ú, 8083 Csákvár
Local Museum
Regional history, local arts, earthenware, finds from the Iron and Stone Age 19869

Csongrád

Csongrádi Múzeum, Tari László Múzeum, Iskola ú 2, 6640 Csongrád - T: (063) 481052, Fax: 48111052. Head: Dr. Judit Szücs
Local Museum - 1956
Local archaeology, local history, navigational artefacts, ethnography 19870

Debrecen

Déri Múzeum, Déri tér 1, 4026 Debrecen, mail addr: POB 61, 4001 Debrecen - T: (052) 417560/561, Fax: 417560, E-mail: deri@derimuz.hu, Internet: http://www.derimuz.hu/DeriMuzeu. Head: Dr. László Selmeczi
Local Museum - 1902
Ethnography, archaeology, local hist, Hungarian art, oriental art, decorative arts, local natural hist, hist of weapons and literature - library, archive 19871

Medgyessy Múzeum, Peterfia ú 28, 4026 Debrecen
Fine Arts Museum
Documentary of the work of the artist: bronze sculptures, maps 19872

Református Kollégiumi és Egyházművészeti Múzeum (Museum of the Reformed College and Ecclesiastical Art), Kálvin tér 16, 4026 Debrecen - T: (052) 414744, Fax: 414744, E-mail: theca@silver.drk.hu. Head: Dr. Botond Gáborjáni Szabó
Historical Museum / Religious Arts Museum - 1963
Memorabilia on the college that was founded in 1538 and on former famous students (Mihály Csokonai Vitéz, Sándor Petoëfi, János Arany etc), religious art, applied art, documents of the Reformed Church in Hungary and history of education 19873

Decs

Sárközi Népművészeti Tájház (Local History Museum of Sárkös), Kossuth ú 34, 7144 Decs
Local Museum
Folk art: costumes, embroidery, weaving 19874

Dunaföldvár

Vármúzeum (Burgmuseum), Rátkai köz 2, 7020 Dunaföldvár - T: 178
Historical Museum
Relics of medieval Dunaföldvár castle 19875

Dunaújváros

Intercisa Múzeum, Városháza tér 4, 2401 Dunaújváros, mail addr: POB 149, 2400 Dunaújváros - T: (025) 408970, Fax: 411315. Head: Dr. Márta Matuss
Local Museum - 1951
Prehistoric, Roman and medieval archaeology, local hist, lapidarium, ethnography - library 19876

Eger

Dobó István Vármuzeum (István Dobó Castle Museum), Vár ú 1, 3300 Eger, mail addr: POB 10, 3301 Eger - T: (036) 312744, Fax: 312450, E-mail: varmuzeum@div.iif.hu, Internet: http://www.div.iif.hu. Head: Dr. Tivadar Petercsák
Local Museum - 1872
Archaeology, hist of Eger Castle, ethnography, relics of the Turkish invasion in Hungary, Baroque art, memorabilia, life and work of the writer Géza Gárdonyi (1863-1922) - library, educational department 19877

Gárdonyi Géza Emlékmúzeum (Géza Gárdonyi Memorial Museum), Gárdonyi ú 28, 3300 Eger - T: (036) 312744, Fax: 312450
Special Museum
Memorabilia on the writer 19878

Érd

Magyar Földrajzi Gyüjtemény (Geographical Collection of Hungary), Budai ú 4, 2030 Érd - T: (023) 363036, Fax: 363036, E-mail: foldrajzi.muzeum@matarnet.hu. Head: Dr. János Kubassek
Historical Museum - 1983
Memorabilia, documents and trophies of Hungarian travellers 19879

Esztergom

Balassa Bálint Múzeum, Mindszenty tér 5, 2500 Esztergom, mail addr: POB 19, 2500 Esztergom - T: (33) 412185, Fax: 412185. Head: Dr. István Horváth
Local Museum - 1894
Archeology, numismatics, applied art, history - library 19880

Főszékesegyházi Kincstár és Könyvtár (Cathedral Treasure Chamber), Szt. István tér 1, 2500 Esztergom - T: (033) 311895
Religious Arts Museum
Coll of textiles and goldworks started in the 11th c - Main Cathedral Library 19881

Keresztény Múzeum (Christian Museum), Mindszenty tér 2, 2500 Esztergom, mail addr: POB 25, 2501 Esztergom - T: (033) 413880, Fax: 413880, E-mail: info@keresztenymuzeum.hu, Internet: http://www.keresztenymuzeum.hu. Head: Pál Cséfalvay
Religious Arts Museum - 1875
Hungarian, Italian and Austrian paintings, tapestries, sculptures - library 19882

Magyar Környezetvédelmi és Vízügyi Múzeum (Hungarian Environmental and Water Management Museum), Kölcsey F. ú 2, 2500 Esztergom - T: (033) 500250, Fax: 500251, E-mail: dunamuz@freemail.hu, Internet: http://www.dunamuzeum.org.hu. Head: Imre Kaján
Science&Tech Museum - 1973
Hist of water conservation with stress on the Danube - library 19883

Vármúzeum, Magyar Nemzeti Múzeum (Castle Museum), Szent István tér 1, 2500 Esztergom, mail addr: PF 364, 1370 Budapest - T: (033) 415986, Fax: 400103, E-mail: rmegom@holop.hu3, Internet: http://www.holop.hu. Head: Dr. Béla Horváth
Historical Museum / Archaeological Museum - 1967
Excavated and reconstructed royal palace from the times of the Hungarian House of the Arpáds, municipal history of Esztergom, a royal seat in the Middle Ages - library 19884

Fertőd

Kastélymúzeum (Castle Museum), Esterházy Kastély, Bartók Béla ú 2, 9431 Fertőd - T: (099) 370971, Fax: 370120. Head: Jolán Bak
Historical Museum - 1959
Historical castle of the Eszterházy family, local documents, furnishings, applied art, memorabilia on Joseph Haydn 19885

Gödöllő

Town Museum, Szabadság tér 5, 2000 Gödöllő - T: (028) 410163
Local Museum 19886

Gyöngyös

Mátra Múzeum, Kossuth ú 40, 3200 Gyöngyös - T: (0637) 311447, Fax: 311447, E-mail: mmuseum@monornet.hu, Internet: http://www.extra.hu/matra_muzeum. Head: Dr. Levente Füköh
Natural History Museum / Ethnology Museum - 1951
Natural science, botany and zoology of the Mátra Mountains, ethnography, hist of hunting, paleontology, entomology, malacology - library 19887

Gyomaendrőd

Kner Nyomdaipari Múzeum (Kner Printing Industry Museum), Kossuth ú 16, 5500 Gyomaendrőd - T: (066) 386172, Fax: 386744, E-mail: knergyoma@bekes.hungary.net, Internet: http://www.lang.hu/gykner.nyomda. Head: Julianna Hudák
Science&Tech Museum - 1970
History of printing, printing press of the Kner family, graphics, prints, furniture - library, archives 19888

Győr

Borsos Miklós Gyűjtemény (Miklós Borsos Collection), Apor Vilmos tér 2, 9022 Győr, mail addr: POB 93, 9002 Győr
Fine Arts Museum - 1979
Works by the Hungarian sculptor Miklós Borsos 19889

Györ Egyházmegyei Könyvtár es Kincstár (Győr Diocese Library and Treasure Chamber), Kaptalandomb 26, 9022 Győr
Religious Arts Museum
Sacral objects, chasuble of King Matthew, jewellery of the Zichy family, medieval and Baroque goldworks 19890

Kovács Margit Múzeum, Apáca ú 1, 9022 Győr, mail addr: POB 93, 9002 Győr
Decorative Arts Museum - 1982
Pottery coll by Kovács 19891

Patikamúzeum (Pharmacy Museum), Széchenyi tér 9, 9022 Győr - T: (096) 320954. Head: Z. Haffner
Historical Museum - 1972
17th c pharmacy (Baroque style, dating from 1667) 19892

Xantus János Múzeum, Széchenyi tér 5, 9002 Győr, mail addr: POB 93, 9022 Győr - T: (096) 310588, Fax: 310731, E-mail: xantus@gymsmuzeum.hu, Internet: http://www.gymsmuzeum.hu. Head: Dr. Eszter Szoényi
Local Museum - 1854
Relics of the ancient town Arrabona, art, archeology, ethnography, numismatics, hist of industry, modern art coll from Györ Arts Museum - library 19893

Gyula

Erkel Ferenc Múzeum, Kossuth Lajos ú 15, 5700 Gyula - T: (066) 361236, Fax: 361236. Head: Péter Havassy
Archaeological Museum / Ethnology Museum / Local Museum / Music Museum - 1868
Archaeology, ethnography, local history, art memorial site for the Hungarian composer (national anthem) Ferenc Erkel - library 19894

Kohán Múzeum, Béke Sugárút 35, 5701 Gyula - T: (066) 361795
Fine Arts Museum - 1978
Memorabilia, life and work of the painter György Kohán 19895

Hajdúböszörmény

Hajdusági Múzeum (Regional Museum), Kossuth ú 1, 4220 Hajdúböszörmény - T: (052) 371038, Fax: 371038. Head: Dr. Miklós Nyakas
Local Museum - 1924
Archaeology, ethnography, local hist, art, primitive paintings - library 19896

Hajduszoboszló

Bocskai István Múzeum, Vöröshadsereg ú 2, 4200 Hajduszoboszló - T: (052) 60311
Local Museum - 1960
Local history, ethnography, numismatics - library 19897

Herend

Herendi Porcelánművészeti, Múzeum Alapitvány (Porcelain Museum), Kossuth ú 140, 8440 Herend - T: (088) 523197, Fax: 523247, E-mail: muzeum@herend.com, Internet: http.//www.museum.herend.com. Head: László Szathmáry
Decorative Arts Museum - 1964
Exhibits from the famous china manufactory, est. 1826, hist of the industry, applied art - library 19898

Hódmezövásárhely

Alfoëldi Galéria, Tornyai János Múzeum, Kossuth tér 8, 6800 Hódmezövásárhely - T: (062) 342277. Head: Imre Nagy
Fine Arts Museum - 1985
Hungarian realistic art from the second half of the 18th c until 1945, paintings by János Tornyai, Menyhért Tóth and Béla Endre 19899

Tornyai János Múzeum, Szántó Kovács János ú 16-18, 6800 Hódmezövásárhely, mail addr: POB 2, 6801 Hódmezövásárhely - T: (062) 344424, Fax: 344424. Head: Imre Nagy
Local Museum - 1904
Archaeology, ethnography, folk art, paintings by János Tornyai, sculptures by Ferenc Medgyessy, modern Hungarian art - library 19900

Hollóháza

Porcelánmúzeum (Porcelainmuseum), Károly ú 11, 3999 Hollóháza - T: (041) 321544
Decorative Arts Museum
History of the porcelain factory 19901

Hollókö

Falumúzeum (Village Museum), Kossuth ú 82, 3176 Hollókö
Open Air Museum 19902

Postamúzeum (Post Office Museum), Kossuth ú 80, 3176 Hollókö - T: (032) 378088
Special Museum 19903

Szövöház (Weavers' House), Kossuth ú 94, 3176 Hollókö
Science&Tech Museum 19904

Hortobágy

Hortobágyi Pásztormúzeum (Shepherd's Museum), 4071 Hortobágy - T: (052) 369119, Fax: 369119, E-mail: hortobagy@tourinform.hu. Head: Zoltánra Gencsi
Folklore Museum - 1965
History of the Puszta and life of the shepherds, clothing and every day objects 19905

Jászberény

Jász Múzeum, Táncsics Mihály ú 5, 5100 Jászberény, mail addr: POB 30, 5101 Jászberény - T: (057) 12753. Head: János Tóth
Local Museum - 1873
Archaeology, ethnography, local hist - library 19906

Kalocsa

Paprika Múzeum, Népmüvészeti Tájház, 6300 Kalocsa
Agriculture Museum
Centre of paprika cultivation, folk art, embroidery 19907

Schöffer-Ház (Museum Nicolas Schöffer), István Király ú 76, 6300 Kalocsa - T: (078) 362861, Internet: http://www.olats.org/schoffer. Head: Lajos Dargay
Fine Arts Museum - 1978
Art, furniture, reliefs, Cybernetic Light Tower - archives 19908

Viski Károly Múzeum, Szent István Király ú 25, 6300 Kalocsa - T: (078) 462351, Fax: 462351, E-mail: viski.karoly@freemail.hu, Internet: http://www.museum.hu/kalocsa/viski. Head: Imre Romsics
Ethnology Museum / Natural History Museum / Folklore Museum - 1932
Ethnography, natural sciences, folk art - library 19909

Kapolnásnyék

Vörösmarty Mihály Emlékmúzeum, Vörösmarty ú, 7475 Kapolnásnyék
Special Museum - 1950
18th c baroque building, birthplace of the poet Mihály Vörösmarty 19910

Kaposvár

Mozimúzeum (Cinematographic Museum), 7400 Kaposvár
Special Museum 19911

Rippl-Rónai Emlékház (Memorial House of Rippl-Rónai), Rippl-Rónai tér 1, 7401 Kaposvár, mail addr: POB 70, 7400 Kaposvár - T: (082) 422144. Head: Dr. István Szabolcs-Király
Fine Arts Museum / Archaeological Museum / Ethnology Museum / Historical Museum - 1978
Archaeology, ethnography, local history, paintings and memorabilia on József Rippl-Rónai, modern Hungarian painter (Impressionism) - library 19912

Somogyi Megyei Múzeumok Igazgatósága (County Museum of Somogy), Foë ú 10, 7400 Kaposvár - T: (082) 312822, Fax: 312822, E-mail: kiraly@kvar.smmi.hu. Head: Dr. István Szabolcs-Király
Local Museum - 1909
Archaeology, ethnography, local hist, paintings by Rippl-Rónai and modern Hungarian art, natural science - library 19913

Kapuvár

Rábaközi Múzeum, Foë tér 1, 9330 Kapuvár - T: (097) 42557. Head: Klara Pamlényi
Local Museum - 1960
Ethnography, local history, art, memorabilia and coll of Pál Pátzay - library 19914

Karcag

Gyoëffy István Nagykun Múzeum, Kálvin ú 4, 5301 Karcag, mail addr: POB 8, 5300 Karcag - T: (059) 312087. Head: Dr. Miklós Nagy-Molnár
Ethnology Museum / Historical Museum - 1906
Ethnography, history, ethnology - library 19915

Kecskemét

Dunamelléki Református Egyházkerület Ráday Múzeuma (Ráday Museum of the Danubian District of the Hungarian Reformed Church), Szabadság tér 7, 6000 Kecskemét - T: (076) 486226, Fax: 486226. Head: Zsuzsa Fogarasi
Religious Arts Museum - 1980
Religious art coll in the Library of Ráday - library 19916

Katona József Múzeum, Bethlen krt 15, 6000 Kecskemét, mail addr: POB 6, 6001 Kecskemét - T: (076) 481350, Fax: 481122. Head: Dr. János Bárth
Local Museum - 1894
Archaeology, ethnography, memorabilia on the dramatist József Katona - library 19917

Kecskeméti Képtár és Tóth Menyhért Emlékmúzeum, Rákóczi ú 1, 6000 Kecskemét - T: (076) 480776. Head: Simon Magdolna
Fine Arts Museum - 1983
19th and 20th c Hungarian art 19918

Magyar Fotográfiai Múzeum, Katona Jósef tér 12, 6000 Kecskemét - T: (076) 483221, Fax: 508259, E-mail: fotomuz@visio.c3.hu, Internet: http://www.fotomuzeum.hu. Head: Károly Kincses
Fine Arts Museum 19919

Naiv Művészek Múzeuma (Museum of Naive Art), Gáspár A. ú 11, 6000 Kecskemét - T: (076) 324767, Fax: 481122. Head: Dr. János Bárth
Fine Arts Museum - 1976 19920

Szórakaténusz Játékmúzeum (Szórakaténusz Toy Museum), Gáspar András ú 11, 6000 Kecskemét - T: (076) 481469, Fax: 481469, E-mail: ifgood@matav.hu. Head: Dr. József Kriston Vizi
Special Museum - 1981
Old periodicals for children, old books, contemporary arts and crafts, toys 19921

Keszthely

Balatoni Múzeum, Múzeum ú 2, 8360 Keszthely - T: (083) 312351, Fax: 312351, E-mail: balatonimuz@freemail.hu, Internet: http://www.museum.hu/keszthely/balatoni. Head: Dr. Róbert Müller
Archaeological Museum / Ethnology Museum - 1898
Archaeology, ethnography of the Lake Balaton area, anthropology, archeobotany, numismatics - library 19922

Festetics-Kastély, Kastély ú 1, 8360 Keszthely - T: (083) 312190, Fax: 315039. Head: László Czoma
Historical Museum / Fine Arts Museum / Decorative Arts Museum - 1974
18th c castle of the Festetics family, first works by Voltaire, Rousseau, Descartes; pieces of furniture, sculptures, paintings - library 19923

Georgikon Majormúzeum (Georgikon Agrarmuseum), Bercsényi ú 67, 8360 Keszthely - T: (083) 311563
Agriculture Museum - 1979
History of agriculture, farm implements in a 18th c building 19924

Helikon Kastélymúzeum (Helikon Castle Museum), Szabadság ú 1, 8360 Keszthely - T: (083) 312190, Fax: 315039
Local Museum - 1974
18th c castle of Festetics family - library 19925

Kiskoërös

Petőfi Emlékmúzeum, Petoëfi tér 1, 6200 Kiskoërös. Head: József Gróf
Special Museum - 1951
Memorabilia on the poet Sándor Petoëfi, ethnographical coll of Slovakia - library 19926

Kiskunfélegyháza

Kiskun Múzeum (Museum of Cumania Minor), Dr. Holló Lajos ú 9, 6100 Kiskunfélegyháza, mail addr: POB 17, 6101 Kiskunfélegyháza - T: (076) 461468, Fax: 462542. Head: Dr. Erzsébet Molnár
Local Museum - 1902
Ethnography, archaeology, hist, prison coll, life and work of the writers Ferenc Móra and Sándor Petoëfi - library 19927

Móra Ferenc Emlékház (Birth Place of Ferenc Móra), Móra Ferenc ú 19, 6100 Kiskunfélegyháza - T: (076) 461468, Fax: 462542. Head: Dr. Erzsébet Molnár
Special Museum - 1972
Memorabilia on the Hungarian writer Ferenc Móra 19928

Kiskunhalas

Csipkeház (Lace House), Kossuth u 37, 6400 Kiskunhalas - T: (077) 421982, 421797, Fax: 523150, E-mail: halasicsipke@emitel.hu, Internet: http://www.hals.hu. Head: Zsuzsanna Kiliti
Decorative Arts Museum
Former lace manufacturer, lace masterpieces 19929

Thorma János Múzeum, Köztársaság u 2, 6400 Kiskunhalas - T: (077) 422864, Fax: 422864, E-mail: muzeum@halas.hu, Internet: http://www.muzeum.halas.hu. Head: Szakál Aurél
Local Museum - 1874
Ethnography, archaeology, applied art, lace coll, local history, works by the Hungarian painter - library 19930

Kisnána

Várrom és Népi Müemlék (Castle Ruin and Folk Monument), Béke ú 22, 3269 Kisnána
Historical Museum - 1968
Relics of the medieval castle Kisnána, historical peasant house 19931

Kisvárda

Rétközi Múzeum, Dimitrov ú 5, 4600 Kisvárda - T: 187. Head: Béla Fehérvári
Local Museum 19932

Vármúzeum, Vár ú 30, 4600 Kisvárda
Local Museum / Ethnology Museum - 1960
Ethnography, local history - library 19933

Komáron

Klapka György Múzeum, Szabadság tér 1, 2900 Komáron - T: (034) 340011
Local Museum
Regional history, Roman lapidary 19934

Kőszeg

Patikamúzeum (Pharmacy Museum), Jurisich tér 11, 9730 Kőszeg, mail addr: POB 4, 9730 Kőszeg - T: (094) 360337. Head: Dr. Csaba Thúroczy
Historical Museum - 1968
Baroque pharmacy of the Jesuits 19935

Városi Múzeum (Municipal Museum), Jurisics tér 6, 9730 Kőszeg - T: (03694) 360240, Fax: 360156. Head: Prof. Dr. Kornél Bakay
Local Museum - 1932
Local history, archaeology, ethnography, applied art Documents on the Turkish Invasion of 1532 - library 19936

Makó

Espersit Ház, József Attila Múzeum, Kazinczy ú 6, 6900 Makó - T: (062) 213540, Fax: 213540, E-mail: info@mfm.u-szeged.hu, Internet: http://www.mfm.u-szeged.hu. Head: Dr. Pál Halmágyi
Local Museum - 1979
Local history, Hungarian literature, exhibition about the poet Attila József 19937

József Attila Múzeum, Felszabadulás ú 4, 6900 Makó - T: (062) 213540, Fax: 213540, E-mail: info@mfm.u-szegfed.hu, Internet: http://www.mfm.u-szeged.hu. Head: Dr. Pál Halmágyi
Special Museum - 1950
Jozsef Pulitzer, Jozsef Galamb and life and works of Ferenc Erdei 19938

Martonvásár

Beethoven Emlékmúzeum (Beethoven-Memorial Museum), Brunszvik ú 2, 2462 Martonvásár - T: (022) 569500, Fax: 460213, E-mail: veiszo@mail.mgki.hu, Internet: http://www.mgki.hu. Head: Ottó Veisz
Music Museum - 1958
18th-19th c mansion of the Brunszvik family, where the famous composer Ludwig van Beethoven visited 19939

Mátészalka

Szatmári Múzeum, Kossuth ú 54, 4700 Mátészalka - T: 11016. Head: Lászlo Cservenyák
Local Museum - 1972
Ethnography, local hist - library 19940

Mezőkövesd

Matyó Múzeum (Local History Museum), Béke tér 20, 3400 Mezőkövesd - T: (040) 11824
Ethnology Museum / Folklore Museum / Local Museum - 1952
Ethnography, folk art, local history - library 19941

Tájház, Mogyoroköz, 3400 Mezőkövesd
Historical Museum
Typically furnished house 19942

Miskolc

Borsod Miskolci Múzeum → Herman Ottó Múzeum

Diósgyoéri Vármúzeum (Burgmuseum Diosgyör), Vár ú 24, 3534 Miskolc - T: (046) 370735, Fax: 530516, E-mail: ADYMUVH@Matavnet.hu. Head: Katalin Kovácsne Ládi
Historical Museum - 1968
History of the medieval castle in restored rooms 19943

Herman Ottó Múzeum, c/o Department of Mineralogy, Kossuth ú 13, 3525 Miskolc - T: (046) 505098, Fax: 555397, E-mail: homin@axelero.hu, Internet: http://www.hermuz.hu. Head: Sándor Szakáll
Natural History Museum - 1980
Minerals 19944

Herman Ottó Múzeum, Görgey Artúr ú 28, 3529 Miskolc, mail addr: POB 4, 3501 Miskolc - T: (046) 361411, Fax: 367975. Head: Dr. Lászlo Veres
Archaeological Museum / Ethnology Museum / Local Museum / Fine Arts Museum - 1899
Archaeology, ethnography, local hist, modern art coll, paintings, drawing history, numismatics - library 19945

Központi Kohászati Múzeum (Central Foundry Museum), Palota ú 22, 3517 Miskolc - T: (046) 79375. Head: Oszkár Szinvavölgyi
Archaeological Museum - 1949
Archaeological foundry of the 9th-10th c, 18th c foundry - library 19946

Magyar Ortodox Múzeum (Hungarian Orthodoxy Museum), Deák F. tér 7, 3525 Miskolc - T: (046) 345892
Religious Arts Museum
Sacral objects of the Hungarian Orthodox Church 19947

Mohács

Kanizsai Dorottya Múzeum, Szerb ú 2, 7700 Mohács - T: (069) 322490. Head: György Sarosácz
Local Museum - 1923
Ethnography, relics from the Turkish invasion in Hungary, history - library 19948

Monok

Kossuth Lajos Emlékmúzeuma, Magyar Nemzeti Múzeum (Kassuth Lajos Memorial Museum), Kossuth ú 18, 3905 Monok, mail addr: PF 364, 1370 Budapest - T: (047) 356156, Internet: http://www.hnm.hu
Historical Museum - 1949
Birthplace of the revolutionary leader Lajos Kossuth, memorial exhibition - library 19949

Mosonmagyaróvár

Hansági Múzeum, Szent István ú 1, 9200 Mosonmagyaróvár - T: (096) 213834, Fax: 212094. Head: Károly Szentkuti
Archaeological Museum / Local Museum / Fine Arts Museum - 1882
Archaeology, 17th-18th c prints, 19th c paintings, lapidarium, local hist - library 19950

Nagycenk

Széchenyi Emlékmúzeum (Széchenyi Memorial Museum), Kiscenki ú 3, 9485 Nagycenk - T: (099) 360023, Fax: 360260. Head: Dr. Attila Környei
Special Museum - 1973
Hist of the Széchenyi family and life of 19th c statesman Count István Széchenyi in his family castle, development of Hungarian transportation 19951

Nagykanizsa

Thury György Múzeum, Erzsébet tér 11, 8801 Nagykanizsa, mail addr: POB 32, 8801 Nagykanizsa - T: (093) 14596. Head: Dr. László Horváth
Local Museum - 1919
Ethnography, archaeology, local hist - library 19952

Nagykőrős

Arany János Múzeum, Ceglédi ú 19, 2751 Nagykőrős, mail addr: POB 29, 2751 Nagykőrős - T: (053) 350810, Fax: 350810, E-mail: PMI/AJMC3HU, Internet: http://www.c3.hu/pmiajm. Head: Dr. László Novák
Local Museum - 1928
Archaeology, ethnography, local history, literary documents of the poet János Arany - library 19953

Nagyvázsony

Kinizsi Vármúzeum (Castle Museum), Kinizsi ú, 8291 Nagyvázsony - T: (088) 31015
Historical Museum - 1956
Relics of a medieval castle 19954

Néprajzi Múzeum (Ethnographical Museum), 8291 Nagyvázsony
Ethnology Museum 19955

Postamúzeum (Post Office Museum), 8291 Nagyvázsony
Special Museum 19956

Nyírbátor

Báthory István Múzeum, Károlyi ú 15, 4300 Nyírbátor, mail addr: POB 28, 4301 Nyírbátor - T: (043) 11341. Head: Dr. László Dám
Local Museum - 1955
Archaeology, ethnography, local hist, art - library 19957

Nyíregyháza

Jósa András Múzeum, Benczúr tér 21, 4400 Nyíregyháza, mail addr: POB 57, 4401 Nyíregyháza - T: (042) 315722, Fax: 315722, E-mail: jam@jam.nyirbone.hu, Internet: http://jam.nyirbone.hu. Head: Dr. Péter Németh
Archaeological Museum / Ethnology Museum / Historical Museum / Fine Arts Museum / Open Air Museum - 1868
Archaeology, ethnography, local hist, art coll by the painter Gyula Benczúr, literary documents of the writer Gyula Krúdy, modern art of the region - library 19958

Opusztaszer

Nemzeti Történeti Emlékpark (National Historic Memory Park), 6769 Opusztaszer - T: (062) 12511
Religious Arts Museum - 1970
13th c church and cloister, cyrcorama by Árpád Feszty about the Hungarian conquest 19959

Orosháza

Szántó Kovács Múzeum, Dózsa György ú 5, 5900 Orosháza - T: (068) 12853
Local Museum - 1947
Ethnography, folk art, archaeology, literary documents of the writer József Darvas - library 19960

Városi Képtár (Municipal Gallery), Thék-Endre u 1, 5900 Orosháza - T: (068) 412523, Internet: http://www.oroshaza.hu/oroshaza/magyar/keptar
Public Gallery 19961

Pákozd

Pákozdi Csata Emlékmüve (Battle of Pákozd Memorial Site and Museum), 8095 Pákozd - T: (022) 315583, Fax: 311734. Head: Dr. Gyula Fülöp
Military Museum
Victory of the Hungarian troops on 29th Sept 1848 19962

Pannonhalma

Panonhalmi Főapátság Gyűjteménye (Abbey of Pannonhalma Collection), Vár ú 1, 9090 Pannonhalma - T: (096) 570142, Fax: 470011. Head: Dr. Silvester Sólymos
Religious Arts Museum / Fine Arts Museum - 1802
Archaeology, applied art, religious art, numismatics, paintings, engravings, prints 19963

Pápa

Dunántúli Református Egyházkerület Tudományos Gyüjteményei Múzeum (Museum of the Transdanubian Reformed Church District), Március 15. tér 9, 8500 Pápa - T: (089) 324240, Fax: 310193, E-mail: ref.lib@papacollege.hu, Internet: http://www.extra.hu/gyujtemenyek. Head: László Köntös
Religious Arts Museum - 1531
Religious art, history of art, archeological coll, Baldacci coll, photographs, 19964

Gróf Esterházy Károly Kastély és Tájmúzeum (Count Charles Esterházy Castle and Regional Museum), Foë tér 1, 8500 Pápa - T: (089) 313584. Head: Dr. Péter László
Local Museum - 1960
Ethnographical, archaeological and industrial coll from the town and the environment - library 19965

Helytörténeti Múzeum, Foë tér 1, 8500 Pápa, mail addr: POB 208, 8501 Pápa - T: (089) 13584. Head: Gabor Ilon
Local Museum - 1960
Local history, archeology, ethnography, art coll, 18th c castle interior - library 19966

Kékfestö Múzeum (Indigoprint Museum), Március 15 tér 12, 8500 Pápa - T: (089) 324390, Fax: 324390, E-mail: Kekfesto.papa@museum.hu, Internet: http://www.museum.hu/papa/kekfesto. Head: Mèri Edina
Science&Tech Museum - 1962
Old blue-dyeing workshop, history of blue-dyeing, 200 years old horse-gin with mangle 19967

Pécs

Amerigo Tot Múzeum, Káptalan ú 2, 7621 Pécs - T: (072) 324822, Fax: 315694, E-mail: jpm@jpm.hu, Internet: http://www.pecs.hu. Head: Zoltán Huszár
Fine Arts Museum
Coll of Amerigo Tot 19968

Csontváry Múzeum, Janus Pannonius ú 11, 7621 Pécs - T: (072) 310544, Fax: 315694, E-mail: jpm@jpm.hu, Internet: http://www.pecs.hu. Head: Zoltán Huszár
Fine Arts Museum - 1973
Works by the expressionist painter Tivadar Csontváry Kosztka 19969

Endre Nemes Múzeum, Káptalan ú 5, 7621 Pécs - T: (072) 310172, Fax: 315694, E-mail: jpm@jpm.hu, Internet: http://www.pecs.hu. Head: Zoltán Huszár
Fine Arts Museum
Coll of Endre Nemes (Surrealistic painting) 19970

Janus Pannonius Múzeum Igazgatòsàga, Kàptalan ú 5, 7601 Pécs, mail addr: POB 158, 7621 Pécs - T: (072) 310172, Fax: 315694, E-mail: jpm@jpm.hu, Internet: http://www.pecs.hu. Head: Zoltán Huszár
Local Museum - 1904
Archaeology, ethnography, local hist, Hungarian art, natural hist - library, educational department 19971

Janus Pannonius Múzeum Természettudományi Osztálya, Janus Pannonius Múzeum, Szabadság út 2, 7623 Pécs, mail addr: c/o Natural History Department of JPM, POB 347, 7601 Pécs - T: (072) 213419, Fax: 315694, E-mail: jpm@jpm.hu, Internet: http://www.pecs.hu. Head: Zoltán Huszár
Natural History Museum - 1951
Natural hist: Trichoptera - Hungary, C Europe (c200 000 units), Lepidoptera - Hungary (c100 000 units), Coleoptera - mostly Hungary (c140 000 units) Mollusca (c10 000 units) 19972

Martyn Ferenc Gyűjtemény, Janus Pannonius Múzeum, Káptalan ú 6, 7621 Pécs - T: (072) 324822, Fax: 315694, E-mail: jpm@jpm.hu, Internet: http://www.pecs.hu. Head: Zoltán Huszár
Fine Arts Museum - 1979
Modern art coll by Ferenc Martyn in a historical building 19973

Mecseki Banyászati Múzeum (Mining Museum), Káptalan ú 2, 7621 Pécs - T: (072) 324822, Fax: 315694, E-mail: jpm@jpm.hu, Internet: http://www.jpm.hu
Science&Tech Museum 19974

Modern Magyar Képtár I, Janus Pannonius Múzeum (Modern Hungarian Gallery I), Káptalan ú 4, 7621 Pécs - T: (072) 324822, Fax: 315694, E-mail: jpm@jpm.hu, Internet: http://www.pecs.hu. Head: Zoltán Huszár
Fine Arts Museum - 1957
Hungarian art coll (1900-1950) 19975

Modern Magyar Képtár II, Janus Pannonius Múzeum (Modern Hungarian Gallery II), Papnövelde ú 5, 7621 Pécs - T: (072) 324822, Fax: 315694, E-mail: jpm@jpm.hu, Internet: http://www.pecs.hu. Head: Zoltán Huszár
Fine Arts Museum - 1957
Hungarian art coll (1955-2001) 19976

Néprajzi Kiállítás, Janus Pannonius Múzeum, c/o Ethnographical Department of JPM, Rákóczi ú 15, 7621 Pécs - T: (072) 315629, Fax: 315694
Ethnology Museum - 1950
Local ethnographical exhibition 19977

Okeresztény Mauzóleum (Early Christian Mausoleum), Szent István tér, 7624 Pécs - T: (072) 312719, Fax: 315694, E-mail: jpm@jpm.hu, Internet: http://www.jpm.hu. Head: Zoltán Huszár
Religious Arts Museum
Burial chambers from the middle of the 4th c 19978

Reneszánsz Kőtár (Renaissance-Lapidarium), Káptalan ú 2, 7621 Pécs - T: (072) 310172, Fax: 315694, E-mail: jpm@jpm.hu, Internet: http://www.jpm.hu. Head: Zoltán Huszár
Archaeological Museum - 1972
Archaeology, Renaissance lapidarium 19979

Román Kori Kőtár (Lapidarium of Roman Age), Dóm tér, 7621 Pécs - T: (072) 324822, Fax: 315694, E-mail: jpm@jpm.hu, Internet: http://www.jpm.hu
Archaeological Museum 19980

Várostörténeti és Munkásmozgalmi Múzeum (Museum of Town History and Labour Movement), Felsömalom ú 9, 7621 Pécs - T: (072) 310165, Fax: 315694, E-mail: jpm@jpm.hu, Internet: http://www.jpm.hu
Local Museum 19981

Vasarely Múzeum, Janus Pannonius Múzeum, Káptalan ú 3, 7621 Pécs - T: (072) 324822, Fax: 315694, E-mail: jpm@jpm.hu, Internet: http://www.pecs.hu. Head: Zoltán Huszár
Fine Arts Museum - 1976
Works by Vasarély (Victor Vásárhelyi, born 1908) in a historical building 19982

Zsolnay Kerámia Kiállítás, Janus Pannonius Múzeum (Zsolnay Ceramic and Porcelain Exhibition of JPM), Káptalan ú 2, 7621 Pécs - T: (072) 324822, Fax: 315694, E-mail: jpm@jpm.hu, Internet: http://www.pecs.hu. Head: Zoltán Huszár
Decorative Arts Museum - 1955
Applied arts, ceramics, porcelain 19983

Rudabánya

Alapítvány Érc és Ásványbányászati Múzeum (Museum of Mining of Metals and Minerals), Petoëfi ú 24, 3785 Rudabánya. Head: Béla Szuromi
Science&Tech Museum - 1956
Mining, hist of the industry - library 19984

Őslénytani Telep (Paleontological Park), 3785 Rudabánya
Ethnology Museum 19985

Salgótarján

Bányászati Múzeum (Mining Museum), Bajcsy-Zs. ú 1, 3100 Salgótarján - T: (032) 317633
Science&Tech Museum 19986

Nógrádi Sándor Múzeum, Nógrádi Sándor tér 8, 3101 Salgótarján, mail addr: POB 3, 3100 Salgótarján - T: (032) 14169, 10800
Local Museum 19987

Nógrádi Történeti Múzeum, Múzeum tér 2, 3100 Salgótarján, mail addr: POB 3, 3100 Salgótarján - T: (032) 10169, Fax: 10819. Head: Dr. István Horváth
Historical Museum - 1959
19-20th c hist of the revolutionary miners' movement, underground mining, industry, literature, art - library 19988

Sárospatak

Rákóczi Múzeum, Magyar Nemzeti Múzeum, Szent Erzsébet u 19, 3950 Sárospatak, mail addr: PF 364, 1370 Budapest - T: (047) 311083, Fax: 311345, E-mail: rakmuzsp@axelero.hu, Internet: http://www.hnm.hu. Head: Dr. Katalin Dankó Jósvai
Archaeological Museum / Folklore Museum / Historical Museum / Fine Arts Museum - 1950
Archaeology, ethnography, history, 17-18th c relics of the Rákóczi family, art coll - library 19989

Római Katolikus Egyházi Gyűjtemény (Roman-Catholic Church Museum), Kádár Kata ú 17, 3950 Sárospatak - T: (041) 11183
Religious Arts Museum - 1969
Applied art, religious art 19990

Sárospataki Református Kollégium Tudomanyos Gyűjteményei Múzeum, Rákóczi ú 1, 3950 Sárospatak - T: (041) 323057. Head: Eszter Pocsainé Eperjesi
Special Museum - 18th c
History of the Sárospatak college, old school equipment, religious art, applied art, folk art 19991

Sárvár

Nádasdi Ferenc Múzeum, Vár ú 1, 9600 Sárvár, mail addr: POB 1, 9601 Sárvár - T: 158. Head: István Söptei
Historical Museum
Late Renaissance and Baroque Hungarian milieu, reconstructed in state rooms of a 16th c castle, ethnography, applied art - library 19992

Sellye

Kis Géza Ormánság Múzeum, Köztársasság tér 6, 7960 Sellye
Decorative Arts Museum / Folklore Museum
Handicrafts and folk art of the region 19993

Siklós

Vármúzeum (Castle Museum), Vajda János tér, 7800 Siklós - T: (072) 13300
Historical Museum - 1952
Castle and prison museum, applied art, lapidarium 19994

Simontornya

Vármúzeum (Castle Museum), Vár tér 10, 7081 Simontornya - T: (0674) 486354, Fax: 486354. Head: Mária Takács
Historical Museum - 1975
Relics of a medieval castle, lapidarium 19995

Sopron

Esterházy-Palota (Esterházy Palais), 9400 Sopron
Local Museum 19996

Fabricius-Ház, Soproni Múzeum (Fabricius House), Foë tér 6, 9400 Sopron, mail addr: POB 68, 9400 Sopron - T: (099) 311327, Fax: 311347, E-mail: smuzeum@mail.c3.hu. Head: Dr. Attila Környei
Decorative Arts Museum - 1963
Items of furniture from the 17-18th c 19997

Középkori O-Zsinagóga, Soproni Múzeum (Medieval Old Synagogue), Új ú 22-24, 9400 Sopron, mail addr: POB 68, 9401 Sopron - T: (099) 311327, Fax: 311347, E-mail: smuzeum@mail.c3.hu. Head: Dr. Attila Környei
Religious Arts Museum - 1976
Jewish religious art and history 19998

Központi Bányászati Múzeum (Central Museum of Mining), Templom ú 2, 9400 Sopron - T: (099) 312667, Fax: 338902. Head: Dr. Kovácsné Bircher Erzsébet
Science&Tech Museum - 1957
Hist of Hungarian coal mining since the 13th c - library 19999

Néprajzi Gyűjtemény, Soproni Múzeum (Ethnography Collection), Deák tér 1, 9400 Sopron, mail addr: POB 68, 9401 Sopron - T: (099) 311463. Head: Dr. Attila Környei
Ethnology Museum - 1867
Ethnography, crafts, literary documents, 18-19th c coll of local hist - library 20000

Pékmúzeum, Soproni Múzeum (Bakers' Museum), Bécsi ú 5, 9400 Sopron. Head: András Nemes
Special Museum - 1975
Local history, ethnography, old baker's shop, relics of bakery 20001

Storno Collection, Soproni Múzeum, Foë tér 8, 9400 Sopron - T: (099) 311327, Fax: 311347, E-mail: smuzeum@mail.c3.hu. Head: Dr. Attila Környei
Fine Arts Museum
Private coll, fine arts (15th-20th c) 20002

Várostörténeti Kiállítás, Soproni Múzeum (Town History Exhibition), Foë tér 8, 9400 Sopron, mail addr: POB 68, 9401 Sopron - T: (099) 311327, Fax: 311347, E-mail: smuzeum@mail.c3.hu. Head: Dr. Attila Környei
Local Museum - 1867
Local hist exhibition and coll (16-20th c), private coll of the Storno family (fine arts, 15-20th c) in original interieur, coll of fine arts - library 20003

Zettl Langer gyűjtemény (Zettl Langer Collection), Balfi ú 11, 9400 Sopron - T: (099) 335123, 311136, Fax: 335123, E-mail: gillie@freemail.hu. Head: Agnes von Langer
Archaeological Museum / Fine Arts Museum - 1882
Roman grave finds, paintings by Veronese, Dürer, Dorfmeister, sketch by Rembrandt 20004

Sóstógyógyfürdő

Sóstói Múzeumfalu (Open Air Museum of Sóstó), Tölgyes út 1, 4431 Sóstógyógyfürdő - T: (042) 479704, Fax: 479704. Head: Dr. István Páll
Open Air Museum - 1970
Hungarian peasant houses and farm buildings with special traditional furniture and old village community buildings 20005

Sümeg

Kisfaludy Emlékmúzeum (Kisfaludy-Memory-Museum), Kisfaludy tér 3, 8330 Sümeg - T: (087) 201
Special Museum - 1913
Literary historical documents on the brother poets Károly and Sándor Kisfaludy 20006

Vármúzeum (Castle Museum), 8330 Sümeg - T: (087) 13750
Historical Museum - 1972
Relics of a medieval castle, local history 20007

Szalafő

Szabadtéri Néprajzi Múzeum (Open Air Museum), 9942 Szalafő
Open Air Museum 20008

Szarvas

Tessedik Sámuel Múzeum, Vajda Péter ú 1, 5540 Szarvas - T: (067) 12960. Head: Dr. József Palov
Local Museum - 1951
Local hist, ethnography, archeology, old mill, Slovakian ethnographic coll - library 20009

Szécsény

Kubinyi Ferenc Múzeum, Ady Endre ú 7, 3170 Szécsény - T: (032) 370143. Head: Dr. Katalin Simán
Archaeological Museum / Historical Museum - 1973
Archaeology, history - library 20010

Szeged

Fekete-Ház, Móra Ferenc Museum Szeged, Somogyi Béla ú 15, 6720 Szeged - T: (062) 425872, Fax: 425033, E-mail: info@mfm.u-szeged.hu, Internet: http://www.mfm.u-szeged.hu. Head: Dr. Gabriella Vörös
Local Museum
Contemporary local history 20011

Jfj. Lele J. Néprajzi Gyűjteménye (Ethnographical Collection of Jr. József Lele), Tápé, Vártó ú 4, 6720 Szeged
Ethnology Museum 20012

Kass Galéria (Kass Gallery), Vár ú 7, 6720 Szeged
Fine Arts Museum
Works by the graphic artist János Kass 20013

Móra Ferenc Múzeum, Roosevelt tér 3, 6720 Szeged, mail addr: POB 474, 6701 Szeged - T: (062) 470370, Fax: 420980, E-mail: info@mfm.u-szeged.hu, Internet: http://www.mfm.u-szeged.hu. Head: Dr. Gabriella Vörös
Archaeological Museum / Ethnology Museum / Local Museum - 1883
Archaeology, ethnography, local hist, natural hist, literary coll, 20th c art, lapidarium - library, educational department 20014

Paprikamúzeum (Red Pepper Museum), Mihálytelek, 6720 Szeged - T: (062) 324745
Agriculture Museum
Equipment for the cultivation and processing of red pepper 20015

Szélmalom (Windmill Museum), Kiskundorozsma, 6720 Szeged
Science&Tech Museum 20016

Székesfehérvár

Budenz-Ház, István Király Múzeum, Arany János ú 12, 8000 Székesfehérvár - T: (022) 13027. Head: Péter Kovács
Fine Arts Museum - 1968
19-20th c art coll, Ervin Ybl coll, 18th c historic building 20017

Csók István Képtár, Bartók Béla tér 1, 8000 Székesfehérvár, mail addr: POB 78, 8002 Székesfehérvár - T: (022) 15583. Head: Péter Kovács
Public Gallery - 1955 20018

Fekete Sas Patikamúzeum (Museum of the Black Eagle Pharmacy), Foë ú 5, 8000 Székesfehérvár, mail addr: POB 78, 8002 Székesfehérvár - T: (022) 15583. Head: Péter Kovács
Historical Museum - 1974
18th c pharmacy 20019

Gorsium Szabadtéri Múzeum (Gorsium Roman Ruin), Tác, 8121 Székesfehérvár - T: (022) 362243, Fax: 311734. Head: Prof. Jenoë Fitz
Open Air Museum / Archaeological Museum - 1963
Lapidarium, relics of the Roman town Gorsium 20020

Országos Aluminiumipari Múzeum (Museum of Hungarian Aluminium Industry), Zombori ú 12, 8000 Székesfehérvár - T: (022) 12465. Head: Dr. Gabor László
Science&Tech Museum - 1971
History of the aluminium industry - library 20021

Palotavárosi Skanzen (Open Air Museum), 8000 Székesfehérvár
Open Air Museum 20022

Schaár Erzsébet Gyűjtemény, Jókai ú 11, 8000 Székesfehérvár, mail addr: POB 78, 8002 Székesfehérvár - T: (022) 15583. Head: Péter Kovács
Fine Arts Museum - 1980 20023

Szent István Király Múzeum (Museum of the King Saint Stephen), Foë u 6, 8002 Székesfehérvár, mail addr: POB 78, 8002 Székesfehérvár - T: (022) 315583, Fax: 311734. Head: Dr. Gyula Fülöp, Vajk Cserményi
Archaeological Museum / Fine Arts Museum - 1873
Prehistoric, Roman and medieval coll, anthropology, ethnography, fragments from the Basilica of King Stephen (975-1038), 20th c art, applied art - library, educational department 20024

Városi Képtár (Municipal Gallery), Oskola ú 10, 8000 Székesfehérvár - T: (022) 329431
Public Gallery 20025

Várostörténeti Múzeum, Uj Magyar Képtár (Town History Museum and New Hungarian Gallery), Megyeház ú 17, 8000 Székesfehérvár
Local Museum / Fine Arts Museum 20026

Szekszárd

Babits Mihály Emlékház (Mihály Babits Memorial Museum), Babits ú 13, 7100 Szekszárd - T: (074) 312154, Fax: 316222, E-mail: wmmm@terrasoft.hu. Head: Dr. Attila Gaál
Special Museum - 1967
Life and work, memorabilia on the poet Mihály Babits in his birthplace 20027

Béri Balogh Adám Múzeum, 7100 Szekszárd
Historical Museum
Ethnography, gallery of Hungarian painters, excavation finds from pre-historic and Roman times 20028

Wosinsky Mór Megyei Múzeum (Mór Wosinsky County Museum), Szent István tér 26, 7101 Szekszárd, mail addr: POB 44, 7101 Szekszárd - T: (074) 316222, Fax: 316222, E-mail: wmmm@terrasoft.hu. Head: Dr. Attila Gaál
Local Museum - 1895
Archaeology, ethnography, literary documents, applied art, art, numismatics, history - library 20029

Szenna

Szabadtéri Néprajzi Gyűjtemény (Ethnographisches Freilichtmuseum), Rákóczi ú 2, 7477 Szenna - T: (082) 317153
Open Air Museum - 1978
Hungarian peasant houses, furniture, textiles of the Somogy district 20030

Szentendre

Ámos-Anna Gyűjtemény, Ferenczy Múzeum (Ámos-Anna Collection), Bogdányi ú 10, 2000 Szentendre, mail addr: c/o Ferenczy Museum, POB 49, 2000 Szentendre - T: (026) 310244, Fax: 310790, E-mail: webmaster@pmmi.hu, Internet: http://www.pmmi.hu. Head: Dr. László Simon
Fine Arts Museum - 1984
20th c art 20031

Barcsay Gyűjtemény, Ferenczy Múzeum (Barcsay Collection), Dumtsa Jenoë ú 10, 2000 Szentendre, mail addr: POB 49, 2000 Szentendre - T: (026) 310244, Fax: 310790, E-mail: webmaster@pmmi.hu, Internet: http://www.pmmi.hu. Head: Dr. László Simon
Fine Arts Museum - 1978
20th c art 20032

Czóbel Béla Múzeum, Templom tér 1, 2000 Szentendre, mail addr: POB 49, 2000 Szentendre - T: (026) 312721, Fax: 310790, E-mail: webmaster@pmmi.hu, Internet: http://www.pmmi.hu. Head: Dr. László Simon
Fine Arts Museum - 1975
Life and work of and paintings by Béla Czóbel 20033

Ferenczy Károly Múzeum, Foë tér 6, 2000 Szentendre, mail addr: POB 49, 2000 Szentendre - T: (026) 310244, Fax: 310790, E-mail: webmaster@pmmi.hu, Internet: http://www.pmmi.hu. Head: Dr. László Simon
Fine Arts Museum - 1951
Archaeology, ethnology, coll of the Szentendre Art School, bequest by the Ferenczy family, local history - library, educational department 20034

Kerényi Jenő Emlékmúzeum, Ferenczy Múzeum (Jenő Kerényi Memorial Museum), Ady Endre ú 5, 2000 Szentendre, mail addr: POB 49, 2000 Szentendre - T: (026) 310244, Fax: 310790, E-mail: webmaster@pmmi.hu, Internet: http://www.pmmi.hu. Head: Dr. László Simon
Fine Arts Museum - 1978
20th c art 20035

Kmetty Múzeum, Ferenczy Múzeum, Fő tér 14, 2000 Szentendre, mail addr: POB 49, 2001 Szentendre - T: (026) 310244, Fax: 310790, E-mail: webmaster@pmmi.hu, Internet: http://www.pmmi.hu. Head: Dr. László Simon
Fine Arts Museum - 1981
20th c art 20036

Kovács Margit Kerámiagyűjtemény, Ferenczy Múzeum, Wastagh György ú 1, 2000 Szentendre, mail addr: POB 49, 2000 Szentendre - T: (026) 310244, Fax: 310790, E-mail: webmaster@pmmi.hu, Internet: http://www.pmmi.hu. Head: Dr. László Simon
Decorative Arts Museum - 1973
Applied art (ceramics) by Margit Kovács, 18th c historic building 20037

Római Kötár (Garden of Roman Ruins), Dunakanyar krt 1, 2000 Szentendre - T: (026) 311190, Fax: 311190, E-mail: kotar@axelero.hu, Internet: http://www.pmmi.hu. Head: Dr. László Simon
Archaeological Museum
Finds of the Roman military camp "Ulcisia Castra" 20038

Szabadtéri Néprajzi Múzeum (Hungarian Open Air Museum), Sztaravodai ú, 2000 Szentendre, mail addr: POB 63, 2001 Szentendre - T: (026) 502500, Fax: 502502, E-mail: sznm@sznm.hu, Internet: http://www.sznm.hu. Head: Dr. Miklós Cseri
Open Air Museum - 1967
Traditional Hungarian peasant houses, furniture, farm buildings and machines - library, educational department, scientific department, archives, technical department, restoration department 20039

Szentendrei Képtár, Fő tér 2-5, 2000 Szentendre, mail addr: POB 49, 2000 Szentendre - T: (026) 310244, Fax: 310790, E-mail: webmaster@pmmi.hu, Internet: http://www.pmmi.hu. Head: Dr. László Simon
Public Gallery - 1977
Modern art exhibitions 20040

Szerb Egyházy Múzeum (Serbian Church Museum), Pátriárka ú 5, 2000 Szentendre - T: (026) 312399, Fax: 314457. Head: Dr. Danilo Kristic
Religious Arts Museum - 1964
Religious art, religious items of the Eastern Church in Hungary 20041

Vajda Lajos Emlékmúzeum, Ferenczy Múzeum (Lajos Vajda Memorial Museum), Hunyadi ú 1, 2000 Szentendre, mail addr: POB 49, 2000 Szentendre - T: (026) 310244, Fax: 310790, E-mail: webmaster@pmmi.hu, Internet: http://www.pmmi.hu. Head: Dr. László Simon
Fine Arts Museum - 1986
20th c art 20042

Szentes

Koszta József Múzeum, Széchenyi Liget 1, 6600 Szentes - T: (063) 313352, Fax: 313352, E-mail: muzeum@szentesinfo.hu. Head: Dr. J. József Szabó
Local Museum - 1897
Archaeology, ethnography, art coll by the painters József Koszta, István Dési Huber, István Drahos, Gábor Csallány - library 20043

Szerencs

Zempléni Muzeum, Várkastély, 3901 Szerencs, mail addr: POB 47, 3900 Szerencs - T: (041) 534. Head: József Siska
Local Museum - 1977
Ethnography, local history, medieval castle - library 20044

Szigetvár

Zrinyi Miklós Vármúzeum (Zrinyi Miklos Castle Museum), Vár ú 1, 7900 Szigetvár - T: (073) 284
Historical Museum - 1917
Hist of the Zrinyi family, hist coll from the period of the Turkish invasion in the 16th c 20045

Szilvásvárad

Lipicai Múzeum (Lipica Museum), 3348 Szilvásvárad
Agriculture Museum
Horse breeding 20046

Szadadtéri Erdei Múzeum (Woodland Museum), 3348 Szilvásvárad
Historical Museum
Documents and equipment from the former forestry 20047

Szolnok

Damjanich János Múzeum, Kossuth tér 4, 5001 Szolnok, mail addr: POB 128, 5001 Szolnok - T: (056) 421602, Fax: 341204. Head: Dr. László Tálas
Local Museum - 1934
Archaeology, ethnography, local hist, coll of the Szolnok Art School - library 20048

Szabadtéri Vízügyi Múzeum (Open Air Museum of Water Supply), Millér, 5000 Szolnok
Open Air Museum / Science&Tech Museum - 1976
Science and technology, water conservation 20049

Szombathely

Savaria Múzeum, Kisfaludy Sándor ú 9, 9701 Szombathely, mail addr: POB 14, 9701 Szombathely - T: (094) 312554, Fax: 313736. Head: Dr. Csaba Thúroczy

Local Museum - 1872
Natural hist, minerals, archaeology, Roman finds,
Iseum, medieval stonework, ethnography - library,
educational department   20050

Smidt Múzeum, Holán E. ú, 9700 Szombathely -
T: (094) 311038. Head: Erzsébet Smidt
Historical Museum - 1968
Medical-historical coll of the surgeon Dr Lajos Smidt
- library   20051

Szombathelyi Képtár (Gallery of Szombathely),
Rákóczi Ferenc ú 12, 9700 Szombathely - T: (094)
13074, Fax: 314096. Head: Nándor Salamon
Fine Arts Museum - 1985
Modern textiles, modern painting, graphics and
sculpture (20th c) - library   20052

Vasi Múzeumfalu, Savaria Múzeum (Ethnographic
Open Air Museum), Árpád ú 30, 9700 Szombathely -
T: (094) 311004
Open Air Museum - 1967
Traditional peasant houses from the Vas
district   20053

Tápiószele

Blaskovich Múzeum, Pest Megyei Múzeumok
Igazgatóságá, Múzeum ú 13, 2766 Tápiószele -
T: (053) 380061, Internet: http://www.pmmi.hu.
Head: Csilla Gócsáné-Móró
Decorative Arts Museum / Fine Arts Museum - 1952
Typical mansion of the lesser nobility with authentic
furniture, art coll of paintings by Hungarian,
Austrian, Italian masters, old books, hunting
trophies, geological rarities, local archeological
finds, diverse pipes   20054

Tata

Görög-Római Szobormásolatok Múzeuma,
Zsinagóga, Rákóczi ú 8, 2892 Tata - T: (034)
381251. Head: Dr. Eva Maria Fülöp
Archaeological Museum / Fine Arts Museum
Copies of Greek and Roman sculptures (7th c B.C.-
2nd c A.D.)   20055

Kuny Domokos Múzeum, Néppark, Kiskastély, 2892
Tata, mail addr: POB 224, 2892 Tata - T: (034)
487888, Fax: 487888. Head: Dr. Éva M. Fülöp
Archaeological Museum / Local Museum / Fine Arts
Museum / Ethnology Museum / Historical Museum -
1912
Archaeology, Roman frescoes, local hist, Roman and
medieval stonework remains, ceramics,
ethnography - library   20056

Német Nemzetiségi Muzeum, Ungarndeutsches
Museum (Hungary-German Museum), Alkotmány ú
1, 2890 Tata - T: (034) 80788
Folklore Museum   20057

Tatabánya

Tatabánya Múzeum, Szent Borbála tér 1, 2800
Tatabánya - T: (034) 310495, Fax: 310495. Head:
Anikó Fürészné-Molnár
Historical Museum / Archaeological Museum /
Science&Tech Museum / Open Air Museum - 1971
Contemporary hist, hist of mining industry, school
hist, archaeology - library   20058

Tiszafüred

Kiss Pál Múzeum, Tariczky Sétány 6, 5350
Tiszafüred - T: (059) 352106. Head: Anikó Füvessy
Local Museum - 1877
Ancient mss of Lajos Kossuth, ancient local books,
newspapers, 19th c pottery, 19th c wooden saddles
- library   20059

Tokaji

Présház (Wine Press), Bem ú 2, 3910 Tokaji - T: (041)
352416
Agriculture Museum
History of local viticulture   20060

Tokaji Múzeum (Town Museum of Tokaji), Bethlen G.
ú 7, 3910 Tokaji - T: (041) 352636,
E-mail: nyirmitel@freemail.hu. Head: Hajnalka Tóth
Local Museum   20061

Túrkeve

Finta Múzeum, Attila ú 1, 5421 Túrkeve - T: (056)
361183. Head: Dr. Julianna Örsi
Fine Arts Museum - 1951
Bequest of the Finta brothers, both sculptors
(20th c)   20062

Vác

Hincz Gyula Állandó Gyüjtemény (Gyula Hincz
Memorial Museum and Exhibition Building),
Káptalan 16, 2600 Vác - T: (027) 313463,
Fax: 315064, E-mail: muvtort@dunweb.hu. Head:
Márta Zombork, Etnology
Fine Arts Museum / Local Museum - 1982
Sculptures and paintings by the artist Gyula Hincz,
archaeological, ethographical, historical
exhibitions   20063

Tragor Ignác Múzeum, Múzeum ú 4, 2600 Vác -
T: (027) 315064, Fax: 315064, E-mail: muzeum@
dunaweb.hu, Internet: http://www.muzeum.vac.hu.
Head: Márta Zomborka Szücsné
Local Museum - 1895
Archaeology, ethnography, local history, fine arts,
applied arts - library   20064

Vaja

Vay Adám Múzeum, Damjanich ú 75, 4562 Vaja -
T: (044) 385297. Head: Sándor Molnár
Historical Museum - 1964
Hist of the Hungarian revolutionary movement in the
18th c, Renaissance castle, local hist, arts -
library   20065

Várpalota

Magyar Vegyészeti Múzeum (Hungarian Chemical
Museum), Szabadság tér 1, 8100 Várpalota -
T: (088) 472391, Fax: 471702, E-mail: vegymuz@
ax.hu, Internet: http://www.kfki.hu/chemonet/hun/
mvm. Head: István Próder
Science&Tech Museum - 1963
Hist of the Hungarian chemical industry -
library   20066

Vásárosnamény

Beregi Múzeum, Rákóczi ú 13, 4800 Vásárosnamény
- T: (044) 182. Head: Dr. Sarolta Felhösné-Csiszár
Local Museum - 1965
Local history, archeology, ethnography   20067

Vértesszőllős

Vértesszőllősi Bemutatóhelye, Magyar Nemzeti
Múzeum (Vértesszőllősi Open-air Exhibition), 2837
Vértesszőllős, mail addr: PF 364, 1370 Budapest -
T: (01) 3382122, Fax: 3177806, Internet: http://
www.hnm.hu. Head: Dr. Viola Dobosi
Archaeological Museum - 1975
Archaeology, paleonlithic settlement   20068

Veszprém

Bajcsy-Zsilinszky Emlékmúzeum (Bajcsy-Zsilinszky
Memorial Museum), Koëvágóörs-Pálköve, 8254
Veszprém
Historical Museum - 1966
Memorial house for Endre Bajcsy-Zsilinszky
progressive Hungarian politician   20069

Bakonyi Múzeum, Erzsebet liget 5, 8200 Veszprém,
mail addr: POB 32, 8201 Veszprém - T: (080) 11358
Local Museum - 1903
Archaeology, historical and ethnographical exhibits
from the Bakony Mountains, natural history, fine
arts, applied arts - library   20070

Laczkó Dezsoë Múzeum, Erzsébet sétány 1, 8201
Veszprém, mail addr: POB 32, 8201 Veszprém -
T: (088) 564310/11, Fax: 426081, E-mail: vmmi@
sednet.hu, Internet: http://www.c3.hu/~vmmuzeum.
Head: Dr. Fodor Zsuzsa
Local Museum - 1903
Ethnography, archaeology, art hist, numismatics,
history - library   20071

Vármúzeum (Castle Museum), Tolbuhin ú 2, 8200
Veszprém - T: (080) 11358
Historical Museum   20072

Vésztő

Csolt Monostor Középkori Romkert, Mágori Domb,
5530 Vésztő
Archaeological Museum   20073

Visegrád

Mátyás Király Múzeum, Magyar Nemzeti Múzeum
(King Matthias Museum), Foë ú 29, 2025 Visegrád,
mail addr: PF 364, 1370 Budapest - T: (026)
398026/252, Fax: 398026, E-mail: mkmvisegrad@
freemail.hu, Internet: http://www.visegrad.hu/
muzeum. Head: Dr. Mátyás Szöke
Archaeological Museum / Historical Museum - 1950
Archaeology, stonework remains, 13th c tower,
Renaissance fountain from the 15th c, late Gothic
palace - library   20074

Zala

Zichy Mihály Emlékmúzeum (Mihály Zichy Memorial
Museum), Zichy Mihály u 20, 8660 Zala - T: (084)
320607. Head: Magdolna Petrus
Fine Arts Museum - 1951
Life, work and memorabilia on the painter Mihály
Zichy   20075

Zalaegerszeg

Göcseji Falumúzeum, Göcseji Múzeum (Village
Museum of Göcsej), Falumúzeum ú 1, 8900
Zalaegerszeg - T: (092) 313494. Head: Dr. László
Vándor
Open Air Museum - 1968
Traditional peasant houses, interiors, mill from the
Göcsaj district   20076

Göcseji Múzeum (Göcsejer-Museum), Batthyány ú 2,
8900 Zalaegerszeg, mail addr: POB 176, 8901
Zalaegerszeg - T: (092) 314537, Fax: 511972,
E-mail: muzeum@dfmk.hu, Internet: http://
alpha.dfmk.hu/~muzeum. Head: Dr. László Vándor
Local Museum - 1950
Archaeology, ethnography, folk art, local hist, art -
library   20077

Magyar Olajipari Múzeum (Museum of the
Hungarian Petroleum Industry), Wlassics Gy ú 13,
8900 Zalaegerszeg - T: (092) 313632, Fax: 311081.
Head: János Tóth
Science&Tech Museum - 1969
Development of the Hungarian oil industry,
technology - library   20078

Zebegény

Szönyi István Emlék Múzeum, Bartóky ú 7, 2627
Zebegény
Fine Arts Museum - 1967
Life, work and memorabilia on the painter István
Szoënyi   20079

Zirc

Bakonyi Természettudományi Muzeum (Natural
History Museum of Bakony Mountains), Rákóczi tér
1, 8420 Zirc - T: (088) 414157, Fax: 414157. Head:
Futó János
Natural History Museum - 1972
Natural hist of the Bakony Mountains area -
library   20080

Iceland

Akranes

Byggdasafn Akraness og Nærsveita (Akanes Folk
Museum), Gardar, 300 Akranes - T: 4311255,
Fax: 4311255, E-mail: akranes-museum@aknet.is,
Internet: http://www.akranes.is/museum. Head: Jón
Allansson
Local Museum - 1959
Local and regional hist   20081

Akureyri

David Stefánsson Memorial Museum, Bjarkarstígur
6, 600 Akureyri - T: 4601450, Fax: 4601460. Head:
Ragnheidur Stefánsdóttir
Historical Museum   20082

Minjasafnida á Akureyri (Akureyri Museum),
Adalstraeti 58, 600 Akureyri - T: 4624162,
Fax: 4612562, E-mail: akmus@nett.is. Head:
Gudrun Kristinsdottir
Local Museum - 1962
photography dept   20083

Náttúrufrædaistofnun Islands, Akureyrarsetur
(Icelandic Institute of Natural History, Akureyri
Division), Hafnarstraeti 97, 602 Akureyri -
T: 4600500, Fax: 4600501, E-mail: kralb@ni.is,
Internet: http://www.ni.is. Head: Kristinn J.
Albertsson
Natural History Museum - 1951
Icelandic and European flora, worldwide shell coll,
Icelandic insects, birds and fungi - library,
herbarium   20084

Nonnahús (Pater Jon Sveinsson Memorial Museum),
Adalstraeti 54a, 602 Akureyri - T: 4623555,
E-mail: nonnahus@ismennt.is. Head: Brynhildur
Pétursdóttir
Historical Museum - 1957
Memorial of the rev. Jón Sveinsson, jesuit priest and
writer of children's books   20085

Sigurhaedir - Hús Skáldsins Museum, Literary
Museum, Eyrarlandsvegur 3, 600 Akureyri -
T: 4626648, Fax: 4626649, E-mail: skald@nett.is.
Head: Erlingur Sigurdarson
Special Museum
Literature exhibitions   20086

Blönduós

Heimilisidnardarsafnid Halldórustofa (Textile
Museum), Árbraut 29, 540 Blönduós - T: 4524067,
Fax: 4524646, E-mail: johstorf@krokur.is,
Internet: http://www.krokur.is/johstorf. Head: Elin S.
Sigurdardóttir
Special Museum - 1976
Handmade textile items, varieties of the Icelandic
national costumes, colourful embroideries, Halldóra
Bjarnadóttir (1873-1981), a pioneer in women's
education   20087

Borgarnes

Byggdasafn Borgarfjardar (Borgarfjördur County
Museum), Bjarnarbraut 4-6, 310 Borgarnes -
T: 4372127, Fax: 4372137, E-mail: gudmars@
ismennt.is. Head: G. Gudmarsson
Fine Arts Museum / Natural History Museum - 1960
Art coll, bird coll   20088

Brú

Byggdasafn Húnvetninga og Strandarmanna (Local
Museum), Reykir, Stadarhreppur, 500 Brú -
T: 4510040, E-mail: peturjo@simnet.is,
Internet: http://www.simnet.is/ofeigur. Head: Petur
Jónsson
Local Museum   20089

Búdardalur

Byggdasafn Dalamanna (Cultural History Museum),
Laugum, 371 Búdardalur. Head: Magnús Gestsson
Historical Museum   20090

Dalvík

Byggdasafn Dalvíkur (Dalvík Local Museum),
Safnahúsid Hvoll, 620 Dalvík - T: 61497
Local Museum - 1987
Jóhann K. Pétursson, Icelands biggest man (2,34m),
cultural hist, Kristjan Eldjárn (president of Iceland
1968-1980)   20091

Egilsstadir

Minjasafn Austurlands (The East Iceland Heritage
Museum), Laufskógar 1, 700 Egilsstadir - T: 471-
1452, Fax: 471-1452, E-mail: minaust@eldhorn.is.
Head: Jóhanna Bergmann
Local Museum - 1943   20092

Eskifjördur

Sjóminjasafn Austurlands (Ship Museum), 735
Eskifjördur - T: 61179. Head: Geir Hólm
Science&Tech Museum   20093

Eyrarbakki

Sjóminjasafnid á Eyrarbakka (Maritime Museum),
Túngötu 59, 820 Eyrarbakki - T: 4831165,
Fax: 4831145, E-mail: sjominjasafn@arborg.is,
Internet: http://www.south.is/husid/
sjominjasafn.html. Head: Thorvaldur H. Gunnarsson
Historical Museum / Special Museum
Boats, fishery, small industry, culture in a maritime
town   20094

Gardabaer

Thjódminjasafn Islands (National Museum of
Iceland), Lyngás 7, 210 Gardabaer - T: 5528888,
Fax: 5302201, E-mail: natmus@natmus.is,
Internet: http://www.natmus.is. Head: Margrét
Hallgrimsdóttir
Local Museum - 1863
library, ethnology department, archaeological
department, photo collections   20095

Hafnarfjördur

Byggdasafn Hafnarfjardar (Hafnarfjördur Museum),
Strandg 50, 220 Hafnarfjördur - T: 5655420,
Fax: 5655438, E-mail: museum@hafnarfjordur.is,
Internet: http://www.hafnarfjordur.is. Head: Björn
Pétursson
Historical Museum - 1953
Sívertsen House (built by Bjarni Sívertsen from
1803-05), Sigga's House (built by Erlendur
Marteinsson in 1902)   20096

Sjóminjasafn Islands (Icelandic Maritime Museum),
Vesturgata 8, 220 Hafnarfjördur - T: 5302200,
5654242, Fax: 5302201, E-mail: sjominjasafn@
natmus.is, Internet: http://www.natmus.is. Head:
Agust Georgsson
Historical Museum - 1986
Rowing boats, fishing gear, models, seafaring, coast
culture   20097

Höfn

Byggdasafn Austur-Skaftafellssýslu (Local
Museum), Gömlu Búd, 780 Höfn - T: 4781833,
Fax: 4781805, E-mail: bga@eldhorn.is,
Internet: http://www.eldhorn.is/syslusafn. Head:
Gísli Sverrir Árnason
Local Museum - 1980
local natural hist dep   20098

Húsavík

Byggdasafnid Grenjadarstad (Grenjadarstadur Folk
Museum), Grenjadarstadur, 641 Húsavík -
T: 8812435, 4641860, Fax: 4642160,
E-mail: safnahus@vortex.is. Head: Gudni
Halldorsson
Local Museum
Old tuf-house, household and farming tools, local
history   20099

Safnahusid Húsavík (Húsavík Museum), Storigardur
17, 640 Húsavík - T: 4641860, Fax: 4642160,
E-mail: safnahus@vortex.is. Head: Gudni
Halldorsson
Local Museum
Local history, natural history, art coll, ships -
archives   20100

Isafjördur

Byggdasafn Vestfjarda (Country Museum),
Austurvegur 9, 400 Isafjördur - T: 3293. Head: Jôn
Sigurpálsson
Local Museum   20101

Keflavík

Byggdasafn Sudurnesja Vatnsnes (Vatnsnes Local
Museum), Vatnsnesvegur 8, 230 Keflavík -
T: 4213155, Fax: 4214667. Head: Gudleifur
Sigurjónsson
Local Museum - 1934
Local and regional hist   20102

Kópavogur

Natural History Museum of Kópavogur, Digranesvegur 12, 200 Kópavogur - T: 5540630, E-mail: nature@skima.is. Head: Hilmar Malmquist
Natural History Museum 20103

Neskaupstadur

Náttúrugripasafnid i Neskaupstad (Museum of Natural History), Miðstræti 1, 740 Neskaupstadur - T: 4771454, E-mail: natgrip@austurland.is. Head: Einar Thorarinsson
Natural History Museum - 1965 20104

Patreksfjördur

Minjasafn Egils Ólafssonar (Egill Olafssons Local Museum), Hnjótur, 451 Patreksfjördur - T: 4561569, Fax: 4561569, E-mail: museum@hnjotur.is, Internet: http://www.hnjotur.is. Head: Johann Asmundsson
Local Museum 20105

Reykjavik

Arbaejarsafn - Reykjavik Museum (Municipal and Open Air Museum), Kistuhylur 4, 110 Reykjavik - T: 5771111, Fax: 5771122, E-mail: abs@reykjavik.is, Internet: http://www.arbaejarsafn.is. Head: Gudny Gerdur-Gunnardottir
Local Museum / Open Air Museum 20106

Åsmundarsafn (Åsmundur Sveinsson Sculpture Museum), Sigtún, 105 Reykjavik - T: 5532155, Fax: 5626191, E-mail: listasafn@reykjavik.is. Head: Eiríkur Thorláksson
Fine Arts Museum - 1982
Sculpture 20107

Listasafn Así, Àsmundarsalur (Labour Union Art Museum), Freyjugötu 41, 101 Reykjavik - T: 5115353, Fax: 5115354, E-mail: listasi@centrum.is. Head: Kristin Gudnadòttir
Fine Arts Museum - 1961
Icelandic art of the 20th c 20108

Listasafn Einars Jónssonar (Einar Jónsson Museum), Njardagata, 121 Reykjavik - T: 5513797, Fax: 5623909, E-mail: skulptur@skulptur.is, Internet: http://www.skulptur.is. Head: Júlíana Gottskálksdóttir
Fine Arts Museum - 1923
Sculpture and painting by Einar Jónsson - sculpture garden 20109

Listasafn Islands (National Gallery of Iceland), Frikirkjuvegur 7, 101 Reykjavik - T: 5159600, Fax: 5159601, E-mail: list@natgall.is, Internet: http://www.listasafn.is. Head: Ólafur Kvaran
Fine Arts Museum - 1884
20th c art Markús Ivarsson coll, works by Gunnlaugur Scheving, Ásgrímur Jónsson coll - library 20110

Listasafn Reykjavíkur (The Reykjavik Art Museum), Flókagötu, 105 Reykjavik - T: 5526131, Fax: 5626191, E-mail: listasafn@reykjavik.is, Internet: http://www.reykjavik.is/listasafn. Head: Eirikur Thorlaksson
Fine Arts Museum - 1973
Erró coll, Kjarval coll, Sveinsson coll - architectural division 20111

Myntsafn Sedlabanka og Thjódminjasafns (Numismatic Museum), Einholti 4, 105 Reykjavik - T: 5699600, Fax: 5699609, E-mail: safnadeild@sedlabanki.is, Internet: http://www.sedlabanki.is. Head: Ólafur Pálmason
Special Museum 20112

Náttúrufrædlistofnun Íslands (Icelandic Institute of Natural History), Hlemmur 3-5, 125 Reykjavik - T: 5900500, Fax: 5900595, E-mail: ni@ni.is, Internet: http://www.ni.is. Head: Jon Gunnar Ottosson
Natural History Museum - 1889
Botany and zoology, geology, invertebrates, mulluscs, amphibians, reptiles, mammals, minerals - library 20113

Norraena Húsid, V. Hringbraut, 101 Reykjavik - T: 17030. Head: Knut Ødegård
Local Museum 20114

Norræna Húsid (Nordic House), v/Hringbraut, Reykjavik, 101 - T: 5517030, Fax: 5526476, E-mail: nh@nordice.is, Internet: http://www.nordice.is
Public Gallery 20115

Nýlistasafnið (Living Art Museum), Vatnsstig 3b, 101 Reykjavik - T: 5514350, Fax: 5614350, E-mail: nylo@nylo.is, Internet: http://www.nylo.is. Head: Sonny Thorbjornsdottir
Fine Arts Museum 20116

Póst- og Símaminjasafnid, Austurgötu 11, Reykjavik - T: 9154321
Special Museum 20117

Safn Ásgrims Jónssonar (Ásgrimur Jónsson Gallery), Bergstadastraeti 74, 101 Reykjavik, mail addr: Pósthólf 668, 121 Reykjavik - T: 5513644, Fax: 5621312, E-mail: list@natgall.is, Internet: http://www.listasafn.is. Head: Júlíana Gottskálksdóttir
Fine Arts Museum 20118

Sigurjón Ólafsson Museum, Laugarnestanga 70, 105 Reykjavik - T: 5532906, Fax: 5814553, E-mail: lso@vortex.is, Internet: http://www.lso.is. Head: Birgitta Spur
Fine Arts Museum - 1984
Works of Sigurjón Ólafsson 20119

Stofnun Arna Magnússonar, Arnagardi v/Sudurgötu, 101 Reykjavik - T: 5254010, Fax: 5254035, E-mail: rosat@hi.is, Internet: http://www.AM.hi.is. Head: Vésteinn Ólason
Folklore Museum - 1971
Medieval manuscripts, folklore 20120

University Art Museum, Oddi, Sudurgata, 101 Reykjavik - T: 91694300
Fine Arts Museum / University Museum 20121

Selfoss

Listasafn Árnesinga -Árnesýsla Art Gallery (Art Museum), Tryggvagata 23, 800 Selfoss - T: 4822703, Fax: 3079, E-mail: listar@isholf.is, Internet: http://www.selfoss.is/listasafn. Head: Hildur Hákonardóttir
Fine Arts Museum - 1964
Art coll of paintings and wood carvings 20122

Seltjarnarnes

Nesstofusafn (Nesstofa Museum), Pósthólf 152, 172 Seltjarnarnes - T: 611016. Head: Kristinn Magnússon
Historical Museum
Medical hist in 1760 mansion 20123

Siglufjördur

Síldarminjasafnid a Siglufirdi (Herring Era Museum of Iceland), Snorrag 15, 580 Siglufjördur - T: 4671604, Fax: 4671888, E-mail: herring@siglo.is, Internet: http://www.siglo.is/herring. Head: Örlygur Kristfinnsson
Special Museum - 1907/91
Herring fishing and industry, tools, equipment, machines, focus on the life and work of the fishermen, workers and owners of the herring companies 20124

Skogar

Byggdasafn Rangæinga (Country Museum), 860 Skogar - T: 78845. Head: Thordur Tomasson
Local Museum 20125

Stykkishólmur

Byggdasafn Snæfellinga og Hnappdæla (Local Museum), Norska Húsid, Hafnargata 5, 340 Stykkishólmur - T: 4381640, Fax: 4381602, E-mail: norskhus@simnet.is. Head: Aldis Sigurdardottir
Local Museum - 1956
Local and regional hist 20126

Varmahlid

Byggdasafn Skagfirdinga (Skagafjördur Folk Museum), Glaumbær, 560 Varmahlid - T: 4536173, Fax: 4538873, E-mail: glaumb@krokur.is, Internet: http://www.krokur.is/glaumb. Head: Sigridur Sigurdardóttir
Special Museum - 1948 20127

Vestmannaeyjar

Byggdasafn (Country Museum), Safnahusinu, 900 Vestmannaeyjar - T: 9811194, Fax: 9811174. Head: Jóhann Fridfinnsson
Local Museum 20128

Fiska- og Náttúrngripasafn Vestmannaeyja (Museum of Natural History), Heidarvegur 12, 900 Vestmannaeyjar - T: 9811997. Head: Kristjan Egilsson
Natural History Museum - 1965
Invertebrates, fossils - aquarium 20129

Vopnafjördur

Minjasafnid Burstarfelli (Burstarfell Local Museum), Burstarfell, 690 Vopnafjördur - T: 4731466. Head: Björg Einarsdóttir
Local Museum
Household tools 20130

India

Agra

Taj Mahal and Fort Akbar, Agra
Archaeological Museum 20131

Ahmedabad

Calico Museum of Textiles, Sarabhai Foundation, The Retreat, Shahi Baug, Ahmedabad 380000 - T: (079) 2868172, Fax: 2865759. Head: Gira Sarabhai
Special Museum - 1949
Representative coll of Indian textile heritage, reconstructed wooden facades - reference library 20132

City Museum, Sanskar Kendra, nr Sardar Bridge, Paldi, Ahmedabad 380007 - T: (079) 6578369, E-mail: history@gujaratworld.com, Internet: http://www.gujaratworld.com/history/museum.html. Head: Kailashnathan
Local Museum / Historical Museum - 2000
Ancient history and art, industrial revolution, textiles, Gandhiism, communities and culture, design, literature, science 20133

Gandhi Smarak Sangrahalaya, Harijan Ashram, Ahmedabad 380027 - T: (079) 7557277, Fax: 7560569, E-mail: gandhiashram@satyam.net.in. Head: Amrutbhai Modi
Special Museum - 1952
Manuscripts of Gandhi's correspondence, books on Gandhiana, negatives of Gandhi, Kusturba and others, Gandhi's writing desk and spinning wheel, life size oil paintings of big and small enlargements of Gandhi 20134

M.C. Mehta Gallery, Bhagtacharya Rd, Sanskar Kendra, Ahmedabad - T: (079) 78369. Head: J. Ramesh
Fine Arts Museum
Miniature painting 20135

Museum of Gujarat Vidya Sabha, c/o B.J. Institute of Learning and Research, R.C. Marg, Ahmedabad 380009 - T: (079) 6588862. Head: Dr. Braratiben K. Shelat
Archaeological Museum / Historical Museum - 1961
Manuscripts in Sanskrit, Prakrit, Hindi, Gujarati, Arabic, and Persian, coins, sculptures, replica and photographs of ancient monuments and sculptures, paintings, stone inscriptions, old documents 20136

Tribal Museum, c/o Tribal Research and Training Institute, Ashram Rd, Gujarat Vidyapith, Ahmedabad 380014 - T: (079) 446148. Head: Dr. T.B. Naik
Ethnology Museum - 1964
Equipment for food gathering, fishing, agriculture, costumes and ornaments, material culture of religion, musical instruments, games, dioramas, maps, paintings, charts and photographs relating to different tribes, Kircho (bamboo musical instruments), Mogradev (wooden crocodile gods), Hunvlo (domestic utensils) - library 20137

Ahmednagar

History Museum, c/o Ahmednagar College, Ahmednagar
Historical Museum - 1965
Specimens of sculptures, coins, pottery, icons, photographs and drawings 20138

Ajmer

Government Museum, near Naya Bazar, Ajmer
Archaeological Museum - 1908
Archaeological objects 20139

Rajputana Museum, Ajmer 305001. Head: R.D. Sharma
Local Museum - 1908
Inscriptions, coins, sculpture, Rajput paintings, arms and armoury of Rajasthan 20140

Alampur

Archaeological Site Museum, Alampur 509152. Head: N. Mallikarjuna Rao
Archaeological Museum - 1953
Sculptures of Western Chalukyan and Kakatiya periods, inscriptions on stone 20141

Aligarh

University Museum of Science and Culture, c/o Aligarh Muslim University, Kennedy House, General Education Centre, Aligarh - T: (0571) 400438. Head: Prof. Alam Iftikhar
Natural History Museum / Archaeological Museum / Historical Museum - 1964
Prehistory, sculptures, terra cottas, paintings, textiles, coins, natural history 20142

Allahabad

Allahabad Museum, Motilal Nehru Park, Kamla Nehru Rd, Allahabad 211002 - T: (0532) 600834. Head: U.S. Tiwari
Fine Arts Museum / Decorative Arts Museum - 1931
Stone sculptures, terra cottas, miniature paintings, modern Indian paintings, seals, sealings, coins, present from Pt. Jawaharlal Nehru, miniature objects, handicrafts, manuscripts, arms and inscriptions 20143

Archaeology Museum, c/o Allahabad University, Allahabad
Archaeological Museum - 1949
Prehistory, prehistoric tools from earliest times to the end of the Pleistocene together with fossils, Mesolithic tools, human and animal skeletons, Neolithic tools and other related antiquities, proto-historic material from different sites, coll from Ghositaram, the famous Buddhist monastery 20144

G.N. Jha Kendriya Sanskrit Vidyapeetha, Chandra Shekhar Azad Park, Allahabad 211002 - T: (0532) 600525, 600957. Head: Prof. Gaya Charan Tripathi
Library with Exhibitions / Historical Museum - 1943
Sanskrit, Hindi, Arabic and Persian manuscripts - manuscripts library of ancient sanskrit texts 20145

Hindi Sangrahalaya, Hindi Sahitya Sammelan, Allahabad
Historical Museum
Printed books, periodicals, manuscripts, coins, letters, photographs, memoir trophies and personal belongings of literary personalities 20146

Zoology Department Museum, c/o University of Allahabad, Allahabad
Natural History Museum - 1910
Different phyla of the animal kingdom - such as stuffed, preserved, dried specimens, articulated skeletons, fossils, models, mounted skeleton of an elephant, camel, stone implements of prehistoric men, rare fossils 20147

Alwar

Government Museum, City Palace, Alwar
Fine Arts Museum / Music Museum / Military Museum - 1941
Arts and handicrafts, paintings, armoury, musical instruments from the Raja's coll 20148

Amaravati

Archaeological Museum, Amaravati 522020. Head: C.L.N. Sastri
Archaeological Museum - 1951
Stupa-slabs, railings, sculpture, inscriptions, coins of gold, silver and lead 20149

Amreli

Amreli Archaeological and Art Museum, Amreli - T: (02792) 221180, Fax: 236770. Head: A.P. Mehta, Hiralal P. Shah
Archaeological Museum / Fine Arts Museum 20150

Shri Girdharbhai Sangrahalaya (Children's Museum), Amreli 365601 - T: (02792) 221180, Fax: 236770. Head: Hiralal Shah
Special Museum - 1955
Educational exhibits, children's museum 20151

Amritsar

Central Sikh Museum, Clock Tower Bldg, Golden Temple, Amritsar. Head: S. Amolak Singh
Religious Arts Museum - 1958
Paintings regarding Sikh hist, relics of Sikh gurus, coins, old manuscripts about Sikh hist 20152

Annamalai Nagar

Zoology Museum, c/o Annamalai University, Annamalai Nagar 608101
Natural History Museum - 1929
South Indian representative invertebrates and lower vertebrates, systematics 20153

Banaras → Varanasi

Banda

Bundelkhand Chhatrasal Museum, Banda
Fine Arts Museum / Decorative Arts Museum / Natural History Museum - 1955
Sculptures, terra cottas, stone implements, beads and seals, coins, anthropological objects, natural science section 20154

Bangalore

Central College Museum, c/o Central College, Bangalore 560001
Natural History Museum / University Museum
Rocks, zoological and botanical specimens, fossils, minerals, specimens of invertebrates and vertebrates, mammals 20155

Karnataka Government Museum and Venkatappa Art Gallery, Kasturba Rd, Bangalore 560001 - T: (080) 2864483, Fax: 2864483. Head: Dr. M.V. Krishnappa, B.M. Chikkamare Gowda
Fine Arts Museum / Museum of Classical Antiquities - 1866
Antiquities from Mohenjodaro, Brahmagiri, Chandravalli, and T.N. Pur, terra cottas from East Bengal, Hoysala, Dravidian, Chola, Chalukya and Pala sculpture, miniature paintings from North India, traditional paintings from Mysore, ivory and ivory inlay articles, sandalwood caskets, old wood carvings, arms and armoury, etc. - temporary exhibitions, auditorium 20156

Visvesvaraya Industrial and Technological Museum, Kasturba Rd, Bangalore 560001 - T: (080) 2864563, Fax: 2864114. Head: K. Vasudeva Bhatta
Science&Tech Museum - 1962
Developments in science and technology and their application to human welfare, scientific, technological and industrial artifacts, working models, steam lorry (1916), music box (1816) - library 20157

Bareilly

Abhai Smarak Panchal Sangrahalaya, 125/5 Kishore Bldgs, Kishore Bazar, Bareilly
Decorative Arts Museum - 1974
Pottery, coins, terra cotta figurines, beads, bone implements 20158

Baripada

Baripada Museum, Baripada
Archaeological Museum - 1903
Palaeolithic and neolithic implements, copper axe-head, sculpture, historical documents, gold, silver and copper coins, seals and beads, terra cotta, stone inscriptions, painted palm-leaf manuscripts 20159

Baroda → Vadodara

Barrackpur

Gandhi Smarak Sangrahalaya, 14 Riverside Rd, Barrackpur
Special Museum - 1961
Photographs portraying Gandhi's life, photocopied letters to Gandhi, press clippings, bulletins and tape recordings 20160

Belkhandi

Belkhandi Museum, Post Office Kalahandi, Belkhandi
Archaeological Museum
Stone sculptures discovered at the site 20161

Bhagalpur

Bhagalpur Museum, Tilka Manjhi Chowk, Bhagalpur
Fine Arts Museum / Decorative Arts Museum - 1976
Stone sculptures, terra cottas, arms 20162

Bhanpura

Local Museum, Bhanpura
Archaeological Museum
Archaeological objects and sculpture 20163

Bharatpur

Government Museum, Inside Fort, Bharatpur
Fine Arts Museum / Decorative Arts Museum - 1944
Sculptures, coins, armoury, zoological specimens, paintings and manuscripts, art and crafts 20164

Bhavnagar

Arts and Crafts Museum, Gandhi Smriti, Bhavnagar
Decorative Arts Museum / Fine Arts Museum - 1963
Arts and crafts of Gujarat State and well known crafts of different States of India 20165

Barton Museum, Gandhi Smriti, Bhavnagar
Fine Arts Museum / Archaeological Museum / Historical Museum - 1895
Arts, antiquities, archaeology, history 20166

Children's Museum, Gandhi Smriti, Bhavnagar
Special Museum - 1959
Coll based on basic training and recreation for children 20167

Gandhi Museum, Gandhi Smriti, Bhavnagar - T: 24024. Head: Himmat Trivedi
Special Museum - 1955
Rare photographs of Mahatma Gandhi, coll of documents and personal relics, audiovisual materials, prayer and lecture records 20168

Bhopal

Birla Museum, New Vidhan Sabha Rd, Satpura, Bhopal 462004 - T: (0755) 551388
Archaeological Museum - 1971
Stone sculptures, terra cottas, coins, manuscripts, prehistoric tools, photographs of monuments of Madhya Pradesh, reproductions of Bhimbetka rock paintings 20169

Central Museum, Bhopal
Fine Arts Museum / Decorative Arts Museum - 1949
Paintings, coins, porcelain, toys of metals and ivory, woodwork, needlework, handicrafts 20170

Madhya Pradesh Tribal Research and Development Institute, 35 Shamla Hills, Bharat Bhavan, Bhopal 462004. Head: Vikas Bhatt
Folklore Museum - 1954
Tribal arts and contemporary work 20171

Regional Science Centre, Banganga Rd, Shamla Hills, Bhopal 462002 - T: (0755) 661655, E-mail: rscbhm@bom6.vsnl.net.in. Head: H. P Mishra
Science&Tech Museum - 1995
Inventions, physical science, planetarium 20172

Bhubaneshwar

Orissa State Museum, Jaydev Marg, Bhubaneshwar 751006 - T: (0674) 52897. Head: Dr. Harish Chandra Das
Archaeological Museum / Folklore Museum / Fine Arts Museum / Natural History Museum - 1932
Archaeology, epigraphy, numismatics, paintings, costumes, ethnology, anthropology, science, manuscripts, particularly of palm leaves - library 20173

Regional Science Centre Bhubaneswar, Pandit Jawaharlal Nehru Marg, Bhubaneswar 751013 - T: (0674) 542795, E-mail: rscbbsr@sancharnet.in. Head: Dr. C. Sukumaran
Science&Tech Museum - 1989
Exhibits on Universe, science, environment, outdoor science park exhibits 20174

Bhuj

Kachchh Museum, Out of Mahadev Gate, Bhuj 370001 - T: 20541. Head: Dr. S.N. Pandey
Fine Arts Museum / Science&Tech Museum / Ethnology Museum / Archaeological Museum - 1877
Arts, crafts and industries of Kachchh, maritime hist, anthropology, archaeology, musical instruments, numismatics, inscriptions of Kshatrapa dynasty (1st and 2nd c) Harappan relics, seals, beads, pottery (2000 BC), aerospace science, memorabilia of India's struggle for freedom - library 20175

Bijapur

Archaeological Museum, Bijapur 587138. Head: H. Telegu
Archaeological Museum - 1912
Antiquities of the period of Adil Shahis (1480-1680), armoury, porcelain and china, coins, miniature paintings, manuscripts 20176

Bikaner

Ganga Government Museum, Museum Bldg, Sagar Rd, Bikaner - T: (0151) 528894. Head: P.C. Bhargava
Fine Arts Museum / Decorative Arts Museum / Natural History Museum - 1937
Arts and crafts, fauna and culture of Bikaner, terracottas, paintings, manuscripts, weapons, textiles of Mughal period, carpets 20177

Bishnupur

Acharya Jogesh Chandra Purakirti Bhavan, Bangiya Sahitya Parisat Bishnupur Branch, POB, Bishnupur 722122. Head: Manik Lal Sinha
Fine Arts Museum / Historical Museum / Folklore Museum - 1951
Art and architecture, prehistoric to contemporary, old manuscripts, folk art 20178

Bodh Ghaya

Archaeological Museum, Bodh Ghaya 824231 - T: 39. Head: S. Singh
Archaeological Museum
Archaeological objects, stone and bronze sculptures 20179

Bombay → Mumbai

Bulandshahar

Government Educational Museum, c/o Government Inter College, Bulandshahar
Decorative Arts Museum
Sculptures, terra cottas, pottery 20180

Burdwan

Museum and Art Gallery, c/o University of Burdwan, Rajbati Post Office, Burdwan 713104 - T: (0342) 2371. Head: Samanta Sailendranath
Fine Arts Museum / Folklore Museum / Decorative Arts Museum - 1965
Indian art and antiques, folk art, European and Indian oil paintings, terra cotta figures and figurines, woodcarvings, manuscripts, coins, bronzes 20181

Calcutta → Kolkata

Calicut → Kozhikode

Cawnpore → Kanpur

Chamba

Bhure Singh Museum, Chamba. Head: H.N. Chopra
Fine Arts Museum / Decorative Arts Museum - 1908
Pahari paintings, Chamba rumal and other textiles, woodcarvings, bronzes, arms, copperplates, historical documents, declarations, coins, manuscripts, sculptures, Rang Mahal section 20182

Chandigarh

Government Museum and Art Gallery, Sector 10-C, Chandigarh 160011 - T: (0172) 742501, Fax: 742501, E-mail: museum@chd.nic.in. Head: Vidya Nand Singh
Fine Arts Museum / Natural History Museum - 1966
Gandhara sculptures, miniatures of the Mughal, Rajasthani, Pahari and Sikh schools and Kangra schools, geological objects, fossils, minerals, painted panels on evolution of life through the ages 20183

Museum of Fine Arts, c/o Punjab University, Chandigarh
Fine Arts Museum - 1968
Contemporary paintings and sculptures, mostly Indian 20184

Chennai

Anatomy Museum, c/o Madras Medical College, Chennai
Special Museum - 1932
Human anatomy, comparative embryology, human skeleton and skeleton parts 20185

Archaeology Museum, c/o Department of Ancient History and Archaeology, University of Madras, Chennai 600005 - T: (044) 5368778 ext 341, Fax: 5366693, Internet: http://www.universityofmadras.edu. Head: Dr. P. Shanmugam
Archaeological Museum / University Museum - 1962
Excavated material and antiquities, palaeolitihics, coins 20186

Fort Museum, Fort Saint George, Chennai 600009 - T: (044) 561127. Head: Dr. D. Jithendradas
Military Museum - 1948
Arms, uniforms, medals, porcelains, coins, manuscripts, paintings, prints, textiles related to East India Company days 20187

Government Museum and National Art Gallery, Pantheon Rd, Egmore, Chennai 600008 - T: (044) 869638. Head: M. Raman
Fine Arts Museum / Archaeological Museum / Ethnology Museum / Music Museum / Natural History Museum - 1851
Art, archaeology, anthropology, numismatics, philately, South Indian bronzes, Buddhist sculptures, folk art, musical instruments, zoology, botany, geology - children's section, library 20188

Madras Christian College Museum, Tambaram, Chennai 600059. Head: Prof. M. Gladstone
Natural History Museum / University Museum - 1835
Zoological specimens from southern India 20189

Museum of the College of Engineering, c/o College of Engineering, Guindy, Chennai
Science&Tech Museum / University Museum - 1920
Models of bridges, dams, girders, railways, culverts, sections of soil, masonry foundations, arches over doors and windows 20190

Chhindwara

State Tribal Museum, Chhindwara 480001 - T: (07162) 42441. Head: Kiran Vijay Singh
Folklore Museum - 1954
Tribal arts, artifacts, crafts 20191

Chitradurga

Local Antiquities Museum, Chitradurga 577501 - T: (08194) 24202, 21716. Head: Shankar S. Athani
Archaeological Museum - 1951
Arms, sculptures, portraits, manuscripts, excavation material from Chandravalli and Brahmagiri, such as neoliths, coins, beads, pottery, seated Dakshabrahma sculpture, hero stone, sculptures 20192

Cochin → Kochi

Coimbatore

Gass Forest Museum, R.S. Puram, Coimbatore, mail addr: c/o Institute of Forest Genetics and Tree Breeding, POB 1061, Coimbatore 641002 - T: (0422) 441540, Fax: 440549. Head: S.R. Madhavan Pillai
Natural History Museum - 1902
Charts on 'Man and Biosphere', films on forestry operations and wildlife, forest flora and fauna, tribal ornaments and weapons - library 20193

Museum of the Agricultural College and Research Institute, c/o Agricultural College and Research Institute, Coimbatore 641002
Agriculture Museum - 1909
Seeds and products of cereals, fibers, minerals, rocks, fungus diseases, models of implements and tools, gold and silver medals, cups, shields, stuffed birds, snakes and poultry 20194

Cuddapah

Bhagavan Mahavir Government Museum, Cuddapah
Historical Museum 20195

Damoh

Purvattatva Sangrahalaya Madhya Pradesh Shasan, Civil Ward 1, Purana Girjaghar, Damoh
Archaeological Museum - 1970
Stone sculptures 20196

Darbhanga

Chandradhari Museum, Dighi Lake, Station Rd, Darbhanga - T: 2191. Head: K.K. Mishra
Decorative Arts Museum - 1957
Bronzes and terra cottas, personal coll of Baba Chandradhari Singh consisting of various paintings, ivory works, bronzes, manuscripts, textiles, coins 20197

Darjeeling

Akshaya Kumar Maitreya Museum, 6 km from Bagdora Airport, Darjeeling, mail addr: North Bengal University PO, Darjeeling 734430 - T: (0353) 581305, 581255, Fax: 581546, E-mail: deanacl@dte.vsnl.net.in. Head: F. Rahaman
Fine Arts Museum / Historical Museum - 1965
Stone, bronze and wooden sculptures, coins, mainly native states of Eastern India, manuscripts, Assamese-Bengali scripts, paintings, miniatures 20198

Bengal Natural History Museum, Darjeeling 734101 - T: (0354) 54308
Natural History Museum - 1903
Butterflies, birds, birds eggs, reptiles and amphibia, fish, insects, invertebrates, mammals 20199

Mountaineering Museum, c/o Himalayan Mountaineering Institute, Jawaharparbat, Darjeeling 734101 - T: (0354) 53803, Fax: 53760, E-mail: cndas@dte.vsnl.net.in. Head: Chandranath Das
Special Museum - 1959
Explorers of 20th c, mountaineering equipment over the ages, topographical models of the Himalaya, details of the Everest region, hist of discovery, attempts and climbs of Mt Everest, flora, fauna, tribal art of Himalayan region, rock samples from Sikkim 20200

Dehradun

Botanical Survey of India, Northern Circle, 3 Lakshmi Rd, Dehradun
Natural History Museum - 1956
Plants, particularly from the Himalayas, insect-catching plants, parasitic plants, alpine cold desert plants, plants of economic importance, medicinal plants, a coll of seeds, fruits and wood samples, large photographs and panels depicting vegetation types of the Himalayas and arid plains 20201

Forest Research Institute and College Museum → F.R.I. Museums

F.R.I. Museums, New Forest, Dehradun 248006 - T: (0135) 755277, Fax: 756865, E-mail: rawatgs@icfre.org, Internet: http://www.icfre.org. Head: G.S. Rawat
Agriculture Museum / University Museum - 1906
Specimens of forest products, forest diseases, forest management and utilisation of forest products, Indian and foreign wood, insect attack, insect coll, wood pathology - aboretum, bambusetum, xylarium 20202

Zonal Museum, 51-7 Hardwar Rd, Dehradun
Ethnology Museum - 1971
Physical and cultural anthropology of North Western India, including the Central and Western Himalayas 20203

Zoological Museum, Northern Regional Station, 218 Kaulagarh Rd, Dehradun 248001 - T: (0135) 28362, Fax: 28362. Head: Dr. Arun Kunar
Natural History Museum - 1960
Fauna of the Northern Region 20204

Delhi

Aitihasic Puratatva Sangrahalaya, Kanya Gurukul, Narela, Delhi 110040
Archaeological Museum - 1963
Coins, copperplates, terra cotta, beads, weapons of the Indus valley civilization, seals and manuscripts 20205

Anthropology Museum, c/o Department of Anthropology, University of Delhi, Delhi 110007 - T: (011) 2515329. Head: Dr. J.S. Bhandari
Ethnology Museum - 1947
Objects of physical and cultural anthropology 20206

Archaeological Museum, Purana Quila, Delhi 110001. Head: Syed Jamal Hassan
Archaeological Museum - 1974
Excavations from Purana Quila 20207

Archaeological Museum Red Fort Delhi, Mumtaz Mahal, Red Fort, Delhi 110006 - T: (011) 267961. Head: S.K. Sharma
Archaeological Museum - 1918
Antiquities connected with the hist of Red Fort, historical coll of the Mughal period, relics of India's War of Independence 20208

Bharatiya Adim Jati Sevak Sangh Museum, Dr. Ambedkar Rd, Delhi 110055 - T: (011) 3532003, 3625492, Fax: 3532003. Head: Banwari Lal Gaur
Ethnology Museum
Tribal costumes and handicrafts, diaromas, artifacts 20209

Crafts Museum, Pragati Maidan, Bhairon Rd, Delhi 110001 - T: (011) 3317641, Fax: 3371515. Head: Dr. Jyotindra Jain
Decorative Arts Museum / Folklore Museum - 1952
Traditional crafts including folk and tribal arts of India, dolls, toys, textiles, jewellery, stone and ivory carvings, bronzes, metalware, pottery, terracottas, basketry, painting, open air village complex - library 20210

Ghalib Museum, Aiwan-E-Ghalib Marg, Delhi 110002
Special Museum - 1969
Ghalib: his age and disciples, social life, Urdu poetry 20211

Indian War Memorial Museum, Red Fort, Mumtaz Mahal, Delhi - T: (011) 327303. Head: Syed Jamal Hassan
Military Museum - 1982
Arms, ammunition, war trophies related to World War I 20212

Indira Gandhi National Centre for the Arts, 1 C.V. Mess, Janpath, Delhi 110 001 - T: (011) 3383895, Fax: 33888280, E-mail: ignca@del3.vsnl.net.in, Internet: http://www.ignca.nic.in. Head: Dr. L.M. Singhvi, Prof. N.R. Shetty
Public Gallery 20213

National Children's Museum, 1 Kotla Rd, Delhi 110002. Head: Dr. Madhu Pant
Special Museum - 1962
Children's art work and artifacts, thematic exhibitions with an educational content, dolls, photography, study kits and working models, masks based on Indian mythology, animal skins 20214

National Gallery of Modern Art, Jaipur House, India Gate, Sher Shah Rd, Delhi 110003 - T: (011) 382835. Head: Dr. Anish Farooqi
Fine Arts Museum - 1954
Contemporary Indian paintings, sculptures, graphics, industrial design, architecture and photography, works by Abanindranath Tagore, Rabindranath Tagore, Jamini Roy, Amrita Sher Gil and others 20215

National Gandhi Museum and Library, Rajghat, Delhi 110002 - T: (011) 3310168, 3311793, Fax: 3311793, E-mail: gandhimk@nda.vsnl.net.in. Head: Dr. Y.P. Anand
Special Museum - 1948
Photographs and relics of Mahatma Gandhi, his vast correspondence, journals, art works and objects, 40,000 books on and by Mahatma Gandhi and his contemporaries, Gandhi's philosophy and India's freedom movement - library, archives, photo studio, picture gallery 20216

National Museum of India, Janpath, Delhi 110011 - T: (011) 3018159, Fax: 3019821. Head: Prof. R.C. Sharma
Archaeological Museum / Ethnology Museum / Fine Arts Museum - 1949
Prehistory, protohistory, sculptures, bronzes, copperplates, coins, miniature paintings, arms, arts, pre-Columbian arts, anthropology, Central Asian coll - Departments of Art, Archaeology, Anthropology, Modelling, Presentation, Publication, Library and Photography 20217

National Museum of Natural History, FICCI Bldg, Barakhamba Rd, Delhi 110001 - T: (011) 3314932, Fax: 3314932. Head: K. Sethuraman
Natural History Museum - 1978
Natural sciences, botany, zoology, ecology, environment - objects enabling visitor to participate by touching and feeling, special facilities for children - library, mobile museum 20218

National Philatelic Museum, Dak Bhavan Parliament St, Delhi 110001 - T: (011) 3032727
Special Museum
Postage stamps especially from India 20219

National Rail Museum, Chanakyapuri, Delhi 110021 - T: (011) 6880939/1816, 3304137, Fax: 6880804, E-mail: rajesh_agrawal@vsnl.com, Internet: http://www.railmuseum.org. Head: Rajesh Agrawal
Science&Tech Museum - 1977
Objects from over 150 years of railway hist in India, vintage locomotives, princely saloons and photographs - library 20220

National Science Centre, Pragati Maidan, near Gate 1, Bhairon Rd, Delhi 110001 - T: (011) 3371263, 3371946, Fax: 3371263, E-mail: nscd@giasdl01.vsnl.net.in, Internet: http://www.nesm.org. Head: P.K. Bhaumik
Science&Tech Museum - 1992
Hist of Indian science, technology and culture, mobile science, hands-on exhibits - science park 20221

Nehru Memorial Museum and Library, Teen Murti House, Delhi 110011 - T: (011) 3015333. Head: Prof. Ravinder Kumar
Special Museum - 1964
Materials from the life and works of Jawaharlal Nehru, Indian's first Prime Minister; Indian struggle for freedom, photo-documentation of national movement - Library 20222

Rabindra Bhavan Art Gallery, 35 Ferozeshah Rd, Delhi. Head: Anand Dev
Fine Arts Museum - 1955
Permanent gallery of the Lalit Kala Akademi, venue of Triennale-India 20223

Shankar's International Dolls Museum, Nehru House, 4 Bahadur Shah Zafar Marg, Delhi 110002 - T: (011) 3316970, Fax: 3721090. Head: Shanta Srinivasan
Special Museum - 1965
Dolls from all over the world 20224

Sulabh International Museum of Toilets, Sulabh Bhawan, Mahavir Enclave, Palam Dabri Marg, Delhi 110045 - T: (011) 5039362, 5032631, Fax: 5034014, E-mail: sulabh@ndb.vsnl.net.in, Internet: http://www.sulabhtoiletmuseum.org. Head: Earl Kessler, Dr. Bindeshwar Pathak
Special Museum 20225

Tibet House Museum, Tibet House, 1 Institutional Area, Lodi Rd, Delhi 110003 - T: (011) 4611515, Fax: 4625536, E-mail: thouse@nde.vsnl.net.in. Head: Doboom Tulku
Ethnology Museum - 1965
Tibetan statues, ritual objects, jewelry, stamps and coins, and manuscripts - library 20226

Deoria

Dr. Raj Bali Pandey Puratatva Sangrahalaya, M.M.M. Siksha Sansthan, Bhatpar Rani, Deoria
Archaeological Museum - 1970
Stone sculpture, stone tools, terra cottas, coins, microlithic stone tools, manuscripts 20227

Government Educational Museum, Deoria
Special Museum - 1950
Plaster casts of historical personalities, terra cottas, specimens of Mohenjodaro and Harrapa, rocks and minerals, stuffed birds and animals, zoological specimens, all kinds of charts and maps, wooden models of irrigation industries, coins, manuscripts, toys, clay models, paintings, metallic images 20228

Dhar

District Archaeological Museum, 12 Cotavad Darwaja, Dhar
Archaeological Museum - 1902
Sculptures, architectural pieces, inscriptions, coins, pottery, art objects, ornaments, photographs, sketches, maps and charts 20229

Dharampur

Lady Wilson Museum, Garden Rd, Dharampur, mail addr: POB 15, Dharampur 369050 - T: (02633) 42055. Head: Dr. S.N. Pandey
Folklore Museum / Natural History Museum / Ethnology Museum / Archaeological Museum - 1928
Tribal art and culture of Gujarat India, and abroad, specimens of stuffed wild animals, zoology, geology, industrial arts from India and abroad, musical instruments, dolls and toys from various countries 20230

Dharwad

Museum of Art and Archaeology, c/o Kernatak University, Dharwad
Fine Arts Museum / Archaeological Museum 20231

Dharwar

Kannada Research Institute Museum, c/o Karnataka University, Dharwar. Head: B.S. Kulkarni
Archaeological Museum - 1939
Prehistoric antiquities, terra cottas, inscriptions, copperplates, sculptures, metal images, wooden figures, paintings, manuscripts 20232

Dhule

I.V.K. Rajwade Sanshodhan Mandal Museum, Rajwade Path, Ln 1, Dhule 424001 - T: (0262) 33848. Head: Dr. P.N. Deshpande
Archaeological Museum / Fine Arts Museum / Local Museum - 1932
Stone sculptures, metal icons, copperplates, coins from India and abroad, manuscripts with paintings, stamps - reference library, archives 20233

Ernakulam

Zoology and Botany Museum, c/o Maharaja's College, Ernakulam
Natural History Museum / University Museum - 1874
Specimens of zoology and botany 20234

Etawah

Government Educational Museum, Government Inter College Compound, Station Rd, Etawah
Special Museum / University Museum - 1957
Original coins, locally collected sculpture pieces (6th c), plaster casts, portraits and sculptures of national leaders, portraits of scientists and literary figures, dioramas, fish, printed copies of Ajanta paintings, dome models, modern paintings and sculptures 20235

Faizabad

Botany Museum, K.S. Saket Mahavidyalaya, Faizabad
Natural History Museum
Specimens of botanical interest, algae, fungipteridophytes 20236

Geography Museum, K.S. Saket Mahavidyalaya, Faizabad
Natural History Museum
Specimens of rocks, minerals, peculiar sand from Comorin 20237

Government J.T.C. Museum, Faizabad
Natural History Museum / Historical Museum - 1952
Animals skeletons, coins, horns of different animals, wooden toys, heads of different animals, stone toys and idols of the part, earthen toys, foreign recent coins 20238

Zoological Museum, K.S. Saket Mahavidyalaya, Faizabad
Natural History Museum
Zoological specimens and photographs 20239

Gangtok

Museum of Icons and Art Objects, c/o Namgyal Institute of Tibetology, Gangtok - T: (0359) 2525. Head: J.K. Rechung
Religious Arts Museum / Fine Arts Museum 20240

Gauhati

Anthropological Museum, c/o Department of Anthropology, Gauhati University, Gopinath Bardoloi Nagar, Gauhati 781014 - T: (0361) 570248, Fax: 570133, E-mail: bapukan@sify.com. Head: B. Choudhury
Ethnology Museum - 1948
Ethnology, all branches of anthropology 20241

Assam Forest Museum, South Kamrup Division, Gauhati. Head: G.N. Bhuyan
Special Museum - 1948-49
Timber, bamboos, canes and various forest products, ivory and lacquer works, medicinal herbs, elephant tusks and rhino horns, models of bridges, buildings 20242

Assam State Museum, Gauhati 781001. Head: Dr. R.D. Choudhury
Historical Museum / Fine Arts Museum - 1940
Stone sculptures, archaeology, paintings, costumes, inscriptions, Padma tankas, coins - library 20243

Commercial Museum, c/o Gauhati University, Gauhati 781014 - T: 88514
Special Museum / University Museum - 1957
Economic development of India, commercial products, minerals and rocks, forest products, handicrafts, industrial and chemical products, agricultural implements, office appliances and labour saving devices, documents, pictures and models, coins 20244

Gauhati Medical College Museum, c/o Gauhati Medical College, Gauhati 781015
Special Museum / University Museum
Science, medicine, anatomy 20245

Gaya

Gaya Museum, Gaya 823001
Archaeological Museum / Ethnology Museum / Natural History Museum / Decorative Arts Museum - 1952
Archaeology, ethnology, geology, natural history, decorative arts, paintings, sketches and photographs, numismatics, arms, manuscripts 20246

Gorakhpur

Archaeological Museum, c/o Department of Ancient History, Archaeology and Culture, Gorakhpur University, Gorakhpur
Archaeological Museum / University Museum - 1958
Coins, sculptures, photographs 20247

Botany Museum, c/o University of Gorakhpur, Gorakhpur
Natural History Museum / University Museum
Different plant groups, insectivorous plants, herbarium representing local flora and fossil specimens 20248

Puratatva Sangrahalaya, Rahul Sankratayan Sansthan, Alinagar, Gorakhpur
Historical Museum - 1967
Sculptures, coins, terra cottas, beads, manuscripts, illustrated manuscripts, palm leaf manuscripts 20249

Zoological Museum, c/o University of Gorakhpur, Gorakhpur
Natural History Museum / University Museum - 1958
All the major vertebrates and invertebrates 20250

Gulbarga

District Museum, Sedam Rd, Gulbarga 585103 - T: (08472) 20608. Head: M.S. Satyan
Archaeological Museum
Archaeological objects, sculptures, inscriptions 20251

Guntur

Archaeological Museum, Nagarjunakonda, Guntur. Head: K. Veerabhadra Rao
Archaeological Museum - 1966
Limestone (early period), granite (medieval period), terra cottas, stuccos, gold, silver and copper coins, pottery, beads, metallic objects, prehistoric stone implements 20252

District Museum, Regional Library opposite A.C. College, Guntur. Head: J. Surya Narayara Rejn
Archaeological Museum - 1975
Sculptures and inscriptions relating to early historic and medieval periods 20253

Gwalior

Archaeological Museum, Gujari Mahal, Gwalior 474003 - T: 328. Head: P.K. Saran
Archaeological Museum - 1922
Sculpture, stone pillars and capitals, sati stones, metal images, terra cotta objects, coins, excavated objects from ancient sites such as Pawaya (Padmavati), Besnagar (Vidisha), Ujjain (Ujjayini) and Maheshwar, copies of Bagh frescoes and paintings 20254

H.H. Maharaja Jayaji Rao Scindia Museum, Museum Jai Vilas Palace, Lashkar, Gwalior 474001
Decorative Arts Museum - 1964
Coll of Royal Family, kitsch 20255

Municipal Museum Gwalior, Moti Mahal Campus, Gwalior 474002 - T: (0751) 322828. Head: M.B. Ojha
Local Museum / Natural History Museum - 1922
Prehistoy, ancient sculpture, brass, copper bronzes, arms and weapons, paintings, modern sculpture, porcelain, glass, ivory, wood, costumes, tapestry, carpet, musical instruments , minerals, coins, crafts 20256

Halebidu

Archaeological Museum, Via Arasikere, Halebidu 573121
Archaeological Museum - 1961
Sculpture, bronzes, copperplates, inscriptions, woodcarvings 20257

Hampi

Archaeological Museum, Hampi
Archaeological Museum
Sculpture and coins from Vijayanagar period 20258

Haora

Ananda Niketan Kirtishala (Rural Museum on Folk Art and Archaeology), Ananda-Niketan, Haora, mail addr: PO Bagnan, Haora 711303. Head: Dipankar Ghoshadhyay
Folklore Museum / Archaeological Museum - 1961
Terra cotta, pottery, temple terra cotta plaques, coins, stone sculptures, folk arts and crafts, Bengali and Sanskrit manuscript copies, card index of ancient temples and mosques, tribal artifacts - library 20259

Central National Herbarium, Botanical Survey of India, Indian Botanical Garden, Haora 711103 - T: (033) 6603235, Fax: 2429330, E-mail: envisbsi@gems.vsnl.net.in. Head: Dr. M. Sanjappa
Natural History Museum - 1793
Plant materials, dried plants, botanical illustrations, maps - library 20260

Sarat Smriti Granthagar, Panitras, Haora
Special Museum - 1956
Manuscripts and articles used by Sarat Chandra Chatterjee, terra cotta, sculptures, coins of various countries, folk art 20261

Hardwar

Archaeological Museum, Gurukul Kangri, Hardwar
Archaeological Museum - 1945
Prehistoric exhibits, sculptures, terra cottas, coins, manuscripts, paintings, arms 20262

State Ayurvedic College Museum, c/o State Ayurvedic College, Gurukul Kangri, Hardwar 249494 - T: (0133) 427563. Head: Dr. Vinod Upadhyay
Natural History Museum / University Museum - 1922
Pharmacy, ayurvedic, herbal medicine and cosmetics 20263

Zoological Museum, c/o Gurukul Kangri University, Hardwar
Natural History Museum / University Museum
Zoological specimens 20264

Hassan

District Museum, Maharaja Park, Hassan. Head: Shivananda V. Rao
Archaeological Museum / Fine Arts Museum - 1977
Archaeological objects, sculptures, inscriptions, arms, coins, paintings 20265

Hooghly

Carey Museum, Serampore, Hooghly, mail addr: c/o Serampore College, POB, Hooghly 712201 - T: 622322. Head: Sunil Kumar Chatterjee
Historical Museum - 1818
Belongings of the founder of Serampore mission, items connected with the early history of the college, rare books and manuscripts - Carey library 20266

College of Textile Technology Museum, c/o College of Textile Technology, 12 William Carey Rd, Serampore, Hooghly
Science&Tech Museum / University Museum - 1959
Textile products 20267

Museum and Art Gallery, c/o Institute Chanderanagar, The Residency, Chanderanagar, Hooghly
Historical Museum / Fine Arts Museum - 1952
Relics of the French in India, including valuable documents, relics of local freedom fighters, bibliographical materials, photographs, paintings, terra cotta, other antiquities 20268

Howrah → Haora

Hyderabad

Andhra Pradesh State Museum, Hyderabad 500034. Head: Dr. V.V. Krishna Sastry
Fine Arts Museum / Decorative Arts Museum - 1930 20269

Khajana Buildings Museum, Golkonda Fort, Golkonda, Hyderabad
Fine Arts Museum - 1960
Sculptures 20270

Qutb Shahi Museum, Golconda, Hyderabad
Archaeological Museum
20271

Salarjung Museum, Hyderabad 500002 - T: (040)
523211. Head: Dr. I.K. Karma
Fine Arts Museum / Decorative Arts Museum - 1951
Western paintings, Indian miniatures, textiles,
bronze, Eastern and European porcelain, jade,
carpets, glass, ivory, clocks, bidri ware, modern art,
marble statues - children's section, library   20272

State Health Museum, Public Garden 11-6-15,
Hyderabad 500004 - T: (040) 232267. Head: S.
Ramakantam
Special Museum / Natural History Museum - 1948
Plastic human heart, 5 specimens of poisonous and
non-poisonous snakes in India, models, objects,
photographs, dioramas, maps, graphics - library,
training center   20273

State Museum, Public Gardens, Hyderabad 500004 -
T: (040) 232267. Head: P. Joginaidu
Decorative Arts Museum / Historical Museum -
1930
Gold coins, Bronze idols, arms and wepons,
decorative art   20274

Yeleswasam Pavilion, Gunfoundry, Hyderabad
500001 - T: (040) 237216
Archaeological Museum - 1961
Material unearthed from the successive excavations
at Yeleswasam   20275

Imphal

Manipur State Museum, Polo Ground, Imphal
795001 - T: 220709. Head: Dr. K. Sobita Devi
Fine Arts Museum / Archaeological Museum /
Natural History Museum / Ethnology Museum - 1969
Art, archaeology, natural history, geology,
anthropology, textiles, cultural hist - library,
archives, children's gallery   20276

Indore

Central Museum, Agra-Bombay Rd, Indore 452001
Archaeological Museum / Fine Arts Museum /
Military Museum - 1929
Archaeological objects, fine arts, arms, coins 20277

Itanagar

Jawaharlal Nehru State Museum, State Museum
Rd, Itanagar 791111 - T: (0360) 212483, 212276.
Head: Dr. D.K. Bora, B. Pertin
Ethnology Museum - 1956
Ethnographic and archaeological objects   20278

Jaipur, Orissa

Jeypore Branch Museum, Jaipur, Orissa
Archaeological Museum - 1976
Sculptures and other archaeological objects 20279

Jaipur, Rajastan

Government Central Museum, Ram Niwas Garden,
Jaipur, Rajastan 302004. Head: R.C. Agarwal
Decorative Arts Museum / Fine Arts Museum /
Natural History Museum - 1886
Metalware, ivory and lacquer work, jewelry, textiles,
pottery, carved wooden objects, arms and weapons,
clay models, sculptures, paintings, educational,
scientific and zoological objects   20280

Maharaja Sawai Man Singh II Museum, City Palace,
Jaipur, Rajastan 302002 - T: (0141) 608055,
Fax: 608169, 603880, E-mail: ctpalace@
pinkline.net, Internet: http://royalfamilyjaipur.com.
Head: Yaduendra Sahai
Fine Arts Museum / Decorative Arts Museum - 1959
Art, miniatures of Mughal and Rajasthani schools,
Persian and Mughal carpets, antique arms and
weapons, textiles and costumes, Mughal glass,
decorative arts, photographs, illuminated
manuscripts of the Razmnama and Ramayana,
astronomical manuscripts and instruments -
library   20281

Jammu

Dogra Art Gallery, Gandhi Bhawan, Dogra Hall,
Jammu, mail addr: POB, Kachi Chawni, Jammu
180001. Head: A.A. Bandey
Fine Arts Museum - 1954
Paintings, especially Phari miniatures, armoury;
Basholi School   20282

Jamnagar

Museum of Antiquities, Lakhoto, Jamnagar 361001
- T: 78125. Head: D.J. Thunga
Archaeological Museum - 1946
Sculptures, paintings, inscriptions, coins, folk art
pieces, natural history   20283

Jaunpur

Archaeological Museum, c/o T.D. College, Jaunpur
Archaeological Museum / University Museum
Sculptures, terra cottas, coins, medals   20284

Botany Museum, c/o T.D. College, Jaunpur
Natural History Museum / University Museum -
1956
All important plant and fossil types   20285

Zoological Museum, c/o T.D. College, Jaunpur
Natural History Museum / University Museum
Zoological exhibits   20286

Jeypore → Jaipur, Rajastan

Jhajjar

Haryana Prantiya Puratatva Sangrahalaya, Gurukul,
Jhajjar
Fine Arts Museum / Decorative Arts Museum - 1961
Coins, inscriptions, copperplates, terra cotta,
sculptures, beads, manuscripts, weapons of the
Indus valley civilization, ancient and modern art
objects   20287

Jhalawar

Government Museum Jhalawar, Jhalawar. Head:
K.L. Meena
Fine Arts Museum / Archaeological Museum /
Decorative Arts Museum - 1915
Sculptures, inscriptions, coins, manuscripts, wood
and ivory carvings, old paintings, minerals   20288

Jhalrapatan

Jhalawar Archaeology Museum, Jhalrapatan
Archaeological Museum   20289

Jhansi

Rani Laxmi Bai Palace Sculpture Collection, Rani
Laxmi Bai Palace, Jhansi
Archaeological Museum - 1970
Hindu and Jain red sandstone images (9th-
12th c)   20290

Jodhpur

Government Museum, Jodhpur
Archaeological Museum / Natural History Museum /
Decorative Arts Museum / Military Museum / Fine
Arts Museum - 1915
Coins, paintings, wood, lacquer items, leather, ivory,
stone, arms, mother of pearl, minerals, glass,
textiles, metal, pottery, antiquities, natural history,
educational apparatus   20291

Sadar Museum, Jodhpur
Archaeological Museum / Fine Arts Museum /
Decorative Arts Museum - 1909
Sculptures, paintings, local arts and crafts, ivory
work, metal work, chundri and leather work of
Jodhpur, manuscripts, documents, carvings, armour,
textiles, pottery   20292

Junagadh

Darbarhall Museum, Diwan Chowk, Junagadh
362001 - T: (0285) 21685. Head: P.V. Dholakia
Decorative Arts Museum / Fine Arts Museum - 1947
Furnishings and household items, paintings   20293

Junagadh Museum, Sakkar Bag, Junagadh 362003 -
T: (0285) 21382. Head: R.R. Goswami
Archaeological Museum / Fine Arts Museum /
Natural History Museum / Folklore Museum - 1901
Archaeology, coins, sculptures, inscriptions,
miniature paintings, manuscripts, silver art, carpets,
glassware, natural history, wooden objects, folk art,
textiles - library, auditorium   20294

Kakinada

Andhra Sahitya Parishat Government Museum,
Veternary Hospital Rd, Ramaraopet, Kakinada
533004 - T: 5619
Archaeological Museum   20295

Kalpi

Mahatma Gandhi Hindi Sangrahalaya, Hindi
Bhawan, Kalpi
Fine Arts Museum / Archaeological Museum - 1950
Sculptures, paintings, terra cotta, metal images,
lithic inscriptions, coins, manuscripts   20296

Kamalapur

Archaeological Museum, Hampi, Kamalapur 583221
- T: (08394) 41561, Fax: 41561. Head: Dr. K.P.
Padhy
Archaeological Museum - 1954
Stone sculptures and architectural pieces of Vijaya
Nagar period, gold and copper coins, palm leaf
manuscripts and copperplates, paintings   20297

Kanpur

Botany Museum, c/o Christ Church College, Kanpur
Natural History Museum / University Museum
Plants of all groups, classes and families, fossils,
herberia, raw plants and plant products   20298

Commercial and Industrial Museum, c/o Directorate
of Industries, Kanpur
Science&Tech Museum / Decorative Arts Museum
Handicrafts, handloom, cottage industry products,
marble, woodcarving, brassware, carpets, silk,
brocades   20299

Zoology Museum, c/o Christ Church College, Kanpur
Natural History Museum / University Museum -
1961
Museum specimens preserved in formalin, stuffed
birds and animals, models   20300

Karimnagar

Gandhi Centenary Museum, opposite RTC Bus
Station Complex, Karimnagar 505001 - T: 43069.
Head: B. Jayarangarao
Archaeological Museum / Fine Arts Museum - 1969
Miniature paintings and paintings of modern art,
material from archaeological excavations   20301

Katora Talab

Chattishgarh Mudra Sangrahalaya (Chattishgarh
Coin and Papermoney Museum), c/o Dr. Singh
Nursing Home, Jhulelal Dham Rd, Katora Talab
492001 - T: (0771) 423866, 423824, 424160,
E-mail: drsingh@mantramail.com. Head: Dr. Bhanu
Pratap Singh
Special Museum - 1999
Indian coins (Satvahana, Mauryan, Kushan,
Indogreek, Guptas, Kalchuri, Sulans, Mouhals etc),
British Ceylon notes, European/ American
coins   20302

Keladi

Keladi Museum, Shimoga Dt, Keladi 577443, mail
addr: c/o Kuvempu University, PO Keladi, Sagar
577401 - T: (08183) 60077, 60140, Fax: 60140.
Head: Dr. K.G. Venkatesh Jois
Archaeological Museum / University Museum -
1960/51
Archaeology rural, prehistoric implements,
sculptures, terra cottas, inscriptions, coins, beads,
ancient palm leaf manuscripts, hist records and
ancient paintings, folklore   20303

Khajuraho

Archaeological Museum, Khajuraho 471606 -
T: (07686) 72320, 74030, Fax: 72320. Head: V.N.
Gupta
Archaeological Museum - 1910
Sculptures, inscriptions and architectural pieces of
Chandella period   20304

Khatkar Kalan

Shaheed-e-Azam Bhagat Singh Museum, Khatkar
Kalan Nawan Shahr
Historical Museum - 1980
Personalia of Singh, material about freedom
movement against British imerialism   20305

Khiching

Khiching Museum, Khiching
Archaeological Museum / Decorative Arts Museum
Stone sculptures, lithic implements, beads,
pottery   20306

Kittur

Kithur Rani Channamma Memorial Museum, Kittur
Fort, Kittur
Archaeological Museum
Archaeological objects, sculptures,
inscriptions   20307

Kochi

Archaeological Museum Cochin, Mattanchery
Palace, Kochi 682002. Head: Dr. Jithendra Das
Archaeological Museum - 1986
Ancient sculpture, copper, bronze and iron
objects   20308

Mattancherry Palace Museum, Archaeological
Survey of India, Kochi 682002
Historical Museum - 1982
Arms and weapons, painting, glass, ivory,
embroidered costumes   20309

Kodagu

Government Museum, Fort, Madikedri, Kodagu
Archaeological Museum / Fine Arts Museum
Sculptures, inscriptions, modern art (paintings),
arms, natural history   20310

Kohima

State Museum, c/o Government of Nagaland, Kohima
Ethnology Museum - 1970
Anthropological specimens   20311

Kolhapur

Kolhapur Museum, Town Hall, Kolhapur
Archaeological Museum - 1946
Finds from Brahmapuri excavations, paintings,
arms, sculptures and miscellaneous works of arts
and stone inscriptions   20312

Kolkata

Academy of Fine Arts Museum, Cathedral Rd,
Kolkata 700071 - T: (033) 444205. Head: Ranu
Mookerjee
Fine Arts Museum / Decorative Arts Museum - 1933
Rabindranath's paintings, manuscripts and personal
belongings, paintings, engravings, miniatures,
sculptures, old textiles, ancient carpets   20313

Asiatic Society Museum, 1 Park St, Kolkata 700016
- T: (033) 240539. Head: Dr. Amalendu De
Fine Arts Museum / Historical Museum - 1784
Rare and illustrated manuscripts, coins, paintings,
inscriptions, sculpture   20314

Asutosh Museum of Indian Art, c/o University of
Calcutta, Centenary Bldg, Kolkata 700073 - T: (033)
343014. Head: Dr. Niranjan Goswami
Fine Arts Museum / Folklore Museum - 1937
Pottery, terracotta from Vishnupur, Sena sculpture,
seals, coins, paintings, folk art, arts of Bengal -
library   20315

Bangiya Sahitya Parisad Museum, 243/1 Acharya
Prafulla Chandra Rd, Kolkata 700006 - T: (033)
3503743. Head: Pradip Chaudhuri
Fine Arts Museum / Decorative Arts Museum /
Historical Museum - 1906
Stone sculpture, terracottas, old paintings, copper
plates, coins (Indo-Greek, Indo-Scythian, Indo-
Parthian, Kusan), old weapons, old banner paintings,
icons, old Bengali, Sanskrit, Persian and Tibetan
manuscripts incl some original manuscripts of
important personalities of India (Vidyasagar,
Vivekananda, R.N. Tagore) - library   20316

Birla Academy of Art and Culture Museum, 108-
109 Southern Av, Kolkata 700029 - T: (033)
4662843. Head: Dr. Archava Roy
Fine Arts Museum / Decorative Arts Museum - 1962
Paintings of the medieval period, miniature
paintings, stone and bronze sculptures,
woodcarvings, terra cottas, textiles, modern art,
archaeological specimens, anthropology - library,
auditorium, exhibition gallery   20317

Birla Industrial and Technological Museum, 19a
Gurusaday Rd, Kolkata 700019 - T: (033) 2476102,
Fax: 2476102, E-mail: bitm@cal2.vsnl.net.in,
Internet: http://www.bitmcal.org. Head: Samares
Goswamy
Science&Tech Museum - 1959
Models and exhibits on various branches of physical
sciences, industry and technology including original
objects - regional science centre, film library,
archives   20318

Crafts Museum, Art in Industry Museum, 9-12 Old
Court House St, Kolkata 700001 - T: (033) 237205.
Head: Ramranjan Chakraborty
Decorative Arts Museum - 1950
Rural arts and crafts including ivories, metal objects
and textiles from different regions of India   20319

Cultural Research Institute, P1/4, CIT Scheme VII-M,
VIP Rd, Kankurgachi, Kolkata 700054 - T: (033)
3379102, Fax: 3379102. Head: Dr. M.K. Chowdhuri
Ethnology Museum - 1955
Different types of artifacts of the tribal folks of West
Bengal   20320

Government Industrial and Commercial Museum,
45 Ganesh Chandra Av, Kolkata 700013 - T: (033)
2365316. Head: S.N. Pal
Historical Museum / Decorative Arts Museum -
1939
Industrial and commercial products of West Bengal
including large, medium and small scale industries
and handicrafts and folk art   20321

Gurusaday Museum, Museum of Bengal Folk Art,
Bratacharigram 743512, mail addr: Joka Post
Office, Kolkata 700104 - T: (033) 4676048,
Fax: 4535972. Head: Justice A.N. Ray
Folklore Museum - 1963
Various types of precious scrolls, paintings
(patachitra), Kalighat pat, terracotta plaques for
temples, stone, wood, brass and bronze sculptures,
figurines, dolls, toys, tribal folk art, musical
instruments, manuscripts, wooden painted
manuscript covers, archaeological specimens,
Kantha and Dhokra art   20322

Indian Museum, 27 Jawaharlal Nehru Rd, Kolkata
700016 - T: (033) 2495699, Fax: 2495696. Head:
Dr. S.K. Chakravarti
Fine Arts Museum / Folklore Museum / Music
Museum / Military Museum / Natural History
Museum - 1814
Miniature paintings, ivory, bead works, textiles,
woodcarvings, bronze, jewelry, temple banners,
scrolls, tribal and folk art, musical instruments,
costumes, masks, arms and weapons, Indus valley
excavated objects, seals, coins, zoology, mammals,
botany - library, herbarium   20323

Marble Palace Art Gallery and Zoo, 46 Muktaram
Babu St, Kolkata. Head: Mrigendra Mallick
Fine Arts Museum / Decorative Arts Museum - 1842
Paintings, bronzes, vases, woodworks, terra cottas,
clocks, chandeliers, mirrors, painted tiles   20324

Municipal Museum, College St Market, North Block,
Kolkata
Special Museum - 1932
Public and civil health and indigenous
products   20325

Nehru Children's Museum, 94/1 Chowringhee Rd,
Kolkata 700020 - T: (033) 2233517, 2236878,
2231551, Fax: 4403890, E-mail: ncm@
cal.vsnl.net.in, Internet: http://
www.nehrumuseum.org. Head: Swdip Srimal
Special Museum - 1972
The Ramayana depicted in 1500 miniature models
in 61 illuminated sets, the Mahabharata depicted in
2000 miniature models in 62 multi-colour and
illuminated sets, dolls and toys, science
section   20326

Netaji Museum, c/o Netaji Research Bureau, 38/2
Lala Lajpat Raj Rd, Kolkata 700020 - T: (033)
756139. Head: Dr. Sisir Kumar Bose
Special Museum - 1961
Photographs, original letters, manuscripts,

paintings, sculptures, films, microfilms, original documents concerning the life, activities and thoughts of Netaji Subhas Bose and Sarat Chandra Bose   20327

Rabindra Bharati Museum, 6/4 Dwarakanath Tagore Ln, Kolkata 700007. Head: Samar N. Bhowmik
Special Museum - 1961
Literary artistic and organisational activities of Rabindranath Tagore and the Tagore family   20328

Regional Labour Institute, Lake Town, Kolkata.
Head: D.B. Deb
Science&Tech Museum - 1965
Exhibits pertaining to industrial safety, hygiene and occupational health   20329

State Archaeological Gallery, 33 Chittaranjan Av, Kolkata 700013
Archaeological Museum - 1962
Prehistory, protohistory, medieval history, stone artifacts, chalcolithic material, pottery and other antiquities, sculptures in stone, metal, ivory, wood, paintings, miniatures, coins, epigraphs, manuscripts   20330

Victoria Memorial Hall, 1 Queen's Way, Kolkata 700071 - T: (033) 2235142, Fax: 2235142, E-mail: victomem@cal2.vsnl.net.in, Internet: http://www.victoriamemoral-cal.org. Head: Prof. C. Panda, D. Phil
Historical Museum / Fine Arts Museum - 1906
Paintings in oil and watercolour, Mughal and Rajput miniatures, prints and lithographs, engravings, drawings, busts and statues, arms and armour, manuscripts, models and portraits of eminent national leaders and their personal relics, objects relating to Indian history of the period 1700-1900   20331

Konarak

Archaeological Museum, Konarak
Archaeological Museum - 1968
13th c sculpture from the Sun Temple complex   20332

Kotah

Museum and Saraswati Bhandar, Kotah
Archaeological Museum / Fine Arts Museum / Military Museum / Folklore Museum - 1944
Sculptures, epigraphs, coins, manuscripts, paintings of Hadoti, Jaipur and Udaipur, arms, costumes   20333

Kozhikode

Regional Science Centre and Planetarium,
Planetarium Rd near Jafferkhan Colony, Kozhikode - T: (0495) 770571, Fax: 765088, E-mail: astropl@md5.vsnl.net.in, Internet: http://www.rscpcalicut.8m.com. Head: V.S. Ramachandran
Science&Tech Museum
Science and technology   20334

V.K. Krishna Menon Museum and Art Gallery,
Malabar Collectors Bungalow, East Hill, Kozhikode - T: (0485) 51253
Fine Arts Museum / Special Museum - 1976
Memorabilia of Sri. V.K. Krishna Menon, paintings (modern, Bengal, Rajastani, Mughal, Chinese, Japanese, Tibetan and realistic school), works by Renound Raja Ravi Varma, carvings in wood, ivory and metals   20335

Lucknow

Army Medical Corps Centre Museum, Army Medical Corps Centre, Lucknow 226001
Military Museum
Old uniforms, swords and equipment, photographs, albums and history of the Army, Navy and Air Force   20336

Bal Sangrahalaya (Children's Museum), Motilal Nehru Marg, Charbagh, Lucknow 226004 - T: (0522) 455761
Special Museum - 1957
Paintings, sculptures, toys, dolls, scientific models, dioramas - library, audio-visual aids   20337

Birbal Sahani Institute of Palaeobotany Museum, 53 University Rd, Lucknow 226007 - T: (0522) 324291, 323206, Fax: 381948, 374528, E-mail: director@bisp-india.org, Internet: http://www.bisp-india.org. Head: Prof. Anshu Kumar Sinha
Natural History Museum - 1946
Plant fossils and specimens of palaeobotanical interest, model of Williamsonia Sewardiana Sahni, geological landscape painting - library, research institute   20338

Botany Museum, c/o Lucknow University, Lucknow
Natural History Museum / University Museum - 1940
Important and rare botanical specimens   20339

College of Arts and Crafts Museum → Museum of Arts and Crafts

Gandhi Museum, Gandhi Bhawan, Mahatma Gandhi Marg, Lucknow 226001
Special Museum - 1973
Photographs, paintings, replica pertaining to Gandhi   20340

Geological Museum, Vasundhara, Sector-E, Aliganj, Lucknow 226020 - T: (0522) 74187, Fax: 76407. Head: K.N. Singh
Natural History Museum - 1961
Rocks, minerals, fossils, models, maps, charts, photographs   20341

Geology Museum, c/o University of Lucknow, Dept. of Geology, University Rd, Lucknow 226007 - T: (0522) 324798, Fax: 222061. Head: Prof. I.B. Singh
Natural History Museum / University Museum - 1947
Indian rock types, minerals, fossils   20342

Jail Training School Museum, Jail Training School, Lucknow 226001
Special Museum - 1973
Models of jails, models of the Kargha factory and flour mill, wooden model of an execution chamber (Phansi Ghar), fetters weighing 30 kg from Rampu, photos of prisons where eminent freedom fighters were kept, coll taken from prisoners, psychological apparatus   20343

Museum of Arts and Crafts, c/o College of Arts and Crafts, University of Lucknow, Tagore Marg, Lucknow - T: 371214, 372381
Decorative Arts Museum / Fine Arts Museum / University Museum - 1911
Ancient arts and crafts coll   20344

Museum of the Department of Anthropology, c/o Department of Anthropology, Lucknow University, Lucknow
Ethnology Museum - 1951
Ethnographic, prehistoric, archaeological, palaeo-anthropological objects   20345

Pathology and Bacteriology Museum, c/o K.G. Medical College, Lucknow
Natural History Museum / University Museum
Specimens of surgical, medical, gynaecological, ophthalmic and other sciences   20346

State Health Institute Museum, K.G. Medical College Campus, Lucknow 226001 - T: (0522) 62236
Special Museum
Coll relating to health science   20347

Uttar Pradesh State Museum, Banarsi Bagh, Lucknow 226001 - T: (0522) 206157, Fax: 206158, E-mail: director@statemuseumlucknow.com, Internet: http://www.statemuseumlucknow.com. Head: Jitendra Kumar
Local Museum - 1863
Sculptures, terracottas, coins, ivory, woodwork, bronzes, metalware, paintings, textiles, miniatures, crafts, natural hist, archaeology, arms and armours, jewellery, manuscripts - conservation lab, photography section, modelling workshop, library   20348

Zoology Museum, c/o University of Lucknow, Lucknow
Natural History Museum / University Museum - 1921
Stuffed mammals, rare mammals, skeletons of mammals   20349

Madras → Chennai

Madurai

Gandhi Memorial Museum, Gandhi Smarak Sangrahalaya, Madurai 625020 - T: (0452) 531060. Head: R. Venkataraman
Special Museum
Relics of Gandhi   20350

Sri Meenakshi Sundaresvara Temple Museum, Madurai
Fine Arts Museum / Decorative Arts Museum - 1937
South Indian bronzes, paintings, jewellery, musical instruments, lamps, wood carvings and other art objects   20351

Malda

Malda Museum, 16 Kalitala 2nd Ln, Malda
Archaeological Museum   20352

Mandapam Camp

Museum of the Central Marine Fisheries Research Station, Mandapam Camp
Special Museum - 1947
Models of fishing gear and equipment used in different parts of India, other marine animals, plants, sea weeds, sea weed products, fish dils and fish manures   20353

Mangalore

Mahatma Gandhi Museum, c/o Canara High School, Mangalore 575004
Natural History Museum / Fine Arts Museum / Ethnology Museum - 1939
Zoology, anthropology, art, coins, manuscripts, sculptures and paintings   20354

Shreemanthi Bai Memorial Government Museum, Bejai, Mangalore 575004. Head: L.S. Krishna Sastry
Fine Arts Museum / Archaeological Museum / Natural History Museum - 1960
Art, archaeology, natural history   20355

Mathura

Government Museum, Dampier Nagar, Mathura 281001 - T: 3191. Head: A.K. Srivastava
Archaeological Museum / Fine Arts Museum / Folklore Museum - 1874
Sculpture, terra cottas, Kushana and Gupta period inscriptions, coins, paintings, bronzes, folk art - reference library   20356

Vrindavan Research Institute Museum, Raman Reti, Vrindavan, Mathura - T: (0565) 443828, Fax: 442476, E-mail: vrivbn@vsnl.com
Library with Exhibitions / Fine Arts Museum
Manuscripts in Sanskrit, Hindi, Bengali, Gujarati, Gurmukhi, Oriya, Urdu and Persian, paintings, sculpture   20357

Meerut

Zoological Museum, c/o Meerut College, Civil Lines St, Meerut 250002 - T: (0121) 664303 ext 219. Head: Prof. K.N. Tyagi
Natural History Museum - 1965
Invertebrate, skeletons and Hill stream fauna, fishes   20358

Midnapore

Sahitya Parishad Museum, Vidyasagar Memorial Hall, Vidyasagar Rd, Midnapore
Archaeological Museum - 1918
Stone sculptures, pottery, seals, coins, manuscripts in Bengali and Sanskrit, panja of the Mughal period, copperplates from the Maharaja Sasanka period (7th c)   20359

Mount Abu

Government Museum, Mount Abu
Archaeological Museum / Fine Arts Museum / Decorative Arts Museum - 1965
Sculptures, paintings, brass, ivory work, embroidery work, woodwork, printing   20360

Mumbai

Dr. Bhau Daji Lad Museum, 91A Dr. Babasaheb Ambedkar Rd, Byculla, Mumbai 400027 - T: (022) 3757943. Head: M. Gandhi
Archaeological Museum / Fine Arts Museum / Decorative Arts Museum / Ethnology Museum / Natural History Museum - 1872
Armour, sculpture, metalware, pottery, stoneware, fine arts, leather work, lacquer work, horn work, ivory, cut glass, manuscripts, paintings, fossils, ethnology, minerals, photographs and maps, Old Bombay coll - library   20361

Grant Medical College Museum, c/o Grant Medical College, Mumbai 400057
Natural History Museum / University Museum - 1845
Pathology museum: forensic medicine, hygiene, public health, anatomy museum: skeletons, bones   20362

Heras Institute of Indian History and Culture, c/o Saint Xavier's College, 5 Mahapalika Marg, Mumbai 400001 - T: (022) 2620665. Head: Dr. Aubrey A. Mascarenhas
Fine Arts Museum / Archaeological Museum - 1926
Indian archaeological finds, Indian Christian art, icons and miniature paintings, sculptures, manuscripts and rare books - library   20363

Jehangir Art Gallery, 161/B Mahatma Gandhi Rd, Mumbai 400023 - T: (022) 243989. Head: Jehangir Sirhirji
Fine Arts Museum   20364

Natural History Museum of Bombay Natural History Society, Hornbill House, Shahid Bhagat Singh Rd, Mumbai 400023 - T: (022) 2821811, Fax: 2837615, E-mail: bnhs@bom4.vsnl.net.in, Internet: http://www.bnhs.org. Head: Dr. A.R. Rahmani
Natural History Museum - 1883
Vertebrates (mammals, birds, reptiles) and insects of the Indian region   20365

Nehru Science Centre, Dr. E. Moses Rd, Worli, Mumbai 400018 - T: (022) 4932668, Fax: 4932668, E-mail: nscm@giasbm01.vsnl.net.in. Head: R.M. Chakraborti
Natural History Museum / Science&Tech Museum - 1985
Science for children, Light & Sight, Sound & Hearing, discovery, evolution, life and work of C.V. Raman, our heritage, children's science park, man and machine, Intel Cyberschool - library, development las, auditorium   20366

Prince of Wales Museum of Western India, 159-161 Mahatma Gandhi Rd, Mumbai 400023 - T: (022) 2844484, Fax: 2045430. Head: Dr. K. Desai
Archaeological Museum / Natural History Museum / Fine Arts Museum / Decorative Arts Museum - 1922
Sculpture, natural hist, Indian miniature paintings, bronzes, Nepalese and Tibetan art, prehistoric and protohistoric objects, decorative arts, Chinese and Japanese porcelain and other antiquities, Indian metalware and modern paintings of the Bombay School, maritime heritage of India - library   20367

Victoria and Albert Museum, Victoria Gardens, Mumbai 400000
Ethnology Museum / Fine Arts Museum / Decorative Arts Museum / Natural History Museum / Historical Museum - 1855

Agriculture, ethnology, religion and mythology, paintings, arms and weapons, industry and industrial products, pottery, geology, relics of old Bombay   20368

Muzaffarnagar

Governmental Educational Museum, Muzaffarnagar
Special Museum - 1959
Coins, terra cottas, sculptures, plaster casts, arts and paintings, dolls, stamps, cannons   20369

Zoology Museum, c/o Sanatan Dharm College, Bhopa Rd, Muzaffarnagar 251001 - T: 6737
Natural History Museum / University Museum - 1970
Invertebrate and vertebrate animals with a separate coll on insects   20370

Mysore

Folklore Museum, c/o University of Mysore, Manasagangotri, Mysore - T: (0821) 22549 ext 64. Head: H. Thipperudraswany
Folklore Museum / University Museum
Paintings, crafts, musical instruments, leather shadow puppets, masks, toys   20371

Sri Jayachamarajendra Art Gallery, Jaganmohan Palace, Mysore 570024 - T: (0821) 23693, Fax: 520031. Head: M. Lakshminarayan
Decorative Arts Museum / Fine Arts Museum - 1924
Oil and water colour paintings, antique clocks, musical instruments, ivory and sandal wood carvings, ceramics and metalware, murals, antique furniture and curios - auditorium   20372

Museum of Art and Archaeology, c/o University of Mysore, Manasagangotri, Mysore 570006 - T: (0821) 22525 ext 37. Head: Dr. T. Dayananda Patel
Fine Arts Museum / Archaeological Museum / University Museum - 1973
Archaeological specimens, sculptures, inscriptions, coins   20373

Museum of the Medical College, c/o Medical College, Mysore
Natural History Museum / University Museum
Anatomical specimens, models and charts, specimens of drugs, paintings of plants, charts and diagrams of medical-legal importance, weapons and toxicological specimens   20374

Nagpur

Central Museum, Museum Rd, Nagpur 440001 - T: (0712) 26231. Head: P.M. Muley
Archaeological Museum / Ethnology Museum / Natural History Museum / Fine Arts Museum - 1864
Archaeology, anthropology, natural hist, art   20375

Nalanda

Archaeological Museum, Nalanda 803111. Head: S.K. Sharma
Archaeological Museum - 1958
Antiquities, sculptures, terracotta figurines, pottery and bronzes   20376

Narendrapur

Our India Project Museum, Ramakrishna Mission Vidyalaya, 24 Parganas, Narendrapur, West Bangal
Natural History Museum - 1964
Minerals, cash crops samples, models   20377

Nasik

Museum of the Sarvajanik Vachanalaya, Peshave Wade, Nasik
Local Museum - 1958
Marathi documents, manuscripts, coins, paintings, arms, maps, playing cards, inscribed images, terra cottas, modern oil and watercolour paintings, statues of historical personages   20378

Old Goa

Archaeological Museum, Old Goa
Archaeological Museum
History of Goa, portraits of Vasco da Gama etc   20379

Padmanabhapuram

Palace and Museum of Antiquities, Padmanabhapuram
Archaeological Museum - 1939
Images of stone, war implements, coins, inscriptions, copperplates   20380

Panaji

Institute Menezes Braganza, POB 221, Panaji 403001 - T: 4143
Fine Arts Museum / Historical Museum - 1871
Paintings and drawings, sculptures, coins and stamps   20381

Patiala

Archaeological Museum of Patiala, Patiala 147001
Archaeological Museum
Anthropology, archaeology, costumes, paintings, ethnography   20382

National Sportsmuseum, Netaji Subhas National Institute, Motibagh, Patiala 147001
Special Museum 20383

Patna

Gandhi Sangrahalaya, Ashok Rajpath, NW Gandhi Maidan, Patna 800001 - T: (0612) 225339, 278760. Head: Dr. Razi Ahmad
Special Museum - 1968
Objects pertaining to Gandhi 20384

Patna Museum, Patna-Gaya Rd, Buddha Marg, Patna 800001 - T: (0612) 235731. Head: Dr. P.K. Jayaswal
Archaeological Museum / Fine Arts Museum / Natural History Museum / Ethnology Museum / Military Museum - 1917
Archaeology, art, natural hist, ethnology, geology, coins, old arms, industrial war trophies, Tibetan paintings 20385

Phulsanda

Phulsanda Religious Arts Museum, Kotwali Rd, Phulsanda, mail addr: c/o Dr. N. Kumar, HIG-3/33 Shraddhapuri, New Sardhana Rd, Meerut 250001 - T: (01343) 60402, 60759, E-mail: satpuruph@cyberbijnor.com. Head: Baba Satpurush, Wale Phulsande
Religious Arts Museum - 1990
Miniature paintings of Hindu gods, goddesses, demigods, Gandharva 20386

Pilani

Birla Museum, Vidya Vihar, Pilani 333031 - T: (0159) 7642158, Fax: 7642175. Head: V.N. Dhaulakhandi
Science&Tech Museum - 1954
Working exhibits on energy, metallurgy, transport, space, mining, electronics, textiles, chemistry, agriculture, populare science, Western & Indian art, old arms and weapons - library, school education center, audiovisual equipment, specialized workshop and studios 20387

Pillalamari

District Museum, Pillalamari 509002
Archaeological Museum / Fine Arts Museum - 1975
Prehistoric artifacts, contemporary arts, miniature paintings, manuscripts, china, coins, bronzes, bidri ware, arms and weapons, inscriptions on stone and stone sculptures from Eastern Vindhyas, Western Chalukya and Rastrakuta periods 20388

Pondicherry

Pondicherry Museum, 2 Saint Louis St, Pondicherry 605001 - T: 336236. Head: K. Rajaram
Local Museum - 1983
Sculpture gallery, archeology section, bronze gallery, geology section, handicrafts section, arms gallery, French India gallery - library 20389

Poona → Pune

Prabhas Patan

Prabhas Patan Museum, Opposite Somanatha Bus Stand, Prabhas Patan 362268 - T: (02876) 32455, 31001, E-mail: prabhmus@bsnl.com. Head: Raj Ratna Goswami
Local Museum - 1951
Sculptures of Somanatha temple, coins of Western Kshatrapas Guptas and medieval Egypt, inscriptions, pottery, photographs, woodcarvings, textiles, embroidery, ornaments, marine specimen, birds, ship models, ethnological coll - library, auditorium 20390

Pudukottai

Government Museum, Big St, Thirugokarnam, Pudukottai 622002 - T: (04322) 22247. Head: Dr. Mohamad J. Raja
Local Museum - 1910
Geology, zoology, arts and industries, anthropology, economic botany, epigraphy, paintings, numismatics, sculptures and bronzes 20391

Pune

Archaeological Museum, c/o Department of Archaeology, Deccan College, Deccan College Rd, Pune 411006 - T: (020) 6693795, Fax: 6692104, E-mail: dakshina@pn2.vsnl.netin. Head: P.P. Dandwate
Archaeological Museum - 1940
Prehistoric stone tools from all India, material of Stone Age period from Africa, Europe, California, Australia and Palestine, excavated finds (e.g. kiln, burials, terracotta, ceramics, copper objects and ornaments, stone objects etc.) from Neolithic, Chalcolithic, Megalithic (Early Iron Age), early historic and medieval periods. Collection of early Indian coins from excavations and explorations, and collection of ethnographic material from Central India. Original fossils of prehistoric period from rivers like Narmada, Godavari, Manjara. 20392

Bharat Itihas Samshodhak Mandal Museum, 1321 Sadashiva, Pune 411030 - T: (0212) 472581. Head: Dr. S.M. Bhave
Historical Museum / Fine Arts Museum - 1910
Marathi, Sanskrit, Persian, Hindi and Kannad documents, paintings, copperplates, stone inscriptions, sculptures, arms, maps, playing cards, dresses, antiquities and remains excavated at Karad (north Satara) 20393

Ethnological Museum, c/o Tribal Research and Training Institute, 28 Queen's Gardens, Pune 411001 - T: (0212) 65941. Head: Dr. G.M. Gare
Ethnology Museum - 1962
Articles of material culture from the tribes of Maharashtra 20394

Mahatma Phule Vastu Sangrahalaya, 1203 Shivajinagar, Ghole Rd, Pune 411005
Local Museum - 1875
Handicrafts, industry, geology, natural history, agriculture, forestry, armoury 20395

Raja Dinkar Kelkar Museum, 1377-1378 Shukrawar Peth, Natu Baug, Pune 411002 - T: (020) 4482101, 4474466, Fax: 4482101, E-mail: sudhanvaranade@hotmail.com, Internet: http://www.rajakel-karmuseum.com. Head: Dr. Hari Govind Ranade
Archaeological Museum / Fine Arts Museum / Historical Museum / Decorative Arts Museum / Music Museum - 1975
Archaeology, art, hist, decorative arts, musical instruments, everyday crafts, lamps, woodwork, sculpture, textiles, writing material, bronzes, leather puppets, miniature paintings - reference library, conservation laboratory 20396

Puri

Archaeological Museum Puri, Puri 752111 - T: (06752) 222. Head: S.K. Goswami
Archaeological Museum - 1968
Ancient sculpture 20397

Purulia

Zilla Samgrahasala, c/o Haripada Sahitya Mandir, POB 6, Purulia 723101 - T: (03252) 23016
Fine Arts Museum / Decorative Arts Museum / Archaeological Museum - 1960
Aculpture, terra cottas, Adibasi musical instruments, Adibasi weapons, wood carvings, old documents and manuscripts, coins, Dokra art, masks, etc., minerals, photographs 20398

Raipur, Karnataka

Mahant Ghasidas Memorial Museum, Raipur, Karnataka
Local Museum - 1875
Archaeology, anthropology, natural history, arts, crafts, paintings 20399

Rajahmundry

Damerla Rama Rao Memorial Art Gallery, Parade Grounds, Rajahmundry. Head: D.V. Rao
Fine Arts Museum 20400

Sri Rallabandi Subbarao Government Museum, Godavari Bund Rd, Rajahmundry 533101 - T: 5619. Head: Dr. V.V. Krishna Sastry
Fine Arts Museum / Archaeological Museum - 1967
Art and archaeology, palm leaf manuscripts, coins, copperplate inscriptions, and other archaeological antiquities 20401

Rajkot

Watson Museum, Jubilee Bagh, Rajkot 360001. Head: Dr. S.K. Bhowmik
Local Museum - 1888
Sculptures and bronzes, miniature paintings and manuscripts, Indian textiles, silver work, copper plate grants of Kshtrapas, science, geology, rocks and minerals, ethnology, embroidery work of Kutch and Kathiawar, musical instruments, Darbar Hall 20402

Ranchi

Anthropology Museum, c/o University of Ranchi, Ranchi
Ethnology Museum - 1953
Ethnographic coll of Central Indian States and of Andaman and Nicobar Islands 20403

Bihar Tribal Welfare Research Institute Museum, Morabadi Rd, Ranchi
Ethnology Museum
Ethnological objects 20404

Roorkee

Geology and Geophysics Museum, c/o University of Roorkee, Roorkee
Natural History Museum / University Museum
Minerals, rocks, fossils, models and charts, fossilized elephant bones and tree from Siwalik 20405

Survey Museum, c/o University of Roorkee, Indian Institute of Technology, Roorkee 247672 - T: (01332) 72349 ext 4421, Fax: 73560, Internet: http://www.rurkui.ernet.in. Head: Dr. D.V. Singh
Science&Tech Museum / University Museum - 1950
Old surveying equipment (1850), latest surveying and mapping equipment 20406

Sanchi

Archaeological Museum, Central Zone, Sanchi 464661. Head: N. Vyas
Archaeological Museum - 1920
Sculpture, iron objects, architectural fragments, terracotta objects, copper objects, coins, inscriptions, Buddhist Hindu pilgrimage centre 20407

Sangaria

Sir Choturam Memorial Museum, Sangaria
Archaeological Museum / Decorative Arts Museum - 1937
Sculptures, terra cottas, metal panels from Rajastan, metal images, wooden and porcelain wares from Chind, coins, armour 20408

Sangli

Sangli State Museum, Sangli - T: (0233) 76913. Head: Dr. A.P. Jamkhedkar
Decorative Arts Museum / Fine Arts Museum - 1954
Paintings, ivory carvings, metalware and various other handicrafts 20409

Santiniketan

Nandan Museum, Kala Bhavan, Visvabharati, Santiniketan
Fine Arts Museum - 1921
Rajput and Mughal miniatures, originals by Rabindranath, Abanindranath, Gaganendranath, Nandalal, Binodebehari, Ramkinkar, terra cotta of Bengal, folk bronzes, Kalighat pata, Chinese, Japanese scroll paintings, original tracings of Ajanta, Bagh, Cochin Murals 20410

Rabindra Bhavana (Tagore Memorial Museum), Post Office, Santiniketan 731235 - T: (03463) 52773, 52751, Fax: 52672, 54066, E-mail: swapan@dwarik.vbharat.ernet.in. Head: Prof. Swapan Majumdar
Special Museum - 1942
Memorabilia of R. Tagore: letters, paintings, manuscripts, newspaper clippings, grammophone records, cine-films, tape recordings - library, archives 20411

Sarnath

Sarnath Museum, Sarnath 221007. Head: Dr. B. Bandyopadhyay
Archaeological Museum - 1904
Buddhist and Hindu coll from 3rd c BC to 12th c AD 20412

Satara

Shri Chhatrapati Shivaji Maharaj Museum, Shetkari Niwas, opposite S.T. Stand, Satara 415002. Head: N.V. Powar
Historical Museum - 1966
History of the Maratha period 20413

Satna

Tulsi Sangrahalaya Ramvan, Satna
Local Museum - 1926
Sculptures, coins, books 20414

Shillong

Zonal Anthropological Museum, Lachumiere, Shillong
Ethnology Museum - 1954
Physical anthropology including palaeanthropology, cultural anthropology, ethnographic specimens 20415

Shimla

Himachal State Museum, Shimla 171004 - T: (0177) 205044, Fax: 226616
Archaeological Museum - 1974
Sculptures, textiles, arts and crafts, musical instruments, paintings, Pahari Miniature Paintings, arms and armour, manuscripts and jewelry, ancient and medieval coins 20416

Shimoga

District Museum, Shimoga
Local Museum
Archaeology, sculptures, inscriptions, paintings, arms, coins 20417

Shirali

Chitrapur Math Museum, Shirali
Local Museum - 1973
Sculptures, bronzes, coins, inscriptions 20418

Shivpuri

District Museum, Shivpuri
Archaeological Museum - 1962
Medieval sculpture 20419

Sibsagar

Sibsagar College Museum, Hiranya Probha Memorial Library and Museum, POB Joysagar, Sibsagar 785665. Head: M. Viswanadham
Historical Museum / University Museum - 1950
Manuscripts of old Assamese literature, copperplates, stone images, sculptures, cutlery and armour, palanquin shafts, Assamese ornaments, costumes, handcrafts of cane or bamboo, old coins, plastercast models, utensils of metallurgical interest 20420

Sikar

Sikar Museum, Sikar
Local Museum - 1945
Sculptures, archaeology, arts and crafts of Shekhawati, old arms and weapons 20421

Srinagar

Sri Pratap Singh Museum, Lalmandi, Srinagar 190008 - T: 32374. Head: M.S. Zahid
Archaeological Museum / Local Museum / Ethnology Museum / Natural History Museum - 1898
Archaeology, miniature paintings, decorative arts, arms, anthropology (models), textiles, minerals, numismatics, manuscripts, natural hist - children's section, library 20422

Srirangapatna

Tipu Sahib Museum, Summer Palace, Dariya-Doulat-Bagh, Srirangapatna 571438. Head: Shivananda V. Rao
Special Museum - 1959
Objects connected with Haidar Ali and Tipu Sultan, paintings and prints, coins and commemorative medals, brass and iron cannons and personal belongings of Tipu 20423

Surat

Sardar Vallabhbhai Patel Museum, Sonifalia, Surat 395003 - T: (0261) 423751, Fax: 422110. Head: Bhamini A. Mahida
Decorative Arts Museum / Fine Arts Museum - 1890
Textiles, costumes, paintings, wood crafts, terra cottas, ivory, coins, manuscripts 20424

Tamluk

Tamralipta Museum and Research Center, Post Office, Tamluk
Decorative Arts Museum / Archaeological Museum - 1973
Pottery, stone tools, bone tools, terra cotta sculptures, figurines, stone and bronze sculptures, manuscripts, coins 20425

Thanjavur

Thanjavur Art Gallery, Palace Bldgs, Thanjavur 613009 - T: (04362) 39823
Fine Arts Museum - 1951
Chola stone sculptures, bronze icons 20426

Thiruvananthapuram

Art Museum, 695001 Thiruvananthapuram - T: 62275. Head: P.R. Chandran
Fine Arts Museum / Decorative Arts Museum - 1855
Local arts and crafts, metal images, wood carvings, ivory works, lamps, musical instruments, numismatics, paintings 20427

Sri Chitra Art Gallery, Gallery of Asian Paintings, Thiruvananthapuram 695001 - T: (0471) 2755. Head: K. Rajendra Babu
Fine Arts Museum - 1935
Modern Indian paintings, Indo-European paintings, works by Raja Ravi Varmi, Mughal and Rajastan miniatures, Persian, Chinese, Japanese paintings, copies of mural paintings - library 20428

Government Museum, 695001 Thiruvananthapuram - T: (0471) 62275. Head: P.R. Chandran
Natural History Museum / Folklore Museum - 1857
Illustrations of local natural hist, customs, geology; Indian arts and crafts - zoological and botanical gardens 20429

Sree Moolam Shastyabdapurti Memorial Institute, Government Press St, Puthenchanthai, Thiruvananthapuram 695001 - T: (0471) 330298, 331358, Fax: 331582
Decorative Arts Museum - 1917
Village and cottage industries products and handicrafts 20430

Tiruchirappalli

Saint Joseph's College Museum, Tiruchirappalli 620002 - T: (0431) 721344, Fax: 721450, E-mail: frsrochesj@yahoo.com. Head: Fr.S. Roche
Natural History Museum / University Museum - 1895
Stuffed birds and animals, butterfly, moth and beetle coll, bottled specimens, stamp and postcard coll, geological specimens, skeletal mounts, coins, gems, pith works, anthropology, culture, ancient armoury, guns 20431

Tirupati

Sri Venkateswara Museum, Tirupati
Archaeological Museum - 1950
Archaeological objects, stone, wooden and metal images, pottery, arms, Rajastan oil paintings, marble statues, coins, inscriptions, albums and charts 20432

Trichur

Archeological Museum, Kollengode House, Chembukau, Trichur
Archaeological Museum - 1947
Megalithic burial jars, pottery wares, beads, iron implements, Stone Age implements, stone sculptures, wooden models of temples, Indus valley specimens, stucco head of Gandhara, copies of mural paintings, coins, bronzes, exhibits from Harappa Civilization 20433

State Museum, Chembukavu, Trichur 680001 - T: 556. Head: K. Raveendran
Natural History Museum / Fine Arts Museum / Archaeological Museum - 1885
Natural hist, zoology, botany, geology, art and industry of the area, archaeological exhibits and old coins - zoological garden 20434

Trivandrum → Thiruvananthapuram

Udaipur

Archaeological Museum, Ahar, Udaipur
Archaeological Museum - 1962
Paleoliths, microliths and relics from excavations, especially from the Ahar mound, medieval sculptures from the Ahar village 20435

Government Museum, Palace Complex, Udaipur
Fine Arts Museum
Sculptures and paintings 20436

Rajkiya Sangrahalaya, Udaipur
Local Museum - 1887
Coins, inscriptions, sculptures, paintings, natural history, local arts, arms 20437

Udupi

Mahatma Gandhi Memorial College Museum, c/o Mahatma Gandhi Memorial College, Kunjibettu, Udupi 576102 - T: (08252) 21159, Fax: 23559, E-mail: rrcmgm-vip@zetainfotech.com
Fine Arts Museum / Historical Museum / University Museum - 1971
Sculptures, bronzes, inscriptions, coins 20438

Ujjain

Vikram Kirti Mandir Museum, c/o Vikram University, Ujjain 456010
Archaeological Museum / Fine Arts Museum / University Museum - 1956
Paintings, coins, fossils, tools, arms and antiquities from the excavation at Kayatha, Bhimbetka and Azad Nagar, Indore, paintings of contemporary artists and a few miniatures 20439

Vadodara

Baroda Museum and Picture Gallery, Sayaji Park, Vadodara 390005 - T: (0265) 793801, 793589, Fax: 431093, E-mail: directormuseum@im.eth.net. Head: V.M. Thakkar
Fine Arts Museum / Natural History Museum - 1894
European paintings, miniature paintings, sculptures, textiles, crafts, woodcarvings, Islamic art, Asian art, Egyptian art, biology, anthropology, ethnology, Indian and foreign coins - children's section 20440

Maharaja Fatesingh Museum, Laxmi Vilas Palace Compound, Vadodara 390001 - T: (0265) 426372, Fax: 431516. Head: R.P. Gaekwad
Fine Arts Museum - 1961
Paintings, sculptures, Graeco-Roman sculptures, Chinese and Japanese art, European applied art, paintings by Raja Ravi Varma and A. Felici and sculptures by A. Felici and P.N. Bose 20441

Medical College Museum, c/o M.S. University of Baroda, Vadodara
University Museum - 1949
Maps, charts, models and specimens of different branches of medical science 20442

Museum of Archaeology, History and Culture, c/o Faculty of Arts, M.S. University of Baroda, Vadodara
Archaeological Museum / Historical Museum
Archaeological, historical and cultural coll, exploration and excavation materials from the early Stone Age to the medieval period 20443

Vaisali

Archaeological Museum, Vaisali
Archaeological Museum - 1971
Sculptures, terra cottas, pottery, seals, bones, metallic objects, weapons 20444

Vallabhvidyanagar

S.P. University Museum, KM Munashi Rd, Vallabhvidyanagar, mail addr: POB 10, Vallabhvidyanagar 388120 - T: 31884. Head: Nandan Shastri
Archaeological Museum / University Museum - 1949
Paleoliths including ancient bricks, coins, copies and photographs of ancient and medieval inscriptions, bronzes, reproductions of ancient and modern paintings, geological specimens of Gujarat, woodworks 20445

University Museum, Sardar Vallabh Bhai Vidyapeeth, Vallabhvidyanagar, mail addr: c/o Sardar Patel University, POB 10, Vallabhvidyanagar 388120 - T: (02692) 32452, Fax: 30238. Head: N.H. Shastri
Archaeological Museum / Historical Museum / Natural History Museum / University Museum - 1949
Archaeology, hist, art, religious objects, basic and natural science 20446

Varanasi

Archaeological Museum, Sarnath, Varanasi 221007. Head: Dr. B. Bandyopadhyay
Archaeological Museum - 1910
3rd c BC to 12th c AD stone sculptures, terracottas stucco, moulded bricks and pottery 20447

Bharat Kala Bhavan, c/o Banaras Hindu University, Varanasi 221005 - T: (0542) 316337, 307620/23, Fax: 316337. Head: Dr. T.K. Biswas
Archaeological Museum / Decorative Arts Museum / Fine Arts Museum / University Museum - 1920
Sculpture (3rd c BC to 18th c), terracotta, coins (6th c BC to 20th c), beads, paintings (10th-20th c), manuscripts, textiles, costumes, decorative arts (metal, ivory, glass, jades, jewellery, arms and armoury), philately, literature - library 20448

Geological Museum, Prof. Rajneth Memorial Museum, c/o Dept. of Geology, Banaras Hindu University, Faculty of Science, Varanasi 221005 - T: (0542) 369239, 307310/11, Fax: 369239, E-mail: m-joshi@satyam.net.in. Head: Mallickarjun Joshi
Natural History Museum / University Museum - 1923
Material of geological interest 20449

Maharaja Banaras Vidya Mandir Museum, Fort Ramnagar, Varanasi
Local Museum - 1964
Arms, ivory, astronomical clock, decorative arts, paintings, manuscripts, palanquins, textiles 20450

Vellore

Government Museum Vellore, Government of Tamilnadu, Fort, Vellore 632004. Head: M. Gandhi
Archaeological Museum / Ethnology Museum / Natural History Museum / Military Museum / Fine Arts Museum - 1985
Archaeological and ethnographical coll, Double Antennae Copper swords, botany and environment, ivory chess board incl boomerang of the Vikrama Sinha, last Kandian King of Sri Lanka, armoury of Arani Jagirdhar, paintings by B. Munirathinam, K.M. Adimoolam and others 20451

Vijayawada

Victoria Jubilee Museum, Bandar Rd, Vijayawada 520002
Archaeological Museum / Fine Arts Museum - 1963
Prehistoric and historic finds, sculpture (2nd-16th c), coins, arms and armaments, 18th and 19th c miniature painting of the Deccani school, bidri ware and celadon ware, manuscripts and modern painting 20452

Wardha

Gandhi Smarak Sangrahalaya, Sevagram, Wardha 442102 - T: (07152) 43526. Head: M. Gandhi
Special Museum - 1936
Memorabilia of Gandhi 20453

Magan Sangrahalaya Samiti, Kumarappa Rd, Maganwadi, Wardha 442201. Head: Devendra Kumar
Science&Tech Museum - 1938
Village industrial products and handicrafts 20454

Indonesia

Ambarawa

Museum Kereta Api (Train Museum), Jalan Setasiun, Ambarawa. Head: Edi Rochmad
Science&Tech Museum - 1978
Railway hist 20455

Museum Palagan Ambarawa, Jalan Mgr. Sugispranoto, Ambarawa
Military Museum - 1974
Military hist, weapons, arms 20456

Ambon

Museum Negeri Maluku Siwa Lima, Jalan Karang Panjang, Ambon. Head: M.S. Supamena
Historical Museum - 1973
Coll referring to Maluccas Islands 20457

Balige

Museum Pemda Balige, Jalan Pansanggranhan 1, Balige. Head: Pareli Simanjuntak
Ethnology Museum
Ethnography 20458

Banda Aceh

Museum Negeri Provinsi D.I. Aceh, Jalan S.A. Mahmudsyah, Banda Aceh 23241 - T: (0651) 21033. Head: Dr. Nasruddin Sulaiman
Local Museum - 1980
History, art, archaeology, ethnography 20459

Bandung

Asian-African Conference Museum, Gedung Merdeka, Jalan Asia Afrika 65, Bandung
Historical Museum
Documents, photos and artifacts relating to political history of Indonesia 20460

Kebon Binatang Taman Sari, Jalan Pattimura VI 56, Bandung
Local Museum 20461

Museum Geologi, Jalan Diponegoro 57, Bandung 40122 - T: (022) 703205, Fax: 702669, E-mail: grdc@melsa.net.id. Head: Dikdik Kosasih
Natural History Museum - 1929
Geology, fossils, rocks and ores, minerals 20462

Museum Mandala Wangsit Siliwangi, Jalan Mayor Lembong 38, Bandung - T: (022) 420339, 350393. Head: Otong Suryana
Military Museum - 1966
Military hist, arms and weapons 20463

Museum Negeri Djawa Barat (West Java Museum), Jalan Oto Iskandar Dinata, Bandung - T: (022) 50976. Head:
Archaeological Museum / Historical Museum - 1974
Archaeology, history of West Java 20464

Post and Giro Museum, Jalan Cilaki 3, Bandung - T: (022) 563379
Special Museum 20465

Bangkalan

Museum Daerah Bangkalan, Jalan Letnan Abdulah 1, Bangkalan. Head: B.U.W. Soejanto
Local Museum / Ethnology Museum
Local history, ethnography 20466

Banjar Baru

Museum Negeri of Lambung Mangkurat, Jalan Jenderal A. Yani Km 36, Banjar Baru - T: (05119) 2453
Local Museum 20467

Banjar Senggulan

Subak Museum, Banjar Senggulan West Bali
Agriculture Museum / Ethnology Museum
Rice farming in Bali, ethnography 20468

Banten

Pra Site Museum, Jalan Mesjid Banten Lama, Banten
Local Museum 20469

Sejarah Mesjid Banten Museum, Jalan Mesjid Banten Lama, Banten
Local Museum 20470

Banyuwangi

Museum Daerah Blambangan, Jalan Sri Tanjung 1, Banyuwangi - T: (0333) 24107. Head: T. Fatimah
Local Museum - 1977
Archaeology, ethnography, hist, mss, numismatics 20471

Bengkalis

Assejarah El Hasyimiah Palace Museum, Jalan Sukaramai Siak Sri Indrapura, Bengkalis
Local Museum 20472

Museum Istant Siak Sri Indapura, Jalan Siak Sri Indapura, Bengkalis
Local Museum / Ethnology Museum
Local history, ethnography 20473

Bengkulu

Museum Negeri of Bengkulu, Jalan Pembangunan Padang Harapan, Bengkulu - T: (0736) 32099
Local Museum 20474

Bima

Museum Asimbugo, Bima
Local Museum 20475

Blitar

Archaeological Museum Blitar, Jalan Sodancho Supriyadi 40, Blitar - T: (0342) 81365
Archaeological Museum 20476

Bogor

Museum Herbarium Bogoriensis, Jalan Juanda 22-24, Bogor 16122 - T: (0251) 322035. Head: Dr. Ekoparoto Walujo
Natural History Museum 20477

Museum Kebun Raya Bogor, Bogor Zoological Museum, Jalan Juanda 9, Bogor, mail addr: POB 110, Bogor - T: (0251) 322177, Fax: 325854. Head: Mohammad Amir
Natural History Museum - 1894
Zoological exhibits from the Indo-Australian region - library 20478

Museum Perjuangan, Jalan Merdeka 28, Bogor
Local Museum 20479

Bukit Tinggi

Museum Bundo Kandung, Jalan Cindur Mato, Bukit Tinggi - T: (0752) 21029
Local Museum / Ethnology Museum
Local hist, ethnography 20480

Museum Kebun Binatang Bukit Tinggi, Jalan Taman Puti Bungsu, Bukit Tinggi
Local Museum 20481

Tridaya Eka Dharma Museum, Jalan Panorama 22, Bukit Tinggi
Local Museum
General coll 20482

Zoological Museum, Jalan Cindur Mato, Bukit Tinggi
Natural History Museum 20483

Cirebon

Museum Kraton Kasepuhan, Jalan Kasepuhan 37, Cirebon - T: (0231) 204001, Fax: 204001. Head: Maulana Pakuningrat
Fine Arts Museum / Ethnology Museum - 1529
Ethnography, art 20484

Pusaka Kanoman Museum, Jalan Dalam Kraton Cirebon, Cirebon
Local Museum 20485

Denpasar

Museum Bali, Jalan Let Kol Wisnu 1, Denpasar - T: (0361) 22680. Head: Putu Budiastra
Archaeological Museum / Local Museum / Ethnology Museum / Folklore Museum / Performing Arts Museum - 1932
Archaeology, local hist, anthropology and ethnography of Bali, local crafts and folk arts, masks, theatrical arts section - library 20486

Puri Gamelan Suar Agung, Jalan Sandat Gg. III 7, Denpasar - T: (0361) 232765, Fax: 235429. Head: I. Ketut Suwentra
Local Museum 20487

Gianyar

Museum Gedung Aca, Jalan Bedulu, Gianyar
Local Museum 20488

Museum Ratna Wartha, Jalan Ubud, Gianyar
Local Museum 20489

Neka Museum and Gallery, Sanggingan St, Gianyar 80571 - T: (0361) 975074, Fax: 975639, E-mail: komaneka@indosat.net.id, Internet: http://www.museumneka.com. Head: Suteja Neka
Fine Arts Museum
Traditional and modern paintings from Bali and other parts of Indonesia 20490

Irian Jaya

Museum Kebudayaan dan Kemajuan Asmat, Jalan Keuskupan Agats, Irian Jaya
Local Museum 20491

Museum Waemena, Jalan Waemena, Irian Jaya
Local Museum 20492

Jakarta

Art Museum, Jalan Fatahillah 6, Jakarta - T: (021) 271062, 671062
Fine Arts Museum 20493

Artha Suaka Museum, Jalan Kebon Sirih 82-84, Jakarta - T: (021) 374108
Local Museum 20494

Djakarta Museum, Pintu Besar Utara 27, Jakarta - T: (021) 22560
Ethnology Museum 20495

Fatahillah Museum → Jakarta History Museum

Jakarta History Museum, Jalan Taman Fatahillah 1, Jakarta 11110 - T: (021) 6929101, Fax: 6902387, E-mail: musejak@indosat.net, Internet: http://www.dismugar.go.id. Head: Dr. Tinia Budiati
Historical Museum 20496

Literary Documentation Centre H.B. Yasin, Jalan Cikini Raya 73, Jakarta 10330 - T: (021) 336641. Head: Dr. Wulan Rujiati Mylyadi
Special Museum - 1977 20497

Military Museum, Jalan Taman Mini Indonesia Indah, Jakarta - T: (021) 8401081
Military Museum 20498

Monumen Nasional (National Monument), Taman Medan Merdeka, Jakarta 10110 - T: (021) 3840451, Fax: 3840451. Head: Dr. Ekki Husein Katili
Historical Museum - 1978
Diorama No.51, depicting milestone in National History 20499

Museum Abri Satriamandala, Jalan Gatot Subroto 14, Jakarta 12710 - T: (021) 5227946, Fax: 5251859
Military Museum - 1972
Military aircraft, tanks, and weapons, dioramas 20500

Museum Adam Malik, Jalan Diponegoro 49, Jakarta - T: (021) 5703246
Local Museum 20501

Museum Bahari (Maritime Museum), Jalan Pasar Ikan 1, Jakarta 14440 - T: (021) 6693406. Head: Dr. W.I. Pandji Indra
Ethnology Museum - 1977
Ethnography 20502

Museum Gedung Juang 45, Jalan Menteng Raya 31, Jakarta 10340 - T: (021) 366141
Ethnology Museum / Local Museum - 1974
Ethnography, local history 20503

Museum Indonesia, Jalan Taman Mini Indonesia Indah, Bogor-Jakarta Hwy, Jakarta 13560 - T: (021) 8400525
Open Air Museum - 1980
Types of houses from 26 provinces, vernacular and religious buildings 20504

Museum Kebun Binatang Ragunan, Jalan Ragunan, Pasar Minggu, Jakarta
Local Museum / Ethnology Museum
Local history, ethnography 20505

Museum Kedokteran (Anatomy Museum), Jalan Salemba Raya 6, Jakarta 10430 - T: (021) 330363. Head: Dr. Alimuddin Tergun
Special Museum - 1946
Anatomy, health care 20506

Museum Kepolisian Negara Republik Indonesia (Criminal Museum), Jalan Trunojoyo 3, Jakarta 12110 - T: (021) 70112652. Head: Dr. Zaidir Djalal
Special Museum - 1958
Hist of crime and crime detection in the area 20507

Museum Komodo, Jalan Taman Mini Indonesia Indah, Jakarta - T: (021) 8400525. Head: Dr. Soenartono Adisumarto
Natural History Museum - 1977
Zoology 20508

Museum Manggala Wanabakti, Jalan Galot Subroto, Jakarta 10270 - T: (021) 58464049. Head: Atang Soemaatmadja
Special Museum - 1983
Forestry 20509

Museum Nasional, Jalan Merdeka Barat 12, Jakarta - T: (021) 3812346, Fax: 3811076, Internet: http://www.museumnasional.org. Head: Dr. Endang Hardiati
Archaeological Museum / Ethnology Museum / Decorative Arts Museum - 1778
Archaeology, anthropology, ethnology and folklore, Chinese and South Asian ceramics, antique Indonesian bronzes 20510

Museum Pancasila Sakti, Jalan Raya Pondok Gede, Jakarta 13810 - T: (021) 8400423. Head: H. Fachrudin
Historical Museum - 1967
Death well where the bodies were hidden, three houses of former Indonesian communist leaders remain in the compound 20511

Museum Sasmita Loka A. Yani, Jalan Lembang, Jakarta - T: (021) 3105183. Head: Herkus Dianto
Historical Museum - 1965
Memorabilia 20512

Museum Sejarah Kebangkitan Nasional, Jalan Abdulrachman Sakti, Jakarta 10410 - T: (021) 356143. Head: Dr. Soegio
Historical Museum - 1974
Hist of National Movement of Independence 20513

Museum Seni Rupa dan Keramik, Jalan Taman Fatahillah, Jakarta 11110. Head: Dr. Sudarmadji
Decorative Arts Museum - 1967 20514

Museum Sumpah Pemuda, Jalan Kramat Raya 106, Jakarta 10450 - T: (021) 3103217. Head: Dr. Achmad Latuconsina
Historical Museum - 1973
History 20515

Museum Takstil, Jalan K. Satsuit Tubun 4, Jakarta 11420 - T: (021) 365367. Head: Sufwandi Margkudilaga
Decorative Arts Museum - 1976 20516

Museum Taman Laut Ancol (Ancol Oceanarium Museum), Jalan Lodan Timur Ancol, Jakarta 14420 - T: (021) 681511, 6452967, Fax: 6452976, E-mail: shrdolphin@yahoo.com, Internet: http://www.ancol.com. Head: Teuku Sahir Syahali
Natural History Museum
Zoology, birds, aquatic, animals, reptiles 20517

Museum Tugu Proklamator, Jalan Proklamasi, Jakarta 10320
Historical Museum - 1945
Hist of Independence 20518

Museum Wayang, Jalan Pintu Besar Selatan 27, Jakarta 11110 - T: (021) 679560
Special Museum - 1974
Puppets 20519

Reksa Artha Museum, Jalan Lebak Bulus I Cilandak, Jakarta - T: (021) 7395000
Local Museum 20520

Taman Prasati Museum, Jalan Tanah Abang I, Jakarta - T: (021) 377907
Local Museum 20521

Tugu Nasional Museum, Jalan Merdeka Utara, Jakarta - T: (021) 340451
Local Museum 20522

Jayapura

Museum Loka Budaya, Jalan Uncen, Sentani Abepura, Jayapura
Local Museum / Ethnology Museum
Local hist, ethnography 20523

Museum Negeri of Irian Jaya, Jalan Raya Sentani Km 17,8, Jayapura
Local Museum 20524

Jepara

Museum Kartini, Jalan Kartini 1, Jepara 59411 - T: 118
Local Museum / Ethnology Museum
Local history, ethnography 20525

Kediri

Archaeological Museum Kediri, Jalan Jend. A. Yani, Kediri
Archaeological Museum 20526

Museum Subak Bali, Sanggulan, Kediri
Agriculture Museum - 1980 20527

Klaten

Sugar Museum, c/o Pabrik Gula Gondang Baru, Klaten - T: (0272) 22328
Agriculture Museum 20528

Klungkung

Gunarsa Museum, Museum Seni Lukis Klasik Bali (Museum of Classical Balinese Painting), Jalan Pertigaan Banda 1, Takmung, Br. Angkan, Klungkung - T: (0366) 22255/56, Fax: 22257, E-mail: gallery@balinetwork.com, Internet: http://www.gunarsa.com. Head: Dr. Nyoman Gunarsa
Fine Arts Museum
Paintings 20529

Kupang

Museum Negeri Propinsi Nusa Tenggara Timur (State Museum of the East Nusa Tenggara Province), Jalan Raya El Tari II, Kota baru, Kupang 85000 - T: (0380) 832471, Fax: 832471. Head: Dr. Yacob Lerrick
Local Museum - 1991
Ethnography, archaeology, history, geology, numismatic, philology, technology, biology, ceramic, handicraft 20530

Museum Undana, Jalan Jenderal Suharto, Kupang
Local Museum 20531

Kutacane

Museum Sepakat Segenep, Jalan Ray Babusalam, Kutacane
Local Museum - 1963 20532

Lampung

Museum Negeri of Lampung, Jalan Teuku Umar, Meneng Bldg, Lampung
Local Museum 20533

Loksumawe

Museum Malikussaleh, Jalan Perdagangan, Komp. SMEA, Loksumawe. Head: Ali Akbar
Local Museum / Ethnology Museum - 1975
Local history, ethnography 20534

Magelang

Museum Diponegoro, Jalan Diponegoro 1, Magelang - T: (0293) 2308
Local Museum / Ethnology Museum
Local hist, ethnography 20535

Museum Soedirman, Jalan Ade Irma Suryani C7, Magelang
Historical Museum - 1976
Dining table set, bed set, special table once used to bathe the corpse of the late General Soedirman 20536

Museum Taruna Akbari Udarat, Jalan Jendral Gatot Subroto, Magelang - T: 2844
Fine Arts Museum - 1975
Art 20537

Malang

Museum Brawijaya, Jalan Ijen 25a, Malang 65112 - T: (0341) 22394. Head: A. Rasjid
Local Museum 20538

Manado

Museum Negeri of North Sulawesi, Jalan W.R. Supratman 72, Manado - T: (0431) 2685, 95123
Local Museum 20539

Museum Wanua Paksinanta, Jalan Ki Hadjar Dewantor 72, Manado - T: (0431) 2685
Historical Museum / Ethnology Museum
History, ethnography 20540

Mataram

Museum Negeri Nusa Tenggara Barat, Jalan Panji Tilar Negara 6, Mataram - T: (0370) 632159, Fax: 637503. Head: Dr. R. Joko Prayitno
Fine Arts Museum / Archaeological Museum - 1982
Art, ethnography, archeology, numismatics, philology, ceramics, history 20541

Medan

Art Museum, Jalan Jati, Medan
Fine Arts Museum 20542

Museum Juang '45, Jalan Pemuda 17, Medan - T: (061) 324110. Head: Nas Sebayang
Historical Museum - 1979
Hist 20543

Museum Negeri Sumatera Utara (North Sumatera Government Museum), Jalan HM Joni 51, Medan 20217 - T: (061) 716792. Head: Suruhen Purba
Historical Museum / Fine Arts Museum / Archaeological Museum / Ethnology Museum - 1976
History, art, archeology of North Sumatra, ethnography 20544

Museum Perjuangan Bukit Barisan, Jalan H. Zainal Arifin 8, Medan - T: (061) 326927
Local Museum - 1970
Local hist, ethnography, military hist 20545

Mojokerto

Museum Purbakala (Municipal Museum), Jalan Jendral A. Yani 18, Mojokerto
Local Museum / Ethnology Museum - 1965
Local history, ethnography 20546

Museum Purbakala Trowulan, Raya Trowulan Km 13, Mojokerto - T: (0321) 61362
Archaeological Museum - 1924
Archaeology 20547

Nganjuk

Statue Museum, Jalan Arca, Nganjuk
Local Museum 20548

North Malaku

Museum Istana Sultan Ternate, Jalan Kabupaten, North Malaku
Local Museum 20549

Padang

Art Museum, Jalan Diponegoro, Padang - T: (0751) 22752
Fine Arts Museum 20550

Museum Negeri Sumatera Barat (West Sumatrian Museum), Jalan Diponegoro Lap Tugu, Padang 25118 - T: (0751) 22316
Ethnology Museum / Fine Arts Museum
Ethnography, art from West Sumatra 20551

Palangkaraya

Museum Balanga, Jalan Tangkiling Km 2, Palangkaraya
Local Museum / Ethnology Museum - 1989
Local history, ethnography 20552

Museum of Central Kalimantan, Jalan Cilik Riwut Km 2,5, Palangkaraya
Local Museum 20553

Palembang

Museum Negeri Propinsi Sumatera Selatan Balaputra Dewa (State Museum of South Sumatra Province Balaputra Dewa), Jalan Srijaya 288, Km 5,5, Palembang 30139 - T: (0711) 411382. Head: Syamsir Alam
Local Museum / Ethnology Museum - 1984
Local hist, ethnography 20554

Sultan Badaruddin Museum, Jalan Pasar Hilir 3, Palembang
Local Museum 20555

Palopo

Museum Batara Guru, Jalan Andi Jemma 1, Palopo
Local Museum 20556

Palu

Museum Negeri of Central Sulawesi, Jalan Sapiri 23, Palu - T: (0451) 22290
Local Museum 20557

Pare-Pare

Museum La Bangenge, Jalan Bau Masseppe 68, Pare-Pare
Local Museum 20558

Pekalongan

Museum Batik (Batik Museum), Jalan Pasar Ratu 30, Pekalongan
Decorative Arts Museum
Decorative arts 20559

Pematangsiantar

Huta Bolon Simanindo Museum, Jalan Kecamatan Simanindo, Pematangsiantar
Special Museum 20560

Museum Simalungun, Jalan Jendral Sudirman 10, Pematangsiantar - T: 21954. Head: T. Moesa Sinaga
Local Museum / Folklore Museum - 1940
Local history, folklore 20561

Zoological Museum, Jalan Kapten M.H. Sitorus 10, Pematangsiantar - T: 21611
Natural History Museum 20562

![Museum Negeri Nusa Tenggara Barat — MATARAM, Jalan Panji Tilar Negara No.6, INDONESIA](advertisement)

Pontianak

Museum Negeri Kalimantan Barat (West Kalimantan Museum), Jalan Jenderal A. Yani, Pontianak - T: (0561) 4600
Local Museum / Ethnology Museum
Local history, ethnography 20563

Purwodadi

Museum Pemerintah Daerah Grobogan, Jalan Pemuda Grobogan, Purwodadi. Head: Endang Koesoemowarni
Local Museum - 1975
Art, Ethnography, Hist 20564

Rembang

Museum Kartini Rembang, Jalan Jendral Gatot Subroto 8, Rembang
Local Museum / Ethnology Museum
Local hist, ethnography 20565

Samosir

Museum Huta Bolon Simanindo, Jalan Huta Bolon, Samosir 22395
Local Museum / Ethnology Museum - 1969
Ethnology, hist 20566

Sanur

Museum Le Mayeur, Sanur. Head: Wayan Suanda
Fine Arts Museum
Works of the Belgian Painter Le Mayeur 20567

Selayar

Museum Nekara, Jalan Jenderal Sudirman 2, Selayar
Local Museum 20568

Semarang

Akpol Museum, Jalan Komplek Akpol Candi Baru, Semarang - T: (024) 411700, 69060
Local Museum 20569

Museum Jamu Nyonya Menir, Jalan Raya Kaligawe Km 4, Semarang - T: (024) 285732
Local Museum 20570

Museum Kebun Binatgang Semarang, Jalan Sriwijaya 29, Semarang
Local Museum 20571

Museum Mandala Bakti, Jalan Merdeka 1, Semarang - T: (024) 311321
Local Museum 20572

Museum Negeri of Central Java, Jalan Abdurrachman Saleh, Semarang - T: (024) 24389
Local Museum 20573

Siaksriinderapura

Museum Asserajah El Hasyimiah, Jalan Sukara Mai, Siaksriinderapura
Fine Arts Museum / Ethnology Museum / Decorative Arts Museum - 1886
Art, ethnography, ceramics 20574

Singaraja

Museum Gedong Kirtya, Jalan Veteran 20, Singaraja. Head: Ketut Sudwidja
Special Museum
Manuscripts of traditional lit 20575

Sintang

Museum Dara Yuanti, Jalan Dara Yuanti, Sintang
Special Museum 20576

Museum Mini Korem, Jalan Sintang, Sintang
Local Museum 20577

Srondol

Museum Rekor Indonesia, Jalan Setiabudi 179, Srondol - T: (024) 312762
Local Museum 20578

Sumedang

Museum Prabu Geusan Ulun, Yayasan Pangeran Sumedang, Jalan Prabu Geusan Ulun 40b, Sumedang 45311 - T: (0261) 201714. Head: H. Djamhir Sumawilaga
Local Museum / Ethnology Museum - 1973
Local history, ethnography 20579

Sumenep

Museum Daerah Sumenep, Jalan Kantor Kabupaten Dati 11, Sumenep
Local Museum
Local history 20580

Sungguminasa

Museum Goa Bala Lompoa, Jalan Sultan Hasanuddin 48, Sungguminasa
Local Museum 20581

Surabaya

Museum Joang '45, Jalan Mayend. Sungkono, Surabaya - T: (031) 67206
Local Museum 20582

Museum Negeri Djawa Timur, Jalan Taman Mayangkara 6, Surabaya 60241 - T: (031) 67037. Head: Dr. Soetjipto
Archaeological Museum / Decorative Arts Museum / Historical Museum
Archeology of East Java, 14th c antiquities, Balinese arts and crafts, Chinese objects, 11th-14th c Hindu and Japanese sculpture, Dutch colonial relics 20583

Museum Tni A.L. Loka Jala Crana, Jalan Komp Akabri Laut Morokrambangan, Surabaya - T: (031) 291092. Head: R. Sutoyo
Historical Museum - 1973
Naval hist, naval weapons 20584

Surakarta

Museum Istana Mangkunegaran, Istana Mangkunegaran, Surakarta
Fine Arts Museum / Decorative Arts Museum - 1918
Art coll, coins, goldsmiths' works, statues of Buddha 20585

Museum Kraton Suaka Budaya, Jalan Dalam Kraton, Surakarta - T: (0271) 2889
Local Museum 20586

Museum Pers, Jalan Gajah Mada 59, Surakarta
Historical Museum / Ethnology Museum
History, ethnography 20587

Museum Pura Mangkunegara, Jalan Dalam Kraton, Surakarta - T: (0271) 2016
Local Museum 20588

Museum Radya Pustaka, Jalan Slamet Riyad 235, Surakarta - T: 2306. Head: K.R.T. Hardjonagoro
Decorative Arts Museum
Decorative arts and crafts 20589

Takengon

Gayo Museum, Jalan Buntul-Buntul, Takengon
Local Museum 20590

Tangawi

Museum Yadnya, Jalan Tangawi, Tangawi
Local Museum 20591

Tanjung Pandan

Museum U.P.T. Balitung, Jalan Melati, Tanjung Pandan - T: (0438) 278
Local Museum 20592

Telanai Pura

Museum Negeri of Jamba, Jalan Urip Sumoharjo 1, Telanai Pura - T: (0741) 268415
Local Museum 20593

Tenggarong

Museum Negeri Kalimantan Timur Mulawarman, Tenggarong - T: 112. Head: Abd. Djabbar
Historical Museum / Ethnology Museum - 1971
History, ethnography 20594

Tidore

Memorial Sultan Tidore Museum, Jalan Salero, Tidore
Local Museum 20595

Ubud

Agung Rai Museum of Art, Ubud 80571 - T: (0361) 974228, Fax: 974229, E-mail: armaubud@denpasar.wasatara.net.id, Internet: http://www.nusantara.com/arma
Fine Arts Museum 20596

Museum Puri Lukisan, Foundation Ratna Wartha, POB 215, Ubud 80571 - T: (0361) 975136, Fax: 975136, E-mail: museumpl@indo.net.id. Head: Tjokorda Bagus Astika
Fine Arts Museum - 1954
Traditional contemporary Balinese painting and sculptures 20597

Ujung Padang

Museum Negeri of La Galigo, Jalan Bateng, Ujung Padang
Local Museum 20598

Watampone

Museum La Pawowoi, Jalan Petta Ponggawe, Watampone
Local Museum 20599

Wua-Wua

Museum Negeri of Southeast Sulawesi, Jalan Saranani, Wua-Wua
Local Museum 20600

Yogyakarta

Hamengku Buwono Palace Museum, Hamengku Buwono Palace, Yogyakarta
Historical Museum / Fine Arts Museum
Paintings, historical materials 20601

Monument Pangeran Diponegoro, Jalan Tegalrejo, Yogyakarta - T: (0274) 3068. Head: Abdul Basir
Historical Museum - 1969
Historical coll 20602

Museum Affandi, Jalan Solo 167, Yogyakarta - T: (0274) 562593. Head: Agung Kusuma
Fine Arts Museum - 1962
Modern and contemporary art 20603

Museum Angkatan Darat, Jalan Bintara Wetan 3, Yogyakarta
Historical Museum / Ethnology Museum
Ethnography, history 20604

Museum Batik (Batik Museum), Jalan Dr. Sutomo 13, Yogyakarta 55211 - T: (0274) 515953, 562338
Decorative Arts Museum - 1977
Decorative arts, handicrafts 20605

Museum Biologi UGM (Biology Museum of the Gadjah Mada University), c/o Gadjah Mada University, Jalan Sultan Agung 22, Yogyakarta - T: (0274) 4011. Head: Dr. Anthon Sukahar
Natural History Museum / University Museum - 1979
Zoology, botany, natural history 20606

Museum Dewantara Kirti Griya (Memorial Museum), Jalan Tamansiswa 31, Yogyakarta 55151 - T: (0274) 377459. Head: Ki Soeharto
Historical Museum - 1970
Memorabilia of Taman Siswa and Ki Hadjar Dewantara 20607

Museum Dharma Wiratama, Jalan Sudirman 47, Yogyakarta - T: (0274) 864178
Local Museum 20608

Museum Dirgantara Mandala, Pangkalan, Lanud Adisucipto, Yogyakarta 55002 - T: (0274) 564466, E-mail: museum_dirgantara@yahoo.com. Head: Y. Supriyatno
Military Museum - 1969
Hist of Indonesian airforce, Japanese, USA and Russian aircrafts 20609

Museum Kraton Yogyakarta, Jalan Dalam Kraton, Yogyakarta - T: (0274) 2036
Fine Arts Museum
Gamelan instruments, paintings, photogr 20610

Museum Pendidikan Islam, Jalan Kapten Tendean 41, Yogyakarta - T: (0274) 4401
Historical Museum
Public affairs, history 20611

Museum Perjuangan, Jalan K.H. Ahmad Dahlan 24, Yogyakarta
Local Museum - 1961
General coll 20612

Museum Sasmita Loka, Jalan Bintaran Wetan 3, Yogyakarta - T: (0274) 2663
Local Museum 20613

Museum Sono Budoyo, Jalan Trikora 27, Yogyakarta - T: (0274) 2775. Head: Dr. Djoko Soekiman
Archaeological Museum / Historical Museum / Fine Arts Museum / Ethnology Museum - 1935
Archaeology, history, art, ethnology 20614

Museum Yogya Kembali, Jalan Desa Kembaran Kab. Sleman, Yogyakarta
Local Museum 20615

Iran

Abadan

Abadan Museum, Abadan
Local Museum
Local history 20616

Ardebil

Chinese House Museum, Alighapoo Sq, Ardebil
Decorative Arts Museum 20617

Birjand

Birjand Museum, Baghe Akbariyyeholeum, Birjand
Historical Museum 20618

Haft Tappeh

Haft Tappeh Museum, Haft Tappeh. Head: Nasser Torki
Archaeological Museum
Excavations from the 'Seven Hills', archaeological finds mainly of the middle Elamite culture with some material from the Parthian and Sassanid period 20619

Hamedan

Buali Museum, Buali Sina Av, Hamedan
Local Museum 20620

Isfahan

Armenian Cathedral and Museum, Julfa, Isfahan, mail addr: POB 81735-115, Isfahan - T: (031) 243471, Fax: 270999. Head: Levon Minassian
Religious Arts Museum - 1930
Armenian manuscript illuminations - library 20621

Chehel Sotun Museum, Isfahan. Head: Karim Nikzad
Local Museum - 1948
Local hist, ethnography, Persian china, paintings, historical frescoes 20622

Karaj

Zoological Museum, c/o Agricultural College, Karaj - T: (0261) 402274, Fax: 224511. Head: Dr. E. Bagheri-Zenouz
Natural History Museum / University Museum - 1925
Zoological coll with particular reference to agriculture - library, conservatory department 20623

Kashan

National Museum of Kashan, Baghe Shah Fin, Amirkabir Av, 8 km South West, Kashan - T: (02521) 4477
Archaeological Museum / Decorative Arts Museum
Archaeological finds from prehistoric to Islamic times, 19th-20th c decorative arts 20624

Kerman

Ethnological Museum of Hammame-e-Ganjalixan, Ganj Alikhan Sq, Kerman - T: (0341) 225577. Head: Hamid Moghimizadeh
Ethnology Museum / Historical Museum - 1971
Anthropology, ethnography, local hist, objects for bathing 20625

Sekkeh Museum (Bank Museum), Ganjali Khan Sq, Kerman
Special Museum 20626

Kermanshah

Moaven Al- Molk Museum, Shahid Haddad Adel Av, Kermanshah - T: (0831) 23777, 76743, Fax: 767401. Head: Nazi Farahmanesh, Asadollah Beiranvand
Historical Museum / Open Air Museum / Ethnology Museum
Anthropology - Central library of cultural heritage organization of Iran 20627

Maku

Baghgheh Chogh Palace, Kakhe Baghgheh Chogh, Maku
Decorative Arts Museum 20628

Maragheh

Maragheh Museum, Owhadis Mausoleum, Maragheh
Local Museum
Ethnography, local history 20629

Marvdashd

Takht-e-Jamshid (Persepolis Museum), Marvdashd
Local Museum 20630

Mashad

Astan-e-Qods-e Razavi Museums, Sahn-e-Imam Khomeini, Mashad - T: (051) 2224570, Fax: 2220845, E-mail: radad@imamreza.or.ir. Head: Mohammad Malek Jafarian
Decorative Arts Museum / Archaeological Museum / Historical Museum / Religious Arts Museum - 1945
Decorative arts and crafts, brocades and rugs of the Safavid period, manuscripts, antique carpets, coins, stamps, Holy Quian 20631

Meshkin Shahr

Meshkin Shahr Museum, Meshkin Shahr
Decorative Arts Museum 20632

Miyandoab

Miyandoab Museum, Parke Shahrdari, Miyandoab
Local Museum 20633

Qazvin

Qazvin Museum, Azadi Sq, Qazvin - T: (0281) 3230. Head: Dawood Fathee
Archaeological Museum
Coins issued in Qazvin, material from the Safavid period 20634

Qom

Qom Museum, Qom - T: 32333, Fax: 26262. Head: M. Fotoghi
Archaeological Museum / Decorative Arts Museum - 1936
Archaeology, rugs and tiles of Safavid period, valuable Korans 20635

Rasht

Rasht Museum, 99 Bisotoon St, Taleghani Av, Rasht
Local Museum - 1940
Anthropology, archaeology, natural history 20636

Sanandaj

Sanandaj Museum, Ameam Khomine Av, Sanandaj - T: (0871) 2268691, Fax: 2253705. Head: Naghme Mohamadi
Folklore Museum / Local Museum - 1975
Regional folk art of Curdistan, Ziwieh castle and Caraftoo cave, Manna tribes 8th c, geology and natural history - Salar saeed-Museum 20637

Shiraz

Pars Museum, Banke Meli Zand Av, Shiraz - T: (071) 24151. Head: Mohammed Hossein Estakhr
Archaeological Museum / Decorative Arts Museum / Fine Arts Museum - 1938
Archaeology, decorative arts, paintings, manuscripts 20638

Takht-e-Jamshid (Persepolis Museum), c/o Institute of Aachaemenid Research, Shiraz 73731. Head: Mansoor Fotchi Chian
Archaeological Museum 20639

Susa

Shush Museum, Susa. Head: Mohammad Ali Yazdanifar
Archaeological Museum 20640

Tabriz

Tabriz Museum, Masjede Kaboud Emam Khomeyni Av, Tabriz - T: (041) 66343. Head: Kazem Notash Sangtarash
Archaeological Museum / Natural History Museum / Historical Museum - 1957
Archaeology, natural history, relics of the constitutional revolution 20641

Teheran

Abgineh Va Sofalineh (Glass and Ceramics Museum of Iran), 57 Si-ye-Tir St, Jomhuri-ye-Eslami Av, Teheran - T: (021) 6708153/54, 6716930, Fax: 6705614. Head: Farzaneh Ghaeny
Decorative Arts Museum / Archaeological Museum - 1980 20642

Carpet Museum of Iran, Dr. Fatemi Av, Kargar Intersection, 14154 Teheran - T: (021) 652703, Fax: 652664. Head: Hossein Hajihassan
Decorative Arts Museum - 1978
Carpets and kilims 20643

Crime Museum, Police Headquarters, Teheran
Special Museum
History of crime in Iran, methods of combatting it, weapons, uniforms 20644

Enqelab Museum (Museum of the Revolution), Tajrish, Sad Abad St, Teheran - T: (021) 283031
Historical Museum 20645

Honarhaye Moaser Tehran (Museum of Contemporary Art), Kargar Av, Teheran - T: (021) 8955754, 8963200, 8951664, Fax: 8965664, E-mail: tmca@irost.com, Internet: http://www.ir-tmca.com. Head: Dr. A.R. Sami-Azar
Fine Arts Museum - 1977 20646

Honarhaye Ziba (Fine Arts Museum), Tajrish, Sad Abad St, Teheran - T: (021) 285021, 282032
Fine Arts Museum 20647

Iran Bastan Museum, 30 Khiaban-e-Imam Khomeini, Khiaban-e-Si-ye Tir, Teheran 11364 - T: (021) 672061. Head: J. Golshan
Archaeological Museum - 1946
library 20648

Javaherat (National Jewelry Treasury of Iran), Ferdowsi Av, Teheran, mail addr: c/o Bank Markazi Jomhouri Islami Iran, POB 11365-8551, Teheran 11354 - T: (021) 64461, Fax: 3112595. Head: S.J. Jalilian
Decorative Arts Museum
Jewelry of the 19th c Iran and gemstones 20649

Kakh-e-Rejat Va Ebrat & Mellat (Reaction and Lesson Palace and National Palace), Tajrish, Sad Abad St, Teheran - T: (021) 282063, 282071
Historical Museum 20650

Kakh Musee-e-Golestan (Golestan Palace Museum), Maidan Panzdah Khordad, Teheran 13445-719, mail addr: POB 11365-9595, Teheran 11149 - T: (021) 312997. Head: Ali Reza Anisi
Decorative Arts Museum - 1966
Part of 19th c royal palaces, porcelain, enamelled tableware, miniatures, ivories, porcelain 20651

Kakhe Muséyé Sabz (Green Palace Museum), Sad-Abad St, Tajrish, Teheran - T: (021) 282031, 287067. Head: Safiye Kargaran
Decorative Arts Museum / Fine Arts Museum - 1981
Jewellery, paintings, textiles, carpets 20652

Museum of Post and Telecomunication Mokhaberat, Emam Khomeyni Av, Teheran 11369, mail addr: POB 5418, Teheran 11365 - T: (021) 6700503, 6709132, Fax: 6709170. Head: Esmail Azimi
Decorative Arts Museum / Special Museum
Postal service, stamps, telecomunication 20653

Muséyé Mardom Shenassi, Panzdah-e, 15 Khordad Sq, Teheran 111414 - T: (021) 310653. Head: Ali Reza Karavani
Ethnology Museum 20654

Muzéyé Honarhaye Melli (Iran National Arts), Baharestan Sq, Kamel-ol-Mulk St, Teheran - T: (021) 316329
Fine Arts Museum / Decorative Arts Museum - 1930
16th-17th c Persian miniatures, ceramics, paintings, ivories, engravings, mosaics 20655

Nezami Museum (Military Museum), Tajrish, Sad Abad St, Teheran - T: (021) 283013
Military Museum 20656

Reza Abbasi Museum, 972 Pole Seyyed Xandan Shariati Av, Teheran - T: (021) 863001/07. Head: Ali-Réza Ebdaai Takallou
Fine Arts Museum / Historical Museum - 1977
Prehistory, history, paintings, calligraphy, applied art 20657

Sabä's House, 92 Zahir-ol-Eslam St, Teheran - T: (021) 3111246. Head: Reza Ismai
Music Museum
Home and memorabilia of Abdul Hassan Sabä, music instruments 20658

Sekkeh (Sepah Bank Coin Museum), Emam Khomeyni Av, Bank-e-Sepah, Teheran - T: (021) 3111091
Special Museum
History of banking, coins 20659

Toos

Toos Museum, Ferdowsi is Mausoleum, Toos
Historical Museum 20660

Urumiyeh

Urumiyeh Museum, Shahid Beheshti Av, Urumiyeh - T: (0441) 27722. Head: Ali Karavani
Local Museum - 1967
Archeology, ethnography 20661

Yazd

Science and Technology Museum, Shahid Ragai St, next to Iranshahr High School, Yazd - T: (0351) 23434. Head: Masoody Jalal
Natural History Museum / Science&Tech Museum - 1989 20662

Iraq

Arbil

Arbil Museum, Arbil
Archaeological Museum
Objects from Iraqi hist up to Arabic-Islamic period 20663

Babylon

Babylon Museum, Babylon
Archaeological Museum - 1949
Objects from prehistoric times to the late Assyrian period, Babylonian and classic relics, models and maps of the ancient city 20664

Baghdad

The Abbasid Palace Museum, Abbasid Palace, Baghdad
Decorative Arts Museum - 1935
Arab antiquities, scale models of important Islamic monumental buildings in Iraq 20665

Al Mada'in Museum, Al Mada'in, Baghdad
Archaeological Museum 20666

Arab Museum, Samaval St, Baghdad
Archaeological Museum
Islamic antiquities, gypsum plaques from Samarra, pottery from Samarra and Wasit, copper vessels, wooden sarcophagus 20667

Baghdad Museum, Sahat Al-Risafi, Baghdad - T: (01) 4165317. Head: Alae Al-Shibli
Ethnology Museum - 1941
Sumerian, Babylonian, Akkadian, Assyrian, Hatrene and Islamic costumes, personal effects of the Royal Family, displays of local popular culture, relics of King Faisal I 20668

Iraq Natural History Research Centre and Museum, Bab Al-Muadham, Baghdad - T: (01) 4165790. Head: H.-A. Ali
Natural History Museum - 1946
Invertebrates, insects, fishes, amphibians and reptiles, birds, mammals, plants, fossils, rocks and minerals - library 20669

Iraqi Museum, Karkh Museum Sq, Salhiya, Baghdad - T: (01) 361215. Head: Rabie Al-Qaisy
Archaeological Museum - 1966/2000
Artifacts from prehistoric period to 19th c - library 20670

Mustansiriya School Collections, c/o Mustansiriya School, Ma'moun St, Baghdad
Historical Museum / University Museum
Restored building of oldest Islamic college in the world (1227-1234 A.D.) housing rich decorations, Arabic calligraphy, historical cartography 20671

Basrah

Basrah Museum, Basrah
Archaeological Museum / Fine Arts Museum - 1975
Middle Eastern antiquities and works of art 20672

Natural History Museum of the University of Basrah, Corniche St, Basrah, mail addr: c/o University of Basrah, POB 432, Basrah - T: (040) 213494. Head: Dr. Khalaf Al-Robaae
Natural History Museum / University Museum - 1971
Flora, fauna of Arabian Gulf, reptiles, amphibia, fish 20673

Kirkuk

Kirkuk Museum, Kirkuk
Archaeological Museum
Prehistoric stone objects, history of civilization in Iraq 20674

Mosul

Mosul Museum, Dawassa, Mosul - T: (060) 2430. Head: Hazim A. Al-Hameed
Archaeological Museum - 1951
Prehistoric agricultural implements, pottery, material from the ruins of Hatra dating back to the 2nd c B.C., finds from excavations at Nimrud 20675

Nergal Gate Museum, Mosul
Archaeological Museum - 1952
Casts of the Royal Assyrian kings, copies of ancient Assyrian sculptures 20676

Nasiriya

Nasiriya Museum, Nasiriya
Archaeological Museum
Near Eastern antiquities, Islamic art 20677

Nimrud

Archaeological Site Nimrud (Calah), Nimrud
Archaeological Museum
Ruins of Assyrian palaces of the 8th and 9th c B.C., ancient Assyrian sculpture 20678

Nineveh

Al Mawsil Museum, Nineveh
Archaeological Museum - 1974
Prehistoric, Sumerian, Assyrian and early Arab periods, Islamic art 20679

Samarra

Samarra Museum, Samarra
Archaeological Museum - 1936
Finds from the ruins of Samarra 20680

Sulaimaniya

Al Sulaimaniya Museum, Sulaimaniya
Archaeological Museum 20681

Ireland

Adare

Adare Trinity Museum, Presbytery, Adare, Co. Limerick - T: (061) 86177, 86208. Head: J. Browne
Historical Museum
Social and domestic life in the Adare area during the past 100 years, historical items relating to the numerous monasteries which once existed in the district 20682

Aran Islands

Ionad Arann Heritage Centre, Cill Ronain, Inis Mor, Aran Islands, Co. Galway - T: (099) 61355, Fax: 61354
Local Museum 20683

Museam na Oileran, Inishmaan, Aran Islands, Co. Galway
Local Museum 20684

Arklow

Arklow Maritime Museum, Saint Mary's Rd, Arklow, Co. Wicklow - T: (0402) 32868
Historical Museum
Story of Arklow's maritime past 20685

Athlone

Athlone Castle Museum, Castle, Athlone, Co. Westmeath - T: (0902) 72191
Historical Museum
Antiquities and material illustrating traditional rural life in the Athlone area 20686

Aughrim

Saint Catherine's National School Museum, Ballinasloe, Aughrim, Co. Galway - T: (091) 73717. Head: Martin J. Joyce
Historical Museum / Archaeological Museum
The museum is on the site of the battlefield and displays bullets, cannonballs and other relics of the battle which decided the Jacobite-Williamite War, Stone Age and Bronze Age archaeological material 20687

Bagenalstown

Hillview Museum, Bagenalstown, Co. Carlow - T: (0503) 21795
Local Museum
Coll of household artifacts and vintage farm machinery 20688

Ballinahown

An Dun Transport and Heritage Museum, Doon, Ballinahown, Co. Offaly - T: (0902) 30106, Fax: 30057, E-mail: connieh@iol.ie, Internet: http://umeandit.com. Head: Kieran Hanniffy, Constance Hanniffy
Science&Tech Museum
Farm implements, vintage cars, post war tractors 20689

Ballinamore

Ballinamore Local Museum, County Library, Ballinamore, Co. Leitrim - T: (078) 44012, Fax: 44425, E-mail: leitrimlibrary@eircom.net. Head: Sean O'Suilleabhain
Local Museum
Archaeology, traditional life of the district, displays of farm equipment and implements - library 20690

Ballybunion

Ballybunion Heritage Museum, Church Rd, Ballybunion, Co. Kerry - T: (088) 654127
Local Museum 20691

Ballyduff

North Kerry Museum, Rattoo, Ballyduff, Co. Kerry - T: (066) 7131000, Fax: 7131744
Local Museum 20692

Ballyferriter

Corca Dhuibhne Regional Museum, Ballyferriter, Co. Kerry - T: (066) 9156333, 9156100, Fax: 9156348, E-mail: mus@cfcdteo.iol.ie, Internet: http://www.corca-dhuibhne.com
Local Museum - 1986
Archaeology, history, geology, traditions, flora, language and literature of the Dingle Peninsula - library, archaeologial and flora survey archive 20693

Ballyheigue

Ballyheigue Maritime Centre, Ballyheigue, Co. Kerry - T: (066) 7133666
Natural History Museum 20694

Ballyjamesduff

Cavan County Museum, Virginia Rd, Ballyjamesduff, Co. Cavan - T: (04985) 44070, Fax: 44332, E-mail: ccmuseum@tinet.ie, Internet: http://homepages.tinet.ie/~ccm. Head: Dominic Egan
Local Museum
Archaeology, geology. folklife, militaria, botany, music, sport, culture, arts and crafts 20695

Ballytore

Ballytore Library and Museum, Old Quaker Meeting House, Ballytore, Co. Kildare
Local Museum 20696

Bantry

1796 Bantry French Armada Exhibition Centre, East Stables, Bantry House, Bantry, Co. Cork - T: (021) 2751796, 2751996, Fax: 2751309
Historical Museum 20697

Bantry House, Bantry, Co. Cork - T: (021) 2750047, Fax: 2750795. Head: E.R.G. Shelswell Withe
Decorative Arts Museum - 1830
French tapestries (18th c) furniture 20698

Bennettsbridge

Mosses Pottery, Bennettsbridge, Co. Kilkenny - T: (056) 27261
Decorative Arts Museum 20699

Birr

Ireland's Historic Science Centre, Rosse Row, Birr, Co. Offaly - T: (0509) 20336, Fax: 21583, E-mail: info@birrcastle.com, Internet: http://www.birrcastle.com. Head: Dr. Downer
Science&Tech Museum - 1996
Astronomical, general scientific, engineering, electrical, photographic, dress and archival collections - Public Records Office of Northern Ireland 20700

Bray

Bray Heritage Centre and Museum, Town Hall, Bray, Co. Wicklow - T: (01) 862539
Local Museum 20701

Bruree

DeValera Museum and Bruree Heritage Centre, Bruree, Co. Limerick - T: (063) 90900, E-mail: brurock@iol.ie, Internet: http://www.bruree.net. Head: Mainchin Seoighe
Historical Museum - 1972
Personal memorabilia from Eamonn de Valera 20702

Buncrana

Dunree Fort, Buncrana, Co. Donegal - T: (077) 61244
Historical Museum 20703

Bunratty

Bunratty Castle and Folkpark, Bunratty, Co. Clare - T: (061) 360788, 361511, Fax: 361020, E-mail: sheedyt@shannon.dev.ie. Head: Tom Sheedy
Agriculture Museum / Ethnology Museum / Open Air Museum / Folklore Museum - 1960
Furnishings, tapestries, pictures, decorative art, agricultural machinery, Talbot coll 20704

Caherdaniel

Derrynane House, Caherdaniel, Co. Kerry - T: (0667) 5113. Head: Michael Maher
Special Museum
O'Connell family portraits and items of furniture, notably in the dining-room and drawing-room, coll of memorabilia and personal possessions of Daniel O'Connell 20705

Cahersiveen

Old Barracks Heritage Centre, Bridge St, Cahersiveen, Co. Kerry - T: (066) 9472777, Fax: 9472993. Head: Carolyn King
Local Museum
Iveragh Peninsula over the past 2000 years 20706

Cape Clear Island

Cape Clear Heritage Centre (temporary closed), Cape Clear Island, Co. Cork - T: (028) 39119, E-mail: ccteo@iol.ie. Head: Éamon Lankford
Local Museum - 1981
Coll of objects relating to the hist of the Island, fishing, farming, handicrafts and domestic life, prehist 20707

Carlow

County Carlow Museum, Town Hall, Centaur St, Carlow - T: (0503) 31759, 31324. Head: Sean O'Leary
Local Museum
Blacksmith's forge, an old-time kitchen and bar, a huckster's shop, a dairy, coll of agricultural implements and craftsmen's tools, displays of ecclesiastical vestments and altar requisites 20708

Carrickmacross

Celebration of Irish Museum, Carrickmacross, Co. Monaghan - T: (042) 9351398. Head: Peadar O'Casaide
Historical Museum
Illustration of the history of the area, farm and household equipment, 18th and 19th c estate surveys and maps, photographs 20709

Carrigtwohill

Fota House, Carrigtwohill, Co. Cork - T: (021) 812555. Head: Christina Neylon
Fine Arts Museum
Coll of Irish landscape paintings, dating from the mid 18th to the mid 19th c, hist of Irish painting during the period, Irish craftmanship, Fota Wildlife Park, Fota Arboretum 20710

Cashel

Bolton Library, GPA Bldg, John St, Cashel, Co. Tipperary - T: (062) 61944, Fax: 62068, E-mail: boltonlibrary@oceanfree.net, Internet: http://www.heritagetowns.com. Head: P. Knowles
Library with Exhibitions
18th c coll, continental printing from 1473 20711

Castlebar

Belcarra Eviction Cottage, Belcarra, Castlebar, Co. Mayo - T: (087) 9090046, E-mail: - marybprendergast@ireland.com, Internet: http://www.museumsofmayo.com. Head: Mary B. Prendergast
Historical Museum
Scene of eviction 1886 20712

Museum of Country Life, National Museum of Ireland Ard-Mhúsaem na hÉireann, Turlough Park, Castlebar - T: (01) 6777444, Fax: 6777828, E-mail: marketing@museum.ie, Internet: http://www.museum.ie. Head: Dr. Patrick Wallace
Folklore Museum / Historical Museum - 2001 20713

Castlerea

Clonalis House, Castlerea, Co. Roscommon - T: (0907) 20014, Fax: 20014. Head: Marguerite O'Conor Nash
Historical Museum - 1878
History and traditions of the O'Conors, including manuscripts and documents, the Coronation Stone of the Kings of Connaught, and the 18th c harp of O'Carolan, last of the Gaelic bards 20714

Celbridge

Castletown House, Teach Chaisleán an Bhaile, Celbridge, Co. Kildare - T: (01) 6288252, Fax: 6271811, E-mail: castletown@ealga.ie, Internet: http://www.heritageireland.ie
Fine Arts Museum / Decorative Arts Museum - 1967
The state rooms incl the 'Pompeian' long gallery, the only surviving 18th c print room in Ireland, recently restored green silk drawing room and magnificent staircase hall with Lafranchini plasterwork, fine coll of 18th c Irish furniture and paintings 20715

Celbridge Motor Museum, Temple Mills House, Celbridge, Co. Kildare - T: (01) 288297. Head: J. Ellis
Science&Tech Museum
Coll of vintage and veteran cars and motorcycles 20716

Church Hill

Glebe House and Gallery, Derek Hill Collection, Church Hill, Co. Donegal - T: (074) 37071, Fax: 37072. Head: Chris Wilson
Fine Arts Museum / Decorative Arts Museum - 1985
Works by Derek Hill (b. 1916), paintings by Annigoni, Bratby, Bonnard, Braque, Picasso, Sutherland and Landseer, as well as works by leading Irish artists, ceramics from Islamic countries and textiles by William Morris 20717

Clonakilty

West Cork Regional Museum, Old Methodist School, Western Rd, Clonakilty, Co. Cork. Head: Michael O'Connell
Local Museum
Local and social history, folklife, Michael Collins coll 20718

Clonfert

Clonfert Museum, Clonfert, Co. Galway
Local Museum 20719

Clonmel

Tipperary S.R. County Museum, The Borstal, Emmet St, Clonmel, Co. Tipperary - T: (052) 25399 ext 3371, Fax: 80390, E-mail: museum@southtippcoco.ie. Head: Pat Holland
Local Museum - 1948
Local history, fine regional art 20720

Cobh

Cobh Museum, High Rd, Cobh, Co. Cork - T: (021) 4814240, Fax: 4811018, E-mail: cobhmuseum@eircom.net
Local Museum - 1970 20721

The Queenstown Story, Cobh Heritage Centre, Cobh, Co. Cork - T: (021) 4813591, Fax: 4813595, E-mail: cobhher@indigo.ie, Internet: http://www.cobheritage.com. Head: Debbie Walsh
Historical Museum
Unique origins, history and legacy are dramatically retold at the Queenstown Story 20722

Cork

Cork Public Museum, Fitzgerald Park, Mardyke, Cork - T: (021) 4270679, Fax: 4270931, E-mail: museum@corkcorp.ie. Head: Stella Cherry
Local Museum - 1910
Archaeology, silver, glass, lace, national and local history 20723

Crawford Municipal Art Gallery, Emmet Pl, Cork - T: (021) 4273377, Fax: 4805043, E-mail: crawfordgallery@eircom.net, Internet: http://www.synergy.ie/crawford. Head: Peter Murray
Fine Arts Museum
20th c paintings and works by artists of the Newlyn School, print coll of 20th c woodcuts 20724

University College Zoological Museum, Prospect Row, Cork - T: (021) 276871, Fax: 270562. Head: Tricha J. Murphy
Natural History Museum / University Museum - 1851
Zoology (two darwin specimens: azara's opossum, patagonian cavy) 20725

Cornafean

Pighouse Collection, Corr House, Cornafean, Co. Cavan - T: (049) 4337248. Head: M.P. Faris
Local Museum
Everyday acquisitions made by members of the Faris family over a period of more than 150 years, Victorian dresses, old bills, household equipment, embroidery 20726

Corofin

Clare Heritage Centre, Church St, Corofin, Co. Clare - T: (065) 6837955, Fax: (065) 6837540, E-mail: clareheritage@eirrum.net, Internet: http://www.clareroots.com. Head: Antoinette O'Bryen
Local Museum
Conditions in Co. Clare in the 19th c, a comprehensive genealogical research service for persons with Clare ancestry 20727

Derrynamuck

Dwyer MacAllister Cottage and Museum, Derrynamuck, Co. Wicklow
Local Museum 20728

Dingle

Dingle Collection, Dingle Heritage Centre, The Quay, Dingle, Co. Kerry - T: (066) 9151787, 9151499
Local Museum 20729

Donabate

Newbridge House, Donabate, Co. Dublin - T: (01) 436534
Local Museum 20730

Donegal

County Donegal Railway Heritage Centre, Old Station House, Donegal - T: (073) 22655, Fax: 23843, E-mail: rrailway@gofree.indigo.ie, Internet: http://www.donegaltown.ie
Science&Tech Museum 20731

Drogheda

Millmount Museum and Tower, Millmount, Drogheda, Co. Louth - T: (041) 9833097, Fax: 9841599, E-mail: info@millmount.net, Internet: http://www.millmount.net. Head: Betty Quinn
Historical Museum
Domestic equipment, handicrafts and craftsmen's tools, 18th and early 19th-c guild and trade banners, geology, archaeology 20732

Dublin

Bank of Ireland Collection, Baggot St, Dublin 4 - T: (01) 785744
Fine Arts Museum
Modern Irish art 20733

Bewley's Café Museum, Bewley's Oriental Café, Grafton St, Dublin 2 - T: (01) 776761
Historical Museum 20734

The Chester Beatty Library, Dublin Castle, Dublin 2 - T: (01) 4070750, Fax: 4070760, E-mail: info@cbl.ie, Internet: http://www.cbl.ie
Library with Exhibitions 20735

Douglas Hyde Gallery, c/o Trinity College, Nassau St, Dublin 2 - T: (01) 6081116, Fax: 6708330, E-mail: dhgallery@tcd.ie, Internet: http://www.douglashydegallery.com. Head: John Hutchinson
Public Gallery / University Museum - 1978
Irish and international contemporary art 20736

Dublin Civic Museum, 58 South William St, Dublin 2 - T: (01) 6794260, Fax: 6775954. Head: Thomas P. O'Connor
Local Museum - 1953
Hist of Dublin in pictures, tapestries, glass, silver decorative objects, numismatics, maps, Dublin trades, industry 20737

Dublin Print Museum, Beggars Bush, Haddington Rd, Dublin 4 - T: (01) 6603770, Fax: 673545, E-mail: npmuseum@iol.ie
Special Museum 20738

Dublin Writers Museum, 18 Parnell Sq N, Dublin 1 - T: (01) 8722077, Fax: 8722231, E-mail: writers@dublintourism.ie, Internet: http://www.visitdublin.com. Head: Robert Nicholson
Special Museum - 1991
Story of the Irish literature - childrens' room 20739

Garda Museum, Garda Headquarters, Phoenix Park, Dublin 8 - T: (01) 771156, 773626
Special Museum
History and traditions of the Constabulary of Ireland (1822-1922), the Dublin Metropolitan Police (1836-1925) and the Garda Síochána, uniforms, insignia, documents, photographs, books and memorabilia of members of the three Forces 20740

Geological Museum, c/o Trinity College, Dept. og Geology, Dublin 2 - T: (01) 6081477, Fax: 6711199, E-mail: wysjckup@tcd.ie, Internet: http://www.tcd.ie/geology/museum.html. Head: Dr. Patrick N. Wyse Jackson
Natural History Museum / University Museum - 1777/1788
Geology, fossils, minerals 20741

Guinness Hopestore Museum, Saint James's Gate, Crane St, Dublin 8 - T: (01) 4084800, 4084965, Internet: http://www.guinness.ie. Head: Ann Lewis
Science&Tech Museum - 1966
History of the Guiness brewing company, brewing technological history, brewing in Ireland, bottles, steam engine models, locomotive, narrow gauge railway engine, labels, bottles, transport history - library 20742

Heraldic Museum, 2 Kildare St, Dublin 2 - T: (01) 6030311, Fax: 6621062, E-mail: herald@nli.ie, Internet: http://www.nli.ie. Head: Brendan O'Donoghue
Historical Museum - 1909
China, glass, wooden and other objects bearing heraldic archievements, ceremonial robes and tabards, banners of chiefs of the name, flags of Irish regiments in French service (18th c), arms of presidents of Ireland, towns and counties, illuminated pedigrees 20743

The Hugh Lane Municipal Gallery of Modern Art, Charlemont House, Parnell Sq N, Dublin 1 - T: (01) 8741903, Fax: 8722182, E-mail: info@hughlane.ie, Internet: http://www.hughlane.ie. Head: Barbara Dawson
Public Gallery
19th and 20th c works of art, paintings by Corot, Constable, Augustus John, Monet and Degas, European stained glass, modern Irish paintings and sculpture, Francis Bacon Studio 20744

Irish Jewish Museum, 3-4 Walworth Rd, Dublin 8 - T: (01) 534754. Head: J. Lynn
Historical Museum / Ethnology Museum
Cultural, commercial and social life of the Jewish people in Ireland 20745

Irish Museum of Modern Art, Royal Hospital, Military Rd, Kilmainham, Dublin 8 - T: (01) 6129900, Fax: 6129999, E-mail: info@modernart.ie, Internet: http://www.modernart.ie. Head: Philomena Byrne
Fine Arts Museum / Public Gallery 20746

Irish Whiskey Corner Museum → The Old Jameson Distillery

James Joyce Museum, Joyce Tower, Sandycove, Dublin 18 - T: (01) 2809265, Fax: 2809265, E-mail: joycetower@dublintourism.ie, Internet: http://www.visitdublin.com. Head: Robert Nicholson
Special Museum - 1962
Joyce's life and career, personal possessions, such as his guitar, waistcoat, travelling trunk and piano, letters and autographs, his works, photos paintings, drawings, one of the two original death-masks made in 1941 - library 20747

Kilmainham Gaol and Museum, Inchicore Rd, Dublin 8 - T: (01) 4535984, Fax: 4532037, E-mail: info@heritageireland.ie, Internet: http://www.heritageireland.ie. Head: Pat Cooke
Historical Museum 20748

Museum of Archaeology, National Museum of Ireland Ard-Mhúsaem na hÉireann, Kildare St, Dublin 2 - T: (01) 6777444, Fax: 6777828, E-mail: marketing@museum.ie, Internet: http://www.museum.ie. Head: Dr. Patrick Wallace
Archaeological Museum / Historical Museum - 1877
Archaeology, history, art, prehistoric gold ornaments and early Christian metalwork, Viking material, Irish and foreign silver, glass, ceramics, textiles, decorative art of Japan and China, natural hist, ethnography 20749

Museum of Childhood, 20 Palmerston Park, Dublin 6 - T: (01) 973223. Head: Joanne Mollereau
Special Museum
Dolls, toys and teddy bears 20750

Museum of Decorative Arts and History, National Museum of Ireland Ard-Mhúsaem na hÉireann, Collins Barracks, Benburb St, Dublin 7 - T: (01) 6777444, Fax: 6777828, E-mail: marketing@museum.ie, Internet: http://www.museum.ie. Head: Dr. Patrick Wallace
Decorative Arts Museum / Historical Museum
Irish and foreign silver, glass, ceramics, textiles, decorative art of Japan and China 20751

Museum of Natural History, National Museum of Ireland Ard-Mhúsaem na hÉireann, Merrion St, Dublin 2 - T: (01) 6777444, Fax: 6777828, E-mail: marketing@museum.ie, Internet: http://www.museum.ie. Head: Dr. Patrick Wallace
Natural History Museum / Historical Museum
Worldwide coll of zoological specimens, ranging from protozoa to mammals, world birds, molluscs, buterflies, big game heads and the fine Blashka glass models of marine life 20752

National Gallery of Ireland, Gailearaí Náisiúnta na hÉireann, Merrion Sq W, Dublin 2 - T: (01) 6615133, Fax: 6619149, E-mail: artgall@eircom.net, Internet: http://www.nationalgallery.ie. Head: Raymond Keaveney, Sergio Benedetti
Fine Arts Museum - 1854
13th-19th c paintings and drawings by European and American artists, Irish artists - education dept, library 20753

National Heritage Museum, Merrion St, Dublin 2 - T: (01) 618811
Historical Museum 20754

National Transport Museum, Howth Castle, Dublin 13 - T: (01) 8480831, Internet: http://www.nationaliansportmuseum.org. Head: W. Kelly
Science&Tech Museum
150 vehicles, incl horse-drawn, electric, steam-powered, trams, buses, commercial vehicles, fire appliances and military transport 20755

National Wax Museum, Granby Row, Parnell Sq, Dublin 1 - T: (01) 726340. Head: Kay Murray
Historical Museum
100 figures, representing two c of Irish history 20756

The Old Jameson Distillery, Bow St, Smithfield, Dublin 7 - T: (01) 8072355, Fax: 8072369, E-mail: ojd@idl.ie, Internet: http://www.whiskeytours.ie. Head: John Callely
Special Museum
Hist and manufacture of Irish whiskey 20757

Pearse Museum, Saint Enda's Park, Grange Rd, Rathfarnham, Dublin 16 - T: (01) 4934208, Fax: 4936120. Head: Pat Cooke
Special Museum - 1979
Documents, photographs, memorabilia, comprehensive view of the life of Patrick Pearse 20758

Plunket Museum of Irish Education, c/o Church of Ireland College of Education, 96 Upper Rathmines Rd, Dublin 6 - T: (01) 4970033, Fax: 4971932, E-mail: library@cice.ie. Head: Susan Parkes
Historical Museum / University Museum - 1990
Irish textbooks, and educational aids from 19th and 20th c 20759

Project Arts Center, 39 East Essex St, Dublin 2 - T: (01) 6796622, Fax: 6792310, E-mail: info@projekt.ie, Internet: http://www.projekt.ie
Public Gallery 20760

Royal College of Surgeons in Ireland Museum, Saint Stephen's Green, Dublin 2 - T: (01) 753816, Fax: 780018. Head: Prof. Mary Leader
Natural History Museum / University Museum - 1820
Bone disease, fetal abnormalities, surgical instruments 20761

University College Dublin Classical Museum, Belfield, Dublin 4 - T: (01) 7068662, Fax: 7061176, E-mail: christina.haywood@ucd.ie. Head: A. Peatfield
Archaeological Museum / University Museum
Greek vases, Roman pottery and glass, Greek and Roman coins, and inscriptions, papyrus fragments, lamps, terracottas, miscellaneous metal items and a sarcophagus 20762

Viking Adventure, Saint Audeon's Church, High St, Dublin 8 - T: (01) 6797099
Religious Arts Museum 20763

Weingreen Museum of Biblical Antiquities, c/o Trinity College, Arts and Social Sciences Bldg, Dublin 2 - T: (01) 6081297, 6082229, Fax: 6774844, E-mail: rodgersz@tcd.ie. Head: Z. Rodgers
Archaeological Museum / University Museum
Excavations at Lachish, Jericho and Jerusalem, material from Buseirah and Tawilan in Jordan, Palestinian pottery, objects of stone, bone, metal, glass, faience and wood 20764

Zoological Museum, c/o Department of Zoology, Trinity College, Dublin 2 - T: (01) 6081679, Fax: 6778094, E-mail: mlinnie@tcd.ie. Head: Martyn J. Linnie
Natural History Museum / University Museum - 1876
Zoology, invertebrates, amphibians, reptiles, mammals, blaschka glass models, great auk 20765

Dun Laoghaire

National Maritime Museum of Ireland, Mariners' Church, Haigh Terrace, Dun Laoghaire, Co. Dublin - T: (01) 2800969, Fax: 2844602. Head: Robert Brennan
Science&Tech Museum - 1977
Irish maritime hist, a French boat from 1796, hist of lighthouse engineering, maps, charts, nautical instruments, marine paintings and pamphlets, ship models 20766

Dungarvan

Dungarvan Museum, Old Town Hall, Saint Augustine St, Dungarvan, Co. Waterford - T: (058) 45960, Internet: http://www.dungarvanmuseum.org
Local Museum
Social, archaeological and economic history of the town 20767

Dunleer

Rathgory Transport Museum, Rathgory, Dunleer, Co. Louth - T: (041) 9838648, 6851389. Head: Paddy Byrne
Science&Tech Museum 20768

Ennis

Clare Museum, Arthur's Row, Ennis, Co. Clare - T: (065) 6823382, Fax: 6842119, E-mail: claremuseum@eircom.net, Internet: http://www.clarelibrary.ie. Head: John Rattigan
Archaeological Museum - 2001
Regional archaeology 20769

De Valera Library and Museum, Harmony Row, Ennis, Co. Clare - T: (065) 6821616, Fax: 6842462. Head: Noel Crowley
Local Museum - 1975 20770

Enniscorthy

Wexford County Museum, Castle, Enniscorthy, Co. Wexford - T: (054) 35926, Fax: 35926, E-mail: wexmus@iol.ie. Head: David Carbery
Local Museum - 1962
Agricultural, military, maritime and industrial history of the town and county of Wexford, a coll of old types of lighting equipment, including stone lamps, rushlight holders, and hob lamps, figureheads from ships lost of the Wexford coast 20771

Fethard

Fethard Park and Folk Museum, Cashel Rd, Fethard, Co. Tipperary - T: (052) 31516, Fax: 31839. Head: Margaret Mullins
Local Museum / Folklore Museum - 1982
Horse-drawn vehicles, carriages, hearses, jaunting cars, traps, delivery cars, horse-drawn agricultural machines, bicycles, perambulators and wheelchairs 20772

Foynes

Foynes Flying Boat Museum, Aras Ide, Foynes, Co. Limerick - T: (069) 65416, Fax: 65416. Head: Margaret O'Shaughnessy
Science&Tech Museum - 1989
Transatlantic aviation 1937-45, flying boats - archives 20773

Galway

Galway Arts Centre, 47 Dominic St, Galway - T: (091) 565886, Fax: 568642, E-mail: gac@indigo.ie, Internet: http://www.galwayartscentre.ie. Head: Helen Carey
Fine Arts Museum
Multidisciplinary arts 20774

Galway City Museum, Spanish Rd, Galway - T: (091) 68151
Local Museum 20775

James Mitchell Museum, c/o National University of Ireland, Dept. of Geology, Galway - T: (091) 524411 ext 2351, 2129, Fax: 750533, E-mail: Patrick.Orr@nuigalway.ie. Head: Dr. Patrick J. Orr, Dr. Martin Feely
Natural History Museum / University Museum
2,500 fossil invertebrate, vertebrate and plant specimens, and 2,000 mineral and rock specimens from locations throughout the world 20776

Músaem Cathrach Na Gaillimhe (Galway City Museum), Spanish Arch, Galway - T: (091) 567641, Fax: 567641. Head: Bill Scanlan
Local Museum - 1972
Hist of the town and its notabilities 20777

Glencolmcille

Glencolmcille Folk Village Museum, Glencolmcille, Co. Donegal - T: (073) 30017, Fax: 30334, E-mail: folkmus@indigo.ie, Internet: http://www.infowing.ie/donegal/Ad/Fr.htm. Head: Shane Gillespie
Local Museum / Folklore Museum / Open Air Museum
3 thatched cottages dating 1700, 1800 and 1900, heritage building giving complete hist of Glencolmcille (first settlers, clans, archaeology, folklore, music, etc.), 1800 schoolhouse 20778

Glenealy

Robert Sheane's Agricultural Museum, Ballydowling, Glenealy, Co. Wicklow - T: (0404) 5608
Agriculture Museum 20779

Gort

Yeats Tower - Thoor Ballylee, Gort, Co. Galway - T: (091) 631436, Fax: 631436. Head: Mary Callanan
Special Museum - 1965
Memorabilia on William Butler Yeats (1865-1939), in his former home 20780

Inniskeen

Inniskeen Folk Museum, Inniskeen, Co. Monaghan - T: (042) 9378109
Folklore Museum
History of the district and its traditional life and customs, a section devoted to the poet, Patrick Kavanagh (1904-67) 20781

Kanturk

Saint Peter's Church Museum, Kanturk, Co. Cork - T: (029) 50598. Head: P.O. Sullivan
Religious Arts Museum
Hist of the area illustrated by maps, photographs, newspapers and diaries, including one of exceptional interest for the years 1840-60 20782

Kilbeggan

Locke's Distillery Museum, Kilbeggan, Co. Westmeath - T: (0506) 32134, Fax: 32134, E-mail: lockesmuseum@iol.ie, Internet: http://www.lockesdistillerymuseum.com. Head: James Mullins
Science&Tech Museum
The oldest licensed pot-still distillery in the world, Irish Whiskey 20783

Kilfenora

Burren Centre, Kilfenora, Co. Clare - T: (065) 7088030, Fax: 7088102, E-mail: burrencenter@tinet.ie, Internet: http://homepage.tinet.ie/~burrencenter. Head: Con Farrell
Local Museum - 1975
Uniqueness of the Burren region, natural and human enviroment 20784

Kilkee

Kilkee Heritage Gallery (closed) 20785

Kilkenny

Butler Gallery, The Castle, Kilkenny - T: (056) 61106, Fax: 70031, E-mail: butlergal@indigo.ie, Internet: http://www.butlergallery.com. Head: Nathalie Weadick
Public Gallery
Irish art 19th-20th c, contemporary art 20786

Rothe House Museum, Parliament St, Kilkenny - T: (056) 22893, 670777, Fax: 22893, 670778. Head: Lex Hyde
Decorative Arts Museum / Local Museum / Folklore Museum - 1966
Pictures and artefacts of Kilkenny's past, costume, furnishing, antiquities, prehistoric and ancient armaments, ornaments, folk tools, historic books, papers - library 20787

Shee Alms House, Rose Inn St, Kilkenny - T: (056) 217055
Special Museum 20788

Killarney

Knockreer House, Killarney, Co. Kerry - T: (064) 31246
Local Museum 20789

Muckross House Gardens and Traditional Farms, National Park, Killarney, Co. Kerry - T: (064) 31440, Fax: 33926, E-mail: mucros@iol.ie, Internet: http://www.muckross-house.ie. Head: P. Dawson
Folklore Museum / Open Air Museum / Agriculture Museum - 1964
Local folklore, traditional crafts, natural hist, local hist - craft centre 20790

Museum of Irish Transport, Scotts Hotel, Killarney, Co. Kerry - T: (064) 34677, Fax: 36656. Head: Denis Lucey
Science&Tech Museum - 1987
19th c bicycles and tricycles, motoring and cycling accessories, components and advertising material, Frederick Wolseley, veteran, vintage and classic cars 20791

Kilmallock

Kilmallock Museum, Kilmallock, Co. Limerick - T: (061) 417826, Fax: 415366
Local Museum 20792

Kilmore Quay

Kilmore Quay Maritime Museum, Kilmore Quay, Co. Wexford - T: (053) 29655, 29832
Science&Tech Museum 20793

Kilmurry

MacSwiney Memorial Museum, Lissarda, Kilmurry, Co. Cork - T: (053) 336144. Head: Mary O'Sullivan
Archaeological Museum / Historical Museum
Archaeology, history and traditional rural life of the area 20794

Kinlough

Kinlough Folk Museum, Kinlough, Co. Leitrim - T: (072) 51586. Head: Patrick Gallagher
Folklore Museum
Hist of the area, with domestic equipment, agricultural implements, craftsmen's tools and weapons, election posters and a poteen still, and a reconstruction of a traditional farmhouse kitchen, photographs of local interest 20795

Kinsale

Kinsale Regional Museum, Kinsale, Co. Cork - T: (021) 4777930, Fax: 4777929, E-mail: kinsalemuseum@ireland.com. Head: Michael Mulcahy
Local Museum - 1940
Hist of the town and include the Charters of the old Kinsale Corporation, relics of the Siege and Battle of 1601-2 and the Siege of 1690, a model of HMS Kinsale, launched in 1700, local coinage, examples of local lace - library 20796

Kinvara

Dunguaire Castle, Kinvara, Co. Galway
Historical Museum 20797

Knightstown

Valentia Island Heritage Centre, Old School, Knightstown, Co. Kerry - T: (066) 9476411. Head: Clare Ring
Local Museum
Transatlantic telegraph cable, marine service at habour, radio and weather stations, lifeboat, local history, archaeology 20798

Knock

Knock Folk Museum, Knock, Co. Mayo - T: (094) 88100, Fax: 88295, E-mail: info@knock-shrine.ie, Internet: http://www.knock-shrine.ie. Head: Grace Mulqueen
Folklore Museum / Religious Arts Museum - 1973
Knock apparition of 1879, places it in context of the lifestyle, people, traditions and costums at that time 20799

Letterkenny

Donegal County Museum, High Rd, Letterkenny, Co. Donegal - T: (074) 24613, Fax: 26522, E-mail: jmccarthy@donegalcoco.ie. Head: Judith McCarthy
Local Museum
Local history, artefacts since prehistory 20800

Limerick

AV Gallery, University of Limerick, Limerick - T: (01) 61202040, Fax: 61202938
Public Gallery / University Museum 20801

The Hunt Museum, Custom House, Rutland St, Limerick - T: (061) 312833, Fax: 312834, E-mail: info@huntmuseum.com, Internet: http://www.ul.ie/~hunt. Head: Peter McNamara
Decorative Arts Museum / Archaeological Museum - 1977
Jewellery, Classical and European archeology, ceramics, medieval art, christian religious art, silver, statuary (polychrome), modern art, fine metalwork, ivory, relics and reliquaries, Chinese and Japanese porcelain, crucifixes, Irish art, medieval stained glass, Georgian architecture in Ireland 20802

King John's Castle, Nicholas St, Limerick - T: (061) 411201, Fax: 472523, E-mail: sheedyt@shannon-dev.ie, Internet: http://www.shennonheritage.com
Historical Museum
Restored castle (1216) 20803

Limerick City Gallery of Art, Pery Sq, Limerick - T: (061) 61310633, Fax: 61415266. Head: Paul M. O'Reilly
Fine Arts Museum
Paintings by Irish artists or by artists with Irish connections, works of Jervas, Carver, Barrett, Mulcahy, Hone, Osbourne, Yeats, Orpen, Keating and Henry - library 20804

Limerick Museum, Castle Ln, Nicholas St, Limerick - T: (061) 417826, Fax: 415266, E-mail: lwalsh@limerickcorp.ie, Internet: http://www.limerickcorp.ie. Head: Larry Walsh
Local Museum - 1916
Local hist, archaeology, natural history, civic insignia, lace, silver, paintings, prints, printing, maps, coins, labour and political history 20805

Listowel

Saint John's Art and Heritage Centre → Saint John's Theatre and Arts Centre

Saint John's Theatre and Arts Centre, The Square, Listowel, Co. Kerry - T: (01) 6822566, Fax: 6823485, E-mail: stjohnstheatre@eircom.net, Internet: http://www.stjohnstheatreustowel.com. Head: Joe Murphy
Public Gallery 20806

Lixnaw

Lixnaw Agricultural Museum, Kiltomey, Lixnaw, Co. Kerry - T: (066) 7132202
Agriculture Museum
Farming implements 20807

Longford

Saint Mel's Diocesan Museum, Presbytery, Longford, Co. Longford - T: (043) 46465. Head: Vincent Connaughton
Religious Arts Museum
Religious, archaeological and folk life material, the 10th-c Crozier of St Mel, a 13th-c French crozier from Limoges, coll of Penal Day Crosses and chalices, medals, coins, ornaments, domestic equipment 20808

Loughrea

Clonfert Diocesan Museum, Saint Brendans Cathedral, Loughrea, Co. Galway - T: (091) 41212. Head: Ignatius Clarke
Religious Arts Museum - 1956
13th, 15th and 17th-c Irish carved wooden figures, 15th to 18th-c vestments, 15th to 19th-c chalices 20809

Lusk

Willie Monks Museum, The Square, Lusk, Co. Dublin - T: (01) 437276. Head: Tom Seaver
Local Museum
Agricultural tools and implements, dairying equipment, a replica of a thatched cottage, furniture, household objects, feature local trades and industries, handicrafts, bulb-growing, paintings, historical events which have taken place in the area 20810

Macroom

Macroom Museum, Castle St, Macroom, Co. Cork - T: (026) 41272. Head: E. O'Riordan
Local Museum
Domestic equipment, craftsmen's tools, farm implements, documents, old photographs 20811

Malahide

Fry Model Railway Museum, Malahide Castle Demesne, Malahide, Co. Dublin - T: (01) 8463779, Fax: 8463723, E-mail: fryrailway@dublintourism.ie, Internet: http://www.visitdublin.com. Head: John Dunne
Science&Tech Museum 20812

Malahide Castle, Malahide, Co. Dublin - T: (01) 8462516, Fax: 8462537, E-mail: malahidecastle@dublintourism.ie, Internet: http://www.visitdublin.ie. Head: Geraldino Lynch
Fine Arts Museum / Historic Site 20813

Maynooth

Carton House, Maynooth, Co. Kildare
Local Museum 20814

College Museum, c/o Saint Patrick's College, Maynooth, Co. Kildare - T: (01) 6285222, Fax: 6289063. Head: Prof. Michael T. Casey
Historical Museum / University Museum - 1930
Original induction coil and other apparatus of Dr. N. Callan, Inventor of the induction coil, ecclesiastical art 20815

Millstreet

Millstreet Local Museum, Carnegie Hall, Millstreet, Co. Cork - T: (029) 70343. Head: Seán Radley
Local Museum - 1980
Coll of photographs, the Liscahane Ogham stone, the social, economic and military hist of the Millstreet area, special section recalling Eurovision Song Contest 1993 which was held in Millst 20816

Monaghan

Heritage Centre of Saint Louis Convent, Louisville, Monaghan, Co. Managhan - T: (047) 83529, 81411
Religious Arts Museum
Hist of the order 20817

Monaghan County Museum, 1-2 Hill St, Monaghan, Co. Monaghan - T: (047) 82928, Fax: 71189, E-mail: comuseum@monaghancoco.ie. Head: Roisin Doherty
Local Museum - 1974
Archeological finds form Lake Dwellings (early historic period), coll of Carrickmacross lace and clones crochet, folklore, local hist, unique 14th c cross known as the 'Cross of Clogher' 20818

Mount Nugent

Crover Folk Museum, Lough St, Mount Nugent, Co. Cavan - T: (049) 8540206. Head: Anita Matthews
Folklore Museum
Hist and character of agriculture and rural life in the area from the 18th c onwards, farm implements and blacksmiths' tools 20819

Mullinahone

Threshing Museum, Carrick Rd, Mullinahone, Co. Tipperary - T: (052) 53144. Head: David O'Brien
Agriculture Museum
Garvie threshing mill dating from the 1920s, a 1930s winnowing machine and elevator, a Jones baler, made in the early 1940s, farming implements, a 1918 McCormack reape r and binder, a 1945 Fordson tractor 20820

Mullingar

Ecclesiastical Museum, Cathedral, Mullingar, Co. Westmeath - T: (044) 48338
Religious Arts Museum
Ecclesiastical exhibits from the Diocese, especially crucifixes, vestments and chalices, dating from c 1600 20821

Mullingar Military Museum, Columb Barracks, Mullingar, Co. Westmeath - T: (044) 48391
Military Museum
Dug-out canoes, fragments of Israeli jets from the Sinai Desert, old battalion flags and pennants, pre-1939 Irish Army full-dress uniform 20822

Nenagh

Castle Brand Visitor Centre, Tyone, Nenagh, Co. Tipperary - T: (067) 31711, Fax: 31659
Local Museum
Cookware 20823

Nenagh District Heritage Centre, Governor's House, Nenagh, Co. Tipperary - T: (067) 32633
Local Museum 20824

Quin

Knappogue Castle, Quin, Co. Clare - T: (061) 368103, Fax: 368889
Local Museum 20825

Rathdrum

Avondale House, Avondale Forest Park, Rathdrum, Co. Wicklow - T: (01) 6615666, Fax: 46111, Internet: http://coillte.ie
Special Museum - 1991
Memorial to Charles Stewart Parnell (1846-91), house built in 1779, contains furnishings of the period, papers and personal possessions 20826

Rathkeale

Irish Palatine Association Museum, Rathkeale, Co. Limerick - T: (069) 63511, Fax: 63511, E-mail: ipass@lircom.net, Internet: http://www.erin.ie/ipa. Head: Austin Bovewizer
Historical Museum
Hist of the German families settled in Ireland in 1709 20827

Robertstown

Robertstown House and Falconry, Robertstown, Co. Kildare
Local Museum 20828

Roscrea

Roscrea Heritage Centre, G.P.A. Damer House, Castle St, Roscrea, Co. Tipperary - T: (0505) 21850. Head: John Cahill
Local Museum - 1983
Farm and household items, prehistory of the Midlands, monastic Midlands 20829

Rosmuck

Patrick Pearse's Cottage, Rosmuck, Co. Galway
Local Museum 20830

Rossnowlagh

Donegal Historical Society Museum, Franciscan Friary, Rossnowlagh, Co. Donegal - T: (072) 51342, 51267. Head: Lucius J. Emerson
Local Museum - 1954
Early firearms and coin coll, Stone Age coll, complete genealogy of the O'Donnell chieftains of Donegal up to present time incl the Spanish and Austrian Branches, European, American and Spanish Armada 20831

Saint Mullins

Saint Mullins Heritage Centre, Saint Mullins, Co. Carlow
Local Museum - 1994
Life and work of St. Mogue, founder of a monastic settlement, local milling and craft industries 20832

Shannon

Lough Gur Village, c/o Shannon Heritage, Shannon 55555 - T: (061) 361511
Open Air Museum
Over 5,000 years of Irish hist 20833

Slane

Francis Ledwidge Cottage and Museum, Slane, Co. Meath - T: (041) 9824544
Local Museum 20834

Sligo

County Museum, Stephen St, Sligo - T: (071) 47190, 42212, Fax: 46798, E-mail: sligolib@iol.ie. Head: Donal Tinney
Archaeological Museum / Historical Museum - 1957
Archaeology and hist of Sligo, The Irish Literary Renaissance 20835

Stradbally

Irish Steam Preservation Society Museum, The Green, Stradbally, Co. Laois - T: (0502) 25444, Fax: 25154, Internet: http://www.irishsteam.ie. Head: Kenneth Graham
Science&Tech Museum - 1968
Coll of steam-powered equipment, including traction engines, road rollers and threshing machines, all built between 1913 and 1940 20836

Straffan

Steam Museum, Lodge Park Heritage Yard, Straffan, Co. Kildare - T: (01) 6273155, Fax: 6273477, E-mail: info@steam-museum.ie, Internet: http://www.steam-museum.ie. Head: Robert Guinnes
Science&Tech Museum - 1988
Richard Guinness coll of historic prototype locomotive models, prototype Richard Trevithick, stationary engines full size working in steam 20837

Straide

Michael Davitt National Memorial Museum, Straide, Co. Mayo - T: (094) 31022, E-mail: davittmuseum@eircom.net, Internet: http://www.museumsofmayo.com/davitt. Head: Nancy Smith
Historical Museum
Land acts, prison records, police files, photo's, personal items, material relating to the land war 20838

Strokestown

Famine Museum, Strokestown Park, Strokestown, Co. Roscommon - T: (078) 33013, Fax: 33712, E-mail: infostrokestownpark.ie, Internet: http://www.strokestownpark.ie
Historical Museum - 1994
Hist of Irish migrants to America in the years of the great famine in 1845-47 20839

Thurles

Thurles Famine Museum, Saint Mary's Church of Ireland, Thurles, Co. Tipperary - T: (0504) 21133
Historical Museum
Displays on the Great Famine (1845-1849) 20840

Tralee

Kerry County Museum, Ashe Memorial Hall, Denny St, Tralee, Co. Kerry - T: (066) 7127777, Fax: 7127444, E-mail: kcmuseum@indigo.ie, Internet: http://www.kerrycountymuseum.com. Head: Helen O'Carroll
Historical Museum
Hist of Kerry and Ireland 20841

Trim

Meath Archaeological and Historical Museum, County Library, Trim, Co. Meath
Archaeological Museum / Historical Museum
Coll of the Meath Archaeological and Historical Society, historical items, especially weapons, prehistoric and early Celtic archaeological material found in the area 20842

Tuam

Tuam Mill Museum, Shop St, Tuam, Co. Galway - T: (093) 24463
Science&Tech Museum
Working models of different types of mill, a selection of quernstones used locally 20843

Tullow

Tullow Museum, Bridge St, Tullow, Co. Carlow - T: (0503) 51702
Local Museum
Hist of the area, domestic equipment, agricultural tools and railway relics 20844

Tully

Irish Horse Museum, Irish National Stud, Tully, Co. Kildare - T: (045) 521617, Fax: 522964, E-mail: stud@irish-national-stud.ie, Internet: http://www.irish-national-stud.ie
Special Museum
Hist of the horse and Irish horse-racing, the farrier, the saddler, the veterinary racing colours, horse-horoscopes, the skeleton of 'Arkle', material relating to famous race horses incl 'Northern Dancer', 'Nijinsky' etc and memorabilia from famous jockeys - Audio-visual display 20845

Waterford

Brother Rice Museum, Mount Sion, Barrack St, Waterford - T: (051) 74390
Special Museum
Life and work of the Waterford merchant, Edmund Ignatius Rice (1762-1844), founder of the Presentation Brothers and the Christian Brothers 20846

Garter Lane Arts Centre, 22a O'Connell St, Waterford - T: (051) 855038, Fax: 871570, E-mail: boxoffice@garterlane.ie, Internet: http://www.garterlane.ie. Head: Caroline Senior
Public Gallery - 1984 20847

Reginalds Tower Museum, The Mall, Waterford - T: (051) 304220
Local Museum 20848

Waterford Treasures at the Granary, Merchant Quay, Waterford - T: (051) 304500, Fax: 304501, E-mail: mail@waterfordtreasures.com, Internet: http://www.waterfordtreasures.com. Head: Eamonn McEneaney
Local Museum - 1999
1000 years of Waterford's hist, traced throzgh artefacts, ranging from Viking up to the present day 20849

Westport

Westport House, Westport, Co. Mayo - T: (098) 25430, Fax: 25206. Head: Earl of Altamont
Decorative Arts Museum / Fine Arts Museum - 1960
Mansion with original furnishings, silver objects, decorative arts, paintings, books, portraits by J. Reynold (1723-1792), 17 paintings by the Irish landscape artist James O'Connor (1819) 20850

Wexford

Irish Agricultural Museum, Johnstown Castle, Old Farmyard, Wexford - T: (053) 42888, Fax: 42213, E-mail: aosullivan@johnstown.teagasc.ie. Head: Dr. A.M. O'Sullivan
Agriculture Museum - 1975
Irish country furniture, rural crafts, farm vehicles, dairy equipment, Great Potato Famine 1845-1847, Ferguson system equipment 20851

Kilmore Quay Maritime Museum, The Quay, Lightship Guillemot, Wexford - T: (053) 29655
Historical Museum
Model ships, pictures, sea antiques 20852

Youghal

Clock Tower Archive Centre, Main St, Youghal, Co. Cork - T: (024) 92926, E-mail: yudc@tinet.ie
Local Museum
Mace, seals, official weights and measures, the original charters of the town, granted by Elizabeth I and James I 20853

Israel

Abu Ghosh

Crusader Church, Church of the Resurrection, Abu Ghosh - T: (02) 525697
Religious Arts Museum
Ceremonial artifacts, archeological findings 20854

Acre

Museum of the Underground Prisoners-Acre, Citadel, 10 Haganah St, Acre - T: (04) 918264
Historical Museum
Life and death in a British prison 20855

Afula

Sturman Institute Museum of Regional Science, Gilboa Community Centers, Afula 18120 - T: (06) 6531605, Fax: 532751. Head: Ofra Keinan
Natural History Museum / Archaeological Museum / Historical Museum - 1941
Stuffed animals of the region, archeology, documents and photogr from the beginning of the colonization of the region by the Jewish pioneers, geology of Gilboa mountains, maps of the colonization and drain of the marshes - Educational dept, archives, libr 20856

Akko

Akko Municipal Museum, El-Jazz'ar St, Akko, mail addr: POB 7, Akko - T: (04) 911764, Fax: 811611. Head: Yossi Adar
Local Museum - 1954
Ancient Turkish bathhouse, crusader excavations 20857

Resistance Museum, Citadel, Akko
Historical Museum
Documents depicting history of the resistance 20858

Almog

House of the Scribe, Jericho Junction, Almog - T: (02) 228465
Archaeological Museum
Replicas of the Dead Sea scrolls 20859

Alumot

Archeological and Land Study Collection, Alumot
Historical Museum / Archaeological Museum
Local history, archeology 20860

Arad

Arad Museum, 28 Ben-Yair St, Arad - T: (057) 957747
Archaeological Museum / Fine Arts Museum
Work of Israeli artists, archaeological discoveries from Tel Arad 20861

Ashkelon

Local Museum, National Parks Authority, Ashkelon, mail addr: POB 7028, Tel Aviv - T: (051) 2058
Archaeological Museum
Roman finds 20862

Avedat

Archeological Site Avedat, National Parks Authority, Avedat, mail addr: POB 7028, Tel Aviv - T: (057) 6361
Archaeological Museum
Nabataean and Byzantine remains 20863

Avihail

Beit Hagdudim (Jewish Legions Museum W.W. I), Avihail - T: (09) 8822212, Fax: 8621619. Head: Dan Oren
Military Museum 20864

Ayelet-Hashahar

Hazor Museum, Ayelet-Hashahar 12200 - T: (06) 934855, Fax: 934777. Head: Jochanan Meyer
Archaeological Museum - 1966
Canaanite and Israelite remains 20865

Bat Yam

Sholem Asch House, 48 Arlosoroff St, Bat Yam
Special Museum
Memorabilia of writer Sholem Asch 20866

Be'eri

Be'eri Archaeological Collection, Mobile Post, Negev, Be'eri 85135 - T: (08) 9949111, Fax: 9949437, E-mail: sifria@beeri.org.il. Head: Rina Havron
Archaeological Museum 20867

Be'ersheva

Negev Museum, Atzma'uth St, Be'ersheva - T: (057) 239105. Head: Galia Gavish
Archaeological Museum / Ethnology Museum - 1954
Local archeology from prehistoric to Arab periods, Beduin ethnology, traditional farm life 20868

Beit Shean

Local Museum of Beit Shean, 1 D St, Beit Shean 10900, mail addr: POB 327, Beit Shean - T: (065) 86221. Head: Arie Eizenberg
Archaeological Museum / Museum of Classical Antiquities - 1949
Artifacts from the Neolithic to the Ottoman period, Roman and Byzantine antiquities, antique domestic utensils - library 20869

Beit Shearim

Museum, Ancient Synagogue and Necropolis, Beit Shearim - T: (04) 931643
Archaeological Museum
Archeology Museum 20870

Bet Alfa

Synagogue, National Parks Authority, Bet Alfa, mail addr: POB 7028, Tel Aviv
Archaeological Museum 20871

Chof Ashkelon

From Holocaust to Revival Museum, Kibbutz Yad Mordekhay, Chof Ashkelon 79145 - T: (08) 6720529, Fax: 6734817, E-mail: museum_y@yadmor.org.il. Head: Vered Bar Semech
Historical Museum - 1968
Documents of Jewish experience in the Holocaust and Israel, Independence war 1948 20872

Deganya Aleph

Bet Gordon, Bet Gordon Institute, Deganya Aleph 15120 - T: (067) 50040. Head: S. Lulav
Natural History Museum - 1935
Birds, reptiles, insects, arthropods, mollusks and plants of the Kinnereth Valley, palaeolithic toos and fossil bones from the Pleistocene site of 'Ubeidiya 20873

Dimona

Municipal Museum, Municipal Bldg, Dimona
Fine Arts Museum
Contemporary and modern art including paintings of French and Belgian schools 20874

Doar-Na Evtach

Archaeological Collection of Youth Village Nitzanim, Doar-Na Evtach 79287 - T: (051) 23168. Head: Aron Waintraub
Archaeological Museum 20875

Eilat

Red Sea Maritime Museum, POB 302, Eilat - T: (07) 931643
Natural History Museum
Marine fauna, marine biology 20876

Ein Harod

Mishkan Le'Omanut (Museum of Art), POB 18965, Ein Harod 18965 - T: (06) 6485701, Fax: 6486306, E-mail: museum@einharodM.org.il, Internet: http://www.sayfur.co.il/mishkan. Head: Galia Bar-Or
Fine Arts Museum / Folklore Museum - 1948
Jewish folk art, works of Israeli artists, works of Jewish artists abroad - library 20877

Ein Hod

Janco-Dada Museum, Ein Hod 30890 - T: (04) 9843152, Fax: 9843152. Head: Raya Zommer
Fine Arts Museum - 1982
Art of Marcel Janco - Youth wing 20878

Emek Hefer

Sharon Museum, Midresht Rupin, Emek Hefer 40250 - T: (09) 688644, Fax: 688644. Head: Eliyahu-Ben Shlomo
Natural History Museum
Butterflies and birds of Israel, natural hist 20879

Ginnosar

Yigal Allon Center, Ginnosar - T: (06) 6721495, Fax: 6722910, E-mail: betalon@netvision.net.il, Internet: http://mahal.zrc.ac.il/alon. Head: Nitzah Kaplan
Historical Museum - 1988
Settlement in Galilee (archaeology, history, ethnography) 20880

Haifa

Art Centre, 24 Shabetai Levi St, Haifa 31451 - T: (04) 8531585. Head: Nissim Tal
Public Gallery 20881

Bet Pinhas Museum of Nature, c/o Biological Institute, Gan Haem, 124 Hatishbi St, Haifa 34455 - T: (04) 372886, Fax: 377019. Head: Pnina Sivan
Natural History Museum - 1950
Bird and skeleton coll, Mediterranean and Red Sea fishes, living reptiles - library 20882

Chagall House, 24 UNO Av, Haifa
Fine Arts Museum
Works of Chagall 20883

Dagon Collection, Archaeological Museum of Grain Handling in Israel, Plumer Sq, Haifa 31003, mail addr: POB 407, Haifa 31003 - T: (04) 8664221, Fax: 8664211. Head: Michael Sharan
Archaeological Museum / Agriculture Museum - 1955
Exhibits depicting grain production and processing from the first Neolithic period to the present 20884

Haifa City Museum, 11 Ben-Gurion Av, Haifa 31451, mail addr: POB 45134, Haifa 33043 - T: (04) 8512030, Fax: 8524433, Internet: http://www.haifamuseum.org.il
Local Museum 20885

Haifa Museum of Art, 26 Shabetai Levi St, Haifa 31451, mail addr: POB 45134, Haifa 33043 - T: (04) 8523255, Fax: 8552714, Internet: http://www.haifamuseums.org.il. Head: Dr. Nissim Tal
Fine Arts Museum - 1951
Painting by contemporary Israeli artists, works by internationally recognized artists, poster coll - library 20886

Israel Oil Industry Museum, 2 Tovim St, Haifa, mail addr: c/o Shemen Ltd., POB 136, Haifa 31001 - T: (04) 654333, Fax: 624898. Head: David Eitam
Science&Tech Museum - 1984
Ancient and modern oil production, restored oil presses 20887

Israel Railway Museum, Haifa East Railway Station, Kikar Faisal, 31014 Haifa - T: (04) 8564293, Fax: 8564310, E-mail: paulc@rail.org.il, Internet: http://www.israrail.org.il
Science&Tech Museum
Hist of local railways, locomotives etc. 20888

Mané-Katz Museum, 89 Jafe Not St, Haifa 34641 - T: (04) 8383482, 8362985, Fax: 8362985. Head: Noa Tarshish
Fine Arts Museum / Decorative Arts Museum - 1977
Painting, drawings and sculpture by Mané-Katz (1894-1962), antique carpets, furniture and Judaica of the artist's private collection 20889

Museum of Prehistory, 124 Hatishbi St, Haifa 34455 - T: (04) 371833
Archaeological Museum - 1962
Natufian figurines from Nahal Oren site on Mt. Carmel, archeological finds from the Tabun Cave and sites in the Jordan Valley 20890

National Maritime Museum, 198 Allenby Rd, Haifa 31451, mail addr: POB 45134, Haifa 33043 - T: (04) 8536622, Fax: 8539286, Internet: http://www.haifamuseums.org.il. Head: Dr. Nissim Tal
Special Museum - 1953
Ship models, marine archeology, mythology and ethnology, ancient scientific instruments, cartography 20891

National Museum of Science, Planning and Technology, Shmaryahu Levin St, Haifa 31448 - T: (04) 8628111, Fax: 8679103, E-mail: museum@mustsee.org.il, Internet: http://www.mustsee.org.il. Head: Prof. Nitsa Movshovitz-Hadar
Science&Tech Museum - 1983
Interactive exhibits, mirrors, airforce, mechanical puzzles, chemistry, computers, visual illusions, radios 20892

Reuben and Edith Hecht Museum, c/o University of Haifa, Main Bldg, Haifa 31905 - T: (04) 8257773, Fax: 8240724, E-mail: mushecht@research.haifa.ac.il, Internet: http://mushecht.haifa.ac.il. Head: Ofra Rimon
Archaeological Museum / Fine Arts Museum / University Museum - 1984
Religious and cult objects from the Chalcolithic through the Byzantine period (emphasis on the Israelite period), Jewish coins, inscribed seals from the biblical period, Art wing: Impressionism and the Jewish Artists in the School of Paris 20893

Tikotin Museum of Japanese Art, 89 Hanassi Av, Haifa 34642 - T: (04) 8383554, Fax: 8379824, E-mail: japanmus@netvision.net.il, Internet: http://www.haifa.gov.il/culture/eng/JapanmuseumEng.html. Head: Ilana Singer
Fine Arts Museum / Decorative Arts Museum - 1959
Japanese art and crafts from ancient to modern times - library, auditorium 20894

Herzliya

Herzliya Museum of Art, 4 Habanim St, Herzliya 46379 - T: (09) 9551011, Fax: 9500043, E-mail: herzmus@netvision.net.il, Internet: http://www.herzliyamuseum.co.il. Head: Dalia Levin
Fine Arts Museum - 1963
Isreali arts, small coll of European arts 20895

Hof Dor

Nahsholim Museum, Kibbutz Nahsholim, Hof Dor - T: (06) 390950
Archaeological Museum
Archaeology of Tel Dor and its harbor 20896

Holon

Mishkan Le'Omanut, 31 Harzfeld St, Holon - T: (03) 882244
Fine Arts Museum - 1960
Contemporary Israeli Art 20897

Hulata

Natural Sciences Museum, Hulata
Natural History Museum 20898

Jerusalem

Archaeological Museum, Rockefeller Bldg, Suleiman Rd, Jerusalem 91000, mail addr: POB 71117, Jerusalem 91710 - T: (02) 6282251, Fax: 6271926, E-mail: ornitil@imj.org.il, Internet: http://www.imj.org.il
Archaeological Museum - 1938
Archaeology of Eretz Israel from earliest times to the end of the Islamic period 20899

Beit Ha'Omanim (Jerusalem Artists House), 12 Shmuel Hanagid St, Jerusalem - T: (02) 6253653, Fax: 6258594, E-mail: artists@internet-zaheiv.net.il, Internet: http://www.interart.co.il/jah. Head: Ruth Zadka
Public Gallery / Fine Arts Museum - 1965
Works by Jerusalem artists 20900

Berman Hall, c/o Jewish National and University Library, POB 34165, Jerusalem 91341 - T: (02) 660351, Fax: 6586315, E-mail: diana@vms.huji.ac.il, Internet: http://sites.huji.ac.il/jnul. Head: Prof. Yoram Tsafrir
Library with Exhibitions 20901

Bible Lands Museum Jerusalem, Corner of Granot and Burla Sts, Jerusalem, mail addr: POB 4670, Jerusalem 91046 - T: (02) 5611066, Fax: 5638228, E-mail: biblelnd@netmedia.net.il, Internet: http://www.blmj.org. Head: Batya Borowski
Archaeological Museum - 1992
Archaeology of ancient Near Eastern, Egypt, and Mesopotamia, special exhibitions on ancient, Near Eastren and classical art 20902

Bloomfield Science Museum Jerusalem, c/o Hebrew University, Museum Blvd, Givat Ram, Jerusalem 91904 - T: (02) 6544888, Fax: 5617937, E-mail: mada@mada.org.il, Internet: http://www.mada.org.il. Head: Maya Halevy
Natural History Museum / Science&Tech Museum / University Museum - 1980
Teaching science through participation 20903

Central Archives for the History of the Jewish People, Hebrew University Campus, Sprintzak Bldg, Jerusalem, mail addr: POB 1149, Jerusalem - T: (02) 5635716, Fax: 5635716, E-mail: archives@vms.huji.ac.il, Internet: http://sites.huji.ac.il/archives. Head: Hadassah Assouline
Historical Museum - 1969
Documents from Jewish communities and organizations around the world 20904

David Palombo Museum, Mount Zion, Jerusalem 91080, mail addr: POB 8110, Jerusalem 91080 - T: (02) 6736640, Fax: 6736113. Head: Ionah Palombo
Fine Arts Museum 20905

Dominus Flevit, Franciscan Custodia di Terra Sancta, Custodia di Terra Sancta, Jerusalem, mail addr: POB 186, Jerusalem 91001 - T: (02) 6274931, Fax: 6289568. Head: Giovanni Frapporti
Archaeological Museum
Jewish tombs, Byzantine church 20906

Ecce Homo, Via Dolorosa, Sisters of Sion, Jerusalem 91190 - T: (02) 6277292, Fax: 6282224, E-mail: eccehomo@inter.net.il, Internet: http://www.webmaster@sion.org/eccehomo.htm. Head: Trudy Nabaura
Archaeological Museum
Archaeology from the Hasmonian, opening canal, from Herodian times (Jesus' period), from Hadrion times, Roman coll 20907

Edward and Helen Mardigian Museum, St of the Armenian Orthodox Patriarchate, Jerusalem - T: (02) 6282331, Fax: 6264862
Historical Museum - 1979
Armenian history and culture 20908

Greek Orthodox Patriarchate Museum, Saint Dimitry St, Jerusalem 91000
Ethnology Museum / Archaeological Museum
Archeology, ethnography, art 20909

Hebrew University Collections of Natural History, c/o Hebrew University, Givat Ram Campus, Jerusalem 91904 - T: (02) 584574, Fax: 584741. Head: Prof. F.D. Por
Natural History Museum / University Museum - 1930
Natural hist of the Middle East, Eastern Mediterranean and Red Sea, petrography and mineralogy, micropalaeontology, palaeontology and mammals, aquatic invertebrates, incl coll of inland waters, mollusca, ichtyology, herpetology, birds, herbarium - herbarium library, molusca library, data bank (in preparation) 20910

Herbert E. Clark Collection of Near Eastern Antiquities, YMCA Bldg, David Hamelech St, Jerusalem
Museum of Classical Antiquities - 1933
Pottery, glass and jewelry, cylinder seals, scarabs, terracotta and bronze figurines 20911

Inland-Water Ecological Laboratory Collection, c/o ESE Department, Hebrew University, Givat Ram Campus, Jerusalem 91904 - T: (02) 6585839, Fax: 6584741. Head: Dr. R. Ortal
Natural History Museum / University Museum - 1977
aquatic sites and aquatic fauna data base 20912

Institute for Jewish Studies, 11 Chaggai St, Jerusalem 95266 - T: (02) 5370305, Fax: 5373537
Historical Museum
Documents, books 20913

International Cultural Center for Youth in Jerusalem, 12 Emek Rephaim Rd, Jerusalem, mail addr: POB 8009, Jerusalem 91000 - T: (02) 664144, 664145. Head: Zvi Dagan
Local Museum 20914

Islamic Museum, El Aqsa Mosque, Jerusalem 91190 - T: (02) 6283286, Fax: 6262442. Head: Khader Salameh
Religious Arts Museum / Historical Museum / Historic Site
Architectural elements and ceremonial art, art books 20915

Islamic Museum Haram Al Sharif, POB 19004, Jerusalem
Religious Arts Museum - 1924
Koran Manuscripts, Islamic ceremonial items, coins, Islamic arts and crafts (Middle Ages) - library 20916

Israel Goor Theater Archive and Museum, c/o Hebrew University, Mount Scopus Campus, Jerusalem - T: (02) 883986
Performing Arts Museum - 1987
Documentation of Israeli and Jewish theater 20917

Israel Museum, Jerusalem, Hakirya, Ruppin Blvd, Jerusalem 91710, mail addr: POB 71117, Jerusalem 91710 - T: (02) 6708811, Fax: 5631833, Internet: http://www.imj.org.il. Head: James Snyder
Religious Arts Museum / Fine Arts Museum / Decorative Arts Museum / Ethnology Museum / Archaeological Museum - 1965
Dead Sea scrolls, archaeology of the Holy Land, Jewish ceremonial art, Jewish ethnography, Israeli art, European art (15th-19th c), modern and contemporary international art, prints, drawings, photography, design, architecture, East Asian arts, art from Africa, Oceania and America 20918

L.A. Mayer Museum for Islamic Art, 2 Hapalmach St, Jerusalem 92542 - T: (02) 5661291, Fax: 5619802, E-mail: islamart@netvision.net.il. Head: Rachel Hasson
Religious Arts Museum / Decorative Arts Museum - 1974
Islamic art of various periods and lands, including metal work, ceramics, jewelry, carpets, miniatures, textiles, weaponry, antique European watches, clocks and music boxes, archeology - library, photographic archive, slide coll 20919

Museum of Jewish Art, Kiryat Banot, 55 Harav Zalman Sorotzkin St, Jerusalem - T: (02) 821298
Religious Arts Museum
Sephardi ritual objects 20920

Museum of Musical Instruments, c/o Jerusalem Academy of Music and Dance, Givat Ram Campus, Jerusalem 91904 - T: (02) 6759911, Fax: 6527713, E-mail: info@jmd.ac.il, Internet: http://www.jmd.ac.il. Head: Claude Abravanel
Music Museum
Musical instruments from various lands and periods 20921

Museum of Natural History, 6 Rehov Mohilever, Jerusalem, mail addr: POB 8234, Jerusalem 91081 - T: (02) 5631116, Fax: 5660666. Head: Sidney Corcos
Natural History Museum - 1961
Exhibits on biological processes, human biology, invertebrates and vertebrates, dioramas representing local habitats - library 20922

Museum of Prehistory, c/o Institute of Archaeology, Hebrew University, Mount Scopus Campus, Jerusalem 91905 - T: (02) 882430. Head: Dr. O. Bar-Yosef
Archaeological Museum / University Museum - 1955
Objects from prehistoric sites in Israel 20923

Museum of Taxes, 32 Agron St, Customs Sq, Jerusalem 91002, mail addr: POB 320, Jerusalem 91002 - T: (02) 6258978, 6703201, Fax: 6258602, E-mail: misim@mof.gov.il, Internet: http://www.mof.gov.il/museum. Head: Mira Dror
Special Museum - 1964
Artifacts and documents relating to levy of taxes - library 20924

Museum of the Studium Biblicum Franciscanum, Via Dolorosa, Jerusalem, mail addr: POB 19424, Jerusalem 91193 - T: (02) 282936. Head: M. Piccirillo
Archaeological Museum - 1923
Roman, Byzantine and Crusader finds, Palestinian numismatics 20925

Pères Blancs - Saint Anne, 19 Mujahidin St, Jerusalem 91190, mail addr: POB 19079, Jerusalem 91190 - T: (02) 6281992, Fax: 6280764, E-mail: mafrpoc@steanne.org, Internet: http://www.steanne.org
Archaeological Museum - 1888/90
Hellenistic and Crusader coll, Cuneiform tablets, oil lamps 20926

Pontifical Biblical Institute Museum, 3 Paul Emile Botta St, Jerusalem, mail addr: POB 497, Jerusalem 91004 - T: (02) 252843, Fax: 241203. Head: Tom Fitzpatrick
Archaeological Museum - 1927
Chalcolithic coll, Egyptian antiquities - library 20927

Ruth Youth Wing, The Israel Museum, POB 71117, Jerusalem 91710 - T: (02) 6708835, Fax: 6708077, E-mail: youthmus@imj.org.il, Internet: http://www.imj.org.il. Head: Nurit Shilo-Cohen
Fine Arts Museum / Archaeological Museum - 1965
Art and archaeological coll, doll coll, temporary exhibitions, childrens art coll - library, teacher's center, multimedia unit, art courses, recycling room 20928

Saint James Museum and Library, Armenian Patriarchate, Jerusalem 91000 - T: (02) 894861, Fax: 894862. Head: Avedis Iprajian
Historical Museum / Religious Arts Museum / Archaeological Museum
Armenian history, Armenian Jerusalem, art and culture, crusader and later archeological finds, Near and Middle Eastern archeology, ceramics, pottery 20929

Samuel Bronfman Biblical and Archeological Museum, Israel Museum, Jerusalem, Hakirya, Jerusalem, mail addr: POB 71117, Jerusalem 91710 - T: (02) 6708812, Fax: 6708906, E-mail: mssilvia@mscc.huji.ac.il, Internet: http://www.imj.org.il. Head: James S. Snyder
Archaeological Museum - 1965
Archeological objects and ancient art from prehistoric to Crusader times, ancient glass, the Hebrew script - Numismatic pavillon, shrine of the book 20930

Schocken Institute of Jewish Research, c/o Jewish Theological Seminary of America, 6 Balfour St, Jerusalem - T: (02) 631288, Fax: 636857. Head: Dr. Shmuel Glick
Historical Museum
Photocopies of the Cairo Genizah, Mahzor Nuremberg - library 20931

Shrine of the Book, Israel Museum, Ruppin Blvd, Jerusalem, mail addr: POB 71117, Jerusalem 91710 - T: (02) 6708862, Fax: 5633695, E-mail: shrine@imj.org.il, Internet: http://www.imj.org.il/shrine. Head: Dr. Adolfo D. Roitman
Archaeological Museum - 1965
Dead sea scrolls, Biblical manuscripts, archaeology of Qumran and Nahal Hever 20932

Sir Isaac and Edith Wolfson Museum, 58 King George St, Jerusalem, mail addr: POB 7440, Jerusalem 91073 - T: (02) 6247908, Fax: 6231810. Head: Estelle Fink
Religious Arts Museum - 1950
Jewish ceremonial art 20933

Skirball Museum of Biblical Archaeology, 13 King David St, Jerusalem 94101 - T: (02) 6203333, Fax: 6251478. Head: Prof. Avraham Biran
Archaeological Museum - 1986
Archaeology of Tel Dan, Tel Gezer, and Aroer 20934

Ticho House, 7 Harav Kook St, Jerusalem 94226, mail addr: POB 71117, Jerusalem 91710 - T: (02) 6245068, 6244186, Fax: 6223218, Internet: http://www.imj.org.il/ticho.html. Head: Irit Salmon
Fine Arts Museum - 1984
Paintings of Anna Ticho, Hanukkah lamps - library, archives, garden 20935

Tower of David Museum of the History of Jerusalem, Jaffa Gate, Jerusalem 91140, mail addr: POB 14005, Jerusalem 91140 - T: (02) 6265333, Fax: 6283418, E-mail: tower@netvision.net.il. Head: Shosh Yaniv
Historical Museum - 1989
History of Jerusalem from the time of the Canaanties Kings to the present, models and dioramas, ancient fortress 20936

The U. Nahon Museum of Italian Jewish Art, 27 Hillel St, Jerusalem 94581 - T: (02) 6241610, Fax: 6253480, E-mail: jija@netvision.net.il, Internet: http://www.jija.org. Head: Nava Kessler
Religious Arts Museum - 1982
Synagogue, ceremonial art, Jewish life Italy - Centro di Studi sull'Ebraismo Italiano 20937

Underground Prisoners' Museum, 1918-1948, Russian Compound, Jerusalem, mail addr: POB 31500, Jerusalem 91314 - T: (02) 6233166, Fax: 6250651, E-mail: achi_y@NetVision.net.il. Head: Y. Achi
Historical Museum - 1965/91
Hist of Jewish underground organizations 20938

Yad Vashem Historical and Art Museum, Har Hazikaron, Jerusalem, mail addr: POB 3477, Jerusalem 91034 - T: (02) 751619, 751620, Fax: 433511. Head: Jehudit Inbar
Historical Museum - 1951
Documentation on victims of the holocaust - library 20939

Kefar Nahum

Capharnaum Ancient Synagogue, Minzar Terra Santa, Kefar Nahum - T: (067) 21059
Religious Arts Museum 20940

Kefar Yehoshua

Beit Hankin, Kefar Yehoshua 30063 - T: (04) 9831277, Fax: 9832378. Head: Ilan Tal
Natural History Museum - 1951 20941

Kfar Tavor

Kfar Tavor Historical Museum, Kfar Tavor - T: (06) 767583
Historical Museum
History of the settlement 20942

Kibbutz Ashdot Yaakov

Beit Uri Ve Rami Nechushtan, Kibbutz Ashdot Yaakov 15150 - T: (06) 757737, 757822, Fax: 757717. Head: M. Neshushtan
Fine Arts Museum - 1958
Loan exhibitions of painting by Jewish artists from France, the U.S. and Israel 20943

Kibbutz Bar Am

Bar David Museum, B.M. Merom Ha Galil, Kibbutz Bar Am 13860 - T: (06) 6988295, (058) 313295, Fax: 6987505, E-mail: ebengal@baram.org.il. Head: Dr. Ely Ben-Gal
Fine Arts Museum - 1982
Judaica, Plastic Art 20944

Kibbutz Chefzi-bah

Beit-Alfa Ancient Synagogue, Kibbutz Chefzi-bah - T: (065) 81675. Head: Ernst R. Salus
Archaeological Museum 20945

Kibbutz Dan

Ussishkin House, Museum for Natural History and Archeology, Kibbutz Dan 12245 - T: (04) 6941704, Fax: 6902755, E-mail: ussishkin@kdan.co.il, Internet: http://teva.org.il/ussiskin. Head: Y. Lev-Ari
Natural History Museum / Archaeological Museum - 1955
Fauna and flora of the Huleh Valley and Mt. Hermon, biblical archaeology of Dan 20946

Kibbutz Ein Dor

Archaeological Museum, at Foot of Mount Tabor, Lower Eastern Galilee, Kibbutz Ein Dor 19335 - T: (06) 768333, Fax: 770650, E-mail: museumed@netvision.net.il. Head: Carmella Arnon
Archaeological Museum - 1986
Memorial to the fallen soldiers of the kibbutz, restored agricultural implements for preparing food as in ancient times (ancient olive and wine presses) 20947

Kibbutz Ein Harod

Bet Sturman, Mobile Post, Gilboa, Kibbutz Ein Harod - T: (065) 81605. Head: A. Levi
Archaeological Museum / Historical Museum / Natural History Museum
Local archeology, modern history of settlement in the Jezreel Valley, zoological coll - archive, study rooms 20948

Kibbutz Gat

Archaeological Museum, Kibbutz Gat - T: (051) 91171. Head: Josef Itai
Archaeological Museum 20949

Kibbutz Hanita

Hanita Wall and Tower Museum, Kibbutz Hanita 22885 - T: (04) 9859677, Fax: 9859990. Head: I. Ben-Barak
Archaeological Museum - 1960
Regional archaeology from the Calcolithic to Byzantine period, hist of Wall and Tower, mosaics from the Byzantine church 20950

Kibbutz Hazorea

Wilfrid Israel Museum for Oriental Art and Studies, Kibbutz Hazorea 30060 - T: (04) 9899566, Fax: 9590860, E-mail: wilfrid@hazorea.org.il, Internet: http://www.wilfrid.org.il. Head: Ehud Dor
Fine Arts Museum - 1951
Far Eastern art 20951

Kibbutz Kefar Gil'adi

Beit Hashomer, Kibbutz Kefar Gil'adi - T: (067) 41565
Historical Museum
Documents, letters, maps and photos depicting the activities of 'Hashomer', an organization of guards which served during the early Jewish settlement - archives 20952

Kibbutz K'far Menahem

Shephela Museum, Kibbutz K'far Menahem 79875 - T: (08) 8501827, Fax: 8508486. Head: Orah Dvir
Fine Arts Museum / Archaeological Museum / Local Museum - 1949
Regional antiquities, modern hist of the settlement, fine arts, children arts 20953

Kibbutz Lahav

Museum for Beduin Culture, Joe Alon Center, Kibbutz Lahav 85335 - T: (08) 9913322, Fax: 9919889, E-mail: triptoz@bezqint.net, Internet: http://www.joealon.org.il. Head: Uzi Halamish
Ethnology Museum - 1985
Daily life of the beduin in the Negev and Sinai - library 20954

Kibbutz Ma'abarot

Local Museum, Kibbutz Ma'abarot 60980 - T: (053) 82836
Archaeological Museum - 1968
Regional archeology, pottery, coins and weapons of various periods - library 20955

Kibbutz Palmachim

Beit Miriam-Museum, Kibbutz Palmachim 76890 - T: (03) 9538281, Fax: 9528966, E-mail: bet_miriam@palmacim.org.il. Head: Zvi Zehavi
Archaeological Museum - 1958
Exhibits from local excavations 20956

Kibbutz Revivim

Mitzpe Revivim Museum, Kibbutz Revivim - T: (057) 965249
Historical Museum
History of Kibbutz Revivim 20957

Kibbutz Ruhama

Archaeological Collection (closed) 20958

Kibbutz Sasa

Local Museum, Kibbutz Sasa 13870 - T: (06) 6988527, Fax: 6988702, E-mail: howard@israntique.org.il. Head: Howard Smithline
Archaeological Museum - 1970
Archeological finds 20959

Kibbutz Sedot Yam

Caesarea Museum, Kibbutz Sedot Yam 38805 - T: (06) 6364367, Fax: 6362211, Internet: http://www.kef-yam.co.il. Head: Rina Angert
Museum of Classical Antiquities - 1951
Classical antiquities 20960

Kibbutz Yif'at

Museum of Pioneer Settlement, Doar Yif'at, Kibbutz Yif'at - T: (06) 30069, Fax: 548974. Head: Avner Galili
Agriculture Museum / Historical Museum - 1967
Agricultural tools and equipment, domestic implements, artifacts depicting founding of the kibbutz movement 20961

Lod

Neot Kedumim, The Biblical Landscape Reserve in Israel, Modi'in Region, between Tel Aviv and Jerusalem, Lod, mail addr: POB 1007, Lod 71100 - T: (08) 9770777, Fax: 9770766, E-mail: gen_info@neot-kedumim.org.il, Internet: http://www.neot-kedumim.org.il. Head: Helen Frenkley
Natural History Museum - 1965
Biblical plants and animals 20962

Lohamei-Hageta'ot

Beit Lohamei Haghetaot, Yad Layeled (Ghetto Fighters' House Museum), M.P. Western Galilee, Lohamei-Hageta'ot 25220 - T: (04) 9958080, Fax: 9958007, E-mail: simstein@gfh.org.il, Internet: http://www.gfh.org.il. Head: Simcha Stein
Historical Museum - 1949
Memorabilia of the holocaust and resistance, paintings and drawings from ghettos and camps, documents - library, archives, Yad Layeled children's holocaust museum 20963

Ma'ayan Barukh

Huleh Valley Regional Prehistoric Museum, Ma'ayan Barukh 12220 - T: (06) 6954611, Fax: 6950724. Head: Amnon Assaf
Archaeological Museum - 1952
Prehistory of the Huleh Valley from the Palaeolithic to the Chalcolithic period, Bronze Age and Roman-Byzantine objects from local excavations, coll of stone grain mills and oil presses, the Earliest Dog, buried with a woman from the Natufian period 12,000 years ago, exhibition of tools that being used in various places in the world that help people understand the tools used in prehistoric times 20964

Midreshet Ruppin

Sharon Museum Emek Hefer, Midreshet Ruppin 40250 - T: (09) 8988644, Fax: 8988644. Head: Eli Ben Shlomo
Natural History Museum - 1956
Butterflies, insects, natural history 20965

Mizpe Ramon

Ramon Visitor's Center, POB 340, Mizpe Ramon 80600 - T: (08) 6588691/98, Fax: 6588620, Internet: http://www.parks.org.il. Head: Oshra Gabay
Local Museum
Technology, geology 20966

Nahariya

Municipal Museum of Archaeology, History, Art and Malacology, Municipality Bldg, Sderot Plaga'aton, Nahariya, mail addr: POB 78, Nahariya 22441 - T: (04) 879863. Head: Laura Cavaglion Bassani
Archaeological Museum / Historical Museum / Fine Arts Museum / Natural History Museum - 1971
Regional archeology, from prehistoric to Byzantine period, sea shell coll 20967

Nahshonim

Center of Nautical and Regional Archaeology, Dora, Nahshonim. Head: Kurt Raveh
Archaeological Museum 20968

Collection of Archaeology and Land Study, Nahshonim
Archaeological Museum 20969

Nazareth

Terra Sancta Museum, Casa Nova St, Nazareth, mail addr: POB 23, Nazareth - T: (06) 54030
Archaeological Museum - 1920
Roman, Crusader and Byzantine remains, coins, glass and antiquities from excavations in the monastery compound 20970

Netanya

International Jewish Sports Hall of Fame, Wingate Institute, Netanya 42902 - T: (09) 8639521, Fax: 8355477, E-mail: prwin@post.tan.ac.il, Internet: http://www.jewishsport.net. Head: Alan Sherman, Effi Yaacobi, Joe Siegman
Special Museum
Coll of olympic and world cup medals, symbols and pins 20971

Nir-David

Museum of Regional and Mediterranean Archaeology, National Park Gan Hashlosha, Nir-David 19150 - T: (06) 6586352, Fax: 6488045, E-mail: mus_gan@netvision.net.il, Internet: http://www.geocities.com.dror_s_1999. Head: Dror Segal
Archaeological Museum - 1963
Greek pottery and sculpture, Estrucan pottery and jewelry, Islamic pottery, archeological finds from Beith Shean Valley, Israelite village life, spinning and weaving - library 20972

Or Yehuda

Babylonian Jewry Museum, 83 Hahagana St, Or Yehuda 60251 - T: (03) 5339278/79, Fax: 5339936. Head: Ygal Loshi
Religious Arts Museum - 1988
Baghdadi Jewish street, Baghdadi Synagogue, the life cycle, community institutions in Baghdad 20973

Petah Tikva

Yad Labanim Museum and Memorial Center, 30 Arlozorov St, Petah Tikva 49100, mail addr: POB 1, Petah Tikva 49100 - T: (03) 9223450, 9052313, Fax: 9223450. Head: M. Marmar
Historical Museum / Fine Arts Museum - 1951
History of Jewish settlement in the city, contemporary art, Israeli art 20974

Qatzrin

Golan Archaeological Museum, Qatzrin - T: (04) 6961350, Fax: 6964665, E-mail: museum@golan.org.il, Internet: http://www.golan.org.il/museum. Head: Nissim Shaul
Archaeological Museum - 1981
Archaeological discoveries from Gamla, an ornamented lintel 20975

Qiryat Shmona

Tel Hai Museum, Kefar Giladi, Qiryat Shmona 12210 - T: (06) 951333, Fax: 951331. Head: Uri Hurvitz
Historical Museum - 1960
Reconstructed settlement, site of Joseph Trumpeldor's defeat by Arab raiders in 1920, photos, documents, models, tools and weapons relating to early modern Jewish settlement of Eretz-Israel 20976

Ramat Gan

Beit Immanuel, 18 Hibbat Zion, Ramat Gan 52105 - T: (03) 788243
Fine Arts Museum
Israeli and Russian painting and sculpture, Far Eastern art 20977

Harry Oppenheimer Diamond Museum, 1 Jabotinsky St, Ramat Gan 52520 - T: (03) 5760219, Fax: 7518515, E-mail: diamus@zahav.net.il. Head: Efraim Raviv
Special Museum - 1986
Israel's diamond industry 20978

Man and the Living World Museum, Park Leumi, Ramat Gan, mail addr: POB 947, Ramat Gan 52109 - T: (03) 6315010, Fax: 6315103, E-mail: musdorit@012.net.il, Internet: http://www.adamvechai.co.il. Head: Dorit Wolenitz
Natural History Museum - 1983
Participatory exhibits of basic biological concepts 20979

Museum of Israeli Art, 144 Abba Hillel Silver St, Ramat Gan 52105 - T: (03) 7527377
Fine Arts Museum - 1987
Painting, sculpture, photography, graphics by Israeli artists 20980

Pirre Gildesgame Maccabi Museum, Kfar Hamaccabiah, Ramat Gan 52105
Special Museum 20981

Ramat Hashofet

Archaeological and Historical Museum, Ramat Hashofet 19238 - T: (04) 9898569, Fax: 9898134
Archaeological Museum 20982

Rehovot

Weizmann Archives and House, c/o Weizmann Institute of Science, POB 26, Rehovot 76100 - T: (08) 9344500, 9344499, Fax: 9344180, E-mail: merav-segal@weizmann.ac.il
Historical Museum - 1958
Historical documents 20983

Yad-Lebanim Memorial Center, Habanim St, Rehovot 76100 - T: (08) 953891. Head: Isaac Elyasiv
Fine Arts Museum 20984

Rishon Le-Zion

Rishon Le-Zion Museum, 4 Ahad Ha'am St, Rishon Le-Zion, mail addr: POB 7, Rishon Le-Zion 75100 - T: (03) 9682435, Fax: 9676934. Head: Itzhak Brenner
Open Air Museum / Historical Museum / Fine Arts Museum / Decorative Arts Museum - 1978/1982
Hist of the early settlement, paintings, sculpture, artistic dolls, fashion - archive, library 20985

Sha'ar Hagolan

Museum of Prehistory, Sha'ar Hagolan 15145 - T: (06) 6650401, Fax: 6677390. Head: Judith Cohen
Archaeological Museum - 1950
Neolithic Yarmukian culture 20986

Shamir

Archeology Museum, Shamir 12135
Archaeological Museum 20987

Shiqmim

Ekron - The Philistine City and it's Culture, Kibbutz Revadim, Shiqmim 79820 - T: (08) 8588913, Fax: 8588796, E-mail: ekron_mu@revadim.org.il. Head: Nathan Eidlin
Archaeological Museum 20988

Tel Aviv

Antiquities Museum of Tel Aviv-Yafo, Eretz Israel Museum, 10 Mifratz Shlomo, Tel Aviv 68038, mail addr: POB 8406, Tel Aviv 61083 - T: (03) 6825375, Fax: 6813624, Internet: http://www.eimuseum.co.il. Head: Tzvi Shacham
Archaeological Museum / Historical Museum
Regional archeology and history, incl ceramics, jewelry, glass, inscriptions and coins 20989

Bank Leumi Museum, 35 Yehuda Halevi St, Tel Aviv - T: (03) 648981
Historical Museum
Story of Bank Leumi 20990

Ben-Gurion House, 17 Ben-Gurion Blvd, Tel Aviv 63454 - T: (03) 5221010, Fax: 5247293, Internet: http://www.ben-gurion-house.org.il. Head: Malka Lif
Special Museum - 1974
Residence of David Ben-Gurion, first Prime Minister of the State of Israel - library 20991

Beth Hatefutsoth (The Nahum Goldmann Museum of the Jewish Diaspora), Rehov Klausner 3, Tel Aviv 61392 - T: (03) 6462020, Fax: 6462050, 6462067, E-mail: bhcurtr@post.tau.ac.il, Internet: http://www.bh.org.il. Head: Dr. David Alexander
Historical Museum - 1978
Photos, models, multi-media presentations depicting Jewish life in the Diaspora, Jewish history, music, communities, lexicon, genealogy - photo archive, genealogy centre, music centre 20992

Bialik-Museum, Bialik St, Tel Aviv - T: (03) 51530. Head: M. Ungerfeld
Local Museum 20993

Ceramics Museum, 2 Levanon St, Ramar Aviv, Tel Aviv, mail addr: POB 17068, Tel Aviv 61170 - T: (03) 64152446, Fax: 6412408, Internet: http:www.ei-museum.co.il. Head: Dr. Irit Ziffer
Archaeological Museum - 1966
Pre-biblical and biblical pottery, local artifacts from late Antiquity to the Middle Ages, Cypriote and Greek coll 20994

Eretz-Israel Museum, 2 Haim Levanon St, Ramat Aviv, Tel Aviv 61170, mail addr: POB 17068, Tel Aviv - T: (03) 6415244, Fax: 6412408, Internet: http://www.eimuseum.co.il. Head: S. Shilo
Archaeological Museum / Historical Museum / Ethnology Museum - 1953
Archaeology, ethnography, history - library 20995

Glass Museum, Eretz-Israel Museum, 2 Haim Levanon St, Ramat Aviv, Tel Aviv 69975, mail addr: POB 17068, Tel Aviv, 61170 - T: (03) 6415244/48, Fax: 6412408, E-mail: Publicmu@netvision.net.il, Internet: http://www.eimuseum.co.il. Head: Henrietta Eliezer-Brunner
Archaeological Museum - 1959
Ancient glass vessels 20996

Helena Rubinstein Pavilion for Contemporary Art, 6 Tarsat Blvd, Tel Aviv 64283 - T: (03) 5287196, Fax: 6958099, Internet: http://www.tamuseum.com. Head: Prof. Mordechai Omer
Fine Arts Museum - 1932 20997

Israel Theater Museum, 3 Melchett St, Tel Aviv, mail addr: POB 17068, Tel Aviv - T: (03) 4152448. Head: J. Gabbai
Performing Arts Museum - 1969
Exhibits on Jewish theater in Israel and abroad, original sketches from productions, 1920-1980, documents from Jewish theater in the underground and camps (WW II) 20998

Jabotinsky Institute, 38 King George St, Tel Aviv, mail addr: POB 23110, Tel Aviv 61230 - T: (03) 5287320, Fax: 5285587, E-mail: Jabo@actcom.co.il, Internet: http://www.jabotinsky.org. Head: Peleg Tamir
Historical Museum
Life and works of Zeev Jabotinsky, leader of Revisionist Zionism, history of the Revisionist Movement 20999

Kadman Numismatic Pavilion, Eretz-Israel Museum, 2 Haim Levanon St, Ramat Aviv, Tel Aviv 69975, mail addr: POB 17086, Tel Aviv 61170 - T: (03) 6415244, Fax: 6412408, E-mail: ceciliameir@hotmail.com, Internet: http://www.eimuseum.co.il. Head: Cecilia Meir
Special Museum - 1962
Hist of money from earliest times to the present, medals, seals, weights and measures, paper money, primitive money 21000

Kibbutz Art Gallery, 25 Dov Hoz St, Tel Aviv, 63416 - T: (03) 5232533, Fax: 5232533, E-mail: nurit@kibbutzgallery.org.il, Internet: http://www.kibbutz-gallery.org.il. Head: Tali Tamir
Public Gallery 21001

Landscapes of the Holy Land Park, Eretz-Israel Museum, 2 Haim Levanon St, Ramat Aviv, Tel Aviv 69975, mail addr: POB 17068, Tel Aviv 61170 - T: (03) 6415244, Fax: 6412408, E-mail: smad_mh@netvision.net.il, Internet: http://www.eimuseum.co.il. Head: E. Ayalon, A. Yosef
Open Air Museum - 1983
Reconstructed flour mill, oil plant and installations, local vegetation 21002

Man and His Work Center in Memory of S. Avitsur, Eretz-Israel Museum, 2 Haim Levanon St, Ramat Aviv, Tel Aviv 69975, mail addr: POB 17068, Tel Aviv 61170 - T: (03) 6415244, Fax: 6412408, E-mail: Gania@001.net.vision.net.il, Internet: http://www.eimuseum.co.il. Head: E. Ayalon
Special Museum - 1982
Tools and implements, reconstructed workshops, material culture, reconstructed operating Bazaar, reconstructed installations 21003

Museonej Zahal, Ministry of Defence, Hakiria, Tel Aviv 61909 - T: (03) 6976320, Fax: 6977258, E-mail: mlenet49@netvision.net.il, Internet: http://www.mod.gov.il/modh1/museums/. Head: S. Keren
Military Museum - 1961 21004

Museum of Ethnography and Folklore, Eretz-Israel Museum, 2 Haim Levanon St, Ramat Aviv, Tel Aviv 69975, mail addr: POB 17068, Tel Aviv 61170 - T: (03) 64152448, Fax: 6412408, Internet: http://www.eimuseum.co.il. Head: N. Behroozy
Folklore Museum / Religious Arts Museum
Jewish folk and ritual objects, costumes of the Jewish communities 21005

Museum of the History of Tel Aviv-Yafo, 27 Rehov Bialik, Tel Aviv - T: (03) 5173052. Head: Z. Sochovolsky
Historical Museum - 1959
Photos, models and maps illustrating the history of the city 21006

Museum Zahal- Beit Eliyahu- Museum Haghna, 23 Rothschild Blvd, Tel Aviv 65122 - T: (03) 5608624, 5600809, Fax: 5666131. Head: Z. Lachish
Military Museum - 1961
Militaria relating to history of State of Israel 21007

Rubin Museum, 14 Bialik St, Tel Aviv - T: (03) 658961
Fine Arts Museum
Life and work of Artist Reuven Rubin 21008

Tel Aviv Museum of Art, 27-29 Sderot Shaoul Hameleeh, Tel Aviv 61332, mail addr: POB 33288, Tel Aviv 61332 - T: (03) 6957361, Fax: 6958099, E-mail: mtalib@tamuseum.com, Internet: http://www.tamuseum.com. Head: Prof. Mordechai Omer
Fine Arts Museum - 1932
European and American art from the 16th c to the present, with emphasis on modern and contemporary art, loan exhibitions - library 21009

Tell Qasile Archaeological Site, Eretz-Israel Museum, 2 Haim Levanon St, Ramat Aviv, Tel Aviv 69975, mail addr: POB 17068, Tel Aviv 61170 - T: (03) 6415244, Fax: 6412408, Internet: http://www.eimuseum.co.il. Head: Harpazi Smadar
Archaeological Museum
Archeological finds of the site 21010

Zoological Museum, c/o Department of Zoology, Tel Aviv University, Tel Aviv 69978 - T: (03) 6409812, 6409012, Fax: 6409403, E-mail: dayant@post.tau.ac.il, Internet: http://www.tau.ac.il/zoology/museum. Head: Prof. T. Dayan
Natural History Museum / University Museum
Local fauna, invertebrates, insects, fish, reptiles, mammals, birds, Red Sea fauna 21011

Tel Yitzhak

Massua-Educational Museum on the Holocaust, Tel Yitzhak 45805 - T: (09) 8999997, Fax: 8997410, E-mail: massuah@netvision.net.il, Internet: http://www.massuah.org. Head: Aya Ben-Nuftali
Historical Museum - 1972
Letters from the time of the Holocaust, post museum, art 21012

Tiberias

Benedictine Monastry - Church of the Multiplication of Loaves and Fish Tabgha, POB 52, 14100 Tiberias - T: (02) 6700400, Fax: 6700401, Internet: http://www.hagia-maria-sion.net. Head: Jeremias Marseille
Archaeological Museum 21013

Museum of the History of Tiberias and the Lake Kinnereth, Tiberias - T: (06) 723788. Head: Zvi Schaiek
Historical Museum - 1950
Objects from ancient synagogues and tombs, 19th c views of the city, history, heritage of Tiberias, Lake Kinnereth (sea of galilee) 21014

Yas'ur

Archaeological Collection, Yas'ur
Archaeological Museum 21015

Yehi'am

Archaeological Collection, Yehi'am
Archaeological Museum 21016

Yesud Hama'ala

Dubrovin Farm Museum, Yesud Hama'ala - T: (06) 937371
Historical Museum
History of the settlement, story of the Dubrovin family 21017

Hula Nature Reserve and Visitors Center, Yesud Hama'ala - T: (06) 961350
Natural History Museum - 1956
Regional ecology 21018

Yotvata

Yotvata Museum and Visitors Center, Yotvata - T: (07) 376018. Head: Eytana Ben-Shimon
Natural History Museum / Archaeological Museum - 1982
Geology, climate, fauna, flora, man in the desert, archeology 21019

Zefat

Beit Hameiri, Old City, Zefat 13110 - T: (06) 971307
Historical Museum
Life in Safed at the turn of the century 21020

Glichenstein Museum, POB 1006, Zefat 13110
Fine Arts Museum
Paintings and sculpture of Hanoch Glichenstein, Haim Vidal Chapira coll 21021

Israel Bible Museum, 1 Hativat Iftach, Zefat 13110, mail addr: POB 4706, Zefat 13110 - T: (04) 69999722, Internet: http://www.israelbiblemuseum.com. Head: Phillip Ratner
Religious Arts Museum - 1984
The Bible through sculpture and painting 21022

Zichron Ya'Akov

Aaronson House, 40 Hameyadim St, Zichron Ya'Akov - T: (063) 99120
Special Museum
Original furnishings and archives of the organizer of the 'Nili' spy network (WW I), herbarium - library 21023

Italy

Acerenza

Museo Diocesano, Largo Seminario, 85011 Acerenza - T: 0971741112. Head: Mario Festa
Religious Arts Museum 21024

Acireale

Pinacoteca dell'Accademia Zelantea, Via Marchese di San Giuliano 17, 95024 Acireale - T: 095604480. Head: Prof. Matteo Fresta
Fine Arts Museum - 1848
Archeology, coins, 17th and 18th c paintings by Sicilian artists 21025

Acquasparta

Raccolta Comunale, Palazzo Cesi, 05021 Acquasparta - T: 0744930644
Local Museum 21026

Acqui Terme e Bagni

Civico Museo Archeologico, Castello dei Paleologi, 15011 Acqui Terme e Bagni - T: 014457555. Head: Luigi Moro
Archaeological Museum 21027

Adrano

Museo Archeologico Etneo, Castello normanno, 95031 Adrano - T: 0957692660
Archaeological Museum
Historical exhibits in an 11th c Norman castle 21028

Adria

Museo Archeologico Nazionale, Via Badini 59, 45011 Adria - T: 042621612, Fax: 042621612. Head: Dr. S. Bonomi
Archaeological Museum - 1905
Attic vases, Roman grave and votive stones, two-wheeled iron chariot of the 4th c B.C., Roman coins, Etruscan bronzes and vases, Roman glass and pottery, pottery of the late Bronze Age 21029

Agliè

Castello Ex-Ducale, Piazza Castello 2, 10011 Agliè - T: 0124330102. Head: Giorgio Fea
Historical Museum
Former ducal residence, 17th c decorations, archeological finds from Tuscolo 21030

Agnone

Museo Emidiano, Chiesa di Sant'Emidio, Corso Vittorio Emanuele 82, 86081 Agnone - T: 086578359. Head: Prof. Filippo La Gamba
Local Museum 21031

Agrigento

Casa Natale di Pirandello, Località Caos, 92100 Agrigento
Historic Site
Books, bibliography, manuscripts and memorabilia of the writer Luigi Pirandello 21032

Museo Archeologico Regionale, Contrada San Nicola, 92100 Agrigento - T: 0922401565, Fax: 092220014. Head: Dr. Gruiseppe Castellana
Archaeological Museum
Archeological finds from excavations of Agrigento, marble sculpture of the Greek period, Attic vases, terra cottas, coins 21033

Museo Civico, Piazza Municipio 361, 92100 Agrigento - T: 092220722
Local Museum
Local history, 14th to 18th c paintings 21034

Museo Diocesano d'Arte Sacra, Annesso al Duomo, 92100 Agrigento
Religious Arts Museum
Priests' vestments, 14th and 15th c frescoes, Byzantine reliquaries, Greek sarcophagus 21035

Aidone

Museo Archeologico di Morgantina, Piazza Torres Trupia, 94010 Aidone - T: 093587307. Head: Dr. Angela Incardona
Local Museum 21036

Aiello del Friuli

Musei Formentini della Civilta, Via Petrarca 1, 33041 Aiello del Friuli - T: 043199507
Local Museum 21037

Ala

Museo Civico 'Luigi Dalla Laita', Via Roma 40, 38061 Ala - T: 0464671120, Fax: 0464671320, E-mail: ala@biblio.infotn.it
Local Museum
Local history and archeology, fossils, minerals, numismatics 21038

Alagna Valsesia

Museo Walser, Località Pedemonte, 13021 Alagna Valsesia - T: 0163922935. Head: Pietro Ferraris
Historic Site - 1976
17th c typical house with period furniture, artifacts and agricultural products 21039

Alassio

Museo di Scienze Naturali 'Don Bosco', Via Don Bosco 12, 17021 Alassio
Natural History Museum - 1950
Fossils, mineralogy, petrography, ornithology, historical-ethnographical material 21040

Alatri

Museo Civico, Corso Vittorio Emanuele 11, 03011 Alatri - T: 0775434995
Local Museum 21041

Alba

Civico Museo Archeologico e di Scienze Naturali 'Federico Eusebio', Via Vittorio Emanuele 19, 12051 Alba - T: 0173290092, Fax: 0173362075. Head: Gianfranco Maggi
Archaeological Museum - 1897
Local prehistoric finds, fossils, molluscs, insects, mammals and birds, herbarium, Roman antiquities, ceramics, tombs, sculpture, decorative fragments - library 21042

Albano Laziale

Museo Civico Albano, Viale Risorgimento 3, 00041 Albano Laziale - T: 069323490, Fax: 069321124, E-mail: albano.urp@flashnet.it. Head: Dr. Giuseppe Chiarucci
Archaeological Museum - 1973 21043

Albenga

Civico Museo Ingauno, Palazzo Vecchio del Comune, Via Nino Lamboglia, 17031 Albenga - T: 018251215, Fax: 0182570434, E-mail: iisl.ingauno@tin.it. Head: Prof. Carlo Varaldo
Archaeological Museum / Local Museum - 1933
Archeological and medieval exhibits, sculpture, tombstones, frescos 21044

Museo del Battistero, Via Nino Lamboglia, 17031 Albenga - T: 018251215, Fax: 0182570434, E-mail: iisl.igauna@tin.it. Head: Prof. Carlo Varaldo
Religious Arts Museum
Baptismal front, 5th and 6th c mosaics 21045

Museo Diocesano, Via dell Episcopio 7, 17031 Albenga - T: 018250288. Head: Fiorenzo Gerini
Religious Arts Museum
Ceramics, silver, paintings 21046

Museo Navale Romano, Piazza San Michele 12, 17031 Albenga - T: 018251215, Fax: 0182570434, E-mail: iisl.ingauno@tin.it. Head: Prof. Carlo Varaldo
Historical Museum
Finds from submarine excavations in the Ligurian Sea, photos and documents of antique ships and naval objects 21047

Albissola Marina

Villa Faraggiana, Via Salomeni 117, 17012 Albissola Marina - T: 019480622, Fax: 032133397
Local Museum 21048

Alessandria

Museo del Cappello, Corso Cento Cannoni 23, 15100 Alessandria - T: 013154241
Decorative Arts Museum
Historical and modern hats, models produced by the hatmaker Borsalino from early to present times 21049

Museo della Battaglia di Marengo, Fraz Spinetta Marengo, Via Genoveva 8a, 15100 Alessandria - T: 0131619589
Historic Site
Documents and model of the battle of Marengo in 1800 21050

Museo e Pinacoteca Civica, Via Tripoli 16, 15100 Alessandria - T: 0131251722, Fax: 0131254681, E-mail: AL0002@biblioteche-reteunitaria.-piemonte.it. Head: Dr. Giulio Massobrio
Local Museum / Fine Arts Museum - 1885
Archeology, paintings, Napoleonic and Renaissance history, numismatics 21051

Alfedena

Museo Civico Aufidenate, Via Corona 2, 67030 Alfedena - T: 086487114
Archaeological Museum
Findings from over 12,000 tombs from the 6th to 4th c B.C. 21052

Allumiere

Museo Civico A. Klitsche de la Grange, Piazza della Repubblica 29, 00051 Allumiere - T: 0766967793, Fax: 0766967793. Head: Dr. Odoardo Toti
Archaeological Museum / Natural History Museum - 1956
Protovillanovian culture, Findings from prehistoric times, Etruscan tomb furnishings, pottery 21053

Altamura

Museo Archeologico Statale, Via Santeramo 88, 70022 Altamura - T: 0803146409, Fax: 0803146409, E-mail: museo.altamura@altanet.it, Internet: http://www.altanet.it/museo. Head: Donata Venturo Rubino
Archaeological Museum - 1987 21054

Altomonte

Museo Civico di Santa Maria della Consolazione, Piazza S. Maria Consolazione, Ex Convento dei Domenicani, 87042 Altomonte - T: 0981948261, Fax: 0981948216, E-mail: informazioni@comune.altomonte.it. Head: Dr. Costantino Belluscio
Historical Museum / Religious Arts Museum 21055

Alzano Lombardo

Museo della Basilica di San Martino, Piazza della Basilica, Parrocchia di Alzano Maggiore, 24022 Alzano Lombardo - T: 035511123
Religious Arts Museum 21056

Amalfi

Museo Civico, Piazza Municipio, 84011 Amalfi - T: 098871066
Local Museum
Historical costumes, nautical instruments, paintings 21057

Museo della Carta, Via delle Cartiere 23, 84011 Amalfi - T: 03288676100, Fax: 089872235, E-mail: jmitalia@amalficoast.it, Internet: http://www.museodellacarta.it. Head: Dr. Emilio De Simone
Historical Museum
Papermill from the middle ages - library 21058

Anacapri

Museo San Michele, Viale Axel Munthe, 80071 Anacapri - T: 0818371401, Fax: 0818373279, E-mail: axelmunthe@capri.it, Internet: http://www.capri.com/axelmunthe. Head: Ann-Marie Kjellander
Historic Site - 1950
House of Axel Munthe, on site of Roman Imperial Villa with Renaissance and 18th c furniture, coll of Etruscan, Egyptian and Roman sculptures, flora and fauna of Capri - garden 21059

Anagni

Museo del Lazio Meridionale, Palazzo di Bonifacio VIII, Via Vittorio Emanuele 236, 03012 Anagni - T: 0775727053
Historical Museum 21060

Museo del Tesoro della Cattedrale, Via Leone XIII, 03012 Anagni - T: 0775727228
Religious Arts Museum
Cathedral treasury, religious art, jewelry, goldsmith work, inscriptions, antique marbles 21061

Ancona

Museo Archeologico Nazionale delle Marche, Via Ferretti 6, 60100 Ancona - T: 0712075390. Head: Prof. Delia Lollini
Archaeological Museum
Exhibits from the paleolithic age to the Roman period, sculpture, frescoes, vases 21062

Museo Diocesano, Vecchio Episcopio, Piazza Duomo 9, 60121 Ancona - T: 07152688, Fax: 071206041. Head: Cesare Recanatini
Religious Arts Museum - 1830
Early Christian and medieval architecture and art from the churches of Ancona, 4th c sarcophagus, 11th c fabrics, four tapestries on cardboard by P.P. Rubens 21063

Pinacoteca Civica 'Francesco Podesti' e Galleria Comunale d'Arte Moderna, Palazzo Bosdari, Via Pizzecolli 17, 60121 Ancona - T: 0712225040, 0712225041, Fax: 0712225048, E-mail: scaann@comune.ancona.it, Internet: http://www.comune.ancona.it. Head: Dr. Michele Polverari
Fine Arts Museum - 1880
14th-18th c paintings, contemporary paintings, paintings by Titian - library 21064

Andria

Museo Diocesano, Piazza Vittorio Emanuele II 23, 70031 Andria - T: 0883592596. Head: Giannicola Agresti
Religious Arts Museum 21065

Angera

Museo Civico Archeologico, Via Marconi 2, 21021 Angera - T: 0331931133. Head: Pierluigi Innocenti
Archaeological Museum 21066

Rocca Borromeo, 21021 Angera - T: 0331931300
Fine Arts Museum
15th c frescoes from the Palazzo Borromeo in Milan 21067

Anghiari

Museo Statale delle Arti e Tradizioni Popolari, Palazzo Taglieschi, Via Mameli 16, 52031 Anghiari - T: 0575788001
Historical Museum 21068

Anticoli Corrado

Civico Museo d'Arte Moderne, Piazza Santa Vittoria, 00022 Anticoli Corrado - T: 077496318. Head: Jacopo Recupero
Local Museum
Paintings, bronzes, sculpture 21069

Aosta

Hospice du Grand Saint Bernard, Gran San Bernardo, 11100 Aosta
Local Museum
Roman articles, minerals, Alpine fauna and flora, history of the Great St. Bernard Pass 21070

Museo Alpino e Archeologico, Via San Orso 10, 11100 Aosta - T: 016541421. Head: Dr. Rosanna Mollo
Archaeological Museum 21071

Museo dell'Accademia di Sant'Anselmo, Musée de l'Académie Saint-Anselme, Via Chambéry 97, 11100 Aosta - T: 0165274876. Head: Omar Borettaz
Historical Museum - 1855
Numismatics, pre-Roman, Roman and medieval exhibits 21072

Tesoro della Cattedrale, Piazza Giovanni XXIII, 11100 Aosta - T: 016531361. Head: Luigi Ganino
Religious Arts Museum
12th to 17th c religious art, reliquaries, jewelry, 12th c mosaics 21073

Tesoro della Collegiata di Sant'Orso, Via Linty 9, 11100 Aosta - T: 016540614. Head: Alberto Maria Careggio
Religious Arts Museum
14th and 15th c religious art 21074

Apice

Museo Civico, P. Carbonara 2, 82021 Apice - T: 0824920082
Local Museum 21075

Aprica

Museo Etnografico, 23031 Aprica - T: 0342746112
Ethnology Museum 21076

Aquileia

Museo Archeologico Nazionale, Via Roma 1, 33051 Aquileia - T: 043191035, 043191016, Fax: 0431919537. Head: Dr. Franca Maselli Scotti
Archaeological Museum - 1882
Roman architecture, mosaics, inscriptions, sculpture - library 21077

Museo Paleocristiano, Piazza Pirano- Localitá Monastero, 33051 Aquileia - T: 043191131, Fax: 0431919537. Head: Dr. Franca Maselli Scotti
Archaeological Museum - 1961
Christian inscriptions, remains of Paleo-Christian architecture, mosaics 21078

Arborea

Museo Archeologico, 09092 Arborea - T: 0783800460
Archaeological Museum 21079

Arcole

Museo Napoleonico, Via Nuova, 37040 Arcole - T: 0457635020, Fax: 0457635532
Historical Museum 21080

Ardea

Raccolta Amici di Manzù, Via di Sant' Antonio 1, 00040 Ardea - T: 069135022. Head: Dr. Livia Velani
Historic Site
Sculptures, drawings, goldwork and engravings by Giacomo Manzù 21081

Arezzo

Museo Archeologico Mecenate, Via Margaritone 10, 52100 Arezzo - T: 057520882, Fax: 057520882. Head: Dr. P. Zamarchi Grassi
Archaeological Museum - 1823
Bronzes, Greek and Etruscan ceramics, goldware, sarcophagi, mosaics 21082

Museo di Casa Vasari, Via XX Settembre 55, 52100 Arezzo - T: 057520295. Head: Dr. Alessandra Griffo
Fine Arts Museum - 1911
Paintings and frescoes by Giorgio Vasari, Tuscan painters, memorabilia 21083

Museo Diocesano, Piazza Duomo, 52100 Arezzo - T: 057523991. Head: Alvaro Bardelli
Religious Arts Museum
Illuminated codices, religous art, paintings, statues 21084

Museo Statale di Arte Medioevale e Moderna, Palazzo Bruno Ciocchi, Via San Lorentino 8, 52100 Arezzo - T: 0575300301, Fax: 057529850
Fine Arts Museum - 1891
15th to 19th c Italian paintings, frescoes, sculpture, majolica, medals, bronzes, ivories, goldsmith art, ancient weapons, coins, glasses 21085

Argenta

Museo Civico, c/o Comune di Argenta, 44011 Argenta - T: 0532808058, Fax: 0532852287, E-mail: ust@comune.argenta.fe.it, Internet: http://www.comune.argenta.fe.it
Local Museum
Local history, archaeology 21086

Museo della Bonifica, c/o Comune di Argenta, 44011 Argenta - T: 0532808058, Fax: 0532852287, E-mail: ust@comune.argenta.fe.it, Internet: http://www.comune.argenta.fe.it
Natural History Museum
Natural history, science and technology 21087

Museo delle Valli d'Argenta, c/o Comune di Argenta, 44011 Argenta - T: 0532808058, Fax: 0532852287, E-mail: ust@comune.argenta.fe.it, Internet: http://www.comune.argenta.fe.it
Natural History Museum
Flora and fauna of the Po delta 21088

Pinacoteca Comunale, Via Aleotti, 44011 Argenta - T: 0532853111
Fine Arts Museum
15th to 18th c frescoes, paintings and sculpture 21089

Arona

Museo Civico Archeologico, Piazza San Graziano, 28041 Arona - T: 0322231232, Fax: 0322242082
Local Museum 21090

Museo Civico di Arona, Piazza De Filippi 1, 28041 Arona - T: 032247602
Archaeological Museum 21091

Arpino

Museo di Palazzo Spaccamela, Via Civitavecchia 55, 03033 Arpino - T: 077684212
Historical Museum 21092

Arquà Petrarca

Casa di Petrarca, Via Valleselle, 35032 Arquà Petrarca - T: 0429718294, Fax: 0429718294, E-mail: musei.comune@padoranet.it, Internet: http://www.padoranet.it/museicivici/monumenti/petrarca.html. Head: Davide Banzato
Historic Site - 1923
Home of scholar-poet Petrarca (1304-1374), furniture, memorabilia 21093

Arsago Seprio

Civico Museo Archeologico, Via R. Vanoni 20, 21011 Arsago Seprio - T: 0331768222. Head: Carlo Mastorgio
Archaeological Museum 21094

Ascea

Scavi Archeologici di Velia, 84046 Ascea
Archaeological Museum 21095

Asciano

Museo d'Arte Sacra, Piazza della Colle giata, Chiesa di Santa Croce, 53041 Asciano - T: 0577718207
Religious Arts Museum
14th and 15th c religious paintings, wooden statues, terra cottas, frescoes 21096

Museo Etrusco, Corso Matteotti, 53041 Asciano - T: 0577718745
Archaeological Museum
Finds of the Etruscan tombs in Poggio Pinci 21097

Ascoli Piceno

Galleria d'Arte Contemporanea, Palazzo Malaspina, Corso Mazzini 224, 63100 Ascoli Piceno - T: 0736250760, Fax: 0736298238. Head: Giuseppe Malatesta
Fine Arts Museum
Painting, sculpture, graphic 21098

Museo Archeologico Statale, Piazza dell'Arringo 1, 63100 Ascoli Piceno - T: 0736253562, Fax: 0736255563
Archaeological Museum - 1779
Prehistoric finds, bronzes, Roman sculpture, mosaics, jewelry, ceramics 21099

Museo della Ceramica, Via Torri 45, 63100 Ascoli Piceno - T: 0736254460
Local Museum 21100

Museo Diocesano, Piazza dell' Arringo 27, 63100 Ascoli Piceno - T: 0736252883, Fax: 0736247708, E-mail: pulchra@mercurio.it, Internet: http://www.ascolipiceno.chiesacattolica.it/museo.htm. Head: Lino Arcangeli
Religious Arts Museum
Religious paintings, ivory, silver and stone sculptures 21101

Pinacoteca Civica, Piazza dell'Arringo, 63100 Ascoli Piceno - T: 0736298213. Head: Prof. Alfio Ortenzi
Fine Arts Museum - 1861
Paintings from the Marches region, paintings by Titian and Tintoretto, 19th c drawings 21102

Ascoli Satriano

Museo Civico, Vicolo Montebello, 71022 Ascoli Satriano - T: 088551117
Local Museum 21103

Asola

Museo Civico Archeologico Goffredo Bellini, Viale Brescia 8, 46041 Asola - T: 0376710542. Head: Giuseppe Furlan
Archaeological Museum 21104

Asolo

Museo Civico, Via Regina Corraro, 31011 Asolo - T: 0423952313. Head: Dr. Corrado Fabris
Local Museum
Archeological section with early Venetian and Roman material, paintings, relics and arms of the Venetian period, room and memorabilia on actress Eleonora Duse 21105

Assisi

Galleria d'Arte Contemporanea, Cittadella Cristiana, Via Ancajani 3, 06081 Assisi - T: 075813231, Fax: 075812445. Head: Toni Bernardini
Religious Arts Museum
800 paintings and sculptures, photographs, prints, children's drawings 21106

Museo Civico e Foro Romano, Via Portica 2, 06081 Assisi - T: 075813053, Fax: 075813716. Head: Dr. Viviana Sonno
Archaeological Museum - 1928
Etruscan and Roman urns, pictures, sculpture, epigraphs, Roman forum 21107

Museo della Basilica Patriarcale S. Maria degli Angeli, 06088 Assisi - T: 07580511, 0758051430, Fax: 0758051418
Religious Arts Museum 21108

Museo e Archivio Capitolare, Piazza San Rufino, 06081 Assisi - T: 075812283. Head: Prof. Dr. Aldo Brunacci
Religious Arts Museum 21109

Museo Sacro, Archivio della Cattedrale di S. Rufino, 06081 Assisi. Head: Prof. Dr. Aldo Brunacci
Religious Arts Museum 21110

Museo-Tesoro Basilica di S. Francesco, Piazza San Francesco 2, 06082 Assisi - T: 075819001, Fax: 075816187, E-mail: chiu@krenet.it, Internet: http://www.romagiubileo.it/assisi. Head: Pasquale Magro
Religious Arts Museum
12th-14th c precious relics, goldsmith art 21111

Pinacoteca Comunale, Piazza del Comune 1, 06081 Assisi - T: 075812579, Fax: 075813716. Head: Dr. Viviana Sonno
Fine Arts Museum
13th-16th c paintings and canvas, detached frescoes 21112

Asti

Centro Nazionale di Studi Alfieriani, Corso Alfieri 375, 14100 Asti - T: 014158284. Head: Roberto Marchetti
Library with Exhibitions 21113

Cripta e Museo di Sant'Anastasio, Corso Alfieri 365a, 14100 Asti - T: 014143745, Fax: 0141399507, E-mail: cultura@comune.asti.it, Internet: http://www.comune.asti.it. Head: Dr. Gemma Boschiero
Fine Arts Museum / Local Museum 21114

Museo Alfieriano, Corso Alfieri 375, 14100 Asti - T: 014158284. Head: Dr. Anita Bogetti
Historic Site - 1937
Birthplace of Vittorio Alfieri, memorabilia and rare editions of his works - library 21115

Museo Archeologico e Paleontologico, Corso Alfieri 2, 14100 Asti - T: 0141353072, 0141399460, Fax: 0141399507, E-mail: cultura@comune.asti.it, Internet: http://www.comune.asti.it. Head: Dr. Gemma Boschiero
Archaeological Museum - 1885
Pre-Roman and Roman archeology, Etruscan antiquities, fossils, mummies 21116

Pinacoteca Civica (temporary closed), Corso Alfieri 357, 14100 Asti - T: 0141594791, Fax: 0141399507, E-mail: cultura@comune.asti.it, Internet: http://www.comune.asti.it. Head: Dr. Gemma Boschiero
Fine Arts Museum - 1903
Ancient, modern and contemporary works of art - library 21117

Atena Lucana

Antiquarium Communale, Viale Kennedy, 84030 Atena Lucana - T: 097576001
Local Museum 21118

Atina

Museo Civico, Piazza Saturno 1, 03042 Atina - T: 077660162
Local Museum 21119

Atri

Museo Capitolare, Annesso Alla Cattedrale, Via Luca d'Atri, 64032 Atri - T: 0858798140. Head: Giuseppe Filippo
Fine Arts Museum - 1914
Wood sculpture, ceramics, religious vestments, goldsmith work, miniatures, old manuscripts, incunabula, 16th-17th c paintings, lapidarium 21120

Avellino

Museo Irpino, Corso Europa, 83100 Avellino - T: 082538582. Head: Consalvo Grella
Fine Arts Museum - 1934
Archeological finds from Iron Age to Roman period, numismatics, religious art, modern section 21121

Avezzano

Museo Lapidario Marsicano, Palazzo Municipale, 67051 Avezzano - T: 08635011. Head: Giorgio Tempesti
Fine Arts Museum 21122

Avola

Museo Civico, Piazza Umberto I 19, 96012 Avola - T: 0931834411
Local Museum
Prehistoric, Graeco-Roman and medieval archeology, paintings, pottery 21123

Badia Polesine

Museo Civico A.E. Baruffaldi, Piazza Vittorio Emanuele II, 45021 Badia Polesine - T: 042552695, Fax: 042551923, E-mail: badiabib@netbusiness.it. Head: Mara Barison
Local Museum / Historical Museum 21124

Bagheria

Galleria d'Arte Moderna e Contemporanea, Via Consolare, pal. Cattolica, 90011 Bagheria - T: 091905438
Fine Arts Museum
Paintings by contemporary artists 21125

Museo Archivio Sacrario di Storia Patria, Villa Cattolica SS. 113, 90011 Bagheria
Historical Museum 21126

Bagnacavallo

Museo Civico, Via Garibaldi 62, 48012 Bagnacavallo - T: 054561256
Local Museum
Painting, archaeology, ethnography 21127

Bagnara di Romagna

Museo d'Arte Sacra, Piazza IV Novembre 2, 48010 Bagnara di Romagna - T: 054566054
Religious Arts Museum 21128

Baranello

Museo Civico, Via Santa Maria, 86042 Baranello - T: 0874460406
Local Museum
Local archeology, paintings, decorative art, coins 21129

Barbarano Romano

Museo Civico, Piazza G. Marconi 21, 01010 Barbarano Romano - T: 0761474778
Local Museum 21130

Bardonecchia

Museo Civico, Via Des Geneys 6, 10052 Bardonecchia - T: 0122999350
Local Museum 21131

Barga

Museo Casa Pascoli, Fraz Castelvecchio Pascoli, Via Caprona 4, 55051 Barga - T: 0583766147
Local Museum 21132

Bari

Gipsoteca del Castello Svevo, Piazza Federico II di Svevia, 70122 Bari - T: 0805214361
Fine Arts Museum
Plaster sculptures of Roman monuments in Sicily 21133

Museo Archeologico Provinciale, Palazzo Ateneo, Piazza Umberto I, 70121 Bari - T: 0805211559. Head: Dr. Giuseppe Andreassi
Archaeological Museum
Prehistoric to Roman history of Apulia, Apulian, Greek and Corinthian pottery, coins and medals 21134

Museo del Dipartimento di Zoologia dell'Università di Bari, Via Orabona 4, 70125 Bari - T: 0805443360, Fax: 0805443358, E-mail: g.scillitani@biologia.uniba.it. Head: Prof. Lidia Scalera Liaci
Natural History Museum 21135

Museo della Basilica di San Nicola, Basilica di San Nicola, 70122 Bari - T: 0805211205. Head: Gerardo Cioffari
Religious Arts Museum
Fragments of sculptures and silver decorations from churches of Bari, liturgical relics 21136

Museo Diocesano, Piazza Odegitria, 70122 Bari - T: 0805210064, Fax: 0805288250, E-mail: - comunicazioni.sociali@odegitria.bari.it, Internet: http://www.odegitria.bari.it. Head: Gaetano Barracane
Religious Arts Museum 21137

Museo Etnografico Africa Mozambico, Convento Cappuccini, Via Gen. Bellomo 94, 70124 Bari - T: 08051610034, Fax: 0805610051. Head: Michele Valerio
Ethnology Museum 21138

Pinacoteca Provinciale di Bari, Via Spalato 19, 70121 Bari - T: 0805412421, Fax: 0805588147, E-mail: pinacotecaprov.bari@tin.it. Head: Clara Gelao
Fine Arts Museum - 1928
11th-19th c Apulian, Venetian and Neapolitan paintings and sculpture (Corrado Giaquinto, Francesco Netti, Filippo Cifariello), Grieco coll: 50 paintings from Fattori to Morandi 21139

Barletta

Museo Civico di Barletta, Corso Cavour 8, 70051 Barletta - T: 0883533005. Head: Prof. Ruggiero Mascolo
Fine Arts Museum - 1929
17th-19th c paintings of the Neapolitan school, Renaissance sculpture, Italian artifacts, local archeology - library 21140

Museo della Cattedrale (temporary closed), Piazza Duomo, 70051 Barletta - T: 0883345522. Head: Giuseppe Paolillo
Religious Arts Museum 21141

Barolo

Museo Civico, Castello Falletti, Piazza Falletti, 12060 Barolo - T: 017356277
Local Museum 21142

Bassano del Grappa

Museo, Biblioteca e Archivio, Museo Civico, Via Museo 12, 36061 Bassano del Grappa - T: 0424522235, 0424523336, Fax: 0424523914, E-mail: museobasa@x-land.it, Internet: http://www-land.it/museobassano. Head: Dr. Mario Guderzo
Fine Arts Museum - 1828
Drawings, engravings, picture gallery, archaeology, numismatics, manuscripts, rare book editions, incunabula, majolica - library, archive 21143

Museo del Ponte degli Alpini, Taverna degli Alpini, 36061 Bassano del Grappa - T: 0424503650
Local Museum 21144

Bastiglia

Museo della Civiltà Contadina, Piazza della Repubblica 54, 41030 Bastiglia - T: 059904063, 059904866, Fax: 059815132, E-mail: socicult@tsc4.com
Local Museum 21145

Bazzano

Museo Civico Archeologico Arsenio Crespellani, Via Contessa Matilde, 40053 Bazzano - T: 051836430, 051831183, Fax: 051836440, E-mail: biblioteca@bazzano.provincia.bologna.it, Internet: http://www.museionline.it/parola/crespell/crespell.htm. Head: Dr. Tiziana Ravasio
Archaeological Museum - 1874
Prehistoric finds from local excavations, Roman objects, bronzes, decorated vases 21146

Bedonia

Museo del Seminario Vescovile, Via San Stefano Raffi, 43041 Bedonia - T: 0525824420, Fax: 0525824621
Archaeological Museum - 1953
Prehistoric to Roman archeological material 21147

Belluno

Museo Civico, Piazza del Duomo 16, 32100 Belluno - T: 0437944836, Fax: 0437944836, E-mail: ggalasso@comune.belluno.it, Internet: http://www.comune.belluno.it. Head: Dr. Giovanna Galasso
Decorative Arts Museum / Fine Arts Museum - 1876
Archeology and science, paintings, small bronzes, drawings, sculptures, medals and coins, china, pottery, jewels after the manners of Belluno 21148

Belvi

Museo Sardo di Scienze Naturali, Via Roma, 08030 Belvi - T: 0784629467. Head: Giuseppe Tolu
Natural History Museum 21149

Bene Vagienna

Museo Civico Archeologico, Palazzo Lucerna di Rovà, Via Roma 125, 12041 Bene Vagienna - T: 0172654152, Fax: 0172654947, E-mail: ufficiocultura@benevagienna.it, Internet: http://www.benevagienna.it. Head: Luciano Oreglia
Local Museum - 1894
Archeology, bronzes, glass, ceramics, Roman architecture 21150

Benevento

Museo del Sannio, Piazza Santa Sofia, 82100 Benevento - T: 082421818, Fax: 082428831. Head: Prof. Elio Galasso
Historical Museum - 1873
Archeology, Roman sarcophagi and vases, medieval and modern art, regional history, numismatics - library 21151

Bentivoglio

Museo della Canape e della Vita Contadina, Fraz Castagnolo Minore, 40010 Bentivoglio - T: 051861504
Historical Museum 21152

Museo della Civiltà Contadina, Villa Smeraldi, Via Santa Marina 35, 40010 Bentivoglio - T: 051891050, Fax: 051898377. Head: Dr. Francesco Fabbri
Agriculture Museum
Tools, farm implements, agricultural objects 21153

Bergamo

Civico Museo Archeologico, Piazza Cittadella 9, 24100 Bergamo - T: 035242839, Fax: 035242839. Head: Dr. Stefania Casini
Archaeological Museum - 1561
Prehistoric, Paleochristian and Langobard findings, Roman statues, reliefs and frescoes, epigraphs - library 21154

Galleria d'Arte Moderna e Contemporanea, Piazza G. Carrara, 24100 Bergamo - T: 035399527, Fax: 035224510. Head: Prof. Vittorio Fagone
Fine Arts Museum 21155

Museo Civico del Risorgimento e della Resistenza, Piazzale Brigata Legnano 12, 24100 Bergamo - T: 035247116. Head: Dr. Roberto Galati
Historical Museum
History and documents on the 'Five Days of Bergamo' in 1848 and of Garibaldi's activity in the town 21156

Museo Civico di Scienze Naturali E. Caffi, Piazza Cittadella 10, 24129 Bergamo - T: 035233513, Fax: 035233154, E-mail: msnbg@tixalinet.it. Head: Dr. Marco Valle
Natural History Museum - 1917
Ornithology, butterflies, herbarium, fossils, minerals, etnography, arachnida, treichoptera - library, didactic section 21157

Museo Diocesano d'Arte Sacra, Via Donizetti 3, 24100 Bergamo - T: 035211001
Religious Arts Museum 21158

Museo Donizettiano, Via Arena 9, 24129 Bergamo - T: 035399269, 035247116, Fax: 035219128, E-mail: donizetti@museostoricobg.org, Internet: http://www.museostoricobg.org. Head: Fabrizio Capitanio
Historic Site - 1902
Memorabilia on the composer Gaetano Donizetti (1797-1848) - archive 21159

Pinacoteca dell'Accademia Carrara, Piazza Carrara 82a, 24100 Bergamo - T: 035399677, Fax: 035224510, E-mail: segr@accademiacarrara.bergamo.it, Internet: http://www.accademiacarrara.bergamo.it. Head: Dr. Francesco Rossi
Fine Arts Museum - 1796
14th to 19th c paintings, 15th c paintings of Venetian, Lombardian and Tuscan schools by Pisanello, Bellini, Botticelli, Mantegna, Lotto and others 21160

Besano

Museo Civico Fossili, Via Prestini 7, 21050 Besano - T: 0332916260, Fax: 0332916568. Head: Dr. Giorgio Teruzzi
Natural History Museum 21161

Besenello

Castel Beseno, 38060 Besenello - T: 0464834600, Fax: 0464239497, E-mail: - castellodelbuonconsiglio@provincal.tn.it. Head: Dr. Franco Marzatico
Historical Museum 21162

Bettona

Pinacoteca e Museo Civico, Palazzetto del Podestà, Piazza Cavour, 06084 Bettona - T: 0759869981
Local Museum - 1958
Paintings of the Umbrian school, works by Perugino, Della Robbia, Di Lorenzo, decorative arts, local history, Etruscan archeology 21163

Bevagna

Antiquarium e Mosaico Romano, Via Porta Guelfa, 06031 Bevagna - T: 0742360123, Fax: 0742361647
Archaeological Museum
Mosaic pavement of the 2nd c antiquities, epigraphs, Roman household objects 21164

Museo di Bevagna, Corso Matteotti 70, 06031 Bevagna - T: 0742360031, Fax: 0742360031
Fine Arts Museum
Paintings by Umbrian masters (Andrea Camassei, Ascensidonio Spacca, Adone Doni, Corrado Giaquinto), Roman coins, archaeological remains 21165

Raccolta Archeological, Corso Matteotti 72, 06031 Bevagna - T: 074262123
Archaeological Museum 21166

Biella

Istituto di Fotografia Alpina Vittorio Sella, San Gerolamo 1, 13900 Biella - T: 0152522445, Fax: 0152522455, E-mail: foundation@bansel.it. Head: Lodovico Sella
Science&Tech Museum / Special Museum - 1948
Mountain photography from 1870 to present time, history of photography from 1839 to modern times, mountain photography coll before 1911 bequested by Agostino Ferrari - library 21167

Museo Civico, Sez. Archeologica, Via Pietro Micca 38, 13051 Biella - T: 01521653, Fax: 01520279
Fine Arts Museum - 1932
Local archaeology, Egyptian antiquities, ancient, modern and contemporary art, 15th and 16th c frescos 21168

Museo Permanente delle Truppe Alpine Mario Balocco, Via Delleani 33, 13051 Biella - T: 015406112, Fax: 015406112. Head: Umberto Carnazzi
Military Museum - 1972 21169

Bisceglie

Museo Civico Archeologico, Via Cardinale dell'Oglio 58, 70052 Bisceglie - T: 0808757576
Archaeological Museum 21170

Bisegna

Museo del Camoscio, Centro di Visita del Parco d'Abruzzo, 67050 Bisegna - T: 086391955. Head: Prof. F. Tassi
Local Museum 21171

Bisuschio

Villa Cicogna Mozzoni, Piazza Cicogna, 21050 Bisuschio - T: 0332470151
Local Museum 21172

Bitonto

Museo Civico E. Rogadeo, Via Rogadeo 52, 70032 Bitonto - T: 0809511877. Head: Dr. Pasquale Cioce
Local Museum
Prehistoric and Graeco-Roman archeological remains of the area, stone tablets, antiquities, paintings 21173

Museo Diocesano, Via del Vescovado 2, 70032 Bitonto - T: 0809511278. Head: Graziano Bellifemine
Religious Arts Museum
Religious art, 15th to 19th c paintings 21174

Bobbio

Castello Malaspina, Via Forte, 29022 Bobbio - T: 052344774
Local Museum
Ranaissance antiquities, furniture and ornaments 21175

Museo dell'Abazzia di San Colombano, Piazza S. Fara, 29022 Bobbio - T: 0523936018, Fax: 0523960484. Head: Roberto Mazzari
Archaeological Museum
Roman to Baroque antiquities and architecture, sculpture 21176

Bogliaco

Museo della Villa Bettoni, Via Bogliaco, 25080 Bogliaco
Fine Arts Museum
Frescoes, portraits and paintings in an 18th c villa 21177

Bolgheri

Museo del Menu, Via dei Colli 3, 57020 Bolgheri - T: 0565762007. Head: Enrico Guagnini
Historical Museum 21178

Bologna

Archivio Storico-Museo dello Studio-Biblioteca, Largo Trombetti 3, 40126 Bologna - T: 051228561, 051259020, Fax: 051259888
University Museum 21179

Biblioteca e Casa di Carducci, Piazza Carducci 5, 40125 Bologna - T: 051347592, Fax: 051347592, E-mail: CasaCarducci@comune.bologna.it. Head: Dr. Pierangelo Bellettini
Special Museum - 1907
Home of poet Giosuè Carducci (1835-1907), manuscripts, his books, personal possessions, furnishings - library, archive 21180

Civico Museo Bibliografico Musicale, Piazza Rossini 2, 40126 Bologna - T: 051221117, Fax: 051221117, E-mail: cmbm@comune.bologna.it, Internet: http://www.comune.bologna.it/cmbm. Head: Dr. Pierangelo Bellettini
Music Museum
15th to 20th c printed music editions, 18th to 19th c pianos, manuscripts of musical theory 21181

Collezioni Comunali d'Arte, Palazzo Comunale, Piazza Maggiore 6, 40126 Bologna - T: 051203526, 051203111, 051203919, Fax: 051232312, E-mail: MuseiCivici4comune.bologna.it, Internet: http://www.comune.bologna.it/Cultura/MuseiCivici/. Head: Prof. Eugenio Riccòmini
Fine Arts Museum - 1936
13th to 19th c Bolognese and Italian paintings, furniture and decorative arts, portrait miniatures, embroidery, laces 21182

Collezioni d'Arte e di Storia della Cassa di Risparmio, Via G.B. Morgagni 3, 40122 Bologna - T: 051230727, Fax: 051232676
Fine Arts Museum - 1978
Stamps, money (15th-20th c) - Library, peridiocals coll 21183

Donazione Putti Biblioteca, Raccolta dell'Istituto Ortopedico Rizzoli, Via Codivilla 9, 40136 Bologna
Historical Museum - 1925
Old books on medical subjects, pictures, prints and autographs of scientists' old surgical instruments, two ivory anatomical manikins, 16th and 18th c globes - library 21184

Gabinetto dei Disegni e delle Stampe, Pinacoteca Nazionale, Via Belle Arti 56, 40126 Bologna - T: 051243222, Fax: 051251368, E-mail: sbas-bo@iperbole.bologna.it. Head: Dr. Marzia Faietti
Fine Arts Museum
Engravings, German, Flemish, Italian and French prints, 16th-19th c Italian drawings 21185

Galleria d'Arte Moderna di Bologna, Piazza della Costituzione 3, 40128 Bologna - T: 051502859, Fax: 051371032. Head: Prof. Peter Weiermair
Fine Arts Museum - 1975
Contemporary art mainly by Emilian and Bolognese painters 21186

Museo Aldrovandiano, Via Zamboni 35, 40126 Bologna - T: 051243420, Fax: 051252110, E-mail: Antonino@bub.unibo.it, Internet: http://www.bub.unibo.it. Head: Dr. Biancastella Antonino
Natural History Museum - 1603/1907
Work of the Italian naturalist Ulisse Aldrovandi, pictures, zoology, botany, geology, mineralogy 21187

Museo Carducciani, Piazza Carducci 5, 40125 Bologna - T: 051347592
Local Museum 21188

Museo Civico Archeologico, Via dell'Archiginnasio 2, 40124 Bologna - T: 051233849, Fax: 051266516, E-mail: mca@comune.bologna.it, Internet: http://www.comune.bologna.it/bologna/musei/archeologico. Head: Dr. Cristiana Morigi Govi
Archaeological Museum - 1881
Topographical section with prehistoric, Etruscan, Gallic and Roman material, Egyptian, Greek, Roman and Etrusco-Italian exhibits, numismatics - library 21189

Museo Civico d'Arte Industriale e Galleria Davia Bargellini, Strada Maggiore 44, 40125 Bologna - T: 051236708, Fax: 051232312, E-mail: MuseiArteAntica@comune.bologna.it, Internet: http://www.comune.bologna.it/Cultura/MuseiCivici. Head: Prof. Eugenio Riccòmini
Decorative Arts Museum - 1928
15th to 19th c locksmith's work in iron and bronze, 18th c Bolognese living style, furniture, 14th to 18th c paintings 21190

Museo Civico del Risorgimemto, Piazza Carducci 5, 40125 Bologna - T: 051225583, Fax: 051225583, E-mail: museorisorgimento@comune.bologna.it, Internet: http://www.comune.bologna.it/museorisorgimento. Head: Dr. Pierangelo Bellettini
Historical Museum 21191

Museo Civico del Risorgimento, Biblioteca-Archivio, Via de' Musei 8, 40124 Bologna - T: 051225583, Fax: 051225583, E-mail: museorisorgimento@comune.bologna.it, Internet: http://www.comune.bologna.it/museorisorgimento. Head: Dr. Pierangelo Bellettini
Library with Exhibitions - 1893
Memorabilia on activities and personalities of the Risorgimento 21192

Museo Civico Medievale, Via Manzoni 4, 40121 Bologna - T: 051203930, 051203111, 051204111, Fax: 051232312. Head: Prof. Eugenio Riccòmini
Fine Arts Museum - 1881
13th to 16th c Bolognese sculpture, arms, glasses, bronces 21193

Museo della Specola, Via Zamboni 33, 40126 Bologna - T: 0516305701, Fax: 0516305700, E-mail: bonoli@bo.astro.it, Internet: http://www.bo.astro.it/dip./Museum. Head: Dr. Fabrizio Bonoli
Historical Museum - 1979
Astronomical instruments from the early 18th c, miscellaneous astronomical instruments from the 13th trough the 19th c, early 18th c observatorium - library, historical archive 21194

Museo delle Navi, Via Zamboni 33, 40126 Bologna - T: 0512099362, Fax: 0512099922, E-mail: smu@ammc.unibo.it, Internet: http://www.unibo.it. Head: Viviana Lanzarini
Science&Tech Museum - 1724
Antique ship models and maps 21195

Museo dell'Istituto di Anatomia Umana Normale, Via Irnerio 48, 40126 Bologna - T: 051244467, 051243103, E-mail: aruggeri@biocfarm.unibo.it. Head: Prof. Alessandro Ruggeri
Natural History Museum / University Museum - 1742
Anatomical wax (18th-19th c) 21196

Museo dell'Istituto di Zoologia, Via San Giacomo 9, 40126 Bologna - T: 051232582
Natural History Museum
Zoology of Mozambique, fish of Brazil, corals, birds of Italy, various continents 21197

Museo dello Studio, Archivo Storico, Largo Trombetti 3, 40126 Bologna - T: 051228561, Fax: 051259888. Head: Dr. Marco Bortolotti
Historical Museum - 1888
Medieval to 19th c hist of Bolognese University life, documents, antiquities, student's life, traditions and culture 21198

Museo di Anatomia Comparata, Via Belmeloro 8, 40126 Bologna - T: 051237301
Natural History Museum 21199

Museo di Anatomia e Istologia Patologica, Via Massarenti 9, 40138 Bologna - T: 051308991
Natural History Museum 21200

Museo di Antropologia, Via Selmi 1, 40126 Bologna - T: 051354190, Fax: 051354191. Head: Prof. Fiorenzo Facchini
Ethnology Museum - 1908
African and Asian masks, deformed skulls 21201

Museo di Architettura Militare, Via Zamboni 33, 40126 Bologna - T: 0512099362, Fax: 0512099922, E-mail: smu@ammc.unibo.it, Internet: http://www.unibo.it. Head: Viviana Lanzarini
Military Museum - 1712
Models of fortifications and guns 21202

Museo di Fisica, Via Irnerio 46, 40126 Bologna - T: 0512091099, Fax: 0512247244, E-mail: museo@df.unibo.it, Internet: http://www.df.unibo.it/museo/welcome.htm. Head: Prof. G. Dragoni
Science&Tech Museum - 1982
Benedetto XIV (1675-1758), Lord George Cowper (1730-1789), Augusto Righi (1850-1920), Quirino Majorana (1871-1957), Gianfranco Sinigaglia (1929-1990) - library, restoration laboratory, photographic laboratory, EDP Centre, educational service 21203

Museo di Mineralogia L. Bombicci, Piazza di Porta San Donato 1, 40126 Bologna - T: 051243556, Fax: 051243336, E-mail: FELICE@GEOMIN.UNIBO.IT. Head: Prof. Claudio D'Amico
Natural History Museum - 1907
Mineralogy, petrography, ornamental stones, ambers, meteorites, old instruments 21204

Museo di Palazzo Pepoli Campogrande, Via Castiglione 7, 40124 Bologna - T: 051229858, 051239031, Fax: 051279926. Head: Dr. Giampiero Cammarota
Fine Arts Museum 21205

Museo di San Domenico, Piazza San Domenico 13, 40124 Bologna - T: 0516400411. Head: Dr. Alfonso D'Amato
Religious Arts Museum - 1956
Religious painting, sculpture and decorative art, goldsmiths' work 21206

Museo di San Giuseppe, Via Bellinzona 6, 40135 Bologna - T: 0513397511, Fax: 0513397699, E-mail: biblio.copp@iol.it. Head: Andrea Maggioli
Religious Arts Museum - 1928
15th-20th c works by Bolognese and Romagnese painters, miniatures, ivories - library, archive 21207

Museo di San Petronio, Presso Basilica San Petronio, Piazza Maggiore, 40124 Bologna - T: 051225442. Head: Mario Fanti
Religious Arts Museum - 1893
History of the Basilica, designs of the facade, 15th and 18th c religious art 21208

Museo di Santo Stefano, Via Santo Stefano 24, 40125 Bologna - T: 051223256. Head: Dr. Romualdo Ziliani
Religious Arts Museum
Roman and Byzantine epigraphs, 14th to 17th c Bolognese paintings 21209

Museo Geologico Paleontologico G. Capellini, Via Zamboni 63, 40127 Bologna - T: 051354555, Fax: 051354522, E-mail: anolraffi@geomin.unibo.it. Head: Prof. S. Raffi
Natural History Museum - 1852
Geology, lithology, paleontology, fossils and rocks mainly from Emilia, Tuscany and Venezia, dinosaurs (Diplodocus, Ichtyosaurus, eggs) - archive, library 21210

Museo Indiano, Via Zamboni 33, 40126 Bologna - T: 0512099362, Fax: 0512099922, E-mail: smu@ammc.unibo.it, Internet: http://www.unibo.it. Head: Viviana Lanzarini
Ethnology Museum - 1903
Ethnographic material, art 21211

Museo Marsiliano, Via Zamboni 35, 40126 Bologna - T: 051243420, Fax: 051252110, E-mail: Antonino@bub.unibo.it, Internet: http://www.bub.unibo.it. Head: Dr. Biancastella Antonino
Historical Museum - 1712/1930
Manuscripts, printed works and possessions of Luigi Ferdinando Marsili, hist, natural hist, military hist, oceanography 21212

Museo Missionario d'Arte Cinese, Via Osservanza 88, 40136 Bologna - T: 051580597, Fax: 051582142, E-mail: frati.ossenvanza@libero.it. Head: Onofrio Gianaroli
Fine Arts Museum
Chinese and New Guinea collections 21213

Museo Ostetrico, Via Zamboni 33, 40126 Bologna - T: 0512099362, Fax: 0512099922, E-mail: smu@ammc.unibo.it, Internet: http://www.unibo.it. Head: Viviana Lanzarini
Science&Tech Museum / Historical Museum - 1757
Dissecting tables, clay models, surgical instruments 21214

Pinacoteca Nazionale, Via Belle Arti 56, 40126 Bologna - T: 051243222, Fax: 051251368. Head: Prof. Andrea Emiliani
Fine Arts Museum - 1808
14th to 18th c Bolognese painting, 15th to 16th c German engravings by Dürer and pupils, Italian Renaissance engravings 21215

Ville delle Rose, Galleria d'Arte Moderna, Via Saragozza 228-230, 40128 Bologna - T: 051502859
Fine Arts Museum 21216

Bolsena

Antiquarium della Chiesa di Santa Cristina, 01023 Bolsena
Archaeological Museum 21217

Museo Territoriale del Lago di Bolsena, Rocca Monaldeschi, 01023 Bolsena - T: 0761798630. Head: Pietro Tamburini
Local Museum - 1991 21218

Bolzano

Merkantilmuseum, Silbergasse 6, 39100 Bolzano - T: 04711945511
Special Museum 21219

Museion - Museo d'Arte Moderna e Contemporanea Bolzano, Via Sernesi 1, 39100 Bolzano - T: 0471980001, 0471977116, Fax: 0471980001, 0471312460, E-mail: info@museion.it, Internet: http://www.museion.it. Head: Andreas Hapkemeyer
Fine Arts Museum - 1987 21220

Museo Civico, Via Cassa di Risparmo 14, 39100 Bolzano - T: 0471974625, Fax: 0471980144, E-mail: museo.civico@comune.bolzano.it, Internet: http://www.comune.bolzano.it/museo_civico. Head: Dr. Stefan Demetz
Local Museum - 1882
Archaeology, ethnography, Baroque paintings from South Tyrolian artists, 13th-16th c local woodcarving, Gothic triptychs and sculptures - library 21221

Bomarzo

Parco dei Mostri, 01020 Bomarzo - T: 0761924029
Fine Arts Museum
Coll of sculptures 21222

Bordighera

Museo Bicknell, Via Romana 39, 18012 Bordighera - T: 0184263601, Fax: 0184266421, E-mail: istituto@iisl.it, Internet: http://www.iisl.it. Head: Prof. Carlo Varaldo
Archaeological Museum - 1888
Herbarium, entomology, copy of prehistoric rock engravings - library 21223

Borghi

Museo Renzi, Via Matteotti 27, 47030 Borghi - T: 0541939028. Head: Sergio Joselu
Local Museum 21224

Borgo a Buggiano

Museo del Santuario del SS. Crocifisso, Corso Indipendenza 56, 51011 Borgo a Buggiano - T: 057232047
Local Museum 21225

Museo dell'Opera, Piazza Pretorio 3, 51011 Borgo a Buggiano - T: 057232850
Local Museum 21226

Borgo Grotta Gigante

Museo di Speleologia, 34010 Borgo Grotta Gigante - T: 040227312. Head: Fabio Forti
Natural History Museum 21227

Borgosesia

Istituto per la Storia della Resistenza e della Societa Contemporanea nelle Province di Biella e Vercelli, Via Sesone 10, 13011 Borgosesia - T: 016321564, Fax: 016321564, E-mail: istituto@storia900bivc.it, Internet: http://www.storia900bivc.it. Head: Piero Ambrosio
Historical Museum - 1974
Documents, photographs and other exhibits on the anti-Fascist, partisan and peasants movements in the province of Biella and Vercelli - library 21228

Museo Etnografico e del Folclore Valsesiano, Via alle Manifatture 10, 13011 Borgosesia - T: 016322505. Head: Dr. Graziella Freschi Conti
Historical Museum 21229

Bormio

Museo Civico, Palazzo De Simoni, Via Buon Consiglio 25, 23032 Bormio - T: 0342904141, Fax: 0342904645. Head: Carlo Ericini
Local Museum
Local history, folk art, ethnographical section 21230

Boscoreale

Antiquarium di Boscoreale, Uomo ed Ambiente nel Territorio Vesuviano, Villa Regina, 80041 Boscoreale - T: 0818707228. Head: Prof. Baldassare Conticello
Archaeological Museum 21231

Botticino

Museo Etnografico della Trinità, Fraz San Gallo, 25080 Botticino - T: 0302691541
Ethnology Museum 21232

Boves

Museo Etnografico delle Alpi Occidentali, Fraz Madonna dei Boschi, Cascina Marquet, 12012 Boves
Ethnology Museum 21233

Bovino

Raccolte di Antichitá, Via Leggieri, 71023 Bovino - T: 0881961013
Local Museum
Roman inscriptions, pottery, bronzes, fossils 21234

Bra

Museo Civico Craveri di Storia Naturale, Via Craveri 15, 12042 Bra - T: 0172412010, Fax: 017244333, E-mail: craveri@comune.bra.cn.it. Head: Ettore Molinaro
Natural History Museum - 1843
Geology, paleontology, zoology, botany, herbarium - archives, library 21235

Museo Vivico Archeologico e Storico, Palazzo Traversa, Via Parpera 4, 12024 Bra - T: 0172423880, Fax: 017244333
Archaeological Museum - 1919
Roman archeological remains of Pollenzo and surroundings 21236

Bracciano

Museo Storico-Aeronautica Militare, Aeroporto L. Bourlot, 00062 Bracciano - T: 06998871, Fax: 0699887445, E-mail: musam@aeronautica.difesa.it, Internet: http://www.aeronautica.difesa.it. Head: Massimo Mondini
Military Museum - 1977
70 Aeroplanes, engines, equipment, weapons, military mementos, uniforms, decorations - Centro Documentazione Umberto Nobile 21237

Breno

Museo Camuno e Biblioteca Civica, Palazzo Comunale, Piazza Ghislandi, 25043 Breno - T: 036422041, Fax: 036422003, E-mail: biblioteca@comune.breno.bs.it, Internet: http://www.voli.bs.it/ifinera/01/musei. Head: Dr. Angelo Giorgi
Local Museum 21238

Brescello

Antiquarium, Via F. Cavallotti, 42041 Brescello - T: 0522687526. Head: Ermes Coffrini
Archaeological Museum - 1960
Roman inscriptions and sculptures from excavations in the ancient town 21239

Brescia

Museo Civico delle Armi L. Marzoli, Parco del Castello, 25100 Brescia - T: 030293292, 0302977800, Fax: 0302400733, Internet: http://www.comune.brescia.it/musei. Head: Dr. Renata Stradiotti
Special Museum
Armour, firearms, armes blanches 21240

Museo Civico di Scienze Naturali, Via Ozanam 4, 25128 Brescia - T: 0302983708, Fax: 0303701048. Head: Pierfranco Blesio
Natural History Museum - 1949
Ornithology, entomology, geology, mineralogy, paleontology, meteorites - library 21241

Museo del Risorgimento, Via Castello 9, 25100 Brescia - T: 0302977800, 03044176, Fax: 0302400733, Internet: http://www.comune.brescia.it/musei. Head: Dr. Renata Stradiotti
Historical Museum / Military Museum - 1887
Documents, relics, prints, arms, local historical paintings of the Risorgimento period 21242

Museo Diocesano d'Arte Sacra, Via Gasparo de Salo 13, 25122 Brescia - T: 0303751064, Fax: 03040233. Head: Ivo Panteghini
Religious Arts Museum - 1978
Ancient fabrics from the 15th-19th c, coll "ex voto" (18th c) 21243

Pinacoteca Civica Tosio Martinengo, Piazza Moretto 4, 25121 Brescia - T: 0303774999, 0302977800, Fax: 0302400733, Internet: http://www.comune.brescia.it/musei. Head: Dr. Renata Stradiotti
Fine Arts Museum - 1832
13th-18th c Italian and foreign paintings, decorative and religous art, masterpieces of Brescian painting 21244

Santa Giulia - Museo della Città, Via dei Musei 81b, 25121 Brescia - T: 0302977800, 0302977834, Fax: 0302400733, Internet: http://www.comune.brescia.it/musei. Head: Dr. Renata Stradiotti
Local Museum / Fine Arts Museum / Archaeological Museum - 1882
Roman, Langobard and Renaissance art, local hist, archaeology 21245

Bressanone

Museo Diocesano e Collezione dei Presepi, Via Palazzo Vescovile 2, 39042 Bressanone - T: 0472830505, Fax: 0472208282, E-mail: brixen@dioezesanmuseum.bz.it, Internet: http://www.dioezesanmuseum.bz.it. Head: Dr. Leo Andergassen
Religious Arts Museum
13th to 18th c local woodcarving and Cathedral treasure, religous art of Roman and baroque eras 21246

Brindisi

Museo Archeologico Provinciale F. Ribezzo, Piazza Duomo, 72100 Brindisi - T: 0831565501/08, Fax: 0831565506, E-mail: provincera@provincera.-brindisi.it. Head: Dr. Angela Marinazzo
Archaeological Museum - 1954
Regional archeological finds, stone fragments, Greco-Roman sculpture, inscriptions, ceramics, terra cottas, mosaics, coins 21247

Brisighella

Casa Malanca, Via Rio Co, 48013 Brisighella - T: 054685435
Local Museum 21248

Museo Civico della Val Lamone, Piazza Marconi 1, 48013 Brisighella - T: 054681225
Local Museum 21249

Museo del Lavoro Contadino, Via Monticino, 48013 Brisighella - T: 054681066. Head: Giorgio Cicognani
Local Museum 21250

Brunico

Stadtgalerie in Bruneck, Bruder-Willram-Str 11, 39031 Brunico - T: 0474411282, Fax: 0474679511, E-mail: stadtgalerie@rolmail.net. Head: Lenka Tresnak
Fine Arts Museum 21251

Südtiroler Landesmuseum für Volkskunde, Herzog-Diet-Str 27, Dietenheim, 39031 Brunico - T: 0474552087, Fax: 0474551764, E-mail: -Volkskundemuseum@provinz.bz.it, Internet: http://www.provinz.bz.it/volkskundemuseen. Head: Dr. Hans Grießmair
Folklore Museum / Ethnology Museum 21252

Budrio

Pinacoteca Civica 'Inzaghi', Via Mentana 9, 40054 Budrio - T: 051801126. Head: Dr. Ferruccio Codicé Pinelli
Fine Arts Museum - 1931
15th to 18th c Bolognese paintings, prints and drawings 21253

Buggiano

Museo dell'Opera, Fraz Buggiano Castello, Piazza Pretorio 6, 51011 Buggiano - T: 057232850
Performing Arts Museum 21254

Museo Parrocchiale del Santuario del Santissimo Crocifisso, Corso Indipendenza 56, 51011 Buggiano - T: 057232047
Religious Arts Museum 21255

Buonconvento

Museo d'Arte Sacra della Val d'Arbia, Via Soccini 17, 53022 Buonconvento - T: 0577806788
Religious Arts Museum 21256

Pinacoteca Parrocchiale, Chiesa Parrocchiale, 53022 Buonconvento
Religious Arts Museum 21257

Raccolta Permanente sulla Lavorazione della Canapa, Via Soccini 34, 53022 Buonconvento - T: 0577806788
Agriculture Museum 21258

Busseto

Casa di Verdi, Località Roncole, 43011 Busseto
Historic Site - 1915
Memorabilia on Giuseppe Verdi (1813-1901) 21259

Museo Civico, Villa Pallavicino, Via Provesi 35, 43011 Busseto - T: 052492230. Head: Nives Guidotti
Local Museum - 1957
16th c historic house with baroque annexes, 15th to 18th c paintings, pottery, furniture 21260

Busto Arsizio

Museo delle Arti Palazzo Bandera, Via Costa 29, 21052 Busto Arsizio - T: 0331321444
Local Museum 21261

Cabras

Antiquarium, 09072 Cabras - T: 0783392370
Archaeological Museum
Archaeological finds 21262

Cagliari

Galleria Comunale d'Arte, Viale Regina Elena, 09124 Cagliari - T: 070490727, Fax: 07042091
Fine Arts Museum - 1927
17th to 20th c Sardinian painting, Oriental decorative arts, folk art of Sardinia 21263

Museo Archeologico Nazionale, Piazza Arsenale, 09100 Cagliari - T: 070655911, Fax: 070658871. Head: Dr. Carlo Tronchetti
Archaeological Museum - 1802
Prehistoric, Punic and Roman archeology of Sardinia, Semitic gems, goldsmith work, Roman glass 21264

Museo Capitolare, Via del Fossario, 09100 Cagliari - T: 070663837
Religious Arts Museum
Material concerning popes, bishops and kings, statues, copper and silverware 21265

Museo di Mineralogia del Dipartimento di Scienza della Terra, Via Trentino 51, 09100 Cagliari - T: 07020061, Fax: 070282236. Head: Prof. Antonio Ulzega
Natural History Museum - 1864 21266

Museo Nazionale Cagliari, Piazza Indipendenza 4, 09127 Cagliari - T: 07054237. Head: Dr. Vincenzo Santoni
Archaeological Museum 21267

Museo Sardo di Antropologia ed Etnografia, Via Porcell 2, 09100 Cagliari - T: 070653839. Head: Prof. Giovanni Floris
Ethnology Museum - 1953
Prehistory and earliest history of Sardinia, Sardinian costumes and folk art 21268

Museo Sardo di Geologia e Paleontologia D. Lovisato, Via Trentino 51, 09100 Cagliari - T: 07020061. Head: Prof. Antonietta Cherchi
Natural History Museum 21269

Pinacoteca Nazionale, Cittadella dei Musei, Piazza Arsenale, 09100 Cagliari - T: 070662496. Head: Francesca Segni Pulvirenti
Fine Arts Museum 21270

Cairate

Museo Civico della Carta, Via Monastero 2, 21050 Cairate - T: 0331360067
Decorative Arts Museum 21271

Cairo Montenotte

Civico Museo, Municipio, 17014 Cairo Montenotte - T: 019502471
Local Museum 21272

Calascibetta

Tesoro della Chiesa di San Pietro, Piazza Madrice, 94010 Calascibetta - T: 093533122
Religious Arts Museum 21273

Calci

Museo di Storia Naturale e del Territorio, Via Roma 79, Certosa, 56011 Calci - T: 050937555, Fax: 050937555, E-mail: strumia@df.unipi.it. Head: Prof. Franco Strumia
Natural History Museum - 1591
Natural history coll 21274

Caldaro

Museo Atesino del Vino, Via dell'oro 1, 39052 Caldaro - T: 0471963168, Fax: 0471963168. Head: Dr. Hans Grießmair
Agriculture Museum - 1955
Hist of regional viticulture, old vineyard tools, wooden barrels and casks, flasks, pots and jugs 21275

Calenzano

Museo dei Soldatino e del Figurino Storico, Via Giotto 5, 50041 Calenzano - T: 0558879441
Historical Museum 21276

Calimera di Lecce

Museo di Storia Naturale, Via Europa, 73021 Calimera di Lecce - T: 0832872301
Local Museum 21277

Caltagirone

Musei Civici e Pinacoteca, Mostra Permanente della Ceramica Moderna, Via Roma 10, 95041 Caltagirone - T: 093341314, Fax: 093357034. Head: Prof. Mario Vaccaro
Local Museum - 1914
Archeological findings of the area, contemporary pottery, fine arts (16th-20th c), ethnology - library, archive 21278

Museo Regionale della Ceramica, Via Volta Libertini 4/5, 95041 Caltagirone - T: 093326668. Head: Dr. Domenico Amoroso
Local Museum 21279

Caltanissetta

Museo Archeologico, Via Colaianni 3, 93100 Caltanissetta - T: 093425936, Fax: 093423932. Head: Dr. Rosalba Panvini
Archaeological Museum 21280

Museo del Folklore, c/o Chiesa San Pio X, Via N. Colajanni, 93100 Caltanissetta - T: 093421013
Folklore Museum
Dioramas of moments in the Passion of Jesus 21281

Museo Mineralogico e delle Zolfare, Viale della Regione 71, 93100 Caltanissetta - T: 0934591280, Fax: 0934592086
Natural History Museum
Minerals, fossils, Sicilian gypsum and sulphur 21282

Camaiore

Museo d'Arte Sacra, Via IV Novembre 71, 55041 Camaiore - T: 0584984182. Head: Arturo Paoli
Religious Arts Museum
Religious art 21283

Camerino

Museo Civico Archeologico, Piazza dei Costanti, 62032 Camerino - T: 0737402310, Fax: 0737402311, E-mail: rivola@camserv.unicam.it, Internet: http://www.museionline.it. Head: Prof. Pierluigi Falaschi
Local Museum / Archaeological Museum
Roman and medieval inscriptions and reliefs, coins, seals, pre-Roman and Roman pottery, paintings by local masters 21284

Museo di Anatomia, Facoltà di Medicina Veterinaria, Istituto di Anatomia degli Animali Domestici, 62032 Camerino
Local Museum 21285

Museo di Geologia, Via Venanzi, 62032 Camerino - T: 07372467
Natural History Museum
Geology, paleontology, petrography, mineralogy 21286

Museo di Scienze Naturali, Via del Bastione 2, 62032 Camerino - T: 073740263, Fax: 073740298. Head: Prof. Alberto Mario Simonetta
Natural History Museum
Comparative anatomy 21287

Museo e Pinacoteca Diocesana, Palazzo Arcivescovile, Piazza Cavour 12, 62032 Camerino - T: 0737630400. Head: Prof. Giacomo Boccanera
Religious Arts Museum
Religious art from local churches including a Madonna by Tiepolo 21288

Pinacoteca Giralamo di Giovanni, Piazza dei Costanti, 62032 Camerino - T: 0737402310, Fax: 0737402311, E-mail: rivola@camserv.unicam.it, Internet: http://www.museionline.it. Head: Prof. Pierluigi Falaschi
Fine Arts Museum
13th and 14th c frescoes, ceramics, 14th and 15th c works by the Camerino school 21289

Camogli

Civico Museo Archeologico, Via Ferrari 41, 16032 Camogli - T: 0185729048, Fax: 0185773504. Head: G.B. Roberto Figari
Archaeological Museum - 1980 21290

Museo Civico Marinaro 'Gio-Bono Ferrari', Via Ferrari 41, 16032 Camogli - T: 0185771570. Head: Prospero Schiffino
Science&Tech Museum
Ship models, paintings of Camogli sailing ships, relics of Garibaldi 21291

Campagnano di Roma

Museo Civico Archeologico, C Vittorio Emanuele 2, 00063 Campagnano di Roma - T: 069042588
Local Museum 21292

Campli

Museo Archeologico, P San Francesco, 64012 Campli - T: 0861569158
Local Museum 21293

Campobasso

Museo del Presepio in Miniatura 'Guido Colitti', Piazza della Vittoria 4, 86100 Campobasso - T: 0874413672. Head: Raffaele Colitti
Religious Arts Museum
Manger scenes from all over the world, manger scene postage stamps 21294

Museo Sannitico Provinciale, Via Chiarizia 10, 86100 Campobasso - T: 08744271, Fax: 0874427216. Head: Dr. Angela Di Niro
Archaeological Museum - 1899
Prehistory, Roman archeology, bronzes 21295

Campobello di Mazara

Museo del Lavoro Contadino, 91021 Campobello di Mazara - T: 0924933111
Historical Museum 21296

Camporgiano

Civica Raccolta di Reperti Archeologici e Ceramiche Rinascimentali, Piazza San Giacomo, Torrione Princ. Rocca Estense, 55031 Camporgiano - T: 0583618888
Archaeological Museum 21297

Canino

Museo Archeologico di Vulci, Località Camino, Castello della Badia, 01011 Canino - T: 0761437787. Head: Dr. Anna Maria Sgubini Moretti
Historical Museum 21298

Canosa di Puglia

Museo Civico Archeologico, Via Varrone 45, 70053 Canosa di Puglia - T: 0883663685, Internet: http://www.canusium.it. Head: Sabino Facciolongo
Archaeological Museum
5th-3rd c BC archeology, pottery, bronzes, Roman sculpture and epigraphs, medieval reports 21299

Caorle

Museo Sacro, Piazza Vescovado 1, 30021 Caorle
Religious Arts Museum 21300

Capaccio

Museo Archeologico Nazionale, Paestum, 84047 Capaccio - T: 0828811023
Local Museum 21301

Capena

Museo Archeologico Capenate e Scavi, Lucus Feroniae, Via Tiberina km 18, 00060 Capena
Archaeological Museum 21302

Capo di Ponte

Centro Camuno di Studi Preistorici, Via Marconi 7, 25044 Capo di Ponte - T: 036442091, Fax: 036442572, E-mail: ccspreist@tin.it, Internet: http://www.rockart-ccsp.com. Head: Prof. Emmanuel Anati
Archaeological Museum 21303

Parco Nazionale delle Incisioni Rupestri, Via Naquane, 25044 Capo di Ponte - T: 036442140, Fax: 036442140. Head: Raffaella Poggiani-Keller
Local Museum 21304

Caprera

Museo Garibaldino, Località La Maddalena, 07024 Caprera
Historic Site
Home of Garibaldi, pesonal possessions, his tomb 21305

Caprese

Museo Michelangelo, Via Capoluogo 3, 32033 Caprese - T: 0575793912
Historic Site
Michelangelo's birthplace, reproductions, outdoor exhibition of works by contemporary sculptors - library 21306

Capri

Museo del Centro Caprense Ignazio Cerio, Piazzetta Cerio 5, 80073 Capri - T: 0818376681, Fax: 0818370858, E-mail: centrocaprense@tin.it. Head: Luca Giordano
Local Museum 21307

Museo Diefenbach, Certosa di San Giacomo, 80073 Capri - T: 0818376218
Local Museum 21308

Caprino Veronese

Museo Civico, Palazzo Carlotti-Municipio, Piazza Roma, 6, 37013 Caprino Veronese - T: 0456209911, Fax: 0456230120. Head: Claudio Facchinetti
Local Museum - 1981 21309

Capua

Museo Provinciale Campano, Via Roma 85, 81043 Capua - T: 0823961402, 0823620076, Fax: 0823620035, E-mail: nsfcen@tin.it. Head: Dr. Riccardo Ventre, Prof. Giuseppe Centore
Religious Arts Museum - 1870
Archaeological section, terracottas, vases, medieval sculpture, architecture, painting, local hist - library 21310

Carditello

Museo dell'Agricoltura Meridionale, Casino Reale di Carditello, 80024 Carditello - T: 0823441545
Agriculture Museum 21311

Carignano

Museo Civico Giacomo Rodolfo, Via Braida 50, 10041 Carignano - T: 0119697838. Head: Dr. Piero Colombino
Local Museum 21312

Carmagnola

Museo Civico di Storia Naturale, Cascina Vigna, Via S. Francesco di Sales, 10022 Carmagnola - T: 0119724390, Fax: 0119724310. Head: Giovanni Boano
Natural History Museum - 1973
Italian birds, Italian and mediterranean reptiles, amphibians, mammals, Italian, mediterranean and african insects, Italian fresh-water fishes, pliocene and quaternary fossils, Italian minerals 21313

Carmignano

Museo Archeologico Comunale, Fraz Artimino, 50042 Carmignano - T: 055879174
Archaeological Museum 21314

Carpi

Museo Civico Giulio Ferrari, Piazza dei Martiri 68, 41012 Carpi - T: 059649315, Fax: 059649206. Head: Alfonso Garuti
Local Museum - 1914
15th-20th c Emilian and Venetian paintings, xylography, local artifacts and craft products, local history exhibits, archeology, historic house - library, photo library 21315

Museo della Xilografia Italiana Ugo da Carpi, Castello dei Pio, 41012 Carpi - T: 059649298, Fax: 059649206
Decorative Arts Museum
Wood cuttings, engravings, ex libris - library 21316

Carpineto Romano

Museo Leoniano, Palazzo Pecci, 00032 Carpineto Romano - T: 06979002
Local Museum 21317

Carrara

Museo Civico del Marmo, Viale XX Settembre, 54033 Carrara - T: 0585845746, Fax: 0585845746, E-mail: sbotti@comune.carrara.it, Internet: http://giove.cnuce.cnr.it/Museo.html. Head: Dr. Marina Babboni
Historical Museum
Modern sculpture collection, Roman collection 21318

Pinacoteca dell'Accademia di Belle Arti, Via Roma 1, 54033 Carrara - T: 058571658. Head: Prof. Floriano Bodini
Fine Arts Museum
Marble sculptures of Roman and medieval period, plaster works, picture gallery 21319

Carrara San Giorgio

Air Museum, Via Castello S Pelagio, 35020 Carrara San Giorgio - T: 0499125008
Local Museum 21320

Casale Monferrato

Museo Civico, Via Cavour, 15033 Casale Monferrato - T: 0142444249, Fax: 0142444312. Head: Germana Mazza
Local Museum
Paintings, wood sculpture, numismatics 21321

Museo d'Arte e Storia Antica Ebraica, Vicolo Salomone Olper 44, 15033 Casale Monferrato - T: 014271807, Fax: 08700406942, E-mail: casaebraica@tiscanet.it, Internet: http://www.jewishheritage.org. Head: Prof. Giulio Bourbon
Historical Museum / Fine Arts Museum - 1969
Silverware, silk, bronzes, documents of Hebrew civilization - conference room, archive 21322

Casalmaggiore

Museo Civico Archeologico, Via Cairoli, 26041 Casalmaggiore - T: 037542309
Archaeological Museum 21323

Casalvieri

Museo Civico Padre Michele Jacobelli, Contrada Jacobelli, 03034 Casalvieri - T: 0776693015
Local Museum 21324

Casamari-Veroli

Museo dell'Abbazia, Abbazia di Casamari, 03020 Casamari-Veroli - T: 0775282371, Fax: 0775281020, E-mail: albertocoratti@tin.it. Head: Silvestro Buttarazzi
Local Museum - 1918
Archeological finds, Roman epigraphs, coins, ceramics, sculpture, paintings 21325

Cascia

Pinacoteca Comunale, Palazzo Santi, Piazza A. Maro, 06043 Cascia - T: 074371223
Fine Arts Museum 21326

Caserta

Museo Vanvitelliano, Palazzo Reale, 81100 Caserta - T: 0823321400, Fax: 0823354516. Head: Dr. Vanda Frizzi
Fine Arts Museum - 1947
18-19th c Italian and Dutch paintings - Biblioteca Palatina 21327

Palazzo Reale, Parco della Reggia, 81100 Caserta - T: 0823321127, Fax: 0823354516. Head: Dr. Vanda Ferolla Frizzi
Fine Arts Museum - 1752
18th c architecture, historical garden with rare plants - library 21328

Casola in Lunigiana

Museo del Territorio dell'Alta Valle dell'Aulella, Scuole Medie, 54014 Casola in Lunigiana - T: 058590361. Head: Fabio Baroni
Local Museum - 1976 21329

Casole d'Elsa

Centro d'Arte Verrocchio, Via San Michele 16, 53031 Casole d'Elsa - T: 0577948312
Fine Arts Museum 21330

Sale della Prepositura, Piazza Liberta 5, 53031 Casole d'Elsa - T: 0577948738
Fine Arts Museum
Sculpture, paitings, silverware 21331

Cassano Ionio

Museo Diocesano, Via Mons Occhiuto, 87011 Cassano Ionio - T: 098171048. Head: Prof. Leonardo Alario
Religious Arts Museum 21332

Castagnole delle Lanze

Museo della Civiltà Contadina dell'Alto Monferrato e della Bassa Langa, Via della Mandolera, 14054 Castagnole delle Lanze - T: 0141878231
Historical Museum 21333

Castel del Rio

Museo della Guerra, P della Repubblica, 40022 Castel del Rio - T: 054295554
Local Museum 21334

Castel di Sangro

Raccolta Municipale, Piazza Plebiscito, 67031 Castel di Sangro - T: 0864854949
Local Museum 21335

Castel Sant'Elia

Museo degli Oggetti Sacri, Santuario Pontificio S. Maria delle Rupi, 01030 Castel Sant'Elia - T: 0761557729
Religious Arts Museum - 1950
Religious art, costumes, ornaments, 12th to 15th c mitres 21336

Castelfiorentino

Pinacoteca, Chiesa di Santa Verdiana, Via Timignano 1, 50051 Castelfiorentino - T: 057164096
Fine Arts Museum
13th and 14th c paintings of the Florentine school, illuminated books 21337

Castelfranco Emilia

Raccolta Civica, Corso Martiri 152, 41013 Castelfranco Emilia - T: 059926724
Historic Site 21338

Castelfranco Veneto

Ca' Corner-Tiepolo, Località Sant'Andrea, 31033 Castelfranco Veneto - T: 0424525103. Head: Baldassare Chiminelli
Fine Arts Museum
Greek, Roman and prehistoric works of art, figurative components by Paolo Veronese and other artists of the Venetian school 21339

Casa del Giorgione, Piazzetta Duomo, 31033 Castelfranco Veneto - T: 0423491240, Fax: 0423720144. Head: Dr. Giacinto Cecchetto
Historic Site 21340

Museo Agricolo, Località Sant'Andrea, Via Lama 2, 31033 Castelfranco Veneto - T: 0424525103. Head: Baldassare Chiminelli
Agriculture Museum 21341

Castellammare di Stabia

Scavi di Stabiae, Loc. San Marco, Via Passeggiata Archeologica, 80053 Castellammare di Stabia - T: 0818714541, Fax: 0818714541, Internet: http://www.pompeiisites.org. Head: Prof. Pietro Giovanni Guzzo
Archaeological Museum 21342

Castellanza

Museo d'Arte Moderna Pagani, Via Gerenzano 70, 21053 Castellanza - T: 0331503113
Fine Arts Museum
Contemporary art 21343

Castell'Arquato

Museo della Collegiata, Chiostro della Chiesa dell'Assunta, 29014 Castell'Arquato - T: 0523805151
Religious Arts Museum
In 14th c cloister, goldsmith's work, paintings, sculpture 21344

Museo Geologico, Via Sforza Caolzio 57, 29014 Castell'Arquato - T: 0523804266, Fax: 0523803982, E-mail: castellarquato@agonet.it, Internet: http://www.commune.castellarquato.pc.it. Head: Dr. Carlo Francou
Natural History Museum - 1961
Geology, paleontology, fossils 21345

Museo Illichiano, Piazza del Comune, 29014 Castell'Arquato - T: 0523805161, Fax: 0523803982
Local Museum 21346

Museo Parrocchiale, 29014 Castell'Arquato
Religious Arts Museum 21347

Castelli

Museo della Ceramica di Castelli, Palazzo Comunale, Via Convento, 64041 Castelli - T: 0861979398. Head: Dr. Giovanni Giacomini
Decorative Arts Museum - 1984
15th to 20th c pottery, archeological section - library, archive 21348

Castelnuovo Calcea

Museo di Civiltà Contadina, Via V. Alfieri 19, 14040 Castelnuovo Calcea - T: 0141957148
Historical Museum 21349

Castelsardo

Museo dell'Intreccio, Castello dei Doria, 07031 Castelsardo - T: 079470138
Local Museum 21350

Castelseprio

Zona Archeologica del Castrum, Via Castelvecchio 58, 21050 Castelseprio - T: 0331820438, Fax: 033189404430. Head: Dr. Angela Surace
Archaeological Museum 21351

Castelvecchio

Museo Casa Pascoli, Via Caprona 4, 61030 Castelvecchio
Local Museum 21352

Castelvetrano

Museo Selinuntino, Via Garibaldi 50, 91022 Castelvetrano - T: 0924904932, E-mail: 0924932188. Head: Dr. Giuseppina Accardi
Archaeological Museum - 1873
6th-4th c B.C. Greek ceramics, Corinthian pottery 21353

Castiglion Fiorentino

Pinacoteca Comunale, Via Del Cassero, 52043 Castiglion Fiorentino - T: 0575657466, Fax: 0575659457, E-mail: icec@ats.it, Internet: http://www.unoinformatica.it/cf_home.htm. Head: Pietro Fusi
Fine Arts Museum - 1920
Umbrian 13th c crucifix, 12th to 15h c goldwork and sacred objects, paintings 21354

Castiglione a Casauria

Domus Clementina, Abbazia Clementina, 65020 Castiglione a Casauria - T: 08588434
Fine Arts Museum
Roman archeological finds, medieval pottery, rare books 21355

Castiglione delle Stiviere

Museo Internazionale della Croce Rossa, Via Garibaldi 50, 46043 Castiglione delle Stiviere - T: 0376638505, Fax: 0376631107, E-mail: micr@dsmnet.it, Internet: http://www.dsmnet.it/micr. Head: Maria Grazia Baccolo
Historical Museum
Exhibits concerning the Red Cross from early to present times, prints and photographs - library 21356

Museo Storico Aloisiano, Via Perati 6, 46043 Castiglione delle Stiviere - T: 0376638062, Fax: 0376671226. Head: Ciro Ferrari
Fine Arts Museum / Decorative Arts Museum
16th to 18th c paintings, portraits, furniture, silverware, decorative arts and other possessions of the Gonzaga family 21357

Castiglione di Garfagnana

Museo della Campagna e della Vita di Ieri, Località San Pellegrino in Alpe, Via del Voltone 15, 55033 Castiglione di Garfagnana - T: 0583649072
Local Museum 21358

Castiglione Olona

Museo della Collegiata, Via Cardinal Branda Castiglioni 1, 21043 Castiglione Olona - T: 0331850280. Head: Fabrizio Cuccurullo
Local Museum 21359

Castignano

Museo Diocesano Inercomunale di Arte Sacra, Piazza San Pietro, 63032 Castignano - T: 0735594960, Fax: 0735577246. Head: Dr. Paola Di Girolami
Religious Arts Museum 21360

Castrovillari

Museo Civico, Via Porta della Catena 2, 87012 Castrovillari - T: 098122260
Local Museum
Archeology from prehistoric to medieval times 21361

Catania

Mineralogy, Petrography and Vulcanology Museum, c/o Dept. of Geological Science, University of Catania, Corso Italia 55, 95129 Catania - T: 0957195752, Fax: 0957195760, E-mail: rcristof@mbox.unict.it. Head: Prof. Renato Cristofolini
Natural History Museum
Mineralogical and petrographical and vulcanological Etnean, Eolian and Vesuvian colls, evaporitic minerals, scientific instruments 21362

Museo Civico Belliniano, Piazza San Francesco 3, 95124 Catania - T: 0957150535. Head: Dr. Ettore Pinto
Music Museum - 1923
Autographs and personal possessions in the home of the composer Vincenzo Bellini, historical documents of the post-Risorgimento period - musical library 21363

Museo Civico Castello Ursino, Piazza Federico di Svevia, 95121 Catania - T: 095345830. Head: Dr. Carmelo Russo
Local Museum - 1934
Remains of the Roman theater of Catania, vases, terra cottas, mosaics, sarcophagi, frescoes, sculpture, Byzantine bas-reliefs and epitaphs, armaments, picture gallery, goldsmith work, religious art, Sicilian coins, historic house - library 21364

Museo di Geologia e Paleontologia, Corso Italia 55, 95129 Catania - T: 0957195764, Fax: 0957195790. Head: I. Di Geronimo
Natural History Museum - 1991
Paleozoic, mesozoic and cenozoic fossil fauna of the world 21365

Museo di Vulcanologia, Corso Italia 55, 95129 Catania - T: 095383730. Head: Prof. Sebastiano Italo Di Geronimo
Natural History Museum
Stones of Italian vulcanoes, mainly Mt. Aetna 21366

Museo Zoologico, Via Androne 81, 95124 Catania - T: 095312355, Fax: 095327990. Head: Prof. Giovanni Costa
Natural History Museum
Fauna from the area and other countries, maritime fauna of the Mediterranean Sea 21367

Catanzaro

Museo Provinciale, Villa Trieste, 88100 Catanzaro - T: 0961720019. Head: Giovanni Bruni
Local Museum - 1879
Prehistoric-Roman archeology, pottery, numismatics, 16th-20th c paintings 21368

Cattolica

Galleria Comunale S. Croce, Via Pascoli 21, 47841 Cattolica - T: 0541967559, Fax: 0541967803, E-mail: ccp@cattolica.net, Internet: http://www.cattolica.net. Head: Dr. Francesco Rinaldini
Fine Arts Museum - 1980 21369

Museo della Regina, Via Pascoli 23, 47841 Cattolica - T: 0541831464, Fax: 0541967803, E-mail: ccp@cattolica.net, Internet: http://www.cattolica.net. Head: Dr. Francesco Rinaldini
Archaeological Museum - 1982 21370

Cava dei Tirreni

Museo della Badia, Via Morcaldi 6, 84010 Cava dei Tirreni - T: 089463922. Head: Eugenio Gargiulo
Local Museum
Roman sarcophagi, illuminated manuscripts, paintings, sculpture 21371

Cavalese

Museo della Comunità di Fiemme, Piazza Cesare Battisti 2, 38033 Cavalese - T: 0462340365, Fax: 0462230800. Head: Dr. Carlo Betta
Local Museum - 1950
Folk art, life and work of the inhabitants of the Val di Fiemme 21372

Cavriana

Museo Archeologico Alto Mantovano, Gruppo Archeologico Cavriana, Villa Mirra, Piazza Castello 5, 46040 Cavriana - T: 037682094. Head: Dr. Loris Freddi, Prof. Adalberto Piccoli
Archaeological Museum 21373

Cecina e Marina

Museo Archeologico, Fattoria La Cinquantino, 57023 Cecina e Marina - T: 0586680145, Fax: 0586611208. Head: Beatrice Gori
Archaeological Museum - 1980
Etruscan and Roman archeology 21374

Museo della Vita e del Lavoro, Fattoria La Cinquantina, 57023 Cecina e Marina - T: 0586680145. Head: Beatrice Gori
Agriculture Museum - 1994
library 21375

Cefalù

Museo della Fondazione Mandralisca, Via Madralisca 15, 90015 Cefalù - T: 092121547, Fax: 092121547
Local Museum - 1866
Sicilian coins, Greek vases, paintings including the 'Portrait of a Man' by Antonello da Messina 21376

Celenza Valfortore

Raccolta Comunale, Largo San Nicola 4, 71035 Celenza Valfortore - T: 0881954016
Local Museum 21377

Cento

Galleria d'Arte Moderna Arnoldo Bonzagni, Palazzo del Governatore, Piazza del Guercino, 44042 Cento - T: 051904196, Fax: 051903079. Head: Dr. Fausto Gozzi
Fine Arts Museum 21378

Pinacoteca Civica, Via Matteotti 16, 44042 Cento - T: 051903640, Fax: 051903079. Head: Dr. Fausto Gozzi
Fine Arts Museum 21379

Centuripe

Museo Civico, Via Ss. Crocifisso, 94010 Centuripe - T: 0935919440, Fax: 0935919417. Head: Dr. Rosario Patané
Archaeological Museum / Local Museum - 1926
Local architecture, Greek and Roman statues, terracottas vases 21380

Ceres

Museo delle Valli di Lanzo, Palazzo Municipale, 10070 Ceres - T: 012353316. Head: Prof. Mario Federico Roggero
Local Museum 21381

Cerignola

Museo del Grano, Via San Tommaso d'Aquino 11, 71042 Cerignola - T: 0885414944
Local Museum 21382

Cerreto di Spoleto

Raccolta Etnografica, Via Dante Alighieri, 06040 Cerreto di Spoleto - T: 074391269, Fax: 074391269. Head: Giampiero Bocci, Prof. Cristina Papa, Maurizio Brunacci, Augusto Lucidi
Folklore Museum 21383

Cerreto Guidi

Museo Villa Medicea, Via della Libertà, 50050 Cerreto Guidi - T: 057155707, Fax: 057155228. Head: Francesca Nannelli
Fine Arts Museum - 1978 21384

Certaldo

Casa del Boccaccio, Via Boccaccio, 50052 Certaldo - T: 0571664208. Head: Prof. Francesco Mazzoni
Historic Site - 1956
Coll of Boccacio's works, secondary literature 21385

Museo di Palazzo Pretorio, Piazza del Vicariato, 50052 Certaldo - T: 05716611
Fine Arts Museum 21386

Certosa di Pavia

Museo della Certosa, Palazzo Ducale, Foresteria, 27012 Certosa di Pavia - T: 0382925613
Religious Arts Museum 21387

Cerveteri

Museo Nazionale Cerite, Castello Ruspoli, 00052 Cerveteri - T: 069940001. Head: Dr. Mario Moretti
Archaeological Museum
Findings from the famous Etruscan necropolis 21388

Cervo

Museo Etnografico del Ponente Ligure, Castello Medievale, 18010 Cervo - T: 0183408197
Ethnology Museum 21389

Cesena

Museo aglie Miniere, Formignano Borello, 47023 Cesena - T: 0547355711, 0547372342, Fax: 0547355720, E-mail: info@cesenainvita.it, Internet: http://www.cesenainvita.it
Local Museum
Local history of the miners village 21390

Museo Archeologico, Piazza Bufalini, 47023 Cesena - T: 0547356327, Fax: 0547356329, E-mail: info@cesenainvita.it, Internet: http://www.cesenainvita.it
Archaeological Museum
Prehistoric and Roman archeological findings from the area 21391

Museo degli Strumenti Musicali, Corso Ubaldo Comandini 3, 47023 Cesena - T: 0547355711, Fax: 0547355719, E-mail: info@cesenainvita.it, Internet: http://www.cesenainvita.it
Music Museum
Documents and Music instruments 21392

Museo del Teatro, Piazza Guidazza, 47023 Cesena - T: 0547355724, Fax: 0547355720, E-mail: info@teatrobonei.it, Internet: http://www.teatrobonei.it
Performing Arts Museum
Theater programs 21393

Museo della Centuriazione, San Giorgio, 47023 Cesena - T: 0547325881/82, Fax: 0547355720, E-mail: info@cesenainvita.it, Internet: http://www.cesenainvita.it
Special Museum
Documents of centuriazione 21394

Museo della Civiltà Contadina Romagnola 'Mario Bocchini', Via Cia degli Ordelaffi, 47023 Cesena - T: 054722409. Head: Dr. Ario Franciosi
Ethnology Museum
Domestic utensils, kitchen, weaving, machines, tools, ceramics, various trades, harness 21395

Museo della Rocca (Fortress Museum), Via Cia degli Ordelacci, Rocca Malatestiana, 47023 Cesena - T: 0547356327, Fax: 0547356329, E-mail: info@cesenainvita.it, Internet: http://www.cesenainvita.it
Historical Museum 21396

Museo dell'Immagine, Via Aldini 26, 47023 Cesena - T: 0547355711, Fax: 0547355719, E-mail: info@cesenainvita.it, Internet: http://www.cesenainvita.it
Fine Arts Museum
Cinematographic archives, photographys of scenery, Antonio Pietrangeli, Vittorugo Contino, Gianvittorio Baldi, Corrado Terzi, Vittorio Bonicelli 21397

Museo di Scienze Naturali, Piazza Zangheri 6, 47023 Cesena - T: 0547356327, Fax: 0547356329, E-mail: info@cesenainvita.it, Internet: http://www.cesenainvita.it
Natural History Museum
Scientific instruments, animals, minerals 21398

Museo di Storia dell'Agricoltura, Rocca Malatestiana, Via Cia degli Ordelarfi 8, 47023 Cesena - T: 0547356327, Fax: 0547356329, E-mail: info@cesenainvita.it, Internet: http://www.cesenainvita.it
Agriculture Museum
History of agriculture, viticulture 21399

Museo Storico dell'Antichità → Museo Archeologico

Pinacoteca Comunale, Via Aldini 26, 47023 Cesena - T: 0547355711, 0547355713, Fax: 0547355720, E-mail: info@cesenainvita.it, Internet: http://www.cesenainvita.it. Head: Dr. Ario Franciosi
Fine Arts Museum
Paintings of local artists 21400

Cherasco

Museo Civico G.B. Adriani, Via Ospedale 40, Palazzo Gotti di Salerano, 12062 Cherasco - T: 0172489101, Fax: 0172489674, E-mail: cherasco2000@tin.it, Internet: http://www.cherasco2000.com. Head: Dr. Bruno Taricco
Local Museum - 1898
Roman archeology, miniatures, paintings, engravings, relics, medals and coins - library 21401

Chianciano Terme

Museo d'Arte Sacra, Via Solferino 38, 53042 Chianciano Terme - T: 05783526
Religious Arts Museum 21402

Sala d'Arte Antica, Via Solferino 38, 53042 Chianciano Terme - T: 057830378
Fine Arts Museum
Works of Sienese and Florentine schools on wood and canvas 21403

Chiari

Pinacoteca Repossi, Via Varisco 9, 25032 Chiari - T: 030711816. Head: Dr. Daniela Vitali
Fine Arts Museum - 1854
Paintings, statues, prints of the Venetian and Flemish schools in the 16th c 21404

Chiavari

Galleria di Palazzo Torriglia, Piazza Mazzini 1, 16043 Chiavari - T: 0185310241. Head: Roberto Zolezzi
Fine Arts Museum 21405

Museo Archeologico per la Preistoria e Protostoria del Tigullio, Via Costaguta, 4, 16043 Chiavari - T: 0185320829, E-mail: museoarchiavari@libero.it. Head: Roberto Maggi
Archaeological Museum - 1985
Prehist, local early iron age - library 21406

Chiavenna

Museo della Valchiavenna e Paradiso, Via Quadrio, 23022 Chiavenna - T: 034332821, Fax: 034334334. Head: Anna Francesca Rota
Local Museum
Local history and natural environment of the Chiavenna Valley 21407

Museo Tesoro della Collegiata di San Lorenzo, Piazza Bormetti, Canonica di San Lorenzo, 23022 Chiavenna - T: 034337152, Fax: 034332117. Head: Guido Scaramellini, Ambrogio Balatti
Religious Arts Museum - 1956
Religious art 21408

Chieri

Capitolo del Duomo, Piazza Duomo, 10023 Chieri
Religious Arts Museum
Treasury of the church, 13th to 16th c Flemish goldwork 21409

Museo Civico Archeologico Romano, Via Palazzo di Città 10, 10023 Chieri - T: 0119424818, Fax: 0119470250
Archaeological Museum 21410

Chiesa in Valmalenco

Museo Storico Etnografico Naturalistico della Valmalenco, Piazza SS. Giacomo e Filippo, 23023 Chiesa in Valmalenco - T: 0342451283. Head: Dr. Giancarlo Carrara
Ethnology Museum 21411

Chieti

Museo Archeologico Nazionale, Villa Comunale 3, 66100 Chieti - T: 087165704, Fax: 087165174. Head: Dr. Maria Rita Sanzi
Archaeological Museum - 1957
6th to 5th c B.C. statues, material from prehistoric Abruzzo, sculpture, epigraphs, mosaics, bronzes, pottery, numismatics 21412

Museo d'Arte C. Barbella, Via Cesare De Lollis 10, 66100 Chieti - T: 0871330873. Head: Dr. Bianca De Luca
Fine Arts Museum
Modern and contemporary paintings 21413

Museo Diocesano Teatino, Chiesa di San Domenico, Corso Marrucino 133, 66100 Chieti - T: 0871330734. Head: Giuseppe Antonio Mariani
Religious Arts Museum - 1957
Religious art, sculpture, 16th to 18th c local painting 21414

Museo Nazionale Archeologico dell'Abruzzo, Villa Comunale, 66100 Chieti - T: 08712909. Head: Dr. Giovanni Scichilone
Archaeological Museum 21415

Museo Provinciale, Tempietto Romano, gia Chiesa di S. Paolo, 66100 Chieti. Head: Prof. Desiderato Scenna
Local Museum 21416

Pinacoteca C. Barbella, Palazzo Martinetti, Via C de Lollis 10, 66100 Chieti - T: 087167554. Head: Dr. Bianca De Luca
Fine Arts Museum 21417

Chiomonte

Pinacoteca G.A. Levis e Museo Archeologico, Via Vittorio Emanuele 75, 10050 Chiomonte - T: 012254504. Head: Aureliano Bertone
Fine Arts Museum 21418

Chiusa

Museo Civico Chiusa, Convento dei Cappuccini, 39043 Chiusa - T: 0472846148, Fax: 0472846148. Head: Dr. Christoph Gasser
Local Museum - 1914/92
Sacral and religious art objects from the 15th-19th c, treasure of Loreto (Spanish and Italian artefacts from the 16th-17th c) 21419

Museo del Villaggio, Fraz Gudon, 39043 Chiusa - T: 0472844001. Head: Ferdinand Gasser
Local Museum - 1973 21420

Chiusi Città

Museo Archeologico Nazionale, Via Porsenna, 53043 Chiusi Città - T: 057820177, Fax: 057820177. Head: Mario Iozzo
Archaeological Museum - 1902
Bucchero Vases, "Canopi", Greek and Etruscan ceramics, Bronze Vases, terracotta, Roman statues - restoring lab 21421

Museo della Cattedrale, Piazza Duomo 7, 53043 Chiusi Città - T: 0578226490
Religious Arts Museum - 1984 21422

Museo Etrusco, Piazza della Cattedrale, 53043 Chiusi Città. Head: Prof. Piero Galeotti
Archaeological Museum 21423

Ciano d'Enza

Castello e Rupe di Canossa, Località Canossa, 46026 Ciano d'Enza - T: 0522878295
Historic Site
Archeological material found in the castle, medieval relics, reproductions of documents depicting the history of the castle 21424

Cicciano

Museo Laboratorio, Via G. Marconi 106, 80033 Cicciano - T: 0818248673
Local Museum 21425

Cingoli

Museo Civico, Piazza Vittorio Emanuele II 1, 62011 Cingoli - T: 0733602877. Head: Paolo Appignanesi
Archaeological Museum
Roman and medieval archeology 21426

Cinto Euganeo

Museo di Cava Bomba, Via Bomba 48, 35030 Cinto Euganeo - T: 042994964
Local Museum 21427

Città della Pieve

Museo di Scienze Naturali, Piazza Plebiscito, 06062 Città della Pieve - T: 0578298033
Natural History Museum 21428

Raccolta d'Arte Diocesano, Cattedrale, Piazza Gramsci, 06062 Città della Pieve - T: 0578298166. Head: Francesco Tassini
Religious Arts Museum 21429

Città di Castello

Fondazione Palazzo Albizzini Collezione Burri, Via Albizzini 1, 06012 Città di Castello - T: 0758554649, 0758559848, Fax: 0758554649, 0758559848, E-mail: burriart@tiscalinet.it, Internet: http://www.cdcnet.net/museo_burri. Head: Prof. Nemo Sarteanesi, Prof. Maurizio Calvesi
Fine Arts Museum - 1981/1990
Works by Alberto Burri in the Albizzini palace (works 1948-1989) and former Tobacco barns (works 1970-1993) - library, Burri archive 21430

Museo Capitolare, Cattedrale, 06012 Città di Castello - T: 0758554705. Head: Prof. Nemo Sarteanesi
Religious Arts Museum
Religious gold and silverwork, sacred vestments, paintings, treasury 21431

Museo delle Tradizioni Popolari, Loc. Garavelle, 06012 Città di Castello - T: 0758552119
Ethnology Museum 21432

Pinacoteca Comunale, Via della Cannoniera 22, 06012 Città di Castello - T: 0758554202. Head: Dr. L. Giombini
Fine Arts Museum
Paintings including works by Signorelli and Raphael, classical, medieval, and Renaissance sculpture, works in terra cotta by Della Robbia, goldsmith's art, 16th c furniture 21433

Raccolta Civica, Via delle Giulianelle, 06012 Città di Castello - T: 0758555687
Local Museum 21434

Cittadella

Pinacoteca del Duomo, Via Marconi, 35013 Cittadella - T: 0495970237
Fine Arts Museum 21435

Civiasco

Museo Comunale E. Durio, Via Ercole Durio 6, 13010 Civiasco - T: 016355700, Fax: 016355700
Local Museum 21436

Cividale del Friuli

Museo Archeologico Nazionale, Piazza Duomo 13, 33043 Cividale del Friuli - T: 0432700700, Fax: 0432700751, E-mail: musarcheo.civ@libero.it.
Head: Paola Lopreato
Archaeological Museum - 1820
Archeological remains from prehistoric to medieval periods, medieval goldwork, lapidary, coins, armaments - library 21437

Museo Christiano e Tesoro del Duomo, Piazza Duomo 5, 33043 Cividale del Friuli - T: 0432731144. Head: Luigi Modotti
Religious Arts Museum - 1950
Baptistery by Callisto, altar by Ratchis and decorative fragments (8th-15th c) 21438

Cividate Camuno

Museo Archeologico di Vallecamonica, Via Nazionale, 25040 Cividate Camuno - T: 0364344301
Archaeological Museum
Roman statues, epigraphs, coins and relics of the area 21439

Civita Castellana

Museo Archeologico dell'Agro Falisco, Forte Sangallo, Via del Forte, 01033 Civita Castellana - T: 076153735. Head: Maria Anna De Lucia Brolli
Archaeological Museum
Etruscan material, especially ceramics from the Necropolis of ancient Falerii 21440

Civitanova Alta

Galleria d'Arte Moderna Moretti, Piazza della Libertà 13, 62013 Civitanova Alta - T: 0733890160, Fax: 0733790356. Head: Bianca Maria Pilotti
Fine Arts Museum - 1972 21441

Civitanova Marche

Museo Storico del Trotto, Ctr Asola 2, 62012 Civitanova Marche - T: 073379179
Local Museum 21442

Civitavecchia

Museo Nazionale Archeologico, Largo Cavour 2, 00053 Civitavecchia - T: 076623604. Head: Dr. Ida Caruso
Local Museum 21443

Civitella Alfedena

Museo del Lupo Appenninico, Centro di Visita del Parco d'Abruzzo, Via Santa Lucia, 67030 Civitella Alfedena - T: 0864890141. Head: Franco Tassi
Natural History Museum 21444

Clusone

Museo Sant'Andrea, Piazza Marinoni 6, 24023 Clusone - T: 034621078
Local Museum
Paintings, ancient coins, antique arms and furniture 21445

Codigoro

Museo Pomposiano, Fraz Pomposa, Abbazia di Pomposa, 44021 Codigoro - T: 0533719060
Local Museum 21446

Coldirodi di Sanremo

Pinacoteca e Biblioteca Rambaldi, Piazza San Sebastiano, 18010 Coldirodi di Sanremo - T: 0184670131. Head: Massimo Ricci
Fine Arts Museum - 1865
Paintings, 16th and 17th c Tuscan paintings - library 21447

Colle di Val d'Elsa

Antiquarium Etrusco, Piazza Duomo, 53034 Colle di Val d'Elsa - T: 0577920015
Archaeological Museum
Local Etruscan remains 21448

Museo Civico e Diocesano d'Arte Sacra, Via del Castello, 53034 Colle di Val d'Elsa - T: 0577923888, Fax: 0577912270, E-mail: colleve@edinet.it.
Internet: http://www.collevaldesa.net
Local Museum
Paintings, canvases, 15th to 18th c relics 21449

Museo d'Arte Sacra, Via del Castello 20, 53034 Colle di Val d'Elsa - T: 0577920180
Religious Arts Museum - 1967
14th c frescoes, 15th to 17th c paintings 21450

Museo Etrusco Ranuccio Bianchi Bandinelli, Palazzo Pretorio, Piazza del Duomo, 53034 Colle di Val d'Elsa - T: 0577920015
Archaeological Museum 21451

Collecchio

Raccolta Guatelli, Fraz Ozzano Taro, Via Nazionale, 43044 Collecchio - T: 0521809100
Fine Arts Museum 21452

Collegno

Museo Archeologico Ad Quintum, Via XX Settembre 10, Fraz Regina Margherita, 10093 Collegno - T: 011781327
Archaeological Museum 21453

Collesalvetti

Pinacoteca Civica Carlo Servolini, 57014 Collesalvetti - T: 050962006
Fine Arts Museum 21454

Collodi

Parco Monumentale di Pinocchio, Via San Gennaro, 51014 Collodi - T: 0572429342
Fine Arts Museum
Monuments, statues, mosaics 21455

Cologna Veneta

Museo Civico Archeologico, Piazza Mazzini, 37044 Cologna Veneta - T: 0442410667, Fax: 0442410811. Head: Prof. Dr. Mario Visentin
Local Museum - 1892
Archeology, Roman-medieval marbles, Roman and Venetian coins, relics of the Risorgimento and World War I 21456

Colorno

Museo Etnografico della Civiltà Contadina, Piazzale Veneto, 43052 Colorno - T: 052181318
Ethnology Museum 21457

Comacchio

Museo Alternativo Remo Brindisi, Lidoi di Spina, Via Nicola Pisano 45, 44022 Comacchio - T: 0533330116. Head: Lino Albani
Fine Arts Museum 21458

Como

Civico Museo Storico G. Garibaldi, Piazza Medaglie d'Oro 1, 22100 Como - T: 031271343, Fax: 031268053. Head: Dr. Lanfredo Castelletti
Historical Museum - 1932
History and archives of the Risorgimento and contemporary periods 21459

Museo Civico Archeologico P. Giovio, Piazza Medaglie d'Oro 1, 22100 Como - T: 031271343, Fax: 031268053. Head: Dr. Lanfredo Castelletti
Archaeological Museum - 1872
Prehistoric material, Roman and medieval stone tablets, medieval arms, Greek vessels, Egyptian material - laboratory 21460

Museo Didattico della Seta, Via Valleggio, 22100 Como - T: 031303180, Fax: 031303180
Local Museum / Science&Tech Museum 21461

Pinacoteca Civica in Palazzo Volpi, Via Diaz, 84, 22100 Como - T: 031269869, Fax: 031240303. Head: Dr. Lanfredo Castelletti
Fine Arts Museum - 1989
14th c frescoes, Carolingian and Romanesque sculptures, paintings (17th c), local artists 21462

Tempio Voltiano, Viale Marconi, 22100 Como - T: 031574705
Historic Site - 1927
Memorabilia and relics on the physicist Alessandro Volta (1745-1827), chronological exhibition of inventions 21463

Comunanza

Museo Diocesano Intercomunale di Arte Sacra, Piazza Santa Catarina, 63044 Comunanza - T: 0735594960, Fax: 0735577246. Head: Dr. Paola Di Girolami
Religious Arts Museum
archive 21464

Conegliano

Museo Civico del Castello, Piazzale Castelvecchio, 31015 Conegliano - T: 043822871, Fax: 0438413313, E-mail: servizio.cultura@comune.conegliano.tv.it
Local Museum
Local history, arms, numismatics, art 21465

Conversano

Museo Civico, Monastero di San Benedetto, 70014 Conversano - T: 0804951975, Fax: 0804953351, E-mail: museo.conversano@tiscali.it, Internet: http://www.media.it/comconv. Head: Vito L'Abbate
Local Museum - 1975
"Scene della Gerusalemme Liberata" by the painter Paolo Finoglio (17th c) 21466

Corbetta

Raccolta Archeologica Alberto Pisani Dossi, Via F. Mussi 38, 20011 Corbetta - T: 029778050. Head: Dr. Carola Risani Dossi
Archaeological Museum
1890 21467

Coreglia Antelminelli

Museo della Figurina di Gesso e del Territorio, Via del Mangano 17, 55025 Coreglia Antelminelli - T: 058378082. Head: Dr. Paolo Tagliasacchi
Local Museum 21468

Corfinio

Museo Capitolare delle Antichità Corfiniesi, Cattedrale di San Pelino, 67030 Corfinio - T: 0864728121
Archaeological Museum - 1880
Archeological findings of local excavations, epigraphs, terra cottas, bronzes, antique arms 21469

Correga Ligure

Museo della Cultura Popolare Contadina, Laboratorio Carbuninna, 15060 Correga Ligure - T: 014399197
Historical Museum 21470

Correggio

Museo Civico Il Correggio, Palazzo dei Principi, Corso Cavour 7, 42015 Correggio - T: 0522693296
Fine Arts Museum - 1918
15th-19th c paintings, 16th c Flemish tapestries, historic house 21471

Corridonia

Pinacoteca, Via Cavour 54, 62014 Corridonia - T: 0733431832. Head: Bianca Maria Pilotti
Fine Arts Museum
14th to 16th c paintings 21472

Cortina d'Ampezzo

Collezione Rimoldi, Corso Italia 67, 32043 Cortina d'Ampezzo - T: 0436866222, Fax: 04362269. Head: Prof. Renato Balsamo
Fine Arts Museum
Modern art 21473

Museo de Ra Regoles, Ciasa de Ra Regoles, Via del Parco 1, 32043 Cortina d'Ampezzo - T: 0436866222, Fax: 04362269
Local Museum 21474

Cortona

Museo Archeologico e Paleontologico di Farneta, Fraz Farneta, 52044 Cortona - T: 0575610010
Archaeological Museum - 1963 21475

Museo dell'Accademia Etrusca, Piazza Signorelli, 52044 Cortona - T: 0575630415, Fax: 0575637248, E-mail: visit@accademia-etrusca.net, Internet: http://www.accademia-etrusca.net. Head: Dr. Paolo Bruschetti
Historical Museum - 1727
Egyptian, Etruscan and Roman antiquities, medieval and modern decorative arts, coins, miniatures, costumes 21476

Museo Diocesano, Chiesa del Gesù, Piazza del Duomo 2, 52044 Cortona - T: 057562830. Head: Giovanni Basanieri
Religious Arts Museum - 1946
Religious art, paintings by Beato Angelico, Sassetta, Signorelli and Lorenzetti, Roman sarcophagus, 16th c goldwork 21477

Cosenza

Museo Civico, Piazza XV Marzo, 87100 Cosenza - T: 098473387. Head: Vincenzo Zumbini
Local Museum
Local archeological finds, prehistoric bronzes 21478

Museo dei Vigili Urbani, Piazza dei Bruzi, 87100 Cosenza - T: 098426802
Local Museum 21479

Museo Tesoro dell'Arcivescovado, Curia, Piazza Giano Parrasio, 87100 Cosenza - T: 098424438
Historical Museum 21480

Costigliole d'Asti

Museo delle Contadinerie, Piazza Castello, 14055 Costigliole d'Asti - T: 0141966289
Historical Museum 21481

Cotignola

Museo Luigi Varoli, Via Sforza 24, 48010 Cotignola - T: 054540111
Local Museum 21482

Courmayeur

Museo Alpino Duca degli Abruzzi, Piazza Abbé Henry 2, 11013 Courmayeur - T: 0165842064
Natural History Museum
Flora, fauna and minerals of the area, photographs 21483

Crema

Museo Civico, Via Dante 49, 26013 Crema - T: 0373257161, Fax: 0373894325. Head: Dr. Carlo Piastrella
Local Museum
Local archeology and history, pottery, furniture 21484

Cremona

Museo Berenziano, Seminario Vescovile, Via Milano 5, 26100 Cremona - T: 037220267, 037221350, Fax: 037229135
Local Museum
Archaeology, paintings, sculpture, numismatics 21485

Museo Civico Ala Ponzone, Palazzo Affaitati, Via Ugolani Dati 4, 26100 Cremona - T: 037229349, Fax: 037222464, E-mail: museo.alaponzone@rccr.cremona.it, Internet: http://www.rccr.cremona.it/doc_comu/mus/mus_ala_ponzone.shtm
Fine Arts Museum / Historical Museum / Archaeological Museum - 1842
Paintings, esp works of the 15th through 20th c prints, drawings and miniatures, archeology, local hist of the Risorgimento 21486

Museo Civico di Storia Naturale, Piazza Marconi 5, 26100 Cremona - T: 037223766. Head: Dr. Cinzia Galli
Natural History Museum - 1877
Mineralogy, ornithology, entomology 21487

Museo della Civiltà Contadina della Valpadana, Cascina Cambonino, Via Castelleone, 26100 Cremona - T: 037221411
Historical Museum 21488

Museo Stradivariano, Palazzo Affaitati, Via Ugolani Dati 4, 26100 Cremona - T: 0372407770 0, Fax: 0372407268, E-mail: museo.alaponzone@rccr.cremona.it, Internet: http://www.rccr.cremona.it/doc_comu/mus/mus_stradivar.shtm. Head: Prof. Andrea Mosconi
Music Museum - 1930
Examples of the famous violin maker Stradivari 21489

Crocetta del Montello

Museo Civico di Storia Naturale, Villa Ancillotto, Via Erizzo, 31035 Crocetta del Montello - T: 042386225. Head: Dr. Antonio Paolillo
Natural History Museum 21490

Crodo

Casa Museo della Montagna, Località Viceno, 28036 Crodo - T: 032461003
Local Museum 21491

Crotone

Museo Archeologico Nazionale, Via Risorgimento, 88074 Crotone - T: 096223082, Fax: 096220179. Head: Dr. Roberto Spadea
Archaeological Museum - 1968
Archeological finds from ancient Crotone 21492

Museo Statale di Crotone, Piazza Risorgimento, 88074 Crotone - T: 096223082, Fax: 096220179. Head: Dr. Roberto Spadea
Local Museum - 1968
Prehistory, numismatics, classical archaeology 21493

Cuglieri

Raccolta Archeologica, Viale Regina Margherita, 09073 Cuglieri - T: 078539623
Archaeological Museum 21494

Cuneo

Museo Casa Galimberti, P Galimberti 6, 12100 Cuneo - T: 0171693344
Local Museum 21495

Museo Civico, Via Santa Maria 10, 12100 Cuneo - T: 0171634175, Fax: 017166137, E-mail: museo@comune.cuneo.it, Internet: http://www.comune.cuneo.it. Head: Dr. Mario Cordero, Livio Mano
Local Museum - 1930
Local history, folk art, religious art, local archaeology, costumes - photographic archive, cartographic archive 21496

Cuorgnè

Mostra Permanente Tuttocarlin, Piazza Morgando 1, 10082 Cuorgnè - T: 0124666058
Local Museum 21497

Cupra Marittima

Museo del Territorio, Palazzo Cipoletti, Via Castello (Marano), 63012 Cupra Marittima - T: 0735778561, 0735778622, Fax: 0735778622, E-mail: archeo@siscom.it
Archaeological Museum 21498

Cutigliano

Museo Etnologico della Montagna Pistoiese, Località Rivoreta, 51024 Cutigliano - T: 057368383
Ethnology Museum 21499

Dalmine

Museo del Presepio, Fraz Brembo, Via XXV Aprile 179, 24044 Dalmine - T: 035563383, Fax: 035563383. Head: Claudio Danesi
Decorative Arts Museum 21500

Deruta

Museo delle Maioliche, Piazza dei Consoli, 06053 Deruta - T: 0759711143. Head: Prof. Marsilio Magnini
Decorative Arts Museum
Original antique majolic articles and reproductions 21501

Desenzano del Garda

Villa Romana a Mosaici, Via Scavi Romani, 25015 Desenzano del Garda - T: 0309143547, Fax: 0309906002, E-mail: sop.arch.lomb@inwind.it. Head: Dr. Elisabetta Roffia
Archaeological Museum - 1970
Pottery, frescos, sculptures 21502

Desio

La Miniera, Via Roma 25, 20033 Desio - T: 0362303850
Science&Tech Museum 21503

Diano Marina

Civico Museo Dianese, Corso Garibaldi, 18013 Diano Marina - T: 0183496542
Local Museum 21504

Dogliani

Museo Storico Archeologico G. Gabetti, Palazzo Comunale, 12063 Dogliani - T: 017370107, Fax: 0173721405. Head: Giuseppe Martino
Archaeological Museum 21505

Dolceacqua

Pinacoteca Giovanni Morscio, Via Patrioti Martiri, 18035 Dolceacqua - T: 018436444
Fine Arts Museum 21506

Domodossola

Museo di Palazzo San Francesco, Piazza Convenzione, 28037 Domodossola - T: 0324242232
Natural History Museum
Mineralogy, zoology, botany, ornithology, numismatics, documents on the Simplon tunnel 21507

Museo di Palazzo Silva, Via Paletta 1, 28037 Domodossola - T: 0324242232
Local Museum - 1860
Local history and life, domestic utensils, 16th to 18th c furniture, costumes, Etruscan material 21508

Museo Immaginario, Via Marconi 7, Corso Dissegna, 28037 Domodossola - T: 032440819, Fax: 032442414
Local Museum 21509

Dozza

Museo della Civiltà Contadina, Piazzale Rocca, 40050 Dozza - T: 0542678089, Fax: 0542678270. Head: Laura Baroni
Historical Museum - 1980 21510

Empoli

Museo Casa Busoni, Piazza della Vittoria 16, 50053 Empoli - T: 0571711122, Fax: 057178236, E-mail: info@centrobusoni.org, Internet: http://www.centrobusoni.org. Head: Marco Vincenzi
Historic Site 21511

Museo Civico di Paleontologia, Piazza Farinata degli Uberti no 10, 50053 Empoli - T: 0571707817, Fax: 0571707910
Natural History Museum - 1984
Pliocene Malacofauna of Tuscany - study center 21512

Museo della Collegiata di Santa Andrea Empoli, Piazza della Propositura 3, 50053 Empoli - T: 057176284, E-mail: terredelrinascimento@comune.vinci.fi.it
Fine Arts Museum - 1859
14th to 17th c Tuscan art, frescoes, paintings, sculpture 21513

Museo Diocesano, Annesso alla Collegiata, 50053 Empoli - T: 057172220. Head: Tommaso Del Vivo
Religious Arts Museum 21514

Enna

Museo Alessi, Via Roma 365, 94100 Enna - T: 0935503165, Fax: 0935503165, E-mail: museoalessi@virgilio.it. Head: Domenico La Bianca
Archaeological Museum / Local Museum / Fine Arts Museum 21515

Museo Archeologico, P Mazzini, 94100 Enna - T: 0935500331
Local Museum 21516

Tesoro del Duomo, Piazza Mazzini, 94100 Enna - T: 0935500940
Religious Arts Museum
Cathedral treasury, gold and silverwork 21517

Erba

Museo Civico, Villa Comunale di Crevenna, Via Ugo Foscolo, 22036 Erba - T: 031615282, Fax: 031615202
Archaeological Museum / Historical Museum - 1961
Prehistory, archeology, ancient tombs cut into granite blocks - library 21518

Ercolano

Scavi di Ercolano, Corso Resina, 80056 Ercolano - T: 0817390963, Fax: 0817777167, E-mail: info@pompeiisites.org, Internet: http://www.pompeiisites.org. Head: Prof. Pietro Giovanni Guzzo
Archaeological Museum 21519

Erice

Museo Civico Antonio Cordici, Piazza Municipio, 91016 Erice - T: 0923869258
Local Museum
Marble, deocrative arts, sculpture, 18th c paintings, wax models 21520

Esino Lario

Museo della Grigna, Via Adamello, 22050 Esino Lario - T: 0341860111
Archaeological Museum - 1935
Gallo-Roman archeology, paleontology, folk art 21521

Este

Museo Nazionale Atestino, Via Negri 9c, 35042 Este - T: 04292085, Fax: 0429610168. Head: Dr. Angela Ruta Serafini
Archaeological Museum - 1902
Prehistoric objects, paleo-Venetian antiquities, Roman sections, paintings, mosaics, historic house, ceramics coll - libraries, archives, restoring laboratory 21522

Etroubles

Museo Biblioteca Comunale, Via Gran S Bernardo 1, 11014 Etroubles - T: 016578308
Local Museum 21523

Fabriano

Museo della Carta e della Filigrana (Fabriano Paper and Watermark Museum), Largo Fratelli Spacca, 2, 60044 Fabriano - T: 0732709297, Fax: 0732709240, E-mail: info@museodellacarta.com, Internet: http://www.museodellacarta.com. Head: Prof. Franco Mariani
Science&Tech Museum - 1985
Filigrane (watermarks) 13th-20th c 21524

Pinacoteca Civica Bruno Molajoli, Via del Poio 18, 60044 Fabriano - T: 0732709255. Head: Dr. Giovanni Moretti
Fine Arts Museum - 1862
16th and 17th c Flemish tapestries, paintings and frescoes of the Fabrian school, Romanesque frescoes (13th c), sculptural wooden groups (14th c) 21525

Faenza

Keramikmuseum, Piazza del Popolo 1, 48015 Faenza - T: 054625231
Fine Arts Museum 21526

Museo Archeologico, Corso Mazzini 93, 48018 Faenza - T: 0546681709, Fax: 0546681709. Head: M. Chiara Guarnieri
Archaeological Museum
Archaeological coll 21527

Museo Civico di Scienze Naturali, Via Medaglie d'Oro 51, 48018 Faenza - T: 0546662425, Fax: 0546662425, E-mail: museofa@supereva.it, Internet: http://www.racine.ra.it/provincia/guidamusei/provinciasito/musei/fa2.htm. Head: Dr. Gian Paolo Costa
Natural History Museum
Paleontology with Brisighella's and Oriolo's vertebrate paleofauna, ornitological coll, 2 entomological colls - botanic garden 21528

Museo del Teatro, Palazzo Milzetti, Via Manfredi 14, 48018 Faenza - T: 054621541, Fax: 0546664907, E-mail: ravfa@sbn.provincia.ra.it, Internet: http://www.racine.ra.it/manfrediana. Head: Dr. Anna Rosa Gentilini
Performing Arts Museum - 1932 21529

Museo Internazionale delle Ceramiche, Viale Baccarini 19, 48018 Faenza - T: 054621240, Fax: 054627141, E-mail: micfaenza@provincia.ra.it, Internet: http://www.micfaenza.org. Head: Prof. Gian Carlo Bojani, Dr. Carmen Ravanelli Guidotti
Decorative Arts Museum - 1908
Hist and technique of ceramic manufacture from prehistoric to modern times, Faenza and international pottery - library 21530

Museo Nazionale dell'Età Neoclassica in Romagna, Via Tonducci 15, 48018 Faenza - T: 054626493, Fax: 054626493. Head: Dr. Anna Colombi Ferretti
Decorative Arts Museum / Historic Site 21531

Museo Torricelliano, Corso Garibaldi 2, 48018 Faenza, mail addr: 179, 48018 Faenza - T: 54625499, E-mail: torricelli@mbox.queen.it, Internet: http://www.unipr.it/torricelliana/torricelliana.html. Head: Prof. Anna Trotti-Bertoni
Natural History Museum - 1947
Live and work of the physicist Evangelista Torricelli (1608-1647), barometers, water gauges, astrolabes 21532

Pinacoteca Comunale Faenza, Via Santa Maria dell' Angelo 1, 48018 Faenza - T: 0546660799, Fax: 0546691679, E-mail: pinacoteca@racine.ravenna.it. Head: Dr. Sauro Casadei
Fine Arts Museum - 1879
Roman lapidary, mosaics, medieval architectural decoration, 14th-20th c local paintings 21533

Falerone

Museo Antiquarium, Piazza della Libertà, 63022 Falerone - T: 0734710115
Archaeological Museum
Archaeologic material of the old Faleria 21534

Museo Civico e Teatro e Serbatoio Romano, Palazzo Comunale, 63022 Falerone
Local Museum
Roman archeology, remains of a Roman theatre, epigraphs, urns 21535

Fano

Museo Civico e Pinacoteca del Palazzo Malatestiano, Piazza xx Settembre 1, 61032 Fano - T: 0721828362. Head: Prof. Franco Battistelli
Local Museum - 1928
15th to 18th c paintings, local relics, numismatics, pottery 21536

Farra d'Isonzo

Museo di Documentazione della Civilta Contadina Friulana, Via Monte Fortino 2, 34070 Farra d'Isonzo - T: 0481888567
Local Museum 21537

Fasano-Savelletri

Museo Archeologico di Egnazia, Via Egnazia 87, 72015 Fasano-Savelletri - T: 0804829056, Fax: 0804829056, Internet: http://www.egnazia.3000.it. Head: Angela Cinquepalmi
Archaeological Museum - 1978 21538

Favara

Museo Comunale A. Mendola, Piazza Cavour 56, 92026 Favara - T: 092234233. Head: Filippo Ferdinando Cilona
Natural History Museum
Minerals, volcanic stones (Vesuvius 1906), stuffed birds and animals, African objects 21539

Feltre

Galleria d'Arte Moderna Carlo Rizzarda, Via del Paradiso 8, 32032 Feltre - T: 0439885241, Fax: 0439885246. Head: Nicoletta Comar
Fine Arts Museum - 1931
Wrought-iron objects by Carlo Rizzarda, 19th and 20th c paintings and sculpture 21540

Museo Civico, Via Luzzo 23, 32032 Feltre - T: 0439885242, Fax: 0439885246. Head: Anna Paola Zugni Tauro
Local Museum - 1903
Roman archeology, local hist, paintings of the Venetian school and antique local furniture 21541

Museo dei Ferri Battuti e Galleria d'Arte Moderna Carlo Rizzarda, Via Paradiso, 32032 Feltre - T: 043989736. Head: Anna Paola Zugni Tauro
Fine Arts Museum 21542

Fénis

Museo del Castello di Fénis, 11020 Fénis - T: 016567963
Local Museum - 1935
Valdostan furniture, domestic utensils, architecture 21543

Ferentino

Museo Civico, Piazzale del Collegio, 03013 Ferentino - T: 0775244001
Local Museum
Local archeology and history 21544

Fermo

Istituto Geografico Polare Silvio Zavatti, Villa Vitali, Viale Trento 29, 63023 Fermo - T: 0734226166, Fax: 0734226166. Head: Gianluca Frinchillucci
Ethnology Museum
Geological samples, Arctic plants and fishes, Eskimo carved ivories, tools, whip for huskies, folk art of the Lapp people, caribou skull - library 21545

Museo Archeologico-Pinacoteca Communale, I Calzecchi Onesti, 63023 Fermo - T: 0734284327, Fax: 0734215231, E-mail: museidifermo@libero.it, Internet: http://www.sistemamuseo.it. Head: Daniela Alessandrini
Local Museum - 1890
Archeology, Roman bronzes, furniture, porcelain, pottery 21546

Museo di Scienze Naturali Tommaso Salvadori, Villa Vitali, Viale Trento 29, 63023 Fermo - T: 0734226166. Head: Dr. Giuliano Liberini
Natural History Museum 21547

Museo Polare → Istituto Geografico Polare Silvio Zavatti

Pinacoteca Comunale, Piazza del Popolo 1, 63023 Fermo - T: 0734284327, Fax: 0734215231, E-mail: museidifermo@libero.it, Internet: http://www.sistemamuseo.it. Head: Daniela Alessandrini
Fine Arts Museum 21548

Ferrara

Casa dell'Ariosto, Via Ariosto 67, 44100 Ferrara - T: 0532208564, Fax: 0532247248. Head: Dr. Anna Maria Visser
Historic Site
The house where the poet Ludovico Ariosto (1474-1533) spent the last years of his live - library (temporarily closed due to restoration) 21549

Casa Romei, Via Savonarola 28, 44100 Ferrara - T: 053240341
Fine Arts Museum - 1952 21550

Civico Museo di Storia Naturale, Via de Pisis 24, 44100 Ferrara - T: 0532203381, Fax: 0532210508, E-mail: museo.storianaturale@comune.fe.it, Internet: http://www.comune.fe.it/storianaturale/index. Head: Dr. Fausto Pesarini
Natural History Museum - 1865
Zoology, mineralogy, geology, paleontology 21551

Museo Civico di Schifanoia, Via Scandiana 23, 44100 Ferrara - T: 053264178, Fax: 0532232944, E-mail: arteantica@comune.fe.it, Internet: http://www.comune.fe.it/musei_aa/schifanoia.htm. Head: Dr. Andrea Buzzoni
Local Museum
14th c Ferrara frescos, Renaissance ceramics, bronzes, coins, codices 21552

Museo d'Arte Moderna e Contemporanea, Palazzo Massari, Corso Porta Mare 9, 44100 Ferrara - T: 0532248303, Fax: 0532205035. Head: Dr. Andrea Buzzoni
Fine Arts Museum - 1994
Fine arts - library 21553

Museo del Duomo, Piazza Cattedrale, 44100 Ferrara - T: 053232969. Head: Vittorio Felisati
Religious Arts Museum
Illuminated hymn books, Flemish tapestries, silver reliquaries 21554

Museo del Risorgimento e della Resistenza, Corso Ercole I d'Este 19, 44100 Ferrara - T: 0532205480, Fax: 0532903586. Head: Gian Paolo Borghi
Historical Museum
Local documents and biographies on the history of the Risorgimento 21555

Museo Giovanni Boldini, Palazzo Massari, Corso Porta Mare 9, 44100 Ferrara - T: 0532248303, Fax: 0532205035. Head: Andrea Buzzoni
Fine Arts Museum - 1935
Works and personal possessions of the Ferrara painter Giovanni Boldini (1842-1931), picture gallery 21556

Museo Lapidario, Via Camposabbionario 1, 44100 Ferrara - T: 053264178, Fax: 0532232944, E-mail: arteantice@comune.fe.it, Internet: http://www.comune.fe.it/musei_aa/schifanoia.htm. Head: Dr. Andrea Buzzoni
Archaeological Museum
Local archaeological finds, antique marbles, Roman epitaphs 21557

Museo Nazionale Archeologico, Via XX Settembre 124, 44100 Ferrara - T: 053266299, Fax: 0532741270
Archaeological Museum - 1935
Pottery from the ancient necropolis of the Graeco-Etruscan city of Spina 21558

Palazzina Marfisa, Corso Giovecca 170, 44100 Ferrara - T: 0532207450, Fax: 0532232944, E-mail: arteantica.comfe@fe.nettuno.it, Internet: http://www.comune.fe.it/musei_aa/schifancia.htm. Head: Dr. Andrea Buzzoni
Decorative Arts Museum / Fine Arts Museum
Original furniture, paintings and musical instruments in a 16th c aristocrat's house 21559

Pinacoteca Nazionale, Corso Ercole I d'Este 31, 44100 Ferrara - T: 0532205844, Fax: 0532204857. Head: Dr. Grazia Agostini
Fine Arts Museum - 1836
14th to 20th c Ferrara painting 21560

Fidenza

Museo Storico del Risorgimento L. Musini, Via Berenini 134, 43036 Fidenza - T: 0524526365. Head: Dr. Carla Cropera
Historical Museum
Local documents on the Risorgimento and World War I 21561

Fiesole

Museo Bandini, Via Giovanni Dupré, 50014 Fiesole - T: 05559477, Fax: 05559080, E-mail: fiesolemusei@tin.it
Fine Arts Museum - 1913
Tuscan paintings, sculpture, della Robbia terracotta works, 15th-17th c paintings 21562

Museo Civico Archeologico, Via Portigiani 1, 50014 Fiesole - T: 05559477, Fax: 05559080, E-mail: fiesolemusei@tin.it, Internet: http://www.ups.it/propart/museo-archeo-fiesole. Head: Dr. Marco De Marco
Archaeological Museum - 1914
Etruscan and Roman finds, urns, pottery, bronzes, sculpture, bones and pottery of the Longobardo region 21563

Museo Dupré, Via Dupré 19, 50014 Fiesole - T: 05559171. Head: Maria Grazia Gardi Dupré
Fine Arts Museum - 1975
Original plaster casts for the sculptures of Giovanni and Amalia Dupré 21564

Museo Etnologico Missionario, Convento San Francesco, 50014 Fiesole - T: 05559175. Head: Dr. Pietro Bragagnolo
Decorative Arts Museum - 1922
Egyptian, Etrusco-Roman and Chinese decorative arts 21565

Figline di Prato

Antiquarium, Pieve di San Pietro, 50040 Figline di Prato - T: 0574460555
Local Museum
Medieval pottery, 15th and 16th c paintings, decorative arts 21566

Museo della Pieve di San Pietro, Via della Chiesa, 50040 Figline di Prato - T: 0574460555
Religious Arts Museum 21567

Filottrano

Museo del Biroccio, Via Beltrami 2, 60024 Filottrano - T: 0717221314. Head: Dr. Glauco Luchetti
Agriculture Museum - 1967 21568

Finale Emilia

Museo Civico, Via Trento Trieste 4b, 41034 Finale Emilia - T: 0535788332. Head: Roberto Ferraresi
Local Museum - 1993
Mineralogy, paleontology, medieval archeology, natural history, ethnology 21569

Museo del Territorio, Viale Stazione, 41034 Finale Emilia - T: 0535788332. Head: Roberto Ferarresi
Historical Museum - 1992
Local and regional history 21570

Museo di Mineralogia e Paleontologia, Via Trento e Trieste 2b, 41034 Finale Emilia - T: 053593509
Local Museum 21571

Finale Ligure

Civico Museo del Finale, Piazza S. Caterina, 17024 Finale Ligure - T: 019690020, Fax: 019681022. Head: Oscar Giuggiola
Archaeological Museum - 1931
Prehistoric archaeology, classic hist, finds from excavations in caves of Finale - library 21572

Firenze

Appartamenti Monumentali, Palazzo Pitti, 50125 Firenze - T: 0552388611, Fax: 0552388613, E-mail: galleriapalatina.galleri@tin.it. Head: Dr. Marco Chiarini
Historical Museum
18th and 19th c furniture and decorations in a 15th c palace, Boboli-gardens 21573

Biblioteca Medicea Laurenziana, Piazza San Lorenzo 9, 50123 Firenze - T: 055210760, 0552111590, 055214443, Fax: 0552302992, E-mail: medicea@unifi.it, Internet: http://www.bml.firenze.sbn.it. Head: Dr. Franca Arduini
Historical Museum / Historic Site - 1571
Greek, Latin, Arab, Hebrew, Persian, Italian, French manuscripts, incunabula, 15th-16th c miniatures, maps, architecture by Michelangelo - library 21574

Capella Brancacci, Piazza del Carmine, Chiesa di Santa Maria, 50124 Firenze - T: 0552382195
Religious Arts Museum 21575

Capelle Medicee, Piazza Madonna degli Aldobrandini 6, 50123 Firenze - T: 0552388602. Head: Licia Bertani
Local Museum 21576

Casa Buonarroti, Via Ghibellina 70, 50122 Firenze - T: 055241752, Fax: 055241698, E-mail: ente@casabuonarroti.it, Internet: http://www.casabuonarroti.it. Head: Dr. Pina Ragionieri
Fine Arts Museum - 1858
Early bas-reliefs, sculptures and drawings by Michelangelo Buonarroti (1475-1564) 21577

Casa di Dante, Via Santa Margherita 1, 50122 Firenze - T: 055283343
Historic Site
Reproductions of documents and memorabilia of Dante's life 21578

Cenacolo del Ghirlandaio, Borgognissanti 42, 50123 Firenze - T: 0552396802
Fine Arts Museum
Coll of paintings by Domenico Ghirlandaio 21579

Cenacolo di San Salvi, Via San Salvi 16, 50135 Firenze - T: 0552388603. Head: Dr. Fausta Navarro
Fine Arts Museum - 1820
16th-18th c paintings, 16th c sculpture and frescos 21580

Cenacolo di Sant'Apollonia, Via XXVII Aprile 1, 50129 Firenze - T: 0552388607, Fax: 0552388699, E-mail: segreteria@sbas.firenze.it, Internet: http://www.sbas.firenze.it. Head: Dr. Rosanna Caterina Proto Pisani
Religious Arts Museum - 1891
15th c frescos and religious art, in a refectory 21581

Cenacolo di Santo Spirito e Fondazione Romano → Fondazione Romano nel Cenacolo di Santo Spirito

Chiesa di Santa Maria Maddalena de Pazzi, Sala Capitolare Crocifissione del Perugino, Borgo Pinti 58, 50121 Firenze - T: 0552478420
Religious Arts Museum
Detached frescoes, paintings by Perugino and his school 21582

Chiostro dello Scalzo, Via Cavour 69, 50129 Firenze - T: 0552388604, Fax: 0552388699, E-mail: segreteria@sbas.firenze.it, Internet: http://www.sbas.firenze.it. Head: Dr. Rosanna Caterina Proto Pisani
Religious Arts Museum 21583

Convento dell'ex-Convento di Sant'Onofrio detto di Fuligno, Via Faenza 48, 50123 Firenze - T: 055286982, Fax: 0552388699, E-mail: segreteria@sbas.firenze.it, Internet: http://www.sbas.firenze.it. Head: Dr. Rosanna Caterina Proto Pisani
Religious Arts Museum - 1855
Refectory with a fresco by Perugino 21584

Donazione Palazzina della Meridiana, Palazzo Pitti, 50125 Firenze - T: 05523885, Fax: 0552388699. Head: Dr. Annamaria Petrioli Tofani
Fine Arts Museum - 1974
Painting, sculpture, furniture, decorative arts 21585

Fondazione Romano nel Cenacolo di Santo Spirito, Piazza Santo Spirito 29, 50125 Firenze - T: 055287043, E-mail: gestione.musei@comune.firenze.it. Head: Dr. Fiorenza Scalia
Religious Arts Museum - 1946
Frescoes, stuccoes, marbles, 11th to 15th c sculptures in the Romano coll including works by Donatello, in a refectory 21586

Fototeca Archivi Alinari, Via della Vigna Nuova 16, 50123 Firenze - T: 055213370, Fax: 055218975
Local Museum 21587

Gabinetto Disegni e Stampe degli Uffizi, Via della Ninna 5, 50122 Firenze - T: 0552388671. Head: Dr. Annamaria Petrioli Tofani
Fine Arts Museum
Prints and drawings 21588

Gabinetto Fotografico, Soprintendenza ai Beni Artistici e Storici, Via Della Ninna 5, 50122 Firenze - T: 05523885, Fax: 0552388699. Head: Dr. Antonio Paolucci
Fine Arts Museum - 1906 21589

Galleria Corsini, Via Parione 11, 50123 Firenze - T: 055450752. Head: Principessa Corsini
Fine Arts Museum 21590

Galleria d'Arte Moderna, Palazzo Pitti, Piazza Pitti 1, 50125 Firenze - T: 055287096. Head: Dr. Ettore Spalletti
Fine Arts Museum - 1924
Italian, mainly Tuscan art of the 19th to 20th c 21591

Galleria degli Uffizi, Piazzale degli Uffizi, 50122 Firenze - T: 0552388651/52, Fax: 0552388694, E-mail: direzione.uffizi@tin.it, Internet: http://www.musa.uffizi.firenze.it. Head: Dr. Annamaria Petrioli Tofani
Fine Arts Museum - 1581
Tuscan, Florentine, Venetian paintings (13th-18th c) incl works by Giotto, Botticelli, Leonardo da Vinci, Masaccio, Fra Angelico, Lippi, Raphael, Titian, paintings by Flemish and German masters, classical sculpture, artists' self-portraits 21592

Galleria del Costume, Palazzo Pitti, 50125 Firenze - T: 0552388713, Fax: 0552388713. Head: Dr. Carlo Sisi
Historical Museum
Period costumes, principally from the 18th to 20th c, fashion accessories 21593

Galleria dell'Accademia, Via Riscasoli 58-60, 50122 Firenze - T: 0552388612, 0552388609, Fax: 0552388609, E-mail: galleriaaccademia@sbas.firenze.it, Internet: http://www.sbas.firenze.it/musei/acca01.htm. Head: Dr. Franca Falletti
Fine Arts Museum - 1784
13th to 16th c paintings, mainly by Tuscan masters, 'David' and six other sculptures by Michelangelo Buonarroti, 19th c plaster models, Russian icons, ancient musical instruments 21594

Galleria dello Spedale degli Innocenti, Piazza Santissima Annunziata 12, 50122 Firenze - T: 0552491708, 0552037323; 0552037308, Fax: 055241663, E-mail: sartini@istitutodegliinnocenti.it, Internet: http://www.istitutodegliinnocenti.it. Head: Giovanni Faenzi
Religious Arts Museum - 1971
Religious painting, works by Ghirlandaio, Luca della Robbia, Piero di Cosimo, Sandro Botticelli, detached frescos, enameled terracotta, building by Filippo Brunelleschi - historical archive 21595

Galleria Palatina, Palazzo Pitti, Piazza Pitti 1, 50125 Firenze - T: 0552388611, Fax: 0552388613, E-mail: galleriapalatina.galleri@tin.it. Head: Dr. Marco Chiarini
Fine Arts Museum
15th to 18th c paintings including Raphael, Titian, Tintoretto, Rubens, van Dyck, Velasquez, 18th and 19th c furniture 21596

Galleria Rinaldo Carnielo, Piazza Savonarola 3, 50132 Firenze - T: 0552398483, Fax: 055288049. Head: Dr. Fiorenza Scalia
Fine Arts Museum
Works by the sculptor Rinaldo Carnielo (1853-1910) 21597

Giardino di Boboli, Piazza Pitti, 50125 Firenze - T: 055218741. Head: Dr. Litta Medri
Open Air Museum 21598

Gipsoteca Istituto d'Arte, Piazzale di Porta Romana 9, 50125 Firenze - T: 055220521, Fax: 0552299809, E-mail: istitutoarte@isa.firenze.it, Internet: http://www.isa.firenze.it. Head: Maria Anna Franceschini
Fine Arts Museum 21599

Istituto e Museo di Storia della Scienza (Museum of History of Science), Piazza dei Giudici 1, 50122 Firenze - T: 055265311, Fax: 0552653130, E-mail: imss@galileo.imss.firenze.it, Internet: http://www.imss.fi.it. Head: Prof. Paolo Galluzzi
Science&Tech Museum - 1927
Astronomy, medicine, physics, historic instruments, optics, mathematics, chemistry, pharmacy - library, archive 21600

Mostra Permanente di Xilografie di Pietro Parigi, Piazza Santa Croce 16, 50122 Firenze - T: 055242783, Fax: 0552480337. Head: Massimiliano G. Rosito
Fine Arts Museum - 1980
library, archive 21601

Musée du Regiment GG.FF., del Drago D'Oro 7, 50124 Firenze - T: 055588104. Head: Antonio Cioci
Military Museum 21602

Museo Archeologico, Via della Colonna 38, 50121 Firenze - T: 05523575, Fax: 055242213. Head: Dr. Francesco Nicosia
Archaeological Museum - 1870
Egyptian, Etruscan and Greco-Roman archeology - library 21603

Museo Bardini, Piazza dei Mozzi 1, 50125 Firenze - T: 0552342427, Fax: 0552625984, E-mail: gestione.musei@comune.firenze.it. Head: Dr. Chiaretta Silla
Fine Arts Museum - 1922
Greek, Roman and medieval sculptures, 14th to 18th c paintings, Renaissance furniture, Oriental rugs, 16th to 18th c weapons 21604

Museo degli Argenti, Museum of Silver, Palazzo Pitti, Piazza Pitti 1, 50125 Firenze - T: 0552388709/761, Fax: 0552388710, E-mail: argenti@sbas.firenze.it. Head: Dr. Marilena Mosco
Decorative Arts Museum - 1919
17th c frescoes, decorative arts, applied arts, jewelry made of precious stones, amber, ivory, gold and silver 21605

Museo del Bigallo, Piazza S. Giovanni 1, 50129 Firenze - T: 0552302885, Fax: 0552302898, E-mail: opera@operaduomo.firenze.it, Internet: http://www.operaduomo.firenze.it. Head: Alfredo Bardazzi
Fine Arts Museum 21606

Museo delle Carrozze, Palazzo Pitti, Piazza Pitti 1, 50125 Firenze - T: 0552388611, 0552388613, Fax: 0552388613
Decorative Arts Museum
Coaches and harnesses of the early 18th c 21607

Museo delle Porcellane, Palazzo Pitti, Piazza Pitti 1, 50125 Firenze - T: 0552388709/761, Fax: 0552388710, E-mail: argenti@sbas.firenze.it. Head: Dr. Marilena Mosco
Decorative Arts Museum - 1963
European porcelain (Napoli, Doccia, Vincennes, Sèvres, Paris, Vienna, Meissen, Berlin, Nymphenburg, Frankenthal) of the 18th and 19th c 21608

Museo dell'Opera di Santa Croce, Piazza Santa Croce 16, 50122 Firenze - T: 0552466105, Fax: 0552466105, E-mail: operasantacroce@tin.it. Head: Dr. Lapo Mazzei
Religious Arts Museum
Cloisters, Chapel of the Pazzi by Brunelleschi (1376-1446), 14th c detached frescoes, Tuscan paintings, Crocifisso di Cimabue 21609

Museo dell'Opera di Santa Maria del Fiore, Piazza Duomo 9, 50122 Firenze - T: 0552302885, Fax: 0552302898, E-mail: opera@operaduomo.firenze.it, Internet: http://www.operaduomo.firenze.it. Head: Dr. Patrizio Osticresi
Fine Arts Museum - 1891
Florentine sculpture, hist and treasury of Cathedral, Michelangelo, Donatello, Arnolfo Di Cambio, Luca Della Robbia, Lorenzo Ghiberti, Filippo Brunelleschi 21610

Museo dell'Opificio delle Pietre Dure, Via degli Alfani 78, 50121 Firenze - T: 05526511, Fax: 055287123. Head: Dr. Giorgio Bonsanti, Dr. Annamaria Giusti
Science&Tech Museum - 1952
Tools and artifacts of stone and semi-precious stones from the 16th to 19th c 21611

Museo di Antropologia ed Etnologia, Via del Proconsolo 12, 50122 Firenze - T: 0552396449, Fax: 055219438, E-mail: musant@unifi.it, Internet: http://www.unifi.it/msn/antrop. Head: Prof. Brunetto Chiarelli
Ethnology Museum - 1869
Skulls of different races, ethnographic objects of Asia, Africa, America, Oceania 21612

Museo di Palazzo Strozzi, Piazza Strozzi, 50123 Firenze - T: 055288342
Fine Arts Museum
History of the Strozzi family and about the construction of their house 21613

Museo di San Marco, Piazza San Marco 3, 50121 Firenze - T: 0552388608, Fax: 0552388704. Head: Dr. Magnolia Scudieri, Dr. Giovanna Rasario
Fine Arts Museum - 1869
Fra Angelico's (1387-1455) frescos and paintings in the Monastery of San Marco, Fra Bartolomeo and the School of San Marco, Domenico Ghirlandaio ('Ultima Cena'), coll of liturgical codices from the 13th-16th c 21614

Museo di Storia della Fotografia Fratelli Alinari, Largo Fratelli Alinari 15, 50123 Firenze - T: 0552395217, Fax: 0552382857, E-mail: museum@alinari.it, Internet: http://www.alinari.it. Head: Claudio De Polo
Fine Arts Museum - 1985 21615

Museo di Storia Naturale Sezione Botanica, Via la Pira 4, 50121 Firenze - T: 0552757462, Fax: 055289006, E-mail: musbot@cesit1.unifi.it, Internet: http://www.unifi.it/msn. Head: Prof. Mauro Raffaell
Natural History Museum - 1842
Herbaria (3,800,000 specimens), historical herbaria, wax models of plants from the 19th c, xylotheca, fossils, materials from plant sources, drawings and manuscripts of famous Italian botanists - library 21616

Museo di Storia Naturale Sezione Geologia e Paleontologia, Via la Pira 4, 50121 Firenze - T: 0552757536, Fax: 055218628, E-mail: muspal@cesit1.unifl.it. Head: Prof. Danilo Torre
Natural History Museum - 1775
Geology, paleontology, fossils - library 21617

Museo di Storia Naturale Sezione Mineralogia, Via la Pira 4, 50121 Firenze - T: 0552757537, Fax: 0552757455, E-mail: musminfi@unifi.it, Internet: http://www.unifi.it/unifi/msn. Head: Curzio Cipriani
Natural History Museum - 1775
Minerals, stones, gems, petrography 21618

Museo di Storia Naturale, Sezione Zoologica La Specola dell'Università degli Studi di Firenze, Via Romana 17, 50125 Firenze - T: 0552288251, Fax: 055225325, E-mail: specola@specola.unifi.it, Internet: http://www.unifit.it/msn. Head: Prof. Marco Vannini
Natural History Museum - 1775
Zoology, anatomic wax preparations 21619

Museo e Chiostri Monumentali di Santa Maria Novella, Piazza Santa Maria Novella, 50123 Firenze - T: 055282187, Fax: 0552625984, E-mail: gestione.musei@comune.firenze.it. Head: Dr. Chiaretta Silla
Religious Arts Museum
Frescos by Paolo Uccello and Andrea di Bonaiuto 21620

Museo e Istituto Florentino di Preistoria, Via San Egidio, 21, 50122 Firenze - T: 055295159, Fax: 055295159. Head: Prof. Francesco Adorno
Archaeological Museum - 1946
Prehistoric finds from all continents 21621

Museo Horne, Fondazione Horne, Via dei Benci 6, 50122 Firenze - T: 055244661. Head: Ugo Procacci
Decorative Arts Museum
Furniture and decorative arts of the 14th to 16th c, painting 21622

Museo Marino Marini, Piazza di San Pancrazio, 50123 Firenze - T: 0552219432, Fax: 055289510, E-mail: museomarinomarini@tiscalinet.it, Internet: http://www.museomarinomarini.it. Head: Dr. Carlo Sisi
Fine Arts Museum 21623

Museo Mediceo della Petraia e Giardino, Via della Petraia 40, 50141 Firenze - T: 055451208. Head: Dr. Isabella Lapi Ballerini
Fine Arts Museum 21624

Museo Nazionale del Bargello, Via del Proconsolo 4, 50122 Firenze - T: 0552388606, Fax: 0552388756, E-mail: museobargello@libero.it. Head: Dr. Beatrice Paolozzi Strozzi
Fine Arts Museum - 1859
14th to 17th c Tuscan sculpture including works by Michelangelo, Cellini and Donatello, applied arts, medals, armaments 21625

Museo Stibbert, Via Frederico Stibbert 26, 50134 Firenze - T: 055486049, Fax: 055486049. Head: Dr. Kirsten Aschengreen Piacenti
Decorative Arts Museum - 1909
European and Oriental armaments, costumes, carpets, tapestries, furniture, porcelain - library 21626

Museo Storico-topografico, Firenze Com'era, Via dell'Oriolo 24, 50122 Firenze - T: 0552616545, Fax: 0552625984, E-mail: gestione.musei@comune.firenze.it, Internet: http://giubileo.comune.fi.it/musei/firenzecomera. Head:

Dr. Chiara Silla
Fine Arts Museum - 1909
Topographical drawings, paintings and prints illustrating the history of Florence 21627

Palazzo Medici Riccardi, Via Cavour 3, 50129 Firenze - T: 0552760340, Fax: 0552760451, E-mail: a.belisario@provincia.fr.it, Internet: http://www.palazzo-medici.it. Head: Alessandro Belisario
Fine Arts Museum
Chapel built by Michelozzo with frescoes by Benozzo Gozzoli (1459), frescoes by Luca Giordano (1680) 21628

Palazzo Vecchio, Piazza della Signoria, 50122 Firenze - T: 05527681, 0552768325, Fax: 0552625984, E-mail: gestione.musei@comune.firenze.it. Head: Dr. Chiaretta Silla
Fine Arts Museum - 1299/1909
14th c palace, Hall of the 'Cinquecento', frescos by Vasari, 14th to 16th c painting and sculpture 21629

Raccolta Alberto Della Ragione e Collezioni del Novecento, Piazza della Signoria 5, 50122 Firenze - T: 055283078, Fax: 0552625984, E-mail: gestione.musei@comune.firenze.it. Head: Dr. Chiara Silla
Fine Arts Museum - 1970
20th c painting and sculpture 21630

Salone Villa Romana, Via Senese 68, 50124 Firenze - T: 055221654
Public Gallery 21631

Fiumicino

Museo delle Navi, Via Alessandro Guidoni, 00054 Fiumicino - T: 066529192, 0665010089
Science&Tech Museum 21632

Foggia

Museo Civico, Piazza V. Nigri 1, 71100 Foggia - T: 0881726245, 0881771823, Fax: 0881673883. Head: Gloria Fazia
Local Museum - 1931 21633

Foligno

Museo Archeologico, Palazzo Trinci, Piazza della Repubblica, 06034 Foligno - T: 0742350734. Head: Piero Lai
Archaeological Museum
Archeological remains of the pre-Roman and Roman period, frescoes, decorations 21634

Follonica

Museo Archeologico, Ex Officine Meccaniche Ilva, 58022 Follonica - T: 056643506
Archaeological Museum 21635

Museo del Ferro e della Ghisa, Ex Officine Meccaniche Ilva, 58022 Follonica - T: 056643506
Science&Tech Museum 21636

Museo del Lavoro, Ex Officine Meccaniche Ilvo, 58022 Follonica - T: 056643506
Local Museum 21637

Museo di Storia Naturale, Ex Officine Meccaniche Ilva, 58022 Follonica - T: 056643506
Natural History Museum 21638

Fondi

Antiquarium, Chiostro di San Francesco, Piazza IV Novembre, 04022 Fondi - T: 0771503604
Local Museum - 1952
Epigraphs, local historic architecture, sculpture coll in a cloister 21639

Fontanellato

Rocca Sanvitale, Piazza Matteotti 1, 43012 Fontanellato - T: 0521822346, 0521829055, Fax: 0521824042, E-mail: fontanellato@tin.it, Internet: http://www.fontanellato.org. Head: Rosanna Rodolfi
Local Museum - 1950
16th and 17th c living style, study room with frescos by Parmigianino (1504-1540) 21640

Forli

Museo Archeologico Antonio Santarelli, Corso della Repubblica 72, 47100 Forli - T: 0543712606, 0543712609, Fax: 0543712616, E-mail: pralu@comune.forli.fo.it. Head: Dr. Franco Fabbri, Dr. Luciana Prati
Archaeological Museum - 1874
Prehistoric, Roman and medieval archeological remains, lapidary, medals, numismatics 21641

Museo del Risorgimento Aurelio Saffi, Corso G. Garibaldi 96, 47100 Forli - T: 0543712606, 0543712609, Fax: 0543712616, E-mail: pralu@comune.forli.fo.it. Head: Dr. Franco Fabbri, Dr. Luciana Prati
Historical Museum - 1888
Local history of the Risorgimento, memorabilia on local participants 21642

Museo delle Ceramiche, Corso della Repubblica 72, 47100 Forli - T: 0543712606, 0543712609, Fax: 0543712616, E-mail: pralu@comune.forli.fo.it. Head: Dr. Franco Fabbri, Dr. Luciana Prati
Decorative Arts Museum - 1940
Ceramics 21643

Museo di San Mercuriale, Piazza Saffi 4, 47100 Forli - T: 054325653
Fine Arts Museum 21644

Museo Etnografico Romagnolo Benedetto Pergoli, Corso della Repubblica 72, 47100 Forli - T: 0543712606, 0543712609, Fax: 0543712616, E-mail: pralu@comune.forli.fo.it. Head: Dr. Franco Fabbri, Dr. Luciana Prati
Ethnology Museum - 1922
Peasant and craftman living style in Romagna, folk art 21645

Museo Ornitologico F. Foschi, Via Pedriali 12, 47100 Forli - T: 054327999
Natural History Museum 21646

Museo Romagnolo del Teatro, Corso G. Garibaldi 96, 47100 Forli - T: 0543712606, 0543712609, Fax: 0543712616, E-mail: pralu@comune.forli.fo.it. Head: Dr. Franco Fabbri, Dr. Luciana Prati
Performing Arts Museum - 1962
History of the Romagnolo Theatre, local authors, actors and musicians 21647

Pinacoteca Civica, Corso della Repubblica 72, 47100 Forli - T: 0543712606, 0543712609, Fax: 0543712616, E-mail: pralu@comune.forli.fo.it. Head: Dr. Franco Fabbri, Dr. Luciana Prati
Fine Arts Museum - 1838 21648

Forlimpopoli

Museo Archeologico Civico, Piazza Fratti 4, nella Rocca Albornoziana, 47034 Forlimpopoli - T: 0543742163, 0543749234, Fax: 0543749247, E-mail: tobial@libero.it, Internet: http://digilander.iol.it/museoforlimpopoli. Head: Tobia Aldini
Archaeological Museum - 1961
Prehistoric, Roman and medieval archaeology, historic house 21649

Formia

Antiquarium Nazionale, Piazza della Vittoria, 04023 Formia - T: 0771770382. Head: Dr. Maria Luisa Veloccia Rinaldi
Archaeological Museum
Roman sculpture, epigraphs and architecture 21650

Fossombrone

Casa Museo-Quadreria, Via Pergamino, 32, 61034 Fossombrone - T: 0721723238, 0721716158, Fax: 0721723205
Fine Arts Museum - 1965
Graphics by Anselmo Bucci 21651

Museo Civico A. Vernarecci, Palazzo Ducale Corte Alta, 61034 Fossombrone - T: 0721723238, 0721716158, Fax: 0721723205
Archaeological Museum - 1901 21652

Francavilla al Mare

Galleria Municipale, Palazzo Comunale, 66023 Francavilla al Mare
Fine Arts Museum
Paintings, mainly by painters of Abruzzo 21653

Frascati

Museo Etiopico, Via Massaia 26, 00044 Frascati - T: 0694286601, Fax: 0694286624, E-mail: capfrase@ofmcap.org. Head: P. Marek Przeczewski
Ethnology Museum
Material collected by Cardinal Massaia during his work in Ethiopia 21654

Museo Tuscolano e Rocca, Piazza Paolo III, 00044 Frascati - T: 069420467
Local Museum - 1903
Prehistoric to Roman archeology, sculpture and decorative arts 21655

Fucecchio

Museo Civico, Poggio Salamartano 1, 50054 Fucecchio - T: 057120349
Local Museum 21656

Funo

Museo della Civilta Contadina e della Canapa, Via Fratelli Rosselli 26, 40050 Funo - T: 051861504
Local Museum 21657

Gaeta

Museo Diocesano, Piazza Duomo, 04024 Gaeta - T: 0771462255. Head: Dr. Giordano Alberto
Religious Arts Museum - 1956
12th to 19th c frescoes and paintings, inscriptions, sculpture 21658

Galatina

Museo d'Arte Pietro Cavoti, Piazza Alighieri 51, 73013 Galatina - T: 0836565340. Head: Dr. Antonio Linciano
Fine Arts Museum 21659

Galeata

Museo Civico Domenico Mambrini, Via Zanetti 10, 47010 Galeata - T: 0543981648
Local Museum
Local archeological finds, sculpture, armaments 21660

Gallarate

Civica Galleria d'Arte Moderna, Palazzo Pubblici Uffici, Viale Milano 21, 21013 Gallarate - T: 0331791266. Head: Prof. S. Zanella
Fine Arts Museum
20th c Italian painting 21661

Museo d'Arte Sacra della Collegiata di Santa Maria Assunta, Corso Italia 3, 21013 Gallarate - T: 0331793611. Head: Dr. Emma Zanella Manara
Religious Arts Museum 21662

Museo della Società Gallaratese di Studi Patri, Via Borgo Antico 4, 21013 Gallarate - T: 0331795092. Head: Angelo Vittorio Mira Bonomi
Historical Museum
Prehistoric and Roman local finds, local history, documents on the Risorgimento 21663

Museo della Tecnica e del Lavoro MV Agusta, Via Matteotti 3, 21013 Gallarate - T: 0331791390
Science&Tech Museum 21664

Gallipoli

Museo Civico, Via de Pace 108, 73014 Gallipoli - T: 0833266177. Head: Prof. Elio Pindinelli
Local Museum
Natural history, ethnography, archeology, painting 21665

Gamboló

Museo Archeologico Lomellino, Castello Litta, Piazza Castello, 27025 Gamboló - T: 0381930781
Local Museum 21666

Gandino

Museo della Basilica, Palazzetto a fianco della Chiesa, Via Loverini, 24024 Gandino - T: 035745508
Religious Arts Museum
Religious art, Flemish tapestries, goldsmith's work of Renaissance and Baroque periods 21667

Ganna

Museo Badia di San Gemolo, Via Perego 3, 21039 Ganna - T: 0332719795
Religious Arts Museum 21668

Gardone Riviera

Museo Dannunziano del Vittoriale, Vittoriale degli Italiani, 25083 Gardone Riviera - T: 036520130, Fax: 036522352. Head: Dr. Luciano De Maria
Historic Site - 1938
Live and work of poet Gabriele D'Annunzio (1863-1938) - library 21669

Garessio

Museo Civico Geo-Speleologico, Piazza Giorgio Carrara, 12075 Garessio - T: 0174803130, 017481122, Fax: 017481081, 017482098, E-mail: garessio@infosys.it, Internet: http://www.garessio.net. Head: Dr. Franco Galleano
Natural History Museum 21670

Garlasco

Museo Archeologico Lomellino, Via della Bozzola 40, 27026 Garlasco - T: 038182141
Archaeological Museum 21671

Garlate

Civico Museo della Seta Abegg, Via Statale 497, 23852 Garlate - T: 0341681306, Fax: 0341650222, E-mail: museoabegg@virgilio.it, Internet: http://www.museoabegg.org. Head: Flavio Crippa
Science&Tech Museum - 1953
Ancient silk technologies 21672

Gattatico

Museo Cervi, Via Fratelli Cervi, 42043 Gattatico - T: 0522678356
Local Museum 21673

Gavardo

Istituzione Museale Gavardese, Piazza San Bernardino 2, 25085 Gavardo - T: 036531021. Head: Rino Simoni
Archaeological Museum - 1956
Paleontology, local prehist, Roman to medieval archaeology, 4th c terracotta vases, mineralogy 21674

Gavinana

Museo Ferrucciano, Piazza Ferrucci, 51025 Gavinana - T: 057366191
Military Museum - 1957
History of the battle of Gavinana, arms - library 21675

Gazzada

Museo di Villa Cagnola, Via Cagnola 17, 21045 Gazzada - T: 0332461304, Fax: 0332463463. Head: Prof. Santino Langé
Fine Arts Museum 21676

Gela

Museo Archeologico Regionale, Corso Vittorio Emanuele 2, 93012 Gela - T: 0933912626. Head: Dr. Rosalba Panvini, Dr. Carla Guzzone
Archaeological Museum - 1958
Prehistoric, Graeco-Roman material from Gela excavations, terra cotta vases, coins 21677

Genga

Frasassi- le Grotte, 60040 Genga - T: 073297211, Fax: 0732972001, E-mail: grotte@frasassi.com, Internet: http://www.frasassi.com. Head: Dr. Giampiero Gabrio Marinelli
Natural History Museum
Caves 21678

Museo Speleopaleontologico, Via Fr S Vittore Terme, 60040 Genga - T: 073290241
Local Museum 21679

Genova

Biblioteca di Storia dell'Arte, Largo Pertini 4, 16121 Genova - T: 0105574722, 0105574702, Fax: 0105574701, E-mail: biblarte@comune.genova.it, Internet: http://www.comune.genova.it/turismo/biblioteche. Head: Elisabetta Papone
Library with Exhibitions - 1908 21680

Civica Galleria d'Arte Moderna (temporary closed), Via Capolungo 3, 16167 Genova - T: 0103726025, Fax: 0105574701, E-mail: museicivici@comune.genova.it. Head: Dr. Maria Flora Giubilei
Fine Arts Museum - 1928
19th and 20th c sculpture mainly by Ligurian masters 21681

Civico Museo Navale, Piazza C. Bonavino 7, 16156 Genova - T: 0106969885, Fax: 0105574701, E-mail: museicivici@comune.genova.it. Head: Dr. Piero Campodonico
Science&Tech Museum / Historical Museum - 1928
Models of ships of various periods, nautical instruments, navigation maps, prints 21682

Galleria di Palazzo Bianco, Via Garibaldi 11, 16124 Genova - T: 0105572013, Fax: 0102475357, E-mail: museicivici@comune.genova.it. Head: Clario Di Fabio
Fine Arts Museum - 1892
Paintings of Genoese masters and other Italian schools from 14th to 18th c, Flemish masters from 15th to 17th c - educational programs department 21683

Galleria di Palazzo Reale, Via Balbi 10, 16100 Genova - T: 0102470640
Fine Arts Museum - 1650
18th c royal style, mirror hall, hall of Arras rugs, paintings, sculpture 21684

Galleria di Palazzo Rosso, Via Garibaldi 18, 16124 Genova - T: 0102476351, Fax: 0102475357, E-mail: museicivici@comune.genova.it, Internet: http://www.comune.genova.it/turismo/musei/rosso.htm. Head: Dr. Piero Boccardo
Fine Arts Museum - 1874
Paintings, frescos, stuccos, prints, drawings, ceramics, numismatics - library 21685

Galleria Nazionale di Palazzo Spinola, Piazza di Pellicceria 1, 16123 Genova - T: 0102705300, Fax: 0102705322. Head: Dr. Farida Simonetti, Dr. Germano Mulazzani
Fine Arts Museum - 1959
Picture gallery in a 17th-18th c palace with paintings by the most important Genoese and Flemish masters, furniture, silver, ceramics - library, archive, didactic section 21686

Istituto ed Orto Botanico Hanbury, Corso Dogali 1c, 16136 Genova - T: 0102099392, Fax: 0102099377. Head: Prof. Paola Profumo
Natural History Museum - 1803
Seeds, drugs, herbarium, flora of Europe, living ferns - library, herbarium, botanical garden 21687

Istituto Policattedra di Ingegneria Navale dell'Università di Genova, Via Montallegro 1, 16145 Genova
Science&Tech Museum / University Museum - 1860
Models of ships, sailing ships and structural detail of merchant ships, submarines, steamer - library, ship structural laboratory, computer center 21688

Museo Americanistico Federico Lunardi, Salita della Santa Maria Santa 43, 16122 Genova - T: 010814737. Head: Prof. Ernesto Lunardi
Archaeological Museum - 1964
Archeological coll of pre-Columbian civilizations, ethnographical items, photographs, ceramic objects of the classic Maya period - library 21689

Museo Bilbioteca dell'Attore, Viale IV Novembre 3, Genova
Performing Arts Museum 21690

Museo Civico di Archeologia Ligure, Villa Durazzo Pallavicini 1, 16155 Genova - T: 0106981048, 0106984045, Fax: 0106974040, E-mail: archligure@mail.comune.genova.it,

Internet: http://www.comune.genova.it
Archaeological Museum - 1928
Ligurian prehistory, Roman and Greek finds, historic house - library 21691

Museo Civico di Storia Naturale G. Doria, Via Brigata Liguria 9, 16121 Genova - T: 010564567, Fax: 010566319. Head: Dr. Roberto Poggi
Natural History Museum - 1867
Zoology, paleontology, mineralogy, botany - library 21692

Museo d'Arte Orientale Edoardo Chiossone, Piazzale Mazzini 4n, 16122 Genova - T: 010542285, Fax: 010580526, E-mail: museicivici@comune.genova.it. Head: Dr. Donatella Failla
Fine Arts Museum - 1899
Japanese and Chinese art 21693

Museo del Risorgimento, Via Lomellini 11, 16124 Genova - T: 0102465843, Fax: 0102541545, E-mail: mazzini05@libero.it. Head: Dr. Leo Morabito
Historical Museum - 1934
Antiquities, documents, journals pertaining to history of the Risorgimento and Europe from the 18th and 19th c - library 21694

Museo del Tesoro della Cattedrale di San Lorenzo, Piazza San Lorenzo, 16123 Genova - T: 0102471831, E-mail: museicivici@comune.genova.it. Head: Clario Di Fabio
Religious Arts Museum - 1956
Treasury of San Lorenzo including relics, copes and goldsmiths' work 21695

Museo dell'Accademia Ligustica di Belle Arti, Largo Pertini 4, 16121 Genova - T: 010581957, Fax: 010587810. Head: Prof. Gianfranco Bruno
Fine Arts Museum
Drawings, frescoes, 16th-19th c Genoese paintings 21696

Museo di Santa Maria di Castello, Salita Santa Maria di Castello 15, 16123 Genova - T: 0102549511, Fax: 01025495244. Head: Giacomo Grasso
Religious Arts Museum - 1959
Religious art, illuminated incunabula and hymnbooks, sculpture, painting (19th c) 21697

Museo di Sant'Agostino, Piazza Sarzano 35r, 16128 Genova - T: 0102511263, Fax: 0102464516, E-mail: museicivici@comune.genova.it. Head: Clario Di Fabio
Fine Arts Museum - 1939
9th to 18th c sculpture - archive 21698

Museo di Storia e Cultura Contadina, Salita al Garbo 47, 16159 Genova - T: 0107401243, Fax: 0105574701, E-mail: museicivici@comune.genova.it. Head: Dr. Patrizia Garibaldi
Historical Museum / Folklore Museum
Coll of objects relating to local rural life in the 19th and 20th c 21699

Museo Etnografico Castello D'Albertis (temporary closed), Corso Dogali 18, 16136 Genova - Fax: 0105574701, E-mail: museicivici@comune.genova.it. Head: Dr. Maria Camilla De Palma
Ethnology Museum - 1932 21700

Museo Giannettino Luxoro, Via Mafalda di Savoia 3, 16167 Genova - T: 010322673, Fax: 0105574701, 010322396, E-mail: museicivici@comune.genova.it, Internet: http://www.comune.genova.it/turismo/musei/luxorowelcome.htm. Head: Dr. Maria Flora Giubilei, Loredana Pessa
Fine Arts Museum - 1945
17th and 18th c Flemish and Genoese paintings, furniture, ceramics, silver ware, Genovese Christmas crib statuettes, Italian ceramics, Chinese ceramics, Genovese silver ware, Genovese furniture, European lace 21701

Palazzo Ducale, Piazza Matteotti 5, 16123 Genova - T: 010563168
Fine Arts Museum 21702

Raccolte di Palazzo Tursi, Via Garibaldi 9, 16124 Genova
Local Museum - 1848
Decorative arts, local antiquities, tapestries, Paganini's violin, letters of Columbus 21703

Raccolte Frugone Villa Grimaldi-Fassio, Via Capolungo 9, 16167 Genova - T: 10322396, Fax: 105574701, E-mail: museicivici@comune.genova.it. Head: Dr. Maria Flora Giubilei
Fine Arts Museum - 1993
Coll of sculpture and paintings by 19th- and 20th-c Italian artists 21704

Giardini Naxos

Museo Archeologico di Naxos, 98030 Giardini Naxos - T: 094251001
Archaeological Museum 21705

Gibellina

Museo Civico di Arte Contemporanea, Via Segesta, 91024 Gibellina - T: 092467428
Local Museum 21706

Gignese

Museo dell'Ombrello e del Parasole, Viale Golf Panorama, 28040 Gignese - T: 032320067
Special Museum
History of umbrellas 21707

Gioia del Colle

Museo Archeologico Nazionale, Corso Vittorio Emmanuele, 70023 Gioia del Colle - T: 0809981305. Head: Dr. Angela Ciancio
Archaeological Museum
Finds from ancient necropoleis 21708

Giulianova

Pinacoteca Comunale V. Bindi, Corso Garibaldi 14, 64021 Giulianova - T: 0858021215, Fax: 0858021215, E-mail: bib.civica.bindi@zerotime.it. Head: Dr. Ludovico Raimondi
Fine Arts Museum - 1972
19th c Neapolitan paintings, autographs 21709

Gorizia

Musei Provinciali di Gorizia, Borgo Castello 13, 34170 Gorizia - T: 0481533926, Fax: 0481534878. Head: Dr. Maria Masau Dan
Local Museum - 1861
Archaeology, numismatics, crafts, items of local traditional life, folk art, textiles, production of silk - historical archives 21710

Museo Provinciale della Grande Guerra, Borgo Castello 13, 34170 Gorizia - T: 0481533926, 0481530382, Fax: 0481534878, E-mail: musei.progo@libero.it, Internet: http://www.provincia.gorizia.it. Head: Dr. Raffaella Sgubin
Historical Museum / Military Museum 21711

Museo Provinciale di Palazzo Attems, Piazza Edmondo de Amicis 2, 34170 Gorizia - E-mail: misei.progo@libero.it, Internet: http://www.provincia.gorizia.it. Head: Dr. Raffaella Sgubin
Local Museum / Fine Arts Museum - 1861
Paintings, stone tablets, history of the war from 1915-1918, archives - library 21712

Gradara

Museo Storico Lisotti Maria, Via Novembre 18, 61012 Gradara
Local Museum 21713

Gradisca d'Isonzo

Enoteca Regionale Permanente la Serenissima, Via Cesare Battisti, 34072 Gradisca d'Isonzo - T: 048199528, Fax: 048199598, E-mail: enoteca@vignetochiamatofriuli.com, Internet: http://www.vignetochiamatofriuli.com. Head: Bruno Augusto Pinat
Agriculture Museum 21714

Galleria Regionale d'Arte Contemporanea L. Spazzapan, Palazzo Torriani, 34072 Gradisca d'Isonzo - T: 0481960816, Fax: 0481531798
Fine Arts Museum 21715

Lapidario Civico, Via Cesare Battisti, 34072 Gradisca d'Isonzo - T: 0481967911, Fax: 0481960622
Archaeological Museum 21716

Gravina di Puglia

Museo Ettore Pomarici Santomasi, Via Museo 20, 70024 Gravina di Puglia - T: 080851021. Head: Franco Tucci
Local Museum
Peasant life and tradition, 17th to 19th c furnishings - library 21717

Grinzane Cavour

Museo dell'Enoteca Regionale Piemontese, Via Castello 5, 12060 Grinzane Cavour - T: 0173262159, Fax: 0173262159
Agriculture Museum 21718

Gropello Cairoli

Museo Archeologico, Via Cairoli 23, 27027 Gropello Cairoli - T: 0382815031. Head: Arnaldo Repetto
Archaeological Museum 21719

Grosseto

Museo Archeologico e d'Arte della Maremma, Piazza A. Baccarini 3, 58100 Grosseto - T: 0564488750, 0564488751, Fax: 0564488753, E-mail: maam@gol.grosseto.it, Internet: http://www.gol.groseto.it.maam. Head: Dr. Mariagrazia Celuzza
Archaeological Museum - 1865
Prehistoric, Etruscan and Roman finds, medieval and modern history, 13th-18th c paintings by the Sienese and Florentine schools - archives, library 21720

Museo di Storia Naturale della Maremma, Via Mazzini 61, 58100 Grosseto - T: 0564414701, 0564488870, Fax: 0564488813, E-mail: msnmare@gol.grosseto.it. Head: Dr. Andrea Sforzi
Natural History Museum - 1960
Minerals, fossils and local fauna - library, vertebrates lab 21721

Grottaferrata

Museo del Monumento Nazionale della Badia Greca di Grottaferrata, Corso del Popolo 128, 00046 Grottaferrata - T: 069459309
Local Museum - 1904
Prehistoric archeology, Greek and Roman sculpture, local finds from the Etruscan, Greek and Roman periods, 13th c frescoes, sacred vestments 21722

Grottaglie

Raccolta dell'Istituto Statale d'Arte per la Ceramica, Via Caravaggio, 74023 Grottaglie - T: 0998667221. Head: Prof. Antonio Arces
Decorative Arts Museum 21723

Grottammare

Museo Diocesano Intercomunale di Arte Sacra, Via San Agostino, 63013 Grottammare - T: 0735594960, Fax: 0735577246. Head: Dr. Paola Di Girolami
Religious Arts Museum - 1999
archive 21724

Gualdo Tadino

Pinacoteca Comunale, Via Calci 84, 06023 Gualdo Tadino - T: 075916647. Head: Prof. A. Santorelli
Fine Arts Museum
Paintings, frescoes 21725

Guardia Sanframondi

Museo di Guardia Sanframondi, 82034 Guardia Sanframondi - T: 0824864013
Local Museum 21726

Guardiagrele

Museo Civico, Via Modesta della Porta, 66016 Guardiagrele - T: 087183445
Local Museum
Roman and Gothic remains and sculptures 21727

Guastalla

Museo della Biblioteca Maldottiana, Corso Garibaldi 54, 42016 Guastalla - T: 0522826294. Head: Giancarlo Bellani
Local Museum - 1934
Local history, coins, medals, autographs, paintings 21728

Gubbio

Museo Diocesano, Palazzo dei Canonici in Duomo, 06024 Gubbio - T: 0759273980, Fax: 0759276316
Religious Arts Museum 21729

Museo e Pinacoteca Comunali, Palazzo dei Consoli, Piazza Grande, 06024 Gubbio - T: 0759274298, Fax: 0759237530. Head: Maria Vispi
Local Museum - 1880
Finds from local excavations, 13th to 17th c paintings, antiquities, Renaissance furniture, ceramics 21730

Museo Francescano, Convento di S. Francesco, 06024 Gubbio - T: 0759273460
Religious Arts Museum
Religious art and artifacts 21731

Gurro

Museo dei Costumi e Tradizioni locali, Palazzo Municipale, 28050 Gurro - T: 032376100. Head: Cirillo Bergamaschi
Historical Museum 21732

Iesi

Museo Civico, Palazzo della Signoria Via Pergolesi, 60035 Iesi - T: 073158659
Archaeological Museum
Archaeology 21733

Pinacoteca Civica, Via XV Settembre, 60035 Iesi - T: 073158659
Fine Arts Museum
Paintings of the Venetian School 21734

Iglesias

Museo Mineralogico, Via Roma 45, 09016 Iglesias - T: 078122304. Head: Prof. Dr. Anna Maria Landis
Natural History Museum
Minerals, stones and fossils of Sardinia 21735

Imola

Collezioni d'Armi e Ceramiche della Rocca Sforzesca, Rocca Sforzesca, Piazza Giovanni dalle Bande Nere, 40026 Imola - T: 0542602609, Fax: 0542602608. Head: Dr. Claudia Pedrini
Decorative Arts Museum - 1973
13th-19th c armaments and medieval ceramics 21736

Collezioni Naturalistiche del Museo Comunale, Via Emilia 80, 40026 Imola
Natural History Museum - 1857
Geology, botany, zoology 21737

Galleria Comunale d'Arte Risorgimento, Via Appia, 40026 Imola - T: 054232632, Fax: 054224350. Head: Alfredo Taracchini
Fine Arts Museum - 1973 21738

Galleria d'Arte Rocca Sforzesca, Via Giovanni dalle Bande Nere, 40026 Imola - T: 054223472
Fine Arts Museum 21739

Musei Comunali di Imola, Via G. Sacchi 4, 40026 Imola - T: 0542602609, Fax: 0542602608, E-mail: musei@comune.imola.bo.it, Internet: http://www.imola.queen.it/eitta/museicomunali. Head: Dr. Claudia Pedrini
Archaeological Museum / Fine Arts Museum 21740

Museo Archeologico e Naturalistico, Via Verdi, 7, 40026 Imola - T: 0542602609, Fax: 0542602608. Head: Dr. Claudia Pedrini
Natural History Museum - 1857
Natural history, geology, botany, zoology, archeology, numismatics, ceramics, ethnography, also of the pre-Columbian period 21741

Museo del Risorgimento, Via Emilia 80, 40026 Imola - T: 0542602609, Fax: 0542602608. Head: Dr. Claudia Pedrini
Historical Museum - 1904
Autographs, medals, portraits, memorabilia on local hist from 1796 to WWI 21742

Museo Diocesano, Palazzo Vescovile, Piazza Duomo 1, 40026 Imola - T: 054222197
Religious Arts Museum 21743

Palazzo Tozzoni, Raccolte e Collezioni d'Arte Comunali, Via Garibaldi 18, 40026 Imola - T: 0542602609, Fax: 0542602626. Head: Dr. Claudia Pedrini
Decorative Arts Museum - 1981
Furnishings, ceramics, paintings, tools 21744

Pinacoteca Civica, Raccolta d'Arte Comunale, Via Emilia 80, 40026 Imola - T: 054223508
Fine Arts Museum 21745

Pinacoteca Comunale, Via G. Sacchi, 4, 40026 Imola - T: 0542602609, Fax: 0542602608. Head: Dr. Claudia Pedrini
Fine Arts Museum - 1938
15th-18th c paintings and contemporary art, Innocenzo da Imola 21746

Imperia

Museo dell'Olivo, Via Garessio 13, 18100 Imperia - T: 018327101, Fax: 018323236
Historical Museum
Hist of olive industry 21747

Museo Navale Internazionale del Ponente Ligure, Piazza Duomo 11, 18100 Imperia - T: 0183651541, 018364572, Fax: 0183651541, E-mail: museonavaleimperia@libero.it, Internet: http://www.cec.it/enti-naval. Head: Flavio Serafini
Historical Museum / Military Museum / Science&Tech Museum 21748

Pinacoteca Civica, Piazza Duomo 6, 18100 Imperia - T: 018361136, Fax: 0183273836
Fine Arts Museum
Antique to modern time painting 21749

Induno Olona

Civico Museo Insubrico di Storia Naturale, Piazza Giovanni XXIII 4, 21056 Induno Olona - T: 0332840611, Fax: 0332202319
Natural History Museum - 1976 21750

Irsina

Museo Archeologico Michele Janora, Piazza San Francesco, 75022 Irsina
Archaeological Museum 21751

Ischia di Castro

Museo Civico Pietro Lotti, Via Roma 4, 01010 Ischia di Castro - T: 0761425455
Local Museum
Local archeology and history 21752

Isernia

Museo Archeologico Romano, Corso Marcelli 48, 86170 Isernia - T: 0865415179
Archaeological Museum - 1958
Sculpture, ruins, antiquities, paleosol of paleolithic settlement 21753

Isola Bella

Museo Borromeo, 28050 Isola Bella - T: 032330556
Fine Arts Museum / Decorative Arts Museum
Painting, furniture, tapestries 21754

Issogne

Castello d'Issogne, 11020 Issogne - T: 012592373, Fax: 012520052
Local Museum
Renaissance paintings and local furniture 21755

Istrana

Villa Lattes, Via N. Sauro 23-24, 31036 Istrana - T: 0422738159
Local Museum 21756

Ivrea

Museo Garda, Piazza Ottinetti 18, 10015 Ivrea - T: 0125410312. Head: Emilio Torra
Natural History Museum
Natural history, ethnography of China, Japan 21757

Jesi

Museo Communale, Palazzo della Signoria, Via Pergolesi, 60035 Jesi - T: 0731538345. Head: Loretta Mozzoni
Local Museum 21758

Pinacoteca Communale, Via XV Settembre, 60035 Jesi - T: 073158659
Fine Arts Museum 21759

La Maddalena

Museo Nazionale del Compendio Garibaldino di Caprera, Isola di Caprera, 07024 La Maddalena - T: 0789727162, Fax: 0789727162. Head: Dr. Marilena Dander
Special Museum - 1978
Home of Garibaldi, personal belongings, his tomb 21760

La Morra

Museo Ratti dei Vini di Alba, Abbazia dell'Annunziata, 12064 La Morra - T: 017350185, Fax: 0173509373. Head: Pietro Ratti, Massimo Martinelli
Agriculture Museum 21761

La Spezia

Museo Archeologico Nazionale, Via Luni, Ortonovo-Luni, 19100 La Spezia - T: 018766811
Archaeological Museum 21762

Museo Civico V. Formentini, Via Curtatone 9, 19122 La Spezia - T: 0187739537. Head: Dr. Marzia Ratti
Local Museum - 1873
Local archeology, ethnography and natural history 21763

Museo Tecnico Navale, Viale Amendola 1, 19122 La Spezia - T: 0187770750, Fax: 0187782555
Science&Tech Museum - 1923
Medieval anchors, guns and weapons, reconstruction of a Roman galley, navigation instruments, manuscripts and maps, military figureheads, models of military Italian ships 21764

Lacco Ameno

Scavi e Museo di Santa Restituta, Piazza Santa Restituta, 80076 Lacco Ameno - T: 081980538. Head: Pietro Mordi
Archaeological Museum - 1974
Ceramics 21765

Lana

Museo Agricolo Alto Adige, Via Brandis 4, 39011 Lana - T: 047354387
Local Museum 21766

Lanuvio

Civico Museo Lanuvio, Via Roma 1, 00040 Lanuvio - T: 069375202. Head: Giuseppe Chiarucci
Local Museum 21767

L'Aquila

Museo di Speleologia Vincenzo Rivera, Via Svolte della Misericordia 2, 67100 L'Aquila - T: 0862414273, Fax: 0862414273. Head: Mauro Panzanaro
Natural History Museum - 1970
Fossils, prehistoric material from the Grotta a Male - library 21768

Museo di Storia Naturale e Museo di Arte e Antichità, Convento di San Giuliano, 67100 L'Aquila - T: 0862314201, Fax: 0862314201. Head: Gabriele Marini
Natural History Museum - 1970 21769

Museo Diocesano, Piazza San Giuseppe, 67100 L'Aquila - T: 086264043. Head: Bernadino Del Coco
Religious Arts Museum
Religious objects, sculpture, paintings including local and Neapolitan masters 21770

Museo Internazionale di Burattini e Marionette, Castello Cinquecentesco, 67100 L'Aquila
Decorative Arts Museum
Over 2 000 marionettes and puppets from different European countries and periods, the coll is being reorganized 21771

Museo Nazionale d'Abruzzo, Castello Cinquecentesco, Viale Benedetto Croce, 67100 L'Aquila - T: 08626331, Fax: 0862413096. Head: Giovanni Bulian
Fine Arts Museum - 1950
Archeology, art from the early Middle Ages to contemporary times, paleontology, numismatics 21772

Museo Paleontologico, Castello Cinquecentesco, Viale B Croce, 67100 L'Aquila - T: 08626331, Fax: 0862413096
Natural History Museum - 1958
Paleontology, elephant fossils - library 21773

Latiano

Museo delle Arti e delle Tradizioni di Puglia, Via G. Verdi 10-12, 72022 Latiano - T: 0831729743
Local Museum 21774

Latina

Antiquarium, Corso Repubblica 134, 04100 Latina - T: 0773690695. Head: Dr. Giuseppe Filipetti
Archaeological Museum
Prehistoric archeology, archaic pottery, Roman remains 21775

Laveno Mombello

Civica Raccolta di Terraglia, Palazzo Perabò, 21014 Laveno Mombello - T: 0332666350, Fax: 0332626042. Head: Albino Reggiori
Decorative Arts Museum - 1968
European and local earthenware from 1880 to 1960 21776

Lecce

Ghen Arte Archivio Museo, CP 303, 73100 Lecce
Local Museum 21777

Museo Missionario Cinese e di Storia Naturale, Via Monte San Michele 4, 73100 Lecce - T: 0832392580. Head: Rosario De Paolis
Fine Arts Museum 21778

Museo Provinciale Sigismondo Castromediano, Viale Gallipoli, 73100 Lecce - T: 0832307415, Fax: 0832304435. Head: Dr. Antonio Cassiano
Archaeological Museum / Decorative Arts Museum - 1868
Regional archeology, Greek vases, Roman statues, ceramics, lamps, medieval antiquities, 15th to 20th c, local painting, decorative arts, numismatics - library 21779

Lecco

Manzoni Villa, Musei Civici, Via Don Guanella, 23900 Lecco - T: 0341481249, Fax: 0341369251, E-mail: villamanzoni@museilecco.org, Internet: http://www.museilecco.org. Head: Gian Luigi Daccó
Historic Site - 1967
Memorabilia of the poet Alessandro Manzoni (1785-1873) in his house - picture gallery 21780

Musei Civici, Torre Viscontea, Piazza XX Settembre, 23900 Lecco - T: 0341369251, 0341481247/49, Fax: 0341369251, E-mail: villamanzoni@museilecco.org, Internet: http://www.museilecco.org. Head: Dr. Gian Luigi Daccò
Historical Museum 21781

Palazzo Belgiojoso, Musei Civici, Corso Matteotti, 23900 Lecco - T: 0341481248, Fax: 0341369251, E-mail: villamanzoni@museilecco.org, Internet: http://www.museilecco.org. Head: Gian Luigi Daccó
Archaeological Museum / Natural History Museum - 1900
Local archaeology, natural hist 21782

Legnago

Museo della Fondazione Fioroni, Via Matteotti 39, 37045 Legnago - T: 044220052. Head: Alberto Bologna
Military Museum / Decorative Arts Museum / Historical Museum - 1958
Weapons, pottery, Italian Risorgimento history 21783

Legnano

Museo Civico G. Sutermeister, Via Mazzini 3, 20025 Legnano - T: 0331543005. Head: Dr. Gabriela Nebuloni
Archaeological Museum
Regional archeology, 15th to 16th c frescoes, vases, arms and armor 21784

Leno

Museo Civico Archeologico e Storico, Palazzo Comunale, 25024 Leno - T: 0309038889
Archaeological Museum 21785

Lentini

Museo Archeologico, Via Piave, 96016 Lentini - T: 095902383
Archaeological Museum
Local archeological finds 21786

Licata

Museo Civico, Piazza Linares 7, 92027 Licata - T: 0922868111. Head: Pietro Meli
Local Museum 21787

Licenza

Museo Oraziano, Palazzo Baronale, Piazza del Palazzo 3, 00026 Licenza - T: 0774499250, Fax: 077446582
Archaeological Museum - 1911
Numismatics, archeology 21788

Lipari

Museo Archeologico Eoliano, Via Castello 1, 98055 Lipari - T: 0909880174, Fax: 0909880175. Head: Dr. Umberto Spigo
Archaeological Museum - 1950
Prehistory and classical material from the Lipari Islands, meridional antiquities 21789

Lissone

Civica Galleria d'Arte Contemporanea, Piazza Libertà, 20035 Lissone - T: 0397397226
Fine Arts Museum 21790

Livorno

Galleria degli ex Voto del Santuario, Santuario di Montenero, 57100 Livorno - T: 0586579033
Religious Arts Museum 21791

Museo Civico Giovanni Fattori, Via San Jacopo in Acquaviva 65, 57127 Livorno - T: 0586808001, Fax: 0586806118, E-mail: museofattori@comune.livorno.it, Internet: http://www.comune.livorno.it. Head: Francesca Giampaolo
Fine Arts Museum - 1896
19th c Tuscan paintings, Byzantine icons, numismatics, archeology - library 21792

Museo Progressivo d'Arte Contemporanea, Villa Maria, Via Redi 22, 57100 Livorno - T: 0586862063
Fine Arts Museum
Contemporary art - library 21793

Museo Provinciale di Storia Naturale, Via Roma 234, 57100 Livorno - T: 0586802294. Head: Gianfranco Barsotti
Natural History Museum - 1929
Ornithology, malacology, entomology, paleontology, mineralogy, botany, ethnology 21794

Livorno Ferraris

Museo Sacrario Galileo Ferraris, Piazza Ferraris 1, 13046 Livorno Ferraris - T: 0161477295
Local Museum 21795

Locri

Antiquarium Statale, Contrada Marasà, 89044 Locri - T: 0964390023
Archaeological Museum - 1971
Prehistorical, Greek and Roman finds, vases, terra cottas, coins, bronzes 21796

Museo Statale di Locri, Strada Statale 106, Km 98, 89044 Locri - T: 096420844. Head: Dr. Claudio Sabbione
Local Museum 21797

Raccolta Privata Scaglione, 89044 Locri - T: 096420207
Archaeological Museum 21798

Lodi

Collezione Gorini, Raccolte Scientifiche dell'Ospedale Maggiore, Piazza Ospedale, 20075 Lodi
Natural History Museum
Preparation, Mummification, anatomy 21799

Museo Civico, Corso Umberto 63, 20075 Lodi - T: 0371420369, Fax: 0371426809. Head: Dr. Luigi Samarati
Local Museum - 1868
Local history and archeology, 14th-20th c paintings, ceramics, pottery of ancient Lodi, wooden altar by the Donati brothers - Archivio Storico Comunale 21800

Museo Diocesano d'Arte Sacra, Via Cavour 31, 20075 Lodi - T: 0371424646. Head: Luciano Quartieri
Religious Arts Museum - 1975 21801

Lonato

Museo della Fondazione Ugo da Como, Via da Como 2, 25017 Lonato - T: 0309130060. Head: Dr. Gaetano Panazza
Local Museum - 1941
Household furnishings and articles concerning typical life of the area, paintings 21802

Lonedo di Lugo

Museo Andrea Piovene, Villa Godi Malinverni, Lonedo di Lugo - T: 0445860561. Head: Pierluigi Malinverni
Natural History Museum - 1908
Fossils, botany, ichthyology 21803

Loreto

Museo Missionario, 42 Via Sisto V, 60025 Loreto - T: 071977396
Local Museum 21804

Museo Pinacoteca Santa Casa, Palazzo Apostolico, Piazza Madonna, 60025 Loreto - T: 071970291, 071977759, Fax: 071970291, E-mail: archivioscasa@libero.it. Head: Floriano Grimaldi
Fine Arts Museum - 1919
Tapestries, ceramics of a 16th c pharmacy, paintings of Lorenzo Lotto, medals, antique furniture - library 21805

Palazzo Apostolico ed Archivio Storico della Santa Casa, Piazza Madonna, 60025 Loreto - T: 071970291, Fax: 071970291, E-mail: archivioscasa@libero.it. Head: Floriano Grimaldi
Religious Arts Museum / Fine Arts Museum 21806

Lovere

Galleria dell'Accademia di Belle Arti Tadini, Piazza Garibaldi 3, 24065 Lovere - T: 035960132
Fine Arts Museum - 1828
From Venetian and Lombardian to 19th c painting incl Bellini, Parmigianino, armaments, numismatics 21807

Lucca

Museo Botanico Cesare Bicchi, Via del Giardino Botanico 14, 55100 Lucca - T: 0583442160. Head: Angelo Lippi
Natural History Museum
Coll of dried plants 21808

Museo Casa Natale Giacomo Puccini, Corte San Lorenzo 9, 55100 Lucca - T: 0583584028
Historic Site 21809

Museo Civico di Storia Naturale de Lucca, Via degli Asili 35, 55100 Lucca - T: 058348280. Head: Mario Cenni
Natural History Museum 21810

Museo di Palazzo Mansi, Via Galli Tassi 43, 55100 Lucca - T: 058355570. Head: Dr. Maria Teresa Filieri
Local Museum - 1868
18th c furnishings and decor 21811

Museo Nazionale di Villa Guinigi, Via della Quarquonia, 55100 Lucca - T: 058346033. Head: Dr. Maria Teresa Filieri
Archaeological Museum / Fine Arts Museum
Roman and Etruscan archeology, pre-Romanesque, Romanesque and Renaissance sculpture and paintings, wood inlays, textiles, medieval goldsmith art 21812

Palazzo Pfanner e Giardino, Via degli Asili 33, 55100 Lucca - T: 03355435756, Fax: 050509417, E-mail: dariopf@tin.it, Internet: http://www.museum.com/jb/museum?id= 12303. Head: Dario Pfanner
Local Museum 21813

Lucera

Museo Civico Guiseppe Fiorelli, Via De Nicastri 74, 71036 Lucera - T: 0881547041, Fax: 0881532035, E-mail: museolucera@tiscalinet.it. Head: Dr. Lisa Pietropaolo
Local Museum - 1905
Local traditions, cribs, terracotta (3th c), mosaics (1st c), intarsia etc. 21814

Lucignano

Museo Civico, Piazza Tribunale 22, 52046 Lucignano - T: 057583801, Fax: 0575838026, E-mail: lucignano@technet.it, Internet: http://www.comune.lucignano.or.it
Local Museum - 1930
14th c Sienese goldsmith work, 14th to 15th c local painting, decorative art 21815

Lugagnano Val d'Arda

Antiquarium e Zona Archeologica, Località Veleia, 29018 Lugagnano Val d'Arda - T: 0523807113
Archaeological Museum
Pre-Roman and Roman findings in Veleia 21816

Lugo

Museo Francesco Baracca, Via Baracca 65, 48022 Lugo - T: 054535071, Fax: 054532804
Historic Site
Memorabilia on local hero Francesco Baracca, historic house 21817

Luino

Museo Civico, Palazzo Verbania, Via Dante Alighieri 6, 21016 Luino - T: 0332532057
Local Museum 21818

Luzzara

Museo Pittori Naif Italiani, Ex Convento Lodigiani, Via Nazionale 28, 42045 Luzzara - T: 0522977283, Fax: 0522976179
Fine Arts Museum 21819

Macerata

Museo della Carrozza, Piazza Vittorio Veneto 2, 62100 Macerata - T: 0733256361, Fax: 0733256361. Head: Dr. Alessandra Sfrappini
Science&Tech Museum - 1962 21820

Museo Marchigiano del Risorgimento G. e D. Spadoni, Piazza Vittorio Veneto 2, 62100 Macerata - T: 07332561, 0733256360, Fax: 0733256338, E-mail: biblioteca@comune.macerata.it. Head: Dr. Alessandra Sfrappini
Historical Museum - 1905
Manuscripts, autographs, portraits, arms, prints illustrating political and military events, local hist from 1789 to 1946 21821

Museo Tipologico del Presepio, Via Pantaleoni 4, 62100 Macerata - T: 0733234035
Religious Arts Museum
Miniature manger scenes 21822

Pinacoteca e Musei Comunali, Piazza Vittorio Veneto 2, 62100 Macerata - T: 0733256361, Fax: 0733256361, 0733256200. Head: Dr. Alessandra Sfrappini
Local Museum / Fine Arts Museum - 1860 21823

Macugnaga

Museo Storico, Fraz Staffa, Via Prati, 28030 Macugnaga - T: 032465009
Historical Museum 21824

Madonna di Tirano

Museo Etnografico Tiranese, Piazza Basilica 30, 23030 Madonna di Tirano - T: 0342701181, Fax: 0342701181, E-mail: museo.tirano@provincia.so.it. Head: Bruno Ciapponi Landi
Ethnology Museum
Ethnography, traditional costumes, customs, and arts of the Valtellina area 21825

Magliano Sabina

Museo Civico, Palazzo Comunale Piazza Garibaldi, 02046 Magliano Sabina - T: 0744919541. Head: Dr. Paola Santoro
Archaeological Museum - 1978
Archaeology 21826

Maglie

Museo Comunale di Preistoria, Via Umberto I, 3, 73024 Maglie - T: 0836423198. Head: Decio De Lorentiis
Archaeological Museum - 1964
Local prehistoric finds, paleontology, miocene fauna - library 21827

Maiolati Spontini

Museo Spontiniano, Via Gaspare Spontini 15, 60030 Maiolati Spontini - T: 0731702972, Fax: 0731701816. Head: Dr. Pierluigi Bertini
Music Museum - 1851
House of the musician Gaspare Spontini, manuscripts 21828

Malè

Museo della Civiltà Solandra, Via Trento 1, 38027 Malè - T: 046391204
Local Museum 21829

Malnate

Museo dei Trasport Italiani, Villa Rachele, Viale Martiri Patrioti, 21046 Malnate - T: 0332425390
Local Museum 21830

Malo

Museo Casabianca, Largo Morandi 1, 36034 Malo - T: 0445602474, Fax: 0445584721, E-mail: info@museocasabianca.com, Internet: http://www.museocasabianca.com
Fine Arts Museum - 1978
Graphics, drawings 21831

Museo della Civiltà Rurale del Vicentino, Cantina Sociale, 36034 Malo - T: 0445602087. Head: Roberto Maistrello
Historical Museum 21832

Mamiano di Traversetolo

Fondazione Magnani Rocca, Via Fondazione Magnani-Rocca 4, 43030 Mamiano di Traversetolo - T: 0521848327, Fax: 0521848337, E-mail: info@magnanirocca.it, Internet: http://www.magnanirocca.it. Head: Simona Tosini Pizzetti
Fine Arts Museum
Paintings by Goya, Filippo Lippi, Dürer, Carpaccio, Renoir, Titian, Rubens, Van Dyck, Monet Cézanne 21833

Mammola

Museo Santa Barbara, Via Santa Barbara, 89045 Mammola - T: 0964414220
Local Museum 21834

Manduria

Antiquarium Municipale, Piazza Garibaldi, 74024 Manduria - T: 099802252, Fax: 0998712097. Head: Gregorio Contessa
Archaeological Museum - 1940
Messapian, Greek and Roman archeology of the area, late medieval ceramics 21835

Raccolta Archeologica, Piazza G Garibaldi 1, 74024 Manduria - T: 099802245. Head: Gregorio Contessa
Archaeological Museum 21836

Manerba del Garda

Museo Civico Archeologico della Val Tenesi, Località Pieve, Via Don Angelo Merici, 25080 Manerba del Garda - T: 0365551007
Archaeological Museum 21837

Manfredonia

Museo Archeologico Nazionale, Castello Svevo-Angioino, 71043 Manfredonia - T: 0884587838, Fax: 0884587838. Head: Marina Mazzei
Archaeological Museum 21838

Mantova

Museo Casa del Mantegna, Via G. Acerbi 47, 46100 Mantova - T: 0376326685
Fine Arts Museum
House of the painter Andrea Mantegna, fragments of original frescoes 21839

Museo Civico di Palazzo Te, Viale del Te, 46100 Mantova - T: 0376323266. Head: Prof. Ugo Bazzotti
Local Museum 21840

Museo dei Burattini, Via T. Tasso, 4, 46100 Mantova - T: 0376381547, Fax: 0376381547. Head: Maurizio Corniani
Performing Arts Museum - 1979
Traditional Italian puppets, puppet theatre, stage-scenery 21841

Museo del Palazzo Ducale, Piazza Sordello 40, 46100 Mantova - T: 0376352111, Fax: 0376366274, Internet: http://www.mantovaducale.it. Head: Dr. Giuliana Algeri
Fine Arts Museum - 1915
250 paintings, frescoes, sinopias, tapestries, numismatics, 'Bridal chamber' with frescoes by Andrea Mantegna 21842

Museo del Risorgimento, Piazza Sordello 42, 46100 Mantova - T: 0376320280. Head: Prof. Rinaldo Salvadori
Historical Museum
Documents and material concerning the Risorgimento up to 1945 21843

Museo di Palazzo d'Arco, Piazza d'Arco 4, 46100 Mantova - T: 0376322242, Fax: 0376369544. Head: Prof. Rodolfo Signorini
Historical Museum 21844

Museo Diocesano, Piazza Virgiliana 55, 46100 Mantova - T: 0376320602, Fax: 0376320602. Head: Ciro Ferrari
Religious Arts Museum 21845

Marciana Marina

Museo Civico Archeologico, Via del Pretorio 66, 57030 Marciana Marina - T: 0565901015
Archaeological Museum 21846

Marianopoli

Museo Archeologico, Piazza Garibaldi, 93010 Marianopoli - T: 0934674357
Archaeological Museum 21847

Marina di Campo

Museo Diocesano di Arte Sacra di Italo Bolano, Chiesa di San Gaetano, Isola d'Elba, 57034 Marina di Campo - T: 0565977764
Religious Arts Museum
Life of Christ by Italo Bolano 21848

Marsala

Museo degli Arazzi delle Madrice, Via Garraffa, 91025 Marsala - T: 0923716295. Head: Mariano Crociata
Religious Arts Museum - 1984 21849

Museo degli Arazzi Fiamminghi, Chiesa Madre, Piazza della Repubblica, 91025 Marsala - T: 0923716295
Decorative Arts Museum
16th c Flemish tapestries 21850

Museo J. Whitaker, Isola di Mothia, 91025 Marsala - T: 0923712598
Archaeological Museum 21851

Marzabotto

Museo Etrusco Pompeo Aria, Via Porrettana Sud 13, 40043 Marzabotto - T: 051932353. Head: Dr. Luigi Malnati
Archaeological Museum - 1831
Archeological findings from the ancient Misa 21852

Maser

Museo delle Carrozze, Villa Barbaro Volpi, 31010 Maser
Science&Tech Museum 21853

Massa

Castello Malaspina, Via del Forte, 54100 Massa - T: 058544774
Local Museum
Archeology of the North Tuscany coast, medieval pottery, furniture 21854

Museo del Duomo, Piazza Duomo 1, 54100 Massa - T: 058542643, Fax: 058542643, E-mail: massacattedrale@interfree.it, Internet: http://massacattedrale.interfree.it. Head: Luca Franceschini
Religious Arts Museum 21855

Massa Fermana

Pinacoteca Comunale, Palazzo Comunale Via Garibaldi 60, 63020 Massa Fermana - T: 0734760127
Fine Arts Museum
Paintings (15th and 16th c) 21856

Massa Lombarda

Centro di Documentazione sulla Storia dell'Agricoltura e della Frutticoltura della Bassa Ravennate "Adolfo Bonvicini", Via Amendola 40, 48024 Massa Lombarda - T: 0545985832/33, Fax: 0545985837, E-mail: cultura@comune.massa-lombarda.ra.it, Internet: http://www.comune.massa-lombarda.ra.it. Head: Francesco Beltrani
Agriculture Museum - 1983 21857

Museo Carlo Venturini, Via Garibaldi 22, 48024 Massa Lombarda - T: 05459858323, Fax: 0545885837, E-mail: cultura@comune.massa-lombardo.ra.it, Internet: http://www.comune.massa-lombarda.ra.it. Head: Francesco Beltrani
Local Museum - 1989 21858

Massa Marittima

Mostra della Civiltà Contadina, Piazza Beccucci, 58024 Massa Marittima - T: 0566902051
Historical Museum 21859

Mostra Permanente della Resistenzo, 58024 Massa Marittima - T: 0566902051
Historical Museum 21860

Museo Archeologico, vlo Todini 1, 58024 Massa Marittima - T: 0566902289
Archaeological Museum 21861

Museo del Risorgimento, Palazzo del Podestà, vlo Todini 1, 58024 Massa Marittima - T: 0566902289
Historical Museum 21862

Museo della Miniera, Via Corridoni, 58024 Massa Marittima - T: 0566902051
Natural History Museum 21863

Museo di Mineralogia, Istituto Tecnico Industriale B. Lotti, Viale Martiri di Niccioleta 1, 58024 Massa Marittima - T: 0566902068. Head: Aldo Bini
Natural History Museum 21864

Museo di Storia e Arte delle Miniere, Pzza Matteotti, 58024 Massa Marittima
Local Museum 21865

Pinacoteca, Palazzo del Podestà, Vicolo Todini 1, 58024 Massa Marittima - T: 0566902289
Fine Arts Museum 21866

Massa Martana

Civico Museo Flaminio Massetano, Ex Convento di Santa Maria della Pace, 06056 Massa Martana - T: 075889210. Head: O.G. Caramazza
Local Museum 21867

Massello

Museo Valdese della Balziglia, Fraz Balziglia, 10060 Massello - T: 0121808816, Fax: 0121808816, E-mail: pawelga@tin.it. Head: Dr. Pawel Gajewski
Religious Arts Museum 21868

Matelica

Museo Piersanti, Via Umberto I 11, 62024 Matelica - T: 073784445. Head: Prof. Piero Allegrini
Religious Arts Museum
13th to 18th c crucifixes, tapestries, goldsmith work 21869

Matera

Museo Nazionale Domenico Ridola, Via D. Ridola 24, 75100 Matera - T: 0835310058, Fax: 0835310058. Head: Dr. Beatrice Arendolbgine
Archaeological Museum - 1911
Prehistoric section, Magna Grecia section, ethnology - library, didactic section 21870

Mazara del Vallo

Museo Civico, Piazza Plebiscito 2, 91026 Mazara del Vallo - T: 0923940266, Fax: 0923908703. Head: Francesca La Malfa
Archaeological Museum - 1931
Prehistoric findings of local interest, amphoras, coins, arms, inscriptions, pottery 21871

Museo Diocesano, Piazza della Repubblica, 91026 Mazara del Vallo - T: 0923941243. Head: Vicenzo De Pasquale
Religious Arts Museum 21872

Medicina

Museo Civico, Palazzo della Comunità, 40059 Medicina - T: 051851158
Local Museum 21873

Meina

Fondazione Europea del Disegno (European Foundation for Drawing), Str Statale 33 del Sempione, 28046 Meina - E-mail: fondazioneeuropeadeldisegno@yahoo.it. Head: Valerio Adami
Fine Arts Museum - 2001
Drawings 20th c 21874

Melfi

Museo Archeologico Nazionale del Melfese, Castello Normanno, 85025 Melfi - T: 0972238726
Archaeological Museum
Local archeology from neolithic to medieval times 21875

Mentana

Museo Garibaldino della Campagna dell'Agro Romano per la Liberazione di Roma 1867, Via Roma s/n, 00013 Mentana - T: 069065573, Fax: 0690627194. Head: Prof. Francesco Guidotti
Historical Museum - 1905 21876

Merano

Merano Arte, Edificio Cassa di Risparmio, Portici 163, 39012 Merano - T: 0473212643, Fax: 0473276147, E-mail: info@kunstmeranoarte.com, Internet: http://www.kunstmeranoarte.com
Public Gallery 21877

Museo della Donna, Portici 68, 39012 Merano
Special Museum 21878

Museo Merano, Museo Civico, Via delle Corse 42a, 39012 Merano - T: 0473236015, Fax: 0473236015, E-mail: egobbi.merandb@gvcc.net, Internet: http://www.gemeinde.meran.bz.it/stadtfuehrer/kultur.htm/. Head: Elmar Gobbi
Local Museum - 1900
Local history and folklore, paintings, archeology, local geology 21879

Mercatello sul Metauro

Museo Parrocchiale della Chiesa Collegiata, Piazza Garibaldi, 61040 Mercatello sul Metauro - T: 072289139
Decorative Arts Museum 21880

Pinacoteca della Chiesa di San Francesco, Piazza San Francesco, 61040 Mercatello sul Metauro - T: 072289139
Fine Arts Museum 21881

Mercogliano

Museo del Santuario di Montevergine, Santuario, 83013 Mercogliano - T: 0825787191. Head: Placido Tropeano
Archaeological Museum 21882

Mergozzo

Antiquarium, Chiesa Parrocchiale di Santa Maria Assunta, 28040 Mergozzo - T: 032380109
Archaeological Museum 21883

Mesagne

Museo Archeologico U. Granafei, Piazza IV Novembre, 72023 Mesagne - T: 0831323542. Head: Prof. Domenico Urgesi
Local Museum - 1913
Prehistory, Roman, medieval materials, vases, bronzes, epigraphs - library 21884

Messina

Museo Regionale, Via della Libertà 465, 98121 Messina - T: 090361292, Fax: 090361294. Head: Dr. Francesca Campagna
Fine Arts Museum / Decorative Arts Museum / Archaeological Museum - 1953
Paintings of the Messina school, sculpture, religious art, polyptych by Antonello da Messina, works by Caravaggio, 16th to 17th c decorative arts, archeology 21885

Museo Zoologico Cambria, S. Agata, Salita Sperone 31, 98166 Messina - T: 090392721, 0906765547, Fax: 090393409
Natural History Museum
Molluscs and vertebrates mainly from Italy 21886

Tesoro del Duomo, Piazza del Duomo, 98100 Messina - T: 090774895. Head: Paolo Romeo
Religious Arts Museum 21887

Metaponto

Museo Archeologico Nazionale, Via Aristea, 75010 Metaponto - T: 0835745327, Fax: 0835745327. Head: Antonio De Siena
Archaeological Museum - 1991
Archeological material concerning the Greek colony 21888

Milano

Biblioteca d'Arte, Castello Sforzesco, 20121 Milano - T: 02877004, Fax: 0272022599, E-mail: bibarte@tin.it, Internet: http://www.bibdarte.it. Head: Dr. Lia Gandolfi
Library with Exhibitions 21889

Cenacolo Vinciano, Convento S. Maria delle Grazie, Piazza S. Maria delle Grazie 2, 20123 Milano - T: 024987588
Fine Arts Museum - 1890
'Last Supper' by Leonardo da Vinci, frescoes, paintings 21890

Civica Galleria d'Arte Moderna, Villa Reale, Via Palestro 16, 20121 Milano - T: 026002819, Fax: 02784688. Head: Dr. Maria Teresa Fiorio
Fine Arts Museum - 1920
19th c Italien paintings, French impressionists, Marino Marini coll, Morandi, Modigliani, Picasso, Matisse - library 21891

Civica Raccolta di Stampe Achille Bertarelli, Castello Sforzesco, 20121 Milano - T: 028693071, Fax: 028693071. Head: Dr. Claudio Salsi
Fine Arts Museum - 1925
800 000 engravings and prints from the 15th c to the present 21892

Civiche Raccolte Archeologiche e Numismatiche di Milano, Castello Sforzesco, 20121 Milano - T: 028053972, Fax: 0286452796, E-mail: Ermanno_Arslan@rcm.inet.it. Head: Dr. Ermanno A. Arslan
Archaeological Museum - 1807
Prehistoric coll from Rome, Greece and Etruria, ceramics, tombstones, numismatic - library 21893

Civiche Raccolte d'Arte Applicata, Castello Sforzesco, 20121 Milano - T: 028745461, Fax: 028693071, E-mail: francesca.tasso@tin.it, Internet: http://www.mimo.it. Head: Dr. Claudio Salsi
Decorative Arts Museum
Furniture, ceramics, tapestries, ivories, glassware, goldsmith work, bronzes 21894

Civico Gabinetto dei Disgeni, Castello Sforzesco, 20121 Milano - T: 026236 ext 3965, Fax: 0286463054. Head: Dr. Maria Teresa Fiorio
Fine Arts Museum 21895

Civico Museo d'Arte Contemporanea, Palazzo Reale, Piazza Duomo 12, 20100 Milano - T: 0262083943, 0286463054, Fax: 0286463054. Head: Dr. Maria Teresa Fiorio
Fine Arts Museum - 1984 21896

Civico Museo Navale Didattico, Via San Vittore 21, 20123 Milano - T: 024816885. Head: Dr. Pietro Fiori
Science&Tech Museum - 1922
Ship models, weapons, iconographic coll - archive 21897

Civico Studio Museo Francesco Messina, Via San Sisto 4a, 20100 Milano - T: 0286453005. Head: Dr. Maria Teresa Fiorio
Local Museum 21898

Collezione Jucker, Via Macchi 28, 20124 Milano - T: 026694690. Head: Gabriella Mercandino Jucker
Fine Arts Museum
19th c Italian painting 21899

Collezioni degli Istituti di Geologia e di Paleontologia, Piazzale Gorini 15, 20133 Milano
Natural History Museum 21900

Erbario dell'Istituto di Scienze Botaniche dell'Università di Milano, c/o Istituto di Scienze Botaniche, Via G. Colombo 60, 20133 Milano
Natural History Museum
Herbarium 21901

Fondazione Antonio Mazzotta, Foro Buonaparte 50, 20121 Milano - T: 02878380, 02878197, Fax: 028693046, E-mail: mazzotta@iol.it, Internet: http://www.mazzotta.it. Head: Gabriele Mazzotta
Association with Coll / Public Gallery - 1994
Works on paper, temporary exhibits 21902

Galleria d'Arte Sacra dei Contemporanei, Via Terruggia 14, 20162 Milano - T: 026421420. Head: Dr. Giulio Madurini
Religious Arts Museum
Religious art 21903

Museo Archeologico, Corso Magenta 15, 20121 Milano
Archaeological Museum
Greek, Etruscan, Roman Barbarian and Gandhara sections 21904

Museo Bagatti Valsecchi, Via Santo Spirito 10, 20121 Milano - T: 0276006132, Fax: 0276014859, E-mail: info@museobagattivalsecchi.org, Internet: http://www.museobagattivalsecchi.org. Head: Dr. Rosanna Pavoni
Fine Arts Museum / Decorative Arts Museum 21905

Museo Cenacolo Vinciano, Piazza S. Maria delle Grazie 2, 20123 Milano - T: 024987588
Local Museum 21906

Museo Civico di Storia Naturale, Corso Venezia 55, 20121 Milano - T: 0288463298, Fax: 0288463281. Head: Enrico Banfi
Natural History Museum - 1838
Paleontology, mineralogy, vertebrate/ invertebrate zoology, ornithology, entomology, botany, palethnology - library 21907

Museo d'Arte Antica, Castello Sforzesco, 20121 Milano - T: 0288463731, Fax: 0288463650, Internet: http://www.mimu.it. Head: Dr. Maria Teresa Fiorio
Fine Arts Museum
Sculpture (from Paleochristian period to 17th c), incl the 'Pietà' Rondanini by Michelangelo, painting (early 14th-18th c), incl works by Mantegna, Correggio, Tintoretto, Lippi, Bellini, Tiepolo 21908

Museo degli Strumenti Musicali, Castello Sforzesco, 20121 Milano - T: 028693071, 02874546, Fax: 028693071, E-mail: francesca.tasso@tin.it, Internet: http://www.mimo.it. Head: Dr. Claudio Salsi
Music Museum - 1958
836 musical instruments 21909

Museo dei Navigli, Via San Marco 40, 20121 Milano - T: 0229001058, Fax: 0229003497
Historical Museum / Science&Tech Museum 21910

Museo del Cinema, Pallazzo Dugnani, Via Daniele Manin 2b, 20121 Milano. Head: Dr. Walter Alberti
Special Museum
History of cinematography, historical records of films 21911

Museo del Collezionista d'Arte, Fondazione Goffredo Matthaes, Via Q. Sella 4, 20121 Milano - T: 0272022488, Fax: 0272023156, E-mail: mcollezionista@ntt.it, Internet: http://www.museodelcollezionista.com. Head: Goffredo Matthaes
Special Museum 21912

Museo del Duomo, Piazza Duomo 14, 20122 Milano - T: 0272022656, Fax: 0272022419. Head: Dr. Ernesto Brivio
Religious Arts Museum - 1953
14th c sculpture, stained glass windows, tapestries, religious art 21913

Museo del Risorgimento e Raccolte Storiche del Comune di Milano, Via Borgonuovo 23, 20121 Milano - T: 0288464170, Fax: 0288464181, E-mail: risorgi@energy.it. Head: Dr. Roberto Guerri
Historical Museum - 1884
Documents of Italian history from 1750 to the present 21914

Museo della Basilica di Santa Maria della Passione, Via Vincenzo Bellini 2, 20122 Milano - T: 02791370. Head: Attilio Cavalli
Religious Arts Museum 21915

Museo delle Armi Antiche, Via Carducci 41, 20125 Milano
Military Museum - 1948
15th to 17th c armaments 21916

Museo di Milano, Via Sant'Andrea 6, 20121 Milano - T: 02783797, Fax: 0272001483. Head: Dr. Roberto Guerri
Historical Museum - 1934
Iconography, topographical maps, prints, 17th c decorations in a historic house 21917

Museo di Paleontologia, c/o Dipartimento Scienze della Terra, Via Mangiagalli 34, 20133 Milano - T: 0223698232, Fax: 0270638261. Head: Dr. Isabella Premoli Silva
Natural History Museum 21918

Museo di Storia Contemporanea, Via Sant'Andrea 6, 20121 Milano - T: 0276006245, Fax: 0272001483. Head: Dr. Roberto Guerri
Historical Museum - 1962
Documents and exhibits concerning history from 1914 to 1945 21919

Museo Manzoniano, Casa del Manzoni, Via Morone 1, 20121 Milano - T: 0286460403, Fax: 02875618, E-mail: manzoni@energy.it. Head: Prof. Gianmarco Gaspari
Special Museum - 1938
Memorabilia and personal books of the poet Alessandro Manzoni (1785-1873) 21920

Museo Marino Marini, Via Palestro 16, 20121 Milano - T: 0276002819. Head: Dr. Maria Teresa Fiorio
Fine Arts Museum 21921

Museo Nazionale della Scienza e della Tecnica Leonardo da Vinci, Via San Vittore 21, 20123 Milano - T: 02485551, Fax: 0248010016, E-mail: museo@museoscienza.org, Internet: http://www.museoscienza.org. Head: Fiorenzo Galli
Science&Tech Museum - 1953
Relics, models and designs with particular emphasis on Leonardo da Vinci's work, airplanes, ships, railways - library, auditorium 21922

Museo Poldi Pezzoli, Via Manzoni 12, 20121 Milano - T: 02794889, Fax: 028690788, E-mail: info@museopoldipezzoli.org, Internet: http://www.museopoldipezzoli.org. Head: Dr. Annalisa Zanni
Fine Arts Museum / Decorative Arts Museum - 1881
14th to 18th c painting, armaments, tapestries, rugs, jewelry, porcelain, glass, textiles, furniture, lace, clocks, sundials - library 21923

Museo Popoli e Culture, Via Mosé Bianchi 94, 20149 Milano - T: 0248320l, Fax: 024695193, E-mail: museo@pimemilano.com, Internet: http://www.pimemilano.com. Head: Massimo Casaro
Folklore Museum - 1910
Works from China, India, Japan, the Far East, bronzes, porcelain, paintings, numismatics, sculpture, ritual objects, tools, musical instruments, folk art, masks, etc from Africa, Papua New Guinea and Amazonas - library 21924

Museo Sacro, Tesoro di Sant'Ambrogio, Piazza Sant'Ambrogio 15, 20123 Milano - T: 0286450895, Fax: 028693839. Head: Dr. Carlo Capponi
Religious Arts Museum - 1949
14th and 15th c goldsmith's works, 15th and 16th c paintings and frescoes, fragments of early 4th and 5th c sculptures 21925

Museo Teatrale alla Scala, Via Filodrammatici 2, 20121 Milano - T: 028053418, Fax: 0286463170, E-mail: scala@energy.it, Internet: http://www.museoteatrale.com. Head: Matteo Sartorio
Performing Arts Museum - 1913
History of theatrical shows from ancient times to the present days, history of the Scala of Milan, Verdi' Manuscripts - library 21926

Padiglione per l'Arte Contemporanea, Via Palestro 14, 20121 Milano - T: 0276009085, Fax: 02783330. Head: Dr. Mercedes Garberi
Fine Arts Museum 21927

Palazzo della Triennale, Viale Alemagna 6, Milano - T: 0276009085
Fine Arts Museum 21928

Pinacoteca Ambrosiana, Piazza Pio XI 2, 20123 Milano - T: 02806921, Fax: 0280692210, E-mail: info@ambrosiana.it. Head: Prof. Gianfranco Ravasi
Fine Arts Museum - 1618
Prints, including many by Dürer, paintings by Titian, Raphael, Caravaggio, drawings by Leonarda da Vinci, Rubens, miniatures, enamels, ceramics 21929

Pinacoteca di Brera, Via Brera 28, 20121 Milano - T: 02722631, Fax: 0272001140. Head: Caterina Bon Valsassina
Fine Arts Museum - 1809
15th to 18th c paintings, mainly of the Lombard and Venetian school, works by Mantegna, Titian, Raphael, Tintoretto, Giovanni Bellini, Veronese, Caravaggio, Tiepolo 21930

Raccolte d'Arte dell'Ospedale Maggiore di Milano, Via Francesco Sforza 28, 20122 Milano - T: 0255038278, Fax: 0258304350. Head: Dr. Paolo Galimberti
Fine Arts Museum
15th to 20th c drawings, statues, pharmacy pottery, objects d'art (bells, clocks, medals, carpets, sets of ancient surgical instruments, ancient furnitures, vestments and wessels for church ceremonies), photographs, core collection of benefactors portraits XVII-XX c 21931

Siloteca Cormio, Piazza San Vittore 21, 20100 Milano - T: 02434154
Natural History Museum
Specimens of wood from all over the world, remains of pile dwellings, objects in wood - library 21932

Società per le Belle Arti ed Esposizione Permanente, Via Turati 34, 20121 Milano - T: 0229004217, Fax: 025511846
Association with Coll 21933

Tesoro del Duomo, Piazza Duomo 18, 20122 Milano - T: 0286463456
Religious Arts Museum
5th to 20th c silver work and ivory, gold and enamelled work, tapestries, religious art 21934

Mileto

Museo Diocesano di Arte Sacra, Palazzo Vescovile, Via Episcopio, 88014 Mileto - T: 0963338397
Religious Arts Museum 21935

Militello in Val di Catania

Museo San Nicolo, Via Umberto I 67, 95043 Militello in Val di Catania - T: 095811251
Local Museum 21936

Minturno

Antiquarium Nazionale, Via Appia 7, 04026 Minturno - T: 0771680093. Head: Dr. Pietro Griffo, Dr. Baldo Conticello
Archaeological Museum
Roman sculpture, terra cottas, coins 21937

Mirandola

Museo Civico, Via Montanari, 5, 41037 Mirandola - T: 053521470, Fax: 053521430. Head: Vittorio Erlindo
Local Museum
Local archeology, room with illustrations of the Pico family 21938

Modena

Centro Museo Universitario di Storia Naturale e della Strumentazione Scientifica, Via Berengario 4, 41100 Modena - T: 0592056954, E-mail: -bartolini.mariagiuseppina@unimo.it. Head: Prof. Maria Giuseppina Bartolini Bussi
Natural History Museum / University Museum - 1989
Zoology from the Modena area, vertebrates of various continents, molluscs, human anatomy, clay and wax anatomical models (1775) fossil vertebrates and invertebrates, mathematical machines, scientific instruments 21939

Galleria Estense, Palazzo dei Musei, Piazza S. Agostino 337, 41100 Modena - T: 059222145, 059235004, Fax: 059230196. Head: Dr. Filippo Trevisani
Fine Arts Museum / Decorative Arts Museum - 1854
Paintings, statues, small bronzes, pottery, ivory, medals, coins, works by Veronese, Tintoretto, Corregio, Bernini, El Greco, Velasquez, Rosa and Reni 21940

Mostra Permanente della Biblioteca Estense, Palazzo dei Musei, Piazza S. Agostino, 337, 41100 Modena - T: 059222248, Fax: 059230195, E-mail: estense@kril.cedoc.unimo.it. Head: Prof. Ernesto Milano
Fine Arts Museum - 14th c
14th to 18th c paintings, illuminated painting by Italian and foreign schools - library 21941

Museo Anatomico, Via Berengario 16, 41100 Modena - T: 059222857
Natural History Museum 21942

Museo Civico Archeologico Etnologico, Largo Porta S. Agostino 337, 41100 Modena - T: 059200100, Fax: 059200110, E-mail: museo.archeologico@comune.modena.it. Head: Andrea Cardarelli
Archaeological Museum - 1871
Prehist, ethnographical objects from South America, Africa, Asia, Oceania 21943

Museo Civico d'Arte, Largo Porta S. Agostino, 41100 Modena - T: 059200100, Fax: 059200110, E-mail: museo.arte@comune.modena.it, Internet: http://www.comune.modena.it/museoarte. Head: Andrea Cardarelli
Fine Arts Museum / Decorative Arts Museum - 1871
Paintings, sculpture religious art, historical instruments, ceramcis, glasses, armaments, textiles 21944

Museo del Risorgimento, Palazzo dei Musei, Piazza S. Agostino, 41000 Modena - T: 059223440
Historical Museum - 1894
Local history, history of the Risorgimento (1750-1870) - library 21945

Museo dell'Istituto di Mineralogia e Petrologia, Via S. Eufemia 19, 41100 Modena - T: 059218062, Fax: 059223605. Head: Elio Passaglia
Natural History Museum - 1927
Zeolites, petrology, regional mineralogy - library 21946

Museo di Paleontologia, Via Università 4, 41100 Modena - T: 0592056527, Fax: 059218212, E-mail: russo@unimo.it. Head: Prof. Antonio Russo
Natural History Museum - 1827
Paleontology, fossils, dinosaurs 21947

Museo di Zoologia, Via Università 4, 41100 Modena - T: 059218302
Local Museum 21948

Museo Lapidario del Duomo, Via Lanfranco 6, 41100 Modena - T: 059216078. Head: Guido Vigarani
Archaeological Museum - 1921
Roman and medieval sculptures and tablets 21949

Museo Lapidario Estense, Palazzo dei Musei, Piazza S. Agostino 337, 41100 Modena - T: 0594395711, Fax: 059230196, E-mail: galleria.estense@interbusiness.it. Head: Dr. Filippo Trevisani
Archaeological Museum - 1828
Roman sculpture, epigraphs, sarcophagi, tombstones 21950

Museo Muratoriano, Via Pomposa 1, 41100 Modena - T: 059241104, Fax: 059241104. Head: Prof. Giorgio Boccolari
Historic Site - 1931
Memorabilia of the historian Ludovico A. Muratori, various editions of his works - library 21951

Modica

Museo Civico, Via Mercè, 97015 Modica - T: 0932945081
Local Museum 21952

Museo Ibleo delle Artie e Tradizioni Popolari, Via Mercè, 97015 Modica - T: 0932945081
Ethnology Museum 21953

Modigliana

Museo Don Giovanni Verità, Corso Garibaldi 27, 47015 Modigliana - T: 054691017. Head: Lorenzo Baldoni
Archaeological Museum / Historical Museum
Archeology, prehistory, documents on the Risorgimento 21954

Mogliano Marche

Museo Parrocchiale, Vicolo Boninfanti, 62010 Mogliano Marche - T: 0733556058
Religious Arts Museum 21955

Museo-Pinacoteca Comunale, Palazzo Forti, Via Roma 54, 62010 Mogliano Marche - T: 0733556824
Fine Arts Museum 21956

Moio della Civitella

Museo della Civiltà Contadina, Scuola Media Statale, 84060 Moio della Civitella - T: 097466113
Historical Museum 21957

Molfetta

Museo Archeologico, Viale Pio XI, 70056 Molfetta - T: 0808852110. Head: Tommaso Tridente
Archaeological Museum
Local archeology, illuminated books, painting 21958

Museo Pinacoteca A. Salvucci, Seminario Vescovile, Piazza Garibaldi 65, 70056 Molfetta - T: 0809971559. Head: Dr. Felice Di Malfetta
Fine Arts Museum - 1984 21959

Molina di Ledro

Museo delle Palafitte, I Molina di Ledro, Via Lungolago, 38060 Molina di Ledro - T: 0464508182. Head: Dr. Michele Lanziger
Archaeological Museum
Reconstructions of the prehistoric dwellers' pile strucutres on Lake Ledro 21960

Monalto Marche

Museo Diocesano Inercomunale di Arte Sacra, Piazza Umberto I 12, 63034 Monalto Marche - T: 0735594960, Fax: 0735577246. Head: Dr. Paola Di Girolami
Religious Arts Museum 21961

Mondavio

Armeria, Piazza Della Rovere, 61040 Mondavio - T: 072197102, Fax: 0721989098, E-mail: proloco.mondavio@provincia.ps.it. Head: Claudio De Santi
Military Museum 21962

Museo di Rievocazione Storica, Piazza Della Rovere, 61040 Mondavio - T: 072197102, Fax: 0721989098, E-mail: proloco.mondavio@provincia.ps.it. Head: Claudio De Santi
Folklore Museum / Historical Museum 21963

Pinacoteca Comunale, Piazza Della Rovere, 61040 Mondavio - T: 072197102, Fax: 0721989098, E-mail: proloco.mondavio@provincio.ps.it. Head: Claudio De Santi
Fine Arts Museum 21964

Monfalcone

Museo Paleontologico, Via Valentinis 134, 34074 Monfalcone - T: 048140014, Fax: 048140014, E-mail: mospeleo@tiscalinet.it, Internet: http://www.fante.speleo.it. Head: Fabio M. Dalla Vecchia
Natural History Museum - 1970
Thin sections of mesozoic carbonate rocks from northern adriatic region, cretaceous fishes, moulds of cretaceous dinosaur footprints from the Istrian peninsula 21965

Monopoli

Collezione Meo-Evoli, Cozzana C. da Sant'Oceano, 154, 70043 Monopoli - T: 080803052
Archaeological Museum 21966

Museo Archeologico, Liceo Classico, Via Europa Libera, 70043 Monopoli - T: 0808872072. Head: Prof. Angelo Menga
Archaeological Museum 21967

Museo della Cattedrale, Basilica della Madonna della Madia, Largo Cattedrale, 70043 Monopoli - T: 080742253. Head: Vicenzo Muolo
Religious Arts Museum 21968

Monrupino

Casa Carsica, Kraška Hiša, Fraz Rupingrande 31, 34016 Monrupino - T: 040631300, Fax: 040366587. Head: E. Kraus
Ethnology Museum - 1968 21969

Monsummano

Museo del Santuario di Santa Maria Santissima della Fontenuova, Piazza Giuseppe Giusti 38, 51015 Monsummano - T: 057251102
Religious Arts Museum 21970

Museo di Casa Giusti, Viale Martini, 51015 Monsummano - T: 057253039
Local Museum 21971

Montagnana

Museo Civico A. Giacomelli, Castel San Zeno, Piazza Trieste, 35044 Montagnana - T: 0429804128, 042981320, Fax: 0429800737, E-mail: comontag@netbusiness.it, Internet: http://www.comune.montagnana.pd.it. Head: Dr. Stefano Baccini
Local Museum - 1974
Pre-Roman and Roman archaeology, ancient ceramics and Venetian painting of the 14th-18th c, music coll 21972

Montalcino

Museo Archeologico, Piazza Cavour 10, 53024 Montalcino - T: 0577848150. Head: Ivo Caprioli
Archaeological Museum
Prehistoriy and Etruscan findings from the area 21973

Museo Civico e Diocesano d' Arte Sacra, Via Ricasoli 10, 53024 Montalcino - T: 0577846014, Fax: 0577849331
Local Museum
14th c paintings by the Sienese school, pottery, majolica ware 21974

Museo Diocesano, Via Ricasoli 31, 53024 Montalcino - T: 0577848168. Head: Augusto Bellugi
Religious Arts Museum
Religious art, paintings and sculptures 21975

Monte San Martino

Pinacoteca dell'Opera Pia Ricci, Via A. Ricci 10, 62020 Monte San Martino - T: 0733660107
Fine Arts Museum 21976

Monte Sant'Angelo

Museo della Basilica di San Michele Arcangelo, Via Reale Basilica, 71037 Monte Sant'Angelo - T: 0884561150, Fax: 0884561150, E-mail: -santuariosanmichele@interfree.it, Internet: http://www.gargano.it/sanmichele. Head: Ladislao Suchy
Religious Arts Museum 21977

Museo delle Arti e Tradizioni Popolari del Gargano Giovanni Tancredi, Piazza San Francesco 15, 71037 Monte Sant'Angelo - T: 0884562098. Head: Antonio Trufini
Ethnology Museum 21978

Montebelluna

Museo Civico di Storia e Scienze Naturali, Via Piave 51, 31044 Montebelluna - T: 0423300456, Fax: 0423602284
Natural History Museum / Archaeological Museum - 1984
Natural history, archeology 21979

Museo dello Scarpone e della Scarpa Sportiva, Via Zuccareda, 31044 Montebelluna - T: 0423303282
Local Museum 21980

Montecatini Terme e Tettuccio

Museo della Propositura di San Pietro, Fraz Montecatini Alto, Via Prataccio 7, Parrocchia, 51016 Montecatini Terme e Tettuccio - T: 057273727
Religious Arts Museum 21981

Montecatini Val di Nievole

Museo della Prepositura, Via Prataccio 7, 51010 Montecatini Val di Nievole - T: 057273727
Religious Arts Museum
Silver work, vestments, 14th c silver reliquary, frescoes 21982

Montechiarugolo

Castello e Raccolta Archeologica, Castello, 43022 Montechiarugolo - T: 0521686600. Head: Stefano Nasi
Archaeological Museum 21983

Montecorice

Museo della Civiltà Contadina, Fraz Ortodonico Cilento, 84060 Montecorice - T: 0974964193. Head: Prof. Cesare Maffia
Historical Museum 21984

Montefalco

Pinacoteca San Francesco, Via Ringhiera Umbra, 06036 Montefalco - T: 0742379598, Fax: 0742379506
Fine Arts Museum
Works by Benozzo Gozzoli, Perugino, frescoes, 13th c decorations 21985

Montefiorino

Museo della Resistenza, Via Rocca 1, 41045 Montefiorino - T: 0536965139
Historical Museum 21986

Montefortino

Pinacoteca Comunale F. Duranti, Palazzo Comunale, Via Roma 21, 63047 Montefortino - T: 0736859101
Fine Arts Museum - 1842
17th c paintings, Tuscan, Venetian and Bolognese schools 21987

Monteleone Sabino

Museo Civico, Palazzo Comunale, 02033 Monteleone Sabino - T: 076584014
Local Museum 21988

Montelupo Fiorentino

Museo Archeologico e della Ceramica Montelupo Fiorentino, Via Bartolomeo Sinibaldi 45, 50056 Montelupo Fiorentino - T: 057151352, Fax: 057151506, E-mail: montelupoceramica@leanet.it, Internet: http://www.museo-montelupo.it. Head: Dr. Fausto Berti
Decorative Arts Museum / Archaeological Museum
Ceramics of Montelupo and Mediterranean, antique italic ceramics, Cypriot and Greek vases, Etruscan aucoheros 21989

Monteprandone

Museo Diocesano Intercomunale di Arte Sacra, Convento Santa Maria delle Grazie, 63020 Monteprandone - T: 0735594960, Fax: 0735577246. Head: Dr. Paola Di Girolami
Religious Arts Museum
archive 21990

Montepulciano

Museo Civico, Via Ricci 15, 53045 Montepulciano - T: 0578716943
Fine Arts Museum - 1905
14th to 17th c Tuscan paintings, illuminated books, terra cottas by Della Robbia 21991

Museo Naturalistico del Lago, Via del Lago 10, 53045 Montepulciano - T: 0578767518
Local Museum 21992

Monterosso Calabro

Museo della Civiltà Contadina ed Artigiana della Calabria, Via G. Marconi 34, 89819 Monterosso Calabro - T: 0963326053, 0963325039, Fax: 0963326053, E-mail: pro.monterosso@tiscalinet.it. Head: Soccorso Capomolla
Agriculture Museum
Farming, costumes, weaving, pottery, wood crafts, blacksmith's work 21993

Monterubbiano

Piccola Raccolta Archeologica, Palazzo Comunale, 63026 Monterubbiano - T: 073459125
Archaeological Museum 21994

Montevarchi

Museo d'Arte Sacra della Insigne Collegiata di San Lorenzo, Via Isidore Del Lungo 4, 52025 Montevarchi - T: 055980468
Local Museum 21995

Museo di Arte Sacra e Tempietto Robbiano, Piazza Varchi, 52025 Montevarchi - T: 055980468. Head: Dr. Emilio Romagnoli
Religious Arts Museum
Paintings, sculpture 21996

Museo Paleontologico, Via Bracciolini 38, 52025 Montevarchi - T: 055981227, Fax: 055981227, E-mail: anademiadelpoggio@technet.it. Head: Michele Sant
Natural History Museum
Fossils, mainly of the Valdarno Superior area 21997

Monticelli d'Ongina

Museo del Po, Museo Civiltà Contadina e Artigina, Castello Pallavicino Casali 10, 29010 Monticelli d'Ongina - T: 0523827185, 0523827195. Head: Giuseppe Fornasari, Casarola Albino
Ethnology Museum / Archaeological Museum / Agriculture Museum / Natural History Museum 21998

Montichiari

Museo Civico Risorgimentale, Piazza del Teatro 16, 25018 Montichiari - T: 030961115
Local Museum 21999

Montodine

Museo Etnografico, Oratorio Don Bosco, 26010 Montodine
Ethnology Museum 22000

Monza

Musei Civici - Museo della Città, Serrone della Villa Reale, Viale Brianza 2, 20052 Monza - T: 039366381, Fax: 039361558, E-mail: musei@comune.monza.mi.it. Head: Dr. Roberto Cassanelli
Local Museum 22001

Museo del Tesoro del Duomo, Via Canonica 8, 20052 Monza - T: 039323404, 039389420, Fax: 039382199, E-mail: duomo.monza@libero.it. Head: Leopoldo Gariboldi
Religious Arts Museum - 1965
5th to 9th c relics, medieval and Renaissance sacred goldwork, parchments, incunabula, rare books 22002

Pinacoteca Civica, Serrone Villa Reale, Viale Brianza 2, 20052 Monza - T: 039322086, Fax: 039361558, E-mail: musei@comune.monza.mi.it. Head: Dr. Roberto Cassanelli
Fine Arts Museum - 1935
16th-17th c paintings, modern art 22003

Morbegno

Museo Civico di Storia Naturale, Via Cortivacci 2, 23017 Morbegno - T: 0342612451, Fax: 0342615528, E-mail: museo.morbegno@provincia.so.it, Internet: http://fc.provincia.so.it/~museo.morbegno/. Head: Fabio Penati
Natural History Museum - 1974
Insects, minerals, birds, mammals, herbarium - library 22004

Morigerati

Museo Etnografico, Fondazione Florenzano, Castello, Via Granatelli 5, 84030 Morigerati - T: 0974982024. Head: Clorinda Florenzano
Ethnology Museum 22005

Napoli

Castel Sant'Elmo, Largo San Martino, 80129 Napoli - T: 0815784030. Head: Dr. Angela Tecce
Historical Museum / Fine Arts Museum 22006

Centro Arte Contemporanea, Via Alvino 13, 80127 Napoli - T: 0815565987
Public Gallery 22007

Collezioni dell'Istituto Universitario Orientale, Piazza S. Giovanni Maggiore 30, 80134 Napoli - T: 0817605403
Archaeological Museum / University Museum 22008

Complesso Museale di Santa Chiara, Via Santa Chiara 49c, 80134 Napoli - T: 0817971256, 0817971261, Fax: 0817971261, E-mail: olchios@mbox.netway.it, Internet: http://www.oltreil-chiostro.org. Head: Giuseppe Reale
Religious Arts Museum - 1995
Religious art, wooden marble sculpture, remains of the thermae (1st-4th c AD) - didactic, graphic and photography department 22009

Galleria dell'Accademia di Belle Arti, Via Santa Maria di Constantinopoli 107a, 80100 Napoli - T: 0815640554, Fax: 0815640592
Fine Arts Museum 22010

Museo Archeologico Nazionale, Piazza Museo, 19, 80135 Napoli - T: 081440166, Fax: 081440013, E-mail: sancmann@interbusiness.it, Internet: http://athena.cib.na.cnr.it/vhf-it/sanc_home.en.html. Head: Prof. Stefano De Caro
Archaeological Museum - 1816
Roman sculpture, painting, bronzes, mural paintings from the excavations of Ercolano, Pompei and Stabiae, domestic utensils, mosaics, vases, ivories, lamps, terra cottas from Pompei and Ercolano, antique technology and engineering 22011

Museo Artistico Industriale, Istituto d'Arte di Napoli, Piazzetta Demetrio Salazar 6, 80132 Napoli - T: 0817645775
Decorative Arts Museum 22012

Museo Civico Gaetano Filangieri, Piazzetta Filangieri, Via Duomo 288, 80132 Napoli - T: 081203175, Fax: 081203175. Head: Dr. Mario Carignani
Decorative Arts Museum / Fine Arts Museum - 1882
Painting, medieval arms, Oriental majolica, porcelain, antique furniture, numismatics, manuscripts - library 22013

Museo dell'Appartamento Storico del Palazzo Reale, Piazza Plebiscito 1, 80132 Napoli - T: 081413888, Fax: 081403561. Head: Filomena Sardella
Decorative Arts Museum - 1950
Tapestries, furniture, ceiling painting by Battistello Caracciolo - Photographic laboratory, filing centre, tapestry restauration centre 22014

Museo delle Carrozze Mario D'Alessandro Marchese di Civitanova, Villa Pignatelli, Via Riviera di Chiaia 200, 80121 Napoli - T: 081669675. Head: Dr. Angela Tecce
Science&Tech Museum 22015

Museo dell'Istituto Statale d'Arte, Piazza Salazar 6, 80132 Napoli
Decorative Arts Museum
Decorative arts and crafts 22016

Museo di Anatomia Veterinaria, Via Veterinaria 1, 80137 Napoli - T: 0815644215/30, Fax: 0815644230, E-mail: paesano@unina.it. Head: Prof. G.V. Pelagalli
Special Museum / University Museum 22017

Museo di Antropologia dell'Università di Napoli, Via Mezzocannone 8, 80134 Napoli - T: 0815802018, Fax: 0812528902, E-mail: fedele@dgbm.unina.it, Internet: http://www.musei.unina.it/Antropologia. Head: Prof. F.G. Fedele
Ethnology Museum / University Museum - 1881
Prehistoric artifacts (mainly lithics) from southern Italy, eastern north America, Troy (Schliemann's gift), about 2,000 human skulls, peruvian mummies 22018

Museo di Capodimonte, Palazzo Reale di Capodimonte, Via Miano 1, 80137 Napoli - T: 0817499111, Fax: 0817445032. Head: Dr. Mariella Utili
Fine Arts Museum / Decorative Arts Museum - 1738
Paintings and sculpture, drawings, prints, ivories, enamels, gold and silver works, tapestry, armaments, medals and bronzes, porcelain - library 22019

Museo di Geologia, Largo San Marcellino 10, 80100 Napoli - T: 081204398
Natural History Museum 22020

Museo di Paleontologia, Largo San Marcellino 10, 80100 Napoli - T: 081204242
Natural History Museum 22021

Museo di Zoologia, Via Mezzocannone 8, 80134 Napoli - T: 0815527089. Head: Prof. Virgilio Botte
Natural History Museum - 1813
Insects, fish, reptiles, birds 22022

Museo Diego Aragona Pignatelli Cortes, Riviera di Chiaja 200, 80122 Napoli - T: 0817612356, Fax: 081669675. Head: Dr. Denise Maria Pagano
Fine Arts Museum / Decorative Arts Museum - 1960
18th c paintings, historic house, carriages 22023

Museo Duca di Martina, Villa Floridiana, Via Cimarosa 77, 80127 Napoli - T: 0815788418. Head: Dr. Flavia Petrelli
Decorative Arts Museum - 1911
Ivories, enamels, bronzes, ceramics, glassware of Murano and Bohemia, European and Far Eastern porcelain - photo archives 22024

Museo e Certosa di San Martino, Largo San Martino 5, 80129 Napoli - T: 0815781769, Fax: 0815781769. Head: Dr. Rossana Muzii
Local Museum - 1866
Neapolitan historical documents, ship models, folklore and costumes, 14th to 19th c paintings and sculpture, majolica, porcelain, glass, miniatures, numismatics, arms 22025

Museo Navale, Via Acton 38, 80133 Napoli - T: 0815513975
Science&Tech Museum 22026

Museo Storico Musicale, c/o Conservatorio di Musica, S. Pietro a Maiella 35, 80138 Napoli - T: 081459255. Head: Prof. Jacopo Napoli
Music Museum 22027

Pinacoteca dei Girolamini, Via Duomo 142, 80138 Napoli - T: 081449139. Head: Giovanni Ferrara
Fine Arts Museum
17th c Neapolitan paintings 22028

Pinacoteca del Pio Monte della Misericordia, Via Tribunali 253, 80139 Napoli - T: 081445517
Fine Arts Museum
Paintings of the Neapolitan school 22029

Raccolta d'Arte Pagliara, Via Suor Orsola 10, 80132 Napoli - T: 081412909
Fine Arts Museum
16th to 19th c drawings, prints and ceramics 22030

Real Museo Mineralogico, Via Mezzocannone 8, 80134 Napoli - T: 0812535163, Fax: 0815518701, E-mail: mghiara@unina.it. Head: Prof. Maria Rosaria Ghiara
Natural History Museum / University Museum
Minerals 22031

Scavi e Museo Archeologico di S. Restituta, Piazza S. Restituta, Lacco Ameno, 80134 Napoli. Head: Canco Pietro Monti
Archaeological Museum 22032

Nemi

Museo delle Navi Romane, Via di Diana 13, 00040 Nemi - T: 069398040, Fax: 069398040, E-mail: soprlazio@libero.it. Head: Dr. Guiseppina Ghini
Archaeological Museum
Recovered Roman ships 22033

Nervesa della Battaglia

Museo di Storia Naturale, Via Bombardieri 1, 31040 Nervesa della Battaglia - T: 0422773231
Natural History Museum 22034

Nicotera

Museo Civico Archeologico, Castello dei Ruffo, 88034 Nicotera - T: 096381013
Archaeological Museum 22035

Museo Diocesano di Arte Sacra, Piazza Duomo 10, 88034 Nicotera - T: 096381308
Religious Arts Museum 22036

Nizza Monferrato

Museo delle Contadinerie Bersano, Piazza Dante 21, 14049 Nizza Monferrato - T: 0141721273
Agriculture Museum
History of viticulture, methods of grape pressing, farm implements and tools 22037

Raccolta Bersano delle Stampe sul Vino, Casa San Marco, Piazza Dante 10, 14049 Nizza Monferrato - T: 0141721088. Head: Laura Bersano
Historical Museum 22038

Nocera Inferiore

Museo Archeologico dell'Agro Nocerino, Piazza Sant'Antonio, 84014 Nocera Inferiore - T: 081929880. Head: Dr. Matilde Romito
Archaeological Museum
Archeological findings of ancient Nuceria, sarcophagi, Roman coins 22039

Nocera Umbra

Pinacoteca Comunale, Piazza Caprera, 06025 Nocera Umbra - T: 0742818846
Fine Arts Museum - 1957
Archeology, paintings, frescoes, library 22040

Nola

Antiquarium del Seminario, Via Seminario 29, 80035 Nola - T: 0815121511, Fax: 0815121511. Head: Giovanni Santaniello
Archaeological Museum
Archeological findings from Cimitile, Cippus Abellanus, epitaphs 22041

Nonantola

Museo Benedettino Nonantolano e Diocesano di Arte Sacra, Via Marconi 3, 41015 Nonantola - T: 059549025, E-mail: secretary@abbazia-nonantola.net, Internet: http://www.abbazia-nonantola.net. Head: Dr. Riccardo Fangarezzi
Religious Arts Museum
Wall paintings, Byzantine crosses, illuminated codices, ancient Thesaurum of the abbey 22042

Norcia

Museo La Castellina, Piazza San Benedetto, 06046 Norcia - T: 0743816404
Local Museum
Local and religious art 22043

Noto

Museo Comunale, Corso V. Emanuele 134, 96017 Noto - T: 0931836462
Fine Arts Museum
Archeology, medieval exhibits, modern art 22044

Novafeltria

Museo Storico Minerario, Fraz Perticara, Via Decio Raggi 26, 61015 Novafeltria - T: 0541917031
Historical Museum 22045

Novara

Civica Galleria d'Arte Moderna Giannoni, Via Fratelli Rosselli 20, 28100 Novara - T: 0321623021, Fax: 032133397. Head: Dr. Maria Laura Tomea Gavazzoli
Fine Arts Museum 22046

Museo Archeologico Remo Fumagalli, Via Fratelli Rosselli 20, 28100 Novara - T: 0321623021, Fax: 032136438. Head: Dr. Maria Laura Tomea Gavazzoli
Archaeological Museum - 1935
Prehist, Celtic culture, Langobard domination 22047

Museo di Storia Naturale Faraggiana-Ferrandi, Via Ferrari 13, 28100 Novara - T: 0321627037, Fax: 032136438. Head: Dr. Maria Laura Tomea Gavazzoli
Natural History Museum - 1937
Natural history section, zoological coll, anthropology section, ethnographic material on East Africa, China and Japan 22048

Museo e Pinacoteca Civica del Broletto, Via Fratelli Rosselli 20, 28100 Novara - T: 0321623021, Fax: 032133397. Head: Dr. Maria Laura Tomea Gavazzoli
Fine Arts Museum / Archaeological Museum - 1874
Paintings, sculptures and drawings of Tuscan, Lombard and Venetian schools, local archeology, 16th to 19th c arms 22049

Museo Lapidario della Canonica del Duomo, Chiostro della Canonica del Duomo, 28100 Novara - T: 0321661635, Fax: 0321661662, E-mail: musei@novaria.org, Internet: http://www.museolapidario.novaria.org. Head: Dr. Paolo Monticelli
Archaeological Museum 22050

Nove

Museo delle Ceramiche, Istituto De Fabris, 36055 Nove - T: 0424590022, Fax: 0424827358. Head: Prof. Nicolo Sebelin
Decorative Arts Museum 22051

Novellara

Museo Civico Gonzaga, Piazzale Marconi 1, 42017 Novellara - T: 0522654242, Fax: 0522652057. Head: Elena Ghidini
Local Museum 22052

Museo della Civiltà Contadina, Piazzale Marconi 1, 42017 Novellara - T: 0522654242, Fax: 0522652057. Head: Elena Ghidini
Historical Museum 22053

Novi Ligure

Museo della Società Storia del Novese, Via Antonio Gramsci 67, 15067 Novi Ligure. Head: Dr. Francesco Melone
Local Museum 22054

Numana

Antiquarium, Via La Fenice, 60026 Numana - T: 0719331162
Archaeological Museum
Greek material from the necropolis of Sirolo and Numana 22055

Nuoro

Museo Civico Speleo-Archeologico, Via L. da Vinci 5, 08100 Nuoro - T: 078433793
Archaeological Museum 22056

Museo Deleddiano, Via Deladda 42, 08100 Nuoro - T: 078434571, Fax: 078437484. Head: Dr. Paolo Piquereddu
Historic Site - 1983 22057

Museo della Vita e delle Tradizioni Popolari Sarde, Via Mereu 56, 08100 Nuoro - T: 078431426. Head: Dr. Paolo Piquereddu
Folklore Museum
Folk art and peasant life of Sardinia, costumes 22058

Oderzo

Museo Civico Archeologico Eno Bellis, Via Garibaldi 63, 31046 Oderzo - T: 0422713333, Fax: 0422713333, Internet: http://www.oderzocultura.it. Head: Dr. Elisa Possenti
Archaeological Museum - 1875
Archeological finds from the area, mosaics, medals 22059

Museo di Storia Naturale Brandolini-Rota e Giol, Via Brandolini 6, 31046 Oderzo - T: 0422712041. Head: Dr. Giuseppe Parpagiola
Natural History Museum 22060

Pinacoteca Comunale Alberto Martini, Via Garibaldi 80, 31046 Oderzo - T: 0422815166
Fine Arts Museum 22061

Offida

Museo Archeologico G. Allevi, Piazza Vittorio Emanuele II 13, 63035 Offida - T: 0736889381. Head: Alberto Piergollini
Archaeological Museum
Local archeology, paintings 22062

Oggebbio

Oskar Schlemmer Theatre Estate and Collection, Via Palermo 6, Cadessino, 28824 Oggebbio - T: 032348468, Fax: 0323491942, E-mail: ramanschlemmer@iol.it, Internet: http://www.schlemmer.org. Head: C. Raman Schlemmer
Fine Arts Museum
Bauhaus exhibits, Indian art, craft, ethnography, photos - C.Raman Schlemmer photo archive 22063

Oleggio

Museo Civico Etnografico, Piazzale della Chiesa 1, 28047 Oleggio - T: 032191323, Fax: 032194505. Head: Gaudenzio Miranda
Ethnology Museum 22064

Museo di Arte Religiosa, Piazzale della Chiesa 1, 28047 Oleggio - T: 032191168. Head: Pietro Parrocchia, Paola Parrocchia
Religious Arts Museum 22065

Orbetello

Antiquarium Comunale, Via Mura di Levante, 58015 Orbetello - T: 0564867451. Head: Gian Piero Soggin
Archaeological Museum
Etruscan and Roman graves, vases, numismatics and bronzes 22066

Oria

Collezione Martini Carissimo, Castello Svevo, 72024 Oria - T: 0831345026
Archaeological Museum 22067

Museo Didattico Zoologico, Santuario San Cosimo alla Macchia, 72024 Oria - T: 0831947542
Natural History Museum 22068

Oristano

Antiquarium Arborense, Via Parpaglia, 09025 Oristano - T: 0783791262, Fax: 0783791229. Head: Giuseppe Pan
Archaeological Museum - 1938
Prehistoric, Punic and Roman archeological findings, Sardinian art and artifacts 22069

Raccolta dell'Opera del Duomo, Piazza Duomo, 09170 Oristano - T: 078378684
Religious Arts Museum 22070

Orte

Museo Diocesano di Arte Sacra, Piazza Colonna 3, 01028 Orte - T: 0761494062. Head: Delfo Gioacchini
Religious Arts Museum
Religious art, paintings, an 8th c mosaic of the Madonna, goldsmith work 22071

Ortisei

Museo della Val Gardena, Union di Ladins (Val Gardena Heritage Museum), Via Rezia 83, 39046 Ortisei - T: 0471797554, Fax: 0471798351, E-mail: museum@val-gardena.com, Internet: http://www.val-gardena.com/english/art/museum-ladin.htm. Head: Robert Moroder
Local Museum / Religious Arts Museum / Natural History Museum
Minerals, geology, zoology and botany of the Dolomites, old wooden toys of Val Gardena, archaeology, religious and profarne sculpture, paintings 22072

Ortona

Pinacoteca M. Cascella, Palazzo Farnese, Passeggiata Orientale, 66026 Ortona - T: 0859067233. Head: Elio Giannetti
Fine Arts Museum 22073

Ortonovo

Museo Archeologico Nazionale di Luni, 19034 Ortonovo - T: 018766811
Archaeological Museum 22074

Orvieto

Museo dell'Opera del Duomo, Palazzo Soliano, Piazza Duomo, 05018 Orvieto - T: 0763342477, Fax: 0763340336. Head: Prof. Romolo Tiberi
Fine Arts Museum
14th c paintings, frescoes, sculpture, medieval art - library 22075

Museo Fondazione C. Faina e Museo Civico Palazzo Faina, Piazza Duomo 29, 05018 Orvieto - T: 0763341216, Fax: 0763341250, E-mail: fainaorv@tin.it, Internet: http://www.museofaina.it. Head: Giuseppe M. Della Fina
Archaeological Museum - 1864
Greek, Etruscan and Roman archeology, numismatics 22076

Osimo

Museo Diocesano di Osimo, Piazza Duomo 3, 60027 Osimo - T: 0717231808, Fax: 0717231133, E-mail: museodiocesano@comune.osimo.an.it, Internet: http://www.comune.osimo.an.it/museo. Head: Flavio Kissi
Religious Arts Museum
Altar pieces, candlesticks, sacred vestments, reliquary 22077

Osoppo

Museo Storico del Forte, Fortezza, 33010 Osoppo
Local Museum 22078

Ossuccio

Antiquarium Lucio Salvio Quintiano, Isola Comacina, 22010 Ossuccio. Head: Luigi Mario Belloni
Archaeological Museum
Archeological findings of the area 22079

Ostia Antica

Castello di Giulio II, Piazza della Rocca, 00119 Ostia Antica - T: 0656358024, Fax: 065651500, E-mail: segreteria.ostia@arti.beniculturali.it, Internet: http://itnw.roma.it/ostia/scavi. Head: Dr. Anna Gallina Zevi
Archaeological Museum - 1940
Archaeology 22080

Museo Ostiense, Viale dei Romagnoli 717, 00119 Ostia Antica - T: 0656358024/26, Fax: 065651500, E-mail: segreteria.ostia@arti.beniculturali.it, Internet: http://itnw.roma.it. Head: Dr. Anna Gallina Zevi
Archaeological Museum
Roman art and sculpture, 2nd c sarcophagi, lead, bronzes, terra cotta, glass, coins, mosaics 22081

Scavi di Ostia, Viale dei Romagnoli 717, 00119 Ostia Antica - T: 0656358099, Fax: 065651500, E-mail: segreteria.ostia@arti.beniculturali.it, Internet: http://itnw.roma.it/ostia/scavi. Head: Dr. Anna Gallina Zevi
Archaeological Museum
Archaeology 22082

Ozzano dell'Emilia

Museo di Anatomia Patologica Veterinaria (Veterinary Pathology and Anatomy Museum), Via Tolara di Sopra 50, 40064 Ozzano dell'Emilia - T: 051792960, 051792970, Fax: 051792970, E-mail: marcato@vet.unibo.it. Head: Paolo Stefano Marcato
Natural History Museum / University Museum - 1807
Veterinary sciences, anatomy, pathology, teratology, plaster models 22083

Museo Zoologico dell'Istituto Nazionale per la Fauna Selvatica, Via Ca' Fornacetta, 9, 40064 Ozzano dell'Emilia - T: 0516512111, Fax: 051796628, E-mail: infsmuse@iperbole.bologna.it. Head: Prof. Mario Spagnesi
Natural History Museum - 1933
Birds, mammals 22084

Ozzano Taro

Raccolta Guatelli, Via Nazionale, 43046 Ozzano Taro - T: 0521809100
Local Museum 22085

Padova

Cappella degli Scrovegni, Piazza Eremitani 8, 35121 Padova, mail addr: Via Porciglia 35 - T: 0498204550, 0498204585, Fax: 0498204566, E-mail: musei@comune.padova.it, Internet: http://www.padovanet.it/museicivici/monumenti/scrovegni.html. Head: Davide Banzato
Fine Arts Museum - 14th c
Frescos by Giotto, sculptures by Giovanni Pisano 22086

Musei Civici agli Eremitani, Piazza Eremitani 8, 35121 Padova, mail addr: Via Porciglia 35, 35121 Padova - T: 0498204550/51, Fax: 0498204585, E-mail: musei@comune.padova.it, Internet: http://www.padovanet.it/museicivici/musei/index.htm. Head: Dr. Davide Banzato
Archaeological Museum / Fine Arts Museum - 1825
Art gallery, works by Giotto, Giorgione, Bellini, Guariento, Tiziano, Tintoretto, Veronese, Romanino, Palma jr., Renaissance bronzes with works by Riccio, Tiziano, Aspetti, J. Sansovino, Emo Capodilista Coll, prehist, pre-Roman and Roman age, Egyptian and Etruscan coll, Merletti and Casuccio, coll, numismatic - library 22087

Museo Aeronautico, Località San Pelagio, Carrara San Giorgio, 35100 Padova - T: 049525883, Fax: 0499125008. Head: Ricciarda Avesani
Science&Tech Museum - 1980
Aircrafts, helicopters, sailplanes, motorsailplanes, documents, books, photographs, from the birth of aviation to today incl also the space - library, archives 22088

Museo Antoniano, Piazza del Santo 11, 35123 Padova - T: 0498225656, Fax: 0498753911. Head: Giovanni Maria Luisetto
Religious Arts Museum - 1907
18th c Venetian painting, 18th c Venetian and French fabrics, Venetian and German goldworks from the 16th-18th c 22089

Museo Bottacin, Piazza Eremitani 8, 35121 Padova - T: 0498204569/570, Fax: 0498204584, E-mail: museo.bottacin@comune.padova.it, Internet: http://www.padovanet.it/museicivici/musei/collezioni/bottacin/index.htm. Head: Dr. Bruno Callegher

Fine Arts Museum - 1865
Greek, Roman and medieval Italian coins and
medals, Renaissance bronzes, seals, 19th and 20th
c paintings, 19th c sculptures - library   22090

**Museo di Geologia e Paleontologia dell'Università
degli Studi di Padova**, Via Giotto 1, 35137 Padova -
T: 0498272050, Fax: 0498272070,
E-mail: museopal@dmp.unipd.it, Internet: http://
www.unipd.it/esterni/wwwgeol/index.html. Head:
Prof. Domenico Rio
Natural History Museum / University Museum
Geology, paleontology   22091

Museo di Scienze Archeologiche e d'Arte, c/o
Università di Padova, Piazza Capitaniato 7, 35139
Padova - T: 0498274611, 0498274576,
Fax: 0498274613, Internet: http://
www.maldura.unipd.it/~discant. Head: Prof. Paolo
Scarpi
Archaeological Museum / Fine Arts Museum
Graeco-Roman art (sculptures and vases), works of
the Italian Renaissance (small sculpture and casts of
Alessandro Vittoria, Bartolomeo Ammannati,
Donatello)   22092

**Museo Diocesano di Arte Sacra San Gregorio
Barbarigo**, Via Duomo 15, 35100 Padova -
T: 0494942060
Religious Arts Museum   22093

Palazzo della Ragione, Via 8. Febbraio, 35122
Padova, mail addr: Via Porciglia 35, 35122 Padova -
T: 0498205006, 0498204513, Fax: 0498204566,
E-mail: musei@comune.padova.it, Internet: http://
www.padovanet.it/museicivici/monumenti/
ragione.html. Head: Dr. Davide Banzato
Historical Museum   22094

Pinacoteca Parrocchiale di San Tomaso Beckett,
Via San Tomaso 3, 35100 Padova - T: 04928768
Fine Arts Museum   22095

Padria

Museo Civico Archeologico, Via Nazionale 1, 07015
Padria - T: 079807018, Fax: 079807323
Archaeological Museum - 1989   22096

Padula

Museo Archeologico della Lucania Occidentale,
Certosa di Padula, 84034 Padula - T: 097577117,
Fax: 097577117. Head: Dr. Matilde Romito
Archaeological Museum - 1957
Archeological findings from the Diano Valley   22097

Paestum

Museo Archeologico Nazionale, Via Aquilia, 84063
Paestum - T: 0828811023. Head: Dr. Laura Rota
Archaeological Museum - 1952
Findings from the excavations of Paestum, bronzes,
sculptures, painted slabs from the necropolis,
including the Diver's tomb   22098

Pagani

Museo Alfonsiano, Basilica di Sant'Alfonso, 84016
Pagani - T: 089916054
Religious Arts Museum   22099

Palazzolo Acreide

Antiquarium, Teatro Greco, 96010 Palazzolo Acreide
- T: 0931871504
Archaeological Museum
Archaeological finds   22100

Casa Museo, Via Machiavelli 19, 96010 Palazzolo
Acreide - T: 0931327380
Agriculture Museum
Peasant life and folk art of Sicily, farm implements,
olive mills, Sicilian puppets, toys   22101

Raccolta Judica, Palazzo Cappellani, 96010
Palazzolo Acreide
Archaeological Museum   22102

Palermo

Antiquarium e Zona Archeologica, Via Solunto,
90124 Palermo
Archaeological Museum   22103

Civica Galleria d'Arte Moderna E. Restivo, Via Turati
10, 90139 Palermo - T: 091588951. Head: Rosa
Maria Giudice
Fine Arts Museum - 1907
19th and 20th c art, mostly by Sicilian artists   22104

Galleria Regionale della Sicilia, Palazzo Abatellis,
Via Alloro 4, 90133 Palermo - T: 0916230033,
Fax: 0916172187. Head: Dr. Vincenzo Abbate
Fine Arts Museum - 1954
Medieval and Renaissance art, paintings by Flemish
and Florentine school, Frescos - library, photo
archives   22105

Mostra Permanente del Tesoro della Cattedrale,
Corso Vittorio Emanuele, 90133 Palermo
Religious Arts Museum
Silver and goldsmith work, precious books, priest
vestments, crown of Constance of Aragon, exhibits
of the Norman Kings   22106

Museo Archeologico della Fondazione Mormino,
Via Libertà 52, 90100 Palermo - T: 0916259519,
Fax: 0916085978. Head: Francesco Mancuso
Archaeological Museum   22107

Museo Archeologico Regionale A. Salinas, Piazza
Olivella, 90133 Palermo - T: 0916116805/07,
Fax: 0916110740. Head: Dr. Carmela Angela Di
Stefano
Archaeological Museum - 1868
Greek, Punic, Roman and Etruscan antiquities,
sculpture and metopes from temple of Selinunte,
Egyptian inscriptions, prehist, oriental coll, marine
archaeology, epigraphy, numismatics - library,
archives   22108

**Museo del Risorgimento Vittorio Emanuele
Orlando**, Piazza S. Domenico 1, 90133 Palermo -
T: 091582774, Fax: 0916113455. Head: Prof.
Francesco Brancato
Historical Museum
Paintings, portraits, prints, medals, sculpture and
relics pertaining to the history of the Risorgimento in
Sicily   22109

Museo di Zoologia della Università di Palermo, c/o
Dipartimento Biologia Animale, Via Archirafi 18,
90123 Palermo - T: 0916230119,
Fax: 0916230144, E-mail: mausar@mbox.unipa.it,
Internet: http://www.unipa.it. Head: Prof. Nicolo
Parrinello
Natural History Museum / University Museum -
1862
Mediterranean fish and molluscs, European birds,
mammalia and reptiles, anatomy, osteology -
library   22110

Museo Diocesano di Arte Sacra, Via Matteo Bonello
2, 90134 Palermo - T: 0916077215/17,
Fax: 0916113642, E-mail: ufbbccee@tin.it,
Internet: http://arcidiocesi.palermo.it/ufficioben-
iculturali. Head: Giuseppe Randazzo
Religious Arts Museum / Decorative Arts Museum -
1927
12th to 18th c paintings by Vasari, Giordano, Novelli
and Velasquez, ceramics, gold and silver plate,
priests' vestments, mosaics, Byzantine icons   22111

Museo Etnografico G. Pitré, Via Duca degli Abruzzi,
90146 Palermo - T: 0916711060. Head: Prof.
Gaetone Falzone
Decorative Arts Museum / Folklore Museum - 1909
Sicilian culture and folk art, Sicilian puppets,
manger scene figures, Sicilian ceramics (19-20th c),
carriages (18th c), costumes (19th c)   22112

Museo Etnografico Siciliano Giuseppe Pitrè, Parco
della Favorita, 1 Viale Duca degli Abruzzi, 90146
Palermo - T: 0917404878, Fax: 0917404880. Head:
Eliana Calandra
Folklore Museum
Manuscripts of Pitré   22113

Museo Geologico G.G. Gemmellaro, Corso Tukory
131, 90134 Palermo - T: 0917041051,
Fax: 0917041041, E-mail: mgup@unipa.it,
Internet: http://www.unipa.it/dipgeopa/museo.htm.
Head: Prof. V. Agnesi
Natural History Museum - 1861   22114

Museo Internazionale delle Marionette, Palazzo
Fatta, Via Butera 1, 90133 Palermo - T: 091328060,
Fax: 091328276
Performing Arts Museum - 1965
Sicilian puppets and marionettes, Oriental
marionettes in amber, parchment and wood, 19th c
manuscripts of plays from Palermo and Naples -
library   22115

Orto Botanico, Via Lincoln 2b, 90133 Palermo -
T: 0916161493, Fax: 0916176089. Head: Prof.
Francesco Maria Raimondo
Natural History Museum - 1795
Wood samples, plants - library   22116

Palestrina

Museo Archeologico Nazionale di Palestrina,
Palazzo Barberini, Piazza della Cortina, 00036
Palestrina - T: 069538100, Fax: 069538100. Head:
Dr. Sandra Gatti
Archaeological Museum - 1956
Local excavations from the temple of Fortuna,
terracottas, mosaics, bronzes, sculptures   22117

Pallanza

Museo del Paesaggio, Museo Storico e Artistico del
Verbano, Palazzo Viani-Dugnani, Via Ruga 44,
28048 Pallanza - T: 0323502418. Head: Prof. Gianni
Pizzigoni
Fine Arts Museum / Archaeological Museum - 1909
Paintings, sculpture, archeology   22118

Palmanova

Museo Civico Storico, Borgo Udine 4, 33057
Palmanova - T: 0432929106. Head: Dr. Gabriella Del
Frate
Local Museum   22119

Palmi

Museo Calabrese di Etnografia e Folklore, Via
Felice Battaglia, 89015 Palmi - T: 0966411080,
0966262250, Fax: 0966411080. Head: Dr. Sergio
Marafioti
Ethnology Museum   22120

Museo d'Arte Moderna, Via Felice Battaglia, 89015
Palmi - T: 0966262250, Fax: 0966411080. Head:
Dr. Sergio Marafioti
Fine Arts Museum   22121

Museo Francesco Cilea, Via Felice Battaglia, 89015
Palmi - T: 0966411080, Fax: 0966411080. Head:
Dr. Sergio Marafioti
Music Museum   22122

Museo Nicola Antonio Manfroce, Via Felice
Battaglia, 89015 Palmi - T: 0966411080,
Fax: 0966411080. Head: Dr. Sergio Marafioti
Local Museum - 1955
Archeological findings from Taurianum, peasant life
and folk art of Calabria, pottery, agricultural
tools   22123

Parma

Casa Museo Toscanini, Via Tanzi 13, 43100 Parma -
T: 0521285499. Head: Dr. Valerio Cervetti
Music Museum
Memorabilia on the conductor Arturo Toscanini
(1867-1957)   22124

Fondazione Museo Glauco Lombardi, Via Garibaldi
15, 43100 Parma - T: 0521233727,
Fax: 0521233727, E-mail: glaucolombardi@
libero.it, Internet: http://www.museolombardi.it.
Head: Dr. Francesca Sandrini
Local Museum
Documents and relics of the Bourbonic period, 18th
c French paintings, documents, relicts and paintings
of Napoleon's and Maria Luigia's period   22125

Galleria Nazionale, Palazzo Pilotta, Piazzale Pilotta
15, 43100 Parma - T: 0521233309, Fax: 206336,
E-mail: sbaspr@libero.it. Head: Dr. Lucia Fornari
Schinachi
Fine Arts Museum - 1752
14th to 19th c paintings, including works by
Correggio, Parmigianino, Van Dyck, artists of the
Parma and Bolognese school, Flemish and French
painters   22126

House of Music-Parma, Piazzale San Francesco,
43100 Parma. Head: Dr. Valerio Cervetti
Music Museum   22127

Museo Archeologico Nazionale, Palazzo Pilotta, Via
della Pilotta 4, 43100 Parma - T: 0521233718.
Head: Dr. Maria Bernabò Brea
Archaeological Museum - 1760
Roman inscriptions, marble works, bronzes, pottery,
material from the pre-Roman period, Egyptian,
Greek and Etruscan coll   22128

Museo Bodoniano, Palazzo della Pilotta, 43100
Parma - T: 0521220423, Fax: 0521235662,
E-mail: luigipelizzoni@yahoo.com
Historical Museum - 1963
Art of printing, rare editions - library   22129

Museo della Farmacia, Via Borgo Pipa 1, 43100
Parma - T: 052133309. Head: Dr. Lucia Fornari
Schinachi
Historical Museum - 1897
Furnishings and objects of an ancient Benedictan
pharmacy, 15th-17th c pots and ceramics   22130

Museo di Arte Cinese ed Etnografico, Centro
Internazionale Arte, Cultura & Società, Via San
Martino 8, 43100 Parma - T: 0521257337,
Fax: 0521960603, E-mail: info@ciacs.it,
Internet: http://www.ciacs.it. Head: Dr. Domenico
Milani
Decorative Arts Museum - 1900
Chinese bronzes, ceramics, porcelains, paintings,
coins, African and Asian ethnography   22131

Museo di Mineralogia e Petrografica, c/o Università
di Parma, Viale delle Scienze 78, 43100 Parma -
T: 0521905326, Fax: 0521905305
Natural History Museum / University Museum
Minerals and rocks of the area   22132

Museo Eritreo Bottego, Via Università 12, 43100
Parma - T: 0521208855, Fax: 0521236465. Head:
Prof. Vittorio Parisi
Local Museum   22133

Museo Etnografico, Via San Martino 8, 43100 Parma
- T: 052154341
Ethnology Museum - 1900
Ethnography, Chinese, Japanese and African art,
African statues in ivory and wood   22134

Museo Paleontologico Parmense, Viale delle
Scienze 78, 43100 Parma - T: 0521905322,
Fax: 0521905305. Head: Prof. Giuseppe Pelosio
Natural History Museum - 1895
Fossils, stones, molluscs - Macropaleontological
laboratory, library   22135

Pinacoteca Giuseppe Stuard, Via Cavestro 14,
43100 Parma - T: 0521231286, 0521218882,
Fax: 0521218875. Head: Prof. Francesco Barocelli
Fine Arts Museum - 1834
Paintings, including early Tuscan artists, Francesi,
Spagnoli, Fiamminghi, coll 'Primitivi Toscani' (3rd-
4th c), Sculptures, north italian furniture (6th-
8th c)   22136

Patti

Zona Archeologica e Antiquarium, Frazione Tindari,
Zona del Teatro greco, 98066 Patti - T: 0941369023
Archaeological Museum
Archaeological material from Tyndaris   22137

Pavia

Musei Civici, Castello Visconteo, 27100 Pavia -
T: 038233853, 0382304816, Fax: 0382303028,
E-mail: museicivici@comune.pv.it, Internet: http://
www.comune.pv.it. Head: Donata Vicini

Local Museum - 1838
Hist of Risorgimento, archeological material,
medieval, Romanesque and Renaissance sculpture,
prints, ethnography   22138

Museo Civico di Storia Naturale, Strada Nuova 65,
27100 Pavia
Natural History Museum
Mineralogy, zoology   22139

Museo del Dipartimento di Scienze della Terra, c/o
Dipartimento di Scienze della Terra, Università di
Pavia, Via Ferrata 1, 27100 Pavia - T: 0382505873,
Fax: 0382505890. Head: Vittorio Tazzoli
Natural History Museum / University Museum -
1779
Mineralogy and petrography   22140

**Museo dell'Istituto di Anatomia Umana e
Patologia**, Via Forlanini 8, 27100 Pavia -
T: 0832392522
Natural History Museum - 1876
Comparative anatomy, embryology,
osteology   22141

Museo di Archeologia, c/o Università di Pavia,
Strada Nuova 65, 27100 Pavia - T: 0382504497,
Fax: 0382504526. Head: Prof. Cesare Saletti
Archaeological Museum / University Museum - 1821
Numismatics, archeology, teaching material,
sculptures, bronzes, architectonic fragments   22142

Museo di Scienze Naturali, Musei Universitari,
Piazza Botta 9, 27100 Pavia - T: 0382506308,
Fax: 0382506308, E-mail: c.museo@unipv.it. Head:
Clementina Rovati
Natural History Museum - 1771
Birds and mammals   22143

Museo Pavese di Scienze Naturali, Castello
Visconteo, 27100 Pavia - T: 038226242. Head: Dr.
Donata Vicini
Natural History Museum   22144

Museo per la Storia dell'Università di Pavia, Strada
Nuova 65, 27100 Pavia - T: 038229724. Head: Prof.
Marco Fraccaro
Historical Museum / University Museum
History of the University of Pavia - library   22145

Pinacoteca Malaspina, Castello Visconteo, 27100
Pavia - T: 038233853, 0382304816,
Fax: 0382303028, E-mail: museicivici@
comune.pv.it, Internet: http://www.comune.pv.it.
Head: Dr. Donata Vicini
Fine Arts Museum - 1835
Medieval art coll, paintings XIVth-XXth c -
library   22146

Pavullo nel Frignano

Civico Museo Archeologico Frignanese, Palazzo
degli Estensi, 41026 Pavullo nel Frignano -
T: 053620809
Archaeological Museum   22147

Pennabilli

Museo Diocesano Antonio Bergamaschi, Seminario
Feretrano, 61016 Pennabilli - T: 0541928415. Head:
Giuseppe Agostini
Religious Arts Museum   22148

Penne

Museo Civico Diocesano, Piazza Duomo, 65017
Penne - T: 0858210525
Religious Arts Museum   22149

Pertica Bassa

**Museo Civico della Resistenza e del Folclore
Valsabbino**, Via Roma 5, 25070 Pertica Bassa -
T: 0365821131, Fax: 0365821195. Head: Prof.
Alfredo Bonomi
Historical Museum / Folklore Museum   22150

Perticara

Museo Storico Minerario, Via D. Raggi 26, 61017
Perticara - T: 0541927576. Head: Fabio Fabbri
Natural History Museum - 1970
Minerals, mining equipment, tools and machinery,
local archeology - library   22151

Perugia

Collegio del Cambio - Museo d'Arte, Corso
Vannuncci 25, 06123 Perugia - T: 0755728599,
Fax: 0755728599, Internet: http://www.perusia.it/
cambio
Fine Arts Museum   22152

Galleria Nazionale dell'Umbria, Palazzo dei Priori,
Corso Vannucci, 06100 Perugia - T: 0755741248,
Fax: 0755741257, E-mail: dizzionegnu@libero.il.
Head: Dr. Vittoria Garibaldi
Fine Arts Museum - 1863
13th to 18th c paintings and sculpture, Francesco di
Giorgio Martini, Beato Angelico, Perugino, jewellery,
costumes - library   22153

Museo Archeologico Nazionale dell'Umbria, Piazza
Giordano Bruno 10, 06100 Perugia -
T: 0755727141, Fax: 0755759682,
E-mail: archeopg@arti.beniculturali.it,
Internet: http://www.archeopg.arti.beniculturali.it.
Head: Dr. Dorica Manconi
Archaeological Museum - 1812
Prehistoric finds from Tuscany, Etruscan and Roman
finds from Perugia   22154

Museo Capitolare di San Lorenzo Chiesa di San Lorenzo, Saladel Dottorato, Piazza IV Novembre, 06100 Perugia - T: 0755723832. Head: Decio Sensi
Religious Arts Museum 22155

Museo dell'Accademia di Belle Arti, Piazza San Francesco al Prato 5, 06123 Perugia - T: 0755730631, Fax: 0755730632. Head: Paolo Mazzerioli
Fine Arts Museum
Gipsoteca, drawings and prints, paintings 22156

Museo dell'Opera del Duomo, Piazza IV Novembre 23, 06100 Perugia
Religious Arts Museum - 1923
Illuminated codices, priest vestments, miniatures and paintings, silverware 22157

Museo di Storia Naturale, Piazza IV Novembre 6, 06100 Perugia - T: 0755725205. Head: Dr. Francesco Saverio Papagno
Natural History Museum 22158

Pesaro

Casa Natale di Rossini, Via Rossini 34, 61100 Pesaro - T: 0721387357
Music Museum
Birthplace of the composer Gioacchino Rossini (1792-1868), autographs and personal possessions, prints and portraits, Rossini Opera Festival 22159

Musei Civici, Pinacoteca, Museo delle Ceramiche, Piazza Toschi Mosca 29, 61100 Pesaro - T: 0721387541, Fax: 0721387524, E-mail: musei@comune.pesaro.ps.it. Head: Gian Carlo Bojani
Fine Arts Museum
Rossini's painting coll, mainly Venetian paintings, including Bellini, ceramics 22160

Museo Archeologico Oliveriano, Via Mazza 96, 61100 Pesaro - T: 072133344, Fax: 0721370365. Head: Prof. Antonio Brancati
Archaeological Museum
Italic, Etruscan, Greek, Roman and Paleochristian remains, coins, medals, coll of ancient maps 22161

Tempietto Rossiniano della Fondazione Rossini, Piazza Olivieri 5, 61100 Pesaro - T: 072130053, Fax: 072131220
Music Museum - 1896
Memorabilia on the composer Gioacchino Rossini (1792-1868), music manuscripts, autographs 22162

Pescara

Museo Civico e Pinacoteca Basilio Cascella, Via Guglielmo Marconi 45, 65100 Pescara - T: 0854283515
Fine Arts Museum 22163

Museo della Casa D'Annunzio, Corso Manthone 101, 65127 Pescara - T: 08560391. Head: Dr. Gerardo Gentile
Special Museum
House of the poet Gabriele D'Annunzio (1863-1938), possessions and relics 22164

Museo delle Genti d'Abruzzo, Via Delle Caserme 22, 65100 Pescara - T: 0854283517. Head: Claudio De Pompeis
Archaeological Museum - 1973 22165

Museo Ittico, Lungofiume Paolucci, 65100 Pescara - T: 0854283516. Head: Gaetano Di Pietro
Natural History Museum 22166

Pescarolo

Museo del Lino, Via G. Mazzini 73, 26033 Pescarolo - T: 0372836193. Head: Casimiro Becchi
Local Museum 22167

Pescasseroli

Museo del Parco Nazionale d'Abruzzo, Centro Visita del Parco d'Abruzzo, Via Santa Lucia, 67032 Pescasseroli - T: 0863910715. Head: Franco Tassi
Natural History Museum 22168

Peschiera del Garda

Museo Palazzina Storica, 37019 Peschiera del Garda
Military Museum
Relics of the World War I 22169

Pescia

Gipsoteca Libero Andreotti, Piazza del Palagio, 6, 51017 Pescia - T: 0572490057, Fax: 0572492255, E-mail: gipsotecapescia@interfree.it. Head: Claudio Stefanelli
Fine Arts Museum - 1992
220 models in plaster by Libero Andreotti 22170

Museo Civico, Piazza Santo Stefano 1, 51017 Pescia - T: 0572490057, Fax: 0572476913, E-mail: gipsotecapescia@interfree.it. Head: Claudio Stefanelli
Fine Arts Museum - 1894
14th to 16th c Tuscan pantings, 14th cent coloured wooden statues, prints by Albrecht Dürer 22171

Museo Civico di Scienze Naturali ed Archeologia della Valdinievole, Piazza Leonardo da Vinci 1, 51017 Pescia - T: 0572477533, Fax: 0572492255. Head: Stefano Petrucci
Natural History Museum / Archaeological Museum - 1976
Fossils, local archaeology and prehist 22172

Museo di Collodi e Pinocchio, Via San Gennaro, 51017 Pescia - T: 0572429342
Local Museum 22173

Pescina

Museo Mazzarino, Viale Francia, 67057 Pescina - T: 0863842156. Head: Maria Pia Quattrociocchi
Local Museum 22174

Pescocostanzo

Museo della Basilica di Santa Maria del Colle, Basilica, 67033 Pescocostanzo - T: 0864641430. Head: Angelo Di Ianni
Religious Arts Museum 22175

Pessione

Museo Martini di Storia dell'Enologia, Piazza Luigi Rossi 2, 10020 Pessione - T: 01194191, Fax: 0119419324
Special Museum - 1961
Wine presses since the 18th c, wine containers in silver and crystal from the 17th throught the 19th c, farm carts, archeological exhibits from Greece, Etruria and South Italy since the 7th c B.C. 22176

Piacenza

Galleria Alberoni, Via Emilia Parmense 77, 29100 Piacenza - T: 0523613198, Fax: 0523613342
Fine Arts Museum - 1761
15th-18th c paintings, incl works by Luca Giordano, Antonello da Messina, Giovanni Paolo Pannini, Domenico Viani, Sebastiano Conca, paintings by Flemish artists, paintings from other European countries, 16th-18th c tapestries 22177

Galleria d'Arte Moderna Ricci-Oddi, Via San Siro 13, 29100 Piacenza - T: 0523320742, Fax: 0523320742, E-mail: riccioddi@libero.it. Head: Prof. Stefano Fugazza
Fine Arts Museum - 1931
19th and 20th c Italian paintings 22178

Musei Civici, Palazzo Farnese, 29100 Piacenza - T: 0523328270, Fax: 0523328270. Head: Dr. Stefano Pronti
Fine Arts Museum / Decorative Arts Museum - 1885
Paintings, graphics, coins, glasses, terra cottas, ceramics 22179

Museo del Risorgimento, Palazzo Farnese, Piazza Cittadella, 29100 Piacenza - T: 0523328270
Historical Museum
Local history of the Risorgimento 22180

Museo del Teatro Municipale, Via Verdi 41, 29100 Piacenza - T: 052324631
Performing Arts Museum - 1804
History of the theatre, librettos, manuscripts, photographs 22181

Museo di Sant'Antonino, Via Chiostro Sant'Antonino 6, 29100 Piacenza - T: 0523320653
Religious Arts Museum
Illuminated codices, miniatures, paintings, vestments 22182

Piadena

Antiquarium Platina, Piazza Garibaldi 3, 26034 Piadena - T: 037598125
Archaeological Museum 22183

Piandimeleto

Museo della Civiltá Contadina, Piazza Conti Oliva 2, 61026 Piandimeleto - T: 0722721528
Historical Museum 22184

Museo delle Scienze della Terra e del Lavoro Contadino, Piazza Conti Oliva 2, 61026 Piandimeleto - T: 0722721493
Natural History Museum 22185

Pianello del Lario

La Raccolta della Barca Lariana, Fraz Calozzo, Via Statale 139, 22010 Pianello del Lario - T: 034487235. Head: Adolfo Premoli Silva
Science&Tech Museum - 1978
Boats 22186

Piazza Armerina

Museo Civico, Via Vittorio Emmanuele, 94015 Piazza Armerina - T: 0935683048
Archaeological Museum 22187

Museo Diocesano, Piazza Duomo 1, 94015 Piazza Armerina - T: 0935680020. Head: Filippo Bognanni
Religious Arts Museum 22188

Villa Romana, Località Casale, 94015 Piazza Armerina - T: 093581036
Local Museum 22189

Piazzola sul Brenta

Museo di Etnomedicina, Collezione A. Scarpa, Villa Simes Contarini, 35016 Piazzola sul Brenta - T: 049550238
Natural History Museum 22190

Piedimonte d'Alife

Museo Civico, Largo San Domenico, 81016 Piedimonte d'Alife - T: 0823911360
Local Museum - 1912
Archeology, sculptural relics, vases, numismatics, ceramics 22191

Museo Internazionale Della Paolera, Via Ercole d'Agnese 72, 81016 Piedimonte d'Alife
Archaeological Museum
Archeological material of China and India, archives 22192

Pienza

Museo Diocesano di Pienza, Corso il Rossellino 30, 53026 Pienza - T: 0578749903, Fax: 0578749071
Religious Arts Museum - 1998
14th and 15th c paintings by the Siena school, 15th and 16th c Flemish tapestries, miniatures 22193

Palazzo Piccolomini, Piazza Pio II 2, 53026 Pienza - T: 057874503
Historical Museum 22194

Pietrasanta

Casa Natale Giosuè Carducci, Via Comunale 138, 55045 Pietrasanta - T: 0584772055, Fax: 0584791982. Head: Dr. Pierluigi Gherardi
Special Museum 22195

Pieve di Cadore

Casa Natale di Tiziano Vecellio, Piazza Tiziano, 32044 Pieve di Cadore - T: 043532262, Fax: 043532858
Fine Arts Museum
Memorabilia on the painter Titian (1489-1576) at his birthplace 22196

Museo della Magnifica Comunità di Cadore, Piazza Tiziano, 32044 Pieve di Cadore - T: 043532262, Fax: 043532858, E-mail: magcomun@tin.it. Head: Prof. Giancandido De Martin
Fine Arts Museum
Works by local painters 22197

Museo Paleoveneto, Piazza Tiziano, 32044 Pieve di Cadore - T: 043532262, Fax: 043532858, E-mail: magcomun@tin.it. Head: Prof. Giancandido De Martin
Archaeological Museum
Local archeology from the 3rd to the 1st c B.C. 22198

Museo Risorgimentale, Piazza Tiziano, 32044 Pieve di Cadore - T: 043532262, Fax: 043532858
Historical Museum
Local history 22199

Pieve di Cento

Pinacoteca Comunale, Piazza Andrea Costa 10, 40066 Pieve di Cento - T: 051975533, Fax: 051974308, E-mail: urp.pieve@provincia.bologna.it. Head: Dr. Artioli Tiberio, Dr. Maria Tasin
Fine Arts Museum - 1980 22200

Pieve Torina

Museo della Nostra Terra, Via Sant'Agostino 4, 62036 Pieve Torina - T: 0737518032. Head: Fernando Mattioni
Local Museum 22201

Pievebovigliana

Museo della Pieve, Via Napoleone 2, 62035 Pievebovigliana
Local Museum
Inscriptions dating back to the 3rd c B.C. 22202

Pinerolo

Museo Civico e Pinacoteca, Piazza Vittorio Veneto 8, 10064 Pinerolo - T: 0121377446. Head: Prof. Dario Seglie
Historical Museum / Folklore Museum - 1905
Local history and folk art 22203

Museo d'Arte Preistorica, Viale Giolitti 1, 10064 Pinerolo - T: 0121794382, Fax: 012175547, E-mail: cesmap@cesmap.it, Internet: http://www.cesmap.it. Head: Prof. Dario Seglie
Archaeological Museum - 1964
Prehistoric art depicting the Italian Alps, the Iberian peninsula, Scandinavia and the French maritime Alps, Rock art of Ningxia (China), India, Arizona (USA), Rep. of Macedonia, Namibia, Siberia, Australia - didactic dept 22204

Museo Didattico di Scienze Naturali, Palazzo Vittone, Via Brignone 3, 10064 Pinerolo - T: 012174477
Natural History Museum 22205

Museo Etnografico del Pinerolese, Palazzo Vittone, Via Brignone 1, 10064 Pinerolo - T: 0121374477. Head: Ezio Giaj
Ethnology Museum 22206

Museo Nazionale dell'Arma della Cavalleria, Via Giolitti 5, 10064 Pinerolo - T: 0121397616. Head: Maria Di Martino
Military Museum - 1961
Ancient and modern arms, uniforms, cavalry relics, Pictures, Bronzes, Silvers, Armoured Vehicles, Wheeled Vehicles, Battleship Vehicles and Carriages - library 22207

Museo Storico Casa del Senato, Via Principi d'Acaja, 10064 Pinerolo - T: 012174505. Head: Nadia Menusan
Local Museum 22208

Pisa

Camposanto e Museo dell'Opera, Piazza Duomo, 56100 Pisa
Fine Arts Museum - 1277
Detaches frescoes, sarcophagi, sculpture 22209

Collezione Titta Ruffo, Teatro Verdi, Via Palestro, 56100 Pisa - T: 050941111, Fax: 050543555, E-mail: pressoff@teatrodipisa.pi.it, Internet: http://www.teatrodipisa.pi.it. Head: Prof. Ilario Luperini
Performing Arts Museum
History of the theatre 22210

Dipartimento di Storia delle Arti dell'Università degli Studi di Pisa, Piazza San Matteo in Soarta 2, Lungarno Mediceo, 56127 Pisa - T: 050542345, 050541801, Fax: 050580128. Head: Prof. Antonio Pinelli
Fine Arts Museum / University Museum 22211

Domus Galilaeana, Via Santa Maria 26, 56126 Pisa - T: 05023726, Fax: 05023726, E-mail: domusgalilaeana@hotmail.com, Internet: http://www.domusgalilaeana.it. Head: Prof. Vincenzo Cappelletti
Special Museum
Memorial house of Galileo Galilei (1564-1642) - library 22212

Domus Mazziniana, Via Mazzini 29, 56100 Pisa - T: 05024174
Special Museum
Manuscripts and relics to the politician Giuseppe Mazzini (1805-1872) 22213

Gabinetto Disegni e Stampe-Dipartimento di Storia delle Arti dell'Università di Pisa, Piazza S. Matteo 2, 56127 Pisa - T: 050587111, Fax: 050580128, E-mail: gds@arte.unipi.it, Internet: http://www.arte.unipi.it. Head: Prof. Antonio Pinelli
Fine Arts Museum - 1958
Prints and drawings, Timpanaro Collection (Fattori, Bartolini, Morandi), Artists' gifts (Accardi, Campigli, Consagra, Fontana, Manzù, Picasso, Munari, Viani, Vedova, Scialoja), engravings from Rome, Calcografia Nazionale, art works by Mario Chiattone 22214

Museo delle Sinopie, Opera della Primaziale Pisana, Piazza Duomo, 56100 Pisa - T: 050560547, Fax: 050561820. Head: Dr. Antonio Lazzarini
Religious Arts Museum 22215

Museo Nazionale di San Matteo, Lungarno Mediceo, Piazetta S. Matteo in Soarta, 56100 Pisa - T: 050541865, Fax: 050500099. Head: Dr. Mariagiulia Burresi
Local Museum - 1949
Archeology, Christian sarcophagi, frescoes, sculptures from Pisa, 13th to 17th c paintings by Tuscan and Pisan schools, Florentine Renaissance painters, coins and medals 22216

Museo Teatrale presso il Teatro Verdi → Collezione Titta Ruffo

Pistoia

Museo Civico, Piazza del Duomo 1, 51100 Pistoia - T: 05733711. Head: Dr. Chiara D'Afflitto
Fine Arts Museum / Decorative Arts Museum
13th c painting, sculpture, ceramics, arms, medals 22217

Museo Clemente Rospigliosi, Ripa del Sale 3, 51100 Pistoia - T: 057328740, Fax: 057328616, E-mail: museodiocesano@deocesi.pistoia.it, Internet: http://www.diocesi.pistoia.it. Head: Luciano Tempestini
Religious Arts Museum - 1990 22218

Museo del Ceppo, Piazza Giovanni XXIII, 51100 Pistoia - T: 0573367821
Local Museum 22219

Museo della Cattedrale di San Zeno e Percorso Archeologico Attrezzato, Palazzo dei Vescovi, Piazza Duomo 5, 51100 Pistoia - T: 0573369272
Religious Arts Museum / Archaeological Museum 22220

Museo Diocesano, Ripa del Sale 3, 51100 Pistoia - T: 057328740, Fax: 057328616, E-mail: museodiocesano@deocesi.pistoia.it, Internet: http://www.diocesi.pistoia.it. Head: Luciano Tempestini
Religious Arts Museum - 1990
Furniture, paintings 22221

Museo Marino Marini, Palazzo del Tau, Corso Silvano Fedi 30, 51100 Pistoia - T: 057331332, Fax: 057330285, E-mail: fmarini@dede.it. Head: Dr. Maria Teresa Tosi
Fine Arts Museum - 1979
Works by Marino Marini (sculptures, bronzes, drawings) 22222

Pizzighettone

Museo Civico, Via Garibaldi 18, 26026 Pizzighettone - T: 0372743347, Fax: 0372743347, E-mail: bibl.pizzighettone@libero.it. Head: Dr. Damiana Tentoni
Local Museum
Local archeology, paintings, weapons 22223

Ploaghe

Pinacoteca, Piazza San Pietro 12, 07017 Ploaghe - T: 079449836
Fine Arts Museum 22224

Pofi

Museo Civico, Via San Giorgio, 03026 Pofi - T: 0775380013
Local Museum 22225

Poggiardo

Museo delle Cripte, Santa Maria degli Angeli, Piazza Pasquale Episcopo, 73037 Poggiardo. Head: Luigi Branca
Religious Arts Museum 22226

Poggibonsi

Museo d'Arte, Fraz Staggia, Collegiata di Maria Assunta, Piazza Grazzini 4, 53036 Poggibonsi - T: 0577930901
Fine Arts Museum 22227

Poggio a Caiano

Museo Villa Medicea, Piazza Medici 14, 50046 Poggio a Caiano - T: 0558770126. Head: Dr. Litta Medri
Historical Museum 22228

Policoro

Museo Nazionale della Siritide, Viale Colombo, 75025 Policoro - T: 0835972154
Archaeological Museum
Archeological findings from the ancient city of Heraclea 22229

Polignano a Mare

Raccolta Archeologica, Viale Rimembranza, 70044 Polignano a Mare - T: 080740144
Archaeological Museum 22230

Pollenza

Museo Civico, Via Roma 32, 62010 Pollenza - T: 0733549387, Fax: 0733549069
Archaeological Museum 22231

Pompei

Museo Sacro, Basilica del Rosario, Piazza B. Longo 1, 80045 Pompei - T: 0818577111, Fax: 0818503357. Head: Giuseppe Adamo
Religious Arts Museum - 1900
Sacred goldsmith work, ancient liturgical books, pottery, porcelain, arms, medals 22232

Museo Vesuviano, Via Colle S. Bartolomeo, 80045 Pompei - T: 0818507255, Fax: 0818632401
Natural History Museum - 1900
Geologic material of the Vesuvius, archeological remains of Pompei, panoramic plan of Pompei 22233

Scavi di Pompei, Porta Marina Inferiore, 80045 Pompei - T: 0818610744, Fax: 0818613183. Head: Prof. Pietro Giovanni Guzzo, Dr. Antonio D'Ambrosio
Archaeological Museum
Excavation finds from the area, domestic utensils and objects pertaining to daily life in the Roman period 22234

Ponte in Valtellina

Museo Parrocchiale di Arte Sacra, Chiesa di San Maurizio, Piazza Luini 12, 23026 Ponte in Valtellina - T: 0342482152
Religious Arts Museum 22235

Ponte San Giovanni

Ipogei dei Volumni, Via Assisana, 06087 Ponte San Giovanni - T: 075393329
Archaeological Museum
Etruscan tomb, urns, pottery 22236

Pontecagnano

Museo Archeologico, Parco Padre Pio, 84098 Pontecagnano - T: 089384037
Archaeological Museum 22237

Museo Nazionale dell'Agro Picentino, Piazza del Risorgimento 14, 84098 Pontecagnano - T: 089383505
Archaeological Museum - 1979
Archaeologic findings 22238

Pontedassio

Museo Storico degli Spaghetti, Via Garibaldi 96, 18027 Pontedassio - T: 018321651
Special Museum
History and technology of the pasta production from the earliest times up to the present, machines, drawings 22239

Pontremoli

Museo delle Statue - Stele Lunigianesi, Castello del Piagnaro, 54027 Pontremoli - T: 0187831439. Head: Prof. Augusto C. Ambrosio
Fine Arts Museum 22240

Ponzone

Museo di Arte Sacra, Piazza Italia, 15010 Ponzone - T: 014478130. Head: Alessandro Buzzi
Religious Arts Museum 22241

Populonia

Museo Etrusco Gasparri, Via San Giovanni, 57020 Populonia - T: 056529407
Archaeological Museum 22242

Pordenone

Museo Civico, Palazzo Ricchieri, Corso Vittorio Emanuele, 33170 Pordenone - T: 0434522507, Fax: 0434522507. Head: Dr. Gilberto Ganzer
Fine Arts Museum - 1970
15th-20th c paintings, sculpture and engravings 22243

Museo Civico delle Scienze, Piazza della Motta 16, 33170 Pordenone - T: 0434392315, Fax: 043426396. Head: Dr. Marco Tonon
Natural History Museum 22244

Portici

Collezioni del Dipartimento di Entomologia e Zoologia Agraria, c/o Università di Napoli, Via Università 100, 80055 Portici - T: 0817755122, Fax: 0817755145. Head: Ermenegildo Tremblay
Natural History Museum / University Museum - 1875
Insects 22245

Porto Torres

Antiquarium, Via di Ponte Romano, 07046 Porto Torres - T: 079514433. Head: Francesca Manconi
Archaeological Museum
Archaeological material 22246

Portoferraio

Museo Il Giardino dell'Arte (Open Air Museum Italo Bolano), San Martino, Isola d'Elba, 57037 Portoferraio - T: 0565914570
Fine Arts Museum / Open Air Museum 22247

Museo Nazionale della Residenza Napoleonica dei Mulini, Piazzale Napoleone 1, 57037 Portoferraio - T: 0565915846, Fax: 0565915846. Head: Dr. Roberta Martinelli
Local Museum 22248

Museo Nazionale della Residenza Napoleonica di Villa San Martino, Villa San Martino, 57037 Portoferraio - T: 0565914688, Fax: 0565914688, Internet: http://www.ambiente.arti.beniculturali.it. Head: Dr. Roberta Martinelli
Historical Museum
Hist of Napoleonic period 22249

Pinacoteca Comunale Foresiana, Salita Napoleone, 57037 Portoferraio - T: 0565937111, Fax: 0565916391. Head: Dr. Giuseppe Battaglini
Fine Arts Museum
Paintings and various works of art 22250

Portogruaro

Museo Nazionale Concordiese, Via Seminario 22, 30026 Portogruaro - T: 042172674
Archaeological Museum - 1887
Archeological findings of the Roman and Christian period 22251

Possagno

Gipsoteca Canoviana e Casa del Canova, Via Canova, 31054 Possagno - T: 0423544323
Fine Arts Museum - 1957
Memorabilia on sculptor Antonio Canova (1757-1822) at his birthplace, models, copies and sketches 22252

Potenza

Museo Archeologico Provinciale, Via Lazio 18, 85100 Potenza - T: 0971444833. Head: Prof. Franco Ranaldi
Archaeological Museum 22253

Museo Provinciale Lucano, Via Malta, 85100 Potenza
Archaeological Museum / Fine Arts Museum / Decorative Arts Museum - 1899
Prehistoric and Roman archeology, arms, bronzes, terra-cottas, coins, picture gallery 22254

Pozza di Fassa

Museo dell'Istituto Culturale Ladino → Museo Ladino di Fassa

Museo Ladino di Fassa, Via Milano 5, 38036 Pozza di Fassa - T: 0462760182, Fax: 0462762651, E-mail: museo@istladin.net, Internet: http://www.istladin.net. Head: Dr. Fabio Chiocchetti
Local Museum - 1975
photo archive 22255

Prali

Museo di Prali e della Val Germanasca, Fraz Ghigo, Via Roma 27, 10060 Prali - T: 0121807519
Local Museum 22256

Prato

Centro per l'Arte Contemporanea Luigi Pecci, Viale della Repubblica 277, 59100 Prato - T: 05745317, Fax: 0574531900, E-mail: pecci@centropecci.it, Internet: http://www.centropecci.it. Head: Bruno Corà
Fine Arts Museum / Open Air Museum - 1988
Works by Mario Merz, Enzo Cucchi, Julian Opie, Fabrizio Plessi, A. Kapoor, Marco Bagnoli, Jannis Kounellis, Michelangelo Pistoletto, Julian Schnabel, Remo Salvatori and others 22257

Galleria Comunale d'Arte, Piazza del Comune, 50047 Prato
Fine Arts Museum - 1858
14th and 15th c Florentine school, 15th to 19th c paintings and sculptures 22258

Galleria di Palazzo degli Alberti, Via degli Alberti 2, 50047 Prato - T: 05746171, Fax: 0574617594, E-mail: cariprato.01@texnet.it
Fine Arts Museum - 1984
Giovanni Bellini, Filippo Lippi, (Michelangelo Merisi da) Caravaggio 22259

Museo Comunale, Palazzo Pretorio, 50047 Prato - T: 0574616303, Fax: 0574616229, E-mail: m.mannini@comune.prato.it, Internet: http://www.po-net.it. Head: Chiesa Bardazzi
Local Museum 22260

Museo del Tessuto (Textile Museum), Piazza del Comune 9, 59100 Prato - T: 0574611503, Fax: 0574444585, E-mail: museodeltessuto@po-net.prato.it, Internet: http://www.po-net.prato.it/tessuto. Head: Guido Pugi
Decorative Arts Museum 22261

Museo dell'Opera del Duomo, Piazza Duomo 49, 50047 Prato - T: 057429339. Head: Claudio Cerretelli
Religious Arts Museum
Frescoes, 16th c paintings, works by Uccello, Lippi, Toscani, sculptures by Donatello 22262

Museo di Pittura Murale, Piazza S. Domenico 8, 50047 Prato - T: 0574460392. Head: Claudio Cerretelli
Fine Arts Museum - 1974
Detached frescoes, sgraffiti, sinopias, didactic presentation of mural painting technique and restoration 22263

Pinacoteca Comunale, Piazza del Comune, 50047 Prato - T: 0574456102. Head: Alessandro Pasquini
Fine Arts Museum - 1858
Paintings, sculptures, drawings and etchings 22264

Quadreria Comunale, Piazza del Comune, 50047 Prato - T: 0574616303, Fax: 0574616229, E-mail: m.mannini@comune.prato.it, Internet: http://www.po-net.it. Head: Chiesa Bardazzi
Fine Arts Museum
Portraits of historical personalities 22265

Predazzo

Museo Civico di Geologia e di Etnografia, Piazza S.S. Filippo e Giacomo 1, 38037 Predazzo - T: 0462502392, Fax: 0462502566. Head: Elio Dellantonio
Natural History Museum - 1972
Geology, paleontology, mineralogy, petrography, ethnography 22266

Premana

Museo Etnografico, Via Roma, 22050 Premana - T: 0341890175. Head: Antonio Codega
Ethnology Museum
History of iron mining, products of iron, tools, crafts, farm implements 22267

Putignano

Museo Civico, Piazza Plebiscito 16, 70017 Putignano - T: 080731140. Head: Pietro Tramonte
Local Museum 22268

Quaranti

Museo del Vino, Via Don Reggio, 14040 Quaranti - T: 014177044
Agriculture Museum 22269

Quarna Sotto

Museo di Storia Quarnese, Piazzale del Municipio, 28020 Quarna Sotto. Head: Ersilio Maggi
Local Museum 22270

Quarto d'Altino

Museo Archeologico Nazionale, Via San Eliodoro 37, 30020 Quarto d'Altino - T: 0422829008, Fax: 0422829008. Head: Dr. Margherita Tirelli
Archaeological Museum - 1960
Finds of the Roman necropolis of Altino - library 22271

Quartu Sant'Elena

Casa Museo Sa Dom'e Farra, Via Capitano Eligio Porcu 143, 09045 Quartu Sant'Elena - T: 070812340. Head: Gianni Musiu
Local Museum 22272

Racconigi

Pinacoteca G.A. Levis, Piazza San Giovanni, 12035 Racconigi - T: 017286406
Fine Arts Museum 22273

Racines

Museo Provinciale della Caccia e della Pesca, Castel Wolfsthurn, Mareta 5, 39040 Racines - T: 0472758121, Fax: 0472758121, E-mail: museo-della-caccia@provincia.bz.it
Science&Tech Museum - 1996 22274

Museo Provinciale delle Miniere, Loc Masseria 32, 39040 Racines - T: 047266364
Science&Tech Museum 22275

Ragogna

Museo Civico, Località San Giacomo di Ragogna, Via Roma, 33030 Ragogna - T: 0432955226, Fax: 0432940951. Head: Dr. Antonio Cerutti
Archaeological Museum / Natural History Museum - 1981
Archeology and natural hist - lapidarium 22276

Ragusa

Castello di Donnafugata, Fraz Donnafugata, 97100 Ragusa - T: 093222405
Fine Arts Museum 22277

Museo Archeologico Ibleo di Ragusa, Via Natalelli 1, 97100 Ragusa - T: 0932622963
Archaeological Museum - 1960
Finds from local excavations 22278

Museo del Parco della Forza, Cava d'Ispica, Parco della Ispica, 97100 Ragusa
Archaeological Museum 22279

Tesoro del Duomo di San Giorgio, Piazza Duomo, 97100 Ragusa - T: 0932220085
Religious Arts Museum 22280

Ramacca

Museo Civico Archeologico, Via G. Marconi 2, 95040 Ramacca - T: 095653106. Head: Dr. Enrico Procelli
Archaeological Museum 22281

Ranco

Museo dei Trasporti Italiani → Museo Europeo dei Trasporti Ogliari

Museo Europeo dei Trasporti Ogliari, Via Alberto 99, 21020 Ranco - T: 0331976614, Fax: 03315461977. Head: Prof. Francesco Ogliari
Science&Tech Museum
Carriages, trains, autobus 22282

Randazzo

Museo Vagliasindi, Casa di Riposo Vagliasindi del Castello, Piazza Rabatà 2, 95036 Randazzo - T: 095921041
Archaeological Museum 22283

Rapallo

Museo del Pizzo al Tombolo, Villa Tigullio, 16035 Rapallo - T: 018563304, Fax: 0185680238. Head: Piera Rum
Ethnology Museum - 1990 22284

Ravello

Antiquarium, Villa Rufolo, 84010 Ravello - T: 089857866, Fax: 089251844. Head: Dr. Angelo Antonelli
Archaeological Museum 22285

Museo del Duomo, Piazza Duomo, 84010 Ravello - T: 089857212
Religious Arts Museum 22286

Ravenna

Museo Arcivescovile, Piazza Arcivescovado 1, 48100 Ravenna - T: 0544218559. Head: Prof. Mario Mazzolti
Religious Arts Museum / Archaeological Museum
Roman and Christian sculptures and inscriptions 22287

Museo Dantesco, Via Dante 4, 48100 Ravenna - T: 054433667, Fax: 0544218476, E-mail: centrodantesco@provincia.ra.it, Internet: http://www.racine.ra.it/centrodantesco. Head: Maurizio Bazzoni
Special Museum
All printed editions of Dante's works (1265-1321), translations, secondary literature, manuscripts 22288

Museo Nazionale, Via Benedetto Fiandrini, 48100 Ravenna - T: 054434424, Fax: 054437391, E-mail: sb2ra@libero.it
Archaeological Museum / Fine Arts Museum / Decorative Arts Museum
Roman and Byzantine sculpture, ivory, stained glass, Byzantine paintings, furniture, bronzes 22289

Museo Ornitologico e di Scienze Naturali, Loggetta Lombardesca, Via di Roma 13, 48100 Ravenna - T: 0544482874, Fax: 0544212092, E-mail: planetario@provincia.ra.it, Internet: http://

www.racine.ra.it/planet. Head: Dr. Franco Gabici
Natural History Museum - 1970
Birds, natural history, eggs, butterflies, shells - scientific library 22290

Museo Strumenti Musicali, Strada St. Adriatica, 48100 Ravenna - T: 0544560547
Music Museum 22291

Pinacoteca Comunale, Via Roma 13, 48100 Ravenna - T: 0544482874, Fax: 0544213641. Head: Gianni Morelli
Fine Arts Museum
16th to 20th c paintings 22292

Recanati

Casa Leopardi, Via Leopardi 14, 62019 Recanati - T: 0717573380, Fax: 0717573380, E-mail: casaleopardi@giacomoleopardi.it, Internet: http://www.giacomoleopardi.it. Head: Anna Leopardi
Library with Exhibitions
Memorabilia on the poet Giacomo Leopardi (1798-1837), manuscripts - library 22293

Museo Diocesano, Via Gregorio XII, 62019 Recanati - T: 071981124. Head: Lauro Cingolani
Religious Arts Museum 22294

Pinacoteca e del Museo B.Gigli, Via Gregorio XII, 62019 Recanati - T: 0717570410, 07175871, Fax: 071982416. Head: Dr. Paolo Pierini
Fine Arts Museum
Paintings by local artists, works by Lorenzo Lotto, modern art gallery, costumes and personal possessions of singer Benjamino Gigli (1890-1957) 22295

Redipuglia

Museo della Guerra e Sacrario della Terza Armata, 34070 Redipuglia
Military Museum
Relics of World War I and the Italian army 22296

Reggio di Calabria

Museo Nazionale di Reggio Calabria, Piazza de Nava 26, 89100 Reggio di Calabria - T: 0965812255, Fax: 096525164
Fine Arts Museum / Archaeological Museum - 1954
Prehistoric, Greek and Roman finds from excavations, vases and terra cottas, coins, bronzes, paintings from the Middle Ages to modern times - library 22297

Reggio Emilia

Galleria Civica Anna e Luigi Parmiggiani, Corso Cairoli 2, 42100 Reggio Emilia - T: 0522451054, Fax: 0522456476, E-mail: musei@munieipio.re.it/, Internet: http://musei.comune.re.it/. Head: Dr. Giancarlo Ambrosetti
Fine Arts Museum - 1933
13th to 18th c European paintings, including works by Veronese, Titian, El Greco, Velazquez, sculpture, woodcarvings, silverware 22298

Musei Civici, Via Spallanzani 1, 42100 Reggio Emilia - T: 0522456477, Fax: 0522456476, E-mail: musei@municipio.re.it/, Internet: http://www.comune.re.it. Head: Dr. Maurizio Festanti
Archaeological Museum - 1799
Local archaeology, natural hist, historical relics, local art 22299

Museo Missionario, Via Ferrari Bonini 2/B, 42100 Reggio Emilia - T: 052233201
Fine Arts Museum 22300

Remedello

Museo Civico Archeologico, Via P. Cappellazzi 1, 25010 Remedello - T: 030957441. Head: Mino Perini
Archaeological Museum 22301

Rende Centro

Museo Civico, Palazzo Zagarese, 87036 Rende Centro - T: 0984443593, Fax: 0984443593, E-mail: museociv@abramo.it. Head: Fiorella Sicilia
Local Museum - 1980
Domestic utensils, costumes, farming, handicraft, musical instruments - libraries, archives 22302

Rezzato

Pinacoteca Internazionale dell'Età Evolutiva, Via IV Novembre 85, 25086 Rezzato - T: 0302792086
Fine Arts Museum 22303

Ribera

Antiquarium e Zona Archeologica, Eraclea Minoa Cattolica Eraclea, 92016 Ribera. Head: Dr. Graziella Fiorentini
Archaeological Museum
Relics found in the excavations, graphic illustrations and topography of the ancient city 22304

Riccione

Museo del Territorio, Viale Lazio 10, 47036 Riccione - T: 0541600504, Fax: 0541600504
Archaeological Museum 22305

Riese Pio X

Museo San Pio X, Via Sarto, 31039 Riese Pio X - T: 0423483050. Head: Paola Vietti
Religious Arts Museum
Memorabilia on Pope Pius X (1903-1914), documents, pontifical robes, personal possessions 22306

Rieti

Museo Civico, Palazzo Comunale, Piazza Vittorio Emanuele II, 02100 Rieti - T: 0746485021
Fine Arts Museum / Archaeological Museum
15th to 18th c paintings, jewelry, local archeology 22307

Tesoro del Duomo, Piazza C. Battisti, 02100 Rieti - T: 0746482720. Head: Prof. Giovanni Maceroni
Religious Arts Museum 22308

Rima San Giuseppe

Museo Della Vedova, Via Della Vedova, 13020 Rima San Giuseppe
Fine Arts Museum 22309

Rimini

Museo della Città, Musei Comunali, Via L. Tonini 1, 47037 Rimini - T: 054121482, 054155414, Fax: 054128692. Head: Dr. Pier Luigi Foschi
Local Museum
Archaeology, antiques, art - Pinacoteca 22310

Museo delle Culture Extraeuropee Dinz Rialto, Castel Sismondo, 41037 Rimini - T: 0541785780, Fax: 054128692. Head: Dr. Pier Luigi Foschi
Ethnology Museum
History, archaeology and art of Africa, Oceania and pre-Columbian, America 22311

Museo e Pinacoteca del Santuario Madonna delle Grazie, Via Santa Maria delle Grazie 10, 47037 Rimini - T: 0541751061, Fax: 0541751582
Ethnology Museum / Fine Arts Museum - 1928
Ethnology, paintings 22312

Museo Missionario Francescano, Convento di S. Maria delle Grazie, Covignano, 47037 Rimini. Head: Mario Balboni
Religious Arts Museum 22313

Rio Marina

Museo Minerario del'Elba, Palazzo Comunale, 57038 Rio Marina - T: 0565962747
Natural History Museum 22314

Ripatransone

Museo Civico Archeologico, Piazza XX Settembre 12, 63038 Ripatransone - T: 073599329, Fax: 07359469. Head: Prof. Antonio Giannetti
Archaeological Museum - 1877 22315

Museo Civico Storico-Etnografico, Palazzo Bonomi, Corso Vittorio Emanuele, 63038 Ripatransone - T: 073599329, Fax: 07359496. Head: Prof. Antonio Giannetti
Historical Museum / Ethnology Museum - 1995
Autographs, hist, weapons 22316

Museo del Vasaio e del Fischietto, Via Garibaldi 42, 63038 Ripatransone - T: 07359338. Head: Innocenzo Peci
Special Museum / Folklore Museum - 1997
Pottery, whistles 22317

Museo della Civiltà Contadina ed Artigiana, Cripta Chiesa San Filippo, 63038 Ripatransone - T: 073597117, Fax: 07359469. Head: Prof. Giuseppe De Angelis
Agriculture Museum - 1990
Crockery, ploughs, kitchen: pottery and equipment 22318

Museo Diocesano Intercomunale di Arte Sacra, Chiesa di Santa Chiara, Corso Vittorio Emanuele, 63038 Ripatransone - T: 073599329, Fax: 07359469. Head: Dr. Paola Di Girolami
Religious Arts Museum - 1999
Clothes, reliquary, silver liturgical objects 22319

Pinacoteca-Gipsoteca Civica, Palazzo Bonomi, Corso Vittorio Emanuele, 63038 Ripatransone - T: 073599329, Fax: 07359469. Head: Prof. Antonio Giannetti
Fine Arts Museum - 1877
Pottery, furniture, plaster casts - archive 22320

Riva del Garda

Museo Civico, La Rocca, Piazza Battisti, 38066 Riva del Garda - T: 0464514490. Head: Mario Matteotti
Archaeological Museum / Local Museum
Local archeology, pile structure, religious art, paintings, natural history, local folk art 22321

Rivoli

Castello di Rivoli Museo d'Arte Contemporanea, Piazza Mafalda di Savoia, 10098 Rivoli - T: 0119565222, Fax: 0119565231, E-mail: info@castellodirivoli.org, Internet: http://www.castello-dirivoli.org. Head: Ida Gianelli, Cesare Annibaldi
Fine Arts Museum 22322

Rivoli Veronese

Museo Napoleonico, Piazza Napoleone, 37010 Rivoli Veronese - T: 0457280179. Head: Dr. Lorenzo Da Pra Galanti
Historical Museum - 1973 22323

Rocca di Mezzo

Museo d'Arte Sacra Cardinale Agnifili, Chiesa di Santa Maria della Neve, 67048 Rocca di Mezzo - T: 0862917557
Religious Arts Museum 22324

Roccalbegna

Raccolta d'Arte, Oratorio SS. Crocifisso, 58053 Roccalbegna - T: 0564989122
Religious Arts Museum 22325

Roma

Antiquarium Comunale, Piazzale Caffarelli 3, 00186 Roma - T: 0667102475, Fax: 0667103118. Head: Dr. Anna Mura Sommella
Archaeological Museum - 1890
Archaeology 22326

Antiquarium Forense, Piazza S. Maria Nova 53, 00185 Roma - T: 066795949
Archaeological Museum
Finds of the prehistoric necropolis in the Roman Forum 22327

Antiquarium Palatino, Piazza Santa Maria Nova 53, 00186 Roma - T: 066795949
Archaeological Museum - 1860
Sculpture, ceramics and pottery found at the Palatine 22328

Casa di Goethe, Via del Corso 18, 00186 Roma - T: 0632650412, Fax: 0632650449, E-mail: info@casadigoethe.it, Internet: http://www.casadigoethe.it. Head: Ursula Bongaerts
Special Museum - 1997
Paintings, prints, manuscripts, photographs illustrating and changing exhibitions, Goethe's travels in Italy 22329

Casa di Pirandello, Via Bosio 15, 00100 Roma - T: 06858047. Head: Prof. Alfredo Barbina
Special Museum
Manuscripts and documents of the writer Luigi Pirandello (1867-1936) - library 22330

Casino dell'Aurora Pallavicini, Via XXIV Maggio 43, Roma - T: 064814344, Fax: 064742615, E-mail: lcapaccioli@saita.it, Internet: http://www.mconline.it. Head: Maria Camilla Pallavicini
Fine Arts Museum
16th and 17th c paintings (Reni, Giordano, Poussin, Brill, Tempesta) 22331

Castello e Museo della Rocca, Località Ostia Antica, 00100 Roma
Archaeological Museum 22332

Cineteca Nazionale, Via Tuscolana 1524, 00174 Roma - T: 06722941
Special Museum 22333

Gabinetto delle Stampe, Piazza S. Pantaleo 10, 00186 Roma - T: 066548393. Head: Dr. Lucia Cavazzi Palladini
Fine Arts Museum 22334

Gabinetto Nazionale delle Stampe, Via delle Lungara 230, 00165 Roma - T: 06699801, Fax: 0669921454. Head: Dr. Michele Cordaro
Fine Arts Museum - 1895
Italian and foreign prints and drawings from the 14th c to present times 22335

Galleria Colonna, Piazza SS. Apostoli 66, 00187 Roma - T: 066784350, Fax: 066794638, E-mail: galleriacolonna@tin.net, Internet: http://www.galleriacolonna.it. Head: Fabio Sanfelice di Bagnoli
Fine Arts Museum - 17th c
15th to 18th c Italian and foreign paintings, including works by Veronese, Tintoretto and Botticelli, sculpture, Italian and foreign furniture 22336

Galleria Comunale d'Arte Moderna e Contemporanea, Via Reggio Emilia 54, 00198 Roma - T: 064742848, Fax: 064742912. Head: Giovanna
Fine Arts Museum - 1925
Modern and contemporary paintings and sculptures, mainly by Roman artists 22337

Galleria dell'Accademia Nazionale di San Luca, Piazza dell'Accademia di San Luca 77, 00187 Roma - T: 066798850, Fax: 066789243. Head: Prof. Carlo Pierrangeli
Fine Arts Museum - 1593
17th-20th c art gallery - library, archive 22338

Galleria Doria Pamphilj, Piazza del Collegio Romano 2, 00186 Roma - T: 066797323, Fax: 066780939, E-mail: info@doriapamphilj.it, Internet: http://www.doriapamphilj.it. Head: Dr. Andrea De Marchi
Fine Arts Museum - 1651
Paintings by Correggio, Tiziano, Claude Lorrain, Filippo Lippi, Annibale Carracci, Michelangelo Merisi da Caravaggio, Diego Velazquez, Raffaello, Pieter Breugel 22339

Galleria Nazionale d'Arte Antica Palazzo Barberini (closed until 2005), Via delle Quattro Fontane 13, 00184 Roma - T: 064814591, 064824184, Fax: 064880560. Head: Dr. Lorenza Mochi Onori
Fine Arts Museum - 1895
12th-18th c paintings, paintings by Simone Martini, Lorenzo Lotto, Titian, Raphael, Bellotto, Caravaggio, Filippo Lippi, Odescalchi coll of arms - library 22340

Galleria Nazionale d'Arte Antica Palazzo Corsini, Via della Lungara 10, 00165 Roma - T: 0668802323. Head: Dr. Silvigliano Alloisi
Fine Arts Museum - 1883
Italian, Dutch and Flemish paintings from the 17th-18th c, paintings by Jusepe de Ribera, Michelangelo Merisi da Caravaggio, Bartolomé Esteban Murillo, Luca Giordano, Fra Angelico, Annibale Carracci, Guido Reni, Nicolas Poussin 22341

Galleria Nazionale d'Arte Moderna-Arte Contemporanea, Viale delle Belle Arti 131, 00196 Roma - T: 06322981, Fax: 063221579. Head: Dr. Bianca Alessandra Pinto
Fine Arts Museum - 1883
19th and 20th c Italian and foreign paintings, sculptures and graphic works, works by Courbet, Monet, van Gogh, Modigliani, Braque, de Chirico, Manzu, Miró, Giacometti, Duchamp - library 22342

Galleria Pallavicini, Palazzo Pallavicini, Via XXIV Maggio 43, 00187 Roma - T: 064744019, Fax: 064882194
Fine Arts Museum 22343

Galleria Spada, Piazza Capodiferro 13, 00186 Roma - T: 066861158. Head: Dr. Roberto Cannata, Maria Lucrezia Vicini
Fine Arts Museum - 1929
16th to 18th c paintings, works by Reni, Titian, Rubens, Brueghel, Roman and 17th c sculpture, decorative arts 22344

Istituto Italiano dei Castelli (IBI), Castel Sant-Angelo, 00193 Roma. Head: Dr. Gaetano Bruni
Historical Museum 22345

Istituto Italiano di Paleontologia Umana (Paleontologic Collection), Piazza Mincio 2, 00198 Roma - T: 068557598, Fax: 068557598
Natural History Museum - 1911
Prehistoric finds, mostly from central and southern Italy, some Neandertal human remains - library 22346

Istituto Nazionale per la Grafica - Calcografia, Via delle Lungara 230, 00187 Roma - T: 066540565. Head: Michele Cordaro
Fine Arts Museum - 1738
Copper engravings, drawings and prints - library 22347

Keats-Shelley House, Piazza di Spagna 26, 00187 Roma - T: 066784235, Fax: 066784167, E-mail: info@keats-shelley-house.org, Internet: http://www.keats-shelley-house.org. Head: Catherine Payling
Special Museum
House where the poet John Keats (1795-1821) died 22348

Mercati Dr. Traiano, Via IV Novembre, 00186 Roma - T: 066841020, Fax: 0667102672
Historical Museum - 1932
Pre- and early history 22349

Monumenti Antichi - Scavi e Carta dell'Agro, Piazza Campitell 7, 00186 Roma - T: 066798254. Head: Prof. Lucas Cozza
Historical Museum 22350

Monumenti Medioevali e Moderni, Piazza Campitelli 7, 00186 Roma - T: 066798104. Head: Dr. Luisa Cordilli Aloisi
Historical Museum 22351

Musei Capitolini, Piazza del Campidoglio, 00186 Roma - T: 0667102071, Fax: 0667103118. Head: Dr. Anna Mura Sommella
Archaeological Museum - 1471
Roman statues, Hellenistic replicas of Greek originals, sarcophagi, portraits, bronze sculptures, equestrian statue of Marcus Aurelius - photo archive 22352

Musei, Gallerie, Gabinetto Stampe e Archivio Fotografico, Piazza S. Egidio, 00186 Roma - T: 065813717. Head: Prof. Cecilia Pericoli
Fine Arts Museum 22353

Museo Aeronautico Caproni di Taliedo, Via Azuni 13, 00196 Roma. Head: Firmina Caproni di Taliedo Guasti
Science&Tech Museum - 1939
Models and historical documents of aviation 22354

Museo Africano, Via Aldovrandi 16, 00197 Roma - T: 06873712
Ethnology Museum - 1929
Art, ethnography, paleontology, prehistory, archaeology of the former colonies 22355

Museo Artistico Industriale, Via Conte Verde 51, 00185 Roma. Head: Prof. Alberto Gerardi
Decorative Arts Museum 22356

Museo Astronomico Copernicano, Viale del Parco Mellini 84, 00136 Roma - T: 0635347056, Fax: 0635347802, E-mail: calisi@aorhp1.rm.astro.it, Internet: http://www.mporzio.astro.it. Head: Prof. Roberto Buonanno
Science&Tech Museum - 1873
Historic astronomical and meteorological instruments, globes, books, pictures, medals, coins, prints concerning to Nicolaus Copernicus (1473-1543) 22357

Museo Barracco, Corso Vittorio Emanuele II 166, 00186 Roma - T: 066886848. Head: Dr. Maria Teresa Nota
Fine Arts Museum - 1902
Evolution of sculpture from Egyptian to Roman styles 22358

Museo Canonica, Viale P. Canonica 2, 00197 Roma - T: 068842279, Fax: 068845702
Religious Arts Museum - 1961
Paintings, marbles, bronzes and plaster models by Pietro Canonica 22359

Museo Centrale del Risorgimento, Vittoriano, Piazza Venezia, 00186 Roma - T: 066793598, 066793526, Fax: 066782572, E-mail: ist.risorgimento@tiscalinet.it, Internet: http://www.risorgimento.it. Head: Prof. Giuseppe Talamo
Historical Museum - 1906
Documents, relics, arms and medals of the Risorgimento 22360

Museo Civico di Zoologia, Via Aldrovandi 18, 00197 Roma - T: 063216586, 063221031, Fax: 063218263, E-mail: info.museo.zoologia@comune.roma.it, Internet: http://www.comune.roma.it/museozoologia. Head: Dr. Claudio Manicastri
Natural History Museum - 1932
Ornithology, malacology, entomology 22361

Museo Criminologico, Via del Gonfalone 20, 00186 Roma - T: 066868849
Special Museum
Documents and relics on the history of criminal investigation, section on capital executions and imprisonments 22362

Museo degli Strumenti della Riproduzione del Suono, Via M. Caetani 32, 00186 Roma - T: 066868364. Head: Dr. Maria Carla Cavagnis Sotgiu
Science&Tech Museum 22363

Museo del Folklore e dei Poeti Romaneschi → Museo di Roma in Trastevere

Museo del Foro d'Augusto (closed) 22364

Museo del Sovrano Ordine Militare dei Cavalieri di Malta, Piazza dei Cavalieri di Malta 3, 00173 Roma
Historical Museum
Relics and documents on the Order of the Knights of Malta 22365

Museo del Tasso, Piazza Sant'Onofrio al Gianicolo 2, 00165 Roma - T: 06657632
Special Museum
Memorabilia on the poet Torquato Tasso (1544-1595) - library 22366

Museo del Teatro Argentina, Via dei Barbieri 22, 00186 Roma - T: 066545006
Performing Arts Museum 22367

Museo della Basilica di San Paolo, San Paolo fuori le Mura, Via Ostiense 186, 00154 Roma - T: 065410341
Religious Arts Museum
Christian epigraphs, medieval frescoes 22368

Museo della Civiltà Romana, Piazza Agnelli 10, 00144 Roma - T: 065926135. Head: Dr. Giuseppina Sartorio Pisani
Historical Museum - 1955
Reproductions, reconstructions and documents depicting the history of Rome 22369

Museo della Comunità Ebraica di Roma, Lungotevere Cenci, 00100 Roma - T: 0668400661, Fax: 0668400684. Head: Dr. Anna Ascarelli Blayer Corcos
Historical Museum - 1977
Ritual silverware, antique sacred furnishings, documents and illustrations about the Jewish community of Rome - historical archive 22370

Museo della Società Geografica Italiana, Via Navicella 12, 00184 Roma - T: 067008279, Fax: 0677079518, E-mail: geomail@tin.it, Internet: http://www.societageografree.it. Head: Prof. Franco Salvatori
Ethnology Museum - 1867
Manuscripts, maps, pictures, busts of conquerors and explorers, arms and various objects of Africa, Asia, America and Australia 22371

Museo della Via Ostiense, Via R. Persichetti 3, Porta San Paolo, 00153 Roma - T: 065743193. Head: Dr. Maria Giuseppina Lauro
Historical Museum 22372

Museo dell'Alto Medioevo, Viale Lincoln 3, 00144 Roma - T: 0654228199, Fax: 0654228130. Head: Dr. Maria Stella Arena
Archaeological Museum - 1967
Findings from the Langobard necropolis of Nocera Umbra and Castel Trosino, medieval pottery and marble reliefs 22373

Museo dell'Arte Classica, Sezione di Archeologia, Piazzale Aldo Moro 5, 00185 Roma - T: 0649913960, Fax: 0649913955, E-mail: - Marcello.Barbanera@uniroma1.it, Internet: http://www.uniroma1.it. Head: Dr. Marcello Barbanera
Archaeological Museum - 1892
Casts of the Egina's sculptures used by Thorvaldsen 22374

Museo delle Cere, Piazza SS. Apostoli 67, Roma - T: 066796482. Head: Alberto Canini
Special Museum
Wax statues of famous persons 22375

Museo delle Mura, Via di Porta San Sebastiano, 00179 Roma - T: 0670475284
Archaeological Museum
Models of the Aurelian Wall and constructional details, inscriptions 22376

Museo delle Origini, Piazzale Aldo Moro 5, 00185 Roma - T: 0649913924, Fax: 0649913653, E-mail: musori@rmcisadu.let.uniroma1.it. Head: Prof. Alessandra Manfredini
University Museum - 1941
Mainly Italian prehistoric material of the Institute of Palethnology 22377

Museo dell'Energia Elettrica, c/o Ente Nazionale per l'Energia Elettrica, Via Giovanni Battista Martini 3, 00198 Roma - T: 0685091, Fax: 0685093771
Science&Tech Museum 22378

Museo dell'Istituto di Patologia del Libro, Via Milano 76, 00184 Roma - T: 06482911, Fax: 064814968. Head: Prof. Carlo Federici
Special Museum - 1938
Antique writing instruments, physically, chemically and biologically damaged books 22379

Museo dell'Istituto Storico e di Cultura dell'Arma del Genio, Lungotevere della Vittoria 31, 00195 Roma - T: 063725446
Military Museum - 1906
Uniforms, models of fortresses, history of the Army communications service and military architecture 22380

Museo di Anatomia Comparata Battista Grassi, Diparti di Biologia Animale e dell'Uomo, Università di Roma, Via A. Borelli 50, 00161 Roma - T: 0649918008, 0649918122, 0649918096, Fax: 064457516, E-mail: - museo.anatomiacomparata@uniroma1.it. Head: Prof. Ernesto Capanna
Natural History Museum - 1870
Large vertebrate skeletons, anatomical preparations of vertebrates and invertebrates, ancient microscopical instruments 22381

Museo di Anatomia Patologica, c/o Università La Sapienza, Viale Regina Elena 324, 00161 Roma - T: 0649970261, Fax: 064461484, E-mail: pgallo@axzma.unizoma1.it. Head: Prof. Pietro Gallo
Natural History Museum / University Museum - 1950
Human pathology, cardiac pathology - slides archives 22382

Museo di Antichità Etrusche e Italiche, c/o Istituto di Etruscologia, Facoltà di Lettere, Piazzale Aldo Moro 5, 00185 Roma - T: 064452239, Fax: 0649913873
Archaeological Museum / University Museum - 1955/62
Etruscan and Italic archaeology and culture 22383

Museo di Antropologia G. Sergi, Diparti di Biologia Animale e dell'Uomo, Università di Roma, Piazzale Aldo Moro 5, 00185 Roma - T: 0649912273, Fax: 0649912769, E-mail: g.manzi@caspur.it. Head: Prof. Gabriella Spedini
Natural History Museum / University Museum
Physical Anthropology, Paleoanthropology, Human Paleontology, historical scientific instruments 22384

Museo di Archeologia Sacra e Profana, Via Appia Antica 136, 00179 Roma - T: 067887035
Archaeological Museum
Paleochristian sarcophagi 22385

Museo di Mineralogia, c/o Dipartimento di Scienze della Terra, Università degli studi La Sapienza, Piazzale Aldo Moro 5, 00185 Roma - T: 0649914887, Fax: 064454729, E-mail: grubessi@axrma.uniroma1.it. Head: Prof. Odino Grubessi
Natural History Museum / University Museum - 1804
Minerals of Latium, single crystals, meteorites 22386

Museo di Paleontologia, c/o Dipartimento di Scienze della Terra, Piazzale Aldo Moro 5, 00185 Roma - T: 0649914315, Fax: 0649914315, E-mail: riccardo.manni@uniroma1.it. Head: Prof. Umberto Nicosia
Natural History Museum / University Museum - 1864
Quaternary mammals of the Mediterranean area, tetrapod footprints, Mesozoic crinoids, echinoids and molluscs, Cenozoic corals, echinoids, foraminifers and molluscs 22387

Museo di Roma, Piazza di San Pantaleo 10, 00186 Roma - T: 066565562, Fax: 0667103118. Head: Prof. Gemma Cortese
Historical Museum - 1930
Scenic reconstructions of Roman life, paintings and drawings, frescoes from the Middle Ages to present times, festival carriages, two coaches from the train of Pope Pius IX, pottery, goldsmith work, all exhibits depicting the history of Rome 22388

Museo di Roma in Trastevere, Piazza S. Egidio 1, 00153 Roma - T: 065813717, Fax: 065884165, E-mail: museodiroma.trastevere@comune.it, Internet: http://www.comune-roma/museodiroma/trastevere. Head: Dr. Maria Elisa Tittoni
Folklore Museum / Fine Arts Museum - 1971 22389

Museo di Storia della Medicina, c/o Facoltà di Medicina e Chirurgia, Viale dell'Università 34a, 00185 Roma - T: 064451721, Fax: 064451721. Head: Prof. Luigi Frati
Natural History Museum / University Museum - 1938
History of medicine, medical instruments 22390

Museo Etrusco di Villa Giulia, Piazzale Villa Giulia 9, 00196 Roma - T: 063226571, 063201951, Fax: 063202010. Head: Dr. A. Maria Moretti, Dr. F. Boitani
Archaeological Museum - 1889
Etruscan and Italian antiquities, bronze sword, sarcophagus, vases, statuettes 22391

Museo Forense, Piazza Santa Maria Nova 53, 00186 Roma - T: 066790333
Special Museum 22392

Museo Francescano, c/o Istituto Storico dei Cappuccini, Circonv Occidentale 6850, GRA km 65, 00163 Roma - T: 0666052518, Fax: 0666162401, E-mail: ist.cap@ofmcap.org, Internet: http://www.istitutostoricoofmcap.org. Head: Servus Gieben
Religious Arts Museum - 1885
Rich coll of paintings, drawings, prints, sculptures, engravings, coins and various articles concerning Franciscan hist and art 22393

Museo Galleria di Villa Borghese, Piazzale Scipione Borghese 5, 00197 Roma - T: 068548577, 068413979, Fax: 068840756. Head: Dr. Alba Costamagna
Fine Arts Museum - 1902
Antique, Baroque and Neoclassical sculptures, a group by Bernini, Canova sculptures, paintings by Raphael, Botticelli, Perugino, Fra Angelico, Titian, Caravaggio, Corregio, Veronese, Rubens, Cranach 22394

Museo Napoleonico, Via Zanardelli 1, 00186 Roma - T: 0668806286, Fax: 068809114, E-mail: napoleonico@comune.roma.it, Internet: http://www.comune.roma.it/museonapoleonico. Head: Dr. Elisa Tittoni Monti
Historical Museum - 1927
Paintings and drawings collected by the Bonaparte family, miniatures, coins and medals, the marriage certificate of Napoleon I and Marie-Louise, relics concerning to the Bonapartes and their relations to Rome 22395

Museo Nazionale d'Arte Orientale, Via Merulana 248, 00185 Roma - T: 064874415, Fax: 064870624, E-mail: orientale@arti.beniculturali.it, Internet: http://www.beniculturali.it. Head: Dr. Donatella Mazzeo
Archaeological Museum - 1958
Sculptures, paintings, ceramics, bronzes and wood carvings from Iran, Afghanistan, Pakistan, India, Tibet, Nepal, China, Corea, Japan and South-East Asia - library, restoration department, photo archive 22396

Museo Nazionale degli Strumenti Musicali, Piazza Santa Croce in Gerusalemme 9, 00185 Roma - T: 067014796, Fax: 067029862. Head: Dr. Antonio Latanza
Music Museum - 1974
Musical instruments from ancient times to the beginning of the 20th c 22397

Museo Nazionale del Palazzo di Venezia, Via del Plebiscito 118, 00186 Roma - T: 0669994318, 0669994319, Fax: 06699994221. Head: Dr. Claudio Strinati
Decorative Arts Museum - 1921
Arms, tapestries, silverware, bronze, ceramics 22398

Museo Nazionale delle Arti e Tradizioni Roma, Piazza Marconi 8, 00144 Roma - T: 065926148, 065910709, 065912669, Fax: 065911848, E-mail: popolari@arti.beniculturali.it, Internet: http://www.popolari.arti.beniculturali.it. Head: Dr. Stefania Massari
Folklore Museum / Fine Arts Museum - 1923
library 22399

Museo Nazionale delle Paste Alimentari (National Museum of Pasta Food), Piazza Scanderbeg 117, 00187 Roma - T: 066991119, 06699120, Fax: 066991109. Head: Giuseppe Giarmoleo
Special Museum
Hist of Pasta, Production Machinery, nutritional info, Pasta in ancient and modern Art 22400

Museo Nazionale di Castel Sant'Angelo, Lungotevere, Castello 50, 00193 Roma - T: 066819111, Fax: 0668191196. Head: Dr. Ruggero Pentrella
Historical Museum - 1925
Ancient arms and armor, Renaissance paintings, decorations, frescoes, period furniture - library 22401

Museo Nazionale Preistorico ed Etnografico Luigi Pigorini, Piazzale G. Marconi 14, 00144 Roma - T: 06549521, Fax: 0654952310, E-mail: pigorini@arti.beniculturali.it, Internet: http://www.pigorini.arti.beniculturali.it. Head: Maria Antonietta Fugazzola Delpino
Archaeological Museum / Ethnology Museum - 1875
Pre- and protohistoric finds, Etruscian finds, Arcaic Votive Roman finds, ethnographic objects from Africa, America, Oceania, Indonesia, anthropological coll - library, archives, conservation and restoration dept 22402

Museo Nazionale Romano-Terme di Diocleziano, Piazza della Finanze, 00185 Roma - T: 064882364, Fax: 064814125, E-mail: info@archeorm.arti.beniculturali.it, Internet: http://www.archeorm.arti.beniculturali.it. Head: Prof. Adriano La Regina
Archaeological Museum - 1889
Greek and Roman sculptures and bronzes, pictures and mosaics, medals and coins 22403

Museo Numismatico della Zecca, Via XX Settembre 97, 00187 Roma - T: 0647613317. Head: Dr. Ariberto Guarino
Special Museum - 1958
Coins from the Middle Ages to present times, Pontifical medals from the 15th c up to now 22404

Museo Nuovo, Piazza del Campidoglio, 00186 Roma - T: 0667102475, Fax: 0667103118. Head: Dr. Anna Mura Sommella
Archaeological Museum
Greek sculptures, sarcophagi, urns and funeral vases 22405

Museo Ostiense, Scavi di Ostia, Via dei Romagnoli 717, 00119 Roma - T: 065650022, 065651405, Fax: 065651500. Head: Anna Gallina Zevi
Archaeological Museum 22406

Museo Palatino, Piazza Santa Maria Nova 53, 00186 Roma - T: 066790333
Archaeological Museum 22407

Museo Sacrario delle Bandiere delle Forze Armate, Vittoriano, Via dei Fori Imperiali, 00100 Roma - T: 0647355002
Military Museum
Relics concerning to the history of the Italian navy, flags, torpedo, documents 22408

Museo Storico dei Bersaglieri, Piazzale Porta Pia, 00198 Roma - T: 06486723
Military Museum - 1887
History of Italian infantry, mainly of the Bersaglieri, uniforms, equipment, armaments 22409

Museo Storico dei Granatieri di Sardegna, Piazza Santa Croce in Gerusalemme 7, 00185 Roma - T: 067028287. Head: Mario Vozzolo
Military Museum - 1924
History of the Sardinian brigade from 17th c to present times 22410

Museo Storico della Fanteria, Piazza Santa Croce in Gerusalemme 9, 00185 Roma - T: 067027971
Military Museum - 1959
Italian uniforms, ancient and modern arms, Alpine and parachute troops, documents, pennons, flags, military valour Medals, plastic models 22411

Museo Storico della Guardia di Finanza, Piazza Armellini 20, 00162 Roma - T: 0644238841. Head: Ferdinando Dosi
Historical Museum - 1937
History of the customs guard and exhibits of current events 22412

Museo Storico della Liberazione di Roma, Via Tasso 145, 00185 Roma - T: 067003866. Head: Prof. Emilio Paolo Taviani
Historical Museum
Rome during the German occupation 1943-1945 22413

Museo Storico della Motorizzazione Militare, Viale dell'Esercito 86, 00143 Roma - T: 065011885. Head: Vittorio Del Falco
Military Museum
Military motorization, lorries, cars, armoured vehicles, motorcycles 22414

Museo Storico dell'Arma dei Carabinieri, Piazza Risorgimento 46, 00192 Roma - T: 066896696
Historical Museum - 1937
History of the Carabinieri, the Italian police - library 22415

Museo Storico delle Poste e Telecomunicazioni, Viale Europa, 190, 00144 Roma - T: 0654602092, Fax: 0659582349. Head: Marcello Cartacci
Science&Tech Museum - 1896
Exhibits and documents concerning to the history of post, telegraph, telephone, radio-television and philately 22416

Museo Storico Nazionale dell'Arte Sanitaria, Lungotevere in Sassia 3, 00193 Roma - T: 066862450, Fax: 066862450. Head: Prof. Dr. Enrico Boheme
Special Museum - 1922
History of medical instruments 22417

Museo Torlonia, Vicolo Corsini 5, 00165 Roma - T: 066561044
Archaeological Museum - 1829
Etruscan archeology, ancient sculptures and paintings arranged by Winckelmann in 1765 22418

Palazzo delle Esposizioni, Via Nazionale 194, 00195 Roma - T: 064885465, Fax: 064870776. Head: Renato Nicolini, Emanuele Bevilecqua
Fine Arts Museum 22419

Piccolo Museo delle Anime del Purgatorio, Lungotevere Prati 12, 00193 Roma - T: 0668806517
Religious Arts Museum 22420

Pinacoteca Capitolina, Piazza Campidoglio, 00186 Roma - T: 0667103069. Head: Dr. Elisa Tittoni Monti
Fine Arts Museum - 1750
14th to 17th c paintings of various schools 22421

Pinacoteca dell'Abbrazia di San Paolo, Via Ostiense 186, 00146 Roma - T: 065410341
Fine Arts Museum
Picture gallery 22422

Quadreria della Cassa Depositi e Prestiti, Piazza al Monte di Pietà, 00186 Roma
Fine Arts Museum - 1857
17th c paintings 22423

Raccolta Lapidaria Capitolina, Piazza del Campidoglio, 00186 Roma - T: 0667102475, Fax: 0667103118. Head: Dr. Anna Mura Sommella
Archaeological Museum
Public inscriptions, votives - photo archive 22424

Raccolta Teatrale del Burcardo, Via del Sudario 44, 00186 Roma - T: 066819471, Fax: 0668194727, E-mail: biblioteca.burcardo@siae.it, Internet: http://www.theatrelibrary.org. Head: Maria Teresa Iovinelli
Performing Arts Museum - 1932
Puppets, masks, costumes, playbills, pamphlets, photos, engravings, prints and other theatre memorabilia 22425

Raccolte dell'Istituto di Clinica delle Malattie Tropicali e Subtropicali, Viale Policlinico, 00161 Roma - T: 06490623. Head: Prof. Antonio Sebastiani
Special Museum
Tropical and subtropical diseases, wax preparations 22426

Raccolte dell'Istituto di Clinica Otorinolaringoiatrica, Viale Policlinico, 00161 Roma - T: 06490051. Head: Prof. Italo De Vincentiis
Special Museum
Otolaryngology 22427

Raccolte dell'Istituto di Clinica Urologica, Viale Policlinico, 00161 Roma
Special Museum
Urology 22428

Raccolte dell'Istituto di Geografia, Piazzale Moro 5, 00185 Roma - T: 0649913932. Head: Prof. Emmanuele Paratore
Natural History Museum
Geography 22429

Raccolte dell'Istituto di Parassitologia, Piazzale Moro 5, 00185 Roma - T: 064455780. Head: Prof. Caio Mario Coluzzi Bartoccioni
Natural History Museum
Parasitology 22430

Raccolte dell'Istituto di Radiologia Medica, Viale Policlinico, 00161 Roma - T: 064455602, Fax: 06490243, E-mail: Roberto.Passariello@mail.uniroma1.it
Science&Tech Museum
Apparatus and instruments of medical radiology from different periods 22431

Raccolte dell'Museo di Merceologia, Via del Castro Laurenziano 9, 00161 Roma - T: 0649766528, Fax: 064452251. Head: Prof. Ernesto Chiacchierini
University Museum
Commerce, trade 22432

Villa della Farnesina, Via della Lungara 230, 00165 Roma - T: 0668801858
Fine Arts Museum - 1510
Renaissance building, 16th c decoration and frescoes, painted ceiling and walls by Raphael, Peruzzi, Sodoma, Sebastiano del Piombo, Giulio Romano 22433

Romagnano Sesia

Museo Storico Etnografico della Bassa Valsesia, Via Torre 2, 28078 Romagnano Sesia - T: 0163833483, Fax: 0163826496. Head: Carlo Brugo
Ethnology Museum / Folklore Museum 22434

Ronca

Museo di Fossili, Via Piazza, 37030 Ronca - T: 0457460260. Head: Prof. Luigi Bertazzolo
Natural History Museum 22435

Rosignano Marittimo

Museo Civico, Castello, 57016 Rosignano Marittimo - T: 0586799232. Head: Dr. Edina Regoli
Local Museum 22436

Rossano

Museo Diocesano, Largo Duomo, 87067 Rossano - T: 0983520282, Fax: 0983520282. Head: Luigi Renzo
Religious Arts Museum - 1952
Paintings, silverware, parchments, Codex Purpureus (6th c) 22437

Rotella

Museo Diocesano Inercomunale di Arte Sacra, Via Ciccolini, 63030 Rotella - T: 0735594960, Fax: 0735577246. Head: Dr. Paola Di Girolami
Religious Arts Museum 22438

Rovereto

Casa di Rosmini, Via Stoppani 1, 38068 Rovereto - T: 0464420788
Local Museum
Ancient house of the Rosmini family, period furniture, paintings - library 22439

Museo Civico di Rovereto, Largo S. Caterina 43, 38068 Rovereto - T: 0464439055, Fax: 0464439487, E-mail: museo@museocivico.rovereto.tn.it, Internet: http://www.museocivico.rovereto.tn.it. Head: Franco Finotti
Local Museum - 1851
Prehistoric archaeology, hist, paleontology, numismatics, natural sciences 22440

Museo d'Arte Moderna e Contemporanea di Trento e Rovereto, Corso Rosmini 58, 38068 Rovereto - T: 0464438887, Fax: 0464430827, E-mail: info@mart.trento.it, Internet: http://www.mart.trento.it. Head: Dr. Gabriella Belli
Fine Arts Museum - 1987
Futurist coll: works by Boccioni, Marinetti, Cangiullo etc - archive, library 22441

Museo Depero, Via della Terra 53, 38068 Rovereto - T: 0464434393, E-mail: info@mart.trento.it, Internet: http://www.mart.trento.it. Head: Dr. Gabriella Belli
Fine Arts Museum - 1957
Futurist paintings, sculptures, tapestries by Fortunato Depero 22442

Museo Storico Italiano della Guerra, Castello di Rovereto, Via Castelbarco 7, 38068 Rovereto - T: 0464438100, Fax: 0464423410. Head: Renzo Brugnoli
Military Museum - 1921
World War I arms and artillery, weapons, uniforms - library 22443

Rovetta

Casa Museo Fantoni, Via Fantoni 1, 24020 Rovetta - T: 034673523. Head: Lidia Rigon
Fine Arts Museum - 1968
Sculptures in clay, wood and marble (16th to 18th c), drawings 22444

Roviano

Museo della Civiltà Contadina Valle dell'Aniene, Palazzo Baronale, 00027 Roviano - T: 0774903143, Fax: 0774903008. Head: Ilaria Candeloro
Agriculture Museum - 1975
Tools, household articles, agricultural implements 22445

Rovigo

Museo Civico delle Civiltà in Polesine → Museo dei Grandi Fiumi

Museo dei Grandi Fiumi, Piazzale San Bartolomeo 18, 45100 Rovigo - T: 042525077, Fax: 0425464546, E-mail: museo.ro@comune.rovigo.it. Head: Prof. Raffaele Peretto
Archaeological Museum / Local Museum - 1978
Archaeology, local history 22446

Museo del Seminario Vescovile, Piazza Vittorio Emmanuele II 14, 45100 Rovigo - T: 042521654, Fax: 042527993. Head: Dr. Antonio Romagnolo
Fine Arts Museum / Archaeological Museum
17th-18th c paintings, archeological finds 22447

Museo dell'Accademia dei Concordi, Piazza Vittorio Emanuele II 14, 45100 Rovigo - T: 042521654. Head: Dr. Adriano Mazzetti
Fine Arts Museum
Paintings of the Venetian school 22448

Rozzano

Museo di Quattroruote, Via A. Grandi 5-7, 20089 Rozzano - T: 02824721, Fax: 0226863093. Head: G. Mazzocchi
Local Museum 22449

Rufina

Museo della Vite e del Vino della Val di Sieve, Villa Poggio Reale, 50068 Rufina - T: 055839377. Head: Alberto Longhi
Agriculture Museum 22450

Russi

Museo Etnografico Romagnolo, Villa Babini, Via M. d'Azeglio 9, 48026 Russi - T: 0544580187. Head: Tino Babini
Ethnology Museum 22451

Rutigliano

Museo Civico Archeologico, Via Leopoldo Tarantini 28, 70018 Rutigliano - T: 080669062. Head: Aurelia D'Amato
Archaeological Museum 22452

Ruvo di Puglia

Museo Nazionale Jatta, Piazza Bovio 35, 70037 Ruvo di Puglia - T: 080812648. Head: Dr. Giuseppe Andreassi
Archaeological Museum - 1820
Finds from local tombs, antique vases (6th to 3rd c B.C.) 22453

Sacile

Museo Civico, Palazzo Flangini Bilia, 33077 Sacile - T: 0434735014
Local Museum 22454

Sagrado

Museo di San Michele, Piazzale Cima 3, 34078 Sagrado - T: 048192002
Military Museum - 1938
Weapons used in World War I 22455

Saint Nicolas

Museo Cerlogne, 11010 Saint Nicolas - T: 016534932. Head: Alexis Bétemps
Special Museum
Literary works by Abbot Cerlogne, exhibits concerning Val d'Aosta dialects 22456

Saint Pierre

Mostra Archeologica Permanente, Castello Sarriod de la Tour, 11010 Saint Pierre - T: 016595122. Head: Dr. Rosanna Mollo
Archaeological Museum 22457

Museo Regionale di Scienze Naturali, Castello di Saint-Pierre, 11010 Saint Pierre - T: 0165903485. Head: Dr. Ivana Grimod
Natural History Museum - 1985
Minerals and rocks, climate and glaciers, flora and vegetation, environments, birds, mammals, insects 22458

Sala Consilina

Museo Archeologico, Via Cappuccini, 84036 Sala Consilina - T: 097521052
Archaeological Museum 22459

Salemi

Mostra di Cimeli del Risorgimento, Convento Gesuitico, Via Francesco d'Aguirre, 91018 Salemi - T: 0924982248, Fax: 0924981663. Head: Paolo Cammarata
Historical Museum - 1960
Armoury and documents of Risorgimento 22460

Salerno

Museo Archeologico Provinciale, Via San Benedetto 28, 84100 Salerno - T: 089231135, Fax: 089225578
Archaeological Museum - 1927
Archeological objects found in the province of Salerno, numismatics 22461

Museo del Duomo, Palazzo Arcivescovile, Via Monterisi 2, 84100 Salerno - T: 089233569
Religious Arts Museum - 1935
12th c ivories, manuscripts, paintings 22462

Museo Parrocchiale di Santa Maria delle Grazie, Via Trotula di Ruggero, 84100 Salerno - T: 089233021
Religious Arts Museum 22463

Salle

Museo Civico Salle, Salle Vecchia, 65020 Salle - T: 085928265
Local Museum 22464

Salò

Museo Civico, Palazzo Municipale, Loggia della Magnifica Patria, 25087 Salò - T: 036520661. Head: Prof. G. Pietro Brogiolo
Local Museum 22465

Museo Storico del Nastro Azzurro, Via Fantoni 49, 25087 Salò - T: 036520804. Head: Alberto Morucci
Military Museum - 1934
Historical articles ranging from the Napoleonic wars to the Resistance 22466

Saluzzo

Museo Civico Casa Cavassa, Via San Giovanni 5, 12037 Saluzzo - T: 017541455, Fax: 017541455, E-mail: cavassa@comune.saluzzo.cn.it. Head: Dr. Elena Pianea
Fine Arts Museum / Decorative Arts Museum
Sculpture, paintings, furnishings 22467

Sammichele di Bari

Museo della Civiltà Contadina, Piazza Caracciolo, 70010 Sammichele di Bari - T: 0808917297. Head: Prof. Vito Donato Bianco
Local Museum 22468

Sampeyre

Museo Etnografico, Via Roma 27, 12020 Sampeyre - T: 0175977148
Ethnology Museum 22469

San Benedetto del Tronto

Musei Sistini del Piceno, Via Forte 16, 63039 San Benedetto del Tronto - T: 0735594960, Fax: 0735577246, E-mail: diocesisbt@katamail.com, Internet: http://www.sanbenedetto-deltronto.chiesacattolica.it/beni.asp. Head: Dr. Paola Di Girolami
Religious Arts Museum - 1999
Chalices, shrines, vestments, furniture, statues, medals - archive 22470

Museo Archeologico Marino, Liceo Scientifico, Viale de Gasperi, 63039 San Benedetto del Tronto - T: 073586855
Archaeological Museum 22471

Museo Ittico Augusto Capriotti, Viale Colombo 98, 63039 San Benedetto del Tronto - T: 073568850
Local Museum 22472

San Benedetto Po

Musei Civici Polironiani, Monastero Benedettino di Polirone, Piazza Teofilo Folengo, 46027 San Benedetto Po - T: 0376623036, Fax: 0376620078. Head: Simona Cirani
Local Museum - 1977
Puppets, agricultural implements, handicraft 22473

San Candido

Museo di San Candido, Via Chorherren 2, 39038 San Candido - T: 0474913132
Local Museum 22474

Stiftsmuseum Innichen, Via Atto 2, 39038 San Candido - T: 0474913418
Religious Arts Museum 22475

San Cesario di Lecce

Museo Civico, Palazzo Ducale, 73016 San Cesario di Lecce - T: 0832631484. Head: Gianfranco Coppola
Local Museum 22476

San Donato Val di Comino

Museo del Capriolo, Centro di Visita d'Abruzzo, 03046 San Donato Val di Comino - T: 086391955
Local Museum 22477

San Gimignano

Basilica Collegiata di Santa Maria Assunta, Piazza del Duomo, 53037 San Gimignano - T: 0577940316, Fax: 0577941056. Head: Valter Pala
Religious Arts Museum 22478

Museo Cappella di Santa Fina → Basilica Collegiata di Santa Maria Assunta

Museo Civico, Piazza del Duomo 2, 53037 San Gimignano - T: 0577990312, Fax: 0577907273, E-mail: cultura@comune.sangimignano.si.it, Internet: http://www.comune.sangimignano.it. Head: Dr. Antonello Mennucci
Fine Arts Museum / Archaeological Museum / Performing Arts Museum 22479

Museo di Arte Sacra, Piazza Pecori 1, 53037 San Gimignano - T: 0577940316, Fax: 0577941056. Head: Valter Pala
Religious Arts Museum - 1915
Wooden statues and crucifixes, religious aricles made of silver and gold 22480

Museo Etrusco, Piazza Pecori, 53037 San Gimignano - T: 0577940687
Archaeological Museum 22481

Pinacoteca Civica, Piazza Duomo 2, 53037 San Gimignano - T: 0577990312, Fax: 0577907273, Internet: http://www.comune.sangimignano.si.it. Head: Dr. Antonello Mennucci
Fine Arts Museum - 1882
Works of Florentine and Sienese schools from the 13th to 15th c 22482

San Ginesio

Pinacoteca Communale, Via Merelli 12, 62026 San Ginesio - T: 0733656068. Head: Prof. Giuseppe Crispini
Fine Arts Museum
Paintings of various schools on canvas and on wood, archeological material 22483

San Giovanni in Galilea

Museo F. Renzi, Via Matteotti, 47030 San Giovanni in Galilea - T: 0541947411
Local Museum 22484

San Giovanni in Persiceto

Pinacoteca Civica, Palazzo SS. Salvatore, Piazza Garibaldi 7, 40017 San Giovanni in Persiceto - T: 051821878, Fax: 051827017
Fine Arts Museum 22485

San Giovanni Valdarno

Museo di Santa Maria delle Grazie, Piazza Masaccio, 52027 San Giovanni Valdarno - T: 0559122445
Fine Arts Museum
15th-19th c paintings of the Florentine school 22486

San Lazzaro di Savena

Museo di Santa Cecilia, Fraz Croara, Abbazia di Santa Cecilia di Croara, 40068 San Lazzaro di Savena - T: 051471751
Religious Arts Museum 22487

San Leo

Museo d' Arte Sacra, 61018 San Leo - T: 0541916306, 0541926967, Fax: 0541926973, E-mail: comune.san-leo@provincia.ps.it, Internet: http://www.incastro.marche.it
Fine Arts Museum
16th-18th c paintings, prints, antique arms, 16th and 17th c furniture 22488

Museo del Forte, 61018 San Leo - T: 0541916302, Fax: 0541926973, E-mail: comune.san-leo@provincia.ps.it, Internet: http://www.incastro.marche.it
Local Museum 22489

San Leonardo in Passiria

Museum Passeier - Andreas Hofer, Sandhof, Via Passiria 72, 39015 San Leonardo in Passiria - T: 0473659086, Fax: 0473657721, E-mail: info@museum.passeier.it, Internet: http://www.passeier.it. Head: Albin Pixner
Local Museum 22490

Talmuseum Andreas Hofer → Museum Passeier - Andreas Hofer

San Lorenzo in Campo

Antiquarium Suasanum, 61047 San Lorenzo in Campo - T: 0721776825. Head: Araldo Angeloni
Archaeological Museum
Tomb requisites, bronzes, coins 22491

Museo Etnografico Africano, 61047 San Lorenzo in Campo - T: 0721776825. Head: Araldo Angeloni
Ethnology Museum
African ritual objects, sculpture and paintings, stuffed animals of Sierra Leone 22492

San Martino della Battaglia

Museo della Battaglia, 25010 San Martino della Battaglia - T: 0309141244
Military Museum - 1939
Uniforms, armaments, local history of the Risorgimento 22493

San Martino in Rio

Museo dell'Agricoltura e del Mondo Rurale, Via Umberto 1, 42018 San Martino in Rio - T: 0522636726, Fax: 0522695986. Head: Lorena Biagini
Agriculture Museum / Folklore Museum 22494

San Mauro Pascoli

Casa del Pascoli, Via G. Pasoli 46, 47030 San Mauro Pascoli - T: 0541931412
Local Museum
Local artifacts 22495

San Michele all'Adige

Museo degli Usi e Costumi della Gente Trentina, Via Mach 2, 38010 San Michele all'Adige - T: 0461650314, Fax: 0461650703, E-mail: mucgt@museosanmichele.it, Internet: http://www.museosanmichele.it. Head: Giovanni Kezich
Folklore Museum - 1968
Ironworks, weaving, wood technology, grinding processing, agriculture, viticulture, alpine pasturing, traditional cooking, heating stoves, peasant life, folk art, religious folk art 22496

San Miniato

Museo Diocesano di Arte Sacra, Piazza del Duomo, 56027 San Miniato - T: 0571418250
Religious Arts Museum
15th-17th c paintings, frescoes, parchments, liturgical items 22497

San Nicolò di Valfurva

Museo Vallivo della Valfurva, Oratorio dei Disciplini, 23030 San Nicolò di Valfurva - T: 0342945784
Local Museum 22498

San Nicolò Ultimo

Talmuseum, 39010 San Nicolò Ultimo
Local Museum
Indigenous animals, furnished rooms, domestic implements, paintings, watches, costumes 22499

San Pellegrino in Alpe

Museo delle Civiltà Contadina, Via del Voltone 15, 55030 San Pellegrino in Alpe - T: 058368291
Local Museum 22500

San Piero a Sieve

Museo della Chiesa Convento del Bosco ai Frati, Convento Francescano, Località Bosco ai Frati, 50037 San Piero a Sieve - T: 055848111
Religious Arts Museum 22501

San Severino Marche

Museo Archeologico G. Moretti, Palazzo Tacchi Venturi, Via Salimbeni 39, 62027 San Severino Marche - T: 0733638095. Head: Prof. Mario Moretti
Archaeological Museum - 1972
Prehistoric section 22502

Pinacoteca Comunale, Palazzo Tacchi Venturi, Via Salimbeni 39, 62027 San Severino Marche - T: 073363097. Head: Prof. Mario Moretti
Fine Arts Museum 22503

San Severo

Museo Alessandro Minuziano, Via Zannotti 90, 71016 San Severo - T: 088223427
Local Museum 22504

San Vito al Tagliamento

Museo Civico, Torre Raimonda, Via Amalteo, 33078 San Vito al Tagliamento - T: 043480405, Fax: 0434877589, E-mail: biblioteca.sanvito@tin.it, Internet: http://www.comune.san-vito-al-tagliamento.pn.it. Head: Angelo Battel
Archaeological Museum 22505

Museo della Vita Contadina "Diogene Penzi", Via Altan 49, 33078 San Vito al Tagliamento - T: 0434833275
Ethnology Museum 22506

Sancto Lucìa de Coumboscuro

Museo Etnografico Coumboscuro della Civiltà Provenzale in Italia, 12020 Sancto Lucia de Coumboscuro - T: 017198771, Fax: 017198771, E-mail: coumboscuroCCP@libero.it. Head: Sergio Arneodo
Ethnology Museum
Peasant life and ethnography of the people in the Cisalpine mountains, weaving, transport, agriculture, liguistic coll - Alpine language library 22507

Sanremo

Museo Archeologico di Palazzo Borea, Via Matteotti 143, 18038 Sanremo - T: 0184531942. Head: Massimo Ricci
Archaeological Museum 22508

Pinacoteca Rambaldi, Local. Coldirodi di Sanremo, Piazza San Sabastiano 15, 18038 Sanremo - T: 0184530131
Fine Arts Museum 22509

Sansepolcro

Museo Civico, Via Aggiunti 65, 52037 Sansepolcro - T: 0575732218, Fax: 0575740338, E-mail: museocivico@technet.it, Internet: http://www.sansepolcro.net. Head: Dr. Francesco Comanducci
Fine Arts Museum / Decorative Arts Museum - 1867
Frescoes by Piero della Francesca, 16th and 17th c paintings, ceramics 22510

Santa Croce Camerina

Museo Archeologico Regionale, Contrada Cammarana, 97017 Santa Croce Camerina - Fax: 0932826002/04. Head: Dr. Giuseppe Voza
Archaeological Museum - 1987 22511

Santa Flavia

Antiquarium, Frazione Solunto Zona Archeologica, Via Porticello, 90146 Santa Flavia - T: 091904557. Head: Prof. Vincenzo Tusa
Archaeological Museum
Archaeological material of Solunto 22512

Santa Maria Capua Vetere

Antiquarium, Anfiteatro Romano, 81055 Santa Maria Capua Vetere - T: 0823798864
Archaeological Museum
Fragments, statues and mosaics from the Campania amphitheatre 22513

Museo del Risorgimento, Piazza Bovio, 81055 Santa Maria Capua Vetere - T: 0823842022
Historical Museum 22514

Santa Maria degli Angeli

Museo della Basilica, 06088 Santa Maria degli Angeli - T: 0758051430, Fax: 0758051418
Religious Arts Museum
14th c convent housing antique vestments, paintings 22515

Santa Maria Maggiore

Museo dello Spazzacamino, Piazza Risorgimento, 28038 Santa Maria Maggiore - T: 032495091
Historical Museum 22516

Santa Marinella

Antiquarium Archeologico di Pyrgi, Castello di Santa Severa, 00058 Santa Marinella - T: 0766740194
Archaeological Museum 22517

Sant'Agata Feltria

Museo di Rocca Fregoso, 61019 Sant'Agata Feltria - T: 0541929645
Local Museum 22518

Sant'Angelo Lodigiano

Museo Cabriniano, Via Cabrini, 20079 Sant'Angelo Lodigiano - T: 037190227. Head: Achille Mascheroni
Religious Arts Museum
Mother Cabrini's birthplace, furnishings, religious articles 22519

Museo del Pane, Piazzetta Bolognini 2, 26866 Sant'Angelo Lodigiano - T: 0371211140/41, Fax: 0371210337, E-mail: fmb@supereva.it, Internet: http://www.fmb.supereva.it. Head: Alberto Dalli
Special Museum 22520

Museo Lombardo di Storia dell'Agricoltura, Piazza Libertà 2, 26866 Sant'Angelo Lodigiano - T: 0371211140, Fax: 026687822, E-mail: frpisani@tin.it. Head: Dr. Giuseppe B. Di Belgiojoso, Dr. Francesca Pisani
Agriculture Museum - 1979
Contribution of the agrarian extra-European civilisations to our agriculture, agriculture prehistory; ancient, medieval, Renaissance, modern history of agriculture, protomechanization in agriculture 22521

Museo Morando Bolognini, Castello Visconteo, Piazzetta Bolognini 2, 26866 Sant'Angelo Lodigiano - T: 0371211140/41, Fax: 0371210337, E-mail: fmb@supereva.it, Internet: http://www.fmb.supereva.it. Head: Alberto Dalli
Decorative Arts Museum - 1933
13th c castle interiors, tapestries 22522

Sant'Anna d'Alfaedo

Museo di Storia Naturale, Via Roma 4, 37020 Sant'Anna d'Alfaedo - T: 0457532502, Fax: 0457532600. Head: Dr. Cherubino Cona
Natural History Museum
Prehistory, fossils 22523

Sant'Antioco

Antiquarium, Via Castello, 09017 Sant'Antioco - T: 078183590. Head: Paolo Bernardini
Archaeological Museum
Findings at the excavation site of a Punis necropolis at Sulcis (5th to 3rd c B.C.) 22524

Sant'Arcangelo di Romagna

Museo degli Usi e Costumi della Gente di Romagna, Via Montevecchi 41, 47038 Sant'Arcangelo di Romagna - T: 0541624703, Fax: 0541622074. Head: Dr. Mario Turci
Folklore Museum 22525

Pinacoteca Civica, Piazza Ganganelli, 47038 Sant'Arcangelo di Romagna - T: 0541626173
Fine Arts Museum 22526

Quadreria Civica, Via Cavallotti 3, 47038 Sant'Arcangelo di Romagna - T: 0541624362, Fax: 0541626464. Head: Dr. Donata Mancini
Fine Arts Museum 22527

Santena

Museo Cavour, Castello di Cavour, 00026 Santena - T: 0119492578. Head: Ippolito Calvi di Bergolo
Historical Museum - 1955
Memorabilia on the Cavour Family and the Risorgimento 22528

Santhià

Galleria d'Arte Moderna, Via dell'Ospedale 11, 13048 Santhià - T: 016194200. Head: Mario Pistono Grand
Fine Arts Museum 22529

Santuario di Montevergine

Galleria e Mostra del Presepe nel Mondo, 83010 Santuario di Montevergine
Fine Arts Museum
Sculpture, gold articles, vestments, manger figures, paintings 22530

Sappada

Museo Etnografico G. Fontana, Borgata Bach 197, 32047 Sappada - T: 0435469126, Fax: 0435469107
Ethnology Museum 22531

Sarnano

Museo dell'Avifauna Appenninica, Via Leopardi 1, 62028 Sarnano - T: 0733659923, Fax: 0733655940, E-mail: comune@sarnano.sinp.net, Internet: http://www.sarnano.com
Natural History Museum 22532

Museo delle Armi e del Martello, Via Leopardi 1, 62028 Sarnano - T: 0733659923, Fax: 0733659940, E-mail: comune@sarnano.sinp.net, Internet: http://www.sarnano.com
Science&Tech Museum 22533

Pinacoteca Comunale, Via Leopardi 1, 62028 Sarnano - T: 0733659923, Fax: 0733659940, E-mail: comune@sarnano.sinp.net, Internet: http://www.sarnano.com
Fine Arts Museum
Renaissance painting, paintings by Crivelli, L'Alunno, Pagani and Folchetti - library 22534

Sarno

Museo Comunale della Valle del Sarno, Santuario di Santa Maria della Foce, 84087 Sarno - T: 081943722
Local Museum 22535

Sarre

Museo del Castello di Sarre, Loc Lalex, 11010 Sarre - T: 0165257027
Historical Museum / Decorative Arts Museum
Decorative arts, local history, furniture - library 22536

Sarsina

Museo Diocesano, Seminario Vescoville, Piazza Plauto, 47027 Sarsina - T: 054794818
Archaeological Museum
Sculptures and Roman finds, coll of 14th c bells 22537

Museo Nazionale Archeologico, Via Cesio Sabino 39, 47027 Sarsina - T: 054794641
Archaeological Museum - 1938
Excavations from the ancient Roman town including sculptures and bronzes, funerary monument and mosaics from the baths, prehistoric sculptures 22538

Sassari

Collezione Entomologica, c/o Istituto di Entomologia Agraria, Via Enrico de Nicola, 07100 Sassari - T: 079229246, Fax: 079229329. Head: Prof. Romolo Prota
Natural History Museum 22539

Museo All'Aperto di Storia dell'Agricultura, c/o Facoltà di Agraria, Fraz Ottava, 07100 Sassari - T: 079390620. Head: Prof. Romolo Prota
Natural History Museum 22540

Museo Archeologico Etnografico Giovanni Antonio Sanna, Via Roma 64, 07100 Sassari - T: 079272203, Fax: 079232666. Head: Dr. Fulvia Lo Schiavo
Archaeological Museum - 1932
Archeology (Central-North Sardinia), ethnography, paintings by Vivarini, medieval and modern art - library 22541

Raccolta dell'Istituto di Mineralogia e Geologia, c/o Facoltà di Agraria, Via Encrico de Nicola, 07100 Sassari - T: 079217430
Natural History Museum - 1963
Minerals, stones, fossils - library 22542

Raccolta Didattica di Animali dell'Istituto di Zoologia, Via Muroni 25, 07100 Sassari - T: 079228663, Fax: 079228663. Head: Prof. A. Casale
Natural History Museum 22543

Sassocorvaro

Museo Civico, Via Crescentini 7, 61028 Sassocorvaro - T: 072276133
Local Museum - 1890
Paintings, history 22544

Museo d'Arte, Via Giuseppe Giusti, 61028 Sassocorvaro - T: 072226144
Fine Arts Museum 22545

Sassoferrato

Galleria Civica d'Arte Moderna e Contemporanea, Via Montanari, 60047 Sassoferrato - T: 073296045. Head: Dr. Stefano Troiani
Fine Arts Museum
Paintings, sculpture, graphic arts 22546

Museo Archeologico, Piazza Matteotti, 60047 Sassoferrato - T: 07329465. Head: Dr. Stefano Troiani
Archaeological Museum 22547

Museo Civico, Piazza Matteotti, 60047 Sassoferrato - T: 07329330. Head: Dr. Stefano Troiani
Local Museum
Prehistory, Roman archeology, art, history 22548

Museo delle Arti e delle Tradizioni Popolari, Palazzo Montanari, 60047 Sassoferrato - T: 07329465. Head: Dr. Stefano Troiani
Folklore Museum 22549

Savigliano

Museo Civico Antonino Olmo e Gipsoteche, Piazza San Francesco 17, 12038 Savigliano - T: 0172712982, Fax: 0172725856. Head: Dr. Rosalba Belmondo
Archaeological Museum / Fine Arts Museum - 1904
Roman finds , paintings of local artists, works in plaster - library 22550

Palazzo Taffini, Via San Andrea 53, 12038 Savigliano - T: 0172711714
Local Museum 22551

Savignano sul Rubicone

Museo Archeologico Romano-Gallico-Etrusco, San Giovanni in Computo, 47039 Savignano sul Rubicone - T: 0541946637
Archaeological Museum
Roman antiquities 22552

Savio

Museo degli Strumenti Musicali Meccanici, Via Romea Sud 481, 48020 Savio - T: 0544560547. Head: Mariagrazia Marini, Marinella Marini
Music Museum
Organs, harmoniums, musical boxes, pianolas, phonographs 22553

Savona

Museo del Santuario di Nostra Signora di Misericordia, Piazza Santuario 6, 17100 Savona - T: 019879025
Religious Arts Museum - 1959
Sacred vessels and vestments (16th-19th c) 22554

Museo della Cattedrale Basilica Nostra Signora Assunta, Piazza del Duomo, 17100 Savona - T: 019825960
Religious Arts Museum 22555

Scaria

Museo Diocesano d'Arte Sacra, Piazza Carloni 8, 22020 Scaria - T: 031840400
Religious Arts Museum 22556

Sciacca

Pinacoteca, Palazzo Comunale, 92019 Sciacca - T: 092522549
Fine Arts Museum
Fine Arts Museum 22557

Selva di Progno

Museo Etnografico dei Cimbri, Via Boschi, 37030 Selva di Progno - T: 0457847050, Fax: 0457847050, E-mail: m.cimbri@netbusiness.it. Head: Giovanni Molinari
Ethnology Museum 22558

Senigallia

Museo dei Centri Storici delle Marche, Piazza del Duca 2, 60019 Senigallia - T: 07163258. Head: Maria Luisa Polichetti
Historical Museum
Regional history 22559

Museo dell'Informazione, Palazzo del Comune, 60019 Senigallia
Special Museum 22560

Museo Pio IX e Pinacoteca d'Arte Sacra Senigallia, Via Mastai 14, 60019 Senigallia - T: 07160649. Head: Angelo Mencucci
Religious Arts Museum 22561

Sepino

Zona Archeologica di Saepinum, 86017 Sepino - T: 087479027
Archaeological Museum - 1979 22562

Seravezza

Museo del Lavoro e della Tradizioni Popolari della Versilia Storica, Palazzo Mediceo, 55047 Seravezza - T: 0584756100
Folklore Museum 22563

Sermoneta

Museo Archeologico, 04010 Sermoneta
Archaeological Museum 22564

Serralunga di Crea

Museo del Santuario di Crea, Santuario di Santa Maria Assunta, 15020 Serralunga di Crea - T: 0142940109
Religious Arts Museum 22565

Serravalle Sesia

Museo di Storia, d'Arte e d'Antichità Don Florindo Piolo, Castello Avondo, Via Torchio, 13037 Serravalle Sesia
Historical Museum / Fine Arts Museum / Archaeological Museum 22566

Sestino

Antiquarium Sestinale, Via Marche 12, 52038 Sestino - T: 0575772718. Head: Fabiola Sarti
Archaeological Museum - 1930
Sculptures, coins, architecture of the region 22567

Sesto al Reghena

Museo dell'Abbazia di Santa Maria in Sylvis, Piazza Castello 3, 33079 Sesto al Reghena - T: 0434699014, Fax: 0434698849, E-mail: abbaziasestopn@libero.it. Head: Giovanni Perin
Religious Arts Museum 22568

Sesto Calende

Museo Civico, Palazzo Comunale, Piazza Mazzini, 21018 Sesto Calende - T: 0331922489, Fax: 0331922486. Head: Angelo Mira Bonomi
Archaeological Museum - 1949
Local finds of Roman and Gallic period, remains of the culture of Golasecca 22569

Sesto Fiorentino

Museo Richard Gihori della Manifattura di Doccia, Viale Pratese 31, 50019 Sesto Fiorentino - T: 0554204952, Fax: 0554204953. Head: Elisabetta Epifori
Decorative Arts Museum - 1737
Porcelain from the local manufacture (1937 to present), terracotta, wax, majolica - library 22570

Sesto in Pusteria

Rudolf Stolz Museum, Via Dolomiti 16, 39030 Sesto in Pusteria - T: 047470323
Historical Museum 22571

Sestri Levante

Pinacoteca Rizzi, Via Cappuccini 8, 16039 Sestri Levante - T: 018541300
Fine Arts Museum - 1960
Paintings of the Venetian and Genoese schools, furniture, pottery 22572

Settignano

Collezione Berenson, 50135 Settignano
Fine Arts Museum 22573

Sezze

Antiquarium Comunale, Largo Bruno Buozzi 1, 04018 Sezze - T: 077388179. Head: Prof. Luigi Zaccheo, Prof. Flavia Pasquali
Archaeological Museum 22574

Sgonico

Museo Speologico, Borgo Grotta Gigante, 34010 Sgonico - T: 040327312. Head: Franco Cucchi
Natural History Museum 22575

Siena

Museo Archeologico Etrusco, Via della Sapienza 3, 53100 Siena - T: 057744293. Head: Dr. Elisabetta Mangani
Archaeological Museum - 1940
Neolithic objects, Attic and Etruscan vases, domestic utensils, metal ornaments and coins 22576

Museo Aurelio Castelli, Convento dell'Osservanza, Via dell'Osservanza, 53100 Siena - T: 0577280250
Fine Arts Museum 22577

Museo Civico, Piazza del Campo 1, 53100 Siena - T: 0577292111. Head: Prof. Dr. Enzo Carli
Fine Arts Museum
Sculptures and monuments, frescoes, coins 22578

Museo della Società di Esecutori di Pie Disposizioni, Via Roma 71, 53100 Siena - T: 0577284300. Head: Dr. Renzo Grassi
Fine Arts Museum - 1938
Sienese paintings 22579

Museo delle Tavolette di Biccherna, Archivio di Stato, Via Banchi di Sotto 52, 53100 Siena - T: 0577247145, Fax: 057744675, E-mail: assiena@comune.siena.it. Head: Dr. Carla Zarrilli
Fine Arts Museum - 1873
Biccherna, small paintings on wood from the 13th through 17th c, documents, illuminated manuscripts 22580

Museo dell'Opera della Metropolitana, Piazza del Duomo 8, 53100 Siena - T: 0577283048, Fax: 0577280626, E-mail: operaduomo@iol.it, Internet: http://www.operaduomo.it. Head: Dr. Mario Lorenzoni
Fine Arts Museum - 1870
Sculptures by Giovanni Pisano, masterpieces from the Sienese school, artworks by gold and silversmiths 22581

Museo di Storia Naturale dell'Accademia dei Fisocritici, Piazza Sant'Agostino 5, 53100 Siena - T: 057747002, Fax: 057747002, E-mail: cancelli@unisi.it; farsi@unisi.it
Natural History Museum - ca 1750
Minerals, rocks, paleontology, fossils of microscopical foraminifera, zoology, mammals, cetaceans, ornithology, terracotta fungi - taxidermy laboratory, library, archive 22582

Pinacoteca Nazionale, Via San Pietro 29, 53100 Siena - T: 0577281161, 0577286143, Fax: 0577270508. Head: Dr. Anna Maria Guiducci
Fine Arts Museum - 1932
13th to 17th c paintings including Duccio, Dürer 22583

Santuario Casa Santa Caterina, Vicolo del Tiratoio 15, 53100 Siena - T: 057744177
Religious Arts Museum 22584

Sigillo

Raccolta Comunale, Palazzo del Comune, Piazza Martiri, 06028 Sigillo - T: 0759177125
Local Museum 22585

Siracusa

Antiquarium del Castello Eurialo, 96100 Siracusa - T: 093169540
Archaeological Museum 22586

Galleria Regionale di Palazzo Bellomo, Via G.M. Capodieci 14-16, 96100 Siracusa - T: 093169511, Fax: 093169529. Head: Dr. Francesca Cicala Campagna
Fine Arts Museum - 1940
Sculpture, paintings of the Sicilian School, works by Antonello da Messina and Antonelliani 22587

Museo Archeologico Regionale Paolo Orsi, Viale Teocrito 66, 96100 Siracusa - T: 0931464022, Fax: 0931462347. Head: Dr. Giuseppe Voza
Archaeological Museum - 1886
Prehist and early hist, Greek, Roman and Paleochristian remains 22588

Solarolo

Museo Civico della Confraternita della SS. Annunziata, Via Foschi, 48027 Solarolo - T: 054651012
Religious Arts Museum 22589

Solferino

Museo della Guerra del 1859, Via Ossario 48, 46040 Solferino - T: 03769141244. Head: Dr. Bruno Bajetta
Military Museum - 1959
Documents on the war of 1859, Gonzaga fortress 22590

Soncino

Museo della Stampa, Casa degli Stampatori, 26029 Soncino - T: 037484883, Fax: 037485333, E-mail: prolocosoncino@tin.it. Head: Mauro Bodini
Fine Arts Museum 22591

Sondrio

Museo Naturalistico Provinciale, Corso Via Veneto, 23100 Sondrio - T: 0342531111, Fax: 0342531277. Head: Bruno Ciapponi Landi
Natural History Museum 22592

Museo Valtellinese di Storia ed Arte, Via M. Quadrio 27, 23100 Sondrio - T: 0342526269, Fax: 0342526270, E-mail: museoso@vol.it. Head: Dr. Angela Dell'Oca Fiordi
Historical Museum / Fine Arts Museum - 1947
Local archaeology and art, esp the coll of Ligari's drawings 22593

Sorrento

Museo Correale di Terranova, Via Correale 48, 80067 Sorrento - T: 0818781846. Head: Marchese Luigi Buccino Grimaldi, Dr. Rubina Cariello
Archaeological Museum / Fine Arts Museum / Decorative Arts Museum - 1924
Greek, Roman and Byzantine marble, inscriptions, fragments, Neapolitan porcelain (17th-18th c) and painting (17th c), manuscripts of Tasso's works 22594

Spello

Collezione Mineralogica, Via San Severino 23, 06038 Spello
Natural History Museum - 1930
Mineralogy 22595

Pinacoteca Civica-Palazzo Canonici, Piazza Matteotti, 06038 Spello - T: 0742301297
Religious Arts Museum
Frescos, paintings (13th-19th c), sacred sculptures, vestments 22596

Pinacoteca Comunale, Piazza della Repubblica, 06038 Spello - T: 0742651221
Fine Arts Museum 22597

Sperlonga

Museo Archeologico Nazionale, Via Flacca, 04029 Sperlonga - T: 077154028. Head: Dr. Baldassare Conticello
Archaeological Museum
Greek and Roman sculptures, terra cotta, vases 22598

Spinetta Marengo

Museo della Battaglia di Marengo, Via Genova 8, 15047 Spinetta Marengo - T: 0131619589
Military Museum 22599

Spoleto

Galleria Communale d'Arte Moderna, Palazzo Rosari Spada, Via Terme, 06049 Spoleto - T: 074345940, Fax: 0743218246. Head: Lamberto Gentili
Fine Arts Museum - 1953
Contemporary painting including Guttuso, Leoncillo, Morlotti, Scanavino, Ceroli 22600

Museo Civico, Piazza del Duomo 3, 06049 Spoleto - T: 0743222209
Local Museum - 1914
Roman inscriptions, medieval and Renaissance sculptures 22601

Museo del Teatro, Via Filitteria 1, 06049 Spoleto - T: 0743223419
Performing Arts Museum
Sketches of scenographies by Cocteau, Moore, Manzù 22602

Museo Diocesano, Palazzo Vescovile, Via A. Saffi 13, 06049 Spoleto - T: 0743221869. Head: Giampiero Ceccarelli
Religious Arts Museum 22603

Pinacoteca Comunale, Via del Municipio, 06049 Spoleto - T: 0743218201, Fax: 0743218246. Head: Lamberto Gentili
Fine Arts Museum - 1871
Painting (13th-15th c), frescoes (15th-16th c), goldsmith work, seals, coins, tapestries (16th c) 22604

Raccolta di Disegni Teatrali, Via Gregorio Elladio, 06049 Spoleto - T: 074328131
Performing Arts Museum 22605

Stenico

Castello di Stenico, 38070 Stenico - T: 046571004, 046571548
Local Museum 22606

Stia

Museo del Castello di Porciano, Fraz Porciano, 52017 Stia - T: 055400517, Fax: 055400506. Head: Martha Specht Corsi
Ethnology Museum - 1978
Old and antique local agricultural and domestic artifacts, medieval archeology coll, photographic documentation on the restoration of the castle, small ethnological coll of native American artifacts 22607

Strà

Villa Nazionale di Strà, Via Pisani, 30039 Strà - T: 049502074, 0499800590. Head: Prof. Dr. Mario Guiotto
Historical Museum 22608

Stradella

Civico Museo Naturalistico Ferruccio Lombardi, Palazzo Comunale, Via Emilia 29, 27049 Stradella - T: 0385249211, Fax: 038543590
Natural History Museum - 1979 22609

Stresa

Museo Pietro Canonica, Palazzo dei Congressi, Piazzale Europa, 28049 Stresa - T: 032330389
Fine Arts Museum 22610

Palazzo Borromeo, Isola Bella, 28049 Stresa - T: 032330556. Head: Giuliano Cardini
Local Museum
Lombard architecture and 17th c paintings, 16th c tapestries, armour, historic house - botanical garden 22611

Stroncone

Museo di Storia Naturale, Via Sebastiano Vici 16, 05039 Stroncone - T: 074460115
Natural History Museum 22612

Stupinigi

Museo d'Arte d'Ammobigliamento, Piazza Principe Amedeo, 10040 Stupinigi - T: 0113581220. Head: Mauriziano Ordine
Fine Arts Museum
Piemontese art and architecture, baroque style building 22613

Sulmona

Museo Civico, Palazzo dell'Annunziata, 67039 Sulmona - T: 086433374. Head: Guido Piccirilli
Fine Arts Museum - 1927
Renaissance architecture, sculptures in wood and stone (14th-16th c), painting (14th-17th c), Roman pottery, jewelry 22614

Susa

Museo Civico, Via del Castello 16, 10059 Susa - T: 012233104. Head: Dr. Laura Carli
Local Museum - 1884
Prehistory, archeology, Roman grave, architectural fragments, folklore 22615

Susegana

Museo dell'Uomo, Via Barriera 35, 31058 Susegana - T: 0438738610
Special Museum 22616

Sutri

Antiquarium Comunale, Palazzo Comunale, 01015 Sutri - T: 0761601212, 0761600867, Fax: 0761601224, E-mail: comunedisutri@mbox.thunder.it. Head: Dr. Carlo Tedeschi
Archaeological Museum
Etruscan, Roman, Greek, medieval sculpture and inscriptions 22617

Museo del Patrimonium, Via di Porta Vecchia 79, 01015 Sutri - T: 0761600867, Fax: 0761601224, E-mail: mazurek.tedeschi@libero.it. Head: Dr. Carlo Tedeschi
Archaeological Museum - 1997
Etruscan, Roman, Greek, medieval sculpture and inscriptions 22618

Suzzara

Galleria Civica d'Arte Contemporanea, Via Guido 48b, 46029 Suzzara - T: 0376535593, Fax: 0376535841, E-mail: galleriacivica.suzzara@ polirone.mn.it, Internet: http://www.polirone.mn.it. Head: Marco Panizza
Fine Arts Museum 22619

Tadasuni

Museo degli Strumenti Musicali Sardi Don Giovanni Dore, Via Adua 7, 09080 Tadasuni - T: 078550113. Head: Giovanni Dore
Music Museum 22620

Taggia

Museo Domenicani, Piazza Cristoforo 6, 18018 Taggia - T: 0184476254, Fax: 0184476203, E-mail: paparone@dmw.it, Internet: http:// www.domenicanitaggia.it. Head: Guiseppe Paparone
Religious Arts Museum
Painting 22621

Tagliacozzo

Museo Orientale, Santuario di Maria SS. d'Oriente, 67069 Tagliacozzo - T: 0863610257. Head: Tommaso Casale
Religious Arts Museum 22622

Taino

Museo Civico di Storia Naturale, Piazza Pajetta 5, 21020 Taino - T: 0331956405
Natural History Museum 22623

Taormina

Antiquarium del Teatro Greco-Romano, Via Teatro Greco, 98039 Taormina - T: 094223220. Head: Dr. Luigi Bernabo Brea
Archaeological Museum
Inscriptions, architectonic fragments, marbles 22624

Taranto

Museo Archeologico Nazionale, Corso Umberto 41, 74100 Taranto - T: 0994532113, Fax: 0994594946. Head: Dr. Giuseppe Andreassi
Archaeological Museum - 1887
Prehistory, Greek and Roman marble and limestone sculpture, Hellenistic finds, ceramics, Corinthian vases, jewelry 22625

Museo Oceanografico dell'Istituto Talassografico, Via Roma 3, 74100 Taranto - T: 0994525434, Fax: 0994594811. Head: Prof. Michele Pastore
Natural History Museum 22626

Museo Provinciale Prodotti della Pesca, Via Fornaci 4, 74100 Taranto - T: 099415498
Special Museum 22627

Tarquinia

Museo Nazionale Archeologico, Palazzo Vitelleschi, Piazza Cavour 1, 01016 Tarquinia - T: 0766856036, Fax: 0766856036. Head: Dr. Maria Cataldi
Archaeological Museum - 1924
Etruscan sarcophagi and remains with figured cemetery stones, tombs with frescoes, Etruscan and Greek vases, bronzes, ornaments 22628

Teggiano

Museo Civico Dianense, Piazza IV Novembre, 84039 Teggiano - T: 097579053. Head: Prof. Arturo Didier
Fine Arts Museum
Romanesque and medieval art, sculptures, frescoes 22629

Teglio

Antiquarium Tellinum, Palazzo Besta, 23036 Teglio - T: 0342780268
Archaeological Museum 22630

Tempio Pausania

Museo Bernardo de Muro, Via Mazzini, 07029 Tempio Pausania - T: 079633349. Head: Maria Antonia Sanna
Local Museum 22631

Raccolta Ornitologica F. Stazza, Piazza San Pietro 7, 07029 Tempio Pausania - T: 079631652
Natural History Museum 22632

Teramo

Museo e Pinacoteca Civici, Villa Comunale, Viale Bovio, 64100 Teramo - T: 0861247772. Head: Dr. Paola Di Felice
Fine Arts Museum - 1979
15th-20th c paintings, 17th c ceramics, modern art picture gallery 22633

Terlizzi

Museo de Napoli, Corso Dante 9, 70038 Terlizzi - T: 0808817577, Fax: 0808813798. Head: Dr. Vito Bernardi
Fine Arts Museum
Paintings and sketches by Michele De Napoli, architectonic fragments 22634

Pinacoteca, Corso Dante 9, 70038 Terlizzi - T: 080817577
Fine Arts Museum 22635

Termini Imerese

Antiquarium di Himera, Strada Statale 113, Località Buonfornello, 90018 Termini Imerese - T: 0918140128, Fax: 0916702070, E-mail: sopripa@regione.sicilia.it
Archaeological Museum
Archaeological finds 22636

Museo Civico, Via dei Museo, 90018 Termini Imerese - T: 0918128279, Fax: 0918128421. Head: Prof. Giuseppe Longo
Archaeological Museum - 1873
Prehistory, architectonic fragments of Roman buildings, geology and mineralogy, coins, Sicilian paintings 22637

Termoli

Galleria Civica d'Arte Contemporanea, Piazza San Antonio, 86039 Termoli - T: 0875712265
Fine Arts Museum
Contemporary art 22638

Terni

Raccolta Archeologica, Piazza Carrara 2, 05100 Terni - T: 0744655656, Fax: 0744549546. Head: Paolo Rinaldi
Archaeological Museum 22639

Terra del Sole

Museo dell'Uomo e dell'Ambiente, Piazza d'Armi 2, 47010 Terra del Sole - T: 0543766766, Fax: 0543766766, E-mail: museo@terradelsole.org, Internet: http://www.terradelsole.org. Head: Renato Giancarlo Zoli
Ethnology Museum - 1971
Wine cycle 22640

Terracina

Museo Civico Archeologico Communale, Palazzo del Comune, Piazza Municipio, 04019 Terracina - T: 0773702220. Head: Dr. Mario Di Mario
Archaeological Museum
Statues, relief work and epigraphs of the Roman period 22641

Terrasini

Museo Civico, Via Cala Rossa 4, 90049 Terrasini - T: 0918682652
Local Museum 22642

Museo Etnografico del Carretto Siciliano, Palazzo d'Ausmal, 90049 Terrasini - T: 091664618
Ethnology Museum 22643

Thiene

Museo del Castello Colleoni Porto, Piazza Ferrarin, 36016 Thiene
Decorative Arts Museum
15th c frescoes, statues, pottery, furniture 22644

Tindari

Antiquarium, 98060 Tindari
Archaeological Museum
Marble sculptures of the Hellenistic period, Greek and Roman articles made of clay 22645

Tirolo di Merano

Landesmuseum Schloß Tirol, Schloßweg 24, 39019 Tirolo di Merano - T: 0473220221, Fax: 0473221132, E-mail: schloss.tirol@ provinz.bz.it. Head: Dr. Siegfried de Rachewiltz
Historical Museum / Archaeological Museum - 1989
History of Tyrol, archaeological coll 22646

Museo Agricolo Brunnenburg/ Landwirtschaftsmuseum, Via Pound 3, 39019 Tirolo di Merano - T: 0473923533, Fax: 0473923533, E-mail: brunnenburg@ rolmail.net, Internet: http://wecome.to/brunnenburg. Head: Dr. Siegfried de Rachewiltz
Agriculture Museum - 1973
Exhibits on bread baking, viticulture, agricultural implements, crafts 22647

Tivoli

Museo Communale, Villa Adriana, 00019 Tivoli - T: 0774290502. Head: Dr. Maria Luisa Veloccia Rinaldi
Fine Arts Museum - 1915
17th c paintings 22648

Villa d'Este, Piazza Trento 1, 00019 Tivoli - T: 077422070
Local Museum 22649

Todi

Museo e Pinacoteca Civica, Piazza del Popolo, 06059 Todi - T: 075882404. Head: Prof. Franco Mancini
Fine Arts Museum / Archaeological Museum / Decorative Arts Museum
Goldsmith work, religious ornaments, archeological findings of Etruscan and Roman objects 22650

Toirano

Museo Preistorico della Val Varatello, Via Parodi, 17020 Toirano - T: 018298062
Archaeological Museum 22651

Tolentino

Museo Civico, Piazza Silveri 2, 62029 Tolentino - T: 0733969996, Fax: 0733969798
Archaeological Museum - 1882
Stone sculptures, ceramics, items from local excavations 22652

Museo delle Ceramiche, Basilica di San Nicola, 62029 Tolentino - T: 0733976311, Fax: 0733976346, E-mail: egidiana@sannicolada-tolentino.it, Internet: http://www.sannicolada-tolentino.it
Decorative Arts Museum - 1930
Vases from Albissola, Deruta, Nove and Castel Durante 22653

Museo dell'Opera del Santuario, Basilica di San Nicola, 62029 Tolentino - T: 0733976311, Fax: 0733976346, E-mail: egidiana@sannicolada-tolentino.it, Internet: http://www.sannicolada-tolentino.it
Religious Arts Museum / Decorative Arts Museum - 1930 22654

Museo Internazionale della Caricatura, Via della Pace 20, 62029 Tolentino - T: 0733901325, Fax: 0733901360. Head: Paolo Valentini
Fine Arts Museum - 1964
Drawings, paintings, statuettes and puppets by the world's most famous caricaturists, humorous journals 22655

Sale Napoleoniche, Palazzo Parisani Bezzi, Via della Pace 20, 62029 Tolentino - T: 0733901325, Fax: 0733901360
Historical Museum - 1909 22656

Tolfa

Museo Civico, Piazza Vittorio Veneto 12, 00059 Tolfa - T: 076692003, Fax: 076692008. Head: Dr. Andrea Zifferero
Archaeological Museum - 1955
Etruscan and Roman and medieval artifacts 22657

Tolmezzo

Museo Carnico delle Arti Populari Michele Gortani, Piazza Garibaldi 2, 33028 Tolmezzo - T: 043343233. Head: Dr. Giorgio Ferigo
Ethnology Museum / Folklore Museum - 1920
Ethnography, local folklore and culture - library, archives 22658

Torgiano

Museo del Vino, Fondazione Lungarotti, Corso Vittorio Emanuele 11, 06089 Torgiano - T: 0759880200, Fax: 0759880300, E-mail: museovino@lungarotti.it, Internet: http://www.lungarotti.it. Head: Dr. Maria Grazia Lungarotti
Agriculture Museum
Wine related works of art (archaeological founds, ceramics, engravings) 22659

Torgnon

Museo Saint Roch, Chiesa Parrocchiale di San Martino, 11020 Torgnon - T: 016640241
Religious Arts Museum 22660

Torino

Armeria Reale, Piazza Castello 191, 10123 Torino - T: 011543889, Fax: 011549547. Head: Dr. Paolo Venturoli
Military Museum - 1837
Arms and armour, dating back to the 13th c, Oriental and exotic armour, famous equestrian armour 22661

Borgo e Castello Medioevale, Parco del Valentino, 10126 Torino - T: 0116699372, Fax: 011655356. Head: Dr. Rosanna Magglo-Serra
Historical Museum 22662

Castello Reggia di Venaria Reale, Piazza del Repubblica 4, Venaria, Torino - T: 011496272
Local Museum 22663

Centro Storico Fiat, Via Chiabrera 20, 10126 Torino - T: 011670474. Head: Antonio Amadelli
Science&Tech Museum
Cars, airplane and ship engines, history of the fiat Company from its very beginning - library 22664

Fondazione Pietro Accorsi, Via Po 55, 10124 Torino - T: 011837688, Fax: 011837688. Head: Giulio Ometto, Dr. Arabella Cifani
Fine Arts Museum 22665

Galleria Civica d'Arte Moderna e Contemporanea di Torino, Via Magenta 31, 10128 Torino - T: 0115629911, Fax: 0114429550, E-mail: gam@ comune.torino.it, Internet: http://www.gam.intesa.it. Head: Prof. Pier Giovanni Castagnoli
Fine Arts Museum - 1959
19th-20th c paintings, graphics and sculptures - library 22666

Galleria dell'Accademia Albertina di Belle Arti, Via Accademia Albertina 8, 10123 Torino - T: 011889020, Fax: 0118125688, E-mail: albertina@alpcom.it, Internet: http:// www.alpcom.it/accademialbertina.torino. Head: Prof. Carlo Giuliano
Fine Arts Museum - 1833
16th-18th c paintings 22667

Galleria Sabauda, Via Accademia delle Scienze 6, 10123 Torino - T: 011547440, 011530501, Fax: 011549547. Head: Dr. Michaela Di Macho
Fine Arts Museum - 1832
Dutch and Flemish paintings, works by the Lombard and Piedmontese schools, sculpture, furniture, jewelry, 15th to 19th c Italian paintings - library, photographs archive 22668

Mole Antonelliana, Via Montebello 20, 10124 Torino - T: 011832874
Historical Museum 22669

Museo Civico d'Arte Antica e Palazzo Madama, Palazzo Madama, Piazza Castello, 10123 Torino - T: 0114429911, Fax: 0114429929, E-mail: palazzo.madama@comune.torino.it, Internet: http://www.comune.torino.it/ palazzomadama. Head: Dr. Enrica Pagella
Decorative Arts Museum - 1863
Metal works, glass, pottery, ceramics, textile works, furniture, miniatures, sculpture, ivory works, drawings, leather, engravings, jewels - library, photo archive 22670

Museo Civico di Numismatica, Etnografia e Arti Orientali, Via Bricherasio 8, 10128 Torino - T: 011541557/608. Head: Dr. Serafina Pennestri
Ethnology Museum 22671

Museo d'Arte Contemporanea, Piazza del Castello, 10098 Torino - T: 0119581547, Fax: 0119561141
Fine Arts Museum
Modern art 22672

Museo d'Arte e Ammobiliamento, Piazza Principe Amedeo, Nichelino, 10042 Torino - T: 0113581220
Decorative Arts Museum 22673

Museo del Piccolo Regio, Piazza Castello 215, 10124 Torino - T: 011549126
Historical Museum 22674

Museo della Fotografia Storica e Contemporanea, Via Avogadro 4, Torino - T: 011546594, Fax: 011544132
Fine Arts Museum 22675

Museo della Marionetta, Teatro Gianduia, Via Santa Teresa 5, 10121 Torino - T: 011530238, Fax: 011530328. Head: Raoul Cristofoli
Performing Arts Museum - 1978
Puppets, scenery, accessories 22676

Museo della Sindone (Museum of Shrouds), Via San Domenico 28, 10122 Torino - T: 0114365832, Fax: 0114319275, E-mail: sindone@tin.it, Internet: http://www.sindone.it. Head: Prof. Bruno Barberis, Dr. Gian Maria Zaccome
Special Museum
Grave-clothes 22677

Museo dell'Agricoltura del Piemonte, Via P. Giuria, 15, 10126 Torino - T: 011657300, 011658129, Fax: 0116502754. Head: L. Quagliotti
Agriculture Museum - 1977 22678

Museo dell'Automobile Carlo Biscaretti di Ruffia, Corso Unità d'Italia 40, 10126 Torino - T: 011677666, Fax: 0116647148, E-mail: museoauto@libero.it, Internet: http:// www.museoauto.org. Head: Rodolfo Gaffino Rossi
Science&Tech Museum - 1957
Automobiles, motor vehicles and chassis, engines, tires, old posters and prints - library, documentation centre, photoarchive 22679

Museo di Anatomia Comparata, Via Giovanni Giolitti 34, 10123 Torino - T: 011831930
Special Museum
Anatomic coll 22680

Museo di Antichita, Collezioni Archeologiche, Via XX Settembre 88c, 10123 Torino - T: 0115211106, Fax: 115213145, E-mail: info@ museoarcheologico.it, Internet: http:// www.museoantichita.it. Head: Dr. Luisa Brecciaroli
Archaeological Museum
Prehistoric weapons, tools and jewels from the Iron and Bronze Ages, Greek pottery, Etruscan coll, Roman sculpture, inscriptions, regional pottery and necropolis 22681

Museo di Antropologia Criminale, Corso Montevecchio 38, 10126 Torino - T: 011535670. Head: Prof. Mario Portigliatti Barbos
Special Museum - 1898
Forensic medicine, skulls, anthropology 22682

Museo di Antropologia ed Etnografia, Via Accademia Albertina 17, 10123 Torino - T: 0118122374. Head: Prof. Emma Rabino Massa
Ethnology Museum - 1923
Skulls, skeletons, brains, fossil casts, pictures of living primates, lithic tools, mummies, ethnographic exhibits of various cultures of the world - library 22683

Museo di Geologia e Paleontologia, Palazzo Carignano, Via Accademia delle Scienze 5, 10123 Torino - T: 0115621179, Fax: 011541755, E-mail: pavia@dst.unito.it, Internet: http:// www.dst.unito.it. Head: Prof. Giulio Pavia
Natural History Museum - 1878
Geology, paleontology, fossiles, mollusks, vertebrates 22684

Museo di Storia Naturale Don Bosco, Viale Enrico Thovez 37, 10131 Torino - T: 0116300629, 0116601066, Fax: 0116300605, 0116602221, E-mail: museo@liceovalsalice.it, Internet: http://www.liceovalsalice.it/museo. Head: Prof. Ezio Fonio
Natural History Museum 22685

Museo di Strumenti del Conservatorio Statale di Musica Giuseppe Verdi, Via Mazzini 11, 10123 Torino
Music Museum 22686

Museo Egizio, Via Accademia delle Scienze 6, 10123 Torino - T: 0115617776, Fax: 0115623157, E-mail: egizio.segreteria@multix.it, Internet: http://www.egizi.artibeniculturali.it. Head: Dr. Anna Maria Donadoni Roveri
Archaeological Museum - 1824
Egyptian hist, sarcophagi, mummies, stelae, statues, papyrus, Ptolemaic and Coptic antiquities, reconstructed Nile temple of the 18th dynasty, complete furnishing of private tomb from Deir El Medina (XVIII Dynasty), papyrus of the kings, Rameses II Statue - education dept, conservation lab, photographic archive, library 22687

Museo Nazionale del Cinema, Fondazione M.A. Prolo - F.I.A.F., Via Montebello 15, 10124 Torino - T: 0118122814, Fax: 0118398501, E-mail: info@museonazionaledelcinema.org. Head: Prof. Mario Ricciardi
Special Museum / Science&Tech Museum - 1953
Pre-cinema exhibits, history of photography, the silent and sound film, cinematographic posters - library, archive, space exhibition, film archive 22688

Museo Nazionale del Risorgimento Italiano, Via Accademia delle Scienze 5, 10123 Torino - T: 0115621147, Fax: 0115624695, E-mail: TO0328@lotuszeg.regione.piemonte.it. Head: Dr. Rosanna Maggio-Serra
Historical Museum
Relics pertaining to the Resistance and the Risorgimento 22689

Museo Nazionale della Montagna Duca degli Abruzzi, Via Giardino 39, 10131 Torino - T: 0116604104, Fax: 0116604622, E-mail: posta@museomontagna.org, Internet: http://www.museomomtagna.org. Head: Aldo Audisio
Historical Museum - 1874
Hist of mountaineering, documents pertaining to the Duke of Abruzzi - documentation centre (photo library), film and video library 22690

Museo Pietro Micca, Via Guicciardini 7, 10121 Torino - T: 011546317
Local Museum
Wooden models of the city and citadel of Turin in various sizes 22691

Museo Regionale di Scienze Naturali, Affiliation Regione Piemonte, Via G. Giolitti, 36, 10123 Torino - T: 01143207302, Fax: 01143207301, E-mail: museo.mrsn@regione.piemonte.it, Internet: http://www.regione.piemonte.it/museoscienzenaturali.htm. Head: Giuliano Bottero
Natural History Museum - 1979
library 22692

Museo Storico Nazionale di Artiglieria, Corso Galileo, Ferraris 0, 10100 Torino - T: 01156034061, Fax: 0115629223
Historical Museum 22693

Museo Zoologico dell'Università di Torino, Via Accademia Albertina 17, 10123 Torino - T: 0118122374, Fax: 0118124561, E-mail: passerin@dba.unito.it. Head: Prof. Emilio Balletto
Natural History Museum
Insects, birds, mammals, fish, reptiles and amphibians, several extinct species 22694

Palazzo Bricherasio, Via Lagrange 20, Torino - T: 0115171660, Fax: 0115629757, E-mail: bricherasio@itanet.com, Internet: http://www.bricherasio.intesa.it. Head: Daniela Magnetti
Fine Arts Museum 22695

Palazzo Reale, Piazzetta Reale 1, Torino - T: 0114361455, Fax: 0114361484, E-mail: sbaap@ambienteto.arti.beniculturali.it, Internet: http://www.ambienteto.arti.beniculturali.it. Head: Daniela Biancolini
Local Museum 22696

Tombe Reali di Casa Savoia, Basilica di Superga, 10132 Torino - T: 0118980083, Fax: 0118987024. Head: Simeone Mareneo
Religious Arts Museum - 1778
Crypt with royal tombs and sculptures - library 22697

Torre Annunziata

Scavi di Oplontis, 80058 Torre Annunziata - T: 0818621755, 0818624081. Head: Prof. Pietro Giovanni Guzzo, Dr. Lorenzo Fergola
Archaeological Museum 22698

Torre del Greco

Museo del Corallo, Piazza Palomba 6, 80059 Torre del Greco - T: 0818811360. Head: Prof. Giuseppe Ciavolino
Decorative Arts Museum
Sculpture, engraved coral, lava, shells, mother-of-pearl and ivory 22699

Torre del Lago Puccini

Museo Pucciniano, Viale Puccini 266, 55048 Torre del Lago Puccini - T: 0584341445, Fax: 024982194, E-mail: casepuccini@tin.it, Internet: http://www.giacomopuccini.it. Head: Simonetta Puccini
Music Museum
House of Giacomo Puccini from 1900 until 1921, the musician's tomb 22700

Torre Pellice

Civica Galleria d'Arte Contemporanea, Via D'Azeglio angolo Vie Dante, 10066 Torre Pellice - T: 012191278. Head: Prof. Giuseppe Mantovani
Fine Arts Museum - 1994 22701

Museo delle Valli Valdesi, Via Beckwith 3, 10066 Torre Pellice - T: 0121932179, Fax: 0121932566, E-mail: centroculturalevaldese@tin.it. Head: Dr. Donatella Sommani
Ethnology Museum - 1889
Ethnographical museum of the Waldensian valleys - library, archives 22702

Torri del Benaco

Museo del Castello Scaligero, Via Fratelli Lavanda 2, 37010 Torri del Benaco - T: 0456296111, Fax: 0456296111
Ethnology Museum 22703

Torri in Sabina

Museo Territoriale dell'Agro Foronovano, Str Provinciale Sabina Vescovio, 02049 Torri in Sabina - T: 076568197
Local Museum 22704

Tortona

Museo Romano, Piazza Arzano 2, 15057 Tortona - T: 0131864273, Fax: 0131811411. Head: Dr. Ugo Rozzo
Archaeological Museum
Roman and medieval artifacts, sculpture, sarcophagi, captals 22705

Trani

Museo delle Carrozze, Piazza Quercia 8, 70059 Trani - T: 088342641
Science&Tech Museum 22706

Museo Diocesano, Piazza Duomo 4, 70059 Trani - T: 0883584632. Head: Dr. Benedetto Ronchi
Religious Arts Museum
14th-17th c paintings, religious ornaments and furnishings 22707

Trapani

Antiquarium, Selinunte, 91100 Trapani
Archaeological Museum
Acropolis with tree temples 22708

Museo Pepoli, Via Pepoli 200, 91100 Trapani - T: 0923535444. Head: Dr. Vincenzo Abbate
Fine Arts Museum
14th-18th c paintings, paintings of the Tuscan school, archeological findings, corals, pottery 22709

Museo Regionale Pepoli, Via Conte Agostino Pepoli 196, 91100 Trapani - T: 0923553269, Fax: 0923535444. Head: Dr. Vincenzo Abbate
Local Museum 22710

Traversetolo

Museo Renato Brozzi, Palazzo Municipale, 43029 Traversetolo
Fine Arts Museum
Sculptures and paintings by Renato Brozzi 22711

Trebisacce

Museo Etnografico, 87075 Trebisacce
Ethnology Museum 22712

Treia

Museo Civico Archeologico, Piazza della Repubblica, 62010 Treia - T: 0733215117
Archaeological Museum 22713

Tremezzo

Museo di Villa Carlotta, Via Regina 2, 22019 Tremezzo - T: 034440405, Fax: 034441011. Head: Prof. Giacomo Elias
Fine Arts Museum - 1927
Sculptures by Canova and Thorvaldsen, paintings by Appiani and Hayez, gobelins 22714

Trento

Castello del Buonconsiglio, Via B. Clesio 5, 38100 Trento - T: 0461233770, Fax: 0461239497, E-mail: castellodelbuonconsiglio@provincie.tn.it, Internet: http://www.buonconsiglio.it. Head: Dr. Franco Marzatico
Fine Arts Museum - 1924
Mss, sculpture, detached frescoes, majolica tiles, china, prints, drawings, paintings, archaeology 22715

Museo d'Arte Moderna e Contemporanea di Trento e Rovereto, Palazzo delle Albere, Via R. da Sanseverino 45, 38100 Trento - T: 0461234860, Fax: 0461234007, E-mail: info@mart.trento.it, Internet: http://www.mart.trento.it. Head: Dr. Gabriella Belli
Fine Arts Museum - 1987
Deposits and donations of important Italian artists (Umberto, Moggioli, Tullio Garbari, Paolo Vallorz), Fausto Melotti's drawings and sculptures 22716

Museo Diocesano Tridentino, Piazza Duomo 18, 38100 Trento - T: 0461234419. Head: Prof. Iginio Rogger
Religious Arts Museum - 1903
Local religious art, archeological finds 22717

Museo Storico, Castello del Buonconsiglio, Via Bernardo Clesio 3, 38100 Trento - T: 0461230482, Fax: 0461237418. Head: Prof. Vincenzo Cali
Historical Museum - 1923
History of the Risorgimento, anti-fascism and the resistance movement 22718

Museo Storico Nazionale degli Alpini, Via Brescia, 38100 Trento - T: 0461827248. Head: Tullio Vidulich
Military Museum
History of the Alpine troops in times of war and peace 22719

Museo Tridentino di Scienze Naturali, Via Calepina 14, 38100 Trento - T: 0461270311, 0461270301, Fax: 0461233830, E-mail: info@mtsn.tn.it, Internet: http://www.mtsn.tn.it. Head: Michele Lanzinger
Natural History Museum - 1846
Prehistory, zoology, botany, minerals, petrography - alpine botanical garden, climatological observatories - botanical garden 22720

Trevi

Raccolta d'Arte di San Francesco, Palazzo Lucarini, Largo Don Bosco, 06039 Trevi - T: 0742381628, Fax: 0742381628
Fine Arts Museum - 1867
Paintings by artists of the Umbrian and Piedmontese schools, medieval and Renaissance sculpture, olive oil cultivation 22721

Trevi Flash Art Museum of International Contemporary Art, Via Lucarini 1, 06039 Trevi - T: 0742381818, Fax: 0742381819
Fine Arts Museum 22722

Treviglio

Museo Civico della Torre, Via Facchetti 14, 24047 Treviglio - T: 0363317506, Fax: 0363317503, E-mail: cultura.treviglio@insieme.net, Internet: http://www.insieme.net. Head: Riccardo Riganti
Local Museum 22723

Trevignano Romano

Museo Civico, Piazza Vittorio Emanuele III, 00069 Trevignano Romano - T: 06999120201, 069991201, Fax: 069999848, E-mail: comune@aconet.it, Internet: http://www.trevignanoromano.it. Head: Dr. Gregorio Bianchini
Archaeological Museum - 1985
Etruscan and Roman remains 22724

Treviso

Casa da Noal, Via Canova 40, 31100 Treviso - T: 0422544895, Fax: 0422591337. Head: Prof. Eugenio Manzato
Decorative Arts Museum / Fine Arts Museum
Furniture, sculptures in wood and marble, musical instruments, pottery 22725

Museo Civico Luigi Bailo, Borgo Cavour 22, 31100 Treviso - T: 0422591337, Fax: 0422591337. Head: Prof. Eugenio Manzato
Archaeological Museum / Fine Arts Museum - 1879
Prehistory, marble statues, frescoes, paintings by Bellini, L. Lotto, Titian, Tintoretto, sculpture by Canova, modern art 22726

Museo della Casa Trevigiana, Via Canova 38, 31100 Treviso - T: 0422544895. Head: Prof. Eugenio Manzato
Local Museum 22727

Museo Diocesano d'Arte Sacra, Via delle Canoniche 9, 31100 Treviso - T: 0422410700, Fax: 0422543926. Head: Umberto Crozzolin
Religious Arts Museum 22728

Museo Zoologico G. Scarpa, Piazzetta Benedetto XI 2, 31100 Treviso - T: 04223247, Fax: 0422324890
Natural History Museum - 1914
2500 specimens of vertebrates, mainly from the Mediterranean area 22729

Trieste

Civico Museo del Castello di San Giusto, Piazza Cattedrale 3, 34121 Trieste - T: 040313636, Fax: 040300687, E-mail: dugulin@comune.trieste.it. Head: Dr. Adriano Dugulin
Decorative Arts Museum / Fine Arts Museum - 1936
Furniture and furnishings of the castle, paintings, arms 22730

Civico Museo del Mare, Via di Campo Marzio 5, 34123 Trieste - T: 040304987, 040304885, Fax: 040302563, E-mail: daprettol@comunetrieste.it, Internet: http://tcd.retecivica.trieste/triestecultura/musei/scientifici/museomare/mareframe/htm. Head: Dr. Sergio Dolce
Natural History Museum - 1904
Models of fishing boats of the Adriatic Sea, Adriatic harbours, nautical instruments 22731

Civico Museo del Risorgimento e Sacrario Oberdan, Via XXIV Maggio 4, 34133 Trieste - T: 040361675, Fax: 040300687, E-mail: dugulin@comune.trieste.it. Head: Dr. Adriano Dugulin
Historical Museum - 1922
History of the Risorgimento, World War I and of Oberdan 22732

Civico Museo della Risiera di San Sabba, Ratto della Pileria 43, 34148 Trieste - T: 040826202, Fax: 040300687, E-mail: dugulin@comune.trieste.it. Head: Dr. Adriano Dugulin
Military Museum / Historical Museum - 1965
Documents and photographs of World War II and especially of the Resistance movement, housed in Italy's one and only concentration camp 22733

Civico Museo di Guerra per la Pace Diego de Henriquez (Town War Museum for Peace), Via Revoltella 37, 34138 Trieste - T: 040948430, Fax: 040944390, E-mail: museodehenriquez@comune.trieste.it, Internet: http://www.retecivica.trieste.it/triestecultura/musei/civicimusei. Head: Dr. Adriano Dugulin
Military Museum / Historical Museum - 1997
Mankind in the light of war events, technological development from prehistoric to modern times (antique 'Zoppolo', pirogue), arms and material of WW II, tanks, heavy artillery, guns, toys, shipmodels 22734

Civico Museo di Storia ed Arte e Orto Lapidario, Via Cattedrale 15, 34121 Trieste - T: 040308686, 040310500, Fax: 040300687, E-mail: dugulin@comune.trieste.it. Head: Dr. Adriano Dugulin
Archaeological Museum / Local Museum - 1873
Numismatics, Roman architecture, Greek gold work, prehistory - library 22735

Civico Museo Morpurgo, Via Imbriani 5, 34122 Trieste - T: 040636969, Fax: 040300687, E-mail: dugulin@comune.trieste.it. Head: Dr. Adriano Dugulin
Local Museum - 1952
Local history, exhibits depicting the lifestyle of the 19th c - library 22736

Civico Museo Revoltella e Galleria d'Arte Moderna, Via Diaz 27, 34123 Trieste - T: 040300938, Fax: 040302742. Head: Dr. Maria Masau Dan
Fine Arts Museum - 1872
19th c furnishings, 19th and 20th c European paintings, sculpture and graphics - library, photo library 22737

Civico Museo Sartorio, Largo Papa Giovanni XXIII 1, 34123 Trieste - T: 040301479, Fax: 040300687, E-mail: dugulin@comune.trieste.it. Head: Dr. Adriano Dugulin
Decorative Arts Museum / Fine Arts Museum - 1949
Furnishings, paintings, ceramics, Trittico di Santa Chiara - library 22738

Civico Museo Teatrale di Fondazione Carlo Schmidl, Via Imbriani 5, 34122 Trieste - T: 040366030, Fax: 0406636969, E-mail: dugulin@comune.trieste.it. Head: Dr. Adriano Dugulin
Music Museum / Performing Arts Museum - 1924
Musical instruments, items related to the theatre in Triest - library 22739

Galleria Nazionale d'Arte Antica, Piazza Libertà 7, 34100 Trieste - T: 04043631, Fax: 04043634. Head: Prof. Franco Bocchieri
Fine Arts Museum 22740

Galleria Storica del Lloyd Triestino, Passeggio S. Andrea 4, 34123 Trieste - T: 0403180111, Fax: 0403180294. Head: Dr. Gianni Usberghi
Historical Museum - 1969
Ship models, advertising sketches, tableware, photos 22741

Museo Civico di Storia Naturale, Piazza Attilio Hortis 4, 34123 Trieste - T: 040301821, 040302563, Fax: 040302563, E-mail: daprettol@comune.trieste.it. Head: Dr. Sergio Dolce
Natural History Museum - 1846
Zoology, botany, geology, minerals, paleontology, anthropology - library 22742

Museo della Fondazione Giovanni Scaramangà di Altomonte, Via Filzi 1, 34132 Trieste - T: 040631585. Head: Dr. Antonio Rossetti de Scander
Fine Arts Museum / Decorative Arts Museum - 1961
Paintings, prints, drawings, ceramics, local history and art - library 22743

Museo Etnografico di Servola, Via del Pane Biano 52, 34146 Trieste - T: 040827248. Head: Dušan Jakomin
Ethnology Museum
Costumes, prints, bedroom and kitchen furnishings, bread-making equipment, tools 22744

Museo Storico del Castello di Miramare, Grignano, 34014 Trieste - T: 040224143, Fax: 040224220, E-mail: info@castello-miramare.it, Internet: http://www.castello-miramare.it. Head: Rossella Fabiani
Decorative Arts Museum - 1955
Furniture and decor depicting a princely residence in the middle of the 19th c - library 22745

Trino

Museo Civico Didattico Gian Andrea Irico, Piazza Garibaldi 7, 13039 Trino - T: 0161829363, Internet: http://www.plurinet.it. Head: Ugo Falabrino
Archaeological Museum / Local Museum - 1975
History of town and trinese printers, coll of 16th c books, archaeological founds (prehistorical to roman/medieval age) 22746

Troia

Museo Civico, Via Regina Margherita 80, 71029 Troia - T: 0881970870, E-mail: comune.troia@isnet.it. Head: Giovanna Velluto
Archaeological Museum
Epigraphic and tomb material, pre-Roman clay pottery, medieval stone tablets 22747

Museo Diocesano e Tesoro della Cattedrale, Palazzo Vescovile, Piazza Cattedrale, 71029 Troia - T: 0881970051. Head: Mario Maitilasso
Religious Arts Museum 22748

Tropea

Raccolta Privata Toraldo di Francia, Via Lauro, 88038 Tropea - T: 096361388
Fine Arts Museum 22749

Tuscania

Museo Nazionale, Chiesa di San Pietro, 01017 Tuscania - T: 0761436196
Archaeological Museum 22750

Udine

Civici Musei e Gallerie di Storia ed Arte, Castello, 33100 Udine - T: 0432501824, 0432502872, Fax: 0432501681, Internet: http://www.comune.udine.it. Head: Dr. Giuseppe Bergamini
Local Museum / Fine Arts Museum - 1906
Archaeology, numismatics, graphics, local paintings, paintings by Carpaccio and Tiepolo, Roman excavations - library, photo archive 22751

Galleria d'Arte Moderna, Piazzale Paolo Diacono 22, 33100 Udine - T: 0432505089, Fax: 0432504219, E-mail: gamud@comune.udine.it, Internet: http://www.comune.udine.it/galleria/mod.htm
Fine Arts Museum - 1895 22752

Museo del Duomo, Metropolitana, Piazza del Duomo, 33100 Udine - T: 0432506830, Internet: http://www.spaziocultura.it/duomoud. Head: Dr. Marino Qualizza
Religious Arts Museum 22753

Museo della Città, Palazzo Torriani, Via Zanon, 33100 Udine - T: 043221193. Head: Dr. Giuseppe Bergamini
Local Museum 22754

Museo Diocesano e Gallerie del Tiepolo, Palazzo Patriarcale, Piazza Patriarcato 1, 33100 Udine - T: 043225003, Fax: 043225003, Internet: http://www.comune.udine.it. Head: Gian Carlo Menis
Religious Arts Museum
Paintings, jewellery, wooden sculptures, devotional stained glass 22755

Museo Friulano di Storia Naturale, Via Grazzano 1, 33100 Udine - T: 0432584711, Fax: 0432584721, E-mail: mfsn@comune.udine.it, Internet: http://www.comune.udine.it. Head: Dr. Carlo Morandini
Natural History Museum - 1866
Minerals, rocks, fossils, prehistoric material, herbarium, invertebrates and vertebrates, mostly from NE Italy, but also some from the rest of Italy, NE Europe and some non European countries - archives, laboratories, library, didactic and expositive section 22756

Ugento

Museo Civico di Paleontologia e Archeologia, Via della Zecca 1, 73059 Ugento - T: 0833555819. Head: Walter Zecca
Archaeological Museum
Paleolithic, mesolithic and neolithic materials 22757

Ultimo

Museo Etnografico, Via San Valburga, 39016 Ultimo - T: 0473795321
Ethnology Museum 22758

Urbania

Museo Civico e Pinacoteca, Corso Vittorio Emanuele 23, 61049 Urbania - T: 0722319985, Fax: 0722319985. Head: Feliciano Paoli
Decorative Arts Museum / Fine Arts Museum - 1631
Pottery, paintings, frescoes, engravings, incunabula - Italian paintings (16th-17th c) 22759

Urbino

Casa Natale di Raffaello, Via Sanzio 57, 61029 Urbino - T: 0722320105, Fax: 0722329695, E-mail: accraff@comune.urbino.ps.it, Internet: http://www.comune.urbino.ps.it/fas.htm. Head: Nino Baldeschi
Fine Arts Museum - 1869
Etchings and reproductions of works by Raphael (Raffaello Sanzio) 22760

Galleria Nazionale delle Marche, Palazzo Ducale, Piazza Duca Federico 1, 61029 Urbino - T: 07222760. Head: Dr. Paolo Dal Poggetto
Fine Arts Museum - 1912
Medieval and Renaissance works of art from town of Urbino and province of Marche, sculpture, majolica, paintings by Uccello, Piero della Francesca, Raphael, Bellini and Titian 22761

Museo del Duomo Albani, Basilica, Piazza Pascoli 1, 61029 Urbino - T: 07222892. Head: Amato Cini
Religious Arts Museum
Frescoes, pottery, sacred objects, paintings 22762

Museo Lapidario, Piazza Duca Federico, 61029 Urbino - T: 07222760
Archaeological Museum 22763

Vacciago di Ameno

Fondazinone Calderara, Via Bardelli 9, 28010 Vacciago di Ameno - T: 0322998192
Fine Arts Museum
Contemporary art 22764

Vado Ligure

Museo Pinacoteca Villa Groppallo, Via Aurelia 72, 17047 Vado Ligure - T: 019883914. Head: Dr. Marisa Pogliani
Fine Arts Museum 22765

Raccolta Archeologica Don Cesare Queirolo, Piazza S. Giovanni Battista 1, 17047 Vado Ligure. Head: Dr. Marisa Pogliani
Archaeological Museum 22766

Valdagno

Galleria Civica, Villa Valle, Viale Regina Margherita 1, 36078 Valdagno - T: 0445428223, Fax: 0445428213, E-mail: cultura@comune.valdagno.vi.it, Internet: http://www.comune.valdagno.vi.it. Head: Prof. Giuliano Menato
Fine Arts Museum - 1973
Contemporary sculpture 22767

Museo di Paleontologia e di Mineralogia, Palazzo Festari, 36078 Valdagno - T: 0445424507, 0445401887, Fax: 0445409724, E-mail: biblioteca@comune.valdagno.vi.it, Internet: http://www.comune.valdagno.vi.it. Head: Dario Savi
Natural History Museum - 1974
Minerals and fossils - library 22768

Valfurva

Museo Vallivo Valfurva, Via San Antonio, 5, 23030 Valfurva - T: 0342945291. Head: Mario Testorelli
Local Museum - 1974
Interior, transport, craft, religious art, war (1915-1918), costumes 22769

Vallada Agordina

Museo di Storia e Cultura della Val del Biois, Municipio, 32020 Vallada Agordina - T: 0437591183
Historical Museum 22770

Vallo di Nera

Raccolta Etnografica, Piazza Santa Maria, 06040 Vallo di Nera - T: 0743912690, Fax: 074391269. Head: Prof. Cristina Papa
Ethnology Museum - 1975
Hemp production and weaving 22771

Valsavarenche

Piccolo Museo Sacro, Fraz. Degioz 68, Chiesa Madonna del Carmine, 11010 Valsavarenche - T: 0165905715. Head: Mario Tringali
Religious Arts Museum - 1981 22772

Varallo Pombia

Museo Archeologico, Villa Soranzo, Via Simonetta 3, 28040 Varallo Pombia - T: 032195355. Head: Stefano Boggio
Archaeological Museum 22773

Varallo Sesia

Museo Calderini, Via Don Maio, 13019 Varallo Sesia - T: 016351424
Natural History Museum
Mineralogy, coll of beetles 22774

Palazzo dei Musei, Via Don Maio 25, 13019 Varallo Sesia - T: 016351424
Local Museum 22775

Riserva Naturale Speciale del Sacro Monte di Varallo, Via Sacro Monte, 13019 Varallo Sesia - T: 016353938, Fax: 016354047, E-mail: riservasacromonte@laproxima.it. Head: Dr. Elena De Filippis
Open Air Museum / Natural History Museum 22776

Varenna

Museo Civico Ornitologico e di Scienze Naturali Luigi Scanagatta, Via 4 Novembre, 23829 Varenna - T: 0341830119, Fax: 0341831210, E-mail: wtcvaren@tin.it. Head: Dr. Alberto Tellini
Natural History Museum - 1962
Birds of the Lake Como area, malacological coll 22777

Varese

Centro di Studi Preistorici ed Archeologici, Piazza della Motta 4, 21100 Varese. Head: Prof. Mario Mirabella Roberti
Archaeological Museum 22778

Museo Civico, Castello di Masnago via Monguelfo, Piazza della Motta 4, 21100 Varese - T: 0332281590. Head: Flaminio Gualdoni
Archaeological Museum
Prehist, archaeology, 18th-19th c 22779

Museo del Santuario e Museo Baroffio, Santa Maria del Monte, 21030 Varese - T: 0332225593
Religious Arts Museum / Fine Arts Museum / Decorative Arts Museum
Paintings, goldwork, sacred vestemnts 22780

Museo Lodovico Pogliaghi, Santa Maria del Monte, 21100 Varese - T: 02806921, Fax: 0280692210, E-mail: info@ambrosiana.it. Head: Gianfranco Ravasi
Fine Arts Museum - 1971 22781

Varese Ligure

Museo Contadino, Fraz Cassego, Scuola Elementare, 19028 Varese Ligure - T: 0187843005
Historical Museum 22782

Varna

Pinacoteca dell'Abbazia di Novacello, Abbazia di Novacello, 39040 Varna - T: 047236189
Religious Arts Museum 22783

Vasto

Museo e Pinacoteca Civici, Piazzale d'Avalos, 66054 Vasto - T: 0873367773. Head: Dr. Francesco Paolo Giovine
Archaeological Museum / Fine Arts Museum - 1849
Excavation objects found in the necropolis of ancient Histonium, 15th-18th c and contemporary paintings 22784

Velletri

Museo Civico, Palazzo Comunale, Via Mameli 6, 00049 Velletri - T: 069641574, 06961581. Head: Anna Germano
Archaeological Museum / Local Museum - 1890
Archeology, Roman sarcophagus 22785

Museo Diocesano, Corso della Repubblica 347, 00049 Velletri - T: 069627217, Fax: 069642095, E-mail: museovelletri@allnet.it, Internet: http://www.museovelletri.com. Head: Fausto Ercolani
Religious Arts Museum
Religious vestments, vases, paintings 22786

Velo Veronese

Museo dei Fossili della Lessinia, Fraz Covolo di Camposilvano, 37030 Velo Veronese - T: 0457835413. Head: Attilio Benetti
Natural History Museum 22787

Venafro

Museo Nazionale, Ex Monastero di Santa Chiara, Corso Garibaldi, 86079 Venafro - T: 0865900363
Historical Museum 22788

Venezia

Ca' d'Oro-Galleria Giorgio Franchetti → Galleria Giorgio Franchetti alla Ca' d'Oro

Casa di Goldoni, Museo Correr, San Tomà 2794, 30125 Venezia - T: 0415236353, Fax: 0415200935. Head: Prof. Giandomenico Romanelli
Performing Arts Museum - 1953
Items used in the Goldoni and Venetian theatre, documents, illustrations - library, theatre 22789

Collezione Casa del Duca, San Samuele, Corte del Duca 3052, 30100 Venezia - T: 0415287903
Fine Arts Museum 22790

Farmacia Conventuale, Convento Cappuccini, Giudecca 194, 30133 Venezia - T: 0415224348, Fax: 0415212773, E-mail: bcve@webgo.it, Internet: http://digilander.iol.it/fraticappuccini/. Head: Gianluigi Pasquale
Historical Museum - 1580/1600
In monastery, 16th c historic pharmacy, 17th-18th c ceramic jars 22791

Gabinetto Stampe e Disegni, Piazza San Marco 52, 30124 Venezia - T: 0415225625, Fax: 0415200935. Head: Prof. Giandomenico Romanelli
Fine Arts Museum 22792

Galleria d'Arte dell'Opera Bevilacqua la Masa, Piazza San Marco 71, 30124 Venezia - T: 0415237819
Public Gallery 22793

Galleria Giorgio Franchetti alla Ca' d'Oro, Cannaregio 3933, 30100 Venezia - T: 0415222349, Fax: 0415222349, E-mail: franchetti.artive@arti.beniculturali.it. Head: Dr. Adriana Augusti
Fine Arts Museum - 1927
Central Italian Paintings of Flemish, German and Netherlan schools (15th-18th c) including Carpaccio, Titian, Tiepolo, Lippi and Bellini, sculpture and bronze (14th-17th c), tapestry, ceramic, medals and coins (15th-18th c) 22794

Gallerie dell'Accademia, Dorsoduro, Campo della Carita, 30121 Venezia - T: 0415222247, 0415212709, Fax: 0415212709, E-mail: accademia.artive@arti.beniculturali.it. Head: Dr. Giovanna Scirè Nepi
Fine Arts Museum - 1807
Venetian painting (13th-18th c) including works by Paolo Veneziano, Bellini, Carpaccio, Giorgione, Veronese, Tintoretto, Tiepolo and Titian 22795

Libreria Sansoviniana, Biblioteca Nazionale Marciana, Piazzetta San Marco 7, 30124 Venezia - T: 0415208788, Fax: 0415238803, E-mail: biblioteca@marciana.venezia.sbn.it, Internet: http://marciana.venezia.sbn.it. Head: Dr. Marino Zorzi
Fine Arts Museum - 1560
Ceiling and wall paintings by Titian, Tintoretto and Veronese, 15th c world map of Fra Mauro - library 22796

Musei Civici Veneziani, San Marco 52, 30124 Venezia - T: 0415225625, Fax: 0415200935, E-mail: mtk.musei@comune.venezia.it, Internet: http://www.museiciviciveneziani.it
Fine Arts Museum 22797

Museo Archeologico Nazionale, Piazzetta San Marco 52, 30124 Venezia - T: 0415225978. Head: Dr. Giovanna Luisa Ravagnan
Archaeological Museum - 1523/1926
Greek and Roman sculpture, jewels, gems and coins, mosaics - library 22798

Museo Civico di Storia Naturale, Santa Croce 1730, 30135 Venezia - T: 0412750206, Fax: 041721000, E-mail: nat.mus.ve@iol.it, Internet: http://www.comune.venezia.it/museicivici/naturale. Head: Dr. Enrico Ratti
Natural History Museum - 1923
Maritime flora and fauna, geology from Monte Bolca - library 22799

Museo Correr, Piazza San Marco 52, 30124 Venezia - T: 0415225625, Fax: 0415200935. Head: Prof. Giandomenico Romanelli
Historical Museum - 1830
Exhibits of Venetian hist and navigation, armaments, costumes, medals and coins, paintings of the Venetian school, paintings by L. Lotto, Bellini, Carpaccio - library 22800

Museo d'Arte Moderna Ca' Pesaro, S. Stae, Canale Grande, 30100 Venezia - T: 041721127. Head: Prof. Giandomenico Romanelli
Fine Arts Museum - 1902
Painting, drawing and sculpture (19th-20th c) 22801

Museo d'Arte Orientale Marco Polo, Palazzo Pesaro, S. Stae, Santa Croce 2078, 30125 Venezia - T: 0415241173. Head: Dr. Adriana Ruggeri Augusti
Decorative Arts Museum 22802

Museo del Risorgimento e dell'Ottocento Veneziano, Piazza San Marco 52, 30124 Venezia - T: 0415225625, Fax: 0415200935. Head: Prof. Giandomenico Romanelli
Historical Museum - 1936
18th c prints and arms, hist of the Risorgimento 22803

Museo del Settecento Veneziano di Ca' Rezzonico, Dorsoduro 3136, 30124 Venezia - T: 0415224543, Fax: 0415200935. Head: Prof. Giandomenico Romanelli
Historical Museum / Fine Arts Museum
Venetian hist and art (17th-18th c) 22804

Museo della Basilica di San Marco, Piazza San Marco 328, 30125 Venezia - T: 0415225205, Fax: 0415208289. Head: Ettore Vio
Religious Arts Museum - 1890
Byzantine art (10th c), tapestries 22805

Museo della Comunità Ebraica, Cannaregio 290b, 30121 Venezia - T: 041715359. Head: Dr. Roberto Bassi
Historical Museum
Items and relics from various Jewish schools 22806

Museo della Congregazione Mechitarista dei Padri Armeni, Isola di San Lazzaro, 30126 Venezia - T: 0415260104, Fax: 0415268690, E-mail: mechitaristi@tin.it. Head: Elia Kilaghbian
Religious Arts Museum / Fine Arts Museum - 1700
Armenian, Egyptian, Roman and Indian art, Armenian, Iranian, Arabic miniatures, manuscripts and modern Armenian paintings, silver works, numismatics, ceramics, paintings of the Venetian school - library, archives, monastic center, academy 22807

Museo della Fondazione Querini Stampalia, Castello 4778, 30122 Venezia - T: 0412711411, Fax: 0412711445, E-mail: quennistampalia@venis.it. Head: Dr. Giorgio Busetto
Fine Arts Museum / Decorative Arts Museum / Music Museum - 1869
Paintings of the Venetian school (Jacopo Palma il Vecchio, Jacopo Palma il Giovane, Pietro Longhi, Gabriel Bella), mss with miniatures, porcelains, musical instruments - library 22808

Museo di Dipinti Sacri Ponte dei Greci, Castello 3412, 30122 Venezia - T: 0415226581, Fax: 0415238248, E-mail: hellenic.inst@gold.gpnet.it. Head: Prof. Chryssa Maltezou
Religious Arts Museum - 1953
Byzantine and post-Byzantine icons: Byzantine (Palaeologean) 14th c, Italian "Trecento" 14th c, Cretan School 16th-18th c 22809

Museo di Torcello, Località Torcello, 30112 Venezia - T: 041730761, Fax: 041730875, E-mail: museo.torcello@provincia.venezia.it, Internet: http://www.provinzia.venezia.it/provinzia/mir/musei/torcello. Head: Dr. Gloria Vidali
Fine Arts Museum / Archaeological Museum - 1870
Medieval mosaics, painting by the Veronese school, archeology - library, archives 22810

Museo Diocesano d'Arte Sacra Santa Apollonia, Castello 4312, 30122 Venezia - T: 0415229166, Fax: 0412702420. Head: Gino Bortolan
Religious Arts Museum 22811

Museo e Centro di Documentazione Fotografica, Palazzo Fortuny, Piazza San Marco 3780, 30124 Venezia - T: 0415221977, Fax: 0415200935. Head: Dr. Sandro Mescola
Fine Arts Museum 22812

Museo Marciano, Chiesa di San Marco, 30100 Venezia - T: 0415225205, Fax: 0415208289. Head: Ettore Vio
Religious Arts Museum 22813

Museo Orientale Ca' Pesaro, Canale Grande, 30100 Venezia - T: 0415241173, Fax: 0415210547. Head: Fiorella Spadavecchia
Fine Arts Museum / Decorative Arts Museum
Painting, sculpture, porcelain, decorative arts from the Far East (17th-19th c) 22814

Museo Storico Navale, Campo S. Biagio 2148, Riva degli Schiavoni, 30122 Venezia - T: 0415200276, Fax: 0415200276
Science&Tech Museum - 1919
Models of historic ships, fishing and rowing boats, models of Chinese and Eastern junks, arms, flags, uniforms, models of fortifications, ship-plans, paintings, shells - library 22815

Museo Vetrario, Località Murano, Fondamenta Giustinian 8, 30124 Venezia - T: 041739586, Fax: 0415200935. Head: Prof. Giandomenico Romanelli
Decorative Arts Museum - 1861
Murano glass from 15th through 20th c, Roman archaeological glass, Renaissance glass 22816

Nuova-Icona, Associazione Culturale per le Arti, Giudecca 454, 30133 Venezia - T: 0415210101, Fax: 0415210101, E-mail: nuovaicona@iol.it. Head: Vittorio Urbani
Association with Coll 22817

Palazzo Ducale, Piazza San Marco 1, 30124 Venezia - T: 0415224951. Head: Umberto Franzoi
Fine Arts Museum
Historic palace, weapons including swords and polearms, paintings by Tintoretto, Titian, Tiepolo and Veronese 22818

Palazzo Grassi, Campo San Samuele 3231, 30124 Venezia - T: 0415235133, Fax: 0415286218, Internet: http://www.palazzograssi.it. Head: Dr. Cesare Annibaldi, Dr. Giuseppe Donegá, Marella Agnelli Caracciolo, Paolo Viti, Pasquale Bonagura
Public Gallery 22819

Peggy Guggenheim Collection, Dorsoduro 701, 30123 Venezia - T: 0412405411, Fax: 0415206885, E-mail: info@guggenheim-venice.it, Internet: http://www.guggenheim-venice.it. Head: Philip Rylands
Fine Arts Museum - 1949
Paintings from the schools of Cubism, Abstraction, Futurism, Surrealism, Abstract Expressionism 22820

Pinacoteca Manfrediana, Dorsoduro 1, 30123 Venezia - T: 0415225558. Head: Antonio Niero
Fine Arts Museum / Archaeological Museum - 1829
Painting, archeology including tombstones and bas-reliefs, sculpture 22821

Scuola Dalmata dei SS. Giorgio e Trifone, Calle dei Furlani Castello 3259, 30122 Venezia - T: 0415228828, Fax: 0415228828. Head: Tullio Vallery
Fine Arts Museum - 1451
Works by Carpaccio, Italian painting, rooms and decorations (16-17th c) 22822

Scuola Grande Arciconfraternita di San Rocco, San Polo 3054, 30125 Venezia - T: 0415234864, Fax: 0415242820, E-mail: snrocco@libero.it. Head: Dr. Ermes Farina
Religious Arts Museum - 1478
Paintings by Tintoretto, Tiziano, Tiepolo, Giorgione - treasury, archive 22823

Scuola Grande Arciconfraternita S.M. del Carmelo, Dorsoduro, Campo Santa Margherita, 30123 Venezia - T: 0415289420. Head: Leomberto Della Toffola
Fine Arts Museum
Paintings of the Venetian School 22824

Scuola Grande di San Giovanni Evangelista, Via San Polo 2454, 30125 Venezia - T: 041718234
Fine Arts Museum
Venetian paintings (16th-18th c) 22825

Venosa

Museo Archeologico Nazionale, Castello Medioevale, 85029 Venosa - T: 097236095. Head: Dr. Antonio Capano
Archaeological Museum - 1991 22826

Ventimiglia

Museo Archeologico Girolamo Rossi, Palazzo Comunale, Forte dell'Annunziata, Via Verdi 41, 18039 Ventimiglia - T: 0184263601, Fax: 0184266421. Head: Prof. Philippe Pergola
Archaeological Museum - 1931
Excavations of ancient city Albintimiulium 22827

Museo e Grotte dei Balzi Rossi, Ponte San Ludovico, 18039 Ventimiglia - T: 018438113
Archaeological Museum
Bones of Cro-Magnon Man, tools, weapons, fossils 22828

Verbania Pallanza

Museo del Paesaggio e Museo Storico Artistico del Verbano e delle Valli Adiacenti, Palazzo Fiani Dugnani, Via Ruga 44, 28048 Verbania Pallanza - T: 0323502418. Head: Prof. Gianni Pizzigoni
Fine Arts Museum 22829

Vercelli

Museo Camillo Leone, Via Verdi 9, 13100 Vercelli - T: 0161253204. Head: Amedeo Corio
Historical Museum / Archaeological Museum - 1907
History of Vercelli from prehistoric period to present, Roman inscriptions, Byzantine icon, mosaics, pre-Columbian vases, incunabula, coins and medals - library 22830

Museo Civico Borgogna, Via Borgogna 1, 13100 Vercelli - T: 016162576
Fine Arts Museum 22831

Museo Francesco Borgogna, Via Antonio Borgogna 8, 13100 Vercelli - T: 0161252776. Head: Francesco Ferraris
Fine Arts Museum
14th-19th c paintings 22832

Veroli

Tesoro della Cattedrale, Cattedrale, 03029 Veroli - T: 0775230024. Head: Antonio Paniccia
Religious Arts Museum 22833

Verona

Galleria Civica d'Arte Moderna e Contemporanea, Palazzo Forti, Via Achille Forti 1, 37121 Verona - T: 0458001903, Fax: 0458003524. Head: Prof. Giorgio Cortenova
Fine Arts Museum - 1937
19th and 20th c artists - Education Department 22834

Museo Africano Missionari Comboniani, Vicolo Pozzo 1, 37129 Verona - T: 0458002418. Head: Elia Toniolo
Ethnology Museum
Items collected by missionaries from Africa, ethnology 22835

Museo Archeologico al Teatro Romano, Rigaste Redentore 2, 37100 Verona - T: 0458000360, Fax: 0458010587. Head: Margherita Bolla
Archaeological Museum - 1924
Roman antiquities, sculptures, mosaics, glassware, pottery, bronze, inscriptions 22836

Museo Canonicale, Piazza Duomo 13, 37121 Verona - T: 045596516. Head: Enrico Maria Guzzo
Religious Arts Museum
Venetian artists 15th to 19th c 22837

Museo Civico di Storia Naturale, Lungadige Porta Vittoria 9, 37129 Verona - T: 0458079400/01, Fax: 0458035639, E-mail: mcsnat@comune.serona.it. Head: Dr. Alessandra Aspes
Natural History Museum - 1926
Paleontology, geology, botany, zoology, entomology, archaeology 22838

Museo degli Affreschi G.B. Cavalcaselle, Via del Pontiere, 37122 Verona - T: 0458000361, Fax: 0458010729, E-mail: castelvecchio@comune.verona.it. Head: Dr. Paola Marini
Fine Arts Museum 22839

Museo delle Carozze dell'Ottocento, Viale del Lavoro 8a, 37100 Verona - T: 045588111. Head: Giuseppe Riccardo Ceni
Science&Tech Museum
Carriages of different types 22840

Museo di Castelvecchio, Corso Castelvecchio 2, 37121 Verona - T: 045594734, 045592985, Fax: 0458010729, E-mail: castelvecchio@comune.verona.it, Internet: http://www.comune.verona.it/castelvecchio/cvsito. Head: Dr. Paola Marini
Fine Arts Museum - 1812
Sculptures, paintings, graphic colls - art library 22841

Museo Lapidario Maffeiano, Piazza Bra 28, 37121 Verona - T: 045590087. Head: Dr. Margherita Bolla
Archaeological Museum - 18th c
Ancient art, epigraphy 22842

Museo Miniscalchi Erizzo, Via San Mammaso 2, 37121 Verona - T: 0458032484, Fax: 0458032484. Head: Gian Paolo Marchini
Fine Arts Museum / Archaeological Museum
Excavations, sculptures, bronzes, paintings of Venetian school 22843

Pinacoteca della Biblioteca Capitolare, Piazza Duomo 13, 37100 Verona - T: 045596516. Head: Alberto Piazzi
Library with Exhibitions 22844

Verucchio

Galleria Comunale d'Arte Moderna, Via Sant'Agostino, 47040 Verucchio - T: 0541668500
Public Gallery 22845

Museo Civico Archeologico, Via Sant'Agostino 14, 47040 Verucchio - T: 0541670280, Fax: 0541679570
Archaeological Museum 22846

Museo Preistorico e Lapidario, Via della Rocca 42, 47040 Verucchio - T: 0541670154
Archaeological Museum 22847

Pinacoteca Comunale, Via Sant'Agostino, 47040 Verucchio - T: 0541670154, Fax: 0541679570
Fine Arts Museum 22848

Vestenanova

Museo dei Fossili, 37030 Vestenanova - T: 045671968
Natural History Museum
Fossils of fish, plants and molluscs 22849

Vetulonia

Museo Archeologico Isidoro Falchi, Piazza Vetluna, 58040 Vetulonia - T: 0564949877. Head: Dr. Celuzza
Archaeological Museum 22850

Viadana

Museo Civico Parazzi, Piazza Matteotti 5, 46019 Viadana - T: 0375833162. Head: Dr. Luigi Rinetti
Fine Arts Museum / Decorative Arts Museum
Frescoes, coins, majolicas, paintings 22851

Viareggio

Museo Villa Puccini, Fraz Torre del Lago Puccini, 55048 Viareggio - T: 0584341445
Music Museum 22852

Vibo Valentia

Museo Archeologico Nazionale, Piazza Garibaldi, 88018 Vibo Valentia - T: 096343350. Head: Dr. Elena Lattanzi, Dr. Maria Teresa Iannelli
Archaeological Museum
Western Greek and Roman finds, vases, terracottas, coins 22853

Vicchio

Museo Beato Angelico, Via Beato Angelico, 50039 Vicchio - T: 0558497023
Religious Arts Museum
Frescoes, religious items 22854

Museo Casa Natale di Giotto, Fraz Vespignano, 50039 Vicchio - T: 055844782
Fine Arts Museum
Birthplace of the fresco-painter Giotto di Bondone 22855

Vicenza

Museo Civico-Pinacoteca di Palazzo Chiericati, Piazza Matteotti 39, 36100 Vicenza - T: 0444321348, Fax: 0444546619
Fine Arts Museum - 1855
Paintings (Paolo Veronese, Hans Memling, Anton van Dyck, Giambattista Tiepolo, Valerio Belli), graphics, etchings, prints, numismatics and sphragistics 22856

Museo del Risorgimento e della Resistenza, Viale X Giugno 115, 36100 Vicenza - T: 0444322998. Head: Dr. Mauro Passarin
Historical Museum - 1983
Risorgimento, World War I, Partisan Resistance Movement - didactic section 22857

Museo Naturalistica-Archeologico, Contrà, S. Corona 4, 36100 Vicenza - T: 0444320440, Fax: 0444325627. Head: Antonio Dallago
Archaeological Museum / Natural History Museum 22858

Vico del Gargano

Museo Civico, Via De Gasperi, 71018 Vico del Gargano - T: 0884993658. Head: Antonio Zaffarano
Archaeological Museum - 1978
Prehistory of Gargano 22859

Vico Equense

Antiquarium, Via San Ciro 16, 80069 Vico Equense - T: 0818015752
Archaeological Museum 22860

Museo Comunale, Corso Umberto I 10, 80069 Vico Equense - T: 0818798343
Local Museum 22861

Vicoforte

Museo Storico Ghislieri, Santuario di Vicoforte, 12080 Vicoforte - T: 0174563107
Local Museum 22862

Vietri

Museo della Ceramica, Villa Guariglia, 84010 Vietri - T: 089211835. Head: Dr. Matilde Romito
Decorative Arts Museum 22863

Vigevano

Civico Museo Archeologico e Pinacoteca, Corso Cavour 82, 27029 Vigevano - T: 038170149
Archaeological Museum / Fine Arts Museum
Paleontology, archeology, history, paintings 22864

Museo del Tesoro del Duomo, Piazza Sant'Ambrogio 14, 27029 Vigevano - T: 038186253. Head: Dr. Pietro Bellazzi
Religious Arts Museum 22865

Museo della Calzatura, Corso Cavour 82, 27029 Vigevano
Historical Museum
History of footwear 22866

Viggiù

Museo Enrico Butti, Viale Varese 2, 21059 Viggiù - T: 0332486510, Fax: 0332488861, E-mail: coviggiu@working.it. Head: Luisa Somaini
Fine Arts Museum
Stone cutter hist 22867

Vignale Monferrato

Enoteca Regionale del Monferrato, Palazzo Callori, Piazza del Popolo 7, 15049 Vignale Monferrato - T: 0142933243, Fax: 0142933243. Head: Dr. Luigi Quartero
Fine Arts Museum 22868

Villa d'Almè

Museo Civico Naturalistico, Via Locatelli Milesi 16, 24018 Villa d'Almè - T: 035541076
Local Museum 22869

Villafranca in Lunigiana

Museo Etnografico della Lunigiana, Via dei Mulini 70, 54028 Villafranca in Lunigiana - T: 0187493417. Head: Germano Cavalli
Ethnology Museum 22870

Villanovaforru

Museo Archeologico Genna Maria, Piazza Costituzione 1, 09020 Villanovaforru - T: 070930048. Head: Ubaldo Badas
Archaeological Museum 22871

Villavallelonga

Museo del Cervo, Centro di Visita d'Abruzzo, 67050 Villavallelonga - T: 0863949261. Head: Franco Tassi
Natural History Museum 22872

Vinci

Museo Leonardiano, Castello dei Conti Guidi, Via della Torre 2, 50059 Vinci - T: 057156055, Fax: 0571567930, E-mail: terredelrinascimento@comune.vinci.fi.it. Head: Romano Nanni
Science&Tech Museum - 1952
Documents on life and work of Leonardo da Vinci (1452-1519), models of machines - library 22873

Vipiteno

Museo Hans Multscher e Museo Civico, Via della Commenda 11, 39049 Vipiteno - T: 0472766464, Fax: 0472767060, E-mail: info@sterzing.net
Fine Arts Museum
Altarpieces painted by Hans Multscher of Ulm (1458), paintings and sculptures 15th-16th c 22874

Museo Provinciale delle Miniere, Via Frundsberg 20, 39049 Vipiteno - T: 0472764875
Local Museum 22875

Virgilio

Museo Archeologico Virgiliano, Fraz Pietole, Via Parma 34, 46030 Virgilio - T: 0376440439. Head: Patrizia Oliveri del Castillo
Archaeological Museum 22876

Viterbo

Museo Civico, Piazza Crispi 2, 01100 Viterbo - T: 0761348275, Fax: 0761348276. Head: Dr. Mario Moretti
Archaeological Museum - 1912
Archeology, sarcophagi, paintings 22877

Vittorio Veneto

Museo del Cenedese, Piazza Flaminio, 31029 Vittorio Veneto - T: 043857103, Fax: 0438946385, E-mail: museocen@tin.it. Head: Dr. Vittorino Pianca
Archaeological Museum / Fine Arts Museum - 1938
Paintings (14th to 16th c), archeology (2000 B.C. - 500 A.C.) 22878

Museo della Battaglia, Piazza Giovanni Paolo, 31029 Vittorio Veneto - T: 043857931, Fax: 0438941421, E-mail: museobattaglia@emmenet.it. Head: Luigi Marson
Historical Museum - 1938
Documents and relics of World War I - library 22879

Vizzola Ticino

Museo Aeronautico Caproni di Taliedo, Via Montecchio 2, 21010 Vizzola Ticino - T: 0331230826
Science&Tech Museum
Aeroplanes, propellers, gliders 22880

Voghera

Museo Civico, Sezione di Scienze Naturali, Via A. Gramsci 1, 27058 Voghera - T: 038343053. Head: Giuseppe Orlandi
Natural History Museum 22881

Museo Paleontologico, Via A. Gramsci 11, 27058 Voghera - T: 038343053
Natural History Museum 22882

Museo Storico, Via Gramsci 1bis, 27058 Voghera - T: 038343636, Fax: 038343403. Head: Giuseppe Beccari
Historical Museum 22883

Volpedo

Museo di Giuseppe Pellizza, Via Rosano 1, 15059 Volpedo - T: 013180141, Fax: 0131806577, E-mail: ivstato@tin.it, Internet: http://www.telnetwork.it/pellizza
Fine Arts Museum 22884

Voltaggio

Pinacoteca dei Cappuccini, Convento dei Padri Cappuccini, 15060 Voltaggio - T: 0109601237
Religious Arts Museum 22885

Volterra

Museo Diocesano di Arte Sacra, Via Roma 13, 56048 Volterra - T: 058886290, Fax: 058884088, E-mail: diocesi@sirt.pisa.it, Internet: http://www.sirt.pisa.it/diocesi. Head: Dr. Umberto Bavoni
Religious Arts Museum - 1936
Sculptures, goldwork, miniatures, embroidery, paintings 22886

Museo Etrusco Guarnacci (Archaeological Park), Via Don Minzoni 15, Fiumi di Volterra, 56048 Volterra - T: 058886347. Head: Prof. Enrico Fiumi
Archaeological Museum
Urns, pottery, vases, archeology 22887

Pinacoteca Comunale, Palazzo Minucci-Solaini, 56048 Volterra - T: 058887580. Head: Dr. Alessandro Furiesi
Fine Arts Museum - 1905
Paintings of the Tuscan school, works by Signorelli, Fiorentino, Ghirlandaio, numismatic coll, medals, ceramics of medieval Period 22888

Zogno

Museo della Valle, Via Furietti 1, 24019 Zogno - T: 034591473. Head: Dr. Vittorio Polli
Historical Museum 22889

Zoppè di Cadore

Museo delle Tradizioni Locali, 32010 Zoppè di Cadore - T: 043778138
Historical Museum 22890

Jamaica

Discovery Bay

Columbus Park, Discovery Bay
Open Air Museum
Cannons, old agriculture and farm equipment, relics of Jamaica's past 22891

Kingston

Bob Marley Museum, 56 Hope Rd, Kingston 6 - T: (876) 927-9152, Fax: (876) 978-4906, E-mail: - marleyfoundation@cwjamaica.com
Music Museum
Life and accomplishments of the musician Robert Nesta Marley - theatre 22892

Coins & Notes Museum → Money Museum

Fort Charles Maritime Museum, Port Royal, Kingston, mail addr: c/o Institut of Jamaica, Museums Division, 12-16 East St, Kingston - T: (876) 922-0620 ext 7, 967-8438. Head: Michael Cooke
Special Museum - 1977
Maritime heritage in Jamaica from 15th - 20th centuries, ship models, paintings, instuments of torture from slavery, shipwright tools, naval instruments - archaeological project 22893

Geology Museum, c/o Institut of Jamaica, Kingston - T: (876) 922-0620 ext 6
Natural History Museum
Rare rocks and minerals 22894

Harry J. Music Museum, 10 Roosevelt Av, Kingston 6 - T: (876) 978-3659
Music Museum 22895

Institute of Jamaica, 10-16 East St, Kingston - T: (876) 922-06206, Fax: (876) 922-1147, E-mail: ioj@mail.infochan.com. Head: Dr. Vivian Crawford
Fine Arts Museum / Ethnology Museum / Historical Museum - 1879
Paintings by Jamaican artists, historical artifacts, craft items and tools 22896

Jamaica Folk Museum, Institute of Jamaica, 12-16 East St, Kingston - T: (876) 922-0620, Fax: (876) 922-1147. Head: Michael Cooke
Folklore Museum - 1961
Traditional craft items, tools, building material and technology from slave/sugar era and post-emancipation period 22897

Mico INAFCA Museum, 1a Marescaux Rd, Kingston 5 - T: (876) 929-2607, Fax: (876) 926-2238, E-mail: C.Packer@U.W.I.Mona.Edu.jm. Head: Dr. Claude Packer
Ethnology Museum / Historical Museum
Ethnology, history 22898

Military Museum, Jamaica Defence Force Museum, 12-14 East St, Kingston - T: (876) 922-0620 ext 6, Fax: (876) 922-1147. Head: Michael Cooke
Military Museum - 1971
Guns of various types, ammunition, uniforms, medals, regimental silverware 22899

Money Museum, c/o Bank of Jamaica, Nethersole Pl, Kingston - T: (876) 922-0750, Fax: 9220416, E-mail: jackiem@boj.org.jm, Internet: http://www.boj.org.jm
Special Museum
Hist of Jamaican tokens, coins and paper money 22900

National Gallery of Jamaica, 12 Ocean Blvd, Kingston - T: (876) 922-1561
Public Gallery 22901

National Museum of Historical Archaeology, Old Naval Hospital, Port Royal, Kingston - T: (876) 922-1287
Archaeological Museum
Hist of the Jamaican people and techniques of excavation 22902

Natural History Museum, c/o Institute of Jamaica, 10-16 East St, Kingston - T: (876) 922-0620/26, Fax: (876) 922-1147, E-mail: nhd.ioj@mail.infochan.com, Internet: http://www.instituteofjamaica.org.jm. Head: Tracy Commock
Natural History Museum
Preserved animals and plants of Jamaica, zoology, Clearinghouse Mechanism, biodibersity - herbarium, discovery room, science library 22903

Zoology Museum, c/o University of the West Indies, Kingston - T: (876) 927-1202
Natural History Museum 22904

Montego Bay

Greenwood Great House Museum, POB 169, Montego Bay - T: (876) 953-1077, Fax: 9531847, E-mail: houdini@cwjamaika.com, Internet: http://www.greenwoodhouse-jamaica.com. Head: Thomas Betton
Decorative Arts Museum
Antique furniture, musical instruments, maps 22905

Hanover Museum, Montego Bay
Local Museum
Hist of the parish 22906

Ocho Rios

Coyaba Gardens and Awarak Museum, Shaw Park, Ocho Rios - T: (876) 974-6235
Historical Museum
Jamaican hist from the Arawak era to the present 22907

Seville Great House and Heritage Park, Saint Ann's Bay, Ocho Rios - T: (876) 972-2191
Historical Museum / Ethnology Museum
Island's hist and culture 22908

Spanish Town

Archaeological Museum, c/o Institute of Jamaica, Old Kings House, Spanish Town Sq, Spanish Town - T: (876) 922-0620 ext 6
Archaeological Museum
Govenor's official residence, artifacts between 1534-1872 22909

Jamaican People's Museum of Craft and Technology, Old Kings House Cultural Complex, Spanish Town Sq, Spanish Town, mail addr: c/o Institute of Jamaica, 12-16 East St, Kingston - T: (876) 922-0620 ext 6, Fax: (876) 922-1147, E-mail: mus.ioj@mail.infochan.com. Head: Michael Cooke
Science&Tech Museum / Historical Museum - 1961
Traditional implements, technology, art and craft from the early and post emancipation period 22910

Japan

Abashiri

Abashiri Kyodo Bijutsukan (Abashiri Municipal Art Museum), 1 Minami-6jo-nishi, Abashiri 093-0016 - T: (01524) 45045
Fine Arts Museum
38 oil paintings by Kaichi Igushi (1911-1955) - galleries 22911

Abashiri Kyodo Hakubutsukan (Abashiri Municipal Museum), 1-1-3 Katsura-machi, Abashiri 093-0041 - T: (0152) 433090. Head: M. Tatewaki
Local Museum - 1936
Local archeology, ethnographical material on life of Ainu, Gilyak, and Oroko peoples, articles of historical and geographical interest 22912

Museums Abashirikangoku, 1-1 Yobito, Abashiri 099-2422 - T: (0152) 452411
Local Museum 22913

Ago

Shima Marineland, Kashikojima, Ago 517-0500 - T: (059) 9431225, Fax: 9431224. Head: Dr. Tadashi Tsujii
Natural History Museum - 1970
Subtropical coral fish, temperate sea fish, and cold-water fish, marine invertebrates from the Japanese coasts, fishes and foreign countries, fossils of aquatic life, penguins - library 22914

Aikawa

Aikawa Local Museum, Sakashita-machi, Aikawa 952-1505
Local Museum
Archeological material, folk art including ceramics, costumes, wooden panel, historical material, samples of calligraphy, local gold mining exhibit 22915

Aira

Matsushita Art Museum, 771, Fukuyama, Fukuyama-cho, Aira 899-4501 - T: (0995) 553350, Fax: 553445, Internet: http://www.synapse.or.jp. Head: Kensuke Matsushita
Fine Arts Museum 22916

Aizuwakamatsu

Fukushima-kenritsu Hakubutsukan (Fukushima Prefectural Museum), 1-25 Joto-machi, Aizuwakamatsu 965-0807 - T: (0242) 286000, Fax: 285986, Internet: http://www.pref.fukushima.jp/frame/hakub.html
Local Museum 22917

Akashi

Akashi-shiritsu Tenmon Kagakukan, 2-6 Hitomaru-cho, Akashi 673-0877 - T: (078) 9195000, Fax: 9196000, E-mail: webmaster@am12.akashi.hyogo.jp, Internet: http://www.am12.akashi.hyogo.jp
Science&Tech Museum
Astronomy, science 22918

Akita

Akita City Art Museum, 1-4 Senshu-koen, Akita 010-0876 - T: (0188) 327575. Head: Josuke Nara
Fine Arts Museum
18th c yoga paintings, local artists, calligraphy 22919

Akita Daigaku Kozangakubu Fuzok u Kogyo Hakubutsukan, c/o Akita University, 28-2, Osawa, Tegata, Akita 010-0851 - T: (0188) 335260
University Museum / Natural History Museum - 1961
Minerals and ores from Japan 22920

Akita-kenritsu Hakubutsukan (Akita Prefectural Museum), 52 Ushiroyama, Kanaashi Niozaki, Akita 010-0124 - T: (0188) 734121, Fax: 734123. Head: Rintaro Takehana
Local Museum
History of the region in dioramas, models, historical material, farm tools and ethnographic material, pottery, fossils, armor, photographs, local natural history, handicrafts, paintings planetarium, lecture hall, conference room 22921

Akita Prefectural Art Gallery, 3-7 Senshuumeitoku-machi, Akita 010-0875 - T: (0188) 343050. Head: Akinobu Hashimoto
Fine Arts Museum
Paintings and drawings by Tsuguji Fujita, Western paintings and prints 22922

Akita Senshu Museum of Art, 2-3-8 Nakadori, Akita 010-0001 - T: (0188) 367860, Fax: 367862. Head: Seiichiro Watanabe
Fine Arts Museum 22923

Akiyo

Akiyoshi-dai Museum of Natural History, Shuho-cho, Akiyo 750-0000
Natural History Museum - 1959
Paleontology, archeology, fossils, geology, earthen vessels and stone implements, cave-dwelling animals - library 22924

Amagasaki

Amagasaki Bunka Art Gallery, 2-7-16 Shouwadori, Amagasaki 660-0881 - T: (06) 4870806, Fax: 3823503. Head: Akira Yamamoto
Public Gallery 22925

Ando

Tomimoto Kenkichi Memorial Museum, Higashiando, Ando 639-1061 - T: (0743) 573300. Head: Isamu Tsujimoto
Decorative Arts Museum
Ceramics and designs by Kenkichi Tomimoto 22926

Aomori

Aomori Kenritsu Kyodokan (Aomori Prefectural Museum), 2-8-14 Hon-cho, Aomori 030-0802 - T: (017) 7771585, Fax: 7771588. Head: Hideo Kobayashi
Folklore Museum / Historical Museum / Natural History Museum
Pottery vessels, exhibits on designing pottery, local historical documents and photographs, lacquer items, costumes, furniture, farm and fishing equipment, straw and wooden utensils, natural history exhibits, display on local industrial growth 22927

Munakata Shikokinenkan (Shiko Munakata Memorial Museum of Art), 2-1-2 Matsubara, Aomori 030-0813 - T: (0177) 774567, Fax: 345611, E-mail: shikokan@infoaomori.ne.jp, Internet: http://www.lantecweb.com/shikokan
Fine Arts Museum - 1974
Prints, paintings and calligraphy of Munakata (1903-75) 22928

Arita

Arita Toji Bijutsukan (Arita Ceramic Museum), 1-4-2 Oodaru, Arita 844-0004 - T: (0955) 423372, Fax: 434185, Internet: http://www.arita.or.jp/aritaware/bijutsukan/toujibi. Head: Takeyoshi Tanaka
Decorative Arts Museum - 1954
Local china and porcelain, documents pertaining to their history, examples of Imari, Kakiemon, Arita, and Nabeshima ware - library 22929

Saga-kenritsu Kyushu Toji Bunkakan (Kyushu Ceramic Museum), 3100-1 Chubu Otsu, Arita 844-8585 - T: (0955) 433681, Fax: 433324
Decorative Arts Museum 22930

Asahi

Ippuku Museum of Art, 6 Fudodo, Shimoniikawa-gun, Asahi 930-0000 - T: (0765) 830100, Fax: 831500. Head: Yukio Kishioka
Fine Arts Museum 22931

Asahikawa

Asahikawa Youth Science Museum, Tokiwa-koen, Asahikawa 070-0044 - T: (0166) 224171
Science&Tech Museum - 1963
Experimental equipment for studies in electricity, atomic energy, astronomy, and the life sciences laboratories - lecture and meeting rooms 22932

Hokkaidoritsu Asahikawa Bijutsukan (Hokkaido Asahikawa Museum of Art), Tokiwa-Koen, Asahikawa 070-0044 - T: (0166) 252577, Fax: 252539, E-mail: asabijutsu.gakugei@pref.hokkaido.jp. Head: Takeshi Sato
Fine Arts Museum - 1982
Paintings and great wood-work object from Northern Hokkaido 22933

Yukara Ori Folkcraft Museum, Takasagodai, Kamui-cho, Asahikawa 070-8061 - T: (0166) 628811, Fax: 622060. Head: Atsushi Nakajima, Kazuhiro Kiuchi
Folklore Museum 22934

Ashikaga

Kurita Bijutsukan (Kurita Museum), 1542 Komaba-cho, Ashikaga 329-4217 - T: (0284) 911026, Fax: 912153. Head: Kurita Hideo
Decorative Arts Museum
Imari and Nabeshima porcelains, raw materials, photographs of the various steps of manufacture 22935

Soun Museum, 2-3768 Midori-cho, Ashikaga 326-0816 - T: (0284) 213808. Head: Suto Yoshihisa
Fine Arts Museum
80 paintings by Tazaki Soun, his personal effects, furniture, house where the artist lived 22936

Ashiya

Emba Museum of Chinese Modern Art, 12-1 Okuike-cho, Ashiya 659-0003 - T: (0797) 380021, Fax: 322797. Head: Tetsukazu Ueno
Fine Arts Museum 22937

Tekisui Art Museum, 13-3 Yama-ashiya-cho, Ashiya 659-0082 - T: (0797) 222228. Head: Tadanari Mitsuoka, Kakutaro Yamaguchi
Fine Arts Museum / Decorative Arts Museum
Chinese bas-reliefs, ceramics, and paintings, Japanese paintings, dolls and ceramic figurines, toys and games, Kyoto ceramic wares, Korean ceramics and paintings 22938

Asuka

Nara-Kokuritsu Bunkazai Kenkyujo Asuka Shiryokan (Asuka Historical Museum, Nara National Cultural Properties Research Institute), 601 Okuyama, Asuka 634-0102 - T: (0744) 543561, Fax: 543563, E-mail: iwamoto@nabunken.go.jp, Internet: http://www.cgc.co.jp. Head: Iwamoto Keisuke
Historical Museum - 1975
Pottery, photographs of the excavation sites, armor and weapons, jewelry, mirrors, photos of the wall paintings of 8th c tomb, Asuka sculpture, 7th c wooden Buddhist temple 22939

Takamatsuzuka Wall Painting Museum, 439 Hirata, Asuka 634-0144 - T: (0743) 573340. Head: Koji Suzuki
Fine Arts Museum 22940

Atami

Kyusei Atami Art Museum, 26-1 Momoyama-cho, Atami 413-0006
Fine Arts Museum / Decorative Arts Museum - 1957
Chinese and Japanese paintings, sculptures, and ceramics, Chinese bronzes, Japanese lacquer, metalwork, and prints, specimens of Japanese and Chinese calligraphy - library 22941

MOA Bijutsukan (MOA Museum of Art), 26-2 Momoyama-cho, Atami 413-8511 - T: (0557) 842511, Fax: 842570, E-mail: www-admin@moa.or.jp, Internet: http://www.moa.or.jp. Head: Yoji Yoshioka
Fine Arts Museum 22942

Azuchi

Shiga-kenritsu Omi Fudoki-No-Oka Shiryokan (Shiga Fudoki-No-Oka Museum), Shimotoyoura, Azuchi - T: (074846) 2424
Local Museum 22943

Beppu

Beppu Daigaku Fuzoku Hakubutsukan (Beppu University Museum of History), 82 Rikushoen, Kita-ijyuu, Beppu 874-0845 - T: (0977) 670101. Head: Prof. Mitsuo Kagawa
Archaeological Museum / University Museum / Historical Museum
Japanese pottery vessels, stone tools from several archeological periods 22944

Bizen

Bizen Pottery Traditional and Contemporary Art Museum, 1659-6 Imbe, Bizen 705-0001 - T: (0869) 641400, Fax: 641400. Head: Saihachi Nakamura
Decorative Arts Museum - 1977
Contemporary Bizen ware, old Bizen ware, potters tools - library 22945

Kei Fujiwara Art Museum, Honami, Bizen 705-0033 - T: (0869) 670638
Decorative Arts Museum
Pottery by Kei Fujiwara 22946

Buzen

Japan Handicrafts Museum, Koishihara Branch, Sarayama, Koishihara, Buzen 828-0044 - T: (0946) 74138
Historical Museum 22947

Chiba

Chiba City Museum of Art, 3-10-8 Chuo, Chuo-ku, Chiba 260-8733 - T: (043) 2212311, Fax: 2212316, E-mail: museum@city.chiba.jp, Internet: http://www.city.chiba.jp/art. Head: Tadashi Kobayashi
Fine Arts Museum - 1995
17th-20th c Japanese paintings, Japanese and Western contemporary art, prints, calligraphy, sculpture, craft, documents for study - library 22948

Chiba-kenritsu Bijutsukan (Chiba Prefectural Museum of Art), 1-10-1 Chuoko, Chuo-ku, Chiba 260-0024 - T: (043) 2428311
Fine Arts Museum 22949

Chiba-kenritsu Chuo Hakubutsukan (Natural History Museum and Institute, Chiba), 955-2 Aoba-cho, Chuo-ku, Chiba 260-8682 - T: (043) 2653111, Fax: 2662481, E-mail: chuohaku@chiba-muse.or.jp, Internet: http://www.chiba-muse.or.jp/natural/
Natural History Museum 22950

Chiba-shi Kasori Kaizuka Hakubutsukan (Kasori Shell Mounds Site Museum), 163 Sakuragi-cho, Chiba 264-0022 - T: (0472) 310129
Ethnology Museum - 1966
Articles from Kasori shell mounds, earthenwares, stone tools, clay objects 22951

Chiba Sogo Museum of Art, 1000 Shinmachi, Chuo-ku, Chiba 260-8557 - T: (043) 2458285, 2452111, Fax: 2458439, E-mail: chibasgo@magical.egg.or.jp, Internet: http://www.chibasogo.co.jp
Fine Arts Museum 22952

Chichibu

Nagatoro Kyukokan, Tatsugafuchi, Nogami-machi, Chichibu 368-0000
Archaeological Museum 22953

Chino

Chino-shi Togariishi Jomon Kokokan (Chino City Togariishi Jomon Archaeology Museum), 4734-132 Toyohira, Chino 391-0213 - T: (0266) 762270, Fax: 762700, Internet: http://www.togariishi.city.-chino.nagano.jp. Head: Atsushi Hama
Archaeological Museum - 1955
Stone and pottery items from excavation sites, small figurines, vases and jars, clay doll "Venus of Jomon", photographs and maps of excavation sites 22954

Musée Marie Laurencin, 4035 Tateshina-Kogen, Chino 391-0395 - T: (0266) 672626, Fax: 672632, E-mail: mml@gb3.so-net.ne.jp, Internet: http://shinshu.online.co.jp/art/laurencin. Head: Masahiro Takano
Fine Arts Museum - 1983
Paintings, water-colours, drawings, prints and illustrated books by Marie Laurencin which cover the whole of her working life from her earliest beginnings to her final years 22955

Chisagata

Utsukushigahara Kogen Bijutsukan (Utsukushigahara Open-Air Museum), Utsukushigahara-Ue, Takeshi-mura, Chisagata 386-0500 - T: (0268) 862331, Fax: 862217, Internet: http://www.fujisankei-g.co.jp/fcg/museum12.htm. Head: Shinya Ueda
Open Air Museum / Fine Arts Museum - 1981
Sculptures by Bourdelle, Miller, Liberman 22956

Chita

Chita-shi Rekishi Minzoku Hakubutsukan (Chita City Museum), 12-2 Midori-machi, Chita 478-0047 - T: (0562) 331571, Fax: 333424. Head: Hideki Hiramatsu
Folklore Museum / Local Museum
Folklore, local history, archaeology, fine arts 22957

Chofu

Chofu City Museum, 3-26-2 Kojima-cho, Chofu 182-0026 - T: (0424) 817656
Local Museum 22958

Mushakoji Saneatsu Memorial Hall, 1-8-30 Wakaba-cho, Chofu 182-0003 - T: (03) 33260648, Fax: 33261330. Head: Hori Kimihiko
Special Museum 22959

Dazaifu

Dazaifu Tenman-gu Hômotsuden (Dazaifu Tenman-gu Treasure House), 1-114 Dazaifu, Dazaifu 818-0100 - T: (092) 9228225. Head: Nobuyoshi Nishitakaesuji
Decorative Arts Museum
Art concerning Michizane Sugawara, to whom the shrine is dedicated, paintings, calligraphy, documents, sculpture, arms and armor, ceramics, lacquer items, masks, metalwork, archeological material 22960

Kanzeon-ji Treasure House, 182 Kanzeonji, Dazaifu 818-0101
Religious Arts Museum - 1959
Buddhist wooden sculptures, Bagaku masks, 8th c bronze bell 22961

Kyushu Rekishi Shiryokan (Kyushu History Museum), 4-7-1 Ishizaka, Dazaifu 818-0118 - T: (092) 9230404, Fax: 9230448. Head: Katsumi Joshihisa
Historical Museum - 1972
Chipped stone tools, Iomon potteries, bronze mirrors, stone figurines, clay figurines (Idaniwa), ridge-end tiles, relief tiles Chinese ceramic wares, gilt bronze Buddha image and container for sutra, Acalanatha with two attendants, pair of Guardian Lions, reduced stupa of King Chien Kung-chu 22962

Eiheiji

Treasure House of the Eiheiji Temple, Eiheiji 910-1200
Religious Arts Museum - 1244
70 buildings, comprising the monastery Eiheiji for the practice of Zen, religious art and furnishings, sculpture and carvings, holy treasure house with writings of Zenji Dogen, the founder of the monastery, 14th c temple bell 22963

Enzan

Shingen-Ko Treasure House, 2280 Koyahiki, Enzan 404-0000 - T: (05533) 34560
Local Museum
Material connected with the Takeda clan, armor, bows and arrows, and swords, fans, lacquer items, documents - garden 22964

Fuchu

Fuchu-shi Kyodono-mori, 6-32 Minami-cho, Fuchu 183-0026 - T: (0423) 687921
Local Museum 22965

Fujimi

Idojiri Kokokan (Idojiri Archaeological Museum), Shinano, Sakai, Fujimi 399-0101 - T: (0266) 642044. Head: Naoji Kobayashi
Archaeological Museum
Prehistoric vessels, stone tools, figurines, full-scale model of prehistoric house furnished with original vessels 22966

Fujinomiya

Fuji Art Museum, 1954 Kamijo, Fujinomiya 418-0116 - T: (0544) 582550, Fax: 584390. Head: Miturn Koyama
Fine Arts Museum / Decorative Arts Museum - 1973
Egyptian stele and Coptic textiles, 19th c European prints, Chinese and Japanese ceramics, lacquer writing boxes, Japanese paintings, calligraphy, prints - library 22967

Fujiyoshida

Entomological Museum of Fujikyu, Fujikyu Highland, Fujiyoshida 403-0000, mail addr: POB 12, Fujiyoshida 403-0000
Natural History Museum - 1968
Largest of exotic Coleoptera in Japan 22968

Fukui

Fukui City Natural Science Museum, Asuwakami-cho, Fukui 918-8006
Natural History Museum
Zoology, botany, mollusks, entomology, mineralogy, fossils 22969

Fukui Fujita Art Museum, 4-15-12 Houei, Fukui 910-0004 - T: (0776) 217710. Head: Yukio Fujita
Fine Arts Museum 22970

Fukui-kenritsu Bijutsukan (Fukui Prefectural Museum of Art), 3-16-1 Bunkyo, Fukui 910-0017 - T: (0776) 250451, Fax: 250452, E-mail: kenpaku@pref.fukui.jp, Internet: http://www.pref.fukui.jp/japanese/institute2.html. Head: Masao Murase
Fine Arts Museum 22971

Fukui-kenritsu Hakubutsukan (Fukui Prefectural Museum), 2-19-15 Omiya, Fukui 910-0016 - T: (0776) 224675, Fax: 224675, E-mail: kenpaku@pref.fukui.jp, Internet: http://www.pref.fukui.jp/dinosaur-fukui/en
Historical Museum / Local Museum
Local archeological material, portraits and memorabilia of local nobles, historical documents, calligraphy, farm tools, household and shop furniture 22972

Fukuoka

Fukuoka-kenritsu Bijutsukan (Fukuoka Prefectural Museum of Art), 5-2-1 Tenjin, Chuo-ku, Fukuoka 810-0001 - T: (092) 7153551, Fax: 7153552
Fine Arts Museum - 1985
Japanese oil paintings, handicrafts, Japanese stile paintings, sculptures, photographs - library 22973

Fukuoka-shi Bijutsukan (Fukuoka Art Museum), 1-6 Ohori-koen, Chuo-ku, Fukuoka 810-0051 - T: (092) 7146051, Fax: 7146145, Internet: http://www.sow.co.jp. Head: Mikio Soejima
Fine Arts Museum / Decorative Arts Museum
Matsunaga coll of ceremony utensils, oil paintings, Kuroda family (local feudal lords) 22974

Fukuoka-shi Hakubutsukan (Fukuoka City Museum), 3-1-1 Momochihama, Sawara-ku, Fukuoka 814-0001 - T: (092) 8455011, Fax: 8455019, E-mail: info@museum.city.fukuoka.jp, Internet: http://museum.city.fukuoka.jp. Head: Keiichi Kuwahara
Local Museum / Historical Museum 22975

Fukushima

Fukushima-ken Bunka Center (Fukushima Cultural Center), 5-54 Kasugacho, Fukushima 960-8116 - T: (0245) 349191
Fine Arts Museum
Japanese paintings, sculpture, handicrafts - lecture hall 22976

Fukushima-kenritsu Bijutsukan (Fukushima Prefectural Museum of Art), 1 Aza Nishi-Yozan Moriai, Fukushima 960-8003 - T: (024) 5315511, Fax: 5310447, E-mail: master@artmuseum.fukushima.fukushima.jp, Internet: http://www.artmuseum.-fukushima.fukushima.jp. Head: Tetsuo Sakai
Fine Arts Museum
Modern Japanese paintings in traditional and Western style, prints, pottery, textiles, sculpture, impressionist and modern American realim paintings, modern Western prints and sculpture 22977

Fukuyama

Fukuyama Auto and Clock Museum, 3-1-22 Kita-yoshizu-cho, Fukuyama 720-0073 - T: (0849) 228188, Fax: 230766, E-mail: kikuya@urban.ne.jp, Internet: http://www.bekkoame.or.jp/~t-kuro/facm
Science&Tech Museum 22978

Fukuyama-Jo Castle Museum, 1-8 Marunouchi, Fukuyama 720-0061 - T: (0849) 222117
Archaeological Museum 22979

Fukuyama Museum of Art, 2-4-3, Nishimachi, Fukuyama 720-0067 - T: (0849) 322345, Fax: 322347, Internet: http://www.hiroshima-u.ac.jp/japanese/fukuyama/f-museum. Head: Masaki Nakano
Fine Arts Museum 22980

Japan Footwear Museum, 4-16-27 Matsunaga-cho, Fukuyama 729-0104 - T: (0849) 346644, Fax: 3417286, E-mail: museum@maruyama.gr.jp, Internet: http://www.maruyama.gr.jp/footandtoy. Head: Mariko Maniyama
Special Museum - 1978
Japanese footgear and footwear, international historic and international footwear 22981

Funabashi

Funabashi Hakubutsukan (Funabashi Municipal Museum), 4-25-19 Yakuendai, Funabashi 274-0077 - T: (0474) 659680
Local Museum 22982

Futatsunashi

Motor Car Museum of Japan, 40 Ikkanyama, Futatsunashi 923-0345 - T: (0761) 434343, Fax: 434444, Internet: http://www.mmjp.or.jp/motorcar-museum-of-japan
Science&Tech Museum 22983

Genkai-Machi

Munakata Taisha Shinpôkan (Museum of Divine Treasures), 2331 Tashima, Genkai-Machi 811-3505 - T: (0940) 621311, Fax: 621315, E-mail: Webmaster@munakata-taisha.or.jp, Internet: htpp://www.munakata-taisha.or.jp/sinpoukan.html. Head: Yoshinori Ohta
Archaeological Museum / Historical Museum / Religious Arts Museum - 1964
Objects from Okinoshima ancient ritual sites, bronce mirrors, jewelry, armour, wessels 22984

Gifu

Gifu-ken Bijutsukan (The Museum of Fine Art, Gifu), 4-1-22 Usa, Gifu 500-8368 - T: (058) 2711313, Fax: 2711313, E-mail: 527213@govt.pref.gifu.jp, Internet: http://www.gifu-art-museum-unet.ocn.ne.jp/. Head: Akihiko Hirako
Fine Arts Museum - 1982 22985

Gotemba

Ferrari Museum, 3373-1 Hakone-michi, Higashi-tanaka, Gotemba 412-0026 - T: (0550) 840550, E-mail: info@ferrari.pos.to, Internet: http://www.ferrari.pos.to
Science&Tech Museum 22986

Sports Car Museum of Japan, 1903 Miyagasaki, Higashi-tanaka, Gotemba 412-0026 - T: (0550) 831600
Science&Tech Museum 22987

Gyoda

Saitama-kenritsu Sakitama Shiryokan, 4834 Saitama, Gyoda 361-0025 - T: (0485) 565430
Decorative Arts Museum
Prehistoric pottery vessels, Kofun pottery cylinders, heads, and torsos 22988

Sakitama Archaeological Hall, Sakitama-jinja, Gyoda 361-0025 - T: (0485) 56111
Archaeological Museum
Prehistoric pottery, pottery cylinders, Sue-ware vessels, armor and swords, mirrors 22989

Hachijo

Hachijo Municipal Museum, 1186 Okago, Hachijo 100-1401 - T: (0499) 623105
Local Museum 22990

Hachinohe

Hachinohe City Museum of Art, 10-4, Oaza Ban-cho, Hachinohe 031-0031 - T: (0178) 458338, Fax: 244531. Head: Uwano Suezo
Fine Arts Museum 22991

Korekawa Archaeological Museum, 3-1 Aza Nakai, Oaza Korekawa, Hachinohe 031-0023 - T: (0178) 961484, Fax: 966361, E-mail: jyomon@hec.hachinohe.ed.jp, Internet: http://www.city.hachinohe.aomori.jp. Head: Masataka Araya
Archaeological Museum - 1963
Archaeological remains from Korekawa-Nakai site (Jomon period), refined potteries, wooden or vegetable implements and laquered items 22992

Hachioji

Hachioji-shi Hakubutsukan (Hachioji City Museum), 33 Ueno-machi, Hachioji 192-0902 - T: (0426) 228939
Local Museum 22993

Murauchi Art Museum, 787 Sanyu-machi, Hachioji 192-0012 - T: (0426) 916301, Fax: 921644. Head: Michimasa Murauchi
Fine Arts Museum 22994

Tokyo Fuji Art Museum, 492-1 Yano-machi, Hachioji 192-0016 - T: (0426) 914511, Fax: 914623, E-mail: tfamintl@fujibi.or.jp, Internet: http://www.fujibi.or.jp. Head: Mitsunari Noguchi
Fine Arts Museum - 1983
Western and Japanese paintings and prints, Western sculpture, ceramics, glass, photographs. Japanese lacquerware, armour, swords 22995

Hadano

Koan Collection, 1-393 Kokakuen, Tsurumaki, Hadano 257-0007
Local Museum
Items of regional interest 22996

Hagi

Hagi Municipal Museum, 522-11 Emukai, Hagi 758-0041 - T: (0838) 256447, Fax: 253142
Local Museum 22997

Ishii Chawan Bijutsukan, 33-Minamifuruhagi-cho, Hagi 758-0077 - T: (08382) 21211. Head: I. Ishii
Fine Arts Museum 22998

Kumaya Bijutsukan (Kumaya Art Museum), 47 Imauonotana-machi, Hagi 758-0052 - T: (0838) 255535
Fine Arts Museum
Japanese paintings, calligraphy, pottery, lacquer items 22999

Haguro

Dewa San-Zan History Museum, 33, Hagurosan, Tôge, Haguro 997-0292 - T: (0235) 622355, Fax: 622352. Head: Hisanobu Ogata
Historical Museum 23000

Hakodate

Hakodate-shiritsu Hakubutsukan (Hakodate City Museum), 17-1 Aoyagi-cho, Hakodate 040-0044 - T: (0138) 235480. Head: M. Ishikawa
Local Museum - 1879
Archaeology, ethnography of the Ainu, Giliak and other native tribes, history, Japanese traditional art, painting, coins - library 23001

Hokkaidoritsu Hakodate Bijutsukan (Hokkaido Hakodate Museum of Art), 37-6 Goryokaku-machi, Hakodate 040-0001 - T: (0138) 566311, Fax: 566381. Head: Toshiya Tanaka
Fine Arts Museum 23002

Hakone

Chokoku no Mori Bijutsukan (Hakone Open-Air Museum), 1121 Ninotaira, Hakone 250-0493 - T: (0460) 021161, Fax: 021169, E-mail: open-air@forest.hakone-oam.or.jp, Internet: http://www.hakone-oam.or.jp. Head: Takatoshi Suzuki
Fine Arts Museum / Open Air Museum - 1969
Late 19th and 20th c Western and Japanese sculpture, contemporary Western and Japanese oil painting, Rosso coll - Sculpture Garden (Henry Moore coll, etc), Picasso Pavilion, Manzu Room 23003

Hakone-Jinja Homotsuden (Hakone Shrine Treasure House), 86 Oshiba, Moto Hakone, Hakone 250-0500 - T: (0460) 36031. Head: Yoshitaka Wakiyama
Religious Arts Museum
Religious sculpture, paintings calligraphy, armor and swords, historical documents 23004

Hakone Souunzan Bijutsukan (Hakone Museum of Art), 1300-493 Gora, Hakone 250-0408 - T: (0460) 022623, 022222, Fax: 020124. Head: Yoji Yoshioka
Decorative Arts Museum - 1952
Pottery and porcelain from China, Japan, Korea, and the Near East, exhibits on ceramic techniques, tools, samples of clay, shards, and photographs, Japanese archeology moss garden, teahouse, bamboo garden - library, bamboo and moss garden 23005

Narukawa Bijutsukan (Narukawa Art Museum), 570 Moto Hakone, Hakone 250-0522 - T: (0460) 36828, Fax: 37620, E-mail: AEA05012@nifty.com, Internet: http://www.narukawamuseum.co.jp
Fine Arts Museum
Modern Japanese paintings 23006

Hakuba

Hakuba Bijutsukan (Hakuba Museum of Art), 2965 Oaza-Hokujo, Hakuba 399-9301 - T: (0261) 726084. Head: Kaname Ishizuka
Fine Arts Museum 23007

Hamamatsu

Hamamatsu City Museum, 4-22-1 Shijimiduka, Hamamatsu 432-8018 - T: (053) 4562208, Fax: 4562275
Local Museum - 1979
Local archeological finds, history, folklore - library 23008

Hamamatsu City Museum of Art, 130 Matsushiro-cho, Hamamatsu 430-0947 - T: (053) 4546801, Fax: 4546829. Head: Tomoaki Amano
Fine Arts Museum - 1971
Japanese, Chinese and European glass painting, ukiyo-e prints 23009

Hamura

Hamura-shi Local Museum, 741 Hane, Hamura 205-0012 - T: (0425) 582561
Local Museum 23010

Hanamaki

Zoshukan (Tibetan Collection at the Kotoku-ji), 95 Minami-kawara-cho, Hanamaki 025-0093 - T: (0198) 34614. Head: Gizo Kamakura
Ethnology Museum
Tibetan objects, including priests robes, hats, prayer wheels, and ritual objects, religious books, bronze statuettes, paintings 23011

Handa

Kamiya Bijutsukan (Kamiya Museum of Art), 10-8-9 Ariwaki-cho, Handa 475-0017 - T: (0569) 292626. Head: Yukio Kamiya
Fine Arts Museum 23012

Hatsukaichi

Itsukushima-jinja Homotsukan (Itsukushima Shrine Treasury), Miyajima-machi, Saeki-gun, Hatsukaichi 738-0013 - T: (0829) 442020. Head: Motoyoshi Nozaka
Religious Arts Museum - 1895
Paintings, calligraphy, sutras, swords and other ancient weapons 23013

Hayama

Yamaguchi Hoshun Memorial Hall, 2320 Isshiki, Hayama 240-0111 - T: (0468) 756094, Fax: 756192, Internet: http://www.jrtf.com/hoshun. Head: Eiji Fukuji
Fine Arts Museum 23014

Higashi-Hiroshima

Higashi-Hiroshima-shiritsu Bijutsukan (Higashi-Hiroshima City Museum of Art), 2-1-3 Hochihonmatsuminami, Higashi-Hiroshima 739-0144 - T: (0824) 285713. Head: Hideaki Masuda
Fine Arts Museum 23015

Higashi-Murayama

Higashi-Murayama Municipal Museum of Provincial History, 1-2-7 Suwa-cho, Higashi-Murayama 189-0021 - T: (0423) 915353
Local Museum 23016

Higashi-Osaka

Higashi-Osaka-shiritsu Kyodo Hakubutsukan (Higashi-Osaka Municipal Local Museum), 18-12 Kamishijo-cho, Higashi-Osaka 579-8052 - T: (0729) 846341. Head: Isao Hashimoto
Local Museum 23017

Higashi-Yatsushiro

Yamanashi-kenritsu Koko Hakabutsukan (Yamanashi Prefectural Archaeological Museum), 923 Shimozone, Nakamichi-cho, Higashi-Yatsushiro 400-1508 - T: (0552) 663881, Fax: 663882, Internet: http://www.aj3.yamanashi.ac.jp/archae
Archaeological Museum 23018

Hiki

Toyama Kinenkan, Shiroi-numa 675, Kawajima-machi, Hiki
Fine Arts Museum - 1970
Japanese paintings, calligraphy, ceramics, lacquer, and textiles, Chinese paintings and ceramics, objects from Egypt, Italy, and the Near East, pre-Inca arts, textiles, and earthenware - library 23019

Hikone

Economical Document Collection, c/o Shiga University, 1-1-1 Nakajima-cho, Bamba, Hikone 522-0069 - T: (07492) 25600
University Museum / Special Museum
Documents concerning economics 23020

Hikone Castle Collection, Kinkame-cho, Hikone 522-0000
Fine Arts Museum 23021

Ii Art Museum, Hikone-jo, Konki-cho, Hikone 522-0061 - T: (07492) 552
Fine Arts Museum
Japanese paintings, calligraphy, ceramics, lacquer items, masks, costumes, furniture, musical instruments, armor and swords 23022

Himeji

Himeji City Museum of Art, 68-25 Hon-machi, Himeji 670-0012 - T: (0792) 222288, Fax: 222290, E-mail: art@city.himeji.hyogo.jp, Internet: http://www.city.himeji.hyogo.jp.art. Head: Tomoya Miyake
Fine Arts Museum - 1983
Oil paintings, watercolours, sketches, prints, sculptures, swords, ceramics, Japanese style paintings 23023

Hyogo-kenritsu Rekishi Hakubutsukan (Hyogo Prefectural Museum of History), 68 Hon-machi, Himeji 670-0012 - T: (0792) 889011, Fax: 889013. Head: Kunihei Wada
Local Museum - 1982
Ancient sculpture, metal art objects, weapons, paintings and scrolls, porce lain and terracotta, costumes, dolls and toys 23024

Hinase

Morishita Art Museum, Nishisakae, Hinase 701-3200 - T: (0869) 720222
Fine Arts Museum 23025

Hirado

Hirado Castle Donjon, Iwanoue-cho, Hirado 859-5121
Military Museum / Decorative Arts Museum
Arms and armor, costumes, Christian relics, rebuilt castle, ceramics 23026

Hirado Kanko Historical Museum, Okubo-cho, Hirado Nagasaki, 859-5102 - T: (0950) 222813, Fax: 222813. Head: Motoko Yamaga
Historical Museum - 1962
Swords and armour, ceramics, paintings, calligraphy, Christian relics, Sokô Yamagas books and related documents, Java letters from Indonesia and items of deported Caucasian-Japanese children in the 17th c 23027

Matsuura Shiryo Hakubutsukan (Matsuura History Museum), 12 Kagamigawa-cho, Hirado 859-5152 - T: (0950) 222236, Fax: 222281
Historical Museum - 1941
Arms and armor, household objects, paintings and screens, calligraphy, lacquer items, ceramics, 25.000 documents, local history exhibits especially on early foreign trade 23028

Saikyo-ji Treasure Hall, 1206 Iwanoue-cho, Hirado 859-5121
Religious Arts Museum - 1977
Buddhist paintings, sculpture, sutras, ceremonial objects, wood blocks - library 23029

Hiraizumi

Chusonji Sankozo (Chusonji Temple Treasury), Chuson-ji, Hiraizumi 029-4100 - T: (0191) 462211
Religious Arts Museum - 1955
Sculpture, gilt-wood coffins, reliquaries, rosaries, shrouds and robes, set s of entire Buddhist canon, metalwork, furniture, late Heian period 23030

Hiraizumi Museum, 81-1 Shirayama, Hiraizumi 029-4100 - T: (019146) 2173
Local Museum - 1955
Chinese Buddhist painting and sculpture, swords, Japanese painting, calligraphy, bronze bell 23031

Motsu-ji Storage House, 48 Aza Osawa, Hiraizumi 029-4100
Religious Arts Museum - 1977
Buddhist paintings and sculpture, music instruments, masks, lacquer utensils, swords, sutras and sutra boxes 23032

Hirakata

Hirakata Gotenyama Art Center, 10-16 Goten-yama-cho, Hirakata 573-1182 - T: (0720) 478351, Fax: 404498. Head: Harue Ishiga
Fine Arts Museum 23033

Tenmon Museum of Art, Yamanoue-Kitamachi 3-1, Hirakata 573-0049 - T: (0720) 410006, Fax: 453012. Head: Yushi Ikeda
Fine Arts Museum 23034

Hiratsuka

Hiratsuka Bijutsukan (Hiratsuka Museum of Art), 1-3-3 Nishi-yawata, Hiratsuka 254-0073 - T: (0463) 352111, Fax: 352741. Head: Minoru Harada
Fine Arts Museum 23035

Hiratsuka-shi Hakubutsukan (Hiratsuka City Museum), 12-41 Sengen-cho, Hiratsuka 254-0041 - T: (0463) 335111
Local Museum 23036

Hirosaki

Hirosaki City Museum, 1-6 Shimoshirogane-cho, Hirosaki 036-8356 - T: (0172) 350700, Fax: 350707. Head: Takeshi Odagiri
Local Museum - 1977 23037

Hiroshima

Health Science Museum, 3-8-6 Senda-machi, Naka-ku, Hiroshima 730-0052 - T: (082) 2469100
Historical Museum 23038

Hermann Hesse Museum, 1-20-31 Inokuchi, Nichi-ku, Hiroshima 733-0842 - T: (082) 2775658
Special Museum 23039

Hiroshima Bijutsukan (Hiroshima Museum of Art), 3-2 Moto-machi, Naka-ku, Hiroshima 730-0011 - T: (082) 2232530, Fax: 2232519, E-mail: office@museum.mighty.co.jp, Internet: http://www.mighty.co.jp/museum. Head: Osamu Hashiguchi
Fine Arts Museum
Modern French (romanticism) and Japanese (western style) paintings 23040

Hiroshima Castle, 21-1 Motomachi, Naka-ku, Hiroshima 730-0011 - T: (082) 2217512, Fax: 2217519. Head: Hironobu Ino
Local Museum / Historic Site - 1958
Arms and armour, local history 23041

Hiroshima Children's Museum, 5-83 Moto-machi, Naka-ku, Hiroshima 730-0011 - T: (082) 2225346, Fax: 2227020, E-mail: webmaster@pyonta.city.-hiroshima.jp, Internet: http://www.pyonta.city.-hiroshima.jp. Head: Hiroshi Okimoto
Special Museum - 1980
Scientific and cultural programmes, exhibits on technology, science, transport, astronomy - planetarium 23042

Hiroshima City Museum of Traditional Provincial Industry, 2-6-20 Ujinamiyuki, Minami-ku, Hiroshima 734-0015 - T: (082) 2536771
Historical Museum / Science&Tech Museum 23043

Hiroshima Heiwa Kinen Shiryokan (Hiroshima Peace Memorial Museum), 1-2 Nakajima-cho, Naka-ku, Hiroshima 730-0811 - T: (082) 2414004, Fax: 5427941, E-mail: hpcf@pcf.city.hiroshima.jp, Internet: http://www.pcf.city.hiroshima.jp/peacesite/. Head: Minoru Hataguchi
Historical Museum - 1955
Actual facts of damages caused by the atomic bomb dropped on Hiroshima, artefacts, articles left by the A-bomb victims, photographs, drawings by survivors - library 23044

Hiroshima-kenritsu Bijutsukan (Hiroshima Prefectural Art Museum), 2-22 Kaminobori-cho, Naka-ku, Hiroshima 730-0014 - T: (082) 2216246, Fax: 2231444, E-mail: hpam@lime.ocn.ne.jp, Internet: http://www.hpam-unet.ocn.ne.jp. Head: Tatsuno Yuichi
Fine Arts Museum
20th c Japanese-style paintings, drawings, sculpture, japanese and asian handicrafts, calligraphy 23045

Hiroshima-shi Gendai Bijutsukan (Hiroshima City Museum of Contemporary Art), 1-1 Hijiyama-Koen, Minami-ku, Hiroshima 732-0815 - T: (082) 2641121, Fax: 2641198, E-mail: hcmca@enjoy.ne.jp, Internet: http://www.hcmca.cf.city.-hiroshima.jp. Head: Yasumaro Yoshinaka
Fine Arts Museum 23046

The Ohsha'joh Museum of Art, 701 Kamegaoka, Ohno-cho, Hiroshima 739-0400 - T: (0829) 563221, Fax: 560661. Head: Michio Umemoto
Fine Arts Museum 23047

Hitachi

Hitachi Kyodo Hakubutsukan (Hitachi City Local Museum), 5-2-22 Miyata-cho, Hitachi 317-0055 - T: (0294) 233231, Fax: 233230. Head: Tsutomu Warigai
Local Museum 23048

Hiwa

Hiwa Museum for Natural History, 119-1 Oaza, Hiwa 727-0300
Natural History Museum - 1951
Natural history exhibits, ivertebrates, mollusks, insects, amphibia, reptiles, mammals, fossils, minerals 23049

Hofu

Amida-ji Treasure Storehouse, 1869 Mure, Hofu 747-0004
Religious Arts Museum
Portraits, pagodas, scrolls, statues 23050

Hofu Tenmangu History Hall, 14-1 Matsuzaki-cho, Hofu 747-0029
Historical Museum
14th c scrolls, portraits, 12th c gilt-bronze reliquary, festival masks, music instruments, mirrors 23051

Mori Hokokai Hakubutsukan (Mori Museum), 1-15-1 Tatara, Hofu 747-0023 - T: (0835) 220001
Fine Arts Museum
Paintings, calligraphy, armor, costumes, lacquer items, documents of the Mori family - gardens 23052

Hokodate

Hokodate Museum of Art, 37-6 Goryokaku-cho, Hokodate 040-0001 - T: (0138) 566311, Internet: http://www.dokyoi.pref.hokkaido.jp/hk-bunka/tennrannkai.htm
Fine Arts Museum - 1986
Arts of Southern Hokkaido, paintings, calligraphies 23053

Hondo

Amakusa Kirishitankan (Amakusa Christian Museum), 19-52 Funeno-machi, Hondo 863-0017 - T: (09692) 23845
Religious Arts Museum 23054

Hotaka

Azumino Mountain Art Museum, 3613-26 Ariake, Hotaka 399-8301 - T: (0263) 834743. Head: Iwao Mizukami
Fine Arts Museum 23055

Rokuzan Bijutsukan (Rokuzan Art Museum), Hotaka 399-8300 - T: (0263) 822094, Fax: 829070. Head: Kaihei Isshi
Fine Arts Museum - 1958
Memorial to the sculptor Ogihara Morie (artistic name "Rokuzan"), his bronzes, oilpaintings, and drawings, Japanese modern sculptures 23056

Hourai

Hourai-choritsu Horaiji-san Shizenkagaku Hakubutsukan (Mount Horaiji Natural History Museum), 6 Moriwaki, Kadoya, Hourai 441-1944 - T: (05363) 51001
Natural History Museum 23057

Mount Horaiji Natural History Museum, 6 Moriwaki, Kadoya, Hourai 441-1944
Natural History Museum - 1963
Exhibits on natural history, invertebrates, insects, amphibia, minerals, fossils 23058

Ibara

Ibara Municipal Denchu Art Museum, 315, Ibara-cho, Ibara 715-8601 - T: (0866) 628787, Fax: 620332. Head: Masatoshi Mori
Fine Arts Museum 23059

Ibusuki

Iwasaki Museum of Art, 3755 Jiyuuni-cho, Ibusuki 891-0403 - T: (0993) 224056, Fax: 243215. Head: Yohachiro Iwasaki
Fine Arts Museum 23060

Ichikawa

Ichikawa Municipal Museum, 2932-1 Kitakokubun, Ichikawa 272-0836 - T: (0473) 732202
Local Museum 23061

Iida

Iida-shi Hakubutsukan (Iida City Museum), 655 Otemachi 2-chome, Iida 395-0034 - T: (0265) 228118, Fax: 225252, E-mail: bihaku@iidanet.or.jp, Internet: http://www.iidanet.or.jp/~bihaku. Head: Tadashi Inoue
Local Museum 23062

Ikaho

Takehisa Yumeji Ikaho Memorial Hall, 544-119 Ikaho, Ikaho 377-0102 - T: (0279) 724788, Fax: 722661. Head: Susumu Kogure
Historical Museum 23063

Ikeda

Itsuo Bijutsukan (Itsuoh Art Museum), 7-17 Tateishi-machi, Ikeda 563-0053 - T: (0727) 513865, Fax: 512427, Internet: http://museum.senri-i.or.jp/itsuo. Head: Akiko Okada
Fine Arts Museum - 1957
Japanese painting, masterpieces of calligraphy, lacquer items, ceramics, porcelain 23064

Ikoma

Horyuji Daihozoden Treasure Museum (Horyuji Temple), 1-1 Horyuji-sannai, Ikaruga-cho, Ikoma 636-01 - T: (0745) 752555. Head: Ryoken Saheki
Religious Arts Museum
Buddhist statues, shrines and other art, temple buildings 23065

Ikomayama Uchu Kagakukan (Mount Ikoma Space Science Museum), 2312-1 Nabata-cho, Ikoma 630-0231 - T: (0743) 742251
Science&Tech Museum / Natural History Museum - 1969
Instruments, models, photographs, illustrations, slides on astronomy, apparatuses 23066

Ikuno, Hyogo

Ikuno Kobutsukan (Ikuno Mineral Museum), 33-5, 1 Otanisuji, Ikuno, Hyogo 679-3300 - T: (079679) 2010
Natural History Museum 23067

Imabari

Ehime Bunkakan (Ehime Cultural Hall), 2-6-2 Koganecho, Imabari 794-0037 - T: (0898) 321063. Head: Ninomiya Kaneichi
Decorative Arts Museum - 1974
Chinese, Japanese, and Korean ceramics, Japanese lacquer items, swords, fragments of Japanese poems - conference room, tea-ceremony room 23068

Imabari City Kono Shiniichi Memorial Culture Hall, 1-4-8 Asahi-machi, Imabari 794-0042
Local Museum
Calligraphy, rare books, local archeological and ethnographic material, pottery, paper money, lacquer household utensils, furniture 23069

Imari

Imari-shi Rekishi Minzoku Shiryokan (Imari Municipal Folk History Museum), 73 Matsushima-cho, Imari 848-0045 - T: (09552) 27105
Folklore Museum / Historical Museum 23070

Ina

Kamiina Museum, Sakura-machi, Ina 396-0000 - T: (0265) 726066
Local Museum 23071

Inawashiro

Dr. Hideyo Noguchi Memorial Hall, Sanshouzawa Inawashio-machi, Inawashiro 969-3282 - T: (0242) 652319
Special Museum - 1939
House where the bacteriologist Dr. Noguchi was born, his bust, personal effects, scientific equipment personal library 23072

Inazawa

Inazawa City Oguiss Memorial Art Museum, 365-8, Maeda, Inazawa-cho, Inazawa 492-8217 - T: (0587) 233300, Fax: 233302. Head: Masatoshi Niwa
Fine Arts Museum 23073

Inuyama

Hakubutsukan Meiji-Mura (Museum Meiji-Mura), 1 Uchiyama, Inuyama 484-0000 - T: (0568) 670314, Fax: 370358, E-mail: webmaster@meitetsu.co.jp, Internet: http://www.meitetsu.co.jp/meiji-vil. Head: Teijiro Muramatsu
Open Air Museum - 1965
62 buildings demonstrating different architectural styles from the 19th and early 20th c re-erected in park (Meiji and Taisho periods 1868-1926), also buildings in Western architectural styles - library 23074

Iwata Senshinkan, 26 Aza Fujimi-cho, Inuyama, Inuyama 484-0081 - T: (0568) 614634. Head: Tadao Iwata
Fine Arts Museum / Decorative Arts Museum
Paintings, calligraphy, tea-ceremony bowls and utensils 23075

Little World Museum of Man, 90-48 Narusawa, Imai, Inuyama 484-0005 - T: (0568) 625611, Fax: 612090
Special Museum 23076

Nihon Monki Senta Hakubutsukan (Museum of the Japan Monkey Centre), 26 Kanrin, Inuyama 484-0081 - T: (0568) 612327, Fax: 626823, E-mail: LDZ05366@nifty.ne.jp, Internet: http://www.meitetsu.co.jp/japan-monkeycentre. Head: Mitsuo Iwamoto
Natural History Museum 23077

Ise

Jingu Museum of Antiquities, Kuratayama, Ise 516-0000 - T: (0596) 221700. Head: Yoshikazu Suzuki
Museum of Classical Antiquities
Calligraphy, documents, lacquer items, masks, arms and armor, ceramics, archeological material, Shinto ceremonial objects, Japanese contemporary paintings - library 23078

Jingu Nogyokan (Jingu Agricultural Museum), Kuratayama, Ise 516-0000. Head: Yasuji Akioka
Agriculture Museum - 1905
Exhibits on agriculture, forestry and fishing, over 40 species of sharks 23079

Kongosho-ji Treasure House, Asama-cho, Ise 516-0021
Religious Arts Museum
Mirrors, pottery and bronze sutra box covers, incense boxes, dishes, scrolls, paintings, calligraphy 23080

Isehara

Sannomiya Local Museum, 1472 Sannomiya, Isehara Kanagawa
Local Museum
Local archeological findings, archaic jewels and rings, swords, household ware, pottery cylinders 23081

Isesaki

Aikawa Kokokan (Aikawa Archaeological Museum), 6-10 Sanko-cho, Isesaki 372-0046 - T: (0270) 250082
Archaeological Museum
Pottery cylinders, stone memorial tablets 23082

Ishigaki

Yaeyama Museum, 4-1 Tonoshiro, Ishigaki 907-0004 - T: (09808) 24712
Local Museum 23083

Ishinomaki

Ishinomaki Culture Center, 1-7-30 Minamihama-cho, Ishinomaki 986-0835 - T: (0225) 942811, Fax: 942811. Head: Hiroshi Abe
Local Museum 23084

Isumi

Chiba-kenritsu Sonan Hakubutsukan (Chiba Prefectural Sonan Museum), 481 Otaki, Otaki-machi, Isumi 298-0216 - T: (0470) 823007, Fax: 824959
Local Museum 23085

Itami

Itami City Museum, 1-1-1 Senzo, Itami 664-0898 - T: (0727) 830582, Fax: 848109. Head: Kunio Wajima
Local Museum - 1972
Folk art, ancient, medieval and modern hist 23086

Itami City Museum of Art, 2-5-20 Miyanomae, Itami 664-0895 - T: (0727) 727447, Fax: 725558, Internet: http://www.city.itami.hyogo.jp/k_bijutsu/bijutsu00.html. Head: Kikuo Ohkouchi
Fine Arts Museum - 1987
Over 2,000 caricature prints, sculptures, satirical works 23087

Ito

Ikeda 20-seiki Bijutsukan (Ikeda Museum of 20th Century Art), 614 Totari Sekiba, Ito 414-0052 - T: (0557) 452211, Fax: 452212, Internet: http://www.nichireki.co.jp/ikeda. Head: Kiichiro Hayashi
Fine Arts Museum
Japanese and Western 20th c paintings under human theme 23088

Kazuaki Iwasaki Space Art Gallery, 9-639 Ohmuro-Kohgen, Ito 413-0235 - T: (0557) 519600, Fax: 519601, E-mail: 7122iwasaki@mail.wbs.ne.jp, Internet: http://www.wbs.ne.jp/bt/kisag
Public Gallery 23089

Itsukaichi

Itsukaichi Folk Museum, 920-1 Itsukaichi-machi, Nishi-tama-gun, Itsukaichi 190-0000 - T: (0425) 964069
Folklore Museum / Ethnology Museum 23090

Iwaki

Iwaki City Art Museum, 4-4, Aza-Donemachi, Taira, Iwaki 970-8026 - T: (0246) 251111, Fax: 251115. Head: Yasuo Taguchi
Fine Arts Museum 23091

Iwakuni

Iwakuni Municipal Museum, 2-7-19 Yokoyama, Iwakuni 741-0081
Local Museum - 1944
Local paintings, photographs, maps, records, and documents, coins, folk art, local archeological finds - library 23092

Nishimura Museum, 2-10-27 Yokoyama, Iwakuni 741-0081 - T: (0827) 410506
Military Museum / Decorative Arts Museum / Open Air Museum
Complete suits of armor, 17th-19th c swords, spears, bows and arrows, lacquer items, furniture, mirrors, music instruments, costumes including No robes and court costumes - park with ancient samurai houses 23093

Iwanai

Arai Memorial Museum of Art, 505 Noduka, Iwanai 045-0024 - T: (0135) 631111, Fax: 631111. Head: Toshizo Arai
Fine Arts Museum 23094

Iwata, Shizuoka

Iwata-shi Kyu Mitsukegakko (Mitsuke School Historical Site), 2452 Mitsuke, Iwata, Shizuoka 438-0086 - T: (0538) 324511. Head: Mamoru Fukuda
Historical Museum - 1953
Educational coll 23095

Izumi

Osaka Prefectural Museum of Yayoi Culture, 443-1 Ikegami-cho, Izumi 594-0083 - T: (0725) 462164
Folklore Museum 23096

Izumo

Izumo Taisha Treasure House, Taisha-machi, Izumo Shimane
Religious Arts Museum
Shinto priest garments, calligraphy, documents and letters, armor and swords, lacquer, models and map of shrine 23097

Izumozaki

Ryokan Kinenken (Ryokan Memorial Gallery), 197 Komeda Oaza, Izumozaki 949-4342 - T: (025878) 78370. Head: Shizuo Sato
Special Museum
Calligraphy and writings of the priest Ryokan (1757-1831), personal effects, portraits, modern museum building designed by Yoshiro Taniguchi 23098

Joetsu

Joetsu-shiritsu Sogo Hakubutsukan (Joetsu Museum), 7-7 Hon-cho, Joetsu 943-0832 - T: (0255) 243120
Local Museum 23099

Kaga

Hazama Inosuke Museum of Art, Fu 23, Hashitate-machi, Kaga 922-0554 - T: (0761) 751627, Fax: 752917. Head: Akio Miyamoto
Fine Arts Museum 23100

Kagoshima

Kagoshima-ken Bunka Center (Kagoshima Cultural Center), 5-3 Yamashita-cho, Kagoshima 892-0816 - T: (0992) 234221
Natural History Museum - 1966
Natural science exhibits, dinosaur fossils 23101

Kagoshima-kenritsu Hakubutsukan (Kagoshima Prefectural Museum), 1-1 Shiroyama-cho, Kagoshima 892-0853 - T: (0992) 236050, Fax: 236080
Local Museum / Natural History Museum - 1954
Local history, natural history, paintings by Japanese artists in the Japanese and Western styles, local ceramics, local ethnographic material 23102

Nagashima Museum, 3-42-18 Take, Kagoshima 890-0045 - T: (0992) 505400, Fax: 505478. Head: Kosuke Nagashima
Special Museum 23103

Shoko Shuseikan Historical Museum, Iso, Yoshino-cho, Kagoshima 892-0871 - T: (099) 2471511, Fax: 2484676, Internet: http://www.minc.ne.jp/shimadzu. Head: Tamura Shozo
Local Museum 23104

Kakegawa

Shiseido Art House, 751-1 Shimomata, Kakegawa 436-0025 - T: (0537) 236122, Fax: 236640, Internet: http://www.shiseido.co.jp
Public Gallery - 1978
Artworks, contemporary art, development of industrial technology, transition of fashion over time 23105

Kakogawa

Kakurin-ji Treasure House, Kakurin-ji, Kakogawa 675-0000 - T: (0794) 226064. Head: Miki Kakusei
Religious Arts Museum
Paintings, sculpture, sutras, ceramics, bronzes, masks, lacquer items 23106

Kamakura

Kamakura Gallery, 2-12-35 Ko-machi, Kamakura 248-0006 - T: (0467) 226163
Fine Arts Museum 23107

Kamakura Kokuhokan (Kamakura Museum, National Treasure House), 2-1-1 Yukinoshita, Kamakura 248-0005 - T: (0467) 220753, Fax: 235953. Head: Tatuto Nuki
Fine Arts Museum / Decorative Arts Museum - 1928
12th-16th c Japanese sculpture, Japanese and Chinese paintings and ceramics, Japanese metalwork, lacquer items, furniture, prints, Ukiyo-e - library 23108

Kamakuragu Homotsu Chinretsujo (Treasure Hall of the Kamakuragu Shrine), Nikaido, Kamakura 248-0002
Religious Arts Museum 23109

Kanagawa-kenritsu Kindai Bijutsukan (The Museum of Modern Art Kamakura), 2-1-53 Yukinoshita, Kamakura 248-0005 - T: (0467) 225000, Fax: 232464, E-mail: exhibition.116@pref.kanagawa.jp, Internet: http://www.planet.pref.-kanagawajp/city/kinbi.htm. Head: Tadayasu Sakai
Fine Arts Museum - 1951
Japanese and foreign art from the 19th c to the present, sculpture, paintings, handicrafts, water colors, drawings, European Old Masters prints - library 23110

Kitakamakura Museum, 2135 Ofuna, Kamakura 247-0056 - T: (0467) 434141
Local Museum 23111

Munakata Prints Museum, 2-19-17 Kamakura-yama, Kamakura 248-0031 - T: (0467) 317642. Head: Pariji Munakata
Fine Arts Museum 23112

Tsurugaoka Hachiman-gu Treasure House, Yukinoshita, Kamakura 248-0005 - T: (0467) 20315. Head: Minoru Okada
Local Museum
Neolithic stone tools, arms and armor, costumes, Bugaku masks, sculpture, 12th c lacquer items, portrait of Yoriyoshi Minamoto, founder of the shrine, his personal possessions 23113

Kaminoyama

Kaisendo Museum, 4-6-8 Yarai, Kaminoyama 999-3134 - T: (0236) 720155, Fax: 720155. Head: Ichi Hasegawa
Military Museum / Decorative Arts Museum - 1951
Chinese lacquer items, Japanese armor, 8th-19th c swords and sword furniture - library 23114

Mokichi Saito Museum, 1421 Aza-Benten, Kita-machi, Kaminoyama 999-3131 - T: (0236) 727227, Fax: 722626. Head: Keizo Suzuki
Special Museum 23115

Kamo, Izu

Choraku Homotsukan (Chorakuji Collection), Shichiken-cho, Shimoda-machi, Kamo, Izu
Fine Arts Museum 23116

Gyokusenji Homotsukan (Gyokusenji Collection), Kakizaki, Shimoda-machi, Kamo, Izu 410-3500
Fine Arts Museum 23117

Shimoda Marine Biological Station, Shimoda-machi, Kamo, Izu
Natural History Museum
Marine biology, invertebrates, mollusks, reptiles 23118

Kamogata

Okayama Tenmon Hakubutsukan (Okayama Astronomy Museum), Chikurinji, Kamogata 719-0200 - T: (086544) 2465
Science&Tech Museum / Natural History Museum - 1960
Models, photographs, displays on astronomy - astronomical observatory 23119

Kanazawa

Honda Museum, 3-1, Dewa-machi, Kanazawa 920-0963 - T: (076) 2610500, Fax: 2610500. Head: Masami Honda
Decorative Arts Museum - 1973
Honda family treasures of household lacquer utensils and chests, costumes, chinaware, arms and armor 23120

Hyakumangoku Bunkaen, Edomura Danpuen, Kitabukuro-cho, Kanazawa 920-1135 - T: (0762) 351337, Fax: 351337. Head: Yoshitada Sakurai
Local Museum 23121

Ishikawa-ken Rekishi Hakubutsukan (Ishikawa Prefectural History Museum), 3-1 Dewa-machi, Kanazawa 920-0963 - T: (0762) 623236, Fax: 621836, E-mail: rekihaku@pref.ishikawa.jp, Internet: http://www.pref.ishikawa.jp/muse/rekihaku. Head: Tsitsugen Torimiya
Historical Museum - 1986
Local historical materials, folklore, natural science 23122

Ishikawa-kenritsu Bijutsukan (Ishikawa Prefectural Art Museum), 2-1 Dewa-machi, Kanazawa 920-0963, mail addr: PC 920-0963, Kanazawa - T: (0762) 317580, Fax: 249550, Internet: http://www.city.kanazawa.ishikawa.jp/kankou/meisyo/kensyuhen/bijutu. Head: Shimasaki Susumu
Fine Arts Museum - 1959
Paintings, ceramics, lacquer wares, dyeing and weaving, calligraphy, bronze sculptures, swords, tea-ceremony utensils, historical documents, No masks and costumes - Museum Hall, library and Museum Shop 23123

Ishikawa-kenritsu Dento Sangyo Kogeikan (Ishikawa Prefectural Museum of Traditional Products and Crafts), 1-1 Kenroku-machi, Kanazawa 920-0936 - T: (0762) 622020, Fax: 628690
Historical Museum 23124

Ishikawa-kenritsu Kyodo Shiryokan (Ishikawa Prefectural Museum), 2-2-5 Hirosaka, Kanazawa 920-0962 - T: (0762) 623236
Local Museum 23125

Kanazawashiritsu Nakamura Kinen Bijutsukan (Nakamura Memorial Art Museum), 3-2-29 Honda-machi, Kanazawa 920-0964 - T: (0762) 2210751, Fax: 2210753, E-mail: nakamuramuse@city.kanazawa.ishikawa.jp, Internet: http://www.city.kanazawa.ishikawa.jp/bunho/nakamura
Fine Arts Museum
Paintings, calligraphy, ceramics, lacquer items, tea-ceremony objects - tea-ceremony house 23126

Seisonkaku, 1-2 Kenrokumoto-machi, Kanazawa 920-0931 - T: (0762) 210580, Fax: 210593. Head: Mitsuo Sato
Fine Arts Museum / Decorative Arts Museum
Paintings and portraits, examples of calligraphy, costumes and accessories, armor, lacquer items, porcelain and pottery, furniture, 19th c Japanese-style building - garden 23127

Kanuma

Kanuma Municipal Art Museum of Kawakami Sumio, 287-14 Mutsumi-cho, Kanuma 322-0031 - T: (0289) 628272, Fax: 628227. Head: Toshinobu Kobayashi
Fine Arts Museum 23128

Karuizawa

Sezon Museum of Modern Art, 2140 Serigasawa, Nagakura, Karuizawa 389-0111 - T: (0267) 462020, Fax: 462021, E-mail: info@smma-sap.or.jp, Internet: http://www.smma-sap.or.jp. Head: Seiji Tsutsumi
Fine Arts Museum 23129

Kasai

Ichijo-ji Treasure House, Sakamoto-cho, Kasai 675-2222
Religious Arts Museum
Japanese sculpture and painting, bronzes, wooden statues of priests, temple masks, a copy of the Hannyako, sutra of wisdom, paintings of Buddhist divinties 23130

Kasama

Nichido Bijutsukan (Nichido Museum of Art), Kasama 309-1600 - T: (0296) 722160, Fax: 725655. Head: Tokushichi Hasegawa
Fine Arts Museum 23131

Kasaoka

Chikkyo Art Museum Kasaoka, 1-17 Rokuban-cho, Kasaoka 714-0087 - T: (0865) 633967, Fax: 634496, E-mail: chikkyo-m@city.kasaoka.okayama.jp, Internet: http://www.city.kasaoka.okayama.jp/chikkyo.htm. Head: Katsusuke Mitani
Fine Arts Museum 23132

Kashihara

Nara-kenritsu Kokogaku Kenkyujo Fuzoku Hakubutsukan (Museum of the Archaeological Institute of Kashihara), 50-2 Unebi-cho, Kashihara 634-0065 - T: (0744) 241185, Fax: 241355
Archaeological Museum
Prehistoric vessels and shards, bone needles, horn and stone implements, pottery, wooden farm tools, bronze bells, swords, mirrors, ornaments, photographs of the excavation sites, roof tiles of different periods 23133

Kashima, Ibaraki

Kashima-jingu Treasure House, 2403 Kyuuchuu, Kashima, Ibaraki 314-0031
Religious Arts Museum
Religious and ceremonial items, 8th c sword and scabbard of a god, 12th c lacquered ornamental saddle, ceramic items, documents, paintings 23134

Kashima, Saga

Yutoku Shrine Museum, 1686 Furueda, Kashima, Saga 849-1321 - T: (09546) 22151
Religious Arts Museum 23135

Kawachi-Nagano

Amanosan Kongo-ji Treasure House, 996 Amano-cho, Kawachi-Nagano 586-0086
Religious Arts Museum
Sculpture, paintings, armor and swords, metalwork, furniture, music instruments, scrolls and documents, mirrors, lacquer boxes - gardens 23136

Kanshin-ji Reihokan (Kanshin-ji Treasure House), 475 Teramoto, Kawachi-Nagano 586-0053. Head: Gyozen Nagashima
Religious Arts Museum
8th-12th c sculptures, documents and scrolls, small bronze figures 23137

Kawagoe

Yamazaki Museum of Art, 4-13 Naka-cho, Kawagoe 350-0065 - T: (0492) 247114, Fax: 268560
Fine Arts Museum 23138

Kawaguchiko

Fuji Visitor Center, Funatsu, Kawaguchiko-machi, Minami-tsuru-gun, Kawaguchiko 401-0301 - T: (0555) 720259, Fax: 720211, E-mail: fuji-v.c@peach.ocn.ne.jp, Internet: http://yamanashi.visitors-net.ne.jp/~fujivisi
Natural History Museum 23139

Kawaguchiko Bijutsukan (Kawaguchiko Museum of Art), 3170 Kawaguchi, Kawaguchiko 401-0304 - T: (0555) 732829, Fax: 767879. Head: Hogara Adachi
Fine Arts Museum 23140

Kawakami

European Folkcraft Museum, Teshikaga, Kawakami 088-32 - T: (01548) 21511, Fax: 22524
Decorative Arts Museum 23141

Kawanishi

Kikusui Handicraft Museum, 2911 Nakakomatsu, Kawanishi 999-0122
Decorative Arts Museum
500 pieces Chinese, Japanese, and Korean ceramics from the prehistoric period to modern times 23142

Kawasaki

Kawasaki Municipal Industrial and Cultural Museum, 2-1-3 Fujimi, Kawasaki-ku, Kawasaki 210-0011
Fine Arts Museum / Decorative Arts Museum / Archaeological Museum
Contemporary Japanese paintings and pottery by Shoji Hamada, local archeological material including pottery and stone implements 23143

Kawasaki-shi Shimin Museum (Kawasaki City Museum), 1-2 Todoroki, Nakahara-ku, Kawasaki 211-0052 - T: (044) 7544500, Fax: 7544533, E-mail: kcm-gaku@rp.catv.ne.jp, Internet: http://www.home.catv.ne.jp/hh/kcm. Head: Yuji Katoh
Local Museum / Fine Arts Museum - 1988
Archaeological, historical and folklore items, graphics, cartoons and comics, photography, prints, film, video 23144

Kawasaki-shiritsu Nihon Minkaen (Kawasaki City Japan House Museum), 7-1-1 Masugata, Tama-ku, Kawasaki 214-0032 - T: (044) 9222181, Fax: 9348652, Internet: http://www.city.kawasaki.jp/sisetu_e/minka.htm. Head: Shuzo Miwa
Open Air Museum - 1967
Open Air Museum of Japanese Traditional Houses 23145

Toshiba Kagakukan (Toshiba Science Institute), 1 Komukai-cho, Saiwai-ku, Kawasaki 210-0903 - T: (044) 5492200, 5112300, Fax: 5201500, Internet: http://www2.toshiba.co.jp/kakan/
Science&Tech Museum
Newest technologies, concepts on electricity, electronic products 23146

Kawashima, Gifu

Naito Kinen Kusuri Hakubutsukan (Naito Museum of Pharmaceutical Science and Industry), Eisai Kawashima Complex, Kawashima, Gifu 501-6195 - T: (058689) 2101, Fax: 2197, Internet: http://www.eisai.co.jp
Special Museum 23147

Kawashima, Saitama

Toyama Kinenkan Fuzoku Bijutsukan (Toyama Memorial Museum), 675, Shirainuma, Kawashima, Saitama - T: (0492) 970007, Fax: 976951. Head: Naoshi Tomobe
Fine Arts Museum 23148

Kikuchi

Kikuchi-Rekishikan (Treasure House of the Kikuchi Shrine), 1257 Waifu, Kikuchi 861-1331
Religious Arts Museum 23149

Kimitsu

Futtsu Oceanographic Museum of Chiba Prefecture, 2280 Futtsu, Futtsu-cho, Kimitsu 299-1100
Natural History Museum
Oceanography 23150

Kiryu

Okawa Bijutsukan (Okawa Museum of Art), 3-69 Kosone-cho, Kiryu 376-0043 - T: (0277) 463300, Fax: 463350. Head: Eiji Okawa
Fine Arts Museum 23151

Kisaradu

Kinreizuka Archaeological Collection, Otayama Koen, Ooda, Kisaradu 292-0044 - T: (0438) 223676. Head: Mitsuru Ishii
Archaeological Museum
Archeological Kofun material from large local burial mound, iron swords and armor, dishes and jars 23152

Kisarazu

Chiba-kenritsu Kazusa Hakubutsukan (Chiba Prefectural Kazusa Museum), 2-16-2 Ota, Kisarazu 292-0044 - T: (0438) 230011, Fax: 232230
Local Museum
Stone tools, pottery vessels, mirrors, tiles, Buddhist sculpture, farm tools, household utensils, material on local literary figures 23153

Kita-mi

Hokumouken Kitami Bunka (Kitami Region Museum of Science, History and Art), 1 Kouen-cho, Kita-mi 090-0015 - T: (0157) 236700, Fax: 318344. Head: Yoshihiro Kumasaka
Natural History Museum / Historical Museum / Fine Arts Museum 23154

Kitaibaraki

Ibaraki Daigaku Izura Bijutsu Bunka Kenkyujo (Ibaraki University Izura Institut of Arts and Culture), 727-2 Izura, Otsu-cho, Kitaibaraki 319-1703 - T: (0293) 460766
Fine Arts Museum / University Museum
Paintings from the early 20th c 23155

Kitakami

Kitakami Municipal Museum, 14-59 Tachibana, Kitakami 024-0043 - T: (0197) 641756, Fax: 641756. Head: Yoshikazu Takata
Local Museum - 1973
Michinoku Folklore Village, historic architecture 23156

Kitakoma

Kiyosato Museum of Photographic Arts, 3545-1222 Kiyosato, Takane-cho, Kitakoma 407-0301 - T: (0551) 485599, Fax: 485445, E-mail: kmopa@comlink.ne.jp, Internet: http://www.comlink.ne.jp/~kmopa
Fine Arts Museum 23157

Kitakyushu

Kitakyushu-shiritsu Bijutsukan (Kitakyushu Municipal Museum of Art), 21-1 Nishi-Sayagatani-machi, Tobata-ku, Kitakyushu 804-0024 - T: (093) 8827777, Fax: 8610959, E-mail: k5200020@city.kitakyushu.jp, Internet: http://www.city.kitakyushu.jp/~k5200020. Head: Gohei Tani
Fine Arts Museum - 1974
Prints of modern foreign artists, sculpture, modern Japanese artists and local artists, Chinese rubbings - library 23158

Kiyose

Kiyose-shi Kyodo Hakubutsukan, 2-6-41 Kami-kiyoto, Kiyose 204-0013 - T: (0424) 938585
Local Museum 23159

Kobe

Hakutsuru Fine Art Museum, 1-1-6 Sumiyoshi-Yamate, Kobe 658-0063 - T: (078) 8516001, Fax: 8516001. Head: Hideo Kano
Fine Arts Museum / Decorative Arts Museum - 1934
Early Chinese bronzes, Chinese pottery and porcelain, Japanese metal ornaments, ritual pendants, lacquer items - library 23160

Hyogo-ken Togei-kan (Hyogo Ceramics Museum), Zentan Kaikan Bldg, 4-5-1 Shimoyamatedori, Chuo-ku, Kobe 650-0011 - T: (078) 3210769
Decorative Arts Museum
Ceramic coll, interior of a house from Takayama - tea-ceremony rooms 23161

Hyogo Kenritsu Bijutsukan (Hyogo Prefectural Museum of Art), 1-1-1, Wakihama-kaigan-dori, Chuo-ku, Kobe 651-0073 - T: (078) 2620901, Fax: 2620903. Head: Shigenobu Kimura, Tokuhiro Nakajima
Fine Arts Museum - 2002
Contemporary Japanese paintings, prints, and sculpture of Western artists 23162

Kobe Fashion Museum, 2-9-1 Koyocho-naka, Higashinada-ku, Kobe 658-0032 - T: (078) 8580050, Fax: 8580058, E-mail: info@fashionmuseum.or.jp, Internet: http://www.fashion-museum.or.jp
Special Museum 23163

Kobe Maritime Museum, Meriken-koen, Hatoba-cho, Chuo-ku, Kobe 650-0042 - T: (078) 3916751, Fax: 3324739, Internet: http://kobe-meriken.or.jp
Science&Tech Museum
port 23164

Kobe-shiritsu Hakubutsukan (Kobe City Museum), 24 Kyo-machi, Chuo-ku, Kobe 650-0034 - T: (078) 3910035, Fax: 3927054. Head: Kazutoshi Sasayama
Local Museum 23165

Kosetsu Bijutsukan (Kosetsu Museum of Art), 285-2 Ishino, Mikage-cho-gunge, Higashinada-ku, Kobe 658-0057 - T: (078) 8410652
Fine Arts Museum - 1972
Japanese and Chinese paintings, calligraphy, scultpure, ceramics, metalwork, Korean pottery 23166

Suma Aqualife Museum, 1-3-5 Wakamiya-cho, Suma-ku, Kobe 654-0049 - T: (078) 7317301, Fax: 7336333. Head: Satoru Sameshima
Natural History Museum - 1987
Aquarium, fossils, aquatic life 23167

Kochi

Chikurin-ji Treasure House, 3577 Godaisan, Kochi 780-8125
Religious Arts Museum
Buddhist sculpture - garden 23168

Kochi-ken Kaitokukan (Kochi Prefectur Cultural Museum), 1-1-20 Marunouchi, Kochi 780-0850 - T: (0888) 245701, Fax: 249931. Head: Yoichi Jakeuchi
Local Museum
Paintings by local artists, folk arts, calligraphies, crafts from Edo-period, arms 23169

Kochi-kenritsu Bijutsukan (Museum of Art, Kochi), 353-2 Takasu, Kochi 781-8123 - T: (088) 8668000, Fax: 668008, E-mail: museum@tosa.net-kochi.gr.jp, Internet: http://www2.net-kochi.gr.jp/~kenbunka/museum. Head: Masanori Kagioka
Fine Arts Museum 23170

Museum in Kochi Park, 1-1-20 Marunouchi, Kochi 780-0850. Head: Tano Masuo
Historical Museum
Autographs, historical material 23171

Yamanouchi-jinja Treasure History Hall, 2-4-26 Takajou-machi, Kochi 780-0862
Religious Arts Museum
Arms and armor of the local daimyos, No masks, tea-ceremony objects, garments 23172

Kodaira

Gas Museum, 2-590 Onuma-cho, Kodaira 187-0001 - T: (0423) 421715
Science&Tech Museum 23173

Musashino Museum, c/o Musashino Art University, 1-736 Ogawa-nishi-machi, Kodaira 187-0035 - T: (042) 3426004/03, Fax: 3426451, E-mail: art-lib@musabi.ac.jp, Internet: http://www.musabi.ac.jp. Head: Yoshiharu Kamino
Fine Arts Museum / University Museum 23174

Kofu

Yamanashi-kenritsu Bijutsukan (Yamanashi Prefectural Museum of Art), 1-4-27 Kugawa, Kofu 400-0065 - T: (0552) 283322, Fax: 283324, Internet: http://www.art-museum.pref.yamanashi.jp. Head: Dr. Takashi Hamada

Fine Arts Museum - 1978
About 70 works by J.-F. Millet, painter of the École de Barbizon (Gustve Courbet, Camille Corot, Théodore Rousseau, Constant Troyon) 23175

Koga

Miho Museum, 300 Momodani, Shigaraki-cho, Koga 529-1814 - T: (0748) 823411, Fax: 823414, E-mail: webmaster@miho.or.jp, Internet: http://www.miho.or.jp
Fine Arts Museum 23176

Shigaraki-yaki Pottery Museum, 11-1, Oaza-Hosohara, Shigaraki-cho, Koga 529 - T: (0748) 821153. Head: Minoru Takita
Decorative Arts Museum 23177

Koganei

Edo-Tokyo Tatemono-En (Edo-Tokyo Open Air Architectural Museum), 3-7-1 Sakuracho, Koganei 184-0005 - T: (042) 3883300, Fax: 3881711, E-mail: enkanri@coral.ocn.ne.jp, engakgei@coral.ocn.ne.jp, Internet: http://www4.ocn.ne.jp/~tatemono. Head: Raijiro Hayashi
Fine Arts Museum 23178

Nakamoura Kenichi Museum of Art, 1-11-3 Naka-cho, Koganei 184-0012 - T: (0423) 849800, Fax: 858161. Head: Tomosaburo Hori
Fine Arts Museum 23179

Tokyo Noko Daigaku Kogakubu Fuzoku Sen'i Hakubutsukan (Museum of Fiber Science and Technology, Tokyo University of Agriculture and Technology), 2-24-16 Naka-machi, Koganei 184-8588 - T: (042) 3887163, Fax: 3887163, E-mail: senhaku@cc.tuat.ac.jp, Internet: http://www.tuat.ac.jp/~museum. Head: Tetsuo Asakura
Science&Tech Museum / University Museum 23180

Kokubunji

Kokubunji Cultural Exhibition Center, 3-10-7 Nishi-moto-machi, Kokubunji 185-0023 - T: (0423) 233231
Local Museum 23181

Kokubunji-shi Bunkazai Hozonkan (Kokubunji Municipal Archaeological Gallery), 1-13-16 Nishi-moto-machi, Kokubunji 185-0023 - T: (0423) 210420
Archaeological Museum
Local prehistorical finds, arrowheads, pottery, sword, tile fragments 23182

Komaki

Menard Art Museum, 5-250, Komaki, Komaki 485-0041 - T: (0568) 755787, Fax: 770626, Internet: http://www.menard.co.jp/06/061j.htm. Head: Koichi Ishikawa
Fine Arts Museum 23183

Komatsu

Komatsu Shiritsu Hakubutsukan (Komatsu City Museum), 19 Marunouchi-koen-machi, Komatsu 923-0903 - T: (0761) 220714, Fax: 217683, E-mail: 3nomaru@po.incl.ne.jp, Internet: http://www.incl.ne.jp/ichihaku. Head: Hideaki Sasaki
Local Museum - 1958
Archeological exhibits incl pottery, swords, metalwork, ethnography, farm tools and farmers clothing, natural hist - library, classroom 23184

Nata-dera Homotsukan (Nata-dera Treasure House), Nata-dera, Awadu-machi, Komatsu 923-0326 - T: (0761) 651602
Religious Arts Museum
Buddhist statues, portable shrine, screen paintings, calligraphy 23185

Komoro

Koyama Keizo Art Museum, 221 Kaikoen-cho, Komoro 384-0000 - T: (0267) 223428
Fine Arts Museum 23186

Koriyama

Koriyama City Museum of Art, 130-2, Oyaji, Yasuhara-machi, Koriyama 963-0666 - T: (0249) 562200, Fax: 562350. Head: Tetsuro Murata
Fine Arts Museum 23187

Kotohira

Kotohira-gu Museum, 892 Kotohira-cho, Kotohira 766-0001 - T: (0877) 752121, Fax: 752125. Head: Mitsushige Kotooka
Local Museum
Japanese painting, calligraphy, sculpture, metalwork, arms and armor, lacquer items, masks, music instruments 23188

Koya

Koyasan Reihokan (Buddhist Museum Koya-San), Koyasan, Koya 648-0211 - T: (0736) 562254. Head: Chikyo Yamamoto
Religious Arts Museum - 1926
Buddhist paintings and images, sutras, old documents 23189

Kuma

Kuma Museum of Art, Oaza Sugou, Kuma 791-1205 - T: (0892) 212881, Fax: 211954. Head: Osamu Kono
Fine Arts Museum 23190

Kumamoto

Hommyo-ji Treasure House, Hanazono, Kumamoto 860-0072 - T: (0963) 20630
Religious Arts Museum
Paintings, calligraphy, swords and armor, ceramics, lacquer items, documents 23191

Kumamoto Castle, 1-1 Hommaru, Kumamoto 860-0002
Historical Museum / Military Museum
Objects connected with the history of the builder of the castle, Kiyomasa Kato, and the Hosokawa clan, items from the Seinan War, weapons and uniforms, prints of the battles and burning of the castle 23192

Kumamoto International Folk Art Museum, Sannomiya-koen, Tatsuda-machi-kami-tatsuda, Kumamoto 862-8004
Folklore Museum
Basketry and straw objects, chests, textiles, ceramics, glass, lacquer items, toys folk arts from Japan, Europe, Central and South America, and Southeast Asia 23193

Kumamoto-kenritsu Bijutsukan (Kumamoto Prefectural Museum of Art), 2 Ninomaru, Kumamoto 860-0008 - T: (096) 3522111, Fax: 3261512, Internet: http://www.kings.co.jp/kumamoto-pref/public/museum. Head: Keichi Sato
Fine Arts Museum 23194

Kumamoto-shiritsu Hakubutsukan (Kumamoto City Museum), 3-2 Furukyo-machi, Kumamoto 860-0007 - T: (096) 3243500, Fax: 3514257. Head: Takao Toyoda
Local Museum - 1952
Natural history, engineering and science exhibits, archeological material, folk arts, tools of the farming and fishing communities, regional crafts - planetarium 23195

Kunisaki

Kunisaki-machi Rekishi Minzoku Shiryokan (Kunisaki History and Folklore Museum), 150-1 Tsurugawa, Kunisaki 873-0503 - T: (0978) 722677
Historical Museum / Folklore Museum 23196

Kurashiki

Japanese Rural Toy Museum, 1-4-16 Chuuou, Kurashiki 710-0046 - T: (086) 4228058
Decorative Arts Museum
Coll of old Japanese folk toys 23197

Kurashiki Archaeological Museum, 1-3-13 Chuo, Kurashiki 710-0046 - T: (086) 4221542. Head: Tadahiko Makabe
Archaeological Museum
Japanese archeological material including stone tools from the neolithic period, pottery, shell and cylindrical stone ornaments, swords, mirrors, earthenware vessels, pottery sutra cases, pre-Columbian pottery, Peruvian textiles 23198

Kurashiki City Art Museum, 2-6-1 Chuo, Kurashiki 710-0046 - T: (086) 4256034, Fax: 4256036, E-mail: kcam@city.kurashiki.okayama.jp. Head: Takenobu Okamoto
Fine Arts Museum
Modern Japanese paintings in traditional Japanese and Western style, contemporary Japanese art 23199

Kurashiki Mingeikan (Kurashiki Museum of Folkcraft), 1-4-11 Chuo, Kurashiki 710-0046 - T: (086) 4221637. Head: Kiyoshi Moriya
Decorative Arts Museum / Folklore Museum
Japanese folk art, American Indian ceramics and baskets, European peasant ceramics and metalwork 23200

Ohara Bijutsukan (Ohara Museum of Art), 1-1-15 Chuo, Kurashiki 710-0046 - T: (086) 4220005, Fax: 4273677, E-mail: info@ohara.or.jp, Internet: http://www.ohara.or.jp. Head: Tadao Ogura
Fine Arts Museum - 1930
17th-20th c Western paintings and sculpture, ceramics and sculptures from Egypt, Persia, and Turkey, Japanese paintings, arts and crafts, French Impressionist masters, textiles, wood-block prints 23201

Torajiro Kojima Memorial Hall, Ohara Museum of Art, 1-1-15 Chuo, Kurashiki 710-0046 - T: (086) 4220005, Fax: 4273677, E-mail: info@ohara.or.jp, Internet: http://www.ohara.or.jp. Head: Tadao Ogura
Fine Arts Museum
Western-style paintings by Torajiro Kojima and the late 19th early 20th c western paintings, oriental antiquities 23202

Kurayoshi

Kurayoshi Museum, 3445-8 Nakano-cho, Kurayoshi 682-0824 - T: (0858) 224409, Fax: 224415. Head: Keimei Ho
Fine Arts Museum / Archaeological Museum - 1972
Contemporary paintings, local archeological items, photographs and drawings, building designed by Toru Kosumi - garden, lecture hall 23203

Kure

Kure Bijutsukan (Kure Museum of Art), 4-9 Saiwai-cho, Kure 737-0028 - T: (0823) 252007. Head: Yoshio Sato
Fine Arts Museum 23204

Kurume

Ishibashi Museum of Art and Asian Gallery, 1015 Nonaka-machi, Kurume 839-0862 - T: (0942) 391131, Fax: 393134, Internet: http://www.ishibashi-museum.gr.jp. Head: Sadao Kitamura, Hiroki Hashitomi
Fine Arts Museum - 1956/96
Western-style Japanese paintings (19th-early 20th c), ceramics 23205

Kushimoto

Okyo and Rosetsu Art Museum, 833 Muryo-ji, Kushimoto 649-3503 - T: (0735) 620468, Fax: 620468. Head: Kohkoh Tohjoh
Fine Arts Museum
Decorative sliding doors, wall scroll paintings, archeological finds consisting of pottery and remnants of a wooden boat 23206

Kushiro

Kushiro Art Museum, 4-1-5 Saiwai-cho, Kushiro 085-0017 - T: (0154) 232381, Fax: 232386, Internet: http://www.dokyoi.pref.hokkaido.jp/hk-bunka/tennrannkai.htm. Head: Hiroshi Araya
Fine Arts Museum - 1998
Regional development of artistic culture, paintings, modern photographic works 23207

Kushiro City Museum, 1-7 Shunkodai, Kushiro 085-0822 - T: (0154) 415809, Fax: 426000, E-mail: ku610601@city.kushiro.hokkaido.jp, Internet: http://www.city.kushiro.hokkaido.jp/museum. Head: Tatsuo Shichita
Local Museum
Ainu material including clothing, lacquer utensils, libation wands, pipes swords, jewelry, cult objects, models of houses, and photographs of Ainu life, archeological pieces including vessels and stone implements 23208

Kyoto

Chishaku-in Temple Storehouse, Higashiyama-Shichijo, Higashiyama-ku, Kyoto 605-0001 - T: (075) 5415361
Decorative Arts Museum
Japanese paintings and screens of the Momoyama period (1573-1615) 23209

Chishaku-in Treasure Hall, Higashi-Kawara-cho, Higashiyama-ku, Kyoto 605-0839
Religious Arts Museum
Buddhist equipment and utensils, documents, paintings, calligraphy, sutras, books 23210

Daigo-ji Treasure Hall, Daigo-ji, Daigo-yama, Fushimi-ku, Kyoto 601-1383 - T: (075) 5710002. Head: Ryuken Sawa
Religious Arts Museum
Religious art, historical documents relating chiefly to Buddhism, calligraphy 23211

Daihoon-ji Treasure House, Shichihonmatsu-dori, Imadegawa-cho, Kamigyo-ku, Kyoto 602-8454
Religious Arts Museum
Sculpture, temple furniture, temple buildings 23212

Daikakuji Temple Treasure House, Osawa-cho, Saga, Ukyo-ku, Kyoto 616-8411 - T: (075) 8710071
Decorative Arts Museum
Decorated room dividers, sculpture, historical documents 23213

Doshisha Neesima Memorabilia Room, Gembu-cho, Kamikyo-ku, Kyoto 602-8580
Fine Arts Museum 23214

Fujii Saisei-kai Yurinkan, 44 Enshoji-cho, Okazaki, Sakyo-ku, Kyoto 606-8344 - T: (075) 7610638, Fax: 7710005. Head: Zenzaburou Fujii
Fine Arts Museum / Decorative Arts Museum
Chinese paintings, calligraphy, Buddhist sculpture, jades, bronzes, pottery and porcelain, lacquer items, costumes, and furniture, Gandhara sculptures, Indian bronzes, Japanese mirrors 23215

Fuzoku Hakubutsukan (Costume Museum), Izutus Bldg, Shin-Hanaya-cho, Shimogyo-ku, Kyoto 600-8185 - T: (075) 3618388
Special Museum
Japanese costumes from ancient to modern time, life-sizes dolls 23216

Garden of Fine Art Kyoto, Hangi-cho, Shimogamo, Sakyo-ku, Kyoto 606-0823 - T: (075) 7242188
Fine Arts Museum / Open Air Museum 23217

Gekkeikan Okura Kinenkan, 247 Minami-hama-cho, Fushimi-ku, Kyoto 612-8045 - T: (075) 6232050, Fax: 6220312, E-mail: k-fukuda@gekkeikan.co.jp, Internet: http://www.gekkeikan.co.jp. Head: Haruhiko Okura
Special Museum 23218

Hadaka no Taisho Kinenkan, 24-2 Rokutan-cho, Toriimoto, Saga, Ukyo-ku, Kyoto 616-8438 - T: (075) 8825115
Local Museum 23219

Hashimoto Kansetsu Memorial Museum, 37 Ishibashi-cho, Jodoji, Sakyo-ku, Kyoto 606-8406 - T: (075) 7510446
Special Museum 23220

Hieizan Natural History Museum, Hieizan, Sakyo-ku, Kyoto 606-0000
Natural History Museum - 1955
Zoology, ornithology, botany 23221

Ike Taiga Museum of Art, 57 Mangoku-cho, Matsuo, Nishikyo-ku, Kyoto 615-8287 - T: (075) 3812832. Head: Yoneyuki Sasaki
Fine Arts Museum
80 paintings and examples of calligraphy by the 18th c buniga painter, Black/white paintings, calligraphy by Ike Taiga (1723-1776) 23222

Imura Art Museum, 29 Matsubara-cho, Shimogamo, Sakyo-ku, Kyoto 606-0804 - T: (075) 7223300
Fine Arts Museum 23223

Insho-Domoto Museum of Fine Arts, 26-3 Kamiyanagi-cho, Hirano, Kita-ku, Kyoto 603-8356 - T: (075) 4630007, 4631348, Fax: 4653099
Fine Arts Museum
The works of the artist Insho Domoto including paintings, prints, and drawings, ceramics, stained glass, tapestries, and metalwork 23224

Kahitsukan - Kyoto Museum of Contemporary Art, 271 Kitagawa, Gion-machi, Higashiyama-ku, Kyoto 605-0073 - T: (075) 5251311, Fax: 5613719, E-mail: kahitsu@kahitsukan.or.jp, Internet: http://www.kahitsukan.or.jp. Head: Yoshitomo Kajikawa
Fine Arts Museum 23225

Kawai Kanjiro's House, 569 Shibutani-dori, Kanei-cho, Higashiyama-ku, Kyoto 605-0875 - T: (075) 5613585, Fax: 5613585. Head: Suyako Kawai
Special Museum / Decorative Arts Museum - 1973
House designed by the famous potter Kanjiro Kawai, his pottery and kiln, sculpture, his writings and samples of calligraphy, notes and books - library 23226

Kitamura Museums, 448-4 Kajii-cho, Imadegawa-sagaru Higashi-iru, Kamigyo-ku, Kyoto 602-0033 - T: (075) 2560637
Local Museum 23227

Kitano Temman-gu Treasure House, Bakuro-cho, Kitano, Kamigyo-ku, Kyoto 602-8386 - T: (075) 4610005
Religious Arts Museum
Paintings, calligraphy, sculpture, lacquer items, metalwork, a few court costumes, ancient scrolls of the legends of the Kitano Tenjin Schrine 23228

Kodai Yuzenen (Yuzen Art Museum), 668 Jumonji, Takatsuji, Inokuma-cho, Shimogyo-ku, Kyoto 600-8353 - T: (075) 8230500
Fine Arts Museum 23229

Komatsu Hitoshi Art Museum, 369 Ohara Ide-cho, Sakyo-ku, Kyoto 601-1246 - T: (075) 7442318
Fine Arts Museum 23230

Kondo Yuzo Memorial Museum, 1-287 Shinmichi, Kiyomizu, Higashiyama-ku, Kyoto 605-0862 - T: (075) 5612917
Special Museum 23231

Koryo Museum of Art, 15 Kamigishi-cho, Shichiku, Kita-ku, Kyoto 603-8400 - T: (075) 4911192
Fine Arts Museum 23232

Koryu-ji Reihoden (Koryu-ji Temple Treasure House), 36 Hachioka-cho, Uzumasa, Ukyo-ku, Kyoto 616-8162 - T: (075) 8611461
Religious Arts Museum
Japanese Buddhist sculpture, calligraphy, documents, 19th c coronation robes and other costumes, 14th c paintings 23233

Kozu Kobunka Museum, Onmae-dori Nishi-agaru, Ichijo, Kamigyo-ku, Kyoto 602-0934 - T: (075) 4618700
Public Gallery 23234

Kuramayama Museum, 1074 Hon-machi, Kurama, Sakyo-ku, Kyoto 601-1111 - T: (075) 7412368
Local Museum 23235

Kyoto Arashiyama Music Box Museum, 1-38 Sagatenryuji Tateishi-cho, Shakado, Saga, Ukyo-ku, Kyoto 616-8375 - T: (075) 8651020
Music Museum 23236

Kyoto City Archaeological Museum, 261-1 Motoisa-cho, Omiyahigashi-iru, Imadegawa-cho Kamigyo-ku, Kyoto 602-0033 - T: (075) 4323245
Archaeological Museum 23237

Kyoto Daigaku Bungakubu Hakubutsukan (Museum of the Kyoto University Faculty of Letters), Yoshida Hon-machi, Sakyo-ku, Kyoto 606-8317 - T: (075) 7532721, Fax: 7532770. Head: Prof. K. Oyama
Archaeological Museum - 1911
Chinese ceramics from neolithic times to the Tang dynasty, early Chinese bronzes and jades, Buddhist sculpture, Japanese pottery, Korean art objects - library 23238

Kyoto-fu Kyoto Bunka Hakubutsukan (Museum of Kyoto), Sanjo Takakura, Nakagyo-ku, Kyoto 604-0000 - T: (075) 2220888, Fax: 2220889, E-mail: mk-pai@mbox.kyoto-inet.or.jp, Internet: http://web.kyoto-inet.or.jp/org/bunpaku
Local Museum 23239

Kyoto Gion Oil Lamp Museum, 540-1 Minamigawa, Gion-machi, Higashiyama-ku, Kyoto 605-0074 - T: (075) 5253812
Decorative Arts Museum 23240

Kyoto Kokuritsu Hakubutsukan (Kyoto National Museum), 527 Chaya-cho, Higashiyama-ku, Kyoto 605-0931 - T: (075) 5411151, Fax: 5310263, E-mail: welcome@kyohaku.go.jp, Internet: http://www.kyohaku.go.jp. Head: Norio Fujisawa

Fine Arts Museum / Decorative Arts Museum / Military Museum - 1889
Japanese and Chinese paintings, calligraphy, group of sutras, sculptures, ceramics, tiles, bronzes, metalwork, lacquer wares, dyeing and weaving, swords and armor, Japanese Buddhist sculpture, archeological material, No robes und kimonoes - library 23241

Kyoto Kokuritsu Kindai Bijutsukan (National Museum of Modern Art Kyoto), Okazaki, Enshoji-cho, Sakyo-ku, Kyoto 606-8344 - T: (075) 7614111, Fax: 7520509, E-mail: info@momak.go.jp, Internet: http://www.momak.go.jp. Head: Takeo Uchiyama
Fine Arts Museum / Decorative Arts Museum - 1963
20th-c art, contemporary Japanese and foreign ceramics, including exhibit of Kanjiro Kawai's works, lacquer wares, metalwork, glass, textiles, sculpture, painting and prints - library 23242

Kyoto Mingei Kan, 2 Kotani-cho, Ichijoji, Sakyo-ku, Kyoto 606-8147 - T: (075) 7912949
Local Museum 23243

Kyoto Museum of Traditional Crafts - Fureaikan, 9-1 Seishoji-cho, Okazaki, Sakyo-ku, Kyoto 606-8343 - T: (075) 7622670
Decorative Arts Museum
Traditional crafts, Arts of Kyoto 23244

Kyoto Museum of World Peace, 56-1 Tojiin-kita-machi, Kita-ku, Kyoto 603-8346 - T: (075) 4658151
Historical Museum 23245

Kyoto Prefectural Museum, Hangi-cho, Shimogamo, Sakyo-ku, Kyoto 606-0823 - T: (075) 7819101. Head: Hideyuki Nabika
Local Museum - 1963
Industrial art works, folk arts, toys, traditional handicrafts, oriental and Japanese instruments, documents - Library, lecture hall, conference room 23246

Kyoto-shi Bijutsukan (Kyoto Municipal Museum of Art), 124 Okazaki Enshoji-cho, Sakyo-ku, Kyoto 606-8344 - T: (075) 7714107, Fax: 7610444. Head: Mitsugi Uehira
Fine Arts Museum - 1933
Contemporary fine arts, Japanese pictures, sculptures, decorative arts exhibits 23247

Kyoto-shi Seishonen Kagaku (Kyoto City Youth Science Center), 13 Ikenouchi-cho, Fukakusa, Fushimi-ku, Kyoto 612-0031 - T: (075) 6421601
Special Museum 23248

Kyoto Yuzen Bunka Kaikan, 6 Mameda-cho, Nishi-kyogoku, Ukyo-ku, Kyoto 615-0801 - T: (075) 3110025
Science&Tech Museum
Yuzen products 23249

Misora Hibari Memorial House, Togetsukyo Kita 50m, Arashiyama, Nishikyo-ku, Kyoto 616-0007 - T: (075) 8645000
Special Museum 23250

Momoyama Art Museum, 192 Gokogu-monzen-cho, Fushimi-ku, Kyoto 612-8039 - T: (075) 6227752
Fine Arts Museum 23251

Museum of Antique Armour Helmets and Swords, 54-1 Shimogamo Kitazono-cho, Sakyo-ku, Kyoto 606-0831 - T: (075) 7127921
Decorative Arts Museum 23252

Museum of the Chado Research Center, Horikawa Teranouchi-agaru, Kamigyo-ku, Kyoto 602-8066 - T: (075) 4316474
Science&Tech Museum 23253

Myôhôin (Treasure House of the Myôhôin Temple), Myohoin-maegawa-cho, Higashiyama-ku, Kyoto 605-0932
Religious Arts Museum
Possessions of Toyotomi-Hideyoshi and many other national treasures 23254

Nakagawa Photo Gallery, 15 Nakamizo-cho, Koyama, Kita-ku, Kyoto 603-8156 - T: (075) 4510505
Fine Arts Museum
Photography 23255

Ningyo no Ie, 12 Butsuhoden-cho, Toriimoto, Saga, Ukyo-ku, Kyoto 616-8434 - T: (075) 8821421
Local Museum 23256

Ninna-ji Temple Treasure House, Ouchi, Omuro, Ukyo-ku, Kyoto 616-8092 - T: (075) 4611155
Religious Arts Museum
Chinese and Japanese paintings, Japanese sculpture, documents including scrolls of Buddhist teachings, Heian medical books, iconographic drawings, lacquer items 23257

Nishijin Textile Center, Horikawa Imadegawa-cho, Kamigyo-ku, Kyoto 602-0033 - T: (075) 4519231
Decorative Arts Museum 23258

No Kaiga Art Museum, 297 Yase, Akimoto-cho, Sakyo-ku, Kyoto 601-1252 - T: (075) 7124757
Fine Arts Museum 23259

Nomura Art Museum, 61 Shimokawara-cho, Nanzenji, Sakyo-ku, Kyoto 606-8434 - T: (075) 7510153, Fax: 7510586, E-mail: nomurams@mx1.alpha-web.ne.jp, Internet: http://www.nomura-museum.or.jp. Head: Harukata Nomura
Fine Arts Museum
Chanoyu, Noh dramas 23260

Omoide Museum, 6-5 Ojoin-cho, Saganisonin Monzen, Ukyo-ku, Kyoto 616-8426 - T: (075) 8620124
Local Museum 23261

Orinasukan, 693 Jofukuji-dori, Kamidachiuri-agaru, Daikoku-cho, Kamigyo-ku, Kyoto 602-8482 - T: (075) 4310020, Fax: 4152590. Head: Takao Watanabe
Special Museum 23262

Raku Museum, 84 Aburanokoji-dori, Aburahashidume-cho, Kamigyo-ku, Kyoto 602-0923 - T: (075) 4140304, Fax: 4140304, E-mail: museum@raku-yaki.or.jp, Internet: http://www.raku-yaki.or.jp. Head: Kichizaemon Raku XV
Decorative Arts Museum 23263

Rakushikan, Museum of Kyoto, Sanjo Takakura, Nakagyo-ku, Kyoto 604-0000 - T: (075) 2510078, Fax: 2310130
Decorative Arts Museum 23264

Rokuharamitsu-ji Treasure House, 2 Hagashi-iru, Matsubara-cho, Higashiyama-ku, Kyoto 605-0063
Religious Arts Museum
Sculpture, portrait statues 23265

Rokuonji (Treasures of the Rokuonji Temple), Kinkakuji-cho, Kita-ku, Kyoto 603-8361
Religious Arts Museum
Famed for its garden and gold pavilion 23266

Ryosan Museum of History, 1 Ryozan-cho, Seikanji, Higashiyama-ku, Kyoto 605-0861 - T: (075) 5313774
Historical Museum 23267

Sakura Bank Exhibition Room, Kyoto Mitsui Bldg, 8 Naginataboku-cho Shijo-dori, Sakai-ku, Kyoto 600-8191 - T: (075) 2318438
Special Museum 23268

Sanjusangendo (National Treasure of the Rengeoin Temple), Higashiyama-shichijo, Higashiyama-ku, Kyoto 605-0000
Religious Arts Museum 23269

Sen'oku Hakukokan Museum (Sumitomo Collection), 24 Shimomiyanomae-cho, Shishigatani, Sakyo-ku, Kyoto 606-8431 - T: (075) 7716411, Fax: 7716099. Head: Dr. Takayasu Higuchi
Archaeological Museum / Fine Arts Museum - 1960
Chinese bronzes, Chinese and Japanese mirrors, Buddhist figures, bells of all periods, Korean mirrors 23270

Shibunkaku Museum of Art, 2-7 Takano, Sekiden-cho, Sakyo-ku, Kyoto 606-8203 - T: (075) 7511777
Fine Arts Museum 23271

Shimazu Foundation Memorial Hall, Kiyamachi Nijo-dori-sanyo-sagaru, Nakagyo-ku, Kyoto 604-8002 - T: (075) 2550980
Special Museum 23272

Shokokuji Jotenkaku Museum, Imadegawa-dori, Karasuma, Higashi-iru, Kamigyo-ku, Kyoto 602-8332 - T: (075) 2410423
Local Museum 23273

Shoren-in Treasure House, Sanjobo-machi, Awadaguchi, Higashiyama-ku, Kyoto 605-0035
Religious Arts Museum - 1153
Rare books, writings, paintings - library 23274

To-ji Homotsukan (To-ji Temple Treasure House), Kujodori, 1 Kujo-cho, Minami-ku, Kyoto 601-8473 - T: (075) 6913325
Religious Arts Museum
Buddhist statues, ancient paintings, some from the 9th c, manuscripts, letters, and documents, lacquer items, sutras 23275

Umekoji Steam Locomotive Museum, Kankiji-cho, Shimogyo-ku, Kyoto 600-8835 - T: (075) 3142996, Fax: 3143054, Internet: http://www.mtm.or.jp/uslm/index.html. Head: Naoki Hirano
Science&Tech Museum 23276

Yatsuhashi-An & Shishu-Yakata, 36 Nishi-koromode-cho, Nishi-kyogoku, Ukyo-ku, Kyoto 615-0877 - T: (075) 3132151
Special Museum 23277

Yogen-In (Treasure Hall of the Yôgen-In Temple), Sanju-sangendômaewari-cho, Higashiyama-ku, Kyoto 605-0941
Religious Arts Museum 23278

Yurinkan Art Museum, 44 Enshoji-cho, Okazaki, Sakyo-ku, Kyoto 606-8344 - T: (075) 7610683
Fine Arts Museum / Decorative Arts Museum - 1926
Rare antique Chinese fine arts and curios, bronzes, jade, porcelain, seals, Buddhist images, pictures, calligraphy 23279

Machida

Machida City Museum, 3562 Hommachida, Machida 194-0032 - T: (0427) 261531
Local Museum
Japanese archeological material, ethnographic items 23280

Machida-shiritsu Kokusai Hanga Bijutsukan (Machida City Museum of Graphic Arts), 4-28-1 Haramachida, Machida 194-0013 - T: (042) 7262771, Fax: 7262840. Head: Shigeru Aoki
Fine Arts Museum - 1987 23281

Mano

Toki No Sato History Hall, 655 Mano-machi, Mano 952-0313
Local Museum
Personal effects of the Emperor Juntoku, calligraphy of the priest Nichiren, fans, exhibit on local gold mining with miners lamps, clothing, and a diorama, ceramics, metalwork, paintings 23282

Marugame

Marugame Bijutsukan (Marugame Museum of Art), 25-1 Nakadu-cho, Marugame 763-0054 - T: (0877) 236326, Fax: 236379. Head: Masahiko Manabe
Fine Arts Museum 23283

Marugame Genichiro-Inokuma (Museum of Contemporary Art), 80-1, Hama-machi, Marugame 763-0022 - T: (0877) 247755, Fax: 247766, E-mail: fvbf3270@infoweb.ne.jp, Internet: http://web.infoweb.ne.jp/MIMOCA/. Head: Takami Sasagawa
Fine Arts Museum 23284

Mashiko

Mashiko Sankokan (Mashiko Ceramics Museum), 3388 Mashiko, Mashiko 321-4217 - T: (0285) 725300
Decorative Arts Museum
Coll of Shoji Hamada, Eastern and estern ceramics, fabrics, furniture, paintings 23285

Matsodo

Matsudo Museum, 671 Sendabori, Matsodo 270-2252 - T: (047) 3848181, Internet: http://www.intership.ne.jp/mcity/english/sight/museum.htm
Local Museum 23286

Matsue

Koizumi Yakumo Kinenkan (Lafcadio Hearn Memorial Museum), 322 Okudani-cho, Matsue 690-0872 - T: (0852) 212147, Fax: 212147. Head: Katsumi Takuwa
Special Museum - 1933
Personal effects of the writer Lafcadio Hearn, books and pictures, his manuscripts, copies of his works - library 23287

Shimane Daigaku Hobungakubu Kokogaku Kenkyushitsu-nai (Shimane University Archaeological Collection), Shimane Daigaku, Matsue 690-0000 - T: (0852) 217100. Head: Yoshiaki Tanaka
Archaeological Museum / University Museum - 1953
Pottery of Kagio Yayoi Burial Mound, pottery and funeral artifacts of Nishidani Yayoi Burial Mound 23288

Shimane-kenritsu Hakubutsukan (Shimane Prefectural Museum), 1 Tono-machi, Matsue 690-0887 - T: (0852) 225750, Fax: 226728, E-mail: kodai@pref.shimane.jp, Internet: http://www2.pref.shimane.jp/kodai. Head: Syo Katsube
Local Museum / Archaeological Museum / Folklore Museum - 1959
Historical heritage, archaeological remains, bronze sword, bronze bell, bronze mirror 23289

Shimane Prefectural Yakumodatsu Fudoki No Oka History Hall, 456 Ooba-cho, Matsue 690-0033
Archaeological Museum
Pottery, stone tools, bone hooks, arrowheads, Kofun Sue ware, horse trappings, pottery cylinders, roof tiles, photographs and drawings of excavation sites 23290

Tanabe Museum of Art, 310-5 Kitahori-cho, Matsue 690-0888 - T: (0852) 262211, Fax: 229130
Fine Arts Museum 23291

Yaegaki-jinja Treasure Storehouse, Sakusa-cho, Matsue 690-0035
Religious Arts Museum - 1965
Unique Shinto wall paintings from the Heian period 23292

Matsumoto

Matsumoto Folk Arts Museum, 1312-1 Shimoganai, Matsumoto 390-0852
Folklore Museum
Folk arts of the mountain regions of Japan, southeast Asian, European, and Near Eastern folk arts, ceramics, lacquer vessels, metalwork 23293

Nakayama Archaeological Museum, Torinouchi, Nakayamadai, Matsumoto 390-0824 - T: (0263) 3822. Head: Iwao Tanaka
Archaeological Museum
Pottery, small figurines, stone implements, swords 23294

Nihon Ukiyo-e Hakubutsukan (Japan Ukiyo-e Museum), 2206-1 Koshiba, Shimadachi, Matsumoto 390-0852 - T: (0263) 474440, Fax: 480208, E-mail: webmaster@cjn.or.jp, Internet: http://www.cjn.or.jp/ukiyo-e
Fine Arts Museum 23295

Nippon Minzoku Shiryokan (Japan Folklore Museum), 4-1 Marunouchi, Matsumoto 390-0873 - T: (0263) 320133
Folklore Museum
Archeological objects including pottery and swords, photos of local excavation sites, historical documents, natural history coll, clocks, dolls, festival objects 23296

Matsusaka

Motoori Norinaga Memorial Hall, 1536-7 Tono-machi, Matsusaka 515-0073 - T: (0598) 210312, Fax: 210371, E-mail: norinaga-m@ma3.justnet.ne.jp
Special Museum 23297

Matsushima

Matsushima Kanrantei Museum, 56 Aza Chonai, Matsushima, Matsushima 981-0213
Local Museum
Archeological finds, local marine shells, 17th-19th c lacquer vessels, armor, and costumes, calligraphy, painting 23298

Zuigan-ji Hakabutsukan (Zuigan Museum), 91 Aza Machiuchi, Matsushima 981-0213 - T: (0223) 542023
Religious Arts Museum
Paintings and portraits, scrolls, sculpture, No and Kyogen masks, temple documents and calligraphy 23299

Matsuyama

Ehime-ken Bijutsukan (Museum of Art, Ehime), Horinouchi, Matsuyama 790-0007 - T: (089) 9320010, Fax: 9320511, E-mail: bijutsu@ehime-iinet.or.jp, Internet: http://joho.ehime-iinet.or.jp/art. Head: Heisaku Harada
Fine Arts Museum
Occidental paintings, sculpture, local paintings 23300

Ehime-kenritsu Hakubutsukan (Ehime Prefectural Museum), Horinouchi, Matsuyama 790-0007 - T: (0899) 341534, Fax: 411454, E-mail: hakubutukan@pref.net-shw.chime.jp. Head: Takao Hino
Natural History Museum - 1959
Japanese otter coll, Stibnite (Ichinokawamin.) 23301

Ehime-kenritsu Rekishi Minzoku Shiryokan (Ehime Prefectural History and Folklore Museum), Horinouchi, Matsuyama 790-0007 - T: (0899) 316393
Historical Museum / Folklore Museum 23302

Matsuyama Municipal Shiki Kinen Museum, 1-30 Dogo Koen, Matsuyama 790-0857 - T: (089) 9315566, Fax: 9343416, Internet: http://www.city.matsuyama.ehime.jp. Head: Takashi Hasegawa
Special Museum - 1986
Poems, Paintings, Scrolls 23303

Nankai Broadcasting Sun Park Museum of Art, 1139 Ido-cho, Matsuyama 791-1114 - T: (0899) 581711, Fax: 572828. Head: Keizo Kadota
Fine Arts Museum 23304

Mihama

Sugimoto Bijutsukan (Sugimoto Art Museum), 1-12-1 Mihamaryokuen, Mihama 470-3232 - T: (0569) 885171, Fax: 885591. Head: Shizuo Honda
Fine Arts Museum 23305

Minami-tsuru

Takamura Art Museum, Takamura, Yamanakako-mura, Minami-tsuru 401-0500 - T: (0555) 620001, Fax: 625000, Internet: http://www.yokogawa.co.jp/Measurement/Yamanashi/art/takamura
Fine Arts Museum 23306

Minamiarima

Hara Castle Memorial Hall, Minamitakaki-gun, Oe, Minamiarima 859-2400 - T: (0957) 857851. Head: Yasumasa Matsuo
Local Museum 23307

Minobu

Minobusan Homotsukan (Kuon-ji Treasure House), Kuon-ji, Minobu 409-2500 - T: (05566) 213, 142. Head: Hishizu Fuji
Religious Arts Museum 23308

Minowa

Minowa Museum, 10286-3 Nakaminowa, Minowa 399-4601 - T: (0265) 794860
Local Museum 23309

Mirasaka

Mirasaka Peace Museum of Art, 2825 Mirasaka, Mirasaka 729-4304 - T: (0824) 442749, Fax: 442745. Head: Masaaki Ooyama
Fine Arts Museum 23310

Misawa

Ogarako Folk Museum, Misawaeki- minami, Misawa 033-8688 - T: (0176) 511111, Fax: 511118, E-mail: hostmaster@komaki-onsen.co.jp, Internet: http://www.komaki-onsen.co.jp. Head: Yukio Sugimoto
Folklore Museum - 1961
Folklore 23311

Mishima

Mishima Taisha Treasure House, 2 Omiya-cho, Mishima 411-0035
Religious Arts Museum
Swords and armor, pottery and stone tools, Nara tiles, mirrors, documents, festival masks 23312

Sano Art Museum, 1-43 Nakata-machi, Mishima 411-0838 - T: (0559) 757278, Fax: 731790. Head: Taeko Watanabe
Fine Arts Museum / Decorative Arts Museum - 1965
Chinese bronzes, pottery, dish ware, Japanese ukiyo-e and contemporary paintings, swords and sword furniture 23313

Mitaka

Hachiro Yuasa Memorial Museum, c/o International Christian University, 3-10-2 Osawa, Mitaka 181-0015 - T: (0422) 333340, Fax: 333485, E-mail: museum-office@icu.ac.jp, Internet: http://subsite.icu.ac.jp/yuasa_museum. Head: Prof. Norihiko Suzuki
Historical Museum / University Museum - 1982
Folk art materials from Japan and prehistoric materials excavated from the ICU campus 23314

Middle Eastern Culture Centre in Japan, 3-10-31 Osawa, Mitaka 181-0015 - T: (0422) 327111
Local Museum 23315

Mito

Ibaraki-ken Kindai Bijutsukan (Museum of Modern Art, Ibaraki), 666-1 Higashikubo Senba-cho, Mito 310-0851 - T: (029) 2435111, Fax: 2439992, E-mail: kinbi@po.net-ibaraki.ne.jp, Internet: http://www.edu.pref.ibaraki.jp/kinbi/. Head: Sadao Kato
Fine Arts Museum - 1988
Paintings, sculpture, handicrafts from the late 19th c to the present 23316

Ibaraki-ken Rekishikan (Ibaraki Prefectural History Museum), 2-1-15 Midori-cho, Mito 310-0034 - T: (0292) 254425
Historical Museum
Exhibit on Shinto festivals, pottery and vessels, sculpture, sutra boxes, paintings, calligraphy, 19th c frame schoolhouse, thatched farmhouse 23317

The Joyo Geibun Center, 1-5-18, Sannomaru, Mito 310-0011 - T: (029) 2316611, Fax: 2248789. Head: Tadao Kanazawa
Fine Arts Museum 23318

Mito Geijutsukan Gendai Bijutsu Center (Art Tower Mito, Contemporary Art Center), 1-6-8 Goken-cho, Mito 310-0063 - T: (029) 2278120, Fax: 2278130, E-mail: webstaff@arttowermito.or.jp, Internet: http://www.arttowermito.or.jp. Head: Mitsuo Yoshida
Fine Arts Museum 23319

Mitsukuni and Nariaki Tokugawa Memorial Collection, 1-3-1 Tokiwa-cho, Mito 310-0033 - T: (0292) 250496. Head: Noriyuki Kashima
Special Museum
Belongings of the second and fifth daimyos, paintings, calligraphy, pipes, pistols, swords, armor, saddles and stirrups 23320

Shokokan Museum, 1-1215-1 Migawa, Mito 310-0912 - T: (0292) 412721
Local Museum 23321

Suifu Meitokukai Foundation Tokugawa Museum, 1-1-1215 Migawa, Mito 310-0912 - T: (0292) 412721, Fax: 430761. Head: Narimasa Tokugawa
Local Museum - 1977
The treasure of the Mito-Tokugawa family including armor and swords, tea-ceremony objects, calligraphy and manuscripts - library 23322

Miyakonojo

Miyakonojo City Museum of Art, 7-18, Himegi-cho, Miyakonojo 885-0073 - T: (0986) 251447. Head: Yoshiharu Aoki
Fine Arts Museum 23323

Miyazaki, Fukui

Fukui-Ken Togeikan (Fukui Prefectural Ceramics Museum), 120-61 Ozowara, Miyazaki, Fukui 916-0273 - T: (0778) 322174, Fax: 322279, E-mail: tougei@ain.pref.fukui.jp, Internet: http://www.pref.fukui.jp. Head: Ogata Masayuki
Decorative Arts Museum - 1971
Old Echizen (from 12th c to 20th c) - pottery workshop, tea-ceremony house, garden 23324

Mizuno Old Ceramics House, 43-28 Kumadani, Miyazaki, Fukui 916-0275 - T: (0778) 2142
Decorative Arts Museum 23325

Miyazaki, Miyazaki-ken

Agricultural Museum, c/o Faculty of Agriculture, Miyazaki University, 3-210 Funasuka, Miyazaki, Miyazaki-ken 880-0031
Agriculture Museum / University Museum - 1930
Natural history, insects and mammals, animals skeletons, agriculture, farm tools, folk crafts - library 23326

Miyazaki-ken Sogo Hakubutsukan (Miyazaki Prefectural Communication Museum), 2-4-4 Jingu, Miyazaki, Miyazaki-ken 880-0056 - T: (0985) 242071, Fax: 242199
Science&Tech Museum 23327

Miyazaki-kenritsu Bijutsukan (Miyazaki Prefectural Art Museum), 3-210 Funatsuka, Miyazaki, Miyazaki-ken 880-0031 - T: (0985) 203792, Fax: 203796, Internet: http://www.pref.miyazaki.jp/kyouiku/bunka/bijutsu. Head: Ikuo Kodama
Fine Arts Museum
Paintings, prints, Italian sculpture, crafts, Surealism art - art library 23328

Museum and Cultural Institute of Miyazaki Prefecture, 2-4-4 Jinguu-cho, Miyazaki, Miyazaki-ken 880-0054 - T: (0985) 242071, Fax: 242199. Head: Kazumaro Yamamoto
Archaeological Museum - 1971
Remains from the Miyazaki burial mounds, works of art by Eikyu, botanical specimens - library, class room, public hall 23329

Mizuho

Mizuhomachi Kyodo Shiryokan, 1962 Ishihata, Mizuho 190-1211 - T: (0425) 575614
Special Museum 23330

Mizunami

Mizunami-shi Kaseki Hakubutsukan (Mizunami Fossil Museum), 1-13 Akiyo-cho, Yamanouchi, Mizunami 509-6132 - T: (0572) 687710, Fax: 661122, E-mail: kaseki@city.mizunami.gifu.jp, Internet: http://www2.city.mizunami.gifu.jp/index.html. Head: Takeharu Toyama
Natural History Museum - 1974
20,000 pieces elasmobranchs fossils, miocene mollusks, amber pieces, 2000 pieces decapod crustacean fossils incl 340 type specimens 23331

Morioka

Iwate-kenritsu Hakubutsukan (Iwate Prefectural Museum), 34 Aza Matsuyashiki Ueda, Morioka 020-0102 - T: (0196) 612831, Fax: 612835. Head: Seiichi Kinno
Fine Arts Museum / Local Museum
Ancient and modern sculpture, weapons, craft objects 23332

Iwate Museum of Art, 12-3 Matsuhaba, Motomiya, Morioka 020-0866 - T: (019) 6581711, Fax: 6581712, E-mail: info@ima.or.jp, Internet: http://www.ima.or.jp. Head: Hideya Sasaki
Fine Arts Museum - 2001 23333

Morioka City Local Hall, 1-14 Atago-cho, Morioka 020-0013 - T: (019) 6545366, Fax: 6533505. Head: Etumasa Ohmura
Local Museum
Archeological finds, local folk arts including baskets and pottery, Nanbu Lord's art crafts, farm tools, ironwork, sutra and documents, Edo-period merchant shop 23334

Morioka Hashimoto Museum of Art, 10 Sainokami, Morioka 020-0000 - T: (0196) 525002. Head: Tsutomu Hashimoto
Fine Arts Museum - 1975
Contemporary Japanese paintings, Barbizon school of paintings, ceramics, sculpture, folk art, reerectes Japanese-style house 23335

Mukaishima

Mukaishima Marine Biological Station, c/o Faculty of Science, Hiroshima University, Onomichi, Mukaishima 722-0000
Natural History Museum / University Museum - 1933
Invertebrates, mollusks, marine biology - library 23336

Muroran

Muroran-shi Seishonen Kagakukan (Muroran Youth Science Museum), 2-2-1 Hon-cho, Muroran 051-0015 - T: (0143) 221058
Special Museum 23337

Musashimurayama

Musashimurayama City Rekishi Minzoku Shiryo-kan, 5-21-1 Honmachi, Musashimurayama 208-0004 - T: (0425) 606620
Local Museum 23338

Nachikatsuura

Kumano Nachi Taisha Treasure House, Nachi-san, Nachikatsuura 649-5301
Religious Arts Museum
Shinto figures, swords, objects from sutra mounds, documents, sutra boxes, mirrors, porcelains, images of the Buddha 23339

Nagakute

Aichi-kenritsu Geijutsu Daigaku Horyuji Kondo Hekiga Mosha Tenjikan, 1-1 Mitsugamine, Oaza Yazako, Nagakute 480-1194 - T: (0561) 621180
Fine Arts Museum / University Museum
Oriental Buddhist wall painting, replicas of wall paintings of the Kondo of Horyu-ji 23340

Toyota Automobile Museum, 41-100 Yokomichi, Nagakute 480-1131 - T: (0561) 635151, Fax: 635159, Internet: http://www.toyota.co.jp/museum. Head: Atsuo Yamamoto
Science&Tech Museum 23341

Nagano

Chihiro Art Museum Azumino, Nishihara, Matsukawa-mura, Kita-Azumi-gun, Nagano 399-8501 - T: (0261) 620772, Fax: 620774, E-mail: chihiroa@seagreen.ocn.ne.jp, Internet: http://www.chihiro.jp. Head: Takeshi Matsumoto
Fine Arts Museum 23342

Kitano Bijutsukan (Kitano Museum of Art), 7963-2 Watauchi, Nagano 381-0000 - T: (0262) 823450, Fax: 822955. Head: Tsuguto Kitauo
Fine Arts Museum
19th c Japanese paintings to the present, guns and armor, lacquer furniture, utensils, Japanese and European ivories - gardens 23343

Nagano-ken Shinano Bijutsukan, Higashiyama Kaiikan (Nagano Prefectural Shinano Art Museum), 1-4-4 Hakoshimizu, Nagano 380-0801 - T: (0262) 322107, Fax: 320050. Head: Dr. Masao Yamamoto
Fine Arts Museum - 1966
Japanese paintings, oil paintings, water colours, drawings, prints, photographies, sculptures, crafts, calligraphies - Higahiyama Kaii Gallery 23344

Zenko-ji Tendai Sect Treasure House, Zenko-ji, Motoyoshi-cho, Nagano 380-0851 - T: (0262) 22460
Religious Arts Museum
Paintings, documents, sculpture, lacquer items, costumes and fashion, calligraphic scrolls by different emperors 23345

Nagaoka

Nagaoka City Local History Hall, 80-24 Oyama-cho, Nagaoka 940-0828
Historical Museum
Items illustrating the history and life of the region, arms and armor, costumes, lacquer items, dolls, clocks exhibit on snow culture including clothing, boots, snowshoes, and skis 23346

Nagaoka Municipal Science Museum, 2-1 Yanagihara-machi, Nagaoka 940-0072 - T: (0258) 320546, Fax: 320561. Head: Hisashi Watanabe
Natural History Museum / Historical Museum
Natural history, zoology, butterflies, local flora, literature and materials on the snow and snow fall, local archeological material 23347

Niigata-kenritsu Kindai Bijutsukan (Niigata Prefectural Museum of Modern Art), 278-14 Aza-Ikake, Miyazeki-machi, Nagaoka 940-2021 - T: (0258) 284111, Fax: 284115, E-mail: kinbi@coral.ocn.ne.jp, Internet: http://www.lalanet.gr.jp/kinbi/index.html. Head: Keizaburo Mizuno
Fine Arts Museum - 1993
Contemporary paintings, sculpture, handicrafts by local artists, Monet, M. Denis, Rodin 23348

Nagasaka

Kiyoharu Shirakaba Museum, 2072 Nakamaru, Nagasaka 408-0036 - T: (0551) 324865, Fax: 322444. Head: Shigeru Takakusa
Special Museum 23349

Nagasaki

Nagasaki Atomic Bomb Museum, 7-8 Hirano-machi, Nagasaki 852-8117 - T: (095) 8441231, Fax: 8465170, E-mail: n_peace@hkg.odn.ne.jp, Internet: http://www.us1.nagasaki-noc.ne.jp/~nacity/na-bomb/museum.html. Head: Yasuro Nanjo
Historical Museum - 1955
Hist exhibits on the atomic bomb dropped on Nagasaki in WWII 23350

Nagasaki-kenritsu Bijutsu Hakubutsukan (Nagasaki Prefectural Art Museum), 1-1-5 Tateyama, Nagasaki 850-0007 - T: (0958) 216700, Fax: 216701, Internet: http://nagasaki.sa-sebo.tao.or.jp/collab/museum
Fine Arts Museum - 1965
Old and contemporary paintings, wood block prints, calligraphy, sculpture, swords, ceramics and porcelain, folk art, medieval-18th c Spanish paintings, prints and sculpture 23351

Nagasaki Municipal Museum, Heiwa Kaikan, 7-8 Hirano-machi, Nagasaki 852-8117 - T: (095) 8458188. Head: Masao Matsuoka
Local Museum - 1941
Artistic handicrafts demonstrating foreign cultural influence, rare books on the history of Nagasaki, prints, art objects of Christanity and trade with Holand and China during the isolation - library 23352

Nagatoro

Saitama-kenritsu Shizenshi Hakubutsukan (Saitama Museum of Natural History), 1417-1 Nagatoro, Nagatoro 369-1305 - T: (0494) 660404, Fax: 691002, E-mail: sizensi@po.kumagaya.or.jp, Internet: http://www.kumagaya.or.jp/~sizensi. Head: Tsutomu Otomo
Natural History Museum - 1981
Mollusks, insects, fossils, minerals, metamorphic rocks, lichen, flore of Saitama 23353

Nagoya, Aichi

Aichi-ken Bijutsukan (Aichi Prefectural Museum of Art), 1-13-2 Higashi-Sakura, Higashi-ku, Nagoya, Aichi 461-8525 - T: (052) 9715511, Fax: 9715604, E-mail: apma-webmaster@aac.pref.aichi.jp, Internet: http://www-art.aac.pref.aichi.jp. Head: Saburoh Hasegawa
Fine Arts Museum - 1992
Modern and contemporary Japanese and Western paintings, prints, and three-dimensional productions 23354

Atsuta-Jingu Museum, 1-1-1 Shingusaka-cho, Jinguu, Atsuta-ku, Nagoya, Aichi 456-0031 - T: (052) 6714151, Fax: 6810538. Head: Yukio Okachi
Religious Arts Museum - 1967
Shinto shrine, historical and ceremonial swords, Bugaku masks, mirrors, Sue ware, temple drums, historical scrolls, textiles and clothing, 20th c Japanese-style paintings 23355

Nagoya/Boston Museum of Fine Arts, 1-1-1 Kanayama-cho, Naka-ku, Nagoya, Aichi 460-0023 - T: (052) 6840786, Fax: 6840738, E-mail: nb@nagoya-boston.or.jp, Internet: http://www.nagoya-boston.or.jp. Head: Toru Asano
Fine Arts Museum 23356

Nagoya Castle Treasure House, 1-1, Honmaru, Naka-ku, Nagoya, Aichi 460-0000 - T: (052) 2311700. Head: Kei Kawaguchi
Local Museum - 1959
Frescoes, fine arts, industrial arts, history, archeology, costumes, maps 23357

Nagoya City Hideyoshi and Kiyomasa Memorial Museum, 25 Aza Chanoki, Nakamura-cho, Nakamura-ku, Nagoya, Aichi 453-0053 - T: (052) 4110035, Fax: 4119987, Internet: http://www.city.nagoya.jp/5okyoiku/hidekiyo. Head: Tokihiro Tsutsumi
Historical Museum - 1967/1991
Belongings and documents connected with the 16th c military dictator of Japan, Toyotomi Hideyoshi and his aid Kiyomasa Kato, his calligraphy, his armor and arms, his clothes, portraits 23358

Nagoya-shi Bijutsukan (Nagoya City Art Museum), 2-17-25 Sakae, Naka-ku, Nagoya, Aichi 460-0008 - T: (052) 2120001, Fax: 2120006, E-mail: artngo@nn.iij4u.or.jp, Internet: http://www.art-museum.city.nagoya.jp. Head: Tatsuo Kobayashi
Fine Arts Museum 23359

Nagoya-shi Hakubutsukan (Nagoya City Museum), 1-27-1 Mizuho-dori, Mizuho-ku, Nagoya, Aichi 467-0806 - T: (052) 8532655, Fax: 8533636, E-mail: ncm-gaku@juno.ocn.ne.jp, Internet: http://www.ncm-jp.com
Local Museum - 1977
Hist of Nagoya from the Stone Age to the present, archeological and ethnographic materials, folk art, fine arts - library, auditoriums 23360

Nagoya-shi Kagakukan (Nagoya City Science Museum), 2-17-1 Sakae, Naku-ku, Nagoya, Aichi 460-0008 - T: (052) 2014486, Fax: 2030788, E-mail: www-adm@ncsm.city.nagoya.jp, Internet: http://www.ncsm.city.nagoya.jp. Head: Dr. Keiji Higuchi
Science&Tech Museum - 1962
Physics, chemistry, engineering, astronomy and space science, telecommunications, steam locomotive, life science, environment, daily life - planetarium, library 23361

Tokugawa Bijutsukan (The Tokugawa Art Museum), 1017 Tokugawa-cho, Higashi-ku, Nagoya, Aichi 461-0023 - T: (052) 9356262, Fax: 9356261, E-mail: info@tokugawa.or.jp, Internet: http://www.cjn.or.jp/tokugawa. Head: Yoshinobu Tokugawa
Fine Arts Museum - 1935
Daimyo (Owari Tokugawa) coll, illustrated tale of Genji, swords, Japanese and Chinese paintings, calligraphy, pottery, tea and incense utensils, rare ceramic pieces, lacquer art, textiles, Noh masks and costumes 23362

Naha

Okinawa-kenritsu Hakubutsukan (Okinawa Prefectural Museum), 1-1 Shuri Onaka-cho, Naha 903-0823 - T: (098) 8842243, Fax: 8864353, E-mail: oki-muse@nirai.ne.jp, Internet: http://w1.nirai.ne.jp/oki-muse
Local Museum - 1946
Local archeological finds, paintings, documents, clothing, boat models, glazed mortuary urns, exhibits on agricultural and fishing communities, Okinawan pottery and lacquer items, calligraphy - library 23363

Nakatsu

Fukuzawa Memorial Hall, Fukuzawa Kinenkan 586, Rusui-machi, Nakatsu 871-0088 - T: (0979) 250063
Historical Museum 23364

Nara

Heijokyuseki Shiryokan, Nara Bunkazaikenkyusho (Heijo Palace Site Museum), 2-9-1 Nijo-cho, Nara 630-8002 - T: (0742) 343931, Fax: 357077, E-mail: webstaff@nabunken.go.jp, Internet: http://www.nabuken.go.jp/shisetsu/hei-shiriyokan/hei-shiriyokan.htm
Historic Site - 1990 23365

Kasuga Taisha (Kasuga Shrine Treasure House), Kasugano-cho, Nara 630-8212 - T: (0742) 227788
Religious Arts Museum
Masks for Bugaku dances, swords and armor, mirrors, lacquer objects, calligraphy, religious paintings, archives, ancient archeological findings - library 23366

Kofukuji Kokuhokan (Kofukuji National Treasure House), 48 Noborioji-cho, Nara 630-8213 - T: (0742) 225370
Religious Arts Museum

Japanese sculptures, bronzes, religious paintings, 10th c scroll, Buddhist statues and sculptures of the Nara period (710-784) and Kamakura period (1192-1333) 23367

Museum Yamato Bunkakan, 1-11-6 Gakuem-Minami, Nara 631-0034 - T: (0742) 450544, Fax: 492929. Head: Akira Mizuta
Fine Arts Museum
Far Eastern antique fine arts, painting, sculpture, calligraphy, lacquer items, metalwork, dyeing and weaving, jewelry, glass, ceramics, textiles - library 23368

Nara City Museum of Photography, 600-1 Takabatake-cho, Nara 630-8301 - T: (0742) 229811
Fine Arts Museum - 1992 23369

Nara-kenritsu Bijutsukan (Nara Prefectural Museum of Art), 10-6 Noborioji-cho, Nara 630-8213 - T: (0742) 233968, Fax: 227032, Internet: http://museum.senri-i.or.jp/nara-museum. Head: Kunisuke Yanagida
Fine Arts Museum / Decorative Arts Museum - 1973
Ukiyo-e prints and paintings, sculpture, 19th-20th c handicrafts, ceramics, textiles, contemporary art 23370

Nara Kokuritsu Hakubutsukan (Nara National Museum), 50 Noborioji-cho, Nara 630-8213 - T: (0742) 227771, Fax: 267218, Internet: http://www.narahaku.go.jp. Head: Hiromitsu Washizuka
Fine Arts Museum - 1895
Buddhist art, paintings, ritual items, 6th-14th c Buddhist statues, relics, scrolls, techniques of temple architecture, handicrafts, calligraphy, roof tiles - garden, teahouse, library 23371

Neiraku Museum, 74 Suimon-cho, Nara 630-8208 - T: (0742) 222173, Fax: 250781. Head: Junsuke Nakamura
Decorative Arts Museum - 1939
Ancient Chinese bronzes, mirrors, Japanese, Chinese and Korean ceramics, old Korean celadon, Japanese art objects - Isuien Japanese landscape garden 23372

Shosoin Treasure Repository, 129 Zoshi-cho, Nara 630-8211 - T: (0742) 262811. Head: Toshio Takebe
Decorative Arts Museum
Repository for personal belongings of Emperor Shomu (8th c AD), inaugural items, manuscripts and sutras, screens, paintings, pottery, glass, lacquer objects, Buddhist religious items, textiles, mirror, 164 masks for Gigaku dances, items from court life 23373

Todai-ji Treasure Hall, 406 Zoshi-cho, Nara 630-8211
Religious Arts Museum - 752
Buddhist treasures, ancient documents, famous images of Buddha, Shosoin Treasure House, personal belongings of Emperor Shomu - library 23374

Toshodai-ji Treasure House, Toshodai-ji, Gojo-cho, Nara 630-8032 - T: (0742) 337900
Religious Arts Museum - 1970
Buddhist statues, paintings, art objects of the Nara period (600-784), the statue of Ganjin 23375

Yakushi-ji Treasure House, 457 Nishinokyo-cho, Nara 630-8042 - T: (0742) 336001, Fax: 336004, E-mail: yksj8@mahoroba.or.jp, Internet: http://www.nanto.com/yakushiji
Religious Arts Museum
Kichijo-tennyo-paintings (heavenly maiden), religious items, bronze images, national treasure 23376

Narita

Naritasan History Museum, Narita-koen, Narita 286-0023 - T: (0476) 220234. Head: Masaji Ohno
Historical Museum - 1947
Paintings, local archeological finds, manuscripts and books, sculpture, botanical specimens, ethnographic items 23377

Naruko

Nippon Kokeshi Museum, 74-2 Shitomae, Naruko 989-6827 - T: (0229) 833600
Local Museum 23378

Narusawa

Kawaguchi-ko Motor Museum, 8545 Fuji-san, Narusawa 401-0322 - T: (0555) 863511, Fax: 863511
Science&Tech Museum 23379

Naruto

Tokushima-kenritsu Torii Kinen Hakubutsukan (Prefectural Torii Memorial Museum), Myokenyama Koen, Muya-cho, Naruto 772-0000 - T: (0886) 864054
Archaeological Museum
Archiological items from Japan, East and Cental Asia, Latin America 23380

Natori

Horsemanship Museum of Takekoma Shrine, Iwanuma-cho, Natori 981-1200
Ethnology Museum
Anthropology, hippology, sports 23381

Niigata

Niigata-kenritsu Kindai Bijutsukan (Niigata Prefectural Museum of Art), 3-1 Ichibambori-dori-cho, Niigata 951-8132 - T: (025) 2253771, Fax: 2282719. Head: Seiro Mayekawa
Fine Arts Museum 23382

Niigata Science Museum, 3-1-1Meike Minami, Niigata 950-0941 - T: (025) 2833331, Fax: 2833336, E-mail: nsm@coral.ocn.ne.jp, Internet: http://www.lalanet.gr.jp/nsm/. Head: Nobumasa Shiga
Science&Tech Museum - 1981
Zoology, botany and environment coll, science and technology, energy - planetarium 23383

Niigata-shiritsu Bijutsukan (Niigata City Art Museum), 5191-9 Nishi-ohata-cho, Niigata 951-8556 - T: (025) 2231622, Fax: 2283051, E-mail: bijutsukan@city.niigata.niigata.jp. Head: Osamu Saito
Fine Arts Museum 23384

Tsurui Museum of Art, 1-2-23 Higashi-odori, Niigata 950-0087 - T: (025) 2473311
Fine Arts Museum 23385

Niimi

Niimi Museum of Art, 361 Nishigata, Niimi 718-0017 - T: (0867) 727851, Fax: 727851. Head: Yoshiharu Henmi
Fine Arts Museum 23386

Nikkou

Nikko Futarasan Jinja Hakubutsukan (Nikko Futarasan Shrine Museum), 2484 Chugushi, Nikkou 321-1661 - T: (0288) 50017. Head: Seika Kitagawa
Religious Arts Museum
Swords and battle gear, portable shrines, ritual items, festival bells, lacquer items, carpenters tools 23387

Nikko Toshogu Treasure House, 2280 Sannai, Nikkou 321-1431 - T: (0288) 540560, Fax: 540061. Head: Hisao Inaba
Religious Arts Museum
Paintings, lacquer items, masks, music instruments, arms and armor, costumes, temple furniture, ritual items, model of temple 23388

Rinno-ji Jokodo Treasure House, Nikkosan, Nikkou 321-1415 - T: (0288) 40531. Head: Eikai Sugawara
Religious Arts Museum
Paintings, sculpture, No masks, metalwork, historical documents and books, swords and armor, lacquer items 23389

Nishinomiya

Egawa Museum of Art, 1-10-40 Karmkotoen, Nishinomiya 662-0813 - T: (0798) 513915, Fax: 513915. Head: Tokusuke Egawa
Fine Arts Museum - 1973
Chinese and Japanese paintings, calligraphy, ceramics, and lacquer items, Korean ceramics 23390

Otani Memorial Art Museum Nishinomiya City, 4-38 Nakahama-cho, Nishinomiya 662-0952 - T: (0798) 330164, Fax: 331699. Head: Shigebumi Tsuji
Fine Arts Museum - 1972
The Otani coll, of Japanese and Western art of the present and recent past - garden 23391

Tatsuuma Archaeological Museum, 2-28 Matsushita-cho, Nishinomiya 662-0962 - T: (0798) 340130, Fax: 340130, E-mail: tatsu-kouko@syd-odn.ne.jp, Internet: http://www.hyogo-intercampus.ne.jp/members/tatsuuma. Head: Hiroshi Kanaseki
Archaeological Museum
Dôtaku, bronze bell and Jômon potteries 23392

Nishiwaki

Okanoyama Museum of Art, 345-1 Kamihie-cho, Nishiwaki 677-0039 - T: (0795) 236223. Head: Kunro Okazawa
Fine Arts Museum 23393

Nogata

Nogata-shi Sekitan Kinenkan (Nogata Municipal Coal Museum), 692-4 Otateyama, Nogata 822-0000 - T: (09492) 52243. Head: Norimitsu Shikada
Science&Tech Museum - 1971
Biggest lump of coal in Japan, oxygen inhalers, models of coal mines 23394

Notojima

Notojima Glass Art Museum, 125-10 Koda, Notojima 926-0211 - T: (0767) 841175, Fax: 841129, E-mail: glass@town.notojima.ishikawa.jp. Head: Tadao Mishima
Decorative Arts Museum
Glass sculptures, Ch'ing dynasty glass, new glass arts 23395

Obihiro

Hokkaidoritsu Obihiro Bijutsukan (Hokkaido Obihiro Museum of Art), 2 Midorigaoka, Obihiro 080-0846 - T: (0155) 226963, Fax: 224233, Internet: http://www.dokyoi.pref.hokkaido.jp/hk-bunka/tennrannkai.htm. Head: Yoshihiro Hasegawa
Fine Arts Museum - 1991
Literature from East Hokkaido authors, carving works for print, calligraphies, print-art 23396

Odawara

Hotoko Ninomiya Jinja Homotsuden (Treasure House of the Hotoku Ninomiya Shrine), 8-10 Johnai, Odawara 250-0014
Religious Arts Museum 23397

Matsunaga Memorial Hall, 943 Itabashi, Odawara 250-0034 - T: (0465) 222962
Fine Arts Museum / Decorative Arts Museum
Earliest existant Japanese paintings, examples of calligraphy by the tea master Sen no Rikyu and others, bronze and wooden sculptures, ceramics, lacquer items, Chinese art coll, including bronzes, paintings, sculpture, and ceramics 23398

Odawara Castle Museum, 6-1 Jonai, Odawara 250-0014
Historical Museum
Copies of portraits of various feudal lords of the castle, documents of the Hojo family, calligraphy and paintings, armor and swords, lacquered toilet seats, maps, painted wooden doors, local products and household utensils 23399

Ogose

Tekiho Memorial Museum of Art, 5 Kosugi, Ogose 350-0422 - T: (0492) 926010, Fax: 925950. Head: Keiichi Nishizawa
Fine Arts Museum 23400

Oita

Oita-kenritsu Geijutsu Kaikan (Oita Prefectural Art Hall), 1-61 Makimidor-machi, Oita 870-0000 - T: (0975) 520077, Fax: 520080. Head: Shigeko Taki
Fine Arts Museum 23401

Okaya

Okaya Sericultural, Equipment and Literature and Silk Museum, 4-1-39, Hon-cho, Okaya 394-0028 - T: (0266) 225854. Head: Masakazu Ito
Local Museum / Agriculture Museum / Special Museum
Archeological material, contemporary paintings, sculpture, and prints, history of silk-spinning and weaving machines 23402

Okayama

Hayashibara Bijutsukan (Hayashibara Museum of Art), 2-7-15 Marunouchi, Okayama 700-0823 - T: (086) 2231733, Fax: 2263089. Head: Ritsuji Okuma
Fine Arts Museum / Decorative Arts Museum - 1964
Chinese and Japanese paintings, lacquer items, and ceramics, Chinese bronzes, Japanese swords and armor, calligraphy, No costumes, Korean ceramics 23403

Okayama-kenritsu Bijutsukan (Okayama Prefectural Museum of Art), 8-120 Tenjin-cho, Okayama 700-0814 - T: (086) 2254800, Fax: 2240648, E-mail: okapm@po.shere.ne.jp, Internet: http://www.pref.okayama.jp/seikatsu/kenbi. Head: Nobuo Miyaji
Fine Arts Museum
Domestic and foreign art activities, art connected with Okayama 23404

Okayama-kenritsu Hakubutsukan (Okayama Prefectural Museum), 1-5 Korakuen, Okayama 703-8257 - T: (086) 2721149, Fax: 2721150. Head: Hasimoto Yasuo
Local Museum
Archaeological and ethnographic material, paintings, swords, pottery, historical documents, religious sculptures and statues, handicrafts 23405

Okayama Shiritsu Oriento Bijutsukan (Okayama Orient Museum), 9-31, Tenjin-cho, Okayama 700-0814 - T: (086) 2323636, Fax: 2325342, E-mail: orient@city.okayama.jp, Internet: http://www.city.okayama.okoyama.jp/kyoiku/orient/index.html. Head: Tsugio Imori
Archaeological Museum 23406

Yumeji Art Museum, 2-1-32 Hama, Okayama 703-8256 - T: (086) 2711000, Fax: 2711000. Head: Motoi Matsuda
Fine Arts Museum 23407

Okazaki

Mitsubishi Automobile Gallery, 1 Nakashingiri, Hashime-cho, Okazaki 444-0908 - T: (0564) 325203
Science&Tech Museum 23408

Oku

Oku Kokokan (Oku Archaeological Collection), Owari, Oku 701-4221
Archaeological Museum 23409

Okutama

Okutama Kyodo Shiryokan, 5 Hara, Nishi-tama-gun, Okutama 198-0223 - T: (0428) 862731
Local Museum 23410

Omachi

Omachi Alpine Museum, 8056-1 Kamisakae-cho, Omachi 398-0000 - T: (0261) 220211, Fax: 220211. Head: Kunio Hirabayashi
Natural History Museum - 1951
Local natural history, mountaineering implements 23411

Ome

Gyokudo Art Museum, 1-1-75 Mitake, Ome 198-0174 - T: (0428) 788335. Head: Yusai Suzuki
Fine Arts Museum - 1961
Paintings and sketches by Gyokudo Kawai, personal effects, photographs of the artist, reproduction of his studio with equipment and furniture, building designed by Isoya Yoshida - garden 23412

Ome Municipal Museum, 1-684 Komaki-cho, Ome 198-0053 - T: (0428) 236859
Local Museum - 1974
Life and history of the region, fishing gear, ceramics, armor, documents, local paintings, folk art 23413

Ome Municipal Museum of Art, 1346-1 Ome, Ome 198-0045 - T: (0428) 241195, Fax: 238229. Head: Tomoyuki Ito
Fine Arts Museum 23414

Omishima

Oyamazumi-jinja Kokuhokan (Oyamazumi Jinja Treasure House), Miyaura, Omishima 794-1304 - T: (0897) 820032. Head: Yashuhisa Mishima
Historical Museum
Earliest known swords and armor (10th c), paintings, shrines, historical documents, oldest mirrors in Japan - library 23415

Omiya

Saitama-kenritsu Hakubutsukan (Saitama Prefectural Museum), 4-219 Takahana-cho, Omiya 330-0803 - T: (048) 6458171, Fax: 6401964, Internet: http://www.pref.saitama.jp/A20/BK00/kenpaku/38.htm
Local Museum
Local archeological finds, sword, models of medieval castles, farm and forestry tools, reconstructed farmhouse interior, early Buddhist sculpture, pottery, contemporary art - library, reconstructred prehistoric huts 23416

Ono

Okugai Hakubutsukan, Gashozukuri Minkaen, 2499 Ogi-machi, Shirakawa-mura, Ono 501-5627 - T: (05769) 61231, Fax: 61830
Open Air Museum / Historical Museum - 1995
Houses with steep rafter roofs 23417

Senko-ji Treasure House, Shimobo Nyukawa-mura, Ono 501
Religious Arts Museum - 1977
Wooden sculpture by the priest Enku, his portrait, his calligraphy, models of temples and farmhouses, local natural history, samples of wood and woodcutters tools 23418

Onomichi

Onomichi Shiritsu Bijutsukan (Onomichi City Museum of Art) (closed for reconstruction until January 2003), 17-19 Nishitsuchido-cho, Onomichi 722-0032, mail addr: 1-15-1 Kubo, Onomichi 722-8501 - T: (0848) 232281, 377630, Fax: 232281, 257293. Head: Akifumi Morishigue
Fine Arts Museum
Japnese art 23419

Osaka

Flanders Center, Osaka Kokusai Koryu Center, 8-2-6 Ue-hon-machi, Tennoji-ku, Osaka 543-0001 - T: (06) 67738850, Fax: 67738855, E-mail: info@flanders.jp, Internet: http://www.flanders.jp/. Head: Bernard Catrysse
Public Gallery 23420

Fujita Museum of Art, 10-32 Amijima-cho, Miyakojima-ku, Osaka 534-0026 - T: (06) 63510582, Fax: 63510583. Head: Masako Fujita
Fine Arts Museum / Decorative Arts Museum - 1951
Chinese and Japanese painting, calligraphy, sculpture, ceramics, lacquer items, textiles, metalwork, Japanes tea-ceremony objects 23421

Idemitsu Museum of Arts Osaka, 3-4-26 Minami-Senba, Chuo-ku, Osaka 542-0081 - T: (06) 62458611, Fax: 62458610, E-mail: si.museo@poem.ocn.ne.jp, Internet: http://www.idmitsu.co.jp/museum. Head: Tadanori Yuba
Fine Arts Museum 23422

Japan Folk Art Museum, 3-7-6 Nanba-naka, Naniwa-ku, Osaka 556-0011 - T: (06) 6416309, Fax: 6336107. Head: Etsuko Kawashima
Folklore Museum 23423

Kanebo Museum of Textiles, 1-5-102 Tomobuchi-cho, Miyakojima-ku, Osaka 534-0016 - T: (06) 9234625
Science&Tech Museum 23424

Kotsu Kagaku Hakubutsukan (Modern Transportation Museum), 3-11-10 Namiyoke, Minato-ku, Osaka 552-0001 - T: (06) 65815771, Fax: 65841309, Internet: http://www.mtm.or.jp

Science&Tech Museum - 1962
Modern means of trasportation, models, equipment, modernizing of the Japanese National Railways 23425

Manno Art Museum, 2-2-3 Nishi Shinsaibashi, Chuo-ku, Osaka 542-0086 - T: (06) 62121517, Fax: 62121519
Fine Arts Museum 23426

Mint Museum, 1-1-7 Temma, Kita-ku, Osaka 530-0043 - T: (06) 3518509
Decorative Arts Museum
Japanese coins from the feudal to the present times 23427

Nanban Bunkakan, 6-2-18 Nakatsu, Kita-ku, Osaka 531-0071 - T: (06) 4510088
Public Gallery 23428

Osaka Castle Museum, 1-1 Osaka-jo, Chuo-ku, Osaka 540-0002 - T: (06) 9413044
Fine Arts Museum / Decorative Arts Museum
Paintings, calligraphy, metalwork, armor and swords, costumes, and documents relating to the history of the castle, ukiyo-e prints, puppets from Osaka Bunraku puppet theater 23429

Osaka Furitsu Gendai Bijutsu Center (Osaka Contemporary Art Center), 3-2-18 Nakanoshima, Kita-ku, Osaka 530-0005 - T: (06) 64456665, Fax: 64477954, Internet: http://paper.cup.com/osaka/genbi.html
Public Gallery 23430

Osaka Human Rights Museum, 3-6-36 Naniwa-nishi, Naniwa-ku, Osaka 556-0026 - T: (06) 5615891
Historical Museum 23431

Osaka International Peace Center, 2-1 Osaka-jo, Chuo-ku, Osaka 540-0002 - T: (06) 9477208
Historical Museum 23432

Osaka Museum of Natural History, 1-23 Nagai-koen, Higashi-sumiyoshi-ku, Osaka 546-0034 - T: (06) 66976221, Fax: 66976225, E-mail: library@mus-nh.city.osaka.jp, Internet: http://www.mus-nh.city.osaka.jp. Head: Takayoshi Nasu
Natural History Museum - 1950
Fossils, local flora and plant fossils, zoology of New Caledonia, paleontology, entomology, herpetology, marine invertebrates, geology - library 23433

Osaka-shiritsu Bijutsukan (Osaka Municipal Museum of Art), 1-82 Chausuyama-cho, Tennoji-ku, Osaka 543-0063 - T: (06) 67714874, Fax: 67714856. Head: Dr. Yutaka Mino
Fine Arts Museum - 1936
Chinese and Japanese paintings, Japanese ceramics and sculptures, Chinese and Korean bronze, mirrors, lacquer items, porcelain, calligraphy, Coptic sculpture, Etruscan pottery, Chinese sculpture, Japanese painting - library 23434

Osaka-shiritsu Hakubutsukan (Osaka City Museum), 1-1 Osaka-jo, Chuo-ku, Osaka 540-0002 - T: (06) 69417177, Fax: 69414064. Head: Kazuhiro Aiso
Local Museum - 1960
Hist and culture of Osaka, archeological material, folk art, pottery, puppets, masks, spinning and weaving exhibit, maps, documents and records of city 23435

Osaka-shiritsu Kindai Bijutsukan Kensetsu Jumbishitsu (Osaka City Museum of Modern Art), 1-3-20, Nakanoshima, Kita-ku, Osaka 530-8201 - T: (06) 62089099, Fax: 62015759
Fine Arts Museum 23436

Osaka-shiritsu Toyo Toji Bijutsukan (Museum of Oriental Ceramics Osaka), 1-1-26 Nakanoshima, Kita-ku, Osaka 530-0005 - T: (06) 62230055, Fax: 62230057, E-mail: toyotoji@moco.or.jp, Internet: http://www.moco.or.jp. Head: Ikutaro Itoh
Decorative Arts Museum 23437

Science Museum Osaka, 4-2-1 Nakanoshima, Kita-ku, Osaka 530-0005 - T: (06) 4445656, Fax: 4445657
Natural History Museum / Science&Tech Museum 23438

Suntory Museum Tenpozan, 1-5-10 Kaigandori, Minato-ku, Osaka 552-0022 - T: (06) 65770001, Fax: 65779200
Fine Arts Museum 23439

Umeda Modern Museum, 2-3-9 Sonezaki, Kita-ku, Osaka 530-0057 - T: (06) 3645165
Local Museum 23440

Yuki Museum of Art, 3-3-9 Hiranomachi, Chuo-ku, Osaka 541-0046 - T: (06) 62030188, Fax: 62031080, Internet: http://www.yuki-museum.or.jp. Head: Takahata Souichi
Fine Arts Museum 23441

Otaru

Kyu Aoyama Bettei, 3-62 Shukuzu, Otaru 047-0047 - T: (0134) 240024
Local Museum 23442

Otaru-shi Hakubutsukan (Otaru Museum), 2-1-20 Ironai, Otaru 047-0031 - T: (0134) 221258, Fax: 332439. Head: Yukiatu Hiroya
Local Museum - 1956
Oceanography, history, archeology, zoology, botany, minerals, art, entomology 23443

Otaru-shi Seishonen Kagakugijutsukan (Otaru Science Center), 1-9-1 Midori, Otaru 047-0034 - T: (0134) 220031, Fax: 271117
Science&Tech Museum / Natural History Museum - 1963
Physics, machines and apparatuses used in engineering, scientific models, educational exhibits 23444

Otsu

Biwa-ko Bunkakan, Uchidehama, Otsu 520-0806 - T: (0775) 228179. Head: Chogoro Kataoka
Local Museum - 1961
Japanese archeological finds from local excavations, Buddhist sculptures, paintings, and ritual objects, Japanese paintings of the Edo period (1615-1868), zoology - library 23445

Omi Shrine Clock Museum, 1-1 Jingu-cho, Otsu 520-0015 - T: (0775) 221907
Special Museum 23446

Shiga-kenritsu Kindai Bijutsukan (Museum of Modern Art, Shiga), 1740-1 Ogaya-cho, Seta Minami, Otsu 520-2122 - T: (077) 5432111, Fax: 5434220, Internet: http://www.biwa.ne.jp/~sg-kinbi. Head: Toru Eiraku
Fine Arts Museum 23447

Tanakami Mineral Museum, Tamakamieda-cho, Otsu 520-2100 - T: (0775) 460163
Natural History Museum 23448

Ranzan

Saitama-kenritsu Rekishi Shiryokan (Saitama Prefectural Historical Museum), 757 Sugaya, Ranzan 355-0221 - T: (049362) 5896
Historical Museum 23449

Rikuzentakata

Rikuzentakada Municipal Museum, Kesen-cho, Rikuzentakata 029-2204
Local Museum 23450

Sabae

Sabae CCI Art Museum, 2-12, Honmachi 3-chome, Sabae 916-8588 - T: (0778) 512800, Fax: 528118. Head: Dr. Toshihiro Sakai
Fine Arts Museum 23451

Saga

Saga-kenritsu Bijutsukan (Saga Prefectural Art Museum), 1-15-23 Jonai, Saga 840-0041 - T: (0952) 243947, Fax: 243947
Fine Arts Museum 23452

Saga-kenritsu Hakubutsukan (Saga Prefectural Museum), 1-15-23 Jonai, Saga 840-0041 - T: (0952) 243947, Fax: 257006. Head: Rikuzou Yamada
Local Museum - 1970
Natural hist, archeological material, folk arts, painting, ceramics, calligraphy - library 23453

Saijo

Saijo Municipal Local Museum, 237-1 Akeyashiki, Saijo 793-0023 - T: (0897) 523199. Head: Syusaku Katakami
Local Museum
Archeological material, paintings, calligraphy, armor, ceramics, natural history, geology 23454

Sakae

Chiba-kenritsu Boso Fudoki-No-Oka (Chiba Prefectual Boso Fudoki-No-Oka Museum), 978 Riyuukakuji, Sakae 270-1506 - T: (0477) 6953126, Fax: 6953140, Internet: http://www.chiba-muse.or.jp. Head: Koushin Ino
Archaeological Museum
Archaeology (Kofun period), remains excavated from burial mounds (Kofun), Haniwa figures, mirrors, swords, jewels 23455

Sakai

Osaka-furitsu Senboku Koko Shiryokan (Osaka Senboku Area Archaelogical Museum), 2-4 Wakamatsudai, Sakai 590-0116 - T: (072) 2910230, Fax: 2910239
Archaeological Museum
Kofun material including Sue-ware vessels, photgraphs of the excavations sites 23456

Sakaide

Kamada Local Museum, 1-1-24 Hon-machi, Sakaide 762-0044 - T: (0877) 462275. Head: Masataka Kamada, Masuo Honda
Local Museum - 1925
Items of regional interest - library 23457

Sakaide Civic Art Museum, 1-3-35 Kotobukicho, Sakaide 762-0043 - T: (0877) 457110, Fax: 464056. Head: Masahiro Ugawa
Fine Arts Museum 23458

Sakata

Homma Museum of Art, 7-7, Onari-cho, Sakata 998-0024 - T: (0234) 244311, Fax: 244311. Head: Nario Komatu
Fine Arts Museum
Japanese paintings and prints, calligraphy, samples of Busons poetry, ceramics - garden 23459

Ken Domon Museum of Photography, Bunka Koen, Iimoriyama, Miyanoura, Sakata 998-0054 - T: (0234) 310028, Fax: 310028. Head: Kousho Watanabe
Science&Tech Museum 23460

Sakura, Chiba

Kawamura Memorial Museum of Art, 631, Sakado, Sakura, Chiba 285-8505 - T: (043) 4982131, Fax: 4982139, E-mail: info@kawamura-museum.com, Internet: http://www.dic.co.jp/museum. Head: Makoto Suzuki
Fine Arts Museum 23461

Kokuritsu Rekishi Minzoku Hakubutsukan (National Museum of Japanese History), 117 Jonai-cho, Sakura, Chiba 285-8502 - T: (043) 3860123, 4860123, Fax: 3864209, 4864209, Internet: http://www.rekihaku.ac.jp. Head: Susumu Ishii
Historical Museum - 1983
Archaeology and folklore coll, natural hist, Japanese history and culture 23462

Sakura City Museum of Art, 210 Shin-machi, Sakura, Chiba 285-0023 - T: (043) 4857851, Fax: 4859892, E-mail: muse@city.sakura.chiba.jp. Head: Maekawa Masahide
Fine Arts Museum - 1994
Modern and contemporary art 23463

Sapporo

Ainu Museum, Hokkaido Daigaku Nogakubu Hakubutsukan, c/o Faculty of Agriculture, Hokkaido University, 2F, Botanic Garden Office, N3 W8, Chuo-ku, Sapporo 060-0003 - T: (011) 2518010, Fax: 2210664, E-mail: admin-exmus@agr.hokudai.ac.jp, Internet: http://www.agr.hokudai.ac.jp/muse. Head: Kiroku Kobayashi
Ethnology Museum / University Museum - 1882
Ainu ethnographic material coll from the late 19th c to early 20th c (canoe, bird-skin clothes, womans leather belt, harpoon heads, sacred altar for the bear ceremony etc) 23464

Clock Tower, Kita 1-jo-Nishi 2, Chuo-ku, Sapporo 060-0001 - T: (011) 2310838
Science&Tech Museum 23465

Hokkaido Bungaku-Kan, 1 Nakajima Koen, Chuo-ku, Sapporo 064-0931 - T: (011) 5625252
Local Museum 23466

Hokkaido Daigaku Nogakubu Hakubutsukan (Museum of the Faculty of Agriculture), c/o Hokkaido University, Kita-3, Nishi-8, Chuo-ku, Sapporo 060-0003 - T: (011) 2518010, Fax: 2210664, E-mail: admin-exmus@agr.hokudai.ac.jp, Internet: http://www.agr.hokudai.ac.jp/muse. Head: Kiroku Kobayashi
Agriculture Museum / University Museum
Animal specimens 23467

Hokkaido Kaitaku Kinenkan (Historical Museum of Hokkaido), 53-2 Konopporo, Atsubetsu-cho, Atsubetsu-ku, Sapporo 004-0006 - T: (011) 8980456, Fax: 8982657, Internet: http://www.pref.hokkaido.jp/kseikatu/ks-kknen/text/home/index.htm. Head: Kazuo Yoshida
Historical Museum / Local Museum - 1971
Regional geology, fossils, ethnology of the Ainu culture, Japanese pinoneer settlement, pottery, models and dioramas of early culture, photgraphs, lacquer, industrial development of region - library 23468

Hokkaido Museum of Literature, 1-4 Nakajima-koen, Chuo-ku, Sapporo 064-0931 - T: (011) 5117655, Internet: http://www.dokyoi.pref.-hokkaido.jp/hk-bunka/tennrannkai.htm
Special Museum - 1995
Literature of North Japan 23469

Hokkaidoritsu Kindai Bijutsukan (Hokkaido Museum of Modern Art), Kita 1, Nishi 17, Chuo-ku, Sapporo 060-0001 - T: (011) 6446881, Fax: 6446885, Internet: http://www.aurora-net.or.jp/art/dokinbi. Head: Takeo Mizukami
Fine Arts Museum - 1977
20th c paintings, drawings, prints and sculptures, 19th-20th c European glass, 20th c Japanese glass - library, lecture hall, audiovisual room, auditorium 23470

Hokkaidoritsu Migishi Kotaro Bijutsukan (Hokkaido Migishi Kotaro Museum of Art), Kita-2, Nishi-15, Chuo-ku, Sapporo 060-0002 - T: (011) 6448901, Fax: 6448902, Internet: http://www.dokyoi.pref.-hokkaido.jp/hk-bunka/tennrannkai.htm. Head: Yasuo Sakai
Fine Arts Museum - 1967
249 paintings and drawings by Kotaro Migishi 23471

Museum of Contemporary Art Sapporo, 2-75, Geijutsunomori, Minami-ku, Sapporo 005-0864 - T: (011) 5925111, Fax: 5910102, E-mail: mocas@artpark.or.jp, Internet: http://www.artpark.or.jp. Head: Takaaki Sasano
Fine Arts Museum 23472

Museum of Winter Sports, 1-3 Nakajima-koen, Chuo-ku, Sapporo 064-0931 - T: (011) 5211002
Special Museum 23473

Sapporo Geijutsu no Mori (Sapporo Art Park), 2-75 Geijutsu no Mori, Minami-ku, Sapporo 005-0864 - T: (011) 5925111, Fax: 5924120, E-mail: info@artpark.or.jp, Internet: http://www.artpark.or.jp. Head: Nobuo Katsura
Fine Arts Museum / Open Air Museum
Arts and crafts 23474

Sapporo Science Center, 5-2-20 Atsubetsu-chuo-1jo, Atsubetsu-ku, Sapporo 004-0051 - T: (011) 8925001
Science&Tech Museum 23475

Sapporo Sculpture Museum, 12-1-41 Miyanomori-4jo, Chuo-ku, Sapporo 064-0954 - T: (011) 6425709, Fax: 6425709. Head: Tetsuo Yoneya
Fine Arts Museum 23476

Sapporo-shi Ashibetsu (Sapporo Local Museum), 4 Kiyota-1jo, Kiyota-ku, Sapporo 004-0841 - T: (011) 8830854
Local Museum 23477

Sapporo Shi Tsukisamu (Sapporo Local Museum), 2-3-9 Tsukisamu, Higashi-2jo, Toyohira-ku, Sapporo 062-0932 - T: (011) 8546430
Local Museum 23478

Sapporo Waterworks Memorial Museum, 4-6-16 Fushimi, Chuo-ku, Sapporo 064-0942 - T: (011) 5618928
Science&Tech Museum 23479

Teine Memorial Museum, 21-3-10 Nishi-machi-minami, Nishi-ku, Sapporo 063-0062 - T: (011) 6611017
Special Museum 23480

Yanaga Hokkaido Museums, 4 Kita-19jo-nishi, Kita-ku, Sapporo 001-0019 - T: (011) 7161358
Local Museum 23481

Sasebo

Palace Huis Ten Bosch Museum, 1-1 Hausutenbosu-machi, Sasebo 859-3243 - T: (0956) 270246, Fax: 270988. Head: Yoshio Anraku
Decorative Arts Museum 23482

Sasebo-shi Bunka Kagakukan (Sasebo Culture and Science Museum), 6-16 Shimanose-cho, Sasebo 857-0806 - T: (0956) 227213
Historical Museum / Natural History Museum 23483

Sawara

Katori-jingu Treasure House, Katori, Sawara 287-0017
Religious Arts Museum
Japanese mirrors, wooden masks, documents pertaining to the history of the shrine 23484

Seki

Gifu-ken Hakubutsukan (Gifu Prefectural Museum), Hyakunen-koen, Oyana, Seki 501-3941 - T: (0575) 283111, Fax: 283110, Internet: http://www.museum.pref.gifu.jp
Local Museum 23485

Sendai

Itsutsubashikan, 1-6-8 Itsutstubashi, Aoba-ku, Sendai 980-0022 - T: (022) 2661451
Local Museum 23486

Kawaguchi Tibetan Collection, c/o Faculty of Literature, Tohoku University, Kawauchi, Aoba-ku, Sendai 980-0862 - T: (022) 2176069, Fax: 2176086
Fine Arts Museum / Decorative Arts Museum
Tibetan paintings, priests robes, reliquaries, prayer wheels, bells, drums, Nepalese bronzes, Indian sculptures 23487

Miyagi-ken Bijutsukan (Miyagi Museum of Art), 34-1 Kawauchi Moto-Hasekura, Aoba-ku, Sendai 980-0861 - T: (022) 2212111, Fax: 2212115. Head: Yoshisaburo Tsugaru
Fine Arts Museum 23488

Nihon Kinzoku Gakkai Fuzoku Kinzoku Hakubutsukan (Metals Museum), Aramaki, Aoba-ku, Sendai 980-0845 - T: (022) 2233685, Fax: 2236312, E-mail: museum@jim.or.jp, Internet: http://wwwoc.nacsis.ac.jp/jim/museum. Head: Dr. Izumi Osamu
Special Museum 23489

Saito Ho-on Kai Shizenshi Hakubutsukan (Saito Ho-on Kai Museum of Natural History), 20-2, Hancho 2-chome, Aoba-ku, Sendai 980-0014 - T: (022) 2625506, Fax: 2625508. Head: Jun-ichi Nishizawa
Natural History Museum - 1933
Geology, mineralogy, paleontology, zoology - library 23490

Sendai Music Box Museum, 2-2-36 Okino, Wakabayashi-ku, Sendai 984-0831 - T: (022) 2855309
Music Museum 23491

Sendai-shi Hakubutsukan (Sendai City Museum), Kawauchi Sannomaruato, Aoba-ku, Sendai 980-0862 - T: (022) 2252557, Fax: 2627947. Head: Naotsugu Hamada
Local Museum - 1961
Portraits, documents, and letters of the family Date, the first feudal lord of the area, family armor and clothing, tea-ceremony objects, lacquer, shikishi and other examples of calligraphy, Christian religious art, 19th c ukiyo-e prints - library 23492

Tohoku Daigaku, Kokoshiryoshitsu (Archaeological Collection, Tohoku University), Tohoku Daigaku, Kawauchi, Aoba-ku, Sendai 980-0862 - T: (022) 221800. Head: Prof. Sutoh Takashi
Archaeological Museum / University Museum
Prehistorical archeological materials, including pottery, fetishes, and figurines, ceramics 23493

Seto

Aichi-ken Toji Siryokan (Aichi Prefectural Ceramics Museum), 234 Minami-Yamaguchi-cho, Seto 489-0965 - T: (0561) 847474, Fax: 844932, Internet: http://www.pref.aichi.jp/touji. Head: Kamei Seiji
Decorative Arts Museum 23494

Seto-shi Rekishi Minzoku Shiryokan (Seto City Folk Historical Material Museum), 1 Higashi-matsuyama-cho, Seto 489-0069 - T: (0561) 820687, Fax: 852653. Head: Kazutoshi Yamakawa
Folklore Museum - 1978
Tools and instruments used before industry ceramics, models of kilns, historical survey of Seto ceramics 23495

Seto Tojiki (Seto Ceramics Center), 1 Kurashiyo-cho, Seto 489-0813 - T: (0561) 824191
Decorative Arts Museum
Traditional and contemporary ceramics, model of old kiln 23496

Shari

Shiretoko Museum, 49 Hon-machi, Shari 099-4113 - T: (01552) 31256, Fax: 31257. Head: Hajime Nakagawa
Local Museum - 1978
Local and regional hist, ornithology, archaeology, zoology, geology, specimens of Stellers sea-eagle and specimens of fishes taken from the coastal area of the sea of Okhotsk 23497

Shibayama

Shibayama Haniwa Hakubutsukan (Shibayama Haniwa Museum), 298 Shibayama, Shibayama 289-1619 - T: (0475) 871250. Head: Tokuei Hamano
Local Museum
Local traditional costumes and accessories, archeological material from 5th c tumili, pottery cylinders, arms and armor, photographs of excavation sites 23498

Shibukawa

Hara Museum ARC, 2844 Kanai, Shibukawa 377-0027 - T: (0279) 246585, Fax: 240449, E-mail: haraarc@mail.wind.ne.jp, Internet: http://www.haramuseum.or.jp. Head: Toshio Hara
Fine Arts Museum 23499

Shido

Shido-dera Treasure House, Shido-machi, Shido 769-2101
Religious Arts Museum
Paintings illustrating history of the temple, calligraphy of literary figures and priests, sculpture 23500

Shido-ji Homotsukan (Shido-ji Treasure House), Shido 769-2100 - T: (0878) 928
Religious Arts Museum 23501

Shiga

Chikubushima Treasure House, Hongon-ji, Chikubushima, Biwa-ko, Shiga 520-0500
Religious Arts Museum
Sutras, paintings, documents, No masks and music instruments 23502

Shimizu

Human Science Museum, Tokai University, 2407 Miho, Shimizu 424-0901 - T: (0543) 342385, Fax: 357095, Internet: http://www.scc.u-tokai.ac.jp/sectu/Kaihaku. Head: Dr. Akira Nagai
Natural History Museum / University Museum
Physiology and morphology of human body - social education center 23503

Tokai Daigaku Kaiyo Kagaku Hakubutsukan (Marine Science Museum, Tokai University), 2389 Miho, Shimizu 424-8620 - T: (0543) 342385, Fax: 357095, E-mail: sectu@scc.u-tokai.ac.jp, Internet: http://www.scc.u-tokai.ac.jp/sectu/kaihaku. Head: Dr. Tadashi Kubota
Natural History Museum / University Museum 23504

Shimonoseki

Akama-jingu Treasure House, Amidaji-cho, Shimonoseki 750-0003
Religious Arts Museum
Items connected with the history of the Gempei War and Emperor Antoku, the 20-volume edition of the Heike Monogatari, paintings, screens 23505

Chofu Museum, 2162, Chofukawabata, Shimonoseki 752-0979 - T: (0832) 450555
Local Museum 23506

Japan-China Peace Negotiations Memorial Hall, Amidaiji-cho, Shimonoseki 750-0003
Historical Museum 23507

Shimonoseki City Art Museum, 1-1 Chofoukuromonhigashi-machi, Shimonoseki 750-0986 - T: (0832) 454131, Fax: 456768. Head: Nagatsugi Zaitsu
Fine Arts Museum 23508

Sumiyoshi-jinja Treasure House, 1162-2 Ichinomiya-hon-machi, Shimonoseki 751-0808
Religious Arts Museum
Wooden statues, calligraphy, shikishi, lacquer items 23509

Shimosuwa

Shimosuwa Museum, 6188-8 Takahama, Shimosuwa 393-0034 - T: (0266) 271627
Local Museum
Archeological items including pottery, swords, and Sue ware, historical fishing boats used in the area, footwear of all kinds, lacquer vessels, arms and armor, exhibits on the life of commoners and samurais 23510

Shinshiyuushin

Shinshu-shinmachi Art Museum, 179 Oaza Shinmachi, Shinshiyuushin 381-2405
Fine Arts Museum
Paintings, watercolors, sculpture, prints, Maruyama coll of calligraphy and paintings 23511

Shiogami

Shiogama Shrine Museum, 1 Ichimoriyama, Shiogami 985-0074 - T: (02236) 21049
Religious Arts Museum - 1965
Festival floats, armor and swords, documents, ceramics, calligraphy, natural history, tools used in collecting salt, fishing gear 23512

Shiojiri

Hiraide Archaeological Museum, 1011-3 Hiraide, Soga, Shiojiri 399-6461 - T: (0263) 521022. Head: Kazuo Kamijo
Archaeological Museum
Pottery, stone implements, Sue-ware bowls, Haji-ware dishes, bronze bells 23513

Shizuoka

Kunozan Toshogu Museum, 390 Negoya, Shizuoka 422-8011 - T: (0542) 372437. Head: Kunio Matsuura
Historical Museum - 1965
Personal effects of Ieyasu Tokugawa and donations by other members of the Tokugawa family, exhibit on military and domestic life of the late 16th-17th centuries 23514

Musée Bernard Buffet, Suruga-daira, Nagaizumi-cho, Sunto-Gun, Shizuoka 411-0931 - T: (0559) 861300, Fax: 875511, E-mail: buffet@buffet-no-mori.or.jp, Internet: http://www.buffet-no-mori.or.jp. Head: Kiheita Okano
Fine Arts Museum 23515

Shizuoka Archaeological Museum, 5-10-5 Toro, Shizuoka 422-8033 - T: (0542) 850476. Head: Masahiro Mochizuki
Archaeological Museum
Wooden items from 200 BC to 250 AD including farming tools, kitchen implements, stools, and dugouts, pottery vessels, bronze bell, stone objects, 19th c farm tools, interior of farmhouse 23516

Shizuoka-kenritsu Bijutsukan (Shizuoka Prefectural Museum of Art), 53-2 Yada, Shizuoka 422-8002 - T: (054) 2635755, Fax: 2635742, E-mail: webmaster@ns.spmoa.shizuoka.shizuoka.jp, Internet: http://www.spmoa.shizuoka.shizuoka.jp. Head: Kenjiro Yoshioka
Fine Arts Museum
Asian and European art since 17th c, Japanese paintings since 17th c, contemporary art, August Rodin sculptures 23517

Sumpu Museum, 15-4 Koya-machi, Shizuoka 420-0852 - T: (054) 2520111, Fax: 2527011. Head: Kunio Shimada
Fine Arts Museum
Japanese-style paintings, calligraphy 23518

Shuuhou

Akiyoshi-choritsu Akiyoshidai Kagaku Hakubutsukan (Akiyoshidai Museum of Natural History), Akiyoshidai, Shuuhou 754-0511 - T: (0837) 620640
Natural History Museum 23519

Soja

Kibi Archaeological Collection, 183 Jitokatayama, Yamate-mura, Soja 719-1100 - T: (08669) 433. Head: Kiyomi Miyaoka
Archaeological Museum
Jomon potterys and stone implements, ceramics, ironwork, roof tiles 23520

Okayama Prefectural Kibiji Local Museum, 1252 Kambayashi, Soja 719-1123
Local Museum - 1976
Kofun material, photographs of the excavation sites, reproductions of the paintings of the 15th c painter Sesshu who was born here 23521

Suita

Kokuritsu Kokusai Bijutsukan (National Museum of Art, Osaka), 10-4 Senri Banpaku-koen, Suita 565-0826 - T: (06) 68762481, Fax: 68783619, E-mail: webinfo@nmao.go.jp, Internet: http://www.nmao.go.jp. Head: Hisao Miyazima
Fine Arts Museum - 1977
Japanese and international contemporary art 23522

Kokuritsu Minzokugaku Hakubutsukan (Minpaku) (National Museum of Ethnology, Minpaku), 10-1 Senri Banpaku-koen, Suita 565-8511 - T: (06) 68762151, Fax: 68750401, Internet: http://www.minpaku.ac.jp. Head: Ishige Naomichi
Ethnology Museum - 1974
Artifacts from East Asia, Oceania, Africa, Europe, and America; peoples, societies, cultures 23523

Osaka Nippon Mingeikan (Japan Folk Crafts Museum Osaka), 10-5 Banpaku-koen, Senri, Suita 565-0826 - T: (06) 68771971, Fax: 68771973. Head: Munemichi Yanagi
Folklore Museum - 1970
Chests, huge pots, straw raincoats and baskets, textiles, pottery, Japanese woodwork, lacquerware 23524

Sukagawa

Center for Contemporary Graphic Art and Tyler Graphics Archive Collection, 1 Miyata, Shiota, Sukagawa 962-0711 - T: (0248) 794811, Fax: 794816, E-mail: ccga-info@mail.dnp.co.jp, Internet: http://www.dnp.co.jp/gallery/contents_e.html
Fine Arts Museum 23525

Sukagawa Municipal Museum, 6 Ikegami-cho, Sukagawa 962-0843 - T: (02487) 53239, Fax: 632157, Internet: http://www.asaka.ne.jp/~skgwyeg
Local Museum 23526

Suwa

Kitazawa Bijutsukan (Kitazawa Museum of Art), 1-13-28 Kogandori, Suwa 392-0027 - T: (0266) 586000, Fax: 586008. Head: Toshio Kitazawa
Fine Arts Museum 23527

Suwa-shi Bitjutsukan (Suwa City Art Museum), 4-1-14 Kogandori, Suwa 392-0027 - T: (0266) 521217. Head: Makio Naito
Fine Arts Museum
Archeological materials, contemporary Japanese painting, sculpture, and handicrafts 23528

Suzuka

Honda Collection Hall, Suzuka-Circuit, 7992 Inou-cho, Suzuka 510-0201 - T: (0593) 787869, Internet: http://www.honda.co.jp/collection-hall
Science&Tech Museum 23529

Tachikawa

Gakkigaku Shiryôkan (Collection for Organology), c/o Kunitachi College of Music, 5-5-1 Kashiwa-cho, Tachikawa 190-8520 - T: (042) 5359574, Fax: 5353631. Head: Prof. Noriko Takano
Music Museum - 1976
Musical instruments 23530

Tadaoka

Masaki Art Museum, 2-9-26 Tadaoka-naka, Senboku-gun, Tadaoka 595-0812 - T: (0725) 216000, Fax: 311773. Head: Masaki Sho
Fine Arts Museum / Decorative Arts Museum
Ceramics, early Indian coins, Gandhara sculpture, paintings, calligraphy, Chinese bronzes, mirrors, jades, tomb tiles, sculptures, objects for tea-ceremony of the Muromachi period (1392-1573) 23531

Tagajou

Tohoku Rekishi Shiryokan (Tohoku Historical Museum), 133 Miyamae, Ukishima, Tagajou 985-0861 - T: (0223) 680101
Historical Museum - 1974
History and culture of the region, prehistorical and historical items, farm tolls, lacquer utensils, clothing, folk arts, old documents, traditional fishing boat - library, archeological research institute 23532

Tagawa

Tagawa Museum of Art, Tagawa City Cultural division, 11-56, Shin-machi, Tagawa 825-0016 - T: (0947) 426161, Fax: 493102. Head: Harumichi Taniguchi
Fine Arts Museum
Local artists 23533

Taisha

Izumo Taisha Shrine Treasure, Kinetsukihigashi, Kiduki-Higashi, Taisha 699-0701 - T: (0853) 533100, Fax: 532515. Head: Takatoshi Senge
Religious Arts Museum 23534

Taishiya

Taish-Machi Kominkan Fuzoku Taisha Kokokan (Taisha Archaeological Collection), 579 Kinezuki-higashi, Taishiya 699-0700
Archaeological Museum 23535

Tajimi

Gifu-ken Tôji Shiryokan (Gifu Prefectural Ceramics Museum), 1-9-4 Higashi-machi, Tajimi 507-0801 - T: (0572) 231191, Fax: 251775, E-mail: shiryoukan@tajimi.com, Internet: http://www.monoyaki.com/siryoukan. Head: Masaya Nishidera
Decorative Arts Museum
Minoyaki ceramics from acient times to modern times 23536

Takamatsu, Kagawa

Kagawa-ken Bunka Kaikan, 1-10-39 Bancho, Takamatsu, Kagawa 760-0017 - T: (0878) 311806, Fax: 311807, E-mail: gs4542@pref.kagawa.jp. Head: Masayuki Miyatani
Fine Arts Museum
Swords, coins 23537

Sanuki Folk Art Museum, 1-20-16 Ritsurin-cho, Takamatsu, Kagawa 760-0073 - T: (0878) 313331. Head: Kunibo Wada
Folklore Museum
Household items, locks, ceramics, decorated oil bottles, toys, dragon masks, carpenters tools, roof tiles 23538

Seto Inland Sea Folk History Museum, 1412-2 Tarumi-cho, Takamatsu, Kagawa 761-8001 - T: (0878) 8814707, Fax: 8814784. Head: Takashi Katayama
Historical Museum / Folklore Museum - 1973
Fishing boats and fishing gear, festivals of the fisher-folk, ship models, farm tools, archeological items including stone tools, pottery, swords, mirrors, coins 23539

Shikoku Minka Hakubutsukan (Rural Residence Museum), 91 Yashimanaka-machi, Takamatsu, Kagawa 761-0112 - T: (0878) 878433111, Fax: 51494. Head: Jatsuo Kato
Local Museum - 1976
Rural Kabuki theater, Augarcaue-Press, house dwelling of the Kono family 23540

Takamatsu City Museum of Art, 10-4 Konya-machi, Takamatsu, Kagawa 760-0027 - T: (087) 8231711, Fax: 8517250. Head: Toshimasa Murakami
Fine Arts Museum - 1949
Japanese contemporary art, lacquerwork, western contemporary prints - library, studio workshop, hi-vision library and theatre 23541

Takaoka

Takaoka Art Museum, 1-1-30, Nakagawa, Takaoka 933-0056 - T: (0766) 201177, Fax: 201178, Internet: http://www.city.takaoka.toyama.jp/english/bijyutu/bijy0100.html. Head: Michio Hisaizumi
Fine Arts Museum - 1994
Local traditional arts and crafts, modern metal works 23542

Takaoka Shiritsu Hakubutsukan (Takaoka Municipal Museum), 1-5 Kojo, Takaoka 933-0044 - T: (0766) 201572, Fax: 201570. Head: Asakura Yoshihiko, Jinbo Seigo
Local Museum - 1971
Contemporary paintings, sculpture, metalwork, lacquer items, textiles, ceramics, general history and local industry 23543

Takaraduka

Tessai Museum, Seicho-ji, Sannai Kiyoshi, Maitani, Takaraduka 665-0831 - T: (0797) 849600. Head: Bishop Sakamoto
Fine Arts Museum
Paintings and examples of calligraphy by the artist Tomioka Tessai, his pottery, sketchbooks 23544

Takasaki

Gunma-kenritsu Kindai Bijutsukan (Museum of Modern Art Gunma), 239 Iwahana-machi, Takasaki 370-1293 - T: (027) 3465556, Fax: 3464064, E-mail: mgakugei@edu-c.pref.gunma.jp, Internet: http://www.edu-c.pref.gunma.jp/kyoui/bijutu01.htm. Head: Prof. Kimio Nakayama
Fine Arts Museum - 1974
Modern and contemporary Japanese art, Chinese and Japanese paintings, modern and contemporary Western art - gallery 23545

Gunma Prefectural Museum of History, 239 Iwahana-machi, Takasaki 370-1293 - T: (027) 3465522, Fax: 3465534, E-mail: grekisi@edu-c.pref.gunma.jp, Internet: http://www.edu-c.pref.gunma.jp/kyoui/grekisi/. Head: Sumio Minegishi
Historical Museum - 1979 23546

Takasaki-shi Bijutsukan (Takasaki Museum of Art), 110-27 Yashima-cho, Takasaki 370-0849 - T: (027) 3246125
Fine Arts Museum
Local paintings 23547

Takayama

Fujii Bijutsu Mingeikan (Folk Craft Museum), Sanmachi Suji, Takayama 506-0006
Decorative Arts Museum
Folk art fron China, Korea and Japan 23548

Hachiga Minzoku Bijutsukan (Hachiga Folk Art Gallery), Shimosanno-machi, Takayama 506-0842
Ethnology Museum / Decorative Arts Museum
Hachiga family coll of ceramics, lacquer items, small figurines, relics of Christianity, and paintings 23549

Hida Kaiun-no-mori (Forest of Seven Lucky Gods), nr Hida Folk Village, Takayama 506-0006
Fine Arts Museum
Huge wooden statues, carved from 1,000 years old trees 23550

Hida Minzoku Kokokan (Archaeology Museum), Sanmachi Suji, Takayama 506-0006
Archaeological Museum
Ninja items 23551

Hida Minzoku-mura (Hida Folk Village), 1-590 Kamiokamoto-cho, Takayama 506-0055 - T: (0577) 334711, Fax: 334714, E-mail: hidafolk@hidanet.ne.jp, Internet: http://www.hidanosato-st.net. Head: Masami Wakitani
Open Air Museum / Folklore Museum - 1959
Farmhouses and their out-buildings, priests residences, house of a village headman, exhibits of farm tools used for various jobs in mountainous areas, clothing, cooking and weaving utensils, traditional crafts 23552

Hida Takayama Bijutsukan (Hida Takayama Museum of Art), 1-124-1 Kamiokamoto-cho, Takayama 506-0055 - T: (0577) 353535, Fax: 353536, Internet: http://www.htm-museum.co.jp
Fine Arts Museum 23553

Hida Takayama Museum, 1-88 Kanda-machi, Takayama 506-0006 - Internet: http://www.htm-museum.co.jp
Decorative Arts Museum
Local lacquer objects including chests, trays, food boxes, bowls, section of a tea-ceremony house, exhibits on carpentry and lacquering, tools 23554

Hida Takayama Shunkei Kaikan (Laquer Ware Museum), Takayama 506-0800
Decorative Arts Museum
Shunkei laquer ware coll, prodution technique 23555

Hirata Kinenkan (Hirata Folk Art Museum), 39 Kaminino-machi, Takayama 506-0846 - T: (0577) 331354, Fax: 328333, E-mail: s-hirata@hidanet.ne.jp, Internet: http://www.hidanet.ne.jp/~s-hirata. Head: Shozo Hirata
Folklore Museum - 1969
Traditional crafts in Hida region, lamps, toys 23556

Inro Bijutsukan, Kami-indino-machi, Takayama 506-0800
Fine Arts Museum
Exquisitely-decorated medicine boxes (called Inro) 23557

Kyodo Gangu-kan (Gallery of Traditional Japanese Toys), Oita Yacho-kan, Takayama 506-0845
Special Museum
Dolls, folk toys 23558

Shishi Kaikan (Lion Dance Ceremony Exhibition Hall), Sakura-machi, Takayama 506-0858
Special Museum
Lion masks used in the lion dance in all Shinto festivals, paintings, swords and armor, lacquer utensils 23559

Takayama Jinya (Historical Goverment House), 1-5 Hachiken-machi, Takayama 506-0012 - T: (0577) 320643, Fax: 320612, E-mail: c27212@govt.pref.gifu.jp
Historic Site 23560

Takayama-shiritsu Hakubutsukan (Takayama Museum of Local History), 75 Kami-ichino-machi, Takayama 506-0845 - T: (0577) 321205
Local Museum / Folklore Museum
Local folk arts, archeological finds from nearby Japanese Alps, local records, firearms, topographic views 23561

Takefu

Echizen-No-Sato Museum, 55-1 Yokawa-cho, Takefu 915-0031 - T: (0778) 272204
Local Museum - 1974
Echizen ware, tiles, gongs, coins, saddles, material on the peasants revolt of 1575 23562

Tako

Childrens Art Museum, 2750 Katori-gun, Tako 289-2200 - T: (0479) 762150. Head: Sakae Ikeda
Fine Arts Museum 23563

Tama

Tama Seiseki Kinenkan (Meiji the Great Memorial Hall of Tama), Renkoji, Tama 206-0021
Historical Museum 23564

Tokyo Kokusai Bijutsukan, 1-33-1 Ochiai, Tama 206-0033 - T: (0423) 389731, Fax: 381046
Fine Arts Museum
Contemporary art, art education (Hi-Vision system) 23565

Tamagawa

Tamagawa Modern Art Museum, 86-4 Ko, Oaza-Ono, Tamagawa 794-0100 - T: (0898) 552738. Head: Osamu Watanabe
Fine Arts Museum 23566

Tamayama

Ishikawa Takuboku Memorial Museum, 9 Shibutami, Tamayama 028-4132 - T: (01968) 31653
Historical Museum 23567

Tateyama

Chiba-kenritsu Awa Hakubutsukan (Chiba Prefectional Awa Museum), 1564-1 Tateyama, Tateyama 294-0036 - T: (0470) 228608, Fax: 228696
Local Museum 23568

Tatsuno

Tatsuno Bijutsukan (Tatsuno Museum of Art), 2407-1 Higuchi, Tatsuno 399-0425 - T: (0266) 430753, Fax: 413976. Head: Koichi Kobayashi
Fine Arts Museum 23569

Tendo

Dewazakura Art Museum, 1-4-1 Hitoichi-machi, Tendo 994-0044 - T: (0236) 545050, Fax: 530600. Head: Seijiro Nakano
Fine Arts Museum 23570

Tenri

Tenri University Sankokan Museum, 250 Morimedo-cho, Tenri 632-8540 - T: (0743) 637721, Fax: 637721. Head: Hidenori Kimura
Archaeological Museum / University Museum - 1930
Japanese and Korean pre-Buddhist antiquities, Chinese art, Near Eastern, Egyptian, and classical antiquity, ethnographic material from North and South America, India, the Near East, Oceania, and Central Africa, Japanese archeological material 23571

Toba

Umi-no Hakubutsukan (Sea Museum), 1-23-11 Toba, Toba 517-0011 - T: (05992) 55141. Head: Ishihara Yoshikata
Natural History Museum 23572

Tokoname

Tokoname Togei Kenkyujyo, Tokoame Institute of Ceramic Art, 7-22 Okujyo, Tokoname 479-0822 - T: (05693) 53970. Head: Takeshi Mizukami
Decorative Arts Museum 23573

Tokushima

Tokushima-kenritsu Hakubutsukan (Tokushima Prefecture Museum), Bunka-no-Mori Koen, Hachiman-cho, Tokushima 770-8070 - T: (088) 6683636, Fax: 6687197, E-mail: museum@staff.comet.go.jp, Internet: http://www.museum.comet.go.jp. Head: Dr. Toshino Amo
Local Museum - 1990
Japanese and South Asian sea shells, Insects of the world, South American fossil vertebrates, archeological materials from Shikoku, Pre-modern art of Tokushima 23574

Tokushima-kenritsu Kindai Bijutsukan (Tokushima Modern Art Museum), Bunka no Mori-sogokoen, Mukoterayama, Hachiman-cho, Tokushima 770-8070 - T: (088) 6681088, Fax: 687198, E-mail: artmuse@staff.comet.go.jp, Internet: http://www.art.comet.go.jp. Head: Kaoru Kawae
Fine Arts Museum - 1990
20th c art (Picasso, Dubuffet, Moore, Yves Klein, Klee, Léger, Artists from Tokushima) 23575

Tokushima Prefectural Local Culture Hall, 2-14 Aiba-cho, Tokushima 770-0835 - T: (0886) 228121, Fax: 228123. Head: Akira Yanamoto
Local Museum 23576

Tokyo

Archaeological Museum of Meiji University, c/o Meiji Daigaku, 1-1 Surugadai, Kanda, Chiyoda-ku, Tokyo 101-8301 - T: (03) 32964432, Fax: 32964364, E-mail: museum@isc.meiji.ac.jp, Internet: http://www.meiji.ac.jp. Head: Saburo Kobayashi
Archaeological Museum / University Museum - 1952
Prehistoric items, pottery, bone implements, hand axe, etc., from different excavation sites - library 23577

Art Gallery of Seikado Library, 2-23-1 Okamoto, Setagaya-ku, Tokyo 157-0076 - T: (03) 37002250. Head: Yoneyama Torataro
Fine Arts Museum / Library with Exhibitions - 1977
Iwasaki family coll of Chinese paintings, Sung printed books, Japanese painting, Buddhist paintings, screens, ukiyo-e prints, calligraphy, swords, and ceramics - library 23578

Asakura Sculpture Gallery, 7-18-10 Yanaka, Taito-ku, Tokyo 110-0001
Fine Arts Museum
Sculpture by Fumio Asakura, his ink paintings, his sculpture tools, in house designed by him - tea-ceremony room, garden 23579

Basho Museum, 1-6-3 Tokiwa, Koto-ku, Tokyo 135-0006 - T: (03) 36311448
Fine Arts Museum 23580

Bridgestone Bijutsukan, Ishibashi Zaidan (Bridgestone Museum of Art, Ishibashi Foundation), 1-10-1 Kyobashi, Chuo-ku, Tokyo 104-0031 - T: (03) 35630241, Fax: 35612130, Internet: http://www.bridgestone-museum.gr.jp. Head: Hideo Tomiyama
Fine Arts Museum - 1952
Japanese modern painting in the Western style, sculpture, prints, 19th c European masters in particular the Impressionists, pottery vessels from the Mediterranean classical world and pre-Columbian Peru - library 23581

Bunkamura Museum of Art, 2-24-1 Dogen-zaka, Shibuya-ku, Tokyo 150-0043 - T: (03) 34779111
Fine Arts Museum 23582

Chichibunomiya Kinen Sports Hakubutsukan (Prince Chichibu Memorial Sports Museum), c/o National Stadium, 10 Kasumigaoka-machi, Shinjuku-ku, Tokyo 160-0013 - T: (03) 340311519, Fax: 34037764, Internet: http://www.ntgk.go.jp. Head: Hiromasa Henmi
Special Museum 23583

Chihiro Art Museum Tokyo, 4-7-2, Shimo-Snakujii, Nerima-ku, Tokyo 177-0042 - T: (03) 39950772, Fax: 39950680, E-mail: chihiro@gol.com, Internet: http://www.chihiro.or.jp. Head: Tetsuko Kuroyanagi
Fine Arts Museum 23584

Chikatetsu Hakabutsukan (Subway Museum), 6-3-1 Higashi-kasai, Edogawa-ku, Tokyo 134-0084 - T: (03) 38785011, Fax: 38785012, Internet: http://www.tokyometro.go.jp/ttjin/5200.html
Science&Tech Museum
Underground railways by Teito Rapid Transit Authority 23585

Commodity Museum of Meiji University, 1-3-1 Surugadai, Kanda, Chiyoda-ku, Tokyo 101-0062 - T: (03) 32964433
Special Museum 23586

Currency Museum, Bank of Japan, Annex Bldg, 1-3-1 Nihonbashi-hongoku-cho, Chuo-ku, Tokyo 103-0021 - T: (03) 32773037, Fax: 32771456, E-mail: cmmail@imes.boj.or.jp, Internet: http://www.imes.boj.or.jp/cm. Head: Tetsu Muto
Historical Museum 23587

Daigo Fukuryu Maru Exhibition Hall, 3-2 Yume-no-shima, Koto-ku, Tokyo 136-0081 - T: (03) 35218494, Fax: 35212900, E-mail: fukuryumaru@msa.biglobe.ne.jp. Head: Shoichiro Kawasaki
Historical Museum 23588

Daimyo Tokei Hakubutsukan (Daimyo Clock Museum), 2-1-27 Yanaka, Taito-ku, Tokyo 110-0001 - T: (03) 38216913
Science&Tech Museum 23589

Department of Historical Manuscripts, c/o National Institute of Japanese Literature, 1-16-10 Yutaka-cho, Shinagawa-ku, Tokyo 142-0042 - T: (03) 37857131, Fax: 37857051. Head: Dr. Hiroshi Koyama
Library with Exhibitions - 1951
Items of local historical interest, books, - archives, library 23590

Drum Museum Taikokan, 2-1-1 Nishi-asakusa, Taito-ku, Tokyo 111-0035 - T: (03) 38425622
Special Museum 23591

Edo-Tokyo Museum, 1-4-1 Yokoami, Sumida-ku, Tokyo 130-0015 - T: (03) 36269974, Fax: 36268001, E-mail: fukyu@edo-tokyo-museum.or.jp, Internet: http://www.edo-tokyo-museum.or.jp. Head: Makoto Takeuchi
Historical Museum / Folklore Museum - 1993
History of the city, the life and culture of their people 23592

Eisei Bunko Museum, 1-1-1 Mejirodai, Bunkyo-ku, Tokyo 112-0015 - T: (03) 39410850, Fax: 39430454. Head: Morisada Hosokawa
Fine Arts Museum - 1950
Paintings and screens, tea-ceremony objects, No robes and masks, Chinese belt buckles, tomb slab, Buddha, bronze mirror, letters, swords and armor 23593

Folk Museum of Meguro-ku, c/o Moriya Educational Hall Shiryo Shitsu, 2-20-17 Gohongi, Meguro-ku, Tokyo 153-0053 - T: (03) 37151531
Folklore Museum 23594

Folk Museum of Ota-ku, 5-11-13 Minami-magome, Ota-ku, Tokyo 143-0025 - T: (03) 37771070
Folklore Museum 23595

Fujita Vente, 4-6-15 Sendagaya, Shibuya-ku, Tokyo 151-0051 - T: (03) 37962486, Fax: 37962205, E-mail: hiranaga@fujita.co.jo, Internet: http://www.fujita.co.jp/vente
Special Museum
Films, lectures 23596

Fune no Kagakukan (Museum of Maritime Science), 3-1 Higashi Yashio, Shinagawa-ku, Tokyo 135-0092 - T: (03) 55001111, Fax: 55001190, Internet: http://www.funenokagakukan.or.jp
Natural History Museum
Exhib in a ferro-concrete repilka of a 60,000 ton liner 23597

Gaimusho, Gaiko Shiryokan (Diplomatic Record Office of the Ministry of Foreign Affairs), 1-5-3 Azabudai, Minato-ku, Tokyo 106-0041 - T: (03) 35854111, Fax: 35854514, Internet: http://www.mofa.go.jp/about/hq/record
Historical Museum 23598

Galerie Taisei, 1-25-1, Nishi-shinjuku, Shinjuku-ku, Tokyo 163-0606 - T: (03) 53815510, Fax: 53815511, E-mail: galerie@pub.taisei.co.jp, Internet: http://www.taisei.co.jp/galerie. Head: Shigeto Kitagawa
Special Museum 23599

Gallery of Horyu-ji Treasures, Tokyo National Museum, 13-9 Ueno-koen, Taito-ku, Tokyo 110-0007 - T: (03) 38221111, Fax: 38229130. Head: Keijirô Inai
Decorative Arts Museum 23600

Gasu no Kagakukan (Gas Science Center), 6-3-16 Toyosu, Koto-ku, Tokyo 135-0061 - T: (03) 35341111, Fax: 35341643, Internet: http://www.tokyo-gas.co.jp/science_museum
Science&Tech Museum
Process of gas supply from generation to delivery 23601

Gotoh Bijutsukan (The Gotoh Museum of Art), 3-9-25 Kaminoge, Setagaya-ku, Tokyo 158-8510 - T: (03) 37030662, Fax: 37030440, Internet: http://www.gotoh-museum.or.jp. Head: Kyuichiro Kinoshita
Fine Arts Museum - 1960
Fine arts and crafts of ancient Japan, China, other Oriental nations 23602

Gotoh Planetarium and Astronomical Museum, 2-21-12 Shibuya, Shibuya-ku, Tokyo 150-0002 - T: (03) 34077409, Fax: 37977354. Head: Sadao Murayama
Natural History Museum - 1957 23603

Hara Bijutsukan (Hara Museum of Contemporary Art), 4-7-25 Kita-Shinagawa, Shinagawa-ku, Tokyo 140-0001 - T: (03) 34450651, Fax: 34730104, E-mail: harainfo@ka2.so-net.ne.jp, Internet: http://www.haramuseum.or.jp. Head: Toshio Hara
Fine Arts Museum - 1979
Works of contemporary art by international artists including video works 23604

Hasegawa Bijutsukan (Hasegawa Art Museum), 1-30-6 Sakura-shin-machi, Setagaya-ku, Tokyo 154-0015 - T: (03) 37018766, Fax: 37090586. Head: Mariko Hasegawa
Fine Arts Museum 23605

Hatakeyama Collection, 2-20-12 Shirokanedai, Minato-ku, Tokyo 108-0071 - T: (03) 34475787, Fax: 34472665. Head: Sadamasa Niyama
Fine Arts Museum
Chinese and Japanese paintings, calligraphy, sculpture, metalwork, and ceramics, Japanese lacquer, tea-ceremony objects, and costumes, Korean ceramics - tea-ceremony room 23606

Idemitsu Bijutsukan (Idemitsu Museum of Arts), 3-1-1 Marunouchi, Chiyoda-ku, Tokyo 100-0005 - T: (03) 32139402, Fax: 32138473, Internet: http://ryowa-oil.co.jp/goannai. Head: Shosuke Idemitsu
Fine Arts Museum / Decorative Arts Museum - 1966
Japanese and Chinese ceramics, samples of calligraphy by literary figures and monks, lacquer items, Chinese bronzes, art objects of the Middle and Near East, paintings and lithographs by Sam Francis and George Rouault 23607

Institute of Nature Study, National Science Museum Tokyo, 5-21-5 Shirokanedai, Minato-ku, Tokyo 108-0072 - T: (03) 34417176
Natural History Museum 23608

Isetan Bijutsukan (Isetan Museum of Art), 3-14-1 Shinjuku, Shinjuku-ku, Tokyo 160-0022 - T: (03) 32252490, Fax: 32252491
Fine Arts Museum 23609

Itabashi Kuritsu Bijutsukan (Itabashi Art Museum), 5-34-27 Akatsuka, Itabashi-ku, Tokyo 175-0092 - T: (03) 39793251, Fax: 39793252, E-mail: bijyutsu@city.itabashi.tokyo.jp, Internet: http://users.goo.ne.jp/itabashiart. Head: Naomitsu Suzuki
Fine Arts Museum 23610

Jitensha Bunka (Bicycle Culture Center), Jitenshakaikan 3, 1-9-3 Akasaka, Minato-ku, Tokyo 107-0052 - T: (03) 35844530, Fax: 35861194, E-mail: bccpost@post0.mind.ne.jp, Internet: http://www.cycle-info.or.jp
Science&Tech Museum 23611

Kagaku Gijutsukan (Science Museum), c/o Japan Science Foundation, 2-1 Kitanomaru-koen, Chiyoda-ku, Tokyo 102-0091 - T: (03) 32122420, Fax: 32123030, E-mail: webmaster@jsf.or.jp, Internet: http://www.jsf.or.jp. Head: Hiroshi Sonoyama
Natural History Museum - 1959
Models, experimental apparatuses, physical sciences, industrial exhibits 23612

Kagu no Hakubutsukan (Furniture Museum), 3-10 Harumi, Chuo-ku, Tokyo 104-0053 - T: (03) 35330098, Fax: 35330098
Decorative Arts Museum
Old japanese furniture 23613

Kami no Hakubutsukan (Paper Museum), 1-1-3 Oji, Kita-ku, Tokyo 114-0002 - T: (03) 39162320, Fax: 59077511, E-mail: home@papermuseum.jp, Internet: http://www.papermuseum.jp. Head: Imamura Tadaya
Science&Tech Museum - 1950

Specimens of ancient handmade paper, various types of paper, both hand-made and machine-made, papermade goods, machines and tools for making paper, the Hyakumanto, the oldest printed matter in the world (770 A.D.) - library, audiovisual and crafts room 23614

Katsushika-ku Kyoiku Shiryokan, 4-21-1 Mizumoto, Katsushika-ku, Tokyo 125-0032 - T: (03) 36075569
Local Museum 23615

Kenji Igarashi Memorial Museum, 2-11-1 Shimo-maruko, Ota-ku, Tokyo 146-0092 - T: (03) 37591336
Special Museum
Dry cleaning and laundering 23616

Kitte no Hakubutsukan (Philatelic Museum), 1-4-23 Mejiro, Toshima-ku, Tokyo 171-0031 - T: (03) 59513331, Fax: 59513332, Internet: http://yushu.or.jp/english/e_pmu. Head: Chuichi Ochiai
Fine Arts Museum 23617

Kodai Orient Hakubutsukan (Ancient Orient Museum), 3-1-4 Higashi-Ikebukuro, Toshima-ku, Tokyo 170-8630 - T: (03) 39893491, Fax: 35903266. Head: Namio Egami
Fine Arts Museum - 1978 23618

Kokugakuin University Archaeological Collection, c/o Kokugakuin Daigaku, 9 Wakagi-cho, Shibuya-ku, Tokyo 150-0000 - T: (03) 34013101
Archaeological Museum / University Museum
Japanese archeological material from pre-ceramic to early historical times, archeological items from China, Korea, and North America, Japanese burial urns, roof tiles, small stone pagodas 23619

Kokuritsu Kagaku Hakubutsukan (National Science Museum), 7-20 Ueno-koen, Taito-ku, Tokyo 110-8718 - T: (03) 38220111, Fax: 58149898, E-mail: webmaster@kahaku.go.jp, Internet: http://www.kahaku.go.jp. Head: Masamine Sasaki
Natural History Museum - 1872
Cross-section of the trunk an a Yaku cedar, Harumi Shibukawa's celestial globe, entire bodies of dinosaur specimens, zoology, botany, anthropology - library 23620

Kokuritsu Seiyo Bijutsukan (The National Museum of Western Art), 7-7 Ueno Koen, Taito-ku, Tokyo 110-0007 - T: (03) 38285131, Fax: 38285135, E-mail: wwwadmin@nmwa.go.jp, Internet: http://www.nmwa.go.jp. Head: Koichi Kabayama
Fine Arts Museum - 1959
European art, French Impressionists, Old Masters paintings, sculpture, print coll - library 23621

Koto-ku Fukagawa Edo Siryokan (Fukagawa Edo Museum), 1-3-28 Shirakawa, Koto-ku, Tokyo 135-0021 - T: (03) 36308625, Fax: 38204379, Internet: http://www.koto-cabletv.co.jp/~koto-ku/edo
Special Museum 23622

Kotsu Hakubutsukan (Transportation Museum), 1-25 Kanda-Suda-cho, Chiyoda-ku, Tokyo 101-0041 - T: (03) 32518481, Fax: 32518489, E-mail: web@kouhaku.or.jp, Internet: http://www.kouhaku.or.jp. Head: Naoki Hirano
Science&Tech Museum - 1921
Railway train, locomotives, motor cars, omnibus, aeroplane, rickshaw, miniature models of vessels - library 23623

Kouseiroudoushou Sangyo Anzen Gijutsukan (National Institute of Industrial Safety Museum), 5-35-1 Shiba, Minato-ku, Tokyo 108-0014 - T: (03) 34523370, Fax: 54430273, E-mail: gcant@jisha.or.jp, Internet: http://www.jaish.gr.jp. Head: Yoshikatsu Kimura
Science&Tech Museum - 1942
Materials on industrial safety 23624

Kumagai Morikazu Museum, 2-27-6 Chihaya, Toshima-ku, Tokyo 171-0044 - T: (03) 39573779
Special Museum 23625

Kume Bijutsukan (Kume Museum of Art), 2-25-5 Kamiosaki, Shinagawa-ku, Tokyo 141-0021 - T: (03) 34911510, Fax: 34916617. Head: Atsuko Kume
Fine Arts Museum 23626

Kunaicho Sannomaru Shozokan (Museum of the Imperial Collections Sannomaru Shozokan), 1-1 Chiyoda, Chiyoda-ku, Tokyo 100-8111 - T: (03) 32131111, Fax: 32131177, Internet: http://kunaicho.go.jp
Fine Arts Museum
Paintings, calligraphy and crafts 23627

Kuroda Kinenshitsu (Kuroda Memorial Hall), 13-27 Ueno-koen, Taito-ku, Tokyo 110-0007 - T: (03) 38232241, Fax: 56855771. Head: Akiyoshi Watanate
Fine Arts Museum - 1930
Of the paintings and sketches of Seiki Kuroda, pioneer of Western painting in Japan - library 23628

Masao Koga Museum, 3-6-12 Uehara, Shibuya-ku, Tokyo 151-0064 - T: (03) 34609051
Special Museum 23629

Matsuoka Museum of Art, 5-12-6, Shiroganedai, Minato-ku, Tokyo 108-0071 - T: (03) 54490251, Fax: 54490252. Head: Mieko Matsuoka
Fine Arts Museum - 1975
Chinese, Korean, Annamese and Japanese ceramics, Japanese traditional paintings, French modern paintings, Gandharan and Indian sculptures 23630

Meguro Gajoen Bijutsukan (Meguro Gajoen Museum of Art), 1-8-1 Shimo-meguro, Meguro-ku, Tokyo 153-0064 - T: (03) 54343820, Fax: 54343947. Head: Toshiro Hosokawa
Fine Arts Museum 23631

Meguro Kiseichukan (Meguro Parasitological Museum), 4-1-1 Shimo-Meguro, Meguro-ku, Tokyo 153-0064 - T: (03) 37167144, Fax: 37162322, E-mail: mpm@mbd.shere.ne.jp, Internet: http://ascaris.med.tmd.ac.jp/mpmE.html. Head: Shunya Kamegai
Natural History Museum - 1953
Natural hist exhibits, parasites of invertebrates and vertebrates, type specimens of helminthes described by the well-known helminthologist Dr. Satyu Yamaguti - library 23632

Meguro Museum of Art, 2-4-36 Meguro, Meguro-ku, Tokyo 153-0063 - T: (03) 37141201, Fax: 37159328. Head: Sadao Kato
Fine Arts Museum - 1987
Artworks of Japanese modern and contemporary artists 23633

Meiji Daigaku Keiji Hakubutsukan (Criminal Museum of the Meiji University), 1-1 Kanda Surugadai, Chiyoda-ku, Tokyo 101-0062 - T: (03) 32964431, Fax: 32964364. Head: Hajime Nabeta
Special Museum / University Museum - 1929
Social science items 23634

Meiji Jingu Homotsuden (Meiji Shrine Museum), 1-1 Yoyogi-kamizono-cho, Shibuya-ku, Tokyo 151-0052 - T: (03) 33795511, Fax: 33795519. Head: Tatumi Date
Decorative Arts Museum - 1921
Treasures and possessions of Emperor Meiji, personal effects of Empress Shoken, memorial picture gallery 23635

Meiji Memorial Picture Gallery, Meiji-jingu Gaien, 9 Kasumigoaka-machi, Shinjuku-ku, Tokyo 160-0013 - T: (03) 34015179, Fax: 34010676
Public Gallery 23636

Memorial Museum of the Kanto Earthquake Disaster, 2-3-25 Yokoami, Sumida-ku, Tokyo 130-0015 - T: (03) 36221208
Historical Museum 23637

Miyagi Michio Memorial Hall, 35 Naka-cho, Shinjuku-ku, Tokyo 162-0835 - T: (03) 32690208
Special Museum 23638

Musashino Ongaku Daigaku Gakki Hakubutsukan (Musashino Academia Museum of Musical Instruments), 1-13-1 Hazawa, Nerima-ku, Tokyo 176-0003 - T: (03) 39921410, Internet: http://www.musashino-music.ac.jp/I/I-3.html
Music Museum
Western classical, Japanese and folk musical instruments 23639

Museum of Contemporary Sculpture, 4-12-18 Naka-meguro, Meguro-ku, Tokyo 153-0061 - T: (03) 37925858, Fax: 37607821. Head: Yasuhiro Watanabe
Fine Arts Museum 23640

Museum of Japanese Sword Fittings, 6-6-11 Hon-komagome, Bunkyo-ku, Tokyo 113-0021 - T: (03) 59766800
Decorative Arts Museum 23641

Nakano Historical Museum, 4-3-4 Egota, Nakano-ku, Tokyo 165-0022 - T: (03) 33199221
Local Museum 23642

Nerima Bijutsukan (Nerima Art Museum), 1-36-16 Nukui, Nerima-ku, Tokyo 176-0021 - T: (03) 35771821, Fax: 35771824. Head: Masafumi Muramatsu
Fine Arts Museum 23643

Nerima Home Town Museum, 1-16-31 Shakujii-dai, Nerima-ku, Tokyo 177-0045 - T: (03) 39960563
Local Museum 23644

New Otani Art Museum, 4-1, Kioi-cho, Chiyoda-ku, Tokyo 102-8578 - T: (03) 32214111, Fax: 32212988, E-mail: museum@newotani.co.jp, Internet: http://www.newotani.co.jp/museum. Head: Kazuhiko Otani
Fine Arts Museum 23645

Nezu Bijutsukan (Nezu Institute of Fine Arts), 6-5-1, Minami-Aoyama, Minato-ku, Tokyo 107-0062 - T: (03) 34002536, Fax: 34002436, E-mail: nezu@nezu-muse.or.jp, Internet: http://www.nezu-muse.or.jp. Head: Kohichi Nezu
Fine Arts Museum / Decorative Arts Museum - 1940
Japanese paintings, calligraphy, sculpture, ceramics, lacquer items, metalwork, Chinese bronzes, Buddhist art, tea-ceremony utensils, Korean ceramics, Chinese clocks 23646

NHK Hoso Hakubutsukan (NHK Broadcasting Museum), 2-1-1 Atago, Minato-ku, Tokyo 105-0002 - T: (03) 54006900, Fax: 54011539, Internet: http://www.nhk.or.jp/bunken/en/h1-e.html
Science&Tech Museum
Development of radio and TV broadcasting in Japan 23647

Nihon Camera Hakubutsukan (Japan Camera Museum), JCII Ichibancho Bldg, 25 Ichiban-cho, Chiyoda-ku, Tokyo 102-0082 - T: (03) 32637110, Fax: 32344650, Internet: http://www.nikon.co.jp/jcii. Head: Mayumi Moriyama
Science&Tech Museum
Cameras, equipment 23648

Nihon Gangu Shiryokan (Japan Toy Museum), 1-36-10 Hashiba, Taito-ku, Tokyo 111-0023 - T: (03) 38745133, Fax: 38713188, Internet: http://www.toynes.or.jp/2-1-1.htm
Special Museum
Toys manufactured in Japan after Meiji period 23649

Nihon Ginko Kin'yu Kenkyujo Kahei Hakubutsukan (Bank of Japan Currency Museum), 1-3-1 Nihonbashi Hongoku-cho, Chuo-ku, Tokyo 103-0021 - T: (03) 32773037, Fax: 32771456, E-mail: cmmail@imes.boj.or.jp, Internet: http://www.imes.boj.or.jp/cm
Special Museum 23650

Nihon Kindai Bungakukan (Museum of Modern Japanese Literature), 4-3-55 Komaba, Meguru-ku, Tokyo 153-0041 - T: (03) 34684181, Fax: 34684185, Internet: http://www1.odn.ne.jp/~bungakukan. Head: Minoru Nakamura
Special Museum 23651

Nihon Mingeikan (Japan Folk Crafts Museum), 4-3-33 Komaba, Meguro-ku, Tokyo 153-0041 - T: (03) 34674527, Fax: 34674537, Internet: http://www.race.u-tokyo.ac.jp/mingeikan. Head: Sori Yanagi
Decorative Arts Museum / Folklore Museum - 1936
Utilitarian works made by unknown craftsmen of Japan, works by Mingei Movement artists, paintings, pottery, porcelain, prints, textiles, lacquer items, masks, toys, furniture, ethnological items, folkcrafts 23652

Nihon Shodo Bijutsukan (Japan Calligraphy Art Museum), 1-3-1 Tokiwadai, Itabashi-ku, Tokyo 174-8688 - T: (03) 39652611, Fax: 39652078
Fine Arts Museum
Examples of 20th-c calligraphy 23653

Nihon Token Hakubutsukan (Japanese Sword Museum), 4-25-10 Yoyogi, Shibuya-ku, Tokyo 151-0053 - T: (03) 33791386, Fax: 33791389. Head: Sadanori Yamanaka
Fine Arts Museum
Swords from all ages, books and photographs 23654

NTT InterCommunication Center, Tokyo Opera City Tower, 3-20-2 Nishishinjukku, Shinjuku-ku, Tokyo 163-1404 - T: (03) 53530800, E-mail: query@ntticc.or.jp, Internet: http://www.ntticc.or.jp
Science&Tech Museum 23655

O Art Museum, 1-6-2 Osaki, Shinagawa-ku, Tokyo 141-0032 - T: (03) 34954040, Fax: 34954192. Head: Sakae Hasegawa
Fine Arts Museum 23656

Odawara Crustacea Museum, 3-11-4 Azabu-10ban, Minato-ku, Tokyo 106-0045
Natural History Museum
Natural sciences, specimens of Crustacea 23657

Okura Shukokan Museum, 2-10-3 Toranomon, Minato-ku, Tokyo 105-0001 - T: (03) 35830781, Fax: 35833831. Head: Noboru Nishitani
Fine Arts Museum / Decorative Arts Museum - 1917
Japanese paintings, sculpture, calligraphy, Chines printed books, ceramics and porcelain, Chinese bronzes, swords, lacquer wares, Noh masks and robes 23658

Ōta Kinen Bijutsukan (Ōta Memorial Museum of Art), 1-10-10 Jingumae, Shibuya-ku, Tokyo 150-0001 - T: (03) 34030880, Fax: 34705994. Head: Motoji Ōta
Fine Arts Museum - 1980
"Actor Kataoka Nizaemon VII in the role of Ki no Natora" by Toshusai Sharaku (wood-block print), "Eight Sights in the Environs of Edo" by Utagawa Hiroshige (wood-block prints), "Three Beauties" by Katsushika Hokusai 23659

Parliamentary Memorial Museum, 1-1-1 Nagata-cho, Chiyoda-ku, Tokyo 100-0014 - T: (03) 35811651
Historical Museum 23660

Ryushi Memorial Hall, 4-2-1 Chuo, Ota-ku, Tokyo 143-0024 - T: (03) 37720680, Fax: 37720680. Head: Kiyoshi Ikefuji
Fine Arts Museum
100 works by the painter Ryushi Kawabata, screens, his colors and brushes, sketches, photographs of the artist, the artists former house 23661

Seiji Togo Memorial Yasuda Kasai Museum of Art, 1-26-1 Nishi-Shinjuku, Shinjuku-ku, Tokyo 160-8338 - T: (03) 33493080/81, Fax: 33493079, Internet: http://www.yasuda.co.jp/museum. Head: Toshihiko Ishii
Fine Arts Museum - 1976
200 works of Seiji Togo, 450 works of other artists 23662

Seikado Library and Art Museum, 2-23-1 Okamoto, Setagaya-ku, Tokyo 157-0076 - T: (03) 37000007, Fax: 37002253, Internet: http://www.mitsubishi.or.jp/e/o/orgm.html. Head: Torataro Yoneyama
Fine Arts Museum
Coll of Yanosuke and Koyata Iwasaki with cultural treasures and about 5,000 artworks 23663

Senshu-Bunko Museum, 2-1-36 Kudan-minami, Chiyoda-ku, Tokyo 102-0074 - T: (03) 32610075, Fax: 32620067. Head: Shigeko Kobayashi
Local Museum 23664

Setagaya-kuritsu Bijutsukan (Setagaya Art Museum), 1-2 Kinuta-koen, Setagaya-ku, Tokyo 157-0075 - T: (03) 34156011, Fax: 34156413, Internet: http://www.setagayaartmuseum.or.jp. Head: Seiji Oshima
Fine Arts Museum
Modern and contemporary art, naive art, outsider art, works of Setagaya City artists 23665

Shensyu Bunko, 2-1-36 Kudan-minami, Chiyoda-ku, Tokyo 102-0074 - T: (03) 32610075
Public Gallery 23666

Shinagawa Historical Museum, 6-11-1 Oi, Shinagawa-ku, Tokyo 140-0014 - T: (03) 37774060
Local Museum 23667

Shirane Memorial Museum, 4-9-2 Higashi, Shibuya-ku, Tokyo 150-0011 - T: (03) 34078615
Special Museum 23668

Shitamachi Museum, 2-1 Ueno Koen, Taito-ku, Tokyo 110-0007 - T: (03) 38237451
Local Museum 23669

Shodo Hakubutsukan (Calligraphy Museum), 2-10-4 Negishi, Taito-ku, Tokyo 110-0003 - T: (03) 38722645
Fine Arts Museum - 1936
Multifarious objects collected by Nakamura demonstrating the history of calligraphy, ancient texts of calligraphy, pottery, jades, bronzes, mirrors, swords, rubbings, coins, inkstones and brushes, stone memorial tablets 23670

Shoto Museum of Art, 14-14, Shoto 2-chome, Shibuya-ku, Tokyo 150-0046 - T: (03) 34659421, Fax: 34606366. Head: Kunio Fujita
Fine Arts Museum 23671

Sogetsu Bijutsukan (Sogetsu Art Museum), 7-2-21 Akasaka, Minato-ku, Tokyo 107-8505 - T: (03) 34089112, Fax: 34081294, E-mail: museum@sogetsu.or.jp, Internet: http://www.sogetsu.or.jp. Head: Akane Teshigara
Fine Arts Museum
Coll by Sofu Teshigahara (founder of Sogetsu school), modern art, ancient Japanese art 23672

Striped House - Museum of Art, 5-10-33 Roppongi, Minato-ku, Tokyo 106-0032 - T: (03) 34058108
Fine Arts Museum 23673

Sugino Gakuen Isho Hakubutsukan (Costume Museum), 4-6-19 Kamiosaki, Shinagawa-ku, Tokyo 141-0021 - T: (03) 34918151 ext. 220
Special Museum 23674

Sumo Hakubutsukan (Sumo Museum), 1-3-28 Yokoami, Sumida-ku, Tokyo 130-0015 - T: (03) 36220366, Internet: http://www.wnn.or.jp/wnn-t/museum
Special Museum
History of Sumo (Japanese wrestling) since 18th c 23675

Suntory Bijutsukan (Suntory Museum of Art), Tokyo Suntory Bldg, 1-2-3 Moto-Akasaka, Minato-ku, Tokyo 107-8430 - T: (03) 34701073, Fax: 34709186, Internet: http://www.suntory.co.jp/sma. Head: Shinichiro Torii
Fine Arts Museum - 1961
Lacquer objects, glassware, costumes, genre screens, woodblock prints, ceramics, masks, iron tea-kettles, 18th-19th c ukiyo-e prints, paintings - tea-ceremony room 23676

Tabako to Shio no Hakubutsukan (Tobacco and Salt Museum), 1-16-8 Jinnan, Shibuya-ku, Tokyo 150-0041 - T: (03) 34762041, Fax: 34765692, Internet: http://www.jnet.ad.jp/www/jt/culture/museum/welcome.html. Head: Katami Ueno
Special Museum - 1978
Japanese woodblock prints, Japanese antique Kiseru pipes, tobacco pouches, tobacco trays, Japanese and foreign cigarette packages, Japanese and foreign salt resources 23677

Tako no Hakubutsukan (Kite Museum), 1-12-10 Nihombashi, Chuo-ku, Tokyo 103-0027 - T: (03) 32752704, 32712465, Fax: 32730575, Internet: http://www.taimeiken.co.jp/tako/f_tako.htm. Head: Masaaki Modegi
Decorative Arts Museum - 1977
Teizo Hashimotos Kites 23678

Teishin Sogo Hakubutsukan (Communications Museum), 2-3-1 Otemachi, Chiyoda-ku, Tokyo 100-0004 - T: (03) 32446811/19, Fax: 32446820, E-mail: www-admin@iptp.go.jp, Internet: http://www.iptp.go.jp/museum_e
Science&Tech Museum - 1955
Historical materials on radio and television broadcasting, mechanics of communications, apparatuses and models, equipment 23679

Tenri Gallery, 1-9 Nishiki-cho, Kanda, Chiyoda-ku, Tokyo 101-0054 - T: (03) 32927025. Head: Akira Yamamoto
Public Gallery
Paintings, art 23680

Tepco Denryookukan (Tepco Electric Energy Museum), 1-12-10 Jinnan, Shibuya-ku, Tokyo 150-0041 - T: (03) 34771191, Fax: 34771399, Internet: http://www5.mediagalaxy.co.jp/denryokukan
Science&Tech Museum
Elecrticity from power generator to consumption 23681

Tepia, Kikai Sangyo Kinenkan (Museum of Industry), 2-8-44 Kita-Aoyama, Minato-ku, Tokyo 107-0061 - T: (03) 54746111, Fax: 54746112, E-mail: webmaster@tepia.or.jp, Internet: http://www.tepia.or.jp
Science&Tech Museum
Technology, mechanical and information industry 23682

Tokyo Central Bijutsukan (Tokyo Central Art Museum), Ginza Boeki Bldg, 2-7-18 Ginza, Chuo-ku, Tokyo 104-0061 - T: (03) 35644600. Head: Masatake Maruyama
Historical Museum / Fine Arts Museum
Contemporary paintings, sculptures, prints, callygraphy, handicrafts 23683

Tokyo Geijutsu Daigaku Daigaku Bijutsukan (The University Art Museum, Tokyo National University of Fine Arts and Music), 12-8 Ueno-koen, Taito-ku, Tokyo 110-8714 - T: (03) 56857755, Fax: 56857805, Internet: http://www.geidai.ac.jp
Fine Arts Museum / University Museum
Paintings, sculptures, crafts 23684

Tokyo Gendai Bijutsukan (Museum of Contemporary Art Tokyo), Toritsu Kiba-koen, 4-1-1 Miyoshi, Koto-ku, Tokyo 135-0022 - T: (03) 52454111, Fax: 52451140, Internet: http://www.tef.or.jp/mot/index-e.html
Fine Arts Museum - 1995 23685

Tokyo Kokuritsu Hakubutsukan (Tokyo National Museum), 13-9 Ueno Koen, Taito-ku, Tokyo 110-8702 - T: (03) 38221111, Fax: 38229130, E-mail: suggestionbox@tnm.go.jp, Internet: http://www.tnm.go.jp
Archaeological Museum / Fine Arts Museum / Decorative Arts Museum - 1872
Japanese archeology, Buddhist paintings, sutras and calligraphy, narrative scrolls, prints, Buddhist sculpture, complete range of Japanese pottery, No and Kyogen masks and costumes, history of arms and armor, lacquer collection, Chinese sculptures, paintings, ceramics, and bronzes, Korean metalwork and ceramics 23686

Tokyo Kokuritsu Kindai Bijutsukan (The National Museum of Modern Art Tokyo), 3 Kitanomaru Koen, Chiyoda-ku, Tokyo 102-8322 - T: (03) 32142561, Fax: 35618100, E-mail: webstaff@momat.go.jp, Internet: http://www.momat.go.jp. Head: Tetsuo Tsujimura
Fine Arts Museum - 1952
Japanese paintings, sculpture, drawings and watercolors, prints, 20th c Japanese crafts, modern and contemporary art, calligraphy - film center, archive 23687

Tokyo Kokuritsu Kindai Bijutsukan Film Center (National Film Center, National Museum of Modern Art), 3-7-6 Kyobashi, Chuo-ku, Tokyo 104-0031 - T: (03) 35610823, Fax: 35610830, Internet: http://www3.momat.go.jp/e_nfc
Special Museum 23688

Tokyo Kokuritsu Kindai Bijutsukan Kogeikan (Crafts Gallery, National Museum of Modern Art Tokyo), 1 Kitanomaru Koen, Chiyoda-ku, Tokyo 102-0091 - T: (03) 32117781, Fax: 32117783, E-mail: cgkanri@momat.go.jp, Internet: http://www3.momat.go.jp/e_crafts. Head: Tetsuo Tsujimura
Decorative Arts Museum - 1977 23689

Tokyo Metropolitan Geijutsu High School Museum, 2-18-58 Ohashi, Meguro-ku, Tokyo 153-0044 - T: (03) 34679494, Fax: 34674991. Head: Michihiro Harima
University Museum 23690

Tokyo Station Gallery, 1-9-1 Marunouchi, Chiyoda-ku, Tokyo 100-0005 - T: (03) 33122763, 32122485, Fax: 32122058, E-mail: tsg@tsg.ejrcf.or.jp, Internet: http://www.ejrcf.or.jp
Fine Arts Museum
Surrealistic art, sculptures, paintings, photographies 23691

Tokyo-to Bijutsukan (Tokyo Metropolitan Art Museum), 8-36 Ueno Koen, Taito-ku, Tokyo 110-0007 - T: (03) 38236921, Fax: 38236920, E-mail: tobi@tef.or.jp, Internet: http://www.tef.or.jp/tmm. Head: Yoshitake Mamuro
Fine Arts Museum - 1926
rented galleries, art studios 23692

Tokyo-to Kindai Bungaku Hakubutsukan (Tokyo Museum of Modern Literature), 4-3-55, Komaba, Meguro-ku, Tokyo 153-0041 - T: (03) 34665150, Fax: 34665195. Head: Kozo Masuda
Special Museum / University Museum
Modern literature 23693

Tokyo-to Shashin Bijutsukan (Tokyo Metropolitan Museum of Photography), 1-13-3 Mita, Meguro-ku, Tokyo 153-0062 - T: (03) 32800031, Fax: 32800033, E-mail: photoinfo@tokyo-photo-museum.or.jp, Internet: http://www.tokyo-photo-museum.or.jp. Head: Tamon Miki
Fine Arts Museum / Science&Tech Museum
Photographic art 23694

Tokyo-to Teien Bijutsukan (Tokyo Metropolitan Teien Art Museum), 5-21-9 Shirokanedai, Minato-ku, Tokyo 108-0071 - T: (03) 34430201, Fax: 34433228, Internet: http://www.tokyo-teleport.co.jp/teien. Head: Masaaki Iseki
Fine Arts Museum
Building in art deco style 23695

Tokyo University Archaeological Collection, c/o Tokyo Daigaku, 7-3-1 Hongo, Bunkyo-ku, Tokyo 113-0033 - T: (03) 38122111. Head: Prof. Keiji Imamura
Archaeological Museum / University Museum 23696

The Tolman Collection, 2-2-18 Shiba-Daimon, Minato-ku, Tokyo 105-0012 - T: (03) 34341300, Fax: 34599282
Fine Arts Museum 23697

Tomioka Museum, 2-13-3, Sanno, Ota-ku, Tokyo 143-0023 - T: (03) 37711054, Fax: 37711054. Head: Reiji Nagasawa
Museum of Classical Antiquities 23698

Ueno Royal Museum, 1-2 Ueno-koen, Taito-ku, Tokyo 110-0007 - T: (03) 38334191, Fax: 38360066, E-mail: http://www.ueno-mori.org. Head: Takatoshi Suzuki
Fine Arts Museum - 1971
Contemporary calligraphy, print coll, paintings 23699

Umezawa Memorial Gallery, 2-9 Surugadai, Kanda, Chiyoda-ku, Tokyo 101-0062
Fine Arts Museum
Umezawas coll of Japanese and Chinese paintings, calligraphy, and ceramics including Korean ceramics 23700

The University Museum, c/o University of Tokyo, 7-3-1 Hongo, Bunkyo-ku, Tokyo 113-0033 - T: (03) 58412802/03, Fax: 58418451, E-mail: web-master@um.u-tokyo.ac.jp, Internet: http://www.um.u-tokyo.ac.jp. Head: Prof. Susumu Takahashi
University Museum / Archaeological Museum / Natural History Museum - 1966
Natural history, authentic specimens of various fields, from Japan and adjacent regions, Western Pacific and Himalayas regions, archaeological colls from Japan, West/East Asia and South America, history of arts and technology 23701

Waseda Daigaku Tsubouchi Hakushi Kinen Engeki Hakubutsukan (Waseda University Tsubouchi Memorial Theatre Museum), 1-6-1 Nishi-Waseda, Shinjuku-ku, Tokyo 169-0051 - T: (03) 52861829, Fax: 52734398, E-mail: enpaku-ml@mn.waseda.ac.jp, Internet: http://www.waseda.ac.jp/enpaku. Head: Torigoe Bunzo
Performing Arts Museum - 1928
Literary works, manuscripts, and personal effects of Tsubouchi, Father of the Japanese Theatre, building modelled after Elizabethan theatre, book, photographs and materials relating to the dramatic arts, coloured wood-block prints - library 23702

Watari-Um (Watari Museum of Contemporary Art), 3-7-6 Jingumae, Shibuya-ku, Tokyo 150-0001 - T: (03) 34023001, Fax: 34057714, E-mail: official@watarium.co.jp, Internet: http://www.watarium.co.jp. Head: Shizuko Watari
Fine Arts Museum 23703

Wocoal Art Center, Spiral, 5-6-23 Minami Aoyama, Minato-ku, Tokyo 107-0062 - T: (03) 34981171, E-mail: info@spiral.co.jp, Internet: http://www.spiral.co.jp
Public Gallery 23704

Yakyu Taiiku Hakubutsukan (Baseball Hall of Fame and Museum), 1-3-61 Koraku, Bunkyo-ku, Tokyo 112-0004 - T: (03) 38113600, Fax: 38115369, E-mail: mailadm@baseball-museum.or.jp, Internet: http://www.baseball-museum.or.jp. Head: Shojiro Ukita
Special Museum 23705

Yamatane Bijutsukan (Yamatane Museum of Art), Sanban-ch KS Bldg, 2 Sanban-cho, Chiyoda-ku, Tokyo 102-0075 - T: (03) 32395911, Fax: 36691954. Head: Tomiji Yamazaki
Fine Arts Museum - 1966
1800 Japanese-style paintings from the 19th c to the present 23706

Yayoi Museum, 2-4-3 Yayoi, Bunkyo-ku, Tokyo 113-0032 - T: (03) 38120012, Fax: 38120699. Head: Takumi Kano
Fine Arts Museum 23707

Yokoyama Taikan Memorial Hall, 1-4-24 Ikenohata, Taito-ku, Tokyo 110-0008 - T: (03) 8211017
Fine Arts Museum
Paintings by Taikan Yokoyama, his painting materials, Yokoyamas coll of ceramics - garden 23708

Tomakomai

Tomakomai-shi Seishonen (Tomakomai Youth Science Museum), 3-1-12 Asahi-machi, Tomakomai 053-0018 - T: (0144) 339158
Special Museum 23709

Tosayamada

Ryuga-Do Cave Museun, 1340 Sakakawa, Tosayamada 782-0005 - T: (0887) 534376, Fax: 532145. Head: Akira Kadowaki
Natural History Museum - 1957
Natural history, amphibia, reptiles, minerals, fossils 23710

Tottori

Tottori Folk Art Museum, 653 Sakae-machi, Tottori 680-0831
Folklore Museum
Chinese, Japanese, Korean, and European ceramics, lacquer vessels, furniture, small stone Buddhist figures 23711

Tottori-kenritsu Hakubutsukan (Tottori Prefectural Museum), 2-124 Higashi-machi, Tottori 680-0011 - T: (0857) 268042, Fax: 268041. Head: Yasuo Kuuioka
Local Museum - 1972
Fine arts, archeological material, folk arts, household implements, reconstructed farmhouse interior 23712

Towa

Yorozu Tetsugoro Memorial Museum of Art, 5-135, Tsuchizawa, Towa 028-0114 - T: (0198) 424402, 424405, Fax: 424405, E-mail: yorozu00@cocoa.ocn.ne.jp. Head: Mizuo Chiba
Fine Arts Museum 23713

Towadako

Towada Natural History Museum, Yasumiya, Towadako 034-0300 - T: (0176) 752121
Natural History Museum 23714

Toyama

Sato Art Museum Toyama, 1-33 Honmaru, Toyama 930-0081 - T: (0764) 329031, Fax: 329080. Head: Sukekuro Sato
Fine Arts Museum 23715

Toyama Kenminkaikan Bijutsukan (Toyama Museum of Art), 4-18 Shinsogawa, Toyama 930-0006 - T: (0764) 323111, Fax: 322024. Head: Toshio Maiwa
Fine Arts Museum 23716

Toyama-kenritsu Kindai Bijutsukan (The Museum of Modern Art Toyama), 1-16-12 Nishinakano-machi, Toyama 939-8636 - T: (076) 4217111, Fax: 4225996, E-mail: bijutsukan01@tym.pref.toyama.jp, Internet: http://www.pref.toyama.jp/branches/3042/3042.htm. Head: Matsuzo Yamaguchi
Fine Arts Museum - 1981
Rouault prints, post-war art, poster coll 23717

Toyama Municipal Folkcraft Village, 1118-8 Anyobou, Toyama 930-0881 - T: (0764) 338270, Fax: 338270. Head: Osami Kouchi
Folklore Museum - 1979
Textiles, ceramics, lacquer items, furniture, clothing, basketry, in reconstructed farmhouse 23718

Toyama Museum, 1-62, Honmaru, Toyama 933 - T: (0764) 327911, Fax: 327911, Internet: http://www.jeims.co.jp/toyama-museum. Head: Tamotsu Takase
Local Museum
Ukiyo-e prints on local medicine, materials illustrating manufacture of medicine, ceramics, tiles, armor, archeological material 23719

Toyohashi

Toyohashi-shiritsu Bijutsukan (Toyohashi City Art Museum), 3 Imahashi-cho, Toyohashi 440-0801 - T: (0532) 512621, Fax: 512624. Head: Masaki Kawai
Fine Arts Museum 23720

Toyonaka

Hashimoto Museum of Art, 2-13-51-103 Terauchi, Toyonaka 560-0872 - T: (06) 8663372, Fax: 8666371. Head: Morimasa Hashimoto
Fine Arts Museum 23721

Nihon Miuka Shuraku Hakubutsukan (Open Air Museum of Old Japanese Farmhouses), 1-2 Hattori Ryokuchi, Toyonaka 560-0873 - T: (06) 68623137, Fax: 68623147
Open Air Museum / Agriculture Museum
Farmhouses, rural buildings, thatched granaries, a rural Kabuki theater, village setting 23722

Toyota, Aichi

Toyota Municipal Museum of Art, 8-5-1 Kozakahon-machi, Toyota, Aichi 471-0034 - T: (0565) 346610, Fax: 314983, Internet: http://www.museum.toyota.aichi.jp. Head: Mitsuhiko Tera
Fine Arts Museum / Decorative Arts Museum - 1995
Modern and contemporary arts, design, craft 23723

Toyota, Hiroshima

Kosanji Temple Museum, 553-2, Setoda, Setoda-cho, Toyota, Hiroshima Hiroshima - T: (08452) 70800, Fax: 73876, E-mail: kgi00652@niftyserve.or.jp. Head: Kozo Kosanji
Religious Arts Museum - 1953
Statue of Amitabha with jewelled crown by Kaikei, portrait of Ki-no-Tsurayuki, from Satake scroll of the thirty-six major poets, Dai-hannyaharamitta-kyo Sutra No. 99, octagonal bronze mirror with Toka flowers and Mandarin ducks design 23724

Tsu

Mie-kenritsu Bijutsukan (Mie Prefectural Art Museum), 11 Otani-cho, Tsu 514-0007 - T: (059) 2272100, 2272232, Fax: 2230570, E-mail: miekenbi@u-net.or.jp, Internet: http://www.u-net.or.jp/~miekenbi. Head: Tetsuo Sakai
Fine Arts Museum - 1953
Works of fine arts, mainly Japanese 23725

Mie-kenritsu Hakubutsukan (Mie Prefectural Museum), 147-2 Komei-cho, Tsu 514-0006 - T: (0592) 282283, Fax: 282283, E-mail: miehaku@museum.fref.mie.jp, Internet: http://www.museum.fref.mie.jp/miehaku
Local Museum 23726

Tsukuba

Ibaraki-ken Tsukuba Bijutsukan (Tsukuba Museum of Art), 2-8 Azuma, Tsukuba 305-0031 - T: (0298) 563711, Fax: 563358, Internet: http://www.edu.pref.ibaraki.jp/board/sisetsu/tsukuba. Head: Yoshio Otsuka
Fine Arts Museum 23727

Tsuruoka

Chido Museum, 10-18 Kachuushin-machi, Tsuruoka 997-0036 - T: (0235) 221199, Fax: 223531. Head: Sakai Tadahisa
Archaeological Museum / Folklore Museum - 1950
Archeological findings with photos and illustrations of excavation sites, uniforms, Japanese and Western clothing, documents, historical photographs, rickshaws, swords and armor, calligraphy, paintings, fishing and farming gear, folk art including backpacks, dolls, lacquer items 23728

Tsuwano

Katsushika Hokusai Bijutsukan, 254 Oaza Ushiroda-Ro, Tsuwano 699-5605 - T: (08567) 21850
Fine Arts Museum
Works by Ukiyo-e artists 23729

Ube

Sekitan Kinenkan (Ube Municipal Coal Museum), Tokiwa-koen, Okiube, Ube 755-0001 - T: (0836) 315281
Science&Tech Museum 23730

Ueda

Shinano Drawing Museum, 300 Higashi, Maeyama, Ueda 386-1436 - T: (0268) 386599, Fax: 388263. Head: Seiichiro Kuboshima
Fine Arts Museum 23731

Ueda Municipal Museum, 3-3 Ninomaru, Ueda 386-0026 - T: (0268) 221274
Local Museum
Arms and armor, chests, scrolls, ceramics, reconstructed farmhouse interior, costumes, local wares, local archeological material 23732

Yamamoto Kanae Memorial Museum, 3-4 Ninomaru, Ueda 386-0026 - T: (0268) 222693
Fine Arts Museum
Oil paintings, watercolors, and drawings by Kanae Yamamoto, his palette and personal effects 23733

Ueno

Basho Memorial Museum, 117-13, Marunouchi, Ueno 518-8770 - T: (0595) 212219, Fax: 212219
Fine Arts Museum
50 scrolls of calligraphy of the famous 27th c haiku poet Matsuo Basho and his pupils, statue of poet who was born here - library 23734

Iga Art and Industry Institute, 6-1, Marunouchi, Ueno 518-0873
Decorative Arts Museum
Art, industrial art 23735

Iga-Ryu Ninja Yashiki (Ninja Museum of Igaryu), Ueno-koen, 117 Marunouchi, Ueno 518-0873 - E-mail: iga-ueno@mxs, meshnet.or.jp, Internet: http://www.sphere.ad.jp/ninja/
Folklore Museum / Local Museum
Clothes, swords, ladders, climbing tools, and other equipment used by the ninja, men serving as spies for the shogunate, costumed mannequins with demon masks 23736

Uji, Kyoto

Asahi-yaki Pottery Museum, 11 Uji-Yamada, Uji, Kyoto 611-0021 - T: (0774) 232511, Fax: 232513, E-mail: info@asahiyaki.com, Internet: http://www.asahiyaki.com. Head: Hosai Matsubayashi
Decorative Arts Museum 23737

Byodo-in Treasure House, 116 Uji-Renge, Uji, Kyoto 611-0021
Religious Arts Museum - 1972
Painted doors, bronze phoenixes, a large bell, wooden Buddhist angels, exhibits about the painted disigns on the wooden beams of the temple 23738

Uodo

Uodu Buried Forest Museum, 814 Shakadou, Uodo 937-0067 - T: (0765) 221049
Natural History Museum 23739

Uodu History and Folklore Museum, 1070 Tenjinyama, Ogawaji, Uodo 937-0022 - T: (0765) 317220
Historical Museum / Folklore Museum 23740

Urahoro

Urahoro-cho Kyodo Hakubutsukan (Urahoro Municipal Museum), 23 Higashi-yama-cho, Urahoro 089-5612 - T: (0155) 762009. Head: Katsuyuki Iemura
Local Museum 23741

Urawa

Saitama-kenritsu Kindai Bijutsukan (Museum of Modern Art Saitama), 9-30-1 Tokiwa, Urawa 336-0001 - T: (048) 8240110, Fax: 8240119, E-mail: momas@saitama-j.or.jp, Internet: http://www.pref.saitama.jp/what/what_23/01.html. Head: Yukito Tanaka
Fine Arts Museum - 1982
20th c and contemporary art by Claude Monet, Camille Pissarro, André Derain, Pablo Picasso, Paul Delvaux, László Moholy-Nagy, Hans Arp, Tsuguharu Fujita, Ei-kyu, Sadamasa Motonage, Ai-o, Yayoi Kusama, Shusaku Arakawa, Yasumasa Morimura, Shigeo Toya, Toshikatsu Endo 23742

Utsunomiya

Tochigi-kenritsu Bijutsukan (Tochigi Prefectural Museum of Fine Arts), 4-2-7 Sakura, Utsunomiya 320-0043 - T: (028) 6213566, Fax: 6213569, Internet: http://www.art.pref.tochigi.jp. Head: Kaku Ishikawa
Fine Arts Museum - 1972
Japanese modern paintings, crafts, sculptures, prints, British modern paintings, sculptures 23743

Tochigi-kenritsu Hakubutsukan (Tochigi Prefectural Museum), 2-2 Mutsumi-cho, Utsunomiya 320-0865 - T: (0286) 341311, Fax: 341310. Head: Kazuo Ikejima
Local Museum - 1971
Arms, paintings, scrolls, manuscripts, mineral coll 23744

Uwajima

Uwajima-shiritsu Date Hakubutsukan (Uwajima Date Museum), 9-14 Goten-machi, Uwajima 798-0061 - T: (0895) 227776
Local Museum 23745

Wakayama

Kii Fudoki-No-Oka Museum, 1411 Iwahashi, Iwase, Wakayama 640-8301 - T: (0734) 716123
Local Museum 23746

Wakayama-kenritsu Hakubutsukan (Wakayama Prefectural Museum), 1-4-14 Fukigami, Wakayama 640-8137 - T: (0734) 368670, Fax: 368662
Historical Museum / Local Museum
Painted room dividers and vertical wall scrolls, paintings, portable shrine, ceramics 23747

Wakayama-kenritsu Kindai Bijutsukan (Museum of Modern Art Wakayama), 1-4-14 Fukiage, Wakayama 640-8137 - T: (073) 4368690, Fax: 4361337, E-mail: post@moma-w.com, Internet: http://www.wakayama.go.jp/prefg/500100/bunkazai/museum1/110.html. Head: Chihiro Tabata
Fine Arts Museum - 1970
Works of modern and contemporary art (Japanese and foreign) and print coll, Pablo Picasso, George Segal, Banka Nonagase, Kigai Kawaguchi, Frank Stella, Mark Rothko, Yuzo Seaki, Kyokichi Tanaka 23748

Warabi

Kyosai Kawanabe Memorial Museum, 4-36-4 Minami-cho, Warabi 335-0003 - T: (048) 4419780, Fax: 4453755, Internet: http://www2.ocn.ne.jp/~kkkb. Head: Kusumi Kawanabe
Fine Arts Museum
Paintings by Kyosai Kawanabe in thruly Japanese tradition 23749

Yahiko

Yahiko-jinja Treasure House, Oaza Yahiko, Yahiko 959-0323
Religious Arts Museum
Paintings, handicrafts, swords, No masks, calligraphy 23750

Yakage

Yakage Museum, 3118-1 Yakage, Yakage 714-1201 - T: (0866) 822110, Fax: 821454. Head: Tetsuya Dansako
Local Museum 23751

Yamagata

Yamagata-kenritsu Hakubutsukan (Yamagata Prefectural Museum), Kajo-koen, 1-8, Kajo-machi, Yamagata 990-0826 - T: (0236) 451111, Fax: 451112
Local Museum - 1970
Archeological finds, ethnographic material, folk art, natural history, local wares, geology 23752

Yamagata Museum of Art, 1-63, Otemachi, Yamagata 990-0046 - T: (023) 6223090, Fax: 6223145, E-mail: yamabi@seagreen.ocn.ne.jp, Internet: http://www.yamagata-art-museum.or.jp. Head: Kyoichi Okazaki
Fine Arts Museum - 1962
Paintings, sculpture, handicraft, bronzes - galleries 23753

Yamaguchi

Yamaguchi Hakabutsukan (Yamaguchi Museum), 8-2 Kasuga-cho, Yamaguchi 753-0073 - T: (0839) 220294, Fax: 220353, Internet: http://www.pref.yamaguchi.jp/e4hakabu.htm. Head: Yasuhisa Yamada
Local Museum - 1912
Historical materials, especially on Yamaguchi prefecture, historical materials of technology, specimens of natural hist 23754

Yamaguchi-kenritsu Bijutsukan (Yamaguchi Prefectural Museum of Art), 3-1 Kameyama-cho, Yamaguchi 753-0089 - T: (0839) 257788, Fax: 257790, Internet: http://www.pref.yamaguchi.jp/e4yamart.htm. Head: Ryosuke Kawano
Fine Arts Museum 23755

Yamanakako

Gallery Abarth, 506-296 Mukoukiritume, Hirano, Yamanakako 401-0502 - T: (0555) 624884, Internet: http://www.gallery-abarth.co.jp
Science&Tech Museum 23756

Yamatokoriyama

Nara-kenritsu Minzoku Hakubutsukan (Nara Prefectural Museum of Folk Culture), 545 Yata-machi, Yamatokoriyama 630-0000 - T: (07435) 33171
Folklore Museum - 1974
Exhibit on the agricultural life of the area before modern equipment, rice culture, tea plantations, lumbering tools, photographs and drawings, household lacquer utensils, clothing baskets, portable shrines 23757

Yasugi

Adachi Museum of Art, 320 Furukawa-cho, Yasugi 692-0064 - T: (0854) 287111, Fax: 286733, Internet: http://www.adachi-museum.or.jp. Head: Takanori Adachi
Fine Arts Museum - 1970
20th c Japanese painting, ceramics, sculpture, woodprints - Japanese garden 23758

Wako Hakubutsukan (Museun of Japanese Steel), 1508, Yasugi-cho, Yasugi 692-0011 - T: (0854) 232500. Head: Tamiya Kishida
Science&Tech Museum
Iron manufacture, traditional techniques, natural hist 23759

Yokogoshi

Northern Culture Museum, 6970 Oaza-Somi, Yokogoshi 950-0205 - T: (025) 3852001, Fax: 3853929. Head: Ito Bunkichi
Fine Arts Museum / Decorative Arts Museum - 1946
Chinese sculpture and ceramics, Japanese paintings, sculpture, ceramics, lacquer items, folk art, and archeology - gardens 23760

Yokohama

Equine Museum of Japan, 1-3 Negishi-dai, Naka-ku, Yokohama 231-0853 - T: (045) 6627581, Fax: 6414604, E-mail: umahaku@bajibunka.jrao.ne.jp, Internet: http://www.bajibunka.jrao.ne.jp. Head: Dr. Akira Tanino
Special Museum - 1977
Japanese saddles and stirrups, clay image figure, scrolls, paintings, ancient and modern sculpture, fossiles - library, Pony center 23761

Hiraki Ukiyo-e Bijutsukan, 2-18-1 Takashima, Nishi-ku, Yokohama 220-0011 - T: (045) 4652233, Fax: 4652234
Fine Arts Museum
Ukiyo-e prints 23762

Iwasaki Museum, 254 Yamate-cho, Naka-ku, Yokohama 231-0846 - T: (045) 6232111, Fax: 6232257
Fine Arts Museum 23763

Kanagawa-kenritsu Hakabutsukan (Kanagawa Prefectural Museum of Cultural History), 5-60 Minami-Nakadori, Naka-ku, Yokohama 231-0006 - T: (045) 2010926, Fax: 2017364, E-mail: fvbi9550@infoweb.or.jp, Internet: http://www2.infoweb.or.jp/kanagawa-museum. Head: Osamu Murakami, Masao Tanaka
Local Museum
Exhibits on local weaving, farming, and fishing, household tools Bunraku puppets, archeological finds with photos and models of excavation sites, late medieval sculpture and painting, models of temples and villas, history of the region 23764

Kanagawa-kenritsu Kanazawabunko Museum (Kanagawa Prefectural Kanazawabunko-Museum), 142 Kanazawa-cho, Kanazawa-ku, Yokohama 236-0015 - T: (045) 7019069, Fax: 7881060, Internet: http://www.planet.pref.kanagawa.jp/city/kanazawa.htm
Fine Arts Museum
Sculptures, paintings, calligraphy, historical documents - library 23765

Kanagawa Prefectural Gallery, 3-1, Yamashita-cho, Naka-ku, Yokohama 231-0023 - T: (045) 6625901 ext 270, Fax: 6413184. Head: Akira Ohno
Public Gallery 23766

Sankei-en Garden, 58-1 Honmoku-sannotani, Naka-ku, Yokohama 231-0824 - T: (045) 6210635, Fax: 6216343, Internet: http://www.sankeien.or.jp. Head: Hidenobu Takahide
Open Air Museum
Villa, teahouses, temple, pagoda, wealthy farmers house, decorative sliding doors - resthouse, gallery 23767

Shin-Yokohama Ramen Hakubutsukan, 2-14-21 Shin-Yokohama, Kohoku-ku, Yokohama 222-0033 - T: (045) 4710503
Local Museum 23768

Silk Hakubutsukan (Silk Museum), 1 Yamashita-cho, Naka-ku, Yokohama 231-0023 - T: (045) 6410841, Fax: 6710727, Internet: http://www.silkmuseum.or.jp. Head: Hiroshi Okazaki
Special Museum 23769

Sogo Museum of Art, 2-18-1, Takashima, Nishi-ku, Yokohama 220-8510 - T: (045) 4652361, Fax: 4652298, E-mail: yokohama_museum@sogo-dept.co.jp. Head: Kan Muto
Fine Arts Museum 23770

Yamauchi Library, 2-3-2 Azamino, Aoba-ku, Yokohama 225-0011 - T: (045) 9011225
Public Gallery 23771

Yokohama Bijutsukan (Yokohama Museum of Art), 3-4-1 Minatomirai, Nishi-ku, Yokohama 220-0012 - T: (045) 2210300, Fax: 2210317, E-mail: master@art-museum.city.yokohama.jp, Internet: http://www.art-museum.city.yokohama.jp
Fine Arts Museum - 1989
Paintings, modern sculpture, metal art objects, photographs 23772

Yokohama Doll Museum, 18 Yamashita-cho, Naka-ku, Yokohama 231-0023 - T: (045) 6719361
Decorative Arts Museum 23773

Yokohama Kaiko Shiryokan (Yokohama History Museum), 3 Nihon Odori, Naka-ku, Yokohama 231-0021 - T: (045) 2012100, Fax: 2012102, Internet: http://city.yokohama.jp/yhspot/kaikou-e.html
Historical Museum 23774

Yokohama Maritime Museum and Nippon-Maru Memorial Park, 2-1-1 Minatomirai, Nishi-ku, Yokohama 220-0012 - T: (045) 2210280, Fax: 2210277, Internet: http://city.yokohama.jp/yhspot/nihon-e.html. Head: Katsuo Midorikawa
Science&Tech Museum - 1989
Ships, marine products, maritime transportation - library 23775

Yokosuka

Kinenkan Mikasa (Memorialship Mikasa), Inaoka, Yokosuka 238-0003 - T: (0468) 225225, Fax: 229822
Military Museum - 1926
Memorial material related to the Russian-Japanese war, historical documents 23776

Yokosuka-shi Hakubutsukan (Yokosuka City Museum), 95 Fukadadai, Yokosuka 238-0016 - T: (0468) 243688, Fax: 243658, Internet: http://www.museum.yokosuka.kanagawa.jp/. Head: Mitsugu Ishida
Local Museum - 1953
Archeological finds with maps and photos, folkloric materials, paleontological specimen, vascular plant marine algae, fungi, insects, fish, luminous organisms - marine biological garden, botanical garden 23777

Yokote

Akita-kenritsu Kindai Bijutsukan (Akita Museum of Modern Art), 62-46 Tomigasawa, Akasaka-cho, Yokote 013-0064 - T: (0182) 338855, Fax: 338858
Fine Arts Museum - 1994
Paintings in Western style or Akita school of Ranga 23778

Yomitanson

Yomitan Township History and Folk Art Hall, 708-4 Aza Zakimi, Yomitanson 579-8052
Historical Museum / Folklore Museum
Local farming and fishing gear, household utensils, Okinawan textiles, costumes, music instruments 23779

Yonago

Sanin Historical Collection, 20 Naka-machi, Yonago 683-0822 - T: (0859) 683227161. Head: Kaneo Itami
Historical Museum - 1940
Exhibits and specimens of historical interest, archeology 23780

Yonago City Museum of Art, 12, Naka-machi, Yonago 683-0822 - T: (0859) 342424, Fax: 330679, E-mail: yonedart@sanmedia.or.jp. Head: Takayoshi Sugimoto
Fine Arts Museum 23781

Yonezawa

Uesugi Shrine Treasure House, 1-4-13 Marunouchi, Yonezawa 992-0052 - T: (0238) 223189. Head: Yoshifumi Daijoji
Religious Arts Museum
Paintings, documents, textiles, 16th c costumes, armor, swords, and spears 23782

Yonezawa Municipal Uesugi Museum, 1-4-13 Marunouchi, Yonezawa 992-0053 - T: (0238) 237302
Local Museum 23783

Yoshino

Nyoirin-ji Treasure House, Nyoirin-ji, Tono-o, Yoshinoyama, Yoshino 639-3115 - T: (0746) 323008. Head: Teishin Kashima
Religious Arts Museum
Paintings, calligraphy, sculpture; armor and swords, objects of historical interest 23784

Yoshimizu-jinja Yoshinoyama (Yoshimizu-jinja Collection), Yoshinoyama, Yoshino 639-3115 - T: (07463) 3024. Head: Ryuhei Nakazawa
Military Museum / Decorative Arts Museum
Paintings, calligraphy, documents, arms and armor, metalwork, lacquer items, music instruments, ceramics, in the former residence of 14th c emperor, his personal effects 23785

Jordan

Al-Karak

Al-Karak Museum for Archaeology and Folklore, Castle, Al-Karak 61110 - T: (03) 351149
Local Museum / Archaeological Museum
Popular life, local history 23786

Al-Mazar

Mazar Islamic Museum, Al-Mazar 61610 - T: (03) 371042
Religious Arts Museum / Folklore Museum
Sculptures, ceramics, coins, antiquities 23787

Amman

Animal Museum, c/o University of Jordan, Dept. of Biological Sciences, Faculty Sciences, POB 1682, Amman 11943 - T: (06) 5843555 ext 2300, Fax: 5840150, E-mail: admin@ju.edu.jo, Internet: http://www.ju.edu.jo
Natural History Museum - 1972 23788

The Anthropological National Folklore Museum, c/o University of Jordan, POB 1682, Amman 11943 - T: (06) 5843555 ext 3739, Fax: 5840150, E-mail: admin@ju.edu.jo, Internet: http://www.ju.edu.jo
Ethnology Museum / Folklore Museum / University Museum - 1980 23789

Biology Museum, c/o University of Jordan, POB 1682, Amman 11943 - T: (06) 5843555 ext 2300, Fax: 5840150, E-mail: admin@ju.edu.jo, Internet: http://www.ju.edu.jo
Natural History Museum / University Museum 23790

Children's Heritage and Science Museum, Haya Arts Center, Shmeisani, Amman 10000
Science&Tech Museum
Sciences, geology, biology, mechanical and electrical items, light 23791

Coins Museum, c/o Central Bank of Jordan, POB 37, Amman 11118 - T: (06) 5630301, Fax: 5638889, 5639730
Special Museum
Coins from pre-Islamic to present time 23792

Geology Museum, Eighth Circle, Amman - T: (06) 5857612, Fax: 5811866
Natural History Museum
Rocks, minerals, geological excavation instruments 23793

Insects Museum, c/o University of Jordan, Dept. of Horticulture and Plant Protection, Faculty Agriculture, POB 1682, Amman 11943 - T: (06) 5843555 ext 3412, Fax: 5840150, E-mail: admin@ju.edu.jo, Internet: http://www.ju.edu.jo
Natural History Museum - 1976 23794

Islamic Museum, King Abdallah Mosque, Amman - T: (06) 5672155, Fax: 5672155
Religious Arts Museum
Pottery, historical photos, King Abdallah 23795

Jordan Archaeological Museum, 2 Jabal Al-Qala'a, Citedel Hill, Amman, mail addr: c/o Department of Antiquities, POB 88, Amman - T: (06) 5638795. Head: Mosa Zayat
Archaeological Museum - 1951
Pottery, metalworks, glass, Jordan antiquities - library 23796

Jordan Folklore and Jewelry Museum, West of Roman Amphitheater, Downtown, Amman, mail addr: c/o Department of Antiquities, POB 88, Amman - T: (06) 5651760. Head: Sa'diya Al-Tel
Folklore Museum - 1972
National traditional costumes and jewelry, mosaics from Jerash and Madaba (5th-6th c) 23797

Jordan Museum of Popular Tradition, East of Roman Amphitheater, Downtown, Amman, mail addr: c/o Department of Antiquities, POB 88, Amman - T: (06) 5630128, Fax: 5651119. Head: Iman Quda
Ethnology Museum / Folklore Museum - 1972
Traditional life, costumes, furnishings, musical instr, handicrafts, jewelry, rugs 23798

Jordan National Gallery of Fine Arts, Jabal Al-Weibdeh, Amman - T: (06) 5630128, Fax: 5651119
Fine Arts Museum
Contemporary Jordan, Arab, Muslim and developing countries paintings, sculptures, ceramics, European oriental paintings 23799

Martyr's Memorial and Military Museum, University Rd, Sports City, Amman - T: (06) 5664240
Military Museum
Military memorabilia from the Great Arab Revolt (1916) to today 23800

Medical Museum, c/o University of Jordan, Faculty Medicine, POB 1682, Amman 11943 - T: (06) 5843555 ext 3412, Fax: 5840150, E-mail: admin@ju.edu.jo, Internet: http://www.ju.edu.jo
Historical Museum - 1980
Specimen of human anatomical organs, pathology 23801

Mosaic Gallery, c/o Department of Antiquities, POB 88, Amman. Head: Nuha Absi
Decorative Arts Museum - 1972
Pieces from the Byzantine era 23802

Aqaba

Museum of Aqaba Antiquities, Aqaba Castle, Aqaba - T: (03) 313731
Historical Museum / Archaeological Museum
Ummayad Islamic archaeological finds, Roman and Byzanine pieces, Sharif Hussein Bin Ali 23803

Irbid

Irbid Archaeological Museum, c/o Yarmouk University, POB 566, Irbid - T: (02) 277066
Archaeological Museum / University Museum 23804

Jordan Natural History Museum, c/o Yarmouk University, POB 566, Irbid - T: (02) 271100 ext 2341
Natural History Museum 23805

Museum of Jordanian Heritage, Irbid, mail addr: c/o Department of Antiquities, POB 88, Amman - T: (06) 5271100 ext 3741
Archaeological Museum 23806

Jarash

Jarash Archaeological Museum, Jarash 26110 - T: (04) 452267
Archaeological Museum 23807

Madaba

Madaba Museum for Archaeology and Folklore, Madaba 17110 - T: (08) 544056
Local Museum / Archaeological Museum
Beti shaabi with oriental architecture, Jordan village handicraft, archaeological finds, mosaics 23808

Petra

Petra Archaeological Museum, Petra 71882 - T: (03) 3360209, 336044, Fax: 336010
Archaeological Museum 23809

Petra Museum, Popular Life Museum, Petra 71882, mail addr: c/o Department of Antiquities, POB 88, Amman
Local Museum 23810

Salt

Es-Salt Archaeological Museum, Salt 19110 - T: (05) 555653
Archaeological Museum 23811

Salt Museum, Popular Life Museum, Salt, mail addr: c/o Department of Antiquities, POB 88, Amman
Local Museum 23812

School Books Museum, Al-Manshyeh, Salt 19117 - T: (05) 3532519, Fax: 3555735
Library with Exhibitions
Arabic, English, Jordanian and Palestinian school books since 1921 23813

Kazakhstan

Aktubinsk

Memorialnyj Muzej Alii Moldagulovoj, Geroiny Sovetskogo Sojuza (Memorial Museum of Alia Moldagulova), Kireeva 7, 463001 Aktubinsk - T: (03132) 28583. Head: G. Akimova
Historical Museum 23814

Almaty

Centralnyj Gosudarstvennyj Muzej Kazachstana (Central State Museum of Kazakhstan), Panfilovcev Park 28, Almaty. Head: Rayan K. Košambekova
Historical Museum / Natural History Museum
History, geology, meteorology of the Kazakh region 23815

The Kasteyev State Museum of Arts of the Republic of Kazakhstan, ul Satpaeva 30a, 480090 Almaty - T: (03272) 478249, Fax: 478669, E-mail: kazart@nursat.kz. Head: Baytursun Esjanovič Umorbeckov
Fine Arts Museum - 1976
Kazach art, Russian art (15th-20th c), Soviet art, Western European art, Oriental art - library 23816

Muzej Narodnych Muzykalnych Instrumentov Kazachstana (Museum of Kazakh Popular Musical Instruments), ul Proletarskaja 24, 480100 Almaty - T: (03272) 616316. Head: N. Murzabekas
Music Museum 23817

National Literary and Memorial Museum-Complex of Sabit Mukanov and Gabit Musrepov, ul M. Tulebaeva 125, 480091 Almaty - T: (03272) 635912. Head: N. Mukanova
Special Museum - 1999 23818

Arkalyk

Istoriko-Kraevedčeskij Muzej (Historical and Regional Museum), Pr Stroitelej30, Arkalyk. Head: M. Birmanova
Local Museum / Historical Museum 23819

Čapaev

Memorialnyj Muzej V.I. Čapaeva (V.I Capaev Memorial Museum), Ul Čapaevskaja36, Čapaev. Head: N.V. Podkuyko
Local Museum 23820

Celinograd

Celinogradskij Istoriko-Kraevedčeskij Muzej (Celinograd Historical and Regional Museum), Ul Oktjabrskaja 57, 473000 Celinograd - T: 21956, 27616. Head: L.G. Yermolenko
Local Museum / Historical Museum 23821

Celinogradskij Muzej Izobrazitelnych Iskusstv (Celinograd Art Museum), Pr Celinnikov 3, 473024 Celinograd - T: 62319. Head: Valentin V. Pak
Fine Arts Museum 23822

Čimkent

Čimkentskij Istoriko-Kraevedčeskij Muzej (Chimkent Historical and Regional Museum), ul Sovetskaja 13, Čimkent. Head: E.B. Kazyhanov
Historical Museum / Local Museum 23823

Otar Memlekettik Archeologicalik Korik Muzej, Al Zarabi 1, Cacelder, Čimkent - T: 21150. Head: A. Ecjanov
Archaeological Museum 23824

Džambul

Džambul Historical and Regional Museum, Tole bi 55, Džambul - T: (0326) 32585
Historical Museum / Local Museum / Fine Arts Museum - 1931
Picture coll of L. Brümmer (1889-1971), coll of ancient sculptures, coll of ancient ceramic plates, dishes, jugs etc 23825

Džambulskij Literaturnyj Memorialnyj Muzej (Dzambul Literary Memorial Museum), Džambul. Head: M. Kozhachev
Special Museum 23826

Gosudarstvennyj Muzej-Reservat Pamjatniki Drevnego Taraza (State Park Museum on the Monuments of Ancient Taraz), Ul Suleymanov 10, Džambul. Head: Azhibay Apsemetov
Historical Museum 23827

Džezkazgan

Istoriko-Kraevedčeskij Muzej Džezkazgana (Dzezkazgan Historical and Regional Museum), Kaumonotes Blvd 26, Džezkazgan. Head: Aleksandr Lobas
Historical Museum / Local Museum 23828

Guriev

Gurievskij Istoriko-Kraevedčeskij Muzej (Guriev Historical and Regional Museum), Ul Ordžonikidze 14, 465050 Guriev. Head: N.A. Aknazarov
Historical Museum / Local Museum 23829

Karaganda

Istoriko-Kraevedčeskij Muzej (Karaganda Historical and Regional Museum), Ul Kirova 38, Karaganda. Head: Valentina Vassilyeva
Historical Museum / Local Museum 23830

Kokčetav

Istoriko-Kraevedčeskij Muzej Kokčetava (Kokcetav Historical and Regional Museum), Ul Kalinina 35, Kokčetav. Head: Valentina Ussenko
Historical Museum / Local Museum 23831

Kzyl-Orda

Istoriko-Kraevedčeskij Muzej Kzyl-Orda (Kzyl-Orda Historical and Regional Museum), Ul Auezov 290, Kzyl-Orda. Head: Kumekbay Karakuzov
Historical Museum / Local Museum 23832

Kuybyshev Republican Memorial Museum, Ul Chapaev 32, Kokchetav, Kzyl-Orda
Historical Museum 23833

Pavlodar

Pavlodarskij Istoriko-Kraevedčeskij Muzej (Pavlodar Historical and Regional Museum), Ul Lenina 129, Pavlodar
Historical Museum / Local Museum 23834

Petropavlovsk

Istoriko-Kraevedčeskij Muzej Vostočnogo Kazachstana (Oriental Kazakh Regional Historical Museum), Ul Lenina 48, Petropavlovsk. Head: Konstantin Ushkov
Historical Museum 23835

Semipalatinsk

Memorialny Literaturny Muzej F.M. Dostoevskogo (F.M. Dostoevskij Regional Commemorative Literary Museum), ul Dostoevskogo 118, 490050 Semipalatinsk - T: (03222) 627942. Head: I.F. Melnikova
Special Museum - 1971
On the writer F.M. Dostoevskij 23836

Respublikanskij Literaturnyij Memorialnyj Muzej Abaja (Abai Commemorative Literary Republican Museum), Ul Lenina 12, 490050 Semipalatinsk. Head: T.S. Ibragimov
Historical Museum - 1940
Kazakh literary history, memorabilia of the poet Ibrahim Abay Kunanbaev - library 23837

Semipalatinskij Istoriko-Kraevedčeskij Muzej (Semipalatinsk Historical and Regional Museum), Ul Abaja 90, 490050 Semipalatinsk - T: (03222) 626732. Head: A.J. Zjablicki
Historical Museum / Local Museum 23838

Sevčenko

Gosudarstvennyj Muzej-Reservat Mangyšlaka Sokroviščа-Zapovedniki Mangyšlaka i Ustyrta (Mangyslak State Park Museum Sites and Monuments of Mangyslak and Ustyrt), Mikrorajon 23, Sevčenko
Historical Museum 23839

Istoriko-Kraevedčeskij Muzej Mangyšlaka (Mangyslak Historical and Regional Museum), Ul Mikrorajon 66, Sevčenko. Head: G. Idrisov
Historical Museum / Local Museum 23840

Shymkent

Otrar State Archaeological Park Museum, Shauldir, 487110 Shymkent - T: (03252) 21150. Head: M. Kojaev
Archaeological Museum - 1980
Archeology, ethnology, art, metalwork, pottery, glass, woodwork, jewellery, coins 23841

Temirtau

Istoriko-Kraevedčeskij Muzej (Historical and Regional Museum), 4th Dept., 472323 Temirtau. Head: A.V. Spassibenko
Historical Museum / Local Museum 23842

Uralsk

Uralskij Istoriko-Kraevedčeskij Muzej (Uralsk Regional and Historical Museum), Ul Lenina 184, Uralsk
Local Museum / Historical Museum 23843

Ust-Kamenogorsk

East Kazakhstan Historical and Regional Museum, Ul Urickogo 40, Ust-Kamenogorsk - T: (03232) 655460. Head: A.V. Mikhalevsky
Historical Museum / Local Museum - 1946
Rocks and minerals, polyanthology, Scythian Saka tribes, ancient art, Old Believers applied arts - Archeological, ethnographical, nature dept 23844

Muzej Narodov Vostočnogo Kazachstana → Vostočno Kazachstanskij Ėtnografičeskij Muzej

Vostočno Kazachstanskij Ėtnografičeskij Muzej (Oriental Kazakh Ethnographical Museum), ul Golovkov 29, 492024 Ust-Kamenogorsk - T: (03232) 264661, Fax: 269099. Head: Nikolai Alekseevič Zaitsev
Ethnology Museum 23845

Kenya

Gilgil

Kariandusi Prehistoric Site Museum, POB 91, Gilgil. Head: Daniel Kipkorir
Archaeological Museum - 1928
Stone Age finds, animal fossils, drawings, casts of skulls, stone axes - national archives 23846

Hyrax Hill

Hyrax Hill Museum, Hyrax Hill, mail addr: POB 9535, Nakuru. Head: Nancy Kiprop
Archaeological Museum
Excavation of three major areas of prehistoric settlements 23847

Kabarnet

Kabarnet Museum, POB 419, Kabarnet - T: (032) 821221. Head: Andrew Cheptum
Local Museum
Material culture of the local peoples 23848

Kapenguria

Kapenguria Museum, POB 383, Kapenguria. Head: Jane Chebitwey
Historical Museum - 1993
Kenya's political development and struggle for independence 23849

Kisumu

Kisumu Museum, Mombasa Rd, Kisumu, mail addr: POB 1779, Kisumu - T: (035) 530804, Fax: 530797, E-mail: kisumuse@arcc.or.ke. Head: Ali Salim Baakabe
Natural History Museum - 1980
Crocodile pond, snake park, traditional Luo homestead, bird's cages and fresh water aquarium, displays of material culture of the peoples of the Western Rift valley and Nyanza Province 23850

Kitale

Kitale Museum, Eldoret Rd, Kitale, mail addr: POB 1219, Kitale - T: (039) 20670. Head: Ibrahim Mahmoud
Historical Museum / Science&Tech Museum - 1926
History, science - library 23851

Lamu

Lamu Museum, POB 48, Lamu - T: (012) 633073, 633201, Fax: 633402. Head: Joseph Cheruiyot
Ethnology Museum / Decorative Arts Museum
Ethnology and folklore, decorative arts, silver and gold work, carved wood 23852

Meru

Meru Museum, Saint Pauls Rd, Meru, mail addr: POB 597, Meru - T: (028) 20482. Head: Peter D. Okwaro
Local Museum - 1973
Material culture of Meru tribe, tools of prehistoric Achulean culture, entomological and ornithological coll from Mt Kenya region - library 23853

Mombasa

Fort Jesus Museum, Nkurumah Rd, Mombasa, mail addr: POB 82412, Mombasa - T: (011) 2312839, 2225934, E-mail: nmkfortj@swiftmombasa.com. Head: Ali Abubakar
Local Museum - 1960
Hist of Kenia, Chinese porcelain, Islamic and local wares from archaeological sites on the coast of Kenya, Arab woodwork and ceramics 23854

Nairobi

Karen Blixen Museum, POB 40658, Nairobi - T: (020) 3882779, E-mail: nml@africaonline.co.ke. Head: Mary Sefu
Special Museum / Decorative Arts Museum 23855

The Museum Studio and Arts Centre, POB 40658, Nairobi - T: (020) 3751515, 3748696, Fax: 3740060, E-mail: info@kuonatrust.org. Head: Lina Karingi
Fine Arts Museum 23856

National Museum Nairobi, Museum Hill, Nairobi, mail addr: POB 40658, Nairobi - T: (020) 3742162, Fax: 3741424, E-mail: nmk@museums.or.ke, Internet: http://www.museums.or.ke. Head: James Maikweki
Natural History Museum
Cultural heritage, neolithic finds, palaeontological, ethnographical, archaeological, bio diversity 23857

National Museums of Kenya, Museum Hill Rd, Nairobi, mail addr: POB 40658, Nairobi - T: (020) 3742131, Fax: 3741424, E-mail: nmk@africaonline.co.ke. Head: Dr. Mohamed Isahakia
Natural History Museum / Ethnology Museum - 1911
Natural hist of Eastern Africa, palaeontology, prehist, archaeology, ethnography, geology, zoology - library 23858

Narok

Narok Museum, POB 468, Narok. Head: Omari Babu
Folklore Museum
Cultural traditions of the Maasai and other speakers of the Maa language, cultural artefacts 23859

Olorgesailie

Olorgesailie Prehistoric Site Museum, 27 Magadi Rd, Olorgesailie, mail addr: POB 40658, Olorgesailie
Archaeological Museum
Stone Age finds 23860

Watamu

Gede Museum and National Monument, Mombasa Rd, Old Malindi, Watamu, mail addr: POB 5067, Malindi - T: (012) 32065. Head: Abdalla Alausy
Archaeological Museum / Decorative Arts Museum
Finds from excavations of the site incl imported Chinese and Islamic porcelains, glass, shell beads, gold and silver jewellery, coins, local pottery 23861

Korea, Democratic People's Republic

Haeju

Haeju Historical Museum, Haeju
Historical Museum 23862

Hamhung

Hamhung Historical Museum, Hamhung. Head: Kim Ik Myon
Historical Museum 23863

Hyangsan

Myohyang-san Museum, Hyangsan. Head: Choi Hyong Min
Local Museum 23864

Pyongyang

Korean Art Gallery, Pyongyang. Head: Kim Sang Choi
Fine Arts Museum
Korean art 23865

Korean Central Ethnographic Museum, Central District, Pyongyang. Head: Jon Moon Jin
Ethnology Museum
Anthropology, ethnography 23866

Korean Central Historical Museum, Central District, Pyongyang. Head: Jang Jong Sin
Historical Museum
Korean hist from prehistory to the 20th c 23867

Korean Revolutionary Museum, Central District, Pyongyang. Head: Hwang Sun Hui
Historical Museum
Historical exhibits from 1850 to the present 23868

Memorial Museum of the War of Liberation, Moranbong District, Pyongyang. Head: Thae Pyong Ryol
Historical Museum
Historic material on the 19th c to the present, exhibits on the war against Japan (1930) and the Korean War 23869

Shinchon

Shinchon Museum, Shinchon. Head: Pak In Chaik
Local Museum 23870

Shinuiju

Shinuiju Historical Museum, Shinuiju. Head: Pak Yong Gwan
Historical Museum 23871

Wonsan

Wonsan Historical Museum, Wonsan. Head: Jo Gang Baik
Historical Museum 23872

Korea, Republic

Andong

Andong Teachers College Museum, c/o Teachers College, Andong 660
Special Museum / University Museum
Teaching coll 23873

Sangji Vocational College Museum, c/o Sangji Vocational College, Yulse-dong, Andong 760-070 - T: (0571) 23021
Special Museum / University Museum
Teaching coll 23874

Asan

Onyang Minsok Pakmulgwan (Onyang Folk Museum), 403-1 Kwongok-dong, Asan 336-030 - T: (041) 5426001/3, Fax: 5426005, E-mail: - oymuseumunitel.co.kr, Internet: http://www.i-museum.kr/onyang. Head: Tak Keun Shin
Folklore Museum - 1978
Traditional arts of Korea, folklore - library, audiovisual room 23875

Cheju

Cheju College Museum, Yongdam 2-dong, Cheju 590 - T: (064) 236140
Special Museum / University Museum
Teaching coll 23876

Cheju-do Folk Craft, Folklore and Natural History Museum, 996-1, Ildo 2-dong, Cheju 590 - T: (064) 222465
Folklore Museum / Natural History Museum
Folk items, plants and native animals from the island of Chejudo 23877

Cheju Folklore Museum, 2505 Samyang 3-dong, Cheju 690-073 - T: (064) 7551976. Head: Song-gi Chin
Folklore Museum - 1964
Domestic tools and utensils, cultural artifacts - library 23878

Cheju National University Museum, Ara I Llong, Cheju 590 - T: (064) 236140, 6141
University Museum 23879

Cheongju

Cheongju University Museum, 36 Naedeok-dong, Cheongju 360-150 - T: (0431) 542111
University Museum - 1967
Local customs and folklore - library 23880

Chinju

Chinju National Museum, 171-1 Namsong-dong, Chinju - T: (055) 7425950. Head: Sunggu Kim
Archaeological Museum - 1984
2900 artifacts from the Kaya Kingdom (A.D. 42-562) 23881

Chonan

Independence Hall of Korea, 230 Namhwa-Ri, Mokchon-Myon, Chonan 330-840 - T: (0417) 5600114, Fax: 5578167. Head: You Chul Park
Historical Museum / Museum of Classical Antiquities / Folklore Museum - 1987
Archaeology, art, anthropology, tribal coll, science, industry, Korean hist against Japanese invasion, books, documents, paintings, calligraphy 23882

Chongju

Cheongju National Museum, 87 Myeongdam-dong, Sangdang-gu, Chongju 360-191 - T: (043) 2520710, 2551632, Fax: 2580711, E-mail: cjmuweb@yahoo.co.kr, Internet: http://cheongju.museum.go.kr. Head: Sugil Go
Archaeological Museum
300 relics from the Paleolith, neolith and bronze age 2,000 artefacts from the Proto-Three kingdoms, Three kingdoms period and Goryeo/ Joseon dynasty 23883

Chonju

Chonbuk University Museum, 1-664-14, Dokjin-dong, Chonju 520 - T: (0652) 703488. Head: Prof. Kwang Cho Shin
University Museum
Teaching coll 23884

Chonju Municipal Museum, Poongnam-dong, Chonju 520 - T: (0562) 65011
Local Museum
Popular art, history of the Paeckche kingdom 23885

Chonju National Museum, 900 Hyoja-dong 2-ga, Wansan-gu, Chonju 560-020 - T: (0652) 2235651
Folklore Museum / Agriculture Museum
3000 folk and agricultural objects 23886

Chunchon

Kang Weon Folk Museums, San 3-2, San Cheon-dong, Chunchon - T: (0361) 502591
Folklore Museum / Ethnology Museum - 1977
Popular art, ethnography 23887

Chungju

Museum of Chungju National University, Iryu-Myon, Chungju 380-702 - T: (0441) 8415095, Fax: 8531236, E-mail: bsan@gukwon.chungju.ac.kr, Internet: http://www.chungju.ac.kr. Head: Il Sung Choi
University Museum - 1980
Crafts, tribal art, aquarium, science and technology 23888

Daejeon

National Science Museum of Korea, 32-2, Kuseong-dong, Yuseong-Ku, Daejeon 305-705 - T: (042) 6017983, Fax: 6017946, E-mail: hcsin@sciencemail.net, Internet: http://www.nsm.go.kr. Head: Seung-Koo Lee
Science&Tech Museum / Natural History Museum / Music Museum - 1990
Archaeological objects, musical instruments, minerals, fossils, zoology and botany coll, environment, technology, industrial products and processes 23889

Gongju

Gongju College of Education Museum, 9-6 Sinkwan-ri-san, Janggi-myun, Gongju
Special Museum / University Museum
Teaching coll 23890

Icheon

Haegang Ceramics Museum, 323-4 Sookwang-Ri, Sindoon-Myeon, Icheon - T: (0336) 342266, Fax: 341629
Decorative Arts Museum 23891

Inchon

Inchon Municipal Museum, 525 Okryon-dong, Inchon - T: (032) 8652570
Local Museum
History of Korea during the second half of the 19th c, local history 23892

Iri

Won Kwang College Museum, 344-2, Sinyong-dong, Iri 510-11 - T: (0653) 522111
University Museum
Teaching coll, Paekche relics, Buddhist art 23893

Jinhae

Naval Academy Museum, Aeng-Gok-dong, Jinhae 645-797 - T: (055) 5425562, 5491180, Fax: 5420033. Head: Kim Joo-Sik
Military Museum
Naval history of Korea, hist of Korean Naval Academy, 23894

Kangchon

Moka Buddhist Art Museum, Eho-ri, Kangchon - T: (031) 8859952
Fine Arts Museum 23895

Kangnung

Edison and Gramophone Museum, 216-4 Songjung-dong, Kangnung - T: (033) 6522500, Fax: 6521198
Music Museum 23896

Kangreung

Kangreung College Museum, Chibyou-dong, Kangreung 210
Special Museum / University Museum
Teaching coll 23897

Kwangdong College Museum, 72-1 Naegok-dong, Kangreung 210 - T: (0391) 377216
Special Museum / University Museum
Teaching coll 23898

Kimje-Gun

Tong-Jin Irrigation Folk Museum, 105 Hyochon-Ri, Kimje-Up, Kimje-Gun - T: (0658) 23121
Agriculture Museum / Folklore Museum - 1983
Traditional farming equipment, folk items 23899

Kongju

Kongju National Museum, 284-1 Chung-dong, Kongju - T: (0416) 8542205, Fax: 8568396, E-mail: Gnmu@Chollian.net, Internet: http://mediart.hcc.ac.kr/~kjm. Head: Dong Suk Kwack
Archaeological Museum / Fine Arts Museum - 1940
Archaeological finds, Korean art 23900

Kwachon

National Museum of Contemporary Art, San 58-1, Makkye-dong, Kwachon 427-080 - T: (02) 5037774/744, Fax: 5039167, Internet: http://www.moca.go.kr. Head: Man-Li Choi
Fine Arts Museum - 1969
Modern and contemporary Korean art 23901

Kwangju

Chonnam University Museum, 318 Yongbong-dong, Kwangju 500
University Museum
Teaching coll 23902

Kwangju Municipal Museum, 1004-4 Yongbbong-dong, Puk-gu, Kwangju - T: (062) 5219041, Internet: http://window.kisc.net/museum
Local Museum
3000 folk items of the southern area of Kwangju 23903

Kwangju National Museum, San 83-3 Maegok-dong, Puk-gu, Kwangju - T: (062) 5717111. Head: Gon Gil Ji
Archaeological Museum
Coll of relics from 2000 - 3000 B.C., Yuan Chinese ceramics 23904

Kyongju

Kuknip Kyongju Pakmulgwan (Kyongju National Museum), 76 Inwang-dong, Kyongju - T: (054) 7725193, Internet: http://www.museum.go.kr/local/kyoungju. Head: Nan Young Lee
Archaeological Museum - 1913
1200 cultural objects of the Silla Dynasty, 6th-7th c funeral offerings 23905

Kyongsan

Yeungnam University Museum, 214 Dae-dong, Kyongsan-eup, Kyongsan 713-800 - T: (053) 827809, 803622
University Museum
Teaching coll including relics of the Silla and Kaya kingdoms 23906

Masan

Kyongnam College Museum, 449 Wolyong-dong, Masan 610
University Museum
Teaching coll 23907

Naesokni

Emileh Museum, 34 Sangpan-ri, Naesokni - T: (043) 5432955
Special Museum 23908

Pochon

Forest Museum, 72 Jig-Dongri, Sohul Myon, Pochon 487-820 - T: (0357) 321448, Fax: 328007. Head: Seung Kul Park
Natural History Museum - 1987
Natural hist coll, botanical garden, aquarium, folk art 23909

Pusan

Dong-a University Museum, 1 Dongdaesin-dong, 3-ga, Soh-gu, Pusan 600 - T: (051) 2430011
University Museum
Teaching coll 23910

Kuknip Pusan Taehak Pakmulgwan (Pusan National University Museum), 30 San Changjun-dong, Gumjung-gu, Pusan 609-735 - T: (051) 5101836, Fax: 5812455. Head: Prof. Suk-Hee Kim
Archaeological Museum / University Museum - 1963
Archeology, cultural relics, ethnology, art objects, historical items from Pusan and Kyongsangnamdo 23911

Pusan Museum, 4-948-1 Taehyon-dong, Nam-gu, Pusan 608 - T: (051) 6246341. Head: Yong Yoon Byoung
Local Museum - 1978
Earthenware of the prehistoric and Kaya Period, ceramics, historical materials, painting, caligraphy, arts and crafts - library, auditorium, research room 23912

Puyo

Kuknip Puyo Pakmulgwan (Puyo National Museum), San 16-1, Tongnam-ri, Puyo - T: (041) 8338561
Archaeological Museum - 1939
6400 cultural articles of the Paeckche Dynasty (18 B.C.-660 A.D.) 23913

Seoul

Agricultural Museum, 75 Chungjong-no, Chung-gu, Seoul - T: (02) 3975676
Agriculture Museum 23914

Artsonje, 144-2 Sekeuk-dong, Chongro-gu, Seoul 110-200 - T: (02) 7338945, Internet: http://www.artsonje.org
Public Gallery 23915

Dan Kook University Museum, 8-3, Hannam-dong-san, Yongsan-gu, Seoul 140 - T: (02) 7970581. Head: Pae Gang Hwang
University Museum
Teaching coll 23916

Dongguk University Museum, 3-26 Pil-dong, Chung-gu, Seoul 100 - T: (02) 22603114
University Museum / Historical Museum 23917

Duksung Womens College Art Museum, 419 Ssangmun-dong, Tobong-ku, Seoul 132 - T: (02) 9151258. Head: Shin Ja Lee
Fine Arts Museum / University Museum - 1971
Folk art and crafts related to customs and manners of women in ancient Korea, modern painting, theatrical masks and costumes - library 23918

Ewha Yoja Taehakkyo Pakmulgwan (Ewha Womens University Museum), 11-1, Daehyon-dong, Sodaemun-gu, Seoul 120 - T: (02) 3603152, Fax: 3603153, E-mail: mailbox@museum.ewha.ac.kr. Head: Hongnam Kim
Decorative Arts Museum / Fine Arts Museum / University Museum - 1935
Gold ornaments, porcelain, paintings of Yi Dynasty, furniture, sculpture - library 23919

Gan-Song Art Museum, c/o Center for the Study of Korean Arts, 97-1 Sungbuk-dong, Sungbuk-gu, Seoul 132 - T: (02) 7620442. Head: Sung Woo Chun
Fine Arts Museum - 1938
Korean art 23920

Great King Sejong Memorial Hall, San 1-157 Chongyangri-dong, Tongdaemun.gu, Seoul - T: (02) 9662571
Historical Museum 23921

Hangguk Minsok-chon (Korean Folk Village), 107 Para-ri, Kihung-up, Yongin-kun, Kyonggi-do, Seoul 449-900 - T: (02) 2832106, Fax: 2814051. Head: Injae Maeng
Folklore Museum - 1973
Korean folklore (included archaeological, historical and folk material) 23922

Hansong Womens College Museum, 2-392-2, Samson-dong, Songbuk-gu, Seoul 132
University Museum
Teaching coll 23923

Hong-ik University Museum, 72-1, Sangsu-dong, Mapo-gu, Seoul 121
University Museum
Teaching coll, modern paintings, history of art, calligraphy 23924

Hwajeong Museum, 273-1 Pyeongchang-dong, Jongno-gu, Seoul 110-012 - T: (02) 22812990/06, Fax: 22872998, E-mail: hahnbit@chollian.net. Head: Dr. Hahn Kwang-ho
Fine Arts Museum
Chinese and Korean art, Tibetian art (Thangka and sculpture) 23925

Joongang University Museum, 221, Heuksok-dong, Kwanak-gu, Seoul 151
University Museum
Teaching coll 23926

Kimchi Field Museum, 159-1 Samsong-dong, Kangnam-gu, Seoul - T: (02) 60026456, Fax: 60026457, E-mail: kimchi@kimchimuseum.co.kr, Internet: http://www.kimchimuseum.co.kr. Head: Nam Seugwoo
Fine Arts Museum / Local Museum
Objects of culture and art of Kimchi 23927

Kookmin College Museum, 861-1, Jongreung-dong, Songbuk-gu, Seoul 132
University Museum
Teaching coll 23928

Korea University Museum, 5-1-2 Anam-dong, Sungbuk-gu, Seoul - T: (02) 9264381
Local Museum / University Museum 23929

Korea War Memorial, 1-8 Yangsandong, Yongsan-gu, Seoul - T: (02) 7093114
Historical Museum 23930

Korean Magazine Museum, 174-1 Chongjin-dong, Chongno-gu, Seoul - T: (02) 7359464
Special Museum 23931

Korean Museum of Contemporary Clothing, 3-13-21 Namsan-dong, Chung-gu, Seoul - T: (02) 3195497
Special Museum 23932

Koryo Taehakyo Pakmulgwan (Korea University Museum), 1, 5ka, Anamdong, Sungbukku, Seoul 136-701 - T: (02) 3290151/52, Fax: 9531528, Internet: http://www.korea.ac.kr. Head: Prof. Se-Young Yoon
Archaeological Museum / University Museum
Archeology, ethnology 23933

Kuknip Kwahak Pakmulgwan (National Science Museum), 2 Waryong-dong, Chongno-gu, Seoul 110 - T: (02) 7625209. Head: Chi-Eun Kim
Natural History Museum - 1926
Natural hist, zoology, reptiles, fossils - library, science classrooms 23934

Kuknip Minsok Pakmulgwan (National Folk Museum), 1 Sejong-no, Jongno-gu, Seoul 110 - T: (02) 7203137, Fax: 7232272, E-mail: hope0921@nfm.go.kr, Internet: http://www.nfm.go.kr. Head: Dr. Jong-chul Rhie
Folklore Museum - 1966
Korean traditional and folk arts 23935

Kuknip Seoul Taehakyo Pakmulgwan (Seoul National University Museum), San 56-1, Sinlim-dong, Kwanak-gu, Seoul 151-742 - T: (02) 8745693. Head: Dr. Mong-Lyong Choi
University Museum
Paintings, calligraphy, archeology, ethnology, exhibits on rural and traditional cultures, shamanism 23936

Kyunghee University Museum, 1 Hoeki-dong, Tongdaemun-gu, Seoul 131 - T: (02) 9610114
Ethnology Museum / University Museum
Ethnography, traditional musical instruments, prehistory 23937

Military Academy Museum, Kongreung-dong, Songbuk-gu, Seoul 132
Military Museum
Ancient and contemporary weapons of all kinds 23938

Museum of Chang-Duk Palace, Chang-Duk Palace, Seoul
Decorative Arts Museum
Costumes, arms, seals, manuscripts of the Yi dynasty, rooms furnished in period style 23939

Museum of Korean Embroidery, 89-4 Nonhyun-dong, Kangnam-gu, Seoul - T: (02) 5155114
Decorative Arts Museum 23940

Myong Ji University Museum, 4-2, Namgajwa-dong, Seodaemun-gu, Seoul 120
University Museum
Teaching coll 23941

National Folklore Museum, Kyongbok Palace, 1 Sejong-no, Chongno-gu, Seoul - T: (02) 7341346
Folklore Museum 23942

National Museum of Korea, Kyongbok Palace, 1-57 Sejong-no, Chongno-gu, Seoul 110 - T: (02) 7202714, 3985000, Fax: 7347255, Internet: http://www.museum.go.kr/. Head: Yang-Ho Chung
Archaeological Museum / Decorative Arts Museum - 1908
Gold crowns and jewelry, Korean pottery, Central Asian Buddhist paintings, archaeological material from Korean sites, Chinese ceramics and other items from Sung and Yuan periods, Chinese material from burials of a Han period Chinese settlement (108-313 A.D.), Central Asian coll of murals - library 23943

Pacific Cultural Museum, 686-5, Shindaebang-dong, Tongjak-Gu, Seoul 156-010 - T: (02) 8323486, Fax: 8412009
Ethnology Museum / Decorative Arts Museum - 1979
Ethnography, crafts, tribal and folk art, medical coll - library, film coll 23944

Postal Museum, 1-21 Chungmuro, Chung-gu, Seoul - T: (02) 7562858
Historical Museum 23945

Samsung Children's Museum, 7-26 Shinchon-dong, Songpa-gu, Seoul - T: (02) 22031871
Historical Museum 23946

Sejong College Museum, 2 Kunja-dong-san, Songdong-gu, Seoul 133
University Museum
Teaching coll 23947

Seoul Municipal Museum of Art, 2-2-1 Shinmun-no, Chongno-gu, Seoul - T: (02) 7362024, Fax: 7232490
Fine Arts Museum 23948

Sokang University Museum, 1 Sinsu-dong, Mapo-gu, Seoul 121
University Museum
Teaching coll 23949

Songsin Teachers College Museum, 2-249-1, Dongson-dong, Songbuk-gu, Seoul 132 - T: (02) 9271001, Fax: 9263120. Head: Lee Hyun Hee
University Museum
Teaching coll 23950

Sookmyung Women's University Museum, 52-12, Chongpa-2ga, Yongsan-gu, Seoul 140-742 - T: (02) 7109134, Fax: 7109267, E-mail: stella@sookmyung.ac.kr, Internet: http://www.museum.sookmyung.ac.kr. Head: Hee-Jae Lee
University Museum
Korean history, ethnographical materials especially relating to women 23951

Straw and Grass Handicraft Museum, 97-9 Chongdam-dong, Kangnam-gu, Seoul - T: (02) 5165585
Historical Museum 23952

Suk Joo-sun Memorial Museum of Korean Folk Arts, c/o Dankook University, San 8-3, Hannam-dong, Yongsan-ku, Seoul 140 - T: (02) 7975121. Head: Joo-sun Suk
Folklore Museum
Shoes, headgear, ornaments, traditional Korean costumes 23953

Sung-Am Archives of Classical Literature, Taesung Bldg, 60-17, 1-ka Taepyong-Ro Chung-Hu, Seoul 100-101 - T: (02) 7365151, Fax: 7358383
Library with Exhibitions - 1974
Books, printing type, wood tags - library 23954

Sung Kyun Kwan University Museum, 3-53, Myungryun-dong, Jongro-gu, Seoul 110 - T: (02) 7625021. Head: Ha Min Byong
University Museum
Teaching coll 23955

Sungjon University Museum, 135 Sangdo-dong, Kwanak-gu, Seoul 151
University Museum
Archaeology, combpattern pottery, earthenware, bronze, mirrors, Mateo Ricchi world map (only remaining copy) 23956

Yonsei University Museum, 134 Sinchon-dong, Sodaemun-gu, Seoul 120 - T: (02) 3612114. Head: Prof. Won-Koo Whang
Archaeological Museum / University Museum - 1965
Palaeolithic and Neolithic implements, palaeontological coll, ceramics - library 23957

Taegu

Kyemyung University Museum, 2139 Taemyong 7-dong, Nam-gu, Taegu 705-030 - T: (053) 6261321. Head: Jong Chull Kim
Archaeological Museum / University Museum
Archaeology, tiles, pottery 23958

Kyongbuk University Museum, 1370 Sangyeok-dong, Buk-gu, Taegu 635 - T: (053) 9522996. Head: Kyong Hyun Mun
Archaeological Museum / University Museum
Paintings, materials from prehistoric and Silla periods 23959

Taegu National Museum, 41 Hwanggum-dong, Susong-gu, Taegu - T: (053) 7686052
Local Museum 23960

Taegu National University of Education Museum, 1999-6, Daemyung-dong, Namgu, Taegu 630 - T: (053) 67014913. Head: Han Keuk
Special Museum / University Museum
Teaching coll 23961

Taejon

Chungnam University Museum, 1 Munhwa-dong-san, Taejon 300 - T: (042) 8220101
University Museum 23962

Tamyang

Tamyang Bamboo Museum, 87-2 Tamju-ri, Tamyang - T: (061) 3814111
Natural History Museum 23963

Uiwang

Railroad Museum, 1-4 Wolam-dong, Uiwang 437-050 - T: (031) 4613610. Head: Young Koog Shin
Science&Tech Museum - 1988 23964

Yangjoo

Total Open-Air Museum, 10-2, Ilyoung-Ri, Changheung-myun, Yangjoo 482-810 - T: (02) 3793994, Fax: 3790252. Head: Joon Eui Noh
Open Air Museum / Fine Arts Museum - 1984
Paintings, modern and period sculpture, books 23965

Yongin

Hoam Art Museum, 204 Kasil-ri, Pogok-myon, Yongin 449-810 - T: (0335) 3201800, Fax: 3201809, E-mail: w3SCF@www.hoammuseum.org, Internet: http://www.hoammuseum.org. Head: Ra Hee Hong Lee
Fine Arts Museum - 1982 23966

Pacific Cultural Museum, 314 Borari, Kihung-up, Yongin - T: (031) 2857215
Folklore Museum 23967

Kuwait

Hawelli

The Tareq Rajab Museum, POB 6156, Hawelli 32036 - T: 5317358, Fax: 5339063, E-mail: museum@trmkt.com, Internet: http://www.trmkt.com
Decorative Arts Museum
Ceramics, manuscripts, metalware, textiles, costumes, silver folk jewellery 23968

Kuwait

Educational Science Museum, Abdulla Mubarek St, Kuwait, mail addr: c/o Ministry of Education, POB 7, 13001 Safat - T: 2421268, Fax: 2446078. Head: Kassim Khodair Kassim
Natural History Museum - 1972
Natural hist, science, oil, astronomy, health - library 23969

Kuwait National Museum, Arabian Gulf St, Kuwait, mail addr: c/o Department of Antiquities and Museums, POB 193, 13002 Safat - T: 2426521, Fax: 2404862. Head: Dr. Fahed Al-Wohaibi
Historical Museum 23970

Sadu House, Arabian Gulf St, Kuwait
Special Museum
Traditional Bedouin weaving 23971

Kyrgyzstan

Biškek

Kyrgyz State Museum of Fine Arts, Pervomaiskaja ul 90, 720000 Biškek. Head: K.N. Uzubalieva
Fine Arts Museum
Contemporary art - library 23972

Memorialnyj Dom-Muzej M.V. Biškek (M.V. Biškek Memorial Museum), ul Frunze 364, 720301 Biškek - T: (03312) 227700. Head: D.N. Nusupova
Military Museum 23973

State Historical Museum of Kyrgyztan, Krasnooktjabrskaja ul 236, 720000 Biškek. Head: N.M. Seytkazieva
Historical Museum
Hist of Kirgiz region from ancient times to the present 23974

Čujsk

Muzej Architektury i Archeologii Vez Burana (Museum of Architecture and Archaeology Tower of Burana), Burano, Čujsk. Head: E.T. Turekanov
Archaeological Museum / Historical Museum 23975

Karacol

Karacolski Istori Kraevedcheskiy Muzeum, Ul Dzerzinskiy, Karacol. Head: D. Mambetova
Local Museum 23976

Oš

Ošskij Objedinennij Istoriko-Kulturnij Muzej-Zaporednik (Osh United Historical Cultural Museum-Preserve), Ul Alebastrova 31, 714000 Oš - T: (033222) 27123. Head: Muchtar Tagaev
Historical Museum 23977

Prževalsk

Memorialnyj Muzej N.M. Prževalskogo (N.M. Przevalsky Regional Museum), Isyk-Kul, Prževalsk. Head: Y.A. Sasymanov
Historical Museum 23978

Przhevalsk Regional Museum, Ul Dzerzhinski 164, Prževalsk. Head: T.P. Ryazonova
Local Museum 23979

Taš-Aryk

Gumbez Manace Literary Ethnographic Museum, Taš-Aryk - T: (032222) 223782, Fax: 225079
Special Museum / Ethnology Museum 23980

Tokmok

Istoriko-Kraevedceskij Muzej (Tokmok Historical and Regional Museum), Ul Triasina 146, 722207 Tokmok - T: 22608. Head: E.N. Chushupal
Historical Museum 23981

Laos

Vientiane

Ho Phakeo, Settathiraj Rd, Vientiane
Historic Site - 1965
Site built in 1563 by King Setthathiraj 23982

Musée National Lao, District Saysettha, Vientiane, mail addr: BP 67, Vientiane
Fine Arts Museum
Painting, books, mss 23983

That Luang, District Saysettha, Vientiane
Historic Site - 1930
Site built by King Saysetthathiraj in 1566 23984

Wat Sisaket, Lane Xang Av, Vientiane
Historic Site - 1828 23985

Latvia

Ādaži

Rīgas Ūdensapgādes Muzejs (Water Supply Museum of Riga), Sūkņu stacija Baltezers, Ādaži, 2164 - T: 7990127, Fax: 7990206. Head: Imants Jakobsons
Science&Tech Museum - 1988 23986

Ainaži

Ainažu Jūrskolas Memoriālais Muzejs (Ainaži Naval College Museum), K. Valdemāra iela 47, Ainaži, 4035 - T: (040) 43349
Historical Museum - 1969 23987

Aizkalne

Raiņa Memorālais Muzejs Jasmuiža (Rainis Memorial Museum Jasmuiža), Jasmuiža, Aizkalne, 5305 - T: (053) 54677, 54688
Special Museum - 1964 23988

Aizkraukle

Aizkraukles Vēstures un Mākslas Muzejs (Aizkraukle History and Art Museum), Kalna ziedi, Aizkraukle, 5100 - T: (051) 23351
Local Museum / Fine Arts Museum - 1973 23989

Aizpute

Meža Muzejs Boju Pilī (Forest Museum in Bojas Palace), Aizpute, 3456 - T: (034) 12054
Natural History Museum - 1972 23990

Alūksne

Alūksnes Novadpētniecības un Mākslas Muzejs (Alūksne Museum of Local Studies and Art), Pils iela 74, Alūksne, 4300 - T: (043) 21363, 23631
Local Museum / Fine Arts Museum - 1959 23991

Ernsta Glika Bībeles Muzejs (Ernst Glück Museum of the Bible), Pils iela 25a, Alūksne, 4301 - T: (043) 23164
Religious Arts Museum - 1991 23992

Apriķi

Apriķu Novada Muzejs (District Museum), Apriķu pamatskola, Apriķi, 3455 - T: (034) 19847, 19851
Local Museum - 1987 23993

Balvi

Balvu Vēstures un Mākslas Muzejs (Balvi History and Art Museum), Vidzemes iela 5a, Balvi, 4500 - T: (045) 22034
Local Museum / Fine Arts Museum - 1989 23994

Bauska

Bauskas Novadpētniecības un Mākslas Muzejs (Bauska History and Art Museum), Kalna 6, Bauska, 3900 - T: (039) 22197, E-mail: bnmuzejs@apollo.lv, Internet: http://www.vip.latnet.lv/LMA/Regions/Bauska/bauska.html. Head: Baiba Šulce
Historical Museum / Fine Arts Museum - 1947
800 works of Soviet, mostly Latvian painters, including 200 paintings by T. Karaša (1915-1975) 23995

Bauskas Pils Muzejs (Bauska Castle Museum), Brīvības Blvd 2a, Bauska, 3901 - T: (039) 23793. Head: M. Skanis
Historical Museum - 1990
Bauskas castle hist, restauration 23996

Bebri

Latvijas Biškopības Vēstures Muzejs (Latvian Museum of the History of Apiculture), Dravas, Bebri, 5135 - T: (051) 64363, 64144
Agriculture Museum - 1984 23997

Voldemāra Jākobsona Memoriālā Māja Muzejs, Galdiņi, Bebri, 5135 - T: (051) 64284, 64275
Fine Arts Museum - 1976 23998

Bērze

Kārļa Ulmaņa Pikšas (Museum of Kārlis Ulmanis Pikšas), Pikšas, Bērze, Bērze, 3712 - T: (037) 32392
Historical Museum - 1993 23999

Bērzgale

Bērzgales Pagasta Vēstures Muzejs (Museum of Bērzgale Parish History), Rītupes iela 34, Bērzgale, 4612 - T: (046) 97544
Special Museum 24000

Burtnieki

Burtnieku Pagasta Briedes Krogs (Briedes Krogs in the Burtnieki Parish), Burtnieki, 4206 - T: (042) 56444, 56570
Agriculture Museum / Ethnology Museum / Local Museum - 1985 24001

Ceraukste

Viļa Plūdoņa Memoriālā Māja Muzejs, Lejenieki, Ceraukste, 3908 - T: (039) 26359
Special Museum - 1963 24002

Cēsis

Alfrēda Kalniņa Memoriālais Muzejs, Rīgas iela 24, Cēsis, 4101
Special Museum - 1979 24003

Cēsu Izstāžu Nams (Exhibition House), Lenču iela 7b, Cēsis, 4101 - T: (041) 23557
Decorative Arts Museum - 1985 24004

Cēsu Vēstures muzejs (Cēsis History Museum), Pils iela 9, Cēsis, 4101 - T: (041) 22615. Head: A. Vanadziņs
Local Museum - 1925
Two parts: Cēsis medieval stone Castle and New Castle, every stage of hist, special archaeological, numismatic and ethnographic coll - library 24005

Daugavpils

Daugavpils Muzeja, Muzeja iela 7, Daugavpils, 5407 - T: (054) 24512, 24073
Local Museum 24006

Daugavpils Muzeja Izstāžu Zāles (Exhibition Hall of Daugavpils Museum), Rīgas iela 20, Daugavpils, 5407 - T: (054) 24512, 24073
Public Gallery 24007

Daugavpils Novadpētniecības un Mākslas Muzejs (Daugavpils Museum of Local Studies and Art), Rīgas iela 8, Daugavpils, 5407 - T: (054) 24155, 22709
Local Museum / Fine Arts Museum 24008

Dobele

Dobeles Novadpētniecības Muzejs (Dobele Museum of Local Studies), Zaļā iela 31, Dobele, 3701 - T: (037) 21309
Local Museum - 1985 24009

Pētera Upīša Piemiņas Muzejs (Museum in Commemoration of Pēteris Upītis), Graudu iela 1, Dobele, 3701 - T: (037) 22294
Natural History Museum - 1979 24010

Drabeši

Āraišu Muzejparks, Ezerpils (Āraiši Museum Park, Lake Fortress), Drabeši, 4140 - T: (041) 97288, 97293
Natural History Museum / Historical Museum / Archaeological Museum - 1983 24011

Druviena

Druvienas Vecā Skola (Druviena Old School), Druviena, 4426 - T: (044) 44550
Historical Museum - 1966 24012

Dundaga

Kubalu Skolas Muzejs (Kubalu School Museum), Kubalu skola, Dundaga, 3270 - T: (032) 42290, 42820
Historical Museum - 1972 24013

Dunte

Minhauzena Muzejs (Muenchausen's Museum), Krogi, Dunte, 4024 - T: (040) 2033
Special Museum - 1983 24014

Ērgļi

Brāļu Jurjānu Memoriālais Muzejs Meņģeļi, Meņģeļi, Ērgļi, 4840 - T: (048) 71077
Special Museum - 1978 24015

Rūdolfa Blaumaņa Memoriālais Muzejs Braki, Braki, Ērgļi, 4840 - T: (048) 71816, 22480
Special Museum - 1959/1992 24016

Gaujiena

Jāzepa Vītola Memoriālais Muzejs (Jazep Vitol Memorial Museum), Anniņas, Gaujiena, 4339 - T: 6546842, Fax: 4357340, E-mail: gaujpag@apollo.lv. Head: Ineta Riepniece
Special Museum - 1963
Exp about life and work of the Latvian composer Jazep Vitol (1863 - 1948) 24017

Gulbene

Gulbenes Vēstures un Mākslas Muzejs (History and Art Museum), Pils iela 5, Gulbene, 4401 - T: (044) 23098
Local Museum / Fine Arts Museum - 1978 24018

Jaunpiebalga

Emīla Dārziņa un Jāņa Sudrabkanal Muzejs, Jāņskola, Jaunpiebalga, 4125 - T: (041) 62354
Special Museum - 1969 24019

Jaunpils

Jaunpils Muzejs (Jaunpils Museum), Jaunpils, 3145 - T: (031) 62262, 62901
Historical Museum - 1993 24020

Jēkabpils

Jēkabpils Vēstures Muzeja Brīvdabas Nodaļa (Open-Air Dept. of the Jēkabpils History Museum), Filozofu iela 6, Jēkabpils, 5200 - T: (052) 32501
Open Air Museum - 1952 24021

Jēkabpils Vēstures Muzeja Mūzikas Vēstures Nodaļa (Dept. of the History of Music of the Jēkabpils History Museum), Brīvības iela 141, Jēkabpils, 5200
Music Museum - 1993 24022

Jēkabpils Vēstures Muzejs (History Museum), Brīvības iela 169-171, Jēkabpils, 5200 - T: (052) 31750, 32205
Historical Museum - 1920 24023

Jelgava

Ādolfa Alunāna Memoriālais Muzejs, Filozofu iela 3, Jelgava, 3001 - T: (030) 21180
Special Museum - 1978 24024

Ģederta Eliasa Jelgavas Vēstures un Mākslas Muzejs (Ģederts Eliass Jelgava History and Art Museum), Akadēmijas iela 10, Jelgava, 3001 - T: (030) 23383, 27948
Local Museum / Fine Arts Museum - 1818 24025

Kurzemes Hercogu Kapenes, Rundāles Pils Muzejs (Family Vault od the Dukes of Courland Exhibition), Lielā iela 2, Jelgava, 3001 - T: (030) 05617, Fax: (039) 2274, E-mail: rpm@eila.lv, Internet: http://www.rpm.apollo.lv. Head: Imants Lancmanis
Historical Museum - 1992
Family history 24026

Latvijas Lauksaimniecības Universitātes Muzejs (Museum of the Latvia Agriculture University), Lielā iela 2, Jelgava, 3001 - T: (030) 25329
University Museum / Agriculture Museum - 1968 24027

Jūrmala

Aleksandra Rusteiķa Memoriālais Muzejs, J. Pliekšāna iela 53, Dzintari, Jūrmala, 2004 - T: (02) 762977
Special Museum - 1992 24028

Jūrmalas Pilsētas Muzejs (Town Museum), Lielais prospekts 24, Priedaine, Jūrmala, 2003 - T: (02) 754660, 751547
Local Museum - 1962 24029

Luda Bērziņa Memoriālais Muzejs, Poruka prospekts 27, Jaundubulti, Jūrmala, 2015 - T: (02) 769152, 760244
Special Museum - 1990 24030

Miervalda Ķemera Muzejs, Durbes iela 21, Ķemeri, Jūrmala, 2012 - T: 7753202. Head: Guntis Bērliņš
Fine Arts Museum - 1990 24031

Raiņa un Aspazijas Memoriālā Vasarnīca (Rainis and Aspazija Memorial Summer Cottage), J. Pliekšāna iela 5-7, Majori, Jūrmala, 2015 - T: (02) 764495, 764295
Special Museum 24032

Kalncempji

Kalncempju Pagasta Novadpētniecības Muzejs Ates Dzirnavās (Kalncempji Parish Museum of Local Studies - Ates Mill), Dzirnavas, Kalncempji, 4342 - T: (043) 45452
Local Museum 24033

Krāslava

Krāslavas Vēstures un Mākslas Muzejs (History and Art Museum), Grāfu Plāteru iela 2, Krāslava, 5600 - T: (056) 23586, 24674
Local Museum / Fine Arts Museum - 1983 24034

Kuldīga

Kuldīgas Novada Muzejs (District Museum), Pils iela 5, Kuldīga, 3301 - T: (033) 23364, 24618
Local Museum - 1935 24035

Lielvārde

Andreja Pumpura Muzejs Lielvārdē (Andrejs Pumpurs Museum in Lielvārde), Kraujas, Lielvārde, 5070 - T: (050) 53759, Fax: 5053759, E-mail: muzejs@lielvarde.lv. Head: Anastasija Neretniece
Special Museum - 1970 24036

Liepa

Eduarda Veidenbauma Memoriālais Muzejs, Kalāči, Liepa, 4128 - T: (041) 95309
Special Museum - 1958 24037

Liepāja

Liepājas Muzeja, Kungu iela 24, Liepāja, 3400
Local Museum 24038

Liepājas Muzeja Izstāžu Zāles (Exhibition Halls of Liepāja Museum), Bāriņu iela 32, Liepāja, 3400
Public Gallery 24039

Liepājas Vēstures un Mākslas Muzejs (Liepāja History and Art Museum), Kūrmājas prospekts 16, Liepāja, 3400 - T: (034) 22327, 22604
Local Museum / Fine Arts Museum - 1911 24040

Limbaži

Limbažu Muzejs (Limbaži Museum), Burtnieku iela 7, Limbaži, 4000 - T: (040) 21432, 21894, Fax: 70894. Head: Janis Ulmis
Local Museum - 1983 24041

Ludza

Ludzas Novadpētniecības Muzejs (Ludza Museum of Local Studies), Kuļņeva iela 2, Ludza, 5700 - T: (057) 23931
Local Museum 24042

Madona

Izstāžu Zāle, Madonas Novadpētniecības un Mākslas Muzejs (Madona Museum of Local Studies and Art), Skolas ielā 10a, Madona, 4801 - T: (048) 22480, 23844
Fine Arts Museum - 1984 24043

Madonas Novadpētniecības un Mākslas Muzejs (Madona Museum of Local Studies and Art), K. Valdemāra bul 18, Madona, 4801 - T: (048) 22480, 23844
Local Museum - 1944 24044

Prof. Aleksandra Bieziņa Muzejs, Sarkani, Dilmani, Madona, 4870 - T: (042) 229270
Special Museum - 1989
Founder of Latvian children' surgery 24045

Mālpils

Latvijas Republikas Meliorācijas un Zemkopības Muzejs (Museum of Land Reclamation and Agriculture of the Latvian Republic), Mālpils, 2152 - T: (02) 925139, 925901
Agriculture Museum - 1967 24046

Meirāni

Jāņa Zābera Memoriālais Muzejs, Vecais Ceplis, Meirāni, 4826 - T: (048) 95345
Special Museum - 1974 24047

Neretas Pagasts

Jāņa Jaunsudrabiņa Muzejs Riekstiņi, Neretas Pagasts, 5118 - T: (051) 76467, Internet: http://ltg.lv/riekstini. Head: Ilze Līduma
Special Museum - 1967 24048

Ogre

Gaidu un Skautu Muzejs (Museum of Guides and Scouts), Mālkalnes prospekts 10, Ogre, 5003 - T: (050) 46145, 23383. Head: Milda Feldmane
Special Museum - 1991
International, national and regional scouting and guiding 24049

Ogres Vēstures un Mākslas Muzejs (Ogre History and Art Museum), Kalna prospekts 3, Ogre, 5001 - T: (050) 24345
Local Museum / Fine Arts Museum - 1980 24050

Pāvilosta

Pāvilostas Novadpētniecības Muzejs (Pāvilosta Museum of Local Studies), Dzintaru iela 1, Pāvilosta, 3466 - T: (034) 98276
Local Museum 24051

Pilcene

Vladislava Loča Latgaliešu Rakstniecības Muzejs (Vladislavs Locis Letigallian Literature Museum), Pilcenes sākumskola, Dricānu pag., Pilcene, 4615 - T: (046) 59102, 25239
Special Museum - 1995 24052

Pilsrundāle

Rundāles Pils Muzejs (Rundāle Palace Museum), Pilsrundāle, 3921 - T: (039) 62274, 62197, Fax: 22274, E-mail: rpm@eila.lv, Internet: http://www-rpm.apollo.lv. Head: Imants Lancmanis
Decorative Arts Museum - 1972 24053

Platone

Eliasu Dzimtas Muzejs Zīlēni (Museum of the Eliasi Family Zīlēni), Zīlēni, Platone, 3021 - T: (030) 23383
Fine Arts Museum - 1987 24054

Pociems

Bārdu Dzimtas Muzejs Rumbiņi (Museum of the Bārda Family Rumbiņi), Rumbiņi, Pociems, 4061
Special Museum - 1993 24055

Preiļi

Preilu Vēstures un Lietišķās Mākslas Muzejs (Preiļi History and Applied Art Museum), A. Paulāna iela 4, Preiļi, 5301 - T: (053) 22731
Local Museum / Fine Arts Museum - 1985 24056

Raiskums

Ungurmuiža (Unguri Manor), Ungurmuiža, Raiskums, 4148 - T: (041) 58223
Historical Museum / Natural History Museum 24057

Rēzekne

Latgales Kultūtvēstures Muzejs (Latgale Culture and History Museum), Atbrīošanas aleja 102, Rēzekne, 4600 - T: (046) 22464, 22778
Decorative Arts Museum / Historical Museum - 1959 24058

Rīga

Andreja Upītša Memoriālais Muzejs (Andrej Upits' Memorial Apartment), Brīvības iela 38, Rīga, 1050 - T: 7289767, Fax: 7289767, E-mail: aupits@latnet.lv. Head: Inese Kaire
Special Museum - 1972 24059

Arzemju Mákslas Muzejs (Museum of Foreign Art), Pils laukums 3, Rīga, 1050 - T: 7228776, Fax: 7228776, E-mail: arzemju.mm@apollo.lv. Head: Daiga Upeniece
Fine Arts Museum
Painting, sculpture, applied art, graphic art - library 24060

Boksa Vēstures Muzejs (Museum of the History of Boxing), J. Endzelīna iela 2, Rīga, 1029 - T: (02) 613832
Special Museum - 1993 24061

Dekoratīvi Lietišķās Mākslas Muzejs (Museum of Decorative Applied Arts), Skārņu iela 10-20, Rīga, 1050 - T: 7229736, 7222235
Decorative Arts Museum - 1989 24062

Ebreji Latvijā (Jews in Latvia), Skolas str 6, Rīga, 1010 - T: 7283484, Fax: 7283484, E-mail: ebreji.latvija@apollo.lv. Head: Margers Vestermanis
Historical Museum - 1996
Documents, books, manuscripts, photos portraying the secular and religious life of Jews in Latvia, clothes rags with concentration camp numbers, objects of Jewish culture 24063

Eduarda Smiļga Teātra Muzejs, E. Smiļga iela 37-39, Rīga, 1002 - T: (02) 611893
Performing Arts Museum - 1976 24064

Farmācijas Muzejs (Museum of Pharmacy), Riharda Vāgnera iela 13, Rīga, 1050 - T: 7213008, Fax: 7216828, Internet: http://www.stn.lv/farmacijas.muzejs. Head: Agris Briedis
Special Museum - 1987
Documents and artefacts from the 17th to 20th century 24065

Frīdriha Candera Memoriālais Muzejs, F. Candera iela 1, Rīga, 1041 - T: 7614113, 6539970, E-mail: vilks@latnet.lv, Internet: http://www.lu.lv/jauna/strukt/muzejs/m_7.html. Head: Dr. Ilgonis Vilks
Special Museum / Science&Tech Museum - 1987 24066

Gustava Šķiltera Memoriālais Muzejs, Daugavgrīvas iela 9, Rīga, 1007 - T: (02) 625364
Fine Arts Museum - 1971 24067

Jāņa Akuratera Muzejs, O. Vācieša iela 6a, Rīga, 1004 - T: (02) 619934
Special Museum - 1991 24068

Jaņa Rozentāla un Rūdolfa Blaumaņa Memoriālais Muzejs, Alberta iela 12, Rīga, 1010 - T: 7331641
Special Museum - 1973 24069

Krišjāņa Barona Memoriālais Muzejs, K. Barona iela 3-5, Rīga, 1011 - T: 7284265
Special Museum - 1983 24070

Lattelekom Muzejs (Museum of Telecommunications), Brīvības iela 33, Rīga, 1010 - T: 7054884/86, Fax: 7240005, E-mail: ilocmeli@exchange.telekom.lv
Science&Tech Museum - 1995 24071

Latvijas Arhitektūras Muzejs (Latvian Architecture Museum), M. Pils iela 19, Rīga, 1050 - T: 7220779, Fax: 7228808, E-mail: Janis.Lejnieks@vkpai.gov.lv, Internet: http://www.arch.museum.lv. Head: Dr. Janis Lejnieks
Decorative Arts Museum - 1994 24072

Latvijas Augstskolu Ķīmijas Vēstures Muzejs (Latvia High Schools' Museum of the History of Chemistry), Kronvalda bulvāris 4, 261. telpa, Rīga, 1586 - T: 7322917
Historical Museum - 1975 24073

Latvijas Dabas Muzejs (Latvian Museum of Nature), K. Barona iela 4, Rīga, 1712 - T: 7226078, 7213291
Natural History Museum - 1955 24074

Latvijas Etnogāfiskais Brīvdabas Muzjs (Ethnographic Open-Air Museum of Latvia), Brīvības iela 440, Rīga, 1056 - T: 7994510, Fax: 7994178. Head: Juris Indāns
Open Air Museum / Ethnology Museum - 1924
Wooden folk architecture of Latvia, ethnography, folk art, metal, textiles, pottery - library, archive, restoration 24075

Latvijas Fotogrāfijas Muzejs (Latvian Photography Museum), Mārstaļu iela 8, Rīga, 1050 - T: 7227231
Science&Tech Museum - 1993 24076

Latvijas Kara Muzejs (Latvian War Museum), Smilšu iela 20, Rīga, 1868 - T: 7228141, Fax: 7228147
Military Museum 24077

Latvijas Kultūras Muzejs Dauderi (Latvian Museum of Culture Dauderi), Sarkandaugavas iela 30, Rīga, 1005 - T: 7392229, Fax: 7392229, E-mail: dauderi@delfi.lv. Head: Dzintra Andrušaite
Historical Museum - 1990 24078

Latvijas Okupācijas Muzejs (Museum of the Occupation of Latvia (1940 - 1991)), Strēlnieku laukums 1, Rīga, 1050 - T: 7212715, Fax: 7229255, E-mail: omf@latnet.lv, Internet: http://www.occupationmuseum.lv. Head: Gundega Michel
Historical Museum - 1993 24079

Latvijas Sorosa fonda Mūsdienu mākslas centrs (Contemporary Art Center of the Soros Foundation), 11. Novembra krastmala 35, Rīga, 1050 - T: 7228478, Fax: 7820252, E-mail: iboiko@sfl-paic.lv
Fine Arts Museum 24080

Latvijas Sporta Muzejs (Latvian Sports Museum), Alksnāja 9, Rīga, 1050 - T: 7225127, 7211365, Fax: 7225127, E-mail: sportmuz@latnet.lv, Internet: http://www.muzeji.lv. Head: Dzintra Grundmane
Special Museum - 1990 24081

Latvijas Ugunsdzēsības Muzejs (Fire-Fighting Museum of Latvia), Hanzas iela 5, Rīga, 1045 - T: 7331334, 7333306, Fax: 7332859, Internet: http://www.ugdd/lv/lv/muzejs. Head: V. Zerdina
Special Museum - 1978 24082

Latvijas Universitātes Botānikas Muzejs (Latvia University Museum of Botany), Kronvalda bulvāris 4, Rīga, 1586 - T: 7325645, 7323307
University Museum / Natural History Museum 24083

Latvijas Universitātes Ģeologijas Muzejs (Latvia University Museum of Geology), Alberta iela 10, Rīga, 1010 - T: 7331766
University Museum / Natural History Museum 24084

Latvijas Universitātes Skaitļošanas Tehnikas Muzejs (Latvia University Museum of Computing Technique and Computing Science), Raiņa bulvāris 29, Rīga, 1586 - T: 7211023
University Museum / Science&Tech Museum 24085

Latvijas Universitātes Vēstures Muzejs (Museum of History of the University of Latvia), Raiņa bulvāris 19, Rīga, 1586 - T: 7228909
University Museum / Historical Museum 24086

Latvijas Universitātes Zoologijas Muzejs (Latvia University Museum of Zoology), Kronvalda bulvāris 4, Rīga, 1586 - T: 7325669
University Museum / Natural History Museum 24087

Latvijas Vēstures Muzejs (History Museum of Latvia), Pils laukumā 3, Rīga, 1050 - T: 7223004, Fax: 7220586, E-mail: museum@history-museum.lv. Head: A. Radins
Historical Museum - 1869
Archaeology, numismatics, ethnography, religious art, decorative art 24088

Mencendorfa Nams (Mentzendorff's House), Grēcinieku iela 18, Rīga, 1957 - T: 7212951, 7222636
Special Museum - 1992 24089

Museum Anatomicum, Kronvalda bulvāris 9, Rīga, 1010 - T: 7325104
Natural History Museum - 1920
How we looked in the past and look today and might look in the future - Dept. of Anthropology 24090

Ojāra Vācieša Memoriālais Muzejs, O. Vācieša iela 19, Rīga, 1004 - T: (02) 618775
Special Museum - 1992 24091

Paula Stradiņa Medicīnas Vēstures Muzejs (Paul Stradin Museum of the History of Medicine), Antonijas iela 1, Rīga, 1360 - T: 7222914, Fax: 7211323, E-mail: museum2@mailbox.riga.lv, Internet: http://www.ltg.lv/x/medicinas.muzejs. Head: Dr. Kārlis-Ēriks Arons
Historical Museum - 1957
Hist of medicine from ancient times to the present, public health, drawings, photographs, 16th-20th c rare medical books - library 24092

Raiņa Literatūras un Mākslas Vēstures Muzejs (Rainis Museum of the History of Literature and Art), Amilšu iela 12, Rīga, 1050 - T: (02) 220134, Fax: 331920. Head: P. Zirnitis
Historical Museum - 1925
Hist of Latvian literature, theatre, music, fine arts and cinema - library, archives 24093

Rīga Motor Museum, S. Eizenšteina iela 6, Rīga, 1079 - T: 7097170, Fax: 7515694, E-mail: rmm@apollo.lv, Internet: http://www.stn.lv/x/rigas.motormuzeis. Head: Edwin Liepins
Science&Tech Museum - 1989 24094

Rīgas Doma Baznīca (Riga Dome Church), Doma laukums, Rīga, 1957 - T: 7224053, 7213213
Religious Arts Museum 24095

Rīgas Kino Muzejs (Riga Film Museum), Šmerla iela 3, Rīga, 1006 - T: 7545099, Fax: 7545099, E-mail: kinomuz@latnet.lv. Head: Inga Perkone
Science&Tech Museum - 1988 24096

Rīgas Tehniskās Universitātes Muzejs (Riga Technical University Museum), Āzenes iela 14/24, Rīga, 1048 - T: (02) 7089485, E-mail: sigitaklezberga@rtu.lv, Internet: http://www.rtu.lv. Head: Alida Zigmunde
University Museum / Historical Museum - 1969 24097

Rīgas Vēstures un Kugniecības muzejs (Museum of History of Riga and Navigation), Palasta 4, Rīga, 1050 - T: 7211358, Fax: 7210226, E-mail: direkt@rigamuz.lv, Internet: http//www.rigamuz.lv. Head: K. Radzina
Historical Museum - 1773
Local history, maritime history, Numismatic coll, silver cabinet, China coll, ship models - publications dept 24098

Valsts Elektrotehniskās Fabrikas Vēstures Muzejs (Museum of the History of the VEF Stock Company), Ropažu iela 1, Rīga, 1039 - T: 7552488
Science&Tech Museum - 1969 24099

Valsts Mākslas Muzejs Izstazu Zale Arsenāls (Exhibition Hall Arsenals of the State Museum of Art), Torna iela 1, Rīga, 1050 - T: 7213695, Fax: 7229570, E-mail: sundari@latnet.lv, Internet: http://www.vmm.lv
Fine Arts Museum
Art of the 2nd half of the 20th c. 24100

Valsts Mākslas Muzeju (State Museum of Art), Kr. Valdemāra iela 10a, Rīga, 1010 - T: 7325021, Fax: 7220714, E-mail: vmm@latnet.lv, Internet: http://www.vmm.lv. Head: Mara Lāce
Fine Arts Museum - 1905
Latvian Fine Art (18th-1940), Latvian graphics, paintings by Nikolai Rerih, Russian Art, communications 24101

Roja

Rojas Jūras un Zvejniecības Muzejs (Roja Museum of Maritime Fishing), Selgas iela 33, Roja, 3264 - T: (032) 69594
Agriculture Museum - 1972 24102

Rūjiena

Ādama Alkšņa Memoriālais Muzejs (Ādams Alksnis Memorial Museum), Rīgas iela 11a, Rūjiena, 4240 - T: (042) 63385
Fine Arts Museum 24103

Rūjienas Izstāžu Zāle (Rūjiena Exhibition Hall), Rīgas iela 34, Rūjiena, 4240 - T: (042) 63175, 63891
Local Museum / Fine Arts Museum - 1992 24104

Sakstagals

Franča Trasuna Muzejs Kolnasāta (Francis Trasuns Museum Kolnasāta), Sakstagals, 4638 - T: (046) 57271, 57216
Special Museum - 1992 24105

Salaspils

Daugavas Muzejs, Dole, Salaspils, 2121 - T: (02) 937616
Local Museum - 1977 24106

Saldus

Saldus Vēstures un Mākslas Muzejs (Saldus History and Art Museum), Striķu iela 22, Saldus, 3800 - T: (038) 22392, 21348
Local Museum / Fine Arts Museum - 1946 24107

Sigulda

Turaidas Muzejrezervāts (Turaida Museum Reserve), Turaidas iela 10, Sigulda, 2147 - T: (029) 71402, Fax: 71797, E-mail: turaida@lis.lv, Internet: http://www.turaida-muzejs.lv. Head: Anna Jurkane
Historical Museum - 1947 24108

Skrīveri

Andreja Upīša Memoriālmāja, Daugavas iela 58, Skrīveri, 5125 - T: (051) 97221
Special Museum - 1952 24109

Staburags

Pētera Barisona Muzejs, Skudras, Staburags, 5128 - T: (051) 44357
Special Museum 24110

Tadaine

Raiņa Muzejs Tadenava, Dunavas pag., Tadaine, 5235 - T: (052) 52522
Special Museum - 1966 24111

Talsi

Lauksaimniecības Tehnikas Muzejs Kalēji (Museum of Farming Equipment Kalēji (The Blacksmiths)), Celtnieku iela 11, Talsi, 3200 - T: (032) 20143, 23616
Science&Tech Museum / Agriculture Museum - 1982 24112

Talsu Novadpētniecības un Mākslas Muzejs (Talsi Museum of Local Studies and Art), Rožu iela 7, Talsi, 3200 - T: (032) 22770, 24541
Local Museum / Fine Arts Museum - 1923 24113

Tērvete

Annas Brigaderes Memoriālais Muzejs, Sprīdīši, Tērvete, 3728 - T: (037) 63352
Special Museum - 1933 24114

Tukums

Durbes Pils (Durbe Palace), Parka iela 7, Tukums, 3101 - T: (031) 23694
Special Museum - 1991 24115

Jaunmoku Pils Muzejs (Jaunmokas Palace Museum), Tukums, 3101 - T: (031) 24572
Historical Museum - 1991 24116

Livonijas Ordeņa Pils Tornis (Tower of the Livonian Order Castle), Brīvības laukums 19a, Tukums, 3101 - T: (031) 23652
Historical Museum - 1995 24117

Tukuma Audēju Darbnīcas (Tukums Weavers' Workshops), Smilšu iela 42, Tukums, 3101 - T: (031) 25539
Science&Tech Museum / Ethnology Museum - 1988 24118

Tukuma Muzejs (Tukums Museum), Dārza iela 11-13, Tukums, 3101 - T: (031) 23652, 24537
Local Museum / Fine Arts Museum - 1936 24119

Valdemārpils

Valdemārpils Mežu Muzejs (Valdemārpils Forest Museum), Priednieki, Valdemārpils, 3260 - T: (032) 76120
Natural History Museum - 1971 24120

Valka

Valkas Novadpētniecības Muzejs (Valka Museum of Local Studies), Rīgas iela 64, Valka, 4700 - T: (047) 22198
Local Museum - 1971 24121

Valle

Brāļu Amtmaņu Muzejs (Museum of Actors and Theater Producers Brothers Amtmaņi), Zvanītāju Bukas, Valle, 5106 - T: (051) 53321, 53444
Performing Arts Museum - 1985 24122

Valmiera

Valmieras Novadpētniecības Muzejs (Valmiera Museum of Local Studies), Bruņinieku iela 3, Valmiera, 4201 - T: (042) 23733, 23620
Local Museum - 1959 24123

Vecpiebalga

Antona Austriņa Memoriālais Muzejs, Kaikaši, Vecpiebalga, 4122
Special Museum - 1990 24124

Brāļu Kaudzīšu Memoriālais Muzejs (Brother Kaudzītes Memorial Museum), Kalna Kaibēni, Vecpiebalga, 4122 - T: (041) 68216, 68251
Special Museum - 1929 24125

Kārļa Skalbes Muzejs, Saulrieti, Vecpiebalga, 4122 - T: (041) 64252
Special Museum - 1987 24126

Ventspils

Herberta Dorbes Muzejs Senču Putekļi (Herberts Dorbe Memorial Museum Senču Putekļi (The Dust of Ancestors)), Ērgļu iela 1, Ventspils, 3600 - T: (036) 25004
Special Museum - 1989 24127

Ventspils Jūras Zvejniecības Brīvdabas Muzejs (Ventspils Open-Air Museum of Maritime Fishing), Riņķu iela 2, Ventspils, 3600 - T: (036) 24467
Open Air Museum / Agriculture Museum - 1954 24128

Ventspils Muzejs (Ventspils Museum), Jāņa 17, Ventspils, 3601 - T: (036) 22031, Fax: 3607025, E-mail: muzejs@vm.apollo.lv, Internet: http://www.ventspils.lv. Head: Aldis Abele
Local Museum / Fine Arts Museum - 1928 24129

Vērgale

Vērgales Pagasta Muzejs (Vērgale Parish Museum), Dambenieki, Vērgale, 3463 - T: (034) 95385
Local Museum - 1992 24130

Vidriži

Emila Melngaiļa Memoriālais Muzejs, Melngaiļi, Vidriži, 4013 - T: (040) 55849
Special Museum - 1984 24131

Leona Paegles Memoriālais Muzejs, Lauči, Vidriži, 4013 - T: (040) 62264
Special Museum - 1959 24132

Viļķene

Ķirbižu Meža Muzejs (Ķirbiži Forest Museum), Viļķene, 4050 - T: (040) 21395, 50324
Natural History Museum - 1989 24133

Zentene

Ernesta Birznieka-Upīša Muzejs Bisnieki, Zentene, 3123 - T: (031) 42473, 24537
Special Museum - 1971 24134

Zirņi

Oskara Kalpaka Muzejs Airīšu Piemiņas Vietā (Oskars Kalpaks Museum in the Memorial Site Airītes), Kalpaki, Zirņi, 3853 - T: (038) 39492
Historical Museum - 1936/1989 24135

Lebanon

Annaya

Saint Sharbel Museum, Monastery, Annaya
Religious Arts Museum / Ethnology Museum
Religious and cultural items, village life in the mountains last century 24136

Beirut

American University of Beirut Museum, Ras Beirut, Beirut - T: (1) 340549, Fax: 340549, E-mail: museum@aub.edu.lb, Internet: http://ddc.aub.edu.lb/projects/museum. Head: Dr. Leila Badre
Archaeological Museum / University Museum - 1868
Flint implements, bronze tools, pottery, glassware, coins, sculpture, cylinder seals 24137

Daheshite Museum, BP 202, Beirut. Head: Dr. A.S.M. Dahesh
Fine Arts Museum
Aquarelles, gouaches, original paintings, engravings, sculptures in marble, bronze, ivory and wood carvings - library 24138

Musée de Préhistoire Libanaise, Beirut, mail addr: c/o Université Saint Joseph, BP 293, Beirut. Head: Prof. Henri Fleisch
Natural History Museum / University Museum - 1963
Natural sciences, prehistory 24139

Musée des Beaux Arts, BP 3939, Beirut - T: (1) 25285. Head: Dr. A.S.M. Dahesh
Fine Arts Museum
Sculptures, paintings 24140

Musée National, Rue de Damas, Beirut - T: (1) 40100 poste 440. Head: Dr. Camile Asmar
Archaeological Museum - 1920
Royal jewelry, arms and statues of the Phoenician epoch, sarcophagus of King Ahiram (13th c B.C.), Greek and Hellenistic sarcophagi, Roman and Byzantine mosaics, Arabic wooden items and ceramics, coins 24141

Musée Nicholas Ibrahim Sursock, Rue de l'Archevèque, Quartier Sursock, Beirut, mail addr: BP 165638, Beirut - T: (1) 334133. Head: Dr. Loutfalla Melki
Fine Arts Museum
Icons, paintings, oriental carpets 24142

Beit-ed-Dine

Musée Al Mathaf El Lubnani, Musée du Liban Féodal, Beit-ed-Dine
Historical Museum / Music Museum
History of the 16th-17th c, musical instruments 24143

Beiteddine

Moussa Castle Museum, Rd Deir-El-Qamar to Beiteddine-Shooff, Beiteddine - T: (5) 500106, 501660, Fax: 501660, 511611, E-mail: moussa@moussacastle.com, Internet: http://www.moussacastle.com.lb. Head: Moussa Al-Maamari
Decorative Arts Museum / Military Museum / Folklore Museum
Lebenese artwork and artifacts, peasant and noble life from past centuries, military, folklore 24144

Bsharri

Gibran Museum, Gibran National Committee, Bsharri - T: (06) 671137, 671044, Fax: (01) 396916, E-mail: k.gibran@cyberia.net.lb
Special Museum
440 Gibran paintings and drawings, 90 copies from the Telfair Museum Savannah (USA) - archives, personal library 24145

Byblos

Fossils Museum, Ancient Souk, Byblos - T: (01) 426703, Fax: 612259. Head: Frédéric Husseini
Natural History Museum
Fossils from Lebanon 24146

Wax Museum, In front of Citadel, Byblos
Historical Museum
Lebanese history 24147

Ehden

Qozhiah Museum, Monastery, Ehden
Religious Arts Museum / Science&Tech Museum
First printing machine of the Arab world and Eastern Mediterranean, religious artwork (19th c), paintings 24148

Jdeidet El-Metn

Lebanon' Marine Wildlife Museum with Collection of Murex, nr Collage La Sagesse, Jdeidet El-Metn
Natural History Museum
Marine wildlife, snails of the Phoenicans (Lebanon's ancestors) 2000 B.C. 24149

Rachana

Rachana Open Air Museum, Rachana - T: (06) 720903, Fax: 720903, E-mail: fbasbous@dm.net.lb. Head: Alfred Basbous
Open Air Museum / Fine Arts Museum
workshop 24150

Shouf

Beiteddine Museum, Beiteddine Palace, Shouf
Ethnology Museum
Clothes, houseware, rifles, swords 24151

Lesotho

Maseru

Lesotho National Museum, POB 1125, Maseru 100 - T: 24862
Local Museum 24152

Morija

Morija Museum, Church St, Morija 190, mail addr: POB 308, Morija 190 - T: 360308, Fax: 360308, E-mail: morija@lesoff.co.za. Head: Stephen J. Gill
Natural History Museum / Ethnology Museum - 1956
Ethnography of Lesotho, geological specimens, Stone Age tools and fossils - archives 24153

Liberia

Cape Mount

Tubman Centre of African Culture, Robertsport, Cape Mount
Ethnology Museum - 1964
African sculpture, weaving, cultural artifacts 24154

Monrovia

Africana Museum, Cuttington University College, Monrovia, mail addr: POB 277, Monrovia. Head: Edward O. N'Gele
Ethnology Museum - 1960
Arts, crafts, ethnography traditional arts and crafts, ethnographical material, 2 traditional houses - research library 24155

National Museum, Broad and Buchanan Sts, Monrovia, mail addr: POB 3223, Monrovia. Head: Burdie Urey-Weeks
Local Museum / Historical Museum - 1962
Liberian culture, ceremonial masks, musical instruments, historical artifacts 24156

Natural History Museum of Liberia, c/o T.J.R. Faulkener College, University of Liberia, Monrovia - T: 224670, Fax: 226418. Head: Charles Steiner
Natural History Museum
Natural history, especially of Liberia 24157

Libya

Benghazi

Benghazi Museum, Department of Antiquities, Benghazi. Head: Dr. Abdullah Shaiboub
Local Museum
Mausoleum of Omar el Mukhtar 24158

Gaigab

Gaigab Museum, Department of Antiquities, Gaigab. Head: Dr. Abdullah Shaiboub
Archaeological Museum 24159

Germa

Germa Museum, Department of Antiquities, Germa. Head: Dr. Abdullah Shaiboub
Archaeological Museum 24160

Leptis Magna

Leptis Magna Museum, Department of Antiquities, Leptis Magna. Head: Dr. Abdullah Shaiboub
Archaeological Museum 24161

Tokra

Tauchira Museum, Department of Antiquities, Tokra. Head: Dr. Abdullah Shaiboub
Archaeological Museum 24162

Tolmeitha

Ptolemais Museum, Department of Antiquities, Tolmeitha. Head: Dr. Abdullah Shaiboub
Archaeological Museum 24163

Tripoli

Archaeological Museum, Department of Antiquities, Assarai al-Hamra, Tripoli. Head: Dr. Abdullah Shaiboub
Archaeological Museum 24164

Epigraphy Museum, Department of Antiquities, Assarai al-Hamra, Tripoli. Head: Dr. Abdullah Shaiboub
Decorative Arts Museum 24165

Ethography Museum, Department of Antiquities, Es saray El-Hamara, Tripoli. Head: Dr. Abdullah Shaiboub
Ethnology Museum 24166

Islamic Museum, Department of Antiquities, Tripoli. Head: Dr. Abdullah Shaiboub
Historical Museum 24167

Natural History Museum, Department of Antiquities, Assarai al-Hamra, Tripoli. Head: Dr. Abdullah Shaiboub
Natural History Museum 24168

Prehistory Museum, Department of Antiquities, Assarai al-Hamra, Tripoli. Head: Dr. Abdullah Shaiboub
Historical Museum 24169

Zanzur

Zanzur Museum, Department of Antiquities, Zanzur. Head: Dr. Abdullah Shaiboub
Archaeological Museum 24170

Liechtenstein

Schaan

DoMuS - Museum und Galerie der Gemeinde Schaan, Rathaus, Landstr 19, 9494 Schaan - T: 2377271, Fax: 2377279, E-mail: domus@schaan.li, Internet: http://www.schaan.li. Head: Eva Pepić
Local Museum / Public Gallery 24171

Vereinigung der Mund- und Fussmalenden Künstler in aller Welt e.V., Im Rietle 25, 9494 Schaan - T: 2321176, Fax: 2327541, E-mail: vdmfk@vdmfk.li, Internet: http://www.vdmfk.com. Head: Marlyse Tovae
Association with Coll 24172

Schellenberg

Wohnmuseum Schellenberg, Aussenstelle des Liechtensteinischen Landesmuseums, Haus Nr. 12, 9488 Schellenberg - T: (00423) 2367550, Fax: 2367552, E-mail: Landesmuseum@llm.li. Head: Norbert W. Hasler
Local Museum - 1994
The oldest preserved wooden residential building within the Lake Constance area, peasant life style from around 1900 24173

Triesenberg

Walser Heimatmuseum, Dorfzentrum, Im Verkehrsbüro, 9497 Triesenberg - T: 2621926, 2655010. Head: Josef Eberle
Local Museum - 1961
Cultural history of the Walser region, including interiors, weaving, farm implements, weights and measures, religious folk art, 17th c Walser house 24174

Vaduz

Kunstmuseum Liechtenstein, Städtle 32, 9490 Vaduz - T: 2350300, Fax: 2350329, E-mail: mail@kunstmuseum.li, Internet: http://www.kunstmuseum.li. Head: Dr. Friedemann Malsch
Fine Arts Museum - 1968 24175

Liechtensteinische Landesbibliothek, Gerberweg 5, 9490 Vaduz - T: 2366362, Fax: 2331419, E-mail: labibl@firstlink.li, Internet: http://www.lbfl.li
Library with Exhibitions 24176

Liechtensteinische Staatliche Kunstsammlung → Kunstmuseum Liechtenstein

Liechtensteinisches Landesmuseum, Städtle 43, 9490 Vaduz, mail addr: Postfach 1216, 9490 Vaduz - T: 2367550, Fax: 2367552, E-mail: landesmuseum@llm.li. Head: Norbert W. Hasler
Archaeological Museum / Historical Museum / Military Museum / Folklore Museum - 1954
Pre- and protohistory (finds from neolithic to alamannic period excavations in Liechtenstein), local history, ecclesiastical sculptures, folklore, numismatics, weapons from the prince's coll, 15th c tavern 24177

Postmuseum des Fürstentums Liechtenstein, Städtle 37, 9490 Vaduz - T: 2366101, Fax: 2366109, E-mail: katrin.frick@abg.llv.li. Head: Hermann Hassler
Special Museum - 1930
Stamp coll, philately, stamps from Liechtenstein, designs, print and colour samples, clichés and stamping machinery, exhibition awards, rare items from all over the world, literature 24178

Sammlungen des Regierenden Fürsten von Liechtenstein, Schloß, 9490 Vaduz - T: 2381200, Fax: 2381271, E-mail: b.capaul@sfl-vaduz.li. Head: Dr. Uwe Wieczorek
Fine Arts Museum
15th-19th c German paintings and sculptures, Rubens coll (sketches, Decius-Mus-Zyklus), weapons, furniture, tapestry, 18th c state carriage made by Nicolas Pineau, 16th-17th c sculpture, Flemish Baroque, 17th c Dutch painting, 14th-18th Italian painting, painting of Viennese Biedermeier 24179

Skimuseum, Bangarten 10, 9490 Vaduz - T: 2321502, Fax: 2321502. Head: Noldi Beck
Special Museum - 1994 24180

Lithuania

Bijotai

Dionizas Poška Hollowed Trunks, Šiauliai Aušros Museum, Baubliai, 5419 Bijotai - Fax: (01) 521638, E-mail: ausros.muz@takas.lt, Internet: http://www.siauliai.aps.lt/ausra
Historical Museum - 1812 24181

Kaunas

Maironis Lithuanian Literature Museum, Rotušės aikstė 13, 3000 Kaunas - T: (07) 207477, Fax: 207477, E-mail: maironio@post.sonexco.com, Internet: http://www1.omnitel.net/maironis. Head: Aldona Ruseckaitė
Special Museum - 1936
Hist of Lithuanian literature from 14th until the end of 20th c, documents related to the poet Jonas Maironis - library 24182

M.K. Čiurlionis National Museum of Art, Vlado Putvinskio 55, 3000 Kaunas - T: (07) 229738, Fax: 204612, E-mail: MKC@takas.lt. Head: Osvaldas Daugelis
Fine Arts Museum - 1921
European and Oriental Art, Lithuanian Folk Art, Ancient Egypt, porcelain, numismatics, devils, works by the Lithuanian painter and composer Mikalojus Konstantinas Čiurlionis (1875-1911) - library 24183

Museum of Pedagogics, Lajsves alleja 24, 3000 Kaunas
Special Museum - 1958
Pedagogics, hist of education, documents, photographs - library 24184

Vytautas The Great War Museum, K. Donelaičio 64, 3000 Kaunas - T: (07) 320765, Fax: 320765, E-mail: janinak@takas.lt. Head: J. Jurevičius
Historical Museum / Military Museum - 1921
Archeology, military history (1236-1994), weapons, numismatics, uniforms, flags, ethnography, photography, church art - library, archives 24185

Pakruojis

Pakruojis Manor House, Šiauliai Aušros Museum, 5419 Pakruojis - Fax: (01) 521638, E-mail: ausros.muz@takas.lt, Internet: http://www.siauliai.aps.lt/ausra. Head: Raimundas Balza
Historic Site - 1988 24186

Šiauliai

Aušros Avenue Mansion, Šiauliai Aušros Museum, Aušros Av 47, 5419 Šiauliai - T: (01) 524391, Fax: 521638, E-mail: ausros.muz@takas.lt, Internet: http://www.siauliai.aps.lt/ausra. Head: Raimundas Balza
Ethnology Museum - 1933
Ethnography 24187

Bicycle Museum, Šiauliai Aušros Museum, Vilniaus St 139, 5419 Šiauliai - T: (01) 524395, Fax: 521638, E-mail: ausros.muz@takas.lt, Internet: http://www.siauliai.aps.lt/ausra. Head: Raimundas Balza
Special Museum - 1980
Coll of bicycles, hist of cycling 24188

Ch. Frenkelis Mansion, Šiauliai Aušros Museum, Vilniaus St 74, 5419 Šiauliai - T: (01) 520116, Fax: 521638, E-mail: ausros.muz@takas.lt, Internet: http://www.siauliai.aps.lt/ausra. Head: Raimundas Balza
Historical Museum - 1994
Art, archaelogy 24189

Photography Museum, Šiauliai Aušros Museum, Vilniaus St 140, 5400 Šiauliai - T: (01) 524396, Fax: 521638, E-mail: siauliai.photo@takas.lt, Internet: http://www.siauliai.aps.lt/ausra. Head: Vilija Ulinskyte
Special Museum - 1973
History of Lithuanian photography 24190

Poet Jovaras House, Šiauliai Aušros Museum, Vytauto St 116, 5400 Šiauliai - T: (01) 524397, Fax: 521638, E-mail: ausros.muz@takas.lt, Internet: http://www.siauliai.aps.lt/ausra. Head: Raimundas Balza
Special Museum - 1985
Memorabilia of the local writer Jovaras, postdard coll 24191

Radio and Television Museum, Šiauliai Aušros Museum, Vilniaus St 174, 5400 Šiauliai - T: (01) 524399, Fax: 521638, E-mail: ausros.muz@takas.lt, Internet: http://www.siauliai.aps.lt/ausra. Head: Raimundas Balza
Science&Tech Museum - 1982
Radio and TV equipment 24192

Šiauliai Aušros Museum, Vytauto 89, 5419 Šiauliai - T: (01) 524390, Fax: 521638, E-mail: ausros.muz@takas.lt, Internet: http://www.siauliai.aps.lt/ausra. Head: Raimundas Balza
Local Museum - 1923
Local and regional history, archaeology, ethnography, art, photography, bicycles, radio and TV history, postcards - library, publishing office, restauration 24193

Venclauskių House, Šiauliai Aušros Museum, Vytauto 89, 5419 Šiauliai - T: (01) 5243900, Fax: 521638, E-mail: ausros.muz@takas.lt, Internet: http://www.siauliai.aps.lt/ausra. Head: Raimundas Balza
Decorative Arts Museum - 1955
Art - publishing office, library 24194

Žaliūkių Windmill, Šiauliai Aušros Museum, Archtektų St, 5400 Šiauliai - T: (01) 524391, Fax: 521638, E-mail: ausros.muz@takas.lt, Internet: http://www.siauliai.aps.lt/ausra. Head: Raimundas Balza
Special Museum - 1967
Milling equipment 24195

Trakai

Trakai Historical Museum, Kestučio 4, Trakai - T: (038) 51274. Head: Virgilijus Poviliūnas
Local Museum - 1948
Hist of the city and castle of Trakai and the surrounding areas 24196

Vilnius

Europos Parkas (Museum of the Centre of Europe), Joneikiškiu k., 4013 Vilnius r. - T: (02) 652368, 502242, Fax: 652368, E-mail: hq@europosparkas.lt, Internet: http://www.europosparkas.lt. Head: Gintaras Karosas
Fine Arts Museum / Open Air Museum - 1993
Large scale works by international artists incl works by, Abakanowicz, LeWitt, Oppenheim, Karosas and Ito 24197

Lietuvos Dailes Muziejus (Lithuanian Art Museum), Didžioji 4, 2001 Vilnius - T: (02) 628030, Fax: 226006. Head: Romualdas Budrys
Fine Arts Museum - 1941
Lithuanian art, Lithuanian folk art, 16th-19th c French, German and English art, amber coll, coll of watches - library, archives, restoration centre 24198

Lietuvos Nacionalinis Muziejus (National Museum of Lithuania), Arsenalo 1, 2001 Vilnius - T: (02) 627774, Fax: 611023, E-mail: muziejus@lnm.lt, Internet: http://www.lnm.lt. Head: Biruté Kulnyté
Local Museum - 1855
Archaeology, ethnography, history, numismatics, iconography - library, archives, publishing house 24199

Lithuanian State Museum, Studenty 8, 2034 Vilnius - T: (02) 355187. Head: K.K. Gaurilius
Local Museum - 1991
Bolshevik genocide, resistance, Gulags 24200

Žeimelis

Žeimelis Žiemgalos Museum, Šiauliai Aušros Museum, Vienybės Sq, 5419 Žeimelis - T: (01) 829145337, Fax: 521638, E-mail: ausros.muz@takas.lt, Internet: http://www.siauliai.aps.lt/ausra. Head: Raimundas Balza
Historical Museum - 1959
Local history and ethnology 24201

Luxembourg

Bech-Kleinmacher

Freilichtmuseum Schwebsingen, 25a Rte du Vin, 5405 Bech-Kleinmacher - T: 69049
Open Air Museum
Memorials to do with Moselle wine 24202

Musée Folklorique et Viticole à Possen, 1 Rue Aloyse Sandt, 5404 Bech-Kleinmacher - T: 23698233, 23697353, Fax: 23697353
Folklore Museum - 1965
History of viticulture, coll of toys, glass and stoves 24203

Bettembourg

Galerie d'Art du Château, Rue du Château, 3201 Bettembourg - T: 518080260/232, Fax: 520039, E-mail: commune@bettembourg.lu, Internet: http://www.tageblatt.lu/betebuerg
Fine Arts Museum 24204

Binsfeld

A. Schiiwesch Musée Rural, A. Schiiwesch Museum für ländliche Kultur, 20 Aloyse Kohnen, 9946 Binsfeld
Local Museum 24205

Brandenbourg

Musée Local, 1 Rue Principale, 9360 Brandenbourg - T: 90475. Head: Josy Schreiner
Local Museum 24206

Clervaux

Musée du Jouet, 9 Grand-Rue, 9710 Clervaux - T: 920228, Fax: 920228
Special Museum 24207

Musée Historique, Château, 9712 Clervaux - T: 91048
Historical Museum
Documents of the Battle of Ardennes, photos by Edward Steichen, models of the most important castles and fortresses of Luxembourg 24208

Diekirch

Musée Municipal, Pl Guillaume, 9233 Diekirch - T: 8087801
Local Museum
Archaeological coll incl two mosaics from the 2nd c BC 24209

Musée National d'Histoire Militaire, 10 Bamertal, 9209 Diekirch - T: 808908, Fax: 804719, E-mail: mnhmdiek@pt.lu, Internet: http://www.nat-military-museum.lu. Head: Roland Gaul
Military Museum - 1984
Local hist during WWII and reconstruction of battle scenes, dioramas, military equipment, vehicles, soldier's belongings, photographs, documents and maps 24210

Dudelange

Musée des Enrôles de Force, Pl de l'Hôtel de Ville, 3590 Dudelange - T: 514389
Military Museum 24211

Musée Municipal, 25 Rue Dominique Lang, 3505 Dudelange - T: 51612138
Local Museum
Paleontology, archaeology, local history, photo gallery Nei Licht 24212

Echternach

Musée de l'Abbaye, Abbaye Bénédictine, 6486 Echternach - T: 72230
Religious Arts Museum - 1987
History of the abbey, book illumination, extracts from the Echternacher Handschriften 24213

Musée de Préhistoire, 2 Rue des Tanneurs, 6491 Echternach - T: 720296
Historical Museum
Prehistory of the human being, production and usage of tools and implements, exhibits from Europe, America, Papua-Newguinea and Morocco 24214

Ehnen

Musée du Vin, 115 Rte du Vin, 5416 Ehnen - T: 760026, Fax: 768451. Head: G. Reuland
Agriculture Museum
Model vineyard with the various types of vine of Luxembourg, old distilleries and wine presses, cooper's gallery 24215

Esch-sur-Alzette

Galerie d'Art d'Esch, 122 Rue de l'Alzette, 4120 Esch-sur-Alzette - T: 547383482, Fax: 542896, E-mail: tpn@villeesch.lu
Public Gallery 24216

Galerie Municipale Dada-Cave, 122 Rue de l'Alzette, 4010 Esch-sur-Alzette - T: 547383508, Fax: 542896, E-mail: tpn@villeesch.lu. Head: Philippe Noesen
Public Gallery 24217

Musée National de la Résistance, Pl de la Résistance, 4041 Esch-sur-Alzette, mail addr: BP 145, 4002 Esch-sur-Alzette - T: 548472, Fax: 542927
Historical Museum - 1956
National resistance in World War II 24218

Ettelbruck

General Patton Memorial Museum, 5 Rue Dr. Klein, 9054 Ettelbruck - T: 810322, Fax: 812586
Military Museum - 1995
General George S. Patten, commander of the 3rd U.S. Army, whose troops liberated the town of Ettelbruck for good on Dec 25th 1944, photographs, documents about the German invasion and occupation 24219

Musée de la Nature, BP 126, 9002 Ettelbruck - T: 818943, 82262. Head: Nicolas Knoch
Natural History Museum 24220

Heiderscheid

Musée Eist Dueref am Laaf van den Joorhonnerten, 15 Rue du Marché, 9158 Heiderscheid
Historical Museum 24221

Luxembourg

Casino Luxembourg - Forum d'Art Contemporain, 41 Rue de Notre-Dame, 2240 Luxembourg - T: 225045, Fax: 229595, E-mail: casino-luxembourg@ci.culture.lu, Internet: http://www.casino-luxembourg.lu. Head: Enrico Lunghi
Public Gallery 24222

Galerie d'Art Contemporain Am Tunnel, 16 Rue Sainte-Zithe, 2763 Luxembourg
Public Gallery 24223

Jean-Pierre Pescatore Collection Villa Vauban, Galerie d'Art de la Ville de Luxembourg, 18 Av Emile Reuter, 2010 Luxembourg - T: 47963033, Fax: 471707, E-mail: d.wagener@musee-hist.lu. Head: Danièle Wagener
Fine Arts Museum - 1966
Paintings by Dutch and Flemish masters of the 17-18th c, French, German and Swiss painting from the 19th c 24224

Musée des Postes et Telecommunications, Coin Rue d'Epernay et Av de la Gare, 2992 Luxembourg - T: 40887322, Fax: 406867, E-mail: pfofftim@pt.lu, Internet: http://www.ept.lu. Head: Guy Rausch
Science&Tech Museum
Development of postal and telecommunications techniques, postman uniforms, letter boxes, telephones, postal stamp coll 24225

Musée des Tramway et Autobus, 63 Rue de Bouillon, 1248 Luxembourg - T: 47962385, Fax: 299209, E-mail: mmedernach@vdl.lu. Head: Marcel Medernach
Science&Tech Museum 24226

Musée d'Histoire de la Ville de Luxembourg, 14 Rue du Saint-Esprit, 2090 Luxembourg - T: 2290501, 47963061, Fax: 471707, E-mail: b.fuge@musee-hist.lu, Internet: http://www.musee-hist.lu. Head: Danièle Wagener
Historical Museum - 1996
Hist of the city of Luxembourg from the 10th c until today, urban development and social hist 24227

Musée d'Instruments Anciens et d'Archives au Conservatoire de Musique, Museum für Musikinstrumente und Archiv des Musikkonservatoriums, 33 Rue Charles Martel, 2134 Luxembourg - T: 47962951
Music Museum
Old musical instruments of various kind 24228

Musée National d'Histoire et d'Art, Marchè-aux-Poissons, 2345 Luxembourg - T: 4793301, Fax: 223760. Head: Paul Reiles
Historical Museum / Fine Arts Museum - 1845
Archaeology, fine arts, folklore, decorative and applied arts, firearms, numismatics, natural history - library 24229

Musée National d'Histoire Naturelle, 25 Rue Munster, 2160 Luxembourg - T: 4622331, Fax: 475152. Head: Norbert Stomp
Natural History Museum - 1988
Botany (herbarium), zoology, ecology, anthropology, paleontology, geology/mineralogy, geophysics (underground Laboratory), human biology 24230

Palais Grand Ducal, Rue du March-aux-Herbes, 1136 Luxembourg - T: 22809
Decorative Arts Museum / Fine Arts Museum
Items of furniture, paintings and wall hangings from the 16th c 24231

Villa Vauban, Galerie d'Art de la Ville de Luxembourg, 18 Av Emile Reuter, 2090 Luxembourg - T: 47963061, Fax: 471707, E-mail: b.fuge@musee-hist.lu. Head: Danièle Wagener
Public Gallery - 1949
Pescatore-Lippmann collection: European painting 17th-19th century 24232

Nospelt

Musée de la Poterie, 3 Rue des Potiers, 8392 Nospelt - T: 300199. Head: Marie Josée Lehnert
Decorative Arts Museum
Potter's implements, typical ceramics from Nospelt, Echternach and Transylvania 24233

Oberkorn

Collection Eugène Pesch, Centre Marcel Noppeney, Rue de Belvaux, 4510 Oberkorn - T: 584343, Fax: 584034/229, E-mail: claude@differdange.lu, Internet: http://www.differdange.lu
Natural History Museum
Minerals, fossils, tools of the pitmen 24234

Galerie d'Art Municipale, Rte de Belvaux, Centre Noppeney, 4510 Oberkorn - T: 584343
Fine Arts Museum 24235

Rumelange

Galerie d'Art Municipale, 99 Grand-Rue, 3730 Rumelange - T: 5631211
Fine Arts Museum 24236

Musée National des Mines Fer Luxembourgeoisie, Carreau de la Mine Walert, 3730 Rumelange - T: 5631211, Fax: 565704. Head: Will Hoffmann
Science&Tech Museum
Industrial history of machines and work implements, closed-down gallery, lives of mine workers 24237

Vianden

Musée d'Art Rustique, Musée Edouard Wolff, 96-98 Grand Rue, 9411 Vianden - T: 834591. Head: Thérèse May, Guy May
Local Museum
Furniture, decorative objects, implements portraying domestic life from 1750-1850 24238

Musée d'Automobiles en Miniature - Den Dinky (Mobile Die Cast Toy Museum), 29 Rue du Sanatorium, 9425 Vianden - T: 84095, Fax: 849461. Head: Nico Berrend
Special Museum - 1986
4.000 new and old models of cars, vans, buses, racing cars and other vehicles 24239

Musée Dicks, 96 Grand Rue, 9411 Vianden - T: 834796
Special Museum
200 dolls and 300 other toys in the house of the Luxembourg poet Edmond de la Fontaine "Dicks" 24240

Musée Victor Hugo (closed until 2002), 37 Rue de la Gare, 9420 Vianden
Special Museum - 1935
House of the French writer Victor Hugo while living in exile in 1871, coll of personal belongings, letters, documents, drawings 24241

Schloß Vianden, Burgmuseum, 48 Grand Rue, 9410 Vianden - T: 84006
Historical Museum
History of the castle: model, maps, drawings and photographs 24242

Weiler-la-Tour

Musée Local, Weiler-la-Tour
Local Museum 24243

Wiltz

Musée de la Bataille des Ardennes, Château de Wiltz, 9516 Wiltz - T: 957442
Military Museum - 1970
American and German weapons and uniforms, documents, photographs and maps reminding of the battle in the Ardenn mountains in winter 1944/45 24244

Musée des Arts et Metiers Anciens, Château de Wiltz, 9516 Wiltz - T: 957444, Fax: 957556, E-mail: siwiltz@pt.lu
Local Museum - 1983
Domestic and traditional implements, tannery 24245

Macedonia

Bitola

Muzej i Galeriya Bitola (Bitola Museum and Gallery), ul Kliment Ohridski bb, 7000 Bitola - T: (097) 35387, Fax: 35292. Head: Nikola Ivanovski
Local Museum
Prehistory, ethnography, antiquities, numismatics, hist of the revolution - library 24246

Kavadarci

Muzej-Galerija Kavadarci, Ul 7-mi Septemvri 58, 1430 Kavadarci - T: 77229
Local Museum 24247

Kruševo

Istoriski Muzej (Historical Museum), Nikole Karev 62, 92520 Kruševo - T: 77126. Head: Viktorija Peti
Historical Museum 24248

Ohrid

Naroden Muzej (National Museum), Ul Boro Sain 10, 6000 Ohrid, mail addr: PP 95, 97000 Ohrid - T: (096) 22318. Head: Nada Novakovska
Archaeological Museum / Ethnology Museum / Historical Museum / Fine Arts Museum - 1951
Archaeology, ethnography, history, art - Archeological museum, gallery of icons, museum of slavic literacy 24249

Prilep

Zavod i Muzej - Prilep, Moše Pijade 142, 7500 Prilep, mail addr: PP 93, 97500 Prilep - T: (098) 211011. Head: Ilija Velkoski
Archaeological Museum / Local Museum - 1955
Archaeology, prehistory, medieval history, numismatics 24250

Skopje

Muzej na Grad Skopje (Museum of the City of Skopje), Mito Hadzi Vasilev bb, 1000 Skopje - T: (02) 115367, Fax: 115367. Head: Klime Korobar
Local Museum - 1949
Local archaeology, prehistory, Middle Ages, 7th-20th c hist, art hist, anthropology - Dept of anthropology, Memorial House, Dept of Historic Armory 24251

Muzej na Makedonija - Arceološki, Etnološki i Istoriski (Museum of Macedonia - Archaeological, Ethnological and Historical), Čurčiska bb, 1000 Skopje - T: (02) 116044, Fax: 116439, E-mail: musmk@mt.net.mk, Internet: http://www.museummk.com. Head: Dr. Dragiša Zdravkovski
Archaeological Museum / Ethnology Museum / Historical Museum / Fine Arts Museum - 1977
Terracotta icons, medieval icons, fresco replicas, folk costumes, jewellery, musical instruments, pottery - library, special laboratories 24252

Muzej na Sovremenata Umetnost Skopje (Skopje Museum of Contemporary Art), Samoilova bb, 1000 Skopje, mail addr: PP 482, 1000 Skopje - T: (02) 117734, 117735, Fax: 110123, E-mail: moca@soros.org.mk. Head: Zoran Petrovski
Fine Arts Museum - 1964
International contemporary art 24253

Prirodonaučen Muzej na Makedonija (Macedonian Museum of Natural History), Bulevar Ilinden 86, 1000 Skopje, mail addr: PP 431, 1000 Skopje - T: (02) 117669, Fax: 116453, E-mail: macmusnh@unet.com.mk, Internet: http://www.members.vienna.at/shrew/Biodiv-Congress.html. Head: Tatjana Boškova
Natural History Museum - 1926
Natural hist, entomology, palaeontology, hydrobiology, botany, ichthyology - library 24254

Umjetnička Galerija (Art Gallery), Krusevska 1, 1000 Skopje, mail addr: PP 278, 91000 Skopje - T: (02) 233904. Head: Viktorija Vaseva Dimeska
Fine Arts Museum - 1948
Medieval Southslavian paintings, icons, Macedonian and Yugoslavian contemporary art, Macedonian coll of 14th - 20th cc - library 24255

Stip

Narodni Muzej (National Museum), ul Toso Aros 10, 2000 Stip
Archaeological Museum / Ethnology Museum / Fine Arts Museum
Archaeology, ethnography, art 24256

Struga

Naroden Muzej Dr. Nikola Nezlobinski (Dr. Nikola Nezlobinski National Museum), Kej 8-mi Novembri 63, 97330 Struga, mail addr: PP 62, 97330 Struga. Head: Naum Panoski
Local Museum - 1938
Archaeology, history, zoology, botany - library 24257

Strumica

Pokrajinski Muzej (Provincial Museum), Ul Nenineva 23, 2400 Strumica
Local Museum
Local history, ethnography 24258

Zavod za Zastita na Spomenicite na Kulturata, Prirodnite Retkosti i Muzej, Institute for Protection of Cultural Monuments, Natural Rarities and Museum, 27 Mart 2, 2400 Strumica - T: (092) 345925, Fax: 345925, E-mail: muzejstr@nic.mpt.com.mk. Head: Aleksandar Cicimov
Local Museum
Coll of 75 golden coins (12th-13th c), coll of medieval ceramics (11th-12th c) 24259

Tetovo

Muzej na Tetovskiot Kraj (Tetovo Regional Museum), Derviska Tekija Arabati Sersem-Ali bb, 1220 Tetovo
Local Museum
Archaeology, ethnography 24260

Titov Veles

Narodni Muzej (National Museum), ul Maršala Tita 22, 91400 Titov Veles, mail addr: PP 96, 91400 Titov Veles - T: 21471. Head: Nikola Tripčev
Local Museum
Archaeology, ethnography, labour movement 1918-1941, National Liberation War 24261

Madagascar

Antananarivo

Musée d' ORSTOM, BP 434, Antananarivo
Natural History Museum - 1947
Zoology, botany, fossils, birds (aviary), herbarium, art works - library 24262

Musée d'Art et d'Archéologie de l'Université d'Antananarivo, 17 Rue Docteur Villette, 101 Antananarivo, mail addr: BP 564, 101 Antananarivo - T: (20) 2225493, Fax: 2232317, E-mail: vohitra@refer.mg. Head: Jean-Aimé Rakotoarisoa
Fine Arts Museum / Archaeological Museum
Art and archaeological coll - library 24263

Musée Historique, Rue Pasteur Ravelojaona, Antananarivo - T: (20) 2220091. Head: Aldine Ravaonatoandro
Historical Museum - 1897
History, art 24264

Musée National de Géologie, Rue Farafaty, Antananarivo, mail addr: BP 322, Antananarivo 101 - T: (20) 2240048, Fax: 2241873, E-mail: mdonna@dts.mg. Head: Ranaivoarivelo Andriamanantena
Natural History Museum 24265

Museum du Parc Tsimbazaza, c/o Parc Botanique et Zoologique de Tsimbaza, Rue Fernand Kassanga, Antananarivo 101 - T: (20) 2231149
Ethnology Museum / Natural History Museum / Open Air Museum
Folklore, archaeology, paleontology, local fauna, pottery, Malagasy art 24266

Salle des Beaux Arts, Palais de la Reine, Antananarivo
Fine Arts Museum 24267

Fianarantsoa

Musée de l'Université de Fianarantsoa, c/o Université de Fianarantsoa, Fianarantsoa - T: (20) 7550802. Head: Clarisse Razafindratsima
Local Museum / University Museum - 1993
Traditional and cultural life - library 24268

Nosy-Bé

Musée du Centre National de Recherches Océanographiques, BP 68, Nosy-Bé 207 - T: (20) 8661373. Head: Jean Maharavo
Natural History Museum - 1974
Marine and brackish water pisces, crustacea, marine shells of echinoderms, coelenterata, molluscs, sponge, marine algae, traditional and artisanal malagasy fishing gear 24269

Toamasina

Musée de la Gendarmerie, Moramanga, Toamasina
Special Museum 24270

Musée Régional, c/o Université de Toamasina, Toamasina - T: (20) 5333400. Head: Fanony Fulgence
Local Museum / University Museum - 1991
Regional customs (fetishes), fishing gear, musical instruments, cooking items, plaiting of mats 24271

Tuléar

Musée de l'Université de Tuléar, c/o Cedratom, Université de Tuléar, BP 185, Tuléar
Science&Tech Museum / University Museum 24272

Malawi

Blantyre

Museum of Malawi, Kamuzu Hwy, Chichiri, Blantyre, mail addr: POB 30360, Blantyre - T: 672438, 675448, 671857, Fax: 676615, E-mail: museums@malawi.net. Head: Dr. M.E.D. Nhlane
Local Museum - 1959
Local and national history, reconstructed traditional hut with furnishings and implements, traditional weaving, iron implements and ceremonial regalia 24273

Mangochi

Lake Malawi Museum, POB 128, Mangochi - T: 584346
Local Museum
Local history and customs, artifacts related to the lake and local fishing 24274

Mzuzu

Mzuzu Museum, POB 138, Mzuzu - T: 332071
Local Museum 24275

Namaka

Mtengatenga Postal Museum, Namaka - T: 675448, 672438, Fax: 676615, E-mail: museums@malawi.net. Head: Dr. Med Nhlane
Special Museum
History of local postal services, housed in traditional carrier's rest hut - post office 24276

Malaysia

Alor Gajah

Museum of Traditional Custumes, Dataran Alor Gajah, 75000 Alor Gajah - T: (06) 2826526, Fax: 2826745
Folklore Museum 24277

Alor Setar

Kedah Royal Museum, Medan bandar, 05400 Alor Setar - T: (04) 7327937
Historical Museum - 1983 24278

Kedah State Art Gallery, Medan Bandar, Jalan Raja, 05400 Alor Setar - T: (04) 7325752
Public Gallery - 1983
Paintings, photographs, musical instruments, handicraft 24279

Muzium Negeri Kedah (Kedah State Museum), Lebuhraya Darulaman, Bakar Bata, 05100 Alor Setar - T: (04) 7331162, Fax: 7305100
Decorative Arts Museum - 1961
Gold and silver flowers, local weapons and ceramics - library 24280

Bedung

Archaeological Museum, Lembah Bujang, 08400 Bedung - T: (04) 4581236
Archaeological Museum - 1983 24281

Gombak

Museum of Aboriginal Affairs, Jalan Pahang, Km 24, 53000 Gombak - T: (03) 6892122
Ethnology Museum - 1987 24282

Ipoh

Geological Survey Museum, Scrivenor Rd, 31400 Ipoh, mail addr: POB 1015, Ipoh - T: (05) 557644/85
Natural History Museum - 1955
Malaysian geological exhibits 24283

Jasin

Agricultural Museum, 75000 Jasin - T: (06) 2826526, Fax: 2826745
Agriculture Museum 24284

Johor Bahru

Abu Bakar Royal Museum, Istana Besar Johor, 80500 Johor Bahru - T: (07) 2230555, Fax: 2248476
Historical Museum 24285

Kepong

Forestry Research Institute Malaysia Museum, 52100 Kepong - T: (03) 6342633
Natural History Museum - 1925 24286

Klang

Gedung Raja Abdullah, Jalan Raja Abdullah, 40100 Klang - T: (03) 3327383
Local Museum
Early hist of Klang to its present state, ethnographic material, photographs 24287

Sultan Abdul Aziz Royal Gallery, Jalan Rusa, 40100 Klang
Fine Arts Museum / Decorative Arts Museum - 1999 24288

Kota Bharu

Muzium Negeri Kelantan (Kelantan State Museum), Jalan Hospital, 15000 Kota Bharu - T: (09) 7482266, Fax: 7473366. Head: Wan Ali Bin Wan Ahmad
Historical Museum - 1982 24289

Kota Kinabalu

Sabah Art Gallery, Jalan Muzium, 88000 Kota Kinabalu - T: (088) 213763/64, Fax: 7615355
Public Gallery - 1984 24290

Sabah Museum, Jalan Muzium, 88300 Kota Kinabalu - T: (088) 253199, 215563, Fax: 240230, E-mail: jmuzium@tm.net.my, Internet: http://www.borneo-online.com.my/museum, http://www.sabah.gov.my/kkbs/muz.htm. Head: Joseph Pounis Guntavid
Ethnology Museum / Historical Museum / Natural History Museum / Archaeological Museum - 1886
Anthropology, archaeology, natural hist (zoology and ethnobotany), historic coll of Sabah - library 24291

Kuah Langkawi

Legends & Heritage Museum, Teluk Yu, 07000 Kuah Langkawi - T: (04) 9591913, Fax: (03) 21613793, E-mail: Misroni@Kraftangan.gov.my, Internet: http://www.kraftangan.com
Decorative Arts Museum - 1995 24292

Kuala Langsar

Perak Royal Museum, Istana Lama Bukit Chandan, 33000 Kuala Langsar - T: (05) 7765500
Historical Museum 24293

Kuala Lumpur

Bak Negara Money Museum, Jalan Dat' Onn, 50480 Kuala Lumpur - T: (03) 2907684, Fax: 2912990
Special Museum - 1989 24294

Balai Seni Lukis Negara (National Art Gallery), Jalan Temerloh, 50400 Kuala Lumpur - T: (03) 4254989, Fax: 4254987. Head: Syed Jamal
Fine Arts Museum - 1958
Painting, sculpture, prints, photographs and crafts 24295

Biomedical Museum, Jalan Pahang, 50588 Kuala Lumpur - T: (03) 2986033, Fax: 2938306, E-mail: environ@gov.my, Internet: http://www.imr.gov.my
Special Museum - 1983 24296

Craft Museum, Sesyen 63, Jalan Conlay 9, 50450 Kuala Lumpur - T: (03) 21613793, Fax: 21613793, E-mail: Misroni@Kraftangan.gov.my, Internet: http://www.kraftangan.com
Decorative Arts Museum - 1995
Handicrafts 24297

Malay Ethnographic Museum, c/o Department of Malay Studies, University of Malaya, 59100 Kuala Lumpur - T: (03) 7555266 ext 421
Ethnology Museum - 1973 24298

Museum of Asian Art, c/o University of Malaya, 50603 Kuala Lumpur - T: (03) 7571061, Fax: 7593985, E-mail: b1othman@umcsd.um.edu.my. Head: Prof. Dr. Othman Yatim
Fine Arts Museum / Decorative Arts Museum - 1974
Southeast Asian textiles and ceramics, classical Indian, Cambodian sculpture, contemporary Malaysian painting, Moghul miniature painting, Malaysian and Indonesian applied arts and crafts, Chinese painting and ceramics, Islamic pottery and metalwork 24299

Muzium Angkatan Tentera, Malaysian Armed Force Museum, Jalan Padang Tembak, 50634 Kuala Lumpur - T: (03) 2921333, Fax: 2939608, E-mail: sm.mmt@mod.gov.my, Internet: http://www.mod.gov.my
Military Museum - 1982 24300

Muzium Negara (National Museum), Jalan Damansara, 50566 Kuala Lumpur - T: (03) 2826255, Fax: 2827294, E-mail: kbb@tm.net.my, Internet: http://www.jma.gov.my. Head: Dr. Kamarul Baharin Bin Buyong
Local Museum - 1963
Ethnology, archaeology, natural hist, anthropology 24301

Muzium Numismatik Maybank, Menara Maybank, Jalan Tun Perak 100, 50050 Kuala Lumpur - T: (03) 20708833, Fax: 20722504, E-mail: publicaffairs@maybank.com.my, Internet: http://www.maybank2u.com. Head: Prakash Mukherjee
Decorative Arts Museum - 1988 24302

Muzium Polis Diraja Malaysia, 5 Jalan Perdana, 50480 Kuala Lumpur - T: (03) 22725689/90, Fax: 22725534. Head: Halal Bin Ismail
Historical Museum - 1961
Exhibits on crime and criminology, police history 24303

Muzium Sejarah National (National History Museum), 29 Jalan Raja, 50566 Kuala Lumpur - T: (03) 26944590, Fax: 26944640. Head: Dr. Kamarul Baharin Bin Buyong
Historical Museum - 1992
History 24304

P. Ramlee Memorial, Jalan Dedap 22, 53000 Kuala Lumpur - T: (03) 40231131, Fax: 40231131, Internet: http://www.arkib.gov.my
Local Museum 24305

Public Service Memorial, Jalan Cenderawasih, 50480 Kuala Lumpur - T: (03) 2945284, Fax: 2945280
Local Museum - 1992 24306

Royal Malaysian Air Force Museum, c/o RMAF Base, Jalan Lapangan Terbang Lama, 50460 Kuala Lumpur - T: (03) 2411133 ext 4129/4198, Fax: 2444134. Head: Dato Muslim Ayob
Military Museum - 1985
Aircraft, aircraft models 24307

Tun Abdul Razak Memorial, Sri Taman, Jalan Perdana, 50480 Kuala Lumpur - T: (03) 26937141, Fax: 26937335. Head: Noriah Jalil
Historical Museum - 1982
Coll pertaining to the late Tun Abdul Razak which includes his biography, contributions to the country and foreign affairs - archives 24308

Tunku Abdul Rahman Memorial, Jalan Dato' Onn, 50480 Kuala Lumpur - T: (03) 2947277
Local Museum 24309

Kuala Terengganu

Muzium Negeri Trengganu, Bukit Losong, 20566 Kuala Terengganu - T: (09) 6221444, Fax: 6231209. Head: Mohamed Yusuf Abdullah
Local Museum - 1977 24310

Kuching

Sarawak Museum, Jalan Tun Haji Openg, 93566 Kuching - T: (082) 44232. Head: Sanib Said
Local Museum - 1886
Ethnology, archaeology, natural history, local history 24311

Sarawak Police Museum, Peti Surat 1564, 93732 Kuching, mail addr: POB 1564, Kuching - T: (082) 440811/19 ext 225
Special Museum - 1971
Crime and criminology in Sarawak 24312

Lumut

Royal Malaysian Naval Museum, c/o KD Pelandok, Pusat Latihan TLDM, 32100 Lumut - T: (05) 683501 ext 2523
Science&Tech Museum - 1984 24313

Malacca

Malacca Museums Corporation, Malacca Heritage Compleks, Stadthuys Bldg, 75000 Malacca - T: (06) 2841934, Fax: 2826745. Head: Khamib Hj. Abab
Military Museum / Decorative Arts Museum / Music Museum - 1954
Arms, jewellery, porcelain, drawings, musical instruments, manuscripts 24314

Melaka

Cultural Museum, Jalan Kota Melaka 7, 75670 Melaka - T: (06) 2826526, Fax: 2826745
Historical Museum / Folklore Museum - 1953
Photos, prints, drawings and specimens illustrating the Portugese, Dutch and English occupations of Malacca, cultural heritage of the Malay Sultanate of Melaka 24315

Galeri Sasterawan Negara (Museum of Literature), nr Seri Melaka, 75670 Melaka - T: (06) 2826645, Fax: 2826745
Special Museum 24316

Kite Museum, Kompleks Werisan Melaka, Jalan Kota, 75670 Melaka - T: (06) 2811289, Fax: 2826745
Fine Arts Museum - 1992 24317

Malaysian Youth Museum, 430 Jalan Laksamana, 75670 Melaka - T: (06) 2826645, Fax: 2826745
Historical Museum 24318

Maritime Museum, Jalan Quayside, 75670 Melaka - T: (06) 2826645, Fax: 2826745
Historical Museum 24319

Memorial Pengisytiharan Kemerdekaan (Proclamation of Independence Memorial), Jalan Parameswara Bandar Hilir, 75670 Melaka - T: (06) 2841231, Internet: http://arkib.gov.my/memorial/mpk.html
Historical Museum - 1985 24320

Museum of Beauty, Kompleks Werisan Melaka, Jalan Kota, 75670 Melaka - T: (06) 2814872, Fax: 2826745
Ethnology Museum - 1992 24321

Museum of History and Ethnography Negeri, Stadhuys, 75670 Melaka - T: (06) 2826645, Fax: 2826745
Local Museum - 1992 24322

Muzium Rakyat (People's Museum), Kompleks Werisan Melaka, Jalan Kota, 75670 Melaka - T: (06) 2814872, Fax: 2826745
Ethnology Museum - 1992 24323

Orang Asli Museum (Malaysian Aboriginal Museum), Air Keroh, 75670 Melaka - T: (06) 2826645, Fax: 2826745
Ethnology Museum 24324

Tentera Laut Diraja Malaysia Muzium (Royal Malaysian Navy Museum), Jalan Quayside, 75670 Melaka - T: (06) 2826645, Fax: 2826745
Military Museum 24325

Tuan Yang Terutama Yang di-Pertua Negeri (Govenor of Melaka's Gallery), Kompleks Werisan Melaka, Jalan Kota, 75670 Melaka - T: (06) 2826526, Fax: 2826745
Historical Museum - 1992
Portraits, costumes, medals 24326

Merbok

Muzium Arkeologi (Archaeological Museum of Lembah Bujang), 08400 Merbok - T: (04) 4572005. Head: Dr. Kamarul Baharin Bin Buyong
Archaeological Museum - 1977
Archaeology 24327

Pekan

Sultan Abu Bakar Museum Pahang, Jalan Sultan Ahmad, 26600 Pekan - T: (09) 4221371, 4221459, Fax: 4221572. Head: Dato Mohamed Mokhtar Bin Abu Bakar
Local Museum - 1976
Cultural and historical materials of the State of Pahang 24328

Pulau Langkawi

Ibrahim Hussein Foundation Museum, Pasir Tengkorak, Jalan Langkawi, 07000 Pulau Langkawi - T: (04) 9594670
Fine Arts Museum - 1999 24329

Pulau Pinang

Museum and Art Gallery, Tingkat 2, Dewan Sri Pinang Lebuh Light, 10200 Pulau Pinang - T: (04) 2613144, Fax: 2613144, E-mail: muzium@ po.jaring.my. Head: Khoo Boo Chia
Local Museum / Public Gallery - 1961 24330

Penang Forestry Museum, Telok Bahang, 11050 Pulau Pinang - T: (04) 2625272, Fax: 2636335, E-mail: jabatanp@sukpp.gov.my. Head: Dr. Mohamed Yunus bin Zakaria
Natural History Museum - 1976
Forest products, wood processing, forest industries, forestry activities 24331

Penang Museum and Art Gallery, Jalan Farquhar, 11050 Pulau Pinang - T: (04) 2613144, Fax: 2613144. Head: Encik Khoo Boo Chia
Local Museum / Public Gallery - 1963
Chinese culture and customs, social, economic and educational exhibits, fishing, weapons 24332

Seremban

Negri Sembilan State Museum, c/o State Secretariat Seremban, Seremban - T: (06) 7631149
Historical Museum - 1954
Weapons, clothing, brasses, musical instruments 24333

Shah Alam

Museum and Art Gallery, c/o School of Art and Design, Mara Institute of Technology, 40450 Shah Alam - T: (03) 5564502
Local Museum / Public Gallery 24334

Sultan Alam Shah Museum, Persiaran Perdagangan, 40000 Shah Alam - T: (03) 5590050, 5597604, Fax: 5501799
Local Museum 24335

Taiping

Muzium Perak, Jalan Taming Sari, 3400 Taiping - T: (05) 8072057, Fax: 8063643. Head: Dr. Kamarul Baharin Bin Buyong
Local Museum - 1886
Ethnology, natural Hist 24336

Maldives

Malé

National Museum, c/o National Centre for Linguistic and Historical Research, Malé - T: 322254, Fax: 326796. Head: Abbas Ibrahim
Local Museum - 1952 24337

Mali

Bamako

Musée National du Mali, Rue du Général Leclerc, Bamako, mail addr: BP 159, Bamako - T: 223486, Fax: 231909, E-mail: musee@malinet.ml. Head: Samuel Sidibé
Natural History Museum / Ethnology Museum
Ethnology, botany, zoology - library 24338

Gao

Musée Régional du Sahel, BP 141, Gao - T: 820031, Fax: 820031
Local Museum 24339

Sikasso

Musée Régional de Sikasso, BP 44, Sikasso
Local Museum 24340

Timbuktu

Centre de Documentation Arabe, Timbuktu
Historical Museum
Historical documents 24341

Malta

Birzebbuga

Ghar Dalam Museum, Bir-id-Deheb Rd, Birzebbuga
Natural History Museum 24342

Gharb

Gharb Folklore Museum, Visitation Sq, Gharb - T: 561929, Fax: 554180. Head: Silvio Felice
Folklore Museum
Old trades 24343

Mdina

Cathedral Museum, Archbishop Sq, Mdina - T: 674697. Head: John Azzopardi
Religious Arts Museum - 1969
Italian, French and Maltese art (14th-18th c), Cathedral silver, prints by Dürer, Italian Baroque music manuscripts, coins 24344

Norman House, Palazzo Falzon, Villegaignon St, Mdina - T: 674512
Special Museum 24345

Mgarr

Ta' Hagrat Copper Age Temples, Mgarr
Archaeological Museum 24346

Rabat

Museum of Roman Antiquities, Rabat
Museum of Classical Antiquities
Roman finds and ruins 24347

Valletta

Museum of Saint John's, Saint John's Sq, Valletta - T: 220536. Head: Dominic Cutajar
Religious Arts Museum 24348

National Museum, Auberge de Provence, Republic St, Valletta - T: 240671. Head: Tancred C. Gouder
Historical Museum / Archaeological Museum 24349

Palace Armoury, Palace of the Grand Masters, Valletta
Military Museum
Arms and armour 24350

Victoria

Archaeology Museum, Bieb I-Imdina St, The Citadel, Victoria - T: 556144, Fax: 559008. Head: Stephen Cini
Archaeological Museum 24351

Folklore Museum, Bernardo De Opuo St, The Citadel, Victoria - T: 562034, Fax: 559008. Head: Saviour Debrincat
Folklore Museum 24352

Natural Science Museum, Il-Kwartier, San Martin St, The Citadel, Victoria - T: 556153, Fax: 559008. Head: Frances Grech
Natural History Museum 24353

The Old Prison, Cathedral Sq, The Citadel, Victoria - T: 565988. Head: John Bajada
Historical Museum / Historic Site 24354

Vittoriosa

Inquisitor's Palace, National Museum of Ethnography, Main Gate St, Vittoriosa - T: 663731, Fax: 663935, E-mail: kenneth.j.gambin@. Head: Kenneth Gambin
Ethnology Museum 24355

Maritime Museum, Naval Bakery, Vittoriosa - T: 21805287, Fax: 21809090, E-mail: antonio.espinosa-rodriguez@magnet.mt. Head: Antonio Espinosa Rodriguez
Historical Museum - 1992
Period models of ships of the order of St. John, Maltese traditional boats, royal navy 24356

Xaghra

Ggantija Prehistoric Temples, Imquades St, Xaghra - T: 553194, Fax: 550107. Head: Alda Xerri
Archaeological Museum / Historic Site 24357

Pomskizillious Museum of Toys, 10 Gnien Xibla St, Xaghra XRA 104, Gozo - T: 562489. Head: Susan Lowe
Special Museum
Toys, games, Edward Lear books and pictures, illustrations 24358

Ta' Kola Windmill, Bambina, Xaghra - T: 561071, Fax: 550107. Head: Victoria Galea
Ethnology Museum 24359

Zabbar

Sanctuary of our Lady of Graces Museum, Mediatrix Sq, Zabbar, mail addr: 4 Sanctuary St, Zabbar ZBR 02 - T: 824383, Fax: 691862, E-mail: geordway@hotmail.com. Head: Anton Cassar
Religious Arts Museum / Military Museum / Historical Museum - 1954
Nautical ex-voto paintings since 16th c, local art and craft - archives 24360

Wickman Maritime Collection, La Capitana, Dwardu Ellul St, Xghajra, Zabbar - T: 690254. Head: Viktor Wickman
Historical Museum - 1953
Development of Maltese maritime trade under British rule 24361

Zurrieg

Palazzo Armeria, Zurrieg - T: 827397
Fine Arts Museum / Decorative Arts Museum
Furnishings, costumes, weapons, paintings 24362

Martinique

Basse-Pointe

Musée de Figurines Végétales, Plantation de Leyritz, 97218 Basse-Pointe - T: 785392, Fax: 789244
Natural History Museum 24363

Fort-de-France

Musée Départemental d'Archéologie Précolombienne et de Préhistoire de la Martinique, 9 Rue de la Liberté, 97200 Fort-de-France - T: 715705, Fax: 730380. Head: Cécile Celma
Archaeological Museum - 1971 24364

Musée Régional d'Histoire et d'Ethnographie, 10 Blvd du Général de Gaulle, 97200 Fort-de-France - T: 638555
Historical Museum / Ethnology Museum 24365

La Trinité

Micromusée, Château Dubuc, Tartane, 97220 La Trinité - T: 644259
Local Museum 24366

Le Carbet

Musée Gauguin, Anse Turin, 97221 Le Carbet - T: 725249
Fine Arts Museum 24367

Les Trois-Ilets

Maison-Musée de la Canne, Pointe Vatable, 97229 Les Trois-Ilets - T: 683204, 683168
Special Museum 24368

Saint-Esprit

Musée des Arts et Traditions Populaires, Rue Cassier-Sainte-Claire, 97270 Saint-Esprit - T: 567651
Folklore Museum 24369

Saint-Pierre

Musée Historique de Saint-Pierre, Pl d'Etsnoz, Villa Sainte-Anne, 97250 Saint-Pierre - T: 781516
Historical Museum 24370

Musée Vulcanologique Franck-Arnold-Perret, Rue Victor Hugo, 97250 Saint-Pierre - T: 781516
Natural History Museum 24371

Sainte-Marie

Musée du Rhum, Distillerie Saint-James, 97230 Sainte-Marie - T: 693002
Special Museum 24372

Mauritania

Nouakchott

Musée National de Nouakchott, BP 1606, Nouakchott - T: (2) 51862
Local Museum 24373

Mauritius

Mahébourg

Historical Museum, Royal Rd, Mahébourg - T: 6319329, Fax: 2125717, E-mail: mimuse@ intnet.mu. Head: S. Abdoolrahaman
Historical Museum - 1950
Naval relics, maps, prints and water colors depicting the scenery and customs of old Mauritius, facsimiles of famous 'Blue Mauritius' postage stamps 24374

Moka

Folk Museum of Indian Immigration, c/o Mahatma Gandhi Institute, Mahatma Gandi Av, Moka
Historical Museum
Indian Artifacts, traditional music instruments, jewelery, household knick-knacks, books - archive 24375

Maison Creole Eureka, Eureka, Moka - T: 4334951, Fax: 2110021
Folklore Museum - 1986
Music, art, antique maps, Chinese and Indian houseware 24376

Old Grand Port

Vieux Grand Port, Royal Rd, Old Grand Port - T: 6344319, Fax: 2125717, E-mail: mimuse@ intnet.mu. Head: S. Abdoolrahaman
Local Museum - 1999
Local history 24377

Plaine Verte

Sir Seewoosagar Ramgoolam Memorial Centre, Sir Seewoosagar Ramgoolam St, Plaine Verte - T: 2420053, Fax: 2125717, E-mail: mimuse@ intnet.mu. Head: S. Abdoolrahaman
Special Museum - 1987
Belongings of Sir S. Ramgoolam 24378

Port Louis

Mauritius Postal Museum, Port Louis
Historical Museum 24379

Natural History Museum, Chaussée, Port Louis - T: 2122815, 2120639, Fax: 2125717, E-mail: mimuse@intnet.mu. Head: S. Abdoolrahaman
Natural History Museum - 1880
Flora and fauna of Mauritius, meteorological exhibits, birds and insects 24380

Souillac

Robert Edward Hart Memorial Museum, Gris Gris, Souillac - T: 6256501, Fax: 2125717, E-mail: mimuse@intnet.mu. Head: S. Abdoolrahaman
Special Museum - 1964
Belongings of poet R.E. Hart, literature 24381

Tyack

B. Bissoondoyal Memorial Centre, Royal Rd, Tyack - T: 6263732, Fax: 2125717, E-mail: mimuse@ intnet.mu. Head: S. Abdoolrahaman
Historical Museum - 1987 24382

Mexico

Acapulco

Museo Histórico de Acapulco, Fuerte de San Diego, Calle Hornitos s/n, 39300 Acapulco - T: (744) 4821114, Fax: 4823828, E-mail: fdsd@ prodigy.net.mx. Head: Julieta Gil Elorduy
Local Museum / Historical Museum
Ancient cultures in Mexico, pre-colonial history of Guerrero, Spanish commercial trade with China/ Philippines, independence of Mexico 24383

Actopán

Museo Regional de Actopán, 42500 Actopán
Ethnology Museum / Historical Museum - 1933
Ethnography, crafts of Otomie Indians 24384

Campeche

Museo Arqueológico, Etnográfico e Histórico del Estado, Calle 8, Campeche
Archaeological Museum / Ethnology Museum / Historical Museum
Archaeology, ethnography and history of Campeche region 24385

Museo de Armas, Calle 8, Campeche
Military Museum
Local history 24386

Museo Regional de Campeche, Calle 59, Campeche. Head: José E. Ortiz Lan
Local Museum - 1985
Archaeology, local hist 24387

Carmen

Museo Regional de Ciudad del Carmen, Carmen
Local Museum
Local history 24388

Chiapa de Corzo

Museo de Laca - Coneculta (Lacquerware Museum), Av Mexicanidad Chiapaneca 10, 29160 Chiapa de Corzo - T: 6160055, Fax: 6160055. Head: María Esther García Ruíz
Decorative Arts Museum / Folklore Museum
Folklore, lacquerware 24389

Ciudad Guzmán

Museo Regional de Ciudad Guzmán, Calle Ángel Conzález 21, Ciudad Guzmán
Local Museum
Folk art, ethnography, local history 24390

Ciudad Madero

Museo de la Cultura Huasteca, Calle 1 de Mayo y Sor J.I. de la Cruz, 89440 Ciudad Madero, mail addr: Apdo 12, 89440 Ciudad Madero - T: (812) 102217, Fax: 102217. Head: Alejandrina Elias Ortiz
Archaeological Museum - 1960
Civilización Huasteca archaeological finds 24391

Colima

Museo Universitario de Culturas Populares, Calle Manuel Gallardo 99, 28000 Colima - T: (312) 26869, Fax: 43380. Head: Juan Carlos G. Reyes
Folklore Museum / University Museum - 1981
Local ethnography 24392

Cuautla

Museo Casa de Morelos, Callejón del Castigo 3, Cuautla. Head: Dolores López Vda. de Bolanos
Local Museum
History of War of Independence, in the house occupied by Morelos during the siege of Cuautla 24393

Dolores Hidalgo

Museo Histórico de Sitio, Av Morelos 1, 37800 Dolores Hidalgo
Historical Museum
Historical building, personal memorabilia of Miguel Hidalgo y Castulo, furniture, pottery 24394

Durango

Museo Regional de Durango, Instituto Juárez, Durango
Local Museum / Folklore Museum
Folk art, local history 24395

Guadalajara

Instituto Mexicano Norteamericano de Jalisco, Calz. Enrique Diaz de Leon 300, Sector Juárez, 44170 Guadalajara - T: (33) 8255838, E-mail: cultural@guadalajara.net
Public Gallery
Modern Mexican and American art 24396

Museo del Estado de Jalisco, Calle Liceo 60, 44100 Guadalajara - T: (33) 6132703, Fax: 6145257
Ethnology Museum / Historical Museum - 1918
Colonial art, history, folk art and cotstumes, archaeology, anthropology 24397

Museo Regional de Guadalajara (Regional Museum of Guadalajara), Calle de Liceo 60, 44100 Guadalajara - T: (33) 6132703, Fax: 6145257. Head: Carlos Beltrán
Local Museum - 1918
Early Mexican objects, folk art and costumes, archeological discoveries, paleontology, paintings from colonial, 17th-20th c - library 24398

Museo-Taller José Clemente Orozco, Calle Aurelio Aceves 27, 44100 Guadalajara. Head: Prof. Margarita V. de Orozco
Fine Arts Museum - 1951
Memorabilia and works of painter Orozco (1883-1949) 24399

Guanajuato

Museo Alfredo Duges de la Universidad de Guanajuato, Calle Lascuraín de Retana 5, 36000 Guanajuato. Head: Prof. Irma B. de Arellano
Natural History Museum / University Museum - 1870
Biology, geology, mineralogy, natural hist 24400

Museo Casa Diego Rivera I.N.B.A., Calle Positos 47, 36000 Guanajuato - T: (473) 21197. Head: Herlinda M. de Villegas
Historic Site 24401

Museo de Historia en la Alhondiga de Granaditas, Calle Mendizábal 6, 36000 Guanajuato - T: (473) 21112. Head: Claudia Canales Ucha
Historical Museum - 1958
History, applied art, memorabilia of painter Hermengildo Bustos, pre-Columbian art, archaeology of Chupícuaro, sculpture 24402

Hermosillo

Museo de Sonora, Hermosillo
Local Museum
History of Sonora region 24403

León

Casa de la Cultura de León, Portal Delicias, Plaza de Fund, 37000 León - T: (477) 43350
Local Museum 24404

Mérida

Museo Arqueológico de Yucatán, Calles 60 y 65, Mérida
Archaeological Museum
Finds of prehistoric, Mayan and Mayapán cultures, ceramics, copper and silver 24405

Museo Regional de Antropología, Palacio Cantón, Calle 43 por Paseo de Montejo, Mérida, mail addr: Apdo 1015, 97127 Mérida. Head: Agustín Peña Castillo
Ethnology Museum - 1920
Finds of prehistoric and Mayan cultures, ceramics, copper, silver, and gold 24406

México

Antiguo Colegio de San Ildefonso, Calle Justo Sierra 16, México 06000 - T: (55) 7024454, Fax: 7025223. Head: Dolores Béistegui
Historical Museum 24407

Antiguo Palacio del Arzobispado, Museo de la SHCP, Calle Moneda 4, México 06020 - T: (55) 5215371, Fax: 5218159, 2281245. Head: Juana Inés Abreu
Decorative Arts Museum 24408

Centro Cultural Isidro Fabela, Plaza de San Jacinto 15, Col. San Angel, 01000 México - T: (55) 55509286, 56162711, Fax: 55509286, E-mail: cifabela@avantel.net. Head: Ana Luisa Valdes Gonzalez Salas
Fine Arts Museum / Historical Museum
Art, history 24409

Centro de la Imagen, Pl de la Ciudadela 2, México 06040 - T: (55) 7096058, Fax: 7091599, 7096095. Head: Patricia Mendoza Ramírez
Fine Arts Museum 24410

Ex Teresa Arte Actual, Lic Primo Verdad 8, Centro Histórico, México 06060 - T: (55) 55229093, 55222721, Fax: 55229093, E-mail: xteresa@avantel.net. Head: Guillermo Santamarina
Fine Arts Museum 24411

Galería de Historia o Museo del Caracol, Castillo de Chapultepec, 1a Sección del Bosque de Chapultepec, México 11580 - T: (55) 55536391, 52863975, Fax: 55536391, E-mail: gale_historia@inah.gob.mx, Internet: http://www.inah.gob.mx/sin_frames/muse/muse03/htme/mume001.htm. Head: Lourdes Mondragón
Historical Museum
Scenes of history events with the use of figures of ceramics (barro), anthropology of Mexico 24412

Galería de la Escuela de Diseño y Artesanias del Instituto Nacional de Bellas Artes, Calle Lucas Balderas 125, 06040 México D.F.. Head: Carlos Cortés Gomez
Fine Arts Museum / Decorative Arts Museum
Paintings 24413

Galería de la Escuela Nacional de Artes Plásticas, Calle Academia 22, 06060 México D.F.
Fine Arts Museum 24414

Galería del Instituto Francés de América Latina, Calle Río Nazas 43, 06500 México - T: (55) 5660777/80. Head: Louis Panabière
Fine Arts Museum
Paintings, drawings and sculpture by Latin American artists 24415

Galería José María Velasco, Calle Peralvillo 55, México - T: (55) 5269157. Head: Elena Olachea
Fine Arts Museum 24416

Museo Anahuacalli, Calle del Museo 150, San Pablo Tepetlapa, Coyoacán, México 04620 - T: (55) 56174310, Fax: 56173797, 56174310. Head: María Dolores Checa
Folklore Museum 24417

Museo Arqueológico de Cuicuilco, Calle Insurgentes Sur, esq Periférico, Col. Isidro Fabela, México 14030 - T: (55) 6069758. Head: Gilberto Marín Vázquez
Archaeological Museum 24418

Museo Arqueológico de Xochimilco, Av Tenotitlan s/n esq Calle La Planta, Santa Cruz Acalpixca, México 16500 - T: (55) 56416847. Head: Hortensia Galindo Rosales
Archaeological Museum 24419

Museo Arqueológico del Cerro de la Estrella, Carretera al Cerro de la Estrelle s/n, Ampliación Veracruziana, México 09860
Archaeological Museum 24420

Museo Casa de Alfonso Reyes, Benjamín Hill 122, Col. Condesa, México 06140 - T: (55) 5152225, Fax: 5152225. Head: Dr. Alicia Reyes
Special Museum 24421

Museo Casa de la Bola, Parque Lira 136, Col. Tacubaya, México 11860 - T: (55) 55158825, 55155582, Fax: 55158825, 55155582, E-mail: casadelabola@hotmail.com. Head: Leonor Cortina, Marcela E. Ramírez
Decorative Arts Museum
15th-19th c European furniture, 15th-19th c European tapestries, 19th c prints, 18th-19th c clocks, 17th and 20th c Mexican paintings, 19th c Chinese and Japanese porcelain 24422

Museo Casa de León Trotsky, Av Río Churubusco 410, Col. Del Carmen, Coyoacán, México 06140 - T: (55) 6588732, 5540687, Fax: 6588732. Head: Jorge Max Rojas Proenzal
Decorative Arts Museum 24423

Museo Casa de Luis Barragán, Calle Francisco Ramírez 14, Tacubaya, México 11870 - T: (55) 5154908. Head: Norma Soto
Decorative Arts Museum 24424

Museo Casa del Risco, Centro Cultural Isidro Fabela, Pl de San Jacinto 15, México 01000 - T: (55) 6162711, Fax: 5509286. Head: Ana Luisa Valdéz González Salas
Natural History Museum 24425

Museo Casa Estudio Diego Rivera y Frida Kahlo, Calle Diego Rivera y Altavista, Col San Angel Inn, Alvaro Obregón, 01060 México - T: (55) 2807596, Fax: 2807596. Head: Blanca Garduño Pulido
Fine Arts Museum - 1986
Permanent exhibition 'Estudio Taller de Diego Rivera' 24426

Museo de Armas, Bosque de Chapultepec, 11580 México
Military Museum
Armaments 24427

Museo de Arte Alvar y Carmen T. de Carrillo Gil, Av Revolución 1608, 01000 México - T: (55) 5503983, 55596289/260, Fax: 55504232, E-mail: macg@www.conet.com.mx, Internet: http://www.conet.com.mx/macg. Head: Osvaldo Sanchez
Fine Arts Museum - 1974
Mexican and international contemporary art - library 24428

Museo de Arte Contemporáneo Internacional Rufino Tamayo, Paseo de la Reforma y Gandhi, Bosque de Chapultepec, 11580 México - T: (55) 2865839, 2863572, 2866519, Fax: 2866539, E-mail: mrtamayo@df1.telmex.net.mx, Internet: http://www.museotamayo.org. Head: María Teresa Márquez
Public Gallery - 1981 24429

Museo de Arte Gráficas Juan Pablos, Calle Galileo 101, Colonia Polanco, México 11580 - T: (55) 2804713, Fax: 2804689. Head: Prof. Luz Sierra Bello
Fine Arts Museum 24430

Museo de Arte Moderno, Paseo de la Reforma y Gandhi, Bosque de Chapultepec, 11580 México - T: (55) 5536233, 2118729, Fax: 5536211, Internet: http://www.cnca.gob.mx/museos.html. Head: Prof. Luis-Martín Lozano
Fine Arts Museum - 1964
Modern and contemporary paintings, sculpture and photography, maily Mexican 24431

Museo de Cera, Calle Londres 6, Col. Juárez, México 06600 - T: (55) 5463784, Fax: 5661093, 5661576. Head: Mario Rabner
Special Museum 24432

Museo de El Carmen, Av Revolución y Callejón Monasterio, San Angel, 01000 México - T: (55) 6161177, 5504896. Head: Laura Espino
Historical Museum / Archaeological Museum
Local archeology 24433

Museo de Geologia, Calle Jaime Torres Bodet 176, Col. Santa María La Ribera, 06400 México - T: (55) 5410116, 5473900, Fax: 5473900. Head: Rodolfo Corona Esquivel
Natural History Museum - 1900
Geology of Mexico and South America, paleontology, mineralogy and petrology 24434

Museo de Higiene, Calle Donceles 39, 06010 México
Special Museum
History of public health 24435

Museo de Historia Natural, Av Constituyentes s/n, Bosque de Chapultepec 2a secc., 11800 México - T: (55) 5156304, 5152222, Fax: 5156882. Head: Marco Barrera Bassols
Natural History Museum - 1964
Biology, entomology, vertebrates and invertebrates, fossils, drawings, photographs - library 24436

Museo de la Basílica de Guadalupe, Pl de las Américas 1, México 07050 - T: (55) 5776022 ext 137, 57816810, Fax: 5775038, E-mail: mubagua@hotmail.com. Head: Jorge Guadarrama
Religious Arts Museum 24437

Museo de la Caricatura, Calle Donceles 99, México 06020 - T: (55) 7029256, 7040459, Fax: 7029256. Head: Guadalupe Rosas Zambrano
Fine Arts Museum 24438

Museo de la Charrería, Calle Isabel la Católica 108, México 06080 - T: (55) 8701559, 8701619 ext 12. Head: Arturo Jiménez Maneja
Folklore Museum 24439

Museo de la Ciudad de México, Calle José María Pino Suárez 30, 06060 México - T: (55) 5229936, 5420487, Fax: 5223640, E-mail: mcm@milenio.com.mx. Head: Conrado Tostado
Local Museum
Local history 24440

Museo de la Indumentaria Luis Márquez Romay, Pl de San Jerónimo 47, México 06080 - T: (55) 7094066, 7095493, Fax: 7095635. Head: Alejandra Dorantes
Special Museum 24441

Museo de la Luz, Calle Ildefonso, esq Del Carmen, México 06020 - T: (55) 7023183/84, Fax: 7024129. Head: Pilar Contreras Irigoyen
Natural History Museum 24442

Museo de la Medicina Mexicana, Calle República del Brasil 33, México 06020 - T: (55) 5297542, 5296416, Fax: 5263853. Head: Virginia Classing de Maria y Campos
Historical Museum 24443

Museo de las Telecomunicationes, Av Lázaro Cárdenas 567, México 03200 - T: (55) 7994614, 6133944. Head: Manuel Rosales Vergas
Science&Tech Museum 24444

Museo del Automóvil, Av División del Norte 3572, San Pablo Tepetlapa, Coyoacán, México 04620 - T: (55) 56170411, 56175663, Fax: 56175052, Internet: http://www.museodelautomovil.com.mx. Head: Arturo Pérez Gutiérrez, Luz María Sánchez Pérez
Science&Tech Museum 24445

Museo del Calzado, Bolívar 27, Cenrto Histórico, México 06000 - T: (55) 55121311, Fax: 55100370, E-mail: zapbor@prodigy.net.mx, Internet: http://elborcegui.com. Head: José Villamayor Coto
Special Museum 24446

Museo del Ejército, Calle Filomeno Mata 6, México 06000 - T: (55) 5123215, 5127586. Head: Nicolás Soto Bastida
Military Museum 24447

Museo del Palacio de Bellas Artes, Av Juarez y Angela Peralta, Colonia Centro, 06050 México - T: (55) 5104384, Fax: 5128614, E-mail: mpba@inba.gob.mx. Head: Alejandra Pería
Fine Arts Museum - 1934
Murals by Diego Rivera, David Alfaro Siqueiros, José Clemente Orozco, Rufino Tamayo, Jorge González Camarena, Manuel Rodriguez Lozano, Roberto Montenegro 24448

Museo del Templo Mayor, Calle Seminario 8, México 06060 - T: (55) 5420606, 5421717. Head: Eduardo Matos Moctezuma
Archaeological Museum 24449

Museo Dolores Olmedo Patiño, Av México 5843, La Noria, Xochimilco, México 16030 - T: (55) 5551016, 5550891, Fax: 5551642. Head: Dolores Olmedo
Historical Museum 24450

Museo Don Benito Juárez, Palacio Nacional, 06000 México - T: (55) 5215366, Fax: 5215366. Head: Daniel Muñoz y Pérez
Historical Museum - 1957
Life and death of Mexican revolutionary Benito Juárez (1806-1872) - library 24451

Museo Estudio Diego Rivera, Diego Riviera 2, esq Altavista, Col. San Angel Inn, 01060 México - T: (55) 5501189, 5501518, Fax: 5501004, 2807596. Head: Blanca Garduño Pulido
Decorative Arts Museum 24452

Museo Franz Mayer, Av Hidalgo 45, Centro Histórico, 06300 México - T: (55) 5182265, Fax: 5212888, E-mail: museo@franzmayer.org.mx. Head: Hector Rivero Borrell
Decorative Arts Museum
Pictures, textiles, ceramics, applied art 24453

Museo Frida Kahlo, Calle Londres 247 esq Allende, Colonia Del C. Coyoacán, México 04100 - T: (55) 5545999, Fax: 6585778. Head: Dolores Olmeda Patiño
Fine Arts Museum
Home of Frida Kahlo and Diego Rivera, paintings by Rivera 24454

Museo José Luis Cuevas, Calle Academia 13, México 06060 - T: (55) 5428959, 5426198, Fax: 5428959. Head: Bertha Riestra de Cuevas
Fine Arts Museum 24455

Museo Legislativo, Av Congreso de la Unión 68, Col. El Parque, México 04500 - T: (55) 6281477. Head: Patricia Moyssen
Historical Museum 24456

Museo Mural Diego Rivera, Pl Solidaridad, 06040 México - T: (55) 5120754, Fax: 5102329
Decorative Arts Museum 24457

Museo Nacional de Antropología, Paseo de la Reforma y Av Ghandhi s/n, 11580 México - T: (55) 2862923, 2685119, Fax: 2861795, E-mail: museo@internet.com.mx, Internet: http://sunsite.unam.mx/antropol. Head: Dr. Mercedes de la Garza Camino
Ethnology Museum - 1864
Anthropology, ethnography, archaeology of Mexico and America - library 24458

Museo Nacional de Arquitectura, Palacio de Bellas Artes, Av Hidalgo 1, Mesanine, México 06050 - T: (55) 7093111, 5217396, Fax: 5124234. Head: Maya Dávalos de Camacho
Fine Arts Museum 24459

Museo Nacional de Arte, Calle Tacuba 8, Colonia Centro, Del. Cuauhtémoc, 06010 México - T: (55) 5217461, 5121684, Fax: 5217320, E-mail: museonal@solar.sar.net. Head: Graciela de la Torre de Reyes Retana
Fine Arts Museum - 1982
Permanent exhibitions, 17th-20th c Mexican art - library 24460

Museo Nacional de Artes e Industrias Populares, Av Juárez 44, 06010 México - T: (55) 5103404. Head: María Teresa Pomar
Folklore Museum / Decorative Arts Museum - 1951
Native pottery, textiles and lacquer, applied arts of México, traditional handicrafts 24461

Museo Nacional de Historia, Castillo de Chapultepec, Av Reforma s/n, 11580 México - T: (55) 5536202, Fax: 5536268. Head: Lara T. Amelia Tamburrino, Margarita Loera Chavez
Historical Museum - 1944
History of Mexico from the Spanish conquest to 1910, ancient and modern arms, Mexican and European porcelain, ceramics, mosaics, jewelry, textiles, paintings, murals, statues, religious art and cultural history, photograpy 24462

Museo Nacional de Historia Natural de la Ciudad de México, Segunda Sección del Bosque de Chapultepec, México - T: (55) 5156304, 5162848, Internet: http://www.arts-history.mx/museos/hisnatur/
Natural History Museum - 1810
Invertebrates, fishes, reptiles, birds, vertebrates, cryptogams - library 24463

Museo Nacional de la Acuarela (National Museum of Watercolours), Calle Salvador Novo 88, Col Coyoacán, México 04000 - T: (55) 55541801, 55541784, Fax: 55541784, E-mail: acuarelamex@terra.com.mx. Head: Alfredo Guati Rojo
Fine Arts Museum
Watercolour painting 24464

Museo Nacional de la Estampa, Av Hidalgo 39, Pl de la Santa Veracruz, 06050 México - T: (55) 5212244, 5104905, Fax: 5212244. Head: Beatriz Vidal de Alba
Fine Arts Museum
Permanent exhibition 'Proceso Historico de la Estampa en México' 24465

Museo Nacional de la Revolución, Pl de la República s/n, 06030 México - T: (55) 5661902, 5462115, Fax: 5462115, E-mail: mnr1910@hotmail.com, Internet: http://www.cultura.d.f.gob.mx. Head: Edna Maria Orozco
Historical Museum 24466

Museo Nacional de las Culturas, Calle de Moneda 13, 06060 México - T: (55) 5420165, Fax: 5420422, E-mail: culturas@prodigy.net.com, Internet: http://www.inah.gob.mx. Head: Leonel Durán Solís
Archaeological Museum / Ethnology Museum - 1965
American and European archaeology, world-wide ethnological coll - library 24467

Museo Nacional de las Intervenciones, Calle General Anaya y 20 de Agosto, Coyoacán, 04120 México - T: (55) 6040699, 6887926, Fax: 6040981. Head: Monica Cuevas y Lara
Historical Museum - 1981
Exhibitions show history of the different foreign invasions that took place in México in 19th c, mexican collonial art 16th-19th c, Churubusco battle 8/20/1847 against the USA - library 24468

Museo Nacional de las Populares, Av Hidalgo 289, Col. Del Carmen Coyacán, México 04100 - T: (55) 5548968, Fax: 6598346, 5548357. Head: Rubin de la Borbolla
Ethnology Museum 24469

Museo Nacional de los Ferrocarriles Mexicanos, Av Jesús García 140, Col. Buenavista, México 06358 - T: (55) 5475851, 3276300 ext 7521. Head: Teresa Márquez Martínez
Science&Tech Museum 24470

Museo Nacional de San Carlos, Puente de Alvarado 50, 06030 México - T: (55) 5668085, 5668342, Fax: 55351256, E-mail: mnsancarlos@inba.gob.mx, Internet: http://www.mnsancarlos.gob.mx. Head: Roxana Valasquez Martinez del Campo
Fine Arts Museum - 1968
14th-19th c European art, primitive and classical paintings and sculptures, coll Olavarrieta, Mayer, Wenner-Green, Pani, Fagoaga, Cardoso 24471

Museo Pedagógico Nacional, Presidente Masaryk 526, México
Special Museum
History of education in Mexico 24472

Museo Postal, Calle Tacuba y Eje Central, Netzahualcoyotl 109, 06080 México - T: (55) 5215260, 7229673, Fax: 5215260, 7229672. Head: Elena Sáinz González
Special Museum - 1897
Postal communication history of México, Philatelic exhibitions - library 24473

Museo Ripley, Calle Londres 6, Col. Juárez, México 06600 - T: (55) 5467670
Special Museum 24474

Museo Serfín de Indumentaria Indígena, Calle Madero 33, México 06000 - T: (55) 5181556, Fax: 5181555, E-mail: eherrera@serfin.com.mx. Head: Elvira Herrera Acosta
Ethnology Museum
Mexican ethnic clothing 24475

Museo Soumaya, Calle Altamirano 46, Pl Loreto, Tizapán, San Angel, México 01090 - T: (55) 6163731, Fax: 5506620. Head: Ana Elena Mallet
Fine Arts Museum 24476

Museo Tecnológico de la Comisión Federal de Electricidad, 2a Sección del Bosque de Chapultepec, México 11870 - T: (55) 5160964/65, Fax: 5165520. Head: Dr. Elia Méndez Lecanda
Science&Tech Museum 24477

Museo Universitario Contemporáneo de Arte, Torre de Rectoría, Insurgentes Sur s/n, Circuito Interior, 04510 México - T: (55) 6220298, 5507863, Fax: 6220399. Head: Rodolfo Rivera Gonzá
Fine Arts Museum / University Museum 24478

Museo Universitario del Chopo, Calle González Martínez 10, Santa María la Rivera, México 06400 - T: (55) 5468490, 5352288. Head: Lourdes Monges
Fine Arts Museum 24479

Papalote, Museo del Niño, 2a sección Bosque de Chapultepec, México 11820 - T: (55) 2371700, Fax: 2371722. Head: Marinela Servitje
Historical Museum 24480

Pinacoteca del Centro de la Profesa, Calle Isabel La Católica 21, México 06000 - T: (55) 5127862. Head: Luis Martín Cano
Fine Arts Museum 24481

Pinacoteca Virreinal de San Diego (San Diego Viceregal Art Gallery), Calle Dr. Mora 7, 06050 México - T: (55) 5102793, Fax: 5122079. Head: Virginia Armella de Aspe
Fine Arts Museum - 1962
Paintings of the colonial era in Mexico, cultural programmes, recitals - library 24482

Universum, Museo de las Ciencias de la UNAM, Edifico de Universum, Zona Cultural, Ciudad Universitaria, México 04510 - T: (55) 56653761, 56224277, Fax: 56653769, E-mail: universu@servidor.unam.mx, Internet: http://www.universum.unam.mx. Head: Julieta N. Fierro Gossman
Science&Tech Museum / University Museum 24483

Monterrey

Museo de Autos y Transporte, Parque Niños Heroes, Monterrey 64000 - T: (81) 3313890, Fax: 3361762
Science&Tech Museum 24484

Museo del Vidrio, 517 Col Treviño, 64570 Monterrey - T: (81) 3291070, 3291052, Fax: 3757649, E-mail: museov@vto.com, Internet: http://museovidrio.vto.com
Decorative Arts Museum
Glass, ceramic art 24485

Museo Regional de Nuevo León, Calle Rafael Jose Verger s/n, 64010 Monterrey - T: (81) 460404. Head: Javier Sanchez Garcia
Local Museum - 1956
Paintings, history, archaeology 24486

Morelia

Casa de Morelos, Morelia
Local Museum
Local history, ethnoghraphy 24487

Museo Regional Michoacano, Calle de Allende 305, 58000 Morelia - T: (443) 120407, Fax: 120407. Head: Eugenio Mercado Lopez
Local Museum - 1886
Archaeology, ethnography and prehist of region - library 24488

Nayarit

Museo Regional, Palacio del Gobierno, Av México 91, Nayarit. Head: Jorge Hernández Moreno
Local Museum
History, archaeology 24489

Oaxaca

Casa de Juárez, Oaxaca
Historical Museum
Memorabilia of Benito Juárez, 19th c painting 24490

Museo de Arte Prehispánico de México Rufino Tamayo, Av Morelos 503, 68000 Oaxaca - T: (951) 64750, Fax: 64750. Head: Prof. Alicia Pesqueira de Esesarte
Fine Arts Museum / Archaeological Museum - 1974
Rufino Tamaya's great disire to make people appreciate mexican prehistoric work as art not as archaeology 24491

Museo de las Culturas de Oaxaca, Ex Convento de Santo Domingo de Guzman, Centro Historico, 68000 Oaxaca - T: (01951) 5162991, Fax: 5162991, E-mail: sdomingo@prodigy.net.mx. Head: Jesus Martínez Arvizu
Archaeological Museum - 1933
Anthropology, ethnography, archaeology, tomb treasures, jewelry 24492

Taller de Artes Plásticas Rufiho Tamayo, Calle Murguia 306, Oaxaca. Head: Prof. Roberto Donis
Fine Arts Museum 24493

Oaxtepec

Ex Convento de Santo Domingo de Guzman, Centro Vacacional IMSS, Domicilio Conocido, Centro, 62738 Oaxtepec - T: (735) 3561960, Fax: 3560093, E-mail: comercvo@yahoo.com.mx, Internet: http://www.imss.gob.mx. Head: Sonia Alexandra Jorquera Caro
Historical Museum - 1988
Regional history pre-colonial and colonial period, insects - herbarium 24494

Pachuca

Museo de la Fotografía, Fototeca del INAH, Exconvento de San Francisco, Calle Casasola s/n, 42050 Pachuca - T: (771) 43653, Fax: 31977. Head: Juan Carlos Valdez
Fine Arts Museum 24495

Patzcuaro

Museo Regional de Artes Populares, Calle Enseñanza y Alcantarillas s/n, Patzcuaro - T: (434) 21029. Head: Rafaela Luft Dávalos
Folklore Museum - 1935
Native Indian arts 24496

Museo Regional de Patzcuaro, Patzcuaro
Local Museum
Regional history and archeology 24497

Puebla

Museo Amparo, Calle 2 Sur 708, Centro Hisrórico, 72000 Puebla - T: (222) 464646, 464210, Fax: 466333, E-mail: amparo@mail.giga.com, Internet: http://www.gigi.com/~amparo
Ethnology Museum
Meeting our roots 24498

Museo de Arte José Luis Bello y González, Av 3 Poniente 302, 72000 Puebla - T: (222) 329475, E-mail: fidel.perez@correoweb.com. Head: Juan Fidel Pérez Espinosa
Fine Arts Museum - 1938
Mexican, Chinese and European paintings and sculptures, decorative arts in ivory, porcelain, wrought iron, pottery, also furniture, religious art, music instruments 24499

Museo de Arte Popular Poblano, Calle 3, Norte 1203, 72000 Puebla
Folklore Museum - 1973
Ceramic crafts, applied art, textiles 24500

Museo de los Fuertes de Guadelupe y Loreto, Fuerte de Loreto, Puebla
Historical Museum
Painting, weapons, medals, coins 24501

Museo Nacional de Ferrocarriles, Calle 11 Norte No 1005, 72000 Puebla
Science&Tech Museum 24502

Museo Regional de Santa Mónica, Av Poniente 103, 72000 Puebla - T: (222) 17207
Fine Arts Museum / Historical Museum - 1940
Painting (17th-19th c), sculpture, furniture 24503

Museo Regional del Estado de Puebla, Casa del Alfeñique, Calle Oriente 4, Norte 416, 72000 Puebla. Head: Juan Armenta Camacho
Local Museum - 1931
Archaeology, history of Puebla province 24504

Querétaro

Museo Regional de Querétaro, Calle Corregidora 3 Sur, 76000 Querétaro - T: (442) 124888, Fax: 122036. Head: Manuel Oropeza Segura
Local Museum - 1936
Hist, religious art - religious historical library 24505

San Luis Potosí

Museo Regional Potosino, Calle Galeana 450, 78000 San Luis Potosí - T: (444) 143572, Fax: 120358. Head: Luz Carregha
Historical Museum - 1952
Huasteca culture, handicraft, in a 18th c Franciscan convent, Colonial coll - library 24506

San Miguel de Allende

Centro Cultural Ignacio Ramírez, Calle Hernández Macias 71, San Miguel de Allende. Head: Prof. Miguel J. Malo Zozaya
Fine Arts Museum / Historical Museum / Archaeological Museum / Folklore Museum
Art, history, archaeology, folklore 24507

Santiago Tuxtla

Museo Regional de Santiago Tuxtla, 95830 Santiago Tuxtla
Local Museum
Local history, ethnography, archeology 24508

Teotihuacán

Museo Arqueológico de Teotihuacán, Piramides, 55800 Teotihuacán
Archaeological Museum - 1922
Regional archaeology, history, ethnography 24509

Tepexpan

Museo de Prehistoria, Tepexpan
Archaeological Museum
Documentation of the time of prehistoric man 24510

Tepic

Museo Regional de Antropologia e Historia de Tepic, Calle Mexico 91 Norte, Tepic. Head: Jorge Hernández Moreno
Ethnology Museum / Historical Museum
History, ethnography of region 24511

Tepotzotlán

Museo Nacional de Virreinato (National Viceroyalty Museum), Plaza Hidalgo 99, 54600 Tepotzotlán - T: (915) 8760245, Fax: 8760332
Fine Arts Museum / Decorative Arts Museum - 1964
Colonial art, painting, chinaware, religious art, sacred vestments, goldwork, silverwork, ancient furniture - library, restauration department 24512

Toluca

Museo Charrería, Toluca
Folklore Museum
Folk costumes 24513

Museo de Arqueología, Calle Santos Degollado 102, Toluca
Archaeological Museum 24514

Museo de Arte Popular, Prolongación de Hidalgo, Toluca
Folklore Museum
Decorative arts 24515

Museo de Ciencias Naturales, Toluca
Natural History Museum
Regional natural history 24516

Museo de las Bellas Artes, Calle de Santos Degollado 102, Toluca. Head: Prof. José M. Caballero Barnard
Fine Arts Museum
Modern Mexican painting, engravings, pre-Columbian sculptures - theatre 24517

Tuxtla Gutiérrez

Museo Regional de Chiapas, Calzada de los Hombres Ilustres s/n, Parque Madero, 29000 Tuxtla Gutiérrez - T: (961) 20459, Fax: 34554. Head: Eliseo Linares Villanueva
Local Museum - 1939
Archaeology, colonial history, anthropology 24518

Museo Zoologico Cesar Domínguez Flores, Calzada Cerro Hueco s/n, El Zapotal, 29000 Tuxtla Gutiérrez - T: (961) 6144701, 6144459, 6144765, Fax: 6144700, E-mail: zoomat@chiapas.net. Head: Pablo Muench Navarro, Margarita Ravelo Virgen
Natural History Museum - 1942
Insects, reptiles, birds, vertebrates 24519

Tzintzuntzan

Museo Etnográfico y Arqueológico, 58440 Tzintzuntzan
Ethnology Museum / Archaeological Museum - 1944
Regional archaeology, ethnography 24520

Uruapán

Museo Regional de Arte Michoacano, Calle Huatápera, Uruapán
Folklore Museum
History, folk art 24521

Villahermosa

Museo de Tabasco, Calle Vincente Guerrero 12, Villahermosa
Archaeological Museum
Archeology, axes, Maya culture, sculpture 24522

Museo La Venta Parque, Villahermosa
Archaeological Museum
Stone heads, altars, stelae 24523

Museo Regional de Antropología Carlos Pellicer Camara, Av Carlos Pellicer 511, 86000 Villahermosa - T: (993) 21803. Head: Julio Cesar Javier Quero
Ethnology Museum 24524

Yuriria

Museo Colonial, Convento de Agustinos, 38940 Yuriria - T: (445) 82036
Fine Arts Museum / Religious Arts Museum
Art, religious art 24525

Moldova

Chişinău

Moldovan State Art Museum, ul Lenina 115, 277012 Chişinău - T: (02) 234496. Head: T.V. Stavila
Fine Arts Museum
Fine art, applied art - library 24526

Ščusev Museum, A. Ščusev Str 77, 277000 Chişinău - T: (02) 244325, 220308, Fax: 243674, E-mail: museum@mnc.md
Special Museum
Coll concerning life and work of the architects Ščusev, A.; Bernadozzi, A.; Kurts, R. 24527

Monaco

Monaco

Collection de Voitures Anciennes de S.A.S. Le Prince de Monaco, Esplanade Rainier III, Fontvieille, 98000 Monaco - T: 92052856, Fax: 92059609
Science&Tech Museum 24528

Musée d'Anthropologie Préhistorique, Blvd du Jardin Exotique, Monaco, 98000 Monaco - T: 93158006, Fax: 93300246, E-mail: ssimone@gouv.mc. Head: Suzanne Simone
Archaeological Museum - 1902
Prehistory, paleontology, human paleontology 24529

Musée de Cires, Historial des Princes de Monaco, 27 Rue Basse, Monaco-Ville, 98000 Monaco - T: 93303905, Fax: 93250073
Historical Museum - 1971
24 Scenes, life size statues from the first Lord of Monaco, François Grimaldi 1297, up to Prince Rainier III and his family 24530

Musée des Souvenirs Napoléoniens et Collection des Archives Historiques du Palais, Pl du Palais, Monaco-Ville, 98015 Monaco Cedex - T: 93251831, Fax: 93508173. Head: Joseph Destefanis
Historical Museum - 1968
Napoleonic souvenirs, palace archives 24531

Musée des Timbres et des Monnaies, Esplanade Rainier III, Fontvieille, 98000 Monaco - T: 93154150, Fax: 93154145
Historical Museum / Decorative Arts Museum - 1996
Stamps since 1885, coins hist of Monaco since 1640 24532

Musée National de Monaco, Collection de Galéa, 17 Av Princesse Grace, Monte-Carlo, 98000 Monaco - T: 93309126, Fax: 92167321, E-mail: musee-national@monte-carlo.mc. Head: Annette Bordeau
Special Museum - 1972
Automatons (Paris, 19th c) and dolls presented in show-cases together with miniature porcelain and period furniture, Neapolitan Chrismas crib, sculptures 24533

Musée Naval, Esplanade Rainier III, Fontvieille, 98000 Monaco - T: 92052848, Fax: 92052858, E-mail: contact@musee_naval.mc, Internet: http://www.naval_museum.mc. Head: Dr. Claude Pallanca
Historical Museum / Science&Tech Museum 24534

Musée Océanographique de Monaco, Institut Océanographique, Av Saint-Martin, Monaco-Ville, 98000 Monaco - T: 93153600, Fax: 92167793, E-mail: rela@oceano.org, Internet: http://www.oceano.mc. Head: Michèle Dufrenne
Natural History Museum - 1910
4,000 tropical and mediterranean fishes, lagoon of the sharks, stuffed animals, skeletons of marine animals - library, aquarium 24535

Palais Princier, Pl du Palais, Monaco-Ville, 98015 Monaco Cedex - T: 93251831, Fax: 93508173
Decorative Arts Museum / Fine Arts Museum
Italian gallery, salon Lois XIV., salon Mazarin 24536

Mongolia

Altanbulag

Muzej Revoljucionnogo Dvizenija (Revolutionary Museum), Altanbulag
Historical Museum - 1971
Mongolian history since 1921 24537

Darhan

Friendship Museum, Darhan
Historical Museum
Founding and development of the industrial city Darhan, Soviet-Mongolian co-operation 24538

Ulaanbaatar

G.K. Zhukov Museum, Ulaanbaatar
Special Museum
Career of Soviet Marshal Zhukov 24539

Military Museum, Ulaanbaatar. Head: P. Byambasüren
Military Museum 24540

Mongolian National Modern Art Gallery, Sukhebaatar Sq 3, Ulaanbaatar - T: (01) 327177, Fax: 313191, E-mail: mnmartgallery@magicnet.mn, Internet: http://www.ulaanbaatar.net/art&culture/natinalgallery. Head: Dashdavaa Enkhtsetseg
Fine Arts Museum - 1989
Mongolian art (painting, sculpture, carvings) 24541

Museum of Mongolian Ethnography, Marx Av, Ulaanbaatar. Head: I. Lhagvasüren
Ethnology Museum 24542

Museum of Religious History, Choyjin Lamyn Hüree, Ulaanbaatar. Head: G. Tövsayhan
Religious Arts Museum
Housed in Choyjin Lamyn Hüree, a former lamasery, Lamaistic relics 24543

National Museum of Mongolian History, Commercial St 2, Ulaanbaatar - T: (01) 326802, Fax: 326802. Head: S. Idshinnorov
Historical Museum - 1924
Prehist, Middle Ages of Mongolia, ethnography, 20th c hist 24544

Natsagdorj Museum (Literary Museum), Friendship Park, Ulaanbaatar - T: (01) 27879
Special Museum
Life and works of the author Dashdorjiyn Natsagdorj (1906-1937) 24545

Natural History Museum, Engels St 46, Ulaanbaatar - T: (01) 324543. Head: P. Erdenebat
Natural History Museum - 1924
Flora and fauna of Mongolia 24546

Palace Museum, Palace, Ulaanbaatar - T: (01) 342195
Historical Museum - 1924
Palace of Bodg Gegeen, Head of the Buddhist Church in Mongolia and Head of State 1911-1924, lamasery 24547

State Central Museum, Ulaanbaatar. Head: A. Perlee
Natural History Museum / Archaeological Museum - 1924
Natural hist, Gobi desert dinosaur eggs and skeletons, art, history, archeology 24548

Suhbaatar and Choybalsam Museum, Ulaanbaatar
Historical Museum
Memorabilia on the two revolutionary leaders Sühbaatar and Choybalsan 24549

Ulan Bator Museum, Ulaanbaatar
Local Museum
Hist of Ulan Bator and its reconstruction 24550

Wildlife Museum, Baygaliyn Hishgiyn ordon, Gandangiyn denj, Ulaanbaatar - T: (01) 3633059, Fax: 360067, E-mail: monsafari@magicnet.mn, Internet: http://www.ulaanbaatar.net/mongolsafari. Head: U. Buyandelger
Natural History Museum 24551

Zanabazar Fine Arts Museum, Barilgachidyn Talbai 46, Ulaanbaatar - T: (01) 26060. Head: D. Gungaa
Fine Arts Museum - 1965
Paintings, sculptures 24552

Morocco

Chefchaouen

Musée Ethnographique, Kasbah Outa Hamman, Chefchaouen - T: (09) 986761
Ethnology Museum
Coll of popular arts and crafts reflecting the life of the Rif enclave and other artefacts from northern Morocco, incl embroidery, wooden caskets, pottery, arms musical instruments 24553

Fez

Musée d'Armes du Bordj Nord, Rue du Batha, Fez - T: (05) 645241. Head: Mohammed Zaim
Historical Museum / Military Museum - 1963
Weapons 24554

Musée du Dar Batha, Pl du Batha Alisco, Fez - T: (05) 634116
Local Museum / Ethnology Museum - 1915
Local and regional hist, ethnology, manuscripts, weapons, Moroccan art, wood, ceramics, textile, carpets, brass 24555

Larache

Musée Archéologique, Larache - T: (09) 912091
Archaeological Museum
Historic artefacts relating to Morrocan tradition incl ancient coins, fishing equipment, musical instruments, statues, jewellery and perfume bottles 24556

Marrakech

Majorelle Museum, Jardin du Majorelle, Marrakech
Fine Arts Museum
Coll of Islamic art housed in the former studio of the French painter Jacques Majorelle 24557

Musée Bert Flint, Rue de la Bahia, Marrakech
Decorative Arts Museum / Folklore Museum
Coll of costumes, jewellery, arms, musical instruments, carpets and furniture, art and popular traditions of the Souss valley and the Sahara 24558

Meknès

Musée de Dar-El-Jamaï, Sahat El-Hadim, Meknès - T: (05) 530863. Head: Hassan Cherradi
Fine Arts Museum / Decorative Arts Museum - 1920
Ethnography, folklore and folk art, wooden sculpture, local handicrafts, Moroccan art 24559

Moulay Idriss

Musée des Antiquités de Volubilis, Volubilis Archaeological Site, 50350 Moulay Idriss - T: (055) 544103, Fax: 544103, E-mail: volubilisarcheosite@yahoo.fr. Head: Dr. Youssef Bokbot
Archaeological Museum
Prehistoric and Roman finds, numismatics, marble and bronze statues 24560

Rabat

Galerie d'Exposition de la Direction des Musées, Bab Er Rouah, Rabat
Public Gallery 24561

Musée Archéologique, 23 Rue Al-Brihi, Chellah, Rabat, mail addr: BP 503, Rabat - T: (07) 7701919, Fax: 7750884. Head: Abdelwahed Ben-Ncer
Archaeological Museum - 1930
Prehistoric excavations, Phoenician and Roman antiquities, Islamic archaeology 24562

Musée de la Kasbah, 23 Rue el Brihi, Rabat. Head: Mohammed Habibi
Archaeological Museum / Folklore Museum
Archaeology and folklore 24563

Musée des Oudaïa, Kasbah des Oudaïa, Rabat - T: (07) 731537. Head: Houceine El-Kasri
Decorative Arts Museum / Folklore Museum - 1915
Moroccan jewelry, pottery, ceramics, Koran manuscripts (13th c) 24564

Musée National d'Histoire Naturelle, Av Ibn Batouta, 10106 Rabat - T: (07) 774548/49, Fax: 774540, E-mail: mouna@israbat.ac.ma, Internet: http://www.israbat.ac.ma
Natural History Museum
Zoology, geology, botany, fossils 24565

Musée Postal, Ministry of Post ant Telecommunication, Rabat
Special Museum - 1970
Moroccan stamps since 1912, envelopes, telephones, telegraph machines incl. Baudot, postal vans 24566

Safi

Musée National de la Céramique (National Ceramics Museum), Citadelle de la Kechla, Safi 46000, mail addr: BP 243, Safi 46000 - T: (04) 463895. Head: Nourddine Safsafi
Decorative Arts Museum - 1990 24567

Tanger

Musée d'Archéologique, d'Arts et d'Folklorique de Tanger, Pl de la Kasbah, Tanger - T: (09) 932097. Head: Mohammed Habibi
Archaeological Museum / Folklore Museum / Fine Arts Museum
Prehistory, Roman antiquities, mosaics, coins, ceramics 24568

Tangier American Legation Museum, 8 Zankat America, Tanger - T: (09) 935317, Fax: 935960. Head: Thor H. Kuniholm
Fine Arts Museum - 1976
Permanent coll of 16th-20th c paintings, etchings, aquatints, prints and maps of Morocco, also documentation and artifacts concerning Moroccan-American relations - research library 24569

Tétouan

Musée Archéologique, 2 Rue Ben H'sain, Tétouan 93000, mail addr: BP 41, Tétouan 93000 - T: (039) 967303. Head: Dr. Amin El-Younsi
Archaeological Museum - 1939
Carthaginian, Roman, Islamic and prehistoric colls from Tamuda, Lixus (mosaics) 24570

Musée d'Art Populaire Marocain, 30 Blvd Mohammed V., Tétouan. Head: Mohamed Serghini
Ethnology Museum / Decorative Arts Museum
Ethnography, folklore, decorative arts 24571

Musée des Arts Traditionnels, Tétouan. Head: Amrani Ahmed
Fine Arts Museum 24572

Musée Ethnographique, Av Skala Bab El-Oukla, Tétouan - T: (09) 970505
Folklore Museum / Ethnology Museum
Ethnography and folk art 24573

Mozambique

Beira

Museum Municipal, Town Hall, Rua Correia de Brito, Beira, mail addr: CP 1702, Beira
Local Museum
Archaeology, ethnology, mineralogy and biology, shells, coins 24574

Manica

Museu Monstruário de Manica, Vila Manica, Manica, mail addr: CP 2, Manica - T: (051) 62168, Fax: 62168. Head: Abdurremane Machon
Natural History Museum
Mineralogy, petrology, geology, zoology, natural history 24575

Maputo

Museu da Revolução, 2999 Av 24 Julho, Maputo - T: (1) 400348
Historical Museum 24576

Museu de Historia da Ocupação Colonial e da Resistencia, Antiga Fortaleza, Maputo, mail addr: CP 2033, Maputo
Historical Museum / Military Museum 24577

Museu de História Natural, Praça da Travessia do Zambeze, Maputo, mail addr: CP 1780, Maputo - T: (1) 491145. Head: Augusto J. Pereira Cabral
Natural History Museum - 1911
Mainly natural hist displays, palaeontology, silverwork of Tete area artisans 24578

Museu Histórico Militar, Praça 7 de Marco, Maputo, mail addr: CP 2033, Maputo
Military Museum - 1955
Old artillery, military equipment and arms, housed in the fortress Nossa Senhora de Conceiçao, relics of former missionary work, religious paintings, furniture 24579

Museu Nacional da Moeda, Rua Consiglieri Pedroso, Maputo, mail addr: CP 2033, Maputo - T: (1) 420290. Head: Maria Inés Nogueira da Costa
Special Museum 24580

Museu Nacional de Arte, 1233 Av Ho Chi Min, Maputo, mail addr: CP 1403, Maputo - T: (1) 422325, 420264, Fax: 425125
Fine Arts Museum 24581

Museu Nacional de Geologia, Instituto Nacional de Geologia, Av Infante de Sagres 2, Maputo, mail addr: CP 217, Maputo. Head: Antonio Manhica
Natural History Museum
Precious stones, mineral and metamorphic and sedimentary rock displays, mostly from formations in Mozambique, archaeology and palaeontology 24582

Museum of Inhaca Island, c/o Department of Biological Sciences, Eduardo Mondlane University, CP 257, Maputo - T: (01) 492142, 490009, Fax: 492176, E-mail: idomio@biologia.uem.mz. Head: Domingos Zefanias Gove
Natural History Museum - 1957
Coll of corals of the East African reef system, marine fishes and insects, marine items - library, meteorological station, diving section, laboratorie s 24583

Matola

Fondaçao Museu Chissano, 32 Rua Torre do Vale, Bairro Sial, Fomento, Matola - T: (1) 752703, Fax: 752703
Local Museum 24584

Nampula

Museu Ferreira de Almeida, Av José Cabral, Nampula, mail addr: CP 12, Nampula
Local Museum
Shells and coral from the nearby coast, silverwork, woodwork, pottery and musical instruments, traditional masks, hunting weapons and utensils 24585

Myanmar

Bago

Museum of the Shwenawdaw Pagoda, Bago
Religious Arts Museum
Old bronzes, modern sacral articles 24586

Kyaukpyu

State Library and Museum, Kyaukpyu
Decorative Arts Museum - 1955
Silver coins, costumes 24587

Mandalay

National Museum of Mandalay, Glass Palace, Mandalay
Local Museum - 1905
19th c history of Mandalay, architectural fragments, art objects 24588

State Museum, Cnr 24th and 80th Sts, Mandalay. Head: U Soe Thein
Fine Arts Museum - 1955 24589

University of Mandalay Collections, Bawdigon Archaeological Museum, Bawdigon, Mandalay - T: (2) 270. Head: U Kyaw Nyein
Ethnology Museum / Fine Arts Museum / Historical Museum - 1904
Ethnography, art, history 24590

Mawlamyine

Mon State Museum, Dawei Tada Rd, Mawlamyine. Head: U Min Khin Maung
Fine Arts Museum - 1955
Paintings, sculptures 24591

State Library and Museum, Mawlamyine
Local Museum - 1955
Local and regional history, architectural fragments 24592

Myohaung

Archaeological Museum, Myohaung
Archaeological Museum
Finds from local excavations 24593

Pagan

Archaeological Museum, opposite Gawdawpalin Temple Bagan, Pagan. Head: U Kyaw Nyein
Archaeological Museum - 1904
Major archaeological site, several 11th-13th c temples and other buildings, coll of material found after the earthquake in 1975 24594

Lacquerware Museum, c/o Lacquerware Training Institute, Pagan
Decorative Arts Museum - 1976
Lacquer pieces, lacquered door panels 24595

Pathein

Pathein Museum, Pathein
Historical Museum / Ethnology Museum
Ethnography, local history 24596

Prome

Prome Museum, High St, Prome
Historical Museum - 1950
Cultural and historical relics of the Burmese kings 24597

Sitture

Rakhine State Museum, Chin Pyan Rd, Kyaung-gyi Quarter, Sitture. Head: Daw Nu Mya Zau
Decorative Arts Museum - 1955
Silver, coins, costumes 24598

Taungdwingyi

Forest Museum, Taungdwingyi
Natural History Museum - 1964
Forestry techniques and products 24599

Taunggyi

Shan State Museum, Min Lan, Thittaw Quarter, Taunggyi. Head: U San Mya
Local Museum - 1957 24600

Yangon

Agricultural Museum, Natmauk Rd, Yangon - T: (1) 51860
Agriculture Museum 24601

Bogyoke Aung San Museum, 25 Bogyoke Museum Rd, Yangon - T: (1) 50600
Military Museum - 1959
Memorabilia of General Aung San 24602

The Buddhist Art Museum, Kaba Aye Pagoda, Yangon - T: (1) 60002, 65425
Religious Arts Museum / Fine Arts Museum - 1956
Buddhist art and archaeology, history of pagodas in Burma - library 24603

Defence Services Museum, Shwedagon Pagoda Rd, Yangon - T: (1) 83014
Military Museum 24604

Health Museum, Municipal Corp Bldgs, Baar St, Yangon
Special Museum
Medicine and hygiene 24605

National Museum of Art and History, 24-26 Pansodan St, Yangon - T: (1) 73706. Head: Dr. Ye Tut, U Kyaw Win
Fine Arts Museum / Archaeological Museum - 1952
Archaeological finds, contemporary painting, crafts, ethnology, Mandalay Lion Throne, regalia of King Thibaw of Mandalay 24606

Natural History Museum, Yangon Zoological Garden, Yangon - T: (1) 72156. Head: Kyaw Nyunt
Natural History Museum - 1968
Mammals, fish, geology, forestry 24607

War Museum, Stewart Rd, Yangon
Military Museum
Militaria 24608

Namibia

Bethanien

Schmelenhaus Museum, Rhenish Mission, Bethanien, mail addr: c/o Namibia Scientific Society, POB 67, Windhoek - T: (061) 225372
Religious Arts Museum
Oldest Mission house in Namibia 24609

Gobabis

Gobabis Museum, 114 Elephant St, Gobabis, mail addr: c/o Deutscher Verein, POB 705, Gobabis - T: (061) 562489, Internet: http://www.natmus.cul.na/nam_mus/gobabis.html. Head: Eimbeck
Local Museum
Items from colonial era, household, farming, school wagon 24610

Grootfontein

Grootfontein Museum, Old Fort, Eric St, Grootfontein, mail addr: POB 234, Grootfontein - T: (067) 242351
Local Museum - 1983
Hand-made bandsaw (1906), wagon building, artefacts and daily life of the Himba tribe and Mbanderu tribe in Botswana with photographs, surveying instruments of past times, minerals, photographic equipment 24611

Helmeringhausen

Helmeringhausen Museum, POB 21, Helmeringhausen - T: (06362) 7. Head: Betrim
Agriculture Museum / Open Air Museum
Open air display of farm implements, machinery and wagon, small display on Karakul farming 24612

Keetmanshoop

Keetmanshoop Museum, Museum Association of Namibia, Rhenish Mission Church, Kaiser St, Keetmanshoop, mail addr: Private Bag 2125, Keetmanshoop - T: (063) 221211 ext 56, Fax: 223818, E-mail: munkhoop@iafrica.com.na. Head: Antoinette Mostert
Music Museum / Natural History Museum
Traditional culture of the local people, natural and agricultural hist 24613

Kolmanskop

Kolmanskop Museum, E of Luderitz, on B4, Kolmanskop, mail addr: POB 357, Luderitz - T: (063) 202719, Fax: 202445. Head: Gino Noli, Marian Scheckle
Local Museum / Science&Tech Museum
Hist of the diamond mining community 24614

Lizauli

Lizauli Cultural Village, S of Mayum filling station, at Kongola, Lizauli, mail addr: POB 142, Katima Mulilo. Head: Munuma Rennox
Local Museum / Open Air Museum - 1992
Arts and crafts, music, iron tool making 24615

Lüderitz

Lüderitz Museum, Diaz St, 9000 Lüderitz, mail addr: POB 512, 9000 Lüderitz - T: (063) 202532, 202346, Fax: 202532. Head: Gisela Scheele-Schmidt
Historical Museum - 1968
Display of diamond mining, minerals from various parts of S.W. Africa, diorama of local sea birds, hist of Lüderitz, tribal arts and crafts, skeleton over 1000 years old, pre-historic animal footprints - aquarium 24616

Maltahohe

Duwisib Castle, POB 132, Maltahohe - T: (06638) 5303, Fax: 5303. Head: Dr. Victoria Nicodemus
Decorative Arts Museum
Antique furniture, works of art and firearms from the 18th and 19th c 24617

Möwe Bay

Möwe Bay Museum, Möwe Bay, mail addr: Private Bag 5001, Swakopmund - T: (0654) 313436. Head: John Paterson
Natural History Museum
Shipwreck items, natural hist of the Skeleton Coast National Park 24618

Okaukuejo

Okaukuejo Museum, Okaukuejo
Natural History Museum
Displays of mammals, snakes and predatory birds, geology of the Etosha Pan 24619

Omaruru

Omaruru Museum, Rhenish Mission Hous, Main St, Omaruru, mail addr: POB 14, Omaruru - T: (064) 570277. Head: Allen Sole
Local Museum
Hist of the mission 24620

Ombalantu

Ombalantu Baobab Tree, Village Centre, 300m S of Asphalt Rd, Ombalantu, mail addr: POB 437, Ombalantu - T: (06751) 51039. Head: Mukulu
Local Museum
Tree where can 20 people sit inside, hist of the area and the local communities, served as a post office and a church and later for former SA army base 24621

Ondangwa

Nakambale Museum, Olukonda National Monument, Ondangwa, mail addr: Privat Bag 2018, Ondangwa - T: (06756) 40241/2, Fax: 40472, 40536, E-mail: elcinmus@iwwn.com.na. Head: Martti Eirola
Local Museum
Displays illustrating past and presents of the church, mission and local cultures of Northern Namibia, Owambo life and culture 24622

Oranjemund

Sperrgebiet Museum, 7th Av, Oranjemund, mail addr: POB 35, Oranjemund - T: (063) 235790, 235183, Fax: 235230
Local Museum
Local history, minerals, mining, fossils, Sperrgebiet ghost towns, NAMDEB diamonds 24623

Outjo

Outjo Museum, Franke Haus Museum, Meesterlaan, Outjo, mail addr: POB 51, Outjo - T: (067) 313013, Fax: 313065, E-mail: outmun@out.namib.com. Head: Karen Rudman
Local Museum
Local hist, natural hist of the area, horn, skin and bone coll of Blok de Wet 24624

Rehoboth

Rehoboth Museum, Old Postmaster's House, Rehoboth, mail addr: Private Bag 1017, Rehoboth - T: (0627) 522954. Head: Martha Gille
Local Museum
Local hist, regional archaeological finds, natural hist, copper mining, ethnological artefacts 24625

Shambyu

Shambyu Museum, 30 km E of Runda, Shambyu, mail addr: POB 2075, Shambyu - T: (067372) 1111. Head: Van Rosmeilen
Folklore Museum
Woodcarving, traditional crafts of Kavango region and Southern Angola, incl stone tools 24626

Swakopmund

Swakopmund Military Museum, Woermanhaus Tower, Bismarck St, Swakopmund, mail addr: POB 998, Swakopmund - T: (064) 402359. Head: Michael McDonald
Military Museum
Military activities in Namibia 24627

Swakopmund Museum, Old Customs House, Strand St, Swakopmund, mail addr: POB 361, Swakopmund - T: (064) 402046, 404324, Fax: 400763. Head: Bjorn Lorck
Local Museum / Natural History Museum - 1951
Flora and fauna of the Namib, fishes, sea birds, seals, mineralogy, relics and documents of German colonial administration, tribal arts and crafts 24628

Tsumeb

Fort Namutoni, Tsumeb
Local Museum 24629

Tsumeb Cultural Village, off B1 Rd, Tsumeb, mail addr: POB 1740, Tsumeb - T: (067) 220787. Head: Taufi
Folklore Museum - 1997
Domestic architecture, ethnic groups, traditional life, dance and story 24630

Tsumeb Museum, Main St, Tsumeb, mail addr: POB 884, Tsumeb - T: (067) 220447. Head: Ilse Schatz
Local Museum
Hist of copper mining in the Tsumeb region, minerals, artefacts, traditional costumes and photographs from the heyday of industry 24631

Walvis Bay

Walvis Bay Museum, Civic Centre, Walvis Bay, mail addr: Private Bag 5017, Walvis Bay - T: (064) 205981. Head: Martie van Heerden, Gert Kruger
Local Museum
Local hist, minerals, natural hist, archaeology, domestic utensils, costumes, furniture 24632

Windhoek

Alte Feste, National Museum of Namibia, Robert Mugabe Av, Windhoek, mail addr: POB 1203, Windhoek - T: (061) 2934437, 2934351, Fax: 228636, E-mail: staff@natmus.edu.na, Internet: http://www.natmus.cul.na. Head: Esther U. Moombolah-Joagoses
Historical Museum / Folklore Museum - 1997
History displays, contemporary culture - Rockart exhibit 24633

Geological Survey Museum, 1 Aviation St, Windhoek - T: (061) 2085111, Fax: 249146, E-mail: info@gsn822.gsn.mme.gov.na. Head: Dr. W. Hegenberger
Natural History Museum
Minerals, fossils, meteorits, geology 24634

National Art Gallery of Namibia, Cnr John Meinert St and Robert Mugabe Av, Windhoek, mail addr: POB 994, Windhoek - T: (061) 231160, 231391, Fax: 240930, E-mail: nagn@mweb.com.na. Head: Annaleen Eins
Fine Arts Museum
Traditional African art, graphic art, John Ndevasia Muafangejo 24635

National Museum of Namibia, 59 Robert Mugabe Av, Windhoek, mail addr: POB 1203, Windhoek - T: (061) 2934437, 2934351, Fax: 228636, E-mail: staff@natmus.cul.na, Internet: http://www.natmus.cul.na. Head: Esther U. Moombolah-Goagoses
Local Museum / Archaeological Museum / Folklore Museum - 1907
Archaeology displays, objects from Nama, Bushman, Herero, Ovambo and other cultures, social hist display, entomology, mammalogy, herpetology, birds, arachnids - library 24636

Owela Display Centre, National Museum of Namibia, Robert Mugabe Av, Windhoek, mail addr: POB 1203, Windhoek - T: (061) 2934351, Fax: 228636, E-mail: staff@natmus.edu.na, Internet: http://www.natmus.cul.na. Head: Esther U. Moombolah-Goagoses
Historical Museum / Ethnology Museum - 1907
Ethnography, natural history, enviromental, traditional village life - touch room for children 24637

State Museum, Carl List Haus, Leutwein St, Windhoek - T: (061) 29391
Natural History Museum 24638

Transnamib Museum, Railway Station, Bahnhof St, Windhoek, mail addr: Private Bag 13204, Windhoek - T: (061) 2982186, 2982624, Fax: 2982495, E-mail: kschullenbach@transnamib.com.na. Head: Konrad Schüllenbach
Science&Tech Museum
History of railways and transport in Namibia 24639

Nepal

Bhaktapur

Picture Gallery, Lal Baithak, Darbar, Bhaktapur - T: 610004
Fine Arts Museum - 1961
Paintings, illustrated manuscripts, murals, stone sculptures 24640

Woodwork Museum, Palace of Fifty-Five Windows, Bhaktapur
Decorative Arts Museum - 1967
Woodworks from all parts of Nepal, carved façade with 55 windows 24641

Kathmandu

Memorial Museum King Tribhuvan, Hanuman Dhoka Palace, Kathmandu
Historical Museum - 1979
Hist of Royal Family 24642

National Museum of Nepal, Museum Rd, Chhauni, Kathmandu - T: (01) 271504, 271478, E-mail: dkkawat@wlink.com.np. Head: Sanu Nani Kansakar
Fine Arts Museum / Local Museum / Natural History Museum / Military Museum - 1928
Arms, historic portraits, decorative art, paintings, sculpture, terra cotta, ethnography, natural hist, Buddhist art gallery, carpetery, photographs - library, conservation laboratory, garden 24643

Natural History Museum, c/o Institute of Science, Tribhuvan University, Anandakuti, Swoyambhu, Kathmandu 44615 - T: (01) 271899. Head: Dr. Keshab Shrestha
Natural History Museum / University Museum - 1975
Botany, zoology, entomology, with special reference to butterflies, ornithology, mammalia, paleontology, ethnobotany - library 24644

Numismatic Museum, Hanuman Dhoka Palace, Kathmandu
Special Museum - 1963
Numismatics 24645

Swayambunath

Swayambunath Museum, Swayambunath
Fine Arts Museum / Archaeological Museum
Art, archeology 24646

Taulihawa

Kapilavastu Museum, Taulihawa
Archaeological Museum
Excavated material associated with the Buddha 24647

Netherlands

Aalten

Museum Frerikshuus, Markt 14, 7121 CS Aalten - T: (0543) 471797, Fax: 471797. Head: J.W.M. Bouwman
Local Museum - 1928
Prehistory, geology, jewels, weaving loom, costumes, coins 24648

Aardenburg

Gemeentelijk Archeologisch Museum, Marktstr 18, 4527 ZG Aardenburg - T: (0117) 475544, 492888, Fax: 492540, E-mail: ArcoWilleboordse@sluis-aardenburg.nl, Internet: http://www.gemeente.sluis-aardenburg.nl. Head: A.C.J. Willeboordse
Archaeological Museum - 1959
Prehistory, esp middle stone-age flint tools, roman pottery, bronzes, numismatics and construction fragments, medieval pottery and ceramics, esp. 12th-14th c herbes and spices-garden with regional-flora 24649

Aarle Rixtel

Heemkamer Barthold Van Hessel, Gemeenschapshuis De Aar, Bosscheweg, 5735 BZ Aarle Rixtel - T: (0492) 381735
Local Museum
Religious standards and vestments, photos, farm implements, paintings 24650

Aduard

Museum Sint-Bernardushof, Hofstr 45, 9831 RB Aduard - T: (050) 4032109
Religious Arts Museum 24651

Alkmaar

Biermuseum de Boom, Houttil 1, 1811 JL Alkmaar - T: (072) 5117033
Special Museum
History of brewing 24652

Het Hollands Kaasmuseum, Waagpl 2, 1811 JP Alkmaar - T: (072) 5114284, Fax: 5117513, E-mail: info@kaasmuseum.nl, Internet: http://www.kaasmuseum.nl
Special Museum
History of cheesemaking 24653

Stedelijk Museum, Doelenstr 5, 1811 KX Alkmaar - T: (072) 5110737, Fax: 5151476. Head: Dr. M.E.A. de Vries
Historical Museum / Archaeological Museum / Decorative Arts Museum - 1875
History, archeological finds, portraits, paintings, sculpture, old silver, porcelain, modern art, antique toys, dolls, tiles 24654

Allingawier

Aldfaers Erf Route, Kanaalweg 4, 8758 LD Allingawier - T: (0515) 231631
Local Museum
Crafts, paintings, folklore, religious art, costume, local and natural history 24655

Almelo

Museum voor Heemkunde Almelo, Korte Prinsenstr 2, 7607 JB Almelo - T: (0546) 816071. Head: S.L. Dronkers
Local Museum - 1975
Tools, textiles, local history, paintures - library 24656

Almere

De Paviljoens, Odeonstr 3, 1325 AL Almere - T: (036) 5450400
Fine Arts Museum
Paintings, sculpture, graphics 24657

Alphen aan den Rijn

Stichting Archeon, Postbus 600, 2400 AP Alphen aan den Rijn - T: (0172) 447744. Head: J. Borgman, Dr. G.J. Verwers
Archaeological Museum 24658

Alphen, Noord-Brabant

Streekmuseum Alphen, Baarleseweg 1, 5131 ZA Alphen, Noord-Brabant - T: (013) 5081821
Science&Tech Museum - 1959 24659

Amen

Bijenteeltmuseum De Bankorf, Amen 33a, 9446 PA Amen
Agriculture Museum
Beekeeping 24660

Amerongen

Amerongs Historisch Museum/ Tabaksmuseum, Burgemeester Van den Boschstr 46, 3958 CD Amerongen - T: (0343) 456500, 451196. Head: D. Pezarro
Historical Museum / Special Museum - 1983
History of tobacco 24661

Kasteel Amerongen, Drostestr 20, 3958 BK Amerongen - T: (0343) 454212, Fax: 563766. Head: Dr. C.L. Paul
Decorative Arts Museum - 1977
Interiors (17th-19th c), portraits, copper, books, tapestries, glass, musical instruments, porcelain, furniture 24662

Amersfoort

Armando Museum, Elleboogkerk, Langegracht 36, 3811 BW Amersfoort - T: (033) 4614088, Fax: 4640550, E-mail: armando.museum@worldonline.nl, Internet: http://www.armandomuseum.nl. Head: Paul Coumans
Fine Arts Museum - 1998 24663

Centrum Beeldende Kunst Provincie Utrecht, Breestr 1, 3811 BH Amersfoort - T: (033) 4618746, Fax: 4614335, E-mail: cbk.pu@planet.nl, Internet: http://www.cbk-utrecht.nl
Public Gallery 24664

Culinair Museum, Kleine Haag 2, 3811 HE Amersfoort
Special Museum
Dinning, interiors 24665

Historische Verzameling Cavalerie → Museum Nederlandse Cavalerie

Mannenzaal van het Sint Pieters en Bloklands Gasthuis, Westsingel 47, 3811 BB Amersfoort - T: (033) 4619987, Fax: 4630254, E-mail: info@museumflehite.nl, Internet: http://www.museumflehite.nl. Head: Dr. Garard Yzereef
Religious Arts Museum / Historical Museum
Religious history 24666

Mondriaanhuis, Museum voor Constructieve en Concrete Kunst, Kortegracht 11, 3811 KG Amersfoort - T: (033) 4620180, Fax: 4614087, E-mail: info@mondriaanhuis.nl, Internet: http://www.mondriaanhuis.nl. Head: Dr. A. de Jongh-Vermeulen
Fine Arts Museum 24667

Museum Flehite Amersfoort, Westsingel 50, 3811 BC Amersfoort - T: (033) 4619987, Fax: 4630254, E-mail: info@museumflehite.nl, Internet: http://www.museumflehite.nl. Head: Dr. Gerard Yzereef
Local Museum - 1878
Bones of prehistoric animals, archeology, local history, furniture, paintings (19th/20th c), porcelain, Gothic sideboard and treasury, genealogical tree of Emperor Charles V, souvenirs of the 17th century Dutch statesman Johan Van Oldenbarnevelt 24668

Museum Jacobs van den Hof, Zuidsingel 14, 3811 HA Amersfoort
Fine Arts Museum
Sculpture 24669

Museum Nederlandse Cavalerie, Bernhardkazerne, Barchman Wuytierslaan 198, 3818 LN Amersfoort, mail addr: Postbus 3003, 3800 DA Amersfoort - T: (033) 4661996, Fax: 4661493, E-mail: cavaleriemuseum@zonnet.nl. Head: J.M.A. Thomas
Military Museum - 1959
Hist of the Dutch cavalry from 1573 to present, WW II vehicles, uniforms, weapons, paintings, miniatures of the Dutch cavalry, armoured cars and tanks used by the cavalry fom 1938 to present 24670

De Zonnehof Museum, Zonnehof 8, 3811 ND Amersfoort
Fine Arts Museum
Sculpture, paintings, graphics 24671

Ammerzoden

Kasteel Ammersoyen, Kasteellaan 7, 5324 JR Ammerzoden - T: (073) 5949582, Fax: 5949583. Head: Dr. C.C.G. Quarles Van Ufford
Decorative Arts Museum - 1976
Castle (14th c) with furniture, paintings (16th-18th c), archeological finds (1400-1870), history of the castle since the Middle Ages 24672

Amstelveel

Gemeentelijk Expositiecentrum Aemstelle, Amsterdamseweg 441, 1181 BP Amstelveel - T: (020) 6432494, 6452333, Fax: 5404461, Internet: http://www.aub.nl
Public Gallery 24673

Amstelveen

Cobra Museum voor Moderne Kunst, Sandbergpl 1-3, 1181 ZX Amstelveen - T: (020) 5475050, 6165772, Fax: 6401251, E-mail: cobra.gallery@cobra-museum.nl, Internet: http://www.cobra-museum.nl
Fine Arts Museum 24674

Museum Jan van der Togt, Dorpstr 50, 1182 JE Amstelveen
Special Museum 24675

Amsterdam

Ajax Museum, Arena Blvd 3, 1101 AX Amsterdam - T: (020) 3111333, 3111446, Fax: 3111447, Internet: http://www.ajax.nl
Special Museum 24676

Allard Pierson Museum Amsterdam, Archeologisch Museum der Universiteit van Amsterdam, Oude Turfmarkt 127, 1012 GC Amsterdam - T: (020) 5252556, Fax: 5252561, E-mail: apm@uba.uva.nl, Internet: http://www.uba.uva.nl/apm. Head: Dr. R.A. Lunsingh Scheurleer
Archaeological Museum / University Museum - 1934
Egyptian, Near Eastern, Greek, Etruscan and Roman archaeology 24677

Amsterdams Historisch Museum, Nieuwezijds Voorburgwal 357, 1012 RM Amsterdam - T: (020) 5231822, Fax: 6207789, E-mail: info@ahm.nl, Internet: http://www.ahm.nl. Head: Pauline W. Kruseman
Historical Museum - 1926
Hist of Amsterdam, portrayed by means of paintings (Civic guards), maquettes, decorative arts, pottery, glass, silver, photographs, maps, archeology, Amsterdam and the Amsterdammers 1800-2000 24678

Amsterdams Openbaar Vervoer Museum, Elandsgracht 150, 1016 VC Amsterdam - T: (020) 4231100, Fax: 4216125
Science&Tech Museum 24679

Anne Frank Huis, Prinsengracht 263, 1016 GV Amsterdam, mail addr: Postbus 730, 1000 AS Amsterdam - T: (020) 5567100, Fax: 6207999, Internet: http://www.annefrank.nl. Head: J.F. Westra
Historical Museum - 1957
Antisemitism, (political) racism, discrimination, multi-ethnic society, racist publications, Anne Frank books, photogr, newspaper clippings - educational services, library 24680

Architektuur Centrum Amsterdam, Waterloopl 213, 1011 PG Amsterdam - T: (020) 6204878, Fax: 6385598, Internet: http://www.arcam.nl
Fine Arts Museum 24681

Artis Geologisch Museum, Plantage Kerklaan 38-40, 1018 CZ Amsterdam - T: (020) 5233400, 5233516, Fax: 5233481, E-mail: geolmuseum@artis.nl, Internet: http://www.artis.nl/inhoud/tl_geol.htm. Head: Dr. J.H. Werner
Natural History Museum - 1934
Geology, mineralogy, ores, fossils - planetarium, zoo, botanical gardens, zoological museum, aquarium 24682

Beurs van Berlage Museum, Damrak 243, 1012 ZJ Amsterdam - T: (020) 5304113, Fax: 6204701, E-mail: info@bvb.nl, Internet: http://www.beursvanberlage.nl
Fine Arts Museum 24683

Bijbels Museum, Herengracht 366-368, 1016 CH Amsterdam - T: (020) 6242436, Fax: 6248355, E-mail: info@bijbelsmuseum.nl, Internet: http://www.bijbelsmuseum.nl. Head: Dr. J.R. Boonstra
Religious Arts Museum
Old bibles, models of tabernacles and temples 24684

Bilderdijkmuseum, De Boelelaan 1105, 1081 HV Amsterdam - T: (020) 6454368
Special Museum - 1908
Memorabilia on W. Bilderdijk (poet, 1756-1831), books, portraits, drawings 24685

Bosmuseum (closed) 24686

Collectie Dr. B. Slingenberg, Keizersgracht 414, 1016 GC Amsterdam - T: (020) 6231391
Local Museum 24687

Collection Guido Van Deth (closed) 24688

EnergeticA, Museum voor Energietechniek, Hoogte Kadijk 400, 1018 BW Amsterdam - T: (020) 4221227, Fax: 4221661, E-mail: cwag@wish.net, Internet: http://www.energetica.nl
Science&Tech Museum
Electricity, gas, elevator 24689

Filmmuseum Foundation Nederlands, Vondelpark 3, 1071 AA Amsterdam, mail addr: Postbus 74782, 1070 BT Amsterdam - T: (020) 5891400, Fax: 6833401, E-mail: info@filmmuseum.nl, Internet: http://www.filmmuseum.nl. Head: Rien Hagen
Special Museum - 1946
Joris Ivens Film Coll, Jean Desmet Coll, filmposters, national and international films, coll films from the tens (1910-1919) - library 24690

Geels & Co. Koffie- en Theemuseum, Woermesstr 67, 1012 HX Amsterdam - T: (020) 6240683, Fax: 6227276
Special Museum 24691

Geelvinck Hinlopen Huis, Herengracht 518, 1017 CC Amsterdam - T: (020) 6390747, Fax: 6242541, E-mail: geelvinck@rusnet.nl, Internet: http://www.geelvinck.org. Head: Dr. A.D.M. Verwey
Decorative Arts Museum
Furniture 17th-19th c, porcelain 18th c, etchings by Rembrandt 24692

The Hash Marihuana Hemp Museum, Oudezijds Voorburgwal 148, 1012 DV Amsterdam - T: (020) 6235961, Fax: 6242433. Head: Ben Dronkers
Special Museum 24693

Heineken Experience, Stadhouderskade 78, 1072 AE Amsterdam - T: (020) 5239666, Fax: 5239738
Special Museum
Beer production 24694

Historisch Documentatiecentrum voor het Nederlands Protestantisme 1800-Heden, c/o Vrije Universiteit Amsterdam, De Boelelaan 1105, 1081 HV Amsterdam - T: (020) 4445270, Fax: 4445611, E-mail: jf.seijlhouwer@dienst.vu.nl, Internet: http://www.vu.nl/hdc. Head: Dr. J. de Bruijn
Historical Museum / University Museum - 1971
Hist of Dutch protestantism 1800 to the present day 24695

Holland Experience, Waterloopl 17, 1011 NV Amsterdam - T: (020) 4222233, Fax: 4222234, E-mail: info@holland-experience.nl, Internet: http://www.holland-experience.nl
Special Museum 24696

Huis Marseille, Stichting voor Fotografie, Keizersgracht 401, 1016 EK Amsterdam - T: (020) 5318989, Fax: 5318988, E-mail: huismarseille@wxs.nl, Internet: http://www.huismarseille.nl. Head: Els Bärents
Public Gallery / Fine Arts Museum - 1999
Historic and modern photographic exhibits 24697

Joods Historisch Museum, Jonas-Daniël-Meyerpl 2-4, 1011 RH Amsterdam, mail addr: Postbus 16737, 1001 RE Amsterdam - T: (020) 6269945, 6254229, Fax: 6241721, Internet: http://www.jhm.nl. Head: Hetty Berg
Religious Arts Museum - 1932/1987
Located in the restored Ashkenazi synagogue complex consisting of four 17th-18th c synagogues, Jewish ceremonial art, Sephardic textiles, Jewish hist in the Netherlands - library 24698

Het Kantenhuis, Kalverstr 124, 1012 PK Amsterdam - T: (020) 6248618, Fax: 6392768
Special Museum
Fan coll 24699

Katten Kabinet, Herengracht 497, 1017 BT Amsterdam - T: (020) 6265378, Fax: 6266764, E-mail: info@kattenkabinet.nl, Internet: http://www.kattenkabinet.nl. Head: Bob Meÿer
Fine Arts Museum
Cats 24700

Kindermuseum, Tropenmuseum, Linnaeusstr 2c, 1092 CK Amsterdam - T: (020) 5688300, Fax: 5688582, E-mail: kindermuseum@kit.nl, Internet: http://www.kit.nl/kindermuseum
Historical Museum 24701

KIT Tropenmuseum, Linnaeusstr 2, 1092 CK Amsterdam, mail addr: Postbus 95001, 1090 HA Amsterdam - T: (020) 5688398, 5688215, Fax: 5688331, E-mail: tropenmuseum@kit.nl, Internet: http://www.tropenmuseum.nl. Head: L.J.B. Schenk
Ethnology Museum - 1910
Ethnography (Asia, Africa, Oceania, South America), artifacts, sculpture and painting, textiles - library 24702

Koninklijk Oudheidkundig Genootschap, Postbus 74888, 1070 DN Amsterdam - T: (020) 6747380, Fax: 6747001, E-mail: KOG@rijksmuseum.nl. Head: Dr. M. Jonker, E. Caljé van den Berg
Historical Museum / Association with Coll 24703

Koninklijk Paleis te Amsterdam (Royal Palace Amsterdam), Nieuwezijds Voorburgwal 147, 1012 RJ Amsterdam - T: (020) 6248698, 6204060, Fax: 6233819, E-mail: info@kon-paleisamsterdam.nl, Internet: http://www.kon-paleisamsterdam.nl. Head: Baron B.W. Huisken
Historical Museum / Decorative Arts Museum - 1979
History of Amsterdam, historical building of Amsterdam, 17th c city hall, Empire furniture 24704

Madame Tussaud's Amsterdam, Dam 20, 1012 NP Amsterdam - T: (020) 5221010, Fax: 6207214, E-mail: madame.tussaud@scenerama.com, Internet: http://www.madame-tussauds.com. Head: Kees Klesman
Special Museum
Wax, molded, portraits 24705

Marc Chagall Kunsthuis, Derde Leliedwarsstr 24, 1015 TE Amsterdam - T: (020) 3307577
Public Gallery 24706

Max Euwe Centrum, Max Euwepl 30, 1017 MB Amsterdam - T: (020) 6257017, Fax: 6392077, E-mail: euwemec@xs4all.nl
Special Museum
Chess and chess player - library 24707

Molen van Sloten (Mill of the Castle), Akersluis 10, 1066 EZ Amsterdam - T: (020) 6690412, Fax: 6151862, E-mail: info@molenvansloten.nl, Internet: http://www.molenvansloten.nl
Science&Tech Museum 24708

Multatuli Museum, Korsjespoortsteeg 20, 1015 AR Amsterdam - T: (020) 6381938, Fax: 6204909, E-mail: multatuli@nl.packardbell.org, Internet: http://home.zonnet.nl/multatuli-museum. Head: J. Van Waterschoot
Special Museum - 1910
Works from and about Multatuli (1820-1887), photographs, manuscripts, books, furniture - library 24709

Museum Amstelkring, Oudezijds Voorburgwal 40, 1012 GE Amsterdam - T: (020) 6246604, Fax: 6381822, E-mail: info@museumamstelkring.nl, Internet: http://www.museumamstelkring.nl. Head: S. Kiers

Religious Arts Museum / Fine Arts Museum / Historical Museum - 1888
Historic house (1661) with attic church from the period of Roman-Catholic Clandestine churches, religious objects, paintings, sculptures, furniture (17th-20th c) 24710

Museum Herengracht, Herengracht 524, 1017 CC Amsterdam - T: (020) 6233246
Local Museum 24711

Museum Het Rembrandthuis, Jodenbreestr 4-6, 1011 NK Amsterdam - T: (020) 5200400, Fax: 5200401, E-mail: museum@rembrandthuis.nl, Internet: http://www.rembrandthuis.nl. Head: Ed de Heer
Fine Arts Museum - 1911
Artist's completely furnished home (17th c) and studio Rembrandt's etchings and some drawings and paintings of his teacher, Pieter Lastman and his pupils - drawings - library, educational department 24712

Museum Suriname, Zeeburgerdijk 21, 1093 SK Amsterdam - T: (020) 4684552, Fax: 4684559, E-mail: museum.suriname@worldonline.nl, Internet: http://home3.worldonline.nl/~mussur
Ethnology Museum 24713

Museum Van Loon, Keizersgracht 672, 1017 ET Amsterdam - T: (020) 6245255, Fax: 4274124, E-mail: info@museumvanloon.nl, Internet: http://www.museumvanloon.nl. Head: T.F. Grever
Decorative Arts Museum - 1973
Furnished 17th-18th century house, Van Loon family portraits and wedding coins 24714

Museum Vrolik, Meibergdreef 15, 1105 AZ Amsterdam - T: (020) 5669111, 5664927, Fax: 6976177, E-mail: museumvrolik@amc.uva.nl, Internet: http://www.uva.nl/voorzieningen/musea/vrolik.html. Head: Dr. R.S. Oostra
Natural History Museum - 1796
Anatomy and embryology of man and vertebrate animals, teratology of man and animals 24715

Museum Willet-Holthuysen, Herengracht 605, 1017 CE Amsterdam - T: (020) 5231870, Fax: 6207789, E-mail: pr@ahm.nl. Head: Pauline W. Kruseman
Decorative Arts Museum - 1896
Typically furnished canal house (1687) with objects of art, glass, porcelain, delftware (17th-18th c), reconstruction of an 18th c garden, Abraham Willet coll (glass, silver, paintings, drawings, sculptures, ceramics) 24716

Museumswerf 't Kromhout, Hoogte Kadijk 147, 1018 BJ Amsterdam - T: (020) 6276777, E-mail: info@nvamf.nl, Internet: http://www.nvamf.nl/kromhout.html
Science&Tech Museum / Open Air Museum
Shipyard history, petroliummotor 24717

Nationaal Spaarpottenmuseum, Raadhuisstr 12, 1016 DE Amsterdam - T: (020) 5567400
Special Museum
Museum of Monexboxes 24718

Nationaal Vakbondsmuseum De Burcht (Labour Union Museum), Henri Polaklaan 9, 1018 CP Amsterdam - T: (020) 6241166, Fax: 6237331, E-mail: vakmus@xs4all.nl, Internet: http://www.deburcht-vakbondsmuseum.nl
Historical Museum 24719

Nederlands Persmuseum, Oost-Indisch Huis, Oude Hoogstr 24, 1012 CE Amsterdam - T: (020) 5253908. Head: D.H. Couvée
Special Museum - 1915
History of the Dutch press, old newspapers, caricatures - library 24720

Nemo, Oosterdok 2, 1011 VX Amsterdam, mail addr: Postbus 421, 1000 AK Amsterdam - T: (020) 5313233, Fax: 5313535, E-mail: info@e-nemo.nl, Internet: http://www.e-nemo.nl. Head: P.G.M. Kijntjes
Science&Tech Museum - 1997
Technology, energy, science, humanity, interactions, interactive exhibits, computer games, theatre and films 24721

New Metropolis → Nemo

NUON Bedrijfsmuseum Amsterdam, Spaklerweg 20, 1096 BA Amsterdam - T: (020) 5973107, Fax: 5971151
Science&Tech Museum
Production and distribution of gas and electricity 24722

Occo Hofje, Nieuwe Keizersgracht 94, 1018 VE Amsterdam - T: (020) 6225219
Fine Arts Museum
Paintings and family portraits (16th-18th c) 24723

Open Haven Museum, KNSM-Laan 311, 1019 LE Amsterdam - T: (020) 4185522, Fax: 4186006
Science&Tech Museum / Open Air Museum
Boats and Shipping 24724

Persmuseum (Press Museum), Zeeburgerkade 10, 1019 HA Amsterdam - T: (020) 6928810, Fax: 4680505, E-mail: info@persmuseum.nl, Internet: http://www.persmuseum.nl. Head: Mariëtte Wolf
Historical Museum - 2001
Netherlands press, newspapers - library 24725

Peter Stuyvesant Stichting, Drentestr 21, 1083 HK Amsterdam - T: (020) 5406252, Fax: 5406357
Fine Arts Museum
Contemporary art and sculpture 24726

Piano en Pianola Museum, Westerstr 106, 1015 MN Amsterdam - T: (020) 6279624, Internet: http://www.pianola.nl. Head: K.P.J. Janse
Music Museum
Automatic pianos and music rolls 24727

Pijpenkabinet & Smokiana, Prinsengracht 488, 1017 KH Amsterdam - T: (020) 4211779, E-mail: info@pijpenkabinet.nl, Internet: http://www.pijpenkabinet.nl. Head: B.R. Goes
Special Museum
Precolumbian pipes, clay and porcelain tobacco pipes, ethnographic pipes, opium pipes, pipemakers' tools 24728

Reflex Miniatuurmuseum, Meibergdreef 9, 1105 AZ Amsterdam - T: (020) 6272832, Fax: 6202590, E-mail: multiple@xs4all.nl, Internet: http://www.reflex-art.nl
Fine Arts Museum 24729

Rijdend Electrisch Tram Museum, Amstelveenseweg 264, 1075 XV Amsterdam - T: (020) 6737538, Fax: 6739980, E-mail: info@trammuseum.demon.nl, Internet: http://huizen.dds.nl/~retm. Head: H. Schulze
Science&Tech Museum 24730

Rijksmuseum (National Museum), Stadhouderskade 42, 1071 ZD Amsterdam, mail addr: Postbus 74888, 1070 DN Amsterdam - T: (020) 6747047, Fax: 6747001, E-mail: info@rijksmuseum.nl, Internet: http://www.rijksmuseum.nl. Head: Prof. R. de Leeuw
Fine Arts Museum - 1800
Dutch painting (15th-19th c), including Frans Hals, Rembrandt ('Nightwatch') and Vermeer, prints and drawings, sculpture and applied arts, delftware, Dresden and Dutch porcelain, history of the Netherlands, Asiatic art - library, printroom 24731

Rijksprentenkabinet, Rijksmuseum, Jan Luykenstr 1a, 1071 XT Amsterdam, mail addr: Postbus 74888, 1070 DN Amsterdam - T: (020) 6747267, 6747000, Fax: 6747001, E-mail: bibliotheek@rijksmuseum.nl, Internet: http://www.rijksmuseum.nl. Head: G. Luijten
Fine Arts Museum - 1800
Dutch graphic art (16th-19th c), Japanese prints, prints of different European schools, drawings by Dutch and foreign artists, portraits and historical prints, prints by Master of the Hausbuch, Seghers and Rembrandt 24732

Scheepvaartmuseum (Maritime Museum), Kattenburgerpl 1, 1018 KK Amsterdam - T: (020) 5232222, Fax: 5232213, Internet: http://www.generali.nl/scheepvaartmuseum. Head: W. Bijleveld
Science&Tech Museum - 1916
Ship models, technical models, ships and mechanical draughts, real ships and ship parts, paintings, prints, drawings, atlases, globes and charts, nautical instruments, arms, coins and other relics related to maritime history of the Netherlands since the 16th century - library 24733

Schriftmuseum J.A. Dortmond, c/o Universiteits-bibliotheek van Amsterdam, Singel 425, 1012 WP Amsterdam - T: (020) 5252476, Fax: 5252311, E-mail: biemans@uba.uva.nl, Internet: http://www.uva.nl/voorzieningen/musea/dortmond.html
Library with Exhibitions / University Museum - 1976
All kinds of manuscripts and handwriting implements give a survey of the history of the art of writing from about 3,000 BC to the present 24734

Stedelijk Museum (Municipal Museum), Paulus Potterstr 13, 1071 CX Amsterdam - T: (020) 5732911, 5732737, Fax: 5732789, E-mail: j.hagman@stedelijk.nl, Internet: http://www.stedelijk.nl. Head: R.H. Fuchs
Fine Arts Museum / Local Museum - 1895
Modern painting and sculpture, video, drawing, graphic work, photography, applied art, industrial design, posters - library 24735

Stichting de Appel, Nieuwe Spiegelstr 10, 1017 DE Amsterdam - T: (020) 6255651, Fax: 6225215, E-mail: info@deAppel.ne, Internet: http://www.deAppel.ne
Fine Arts Museum 24736

Tattoo Museum, Oudezijds Achterburgwal 130, 1012 DT Amsterdam - T: (020) 6251565, Fax: 6204634, E-mail: info@tattoomuseum.com, Internet: http://www.tattoomuseum.com
Special Museum - 1996 24737

Theater Museum, c/o Theater Instituut Nederland, Herengracht 168, 1016 BP Amsterdam - T: (020) 5513300, Fax: 5513303, E-mail: info@tin.nl, Internet: http://www.tin.nl. Head: Dr. K. Vuyk
Performing Arts Museum - 1925
Dutch theatre history, cabaret, costumes, documents, photographs, graphics, drawings, models, paintings, curiosa, memorabilia, puppets, manuscripts, books, posters, press clippings, programs, miniature stage of Baron H. van Slingelandt - libraries 24738

Theo Thijssen Museum, Eerste Leliedwarsstr 16, 1015 TA Amsterdam - T: (020) 4207119, Internet: http://members.tripod..com/~theothijssen
Special Museum / Historical Museum
Life of author, teacher and politican T. Thijssen 24739

Universiteitsmuseum De Agnietenkapel, Oudezijds Voorburgwal 231, 1012 EZ Amsterdam - T: (020) 5253339, Fax: 5253378, E-mail: agnieten@agnieten.uva.nl, Internet: http://www.uva.nl/voorzieningen/musea/agniet.html. Head: A.M.Th. Schilder
Historical Museum / University Museum - 1923
History of the university and student life, paintings, portraits, medals, documents 24740

Van Gogh Museum, Paulus Potterstr 7, 1071 CX Amsterdam, mail addr: Postbus 75366, 1070 AJ Amsterdam - T: (020) 5705200, Fax: 6735053, E-mail: info@vangoghmuseum.nl, Internet: http://www.vangoghmuseum.nl. Head: John Leighton
Fine Arts Museum - 1974
About 200 paintings and 500 drawings by Vincent Van Gogh (1853-1890), 700 letters to his brother Theo, works by Emile Bernard, Gauguin, Toulouse-Lautrec, Monticelli - library 24741

Verzetsmuseum Amsterdam (Dutch Resistance Museum), Plantage Kerklaan 61a, 1018 CX Amsterdam - T: (020) 6202535, Fax: 6202960, E-mail: info@verzetsmuseum.org, Internet: http://www.verzetsmuseum.org. Head: A,G.J. van Seters
Historical Museum - 1985
Hist of the resistance in the Netherlands during WW II 24742

Vredes Museum (Peace Museum Project), Minahassastr 1, 1094 RS Amsterdam - T: (020) 6681868, Fax: 6681868, E-mail: vredesmuseum@worldmail.nl, Internet: http://www.vredesmuseum.nl. Head: Dr. Hans Wiebenga
Historical Museum
Items against war and for non-violence 24743

Het Waaierkabinet, Prinsengracht 1083, 1017 JH Amsterdam - T: (020) 6234410. Head: Felix Tal
Decorative Arts Museum - 1948
Coll of Chinese and Japanese fans and fans from various centuries 24744

Werkspoor Museum, Oostenburgergracht 77, 1018 NC Amsterdam - T: (020) 6251035/37, Fax: 6253970, Internet: http://www.storkgroup.com/profiel/geschiedenis/werkspoor. Head: Dr. H.J.M. Stevens Hardeman
Historical Museum - 1950
History of the East-Indian Company at Oosterburg (1663 to the beginning of the 19th c), local history, pictures, photographs, models of steam engines, models of trains, Werkspoor's activities depicted by various artists 24745

Het Wijnkopersgildehuys, Koestr 10-12, 1012 BX Amsterdam - T: (020) 6231210. Head: W.P.A.M. Kaijt
Historical Museum
Guildhall of the wine merchants (1633), interior, paintings, glass 24746

Woonbootmuseum (Houseboatmuseum), Prinsengracht, tegenover Nr 296, 1016 HW Amsterdam - T: (020) 4270750, Fax: 4270750, E-mail: info@houseboatmuseum.nl, Internet: http://www.houseboatmuseum.nl. Head: V. Van Loon
Special Museum 24747

Zoölogisch Museum Amsterdam, Mauritskade 61, 1092 AD Amsterdam, mail addr: c/o Universiteit van Amsterdam, Postbus 94766, 1090 GT Amsterdam - T: (020) 5255422, Fax: 5255402, E-mail: dunselma@science.uva.nl, Internet: http://www.bio.uva.nl/zma. Head: Dr. W. Los
Natural History Museum - 1838
Zoology, ornithology, entomology, herpetology, mammals, malacology, crustacea 24748

Andijk

Museum Saet en Cruyt, Dijkweg 319, 1619 JH Andijk - T: (0228) 592227, Fax: 592227. Head: M. Dekker
Agriculture Museum
Agriculture, seed-industry 24749

Poldermuseum Het Grootslag, Dijkweg 318, 1619 JH Andijk - T: (0228) 592227
Science&Tech Museum
Old mill (1860) with implements 24750

Anjum

Koren en Pel Molen De Eendracht, Mounebuorren 18, 9133 MB Anjum - T: (0519) 321926, Fax: 321717. Head: K. Moes
Science&Tech Museum - 1889
Restored mill, models and photos from different mills in Frisia, shell coll, fossiles, minerals 24751

Apeldoorn

Historisch Museum Apeldoorn, Raadhuispl 8, 7311 LK Apeldoorn, mail addr: Postbus 9033, 7300 ES Apeldoorn - T: (055) 5216129, Fax: 5225456, E-mail: hmapeldoorn@wxs.nl. Head: Joh Boerema
Local Museum
Prehistoric finds, pottery (mainly 19th c), agriculture, paper industry, costumes 24752

Museum van de Kanselarij der Nederlandse Orden, Koninklijk Park 1, 7315 JA Apeldoorn - T: (055) 5212224. Head: Dr. A.W. Vliegenthart, W.W.G. Steurbaut
Special Museum
Medals of honour 24753

Nederlands Politie Museum, Arnhemseweg 346, 7334 AC Apeldoorn, mail addr: Postbus 3008, 7303 GE Apeldoorn - T: (055) 5430691, Fax: 5431027, E-mail: nederlands@politiemuseum.nl, Internet: http://www.politiemuseum.nl. Head: T.R. Pauka
Special Museum / Historical Museum - 1991
History of Netherlands police 24754

Paleis Het Loo - Nationaal Museum, Koninklijk Park 1, 7315 JA Apeldoorn - T: (055) 5772400, Fax: 5219983, E-mail: info@paleishetloo.nl, Internet: http://www.paleishetloo.nl. Head: Dr. J.R. ter Molen
Historical Museum / Museum of Classical Antiquities - 1970
Hist of the House of Orange Nassau and its impact on the Netherlands, portraits, paintings, furniture, documents, prints, ceramics, sledges, carriages and vintage cars, ornamental cabinet, silver furniture, table, mirror and candlestands, Chancery of the Netherlands Orders of Knighthood 24755

Van Reekum Museum, Raadhuispl 8, 7311 LK Apeldoorn - T: (055) 5219155, Fax: 5225456, E-mail: van.reekum@worldonline.nl, Internet: http://www.apeldoorn.nl/vanreekum. Head: Joh Boerema
Fine Arts Museum
Graphic arts, photography - library 24756

Appelscha

Culinair Historisch Museum De Vleer, Vaart Zuidzijde 75, 8426 AG Appelscha
Special Museum
Dinning history 24757

Natuurhistorisch Museum en Aquarium Octopus, Bosberg 1, 8426 GJ Appelscha - T: (0516) 431410, 432043
Natural History Museum
Natural History 24758

Appingedam

Museum Stad Appingedam, Wijkstr 25, 9901 AE Appingedam - T: (0596) 680168, Fax: 681405. Head: M.F. Van Klinken
Local Museum / Historical Museum - 1942
Local hist, costumes, documents, pictures, photographs, silver objects, Chinese porcelain, topographical and urban developments 24759

Arnemuiden

Museum Arnemuiden, Langstr 28-35, 4341 EE Arnemuiden - T: (0118) 603175
Local Museum
Local history, old costume, phothgraphs, paintings, fishery history, shipmodels 24760

Old Aircraft Museum, Calandweg 2, 4341 RA Arnemuiden
Science&Tech Museum
Aviation, flying Gyrocopter 24761

Arnhem

Arnhems Oorlogsmuseum 1940-45, Kemperbergerweg 780, 6816 RX Arnhem
Military Museum / Historical Museum
World war II, militaria 24762

Gemeentemuseum Arnhem, Utrechtseweg 87, 6812 AA Arnhem - T: (026) 3512431
Local Museum 24763

Historisch Museum Grenadiers en Jagers, Deelenseweg 20, 6816 TS Arnhem, mail addr: Postbus 9210, 6800 HM Arnhem - T: (026) 3533369. Head: H. Coopmans
Military Museum - 1885
History of the grenadiers and hunters, regimental coll of uniforms, weapons, paintings of the Dutch foot guards from 1829 to the present - library 24764

Historisch Museum Het Burgerweeshuis, Bovenbeekstr 21, 6811 CV Arnhem - T: (026) 4426900, Fax: 4436315. Head: Dr. L. Brandt Corstius
Local Museum
Local history, Chinese porcelain, pottery from Delft and Arnhem, ceramics, glasses, silver, graphics and illustrations by regional artists 24765

Huis Zypendaal, Zypendaalseweg 44, 6814 CL Arnhem - T: (026) 3552555
Decorative Arts Museum
Furniture, memorabilia of the Arnhem noble family Brantsen van de Zyp 24766

Inter Art - Sonsbeek Art and Design, Tellegenlaan 3, 6814 BT Arnhem - T: (026) 3512255, Fax: 4465201, E-mail: inter.art@unicall.be. Head: Stefaan Delbaere
Public Gallery
Paintings, graphics, sculptures, glass art 24767

Koninklijk Tehuis voor Oud-Militairen en Museum Bronbeek, Velperweg 147, 6824 MB Arnhem - T: (026) 3840840, Fax: 3840890, E-mail: ktomm.bronbeek@army.dnet.mindef.nl. Head: R. Harting
Military Museum / Historical Museum - 1863
Ethnography of the former Netherlands East Indies, hist of the former Royal Netherlands East Indian Army, uniforms, portraits, paintings, medals of honor, flags, arms - library 24768

Museum voor Moderne Kunst (Museum of Modern Art), Utrechtseweg 87, 6812 AA Arnhem - T: (026) 3512431, Fax: 4435148, Internet: http://www.mmkarnhem.nl. Head: M. Meijer
Fine Arts Museum - 1920
Paintings (16th-20th c), neorealists (Dick Ket, Pyke Koch, Raoul Hynckes, Carel Willink, Wim Schuhmacher), contemporary Dutch art, 20th c applied art, Dutch contemporary jewelry 24769

Nederlands Openluchtmuseum, Schelmseweg 89, 6816 SJ Arnhem - T: (026) 3576111, Fax: 3576147, E-mail: info@openluchtmuseum.nl, Internet: http://www.openluchtmuseum.nl. Head: J.A.M.F Vaessen
Open Air Museum - 1912
90 buildings (farms, houses, workshops, mills) from all over the country, folk costumes, popular art, crafts, ceramics, agriculture, HollandRama - library 24770

Nederlands Wijnmuseum, Velperweg 23, 6824 BC Arnhem - T: (031 264424042, Fax: 264458884, E-mail: info@wijnmuseum.nl, Internet: http://www.wijnmuseum.nl. Head: M.G. Donders Van den Aardweg
Special Museum - 1983
Hist of winegrowing, corkscrews 24771

Arum

Rock 'n Roll Museum Arum, Van Camminghaweg 28-30, 8822 WD Arum - T: (0517) 642217, Internet: http://www.rockmuseum.nl. Head: Th. P. Dasbach
Music Museum
Music, dance 24772

Asselt

Folkloristisch Museum, Pastoor Pinckerstr, 6071 NW Asselt - T: (0475) 501501. Head: Dr. A. Van Rijswigck
Folklore Museum - 1927
Archeological finds, domestic utensils, earthenware, religious objects (also Jewish) 24773

Assen

Atelier Kea Homan, Esstr 49, 9401 NT Assen
Fine Arts Museum
Graphics 24774

Draaiorgelmuseum, Rode Heklaan 3, 9401 SB Assen - T: (0592) 345885, 350076, Fax: 350205, E-mail: pb0.ajt@12move.nl. Head: G. Hulshof
Music Museum
Music, barrel-organs 24775

Drents Museum, Brink 1, 9401 HS Assen, mail addr: Postbus 134, 9400 AC Assen - T: (0592) 312741, Fax: 317119, E-mail: info@drentsmuseum.nl, Internet: http://www.drentsmuseum.nl. Head: Dr. G.G. Horstmann, Dr. V.T. Van Vilsteren, Dr. J.J. Heij, Dr. P. Schonewille, J. Beuker, Dr. M. de Bois
Historical Museum - 1854
Regional prehistory and history, documents about historic monuments in the province of Drenthe, Netherlands art around 1900, costumes, rooms with period furniture, coins, oldest canoe in the world (6,000 BC), wooden disk wheels (2,000 BC) - discovery room for children 24776

Museum APZ-Drenthe, Dennenweg 9, 9404 LA Assen
Science&Tech Museum 24777

Provinciaal Museum van Drenthel → Drents Museum

Stoottroepen Museum, Balkenweg 3, 9405 CC Assen
Religious Arts Museum
Reliogious art, militaria 24778

Asten

Nationaal Beiaardmuseum, Ostaderstr 23, 5721 WC Asten - T: (0493) 691865, Fax: 697079, E-mail: alehr@iaehv.nl, Internet: http://www.carillon-museum.nl. Head: Dr. André Lehr
Special Museum - 1969
All kinds of bells from all over the world, carillons, tower clocks, carillon mechanisms, archeology and ethnology in connection with bells - library 24779

Natuurhistorisch Museum de Peel, Ostaderstr 23, 5721 WC Asten - T: (0493) 691865, Fax: 697079, E-mail: algemeen@museumdepeel.nl, Internet: http://www.museumdepeel.nl. Head: W.A.G. Dibbets
Natural History Museum - 1973
Ornithology, entomology, mammals, fish, botany, palaeontology, gardens, reptiles and amphibians 24780

Axel

Streekmuseum Het Land van Axel, Noordstr 11-13, 4571 GB Axel
Local Museum - 1939
19th century farmers' costumes, old farm carts, folk costumes, jewels, utensils, furniture from 1860 and 1900, school books (18th-19th c) 24781

Witte's Museum, Bastionstr 45, 4571 ES Axel
Special Museum
Cartography 24782

Baarn

Baarnse Oudheidkamer, Burg. Penstr 4, 3741 AH Baarn. Head: A. Van der Mersch
Historical Museum
Local history 24783

Kasteel Groeneveld, Groeneveld 2, 3744 ML Baarn - T: (035) 5420446, Fax: 5421819, E-mail: groeneveld@ifa.agro.nl, Internet: http://www.kasteelgroeneveld.nl. Head: Dr. S. H. Visser
Fine Arts Museum
Castle with art-exhibitions 24784

Oranje Museum, Lt. Gen. Van Heutszlaan 7, 3743 JL Baarn - T: (035) 65422776
Historical Museum
Museum of the Dutch Royal Family: photographs and crockery 24785

Bakel

Museum de Tolbrug, Neerstr 11, 5761 RE Bakel - T: (0492) 341819
Local Museum 24786

Bakkum

Wegwijs Museum, Van Oldenbarneveldtweg 40, 1901 NZ Bakkum - T: (0251) 652243
Local Museum 24787

Bant

Kijk- en Luistermuseum, Schoterpad 1, 8314 RA Bant
Fine Arts Museum
Paintings showroom 24788

Barger Compascuum

Veen Park, Berkenrode 4, 7884 TR Barger Compascuum - T: (0591) 324444, Fax: 349122. Head: J.H.G. Keuter
Open Air Museum
Houses of peat workers (around 1920), school, bakery with petrol heated oven, windmill, agricultural implements, domestic utensils 24789

Barneveld

Pluimvee Museum, Hessenweg 2a, 3771 RB Barneveld - T: (0342) 400073, Fax: 401262, E-mail: pluimvee.museum@worldonline.nl, Internet: http://www.pluimveemuseum.com
Agriculture Museum
Poultry-farming 24790

Veluws Museum Nairac, Langstr 13, 3771 BA Barneveld - T: (0342) 415666, Fax: 490943, E-mail: museumnairac@introweb.nl, Internet: http://www.barneveld.com/nairac. Head: P.C. Van Leeuwen
Local Museum - 1875
Prehistoric and archeological finds, glasses, coins, furniture, old local costumes - library 24791

Beek

Carnavalmuseum, Fattenbergstr 55, 6191 EP Beek
Special Museum 24792

Heemkundemuseum Beek, Sint-Martinusstr 12, 6191 TL Beek
Local Museum
Craftmen's instruments and agricultural implements, local history, archeology 24793

Beek en Donk

Oud Raadhuis, Heuvelplein 8, 5741 JK Beek en Donk - T: (0492) 462345
Local Museum
Town Hall 24794

Beers, Friesland

Stinzenmuseum, Tsjerke en Uniastate Beers, Tsjerkepaad 3, 9025 BJ Beers, Friesland. Head: O. Faber
Historical Museum - 1963
Heraldic figures and coats-of-arms, items relating to swan hunting, pictures of old gates 24795

Beilen

De Klomphoek, Brunstingerstr 43, 9411 EJ Beilen
Local Museum
Local history, crafts 24796

Oudheidkamer Beilen, Kampstr 2, 9411 HD Beilen, mail addr: Kievitlaan 13, 9411 HD Beilen - T: (0593) 523334. Head: W. Bakker
Archaeological Museum / Historical Museum / Folklore Museum
Porcelain, silver, paintings 24797

Bellingwolde

Beeldentuin Belling Garde, Hoofdweg 244, 9695 AV Bellingwolde
Fine Arts Museum
Ceramics, paintings, sculpture 24798

Craftselijke Zadelmakerij Museum, Rhederweg 21, 9695 CA Bellingwolde
Historical Museum
Crafts, saddles 24799

Streekmuseum De Oude Wolden, Hoofdweg 161, 9695 AB Bellingwolde
Archaeological Museum
Prehistoric finds, fossils, tools, costumes, crafts 24800

Beneden Leeuwen

Historisch Museum Tweestromenland, Pastoor Zijlmansstr 3, 6658 EE Beneden Leeuwen, mail addr: Heuvel 107, 6651 DC Druten - T: (0487) 517282, E-mail: mw@tweestromenland-museum.myweb.nl
Historical Museum - 1986
Local history 24801

Bennekom

Kijk en Luister Museum, Kerkstr 1, 6721 VA Bennekom - T: (0318) 414629. Head: J.V.D. Hazel, M.V.D. Hazel Mulder, H. Gijsbertsen
Local Museum - 1955
History of Bennekom and the environs 24802

Tute-Natura, Bosbeekweg 19, 6721 MH Bennekom
Natural History Museum - 1973
Plants, birds, natural history, prehistory 24803

Berg en Dal

Afrika Museum, Postweg 6, 6571 CS Berg en Dal - T: (024) 6842044, 6841211, Fax: 6841922, E-mail: directie@afrikamuseum.nl, Internet: http://www.afrikamuseum.nl. Head: Dr. C.M.S. Eisenburger
Ethnology Museum - 1954
African ethnology, African arts, Yoruba coll, nail fetish, Edan figures, Ogboni coll, Senufo maternity, Angola tombstones - library, educational center, open air area 24804

Bergeijk

Automusa, Standerdmolen 3, 5571 RN Bergeijk - T: (0497) 571003, Fax: 575082, E-mail: info@automusa.nl, Internet: http://www.automusa.nl
Science&Tech Museum 24805

Eicha-Museum, Eerselsedijk 4, 5570 CM Bergeijk, mail addr: c/o Cultureel Centrum De Kattendans, Postbus 140, 5570 AB Bergeijk - T: (0497) 575986, Fax: 575647. Head: Johan Biemans
Archaeological Museum
Prehistorical finds, earthenware, Merovingian ornaments and glass 24806

Hondenmuseum, Weebosch 78, 5571 LZ Bergeijk
Special Museum
Dogmuseum 24807

Muzen Museum voor Creatief Werk, De Hof, Dennendreef 7, 5571 AK Bergeijk
Fine Arts Museum
Naive painting and works by juvenile artists, tapestries from Egypt, Italy and the Netherlands, musical instruments 24808

Witrijtmuseum, Witrijt 10, 5571 XH Bergeijk - T: (0497) 512625
Local Museum 24809

Bergen, Noord-Holland

Gemeentemuseum 't Sterkenhuis, Oude Prinsweg 21, 1861 CL Bergen, Noord-Holland. Head: A.J.M. Leijen
Local Museum - 1903
Local hist, archaeological finds, historical room with porcelain, costumes, textiles, graphics 24810

Museum Kranenburgh, Hoflaan 26, 1861 CR Bergen, Noord-Holland - T: (072) 5898927
Special Museum 24811

Bergen op Zoom

Gemeentemuseum Het Markiezenhof, Steenbergsestr 8, 4611 TE Bergen op Zoom - T: (0164) 242930
Local Museum 24812

Bergum

Streekmuseum Volkssterrenwacht, Menno Van Coehoornweg 9, 9251 LV Bergum - T: (0511) 465544
Local Museum 24813

Best

Klompenmuseum De Platijn, Broekdijk 16, 5681 PG Best - T: (0499) 371247. Head: H. Van Laarhoven
Special Museum
Shoestore with clogs 24814

Biddinghuizen

Het Nederlands Sportmuseum, Spijkweg 30, 8256 RJ Biddinghuizen - T: (0321) 331256
Special Museum
Museum of Sports 24815

Birdaard

Ruurd Wiersma Hus, Mounewei 6-7, 9111 HB Birdaard
Fine Arts Museum
Paintings 24816

Bleiswijk

Oudheidkamer Bleiswijk, Dorpsstr 89, 2665 BH Bleiswijk - T: (010) 5214111
Historical Museum
Implements 24817

Bloemendaal

Museum Meerenberg, Brederodelaan 10, 2061 JS Bloemendaal - T: (023) 5130307
Local Museum 24818

Blokzijl

Het Gildenhuys, Kerkstr 7, 8356 DN Blokzijl - T: (0527) 291381, 291206. Head: C.E. Koopmans-Witt
Local Museum
Local history of Blokzijl and the relation to water 24819

Bodegraven

Kaasmuseum Bodegraven, Spoorstr 15, 2411 ED Bodegraven - T: (0172) 650909
Special Museum 24820

Boekel

Kachelmuseum De Drie Kronen, Volkelseweg 8, 5427 RB Boekel - T: (0492) 321595
Special Museum
Tiles 24821

Bolsward

It Gysbert Japicxhûs Museum, Wipstr 6, 8701 HZ Bolsward - T: (0515) 573990, Fax: 577204, E-mail: gysbert@tekstwinkelmuseum.tmfweb.nl. Head: B. Miedema
Special Museum
Frysian, Netherlandish, German and English literature 24822

Oudheidkamer in het Stadhuis, Jongemastr 2, 8701 JD Bolsward - T: (0515) 578787, Fax: 576688
Local Museum - 1949
Local history, porcelain, furniture, missal from 1475, silver, coins, pewter, council chamber 24823

Borculo

Boerderijmuseum De Lebbenbrugge, Lebbenbruggedijk 25, 7271 SB Borculo - T: (0545) 272246
Agriculture Museum - 1926
19th century farm with interiors 24824

Brandweermuseum en Stormrampmuseum, Hofstr 5, 7271 AP Borculo - T: (0545) 272848, Fax: 271405. Head: W. Tijdink
Science&Tech Museum - 1900
Various firefighting material from 1648 to the present, uniforms, medals, coins 24825

Museum Batjuchin, Molenstr 15, 7271 BJ Borculo - T: (0545) 272847
Local Museum 24826

Museum 't Los Hoes, Burg. Bloemersstr 1, 7271 DA Borculo - T: (0545) 272200, Fax: 271666. Head: B.H. de Wit
Natural History Museum - 1980
Ultra violet minerals, paleontological collections, local paleontological collections 24827

Openbaar Vervoer Museum, Steenstr 30, 7271 BP Borculo - T: (0545) 274144
Science&Tech Museum 24828

Borger

Nationaal Hunebedden Infocentrum, Bronnegerstr 12, 9531 TG Borger - T: (0599) 236374
Historical Museum - 1967
Barrows 24829

Borgercompagnie

Museum Lammert Boerma, Borgercompagnieweg 44-46, 9632 TD Borgercompagnie - T: (0590) 39330, Internet: http://www.museum.boerma.com. Head: J. Steneker
Special Museum 24830

Borne

Bussemakerhuis, Ennekerdijk 11, 7622 ED Borne - T: (074) 2669636, Fax: 2669636. Head: Dr. P. Bakels
Historical Museum / Local Museum / Library with Exhibitions 24831

Boskoop

Boomkwekerijmuseum, Reijerskoop 54, 2771 BR Boskoop - T: (0172) 217756, Fax: 217756
Natural History Museum
Hist and techniques of tree-propagation 24832

Bosschenhoofd

Vliegend Museum Seppe, Pastoor van Breugelstr 93e, 4744 RC Bosschenhoofd - T: (0165) 321335, Fax: 548611, E-mail: airmad@planet.nl, Internet: http://www.museum.tmfweb.nl
Science&Tech Museum 24833

Bourtange

De Baracquen Museum voor Bourtanger Bodemvondsten, Meestr 3, 9545 PJ Bourtange - T: (0599) 354600
Local Museum
Local history 24834

Het Nieuwe Kruithuis, Commandeurstr 1, 9545 PJ Bourtange - T: (0599) 354600
Historical Museum
History of Bourtange 24835

Synagoge, Batterijenstr 1, 9545 PP Bourtange - T: (0599) 354238
Historical Museum - 1974
History of the jews in Bourtange 24836

Boxtel

Oertijdmuseum, De Groene Poort, Bosscheweg 80, 5283 WB Boxtel - T: (0411) 616861, Fax: 616862, E-mail: oertijdmuseum.degroenepoort@wxs.nl, Internet: http://www.home.wxs.nl/oertijdmuseum.-degroenepoort. Head: Dr. R.H.B. Fraaye
Natural History Museum 24837

Breda

De Beyerd, Centrum voor Beeldende Kunst, Boschstr 22, 4811 GH Breda - T: (076) 5299900, Fax: 5299929, E-mail: debeyerd@breda.nl. Head: F. Tiesing
Fine Arts Museum / Public Gallery 24838

Bierreclamemuseum, Haagweg 375, 4813 XC Breda
Special Museum
Advertising for beer, graphics 24839

Breda's Museum, Parade 12-14, 4811 DZ Breda, mail addr: Postbus 1173, 4801 BD Breda - T: (076) 5299300, Fax: 5299311, E-mail: breda.museum@wxs.nl, Internet: http://www.breda-museum.nl. Head: Dr. J.F. Grosfeld
Historical Museum / Religious Arts Museum / Archaeological Museum - 1903
Mainly hist of the Barony of Breda, pictures, weapons, silver, fire brigade, costumes, folklore, coins, ceramics, historical-topographical globe, legal hist, archaeology, art and industry 24840

Generaal Maczek Museum, De La Reijweg 95, 4818 BA Breda - T: (076) 5274089, E-mail: info@maczekmuseum.nl, Internet: http://www.maczekmuseum.nl. Head: F.C.K. Ruczynski
Military Museum - 1984
Liberation 1944/45 of parts of Holland by the 1st Polish Armoured Division under General S. Maczek - archive 24841

Museum Oorlog en Vrede, Ginnekenweg 76, 4818 JH Breda - T: (076) 5213456. Head: W. Mol
Military Museum / Historical Museum
Objects relating to World War II 24842

Nederlands Centrum voor Handwerken, Spinveld 13a, 4815 HR Breda
Decorative Arts Museum
Arts and crafts 24843

Breezand

Museum Anna Paulowna, Zandvaart 15, 1764 NJ Breezand - T: (0223) 523155
Special Museum 24844

Breskens

Visserijmuseum, Kaai 1, 4511 RC Breskens - T: (0117) 383656
Special Museum
Fishing 24845

Breukelen

Ridderhofstad Gunterstein, Zandpad 48, 3621 NE Breukelen
Historical Museum
Manuscripts by Louis Napoleon and statesman Johan von Oldenbarneveldt (1547-1619), travel reports, topography, coins, furniture, family portraits 24846

Brielle

Historisch Museum Den Briel, Markt 1, 3231 AH Brielle - T: (0181) 475475, Fax: 475476
Local Museum
Local history 24847

Broek op Langedijk

Museum Broeker Veiling, Museumweg 2, 1721 BW Broek op Langedijk, mail addr: Postbus 1, 1720 AA Broek op Langedijk - T: (0226) 313807, Fax: 318304, E-mail: broekker@xs4all.nl, Internet: http://www.noord-holland-tourist.nl/nl/museumplein/broekker.htm. Head: J.C.M. Van Daelen
Agriculture Museum - 1974
Oldest European vegetable auction hall, agricultural implements 24848

Brouwershaven

Brouws Museum, Haven Zuidzijde 14-15, 4318 AJ Brouwershaven
Local Museum
Cartography, coins, maritime history, paintings, local history 24849

Grote- of Sint Nicolaaskerk, Kerkpad 2, 4318 EG Brouwershaven
Local Museum / Religious Arts Museum
Architecture, sculpture, paintings, local history 24850

Bruinisse

Oudheidkamer, Oudestr 27, 4311 AV Bruinisse - T: (0111) 481223. Head: J. Jumelet
Local Museum - 1968
Household objects, costumes (18th-19th c), objects relating to the mussel and shrimp trade 24851

Visserijmuseum, Oudestr 23, 4311 AV Bruinisse - T: (0111) 482485
Special Museum
Shells, history of fishing 24852

Brummen

Collectie in het Gemmeentehuis, Engelenburgerlaan 31, Brummen - T: (0575) 562233
Decorative Arts Museum
Silver of the Sint-Jansgilde 24853

Brunssum

Verzameling Oudheidkundige Vondsten in het Ontmoetingscentrum, Lindeplein 2B, 6444 AT Brunssum - T: (045) 5278422, Fax: 259879
Archaeological Museum - 1977
Earthenware (1025-1450) of local production, Roman finds, coins 24854

Budel

Museum voor het Radiozendamateurisme Jan Corver, Broekkant 1, 6021 CR Budel - T: (0495) 430342
Science&Tech Museum 24855

Bunnik

Oud Amelisweerd Museum, Koningslaan 9, 3981 HD Bunnik - T: (030) 2362362, Fax: 6570653, E-mail: rtjan@centraalmuseum.nl, Internet: http://www.centraalmuseum.nl. Head: R. Tjan
Historical Museum 24856

Portanje's Vespa Scooter en Nostalgie Collectie, Stationsweg 41, 3981 AB Bunnik - T: (030) 6563838, Fax: 6563838, E-mail: k.portanje@consunet.nl, Internet: http://www.portanje.com. Head: B.K. Portanje
Science&Tech Museum 24857

Bunschoten Spakenburg

Historische Expositie Klederdracht en Visserijmuseum, Kerkstr 20, 3751 AR Bunschoten Spakenburg
Special Museum
Dolls with historical costumes dating back 1780 24858

Spakenburgs Museum 't Vurhuus, Oude Schans 47, 3752 AH Bunschoten Spakenburg - T: (033) 42983319
Local Museum
Interior, costumes 24859

Buren, Friesland

Landbouw- en Juttersmuseum Swartwoude, Hoofdweg 1, 9164 KL Buren, Friesland
Agriculture Museum / Special Museum
Hunting, agriculture, costumes, arts and crafts 24860

Buren, Gelderland

Boerenwagenmuseum, Achter Bonenburg 1, 4116 BD Buren, Gelderland - T: (0344) 571431, 572493
Science&Tech Museum 24861

Museum van de Koninklijke Marechaussee, Weeshuiswal 9, 4116 BR Buren, Gelderland - T: (0344) 571256, Fax: 572009. Head: F.J. Van Lier
Special Museum - 1936
Paintings, prints, uniforms, documents and weapons concerning the royal gendarmes and the Netherlands Police 24862

Burgh Haamstede

Tentoonstellingsruimte 't Oute Hus, J J Boeijesweg 6, 4328 HB Burgh Haamstede
Public Gallery
Paintings 24863

Bussum

Collectie A. Veltman, Koningslaan 37, 1405 GK Bussum - T: (035) 6912812
Decorative Arts Museum 24864

Cadier en Keer

Afrika Centrum, Rijksweg 15, 6267 AC Cadier en Keer - T: (043) 4077383, Fax: 4077374, E-mail: museum@afrikacentrum.nl, Internet: http://www.afrikacentrum.nl. Head: J. Demarteau
Ethnology Museum - 1959
Art objects and domestic articles from Western Africa - documentation center 24865

Castricum

Fort Kijkduin, Dorpsstr 65, 1901 NZ Castricum - T: (0251) 652422
Natural History Museum 24866

Coevorden

Drenthe's Veste Stedelijk Museum, Haven 4-6, 7741 JV Coevorden - T: (0524) 516225, E-mail: gemeente@gem.coevorden.nl, Internet: http://www.coevorden.nl
Local Museum
Local history, costumes 24867

Cruquius

Museum de Cruquius, Cruquiusdijk 27, 2142 ER Cruquius - T: (023) 5285704, Fax: 5285704, Internet: http://www.noord-holland-tourist.nl/nl/museumplein. Head: N.F. Faber Wittenberg
Science&Tech Museum - 1933
Steam engine and tools, sketch of the Netherlands as Polderland, dike construction, windmill modells, maps 24868

Cuijk

Amerika Museum Nederland, Grotestr 62, 5431 DL Cuijk - T: (0485) 316221, E-mail: p.schoonhoven@betuwe.net, Internet: http://www.amerikamuseum.nl. Head: W. Schoonhoven Okken
Ethnology Museum - 1971
Pre-Columbian art (Mexico and the High Andes), Canadian Indians, the Central Eskimo culture, modern South American Indian material 24869

Culemborg

Jan Van Riebeeckhuis, Achterstr 26-30, 4101 BB Culemborg, mail addr: Postbus 169, 4000 AD Tiel - T: (0344) 612230, Fax: 631504, E-mail: info@regionaalarchiefrivierenland.nl, Internet: http://www.regionaalarchiefrivierenland.nl. Head: W. Veerman
Special Museum - 1971
Birthplace of the explorer Jan Van Riebeeck, furniture, domestic utensils - city archives, printroom and historical library 24870

Museum Elisabeth Weeshuis, Heerenstr 29, 4001 BR Culemborg - T: (03450) 13912. Head: P.W. Schipper
Decorative Arts Museum - 1928
Antiquities of Culemborg and environs, topography, pottery, silver, history of government and laws, portraits of royalty (16th-18th c), religious paintings (16th c) 24871

Dalen

De Drentse Glasbloazer, Burgemeester Ten Holtewg 10a, 7751 CS Dalen
Decorative Arts Museum
Glass art 24872

De Koog

EcoMare, Ruyslaan 92, 1796 AZ De Koog - T: (0222) 317741, Fax: 317741, E-mail: info@ecomare.nl, Internet: http://www.ecomare.nl. Head: Dr. J. Kuiper
Natural History Museum - 1930
Hist and evolution of the tidal shallows of thw Wadden sea area, the island Texel and the North Sea, human use 24873

De Rijp

Museum in 't Houtenhuis (Wooden House Museum), Jan Boonpl 2, 1483 BL De Rijp - T: (0299) 671286, E-mail: museum@houtenhuis.nl, Internet: http://www.houtenhuis.nl. Head: Jenny Mulder
Local Museum - 1937
Objects relating to whaling and herring industry, finds (17th-18th c), folk-art, landscape, wood construction 24874

Museum Jan Boon, Rechtestr 146, 1483 BG De Rijp - T: (0299) 671451
Local Museum 24875

De Steeg

Kasteel Middachten, 6994 JC De Steeg - T: (026) 4954998, Fax: 4955115. Head: N.W. Conijn
Decorative Arts Museum
Old castle with interior (17th c) 24876

De Waal

Agrarisch en Wagenmuseum, Hogereind 4-6, 1793 AG De Waal - T: (0222) 312951, 318622
Agriculture Museum / Science&Tech Museum - 1964
Sleighs and coaches, tools, agricultural implements, Trafic from perambulator until bearer and hearse 24877

Delden

Zoutmuseum Delden, Langestr 30, 7491 AG Delden - T: (074) 3764546. Head: R.H.A. Klumpers
Special Museum - 1985
Exposition about salt, pepper and salt-cellars (shakers) 24878

Delft

Delft Volkenkundig Diorama Museum, Fortuynstr 1, 2611 MV Delft, mail addr: Werkplaats 7, 2611 MV Delft - T: (015) 2131062
Archaeological Museum
Greek and Roman dwellings, roman reliefs - library 24879

Hofje Van Gratie, Van der Mastenstr 28, 2611 NZ Delft - T: (015) 2124236. Head: J. Graswinkel
Historical Museum - 1957
Portraits of regents' families, furniture, earthenware 24880

Koninklijk Nederlands Leger- en Wapenmuseum, Armamentarium, Korte Geer 1, 2611 CA Delft - T: (015) 2150500, Fax: 2150544, Internet: http://www.legermuseum.nl. Head: J.A. Buijse
Military Museum - 1913
Military history of the Netherlands, weapons from prehistory to present, uniforms, flags, paintings - library 24881

Mineralogisch-Geologisch Museum, Mijnbouwstr 120, 2628 RX Delft - T: (015) 2786021, Fax: 2781189, E-mail: m.m.vantooren@ta.tudelft.nl, Internet: http://www.ta.tudelft.nl/museum.html. Head: M.M. van Tooren
Natural History Museum - 1912
Mineralogy, paleontology, petrology, economic geology, Prof. Dr. G.A.F. Molengraaff (1860-1942) 24882

Museum Lambert Van Meerten, Oude Delft 199, 2611 HD Delft - T: (015) 2602358, Fax: 2138744. Head: Dr. D.H.A.C. Lokin
Decorative Arts Museum / Historic Site - 1909
Glazed eathenware (majolica), silver from Delft, two 17th-century windows with metalwork, furniture, paintings (17th c) 24883

Museum Nusantara, Museum voor het Indonesisch Cultuurgebied, Sint-Agathaplein 4, 2611 HR Delft - T: (015) 2602358, Fax: 2138744, E-mail: gemeentemusea@delft.nl. Head: Dr. D.H.A.C. Lokin
Ethnology Museum - 1864
Ethnology of Indonesia, arts and handicrafts of the various islands, Indonesian textiles, Wajang puppets and gamelan orchestra, house and ship models, objects related to the colonial hist, the V.O.C. - library 24884

Museum Paul Tétar Van Elven, Koornmarkt 67, 2611 EC Delft - T: (015) 2124206, E-mail: lidythijsee@hotmail.com. Head: L. Thijsse
Fine Arts Museum / Decorative Arts Museum - 1927
Furnished house of painter Paul Tétar van Elven (1823-1896), paintings (19th c), furniture, porcelain, Delft pottery 24885

NMI-Museum IJkwezen, Ezelsveldlaan 61, 2611 RV Delft - T: (015) 2138311, Fax: 2612971. Head: J.G. Tuinder
Special Museum - 1963
Weights, measures, linear measures, gasmeters - library 24886

Stedelijk Museum Het Prinsenhof, Sint-Agathapl 1, 2611 HR Delft - T: (015) 2602358, Fax: 2138744. Head: Dr. D.H.A.C. Lokin
Historical Museum / Decorative Arts Museum / Fine Arts Museum / Historic Site / Local Museum - 1948
Paintings of local artists (Cornelius Van Vliet, Gillis de Berch, Willem Van Aelst, Daniel Vosmaer, Jan Tengnagel), portraits (16th-18th c), tapestries, Delft pottery and silver, pictures and weapons relating to Prince William's war against Spain, W.J. Rust coll of earthenware, European porcelain, religious art - library 24887

Studieverzameling, Technische Universiteit Delft, Faculteit Elektrotechniek, Mekelweg 4, 2628 CD Delft - T: (015) 2785757, E-mail: conservator@historia.et.tudelft.nl, Internet: http://historia.et.tudelft.nl
Science&Tech Museum / University Museum
Gyroscopic compasses, vacuum tubes, machines, parts and materials relating to electrotechnology and electronics, radio, radar, telecommunication, valve sets, surveying, measuring equipment and instruments, telephone equipment 24888

Techniek Museum Delft, Ezelsveldlaan 61, 2611 RV Delft - T: (015) 2138311, Fax: 2134976, E-mail: museum@cmg.tudelft.nl, Internet: http://www.museum.tudelft.nl. Head: Dr. H.G. Heijmans
Science&Tech Museum - 1975
Combustion engines, steam engines, machine tools, holography, computer hist, optical illusions, measuring and gauging instruments (by the Netherlands Bureau of Standards) 24889

Wijnmuseum De Keyser onder 't Boterhuys, Markt 17a, 2611 GP Delft. Head: Daan Van Geenen
Special Museum
Winemuseum 24890

Delfzijl

Museum Delfzijl, Zeebadweg 7, 9933 AV Delfzijl - T: (0596) 612318
Local Museum
aquarium 24891

Den Burg

Oudheidkamer, Kogerstr 1, 1791 EN Den Burg - T: (0222) 314956, Fax: 310456. Head: J. Kuiper
Local Museum - 1955
History and folklore of Textel, pictures, porcelain, tiles, underwater archeology, maritime history 24892

Den Haag

Beelden aan Zee, Harteveltstr 1, 2586 EL Den Haag - T: (070) 3585857, Fax: 3584050, E-mail: info@beeldenaanzee.nl, Internet: http://www.beeldenaanzee.nl
Fine Arts Museum 24893

Collectie D.H.G. Bolten, Statenlaan 4, 2582 GL Den Haag - T: (070) 3553186
Decorative Arts Museum 24894

Collectie H.H.F. Salomon (closed) 24895

Gemeentemuseum Den Haag, Stadhouderslaan 41, 2517 HV Den Haag, mail addr: Postbus 72, 2501 CB Den Haag - T: (070) 3381111, Fax: 3557360, E-mail: post@gm.denhaag.nl, Internet: http://www.gemeentemuseum.nl. Head: W. Van Krimpen
Fine Arts Museum / Decorative Arts Museum / Music Museum - 1862/1935
Modern art (19th-20th c, including Mondrian drawings and paintings), applied art, musical instruments, prints, library and archives of composers, fashion - Closed to the public from 01/97 to 10/98 due to restoration - art hist and music library, education department 24896

Haags Historisch Museum, Korte Vijverberg 7, 2513 AB Den Haag - T: (070) 3646940, Fax: 3646942, E-mail: info@haagshistorischmuseum.nl, Internet: http://www.haagshistorischmuseum.nl. Head: Drs. M.P. Van Maarseveen
Historical Museum - 1988
Topographical paintings, prints, drawings, models, silverware, doll's houses 24897

Haags Openbaar Vervoer Museum, Parallelweg 224, 2526 NL Den Haag - T: (070) 4451559, Fax: 4450472
Science&Tech Museum 24898

Iconografisch Bureau, Prins Willem-Alexanderhof 26, 2595 BE Den Haag - T: (070) 3836908. Head: Dr. K. Schaffers Bodenhausen
Library with Exhibitions 24899

Indisch Herinneringscentrum, Waldeck Pyrmontkade 906, 2518 JV Den Haag - T: (070) 3637443
Historical Museum 24900

Kikkermuseum (Frog Museum), Frederik Hendriklaan 38, 2582 BD Den Haag - T: (070) 3554385
Special Museum 24901

Het Koetshuis, Hooikade 23, 2514 BJ Den Haag - T: (070) 3183783
Historical Museum 24902

Koninklijk Kabinet van Schilderijen, Mauritshuis (Royal Picture Gallery), Korte Vijverberg 8, 2513 AB Den Haag - T: (070) 3469244, 3023456, Fax: 3653819, E-mail: communicatie@mauritshuis.nl, Internet: http://www.mauritshuis.nl. Head: F.J. Duparc
Fine Arts Museum - 1820
Flemish painting (15th-17th c), Dutch painting (16th-18th c), portrait miniatures (16th-18th c, esp from England 24903

Letterkundig Museum en Kinderboekenmuseum, Koninklijke Bibliotheek, Prins Willem-Alexanderhof 5, 2595 BE Den Haag - T: (070) 3140911, Fax: 3140450, E-mail: info@kb.nl, Internet: http://www.letmus.nl. Head: Dr. W. Van Drimmelen
Library with Exhibitions 24904

Loosduins Museum De Korenschuur, Margaretha Van Hennebergweg 2a, 2552 BA Den Haag - T: (070) 3973342, Fax: 3973342, E-mail: loosduinen@planet.nl, Internet: http://www.loos.duinsmuseum.nl. Head: C.M. de Beus
Local Museum
Local history 24905

Louis Couperus Museum, Javastr 17, 2582 AB Den Haag - T: (070) 3640653
Special Museum 24906

Museon, Stadhouderslaan 41, 2517 HV Den Haag - T: (070) 3381338, Fax: 3381339, E-mail: info@museon.nl, Internet: http://www.museon.nl. Head: B. Molsbergen, B. Crezee
Natural History Museum / Science&Tech Museum / Historical Museum - 1904
Educational museum with a series of exhibits on five main areas: geology, natural history, history, science and technology 24907

Museum Bredius, Lange Vijverberg 14, 2513 AC Den Haag - T: (070) 3620729, Fax: 3639978, E-mail: info@museumbredius.nl, Internet: http://www.museumbredius.nl
Fine Arts Museum - 1923
Dutch art (17th c), incl paintings and drawings by Rembrandt, Salomon van Ruisdael, Jan Steen, applied arts 24908

Museum de Gevangenpoort, Buitenhof 33, 2513 AH Den Haag - T: (070) 3460861, Fax: 3614262, E-mail: info@gevangenpoort.nl, Internet: http://www.gevangenpoort.nl. Head: Dr. M.P. Van Maarseveen
Special Museum - 1882
Medieval prison with torture instruments, documentation on former judicial practices, memorabilia on some former prisoners especially the brothers Cornelis and Jan de Witt (1625-1672) 24909

Museum Het Paleis, Lange Voorhout 74, 2514 EH Den Haag - T: (070) 3624061
Decorative Arts Museum 24910

Museum Meermanno-Westreenianum, Prinsessegracht 30, 2514 AP Den Haag - T: (070) 3462700, Fax: 3630350, E-mail: info@meermanno.nl, Internet: http://www.meermanno.nl. Head: M.C. Van der Sman
Special Museum - 1849
Books, manuscripts, incunabula, modern typography, antiquities from Egypt, Greece and Rome 24911

Museum Mesdag, Van Gogh Museum Amsterdam, Laan van Meerdervoort 7f, 2517 AB Den Haag, mail addr: Postbus 75366, 1070 AJ Amsterdam - T: (070) 3621434, Fax: 3614026, E-mail: mumesdag@xs4all.nl. Head: J. Leighton
Fine Arts Museum - 1903
Paintings of Barbizon school and The Hague school (19th c), Italian, Hungarian paintings, paintings from the Netherlands, Rozenburg and Chinese ceramics, Japanese bronzes 24912

Museum Scheveningen, Neptunusstr 92, 2586 GT Den Haag - T: (070) 3500830, Fax: 3503080. Head: G.J.M.M. Groenewoud
Historical Museum - 1952
History of fishing and related trades, models of ships, instruments, costumes, paintings, ornaments, jewels, bathing culture - Centre of family history 24913

Museum van het Ambacht, Boekhorststr 121, 2512 CC Den Haag - T: (070) 3637753. Head: Robert C.G.A. Stahlecker
Science&Tech Museum
History of handicraft 24914

Museum voor Communicatie (Museum of Communication), Zeestr 82, 2518 AD Den Haag - T: (070) 3307500, Fax: 3608926, E-mail: info@muscom.nl, Internet: http://www.muscom.nl. Head: G. Beauchez
Special Museum - 1929
Stamps from all over the world, sketches, models and machines relating to technical post office equipment, transportation and telecommunication - library 24915

Museumschip Mercuur, Dr. Lelykade 21, 2583 CL Den Haag
Military Museum / Science&Tech Museum
War ship, militaria 24916

Nationaal Schaakmuseum, Van Speijkstr 1, 2518 EV Den Haag - T: (070) 3643023
Special Museum 24917

Nationaal Zeebiologisch Museum Scheveningen, Strandweg 13, 2586 JK Den Haag - T: (070) 502528, Fax: 3549980. Head: P. Sloof Vermeij
Natural History Museum - 1979
Shells, crabs, crustaceans, coral reef, sea turtles, ethnographics 24918

Nederlands Kansspelmuseum, Paleisstr 5, 2514 JA Den Haag - T: (070) 3021500, Fax: 3021676
Special Museum 24919

Odigia Ikonen-Museum, Molenstr 6, 2513 BK Den Haag - T: (070) 3924000, Fax: 3465892
Fine Arts Museum 24920

Panorama Mesdag, Zeestr 65, 2518 AA Den Haag - T: (070) 3106665, 3644544, Fax: 3450431, E-mail: info@panorama-mesdag.com, Internet: http://www.panorama-mesdag.com. Head: Dr. M.A. de Jong
Fine Arts Museum - 1881
Panorama of Scheveningen (1880) painted by Hendrik W. Mesdag (1831-1915), his wife, Th. de Bock, Breitner and Blommers. Paintings, watercolours and studies by Mesdag and his wife 24921

Politiemuseum, Burg de Monchijplein 19, 2585 BD Den Haag - T: (070) 3104911
Special Museum 24922

Popmuseum, Koninginnegracht 51b, 2514 AE Den Haag - T: (070) 3603337
Music Museum
Museum of Popmusic 24923

Rijksarchief, Prins Willem-Alexanderhof 20, 2509 LM Den Haag - T: (070) 3315550, 3315400, Fax: 3315499. Head: Dr. J.E.A. Boomgaard
Historical Museum 24924

Rijksbureau voor Kunsthistorische Documentatie (Netherlands Institute for Art History), Prins Willem-Alexanderhof 5, 2509 LK Den Haag - T: (070) 3339777, Fax: 3339789, E-mail: secretariaat@rkd.nl, Internet: http://www.rkd.nl. Head: Dr. R.E.O. Ekkart
Fine Arts Museum - 1932
library 24925

Rijksmuseum Hendrik Willem Mesdag, Laan van Meerdervoort 7f, 2517 AB Den Haag - T: (070) 3635450. Head: R. de Leeuw
Fine Arts Museum 24926

Schilderijenzaal Prins Willem V, Buitenhof 35, 2513 AH Den Haag - T: (070) 3624444, Fax: 3653819, E-mail: communicatie@mauritshuis.nl, Internet: http://www.mauritshuis.nl. Head: F.J. Duparc
Fine Arts Museum
Paintings including works by Jan Brueghel the younger, Potter, N. Berchem, Jan Steen 24927

Stroom - Haags Centrum voor Visueel Kunst, Spui 193-198, 2511 BN Den Haag - T: (070) 3658985, Fax: 3617962, E-mail: info@stroom.nl, Internet: http://www.strom.nl. Head: Lily Van Ginneken
Fine Arts Museum 24928

Volksbuurtmuseum, Hobbemastr 120, 2526 JS Den Haag - T: (070) 3898186, Internet: http://www.volksbuurtmuseum.nl
Folklore Museum 24929

Vredespaleis, Carnegiepl 2, 2517 KJ Den Haag - T: (070) 3024242, Fax: 3024132, E-mail: carnegie@wxs.nl. Head: W.A. Hamel
Historical Museum 24930

Yi Jun Peace Museum, Wagenstr 124a, 2512 BA Den Haag - T: (070) 3562510
Historical Museum 24931

Den Ham

Middendorpshuis, Meersendijk 4, 7683 PC Den Ham - T: (0546) 671778, E-mail: middendorpshuis@hotmail.com. Head: G. Hengstman
Historical Museum - 1972
Coll with historical background 24932

Den Helder

Käthe Kruse-Poppenmuseum, Binnenhaven 25-26, 1781 BK Den Helder - T: (0223) 616704, Fax: 684201, E-mail: kathekrusemuseum@planet.nl. Head: Tiny Riemersma
Special Museum 24933

Marinemuseum, Hoofdgracht 3, 1781 AA Den Helder - T: (0223) 657534, Fax: 657282, E-mail: info@marinemuseum.nl, Internet: http://www.marinemuseum.nl. Head: H. de Bles
Military Museum - 1962
Naval coll, ship models, naval uniforms, weapons, portraits, pictures, orders of knighthood and other decorations, flags, navigational instruments, maps and 3 museumships, the submarine 'Tonijn'(1961) and the minesweeper 'Abraham Crijnssen'(1936), ironclad ramship 'Schorpioen' (1868) 24934

Nationaal Reddingmuseum Dorus Rijkers, Bernhardpl 10, 1781 HH Den Helder, mail addr: Postbus 346, 1780 AH Den Helder - T: (0223) 618320, Fax: 610792, E-mail: info@reddingmuseum.nl, Internet: http://www.reddingmuseum.nl. Head: M.C. Kedde
Science&Tech Museum - 1981
Lifeboats, life saving appliances, models, paintings, photographs, navigation instruments, means of communication and buoys, hist of Dutch lifeboat service - library 24935

Den Oever

Wieringer Museumboerderij, Hofstr 36, 1779 CD Den Oever - T: (0227) 511351, Fax: 511351. Head: M. Teeuwisse
Agriculture Museum - 1965
Old farm in West-Friesian style with inventory, equipment, old tiles, painted panels, modern art - theater and cinema 24936

Denekamp

Huize Keizer, Kerkplein 2, 7591 DD Denekamp - T: (0541) 351205
Local Museum
Local history, interior 24937

Museum Natura Docet, Oldenzaalsestr 39, 7591 GL Denekamp - T: (0541) 351325, Fax: 353592, E-mail: info@naturadocet.nl, Internet: http://www.naturadocet.nl. Head: A.B. Wittgen
Natural History Museum - 1911
Fossils, migrant birds and mammals from the eastern Netherlands, shells, insects, erratic boulders, butterflies - library 24938

Singraven, Molendijk 37, 7591 PT Denekamp - T: (0541) 351906
Fine Arts Museum / Decorative Arts Museum - 1968
Paintings (17th c), French and English pictures, 17th to 18th century furniture, gobelins, Delft pottery 24939

Deurne

Gemeentemuseum De Wieger, Oude Liesselseweg 29, 5751 WN Deurne - T: (0493) 322930, Fax: 323031. Head: R. Smolders
Fine Arts Museum - 1965
Former residence of artist Hendrik Wiegersma (1891-1969), paintings, bronzes, silver engravings by Wiegersma, sculptures and paintings of his contemporaries 24940

Deventer

Automuseum Deventer, Sluisstr 6, 7411 EG Deventer - T: (0570) 671179, Fax: 670027, E-mail: info@automuseumdeventer.nl, Internet: http://www.automuseumdeventer.nl. Head: J.A. Bruijn
Science&Tech Museum 24941

Historisch Museum Deventer (temporary adress until autumn 2004), Grote Kerkhof 1, 7411 KT Deventer - T: (0570) 693783, 693780, Fax: 693788, E-mail: info@deventermusea.nl, Internet: http://www.deventer.nl/frm/frm.stadencultuur-home.html. Head: N. Herweijer
Historical Museum - 1913
Prehistoric ceramics, numismatics, folklore, design, graphics, paintings, tools, construction fragments, history of Deventer, topography, bicycles, paintings by Gerard Terborch and Hendrik Terbrugghen 24942

Museum De Waag → Historisch Museum Deventer

Speelgoed- en Blikmuseum (Toy and Tinplate Museum), Brink 47, 7411 BV Deventer - T: (0570) 693783, 693786, Fax: 693788, E-mail: info@deventermusea.nl, Internet: http://www.deventer.nl/frm/frm.stadencultuur-home.html. Head: N. Herweijer
Special Museum - 1982
Toys, children's books, furniture in miniature, Tins, mechanical toys, trains 24943

Diepenheim

Plumershuuske, Grotestr 49, 7478 AB Diepenheim - T: (0547) 351622, Fax: 351365
Science&Tech Museum
Craftsmen's tools and equipment 24944

Diever

Museum Radio-Wereld, Achterstr 9, 7981 AS Diever - T: (0521) 592386
Science&Tech Museum 24945

Schultehuis, Brink 7, 7981 BZ Diever - T: (0521) 591290. Head: Dr. G. Overdiep
Decorative Arts Museum - 1935
Furniture and porcelain dating back to 1600 24946

Doesburg

Museum De Roode Tooren, Museum voor Stad en Ambt Doesburg, Roggestr 9-11, 6981 BJ Doesburg, mail addr: Postbus 1, 6980 AA Doesburg. Head: C.M. Rabeling
Archaeological Museum
Archeological finds, medieval relics 24947

Doetinchem

Museum 't Gevang, Nieuwstad 74-76, 7001 AE Doetinchem - T: (0341) 335557. Head: A.X. Kisman
Historical Museum
Jail (17th c), cooper's workshop 24948

Museum van Geologie Migena, Kruisbergseweg 116, 7009 BS Doetinchem - T: (0341) 333818
Natural History Museum
Minerals, fossils, finds 24949

Stadsmuseum Doetinchem, Grutstr 27, 7001 BW Doetinchem - T: (0314) 335557, Fax: 335557. Head: A.K. Kisman
Local Museum
Archeological findings, school room (1930) 24950

Dokkum

Natuurmuseum Dokkum, Kleine Oosterstr 12, 9101 KK Dokkum - T: (0519) 297318, Fax: 297318, E-mail: natuurmuseum.dokkum@freeler.nl. Head: J. de Vries
Natural History Museum - 1953
Birds, mammals, dioramas - library 24951

OerKa Irene Verbeek Museum, Terpkenlije te Raand, 9101 AK Dokkum, mail addr: Postbus 85, 9950 AB Winsum - T: (0516) 512187, Fax: 522167, E-mail: ireneverbeek@hetnet.nl. Head: Dr. S.H.M. Tromp
Fine Arts Museum
Sculpture, printed art, graphics, paintings 24952

Streekmuseum Het Admiraliteitshuis, Diepswal 27, 9101 LA Dokkum - T: (0519) 293134. Head: G.I.W. Dragt
Local Museum - 1937
Objects about Dokkum and the environs, silver, ceramics, toys, costumes, topography - library 24953

Dongen

Dongha Museum, Kerkstr 33, 5101 BB Dongen - T: (0162) 387194, Fax: 387194, E-mail: info@donghamuseum.nl, Internet: http://www.donghamuseum.nl. Head: P. den Boer
Historical Museum / Science&Tech Museum 24954

Doorn

Kasteel Huis Doorn, Langbroekerweg 10, 3941 MT Doorn - T: (0343) 421020, Fax: 420573, E-mail: kasteel.huis.doorn@wxs.nl, Internet: http://www.huisdoorn.nl. Head: Dr. Th.L.J. Verroen
Decorative Arts Museum - 1950
Furniture, paintings, porcelain, gold and silver possessed by the German Emperor Wilhelm II (1859-1941), snuffboxes of Frederic the Great, King of Prussia (1712-1786) 24955

Maarten Maartenshuis, Amersfoortseweg 98, 3941 EP Doorn - T: (0343) 473322, Fax: 473464, E-mail: info@sbi.nl. Head: Dr. M.E.M. Doorewaard
Special Museum 24956

Oudheidkamer Doorn, Raadhuispl 2, 3941 BW Doorn - T: (0343) 473100
Local Museum
Castle 24957

Doornenburg

Kasteel De Doornenburg, 6686 Doornenburg - T: (0481) 421456. Head: J. Derksen
Decorative Arts Museum
Castle with furniture (mainly early 16th c), armaments, engravings, maps 24958

Doorwerth

Museum voor Natuur- en Wildbeheer, Nederlands Jachtmuseum, Kasteel Doorwerth, Fonteinallee 2, 6865 ND Doorwerth, mail addr: Postbus 11, 6865 ZG Doorwerth - T: (026) 3390698, Fax: 3390712, E-mail: natmusdwxs4all.nl, Internet: http://www.natuurmuseumdoorwerth.nl. Head: J.A. Zoer
Natural History Museum - 1968
Natural history, hunting, shooting and trapping, exhibitions on hunting in the Dutch Low Countries in the past 24959

Dordrecht

Dordrechts Museum, Museumstr 40, 3311 XP Dordrecht, mail addr: Postbus 1170, 330 BD Dordrecht - T: (078) 6482148, Fax: 6141766, E-mail: DordrechtsMuseum@kun.dordrecht.nl, Internet: http://www.museum.dordt.nl
Fine Arts Museum - 1842
Dutch pupils of Rembrandt (17th c), Ary Scheffer Coll ('Portrait of Chopin'), Amsterdam and Hague School, Dutch impressionists, Jan van Goyen 'View of Dordrecht'. coll of Dutch Modern Art - library, film room, restoration-workshop 24960

Het Fluytenlusthof, Violenstr 34, 3314 ZX Dordrecht - T: (078) 6311993
Local Museum 24961

Lips Slotenmuseum, Merwedestr 48, 3313 CS Dordrecht, mail addr: Postbus 59, 3300 AB Dordrecht - T: (078) 6394041, Fax: 6394595. Head: S. Mannesse
Science&Tech Museum - 1930
Locks, safes, keys, treasuries 24962

Museum 1940-1945, Nieuwe Haven 26, 3300 Dordrecht - T: (078) 6130172
Historical Museum
Museum of the German Occupation 1940-45 24963

Museum Newton, Blekersdijk 62, 3311 LE Dordrecht - T: (078) 6144542
Natural History Museum 24964

Museum Simon van Gijn, Nieuwe Haven 29, 3311 AP Dordrecht, mail addr: Postbus 706, 3300 AS Dordrecht - T: (078) 6133793, Fax: 6317913. Head: P.J. Reinders
Decorative Arts Museum - 1925
Local silver, ship models, reproductions, costumes, toys, furniture, glass, porcelain, coins, pewter, stamps, building fragments, pottery, furniture, rugs (18th c) 24965

Museum voor Poppenspelcollecties, Steegoversloot 37, 3311 PM Dordrecht - T: (078) 147570
Special Museum
Puppets, marionettes 24966

Naaimachine Museum, Singel 66, 3311 SJ Dordrecht - T: (078) 6142678
Science&Tech Museum
Sewing-Machine Museum 24967

Nationaal Landschapskundig Museum, Reeweg 145, 3312 CN Dordrecht - T: (078) 6147476
Natural History Museum 24968

Drachten

Minimuseum De Trapper, Kuinder 29, 9204 AB Drachten - T: (0512) 517111
Science&Tech Museum
Bicycles 24969

Museum Smallingerland, Museumpl 2, 9203 DD Drachten - T: (0512) 515647, Fax: 541445. Head: Jaap C.N. Bruintjes
Fine Arts Museum - 1936
Prehistory, traditional and modern art, dadaism (Theo van Doesburg, Kurt Schwitters) - library 24970

Dreischor

Streek- en Landbouwmuseum Schouwen-Duiveland, Molenweg 3, 4315 CE Dreischor - T: (0111) 402303, Fax: 402303
Agriculture Museum / Folklore Museum 24971

Driebergen-Rijsenburg

Museum 't Schilderhuis, Van Rijckevorselstr 2, 3972 ER Driebergen-Rijsenburg - T: (0343) 517588, Fax: 532074, E-mail: schilderhuis@hetnet.nl, Internet: http://www.schilderhuis.nl. Head: W.J.M. Schaatsenberg
Military Museum - 1969
library, archives 24972

Nederlands Speelgoedmuseum, Prins Hendriklaan 1, 3972 EV Driebergen-Rijsenburg - T: (0343) 513626
Special Museum
Museum of Toys 24973

Dronten

Jael Stichting, Ellerweg 3, 8251 RJ Dronten - T: (0321) 312329
Local Museum 24974

Drouwen

Expositie Versteend Leven, Alinghoek 7, 9533 PD Drouwen
Ethnology Museum
Archeology, geology, arts and crafts 24975

Telefoonmuseum, Gasselterstr 7, 9533 PC Drouwen
Science&Tech Museum 24976

Dwingeloo

Kinderwagens van toen, Zuidenweg 21, 7991 AL Dwingeloo
Special Museum
Prams 24977

Planetron - Aards Paradijs, Drift 11b, 7991 AA Dwingeloo - T: (0521) 593535, Fax: 349122. Head: G. de Leeuw
Open Air Museum / Local Museum 24978

Pottenbakkerij De Brinksteen, Entingheweg 1, 7991 CB Dwingeloo
Decorative Arts Museum
Pottery, ceramics, graphics 24979

Wiechers Woon Oase, Entingheweg 15, 7991 CC Dwingeloo
Decorative Arts Museum
Paintings, ceramics 24980

Echt

Gemeentemuseum Echt, Nieuwe Markt 55, 6101 CV Echt
Local Museum
Local history 24981

Edam

Edams Museum, Dampl 18, 1135 BK Edam - T: (0299) 372431. Head: G.H. Conijn
Local Museum - 1895
Furnished rooms, kitchen and cellar, local and regional history, Fris pottery, etchings as discovery 24982

Ede

Museum Oud-Ede, Museumplein 7, 6711 NA Ede
Local Museum - 1938
Farm (1700) with inventory, archeology (prehistoric and medieval), craftmen's tools, domestic utensils, costumes, local history 24983

Museum Verbindingsdienst, Elias Beeckmankazerne, Nieuwe Kazernelaan 10, 6711 JC Ede - T: (0318) 619110 ext 2306, E-mail: info@museumverbindingsdienst.nl, Internet: http://www.museumverbindingsdienst.nl. Head: Aden Boer
Military Museum
Military morse printers, telephones, photographs , radio equipment and uniforms 24984

Ee

Vlasbewerkingsmuseum It Braakhok, Foeke Sjoerdsstrijtte 4a, 9131 LB Ee - T: (0519) 51325
Agriculture Museum
Cultivation of flax 24985

Eefde

Militair Historisch Museum De Veteraan, Koffiestr 9, 7211 AB Eefde - T: (0575) 514209
Military Museum
Military history (1935-1945) 24986

Eelde

Klompenmuseum Gebr. Wietzes, Wolfhorn 1a, 9761 BA Eelde - T: (050) 3091181, E-mail: vdhof@worldonline.nl, Internet: http://www.klompenmuseum.nl. Head: J. Tent
Special Museum 24987

Museum voor Figuratieve Kunst, Hoofdweg 76, 9761 EK Eelde
Fine Arts Museum
Sculpture, graphics, paintings 24988

Wietzes Stichting → Klompenmuseum Gebr. Wietzes

Eenrum

Abraham's Mosterdmakerij, Molenstr 5, 9967 SL Eenrum
Special Museum
Crafts, mustard production, natural and local history 24989

Eerbeek

Speelgoedmuseum De Brug, Brummenseweg 16, 6961 LR Eerbeek - T: (0313) 651316, Fax: 650824
Special Museum
Dolls and puppets 24990

Eernewoude

Museum It Kokelhus van Jan en Sjut, It Fliet 14-16, 9264 TD Eernewoude - T: (0511) 59376
Decorative Arts Museum - 1956
18th century house with living room furnished in the original style, biblical figures 24991

Eersel

Oudheidkamer, Kapelweg 2, 5521 AN Eersel. Head: J.H. Lenaers
Archaeological Museum 24992

Streekmuseum De Acht Zaligheden, Kapelweg 2, 5521 JJ Eersel - T: (0497) 515649. Head: J.H. Lenaers
Agriculture Museum - 1980
Old farm with interiors and farm equipment from the beginning of the 20th century, gardens with flowers, herbs, vegetables and trees, field with animal food, old game called beugelspel - library 24993

Eext

Dorpsmuseum De Kluis, Middenstr 3, 9463 PP Eext
Local Museum
Local history, archaeology, crafts 24994

Egmond aan Zee

Museum van Egmond, Zuiderstr 7, 1931 GD Egmond aan Zee. Head: P. Verschuur
Local Museum - 1951
Local hist and hist of fishery, pictures, photos, paintings 24995

Egmond Binnen

Museum Abdij van Egmond, Sint-Adelbertabdij, Abdijlaan 26, 1935 BH Egmond Binnen - T: (072) 5061415. Head: Dr. P.-J. Berghout
Archaeological Museum
Objects found around the abbey (early Middle Ages to the 16th c), earthenware, tiles, coins, textiles 24996

Eibergen

Historisch Museum de Scheper, Hagen 24, 7151 CA Eibergen - T: (0545) 471050, E-mail: vuurrever@hetnet.nl, Internet: http://home.hetnet.nl/descheper. Head: Dr. H. Schepers
Historical Museum
Archeology, geology, Menno ter Braak, Willem Sluyter 24997

Eindhoven

DAF Automobiel Museum, Tongelresestr 27, 5613 DA Eindhoven - T: (040) 2444364, 2144520, Fax: 2144370
Science&Tech Museum 24998

Edelsteenslijperij de Steenarend, Strijpsestr 63-65, 5616 GL Eindhoven
Special Museum
Gems grinding 24999

Kunstenaarscentrum De Fabriek, Baarsstr 38, 5615 RG Eindhoven - T: (040) 2551530
Fine Arts Museum
Architecture, sculpture 25000

Milieu Educatie Centrum (Ecological Education Centre), Genneperweg 145, 5644 RS Eindhoven
Natural History Museum 25001

Museum Kempenland, Steentjeskerk, Sint-Antoniusstr 5-7, 5616 RT Eindhoven - T: (040) 2529093, Fax: 2522344, Internet: http://www.dse.nl/kempenland.tmp. Head: Peter Thoben
Fine Arts Museum / Local Museum - 1920
Local and regional history of culture, paintings, photographs of Brbant and Flemish sculpture 19th and 20th c 25002

Museum of Historical Philips Products, Hurksestr 19, 5652 AH Eindhoven - T: (040) 2723308, Fax: 2723361, E-mail: psalon2@ehv.sc.philips.com
Science&Tech Museum 25003

Het Philips Gloeilampenfabriekje anno 1891, Emmasingel 31, 5611 AZ Eindhoven
Science&Tech Museum / Historical Museum 25004

Prehistorisch Openluchtmuseum, Boutenslaan 161b, 5644 TV Eindhoven - T: (040) 2522281
Archaeological Museum / Open Air Museum 25005

Presentatieruimte de Overslag, Hofstr 89, 5641 TC Eindhoven - T: (040) 2815503, Fax: 2822131, E-mail: overslag@iae.nl, Internet: http://www.iae.nl/user/overslag. Head: M. Vetter
Public Gallery
Installations, inderdisciplinary arts 25006

Studiecentrum Perk, Visserstr 13, 5612 BS Eindhoven
Fine Arts Museum
Arts and crafts 25007

Ton Smits Huis, Jacob Reviuslaan 25, 5644 TP Eindhoven - T: (040) 114786
Fine Arts Museum
Painting by Ton Smits 25008

Van Abbemuseum (closed, re-open December 2002), Bilderdijklaan 10, 5611 NH Eindhoven, mail addr: Postbus 235, 5600 AE Eindhoven - T: (040) 2755275, 2758522, Fax: 2460680, E-mail: communication@vanabbemuseum.nl, Internet: http://www.vanabbemuseum.nl. Head: J. Debbaut
Fine Arts Museum - 1936
Lissitzky Coll, 20th century art, Moholy-Nagy 'Lightmachine', Marc Chagall 'Hommage à Appolinaire', Joseph Beuys 'Environment' - library 25009

Elburg

Cars of Yester Year, J.P. Broekhovenstr 15, 8081 HB Elburg
Science&Tech Museum
Carmuseum 25010

Gemeentemuseum Elburg, Jufferenstr 6-8, 8081 CR Elburg - T: (0525) 681341, E-mail: peter@hpveluwe.nl, Internet: http://www.hpveluwe.nl. Head: P. Van Beek
Local Museum
Paintings on fishery and landscape, navigation instruments, planetarium, silver, coins 25011

Elsloo

Streekmuseum Schippersbeurs, Op den Berg 4-6, 6181 GT Elsloo - T: (046) 4376052, E-mail: info@streekmuseumelsloo.nl, Internet: http://www.streekmuseumelsloo.nl. Head: H. Dobbelstein
Local Museum - 1961
Prehistoric finds, Neolithic, Roman, Gallo-Roman objects, household and farming articles, bandceramics, weaving, basketry, brickmaking, beekeeping, butter and milk production, daily life about 1880 25012

Elst

Museum onder de N.H. Kerk, Sint-Maartenstr 32b, 6661 DA Elst - T: (0481) 371357, 378096. Head: R. Van den Berg
Archaeological Museum
Finds from Gallo-Roman temples, animals' skulls 25013

Emmen

Centrum Beeldende Kunst Emmen, Raadhuispl 1, 7811 AP Emmen - T: (0591) 685820, Fax: 685966, E-mail: cbk@emmen.nl, Internet: http://www.emmen.nl. Head: H. Rynierse
Fine Arts Museum
Paintings, ceramics, sculpture, graphics 25014

Galerie de Lange, Westenesscherstr 56, 7814 TA Emmen - T: (0591) 640147, Fax: 640147
Public Gallery 25015

Museum Radiotron, Marktpl 17, 7815 LW Emmen, mail addr: E. Van Drielstr 28, 7815 LW Emmen - T: (0591) 611783
Science&Tech Museum
Old radiosets, phonographes and cameras 25016

Enkhuizen

Museum van Historische en Moderne Wapens, Zwaanstr, 1601 KM Enkhuizen - T: (0228) 33650, 35508
Military Museum
All kinds of weapons from prehistorical times to the present 25017

Stedelijk Waagmuseum (closed) 25018

Zuiderzeemuseum, Wierdijk 12-22, 1601 LA Enkhuizen, mail addr: Postbus 42, 1600 AA Enkhuizen - T: (0228) 351111, Fax: 351212, E-mail: netpost@zuiderzeemuseum.nl, Internet: http://www.zuiderzeemuseum.nl. Head: K.A. Weeda
Local Museum / Open Air Museum / Science&Tech Museum - 1948
Objects relating to the Zuiderzee area, the coast and the islands, navigation, fishing and related trades, ships and ship models, paintings, fisherman's tools, costumes, open air coll of 130 houses from the Zuiderzee area - library 25019

Ens

Museum Schokland, Middelbuurt 3, 8307 RR Ens - T: (0527) 251396, Fax: 251286, E-mail: museum@beleef-schokland.nl, Internet: http://www.beleef-schokland.nl. Head: H. Bloem
Archaeological Museum / Historical Museum - 1947
Archaeology, geology, finds from the IJsselmeer-polders, hist of the population of the former island 25020

Enschede

Museum Jannink, Haaksbergerstr 147, 7513 EL Enschede - T: (053) 4319093, Fax: 4305492. Head: H.A.C. Bloemen
Historical Museum - 1959
Living and working in Twente 25021

Natuurmuseum Enschede, M.H. Tromplaan 19, 7511 JJ Enschede - T: (053) 4807680, Fax: 4300176, E-mail: info@natuurmuseumenschede.nl, Internet: http://www.natuurmuseumenschede.nl. Head: F. Van Stuivenberg
Natural History Museum - 1921
Zoology, botany, geology of eastern parts of the Netherlands, fossils - astronomical observatory, library, educational center, bee-keeping, aquariums, terrariums 25022

Publiekscentrum voor Beeldende Kunst, Noorderhagen 2a, 7511 EL Enschede - T: (053) 4310041, Fax: 4327653, Internet: http://www.loketenschede.nl. Head: O.D. Wandrooij
Public Gallery 25023

Rijksmuseum Twenthe, Lasondersingel 129-131, 7514 BP Enschede - T: (053) 4358675, Fax: 4359002, E-mail: info@rijksmuseum-twenthe.nl, Internet: http://www.rijksmuseum-twenthe.nl. Head: Dr. D.A.S. Cannegieter
Fine Arts Museum - 1930
Medieval religious manuscripts, sculptures and paintings, gobelins (17th c), portraits and landscapes (16th-19th c), silver toys, glass, gold and silver jewels, Delft pottery (18th c) modern and contemporary art - library 25024

Traditiekamer Vliegbasis Twenthe, Zuidkamp 54, 7522 PT Enschede - T: (053) 350705
Science&Tech Museum
History of aeroplanes 25025

Zandlopermuseum Glanerbrug, Cornelis Houtmanstr 39, 7534 BL Enschede
Science&Tech Museum
Sand-glass 25026

Enter

Oudheidkamer, Dorpsstr 42, 7468 CC Enter - T: (0547) 382938
Local Museum
Local history 25027

Epe

Hagedoorns Plaatse, Ledderweg 11, 8162 SZ Epe, mail addr: Stationsweg 18, 8166 KB Emst - T: (0578) 627162. Head: Elke Tetterode Ravestein
Agriculture Museum - 1978
Old farm (1715) with interior and implements 25028

Veluws Klederdrachtenmuseum, Markt 5, 8161 CL Epe, mail addr: Stationsweg 18, 8166 KB Emst - T: (0578) 627162. Head: Elke Tetterode Ravestein
Folklore Museum - 1983
Clothing 25029

Erica

Industrieel Smalspoor Museum, Griendtsveenstr 150, 7887 TK Erica - T: (0591) 303061, Fax: (0599) 235816, E-mail: fuborail@tref.nl, Internet: http://get.to/smalspoor. Head: C.D. Fuller
Science&Tech Museum
70 diesel narrow gauge loco's, dump cars 25030

Ermelo

Gemeentelijke Oudheidkamer, Raadhuisplein 2, 3851 NT Ermelo, mail addr: Postbus 500, 3850 AM Ermelo - T: (0341) 567321, Fax: 567369. Head: G.P. v. d. Mewlen
Archaeological Museum
Prehistoric finds, mammoth skeleton 25031

Traditiekamer Regiment Stoottroepen, Generaal Spoorkazerne, Leuvenumseweg 88, 3852 AV Ermelo - T: (0341) 423911
Military Museum
History of the Stoottroepen Regiment 25032

Etten Leur

Grafisch Historisch Centrum, Leeuwerik 8, 4872 PH Etten Leur - T: (076) 5034826. Head: J.C.P. Valentin
Science&Tech Museum - 1976
History of printing 25033

Oudheidkundig Museum Jan Uten Houte, Paulushofje Markt 55-61, 4875 CC Etten Leur - T: (076) 5014244. Head: C.J.M. Leijten
Historical Museum - 1964
Reconstructed inn, interior (19th c), chapel (18th c), with altar of a clandestine church, costumes, crafts, weights and measures, agricultural implements 25034

Exloo

Museum Bebinghehoes, Zuiderhoofdstr 6-8, 7875 BX Exloo - T: (0591) 549242, 549828. Head: F. Koster
Agriculture Museum - 1974
Peat-cutting instruments, domestic utensils, arts and crafts 25035

Exmorra

Fries Landbouw Museum, Dorpsstr 72, 8759 LE Exmorra - T: (0515) 575995
Agriculture Museum
Agricultural machineries 25036

Ezinge

Museum Wierdenland, Torenstr 12, 9891 AG Ezinge
Local Museum
Archeology, local history, technology 25037

Franeker

Kaatsmuseum (Ballmuseum), Voorstr 2, 8801 LC Franeker
Special Museum
Sport, medals 25038

Museum 't Coopmanshûs, Voorstr 49-51, 8801 LA Franeker - T: (0517) 932192. Head: Germa Van Heerbeek
Local Museum - 1921
History of the former university (1585-1811) and Atheneum (1815-1843), coll Anna Maria Van Schurmann (1607-1678), wooden artefacts by Von Schlumbach, porcelain and silver, Mechanical works of art, miniatures - library 25039

Frederiksoord

Klokkenmuseum, Maj. Van Swietenlaan 17, 8382 CE Frederiksoord - T: (0521) 381577. Head: G.L. Tasma
Science&Tech Museum - 1973
Clocks and watches, all types of the Frisian clock (1500-1900), tools 25040

Museum De Koloniehof, Koningin Wilhelminalaan 87, 8382 GC Frederiksoord
Local Museum
Local history, natural history, crafts, coins 25041

Gasselternijveen

Scheepvaartmuseum, Hoofdstr 48, 9514 BG Gasselternijveen
Historical Museum
Maritime history 25042

Geertruidenberg

Stedelijke Oudheidkamer De Roos, Markt 46, 4931 BT Geertruidenberg - T: (0162) 517689, E-mail: hans.oomen@zonnet.nl
Local Museum 25043

Geervliet

Oudheidkamer Geervliet, Bernisseweg 13, 3211 AB Geervliet - T: (0181) 661597
Local Museum
Antiquities, utensils especially from the environs of Putten island 25044

Gees

Atelier Na-iem, Dorpsstr 2, 7863 PC Gees
Historical Museum
Crafts 25045

Geldrop

Gemeentelijke Oudheidkamer, Kasteel Mierloseweg 1, Geldrop - T: (040) 2867666
Archaeological Museum - 1964
Archeology, portraits (19th c), photographic material on economic, social and cultural life of Geldrop, tools 25046

Geleen

Schoolmuseum Geleen, Groenstr 44, 6162 ER Geleen - T: (04494) 2441
Special Museum 25047

Gemert

Boerenbondsmuseum, Pandelaar 106, 5421 NJ Gemert - T: (0492) 366444, Fax: 392060, E-mail: info@boerenbondsmuseum.nl, Internet: http://www.boerenbondsmuseum.nl. Head: Riek Hurkmans
Agriculture Museum 25048

Genemuiden

Stedelijke Oudheidkamer, Hoek 27, 8281 AW Genemuiden - T: (038) 382368
Local Museum
Local history, furniture, tools and parts of machinery related to the local industry 25049

Gennep

Museum Het Petershuis, Niersstr 2, 6591 CB Gennep - T: (0485) 514400
Local Museum 25050

Giessenburg

Reghthuys, Dorpsstr 10, 3381 AG Giessenburg - T: (0184) 652872. Head: H. Harrewijn
Local Museum 25051

Giethoorn

Coop'ren Duikhelm, Binnenpad 62, 8355 BV Giethoorn - T: (0521) 362211
Local Museum 25052

Histo-Mobil, Cornelisgracht 42, 8355 CH Giethoorn - T: (0521) 361498, Fax: 362423. Head: Erik Maat
Science&Tech Museum - 1986
Old vehicles, agricultural machinery, old household appliances, horse carriages, bikes, motorbikes, trains, oil cans and farm equipment 25053

Museum De Speelman, Binnenpad 123, 8355 BV Giethoorn - T: (0521) 361776, Fax: 361776. Head: V.M.L. da Costa
Music Museum - 1980
Music instruments, musical boxes (1800-1925), life of street musicians in former times 25054

Oude Aarde, Binnenpad 43, 8355 BR Giethoorn - T: (0521) 361313, Fax: 362105. Head: Leo Van der Zalm
Natural History Museum - 1969
Local history, minerals (crystals, gems), reptiles 25055

Uus't Olde Maat, Binnenpad 52, 8355 BT Giethoorn - T: (0521) 362244
Local Museum 25056

Goedereede

Museum in de Toren, Ireneweg 4, 3252 BN Goedereede, mail addr: Ireneweg 4, 3253 BK Ouddorp - T: (0187) 681594
Local Museum
Local finds, costumes 25057

Goes

Museum voor Zuid- en Noord-Beveland, Singelstr 13, 4461 HZ Goes - T: (0113) 228883. Head: Frank de Klerk
Local Museum - 1850/1865
Archeology, antiquities, costumes, silverwork, coins, instruments of torture, town views, paintings, toys 25058

Stoomtrein Goes-Borsele, Stephensonweg 9, 4462 GM Goes - T: (0113) 270705
Science&Tech Museum 25059

Goirle

Heemerf De Schutsboom, Nieuwe Rielseweg 41-33, 5051 PD Goirle - T: (013) 5348972, E-mail: - devijerheertganghen@aaaw.demon.nl, Internet: http://www.aaaw.demon.nl
Local Museum - 1937
Archeology, coins, cultural, social and economic life of the Catholic Netherlands (1853-1953), local history and industries 25060

Goor

Oudheidkamer Goor, Stationslaan 1, 7471 AP Goor - T: (0547) 260079
Local Museum 25061

Gorredijk

Streekmuseum Opsterland, Hoofdstr 39, 8401 BW Gorredijk
Local Museum - 1961
Geology, archeology, crafts, farm tools, peat cutting, cable car reproduction (1896), textiles 25062

Gouda

Museum De Goudse Glazen, Achter de Kerk 15a, 2801 JX Gouda
Special Museum 25063

Museum De Moriaan, Westhaven 29, 2801 JX Gouda - T: (0182) 588444, Fax: 588671. Head: Dr. N.C. Sluijter Seijffert
Special Museum - 1937
Inventory of a tobacco shop, pipes, earthenware Art Nouveau (Gouda plateel) 25064

Museum Het Catharina Gasthuis, Oosthaven 9, 2801 PB Gouda - T: (0182) 588440, Fax: 588671. Head: Dr. N.C. Sluijter Seijffert
Local Museum / Fine Arts Museum - 1874
French and Dutch painting (19th c), ancient medical instruments, pharmacy, toys, religious art and vestments, silver, coins, 16th and 17th c paintings modern art, decorative arts (late 16th-20th c) 25065

Stadsgalerie Gouda, Achter de Kerk 10, 2801 JX Gouda - T: (0182) 527273, Fax: 520215
Public Gallery 25066

Verzetz Museum Zuid-Holland, Turfmarkt 30, 2801 HA Gouda - T: (0182) 520385, Fax: 583825, E-mail: verzetsmuseum-zh@wxs.nl. Head: Marie-Thérèse Konsten
Historical Museum - 1985
History of resistance of fascism and jew baiting, present forms of fascism 25067

Gramsbergen

Gemeentelijke Oudheidkamer, Esch 1, 7783 CG Gramsbergen - T: (0524) 261241/43
Local Museum - 1948
History of Gramsbergen and the environs, prehistoric finds (found in the field of battle 1927) 25068

Grijpskerke

Imkerijmuseum Poppendamme, Poppendamseweg 3, 4364 SL Grijpskerke
Agriculture Museum
Breeding of bees, apiculture 25069

Zijdemuseum (Silkmuseum), Kerkstr 1, 4364 AJ Grijpskerke - T: (0118) 593305
Special Museum 25070

Groenlo

Grolsch Museum, Goudsmitstr 6, 7141 AX Groenlo - T: (0544) 461247. Head: G.H. Harbers
Local Museum
Urns, pottery and other finds, weapons, weaving loom, fire-fighting, religious painting 25071

Stoomhoutzagerij, Winterswijkseweg 49, 7141 CR Groenlo, mail addr: Markulzenweg 21, 7141 CR Groenlo - T: (0315) 651662
Science&Tech Museum
Bicycle factory 25072

Groesbeek

Bevrijdingsmuseum 1944, Wijlerbaan 4, 6561 KR Groesbeek - T: (024) 3974404, Fax: 3976694. Head: F. Boshouwers
Military Museum - 1987
Hist of the landing of the allied troops in Nijmegen 1944, 'Operation Market Garden', 'Operation Veritable' 25073

Groningen

Centrum Beeldende Kunst (Centre for Visual Arts), Trompsingel 27, 9724 DA Groningen - T: (050) 3680160, Fax: 3680169, Internet: http://www.cbkgroningen.nl
Public Gallery
Paintings, sculpture, ceramics, graphics 25074

Filmhistorisch Museum, Gedempte Zuiderdiep 137-139, 9711 HE Groningen - T: (050) 140659
Special Museum
History of filmcameras and -projectors 25075

Grafisch Museum Groningen, Rabenhauptstr 65, 9725 CC Groningen - T: (050) 5256497, E-mail: info@grafischmuseum.nl, Internet: http://www.grafischmuseum.nl. Head: D.E. Loman
Science&Tech Museum
Graphic Museum 25076

Groninger Museum, Museumeiland 1, 9711 ME Groningen - T: (050) 3666555, Fax: 3120815, E-mail: info@groninger-museum.nl, Internet: http://www.groninger-museum.nl. Head: Kees Van Twist
Fine Arts Museum / Decorative Arts Museum / Archaeological Museum / Museum of Classical Antiquities - 1894
Regional finds, local silver, oriental ceramics, Dutch and Flemish drawings and paintings including Rembrandt, Rubens and Fabritius, contemporary art and design - library 25077

Minimuseum, Ubbo Emmiusstr 34 a, 9711 CC Groningen
Local Museum
Local history, paintings, military history 25078

Museum De Cateraars, Florakade 498, 9713 ZP Groningen - T: (050) 3120714
Special Museum 25079

Museumproject AZG, Hanzepl 1, 9713 GZ Groningen
Historical Museum
Medical history 25080

Natuurmuseum Groningen, Praediniussingel 59, 9711 AG Groningen, mail addr: Postbus 1145, 9701 BC Groningen - T: (050) 3676170, Fax: 3189676, E-mail: groningen@natuurmuseum.org, Internet: http://www.natuurmuseum.org. Head: Kees van der Meiden
Natural History Museum - 1932
Biology, birds, insects, wild mammals, fresh water aquaria, shells from the North Sea basin, geology, Saalian erratic boulders, fossils - library, educational center 25081

Niemeyer Tabaksmuseum, Brugstr 24, 9711 HZ Groningen - T: (050) 3122202, Fax: 3183751, E-mail: jw.vanveen@noordelijkscheep-vaartmuseum.nl
Special Museum - 1954
History of tobacco and its use in Western Europe from 1500 until 1930, pre-Columbian pipes 25082

Noordelijk Scheepvaartmuseum, Brugstr 24-26, 9711 HZ Groningen - T: (050) 3122202, Fax: 3183751, E-mail: info@noordelijkscheep-vaartmuseum.nl, Internet: http://www.noordelijk-scheepvaartmuseum.nl. Head: G.M.W. Acda
Science&Tech Museum - 1932
Maritime history of the Netherlands, ship models, maps, instruments, paintings, ship decoration 25083

Universiteitsmuseum, Zwanestr 33, 9712 CK Groningen, mail addr: Postbus 72, 9700 AB Groningen - T: (050) 3635562, E-mail: museum@ub.rug.nl, Internet: http://www.rug.nl/museum. Head: F.R.H. Smit
University Museum - 1934
Hist of the State University of Groningen, student life, development of the sciences and education, coll of documents, scientific instruments, minerals and fossils - library, documentation center 25084

Volkenkundig Museum Gerardus van der Leeuw, c/o Rijksuniversiteit Groningen, Nieuwe Kijk in 't Jatstr 104, 9712 SL Groningen - T: (050) 3635791, Fax: 3636200, E-mail: volkkmus@theol.rug.nl, Internet: http://home.hetnet.nl/gerardus2001. Head: Dr. V. Arnoldus Schröder
Ethnology Museum / University Museum - 1968
Cultures of the so-called illiterate peoples (especially Indonesia, the Pacific and Africa south of the Sahara), archeology of Egypt 25085

Grouw

Mineralogisch Museum, Leechlaan 22, 9001 ZH Grouw - T: (0566) 623636
Natural History Museum
Mineralogy 25086

Museum de Trije Gritenijen, Stationsweg 1, 9001 ED Grouw - T: (0566) 623911, 621364
Local Museum
Local history, paintings, ceramics, literature, silver 25087

Haaksbergen

Museum Buurt Spoorweg, Stationsstr 3, 7481 JA Haaksbergen - T: (053) 5721516, Fax: 5741196. Head: B. Heerink
Science&Tech Museum
Railroads 25088

Haarlem

Archeologisch Museum Haarlem, Grote Markt 18k, 2011 RD Haarlem - T: (023) 5113000
Local Museum / Archaeological Museum 25089

Corrie ten Boomhuis, Barteljorisstr 19, 2011 RA Haarlem
Military Museum
Weapons, interior 25090

Frans Hals Museum, Groot Heiligland 62, 2011 ES Haarlem, mail addr: Postbus 3365, 2001 DJ Haarlem - T: (023) 5115775, Fax: 5115776, E-mail: franshalsmuseum@haarlem.nl, Internet: http://www.franshalsmuseum.nl. Head: K.J.J. Schampers
Fine Arts Museum / Decorative Arts Museum - 1913
Paintings since the 16th century, group portraits by Frans Hals (1580-1666) and others, Tulip-book by Judith Leyster, old doll's house, coll of Haarlem silver, old furniture, old pharmacy, copper, tin, porcelain, glass, numismatics, pottery, style of living, old bed curtains 25091

De Hallen, Grote Markt 16, 2011 RD Haarlem - T: (023) 5115775, Fax: 5115776, E-mail: franshalsmuseum@haarlem.nl, Internet: http://www.franshalsmuseum.nl. Head: K.J.J. Schampers
Public Gallery
Paintings, prints, ceramics, graphics, sculpture, photography 25092

Historisch Museum Zuid-Kennemerland, Groot Heiligland 47, 2011 EP Haarlem - T: (023) 5422427, E-mail: historischmuseum@zonnet.nl
Historical Museum
History of Haarlem - photo archive 25093

Museum Enschedé, Jan van Krimpenweg 19, 2031 CG Haarlem - T: (023) 5184493, Fax: 5325550, E-mail: museum.enschede@planet.nl, Internet: http://www.joh-enschede.nl. Head: Johan de Zoete
Science&Tech Museum - 1904
History of printing, printing art, historic and modern printing machinery, documents, banknotes, stamps, security printing 25094

NZH Vervoer Bedrijfsmuseum, Leidsevaart 396, 2014 HM Haarlem - T: (023) 5152626
Historical Museum 25095

Schatkamer van de Kathedrale Basiliek Sint-Bavo (Museum of Religious Art), Leidse Vaart 146, 2014 HE Haarlem - T: (023) 5533377. Head: P.M.J. Stuyt
Religious Arts Museum - 1973
Treasure Chamber, gold and silver (15th c to present) 25096

Spaarnestad Fotoarchief, Groot Heiligland 47, 2011 EP Haarlem - T: (023) 5185150
Fine Arts Museum 25097

Teylers Museum, Spaarne 16, 2011 CH Haarlem - T: (023) 5319010, Fax: 5342004, E-mail: teyler@euronet.nl, Internet: http://www.teylersmuseum.nl. Head: Dr. M. Scharloo
Fine Arts Museum / Historical Museum / Science&Tech Museum - 1778
Paintings, drawings, scientific instruments, fossils, minerals, medals, coins - library, study room art coll, educational service 25098

Theo Swagemakers Museum, Stoofsteeg 6, 2011 TE Haarlem - T: (023) 5327761, Fax: (020) 6598693, E-mail: swagemakersmuseum@galeriepietershuis.nl, Internet: http://www.swagemakersmuseum.nl. Head: L.J.M. Moons
Fine Arts Museum
Paintings, watercolours, gouches by T. Swagemakers 25099

Haarzuilens

Kasteel de Haar, Collectie Th. Baron Van Zuylen Van Nijevelt Van de Haar, Kasteellaan 1, 3455 RR Haarzuilens - T: (030) 6773801, Fax: 6775827, E-mail: de_haar@euronet.nl, Internet: http://www.kasteeldehaar.nl. Head: M.L. Van Dedem
Decorative Arts Museum / Historical Museum - 1925
Family portraits, furniture from the Netherlands, England, France and Italy, Persian rugs, Flemish gobelins (14th-15th c), paintings (14th-19th c), chinese and japanese porcelain 25100

Haastrecht

Museum van de Stichting Bisdom van Vliet, Hoogstr 166, 2851 BE Haastrecht - T: (0182) 501354. Head: R.N.S. Verhoeff
Decorative Arts Museum - 1923
Family house (19th c) with complete original furniture 25101

Haelen

Streekmuseum Leudal, Sint Elisabethshof, Roggelseweg 58, 6081 NP Haelen
Local Museum
Local history, archeology, ceramics, crafts, natural history 25102

Halfweg

Stoomgemaal Halfweg (Steam Mill), Haarlemmermeerstr 4, 1165 HJ Halfweg - T: (020) 4974396
Science&Tech Museum 25103

't Harde

Nederlands Artillerie Museum, Eperweg 149, 8084 HE 't Harde - T: (0525) 657310, Fax: 657311
Military Museum
History of the Netherlands artillery 25104

Hardenberg

Huize Nijenstede, Hessenweg 51, 7771 RD Hardenberg - T: (0523) 261734. Head: G.J. Mullers Bast
Folklore Museum
Folk art 25105

Museum Hardenberg, Voorstr 34, 7772 AD Hardenberg - T: (0523) 265624, E-mail: info@historiekamer.nl, Internet: http://www.historiekamer.nl
Local Museum
Prehistoric finds, fossils, coins, farm implements, old Saxon kitchen, smithy - archives 25106

Harderwijk

Veluws Museum van Oudheden, Donkerstr 4, 3841 CC Harderwijk, mail addr: Postbus 61, 3841 CC Harderwijk - T: (0341) 414468, Fax: 415128. Head: W. Lodewijk
Local Museum - 1952
Coins of Gelderland made in Harderwijk, academical dissertations of the University of Gelderland in Harderwijk, archeological finds of the North and West Veluwe, seal of Harderwijk with so-called kogge-ship (14th c) 25107

Harkema

Themapark Openluchtmuseum De Spitkeet, Betonwei 32, 9281 KT Harkema
Local Museum / Open Air Museum
Local history, flora and fauna, agriculture, textiles 25108

Harlingen

Gemeentemuseum Het Hannemahuis, Voorstr 56, 8861 BM Harlingen - T: (0517) 413658. Head: H.P. ter Avest
Local Museum - 1957
Harlinger history, silver, paintings (17th-19th c), tiles, ship models, steamers in Harlingen town history 25109

Harlinger Aardewerk Museum, Zoutsloot 43, 8861 SV Harlingen - T: (0517) 413341, Fax: 413341
Decorative Arts Museum
Frisian ceramics (Makkum, Harlingen, Bolsward, Frisian delftware), carven pottery (Lemmer, Workum, Sneek) 25110

Hasselt

Oude Stadhuis, Markt 1, 8061 GG Hasselt - T: (038) 4771600, Fax: 4773712
Local Museum
Town hall (15th-16th c), history of Hasselt, paintings (17th c), weapons 25111

Hattem

Anton Pieck Museum, Achterstr 46-48, 8051 ES Hattem - T: (038) 4442192, Fax: 4442192, E-mail: - antonpieckmuseum@hetnet.nl. Head: A. Nit
Fine Arts Museum
General survey of work of Anton Pieck, graphics, drawings, paintings 25112

Nederlands Bakkerijmuseum Het Warme Land, Kerkhofstr 13, 8051 GG Hattem - T: (038) 4441715, Fax: 4446784. Head: J.E. Barendsen
Special Museum - 1977
Municipal bakery (15th-16th c) with interior and shop, pottery, utensils and models, milling hist from prehistory, middle ages until present times - library 25113

Streekmuseum Hattem, Achterstr 48, 8051 GC Hattem - T: (038) 4442897
Local Museum - 1949
Local history, agricultural tools, costumes, archeology (prehistoric and medieval) 25114

Havelte

Ontmoetingscentrum de Veldkei, Expositie, Veldkamp 77, 7971 BX Havelte
Decorative Arts Museum
Glass art 25115

Hazerswoude Dorp

Gemeentemuseum, Dorpsstr 66, 2391 HG Hazerswoude Dorp
Local Museum
Local history 25116

's-Heer Abtskerke

Stichting Zeeland 1939-1945, Sinoutskerke 2, 4444 RT 's-Heer Abtskerke
Historical Museum
World war II 25117

Heerde

Oudheidkamer Heerde, Dorpsstr 55, 8181 HN Heerde - T: (0578) 694404
Local Museum
Stones, paintings by J.B. Kleintjes 25118

's-Heerenberg

Gouden Handen, Emmerikseweg 13, 7041 AV 's-Heerenberg - T: (0314) 662343, Fax: 62343. Head: J.H.A. Lohmann
Fine Arts Museum - 1975
Native art, icons, sculptured candles, evolution of mankind, including model of cave men in authentic settings 25119

Stichting Huis Bergh, Hof van Berg 8, 7041 AC 's-Heerenberg, mail addr: Postbus 155, 7040 AD 's-Heerenberg - T: (0314) 661281, Fax: 663830). Head: J.B. Meyer
Decorative Arts Museum / Fine Arts Museum - 1946
Castle (15th-17th c) with furniture, sculptures, carvings, book bindings, manuscripts, weapons, coins, regional topography and cartography, geology, paintings of Dutch, German and Italian masters (14th-18th c) 25120

Heerenveen

Ferdinand Domela Nieuwenhuis Museum, Minckelersstr 11, 8442 CE Heerenveen - T: (0513) 623408, Fax: 645782, E-mail: info@fdnmuseum.nl, Internet: http://www.fdnmuseum.nl. Head: Dr. M. Albers
Special Museum / Historical Museum - 1925
Life and work of F.D. Niewenhuis for socialism, labour movement 25121

Historisch Museum Heerenveen → Museum Willem van Haren

Museum Willem van Haren, Minckelersstr 11, 8442 CE Heerenveen - T: (0513) 623408, Fax: 627453, E-mail: museum@willemvanharen.nl, Internet: http://www.willemvanharen.nl. Head: Dr. M. Albers
Local Museum - 1982
19th c pharmacy, turf digging and cutting equipment, silver from Heerenveen, town model model from 1830 25122

Heerewaarden

Milieucentrum De Grote Rivieren, Langestr 38, 6624 AB Heerewaarden - T: (0487) 572831
Local Museum
Local history 25123

Heerhugowaard

Poldermuseum Den Huijgen Dijck, Huijgendijk 17, 1703 RG Heerhugowaard, mail addr: Postbus 220, 1700 AE Heerhugowaard - T: (072) 5741159
Science&Tech Museum - 1979
Old pumps 25124

Heerlen

Museum La Diligence, Zandweg 179, 6419 PK Heerlen - T: (045) 5412629, Fax: 5427514, E-mail: diligence@cuci.nl, Internet: http://www.ladiligence.nl. Head: C. Van Tilburg
Special Museum
Coache, Curiosity 25125

Stadsgalerij Heerlen, Raadhuisplein 19, 6411 HK Heerlen - T: (045) 5604449, Fax: 5717475, E-mail: stadsgalerij@heerlen.nl, Internet: http://www.stadgalerijheerlen.nl. Head: Dr. J.W. Van Oosterzee-Beeling
Fine Arts Museum
Dutch contemporary art: Cobra, post-Cobra, abstract expressionism 25126

Thermenmuseum, Coriovallumstr 9, 6411 CA Heerlen - T: (045) 5605100, Fax: 5603915, E-mail: info@thermenmuseum.nl, Internet: http://www.thermenmuseum.nl. Head: Dr. J.W. Jansen
Archaeological Museum - 1977
Roman provincial archeology, excavation of a Roman bath (2nd-4th c) under the roof of a modern building - library 25127

Heeswijk Dinther

Museumboerderij, Meerstr 20, 5473 VW Heeswijk Dinther
Local Museum 25128

Heeze

Collectie H.N.C. Baron Van Tuyll Van Serooskerken Van Heeze en Leende, Kasteel Heeze, 5591 HC Heeze - T: (040) 221754
Fine Arts Museum 25129

Heilig Landstichting

Bijbels Openluchtmuseum, Profetenlaan 2, 6564 BL Heilig Landstichting - T: (024) 3823110, Fax: 3823111. Head: Dr. J. Van Laarhoven
Open Air Museum - 1911
Reconstructions of houses and daily life in the Palestine up to the Roman Period, objects relating to biblical countries and their cultures, cribs 25130

Heiligerlee

Klokkengieterij Museum, Provincialeweg 46, 9677 PD Heiligerlee - T: (0597) 421799
Science&Tech Museum
Old bellfoundry with tools 25131

Museum Slag bij Heiligerlee, Provincialeweg 55, 9677 PB Heiligerlee
Local Museum
Local history, community 25132

Museumboerderij Welgelegen, Dijkstilsterweg 4, 9965 TH Heiligerlee - T: (0595) 571430
Agriculture Museum
Farm with implements 25133

Heinenoord

Streekmuseum Hoeksche Waard, Hofweg 13, 3274 BK Heinenoord - T: (0186) 601535, Fax: 604587, Internet: http://www.streekmuseum.hw.nl. Head: B. Kolbach
Local Museum - 1968
Local history, jewels, costumes, agricultural instruments in their original workshops, topography, crafts tools 25134

Heinkenszand

't Kunstuus, Dorpsstr 43, 4451 BB Heinkenszand - T: (0113) 562996, Internet: http://www.kunstuus.nl
Fine Arts Museum 25135

Heino

Hannema-de Stuers Fundatie, Kasteel Het Nijenhuis, 8131 RD Heino - T: (0572) 391434, Fax: 393515, E-mail: info@museumhsf.nl, Internet: http://www.museumhsf.nl. Head: Dr. A.C.M. Grondman
Fine Arts Museum - 1957
Paintings, designs, sculptures, furniture (17th-20th c), Chinese ceramics - museum library 25136

Hellevoetsluis

Museum Gesigt van 't Dog, Oostzanddijk 24, 3221 AL Hellevoetsluis - T: (0181) 318732
Local Museum
Local history 25137

Nationaal Brandweermuseum, Industriehaven 8, 3221 AD Hellevoetsluis - T: (0181) 314479, Fax: 324639. Head: C. Van Egmond
Science&Tech Museum - 1920
Firefighting material, vehicles and engines since 1550 25138

Rijdend Tram Museum, Struijtse Zeedijk 1, 3224 AN Hellevoetsluis, mail addr: Postbus 5, 3220 AA Hellevoetsluis - T: (0181) 315919
Science&Tech Museum
Coll of narrow-gange tramway material 25139

Helmond

Gemeentemuseum Helmond, Kasteelplein 1, 5701 PP Helmond - T: (0492) 587716, Fax: 587717, E-mail: mushelm@iae.nl. Head: J. Bongaarts
Fine Arts Museum - 1923
Modern art, coll of fine arts "men and work", city hist 25140

ID Galerie, Heistr 86-94, 5701 HR Helmond - T: (0492) 522324, Fax: 554377, E-mail: p.van.duppen@hccnet.nl, Internet: http://www.interieurvanmierio.nl
Public Gallery 25141

Jan Vissermuseum, Museum voor Landbouw, Keizerin Marialaan 5, 5702 NR Helmond - T: (0492) 548504
Agriculture Museum
Agricultural implements 25142

Hengelo

Historisch Museum Hengelo, Beekstr 51, 7551 DP Hengelo - T: (074) 2594216, Fax: 2594217, E-mail: oaldhengel@tref.nl, Internet: http://www.oaldhengel.nl
Historical Museum
Local history 25143

Museum Heim, Bornsestr 7, 7556 BG Hengelo - T: (074) 2430054
Local Museum 25144

's-Hertogenbosch

Gemaal Caners, Krommenhoek 10, 5236 BE 's-Hertogenbosch
Science&Tech Museum
Polder mill, water 25145

Kapucijnenmuseum, Van der Does de Willeboissingel 12, 5211 CB 's-Hertogenbosch - T: (073) 6130155, Fax: 6148839
Religious Arts Museum
History of the Capuchins in Netherlands 25146

Museum Hertogsgemaal, Rosmalensedijk 10, 5236 BD 's-Hertogenbosch
Local Museum
Local history, archaeology, ceramics, coins 25147

Museum Slager, Choorstr 16, 5211 KZ 's-Hertogenbosch - T: (073) 133216, Internet: http://www.museumslager.nl. Head: H. Bergé
Fine Arts Museum - 1968
Works by members of the Slager family (1841-1994), landscape, stillife, townscape, and portraits of the family 25148

Museum voor Hedendaagse Kunst Het Kruithuis (temporary closed, reconstruction), Hekellaan 2, 5211 LX 's-Hertogenbosch - T: (073) 6122188, Fax: 6130337, E-mail: inform@museumhetkruithuis.nl, Internet: http://www.museumhetkruithuis.nl. Head: Yvònne G.J.M. Joris
Fine Arts Museum - 1956
International coll of modern and contemporary ceramics, international coll of jewelleries (since 1945) - (above address temporary, was Citadellaan 7) 25149

Noordbrabants Museum, Verwersstr 41, 5200 BA 's-Hertogenbosch - T: (073) 6877800, Fax: 6877899, E-mail: info@noordbrabantsmuseum.nl. Head: Margriet Van Boven
Fine Arts Museum - 1987
Hist of North Brabant, works by artists living in the area, late medieval sculpture, flower still-life paintings - sculpture garden 25150

Nova Zembla, Lederstr 9 - 11, 5223 AW 's-Hertogenbosch
Fine Arts Museum
Sculpture, paintings 25151

Oeteldonks Gemintemuzejum, Hinthamerstr 27, 5211 ME 's-Hertogenbosch
Local Museum 25152

Orangerie, Sint Josephstr 15a, 5211 NH 's-Hertogenbosch
Fine Arts Museum
Sculpture, paintings 25153

Sint Jansmuseum De Bouwloods, Torenstr 16, 5211 KK 's-Hertogenbosch
Religious Arts Museum
Crafts, architecture, sculpture, religious art 25154

Zwanenbroedershuis, Illustre Lieve Vrouwe Broederschap, Hinthamerstr 94, 5211 MS 's-Hertogenbosch - T: (073) 6137383, Fax: 6122152
Religious Arts Museum - 1318
Religious art, tin, coins 25155

Heumen

Brouwerijmuseum Raaf, Rijksweg 232, 6582 AB Heumen - T: (080) 581177
Science&Tech Museum
Breweries 25156

Hillegom

Den Hartogh Ford Museum, Haarlemmerstr 36, 2181 HC Hillegom - T: (0252) 518118, Fax: 517615, E-mail: denhartogh.fordmuseum@classics.nl, Internet: http://www.classics.nl
Science&Tech Museum 25157

Hilvarenbeek

Museum De Doornboom, Doelenstr 53, 5081 CK Hilvarenbeek - T: (013) 5054093
Science&Tech Museum
Windmill, old tools 25158

Museumbrouwerij De Roos, Vrijthof, Sebastiaanstr 4, 5081 ZG Hilvarenbeek - T: (013) 5055045, E-mail: museumbrouwerij.deroos@wxs.nl
Science&Tech Museum 25159

Nationaal Likeur- en Frisdrankenmuseum Isidorus Jonkers, Varkensmarkt 22, 5081 CP Hilvarenbeek - T: (013) 5053119, E-mail: info@likeur-frismuseum.org, Internet: http://www.likeur-frismuseum.org
Special Museum
Old liqueur-factory with implements relating to distillation 25160

Hilversum

Goois Museum, Kerkbrink 6, 1217 SP Hilversum - T: (035) 6292826
Local Museum - 1969
Regional archeology and geology of Gooi, antiquities of Gooi, topographic atlas of Gooi 25161

Omroepmuseum en Smalfilmmuseum, Oude Amersfoortseweg 121-131, 1212 AA Hilversum - T: (035) 6885888, 6856633
Science&Tech Museum
archive 25162

Hindeloopen

Het Eerste Friese Schaatsmuseum, Kleine Weide 1-3, 8713 KZ Hindeloopen - T: (0514) 521683
Special Museum
First Frisian Museum of Iceskating 25163

Hidde Nijland Museum, Dijkweg 1, 8713 KD Hindeloopen - T: (0514) 521420
Local Museum - 1919
Local interiors (18th c), painted furniture, local costumes, history of the town and navigation 25164

Hippolytushoef

Museum Hippolytushoef, Stroeerweg 39, 1777 NE Hippolytushoef - T: (0227) 511353
Local Museum 25165

Hoenderloo

Jachthuis Sint-Hubertus, Apeldoornseweg 250, 7351 TA Hoenderloo - T: (0318) 595922, Fax: 592248, E-mail: park@hogeveluwe.nl, Internet: http://www.hogeveluwe.nl. Head: P. Schenk
Historic Site
Hunting seat (1914-1920) with original interior and art coll 25166

Hoensbroek

Kasteel Hoensbroek, Klinkertstr 118, 6433 PB Hoensbroek - T: (045) 5227272, Fax: 5211427, E-mail: museum@kasteelhoensbroek.nl, Internet: http://www.kasteelhoensbroek.nl. Head: F.W. Jansen
Decorative Arts Museum
Castle (from the 14th/17th/18th c) decorated with furniture and objects 25167

Hollum

Cultuur-Historisch Museum Sorgdrager, Herenweg 1, 9161 AM Hollum - T: (0519) 554477, Fax: 542136, E-mail: historisch.museum@ameland.nl, Internet: http://www.ameland.nl/toerisme/musea
Local Museum
Captain's house of 1751 with interior, folk art 25168

Reddingsmuseum Abraham Fock, Oranjeweg 18, 9161 CC Hollum - T: (0519) 554243
Historical Museum 25169

Holten

Natuurdiorama Holterberg, Holterbergweg 12, 7451 JL Holten - T: (0548) 361979, Fax: 367638
Natural History Museum - 1938
European mounted birds and mammals, dioramas 25170

Honselersdijk

Westlands Museum voor Streek- en Tuinbouwhistorie, Middel Broekweg 154, 2675 KL Honselersdijk - T: (0174) 621084, Fax: 642414, E-mail: info@westlandsmuseum.nl, Internet: http://www.westlandsmuseum.nl. Head: A.A.G. Immerzeel
Agriculture Museum / Historical Museum - 1908
Archeological finds from late Stone Age till Middle Ages, hist of seven villages from Westland region, hist of gardening in glasshouses, coll of gardening tools, reconstruction of an historical garden with glasshouses 25171

Hoofddorp

Historisch Museum Haarlemmermeer, Kruisweg 1403, 2131 MD Hoofddorp - T: (023) 5620437
Historical Museum 25172

Hoogeveen

Glasmuseum, Brinkstr 5, 7902 AC Hoogeveen - T: (0528) 220999, Fax: 220981, E-mail: info@glasmuseum.nl, Internet: http://www.glasmuseum.nl. Head: C. Van Olst
Decorative Arts Museum 25173

Hooghalen

Herinneringscentrum Kamp Westerbork, Oosthalen 8, 9414 TG Hooghalen
Military Museum
War history, memorabilia 25174

Hoogwoud

Museumboerderij Westfrisia, Koningspade 31, 1718 MP Hoogwoud - T: (0226) 351431
Agriculture Museum / Local Museum
Agricultural implements 25175

Hoorn

Collectie J.E. de Visser, Binnenluiendijk 3, 1621 ME Hoorn - T: (0229) 215783
Special Museum 25176

Museum van de Twintigste Eeuw (Museum of the Twentieth Century), Bierkade 4-4a, 1621 BE Hoorn - T: (0229) 214001
Historical Museum 25177

Museumstoomtram Hoorn-Medemblik, Tramstation Van Dedemstr 8, 1624 NN Hoorn, mail addr: Postbus 137, 1620 AC Hoorn - T: (0229) 214862, Fax: 216653, E-mail: info@museumstoomtram.nl, Internet: http://www.museumstoomtram.nl. Head: J. Nieweg
Science&Tech Museum
Old trams with steam engines 25178

Speelgoedmuseum De Kijkdoos (Toys Museum), Italiaanse Zeedijk 106, 1621 AK Hoorn - T: (0229) 217589. Head: A. Kuiper
Special Museum 25179

Westfries Museum, Rode Steen 1, 1621 CV Hoorn, mail addr: Achterom 2, 1621 KV Hoorn - T: (0229) 280022, Fax: 280029, E-mail: info@wfm.nl, Internet: http://www.wfm.nl. Head: R.J. Spruit
Historical Museum - 1879
Hist of Hoorn, West-Friesland and navigation, archeological finds, paintings (17th-19th c), drawings, maps, coins, furniture, interiors (18th-19th c), tin, glass, pottery, tiles (17-18th c), costumes (18th-19th c), contemporary Westfrisian naive painting, painted map of Batavia (1627) 25180

Horst

Koperslagersmuseum Van der Beele, Gasthuisstr 46, 5961 GB Horst - T: (077) 3985621, Fax: 3985621. Head: P. Van der Beele
Special Museum - 1983
Objects relating to copper, Old coppersmith's tools 25181

Nationaal Asperge- en Champignonmuseum De Locht, Koppertweg 5, 5962 AL Horst - T: (077) 3987320
Natural History Museum 25182

Oudheidkamer Horst, Steenstr 2, 5961 EV Horst - T: (077) 396540
Local Museum
Archeological finds, agricultural implements, local history 25183

Houten

Topografische en Oudheidkundige Verzameling, Het Kant 2, 3995 DZ Houten, mail addr: Postbus 30, 3990 DA Houten - T: (030) 26392611, Fax: 6392899
Historical Museum 25184

Houwerzijl

De Theefabriek, Hoofdstr 15-17, 9973 PD Houwerzijl
Special Museum
Tea production 25185

Huijbergen

Wilhelmietenmuseum, Staartsestr 2, 4635 BB Huijbergen - T: (0164) 642650, Fax: 642470, E-mail: cfh@xs4all.nl. Head: Eduard Quint
Religious Arts Museum
Religious art and history, documents (14th-19th c) 25186

Huizen

Bakkerijmuseum, Schippersstr 5, 1271 VB Huizen - T: (035) 5250223
Special Museum 25187

Huizer Klederdrachtmuseum, Havenstr 81, 1271 AD Huizen - T: (035) 6969080
Folklore Museum
Museum of Huizer Costumes 25188

Hulst

Streekmuseum De Vier Craftsen, Steenstr 28, 4561 AS Hulst
Local Museum
Archeology, costume, agriculture, milling 25189

Ijmuiden

Pieter Vermeulen Museum, Moerbergplantsoen 20, 1972 XG Ijmuiden - T: (0255) 536726. Head: S.J. Herder Brouwer
Local Museum - 1952
Natural history, shells, birds, algae of the coast, food web of the North Sea, fishery, port sketch, ship model - library, garden 25190

Zee- en Havenmuseum de Visserijschool, Havenkade 55, 1973 AK Ijmuiden - T: (0255) 538007
Historical Museum 25191

Ijsbrechtum

Epema-State, Epemawei 6-8, 8633 KS Ijsbrechtum - T: (0515) 412475
Local Museum
Medieval Friese site with interior, porcelain and portraits 25192

Ijsselstein

Stadsmuseum Ijsselstein, Walkade 2, 3401 DS Ijsselstein - T: (030) 6886800
Local Museum
Local history, archeology, industrial development, ceramics, glass art, religious art, coins, paintings, maps, agriculture, milling, textiles, militaria, turtore instruments 25193

Ijzendijke

Streekmuseum West Zeeuws-Vlaanderen, Markt 28, 4515 BB Ijzendijke - T: (0117) 301200
Local Museum 25194

Janum

Kerkmuseum Janum, Kerkstr 4, 9107 GH Janum
Religious Arts Museum
Archeology, religious art 25195

Joure

Museum Joure, Geelgietersstr 1-11, 8501 CA Joure, mail addr: Postbus 75, 8500 AB Joure - T: (0513) 412283, Fax: 419653, E-mail: info@museumjoure.nl, Internet: http://www.museumjoure.cybercomm.nl. Head: H.B. ten Wolde
Local Museum - 1976
Tobacco, coffee, tea, clockmaker's shop, brass castings, bakery, graphic coll, goldsmith's shop, Frisian clocks, nature dept 25196

Oldtimercentrum Select, Madame-Curieweg 4, 8501 XC Joure - T: (0513) 415499, Fax: 412561
Science&Tech Museum 25197

Kampen

Frans Walkate Archief/ SNS Historisch Archief, c/o SNS Bank, Burgwal 43, 8261 EP Kampen - T: (038) 3392351, 3392266, Fax: 3392354, E-mail: info@walkate-archief.nl, Internet: http://www.walkate-archief.nl. Head: H. Harder
Local Museum - 1938
Works of local painters, topography, town hist, photographs, modern art 25198

Kamper Tabaksmuseum, Botermarkt 3, 8261 GR Kampen - T: (038) 43325353
Special Museum 25199

Stedelijk Museum Kampen, Oudestr 158, 8261 CZ Kampen, mail addr: Postbus 5009, 8260 GA Kampen - T: (038) 43317361, Fax: 43326849. Head: E.F.L.M. Van der Werdt
Local Museum - 1947
Coins, paintings, local silver collection, a horn with silver decorations either from the skippers of 'St. Anne' or the 'Rhineskippersguild' (1369), costumes, ceramics, archaeological finds, restored buckwheat mill, Barent Avercamp, Mechteld Toe Boelop - library 25200

Kapelle

Fruitteeltmuseum, Biezelingseweg 10, 4421 PM Kapelle
Agriculture Museum
Fruits production 25201

Kattendijke

Pottenbakkerij Museum, Dorpsstr 8 - 10, 4474 AD Kattendijke
Decorative Arts Museum
Arts and crafts, pottery 25202

Katwijk aan Zee

Katwijks Museum, Voorstr 46, 2225 ER Katwijk aan Zee - T: (071) 4013047, Fax: 4017707. Head: G. Van Kruistum
Local Museum - 1966
Local art and history, folklore, costumes, lace - library 25203

Keijenborg

Klompen Museum, Uilenesterstr 10a, 7256 KD Keijenborg - T: (0575) 463030
Special Museum
Museum of Wooden Shoes 25204

Kerkdriel

Oudheidkamer Maasdriel, Teisterbandstr 38, 5331 CR Kerkdriel - T: (0418) 631852
Local Museum
Local history 25205

Kerkrade

Industrion Museum for Industry and Society, Museumpl 2, 6461 MA Kerkrade, mail addr: Postbus 164, 6460 AD Kerkrade - T: (045) 5670809, Fax: 5463848, E-mail: info@industrion.nl, Internet: http://www.industrion.nl. Head: A.F. Magielsen
Science&Tech Museum - 1992
Mining lamps, fossils, minerals, wooden water pump (18th c), glass, ceramic, printing, paper, metal, chemical, nutrition industries, Crossley Motors - library, auditorium 25206

Klarenbeek

Haardplatenmuseum Klarenbeek, Oude Broekstr 12, 7382 AR Klarenbeek - T: (055) 3011747, Fax: 3011046, E-mail: brascamp@tref.nl, Internet: http://www.brascamp.com. Head: M.H. Brascamp
Special Museum
Fire backs 25207

Kloosterburen

Oldtimermuseum De Ronkel, Hoofdstr 46, 9977 RE Kloosterburen
Science&Tech Museum
Cars, motors, toy-money 25208

Kollum

Oudheidkamer/ Museum Mr. Andreae, Eyso de Wendtstr 9-11, 9291 ES Kollum - T: (0511) 452833
Local Museum
Photostudio (1900), store, church, furnished stile room, clothing, school room, changing summer exhibitions 25209

Koog aan de Zaan

Molenmuseum, Museumlaan 18, 1541 LP Koog aan de Zaan - T: (075) 6288968. Head: A.F. Neuhaus
Science&Tech Museum / Local Museum - 1925
Paintings, fragments, models, work instruments relating to industry and watermills, weaving tools, mill panorama copies of all sorts of industrial/water mills 25210

Oliemolen Het Pink, Pinkstr 12, 1544 BB Koog aan de Zaan, mail addr: 't Weethuis, Lagedijk 39, 1544 BB Zaandijk - T: (075) 6215148, Fax: 6215148
Science&Tech Museum - 1925
Mill from 1620 with original inventory, models, work benches 25211

Krimpen aan den IJssel

Streekmuseum Crimpenerhof, Ijsseldijk 312, 2922 BM Krimpen aan den IJssel - T: (0180) 514866, Fax: 518931, E-mail: - streekmuseumcrumpenerhof@planet.nl. Head: Dr. J.F Nauta
Agriculture Museum / Folklore Museum - 1964
Farm from about 1730 with farm implements and interiors, ship building, stone bakery, pottery 25212

Laag Keppel

Margaretha Museum, Rijksweg 75, 6998 AG Laag Keppel - T: (0314) 381725
Local Museum 25213

Landsmeer

Grietje Tump Museum, Zuideinde 69, 1121 DD Landsmeer - T: (020) 6313455, Internet: http:// www.hollandmuseums.nl
Historical Museum
Common things, textiles, costume, curiosa 25214

Laren, Gelderland

Huis Verwolde, Jonker Emilelaan 4, 7245 TL Laren, Gelderland - T: (0573) 401825, Internet: http:// www.hgl-vgl.nl. Head: B.H. Pyl
Local Museum / Decorative Arts Museum - 1982
Country-house (1762) with a china room, nursery and kitchen 25215

Laren, Noord-Holland

Geologisch Museum Hofland, Hilversumseweg 51, 1251 EW Laren, Noord-Holland - T: (035) 5382520
Natural History Museum
Geology, fossils, minerals, archaeology, prehist, mining 25216

Singer Museum, Oude Drift 1, 1251 BS Laren, Noord-Holland - T: (035) 5315656, Fax: 5317751, E-mail: museum@singerlaren.nl. Head: E.J.C. Raassen Kruimel
Fine Arts Museum - 1956
International coll of paintings from the schools of Amsterdam, Den Haag and Laren, coll of the American painter William H. Singer, coll of French paintings (19th c), coll of Dutch and French sculptures 25217

Lauwersoog

Expozee, Strandweg 1, 9976 VS Lauwersoog - T: (0519) 349045, Fax: 349304. Head: P.A. Malewicz
Science&Tech Museum
Land reclamation and dike construction 25218

Leek

Joodse Schooltje, S.-Leviestr 10, 9351 BM Leek - T: (0594) 517266, E-mail: samuel_levie@ yahoo.com. Head: A. Klein
Special Museum
Education, costume 25219

Nationaal Rijtuigmuseum (National Carriage Museum), Nienoord 1, 9351 AC Leek - T: (0594) 512260, Fax: 517921, E-mail: rijtuigmuseum@ tref.nl, Internet: http://www.rijtuigmuseum.nl. Head: L.L.M. Eekhout
Science&Tech Museum - 1958
Carriages, sleighs, (17th-20th c), paintings, graphics, travel accessories - library 25220

Leens

Landgoed Verhildersum Museum, Wierde 40, 9965 TB Leens - T: (0595) 571430
Local Museum - 1966
Castle (1398-1400, rebuilt 16th c), interiors and style of living (18th-19th c), portraits, agricultural implements, local history and art 25221

Museumboerderij, Dijkstilsterweg 4, 9965 TH Leens
Local Museum
Crafts, folklore, costume, natural history, agriculture, local history 25222

Leerdam

Museum 't Poorthuis, Kerkstr 91, 4140 AA Leerdam - T: (0345) 3075
Local Museum - 1965
History of Leerdam, crafts instruments, wheel making 25223

Nationaal Glasmuseum (National Glass Museum), Lingedijk 28, 4142 LD Leerdam - T: (03451) 13662, Fax: 13662. Head: T.G. te Duits
Special Museum - 1953
Old and modern glass from the Netherlands and other countries, single pieces made by artists in the Leerdam glassworks 1925-1980 - library 25224

Oude Raadhuis, Kerkstr 18, 4141 AW Leerdam - T: (0345) 613057. Head: M.A.C. Boomstra Van Raak
Local Museum 25225

Leeuwarden

Fries Letterkundig Museum, Grote Kerkstr 212, 8911 EG Leeuwarden - T: (058) 2120834, Fax: 2132672. Head: T.J. Steenmeijer Wielenga
Special Museum - 1959
Objects about literature of Friesland including manuscripts, letters, portraits, paintings, posters, programs, Pieter Jelles Troelstra coll, his wife Nynke Van Hichtum and other members of the Troelstra family, Mata Hari - library 25226

Fries Museum, Turfmarkt 11, 8911 KS Leeuwarden - T: (058) 2555500, Fax: 2132271, E-mail: info@ friesmuseum.nl, Internet: http:// www.friesmuseum.nl. Head: Dr. Cees Van't Veen
Local Museum / Archaeological Museum / Fine Arts Museum / Military Museum / Decorative Arts Museum - 1881
Regional antiquities, archaeology, Middle Ages, paintings, portraits, silver (16th-19th c), folk arts, numismatics, topographic atlas of Friesland, copper engravings, resistance in WW II, modern art, Mata Hari Gallery, textile and costume 25227

Fries Natuurmuseum, Schoenmakersperk 2, 8911 EM Leeuwarden - T: (058) 2129085, Fax: 2131365, E-mail: fries.natuurmuseum@wxs.nl, Internet: http://home.wxs.nl/~fries.natuurmuseum. Head: Dr. H. Wÿnandts
Natural History Museum - 1923
Geology, flora and fauna of Friesland and the environs, birds, eggs, insects, shells, herbarium - library 25228

Museum De Grutterswinkel, Nieuwesteeg 5-7, 8911 DT Leeuwarden
Historical Museum
Crafts, interior, dinning 25229

Museum Nanning Hendrik Bulthuis, Huizum Dorp 11, 8934 BP Leeuwarden
Historical Museum
Sculpture, maritime history 25230

Nationaal Keramiekmuseum Het Princessehof (National Ceramicmuseum), Grote Kerkstr 11, 8911 DZ Leeuwarden - T: (058) 2948958, Fax: 2948958, E-mail: info@princessehof.nl, Internet: http:// www.princessehof.nl. Head: Cees van 't Veen
Decorative Arts Museum / Special Museum / Historic Site - 1917
Ceramics from Asia, Europe, South America and Persia, tiles from Europe and the Middle East, modern ceramics, other applied arts, fine arts from the Netherlands (20th c), stoneware, earthenware, modern art gallery "The Prince of Leeuwarden" - library 25231

Pier Pander Museum, Prinsentuin 1, 8911 DZ Leeuwarden - T: (058) 2948958, Fax: 2948968, E-mail: info@princessehof.nl. Head: Dr. Cees van't Veen
Fine Arts Museum - 1924
Sculptures by Pier Pander and monument to the artist (1864-1919) 25232

Verzetsmuseum Friesland (Resistance Museum Friesland), Turfmarkt 11, 8911 KS Leeuwarden - T: (058) 2120111, Fax: 2132271, E-mail: info@ verzetsmuseum.nl, Internet: http:// www.verzetsmuseum.nl. Head: G. Koopmans
Military Museum / Historical Museum
Documentation on World War II - library 25233

Leiden

Academisch Historisch Museum der Universiteit Leiden, Rapenburg 73, 2311 GJ Leiden - T: (071) 5277242. Head: Prof. Dr. W. Otterspeer
University Museum - 1930
University history, portraits, documentation - archive 25234

Anatomisch Museum, Wassenaarseweg 62, 2333 AL Leiden, mail addr: c/o Rijksuniversiteit Leiden, Postbus 9602, 2300 RC Leiden - T: (071) 5276677, Fax: 5276680. Head: Prof. H. Beukers
Natural History Museum - 1593 25235

Het Koninklijk Penningkabinet (Royal Coin Cabinet), Rapenburg 28, 2311 EW Leiden, mail addr: Postbus 11028, 2301 EA Leiden - T: (071) 5120748, 5160999, Fax: 5128678, E-mail: museum@ penningkabinet.nl. Head: M. Scharloo
Special Museum - 1816
Coins, medals, papermoney and rubber stamps 25236

Modelbouwmuseum, Noordeinde 2a, 2311 CD Leiden - T: (071) 5124567
Special Museum 25237

Molenmuseum De Valk, 2e Binnenvestgracht 1, 2312 BZ Leiden - T: (071) 5165353, Fax: 5134805, E-mail: devalk@molenmuseum.myweb.nl, Internet: http://www.molenmuseum.myweb.nl. Head: H. Van der Lelie
Science&Tech Museum - 1966
Mill (1743) with original machinery, tools and implements, mill models, documentation 25238

Museum Boerhaave, Lange Sint-Agnietenstr 10, 2312 WC Leiden, mail addr: Postbus 11280, 2301 EG Leiden - T: (071) 5214224, Fax: 5120344, E-mail: presentatie@museumboerhaave.nl, Internet: http://www.museumboerhaave.nl. Head: Dr. G.A.C. Veeneman
Historical Museum / Science&Tech Museum - 1928
Hist of science and medicine, microscopes, telescopes, medical instruments, electric machines, physical demonstration models (18th c, van 's-Gravesande and Musschenbroek coll), Ehrenfest-Archives, quadrant of Snellius, microscope of Antoni van Leeuwenhoek, lenses by Chr. Huygens, heliumliquefactor of Kamerlingh Onnes - library 25239

Naturalis, Nationaal Natuurhistorisch Museum, Darwinweg 2, 2333 CR Leiden, mail addr: Postbus 9517, 2300 RA Leiden - T: (071) 5687600, Fax: 5687666, E-mail: naturalis@naturalis.nnm.nl, Internet: http://www.naturalis.nl. Head: W.G. Van der Weiden
Natural History Museum - 1820
Mammals, ornithology, entomology, crustacea, fish, herpetology, worms, mollusca, petrography, mineralogy, paleontology - library, nature information centre 25240

Prentenkabinet der Universiteit Leiden, Rapenburg 65, 2311 GJ Leiden - T: (071) 5272700, Fax: 5272615, E-mail: I.Th.Leyerzapf@ Rullet.Leidenuniv.nl, Internet: http:// www.let.leidenuniv.nl/PKL/facade.htm. Head: Dr. I.Th. Leijerzapf
Fine Arts Museum / University Museum - 1815
Drawings of the Dutch and Flemish schools, European prints, book illustrations, dutch photography (1839-today) - library 25241

Rijksmuseum van Oudheden (National Museum of Antiquities), Rapenburg 28, 2311 EC Leiden, mail addr: Postbus 11114, 2301 EC Leiden - T: (071) 5163163, E-mail: info@rmo.nl. Head: J.R. Magendans
Archaeological Museum - 1818
Egyptian sculptures and decorative arts, Nubian Temple rebuilt in special hall, coll from Palestine, Mesopotamia, Persia, Greek, Roman, Cypriot and Etruscan antiquities, prehistory and early hist of the Netherlands - library 25242

Rijksmuseum voor Volkenkunde (National Museum of Ethnology), Steenstr 1, 2312 BS Leiden, mail addr: Postbus 212, 2300 AE Leiden - T: (071) 5168800, Fax: 5128437, E-mail: info@rmv.nl, Internet: http://www.rmv.nl. Head: Dr. S.B. Engelsman
Ethnology Museum - 1837
Ethnology (Indonesia, Oceania, China, Japan, Korea, West-, Central- South- and Southeast-Asia, Arctic regions, The Americas, Africa), archeology from Java (Hindu-Javanese art), Japanese art (prints and drawings), pre-Columbian art, bronze from Benin and other African art, Buddhist art, the 'Leyden Plate' (oldest contemporaneously dated inscription from the Maya civilisation) - library 25243

Stedelijk Museum De Lakenhal, Oude Singel 28-32, 2312 RA Leiden - T: (071) 5165360, Fax: 5134489, E-mail: postbus@lakenhal.nl, Internet: http:// www.lakenhal.nl. Head: Dr. H. Bolten Rempt
Fine Arts Museum - 1874
Paintings by Lucas van Leyden (1489-1533), Rembrandt, Jan Steen, Jan van Goyen, sculptures, glass, silver, period rooms (17th-19th c), local archaeological finds and modern art - library 25244

Wagenmakersmuseum, Oude Varkensmarkt 13, 2311 VN Leiden
Science&Tech Museum
Implements for carriage making 25245

Leiderdorp

Oudheidkamer Leiderdorp, Ericalaan 3b, 2351 CW Leiderdorp - T: (071) 5410976
Local Museum
Local history 25246

Lelystad

Nationaal Ruimtevaart Museum (National Space Museum), Kempenaar 33, 8231 DN Lelystad - T: (0320) 280000, Fax: 234636, E-mail: space.center@wxs.nl, Internet: http:// www.nationaalruimtevaartmuseum.nl. Head: H. Van Wezel
Science&Tech Museum
Museum of Astronautics 25247

Nederlands Sportmuseum, Museumweg 10, 8242 PD Lelystad
Special Museum
Sports history 25248

Nieuw Land Poldermuseum, Oostvaardersdijk 1-13, 8244 PA Lelystad - T: (0320) 260799, Fax: 260436. Head: Dr. N.F. Abcouwer
Science&Tech Museum - 1976
Land reclamation in Ijsselmeer - library, slide shows, films 25249

Vliegend Museum Lelystad, Airport, Maraboeweg 12, 8218 NV Lelystad - T: (0320) 288699, E-mail: vml@solcon.nl, Internet: http:// www.solcon.nl/vml. Head: Alexander Waning
Science&Tech Museum
Aeroplanes 25250

Zep/Allon Museeum, Karperweg 12, 8221 RB Lelystad
Science&Tech Museum
Aviation history 25251

Lemmer

Indian Museum, Indian Pl, Lemsterhoek, 8531 XH Lemmer - T: (0514) 563244, Fax: 563244. Head: Tony Leenes
Science&Tech Museum
Ca. 40 "Indian" motorcycles 25252

Oudheidkamer Lemster Fiifgea, Nieuwburen 1, 8531 EE Lemmer - T: (0514) 561619, 562055
Local Museum
Local history, fishing, peat cutting 25253

Lent

Wijnmuseum, Bemmelsedijk, 6663 KZ Lent - T: (024) 3231746
Special Museum
Museum of Wines 25254

Leylstad

Nationaal Scheephistorisch Centrum, Batavia-werf, Oostvaardersdijk 1-9, 8200 AC Leylstad - T: (0320) 261409, Fax: 261360, E-mail: info@bataviawerf.nl, Internet: http://www.bataviawerf.nl. Head: Janneke Kuysters
Science&Tech Museum - 1998 25255

Lievelde

Avog's Crash Museum, Europaweg 34, 7137 HN Lievelde - T: (0544) 461480, E-mail: pmonasso.avog.acm@hetnet.nl. Head: J.J.M. Geerdinck
Military Museum - 1981
Aircraft equipment from World War II 25256

Openluchtmuseum Erve Kots, Eimersweg 4, 7137 HG Lievelde - T: (0544) 371691, Fax: 77676. Head: G.J. Weenink
Open Air Museum - 1936
Prehistoric finds, household objects, tools 25257

Loosdrecht

Kasteel-Museum Sypesteyn, Nieuw-Loosdrechtsedijk 150, 1231 LC Loosdrecht - T: (035) 5823205, Fax: 5828657, E-mail: info@ sypesteyn.nl, Internet: http://www.sypesteyn.nl. Head: A.W. Oosthoek-Bogaard
Fine Arts Museum - 1927
Art (16th-18th c), paintings, family portraits, furniture, weapons, clocks, porcelain, glasses, silver, pottery, founder and collector C.H.C.A. van Sypesteyn 25258

Loppersum

Spoor- en Tramwegverzameling, Raadhuisstr 7, 9919 AK Loppersum
Science&Tech Museum
Trams, militaria 25259

Luijksgestel

Bakkerijmuseum De Grenswachter, Kapellerweg 15, 5575 BG Luijksgestel - T: (0497) 541314, E-mail: info@bakkerij-museum.nl, Internet: http:// www.bakkerij-museum.nl. Head: R. Ivens
Special Museum 25260

Lunteren

De Koepel, Boslaan 92, 6741 KG Lunteren - T: (0318) 482549
Natural History Museum
Geology, flora and fauna 25261

Lutjegast

Abel Tasman Kabinet, Kompasstr 1, 9866 AP Lutjegast
Local Museum
Local history 25262

Luttelgeest

Museum Orchideën Hoeve, Oosterringweg 34, 8315 PV Luttelgeest - T: (0527) 202875
Local Museum 25263

Maarsbergen

Kaasboerderijmuseum de Weistaar, Rottegatsteeg 6, 3953 MN Maarsbergen - T: (033) 281943
Special Museum
History of butter and cheesemaking 25264

Museum Valkenheide, Valkenheide 26, 3953 MD Maarsbergen
Historical Museum
Crafts 25265

Maarssen

Museum Maarssen, Diependaalsedijk 19b, 3601 GH Maarssen, mail addr: Postbus 130, 3600 AC Maarssen - T: (0346) 554440
Local Museum - 1995
Local history 25266

Nederlands Drogisterij Museum, Dutch Drugstore Museum, Diependaalsedijk 19c, 3601 GH Maarssen - T: (0346) 555253, Fax: 8509615, E-mail: drogmuseum@tref.nl, Internet: http://www.drogisterijmuseum.nl. Head: Koos Koster
Historical Museum 25267

Maasland

Museum De Schilpen, 's-Herenstr 24, 3155 SK Maasland - T: (010) 5913042
Local Museum
Local history 25268

Maassluis

Gemeentemuseum, Zuiddijk 16, 3143 AS Maassluis - T: (010) 5913813, Fax: 5924950. Head: Esther Bánki, M. Van Rijnswall
Fine Arts Museum - 1933
Modern art after 1900, local hist, Jeanne Bieruma Oosting, Jan van Heel, Otto de Kat - library 25269

Nationaal Sleepvaartmuseum, Hoogstr 1-3, 3142 EA Maassluis - T: (010) 5912474, Fax: 5919501, E-mail: paulalers@hetnet.nl. Head: L. Timmermans
Science&Tech Museum
Ship models, hist of Dutch towing industry 25270

Maastricht

Bonnefantenmuseum, 250 Av Ceramique, 6221 KX Maastricht, mail addr: Postbus 1735, 6201 BS Maastricht - T: (043) 3290190, Fax: 3290199, E-mail: info@bonnefanten.nl, Internet: http://www.bonnefanten.nl. Head: Alexander Van Grevenstein
Fine Arts Museum - 1865/1968
Old Masters: sculptures from regional schools (13th-16th c), Italian paintings, German painting and sculpture, Maastricht silverware, Southern Netherlandish paintings (16th-17th c), contemporary art: minimal art and Arte Povera movement (Sollewit, R. Secra, M. Merz) - library 25271

Museum De Helpoort, Sint-Bernardusstr, 6200 AE Maastricht, mail addr: Postbus 230, 6200 AE Maastricht - T: (043) 317550, 317803, 316752. Head: A.F. Henar
Archaeological Museum / Natural History Museum
Archeology, geology 25272

Museum voor Devotieprentjes en andere Devotionalia, Stichting Santjes en Kantjes, Cörversplein 14, 6221 EZ Maastricht - T: (043) 3251851. Head: J. Goessen
Religious Arts Museum 25273

Natuurhistorisch Museum Maastricht, De Bosquetpl 6-7, 6211 KJ Maastricht, mail addr: Postbus 882, 6200 AW Maastricht - T: (043) 3505490, Fax: 3505475, E-mail: mail@nhmmaastricht.nl, Internet: http://www.nhmmaastricht.nl. Head: D.Th. de Graaf
Natural History Museum - 1912
Fossils, local flora and fauna, geology, paleontology, entomology - library 25274

Schatkamer van de Basiliek van Onze Lieve Vrouwe, Onze Lieve Vrouweplein 8, Maastricht - T: (043) 251851
Religious Arts Museum
Religious art and objects 25275

Schatkamer van de Sint-Servaasbasiliek, Keizer Karelplein 6, 6211 TC Maastricht - T: (043) 210490. Head: L.M. Tagage
Religious Arts Museum - 827
Art from ca 900-1300, important coll of silks from ca 500-1200, goldsmithy of the "Meuse-Region" about 1100 25276

Sint-Pieters Museum op de Lichtenberg, Lichtenbergweg 2, 6212 NG Maastricht
Special Museum 25277

Spaans Gouvernement Museum, Vrijthof 18, 6211 LD Maastricht - T: (043) 3211327, Fax: 3214384, E-mail: museum.spaans.gouvernement@wxs.nl. Head: Monique F.A. Dickhaut
Decorative Arts Museum - 1973
Residence of Dukes of Brabant, Wagner-De Wit coll of antique furniture, clocks, sculptures, paintings, ceramics of the 18th c 25278

Ut Hoes met de Kiekdoes, Bogaardenstr 43, 6211 SN Maastricht - T: (043) 3211325. Head: Pieke Dassen
Performing Arts Museum
Old raree-shows 25279

Makkum

Fries Aardewerkmuseum De Waag, Pruikmakershoek 2, 8754 ET Makkum - T: (0515) 21349, Fax: 232555. Head: Pieter Jan Tichelaar
Decorative Arts Museum - 1960
Tin glazed earthenware and tiles, delftware 25280

Markelo

Museum Eungs Schöppe, Goorseweg 1, 7475 AX Markelo - T: (0547) 363536
Local Museum
Clothing, household articles 25281

Marken

Marker Museum, Kerkbuurt 44-47, 1156 BL Marken - T: (0299) 601904. Head: G. Appel
Local Museum - 1981
Costumes, paintings (R. Pijnenburg) 25282

Marssum

Heringastate, Slotlaene 1, 9034 HM Marssum - T: (058) 251231. Head: J.G. Beversluis
Decorative Arts Museum
16th century nobleman's seat, furniture and paintings (17th c), silver (1880), bedsteads (16th c) 25283

Medemblik

Kasteel Radboud, Oudevaartsgat 8, 1671 HM Medemblik, mail addr: Postbus 7, 1670 AA Medemblik - T: (0227) 541960, Fax: 542924
Historical Museum
Old castle (13th c) with interior and paintings 25284

Nederlands Stoommachinemuseum, Oosterdijk 4, 1671 HJ Medemblik - T: (0227) 544732, Fax: 540391, E-mail: info@stoomachinemuseum, Internet: http://www.stoommachinemuseum.nl. Head: J.F. Maret
Science&Tech Museum
Museum of Steam Engines 25285

Oude Bakkerij, Nieuwstr 8, 1671 BD Medemblik - T: (0227) 545014
Special Museum
Old Bakery 25286

Oudheidkamer, Torenstr 15, 1671 CN Medemblik - T: (0227) 541943. Head: J. Van Leverink
Local Museum - 1964
Local history 25287

Meerssen

Natuur Historisch Museum en Heemkunde Centrum, Markt 27a, 6231 LR Meerssen
Local Museum
Local and natural history, crafts, archeology, geology, agriculture 25288

Meppel

Drukkerijmuseum Meppel, Kleine Oever 11, 7941 BK Meppel - T: (038) 43358259
Science&Tech Museum
Hist of printing 25289

Meppeler Expositie Centrum, Hoofdstr 22, 7941 AG Meppel
Public Gallery
Ceramics, sculpture, paintings, graphics 25290

Middelburg

Multi Colour Museum, Torenweg 4 a, 4337 PD Middelburg
Decorative Arts Museum
Costumes, arts and crafts 25291

Vleeshal, Lange Noordstr 8, 4331 CD Middelburg
Public Gallery
Arts and crafts 25292

Zeeuws Museum, Abdij 3, 4331 BK Middelburg, mail addr: Postbus 378, 4330 AJ Middelburg - T: (0118) 626655, Fax: 638998. Head: Dr. I.V.T. Spaander
Historical Museum - 1769
2000 years of Zealand hist, from archeology to contemporary art - library, Rooseveld study center 25293

Middelharnis

Rien Poortvlietmuseum, Raadhuisstr 1, 3241 CP Middelharnis - T: (0187) 486725
Decorative Arts Museum
Work of R. Poortvliet 25294

Middelstum

Museum Bakkerij Mendels, Kerkstr 3, 9991 BL Middelstum - T: (0595) 551248, E-mail: emeiborg@hetnet.nl. Head: W. Tommassen, E. Meiborg
Special Museum
Historical bakery (16th-17th c) with interior (1829) and equipment 25295

Middenbeemster

Huize Betje Wolff, Middenweg 178, 1462 HL Middenbeemster, mail addr: Postbus 73, 1462 ZH Middenbeemster - T: (0299) 681968
Agriculture Museum - 1936
Furnished living room (18th-19th c), objects relating to dairy economy and cattle breeding 25296

Moddergat

Museum 't Fiskershúske, Fiskerspaad 4-8a, 9142 VN Moddergat - T: (0519) 58454, Fax: 589512. Head: G.I.W. Dragt
Local Museum - 1965
Three fishermen's houses with 19th century interiors, fishing equipment, costumes, folk art, history of the Frisian rescue work, lifeboat models, rescue articles, medals, pictures 25297

Monnickendam

Gouwzeemuseum 't Havenland, Havenstr 20, 1141 AX Monnickendam - T: (0299) 651582. Head: D. Oosterbaan
Local Museum 25298

Montfoort

Art of Velvet Gallery De Stierenstal, Willeskop 134, 3417 MG Montfoort - T: (0348) 471796, Fax: 471796, E-mail: h.ferree@planet.nl
Special Museum 25299

Moordrecht

't Oude Ambachtshuis, Dorpsstr 60, 2841 BK Moordrecht - T: (0182) 378197
Science&Tech Museum
Craftsmanhouse 25300

Naarden

Comenius Museum, Kloosterstr 33, 1411 RS Naarden - T: (035) 6943045, Fax: 6941949, E-mail: info@comeniusmuseum.nl, Internet: http://www.comeniusmuseum.nl. Head: Lies Netel
Special Museum - 1992
Writings of Jan Amos Comenius (1592-1670) and objects relating to the philosopher, pedagogue and theologian 25301

Het Nederlands Vestingmuseum, Westwalstr 6, 1411 PB Naarden - T: (035) 6945459, Fax: 6943511, E-mail: info@vestingmuseum.nl, Internet: http://www.vestingmuseum.nl. Head: F.M. Fox
Military Museum - 1955
Hist of fortress Turfpoort and its casemates (17th-19th c), watercolours, pictures, maps, historic dioramas, canons, uniforms, water defence lines 25302

Nagele

Museum Nagele, Ring 23, 8308 AL Nagele
Local Museum
Local history, architecture, paintings, graphics 25303

Nederweert Eind

Limburgs Openluchtmuseum Eynderhoof, Milderspaat 1, 6034 PL Nederweert Eind
Local Museum / Open Air Museum
Local history, natural history, crafts, archeology, architecture, industrial development 25304

Nes

Natuurmuseum, Strandweg 38, 9163 ZM Nes - T: (0519) 542737, Fax: 542136
Natural History Museum 25305

Niebert

Schilder- en Bakkerijmuseum 't Steenhuis, 't Pad 15a, 9365 TA Niebert
Fine Arts Museum / Special Museum
Paintings, interieur, baking, history 25306

Nieuw Buinen

Keramisch Museum Goedewaagen, Glaslaan 29a, 9521 GG Nieuw Buinen - T: (0599) 616030, Fax: 621210, E-mail: info@goedewaagen.nl, Internet: http://www.goedewaagen.nl. Head: S.J. Kamer
Decorative Arts Museum
Ceramics, crafts, art deco 25307

Nieuw Roden

Kunstpaviljoen, Zevenhuisterweg 4b, 9311 VB Nieuw Roden
Public Gallery
Painting, sculpture, graphics, ceramics, textiles 25308

Nieuw Vossemeer

A.M. de Jongmuseum, Voorstr 29, 4681 AC Nieuw Vossemeer - T: (0167) 502350
Special Museum - 1968
Drawings, letters, photos and books of writer A.M. de Jong (1888-1943) 25309

Nieuwe Niedorp

Noord-Hollands Motoren Museum, Schulpweg 19, 1733 AT Nieuwe Niedorp - T: (0226) 413571
Science&Tech Museum 25310

Nieuwe Pekela

Kapiteinshuis Pekela, D. Sicco Tjadenstr 95-96, 9663 RD Nieuwe Pekela
Local Museum
Local history, ship building 25311

Nieuwegein

Historisch Museum Warsenhoeck, Geinoord 12, 3432 PE Nieuwegein - T: (030) 260332396
Historical Museum 25312

Oudheidkamer Vreeswijk, Fort Vreeswijk 1b, 3433 ZZ Nieuwegein
Historical Museum
Fort history 25313

Nieuweschans

Naaimachinemuseum, Hoofdstr 29, 9693 AC Nieuweschans
Special Museum
Sewing machines 25314

Vestingmuseum, Eerste Kanonnierstr 2, 9693 EB Nieuweschans - T: (0597) 542249
Historical Museum
Carts, picture postcards 25315

Nieuwkoop

Smederij Museum, Zuideinde 33, 2421 AE Nieuwkoop - T: (4551) 1393
Science&Tech Museum 25316

Nieuwleusen

Zo Was 'T, Backxlaan 16, 7711 AG Nieuwleusen - T: (0529) 481583
Local Museum
Local history 25317

Nieuwolda

Kinderwagenmuseum, Hoofdweg 25, 9944 EA Nieuwolda - T: (0596) 541941
Special Museum
Baby carriages, children's wear 25318

Museumgemaal de Hoogte, De Streep 18, 9944 BP Nieuwolda
Science&Tech Museum
Watermill 25319

Nij Beets

Openlucht Laagveenderij Museum Damshûs, Domela Nieuwenhuisweg 49, 9245 VB Nij Beets - T: (0512) 461599. Head: J.G. Dijkstra
Open Air Museum - 1960
Room of a peat cutter (1870), tools 25320

Nijmegen

Anatomisch Museum Nijmegen, Geert Grooteplein-Noord 21, 6525 EZ Nijmegen
Historical Museum
Anatomy, medicine 25321

Museum de Stratemakerstoren, Waalkade 83-84, 6511 XR Nijmegen
Local Museum
Local history, archeology, architecture, militaria 25322

Museum Het Valkhof, Kelfkensbos 59, 6511 TB Nijmegen, mail addr: Postbus 1474, 6501 BL Nijmegen - T: (024) 3608805, Fax: 3608656, E-mail: mhv@museumhetvalkhof.nl, Internet: http://www.museumhetvalkhof.nl. Head: Dr. M. Brouwer
Archaeological Museum / Fine Arts Museum / Historical Museum
Ancient and modern art, archaeology - library 25323

Nationaal Fietsmuseum Velorama (National Bicycle Museum Velorama), Waalkade 107, 6511 XR Nijmegen - T: (024) 3604970, Fax: 3607177. Head: G.J. Moed
Science&Tech Museum - 1981
Bicycles 25324

Natuurmuseum Nijmegen, Gerard Noodtstr 121, 6511 ST Nijmegen - T: (024) 3297070, Fax: 3297079, E-mail: info@natuurmuseum.nl, Internet: http://www.natuurmuseum.nl. Head: G. Mangnus
Natural History Museum
Formerly Jewish synagogue with coll of natural history 25325

Nijmeegs Volkenkundig Museum, Thomas van Aquinostr 1, 6525 GD Nijmegen - T: (024) 3615577, E-mail: f.hoekstra@maw.kun.nl, Internet: http://www.kun.nl/nvm
Ethnology Museum 25326

Van 't Lindenhoutmuseum, Scherpenkampweg 21, 6545 AK Nijmegen - T: (080) 770417
Historical Museum
History of the local orphanage 25327

Nisse

Het Trekkermuseum, Palmboomseweg 3, 4443 RM Nisse
Science&Tech Museum
Industrial tractor production 25328

Noordbergum

Scherjon's Klompenmakerij en Museum, Dokter IJpeijlaan 8, 9257 MR Noordbergum - T: (0511) 472336, Fax: 473400, E-mail: scherjons-klompen@wxs.nl
Special Museum
History of clogs 25329

Noordbroek

Aardewerkverzameling Petrus Pegout, Noorderstr 2, 9635 TG Noordbroek
Decorative Arts Museum
Ceramics, pottery 25330

Nederlands Strijkijzer-Museum, Noorderstr 4, 9635 TG Noordbroek - T: (0598) 452075, Fax: 451181, E-mail: strijkijzer@dolfijn.nl, Internet: http://www.noordbroek.com/strijkijzer.html. Head: G.J. den Besten
Historical Museum - 1982
Old farm house (1576) with coll of flat and smoothing irons, crimping machines, mangling boards, linnen presses 25331

Noorden

Poldermuseum, Simon van Capelweg 123, 2431 AE Noorden - T: (0172) 408174
Local Museum
Local history 25332

Noordhorn

Kostuummuseum De Gouden Leeuw, Langestr 48, 9804 PL Noordhorn
Special Museum
Ceramics, folklore, textiles, costume 25333

Noordwijk, Zuid-Holland

Jan Verwey Natuurmuseum, Weteringkade 27, 2201 SK Noordwijk, Zuid-Holland
Natural History Museum
Minerals, fossils 25334

Museumsboerderij Oud Noordwijk, Jan Kroonsplein 4, 2202 JC Noordwijk, Zuid-Holland - T: (071) 3617884, E-mail: gon@tiscalimail.nl. Head: W. Baalbergen
Local Museum - 1961
18th century farm with complete interior (19th c), costumes, models of fishing boats, coll of shells found in the North Sea, photographs, drawings, pottery 25335

Space Expo, Keplerlaan 3, 2201 AZ Noordwijk, Zuid-Holland - T: (071) 3646446, Fax: 3646453, E-mail: mailnse@estec.esa.nl, Internet: http://www.space-expo.nl. Head: Arthur O. Eger
Science&Tech Museum - 1990 25336

Noordwolde Fr

Nationaal Vlechtmuseum, Mandehof 7, 8391 BG Noordwolde Fr
Special Museum
Arts, wickerworks 25337

Nuenen

Van Gogh Documentatiecentrum, Gemeentehuis, Papenvoort 15, 5671 CP Nuenen - T: (040) 2631668, Fax: 2833165. Head: T. de Brouwer
Fine Arts Museum
Photos and reproductions of Van Gogh's works, documents on his stay at Nuenen 1883-1885 25338

Nuis

't Rieuw, Oudeweg 15b, 9364 PP Nuis
Local Museum
Crafts, archeology, art, agriculture 25339

Nunspeet

Veluws Diorama, Marktstr 17-19, 8071 GV Nunspeet - T: (0341) 2832500. Head: H. Jung
Natural History Museum - 1957
Mounted birds, mammals, botany 25340

Zandenbos, Eperweg 132, 8072 PL Nunspeet - T: (0341) 252996, Fax: 263877
Natural History Museum 25341

Oirschot

Landbouwmuseum Hand en Span, Rijkesluisstr 56, 5688 ED Oirschot - T: (0499) 571291
Agriculture Museum
Agricultural implements (1800-1940) 25342

Museum De Vier Quartieren, Museum van het Brabantse Volksleven 1795-1945, Sint-Odulphusstr 11, 5688 BA Oirschot - T: (0499) 550599, Fax: 577633, E-mail: info@vvvoirschot.nl, Internet: http://www.vvvoirschot.nl. Head: M. Gloudemans
Local Museum / Agriculture Museum / Religious Arts Museum - 1976
Folk art of Brabant (18th-19th c), religious art, tools and implements used in the area of Den Bosch 25343

Oldeboorn

Aldheidskeamer Uldrik Bottema, Waechstege 1, 8495 JD Oldeboorn
Local Museum
Local history 25344

Oldenzaal

Historisch Museum Het Palthe Huis, Marktstr 13, 7571 ED Oldenzaal - T: (0541) 513482
Local Museum - 1907
Archeology, prehistory, fossils, heraldic figures, pipes, old library, farm kitchen, mirrors, sundial, period rooms 25345

Kunstcentrum De Waagh, Waagstr 4, 7571 EA Oldenzaal - T: (0541) 535151
Public Gallery 25346

Sint-Plechelmusbasiliek met Schatkamer, Sint-Plechelmuspl 4, 7571 CC Oldenzaal - T: (0541) 514794. Head: J.B.A. Velers
Religious Arts Museum
Religious objects, memorabilia of St. Plechelmus, vestments 25347

Olst

Geologisch Streek-Museum de IJsselvallei, Eikelhofweg 12, 8121 RC Olst - T: (0570) 563633. Head: A.J.G. Verhaard
Natural History Museum - 1980
Geological and palaeological material 25348

Letterkundig Museum, Diepenveenseweg 1, 8121 DV Olst
Special Museum
Documents on literary history of the Netherlands and Flanders 25349

Ommen

Nationaal Tinnen Figuren Museum, Markt 1, 7731 DB Ommen - T: (0529) 454500, Fax: 453552, E-mail: info@tinfigmuseum.nl, Internet: http://www.tinfigmuseum.nl
Special Museum 25350

Streekmuseum Ommen, Gemeentehuis, Den Oordt 7, 7731 CM Ommen - T: (0529) 453487
Local Museum
Local costumes, vessels, jewels, geology, prehistory, tools, parts of restored wood and corn mills 25351

Onstwedde

Slaait'n Hoes, De Horn 5, 9591 AE Onstwedde - T: (0599) 332232
Local Museum
Local history, costume 25352

Oosterbeek

Airborne Museum Hartenstein, Utrechtseweg 232, 6862 AZ Oosterbeek - T: (026) 3337710, Fax: 3391785, E-mail: info@airbornemuseum.nl, Internet: http://www.airbornemuseum.nl. Head: W. Boersma
Historical Museum - 1949
Objects relating to the battle of Arnhem in September 1944 - library, archive 25353

Oosterend

Kazemattenmuseum, c/o Stichting Kornwerderzand, Sibadaweg 12, 8734 HE Oosterend - T: (0515) 231346, Fax: 232143, E-mail: kazemat@worldonline.nl. Head: F.G. de Boer
Military Museum - 1985
Casemates, cannons and kitchen equipment of the Second World War 25354

Oosterhout

Bakkerij Museum, Klappeijstr 47-49, 4901 HD Oosterhout - T: (0162) 429700
Special Museum
Bakery Museum 25355

Brabants Museum Oud Oosterhout, Bredaseweg 129, 4904 SB Oosterhout - T: (0162) 426815, E-mail: rene.seur@hetnet.nl
Local Museum 25356

Collectie Militaire Traditie, Dorpsstr 33, 6678 BE Oosterhout - T: (0481) 481566
Military Museum
Military uniforms, documents of the Netherlands forces until 1940 25357

Speelgoedmuseum Op Stelten, Sint Vincentiusstr 86, 4901 GL Oosterhout - T: (0162) 452815, Fax: 452413
Special Museum
Toys (1750-1950), puppets 25358

Oostkapelle

Fossielenmuseum, Molenweg 36, 4356 AB Oostkapelle - T: (0118) 592620. Head: William J. Phaff
Natural History Museum - 1977 25359

Zeeuws Biologisch Museum, Duinvlietweg 6, 4356 ND Oostkapelle - T: (0118) 582620, Fax: 582664. Head: Bert Van de Hoef
Natural History Museum - 1977
Natural history, ornithology, butterflies, marine hydrobiology - library, educational dept 25360

Oostvoorne

Oldtimermuseum De Rijke, Industrieterrein Pinnepot, 3233 ER Oostvoorne - T: (0181) 483876, Fax: 486143
Science&Tech Museum 25361

Oostwold, Leek

Mineralenexpositie De Siersteen, Hoofdstr 197, 9828 PA Oostwold, Leek
Natural History Museum
Minerals, crafts 25362

Ootmarsum

Museum Ton Schulten, Kerkpl 16-17, 7631 EV Ootmarsum - T: (0541) 291763, Fax: 291326, E-mail: info@tonschulten.nl, Internet: http://www.tonschulten.nl. Head: Ton Schulten
Fine Arts Museum
Paintings 25363

Openluchtmuseum Ootmarsum, Smithuisstr 2, 7631 GH Ootmarsum - T: (0541) 293099, Fax: 295008, E-mail: info@openluchtmuseumootmarsum.nl, Internet: http://www.openluchtmuseu-mootmarsum.nl. Head: J.C. Tip
Open Air Museum 25364

Stadsgalerie Engels Tuin, Hazelrot 3, 7631 BK Ootmarsum - T: (0541) 293555
Public Gallery 25365

Orvelte

Gereedschapmuseum, Schoolstr 1, 9441 PE Orvelte - T: (0593) 322251
Science&Tech Museum
Tools 25366

Museum Orvelte, Dorpsstr 1a, 9441 PD Orvelte - T: (0593) 322335, Fax: 322377, E-mail: vvvorvelte@hetnet.nl
Local Museum 25367

Ospel

Bezoekerscentrum Mijl Op Zeven, Moostdijk 15, 6035 RB Ospel - T: (0495) 641497, Fax: 466238, Internet: http://www.staatsbosbeheer. Head: I. Davidse
Natural History Museum - 1966
Local flora and fauna, hist of peat cutting 25368

Bromfietsmuseum De Peel, Ommelpad 12, 6035 PC Ospel - T: (0465) 663397, Fax: 663521
Science&Tech Museum 25369

Peelmuseum, Cassaweg 1a, 6035 PP Ospel - T: (0495) 641246
Natural History Museum
Peat cutting, local flora and fauna, craftmen's and agricultural implements, costumes 25370

Oss

Jan Cunen Museum → Museum Jan Cunen

Museum Jan Cunen, Molenstr 65, 5341 GC Oss - T: (0412) 629336, Fax: 629335, E-mail: museumjancunon@on.nl, Internet: http://www.museumjancunen.nl. Head: Edwin JacobsVan Esch
Performing Arts Museum - 1935
Local and regional history(19th c), contemporary art, fine arts 25371

Otterlo

Kröller-Müller Museum, Houtkampweg 6, 6731 AW Otterlo, mail addr: Postbus 1, 6730 AA Otterlo - T: (0318) 591241, Fax: 591515, E-mail: information@kmm.nl, Internet: http://www.kmm.nl. Head: Dr. E.J. Van Straaten
Fine Arts Museum - 1938
Van Gogh, Van der Leck, contemporary sculptures, a.o. Hepworth, Moore, Serra, Lipchitz, realism, impressionism, cubism, abstract art, large sculpture park 25372

Nederlands Tegelmuseum, Eikenzoom 10, 6731 BH Otterlo - T: (0318) 591519, Fax: 592000. Head: G.J. Brussee
Decorative Arts Museum - 1961
Tiles from 1300 till today 25373

Oud-Zuilen

Slot Zuylen, Tournooiveld 1, 3611 AS Oud-Zuilen - T: (030) 2440255. Head: W.R.A. Baron Van Tuyll Van Serooskerken
Decorative Arts Museum - 1952
Medieval inventory, gobelins, history, china porcelain, glass 25374

Ouddorp

Ouddorps Raad- en Polderhuis, Raadhuisstr 4, 3253 AN Ouddorp, mail addr: Duinkerkerweg 25, 3253 AJ Ouddorp - T: (0187) 682425
Archaeological Museum / Decorative Arts Museum
Archeology, interior 25375

Rijdend Tram Museum, De Punt 8, 3253 MC Ouddorp - T: (0187) 683052
Science&Tech Museum
Tramway 25376

Oude Pekela

Westerwolds Crashmuseum, Schipperswijk 12, 9665 PM Oude Pekela - T: (06) 28937619, E-mail: c.timmerad@12move.nl
Historical Museum / Science&Tech Museum
Aviation history 25377

Oudemirdum

Natuur Streekmuseum Klif en Gaast, Brink 4, 8567 JD Oudemirdum - T: (05147) 1777
Natural History Museum - 1991
Fauna and flora of the environs, Culture and recreative possibilities of the environs 25378

Oudenbosch

Natuurhistorisch en Vogelmuseum, Darinkveld 37, 4731 UK Oudenbosch - T: (0165) 22751
Natural History Museum
Ornithology, ethnography (Indonesia, Africa, China) 25379

Nederlands Zouavenmuseum, Markt 31, 4731 HM Oudenbosch - T: (0165) 313448, E-mail: info@zouavenmuseum.nl, Internet: http://www.zouavenmuseum.nl. Head: M.C. Zonneveld-Kouters
Religious Arts Museum
Religious history 25380

Ouderkerk Amstel

Oudheidkamer, Kerkstr 4-6, 1191 JB Ouderkerk Amstel - T: (020) 4964365
Local Museum 25381

Oudeschans

Vestingmuseum Oudeschans, Achterstr 2, 9696 XJ Oudeschans
Local Museum
Local history 25382

Oudeschild

Maritiem en Jutters Museum, Barentszstr 21, 1792 AD Oudeschild - T: (0222) 314956, Fax: 310456, E-mail: texelsmuseum@miconnet.nl, Internet: http://www.miconnet.nl/ntexelm. Head: B. Van Tilburg
Science&Tech Museum / Historical Museum / Natural History Museum - 1980
Navigation hist, paintings, ship models, underwater archeology, maritime hist, rescue and pilot services, natural hist, aquaria, marine animals, living seals 25383

Oudewater

De Heksenwaag, Leeuweringerstr 2, 3421 AC Oudewater - T: (0348) 563400. Head: Dr. B. Griepink
Local Museum - 1943
Topography, paintings, old customs, coins, weights 25384

Oudkerk

De Klinze, Van Sminiaweg 36, 9064 KG Oudkerk - T: (058) 25252
Local Museum 25385

Ouwerkerk

Minischeepvaartmuseum, Viane 1, 4305 RL Ouwerkerk
Historical Museum
Marine history, ships 25386

Overloon

Nationaal Oorlogs- en Verzetsmuseum (National War- and Resistance Museum), Museumpark 1, 5825 AM Overloon - T: (0478) 641250, 641820, Fax: 642405, E-mail: overloon@oorlogsmuseum.nl, Internet: http://www.oorlogsmuseum.nl. Head: Dr. S.N. Temming
Military Museum / Historical Museum - 1946
Military vehicles, guns, uniforms, Auschwitz-realia, Drawings (Buchenwald) by Heuzi Piech 25387

Overveen

Achter de Zuilen, Bloemendaalseweg 158, 2051 GJ Overveen - T: (023) 5225655, E-mail: ehfeith@planet.nl
Public Gallery 25388

Papendrecht

Museum voor Moderne Kunst, Markt 2, 3351 AZ Papendrecht - T: (078) 6158695
Fine Arts Museum 25389

De Rietgors, Museum voor Moderne Kunst, P.C. Hooftlaan 180, 3351 ER Papendrecht - T: (078) 6158695, Fax: 6158695. Head: I.A.M. Knapen
Fine Arts Museum - 1967
Cobra (Karel Appel, P. Alechinsky, Corneille, D. Henkes) 25390

Petten

De Dijk Te Kijk, Strandweg, 1755 LH Petten, mail addr: c/o Hoogheemraadschap Noordhollands Noorderkwartier, Postbus 22, 1800 AA Petten - T: (0299) 360611. Head: K. Woestenburg
Science&Tech Museum
Information about dikes 25391

Piaam

't Fûgelhûs, Natuurhistorisches Museum, Buren 6, 8756 JP Piaam - T: (0515) 232161. Head: G. Van der Velde Hiemstra
Agriculture Museum - 1972
Photos of poultry, slides 25392

Pieterburen

Koffie- en Winkelmuseum, Hoofdstr 101, 9968 AC Pieterburen
Special Museum
Coffie, costume, puppet-houses, tobacco, textiles 25393

Poederoijen

Slot Loevestein, Loevestein 1, 5307 TG Poederoijen - T: (0418) 671375
Decorative Arts Museum / Fine Arts Museum
Castle (1357-68) with furniture, paintings and prints 25394

Purmerend

Caddy's Diner, Verzetslaan 3, 1447 XX Purmerend - T: (0299) 422049, Fax: 422049
Science&Tech Museum 25395

Purmerends Museum, Stadhuis, Kaasmarkt 20, 1441 BG Purmerend - T: (0299) 472718, Fax: 428755, E-mail: info@purmerendsmuseum.nl, Internet: http://www.purmerendsmuseum.nl. Head: S. Van den Berg
Local Museum / Decorative Arts Museum
Pottery (1895-1907), local history, handicrafts, design 25396

Raamsdonksveer

Het Nationaal Automobielmuseum, Steurweg 8, 4941 AL Raamsdonksveer - T: (0162) 1585400, Fax: 120890. Head: E.V.N. Louwman
Science&Tech Museum - 1968
Passenger cars, commercial vehicles, cycles, motorcycles, carriages, toys, posters, automobiles 25397

Reeuwijk

Oudheidkamer Reeuwijk, Oudeweg 3, 2811 NM Reeuwijk - T: (0182) 393773
Local Museum
Local history 25398

Rendswoude

Oudheidkamer, Dorpsstr 4, 3927 BD Rendswoude - T: (0318) 571151
Local Museum
Local history 25399

Renesse

Bliksemmuseum De Blikvanger, Capelweg 18, 4325 BT Renesse - T: (0111) 461794
Special Museum 25400

Doe- en Activiteitencentrum Ecoscope, Wilhelminaweg 2, 4325 BE Renesse
Special Museum
Architecture, paintings, geology, flora and fauna natural history, agriculture, ecology 25401

Renswoude

Oudheidkamer Renswoude, Dorpsstr 4, 3927 BD Renswoude
Local Museum
Local history 25402

Reusel

Radio Amateur Museum, Kruisstr 23, 5541 CH Reusel - T: (0497) 644280, E-mail: - radio.amateur.museum@wanadoo.nl, Internet: http://www.brabantmuseumland.nl/reusel. Head: F.J.J. Driesens
Science&Tech Museum
Dutch radios, amateur build radios - library 25403

Rhenen

Streekmuseum Het Rondeel, Kerkstr 1, 3911 LD Rhenen - T: (0317) 612077
Local Museum - 1910
Historical coll of Rhenen, summer residence of Frederic V and Mary Stuart, archeology, jewels, porcelain, tiles, guild silver, sketches, graphics, modern art 25404

Ridderkerk

Oudheidkamer Ridderkerk, Kerksingel 26, 2981 EH Ridderkerk - T: (0180) 430615
Local Museum
Local history 25405

Rijnsburg

Museum Oud-Rijnsburg, Oude Vlietweg 6, 2231 CN Rijnsburg, mail addr: Postbus 266, 2230 AG Rijnsburg - T: (071) 4022961
Local Museum
Local history 25406

Het Spinozahuis, Spinozalaan 29, 2231 SG Rijnsburg
Library with Exhibitions - 1899
Reconstruction of the library of the philosopher B. de Spinoza (1632-1677), editions of his works, works relating to him, portraits, old instruments for grinding lenses 25407

Rijssen

Pelmolen Museum, Pelmolenpad 9a, 7461 PR Rijssen - T: (0548) 533339
Science&Tech Museum
Old mill 25408

Rijssens Museum, Kasteellaan 1, 7461 PV Rijssen, mail addr: Postbus 296, 7460 AG Rijssen - T: (0548) 514261
Local Museum - 1951
Town views, photographs, agricultural and industrial (jute) implements and tools, dolls with costumes, coins, Delft pottery 25409

Rijswijk, Zuid-Holland

Museum Rijswijk Het Tollenshuis, Herenstr 67, 2282 BR Rijswijk, Zuid-Holland - T: (070) 3903617, Fax: 3368880, E-mail: musryszh@xs4all.nl, Internet: http://www.museumryswyk.nl. Head: A.D. Kwakernaak
Local Museum - 1940
Archeological finds, paintings, furniture, local history, contemporary art 25410

Rockanje

Duinhuisjes, Duinstr 18, 323 NK Rockanje - T: (0181) 482749
Open Air Museum
Little Dunehouses 25411

Roden

Jelly van den Bosch Museum, Hoppad 19, 9301 PG Roden
Fine Arts Museum
Graphic art, paintings 25412

Museum Havezate Mensinge, Mensingheweg 7, 9301 KA Roden - T: (050) 5015030
Local Museum
Local history, ceramics, paintings 25413

Museum Kinderwereld, Brink 31, 9301 JK Roden - T: (050) 5018851, Fax: 5015713, E-mail: kinderwereld@capitolonline.nl, Internet: http://www.kinderwereld.net. Head: R. Valenteijn
Special Museum
Antique toys 25414

Roderwolde

Nederlands Graanmuseum, Hoofdstr 60, 9315 PC Roderwolde - T: (050) 5032198
Science&Tech Museum
Old mill (1892) with inventory 25415

Olie- en Korenmolen Woldzigt, Hoofdstr 58, 9315 PC Roderwolde
Local Museum
Local history, agriculture, oil- and corn mill 25416

Roermond

Stedelijk Museum Roermond (Municipal Museum Roermond), Andersonweg 4, 6041 JE Roermond - T: (0475) 333496, Fax: 336299
Decorative Arts Museum / Local Museum - 1932
Contemporary and historical art and design, works by Pierre Cuypers and Hendrik Luyten 25417

Rolde

Streekmuseum Het Dorp van Bartje, Balloerstr 2a, 9451 AK Rolde
Local Museum
Local history, archeology 25418

Roosendaal

Museum De Ghulden Roos, Molenstr 2, 4701 JS Roosendaal - T: (0165) 536916, Fax: 536916. Head: S.L. Verster
Decorative Arts Museum / Fine Arts Museum / Folklore Museum - 1932
Folklore, stoneware (15th-18th c), glass, Delft pottery, porcelain from Asia, toys, paintings and drawings by Alfred Ost, hist of Roosendaal 25419

Rosmalen

Autotron, Graafsebaan 133, 5248 NL Rosmalen - T: (073) 5233300, Fax: 5216795, E-mail: info@autotron.nl, Internet: http://www.autotron.nl. Head: J. Blijenberg
Science&Tech Museum - 1972
Coll of over 100 automobiles, automotive-industry (AutoDome) 25420

Huis van de Toekomst, Graafsebaan 133, 5248 NL Rosmalen - T: (073) 5219050
Science&Tech Museum
House of the future 25421

Rotterdam

Belasting en Douane Museum, Parklaan 14-16, 3016 BB Rotterdam - T: (010) 4400200, Fax: 4361254, E-mail: info@belasting-douanemus.nl, Internet: http://www.belasting-douanemuseum.nl. Head: Dr. L.A. Peeperkorn-van Donselaar
Historical Museum - 1937
History of taxes from ancient times to the present, paintings, prints, furniture, ceramics, pewter, coins, medals, fiscal seals and stamps, instruments, tools, measures and weights, assessment materials, playing cards, round games, uniforms, weapons, means of smuggling - library 25422

Chabot Museum, Museumpark 11, 3015 CB Rotterdam - T: (010) 4363713, Fax: 4360355, E-mail: mail@chabotmuseum.nl, Internet: http://www.chabotmuseum.nl. Head: C. Grootveld-Parrée
Fine Arts Museum - 1993
Paintings by Hendrik Chabot (1894-1949), war cycle 1940-1945, sculptures 1923-1939, Dutch expressionism - educational center 25423

De Dubbele Palmboom, Historisch Museum Rotterdam, Voorhaven 12, Delfshaven, 3024 RM Rotterdam - T: (010) 4761533, Fax: 4782376
Local Museum
Ancient crafts and social life, silver (18th-19th c) 25424

Hilleshuis Museum, Riederlaan 200, 3074 CL Rotterdam - T: (010) 4198698
Decorative Arts Museum 25425

Historisch Museum Rotterdam Het Schielandhuis, Korte Hoogstr 31, 3011 GK Rotterdam - T: (010) 2176767, Fax: 4334499, E-mail: info@hmr.rotterdam.nl, Internet: http://www.hmr.rotterdam.nl. Head: H. Walgenbach
Historical Museum
Hist and art hist of Rotterdam 25426

Home of History, Van Zandvlietpl 1, 3077 AA Rotterdam
Local Museum
Local history, architecture, sport, militaria 25427

KinderKunstHal Villa Zebra, Museumpark 30, 3015 CX Rotterdam - T: (010) 2411717, Fax: 2411710, E-mail: post@villazebra.nl, Internet: http://www.villazebra.nl. Head: Jet Manrho
Fine Arts Museum
Graphics, drawings 25428

Kunsthal Rotterdam, Museumpark, Westzeedijk 341, 3015 AA Rotterdam, mail addr: Postbus 23077, 3001 KB Rotterdam - T: (010) 4400300, Fax: 4367152, E-mail: communicatie@kunsthal.nl, Internet: http://www.kunsthal.nl. Head: W. Pijbes
Fine Arts Museum
Modern and contemporary art, photography, design, Western art 25429

Mariniersmuseum der Koninklijke Marine, Wijnhaven 7-9, 3011 WH Rotterdam - T: (010) 4129600, Fax: 4333619. Head: M.F. Groen
Military Museum
Hist of Corps Mariniers 25430

Maritiem Buitenmuseum, Leuvehaven 50-72, 3011 EA Rotterdam - T: (010) 4048072, Fax: 4333619, Internet: http://www.buitenmuseum.nl
Open Air Museum 25431

Maritiem Museum Rotterdam, Leuvehaven 1, 3011 EA Rotterdam - T: (010) 4132680, Fax: 4137342, E-mail: publ@maritiemmuseum.nl, Internet: http://www.maritiemmuseum.nl. Head: C.O.A. Schimmelpenninck Van der Oije
Science&Tech Museum - 1873
Ship models (15th-20th c), construction designs, globes, atlases, maps, navigation instruments, paintings, ship decorations, documents relating to the history of navigation and maritime constructions, fishing boat models - library, visitor service 25432

Museum Boijmans Van Beuningen, Museumpark 18-20, 3015 CX Rotterdam, mail addr: Postbus 2277, 3000 CG Rotterdam - T: (010) 4419400/470, Fax: 4360500, E-mail: info@boijmans.rotterdam.nl, Internet: http://www.boijmans.rotterdam.nl. Head: C.P.E. Dercon, H. Bongers
Fine Arts Museum - 1847
Div: applied art, Renaissance and baroque, paintings from the Netherlands (15th-17th c), Italy (14th-16th c), France, modern art, expressionists and surrealists, impressionists, realists, sculpture, pop art and photorealism, industrial design 25433

Museum Oud Overschie, Overschiese Dorpsstr 136-138, 3043 CV Rotterdam - T: (010) 4157678
Local Museum
Local history 25434

Museum voor Keramiek Pablo Rueda Lara, Aelbrechtskolk 10, 3024 RE Rotterdam
Decorative Arts Museum
Ceramics 25435

Museumwoning de Kiefhoek, Hendrik Idopl 2, 3073 RC Rotterdam
Special Museum
Architecture, household 25436

Nationaal Schoolmuseum, Nieuwemarkt 1a, 3011 HP Rotterdam - T: (010) 4045425, Fax: 2331801, E-mail: info@schoolmuseum.nl, Internet: http://www.schoolmuseum.nl. Head: Jaap ter Linden
Special Museum - 1979
History of education in Netherlands 25437

Natuurmuseum Rotterdam, Westzeedijk 345, 3015 AA Rotterdam, mail addr: Postbus 23452, 3001 KL Rotterdam - T: (010) 4364222, Fax: 4364399, E-mail: natuurmuseum@nmr.nl, Internet: http://www.nmr.nl. Head: Dr. J.W.F. Reumer
Natural History Museum - 1927
Plio-Pleistocene, Miocene, Oligocene and Eocene mollusca, marine and land mollusca from Europe and the Indo-Australian region, Pleistocene mammalia from the Netherlands, European, Neotropical and IndoAustralian hymenoptera, aculeata, coleoptera and lepidoptera, European birds and mammals, geology, botany, European marine invertebrates, urban flora - library 25438

Nederlands Architektuurinstituut, Museumpark 25, 3015 CB Rotterdam - T: (010) 4401200, Fax: 4366975, E-mail: info@nai.nl, Internet: http://www.nai.nl. Head: Aaron Betsky
Special Museum 25439

Nederlands Economisch Penningkabinet, c/o Erasmusuniversiteit, Burgemeester Oudlaan 50, 3062 PA Rotterdam - T: (010) 4081773, Fax: 4089088, E-mail: onderwater@oos.eur.nl. Head: Prof. G.W. de Wit
Special Museum - 1961
Medals relating to the economic life of Rotterdam and to public works 25440

Nederlands Foto Instituut, Witte de Withstr 63, 3012 BN Rotterdam
Fine Arts Museum
Paintings, photography 25441

De Ontdekhoek Kindermuseum, Pannekoekstr 55, 3011 LC Rotterdam - T: (010) 4143103
Special Museum 25442

Oorlogsverzetsmuseum Rotterdam, Veerlaan 82-92, 3072 ZZ Rotterdam - T: (010) 4840931, Fax: 4859326, E-mail: ovmrotterdam@hetnet.nl. Head: Constanze Endenburg
Military Museum 25443

Openbaar Vervoer Museum, Oostpl 165, 3011 KZ Rotterdam - T: (010) 4330762
Science&Tech Museum 25444

Openlucht Binnenvaartmuseum, Koningsdam 1, 3011 TN Rotterdam - T: (010) 4334430
Science&Tech Museum / Open Air Museum 25445

Scouting Museum de Ducdalf, Heemraadssingel 129, 3022 CD Rotterdam - T: (010) 4775911, Fax: 4779972, E-mail: info@scoutmuseum.nl, Internet: http://www.scoutmuseum.nl. Head: R.G. Eikenoord
Special Museum
Scouting history 25446

Stichting Atlas Van Stolk, Korte Hoogstr 31, 3011 GK Rotterdam - T: (010) 2176724, Fax: 4334499, E-mail: hmr@rotterdam.nl. Head: Dr. J.C. Nix
Library with Exhibitions - 1835
Drawings, engravings, photos concerning the history of the Netherlands, pictures of daily life, historical events and persons (including illustrated books, maps, allegorical prints and caricatures) - room for slideshows 25447

Toy-Toy Museum, Groene Wetering 41, 3062 PB Rotterdam - T: (010) 4525941, Fax: 4524014
Special Museum
Ancient toys and puppets 25448

Tram Museum Rotterdam, Nieuwe Binnenweg 362, Rotterdam, mail addr: Postbus 97620, 2509 GA Den Haag - T: (079) 3311038. Head: J.J.G. Koopmans
Science&Tech Museum - 1965 25449

Wereldmuseum Rotterdam, Willemskade 25, 3016 DM Rotterdam - T: (010) 2707172, Fax: 2707182, E-mail: www.secr@wereldmuseum.rotterdam.nl, Internet: http://www.wereldmuseum.rotterdam.nl. Head: Stanley Bremer
Ethnology Museum - 1885
Ethnological coll from Indonesia, Oceania, the realm of Islam, Asia, Africa, the Americas, contemporary and historical cultures - library, theatre 25450

Witte de With, Centrum voor Hedendaagse Kunst (Centre for Contemporary Art), Witte de Withstr 50, 3012 BR Rotterdam - T: (010) 4110144, Fax: 4117924, E-mail: info@wdw.nl, Internet: http://www.wdw.nl. Head: Catherine David
Fine Arts Museum
Modern and contemporary art 25451

Het Zakkendragershuisje, Historisch Museum Rotterdam, Voorstr 13-15, 3024 RS Rotterdam - T: (010) 4772664. Head: C.J. du Ruy Van Beest Holle
Science&Tech Museum - 1966
Pewterer's workshop, bronze casting moulds (esp. 17th c), stamps 25452

Rozendaal

Kasteel Rosendael, Rosendael 1, 6891 DA Rozendaal - T: (026) 3644645
Decorative Arts Museum
Historic country house, special coll of furniture, silver and porcelain 25453

Ruinen

Pasmans Huus, Oosterstr 16, 7963 AC Ruinen
Local Museum
Local history, folklore, textiles 25454

Ruinerwold

Het Koptisch Museum, Haakswold 5, 7961 LC Ruinerwold
Decorative Arts Museum
25455

Museumboerderij de Karstenhoeve, Dr. Larijweg 21, 7961 NL Ruinerwold - T: (0522) 481447. Head: A. Hoorn Bakker
Agriculture Museum - 1954
Farm (18th c) with complete inventory 25456

Pottenbakkerij Het Ovenhuis, Doctor Larijweg 89, 7961 NP Ruinerwold
Decorative Arts Museum
Pottery, ceramics 25457

Zomerkoestal uut 't Wold, Doctor Larijweg 74, 7961 NN Ruinerwold
Natural History Museum
Natural history, sculpture, geology 25458

Santpoort

Ruïne van Brederode, Velserenderlaan 2, 2082 LA Santpoort - T: (023) 5378763
Archaeological Museum
Archeological objects found in the environs of the ruin, earthenware, weights and measures, glass 25459

Sappemeer

Museumwerf Wolthuis, Noorderstr 308, 9611 AH Sappemeer - T: (0598) 616393
Science&Tech Museum
Old shipyard 25460

Sassenheim

Sikkens Schildersmuseum, Wilhelminalaan 1, 2171 CS Sassenheim - T: (0252) 221089, Fax: 220272. Head: C.P. Tromp
Fine Arts Museum - 1981
Coll illustrating the history of the painting trade and paint industry, coll of wallpaper hist - library 25461

Schagen

Automuseum Schagen, Lagedijkerweg 1a, 1742 NB Schagen - T: (0224) 215101
Science&Tech Museum 25462

Museumboerderij Vreeburg, Loet 14, 1741 BP Schagen - T: (0224) 216906
Science&Tech Museum / Local Museum 25463

Somme Museum, Slotplein 2, 1741 VA Schagen - T: (0224) 213248
Military Museum
Implements, uniforms 25464

Schagerbrug

Oude Ambacht, Schoolstr 14, 1751 CG Schagerbrug - T: (0224) 573007
Local Museum 25465

Oudheidkamer Zijpe, Schagerweg 97, 1751 CB Schagerbrug - T: (0224) 571941
Local Museum
Carts, engravings 25466

Schermerhorn

Museum-molen, Noordervaart 2, 1636 VL Schermerhorn - T: (072) 5021519, Fax: 5021580, E-mail: info@museummolen.nl, Internet: http://www.museummolen.nl. Head: A. Dorst
Science&Tech Museum - 1968
17th century mill with original interior 25467

Schiedam

Kunstcentrum Pand Paulus, Korte Haven 125, 3111 BJ Schiedam - T: (010) 4261557
Fine Arts Museum 25468

Nationaal Coöperatie Museum, Lange Haven 84, 3111 CH Schiedam, mail addr: Stadhouderslaan 26, 3136 BN Vlaardingen - T: (010) 4270920
Historical Museum
Local history 25469

Nederlands Gedistilleerd Museum De gekroonde Brandusketel, Lange Haven 74-76, 3112 GH Schiedam - T: (010) 4269066, Fax: 4732780. Head: P.Th. Tjabbes
Special Museum
Hist of the Genever industry 25470

Stedelijk Museum, Hoogstr 112, 3111 HL Schiedam - T: (010) 2463666, Fax: 2463664, E-mail: stedelijk.museum.schiedam@kabelfoon.nl. Head: D.A. Wind
Fine Arts Museum - 1899
Post-1945 painting and graphics, American pop art, contemporary sculpture and ceramics, works from the Cobra movement, Abstract Expressionism, radical painting and systematic art 25471

Schijndel

Museum Jan Heestershuis, Pompstr 17, 5481 BL Schijndel - T: (073) 5492276
Fine Arts Museum
Prints, paintings by Jan Heesters 25472

Schinveld

Gemeentemuseum Onderbanken, Kloosterlaan 7, 6451 EN Schinveld
Local Museum
Local history, archeology, ceramics, crafts, glass art 25473

Schiphol

Dutch Dakota Association Exhibition, Thermiekstr 152, Hangar 3, 1117 Schiphol - T: (020) 3747700, Fax: 4050221, E-mail: dda@xs4all.nl, Internet: http://www.xs4all.nl/~dda. Head: A.C. Groeneveld
Science&Tech Museum
Collection of Dakota Aeroplanes 25474

Nationaal Luchtvaart Museum Aviodome (National Aviation Museum Avidome), Westelijke Randweg 201, 1118 CT Schiphol - T: (020) 4068000, Fax: 4068001, E-mail: info@aviodome.nl, Internet: http://www.aviodome.nl. Head: A.P.J. Van der Holst
Science&Tech Museum - 1971
Evolution of aviation in the past, present and future 25475

Schipluiden

Regthuis t'Schou, Vlaardingskade 57, 2636 BD Schipluiden - T: (015) 3808311
Local Museum 25476

Schoonebeek

Museum Zwaantje Hans Stockman's Hof, Burgemeester Osselaan 5, 7761 BS Schoonebeek
Local Museum
Local history, archaelogy, crafts, coins 25477

Schoonhoven

Nederlands Goud-, Zilver- en Klokkenmuseum, Kazernepl 4, 2871 CZ Schoonhoven - T: (0182) 385612, Fax: 385855. Head: Dr. G.W.M. Jager
Decorative Arts Museum - 1902
Gold and silver objects, clocks, watches, tools, books, documents - library 25478

Schoonhovens Edelambachtshuys, Haven 13, 2871 CK Schoonhoven - T: (0182) 32614, Fax: 386371, E-mail: info@rikkoertjuweliers.nl, Internet: http://www.rikkoertjuweliers.nl. Head: A. Rikkoert
Decorative Arts Museum
Silver 25479

Schoonoord

Openluchtmuseum Ellert en Brammert, Tramstr 73, 7848 BJ Schoonoord - T: (0591) 382746, Fax: 382746, Internet: http://www.ellerten-brammert.nl. Head: C. Akker
Open Air Museum - 1954
Saksian farm, social life around 1900, geology 25480

Sellingen

Museum Sint Sellian, Dorpsstr 15a, 9551 AB Sellingen
Religious Arts Museum
Interieurs 25481

Simpelveld

Zuid-Limburgse Stoomtreinmaatschappij, Stationsstr 20-22, 6369 ZH Simpelveld - T: (045) 5440018, Fax: 5440081
Science&Tech Museum 25482

Sint Anna ter Muiden

Streeklandbouwmuseum Agrimuda, Greveningseweg 1, 4524 JK Sint Anna ter Muiden - T: (0117) 462844, Fax: 492549, E-mail: ArcoWillebuordse@sluis-aardenburg.nl, Internet: http://www.gemeente.sluis-aardenburg.nl. Head: M. Grbic
Agriculture Museum - 1973
Agricultural history of the Zeeuws-Vlaanderen area, old barns b.e. (1740), plow used only in this area (Wale Ploeg 1610-1900) 25483

Sint Annaland

Streekmuseum Tholen en Sint-Philipsland, Bierensstr 6, 4697 GE Sint Annaland - T: (0166) 652649. Head: M.A. Geuze
Agriculture Museum - 1973
Farm interior, costumes, agricultural implements, topographical and religious prints, toys, pottery, tiles 25484

Sint Geertruid

Limburgs Miniatuurmuseum, Schoolstr 5 7, 6265 AR Sint Geertruid
Local Museum
Archeology, folklore, architecture, geology, folk art 25485

Sint Jacobiparochie

Museum Kuipers, de Vriesstr 3, 9079 KK Sint Jacobiparochie - T: (0518) 491809
Local Museum 25486

Sint Jansteen

Speelgoedmuseum De Kindertijd, Hoofdstr 25, 6564 AM Sint Jansteen - T: (0114) 310313
Special Museum
Toys (1850-1955), children's books 25487

Sint Michielsgestel

Oudheidkundig Museum, Theerestr 42, 5271 GD Sint Michielsgestel - T: (073) 5517903
Archaeological Museum - 1992
Roman antiquities, pottery, coins, bronze, glass, reconstructions of a Roman grave, well and kiln, coll of Roman mortaria stamps 25488

Sint Odilienberg

Roerstreekmuseum, Kerkpl 10, 6077 AA Sint Odilienberg - T: (0475) 532895
Local Museum
Local history, archeology (prehistoric, Roman and medieval), geology, zoology, ornithology, entomology, coins, crafts 25489

Sint Oedenrode

Christ Boelens Jukeboxen Museum, Hulst 10, 5492 SB Sint Oedenrode - T: (0413) 476666, Fax: 476464, E-mail: christ@jukeboxen.nl, Internet: http://www.jukeboxen.nl. Head: Christ Boelens
Music Museum
Collection Jukeboxes 25490

Museum Sint-Paulusgasthuis, Kerkstr 20, 5492 AH Sint Oedenrode - T: (04138) 4100
Local Museum 25491

Oda Museum, Kofferen 43, 5492 BM Sint Oedenrode - T: (0413) 480911
Local Museum
Smithy (1920) 25492

Sittard

Stedelijk Museum Het Domein, Limburgs Centrum voor Fotografie, Kapittelstr 6, 6131 ER Sittard, mail addr: Postbus 18, 6130 AA Sittard - T: (046) 4513460, Fax: 4529111, E-mail: het.domein@wxs.nl, Internet: http://www.hetdomein.nl. Head: Stijn Huijts
Fine Arts Museum - 1993
Contemporary art and photography, local and regional hist 25493

Sliedrecht

Nationaal Baggermuseum, Molendijk 204, 3361 ER Sliedrecht - T: (0184) 414166, Fax: 410289, E-mail: baggermuseum@tref.nl, Internet: http://www.baggermuseum.nl. Head: J.J.A. Wijn
Science&Tech Museum - 1973
Technical and ship models, fotographs, pictures, paintings, technical drawings, dredged objects, dredgers 25494

Sliedrechts Museum, Kerkbuurt 99, 3361 BD Sliedrecht - T: (0184) 413404. Head: W. Bos
Local Museum - 1964
Local history, instruments for water construction, hoop and rope works 25495

Slochteren

Fraeylemaborg, Hoofdweg 30, 9621 AL Slochteren - T: (0598) 421568, Fax: 423045, E-mail: fraeylemaborg@fmog.nl, Internet: http://www.fraeylemaborg.nl. Head: H. Van Harten Boers
Decorative Arts Museum
Small restored castle (15th-18th c), prints particularly concerning the Royal Dutch family, furniture and paintings of 18th and 19th c, Asian porcelain 25496

Museum '40-'45, Hoofdweg 56, 9621 AM Slochteren
Historical Museum
Militaria, World war II 25497

Politie-Petten Museum, Zuiderweg 3, 9621 BK Slochteren - T: (050) 5873257, 5413261, Fax: 5871099, E-mail: h_buurma@hotmail.com. Head: Hilbrand Buurma
Special Museum
Police caps from all over the world 25498

Sloten

Museum Stedhûs Sleat, Heerenwal 48, 8556 XW Sloten - T: (0514) 531541, Fax: 531898. Head: Dr. M. Albers
Local Museum - 1984
Cinematografic material, topography, paintings, weapons, flags, tools, fans, clocks, magic laterns 25499

Sluis

Oudheidkundige Verzameling, Groote Markt 1, 4524 CD Sluis - T: (0117) 475560, Fax: 492540, E-mail: ArcoWilleboordse@sluis-aardenburg.nl, Internet: http://www.gemeente.sluis-aardenburg.nl. Head: D. Gÿsel-Dewaele
Local Museum - 1877
Town hall (14th c), paintings (16th-17th c), tapestries (17th c), grave fragments, archaeological finds 25500

Streeklandbouwmuseum Agrimuda, Greveningseweg 1, 4524 JK Sluis - T: (0117) 462844, 475544, Fax: 492540, E-mail: arcowilleboordse@sluis-aardenburg.nl, Internet: http://www.sluis-aardenburg.nl. Head: Arco Willeboordse
Agriculture Museum
Crafts, costume, agriculture, carriages 25501

Sneek

Fries Scheepvaart Museum, Kleinzand 14, 8601 BH Sneek - T: (0515) 414057, Fax: 434155, E-mail: fsm@freemail.nl, Internet: http://www.friesnet.nl/musea/fsm.htm
Science&Tech Museum / Historical Museum - 1938
History of navigation in Friesland, ship models, navigation instruments, maps, coins, paintings, archeology, topography, silver - period rooms 25502

Schutterskamer, Stadhuis, Marktstr 11, 8600 HA Sneek - T: (0515) 485555, Fax: 483374, Internet: http://www.sneek.nl
Military Museum - 1950
Historic townhall (1761) 25503

Soest

Galerie Anna Paulownahuis, Burgemeester Grothestr 51, 3761 CL Soest - T: (035) 6021983
Public Gallery 25504

Museum Oud Soest, Steenhoffstr 46, 3764 BM Soest - T: (035) 6023878
Local Museum - 1905
Coach making, old trades and shops 25505

Soesterberg

Militaire Luchtvaart Museum, Kamp van Zeist 2-4, 3769 DL Soesterberg, mail addr: Postbus 184, 3769 ZK Soesterberg - T: (0346) 353815, Fax: 351143, E-mail: info@mlm.af.dnet.mindef.nl, Internet: http://www.militaireluchtvaartmuseum.nl. Head: Dr. J.A.M.M. Janssen
Military Museum - 1968
7 pre-war aircraft, 7 aircraft Naval Air Service, 25 aircraft Royal Netherlands Air Force, Complete coll engines of piston and jet propulsion, uniforms, artifacts, ground equipment, missiles - library, archive 25506

Sommelsdijk

Streekmuseum Goeree en Overflakkee, Kerkstr 2, 3245 AK Sommelsdijk - T: (0187) 43778
Archaeological Museum - 1956
Roman finds, objects relating to fishery, navigation and militia, folk costumes, living style 25507

Spanbroek

Frisia Museum, Spanbroekerweg 162, 1715 GV Spanbroek - T: (0226) 351111, Fax: 351859, E-mail: receptie@frisia-museum.nl, Internet: http://www.frisia-museum.nl. Head: Dr. Emily Ansenk
Fine Arts Museum
Magical realism, 20th c realistic art, pittura metafysica, surrealism 25508

Spijkenisse

Clown Pepie Museum, Roerdomphoek 21, 3201 HM Spijkenisse - T: (0181) 619721
Performing Arts Museum 25509

Stadskanaal

Museum Musica, Scheepswerfkade 34-35, 9503 PB Stadskanaal
Music Museum
Paintings, musical instruments, clocks 25510

Museumspoorlijn Star, Stationsstr 3, 9503 AD Stadskanaal - T: (0599) 651890, Fax: 653003, E-mail: www.info@stadskanaalrail.nl, Internet: http://www.stadskanaalrail.nl
Science&Tech Museum
Tramway history 25511

Streekhistorisch Centrum, Ceresstr 2, 9502 EA Stadskanaal - T: (0599) 612649
Local Museum
Documents on navigation, potatoe industry, crafts 25512

Staphorst

Museumboerderij, Gemeenteweg 67, 7951 CE Staphorst, mail addr: Binnenweg 26, 7951 DE Staphorst - T: (0522) 462526
Local Museum
Weaving works, interior 25513

Steenwijk

Kermis- en Circusmuseum Steenwijk, Onnastr 3, 8331 HK Steenwijk - T: (0521) 518687
Special Museum 25514

Oudheidkamer, Markt 64, 8331 HK Steenwijk - T: (05210) 12641
Local Museum
Local history 25515

Steijl

Missiemuseum Steijl, Sint-Michaelstr 7, 5935 BL Steijl - T: (077) 3261499, Fax: 3261498, E-mail: missiemuseum@steyler.nl. Head: G.M. Coppus
Ethnology Museum / Religious Arts Museum / Natural History Museum - 1882
Coll Schmutzer, Christian Javanese woodcarvings (1924-1927) made by Sundanese sculptor Iko in order of Jos. Schmutzer 25516

Stein

Archeologiemuseum, Hoppenkampstr 14a, 6171 VP Stein - T: (046) 338919, Internet: http://www.rucosoft.demon.nl/archeologie.html. Head: M. Deriks
Archaeological Museum - 1967
Gallery-tomb of the Seine-Oise-Marne-culture (dated from about 2850 BC), prehistoric finds from Stein and the environs 25517

Stellendam

Delta Expo, Haringvlietsluizen, 3251 LD Stellendam
Science&Tech Museum - 1972
Exposition of the Delta-works - educational center, library 25518

Sterksel

Peter Van den Braken Centrum, Turven 12, 6029 PD Sterksel - T: (040) 221004
Fine Arts Museum
Netherlandish paintings 25519

Stevensweert

Streekmuseum Stevensweert/ Ohé en Laak, Jan Van Steffeswertpl 1, 6107 BZ Stevensweert - T: (0475) 551693
Local Museum - 1983
Local history 25520

Strijen

Het Land van Strijen, Kerkstr 47, 3291 AK Strijen - T: (078) 6741502, 6742118. Head: A.G. Voordendaf
Local Museum
Local history, WW II, waterfloods, art exhibitions, blacksmith, archeology from 2200 before Christ till 19th c 25521

Surhuisterveen

Munt- en Penningkabinet van de Spaar- en Voorschotbank, Jan Binneslaan 9a, 9231 CA Surhuisterveen
Special Museum
Coins, medals 25522

Susteren

Volkskundig Educatie Museum, Op de Pas 6, 6114 RA Susteren
Local Museum
Ethnology, folklore, ceramics, paintings, medicine, glass, religious art, education 25523

Swalmen

Volkskundig en Voorhistorisch Museum, Pastoor Pinckersstr, 6071 NW Swalmen - T: (0475) 501501, 501298. Head: Dr. A. Van Rijswijck
Ethnology Museum / Archaeological Museum
Early History 25524

Tegelen

Pottenbakkersmuseum (Pottery Museum), Kasteellaan 8, 5932 AG Tegelen - T: (077) 3260213, Fax: 3260214
Decorative Arts Museum
Earthenware (19th c), tobacco-boxes, sculptures, decorated dishes, modern ceramics 25525

Ter Apel

Museum Kloster Ter Apel, Boslaan 3-5, 9561 LH Ter Apel - T: (0599) 581370, Fax: 587140, E-mail: receptie@museumklooster-terapel.com, Internet: http://www.museumklooster-terapel.com. Head: A. Kuper
Religious Arts Museum - 1989
15th c cloister, inventory, constuction fragments, stained glass, tower clock (17th c), coll. paraments (19th c) - Herb garden 25526

Poppenmuseum, Rundestr 29, 9561 PS Ter Apel
Special Museum
Puppet-houses 25527

Terhorne

Museum Kameleon Dorp en Museum Hans Brinker, Buorren 43, 8493 LC Terhorne
Folklore Museum
Printing art, folklore, literature 25528

Terneuzen

Schoolmuseum, Vissteeg 4, 4531 EX Terneuzen
Historical Museum
Local history, education 25529

Schooltijd Schoolmuseum, Tuinpad 4, 4531 EW Terneuzen
Historical Museum
Education 25530

Thorn

Het Land van Thorn/ Panorama Thorn, Wijngaard 14, 6017 AG Thorn - T: (0475) 562761
Local Museum 25531

Museum in de Stiftkerk, Wijngaard 11, 6017 AG Thorn - T: (0475) 561410, 562241, Fax: 561736, E-mail: hamanspwfm@planet.nl. Head: Dr. P. Hamans
Religious Arts Museum - 1931
Liturgical objects, portraits, silver 25532

Tiel

Museum Sacrum, Prinses Irenelaan 10, 4002 AR Tiel - T: (0344) 618926
Religious Arts Museum 25533

Streekmuseum De Groote Sociëteit, Plein 48, 4001 LJ Tiel - T: (0344) 614416, Fax: 664114, E-mail: museumtiel@hetnet.nl
Decorative Arts Museum
Interiors, topography, coins, tin, copper, porcelain 25534

Tijnje

Eerste Nederlandse Opel Automuseum, Riperweg 26a, 8406 AJ Tijnje - T: (0513) 571401, 571119, Fax: 571702
Science&Tech Museum 25535

Tilburg

Het Koetsmuseum, Broekstr 9, 5018 TD Tilburg - T: (013) 5433760
Science&Tech Museum
Old Carriages 25536

Maison du Vin (closed) 25537

Muziekinstrumentenmakersmuseum, Nijverstr 4a, 5041 AH Tilburg - T: (013) 5423525
Music Museum 25538

Natuurmuseum Brabant, Spoorlaan 434, 5038 CH Tilburg, mail addr: Postbus 924, 5000 AX Tilburg - T: (013) 5353935, Fax: 5351090, E-mail: info@natuurmuseumbrabant.nl, Internet: http://www.natuurmuseumbrabant.nl. Head: Dr. F.J.M. Ellenbroek
Natural History Museum - 1933
Birds, mammals, insects, fossils, plants - library, department of education 25539

Nederlands Textielmuseum (Dutch Textile Museum), Goirkestr 96, 5046 GN Tilburg - T: (013) 5367475, Fax: 5363240, E-mail: textielmuseum@tilburg.nl, Internet: http://www.textielmuseum.nl. Head: C.E.M. Reinders
Science&Tech Museum / Decorative Arts Museum - 1958
Textile art, textile design, industrial machines - library 25540

De Pont, Stichting voor Hedendaagse Kunst, Wilhelminapark 1, 5041 EA Tilburg, mail addr: Postbus 233, 5000 AE Tilburg - T: (013) 5438300, Fax: 5420952, E-mail: info@depont.nl, Internet: http://www.depont.nl. Head: Hendrik Driessen
Fine Arts Museum
Museum of Modern and Contemporary Arts 25541

Poppen- en Speelgoedmuseum, Telefoonstr 13-15, 5038 DL Tilburg - T: (013) 5436305, Fax: 5424234, E-mail: poppenmuseum@hetnet.nl, Internet: http://www.poppenmuseum.nl. Head: H.H Bechers
Special Museum
Museum of Dolls en Puppets, toys 25542

Scryption, Museum voor Schriftelijke Communicatie, Spoorlaan 434a, 5038 CH Tilburg - T: (013) 5800821, E-mail: scryption@tref.nl, Internet: http://www.tref.nl/tilburg/scryption. Head: R.R. Berkel
Science&Tech Museum - 1949
Various writing and typing apparati, typewriters, calculating machines, fountain pens, inkwells and office equipment - library 25543

Uden

Museum voor Religieuze Kunst, Vorstenburg 1, 5401 AZ Uden - T: (0413) 263431, Fax: 253706, E-mail: info@museumvoorreligieuzekunst.nl, Internet: http://www.museumvoorreligieuzekunst.nl. Head: Dr. L.C.B.M. Van Liebergen
Religious Arts Museum
Religious objects and art, paintings, manuscripts (15th-16th c) 25544

Uithuizen

Internationaal Museum 1939-1945, Dingeweg 1, 9981 NC Uithuizen - T: (0595) 434100, Fax: 431837, E-mail: mus39-45@tref.nl, Internet: http://www.museum11939-1945.nl
Historical Museum 25545

Kantmuseum, Oude Dijk 7, 9981 TH Uithuizen
Historical Museum
Arts and crafts, textiles 25546

Museum Menkemaborg, Menkemaweg 2, 9981 CV Uithuizen - T: (0595) 431970, Fax: 434774, E-mail: menkemaborg@castel.nl, Internet: http://www.menkemaborg.nl. Head: I.M. Stamhuis
Decorative Arts Museum / Historic Site - 1700
Castle (17th-18th c) with complete inventory, portraits, carved mantelpieces (about 1700), furniture, glass, silver, formal garden with maze, reconstructed after 1700 plan, and kitchen gardens 25547

Uithuizermeeden

Het Hoogeland Museum, Hoofdstr 13, 9982 AA Uithuizermeeden
Historical Museum
Crafts, textiles 25548

Ulvenhout

Heemkundemuseum Paulus Van Daesdonck, Pennendijk 1, 4851 VL Ulvenhout, mail addr: Postbus 89, 4850 AB Ulvenhout - T: (076) 5612742. Head: C.J.M. Leyten
Folklore Museum
Interior, costumes 25549

Urk

Het Oude Raadhuis, Wijk 2-4, 8321 EP Urk - T: (0527) 683262, Fax: 687444, E-mail: museum@opurk.nl, Internet: http://www.museum.opurk.nl
Local Museum 25550

Visserijtentoonstelling Hulp en Steun, Westhavenkade, Heerenkamp 15, 8321 BW Urk
Special Museum
History of fishery at Urk, local costumes and folk art, fossils 25551

Utrecht

Aboriginal Art Museum, Oudegracht 176, 3511 NP Utrecht - T: (030) 2380100, Fax: 2380102, E-mail: info@aamu.nl, Internet: http://www.aamu.nl
Fine Arts Museum
Paintings, ethnic art 25552

Amev Verzekeringsmuseum, Archimedeslaan 10, 3584 BA Utrecht - T: (030) 2573105
Special Museum
History of insurances 25553

Archaeologische Verzameling der Rijksuniversiteit, Lange Nieuwstr 106, 3512 PN Utrecht, mail addr: Kromme Nieuwegracht 29, 3512 HD Utrecht - T: (030) 2536030, Fax: 2536167, E-mail: joop.j.derksen@let.uu.nl. Head: J.J.V.M. Derksen
Archaeological Museum / University Museum - 1928
Greek and Roman antiquities 25554

Centraal Museum Utrecht, Nicolaaskerkhof 1, 3512 XC Utrecht, mail addr: Postbus 2106, 3500 GC Utrecht - T: (030) 2362362, Fax: 2332006, E-mail: info@centraalmuseum.nl, Internet: http://www.centraalmuseum.nl. Head: Dr. K.M.T. Ex
Fine Arts Museum / Decorative Arts Museum - 1838
Paintings, sculptures, designs, graphics (mainly artists of Utrecht 15th-19th c), furniture, doll's house (1680), ceramics, porcelain, silver, numismatics, costumes (18th-19th c), lace, textiles, art objects relating to the history of Utrecht, archeology, ship (800), architectural fragments 25555

Corpsmuseum van het Utrechtsch Studenten Corps, Janskerkhof 14, 3512 BL Utrecht - T: (030) 2360800, Fax: 2360810, E-mail: senaat.usc@wxs.nl, Internet: http://www.usc.nl. Head: H.R. Eekhof
Historical Museum / University Museum 25556

Moluks Historisch Museum, Kruisstr 313, 3581 GK Utrecht - T: (030) 2367116, Fax: 2328967, E-mail: info@museum-maluku.nl, Internet: http://www.museum-maluku.nl. Head: W. Manuhutu, H. Smeets
Ethnology Museum - 1990 25557

Museum Catharijneconvent, Lange Nieuwstr 38, 3512 PH Utrecht, mail addr: Postbus 8518, 3503 RM Utrecht - T: (030) 2313835, Fax: 2317896, E-mail: - catharijneconvent@wxs.nl, Internet: http://www.catharijneconvent.nl. Head: K. Reichardt
Religious Arts Museum / Historical Museum / Fine Arts Museum - 1978
Cultural hist of Christianity in the Netherlands, paintings, sculptures, manuscripts, textiles, minor arts, Carolingian ivory chalice, Aachen, ivory icon with the Hodogetria, Constantinopel (beginning of the 9th c), Rembrandt van Rijn 'The baptism of the eunuch' - library, educational center 25558

Museum Diergeneeskunde, Yalelaan 1, 3584 CL Utrecht, mail addr: Postbus 80150, 3508 TD Utrecht - T: (030) 2534675. Head: Dr. P. Koolmees
Historical Museum - 1954
Hist of education in veterinary sciences in the Netherlands, veterinary instruments, hist of veterinary practice 25559

Museum voor het Kruideniersbedrijf, Hoogt 6, 3512 GW Utrecht, mail addr: Postbus 1442, 3500 BK Utrecht - T: (030) 2316628. Head: B.W. Timmerman
Agriculture Museum
Grocery from 1873 with colonial produce 25560

Nationaal Museum van Speelklok tot Pierement, Buurkerkhof 10, 3511 KC Utrecht - T: (030) 2312789, Fax: 2322285, E-mail: post@museumspeelklok.nl, Internet: http://www.museumspeelklok.nl. Head: Dr. H.M. Blankenberg
Music Museum - 1958
Automatic musical instruments 25561

Het Nederlands Muntmuseum, Leidseweg 90, 3531 BG Utrecht, mail addr: Postbus 2407, 3500 GK Utrecht - T: (030) 2910410, Fax: 2910467, E-mail: museum@coins.nl, Internet: http://www.muntmuseum.nl. Head: Albert A.J. Scheffers
Special Museum - 1845
Coins and medals especially from the Netherlands (1st c AD to present), weights and measures, minting-tools, space and machines - library 25562

Nederlands Spoorwegmuseum (The Dutch Railway Museum), Maliebaanstation 16, 3581 XW Utrecht - T: (030) 2306206, Fax: 2318286, E-mail: info@spoorwegmuseum.nl, Internet: http://www.spoorwegmuseum.nl. Head: Dr. P.M.L. Van Vlijmen
Science&Tech Museum - 1927
History of the railway and tramway, especially in the Netherlands, sketches, originals, models, instruments, graphics, drawings, photographs, numismatics, prints, locomotives, electric tram engines, horse and buggy steam trams, signals, special trains for kids 25563

Nederlands Waterleidingmuseum, Lauwerhof 29, 3512 VD Utrecht, mail addr: Postbus 40205, 3504 AA Utrecht - T: (030) 2321152, Fax: 2487474. Head: J.A.L de Meyere
Science&Tech Museum
History of water-supply 25564

Palaeobotanisch Museum, Budapestlaan 4, 3584 CD Utrecht - T: (030) 2532629, 2532799, Fax: 2535096, E-mail: j.vanderburgh@bio.uu.nl. Head: Dr. J. Van der Burgh
Natural History Museum - 1977
library 25565

Poppenhuis Carmen, Wittevrouwensingel 102, 3514 AM Utrecht
Special Museum 25566

Rietveld Schröderhuis, Centraal Museum Utrecht, Prins Hendriklaan 50a, 3583 EP Utrecht - T: (030) 2362310, Fax: 2332006, Internet: http://www.centraalmuseum.nl
Local Museum
House designed by Gerrit Rietveld 25567

Universiteitsmuseum Utrecht, Lange Nieuwstr 106, 3512 PN Utrecht - T: (030) 2538008, Fax: 2538700, E-mail: peter.dehaan@museum.uu.nl, Internet: http://www.museum.uu.nl. Head: Drs. Peter de Haan
Natural History Museum / Science&Tech Museum / University Museum - 1938
Permanent historical coll of scientific and medical instruments, microscopes, zoological specimen, portraits, medals, books, curiosities 25568

Volksbuurtmuseum Wijk, Waterstr 27, 3511 BW Utrecht
Local Museum / Folklore Museum
Local history, folklore, crafts, paintings, industrial development 25569

Vaals

Kopermolen, Van Clermontplein 11, 6291 AT Vaals - T: (043) 304668
Science&Tech Museum 25570

Vaassen

Kasteel Cannenburch, M. Van Rossumplein 4, 8171 EB Vaassen - T: (0578) 571292. Head: Dr. C.C.G. Quarles Van Ufford
Decorative Arts Museum - 1951
Castle (14th c), interior, family portraits of Gelderland (16th-19th c), ceramics 25571

Valkenburg

Museum der Katakombenstichting, Plenkerstr 55, 6301 GL Valkenburg - T: (043) 6012554, Fax: (046) 4421443. Head: Bert Heggen
Religious Arts Museum - 1910
Religious objects from ancient Rome, reconstructed Roman catacombs 25572

Steenkolenmijn Daalhemergroeve, Daalhemerweg 31, 6301 BJ Valkenburg - T: (043) 6012491, Fax: 16550, E-mail: ecaselli@xs4all.nl, Internet: http://www.steenkolenmijn.nl. Head: E.M.H.C.M. Caselli Wijsbek
Science&Tech Museum - 1917
Reconstructed coal mine with original tools and machines, fossils 25573

Streekmuseum Land van Valkenburg, Grotestr 31, 6301 CW Valkenburg - T: (043) 6016394. Head: Dr. N. Beuken
Local Museum - 1951
Marlstone building, geology, citizen soldiery, devotional objects, pharmacy, archaeology, carneval, flintstone, contemporary art, extraordinary clocks 25574

Valkenswaard

Museum Van Gerwen-Lemmens, Leenderweg 71, 5555 CA Valkenswaard - T: (040) 2012162, Fax: 2044813, E-mail: ch.gerwen@wxs.nl. Head: Dr. Ch. Van Gerwen
Religious Arts Museum - 1980
Religious Art, sculpture and textile 25575

Veendam

Porselein Dierenpark, Landbouwstr 27, 9643 GA Veendam - T: (0598) 625333
Decorative Arts Museum
Animals of porcelain 25576

Het Veenkoloniaal Museum, Winkler Prinsstr 5, 9641 AR Veendam - T: (0598) 616393, Fax: 616590, E-mail: info@veenkoloniaalmuseum.nl, Internet: http; // www.veenkoloniaalmuseum.nl. Head: Petra Maters
Local Museum - 1939
Local history, documents, reproductions, books, library Winkler Prins and Geert Teis, English and Russian ceramics (18th c), photos of the local surroundings, old maps, ship models and many objects regarding shipping and sea history of the marsh colonies - library 25577

Verzamelmuseum, Beneden Oosterdiep 60, 9641 AJ Veendam - T: (0598) 621122, Fax: 616688. Head: E.A. Luten Schuitema
Decorative Arts Museum 25578

Veenendaal

Historisch Museum Het Kleine Veenlo, Markt 10, 3901 DN Veenendaal - T: (0318) 550010
Local Museum 25579

Veenhuizen

Gevangenismuseum Veenhuizen, Hoofdweg 8, 9341 BH Veenhuizen - T: (0592) 388264
Local Museum
Local history, prision 25580

Veenklooster

Agrarisch Bedrijfsmuseum De Brink, Kleasterwei 2, 9297 WS Veenklooster - T: (0511) 443992
Agriculture Museum
Agricultural machinery from 1800 25581

Fogelsangh State, Kloosterweg 1, 9297 WT Veenklooster - T: (0511) 441970. Head: R. Vos
Decorative Arts Museum - 1963
Old glass, porcelain, family portraits, furniture, old kitchen, coppersmith's shop with workshop, toys, carriage house with carriages, hunting room 25582

Veere

De Schotse Huizen, Kaai 27, 4351 AA Veere - T: (0118) 501744, Fax: 501744. Head: J. Van den Broeke
Local Museum - 1947
Topography of Veere, crafts, costumes of Zeeland, Chinese and Japanese ceramics, jewelry, porcelain, fishery, pictures, furniture 25583

Vierschaar Museum, Stadhuis, Markt 5, Veere, mail addr: Postbus 1000, 4357 ZV Koudekerke - T: (0118) 555444, Fax: 555433
Local Museum - 1881
Hall with Gobelin tapestries and paintings, guild pieces, laws, historical objects 25584

Veldhoven

Gemeentelijk Museum 't Oude Slot, Hemelrijken 6, 5502 HM Veldhoven - T: (040) 2533160. Head: P. Mols
Local Museum / Archaeological Museum - 1964
Pre-industrial implements and domestic utensils (16th-19th c), local archeological finds (prehistory to middle ages) 25585

Velp

Historische Kruidenierswinkel Fa. Wijlhuizen, Emmastr 10, 6881 ST Velp
Historical Museum
Historical grocer's shop with coffee and peanut roaster 25586

Velsen Zuid

Museum Beeckestijn, Rijksweg 136, 1981 LD Velsen Zuid - T: (0255) 512091, Fax: 61515
Decorative Arts Museum - 1969
Interiors (18th-19th c), paintings (17th-19th c), fans (18th-19th c) 25587

De Romeinen in Velsen, Oude Raadhuis, Torenstr 7, 2011 KR Velsen Zuid, mail addr: Parklaan 39, 2011 KR Haarlem - T: (023) 5320788
Archaeological Museum
Roman history 25588

Venhuizen

Schaatsmuseum, Kerkeveld 4, 1606 AV Venhuizen - T: (0228) 541790
Historical Museum 25589

Venlo

Limburgs Museum, Keulsepoort 5, 5911 BX Venlo - T: (077) 3522112, Fax: 3548396, Internet: http:// limburgsmuseum.nl. Head: Dr. Jos Schatorje
Local Museum / Folklore Museum
Regional history, folklore, ceramics, crafts, archeology, industrial development, religious art, costume, paintings 25590

Museum Van Bommel Van Dam, Deken Van Oppensingel 6, 5911 AD Venlo - T: (077) 3513457, Fax: 3546860, E-mail: info@vanbommelvandam.nl, Internet: http://www.vanbommelvandam.nl. Head: Th.G.M.J. Voragen
Fine Arts Museum - 1971 25591

Venray

Geschied- en Oudheidkundig Museum 't Freulekeshuus, Eindstr 8, 5801 CR Venray - T: (0478) 583880, Fax: 641084, E-mail: info@museumvenray.nl. Head: Dr. M.H.J. Van Dorst
Historical Museum
Local history, archeology (stone ages, Roman and Merovingian times), coins (15th-17th c) 25592

Odapark, Merseloseweg 117, 5801 CC Venray - T: (0478) 513690, Fax: 533999, E-mail: info@odapark.com, Internet: http://www.odapark.com. Head: F. Welschen
Public Gallery
Sculptures, modern art 25593

Vianen

Stedelijk Museum Vianen, Voorstr 97, 4132 AP Vianen - T: (0347) 371648. Head: Prof. R.A.P. Tielman
Local Museum - 1969
Archeological finds, tin, bronze, silver, furniture, paintings, porcelain, Delft pottery, local and regional hist 25594

Vinkeveen

Museum in de Veenen, Herenweg 240, 3645 DW Vinkeveen - T: (0297) 22223
Historical Museum
History of peatdigging with implements 25595

Vlaardingen

Muziekinformatie- en Documentatiecentrum Ton Stolk, Westhavenkade 45, 3131 AE Vlaardingen - T: (010) 4347240, E-mail: tonstolk@zonnet.nl, Internet: http://www.tonstdk.nlk. Head: Ton Stolk
Music Museum
Music instruments, music autographs 25596

Streekmuseum Jan Anderson, Kethelweg 50, 3135 GM Vlaardingen - T: (010) 4343843, Fax: 4343843. Head: J. Anderson
Local Museum
Local history, folk art, toys 25597

Visserijmuseum, c/o Instituut voor de Nederlandse Zeevisserij, Westhavenkade 53-54, 3131 AG Vlaardingen - T: (010) 4348722, Fax: 4604152, E-mail: Visserijmuseum@wxs.nl, Internet: http:// www.visserijmuseum.nl. Head: Dr. J.P. ter Brugge
Science&Tech Museum / Historical Museum - 1962
Fishery, ship models, fishing gear and techniques, fish detection and navigation, interiors, costumes, folk art - documentation centre, library, 25598

Vledder

Miramar Zeemuseum, Vledderweg 25, 8381 AB Vledder - T: (0521) 381300, E-mail: info@miramar-zeemuseum.nl, Internet: http://www.miramar-zeemuseum.nl. Head: A. Nicola
Natural History Museum
Shells from various oceans, coral, fish embryo fossils, starfish, marine birds, dioramas 25599

Museum Hedendaagse Grafiek en Glaskunst, Brink 1, 8381 BE Vledder - T: (0521) 383352, Fax: 383354, E-mail: postmaster@museums-vledder.nl, Internet: http://www.museums-vledder.nl. Head: Dr. H.A. Plenter
Fine Arts Museum
Graphic art, sculpture, paintings, glass art 25600

Museum voor Valse Kunst, Brink 1, 8381 BE Vledder - T: (0521) 383352, Fax: 383354, E-mail: postmaster@museums-vledder.nl, Internet: http://www.museums-vledder.nl. Head: Dr. H.A. Plenter
Fine Arts Museum
Sculpture, glass art, graphics, paintings 25601

Vledderveen, Drente

Hans van Riessen Museum, Jan van der Veenweg 2, 8385 GT Vledderveen, Drente
Decorative Arts Museum
Arts and crafts 25602

Vlieland

De Noordwester, Dorpsstr 150, 8899 AN Vlieland - T: (0562) 451700, Fax: 451895
Natural History Museum - 1984
Birds, shells, sea fish, objects from the beach and wrecks 25603

Het Trompshuys, Dorpstr 99, 8899 AD Vlieland, mail addr: Postbus 14, 8899 ZN Vlieland - T: (0562) 451600, Fax: 451600. Head: Bert Huiskes
Fine Arts Museum - 1958
Dutch paintings (Betzy R. Akersloot-Berg, Hendrik Willem Mesdag), Max Liebermann 25604

Vlijmen

Aansteker- en Lucifermuseum, Beneluxlaan 45, 5251 LD Vlijmen - T: (073) 5117102. Head: Frans Van der Heijden
Special Museum
Museum of Cigarettelighters and Matches 25605

Vlissingen

Stedelijk Museum Vlissingen → Zeeuws Maritiem Muzeeum

Zeeuws Maritiem Muzeeum, Nieuwendijk 11, 4381 CG Vlissingen - T: (0118) 412498, Fax: 430307, E-mail: info@lampsinshuis.com. Head: Dr. W.I.M. Weber
Historical Museum - 2002
Maritime history of Zeeland, maritime archaeology, paintings, ship models, tiles 25606

Volendam

Volendams Museum, Zeestr 37, 1131 ZD Volendam - T: (0299) 364564. Head: Hein Veerman
Local Museum
Local history, furniture, costumes, coins 25607

Vollenhove

Oudheidkamer Brederwiede, Bisschopstr 24, 8325 BC Vollenhove, mail addr: Moespot 13, 8325 PB Vollenhove - T: (0527) 241700
Local Museum
Local history, carts 25608

Voorburg

Huygens Museum Hofwijck, Westeinde 2a, 2275 AD Voorburg - T: (070) 3872311, Fax: 3867257. Head: E. de Heen
Local Museum - 1928
Family portraits, sculptures and documents concerning the Huygens family 25609

Museum Swaensteijn, Herenstr 101, 2271 CC Voorburg - T: (070) 3861673, Fax: 3874185, E-mail: swaensteyn@zonnet.nl. Head: Dr. Alexandra E. Oostdijk
Historical Museum - 1961
Topography of Voorburg, local history and art 25610

Voorschoten

Kasteel Duivenvoorde, Laan van Duivenvoorde 4, 2252 AK Voorschoten - T: (071) 5613752, Fax: 5617638. Head: Dr. T.G.D. Steenbeek
Decorative Arts Museum - 1960
Castle (17th c) with interior (17th-19th c), family portraits, porcelain 25611

Vorchten

Poppenspe(e)lmuseum, Kerkweg 38, 8193 KL Vorchten - T: (0578) 631329, 560239, Fax: 631329, 560621, E-mail: info@poppenspelmuseum.nl, Internet: http://www.poppenspelmuseum.nl. Head: O.J.E. Von der Mieden
Performing Arts Museum / Special Museum - 1983
Dolls, puppets, books, prints, photographs - library 25612

Vries

Kerkmuseum De Klokkengieterij, Brink 3, 9481 BE Vries - T: (0592) 52160. Head: Dr. L.A. de Groot
Religious Arts Museum
Church (11th c) with Gothic choir (1425), model of regional bell foundry (1577), sarcophagi 25613

Vriezenveen

Museum Oud Vriezenveen, Westeinde 65, 7671 CD Vriezenveen - T: (0546) 563476. Head: T. Jansen Bramer
Local Museum - 1953
Prehistoric finds, fossils, agricultural implements, craftmen's tools, pottery (16th-18th c), farm kitchen with antique furniture, memorabilia on relations to Czarist Russia 25614

Veenmuseum Wester-Haar-Vriezenveensewijk, Paterswal 9, 7671 TB Vriezenveen - T: (0523) 52520
Natural History Museum
Implements of peat-bog Workers 25615

Vught

Nationaal Monument Kamp Vught, Lunettenlaan 600, 5263 NT Vught - T: (073) 6560835
Military Museum
History of the Pioneer Corps 25616

Oudheidkamer, Taalstr 88, 5261 BH Vught
Local Museum
Local history, crafts, toys 25617

Waalwijk

Nederlands Leder- en Schoenenmuseum (Dutch Leather and Shoe Museum), Elzenweg 25, 5144 MB Waalwijk - T: (0416) 332738, Fax: 344176, E-mail: schoenenmuseum@tref.nl, Internet: http:// www.tref.nl/waalwijk/schoenenmuseum. Head: Dr. W. Blok
Special Museum - 1954
Historic and exotic shoes of all cultures, modern shoes, old work instruments, other leather wares, old shoemaker's living room and workshop of Brabant, paintings, silver of the old shoemakers' corps - documentary centre on leather 25618

Wageningen

Casteelsche Poort, Bowlespk 1a, 6701 DN Wageningen - T: (0317) 421436
Historic Site 25619

International Soil Reference and Information Centre, Duivendaal 9, 6700 AR Wageningen, mail addr: Postbus 353, 6700 AJ Wageningen - T: (0317) 471711, Fax: 471700, E-mail: soil@isric.nl, Internet: http://www.isric.nl. Head: Dr. L.R. Oldeman
Natural History Museum - 1966
About 900 soil profiles and relevant information from over 70 countries in the world - library, map coll 25620

Nationaal Museum Historisch Landbouwtechniek (Museum of Historical Agricultural Engineering), Droevendaalsesteeg 50, 6708 PB Wageningen - T: (0317) 415774. Head: J.W. Van Brakel
Agriculture Museum - 1980
Agricultural machinery - library 25621

Warffum

Openluchtmuseum Het Hoogeland, Schoolstr 4, 9989 AG Warffum - T: (0595) 422233, Fax: 424951. Head: K. Strengers Olde Kalter
Open Air Museum - 1959
Folk art, style of living, history of fashion, textiles, historic clothes (costumes and underclothing), school curiosities, Dutch inn - library 25622

Warga

Museum Ald Slot, Ald Slotwei 1-5, 9005 NK Warga
Decorative Arts Museum
Interior, ceramics, paintings 25623

Wartena

It Earmhus en Oud Friese Greidboerderij, Hellingpaed 3, 9003 LW Wartena, mail addr: De Bleek 9, 9003 MH Wartena - T: (058) 251673
Special Museum
History of fishery 25624

Wateren

Natuurmuseum het Drents-Friese Woud, Wateren 13, 8438 SB Wateren
Natural History Museum
Regional flora and fauna, archeology 25625

Waterhuizen

Blokwachterswoning Waterhuizen, Waterhuizen 4, 9609 PA Waterhuizen
Science&Tech Museum
Tramway 25626

Wedde

Museum Grootmoeders Keuken, Hoofdweg 10, 9698 AE Wedde
Decorative Arts Museum
Ceramics, glaskunst, interieurs 25627

Museum voor Naaldkunst, Hoofdweg 8, 9698 AE Wedde - T: (0597) 562614. Head: H. Stevan Bathoorn
Special Museum
Needlework 25628

Weert

Gemeentemuseum De Tiendschuur, Recollectenstr 5, 6001 AJ Weert - T: (0495) 552610, Fax: 541554, E-mail: museumweert@planet.nl. Head: J. Van Cauteren
Local Museum - 1936
Natural history, antiquities relating to Weert and environs, prehistory, pictures, numismatics, old town views, rifle and trade organizations, folklore, local art 25629

Gemeentemuseum voor Religieuze Kunst, Markt 7, 6001 EJ Weert - T: (0495) 531920, Fax: 541554, E-mail: museumweertplanet.nl. Head: J. Van Cauteren
Religious Arts Museum
Religious art 25630

Weesp

Gemeentemuseum, Nieuwstr 41, 1381 BB Weesp - T: (0294) 491245, Fax: 414251, E-mail: azondergeld@weesp.nl, Internet: http:// www.weesp.nl
Local Museum - 1911
Local history, porcelain (1759-1768), paintings, topography 25631

Molen De Vriendschap, Utrechtseweg 11a, 1381 GR Weesp - T: (0294) 417024
Science&Tech Museum 25632

Werkendam

Biesbosch Museum, Hilweg 2, 4251 MT Werkendam - T: (0183) 504009, Fax: 505727, E-mail: bbmuseum@euronet.nl, Internet: http://www.biesboschmuseum.nl
Local Museum
Local history 25633

Wesepe

Robot Speelgoedmuseum, Raalterweg 83, 8124 AG Wesepe - T: (0570) 531389
Special Museum
History of tools 25634

West Terschelling

Centrum voor Natuur en Landschap, Burgemeester Redekerstr 11, 8881 BZ West Terschelling - T: (0562) 442390
Natural History Museum - 1954
Regional flora, fauna, aviflora and environment - sea aquarium, education center 25635

Gemeentemuseum 't Behouden Huijs, Commandeurstr 30, 8881 BB West Terschelling - T: (0562) 442389, Fax: 443719, E-mail: behoudenhuys@euronet.nl, Internet: http://www.behouden-huys.nl. Head: G.A. de Weerdt
Historical Museum / Folklore Museum 25636

Westdorpe

Oudheidkundig Museum, Brouwerij De Witte Leeuw, Singel 46, 4554 CP Westdorpe - T: (0115) 41183
Local Museum 25637

Westerbork

Museum - Herberg de Ar, Hoofdstr 42-44, 9431 AE Westerbork - T: (0593) 331533
Local Museum
Household articles 25638

Museum van Knipkunst, Hoofdstr 16, 9431 KN Westerbork - T: (0593) 331381
Fine Arts Museum
Cutting art 25639

Westeremden

Expositieruimte De Weem, Abt Emopad 2, 9922 PJ Westeremden
Fine Arts Museum / Decorative Arts Museum
Paintings, decorative art 25640

Wijk bij Duurstede

Museum Dorestad, Muntstr 42, 3961 AL Wijk bij Duurstede - T: (0343) 571448, Fax: 554342. Head: Lisette Le Blanc
Local Museum - 1926/1973
Local and regional antiquities, prehistory, topography, coins, sketch of the castle of Duurstede 25641

Wijngaarden

Oudheidkamer, Dorpsstr 17, 3366 BC Wijngaarden, mail addr: Molenhoek 3, 2973 AG Molenaarsgraaf - T: (0184) 641293
Local Museum
Local history 25642

Winkel

Parfumflessenmuseum, Dorpsstr 33, 1731 RB Winkel - T: (0224) 541578
Special Museum 25643

Winschoten

Museum Stoomgemaal Winschoten, Oostereinde 4, 9672 TC Winschoten - T: (0597) 425070
Science&Tech Museum
Steam engines and electric motors 25644

Nationaal Ambulance- en Eerste Hulpmuseum (temporary closed), Papierbaan 2, 9672 BH Winschoten - T: (0597) 422000, Fax: 186511
Historical Museum 25645

Noordelijk Busmuseum, P. van Dijkstr 5, 9672 AJ Winschoten - T: (0597) 424776
Science&Tech Museum
Hist of local busservice 25646

Winterswijk

Museum Freriks, Groenloseweg 86, 7101 AK Winterswijk - T: (0543) 533533, E-mail: jan.tjalkens@t-online.de, Internet: http://www.freriks.nl. Head: Paul Puntman
Local Museum - 1975
Geology, natural history, local history, folklore, fine arts - library 25647

Woerden

Gemeentemuseum → Stadsmuseum Woerden

Klein Saab Museum d'Oude Bolneus, Gedempte Binnengracht 27, 3441 AE Woerden - T: (0348) 415573, Fax: 415573
Science&Tech Museum 25648

Stadsmuseum Woerden, Kerkpl 6, 3441 BG Woerden - T: (0348) 431008, Fax: 432255, E-mail: stadsmuseumwoerden@planet.nl, Internet: http://www.stadsmuseumwoerden.nl. Head: F.M. de Graaf
Fine Arts Museum / Local Museum - 1986
16th-17th c buildings, weapons, archeology, facade stones, topography, paintings and works of artists born in Woerden (Leo Gestel, C. Vreedenburgh, Jan Kriege, H. van Kempen, H. Van Swanevelt) 25649

Wolvega

Oudheidkamer Windlust, Zilverlaan 1, 8471 DX Wolvega - T: (0561) 62709. Head: W. Piek
Local Museum - 1955
Mill (1888), local history, photographs, portraits, tools, topography 25650

Wommels

Museum Striid tsjin it Wetter, Ald Hiem 2, 8731 BR Wommels
Local Museum
Local history, archeology 25651

Workum

Jopie Huisman Museum, Noard 6, 8711 AH Workum - T: (0515) 543131, Fax: 543850, E-mail: info@jopiehuismanmuseum.nl, Internet: http://www.jopiehuismanmuseum.nl. Head: Baukje Scheppink
Fine Arts Museum - 1986
Paintings by Jopie Huisman 25652

Museum voor Kerkelijke Kunst, Noard 173, 8711 AE Workum
Religious Arts Museum
Religious art, paintings of J.V. Janning 25653

Museum Warkums Erfskip, Merk 4, 8711 CL Workum - T: (0515) 543155
Local Museum - 1966
Pottery, tiles, silver, old tools and instruments, historic engravings, scale models of mills and ships 25654

Tweewielermuseum Tankstop, Noord 118, 8711 AL Workum - T: (0515) 542940
Science&Tech Museum 25655

Woubrugge

Museum Van Hemessen, Dokter Lothlaan 1, 2481 AB Woubrugge - T: (0172) 518540
Local Museum 25656

Woudrichem

Visserij- en Cultuurhistorisch Museum, Kerkstr 41, 4285 BA Woudrichem - T: (0183) 303336
Special Museum / Local Museum
Fishing instruments, ship models, two original trawlers 25657

Wouw

Brandweermuseum, Wouwse Plantage, Plantage-Centrum 1, 4725 SR Wouw - T: (0165) 303252, Fax: 303252
Science&Tech Museum
Fire rescue equipment 25658

Den Groenen Zonck, Roosendaalsestr 43, 4724 AB Wouw - T: (0165) 302290
Science&Tech Museum
History of printing 25659

Yde

Brink 7 Galerij, Brink 7, 9494 PG Yde - T: (050) 4061580
Public Gallery 25660

Yerseke

Museum Yerseke, Kerkpl 1, 4401 ED Yerseke
Local Museum
Local and natural history, crafts, food, fishery 25661

Zaamslag

Schelpen Museum, Plein 3, 4543 BH Zaamslag, mail addr: Rozemarijnstr 2, 4543 BV Zaamslag - T: (0115) 431233
Natural History Museum
Shells, skeletons 25662

Zaandam

Czaar Peterhuisje, Krimp 23, 1506 AA Zaandam - T: (075) 6160390
Historical Museum
Objects relating to Czar Peter (who stayed here in 1697) and his family, paintings, furniture, memories of important persons who have visited the house 25663

In de Gecroonde Duijvekater, Zeilenmakerspad 4, 1509 BZ Zaandam - T: (075) 6173522
Local Museum 25664

Museum van het Nederlandse Uurwerk, Kalverringdijk 3, 1509 BT Zaandam - T: (075) 6179769, Fax: 6157786, Internet: http://go.to/dutchclock. Head: P.P.H. Van Leeuwen
Science&Tech Museum - 1976
Amsterdam longcase clocks (1730-1775), clocks from the Zaan-region (1688-1785), Frisian clocks (1736-1850), oldest known Dutch longcase clock (1675), oldest known Dutch domestic clock with chimes (1685), Regulator (Amsterdam, 1840), oldest known pendulum-clocks (1657-1662) 25665

Museumwinkel Albert Heijn, Kalverringdijk 5, 1509 BT Zaandam - T: (075) 6593026
Local Museum 25666

Noorderhuis, Kalverringdijk 17, 1509 BT Zaandam - T: (075) 6173237
Local Museum 25667

Politiemuseum, Westzijde 109, 1506 GB Zaandam - T: (075) 6352066
Special Museum
Museum of the Police 25668

De Zaanse Schans, Zeilenmakerspad 4, 1500 Zaandam - T: (075) 173522
Open Air Museum
Several historic houses and mills reconstructed at this site, bakery, grocer's shop, house with Dutch clocks 25669

Zaandijk

Zaanlandse Oudheidkamer, Lagedijk 80, 1544 BJ Zaandijk - T: (075) 217622
Local Museum - 1899
Enivornments of Zaandijk, trades, living style, topography, ship models, folklore, costumes, toys - library 25670

Zaltbommel

Maarten Van Rossum Museum, Nonnenstr 5, 5301 BE Zaltbommel - T: (0410) 512617. Head: P. Schipper
Local Museum - 1905
Local and regional antiquities, paintings, sketches, plates, pastels, photographs, manuscripts, copper, tin, weapons, coins, facade stones, construction fragments, old furniture, porcelain, glass, pottery, relics, books - library 25671

Zandvoort

Zandvoorts Museum, Swalluëstr 1, 2042 KA Zandvoort, mail addr: Postbus 331, 2040 AH Zandvoort - T: (023) 5740280, E-mail: museum@zandvoort.nl
Historical Museum / Folklore Museum
Local history, engravings 25672

Zeddam

Museum van Zwerfstenen in de Rosmolen, Bovendorpsstr 5, 7038 CH Zeddam - T: (0314) 651117, Internet: http://www.sintoswaldusgilde.nl
Special Museum
Coll of mill stones 25673

Zeelst

Gemeentelijk Museum 't Oude Slot, Hemelrijken 14, 5502 JC Zeelst - T: (040) 533160
Archaeological Museum - 1967
Local archeological finds (prehistory to Middle Ages) 25674

Zeist

Van de Poll-Stichting, Griffenstijnse Laan 77, 3703 AD Zeist - T: (030) 26917375
Local Museum
Topographic atlas, local historical documents 25675

Zeister Slot, Zinzendorflaan 1, 3703 CE Zeist - T: (030) 26910814, 26928222
Decorative Arts Museum
Castle (17th c) with interiors 25676

Zelhem

Boerenmuseum Zelhem, Ferdinand-Bol-Str 2, 7021 DX Zelhem, mail addr: Meeneweg 16, 7021 HN Zelhem - T: (0314) 621387
Agriculture Museum
Old farmhouse with inplements and interior 25677

Zevenaar

Buitenmolen Museum, Molenstr 63, 6901 CC Zevenaar - T: (0316) 340607
Science&Tech Museum
Old Mill 25678

Liemers Museum, Stationspl 4, 6901 BE Zevenaar, mail addr: Postbus 2059, 6900 CB Zevenaar - T: (0316) 333615, Fax: 540813. Head: Drs. I.J.A. Mens
Local Museum - 1981
Local history, roman finds 25679

Peter Stuyvesant Stichting, Kerkstr 27, 6901 AA Zevenaar, mail addr: Postbus 12, 6900 AA Zevenaar - T: (0316) 524550
Fine Arts Museum
Contemporary painting and sculpture 25680

Zevenbergen

Heemkundekring Willem Van Strijen, Zuidhaven 17, 4761 BM Zevenbergen - T: (0168) 324075. Head: A.C. Beumer
Local Museum - 1980
Clothes, work instruments, farm tools, porcelain, pottery, crystal, silver, maps, room with interior, kitchen 25681

Zierikzee

Burger Weeshuis, Poststr 45, 4301 AB Zierikzee - T: (0111) 412683. Head: A.S.M. Braat
Decorative Arts Museum - 1860
16th c orphanage, regents' room, walls in Louis XV covering, gold leather (1725), tin, paintings 25682

Maritime Museum Zierikzee, Mol 25, 4301 JC Zierikzee, mail addr: Postbus 5555, 4300 JA Zierikzee - T: (0111) 454464, Fax: 454497, E-mail: museum@schouwen-duiveland.nl, Internet: http://www.schouwen-duiveland.nl. Head: M.M. Van Meerten
Science&Tech Museum - 1971
Paintings, ship models, old sea charts, musselfishing and oysterfishing attributes, prehistorical bones 25683

Stadhuismuseum, Meelstr 8, 4301 EC Zierikzee, mail addr: Postbus 5555, 4300 JA Zierikzee - T: (0111) 454464, Fax: 454497, E-mail: museum@schouwen-duiveland.nl, Internet: http://www.schouwen-duiveland.nl. Head: M.M. Van Meerten
Local Museum - 1930
History of Zierikzee and its trades, commerce, agriculture, fishing, pictures, local silver, crystal, porcelain, pottery, ship models 25684

Verpleeghuis Cornelia, Lange Blokweg 2, 4301 NW Zierikzee
Fine Arts Museum
Sculpture, paintings, arts and crafts 25685

Zoelen

Imkerijmuseum de Zoete Inval, Hogestr 1, 4011 KA Zoelen - T: (0344) 682249
Agriculture Museum
Bee-farming Museum 25686

Zoetermeer

Historisch Museum 't Oude Huis → Stadsmuseum Zoetermeer

Stadsmuseum Zoetermeer, Dorpsstr 7, 2712 AB Zoetermeer - T: (079) 164735, Fax: 166258, E-mail: info@stadsmuseumzoetermeer.nl, Internet: http://www.stadsmuseumzoetermeer.nl. Head: J. Van der Ploeg
Historical Museum - 1976
Recent mass-cultural products - archive 25687

Zoutelande

Zeeuws Poppen- en Klederdrachten Museum, Duinweg 9, 4374 EA Zoutelande
Special Museum / Folklore Museum 25688

Zoutkamp

Visserijmuseum Zoutkamp, Reitdiepskade 11, 9974 PJ Zoutkamp
Historical Museum
Fishery 25689

Zuidhorn

Museum Historische Buitenboordmotoren, Oostergast 19, 9801 AK Zuidhorn
Science&Tech Museum
Motors of ships, ship building 25690

Zuidlaren

Molenmuseum De Wachter, Havenstr 36, 9471 AM Zuidlaren
Science&Tech Museum
Mill 25691

Zuidwolde, Drenthe

Cultuur Historisch Museum, Tonckensstr 49, 7921 KB Zuidwolde, Drenthe - T: (0528) 373332
Historical Museum 25692

Museumboerderij New Greenwich Village, Willem Moesweg 25, 7924 PA Zuidwolde, Drenthe - T: (0528) 372388. Head: John H. Cordell
Fine Arts Museum / Decorative Arts Museum - 1957
Wood carving, tapestries, fine arts 25693

Zuidwolde, Groningen

Van-der-Werf's Wedgwoodmuseum, Boterdiep Westzijde 38, 9785 AK Zuidwolde, Groningen
Historical Museum 25694

Zundert

Van Gogh Centrum, Molenstr 170, 4881 GG Zundert - T: (076) 5971999. Head: L. Bindels
Historical Museum
House were Vincent Van Gogh was born (30.03 1853) 25695

Zutphen

Museum Henriette Polak, Zaadmarkt 88, 7201 JL Zutphen - T: (0575) 51687, Fax: 544088, E-mail: stedelijkemuseazutphen@tebenet.nl
Fine Arts Museum - 1975
Modern Dutch figurative art 25696

Stedelijk Museum Zutphen, Rozengracht 3, 7201 JL Zutphen - T: (0575) 516878, Fax: 544088, E-mail: stedelijkemuseazutphen@tebenet.nl
Local Museum - 1866

Archeology, construction fragments, maps, topography, silver, glass, numismatics, tiles, pharmacy, toys, costumes, Gothic hall, paintings, medieval art coll 25697

Zwanenburg

Amsterdams Automuseum, Zwanenburgerdijk 281, 1161 NL Zwanenburg - T: (020) 4977291, Fax: 4977723, E-mail: info@amsterdams-automuseum.nl, Internet: http://www.amsterdams-automuseum.nl
Science&Tech Museum 25698

Zwartsluis

Schoonewelle, Centrum Natuur en Ambacht, Museumlaan 2, 8064 XN Zwartsluis - T: (030) 23066555
Natural History Museum - 1958
Birds, mammals, butterflies, eggs 25699

Zwijndrecht

General George C. Marshall Museum, Noordweg 15a, 3336 LH Zwijndrecht - T: (078) 6205880, Fax: 6205881
Military Museum / Science&Tech Museum 25700

Zwolle

Harley-Davidson en Indian Museum, Oude Almeloseweg 2-4, 8025 AP Zwolle - T: (0384) 534136, Fax: 531475
Science&Tech Museum 25701

Museum de Stadshof, Blijmarkt 18-20, 8011 NE Zwolle - T: (038) 4232616
Local Museum 25702

Stedelijk Museum Zwolle, Melkmarkt 41, 8011 MB Zwolle, mail addr: Postbus 1130, 8001 BC Zwolle - T: (038) 4214650, Fax: 4219248, E-mail: muszwol@museum.zwolle.nl, Internet: http://www.museum.zwolle.nl. Head: H.J. Aarts
Local Museum - 1884
Prehistory, paintings and drawings, silver, furniture, porcelain, glass, interiors from 17th and 18th c, coins, objects concerning the history of Zwolle and Overijssel, history, old and modern art - library 25703

Netherlands Antilles

Curaçao

Curaçao Museum, Van Leeuwenhoekstr, Curaçao - T: (09) 4623873, Fax: 4623777. Head: D. Engels
Local Museum - 1946
Local hist, paintings, furniture, Indian coll 25704

New Caledonia

Bourail

Musée Historique, Rue Simone Drémon, Bourail - T: 441646, Fax: 447033
Historical Museum
History, rural life, trade 25705

Nouméa

Musée Néo-Calédonien, Baie de la Moselle, Angle Av du M. Foch et Rue E. Porcheron, Nouméa - T: 272342, 274179
Archaeological Museum / Fine Arts Museum / Folklore Museum 25706

New Zealand

Akaroa

Te Whare Taonga O Akaroa (Akaroa Museum), Lavaud St, Akaroa 8161 - T: (03) 3041013, Fax: 3041013, E-mail: akmus@xtra.co.nz. Head: Lynda Wallace
Local Museum - 1964
General hist, whaling, French settlement 1840, Maori artifacts (Taonga), four historic buildings 25707

Alexandra

Alexandra Museum, Kelman St, Alexandra 9181 - T: (03) 4486230, Fax: 4486230, E-mail: alex.museum@xtra.co.nz. Head: Gillian Grant
Local Museum - 1959
Gold mining, pioneers' life, photographs - photographic and paper archives 25708

Vallance Cottage, Samson St, Alexandra 9181 - T: (03) 4486230, Fax: 4486230, E-mail: alex.museum@xtra.co.nz. Head: Gillian Grant
Local Museum
Restored miner's cottage 25709

Arrowtown

Lakes District Museum, 49 Buckingham St, Arrowtown 9691 - T: (03) 4421824, Fax: 4420835, E-mail: museum@queenstown.co.nz, Internet: http://www.museumqueenstown.com. Head: David Clarke
Local Museum - 1948
Gold, minerals, gold-miners' tools and implements, relics of Chinese miners, domestic utensils, photographs, books and documents, vehicles - art gallery 25710

Ashburton

Ashburton Aviation Museum, Airport, Seafield Rd, Ashburton 8300 - T: (03) 3083262, Fax: 3083082, E-mail: neil.stuckey@xtra.co.nz. Head: Jim Chivers
Science&Tech Museum - 1974 25711

Ashburton Museum, Baring Sq E, Ashburton 8300 - T: (03) 3083167, E-mail: museum@ashburton.co.nz. Head: Rita Wright
Local Museum 25712

Ashburton Vintage Car Club Museum, POB 382, Ashburton 8300 - T: (03) 3084595, Fax: 3037125. Head: Milner Jacob
Special Museum 25713

Museum of Woodwork and Ornamental Turning, 103 Alford Forest Rd, Ashburton 8300 - T: (03) 3086611, Fax: 3081905, E-mail: puzzle@xtra.co.nz. Head: Bob Lynn
Decorative Arts Museum - 1981
Woodworking tools, named pieces of wood, antique lathes, Ornamentel turning lathes, woodworking bks 25714

Plains Vintage Railway and Historical Museum, Tinwald Domain, Maronan Rd, Ashburton 8300, mail addr: POB 5051, Ashburton 8300 - T: (03) 3089600, Internet: http://www.ashburton.co.nz/plainsrailway. Head: Ron Hayward
Science&Tech Museum / Historical Museum - 1973 25715

Auckland

Alberton, 100 Mount Albert Rd, Auckland 1003 - T: (09) 8467367, Fax: 8461919, E-mail: alberton@historic.org.nz, Internet: http://www.historic.org.nz
Special Museum
Furnishings, Kerr Taylor family 25716

Artspace, 300 Karangahape Rd, Auckland - T: (09) 3034965, Fax: 3661842, E-mail: artspace@artspace.org.nz, Internet: http://www.artspace.org.nz. Head: Robert Leonard
Public Gallery - 1987
Contemporary art 25717

Auckland Art Gallery - Toi o Tāmaki, 5 Kitchener St, Auckland 1036 - T: (09) 3077700, Fax: 3021096, E-mail: gallery@akcity.govt.nz, Internet: http://www.akcity.govt.nz/around/placesartgallery. Head: Chris Saines
Fine Arts Museum - 1888
Old master paintings, drawings, prints, Mackelvie coll, European paintings, prints, sculpture (12th-20th c), British drawings, drawings by Thomas Rowlandson, New Zealand paintings, drawings, prints, sculpture (19th-20th c) - library 25718

Auckland Museum and Auckland War Memorial Museum, Domain Dr, Auckland 1000, mail addr: Private Bag 92018, Auckland 1030 - T: (09) 3090443, Fax: 3799956, E-mail: marketing@akmuseum.org.nz, Internet: http://www.akmuseum.org.nz. Head: Dr. Rodney Wilson
Local Museum - 1852
Maori and Pacific archeology and ethnology, natural history, applied arts, military history, Maori war canoe and meeting house, N.Z. social history - library, natural history resource centre, military archives 25719

Auckland Society of Arts Gallery, 32 Lorne St, Auckland 1000 - T: (09) 784160, 3794170, Fax: 3794170. Head: Elaine Mayer
Public Gallery 25720

Crystal Mountain - Crystal & Mineral Gallery & Museum, 80 Candia Rd, Swanson, Auckland 1008 - T: (09) 8335033, Fax: 8335044, E-mail: info@crystalmountain.co.nz, Internet: http://www.crystal-mountain.co.nz. Head: Abrelino Nogueira, Sandy Nogueira
Special Museum 25721

Ernest and Marion Davis Medical History Museum, c/o Department of Endocrinology, Auckland Hospital, Park Rd, Auckland 1030 - T: (09) 3074949 ext 6000, Fax: 3074993, E-mail: emdavislib@xtra.co.nz. Head: Prof. H.K. Ibbertson, Prof. I.M. Holdaway
Special Museum - 1965
Ancient medical texts, apothecary jar coll, medical instruments, pictorial displays of medical hist - medical history library 25722

Ewelme Cottage, 14 Ayr St, Parnell, Auckland 1001 - T: (09) 3790202, Fax: 3790202
Special Museum
Family related items of 105 years 25723

Geology Museum, 23 Symonds St, Auckland 1001, mail addr: c/o Department of Geology, University of Auckland, Private Bag 92019, Auckland 1030 - T: (09) 3737999 ext 7431, Fax: 3737435, E-mail: n.hudson@auckland.ac.nz. Head: Dr. Neville Hudson
Natural History Museum / University Museum - 1883
Fossils, rocks, minerals 25724

George Fraser Gallery, University of Auckland, 25 Princes St, Auckland 1001 - T: (09) 3677163
Public Gallery 25725

Highwic, 40 Gillies Av, Epsom, Auckland 1003 - T: (09) 5245729, Fax: 5245575, E-mail: highwic@historic.org.nz, Internet: http://www.historic.org.nz
Special Museum 25726

Journey's End Cottage and Laishley House, Onehunga Fencible, 3/40 Woodward Av, Mangere Bridge, Auckland 1006 - T: (09) 6369532. Head: Colin Freland
Local Museum 25727

Kinder House, 2 Ayr St, Parnell, Auckland 1001 - T: (09) 3794008
Special Museum 25728

Melanesian Mission House, 2 Tamaki Dr, Auckland - T: (09) 589250. Head: R.W. Macklin
Religious Arts Museum 25729

Montery Park Motor Museum, Upper Harbour Dr, Hobsonville, Auckland 1008 - T: (09) 4169282
Science&Tech Museum 25730

Museum of Puppets, c/o New Zealand Puppet Theatre, POB 6893, Auckland 1036 - T: (09) 3095755, Fax: 3033611. Head: Evan Blackman
Performing Arts Museum 25731

Museum of Transport and Technology, Great North Rd, Western Springs, Auckland - T: (09) 8460199, Fax: 8464242, E-mail: motatadmin@internet.co.nz, Internet: http://www.motat.org.nz. Head: John Syme
Science&Tech Museum - 1964
Transport especially aviation, trams, road, steam engineering, industrial and domestic technology, engineering, printing, business and office equipment, colonial village - library 25732

National Racing Museum, POB 852, Auckland 1015 - T: (09) 5244069. Head: Stuart Fergusson
Special Museum 25733

New Zealand Fleet Air Arm Museum, Great North Rd, Western Springs, Auckland, mail addr: c/o Museum of Transport and Technology, POB 9364, Auckland - T: (09) 5240371, Fax: 3031089. Head: David Allison
Science&Tech Museum 25734

New Zealand Fungal Herbarium, 120 Mount Albert Rd, Auckland - T: (09) 8154200, Fax: 8497093, E-mail: MckenzieE@landcare.cri.nz, Internet: http://www.nzfungi.landcare.cri.nz. Head: Dr. Eric McKenzie
Natural History Museum - 1936
Herbarium specialising in pathogenic plant fungi, New Zealand rusts, smuts, gasteromycetes, polyporaceae, thelephoraceae, hypocreales and hyphomycetes, about 1100 type specimens, G.H. Cunningham, R.F.R. McNabb, J.M. Dingley, G.J. Samuels - library 25735

New Zealand National Maritime Museum, Corner Quay & Hobson Sts, Auckland 1001 - T: (09) 3730800, Fax: 3776000, E-mail: museum@nzmaritime.org, Internet: http://www.nzmaritime.org. Head: R.C. Croker
Special Museum 25736

Oratia Folk Museum, 527 West Coast Rd, Oratia, Auckland 1007 - T: (09) 8187816. Head: David Harre
Folklore Museum 25737

Tainui Folk Museum and Garden of Memories, 9 Drake Rd, Howick, Auckland 1705 - T: (09) 5344334. Head: Taini Drummond
Folklore Museum 25738

Balclutha

South Otago Historical Museum, 1 Renfrew St, Balclutha 9200 - T: (03) 4182382. Head: D.B. Telford
Historical Museum 25739

Blenheim

Brayshaw Museum Park, Arthur Barkar Pl, mail addr: POB 308, Blenheim 7315 - T: (03) 5781712, Fax: 5781739, E-mail: info@marlborough-museum.org.nz. Head: D. Cordes
Local Museum
Beavertown replica of Blenheim in 1900's - archives 25740

Bluff

Bluff Maritime Museum, 227 Foreshore Rd, Bluff, mail addr: POB 9, Bluff 9531 - T: (03) 2127534, Fax: 2127534. Head: Teresa MacDonald
Special Museum - 1992 25741

Cambridge

Cambridge Museum, Old Courthouse, Victoria St, Cambridge 2351 - T: (07) 8273319, E-mail: parkere@i4free.co.nz. Head: Eris Parker
Local Museum
Cambridge genealogies 25742

Cheviot

Cheviot Museum, Hall St, Cheviot 8271 - T: (03) 3198536. Head: Aubrey Cropp
Local Museum - 1978
Archives, incl local families hist, photogr, display and information on Moas, local memorabilia 25743

Christchurch

Belfast Museum, Kapuatohe Historic Reserve, c/o Papanui Service Centre, POB 5142, Christchurch 8015 - T: (03) 3528117, Fax: 3521308, E-mail: sharon.ogden@ccc.govt.nz. Head: Sharon Ogden
Local Museum 25744

Canterbury Museum, Rolleston Av, Christchurch 8001 - T: (03) 3665000, Fax: 3665622, E-mail: info@cantmus.govt.nz. Head: Anthony Wright
Local Museum - 1870
Geology, zoology, fossil birds, ethnology, archeology, Asian and European decorative arts, costume, Canterbury hist, Antarctic hist, manuscripts, pictures, photographs, stamps of New Zealand, documentary hist, human hist, natural hist - library 25745

Centre of Contemporary Art, 66 Gloucester St, Christchurch 8015, mail addr: POB 772, 8015 - T: (03) 3667261, Fax: 3667167, E-mail: director@coca.org.nz, Internet: http://www.coca.org.nz. Head: Warren Feeney
Fine Arts Museum - 1880
Contemporary New Zealand art 25746

Christchurch Art Gallery, Botanic Gardens, Rolleston Av, Christchurch 8015 - T: (03) 3650915, Fax: 3653942, E-mail: art.gallery@ccc.govt.nz, Internet: http://www.mcdougall.org.nz. Head: P. Anthony Preston
Fine Arts Museum - 1932
European paintings (17th-20th c), British paintings and watercolours (18th-20th c), New Zealand paintings, watercolours, sculpture and pottery (19th-20th c) - education department, archive 25747

Dr. Heins Classic Car Collection, 376 Main S Rd, 9 Chappie Pl, Christchurch 2001 - T: (03) 3442222, Fax: 3442288, E-mail: dr.heins.classic@xtra.co.nz, Internet: http://www.classics.co.nz. Head: Dr. Heins
Science&Tech Museum
Cars 25748

The DVD Military Collection, 1/70 Gloucester St, Christchurch 8001 - T: (03) 3668323
Military Museum 25749

Ferrymead Heritage Park, Ferrymead Park Dr, Christchurch 8002 - T: (03) 3841970, Fax: 3841725, E-mail: info@ferrymead.org.nz, Internet: http://www.ferrymead.org.nz. Head: B. Lintott
Historical Museum / Local Museum - 1965
Fire display, Dinni coll of mechanical musical instruments, technology, transport 25750

Kaiapoi Historical Museum, 19 Norrie St, Redwood, Christchurch 8252 - T: (03) 3524675
Historical Museum 25751

Lyttelton Historical Museum, Gladstone Quay, Lyttelton, Christchurch 8012 - T: (03) 3288972. Head: Baden N. Norris
Historical Museum - 1965
Maritime display, antarctic display, local history 25752

Order of Saint John Museum, 150 Saint Asaph St, Christchurch 8001, mail addr: POB 1443, Christchurch 8015 - T: (03) 3664776, Fax: 3537112, E-mail: enquiries@stjohnnrsi.org.nz. Head: Beverley Booth
Special Museum
Medical history, first aid, ambulance service 25753

Robert McDougall Art Gallery → Christchurch Art Gallery

Royal New Zealand Air Force Museum, Main South Rd, Christchurch 800 A - T: (03) 3439532, Fax: 3439533, E-mail: info@afw.co.nz, Internet: http://www.afw.co.nz. Head: David Provan
Military Museum - 1987
Aircraft coll/Supermarine Spitfire, De Havilland Mosquito etc - archives, education 25754

Royal New Zealand Army Medical Corps Museum, Health Services School, Burnham Military Camp, Christchurch 8191 - T: (03) 3630099, Fax: 3630209, E-mail: K.treanor@netaccess.co.nz. Head: M.J. Withers
Military Museum - 1966 25755

Saint Andrews College Museum, 347 Papanui Rd, Christchurch 8005 - T: (03) 3559045, Fax: 3550100, E-mail: museum@stac.school.nz, Internet: http://www.stac.school.nz. Head: Jan Hampton
University Museum - 1989
General memorabilia of College from 1916, photogr, clothing, medals, china, and displays 25756

Sumner/Redcliffs Historical Museum, c/o 5 Main Rd, Redcliffs, Christchurch 8008 - T: (03) 3841159. Head: M. Rule
Historical Museum 25757

Yaldhurst Museum of Transport and Science, School Rd, Yaldhurst, Christchurch 8005 - T: (03) 3427914, Fax: 3427916, E-mail: museum@ihug.co.nz, Internet: http://members.xoom.com/carmuseum. Head: Grant Cooper
Science&Tech Museum 25758

Clyde

Clyde Historical Museums, POB 11, Clyde - T: (03) 4492092. Head: A.M. Paton
Historical Museum - 1878
Mining, gold nuggets, gold sand, gold coins and jewelry, minerals, dock leg-irons, goal door, pioneer household goods, clothing, books, crystal chandelier, horse-drawn vehicles, farm implements, fully-equipped manual herb processing factory 25759

Vincent County and Dunstan Goldfields Historical Museum, Dunston Court House, Blythe St, Clyde 9180
Historical Museum 25760

Coalgate

Glentunnel Museum, Whitecliffs Rd, Coalgate 8170 - T: (03) 3182791. Head: Sally Spence
Local Museum 25761

Coromandel

Coromandel School of Mines Museum, Rings Rd, Coromandel - T: (07) 8668987, E-mail: argentum@wave.co.nz. Head: D.M. Phillip
Historical Museum - 1887
Geological specimens, mining, photographs and mining books, plans newspapers, local/ family history 25762

Cromwell

Cromwell Museum, 44 The Mall, Cromwell 9191 - T: (0294) 4450212, Fax: (03) 4451319. Head: El Bisset, Helen Scotes
Science&Tech Museum - 1962
Chinese goldmining, dredging (Gold), pioneer women, hotels 25763

Cust

Cust Museum, Main Rd, Cust 8254 - T: (03) 3125720. Head: Bernard Kingsbury
Local Museum - 1990 25764

Darfield

Hororata Historic Museum, Isherwood, RD, Darfield 8172 - T: (03) 3186876. Head: Les Nell
Historical Museum 25765

Dargaville

Dargaville Museum, Harding Park, Dargaville - T: (09) 4397555, Fax: 4397133, E-mail: darg.museum@xtra.co.nz, Internet: http://www.kauricoast.co.nz. Head: Nick Puharich
Historical Museum / Local Museum - 1960
Maori artifacts, kauri gum, local historical photographs, pioneer and early shipping relics, shipwreck displays, Rainbow Warrior Masts, pre-Maori carving (2000 years old) 25766

Devonport

Royal New Zealand Navy Museum, Spring St, Devonport 1330 - T: (09) 4455186, Fax: 4455046. Head: Peter Dennerly
Military Museum - 1974 25767

Dunedin

Anatomy Museum, c/o Department of Anatomy and Structural Biology, University of Otago, POB 913, Dunedin 9015 - T: (03) 4797361, Fax: 4797254, E-mail: tracy.connolly@stonebow.otago.ac.nz, Internet: http://www.otago.ac.nz/anatomy. Head: Tracy Connolly
University Museum / Historical Museum - 1874
Anatomy teaching specimens, health science, medicine 25768

Dunedin Hospital Museum, Otago Medical School, Great King St, Dunedin 9001 - T: (03) 4791700, Fax: 4747623
Special Museum 25769

Dunedin Museum of Transport and Technology, POB 1356, Dunedin 9015 - T: (03) 4657775. Head: Eric Brodie
Science&Tech Museum 25770

Dunedin Public Art Gallery, The Octagon, Dunedin 9001 - T: (03) 4743240, Fax: 4743250, E-mail: dpagmail@dcc.govt.nz, Internet: http://www.thecityofdunedin.govt.nz. Head: Priscilla Pitts

Public Gallery - 1884
British portraits (late 17th to early 19th c), British landscapes (18th-20th c), Smythe Coll of British watercolours (18th-19th c), British Victorian genre painting, British contemporary painting, European masters, chiefly Italian, French and Flemish (late Middle Ages to 18th c), contemporary New Zealand painting and sculpture, contemporary Australian painting, antique furniture, silver, glass, porcelain and oriental rugs, Japanese prints - conservation laboratory 25771

Dunedin Public Libraries Artprint Collection, 230 Moray Pl, Dunedin - T: (03) 4743690, Fax: 4743660, E-mail: library@dcc.govt.nz, Internet: http://www.citydunedin.govt.nz/library. Head: Allison Dobbie
Library with Exhibitions 25772

Engine House, Dunedin Gasworks Museum Trust, Braemar, Dunedin 9015, mail addr: Box 5929, Dunedin 9015 - T: (03) 4555063. Head: W.J. Cowan
Science&Tech Museum - 1988
Buildings and machines from New Zealands first gasworks, working industrial museum with steam exhausters 25773

Fletcher House, Portobello Rd, Broad Bay, Dunedin 9003 - T: (03) 4780180. Head: Allan Gilbert
Local Museum 25774

Geology Museum of the University of Otago, Leith St, Dunedin 9015 - T: (024) 771640 ext 606, Fax: 4797527. Head: Prof. J.D. Campbell, Dr. R. Ewan Fordyce
Natural History Museum / University Museum
New Zealand fossils, fossil whales, dolphins, penguins 25775

Naval Reserve Association Museum, 211 Saint Andrews St, Dunedin 9001
Historical Museum 25776

Otago Military Museum, Kensington Army Hall, Bridgman St, Dunedin 9030 - T: (03) 4884345, Fax: 4884385, E-mail: connors@clear.net.nz. Head: Brian Connor
Military Museum 25777

Otago Museum, 419 Great King St, Dunedin 9030 - T: (03) 4747474, Fax: 4775993, E-mail: mail@otagomuseum.govt.nz, Internet: http://www.otagomuseum.govt.nz. Head: Shimrath Paul
Local Museum - 1868
Zoology, geology, botany, physical anthropology, archaeology, ethnology, technology, decorative arts Egyptian, classical and West-European antiquities, Southern Maori material 25778

Otago Peninsula Museum, Harington Point Rd, Portobello, Dunedin 9021 - T: (03) 4780255, Fax: 4780655, E-mail: virginiamarriott@yahoo.com. Head: Warren Morris
Local Museum 25779

Otago Settlers Museum, 31 Queens Gardens, Dunedin 9030 - T: (03) 4775052, Fax: 4778360, E-mail: settler@es.co.nz, Internet: http://www.CityofDunedin.com. Head: Priscilla Pitts
Historical Museum - 1898
Decorative arts and photographs, portrait coll of early European settlers, whaling, goldmining, Maori Kai/Tahu settlement and development, road transport, locomotives - library, archives 25780

Otago Vintage Machinery Club Museum, 24 Quarry Rd, Green Island, Dunedin 9001 - T: (03) 4883105. Head: John King
Science&Tech Museum 25781

Otakou Marae Museum, Tamatea Rd, Dunedin 9021 - T: (03) 4780352, Fax: 4780354, E-mail: otakou@clear.net.nz. Head: Hoani Langsbury
Local Museum
Local hist 25782

Theomin Gallery, Olveston Dunedin's Historic Home, 42 Royal Terrace, Dunedin 9001 - T: (03) 4773320, Fax: 4792094, E-mail: olvestor@xtra.co.nz, Internet: http://www.visit-dunedin.co.nz/olvestor.html. Head: G.D. Barron
Decorative Arts Museum - 1967
Jacobean style home, antique furniture, pictures, silverware, porcelain, carved ivory, Japanese artifacts, weapons, inro, embroidery 25783

Eketahuna

Eketahuna and Districts Museum, Bengston St, Eketahuna 5480 - T: (06) 3758550, Fax: 3758519. Head: Avis Cooper
Local Museum - 1979
Match Box coll 25784

Featherston

Featherston Heritage Museum, Cnr Lyon and Fitzherbert Sts, Featherston 5952 - T: (06) 3089458. Head: Raymond Clapperton
Local Museum - 1992
Featherston Military Camp, WW I and WW II, Japanese Prisoner of War Camp Featherston 25785

Featherston Memorabilia Museum, 5 Woodward St W, Featherston 5952 - T: (06) 3089352. Head: Ken Burgiss
Local Museum - 1985
Bottles, food packaging, telephones 25786

Fell Engine Museum → Fell Locomotive Museum

Fell Locomotive Museum, Cnr Lyon and Fitzherbert Sts, Featherston 5952 - T: (06) 3089379, Fax: 3089487, E-mail: ian.miles@xtra.co.nz. Head: Noel Meek
Science&Tech Museum
Fell railway system for the Rimutaka Incline 25787

Kahutara Canoes and Taxidermy Museum, Kahutara, off Lake Ferry Rd 1, Featherston - T: (06) 3088453, Fax: 3088453. Head: John McCosh
Natural History Museum - 1985
Rock coll, insect coll, birds, collection of exotic animals 25788

Foxton

Foxton Museum, 5 Ravensworth Pl, Foxton 5551 - T: (06) 3636846. Head: Tony Hunt
Local Museum 25789

National Museum of Audiovisual Arts and Sciences, Memorial Hall, Foxton 5551 - T: (06) 3636638. Head: Peter Edwards
Fine Arts Museum 25790

National Trolleybus Museum, Main St, Foxton 5551 - T: (06) 3636656. Head: Ian Little
Science&Tech Museum 25791

Gisborne

East Coast Museum of Technology, POB 971, Gisborne 3815 - T: (06) 8689284. Head: Murray Goodwin
Science&Tech Museum
Transport, agriculture, industry, business, domestic items and fire engines 25792

Gisborne Museum and Arts Centre → Tairawhiti Museum

Tairawhiti Museum, 18-22 Stout St, Gisborne 3815, mail addr: POB 716, Gisborne 3815 - T: (06) 8673832, Fax: 8672728, E-mail: gmac@clear.net.nz. Head: Michael Spedding
Local Museum / Fine Arts Museum - 1954
Maori artifacts, local bygones, photographs, documents, New Zealand paintings, geology, natural history, examples of East Coast Maori carving, maritime history and technology - library, studios (artists, potters, photographers), area for concerts 25793

Golden Bay

Golden Bay Museum and Gallery, Commericial St, Takaka, Golden Bay 7172 - T: (03) 5259990, Fax: 5259990. Head: Mary Crockford
Local Museum
Abel Tasman display 25794

Gore

Eastern Southland Gallery, Cnr Hokonui Dr and Norfolk St, Gore 9700, mail addr: POB 305, Gore 9700 - T: (03) 2089907, Fax: 2081210. Head: Jim Geddes
Public Gallery - 1983
Art works, craft work, historical displays 25795

Gore Airforce Museum, 43 Maitland St, Gore 9700 - T: (03) 2085354, Fax: 2085354. Head: Roy Richardson
Military Museum - 1989
Wartime photogr, books, uniforms, mainly WWII, Tiger Moth Cessna Agwagon VP-2, Hughes 300 Helicopter - aviation research (on request) 25796

Gore Historical Museum and Hokonui Heritage Research Centre, Cnr Hokonui Dr and Norfolk St, Gore 9700 - T: (03) 2087032, Fax: 2089908, E-mail: heritage@goredc.govt.nz. Head: W. Hamilton
Historical Museum - 1988
Colonial costumes, local hist 25797

Greymouth

Greymouth RSA War Museum, 187 Tainui St, Greymouth
Military Museum 25798

Shantytown, West-Coast-Living Heritage, Greymouth 7870 - T: (03) 7626634, Fax: 7626649, E-mail: shantytown@xtra.co.nz, Internet: http://www.shantytown.co.nz
Open Air Museum - 1971
Historic replica gold mining town, steam trains (1897 and 1913), horsedrawn vehicles, 1866 church, horsedrawn rides - library 25799

Greytown

Cobblestones Museum, Main St, Greytown 5953 - T: (06) 3049687, Fax: 3797399. Head: G. Croton
Local Museum / Historical Museum - 1965 25800

Hamilton

Agricultural Heritage Museum, Mystery Creek Rd, Hamilton, mail addr: Private Bag 3015, Hamilton - T: (07) 8437990, Fax: 8438572, E-mail: terryh@mysterycreek.co.nz, Internet: http://www.mysterycreek.co.nz. Head: Kerry Clarkin
Agriculture Museum 25801

Te Kauri Lodge Museum, POB 7030, Hamilton 2001 - T: (07) 8710625. Head: Jenny West
Natural History Museum 25802

Waikato Museum of Art and History, Grantham at Victoria St, Hamilton 2020 - T: (07) 8386533, Fax: 8386571, E-mail: museum@hcc.govt.nz, Internet: http://www.hpl.govt.nz/waimuse. Head: Jenny Cave
Fine Arts Museum / Historical Museum - 1970
New Zealand archeology and hist, Pacific ethnology and traditional arts, New Zealand, Australian painting, prints, drawings and sculpture, Te Winika-Maori war canoe, Tainui Maori Culture - library, archive 25803

Havelock

Havelock Museum, Main Rd, Havelock 7154 - T: (03) 5742176, Fax: 5742276, E-mail: ritacollet@paradise.co.nz. Head: Philip Steel
Historical Museum - 1968
Saw milling equipment, old steam and conbustion engines, bottle coll, minerals 25804

Hawarden

Waipara County Historical Society Museum, Hawarden 8274 - T: (03) 3144403
Historical Museum 25805

Hawera

Tawhiti Museum, 47 Ohangai Rd, Hawera 4800 - T: (06) 2786837. Head: Nigel Ogle
Local Museum 25806

Helensville

Helensville and District Pioneer Museum, 4 Porter Crescent, Helensville 1250 - T: (09) 4207881. Head: John Pyatt
Local Museum 25807

Hokitika

West Coast Historical Museum, Corner of Tancred and Hamilton St, Hokitika 7900 - T: (03) 7556898, Fax: 7555011, E-mail: hokimuseum@xtra.co.nz, Internet: http://www.westlanddc.govt.nz. Head: Julia Bradshaw
Local Museum - 1960
Hist of the region, gold mining, Maori history and greenstone, European settlement, photos, maps - library, archives for historical and genealogical research 25808

Invercargill

Anderson Park Art Gallery, McIvor Rd, Invercargill 9515 - T: (03) 2157432. Head: Joyce Robins
Public Gallery - 1951
New Zealand contemporary paintings, watercolours of Invercargill (19th-20th c), European paintings, Anderson family 25809

Southland Fire Service Museum, POB 192, Invercargill 9515 - T: (03) 2179235. Head: A.K. Turner
Science&Tech Museum 25810

Southland Museum and Art Gallery, Gala St, Invercargill 9515 - T: (03) 2189753, Fax: 2183872, E-mail: office@southlandmuseum.co.nz, Internet: http://www.southlandmuseum.co.nz. Head: David J. Woodings
Archaeological Museum / Fine Arts Museum / Local Museum / Natural History Museum - 1871
Maori artifacts, geology, live tuatara, sub-fossil moa bones, regional/national/international fine arts 25811

Kaeo

Whangaroa County Museum, Leigh St, State Hwy 10, Kaeo 0471 - T: (09) 4050050. Head: Daphnea Gates
Local Museum - 1979
Material on the shipwreck-massacre of ship 'Boyd' in 1809 in Whangaroa Harbour, woman's suffrage, timber milling, Maori Taonga treasures 25812

Kaiapoi

National Scout Museum, 12 Williams St, Kaiapoi 8252 - T: (03) 3278007, Fax: 3275210. Head: Peter C. Henwood
Historical Museum - 1987
Scouting hist - library, archive 25813

Kaikohe

Kaikohe Pioneer Village and Museum, Recreation Rd, Kaikohe 0400 - T: (09) 4010816. Head: Jo Hoani, Clive Smith
Historical Museum 25814

Kaikoura

Kaikoura District Museum, 14 Ludstone Rd, Kaikoura 8280 - T: (03) 3197440, E-mail: kk.museum@xtra.co.nz. Head: Pam Garbes
Historical Museum - 1968
Maori coll, early colonial items, photographs - archives 25815

Kaitaia

Far North Regional Museum, 6 South Rd, Kaitaia 0500 - T: (09) 4081403, Fax: 4081403,

Internet: http://www.nzmuseums.co.nz/museums/far_north_regional.html. Head: Michael P.S. Ibbotson
Local Museum - 1969
Colonial room of local furniture, Maori culture room, artifacts and implements, photographic coll, local mounted birds, shells and fossils, kauri gum coll, de Surville anchor, early Missionary activity - archive 25816

Wagener Museum, Houhora Heads, Kaitaia 0555 - T: (09) 4098850, Fax: 4098880. Head: Eric Wagener
Local Museum 25817

Karamea

Karamea Museum, Waverley St, Karamea 7650 - T: (03) 7826812
Local Museum 25818

Kawhia

Kawhia Regional Museum Gallery, Kaora St, Kawhia 2451 - T: (07) 8710714. Head: Diana Ferris
Local Museum 25819

Kerikeri

Society for Preservation of the Kerikeri Stone Store Area Visitor Centre, Rewas Village, Landing Rd, Kerikeri 0470 - T: (09) 4076454, Fax: 4076454, E-mail: g-brown@paradise.net.nz. Head: G.B. Brown
Open Air Museum / Natural History Museum / Historical Museum - 1969
Pre European unfortifies Maori village replica, local history, use of plants by the Maori - Discoverers garden 25820

Kurow

Upper Waitaki Pioneer Museum and Gallery, Te Akatarawa Sta, Kurow 8951 - T: (03) 4360556. Head: W. Cleave
Local Museum 25821

Lawrence

Tuapeka Goldfields Museum, 17 Ross Pl, Lawrence 9153 - T: (03) 4859222, Fax: 4859222. Head: Rodger Anderson
Local Museum 25822

Lower Hutt

Dowse Art Museum, 45 Laings Rd, Lower Hutt 6009 - T: (04) 5706500, Fax: 5695877, E-mail: dowse@huttcity.govt.nz, Internet: http://www.dowse.hutt-city.govt.nz. Head: Tim Walker
Decorative Arts Museum - 1971
New Zealand craft (ceramics, glass, textiles, wood, body adornment), New Zealand contemporary photography 25823

Institute of Geological and Nuclear Sciences, 69 B Gracefield Rd, Lower Hutt 6009 - T: (04) 5101444, Fax: 5104600. Head: Andrew West
Natural History Museum - 1865
New Zealand rock types, samples from Antarctica, sub-Antarctic Islands, Pacific, marine fossil invertebrates, molluscs, fossil plant coll, minerals, drill core coll - library 25824

Silver Stream Railway Museum, Eastern Hutt Rd, Taita Gorge, Lower Hutt 6009 - T: (04) 5637348, Fax: 9715747, Internet: http://www.silversteam-railway.org.nz. Head: Kieth Davis
Science&Tech Museum 25825

Te Whare Whakaaro o Pito-one (Petone Settlers Museum), The Esplanade, Petone, Lower Hutt 6009, mail addr: Private Bag 31912, Lower Hutt 6009 - T: (04) 5688373, 5688716, Fax: 5688933, E-mail: contact@huttcity.govt.nz, Internet: http://www.huttcity.govt.nz. Head: David Mealing
Local Museum - 1977
Photography, pictures, toys, games, dolls, porcelain, ceramics, silver, costumes, textiles, maps 25826

Lumsden

Lumsden and District Museum, Diana Street, Kumsden Information Centre, Lumsden - T: (03) 2487713
Local Museum 25827

Mapua

Mapua Fire Engine Museum, 3 Toru St, Mapua 7150 - T: (03) 5402794. Head: Greg Olsen
Science&Tech Museum 25828

Marton

Marton Historic Village Museum, Wellington Rd, Marton 5151 - T: (06) 3278623. Head: Paul Melody
Open Air Museum - 1978 25829

Masterton

Mount Bruce Pioneer Museum, RD 1, Masterton 5921 - T: (06) 3725859, Fax: 3725859, E-mail: h.christensen@xtra.co.nz. Head: Henry Christensen
Local Museum - 1984 25830

Museum of Childhood, 40 Makora Rd, Masterton 5900 - T: (06) 3774743. Head: Diana Stidolph
Special Museum - 1967 25831

Vintage Aircraft Museum, Hood Aerodrome, Masterton 5901 - T: (06) 3773466
Science&Tech Museum 25832

Wairarapa Museum and Art Gallery, Bruce St, Masterton 5900 - T: (06) 3771210, Fax: 3771210, E-mail: artsandhistory@xtra.co.nz. Head: Richard Arlidge
Fine Arts Museum / Local Museum - 1969
Contemporary New Zealand prints, paintings and sculptures, Taonga Maori of the Wairarapa 25833

Matakohe

The Kauri Museum, Church Rd, Matakohe, Matakohe 0584 - T: (09) 4317417, Fax: 4316969, E-mail: admin@kauri-museum.com, Internet: http://www.kauri-museum.com. Head: Roger Mulvay
Local Museum - 1962
Regional hist, Kaurigum, Kauri and other native timbers, artifacts of industry associated with Kauri timber and gum, house completely furnished with Kauri furniture, early school, church and post office, Kauri theme exhibition 25834

Matamata

Firth Tower Historical Reserve, Tower Rd, Matamata 2271 - T: (07) 8819050, Fax: 8885049, E-mail: bhamlin@mpdc.govt.nz
Historical Museum - 1978
Josiah Firth 25835

Methven

Methven Museum, 15 McDonald St, Methven 5031 - T: (03) 3028391. Head: Angela Grieve
Local Museum 25836

Milton

Tokomairiro Historical Society Museum, 53 Union St, Milton 9250 - T: (03) 4178291, Fax: 4177117, E-mail: miltoninfo@xtra.co.nz. Head: N. Allison
Historical Museum - 1966 25837

Morrinsville

Morrin Museum, 53a Lorne St, Morrinsville 2251 - T: (07) 8897888, Fax: 8895472, E-mail: mgribb@ihug.co.nz, Internet: http://homepage.ihug.co.nz/~mgribb/start.htm. Head: Michael Gribble
Local Museum - 1969 25838

Motueka

Motueka District Museum, 140 High St, Motueka 7161 - T: (03) 5287660, Fax: 5287660, E-mail: savepast@ihug.co.nz. Head: Judy Klaus
Local Museum 25839

Murchison

Murchison Museum, Fairfax St, Murchison 7191 - T: (03) 5239392, Fax: 5239392. Head: Graeme Bradley
Local Museum 25840

Napier

Hawke's Bay Museum, 9 Herschell St, Napier 4001 - T: (06) 8357781, Fax: 8353984, E-mail: hbec@inhb.co.nz. Head: Lynne Trafford
Local Museum - 1989
Maori and Polynesian artifacts, early New Zealand home and farm equipment, antique furniture, porcelain and silver, New Zealand painting, sculpture and pottery, relics of the earthquake in Hawke's Bay (1931), Art Deco, textiles and costumes, NZ Dinosaur exhibits and colls - archive, library 25841

Naseby

Maniototo Early Settlers Museum, Corner Leven and Earn Sts, Naseby 9071 - T: (03) 4449558, Fax: 4449558. Head: Kay Dundass
Local Museum
Gold specimen, implements for gold coll and weighing, household articles of gold-mining days, photographic coll, Maniototo hist - family history research 25842

Nelson

Bishop Suter Art Gallery → The Suter, Te Aratoi o Whakatu

Nelson Provincial Museum, Hillford St, Stoke, Nelson, 7001, mail addr: POB 853, Nelson, 7015 - T: (03) 5479740, Fax: 5478549, E-mail: enquiries@museum.np.org.nz. Head: Wayne P. Marriott
Local Museum - 1841
Cultural hist, specialising in photographic coll - archive 25843

The Suter, Te Aratoi o Whakatu, Bridge St, Nelson 7035 - T: (03) 5484699, Fax: 5481236, E-mail: suter@netaccess.co.nz, Internet: http://www.thesuter.org.nz. Head: Helen Telford
Fine Arts Museum - 1898
Watercolours by John Gully (1819-1888), J.C. Richmond (1827-1898), contemporary English and European works 25844

New Plymouth

Bowls New Zealand Museum, Dean Park, Brooklands Rd, New Plymouth 4600 - T: (06) 7580284, Fax: 7580284. Head: Bob Vinsen
Special Museum - 1978
Hist of NZ bowls from 1861, tributes to past and present bowlers, hist of internat events 25845

Govett-Brewster Art Gallery, Queen St, New Plymouth 4600, mail addr: POB 647, New Plymouth 4600 - T: (06) 7585149, Fax: 7580390, E-mail: mail@govettbrewster.org.nz, Internet: http://www.govettbrewster.org.nz. Head: Gregory Burke
Fine Arts Museum - 1969
Contemporary art from New Zealand and other countries, Len Lye coll/archive - library 25846

Hurworth Cottage, Historic Places Trust, 906 Carrington Rd, RD 1, New Plymouth 4601 - T: (06) 7533593, Fax: 7533592, E-mail: information@historic.org.nz, Internet: http://www.historic.org.nz. Head: Margaret Bell
Historical Museum - 1855/1976
Library 25847

Puke Ariki - Taranaki Museum, War Memorial Bldg, Brougham St, New Plymouth 4615 - T: (06) 7584544, Fax: 7587427, E-mail: enquiries@pukeariki.com, Internet: http://www.pukeariki.com. Head: Suzanne Porter
Local Museum - 1847
Maori wood carvings of Taranaki dating from pre 1830, household relics, weapons, tools, items of early settlement, natural hist, art coll, photos - district library, archives 25848

Norsewood

Norsewood Pioneer Museum, POB 52, Norsewood 5491 - T: (06) 3740721. Head: D. Charlton-Jones
Historical Museum - 1965
Early settlers' household, farming and milling equipment, history of the Scandinavian settlement 25849

Oamaru

Forrester Gallery, 9 Thames St, Oamaru 8900 - T: (03) 4341653, Fax: 4341654, E-mail: - forrestergallery@xtra.co.nz. Head: Warwick Smith
Fine Arts Museum - 1983
Coll and care of works of art and architectural drawings related to North Otago and New Zealand, programme of exhibitions and cultural events 25850

North Otago Museum, 60 Thames St, Oamaru 8900 - T: (03) 4341652, Fax: 4341649, E-mail: museum@waitaki-dc.govt.nt, Internet: http://www.northotago-museum.co.nz. Head: Bruce McCulloch
Local Museum - 1882
George Meek coll of pioneer and early settlers' domestic and industrial articles, historical photographs, Oamaru limestone, Timaru and Temuka pottery - archives 25851

Okains Bay

Okains Bay Maori and Colonial Museum, Main Rd, Okains Bay 8161 - T: (03) 3048611. Head: Murray Thacker
Open Air Museum / Ethnology Museum / Local Museum - 1961
Maori coll (archeological and ethnological), including a meeting house and a store house, colonial coll of cottages, farming implements, transport vehicles 25852

Ongaonga

Ongaonga Old School Museum, Bridge St, Ongaonga 4170 - T: (06) 8566749, Fax: 8566748. Head: Shona Simpson
Historical Museum - 1966
Furnished classroom (1975-1886), local history, firearms from Maori wars, kitchen utensils, sewing machines, historic sword, New Zealand newspaper from 1879, phonograph, photographs 25853

Opotiki

Opotiki Heritage and Agricultural Society Museum, 123 Church St, Opotiki 3092 - T: (07) 3155193, E-mail: alan.l.rowe@xtra.co.nz, Internet: http://www.opotiki.org/ohas.html. Head: Alan L. Rowe
Local Museum / Agriculture Museum 25854

Otautau

Otautau and District Local History Museum, 146 Main St, Otautau 9653 - T: (03) 2258748, E-mail: soren.otautau@paradise.co.nz. Head: Russell Wesney
Local Museum 25855

Outram

Taieri Historical Museum, McLeod Rd R.D.1, Outram 9055 - T: (03) 4862701, (025) 733035, Fax: 4862701, E-mail: neil.gamble@extra.co.nz. Head: R.J. Beardsmore
Historical Museum - 1972 25856

Owaka

Catlins Historical Museum, 8 Waikawa Rd, Owaka 9251 - T: (03) 4158490, E-mail: deversons@actrix.gen.nz, Internet: http://www.nzmuseums.co.nz/museums.catlins.html. Head: R. Hewson
Local Museum 25857

Oxford

Oxford Museum, 7a Bay Rd, Oxford 8253 - T: (03) 3124533. Head: Margaret Ivory
Local Museum - 1980 25858

Paeroa

Paeroa and District Historical Society Museum, 37 Belmont Rd, Paeroa 2951 - T: (064) 78628486, Fax: 78628486. Head: Graham C. Watton
Historical Museum 25859

Pahiatua

Pahiatua and District Museum, 66 Sedcole St, Pahiatua 5470 - T: (06) 3768479, 3768413. Head: I. Eddie
Local Museum 25860

Paihia

Waitangi Treaty House, Waitangi National Reserve, Paihia - T: (09) 4027437, Fax: 4028303. Head: P.D. Jackson
Historical Museum - 1932
Site of Treaty of Waitangi, carved Maori meeting house and war canoe, exhibits of New Zealand historical interest up to 1840, visitor centre complex an audio-visual programme on signing of treaty between Maori Chiefs and British Crown 25861

Pakuranga

Howick Historical Village, Bells Rd, Howick, Pakuranga 1731 - T: (09) 5769506, Fax: 5769708, E-mail: fencible@ihug.co.nz, Internet: http://www.fencible.org.nz. Head: A.J. La Roche
Open Air Museum - 1962
Early history of Auckland 1840-1880, esp. Fencible immigration, Maori and European buildings 25862

Palmerston North

Manawatu Art Gallery, 398 Main St, Palmerston North 5330 - T: (06) 3588188, Fax: 3588849, E-mail: mail@mag.org.nzn, Internet: http://www.mag.or.nz. Head: Julie Catchpole
Fine Arts Museum - 1959
Paintings, watercolours, prints, ceramics and sculptures by New Zealand artists 25863

Rugby Museum, 87 Cuba St, Palmerston North 5315 - T: (06) 3586947, Fax: 3586947, E-mail: info@rugbymuseum.co.nz, Internet: http://www.rugbymuseum.co.nz. Head: Bob Luxford
Special Museum - 1970 25864

Science Centre and Manawatu Museum, Te Whare Pupuri Taonga o Manawatu, Te Aweawe Complex, 396 Main St, Palmerston North 5330 - T: (06) 3555000, Fax: 3583552. Head: Julie Catchpole
Natural History Museum / Folklore Museum - 1994
Rangitane Maori cultural objects - research library, teacher resource room 25865

Papakura

Papakura and District Historical Society Museum, Accent Point Bldg, 28 East St, Papakura 1703 - T: (09) 9782600, Fax: 9782607, E-mail: pmuseum@ihug.co.nz. Head: Jocelyn Brown
Local Museum 25866

Paraparaumu

Museum of Aviation, Paraparaumu Airport, Kapiti Rd, Raumati, Paraparaumu 6450 - T: (04) 2998965. Head: Patrick H. Pallin
Science&Tech Museum - 1993
Pioneer aviators 25867

Southward Museum, Otaihanga Rd, Paraparaumu 6450 - T: (04) 2971221, Fax: 2970503. Head: Stan Bellamore
Science&Tech Museum - 1979
English, European and USA cars all years to 1970 25868

Patea

South Taranaki Regional Museum, 127 Egmont St, Patea 5181 - T: (06) 2738084 ext 826. Head: G.L. Baker
Local Museum - 1974
Documents relating to local military settlement, Maori carvings depicting the arrival of the Aotea canoe and history of the Ruanui and Ngarauru tribes, vehicles, machinery, farm implements - library and archives 25869

Picton

Picton Community Museum, London Quay, Picton 7372 - T: (03) 5738283. Head: Mike Taylor
Local Museum - 1964
Early (1827-1911) and Perano (1911-1964) whaling, Maori section, shells, photographs 25870

Piopio

Piopio and District Museum, Ruru St, Piopio 2555 - T: (07) 8778293. Head: John L. Petre
Local Museum
Early settler artifacts and photographs 25871

Pleasant Point

Pleasant Point Railway and Historical Society Museum, Railway Station, Main Rd, Pleasant Point 8772 - T: (03) 6862269, Fax: 6862269, Internet: http://www.timarn.com/railway. Head: Marian Blanchard
Science&Tech Museum / Historical Museum - 1970
NZ's only restored half-birdcage carriage built 1895, steam and diesel locomotives, restored railway carriages and freight wagons, local history - old time movie theatre 25872

Porirua

New Zealand Police Museum, c/o Royal New Zealand Police College, Papakowhai Rd, Porirua 6220 - T: (04) 2383141, Fax: 2370129, E-mail: museum@police.govt.nz. Head: Bronwyn Grant
Historical Museum - 1908
NZ medals, firearms, crimes, police vehicles and motorbikes, uniforms, tools, technologies - forensic museum 25873

Pataka Porirua Museum of Arts and Cultures, Cnr Norrie and Parumoana Sts, Porirua 6220 - T: (04) 2371511, Fax: 2374527, E-mail: pataka@pcc.govt.nz, Internet: http://www.pataka.org.nz. Head: Helen Kedgley, Bob Maysmor
Local Museum / Fine Arts Museum - 1998
Local hist, contmporary Maori-, Pacific- and New Zealand- Art, mechanical music instruments 25874

Porirua Hospital Museum, Kenepuru Dr, Porirua 6220, mail addr: POB 50-264, Porirua 6220 - T: (04) 2374589 ext 7541, Fax: 2374269, E-mail: fphm@ihug.co.nz, Internet: http://www.converge.org.nz/fphm. Head: Dr. Helen Bichan
Special Museum - 1987
Mental health, mental illness, mental disability 25875

Porirua Museum → Pataka Porirua Museum of Arts and Cultures

Port Chalmers

Port Chalmers Museum, Beach St, Port Chalmers - T: (03) 4728233, E-mail: pcmuseum@xtra.co.nz. Head: Rowan Carroll
Local Museum - 1913/1987
Local and maritime history 25876

Puhoi

Puhoi Historical Society Museum, Puhoi Store, Puhoi 1240 - T: (09) 4220816, Fax: 4220816. Head: Norman Golding
Local Museum
Bohemian settlement (settled 1863), photos, family records etc. 25877

Putaruru

Putaruru Timber Museum, POB 103, Putaruru 2321 - T: (07) 8837621, Fax: 8837621. Head: Tony Robben
Natural History Museum
History of timber industry 25878

Raglan

Raglan and District Museum, 22 Kaitoke St, Raglan 2021 - T: (07) 8257195, Fax: 8257054
Local Museum 25879

Rangiora

Rangiora Museum, Good St, Rangiora 8254 - T: (03) 3137592. Head: Ann Jelfs
Local Museum
Local history 25880

Reefton

Black's Point Museum, Black's Point, Main Hwy, Reefton 8290 - T: (03) 7328808. Head: Colin Watts
Local Museum
Wesley Church, gold mining equipment, early Reefton papers 25881

Renwick

Renwick Museum, 58 High St, Renwick 7352
Local Museum - 1931
Model smithy and tools, pioneer tavern, early colonial artifacts - library 25882

Riverton

Wallace Early Settlers Museum, Palmerstow St, Riverton 9654 - T: (03) 2348520. Head: Blanche Ward
Historical Museum 25883

Rotorua

Rotorua Museum of Art and History, Te Whare Taonga o te Arawa, Government Gardens, Albert Dr, Rotorua 3220 - T: (07) 3494350, Fax: 3492819, E-mail: rotoruamuseum@rdc.govt.nz, Internet: http://www.rotoruamuseum.co.nz. Head: Greg W. McManus
Fine Arts Museum / Historical Museum - 1969
Historical and contemporary New Zealand fine art, treasures of the Te Arawa, photogr - library 25884

Te Amorangi Trust Museum, 43-45 Robinson Av, Rotorua 3230 - T: (07) 3459525, E-mail: bryon.w@xtra.co.nz. Head: B. Somervell
Local Museum - 1968
Indigenous logging in Rotorua area 25885

Roxburgh

Teviot District Museum, 37 Branxholm St, Roxburgh 9156 - T: (03) 4468494. Head: D.A. Lusby
Local Museum 25886

Russell

Pompallier House, The Strand, Russell - T: (09) 4037861, Fax: 4038588
Historical Museum 25887

Russell Museum, 2 York St, Russell 0255 - T: (09) 4037701, Fax: 4037701, E-mail: rslmuseum@xtra.co.nz, Internet: http://www.nzmuzeums.co.nz/museums/russell.museum.html
Local Museum - 1954
Maori artifacts, whaling, 5th scale model of Cook's 'Endeavour', pioneer and colonist items 25888

Shannon

Shannon Railway Station Museum, Plinner Terrace, Shannon 55555 - T: (06) 3627343. Head: Betty Rosanowski
Science&Tech Museum 25889

Silverdale

Pioneer Village, Wainui Rd, Silverdale 1461, mail addr: POB 27, Orewa 1461 - T: (09) 4268272, Fax: 4268272. Head: Graham Robinson
Open Air Museum / Local Museum / Historical Museum 25890

Stewart Island

Rakiura Museum, Ayr St, Stewart Island 9530 - T: (03) 2191049, Fax: 2191022. Head: Elaine Hamilton
Local Museum - 1960
Maori and European settlement, whaling, milling, fishing, boatbuilding, natural history 25891

Taihape

Taihape and District Museum, Huia St, Taihape 5457 - T: (06) 3880297/089, Fax: 3881488, E-mail: cjgilbert@xtra.co.nz. Head: B. Jensen
Local Museum - 1970
China coll depicting early Taihape street scenes 25892

Takaka

Rockville Machinery Museum, Waitapu Rd, Takaka 7171 - T: (03) 5259030. Head: Paul Sangster
Science&Tech Museum 25893

Taupo

Taupo District Museum of Art and History, Story Pl, Taupo 3300 - T: (07) 3784167. Head: Ken Niven
Fine Arts Museum / Historical Museum
Complete Coll of (1/72 scale) aircraft that took part in World War II, topographic map of Taupo District to exact scale 1:40,000 including "Tongariro National Park", and North Island volcanic mountain group 25894

Tauranga

Brain-Watkins House, 233 Cameron Rd, Tauranga 3001 - T: (07) 5781835. Head: Alan Lambourn
Local Museum 25895

Tauranga Historic Village Museum, 1010 Tyne St, Mount Maunganui, Tauranga 3002 - T: (07) 5781302, Fax: 5781822. Head: Max Mason
Open Air Museum - 1977
Historic Maori village township, restored vintage tractors 25896

Te Awamutu

Te Awamutu Museum, 135 Roche St, Te Awamutu 2400 - T: (07) 8714326, Fax: 8714328, E-mail: tamuseum@ihug.co.nz, Internet: http://www.tamuseum.org.nz. Head: Tracy Sibson
Local Museum - 1935
Maori and local hist, Tainui treasure 'Uenuku', Tim and Neil Finn display - library, archives 25897

Te Kauwhata

Waikare Historical Society Museum, Homestead Rise, Aparangi, Te Kauwhata 2152 - T: (07) 8263318. Head: R.P. Moorfield
Historical Museum - 1974 25898

Te Kuiti

Te Kuiti and District Historical Society Museum, POB 150, Te Kuiti 2500 - T: (07) 8787582. Head: Jim O'Halloran
Local Museum 25899

Temuka

Temuka Courthouse Museum, 2 Domain Av, Temuka 8752 - T: (03) 6157103. Head: Tess Daly
Local Museum - 1982 25900

Thames

Thames School of Mines and Mineralogical Museum, 101 Cochrane St, Thames 2801 - T: (07) 8686227, Fax: 8686995, E-mail: -thamesschoolofmines@historic.org.nz, Internet: http://www.historic.org.nz
Science&Tech Museum / Natural History Museum - 1886
Ores, minerals, metals, rocks, fossils, shells, semiprecious stones, carved kauri gum, models of mining machinery, metallurgical samples, tools, photographs of mining period 25901

Timaru

Aigantighe Art Gallery, 49 Wai-iti Rd, Timaru - T: (03) 6884424, Fax: 6848346, E-mail: aigant@es.co.nz. Head: Dr. Fiona Ciaran
Fine Arts Museum - 1956
New Zealand and British paintings, prints, drawings, sculpture, pottery (C.F. Goldie, Frances Hodgkins) 25902

South Canterbury Museum, 4 Perth St, Timaru 8615, mail addr: PO Box 522, Timaru 8615 - T: (03) 6842212, Fax: 6842212, E-mail: museum@tindc.govt.nz. Head: Philip Howe
Local Museum - 1952
Local nature specimens, Maori artefacts, 19th and 20th century social history artefacts, archival documents, photographs 25903

Tokanui

Waikawa District Museum, RD 1, Tokanui 9671 - T: (03) 2468489
Local Museum - 1975
Maori artifacts, early colonial shipping and whaling articles and various colonial items, photos of early settlers, district hist 25904

Tokomaru

Tokomaru Steam Engine Museum, Main Rd, Hwy 57, Tokomaru 5450 - T: (06) 3298867, Fax: 3298840, E-mail: tokumarusteam@xtra.co.nz, Internet: http://www.tokomarusteam.com.nz. Head: Colin Stevenson
Science&Tech Museum - 1970
Working steam engines, working scale models, railway system - library 25905

Tuatapere

Tuatapere Bushmans Museum, Main St, Tuatapere 9655 - T: (03) 2266399
Local Museum 25906

Waiau

Amuri Historical Museum, Highfield Rd, Waiau 8275 - T: (03) 3156010. Head: P.S. Northcote
Historical Museum 25907

Waiheke Island

Waiheke Island Historical Society Museum, POB 206, Waiheke Island 3090. Head: Kit Nelson
Historical Museum 25908

Waihi

Waihi Arts Centre and Museum Association, Kenny St, Waihi 3061 - T: (08163) 8638386, Fax: 8638426, E-mail: wacma@xtra.co.nz. Head: D.C. Lockwood
Local Museum - 1962
Local gold mining history, Ohinemuri district history, geological specimens, maps, photographs, paintings 25909

Waikaia

Switzers Museum, Blaydon St, Waikaia 9755 - T: (03) 2027746
Local Museum
Bottle House, gold mining hist 25910

Waikouaiti

Waikouaiti Museum, Main Rd and Kildare St, Waikouaiti 9063 - T: (03) 4657736, Fax: 4657736. Head: Marie Harrison
Local Museum - 1966
Greenstone, moa bones, trypot whaleboat oars 25911

Waimate

Waimate Historical Museum, 28 Shearman St, Waimate 8791 - T: (0519) 6897832, E-mail: wtemus@xtra.co.nz, Internet: http://www.waimate.org.nz/museum. Head: J.A. Foley
Historical Museum - 1954
Pioneer household and farm implements, machinery, militaria from mid- 1800's through to twentieth c, clock coll, photographic coll, historic memorabilia, horse-drawn vehicle coll - archives, library 25912

Waiouru

Queen Elizabeth II Army Memorial Museum, State Hwy 1, Waiouru 5164 - T: (06) 3876911, Fax: 3876319, E-mail: armymuseum@xtra.co.nz, Internet: http://www.army.mil.nz. Head: V.L. Pomana
Military Museum - 1978
General Sir Alexander Godley's orders, decorations, medals, sword and uniform, Cpt Charles Upham medal group, NZ war history - Kippenberger Pavillion, archive, library 25913

Waipawa

Central Hawke's Bay Settlers Museum, High St, Waipawa 4170 - T: (06) 8577288
Local Museum 25914

Waipu

Waipu Centennial Trust Board, 36 The Centre, Waipu 0254 - T: (09) 4320746, Fax: 4320746, E-mail: waipu9@xtra.co.nz
Local Museum - 1953
Local pioneering relics, kauri gum, polished and unpolished, genealogies, documents, photographs of Nova Scotian Pioneers who settled in Waipu in 1853 25915

Waipukurau

Waipukurau Museum, 13 Francis Drake St, Waipukurau 4176 - T: (06) 8589529. Head: E.B. Jones
Local Museum 25916

Wairoa

Wairoa District Museum, Marine Parade, Wairoa 4192 - T: (06) 8383108, Fax: 8388847. Head: Tearoha Cooper
Local Museum - 1974 25917

Waitangi

Chatham Islands Museum, Waitangi 8030 - T: (03) 3050033. Head: Terry Melville
Local Museum 25918

Waitomo Caves

Waitomo Museum of Caves, 21 Waitomo Caves Rd, Waitomo Caves 2566 - T: (07) 8787640, Fax: 8786184, E-mail: waitomomuseum@xtra.co.nz, Internet: http://www.waitomo-museum.co.nz. Head: Peter Dimond
Natural History Museum - 1971
Sub fossil bird bone coll, Caves hist 25919

Waiuku

Waiuku Museum, 13 King St, Waiuku 1852 - T: (09) 2358698. Head: Rachel Gillies
Local Museum - 1966
Farm implements, clothing, local hand-crafted furniture, Maori carving, local photographs 25920

Wakefield

Pigeon Valley Steam Museum, Pigeon Valley, 2 km from Wakefield, Wakefield 7181, mail addr: 51 Norwich St, Stoke, Nelson 7001 - T: (03) 5479976. Head: Ken Ivory
Science&Tech Museum
Steam and agricultural machinery 25921

Wanaka

New Zealand Fighter Pilots Museum, POB 218, Wanaka 9192 - T: (03) 4437010, Fax: 4437011. Head: Ian J. Brodie
Military Museum 25922

Wanganui

Sarjeant Gallery - Te Whare o Rehua, Queen's Park, Wanganui 5015 - T: (06) 3490506, Fax: 3490507, E-mail: billm@sarjeant.org.nz, Internet: http://www.sarjeant.org.nz. Head: Bill Milbank
Fine Arts Museum - 1919
Drawings by Bernadino Poccetti ('Passion of our Lord Jeses Christ' 1548-1612), early New Zealand and 19th-20th c British and European oils, watercolours and prints, WWI cartoons, posters, works by leadind contemporary artists from NZ 25923

Whanganui Regional Museum, Watt St, Wanganui 5015 - T: 3476512, Fax: 3476512, E-mail: info@museum.queenspark.org.nz, Internet: http://www.wanganui-museum.org.nz. Head: Sharon Dell
Local Museum - 1895
Maori and Polynesian artifacts, Maori canoes, New Zealand birds, whale skeletons, fish, shells, minerals, entomology, firearms, medals and coins, early colonial material, local hist, Maori ornaments and weapons, photographs, archives - reference library 25924

Whanganui Riverboat Centre Museum, 1a Taupo Quay, Wanganui - T: (06) 3471863, Fax: 3471863, E-mail: Riverboatswanganui@clear.net.nz, Internet: http://www.wanganui.org.nz/riverboats. Head: Libby Gray
Historical Museum - 1994
Riverboats, local hist, steam paddlewheeler 25925

Ward

Ward Museum, POB 26, Ward 7350 - T: (03) 5756885. Head: H. Thomson
Local Museum 25926

Warkworth

Warkworth and District Museum, Tudor Collins Dr, Warkworth 1241 - T: (09) 4257093, Fax: 4257058, E-mail: warkworthmuseum@xtra.co.nz, Internet: http://www.wwmuseum.orcon.net.nz. Head: Ian Ferguson
Local Museum - 1980 25927

Wellington

Alexander McKay Geological Museum, c/o Victoria University, POB 600, Wellington 6020 - T: (04) 4715345 ext 8378, Fax: 4951586. Head: Dr. Michael Hannah
Natural History Museum / University Museum 25928

City Gallery Wellington, Civic Sq, Wellington 6015 - T: (04) 8013952, Fax: 8013950, E-mail: art.gallery@wcc.govt.nz, Internet: http://www.city-gallery.org.nz. Head: Paula Savage
Public Gallery - 1970's 25929

Colonial Cottage Museum, 68 Nairn St, Wellington 6015 - T: (04) 3849122, Fax: 3849202, E-mail: admin@coloniacottagemuseum.co.nz, Internet: http://www.coloniacottagemuseum.co.nz. Head: Kim Townley
Historical Museum 25930

Kapiti Coast Museum Waikanae, 9 Elizabeth St, Waikanae, Wellington 6010 - T: (04) 2932359. Head: Neville Harris
Local Museum - 1983
Domestic radio receivers, amateur radio equipment - communication section, amateur radio station 25931

Katherine Mansfield Birthplace, 25 Tinakori Rd, Thorndon, Wellington 6001 - T: (04) 4737268
Special Museum 25932

Kura Gallery, 19 Allen St, Wellington 6001 - T: (04) 8024934
Public Gallery 25933

Museum of Wellington, City and Sea, Queens Wharf, Jervois Quay, Wellington 6015 - T: (04) 4728904, Fax: 4961949, E-mail: museum@mowcas.co.nz, Internet: http://www.bondstore.co.nz. Head: John Gilberthorpe
Local Museum - 1972
General marine coll incl art, shipping ephemera, maritime objects, photos, Union Steam Ship Company, Wellinton Harbour Board, interisland ferry Wahine and its disaster, Local social history - library, archives, research service 25934

National Cricket Museum, c/o Wellington Cricket Association, Old Stand, Basin Reserve, Wellington 6015 - T: (04) 3856602, Fax: 3843498, E-mail: - national.cricket.museum@paradise.net.nz. Head: Stanley Cowman
Special Museum - 1987 25935

New Zealand Academy of Fine Arts Gallery, 1 Queens Wharf, Wellington - T: (04) 4998807, Fax: 4992612, E-mail: nzafa@xtra.co.nz, Internet: http://www.nzafa.com. Head: Philip Markham
Public Gallery - 1882
New Zealand artists, New Zealand visual arts 25936

New Zealand Centre for Photography, c/o Portrait Gallery, Bowen House, Cnr Lambton Quay and Bowen St, Wellington 6001 - T: (04) 9151507, Fax: 9151507, E-mail: centrephot@clear.net.nz, Internet: http://nzcp.wellington.net.nz. Head: David Langman
Fine Arts Museum 25937

New Zealand Olympic and Commonwealth Games Association Museum → Olympic Museum

New Zealand Portrait Gallery, Bowen House, Cnr Lambton Quai and Bowen St, Wellington 6005, mail addr: POB 17096, Wellington 6005 - T: (04) 4768806, Fax: 4728874, E-mail: wrw@nzportgal.org.nz, Internet: http://www.nzportgal.org.nz
Fine Arts Museum 25938

New Zealand Post Collection Museum, Te Puni Mail Centre, Petone, Wellington 6320 - T: (04) 5680270, Fax: 5680231. Head: Eric Adank
Special Museum
Stamps, associated artwork and postal artifacts 25939

Oceania Design, 41A Willis St, Wellington 6001 - T: (04) 4999588
Public Gallery 25940

Olympic Museum, New Zealand Olympic Commitee, 97-99 Courtenay Pl, Wellington 6015 - T: (04) 3850070, Fax: 3850090, E-mail: charles@olympic.org.nz, Internet: http://www.olympic.org.nz/museum. Head: Charles Callis
Special Museum
NZ Olympic movement, Commonwealth Games 25941

Paekakariki Railway Museum, Engine Shed, SH 1, Paekakariki, Wellington 6010 - T: (04) 2928296, Fax: 2928296. Head: Christine Johnson
Science&Tech Museum 25942

Petone Settlers Museum, The Esplanade, Petone, Wellington 6008 - T: (04) 5688373
Local Museum 25943

Rimu Street Gallery, 26 Rimu St, Rona Bay, Wellington 6008
Public Gallery 25944

Salvation Army Archives and Museum, 204 Cuba St, Wellington 6015 - T: (04) 3820732, Fax: 8026259, E-mail: archives@nzf.salvationarmy.org. Head: Alan Robb
Religious Arts Museum - 1990
Salvation Army publications and uniforms 25945

Si Salon, 95 Customhouse Quay, Wellington 6001 - T: (04) 4996620
Public Gallery 25946

Tamarillo, 102 Wakefield St, Wellington 6001 - T: (04) 4736095
Public Gallery 25947

Te Papa, Museum of New Zealand Te Papa Tongarewa, Cable St, Wellington 6020 - T: (04) 3817000, Fax: 3817070, E-mail: mail@tepapa.govt.nz, Internet: http://www.tepapa.govt.nz. Head: Cheryll Sotheran
Natural History Museum / Ethnology Museum / Historical Museum - 1865
Mammals, esp marine mammals, birds, reptiles, fishes, mollusca, crustacea, echinoderms, insects, plants, ethnology of New Zealand and the Pacific, colonial hist, fine arts - library 25948

Westpac Banking Corporation Archive and Museum, POB 691, Wellington 6015 - T: (04) 4773868, Fax: 4773520. Head: Pauline Porteous
Special Museum - 1979 25949

Wellsford

Albertland and Districts Museum, Memorial Park, Wellsford - T: (09) 4238181, Fax: 4238181. Head: Bette Lamont
Local Museum
Domestic utensils, farm implements, tools, Maori artifacts, press, photographs from the pioneer period, Harold Marsh photograph coll (1900-1948) 25950

Whakatane

Whakatane District Museum and Gallery, Boon St, Whakatane 3080 - T: (07) 3079805, Fax: 3088796, E-mail: museum@whakatane-dc.govt.nz, Internet: http://www.browserbuys.co.nz/whakatane-museum-home.htm. Head: Roy Gould
Historical Museum / Fine Arts Museum - 1972
Maori artifacts, pioneer relics, Ellis coll of New Zealand books - archives, research library 25951

Whangarei

Claphams Clock Museum, Town Basin, Whangarei 0130, mail addr: Private Bag 9023, Whangarei 0130 - T: (09) 4383993, Fax: 4383993. Head: Roger Schofield
Science&Tech Museum - 1900
Clocks and watches, Dan Rey clock (1650), Grand Sonnerie clock (1800), Viennese hand-painted clock on a French rose onyx base (1840) 25952

Whangarei Art Museum, Te Wharetaonga o Whangarei, Cafler Park Rose Gardens, Water St, Whangarei 0130 - T: (09) 4307240, Fax: 4307240, E-mail: whgartmuseum@xtra.co.nz. Head: Scott Pothan
Fine Arts Museum 25953

Whangarei Museum, State Hwy 14, Te Mai, Whangarei 0115 - T: (09) 4389630, Fax: 4389630, E-mail: admin@whangareimuseum.org.nz, Internet: http://www.whangareimuseum.org.nz. Head: Stefan Tengblad
Local Museum - 1972
Industrial design, Taonga Maori, live, flora and fauna, telephone and gramophone 25954

Whitianga

Mercury Bay and District Museum, 12 The Esplanade, Whitianga 2856 - T: (07) 8665995, Fax: 8665995. Head: Gene Horne
Local Museum - 1972 25955

Woodville

Woodville Pioneer Museum, 62 Ormond St, Woodville 5473 - T: (06) 3765677. Head: Freda O'Brien
Local Museum - 1970
Model T Fire Engine and Commer fire engine - ex Woodville volunteer fire brigade and other equipment, railway equipment/ memorabilia, Tom and Bessie Spinett's Teapot, Coll - camera, telephone, bottles (Brewers & Cordial) 25956

Wyndham

Wyndham Museum, 40 R. Beange, Redan No 2 Rd, Wyndham 9758 - T: (03) 2064285. Head: W.O. Hunter
Local Museum 25957

Nicaragua

Chontales

Museo Gregorio Aguilar Barea, Calle Juigalpa, Chontales. Head: Gustavo M. Villanueva
Local Museum
Local history, ethnography 25958

Granada

Museo Arqueológico, Colegio Centro América, Granada
Archaeological Museum 25959

Managua

Museo Nacional de Nicaragua, Palacio Nacional de la Cultura, Managua, mail addr: Apdo 416, Managua - T: 2224820, Fax: 2224820, E-mail: mnndc@ibw.com.ni. Head: Egdar Espinoza Pérez
Archaeological Museum / Historical Museum - 1896
Archaeology, history, natural hist - library 25960

Masaya

Museo Tenderi, Villa Nindirí, Masaya
Local Museum
Local hist, ethnography 25961

Niger

Niamey

Musée National du Niger, BP 248, Niamey - T: 734321. Head: Albert Ferral
Local Museum - 1959
Prehist, archaeology, costumes, crafts, tribal houses, history 25962

Zinder

Musée Régional de Zinder, BP 614, Zinder
Local Museum 25963

Nigeria

Aba

National Museum of Colonial History, 6 Ikot Ekpene Rd, Aba, mail addr: PMB 7116, Aba - T: (082) 221863. Head: Dr. Omotoso Eluyemi
Historical Museum 25964

Abeokuta

National Museum of Abeokuta, PMB 2004, Abeokuta - T: (039) 232508
Local Museum 25965

Abuja

Didi Museum, Plot 175 Akin Adesola St, Victoria I, Abuja - T: (09) 612845
Local Museum 25966

National Museum, Abuja, Plot 2018, Cotonou Crescent, Wuse Zone 6, Abuja, mail addr: PMB 171, Garki, Abuja - T: (09) 5238254, 5230823, Fax: 5238254. Head: Dr. Omotoso Eluyemi
Historical Museum - 1997 25967

Akure

National Museum of Akure, Old Local Government Secretariat, Akure, mail addr: PMB 664, Akure
Local Museum 25968

Argungu

Kanta Museum Argungu, Gidan Yakubu Nabame Argungu, Argungu
Ethnology Museum
Weapons, ancient metal pots 25969

Benin

National Museum Benin, King's Sq, Benin, mail addr: PMB 1115, Benin - T: (052) 201130. Head: Prof. Ade Obayemi
Decorative Arts Museum - 1973
Local antiquities, bronzes, terracotta, intrinsic artworks, cast iron pieces, Old Benin Empire, 25970

Calabar

National Museum of Calabar, Old Residency, Calabar, mail addr: PMB 1180, Calabar - T: (087) 223476, Fax: 220111
Local Museum 25971

Enugu

National Museum of Enugu, 65 Abakaliki Rd, Enugu, mail addr: PMB 1285, Enugu - T: (042) 255280. Head: Felicia Anyaegbuna
Local Museum
Ethnography, history, economics, politics, warfare, arts & Crafts 25972

Esie

National Museum - House of Images Esie, PMB 301, Esie - T: (031) 701047. Head: Daniel O. Kekeke
Archaeological Museum - 1945
Soapstone sculptures of Esie 25973

Ibadan

Museum of the Institute of African Studies, c/o University of Ibadan, Ibadan
Ethnology Museum / Archaeological Museum / University Museum
Ethnographic and archaeological exhibits 25974

Zoology Museum, c/o University of Ibadan, Ibadan. Head: Johnson Fagbohunmi
Natural History Museum / University Museum
Vertebrate and invertebrate specimens, particularly of tropical species for teaching and research 25975

Ife

National Museum Ile-Ife, Enuwa Sq, Ife - T: (036) 230150, E-mail: ifemuseum@ganet.city.ng. Head: Bode Adesina
Archaeological Museum
Archaeology of ancient Ife, bronze and terracotta sculpture, history of Western Nigeria 25976

Natural History Museum, c/o Obafemi Awolowo University, Ife - T: (036) 232227, E-mail: misawumi@oauife.edu.ng. Head: Dr. M.A. Isawumi
Natural History Museum / Archaeological Museum - 1972
Research, teaching, exhibition and identification of animal and plant specimens, botanical, entomological, geological and zoological coll, archaeological coll 25977

Ikwuano

National War Museum of Umauhia, Ebitu Amafor, Ikwuano, mail addr: PMB 7074, Umauhia - T: (088) 222485
Military Museum - 1985
Ojukwu bunker, voice of Biafra, Nigerian civil war (1966- 1970), pre-colonial weapons 25978

Ilorin

Esie Museum, Esie via Ora, Ilorin, mail addr: PMB 301, Ilorin
Museum of Classical Antiquities - 1945
Stone antiques 25979

Ilupeju

Aaragon Museum, 205 Ikorodu Rd, Obanikoro, Ilupeju - T: 821040
Local Museum 25980

Jos

Jos National Museum and Museum of Traditional Nigerian Architecture, opposite Zoo, Jos, mail addr: POB 2031, Jos - T: 54005. Head: M. Dandaura
Local Museum - 1952
Archaeology, ethnography, terracotta Nok figurines, Benin-Ife-Yoruba works, traditional architecture - library 25981

Museum of the Institute of African Studies, c/o University of Ife, PMB 2031, Jos. Head: M. Akanbiemu
Ethnology Museum / Archaeological Museum - 1965
Archaeology, ethnology, terracotta, masks and Yoruba cult objects - library 25982

Kaduna

National Museum Kaduna, Ali Akilu Rd, Kaduna, mail addr: PMB 2127, Kaduna - T: (062) 211180, Fax: 2633890. Head: Dr. K.S. Chafe
Archaeological Museum / Ethnology Museum - 1975
Archaeology and ethnography, houses the 'Craft Village' where traditional hairplaiting, weaving, pottery, calabash decoration, wood carving, brass casting and smithery are done - library 25983

Kano

Gidan Makama Museum, POB 2023, Kano - T: (064) 645170
Folklore Museum / Ethnology Museum - 1959
Ethnography, folklore, local art 25984

Lagos

Aaragon Museum, Lawn Tennis Club, Race Course, Lagos
Special Museum 25985

Centre for Black and African Art and Civilization, National Theatre, Lagos, mail addr: PMB 12794, Lagos - T: (1) 831734, Fax: 2694413. Head: Prof. U. Edebiri
Fine Arts Museum - 1978

Nigerian art, Black and African art, Africa and the origin of man, African architectural technology, the art of Black Australia, Zimbabwe house, Angola house - library, archives, audio-visual dept 25986

National Museum, Lagos, Onikan Rd, Lagos, mail addr: PMB 12556, Lagos - T: (01) 2634040, 2631934, Fax: 2633890. Head: Dr. Omotoso Eluyemi
Ethnology Museum / Archaeological Museum / Decorative Arts Museum - 1957
Ethnology, archaeology, Nok and Ife terracottas, Ife, Igbo-Ukwu and Benin bronzes, history, ethnography - library 25987

Makurdi

National Museum Makurdi, G.P. 4, Ahmadu Bello Way, Makurdi, mail addr: PMB 102294, Makurdi - T: (044) 31297. Head: J.Y. Dauda
Local Museum - 1988
History, archeology, ethnography, wooden objects, masks, textiles, terracotta, metal objects - research and training dept 25988

Nsukka

Archaeology Museum, c/o Department of Archaeology, University of Nigeria, Nsukka - T: (042) 771911
Archaeological Museum 25989

Oron

National Museum, Oron, PMB 1004, Oron. Head: Aniefiok Udo Akpan
Folklore Museum - 1959
Traditional carvings from the Oron area 25990

Oshogbo

Ataoja, Oba Oyewale Matanmi's Palace, National Commission for Museums and Monuments, Ataoja' Palace, Oja-Oba, Oshogbo, mail addr: PMB 4376, Oshogbo - T: (035) 241471. Head: Oluremi Funsho Adedayo
Local Museum / Historical Museum / Natural History Museum - 1988
Wood and metal sculpture, representations of Yoruba gods and godnesses, embroidery, plants, animals leather and brass works, drums, ritual objects 25991

Museum of Antiquities, 27 Catholic Mission Rd, Oshogbo
Decorative Arts Museum
Local ceremonial artifacts, costumes 25992

Museum of the Institute of African Studies, 25 Aiyetoro Rd, Ikirun Byepass, Oshogbo, mail addr: PMB 4376, Oshogbo - T: (035) 232874
Ethnology Museum - 1966
Wood and metal sculpture, bead work and embroidery, leather applique and brass work, drums, ritual objects and Afikpo Ibo masks 25993

Owo

Owo Museum, POB 84, Owo. Head: Ola Abejide
Folklore Museum - 1959
Handicraft, ethnographic Yoruba finds 25994

Port Harcourt

National Museum of Port Harcourt, 2 Harley St, Port Harcourt, mail addr: PMB 5166, Port Harcourt - T: (084) 333406
Local Museum 25995

Uyo

National Museum Uyo, Wellington Bassey Way, Uyo, mail addr: PMB 1109, Uyo - T: (085) 203077. Head: Violetta I. Epko
Local Museum - 1989
State creation, women organizations, material culture, traditional kitchen - library, education centre 25996

Niue

Alofi

Huanki Cultural Centre, POB 67, Alofi. Head: Phyllis E. Richmond-Rex
Historical Museum - 1989
Old artefacts, handicraft 25997

Norfolk Island

Kingston

Norfolk Island Museum, Kingston - T: 672323088, Fax: 672323177
Local Museum
Pier store, Royal engineers office, Sirius Maritime Museum, No. 10 Quality Row House 25998

Norway

Ådalsbruk

Klevfos Industrimuseum, 2345 Ådalsbruk - T: 62590505, Fax: 62590505
Science&Tech Museum
Primitive old pulp- and papermill 25999

Ängelholm

Banmuseet, 262 52 Ängelholm - T: (0431) 442170, Fax: 442179, E-mail: lars-olov.karlsson@banverket.se, Internet: http://www.banverket.se. Head: Andreas Dreyer
Science&Tech Museum 26000

Åfjord

Åfjord Bygdetun, 7170 Åfjord
Local Museum
Old cottage and local history items 26001

Ål

Ål Bygdemuseum, Leksvold, 2 km from Hwy 7, 3570 Ål - T: 32081770
Open Air Museum - 1924
Old farm-yard with two 18th c cottages, 15 buildings, including old school house, grinding mill, cottage (17th c), 'rose-painting' coll 26002

Ålen

Ålen Bygdetun, nr Hwy 30, 7480 Ålen
Local Museum
Local history, utensils and implements, old cottage 26003

Ålesund

Ålesunds Museum, Rasmus Rønnebergsg 16, 6002 Ålesund - T: 70123170, Fax: 70121141, E-mail: museum@mr.telia.no
Local Museum - 1903
Local history, natural history, social history, archaeology section, seafaring, fishing and arctic hunting - library 26004

Sunmøre Museum, Borgundgavlen, 6015 Ålesund - T: 70174000, Fax: 70174001, E-mail: museum@sunnmore.museum.no, Internet: http://www.sunnmore.museum.no. Head: Tor Erik Standal
Local Museum - 1931
Boats and fishing implements, regional prehistory, agriculture, handicrafts, copies of 3 prehistoric ships (600 AD) in full scale, about 50 old houses grouped in farmyards - library 26005

Alsvåg

Øksnes Bygdemuseum, 8432 Alsvåg - T: 76131485, Fax: 76131485
Local Museum
Local rural life, 18th c manor 26006

Alta

Alta Museum, Altav 19, 9500 Alta - T: 78435377, Fax: 78435829. Head: Hans Christian Søborg
Local Museum
Rock carvings (World heritage), northern lights observatory, military display 26007

Alvdal

Nordre Husan, Osterdal Valley, North of Alvdal Village on Hwy 30, 2560 Alvdal
Open Air Museum
Mountain village farmyard consisting of sixteen houses (many from the 17th c) on their original sites 26008

Åmot

Modums Blaafarveværk, 3340 Åmot - T: 32782800, Fax: 32782700, E-mail: info@blaa.no, Internet: http://www.blaa.no. Head: Tone Sinding Steinsvik
Historical Museum
19th c workers's houses at the Modum cobalt mines (1773 - 1893) and Haugfoss works, smalt production, local history section, art gallery, Th. Kittelsen museum - annual art exhibition 26009

Åndalsnes

Ner Hole Museum, Close to the E 69, Nedre Hole, 6300 Åndalsnes
Open Air Museum - 1950
Stonebuilt farmhouse (1814) and other buildings 26010

Andenes

Polarmuseet, Old Doctor's House, 8480 Andenes - T: 76142088
Historical Museum
Exhibits related to Svalbard, Polar expeditions section, sealing and trapping in the Arctic 26011

Aremark

Aremark Historielag, Hwy 21, 1770 Aremark. Head: Knud Selmer Olsen
Local Museum - 1964
Grain mill (1885) 26012

Arendal

Aust-Agder Museet, Langsæ Gård, Parkv 16, 4800 Arendal - T: 37022422. Head: Ulf Hamran
Local Museum - 1832
Maritime section, prehistory, ethnography, geology, coins and medals, furniture, arts and crafts 26013

Merdøgård, Merdøy Island, 4800 Arendal - T: 37022422. Head: Ulf Hamran
Open Air Museum - 1930
18th c captain's or 'skipper's' house, demonstrating the close connection between domestic life and house furnishing in Southern Norway, Holland and England in the days of the sailing vessels 26014

Årnes

Gamle Hvam Museum, Hwy 173, 2150 Årnes - T: 63909609, Fax: 63909503, E-mail: post@gamlehvam.museum.no, Internet: http://www.gamlehvam.museum.no
Open Air Museum - 1915
18th c farmyard with 12 old buildings, furnishing and equipment, coll of agricultural machinery from 1800 to the 1970's, traditional garden plants 26015

Ås

Norsk Landbruksmuseum (Norwegian Museum of Agriculture), Norges Landbrukshøgskole, 1432 Ås - T: 64949995, Fax: 64949996, E-mail: - norsk.landbruksmuseum@nlm.nlh.no, Internet: http://org.nlh.no/nlm. Head: Elisabeth Koren
Agriculture Museum - 1984
Agriculture, breeding (rare breeds) - research centre 26016

Åsgårdstrand

Munchs Hus (Munch's house), Munchs gate 25, 3179 Åsgårdstrand - T: 33082131, 33085372, Fax: 33085002, E-mail: kulturkontoret@borre.kommune.no, Internet: http://www.borre.kommune.no/kulturkontoret/munchhus.html
Special Museum / Fine Arts Museum
House of Edvard Munch where he created his best known paintings 26017

Askim

Askim Bygdemuseet, E 18, outskirts, 1800 Askim - T: 69884779
Open Air Museum - 1939
Courtyard with 7 old farm houses, equipped with furniture and utensils 26018

Aurland

Aurland Bygdetun, Onstadstova, 5745 Aurland
Special Museum
Sheriff's home with a coll of mementoes from Per Sivle (Norwegian poet 1857-1904) 26019

Bagn

Bagn Bygdesamling, E 16, Islandmoen Farm, 2930 Bagn - T: 61347749, Fax: 61347749. Head: Trond Braaten
Open Air Museum - 1914
Fourteen old farm houses, local hist artifacts, schoolmuseum, war in Bagn 1940-45 26020

Ballangen

Ballangen Bygdemuseet, nr E 6, 8540 Ballangen - T: 76929120, Fax: 7692921, E-mail: radmann@ballangen.kommune.no. Head: Ivar Skoglund
Local Museum - 1962
Local history, mine history of the pit Bjoerkaasen Gruver (1914 - 1964) 26021

Bardu

Troms Forsvarsmuseum, Setermoen, 9360 Bardu - T: 77185658, Fax: 77185651, E-mail: administration@midt-troms.museum.no, Internet: http://www.midt-troms.museum.no. Head: Finn Fossum
Military Museum 26022

Bergen

Bergen Billedgalleri, Bergen Kunstmuseum (The City Art Collection, Bergen Art Museum), Lars Hillesg 10, 5016 Bergen - T: 55568000, Fax: 55568011, E-mail: post@bergenartmuseum.no, Internet: http://www.bergenartmuseum.no. Head: Audun Echoff
Public Gallery / Fine Arts Museum - 1878
Norwegian paintings and sculptures from the 19th and 20th c, European art, J.C. Dahl, Russian and Greek icons from 14th c - library 26023

Bergen Museum, c/o Universitetet i Bergen, Harald Hårfagresgt 1, 5020 Bergen - T: 55589360, Fax: 55589364, E-mail: kare.hesjedal@bm.uib.no, Internet: http://www.bm.uib.no. Head: Kåre Hesjedal
Natural History Museum / Historical Museum / University Museum - 1825
Anthroplogy, archaeology, botany, geology, Norwegian culture, folk art, zoology 26024

Bergens Sjøfartsmuseum (Bergen Maritime Museum), Haakon Sheteligspl 15, 5007 Bergen - T: 55549600, Fax: 55549610, E-mail: - bergens.sjoefartsmuseum@bsj.uib.no. Head: Atle Thowsen
Special Museum / Science&Tech Museum - 1921
Hist of shipping, models incl Norwegian smallcrafts, plans, drawings, pictures, banners from shipyards - library, archives 26025

Bergens Teatermuseet, Villav 5, 5007 Bergen - T: 55212963. Head: Kari Gaarder Losnedahl
Performing Arts Museum 26026

Bergens Tekniske Museet, Thormøhlens g 23, 5006 Bergen - T: 55961160
Science&Tech Museum
Tram depot from 1912, printing press, museum tramway, steam engines, railway carriages 26027

Bryggens Museum, Dreggsallmenning 3, 5835 Bergen - T: 55588010, Fax: 55588050, E-mail: eli.rodseth@bmu.uib.no, Internet: http://www.uib.no/bmu. Head: Dr. Anne Ågotnes
Historical Museum / Archaeological Museum - 1976
Medieval archaeology, cultural and economic hist of Bergen and Western Norway throughout the Middle Ages 26028

Håkonshallen og Rosenkrantztårnet, Bryggens Museum (Håkon's Hall and The Rosenkrantz Tower), Bergenhus Festning, 5003 Bergen - T: 55316067, 55588010, Fax: 55588050, E-mail: eli.rodseth@bmu.uib.no/haakon.htm, Internet: http://www.bryggens.museum.no. Head: Dr. Anne Ågotnes
Historic Site
Håkonshallen (Royal Ceremonial Hall, 1248-61) in Gothic style, Rosenkrantztårnet (Tower, 1562-67) built around a medieval core, several 18th c buildings 26029

Det Hanseatiske Museet og Schøtstuene, Finnegårdsg 1a, 5003 Bergen - T: 55314189, Fax: 55311126, E-mail: hanseat@online.no, Internet: http://www.hanseatisk.museum.no. Head: Marco Trebbi
Local Museum - 1872
One of the oldest and best preserved wooden buildings in Bergen, furnished in the style of the 1700's depicting the life of a Hanseatic merchant, Schøtstuene: old assembly rooms where Hanseatic merchants gathered for warm meals, court meetings and teaching apprentices 26030

De Kulturhistoriske Samlinger, c/o Universitetet i Bergen, Haakon Shetelígs Pl 10, 5007 Bergen - T: 55580000, Fax: 55589656, Internet: http://www.bm.vib.no. Head: Kåre Hesjedal
Historical Museum / University Museum - 1825
Pre- and proto-hist, medieval archaeology and architecture, antiquities, hist of art, Norwegian folk art, cultural anthropology, post-medieval social history, ecclesiastical art, ethnography - library 26031

Museet Gamle Bergen (Old Bergen Museum), Sandviken, Elsesro, 5035 Bergen - T: 55257850, Fax: 55257850. Head: T. Fett
Open Air Museum - 1934
18th and 19th c buildings, furnishings 26032

Naturhistoriske Samlinger, Bergen Museum, Musépl 3, 5007 Bergen - T: 55582920, Fax: 55589180, E-mail: bergen.museum@bm.uib.no, Internet: http://www.bm.uib.no. Head: Bjarne A. Meidell
Natural History Museum / University Museum - 1825/1948
Zoology, botany, geology, minerals, Norwegian and non-Norwegian fauna skeletons of large whales, entomology, marine invertebrates, asteology - library 26033

Norges Fiskerimuseet, Bontelabo 2, 5003 Bergen - T: 55321249, Fax: 55318984. Head: Anders Haaland
Special Museum - 1880
Fishery in Norway, models illustrating various fishing methods, old gear, boat models 26034

Rasmus Meyers Samlinger, Bergen Kunstmuseum (Rasmus Meyer Collections, Bergen Art Museum), Rasmus Meyers Allé 7, 5015 Bergen - T: 55568000, Fax: 55568011, E-mail: post@bergenartmuseum.no, Internet: http://www.bergenartmuseum.no. Head: Audun Echoff
Decorative Arts Museum / Fine Arts Museum - 1916
Norwegian art from the 17th c to 1915, for example, J.C. Dahl, Tidemand, Gude, Werenskiold, Chr. Krohg, coll of works by Edvard Munch, old Bergen interiors 26035

Stenersens Samling, Bergen Kunstmuseum (The Stenersen Collection, Bergen Art Museum), Rasmus Meyers Allé 3, 5016 Bergen - T: 55568000, Fax: 55568011, E-mail: post@bergenartmuseum.no, Internet: http://www.bergenartmuseum.no. Head: Audun Echoff
Fine Arts Museum - 1973
Modern art, incl works by Paul Klee, Edvard Munch, Pablo Picasso, Max Ernst, Lionel Feininger, Jorn, Wassilij Kandinsky, Miró, Nesch, Poliakoff, de Stal, Tamayo, Tobey, Vasarely, Vieira da Silva, Wols, and others - library 26036

Vestlandske Kunstindustrimuseum (West Norway Museum of Decorative Art), Nordahl Brunsg 9, 5014 Bergen - T: 55325108, Fax: 55317455, E-mail: post@vk.museum.no, Internet: http://www.vk.museum.no. Head: Jorunn Haakestad
Decorative Arts Museum - 1887
Applied and decorative arts, Norwegian and European furnishings, goldsmith's work, costumes, textiles, ceramics, glass, porcelain, silver (Renaissance to the present), antiquities, photographs, J.W.N. Munthe's Chinese coll - library 26037

Billingstad

Norges Birøkterlags Museet (Norwegian Beekeepers Association Museum), Bergerv 15, 1362 Billingstad - T: 66845315, Fax: 66848905. Head: Aasne Aarhus
Agriculture Museum - 1890
Development of beekeeping in Norway 26038

Bjarkøy

Bjarkøy Museet, 9426 Bjarkøy - T: 77090117
Local Museum 26039

Bjerka

Hemnes Bygdetun, Lillebjerka, on E 6, 8643 Bjerka
Open Air Museum - 1967
Nine buildings including an open-hearth cottage (1830) illustrating 19th c peasant life 26040

Bjugn

Bjugn Bygdatun, Mølnargården, 7159 Bjugn - T: 72528956
Local Museum / Natural History Museum
Rural life, boats, fishing, regional geology, birds 26041

Bleikvasslia

Malla Bleikvasslis Samlinger, nr Hwy 806, 8647 Bleikvasslia
Local Museum
Local history, domestic utensils, harness items and carts, implements and tools 26042

Bø i Telemark

Bø Bygdemuseet, Oterholt, 3800 Bø i Telemark - T: 35930061
Local Museum
Rural life 26043

Bodø

Kjerringøy Gamle Handelssted, Nordland Fylkesmuseet, Kjerrinøy, Prinsensg 116, 8005 Bodø - T: 75521640, Fax: 75525805, E-mail: nordmus@online.no, Internet: http://www.museumsnett.no/nordlandsmuseet. Head: Harry Ellingsen
Open Air Museum
Old trading post (ca. 1800) with many furnished buildings forming a courtyard 26044

Nordlandsmuseet, Prinsensg 116, 8005 Bodø - T: 75521640, Fax: 75525805, E-mail: nordmus@online.no, Internet: http://www.museumsnett.no/nordlandsmuseet. Head: Harry Ellingsen
Local Museum / Natural History Museum / Archaeological Museum - 1888
Fisheries, traditional boats, local hist, weapons, life in Nordland County, social hist, natural hist and archaeology, Bodo's history since 1816 - library, open air museum, trading station 26045

Borge Sarpsborg

Roald Amundsens Minne, Hwy 111, West of Sarpsborg, 1700 Borge Sarpsborg
Special Museum - 1972
Birthplace and chidhood home of arctic explorer Roald Amundsen 26046

Borkenes

Kvæford Bygdetun, at Rå, nr Hwy 849, 9410 Borkenes - T: 77093444
Open Air Museum - 1955
Four old farm buildings, two waterpowered grinding mills (1861/1880) 26047

Trastad Samlinger, 9475 Borkenes - T: 77093424, Fax: 77093424, E-mail: tskudal@online.no, Internet: http://www.museumsnett.no/trastad. Head: Tina M. Skudal
Fine Arts Museum / Decorative Arts Museum / Historical Museum - 1996
Largest central institution of Norway for physically and mentally disabled, hist of the disabled, the world largest coll of art and handicraft made by disabled, art by Herleik Kristiansen and Torstein Nilsen - art gallery 26048

Børsa

Skaun Bygdamuseum, Skaun Kommune, 7353 Børsa - T: 72867200, 72864884, Fax: 72867201
Open Air Museum
Rural life, farm, school from 1878, church from 1180 26049

Bøverbru

Toten Økomuseum (Toten Ecomuseum), Stenberg Farm, between Hwys 4 and 33, 2846 Bøverbru - T: 61196500, 61169500, Fax: 61196500, 61169580
Open Air Museum - 1931
Stenberg farm (1790) with a ring of farm buildings around the courtyard, local antiquities, church art, old crafts, costumes, implements, carriages 26050

Brevik

Brevik Bymuseum, Kirkev 4, 3950 Brevik - T: 35549200, Fax: 35549200. Head: Kirsten Tangen
Local Museum - 1975
Town hall (1760), grocery shop, war collection, pharmacy, post office 26051

Brøstadbotn

Dyrøy Bygdemuseet, Postboks 80, 9340 Brøstadbotn - T: 77188106
Local Museum 26052

Bryne

Garborgheimen - Knudaheio, nr Hwy 505, East of Bryne, 4341 Bryne - T: 51776160, Fax: 51776161, E-mail: storstova.bryne@rl.telia.no
Special Museum
Two small houses commemorating the poet Arne Garborg, Garborgheimen, 19th c Jæren house, is his birthplace, from 1848, Knudaheio, a few kilometers to the east, was built by the poet in 1899 26053

Bygland

Bygland Museet, Setesdal, on Hwy 39, 4745 Bygland - T: 37934700, Fax: 37935228
Open Air Museum - 1937
Open-hearth cottage (1650), 5 other timbered buildings 26054

Bykle

Huldreheimen, North of Hwy 12, 4694 Bykle
Open Air Museum
Open-hearth cottage, two storehouses, grinding mill and seter house, all furnished 26055

Dalen i Telemark

Anne Grimdalens Minne, Grimdalen Farm, nr Hwy 45, 3880 Dalen i Telemark - T: 35077797
Fine Arts Museum
300 of Anne Grimdalen's sculptures 26056

Dokka

Lands Museet, Villav, nr Hwy 35, 2870 Dokka - T: 61110687. Head: Alastair Brown
Open Air Museum - 1927
Fourteen old farmhouses and local history artifacts, over 30 old buildings representing an inlands agricultural/forestry district, together with artefacts, archive and photograph coll - library, local historical archive 26057

Drammen

Drammens Museum for Kunst og Kulturhistorie, Fylkesmuseum for Buskerud, Konnerudg 7, 3045 Drammen - T: 32200930, Fax: 32200949. Head: Åsmund Thorkildsen
Local Museum / Folklore Museum - 1908
Glass from the Nøstetangen factory, Rose-garden-tapestry, by Frida Hansen, ethnology, civil and peasant culture, applied art, folk art, ecclesiastical art, maritime section, agriculture, textiles, Gamle Marienlyst manor (1770) furnished with period interiors, arms, flags, and uniforms 26058

Kunstmuseet, Drammen Kunstforening, Gml. Kirkepl 7, 3001 Drammen - T: 32806399, Fax: 32806370. Head: Øystein Loge
Fine Arts Museum - 1867
Art coll 26059

Drangedal

Drangedal Bygdetun, 3750 Drangedal - T: 35997000, Fax: 35997099, E-mail: -drangedal.kommune@online.no. Head: Gunnar Skarstøl
Open Air Museum - 1962
18 old buildings 26060

Drøbak

Follo Museum, Seiersten, 1440 Drøbak - T: 64939990, Fax: 64933319, E-mail: follmuse@online.no
Open Air Museum - 1948
Old buildings, artifacts, boats 26061

Egersund

Dalane Folkemuseum, Slettebø, 4379 Egersund - T: 51491479, Fax: 51498866, E-mail: dalfolke@rl.telia.no, Internet: http://www.museumsnett.no/dalanefolkemuseum. Head: Leif Dybing
Local Museum - 1910
Old houses (1850), interiors, old workshops, tools, agricultural implements, local history - library 26062

Egersund Fayancemuseum, Elganev 1, Eie, 4371 Egersund - T: 51491479, Fax: 51498866, E-mail: dalfolke@rl.telia.no, Internet: http://www.museumsnett.no/dalanefolkemuseum. Head: Leif Dybing
Decorative Arts Museum - 1986 26063

Eggedal

Hagan, 3359 Eggedal
Fine Arts Museum
Home of the painter Christian Skredsvig with his studio and some of his painting 26064

Tveitens Samlinger, 3359 Eggedal
Local Museum - 1964
Implements pertaining to local history, three old houses, Eggedal mill 26065

Eidsberg

Eidsberg og Mysen Historielag, Folkenborg, 1880 Eidsberg
Historical Museum 26066

Eidskog

Eidskog Museum, Eidskog, mail addr: Box 86, 2230 Skotterod - T: 62833600, 62839290
Local Museum / Open Air Museum 26067

Eidsvoll Verk

Eidsvoll 1814 - Rikspolitisk Senter, Eidsvoll Bygningens Nasjonalhistoriske Samlinger (Norwegian Center for Constitutional History), Carsten Ankersv, 2074 Eidsvoll Verk - T: 63922210, Fax: 63922211, E-mail: kontor@eidsvoll1814.museum.no, Internet: http://www.eidsvoll1814.museum.no. Head: Thore Desserud
Historical Museum
Building presented to the Norwegian Storting (1851), memorial of May 17th, 1814 (Constitution Day), originally furnished Assembly Hall (Rikssalen), portrait gallery, hist coll, documents 26068

Eidsvoll Bygdemuseet (Eidsvoll Rural Museum), Hammerstad, E 6 Hwy, 2080 Eidsvoll Verk - T: 63960505, Fax: 63961280. Head: Bjørn Sverre Hol Haugen
Open Air Museum - 1950
Local farm equipment, utensils, furniture, 26 old buildings of all kinds, iron foundry - Eidsvoll photo archive 26069

Eidsvollsminnet → Eidsvoll 1814 - Rikspolitisk Senter

Elverum

Glomdalsmuseet, West Banks of the Glomma River, 2400 Elverum - T: 62419100, Fax: 62415882, E-mail: glmuseet@online.no. Head: Jan Hoff Jørgensen
Open Air Museum / Local Museum - 1911
Eighty old farmhouses arranged in courtyards, fireproof building with systematic coll, Tynset farm, Rendalen farm, Åmot farm, and Solør farm, Stemsrud building 26070

Norsk Skogbruksmuseum (Norwegian Forestry Museum), Solørv 151, 2407 Elverum - T: 62409000, Fax: 62409050, E-mail: post@skogmus.no, Internet: http://www.skogmus.no. Head: Yngve Astrup
Agriculture Museum - 1954
Norwegian forestry, logging and timber transport, hist of Norwegian hunting and trapping, Norwegian fauna, stuffed animals and birds, weapons, freshwater fishing, fishing traps, sport fishing, flies for trout and salmon - library, lecture hall, aquarium, open-air museum 26071

Enebakk

Enebakk Museet, Hwy 120, Southeast of Oslo, 1835 Enebakk
Open Air Museum - 1931
Farmhouse, storehouse, kiln, barn, cowshed and stable 26072

Engerdal

Blokkodden Villmarksmuseet, Kulturkontoret, Engerdal Kommune, 2440 Engerdal - T: 62458000, Fax: 62458057
Local Museum 26073

Evenskjer

Skånland Museet, Steinsland, 9440 Evenskjer - T: 77088255, Fax: 77088485, E-mail: elisabeth.oien@skanland.kommune.no, Internet: http://www.skanland.kommune.no/a-index.htm
Local Museum / Agriculture Museum / Ethnology Museum - 1982
Rural life, Sami dwellings 26074

Eydehavn

Eydehavn Museet, Nesbyen, 4810 Eydehavn - T: 37030800
Local Museum
Industrial social hist, 1920 worker's home 26075

Fåberg

Norsk Vegmuseum (Norwegian Road Museum), Hunderfossen, 2625 Fåberg - T: 61274450, Fax: 61274460, E-mail: knut-age.dalbak@vegdir.vegvesen.no, Internet: http://www.vegvesen.no/kampanje/vegmus/vegmus.stm. Head: Geir Paulsrud
Science&Tech Museum - 1992
Road construction and maintenance, hist of road travel 26076

Fagernes

Valdres Folkemusum, Tyinvegen 27, 2900 Fagernes - T: 61359900, Fax: 61359901, E-mail: vfmuseum@online.no, Internet: http://www.valdresmuseum.no. Head: Ingar Rarhein
Folklore Museum / Open Air Museum - 1901
70 old houses, exhibitions illustrating life in the mountains, hunting and fishing, medieval tapestries and chests, old silver and textiles, folk music instruments, weapons, ethnography - library, local history archive, local genealogical centre, folk music archives and workshop 26077

Fana

Hordamuseet, Hordnesv 24, 5244 Fana - T: 55112900, Fax: 55112901, E-mail: post@horda.museum.no, Internet: http://www.museumsnett.no/hordamuseet. Head: Ole Mikal Olsen
Agriculture Museum / Open Air Museum / Folklore Museum - 1945
Interplay between agriculture and fishing, traditional buildings and rural life 26078

Fannrem

Orkdal Bygdetun, Torshus Folkehøgskole, on Hwy 65, 7320 Fannrem - T: 72480000. Head: Erik Skjølberg
Decorative Arts Museum - 1929
Three old houses with furniture and utensils 26079

Fetsund

Fetsund Lensemuseet, Lundv 3, 1900 Fetsund - T: 63880911, Fax: 63882700, E-mail: post@fetsundlenser.no
Historical Museum
Timber rafting hist, authentic timber worker houses, nature exhibition 26080

Finnsnes

Lenvik Bygdemuseet, Bjorelvnes, 9301 Finnsnes, mail addr: Boks 165, 9305 Finnsnes - T: 77871965, Fax: 77871966, E-mail: lenmus@c2i.net. Head: Kåre William Rauø
Agriculture Museum
Fisheries, rural life 26081

Flekkefjord

Flekkefjord Museum, Dr. Kraftsg 15, 4400 Flekkefjord - T: 38322659, Fax: 38323006, E-mail: flmuseum@online.no. Head: Arild Johannessen
Local Museum - 1924
18th c house in the Dutch Quarter, furniture, porcelain, textiles, silver, exhibition of the archaeological prehistory of the area, exhibition of Cultural and trade connection between South-Norway and the Netherlands in 15 & 16th c 26082

Florø

Kystmuseet i Sogn og Fjordane, Brendøyvägen, mail addr: Postboks 94, 6901 Florø - T: 57742233, Fax: 57742680, E-mail: museum@kyst.museum.no, Internet: http://www.sognogrjordane.kulturnett.no/kystmuseet. Head: Kristian Jansen
Local Museum - 1980
Traditional fishing life, boat coll, oldest sloop in Norway, oil in the North sea, sea-birds, herring fishery 26083

Foldereid

Leirvika Bygdesamling, nr Hwy 770, 7975 Foldereid
Local Museum - 1906
Two old buildings furnished with utensils, implements and books 26084

Folldal

Folldal Bygdetun, Streitlien Uppigard, 2580 Folldal - T: 62491000, Fax: 62490568, Internet: http://www.museumsnett.no/falldalbygdetun
Local Museum
Decorated traditional buildings, Folldal and Dovre area, old waterdriven saw, mill, school museum 26085

Folldal Gruver, Folldal Verk, 2580 Folldal - T: 62490505, Fax: 62480666
Science&Tech Museum
Local mining hist 26086

Follebu

Aulestad, Karoline og Bjørnstjerne Bjørnsons Hjem, 2656 Follebu - T: 61224110, Fax: 61223083, E-mail: Aulestad@maihaugen.museum.no, Internet: http://www.maihaugen.no/aulestad. Head: Olav Aaraas
Special Museum - 1934
Home of Karoline and Bjørnstjerne Bjørnson, memorabilia of the poet and Nobel Prize winner (1903) and his family (1875-1910), authentic interior, Norwegian ethnology 26087

Førde

Sunnfjord Museum, Mo, E39, 6800 Førde - T: 57721220, Fax: 57721229, E-mail: post@sunnfjord.museum.no, Internet: http://sognogfjordane.kulturnett.no/sunnfjordmuseum. Head: Gunnhild Systad
Agriculture Museum / Folklore Museum / Open Air Museum - 1910
Old farmyard, cottage (1500), and other farm buildings with utensils and implements, exhibition hall with coll of woodcarving, textiles and costumes, bridal crowns 26088

Føresvik

Bokn Bygdemuseet, Håland, 4290 Føresvik - T: 52748500
Agriculture Museum
Fishery, agriculture on Bokn Island 26089

Fredrikstad

Fredrikstad Museet, Isegran, 1600 Fredrikstad - T: 69306875, Fax: 69340311, E-mail: tola@fredrikstad.kommune.no, Internet: http://www.hiof.no/fredrikstad-museum. Head: T. Thogersen
Local Museum - 1903
Local history exhibits, military objects, maritime exhibits and boats - arts and crafts center 26090

Frosta

Frosta Bygdemuseet, nr Hwy 753, 7633 Frosta. Head: Kjell Andersen
Local Museum - 1909
Local history items, two old buildings 26091

Fyresdal

Fyresdal Bygdemuseet (Fyresdal Open Air Museum), nr Hwy 355, 3870 Fyresdal - T: 35041455, Fax: 35041203
Open Air Museum - 1909
Old cottages, loft, grinding mill, sauna, court room, local artifacts, old ship, bakery, sawmill 26092

Geilo

Dagali Museum, Dagali, 3580 Geilo - T: 32093793. Head: Kåre Sønsterud
Folklore Museum
Various buildings, grinding mill (1774), barn (ca. 1740), stable, kiln, cowshed with implements (18th c), school and church cottage (1850-70), furniture, arms - exhibition hall 26093

Gjettum

Samvirkemuseet, Dr. Høstsv 35, 1346 Gjettum - T: 67543653, Fax: 67514031
Historical Museum
Norway's first cooperative store 26094

Gjøvik

Eiktunet Kulturhistorisk Museum (Eiktunet Museum of Local History), Øverbyv 108, 2825 Gjøvik - T: 61172998, Fax: 61170646. Head: Lissie Norland
Local Museum
Burial mounds and other remains from farm settlements dating back to 200 AD, 33 buildings from the 18-19th c incl a central farm yard, a school- house, a small cottars farmstead, a watermill and summer dairy farm 26095

Gol

Gol Bygdemuseet, Hallingdal Folk High School, 1 km North of Hwy 7, 3550 Gol
Agriculture Museum / Open Air Museum
Skaga farm, consisting of seven old houses and three rebuilt houses 26096

Granvin

Granvin Bygdemuseet, 5736 Granvin - T: 56525117, Fax: 56525444
Local Museum - 1920
Brynjulfstova cottage, items of local interest, Kapteinsgården (18th c) 26097

Gratangen

Nordnorsk Fartøyvernsenter og Båtmuseum (North Norwegian Vessel Preservation Center and Boatmuseum), 9470 Gratangen - T: 76920370, Fax: 76920390, E-mail: nfsenter@online.no. Head: Sverre Nordmo
Science&Tech Museum - 1955
Sverre Nordmos coll of old boats and fishing gear 26098

Grimstad

Ibsenhuset og Grimstad Bymuseet, Henrik Ibseng 14, 4890 Grimstad - T: 37044653, Fax: 37043090, E-mail: ibsenhuset@czi.net, Internet: http://www.ibsen.org. Head: Rolf Erik Nilsen
Special Museum - 1916
Apothecary's shop (1839) with original furnishings, where Henrik Ibsen worked and where his first play 'Catilina' was written, local history, maritime section 26099

Halden

Halden Historiske Samlinger, Rød Herregård, 1771 Halden - T: 69185411, Fax: 69186570. Head: Ole Rømer Sandberg
Historical Museum - 1896
Haldens Minders Museum, Idd Bygdemuseum, Berg Bygdetun, Rød Herregård, Industrimuseet i Tistedalen 26100

Halsnøy Kloster

Klostertunet, Isl. Halsnøy, E. Leirvik, 4555 Halsnøy Kloster
Historic Site - 1958
Ruins of the Halsnøy Monastery (1164), fishery department with boats and gear (belonging to the Sunnhordland Folkemuseum) 26101

Haltdalen

Haltdalen Bygdetun, Heksem Farm, 7487 Haltdalen
Open Air Museum
Old farmhouse, cowshed and storehouse 26102

Hamar

Hedmarksmuseet og Domkirkeodden, Mjøsa, Strandv 100, 2315 Hamar - T: 62542700, Fax: 62542701, E-mail: admin@hedmarksmuseet.museum.no, Internet: http://www.hedmarksmuseet.museum.no. Head: Steinar Bjerkestrand
Local Museum / Folklore Museum / Open Air Museum - 1902
Ruins of the medieval cathedral with its modern glass-cover (the glass-cathedral) and the bishop's residence, Viking exhibition, herb garden and an open air museum with 60 old buildings containing local hist exhibition - photo library 26103

Norsk Jernbanemuseum (Norwegian Railway Museum), Strandveien 132, 2316 Hamar - T: 62513160, Fax: 62529699, E-mail: norsk.jernbanemuseum@jbv.no, Internet: http://www.norsk-jernbanemuseum.no. Head: Dr. Andreas Dreyer
Science&Tech Museum / Open Air Museum - 1896
Coll illustrating the development of Norway's railways, old locomotives and carriages, 300-meter railway track with old stations and signal arrangements 26104

Harmarøy

Hamarøy Bygdetun, Postboks 44, 8294 Hamarøy - T: 75770294
Open Air Museum
Rural life, trading centre with 1880 and 1920 interiors 26105

Harstad

Trondarnes Distriktmuseum, Verftsg 1, 9401 Harstad - T: 77065190, Fax: 77061694. Head: Øystein Normann
Local Museum
Industrial hist of Harstad, heritage trails 26106

Haugesund

Haugesund Billedgalleri (Haugesund Art Gallery), Erling Skjalgssonsg 4, 5501 Haugesund - T: 52723471, Fax: 52729442, E-mail: billedga@online.no, Internet: http://www.haugesund-billedgalleri.net. Head: Martin Worts
Fine Arts Museum - 1973
Art from the Western part of Norway (Norvald Valand, Fredrik Kolstø), Folgerø Coll of Classical music - library 26107

Karmsund Folkemuseum, Skaareg 142, 5527 Haugesund - T: 52709360, Fax: 52709369, Internet: http://www.museumsnett.no/karmsundfolkemuseum. Head: Carl E. Buch

Folklore Museum / Local Museum - 1925
Ethnographical objects, town department, maritime section, prehistory and social history of the area 26108

Hemnes i Høland

Aurskog-Høland Bygdetun, Braate, 1970 Hemnes i Høland
Open Air Museum
Seven old farmhouses, items illustrating life in these forest districts in earlier times 26109

Hemsedal

Hemsedal Bygdatun, Øvre Løken, 3560 Hemsedal - T: 31408800, Fax: 31408830, E-mail: hemsedal.kommune@hemsedal.kommune.no. Head: Sissel Carlstrøm
Open Air Museum - 1956
Old farmhouses 26110

Hidrasund

Fedrenes Minne, Rasvåg, 4432 Hidrasund - T: 38372275
Local Museum - 1944
Local curiosities and antiquities - library 26111

Hjelmeland

Vigatunet, Ryfylkemuseet, Vigatunet, Hwy 13, 4130 Hjelmeland - T: 52792950
Agriculture Museum
Historical fruit garden 26112

Hol i Hallingdal

Hol Bygdemuseet, Hagafoss, nr Hwy 7, 3576 Hol i Hallingdal - T: 32089100, Fax: 32089395
Open Air Museum - 1914
Hole farmyard with 16 old houses, the Nestegard and Raunsgard cottages with remarkable 'rose painting' 26113

Holmestrand

Holmestrand Museum, Nils Kjærsg 4, 3080 Holmestrand - T: 33053922
Local Museum - 1929
Local history, maritime history, fine arts, Holst House (1756) 26114

Holmsbu

Holmsbu Billedgalleri, 3484 Holmsbu
Public Gallery - 1973
Paintings from most periods in Henrik Sørensen's life, works by his Holmsbu friends, Oluf Wold Torne and Thorvald Erichsen 26115

Homborsund

Nørholm, nr E 18, 6 km West of Grimstad, 4897 Homborsund
Special Museum
Nobel Prize winner Knut Hamsun's farm (1918), now a memorial museum with his books, paintings and other belongings 26116

Hommelstø

Velfjord Bygdemuseum, Strøm, nr Hwy 76, 8960 Hommelstø - T: 75024334, Fax: 75024334. Head: Ivar Seip
Open Air Museum / Folklore Museum - 1953
12 old houses, systematic coll incl Lapp section 26117

Hønefoss

Ringerikes Museet, Norderhov, 3500 Hønefoss - T: 32135197. Head: Preben L. Johannessen
Special Museum - 1923
Items connected with P.Chr. Asbjørnsen and Jørgen Moe, the earliest collectors of Norwegian folk tales, section dealing with the resistance movement during World War II, old rectory office, Riddergården House including eight buildings 26118

Honningsvåg

Nordkappmuseet, Fiskeriveien 4, 9751 Honningsvåg - T: 78472833, Fax: 78472032, E-mail: nordkapp@online.no, Internet: http://www.museumsnett.no/nordkappmuseum. Head: Kjersti Skavhaug
Local Museum / Historical Museum
Fishery, North Cape tourism, every day life on the Arctic coast of Finnmark 26119

Hornindal

Anders Svors Museet, Hwy 60, Grodås, 6790 Hornindal
Fine Arts Museum
Approximately 400 works by the sculptor Anders Svor (1864-1929) 26120

Horten

Marinemuseet (Royal Norwegian Navy Museum), Karljohansvern, 3191 Horten - T: 33033397, Fax: 33033505. Head: Steinar Sandvold
Military Museum - 1853
History of the Norwegian Navy, ship models, weapons, curiosities, the world's first torpedo boat, 'RAP' (1873) 26121

Norsk Museum for Fotografi - Preus Fotomuseum, Karljohansvern, 3192 Horten - T: 33031630, Fax: 33031640, E-mail: post@foto.museum.no, Internet: http://www.foto.museum.no. Head: Øivind Storm Bjerke
Fine Arts Museum - 1995
History, technology and art of photography, historic and contemporary photographs 26122

Hovdebygda

Ivar Aasen-tunet, Indrehovdevegen 176, 6160 Hovdebygda - T: 70047570, Fax: 70047571, E-mail: admin@aasentunet.no, Internet: http://www.aasentunet.no. Head: Ottar Grepstad
Local Museum - 2000 26123

Høvikodden

Henie Onstad Kunstsenter, 1311 Høvikodden - T: 67804800, Fax: 67543270, E-mail: henie.onstad@hok.no, Internet: http://www.henieonstad.no. Head: Jan Feldberg, Gavin Jantjes
Fine Arts Museum
20th c painting, theater, dance, and cinema exhibitions, outdoor sculptures 26124

Høydalsmo

Lårdal Bygdemuseum (Lårdal Rural Museum), nr Hwy 45, North of Dalen, 3860 Høydalsmo - T: 35077331. Head: Aanund Olsnes
Open Air Museum / Folklore Museum - 1950
30 houses, folk art, whetstone quarry - stave church 26125

Hurdal

Hurdal Bygdetun, Garsjoen, North of Lake Hurdal, 2090 Hurdal - T: 63989126, 91108653, E-mail: thor.trapness@netcom.no. Head: Thor Trapness
Local Museum - 1971
Local hist, 17th c inn and post office, sawmill, hill farm 26126

Hvalstad

Asker Museum, Otto Valstadsv 19, 1395 Hvalstad - T: 66790011, Fax: 66781520, E-mail: asker.museum@asker.kommune.no. Head: Frederikke Hegnar von Ubisch
Local Museum
Old buildings and furniture, paintings, local antiquities 26127

Jaren

Hadeland Folkemuseum, Brandbu, nr Hwy 4, 2770 Jaren - T: 61334012, Fax: 61334157, E-mail: hadeland.folkemuseum@online.no. Head: Katja Nicolaysen
Open Air Museum / Folklore Museum - 1913
Romanesque Tingelstad church (ca. 1220) with Renaissance interior, open-air section with 28 old houses representative of the area, mechanical weavery, coll of Stone Age finds, grocery store 26128

Jessheim

Ullensaker Bygdetun, Ullensaker Rådhus, 2050 Jessheim
Local Museum
Local history 26129

Kabelvåg

Lofotmuseet, Kabelvåg Fiskerimuseum, Storvagan, 8310 Kabelvåg - T: 76078223, Fax: 76078765, E-mail: lofotmus@online.no, Internet: http://www.museumsnett.no/lofotmuseet
Ethnology Museum - 1936
Exhibits illustrating the life and work of the Lofoten fishermen 26130

Kanestraum

Straumsnes Museum, Kanestraum Quay, Hwy 65, Kvisvik, 6674 Kanestraum - T: 71532574. Head: J. Ljøkjell
Local Museum - 1922
Items of local interest 26131

Kapp

Toten Økomuseum (Toten Ecomuseum), 2858 Kapp - T: 61169500, Fax: 61169580, E-mail: post@totenmuseet.no, Internet: http://www.totenmuseet.no. Head: Torveig Dahl
Agriculture Museum / Open Air Museum / Public Gallery
Governor's farm (1800), school (1844), local industry - archives, art gallery, documentation centre 26132

Karasjok

De Samiske Samlinger, Museumsg 17, 9730 Karasjok - T: 78469950, Fax: 78469955, E-mail: svd@trollnet.no. Head: Berit Åse Johnsen
Open Air Museum / Folklore Museum - 1939
Exhibits illustrating the life and work of the Lapps on

the Finnmark plateau and outside of Finnmark, open-air museum including farms typical of the various Lapp livelihoods, such as fishing and the herding of reindeer 26133

Kaupanger

De Heibergske Samlinger - Sogn Folkemuseum, 6854 Kaupanger - T: 57678206, Fax: 57678511, E-mail: sogn-folkemuseum@dhs.museum.no, Internet: http://www.dhs.museum.nomuseumsnett/default.htm. Head: Aage Engeseter
Open Air Museum / Folklore Museum - 1909
35 buildings from different parts of Sogn, dating from the Middle Ages to the present, textiles, costumes, country craft, household goods, farming tools, trade and religious life, farm from the middle of the 19th c, Sogn Fjordmuseum with exhibits from the fjord culture, including a boat coll and a reconstructed boatbuilder's workshop 26134

Kautokeino

Guovdageainnu Gilisillju, 9520 Kautokeino - T: 78485800, Fax: 78485890
Local Museum
Sami hist camp, reindeer herding, riverboat cruises 26135

Kirkenær

Gruetunet, 1 km from Kirkenær Village on Hwy 3, 2260 Kirkenær - T: 62947315, Fax: 62947315
Local Museum / Open Air Museum - 1942
Fourteen buildings, local history 26136

Kirkenes

Sør-Varanger Museum, Grenselandmuseet, Føtevannslia, 9900 Kirkenes - T: 78994880, Fax: 78994890, E-mail: grensland.museet@online.no, Internet: http://www.museumsnett.no/sor-varangermuseum. Head: Silja Arvola
Historical Museum - 1967
Greek-Orthodox chapel (1565) in Neiden on Hwy 645 km West of Kirkenes, kirkenes under the second world war, Bjørklund farm near Svanvik 40 km south of Kirkenes, multi-ethnic society between the borders of Finland and Russia 26137

Kleppe

Klepp Bygdemuseum, Haugabakkav 9, POB 25, 4358 Kleppe - T: 51429860, 51425076, Fax: 51429877, E-mail: kultur.etat@klepp.kommune.no, Internet: http://www.klepp.kommune.no. Head: Hege Skotheim
Local Museum - 1954
Old building, local history artifacts 26138

Kollungtveit

Grindheim Bygdemuseum, Sveindal, off Hwy 9, 4545 Kollungtveit
Local Museum - 1926
Old timbered building, fully furnished 26139

Kongsberg

Den Kongelige Mynts Bedriftsmuseum, Hytteg 3, 3601 Kongsberg - T: 32733260, Fax: 32730263
Special Museum
Numismatic industry and coll 26140

Kongsberg Ski Museum, Department of Norwegian Mining Museum, Hytteg 3, 3616 Kongsberg - T: 32723200, Fax: 32723210, E-mail: bergverksmuseet@bvm.museum.no, Internet: http://www.kongsberg.net/bergverksmuseet. Head: Magne Bråthen
Special Museum - 1985
150 years ski sport hist, trophy coll, hist of skiing in general, ski expeditions to North and South Pole 26141

Kongsberg Våpenfabrikks Museum, Hytteg 3, 3616 Kongsberg - T: 32723200, Fax: 32723210, E-mail: fs@bvm.museum.no, Internet: http://www.kongsberg.net/bergverksmuseet. Head: Liv Håskoll Haugen
Military Museum / Science&Tech Museum
Weapons and equipment developed and produced by Norway's largest armament factory since 1814, firms in aircraft engine parts, subsea installations and maritime electronics - archive, photo coll, coll of technical drawings 26142

Lågdalsmuseet, Museum for Kongsberg, Numedal and Øvre-Eiker, Tillischbakken 8, 3613 Kongsberg - T: 32733468, Fax: 32724171, E-mail: - laagdalsmuseet.kongsberg@eunet.no, Internet: http://www.kongsberg.net/laagdalsmuseet. Head: Haakon Livland
Open Air Museum - 1924
39 old lofts and cottages from Uvdal, Nore, Flesberg, Rollag, Sandsvær, and Kongsberg 26143

Norsk Bergverksmuseum (Norwegian Mining Museum), Hytteg 3, 3616 Kongsberg - T: 32733260, Fax: 32730263, Internet: http://www.kongsberg.net/bergverksmuseum. Head: Liv Håskoll Haugen
Science&Tech Museum - 1938
Hist of the silver mines (1623-1958), silver mineral coll, Norwegian minerals and ores, mining equipment, minting equipment, Norwegian coins and medals, winter sport equipment, trophies 26144

Kongsvinger

Kongsvinger Museum, Vollg 10, 2200 Kongsvinger - T: 62819269
Local Museum
19th c home of Government official, museum of women's hist 26145

Koppang

Stor-Elvdal Museum, 2480 Koppang - T: 62464605, Fax: 62464607
Local Museum
Rural life museum 26146

Kragerø

Berg-Kragerø Museum, Lovisenbergv 45, 3770 Kragerø - T: 35981453. Head: Jean Aase
Fine Arts Museum / Decorative Arts Museum - 1927
Manor with furniture, paintings, maritime hist - Th. Kittelsen House 26147

Kristiansand

Agder Naturmuseum og Botaniske Hage, Gimlev 23, Gård, 4630 Kristiansand S, mail addr: Postboks 1018, 4602 Lundsiden - T: 38092388, Fax: 38092378. Head: Ovin G. Udø
Natural History Museum - 1828
Succulent coll, natural history of South Norway - botanical garden 26148

Christianssands Billedgalleri, Rådhusg 11, 4601 Kristiansand S - T: 38025853
Fine Arts Museum - 1902
Paintings, drawings, graphic art, sculptures 26149

Vest-Agder Fylkesmuseum, Vigev 22b, 4633 Kristiansand S - T: 38090228, 38091065, Fax: 38090599, E-mail: ekspedisjonen@vaf.museum.no, Internet: http://www.museumsnett.no/vafymuseum. Head: Jan Henrik Munksgaard
Open Air Museum / Local Museum - 1903
Old farmyards and town houses incl. workshops, maritime exhibition, cultural hist, ethnography, folklore - library 26150

Kristiansund

Nordmøre Museum, Knudtzondalen, 6500 Kristiansund - T: 71671578. Head: Sverre J. Svendsen
Local Museum - 1894
Local history, archaeology, ethnography, folklore, fishery department, old farmhouses 26151

Kvernes

Gamle Kvernes Bygdemuseum, Averøy Island, 6540 Kvernes - T: 71514066. Head: Kaare Bøe
Open Air Museum - 1941
12 old buildings, including cottages, storehouses (17th c), fishery section, archeological section - library 26152

Kvikne

Bjørgan Prestegård, 2592 Kvikne - T: 62484044
Special Museum
Birthplace of Bjørnstjerne Bjørnson 26153

Kviteseid

Kviteseid Bygdetun, nr Hwy 39, 3850 Kviteseid - T: 35053111
Open Air Museum - 1972
Farmhouse (1739), lofts (17th and 18th c), barn, cowshed, sauna, smithy, and grinding mill (18th c), domestic utensils, farm implements, medieval church with painted ceiling and Rococo decoration, Gunnar Utsonds skulptur coll 26154

Langesund

Cudrio Kystmuseum, Cudrios g 5, 3971 Langesund - T: 35577700, Fax: 35577770
Local Museum
18th c farm, wedding costumes 1860-1910 26155

Larvik

Herregården Museum, Larvikmuséene, Herregårdsletta 6, 3257 Larvik - T: 33130404, Fax: 33130454, E-mail: larvikmuseene@larvik.kommune.no. Head: Arnfinn Malme
Decorative Arts Museum - 1916
Period furnishings of an aristocratic, 17th c Scandinavian home, former residence of the Danish governor Ulrich Frederik Gyldenløve (1677) 26156

Larvik Sjøfartsmuseum, Larvikmuséene (Larvik Maritime Museum), Kirkestredet 5, Skottebrygga, 3251 Larvik - T: 33126298. Head: James Ronald Archer
Science&Tech Museum - 1926
Maritime hist of the area, featuring the boat builder Colin Archer, Magnus Andersen, who sailed in 1893 with a copy of the Gokstad Viking ship across the North Atlantic, and Thor Heyerdahl's Kon-Tiki and RA expeditions, whaling 26157

Leinøy

Herøy Kystmuseum, 6094 Leinøy - T: 70085290
Local Museum
Coastal life, 7th c boat 26158

Leka

Leka Bygdemuseum, 7994 Leka - T: 74399763
Local Museum - 1962
Two old buildings, fishery section with 5 different types of boats and fishing gear, Herlaugshaugen burial mound from the Viking period, the second largest of its kind in Norway 26159

Leknes

Vestvågøy Museum, Fygleveien 109, 8370 Leknes - T: 76080043, Fax: 76086143, E-mail: vvmuseum@online.no, Internet: http://home.sol.no/~vvmuseum. Head: Hege Sofie Bull
Local Museum / Open Air Museum - 1962
Local hist, fishing gear, rural artifacts, school items, fishermen's shed ('rorbu'), Nordland boats 26160

Leksvik

Leksvik Bygdesamling, 2 km from the Village, 7120 Leksvik
Local Museum - 1949
Two old buildings, local history artifacts 26161

Levanger

Falstadminnet, The Falstad Memorial, Gimlev 3, 7600 Levanger - T: 74083266, Fax: 74095212, E-mail: rnilssen@online.no, Internet: http://home.sol.no/~trn1000/falstad.htm
Military Museum
WW II relics, human rights issues 26162

Levanger Museum, Gimlev 3, 7600 Levanger - T: 74083266, Fax: 74095212. Head: Susan Matland
Local Museum - 1984
Photographs, local rural life - photo archive 26163

Lillehammer

Lillehammer Kunstmuseum (Lillehammer Art Museum), Stortorget 2, 2602 Lillehammer - T: 61054460, Fax: 61251944, E-mail: post@lillehammerartmuseum.com, Internet: http://www.lillehammerartmuseum.com. Head: Svein Olav Hoff
Fine Arts Museum - 1927
19th and 20th c Norwegian paintings, drawings, graphic arts, sculpture, works of the 'Lillehammer colony' incl Thorvald Erichsen and Einar Sandberg - library 26164

Maihaugen, De Sandvigske Samlinger, Maihaugveien 1, 2609 Lillehammer - T: 61288900, Fax: 61288901/915, E-mail: post@maihaugen@museum.no, Internet: http://www.museumsnett.no/maihaugen/lblve/. Head: Ågot Gamhersvik
Local Museum / Open Air Museum / Folklore Museum - 1887
Regional museum of rural life, textiles, church art, ethnology, open air museum with old farms and Garmo stave church (about 1200), old workshops, Norwegian history exhibition (1993) - library 26165

Lillesand

Lillesand By-og Sjøfartsmuseum (Lillesand Town and Maritime Museum), Carl Knudsen Gården, 4790 Lillesand - T: 37270430, Fax: 37261599. Head: Alvhild Gulbrandson
Local Museum - 1967
Local culture, patrician house (ca. 1830) with furnishings and decoration, shipbuilding and seamanship 26166

Limingen

Røyrvik Bygdatun, 7894 Limingen - T: 74335100, Fax: 74335159
Open Air Museum
Mountain farming, sami gallery 26167

Løkken Verk

Gammelgruva, Orkla Industrimuseum (The Old Mine), 7332 Løkken Verk - T: 72499100, Fax: 72499101, E-mail: post@oi.no, Internet: http://www.oi.no. Head: Asle B. Bjørgen
Science&Tech Museum - 1985
Museum mine, mining methods from 1654, old blasting techniques, Mining hist from 17th c, geology coll 26168

Thamshavnbanen, Orkla Industrimuseum, 7332 Løkken Verk - T: 72499100, Fax: 72499101, E-mail: post@oi.no, Internet: http://www.oi.no. Head: Asle B. Bjørgen
Science&Tech Museum - 1983
First electric railway in Norway 1908, mining train and the world's oldest AC-powered railroad in work, passenger transportation, original engines from 1908 26169

Lom

Lom Heimbygdslag, nr Hwys 15 and 55, 2686 Lom - T: 61211000, Fax: 61211770. Head: Torgeir T. Garmo
Local Museum - 1925
St. Olav's cottage (1021), Glømsdal cottage (1761), eleven other buildings, poet Olav Aukrust's coll 26170

Norsk Fjellmuseum (Norwegian Mountain Museum), Postboks 5, 2688 Lom - T: 61211600, Fax: 61211730, E-mail: post@fjell.museum.no, Internet: http://www.fjell.museum.no
Natural History Museum 26171

Lonevåg

Havråtunet, Havrå between Haus and Bruvik, 5282 Lonevåg - T: 56392410. Head: Randi Andersen
Open Air Museum / Agriculture Museum - 1973
Havråtunet - an original hamlet of 36 wooden houses dating from c 1300 in an area of only 100 x 50 m, surroundings still mostly intact as earlier cultivated in Western Norway, ie. as strip farming incl potato fields, fruit bushes, fields and woodland 26172

Osterøy Museum, Gjerstad on the Island of Osterøy, 5258 Lonevåg - T: 56392410, Fax: 56392410. Head: Randi Andersen
Open Air Museum - 1920
Ten wooden houses from the island dating from c 1500, including a fine two-storey reception house ("loft"), farm buildings, school and smithy, old rural craft implements from local traditions such as house-building, tanning, woodworking, clothes/costumes 26173

Longyearbyen

Svalbard-Museum, 9170 Longyearbyen - T: 79021384
Local Museum - 1981 26174

Lørenskog

Lørenskog Bygdetun, Kjenn School, Hasselv, 1470 Lørenskog
Local Museum
Local history 26175

Lundenes

Grytøy Bygdetun, Grytøy Island, 9420 Lundenes - T: 77079218
Open Air Museum - 1965
Large dwelling, storehouse, boathouse containing boats and fishing gear, local history exhibits 26176

Mandal

Mandal Bymuseum, Andorsengården, 4501 Mandal - T: 38262011, Fax: 38263386. Head: Knuth Lindseth
Fine Arts Museum - 1954
Art gallery: paintings by Adolph Tidemand and Amaldus Nielsen, local maritime museum, Andorsengården (1801) 26177

Mandal og Opplands Folkemuseum, Øyslebø, nr Hwy 455, 4500 Mandal - T: 38262220
Open Air Museum / Folklore Museum - 1912
Old buildings, old farmhouse from Åseral 26178

Olav Holmegaards Samlinger, c/o Mandal Bymuseum, Andorsengården, 4500 Mandal
Decorative Arts Museum
Furniture, textiles, domestic utensils and implements 26179

Melbu

Vesterålen Bygdemuseum, nr Hwy 19, 8490 Melbu - T: 76157556, Fax: 76158265. Head: Geir Remen
Open Air Museum - 1923
Old buildings, exhibits illustrating arts and crafts, social history 26180

Meråker

Meråker Bygdemuseum, nr Meråker Station, 1 km from E 14, 7530 Meråker - T: 74812173, Fax: 74812051, E-mail: nin-fr@online.no. Head: Bjørn R. Krogstad
Local Museum - 1950
12 old buildings, among them a smithy, a 'seter' cottage, hist and domestic artifacts (summer dairy, mill) 26181

Mo i Rana

Rana Museum, Cultural History Department, Fridtjof Nansensg 22, 8601 Mo i Rana, mail addr: Postboks 173, 8601 Mo i Rana - T: 75146170, Fax: 75146171, E-mail: kulturhistorisk@rana.museum.no. Head: Per Ole Syvertsen
Local Museum - 1910
Local history, folklore, old buildings, mining, industrial history, Sami culture - library 26182

Rana Museum, Natural History Department, Moholmen 1, 8601 Mo i Rana, mail addr: Postboks 173, 8601 Mo i Rana - T: 75146170, Fax: 75146171, E-mail: kulturhistorisk@rana.museum.no. Head: Per Ole Syvertsen
Natural History Museum 26183

Stenneset Bygdetun, Rana Museum (Stenneset Open Air Museum), on Hwy 805, 8600 Mo i Rana, mail addr: Postboks 173, 8601 Mo i Rana - T: 75146170, Fax: 75146171
Open Air Museum / Agriculture Museum
Old rectory, small farmyard 26184

Moen

Fossmotunet - Målselv Bygdemuseum, Fossmo, 4 km East of Bardufoss and E 6, 9321 Moen, mail addr: Boks 75, 9329 Moen - T: 77832010, Fax: 77832009, E-mail: tore.hauge@midt-troms.museum.no, Internet: http://www.midt-troms.museum.no. Head: Tore Hauge
Open Air Museum - 1969
Farmhouse (1824), smithy, storehouse, tools and rural utensils 26185

Kongsvold Bygdetun, Målselv Bygdetun, Kongsli, Øverbygd E of Hwy 87 and N of Lake Lille Rostavatn, 9329 Moen - T: 77831100. Head: Gunnar Kaasen
Open Air Museum - 1947
Konglistua cottage (1840), domestic utensils 26186

Molde

Fiskerimuseet på Hjertøya, Per Amdamsv 4, 6413 Molde - T: 71202460, Fax: 71202461, E-mail: post@romsdal.museum.no. Head: Jarle Sanden
Open Air Museum
Small fishing village with shore houses, boathouses, cod-liver oil refinery 26187

Romsdalsmuseet, Per Amdamsv 4, 6413 Molde - T: 71202460, Fax: 71202461, E-mail: post@romsdal.museum.no. Head: Jarle Sanden
Open Air Museum 26188

Morgedal

Olav Bjaalandmuseet, E 76, 3848 Morgedal
Special Museum - 1966
Coll of Olav Bjåland, a member of Roald Amundsen's South Pole expedition, tradition of skiing in Morgedal 26189

Sondre Nordheimstova, Hills 1,5 km off E 76, 3848 Morgedal
Special Museum
Birthplace of the pioneer of modern skiing, Sondre Nordheim (1825-97) 26190

Mosjøen

Vefsn Museum, Austerbygdv 3, 8650 Mosjøen - T: 75172000, Fax: 75172001. Head: Hans Pedersen
Open Air Museum - 1909
Old church (1735), old buildings 26191

Moss

Rabekk Museum, Rabekk Manor, 1522 Moss, mail addr: Postboks 636, 1522 Moss - T: 69275701, E-mail: tvin@online.no, Internet: http://tvin.home.online.no. Head: Tor Vinje
Local Museum - 1966
Local history, artifacts 26192

Mosterøy

Utstein Kloster, 4156 Mosterøy - T: 51724705, Fax: 51724708, E-mail: utstein@online.no, Internet: http://www.utstein-kloster.no
Religious Arts Museum - 1965
Augustinian monastery (13th c) 26193

Mosvik

Mosvik - Sæteråsgården, nr Hwy 755, 7690 Mosvik
Local Museum - 1960
Farmhouse, artifacts 26194

Mysen

Folkenborg Museum, Eidsberg og Mysen Historielag, Folkenborgv, 1850 Mysen - T: 69891391. Head: Bjørn K. Høie
Local Museum - 1936
Local history, farmhouse (1720), cottage, storehouse, smithy, implement house (ca. 1780) 26195

Nå

Agatunet (Aga Village), Aga, 5776 Nå - T: 53662214, 48023658, Fax: 53663090. Head: Guttorm A. Rogdeberg
Open Air Museum / Public Gallery / Agriculture Museum - 1938
Home of Sir Sigurd Brynjulvson, counsellor to the King and Magistrat of Western Norway, ca 1240-1303, the queens appletree, Lagmannstove, the oldest town house in Norway, 30 different houses built like an European village - workshop for weavers and rose-painting 26196

Nærbø

Jærmuseet, Kvia, 4365 Nærbø, mail addr: Postboks 250, 4367 Nærbø - T: 51433189, Fax: 51434767, E-mail: jaermus@c2i.net, Internet: http://www.museumsnett.no/jaermuseet. Head: Målfrid Snørteland
Agriculture Museum
Agriculture, machinery, breeding, farming, prehistoric site 26197

Namsos

Namsdalsmuseet, Kjærlighetsstien 1, 7800 Namsos - T: 74274072. Head: Geir A. Grøtan
Open Air Museum / Folklore Museum - 1925
Five old buildings forming a courtyard, Lapp culture section, old tools and implements illustrating rural life in the district, Namdal fembøring (big open fishing boat) 26198

Nord-Trøndelag Fylkesgalleri (County Gallery), Kulturhuset, 7800 Namsos - T: 74275900, Fax: 74275090. Head: Asbjørn Hagerup
Fine Arts Museum - 1987
Norwegian and int art 26199

Narvik

Nordland Røde Kors Krigsminnemuseum (Nordland Red Cross War Museum), Torghallen, 8501 Narvik, mail addr: Postboks 513, 8507 Narvik - T: 76944426, Fax: 76944560, E-mail: kmmu@online.no, Internet: http://www.museumsnett.no. Head: Ulf E. Torgersen
Military Museum / Historical Museum - 1964
German invasion (9th April 1940) , fights at sea, land and the air with British, French, Polish, German and Norwegian forces, German occupation of Norway 1940-1945 26200

Ofoten Museum, Parkhallene, 8501 Narvik - T: 76944732. Head: Lars Slettjord
Science&Tech Museum / Folklore Museum - 1981
Kiruna-Narvik railway, costumes (1910-1950) 26201

Nesbyen

Hallingdal Folkemuseum, Møllevegen, 3541 Nesbyen - T: 32071485, Fax: 32071498, E-mail: firmapost@hallingdal-folkemuseum.no, Internet: http://www.museumsnett.no/hallingdal. Head: Torill Thømt
Open Air Museum / Folklore Museum / Ethnology Museum - 1899
Old timber buildings, including the medieval loft from Stave, Trøymstua, and the 18th c Villandsstua, textiles, weapons, rose painting, folk costumes, ethnography and folklore, Skrattegard loghouse built in North Dakota in 1882 26202

Nordli

Gamstuggu Nordli, Hwy 74, 7882 Nordli - T: 74337160, Fax: 74337290. Head: Karl A. Fagerli
Local Museum
Two old houses, local history artifacts 26203

Norheimsund

Kvam Bygdemuseum, Öystese, Vikøy and Ålvik, 5600 Norheimsund - T: 51551200, Fax: 56551720. Head: Helene Moe
Local Museum - 1917
Torstein house (1861), a boathouse, a churchboat from Fiske, nearby the old Vavollen farm with storehouse (18th c) and 'open-hearth' cottage with original interior 'kroting' decorations (geometrical festive decor applied to sooted logs with a mixture of chalk and water) 26204

Mons Breidvik Galleries, Town Hall of Kvam County, 5600 Norheimsund - T: 56551200, Fax: 56551720. Head: Helene Moe
Public Gallery
Works by the painter and graphic artist Mons Breidvik (1881-1950) 26205

Notodden

Heddal Bygdetun, 3676 Notodden - T: 35020840
Open Air Museum - 1950
17 old houses arranged as a courtyard (close to Heddal stave church) 26206

Oppdal

Oppdal Bygdemuseum, 7340 Oppdal - T: 72401000, Fax: 72401001. Head: Arild Hoel
Open Air Museum - 1937/53
Sixteen old buildings, including storehouses, a smithy, a steam bath, a grinding mill, a threshing barn (1656), woodcarvings, utensils and implements 26207

Opphaug

Austråt Slott, Ørlandet, 4 km from Hwy 719, 7140 Opphaug
Historical Museum
Castle (mid 17th c), said to be the most original work of the Norwegian Renaissance period, church from about 1200 26208

Ørje

Haldensvassdragets Kanalmuseum, Ørje Brug, 1870 Ørje - T: 69811021, Fax: 69813429, E-mail: post@kanalmuseet.no, Internet: http://www.kanalmuseet.no. Head: Reni Braarud
Science&Tech Museum
Forestry, river rafting, canal transport, locks 26209

Orkanger

Orkdal Bygdemuseum, Postboks 83, 7310 Orkanger - T: 72480000, Fax: 72481910
Local Museum 26210

Ørnes

Meløy Bygdemuseum, Øde, Reipå, 8150 Ørnes - T: 75755940, Fax: 75755042, E-mail: trine.iversen@meloy.kommune.no, Internet: http://www.meloy.kommune.no. Head: Trine Groenn Iversen
Local Museum
Farmer and fisher around 1900, school 26211

Ørsta

Brudavollen Bygdetun, Hwy 655, Høgebru, 6150 Ørsta - T: 70066644, 70066764. Head: Borghild Brekke
Open Air Museum - 1959
Five old buildings in their original settings 26212

Os i Østerdalen

Oddentunet, Narjordet, 2550 Os i Østerdalen - T: 62470300, Fax: 62470340, E-mail: os.kommune@cti.net
Agriculture Museum
Historic farm, decorations from 1820 26213

Oslo

Astrup Fearnley Museet for Moderne Kunst, Dronningens g 4, 0107 Oslo - T: 22936060, Fax: 22936065, E-mail: af-museet@fearnleys.no, Internet: http://www.af-moma.no
Fine Arts Museum - 1993
Modern art (Anselm Kiefer, Damien Hirst) 26214

Bogstad Gård (Bogstad Manor), Sørkedalen 826, 0758 Oslo - T: 22065200, Fax: 22065201, E-mail: bogstad@bogstadgard.no, Internet: http://www.hellebard.norskfolke.museum.no/bogstad. Head: Else Espeland
Decorative Arts Museum - 1955
18th c manor with original 18th and 19th c interiors 26215

Botanisk Museum, Universitetets Naturhistoriske Museer (Botanical Museum), Sars G 1, 0562 Oslo, mail addr: Boks 1172 Blindern, 0318 Oslo - T: 22851600, Fax: 22851835, E-mail: nhm-museum@nhm.uio.no, Internet: http://www.nhm.uio.no/botanisk/bot-mus/. Head: Prof. Dr. Elen Roaldset
Natural History Museum / University Museum - 1814
Extensive herbarium of Norwegian flora 26216

Etnografisk Museum, Universitetets Kulturhistoriske Museer (Ethnographic Museum, University Museum of Cultural Heritage), Frederiksg 2, 0164 Oslo 1 - T: 22859964, Fax: 22859960, E-mail: info@ukm.uio.no, Internet: http://www.ukm.uio.no. Head: Dr. Egil Mikkelsen
Ethnology Museum / University Museum - 1857
Ethnographical coll from Africa, Asia, the Americas, the Arctic and Oceania - library 26217

Filmmuseet, Dronningensgt 16, 0105 Oslo - T: 22474500, Fax: 22474598, E-mail: utstillinger@nfi.no, Internet: http://www.nfi.no. Head: Ole A. Werring
Performing Arts Museum 26218

Forsvarsmuseet (Armed Forces Museum), Akershus, Oslo Mil, 0015 Oslo - T: 23093582, Fax: 23093190, E-mail: fmu@c2i.net, Internet: http://www.fmu.mil.no. Head: Rolf Scheen
Military Museum - 1860
Weapons, uniforms, military equipment, military hist, documentation from Viking period to World Wars I and II - library, photoarchives 26219

Frammuséet, Bygdøynes, 0286 Oslo - T: 23282950, Fax: 23282951, Internet: http://www.fram.museum.no
Special Museum - 1936
3-masted schooner 'Fram' (built by Colin Archer in 1892), the ship used by Fridtjof Nansen, Roald Amundsen, and Otto Sverdrup on their expeditions, arctic and antarctic equipment displayed an board 26220

Geologisk Museum, Universitets Naturhistoriske Museer, Sars' gate 1, 0562 Oslo, mail addr: Boks 1172 Blindern, 0318 Oslo - T: 22851670, Fax: 22851810, E-mail: nhm-museum@nhm.uio.no, Internet: http://www.nhm.uio.no/palmus. Head: Prof. Dr. Elen Roaldset
Natural History Museum / University Museum - 1916
Prehistoric animal and plant life, fossils from Cambro-Silurian beds of Norway and from Precambrian to Tertiary beds of Svalbard Pleistocene fossils, sea scorpion, coll of trilobites, agnathes, primitive fishes 26221

Historisk Museum, Universitetets Kulturhistoriske Museer (The Historical Museum, University Museum of Cultural Heritage), Frederiksg 2, 0164 Oslo - T: 22859912, Fax: 22859920, E-mail: info@ukm.uio.no, Internet: http://www.ukm.uio.no. Head: Dr. Egil Mikkelsen
Historical Museum / University Museum
Ethnographic Museum, Antiquities Collection, Coin Collection 26222

International Museum of Children's Art, Lille Frønsv 4, 0369 Oslo - T: 22468573, Fax: 22692910. Head: Rafael Goldin
Fine Arts Museum
International coll of fine arts made by children (age: 2-18 years), displaying masterworks and thematical exhibitions from a total coll counting more than 100.000 items from 150 countries, dolls 26223

Kon-Tiki Museum, c/o Institute for Pacific Archaeology and Cultural History, Bygdøynesv 36, 0286 Oslo 2 - T: 23086767, Fax: 23086760, E-mail: kon-tiki@online.no, Internet: http://www.kon-tiki.no. Head: Maja Bange
Archaeological Museum / Historical Museum - 1949
Archaeology, arts and crafts, the balsa raft Kon-Tiki (1947), the papyrus boat Ra II (1970), the vessel Tigris, stone sculptures from the secret caves of the Easter Island, replica of an Easter Island statue (9,2 meters), boat models, aquarium - library, research department 26224

Kunstindustrimuseet i Oslo (Museum of Decorative Arts and Design in Oslo), Sankt Olavsg 1, 0165 Oslo 1 - T: 22036540, Fax: 22113971, E-mail: museum@kunstindustrimuseet.no, Internet: http://www.kunstindustrimuseet.no. Head: Martin Biehl
Decorative Arts Museum - 1876
Goldsmith's and silversmith's work, woven tapestry (Baldishol tapestry, ca 1200), glass and faience, furniture from different periods, textiles and costumes (incl coll of Norwegian Royal costumes), 20th c Scandinavian crafts and design - library 26225

Museet for Samtidskunst (National Museum of Contemporary Art), Bankpl 4, 0034 Oslo - T: 22335820, Fax: 22862220, E-mail: info@mfs.museum.no, Internet: http://www.museumsnett.no/mfs. Head: Per Bj. Boym
Fine Arts Museum - 1990
Modern art, 1945 until today 26226

Myntkabinett, Universitetets Kulturhistoriske Museer (The Coin Collection, University Museum of Cultural Heritage), Frederiksg 2, 0164 Oslo 1 - T: 22859912, Fax: 22859920, E-mail: info@ukm.uio.no, Internet: http://www.ukm.uio.no. Head: Dr. Egil Mikkelsen
University Museum / Decorative Arts Museum - 1817
Coll of coins and medals of the last 1000 years - library 26227

Nasjonalgalleriet (The National Gallery, Oslo), Universitetsg 13, 0033 Oslo, mail addr: Postboks 8157, 0033 Oslo - T: 22200404, Fax: 22361132, E-mail: nga@nasjonalgalleriet.no, Internet: http://www.nasjonalgalleriet.no. Head: Anniken Thue
Fine Arts Museum - 1836
Norwegian art, especially 19th and 20th c painting and sculpture, works from other Scandinavian countries, French art since Delacroix, some old masters, Russian icons, Graeco-Roman sculptures, casts of antique, medieval, and Renaissance sculpture, prints and drawings - library, print dept 26228

Norges Hjemmefrontmuseum (Norway's Resistance Museum), Bygn 21, Oslo Mil, Akershus, 0015 Oslo - T: 23093138, Fax: 23093137, E-mail: -norges.hjemmefrontmuseum@os.telia.no, Internet: http://www.nhm.mil.no. Head: Arnfinn Moland
Historical Museum / Military Museum - 1966
Authentic documents, photos, models, weapons and equipment pertaining to the Resistance during the Occupation years 1940-45, fortress and castle which were rebuilt by Christian IV (1630), royal tombs - library, historical archives 26229

Norsk Arkitekturmuseum (The Norwegian Museum of Architecture), Kongens g 4, 0153 Oslo - T: 22424080, Fax: 22424106, E-mail: post@arkitektur.museum.no, Internet: http://www.arkitektur.museum.no. Head: Ulf Grønvold
Fine Arts Museum - 1975
Hist of architecture 26230

Norsk Farmasihistorisk Museum, Museumsv 10, Bygdøy, 0287 Oslo 2 - T: 22123700, Fax: 22123777, E-mail: webmaster@norskfolke.museum.no, Internet: http://www.norskfolke.museum.no. Head: Olav Aaraas
Special Museum - 1963
History of pharmacy in Norway, starting with Svaneapotek in Bergen (1595), development of the pharmaceutical industry 26231

Norsk Folkemuseum (Norwegian Folk Museum), Museumsv 10, 0287 Oslo 2 - T: 22123700, Fax: 22123777, E-mail: nf@norskfolke.museum.no, Internet: http://www.norskfolke.museum.no. Head: Olav Aaraas
Folklore Museum - 1894
Norwegian people's life from the Reformation to the present, rural and urban, Gol stave church, Raulandstua, furniture, household items, folk art and folk dresses, clothing, tapestries, farming implements, logging gear, trappings, conveyances, childhood, the first parliament halls of Norway, ecclesiatic, Lappish (Sami) section, photos - library, research dept. 26232

Norsk Sjøfartsmuseum (Norwegian Maritime Museum), Bygdøynesveien 37, 0286 Oslo 2 - T: 24114150, Fax: 24114151, E-mail: fellespost@norsk-sjofartsmuseum.no, Internet: http://www.museumsnett.no/nsm. Head: Aagot Gammersvik
Science&Tech Museum - 1914
Ship models, ship portraits, navigational instruments, underwater finds, a first class accomodation from a passenger steamer, a

deckhouse from a sailing ship, Norwegian coastal crafts, the polar ship 'Gjøa', archives of logbooks, manuscripts, photogr - library, marine archaeological dept 26233

Norsk Teknisk Museum (Norwegian Museum of Science and Technology), Kjelsaasv 143, 0491 Oslo - T: 22796000, Fax: 22796100, E-mail: post@tekniskmuseum.no, Internet: http://www.tekniskmuseum.no. Head: Gunnar Nerheim
Science&Tech Museum - 1914
Technology, handicrafts, industry, communications, Norwegian inventions, working models, model railway, vintage cars - library 26234

Norsk Tollmuseum (Customs House), Tolbug 1a, 0032 Oslo, mail addr: Postboks 8122, 0032 Oslo - T: 22346876, Fax: 22177148, E-mail: - jon.agust.eggertsson@toll.no, Internet: http://www.norsktollerforbund.no/norsk_tollmuseum.htm
Historical Museum - 1915
Development of the Norwegian Customs Service 26235

Norsk Veterinærmedisinsk Museum, c/o The Norwegian School of Veterinary Science, Ullevålsv 72, 0164 Oslo 1 - T: 22964500, Fax: 22565704, E-mail: kristian.ingebrigtsen@veths.no. Head: Kristian Ingebrigtsen
University Museum / Historical Museum - 1967
Veterinary sciences - library 26236

Oscarshall, Bygdøy, Oscarshallv, 0287 Oslo 2 - T: 22437749
Fine Arts Museum
Neo-Gothic summer residence (1850) with a beautiful garden, portrait gallery, paintings from the Norwegian romantic period 26237

Oslo Bymuseum (Oslo City Museum), Frognerv 67, 0266 Oslo - T: 22430645, Fax: 22434891, E-mail: oslbymus@online.no. Head: Trond Gjerdi
Local Museum - 1905
Pictures, photos, models of old buildings relating to the history of Oslo as city and capital of Norway - library, photoarchives 26238

Oslo Kommunes Modellsamling, c/o Oslo Byplankontor, Trondheimsv 5, 0560 Oslo 1 - T: 22207210. Head: Finn Kluge
Special Museum
Municipal coll of town plans and models 26239

Oslo Middelalderpark (Oslo Medieval Park), Oslog, Oslo - T: 22194468, Fax: 22674466, E-mail: Oslo.Ladegaard@sensewave.com. Head: Anne Louise Lien, Ann-Katrin Olsen
Open Air Museum
Ruins of St. Hallvard's Church, the Cross Church, and the Olav Monastery (Middle Ages), St. Clemens Church, St. Marys Church and the King's Castle, Ladegården (1725, built on the ruins of the bishop's palace), Bishop Nikolas Chapel (ca. 1200), rooms preserved from the Olav Monastery, medieval masonry and stones, reconstructed medieval shoreline 26240

Paleontologisk Museum → Geologisk Museum

Postmuseet, Kirkeg 20, 0153 Oslo - T: 23148059, Fax: 23148855. Head: A. Woll
Special Museum - 1947
Complete coll of Norwegian stamps, 350 years of Norwegian post office history 26241

Riksantikvaren, Directorate for Cultural Heritage, Dronningens g 13, 0034 Oslo - T: 22940400, Fax: 22940404, E-mail: riksantikvaren@ra.no, Internet: http://www.riksantikvaren.no. Head: Nils Marstein
Fine Arts Museum - 1912
Surveys and original drawings of ancient Norwegian architecture, about 500.000 photographs of listed houses and churches, surveys of 30 stave churches - library, archive 26242

Skimuseet, Kongevein 5, 0787 Oslo - T: 22923200, Fax: 22923270, E-mail: skimuseet@skiforeningen.no, Internet: http://www.skimuseet.com. Head: Karin Berg
Special Museum
History of skiing in Norway, skis, bindings, and poles from the earliest days, equipment used by Nansen and Amundsen in their polar expeditions, photos, prizes, and medals 26243

Stenersenmuseet, Munkedamsveien 15, 0125 Oslo - T: 23493600, Fax: 23493610, E-mail: post@stenersen.museum.no, Internet: http://www.stenersen.museum.no. Head: Østein Ustvedt
Fine Arts Museum - 1994
Paintings, drawings, watercolors, prints, coll by Munch, 3 permanent art colls, changing exhibits 26244

Teatermuseet i Oslo, Christiania Torv 1, 0151 Oslo - T: 22426509, Fax: 22424562, E-mail: teaterm@online.no, Internet: http://www.home.sol.no/~teaterm. Head: Ragnhild Wang, Lucie Lovén
Performing Arts Museum - 1939
Material associated with theatrical life in Oslo 26245

Universitetets Oldsaksamling, Universitetets Kulturhistoriske Museer (Antiquities Collection, University Museum of Cultural Heritage), Frederiksg 2, 0164 Oslo 1 - T: 22859912, Fax: 22859920, E-mail: info@ukm.uio.no, Internet: http://www.ukm.uio.no. Head: Dr. Egil Mikkelsen
Archaeological Museum / University Museum / Historical Museum - 1829
Norway's archaeological heritage, esp. Viking coll, swords, jewellery, household utilities, medieval painted wooden objects of religious art - library 26246

Vetrinærmuseet → Norsk Veterinærmedisinsk Museum

Vigeland-Museet, Nobelsg 32, 0268 Oslo 2 - T: 22542530, Fax: 22542540, E-mail: post@vigeland.museum.no, Internet: http://www.vigeland.museum.no. Head: Lise Mjøs
Fine Arts Museum - 1947
Works by the sculptor Gustav Vigeland, bronzes, plaster models for monumental sculptures, models in clay, drawings and woodcuts 26247

Vikingskiphuset, Universitetets Kulturhistoriske Museer (Viking Ship Museum, University Museum of Cultural Heritage), Huk Aveny 35, Bygdøy, 0287 Oslo 2 - T: 22135280, Fax: 22135281, E-mail: info@ukm.uio.no, Internet: http://www.ukm.uio.no. Head: Dr. Egil Mikkelsen
Historical Museum / University Museum
Three Viking ships excavated at Oseberg, Gokstad and Tune, finds from the Oseberg mound including sledges, a ceremonial carriage, carved dragon heads, household utensils and other sepulchral relics connected with the 'Oseberg Queen' 26248

Zoologisk Museum, Universitetets Naturhistoriske Museer (Zoological Museum), Sars G 1, 0562 Oslo 5, mail addr: Boks 1172 Blindern, 0318 Oslo - T: 22851700, Fax: 22851709, E-mail: nhm-museum@nhm.uio.no, Internet: http://www.nhm.uio.no. Head: Prof. Dr. Elen Roaldset
Natural History Museum / University Museum - 1813
Zoology, geology, paleontology, botanic - botanical garden, library 26249

Øystese

Ingebrigt Vik's Museum, 5610 Øystese - T: 56552269
Fine Arts Museum 26250

Paradis

Gamlehaugen, 5231 Paradis - T: 55925120, Fax: 55925133, E-mail: henry.lie@statsbygg.no. Head: Einar Skarsbø
Special Museum - 1925
Home of Christian Michelsen, Norway's Prime Minister in 1905, now a royal residence, with old interiors and memorabilia of the year 1905, when the union with Sweden was disbanded 26251

Troldhaugen - Edvard Grieg Museum, Trolnaugv 65, 5232 Paradis - T: 55910710, Fax: 55911395, E-mail: trold@online.no, Internet: http://www.bergen.by.com/museum/troldhaugen. Head: Erling Dahl
Music Museum - 1928
Victorian home of Edvard and Nina Grieg, urn containing the composer's burial remains - concert hall 26252

Porsgrunn

Porsgrunn Bymuseum og Sjofartmuseet Raschebakken → Stiftelse Porsgrunnsmuseene

Stiftelse Porsgrunnsmuseene, Raschebakken 1, 3921 Porsgrunn - T: 35555797, Fax: 35555797, E-mail: porsgrunn.bymuseum@c2i.net. Head: Aasmund Beier
Decorative Arts Museum - 1930
Porsgrunn Porcelain Factory, fine china, customs house (1661), maritime gallery 26253

Prestfoss

Sigdal og Eggedal Museum, Hwy 287, 20 km North of Åmot, 3350 Prestfoss - T: 32710490, Fax: 32710642. Head: Håvard Støvern
Open Air Museum - 1944
Old buildings incl rose-painted cottage (1799), implements 26254

Råde

Råde Bygdetun, 1640 Råde. Head: Eigil Tangen
Local Museum - 1949
Textile coll from home-produced flax, three old farm houses 26255

Rakkestad

Rakkestad Bygdetun, Bygdetunv, 1890 Rakkestad. Head: Per Kr. Filtvedt
Open Air Museum - 1950
Five old houses illustrating farming life and work in the past 26256

Rauland

Myllargut-Heimen, nr Lake Totak, Hwy 362, Arabygdi, 3864 Rauland
Music Museum - 1951
Cottage where Thorgeir Øygarden Augundson (1801-72), the best-known Norwegian fiddler, spent his last years 26257

Rendalen

Jacob Breda Bullmuseet, 2485 Rendalen - T: 62468500, Fax: 62468507, E-mail: postmottak@rendalen.kommune.no, Internet: http://www.rendalen.kommune.no. Head: Ole Bjørn Salvesen
Historical Museum / Music Museum - 1964
Birthplace and residence of Jacob Breda Bull from 1853 to 1869 26258

Rennebu

Rennebu Bygdetun, nr Hwy 700, 7393 Rennebu - T: 72426122. Head: Birgit Foss
Open Air Museum / Local Museum - 1953
Old farmyard with 7 buildings on the original site, local history items 26259

Rennesøy

Rennesøy Bygdemuseum, 4150 Rennesøy - T: 51723305, Fax: 51513761
Local Museum - 1966
Old wind mill, Colter's farm 26260

Rindal

Rindal Bygdemuseum, Langkloppan, 6657 Rindal, mail addr: Postboks 47, 6657 Rindal - T: 71665111, 71665329, Fax: 71645663
Local Museum 26261

Rindalsskogen

Rindal Bygdemuseum, near Hwy 65, 7358 Rindalsskogen
Open Air Museum - 1950
Old farmhouses, local artifacts 26262

Risøyhamn

Andøymuseet, 9490 Risøyhamn, mail addr: Postboks 11, 8483 Andenes - T: 76142088, Fax: 76142313. Head: Kjersti Haugen Aashagen
Open Air Museum / Natural History Museum - 1933/1967
5 old buildings, pre-quaternary fossils and the famous skeleton of an ichthyosaur, polar fishing, architecture, Hilmar Nøis, Helmer Hansen - The Polar Museum and 'The Old Andøymuseet' 26263

Rissa

Rissa Bygdemuseum, on Hwy 717, Reinskloster, 7100 Rissa - T: 73855560. Head: Kjersti Karijord Snørvik
Open Air Museum
Old cottage (ca. 1720), ruins of the Reinskloster monastery (ca. 1250), old dairy, Norway's first dairy museum 26264

Rjukan

Norsk Industriarbeidermuseet (Norwegian Industrial Workers' Museum), Postboks 52, 3660 Rjukan - T: 35095153, Fax: 35095139, E-mail: - norskindustriarbmus@telnet.no. Head: Bjørn Eduardsen
Historical Museum - 1987
Former Norsk Hydro power station, hist of the local workers' movement, wartime occupation by the Germans, the Hydro-Rjukan coll (1907-91), Elkem Asa coll (1920-80), Hydro-Rjukan Archives (1907-91) - photo archives, archives 26265

Rjukan og Tinn Museum, Bjørkhaug, 3660 Rjukan - T: 35095153, Fax: 35095139. Head: Tor Odden
Folklore Museum / Military Museum - 1928
Øverland East and Øverland West courtyards, implements, folk art, textiles, weapons, cabin used by the heavywater plant saboteurs from Hardangervidda (1943) including weapons, maps and equipment, Øverland school house 26266

Roan

Roan Bygdetun, 7180 Roan
Local Museum
Brandsøy cottage (ca. 1770), containing some interesting items 26267

Rognan

Saltdal Bygdetun, Postboks 91, 8250 Rognan - T: 75690660, Fax: 75691405
Local Museum
Local farm life, boats, WW II exhibits 26268

Rollag

Rollag Bygdetun, 3626 Rollag
Open Air Museum - 1946
Six timber buildings, old rectory (17th c) with a bishop's cottage and a storehouse (18th c) 26269

Rolvsøy

Hans Nielsens Hauges Minne, Hwy 109, 1700 Rolvsøy
Special Museum
Birthplace of the evangelist Hans Nielsen Hauge, memorabilia and personal items, books and leaflets 26270

Røros

Ratvolden, Rugeldalen, 7460 Røros - T: 72414619, Fax: 72414660
Special Museum
Home of the famous Norwegian author Johan Falkberget (1897-1967) 26271

Rørosmuseet, Malmpl, 7460 Røros, mail addr: Postboks 224, 7374 Røros - T: 72406170, Fax: 72406180, E-mail: museumspost@rorosmuseet.museum.no. Head: John A. Bryde
Local Museum - 1930
Smelting works (models of hoists, water wheels, horse-drawn capstans and smelting furnaces), Olav's Mine (preserved copper mine, mining operations and working conditions, local folk costumes 26272

Rørvik

Woksengs Samlinger, Postboks 177, 7900 Rørvik - T: 74390441, Fax: 74390465. Head: Sigmund Alsaker
Local Museum - 1974
Local history, exhibits about the coast 26273

Rosendal

Baroniet Rosendal, Hwy 13, Hardanger Fjord, 5470 Rosendal - T: 53482999, Fax: 53482998, E-mail: info@baroniet.no, Internet: http://www.baroniet.no. Head: Anne Grete Honerød
Fine Arts Museum / Decorative Arts Museum
Rosendal chateau (17th c) with a beautiful park and garden 26274

Rysstad

Rygnestadtunet, Postboks 24, 4748 Rysstad - T: 37936303, Fax: 37936323, E-mail: setesdalsmuseet@c2i.net. Head: Anna Stella Karlsdottir
Open Air Museum - 1938
Farmstead, 16th c houses, appears in legends 26275

Setesdalsmuseet, 4748 Rysstad - T: 37936303, Fax: 37936323, E-mail: setesdalsmuseet@c2i.net. Head: Anna Stella Karlsdottir
Historical Museum - 1938
Regional art, costumes 26276

Sagstua

Sagstua Skolemuseum, Sigurd Hoels Hjem, 2120 Sagstua - T: 62971992
Special Museum
School from 1855, home of the author Sigurd Hoel 26277

Sakshaug

Inderøy Bygdemuseum, close to Hwy 755, 7670 Sakshaug - T: 74153050
Open Air Museum - 1924
Four old buildings illustrating life on the Inderøy peninsula in former times 26278

Salangsdalen

Bardu Bygdetun, Lundamo, E 6, 9360 Salangsdalen - T: 77832010, Fax: 77832009, E-mail: tore.hauge@midt-troms.museum.no, Internet: http://www.midt-troms.museum.no. Head: Tore Hauge
Open Air Museum - 1965
Old farmyard (1860) with 5 original buildings 26279

Sand

Ryfylkemuseet, Nordenden 14, 4230 Sand - T: 52792950, Fax: 52792951, E-mail: post@ryfylkemuseet.no. Head: Roy Höibo
Local Museum / Open Air Museum - 1981 26280

Sandane

Nordfjord Folkemuseum, Gota 16, 6823 Sandane - T: 57866122, Fax: 57866435, E-mail: nfmuseum@firda.net, Internet: http://www.sognogfjordane.-kulturnett.no. Head: Aslaug Nesje Bjørlo
Open Air Museum - 1920
Folk arts and folklore, agricultural implements, old buildings 26281

Sandefjord

Kommandør Chr. Christensen's Hvalfangst Museum (Commander Chr. Christensen's Whaling Museum), Museumg 39, 3210 Sandefjord - T: 33484650, Fax: 33463784, E-mail: sfjmus@vestfoldnett.no. Head: Jan Erik Ringstad
Historical Museum - 1917
Development of whaling from primitive methods to pelagic whaling and whale factory ships in the Antarctic - reference library, whaling centre 26282

Sandefjord Bymuseum (Sandefjord Town Museum), Hystadv 21, 3213 Sandefjord - T: 33484650, Fax: 33463784, E-mail: sfjmus@vestfoldnett.no. Head: Jan Erik Ringstad
Local Museum - 1898
Local history, arts and crafts coll, Pukkestad vicarage (1792) 26283

Sandefjord Sjøfartsmuseum (Sandefjord Maritime Museum), Prinsensg 18, 3211 Sandefjord - T: 33484650, Fax: 33463784, E-mail: sfjmus@vestfoldnett.no. Head: Jan Erik Ringstad
Special Museum - 1957
Pictures and paintings, models of windjammers, Roald Amundsen coll, maritime history, horology, navigation, Viking exhibition 26284

Sandnes

Jonas Øglands Bedriftsmuseum, Holbergs g 16, 4301 Sandnes - T: 51660462, Fax: 51660466
Science&Tech Museum
Hist of manufacturing company (bicycles, clothes), working conditions of 1930 26285

Sandnessjøen

Petter Dass-Museet på Alstahaug (Petter Dass-Museum at Alstahaug), Postboks 164, 8001 Sandnessjøen - T: 75044055, Fax: 75043399. Head: Gunnar Berntsen
Special Museum - 1988
Parsonage of 17 c poet P. Dass, 12th c church, fishery, rural life 26286

Sarpsborg

Borgarsyssel Museum, Gamlebyg 8, 1700 Sarpsborg - T: 69155011, Fax: 69156130
Archaeological Museum - 1921
Ruins of St. Nicholas church (ca. 1100), old buildings (1660-1825), complete farm (Middle Ages), prehistoric archaeological exhibition, baptismal fonts, high seat panels, Østfold Gallery: silver, stoneware (Herrebø), rose-painting - library 26287

Seierstad

Fosnes Bygdemuseum, 7815 Seierstad - T: 74286899
Local Museum 26288

Selbu

Selbu Bygdemuseum, Mebonden, nr Hwy 705, 7580 Selbu - T: 73816700, Fax: 73816750, Internet: http://www.selbunett.no/skommune/museum
Local Museum - 1925
Furniture, implements, mineral coll, decorated walls by Bjarne Rise, Selbu-knitting, open-air section at Kalvåa 26289

Singsås

Singsås Bygdemuseum, 7494 Singsås - T: 72435421
Local Museum - 1935
Local history, implements and utensils, old schoolhouse 26290

Sjøvegan

Salangen Bygdetun, Øvre Salangen, 9350 Sjøvegan - T: 77172181, Fax: 77171562, E-mail: - Grethe.Davidsen.kleppe@salangen.kommune.no
Local Museum - 1984
Farm, shoemaker's workshop, carpenter's tools 26291

Skårer

Lørenskog Bygdemuseum, Postboks 304, 1471 Skårer - T: 67973555, Fax: 67971895
Agriculture Museum / Local Museum
Agriculture, forestry 26292

Skarnes

Odalstunet, Hwy 2, 2100 Skarnes - T: 62965306
Open Air Museum
Courtyard consisting of several old farmhouses 26293

Skedsmokorset

Skedsmo Bygdetun, Hwy 120, E 6, 2020 Skedsmokorset
Local Museum
Huseby farm with main building, cottage and storehouse, dwellings of government officials (19th c) 26294

Skei i Jølster

Astruptunet, Jølster Kommune, 6841 Skei i Jølster, mail addr: Boks B, 6841 Skei i Jølster - T: 57726144, 57726782, Fax: 57726141, E-mail: astruptunet@astruptunet.com, Internet: http://www.astruptunet.com. Head: Solveig Berg Lofnes
Fine Arts Museum 26295

Midttunet, Jølster Kommune, 6841 Skei i Jølster, mail addr: Boks B, 6841 Skei i Jølster - T: 57726140, Fax: 57726141. Head: Solveig Berg Lofnes
Ethnology Museum / Local Museum 26296

Skien

Fylkesmuseet for Telemark og Grenland, Brekkeparken, Øvregt 41, 3715 Skien - T: 35523594, Fax: 35520159, E-mail: post@telemark.museum.no. Head: Vibeke Mohr
Folklore Museum / Open Air Museum - 1909
Folk art, agriculture, horticulture, forestry, handicrafts, navigation, communications, church art, local hist, Ibsen section, open-air museum with several log houses (medieval to 19th c), incl Borgestua (1584) and Rambergstua, decorated with 'rose-painting' (1788), Brekkeparken (planned by Pries, completed in 1816), Søndre Brekke (1780) with furnishings from the 17th, 18th, and 19th c, section for the presentation of rose-painting, woodcarving, folk costumes, weaving, embroidery and silversmith's work - library 26297

Ibsens Venstøp, Venstøphøgda 74, 3721 Skien - T: 35523594, Fax: 35520159, E-mail: post@telemark.museum.no
Special Museum
Place where the Ibsen family lived from 1835 to 1843, marionette theater Henrik Ibsen used to show his dramatic abilities for the first time - multimedia exhibition 26298

Skiptvet

Nes Lensemuseum, Nesveien 265, 1816 Skiptvet - T: 69809011, Fax: 69809052, E-mail: kultur.oppvekst@skiptvet.kommune.no, Internet: http://www.skiptvet.kommune.no. Head: Harald Frorud
Science&Tech Museum - 1984
Power station, smithy with forge, joiner's workshop, dining hut and a saw 26299

Skiptvet Bygdemuseum (Local Museum), Storveien 26, 1816 Skiptvet - T: 69809011, Fax: 69809052, E-mail: kultur.oppvekst@skiptvet.kommune.no, Internet: http://www.skiptvet.kommune.no. Head: Harald Frorud
Local Museum - 1944
Farmyard with farmhouse, barn, storehouse, kiln and smithy, furniture, domestic utensils 26300

Skogn

Skogn Bygdetun, E 6, 7620 Skogn
Local Museum - 1918
Ammestua house (ca. 1600), where mothers used to breastfeed their children before baptism, large burial mound from the Viking period 26301

Skotselv

Bakke Bygdeminnelag, Skotselv Skole, 3330 Skotselv - T: 32756058. Head: Jon Magne Aas
Local Museum
Stoves and other items made by the Hassel iron works, furniture and household utensils from the parish of Øvre Eiker, Düvelgården House 26302

Skulestadmo

Voss Folkemuseum, Mølstervegen 143, 5710 Skulestadmo - T: 56511511, Fax: 56518815, E-mail: voss.museum@c2i.net, Internet: http://home.c2i.net/voss-folkemuseum. Head: Dag H. Saeverud
Open Air Museum - 1917
Mølster farm, including 20 houses, most of them from the 18th c, barn (1680), two medieval 'lofts', artifacts illustrating life and work at Voss through the ages 26303

Slemmestad

Cementmuseet Slemmestad, Vaterlandsv 13, 3470 Slemmestad - T: 31281484, Fax: 31281130, E-mail: slemmestad@royken.folkebibl.no, Internet: http://www.royken.folkebibl.no. Head: Liv Holmesland
Science&Tech Museum
Cement industry museum, geological coll 26304

Smøla

Smøla Museum, Postboks 34, 6571 Smøla - T: 71540400, Fax: 71540444, E-mail: tbandresen@hotmail.com. Head: Thomas Bjorkan Andresen
Local Museum
Farmer-fisherman's way of life 26305

Snåsa

Snåsa Bygdamuseum, Vonheim, 7760 Snåsa - T: 74151490
Local Museum
Rural life, shoemaker workshop, tapestry - Photo archive 26306

Sørsamiske Samlinger, Vinje School, nr Hwy 763, 7760 Snåsa - T: 74151522. Head: Sigbjørn Dunfjeld
Folklore Museum
Coll of arts and crafts illustrating Lapp culture 26307

Søgne

Søgne Bygdemuseum, Rådhuset, 4682 Søgne - T: 38055555, Fax: 38055516
Local Museum - 1907
16th-18th c articles of farmers and countrymen used in this rural district 26308

Soknedal

Soknedal Museumslag, E 6, 7450 Soknedal
Local Museum
Old buildings, local history artifacts 26309

Sørkjosen

Nord-Troms Museum, Postboks 13, 9086 Sørkjosen - T: 77765868, Fax: 77767020. Head: Tore Hauge
Local Museum
Coastal sami farm 18th c 26310

Sørli

Sørli Museum, Hwy 765, 7884 Sørli - T: 74343411, Fax: 74343410, E-mail: lierne@online.no
Local Museum
Farmhouse, storehouse, local history, a hunting-box 26311

Sørumsand

Urskog-Hølandsbanen, Hwy 171, Northeast of Oslo, 1920 Sørumsand - T: 63868150, Fax: 63827121, E-mail: tertitten@sorum.online.no, Internet: http://www.tertitten.no. Head: Finn Halling
Science&Tech Museum
Narrow gauge railway, steam engine, 4 km tracks operation 26312

Sørvågen

Fiskerværsmuseet (Norwegian Fishing Village Museum), Å i Lofoten, 8392 Sørvågen - T: 76091488, Fax: 76091566, E-mail: nfmuseum@lofoten-info.no, Internet: http://www.lofoten-info.no/nfmuseum. Head: Ottar Schiøtz
Open Air Museum / Local Museum
Fisheries, local culture 26313

Sørvik

Sandtorg Bygdetun, 9433 Sørvik - T: 77076364, Fax: 77076440
Local Museum - 1960
Fishery, 19th c rural life, sheriffs house, prison 26314

Spydeberg

Galtebosamlingen, Rd to Lake Lysern, North of the Village, 1820 Spydeberg
Military Museum
Weapons 26315

Spydeberg Bygdetun, Hov N Spydeberg and E 18, 1820 Spydeberg
Open Air Museum - 1938
Farmyard with five old buildings, Iron Age burial mounds 26316

Stadsbygd

Kystmuseet Staværingen → Museet Kystens Arv

Museet Kystens Arv (The Coastal Heritage Museum), Prestelva, 7105 Stadsbygd - T: 73855560, Fax: 73855751, E-mail: kystens.arv@rissa.online.no, Internet: http://www.museumsnett.no/mka. Head: Bernt Brevik
Local Museum / Science&Tech Museum
Local fishing, boatbuilding, boat coll with 32 unique boats, 52 feet long "The Last Viking", fisheries in Lofoten - the monastery of Rein, archives for Northern emigration, outdoor Amfi 26317

Stavanger

Arkeologisk Museum i Stavanger, Museum of Archaeology Stavanger, Peder Klowsg 30a, 4002 Stavanger - T: 51846000, Fax: 51846199, E-mail: AMS@Ark.museum.no, Internet: http://www.ark.museum.no. Head: Roy Høibo
Archaeological Museum - 1975
Archaeology, reconstructed Iron Age farm at Ullandhaug, reconstructed Bronze Age village at Landa, natural sciences species coll - library, archives, exhibition, lectures 26318

Norsk Hermetikkmuseum (Norwegian Canning Museum), Øvre Strandg 88a, 4010 Stavanger - T: 51526591, Fax: 81842701, E-mail: piers.crocker@stavanger.museum.no, Internet: http://www.stavanger.museum.no. Head: Piers Crocker
Science&Tech Museum / Local Museum
Former canning factory, sardine industry, production demonstrated, sardine labels 26319

Rogaland Kunstmuseum i Stavanger (Rogaland Museum of Fine Arts), Tjensvoll 6, 4021 Stavanger - T: 51530900, Fax: 51530520, E-mail: post@rogaland-kunst.museum.no. Head: Ellen Sæthre
Fine Arts Museum - 1966
Coll of Norwegian painting, sculpture and graphics, works by the great Stavanger painter Lars Hertervig, Halvdan Hafsten coll, Norwegian art 1930-70 26320

Stavanger Maritime Museum, Nedre Strandgt 178-179, 4010 Stavanger - T: 51842700, Fax: 81842701, E-mail: firmapost@stavanger.museum.no, Internet: http://www.stavanger.museum.no. Head: Harald Hamre
Historical Museum / Local Museum
Development of shipping, habour traffic, commerce, ship building 26321

Stavanger Museum, Muség 16, 4010 Stavanger - T: 51842700, Fax: 51842701, E-mail: firmapost@stavanger.museum.no, Internet: http://www.stavanger.museum.no. Head: Ove Magnus Bore
Historical Museum / Natural History Museum - 1877
Cultural history, ethnography, zoology, Ledaal Mansion (1800) furnished in the styles of 1800-1865, Breidablikk (manor house 1881), - library 26322

Vestlandske Skolemuseum, Veumv, 4016 Stavanger, mail addr: Postboks 1075, Hillevag, 4004 Stavanger - T: 51585372. Head: Elin Trollerudoy
Special Museum - 1925
Old and new school equipment, means of instruction, pedagogical books 26323

Steinkjer

Egge Museum, Fylkesmannsgården, 7715 Steinkjer - T: 74163110, Fax: 74169693, E-mail: post@eggemuseum.no, Internet: http://www.eggemuseum.no. Head: Bodil Østerås
Open Air Museum / Agriculture Museum - 1929
11 old buildings from 1759-1895, incl dwelling-house, barn, cowhouse/horsestable, cooking-house, storehouse, smithery, bathhouse, drye-house, mill, log cabin and cotter's farm, domestic utensils, farm implements, burial moulds, Bardal rockcarving field 26324

Stjørdal

Stjørdal Museum KF, Vaernes, 7501 Stjørdal - T: 74827021, Fax: 74821478, E-mail: museet@stjordal.kommune.no, Internet: http://www.bergkunst.net. Head: Siri Schrøder Vesterhjær
Local Museum - 1956
Vicar home and garden (1800), village home (1910) incl shed and storehouse, smithy and open-hearth 'seter' hut, rock art 26325

Stokke

Stokke Bygdetun, Bokemoa, 3160 Stokke - T: 33337848
Local Museum
Rural life, whaling guns 26326

Stokmarknes

Hurtigrutemuseet, W.D. Halsg 1, 8450 Stokmarknes - T: 76152822, Fax: 76152953
Science&Tech Museum
Coastal Hurtigrute steamer hist, ship models 26327

Stonglandseidet

Sør-Senja Museum, 9392 Stonglandseidet - T: 77854677, Fax: 77854712, E-mail: senjamus@online.no. Head: Yngvar Ramstad
Local Museum - 1977
Two Sami homestead, fishing, farming, military 26328

Stord

Sunnhordland Folkemuseum og Sogelag, Township Leirvik, on Stord, 5401 Stord - T: 53413899, Fax: 53413870, E-mail: tlm@sunnhordland.museum.no. Head: Tore Lande Moe
Folklore Museum / Open Air Museum - 1913
Display featuring agriculture, forestry, fishery and life in prehistoric times, coll of sculptures by Torleiv Agderstein, farm buildings, two open hearth huts, a "lemstove", a school, a country store and a beach fisherman's rented hut 26329

Sulitjelma

Sulitjelma Gruvemuseum, 8230 Sulitjelma - T: 75643026. Head: Aksel Johnsen
Special Museum - 1970
Life and work in the mines 26330

Sund i Lofoten

Fiskerimuseet og Kunstsmie i Sund, 8384 Sund i Lofoten
Local Museum - 1966
Old boats, fishing gear, engine (1908) still in operation, curiosities 26331

Sunndalsøra

Sunndal Bygdemuseum, Leikvin, 6600 Sunndalsøra - T: 71691236, Fax: 71699001, E-mail: sunndal@eunet.no. Head: Odelbjørn Sisdal
Local Museum - 1935
Viking burial site, rural life, 19th c English tourism souvenirs, old Sunndal farm, chapel, local history artifacts, exhibition about English salmon fishing in Western Norway during the 19th c 26332

Surnadal

Surnadal Bygdemuseum, Hwy 620, 6650 Surnadal - T: 71761411
Local Museum 26333

Svartskog

Roald Amundsens Hjem Uranienborg, Roald Amundsensv 192, 1420 Svartskog - T: 67123650, Fax: 67122635. Head: Odd Rogne
Special Museum - 1934
Memorabilia of Roald Amundsen 26334

Svelvik

Svelvik Museum, Kirkegaten, 3060 Svelvik - E-mail: mortencs@online.no, Internet: http://home.sol.no/leiftang/museum.no.html. Head: Morten Chr. Stensholt
Local Museum - 1937

Coll commemorating the windjammer days, and the national celebrity, author and businessman Elias Kræmmer, coll from the local fire dept with a 1941 Opel Blitz truck 26335

Sykkylven

Sykkylven Naturhistorisk Museum, 6230 Sykkylven - T: 70246500, Fax: 70246501, E-mail: kultur@sykkylven.kommune.no, Internet: http://.www.sykkylven.kommune.no
Natural History Museum
Birds and animals of Norway and Svalbard 26336

Tennevoll

Krambuvika Bygdemuseum, Soløy i Lavangen, 9465 Tennevoll - T: 77175471
Local Museum
Agriculture, fisheries, wharf and farm buildings 26337

Tingvatn

Hægebostad Bygdemuseum, nr Hwy 43, Lyngdal Valley, 4595 Tingvatn - T: 38349100
Local Museum - 1961
Old moot-place with burial mounds and stone monuments from the Iron Age 26338

Tingvoll

Tingvoll Bygdemuseum, 1,5 km from Hwy 16, 6630 Tingvoll - T: 71531627. Head: Olav Bekken
Local Museum - 1937
Old farmhouse, storehouse, barn, stable, gate-saw, grinding mill, furniture, utensils and implements 26339

Tolga

Sætersgårds Samlinger Dølmotunet, Dølmotunet Tolga, 2540 Tolga - T: 62496514, 62496423, Fax: 62496597, E-mail: eivind.moen@tolga.kommune.no, Internet: http://www.tolga.komune.no. Head: Eivind Moen
Agriculture Museum / Local Museum
Historic farm 26340

Tønsberg

Vestfold Fylkesmuseum, Farmannsv 30, 3111 Tønsberg - T: 33312919, Fax: 33318909. Head: Per Thoresen
Open Air Museum / Agriculture Museum / Folklore Museum - 1939
Medieval to 18th c farm buildings with an agricultural section, whaling department, maritime department, local history and ethnography section, prehistoric section, the Viking ship from Klåstad - library 26341

Tresfjord

Tresfjord Museum, nr E 69, 6380 Tresfjord - T: 71184466
Open Air Museum - 1943
Five old houses with furnishings, open-hearth cottage (1650) 26342

Trøgstad

Trøgstad Bygdemuseum, Skjønhaug Village, Hwy 22, 1860 Trøgstad - T: 67926597, 67926179. Head: Maren-Otte Mellbye
Local Museum / Folklore Museum - 1928
Local history, folklore, 18th c farmhouses 26343

Tromsø

Nordnorsk Kunstmuseum (Art Museum of Northern Norway), Sjøg 1, 9260 Tromsø - T: 77680090, Fax: 77685840, E-mail: nnkm@online.no, Internet: http://www.museumsnett.no/nordnorsk-kunstmuseum. Head: Anne Aaserud
Fine Arts Museum 26344

Polarmuseet i Tromsø (Polarmuseum in Tromsø), Søndre Tollbug 11, 9001 Tromsø - T: 77684373, Fax: 77611720. Head: Torbjorn Trulssen
Historical Museum - 1978
Coll pertaining to hunting in the Arctic, exhibits on scientific expeditions, Helmer Hansen's skis, finds from Wilhelm Barent's winter camp at Novaja Zemlja, a few items from the arctic explorers Roald Amundsen and Fritjof Nansen 26345

Tromsø Folkemuseum, Folkeparken, 9000 Tromsø - T: 77683714
Open Air Museum / Folklore Museum - 1952
Seven houses, local history exhibitions 26346

Tromsø Universitets Museum, c/o Universitetet i Tromsø, Lars Thøringsv 10, 9037 Tromsø - T: 77645000, Fax: 77645520, E-mail: else@imv.uit.no. Head: Else Bottengård
University Museum / Natural History Museum - 1872
Cultural hist, archaeology, Sami ethnography, botany, zoology, marine biology, geology, folk music, ecclesiastical art 26347

Trondheim

Erkebispegården (Archbishop's Palace), 7000 Trondheim - T: 73539160, Fax: 73890808, E-mail: postmottak.ndr@kirken.no, Internet: http://www.nidarosdomen.no. Head: Oeyvind Lunde
Historical Museum / Archaeological Museum / Religious Arts Museum
Oldest secular building still standing in Scandinavia (ca. 1160), Armoury: military museum, Resistance Museum 26348

Kriminalmuseet → Trondheim Politimuseum

Nordenfjeldske Kunstindustrimuseum (National Museum of Decorative Arts), Munkeg 5, 7013 Trondheim - T: 73808950, Fax: 73808951, E-mail: nkmuseum@nkim.museum.no, Internet: http://www.nkmuseum.nkim.museum.no. Head: Jan-L. Opstad
Decorative Arts Museum - 1893
Design, arts and crafts from the early 1600s up to the present, Norwegian and foreign applied art, furniture, silver, glass, ceramics, textiles and metalwork, 20th c Art Nouveau movement, works of the Belgian architect Henry Van de Velde, tapestry by Hannah Ryggen and Synnøve Anker Aurdal, glass by Benny Motzfeld 26349

Ringve Museum, Lade Allé 60, 7441 Trondheim - T: 73922411, Fax: 73920422, E-mail: firmapost@ringve.museum.no, Internet: http://www.ringve.com. Head: Peter Andreas Kjeldsberg
Music Museum - 1952
Valuable instruments from all over the world, Mozart room, Beethoven room, Chopin room, Tchaikovsky room, Ringve Great House (1860) with period interiors, historic musical stations and traditional instruments from all corners of the world in a new and modern exhibition - concert hall, botanical garden, museumshop 26350

Stiftsgården, Munkeg 23, 7000 Trondheim - T: 73522473, Fax: 73542534
Decorative Arts Museum
Rococo house from the 1770's, the second largest wooden building in Scandinavia, with wrought iron work on stairways, painted wall hangings, beautiful old furniture, and the manor garden with lime trees 26351

Trøndelag Folkemuseum, Sverresborg Allé, 7020 Trondheim - T: 73890100, Fax: 73890150, E-mail: tfadm@t-online.no, Internet: http://www.trondelag.folkemuseum.no. Head: Peter Søholt
Open Air Museum / Folklore Museum - 1909
60 old buildings, old town and countryside buildings from the 18th and 19th c, Norway's northern-most stave church (1170), skimuseum, folk art, wood carving, painting, textiles, and everyday utensils, exhibit images of life 26352

Trøndelag Kunstgalleri/Trondheim Kunstmuseum, Bispeg 7b, 7000 Trondheim - T: 73538180, Fax: 73538170, E-mail: kunst@tkm.museum.no. Head: Randi N. Lium
Fine Arts Museum - 1845
Norwegian painting, especially from the 19th and 20th c, Edvard Munch room (25 graphic works), European painting 26353

Trondheim Politimuseum, Kongensg 95, 7012 Trondheim - T: 73899203, E-mail: -norsk.rettsmuseum@c2i.net, Internet: http://www.trondheim.politiet.no
Special Museum - 1918
Items and curiosities connected with the history of the Trondheim police force 26354

Vitenskapsmuseet (Museum of Natural History and Archaeology), c/o Norges Teknisk-Naturvitenskapelige Universitet, Erling Skakkes g 47, 7491 Trondheim - T: 73592145, Fax: 73592136, E-mail: post@vm.ntnu.no, Internet: http://www.ntnu.no.vmuseet. Head: Astrid Langratn
Archaeological Museum / Natural History Museum / University Museum - 1760
Natural hist, geology, religious artefacts, Southern Lapp culture, archaeology (Stone, Bronze and Viking Ages), Trondheim in the Middle Ages - library 26355

Trysil

Trysil Bygdemuseum, 2420 Trysil - T: 62451300, Fax: 62450233
Open Air Museum - 1901
20 buildings incl dwelling houses, barn, cowsheds, mountain dairy farm, sawmill, sauna, flour mill, forge, log cabin 26356

Tuddal

Tuddal Bygdetun, 3697 Tuddal
Open Air Museum
Old buildings 26357

Tydal

Tydal Bygdetun, Hwy 705, 7590 Tydal - T: 74815300, Fax: 74815545. Head: Ingeborg Berggård
Local Museum - 1929
Storaunstuggu cottage (1666), items connected with the fateful retreat of the Swedish army from the Trøndelag district in 1718 26358

Tylldalen

Tylldalen Bygdetun, Prestgarden, 2510 Tylldalen - T: 62486116
Agriculture Museum
Farm 26359

Tynset

Tynset Bygdemuseum, Kongsv 6, 2501 Tynset, mail addr: Postboks 150, 2501 Tynset - T: 62480870, Fax: 62480666
Local Museum - 1923
Furnished old cottages illustrating life and work of a mountain community, antiquities, skis, weapons, books and newspapers 26360

Undheim

Time Bygdemuseum, 4342 Undheim - T: 51776160, Fax: 51776161
Local Museum
Local history 26361

Utne

Hardanger Folkemuseum, Neset, 5797 Utne - T: 53666900, Fax: 53666062, E-mail: hardemuse@newmedia.no, Internet: http://www.hardanger.museum.no. Head: Ågot Gammersvik
Folklore Museum / Open Air Museum - 1911
Modern exhibition and administration building where there are regular theme exhibitions as well as permanent exhibitions of traditional crafts and folk art, outdoor coll with buildings from the 13th c to present 26362

Uvdal i Numedal

Nore og Uvdal Bygdetun, 3632 Uvdal i Numedal - T: 32742760, Fax: 32742761, E-mail: postmottak@nore-og-uvdal.kommune.no
Local Museum - 1960
Local history, parson's cottage and a loft 26363

Vaagaamo

Håkenstad Gardsmuseum, 2 km North of the Village, 2680 Vaagaamo
Open Air Museum
Ten preserved buildings (mostly 18th c), room furnishings, utensils illustrating life at this estate during different periods 26364

Vadsø

Vadsø Museum - Ruija Kvenmuseum, Hvistendahlsg 31, 9800 Vadsø - T: 78942890, Fax: 78942899, E-mail: museum@vadso.kommune.no, Internet: http://www.museumsnett.no/vadsomuseet. Head: Sigrid Skarstein
Local Museum - 1971
Tuomainen house (1850): life of the Finnish immigrants in the 18th/19th c, Esbensen house (1850): merchant complex, Kjeldsenbruket: fish merchant complex 26365

Vågåmo

Bygdetunet Jutulheimen, Vågå Historielag, nr the Village, Hwy 15, 2680 Vågåmo - T: 61237189. Head: Jehans Storvik
Open Air Museum - 1957
Several old Vågå farmhouses with furniture and implements, Jo Visdal 26366

Vanse

Lista Museum, 4560 Vanse, mail addr: PL 122, 4552 Farsund - T: 38393440, Fax: 38392309, E-mail: lista-museum@sensewave.com. Head: Ole Madsen
Local Museum - 1921
Archaeology, agriculture, shipping, art, captain's house water mills, war history - sea-rescue station 26367

Varangerbotn

Varjjat Sámi Musea, Varanger Samiske Museum, 9840 Varangerbotn - T: 78959920, Fax: 78959930, E-mail: info@varanger-samiske.museum.no, Internet: http://www.museumsnett.no/vsm. Head: Kjersti Schanche
Historical Museum / Ethnology Museum
Sami museum, prehistoric site, sacrificial site, pre-Christian Sami graves, Sami ethnographical material, coastal Sami hist and prehist, Sami handicraft 26368

Vardø

Vardømuseene, Per Larssensg 32, 9950 Vardø - T: 78988075, Fax: 78988075. Head: Ole Lindhartseni
Local Museum - 1874
Vardøhus fortress (1737), cultural, military and natural hist coll, curiosities, culture hist 26369

Varhaug

Grødaland Bygdetun, Hå Municipality, 4368 Varhaug - T: 51436150, Fax: 51431211. Head: Eva Watne
Local Museum - 1936
Early 18th c farm, stave-built barns, architecture (oldest example of the traditional farm buildings from this part of Norway) 26370

Hå Bygdemuseum, Kommunehuset at Varhaug Station, 4368 Varhaug - T: 51436150, Fax: 51431211
Local Museum - 1954
Local history artifacts 26371

Hå Gamle Prestegard, Obrestad, 4360 Varhaug - T: 51433944, Fax: 51431211. Head: Eva Watne
Archaeological Museum / Fine Arts Museum - 1983
18th c parsonage, archaeology, contemporary art 26372

Varteig

Varteig Bygdemuseum, nr Hwy 111, North of Sarpsborg, 1735 Varteig
Local Museum - 1933
Cultural-historical coll from Varteig parish 26373

Vatnestrom

Iveland og Vegusdal Bygdemuseum, Fjermedal, 4730 Vatnestrom - T: 37961941. Head: Torkell Fjermedal
Local Museum - 1974
Rural life, prehistoric site 26374

Vega

Vega Bygdemuseum, Postboks 23, 8980 Vega - T: 75035102. Head: Per Morten Gullsvåg
Local Museum - 1976
Local history 26375

Vennesla

Setesdalsbanen Stiftelsen, Grovane, 4700 Vennesla - T: 38156482, Fax: 38156721, E-mail: post@setesdalsbanen.no, Internet: http://www.setesdalsbanen.no. Head: Aslak Wegge
Science&Tech Museum - 1964
Grovane station on the Sørland Railway, narrow-gauge Setesdal Railway remains, some steam engines, 5 km long track, bridges and tunnels 26376

Vennesla Bygdemuseum, Grovane, nr Hwy 405, 4700 Vennesla - T: 38156482. Head: Carl F. Thorsager
Local Museum - 1952
Two old buildings and local artifacts 26377

Verdal

Stiklestad Nasjonal Kultursenter (Stiklestad National Cultural Center), 7650 Verdal - T: 74044200, Fax: 74044210, E-mail: stiklestad@snk.no, Internet: http://www.stiklestad.no. Head: Turid Hofstad
Local Museum / Historic Site / Open Air Museum - 1926
Stiklestad medieval church, where St. Olav fell in battle in 1030, group of farm buildings including large, partly furnished dwelling (1793), modern building with different historical exhibitions 26378

Vesterøy

Kystmuseet Hvaler, Postboks 44, 1684 Vesterøy - T: 69376647, E-mail: Kystmuseet@hvaler.online.no, Internet: http://www.museumsnett.no/hvaler. Head: Morten Kielland
Science&Tech Museum
Old ships, fishery, navigation 26379

Vik i Helgeland

Sømna Bygdetun, Postboks 178, 8924 Vik i Helgeland - T: 75029283, Fax: 75029306
Local Museum
Fishery, rural life, cabin, store 26380

Vikebukt

Landbruksmuseet for Møre og Romsdal, Gjermundnes, 6392 Vikebukt - T: 71189155, Fax: 71189170, E-mail: landpgj@online.no. Head: Anne-Marie Førde
Agriculture Museum
Horse-drawn farming equipment, agricultural implements, tractors, herbal coll 26381

Vingelen

Vingelen Kirke- og Skolemuseum, 2542 Vingelen - T: 62494521, Fax: 62480870
Religious Arts Museum / Special Museum
Church art and school hist 26382

Vinje

Øyfjell Bygdemuseum, Øfjell, 3890 Vinje - T: 35073800
Local Museum 26383

Vinjestova, E 134, 3890 Vinje - T: 35072553, Fax: 35072633, E-mail: Plassen@online.no
Special Museum - 1904
Cottage (1824) where the poet Å.O. Vinje (1818-70) grew up 26384

Volda

Volda Bygdetun, Haueleitet, 6101 Volda - T: 70077854
Local Museum - 1911
Old farmhouses and a storehouse, items of local interest 26385

Oman

Muscat

Oman Natural History Museum, Al Khuwayn, Muscat, mail addr: POB 668, Muscat - T: 605400, Fax: 602735. Head: Said Ali Said Al-Farsi
Natural History Museum - 1983
National Shell and Coral Coll, National Insect and Osteological coll (esp cetacea) - National Herbarium of Oman, botanical garden 26386

Qurm

Qurm Museum, Qurm, mail addr: c/o Ministry of National Heritage and Culture, POB 668, Muscat
Archaeological Museum / Ethnology Museum - 1974
Archeology, ethnology 26387

Ruwi

National Museum at Ruwi, Ruwi
Historical Museum 26388

Pakistan

Abbottabad

Pakistan Forest Museum, Abbottabad
Natural History Museum - 1952/1966
Forest products 26389

Bhawalpur

Bahawalpur Museum, Library Rd, Bhawalpur
Archaeological Museum / Ethnology Museum - 1971
Archeology, ethnology 26390

Natural History Museum, Bhawalpur
Natural History Museum - 1945
Natural History, applied arts 26391

Chakdara

Chakdara Museum, Chakdara
Archaeological Museum - 1970
Archeology, terra cotta - library 26392

Dokri

Museum of Archaeological Site Moenjodaro, Dokri - T: (07443) 272
Archaeological Museum - 1924
Excavations from Moenjodaro including a statuary, seals, household objects, personal ornaments, ivory, bone and shell objects, painted and plain pottery (2500-1500 B.C.), fresco paintings 26393

Faisalabad

Agricultural Museum, c/o Agricultural University, Faisalabad
Agriculture Museum - 1907
History of agriculture in Pakistan, economic crops, agricultural implements 26394

Guddu

Guddu Barrage Museum, Guddu
Archaeological Museum
Exhibits collected during the construction of the dam 26395

Harappa

Archaeological Museum Harappa, Harappa 57171 - T: 323539. Head: Mohammad Bahadar Khan
Archaeological Museum - 1927
Indus Valley objects including a human skeleton, pottery, archaeological material from 2500-1500 B.C. 26396

Hyderabad

Education Museum, c/o Sind University Hyderabad, Hyderabad
University Museum - 1959
Education 26397

Hyderabad Museum, Hyderabad
Fine Arts Museum / Archaeological Museum / Ethnology Museum - 1971
Arts, crafts, archeology, anthropology 26398

Sind Provincial Museum, National Hwy, New Eidgah, Hyderabad - T: (0221) 24463, 27057. Head: Zafar Kazmi
Archaeological Museum / Historical Museum
Archaeology of the Indian valley, Buddhist and Islamic periods in Sind, arts and crafts, struggle for independence 26399

Islamabad

Lok Virsa, Shakar Parian Hills, Garden Av, Islamabad, mail addr: c/o National Institute of Folk and Traditional Heritage, POB 1184, Islamabad - T: (051) 823883, Fax: 813756
Folklore Museum / Decorative Arts Museum - 1973
Folk art and crafts central asia and ethnic tribes - research library 26400

Pakistan Museum of Natural History, Garden Av, Shakar Parian, Islamabad 44000 - T: (051) 219938, E-mail: pmnh@sdnpk.undp.org. Head: Dr. Shazad A. Mufti
Natural History Museum - 1978
Fossils of Siwalik area, semi-precious stones of North West Pakistan, medically important plants and insects, fishes, amphibians, reptiles and mammals of the northern mountain region of Pakistan - Botanical, zoological, earth sciences and public services 26401

Karachi

Aiwen e Rifat Museum and Art Gallery, 27A Al Asif, Central Union Commercial Area, Shahid-e-Millat Rd, Karachi. Head: Muhammad Ishtiaq Khan
Fine Arts Museum
Paintings, applied arts, handicrafts 26402

Archaeological Museum, c/o Karachi University, Karachi
Archaeological Museum / University Museum - 1955
Coll from sites througout Pakistan 26403

National Museum of Pakistan, Burns Garden, Victoria Rd, Karachi 74200 - T: (021) 2113412. Head: Pervin T. Nasir
Archaeological Museum / Decorative Arts Museum / Ethnology Museum - 1950
Archeology from the Stone Age to the Mughal period (16th-19th c A.D.), Indus Valley material (3000-1500 B.C.), Gandhara sculptures (1st-4th c A.D.) depicting the life of Buddha, calligraphy, ceramics and glassware, coins, ethnography 26404

Natural History Museum, c/o Karachi University, Karachi
Natural History Museum / University Museum - 1950
Natural history of Pakistan 26405

Quaid-i-Azam Birthplace and Museum, Wazir Mansions, Karachi - T: (021) 411264. Head: Tahir Saeed
Special Museum - 1953
Birthplace of Quaid-i-Azam Mohammad Ali Jinnah, the founder of Pakistan (born 1876), furniture and law books - library 26406

Lahore

Chughtai Museum Trust, Mian Salah Mimar Ln, 4 Garden Town, Lahore 54600 - T: (042) 5850733, Fax: 5838373. Head: Arif Rahman Chughtai
Fine Arts Museum - 1975
Coll of M.A. Rahman Chughtai (1897-1975), Modern Master of the East and National Painter of Pakistan, comprising of Islamic miniatures, Ino-Pakistani miniatures, Islamic calligraphy, manusscripts, Japanese woodcuts, coll of Punjab miniatures - library 26407

Industrial and Commercial Museum, Poonch House, Multan Rd, Lahore - T: (042) 66209. Head: Mushtaq Ahmad
Science&Tech Museum - 1950
National resources and their utilisation in the field of industry and commerce, arts and crafts - library 26408

Iqbal Museum, Javed Manzil, Allama Iqbal Rd, Lahore - T: (042) 6367046
Special Museum - 1977
Home of the poet and philosopher Allama Sheikh Muhammad Iqbal, original manuscripts and personal belongings 26409

Lahore Fort Museum, Lahore Fort, Lahore - T: (042) 56747. Head: Saeed-Ur Rahman
Military Museum / Historical Museum - 1928
Sikh arms and armour, drums, banners, quilts, chakras, Princess Bamba coll of oil paintings, watercolors, photographs and metallic objects, portraits of Sikh princes, the fort is a monument of the Mughal period 26410

Lahore Museum, Shahrah-e-Quaid-e-Azam, Lahore - T: (042) 9210805, 9211819, Fax: 9210810. Head: Dr. Anjum Rehmani
Decorative Arts Museum / Folklore Museum / Local Museum - 1855
Archaeology, history, art, Buddhist, Bramanical and Jain sculptures, pottery, metalware, arms, carpets, rugs, calligraphy, woodwork, contemporary paintings and crafts, Napalese, Tibetan a.o. objects incl a copper and brass statuary, banners, ornaments, Mughal and Pahari miniatures, Muslim coins and costumes, folk arts, models of some monuments 26411

National Museum of Science and Technology, G.T. Rd, Lahore 54890 - T: (042) 6822006, 6841030, Fax: 6822023, E-mail: sajid@nmst.brain.net.pk. Head: Sajid Anwar Malik
Science&Tech Museum - 1965
Engines, fluid mechanics, light and sound, magnetism and electricity, mechanics, behavioral psychology, meteorology, astronomy and time, human anatomy, natural hist, biology, computers and rockets - library 26412

Natural History Museum, c/o Government College, Lahore
Natural History Museum / University Museum - 1909 26413

Punjab Archives Museum, c/o Punjab Civil Secretariat, Lahore - T: (042) 9210755, Fax: 9212241. Head: Nazir Ahmad Chaudhary
Historical Museum - 1924
library, archives 26414

Zoological Museum, Zoological Garden, Lahore. Head: M. Ikramullah Khan
Natural History Museum 26415

Mangla

Dam Site Museum, Mangla
Natural History Museum - 1967
Natural history, geology, archeology 26416

Moen-Jo-Daro

Archaeological Museum Moen-Jo-Daro, PO Dokri, Moen-Jo-Daro - T: (07443) 272. Head: Saeed Khan Jatoi
Archaeological Museum
Finds from the prehistoric site, then the largest city in Indus valley 26417

Peshawar

Archaeological Museum Peshawar, c/o University of Peshawar, Peshawar - T: 8287. Head: Prof. Farzaud Durrani
Archaeological Museum / University Museum - 1964
Archaeologic materials from regional sites, coins 26418

Forest Museum, c/o Pakistan Forest Institute, Peshawar
Natural History Museum - 1952
Forest and allied products 26419

Islamia College Museum, c/o Islamia College, Peshawar
Natural History Museum / University Museum - 1934
Zoological coll 26420

Peshawar Museum, Peshawar - T: (0521) 74452. Head: Aurangzeb Khan
Local Museum - 1906
Excavations from various sites in the ancient Gandhara region, stone inscriptions in Kharoshti, Sarda, Kufic and Persian characters, specimens of Kashmir papier-mâché, needlework, Persian manuscripts, ethnography, wooden effigies from Kafiristan 26421

Quetta

Archaeological Museum of Baluchistan, Tola Ram Rd, Quetta
Archaeological Museum - 1972
Regional excavations, weapons, ceramics 26422

Geological Museum, Quetta
Natural History Museum
Geology, palaeontology, mineralogy 26423

Rawalpindi

Botanical Museum, c/o Gordon College Rawalpindi, Rawalpindi
Natural History Museum / University Museum - 1930
Himalayan plants and fossil plants 26424

Pakistan Army Museum, Eftikhar Khan Rd, Rawalpindi
Military Museum - 1962
Old weapons, colors and standards, uniforms and medals, paintings 26425

Saidu Sharif

Archaeological Museum Saidu Sharif, Saidu Sharif. Head: Nazir Ahmad Khan
Archaeological Museum - 1959
Archeology, ethnology 26426

Swat

Archaeological Museum, Swat - T: (0536) 4100. Head: Dr. Mohammad Ashraf
Archaeological Museum - 1963
Excavations from Butkara I, Panr and Udegram including Buddhist objects and specimens of Gandhara sculptures (1st c B.C.-7th c A.D.), pre-Buddhist material, ethnology 26427

Taxila

Archaeological Museum, Taxila - T: (0596) 2495. Head: Gulzar Muhammad Khan
Archaeological Museum - 1928
Ghandara sculptures in stone, stucco and terra cotta, pottery, household vessels, toilet articles, gems, jewelry, coins, inscriptions, tools and implements, weapons - library 26428

Umarkot

Archaeological Museum Umarkot, Umarkot. Head: Mazhar Ali
Archaeological Museum - 1968
Birthplace of the Mughal Emperor Akbar, manuscripts, paintings, Imperial documents, coins and armory relating to the Mughal period and to Akbars reign 26429

Palestine

Al-Bireh

Palestine Folklore Museum, Samieha Khalil St, Al-Bireh - T: (02) 2401123, 2402876, Fax: 2401544, E-mail: usra@palnet.com, Internet: http://www.intertech-pal.com/inash/Arabic/accomplishment/folklore.html. Head: Abdul Aziz H. Abu Hadba
Folklore Museum
Coll of traditional costume, pottery, household and agricultural implements 26430

Popular Art Centre, Al-Ein St 3, Al-Bireh - T: (02) 2953891, Fax: 2952851, E-mail: pac@palnet.com, Internet: http://www.popularartcentre.org. Head: Khaled Elayyan
Folklore Museum / Fine Arts Museum 26431

Jerusalem

Musée de l'Ecole Biblique et Archéologique Française, 6 Nablus Rd, Jerusalem, mail addr: POB 19053, Jerusalem - T: (02) 6264468/69 ext 220, Fax: 6282567, E-mail: humbert@ebaf.edu. Head: Jean-Baptiste Humbert
Archaeological Museum - 1890
Finds from regular excavations in Palestine, archaeological colls from Near-Eastumismatics, mosaics - library 26432

Panama

David

Museo de la Historia de la Cultura José de Obaldía, Av 8a, Este Casa 57, David - T: 757839. Head: Prof. Mario Molina
Historical Museum 26433

Guarraré

Casa Manuel F. Zárate, Guarraré
Ethnology Museum / Folklore Museum
Popular art of Panamá, ethnography 26434

Natá

Parque Arqueológico El Caño, Natá
Archaeological Museum
Archaeological finds from various excavations 26435

Panamá City

Museo Afro Antillano, Calle 24 y Av Justo Arosemena, 662 Panamá City - T: 625348
Ethnology Museum / Historical Museum
Ethnography, local history 26436

Museo Antropológico Reina T. de Araúz, Plaza de Mayo 5, 662 Panamá City - T: 620415. Head: Romualda Lombardo
Ethnology Museum
Anthropology, ethnography 26437

Museo Belisario Porras, Av Belisario Porras, Las Tablas, 662 Panamá City - T: 946326
Special Museum
Life and work of the political leader Belisario Porras 26438

Museo de Arte Contemporáneo, Instituto Panameño de Arte, 662 Panamá City, mail addr: Apdo 4211, 5 Panamá City - T: 2628012, Fax: 2623376. Head: Alida de la Lima
Fine Arts Museum - 1962
Contemporary art, silkscreen and etching shop - library 26439

Museo de Arte Religioso Colonial, Catedral, Casco Viejo Calle 3a, 662 Panamá City
Religious Arts Museum
Religious art of the colonial period 26440

Museo de Ciencias Naturales, Av Cuba, Calles 29 y 30, 662 Panamá City - T: 250645, Fax: 2250645. Head: Nuria E. de Barillas
Natural History Museum
Paleontology, native and foreign reptiles, entomology, marine biology 26441

Museo de Herrera, Calle Manuel María Correa y Av Julio Arjona Chitré, 662 Panamá City
Historical Museum 26442

Museo de Historia de Panamá, Palacio Municipal, Plaza de la Catedral, 662 Panamá City - T: 286231
Historical Museum
History of Panamá 26443

Museo de Historia Natural, Calle 29 y 30 No 2939, 662 Panamá City, mail addr: Apdo 662, Zona 1, 662 Panamá City
Natural History Museum - 1975
Birds, mollusks and fossils 26444

Museo de la Historia y la Tradición, Calle San Antonio, Penonomeña Penonomé, 662 Panamá City - T: 978490
Historical Museum 26445

Museo de la Nacionalidad, Calle José Vallarino 3370, Los Santos, 662 Panamá City - T: 968192
Historical Museum 26446

Museo del Canal Interoceanico de Panamá (Interoceanic Canal Museum of Panamá), Entre Calle 5ta y 6ta, Panamá City - T: 2111994/95, Fax: 2111649/50, E-mail: pcmuseum@sinfo.net. Head: Dr. Angeles Ramos Baquero
Science&Tech Museum / Historical Museum - 1997
Documents, history and memorabilia of canal construction, 19th c paintings, historic boats, medals, history of Panama 26447

Museo Nacional de Panamá, Esquina Av Cuba y Calle 30, 662 Panamá City - T: 250645, Fax: 250646. Head: Nuria E. de Barillas
Natural History Museum - 1925
Geology, paleontology, vertebrates, invertebrates 26448

Parita

Museo de Arte Religioso, Iglesia de Santo Domingo, Calle La Parita, 662 Parita
Religious Arts Museum
Religious art 26449

Papua New Guinea

Boroko

Papua New Guinea National Museum and Art Gallery, POB 5560, Boroko - T: 3252405, 3252458, Fax: 3251779, E-mail: pngmuseum@global.net.pg. Head: Soroi Marepo Eoe
Ethnology Museum / Natural History Museum / Fine Arts Museum - 1954
Cultural anthropology, ethnology, natural history, contemporary art, modern history - library 26450

Goroka

J.K. MacCarthy Museum, POB, Goroka - T: (0675) 731502, Fax: 7322987. Head: Theodore Mawe
Ethnology Museum - 1966
Ethnography, anthropology, arts, handicrafts 26451

Yomba

Madang Museum, Culture and Tourism Centre, mail addr: POB 2025, Yomba - T: 823199. Head: Austin Edo
Local Museum - 1981 26452

Paraguay

Asunción

Centro Cultural Paraguayo-Americano, Av España 352, Asunción - T: (021) 24772, 24831
Public Gallery 26453

Centro de Artes Visuales, Museo del Barro, Emeterio Mirando y Calle Uno, Isla de Francia, Asunción - T: (021) 607996, Fax: 607996, E-mail: museobarro@quanta.com.py. Head: Carlos Colombino, Osvaldo Salerno, Ticio Escobar
Public Gallery / Fine Arts Museum 26454

Colección Carlos Alberto Pusineri Scala, Calle Hernandarias 1313, Asunción
Historical Museum - 1950
Colonial and military history, archaeology, numismatics, anthropology 26455

Museo Bernardino Caballero, Parque Caballero, Asunción - T: (021) 223549
Fine Arts Museum 26456

Museo de Cerámica y Bellas Artes Julián de la Herreria, Calle Estados Unidos 1120, Asunción. Head: Josefina Pla
Fine Arts Museum / Decorative Arts Museum - 1938
Ceramics, fine arts, folk art - library 26457

Museo de Ciencias Naturales, Colegio Internacional, Calle Rio de Janeiro, Asunción - T: (021) 200575
Natural History Museum
Botany, geology, zoology 26458

Museo de Historia Natural del Paraquay, Jardín Botánico, Calle Santisima Trinidad, Asunción
Natural History Museum - 1921
Natural history, archaeology 26459

Museo de la Casa de la Independencia, Calle 14 de Mayo y Presidente Franco, Asunción - T: (021) 493918. Head: Prof. Carlos Alberto Pusineri Scala
Historical Museum - 1965
Colonial history 26460

Museo del Barro, Grabadores del Cabichi, esq Emeterio Miranda y Malas López, Asunción - T: (021) 607996, Fax: 607996, E-mail: museobarro@quanta.com.py. Head: Carlos Colombino
Decorative Arts Museum 26461

Museo Etnográfico Andrés Barbero, España 217, Calle Mompox, Asunción - T: (021) 441696, Fax: 441696, E-mail: museoetn@pla.net.py, Internet: http://www.pla.net.py/home/museoetn. Head: Prof. Adelina Pusineri
Ethnology Museum - 1929
Ethnography, archaeology, mineralogy, Guarani urns and earthenware of Indian tribes - library 26462

Museo Histórico Militar, Av Mariscal López 140, Asunción. Head: Manuel Wenceslao Chaves
Military Museum
Military artifacts 26463

Museo Mons Juan Sinforiano Bogarin, Av Kubitschek y Cerro Corá, Asunción
Religious Arts Museum
Religious art 26464

Museo Nacional de Bellas Artes y Antigüedades, Calle Mariscal Estigarribia e Iturbe, Asunción - T: (021) 447716. Head: José Laterza Parodi
Fine Arts Museum
Paintings and sculptures 26465

Concepción

Centro Cultural Paraguayo-Argentino, Av Humaitá 212, Concepción - T: (031) 2371
Public Gallery 26466

Itaugua

Museo Iconográfico, Itaugua
Religious Arts Museum
Religious art, local history 26467

Yaguarón

Museo Doctor Francia, Yaguarón. Head: Dr. Julio César Chaves
Historical Museum - 1968
Furniture and domestic articles in an 18th c house 26468

Peru

Ancash

Museo Arqueológico Regional de Ancash, Av Pedro García Villón 725, Ancash - T: 721551. Head: Dr. Odón Rosales Huatuco
Archaeological Museum - 1936
Finds from Huarás, stone carvings, megalithic statues 26469

Arequipa

Museo Arqueologico José María Morante de la Universidad Nacional de San Augustín de Arequipa, Av Independencia s/n, Ciudad Universitaria, Arequipa - T: (054) 229719, Fax: 237808. Head: Prof. Miguel Baldarrago Umpire
Archaeological Museum / University Museum - 1933
Archaeology, hist, ceramics, furniture 26470

Museo de Cayma, Arequipa
Local Museum
Archaeology, history, ethnology 26471

Ayacucho

Museo Histórico Regional de Ayacucho, Jirón, Calle 28 de Julio Noi 106, Ayacucho. Head: César O. Prado
Historical Museum - 1954
History, archaeology, crafts, anthropology, religious art, colonial art, pre-Columbian ceramics, folk art, numismatics - library 26472

Callao

Museo Histórico Militar del Perú, Castillo del Real Felipe, Callao - T: 294793. Head: Oscar Diez Valdez
Military Museum - 1946
Military history of Perú since 1730 26473

Museo Histórico Naval del Perú, Av Jorge Chávez 123, Callao - T: 294793. Head: Alfonso Aguero Moras
Historical Museum - 1958
Naval history of Peru, uniforms, ship models maps - library 26474

Casma

Museo Regional de Casma Max Uhle, Carretera Panamericana Norte km 370, Casma - T: 185. Head: Lorenzo Samaniego Román
Local Museum 26475

Cusco

Museo de la Universidad, Calle Tigre 165, Cusco. Head: Dr. Luis A. Pardo
Archaeological Museum / University Museum
Archaeological finds from sites in the region 26476

Museo Histórico Regional - Casa Garcilaso Cusco, Calle Heladeros s/n, Cusco - T: (084) 223245, Fax: 223831, E-mail: casagarcilaso@peru.com. Head: Miguel Angel Cornejo Gutiérrez
Historical Museum - 1946
History, native art, Peruvian colonial art - Conservation, research 26477

Huancayo

Museo Arqueológico Frederico Galvez Durand de la Gran Unidad Santa Isabel, Calle Huancas 251, Huancayo
Archaeological Museum - 1952
Archaeological finds from Nazca and other Peruvian cultures, weaving, gold and bronze ornaments, fossils 26478

Huánuco

Museo y Biblioteca Leoncio Prado, Calle 2 de Mayo de Tarapacá, Huánuco. Head: Ricardo E. Flores
Ethnology Museum - 1945
Ethnology 26479

Ica

Museo Cabrera, Plaza de Armas, Calle Bolívar 174, Ica. Head: Dr. Javier Cabrera
Archaeological Museum - 1966
Coll of ancient engraved stones and pottery - library 26480

Museo Regional de Ica, Prolongación Ayabaca, Cuadra 8, Urbanización San Isidro, Ica - T: (034) 234383, Fax: 232881. Head: Susana Arce Torres
Local Museum - 1946
Archaeology, hist 26481

Lambayeque

Museo Arqueológico Regional Brüning, Av Huamachuco s/n, Lambayeque
Archaeological Museum - 1924
Gold and silver objects, textiles, ceramics, wood and stone, two blue and black granite mortars in Chavin style 26482

Lima

Centro de Arte Visuales, Nicolas de Ribera El Viejo 149, Lima 1 - T: (01) 4270935, Fax: 4260918, E-mail: bienaldelima@munlima.gob.pe, Internet: http://www.bienaldelima.com.pe. Head: Luís Lama
Public Gallery
Contemporary art 26483

Colección de Arte Popular de Elvira Luza, Calle Hernán Velarde 199, Lima - T: (01) 245122
Folklore Museum
Folk art 26484

Fundacion Museo Amano, Calle del Retiro 160, Miraflores, Lima 18 - T: (01) 412909, Fax: 421007
Decorative Arts Museum
Textiles, decorative art, weaving, ceramics, archeology 26485

Museo Aeronáutico del Perú, Av Arequipa 5200, Miraflores, Lima - T: (01) 455240
Science&Tech Museum 26486

Museo Arqueológico Rafael Larco Herrera, Av Bolívar 1515, Pueblo Libre, Lima - T: (01) 4611312, 4611835, Fax: 4615640, E-mail: museolarco@tsi.com.pe, Internet: http://museolarco.perucultural.org.pe. Head: Isabel Larco de Alvarez Calderon
Archaeological Museum - 1926
Gold and silver objects, copper, ceramics, textiles, erotic coll - library 26487

Museo de Arqueología Josefina Ramos de Cox, c/o Instituto Riva-Agüero, Pontificia Universidad Católica del Perú, Calle Jirón de la Unión 554, Lima 1
Archaeological Museum / University Museum 26488

Museo de Arqueología y Antropología de la Universidad Nacional Mayor de San Marcos, Parque Universitario, Av Nicolás de Piérola 1222, Lima 1 - T: (01) 4278155, Fax: 4280052, 4277699, E-mail: arqlperu@mail.geocities.com. Head: Dr. Ruth Shady Solís
Archaeological Museum / University Museum - 1919
Caral, Nasca, Chavin, Moche, Chimu, Lima and other colls 26489

Museo de Arte, Paseo Colón 125, Lima - T: (01) 4234732, Fax: 4236332, E-mail: artelima@tsi.com.pe, Internet: http://www.tsi.com.pe/artelima. Head: Pedro Pablo Alayza
Fine Arts Museum / Decorative Arts Museum - 1961
Pre-Columbian native arts, colonial furniture, paintings, sculptures, religious art, 19th-20th c paintings and furniture 26490

Museo de Arte Italiano, Paseo de la República 250, Lima 1 - T: (01) 4239932, Fax: 4239932. Head: Irene Velaochaga Rey
Fine Arts Museum - 1921
Italian paintings and sculpture - library 26491

Museo de Arte Religioso de la Basílica Catedral, Catedral de Lima, Plaza de Armas s/n, Lima - T: (01) 287289
Religious Arts Museum 26492

Museo de Arte Virreynal del Convento de San Francisco, Calle Jirón Ancash s/n, Lima - T: (01) 275254
Religious Arts Museum 26493

Museo de Arte y de Historia de la Universidad Nacional Mayor de San Marcos, Parque Universitario 1225, Lima 1 - T: (01) 274870. Head: Alfonso Castrillon
Fine Arts Museum / Historical Museum / University Museum 26494

Museo de Historia Natural, Av Arenales 1256, Lima, mail addr: c/o Universidad Mayor de San Marcos, Apdo 14-0434, Lima 14 - T: (01) 4710117, Fax: 2656819, E-mail: museohn@unmsm.edu.pe. Head: Dr. Niels Valencia
Natural History Museum - 1918
Botany, zoology, minerals, fosils - library 26495

Museo de los Combatientes del Morro de Arica, Calle Jirón Cailloma 125, Lima - T: (01) 270958
Military Museum 26496

Museo de Oro del Perú y Armas del Mundo, Av de Molina 1110, Monterrico, Lima - T: (01) 352917
Archaeological Museum / Military Museum - 1924
Pre-Columbian gold objects, Pre-Columbian, European and Oriental weapons 26497

Museo del Banco Central de Reserva, Esquina Lampa y Ucayali, Lima - T: (01) 4276250, Fax: 4275880, E-mail: museo@bcrp.gob.pe. Head: Cecilia Bákula
Special Museum
Archaeology, ethnology, history, numismatic arts 26498

Museo del Convento de los Descalzos, Alameda de los Descalzos s/n, Rimac, Lima - T: (01) 813434
Religious Arts Museum 26499

Museo Geológico de la Universidad Nacional de Ingeniería del Perú, Av Tupac Amaru, Lima. Head: Julio V. Davila
Natural History Museum / University Museum - 1891
Geology, mineralogy 26500

Museo Nacional de Antropología y Arqueología, Pueblo Libre, Plaza Principal, Lima - T: (01) 635070. Head: Hermilio Rosas la Noire
Ethnology Museum / Archaeological Museum - 1822
Pre-Inca and Inca finds 26501

Museo Nacional de Historia, Pueblo Libre, Plaza Bolívar, Lima - T: (01) 632009. Head: Dr. César Coloma Porcari
Historical Museum - 1836
Paintings, arms, pictures from Colonial to Republican times - library 26502

Museo Nacional de la Cultura Peruana, Av Alfonso Ugarte 650, Lima 1, mail addr: Apdo 3048, Lima 100 - T: (01) 4235892, Fax: 4235892, E-mail: mncp@terra.com.pe, Internet: http://www.museodelacultura.perucultural.org.pe. Head: Sara Acevedo Basurto
Ethnology Museum - 1946
Anthropology, folklore, ceramics, textiles, folk costumes, folk wood-carvings, paintings and drawings, music instruments, domestic and religious objects, Amazonican art - library, research dept., Peruan art institute 26503

Museo Numismático de la Casa Nacional de la Moneda, Av Pardo 731, Miraflores, Lima
Special Museum 26504

Museo Pachacamac, Antigua Panamericana sur km 31, Lurin, Lima - T: (01) 4300168, Fax: 4300168, Internet: http://www.pachacamac.perucultural.com.pe. Head: Giancarlo Marcode Flores
Archaeological Museum 26505

Museo Postal y Filatélico de Correos del Perú, Correos del Perú-Lima, Lima - T: (01) 287931. Head: Dora Ibérico Castro
Special Museum - 1931
Postal history, postage stamps, numismatics 26506

Museo Taurino de la Plaza de Acho, Calle Maranón 569, Rimac, Lima - T: (01) 278741
Historical Museum 26507

Museo Tribunal de la Santa Inquisición, Plaza Bolívar, Calle Jirón Junín 548, Lima
Historical Museum 26508

Pedro de Osma Museo, Av Pedro de Osma 421, Lima 4 - T: (01) 4670141, Fax: 4670063, 22, E-mail: museosma@chavin.rcp.net.pe. Head: Pedro Gjurinovic Canevaro
Fine Arts Museum - 1980 26509

Pinacoteca Municipal Ignacio Merino, Plaza Mayor de Lima, Conde de Superunda 169-505, Lima - T: (01) 4276080, Fax: 4272151, E-mail: mhl-patrim@munlima.gob.pe, Internet: http://www.munlima.gob.pe/educycultura. Head: Alex Faruk Salomón Zuebi
Fine Arts Museum
Paintings, wood-carvings, Wahol ceramics 26510

Nasca

Museo Didáctico Antonini, Av de la Cultura 600, Nasca - T: (034) 523444, Fax: 523100, E-mail: cahvachi@terra.com.pe, Internet: http://digilander.iol.it/mdantonini. Head: Giuseppe Orefici
Archaeological Museum - 1999 26511

Pisco

Museo de Sitio de Paracas Julio C. Tello, Pisco - T: (034) 232881, Fax: 232881. Head: Rubén García Soto
Archaeological Museum - 1964 26512

Trujillo

Museo Arqueológico de la Universidad de Trujillo, Calle Bolívar 446, Trujillo. Head: Dr. Jorge Zevallos Quinones
Archaeological Museum / University Museum - 1939
Ceramics, metals, wood, stone, textiles - library 26513

Philippines

Badoc

Juan Luna Shrine, Badoc. Head: Dr. Leonila B. Arzadou
Fine Arts Museum - 1976
Reproductions of Juan Lunas paintings, artifacts and relics related to the history of the town 26514

Baguio

Baguio-Mountain Province Museum Foundation, Ministry of Tourism Compond, Government Park Rd, Baguio 2600 - T: (442) 7902. Head: Leonora P. San Agustin
Ethnology Museum - 1977
Ethnography of the benguet, Ifugao, Apayao and Kalinga tribes, some artifacts of the Tingguian and Gaddang tribes 26515

Bibak Museum, Benguet, Ifugao Bontoc, Apayao and Kalinga Museum of Culture, c/o University of Baguio, Baguio 2600
Historical Museum 26516

Saint Louis University Museum, POB 71, Baguio 2600 - T: (074) 4423043. Head: Isikias T. Picpican
Ethnology Museum / Natural History Museum / University Museum
Ethnology, natural history 26517

Batan

Kalantiaw Shrine, Aklan, Batan, mail addr: POB 3398, Manila
Historical Museum - 1957
Memorial to Datu Benhadara Kalantiaw, first Filipino lawgiver 26518

Bolinao

Bolinao Museum, Bolinao 2406 - T: (075) 5542065. Head: Gina C. de Vera
Local Museum - 1976
Local history, archaeology 26519

Bontoc

Bontoc Museum, Bontoc. Head: Nieves Valdés
Ethnology Museum / Open Air Museum - 1980
Ethnography, tribal art, specimens of native houses, farming and fishing implements, musical instruments, fossils and rocks coll, household objects, war implements, native dresses, basketry, ornaments, antique jazz and ceramic pieces 26520

Butuan

Butuan Regional Museum, Butuan 8600. Head: Bernardinito C. Galpo
Local Museum - 1978
Prehist finds, miniatures, manuscripts, musical instruments, fossils, minerals, industrial processes 26521

Cagayan de Oro

Xavier University Museum (Museo de Oro), c/o Xavier University, Corrales Av, Cagayan de Oro 9000 - T: (08822) 723818/116 local 2403, Fax: 726355
Ethnology Museum / Archaeological Museum / Historical Museum / Folklore Museum / Religious Arts Museum / University Museum
Altar paraphenalia in silver, gold and bronze, religious figurines, painting of religious scenes and local natural events - archives, library 26522

Calamba

Rizal Shrine, Rizal St, Calamba 4027, mail addr: POB 3398, Manila - T: (049) 5452010. Head: Luisa S. Valeza
Historical Museum - 1948
Originals and replicas of relics and memorabilia related to Dr. José Rizal, national hero of the Philippines - library 26523

Cebu

CAP Art Center and Don Sergio Osmeña Memorabilia, 60 Osmeña Blvd, Cebu 6000 - T: (032) 2536519, Fax: 2538102. Head: Mary Faelnar Abad
Special Museum / Fine Arts Museum - 1985
Belongings of Don Sergio Osmeña (e.g. paintings, books, Cadillac car, suits, photographies, posters, Don Sergio Osmeña stamps, bust sculpture), McArthurs room and elevator (OTIS) 26524

Saint Theresa's College Folklife Museum, Ramon Aboitiz St, Cebu 6000 - T: (032) 2536337, Fax: 2536351. Head: Maria Delia Coronel
Folklore Museum
Ethnography, folklore, literature 26525

University Museum, c/o University of San Carlos, P. del Rosario St, Cebu 6000 - T: (032) 2531000, Fax: 54341, 2537989, E-mail: uscmusm@pinya.usc.edu.ph. Head: Marlene Soccoro R. Samson
Local Museum / University Museum - 1967
Magsuhot coll of terracotta burial and funerary vessels, religious art, ethnographic material - library 26526

Dapitan

Rizal Shrine Talisay, Dapitan
Historical Museum - 1945
Replicas of relics and memorabilia related to Dr. José Rizal, national hero of the Philippines 26527

Dumaguete

Anthropology Museum, c/o Silliman University, Dumaguete 6501 - T: 3445. Head: Dr. Angel C. Alcala, Dr. Hubert Reynolds
Ethnology Museum / University Museum - 1970
Metal Age pottery, metal implements, late Neolithic and early Iron Age carved limestone - library 26528

Iloilo City

Iloilo Museum, Bonifacio Dr, Iloilo City 5901 - T: (033) 72986. Head: Carlos L. Jalandoni
Local Museum - 1972
Artifacts from Pasnay Island, elephant fossils from Iloilo, gold-leaf masks, porcelain, stoneware, colonial sculpture 26529

Intramuros

Phillipines Sports Hall of Fame, Palacio del Gubernador, Intramuros, Manila
Special Museum 26530

Rizal Shrine, Fort Santiago, Intramuros, mail addr: POB 3398, Manila 2801
Historical Museum - 1951
Relics and memorabilia related to Dr José Rizal, national hero of the Philippines 26531

San Agustin Museum Intramuros, General Luna St, Intramuros 1002, mail addr: POB 3366, Manila 1002 - T: (02) 5274060/61, 5266794, Fax: 5274060. Head: Dr. Pedro G. Galende
Religious Arts Museum - 1976
Religious artifacts, history of Christianity 26532

Jolo

Sulu Ethnological Museum, c/o Notre Dame Jolo College, Jolo 7901
Ethnology Museum / University Museum
Anthropology, ethnography 26533

Kabacan

Cultural Museum, State University Museum, c/o Mindanao Institute of Technology, Kabacan 9600. Head: Daniel L. Lacerna
Ethnology Museum / University Museum 26534

Kawit

Aguinaldo Shrine, General Tirona St, Kawit 4104, mail addr: POB 3398, Manila - T: (095) 4352611. Head: Rosalinda M. Aguinaldo
Historical Museum - 1964
Relics and memorabilia related to the Philippine revolution 26535

Magsingal

Ilocaniana Cultural Museum, 0405 Magsingal
Local Museum 26536

Magsingal Regional Museum, Magsingal 0405
Local Museum 26537

Makati

Ayala Museum, Makati Av, Makati, mail addr: POB 259, Makati - T: (0632) 8121191, Fax: 8173209. Head: Sonia P. Ner
Historical Museum - 1974
Social and cultural hist of the Philippines, dioramas, boat room, Fernando Amorsola (artist) gallery and Carlos P. Romulo (diplomat) memorabilia 26538

Kasiyahan (General Carlos P. Romulos Private Museum and Library), Makati - T: (02) 886795
Special Museum 26539

Philippine Army Museum and Library, Mac Arthur Av corner Memorial Rd, Fort Andres Bonifacio, Makati
Military Museum 26540

Malacañang

Philippine Presidential Museum, Malacañang Palace, Malacañang 1005 - T: (02) 5212301. Head: Eva Toledo
Historical Museum
President Ferdinand E. Marcos coll, local history, natural history, folklore 26541

Malate

Carfel Seashell Museum, Carfel, 1786 A. Mabini St, Malate
Natural History Museum - 1973
Shells and fossils 26542

Malolos

Barasoain Historical Landmark, Malolos 2601
Historical Museum - 1973
Religious relics, exhibit on important events in Philippine history 26543

Hiyas Ng Bulakau Museum (Bulakan Provincial Museum), Malolos 3000 - T: 7974477. Head: Amelia M. Aquino
Local Museum - 1971
Archaeology, history, ethnography 26544

Mandaluyong

Barangay Museum, Namayan, Mandaluyong 3119
Ethnology Museum
Ethnography of the Philippines 26545

Vargas Museum and Art Gallery, c/o Jorge V. Vargas Filipiniana Foundation, 211 Shaw Bd, Mandaluyong 3119 - T: (02) 792912
Fine Arts Museum
Works by Philippine artists 26546

Manila

Ateneo Art Gallery, c/o Ateneo de Manila University, Manila
Fine Arts Museum / University Museum 26547

Bayanihan Folks Arts Center, Philippine Womens University Museum, Taft Av, Manila 2801 - T: (02) 583187. Head: Dr. Letitia P. de Guzman
Folklore Museum / University Museum
Artifacts, wares, instruments and costumes from Mindanao and Igorot tribes, Maria Clara costumes and prints 26548

Carlos P. Garcia Memorabilia, c/o National Library Filipiniana Division, T.M. Kalaw St, Manila 2801
Historical Museum
Personal memorabilia of President Carlos P. Garcia 26549

Casa Manila, Intramuros Administration Museum, Plaza San Luis Complex, General Luna St corner Real St, Intramuros, Manila 1002 - T: (02) 487412, Fax: 461188. Head: Rene Luis S. Mata
Historical Museum - 1979
Colonial furniture, house details, religious art, Spanish, American and Japanese weapons, military uniforms (Spanish), textiles, household items, colonial costumes, jewelry, photographs etc 26550

Centro Escolar University Museum and Archives, Mendiola St, Manila 2804 - T: (02) 497631. Head: Marina Dayrit
Historical Museum / University Museum
Personal belongings of university members including togas, albums, certificates of awards and publications 26551

Malacañang Palace Presidential Museum, J.P. Laurel St, San Miguel, Manila - T: (02) 5212301. Head: Edna S. Gaffud
Historical Museum - 1986
Memorabilia of all former Philippine presidents - library 26552

Manila Police Department Museum, Felipe II St, Binondo, Manila 2801, mail addr: c/o National Commission for Culture and Arts, 633 Gen. Luna St, Intramuros, Manila 1600 - T: (02) 2444984, E-mail: esqbase@skyinet.net. Head: Joven Mandanas Esquito
Military Museum - 1970
Relicts since 1901 26553

Metropolitan Museum of Manila, Bangko Sentral ng Pilipinas Complex, Roxas Blvd, Manila 2801 - T: (02) 5361566, 5237855, Fax: 5361566, E-mail: art4all@info.com.ph. Head: Corazon S. Alvina
Fine Arts Museum - 1976
Paintings, sculptures, Philippinian art hist (late 20th c) 26554

Munting Museo Ng Namayan, Claro Castaneda, Saint Mandaluyong, Manila 3119 - T: (02) 700774. Head: Norberto S. Arcangel
Special Museum 26555

Museo ng Bangko Sentral ng Pilipinas (Museum of the Central Bank of the Philippines), A. Mabini St, Malate, Manila 1004 - T: (02) 5249534, Fax: 5236210, 5232388, E-mail: -ssdelacruzabsp.gov.ph. Head: Fe M. de la Cruz
Special Museum - 1974
Numismatics coll on the evolution of Philippine money, primitive money, foreign currencies, medals, commemorative coins 26556

Museo ng Kalinangang Pilipino (Museum of Philippine Humanities), Roxas Blvd, Manila, mail addr: POB 310, Manila 1099 - T: (02) 8325094, Fax: 8330267, 5515960, E-mail: ccp@ccpap.admu.edu.ph. Head: Sid Gomez Hildawa
Ethnology Museum - 1988
Ethnic Philippine jewelries, textiles, weaponry, pottery, household utensils, Asian musical instruments and other assorted artifacts 26557

Museo ng Maynila (Museum of the City of Manila), South Rd, nr Roxas Blvd, Ermita, Manila - T: (02) 5367388, Fax: 5367388. Head: Monina Katherina Borja-Santiago
Local Museum
Local history 26558

Museum of Philippine Art, Rizal Park SW, Former Elks Club Bldg, Manila 2801 - T: (02) 476556
Fine Arts Museum 26559

Museum of Philippine Costumes, Metropolitan Theatre, Arroceros St, Manila - T: (02) 484721 local 243. Head: Conchita Sunico
Folklore Museum
Tribal costumes, Philippine ambroidery, beadwork and appliqué 26560

National Historical Institute, T.M. Kalaw St, Ermita, Manila 2801 - T: (02) 509952, 590646, 581159. Head: Dr. Serafin D. Quiason
Historical Museum 26561

National Museum of the Philippines, P. Burgos St, Rizal Park, Manila, mail addr: POB 2659, Manila 1000 - T: (02) 5271215, Fax: 5270306, E-mail: nmuseum@i-next.net, Internet: http://members.tripod.com/philmuseum. Head: Gabriel S. Casal
Fine Arts Museum / Ethnology Museum / Archaeological Museum / Natural History Museum - 1901
Fine arts, anthropology, ethnographical, archaeological, historical, zoological, botanical, geological exhibits - planetarium 26562

Philippine National Railway Museum, Tutuban Railway Terminal, Divisoria, Manila 2807 - T: (02) 210011 local 200. Head: Sally Bundoc
Science&Tech Museum
History of the Philippine railway system 26563

Philippine Science Centrum, Up-Manila Compound, Pedro Gil St, Ermita, Manila, mail addr: POB 1832, Manila - T: (02) 5258752, Fax: 5258418, E-mail: pfst@philonline.com.ph, Internet: http://www.philoline.com/~pfst/pfstweb.htm. Head: Leticia Moran-Zerda
Natural History Museum - 1984
Interactive science exhibitions - galleries, science educational programs 26564

Quezonia Museum, National Library Bldg, T. Kalaw St, Manila 2801
Local Museum 26565

Ramón Magsaysay Memorabilia, RM Center, Roxas Blvd, Manila 1004 - T: (02) 5213166/85, Fax: 5218105, E-mail: rmaf@rmaf.org.ph, Internet: http://www.rmaf.org.ph. Head: Carmencita T. Abella
Historical Museum
President Ramon Magsaysay 1954-1957 26566

Resurreccion Memorial Museum, Ilocos Museum of Music and Fine Arts, 21 Calle Real, Luna La Union, Manila, mail addr: POB 3016, Manila. Head: Teodoro F. Resurreccion
Fine Arts Museum
Graphics, paintings 26567

Santa Ana Archaeological Site and Liturgical Arts Museum, Pl Felipe Calderon, Manila 2802
Archaeological Museum / Religious Arts Museum
Excavated pre-Spanish 13th c graveyard, polychrome religious images from churches of the 17th and 18th c 26568

University of Santo Tomas Museum of Arts and Sciences, c/o University of Santo Tomas, Main Bldg, Calle España, Manila 1008 - T: (02) 781815, 7409718, 7313101 local 337, Fax: 7409718, E-mail: isidro.a@ustcc.ust.edu.ph. Head: Isidro Abaño
Fine Arts Museum / Natural History Museum / University Museum - 1872
Anthropology, natural sciences, specimens, mineralogy, petrology, ethnological material, coins, medals, religious paintings and sculptures, portraits, costumes, furniture, architectural fragments (18th-19th c) 26569

Marawi

Aga Khan Museum, c/o Mindanao State University, Marawi 9700 - T: 60. Head: Dr. Mamitua Saber
Ethnology Museum - 1962
Artifacts relating to socio-cultural life of Philippine Muslims 26570

Muñoz

Central Luzon State University Museum, c/o Central Luzon State University, Muñoz 3120 - T: 599557. Head: Dr. Teresita R. Maquiso
University Museum
Historical coll 26571

Naga

University of Nueva Caceres Museum, Jaime Hernandez Av, Naga 4400 - T: (054) 737881, Fax: 8111015, E-mail: dhs@unc.edu.ph. Head: Clodualdo N. Ceron
Local Museum / Historical Museum / University Museum - 1952

Don Jaime Hernandez coll on the Philippine Commonwealth and the Republic, Dolores Sison's chain and doll coll, Filipiniana colls - Bicol archival library 26572

Pandacan

Mabini Shrine, Malacañang Compound, Pandacan 2802, mail addr: POB 3398, Manila
Historical Museum - 1968
Relics and memorabilia related to Apolinario Mabini (brains of the Philippine revolution) 26573

Pasay

Aurelio Sevilla Alvero Library and Museum, 111 P. Manahan St, Pasay 3129. Head: Lucila A. Salazar
Local Museum
Art, local history, classical antiquities, ethnology, natural history, folklore - library 26574

Cultural Center of the Philippines, Visual Arts Division, Roxas Blvd, Pasay 1307, mail addr: POB 310, Manila 1000 - T: (02) 8323702, Fax: 8323702, E-mail: ccp@ccp.admu.edu.ph, Internet: http://www.admu.edu.ph/ccp. Head: Sid Gómez Hildawa
Association with Coll
Sculpture, modern painting, wood and pottery 26575

Kailokuan Historical Ilocano Museum, Vigan House, Nayong Pilipino, Pasay 3129
Local Museum
Art, culture and industry of the Ilocano people, antiquities 26576

Panamin Museum (Museum of Philippine Traditional Cultures), Muslim Region, Nayong Pilipino, Pasay 3129 - T: (02) 8323759
Folklore Museum / Decorative Arts Museum 26577

Philippine Air Force Museum, Col Jesus Villamor Air Base, Pasay 1309 - T: (02) 8323498, Internet: http://www.philairforce.homepage.com/museum.html. Head: Malikil N. Abdulgapul
Military Museum - 1974
15 different kinds of real aircraft static display, Aircraft Picture Frame, dioramas, weapons, ammunitions, firearms of WW II, uniforms - exhibit department, aircraft park 26578

Philippine Lepidoptera, Bohol House, Nayong Pilipino, Pasay 3129
Natural History Museum
Butterflies 26579

Philippine Marine and Terrestrial Fauna, Badjao House, Nayong Pilipino, Pasay 3129
Natural History Museum 26580

Philippine Marine Life and Philippine Shells, Samal House, Nayong Pilipino, Pasay 3129
Natural History Museum 26581

Pasig

Lopez Memorial Museum, Benpres Bldg, Exchange Rd, Pasig 1600 - T: (02) 6359545, Fax: 6312417, E-mail: pezseum@skyinet.net. Head: Mariles E. Matias
Special Museum / Fine Arts Museum
Paintings by Filipino painters, letter and manuscripts of José Rizal - library 26582

Piddig

Piddig Museum, Piddig 0315
Local Museum 26583

Puerto Princesa

Palawan Teachers College Museum, Tiniguiban Heights, Puerto Princesa
Ethnology Museum / University Museum - 1976
Ethnography 26584

Quezon City

Asian Center Museum, c/o University of the Philippines, Diliman, Quezon City 1101 - T: (02) 976601, Fax: 961821. Head: Prof. Aurora Roxas Lim
Ethnology Museum / University Museum - 1974
Philippine ethnographic material 26585

Ateneo Art Gallery, Ateneo de Manila University, Katipunan Av, Loyola Heights, Quezon City 1108, mail addr: POB 154, Quezon City 1108 - T: (02) 4266001 ext 4160, 4266488, Fax: 4266088, E-mail: yoelya@admin.edu.ph. Head: Prof. Emmanuel Torres
Fine Arts Museum / University Museum - 1960
Post World War II Philippine painting 26586

Quezon Memorial Shrine, Diliman, Quezon City, mail addr: POB 3398, Manila
Historical Museum - 1945
Relics and memorabilia of the late president Manuel L. Quezon, a Filipino patriot, revolutionist, statesman and first president of the Commonwealth of the Philippines 26587

University Museum of Anthropology, University of the Philippines Arts and Sciences Bldg, Diliman, Quezon City 3004. Head: Natividad Noriega
Ethnology Museum / University Museum
Archeology, ethnology 26588

Sampaloc

Museums of Filipinana and Rizaliana, c/o Arallano University, Sampaloc
Historical Museum / Ethnology Museum
History, ethnography 26589

San Miguel

Marcos Foundation Museum, Ang Maharlika, 838 General Solano St, San Miguel 2804. Head: Daniel W. Tantoco
Historical Museum
Historical coll 26590

San Pablo

Escudero Private Museum, Villa Escudero, San Pablo 3723, mail addr: c/o Aera Memorial Foundation Inc., POB 4, San Pablo 4000. Head: Conrado A. Escudero
Fine Arts Museum / Historical Museum / Archaeological Museum
Art, local history, archeology, religious art - library 26591

Santo Tomás

Malvar Historical Landmark, Santo Tomás
Military Museum - 1974
Photographic exhibit on the Filipino-American War (1899-1901) 26592

Sarrat

Sarrat Museum, Sarrat
Local Museum
Local ethnography and history 26593

Taal

Apacible Historical Landmark, Marcela M. Agoncillo St, Taal, mail addr: POB 3398, Manila
Historical Museum - 1976
Relics and memorabilia related to the late Galicano and Leon Apacible (local heroes) 26594

Marcela M. Agoncillo Historical Landmark, Taal
Historical Museum - 1980
Relics and memorabilia related to Doña Marcela M. Agoncillo, who created the first Filipino flag 26595

Tacloban

Divine Word University Museum, Av Vateranos, Tacloban 7101 - T: (053) 3213758. Head: Raul D. Agner
Historical Museum / University Museum
Inscriptions, statues of saints, weapons 26596

Leyte-Samar Museum, Romualdez Hall, Tacloban 7101 - T: (053) 3212307
University Museum 26597

Tagbilaran

Bohol Museum, 10 Rocha St, Tagbilaran 6300 - T: 2642. Head: Salome D. Ramos
Local Museum - 1981
Crafts, tribal art, ethnography 26598

Tanauan Batangas

José P. Laurel Memorial Museum, Tanauan Batangas
Special Museum
Documents and personal possessions of J.P. Laurel (1890-1960) - library 26599

Tawi-Tawi

Tawi-Tawi Ethnological Museum, c/o WMSU-Sulu College of Technology and Oceanography, San Jose Rd, Tawi-Tawi 7602. Head: Orlando B. Cuartocruz
Ethnology Museum
Ethnography, anthropology 26600

Tawi-Tawi Technological Museum, c/o WMSU-Sulu College of Technology and Oceanography, Bongao, Tawi-Tawi 7602
Science&Tech Museum 26601

Tuguegarao

Cagayan Provincial Museum, Tuguegarao 1101 - T: (08822) 4461800. Head: Lusia Battung
Archaeological Museum
Palaeolithic site, excavations 26602

Vigan

Ayala Museum, Crisologo House, Vigan 0405 - T: 2461
Historical Museum
Materials relating to important Ilocanos and Ilocano writers, artefacts of Crisologo family 26603

Laoag Museum, Vigan 0405
Local Museum
Local history, ethnography 26604

University of Northern Philippines Museum, Vigan 0405
Ethnology Museum / Archaeological Museum / University Museum
Ethnography, archaeology 26605

Vigan Museum, Padre Burgos Residence, Vigan 0405. Head: Perlita A. Foz
Historical Museum / Fine Arts Museum
Memorabilia of the national hero Fr. José Burgos, archaeology 26606

Vinzons

Vinzons Historical Landmark, Vinzons Av, Vinzons. Head: Norma A. Mago
Special Museum - 1974
Relics and memorabilia of the late Wenceslao Q. Vinzons (World War II hero) 26607

Zamboanga

National Museum, Region IX Branch, Fort Pilar, Zamboanga - T: (062) 9916029. Head: Eufemia B. Catolin
Ethnology Museum - 1986
Ethnological coll, underwater archeology, natural sciences 26608

Poland

Alwernia

Muzeum Pożarnictwa, ul K. Korycińskiego 1, 32-066 Alwernia - T: (012) 2831208. Head: Czesław Nawrocki
Historical Museum - 1953
Fire engines, fire protection equipment 26609

Antonin

Salon Muzyczny im. Fryderyka Chopina, Centrum Kultury i Sztuki w Kaliszu (Memorial Room), 63-422 Antonin - T: (062) 7348169, Fax: 7361651. Head: Jan Siwek
Historic Site
Room in Pałac Radziwiłłów, where the composer Chopin (1810-1849) lived in 1829, sheet music, furniture 26610

Augustów

Muzeum Ziemi Augustowskiej, ul Hoża 7, 16-300 Augustów - T: (087) 6432754. Head: Eliza Ramut
Local Museum - 1968
Ethnography (fishing, farming, stockbreeding, apiculture, hunting, smithing, weaving, pottery, housekeeping), documents (history of Augustów region and town) 26611

Baranów Sandomierski

Muzeum Zaglebia Siarkowego → Muzeum Zamek

Muzeum Zamek, Zamek w Baranowie Sandomierskim (Museum of the Castle Basin), ul Zamkowa 20, 39-450 Baranów Sandomierski - T: (015) 8118040, 8118039, Fax: 8118039, 8118063, E-mail: zamek.baranow@motronik.com.pl, Internet: http://www.baranow.motronik.com.pl. Head: Adam Zwolak
Local Museum - 1966
Local and regional hist, geology, archaeology, 16th-17th c mannerism castle 26612

Barczewo

Muzeum Feliksa Nowowiejskiego (The Feliks Nowowiejski Museum), ul Mickiewicza 13, 11-010 Barczewo - T: (089) 148549. Head: Elżbieta Gliszczyńska
Music Museum - 1961
Memorabilia on the composer Feliks Nowowiejski (1877-1946) in his birthplace, local history 26613

Bardo

Muzeum Sztuki Sakralnej, ul Wolności 5, 57-256 Bardo - T: (074) 152043
Fine Arts Museum 26614

Barlinek

Muzeum Regionalne, ul Niepodległości 17, 74-320 Barlinek - T: (095) 461889. Head: Ewa Rogozińska
Local Museum 26615

Bartne

Zabytkowa Cerkiew w Bartnem, Muzeum Budownictwa Ludowego w Szymbarku (Orthodox Church in Bartne), Sękowa, 38-307 Bartne. Head: Józef Madzik
Religious Arts Museum - 1975
19th c wooden Orthodox church, stonecutting 26616

Będzin

Muzeum Zagłębia, ul Świerczewskiego 15, 42-500 Będzin - T: (032) 2677707, Fax: 2677707, E-mail: muzeumzaglebia@arg.pl, Internet: http://www.muzeum-zaglebia.arg.pl. Head: Anna Smogór
Local Museum 26617

Bełchatów

Muzeum Regionalne, ul 1 Maja 45, 97-400 Bełchatów - T: (044) 324496. Head: Bogusław Dziedzic
Local Museum 26618

Bęsia

Muzeum Młynarstwa Powietrznego, Wiatrak Kolno Mazurskie, 11-308 Bęsia - T: (089) 5277050. Head: Dr. Irena Modrzejewska
Historical Museum 26619

Biała Podlaska

Galeria Okręgowe, ul Sawickiej 21, 21-500 Biała Podlaska - T: (057) 435627. Head: Anna Kubiak
Religious Arts Museum 26620

Muzeum Okręgowe, ul Warszawska 12, 21-500 Biała Podlaska - T: (057) 434128, 435556, Fax: 434128. Head: Celestyn Wrębiak
Local Museum - 1966
Horse theme in modern paintings, icones, Polish modern medals, tapestry, costumes sculptures - Gestapo Prison 26621

Białowieża

Muzeum Przyrodniczo-Leśne, Białowieza National Park (Museum of Natural History), Park Pałacowy, 17-230 Białowieża - T: (085) 6812275, Fax: 6812323, E-mail: bpn@lynx.bpn.bialowieza.pl. Head: Bogdan Jaroszewicz
Natural History Museum - 1920
Geography, botany, zoology, ornithology, entomology, ethnology - library 26622

Białystok

Muzeum Historyczne, Muzeum Okręgowego w Białymstoku (Historical Museum), ul Warszawska 37, 15-062 Białystok - T: (085) 7416591. Head: Aleksander Antoniuk
Historical Museum 26623

Muzeum Ruchu Rewolucyjnego, Oddział Muzeum Okręgowego w Białymstoku, ul Warszawska 37, 15-062 Białystok - T: (085) 416591
Local Museum 26624

Muzeum Wojska (Military Museum), ul Kilińskiego 7, 15-089 Białystok - T: (085) 7415448, Fax: 7415448, E-mail: muzeum_wojska@bialystok.home.pl. Head: Dr. Krzystof Filipow
Military Museum 26625

Państwowe Muzeum w Białymstoku (District Museum), Rynek Kościuszki 10, 15-426 Białystok - T: (085) 7421473. Head: Andrzej Lechowski
Local Museum - 1949
Archaeology, 18th-20th c historical documents, Polish paintings, ethnography - Departement in Tykocin 26626

Biecz

Muzeum Regionalne (Regional Museum), ul Węgierska 2, 38-250 Biecz. Head: Marta Bartuś
Local Museum - 1953
Archeology, history, art, old prints, coins, 500 year-old potter's kiln, guild documents, 15th c Gothic Madonna, life and work of the historian Marcin Kromer (1512-1589), late Renaissance house 26627

Bielsk Podlaski

Muzeum Martyrologii (Museum of Martyrdom), ul Hołowieska 18, 17-100 Bielsk Podlaski - T: (085) 302241. Head: Mikołaj Budka
Historical Museum
Struggle and martyrdom of the inhabitants of Bielsk county during the Nazi occupation 26628

Muzeum w Bielsku Podlaskim, Muzeum Podlaskie w Białmystoku, ul Mickiewicza 45, 17-100 Bielsk Podlaski - T: (085) 7302244. Head: Alina Dębowska
Local Museum 26629

Prywatne Muzeum Etnograficzno-Historyczne, ul Wiejska 48, 17-100 Bielsk Podlaski - T: (085) 306553. Head: Doroteusz Fionik
Folklore Museum 26630

Bielsko-Biała

Muzeum Okręgowe, Zamek, ul Wzgórze 16, 43-300 Bielsko-Biała - T: (033) 125353, Fax: 125353. Head: Dr. Jerzy Polak
Local Museum - 1897
Applied weaving art, ethnology, arts, paintings and sketches by Julian Fałat (1853-1929), relics of the ancient towns Bielsko and Biała, tin coll, old textile machines 26631

Muzeum Techniki Włókienniczej, Muzeum Okręgowego w Bielsku-Białej, ul Sukiennicza 7, 43-300 Bielsko-Biała - T: (033) 122367. Head: Juliusz Kokot
Science&Tech Museum 26632

Bieżuń

Muzeum Regionalne, ul Zamkowa 2, 09-320 Bieżuń
Folklore Museum 26633

Biłgoraj

Muzeum Regionalne (Regional Museum), 23-400 Biłgoraj
Local Museum - 1967
Local history, costumes, sieve-making industry, resistance movement during World War II 26634

Muzeum Rzemiosł Ludowych w Biłgoraju, Plac Wolności 16, 23-400 Biłgoraj - T: (084) 3841
Local Museum 26635

Skansenowska Zagroda Sitarska, ul Krasickiego 32, 23-400 Biłgoraj - T: (084) 862733
Open Air Museum 26636

Bobowa

Muzeum Parafialne, Filia Muzeum Diecezjalnego w Tarnowie, 38-350 Bobowa - T: (018) 511 81 162. Head: Stanisław Chrzan
Religious Arts Museum 26637

Bochnia

Muzeum w Bochni im. Prof. Stanisława Fischera, Rynek 20, 32-700 Bochnia - T: (014) 6122426, 6123285, E-mail: muzeum@bochnia.pl, Internet: http://www.muzeum.bochnia.pl. Head: Jan Flasza
Local Museum 26638

Bodzentyn

Zabytkowa Zagroda Świętokrzyska, ul 1-go Maja 12, 26-010 Bodzentyn
Folklore Museum 26639

Bogatynia

Muzeum Górnicze (Mining Museum), 59-916 Bogatynia - T: (075) 7735300, Fax: 7733000, E-mail: biuletyn.turowa@kwbturow.com.pl. Head: Stanisław Żuk
Natural History Museum / Science&Tech Museum - 1971
Fossils, mining technology, paleontology, hist of the mine 26640

Bogdaniec

Muzeum Budownictwa i Techniki Wiejskiej, Muzeum w Gorzowie Wielkopolskim, ul Leśna 22, 66-450 Bogdaniec
Science&Tech Museum 26641

Bolesława

Muzeum Bolesława Prusa, Pałac Małachowskich, 24-140 Bolesława - T: 272
Special Museum 26642

Muzeum Stefana Żeromskiego, ul Żeromskiego 8, 24-140 Bolesława - T: 114780
Special Museum 26643

Bolesławiec

Muzeum Ceramiki (Museum of Ceramics), ul Mickiewicza 13, 59-700 Bolesławiec - T: (075) 7323857, Fax: 7323857, E-mail: poczta@muzeum-ceramiki.art.pl, Internet: http://www.muzeum-ceramiki.art.pl. Head: Teresa Wolanin
Decorative Arts Museum - 1909
Local ceramics, local and European stoneware - library 26644

Szkolne Muzeum Morskie (School Marine Museum), ul Brody 12, 59-700 Bolesławiec - T: (075) 7322458. Head: Wanda Kulczycka
Local Museum - 1965
Ship models, marine biology, handicraft, musical instruments, navigation 26645

Bolków

Muzeum-Zamek w Bolkowie, Muzeum Okręgowego w Jeleniej Górze (Castle Museum in Bolków), ul Księcia Bolka, 58-575 Bolków - T: (075) 7413297. Head: Adam Łaciuk
Local Museum - 1900
Local hist, hunting in Lower Silesia, 14th c castle 26646

Brodnica

Muzeum Regionalne, ul Zamkowa 1, 87-300 Brodnica - T: (0511) 83698. Head: Waldemar Gęsicki
Local Museum 26647

Brzeg

Muzeum Piastów Śląskich (Museum of the Silesian Piasts), pl Zamkowy 1, 49-300 Brzeg - T: (077) 4163257, Fax: 4164210, Internet: http://www.zamekbrzeg.pl. Head: Paweł Kozerski
Historical Museum - 1945
History of the Piast dynasty in the Silesian area, historical relics, numismatics, manuscripts, old prints, parchment documents, sarcophaguses, medieval, renaissance, baroque paintings, sculpture, crafts 26648

Brzeziny

Muzeum Regionalne, ul Piłsudskiego 49, 95-060 Brzeziny - T: (046) 8743382. Head: Elżbieta Putyńska
Local Museum - 1972
Tailoring 26649

Brzozów

Muzeum Regionalne im. Adama Fastnachta, Rynek 10, 36-200 Brzozów - T: (013) 4341869, 856, Fax: 4341856, E-mail: wiadbrzoz@pro.onet.pl, Internet: http://www.brzozow.com.pl. Head: Halina Kościńska
Local Museum 26650

Bydgoszcz

Muzeum Okręgowe im. Leona Wyczółkowskiego (Leon Wyczółkowski Regional Museum), ul Gdańska 4, 85-006 Bydgoszcz - T: (052) 227576, Fax: 227576. Head: Małgorzata Winter
Local Museum - 1923
Archaeology, hist, numismatics, coll of the painter Leon Wyczółkowski (1852-1936), incl paintings, drawings, prints, works by the painter Maksymilian Antoni Piotrowski (1813-1875), works by the painter Walter Leistikow (1865-1908), 19th-20th c Polish paintings 26651

Muzeum Oświaty w Bydgoszczy (Bydgoszcz Country Educational Museum), ul Bałtycka 59, 85-707 Bydgoszcz - T: (052) 3426590, Fax: 3411984. Head: Alicja Gorzycka
Historical Museum - 1985
Ancient school equipment (desks, blackboards, pictures), ancient school certificates, handbooks, documents about teachers, professional life, (from beginning of 20th c to present) - library 26652

Muzeum Tradycji Pomorskiego Okręgu Wojskowego, ul Czerkaska 1, 85-915 Bydgoszcz - T: (052) 782026. Head: Wojciech Zawadzki
Local Museum 26653

Bystra

Muzeum Juliana Fałata, Oddział Muzeum Okręgowego w Bielsku-Białej, ul J. Fałata 48, 43-360 Bystra - T: (033) 361
Special Museum 26654

Bystrzyca Kłodzka

Muzeum Filumenistyczne (Matches Museum), ul Mały Rynek 1, 57-500 Bystrzyca Kłodzka - T: (074) 110637. Head: Iwona Mokrzanowska
Local Museum / Special Museum
Local history, local production of matches 26655

Bytom

Muzeum Górnośląskie (The Upper Silesian Museum), pl Jana III Sobieskiego 2, 41-902 Bytom - T: (032) 2818294, 2819733, Fax: 2813401, E-mail: mgbytom@us.edu.pl, Internet: http://www.muzeum.bytom.pl. Head: Mieczysław Dobkowski
Local Museum - 1927
Div of Art: Polish painting, Polish contemporary art, foreign painting, graphic art, guild art, applied arts, Div of Archeology: exhibits from the Bronze Age, Hallstatt, Roman period, Middle Ages, Div of Ethnography: folk costumes, laces, tools, Div of History: hist of Upper Silesia, Div of Natural History: geology, zoology, botany 26656

Bytów

Muzeum Zachodnio-Kaszubskie (Museum of Western Kashubia), ul Zamkowa 2, 77-100 Bytów - T: (0593) 2623, Fax: 2623. Head: Janusz Kopydłowski
Local Museum - 1972
Ethnography, local hist, old castle 26657

Cedynia

Muzeum Regionalne (Regional Museum), pl Wolności 8, 74-130 Cedynia. Head: Czesław Kroczak
Archaeological Museum - 1966
Exhibits from the excavations of the castle in Cedynia 26658

Chełm

Galeria Okręgowe, ul Św. Mikołaja 4, 22-100 Chełm - T: (082) 55958
Fine Arts Museum 26659

Muzeum Okręgowe w Chełmie (District Museum in Chełm), ul Lubelska 55, 22-100 Chełm - T: (082) 652693. Head: Longin Tokarski
Local Museum / Natural History Museum / Archaeological Museum - 1892
Relics from Stone Age, local history, painting, applied art, flora and fauna, fossils - library 26660

Chełmno

Muzeum Byłego Obozu Zagłady w Chełmnie nad Narem (Holocaust Museum), 62-663 Chełmno - T: (056) 14710. Head: Stanisław Klapczyński
Historical Museum
Hist of the concentration camp in Chełmno 26661

Chlewiska

Zabytkowa Huta Żelaza, Filia Muzeum Techniki w Warszawie (Ancient Foundry), 26-510 Chlewiska. Head: Stanisław Turek
Science&Tech Museum
Foundry equipment, old mouldings 26662

Chochołów

Muzeum Powstania Chochołowskiego, 34-513 Chochołów - Internet: http://www.muzeum.za-kopane.top.pl. Head: Anna Kozak
Ethnology Museum 26663

Chojnice

Muzeum Historyczno-Etnograficzne (Historical-Ethnographical Museum), ul Podmurna 15, 89-600 Chojnice - T: (052) 3974392, 3972319, Fax: 3972319, E-mail: mhech@wp.pl. Head: Dr. Janina Cherek
Historical Museum / Ethnology Museum - 1932
Archeology, hist of the town and country, ethnography from Southern Kashubia, sports incl a wooden bicycle from 1860 26664

Muzeum Oddział im. Albina Makowskiego, ul Drzymay 5, 89-600 Chojnice - T: (0531) 73626. Head: Dr. Janina Cherek
Local Museum 26665

Chojnów

Muzeum Regionalne (Municipal Museum), pl Zamkowy 3, 59-225 Chojnów - T: (076) 8188353. Head: Jerzy Janus
Local Museum - 1908
Burial remains from 2000 BC, urns, regional, industry and crafts, smithery, furniture, flax processing tools, 16th c sgraffitos, weapons, painting, coll of tiles, ancient coins 26666

Chorkówka

Muzeum Przemysłu Naftowego w Bóbrce (Museum of Petroleum Industry in Bóbrka), Bóbrka, 38-458 Chorkówka - T: (013) 4333478
Open Air Museum / Science&Tech Museum 26667

Choroszcz

Muzeum Wnętrz Pałacowych w Choroszczy, Muzeum Podlaskie w Białymstoku (Museum of Palace Interior), Pałac, 16-070 Choroszcz - T: (085) 7191233. Head: Anna Dąbrowska
Fine Arts Museum - 1973
Palace interior, furniture, paintings, sculptures, clocks, china 26668

Chorzów

Górnośląski Park Etnograficzny, ul Parkowa 1, 41-500 Chorzów - T: (032) 410718, Fax: 415501. Head: Barbara Heidenreich
Ethnology Museum 26669

Muzeum w Chorzowie, ul Powstańców 25, 41-500 Chorzów - T: (032) 2413104, Fax: 2413926, E-mail: chorzow@kustosz.com.pl, Internet: http://www.kustosz.com.pl/m-chorz.htm. Head: Daniela Sawicka-Oleksy
Local Museum - 1925
Silesian folk costumes, chests, carvings, interiors, farm implements, local history, numismatics, art 26670

Chrzanów

Muzeum w Chrzanowie, ul Mickiewicza 13, 32-500 Chrzanów - T: (035) 351 73. Head: Jerzy Motyka
Local Museum - 1960
History, judaica, ethnography, nature - library, archives 26671

Ciechanów

Muzeum Okręgowe (District Museum), ul Sienkiewicza 79, 06-400 Ciechanów - T: (023) 725346, Fax: 725346. Head: Hanna Długoszewska-Nadratowska
Historical Museum 26672

Ciechanowiec

Muzeum Rolnictwa im. ks. Krzysztofa Kluka (Jan Krzysztof Kluk Museum of Agriculture), ul Pałacowa 5, 18-230 Ciechanowiec - T: (086) 2771328, Fax: 2771328. Head: Kazimierz Uszyński
Agriculture Museum - 1963
Local hist, farm implements, mediums of village carriage, domestic utensils, village handicrafts, hist of animal husbandry, hist of plant cultivation, memorabilia on J.K. Kluk, Museum of Veterinary, open air ethnographical museum (40 buildings), herb garden - library 26673

Muzeum Weterynarii, Oddział Muzeum Rolnictwa im. K. Kluka w Ciechanowcu, 18-230 Ciechanowiec - T: (086) 2771328, Fax: 2771328
Special Museum 26674

Cieszyn

Galerie Muzeum w Cieszynie, ul Regera 6, 43-400 Cieszyn - T: (033) 521577, Fax: 521577. Head: Małgorzata Płazak
Local Museum - 1802
Archeology, geography, ethnography, folk art, art, history, photographs - library 26675

Czarnolas

Jan Kochanowski Muzeum, Jacek Malczewski Muzeum Radom, 26-702 Czarnolas - T: (048) 6772005. Head: Renata Pogorzelska
Historic Site - 1976
Local history, Polish Poets, works of Poland's greatest Renaissance poet Jan Kochanowski (1530-1584), 19th c country house of the Jabłonowski family 26676

Częstochowa

Muzeum 600-lecia Jasnej Góry, ul Kordeckiego 2, 42-200 Częstochowa - T: (034) 45087/88 w. 283
Religious Arts Museum 26677

Muzeum Częstochowskie, pl Biegańskiego 45, 42-200 Częstochowa - T: (034) 244424. Head: Andrzej Zembik
Local Museum - 1905
Natural hist, archeology, ethnography, history, art hist 26678

Muzeum Górnictwa i Hutnictwa Rud Żelaza, Muzeum Częstochowskiego (Museum of Iron Ore Mining), Park im. S. Staszica, 42-200 Częstochowa. Head: Krystyna Małuszyńska
Science&Tech Museum
Hist of iron ore mining 26679

Muzeum Tradycji i Perspektyw Huty im. B. Bieruta, ul Łukasińskiego 26, 42-207 Częstochowa - T: (034) 38804, 37202
Local Museum 26680

Zbiory Sztuki na Jasnej Górze (Jasna Góra Treasury), ul Kordeckiego 2, 42-200 Częstochowa - T: (034) 245087. Head: Jan Golonka
Religious Arts Museum
Religious art, liturgical vestments and vessels, votive shields, jewelery, orders, coins and medals, bequest by Sigismund I and Sigismund Augustus, Queen Bona, Sigismund III 26681

Człuchów

Muzeum Regionalne, Aleje Wojska Polskiego 3, 77-300 Człuchów - T: (0597) 425 86. Head: Ewa Homa-Rożek
Local Museum
Regional history, archeology, art, Gothic castle 26682

Darłowo

Muzeum w Darłowie, Zamek Książąt Pomorskich, ul Zamkowa 4, 76-150 Darłowo - T: (094) 142351. Head: Ewa Bielecka
Local Museum - 1923
Geology, natural history, archeology, ethnography, history, applied art, fine art, 12th c castle 26683

Dęblin

Ośrodek Historii Dęblińskiego Węzła Kolejowego, Stacja osobowa PKP, 08-520 Dęblin. Head: Jerzy Walberczyk
Local Museum 26684

Dębno

Muzeum Wnętrz Zabytkowych, Muzeum Okręgowego w Tarnowie, Zamek, 32-852 Dębno - T: (014) 6658035. Head: Lidia Luchter-Krupińska
Local Museum - 1978
Local history, 15th c Gothic castle, furniture, China coll 26685

Dobczyce

Muzeum Regionalne Polskiego Towarzystwa Turystyczno-Krajoznawczego im. Władysława Kowalskiego (Regional Museum of the Polish Tourist Association), Stare Miasto, 32-410 Dobczyce - T: (012) 2711455. Head: Gwalbert Kozubek
Local Museum - 1964
Archeological finds, ceramics, tools, arms, domestic utensils, coins, old books, costumes 26686

Dobra

Muzeum Parafialne, Muzeum Diecezjalne w Tarnowie (Parish Museum), 34-642 Dobra - T: (018) 378811. Head: Władysław Tarasek
Local Museum - 1955
Sacral art, folk art, local archival material 26687

Dobre

Społeczne Muzeum Konstantego Laszczki, ul Szkolna 3, 05-307 Dobre - T: 71178
Fine Arts Museum 26688

Dobrzyca

Pałac w Dobrzycy, Muzeum Narodowe w Poznaniu, ul Pleszewska 5, 63-330 Dobrzyca - T: (862) 414111
Local Museum 26689

Dominowo

Rezerwat Archeologiczny-Gród Piastowski w Gieczu, Oddział Muzeum Pierwszych Piastów na Lednicy, Grodziszczko 2, 63-012 Dominowo
Archaeological Museum 26690

Dukla

Muzeum Historyczne - Pałac w Dukli (History Museum-Palace in Dukla), Trakt Węgierski 5a, 38-450 Dukla - T: (013) 4330085, Fax: 4330236. Head: Stanisław Blazewiczea
Historical Museum - 1964
Hist of the battle of Dukla in 1915 and 1944, lodged in a 17th c palace, rebuilt in Rococo style by the Mniczech family in 1764, hist of St.Jan of Dukla 26691

Duszniki Zdrój

Muzeum Papiernictwa (Museum of the Paper Industry), ul Kłodzka 42, 57-340 Duszniki Zdrój - T: (074) 669248, Fax: 669020. Head: Bożena Makowska
Science&Tech Museum
Hist of the paper industry in Poland and around the world, old paper mill, tools and watermarks, manifacture of hand-made paper - manufacture department 26692

Elbląg

Muzeum w Elblągu, Bulwar Zygmunta Augusta 11, 82-300 Elbląg - T: (055) 2324317, Internet: http://elblag.softel.elblag.pl/muzeum.htm. Head: Kazimierz Arbart
Local Museum - 1954
Archeological finds, incl 13th c baptismal font, medieval sword crafts, art, iconography, local hist 26693

Frombork

Muzeum Mikołaja Kopernika (Nicolaus Copernicus Museum), ul Katedralna 18, 14-530 Frombork - T: (055) 2437218, 2437396, Fax: 24372188, E-mail: frombork@softel.elblaq.pl, Internet: http://www.frombork.art.pl. Head: Henryk Szkop
Natural History Museum - 1948
Life, scientific work and activities of N. Copernicus, paintings, sculptures, prints, numismatics, medals, observation instruments - library 26694

Gąsawa

Muzeum Archeologiczne w Biskupinie, Biskupin 17, 88-400 Gąsawa - T: (052) 3025025, Fax: 3025420, E-mail: muzeum@biskupin.pl, Internet: http://www.biskupin.pl. Head: Wiesław Zajączkowski
Archaeological Museum 26695

Gdańsk

Centralne Muzeum Morskie (Polish Maritime Museum), ul Ołowianka 9-13, 80-751 Gdańsk - T: (058) 3018611, 3018612, Fax: 3018453, E-mail: sekretariat@cmm.pl. Head: Dr. Jerzy Litwin
Science&Tech Museum - 1960
Hist of shipbuilding, hist of maritime shipping, ship models, marine fine arts, hist of yachting, underwater archeology, working boats - library, conservation of archaeological items 26696

Centrum Sztuki Współczesnej Łaźnia (Laznia Centre for Contemporary Art), ul Jaskółcza 1, 80-767 Gdańsk - T: (058) 3052680, 3202976, Fax: 3052680, E-mail: office@laznia.pl, Internet: http://www.laznia.pl. Head: Małgorzata Lisiewicz
Fine Arts Museum
Installations, photography, objects, art in public space, site-specific realisations, media art, sculpture, sound and light art, painting 26697

Dom Uphagena, Muzeum Historyczne Miasta Gdańska, ul Długa 12, Gdańsk - T: (058) 3012371, Fax: 3012371, E-mail: dom.uphagena@mhmg.gda.pl. Head: Ewa Szymańska
Local Museum 26698

Dwór Artusa, Muzeum Historii Miasta Gdańska, ul Długi Targ 45, 80-830 Gdańsk - T: (058) 314359. Head: Edward Śledź
Historical Museum 26699

Gdańska Galeria Fotografii, Muzeum Narodowego (Gdańsk Photography Gallery), ul Grobla I 3-5, 80-834 Gdańsk - T: (058) 3017147, Fax: 3011125, E-mail: info@muzeum.narodowe.gda.pl, Internet: http://www.muzeum.narodowe.qda.pl/html/galeria.html. Head: Stefan Figlarowicz
Fine Arts Museum 26700

Muzeum Archeologiczne (Archaeological Museum), ul Mariacka 25/26, 80-958 Gdańsk - T: (058) 3015031, Fax: 3015228, E-mail: mag@archeologia.pl, Internet: http://www.archeologia.pl. Head: Henryk Paner
Archaeological Museum - 1953
Coll from the later Stone Age to the modern times, face urns of the Earl Pomeranian Culture, artistic metal craft of the Wielbark Culture, prehistoric and medieval amber articles, craft of early medieval Gdańsk, early medieval stave boat, Sudan ethno-archeological coll - educational department, library, archive 26701

Muzeum Archidiecezjalne w Oliwie, ul Cystersów 16, 80-330 Gdańsk - T: (058) 5520051, Fax: 5522775, E-mail: kuria@diecezja.gda.pl.. Head: Alina Szpakiewicz
Religious Arts Museum 26702

Muzeum Etnografii, Muzeum Narodowe (Ethnological Museum), ul Cystersów 19, 80-330 Gdańsk - T: (058) 5524139, Fax: 5524637. Head: Wiktoria Blacharska
Ethnology Museum 26703

Muzeum Historii Miasta Gdańska (Museum of History of the City of Gdańsk), ul Długa 47, 80-831 Gdańsk - T: (058) 3014871, Fax: 3014871. Head: Adam Koperkiewicz
Historical Museum - 1970
Cultural hist of Gdańsk with special reference to current town activities, coins, medals from the Gdańsk mint 26704

Muzeum Narodowe (National Museum), ul Toruńska 1, 80-822 Gdańsk - T: (058) 3016804, Fax: 3011125, E-mail: info@muzeum.narodowe.gda.pl, Internet: http://www.muzeum.narodowe.gda.pl. Head: Tadeusz Piaskowski
Local Museum - 1872
Div of Polish Art: medieval art, modern art, Div of Foreign Art: 17th c Flemish and Dutch painting, Italian painting, French painting, contemporary art, Div of Decorative Art: textiles, furniture, ceramics, goldsmithery, exhibits from the Middle Ages, Renaissance, Baroque, Rococo, Neoclassicism, Div of Prints: contains ca 6000 items, Kabrun coll and Giełziński coll incl foreign and Polish art - library 26705

Muzeum Poczty i Telekomunikacji Oddział w Gdańsku (Mail and Telecommunication Museum), pl Obrońców Poczty Polskiej 1-2, 80-801 Gdańsk - T: (058) 3017611, Fax: 3017611. Head: Wiesław Wołodko
Science&Tech Museum / Historical Museum - 1979
Coll of early telephones and telegraphs hist of Polish National Post Defense on Sept 1st 1939 in Gdansk 26706

Muzeum Sportu i Turystyki Ziemi Gdańskiej, Muzeum Historii Miasta Gdańsk, ul Podmurze 2, 80-835 Gdańsk - T: (058) 314871, Fax: 314871
Historical Museum 26707

Oddział Sztuki Współczesnej, Muzeum Narodowe w Gdańsku (Museum of Contemporary Art), ul Cystersów 18, 80-330 Gdańsk - T: (058) 5521271, Fax: 5524637. Head: Jerzy Bradtke
Fine Arts Museum - 1965
Coll of contemporary Polish art in a historical baroque palace 26708

Statek-Muzeum Dar Pomorza, Centralne Muzeum Morskie (Museum Ship Dar Pomorza), ul Ołowianka 9-13, 80-751 Gdańsk - T: (058) 6202371, Fax: 6202477, E-mail: sekretariat@cmm.pl. Head: Dr. Jerzy Litwin
Science&Tech Museum - 1981
Hist of the ship "Dar Pomorza" 26709

Statek-Muzeum Sołdek, Centralne Muzeum Morskie (Museum Ship Sołdek), ul Ołowianka 9-13, 80-751 Gdańsk - T: (058) 3018611, Fax: 3018453, E-mail: sekretariat@cmm.pl. Head: Dr. Jerzy Litwin
Science&Tech Museum - 1981
Hist of the ship "Sołdek" 26710

Twierdza Wisłoujście, Muzeum Historii Miasta Gdańska, ul Stara Twierdza 1, Gdańsk - T: (058) 431405
Historical Museum 26711

Westerplatte, Muzeum Historii Miasta Gdańska, Gdańsk - T: (058) 436972
Local Museum 26712

Wieża Więzienna i Katownia, Muzeum Historii Miasta Gdańska, ul Targ Węglowy 50, Gdańsk - T: (058) 314733
Local Museum 26713

Zabytkowa Kuźnia Wodna, Filial Muzeum Techniki w Warszawie, ul Bytowska 1, 80-328 Gdańsk - T: (058) 525151. Head: Zbigniew Wilk
Science&Tech Museum 26714

Gdynia

Domek Abrahama, Muzeum Miasta Gdyni, ul Starowiejska 30, Gdynia - T: (058) 219073
Local Museum 26715

Muzeum Marynarki Wojennej (Navy Museum), ul Skwer Kościuszki, 81-912 Gdynia - T: (058) 263565, 263745, 263984. Head: Zbigniew Wojciechowski
Military Museum
Model of the Gdańsk ship 'Mars' (built 1697), the Navy in the period between the two World Wars, the WWII period, naval warfare, heavy arms and guns 26716

Muzeum Miasta Gdyni (Museum of The City of Gdynia), ul Starowiejska 30, 81-356 Gdynia - T: (058) 219073. Head: Stefania Lemańska
Historical Museum 26717

Muzeum Oceanograficzne i Akwarium Morskie, Al Zjednoczenia 1, 81-345 Gdynia - T: (058) 6217021, E-mail: muzeum@mir.gdynia.pl, Internet: http://www.mir.gdynia.pl/akw/muz_akw.htm. Head: Kazimierz Siudziński
Natural History Museum 26718

Pawilon Wystawowy, Muzeum Miasta Gdyni, ul Waszyngtona 21, 81-342 Gdynia - T: (058) 204730
Public Gallery 26719

Statek-Muzeum Dar Pomorza, Centralne Muzeum Morskie w Gdańsku (Museum Ship Dar Pomorza), Nabrzeże Pomorskie, 81-345 Gdynia - T: (058) 6202371. Head: Prof. Andrzej Zbierski
Science&Tech Museum - 1982
Hist of the ship, temporary exhibitions 26720

Giecz

Gród Piastowski w Gieczu, Archeologiczny Muzeum Pierwszych Piastów na Lednicy (Archeological Reserve), 63-012 Giecz - T: (0667) 59222. Head: Edwin Dzięciołowski
Archaeological Museum
Hist of the castle, exhibits from the early Middle Ages 26721

Gliwice

Muzeum Geologii Złóż im. Czesława Poborskiego, Politechnika Śląska (Silesian Technical University Cz. Poborski Mineral Deposits Museum), ul Akademicka 2, 44-100 Gliwice - T: (032) 2372289, Fax: 2372290, E-mail: muzgeol@zeus.polsl.gliwice.pl. Head: Krzysztof Lysogórski
Natural History Museum - 1961
Coll of rocks, metall ores from European deposits, zinc and lead ores from upper Silesian deposits 26722

Muzeum w Gliwicach, ul Dolnych Wałów 8a, 44-100 Gliwice - T: (032) 2310854, Fax: 2307366, E-mail: muzeumwgliwicach@wp.pl. Head: Grazyna Przybył
Local Museum - 1905
Archeology, history 13th-20th c, social and cultural activities on Upper Silesia betweem WWI and WWII, ethnography, art, casts, glass, handicraft, silver jewellery, goldsmith's trade, Western European painting and graphics - library 26723

Głogów

Muzeum Archeologiczno-Historyczne (Archaeology and History Museum), ul Brama Brzostowska 1, 67-200 Głogów - T: (076) 8341081, Fax: 8333038. Head: Leszek Lenarczyk
Archaeological Museum - 1967
Local hist, archaeology, Piast castle from the 13th-18th c, numismatics - library 26724

Głogówek

Muzeum Jana Cybisa, Muzeum Śląska Opolskiego w Opolu, Zamek, 48-250 Głogówek - T: (077) 500
Fine Arts Museum 26725

Muzeum Regionalne (Regional Museum), ul Słowackiego 1, 48-250 Głogówek - T: (077) 4373500. Head: Albert Szyndzielorz
Local Museum 26726

Głsawa

Muzeum w Biskupinie, Państwowy Muzeum Archeologicznego w Warszawie (Museum in Biskupin), Biskupin, 88-410 Głsawa - T: (0534) 25025, Internet: http://gray.logonet.com.pl/bydgoszcz/biskupin.html. Head: Wiesław Zajączkowski
Archaeological Museum - 1958
Partly reconstruction of the settlement, exhibition pavilion, farmer's hut from the end of XVIII AD, cattle, horses and sheep flock within the experimental archaeology area - ancient timber conservation laboratory, experimental archaeology area 26727

Gniew

Zamek, Muzeum Archeologiczne, ul Zamkowa 1, Gniew - T: (069) 352537
Local Museum 26728

Gniezno

Muzeum Początków Państwa Polskiego (Museum of the Origin of the Polish State), ul Prof. J. Kostrzewskiego 1, 62-200 Gniezno - T: (061) 4264641, Fax: 4264841, E-mail: mppp@gniezno.home.pl, Internet: http://www.mppp.home.pl. Head: Stanisław Pasiciel
Local Museum - 1956
Gothic and Renaissance tiles from Gniezno, archaeology, hist - library, archives 26729

Gołotczyzna

Muzeum im. Aleksandra Świętochowskiego, ul Świętochowskiego 4, 06-430 Gołotczyzna - T: (023) 713078. Head: Grzegorz Roszko
Special Museum
Life and work of the writer-publicist Aleksander Świętochowski (1849-1938) in his former home 26730

Golub-Dobrzyń

Muzeum Regionalne PTTK (Museum of the Dobrzyń Region), Zamek, 87-400 Golub-Dobrzyń - T: (056) 832455, Fax: 832666. Head: Zygmunt Kwiatkowski
Local Museum - 1967
Archeology, history, numismatics, in a 14th c Gothic castle 26731

Gołuchów

Muzeum-Zamek w Gołuchowie (Castle-Museum in Gołuchów), 63-322 Gołuchów - T: (062) 17013. Head: Danuta Marek
Fine Arts Museum - 1962
16th c castle of the Leszczyński family, rebuilt in the French Renaissance style for princess Izabella Czartoryski in the 2nd half of the 19th c by Maurice Ouradou, West European painting (eg by the Portuguese painter Alonso Coello), and Polish painting, furniture, interior decoration, fabrics and antique vases 26732

Gorlice

Muzeum Regionalne (Regional Museum), ul Wąska 7-9, 38-300 Gorlice - T: (018) 522615. Head: Leszek Brzozowski
Local Museum - 1957
Exhibits from World War I (Battle of Gorlice 1915) 26733

Gorzeń Górny

Muzeum Emila Zegadłowicza, Gorzeń Górny 1, Wadowice, 34-100 Gorzeń Górny - T: (033) 33966. Head: Adam Zedgadłowicz
Historic Site - 1946
Memorabilia on the writer E. Zegadłowicz (1888-1941) in his former home, engravings, drawings - archives 26734

Gorzów Wielkopolski

Muzeum w Gorzowie Wielkopolskim, ul Warszawska 35, 66-400 Gorzów Wielkopolski - T: (095) 322843. Head: Zdzislaw Linkowski
Local Museum - 1945
Natural history, general history, regional geography and history, archeology, ethnography, art, technology - library 26735

Gostyń

Muzeum w Gostyniu, ul Wrocławska 257, 63-800 Gostyń - T: (065) 721297. Head: Andrzej Grześkowiak
Local Museum - 1967
Local history 26736

Grabonóg

Muzeum im. Edmunda Bojanowskiego w Grabonogu, Piaski, 63-820 Grabonóg - T: (065) 719708. Head: Teresa Sroka
Local Museum 26737

Grodzisk Mazowiecki

Muzeum Regionalne Polskiego Towarzystwa Turystyczno-Krajoznawczego (Museum of the Polish Tourist Association), ul Parkowa 1, 05-825 Grodzisk Mazowiecki - T: (022) 555057. Head: Janusz Szczepan Sobieraj
Local Museum - 1961
Local hist in an 18th c farmstead 26738

Grójec

Społeczne Muzeum Sadownictwa, ul Mogielnicka 28, 05-600 Grójec - T: (0488) 3572
Special Museum 26739

Grudziądz

History of Grudziądz, ul Spichrzowa 9, granary, 86-300 Grudziądz - T: (056) 4659063
Local Museum 26740

Muzeum w Grudziądzu, ul Wodna 3-5, 86-300 Grudziądz - T: (056) 4659063/64/65, Fax: 4659066, Internet: http://www.grudziaz.com/muzeum. Head: Ryszard Boguwolski
Ethnology Museum - 1884
Local hist, 19th-20th c Polish painting, contemporary Pomeranian painting, numismatics, natural hist, in 17th-18th c cloister, archaeological objects from the Stone Age to the Middle Ages 26741

Grybów

Muzeum Parafialne, Muzeum Diecezjalnego w Tarnowie (Parish Museum), ul Kościelna 3, 33-330 Grybów - T: (018) 450262. Head: Adam Kaźmierczyk
Local Museum 26742

Hel

Muzeum Rybołówstwa, Centralne Muzeum Morskie w Gdańsku (Fishery Museum), Bulwar Nadmorski im. Demela 2, 84-150 Hel - T: (058) 6750552, Fax: 6750905, E-mail: sekretariat@cmm.pl. Head: Dr. Jerzy Litwin
Ethnology Museum - 1972
Natural hist, fishing equipment, hist of navigation, in a 15th Gothic church 26743

Hrubieszów

Muzeum im. Stanisława Staszica, Muzeum Okręgowego w Zamościu, ul 3 Maja 11, 22-500 Hrubieszów - T: (0838) 2783. Head: Helena Bojarczuk
Local Museum

Local hist, archeology, ethnography, memorabilia on the poet and political leader Stanisław Staszic (1755-1826), in a baroque-classicistic mansion from the end of the 18th c 26744

Iłża

Muzeum Regionalne, ul Błazińska 1, 27-100 Iłża - T: (048) 162929. Head: Beata Bujakowska
Local Museum 26745

Inowrocław

Muzeum im. Jana Kasprowicza, pl Klasztorny 2, 88-100 Inowrocław - T: (0536) 75873. Head: Janina Sikorska
Historical Museum - 1931
History of Inowrocław and the West Kuyavy region, Lusatian culture, tomb from Opoki, modern art, memorabilia of Stanisław Przybyszewski, Jan Kasprowicz (1860-1926), salt mining 26746

Iwanowice

Muzeum Regionalne PTTK i Urzędu Gminy, 32-263 Iwanowice - T: (012) 222094. Head: Antoni Walaszczyk
Local Museum 26747

Iwkowa

Muzeum Parafialne, Filia Muzeum Diecezjalnego w Tarnowie, 32-861 Iwkowa. Head: Włodzimierz Maziarka
Fine Arts Museum 26748

Jaracz

Muzeum Historii Młynarstwa i Wodnych Urządzeń Przemysłu Wiejskiego w Jaraczu, Muzeum Narodowego Rolnictwa i Przemysłu Rolno-Spożywczego w Szreniawie, 64-600 Jaracz - T: (067) 610515. Head: Wiesław Płotkowiak
Science&Tech Museum - 1981
Watermill with machinery, tools and implements, models of different types of windmills, milling history in Poland 26749

Jarocin

Muzeum Regionalne, Rynek 1, 63-200 Jarocin - T: (062) 473449. Head: Eugenunsz Czarny
Local Museum - 1960
Ethnography, farm implements, archeology of the Lusatian culture, history, numismatics 26750

Jarosław

Muzeum w Jarosławiu, ul Rynek 4, 37-500 Jarosław - T: (0194) 5437. Head: Joanna Kociuba
Local Museum - 1925
17th-18th c costumes, furniture, domestic utensils 26751

Jasło

Muzeum Regionalne, ul Kadyiego 11, 38-200 Jasło - T: (013) 442359. Head: Afred Sepioł
Local Museum - 1969
Local hist, crafts and guilds, icons, Gothic and baroque sculptures, documents from the Nazi period, painting (17th-20th c), numismatics, folk art 26752

Jawor

Muzeum Regionalne, ul Klasztorna 6, 59-400 Jawor - T: (076) 8702321. Head: Anna Grynszpan
Local Museum - 1929
Local hist, archeology, militaria, applied art, ethnography of the Sub-Sudeten region and Lower Silesia 26753

Jaworzno

Muzeum Miasta Jaworzna, ul Pocztowa 5, 43-600 Jaworzno - T: (035) 7519162, Fax: 7519162, E-mail: muzeum@um.jaworzno.pl. Head: Przemysław Dudzik
Local Museum 26754

Jedlicze

Muzeum Marii Konopnickiej w Żarnowcu, Żarnowiec, 38-460 Jedlicze - T: (013) 4352013. Head: Zdzisław Łopatkiewicz
Special Museum - 1960
Memorial to the poetess and novelist Maria Konopnicka (1842-1910), in a 18th c house - library 26755

Jędrzejów

Państwowe Muzeum im. Przypkowskich, pl Kościuszki 7/8, 28-300 Jędrzejów - T: (0498) 61156. Head: Piotr Maciej Przypkowski
Local Museum - 1962
Time measurements, sundials, astronomical and gnomonic instruments, gastronomy, kitchen utensils, graphic arts, bookplates, photography, historical interiors - library 26756

Jelenia Góra

Dom Gerharta Hauptmanna (Gerhart Hauptmann's House), Ul Michałowicka 32, Jagniątków, 58-570 Jelenia Góra - T: (075) 7553286, Fax: 7556395, E-mail: kontakt@dom-gerharta-hauptmanna.pl, Internet: http://www.dom-gerharta-hauptmanna.pl. Head: Robert Szuber
Historic Site / Special Museum
House, where the Nobel Prize winner Gerhart Hauptmann lived and worked until his death in 1946 26757

Muzeum Okręgowe (District Museum), ul Jana Matejki 28, 58-500 Jelenia Góra - T: (075) 7523465. Head: Stanisław Firszt
Local Museum - 1889
Glassmaking and glasspainting, weaving, ethnography, folk furniture, ancient and contemporary engravings, Silesian ancient handicraft - library 26758

Muzeum Przyrodnicze (Natural History Museum), ul Wolności 268, 58-560 Jelenia Góra - T: (075) 7551506, 7557400, Fax: 7551506, E-mail: muzeum@skrzynka.pl. Head: Andrzej Paczos
Natural History Museum - 1920
Natural hist, mammals, birds, insects, invertebrates, fungi, minerals - library 26759

Muzeum Przyrodnicze Karkonoskiego Parku Narodowego, ul Chałubińskiego 23, 58-570 Jelenia Góra - T: (075) 7553726, Fax: 7553348, E-mail: mskpn@eta.pl. Head: Tatiana Mochola
Natural History Museum 26760

Jugowice

Muzeum Regionalne w Zagórzu Śląskim, Zamek Grodno, Zagórze Śląskie, 58-321 Jugowice - T: 360
Local Museum 26761

Kalisz

Centrum Rysunku i Grafiki im. Tadeuza Kulisiewicza, Muzeum Okręgowego Ziemi Kaliskiej w Kaliszu, ul Kolegialna 4, 62-800 Kalisz - T: (062) 572999. Head: Hanna Jaworowicz
Fine Arts Museum 26762

Muzeum Okręgowe Ziemi Kaliskiej (Museum of the Kalisz Region), ul Kościuszki 12, 62-800 Kalisz - T: (062) 5030203, 5030155, Fax: 5030155, E-mail: muzeum@info.kalisz.pl, Internet: http://www.info.kalisz.pl/muzeum. Head: Jerzy Aleksander Splitt
Local Museum - 1906
Roman finds, early medieval period, ceramics, tombstone, coins from the 11th-12th c, local hist, crafts, documents from the Nazi period, Central European and exotic butterflies, farm implements, folk costumes, lace making, African coll, works of the Polish graphic artist Tadeusz Kulisiewicz (1889-1988), fine arts coll - library, centre for graphics and drawing 26763

Rezerwat Archeologiczny na Zawodziu, Muzeum Okręgowego Ziemi Kaliskiej w Kaliszu, ul Bolesława Pobożnego 101, 62-800 Kalisz - T: (062) 5030203, 5030155, Fax: 5030155, E-mail: muzeum@info.kalisz.pl, Internet: http://www.info.kalisz.pl/muzeum. Head: Leszek Ziąbka
Archaeological Museum 26764

Kamienna Góra

Muzeum Tkactwa Dolnośląskiego (Museum of Lower Silesian Weaving), pl Wolności 11, 58-400 Kamienna Góra - T: (075) 7442275, Fax: 7442275. Head: Leokadia Ewa Kosiba
Folklore Museum - 1932
Local and regional history, crafts, weaving, carving, wooden sculptures, silver coins, house dating back to 1650 26765

Kamionka

Muzeum Zamoyskich w Kozłówce, Pałac, 21-132 Kamionka - T: (081) 8527588, 8527091, Fax: 8527988, E-mail: kozlmuz@platon.man.lublin.pl, Internet: http://www.muzeumkozlowka.lublin.pl. Head: Krzysztof Kornacki
Fine Arts Museum - 1944
Coll of the Zamoyski Family, Socialist Realism Art - library 26766

Kampinos

Muzeum Puszczy Kampinoskiej Granica (Museum of the Kampinoska Forest), Granica, 05-085 Kampinos - T: (022) 7250123. Head: Ludwika Kwiadas-Wierzbicka
Natural History Museum - 1964
Animals, plants, trees, historic and geological charts, historical weapons, documents - open-air museum of folk architecture 26767

Karpacz

Muzeum Sportu i Turystyki Regionu Karkonoszy, ul Kopernika 2, 58-540 Karpacz - T: (075) 7619652, Fax: 7619652, E-mail: muzeum.turystyki@karpacz.pl, Internet: http://www.karpacz.pl/kultura/muz_sp.html. Head: Zbigniew Kulik
Historical Museum 26768

Muzeum Zabawek ze Zbiorow Henryka Tomaszewskiego (Henryk Tomaszewski Toy Museum), ul Karkonoska 5, 58-540 Karpacz - T: (075) 7618523
Special Museum 26769

Parafia Ewangelicko - Augsburska Wang (Vang Church), ul Śnieżki 8, 58-550 Karpacz - T: (075) 7619228, Fax: 7619228, E-mail: wang@sponsor.com.pl. Head: Edwin Pech
Religious Arts Museum - 1844
Early 13th c wooden church with carvings, moved to the present location from Vang, Province of Valdres, Norway 26770

Kartuzy

Muzeum Kaszubskie (Kashubian Museum), ul Kościerska 1, 83-300 Kartuzy - T: (058) 6811442, Fax: 68110378, E-mail: muzeum@muzeum-kaszubskie.gda.pl, Internet: http://www.muzeum-kaszubskie.gda.pl. Head: Norbert Maczulis
Ethnology Museum - 1932
Ethnography, fishing, farming, furniture, ceramics, masks, musical instruments, rare Kashubian painting on glass 26771

Katowice

Harcerskie Muzeum Etnograficzne przy Szkole Podstawowej nr 11 w Katowicach, ul Nasypowa 16, 40-551 Katowice - T: (032) 571585. Head: Paweł Nowojski
Ethnology Museum - 1972 26772

Muzeum Archidiecezjalne (Archidiocesan Museum), ul Jordana 39, 40-043 Katowice - T: (032) 2516703, Fax: 2514830, E-mail: muzeum@quest.kuria.katowice.pl. Head: Henryk Pyka
Religious Arts Museum 26773

Muzeum Biograficzne im. Pawła Stellera, Muzeum Historii Katowic, ul Andrzeja 13, 40-061 Katowice - T: (032) 512683
Fine Arts Museum 26774

Muzeum Historii Katowic (Museum of History of Katowice), ul Ks. Józefa Szafranka 9, 40-025 Katowice - T: (032) 2562134, Fax: 2562134. Head: Jadwiga Lipońska-Sajdak
Historical Museum 26775

Muzeum Prawa i Prawników Polskich, ul Andrzeja 16, 40-061 Katowice - T: (032) 511421 w. 81
Local Museum 26776

Muzeum Śląskie, Aleja Wojciecha Korfantego 3, 40-005 Katowice - T: (032) 2599804, Fax: 2599804. Head: Dr. Lech Szaraniec
Local Museum - 1924/1985
Polish painting 1800-1939, Polish comtemporary painting, graphics, Polish posters, Polish nonprofessional art, Silesian ethnography 26777

Kazimierz Dolny

Muzeum Nadwiślańskie, ul Podzamcze 12a, 24-120 Kazimierz Dolny - T: (081) 810288, Fax: 810277. Head: Jerzy Żurawski
Local Museum - 1963
Iconography, local and regional hist, archeology, painting, drawing, graphics, in a 16th c Renaissance house - Goldsmithery museum 26778

Muzeum Przyrodnicze, Muzeum Nadwiślańskie (Museum of Nature), ul Puławska 54, 24-120 Kazimierz Dolny - T: (081) 8810326, Fax: 8810277, E-mail: muzeum@muzeumprzyrodnicze.kazimierz-dolny.pl, Internet: http://www.muzeumprzyrodnicze.kazimierz-dolny.pl. Head: Wiktor Kowalczyk
Natural History Museum - 1982 26779

Muzeum Sztuki Złotniczej, ul Senatorska 11, 24-120 Kazimierz Dolny - T: (081) 810104. Head: Tadeusz Rozłowski
Fine Arts Museum 26780

Kcynia

Palucka Izba Muzealna, Muzeum Okręgowego im. Leona Wyczółkowskiego w Bydgoszczy, ul Poznańska 49, 89-240 Kcynia. Head: Danuta Kosznik
Ethnology Museum 26781

Kępno

Muzeum Regionalne PTTK, ul Sienkiewicza 11, 63-600 Kępno - T: (0647) 22283
Local Museum 26782

Muzeum Ziemi Kępińskiej, ul Kwiatowa 30, 63-600 Kępno - T: (0647) 23611. Head: Jerzy Wojciechowski
Archaeological Museum - 1936
Archeology, ethnography, history, art culture 26783

Kętrzyn

Muzeum im. Wojciecha Kętrzyńskiego, pl Zamkowy 1, 11-400 Kętrzyn - T: (0886) 3282. Head: Mariusz Wyczółkowski
Local Museum - 1945
Neolithic archeology, 15th-17th c sculptures, painting, numismatics, furniture, Meissen porcelain, natural history, geology, lodged in a 14th c Gothic castle 26784

Kęty

Muzeum w Kętach, Muzeum Okręgowego w Bielsku-Białej, ul Żwirki i Wigury 2, 32-650 Kęty - T: (033) 453107. Head: Teresa Kuźma
Local Museum 26785

Kielce

Muzeum Lat Szkolnych Stefana Żeromskiego (Museum of Stefan Żeromski's School Years), ul Jana Pawła II 5, 25-013 Kielce - T: (041) 3445792. Head: Kazimiera Zapałowa
Special Museum - 1965
Memorabilia on the poet Stefan Żeromski (1864-1924), manuscripts of his works 26786

Muzeum Narodowe w Kielcach (National Museum in Kielce), pl Zamkowy 1, 25-010 Kielce - T: (041) 3444014, Fax: 3448261, Internet: http://complex.complex.com.pl/kielce/szlak.htm. Head: Alojzy Oborny
Historical Museum / Fine Arts Museum - 1908
Paintings from the 18th-20th c, Polish Sarmatian portraits, works by Misiowski, Orłowski, Grassi, Lampi, interior exhibits from the 17th-18th c, ethnographic exhibiton, folk culture from Kielce County, the Łsogory region, agriculture, weaving, crafts, recent hist of the region of Kielce, archeology, natural hist, graphics, numismatics, arms - Departement in Oblęgorek 26787

Muzeum Pamięci Narodowej lata 1939 -1956 (National memorial), ul IX Wieków Kielc 3 p. 501, 25-516 Kielce - T: (041) 21982. Head: Andrzej Jankowski
Local Museum 26788

Muzeum Wsi Kieleckiej, ul Jana Pawła II 6, 25-013 Kielce - T: (041) 3449297, Fax: 3449297. Head: Andrzej Szura
Ethnology Museum 26789

Muzeum Zabawkarstwa, ul Kościuszki 11, 25-310 Kielce - T: (041) 3444078. Head: Ryszard Zięzio
Historical Museum - 1979 26790

Muzeum Zakładowe im. St. Staszica Kieleckiej Fabryki Pomp "Białogon", ul Druckiego-Lubeckiego 1, 25-818 Kielce - T: (041) 682 02
Science&Tech Museum 26791

Muzeum Zbiorów Geologicznych (Museum of Geologic Collection), ul Zgoda 21, 25-953 Kielce - T: (041) 3612537, Fax: 3612493. Head: Jolanta Studencka
Natural History Museum - 1963
Rock, fossil and mineral coll from Góry Swiętokrzyskie (Holy Cross Mts) 26792

Rocznik Muzeum Narodowego w Kielcach, Pl Zamkowy 1, 25-010 Kielce - T: (041) 3446764, 3444014, Fax: 3448261, E-mail: muzeum@kielce.uw.gov.pl, Internet: http://www.kielce.uw.gov.pl/muzeum
Fine Arts Museum / Local Museum 26793

Kłodzko

Muzeum Ziemi Kłodzkiej (Museum of the Kłodzko Region), ul Łukasiewicza 4, 57-300 Kłodzko - T: (074) 673570, Fax: 673570. Head: Krystyna Toczyńska Rudysz
Local Museum - 1963
Archeology, hist, ethnography, contemporary painting, glass painting, sacral art, seal presses of the town Kłodzko, coll of travelling excritoires, numismatics, modern glass art, Silesian clocks - library 26794

Kluczbork

Muzeum im. Jana Dzierzona (Jan Dzierżoń Museum), ul Zamkowa 10, 46-200 Kluczbork - T: (077) 4182707. Head: Roman Pastwinski
Historical Museum - 1959
Primitive beehive from the 1st c BC, local hist, memorials of Dr. Jan Dzierzon, archeology, apiculture 26795

Kluki

Muzeum Wsi Słowińskiej w Klukach, Muzeum Pomorza Środkowego w Słupsku (Slovintzian Homestead), 76-214 Kluki - T: (059) 117344. Head: Henryk Soja
Open Air Museum - 1963
Household items, Slovinian furniture, fishing equipment, tools for digging the peat out 26796

Kolbuszowa

Muzeum Kultury Ludowej (Folk Museum), ul Kościuszki 2, 36-100 Kolbuszowa - T: (017) 271296. Head: Mirosław Górski
Ethnology Museum - 1958
Folk pottery, costumes, open-air museum of architecture of the Lasowiaks and Rzeszowiaks (45 objects), plaiting, farm implements coll, furniture, folk art (sculpture, bass-relief), fire-fighting coll - library, archives 26797

Koło

Muzeum Technik Ceramicznych, ul Kajki 44, 62-600 Koło - T: (063) 721559. Head: Dr. Józef Stanisław Mujta
Decorative Arts Museum - 1972
Porcelain and ceramics, ethnography, regional history 26798

Kołobrzeg

Muzeum Miasta Kołobrzegu, Muzeum Oręża Polskiego, ul Armii Krajowej 13, 78-100 Kołobrzeg - T: (0965) 22091. Head: Barbara Zabel
Local Museum 26799

Muzeum Oręża Polskiego (Polish Army Museum), ul Armii Krajowej 13, 78-100 Kołobrzeg - T: (0965) 22091. Head: Hieronim Kroczyński
Local Museum - 1963
Military history, local history 26800

Komorniki

Muzeum Narodowe Rolnictwa i Przemysłu Rolno-Spożywczego w Szreniawie (National Museum of Agriculture and Food Industry), Dworcowa 5, 62-052 Komorniki - T: (061) 8107629, Fax: 8107642. Head: Dr. Henryk Nowacki
Agriculture Museum - 1964
Hist of agriculture, hunting, rural crafts, processing and agricultural-food industry in Poland, objects, models, documents - library 26801

Konin

Muzeum Okręgowe (District Museum), ul Muzealna 6, 62-505 Konin - T: (063) 427431. Head: Dr. Lucja Paulicka-Nowak
Local Museum - 1956
Geology, mineralogy, paleontology, archeology (Mesolithic and Neolithic period), local history, militaria, numismatics, ethnography 26802

Kórnik

Muzeum Biblioteki Kórnickiej, Polish Academy of Sciences (Museum of the Kórnik Library), ul Zamkowa 5, 62-035 Kórnik - T: (061) 8170081, Fax: 171930, E-mail: bkpan@amu.edu.pl, Internet: http://www.bkpanpoznan.pl. Head: Prof. Dr. Stanisław Sierpowski
Library with Exhibitions / Local Museum
Artistic craft, etthnography, archaeology, graphics, paintings, numismatics, natural history 26803

Kościan

Muzeum Regionalne (Regional Museum), Rynek 1, 64-100 Kościan - T: (065) 5122934, Fax: 5122700. Head: Eugeniusz Śliwiński
Local Museum 26804

Kosów Lacki

Muzeum Walki i Męczeństwa w Treblince, Muzeum Okręgowego w Siedlcach (Holocaust Museum of Treblinka), Treblinka, 08-330 Kosów Lacki. Head: Edward Kopówska
Historic Site 26805

Koszalin

Muzeum Okręgowe (District Museum), ul Młyńska 37, 75-429 Koszalin - T: (094) 43 20 11. Head: Juliusz Sienkiewicz
Local Museum - 1924
Archeology, ethnography, applied arts 26806

Koszuty

Muzeum Ziemi Średzkiej, 63-022 Koszuty - T: (0667) 51023, Fax: 51023. Head: Tadeusz Osyra
Decorative Arts Museum - 1966
Furniture, paintings and decorative artifacts from the original manor house 26807

Kozienice

Muzeum Regionalne (Regional Museum), ul Parkowa 5B, 26-900 Kozienice - T: (048) 143372. Head: Krzysztof Reczek
Local Museum - 1974
Local ethnology, folk arts, regional hist, hippology 26808

Kraków

Dom Jana Matejki, Muzeum Narodowego w Krakowie, ul Floriańska 41, 31-019 Kraków - T: (012) 4225926, 4230408, Fax: 4312373, E-mail: dommatejki@muz-nar.krakow.pl. Head: Malgorzata Buyko
Local Museum 26809

Dom Józefa Mehoffera, Muzeum Narodowe, ul Krupnicza 26, Kraków - T: (012) 4211143
Special Museum 26810

Dzieje i Kultura Żydów Krakowskich (Muzeum Historycznego Miasta Krakowa), ul Szeroka 24, Stara Synagoga, 31-053 Kraków - T: (012) 660534, 660544
Local Museum 26811

Dzieje Teatrów Krakowskich, Muzeum Historycznego Miasta Krakowa, ul Szpitalna 21, 31-024 Kraków - T: (012) 226824
Local Museum 26812

Gabinet Prof. K. Sosnowskiego, Ośrodek Muzealny KTG, ul Westerplatte 15-16, 31-033 Kraków - T: (012) 229566
Special Museum 26813

Gabinet Rycin Polskiej Akademii Umiejętności w Krakowie (Print Room of the Polish Academy of Arts and Sciences), ul Sławkowska 17, 31-016 Kraków - T: (012) 4227066, Fax: 4225422, E-mail: office@pau.krakow.pl. Head: Krysztof Krużel
Fine Arts Museum
European prints 15th - 19th cc. 26814

Galeria Międzynarodowego Centrum Kultury, Rynek Główny 25, 31-008 Kraków - T: (012) 4218601, 4217700, Fax: 4218571, 4217844, E-mail: ejpurchl@cyf-kr.edu.pl
Fine Arts Museum 26815

Galeria Polskiego Malarstwa i Rzeźby XIX w., Rynek Główny 1, 31-042 Kraków - T: (012) 4221166
Fine Arts Museum 26816

Galeria Sztuki Polskiej XIX w. w Sukiennicach, Muzeum Narodowego w Krakowie, Rynek Główny 1/3, 31-042 Kraków - T: (012) 221166. Head: Tadeusz Dziurzyński
Fine Arts Museum - 1879
Polish painting and sculpture from 1764 to the end of the 19th c 26817

Kamienica Szołayskich, Muzeum Narodowego w Krakowie (Szołayski House), pl Szczepański 9, 31-011 Kraków - T: (012) 4227021. Head: Jan Barcik
Fine Arts Museum
Gallery of Polish painting and sculpture, the coll from the 15th-16th c ranks among the most valuable in Poland 26818

Manggha Centrum Sztuki i Techniki Japońskiej, Muzeum Narodowe w Krakowie, ul Konopnickiej 26, Kraków - T: (012) 2672703, 2673753, Fax: 2674079, E-mail: centrum@manggha.krakow.pl, Internet: http://www.manggha.krakow.pl. Head: Bogna Dziechiaruk-Maj
Fine Arts Museum 26819

Muzeum Archeologiczne w Krakowie (Archaeological Museum in Cracow), ul Senacka 3, 31-002 Kraków - T: (012) 4227560, Fax: 4227761, Internet: http://www.krakow.pl/muzea/archeol/index.htm. Head: Dr. Jacek Rydzewski
Archaeological Museum - 1850
Paleolithic and Mesolithic Age, Neolithic and early-Bronze Age, Lusatian Culture, La Tène and Roman Periods, early Middle Ages, Middle Ages, Mediterranean and Non-European archaeology - scientific and educational section, workroom for research in metallography, library 26820

Muzeum Archeologiczne w Krakowie, Oddział w Nowej Hucie (Archaeology Museum in Cracow), Osiedle Zielone 7, 31-968 Kraków - T: (012) 440940. Head: Dr. Jacek Rydzewski
Archaeological Museum 26821

Muzeum Archidiecezjalne w Krakowie (Archidiocesan Museum in Cracov), ul Kanonicza 19-21, 31-002 Kraków - T: (012) 4218963, Fax: 4227523, Internet: http://info.cyf-kr.edu.pl/WK/PL/kultura/muzea/muzea/Archidiecezjalne/archidi.htm. Head: Dr. Józef Andrej Nowobilski
Religious Arts Museum 26822

Muzeum Czartoryskich, Muzeum Narodowe w Krakowie (Czartoryski Museum), ul Św. Jana 19, 31-017 Kraków - T: (012) 4225566, Fax: 4226137, Internet: http://www.gwc.net/czartor. Head: Prof. Janusz A. Ostrowski
Fine Arts Museum - 1801
Excavations from Mesopotamia, Ancien Egypt, Greek art, Roman art, permanent exhibition of the Czartoryski Coll, Decorative Art, Venetian glassware, 16th-18th c Czech, Silesian, Polish and German glassware, Italian and Spanish majolica, Viennese, Meissen, Polish and French porcelain, Persian rugs, furniture, 550 paintings (eg 'The Lady with the Ermine' by Leonardo da Vinci), miniatures and sculptures, The Armoury, Prints Cabinet: about 35,000 prints, drawings, watercolours by Polish and foreign artists - Czartoryski Library 26823

Muzeum Czynu Niepodległościowego, Al Maja 7, 30-960 Kraków - T: (012) 225566, Fax: 226137
Historical Museum 26824

Muzeum Czynu Zbrojnego Pracowników Huty im. Tadeusza Sendzimira, Os. Górali 23, 31-961 Kraków - T: (012) 6443517. Head: Władysław Sadowski
Military Museum 26825

Muzeum Dzieje i Kultura Żydów, Muzeum Historyczne Miasta Krakowa (Museum of History of the City of Cracow, Jewish Department), ul Szeroka 24, 31-053 Kraków - T: (012) 4220962, Fax: 4220962, E-mail: alteszul@poczta.onet.pol. Head: Eugeniusz Duda
Historical Museum - 1958
Jewish ceremonial art 26826

Muzeum Emeryka Hutten-Czapskiego, Muzeum Narodowego w Krakowie (Emeryk Hutten-Czapski Museum), ul Józefa Piłsudskiego 12, 31-109 Kraków - T: (012) 222733, Fax: 225434. Head: Iwona Korzeniewska
Historical Museum
Numismatics, prints, drawings, watercolours, old Books and manuscripts - library 26827

Muzeum Etnograficzne (Ethnographical Museum), pl Wolnica 1, 31-060 Kraków - T: (012) 6565601, Fax: 6563612. Head: Maria Zachorowska
Ethnology Museum - 1910
Polish folk culture, non-European ethnographical coll from Asia, Africa, South America, 18th-19th c coll Siberia, Indonesia and Cameroon - library, archives 26828

Muzeum Farmacji, Collegium Medicum Uniwersytetu Jagiellońskiego (Museum of Pharmacy, Collegium Medicum at the Jagiellonian University), ul Floriańska 25, 31-019 Kraków - T: (012) 4219279, E-mail: Muzeum.Farmacji.UJ@mp.pl. Head: Dr. Leszek Jan Ekiert
Special Museum / Science&Tech Museum - 1946
Hist and development of pharmacy, interiors of old pharmacies, pharmacy celler and laboratory from the 17th c, herbarium and drying room, drug trade, receptacles, antique apothecary jars - library, archives 26829

Muzeum Geologiczne, Wydziału Geologii, Geofizyki i Ochrony Środowiska AGH (Museum of the Academy of Mining and Metallurgy), Al Mickiewicza 30, 30-059 Kraków - T: (012) 172365, Fax: 332936. Head: Remigiusz Molenda
Science&Tech Museum - 1959
Mathematics, physics, chemistry, geology, mining, electrotechnology, metallurgy, ceramics - library 26830

Muzeum Geologiczne Instytutu Nauk Geologicznych Polska Adademia Nauk (Laboratory and Museum of Geology of Younger Structures of the Polish Academy of Sciences), ul Senacka 1-3, 31-002 Kraków - T: (012) 4221910, 4228920, Fax: 4221609, E-mail: ndlaptas@cyf-kr.edu-pl. Head: Dr. Andrzej Łaptaś
Natural History Museum
Exhibits from Poland with special emphasis on Southern Poland 26831

Muzeum Historii Fotografii, ul Józefitów 16, 30-045 Kraków - T: (012) 6345932, Fax: 6330637, E-mail: foto@mhf.krakow.pl, Internet: http://www.mhf.krakow.pl. Head: Maciej Beiersdorf
Historical Museum 26832

Muzeum Historyczne Miasta Krakowa (History Museum of the City of Cracow), Rynek Główny 35, 31-011 Kraków - T: (012) 223264. Head: Andrzej Szczygieł
Historical Museum - 1899
Hist of Polish Jews, Polish martyrdom (1939-1945), hist of theatre in Cracow, hist of printing in Cracow, coll of clocks, arms, paintings, graphics, old photographs, crafts, cribs 26833

Muzeum Katedralne Jana Pawła II, ul Wawel 2, 31-001 Kraków - T: (012) 222643. Head: Maria Rojek
Religious Arts Museum - 1978
Copies of Kings crowns, coronations copes, liturgical vestments, vestments of John Paul II, pope 26834

Muzeum Lotnictwa Polskiego (Polish Aviation Museum), Al Jana Pawła II 39, 30-969 Kraków - T: (012) 4127855, Fax: 4127855, E-mail: muzlot@bci.krakow.pl, Internet: http://www.muz-lotnictwa.krakow.pl./muzeum_home.html. Head: Krzysztof Radwan
Science&Tech Museum - 1967
Aircraft and aero engines exhibited at the former Rakowice-Czyżyny airport - library, restoration dept, photo archives 26835

Muzeum Narodowe, Biblioteka Czartoryskich, ul Św. Marka 17, 31-018 Kraków - T: (012) 4224079/1172, E-mail: bczart@poland.com. Head: Jolanta Lenkiewicz
Library with Exhibitions 26836

Muzeum Narodowe w Krakowie (National Museum in Cracow), al 3 maja 1, 30-062 Kraków - T: (012) 6343377, Fax: 6339767, E-mail: dyrekcja@muz-nar.krakow.pl, Internet: http://www.nar-krakow.pl. Head: Zofiasz Gołubiew
Historical Museum / Fine Arts Museum - 1879
Polish painting and sculpture from early middle ages till today, Polish drawings, etchings, aquarelles, applied art, arms and armour, Far Eastern art, numismatics, prints, textiles, costumes, European paintings, European applied art - library 26837

Muzeum Odona Bujwida, Lubicz 34 m. 8, Kraków - T: (012) 4215329
Special Museum 26838

Muzeum Pamięci Narodowej, pl Bohaterów Getta 18, Kraków - T: (012) 6565625
Historical Museum 26839

Muzeum Przyrodnicze Instytutu Systematyki i Ewolucji Zwierząt PAN (Natural Science Museum of the Polish Academy of Sciences), ul Sebastiana 9, 31-049 Kraków - T: (012) 4228937, Fax: 4222791. Head: Prof. Wiesław Krzemiński
Natural History Museum - 1863
Entomology, mammals, reptiles, amphibians from the Pliocene and Pleistocene 26840

Muzeum Stanisława Wyspiańskiego, Muzeum Narodowego w Krakowie, ul Kanonicza 9, 31-002 Kraków - T: (012) 4228337. Head: Marta Romanowska
Fine Arts Museum 26841

Muzeum Teatralne, Muzeum Historycznego m. Krakowa, ul Szpitalna 21, 31-024 Kraków - T: (012) 4226824. Head: Krystyna Solańska
Historical Museum 26842

Muzeum Ubezpieczeń (Insurance Museum), ul Dunajewskiego 3, 31-133 Kraków - T: (012) 4228216, Fax: 4215060. Head: Marianna Halota
Historical Museum - 1987
More than 38,000 exhibits from different insurance firms from Poland and foreign countries (insurance policies, prints, memorial medals, photographies, periodicals etc), coll of industrial, economic and prevential insurances from 1803 - library 26843

Muzeum Uniwersytetu Jagiellońskiego Collegium Maius (Jagiellonian University Museum), ul Jagiellońska 15, 31-010 Kraków - T: (012) 4220549, 4221033, Fax: 4222734, E-mail: info@maius.in.uj.edu.pl, Internet: http://www.uj.edu.pl/Muzeum. Head: Prof. Dr. Stanisław Waltoś
University Museum - 1867
Portrait gallery, sculptures, prints, numismatics, goldsmithery, textiles, ancient art, instruments, globes, scientific instruments 26844

Muzeum w Dworkuk Matejki, ul Wańkowicza 25, Kraków - T: (012) 6445674
Special Museum 26845

Muzeum Zoologiczne Instytutu Zoologii Uniwersytetu Jagiellońskiego (Zoological Museum of the Jagiellonian University), ul R. Ingardena 6, 30-060 Kraków - T: (012) 6336377 ext 2416, Fax: 6343716, E-mail: wojt@zuk.iz.uj.edu.pl. Head: Prof. Janusz Wojtusiak
Natural History Museum - 1782/1969
Natural hist, zoology, Nowicki coll of Diptera and fishes, shells, Lepidoptera of African, Neotropical and Palaearctic regions 26846

Oddział Zbiorów Graficznych i Kartograficznych, Biblioteka Jagiellońska (Graphic and Cartographical Collections of the Jagiellonian Library), Al Mickiewicza 22, 30-059 Kraków - T: (012) 6336377, Fax: 6330903, E-mail: hordynsk@if.uj.edu.pl
Fine Arts Museum
Prints, drawings, exlibris, photography, postcards 26847

Ośrodek Biograficzny Komisji Turystyki Górskiej, Gabinet prof. Kazimierza Sosnowskiego, ul Westerplatte 15, 21-033 Kraków - T: (012) 4227431. Head: Andrzej Matuszczyk
Fine Arts Museum 26848

Pałac Sztuki w Krakowie, pl Szczepański 4, Kraków - T: (012) 4226616, E-mail: ysrzepin@kinga.cyf-kr.edu.pl, Internet: http://www.palac-sztuki.krakow.pl
Fine Arts Museum 26849

Regionalne Muzeum Młodej Polski PTTK Rydlówka, ul W. Tetmajera 28, 31-352 Kraków - T: (012) 6370750, Fax: 6370750. Head: Maria Rydel
Local Museum 26850

Stara Synagoga → Muzeum Dzieje i Kultura Żydów

Walka i Męczeństwo Polaków w latach 1939-1945, Muzeum Historyczne Miasta Krakowa (Historical Museum of the city of Cracow - The Fight and Martyrdom of the Poles in 1939-1956), ul Pomorska 2, 30-039 Kraków - T: (012) 6331414. Head: Jacek Salwiński
Historical Museum
Documents and photographs presenting Cracow during World War II and after war, Gestapo cells in Cracow 26851

Zamek Królewski na Wawelu - Państwowe Zbiory Sztuki (Wawel Royal Castle - State Art Collections), Wawel 5, 31-001 Kraków - T: (012) 4225155, Fax: 4221950, E-mail: zamek@wawel.krakow.pl, Internet: http://www.wawel.krakow.pl. Head: Prof. Jan Ostrowski
Fine Arts Museum - 1930
King Sigismund Augustus' 16th c coll of Flemish tapestries, of Oriental tents and carpets, armoury, Royal Treasury and memorabilia, Italian and Netherlandish painting, furnishings of the Royal Chambers / Italian furniture and ceramics, Delft ceramics, Archaeological coll - library 26852

Kraśnik

Muzeum 24 Pułku Ułanów, Muzeum Regionalnego w Kraśniku, ul Piłsudskiego 7, 23-200 Kraśnik - T: (081) 8845031. Head: Zbigniew Wichrowski
Military Museum 26853

Muzeum Regionalne, Muzeum Lubelskiego w Lublinie (Regional Museum), ul Klasztorna 3, 23-200 Kraśnik - T: (081) 8843485. Head: Zbigniew Wichrowski
Local Museum 26854

Krasnobród

Parafialne Muzeum Regionalne (Regional Parish Museum), ul Tomaszowska 16, 22-440 Krasnobród - T: (084) 8327098. Head: Roman Marszalec
Local Museum 26855

Krasnystaw

Muzeum Regionalne (Regional Museum), ul J. Piłsudskiego 3, 22-300 Krasnystaw - T: (082) 5763663, E-mail: muzekrasQpolbox.com, Internet: http://free.polbox.pl/m/muzekras. Head: Władysław Fedorowicz
Local Museum - 1958
History, archeology, ethnography, numismatics, natural history, esp. archeology and primaeval history of the town, Polish portrait of the 18th and early 19th cc., artistic handycrafts (18th-early 20th cc.), in a former Jesuit monastery 26856

Krośniewice

Muzeum im. Jerzego Dunin-Borkowskiego (Jerzy Dunin-Borkowski Museum), Plac Wolności 1, 99-340 Krośniewice - T: (042) 523347, Fax: 547782. Head: Kazimierz Śwircz
Local Museum - 1978
Painting, graphic art and drawing, numismatics, applied art, arms, old prints - archives, library 26857

Krosno

Muzeum Misyjne (Mission Museum), ul Łukasiewicza 62, 38-400 Krosno - T: (013) 4321676. Head: Maria Motyka
Religious Arts Museum 26858

Muzeum Okręgowe (District Museum), ul Piłsudskiego 16, 38-400 Krosno - T: (013) 4321376, Fax: 4324301. Head: Jan Gancarski
Local Museum - 1954
Archeology, history of lighting, history of oil exploration, local history, art, contemporary glass coll 26859

Muzeum Rzemiosła (Folk Art Museum), ul Piłsudskiego 17, 38-400 Krosno - T: (013) 4324188. Head: Ewa Mańkowska
Folklore Museum 26860

Krotoszyn

Muzeum Regionalne PTTK im. Hieronima Ławniczaka (Museum of the Krotoszyn Region), Mały Rynek 1, 63-700 Krotoszyn - T: (064) 52615. Head: Helena Kasperska
Local Museum - 1957
Ethnography, history, archeology 26861

Muzeum Ziemi Krotoszyńskiej, pl 1 Maja 1, 63-700 Krotoszyn - T: (064) 2615
Local Museum 26862

Krynica

Muzeum Nikifora, Galeria Sztuki Romanówka, Bulwary Dietla 19, 33-380 Krynica - T: (018) 715303. Head: Wacław Kawiorski
Fine Arts Museum 26863

Muzeum Parafialne, Muzeum Diecezjalnego w Tarnowie (Parish Museum), ul Kościelna 2, 33-380 Krynica - T: (018) 712388. Head: Kazimierz Markowicz
Religious Arts Museum 26864

Krzemionki koło Ostrowca

Rezerwat Archeologiczny i Muzeum w Krzemionkach k. Ostrowca, Muzeum Historyczno-Archeologicznego w Ostrowcu (Archeological Reserve), Ostrowiec Świętokrzyski, 27-400 Krzemionki koło Ostrowca - T: (047) 620978, Fax: 653651. Head: Czesław Zybała
Archaeological Museum - 1922
Exhibition depicting flint mining and processing in the later Stone Age (c 2000 BC) 26865

Krzeszowice

Muzeum Ziemi Krzeszowickiej, ul Krakowska 30, Krzeszowice - T: (012) 2821494
Local Museum 26866

Kudowa Zdrój

Skansen Kultury Ludowej Pogórza Sudeckiego, ul Pstrążna 13, 57-350 Kudowa Zdrój - T: (074) 662843. Head: Dr. Euzebiusz Gil
Open Air Museum 26867

Kutno

Muzeum Regionalne (Regional Museum), pl Piłsudskiego 21, 99-300 Kutno - T: (024) 547964. Head: Maurycy Żmuda
Local Museum 26868

Kwidzyn

Muzeum w Kwidzynie, Muzeum Zamkowego w Malborku (Castle Museum), ul Katedralna 1, 82-500 Kwidzyn - T: (055) 793889, Fax: 793889. Head: Dr. Antoni J. Pawłowski
Archaeological Museum - 1950
Archaeology, history, applied arts, ethnography, natural hist 26869

Lanckorona

Izba Muzealna im. Antoniego Krajewskiego, Rynek, 34-143 Lanckorona
Local Museum - 1975 26870

Łańcut

Muzeum Zamek w Łańcucie, ul Zamkowa 1, 37-100 Łańcut - T: (017) 2252008, Fax: 2252012, E-mail: dyrektor@zamek.dnet.pl. Head: Wit Karol Wojtowicz
Historical Museum - 1944
Interiors from the 17th-20th c (Zodiac Hall, Ceiling Hall, Rococo Salon, Boucher drawing room, Chinese room, Ballroom), Art Coll: Polish and foreign art, majolica, porcelain, carriages, carriages, icon coll - library, synagoge 26871

Lębork

Muzeum w Lęborku, ul Młynarska 14/15, 84-300 Lębork - T: (059) 622414. Head: Elżbieta Kal
Local Museum - 1952
Archeology, furniture, arms, minerals 26872

Łęczna

Muzeum Regionalne, Muzeum Lubelskiego w Lublinie, ul Bóżnicza 17, 21-010 Łęczna - T: (081) 7520869. Head: Józefa Ewa Leśniewska
Local Museum - 1966
Local hist, ethnography, archeology, hist of art, military hist, in a 17th c synagogue 26873

Łęczyca

Muzeum w Łęczycy, ul Zamkowa 1, 99-100 Łęczyca - T: (0114) 2543. Head: Anna Dłużwska-Sobczak
Local Museum - 1949
History, ethnography, natural hist, in a 14th c castle 26874

Lednogóra

Muzeum Pierwszych Piastów na Lednicy, Dziekanowice 32, 62-261 Lednogóra - T: (061) 4275010, Fax: 4275020, E-mail: mpp@info.poznan.pl. Head: Andrzej Kaszubkiewicz
Open Air Museum - 1969
Weapons (10th-12th c), relics of castle from 10th-11th c, folk architecture of Wielkopolska region (18th-20th c) - library, archive, paleoecological laboratory 26875

Wielkopolski Park Etnograficzny, Muzeum Pierwszych Piastów na Lednicy, Dziekanowice 23, 62261 Lednogóra - T: (061) 2475040, Fax: 2475020, E-mail: mpp@info.poznan.pl. Head: Antoni Pełczyk
Open Air Museum 26876

Legnica

Muzeum Miedzi (Copper Museum), ul Partyzantów 3, 59-220 Legnica - T: (076) 8620289, 8624949, Fax: 8620289, E-mail: muzeum-miedzi@kki.net.pl. Head: Andrzej Niedzielenko
Local Museum - 1962
Archeology, utilitarian and artistic objects of copper, technology of copper production, local history, 19th-20th c Polish painting, contemporary copper sculpture, in a baroque palace from the 18th c 26877

Legnickie Pole

Muzeum Bitwy Legnickiej, Muzeum Miedzi w Legnicy (Museum of the Battle of Legnica), pl Henryka Pobożnego 3, 59-241 Legnickie Pole - T: (076) 8582398, Fax: 8620289. Head: Walentyna Trzepacz
Historical Museum - 1961
Hist of the battle with the Tatars in 1241, in a former 13th-14th c sacral edifice 26878

Leśnica

Muzeum Czynu Powstańczego, Muzeum Śląska Opolskiego w Opolu, ul Powstańców Śląskich 1, 47-150 Leśnica - T: (077) 617966. Head: Dr. Zyta Zarzycka
Historical Museum - 1964
Hist of the revolutionary movement against the Germans in the Nazi period 26879

Leszno

Muzeum Okręgowe w Lesznie (District Museum in Leszno), pl dra Metziga 17, 64-100 Leszno - T: (065) 5206781, Fax: 5292986. Head: Witold Omieczyński
Local Museum - 1950
Local hist, hist of the Leszczyński family in the 16th-17th c and Sułkowski family in the 18th c, folk costumes, furniture, farm implements, weaving implements, Polish painting 26880

Letnica

Lubuskie Muzeum Wojskowe w Zielonej Górze z/s w Drzonowie, Drzonów 54, 66-014 Letnica - T: (068) 3211856, Fax: 3211829, Internet: http://free.polbox.pl/l/leszekch. Head: Dr. Włodzimierz Kwaśniewicz
Military Museum 26881

Leżajsk

Muzeum Prowincji oo Bernardynów, pl Mariacki 8, 37-300 Leżajsk - T: (0195) 20006
Religious Arts Museum 26882

Lidzbark

Muzeum Pożarnictwa, ul Nowy Rynek 15, 13-230 Lidzbark - T: (0215) 61568. Head: Maksymilian Anger
Local Museum 26883

Lidzbark Warmiński

Muzeum Warmińskie, Muzeum Warmii i Mazur w Olsztynie, pl Zamkowy 6, 11-100 Lidzbark Warmiński - T: (089) 7672111. Head: Edward Radtke
Local Museum 26884

Limanowa

Muzeum Regionalne Ziemi Limanowskiej, ul Józefa Marka 13, 34-600 Limanowa - T: (018) 372042. Head: Jan Wielek
Local Museum 26885

Lipce Reymonotowskie

Muzeum im. Władysława St. Reymonta, Muzeum Okręgowego w Żyrardowie, ul Wiatraczna 10, 96-127 Lipce Reymonotowskie - T: (046) 756112. Head: Zbigniew Nagiełło
Local Museum 26886

Liw

Muzeum Zbrojownia (Museum-Armoury), ul S. Batorego 2, 07-121 Liw - T: (025) 7925717, Fax: 7925717, E-mail: zamekliw@poland.com. Head: Anna Ambroż
Military Museum - 1963
Arms and weapons from the 15th-20th c, coll of Polish sarmatian painting from the 17th-18th c, in a 15th c Gothic castle and in a 18th c Baroque manorhouse 26887

Łódź

Centralne Muzeum Włókiennictwa (Central Museum of Textiles), ul Piotrkowska 282, 93-034 Łódź - T: (042) 6843355, Fax: 6843355, E-mail: ctmustex@muzeumwlokiennictwa.muz.pl. Head: Norbert Zawisza
Historical Museum - 1960
Hist of textiles, folk weaving, hist of textile technology, hist of textile industry, modern tapestry, Garments of 19th & 20th cc - library 26888

Miejska Galeria Sztuki, ul Wólczańska 31, 90-607 Łódź - T: (042) 6327995, Fax: 6303372, E-mail: wystawy@miejskagaleria.lodz.pl, Internet: http://www.miejskagaleria.lodz.pl
Public Gallery
Painting, graphic art 26889

Muzeum Archeologiczne i Etnograficzne (Archaeological and Ethnographic Museum), pl Wolności 14, 91-415 Łódź - T: (042) 6328440, Fax: 6329714. Head: Prof. Ryszard Grygiel
Archaeological Museum - 1929
Archeology, Paleolithic Age, Neolithic Age, Bronze Age, early Iron age, late La Tène and Roman periods, period of the Great Migration and Middle Ages, numismatics, ethnography - library, radiocarbon workshop, conservation section 26890

Muzeum Archidiecezji Łódzkiej (Łódź Archidiocesan Museum), ul Skorupki 1, 90-458 Łódź - T: (042) 375844, Fax: 361696. Head: Jerzy Spychała
Religious Arts Museum 26891

Muzeum Historii Miasta Łodzi (Museum of History of the City of Łódź), ul Ogrodowa 15, 91-065 Łódź - T: (042) 6540323, Fax: 9540202/323, E-mail: poznansk@poznanskipalace.pl, Internet: http://www.poznanskipalace.muz.pl. Head: Ryszard Czubaczyński
Local Museum - 1975
Artur Rubinstein coll - library 26892

Muzeum Historii Ruchu Rewolucyjnego w Łodzi, ul Gdańska 13, 90-706 Łódź - T: (042) 336442
Historical Museum 26893

Muzeum Kinematografii, pl Zwyciestwa 1, 93-502 Łódź - T: (042) 740957. Head: Dr. Antoni Szram
Special Museum 26894

Muzeum Książki Artystycznej, ul Tymienieckiego 24, Łódź - T: (042) 6748968
Special Museum 26895

Muzeum Martyrologii i Walki, Oddział Muzeum Historii Ruchu Rewolucyjnego w Łodzi, Radogoszcz, ul Zgierska 147/151, 91-490 Łódź - T: (042) 57 93 34
Local Museum 26896

Muzeum Polskiej Wojskowej Służby Zdrowia, ul Gen. Żeligowskiego 7-9, 90-752 Łódź - T: (042) 339660. Head: Dr. Czesław Jésman
Local Museum 26897

Muzeum Przyrodnicze Uniwersytetu Łódzkiego (Museum of Natural History of the Łódź University), ul Kilińskiego 101, 90-011 Łódź - T: (042) 6390493, 6390490, 6390489, E-mail: jbanb@biol.uni.lodz.pl, Internet: http://taxus.biol.uni.lodz.pl/muzeum.htm. Head: Prof. Jerzy Bańbura
Natural History Museum - 1930
Paleontology, zoology, entomology 26898

Muzeum Sportu i Turystyki (Museum of Sport and Tourism), ul Skorupki 21, 90-532 Łódź - T: (042) 368358. Head: Dr. Andrzej Bogusz
Special Museum - 1981
Olympic prizes (medals and diplomas), special coll, sport art (pictorial art, graphic art, sculptures), sports accessories of 19th and 20th c, bicycles, light athletics accessories - library, archive 26899

Muzeum Sztuki w Łodzi (Museum of Art in Łódź), ul Więckowskiego 36, 90-734 Łódź - T: (042) 6339790, Fax: 6329941, E-mail: muzeum@muzeumsztuki.lodz.pl, Internet: http://www.muzeumsztuki.lodz.pl. Head: Mirosław Borusiewicz
Fine Arts Museum - 1930
International and Polish contemporary and modern art, esp constructivism of the 1930s (Władysław Strzemiński, Katarzyna Kobro, Henryk Stażewski) - Residence Księży Młyn - Interior of the end of 19th c 26900

Rezydencja Księży Młyn, Muzeum Sztuki w Łodzi, ul Przędzalniana 72, 90-338 Łódź - T: (042) 6749698, Fax: 6749982, E-mail: museumct@krysia.um.lodz.pl. Head: Mirosław Borusiewicz
Fine Arts Museum 26901

Łomża

Muzeum Północno-Mazowieckie, ul Krzywe Koło 1, 18-400 Łomża - T: (086) 2165192, Fax: 2165192. Head: Jerzy Jastrzębski
Local Museum - 1948
Early medieval archaeology, regional hist and art, numismatics, ethnography, folk sculpture, amber, paraffin lamps 26902

Łopuszna

Muzeum Kultury Szlacheckiej (The Manor House in Łopuszna), 34-432 Łopuszna - T: (018) 2653919, Internet: http://www.muzeum.zakopane.top.pl. Head: Małgorzata Ronowicz
Local Museum
Typical furnishings of a Polish Manor in the Podhale region, art, applied art 26903

Łosice

Muzeum Regionalne w Łosicach, ul Siedlecka 7, 08-200 Łosice - T: (057) 377
Ethnology Museum 26904

Łowicz

Muzeum w Łowiczu, Rynek Kościuszki 4, 99-400 Łowicz - T: (046) 373928. Head: Walerian Warchałowski
Local Museum - 1959
Prehistoric and early-historic archeology, history, ethnography, open-air centre of folk architecture, natural history 26905

Lubaczów

Muzeum w Lubaczowie, ul Sobieskiego 4, 37-600 Lubaczów - T: (010) 321802. Head: Zygmunt Kubrak
Local Museum
Archaeology, history, numismatics, ceramics, ethnography 26906

Lubań

Muzeum Regionalne (Regional Museum), Rynek 1, 59-800 Lubań - T: (075) 7223213. Head: Bożena Adamczyk-Pogorzelska
Local Museum 26907

Lubartów

Muzeum Regionalne, Muzeum Lubelskiego w Lublinie, ul Kościuszki 28, 21-100 Lubartów - T: (0836) 2808. Head: Anna Żmuda
Local Museum - 1970
Ethnography, numismatics, history, archeology, 19th c ceramics manifactury 26908

Lublin

Dworek Wincentego Pola, Oddział Muzeum Lubelskiego w Lublinie, ul Kalinowszczyzna 13, 20-129 Lublin - T: (081) 772413. Head: Władysława Wojtysiak
Local Museum 26909

Muzeum Archidiecezjalne Lubelskie (Lublin Archidiocesan Museum), ul Filaretów 7, 20-609 Lublin - T: (081) 5251201, E-mail: muzeum@kuria.lubin.pl, Internet: http://www.kuria.lublin.pl/str-muze.htm. Head: Eugeniusz Kościołko
Religious Arts Museum 26910

Muzeum Diecezjalne Sztuki Religijnej, ul Podwale 15, 20-117 Lublin - T: (081) 21871
Fine Arts Museum 26911

Muzeum-Dworek Wincentego Pola, Muzeum Lubelskiego w Lublinie, ul Kalinowszczyzna 13, 20-129 Lublin - T: (081) 7472413. Head: Władysława Wojtysiak
Special Museum - 1972
Bibliographical coll relating to Wincenty Pol (1807-1872), poet, writer and scientist in the field of geography, coll of old Polish globes 26912

Muzeum Historii Miasta Lublina, Muzeum Lubelskiego w Lublinie (Museum of the History of Lublin), pl Łokietka 3, 20-109 Lublin - T: (081) 5326001. Head: Jadwiga Chmielak
Local Museum 26913

Muzeum Katolickiego Uniwersytetu Lubelskiego im. Ks. Władzińskiego, Al Racławickie 14, 20-950 Lublin
University Museum 26914

Muzeum Literackie im. Józefa Czechowicza, Muzeum Lubelskiego w Lublin (Józef Czechowicz Museum), ul Narutowicza 10, 20-004 Lublin - T: (081) 5320277. Head: Ewa Łos
Special Museum - 1968
Memorabilia on the poet Józef Czechowicz (1903-1939), in a 17th c cloister 26915

Muzeum Lubelskie (District Museum), ul Zamkowa 9, 20-117 Lublin - T: (081) 5321743, Fax: 5321743, E-mail: dyrektor@zamek-lublin.pl, Internet: http://www.zamek-lublin.pl. Head: Zygmunt Nasalski
Local Museum - 1906
Archeology, ethnography, Polish and foreign painting, graphics and applied art, numismatics, iconographic coll, history, military coll - library, conservation dept, The Chapel of Lublin Castle (Gothic architecture, Russo-Byzanthine frescoes from 1418) 26916

Muzeum Martyrologii Pod Zegarem, Muzeum Lubelskiego w Lublinie, ul Uniwersytecka 1, 20-029 Lublin - T: (081) 5333678
Historical Museum 26917

Muzeum Wsi Lubelskiej, al Warszawska 96, 20-833 Lublin - T: (081) 5338513, Fax: 5333051, E-mail: skansen@skansen.lublin.pl. Head: Dr. Mieczysław Kseniak
Open Air Museum / Agriculture Museum - 1970
Vernacular, wooden architecture, furnishing, household equipment agricultural tools 26918

Państwowe Muzeum na Majdanku (State Museum at Majdanek), ul Droga Męczenników Majdanka 67, 20-325 Lublin - T: (081) 7442640, Fax: 7440526, E-mail: majdanek@lu.onet.pl, Internet: http://www.majdanek.pl. Head: Edward Balawejder
Historical Museum - 1944
Former concentration camp, gas chambers, crematorium, prisoners' barracks, hist of the Nazi policy of extermination, resistance movement, archives, documents, photogr, modern graphic, painting, sculpture - library, archives 26919

Luboń

Muzeum Martyrologiczne w Żabikowie, ul Niezłomnych 2, Luboń - T: (061) 8130681, Fax: 8103411. Head: Andrzej Beryt
Historical Museum 26920

Łuków

Muzeum Regionalne (Regional Museum), ul Piłsudskiego 19, 21-400 Łuków - T: (0255) 2716. Head: Longin Kowalczyk
Local Museum - 1964
Folk art, weaving, local hist, documents from the years of Nazi occupation 26921

Malbork

Muzeum Zamkowe (Castle Museum), ul Starościńska 1, 82-200 Malbork - T: (055) 723364, Fax: 2722405, Internet: http://www.malbork.pl/zamek. Head: Mariusz Mierzwiński
Historic Site - 1961
Arms, medals, history of the castle, amber coll, archeology, medieval sculptures, numismatics, in a 13th-14th c castle, built by the Teutonic Knights, medieval archit. details coll, old engravings and modern ex-libris coll, old stove tiles coll, old stained-glass windows coll 26922

Miechów

Muzeum Kościuszkowskie PTTK, ul Racławicka 26, 32-200 Miechów - T: (0498) 327 08. Head: Radosław Kluza
Local Museum - 1908
Natural history, geology, prehistoric archeology, local history, numismatics 26923

Muzeum Regionalne PTTK (Regional Museum), ul Sobieskiego 4, 32-200 Miechów - T: (0498) 305 28. Head: Ewa Kilian
Local Museum 26924

Międzychód

Muzeum Regionalne, ul 17 stycznia 100, 64-400 Międzychód - T: 701
Local Museum 26925

Międzyrzecz

Muzeum w Międzyrzeczu, ul Podzamcze 2, 66-300 Międzyrzecz - T: (095) 412567. Head: Joanna Patorska
Local Museum - 1946
Archeology, ethnography, history of art, applied arts, in a 17th-18th c building, portraits found on the coffin second half of the 17th c - first half of the 18th c - Departement in Pszczew 26926

Międzyzdroje

Muzeum Przyrodnicze Wolińskiego Parku Narodowego im. Prof. Adama Wodziczki (Adam Wodziczko Natural History Museum of Wolin Natural Park), ul Niepodległości 3, 72-510 Międzyzdroje - T: (097) 3280737, Fax: 3280357. Head: Lech Zużałek
Natural History Museum - 1962
Flora and fauna of Wolin island, geology, dendrology, entomology, ornithology, nature of the Baltic Coast 26927

Mielec

Jadernówka, Fotograficzny Muzeum Regionalnego w Mielcu, ul Jadernych 19, 39-300 Mielec - T: (0196) 2271. Head: Janusz Zborowski
Fine Arts Museum 26928

Muzeum Regionalne (Regional Museum), ul Legionów 73, 39-300 Mielec - T: (0196) 4232. Head: Janusz Zborowski
Local Museum - 1978
Regional coll, photographic coll, judaica, archeology, numismatics 26929

Mikołajki

Muzeum Reformacji Polskiej, Muzeum Okręgowego w Suwałkach, ul Kolejowa 6, 11-730 Mikołajki - T: (0878) 16087. Head: Władysław Pilchowski
Local Museum - 1973
Documents of the Reformation from the 16th c in all languages 26930

Mirosławiec

Muzeum Walk o Wał Pomorski przy Miejsko-Gminnym Ośrodku Kultury, ul Parkowa 1, 78-650 Mirosławiec - T: (067) CR587411. Head: Zofia Kobusiewicz
Local Museum 26931

Mława

Muzeum Ziemi Zawkrzańskiej (Museum of the Zawkrzańska Region), ul 3 Maja 5, 06-500 Mława - T: (023) 543348. Head: Andrzej Grzymkowski
Local Museum - 1926
Archaeology, history, art, numismatics, natural hist, paintings by W. Piechowski 26932

Morąg

Muzeum im. J.G. Herdera w Morągu, Oddział Muzeum Warmii i Mazur w Olsztynie, ul Dąbrowskiego 54, 14-300 Morąg - T: (089) 7572848. Head: Magdalena Bartoś
Local Museum 26933

Muzeum Warmii i Mazur w Olsztynie, Oddzial w Meragu → Muzeum im. J.G. Herdera w Morągu

Mosina

Ośrodek Muzealno-Dydaktyczny Wielkopolskiego Parku Narodowego (Museum-Didactic Centre of Wielkopolski National Park), Jeziory, 62-050 Mosina - T: (061) 8136299, Fax: 8136299, E-mail: wpnarod@optimus.poznan.pl, Internet: http://www.city.poznan.pl. Head: Zygfryd Kowalski
Natural History Museum - 1952
Natural hist, environmental sciences 26934

Mrągowo

Muzeum Ziemi Mrągowskiej, Muzeum Warmii i Mazur w Olsztynie, ul Ratuszowa 5, 11-700 Mrągowo - T: (089) 7412812. Head: Alina Wierzbicka
Local Museum 26935

Mrówki

Skansen Archeologiczny w Mrówkach, Muzeum Okręgowego w Koninie (Open Air Museum for Archeology), 62-550 Mrówki - T: (063) CR701555. Head: Krzyštof Gorczyca
Archaeological Museum / Open Air Museum
Departement of the District Museum in Konin 26936

Muszyna

Muzeum Regionalne PTTK, ul Kity 26, 33-370 Muszyna - T: (018) 714140. Head: Barbara Rucka
Local Museum - 1958
Folklore, folk art, local history, in a 15th c building 26937

Myślenice

Muzeum Regionalne, ul Sobieskiego 3, 32-400 Myślenice - T: (012) 2720211. Head: Irena Kuczek
Local Museum - 1953
Ethnology, folk art, costumes, local history, archeology, natural history 26938

Myślibórz

Muzeum Regionalne, Ośrodek Edukacji Plastycznej i Historycznej, ul Bohaterów Warszawy 74, 74-300 Myślibórz - T: (095) 472448. Head: Ryszard Jobke
Local Museum 26939

Mysłowice

Entralne Muzeum Pożarnictwa, ul Stadionowa, 41-400 Mysłowice - T: (032) 1223733. Head: Feliks Barbarowicz
Historical Museum 26940

Muzeum Pożarnictwa, ul Powstańców 27, 41-400 Mysłowice - T: (032) 225388
Special Museum 26941

Nakło nad Notecią

Muzeum Ziemi Krajeńskiej, ul Pocztowa 14, 89-100 Nakło nad Notecią - T: (052) 853249. Head: Robert Tomaszewski
Local Museum - 1964
Archeology, local hist 26942

Nałęczów

Muzeum Bolesława Prusa (Bolesław Prus Museum), Al Małachowskiego 2, 24-140 Nałęczów - T: (081) 5014552. Head: Halina Lubomiła Bukowska
Historic Site - 1961
Life and literary work of the Polish positivist, B. Prus (1847-1912), manuscripts, photographs, books, periodicals, foreign language editions 26943

Muzeum Stefana Żeromskiego (Stefan Żeromski Museum), ul Stefana Żeromskiego 2, 24-140 Nałęczów - T: (081) 5014780. Head: Maria Mironowicz-Panek
Special Museum - 1928
Memorabilia on the poet Stefan Żeromski (1864-1925) in his summer house 26944

Namysłów

Muzeum w Namysłowie, Namysłowskiego Ośsodka Kultury, ul Chrobrego 30b, 46-100 Namysłów - T: (077) 4101211. Head: Jadwiga Kawecka
Local Museum 26945

Nieborów

Pałac Radziwiłłów w Nieborowie, Muzeum Narodowego w Warszawie (The Radziwill Palace in Nieborów), 99-416 Nieborów - T: (046) 8385623/35, Fax: 385635. Head: Ewa Swiecka
Local Museum - 1945
Palace of Nieborów: 17th-19th c interiors, Greek and Roman sculptures, Helena Radziwill coll, lapidarium, Polish and foreign painting, decorative art, majolica, 18th c Park in Arkadia, pseudo-antique and romantic edifices - library 26946

Niedzica

Muzeum Zamku w Niedzicy (Castle Museum), Zamek, 34-441 Niedzica - T: (018) 2629473, 2629480/489, Fax: 2629480. Head: Dr. Jerzy Baranowski
Historical Museum / Folklore Museum - 1964
Old furniture, 17th-19th c portrait gallery, in a 14th-15th c Gothic castle, folklore coll 26947

Niepołomice

Muzeum Sztuki Nowoczesnem (Museum of Modern Art), Ul Zamkowa 2, 32-005 Niepołomice - T: (012) 4210278, Fax: 4210278, E-mail: potocka@bunkier.com.pl. Head: Maria Anna Potocka
Fine Arts Museum 26948

Nieszawa

Muzeum im. Stanisława Noakowskiego, Muzeum Ziemi Kujawskiej i Dobrzyńskiej (Stanisław Noakowski Museum), ul A. Mickiewicza 6, 87-730 Nieszawa - T: (054) 831168. Head: Ryszard Lewandowski
Fine Arts Museum - 1983
Drawings, designes and souvenirs of Stanisław Noakowski, exposed in the house he was born in 26949

Nowa Ruda

Muzeum Górnictwa Podziemnego (Mining Museum), ul Obozowa 4, 57-401 Nowa Ruda - T: (074) 8723501, 8724624, Fax: 8724624
Science&Tech Museum 26950

Muzeum Prof. Josepha Wittiga, ul Słupiecka 42, 57-400 Nowa Ruda - T: (074) 8724624, Fax: 8724624
Special Museum 26951

Nowa Słupia

Muzeum Starożytnego Hutnictwa Świętokrzyskiego im. prof. M. Radwana, Muzeum Techniki w Warszawie (Museum of Ancient Metallurgy), ul Świętokrzyska 59, 26-006 Nowa Słupia - T: (041) 177018. Head: Lucyna Spelak
Science&Tech Museum
Hist of metallurgy in the region of the Świętokrzyskie Mountains, furnaces, documents and mementoes connected with the struggle for independence and World War II 26952

Nowa Sól

Muzeum Miejskie, ul Muzealna 20, 67-100 Nowa Sól - T: (068) 873640, Fax: 3873640, E-mail: muzeum@gamma.com.pl, Internet: http://www.gamma.com.pl/muzeum. Head: Krystyna Bakalarz
Natural History Museum - 1947
Natural history, archeology, militaria, numismatics, ethnology, in a 19th c palace 26953

Nowe Miasto Lubawskie

Muzeum Ziemi Lubawskiej, ul 19 Stycznia 17a, 13-300 Nowe Miasto Lubawskie - T: (0511) 42824. Head: Zbigniew Ewertowski
Local Museum - 1959
Ethnography, domestic utensils, ceramics, archeology, history, in a 14th c Gothic building 26954

Nowe Miasto nad Pilicą

Muzeum Regionalne, ul Koźmińskiego 7, 26-420 Nowe Miasto nad Pilicą - T: (048) 751011. Head: Jerzy Porada
Local Museum - 1961
Local history 26955

Nowogród

Skansen Kurpiowski im. Adama Chętnika, Muzeum Regionalne (Adam Chętnik Memorial Kurpic Region Open Air Museum), ul Zamkowa 25, 18-414 Nowogród - T: (086) 176562. Head: Urszula Kuczyńska
Open Air Museum - 1927
Apiculture, beehives, apiarian equipment, farm implements, handmills, domestic utensils 26956

Nowy Barkoczyn

Muzeum Hymnu Narodowego, Muzeum Narodowego w Gdańsku (Józef Wybicki Memorial Museum), Bedomin 16, 83-422 Nowy Barkoczyn - T: (058) 877424, Fax: 877424. Head: Henryk Wawrzyk
Historical Museum - 1978
Birthplace of Józef Wybicki (1747-1822), political leader, author of the Polish national anthem 26957

Nowy Sącz

Galeria Sztuki Dawna Synagoga, Muzeum Okręgowego w Nowym Sączu, ul Berka Joselewicza 12, 33-300 Nowy Sącz - T: (018) 421315. Head: Marek Wcześny
Fine Arts Museum - 1982
Contemporary art, art of Nowy Sacz, contemporary Polish pastel drawings, Judaica, interiors of middle-class house, Maria Ritter's paintings 26958

Muzeum Okręgowe (District Museum), ul Lwowska 3, 33-300 Nowy Sącz - T: (018) 4437708, Fax: 4437865, E-mail: domgotycki@poczta.onet.pl, Internet: http://www.nowy.sacz.pl/muzeum. Head: Wacław Kawiorski
Local Museum - 1938
Archaeology, numismatics, religious art, photos 26959

Sądecki Park Etnograficzny, Muzeum Okręgowego w Nowym Sączu, ul Wieniawy Długoszowskiego 83b, 33-300 Nowy Sącz - T: (018) 426412. Head: Wacław Kawiorski
Ethnology Museum 26960

Nowy Targ

Muzeum Podhalańskie PTTK, ul Sobieskiego 2, 34-400 Nowy Targ - T: (0187) 62377. Head: Stanisław Marek
Local Museum - 1962
History, ethnography, interiors 26961

Nowy Tomyśl

Muzeum Wikliniarstwa i Chmielarstwa, Muzeum Narodowego Rolnictwa i Przemysłu Rolno-Spożywczego w Szreniawie, Park Kultury i Wypoczynku, 64-300 Nowy Tomyśl - T: (0666) 22311. Head: Andrzej Chwaliński
Science&Tech Museum 26962

Nowy Wiśnicz

Muzeum Pamiątek po Janie Matejce "Koryznówka", 32-720 Nowy Wiśnicz - T: (014) 6128374. Head: Maria Serafińska-Domańska
Special Museum 26963

Nysa

Muzeum w Nysie, ul Biskupa Jarosława 11, 48-300 Nysa - T: (077) 4332083. Head: Elina Romińska
Local Museum - 1897
Archaeology, paintings, graphics, handicraft, furniture from Gothic to Biedermeier style, pewter, ceramics, history, guild documents, military accessories, photographs of Nysa and vicinity 26964

Oblęgorek

Muzeum Henryka Sienkiewicza w Oblęgorku, Muzeum Narodowe w Kielcach (Henryk Sienkiewicz Museum), Strawczyn, 26-067 Oblęgorek - T: (041) 110426. Head: Ireneusz Rębosz
Special Museum - 1958
Memorial to the writer Henryk Sienkiewicz (1846-1916), interiors, photographs, letters, portraits, translations 26965

Ochla

Muzeum Etnograficzne w Zielonej Górze z Siedzibą w Ochli, 66-006 Ochla 8 - T: (068) 211591. Head: Dr. Barbara Kołodziejska
Ethnology Museum 26966

Odporyszów

Muzeum Parafialne im. Jana Wnęka w Odporyszowie, Muzeum Diecezjalnego w Tarnowie, Żabno, 33-240 Odporyszów - T: (014) 456984. Head: Henryk Surma
Local Museum 26967

Ogródek

Muzeum im. Michąla Kajki w Ogródku, Muzeum Okręgowego w Suwałkach, Klusy, 19-323 Ogródek - T: (087) 237425. Head: Elżbieta Nieszczerzewska
Local Museum 26968

Ojców

Muzeum im. prof. Władysława Szafera, Willa Łokietek, 32-047 Ojców - T: (012) 3892040, Fax: 3892006. Head: Józef Partyka
Natural History Museum 26969

Muzeum Regionalne PTTK, 32-047 Ojców - T: (012) 3892036. Head: Andrzej Uracz
Local Museum - 1965
Local and natural hist, geology, archeology 26970

Olesno

Muzeum im. Jana Nikodema Jaronia (Nikodem Jaroń Regional Museum), Rynek 20, 46-300 Olesno - T: (034) 582438. Head: Wojciech Łonak
Local Museum - 1960
Ethnography, farmhouse interior, hist of the struggle for national liberation in the 19th-20th c 26971

Olkusz

Muzeum Afrykanistyczne im. dra Bogdana Szczygła, ul Szpitalna 32, 32-300 Olkusz - T: (035) 432226. Head: Grażyna Praszelik-Kocjan
Fine Arts Museum 26972

Muzeum Pożarnictwa Ziemi Olkuskiej, ul Floriańska 5, 32-300 Olkusz - T: (032) 6432845. Head: Marian Konieczny
Science&Tech Museum 26973

Muzeum Regionalne PTTK im. Antoniego Minkiewicza, Rynek 20, 32-300 Olkusz - T: (035) 434227, Fax: 434227. Head: Barbara Stanek
Local Museum
Prehist and hist of Olkusz, silver mining 26974

Olsztyn

Muzeum Warmii i Mazur (Warmia and Mazuries Museum), ul Zamkowa 2, 10-074 Olsztyn - T: (089) 5279596, Fax: 5272039, E-mail: muzeum@mailbox.olsztyn.pl, Internet: http://www.olsztyn.pl. Head: Janusz Cygański
Local Museum - 1945
Archeology, ethnography, medieval and modern art, contemporary art, decorative and applied arts, natural history, regional history - library, departments in Lidzbark Warmiński, Morąg, Mrągowo, Reszel, Szczytno, Stębark 26975

Olsztynek

Muzeum Budownictwa Ludowego - Park Etnograficzny w Olsztynku (Museum of Folk Architecture - Ethnographic Park in Olsztynek), ul Sportowa 21, 11-015 Olsztynek - T: (089) 5192164, Fax: 5192164. Head: Tadeusz Kufel
Open Air Museum - 1913
56 examples of regional architecture from Ermland, Masuren, Oberland, Barten, Sambinen and Memelland, interiors, tools, folk art - library 26976

Opatówek

Muzeum Historii Przemysłu, ul Kościelna 1, 62-860 Opatówek - T: (062) 5618626. Head: Roman Hauk
Local Museum - 1981
Polish pianos, industrial laces and embroideries, 19th c machines - library 26977

Opinogóra

Muzeum Romantyzmu (Museum of Romanticism), ul Krasińskiego 5, 06-406 Opinogóra - T: (023) 717025. Head: Janusz Królik
Special Museum - 1961
History of the period of Romanticism, mementoes connected with Zygmunt Krasiński (1812-1859), one of the leading poets of Polish Romanticism, in a small 19th c Neo-Gothic castle 26978

Opoczno

Muzeum Regionalne, pl Zamkowy, 26-300 Opoczno - T: (044) 552319. Head: Jan Łuczkowski
Local Museum
Local hist, folk art, ethnography, in a Gothic castle 26979

Opole

Centralne Muzeum Jeńców Wojennych w Łambinowicach -Opolu (Central Museum of Prisoners of War), ul Minorytów 3, 45-017 Opole - T: (077) 4537872, 4539216, Fax: 4537872, E-mail: cmjw@polbox.com, Internet: http://www.uni.opole.pl./cmjw. Head: Dr. Czesław Wawrzyniak
Historical Museum - 1964
Remains the of prisoners of war camp, cemetery where 60,000 prisoners of war from Soviet Union are buried 26980

Muzeum Diecezjalne w Opolu (Diocesan Museum), ul Bolesława Kardynała Kominka 1a, 45-032 Opole - T: (077) 4530015, 456015. Head: Dr. Piotr Maniurka
Religious Arts Museum 26981

Muzeum Śląska Opolskiego (Museum of Silesia Opole), Mały Rynek 7, 45-020 Opole - T: (077) 4544611, Fax: 4536677, E-mail: mso@po.opole.pl, Internet: http://www.opole.pl/muzea/mso. Head: Elwira Holc
Local Museum - 1900
Archaeology, hist of the city and region of Opole, medieval and modern sculptures, Polish painting of the 19th-20th c, natural hist, local ethnography 26982

Muzeum Wsi Opolskiej (Museum of the Opole Countryside), ul Wrocławska 174, 45-835 Opole - T: (077) 4743021, 4572349, Fax: 4743021, E-mail: mwsio@uni.opole.pl, Internet: http://www.uni.opole.pl/mwo. Head: Jarosław Gałęza
Open Air Museum - 1961
Wooden architecture, interiors, tools, agricultural equipment, folk costumes 26983

Oporów

Muzeum w Oporowie, 99-322 Oporów - T: (024) 521822. Head: Grażyna Majewska
Local Museum - 1949
Fine art coll 17th-19th c, (painting and decorative art including furniture) in a 15th c, Gothic castle 26984

Osiek nad Notecią

Muzeum Kultury Ludowej, Muzeum Okręgowego w Pile (Folk Art Museum), ul Dworcowa 10, 89-333 Osiek nad Notecią - T: (067) 864051. Head: Stefan Rola
Folklore Museum 26985

Ostrołęka

Muzeum Okręgowe (District Museum), pl Gen. J. Bema 8, 07-400 Ostrołęka - T: (029) 5443. Head: Bernard Kielak
Local Museum 26986

Ostrów Wielkopolski

Muzeum Miasta Ostrowa Wielkopolskiego, Rynek-Ratusz, 63-400 Ostrów Wielkopolski - T: (062) 5928052, 5928062, E-mail: muzeum@muzeum.ostrow-wielkopolski.pl, Internet: http://www.muzeum.ostrow-wielkopolski.pl. Head: Witold Banach
Local Museum 26987

Ostrowiec Świętokrzyski

Muzeum Historyczno-Archeologiczne, ul Świętokrzyska 37, 27-400 Ostrowiec Świętokrzyski - T: (047) 653651, Fax: 653651. Head: Wojciech Kotasiak
Local Museum - 1966
Local hist, hist of regional metallurgy, porcelain and faience production, in a 19th c palace of the Wielopolski family 26988

Ostrzeszów

Muzeum Regionalne, Rynek 19, 63-500 Ostrzeszów - T: (064) 7302042. Head: Mirosława Rzepecka
Local Museum 26989

Oświęcim

Państwowe Muzeum w Oświęcimiu-Brzezince (State Museum of Oświęcim-Brzezinka (Auschwitz-Birkenau)), ul Więźniów Oświęcimia 20, 32-603 Oświęcim - T: (033) 432022, Fax: 431934. Head: Jerzy Wróblewski
Historical Museum - 1947
Memorial of the Martyrdom of the Polish Nation on the grounds of the former concentration camp Auschwitz-Birkenau, established in 1940. About four million people of various nationalities were murdered in the camp, history of extermination, photographs, documents, camp prison, torture cells, instruments of torture, gas chambers, crematoria - library 26990

Ożarów

Muzeum Wnętrz Dworskich, Muzeum Ziemi Wieluńskiej (Museum of Interial Manor), 98-342 Ożarów - T: (0199) 11724. Head: Bogusława Wiluś
Fine Arts Museum - 1981
Manor house from 1757, Polish portraits, furniture, carpets, silver, embroidery, laces, porcelain, glass, hunting weapons, docs, books 26991

Pabianice

Muzeum Miasta Pabianice, Stary Rynek 1-2, 95-200 Pabianice - T: (042) 153982. Head: Urszula Maria Jaros
Local Museum - 1907
Archeology and history, ethnography (coll of Central Africa and Asia), folk art of the region, natural history, in a 16th c estate 26992

Paczków

Muzeum Gazownictwa, ul Pocztowa 6, 48-370 Paczków - T: (077) 4316834. Head: Adam Król
Science&Tech Museum 26993

Pakość

Muzeum Parafialne, ul Inawrocławska 3, 88-170 Pakość - T: (0536) 518543
Local Museum 26994

Palmiry

Muzeum Walki i Męczeństwa w Palmirach, Muzeum Historyczne Miasta Starego Warszawy (Museum of War and Martyrology in Palmiry), Czosnów, 05-152 Palmiry - T: (022) 7850046. Head: Prof. Janusz Durko
Historical Museum - 1973 26995

Paszyn

Muzeum Parafialne im. Ks. Edwarda Nitki, Filia Muzeum Diecezjalnego w Tarnowie (Parish Museum), 33-327 Paszyn - T: (018) 432524. Head: Stanisław Janas
Religious Arts Museum 26996

Pelplin

Muzeum Diecezjalne (Diocesan Museum), ul ks. Biskupa Dominika 11, 83-130 Pelplin - T: (069) 1361221, Fax: 361699. Head: Dr. Roman Ciecholewski
Religious Arts Museum - 1928
Medieval painting and sculpture from Pomerania, in an episcopal palace 26997

Pieniężno

Muzeum Misyjno-Etnograficzne, Seminarium Duchownego Księży Werbistów, Kolonia 19, 14-520 Pieniężno - T: (055) 436031, Fax: 436702. Head: Dr. Eugeniusz Śliwka
Ethnology Museum 26998

Piła

Museum Okręgowe im. Stanisława Staszica, ul Chopina 1, 64-920 Piła - T: (069) 127137. Head: Jan Niedźwiecki
Local Museum
Local history, archeology - Dept. in Osiek nad Notecią 26999

Muzeum Stanisława Staszica, ul Browarna 18, 64-920 Piła - T: (067) 131567. Head: Józef Olejniczak
Special Museum - 1951
Memorial to Stanisław Staszic (1755-1826) in his birthplace, letters, first editions of his publications, natural history, drawings, Staszic's geological maps 27000

Pińczów

Muzeum Regionalne (Regional Museum of Pinczov), ul J. Piłsudskiego 2a, 28-400 Pińczów - T: (0496) 3572472, Fax: 3577353, E-mail: mrpinczow@wp.pl. Head: Jerzy Znojek
Local Museum - 1963 27001

Piotrków Trybunalski

Muzeum Okręgowe, pl Zamkowy 4, 97-300 Piotrków Trybunalski - T: (044) 477046. Head: Stanisław Gąsior
Local Museum - 1908
Archeology, history, art, numismatics, ethnography - Departement in Polichno 27002

Pisz

Muzeum Ziemi Piskiej, Oddział Muzem Okręgowego w Suwałkach, pl Dzierżyńskiego 8, 12-200 Pisz - T: (0117) 322 64. Head: Mieczysław Kulęgowski
Natural History Museum 27003

Płock

Muzeum Diecezjalne (Diocesan Museum), ul Tumska 3a, 09-402 Płock 6 - T: (024) 2622623, 2624323. Head: Bronisław Gwiazda
Religious Arts Museum - 1903
Sculpture, Italian, Dutch, French, Spanish and Polish painting, woodcuting, goldsmithery, textiles, liturgical garments, glassware and ceramics, history 27004

Muzeum Mazowieckie w Płocku (Mazovian Museum in Płock), ul Tumska 2, 09-402 Płock - T: (024) 2624491, Fax: 2624493, E-mail: muzeum@free.plock.pl. Head: Tadeusz Zaremba
Local Museum - 1821
Polish painting, applied art, contemporary art, art Nouveau, Art Dèco, folk sculpture, history of the region, archeology,ethnography, numismatics - archives, library, granary 27005

Poddębice

Regionalna Izba Muzealna, 99-200 Poddębice - T: (043) 782991. Head: Paweł Duraj
Local Museum - 1961
Local history, in a historical late-Renaissance palace 27006

Podegrodzie

Muzeum Lachów Sądeckich im. Zofii i Stanisława Chrząstowskich, Sądecki Park Etnograficznego w Nowym Sączu, 33-386 Podegrodzie - T: (018) 459033. Head: Wacław Kawiorski
Local Museum - 1961
Folk art and culture, crafts, farm implements 27007

Podkowa Leśna

Muzeum im. Anny i Jarosława Iwaszkiewiczów w Stawisku, ul Gołębia 1, 05-807 Podkowa Leśna - T: (022) 7589363, Fax: 7291421. Head: Oskar Koszutski
Fine Arts Museum 27008

Polanica Zdrój

Mission and Folklore Museum, ul Reymonta 1, 57-320 Polanica Zdrój - T: (074) 681317
Ethnology Museum
Folklore from Peru, Zaïre and Polynesia 27009

Muzeum Kamieni Szlachetnych (Precious Stones Museum), ul Bolesława Chrobrego 5, 57-320 Polanica Zdrój - T: (074) 681119
Special Museum 27010

Polichno

Muzeum Czynu Partyzanckiego, Muzeum Okręgowe w Piotrkowie Trybunalskim (Museum of Partisan Struggle), 97-322 Polichno - T: (044) 464769. Head: Zofia Rell
Historical Museum
Hist of the partisan struggle, maps, uniforms, mementoes 27011

Poręba Wielka

Muzeum Biograficzne Władysława Orkana, Muzeum im. Wł. Orkana w Rabce (Władysław Orkan's House 'Orkanówka'), Poręba Wielka 109, 34-635 Poręba Wielka - T: (018) CR 378811. Head: Jadwiga Zapałowa
Historic Site - 1979
Memorabilia of the poet Władisław Orkan (1875-1930), family belongings 27012

Poznań

Galeria Miejeska Arsenał (Arsenal Municipal Gallery), Stary Rynek 3, 61-772 Poznań - T: (061) 8529502, E-mail: office@arsenal.info.poznan.pl, Internet: http://arsenal.info.poznan.pl. Head: Wojciech Makowiecki
Public Gallery 27013

Mieszkanie-Pracownia Kazimiery Iłłakowiczówny, Biblioteka Raczyńskich, c/o Oddział Biblioteki Raczyńskich, ul Gajowa 4, Poznań - T: (061) 8473645. Head: Wioletta Sytek
Special Museum 27014

Muzeum Akademii Medycznej (Academic Museum of Medicine), Ul Sieroca 10, 61-000 Poznań - T: (061) 8522544. Head: Roman Meissner
Historical Museum 27015

Muzeum Archeologiczne (Archaeological Museum), Pałac Górków, Ul Wodna 27, 61-781 Poznań - T: (061) 8528251, 8526430, Fax: 8531010, E-mail: muzarp@man.poznan.pl, Internet: http://www.muzarp.poznan.pl. Head: Prof. Lech Krzyżaniak
Archaeological Museum - 1857
Archaeological relics from the Stone Age, Bronze Age, Iron Age and medieval period, Neolithic and Predynastic periods of the Sudan and Egypt - library 27016

Muzeum Archidiecezjalne (Archdiocesan Museum), ul Ks. I. Posadzego 2, 61-108 Poznań - T: (061) 8526195. Head: Marian Lewandowski
Religious Arts Museum - 1893
Sacral painting and sculptures, applied art, textiles, numismatics - library 27017

Muzeum Armii Poznań, Wielkopolskie Muzeum Walk Niepodległościowych w Poznaniu (Museum of the Poznań Army), Cytadela - Mała Śluza, 61-663 Poznań - T: (061) 8204503. Head: Jarosław Bączyk
Historical Museum - 1982
Hist of the Polish Armed Forces 1918-39 27018

Muzeum Broni Pancernej (Tank Museum), Ul Wojska Polskiego 84, 61-000 Poznań - T: (061) 8575166. Head: Tomasz Ogrodniczak
Military Museum
Tanks from the WW II 27019

Muzeum Etnograficzne, Muzeum Narodowego w Poznaniu (Museum of Folk Culture and Art), Ul Grobla 25, od Ul Mostowej 7, 61-858 Poznań - T: (061) 8523006, Fax: 8515898. Head: Maria Kośko
Ethnology Museum - 1911
Carved roadside posts from Great Poland, folk painting and sculpture, costumes, ceramics, exhibits from New Guinea, Africa, Asia, pre-Columbian Central American ceramics 27020

Museum-Fort VII, Oddział Muzeum Historii Ruchu Robotniczego w Poznaniu, ul Polska, 60-595 Poznań - T: (061) 8483138
Local Museum 27021

Muzeum Historii Miasta Poznania, Muzeum Narodowe w Poznaniu (Museum of the History of the City of Poznań), Stary Rynek 1, 61-772 Poznań - T: (061) 8525613, 8528011, Fax: 8515898. Head:

Magdalena Mrugalska-Banaszak
Local Museum - 1954
Hist of the town from the 13th c to the present day, in 13th-14th c city hall, Renaissance Town Hall rebuilt by G.B. Quadro 27022

Muzeum Instrumentów Muzycznych, Muzeum Narodowe w Poznaniu, Stary Rynek 45, 61-772 Poznań - T: (061) 8520857, Fax: 8515898. Head: Janusz Jaskulski
Music Museum - 1945
Coll of over 1600 musical instruments, 16th-20th c Polish string instruments, memorials of Frédéric Chopin, folk instruments, musical instruments from archaeological excavations, membraphones, idiophones, cordophones - library 27023

Muzeum Literackie Henryka Sienkiewicza, c/o Oddział Biblioteki Raczyńskich, Stary Rynek 84, 61-772 Poznań - T: (061) 8522496. Head: Ignacy Moś
Special Museum 27024

Muzeum Martyrologii Wielkopolan w Forcie VII, Wielkopolskiego Muzeum Historycznego w Poznaniu (Museum of Martyrdom), Al Polska, 60-595 Poznań - T: (061) 8483138. Head: Leszek Wróbel
Historical Museum
Memorabilia and documents on WWII and Nazi occupation 27025

Muzeum Motoryzacji Automobilklubu Wielkopolski, Pod Rondem Kaponiera, 61-000 Poznań - T: (061) 8476359
Science&Tech Museum 27026

Muzeum Narodowe, Galeria Malarstwa i Rzeźby (National Museum), Al Marcinkowskiego 9, 61-745 Poznań - T: (061) 8568000, 8525969, Fax: 8515898, E-mail: mnpweb@info.com.pl, Internet: http://mnp.info.poznan.pl/main.html. Head: Wojciech Suchocki
Fine Arts Museum - 1857
Medieval art, European paintings 14th-19th c, Polish paintings 15th-20th c, prints, drawings, sculpture, numismatics, modern art 27027

Muzeum przy Zakładach Metalowych im. Hipolita Cegielskiego, ul 28 Czerwca 1956 r. 219, 61-485 Poznań - T: (061) 8312440, Fax: 8333149. Head: Bolesław Januszkiewicz
Science&Tech Museum - 1966
Machinery, development of industrial technology, hist of the labour movement 27028

Muzeum Sztuk Użytkowych, Muzeum Narodowe w Poznaniu (Museum of Applied Arts), Góra Przemysła 1, 61-768 Poznań - T: (061) 8522035, 8568185, Fax: 8515898, E-mail: mnoffice@man.poznan.pl, Internet: http://mnp.info.poznan.pl, http://www.info.poznan.pl/Culture-Museums/AppliedArt. Head: Zygmunt Dolczewski
Decorative Arts Museum - 1965
Small coll of early Meissen Porcelain, Venetian, Bohemian, German and Silesian glassware, clocks, arms, silver and tin tablewares, Polish gold sashes, tapestries, East carpets, Japanese tsubas, Far East ceramics, European miniatures and snuff-boxes 27029

Muzeum Uzbrojenia - Cytadela Poznańska, Wielkopolskie Muzeum Walk Niepodległościowych w Poznaniu (Museum of the Poznań-Citadel), Ul Armii Poznań, 61-663 Poznań - T: (061) 8204503. Head: Jan Wieczorek
Historical Museum - 1965
Hist of the Citadel, hist of Polish aviation - open air park 27030

Muzeum Wiedzy o Środowisku, ul Bukowska 19, 60-809 Poznań - T: (061) 8475601, Fax: 8473668. Head: Prof. Dr. Lech Ryszkowski
Natural History Museum 27031

Pracownia - Muzeum Józefa Ignacego Kraszewskiego, Biblioteka Raczyński (Jozef I. Kraszewski Museum), ul Wroniecka 14, Poznań - T: (061) 8551244. Head: Krzysztof Klupp
Special Museum / Library with Exhibitions 27032

Wielkopolskie Muzeum Wojskowe, Muzeum Narodowe w Poznaniu (The Wielkopolskie Military Museum), Stary Rynek 9, 61-772 Poznań - T: (061) 8526739, Fax: 8515898. Head: Tadeusz Jeziorowski
Military Museum - 1919
Polish and foreign weapons and armaments, liberation struggles in Poland (1794, 1830-31, 1848, 1863, 1918-19), uniforms, banners, military signs - archives, library 27033

Zbiory Sprzętu Ratownictwa Kolejowego, Ul Kolejowa 23, 61-000 Poznań - T: (061) 8635419. Head: Jacek Piątek
Science&Tech Museum 27034

Prudnik

Muzeum Ziemi Prudnickiej, ul Chrobrego 11, 48-200 Prudnik - T: (077) 4363808, Internet: http://www.prudnik.umig.gov.pl/kultura/muzeum.htm. Head: Urzula Rzepiela
Local Museum - 1959
Local hist 27035

Pruszków

Muzeum Starożytnego Hutnictwa Mazowieckiego (Museum of Ancient Mazovian Metallurgy), pl Jana Pawła II 2, 05-800 Pruszków - T: (022) 7587266, Fax: 7587266. Head: Stefan Woyda
Archaeological Museum - 1975
West Mazovian archaeological sources concerning ancient metallurgy from the period of Roman influences 27036

Przasnysz

Muzeum Historyczne, Muzeum Okręgowego w Ostrołęce, Ratusz, Rynek 1, 06-300 Przasnysz - T: (0478) 2866. Head: Janina Żbikowska
Local Museum 27037

Przemyśl

Muzeum Archidiecezjalne (Garden Museum), Pl Czackiego 2, 37-700 Przemyśl - T: (016) 6716454, Fax: 6716425. Head: Zbigniew Bielamowicz
Religious Arts Museum / Natural History Museum - 1902
Painting, sculpture, applied arts, liturgical garments, in a 17th c church, gardening 27038

Muzeum Narodowe Ziemi Przemyskiej, Pl T. Czackiego 3, 37-700 Przemyśl - T: (016) 6789335, 6750152, Fax: 6789335
Local Museum 27039

Przeworsk

Muzeum Pożarnicze, Dział Muzeum w Przeworsku, Park Miejski 6, 37-200 Przeworsk - T: (010) 3165
Special Museum 27040

Muzeum w Przeworsku, Zespół Pałacowo-Parkowy, Pałac Lubomirskich, Park 2, 37-200 Przeworsk - T: (016) 6487145, Fax: 6488642. Head: Ewa Zaremba
Fine Arts Museum / Decorative Arts Museum / Science&Tech Museum / Local Museum / Folklore Museum - 1978
Dept of palace interior and palace carriages, dept of town and regional hist, dept of fire guard hist (palace stable) 27041

Przysucha

Muzeum im. Oskara Kolberga, Muzeum Wsi Radomskiej w Radomiu, ul WOP 11, 26-400 Przysucha - T: (048) 752248. Head: Katarzyna Markiewicz
Fine Arts Museum 27042

Pszczew

Muzeum Regionalne, Muzeum w Międzyrzeczu, 66-330 Pszczew - T: (095) 150. Head: Włodzimierz Nowak
Local Museum 27043

Pszczyna

Muzeum Skansen, Aleja Parkowa, 43-200 Pszczyna - T: (032) 2103493. Head: Aniela Kraciak
Local Museum 27044

Muzeum Zamkowe (Castle Museum), ul Brama Wybrańców 1, 43-200 Pszczyna - T: (032) 4490888, 2103037, Fax: 4490333, E-mail: kancelaria@muzeum.pszczyna.top.pl, Internet: http://www.muzeum.pszczyna.top.pl. Head: Dr. Maciej Kluss
Fine Arts Museum - 1946
Original 19th c interiors, arms, hunting trophies, miniatures 27045

Regionalne Muzeum Prasy i Drukarstwa Śląskiego, ul Piastowska 26, 43-200 Pszczyna - T: (032) 2213
Science&Tech Museum 27046

Puck

Muzealne Zbiory Rybackie im. Józefa Budzisza, ul Morska 13, Puck - T: (058) 732972
Local Museum 27047

Muzeum Ziemi Puckiej (Museum of the Puck Region), pl Wolności 28, 84-100 Puck - T: (058) 6732996/229, Fax: 6732229, E-mail: mzpuck@poczta.onet.pl. Head: Mirosław Kuklik
Ethnology Museum / Local Museum
Kashubian ethnography, hist of the Puck region 27048

Szpitalki, Muzeum Ziemi Puckiej, ul Wałowa 11, Puck - T: (058) 732229
Local Museum 27049

Puławy

Muzeum Oświatowe, Szkolne Schronisko Młodzieżowe Muzeum Oświatowe w Puławach, ul Włostowicka 27, 24-100 Puławy - T: (081) 8877129. Head: Ewa Szpakowska
Local Museum - 1987
Old schoolbooks, photos, documents, old certificates 27050

Muzeum Regionalne PTTK, ul Czartoryskich 6a, 24-100 Puławy - T: (081) 878674. Head: Józef Gądor
Local Museum - 1949
Archeology, ethnography, graphics, paintings, furniture 27051

Pułtusk

Muzeum Regionalne, Rynek 1, 06-106 Pułtusk - T: (0238) 3132. Head: Anna Henrykowska
Local Museum 27052

Puszczykowo

Muzeum-Pracownia Literacka Arkadego Fiedlera, ul Słowackiego 1, 62-041 Puszczykowo - T: (061) 133794. Head: Marek Fiedler
Special Museum - 1973 27053

Pyzdry

Muzeum Regionalne (Museum of the Region of Pyzdry), pl Kaliski 25a, 62-415 Pyzdry - T: (063) 768107. Head: Robert Michał Czerniak
Local Museum - 1957
Arms, guild books, documents, costumes, numismatics, local history 27054

Rabka

Muzeum im. Władysława Orkana (Wladyslaw Orkan's Museum), ul Sadecka 6, 34-700 Rabka - T: (187) 2676289, Fax: 2676365. Head: Maria Sokól-Augustyńska
Folklore Museum - 1936
Fishing, hunting, sheepherding, crafts, costumes, folk culture, folk art - Departement in Poręba Wielka 27055

Racibórz

Muzeum w Raciborzu, ul Rzeźnicza 15, 47-400 Racibórz - T: (032) 4154901, Fax: 4154901. Head: Joanna Muszała-Ciałowicz
Local Museum - 1927
Archaeology, ethnography, art, history, egyptology 27056

Radom

Jacek Malczewski Muzeum, Rynek 11, 26-600 Radom - T: (048) 3622114, Fax: 3623481, E-mail: - jacek_malczewski_museum@wp.pl. Head: Janusz Pulnar
Local Museum - 1923
19th-20th c Polish painting, ethnography, archeology, natural history, ornithology, paleontology 27057

Muzeum Sztuki Współczesnej, Muzeum im. Jacka Malczewskiego w Radomiu (Museum of Modern Art), Rynek 4-5, 26-600 Radom - T: (048) 3622550, Fax: 3623481, E-mail: - museum_modernart_radom@wp.pl. Head: Mieczysław Szewczuk
Fine Arts Museum - 1990
Polish modern art after 1945 27058

Muzeum Wsi Radomskiej, ul Szydłowiecka 30, 26-600 Radom - T: (048) 25591. Head: Małgorzata Jurecka
Local Museum 27059

Radomsko

Muzeum Regionalne, ul Narutowicza 1, 97-500 Radomsko - T: (044) 835651. Head: Bożena Błaszczyk
Local Museum - 1970
Folk art, archaeology 27060

Radzyn Chełmiński

Muzeum Regionalne, Muzeum Ziemi Bydgoskiej im. L. Wyczółkowskiego, Radzyn Chełmiński
Local Museum
Local history in the 13th-14th c castle of the Teutonic Knights 27061

Rakoniewice

Wielkopolskie Muzeum Pożarnictwa PTTK, ul Kościelna 1, 64-067 Rakoniewice - T: (0666) 41158
Local Museum 27062

Rawa Mazowiecka

Muzeum Ziemi Rawskiej, ul Łowicka 26, 96-200 Rawa Mazowiecka - T: (0492) 4569. Head: Joanna Sienkiewicz
Local Museum - 1966
Archeology, numismatics, ethnography - library 27063

Rawicz

Muzeum Ziemi Rawickiej, Rynek 1, Ratusz, 63-900 Rawicz - T: (065) 453575. Head: Bożena Rawluk-Raus
Local Museum - 1972
Archeology, history, ethnography 27064

Reszel

Galeria Zamek w Reszlu, Muzeum Warmii i Mazur w Olsztynie, ul Podzamcze 3, 11-440 Reszel - T: (089) 7550109. Head: Jolanta Marschall
Public Gallery 27065

Rogalin

Muzeum Narodowe w Poznaniu, Oddział w Rogalinie, ul Arciszewskiego 21, 62-022 Rogalin - T: (061) 138030, Fax: 138357. Head: Joanna Nowak
Fine Arts Museum - 1949
French, Dutch and Polish furniture 17th-20th c, Meissen, Polish and Russian porcelain, Polish painting and sculpture, French and German painting 19th - 20th c, French garden and English park 27066

Rogierówko

Punkt Etnograficzny w Rogierówku, Muzeum Pierwszych Piastów na Lednicy w Lednogórze, ul Podgórna 2, 60-480 Rogierówko - T: (061) 482051. Head: Tadeusz Marszewski
Ethnology Museum 27067

Rogów

Muzeum Lasu i Drewna przy Lesnym Zakładzie Doświadczalnym SGGW (Warsaw Agriculture University Experimental Forest Station - Museum of Forestry and Wood), ul Akademicka 20, 95-063 Rogów - T: (046) 8748374, Fax: 8748374, E-mail: cepl@witch.sggw.waw.pl. Head: Marek Sławski
Natural History Museum 27068

Rogoźnica

Państwowe Muzeum Gross-Rosen w Rogoźnicy, ul Starachowicka 9a, 58-300 Rogoźnica, mail addr: 58-152 Goczałków - T: (074) 551807, 541961. Head: Aleksandra Rudy
Historical Museum 27069

Rogoźno

Muzeum Regionalne im Wojciechy Dutkiewicz, Rogozińskie Centrum Kultury, pl K. Marcinkowskiego 1, 64-610 Rogoźno - T: (067) 2618078. Head: Lucyna Bełch
Local Museum - 1983
Local hist, memorabilia of Wojciecha Dutkiewicz, natural hist, folk culture site 27070

Romanów

Muzeum Józefa Ignacego Kraszewskiego (Józef Kraszewski Museum), Sosnówka, 21-518 Romanów - T: (057) CR 3792110. Head: Anna Czchodzińska-Przybysławska
Special Museum - 1962
Memorial to the writer J.I. Kraszewski (1812-1887), manuscripts, paintings, drawings, photos, various editions of his works 27071

Ruda Śląska

Muzeum Miejskie im. Maksymiliana Chroboka, ul Wolności 26, 41-700 Ruda Śląska - T: (032) 2484457, Fax: 2484457. Head: Michal Lubina
Historical Museum / Folklore Museum 27072

Russów

Oddział Literacki im. Marii Dąbrowskiej w Russowie, Muzeum Okręgowe Ziemi Kaliskiej w Kaliszu, Zelazków, 62-817 Russów - T: (062) 7691265, E-mail: muzeum@info.kalisz.pl, Internet: http://www.infokalisz.pl/Muzeum. Head: Grażyna Przybylska
Special Museum
Furniture, belongings of the writer Maria Dąbrowska, historic buildings 27073

Rybnik

Muzeum w Rybniku, Rynek 18, 44-200 Rybnik - T: (036) 4221423, Fax: 4225643, E-mail: muzeum@muzeum.rybnik.pl, Internet: http://www.muzeum.rybnik.pl. Head: Genowefa Grabowska
Local Museum - 1958
Ethnography, archeology, history and culture of the region, coal mining 27074

Ryn

Muzeum Regionalne im. Albina Nowickiego, pl Wolności 2, 11-520 Ryn - T: (0878) 180 61. Head: Wiesława Chmielewska
Local Museum 27075

Rypin

Muzeum Ziemi Dobrzyńskiej, ul Warszawska 20, 87-500 Rypin - T: (054) 2514
Local Museum 27076

Rzepiennik Strzyżewski

Muzeum Parafialne, Filia Muzeum Diecezjalnego w Tarnowie (Parish Museum), 33-163 Rzepiennik Strzyżewski. Head: Dr. Władysław Bochenek
Religious Arts Museum 27077

Rzeszów

Muzeum Etnograficzne im. Franciszka Kotuli, Muzeum Okręgowego w Rzeszowie, ul Rynek 6, 35-064 Rzeszów - T: (017) 8620217. Head: Dr. Krzysztof Ruszel
Ethnology Museum 27078

Muzeum Okręgowe (District Museum), ul 3 Maja 19, 35-030 Rzeszów - T: (017) 8535278. Head: Sylwester Czopek
Local Museum - 1935
Archaeology, ethnography, art, applied art, history, mementoes - library 27079

Sadowne

Muzeum Regionalne Ziemi Sadowieńskiej, ul Kościuszki, 07-140 Sadowne - T: (025) 75323838. Head: Leszek Sówka
Local Museum 27080

Sandomierz

Muzeum Diecezjalne Sztuki Kościelnej (Diocesan Museum), ul Długosza 9, 27-600 Sandomierz - T: (015) 322304. Head: Roman Chwałek
Religious Arts Museum - 1905
Archaeology, 18th-19th c glass painting, ceramics, old Polish noblemen's national dress, furniture, 15th-19th c religious painting of the Cracow school, tapestry, textiles 27081

Muzeum Historii Polskiego Ruchu Ludowego w Warszawie, Oddział w Sandomierzu, ul 11 Listopada 1, 27-600 Sandomierz - T: (015) 322141. Head: Stanisław Kos
Historical Museum 27082

Muzeum Literatury im. Jarosława Iwaszkiewicza, Muzeum Okręgowego w Sandomierzu, ul Katedralna 5, 27-600 Sandomierz - T: (015) 322147. Head: Jerzy Krzemiński
Special Museum 27083

Muzeum Okręgowe (District Museum), Rynek 10, 27-600 Sandomierz - T: (015) 322265. Head: Zofia Czub
Local Museum - 1956
Archaeology, ethnography, numismatics 27084

Sanok

Muzeum Budownictwa Ludowego (Museum of Folk Architecture), ul Traugutta 3, 38-500 Sanok - T: (013) 4630934, Fax: 4635381, E-mail: skansen.sanok@pro.onet.ol. Head: Jerzy Ginalski
Local Museum / Open Air Museum - 1958
The museum represents the ethnic group of Dolinianie, Pogórzanie, Łemkowie and Bojkowie, folk architecture, churches, cottages, water-mill and windmill, beehives, Carpathian icons - library, archive 27085

Muzeum Historyczne w Sanoku, ul Zamkowa 2, 38-500 Sanok - T: (013) 4630609, Fax: 4630609. Head: Wiesław Banach
Historical Museum - 1934
Archeology, numismatics, orthodox church art (Poland's largest coll of icons, dating from the 14th to the 19th c), painting gallery, ethnography, weapons and arms - library 27086

Sękowa

Ośrodek Budownictwa Ludowego w Szymbarku z filia w Bartnem, Muzeum Budownictwa Ludowego w Szymbarku (Open Air Museum of Szymbark and branch in Bartnem), Cerkiew, 38-307 Sękowa - T: 114. Head: Anna Bak
Open Air Museum - 1986
Ethnography 27087

Siedlce

Muzeum Diecezjalne (Diocesan Museum), ul Swirskiego 56, 08-110 Siedlce - T: (025) 6449865, Fax: 6417532, E-mail: muzeum_diecazjalne@siedlce.opoka.org.pl, Internet: http://www.muzeum.siedlce.pl. Head: Henryk Drozd
Religious Arts Museum 27088

Muzeum Okręgowe (Museum of the Region of Podlasie), ul Świerczewskiego 1, 08-110 Siedlce - T: (025) 24224, Fax: 27470. Head: Zofia Czapska
Local Museum
History, folk art, in an 18th c baroque city hall - Departement in Treblinka 27089

Sielpia

Muzeum Zagłębia Staropolskiego w Sielpi, Muzeum Techniki w Warszawie (Museum of the Old Poland Basin), Dziebałtów, 26-231 Sielpia - T: (0411) 21293. Head: Dr. Jerzy Jasiuk
Special Museum - 1934
Old machines, art, engineering, castings 27090

Siemiatycze

Muzeum Regionalne Siemiatycki Ośrodek Kultury, ul Zaszkolna 1, 17-300 Siemiatycze - T: (085) 552308. Head: Zenon Sielewonowski
Local Museum 27091

Sieradz

Muzeum Okręgowe, ul Dominikańska 2, 98-200 Sieradz - T: (043) 271639. Head: Czesław Rutkowski
Local Museum - 1953
Relics of Lusatian culture, folk art, Polish painting, Walewski's coll, documents about Sieradz - library 27092

Sierpc

Muzeum Wsi Mazowieckiej (Museum of Masovien Village), ul Narutowicza 64, 09-200 Sierpc - T: (024) 752883, Fax: 752883. Head: Jan Rzeszotarski
Open Air Museum - 1971
Folk architecture, interior, folk sculpture, ethnography, local hist - library, archives 27093

Skarżysko-Kamienna

Muzeum im. Orła Białego, ul Słoneczna 90, 26-110 Skarżysko-Kamienna - T: (047) 531331. Head: Andrzej Lange
Military Museum - 1969
Militaria, World War II 27094

Sławków

Muzeum Regionalne, Dział Kultury Dawnej Miejskiego Ośrodka Kultury, ul Rynek 9, 42-533 Sławków - T: (032) 1931396. Head: Barbara Noryńska
Local Museum 27095

Słońsk

Muzeum Martyrologii (Sonnenburg), ul 3 Lutego 54, 66-436 Słońsk - T: 66436. Head: Tadeusz Demski
Local Museum 27096

Słupca

Muzeum Regionalne, Filia Muzeum Okręgowego w Koninie, ul Warszawska 53, 62-400 Słupca - T: (063) 752640. Head: Andrzej Łukaszewski
Local Museum 27097

Słupsk

Muzeum Pomorza Środkowego (Museum of Central Pomerania), ul Dominikańska 5-9, 76-200 Słupsk - T: (059) 8424081/82, Fax: 8426518, E-mail: mariwoj@polbox.com, Internet: http://www.mars.slups.pl/mps. Head: Mieczysław Jaroszewicz
Local Museum - 1948
Regional hist and culture (14th-20th c), old and contemporary local folk art, Polish art (19th-20th) - Slovinian village - open air museum in Kluki 27098

Smołdzino

Muzeum Przyrodniczo-Leśne Słowińskiego Parku Narodowego (Museum of Natural History and Forest), ul Mostnika 1, 76-214 Smołdzino - T: (059) 116204. Head: Mariusz Zielonka
Natural History Museum - 1974
Birds, mammals, insects, minerals 27099

Sobibór

Muzeum Byłego Obozu Zagłady w Sobiborze, Muzeum Pojezierza Łęczyńsko-Włodawskiego, 22-231 Sobibór - T: (082) 5719867. Head: Krzysztof Skwirowski
Historical Museum 27100

Sobótka

Muzeum Gazownictwa, ul Czysta 1, 55-050 Sobótka - T: (071) 3162756
Science&Tech Museum
Gas work 27101

Muzeum Ślężańskie im. Stanisława Dunajewskiego, ul Św. Jakuba 18, 55-050 Sobótka - T: (071) 3162622, Fax: 3162622. Head: Wojciech Fabisiak
Local Museum - 1962
Archaeology, art, natural hist, local hist, lapidarium, in a 16th c building 27102

Sochaczew

Muzeum Fryderyka Chopina w Żelazowej Woli (Frédéric Chopin's House), 96-503 Sochaczew - T: (046) 8633300, Fax: 8634076. Head: Tadeusz Owczuk
Historic Site - 1932
Memorial to the composer F. Chopin in his birthplace, documents, furniture 27103

Muzeum Kolei Wąskotorowej, Muzeum Kolejnictwa w Warszawie (Narrow Gauge Railway Museum), ul Towarowa 7, 96-500 Sochaczew - T: (0494) 22405 w. 341. Head: Czesław Gwara
Science&Tech Museum - 1985
Narrow gauge rolling stock built between 1880 and 1950 27104

Muzeum Ziemi Sochaczewskiej, ul Kościuszki 2, 05-900 Sochaczew - T: (494) 233 09, 226 70. Head: Maciej Wojewoda
Local Museum 27105

Sopot

Muzeum Stutthof w Sztutowie, Oddział w Sopocie (Museum Stutthof, Department in Sopot), ul Kościuszki 63, 81-703 Sopot - T: (058) 512987. Head: Mirosława Godlewska
Historical Museum 27106

Sosnowiec

Muzeum Geologiczne Obszaru Górnośląskiego Instytutu Geologicznego, ul Białego 1, 41-200 Sosnowiec - T: (032) 662036
Science&Tech Museum 27107

Muzeum w Sosnowcu, ul Chemiczna 12, 41-200 Sosnowiec - T: (032) 660262, Fax: 667944. Head: Zbigniew Studencki
Natural History Museum 27108

Śrem

Muzeum Śremskie, ul Mickiewicza 89, 63-100 Śrem - T: (0667) 2835938. Head: Mariusz Kondziela
Local Museum 27109

Środa Śląska

Muzeum Regionalne (Regional Museum), pl Wolności 3, 55-300 Środa Śląska - T: (071) 3172795, Fax: 3172795. Head: Jacek Czajka
Local Museum - 1964
Local hist, woodwork 27110

Średzki Ośrodek Kultury Galeria, Pl Wolności 86, Środa Śląska - T: (071) 3172228
Local Museum 27111

Stara Kuźnica

Zabytkowa Kuźnia Wodna w Starej Kuźnicy, Filia Muzeum Techniki w Warszawie, Stara Kuźnica 46, 26-206 Stara Kuźnica. Head: Stanisław Niewęgłowski
Science&Tech Museum
Old forge driven by water, 18th c equipment 27112

Starachowice

Muzeum Regionalne PTTK, ul Krywki 1, 27-200 Starachowice - T: (047) 746268, Fax: 746268. Head: Edward Imiela
Local Museum 27113

Stargard

Muzeum w Stargardzie, Rynek Staromiejski 2-4, 73-110 Stargard - T: (091) 5772556, 5783835, Fax: 5772556, E-mail: info@muzeum-stargard.pl, Internet: http://www.muzeum-stargard.pl. Head: Slawomir Preiss
Local Museum - 1908/1960
Archeology, history, art, militaria, connected with the town 27114

Stary Sącz

Muzeum Regionalne im. Seweryna Udzieli (Regional Museum), Rynek 6, 33-340 Stary Sącz - T: (018) 4460094. Head: Jan Koszkul
Local Museum - 1947
Folk sculptures from the 18th-19th c, crafts, ceramics, local hist 27115

Stębark

Muzeum Bitwy Grunwaldzkiej, Muzeum Warmii i Mazur w Olsztynie (Museum of the Battle of Grunwald), Grunwald - Pole Bitwy, 14-108 Stębark - T: (089) 6472227/28. Head: Romuald Odoj
Military Museum / Archaeological Museum - 1960
Militaria, archeological finds from the Battle of Grunwald 1410 27116

Stęszew

Muzeum Regionalne w Stęszewie, Rynek 8, 62-060 Stęszew - T: (061) 134012. Head: Jan Stanisław Szurek
Local Museum - 1970
Banner collection, medals, local and regional hist, ethnographical coll, handicraft, national costumes, national insurrections, ethnology - archives, picture gallery 27117

Stryszów

Muzeum-Dwór w Stryszowie, Zamku Królewskiego na Wawelu w Krakowie, 34-146 Stryszów 508 - T: (033) 37489. Head: Witold Kaczmarczyk
Local Museum 27118

Strzyżów

Muzeum Społeczne, ul Mickiewicza 10, 38-100 Strzyżów - T: (017) 62 22 19. Head: Adam Kluska
Local Museum
Local history 27119

Sucha Beskidzka

Muzeum Regionalne, ul Zamkowa 1, 34-200 Sucha Beskidzka. Head: Aleksander Krzeszowiak
Archaeological Museum 27120

Sulejów

Izba Regionalna Polskiego Towarzystwa Turystyczno-Krajoznawczego (Regional Room of the PTTK), 97-330 Sulejów - T: (044) 16. Head: Zofia Gwarda
Local Museum
Finds from the former Cistercian abbey, stone heraldry, local ceramics, wooden sculptures, paintings, numismatics, ethnography, memorials of the writer Lucjan Rudnicki 27121

Sulmierzyce

Muzeum Ziemi Sulmierzyckiej im. S.F. Klonowica (S.F. Klonowic Museum of the Sulmierzyce Region), Stary Ratusz, 63-750 Sulmierzyce - T: 53. Head: Grzegorz Stawowy
Local Museum - 1957
Stone and Bronze Age finds, costumes, crafts, guilds, local history, in a wooden Town Hall dated 1743 27122

Sułoszowa

Muzeum Zamkowe w Pieskowej Skale, Zamku Królewskiego na Wawelu (Castle Museum), Pieskowa Skała, 32-045 Sułoszowa - T: (012) 226866. Head: Ewa Mikołajska
Fine Arts Museum - 1971
European art from the Middle Ages to the 20th c, van der Helst, Tiepolo, Magnasco, Delacoix - library 27123

Supraśl

Punkt Muzealny w Supraśli, Muzeum Okregowego w Białymstoku, ul Konarskiego 4, 16-080 Supraśl - T: (085) 183506. Head: Ewa Karpowicz
Fine Arts Museum 27124

Suwałki

Muzeum Marii Konopnickiej, Muzeum Okręgowego w Suwałkach, ul Kościuszki 31, 16-400 Suwałki - T: (087) 664133. Head: Zygmunt Filipowicz
Fine Arts Museum 27125

Muzeum Okręgowe (Suwałki Province Museum), ul Kościuszki 81, 16-400 Suwałki - T: (087) 5665750, Fax: 5651396, E-mail: muzsuw@alpha.net.pl. Head: Jerzy Brzozowski
Local Museum
Unique archeological artefacts of stone and iron ages, coll of paintings of Alfred Nierusz-Kowalski, exhibition about the Polish writer Maria Konopnicka - sections of archeology, geology, ethnography, history, art, literature 27126

Swarzędz

Skansen Pszczelarski, ul Poznańska 35, 62-020 Swarzędz - T: (061) 173147, Fax: 172565. Head: Krzysztof Gozdowski
Open Air Museum - ca 1960
Early wooden hives, with carved and ornamented logs, and carved human and animal figures, beekeeping material - library 27127

Świątniki

Pałac w Rogalinie, 62-022 Świątniki - T: (061) 138030
Local Museum 27128

Świdnica

Muzeum Archeologiczne Środkowego Nadodrza, ul Długa 27, 66-008 Świdnica - T: (068) 273113. Head: Dr. Adam Kołodziejski
Archaeological Museum - 1982
Pre-Columbian art (pottery and sculpture) 27129

Muzeum Dawnego Kupiectwa (Museum of Old Silesian Trade), Rynek 37, 58-100 Świdnica - T: (074) 521291. Head: Wiesław Rośkiewicz
Local Museum - 1967
Crafts, weights and measures, local history 27130

Świebodzin

Muzeum Regionalne (Regional Museum of Świebodzin), Ratusz 1, 66-200 Świebodzin - T: (068) 3823101, Fax: 3823007. Head: Marek Nowacki
Local Museum - 1971 27131

Świętochłowice

Muzeum Miejskie, ul Dworcowa 14, 41-600 Świętochłowice - T: (032) 452388. Head: Zofia Brachaczek
Local Museum 27132

Święty Krzyż

Muzeum Misyjne Misjonarzy Oblatów MN, Klasztor Św. Krzyża, Bieliny, 26-004 Święty Krzyż - T: (041) 177021. Head: Franciszek Bok
Religious Arts Museum 27133

Muzeum Przyrodniczo-Leśne Świętokrzyskiego Parku Narodowego (Peasant House), Bieliny, 26-004 Święty Krzyż - T: (041) 177087. Head: Jerzy Chodasiewicz
Ethnology Museum
Ethnography, larchwood peasant house from 1789, domestic utensils 27134

Świnoujście

Muzeum Rybołówstwa Morskiego, pl Rybaka 1, 72-600 Świnoujście - T: (097) 3212426. Head: Dr. Józef Pluciński
Local Museum 27135

Szamotuły

Muzeum-Zamek Górków, Państwowa Instytucja Kultury, ul Wroniecka 30, 64-500 Szamotuły - T: (0668) 2925716, Fax: 25716. Head: Marek Szczepański
Local Museum - 1957
Archeology, ceramics of the Lusatian Culture, ethnography, history, applied art, numismatics, in a 16th c Gothic tower 27136

Szczawa

Muzeum 1 Pułku Strzelców Podhalańskich Armii Krajowej, Muzeum Diecezjalnego w Tarnowie, 34-607 Szczawa - T: (018) 324026. Head: Zygmunt Warzecha
Military Museum 27137

Szczawnica

Muzeum Pienińskie im. Józefa Szalaya, Muzeum Okręgowego w Nowym Sączu, pl Dietla 7, 34-460 Szczawnica - T: (0187) 22258. Head: Jolanta Jarocka-Bieniek
Local Museum - 1972
Local hist, ethnography 27138

Szczecin

Galeria Sztuki, Dział Muzeum Narodowego w Szczecinie (Museum of Modern Art), ul Staromłyńska 1, 70-561 Szczecin - T: (091) 4335066, Fax: 4347894, E-mail: biuro@muzeum.szczecin.pl, Internet: http://www.muzeum.szczecin.pl. Head: Marta Poszumska
Fine Arts Museum 27139

Muzeum Archidiecezjalne (Archidiocesan Museum), ul ks. Kardynała Stefana Wyszyńskiego 19, 70-200 Szczecin - T: (019) 339094. Head: Roman Kostynowicz
Religious Arts Museum 27140

Muzeum Geologiczne Uniwersytetu Szczecińskiego, Al Jedności Narodowej 22a, 70-453 Szczecin - T: (091) 4891689, Fax: 4342992, E-mail: petromin@univ.szczecin.pl, Internet: http://www.univ.szczecin.pl/wnp/muzgeo. Head: Dr. Bernard Cedro
Natural History Museum 27141

Muzeum Historii Medycyny i Farmacji, ul Rybacka 1, 70-204 Szczecin - T: (091) 4336357, Fax: 4335660. Head: Prof. Tadeusz Brzeziński, Dr. Aleksandra Kładna
Natural History Museum 27142

Muzeum Historii Miasta, Muzeum Narodowego w Szczecinie, ul Mściwoja 8, 70-533 Szczecin - T: (091) 880249. Head: Dr. Bogdana Kozińska
Local Museum - 1975
City map coll, military coll, decorative art 27143

Muzeum Morskie, Muzeum Narodowego w Szczecinie, ul Wały Chrobrego 3, 70-500 Szczecin - T: (091) 336018, Fax: 347894. Head: Prof. Dr. Władysław Filipowiak
Natural History Museum 27144

Muzeum Narodowe (National Museum), ul Staromłyńska 27, 70-561 Szczecin - T: (091) 336070, Fax: 347894. Head: Prof. Dr. Władysław Filipowiak
Fine Arts Museum / Decorative Arts Museum / Historical Museum / Archaeological Museum - 1945
13th-15th c sculptures, painting, applied art, folk carving, religious art, prints, crafts, Pomeranian goldsmithery, jewels, models of sailing vessels from the 13th to the 19th c, present-day shipping, Pomeranian folk art, West African coll, ceramics, musical instruments, Neolithic and Bronze Age exhibits, Roman finds, 9th c Slav boat, history, numismatics - library 27145

Szczecinek

Muzeum Regionalne, ul ks. Elżbiety 6, 78-400 Szczecinek - T: (0966) 40977. Head: Jerzy Dudź
Local Museum - 1958
Archeology, local history, in a 16th c tower 27146

Szczyrzyc

Muzeum Klasztorne OO Cystersów (Cistersian Monastery Museum), 34-623 Szczyrzyc - T: (018) 3320004. Head: Antoni Jędrzejewski
Religious Arts Museum - 1954
Religious art, painting, sculptures, liturgical vestments, prints, arms, applied arts, in an old 16th-19th c Cistercian monastery 27147

Szczytno

Muzeum Mazurskie, Muzeum Warmii i Mazur w Olsztynie (Maruzian Museum), ul Sienkiewicza 1, 12-100 Szczytno - T: (089) 6242437. Head: Stanisława Ostaszewska
Local Museum
Ethnography, archeology, history, natural science 27148

Szklarska Poręba

Muzeum Energetyki Jeleniogórskiej, ul Jeleniogórska 2, 58-580 Szklarska Poręba - T: (075) 7172121
Science&Tech Museum 27149

Muzeum Mineralogiczne, ul Kilińskiego 20, 58-580 Szklarska Poręba - T: (075) 7173537. Head: Renata Sokołowska
Natural History Museum 27150

Muzeum w Szklarskiej Porębie Hoffmanna, ul Matejki 23, 58-580 Szklarska Poręba - T: (075) 7172752
Local Museum 27151

Sztutowo

Państwowe Muzeum Stutthof (State Museum Stutthof), ul Muzealna 6, 82-110 Sztutowo - T: (055) 2478353, Fax: 2478358. Head: Janina Grabowska-Chałka
Historical Museum - 1960
Former concentration camp Stutthof, gas chambers, women's barracks, barbed-wire fences, watch tower, crematorium 27152

Szydłów

Muzeum Regionalne, ul Szkolna 8, 28-125 Szydłów - T: (049) 545146. Head: Iwona Baran
Local Museum - 1961
Archeology, militaria, geology, in a Treasury, built 1528 27153

Szydłowiec

Muzeum Ludowych Instrumentów Muzycznych (Museum of Folk Musical Instruments), ul Sowińskiego 2, 26-500 Szydłowiec - T: (048) 171789, Fax: 171789, Internet: http://www.radom.net/mlim. Head: Maria Jost-Prześlakowska
Music Museum - 1969
Folk musical instruments representing all ethnographic regions, displayed in a 16th c castle 27154

Tarnobrzeg

Muzeum Historyczne Miasta Tarnobrzega (Historical Museum of Tarnobrzeg), ul St. Pawłowskiego 14, 39-400 Tarnobrzeg - T: (015) 8234556. Head: Adam Wójcik
Local Museum 27155

Tarnów

Dwór w Dołędze, Muzeum Okręgowego w Tarnowie, Dołęga 10, Zaborów, 32-821 Tarnów - T: (014) 715414. Head: Władysław Konieczny
Local Museum - 1981 27156

Muzeum Diecezjalne (Diocesan Museum), pl Katedralny 6, 33-100 Tarnów - T: (014) 219993. Head: Dr. Władysław Szczebak
Fine Arts Museum - 1888
Gothic art (painting, sculptures), applied arts, crafts, folk art, modern Polish painting - Departements in Odporyszów, Paszyn, Rzepiennik Strzyżewski, Szczawa and Szczyrzyc 27157

Muzeum Etnograficzny, Muzeum Okręgowego w Tarnowie, ul Krakowska 10, 33-100 Tarnów - T: (014) 6220625, Internet: http://www.tarnow.pl/muzea/okregowe/muz_etno.htm. Head: Anna Bartosz
Ethnology Museum - 1984
Gipsy culture, folk art 27158

Muzeum Okręgowe (Regional Museum), Rynek 20/21, 33-100 Tarnów - T: (014) 212149, Fax: 6261585, E-mail: muzeum@tarnow.ipl.net, Internet: http://muzeumtarnow.w.pl. Head: Adam Bartosz
Local Museum - 1927
17th-18th c Polish painting, 19th-20th c Polish painting, 18th-20th c ex-libris, 17th-19th c military coll, documents Polish and European porcelain 18th-19th c, Polish glass 18th-19th c, Gypsie and Roma culture - library 27159

Muzeum Okręgowe Zabytków Techniki, Drogownictwa przy Rejonie Dróg Publicznych w Tarnowie (Road Museum), 33-230 Tarnów. Head: Marceli Bochenek
Science&Tech Museum - 1985
Open air road machines coll 27160

Tarnowskie Góry

Muzeum w Tarnowskich Górach (Regional Museum of Tarnowskie Góry), Rynek 1, 42-600 Tarnowskie Góry - T: (032) 2852607, Fax: 2852607. Head: Zofia Krzykowska
Local Museum - 1958
Local history, paintings, local silver mining, ethnography, coll of free mason's 27161

Tczew

Muzeum Wisły, Centralny Muzeum Morskiego w Gdańsku (Vistula River Museum), ul 30 Stycznia 4, 83-110 Tczew - T: (058) 5310705, Fax: 3018453, E-mail: sekretariat@cmm.pl. Head: Dr. Jerzy Litwin
Ethnology Museum - 1979
Working boats, ship models, fine arts, fishing equipment 27162

Tomaszów Lubelski

Muzeum Regionalne im. Janusza Petera, ul Zamojska 2, 22-600 Tomaszów Lubelski - T: (0832) 3720. Head: Eugeniusz Hanejko
Local Museum - 1962
Archeology, ethnography, history 27163

Tomaszów Mazowiecki

Muzeum w Tomaszowie Mazowieckim, ul POW 11/15, 97-200 Tomaszów Mazowiecki - T: (044) 7244848, Internet: http://www.audax.com.pl/tomaszow/muze.htm. Head: Wiesława Bogurat
Local Museum - 1927
Ethnography, history, natural science, archaeology 27164

Toruń

Dom Eskenów, Muzeum Okręgowe w Toruniu, ul Łazienna 16, 87-100 Toruń - T: (056) 6227038, Fax: 6224029. Head: Roman Domagała
Local Museum
Polish modern art, militaria, archaeology, Toruń in the 19th c 27165

Galeria i Ośrodek Plastycznej Twórczości Dziecka, ul Rynek Nowomiejski 17, 87-100 Toruń - T: (056) 275 34
Public Gallery 27166

Galeria Sztuki Wozownia (Art Gallery Wozownia), ul Rabiańska 20, 87-100 Toruń - T: (056) 6226339, Fax: 6210929, E-mail: wozownia@wp.pl, Internet: http://www.wozownia.hg.pl. Head: Anna Jackowska
Fine Arts Museum - 1950
Paintings, graphics, photographs, Polish contemporary art 27167

Muzeum Etnograficzne, ul Wały Sikorskiego 19, 87-100 Toruń - T: (056) 6223649. Head: Roman Tubaja
Ethnology Museum - 1959
Fishing implements, hunting, domestic utensils, folk art, furniture, ceramics, spoken folklore (fables, legends, proverbs, folk dances), costumes, homestead from the Kuyavia region 27168

Muzeum Mikołaja Kopernika, Muzeum Okręgowego w Toruniu, ul Kopernika 15-17, 87-100 Toruń - T: (056) 6226748. Head: Janina Mazurkiewicz
Historical Museum - 1960
Two burgher houses from the 14th and 15th c, house at ul Kopernika 15: furniture, applied art, medieval architectonic decoration, house at ul Kopernika 17: birth house of N. Copernicus, old books, astronomical instruments, portraits, prints, documents 27169

Muzeum Okręgowe w Toruniu (District Museum in Toruń), Rynek Staromiejski 1, Ratusz, 87-100 Toruń - T: (056) 6224027, Fax: 6224029. Head: Michał Woźniak
Local Museum / Fine Arts Museum - 1861
From medieval to modern art, archaeology, history, ruins of the Teutonic Knights castle, far eastern art, Nicholas Copernicus - library, conservation laboratory 27170

Rocznik Muzeum w Toruniu, ul Rynek Staromiejski 1, 87-100 Toruń - T: (056) 6227038
Fine Arts Museum / Local Museum 27171

Sztuka Dalekiego Wschodu, Muzeum Okręgowe w Toruniu (Far Eastern Art Museum), Rynek Staromiejski 35, 87-100 Toruń - T: (056) 6227038, Fax: 6224029, E-mail: dzialsztuki@wp.pl, Internet: http://www.muzeum.torun.pl. Head: Anna Kosicka
Fine Arts Museum
Decorative arts and crafts, applied arts, art of China, Japan, India, Siam, Tibet, and Vietnam, precious and semi-precious stones, painting, graphics, fabrics and furniture, ceramics, arms, sculpture 27172

Tropie

Muzeum Parafialne, Filia Muzeum Diecezjalnego w Tarnowie, 33-315 Tropie. Head: Stanisław Pietrzak
Religious Arts Museum 27173

Trzcianka

Muzeum im. Wiktora Stachowiaka, ul Żeromskiego 36a, 64-980 Trzcianka - T: (067) 162446. Head: Jan Dolata
Local Museum - 1958
Archeology, history 27174

Trzcianne

Krzysztof Kawenczynski Muzeum, Budy, Sucha Barc, 19-225 Trzcianne - T: (086) 2195009
Historical Museum
Household furnishings, old books, grammophone and domestic utensils housed in the owner's home 27175

Tuchola

Muzeum Borów Tucholskich, Muzeum Okręgowego im L. Wyczółkowskiego w Bydgoszczy (Tuchola Wood Museum), ul Podgórna 1, 89-500 Tuchola - T: (0531) 43712. Head: Janusz Kochanowski
Local Museum - 1980
Coll of animals and plants 27176

Turek

Muzeum Rzemiosła Tkackiego, pl Wojska Polskiego 1, 62-700 Turek - T: (063) 784160. Head: Grażyna Piasecka
Ethnology Museum 27177

Tykocin

Muzeum w Tykocinie, Muzeum Okręgowego w Białymstoku, ul Kozia 2, 16-080 Tykocin - T: (085) 181613. Head: Ewa Maria Wroczyńska
Local Museum 27178

Tylawa

Muzeum Kultury Łemkowskiej w Zyndranowej, Zyndranowa 1, 38-454 Tylawa - T: (013) 4330712. Head: Teodor Gocz
Open Air Museum - 1968
Original lemko farmhouse, folkart 27179

Ustrzyki Dolne

Muzeum Przyrodnicze Bieszczadzkiego Parku Narodowego (Bieszczady National Park Museum), ul Bełzka 7, 36-700 Ustrzyki Dolne - T: (013) 4611091. Head: Tomasz Winnicki
Natural History Museum - 1968
Coll of red deer antlers 27180

Uzarzewo

Muzeum Narodowe Rolnictwa i Przemysłu Rolno-Spożywczego, ul Akacjowa 12, 62-006 Uzarzewo, Kobylnica - T: (0461) 8179211
Agriculture Museum 27181

Muzeum Przyrodniczo-Łowieckie (Museum of Nature and Hunting), Akacjowa 12, 62-006 Uzarzewo, Kobylnica - T: (061) 8181211. Head: Anna Makarewicz
Natural History Museum 27182

Wąchock

Muzeum Cystersów (Cistercian Museum), ul Kościelna 14, 27-215 Wąchock - T: (047) 715066. Head: Alberyk Siwek
Religious Arts Museum 27183

Wadowice

Dom Rodzinny Ojca Świętego Jana Pawla II, ul Kościelna 7, 34-100 Wadowice - T: (033) 32662. Head: Innocenta Boarowy
Historical Museum 27184

Wągrowiec

Muzeum Regionalne (Regional Museum), ul Opacka 15, 62-100 Wągrowiec - T: (067) 620321. Head: Zofia Zawol
Local Museum 27185

Wałbrzych

Muzeum Przemysłu i Techniki, Muzeum w Wałbrzychu (Museum of Industry and Technic), ul Wysockiego 28, 58-304 Wałbrzych - T: (074) 8422039, Fax: 8422039. Head: Jerzy Kosmaty
Science&Tech Museum 27186

Muzeum w Wałbrzychu, ul 1 Maja 9, 58-300 Wałbrzych - T: (074) 8424845, 8434146, Fax: 8424845, E-mail: walbrzych@kustosz.com.pl. Head: Stanisław Zydlik
Natural History Museum - 1908
Natural history, mining, geology, china 27187

Wałcz

Muzeum Ziemi Wałeckiej, ul Pocztowa 14, 78-600 Wałcz - T: (067) 582591. Head: Dobrochna Szymańska
Local Museum 27188

Warka-Winiary

Muzeum im. Kazimierza Pułaskiego (Kazimierz Pułaski Museum), ul K. Pułaskiego 12, 05-660 Warka-Winiary - T: (0488) 72267. Head: Anna Kornatek
Historical Museum - 1967
Memorial to General Kazimir Pułaski, hero of Polish and American history, his role in the War of Independence, memorials to 19th c political émigrés 27189

Warszawa

Biblioteka, Muzeum i Archiwum Warszawskiego Towarzystwa Muzycznego im. Stanisława Moniuszki (Library, Museum and Archives of the Stanisław Moniuszko Warsaw Musical Society), ul Zakroczymska 2, 00-225 Warszawa - T: (022) 8315011, Fax: 8315011. Head: Andrzej Spoz
Music Museum - 1871
Musical manuscripts of various Polish composers: S. Moniuszko, M. Kamieński, J. Stefani, M. Karłowicz, Z. Noskowski, J. Elsner, I.F. Dobrzyński, F. Chopin, letters, musical editions - library 27190

Biblioteka Narodowa (National Library), pl Krasińskich 3/5, 00-207 Warszawa - T: (022) 8313241, Fax: 6355567. Head: Alicja Żendara
Library with Exhibitions
Drawings, engravings, Potocki Willanów Coll, Krasinski, Czetwertyński, Schaffgotsch, Ossoliński, Zamoyski Colls, exlibris, photos, postcards - library 27191

Biblioteka Sejmowa, Wydzial Muzealiów, ul Wiejska 4, 00-902 Warszawa - T: (022) 6942494. Head: Joachim Bieńkowski
Local Museum 27192

Centrum Sztuki Współczesnej-Zamek Ujazdowski (Centre for Contemporary Art, Ujazdowski Castle), al Ujazdowskie 6, 00-461 Warszawa - T: (022) 6281271 w. 135, Fax: 6289550. Head: Wojciech Krukowski
Fine Arts Museum - 1986
Contemporary Polish and foreign art - library, theatre, archive 27193

Gabinet Numizmatyczny Mennicy Państwowej, ul Pereca 21, 00-848 Warszawa - T: (022) 6564229. Head: Tomasz Bylicki
Special Museum 27194

Gabinet Rycin Biblioteki Uniwersyteckiej w Warszawie (Print Room of the Warsaw University Library), ul Dobra 56/66, 00-312 Warszawa - T: (022) 5525830, Fax: 5525659, E-mail: gabryc@mail.uw.edu.pl, Internet: http://www.buw.uw.edu.pl. Head: Wanda M. Rudzińska
Fine Arts Museum - 1818
European prints and drawings from the 16th-18th c, architectural drawings (mainly Polish) from the 17th-18th c, European and Polish prints and drawings from the 19th-20th c 27195

Konteksty. Polska Sztuka Ludowa, ul Długa 26-28, 00-950 Warszawa - T: (022) 8313271 ext. 243, Fax: 6354900, E-mail: kontexty@mercury.ci.uw.edu.pl, Internet: http://www.konteksty.pl
Ethnology Museum 27196

Mauzoleum Walki i Męczeństwa 1939-1945, Muzeum Niepodległości w Warszawie (Mausoleum of Struggle and Martyrdom), ul Szucha 25, 00-580 Warszawa - T: (022) 6294919. Head: Barbara Izdebska
Historical Museum
Documents, instruments of torture, in a former Gestapo building 27197

Muzeum Adwokatury Polskiej (Polish Bar Museum), ul Świętojerska 16, 00-202 Warszawa - T: (022) 8310376, Fax: 6352709. Head: Dr. Andrzej Stoga
Historical Museum - 1983
Old prints concerning the development of Polish law documents illustrating Polish lawyers activities before, during and after World War II, the fight of Polish lawyers against Nazi occupation and Soviet occupation - library, archive 27198

Muzeum Akademii Sztuk Pięknych w Warszawie, ul Krakowskie Przedmieście 5, 00-068 Warszawa - T: (022) 262167, Fax: 262167. Head: Maryla Sitkowska
Fine Arts Museum - 1985
Students' and professors' works from about 1955 27199

Muzeum Andrzeja Struga, Muzeum Literatury w Warszawie (Museum of Andrzej Strug), Al Niepodległości 210 m 10a, 00-608 Warszawa - T: (022) 250971. Head: Maria Mirzejewska
Special Museum - 1981
Literary works, letters, memorabilia 27200

Muzeum Archidiecezji Warszawskiej, ul Solec 61, 00-424 Warszawa - T: (022) 6213414, Fax: 6213414. Head: Andrzej Przekazinski
Religious Arts Museum 27201

Muzeum Azji i Pacyfiku (The Asia and Pacific Museum), ul Solec 24, 00-403 Warszawa - T: (022) 6296724, Fax: 6219470, E-mail: plawmaip@qdnet.pl, Internet: http://www.muzeumazji.pl. Head: Andrzej Wawrzyniak
Fine Arts Museum - 1973
Indonesian and Indian arts, handicrafts etc - library, galleries 27202

Muzeum Cechu Rzemiosł Skórzanych im. Jana Kilińskiego, ul Wąski Dunaj 10, 00-256 Warszawa - T: (022) 8319673. Head: Lidia Eberle
Science&Tech Museum - 1973
Instruments of harness and shoe makers 27203

Muzeum Drukarstwa Warszawskiego, Muzeum Historyczne Miasta Starego Warszawy, ul Łucka 1-5, 00-842 Warszawa - T: (022) 6206042. Head: Wanda Szaniawska
Science&Tech Museum 27204

Muzeum Ewolucji Instytutu Paleobiologii PAN (Museum of Evolution of the Palaeobiological Institute of the Polish Academy of Science), pl Defilad 1, 00-110 Warszawa - T: (022) 6566637, Fax: 221652. Head: Dr. Krzysztof Małkowski
Natural History Museum - 1985 27205

Muzeum Fryderyka Chopina, Towarzystwo im. Fryderyka Chopina (Frederick Chopin Museum), ul Okólnik 1, 00-368 Warszawa - T: (022) 8265935, Fax: 8279599, E-mail: info@chopin.pl, Internet: http://www.chopin.pl. Head: Hanna Wróblewska-Straus
Music Museum - 1935
Works of Chopin, first editions, letters, autographs, portraits, works by various composers - library, tape library, photographic coll 27206

Muzeum Gazownictwa przy Gazowni Warszawskiej (Museum of Warsaw Gaswork), ul Kasprzaka 25, 01-224 Warszawa - T: (022) 6326732 w. 223, Fax: 6326527. Head: Zygmunt Marszałek
Science&Tech Museum - 1977
Gasmeters, exhaustors, gas equipment, docs 27207

Muzeum Geologiczne Państwowego Instytutu Geologicznego (Geological Museum of the Polish Geological Institute), ul Rakowiecka 4, 00-975 Warszawa - T: (022) 6468335, 8495351 ext. 503, 348, Fax: 8495351/231, E-mail: wmiz@pgi.waw.pl, Internet: http://www.pgi.waw.pl/muzeum. Head: Dr. Włodzimierz Mizerski
Natural History Museum - 1919
Exhibition of Poland's minerals and rocks, stratigraphy of Poland, paleontology, geology, mineral resources, energy resources, regional traces of Jurassic dinosaurs - archive 27208

Muzeum Historii Polskiego Ruchu Ludowego, al Wilanowska 204, 02-730 Warszawa - T: (022) 437873, 433876, Fax: 433876. Head: Józef Czajkowski
Historical Museum 27209

Muzeum Historyczne Miasta Starego Warszawy (Historical Museum of the Old City of Warsaw), Rynek Starego Miasta 28-42, 00-272 Warszawa - T: (022) 6351625, Fax: 8319491. Head: Prof. Janusz Durko
Historical Museum - 1936
Hist of Warsaw from the 10th c to the present day, Ludwik Gocel Coll - library 27210

Muzeum i Instytut Zoologi PAN (Museum and Institute of Zoology of the Polish Academy of Science), ul Wilcza 64, 00-679 Warszawa - T: (022) 6287304, Fax: 6296302, E-mail: office@qmiiz.waw.pl, Internet: http://www.miiz.waw.pl. Head: Prof. Wieslaw. Bogdanowicz
Natural History Museum - 1819
Zoological coll - library, archives 27211

Muzeum Ignacego Jana Paderewskiego i Wychodźstwa Polskiego w Ameryce, Muzeum Narodowego w Warszawie (The I.J. Padarowski and Polish Americans Museum), ul Szwoleżerów 9, 00-460 Warszawa - T: (022) 6253927, Fax: 6226434. Head: Andrzej Maciejewski
Historical Museum - 1988
Works of art, Japanese and Chinese art, instruments, docs, memorabilia of great Polish emigrants - concert hall 27212

Muzeum Karykatury (Caricature Museum), ul Kozia 11, 00-070 Warszawa - T: (022) 278895. Head: Wojciech Chmurzyński
Fine Arts Museum 27213

Muzeum Katyńskie, ul Powsińska 13, Warszawa - T: (022) 8426611, Fax: 8426611. Head: Sławomir Błazewicz
Historical Museum 27214

Muzeum Kolejnictwa, ul Towarowa 1, 00-958 Warszawa - T: (022) 6200480, Fax: 6200480. Head: Janusz Sankowski
Science&Tech Museum - 1972 27215

Muzeum Kolekcji im. Jana Pawła II, Fundacji Carroll Porczyńskich, pl Bankowy 1, 00-139 Warszawa - T: (022) 6202725, Fax: 6200991. Head: Dr. Bogdan Kurant
Religious Arts Museum / Fine Arts Museum 27216

Muzeum Łazienki Krolewskie (Royal Lazienki Museum), ul Agrykola 1, 00-460 Warszawa - T: (022) 6218212, Fax: 6296945, E-mail: -lazienkikrolewskie@pro.onet.pl, Internet: http://www.webmarket.com.pl/lazienki. Head: Prof. Marek Kwiatkowski
Fine Arts Museum
Includes the Palace on the Isle (18th c), White Cottage (18th c), Old Orangery with the old theatre (18th c), Stanysław Augustus Coll of gems, Gallery of Polish Sculpture, Officer-Cadet School (1788), interiors, sculptures, painting, furniture 27217

Muzeum Literatury im. Adama Mickiewicza (Museum of Literature), Rynek Starego Miasta 18/20, 00-272 Warszawa - T: (022) 8314061/62, Fax: 8317692, E-mail: muzeum.literatury@poczta.wp.pl. Head: Janusz Odrowąż-Pieniążek
Special Museum - 1951
Permanent biographical exhibition on Adam Mickiewicz (1798-1855), mementoes of Julian Tuwim, Leopold Staff, manuscripts by Polish authors of the 18th-20th c, portraits, art and historical relics - library 27218

Muzeum Łowiectwa i Jeździectwa (Museum of Hunting and Horsemanship), ul Szwoleżerów 9, 00-464 Warszawa - T: (022) 6284205, Fax: 6284699, E-mail: mlij@muz-low.com.pl, Internet: http://www.muz-low.com.pl. Head: Piotr Świda
Natural History Museum - 1983 27219

Muzeum Marii Dąbrowskiej, ul Polna 40 m 31, Warszawa - T: (022) 253113
Special Museum 27220

Muzeum Marii Skłodowskiej-Curie (Marie Curie Museum), ul Freta 16, 00-227 Warszawa - T: (022) 318092, Fax: 311304. Head: Margaret Sobiesznak-Marcimak
Historic Site - 1967
Memorial to the scientist Marie Curie (1867-1934) in her birthplace - library, picture archives 27221

Muzeum Miar - Zbiory Metrologiczne Głównego Urzędu Miar (Metrological Coll of the Central Bureau of Standards), ul Elektoralna 2, 00-139 Warszawa - T: (022) 6200241 w. 503. Head: Elżbieta Wiśniewska
Science&Tech Museum - 1952
Hist of metrology, weights and measures 27222

Muzeum Narodowe w Warszawie (National Museum in Warsaw), al Jerozolimskie 3, 00-495 Warszawa - T: (022) 6211031, 6225665, Fax: 6228559, E-mail: Folga@mnw.art.pl, Internet: http://www.mnw.art.pl. Head: Ferdynand B. Ruszczyc, Dorota Folga-Januszewska
Fine Arts Museum - 1862
Antique art (Ancient Egypt, Near East, Antique), Early Medieval Nubian frescos from Faras (Pachoras), oriental art, European medieval art, Polish painting, European Old Masters, prints, drawings, photographs, decorative art, modern art, contemporary art - Departement in Nieborów 27223

Muzeum Niepodległości (Museum of Independence), al Solidarności 62, 00-240 Warszawa - T: (022) 8269091, Fax: 8270323, E-mail: astawarz@interia.pl, Internet: http://www.museum.zk.pl. Head: Dr. Andrzej Stawarz
Historical Museum - 1990
Independence movement hist, coll in memory of Joseph Pilsudski, Coll Leopolis, Coll of Sybiraks, Coll of General W. Sikorski - library 27224

Muzeum-Pałac w Wilanowie (Palace Museum of Warsaw-Wilanów), ul S.K. Potockiego 10-16, 02-958 Warszawa - T: (022) 428101, Fax: 423116, E-mail: wilanowm@plearn.edu.pl, Internet: http://sunsite.icm.edu.pl/art/wilanow. Head: Teresa Perkowska-Pocheć
Fine Arts Museum - 1805
17th-19th c palace, 17th-19th c interiors, Polish and European paintings 17th-19th c, gallery of Polish portraits 16th-19th c, 16th-19th c porcelain, enamels, textiles, goldsmithery, gardens 17th-19th c - library, conservation ateliers 27225

Muzeum Plakatu w Wilanowie, Muzeum Narodowego w Warszawie (The Poster Museum at Wilanów), ul Kostki Potockiego 10/16, 02-958 Warszawa - T: (022) 8422606, 8424848, Fax: 8422606, E-mail: plakat@mnw.art.pl. Head: Maria Kurpik
Decorative Arts Museum - 1968
56000 speciments of Polish and foreign posters, applied graphic art, coll of posters from International Poster Biennale - Warsaw, since 1966 up to today 27226

Muzeum Politechniki Warszawskiej, pl Politechniki 1, 00-061 Warszawa - T: (022) 6607493. Head: Edward Domański
Science&Tech Museum 27227

Muzeum Powstania Warszawskiego, Muzeum Historycznego Miasta Starego Warszawy (Museum of the Rebellion of Warsaw), Rynek Starego Miasta 28, 00-272 Warszawa - T: (022) 6351625 w. 124. Head: Izabella Klemińska
Historical Museum 27228

Muzeum Przemysłu, Muzeum Techniki w Warszawie (Museum of Trade and Industry), ul Żelazna 51/53, 00-852 Warszawa - T: (022) 6202409. Head: Edward Mierkiewicz
Science&Tech Museum 27229

Muzeum Rzemiosł Artystycznych i Precyzyjnych (Museum of Clocks and Handicrafts), ul Piekarska 20, 00-264 Warszawa - T: (022) 319628. Head: Michał Śniegocki
Science&Tech Museum - 1966
Crafts and guilds, old clocks, jewellry, optics, engravings, goldsmithery 27230

Muzeum Rzeźby im. Xawerego Dunikowskiego, Muzeum Narodowe w Warszawie (Xawery Dunikowski Museum of Sculpture), ul Puławska 113a, 02-595 Warszawa - T: (022) 8431586, Fax: 8431586, E-mail: biuromrz@mnw.art.pl. Head: Radosław Mleizko
Fine Arts Museum - 1965
Memorial to the artist Xawer Dunikowski (1875-1964), coll of 3200 Polish and European sculptures 16th - 20th c, paintings, in an 18th c palace 27231

Muzeum Sejmu, ul Wiejska 4-6, 00-489 Warszawa - T: (022) 6287001 w. 494
Local Museum 27232

Muzeum Sportu i Turystyki (Museum of Sports and Tourism), ul Wawelska 5, 02-034 Warszawa - T: (022) 8254851, 8250405, Fax: 8250407. Head: Dr. Iwona Grys
Historical Museum - 1952
Sports and tourism equipment, documents and mementoes, medals and prizes in the field of sports and tourism, fine arts, music, literature devoted to sports and tourism - photo archives, library 27233

Muzeum Teatralne (Theatre Museum), pl Teatralny 1, 00-950 Warszawa - T: (022) 6920211/756, Fax: 8260423, 8265012, E-mail: muzeum@teatrwielki.pl, Internet: http://www.teatrwielki.pl. Head: Dr. Andrzej Kruczyński
Performing Arts Museum - 1957
Hist of Polish theatre since the 18th c, mementoes of Polish actors, posters, photographs, manuscripts, stage costumes, stage designs, paintings, drawings sculptures 27234

Muzeum Techniki w Warzawie (Museum of Technology in Warsaw), Pałac Kultury i Nauki, pl. Defilad 1, 00-901 Warszawa - T: (022) 6204710, Fax: 6204710. Head: Jerzy Jasiuk
Science&Tech Museum - 1955
Hist of technology, technological progress, mining, metallurgy, transportation, astronautics, forestry, timber industry, food industry, telecommunication, energetics, geodesy, chemistry, ecology - library, planetarium 27235

Muzeum Uniwersytetu Warszawskiego, ul Krakowskie Przedmieście 32, Warszawa - T: (022) 5520107, Fax: 5521547, E-mail: muzeum.uw@mercury.ci.uw.edu.pl, Internet: http://www.uw.edu.pl. Head: Dr. tomasz Straczek
University Museum 27236

Muzeum Więzienia Pawiak, Muzeum Niepodległości w Warszawie (Pawiak Prison Museum), ul Dzielna 7, 00-162 Warszawa - T: (022) 311317. Head: Barbara Izdebska
Historical Museum - 1965
Hist of the prison in the Tsarist times, martyrdom of political prisoners in the years of the Nazi occupation 27237

Muzeum Władysława Broniewskiego, Muzeum Literatury im. Adama Mieckiewicza w Warszawie (Władisław Broniewski Museum), ul J. Dąbrowskiego 51, 02-561 Warszawa - T: (022) 450328. Head: Sławomir Kędzierski
Special Museum - 1963
Memorial to the contemporary poet W. Broniewski, manuscripts, letters, first editions - library 27238

Muzeum Wojska Polskiego (Polish Army Museum), al Jerozolimskie 3, 00-902 Warszawa 133 - T: (022) 6295271, Fax: 6295273, E-mail: muzeumwp@wp.mil.pl. Head: Dr. Jacek Macyszyn
Military Museum - 1920
Weapons, uniforms, banners, decorations, militaria, coll of modern paintings, sculptures and graphics, oriental, weapons hall - library 27239

Muzeum Wojska Polskiego Galeria Sztuki, ul Krakowskie Przedmieście 11, 00-068 Warszawa - T: (022) 6835013
Fine Arts Museum 27240

Muzeum Woli, Muzeum Historycznego Miasta Starego Warszawy, ul Srebrna 12, 00-810 Warszawa - T: (022) 6243733, Fax: 6249021, E-mail: mhw@zabytki.pl. Head: Karol Mórawski
Historical Museum - 1974
Posters, photographs, silver plate coll from Warsaw - archives 27241

Muzeum X Pawilonu Cytadeli Warszawskiej, Muzeum Niepodlegkośei (Museum of the 10th Pavilion of the Warsaw Citadel), ul Skazańców 25, 01-532 Warszawa - T: (022) 392383, 391268. Head: Jerzy Wagrodzki
Special Museum
Hist coll in a citadel, established by the Tsarist government in 1835-39 after the November Uprising 27242

Muzeum Ziemi Polskiej Akademii Nauk (Museum of Earth Science of the Polish Academy of Sciences), Al Na Skarpie 20-26, 00-488 Warszawa - T: (022) 6298061/64, Fax: 6297497, Internet: http://psm.ci.uw.edu.pl/alf/mz. Head: Dr. Krzysztof Jakubowski
Natural History Museum - 1946
Geological sciences, mineralogy, petrography, amber, paleobotany, paleozoology, zoology, hist of geology - library 27243

Muzeum Żoliborza, ul Duracza 19, Warszawa - T: (022) 354355
Special Museum 27244

Muzeum Żydowskiego Instytutu Historycznego w Polsce (Museum of the Jewish Historical Institute), ul Tłomackie 3/5, 00-090 Warszawa - T: (022) 8279221, Fax: 8278372, E-mail: secretary@jewishinstitute.org.pl, Internet: http://www.jewishinstitute.org.pl. Head: Felix Tych
Historical Museum - 1948
Works of fine arts by Jewish artists (paintings, sculptures, graphic arts), historic objects (mostly from the years of holocaust), ritual art objects 27245

Państwowe Muzeum Archeologiczne (State Archaeological Museum), ul Długa 52, 00-241 Warszawa - T: (022) 8313221, Fax: 8315195, E-mail: pma@ternet.pl, Internet: http://www.sswtm.mnw.art.pl/pma. Head: Dr. Jan Jaskanis
Archaeological Museum - 1923
Paleolithic and Mesolithic periods, Neolithic period and early Bronze Age, Bronze and early Iron Age, late La Tène and Roman periods, early Medieval period, middle Ages and later times, archaeological material of Baltic peoples' cultures - Biskupin Open Air Museum 27246

Państwowe Muzeum Etnograficzne (State Ethnographic Museum), ul Kredytowa 1, 00-056 Warszawa - T: (022) 8277641, Fax: 8276669. Head: Dr. Jan Witold Suliga
Ethnology Museum - 1875/1946
Basic economy and handicrafts, weaving, costumes, embroidery and lace, folklore, painting, graphic art and cut-out art, sculpture, non-European cultures - library 27247

Salonik Chopinów, Filia Muzeum Towarzystwa im. Fryderyka Chopina w Warszawie, ul Krakowskie Przedmieście 5, 00-068 Warszawa - T: (022) 8266251 w. 267, Fax: 8279599, E-mail: info@chopinnn.pl, Internet: http://www.chopin.pl. Head: Hanna Wróblewska-Straus
Music Museum
Salon of the composer Frédéric Chopin (1810-1849), home of Chopin 1827 - 1830 27248

Zamek Królewski w Warszawie - Pomnik Historii i Kultury Narodowej (Royal Castle in Warsaw - National History and Cultural Memorial), pl Zamkowy 4, 00-277 Warszawa - T: (022) 6572170, Fax: 6572271, E-mail: zamek-krolewski.art.pl, Internet: http://www.zamek-krolewski.art.pl. Head: Prof. Andrzej Rottermund
Fine Arts Museum - 1980
Polish portraits 16th-19th c, European and Polish furniture and decorative arts, numismatic coll, oriental rugs coll, archaeological coll - library, archives 27249

Zbiory Metrologiczne Głównego Urzędu Miar (Metrological Collection - Central Office of Measures), ul Elektroralna 2, 00-139 Warszawa - T: (022) 200241 w. 503. Head: Jerzy Mikoszewski
Special Museum / Science&Tech Museum 27250

Warta

Muzeum Miasta i Rzeki Warty (Warta and River Warta Museum), ul 20 Stycznia 26, 98-290 Warta - T: (041) 294178. Head: Barbara Cichecka
Local Museum - 1981
Material relating to the life of the pilot Stanislaw Skarżyński, archaeology of storage "Jeziorsko" 27251

Wasilków

Białostockie Muzeum WSI, Państwowe Muzeum w Białymstoku, Szosa do Augustowa, 16-010 Wasilków - T: (085) 7436082
Open Air Museum 27252

Wdzydze Kiszewskie

Muzeum - Kaszubski Park Etnograficzny im. Til Gulgowskich we Wdzydzach (Museum Ethnografic Park in Wdzydze), 83-400 Wdzydze Kiszewskie - T: (058) 86861130, 6861288, Fax: 6861130, E-mail: muzeumwdzydze@qkki.net.pl. Head: Teresa Lasowa
Ethnology Museum - 1906
Buildings from Casubian area, Kociewie, manor houses, church, historical machinery 27253

Węgorzewo

Muzeum Kultury Ludowej (Ethnology Museum), ul Portowa 1, 11-600 Węgorzewo - T: (0117) 73242. Head: Barbara Grąziewicz-Chludzińska
Ethnology Museum 27254

Wejherowo

Muzeum Piśmiennictwa i Muzyki Kaszubsko-Pomorskiej (Museum of Kashubian and Pomeranian Literature and Music), ul Zamkowa 2a, 84-200 Wejherowo - T: (058) 6722956, 6722566, Fax: 6722956. Head: Bogusław Breza
Historical Museum - 1968
Manuscripts and old prints of the Cashubian writers 27255

Wenecja

Muzeum Kolei Wąskotorowej w Wenecji, Muzeum Ziemi Pałuckiej w Żninie, Gąsawa, 88-410 Wenecja - T: (0534) 251150. Head: Andrzej Rosiak
Science&Tech Museum 27256

Widawa

Muzeum Parafialne, Rynek Kościuszki 14, 98-170 Widawa - T: (0198) 19. Head: Kazmimierz Pacholik
Religious Arts Museum 27257

Wiele

Muzeum Ziemi Zaborskiej; Galeria Sztuki Ludowej, ul Dąbrowska 32, 89-654 Wiele - T: 87 34 70
Ethnology Museum 27258

Wieliczka

Muzeum Żup Krakowskich (Museum of the Cracow Salt Mines), ul Zamkowa 8, 32-020 Wieliczka - T: (012) 4221947, Fax: 2783028, E-mail: podziemne@muzeum.wieliczka.pl, Internet: http://www.muzeum.wieliczka.pl. Head: Prof. Antoni Jodłowski
Special Museum - 1951
Underground museum, historical part of the medieval salt mine, 17th-19th c mining excavation, Chapel of St. Kinga carved in salt, historical exhibits relating to geology, natural hist, hist of mining, archaeology - library, archive, dept of mining maps 27259

Wieluń

Muzeum Ziemi Wieluńskiej, ul Narutowicza 13, 98-300 Wieluń - T: (043) 8434334, Fax: 8434334, E-mail: mzw@poland.com. Head: Bogusław Abramek
Local Museum - 1964
Archaeology, hist, ethnography, numismatics, in a former monastery, 18th-19th c art coll - Department in Ożarów - Manorial Interior Museum 27260

Wierzchosławice

Muzeum Dom Wincentego Witosa, 33-122 Wierzchosławice - T: (014) 797040. Head: Janina Kupiec
Historical Museum - 1971
Memorabilia of W. Witos, peasant life, polish history, local ethnography 27261

Wisła

Muzeum Beskidzkie im. A. Podżorskiego, Muzeum w Cieszynie (Museum of the Beskid Mountains), ul P. Stellera 1, 43-460 Wisła - T: (033) 552250. Head: Małgorzata Kiereś
Ethnology Museum - 1964
Folk culture of the Beskid highlanders, costumes, folk art, farm implements, domestic utensils 27262

Wiślica

Muzeum Regionalne, ul Okopowa 27, 28-160 Wiślica - T: (049) 792089. Head: Ewa Czerw
Local Museum
Archeology, local history 27263

Władysławowo

Izba Pamięci gen. Józefa Hallera, Nadmorski Park Krajobrazowy, ul Morska 6, Władysławowo - T: (058) 740685
Special Museum 27264

Muzeum Latarnictwa, Rozewie, 84-120 Władysławowo - T: (058) 749542
Local Museum 27265

Muzeum Przyrodnicze, Nadmorski Park Krajobrazowy, ul Morska 6, Władysławowo - T: (058) 740685
Natural History Museum 27266

Włocławek

Muzeum Etnograficzne, Ziemi Kujawskiej i Dobrzyńskiej (Ethnographical Museum), ul Bulwary 6, 87-800 Włocławek - T: (054) 323001. Head: Krystyna Iwona Pawłowska
Ethnology Museum - 1986
Ancient folk art, embroidery, costumes, folk furniture, interior houses equipment, handicraft 27267

Muzeum Historii Włocławka, Muzeum Ziemi Kujawskiej i Dobrzynskiej, ul Szpichlerna 19, 87-800 Włocławek - T: (054) 326753. Head: Pawel Sobczyk
Local Museum - 1972
Medieval handicraft, arms and medals (16th, 19th and 20th c), ancient coins 27268

Muzeum Ziemi Kujawskiej i Dobrzyńskiej (Museum of the Kujawy and Ziemia Dobrzyńska), ul Słowackiego 1a, 87-800 Włocławek - T: (054) 323625, 323243, Fax: 323625. Head: Dr. Agnieszka Kowalewska
Decorative Arts Museum - 1909
Ancient and modern faience esp from Włocławek 27269

Wojewódzkie Muzeum Pożarnictwa, ul Bohaterow Strajku 1936, 87-800 Włocławek - T: (054) 27441
Local Museum 27270

Zbiory Sztuki, Muzeum Ziemi Kujawskiej i Dobrzyńskiej (Fine Arts Museum), ul Zamcza 10-12, 87-800 Włocławek - T: (054) 325061. Head: Krystyna Kotula
Fine Arts Museum - 1989
Ceramic sculpture by Stanisław Zagajewsky and Wacław Bebnowski, 18th-20th c Polish painting esp portraits, handicraft 27271

Włodawa

Muzeum Pojezierza Łęczyńsko-Włodawskiego, ul Czerwonego Krzyża 7, 22-200 Włodawa - T: (082) 5722178, Fax: 5722178, E-mail: marekbem@kki.net.pl. Head: Marek Bem
Ethnology Museum / Historical Museum 27272

Wodzisław Śląski

Muzeum w Wodzisławiu Śląskim, ul W. Kubsza 2, 44-300 Wodzisław Śląski - T: (036) 4552574, Internet: http://www.kutosz.com.pl/m-wodz.htm. Head: Barbara Kordowska
Local Museum 27273

Wola Okrzejska

Muzeum Henryka Sienkiewicza, 21-480 Wola Okrzejska. Head: Antoni Cybulski
Historic Site - 1966
Memorial to the poet H. Sienkiewicz (1846-1916), in a historical farmstead where he was born 27274

Wolin

Muzeum Regionalne im. Andrzeja Kaube (Regional Museum of Andrzeja Kaube), ul Zamkowa 24, 72-500 Wolin - T: (0936) 617 63. Head: Karol Kruk
Archaeological Museum - 1966
Archeology, local history of Wolin from the 9th to the 12th c 27275

Wolsztyn

Muzeum Regionalne im. Marcina Rożka, ul 5 Stycznia 34, 64-200 Wolsztyn - T: (068) 3842648, E-mail: kochroz@wp.pl. Head: Zofia Chwalisz
Local Museum - 1968
Memorial to the artist Marcin Rożek, murdered by the Nazis in 1944, sculptures, paintings, photographs 27276

Wróblew

Muzeum Walewskich w Tubądzinie, Muzeum Okręgowe w Sieradzu (Museum of the Walewski Family in Tubadzin), 98-285 Wróblew - T: (043) 8213726, Internet: http://www.tubadzin.co.pl/muzeum/muzeum.htm. Head: Bogdan Cieślak
Fine Arts Museum - 1984
Portraits of the members of Walewski's family form the 17th- 20th cent., furniture (18th and 19th cent.) 27277

Muzeum Wnetrz Dworskich w Tubadzinie → Muzeum Walewskich w Tubądzinie

Wrocław

Muzeum Archeologiczne (Archaeological Museum), ul Kazimierza Wielkiego 35, 50-077 Wrocław - T: (071) 3442820, Fax: 3442829. Head: Dr. Jerzy Lodowski
Archaeological Museum - 1945
Stone Age and Early Bronze Age, Bronze Age (Lusatian Culture), Iron Age, Early Medieval and Medieval Age, Mediterranean Archeology - library, laboratory 27278

Muzeum Archidiecezjalne we Wrocławiu (Archdiocesan Museum in Wrocław), ul Kanonia 12, 50-329 Wrocław - T: (071) 3221755, Internet: http://www.archidiecezja.wroc.pl. Head: Dr. Józef Pater
Religious Arts Museum
Gothic sculpture and painting, liturgical garments, goldsmithery, Gothic altarpieces - library 27279

Muzeum Architektury (Museum of Architecture), ul Bernardyńska 5, 50-156 Wrocław - T: (071) 3448278, Fax: 3446577, E-mail: muzeum@ma.wroc.pl. Head: Jerzy Ilkosz
Fine Arts Museum - 1965
Architecture (ancient, medieval, modern), town planning, drawings, engravings, models, photographs, in a 15th-16th c Bernardine monastery - library 27280

Muzeum Arsenal, ul Cieszyńskiego 9, 50-136 Wrocław - T: (071) 3441571. Head: Marek Burak
Special Museum
Armory 27281

Muzeum Etnograficzne, Muzeum Narodowe w Wrocławiu, ul Kazimierza Wielkiego 35, 50-077 Wrocław - T: (071) 3443313. Head: Dr. Magdalena Rostworowska
Ethnology Museum - 1953
Farming, animal husbandry, hunting and fishing, weaving, smithery, pottery, folk art, Lower Silesian culture 27282

Muzeum Geologiczne Instytutu Nauk Geologicznych Uniwersytet Wrocławski im. Henryka Teisseyre (Geological Museum, University of Wrocław), ul Cybulskiego 30, 50-205 Wrocław - T: (071) 3201327, Fax: 3201371. Head: Prof. Andrzej Grodzicki
Natural History Museum - 1863
Stratigraphical, palaeontological coll, regional coll 27283

Muzeum Historyczne w Wrocławiu, Muzeum Miejskie Wrocławia (Historical Museum in Wrocław), ul Sukiennice 14/15, 50-107 Wrocław - T: (071) 3445730, Fax: 3444785, E-mail: MUZEUM_MIEJSKIE@AGE.pl, Internet: http://www.muzeum.miejskie.wroclaw.pl. Head: Dr. Maciej Łagiewski
Local Museum - 1970
Hist of Wrocław, in the historic building of the Old Town Hall dating back to the 13th c, rich Gothic and early Renaissance sculptural decorations, Polish and Silesian military, craft, silver, pewter 27284

Muzeum Mineralogiczne Instytutu Nauk Geologicznych, Uniwersytutu Wrocławskiego (Mineralogical Museum of the Institute of Geological Sciences), ul Cybulskiego 30, 50-205 Wrocław - T: (071) 3759206, Fax: 3759371, E-mail: mmin@ing.uni.wroc.pl. Head: Prof. Michał Sachanbiński
Natural History Museum
Mineralogy, gemmology, meteorites 27285

Muzeum Narodowe (National Museum), pl Powstańców Warszawy 5, 50-153 Wrocław - T: (071) 33725150, 3438830, Fax: 3435643, E-mail: MuzeumNarodowe@wr.onet.pl. Head: Mariusz Hermansdorfer
Fine Arts Museum - 1947
Medieval Silesian art, Silesian art 16th-19th c, Polish painting, foreign painting sculpture, Polish photography, graphic art, applied art, contemporary art, arms, material culture, numismatics and sphragistics, ethnological coll, the panoramic painting "The Battle at Racławice", oriental arts - library, archives 27286

Muzeum Poczty i Telekomunikacji (Post and Telecommunication Museum), ul Krasińskiego 1, 50-954 Wrocław - T: (071) 3436765, Fax: 3441822. Head: Jadwiga Bartków-Domagala
Special Museum - 1921
Paintings, prints, plans of postal and telecommunication connections, uniforms, philatelic coll, 18th c post office, 16th c mail coffer, stagecoaches - library, archive 27287

Muzeum Przyrodnicze Uniwersytetu Wrocławskiego (Museum of Natural History), ul H. Sienkiewicza 21, 50-335 Wrocław - T: (071) 3225044, Fax: 3225044, E-mail: muzsekr@biol.uni.wroc.pl, Internet: http://www.biol.uni.wroc.pl/muzsekr/index.html. Head: Prof. Andrzej Wiktor
Natural History Museum - 1814
Zoology, insects, corals, birds, mollusks, fishes, plants - library 27288

Muzeum Sztuki Medalierskiej (Museum of Medallic Art), Rynek 6, 50-108 Wrocław - T: (071) 3443983. Head: Zdzisław Olszanowski
Decorative Arts Museum - 1965
Polish and foreign medals, medallions, decorations, insignia, stamps, drawings and sketches for medals - library 27289

Muzeum Wojsk Inżynieryjnych, Wyższej Szkoły Oficerskiej Wojsk Inżynieryjnych, ul Obornicka 108, 50-961 Wrocław - T: (071) 3433639. Head: Wojciech Leszczyński
Science&Tech Museum 27290

Stary Cmentarz Żydowski, Muzeum Historycznego we Wrocławiu (Old Jewish Cementery), ul Ślężna 37/39, 53-301 Wrocław - T: (071) 678236. Head: Tadeusz Włodarczyk
Historic Site 27291

Zbiory Muzealne Biblioteki Zakładu Narodowego im. Ossolińskich (Museums Collection of the Ossoliński Library), ul Szewska 37, 50-139 Wrocław - T: (071) 3444771. Head: Gabriela Sukiennik
Historical Museum / Library with Exhibitions - 1826
Numismatics, medalography, sphragistics, heraldry 27292

Wronki

Muzeum Regionalne (Regional Museum), ul Szkolna 2, 64-510 Wronki - T: (067) 540617. Head: Bogdan Tomczak
Local Museum 27293

Września

Muzeum Regionalne im. Dzieci Wrzesińskich (Children of Września Regional Museum), ul Dzieci Wrzesińskich 13, 62-300 Września - T: (066) 4360192. Head: Hanna Bachorz
Local Museum - 1961
Local history, especially from the period of the revolution of 1848 27294

Wschowa

Muzeum Ziemi Wschowskiej (Museum of Wschowa Region), pl Zamkowy 2, 67-400 Wschowa - T: (065) 402560. Head: Władysław Czyżyk
Local Museum
Local history, numismatics, furniture, portraits, old books, first editions of works by Elżbieta Drużbacka, in 17th c baroque house 27295

Wygiełzów

Nadwiślański Park Etnograficzny w Wygiełzowie i Zamek w Lipowcu, Muzeum w Chrzanowie, Babice, 32-551 Wygiełzów - T: (035) 134062. Head: Henryka Haduch
Open Air Museum 27296

Wyszków

Muzeum Miejskie, Muzeum Okręgowego w Ostrołęce, Al Róż 2, 07-200 Wyszków - T: (0216) 24201 w. 276. Head: Beata Sokołowska
Historical Museum 27297

Zaborów

Muzeum Okręgowe, Tarnów Oddział - Dwór w Dołędze, Dołęga 10, 32-821 Zaborów - T: (014) 6715414. Head: Władysław Konieczny
Local Museum 27298

Zabrze

Muzeum Górnictwa Węglowego (Coal Mining Museum), ul 3 Maja 19, 41-800 Zabrze - T: (032) 2718831, 2716591, Fax: 2718831, 2716591 w. 43, E-mail: mgw@promarcos.com.pl, Internet: http://www.promarcos.com.pl/guido. Head: Krystyna Barszczewska
Science&Tech Museum - 1979
Mining lamps, mining pumps - one of them from 80s of the 18th c, mine surveying, mine rescue work, mining culture: miners' uniforms, instruments, pictures, sculptures and mining standards 27299

Muzeum Miejskie, pl Krakowski 9, 41-800 Zabrze - T: (032) 1715680. Head: Bernard Szczech
Local Museum - 1935
Hist of Upper Silesia, ethnography, art, amateur art (coal sculpture) 27300

Skansen Górniczy Królowa Luiza, Muzeum Górnictwa Węglowego w Zabrzu (Mining Skansen Museum Queen Louise), ul Wolności 402, 41-800 Zabrze - T: (032) 3701127, Fax: 2718831, 2716591 w. 43, E-mail: mgw@promarcos.com.pl, Internet: http://www.promarcos.com.pl/guido. Head: Jan Gustaw Jurkiewicz
Science&Tech Museum - 1993
Machine's building, hoist tower and shaft top from the 70s of 19th c, original mining excavations from a hard coal mine from the end of 19th c, and present excavations with machines and equipment, unique steam winding-machine from 1915, still working 27301

Żagań

Muzeum Martyrologii Alianckich Jeńców Wojennych (Museum of the Martyrdom of Allied Prisoners of War), ul Lotników Alianckich 9, 68-100 Żagań - T: (068) 773577. Head: Elżbieta Ciepiela
Historical Museum
Documents and mementoes illustrating the martyrdom of prisoners of war during World War II, in a former Stalag VIIIc camp 27302

Zagórze Śląskie

Muzeum Regionalne PTTK w Zagórzu Śląskim Zamek Grodno, 58-321 Zagórze Śląskie - T: 360. Head: Jan Sakwerda
Local Museum
14th c castle, arms, local history 27303

Zakopane

Galeria Sztuki im. W. i J. Kulczyckich, Muzeum Tatrzańskiego w Zakopanem (W. and J. Kulczyckich Art Gallery), Koziniec 8, 34-500 Zakopane - T: (0165) 12936. Head: Marta Nodzyńska
Fine Arts Museum - 1981
Art 27304

Galeria Władysława Hasiora, Muzeum Tatrzańskiego w Zakopanem, ul Jagiellońska 18 b, 34-500 Zakopane - T: (018) 2066871, Fax: 2063872, E-mail: museum@zakopane.top.pl, Internet: http://www.muzeum.zakopane.top.pl. Head: Tereza Jabłońska
Public Gallery 27305

Muzeum Jana Kasprowicza, Stowarzyszenia Przyjaciół Twórczości J.Kasprowicza, Harenda 12a, 34-500 Zakopane - T: (0165) 684 26. Head: Zdzisława Zając
Special Museum - 1950
Memorial to the poet Jan Kasprowicz (1860-1950), representative of the "Young Poland" Movement 27306

Muzeum Karola Szymanowskiego, Muzeum Narodowego w Krakowie, ul Kasprusie 19, Willa Atma, 34-500 Zakopane - T: (0165) 3150
Special Museum 27307

Muzeum Kornela Makuszyńskiego, Muzeum Tatrzańskiego w Zakopanem (Kornel Makuszyński Museum), ul K.Przerwy-Tetmajera 15, 34-500 Zakopane - T: (018) 2012263, E-mail: museum@zakopane.top.pl, Internet: http://www.muzeum.zakopane.top.pl. Head: Teresa Jabtonska
Special Museum - 1966
Memorial to the writer Kornel Makuszynski (1884-1953) in his former home, villa Opolanka 27308

Muzeum Tatrzańskie im. Tytusa Chałubińskiego (Tytus Chałubiński Tatra Museum), ul Krupówski 10, 34-500 Zakopane - T: (018) 2015205, 2012935, Fax: 2063872, E-mail: museum@zakopane.top.pl, Internet: http://www.muzeum.zakopane.top.pl. Head: Teresa Jabłońska
Local Museum - 1888
Ethnography and natural hist from the Tatra Mountains region - library 27309

Muzeum-Zbiory Ludoznawcze im. Stefana i Tadeusza Szymańskich, ul Bulwary Słowackiego 2, 34-501 Zakopane - T: (0165) 38 72
Natural History Museum 27310

Zamość

Martyrologiczny Punkt Upamiętnienia - Rotunda, ul Męczenników Rotundy, 22-400 Zamość. Head: Andrzej Urbański
Local Museum 27311

Muzeum Okręgowe, ul Ormiańska 30, 22-400 Zamość - T: (084) 386494, Fax: 384202. Head: Andrzej Urbański
Local Museum - 1925
Furniture, numismatics, costumes, ceramics, carvings, painting - archives 27312

Okręgowe Muzeum Techniki Drogowej i Mostowej Okręgu Lubelskiego przy Zarządzie Dróg w Zamościu, ul Szczebrzeska 69, 22-400 Zamość - T: (084) 3415, Fax: 3644. Head: Czesław Sobótek
Science&Tech Museum 27313

Zawoja

Muzeum Przyrodnicze Babiogórskiego Parku Narodowego (Natural History Museum of Babia Góra National Park), 34-223 Zawoja - T: 110. Head: Janina Parusel
Natural History Museum - 1957
Protection of nature in Babia Góra, plants and animals under protection, geology, hydrology, ethnography of the Western Carpathians - library, scientific laboratory 27314

Zbąszyń

Muzeum Regionalne Ziemi Zbąszyńskiej PTTK (Regional Museum of the Zbąszyń Region), ul Garczyńskich 6, 64-360 Zbąszyń - T: (068) 846356. Head: Franciszek Zierke
Local Museum - 1965
Folk art, musical instruments, in a 13th c castle 27315

Zduńska Wola

Muzeum Historii Miasta, ul Stefana Prawdzic-Złotnickiego 7, 98-220 Zduńska Wola - T: (043) 234843. Head: Jerzy Chrzanowski
Historical Museum 27316

Żerków

Muzeum im. Adama Mickiewicza w Śmiełowie, Muzeum Narodowe w Poznaniu (Adam Mickiewicz Museum at Śmiełów), 63-210 Żerków - T: (062) 7403164. Head: Andrzej Kostołowski
Local Museum - 1975
Art and literature, interior of the neoclassical palace built in 1797, 17th-19th c painting, memorabilia of Adam Mickiewicz, one of the greatest Polish poets, and his visit at Śmiełow 27317

Zgierz

Muzeum Miasta Zgierza, ul Dąbrowskiego 21, 95-100 Zgierz - T: (042) 163792. Head: Anna Walaszczyk
Decorative Arts Museum / Historical Museum 27318

Ziębice

Muzeum Sprzętu Gospodarstwa Domowego, Rynek 44, 57-220 Ziębice - T: (074) 8191378, Fax: 8191378, E-mail: msgd@wp.pl. Head: Jarosław Zurawski
Local Museum - 1931
Applied art, ethnography, coll of Joseph Langer 27319

Zielona Góra

Muzeum Ziemi Lubuskiej (Museum of the Lubusz Region), Al Niepodległości 15, 65-048 Zielona Góra - T: (068) 3272345, 3202678, Fax: 3246561, E-mail: muzeum@man.zgora.pl, Internet: http://www.zgora.pl/muzeum. Head: Dr. Andrzej Toczewski
Local Museum / Fine Arts Museum - 1946
Wine making, medieval art, history, modern art 27320

Złota

Muzeum Parafialne, Muzeum Diecezjalnego w Tarnowie (Parish Museum), 32-859 Złota - T: (0192) 54500 w. 57. Head: Stanisław Kąsziołka
Religious Arts Museum 27321

Złotów

Muzeum Ziemi Złotowskiej, ul Wojska Polskiego 2a, 77-400 Złotów - T: (067) 632872. Head: Małgorzata Chołodowska
Local Museum
Local hist, archeology, ethnography 27322

Złoty Stok

Muzeum Górnictwa i Hutnictwa Kopalina Złota (Mining and Iron Works Museum), ul Złota 7, 57-000 Złoty Stok - T: (074) 175508
Science&Tech Museum 27323

Żnin

Muzeum Ziemi Pałuckiej, pl Wolności 1, 88-400 Żnin - T: (0534) 20293, Fax: 20293. Head: Andrzej Rosiak
Local Museum - 1963
Local hist, archeology, applied art, ethnography, mementoes of the Renaissance poet Klemens Janicki (1516-1543), the author and educator Erazm Glicznęr (1535-1608), the scientist Jan Śniadecki (1756-1820) and Jędrzej Śniadecki (1768-1838) 27324

Zubrzyca Górna

Orawski Park Etnograficzny, 34-484 Zubrzyca Górna - T: (0187) 52709. Head: Eugeniusz Moniak
Ethnology Museum - 1955
Original old manor of the Moniak family, 18th c peasant cottage from Jablonka, old inn, furnishing 27325

Żyrardów

Muzeum Okregowe (District Museum), ul Karola Dittricha 1, 96-300 Żyrardów - T: (046) 8554179, 8548180, Fax: 8553313. Head: Dr. Jerzy Naziebło
Local Museum - 1961
Local history, development of the linen industry, local social and culture conditions, lodged in a 19th c palace of linen factory's owners, paintings of Józef Rapacki (1871-1929) 27326

Żywiec

Muzeum w Żywcu, ul Kościuszki 5, 34-300 Żywiec - T: (033) 612124, Fax: 612124. Head: Barbara Rosiek
Local Museum - 1927
Local hist, guild art, ethnography, natural history, archeology - library 27327

Portugal

Abrantes

Museu D. Lopo de Almeida, Igreja de Santa Maria do Castelo, 2200-366 Abrantes - T: 241371724, Internet: http://www.cm-abrantes.pt
Archaeological Museum 27328

Alcácer do Sal

Museu Municipal Pedro Nunes, Praça Pedro Nunes, 7580 Alcácer do Sal - T: 265622565/67, 265622603. Head: Dr. João Carlos Lázaro Faria
Archaeological Museum 27329

Alcochete

Museu Municipal, Rua Dr. Cipriào de Figueiredo, 2890 Alcochete
Local Museum
Local hist, salt making museum, boat museum 27330

Alenquer

Museu Hipólito Cabaço, Câmara Municipal, 2580 Alenquer - T: 263730900, Fax: 263711504. Head: João José Fernandes Gomes
Local Museum - 1945
Archeology, history and ethnography 27331

Alpiarça

Casa-Museu dos Patudos, Rua José Relvas, 2090 Alpiarça - T: 243558321, 243556444, Fax: 243555339. Head: Dr. Nuno Saldanha
Fine Arts Museum / Decorative Arts Museum - 1905
Spanish, Italian, English, and Dutch painting, Oriental ceramics, European and Oriental furniture, Portuguese and Oriental textiles - library, historical archive 27332

Alverca do Ribatejo

Museu do Ar, Largo dos Pioneiros, 2615-174 Alverca do Ribatejo - T: 219582782, 219581294, Fax: 219571931, E-mail: museudoar@mail.telepac.pt, Internet: http://www.emfa.pt/museu/pagia.asp. Head: Albano Fernandes
Historical Museum - 1969
Aeroplanes, engines, armament, scale models, medals, stamps, photos - library 27333

Amarante

Museu Municipal Amadeo de Souza-Cardoso, Alameda Teixeira de Pascoaes, 4600-011 Amarante - T: 255420233, Fax: 255420203, E-mail: cma.gabimprensa@mail.telepac.pt, Internet: http://www.geira.pt/MMASoutaCardoso
Fine Arts Museum
Art of Portuguese school, 20th c painting and sculpture 27334

Amares

Museu do Santuário de Nossa Senhora da Abadia, Bouro, Santa Maria, 4720 Amares - T: (053) 37197
Religious Arts Museum
Hist of the Abbey 27335

Angra do Heroísmo

Museu de Angra do Heroísmo, Convento de S. Francisco, Ladeira de São Francisco, 9701-875 Angra do Heroísmo - T: 295213147, 295213148, Fax: 295213137, E-mail: museu.angra@mail.telepac.pt. Head: Dr. José Olívio Mendes da Rocha
Local Museum
Painting, sculpture, drawing and prints, furniture and decorative arts, miltary equipment, maps 27336

Avanca

Casa-Museu Egas Moniz, Casa do Marinheiro, 3860 Avanca. Head: B. de Melo
Decorative Arts Museum
Furniture and applied arts 27337

Aveiro

Museu de Aveiro, Av Santa Joana, 3810-329 Aveiro - T: 234423297, 234383188, Fax: 234421749, E-mail: maveiro@ipmuseus.pt. Head: Maria Isabel de Sousa Pereira
Local Museum / Fine Arts Museum / Religious Arts Museum - 1911
Sculpture and painting (15th-18th c), textiles, carved wood, religious objects, ceramics 27338

Azambuja

Museu de Azambuja, 2050 Azambuja - T: 263402258, Fax: 263402124. Head: Americo G. Cardoso Botelho
Ethnology Museum - 1964
Ethnography of former colonies 27339

Barcelos

Museu de Olaria, Rua Cónego Joaquim Gaiolas, 4750-306 Barcelos - T: 253824741, Fax: 253809661, E-mail: molaria@um.geira.pt, Internet: http://www.geira.pt/molaria. Head: Dr. Maria Claúdia C. Milhazes
Ethnology Museum / Decorative Arts Museum
Pottery, ethnography 27340

Beja

Museu da Rainha Dona Leonor, c/o Convento Nossa Senhora da Conceição, Largo Conceição, 7800-131 Beja - T: 284323351. Head: Dr. José Carlos Oliveira
Archaeological Museum - 1892
Manuelinic finds, 15th-18th c painting, costumes, visigothic art 27341

Braga

Museu Regional de Arqueologia D. Diogo de Sousa, Rua Bombeiros Voluntários, 4700-025 Braga - T: 253273706, 253615844, Fax: 253612366, E-mail: mdds@um.geira.pt, Internet: http://www.geira.pt/mdds. Head: Isabel Silva
Archaeological Museum 27342

Tesouro da Sé Primaz, Rua Sé Primaz, 4700 Braga. Head:
Religious Arts Museum
Sculpture, religous artifacts. 27343

Bragança

Museu Regional Abade de Baçal, Rua Abílio Bessa 27, 5300-011 Bragança - T: 273323242, 273332004. Head: Dr. Maria de Lourdes Coelho Bartholo
Local Museum 27344

Caldas da Rainha

Museu de José Malhoa, Parque Dom Carlos I, 2500 Caldas da Rainha - T: 262831984, Fax: 262843420. Head: Paulo Henriques
Fine Arts Museum - 1933
Painting, sculpture and drawing of the Portuguese naturalist and academic art from 19th and 20th c, importants nucleus of paintings by José Malhoa (1855-1933) and official monumental sculptures of 20th c - library, educational dept 27345

Caramulo

Museu do Caramulo, Rua Jean Lurçat, 3475-031 Caramulo - T: 232861270, Fax: 232861490, E-mail: info@museu-caramulo.net, Internet: http://www.museu-caramulo.net. Head: João Lacerda
Fine Arts Museum / Decorative Arts Museum / Science&Tech Museum
Portugese and European fine arts, decorative arts, automobile coll 27346

Cartaxo

Museu Rural e do Vinho do Concelho, Quinta das Pratas, 2070 Cartaxo - T: 243702372
Agriculture Museum
Wine-making, agriculture 27347

Cascais

Museu Condes de Castro Guimarães, Av Rei Humberto de Itália II, Gandarinha, 2750-641 Cascais - T: 214825404, Fax: 214825404. Head: Maria José Rego Sousa
Decorative Arts Museum - 1930
Prehistoric ceramics, furnishings and decorative objects, visual arts - library, archive 27348

Museu do Mar - Rei D. Carlos, Rua Júlio Pereira de Mello, 2754-501 Cascais, mail addr: Praça 5 de Outubro, 2754-501 Cascais - T: 214861377, 214836268, Fax: 214836268. Head: Dr. João Carlos Camacho
Local Museum
Marine biology, roman amphores, guns 7th c, navigation and seamanship, underwater archaeology, King Carlos I - library 27349

Castelo Branco

Museu de Francisco Tavares Proença Júnior, Largo Dr. José Lopes Dias, 6000-171 Castelo Branco - T: 272344277, Fax: 272327880, E-mail: mftpj@ipmuseus.pt, Internet: http://www.ipmuseus.pt. Head: Dr. Ana Margarida Serra Ferreira
Archaeological Museum / Local Museum / Decorative Arts Museum - 1910
Memories of the diocese, religious icons and portraits, traditional textile technology (linen/silk), embroidered fabrics, tapestry, archaeology, art, costumes 27350

Chaves

Museu Municipal de Chaves, Rua C.M. de Chaves, 5400 Chaves - T: 276321965, 276321966, 276321967
Local Museum
Archeology, numismatics, ceramics, arts 27351

Coimbra

Museu Antropológico, c/o Instituto de Antropologia, Universidade de Coimbra, Barrio Sousa Pinto, Rua Arco de Traição, 3000-056 Coimbra - T: 239829051/52, Fax: 239823491. Head: Prof. Dr. Paulo Gama Mota
Ethnology Museum / University Museum - 1885
Anthropology of Angola and Brasil - library 27352

Museu de Arte Sacra da Universidade, Cidade Universitaria, 3000 Coimbra
Religious Arts Museum / University Museum
Liturgical objects, icons, etc. 27353

Museu de Física, c/o Departamento de Física, Faculdade de Ciências, Universidade de Coimbra, 3004-516 Coimbra - T: 239410600, Fax: 239829158, E-mail: museufisica@ci.uc.pt, Internet: http://www.fis.uc.pt/museu. Head: Prof. Dr. Armando Ponce de Leão Policarpo
Science&Tech Museum / University Museum - 1772
Scientific instruments, Giovanni dalla Bella, João Jacinto de Magalhães 27354

Museu de História Natural, c/o Faculdade de Ciências e Tecnologia, Universidade de Coimbra, Largo Marquês de Pombal, 3004-517 Coimbra - T: 239834729, Fax: 239826798. Head: Prof. Arsélio Pato de Carvalho
Natural History Museum / University Museum - 1772
Portuguese, European and overseas zoological, anthropological, botanical, mineralogical and geological coll - library 27355

Museu e Laboratório Zoológico, c/o Universidade de Coimbra, Largo do Marquez de Pombal, Cidade Universitaria, 3004-517 Coimbra - T: 239834729/31. Head: Prof. Arsélio Pato de Carvalho
Natural History Museum / University Museum 27356

Museu Mineralógico e Geológico, Secção do Museu de História Natural, c/o Faculdade de Ciências, Universidade de Coimbra, Praça Marquês de Pombal, 3000-272 Coimbra - T: 239823022, Fax: 239837711, E-mail: mmguc@ci.uc.pt. Head: Carlos António Regêncio Macedo
Natural History Museum / University Museum - 1885
Minerals, rocks and fossils 27357

Museu Nacional de Machado de Castro, Largo Dr. José Rodrigues, 3000-236 Coimbra - T: 239823727, Fax: 239822706, E-mail: mnmc@ipmuseus.pt, Internet: http://www.ipmuseus.pt. Head: Adília Alarcão
Fine Arts Museum / Decorative Arts Museum / Religious Arts Museum - 1911
Works of art, furniture, carpets, ceramics, religious ornaments from churches and moasteries of the region, sculptures, goldsmith's art, textiles, faïances, oriental coll - conservation dept 27358

Condeixa-a-Nova

Museu Monográfico de Conimbriga, Ap. 54, 3151-999 Condeixa-a-Nova - T: 239949110, Fax: 239941474, E-mail: mmconimbriga@ipmuseus.pt, Internet: http://www.ipmuseus.pt/portu/museus/cominbr.htm. Head: Dr. Virgilio H. Correia
Archaeological Museum - 1962
Exhibits relating to the site of the Roman town of Conimbriga 27359

Elvas

Museu Arqueológico e Etnológico António Tomás Pires, Largo do Colégio, 7350-018 Elvas - T: 245622402, Fax: 245629060
Archaeological Museum / Ethnology Museum - 1880
Archaeology, handicraft, ceramics, religious art, folk art, numismatics, medals 27360

Estoril

Casa Verdades de Faria, Museu da Música Regional Portuguesa, Av Sabóia 1146b, Monte Estoril, 2765-277 Estoril - T: 214680477, Fax: 214866183. Head: Maria da Conceição Correia
Music Museum 27361

Evora

Museu de Evora, Largo Conde Vila Flor, 7000-804 Evora - T: 266702604, Fax: 266708094, E-mail: mevora@ipmuseus.pt, Internet: http://www.ipmuseus.pt. Head: Dr. Joaquim Oliveira Caetano
Archaeological Museum / Fine Arts Museum / Decorative Arts Museum - 1915
Roman sculptures, art of the Middle Ages, Renaissance art, furniture, Flemish, Portuguese, Dutch paintings, ceramics, religious and domestic silver 27362

Faro

Colecção Maritima do Comandante Ramalho Ortigão, Departamento Marítimo do Sul, 8000 Faro - T: 289803601. Head: Carlos Saraiva da Costa Pecorelli
Special Museum - 1931
Model ships, fishing gear, marine paintings 27363

Museu Antonino, Ermida de Santo António do Alto, 8000 Faro
Religious Arts Museum - 1933
Liturgical objects 27364

Museu Arqueológico e Lapidar do Infante D. Henrique (Archeologic Museum of Faro), Praça Dom Afonso III, 8000-173 Faro - T: 289897400/02, Fax: 289802326, E-mail: museu.faro@clix.pt, Internet: http://www.cmf.pt. Head: Conceição Pinto
Archaeological Museum - 1894
History, archeology, ethnography, paintings, Roman and Arabian pottery, Roman mosaic pavement 27365

Figueira da Foz

Museu Municipal Dr. Santos Rocha, Rua Calouste Gulbenkian, 3080-084 Figueira da Foz - T: 233402840, Fax: 233402848. Head: Maria Isabel de Sousa Pereira
Local Museum - 1894
Archeology, ethnology, anthropology 27366

Funchal

Museu da Quinta das Cruzes, Calçada do Pico 1, 9000-206 Funchal - T: 291741382. Head: Amandio Souza
Decorative Arts Museum - 1946
Silver, furniture, pottery, prints 27367

Museu Diocesano de Arte Sacra, Rua do Bispo 21, 9000-073 Funchal - T: 291228900
Religious Arts Museum 27368

Museu Municipal do Funchal (História Natural), Rua da Mouraria 31, 9004-546 Funchal - T: 291229761, Fax: 291225180. Head: M.J. Biscoito
Natural History Museum - 1929
Fishes and crustaceans of Madeira - library 27369

Guimarães

Museo Arqueológico de Martins Sarmento, Rua de Paio Galvão, 4814-509 Guimarães - T: 253415969, Fax: 253415969, E-mail: sms@mail.telepac.pt, Internet: http://www.geira.pt/ms. Head: Joaquim A. Santos Simões
Archaeological Museum 27370

Museu de Alberto Sampaio, Rua Alfredo Guimarães, 4810-251 Guimarães - T: 253423910, Fax: 253423919, E-mail: masampaio@ipmuseus.pt, Internet: http://www.ipmuseus.pt/portu/museus/sampaio.htm. Head: Isabel Maria Fernandes
Fine Arts Museum / Decorative Arts Museum - 1928
Goldsmithy, 14th-16th c sculpture, sarcophagi, altars, 15th-18th c religious paintings, woodcarving works, Portuguese and Delft faience - library 27371

Paço dos Duques de Bragança, 4810-245 Guimarães - T: 253412273, Fax: 253517201. Head: Dr. Maria da Concerção Mendes Marques
Decorative Arts Museum - 1959
Furnishings, interiors and artworks from the 15th to the 18th c - Educational services 27372

Lagos

Museu Dr. José Formosinho, Rua Carlos Alberto da Silveira, 8600-594 Lagos - T: 282762301, E-mail: jcrformosinho@mail.telepac.pt, Internet: http://www.terravista.pt/MeiaPraia/4884/. Head: José Ramos Formosinho
Local Museum - 1932
Archaeology, ethnology, numismatics, painting, religious art 27373

Lajes do Pico

Museu dos Baleeiros, Rua dos Baleeiros 13, 9930 Lajes do Pico - T: 292672276, Fax: 292679020. Head: Francisco Medeiros
Ethnology Museum - 1988
Whaling, farming, scrimshaw - library, archives 27374

Lamego

Museu de Lamego, Largo de Camões, 5100 Lamego - T: 254612008, Fax: 254655264, E-mail: ipm@individual.eunet.pt, Internet: http://www.ipmuseus.pt. Head: Agostinho Ribeiro
Fine Arts Museum - 1917
Painting, sculpture, tapestries, and religious decorative objects 27375

Leiria

Museu de Leiria, Edificio dos Paços do Concelho, Largo da República, 2410-160 Leiria
Decorative Arts Museum 27376

Lisboa

Casa-Museu Dr. Anastácio Gonçalves, Av 5 de Outubro 6-8, 1050-055 Lisboa - T: 213540923, Fax: 213548754, E-mail: cmag@ipmuseus.pt. Head: Maria Antonia Pinto de Hatas
Fine Arts Museum / Decorative Arts Museum
Studio of the painter José Malhoa, Chinese porcelain XXII-XIX c, Portuguese paintings late 19th to half 20th c, Portuguese furniture and European furniture 17th-19th c 27377

Centro de Arte Moderna da Fundação Calouste Gulbenkian, Rua Dr. Nicolau Bettencourt, 1050-058 Lisboa - T: 217935131, Fax: 217939294. Head: José A. Sommer Ribeiro
Fine Arts Museum - 1979
Portuguese and foreign modern art, documentation and research depts, workshops, outdoor amphitheatre 27378

Exhibition Centre, Centro Cultural de Belém, Praça do Império, 1449-003 Lisboa - T: 213612400, Fax: 213612570, E-mail: ccb.exhib.cent@mail.telepac.pt, Internet: http://www.ccb.pt. Head: A. Margarida Veiga
Decorative Arts Museum
Design 27379

Fundação Ricardo do Espírito Santo Silva, Largo das Portas do Sol 2, 1100-411 Lisboa - T: 218862183, Fax: 218872173, E-mail: fressmuseu@mail.telepac.pt, Internet: http://www.fress.pt. Head: Dr. Maria João Espírito Santo Bustorff Silva
Decorative Arts Museum / Fine Arts Museum - 1953
Furnishings, silver, porcelain and rugs, painting (15th-19th c) 27380

Instituto Português do Património Arquitectónico e Arqueológico, Palácio Nacional da Ajuda, Calçada da Ajuda, 1300 Lisboa - T: 213631677, Fax: 213637047. Head: Dr. Luis Ferreira Calado
Fine Arts Museum / Archaeological Museum 27381

Jardim-Museu Agrícola Tropical, Largo dos Jerónimos, 1400-209 Lisboa - T: 213620210, Fax: 213631460, E-mail: iict@iict.pt. Head: C.M. Bugalho Semedo
Agriculture Museum - 1906
Agriculture in overseas zones, wood coll - library 27382

Museu Agrícola Tropical → Jardim-Museu Agrícola Tropical

Museu Antoniano, Igreja de Santo António, Largo Sé, 1100-585 Lisboa - T: 218860447, Fax: 217571858, E-mail: museudacidade@mail.telepac.pt. Head: Ana Cristina Leite
Religious Arts Museum - 1962
Iconography, sculpture, liturgical objects, engravings, tiles, painting 27383

Museu Arqueológico, Largo do Carmo, 1200-092 Lisboa. Head: Dr. Elisabeth Cabral
Archaeological Museum - 1866
Prehistoric finds, Spanish, Portugese and Dutch ceramic tiles, armaments, sarcophagi, numismatics 27384

Museu Calouste Gulbenkian, Av Berna 45a, 1067-001 Lisboa - T: 217823421, Fax: 217823032, E-mail: nvsilva@gulbenkian.pt, Internet: http://www.gulbenkian.pt. Head: Dr. João Castel-Branco Pereira
Fine Arts Museum / Decorative Arts Museum - 1960
Islamic and Far Eastern art, European paintings (14th-20th c), French decorative arts 18th c, Lalique jewellery 27385

Museu da Agua da Epal, c/o Empresa Portuguesa das Aguas Livres S.A., Rua Alviela 12, 1170-012 Lisboa - T: 218100215, Fax: 218129134, E-mail: margarida.santos@epal.pt, Internet: http://www.epal.pt. Head: Dr. Margarida Ruas dos Santos
Science&Tech Museum - 1987
Aqueduct and water reservoir 27386

Museu da Agua Manuel da Maia → Museu da Agua da Epal

Museu da Cidade, Campo Grande 245, 1700-091 Lisboa - T: 217571725, 217571727, Fax: 217571858, E-mail: museudacidade@mail.telepac.pt, Internet: http://portugal.hpv.pt/lisboa/mcd. Head: Ana Cristina Leite
Local Museum - 1941
Archaeology, painting, engravings, sculpture, tiles, model of Lisboa, ceramics - educational services 27387

Museu da Liga dos Combatentes da Grande Guerra, Rua de João Pereira da Rosa 18, 1249-032 Lisboa
Military Museum
Memorabilia from the First World War, African art 27388

Museu das Comunicações, Rua do Instituto Industrial 16, 1200-225 Lisboa - T: 213935000, Fax: 213935006, E-mail: museu@fpc.pt, Internet: http://www.fpc.pt
Science&Tech Museum - 1997
Portugese coll of stamps, philatelic, postal and telecommunications patrimony 27389

Museu de Arte Popular, Av Brasília, 1400-038 Lisboa - T: 213011282, Fax: 213011282. Head: Elisabeth Costa
Folklore Museum - 1948
Ceramics, dolls, textiles, costumes, etc. 27390

Museu de Marinha, Praça do Império, 1400-206 Lisboa - T: 213620019, Fax: 213631987. Head: José Martins e Silva
Science&Tech Museum - 1863
Ships, nautical instruments, cannons, uniforms, paintings, models, original royal barges, original river boats, original seaplanes - library, photographic archive, ship and boat plans archive 27391

Museu de São Roque, Largo Trindade Coelho, 1200-470 Lisboa - T: 213235380, 213421966, Fax: 213235060, E-mail: secretaria-geral@misericordiadelisboa.pt. Head: Dr. Teresa Morna
Religious Arts Museum - 1905
Religious paintings, objects, 18th c robes and vessels, Portuguese painting from 16th c, Portuguese and Italian (18th c) silver 27392

Museu do Chiado, Rua Serpa Pinto 4, 1200-444 Lisboa - T: 213432148, Fax: 213432151, E-mail: mchiado@ipmuseus.pt, Internet: http://www.ipmuseus.pt/html/museus/netdex3.html. Head: Dr. Pedro Lapa
Fine Arts Museum 27393

Museu e Laboratório Mineralógico e Geológico, c/o Facultade de Ciências de Lisboa, Rua Escola Politécnica 58, 1250-102 Lisboa
Natural History Museum / University Museum 27394

Museu Etnográfico da Sociedade de Geografia de Lisboa, Rua Portas de Santo Antão 100, 1150-269 Lisboa - T: 213425401, Fax: 213464553. Head: Prof. João Pereira Neto, Dr. José Queiroz
Ethnology Museum - 1875
Musical instruments from former overseas provinces, armaments and costumes, fine arts 27395

Museu Geológico, Instituto Geológico e Mineiro, Rua da Academia das Ciências 19, 1249-280 Lisboa - T: 213463915, Fax: 213424609, E-mail: museugeol.igm@mail.telepac.pt, Internet: http://www.igm.pt. Head: J. Brandão
Natural History Museum - 1848
Paleontology, archaeology 27396

Museu Instrumental, Rua Ocidental do Campo Grande 83, 1700-088 Lisboa
Music Museum - 1977
Several rare wind instruments, Asiatic and Portuguese folk instruments, two unique Portuguese made harpsichords and Portuguese clavichords 27397

Museu Militar de Lisboa, Largo do Museu de Artilharia, 1100-366 Lisboa - T: 218842513/569, Fax: 218842556. Head: António Rodrigues da Graça
Military Museum - 1851
Firearms and cannons from the 14th c to WW I, armos 27398

Museu Nacional de Arqueologia (National Archaeological Museum), Praça do Império, Belém, 1400-206 Lisboa - T: 213620000, Fax: 213620016, E-mail: mnarqueologia@ipmuseus.pt. Head: Luís Raposo
Archaeological Museum - 1893
Jewellery, ancient gold ware, Egyptian coll, pre-Latin and Latin epigraphs, written documentation - library 27399

Museu Nacional de Arte Antiga, Rua das Janelas Verdes, 1249-017 Lisboa - T: 213912800, Fax: 213973703, E-mail: mnarteantiga@ipmuseus.pt, Internet: http://www.ipmuseus.pt. Head: José Luís Porfirio
Fine Arts Museum / Decorative Arts Museum - 1884
Portuguese and European paintings, Portuguese and Oriental sculpture coll and decorative art, drawings and prints - library, educational service 27400

Museu Nacional de Etnologia, Av Ilha da Madeira, 1400-203 Lisboa - T: 213015264, Fax: 213013994. Head: Joaquim Pais de Brito
Ethnology Museum - 1965
Visual anthropology, Portugal, Africa, Timor, Goa, Amazonia 27401

Museu Nacional de História Natural, c/o Faculdade de Ciências, Universidade de Lisboa, Rua Escola Politécnica 58, 1250-102 Lisboa - T: 213961521, Fax: 213605850. Head: Prof. A.M. Galopim de Carvalho
Natural History Museum - 1859
Mineralogy and geology, botany, zoology, and anthropology, palaeontology - library 27402

Museu Nacional do Teatro, Estrada do Lumiar 12, 1600-495 Lisboa - T: 217572547, Fax: 217575714. Head: Dr. Vitor Pavão dos Santos
Performing Arts Museum - 1985
Costumes, stage and costume designs, books, paper clippings, photos, programmes, playbills, posters - library, archives paper and textile restoring depts 27403

Museu Nacional do Traje, Largo Júlio de Castilho, 1600-483 Lisboa - T: 217590318, Fax: 217591224
Decorative Arts Museum - 1977 27404

Museu Nacional dos Coches, Praça Afonso de Albuquerque s/n, 1300-004 Lisboa - T: 213610850, Fax: 213637246, 213632503, E-mail: mncoches@ipmuseus.pt, Internet: http://www.ipmuseus.pt. Head: Dr. Silvana Bessone
Science&Tech Museum - 1905
Royal coaches, carriages, sedan chairs, litters, 17th-20th c arts, harness, portraits of the Royal Family, paintings, engravings - library, educational service 27405

Museu Numismático Português, Casa de Moeda, Av António José de Almeida, 1000-042 Lisboa - T: 217810700, E-mail: mramos@incm.pt, Internet: http://www.incm.pt. Head: Margarida Ramos
Special Museum - 1934
Portugese, Roman, Visigoth, and Iberian coin coll, coins from former colonies 27406

Museu Palácio Nacional da Ajuda, Largo da Ajuda, 1300-018 Lisboa - T: 213637095, Fax: 213648223. Head: Isabel Silveira Godinho
Decorative Arts Museum / Fine Arts Museum - 1938
Furnishings and interiors (18th-19th c) sculpture and painting, drawings, textiles, ceramic and porcelain, metal, glass and cristal, silver, jewelry 27407

Museu Rafael Bordalo Pinheiro, Campo Grande 382, 1700-097 Lisboa - T: 217590816, Fax: 217571858, E-mail: museudacidadeqmail.telepac.pt. Head: Ana Cristina Leite
Fine Arts Museum / Decorative Arts Museum - 1916
Caricatures and satirical documents, painting and ceramics - library 27408

Museu Restauraçao, Palacio de la Independência, Largo Sã Domingos, 1150-320 Lisboa
Fine Arts Museum 27409

Museu Tauromáquico, Praça de Toiros do Campo Pequeno, 1000-082 Lisboa
Special Museum
History of bullfighting, documents on famous national and international bullfighters 27410

Loures

Museu Municipal, Quinta do Conventinho, 2674-501 Loures - T: 219939600, Fax: 219839696, E-mail: c.Loures.dpc@mail.telepac.pt, Internet: http://www.c.m-loures.pt
Local Museum 27411

Mafra

Palácio Nacional de Mafra, 2640 Mafra - T: 261817550, Fax: 261811947. Head: Maria Margarida V. Montenegro Carneiro
Fine Arts Museum / Religious Arts Museum - 1910
18th religious arts coll, painting coll, sculpture and coll of books - library, Basilica, Palace (Royal residence), Convent 27412

Minde

Museu de Roque Gameiro, 2395 Minde
Fine Arts Museum
Works of Roque Gameiro and his family, ethnographic coll 27413

Nazaré

Museu Etnográfico e Arqueológico do Dr. Joaquim Manso, Rua D. Fuas Roupinho, Sítio da Nazaré, 2450-065 Nazaré - T: 262561246, 262561687. Head: João de Loureiro Saavedra Machado
Ethnology Museum / Archaeological Museum - 1976
Ethnography and archaeology 27414

Obidos

Museu Municipal de Óbidos, Praça de Santa Maria, 2510 Obidos - T: 262955010
Fine Arts Museum - 1970
Paintings of Josepha d'Óbidos 18th c, archaeology, religious art, arms of the war between Portugal and France 27415

Ovar

Museu de Ovar, Rua Heliodoro Salgado 9, 3880 Ovar - T: 234572822
Local Museum
Contemporary painting and ceramics, ethnography 27416

Pinhel

Museu Municipal, 6400 Pinhel
Local Museum
Archeology, applied arts, numismatics 27417

Ponta Delgada

Museu de Carlos Machado, Monastère de Santo André, Rua João Moreira, 9500-075 Ponta Delgada - T: 296283814, Fax: 296629504, E-mail: museu.c.machado@mail.telepac.pt, Internet: http://www.azoresnet.com/museus/mcm. Head: António Manuel Silva de Oliveira
Fine Arts Museum / Ethnology Museum / Natural History Museum
Fine arts, ethnography, natural history 27418

Portalegre

Museu Municipal de Portalegre, Rua José Maria da Rosa, 7300-110 Portalegre - T: 245300120 ext 344, Fax: 245330235, E-mail: cm.portalegre@mail.telepac.pt. Head: Dr. Sónia Alves
Local Museum - 1918
Religious and decorative arts, jewellery, paintings 27419

Porto

Casa de Vitorino Ribeiro, Rua Joaquim Vitorino Ribeiro 148, 4350-207 Porto - T: 225022422
Decorative Arts Museum / Ethnology Museum
Applied arts, ethnography 27420

Casa Museu Guerra Junqueiro, Rua de Dom Hugo 32, 4050-305 Porto - T: 222053644, 222003689, Fax: 226068534. Head: Maria João Vasconcelos
Decorative Arts Museum
Applied arts, belongings of the poet Guerra Junqueiro 27421

Casa-Museu Teixeira Lopes e Galerias Diego de Macedo, Plaça Teixeira Lopes 32, 4150-727 Porto
Fine Arts Museum - 1933
Sculpture 19th c, paintings 19th-20th c, African art - library 27422

Casa-Oficina de António Carneiro, Rua de António Carneiro 363, 4300-027 Porto - T: 225379668, 225375782. Head: Maria João Vasconcelos, Maria da Luz Paula Marques
Fine Arts Museum - 1973
Works of the painters António Carneiro and his son Carlos Carneiro 27423

Museu de Arte Contemporânea - Fundação de Serralves → Museu de Serralves

Museu de Etnografia e História, Largo São João Novo 11, 4050-554 Porto - T: 222002010
Ethnology Museum / Historical Museum
Local ethnography and history 27424

Museu de História Natural, c/o Faculdade de Ciências, Praça Gomes Teixeira, 4050-290 Porto - T: 223401400, Fax: 222056456, E-mail: fsborges@fc.up.pt, Internet: http://www.up.pt. Head: Prof. F. Sodré Borges
Natural History Museum / University Museum - 1916/1996
Mollusks, insects, birds, minerals, fossils, archaeology, ethnography 27425

Museu de Serralves, Fundação de Serralves, Rua Don João de Castro 210, 4150-417 Porto - T: 226156500, Fax: 226156533, E-mail: serralves@mail.telepac.pt, Internet: http://www.serralves.pt. Head: Teresa Parício Gouveia
Fine Arts Museum - 1999 27426

Museu do Carro Eléctrico, Alameda Basílio Teles 51, 4150-127 Porto - T: 226158185, Fax: 225071150, E-mail: cpimentel@stcp.pt, Internet: http://www.stcp.pt. Head: Cristina Pimentel
Science&Tech Museum
Trolley transportation, trams 27427

Museu Eng. António de Almeida, Rua Tenente Valadim 231, 4100-479 Porto - T: 226067418, Fax: 226004314, E-mail: fundacao@feaa.pt, Internet: http://www.feaa.pt. Head: Dr. Fernando Aguiar Branco
Decorative Arts Museum - 1969
Numismatic coll composed of Greek, Roman, Byzantine, French and Portuguese gold coins, Saxon porcelains - library 27428

Museu Nacional de Soares dos Reis, Palacio dos Carrancas, Rua de Dom Manuel II, 4050-342 Porto - T: 223393770, Fax: 222082851. Head: Laura Mónica Bessa Luis Baldaque, Dr. Lúcia de Matos
Decorative Arts Museum / Fine Arts Museum - 1836
Medieval sculpture, decorative arts, 19th c Portuguese painting and sculpture, foreign painting (16th to 20th c) 27429

Museu Romântico da Quinta da Macieirinha, Rua de Entrequintas 220, 4050-239 Porto - T: 226091131
Fine Arts Museum 27430

Queluz

Palacio Nacional de Queluz, Largo do Palácio, 2745-191 Queluz - T: 214343860, Fax: 214343878, E-mail: pmqueluz@ippar.pt. Head: Ana Flores
Decorative Arts Museum - 1941
Furnishings and interiors (18th-19th c) 27431

Santarém

Museu Municipal de Santarém, Largo Zeferino Sarmento, 2000-121 Santarém - T: 243304462/400, Fax: 243304449, E-mail: cmscultsocia@mail.telepac.pt
Archaeological Museum / Local Museum
Medieval sculpture and art, archeological fragments 27432

Santiago do Cacém

Santiago do Cacém Museu Municipal, Largo Município, 7540 Santiago do Cacém - T: 269827375
Local Museum
Local life and traditions 27433

Santo Tirso

Museu Municipal Abade Pedrosa, Rua Unisco Godinis 100, 4780 Santo Tirso - T: 252856091, Fax: 252859267. Head: Alvaro de Brito Moreira
Archaeological Museum - 1989
Prehistoric, Classic and medieval archaeology 27434

São Mamede de Infesta

Casa-Museu Abel Salazar da Universidade do Porto, Rua Abel Salazar, 4465-012 São Mamede de Infesta - T: 229010827. Head: Prof. Nuno Grande
University Museum / Fine Arts Museum 27435

Seixal

Museu Municipal do Seixal Núcleo Sede, Praceta Francisco Adolfo Coelho, Torre da Marinha, 2840 Seixal - T: 212225300, 212217596, Fax: 212225301, E-mail: ecomuseu.cms@mail.telepac.pt. Head: Filipe Graça
Local Museum - 1982
Local hist, traditional boats of the River Tagus, Roman and industrial archaeology 27436

Setúbal

Museu de Setúbal - Convento de Jesus - Galeria de Arte Quinhentista, Rua Balneário Dr. Paula Borba, 2900-261 Setúbal - T: 265537890, Fax: 265537893. Head: Fernando António Baptista Pereira
Fine Arts Museum / Archaeological Museum / Historical Museum - 1961
Painting (important 16th c Portuguese works), sacred and applied arts, archeology 27437

Museu Oceanográfico, Portinho da Arrábida, 2900 Setúbal - T: 265524032. Head: Ricardo Luís Paiva
Natural History Museum - 1955
Fish and fishing 27438

Silves

Museu Municipal de Arqueologia, Travessa Portas de Loulé, 8300-189 Silves - T: 282444832, Fax: 282442650
Archaeological Museum 27439

Sintra

Museu Anjos Teixeira, Volta do Duche, Rio do Porto, 2710-631 Sintra - T: 219240648
Local Museum 27440

Museu Arqueológico de São Miguel de Odrinhas, Av Prof. Dr. Dom Francisco de Almeida, 2710 Sintra - T: 2196135747, Fax: 219613578. Head: José Cardim Ribeiro
Archaeological Museum 27441

Palácio Nacional da Pena, 2710 Sintra - T: 219230227, 219240861, Fax: 219234375. Head: José Manuel Martins Carneiro
Decorative Arts Museum
Furnishings and interiors in 9th c electic style, decorative arts and ceramics !Furnishings and interiors ????? (17th-18th c) - Education Dept 27442

Quinta das Cruzadas, Centro de Exposições, Arte e Multimédia, Quinta das Cruzadas, Linhó, 2710-444 Sintra - T: 219239320, Fax: 219249424
Public Gallery 27443

Tomar

Museu Luso-Hebraico de Albraão Zacuto, Rua da Judiaria 85, 2300 Tomar
Religious Arts Museum
Funerary sculpture from the ancient synagogue of Tomar 27444

Museu Municipal Polinucleado de Tomae, Av de Cândido Madureira, 2300-550 Tomar - T: 249329811, Fax: 249329809
Fine Arts Museum
Contemporary painting and sculpture, matchbox design, medievial archaeology 27445

Torres Novas

Museu Carlos Reis, Largo do Salvador, 2350 Torres Novas - T: 249822480. Head: Jorge M. de Abreu
Fine Arts Museum / Religious Arts Museum / Archaeological Museum / Historical Museum / Ethnology Museum - 1937
Fine arts, religious art, archaeology, history, ethnography, numismatics 27446

Viana do Castelo

Museu Municipal de Viana do Castelo, Largo de São Domingos, 4900-330 Viana do Castelo - T: 258820377, Fax: 258824223. Head: Dr. António Matos Reis
Decorative Arts Museum / Fine Arts Museum - 1888
Antique Portuguese pottery (XVII, XVIII and XIX c), Indo-Portuguese furniture, Portuguese furniture of XVII and XVIII c 27447

Vila do Conde

Agricultural Museum of Entre Douro e Mino, Agrarian Region, Rua de Agraria, Lugar de Castro, Vairão, 4480 Vila do Conde - T: 252660450, Fax: 252660455, E-mail: ddirp@draedm.min-agricultura.pt, Internet: http://www.geira.pt/maedourominho. Head: Abraã9 Veloso
Agriculture Museum
Traditional agriculture of the region 27448

Vila Nova de Gaia

Casa-Museu Teixeira Lopes, Rua Teixeira Lopes 32, 4400-320 Vila Nova de Gaia. Head: Manuel Teixeira Lopes
Fine Arts Museum 27449

Vila Viçosa

Museu-Biblioteca da Fundacão de Casa de Bragança, Terreiro do Paço Ducal 6, 7160-251 Vila Viçosa - T: 268980659, Fax: 268989808, E-mail: -palaeiovilavicosa@clix.pt. Head: Maria de Jesus Monge
Decorative Arts Museum - 1945
Flemish, Spanish and Portuguese tiles, majolica, porcelain, tapestries, furniture, pastels and water-colours of King D. Carlos, arms (since 16th c) - library, archives, music archives 27450

Viseu

Casa-Museu de Almeida Moreira, Rua Soar de Cima, 3500-211 Viseu - T: 232423769, E-mail: mgv@ipmuseus.pt. Head: Dr. Alberto Correia
Fine Arts Museum - 1962
Paintings, ceramics, furniture, arms 27451

Museu de Grão Vasco (interim until end of reconstruction in 2003), Paço dos Três Escalões, 3500-195 Viseu - T: 232422049, Fax: 232421241, E-mail: mgv@ipmuseus.pt. Head: Dr. Alberto Correia
Fine Arts Museum - 1916
Portuguese painting, sculpture, furniture, ceramics, textiles 27452

Puerto Rico

Barranquitas

Luis Muñoz Rivera Museum, Calle Padre Berrios 9, Barranquitas, PR 00794 - T: (787) 857-0230, Fax: (787) 857-0230. Head: Awilda Palau
Historical Museum - 1916
Mural representing the civic and political life of the patriot, articles, documents and photographs related to the life and death of Don Luis Muñoz Rivera - library 27453

Bayamon

Dr. Jose Celso Barbose Museum, Calle Barbosa 16, Bayamon, PR 00901, mail addr: c/o Instituto de Cultura, Apdo. 9024184, San Juan 00902-4184 - T: (787) 723-6246, Fax: (787) 723-1822. Head: Dr. José Ramon DeLatorre-Martinez, Sandra Cintoron
Local Museum / Decorative Arts Museum
Local hist 27454

Guaynabo

Caparra Museum and Historic Park, Carretera 2, Guaynabo - T: (787) 724-5477, 724-0700, Fax: (787) 723-1822. Head: Ramon E. Rivera Caliz
Local Museum
Ruins of Caparra, the first spot of colonization in Puerto Rico 27455

Gurabo

Turabo University Museum, POB 3030, Gurabo, PR 00778 - T: (787) 743-7979 ext 4135, Fax: (787) 743-7979 ext 4149, E-mail: jpasto@caribe.net. Head: Juan A. Pastoriza
Archaeological Museum / University Museum - 1981
Archaeology of the eastern part of Puerto Rico, folkloric arts and crafts artifacts, ethnological representation of the region in the 19th c - library 27456

Mayagüez

Marine Sciences Museum, c/o Department of Marine Sciences, University of Puerto Rico, POB 9013, Mayagüez, PR 00681 - T: (787) 832-4040 ext 3443, 265-3838, Fax: (787) 899-5500, 265-5408, E-mail: director@cima.uprm.edu, Internet: http://cima.uprm.edu. Head: Dr. Nilda E. Aponte
Natural History Museum / University Museum - 1954
Invertebrates, fishes, shells, copepoda, tropical algae, marine science and biology - research library 27457

Ponce

Hacienda Buena Vista, Rte 10, km 16.8, Ponce, PR 00731-9705, mail addr: POB 9023554, San Juan, PR 00902-3554 - T: (787) 284-7020, Fax: (787) 722-5872, E-mail: fideicomiso@fideicomiso.org, Internet: http://www.fideicomiso.org. Head: Francisco Javier Blanco
Local Museum - 1987
Vives family records, documents, business papers and photographs, gardens, trails, reconstructed coffee processing machinery - library 27458

Museo de Arte de Ponce, 2325 Av Las Américas, Ponce, PR 00732, mail addr: POB 9027, Ponce, PR 00732-9027 - T: (787) 848-0505, 840-1510, Fax: (787) 841-7309, E-mail: map@caribe.net. Head: Dr. Carmen T. Ruiz Fischler
Fine Arts Museum / Decorative Arts Museum - 1959
Paintings, sculptures, archaeology, Oriental and pre-Columbian ceramics, glassware - conservation lab, library 27459

Museo de la Historia de Ponce, Calle Isabel 51-53, Ponce, PR 00732 - T: (787) 844-7071
Local Museum 27460

San Juan

Caribbean Primate Research Center Museum, Medical Sciences Campus, San Juan, PR 00936-5067, mail addr: c/o University of Puerto Rico, POB 365067, San Juan, PR 00936-5067 - T: (787) 753-8656, Fax: (787) 753-8656, E-mail: cprcmuseum@rcm.upr.edu. Head: Dr. Jean E. Turnquist
Natural History Museum / University Museum - 1982
Primate skeletal collection consisting of cranial and post-cranial elements, primarily rhesus macques (Macaca mulatta) incl known animals from the Cayo Santiago colony (CPRC) in Puerto Rico and their accompanying genealogical database - library 27461

Casa Blanca Museum, Calle San Sebastian 1, San Juan, PR 00901, mail addr: Apdo 4184, San Juan, PR 00902-4184 - T: (787) 724-4102, Fax: (787) 724-7837. Head: José Ramón de la Torre

Local Museum - 1975
Domestic life in San Juan during the first three centuries Spanish colonization, furniture, household decorations 27462

Museo de Arte Contemporáneo de Puerto Rico, Universidad del Sagrado Corazón, Edificio Barat, Santurce, San Juan, mail addr: Apdo 362377, San Juan - T: (787) 268-0049, 727-7996, Fax: (787) 727-7996, E-mail: macdpr@caribe.net, Internet: http://www.museocontemporaneopr.org. Head: Maria E. Somoza
Fine Arts Museum 27463

Museo de Las Américas, Cuartel de Ballaja, El Morro, San Juan, PR 00901, mail addr: POB 9023634, Old San Juan, PR 00902-3634 - T: (787) 724-5052, Fax: (787) 722-2848, E-mail: musame@prtc.net, Internet: http://www.museolosamericas.org. Head: Dr. Ricardo E. Alegria
Fine Arts Museum / Folklore Museum - 1992
Folk art from the Americas, African heritage 27464

Museo del Niño, Calle Cristo 150, San Juan, PR 00901 - T: (787) 725-7214, 722-3791, Fax: (787) 723-2058. Head: Carmen L. Vega
Special Museum - 1987 27465

Museum of History, Anthropology and Art, Ponce de Léon Av, San Juan, PR 00931, mail addr: c/o University of Puerto Rico, POB 21908 UPR, San Juan, PR 00931-1908 - T: (787) 763-3939, Fax: (787) 763-4799, E-mail: galomar@rrpac.upr.ciu.edu
Archaeological Museum / Historical Museum / Fine Arts Museum / University Museum - 1940
Puerto Rican paintings, prints and drawings, archaeology, folk art, history, philately, numismatics - library, archive of Artists, slide coll 27466

Museum of Military and Naval History, Fort San Jeronimo beside Caribe Hilton Hotel, San Juan, PR 00905, mail addr: POB 4184, San Juan, PR 00905 - T: (787) 723-6246. Head: Victor M. Gerena
Military Museum - 1962
Armory, flags, uniforms 27467

Museum of the Puerto Rican Family of the 19th Century, Calle Fortaleza 319, San Juan, PR 00901, mail addr: Apdo 4184, San Juan, PR 00902-4184 - T: (787) 724-0700, 724-5477. Head: Sandra Cintron, José Ramonde Lastorres Martinez
Local Museum / Decorative Arts Museum - 1964
Puerto Rican 19th c furniture 27468

Popular Arts Museum, Calle Cristo 253, San Juan, PR 00901, mail addr: Apdo 4184, San Juan, PR 00902-4184 - T: (787) 724-5477, 724-0700, Fax: 724-8393. Head: Miriam Vargas
Fine Arts Museum / Folklore Museum
Graphics, paintings, sculpture, 18th and 19th c works by Puerto Rican artists 27469

San Juan National Historic Site, Norzagaray 501, Fort San Cristobal, San Juan, PR 00901 - T: (787) 729-6777, Fax: (787) 724-6665, E-mail: milagrosflores@nps.gov, Internet: http://www.nps.gov/saju. Head: Paul B. Hartwig
Military Museum / Local Museum - 1949
Old Spanish uniform items, weapons, coins, ceramics, construction plans, rare books, period furnishings, troop quarters - library, military archives 27470

Vega Baja

Museo Casa Alonso, Calle Betances 34, Vega Baja, PR 00693 - T: (787) 858-6447, 858-7113
Local Museum
Art, history, cultura 27471

Qatar

Doha

Qatar National Museum, Old Emiri Palace Complex, Doha. Head: Ibrahim Jaber Al-Jaber
Ethnology Museum / Archaeological Museum / Historical Museum - 1975
Ethnography, archaeo-history, geology, botany, zoology, jewellery, numismatics, perfumery 27472

Réunion

Cilaos

Musée-Ecole de Broderie, 4 Rue des Ecoles, 97413 Cilaos - T: 317748
Special Museum 27473

Piton-Saint-Leu

Muséum Agricole et Industriel de Stella Matutina, 6 Allée des Flamboyants, 97424 Piton-Saint-Leu - T: 341624, Fax: 341266, E-mail: seml@oceanes.fr, Internet: http://www.reunienmuseo.com. Head: Hugues Payet
Agriculture Museum / Science&Tech Museum 27474

Saint-Denis

Musée Léon Dierx, 28 Rue de Paris, 97400 Saint-Denis, mail addr: BP 395, 97400 Saint-Denis - T: 202482, Fax: 218287. Head: Jean-Paul Le Maguet
Fine Arts Museum - 1912
Paintings, sculptures, French impressionists, stamps, contemporary art exhibitions - documentation service 27475

Muséum d'Histoire Naturelle, Rue Poivre, 97400 Saint-Denis - T: 200219, Fax: 213393, E-mail: museum@cg974.fr, Internet: http://www.cg974.fr. Head: Sonia Ribes
Natural History Museum - 1854
Natural history, zoology, ornithology, mineralogy - library 27476

Saint-Gilles-les-Hauts

Musée Historique, Domaine Panon-Desbassayns, 97435 Saint-Gilles-les-Hauts - T: 556410, Fax: 555191. Head: Jean Barbier
Historical Museum - 1976 27477

Saint-Paul

Musée Historique de Saint-Gilles-les-Hauts, 97435 Saint-Paul - T: 556410, Fax: 555191. Head: Jean Barbier
Historical Museum - 1973
Local hist, furniture, portraits, sailing ships, porcelain from China (esp Chinese blue and white ceramics), coll on the stay of Paul and Virginie 27478

Romania

Adamclisi

Muzeul de Arheologie Adamclisi (Museum of Archaeology Adamclisi), 8634 Adamclisi - T: (041) 618763. Head: Dr. Adrian Rădulescu
Archaeological Museum - 1977
Archaeology, lapidarium 27479

Agnita

Muzeul de Istorie "Valea Hartibaciului", Str 1 Decembrie 29, 2475 Agnita - T: (069) 512759. Head: Lucia-Letitia Rodina
Historical Museum - 1957
Archaeology, numismatics, art, ethnography 27480

Aiud

Muzeul de Istorie Aiud (Aiud Museum of History), Piaţa Republicii 24, 3325 Aiud - T: (058) 861849. Head: Matilda Takacs
Historical Museum - 1880
Archaeology, numismatics, history, ethnography, housed in a 16th c building - library 27481

Muzeul de Ştiinţele Naturii Aiud (Aiud Natural History Museum), Str 11 Iunie 1 Bethlen Gabor 1, 3325 Aiud - T: (058) 681748. Head: Ana Herta
Natural History Museum - 1796
Mineralogy, palaeontology, zoology, herbarium - library 27482

Alba Iulia

Muzeul Naţional Al Unirii Alba Iulia, Str Mihai Viteazul 12-14, 2500 Alba Iulia - T: (0968) 813300, Fax: 811833. Head: Horea Ciugudeaxi
Historical Museum - 1887
Archaeology, numismatics, national union of 1918, ethnography, art - library 27483

Alexandria

Muzeul Judeţean de Istorie Teleorman (Teleorman District Museum of History), Str Dunării 137, 0700 Alexandria - T: (047) 322141. Head: Ecaterina Ţânţăreanu
Local Museum - 1951
Archaeology, numismatics, history, ethnography 27484

Arad

Muzeul Judeţean Arad (Arad District Museum), Piaţa G. Enescu 1, 2900 Arad - T: (057) 216499. Head: George Pascu Hurezan
Local Museum - 1893
Archaeology, history, Romanian and European art, ethnography 27485

Avram Iancu

Muzeul Avram Iancu, 3393 Avram Iancu - T: 11853
Local Museum - 1924
Letters, documents and weapons dedicated to the revolutionary fighter Avram Iancu (1824-1872), in his birthplace 27486

Bacău

Complexul Muzeal de Stiintele Naturii Bacău, Str Gh. Vrânceanu 44, 5500 Bacău - T: (034) 112006, Fax: 112006. Head: Dr. Niculae Barabas
Natural History Museum - 1959
Evolution, flora and fauna - library 27487

Muzeul Judeţean de Istorie Iulian Antonescu Bacău (Bacău District Museum of History Iulian Anntonescu), Str 9. Mai 7, 5500 Bacău - T: (034) 112444, Fax: 12444, E-mail: mistbc@cybernet.ro. Head: Marin Lăcrămioara
Historical Museum - 1957
History, art, ethnography, literature - history 27488

Baia Mare

Muzeul de Mineralogie Baia Mare (Mineralogy Museum Baia Mare), B-dul Traian 8, 4800 Baia Mare - T: (062) 227517, Fax: 227517, E-mail: muzmin@sintec.ro. Head: Victor Gorduza
Natural History Museum - 1889 27489

Muzeul Judeţean Maramureş (Maramureş District Museum), B-dul Traian 8, 4800 Baia Mare - T: (062) 411927. Head: Ion Igna
Local Museum - 1899
Archaeology, local and Transylvanian hist, mining, ethnography, natural science, classical and contemporary painting - library 27490

Baileşti

Muzeul Cimpiei Baileştitor, Str Carpati 68, 1225 Baileşti - T: 12342. Head: Constantin Cîşlaru
Local Museum - 1965
Local hist, archaeology, ethnography, agriculture 27491

Beiuş

Muzeul Etnografic Beiuş (Ethnological Museum), Piaţa Samuil Vulcan, 3600 Beiuş - T: 12247. Head: Nicolae Branda
Ethnology Museum - 1958
Ethnography, folk art, hist 27492

Bicaz

Complexul Muzeal Judeţean Neamţ, Str Barajului 1, 5650 Bicaz - T: (033) 17496
Local Museum - 1960
Archaeology, documents and models of the Bicaz hydropower station, ethnography, local art 27493

Birlad

Muzeul V. Pîrvan, Str Sterian Dumbrava 1, 6400 Birlad - T: (0984) 12403. Head: Nicoleta Arnawtu
Local Museum - 1914
Archaeology, numismatics, local history, natural science, art 27494

Bistriţa

Muzeul Judeţean Bistriţa-Năsăud (Bistriţa-Nasaud Regional Museum), Str General Grigore Bălan 19, 4400 Bistriţa - T: (063) 211063. Head: Dr. Ioan Chintăuan
Local Museum - 1950
Archaeology, numismatics, regional hist, ethnography, natural sciences and fine arts 27495

Blaj

Muzeul de Istorie Blaj, Str Armata Rosie 2, 3175 Blaj - T: 11853. Head: Cornel Tatai
Local Museum - 1850
Archaeology, history, housed in a 17th c building 27496

Botoşani

Muzeul Judeţean Botoşani, Str Unirii 13, 6800 Botoşani - T: (031) 513446. Head: Lucia Pârvan
Local Museum - 1955
Archaeology, numismatics, local hist, ethnography, natural science, art - library 27497

Brad

Muzeul de Istorie şi Etnografie Brad (Brad History and Ethnography Museum), 2775 Brad. Head: Mihai David
Historical Museum / Ethnology Museum - 1987 27498

Brăila

Muzeul Brăilei, Piaţa Traian 3, 6100 Brăila - T: (039) 614725, Fax: 614725. Head: Ionel Cândea
Local Museum - 1881
Archaeology, local hist, documents related to the writer Panait Istrati and the literary criticist Dumitru Panaitescu-Perpessicius, ethnography, natural science, art 27499

Bran

Muzeul Bran, Str Traian Mosoiu 498, 2229 Bran - T: (068) 236538. Head: Raul Mihai
Local Museum - 1957
Medieval hist, weapons, tools, furniture, local hist, ethnography, medieval art, open air ethnography park 27500

Braşov

Braşov Country Museum od History, Piaţa Sfatului 30, 2200 Braşov
Historical Museum 27501

Gheorghe Dima Memorial House, Piaţa Sfatului 25, 2200 Braşov
Special Museum 27502

Muzeul a Primei Scoli Româneşti din Şchei Braşovului (Museum of First Romanian School of Braşov), Piaţa Unirii 1, 2200 Braşov - T: (068) 143879. Head: Dr. Vasile Olteanu
Historical Museum - 1933
Ancient books, documents, manuscripts, medieval art, housed in the building of the first Romanian school (15th c) 27503

Muzeul de Artă, B-dul Eroilor 21, 2200 Braşov - T: (068) 140138. Head: Titus Haşdeu
Fine Arts Museum - 1950
Romanian and foreign art 27504

Muzeul de Etnografie Braşov (Braşov Ethnographical Museum), B-dul Eroilor 21a, 2200 Braşov - T: (068) 152252. Head: Ligia Fulga
Ethnology Museum - 1990
Textiles, costumes, pottery, furniture, icons on glass, glasses and jugs made of glass, painted eggs 27505

Muzeul Judeţean de Istorie Braşov, Str 23 August 30, 2200 Braşov - T: (068) 472350, Fax: 472350. Head: Radu Ştefănescu
Historical Museum - 1908
Archaeological finds, numismatics, history, ethnography, housed in the medieval city hall (15th c) 27506

Bucureşti

Colecţia Theodor Aman, Muzeul de Istorie şi Artă al Municipiului Bucureşti, Str C.A. Rosetti 8, 70746 Bucureşti - T: (01) 6145812. Head: Nicolae Delaport
Fine Arts Museum - 1908
Paintings, drawings, original furnishings, house of painter Teodor Aman (1831-1891) 27507

Muzeul Arhivelor Statului, Str Arhivelor 2, Bucureşti
Historical Museum - 1957
Ancient books, documents, manuscripts, engravings regarding Romanian history 27508

Muzeul Cecilia şi Frederic Storck, Str Vasile Alecsandri 16, 71112 Bucureşti - T: (01) 6117889. Head: Nicolae Delaport
Fine Arts Museum - 1951
Exhibits in connection with the sculptor Karl Storck (1820-1877), his sons Carl (1854-1926) and Frederic (1872-1924) and his wife Cecilia Storck, history of fine arts in Romania 27509

Muzeul Colecţiilor de Artă, Calea Victoriei 111, 71102 Bucureşti - T: (01) 6596693. Head: Dr. Alexandru Cebucoprea
Fine Arts Museum - 1978
Romanian art (19th-20th c), Oriental art works 27510

Muzeul Comunităţilor Evreieşti din România (Museum of the Jewish Communities in Romania), Str Mămulari 3, Sector 3, 70468 Bucureşti - T: (01) 6150837, Fax: 3120869. Head: Beatrice Stambler
Historical Museum - 1978 27511

Muzeul Curtea Veche, Palaţul Voievodal, Str 30 Decembrie 18-22, 70002 Bucureşti - T: (01) 6140375
Archaeological Museum - 1972
Archaeology, housed in a 15th c palace 27512

Muzeul de Artă Feudala D. Minovici, Str Dr. Nicolae Minovici 3, 71557 Bucureşti - T: (01) 6571505. Head: Dr. Alexandru Cebuc
Fine Arts Museum 27513

Muzeul de Istorie Naturala Grigore Antipa, Soseaua Kiseleff 1, 79744 Bucureşti 2 - T: (401) 3128826/63, Fax: 3128886, E-mail: ghantipa@pcnet.pcnet.ro, dmurariu@opensys.ro. Head: Dr. Dumitru Murariu
Natural History Museum - 1834/1908
Fauna of all continents, molluscs, butterflies, fossils, skeletons, minerals, insects, birds, mammals - library 27514

Muzeul de Istorie şi Artă al Municipiului Bucureşti (The History and Art Museum of Bucarest), I.C. Bratianu Blvd 2, 70058 Bucureşti - T: (01) 3156858, 3138515, Fax: 3102562, E-mail: mistorie@sunu.rnc.ro
Historical Museum / Fine Arts Museum / Archaeological Museum - 1921
Archaeological finds, numismatics, history of the city, documents, maps - pinacotheque, restoration, library 27515

Muzeul de Istorie şi Artă al Municipiului Bucureşti, Secţia Cornel Medrea, Str General Budisteanu 16, 70744 Bucureşti - T: (01) 666592597. Head: Nicolae Delaport
Fine Arts Museum - 1948
Works by sculptor Cornel Medrea (1888-1964) 27516

Muzeul Gheorghe Tattarascu, Str Domnita Anastasia 7, 70623 Bucureşti - T: (01) 6141006
Special Museum - 1955 27517

Muzeul Hrandt Avakian, Muzeul Naţional de Artă al României, Str Ion Mincu 19, 71301 Bucureşti - T: (01) 2234936, Fax: 3124327, E-mail: national@art.museum.ro, Internet: http://art.museum.ro. Head: Roxana Theodorescu
Fine Arts Museum / Decorative Arts Museum
Paintings, watercolours, Chinese and Japanese decorative art 27518

Muzeul K.H. Zambaccian, Muzeul Naţional de Artă al României, Str Muzeul Zambaccian 21a, Bucureşti - T: (01) 2301920
Fine Arts Museum - 1946
Romanian/ European art from 1st half of the 20th c 27519

Muzeul Literaturii Române (Museum of the Romanian Literature), Blvd Daçia 12, Sector 1, 71116 Bucureşti - T: (01) 6503395, Fax: 6503395. Head: Alexandru Dan Condeescu
Special Museum
Hist of literature in Romania, documents, manuscripts, rare editions - library 27520

Muzeul Militar Naţional (National Military Museum), Str Mircea Vulcanescu 125-127, Sector 1, 77116 Bucureşti - T: (01) 6373830, Fax: 6387630. Head: Ilie Schipor
Military Museum - 1923
Archaeology, weapons, trophies, flags, documents, photos, military costumes, military history - library, archives 27521

Muzeul Naţional al Pompierilor (National Fire Fighters' Museum), Blvd Ferdinand I 33, Sector 2, 73241 Bucureşti - T: (01) 2522884, Fax: 2420990. Head: Prof. Ion Panţuru
Science&Tech Museum - 1963
Development of fire fighting in Romania 27522

Muzeul Naţional Cotroceni (Cotroceni National Museum), B-dul Geniului 1, 76238 Bucureşti - T: (01) 637411, Fax: 3131618. Head: Dr. Eleonora Cofas
Fine Arts Museum - 1991
Roamanian art, medieval architecture, decorative art 27523

Muzeul Naţional de Artă al României (National Museum of Art of Romania), Calea Victoriei 49-53, 70101 Bucureşti - T: (01) 3155193, 3133030, Fax: 3124327, E-mail: theodorescu@art.museum.ro, Internet: http://art.museum.ro. Head: Roxana Theodorescu
Fine Arts Museum - 1948
Romanian and international art, painting, sculpture, prints, woodcarving, embroidery, jewelry, ceramics, tapestries, ancient books, porcelain, furniture, - library, restoration lab 27524

Muzeul Naţional de Istorie a României, Calea Victoriei 12, 79740 Bucureşti - T: (01) 3158207, 3157055, Fax: 3113356, E-mail: mnir@mailbox.ro, Internet: http://www.mnir.ro. Head: Dr. Criş Muşeţeanu
Historical Museum / Archaeological Museum - 1968
Archaeology, Stone and Bronze Age finds, Daco-Getic, Greek and Roman objects, numismatics, medieval tools and weapons, icons, inscriptions, lapidarium, documents 27525

Muzeul Naţional George Enescu (National Museum George Enescu), Calea Victoriei 141, 71102 Bucureşti - T: (01) 6596365, Fax: 3129182. Head: Ilinca Dumitrescu
Music Museum
Life and works of George Enescu (1881-1955), the most important Romanian composer, Romanian music in general 27526

Muzeul Satului (Village Museum), Soseaua Kiseleff 28-30, 71321 Bucureşti - T: (01) 2229110, Fax: 2229068, E-mail: muzeulsatului@xnet.ro, Internet: http://www.cimec.ro/muzee/muzsat. Head: Prof. Paul H. Stahl
Ethnology Museum / Open Air Museum - 1936
Architectural munuments, devices, tools, ceramics, furniture, costumes, carpets, textiles, icons, religious objects, etnographical coll 27527

Muzeul Taranului Român (Romanian Peasants Museum), Soseaua Kiseleff 3, 71268 Bucureşti - T: (01) 6505360, Fax: 3129875, E-mail: muztar@rnc.ro, Internet: http://www.itc.ro/mtr/tar_e.htm. Head: Horia Bernea
Folklore Museum 27528

Muzeul Teatrului National, Blvd N. Balcescu 1, 70111 Bucureşti - T: (01) 6139175. Head: Lidia Munteanu
Performing Arts Museum - 1942
History of the Romanian theater, documents on actors, stage sets, costumes, programmes, Romanian playwrights 27529

Muzeul Tehnic Prof. Ing. Dimitrie Leonida, Str Candiano Popescu 2, 75206 Bucureşti - T: (01) 6237777. Head: Nicolae Diaconescu
Science&Tech Museum - 1909
Old tools, modern equipment, documents, Romanian inventions - library 27530

Muzeul Theodor Pallady, Muzeul Naţional de Artă al României, Str Spatarului 22, 70242 Bucureşti - T: (01) 2114979
Fine Arts Museum
Prints, drawings, paintings, European and Oriental art, furniture 27531

Bumbeşti-Jiu

Muzeul Arhitecturii Populare din Gorj, Muzeul Judeţean Gorj (Gorj Museum of Folk Architecture), 1434 Bumbeşti-Jiu. Head: Prof. Vasile Petre
Folklore Museum - 1968 27532

Buzău

Muzeul Judeţean Buzău (Buzău District Museum), Str Nicolae Balcescu 50, 5100 Buzău - T: (038) 435127. Head: Valeriu Bălcescu
Local Museum - 1951
Archaeology, numismatics, medieval and modern hist of the region, ethnography, folk art, contemporary Romanian art 27533

Calafat

Muzeul Orăşenesc Calafat, Str 30 Decembrie 6, 1275 Calafat - T: (051) 12342. Head: Iulia Ghita
Folklore Museum 27534

Călăraşi

Muzeul Dunării de Jos (Lower Danube Museum), Str Progresului 84, 8500 Călăraşi - T: (042) 113161. Head: Marian Neagu
Local Museum - 1951
History, ethnography, modern Romanian arts 27535

Caracal

Muzeul Orăşenesc Caracal, Blvd Republicii 61, 0800 Caracal - T: 17262. Head: Stefan Chitu
Archaeological Museum 27536

Muzeul Romanaţiului Caracal (Caracal Museum of the Romanaţi), Str Libertăţii 26, 0800 Caracal - T: (049) 511344. Head: Paul Lică
Local Museum - 1951
History, ethnography, art - lapidarium 27537

Caransebeş

Muzeul Judeţean de Etnografie şi a Regimentului de Graniţă-Caransebeş (Caransebeş Border District Ethnographic and Regimental Museum), Str Gen. Ion Dragalina 2, 1650 Caransebeş - T: (055) 512193. Head: Dr. Petre Bona
Ethnology Museum / Local Museum / Archaeological Museum - 1929
Archaeology, hist of the area, ethnography 27538

Carei

Complexul Muzeal Judeţean Satu Maru, Secţia de Istorie şi Stiintele Naturii Carei, Str 25 Octombrie 1, 3825 Carei - T: (061) 37526. Head: Nete Ercosan
Natural History Museum 27539

Cîmpina

Expozitia Memoralia Nicolae Grigorescu, Complexul Muzeal Judeţean Prahova, Str 23 August 166, 2150 Cîmpina - T: (0971) 12535. Head: Stefan Dumitrescu
Fine Arts Museum - 1955
Documents on painter Nicolae Grigorescu (1838-1907), paintings, letters 27540

Memorial Museum B.P. Hasdeu, Carol I 199, 2150 Cîmpina - T: (044) 335599, Fax: 371458, E-mail: primarie@interplus.ro, Internet: http://www.cimec.ro/Muzee/.hasdeu./index.htm. Head: Jenica Tabacu
Special Museum - 1965
Documents on the life and activity of the scientist, professor, writer and historian B.P. Hasdeu (1838-1907), exhibits related to his daughter Julia (1869-1888) 27541

Cîmpulung

Muzeul Orăşenesc Cîmpulung Muscel, Secţia de Istorie şi Secţia de Artă Plastica, Str Negru Voda 127, 0425 Cîmpulung - T: (048) 11737. Head: Dr. Vasile Trimbaciu
Local Museum - 1951
Archaeology, lapidarium, ethnography, folk art, modern Romanian art, natural science 27542

Muzeul Zonal Cîmpulung, Str Negru Vodă 119, 0425 Cîmpulung - T: (048) 11737. Head: Stefan Trâmbaciu
Local Museum - 1880
History, arts natural science, ethnography, folk art 27543

Cîmpulung Moldovenesc

Muzeul Artei Lemnului, Wooden Art Museum, Calea Transilvaniei 10, 5950 Cîmpulung Moldovenesc - T: (030) 311378. Head: Marcel Zahanciuc
Fine Arts Museum - 1936
Ethnography, history, folk art 27544

Muzeul Orăşanesc Cîmpulung Moldovenesc, Str 7 Noiembrie 10, 5950 Cîmpulung Moldovenesc - T: (030) 16439
Local Museum
Ethnography, woodcarving, local history 27545

Ciucea

Muzeul Memorial Octavian Goga, Str Principala, 3539 Ciucea - T: 12344. Head: Aurel Jurca
Folklore Museum 27546

Cluj-Napoca

Muzeul de Istorie a Farmaciei Cluj-Napoca, Piaţa Libertăţii 28, 3400 Cluj-Napoca - T: (064) 197567, Fax: 191718, E-mail: museum@cs.ubbcluj.ro. Head: Eva Crişan
Historical Museum - 1963
Pharmaceutical equipment and documents, medical equipment 27547

Muzeul Etnografic al Transilvaniei (Ethnographical Museum of Transylvania), Str Memorandumului 21, 3400 Cluj-Napoca - T: (064) 192344, Fax: 192148, E-mail: metnog@others.ubbcluj.ro, Internet: http://www.culture.ro/pages/met/indexhtml. Head: Tiberiu Graur
Ethnology Museum - 1922
Handicrafts, pottery, woodcarving, costumes, folk art, open-air ethnographical museum (Hoia) 27548

Muzeul Memorial Emil Isac, Str 1 Mai 23, 3400 Cluj-Napoca - T: (064) 12344
Special Museum - 1955
Manuscripts, documents, letters, photos and books dedicated to the poet Emil Isac (1886-1954) 27549

Muzeul National de Artă Cluj-Napoca, Piata Unirii 30, 3400 Cluj-Napoca - T: (064) 116952. Head: Dr. Livia Drăgoi
Fine Arts Museum - 1951
Romanian and European art of medieval, modern and contemporary times, housed in an 18th c palace - library 27550

Muzeul Naţional de Istorie a Transilvaniei, Str C. Daicoviciu 2, 3400 Cluj-Napoca - T: (064) 195677, Fax: 191718, E-mail: secretariat@mnit.museum.utcluj.ro, Internet: http://www.museum.utcluj.ro. Head: Prof. Dr. Ioan Piso
Historical Museum - 1859
Archaeology, numismatics, lapidarium, weapons, jewelry, maps, rare books, history of Transylvania - library 27551

Muzeul Zoologic al Universităţii Babeş-Bolyai (Zoological Museum of the Babeş-Bolyai University), Str Clinicilor 5-7, 3400 Cluj-Napoca - T: (064) 191483, 195739, Fax: 431858, E-mail: dceuca@biolog.ubbcluj.ro. Head: Dr. Ioan Coroiu
Natural History Museum - 1859 27552

Constanţa

Complexul Muzeal de Stiinţe ale Naturii Constanţa (Natural History Museum Complex), B-dul Mamaia 255, 8700 Constanţa - T: (041) 547055, Fax: 831553, E-mail: delfinariu@cjc.ro. Head: Gabriela Plotoagă
Natural History Museum - 1958
Black Sea fauna, zoology, ichthyology - aquarium, dolphinarium, planetarium, observatory 27553

Muzeul de Artă Constanţa, Blvd Tomis 84, 8700 Constanţa - T: (041) 617012, Fax: 617012. Head: Dr. Doina Păuleanu
Fine Arts Museum - 1961
Modern Romanian art 27554

Muzeul de Artă Populară (Folk Art Museum), B-dul Tomis 32, 8700 Constanţa - T: (041) 616133. Head: Maria Magiru
Folklore Museum 27555

Muzeul de Istorie Naţională şi Archeologie (Museum of National History and Archaeology), Piaţa Ovidiu 12, 8700 Constanţa - T: (041) 614562. Head: Dr. Adrian Radulescu
Natural History Museum / Archaeological Museum - 1879
Archaeology, numismatics, lapidarium, mosaics, jewelry of the Greek-Roman period in Dobruja, local history, midieval and modern history - library 27556

Muzeul Marinei Române (Romanian Naval Museum), Str Traian 53, 8700 Constanţa - T: (041) 619035, Fax: 619035. Head: Ion Ionescu
Special Museum - 1969
Navy history, maps, documents, uniforms, archaeological finds, coll of decoration, underwater weapons - library 27557

Corabia

Muzeul de Arheologie şi Etnografie Corabia (Corabia Archaeological and Ethnographical Museum), Str Cuza Vodă 65, 0875 Corabia - T: (049) 561364. Head: Dr. Florea Bâciu
Archaeological Museum / Ethnology Museum - 1951
Archaeological finds, coins, ethnography, folk art 27558

Coşbuc

Muzeul Memorial George Coşbuc, 4518 Coşbuc
Special Museum - 1949
Books, manuscripts, photos and documents on life and work of the poet George Coşbuc (1866-1919) 27559

Craiova

Muzeul de Artă Craiova (Craiova Art Museum), Str Calea Unirii 15, 1100 Craiova - T: (051) 412342, Fax: 412342. Head: Prof. Paul Rezeanu
Fine Arts Museum - 1908
Romanian art (17th-20th c), European paintings, sculptures by Constantin Brâncuşi - laboratory of restoration 27560

Muzeul Olteniei, Str Madona Dudu 44, 1100 Craiova - T: (051) 418631, Fax: 411674. Head: Adrian Năstase
Local Museum - 1951
Archaeological finds, numismatics, hist of the area, ethnography, folk art - library 27561

Cristuru Secuiesc

Complexul Muzeal Harghita, Secţia de Istorie, Artă, Etnografie, Stiintele Naturii, Str Liberitatii 45, 4180 Cristuru Secuiesc - T: 11727
Historical Museum / Fine Arts Museum / Ethnology Museum / Natural History Museum - 1946
Archaeology, numismatics, ethnography, folk art, natural science 27562

Curtea de Argeş

Muzeul de Istorie şi Etnografie (History and Ethnography Museum), Str Negru Vodă 2, 0450 Curtea de Argeş - T: (051) 11446. Head: Nicolae Moisescu
Historical Museum / Ethnology Museum - 1958
Local hist, archaeology, ethnography, folk art 27563

Dej

Muzeul Municipal Dej, Piata Bobilna 16, 4650 Dej - T: (064) 211790226, Fax: 212388. Head: Prof. Emil Lažar
Local Museum 27564

Deva

Muzeul Civilizaţiei Dacice şi Române (Museum of Dacian and Roman Civilisation), Str 1 Decembrie 39, 2700 Deva - T: (054) 215409, 212200, Fax: 212200. Head: Adriana Rusu Pescaru
Historical Museum - 1882
Archaeology, finds of the Dacian and Roman periods, lapidarium, medieval and modern history, ethnography, folk art, geology, mineralogy, natural science, housed in a 16th c building 27565

Doftana

Muzeul Doftana, Doftana
Local Museum - 1952
History of the revolutionary movement, photos, documents, personal belongings of political prisoners, housed in former prison 27566

Dorohoi

Complexul Muzeal Judeţean Botosani, Secţia de Stiintele Naturii, Str Al. Ion Cuza 43, 6850 Dorohoi - T: 11773
Natural History Museum - 1953
Mineralogy, geology, local fauna 27567

Expozitia Memoriala George Enescu, Complexul Muzeal Judeţean Botosani, Str Republicii 81, 6850 Dorohoi - T: 13446
Music Museum - 1957
Documents, letters and photos on the life and work of the Romanian musician George Enescu (1881-1955) 27568

Drobeta-Turnu Severin

Muzeul Regiunii Porţilor de Fier (Regional Museum Iron Gates), Str Independenţei 2, 1500 Drobeta-Turnu Severin - T: (052) 812177. Head: Ion Stîngă
Local Museum - 1912
Local and regional hist, folk art, flora and fauna of the aerea, geology, archaeology, lapidarium, Romanian art, paleontology, mineralogy 27569

Făgăraş

Muzeul din Făgăraş, Str Mihai Viteazul 1, 2300 Făgăraş - T: 11862
Local Museum - 1954
Archaeology, medieval testimonies, ethnography, folk art, housed in a 14th c fortress 27570

Fălticeni

Muzeul Orăşanesc Fălticeni, Str 23 August 2, 5750 Fălticeni - T: 41370
Local Museum - 1914
Cultural history, literature, ethnography, folk art, regional flora and fauna 27571

Flamînzi

Muzeul Rascoala Taranilor din 1907 - Flamînzi, 6840 Flamînzi
Local Museum 27572

Focsani

Complexul Muzeal Judeţean Vrancea, B-dul Gării 5, 5300 Focsani - T: (037) 622890. Head: Horia Dumitrescu
Natural History Museum - 1951
Natural hist, herbarium 27573

Muzeul Judeţean de Istorie şi Etnografie, Blvd Garii 1, 5300 Focsani - T: (037) 622790. Head: Horia Dumitrescu
Historical Museum / Ethnology Museum - 1951
Archaeology, numismatics, ethnography and folk art 27574

Galaţi

Complex Muzeal de Stiintele Naturii (Natural Sciences Museum Complex), Str Domneasca 91, 6200 Galaţi - T: (036) 411898, Fax: 414475, E-mail: cmsngl@compro.ro. Head: Aurora Marcu
Natural History Museum - 1956
Regional fauna, zoology, botany - botanical gardens, zoo 27575

Muzeul de Artă Vizuale (Museum of Visual Arts), Str Domnească 141, 6200 Galaţi - T: (036) 413452. Head: Ion Simion Mărculescu
Fine Arts Museum - 1966
Modern and contemporary Romanian art 27576

Muzeul Judeţean de Istorie (District Museum of History), Str Maior Iancu Fotea 2, 6200 Galaţi - T: (036) 414228. Head: Ştefan Stanciu
Local Museum - 1939
Archaeology, numismatics, ethnography, folk art - library 27577

Gheorghe Gheorghiu-Dej

Complexul Muzeal Judeţean Bacău, Secţia de Istorie, Str Aleea Parcului 3bis, 5450 Gheorghe Gheorghiu-Dej - T: 12444. Head: Constantin Eminovici
Historical Museum 27578

Gheorghieni

Complexul Muzeal Harghita, Secţia de Istorie, Secţia de Etnografie şi Secţia de Stiintele Naturii, Str Republicii 1, 4200 Gheorghieni - T: 11727
Historical Museum / Ethnology Museum / Natural History Museum 27579

Gherla

Muzeul de Istorie Gherla (Gherla History Museum), Str Mihai Viteazul 6, 3475 Gherla - T: (064) 241947, Fax: 241666. Head: Rodica Pintea
Local Museum - 1881
Local hist - library 27580

Giurgiu

Muzeul Judeţean Giurgiu, Str Constantin Dobrogeahu Gherea 3, 8375 Giurgiu - T: (046) 216801. Head: Vasile Barbu
Local Museum - 1950
History, ethnography 27581

Gura Humorului

Muzeul Etnografic Gura Humorului, B-dul Bucovinei 21, 5900 Gura Humorului - T: (030) 231108. Head: Elvira Romaniuc
Ethnology Museum - 1956
Folk art of the area - library 27582

Hunedoara

Muzeul Castelul Corvinestilor, Str Curtea Corvinestilor 1-3, 2750 Hunedoara - T: (054) 715409. Head: Elena Buchariu
Historical Museum - 1956
Archaeological finds, inscriptions, sculptures, medieval history, weapons, housed in a 14th c castle 27583

Huşi

Muzeul Orăşenesc Huşi, Str Republicii 8, 6575 Huşi - T: (035) 411626
Local Museum 27584

Iaşi

Expoziţia Permanentă Mihai Eminescu, Grădina Copou, 6600 Iaşi
Local Museum - 1989 27585

Muzeul de Artă (The Art Museum), Piaţa Ştefan cel Mare şi Sfânt 1, 6600 Iaşi - T: (032) 218383, Fax: 218383, E-mail: palatis@mail.opsynet.com, Internet: http://www.home.dntis.ro/~palatis/uk. Head: Ivona Elena Cernat
Fine Arts Museum - 1860
European Art, Romanian modern and contemporary art 27586

Muzeul de Istorie al Moldovei (Moldavian History Museum), Piaţa Ştefan cel Mare şi Sfânt 1, 6600 Iaşi - T: (032) 218383, Fax: 218383, E-mail: palatis@mail.dntis.ro, Internet: http://www.home.dntis.ro/~palatis/uk. Head: Dr. Văcaru Silviu
Historical Museum - 1916
Archaeology, medieval, modern and contemporary hist of Moldavia 27587

Muzeul de Istorie Naturală Iaşi (Iaşi Natural History Museum), Str Independentei 16, 6600 Iaşi - T: (032) 218337, E-mail: grigore@uaic.ro. Head: Prof. Dr. I. Ion
Natural History Museum / University Museum - 1834
Mineralogy, fossils, botany, zoology 27588

Muzeul Etnografic al Moldovei (The Ethnological Museum of Moldavia), Piaţa Ştefan cel Mare şi Sfânt 1, 6600 Iaşi - T: (032) 218383, Fax: 218383, E-mail: palatis@mail.dntis.ro, Internet: http://www.home.dntis.ro/~palatis/uk/index.htm. Head: Rodica Ropot
Ethnology Museum - 1943
Traditional wood art, traditional agricultural tools, coll of interior textiles, clothes and carpets, traditional masks, ceramics 27589

Muzeul Literaturii Române (Museum of Romanian Literature), Str Vasile Pogor 4, 6600 Iaşi - T: (032) 145760, Fax: 213210. Head: Lucian Vasiliu
Special Museum - 1971
Hist of literature in Moldavia, ancient prints, books, documents, photos 27590

Muzeul Memorial Bojdeuca Ion Creangă (Memorial Museum Ion Creangă's Cottage), Str Simion Bărnuţiu 4, 6600 Iaşi - T: (032) 115515. Head: Constantin Parascan
Special Museum - 1918
Documents, photos, books, personal objects of writer Ion Creangă (1837-1889) - documentary exhibition, documentary library 27591

Muzeul Ştiinţei şi Tehnicii " Ştefan Procopiu" ("Ştefan Procopiu" Science and Technical Museum), Piaţa Ştefan cel Mare şi Sfânt 1, 6600 Iaşi - T: (032) 218383, Fax: 218383, E-mail: palatis@mail.opsynet.com, Internet: http://www.home.dntis.ro/~palatis/uk/index.htm. Head: Lenuta Chirită
Science&Tech Museum - 1955
Technique, musical automates, mineralogy, photo apparatus, meteorology apparatus, telecommunications, ccomputers 27592

Muzeul Teatrului, Str Vasile Alecsandri 3, 6600 Iaşi - T: (032) 115760
Performing Arts Museum - 1976
History of theater, documents, photos 27593

Muzeul Unirii, Str Alexandru Lăpuşneanu 14, 6600 Iaşi - T: (032) 116414
Historical Museum - 1955
Medieval and modern historical documents, paintings, sculptures, maps, documents referring to the Union of 1859 27594

Ipoteşti

Expozitia Memoriala Mihai Eminescu, Complexul Muzeal Judeţean Botosani, 6814 Ipoteşti - T: 13446. Head: Paul Sadurschi
Special Museum - 1950
Documents, books, photos personal objects of poet Mihai Eminescu (1850-1889) 27595

Lipova

Muzeul Judeţean Arad, Secţia de Artă, Str N. Balcescu 21, 2875 Lipova - T: (057) 516499
Fine Arts Museum - 1952
Archaeological finds, history, ethnography, folk art 27596

Lugoj

Muzeul de Istorie şi Etnografie Lugoj, Str Nicolae Balcescu 2, 1800 Lugoj - T: (056) 334818. Head: Mircea Rusu
Local Museum - 1905
Archaeology, history, cultural history, ethnography 27597

Lupsa

Muzeul Etnografic Lupsa, 3380 Lupsa - T: 11853
Ethnology Museum - 1939
Handicrafts, costumes, woodcarvings 27598

Măldăreşti

Muzeul Judeţean Vilcea, Secţia de Etnografie, 1052 Măldăreşti - T: 18128. Head: Sergiu Purice
Ethnology Museum 27599

Mangalia

Muzeul de Arheologie Mangalia, Str Izvorului 3, 8727 Mangalia - T: (041) 753580, Fax: 752872, E-mail: callatis@impromex.ro. Head: Valeriu Georgescu
Archaeological Museum - 1925
Numismatics, history of the ancient city of Callatis 27600

Medgidia

Muzeul National de Istorie Nationala, Arheologie şi Artă Constanţa, Aleea Trandafirilor 1, 8650 Medgidia - T: (041) 810851. Head: Dr. Adrian Radulescu
Historical Museum / Fine Arts Museum / Archaeological Museum - 1964
Contemporary Romanian art 27601

Mediaş

Muzeul Municipal Medias, Str Viitorului 46, 3125 Mediaş - T: (069) 841299, Fax: 820506. Head: Dr. Peter Weber
Local Museum - 1950
Archaeology, hist of the area, ethnography, art, natural science 27602

Miercurea Ciuc

Muzeul Secuiesc al Ciucului, Csiki Székékely Múzeum (Ciuc Szekler Museum), Piaţa Cetăţii 2, 4100 Miercurea Ciuc - T: (066) 811727, Fax: 811727. Head: Andras Szabo
Local Museum - 1930
Archeology, history, ethnography, folk art, sculpture, housed in a 17th c building - Imre Nagy Galery 27603

Mirceşti

Expozitia Memoriala Vasile Alecsandri, Complexul Muzeal Iaşi, 5731 Mirceşti - T: 47402
Special Museum - 1957
Books, manuscripts, photos, personal objects of the poet Vasile Alecsandri (1821-1890), in his country house 27604

Moreni

Muzeul Judeţean Dimbovita, Expozitia Permanenta Lupta Revolutionara a Petrolistilor din Zona Moreni, Str 11 Iunie 2, 0271 Moreni - T: 12877
Local Museum 27605

Năsăud

Muzeul Năsăudean, Str Grănicerilor 19, 4500 Năsăud - T: (063) 362967. Head: Ioan Radu Nistor
Local Museum - 1931
Archaeology, history, ethnography, natural science, housed in an 18th c building 27606

Muzeul Năsăudean, Secţia de Expozitia Memoriala Liviu Rebreanu, Cartierul Liviu Rebreanu, 4500 Năsăud
Special Museum 27607

Negreşti Oaş

Muzeul în Aer Liber (Open Air Museum of the Oaş Land), Str Livezilor 3-5, 3919 Negreşti Oaş - T: (061) 854860, Fax: 854839. Head: Prof. Remus Vârnav
Open Air Museum - 1965 27608

Muzeul Tării Oaşului (Museum of the Oaş Land), Str Victoriei 140, 3919 Negreşti Oaş - T: (061) 854839, Fax: 854839. Head: Prof. Remus Vârnav
Local Museum - 1965
Ethnography, folk art, fine arts 27609

Odorheiul Secuiesc

Haáz Rezsö Museum, Str Kossuth Lajos 29, 4150 Odorheiul Secuiesc - T: (066) 218375, Fax: 218375, E-mail: agnesh@sco.com. Head: Eugen Zepeczaner
Local Museum / Archaeological Museum / Ethnology Museum - 1772/1949
Archaeological finds, history of the area, ethnography 27610

Olteniţa

Muzeul de Arheologie Olteniţa (Archeology Museum Olteniţa), Str Arges 101, 8350 Olteniţa - T: (042) 511174, Fax: 511174, E-mail: muz.arhe.oltenita@qk.ro. Head: Done Serbanescu
Archaeological Museum - 1957
Archaeology 27611

Oradea

Expozitia Memoriala Ady Endre, Complexul Muzeal Judeţean Bihor, Parcul Traian 10, 3700 Oradea - T: (059) 112724
Special Museum - 1955
Documents, photos, books, personal objects of the revolutionary Hungarian poet Ady Endre (1877-1919) 27612

Expozitia Memoriala Iosif Vulcan, Complexul Muzeul Judeţean Bihor, Str Iosif Vulcan 16, 3700 Oradea - T: (059) 112724
Special Museum - 1965
Memorabilia of writer Iosif Vulcan (1841-1907) 27613

Muzeul Tării Crişurilor (Criş County Museum), B-dul Dacia 1-3, 3700 Oradea - T: (059) 479917, Fax: 479918. Head: Aurel Chiriac
Local Museum - 1896
Archaeology, hist, ethnography, folk art, housed in an 18th c palace, natural hist, folk, Romanian and Universal art 27614

Orăştie

Muzeul de de Etnografie şi Artă Populară Orăştie (Ethnography and Folk Art Museum), Str Aurel Vlaicu 17, 2600 Orăştie. Head: Cosma Aurelian
Ethnology Museum / Folklore Museum - 1952
History, ethnography, folk art 27615

Petroşani

Muzeul Mineritului (Mining Museum), Str Nicolae Balcescu 21, 2675 Petroşani - T: (054) 541744. Head: Dumitru Peligrad
Local Museum - 1961 27616

Piatra Neamţ

Muzeul de Artă Piatra-Neamţ, Complexul Muzeal Judetean Neamţ (Piatra-Neamţ Art Museum), Piaţa Libertăţii 1, 5600 Piatra Neamţ - T: (033) 216808. Head: Violeta Şerban
Fine Arts Museum - 1980
Romanian art 27617

Muzeul de Etnografie Piatra-Neamţ, Complexul Muzeal Judetean Neamţ (Piatra-Neamţ Ethnography Museum), Piaţa Libertăţii 1, 5600 Piatra Neamţ - T: (033) 216808. Head: Florentina Buzenschi
Ethnology Museum 27618

Muzeul de Ştiinte Naturale, Complexul Muzeal Judeţean Neamţ, Str Petru Rares 26, 5600 Piatra Neamţ - T: (033) 224211. Head: Maria Apetrei
Natural History Museum - 1965
Fossils, minerals, geology, flora and fauna of the Carpathians 27619

Muzeul Judeţean de Istorie, Complexul Muzeal Judetean Neamţ (History Museum of Piatra Neamţ County), Str Mihai Eminescu 10, 5600 Piatra Neamţ - T: (033) 217496, Fax: 217496, E-mail: Muzeu.PNeamt@decebal.ro. Head: Gheorghe Dumitroaia
Archaeological Museum / Historical Museum - 1934
Archaeological finds, history, ethnography 27620

Piteşti

Muzeul Judeţean Argeş (The District Argeş Museum), Str Armand Calinescu 44, 0300 Piteşti - T: (048) 220254, Fax: 220254, E-mail: museuarg@geostar.ro. Head: Dr. Radu Stancu
Local Museum - 1928
Archaeology, numismatics, history, ethnography, art, natural science, housed in an 14th c building - gallery of naive art 27621

Ploieşti

Muzeul de Artă Ploieşti, B-dul Indepependenţei 1, 2000 Ploieşti - T: (044) 125775. Head: Ruxandra Ionescu
Fine Arts Museum - 1929
Classical and contemporary Romanian art 27622

Muzeul de Biologie Umanăn Prahova, Human Biology Muiseum, Str CaÔElin Cătălin 1, 2000 Ploieşti - T: (044) 121200. Head: Prof. Emilia Iancu
Natural History Museum - 1956 27623

Muzeul de Istorie şi Arheologie Prahova (Prahova Museum of History and Archaeology), Str Toma Caragiu 10, 2000 Ploieşti - T: (044) 114437, Fax: 114437. Head: Maria Dulgheru
Historical Museum / Archaeological Museum - 1953
Archaeology, numismatics, history, ethnography - library 27624

Muzeul de Stiinţele Naturii Ploieşti, Str 6 Martie 1, 2000 Ploieşti
Natural History Museum - 1956
Natural resources, regional flora and fauna 27625

Muzeul National al Petrolului, National Oil Company Petrom (National Oil Museum), Str Dr. Bagdasar 8, 2000 Ploieşti - T: (044) 123564, 197585, Fax: 119542, E-mail: mnpetrol@go.ro. Head: Gabriela Tănăsescu
Science&Tech Museum - 1961
Hist of the use of oil, oil drilling, modern technology, geology, documents, photos - library 27626

Poiana Sibiului

Muzeul Etnografic Poiana Sibiului, Poiana Sibiului
Ethnology Museum - 1935
Ethnography, folk art 27627

Rădăuţi

Muzeul Etnografic Rădăuţi, Piaţa Unirii 63, 5875 Rădăuţi - T: (030) 762565. Head: Dragoş Cuseac
Ethnology Museum - 1920 27628

Muzeul Tehnicii Populare Bucovinene, Piaţa Republicii 65, 5875 Rădăuţi
Folklore Museum - 1920
Woodcarvings, costumes, handicrafts 27629

Răşinari

Muzeul Etnografic, Str Muzeului 183, 2439 Răşinari. Head: Zoe Buciu
Ethnology Museum 27630

Reghin

Muzeul de Etnografie şi Artă Populară, Str Vînătorilor 51, 4225 Reghin - T: (065) 512571, E-mail: muzeureghin@xnet.ro. Head: Maria Borzan
Ethnology Museum / Folklore Museum / Open Air Museum - 1960
Folk art, open air ethnography park - library 27631

Reşiţa

Muzeul Banatului Montan (Museum of Montaneus Banat), Blvd Republicii 10, 1700 Reşiţa - T: (055) 221077, Fax: 226500. Head: Ţeicu Dumitru
Local Museum - 1962
Archaeology, numismatic, hist, art 27632

Rîmnicu Sărat

Muzeul Mixt Rîmnicu-Sărat, Str Mare 132, 5250 Rîmnicu Sărat - T: (038) 535127. Head: Mihau Ceausu
Local Museum - 1960
History, ethnography, local art 27633

Rîmnicu Vîlcea

Muzeul Judeţean Rîmnicu Vîlcea (Rîmnicu Vîlcea District Museum), Calea Traian 157-159, 1000 Rîmnicu Vîlcea - T: (050) 718121. Head: Petre Bardasu
Local Museum - 1955
Archaeology, history, ethnography, art, open air ethnography museum 27634

Roman

Muzeul de Istorie şi Artă Roman, Cuza-Vodă Nr 9, 5550 Roman - T: (033) 727726, Fax: 727726. Head: Vasile Ursachi
Historical Museum / Archaeological Museum - 1957
Archaeology, history, art 27635

Muzeul de Stiinţele Naturii, Str Proletariatului 4, 5550 Roman - T: (033) 721521. Head: Constantin Tarabuta
Natural History Museum - 1965
Flora and fauna of the area 27636

Roşiori de Vede

Muzeul din Roşiorii de Vede, Str Dunarii 54, 0600 Roşiori de Vede
Local Museum - 1965
Archaeology, history, ethnography, art 27637

Sacueni

Muzeul Sacuieni, Str Libertatii 1, 3750 Sacueni - T: 12724. Head: Wilhelm Iulia
Local Museum 27638

Sarichioi

Peasant Farm Museum, Enisala, Sarichioi
Agriculture Museum / Folklore Museum 27639

Sarmizegetusa

Muzeul Arheologic Sarmizegetusa, Muzeul Civilizaţiei Dacice şi Romane Deva, 2662 Sarmizegetusa - T: (054) 776418, Fax: 776418, E-mail: muzeu_sarmiz@smart.ro. Head: Secţie-Băeştean Gică
Archaeological Museum / Open Air Museum - 1924
Lapidarium, inscriptions, coins, ancient art, at the site of a former Roman city 27640

Sat Coltau

Expozitia Memoriala Petőfi Sándor, Complexul Muzeal Maremures, Comuna Bacaliseni, 4862 Sat Coltau
Special Museum 27641

Satu Mare

Muzeul Judeţean Satu Mare (Satu Mare District Museum), B-dul Vasile Lucaciu 21, 3900 Satu Mare - T: (061) 737526, Fax: 736761. Head: Viorel Ciubota
Local Museum - 1890
Archaeology, hist, ethnography, folk art, Romanian painting, art objects, natural science, archaeological sites - restoration laboratory, history library 27642

Săveni

Colecţia de Arheologie Saveni, Complexul Muzeal Judeţean Botosani, Str Republicii 140, 6875 Săveni - T: 13446
Archaeological Museum 27643

Sebeş

Muzeul Mixt Sebeş, Parcul 8 Mai 4, 2575 Sebeş - T: (058) 711853
Local Museum - 1951
History, ethnography, natural science, housed in a 15th c building 27644

Sfîntu Gheorghe

Muzeul National Secuisec (Szekler National Museum), Kós Károly Str 10, 4000 Sfîntu Gheorghe - T: (067) 312442, Fax: 312442, E-mail: digital@cosys.ro, Internet: http://www.cosys.ro/siculica. Head: Konya Adam
Local Museum - 1879
Archaeology, hist, ethnography, modern Romanian and Hungarian art, natural sciences, numismatics, science and technology - art gallery, library 27645

Sibiu

Complexul Naţional Muzeal Astra (National Astra Museum), Piaţa Mică 11, 2400 Sibiu - T: (069) 218195, 242599, Fax: 218060, E-mail: astra@sbx.logicnet.ro, Internet: http://www.astra.museum.com. Head: Corneliu-Ioan Bucur
Folklore Museum - 1905
Romanian monuments of architecture and traditional (preindustrial) installations, Romanian folk art, Non-European ethnography (Franz Binder coll and other objects) - ASTRA Film Studio, restoration and conservation lab, ethnographical and anthropological library, ethnographical archive, craft stores, PR dept, education dept 27646

Muzeul de Istorie Naturală din Sibiu, Muzeul Naţional Brukenthal (Sibiu Natural History Museum), Str Cetăţii 1, 2400 Sibiu - T: (069) 436868. Head: Gh. Ban
Natural History Museum - 1849
Zoology, botany, paleontology, mineralogy, flora and fauna, open air ethnography section - library 27647

Muzeul Naţional Brukenthal (Brukenthal National Museum), Piaţa Revoluţiei 4, 2400 Sibiu - T: (069) 4217691. Head: Alexandru Lungu
Archaeological Museum / Fine Arts Museum - 1817
Archaeology, numismatics, rare prints, folk art, modern and contemporary Romanian art, European art, lapidarium 27648

Sighetu Marmaţiei

Muzeul Maramuresului, Str Libertatii 16, 4925 Sighetu Marmaţiei - T: (062) 311521, Fax: 311521, E-mail: muzeukm0@sintec.ro. Head: Mihai Dăncuş
Folklore Museum - 1883
Folk art, costumes, icons, handicrafts, woodcarvings of the Maramures area, open air museum, archeology coll (esp bronce age), flora and fauna of Maramures, etnographic coll conc the Jewish, Hungarian and Slavonic minorities 27649

Sighişoara

Muzeul de Istorie Sighişoara, Piaţa Muzeului 1, 3050 Sighişoara - T: (065) 771108, 771514. Head: Adriana Antihi
Local Museum - 1899
Archaeological finds, coins, hist of guilds, tools, weapons, documents, clocks, medieval farmacy 27650

Sinaia

Muzeul Peleş, Str Peleşului 2, 2180 Sinaia - T: (044) 310918, Fax: 312416. Head: Gabriela Popa
Fine Arts Museum / Local Museum / Decorative Arts Museum - 1953
Art, paintings, sculptures, weapons, tapestries, porcelain, furniture, carpets, stained-glass windows 27651

Slatina

Muzeul Judeţean de Istorie şi Etnografie, Str Ionascu 75, 0500 Slatina - T: (049) 422259. Head: Aurelia Groşu
Historical Museum / Ethnology Museum - 1953
Archaeology, history, ethnography, folk art 27652

Slobozia

Muzeul Judeţean Ialomiţa, Str Matei Basarab 30, 8400 Slobozia - T: (043) 230054, Fax: 230054. Head: Emilia Corbu
Historical Museum - 1971
Archaeology, Ethnography, History 27653

Stefaneşti

Complexul Muzeal Goleşti, 0343 Stefaneşti - T: (048) 266364, Fax: 266364. Head: Prof. Constantin Iliescu
Historical Museum / Open Air Museum / Folklore Museum - 1943/1966
Documents, personal objects of the Golescu family, Goleşti residence (built in 1640), ethnography, folk art, open air ethnography museum, wine and fruit growing 27654

Suceava

Muzeul National al Bucovinei (Bucovina National Museum), Str Stefan cel Mare 33, 5800 Suceava - T: (030) 716439, Fax: 716439. Head: Pavel Blaj
Archaeological Museum / Historical Museum / Ethnology Museum / Fine Arts Museum / Natural History Museum / Music Museum - 1900
Archaeology, numismatics, history, ethnography, art, natural science, documents on composer Ciprian Porumbescu (1853-1883) 27655

Tecuci

Muzeul Mixt Tecuci, Str 23 August 37, 6300 Tecuci. Head: Nicolae Radulescu
Local Museum - 1934
Archaeology, history, natural science 27656

Timişoara

Muzeul Banatului (Museum of the Banat), Piaţa Huniade 1, 1900 Timişoara - T: (056) 191339, 201321, Fax: 201321, E-mail: root@mbt.dnttm.ro, Internet: http://www.infotim.ro/patrimcb/tm/timisoar/muzban. Head: Dr. Florin Draşovean
Local Museum / Open Air Museum - 1872
Archaeology, numismatics, lapidarium, history, ethnography, folk art, Romanian and foreign art, natural science, open air ethnography section, housed in a 14th c castle 27657

Tîrgovişte

Complexul Monumental Curtea Veche, Str Nicolae Bălcescu 221, 0200 Tîrgovişte - T: (045) 612877
Archaeological Museum - 1967
Archaeology, documents referring to the city, housed in a 14th c building 27658

Complexul Muzeal Judeţean Dîmboviţa (Dîmboviţa District Museum Complex), Str Justitiei 3-5, 0200 Tîrgovişte - T: (045) 612877. Head: Gheorghe Bulei
Local Museum - 1940
Archaeology, numismatics, history, ethnography, literature, art 27659

Muzeul de Artă, Str Nicolae Balcescu 219-231, 0200 Tîrgovişte - T: (045) 612877
Fine Arts Museum 27660

Muzeul Judeţean Dîmboviţa, Secţia Tiparului şi al Cartii Vechi Româneşti, Str Justitiei 5, 0200 Tîrgovişte - T: (045) 612877. Head: Gabriela Nitulescu
Historical Museum - 1967
Cultural history, history of printing, old Romanian books 27661

Tîrgu Jiu

Muzeul de Artă, Muzeul Judeţean Gorj (Art Museum), Parcul Central, 1400 Tîrgu Jiu - T: (053) 218550. Head: Carmen Silvia Şocu
Fine Arts Museum
Romanian contemporary art, sculptures by Brâncuşi 27662

Muzeul de Istorie şi Arheologie, Muzeul Judeţean Gorj (History and Archaeology Museum), Str Geneva, 1400 Tîrgu Jiu - T: (053) 212044
Historical Museum / Archaeological Museum - 1894
library 27663

Muzeul Judeţean Gorj (Gorj District Museum), Str Geneva 8, 1400 Tîrgu Jiu - T: (053) 212044. Head: Prof. Vasile Marinoiu
Local Museum 27664

Tîrgu Mureş

Muzeul de Arheologie şi Istorie, Muzeul Judeţean Mureş (Archaeology and History Museum), Str George Enescu 2, 4300 Tîrgu Mureş - T: (065) 432512
Archaeological Museum / Historical Museum 27665

Muzeul de Artă, Muzeul Judeţean Mureş (Art Museum), Str George Enescu 2, 4300 Tîrgu Mureş - T: (065) 432179
Fine Arts Museum
19th and 20th c art 27666

Muzeul Judeţean Mureş, Str Horea 24, 4300 Tîrgu Mureş - T: (065) 425634. Head: Valer Pop
Historical Museum / Fine Arts Museum / Natural History Museum - 1886
Classical and contemporary art, Romanian art, Hungarian paintings, plastic art, archaeology, history, numismatics, ethnography, natural science, Ion Vlasiu Art Gallery 27667

Tîrgu Neamţ

Muzeul de Istorie si Etnografie, Complexul Muzeal Judeţean Neamţ, Stefan col Mare 37, 5675 Tîrgu Neamţ - T: (033) 790594. Head: Vitalie Josanu
Local Museum 27668

Tîrgu Secuiesc

Muzeul Judeţean Covasna, Secţia de Istorie, Piaţa Armata Rosie 10, 4050 Tîrgu Secuiesc - T: (067) 314367
Historical Museum 27669

Topalu

Muzeul de Artă Dinu şi Sevasta Vintilă, Topalu
Fine Arts Museum - 1960
Paintings, sculptures by Romanian artists 27670

Tulcea

Art Museum, Eco-Museal Research Institute of Tulcea, Str Alexandru Sahia 2, 8800 Tulcea
Fine Arts Museum 27671

Ethnographic Museum, Eco-Museal Research Institute of Tulcea, Str 9 Mai 4, 8800 Tulcea
Ethnology Museum 27672

History and Archaeology Museum, Eco-Museal Research Institute of Tulcea, Str Gloriei, Parcul Monumentul Independentei, 8800 Tulcea
Archaeological Museum 27673

Natural Science Museum, Eco-Museal Research Institute of Tulcea, Str 14 Noiembrie 3, 8800 Tulcea - T: (040) 513231, 515375, Fax: 513231, E-mail: icemtl@tlx.ssitl.ro. Head: Simion Gavrila
Natural History Museum - 1949
Flora and fauna of the region 27674

Turda

Muzeul Municipal Turda, Str B.P. Hasdeu 2, 3350 Turda - T: (064) 312344. Head: Claudia Luca
Local Museum - 1951
Archaeology, history, ethnography, housed in a 15th c palace 27675

Urlaţi

Complexul Muzeal Judeţean Prahova, Secţia de Artă Urlaţi, Str Orzoaia de Sus 12, 2041 Urlaţi - T: (044) 244937. Head: Zoe Stoicescu Apostolache
Fine Arts Museum 27676

Muzeul Etnografic Urlaţi, Str Orzoaia de Sus 12, 2041 Urlaţi
Ethnology Museum - 1955
Ethnography, folk art 27677

Valenii de Munte

Expozitia Memoriala Nicolae Iorga, Complexul Muzeal Judeţean Prahova, Str George Enescu 3, 2100 Valenii de Munte - T: 44937. Head: Zoe Stoicescu Apostolache
Special Museum - 1965
Documents, photos, furniture of the historian Nicolae Iorga (1871-1940), in his country house 27678

Vaslui

Muzeul Stefan Cel Mare (Stefan Cel Mare Museum), Piaţa Independenţei 1, 6500 Vaslui - T: (035) 311626. Head: Constantin Popescu
Local Museum - 1974
Local hist, archaeology, art, ethnography - library 27679

Vatra Dornei

Muzeul Orăşanesc Vatra Dornei, Str 7 Noiembrie 17, 5975 Vatra Dornei - T: (030) 316439. Head: Simion Hoja
Natural History Museum - 1957
Geology, flora and fauna of the area 27680

Zalău

Muzeul Judeţean de Istorie şi Artă Zalău, Str Unirii 9, 4700 Zalău - T: (060) 612223, Fax: 661706. Head: Alexandru Matei
Historical Museum / Fine Arts Museum - 1951
Archaeology, numismatics, lapidarium, history, ethnography, folk art, contemporary Romanian art - library 27681

Russia

Abramcevo

Muzej-usadba Abramcevo (Abramtsevo Estate Museum), 141352 Abramcevo - T: (095) 5845533, Fax: 5845533. Head: Ivan Alekseevič Ribakov
Fine Arts Museum
Russian fine art, art history, literature, theatre 27682

Aginskoe

Aginskij Okružnoj Kraevedčeskij Muzej (Regional Museum), Aginskoe
Local Museum - 1961
Local history, economics, natural history - library 27683

Aksaj

Muzej Istorii Aksaja, ul Gulaeva 110, 346700 Aksaj - T: 123635
Local Museum 27684

Archangelsk

Archangelskij Oblastnoj Kraevedčeskij Muzej (Arkhangelsk State Museum), pl V.I. Lenina 2, 163061 Archangelsk - T: 36679. Head: J.P. Prokopev
Historical Museum - 1737
Hist of the Northern Coast area, art, ethnography - library 27685

Archangelskij Oblastnoj Muzej Izobrazitelnych Iskusstv (Arkhangelsk State Museum of Fine Arts), nab Lenina 79, 163061 Archangelsk. Head: M.V. Mitkevič
Fine Arts Museum
Ancient North and Western European Art - library 27686

Archangelskoe

Muzej-usadba Archangelskoe (Country Estate Museum Arkhangelskoe), 143420 Archangelskoe - T: (095) 5602231
Local Museum - 1919
History, ancient hist, military hist, archeology - library 27687

State Museums Association "The Artistic Culture of the Russian North" (Regional Museum of Fine Art), Pl Lenina 2, Archangelskoe 61 - T: (8182) 432673. Head: V.M. Mitkevich
Fine Arts Museum - 1960
Ancient Russian art (14th-18th c), Northern applied and folk arts, Russian classic and modern art - library 27688

Arzamas

Arzamasskij Istoriko-chudožestvennyj Muzej, ul Kosmonavtov 39a, 607220 Arzamas
Local Museum - 1956 27689

Ašaga-stal

Stalsky Memorial Museum, Ašaga-stal
Special Museum
Hist of Dagestan literature - library 27690

Astrachan

Astrachanskaja Gosudarstvennaja Galereja im. B.M. Kustodieva (Astrakhan State Gallery B.M. Kustodiev), ul Sverdlova 81, Astrachan - T: 226665, Fax: 226665. Head: L.J. Ilina
Fine Arts Museum - 1918
Coll of works of Russian painters, sculptors and graphic artists - library 27691

Astrachanskij Oblastnoj Kraevedčeskij Muzej (Astrakhan Regional Museum), Sovetskaja 15, Astrachan
Local Museum - 1836
Local hist, economics, natural hist - library 27692

Azov

Archeologičeskij Muzej, Rostovskij Oblastnyj Muzej Kraevedčenija, 346723 Azov - T: 20249
Archaeological Museum - 1958 27693

Azovskij Kraevedčeskij Muzej, ul Moskovskaja 38-40, 346740 Azov - T: 30771
Local Museum - 1959 27694

Balachna

Balachninskij Kraevedčeskij Muzej (Regional Museum), pr Revolyutsii 17, 606400 Balachna - T: 2170
Local Museum - 1927
Coll of local tiles (17-19th c) and mugs (19-20th c) 27695

Barabinsk

Barabinskij Kraevedčeskij Muzej (Regional Museum), ul Kirova 3, 632300 Barabinsk - T: 5672
Local Museum 27696

Barnaul

Altajskij Gosudarstvennyj Chudožestvennyj Muzej
→ Gosudarstvennyj Chudožestvennyj Muzej Altajskogo Kraja

Altajskij Gosudarstvennyj Kraevedčeskij Muzej (Altai State Regional Studies Museum), ul Polzunova 46, 656099 Barnaul 43 - T: (03852) 234551, 234943, Fax: 234551, E-mail: agkm@chat.ru, ieu@dcn-asu.ru, Internet: http://www.museum.ru/museums/asrsm. Head: L. Leonova
Local Museum - 1823
Local hist, economics, culture, natural hist, archaeology, ethnography, space, military hist, agriculture, science and technology, photo coll - library 27697

Gosudarstvennyj Chudožestvennyj Muzej Altajskogo Kraja (The State Art Museum of Altay Region), pr Lenina 88, Barnaul - T: (03852) 220265, Fax: 220265, E-mail: muzei@ab.rum2090@mail.museum.ru, Internet: http://www.ab.ru/~muzei, http://www.museum.ru/m2090. Head: Inna Konstantinovna Galkina
Decorative Arts Museum - 1958
Large coll, from 18th c onward, of wood carvings, ceramics, national costumes - library 27698

Belgorod

Belgorod-Dnestrovskij Kraevedčeskij Muzej (Belgorod-Dnestrovski Regional Museum), ul Timirjazeva 19, Belgorod
Local Museum
Ethnography, history, economics, natural history 27699

Belinskij

Gosudarstvennyj Memorialnyj Muzej V.G. Belinskogo (V.G. Belinski State Memorial Museum), ul Belinskogo 11, 442250 Belinskij - T: 21981. Head: I.A. Gerasikin
Special Museum - 1938
Home, life and work of the literary critic Vissarion Grigorevich Belinski 27700

Berezniki

Bereznikovskij Istoriko-kraevedčeskij Muzej, Pr Lenina 43, 618400 Berezniki - T: 394663
Local Museum - 1924 27701

Bijsk

Bijskij Kraevedčeskij Muzej B.V. Bianki (B.V. Bianki Local Museum), ul Sovetskaja 42, Bijsk
Local Museum - 1920
Local history, economics, culture, natural history - library 27702

Blagoveščensk

Amurskij Oblastnoj Muzej Kraevedenija (Regional Museum), Internacionalnyj per 6, Blagoveščensk
Local Museum - 1896
History, natural history, culture - library 27703

Bolšoe Muraškino

Bolšemuraškinskij Rajonnyj Istoriko-kraevedčeskij Muzej, Ul Svobodij 90, 606330 Bolšoe Muraškino - T: 21944
Local Museum
Precious Russian and intl medals (1872-1913), coll of weapons, material on protopope Avvakum 27704

Borodino

Gosudarstvennyj Borodinskij Voenno-istoričeskij Muzej (Borodino State Museum of War and History Museum), 143240 Borodino - T: (09638) 51057, Fax: 51057, E-mail: borodino@rosmail.ru, Internet: http://www.borodino.ru. Head: Alise D. Kachalova
Military Museum - 1839
Campaign of 1812, the Battle of Borodino and the World War II, documents - library 27705

Brjansk

Brjanskij Gosudarstvennyj Chudožestvennyj Muzej (Bryansk State Museum of Fine Arts), ul Gagarina 19, Brjansk. Head: B.F. Faenkov
Fine Arts Museum 27706

Brjanskij Gosudarstvennyj Obedinennyj Kraevedčeskij Muzej (Bryansk State Museum of Local Lore), Partizanskaja pl 6, 241011 Brjansk - T: (0832) 446398, E-mail: peresvet@online.debryansk.ru. Head: Vladimir P. Alekseev
Historical Museum - 1945
Natural history, history, economics, culture - library 27707

Buguruslan

Buguruslanskij Istoriko-kraevedčeskij Muzej, ul Krasnogvardeiskaja 62, 461600 Buguruslan - T: 76383
Local Museum - 1930 27708

Buzuluk

Buzulukskij Istoriko-kraevedčeskij Muzej, ul Lenina 56, 461010 Buzuluk
Local Museum - 1955
Archeology, paintings, local journals (1850-1917), samovars, coins, medals, photographies 27709

Čajkovskij

Čajkovskij Kraevedčeskij Muzej, Ul Mira 21, 617740 Čajkovskij - T: 394663
Local Museum - 1963 27710

Čeboksary

Čuvašskij Chudožestvennyj Muzej (Chuvash Art Museum), ul Kalinina 60, 428008 Čeboksary - T: 220704. Head: N. Sadjukov
Fine Arts Museum - 1939
Fine art, mainly modern Russian, Soviet and Chuvash artists, traditional Chuvash decorative art - library 27711

Čeljabinsk

Čeljabinskaja Gosudarstvennaja Kartinnaja Galerija (Chelyabinsk State Picture Gallery), ul Truda 92a, 454001 Čeljabinsk - T: (03512) 330682. Head: I.F. Tkačenko
Public Gallery 27712

Čeljabinskij Oblastnoij Kraevedčeskij Muzej (Regional Museum), ul Kirova 60a, 454000 Čeljabinsk - T: 337291. Head: Andrej Grigorjevič Sanvenko
Local Museum - 1924
Local hist, economics, culture - library 27713

Čerdyn

Čerdynskij Kraevedčeskij Muzej A.A. Puškina, ul Lenina 69, 618600 Čerdyn - T: 21307
Local Museum 27714

Chabarovsk

Dalnevostočnyj Chudožestvennyj Muzej (Far Eastern Art Museum), ul Ševčenko 7, Chabarovsk - T: (04212) 327258, Fax: 327258, E-mail: museum@mail.ru, Internet: http://www.art-museum.khv.ru. Head: Valentina Aleksandrovna Zaporožskaja
Fine Arts Museum - 1931
Art - library 27715

Muzej Iskusstv (Art Museum), ul Karla Marksa 21, 680000 Chabarovsk
Fine Arts Museum 27716

Chanty-Mansijsk

Chanty-Mansijskij Okružnoj Kraevedčeskij Muzej (Chanty-Mansijsk Regional Museum), Komsomolskaja ul 9, Chanty-Mansijsk
Local Museum - 1936
History, natural history, economics, culture - library 27717

Dobrjanka

Dobrjanskij Istoričeskij Muzej, Permskij Oblastnyj Kraevedčeskij Muzej, Ul Lenina 3, 618710 Dobrjanka - T: (3422) 342569
Local Museum 27718

Dzeržinsk (Nižegorod)

Dzeržinskij Gorodskoj Kraevedčeskij Muzej (Dzeržinsk City Museum), Pr Dzeržinskogo 8, 606000 Dzeržinsk (Nižegorod)
Local Museum - 1932
Paintings and graphics by N.K. Guselnikov (1910-1957), 191 bombs from different countries 27719

Ekaterinburg

Ekaterinburgskaja Kartinnaja galerija (Ekaterinburg Picture Gallery), ul Vainera 11, Ekaterinburg L-14. Head: E.V. Chamcov
Fine Arts Museum - 1746
Painting, metal objects, Western European, Russian and Soviet art - library 27720

Oblastnoj Kraevedčeskij Muzej (Museum of Local History and Nature), ul Malyševa 46, 620151 Ekaterinburg - T: (3432) 764719, Fax: 764718, E-mail: radio@dialup.mplik.ru, Internet: http://www.uralregion.ru/radio. Head: Valeri K. Ufimcev
Local Museum - 1870
Social, cultural, natural, political hist of the region, handicrafts, furnishings, domestic utensils, textiles, woood, rare books, numismatics, archaeoogy, exotic coll, cult objects - library, archive, restauration workshops, taxidermy laboratory, planetarium 27721

State Amalgamated Museum of the Writers of the Ural, Ul Tolmačeva 41, 620151 Ekaterinburg - T: (3432) 517281. Head: L.A. Chudjakova
Special Museum - 1940/1980
Material on the life and work of Mamin-Sibiryak, Bazhov, and contemporary writers of the Urals - library 27722

Uralskij Geologičeskij muzej V.V. Vachrušev (Ural Geological Museum V.V. Vakhrushev), ul Kuibyševa 30, 620120 Ekaterinburg - T: (3432) 223109, Fax: 294838. Head: Juri A. Polenov
Natural History Museum - 1937
Gold and minerals from Ural 27723

Ėlista

Kalmyckij Respublikanskij Kraevedčeskij Muzej im. Prof. N.N. Palmova, Teatralnyj per 2, Ėlista
Historical Museum - 1961
History, natural history, economics, culture - library 27724

Gagarin

Memorialnyj Muzej Jurija Gagarina (Yurii Gagarin Memorial Museum), ul Gagarina, Gagarin - T: (08135) 41926, Fax: 48837, E-mail: gagarinm@sci.smolensk.ru, Internet: http://www.sci.smolensk.ru/users/gread. Head: Maria Stepanova
Local Museum - 1970
Life and work of the cosmonaut Yurii Gagarin, hist of Gagarin town and region 27725

Gorno-Altajsk

Gorno-Altajskij Oblastnoj Kraevedčeskij Muzej (Regional Museum), Socialističeskaja 35, Gorno-Altajsk
Local Museum - 1920
Local history, economics, natural history - library 27726

Gorodec

Gorodeckij Kraevedčeskij Muzej (Gorodec Regional Museum), Ul Lenina 11, 606430 Gorodec - T: 22849
Local Museum - 1917
Wood carvings, gold embroidery (18-19th c), local decorative and applied art, works by local painters, clay toys by the Sirotkin dynasty, handmade books by calligrapher I.G. Blinov 27727

Irkutsk

Irkutskij Oblastnoj Kraevedčeskij Muzej (Regional Museum), ul Karla Marksa 2, Irkutsk - T: (3952) 335916. Head: L.M. Kolyesnik
Local Museum - 1782
Coll gathered by members of the East-Siberian dept of the Russian Emperial Geographical Society in China, in Mongolia and, in particular, in Siberia - scientific library 27728

Muzej Iskusstv (Art Museum), ul Karla Marksa 23, 664000 Irkutsk
Fine Arts Museum 27729

Iskitim

Iskitimskij Kraevedčeskij Muzej (Regional Museum), ul Koroteeva 28, 633210 Iskitim - T: 42086
Local Museum - 1972
Natural history, ethnography, local history 27730

Ivanovo

Ivanovskij chudožestvennyj muzej (Ivanovski Art Museum), pr Lenina 33, 153002 Ivanovo - T: 26504. Head: L.V. Volovenskaja
Fine Arts Museum - 1960
Greek, Roman and Ancient Egyptian art, icons, 18th-20th c Russian art - library 27731

Ivanovskij Oblastnoj Kraevedčeskij Muzej (Ivanovo Regional Museum), ul Baturina 6/40, Ivanovo
Local Museum - 1915
History and economic development of the region, iron, chemical and textile industries, popular art, costumes, paintings - library 27732

Izborsk

Izborskij Gosudarstvennyj Istoriko-architekturnyj i Prirodnij Landšaftny Muzej Zapovednik Izborsk (Natural and Historically Architectural State Museum Izborsk), Pechorskaja ul 39, 181518 Izborsk - T: (248) 96696, Fax: 96696. Head: Leonid Panov
Historical Museum / Natural History Museum - 1964
Fortified building - historical archives 27733

Iževsk

Udmurtskij Respublikanskij Kraevedčeskij Muzej (Regional Museum), ul V. Sivkova 180, Iževsk
Local Museum - 1930
History, economics, natural history, ethnography - library 27734

Jakutsk

Chudožestvennyj muzej (Art Museum), ul Maxima Ammosova 14, Jakutsk
Fine Arts Museum 27735

Jakutskij Muzej Izobrazitelnych Iskusstv (Jakutsk Museum of Fine Arts), ul Chabarova 27, 677000 Jakutsk - T: 27798. Head: N.M. Vasileva
Fine Arts Museum - 1928
17th-20th c Western European, Russian and Soviet art, folk art 27736

Jakutskij Respublikanskij Kraevedčeskij Muzej, Muzejnyj per 2, Jakutsk
Local Museum 27737

Muzej Istorii i Kultury Čelovečestva, Jakutskij gosudarstvennyj muzej (Museum of History and Culture of the Peoples), ul Lenina 5, Jakutsk 20 - T: (41122) 23753, Fax: 23753. Head: Ertyukova Nadezda Semenovna
Ethnology Museum - 1891
Subjects of the Polar expedition by guidance of Eduard toll, materials of christianity and culture - library 27738

Jaroslavl

Gosudarstvennyj Muzej Architektury i Iskusstva, Pl Podbelskogo 25, 150000 Jaroslavl - T: 220272
Decorative Arts Museum / Fine Arts Museum 27739

Jaroslavskij Istoričeskij Muzej-zapovednik (Jaroslavl Historical and Architectural Museum-Preserve), Bogojavlenskaja pl 25, 150000 Jaroslavl - T: (0852) 304072, 303537, Fax: 305755, E-mail: galla@uniyar.ae.ru, Internet: http://www.yarmp.yar.ru. Head: Benjamin Ivanovič Lebedev
Local Museum - 1865
Local hist, manuscripts, documents - library 27740

Jasnaja Poljana (Tula)

Gosudarstvennyj Muzej L.N. Tolstogo "Jasnaja Poljana" (Museum-estate of L.N. Tolstoj "Yasnaya Polyana"), 301214 Jasnaja Poljana (Tula) 301214 - T: (0872) 386710, Fax: 386710, E-mail: yaspol@tula.net, Internet: http://www.tolstoy.ru/yaspol. Head: Vladimir I. Tolstoj
Special Museum - 1921
Memorabilia of the writer Lev Nikolaevich Tolstoi (1828-1910) in his former house and estate - library, publishing house, gallery 27741

Kaliningrad

Amber Museum, pl Maršala Vasilevskogo 1, 236000 Kaliningrad - T: (0112) 461220
Natural History Museum 27742

Bunker Museum, Universitetskaja ul, 236000 Kaliningrad - T: (0112) 460593
Historical Museum 27743

Museum of History and Art, Kliničeskaja ul 21, 236000 Kaliningrad - T: (0112) 453844
Historical Museum / Natural History Museum / Fine Arts Museum 27744

Muzej Mirovogo Okeana (Museum of the World Ocean), Naberežnaja Petra Velikogo 1, 236006 Kaliningrad - T: (0112) 436302, Fax: 340211, E-mail: postmaster@vitiaz.koenig.ru, Internet: http://www.vitiaz.ru. Head: Svetlana G. Sivkova
Natural History Museum / Science&Tech Museum 27745

State Art Gallery, Moskovskij pr 60-62, 236000 Kaliningrad - T: (0112) 467166
Public Gallery / Fine Arts Museum 27746

Kaluga

Gosudarstvennyj Muzej Istorii Kosmonavtiki im. K.E. Ciolkovskogo (State Museum of the History of Cosmonautics K.E. Tsiolkovsky), ul Koroleva 2, Kaluga - T: (084) 2574333, Fax: 2574333, E-mail: mkosmos@kaluga.ru. Head: E. Kouzin
Science&Tech Museum - 1967
Aviation, aeronautics, cosmonautics, manned spaceships, works of the astronautical scientist Konstantin Eduardovich Tsiolkovski - library 27747

Kalužskij Oblastnoj Chudožestvennyj Muzej (Kaluga Regional Art Museum), ul Lenina 104, 248600 Kaluga - T: (0842) 563660, E-mail: artmuseum@kaluga.ru, Internet: http://users.kaluga.ru/artmuseum/. Head: T.V. Morozova
Fine Arts Museum - 1918
Sculpture, paintings, drawings - library 27748

Kalužskij Oblastnoj Kraevedčeskij Muzej (Kaluga Regional Museum), ul Puškina 14, Kaluga
Local Museum - 1917
History, economics, natural history, ethnography - library 27749

Kazan

Gosudarstvennyj Tatarskij Muzej (Tatar State Museum), Kremlevskaja ul 2, 420111 Kazan - T: (8432) 321484, Fax: 321484. Head: G.S. Mychanov
Local Museum - 1894
Art, natural hist, cultural hist of the Tatar region - library 27750

Kazanskij Memorialnyj Muzej im. A.M. Gorkogo (Gorki Memorial Museum), ul Gorkogo 10, Kazan
Special Museum - 1950
Memorabilia of the writer Maksim Gorki, literary hist - library 27751

Tatarskij Gosudarstvennyj Muzej Izobrazitelnych Iskusstv (Tatar State Museum of Fine Arts), ul Karla Marksa 64, 420015 Kazan - T: (8432) 366921, Fax: 361865, E-mail: finearts@bancorp.ru. Head: Anatoli A. Slastunin
Fine Arts Museum
Fine art, contemporary art 27752

Tatarskij Istoričeskij Muzej (Tatar Historical Museum), Ul Uljanova 58, 420000 Kazan
Historical Museum
10,000 exhibits incl documents, photographs, works of art and other exhibits relating to Lenin's life 27753

Kemerovo

Kemerovskij Oblastnoj Kraevedčeskij Muzej (Regional Museum), Sovetskij pr 89, Kemerovo
Local Museum - 1957
History, ethnography, economics, natural history, culture - library 27754

Kirov

Kirovskij Muzej im. Viktora i Appolinarisa Vasnecovych (Kirov Victor and Appolinaris Vasnetsov Museum), Ul Karla Marksa 70, 610000 Kirov - T: 622646. Head: Alla A. Noskova
Fine Arts Museum - 1910
Russian and West European sculpture, paintings, engravings and decorative art - library 27755

Kirovskij Oblastnoj Kraevedčeskij Muzej (Kirov Regional Museum), Ul Lenina 82, Kirov
Local Museum / Special Museum - 1918
Contemporary literature of the Urals and Siberia, local hist, natural hist - library 27756

Kislovodsk

Memorialnyj Muzej-usadba Chudožnika N.A. Jarošenko (Memorial Estate Museum), ul Jarošenko 3, 357741 Kislovodsk - T: (33113) 35158
Fine Arts Museum - 1962
Fine art, life and work of the painter Nikola Yaroshenko - library 27757

Kiži

Gosudarstvennyj Istoriko-architekturnyj i Etnografičeskij Muzej-zapovednik Kiži (State Open Air Museum Kizhi of Architecture, History and Ethnography), ul Neglinskaja 23, 185000 Kiži - T: 70087, Fax: 72297. Head: Michail Vasilevič Lapatkin
Open Air Museum - 1969
Architectural wooden ensemble of churches and Russian houses of the 16th and 17th c, folk art - Regional childrens museum center 27758

Klin

Gosudarstvennyj Dom-muzej P.I. Čajkovskogo (P.I. Tchaikovsky State Memorial House), ul Čajkovskogo 48, 141600 Klin - T: (09624) 58196, Fax: 58467, E-mail: gdmch@dol.ru, Internet: http://www.museum.ru/m443. Head: G.I. Belonovich
Music Museum - 1894
Memorabilia of P.I. Tchaikovsky, documents, records, books, sheet music - library 27759

Komsomolsk-na-Amure

Muzej Izobrazitelnych Iskusstv (Museum of Fine Arts), pr Mira, Komsomolsk-na-Amure. Head: E.J. Turčinskaja
Fine Arts Museum 27760

Končanskoe-Suvorovskoe

Muzej-zapovednik A.V. Suvorova, 174435 Končanskoe-Suvorovskoe - T: 96133. Head: Valentina Pavlovna Mališeva
Historical Museum - 1942
Memorabilia of the commander-in-chief Aleksandr Vasilevich Suvorov, military hist - library 27761

Korablino

Korablinkskij Kraevedčeskij Muzej, ul Sadovaja, 391220 Korablino - T: 2968
Local Museum 27762

Kostroma

Kostromskij Istoriko-architekturnyj Muzej-zapovednik (Kostroma Historical and Architectural Museum), Prosveščenija 1, Kostroma 4
Historical Museum - 1885
History, ethnography, architecture, archeology, art - library 27763

Kostromskij Muzej Izobrazitelnych Iskusstv (Kostroma Museum of Fine Arts), pr Mira 5, Kostroma. Head: V.J. Ignatev
Fine Arts Museum - 1913
Russian art, Ancient Russian religious books, work of Y. Chestnyakov 27764

Krasnodar

Krasnodarskij Chudožestvennyj Muzej im. F.A. Kovalenko (Kovalenko Art Museum), Krasnaja 13, Krasnodar - T: (8612) 685835, Fax: 685835, E-mail: M1446@mail.museum.ru, Internet: http://www.mail.museum.ruµ1446. Head: Tatjana Michailovna Kondratenko
Fine Arts Museum - 1904
17th-20th c Russian and European art, Russian, W-European and Japanese engraving - library, archive 27765

Krasnojarsk

Krasnojarskij Chudožestvennyj Muzej (Krasnoyarsk Arts Museum), ul Parižkoj Kommuny 20, 660097 Krasnojarsk - T: 272558. Head: A.F. Efimovskij
Fine Arts Museum - 1958
Fine art, decorative and applied art - library 27766

Krasnojarskij Kraevoj Muzej (Krasnojarsk Regional Museum), ul Dubrovinskogo 84, 660000 Krasnojarsk 49
Local Museum - 1889
History, economics, ethnography, natural hist - library 27767

Kudymkar

Komi-Permjackij Okružnoj Muzej (Regional Museum), ul Sovetskaja 31, 617000 Kudymkar - T: 20948
Local Museum - 1921
History, economics, ethnography, natural history, culture - library 27768

Kungur

Kungurskij Kraevedčeskij Muzej, ul Gogolja 36, 617400 Kungur - T: (0271) 24394. Head: Faina Sergeevna Bratilova
Local Museum - 1911
National costumes, numismatics, ceramics, art works made of the Ural minerals and soft rock stones, coll of applied and folk art, coll of painting and drawing works, archaeological coll, coll of Samovars, coll of photodocuments, coll of phalerae - library, archives 27769

Kurgan

Istoriko-kraevedčeskij Muzej Taldy-Kurgana (Taldy-Kurgan Historical and Regional Museum), ul Abaja 231, 640000 Kurgan. Head: A.Z. Lian
Local Museum / Historical Museum 27770

Kurganskij Oblastnoj Kraevedčeskij Muzej (Regional Museum), ul Volodarskogo 42, Kurgan
Local Museum - 1950
Local history, ethnography, economics, natural history - library 27771

Kursk

Kurskaja Kartinnaja Galerija (Kursk Art Gallery), ul Sovetskaja 3, 305016 Kursk - T: (071) 2223936, E-mail: gallery@pub.sovtest.ru, Internet: http://www.museum.ru. Head: I.A. Pripačkin
Fine Arts Museum - 1935
19th-20th c Russian art - library 27772

Kurskij Oblastnoj Kraevedčeskij Muzej (Kursk Regional Museum), ul Lunačarskogo 6, Kursk
Local Museum - 1903
Local hist, natural hist - library 27773

Kyzyl

Tuvinskij Respublikanskij Kraevedčeskij Muzej im. 60 Bogatyrej (Regional Museum), ul Lenina 7, Kyzyl
Local Museum - 1930
History, economics, ethnography, natural history - library 27774

Lermontov

Lermontovskij Gosudarstvennyj Muzej Tarchany (Lermontov State Museum Tarkhany), 442240 Lermontov - T: (053) 21203, Fax: 22234, E-mail: muslerm@sura.ru, Internet: http://www.sura.ru/tarhany. Head: T.M. Melnikova
Special Museum - 1939
Life and work of the poet Mikhail Yurevich Lermontov 27775

Lipeck

Lipeckij Oblastnoj Kraevedčeskij Muzej (Lipetsk Regional Museum), pl Lenina 25, 398050 Lipeck - T: (074) 240286. Head: Lidija P. Katerinkino
Local Museum - 1909
Local history, natural history, economics, documents related to socialist politician Georgy Plekhanov (1856-1918) - library 27776

Lomonosov

Coasting Hill Pavilion, Verchnyj park, Lomonosov - T: (812) 4224796, Fax: 4231618. Head: N.I. Karmazin
Decorative Arts Museum - 1959
Original interiors (1762-1774), A. Rinaldi Rococo style, wall paintings, porcelain, artificial marbel floors, art, porcelain, furniture 27777

Dvorets-muzej Petra III (Palace Museum of Peter the III), Verchnyj park, 189510 Lomonosov - T: (812) 4224796, Fax: 4231618. Head: N.I. Karmazin
Decorative Arts Museum - 1953
Palace, built by A. Rinaldi 1758-1762, original interiors, porcelain, furniture, wood carvings, enamels, pictures on silk, stucco work 27778

Gosudarstvennyj Muzej Istorii, Iskusstva i architektury (State Museum of History, Art and Architecture), Pr Junogo Lenina 48, 189510 Lomonosov - T: 4734796
Historical Museum / Fine Arts Museum 27779

Kitajskij Dvorec-muzej (China Palace Museum), Verchnyj park, Lomonosov - T: (812) 4224796, Fax: 4231618. Head: N.I. Karmazin
Fine Arts Museum - 1922
Original interiors (1762-1768), A. Rinaldi Rococo style, plafonds, wall paintings, embroidery, panels, unique inlaid parquetry, painting, furniture, porcelain, wood carvings, art modelling, enamel 27780

Machačkala

Dagestanskij Chudožestvennyj Muzej (Dagestan Museum of Fine Arts), ul Markova 45, Machačkala
Fine Arts Museum 27781

Malojaroslavec

Malojaroslavskij Muzej Voennoj Istorii 1812 Goda (Maloyaroslavets Museum of History of the War of 1812), Moskovskaja ul 27, 249050 Malojaroslavec - T: 22711. Head: N.V. Kotljakova
Military Museum - 1939
Regional hist, relics of 1812 campaigns - library 27782

Melichovo

Memorialnyj Muzej A.P. Čechova (Memorial Museum A.P. Chekhov), 142326 Melichovo - T: (8272) 23610, Fax: 24079. Head: Juri Alexandrovič Bičkov
Special Museum
Memorabilia of the writer Anton Pavlovich Chekhov - library 27783

Miass

Natural Science Museum of the Ilmen State Reserve, 456301 Miass - T: (035135) 54890, Fax: 50286, E-mail: founds@imin.urc.ac.ru. Head: Dr. S.N. Nikandrov
Natural History Museum - 1930
Mineralogical wealth of the Ilmen Preserve, the grounds of which contain almost all the known minerals - library 27784

Michajlov

Michajlovskij istoričeskij muzej, ul Maršala Golikova, 6, 391710 Michajlov - T: (09130) 21375
Historical Museum - 1979 27785

Michajlovskoe

Puškinskij Gosudarstvennyj Zapovednik (Pushkin State Preserve), Novorževskaja ul 21, 181370 Michajlovskoe, Puškinskie Gory - T: (081146) 22560, Fax: 22641, E-mail: museum@pushkin.pskov.ru, Internet: http://www.pushkin.pskov.ru. Head: Georgij N. Vasilevič
Special Museum / Local Museum - 1922
Memorabili (28.000 exhibits) of the poet A.S. Puškin (1799 - 1837) in his former estate - library 27786

Minusinsk

Minusinskij Muzej im. N.M. Martjanova, ul Lenina 60, Minusinsk
Local Museum - 1878
Local history, natural history - library 27787

Moskva

Almaznyj fond, Gosudarstvennyj Muzej Moskovskogo Kremlja, Kreml, 103073 Moskva - T: (095) 2292036
Decorative Arts Museum
Russian and foreign jewelry, insignia 27788

Archangelskij Sobor, Gosudarstvennyj Muzej Moskovskogo Kremlja (Archangelsk Cathedral), Moskovskij Kreml, 103012 Moskva
Religious Arts Museum 27789

Blagoveščenskij Sobor, Gosudarstvennyj Muzej Moskovskogo Kremlja (Cathedral of the Annunciation), Sobornaja pl, 101000 Moskva - T: (095) 2030349, Fax: 2024256
Religious Arts Museum 27790

Centralnyj Dom Chudožnikov (Central House of Artists), Krymskij Val 10, 117049 Moskva - T: (095) 2389843, Fax: 2389810, E-mail: art@cha.ru, Internet: http://www.cha.ru
Public Gallery 27791

Centralnyj Muzej Aviacii i Kosmonavtiki (Central Museum of Aviation and Cosmonautics), Krasnoarmejskaja ul 4, 125167 Moskva - T: (095) 2125461, Fax: 2127301. Head: P.F. Vjalikov
Science&Tech Museum - 1924
Development of aeronautics and astronautics, original aircrafts, spacecraft, space exploration vehicles, instruments - library 27792

Centralnyj Muzej Drevnerusskoj Kultury i Isskustva im. Andreja Rubleva (Andrey Rublev Museum of Ancient Russian Art), Andronevskaja pl 10, 107120 Moskva - T: (095) 2781467, Fax: 2785055. Head: G.V. Popov
Fine Arts Museum - 1947
Icons, applied art, manuscripts, old printed books - library 27793

Centralnyj Muzej Federalnoj Pograničnoj Služby RF (Central Museum of Frontier-Guard Regiments of Russia), Jauzskij bul 13, 101000 Moskva - T: (095) 9164162
Military Museum
Historical materials till 1917, war period to present 27794

Centralnyj Muzej MVD Rossii (Central Museum of the Ministry of Interior of Russia), Seleznëvskaja ul 11, 103030 Moskva - T: (095) 9780659
Special Museum 27795

Centralnyj Muzej Velikoj Otečestvennoj Vojny (Great Patriotic War Museum), ul Bratev Fončenko 11, 101000 Moskva - T: (095) 1420209, Fax: 1455558
Historical Museum / Military Museum 27796

Centralnyj Muzej Vooružennych Sil (Central Museum of the Armed Forces), ul Sovetskoj Armii 2, 129110 Moskva - T: (095) 2814877, Fax: 2817735. Head: Aleksandr K. Nikonov
Military Museum - 1919
Military exhibits - library 27797

Centralnyj Muzej Vserossijskogo Obščestva Slepych (Central Museum of the Russian Association of Blind People), ul Kuusinena 19a, 125252 Moskva - T: (095) 9433457
Special Museum 27798

Cerkov Pokrova v Filjach (Pokrov Church Museum), Novozavodskaja ul 6, 121087 Moskva - T: (095) 1484552, Fax: 1487947
Religious Arts Museum 27799

Cerkov Rispoloženija, Gosudarstvennyj Muzej Moskovskogo Kremlja (Rispolozhensky Cathedral), Moskovskij Kreml, 103012 Moskva. Head: I.A. Rodimceva
Religious Arts Museum
Icons, collection of wooden sculptures, religious art, in a cathedral built in 1485 27800

Cerkov Troicy v Nikitnikach, Gosudarstvenny Istoričeski muzej (Trinity Church in Nikitniki), Per Nikitnikov 3, 103012 Moskva - T: (095) 2985018. Head: G.U. Elkin
Religious Arts Museum - 1924
17th century Russian architecture and painting 27801

Darvinovskij Muzej (Darwin Museum), Ul Vavilova 57, 117292 Moskva - T: (095) 1353384, 1353386, Fax: 1353384, E-mail: darwin@museum.ru, Internet: http://www.darwin.museum.ru. Head: Anna I. Klukina
Natural History Museum - 1907
Hist and development of the Darwinian theory, evolution of life, variability of the animal 27802

Decembrists Museum, Staraja Basmannaja ul 23, Moskva - T: (095) 2619070
Special Museum 27803

Detskij Muzej Buratino-Pinokkio, 2-aja Parkovaja ul 18, 111037 Moskva - T: (095) 1640576
Special Museum 27804

Dom-muzej A.N. Ostrovskogo (Ostrovsky House Museum), Malaja Ordynka ul 9, 101000 Moskva - T: (095) 9538684
Special Museum
Mansion wher the Russian playwright was born in 1823, exhibits describing live and traditions of old Moscow, development of the theatre, documents, photos, sketches, costumes, etc. 27805

Dom-muzej F.I. Šaljapina (Shalyapin House Museum), Novinskij bul 25, 101000 Moskva - T: (095) 2056236
Music Museum
House of the famous Russian singer 27806

Dom-muzej K.S. Stanislavskogo, Muzej Moskovskogo Chudožestvennogo Akademičeskogo teatra (K.S. Stanislavsky House Museum), Leontjevskij per 6, 103009 Moskva - T: (095) 2292442. Head: G.G. Šneiter
Special Museum - 1940
Memorabilia of Konstantin Stanislavsky 27807

The State Historical Museum
Red Square 1/2

St. Basil Cathedral
Red Square 2

The New Virgin Nunnery
Novodevichy proezd 1

Romanovs Chambers in Zariadie
Varvarka ulitsa, 10

The State Historical Museum

with its three branches is the national museum of Russia. The museum collection comprise more than 4,5 million objects of fine and applied arts, archaeology, textiles and costumes, furniture, jewelry, metalwork, old printed books and manuscripts, coins and medals, hand-drawn and printed maps, ceramics and glass, arms and 15 million sheets of unique documentary archive. The museum has also a rich library of rare Russian and European editions. In the museum exhibition halls, each of which is decorated in the style of definite history epoch, there are presented the objects of history and culture of Russia from ancient times to the beginning of the XX century.

Offices: Red Square 1/2, Moscow 103012, Russia

Tel.: (7-095) 292-22-69,
Fax: (7-095) 925-95-27
internet: www.shm.ru

Dom-muzej M.I. Cvetaevoj (Tsvetaeva House Museum), Borisoglebskij per 6, 101000 Moskva - T: (095) 2023543, Fax: 2033280
Special Museum
Home of the Russian poet, personal belongings, rare publications, books 27808

Dom-muzej M.Ju. Lermontova (Lermontov Apartment Museum), Malaja Molčanovka ul 2, 101000 Moskva - T: (095) 2915298
Special Museum 27809

Dom-muzej M.N. Ermolovoj (Ermelova House Museum), Tverskoj bul 11, 101000 Moskva - T: (095) 2900215
Special Museum
House of the famous actress 27810

Dom-muzej N.V. Gogolja, Gorodskaja biblioteka - kulturnyj centr N.V. Gogolja (N.V. Gogol House Museum - City Library - Culture Centre), Nikitskij bul 7A, 121019 Moskva - T: (095) 2911550, Fax: 2911550. Head: V.P. Vikulova
Special Museum - 1974
Life and work of Gogol, Gogol special coll of 600 vols and manuscript room - library 27811

Farmacevtičeskij muzej (Pharmaceutical Museum), Ul Krasikova 34, 117418 Moskva - T: (095) 1209151. Head: B.M. Salo
Science&Tech Museum
Hist of pharmacy 27812

Gosudarstvennaja Kollekcija Unikalnych Muzykalnych Instrumentov, Malyj Vlassevskij per 4, 121002 Moskva - T: (095) 2419675, Fax: 2419769
Music Museum 27813

Gosudarstvennaja Tretjakovskaja Galerja (The State Tretjakov Gallery), Lavrušinskij per 10, 109017 Moskva - T: (095) 2307788, 9535223, Fax: 2331051. Head: P.I. Lebedeev
Fine Arts Museum - 1856
Coll of 40,000 Russian icons and works of Russian and Soviet painters, sculptors graphic artists from the 11th c to modern times - library 27814

Gosudarstvennyj Biologičeskij Muzej im. K.A. Timirjazeva (K.A. Timiryazev State Museum of Biology), Malaja Gruzinskaja ul 15, 123242 Moskva - T: (095) 2525542, Fax: 2556321, E-mail: gbmt@aha.ru, M283@mailmuseum.ru, Internet: http://www.museum.ru/M283. Head: Elena Čusova
Natural History Museum
Natural science, biology, evolution of life - library 27815

Gosudarstvennyj Centralnyj Muzej Musykal'noj Kultury im. M.I. Glinki (M.I. Glinka State Central Museum of Music), Ul Fadeeva 4, 125047 Moskva - T: (095) 9723237, 2511066, Fax: 9723255, 2511368, E-mail: glinkaqcityline.ru, Internet: http://www.museum.ru/M305. Head: A.D. Panjuškin
Music Museum - 1943
Manuscripts, memorabilia of musicians, musical instruments, records, sheet music, fine art - library, archives 27816

Gosudarstvennyj Centralnyj Muzej Sovremennoj Istorii Rossii (State Central Museum of Contemporary History of Russia), Tverskaja ul 21, 103050 Moskva - T: (095) 2995217, Fax: 2998515, E-mail: 9055.g23@23.relcom.ru. Head: Dr. T.G. Šumnaja
Historical Museum - 1917
Hist of the revolution in Russia, hist of the contemporary society - library 27817

Gosudarstvennyj Centralnyj Teatralnyj Muzej im. Bachrušina (State Central Theatre Museum A.A. Bakhrushin), Ul Bachrušina 31, 113054 Moskva - T: (095) 9534470, Fax: 9534848. Head: V.V. Gubin
Performing Arts Museum - 1894
Materials on the hist and theory of theatre, especially Russian theatre, manuscripts of Ostrowskij, Lenski, Stanislavski, Meyerhold, Eundova, Vachtangov, Komissarchevskaya, Sobinov, etc - library, dept of fine arts, archives, dept of photographies 27818

Gosudarstvennyj Geologičeskij Muzej im V.I. Vernadskogo (Vernadsky State Geological Museum), Mochovaja ul 11, zdanie 2, 103009 Moskva - T: (095) 2035387, Fax: 2035287, E-mail: info@sgm.ru, Internet: http://www.sgm.ru. Head: Dmitry V. Rundqvist
Natural History Museum - 1755
Paleobotany, geological processes, mineralogy (rocks, ores), meteorites, paleofauna and paleoflora, memorial coll (Pavlov, Vernadsky) - library 27819

Gosudarstvennyj Istoričeskij Muzej (State Historical Museum), Krasnaja pl 1-2, 103012 Moskva - T: (095) 2923731, Fax: 9214311. Head: Dr. A.I. Škurko
Historical Museum - 1872
Russian hist from prehist to the present - library, archives, photograph and holograph lab, restoration workshops 27820

Gosudarstvennyj Istoriko-architekturnyj, Chudožestvennyj i Prirodnyj Muzej-Zapovednik Caricyno (State Museum of History, Architecture, Art and Nature Tsaritsyno), Dolskaja ul 1, 101000 Moskva - T: (095) 3210743
Historical Museum / Fine Arts Museum / Natural History Museum 27821

Gosudarstvennyj Literaturnyj Muzej (State Literature Museum), Ul Petrovka 28, 103051 Moskva - T: (095) 9213857, Fax: 9233022, E-mail: litmuz@orc.ru. Head: Natalja Vladimirovna Šachalova
Special Museum - 1934
Various coll of hist of Russian and Soviet literature, coll of graphics - library; museum silver age of Russian literature; Russian literature of the 1840s; Soviet literature memorial house-museums of diff. writers 27822

Gosudarstvennyj Muzej A.S. Puškina (A.S. Pushkin State Museum), Ul Prečistenka 12, 119034 Moskva - T: (095) 2015674, Fax: 2024354. Head: E. Bogatyrev
Special Museum / Fine Arts Museum - 1957
Memorabilia of the poet A.S. Pushkin, books, manuscripts, permanent exhibitions on his life and work, 19th c fine art - library, cinema and lecture hall 27823

Gosudarstvennyj Muzej Detskich Teatrov (National Children's Theatres Museum), ul Sovetskoj Armii 12, 129110 Moskva - T: (095) 2891554
Performing Arts Museum
Hist of children's puppet, musica and drama theatres 27824

Gosudarstvennyj Muzej Kolomenskoe (State Museum-Reserve Kolomenskoye), Pr Andropova 39, 115487 Moskva - T: (095) 1125217, 1152179, Fax: 1120414, E-mail: kolomen@museum.ru. Head: Ljudmila P. Kolesnikova
Historic Site
Summer residence of Moscow Grand Princes and Russian Tsars, 16. and 17th c; coll. of ancient Russian icons 27825

Gosudarstvennyj Muzej L.N. Tolstogo (L.N. Tolstoy State Museum), Ul Pjatnickaja 12, 113035 Moskva - T: (095) 9516440. Head: L.M. Lubimova
Special Museum - 1911
Original works of the writer Lev Tolstoy (1828-1910), manuscripts, archival material on Tolstoy and his circle, paintings, sculptures, photographs 27826

Gosudarstvennyj Muzej L.N. Tolstogo (L.N. Tolstoy State Museum), Ul Prečistenka 11, 119034 Moskva - T: (095) 2013811, Fax: 2029338. Head: L.M. Lubimova
Special Museum - 1911
Original works of the writer Lev Tolstoy (1828-1910), manuscripts, archival material on Tolstoy and his circle, paintings, sculptures, photographs - archive, library 27827

Gosudarstvennyj Muzej-masterskaja Skulptora A.S. Golubkinoj (State Studio Museum of the Sculptor A.S. Golubkina), Bolšoj Levšinskij per 12, 101000 Moskva - T: (095) 2015682
Fine Arts Museum
Paintings, graphics, sculptures, documents, photos 27828

Gosudarstvennyj Muzej Moskovskogo Kremlja (Moscow Kremlin State Museum), Kreml, metro Biblioteka im. Lenina, 103012 Moskva - T: (095) 2023776, Fax: 9216323
Local Museum / Historic Site 27829

Gosudarstvennyj Muzej Oborony Moskvy (Defence of Moscow Museum), Mičurinskij pr, Olimpijskaja derevnja 3, 101000 Moskva - T: (095) 4376066, 4300549, Fax: 4376074, 4319008. Head: Alla Stepanovna Lukičeva
Historical Museum / Military Museum
Moscow Battle of World War II; coll of paintings and front made graphics, soldiers' personal correspondence 27830

Gosudarstvennyj Muzej Vadima Sidura (Vadim Sidur State Museum), Novogireevskaja ul 37, 101000 Moskva - T: (095) 9185181, Fax: 9185633
Fine Arts Museum
Sculptures, paintings and graphics by Vadim Sidur 27831

Gosudarstvennyj Muzej V.V. Majakovskogo (V.V. Mayakovsky State Museum), Lubjanskij proezd 3, 101000 Moskva - T: (095) 9282569, Fax: 9286092. Head: Svetlana S. Strižnikova
Special Museum - 1937
Memorabilia of V.V. Mayakovski in the house where the poet lived from 1919 to 1930, manuscripts, documentary material, notebooks - library 27832

Gosudarstvennyj Muzej Životnovodstva im Akademika E.F. Liskuna (Liskun State Museum of Cattle Breeding), Timirjazevskaja ul 48, 129550 Moskva - T: (095) 9763870
Agriculture Museum 27833

Gosudarstvennyj Naučno-issledovatelskij Muzej Architektury im. A.V. Ščuseva (Shchusev State Museum of Architecture), Pr Vozdviženka 5, 121019 Moskva - T: (095) 2900551, Fax: 2912109, E-mail: Muar@muar.ru, Internet: http://www.muar.ru. Head: David A. Sarkisjan
Fine Arts Museum - 1934
Hist of architecture, outstanding contemporary work, monumental sculpture and painting, coll and care of documents on architecture and town planning, architectural drawings, photography - library 27834

Guelman Gallery, ul Malaja Poljanka 7, 109180 Moskva - T: (095) 2388492, Fax: 2002216, E-mail: marat@guelman.ru, guelman@gallery.ru
Fine Arts Museum / Public Gallery 27835

Gumanitarnyj Centr-muzej Tvorčestva Autsajderov (Museum of the Work of Outsiders), Izmajlovskij bul 30, 111023 Moskva - T: (095) 4656304, 1643738, Fax: 1643738
Special Museum 27836

Kulturnyj Centr-muzej V.S. Vysockogo (V.S. Vysockij cultural centre and museum), Nižnij Taganskij tupik 3, 109004 Moskva - T: (095) 9157578
Special Museum 27837

Manežnaja Exhibition Hall, Manežnaja pl 1, Moskva - T: (095) 2028976, Fax: 2025242
Public Gallery 27838

Memoralnyj Muzej-kvartira A.S. Puškina (A.S. Puškin Memorial Apartment Museum), ul Arbat 53, 101000 Moskva - T: (095) 2412246, Fax: 2414212
Special Museum 27839

Memorialnyj Dom-muzej akademika S.P. Koroleva (S.P. Korolev House Museum), 6-oj Ostankinskij per 2, 129515 Moskva - T: (095) 2860181, Fax: 2860181, E-mail: kosmonav@mtu-net.ru, Internet: http://www.museum.ru/kosmonav. Head: Larissa Filina
Science&Tech Museum 27840

Memorialnyj Dom-muzej Gercena (Herzen Memorial House Museum), Sivcev Vražek per 27, 101000 Moskva - T: (095) 2415859, Fax: 2411796. Head: Irena A. Jelvakova
Special Museum 27841

Memorialnyj Dom-muzej P.D. Korina (Korin Memorial House Museum), Malaja Pirogovskaja ul 16, 101000 Moskva - T: (095) 2451190
Fine Arts Museum
House and studio of the painter Korin from 1934 till 1967 27842

Memorialnyj Dom-muzej V.M. Vaznecova, Gosudarstvennaja Tretjakovskaja Galereja (V.M. Vasnetsov Memorial House Museum), Per Vaznecova 13, 129090 Moskva - T: (095) 2811329
Fine Arts Museum / Decorative Arts Museum
Furniture, applied art, paintings 27843

Memorialnyj Muzej A.N. Skrjabina (A.N. Skryabin Museum), Bolšoj Nikolopeskovskij per 11, 121002 Moskva - T: (095) 2410302, Fax: 2411901. Head: Rybakova
Music Museum - 1919
Memorabilia of the composer Aleksandr N. Skryabin, letters, Skryabins personal library, tape archives of his compositions performed by Skryabin himself and other famous artists, in the house where the composer lived and died - library 27844

Memorialnyj Muzej Kosmonavtiki (Memorial Museum of Cosmonautics), Pr Mira, Alleja Kosmonavtov 111, Moskva - T: (095) 2831837, 2826171, Fax: 2828212, E-mail: mmcrus@glasnet.ru, Internet: http://www.museum.ru/kosmonav. Head: Juri Solomko
Science&Tech Museum
Cosmonautics, objects of technical, historical and biographical interest 27845

Memorialnyj Muzej-kvartira A.M. Vasnecova (Vasnetsov Apartment Museum), Furmannyj per 6, 101000 Moskva - T: (095) 2089045
Special Museum 27846

Memorialnyj Muzej-Masterskaja Skulptora S.T. Konenkova (Memorial Studio Museum of the Sculptor S.T. Konenkov), Tverskaja ul 17, 103009 Moskva - T: (095) 2294472
Fine Arts Museum
Sculptures, drawings, photos, documents 27847

Meždunarodnyj Centr-Muzej im. N.K. Rericha (International Centre - Museum of N.K. Roerich), Malyj Znamenskij per 3/5, 121019 Moskva - T: (095) 2036419, Fax: 2037184, E-mail: icr.moscow@mtu-net.ru, Internet: http://www.roerich-museum.ru. Head: Ljudmila Vasiljevna Šapošnikova
Fine Arts Museum / Local Museum
Life and work of the members of the Roerich family 27848

Mineralogičeskij Muzej im. A.E. Fersmana Akademii Nauk Rossii (Fersman Mineralogical Museum of the Academy of Sciences of Russia), Leninskij pr 18, 117071 Moskva - T: (095) 9543900, Fax: 9524850, E-mail: DMZ@MINMUZ.msk.su, Internet: http://www.fmm.ru. Head: Prof. M.I. Novgorodova
Natural History Museum - 1716 27849

Moskovskaja gosudarstvennaja kartinnaja galereja A. Šilova, ul Znamenka 5, 121019 Moskva - T: (095) 20342085, Fax: 2036975
Fine Arts Museum 27850

Moskovskij Dom Fotografii, ul Ostoženka 16, 121034 Moskva - T: (095) 2020610, Fax: 2024346
Special Museum / Public Gallery 27851

Moskovskij Gosudarstvennyj Muzej S.A. Esenina (Moscow State Esenin Museum), Bolšoj Stročenovskij per 2, 113054 Moskva - T: (095) 9549764, 9581674, Fax: 9581674, E-mail: esenynm@cnt.ru. Head: Svetlana N. Šetrakova
Special Museum 27852

Moskovskij Literaturnyj Muzej-Centr K.G. Paustovskogo, Starye Kuzminki 17, Moskva - T: (095) 1727791, Fax: 1727791, E-mail: m385@mail-museum.ru, Internet: http://www.city-kgp.nm.ru. Head: Ilja Iljič Komarov
Special Museum 27853

Municipalnyj Muzej Naivnogo Iskusstva (Municipal Museum of Naive Art), Sojuznyj pr 15a, 111396 Moskva - T: (095) 3010348, Fax: 3031514, E-mail: museumofnaiveart@cityline.ri. Head: Vladimir Grozin
Fine Arts Museum 27854

Muzej A.D. Sacharova (A.D. Sacharov Museum Apartment), ul Zemljanoj val 57, 109004 Moskva - T: (095) 9234401, 9172653, Fax: 9172653
Special Museum 27855

Muzej A.M. Gorkogo (A.M. Gorki Museum), Povarskaja ul 25a, 121069 Moskva - T: (095) 2905130. Head: L.P. Bykovceva
Special Museum - 1937
Memorabilia of the writer Maksim Gorki - library 27856

Muzej Archeologii Moskvy (Moscow Archaeology Museum), Manežnaja pl 1, 101000 Moskva - T: (095) 2920226, Fax: 2920346
Archaeological Museum 27857

Muzej A.S. Makarenko (Makarenko Museum), Poklonnaja ul 16, 121170 Moskva - T: (095) 1480835, E-mail: m372@mail.museum.ru, Internet: http://www.museum.ru/m372. Head: Vladimir Vasilevič Morozov
Special Museum
Life of the famous Russian educator A.S. Makarenko 27858

Muzej-čitalnja N.V. Fëdorova (N.V. Fedorov Library-Museum), ul Profsojuznaja 92, 117485 Moskva - T: (095) 3355722, Fax: 3353355
Special Museum 27859

Muzej Ekslibrisa, Pušečnaja ul 7/5, 103031 Moskva - T: (095) 9282998, Fax: 9214626
Special Museum 27860

Muzej Etnografičeskogo Kostjuma na Kuklach (Museum of Ethnographic Costumes on Dolls), Sudostroitelnaja ul 28, 115407 Moskva - T: (095) 1148123, 1166066, Fax: 1166066, E-mail: ivannikova_l@mail.ruM1660@mail.museum.ru, Internet: http://www.Museum.ru/M1660. Head: Ljudmila Ivannikova
Decorative Arts Museum
Russian national costumes 27861

Muzej Gosudarstvennogo Akademičeskogo Bolšogo Teatra Rossii (State Academic Bolshoi Theatre Museum), Teatralnaja pl 2, 103009 Moskva - T: (095) 2920025. Head: V.I. Zarubin
Performing Arts Museum - 1920
Hist of the Bolshoi theatre, documents, objects 27862

Muzej Gosudarstvennogo Akademičeskogo Malogo Teatra (Museum of the State Academic Maly Theatre), Teatralnaja pl, 103009 Moskva - T: (095) 2218548, Fax: 9210350. Head: N.I. Sorokina
Special Museum - 1932
Hist of the theatre, documents - library 27863

Muzej Gosudarstvennogo Centralnogo Teatra Kukol pod Rukovodstvom Narodnogo Artista S.V. Obrazcova (Obrazcov Central State Puppet Theater Museum), Sadovo Samotečnaja ul 3, Moskva - T: (095) 2998910, Fax: 2998910. Head: Dr. Boris Goldovski
Performing Arts Museum - 1937
Hist of the puppet theater in Russia and other countries - library 27864

Muzej Gosudarstvennogo Prirodnogo Nacionalnogo Parka Losinogo Ostrova (Museum of the National Park of the Losiny Island), ŠcČëlkovskoe šosse, 21 km, 111523 Moskva - T: (095) 4657986
Natural History Museum 27865

Muzej Grebnych Vidov Sporta, 1-aja Krylatskaja ul 2, 121552 Moskva - T: (095) 1493364, Fax: 1412351
Special Museum 27866

Muzej Igorja Talkova (Igor Talkov Museum), Černigovskij per 9, 101000 Moskva - T: (095) 9512631
Special Museum 27867

Muzej im. N.A. Ostrovskogo (N.A. Ostrovski Museum), Tverskaja ul 14, 103009 Moskva - T: (095) 2293134
Special Museum - 1940
Memorabilia of the writer N.A. Ostrovski in his former home 27868

Muzej Iskusstva Narodov Vostoka (State Museum of Oriental Art), Nikitskij bul 12a, 121019 Moskva - T: (095) 2910341, Fax: 2024846, E-mail: gmwinter@orc.ru. Head: Dr. V.A. Nabatchikov
Fine Arts Museum - 1918
Middle and Far Eastern art, art of the central Asian republics and Zakavkazie, carpets, fabrics, ceramics - library 27869

Muzej Istorii Moskovskogo Metropolitena (Historical Museum of the Moscow Metro), Chamovničeskij Val 36, 119048 Moskva - T: (095) 2227309. Head: V. Bolotov
Science&Tech Museum / Historical Museum
History of the Moscow Metro 27870

Muzej Istorii Moskvy (Museum of the History of Moscow), Novaja pl 12, 103012 Moskva - T: (095) 9243145, Fax: 9243145, E-mail: msm.mscw@cityline.ru, Internet: http://www.museum.ru/moscow/mainmenu.htlm. Head: Galina I. Vedeznikova
Historical Museum - 1896
Hist of Moscow, economics, urban planning, architecture - library 27871

Muzej Istorii Otečestvennogo Predprinimatelstva, Stremjannyj per 28, korp 1, 113054 Moskva - T: (095) 2379231
Special Museum / Historical Museum 27872

Muzej Istorii Razvitija Mosenergo (Museum of Development of Moscow Power Supply), Raušskaja nab 8, 113035 Moskva - T: (095) 9572639
Science&Tech Museum
Hist of the development of electric power industry in Russia, charts, maps, models 27873

Muzej Istorii Vojsk Moskovskogo Voennogo Okruga (Museum of the History of Moscow District Military Regiments), 1-yj Krasnokursantskij proezd 1, 101000 Moskva - T: (095) 2615576
Military Museum
Hist of the Russian and Soviet army from 1864 till present 27874

Muzej Izobrazitelnych Iskusstv im. A.S. Puškina (Pushkin Museum of Fine Arts), ul Volchonka 12, 121019 Moskva - T: (095) 2036974, Fax: 2034674, E-mail: finearts@gmii.museum.ru, Internet: http://www.museum.ru/gmii. Head: Irina A. Antonova
Fine Arts Museum - 1912
Ancient Eastern, Greek, Roman, Byzantine, European and American art, numismatics, sculpture, graphics - library 27875

Muzej Keramiki i Usadba Kuskovo XVIII Veka (State Ceramics Museum and 18th Century Kuskovo Estate), Ul Junosti 2, 111402 Moskva - T: (095) 3700150, Fax: 9186540. Head: Elena S. Eritsyan
Decorative Arts Museum
Coll of art, ceramics, glass, porcellain, Russian carpets, furniture 27876

Muzej Kino (Cinema Museum), Družinnikovskaja ul 15, 123242 Moskva - T: (095) 2559681
Special Museum 27877

Muzej klassičeskogo i sovremennogo iskusstva (Classical and Modern Art Museum), Bolšoj Afanasevskij per 15, 121019 Moskva - T: (095) 2021547, Fax: 2910423, E-mail: burganov@mail.ru, Internet: http://www.mtu-net.ru/burganov. Head: Aleksandr Burganov
Fine Arts Museum 27878

Muzej Knigi, Rossijskaja gosudarstvennaja biblioteka (Book Museum), ul Vozdviženka 3, 101000 Moskva - T: (095) 2228672
Decorative Arts Museum
Prints 15th-20th c, antique pens, paper knives, bookmarks, inkpots 27879

Muzej Konevodstva (Horse-Breeding Museum), Timirjazevskaja ul 44, 101000 Moskva - T: (095) 9761003
Special Museum
Hist of horse-breeding 27880

Muzej Košek (Cats Museum), Rublëvskoe šosse 109, korp 1, 121552 Moskva - T: (095) 1415455, Fax: 1415424
Special Museum 27881

Muzej Krutickoe Podvore, Krutickaja ul 11, 109044 Moskva - T: (095) 2764981
Local Museum 27882

Muzej-kvartira A.M. Gorkogo (A.M. Gorki House Museum), Malaja Nikitskaja ul 6, 121069 Moskva - T: (095) 2900535. Head: L.P. Bykovceva
Special Museum - 1965
Memorabilia of the writer Maksim Gorki, his private library, his coll of Oriental arts 27883

Muzej-kvartira A.N. Tolstogo (Alexey Tolstoy Apartment Museum), ul Spiridonovka 2, 110000 Moskva - T: (095) 2900956
Special Museum 27884

Muzej-kvartira A.P. Čechova, Gosudarstvennyj Literaturnyj Muzej (A.P. Chekhov Apartment Museum), Sadovaja-Kudrinskaja ul 6, 103001 Moskva - T: (095) 2913837
Special Museum - 1954
Memorabilia of the writer Anton Pavlovich Chekhov in his former home 27885

Muzej-kvartira Dirižëra N.S. Golovanov (House-Museum f the conductor N.S. Golovanov), Brjusov per 7, 103009 Moskva - T: (095) 2297083
Music Museum 27886

Muzej-kvartira F.M. Dostoevskogo, Gosudarstvennyj literaturnyj muzej (F.M. Dostoevsky Apartment Museum), ul Dostoevskogo 2, 103030 Moskva - T: (095) 2811085. Head: Galina B. Ponomareva
Special Museum - 1928
Memorabilia of the writer F.M. Dostoevsky in his former home 27887

Muzej-kvartira K.A. Timirjazeva (K.A. Timiryazev Apartment Museum), Romanova pereulok 2/2/29, 103009 Moskva - T: (095) 2028064. Head: A.A. Druček
Science&Tech Museum - 1942
Memorabilia of the scientist Kliment Arkadevich Timiryazev (1843-1920), natural history, evolutionary theory, physiology - library 27888

Muzej-kvartira Lunačarskogo (Lunacharski Apartment Museum), ul Vesnina 9, 121002 Moskva - T: (095) 2410877. Head: Boris N. Antipenkov
Special Museum
Flat where Lunacharski, the writer and first minister of public education and art lived from 1918 to 1920 27889

Muzej-kvartira S.B. Goldenvejzera (A.B. Goldenveyser Museum Apartment), Tverskaja ul 17, 103009 Moskva - T: (095) 2292929
Special Museum 27890

Muzej-kvartira V.I. Nemiroviča-Dančenko, Muzej Moskovskogo Chudožestvennogo Akademičeskogo Teatra (V.I. Nemirovich-Danchenko Apartment Museum), Gliniščevskij per 5-7, 103009 Moskva - T: (095) 2095391. Head: M.T. Bogomolova
Special Museum - 1944
Memorabilia of the theatre founder Vladimir Nemirovich-Danchenko 27891

Muzej-kvartira V.S. Mejercholda (V.S. Meyerhold Museum), Brjusov per 12, 103009 Moskva - T: (095) 2295322
Special Museum 27892

Muzej Ličnych Kollekcij (Museum of Private Collections), ul Volchonka 14, 121019 Moskva - T: (095) 2028481
Special Museum 27893

Muzej Mecenatov i Blagotvoritelej Rossii (Museum of Patrons and Benefactors of Russia), Donskaja ul 9, 117049 Moskva - T: (095) 2375349, Fax: 9563105
Special Museum 27894

Muzej Morskogo Flota, Mintrans RF (Museum of the Ocean Fleat), ul Admirala Makarova 4, 125212 Moskva - T: (095) 1508494
Special Museum 27895

Muzej Moskovskogo Chudožestvennogo Akademičeskogo Teatra (Moscow Art Academic Theatre Museum), Kamergerskij pereulok 3a, 103009 Moskva - T: (095) 2290080, Fax: 2292087, E-mail: korchevn@mxat.ru, Internet: http://www.mxat.ru. Head: I.L. Korčevnikova
Performing Arts Museum - 1923
Hist of the theatre - library, memorial places of Stanislavsky and Nemirovich-Danchenko 27896

Muzej Moskovskoj Konservatorii, Bolšaja Nikitskaja ul 13, 103009 Moskva - T: (095) 2290098
Special Museum 27897

Muzej na Poklonnoj, ul Bratev Fončenko 11, 121170 Moskva - T: (095) 4498039, Fax: 1455558 27898

Muzej Narodnogo Iskusstva (Folk Art Museum), Leontevskij per 7, 103009 Moskva - T: (095) 2901683. Head: G.A. Jakovleva
Folklore Museum / Fine Arts Museum - 1885
Folk art, ancient and modern applied art, decorative art 27899

Muzej Narodnoj Grafiki (Museum of Folk Graphics), Malyj Golovin per 10, 101000 Moskva - T: (095) 2085182, Fax: 9230213. Head: Viktor Penzin
Special Museum 27900

Muzej Obščestva Krasnogo Kresta Rossii (Museum of the Red Cross Organisation of Russia), Čeremuškinskij proezd 5, 117036 Moskva - T: (095) 1260922, Fax: 3107048
Special Museum 27901

Muzej Obščestva Sporta Dinamo-Moskva (Museum of the Association of Sports Dynamo Moscow), Leningradskij pr 36, 125167 Moskva - T: (095) 2127151
Special Museum 27902

Muzej Obščestvennogo Pitanija, Rogožskij Bolsoj per 17, 109147 Moskva - T: (095) 9129632
Special Museum 27903

Muzej Ochoty i Rybolovstva (Museum of Hunting and Fishing), Golovinskoe šosse 1A, 125212 Moskva - T: (095) 7853333, Fax: 4591895, E-mail: ruhunt@ore.ru. Head: Galina Semenova
Special Museum
Hisdtory of hunting and fishing in Russia, taxidermic mounts and groups, Russian hunting guns, Siberian roe deer, maral, Caribian antlers, skins of wolf, lynx, bear, wild boar tusks 27904

Muzej-panorama Borodinskaja Bitva (Kutuzov's Hut and Battle of Borodino Panorama), Kutuzovskij pr 38, 101000 Moskva - T: (095) 1481925, Fax: 1489489
Military Museum
Battle of Borodino 1812 27905

Muzej Parka Iskusstv na Krymskoj Naberežnoj, Krymskij val 10/14, 117049 Moskva - T: (095) 2903389
Special Museum 27906

Muzej Pograničnoj Ochrany (Museum of Frontier Guards), Bolšaja Bronnaja ul 23, 101000 Moskva
Military Museum
Hist of Soviet frontier guard 27907

Muzej Revoljucii (Museum of the Revolution), Tverskaja ul 21, 103050 Moskva - T: (095) 2995217, Fax: 2998515. Head: Dr. T.G. Šumnaja
Historical Museum - 1917
Hist of the Revolution, labour movement 27908

Muzej Sporta v Lužnikach (Sport Museum at Luzhniki), Lužneckaja nab 24, 101000 Moskva - T: (095) 2010072, Fax: 2010813
Special Museum / Historical Museum
Hist of the development of Sport and Olympic games 27909

Muzej Staryj Anglijskij Dvor (Old English Court Museum), ul Varvarka 4A, 103012 Moskva - T: (095) 2983952
Special Museum / Historical Museum 27910

Muzej-studija Radioteatra, Bolšoj Ovčinnikovskij per 17/1 kv 5, 113184 Moskva - T: (095) 9535764
Special Museum 27911

Muzej Teatra Operetty (Operetta Theatre Museum), Bolšaja Dimitrovka ul 6, 101000 Moskva - T: (095) 2926377
Performing Arts Museum 27912

Muzej Tropinina i Moskovskich Chudožnikov Ego Vremeni (Museum of Tropinin and His Contemporaries), Ščetininskij per 10, 101000 Moskva - T: (095) 9539750
Fine Arts Museum
Memorial exhibits and paintings by Tropinin, Russian art 27913

Muzej Unikalnych Kukol (The Museum of Unique Dolls), ul Malaja Dmitrovka 9, 103006 Moskva - T: (095) 2992800/9385, Fax: 2999385
Decorative Arts Museum 27914

Muzej-Usadba L.N. Tolstogo v Chamovnikach (L.N. Tolstoy Country Estate Museum), ul Lva Tolstogo 21, 119021 Moskva - T: (095) 2469444. Head: A.V. Salomatin
Special Museum
Memorabilia of the writer Lev N. Tolstoi in his former home, original interiors 27915

Muzej V.I. Lenina, Gosudarstvennyj Istoričeskij Muzej (Lenin Museum), Krasnaja pl 1-2, 103012 Moskva - T: (095) 9244529, Fax: 9259527. Head: T.G. Koloskova
Historical Museum - 1924
Contains ca 75 000 items including personal belongings, documents, photographies, works of art, gifts relating to to the life and work of Lenin (1870-1924), Stalin and other Soviet Communist leaders - library 27916

Muzej Vody (Water Museum), Sarinskij proezd 13, 109044 Moskva - T: (095) 2769213
Special Museum 27917

Muzej Zavoda Moskvič (Moskvitch Factory Museum), Volgogradskij pr 42a, 109316 Moskva - T: (095) 2778444, Fax: 2740049
Science&Tech Museum 27918

Muzej Zemlevedenija Moskovskogo Gosudarstvennogo Universiteta M.V. Lomonosova (Museum of Earth Science of the M.V. Lomonosov Moscow State University), Universitetskaja pl 1, Vorobevy gory, 119899 Moskva - T: (095) 9392976, Fax: 9391594. Head: Prof. S.A. Ušakov
Natural History Museum / University Museum - 1955
Earth science, climatology, water resources, soil science, fauna, flora, zoology - library 27919

Naučno-issledovatelskij Institut i Muzej Antropologii im. D.N. Anučina, Moskovskij Gosudarstvennyj Universitet (Anthropological Institute and Museum D.N. Anuchin), Mochovaja ul 18, 103009 Moskva - T: (095) 2035067, Fax: 2033554. Head: Prof. Dr. V.P. Čecov
Ethnology Museum - 1879
Anthropology, archeology, coll from Africa, Mesolithic burial remains from the Dnieper region, ethnography - library 27920

Naučno-memorialnyj Muzej N.E. Žukovskogo (N.E. Zhukovsky Memorial Museum), ul Radio 17, 107005 Moskva - T: (095) 2664230, Fax: 2710019. Head: V.I. Maslov
Special Museum - 1956
Hist of aviation science and technique - library, archives 27921

N.G. Rubinstein Museum, c/o Moskovskij konservatorij, Bol'saja Nikitskaja 13, 103871 Moskva - T: (095) 2299098, Fax: 2299098, Internet: http://www.mosconsv.rus/contents/museumr.html. Head: Dr. E. Gurevič
Music Museum - 1912
Coll of antique string instruments, manuscripts, paintings, sculptures, memorabilia 27922

Novaja Tretjakovskaja Galerja (New Tretyakov Gallery), Krymskij Val 10-14, 117049 Moskva - T: (095) 2381378, 2382054
Fine Arts Museum 27923

Novodevičij Monastyr, Gosudarstvennyj Istoričeskij Muzej (New Virgin Nunnery), Novodevičij proezd 1, 119435 Moskva - T: (095) 2468526, 2452954. Head: V.G. Veržbitskij
Religious Arts Museum - 1922
16th-17th c fine and applied arts, religious art, in the 16th c cathedral of a former monastery 27924

Ogni Moskvy - Muzej Istorii Gorodskogo Osveščenija, Armjanskij per 3, 101000 Moskva - T: (095) 9247374
Special Museum 27925

Ore-Petrographic Museum, Institute of Geology of Ore Deposits, Petrography, Mineralogy and Geochemistry of RAS, Staromonetnyj per 35, 109017 Moskva - T: (095) 2308292, Fax: 2302179, E-mail: pavlov@igem.ru, Internet: http://www.Museum.com./jb/museum?id= 18545. Head: V.A. Pavlov
Natural History Museum - 1934 27926

Oružejnaja Palata, Gosudarstvennyj Muzej Moskovskogo Kremlja (Armoury), Kreml, 103073 Moskva - T: (095) 2020052, 9245503, Fax: 9216323, E-mail: head@kremlin.museum.ru, Internet: http://www.kremlin.museum.ru. Head: Dr. Elena Gagarina
Decorative Arts Museum - 1806
Russian and foreign applied art, arms and armour, jewelry, textiles, garments, embroidery, insignia, enamels, religious art, harnesses, sattles, couches, rare books 27927

Ostankinskij Dvorec-muzej (Ostankino Palace Museum), 1-ja Ostankinskaja ul 5, 129515 Moskva - T: (095) 2866288, 2834645, Fax: 2860288. Head: Elvea Aleksandrovna Komlerova
Fine Arts Museum - 1927
Fine art, applied art, ethnography, folk art, archeology - library 27928

Otraženie - Muzej Voskovych Figur (Waxworks Museum), Tverskaja ul 14, 102009 Moskva - T: (095) 2298552
Special Museum 27929

Palaty v Zarjade XVI - XVII Vekov, ul Varvarka 10, 103012 Moskva - T: (095) 2983706
Special Museum 27930

Paleontologičeskij Muzej im. Ju.A. Orlova (Paleontology Museum), Profsojuznaja ul 123, 117647 Moskva - T: (095) 3391500, Fax: 3390577, E-mail: aroza@paleo.msk.su. Head: Aleksej Rozanov
Natural History Museum - 1930
Fossil inververtebrate and vertebrate animals and fossil plants 27931

Patrijaršie Palaty, Gosudarstvennyj Muzej Moskovskogo Kremlja (Seat of the Patriarch), Kreml, 103073 Moskva - T: (095) 2024256
Special Museum / Religious Arts Museum 27932

Podpolnaja Tipografija CK RSDRP, Lesnaja ul 55, 103055 Moskva - T: (095) 2503074
Special Museum / Historical Museum 27933

Pokrovskij Sobor-chram Vasilija Blažennogo, Gosudarstvennyj Istoričeskij Muzej (Saint Basil Cathedral), Krasnaja pl, 103012 Moskva - T: (095) 2983304. Head: G.V. Sharygin
Religious Arts Museum - 1923
Unique coll of 16-19th century icons and applied arts 27934

Politechničskij Muzej (Polytechnical Museum), Novaja pl 3-4, 101000 Moskva - T: (095) 9250614, 9230756, 9215294, Fax: 9251290. Head: Prof. Dr. Gurgen G. Grigorian
Science&Tech Museum - 1872
Hist and development of science and technology 27935

Povčenno-agronomičeskij Muzej im. V.R. Viljamsa (Soil and Agronomy Museum W.R. Williams), Timirjazevskaja ul 55, 101000 Moskva - T: (095) 9760280
Agriculture Museum
Soils from all over former USSR 27936

Presnja Istorika-memorialnyj Muzej, Bolšoj Predtečenskij per 4, 123242 Moskva - T: (095) 2523035
Historical Museum / Historic Site 27937

S.A. Otkrytka, ul Burakova 1-2, 105118 Moskva - T: (095) 3668968, Fax: 3668968. Head: Maria Katkova
Public Gallery 27938

Samocvety, ul Narodnogo Opolčenija 29, 123154 Moskva - T: (095) 1975401, Fax: 1976763
Special Museum 27939

State Exhibition Hall Zamoskvorechie, Serpuchovskij Val 24, 117419 Moskva - T: (095) 9543009, 9523008, Fax: 9542300. Head: Larisa Rybnikova
Public Gallery 27940

Učebno-chudožestvennyj Muzej im. I.V. Cvetaeva (I.V. Tsvetaev Art Museum), ul Čajanova 15, 125047 Moskva - T: (095) 2506197
Fine Arts Museum 27941

Uspenskij Sobor, Gosudarstvennyj Muzej Moskovskogo Kremlja (Cathedral of the Assumption), Sobornaja pl, 101000 Moskva
Religious Arts Museum
Icons of the 14th-17th c, mosaics, throne of Ivan the Terrible, in a cathedral built 1479 27942

Vserossijskij Muzej Dekorativno-Prikladnogo i Narodnogo Iskusstva (All-Russian Decorative and Folk Art Museum), Delegatskaja ul 3, 101000 Moskva - T: (095) 9210139, Fax: 9230620
Decorative Arts Museum
Russian jewellery, handicrafts, applied art 27943

Vystavočnye Zaly v Dome Aksakovych (Exhibition Halls in Aksakov's House), Sivcev Vražek per 30, 101000 Moskva - T: (095) 2411710, 2418008
Special Museum
Documents and materials on the life and creative work of the famous Russian writers Aksakov, Gogol, Tolstoy and Dostoevsky 27944

Zoologičeskij Muzej Moskovskogo Gosudarstvennogo Universiteta M.V. Lomonosova (Museum of Zoology of the M.V. Lomonosov Moscow State University), Bolšaja Nikitskaja ul 6, 103009 Moskva - T: (095) 2036493, 2033569, Fax: 2032717, E-mail: MI634@mail.museum.ru, Internet: http://www.museum.ru/MI634. Head: Dr. Olga L. Rossolimo
Natural History Museum
Systematics, speciation, zoogeography, faunistic investigations - library 27945

Zverevskij Centr Sovremennogo Iskusstva (Sverev Center of Modern Art), Novorjazanskaja ul 29, 107066 Moskva - T: (095) 2611210, 2656166, Fax: 2656166
Fine Arts Museum / Public Gallery 27946

Murmansk

Murmanskij Oblastnoj Kraevedčeskij Muzej, pr Lenina 54, Murmansk
Local Museum - 1927
Settlement and development of the region, early Russian navigators of the Arctic, tools and ornaments from early inhabitants of the area - library 27947

Nalčik

Gosudarstvennyj Obedinennyj Muzej Kabardino-Balkarii (National Museum of Kabardino-Balkarian Republik), ul M. Gorkogo 62, 360022 Nalčik - T: 53942. Head: Z. Pashtov
Local Museum - 1921
Natural history, local history, economics, culture - library, picture gallery 27948

Kabardino-Balkarskij Chudožestvennyj Muzej (Kabardino-Balkar Art Museum), Pr Lenina 35, 360000 Nalčik. Head: I.Z. Batašov
Fine Arts Museum 27949

Nižnij Novgorod

Gaz Factory Museum, Pr Lenina, GAZ Personnel Training Bldg, 603046 Nižnij Novgorod - T: (8312) 561438, 561070, Fax: 985010
Science&Tech Museum 27950

Gosudarstvennyj Muzej A.M. Gorkogo (The Badge of Honour State Museum of A.M. Gorky), ul Minina 26, 603155 Nižnij Novgorod - T: (08312) 361529, Fax: 361529, E-mail: danco@uic.nnov.ru, Internet: http://www.museum.nnov.ru/danco. Head: Tamara Aleksandrovna Ryžova
Special Museum - 1928
Memorabilia of the writer Maksim Gorky, literary hist, original furnishings - library 27951

Nižegorodskij Chudožestvennyj Muzej (Nizhni Novgorod Art Museum), Kreml zd 3, 603082 Nižnij Novgorod - T: (08312) 390855, Fax: 336085, E-mail: art@museum.nnov.ru, Internet: http://www.museum.nnov.ru/art. Head: N.N. Krivova
Fine Arts Museum
Russian and Western European artist - library 27952

Nižegorodskij Istoričeskij Muzej (Mizhni Novgorod Historical Museum), nab Ždanova 7, 603005 Nižnij Novgorod - T: (08312) 332379
Local Museum - 1896
Archeology, hist of the Central Volga area dating back to ancient times, architecture, ethnography, costumes, decorative arts, porcelain - library 27953

Nižnij Tagil

Nižnetagilskij Muzej-Zapovednik Gornozavodskogo Dela Srednego Urala (Nizhny Tagil Museum-Reserve of Mininf and Metallurgy in the Middle Urals), pr Lenina 1a, 622001 Nižnij Tagil - T: (03435) 416404, 416401, 416412, Fax: 416465, E-mail: museum@museum.unets.ru, Internet: http://geg.chem.usu.ru:8080. Head: Ivan Grigorjevič Semionov
Local Museum - 1840
Collections concerning history, natural history, economics, culture, archeology, ethnology, applied arts - Museum-works, Regional History Museum, Museum of Ethnology, Natural History Museum, Applied Arts Musueum, Literary Museum 27954

Novgorod

Kraevedčeskij Muzej Novgorodskogo Rajona, Pervomajskaja ul 2, 173000 Novgorod - T: (05241) 91943, 99632
Local Museum 27955

Muzej A.V. Suvorova, Pervomajskaja ul 2, 173000 Novgorod - T: (05241) 98533/76
Local Museum 27956

Novgorodskij Gosudarstvennyj Muzej-zapovednik (Novgorod State Museum Reservation), Kreml 11, 173007 Novgorod - T: (0816) 73608, Fax: 73608. Head: Nikolaj N. Grynëv
Local Museum - 1865
History, manuscripts, Russian art, decorative and folk art, rare books, numismatics, costumes, - library 27957

Novočerkassk

Dom-muzej M.B. Grekova (M.B. Grekov House-Museum), ul Grekova 124, Novočerkassk - T: (086352) 24320, Fax: 24114. Head: Galina Erašova
Local Museum / Public Gallery 27958

Novočerkasskij Muzej Istorii Donskich Kazakov (Novocherkassk Museum of the History of the Don Cossacks), Sovetskaja ul 38, 346430 Novočerkassk - T: 24114. Head: L.A. Gurov
Historical Museum - 1899
Hist of the Don Cossacks, exhibition on Stepan Timofeevich Razin, the 17th c leader of the peasant liberation movement - library 27959

Novokuzneck

Kemerovskij Oblastnoj Muzej Sovetskogo Izobrazitelnogo Iskusstva (Regional Museum of Soviet Fine Art), ul Kirova 62, 654018 Novokuzneck - T: 476848, 472886
Fine Arts Museum - 1963
Fine art, Soviet art - library 27960

Novorossijsk

Novorossijskij Gosudarstvennyj Istoričeskij Muzej Zapovednik (Novorossiysk State Historical Preserve), ul Sovetov 58, 353900 Novorossijsk, Krasnoyarski krai - T: (08617) 252457, 610027, Fax: 251854. Head: Larisa Aleksandrovna Kolbasina
Local Museum - 1916
Local and regional history, maritime coll, ethnographic and numismatic coll, paintings, orders and medals, hist gold and silver, memorabilia of the writer N. Ostrovsky, arms and military equipment of WW II, - library, N. Ostrovsky-Museum, Memorials "Heroes of the Great Patriotic War" and "Death Valley" 27961

Novosibirsk

Novosibirskaja Oblastnaja Kartinnaja Galereja (Novosibirsk Region Picture Gallery), Krasny pr 5, 630093 Novosibirsk - T: (3832) 222267. Head: Juri A. Vorobjev
Fine Arts Museum - 1958
Painting, sculpture - library 27962

Novosibirskij Oblastnoj Kraevedčeskij Muzej (Regional Museum), Krasnyj pr 23, 630099 Novosibirsk - T: (3832) 225421
Local Museum - 1920
Natural history, history and economic development of the region, decorative and applied art, numismatics, ethnology - library 27963

Novotroick

Novotroickij Istoriko-kraevedčeskij Muzej, Sovetskaja ul 82, 462359 Novotroick - T: 43495
Local Museum - 1988
Paintings, graphics, sculptures, precious stones and metals, weapons, textiles, archeology, anthropology, botanical and zoological coll - library (lit on geology) 27964

Omsk

Omskij Gosudarstvennyj Obedinennyj Istoričeski i Literaturnyj Muzej, ul Lenina 23a, 644024 Omsk - T: (03812) 313221
Historical Museum - 1879
Arab, Chinese, Siberian and Russian coins (17-20th c), archeology, ethnography, traditional copper artefacts, Siberian icons, Russian and West European engravings, works by painters from Omsk (1910-1920 and contemporary), weapons, guns, history of Siberia, local history - library 27965

Omskij Muzej Izobrazitelnych Iskusstv (Omsk Fine Art Museum), ul Lenina 23, 644024 Omsk. Head: A.A. Gerzon
Fine Arts Museum 27966

Omskij Oblastnoj Kraevedčeskij Muzej, ul Lenina 23, Omsk
Local Museum 27967

Orël

Bunin Museum, Gosudarstvennyj literaturnyj muzej im. I.S. Turgeneva, Oktjabrskaja pr 9, 302000 Orël - T: (3532) 60774
Local Museum - 1991 27968

Dom-muzej N. Andreeva, Gosudarstvennyj literaturnyj muzej im. I.S. Turgeneva (N. Andreev House Museum), Puškarnaja ul 41, 302000 Orël - T: (3532) 64824
Local Museum - 1991 27969

Dom-muzej N.S. Leskova, Gosudarstvennyj literaturnyj muzej im. I.S. Turgeneva (N.S. Leskov House Museum), ul Oktjabrskaja 9, 301028 Orël - T: 63304
Special Museum - 1974 27970

Gosudarstvennyj Literaturnyj Muzej im. I.S. Turgeneva (I.S. Turgenev State Literary Museum), ul Turgeneva 11, 302000 Orël - T: (3532) 63528, 62737. Head: V.V. Safronova
Special Museum - 1918
Life and work of the writer Ivan Sergeevich Turgenev (1818-1883), photos, art works, personal memorabilia, original furniture from his home in Spasskoe Lutovino - library 27971

Muzej-Diorama Orlovskaja Nastupatelnaja Operacija, ul Normandija-Neman 1, 302000 Orël - T: 55090
Military Museum 27972

Muzej im. T.N. Granovskogo, Gosudarstvennyj Literaturnyj Muzej im. I.S. Turgeneva (T.N. Granovsky Museum), ul 7-ogo Nojabrja 24, 302000 Orël - T: 62737
Local Museum - 1985
Public figures born in Orel - library 27973

Orlovskaja Kartinnaja Galereja (Orel Art Gallery), ul Saltykova-Ščedrina, Orël. Head: N.G. Antipov
Public Gallery
Fine art, painting 27974

Orlovskij Oblastnoj Kraevedčeskij Muzej (Regional Museum), ul Gostinaja 2, 302001 Orël - T: (0862) 56791, 56793, Fax: 66006, E-mail: ormuseum@orel.ru. Head: Valentina Vasiljevna Titova
Local Museum - 1897
Hist of the Orel region, furniture, paintings, natural hist - Museum-Diorama "Orel Offensive Operation in 1943", library 27975

Orenburg

Kraevedčeskij Muzej Istorii Orenburga, ul Naberežnaja 29, 460014 Orenburg - T: 476725
Local Museum 27976

Orenburgskij Muzej Izobrazitelnych Iskusstv (Orenburg Museum of Fine Arts), ul Pravdy 6, Orenburg - T: (3532) 476483. Head: L.B. Popova
Fine Arts Museum - 1961
Contemporary art, Orenburg hand-made down shawls ("pautinkas") 27977

Orenburgskij Oblastnoj Kraevedčeskij Muzej (Regional Museum), Sovetskaja 28, 460000 Orenburg - T: 470743
Local Museum - 1830
Coll of womens costumes in Orenburg and surroundings (18-19th c), handwritten and rare books (16-19th c), Russian and foreign coins (16-19th c), canon used by E. Pugachevs uprising peasants army, Pushkins death mask - library 27978

Orsk

Orskij Istoriko-kraevedčeskij Muzej, pr Lenina 46, 462404 Orsk - T: 24615
Local Museum - 1939
Archeology, coll of colourful jaspers from Orsk, jasper artefacts, sports coll 27979

Osa

Osinskij Kraevedčeskij Muzej, ul Sverdlova 2, 618120 Osa - T: (034291) 23607. Head: Galina Ivanova Klykova
Local Museum - 1987 27980

Palech

Muzej Krestovosdviženskaja Cerkov, Palech
Religious Arts Museum 27981

Muzej Palechskogo Remesla (Museum of Palekh Handicrafts), ul Bakanova 50, Palech. Head: G.M. Melnikov
Decorative Arts Museum
Costumes, pottery, woodcarvings 27982

Pavlovo

Pavlovskij Istoričeskij Muzej, ul Krasnoarmeiskaja 6, 606130 Pavlovo - T: 332379
Historical Museum - 1936
Various metal instruments, paintings, documents, photos 27983

Pavlovsk

State Museum Pavlovsk Palace and Park, ul Revoljucii 20, 196621 Pavlovsk - T: (812) 4702155, Fax: 4651104, E-mail: admin@pavlovskart.spb.ru, Internet: http://www.pavlovskart.spb.ru. Head: Nicolaï S. Trétiakov
Fine Arts Museum
The late 18th-19th c Pavlovsk Palace and Park of landscape style, former summer residence of Emperor Paul I, interior of decorative and applied arts, furniture, porcelain, tapestries, crystal glass works by European and Russian masters, coll of paintings and antiques 27984

Penza

Literaturnyj Muzej, ul Kirova 3, 440010 Penza - T: 668410
Special Museum 27985

Penzenskaja Kartinnaja Galerija (Penza Picture Gallery), Sovetskaja ul 3, 660026 Penza - T: 666400. Head: Valerij Sazonov
Fine Arts Museum - 1892
library 27986

Penzenskij Gosudarstvennyj Obedinenyj Kraevedčeskij Muzej (Regional Museum), Krasnaja 73, 440026 Penza - T: 663414. Head: A.N. Batova
Local Museum - 1905
History, economics, natural history, ethnography - library 27987

Pereslavl-Zalesskij

Pereslavl-Zalesskij Historical and Art Museum, Museum pereulok 4, 152140 Pereslavl-Zalesskij - T: 21910
Religious Arts Museum 27988

Perm

Permskaja Gosudarstvennaja Chudožestvennaja Galereja (Perm State Art Gallery), Komsomolskij pr 4, 614000 Perm - T: (03422) 122250, 122395, 122623, Fax: 122250, E-mail: pgallery@perm.raid.ru. Head: N.V. Beljaeva

Fine Arts Museum - 1922
Coll of Russian icons (16-18th c), Perm wooden sculpture, golden embroidery, Russian art (18-20th c), applied arts - library 27989

Permskij Oblastnoj Kraevedčeskij Muzej (Regional Museum), Komsomolskij pr 6, 614000 Perm - T: (03422) 342569
Local Museum - 1890
Archaeology, ethnography, natural hist, numismatics, pictorial and plastic arts, science and technology monuments, paleontology - library 27990

Petrokrepost

Muzej-pamjatnik Šlisselburgskaja Krepost, Gosudarstvennyj muzej istorii Leningrada (Fortress Museum Shlisselburg), Petrokrepost - T: 2384779, 2384511
Military Museum - 1918
Historical fortress built 1323, military history, former political prison 27991

Petrozavodsk

Karelskji Gosudarstvennyj Kraevedčeskij Muzej (Karelian State Regional Museum), pl Lenina 1, 185035 Petrozavodsk - T: (0814) 70240, Fax: 73540. Head: O.A. Sokolova
Local Museum - 1871
Ethnography, geology, archaeology, decorative and applied arts, folk art, natural hist - library, archives 27992

Kizhi State Open-Air Museum of History, Architecture and Ethnography, Dzeržinskyj ul 39, 185610 Petrozavodsk - T: 70087. Head: O.A. Nabokova
Historical Museum / Fine Arts Museum / Ethnology Museum - 1961
Wooden architecture, history, ethnography, early Russian and Karelian painting and folklore - library 27993

Muzej Izobrazitelnych Iskusstv Karelii (Karelian Museum of Fine Arts), pr Karla Marksa 8, 185610 Petrozavodsk - T: (08142) 769860, Fax: 782578, E-mail: galptz@karelia.ru, Internet: http://www.karelia.ru/~fine_art/museum/mus.htm. Head: N.I. Vavilova
Fine Arts Museum - 1960
15th-18th c icons, works of contemporary Karelian artists - library 27994

Pjatigorsk

Gosudarstvennyj Literaturno-memorialnyj Muzej im. M.Ju. Lermontova (Lermontov State Literary Memorial Museum), Lermontovskaja ul 4, 357500 Pjatigorsk - T: 52710. Head: Ludmila Ivanovna Morozova
Special Museum - 1912
Memorabilia of the poet Mikhail Yurevich Lermontov - library 27995

Pjatigorskij Kraevedčeskij Muzej (Pjatigorsk Regional Museum), ul Sakko i Vancetti 2, 357501 Pjatigorsk - T: 54525, 51858. Head: Lidiya Ivanovna Krasnokutskaja
Local Museum - 1906
Natural history, history, economics, culture - library 27996

Polibino

Polibinskij Memoralnyj Muzej S.V. Kovalevskoj, 182157 Polibino - T: (0253) 29523. Head: Valentina R. Pavlovna
Special Museum - 1986
Memorabilia of the mathematician and writer Sofiya Vassilevna Kovalevskaya (1850-1891), applied arts, journals from the 19th c 27997

Pskov

Pskovskij Istoričeskij, Architekturnyj i Chudožestnennyj Muzej (Pskov Museum of History, architecture and art), ul Nekrasova 7, 180000 Pskov - T: 22518. Head: Aleksandr Golyšev
Historical Museum / Fine Arts Museum - 1876
Hist and ethnography of Russia, icons, Russian art 27998

Puškin

Gosudarstvennyj Muzej Carskoje Selo (State Museum Tsarky village), Sadovaja ul 7, 189690 Puškin - T: (812) 4666669, Fax: 4652196. Head: Ivan Petrovič Sautov
Open Air Museum - 1918
Russian garden architecture, sculptures, costumes, coaches 27999

Muzej-dača A.S. Puškina (A.S. Pushkin Country House Museum), Puškinskaja ul 2, Puškin
Special Museum - 1958
Memorial to the poet Aleksandr Sergeevich Pushkin, original interiors 28000

Muzej Licej, Nacionalnyj Muzej Puškina (Lyceum Museum), Komsomolskaja ul 1, Puškin
Special Museum - 1949
Exhibits illustrating the life and work of the poet Aleksandr Sergeevich Pushkin and his epoch, portraits, rare books, manuscripts and drawings by the poet, in a lyceum where the poet studied from 1811 to 1817 - library 28001

Puškinskie Gory

Svjatogorskij Monastyr, 181388 Puškinskie Gory - T: 23188
Religious Arts Museum
Icons (17-19th c), bells (16-19th c), rare books (17-18th c) 28002

Repino

Muzej-usadba I.E. Repina (I.E. Repin Country House Museum), Usadba Penaty, 189648 Repino - T: 2316828. Head: Jelena Kirillina
Fine Arts Museum - 1940
Memorabilia of Ilya Efimovich Repin in the country house where the painter lived from 1900 to 1930, original interiors, park, artists grave 28003

Rjazan

Dom-muzej Akademika I.P. Pavlova, ul Pavlova 23-25, 390000 Rjazan - T: 776272
University Museum 28004

Rjazanskij Gosudarstvennyj Istoriko-architekturnyj Muzej-zapovednik (Ryazan Historical-Architectural Museum Reservation), Kreml 118, 390000 Rjazan - T: 774769
Fine Arts Museum / Historical Museum - 1884
Over 108,000 items describing the history, culture and art of the peoples of Russia 28005

Rjazanskij Kraevedčeskij Muzej (Ryazan Regional Museum), Kreml 15, 390000 Rjazan
Local Museum - 1918
History, economics, natural hist, ethnography - library 28006

Rjazanskij Oblastnoj Chudožestvennyj Muzej (Ryazan Regional Art Museum), ul Svoboda 57, 390000 Rjazan - T: (0912) 779500. Head: Vladimir Alexandrovič Ivanov
Fine Arts Museum - 1913
19th-20th c Russian paintings, applied arts - library 28007

Roslavl

Roslavskij Istoričeskij Muzej (Roslavl Historical Museum), ul Proletarskaja 63, 216500 Roslavl - T: 31849. Head: Maja I. Ivanovna
Local Museum - 1920
History, economy and culture of the Russian people from earliest times - library 28008

Rostov-na-Donu

Muzej Izobrazitelnych Iskusstv (Museum of Fine Arts), ul Puškina 115, 344007 Rostov-na-Donu - T: (8632) 665907. Head: Galina Sergeevna Alimurzaeva
Fine Arts Museum - 1938
19th-20th c paintings by Russian artists - library 28009

Rostovskij Oblastnoj Muzej Kraevedenija, ul Èngelsa 79, 344006 Rostov-na-Donu - T: (8632) 650111
Local Museum - 1910
History, archaeology of the area, coll of 11th-12th c stone idols worshipped by nomads, Russian art, costumes - library 28010

Salechard

Okružnoj Kraevedčeskij Muzej, Jamalo-Neneckogo Nacionalnogo okruga (Regional Museum), ul Sverdlova 14, Salechard
Local Museum - 1902
History, ethnography, economics, natural history - library 28011

Samara

Samarskij Chudožestvennyj Muzej (Samara Art Museum), pl Kujbyševa, Dvorec Kultury, 443001 Samara. Head: Anneta Ju. Bass
Fine Arts Museum - 1897
19th-20th c Russian art - library 28012

Samarskij Memorialnyj Muzej im. A.M. Gorkogo (Samara A.M. Gorky Memorial Museum), ul St Razina 126, 443000 Samara
Special Museum - 1946
Life and work of Maksim Gorki and other literary figures, original furniture, literary hist - library 28013

Samarskij Oblastnoj Kraevedčeskij Muzej (Regional Museum), Frunze ul 159, 443010 Samara - T: 332519, 334188
Local Museum - 1880
Local history, costumes, handicrafts, housing, ethnography - library 28014

Sankt-Peterburg

Botaničeskij Muzej (Botanical Museum), ul Professora Popova 2, 197022 Sankt-Peterburg - T: (812) 2348439. Head: L. Ju. Budancev
Natural History Museum - 1823 28015

Centralnyj Geologorazvedočnyj Muzej im. F.N. Černyševa (F.N. Chernyshev Central Geological and Prospecting Museum), Srednyj Pr 74, 199026 Sankt-Peterburg - T: (812) 2180634, Fax: 3215399. Head: A.M. Karpunin
Natural History Museum - 1923
Geological sciences, paleontology, petrology, geological education 28016

Centralnyj Muzej Pochvovedenija im. V.V. Dokučaeva (Dokuchaev Central Soil Museum), Birževoj Proezd 6, 199034 Sankt-Peterburg - T: (812) 3285602, Fax: 3285602, E-mail: soil@ba5289.spb.edu, Internet: http://www.soilmuseum.by.ru. Head: Dr. B.F. Aparin
Natural History Museum - 1904 28017

Centralnyj Muzej Svjazi im. A.S. Popova (A.S. Popov Central Museum of Communication), ul Počtamskaja 7, 190000 Sankt-Peterburg - T: (812) 3154873, Fax: 3154873, E-mail: bakayutova@ptti.ru, Internet: http://www.minsvyaz.ru. Head: Lyudmila Bakayutova
Science&Tech Museum - 1877
Hist of communication technology, state postage stamp coll 28018

Centralnyj Muzej Železnodorožnogo Transporta (Central Museum of Railway Transport), Sadovaja ul 50, 190068 Sankt-Peterburg - T: (812) 3151476. Head: G.P. Zakrevskaja
Science&Tech Museum - 1813
Hist of railway transportation in Russia, miniature models of engines, carriages and bridges, machines for railway construction, communication and railway automatic apparatus, documents, photos - Museum of Native Bridgebuilding, Museum of Natural Engines and Carriages 28019

Centralnyj Voenno-morskoj Muzej (Central Naval Museum), Birževaja Pl 4, 199034 Sankt-Peterburg - T: (812) 3282502, Fax: 3282701, E-mail: museum@mail.admiral.ru, Internet: http://www.museum.navy.ru. Head: E.N. Korčagin
Military Museum - 1709
More than 700,000 items of relics and other materials from the Russian and Soviet Navies, departments of hist of the Russian Navy, hist of the Soviet Navy, hist of the Navy in the 1941-45 period, hist of the Navy in the post-war period - library 28020

Dom-muzej Petra I (Peter the Great House Museum), Petrovskaja Nab 6, 197046 Sankt-Peterburg - T: (812) 2324576
Local Museum - 1930
Little wooden home (built 1703) where Peter the Great stayed during the construction of the Peter and Paul Fortress, 18th c furniture 28021

Dvorec-Muzej Petra I (Museum Palace of Peter the Great), Letnij Sad, 191186 Sankt-Peterburg - T: (812) 3129666, Fax: 3129666, E-mail: letnisad@infopro.spb.su. Head: T.D. Kozlova
Fine Arts Museum - 1934
18th c architecture and sculpture, original interiors, decorative and applied art 28022

Gornyj Muzej (Mining Museum), c/o Saint Petersburg State Mining Institute, Technical University, Vasilevskij Ostrov, 21-ja Linija 2, 199106 Sankt-Peterburg - T: (812) 3214082, Fax: 3277359, E-mail: SPMI@mail.wplus.net. Head: Janna Polyarnaya
Science&Tech Museum - 1773
Specimen of minerals (incl natural and artificial), rocks, ores, fossils, meteorites. articles made of gemstone, industrial goods, coll of historical technique in models of the 19th and early 20th c, coll of edged weapons (Zlatoust Arms Factory) 28023

Gosudarstvennyj Eremitage (State Hermitage Museum), Dvorcovaja Nab 34-36, 191186 Sankt-Peterburg - T: (812) 3113420, 2129545. Head: Michail Piotrovski
Fine Arts Museum - 1764
Richest coll in Russia of the art of prehistoric, ancient, Greek, Roman and medieval times, drawings, engravings, Italian, Dutch, Spanish, French and German paintings including works by Leonardo da Vinci, Raphael, Titian, Rubens, Rembrandt, applied arts, numismatics, arms 28024

Gosudarstvennyj Memorialnyj Muzej im. A.V. Suvorova (State Memorial A.V. Suvorov Museum), ul Saltykova-Ščedrina 43, 193015 Sankt-Peterburg - T: (812) 2742628, 2793913, Fax: 2742850. Head: Alexander Kouzmin
Military Museum - 1904
Russian military hist, exposition on the great Russian commander-in-chief Aleksandr Vasilevich Suvorov, military painting, documents, tin soldiers 28025

Gosudarstvennyj Memorialnyj Muzej Oborony i Blokady Leningrada (The State Museum of the Defense and Siege of Leningrad), Soljanoj Per 9, 191028 Sankt-Peterburg - T: (812) 2737647, Fax: 2758482
Historical Museum 28026

Gosudarstvennyj Muzej Istorii Religii (State Museum of the History of Religion), Kazanskaja Pl 2, 191186 Sankt-Peterburg - T: (812) 3123586, Fax: 3119483, E-mail: history@relig-museum.ru. Head: Stanislav A. Kučinskij
Religious Arts Museum - 1932
Origin of Christianity, objects relating to various sects and denominations, documents, books, religious art, 19th c church - library 28027

Gosudarstvennyj Muzej Istorii Sankt-Peterburga (State Museum of the History of Saint Petersburg), Petropavlovskaja Krepost 3, 197046 Sankt-Peterburg - T: (812) 2384511, Fax: 2384243, E-mail: direct@ppk.spb.su. Head: B.S. Arakčeev
Historical Museum - 1907
Hist and development of local city planning and construction, architectural and cultural hist of St. Petersburg, rare book and drawings of buildings of St. Petersburg up to 1836, objects of art, items of everyday use from 18th c, posters, photographies, rare documents - Shlisselburg Fortress, Printing Museum, Rumjantsevsky Mansion 28028

Gosudarstvennyj Muzej Političeskoj Istorii Rossii (State Museum of Political History of Russia), Ul Kujbyševa 4, 197046 Sankt-Peterburg - T: (812) 2337266, Fax: 2337200, E-mail: polithist@soros.spb.ru, Internet: http://www.museum.ru/museum/polit_hist. Head: Evgenij Artëmov
Historical Museum - 1919
Hist of the 1917 Revolution, Russian Civil War and WWII, development of socialism in the USSR, banners of 1917, posters, porcelain, documents, photographs - library 28029

Gosudarstvennyj Muzej Teatralnogo i Musykalnogo Iskusstva (Saint Petersburg State Museum of Theatre and Music), Pl Ostrovskogo 6, 191011 Sankt-Peterburg - T: (812) 3155243, 3101029, 3123070, Fax: 3147746, E-mail: theatre@museums.org.ru. Head: I.V. Evstigneeva
Performing Arts Museum - 1918
History of the theatre in Russia, and other countries, documents, records, photographs, memorabilian posters, ballet shoes, fine art coll with sketches, paintings, drawings, sculptures, coll of costumes of the Russia Imperial Theatre 28030

Gosudarstvennyj Muzej Velikoj Oktjabrskoj Socialističeskoj Revoljucii, ul Kujbyševa 4, 197046 Sankt-Peterburg - T: (812) 2389720. Head: M.P. Potiforova
Historical Museum 28031

Gosudarstvennyj Muzej Zapovednik Petergof (Peterhof State Museum Reserve), Rasvodnaja ul 2, Sankt-Peterburg 198516 - T: (812) 4277425, Fax: 4279330, E-mail: admin@peterhof.org, Internet: http://www.peterhof.org. Head: V.V. Znamenov
Historic Site / Open Air Museum / Historical Museum / Decorative Arts Museum / Fine Arts Museum - 1918
Coll of paintings, sculpture, porcelain, bronze etc - library, archives 28032

Gosudarstvennyj Russkij Muzej (State Russian Museum - Mikhailovsky Palace), Michailovskij Dvorec, Inženernaja ul 2, 191011 Sankt-Peterburg - T: (812) 3811615, Fax: 3144153, E-mail: info@rusmuseum.ru. Head: Vladimir Gusev
Decorative Arts Museum / Fine Arts Museum
11th-20th c Russian art, Soviet art, painting, drawings and sculpture, apllied and folk art, coins, medals, engravings; Marble Palace, Sroganov Palace, Engineer's Palace - archive 28033

Gosudarstvennyj Russkij Muzej (State Russian Museum - Benois Wing), Korpus Benua, Naberežnaja kanala Griboedova 2, 191011 Sankt-Peterburg - T: (812) 3811615, Fax: 3144153, E-mail: info@rusmuseum.ru. Head: Vladimir Gusev
Decorative Arts Museum - 1898
11th-20th c Russian art, Soviet art, painting, drawings and sculpture - archive 28034

Inženernyj (Michailovskij) Zamok, Gosudarstvennyj Russkij Muzej (State Russian Museum - Saint Michael's or Engineer's Palace), Sadovaja ul 2, 191011 Sankt-Peterburg - T: (812) 3134173, E-mail: info@rusmuseum.ru
Decorative Arts Museum / Fine Arts Museum
11th-20th c Russian art 28035

Isaakievskij Sobor (Saint Isaacs Cathedral), Isaakievskaja Pl, 190000 Sankt-Peterburg - T: (812) 3159732. Head: Georgij P. Butikov
Fine Arts Museum / Decorative Arts Museum - 1931
Religious art, decorative art, painting, sculpture, mosaics, medals, engravings 28036

Kunstkamera → Muzej Antropologii i Etnografii im. Petra Velikogo

Kvartira-muzej N.A. Nekrassova (N.A. Nekrassov Apartment Museum), Litejnyj Pr 36, 191104 Sankt-Peterburg - T: (812) 2720165
Special Museum
Life and work of the poet Nikolai A. Nekrassov in his former home 28037

Literaturno-memorialnyj Muzej F.M. Dostoevskogo (Dostoevsky Literary-Memorial Museum), Kuznečnyj Per 5, 191002 Sankt-Peterburg - T: (812) 3114031, Fax: 1120003, E-mail: ashimbaeva@md.spb.ru, Internet: http://www.md.spb.ru. Head: N. Ašimbaeva
Special Museum - 1971
The house where the author lived 1878-1881, manuscripts, documentary material, memorial items - library 28038

Literaturnyj Muzej Instituta Russkoj Literatury (Literary Museum of the Institute of Russian Literature), Nab Makarova 4, 199034 Sankt-Peterburg - T: (812) 2180502. Head: T.A. Komarova
Special Museum - 1899
Literary hist of Russia and the USSR, objects relating to Radishchev, Lermontov, Gogol, Dostoevski, Turgenev and other Russian writers - library 28039

Memorialnyj Muzej A.S. Popova (Memorial Museum of A.S. Popov), ul Professora Popova 5, 197376 Sankt-Peterburg - T: (812) 2345900, Fax: 3462758, 2345900, E-mail: VRIA@eltech.ru, Internet: http://www.eltech.ru. Head: Dr. Larissa Igorevna Zolotinkina
Science&Tech Museum / University Museum - 1948
Memorabilia of the scientist and inventor of the wireless telegraph Aleksandr Stepanovich Popov, documents, manuscripts, devices - archives 28040

Memorialnyj Muzej-kvartira Rimskogo-Korsakova (Memorial Museum Apartment of Rimsky-Korsakov), Zagorodnyj Pr 28, 191002 Sankt-Peterburg - T: (812) 1133208, Fax: 1133208, E-mail: RIMKOR@comset.net. Head: D. Čirkova
Special Museum 28041

Memorialnyj Muzej Šaljapina (Shalyapin Memorial Museum), Graftio ul 2b, 197022 Sankt-Peterburg - T: (812) 2341056. Head: Z. Getman
Special Museum - 1975 28042

Mramornyj Dvorec, Gosudarstvennyj Russkij Muzej (State Russian Museum - Marble Palace), Milionnaja ul 5/1, 191011 Sankt-Peterburg - T: (812) 3129196, E-mail: info@rusmuseum.ru
Decorative Arts Museum / Fine Arts Museum
11th-20th c Russian art 28043

Museum of the Mussorgsky State Academic Opera and Ballet Theatre, pl Iskusstv 1, Sankt-Peterburg - T: (812) 3181982, Fax: 3147284. Head: M. Kortunova
Performing Arts Museum - 1935
Coll of materials (sketches, posters, etc.) depicting the history of the theatre and its work 28044

Muzej Akademii Chudožestv (Museum of the Academy of Art), Universitetskaja Nab 17, 199034 Sankt-Peterburg - T: (812) 2136496
Fine Arts Museum 28045

Muzej Antropologii i Etnografii im. Petra Velikogo (Peter the Great Museum of Anthropology and Ethnography (Kunstkamera)), Universitetskaja Nab 3, 199034 Sankt-Peterburg - T: (812) 3280712, 3281412, Fax: 3280811, E-mail: Museum@kunstkamera.ru, Internet: http://www.kunstkamera.ru. Head: Prof. Čuner Taksami
Ethnology Museum - 1879
Ethnography, archeology, anthropology (North and South America, Australia, Oceania, the Near East, Central Eastern, South-East Asia, Siberia, Africa, Europe), coll by J. Cook, I. Voznesensky, N.N. Miklukho-Maklay, A. Frich, V. Junker, P. Kozlov, V. Alexeyev, A. Grubauer etc. 28046

Muzej Chleba (Museum of Bread), Ligovskij pr 73, 190000 Sankt-Peterburg - T: (812) 1641110
Special Museum
Hist of the bread baking industry in Russia 28047

Muzej Cirkovogo Iskusstva (State Circus Museum), nab Fontanki 3, 191011 Sankt-Peterburg - T: (812) 3134413, Fax: 3148059, E-mail: circusmuseum@aport.ru. Head: Natalja Kuznecova
Performing Arts Museum - 1928
80,000 exhibits of plans, sketches, paintings, posters, programs, clippings, magazines, dresses, videos - library 28048

Muzej Dekorativno-prikladnogo Iskusstva (Museum of Applied Art), Soljanoj Per 3, 191028 Sankt-Peterburg - T: (812) 2733258
Decorative Arts Museum
Artistic handicraft, applied art from 1,000 BC to present 28049

Muzej D.I. Mendeleeva (D.I. Mendeleev Museum), Mendeleevskaja Pr 2, 199034 Sankt-Peterburg - T: (812) 2189744, Fax: 2181346, E-mail: igor@mdim.lgu.spb.su. Head: Prof. I.S. Dmitriev
Special Museum - 1911
Memorabilia of Dmitri Ivanovich Mendeleev (1834-1907), scientific archives, in the flat where the scientist lived from 1866 to 1890 28050

Muzej Gosudarstvennogo Akademičeskogo Marijnskogo Teatra Opery i Baleta (Museum of the State Academic Mariinsky Theater), Teatralnaja pl 1, 190000 Sankt-Peterburg - T: (812) 3264174, Fax: 3141744, E-mail: svetashab@mariinsky.spb.ru, Internet: http://www.mariinsky.ru. Head: Svetlana Šabanova
Performing Arts Museum
Music documents, hist of the performing arts, hist objects scenery and costume designs - library 28051

Muzej im. M.V. Lomonosova (M.V. Lomonosov Museum), Universitetskaja Nab 3, 199034 Sankt-Peterburg - T: (812) 3281011, Fax: 3280811. Head: E.P. Karpeev
Science&Tech Museum - 1947
Scientific instruments, astronomic equipment (18th-19th c), the Great Gottorf Globe-Planetarium 1656, memorabilia objects of the Russian encyclopaedist Mikhail Vasilevich Lomonosov (1711-1765) - library 28052

Muzej im. S.M. Kirova (S.M. Kirov Museum), Kamennoostrovskij Pr 26-28, 197101 Sankt-Peterburg - T: (812) 3461481
Historical Museum - 1938
Memorabilia of the Soviet politician Sergei Mironovich Kirov (1886-1934), documents, photographs, paintings, sculpture 28053

Muzej Istorii Milicii (Militia History Museum), Poltavskaja ul 12, 193167 Sankt-Peterburg - T: (812) 2777825, 2794233, Fax: 2794219. Head: Igor Michailov
Special Museum
Hist of the Department of Criminal Investigation 28054

Muzej Kirovskogo Zavoda (Museum of the Kirov Works), Pr Staček 72, Dvorec Kultury, 190000 Sankt-Peterburg
Historical Museum - 1962
Labour movement, documents on the 1917 Revolution and World War II, rare photographs, contemporary hist 28055

Muzej Krejsera Avrora, Centralnyj Voenno-morskoj muzej (Cruizer Aurora Museum), Petrogradskaja Nab, bliz mosta Svobody, 197046 Sankt-Peterburg - T: (812) 2308440, Fax: 3282701, E-mail: museum@mail.admiral.ru, Internet: http://www.museum.navy.ru. Head: Lev Davidovyč Černavin
Historical Museum - 1956
History of the 1917 October Revolution and the historical role of the cruiser Avrora, veteran of Russian-Japanese war and World War I and II 28056

Muzej-kvartira A. Puškina, Nacionalnyj Muzej Puškina (A. Pushkin Apartment Museum), Nab Mojki 12, 191186 Sankt-Peterburg - T: (812) 3113531, Fax: 3113801, E-mail: vmp@mail.admiral.ru, Internet: http://www.pushkin.ru. Head: Galina Michailovna Sedova
Special Museum
Life and work of the poet A.S. Pushkin in the flat where the poet died, original interiors, documents, manuscripts 28057

Muzej-kvartira I.I. Brodskogo, Research Museum of the Russian Academy of Arts (The Isaak Brodsky Apartment Museum), Pl Iskusstv 3, 191011 Sankt-Peterburg - T: (812) 3143658, 3125824, Fax: 3236169, E-mail: M167@mail.museum.ru, Internet: http://www.museum.ru/M167. Head: N.M. Balakina
Fine Arts Museum - 1949
Memorabilia of the painter Isaak Izrailevič Brodski (1884-1939), drawings, paintings, documents, the artists original studio, coll of Russian paintings and drawings from the 19th-20th c 28058

Muzej Muzykalnych Instrumentov (Museum of Musical Instruments), Isaakievskaja Pl 5, 190000 Sankt-Peterburg - T: (812) 3145345
Music Museum
1900 28059

Muzej Pečati (Museum of Printing), Mojkij nab 32, 190000 Sankt-Peterburg - T: (812) 3120977
Decorative Arts Museum 28060

Muzej Skulptury (Museum of Sculpture), Pl Alexsandra Nevskogo 1, 193107 Sankt-Peterburg - T: (812) 2742635, Fax: 2742579. Head: N.H. Belova
Fine Arts Museum
Largest coll of Russian sculpture, documents on architecture and town planning, architectural drawings 28061

Muzej Zdravoochranenija (Museum of Public Health), ul Italianskaja 25, 191011 Sankt-Peterburg - T: (812) 2126070, Fax: 3117033. Head: Galina A. Vladimirova
Natural History Museum - 1918
Anatomy, physiology, preventive medicine, hygiene - medical public library 28062

Nacionalnyj Muzej Puškina (National Pushkin Museum), Nab Mojki 12, 191186 Sankt-Peterburg - T: (812) 3113801, Fax: 3113801, E-mail: vmp@mail.admiral.ru, Internet: http://www.pushkin.ru. Head: Sergej Michailovič Nekrasov
Special Museum - 1879
Life and work of the poet and his epoch 28063

Petropavlovskaja Krepost (Peter and Paul Fortress), pl Revoljutsii, Sankt-Peterburg - T: (812) 2384511, Fax: 2384243, E-mail: direct@ppk.spb.su. Head: Natalja Dementieva
Historic Site - 1924
Military hist, 18th c church, various buildings showing the hist and architectural hist of St. Peterburg 28064

Rossijskij Ėtnografičeskij muzej (Russian Museum of Ethnography), Inženernaja ul 4/1, 191011 Sankt-Peterburg - T: (812) 3158502, Fax: 3158502, E-mail: rme@infopro.spb.su, Internet: http://www.ethnomuseum.ru. Head: V.M. Grusman
Ethnology Museum - 1901
19th-20th c ethnographical exhibits, crafts, contemporary folk art 28065

Russkij Gosudarstvennyj Muzej Arktiki i Antarktiki (Russian State Museum of the Arctic and Antarctic), ul Marata 24a, 191040 Sankt-Peterburg - T: (812) 1131998, Fax: 1646818. Head: V.I. Bojarskij
Natural History Museum - 1937
Hist of the Soviet expeditions to the Arctic and Antarctic, documents, original equipment, polar aviation, natural hist, in a 19th c church - library 28066

Stroganovskij Dvorec, Gosudarstvennyj Russkij Muzej (State Russian Museum - Stroganov Palace), Nevskij pr 17, 191011 Sankt-Peterburg - T: (812) 3112360, E-mail: info@rusmuseum.ru
Fine Arts Museum
11th-20th c Russian art 28067

Svjato-Troickij Sobor (Cathedral of the Holy Trinity), Pl Aleksandra Nevskogo, Monastyrkij Nab 1, 190000 Sankt-Peterburg - T: (812) 2740409, 2744464
Religious Arts Museum
Complex of 16 religious buildings 28068

Voenno-istoričeskij Muzej Artillerii, Inženernych Vojsk i Vojsk Svjazi (Museum of Artillery, the Corps of Engineers and the Signal Corps), Alexandrovskij Park 7, 197046 Sankt-Peterburg - T: (812) 2384704, Fax: 2384704. Head: V.M. Krylov
Military Museum - 1756
Hist of Russian and Soviet artillery, exhibits from the War of 1812, military techniques, weapons, flags, uniforms 28069

Voenno-medicinskij Muzej (Military Medical Museum), Lazaretnyj Per 2, 191180 Sankt-Peterburg - T: (812) 3155358, Fax: 3102025. Head: Prof. Dr. Anatolij A. Budko
Historical Museum / Military Museum - 1942
Hist of Russian and Soviet medicine since the 14th c, documents, relics, manuscripts, instruments, pictures, sculptures, photographs - archives of military medical documents 28070

Vystavočnyj Zal Sojuza Chudožnikov Rossii (Exhibition Hall of the Artists' Union of Russia), Sverdlovskaja Nab 64, 190000 Sankt-Peterburg - T: (812) 2240633
Public Gallery 28071

Zoologičeskij Muzej Akademii Nauk (Academy of Sciences Museum of Zoology), Universitetskaja Nab 1, 199034 Sankt-Peterburg - T: (812) 2180112, Fax: 1140444, E-mail: prl@zisp.spb.su. Head: R.L. Potapov
Natural History Museum - 1832
Natural sciences, zoology, evolution of fauna 28072

Saransk

Mordovskij Muzej Izobrazitelnych Isskustv (Mordovian Museum of Fine Arts), Kommunističeskaja ul 61, 430000 Saransk - T: (08342) 175638, Fax: 175638. Head: M.N. Baranova
Fine Arts Museum - 1960
Painting, sculpture, prints, decorative art - library 28073

Respublikanskij Kraevedčeskij Muzej Mordovii (Regional Museumn), Moskovskaja 48, Saransk
Local Museum - 1918
History, ethnography, natural history, economics - library 28074

Saratov

Memorialnyj Muzej Černyševskogo (Chernyshevski Memorial Museum), ul Černyševskogo 142, 410002 Saratov - T: (08452) 263583, Fax: 243367. Head: G.P. Murenina
Special Museum - 1920
Memorabilia of the writer Nikolai Gavrilovich Chernyshevski, documents - library 28075

Radiščev Chudožestvennyj Muzej (Radishchev Art Museum), ul Radiščeva 39, 410600 Saratov - T: (08452) 241918. Head: Galina Kormakulina
Fine Arts Museum - 1885
Alexei Bogolubov coll, icons and 18th-19th c wooden sculpture from Volga region, Russian art, Russian and Western graphics - library, archive 28076

Saratovskij Kraevedčeskij Muzej (Saratov Museum of Local History, Nature and Culture), ul Lermontova 34, Saratov - T: (08452) 262231, Fax: 262231, E-mail: centraloffice@comk.ru, Internet: http://www.comk.ru. Head: Nikolaj Malov
Local Museum - 1886
History, ethnography, natural history, economics, archeology - library, ethnographic coll 28077

Sebež

Sebežskij Muzej Prirody, Proletarskaja ul 21, 182250 Sebež
Natural History Museum
Natural history, ecology 28078

Semenov

Semenovskij Gosudarstvennyj Kraevedčeskij Muzej, ul Matveeva 4, 606600 Semenov - T: 332379
Local Museum - 1934
Paintings (19-20th c) 28079

Sergač

Sergačskij Kraevedčeskij Muzej (Regional Museum), ul Leninskaja 33, 607510 Sergač - T: (083191) 22151. Head: Nina Ivanovna Soldatova
Local Museum - 1967
Old photographs, manuscripts, fine art and religious art 28080

Sergiev Posad

Chudožestvenno-pedagogičeskij Muzej Igruški (Art Pedagocical Museum of Toys), Pr Krasnoj Armii 115, 141300 Sergiev Posad, Moskovskaja obl.
Decorative Arts Museum 28081

Sergievo-Posadskij Gosudarstvennyj Istoriko-chudožestvennyj Muzej Zapovednik (Sergiev-Posad State History and Art Museum-Reserve), pr Krasnoj armii 144, 141300 Sergiev Posad, Moskovskaja obl. - T: (09654) 41358, Fax: 7862708, E-mail: sergiev@divo.ru, Internet: http://www.musobl.divo.ru. Head: Feliks H. Makoev
Historical Museum / Fine Arts Museum / Decorative Arts Museum - 1920
The museum occupies some of the buildings of the Trinity-Sergius Lavra monastery, Russian art from the 14th c to the present 28082

Serpuchov

Serpuchovskij Muzej Istorii i Iskusstva (Museum of History and Art), Čekhova 87, 142206 Serpuchov - T: 21833. Head: Aleksandr Ivanovich Kurochkin
Fine Arts Museum / Historical Museum
19th-20th c Russian paintings, West European art, graphics 28083

Smolensk

Smolenskaja Galerja, ul Krupskoj 7, Smolensk
Public Gallery 28084

Smolenskij Muzej-Zapovednik (Smolensk State Museum-Preserve), B. Sovetskaja 11, Smolensk - T: (0812) 237373, Fax: 237346, E-mail: smolmuz@sci.smolensk.ru, Internet: http://admin.smolensk.ru/turizm/muz_zap. Head: Nadežda Volosenkova
Local Museum - 1888
Local history, archaeology, prominent personalities of the region, memorabilia of the composer Michail Glinka and of the sculptor S. Konenkov, memorabilia of the cosmonaut Gagarin, decorative and applied art 17th - 20th cc, folk art, Western Europe paintings - library 28085

Smolenskij Sobor, Novodevičij muzej (Smolensk Cathedral), Sobornyj dvor 5, 214000 Smolensk - T: (0812) 30757
Religious Arts Museum 28086

Solikamsk

Solikamskij Gorodskoj Kraevedčeskij Muzej (Municipal Museum), ul Naberezhnaya 82, 618500 Solikamsk - T: 394663
Local Museum - 1929 28087

Spasskoe-Lutovinovo

Dom-muzej I.S. Turgeneva, Gosudarstvennyj Muzej I.S. Turgeneva Orel (I.S. Turgenev House Museum), Spasskoe-Lutovinovo
Special Museum
Memorabilia of the writer Ivan Sergeevich Turgenev in his country estate, literary history 28088

Staraja Russa

Starorusskij Kraevedčeskij Muzej (Old Russian Regional Museum), ul Vozroždenija 1, 175200 Staraja Russa - T: 21816
Local Museum / Fine Arts Museum - 1919
Paintings, sculpture 28089

Staročerkassk

Staročerkasskij Istoriko-architekturnyj Muzej-zapovednik, 346700 Staročerkassk - T: 29748
Historical Museum 28090

Staročerkasskij Muzej, Novočerkasskij muzej istorii donskich kozakov (Local Museum), Staročerkassk
Local Museum
History of the Don Cossacks, exhibition on Stepan Timofeevich Razin, 17th c leader of the peasant liberation movement 28091

Stavropol

Kraevedčeskij Muzej, Bul Lenina 22, 355000 Stavropol - T: (86522) 337712
Local Museum 28092

Stavropolskij Kraevedčeskij Muzej (Stavropol Regional Museum), ul Dzerdžinskogo 135, 355000 Stavropol
Local Museum - 1904
History, ethnography, natural history, economics - library 28093

Stavropolskij Muzej Izobrazitelnych Iskusstv (Stavropol Museum of Fine Arts), ul Dzerdžinskogo 115, 355000 Stavropol - T: 30005. Head: Z.A. Belaja
Fine Arts Museum - 1962
Paintings and drawings by Russian artists 28094

Syktyvkar

Nacionalnaja Galereja Respubliki Komi (The National Gallery of the Komi Republic), ul Kirova 44, 167981 Syktyvkar - T: (8212) 426066, Fax: 426066, E-mail: ngrk@online.ru. Head: Svetlana A. Beljaeva
Fine Arts Museum
Coll of Western European art, Old Russian art (icons, casting), Russian art, Russian Avantgarde, Soviet pictorial art, Komi pictorial art 28095

Respublikanskij Kraevedčeskij Muzej Komi (Regional Museum), ul Ordzonikidze 2, Syktyvkar
Local Museum - 1911
History, ethnography, economics, natural history - library 28096

Syzran

Syzranskij Gorodskoj Kraevedčeskij Muzej, per Dostoevskogo 34, 446001 Syzran - T: 23355
Local Museum - 1925 28097

Taganrog

Taganrogskij Gosudarstvennyj Literaturnyj i istoriko-architekturnyj Muzej-zapovednik, ul Oktjabrskaja 9, 347900 Taganrog - T: 63496
Historical Museum - 1983 28098

Taganrogskij Kraevedčeskij Muzej (Taganrog Municipal Museum), ul Gluško 13, 347900 Taganrog - T: 63363
Local Museum - 1898 28099

Taganrogskij Muzej im. A.P. Čechova (A.P. Chekhov Museum Taganrog), ul Oktjabrskaja 9, 347900 Taganrog - T: 62745
Special Museum - 1960
Rooms arranged as they were when Chekhov lived there in his childhood 28100

Talaškino

Muzej Prikladnogo Iskusstva (Museum of Applied Art), Teremok, Talaškino
Decorative Arts Museum 28101

Tambov

Tambovskaja Kartinnaja Galereja (Tambov Picture Gallery), ul Sovetskaja 97, 392000 Tambov. Head: Tamara Nikolaevna Šestakova
Public Gallery
Painting, contemporary art 28102

Tambovskij Oblastnoj Kraevedčeskij Muzej (Regional Museum), Oktjabrskaja pl 4, Tambov
Local Museum - 1918
History, ethnography, economics, natural history - library 28103

Tara

Tarskij Istoriko-architekturnyj Muzej, pr Karla Marksa 8, 646500 Tara
Historical Museum 28104

Tatarsk

Tatarskij Kraevedčeskij Muzej (Regional Museum), ul Telegina 52, 632120 Tatarsk
Local Museum 28105

Tichvin

Gosudarstvennyj Dom-muzej N.A. Rimskogo-Korsakova (Rimski-Korsakov Memorial House), ul Rimskogo-Korsakova 13, 187500 Tichvin - T: 11509, 11267. Head: Anna Alekseevna Stepanova
Music Museum - 1944
Life and work of the composer Nikolai Andreevich Rimski-Korsakov in his birthplace - library, archive 28106

Tjumen

Tjumenskaja Kartinnaja Galereja (Tjumen Picture Gallery), ul Respublika 29, 625000 Tjumen. Head: I.S. Terentev
Public Gallery
Fine art, contemporary art 28107

Tobolsk

Tobolskaja Kartinnaja Galereja (Tobolsk Picture Gallery), pl Krasnaja 2, 626100 Tobolsk
Public Gallery
Paintings 28108

Tobolskij Gosudarstvennyj Istoriko-architekturnyj Muzej-zapovednik (Tobolsk State Historical Museum), Krasnaja pl 2, 626100 Tobolsk
Historical Museum - 1870
History of Siberia - library 28109

Tomsk

Tomskij Oblastnoj Kraevedčeskij Muzej (Regional Museum), pr Lenina 75, Tomsk
Local Museum - 1922
History, ethnography, economics, natural history - library 28110

Tula

Tulskij Muzej Izobrazitelnych Iskusstv (Tula Museum of Fine Arts), ul Engelsa 64, 300012 Tula - T: (0872) 354272, Fax: 354272, E-mail: artmuseum@tula.net. Head: Marina Nikolaevna Kuzina
Fine Arts Museum - 1919
Fine art, contemporary art - library 28111

Tulskij Oblastnoj Kraevedčeskij Muzej (Tula Museum of Regional Studies), ul Sovetskaja 68, 300000 Tula - T: (0872) 362208. Head: N.B. Nemova
Local Museum - 1919
Local hist, materials on the 1917 October Revolution, samovars, costume, manuscripts, accordeons, embroidery, archaeology - library 28112

Tver

Tverskaja Oblastnaja Kartinnaja Galereja (Tver Regional Art Gallery), Sovetskaja ul 3, 170640 Tver - T: (0822) 332561, Fax: 332561, E-mail: Art@tversu.ru, Internet: http://www.galleru.tversu.ru. Head: Tatjana Savvateevna Kujukina
Fine Arts Museum - 1937
Fine art, contemporary art - library 28113

Tverskoj Gosudarstvennyj Obedinennyj Muzej (Tver State Museum), ul Sovetskaja 5, 170640 Tver - T: (0822) 335127, Fax: 333790, E-mail: museum@tversu.ru, Internet: http://www.museum.tver.ru. Head: Jurij Michailovič Bošniak
Local Museum - 1866
History, economics, ethnography, natural history - library 28114

Ufa

Baškirskij Gosudarstvennyj Chudožestvennyj Muzej im. M.V. Nesterova (Bashkirian State Art Museum), ul Gogolja 27, 450025 Ufa - T: (3472) 234236
Fine Arts Museum - 1919
Art, manuscripts - library 28115

National'nyj Muzej Respubliki Baškortostan (National Museum of Bashkortistan), ul Sovjetskaja 14, 450008 Ufa - T: (3472) 221250, Fax: 234451, E-mail: Nmuseum@soros.bashedu.ru, Internet: http://museum.ufanet.ru
Local Museum 28116

Respublikanskij Kraevedčeskij Muzej Bashkirskoj, ul Oktyabrskoj revolyutsii 10, Ufa - T: (3472) 234451. Head: Ilvar Akbulatov
Local Museum - 1864
History, ethnography, economics, natural history - library 28117

Uglič

Istoričeskij Muzej (Historical and Art Museum), Kreml 3, 152620 Uglič - T: (08532) 51757, E-mail: uglmus@yaroslavl.ru. Head: Viktor Erochin
Historical Museum
Russian history and art 28118

Ulan-Udė

Respublikanskij Kraevedčeskij Muzej im. M.I. Changalova Burjatii, Profsojuznaja 29, Ulan-Udė
Local Museum - 1923
History, ethnography, economics, natural history - library 28119

Uljanovsk

Muzej Gončarova (Goncharov Museum), ul Gončarova 20, 432700 Uljanovsk - T: (8422) 313481, Fax: 314181, E-mail: M1785@mail.museum.ru. Head: Antonina Vasilevna Lobkareva
Special Museum 28120

Muzej Karamzinskaja Obščestvennaja Biblioteka (Karamzin Public Library Museum), ul kommunističeskaja 3, 4327000 Uljanovsk - T: (08422) 313686, Fax: 413780, E-mail: lib@mv.ru. Head: Ljudmila Ivaškina
Library with Exhibitions 28121

Uljanovskij filial Centralnogo muzeja V.I. Lenina, ul Lenina 58, 432700 Uljanovsk
Local Museum 28122

Uljanovskij Oblastnoj Kraevedčskij Muzej im. I.A. Gončarova, bul Novyj Venec 3-4, Uljanovsk
Local Museum - 1895
History, ethnography, economics, natural history - library 28123

Vetluga

Vetlužskij Kraevedčeskij Muzej (Regional Museum), ul Lenina 1a, 606860 Vetluga - T: 22560
Local Museum - 1918
Coll of rare books (18th c), ethnology, coll of bronze canons of field marshal N.I. Repnin (president of the council of war under Peter I) 28124

Vladikavkaz

Respublikanskij Muzej Kraevedenija Severnoj-Osetii (Republican Museum), pr Mira 11, Vladikavkaz
Local Museum - 1961
Regional history, ethnography, archaeology, botany, zoology, geology - library 28125

Severoossetinskij Literaturnyj Muzej im. K.L. Četagurova (K.L. Chetagurov North-Ossetian Literary Museum), Butirina, 362000 Vladikavkaz - T: (086722) 36222. Head: E.A. Kesaeva
Special Museum - 1979
Caucasian poetry and literature, memorabilia of the poet Konstantin Levanovich Chetagurov 28126

Vladímir

Muzej, ul III Internacionala 43, Vladímir
Folklore Museum 28127

Vladimiro-Suzdalskij istoriko-chudožestvennyj i architekturnyj muzej-zapovednik (Vladimir-Suzdal Museum of Art History and Architecture), ul III Internatsionala 58, Vladímir
Fine Arts Museum - 1862
History, archeology, art, architecture - library 28128

Vladivostok

Muzej-Akvarium, Tichookeanskogo naučno-issledovatelskogo instituta rybnogo chozjajstva i okeanografii (TINRO) (Museum-Aquarium Pacific Research Institute of Fisheries and Oceanography), ul Batareinai 4, 690600 Vladivostok - T: (4232) 255965, Fax: 257783. Head: Gennadij N. Kurganskij
Natural History Museum - 1925
Marine biology, ichthyology, molocology, biology of sea mammals, flora and fauna of the Pacific Ocean 28129

Primorskij Kraevedčeskij Muzej im. V.K. Arseneva, ul 1-ja Maja 6, Vladivostok
Local Museum - 1936
History, ethnography, economics, natural history - library 28130

Voejkovo

Metereological Museum of the Central Geophysical Observatory, Voejkovo. Head: A.A. Vasilev
Natural History Museum 28131

Volgograd

Gosudarstvennyj Muzej-panorama Stalingradskaja Bitva (State Museum-Panorama Battle of Stalingrad), ul Čujkova 47, 400053 Volgograd - T: (8442) 347272, Fax: 347241, E-mail: panorama@volgadmin.ru, Internet: http://www.volgadmin.ru/panorama. Head: Boris Usik
Military Museum / Historical Museum - 1937
132.000 items feature the defence of the city during the Civil War (1918-1920) and the Battle of Stalingrad (1942-1943), weapons, military equipment, medals, drawings, hall, devoted to the war in Afganistan - library, cinema 28132

Volgogradskij Oblastnoj Kraevedčeskij Muzej, pr V.I. Lenina 39, 400000 Volgograd
Local Museum - 1924
History, ethnography, economics, natural history - library 28133

Vologda

Vologda Historical, Architectural and Artistic Museum Reserve, Orlov 15, 160000 Vologda - T: 722283. Head: L.D. Korotajeva
Historical Museum - 1885
History, ethnography, nature, literature, decorative and applied art, old Russian painting, modern art of the Vologda region, permanent exhibitions - library 28134

Vologodskaja Kartinnaja Galereja (Vologda Art Gallery), Kremlevskaja pl 2, 160000 Vologda. Head: S.G. Ivenskij
Public Gallery - 1953
Fine art, contemporary art - library 28135

Vologodskij Kraevedčeskij Muzej, ul Majakovskogo 15, Vologda
Local Museum - 1923
History, ethnography, economics, natural history - library 28136

Voronež

Voronežskij Chudožestvennyj Muzej (Voronezh Art Museum), pr Revoljucii 18, 394000 Voronež - T: 552843. Head: Vladimir Ustinov
Fine Arts Museum - 1933 28137

Voronežskij Oblastnoj Kraevedčeskij Muzej (Regional Museum), ul Plechanovskaja 29, 394018 Voronež - T: 520395. Head: T.V. Frolova
Local Museum - 1894
History, ethnography, economics, natural history 28138

Vyra

Muzej Stancionnyj Smotritel (Postmaster Museum), Vyra
Special Museum - 1980
Museum connected with Pushkins short story "Stantsionny smotritel" ("Postmaster"), in a former post house, described by the poet in his story, original interiors, samovar, travel document of A.S. Pushkin dated 5.5.1829, harnessry 28139

Rwanda

Butare

Musée National, BP 630, Butare - T: 30810, 30811, Fax: 30834. Head: Simon Ntigashira
Local Museum - 1953
Ethnology, archaeology, geology, botany, basket-works, carvings, handicrafts 28140

Kabgayi

Musée de Kabgayi, Evêché de Kabgayi, Kabgayi, mail addr: BP 66, Kabgayi - T: 62104. Head: Pierre Boutry
Local Museum - 1943
Ethnography, lances, pottery, basketry, mineralogy, geology, art 28141

Kigali

Musée Géologique du Rwanda, Av de la Justice, Kigali, mail addr: BP 73, Kigali - T: 73401, Fax: 75465. Head: Albert Ndacyayisenga
Natural History Museum - 1977
Rocks, minerals, photographs 28142

St. Lucia

Castries

Pigeon Island, POB 595, Castries - T: (758) 452-5005, Fax: (758) 453-2791. Head: Paul Jackson
Historical Museum / Natural History Museum - 1994
History, geology and natural history 28143

St. Pierre and Miquelon

Saint-Pierre

Musée de Saint-Pierre, 15 Rue du Docteur Dunan, 97500 Saint-Pierre - T: 413035, Fax: 413035
Natural History Museum / Local Museum 28144

Samoa

Apia

National Museum and Culture Centre, Apia
Local Museum - 1984
library, theatre and craft workshops 28145

Vailima

Robert Louis Stevenson Museum, Vailima
Special Museum
Stevenson's house and estate 28146

San Marino

San Marino

Galleria Nazionale di Arte Moderna e Contemporanea, Loggia dei Balestrieri, Scala Bonetti 2, 47890 San Marino - T: 882670, Fax: 882679. Head: Dr. Francesca Michelotti
Fine Arts Museum
Modern and contemporary art 28147

I Torre Guaita, Via Salita delle Rocca, 47031 San Marino - T: 991369
Historical Museum
Tower history 10th-17th c 28148

Museo Auto d'Ecopa, Via dei Boschetti, Borgo Maggiore, 47000 San Marino - T: 906292
Science&Tech Museum 28149

Museo delle Armi Antiche, II Torre Castello alla Cesta, Salita alla Cesta, 47890 San Marino - T: 991295. Head: Dr. Francesca Michelotti
Military Museum - 1956
Antique firearms from the 13th-19th c 28150

Museo delle Armi Moderne, Contrada della Pieve 27, 47031 San Marino - T: 991999
Military Museum 28151

Museo delle Cere - Strumenti di Tortura, Via Lapicidi Marini 17, 47890 San Marino - T: 992940
Historical Museum - 1966
History of the Risorgimento 28152

Museo delle Curiosità, Via Salita delle Rocca 26, 47000 San Marino - T: 992437, 991075
Special Museum 28153

Museo di Stato, Piazzetta del Titano 1, 47890 San Marino - T: 883835, 882670, Fax: 882679, E-mail: museodistato@omniway.sm. Head: Dr. Francesca Michelotti
Local Museum
Furniture, pottery, numismatics, archaeology, paintings 28154

Museo Postale, Filatelico-Numismatico, Piazza Grande Borgo Maggiore, 47893 San Marino - T: 883469
Special Museum - 1972
Stamps, coins 28155

Museo San Francesco, Via Basilicius 33, 47890 San Marino - T: 885132
Fine Arts Museum
Ancient and modern works, incunabula 28156

Palazzo Pubblico, Opera di Francesco Azzurri 1884-1894, Sede del Governo, Piazza della Libertà, 47890 San Marino - T: 885370
Historical Museum 28157

Sao Tome and Principe

São Tomé

Museu Nacional, Praça de Juventude, São Tomé, mail addr: CP 87, São Tomé - T: 21874
Fine Arts Museum / Folklore Museum - 1975
African art, religious art 28158

Saudi Arabia

Jeddah

King Abdul Aziz University Museum, POB 1540, Jeddah 21441 - T: (02) 6400000, Fax: 6404000
University Museum 28159

Riyadh

Geological Museum, c/o University of Riyadh, Almilaz, Riyadh - T: (01) 4676243, Fax: 4676345. Head: A.A. El-Khayal
Natural History Museum - 1958
Geology and Paleontology of Saudi Arabia 28160

King Saud University Museum, University, Riyadh - T: (01) 4678135
Archaeological Museum / University Museum
University's archaeological excavations at Al-Fao and Rabdhah, pre-Islamic city 300BC - 300AD 28161

National Museum, c/o Deputy Ministry for Antiquities and Museums, POB 3734, Riyadh 11481 - T: (01) 4036010, Fax: 4029976. Head: Ali S. Al-Moghanam
Historical Museum / Archaeological Museum - 1978/1999
Stone Age, Age of Trade, After the Revelation (development of Islam), First and Second Saudi States, unification of the Kingdom of Saudi Arabia by King Abdulaziz al-Saud 28162

National Museum for Trading, POB 126, Riyadh 11411 - T: (01) 4632517
Historical Museum 28163

Oriental Museum for Carpets, POB 20803, Riyadh 11465 - T: (01) 4025207
Historical Museum 28164

Senegal

Dakar

Musée d'Archéologie, Rue Malavois, Gorée, Dakar
Archaeological Museum
Archaeology of West Africa 28165

Musée d'Art Africain, 1 Pl Soweto, Dakar - T: 214015, Fax: 244918. Head: Amadou Tahirou Diaw
Fine Arts Museum / Ethnology Museum - 1936
African art, sculpture, ethnology 28166

Musée Dynamique, Blvd Martin Luther King, Dakar, mail addr: BP 3308, Dakar - T: 220798
Decorative Arts Museum 28167

Musée Géologique, Rte de l'Université, Dakar, mail addr: BP 1238, Dakar - T: 320726, Fax: 320852. Head: Baidy Diene
Natural History Museum - 1963
library 28168

Gorée

Maison des Esclaves, Gorée - T: 20970
Historical Museum 28169

Musée de la Mer, Gorée. Head: Dr. Seck
Natural History Museum - 1959
Oceanography, marine biology 28170

Musée Historique, Rue Malavois, Gorée. Head: Dr. Abdoulaye Camara
Historical Museum / Archaeological Museum
Archeology, prehistory, slavery, modern hist 28171

Saint-Louis

Centre de Recherches et de Documentation du Sénégal, Rue Neuville, Pointe-Sud, Saint-Louis, mail addr: BP 382, Saint-Louis - T: 611050. Head: Abdoul Hadir Aidara
Local Museum - 1943
Zoology, botany, geology, anthropology, history, art 28172

Seychelles

Victoria

National Museum, 5th June Av, Victoria, mail addr: POB 720, Victoria - T: 321333, Fax: 323183, E-mail: seymus@seychelles.net. Head: Stella Doway
Historical Museum - 1964
History, natural hist, Stone of Possession 28173

Sierra Leone

Freetown

Sierra Leone National Museum, Cotton Tee Bldg, Freetown, mail addr: POB 908, Freetown - T: (22) 223555. Head: Celia A.B. Nicol
Local Museum
Archaeology, ethnology, chieftaincy regalia, Secret Society's parapheralia 28174

Singapore

Singapore

Art Museum and Exhibition Gallery, c/o National University of Singapore, 10 Kent Ridge Crecent, 119260 Singapore
Fine Arts Museum 28175

Asian Civilisations Museum, National Museums of Singapore, 39 Armenian St, Singapore 179939 - T: 3323015, Fax: 3327993, E-mail: nhb_acm@nhb.gov.sg, Internet: http://www.nhb.gov.sg. Head: Dr. Kenson Kwok
Ethnology Museum - 1997 28176

Fort Siloso, Jetty Rd, Sentosa, Singapore - T: 2750388, Fax: 2750161. Head: Lisa Lim
Military Museum - 1975
History of Fort, Malay traditions, weapons 28177

Lee Kong Chian Art Museum, c/o National University of Singapore, Block AS6, 10 Kent Ridge Crescent, Singapore 119260 - T: 8746917, 8746496, Fax: 8722632, E-mail: uamhead@nus.edu.sg, Internet: http://www.nus.edu.sg/museums. Head: Angela Sim
University Museum / Fine Arts Museum - 1970
Painting and calligraphy from 14th c on, ceramics, archaic jade, bronzes, sculpture - reference library on Chinese art 28178

Maritime Museum, Singapore, mail addr: c/o Port of Singapore Authority, POB 300, Singapore 911141 - T: 2750133, 2750134, Fax: 2744677
Special Museum - 1975
Paintings, ship models, fishing artifacts, local watercraft, charts, photographs, coins and medals - library 28179

Ng Eng Teng Gallery, c/o National University of Singapore, Block AS6, 10 Kent Ridge Crescent, Singapore 119260 - T: 8744333, 8744308, Fax: 8722632, E-mail: uamhead@nus.edu.sg, Internet: http://www.nus.edu.sg/museums. Head: Angela Sim
University Museum / Fine Arts Museum - 1997
Donated artworks by Ng Eng Teng, sculptures, paintings, drawings, studio pottery, maquettes 28180

Singapore Art Museum, 71 Bras Basah Rd, Singapore 189555 - T: 3323222, Fax: 3347919, E-mail: Santha-Anthony@nhb.gov.sg, Internet: http://www.nhb.gov.sg. Head: Kian Chow Kwok
Fine Arts Museum
Visual Art, modern and contemporary Asian art 28181

Singapore History Museum, National Museums of Singapore, 93 Stamford Rd, Singapore 178897 - T: 3380000, Fax: 3323568, Internet: http://www.museums.org.sg. Head: How Seng Lim
Historical Museum
Prehistory of Southeast Asia, hist of Singapore with a coll of historical paintings, photographs, prints and maps 28182

Singapore Science Centre, 15 Science Centre Rd, Singapore 609081 - T: 4252500, Fax: 5659533, E-mail: webmaster@sci-ctr.edu.sg, Internet: http://www.sci-ctr.edu.sg. Head: Dr. Chew Tuan Chiong
Science&Tech Museum - 1977
Physical sciences, life sciences, aviation, space science, mathematics, information technology 28183

Slovakia

Antol

Museum of Forestry, 969 72 Antol - T: (0859) 23932
Agriculture Museum 28184

Banská Bystrica

Museum of Literature and Music, State Scientific Library Banská Bystrica, Lazovna 44, 975 90 Banská Bystrica - T: (048) 4123690, 4155023, Fax: 4123690, E-mail: lhmbb@svkbb.sk. Head: Dr. Mariana Bardiová
Music Museum 28185

Muzeum Slovenského Narodného Povstania (Museum of the Slovakian National Uprising), Kapitulská 23, 974 00 Banská Bystrica - T: (088) 52529. Head: Dr. Ján Stanislav
Historical Museum - 1955
Hist of the Slovakian anti-Faschist struggle in World War II 28186

Štátna Galéria (State Gallery), Dolná 8, 975 90 Banská Bystrica - T: (088) 4124167, Fax: 4126080, E-mail: sgbb@isternet.sk, Internet: http://www.isternet.sk/sgbb. Head: Branislav Rezník
Fine Arts Museum - 1956
Graphic art and sculpture (modern and contemporary works by Slovak and foreign artists), printing (19th-20th c), applied art by contemporary Slovak artists - library, archive 28187

Stredoslovenské Múzeum (Museum of Central Slovakia), nám SNP č 4, 975 90 Banská Bystrica - T: (048) 4125895/96, Fax: 4155077, E-mail: smbb@stonline.sk. Head: Milan Šoka
Local Museum - 1889
Archaeology, mining, natural sciences, paintings, ethnography, local hist - library 28188

Banská Štiavnica

Slovenské Banské Múzeum (Slovak Mining Museum), ul Kammerhofská 2, 969 01 Banská Štiavnica - T: (0859) 6911541, Fax: 6912764. Head: Ján Novák
Science&Tech Museum / Fine Arts Museum / Local Museum - 1900
Mining, minerals of Banská Štiavnica Ore Field, historical weapons, Gothic fine art, prints (15th-18th c), ethnology, modern art, native artists 28189

Bardejov

Šarišské Múzeum (Saris Museum), Radničné nám 13, 085 01 Bardejov - T: (054) 4724966, Fax: 4724966, E-mail: sarmus@nextra.sk, Internet: http://home.nextra.sk/sarmus. Head: Dr. František Gutek
Local Museum - 1903
Gothic embroidery, religious art, folk art, ceramics, painting, local hist, entomology, ornithology, zoology, icons, crafts and guilds 28190

Bardejovské Kúpele

Múzeum, 086 31 Bardejovské Kúpele
Open Air Museum / Ethnology Museum
Ethnography 28191

Betliar

Slovenské Národné Múzeum - Múzeum Betliar, Kaštielská 6, 049 21 Betliar - T: (058) 7983118, Fax: 7983195, E-mail: muzeum.betliar@stonline.sk. Head: Eva Lazárová
Fine Arts Museum / Archaeological Museum / Military Museum - 1949
Furnishings, painting, arms, hunting trophies, in a 18th c palace - library 28192

Blatnica

Karol Plicka Museum, 038 15 Blatnica - T: (0842) 31011
Local Museum 28193

Bojnice

Múzeum, Hrad, ul Zámok a Okolie č 1, 972 01 Bojnice. Head: Ján Papco
Local Museum - 1950
Nitra Valley geology, geography, prehistoric archeology, weaving, furniture, fine arts, in a 13th c castle 28194

Bratislava

Antická Gerulata v Rusovciach, Mestské Múzeum v Bratislave, Gerulatská 69, 851 10 Bratislava - T: (07) 62859332, 54434742, Fax: 54434631, E-mail: mmba@bratislava.sk, Internet: http://www.bratislava.sk. Head: Peter Hyross
Archaeological Museum
Roman military camp, the only one in Slovak 28195

Archeologické Múzeum, Slovenské Národné Múzeum (Archeology Museum of the Slovak National Museum), Žižkova 12, 814 36 Bratislava - T: (02) 54413680, Fax: 54410772. Head: Dr. Štefan Holčík
Archaeological Museum - 1969
Prehistory, protohistory, Middle Ages, Egyptian coll - library, laboratories, photolaboratory 28196

Esterházyho Palác, Slovenská Národná Galéria (Esterhazy Palais), Námestie L'Štúra 4, 815 13 Bratislava - T: (07) 544320812, 54431703, Fax: (07) 54433971
Fine Arts Museum 28197

Etnografická Expozícia - Vajnory House, Mestské Múzeum v Bratislave, Vajnory, Rolnícka 185, 813 00 Bratislava - T: (07) 54434742, Fax: 54434631, E-mail: mmba@bratislava.sk, Internet: http://www.bratislava.sk. Head: Dr. Peter Hyross
Ethnology Museum 28198

Expozícia Historických Hodín, Mestské Múzeum v Bratislave (Museum of Historic Clocks), Židovská 1, 800 00 Bratislava - T: (02) 54411940, Fax: 54434631, E-mail: mmba@bratislava.sk, Internet: http://www.bratislava.sk. Head: Dr. Peter Hyross
Special Museum
Clocks from 17th to 20th c, famous rococo building 28199

Expozícia Zbraní a Mestského Opevnenia, Mestské Múzeum v Bratislave (Museum of Arms and City Fortification), Michalská 24, 800 00 Bratislava - T: (02) 54433044, Fax: 54434631, E-mail: mmba@bratislava.sk, Internet: http://www.bratislava.sk. Head: Dr. Peter Hyross
Historical Museum
Bratislava's fortification and historical fights concerning the city, arms and exhibits of the Bratislava moulders and gunsmiths 28200

Farmaceutická Expozícia, Mestské Múzeum v Bratislave (Museum of Pharmacy) (temporary closed), Lekáreň Červený rak, Michalská 26, 800 00 Bratislava - Fax: (02) 54434631, E-mail: mmba@bratislava.sk. Head: Peter Hyross
Historical Museum
History of Pharmacy, pharmaceutical equipment 28201

Galéria Mesta Bratislavy (Municipal Gallery of Bratislava), Františkánske nám 11, 815 35 Bratislava - T: (02) 54435102, Fax: 54432611, E-mail: gmb@nextra.sk, Internet: http://www.savba.sk/logos/list-e.html. Head: Dr. Ivan Jančár
Fine Arts Museum
Pálffy palace: 19th-20th c Slovak and European paintings and sculptures, Gothic art; Mirbach palace: Baroque paintings, sculptures, graphics and contemporary Slovak art - library 28202

Historické Múzeum, Slovenské Národné Múzeum (History Museum), Vajanského nám 2, 814 36 Bratislava - T: (07) 5341600, Fax: 5314981. Head: Dr. Peter Hyross
Historical Museum - 1924
Hist of Slovakia, coll from the 16th c up to the present day, coins and medals, drawings, prints, sculptures, paintings, folk art (wood, ceramics, glass, metal, stone) - laboratories, photolaboratory, library, archives 28203

Hudobná Expozícia - Rodný Dom J.N. Hummela, Mestské Múzeum, Klobučnícka 2, 815 18 Bratislava - T: (02) 54434742, Fax: 54434631, E-mail: mmba@bratislava.sk, Internet: http://www.bratislava.sk. Head: Dr. Peter Hyross
Music Museum - 1937
Life and work of the composer J.N. Hummel (1778-1837) in his birth house, original spinets, pianos 28204

Hudobné Múzeum (Music Museum), Hrad, Bašta Luginsland, 814 36 Bratislava - T: (07) 54413349, Fax: 54413349, E-mail: musica@internet.sk, Internet: http://www.snm.sk. Head: Dr. Jana Kalinayová
Music Museum - 1965
Music instruments especially from Slovakia, small coll of non-European instruments, music coll 14th-20th c - laboratory, photothèque, archives, library 28205

Ivé Múzeum Obchodu, Sasinkova 19, 800 00 Bratislava - T: (07) 5415721
Special Museum 28206

Krajanské Múzeum MS Bratislava, Štefanikova 25, 811 05 Bratislava - T: (07) 321618
Local Museum 28207

Literárna Expozícia - Múzeum Janka Jesenského, Mestské Múzeum v Bratislave, Somolického 2, 811 05 Bratislava - T: (02) 54434742, Fax: 54434631, E-mail: mmba@bratislava.sk, Internet: http://www.bratislava.sk. Head: Dr. Peter Hyross
Special Museum - 1948
Memorabilia of the writer Janko Jesenský (1874-1945) in his former home, books, manuscripts, photographs, furniture - library 28208

Mestské Múzeum v Bratislave (City Museum Bratislava), Primaciálne nám 3, 815 18 Bratislava - T: (02) 54434742, Fax: 54434631, E-mail: mmba@bratislava.sk, Internet: http://www.bratislava.sk. Head: Dr. Peter Hyross
Historical Museum - 1868
Local hist, folk art, crafts, furnishings, tools, archaeology, viticulture, literature, musical instruments, historic weapons, coins, costumes, pharmacy, numismatics, historical clocks, religious art 28209

Múzeum Polície Slovenskej republiky (Museum of the Police of the Slovak Republic), Gundulicová 2, 812 72 Bratislava - T: (07) 0961056080, Fax: 0961059011. Head: Dr. Zuzanah Slamenová
Special Museum 28210

Múzeum Telesnej Kultúry Bratislava, Trnavská ul 29a, 831 04 Bratislava - T: (07) 44372427
Special Museum 28211

Múzeum Umeleckých Remesiel, Mestské Múzeum v Bratislave (Museum of Arts and Crafts), Beblavého 1, Bratislava - T: (02) 54412784, Fax: 54434631, E-mail: mmba@bratislava.sk, Internet: http://www.bratislava.sk. Head: Dr. Peter Hyross
Decorative Arts Museum
Arts and crafts 15th to 20th c, furniture, ceramics, glass textile, religious objects, silver 28212

Múzeum V.I. Lenina, ul Obrancov Mieru 21a, 801 00 Bratislava
Historical Museum 28213

Múzeum Židovskej Kultúry (Museum of Jewish Culture), Židovská 17, 811 01 Bratislava - T: (02) 54418507, Fax: 59349145, E-mail: mzk@snm.sk, Internet: http://www.snm.sk. Head: Prof. Pavol Meštan
Historical Museum / Special Museum 28214

Prírodovedné Múzeum, Slovenské Národné Múzeum (Natural History Museum), Vajanského náb č 2, 814 36 Bratislava - T: (07) 366623, Fax: 366653. Head: Dr. Eva Nelišerová
Natural History Museum - 1924
Botany, zoology, mineralogy, petrology, paleontology, paleozoology, paleobotany, anthropology - libraries, laboratories, photolaboratory 28215

Slovenská Národná Galéria (Slovak National Gallery), Riečna 1, 815 13 Bratislava - T: (07) 54432081/82, 54430437, Fax: 54433971, E-mail: gr@sng.sk, Internet: http://www.sng.sk. Head: Dr. Katarína Bajcurová
Fine Arts Museum - 1948
Paintings, sculpture, prints, drawings, applied art, naive art, architecture - library, archives, restoration studio, branches: Castle Zvolen, Castle Strážky (Spišská Belá), Ludovít Fulla Gallery (Ružomberok),, Vermess-Villa (Dunajská Streda), Gallery of Naive Art 28216

Slovenské Národné Múzeum (Slovak National Museum), Vajanského náb 2, 814 36 Bratislava - T: (07) 366944 kl 141, Fax: 366653. Head: Dr. Branislav Matoušek
Archaeological Museum / Historical Museum / Natural History Museum / Music Museum - 1924
Archeology, history, natural sciences, musicology - library, archives, museological information centre 28217

Vodné Kasárne, Slovenská Národná Galéria (Water Barracks), Rázusovo Nábrežie 2, 815 13 Bratislava - T: (07) 544320812, 54431703, Fax: (07) 54433971
Fine Arts Museum 28218

Brezno

Horehronské múzeum (Museum of the region of the Upper Hron), nám Gen. M.R. Štefánika 55, 977 26 Brezno - T: (048) 6112453, Fax: 6114633, E-mail: hormuz@naex.sk. Head: Ján Weiss
Local Museum - 1960
Ethnography, local hist 28219

Brodzany

Slovanské Múzeum A.S. Puškina, 985 42 Brodzany - T: (0815) 487272
Special Museum 28220

Čadca

Kysucke Muzeum, Palárikov dom, 022 01 Čadca. Head: Pavel Kužma
Local Museum
Local history 28221

Častá

Múzeum Červený Kameň (Museum Castle Red Rock), Hrad Červeny Kamen, 900 89 Častá - T: (033) 6495317, Fax: 64951322, E-mail: muzeumca@stonline.sk, Internet: http://www.snm.sk/ck. Head: Dr. Jaroslav Hájiček
Historic Site - 1950
Original furnishing, arms, ceramics, porcelain, sculpture paintings (16th-19th c) 28222

Červený Kláštor

Múzeum Červený Kláštor, 059 06 Červený Kláštor - T: (0964) 4822955, Fax: 4322302, E-mail: muzeum@sl.sinet.sk. Head: Monika Pavelcikova
Religious Arts Museum
Cloister history, religious art, furnishing, Hussite armaments, ethnography, in a 14th c cloister 28223

Detva

Podpolianske Múzeum Detva, nám SNP 1, 962 12 Detva - T: (0855) 355229, 355212
Historical Museum 28224

Dolná Strehová

Múzeum Bábkarských Kutúr a Hračiek Hrad Modrý Kameň, expozícia Dolná Strhová, 991 02 Dolná Strehová - T: (0845) 4897189
Local Museum
Local hist, memorial to the writer Imre Madách (1823-1864) and literary personalities 28225

Dolný Kubín

Oravská Galéria (Orava Gallery), Hviezdoslavovo nám 11, 026 01 Dolný Kubín - T: (043) 5863212, Fax: 5864395, E-mail: ogaleria@nextra.sk, Internet: http://www.oravskagaleria.sk. Head: Eva Luptáková
Fine Arts Museum - 1965
Painting, sculpture, graphics, drawing, folk art, a church in Slanica standing on elevation surrounded by waters of the Orava Dam 28226

Oravské Muzeum Pavla Országha Hviezdoslava, Hviezdoslavovo nám 7, 026 01 Dolný Kubín - T: (0845) 2056. Head: Dušan Karaska
Special Museum - 1868
Memorial to the poet Pavel O. Hviezdoslav (1849-1921) - library 28227

Dunajská Streda

Slovakian National Gallery, Villa Vermes, Gorkého 2, 929 01 Dunajská Streda - T: (0709) 22169
Public Gallery 28228

Žitnoostrovské Múzeum, Malinovského 22, 929 01 Dunajská Streda - T: (0709) 22402
Local Museum
Local hist 28229

Filakovo

Městské Múzeum Filakovo, Hlavná ul 14, 986 01 Filakovo - T: (0863) 82619
Local Museum 28230

Novohradské Múzeum, Zápotockého 14, 986 01 Filakovo
Local Museum
Local history 28231

Galanta

Vlastivedné Múzeum v Galante, Hlavná 976/8, 924 00 Galanta - T: (031) 7805535, Fax: 7805535, E-mail: muzeumgalanta@ba.telecom.sk. Head: Jozef Keppert
Local Museum
Local history, ethnology, archeology 28232

Gelnica

Banícke Múzeum (Mining Museum), Banícke nám 6, 056 01 Gelnica
Science&Tech Museum - 1938
Mineralogy, mining history and technology, local history 28233

Hlohovec

Vlastivedné Múzeum v Hlohovci, Komenského 15, 920 01 Hlohovec - T: (07) 300337, Fax: 300337, E-mail: vmh@slovanet.sk. Head: Ivan Pastorek
Local Museum - 1959
Natural sciences, history 28234

Holíč

Slovakian National Museum, Hrad, 908 51 Holíč - T: (0801) 2139
Local Museum 28235

Humenné

Okresné Vlastivedné Múzeum (Museum of National History), Slobody nám 8, 066 01 Humenné - T: (0933) 2240. Head: Ján Lukáč
Historical Museum - 1960
Ethnography, folk art, in a 17th c Renaissance palace 28236

Ilava

Městské Múzeum, Ružová, 019 01 Ilava - T: (0827) 65198. Head: Dr. Teodor Kohút
Local Museum
Local history 28237

Kežmarok

Museum of Home Décor, Múzeum v Kežmarku, Hlavne nám 55, 060 01 Kežmarok - T: (0968) 2906. Head: Stanislav Gaborčík
Decorative Arts Museum 28238

Múzeum v Kežmarku (Museum of Kežmarok), Hradné nám 42, 060 01 Kežmarok - T: (0968) 4522618, Fax: 4523526, E-mail: muzeum@nextra.sk. Head: Stanislav Gaborčík
Local Museum - 1928
Archeology, art hist, ethnography, hist, literary hist, numismatics 28239

Podtatranské Muzeum → Múzeum v Kežmarku

Komárno

Podunajské Múzeum (Danubian Museum), ul Palatínova 13, 94501 Komárno - T: (035) 7731476, Fax: 7731476. Head: Jozef Csütörtöky
Local Museum - 1886
Natural hist of the area, hist of the town Komárno, archeology (roman and celtic coll), culture of the Hungarian minority in Slovakia, Hungarian artists in Slovakia 28240

Košice

Galéria J. Jakobyha, Hlavná 72, 040 01 Košice - T: (095) 6221187
Fine Arts Museum 28241

Slovenské Technické Múzeum (Slovak Technical Museum), ul Hlavná 88, 043 82 Košice - T: (055) 6223665, Fax: 6225965, E-mail: labanic@stm-ke.skstm-ke@stm-ke.sk, Internet: http://www.stm-ke.sk. Head: Eugen Labanič
Science&Tech Museum - 1947
Aviation, railway, communications, cinematography, photography, metallurgy, physics, astronomy, mining, cartography, geodesy, motors, transport 28242

Východoslovenské Múzeum (Museum of Eastern Slovakia), Hviezdoslavova 3, 041 36 Košice - T: (095) 6220309, Fax: 6228696, E-mail: vsmuz@stonline.sk, Internet: http://www.kosice.sk. Head: Dr. Róbert Pollák
Local Museum - 1872
History, hist of art, zoology, botany, geology, archeology, ethnography, religious art - library 28243

Kremnica

NBS-Múzeum Mincí a Medailí (Museums of Coins and Medals), Štefánikovo nám 10, 967 01 Kremnica - T: (0857) 6742121, Fax: 6742121, Internet: http://www.nbs.sk. Head: Mariana Novotná
Special Museum - 1889
Local hist, numismatics, coins, struck and cast medals, Town castle 28244

Krompachy

Múzeum Krompachy, Dru Stevná 4, 053 42 Krompachy - T: (0965) 972533
Local Museum 28245

Krupina

Múzeum, 963 01 Krupina
Local Museum
Local history 28246

Levice

Tekovské Muzeum, ul Velkého Októbra, 934 01 Levice - T: (0813) 21589
Natural History Museum / Historical Museum / Archaeological Museum / Ethnology Museum - 1927
Natural sciences, history, archeology, numismatics, art hist, ethnography 28247

Levoča

Museum of Special Educational System, nám Majstra Pavla 28, 054 01 Levoča - T: (0966) 2863
Special Museum 28248

Spišské Múzeum, nám Majstra Pavla 40, 054 01 Levoča - T: (053) 4512786, Fax: 4512824, E-mail: muzeumle@isternet.sk. Head: Dr. Mária Novotná
Local Museum / Historical Museum - 1884
Local hist, arms, guild relics, religious art, art history, ethnography - library, archives 28249

Liptovský Hrádok

Národopisné Múzeum Liptova (Ethnographical Museum of Liptov), 033 01 Liptovský Hrádok - T: (0844) 222485. Head: Dr. Iveta Zuskinová
Ethnology Museum - 1958
Costumes, agriculture, alpine farming, wooden objects, folklore, in an 18th c former courthouse, folk art - open-air museum Pribylina 28250

Liptovský Mikuláš

Janošík Prison Museum, Palúdzka, 031 01 Liptovský Mikuláš - T: (0849) 22061
Special Museum 28251

Múzeum Janka Krála, nám Osvoboditelov 31, 031 01 Liptovský Mikuláš - T: (0849) 22554. Head: Dr. Elena Medzihradská
Historical Museum - 1955
History of literature, books 28252

Oblastná Galéria P.M. Bohúňa (District Art Gallery), Tranovského 3, 031 01 Liptovský Mikuláš - T: (0849) 3158
Fine Arts Museum
Medieval, national and modern art, applied arts 28253

Slovenské Múzeum Ochrany Prírody a Jaskyniarstva (Slovak Museum of Nature Protection and Speleology), Školská 4, 031 01 Liptovský Mikuláš - T: (044) 5522061, Fax: 5514381, E-mail: smopaj@smopaj.sk. Head: Dana Šubová
Natural History Museum - 1904
Minerals, rock formations, speleothems, paleonthologic and archeological finds from caves, memories of nature protection and speleology in Slovakia 28254

Lučenec

Novohradská Galéria, Kubinyiho nám č 3, 984 01 Lučenec - T: (0863) 4332501
Fine Arts Museum 28255

Novohradské Múzeum, Kubínyiho nám 3, 984 01 Lučenec - T: (0863) 4332502, Fax: 4332980. Head: Iveta Kaczarová
Decorative Arts Museum - 1954
Pottery, glass 28256

Malacky

Městské Múzeum Michala Tillnera, Družstevná 12, 901 01 Malacky - T: (0703) 7722155, Fax: 7722110. Head: Dr. Rudolf Irša
Local Museum
Local hist 28257

Markušovce

Nábytkové Muzeum (Furniture Museum), Letohrádok Dardanely, 053 21 Markušovce - T: (0965) 98212. Head: Dr. Ladislav Spalek
Decorative Arts Museum / Music Museum - 1959
Furniture, living style of Eastern Slovakia, especially of the Spiš area, portraits, painting, decorative art, porcelain, glass, wall paintings, in a 17th c Renaissance palace, music instruments - music museums 28258

Martin

Etnografické Múzeum, Slovenské Národné Múzeum (Ethnographic Museum of the Slovak National Museum), Malá Hora 2, 036 80 Martin - T: (0842) 4131011/12, Fax: 4220290, E-mail: snm-eem@bb.telecom.sk. Head: Dr. Mária Halmová
Ethnology Museum - 1893
Ethnology, agriculture and shepherd's objects, handicraft, costumes, folk art, decorative arts, cultural and national history, archeology - library, open air museum 28259

Martin Benka Museum, Kuzmanyho 34, 036 01 Martin - T: (0842) 4131390, E-mail: snm-em@bb.telecom.sk
Local Museum 28260

Museum of the Slovakian Village, Jahodnícke háje, 036 01 Martin - T: (0842) 4139491, Fax: 4132683, E-mail: snm-em@bb.telecom.sk
Local Museum 28261

Slovenské Národné Literárne Múzeum, Slovenská Narodná Knižnica (Slovak National Literary Museum of the Slovak National Library), Mudroňova 35, 036 01 Martin - T: (043) 4134036, 4134152, Fax: 4134036, E-mail: snlm@snk.sk, Internet: http://www.snk.sk. Head: Jozef Benovsky
Special Museum
History of Slovakian literature 28262

Turčanska Gallery, Daxnerova, 036 01 Martin - T: (0842) 30427
Local Museum 28263

Turčianske Múzeum Andreja Kmeta (Museum of Andrej Kmet), Kmet'ova 20, 036 01 Martin - T: (0842) 30639. Head: Dr. Jozef Mlynarčík
Natural History Museum - 1964
Natural sciences, history, memorabilia of A. Kmet, Slovakian museologist 28264

Medzilaborce

Warhol Family Museum of Modern Art, ul Andy Warhola 749, 068 01 Medzilaborce - T: (0939) 21059, Fax: 21069. Head: Nataša Hrisenková
Fine Arts Museum - 1991
Paintings of Andy Warhol, paintings of Paul Warhol, Ruthenian contemporary art, paintings of Ultra Violet - library, archive 28265

Michalovice

Zemplińske Múzeum, Kostolná nám 1, 071 01 Michalovice - T: (0946) 21335, Fax: 31086. Head: Dr. Lýdia Gačková
Local Museum - 1957
Fauna, archeology, art, religious objects, ethnography, hist of pottery, wine making 28266

Modra

Muzeum Ludovita Štúra, Štúrova ul 54, 900 01 Modra - T: (0704) 922765, Fax: 92244. Head: Olga Pavúková
Special Museum
Memorabilia of the writer Ludovit Štúr (1815-1856), literary history 28267

Modrý Kameń

Múzeum Bábkarských Kultúr a Hračiek Hrad Modry Kameň, Zámocká 1, 992 01 Modrý Kameń - T: (0854) 4870194. Head: Dr. Vladimír Siváček
Special Museum
Toys and puppets, local hist 28268

Myjava

Múzeum Slovenských Národných Rád, Slovenského Národného Múzea (Museum of the Slovak National Councils), 907 01 Myjava - T: (0802) 902256. Head: Blanka Landová

Historical Museum - 1968
History of the Slovak National Councils, history and etnography of the Myjava region - library, laboratory 28269

Námestovo

Oravská galéria (Orava Gallery), Slanicky ostrov, 029 01 Námestovo - T: (043) 5522401, E-mail: ogaleria@nextra.sk, Internet: http://www.oravskagaleria.sk. Head: Eva Luptáková
Fine Arts Museum 28270

Nitra

Misijné Múzeum Nitra, ul Na Kalvarii, 950 50 Nitra - T: (087) 416928, 417797
Local Museum 28271

Ponitrianske Múzeum, Štefánikova 1, 949 01 Nitra - T: (087) 514253. Head: Anton Števko
Local Museum - 1886
Local hist, zoology, botany 28272

Slovenské Polnohospodárske Múzeum (Slovenian Agricultural Museum), 949 01 Nitra
Agriculture Museum - 1960
Development of farming in Slovakia, animal husbandry, vegetable growing, farm implements, agricultural machinery, apiculture, in a 17th c cloister 28273

Nová Baňa

Pohronské Múzeum v Novej Bani, Bernolákova 2, 968 01 Nová Baňa - T: (0858) 6855178, Fax: 6855178. Head: Gejza Trgina
Local Museum 28274

Nové Mesto nad Váhom

Podjavorinské Muzeum, nám Slobody 10, 915 01 Nové Mesto nad Váhom
Natural History Museum / Historical Museum / Ethnology Museum - 1930
Natural sciences, history, ethnography, in an 18th c baroque building 28275

Nové Zámky

Vlastivedné Múzeum (Home Knowledge Museum), Pribinova 5, 940 01 Nové Zámky - T: (0817) 27845, Fax: 27845. Head: Štefan Vida
Archaeological Museum / Fine Arts Museum / Ethnology Museum - 1935
Archeology, art hist, numismatics, ethnography 28276

Oščadnica

Kysuce Gallery, Hrad, 023 01 Oščadnica - T: (0824) 21386
Public Gallery 28277

Pezinok

Malokarpatské Vinohradnicke Múzeum (Little Carpathian Vine-Growing Museum), ul M.R. Štefánika 4, 902 01 Pezinok - T: (0704) 3347. Head: Hana Dolská
Agriculture Museum - 1960
Vine-growing exhibits, housed in a 16th c building 28278

Slowakische Nationalgalerie, Cajlanská 255, 902 01 Pezinok - T: (0704) 6404035
Public Gallery 28279

Pieštany

Balneologické Múzeum (Balneological Museum), Bethovenova 5, 921 01 Pieštany - T: (033) 7722875, Fax: 7722875, Internet: http://www.balneomuzeum.sk. Head: Dr. Vladimír Krupa
Special Museum - 1933
Archeological finds, numismatics, medical equipment from the bequest of the first bath physician Dr F. Scherer, ethnography, stained glass, wood sculptures, embroidery, natural history, balneology, history of Slovakian bath 28280

Poltár

Městské Múzeum Poltár, ul Dryby 43, 987 01 Poltár - T: (095) 6223073
Local Museum 28281

Poprad

Podtatranské Múzeum, Vajanského 72, 058 00 Poprad - T: (092) 721868, 721924, E-mail: muzeumpp@isternet.sk. Head: Dr. Peter Roth
Local Museum - 1876
Natural sciences, archeology, history, numismatics, geology, mineralogy, paleontology, botany, zoology, ethnology 28282

Tatranská Galéria, Alžbetina 30, 058 01 Poprad - T: (092) 65315, Fax: 721670. Head: Dr. Anna Ondrušeková
Fine Arts Museum - 1960
photography section 28283

Považská Bystrica

Local Museum, Kaštiel Orlové, 017 01 Považská Bystrica - T: (0822) 25718
Local Museum 28284

Prešov

Šarišská Galéria (Gallery of Šariš), Hlavná 51, 080 01 Prešov - T: (091) 725423, Fax: 734038. Head: Marta Hrebíčková
Fine Arts Museum - 1956
Art 28285

Vlastivedné Múzeum, Hlavná 86, 080 01 Prešov - T: (091) 34708. Head: Dr. Ján Ordoš
Local Museum - 1945
Geology, botany, zoology, ecological units, marine birds, archeology, Celtic and Slavic economic history, local history, in a Renaissance house 28286

Rajec

Městské Múzeum Rajec, nám SNP 15, 015 01 Rajec - T: (0823) 422198, 422067
Local Museum 28287

Rimavská Sobota

Gemersko-Malohontské Múzeum, nám Mihálya Tompu 24, 979 01 Rimavská Sobota - T: (0866) 5622944, Fax: 5621387. Head: Svetlana Bornayová
Local Museum - 1882
Archaeology, regional ceramics, Egyptian mumy, numismatics, ethnology, hist, natural hist, burial urns of the Baden Culture, crafts - library, archives 28288

Rožňava

Banicke Múzeum (Mining Museum), Šafárikova 31, 048 01 Rožňava - T: (0942) 23710. Head: Jozef Csobádi
Science&Tech Museum - 1902/1944/1956
Medieval mining technology, mining equipment, local history, geology, speleology 28289

Ružomberok

Liptovské Muzeum, nám Š.N. Hýroša, 034 50 Ružomberok. Head: Dr. Ladislav Cserei
Local Museum - 1912
Geology, mineralogy, botany, zoology, history, ethnography, costumes, art, local history 28290

Nationalny Galeria, Makovického 1, 034 50 Ružomberok - T: (0848) 24868
Public Gallery 28291

Sabinov

Městské Muzeum, nám Slobody 100, 083 01 Sabinov - T: (0934) 3413
Local Museum - 1954
Natural science, archeology, history, ethnography 28292

Šahy

Múzeum a Galéria Hont Šahy, ul J. Rotaridesa 13, 936 91 Šahy - T: (0812) 2230, 2365
Local Museum / Fine Arts Museum 28293

Senica

L. Novomeský Museum, Sadova, 905 01 Senica - T: (0802) 3080
Local Museum 28294

Skalica

Záhorské muzeum, nám Slobody 13, 909 01 Skalica - T: (034) 6644230, Fax: 6644230, E-mail: zahorskemuzeum@zahorskemuzeum.sk, Internet: http://www.zahorskemuzeum.sk. Head: Viera Drahošova
Local Museum - 1905
Folklore Art, archeology, history, ethnography, costumes, ceramics 28295

Smižany

Regional Ethnographic Museum, Krátka 5, 053 11 Smižany - T: (0965) 31291
Local Museum 28296

Sobotište

Múzeum Samuela Jurkovia Sobotište, 906 05 Sobotište - T: (0802) 82102, Fax: 82232
Special Museum 28297

Spišská Béla

Múzeum Michala Greisigera, Hviezdoslavova 21, 085 01 Spišská Béla - T: (0969) 91322, Fax: 91443
Local Museum
Local history 28298

Oddelenie Technické Múzeum Košice, J.M. Petzval dům, 059 01 Spišská Béla - T: (0968) 91307. Head: Antónia Rončkevičová
Science&Tech Museum
Development of optical sciences, memorabilia on the optician and photograph Johann Petzval (1807-1891) in his birth house 28299

Spišská Nová Ves

Museum Spiša (Museum of Spiš), Letná 50, 052 01 Spišská Nová Ves - T: (0965) 4423757, Fax: 4426785, E-mail: muzspisa@spisnet.sk. Head: Dr. Ladislav Spalek
Local Museum - 1951
Local history, natural history 28300

Stará Lubovňa

Gallery of Plastic Arts, Hrad, 064 01 Stará Lubovňa - T: (0962) 22422
Public Gallery 28301

Okresné Vlastivedné Múzeum (District Motherland Museum at Stará Lubovňa), Hrad, Zamocká 20, 064 01 Stará Lubovňa - T: (0963) 22422, Fax: 22302. Head: Rudolf Žiak
Local Museum - 1956
Local history, art, ethnography, crafts, sacral art, in a 17th castle 28302

Stupava

Múzeum Ferdiša Kostku, ul F. Kostku 25, 900 31 Stupava - T: (07) 934882. Head: Magda Kostková
Fine Arts Museum - 1968
Memorabilia of the artist Fertiš Kostka in his birth house, his old ceramic atelier 28303

Svätý Anton

Múzeum vo Sv. Antone, Kaštiel, 969 72 Svätý Anton - T: (045) 6913932, 6921954, Fax: 6921955, E-mail: manton3@stonline.sk. Head: Marian Číž
Local Museum - 1954
Historical interior of Mansion, original furniture, paintings, graphics, hunting trophies, zoology 28304

Svätý Jur

Vlastivedné a Literárne Múzeum, Letohradská 16, 900 21 Svätý Jur - T: (07) 44971204, 44970476. Head: Beata Vlasáková
Special Museum - 1952
Memorabilia of the writer Peter Jilemnický (1901-1949) in his own home, town hist 28305

Svidník

Dukelské Múzeum, 089 01 Svidník - T: (0937) 21398. Head: Dr. Jozef Rodák
Military Museum - 1965
Memorial to the Battle of Dukla, commemorative lay-out of the Dukla battlefield as an open air military reservation, firing posts, headquarters, restored bunkers - library 28306

Múzeum Ukrajinsko-Rusínskej Kultúry (Museum of Ukrainian-Ruthenian Culture), Centrálna 258, 089 01 Svidník - T: (0937) 7521365, Fax: 7521569, E-mail: murk@bj.psg.sk. Head: Dr. Miróslav Sopóliga
Ethnology Museum - 1956
Historical coll: social and political struggle of the Ukrainian - Ruthenian of Eastern Slovakia, Ethnographical coll: folk art, costumes, crafts, Icon coll: 'The Day of Judgement' (three panel paintings), icons from Slovakia 28307

Tajov

Jozef Gregor Tajovský Memorial House, 976 34 Tajov - T: (088) 9742
Local Museum 28308

Tatranská Lomnica

Múzeum Tatranského Národného Parku (Museum of Tatra National Park), 059 60 Tatranská Lomnica - T: (0969) 4467951, Fax: 4467958, E-mail: zamecnik@vstanap.sk. Head: Mikulas Michalčik
Natural History Museum - 1957
Geology, botany, zoology, history, mountain tourism, recreation and sport, ethnography, plant coll of vascular plants, lichens, mosses and historical coll from the 19th c, coll of endangered animals - library, archives, photoarchive, botanical garden 28309

Topolčany

Vlastivedné Muzeum, ul D. Jurkoviča, 955 01 Topolčany - T: (0815) 23253. Head: Dr. Blažena Smotláková
Local Museum - 1961
Anthropology, numismatics, history 28310

Trenčín

Trenčianske Múzeum, Mierové nám 46, 911 00 Trenčín - T: (0831) 35589. Head: Ferdinand Brunovský
Local Museum - 1877
Natural sciences, archeology, Roman and Slavic relics, local history, Turkish items, decorative art, crafts, Holuby and Brančik coll of insects and plants, in a 17th c baroque castle - library 28311

Trnava

Západoslovenské Múzeum v Trnave (Westslovakian Museum in Trnava), Muzejné nám 3, 918 09 Trnava - T: (033) 5512913/4, Fax: 5512911, E-mail: zsm@tt.sknet.sk. Head: Dr. Tibor Díte
Local Museum - 1954
Natural sciences, archeology, ethnography, numismatics, history, Š.C. Parrák's ceramic coll, East Asian relics, Samurai armaments, coll of the Tokyo Imperial Foundry, Slovak bells coll, M. Schneider-Trnavský's inheritance, book plates, dobro, books - library 28312

Tvrdošín

Gáleria Marie Medvedckej, Oravská galéria (Orava Gallery), Medvedzie 1/1, 029 01 Tvrdošín - T: (0846) 5322793, E-mail: ogaleria@nextra.sk, Internet: http://www.oravskagaleria.sk
Fine Arts Museum
Paintings of Maria Medvedcka 28313

Uhrovec

Local Museum L. Štúra, 956 41 Uhrovec - T: (0832) 94247
Local Museum 28314

Ždiar

Múzeum, 059 55 Ždiar
Ethnology Museum / Folklore Museum
Ethnography, folk art 28315

Žilina

Považské Múzeum (Museum of the Považie Region), Budatín, 010 03 Žilina - T: (041) 5001511, Fax: 5001512, E-mail: muzeum@psgnetza.sk. Head: Dr. Marián Mrva
Local Museum / Special Museum - 1942
Zoology, botany, geology, archeology and hist of Northwest Slovakia, ethnology, hist of transport, hist of the tinker's trade 28316

Zlaté Moravce

Městské Múzeum, nám Osvoboditelov 1, 953 01 Zlaté Moravce
Local Museum - 1896
Natural science, archeology, history 28317

Zvolen

Lesnícke a Drevárske Múzeum, 960 01 Zvolen - T: (0855) 5321886, Fax: 5320649, E-mail: muzeum@ldmzvolen.sk, Internet: http://www.ldmzvolen.sk. Head: Želmíra Šípková
Special Museum - 1942
Archaeology, numismatics, art hist, ethnography, forestry 28318

Slovenská Národná Galéria, Nam SNP, Zámek, 960 01 Zvolen - T: (0855) 24311
Public Gallery 28319

Slovenia

Ajdovščina

Pilonova Galerija (Pilon Gallery), Prešernova 3, 5270 Ajdovščina - T: (05) 3661131, Fax: 3661131, E-mail: pilonova.galerija@siol.net. Head: Irene Mislej
Fine Arts Museum - 1974
Art works by the painter and photograph Veno Pilon (1896-1970), international art colony Vipavski Križ, drawings by France Mihelič - archives 28320

Begunje na Gorenjskem

Muzeji Radovljiške Občine (Memorial Museum of Hostages), Begunje 55, 4275 Begunje na Gorenjskem, mail addr: Linhartov Trg 1, 4240 Radovljica - T: (04) 5333790, 5320520, Fax: 5320524, E-mail: muzeji.radovljiske.obcine@siol.net. Head: Verena Štekar Vidic
Historical Museum - 1960
Exhibits on Gorenjsko hostages in World War II 28321

Bled

Muzej na Blejskem Gradu (Museum in The Bled Castle), 4260 Bled - T: (04) 5741230, Fax: 5741230, E-mail: info@dzt.bled.si, Internet: http://www.bled.si. Head: Mirko Ulčar
Historical Museum
11th-19th c local history, weapons 28322

Bohinjska Bistrica

Muzej Tomaža Godca, Gorenjski Muzej Kranj (Museum of Alpine Farming), Zoisova 1, 4264 Bohinjska Bistrica - T: (04) 5721763, Fax: 2013951, E-mail: info@gorenjski-muzej.si, Internet: http://www.gorenjski-muzej.si. Head: Barbara Ravnik Toman
Archaeological Museum / Special Museum / Historical Museum / Military Museum - 1979
Archeological exhibition, war-museum of the Isonzo front 1915 - 1917, leather-tanning exhibition 28323

Bohinjsko Jezero

Planšarski Muzej, Gorenjski Muzej (Museum of Alpine Farming), Stara Fužina 181, 4265 Bohinjsko Jezero, mail addr: Tomšičeva 44, 4000 Jezero Kranj - T: (04) 5723095, Fax: 2013951, E-mail: info@gorenjski-muzej.si, Internet: http://www.gorenjski-muzej.si. Head: Barbara Ravnik Toman
Agriculture Museum - 1971
Cheese manufactory 28324

Brežice

Posavski Muzej Brežice (Posavje Museum), Cesta Prvih Borcev 1, 8250 Brežice, mail addr: P.P. 5, 8250 Brežice - T: (07) 4961271, Fax: 4961271, E-mail: Ivan.Kastelic@quest.arnes.si, Internet: http://www.posavski-muzej.si. Head: Tomaž Teropšić
Archaeological Museum / Ethnology Museum / Historical Museum - 1949
Archaeology, ethnography, hist, Baroque art, relics on the peasant revolt in 1573 and National Liberation War (1941-1945) - library 28325

Celje

Muzej Novejše Zgodovine Celje (Museum of Recent History Celje), Prešernova ul 17, 3000 Celje - T: (03) 4286410, Fax: 4286411, E-mail: mnzc@guest.arnes.si, Internet: http://www2.arnes.si/~cemnzc. Head: Prof. Marija Počivavšek
Historical Museum - 1963
Life in Celje 1900-2000, coll of Slovene dental surgery, Josip Pelican's Photographic studio - Children's museum 28326

Pokrajinski Muzej Celje (Regional MuseumCelje), Muzejski trg 1, 3000 Celje - T: (03) 5442633, Fax: 5443384, E-mail: info@pokmuz-ce.si, Internet: http://www2.arnes.si/~pokmuzce/index1.htm. Head: Darja Pirkmajer
Local Museum - 1882
Archaeology, ethnology, fine and decorative arts, numismatics - library, Šempeter (Roman Necropolis), Rifnik (Archaeological Park) 28327

Idrija

Mestni Muzej Idrija (Idrija Municipal Museum), Ul Prelovčeva 9, 5280 Idrija - T: (05) 3726600, Fax: 3773580, E-mail: tajnistvo@muzej-idrija-cerkno.si, Internet: http://www.muzej-idrija-cerkno.si. Head: Ivana Leskovec
Local Museum - 1953
Gewerkenegg castle; hist of the mercury mine and the town of Idrija; mine pumping device; miners house; partisan printing house and Franja partisan hospital; birth house of the writer France Bevk 28328

Jesenice

Muzej Jesenice, Prešernova 45, 4270 Jesenice. Head: Nataša Kokošinek
Local Museum / Science&Tech Museum - 1992
Hist of mining and railroads, labour movement, hist, coll of fossils - archive 28329

Kamnik

Kamniški Muzej (Kamnik Museum), Muzejski Pot 3, 1240 Kamnik - T: (01) 8391313. Head: Mirina Zupančič
Local Museum
Archaeology, ethnography, furniture, history 28330

Kobarid

Kobariški Muzej (Kobarid Museum), Gregorciceva ul 10, 5222 Kobarid - T: (05) 3885055, Fax: 3885055. Head: Jože Šerbec
Historical Museum - 1990
Memorabilia of the battle of Kobarid in October 1917 28331

Kočevje

Pokrajinski Muzej (Provincial Museum), Ul Prešernova 11, 1330 Kočevje - T: (01) 8955114, 8950330, Fax: 8950305, E-mail: muzej@pmk-kocevje.si. Head: Ivan Kordiš
Local Museum - 1953
Dept. of ethnography, archaeology, movement and history of revolution, art - library 28332

Koper

Obalne Galerije - Galerija Loža, Trg Titov 1, 6000 Koper - T: (05) 6274837, E-mail: galerijameduza@guest.arnes.si. Head: Toni Biloslav
Public Gallery / Fine Arts Museum
Sculpture and paintings by regional artists 28333

Pokrajinski Muzej Koper (Koper Regional Museum), Ul Kidričeva 19, 6000 Koper - T: (05) 6271364, Fax: 6276484. Head: Salvator Zitko
Local Museum - 1911
Ethnography, art, labour movement, hist - lapidarium, memorial room of G. Tartini 28334

Kostanjevica na Krki

Galerija Božidar Jakac, Grajska Cesta 45, 8311 Kostanjevica na Krki - T: (07) 4987008, Fax: 4987335, E-mail: info@galerija-bj.si, Internet: http://www.galerija-bj.si. Head: Bojanj Božič
Fine Arts Museum 28335

Kranj

Galerija Mestne Hiše (Town Hall Art Gallery), Glavni trg 4, 4000 Kranj - T: (04) 2013950, Fax: 2013951, E-mail: info@gorenjski-muzej.si, Internet: http://www.gorenjski-muzej.si. Head: Barbara Ravnik Toman
Fine Arts Museum - 1963 28336

Gorenjski Muzej Kranj, Glavni trg 4, 4000 Kranj - T: (04) 2013950, Fax: 2013951, E-mail: info@gorenjski-.muzej.si, Internet: http://www.gorenjski-muzej.si. Head: Barbara Ravnik Toman
Fine Arts Museum / Archaeological Museum / Decorative Arts Museum / Folklore Museum - 1963
Gallery of works by the sculptor Alojz Dolinar, archaeological coll, painted furniture, folk art - library, photo-archive 28337

Prešernov Spominski Muzej (Memorial Museum of France Prešeren), Prešernova 7, 4000 Kranj - T: (04) 2013950, Fax: 2013951, E-mail: inf@gorenjski-muzej.si, Internet: http://www.gorenjski-muzej.si. Head: Barbara Ravnik Toman
Special Museum - 1963
Literary and art hist, memorabilia on the Slovenian poet France Prešeren 28338

Kropa

Muzeji RadovlJiške Občine (Iron Forging Museum), Kropa 10, 4245 Kropa - T: (04) 5336717, Fax: 5315049. Head: Verena Štekar Vidic
Science&Tech Museum - 1952
Iron forging items, artistic smiths of Kropa, presentation of making hand made nails 28339

Laško

Muzejska Zbirka Laško (Laško Museum Collection), Askercev trg 4, 3270 Laško. Head: Jože Majcen
Local Museum
Ethnography, history of the city 28340

Ljubljana

Arhitekturni Muzej Ljubljana, Karunova 4, 1000 Ljubljana - T: (01) 2513008. Head: Peter Krečič
Fine Arts Museum 28341

Cankarjev Dom, Kidričev Park 1, 1000 Ljubljana - T: (01) 2521121, Fax: 2524279. Head: Mitja Rotovnik
Historical Museum 28342

Galerija Škuc, Stari trg 21, 1000 Ljubljana - T: (01) 2516540, 4213140, Fax: 2516540, E-mail: galerija.skuc@guest.arnes.si, Internet: galerija.skuc-drustvo.si. Head: Joško Pajer
Public Gallery 28343

Mala Galerija (The Small Galery), Slovenska 35, 1000 Ljubljana - T: (01) 2416800, Fax: 2514120, E-mail: info@mg-lj.si, Internet: http://www.mg-lj.si. Head: Zdenka Badovinac
Public Gallery 28344

Meðunarodni Grafični Likovni Centar (International Center of Graphic Arts), Pod turnom 3, 1000 Ljubljana - T: (01) 2413800, Fax: 2413821, E-mail: info@mglc-lj.si. Head: Lilijana Stepančič
Public Gallery / Fine Arts Museum - 1986
Contemporary and modern prints and artist's books - print workshop 28345

Mestna Galerija Ljubljana (City Art Museum), Mestni trg 5, 1000 Ljubljana - T: (01) 2411770, Fax: 2411782, E-mail: mestna.galerija-lj@siol.net, Internet: http://www.mestna-galerija.si. Head: Aleksander Bassin
Fine Arts Museum
Contemporary art, ceramics, book illustrations, posters 28346

Mestni Muzej Ljubljana, Gosposka 15, 1000 Ljubljana - T: (01) 2522930, Fax: 2522946, E-mail: tajnistvo@mm.lj.si, Internet: http://www.mm-lj.si. Head: Taja Čepič
Local Museum / Decorative Arts Museum / Archaeological Museum / Historical Museum - 1935
Furniture, arts and crafts, local topography, militaria, archaeology, finds from Celtic-Illyrian and Roman periods 28347

Moderna Galerija (Museum of Modern Art), Tomšičeva 14, 1000 Ljubljana, mail addr: P.P. 265, 1001 Ljubljana - T: (01) 2514101, Fax: 2514120, E-mail: info@mg-lj.si, Internet: http://www.mg-lj.si. Head: Zdenka Badovinac
Fine Arts Museum / Public Gallery - 1948
20th c Slovenian and international art - library, archive 28348

Muzej Novejše Zgodovine Slovenije (National Museum of Contemporary History), Celovška cesta 23, 1000 Ljubljana - T: (01) 3009610, Fax: 4338244, E-mail: uprava@muzej-nz.si, Internet: http://www.muzej-nz.si. Head: Marjeta Mikuž
Historical Museum - 1948
Arms, uniforms and medals of partisans and occupying armies, history of resistance movement 1941-45, documents, collections of both world wars, photographs, works of art 28349

Narodna Galerija (National Gallery of Slovenia), Puharjeva 9, 1000 Ljubljana, mail addr: P.P. 432, 1001 Ljubljana - T: (01) 2415434, Fax: 2415403, E-mail: info@ng-slo.si, Internet: http://www.ng-slo.si. Head: Dr. Andrej Smrekar
Fine Arts Museum - 1918
Paintings and sculpture (13th to 19th c), medieval frescoes, Slovenian impressionist art (18th to 20th c), Slovenian graphics, photographies, documents - library 28350

Narodni Muzej Slovenije (National Museum of Slovenia), Prešernova 20, 1000 Ljubljana, mail addr: P.P. 529-X, 1000 Ljubljana - T: (01) 2414400, Fax: 2414422, E-mail: kos.peter@narmuz-lj.si, Internet: http://www.narmuz-lj.si. Head: Dr. Peter Kos
Historical Museum / Archaeological Museum / Decorative Arts Museum / Fine Arts Museum - 1821
Prehistoric archaeological finds, applied art, history, numismatics, graphic arts, early Slavic material, relief of the Battle of Sisak against the Turks, Balkan coins - library 28351

Pharmaceutical and Medical Museum of Bohuslav Lavička, LEK, Verovškova 57, 1000 Ljubljana - T: (01) 5340161
Special Museum 28352

Pivovarski Muzej (Brewery Museum), Pivovarniška ul 2, 1000 Ljubljana - T: (01) 4717340, Fax: 4717344, E-mail: Pivovarski.muzej@pivo-union.si, Internet: http://www.pivo-union.si. Head: Helena Jenko
Science&Tech Museum 28353

Prirodoslovni Muzej Slovenije (Slovenian Museum of Natural History), Prešernova 20, 1000 Ljubljana, mail addr: P.P. 290, 1000 Ljubljana - T: (01) 2410944, Fax: 2410953, E-mail: biblioteka@pms-lj.si, Internet: http://www2.pms-lj.si. Head: Dr. Bredaa Činč-Juhant
Natural History Museum - 1821
Botany, entomology, herpetology, coll of minerals, herbaria, coll. of mammals, paleontology - library, audio-visual dept 28354

Slovenski Etnografski Muzej (Slovene Ethnographic Museum), Metelkova 2, 1000 Ljubljana - T: (01) 4343235, Fax: 4325377, E-mail: etnomuz@etno-muzej.si, Internet: http://www.etno-muzej.si. Head: Inja Smerdel
Ethnology Museum - 1923
Slovenian and non-european ethnography, cultural history, crafts 28355

Slovenski Gledališki Muzej (Slovenian Theatre Museum), Ul Cankarjeva 11, 1000 Ljubljana - T: (01) 2510142. Head: Bojan Kavčič
Performing Arts Museum
Theater, textbooks, manuscripts, programs, costumes, scenery 28356

Slovenski Šolski Muzej (Slovenian School Museum), Plečnikov trg 1, 1000 Ljubljana - T: (01) 2513024, Fax: 2513024, E-mail: Solski.muzej@Guest.ARnes.si, Internet: http://www.ssolski-muzej.si. Head: Branko Šuštar
Historical Museum - 1938
School and education in present time - library 28357

Tehniški Muzej Slovenije (Technical Museum of Slovenia), Parmova 33, 1000 Ljubljana, mail addr: P.P. 3525, 1001 Ljubljana - T: (01) 4361606, 4362269, Fax: 4361606, E-mail: orest.jarh@tms.si, Internet: http://www.tms.si. Head: Dr. Orest Jarh
Science&Tech Museum - 1953
Forestry and wood technology, hunting, smithwork, textiles, transportations, electrotechnology, fishing, agricultural technology, post and telecommunications, wheatmill, horsemill, veneer workshop, sawmill 28358

Tobačni Muzej (Tobacco Museum), c/o Mestni Muzej Ljubljana, Gosposka 15, 1000 Ljubljana - T: (01) 2522930, Fax: 2522946, E-mail: tajnistvo@mm-lj.si. Head: Taja Čepič
Agriculture Museum - 1992 28359

Zemljepišni Muzej Slovenije (Geographical Museum of Slovenia), Trg Francoske Revolucije 7, 1000 Ljubljana - T: (01) 2513458. Head: Rado Genorio
Special Museum - 1946
Maps, geography of Slovenia 28360

Zgodovinski Arhiv i Muzej Univerze v Ljubljani (Historical Archive and University Museum of Ljubljana), Kongresni trg 12, 1000 Ljubljana - T: (01) 4254055, E-mail: joze.ciperle@uni-lj.si, Internet: http://www.uni-lj.si
University Museum / Historical Museum 28361

Maribor

Muzej Narodne Osvobodite (Maribor National Liberation Museum), Ul Heroja Tomšiča 5, 2000 Maribor - T: (02) 2511671, Fax: 2527394. Head: Dr. Marjan Žnidarič
Historical Museum - 1958
National Liberation War (1941-1945), documents, photographs, publications of the Partisan Movement, hist of Maribor, memorial material from 1918-91, scouts and woodcrafts, falcons and eagles in Slovenia - archives 28362

Pokrajinski Muzej (Regional Museum), Grajska ul 2, 2000 Maribor - T: (02) 2511851, Fax: 2527777. Head: Vili Vuk
Local Museum - 1903
Local hist, archaeology, ethnography, topography, cultural hist, art, uniforms, costumes, goldsmith art - library 28363

Razstavni Salon Rotovž (Rotovž Gallery), Trg B. Kraigherja 3, 2000 Maribor - T: (02) 2510494, 2502543, Fax: 2502544, E-mail: breda.kolar@umetnostnagalerija.si; simona.vidmar@umetnostna-galerija.si, Internet: http://www.umetnostna-galerija.si. Head: Meta Gabršek Prosenc
Fine Arts Museum 28364

Umetnostna Galerija Maribor (Art Gallery Maribor), Strossmayerjeva 6, 2000 Maribor - T: (02) 2295860, 2295861, Fax: 2527784, E-mail: uprava@umetnostnagalerija.si, Internet: http://www.umetnostnagalerija.si. Head: Meta Gabršek Prosenc
Fine Arts Museum - 1954
19th-20th c paintings, graphics and sculpture of Northeast Slovenia 28365

Metlika

Belokranjski Muzej (Bela County Museum), Trg Svobode 4, 8330 Metlika - T: (07) 3058177, Fax: 3058177. Head: Andreja Brancelj
Local Museum - 1951
Archaeology, ethnography, cultural hist, art, 20th c hist 28366

Slovenski Gasilski Muzej (Slovenian Museum of Firefighting), Trg Svobode 4, 8330 Metlika - T: (07) 3058697
Science&Tech Museum - 1969
Development of fire fighting in Slovenija 28367

Mojstrana

Triglavska Muzejska Zbirka, Triglavska 50, 4281 Mojstrana - T: (04) 5891035, Fax: 5895101, E-mail: pd.dovje-mojstrana@siol.net. Head: Miro Eržen
Special Museum
Alpine coll 28368

Murska Sobota

Galerija Murska Sobota (Gallery of Murska Sobota), Kocljeva 7, 9000 Murska Sobota - T: (02) 5211008, Fax: 5221143, E-mail: franc.obal@guest.arnes.si. Head: Franc Obal
Fine Arts Museum - 1965
Contemporary Slovenian and foreign fine arts (paintings, graphics, sculptures), small sculptures from 13 biennials of small sculpture from 1973 onwards, coll of 100 works (drawings and graphics) by Nande Vidmar(1899-1981) 28369

Pokrajinski Muzej (Regional Museum), Trubarjev Drevored, 9000 Murska Sobota - T: (02) 5271706, Fax: 5211155, E-mail: Irena.Savel@guest.arnes.si, Internet: http://www.pok.muzej-ms.si. Head: Irena Savel
Local Museum
Regional cultural heritage 28370

Nazarje

Galerija Jaki, 3331 Nazarje
Fine Arts Museum
Paintings by Yugoslav artists 28371

Nova Gorica

Goriški Muzej (Museum of Gorica), Grajska 1, 5000 Nova Gorica - T: (05) 3027131, Fax: 3027130. Head: Slavica Plahuta
Local Museum - 1952
Local history, ethnography, art, history - library 28372

Novo Mesto

Dolenjski Muzej Novo Mesto (Museum of the Dolenjsko Region), Ul Muzejska 7, 8000 Novo Mesto - T: (07) 3731111, Fax: 3731112, E-mail: dolenjski.muzej@quest.arnes.si, Internet: http://www.dol-muzej.com. Head: Zdenko Picelj
Local Museum - 1950
Archaeology, hist, cultural hist, ethnology - art gallery 28373

Piran

Obalne Galerije - Mestna Galerija, Trg Tartinijev, 6330 Piran - T: (05) 6730380, Fax: 6732690, E-mail: obalne.galerije@guest.arnes.si. Head: Toni Biloslav
Fine Arts Museum / Public Gallery
Sculpture and painting by regional and inetrnational artists 28374

Pomorski Muzej Sergej Mašera (Maritime Museum), Cankarjevo Nabr 03, 6330 Piran, mail addr: POB 103, 6330 Piran - T: (05) 6710040, Fax: 6710050, E-mail: muzej@pommuz-pi.si, Internet: http://www2.arnes.si/~kppomm. Head: Flavio Bonin
Historical Museum - 1954
Boats, shipping, naval history, fisheries, salt making, maritime archeology - Salt Pans Museum, Traditional Oilery Coll 28375

Postojna

Notranjski Muzej Postojna (Notranjska Museum), Ljubljanska 10, 6230 Postojna, mail addr: P.P. 124, 6230 Postojna - T: (07) 7264210, 7261346. Head: Valentin Schein
Local Museum - 1990
Karstology, speleology, archaeology, cultural hist, local hist, ethnology, biology - library 28376

Predjamski

Muzejska Zbirka v Predjamskom Gradu (Castle Museum), 6230 Predjamski
Local Museum
Archaeology, cultural history, history of the revolution 28377

Ptuj

Pokrajinski Muzej Ptuj (Regional Museum), Muzejski trg 1, 2250 Ptuj - T: (02) 7879230, 7480350, Fax: 7879245, E-mail: muzej-ptuj.uprava@siol.net. Head: Prof. Aleš Arih
Local Museum - 1893
Archaeology, art, local hist, cultural hist, ethnography, viticulture, three temples of Mithras 28378

Radovljica

Čebelarski Muzej, Muzeji Radovljiške Občine (Beekeeping Museum), Linhartov trg 1, 4240 Radovljica - T: (04) 5320520, Fax: 5320524, E-mail: muzeji.radovljiske.obcine@siol.net. Head: Verena Štekar-Vidic
Agriculture Museum - 1959
Illustrated front-boards of beehives, beekeeping tools, unique items of Slovene folk art 28379

Galerije Sivčeva Hiša, Linhartov trg 22, 4240 Radovljica - T: (04) 5320520, Fax: 5320524, E-mail: muzeji.radovljiske.obcine@siol.net. Head: Verena Štekar-Vidic
Public Gallery 28380

Ravne na Koroškem

Koroški Muzej Ravne na Koroškem, Na Gradu 5, 2390 Ravne na Koroškem - T: (02) 8215260, Fax: 8221634, E-mail: karla.oder@guest.arnes.si, Internet: http://www.koroski-muzej.si. Head: Karla Oder
Local Museum
Ethnography, mining, railroads, forestry 28381

Prežihov Spominski Muzej, Preški vrh 13, 2390 Ravne na Koroškem - T: (02) 8222988, Fax: 8221634, E-mail: karla.oder@guest@arnes.si, Internet: http://www.koroski-muzerj.si. Head: Karla Oder
Ethnology Museum 28382

Ribnica na Dolenjskem

Ribniški Muzej, Škrabčev Trg 21, 1310 Ribnica na Dolenjskem - T: (01) 8361179, Fax: 8361938. Head: Vesna Horžen
Local Museum / Ethnology Museum / Archaeological Museum
Local history, archaeological coll 28383

Rogoška Slatina

Muzejska Zbirka, Zdravilišče, 3250 Rogoška Slatina
Fine Arts Museum
Paintings, graphics, cultural history 28384

Škofja Loka

Loški Muzej (Museum of Škofja Loka), Grajska Pot 13, 4220 Škofja Loka - T: (04) 5127010/7161, Fax: 5127160, E-mail: Loski.muzej@guest.arnes.si, Internet: http://www2.arnes.si/~krlmuz1s. Head: Franc Podnar
Local Museum - 1939
Local, cultural, art hist, natural hist, archaeology, ethnology, town and castles under the governance of Freising bishops, medieval trade guilds, Ivan Tavčar's memorial room, Kalan's furniture from 18th c, ceramics, copies of Gothic wall paintings, Baroque golden altars 28385

Slovenj Gradec

Galerija Likovnih Umetnosti (Art Gallery), Glavni trg 24, 2380 Slovenj Gradec - T: (02) 8822131, 8841283, Fax: 8822130, E-mail: galerija@glu-sg.si, Internet: http://www.glu-sg.si. Head: Karel Pečko, Milena Zlatar
Fine Arts Museum
Sculpture and paintings by south slavic artists 28386

Muzej Ljudske Revolucije Slovenj Gradec (Museum of the Slovenian Revolution), Glavni trg 24, 2380 Slovenj Gradec. Head: Marjan Linasi
Historical Museum
History of the Revolution 28387

Sokličev Muzej (Soklič Museum), Trg Osvoboditve 5, 2380 Slovenj Gradec - T: (02) 8841505. Head: Peter Leskovar
Ethnology Museum / Archaeological Museum / Local Museum
Ethnology, archaeology, regional cultural history 28388

Umetnostni Paviljon → Galerija Likovnih Umetnosti

Šoštanj

Napotnikova Galerija, Osnovna Škola Biba Röck, 3325 Šoštanj
Fine Arts Museum
Contemporary painting 28389

Srednja Vas v Bohinju

Oplenova Hiša, Gorenjski Muzej Kranj (Museum of Alpine Farming), Studor 16, 4267 Srednja Vas v Bohinju - T: (04) 5723522, Fax: 2013951, E-mail: info@gorenjski-muzej.si, Internet: http://www.gorenjski-muzej.si. Head: Barbara Ravnik Toman
Agriculture Museum - 1991 28390

Tolmin

Tolminski Muzej (Tolmin Museum), Mestni trg 4, 5220 Tolmin - T: (05) 3811360, Fax: 3811361, E-mail: muzej@tol-muzej.si, Internet: http://tol-muzej.si. Head: Damjana Fortunat Černilogar
Local Museum / Archaeological Museum / Ethnology Museum - 1951
Local hist, archaeology, ethnography, cultural hist - library, archives, depot 28391

Trbovlje

Muzej Ljudske Revolucije Trbovlje, Ul 1. Junija 15, 1420 Trbovlje. Head: Nevenka Troha
Historical Museum
History of the workers' movement in the local coalfield 28392

Trebnje

Galerija Likovnih Samorastnikov (Culture Gallery of Naive Artists), Baragov trg 7a, 8210 Trebnje - T: (07) 3482100, Fax: 3482102, E-mail: info@ciktrebnje.si, Internet: http://www.ciktrebnje.si. Head: Darinka Tomplak
Fine Arts Museum - 1972 28393

Tržič

Kurnikova Hiša, Kurnikova Pot 2, 4290 Tržič - T: (04) 5923810, Fax: 5923811, E-mail: trziski.muzej@guest.arnes.si. Head: Melanija Primozic
Ethnology Museum
Ethnography 28394

Tržiški Muzej, Muzejska ul 11, 4290 Tržič - T: (04) 5923810, Fax: 5923811, E-mail: trziski.muzej@guest.arnes.si. Head: Melanija Primozic
Local Museum - 1964
Crafts, shoemaking, leather, textiles 28395

Velenje

Muzej Velenje (Velenje Museum), Ljubljanska 45, 3320 Velenje - T: (03) 8982634, Fax: 8982640, E-mail: damijan.kljajic@guest.ames.si, Internet: http://www2.pms-lj.si/velenje. Head: Damijan Kljajić
Local Museum 28396

Zavičajni Muzej, Ul Ljubljanska 54, 3320 Velenje
Science&Tech Museum
Mining, local history 28397

Vinica

Rojstna Hiša Pesnika Otona Župančiča (Oton Župančič Collection), 8344 Vinica
Historical Museum
Memorabilia on poet Oton Župančič 28398

Vrhnika

Spominska Zbirka Pisatelja Ivana Cankarja, Na Klancu 1, 1360 Vrhnika, mail addr: c/o ZLKD, Tržaška 25, 1360 Vrhnika - T: (01) 7553648, Fax: 7553648, Internet: http://welcome.to/vrhnika
Special Museum - 1948
Literature, memorabilia of the writer Ivan Cankar 28399

Vrsno

Rojstna Hiša Simona Gregorčiča (Simon Gregorčič Collection), 5222 Vrsno
Local Museum
Local history, ethnography 28400

Zagorje

Muzejska Zbirka NOB, 1410 Zagorje
Historical Museum
History of the National Liberation War 28401

Solomon Islands

Honiara

Soloman Island National Museum and Cultural Centre, POB 313, Honiara - T: 23351. Head: Lawrence Foanaota
Historical Museum / Folklore Museum / Fine Arts Museum - 1969
Prehistory, language and oral tradition, music, dance, architecture 28402

Somalia

Mogadishu

Somali National Museum, Corso Republica, Mogadishu, mail addr: POB 6917, Mogadishu - T: (1) 21041. Head: Ahmed Farah
Local Museum - 1934
Ethnology, traditional Somali objects, Arab metal work, weapons, jewelry, documents and old Arab books, numismatics, philately, natural history, fossils, minerals - library 28403

South Africa

Adelaide

Our Heritage Museum, Queen St, Adelaide 5760
Decorative Arts Museum / Agriculture Museum - 1967
Victorian, Jacobean and Voortrekker furniture, silver, glass and china, farm implements, wagons and carts 28404

Alice

F. S. Malan Ethnological Museum → University of Fort Hare Museum

University of Fort Hare Museum, Private Bag X1314, Alice 5700 - T: (040) 6022269, Fax: 6531926. Head: Reginald Letsatsi
Ethnology Museum / University Museum - 1989
Artifacts from Cape Nguni, Zulu and Sotho tribes, implements and ornaments, works by contemporary African artists 28405

Aliwal North

Aliwal North Museum, Aliwal North - T: (0551) 2441
Local Museum
Local hist 28406

Auckland Park

Gencor Art Gallery, c/o Rand Afrikaans University, POB 525, Auckland Park 2006 - T: (011) 4892099, Fax: 4892099, E-mail: aed@adfin.rau.ac.za. Head: Annali Cabano-Dempsey
Public Gallery / University Museum 28407

Barberton

Barberton Museum, 36 Pilgrim St, Barberton 1300, mail addr: Private Bag X1626, Barberton 1300 - T: (013) 7124208/281, Fax: 7124208/281. Head: A.R. Bornman
Local Museum - 1898
Relics of the Lowveld goldrush during the 1880s, mining and geology, cultural hist, ethnology (Swazi), archaeology, transport - two house museums (Belhaven and Stopforth House) 28408

Barkley East

Barkley East Museum, Barkley East 5580 - T: (04542) 63, Fax: 350
Local Museum
Local history and geology, early transportation 28409

Beaufort West

Beaufort West Museum, 87-91 Donkin St, Beaufort West 6970, mail addr: POB 370, Beaufort West 6970 - T: (023) 4152308, Fax: 4152121, E-mail: bwesmuseum@telkomsa.net. Head: Sandra Smit
Local Museum - 1976
Local hist, 19th c firearms, domestic implements, furnishings, Chris Barnard Exhibition (Prof. Chris Barnard's coll) 28410

Bellville

Mayibuye Centre Collection, University of the Western Cape, Private Bag X17, Bellville 7434 - T: (021) 9592935, Fax: 9593411. Head: Anthea Josias
Fine Arts Museum / University Museum - 1992
South African art, films, tapes, videos, posters, banners - photographic archive 28411

Bethlehem

Bethlehem Museum, 7 Muller St East, Bethlehem 9700, mail addr: POB 551, Bethlehem 9700 - T: (058) 3033477, Fax: 3035076
Local Museum - 1964
Items of local historic import, farm implements, objects from early railway transport 28412

Bethulie

Pellisier House Museum, 1 Voortrekker St, Bethulie 9992 - T: (051762) 68. Head: R. Botha
Local Museum - 1979
Household artifacts (1830-1872), photos, ox-waggons and other vehicles 28413

Bloemfontein

A.C. White Gallery, Municipal Theatre, Charles and Markgraaf Sts, Bloemfontein 9301
Fine Arts Museum
Works of contemporary South African artists 28414

First Raadsaal Museum, 95 Saint George St, Bloemfontein 9301, mail addr: POB 266, Bloemfontein 9301 - T: (051) 479609 ext 259, Fax: 479681. Head: Dr. C.M. Engelbrecht
Historical Museum - 1877
Cultural hist 28415

Freshford House Museum, 21 Kellner St, Bloemfontein 9301, mail addr: POB 266, Bloemfontein 9300 - T: (051) 4479609, Fax: 4476273. Head: Dr. C.M. Engelbrecht
Historical Museum - 1897
Cultural hist 28416

Johannes Stegmann Art Gallery, c/o University of the Orange Free State, POB 339, ITB 211, Bloemfontein 9300 - T: (051) 4012706, Fax: 4483942, E-mail: joubertj@rs.uovs.ac.za. Head: Jeanne Joubert
Fine Arts Museum / University Museum 28417

Military Museum Fort, 116 Church St, Bloemfontein 9300 - T: (051) 4475478, Fax: 4054259
Military Museum 28418

Museum Old Presidency, 17 President Brand St, Bloemfontein 9300, mail addr: Private Bag X20543, Bloemfontein 9300 - T: (051) 4480949, Fax: 4054259. Head: T.A. Lubbe
Historical Museum / Decorative Arts Museum / Museum of Classical Antiquities / Historic Site - 1885
Late Victorian furniture, antique Persian, Eastern, Chinese carpets 28419

Nasionale Afrikaanse Letterkundige Museum en Navorsingsentrum, Old Government Bldg, Pres Brand St, Bloemfontein 9301, mail addr: Private Bag X20543, Bloemfontein 9300 - T: (051) 4054013, Fax: 4054873. Head: T.A. Lubbe
Special Museum - 1973
Manuscripts, books, letters and photos illustrating history of Afrikaans language, exhibits on individual literary figures - library 28420

National Museum Bloemfontein, 36 Aliwal St, Bloemfontein 9301 - T: (051) 4479609, Fax: 4476273, E-mail: direk@nasmus.co.za, Internet: http://www.nasmus.co.za. Head: Dr. C.M. Engelbrecht
Archaeological Museum / Fine Arts Museum / Ethnology Museum / Natural History Museum / Historical Museum - 1877
Anthropology, natural hist, local hist, Florisbad skull, Euskelosaurus fossil, Diarthognathus, Homoiceras horn cores, Hottentot skulls, Achilleoceras fossil, Malvern meteorite, early Blomfontein street scene, live bee-hive and invertebrates - library 28421

National Music Museum, President Brand St, Bloemfontein 9301, mail addr: Private Bag X20543, Bloemfontein 9300 - T: (051) 4054013. Head: T.A. Lubbe
Music Museum
Manuscripts, books, documents, grammophone records, exhibits on composers and musicians 28422

National Theatre Museum, President Brand St, Bloemfontein 9301, mail addr: Private Bag X20543, Bloemfontein 9300 - T: (051) 4054013. Head: T.A. Lubbe
Performing Arts Museum - 1974
Manuscripts, books, plays, documents, letters, posters, exhibits on theatre personalities 28423

Oliewenhuis Art Museum, 16 Harry Smith St, Bloemfontein 9301, mail addr: POB 266, Bloemfontein 9300 - T: (051) 4479609, Fax: 4479283, E-mail: oliewen@nasmus.ca.za, Internet: http://www.nasmus.co.za/oliewenh/olwh.htm. Head: Dr. C.M. Engelbrecht
Fine Arts Museum - 1985
Contemporary South African art, works by Willem Boshoff, (wooden sculptures), works on loan 28424

War Museum of the Boer Republics, National Women's Monument Grounds, Bloemfontein 9301, mail addr: POB 704, Bloemfontein 9300 - T: (051) 4473447, Fax: 4471322, E-mail: museum@anglo-boer.co.za, Internet: http://www.anglo-boer.co.za. Head: F.J. Jacobs
Military Museum - 1931
Oils and drawings of Boer generals, leaders and war scenes of Anglo-Boer war 1899-1902, arms, uniforms, flags and maps, memorabilia, busts, photographs 28425

Boshof

Museum Chris Van Niekerk, 2 Voortrekker St, Boshof 8340, mail addr: Private Bag X20543, Bloemfontein 9300 - T: (053) 5410014, Fax: 5410360. Head: T.A. Lubbe
Historical Museum - 1981
Senator Chris Van Niekerk, Anglo-Boer war, Afrikaans folk dancing, leading personalities from Boshof 28426

Bredasdorp

Shipwreck Museum, 6 Independent St, Bredasdorp 7280, mail addr: POB 235, Bredasdorp 7280 - T: (02842) 41240, Fax: 41240, E-mail: swm@xsinet.co.za. Head: A.J. Swart
Historical Museum - 1975
Shipwrecks exhibits housed in old church, furniture and figure heads out of shipwrecks 28427

Brooklyn

Anton Van Wouw House, University of Pretoria, 299 Clarke St, Brooklyn 0181 - T: (012) 4607422. Head: Joey Ernst
Fine Arts Museum
Works of Anton van Wouw 28428

Burgersdorp

Burgersdorp Cultural Historical Museum, 49 Piet Retief St, Burgersdorp 9744 - T: (051) 6531738, Fax: 6531738. Head: Dalene Bredenkamp
Local Museum - 1970
Early settlement, culture of the English, Afrikaners and Xhosa, two typical Karoo houses, first Theological School of the Reformed Church, Dutch and English furniture, dinner-ware, gun and ammunition, photos, books, vehicles, Voortrekker implements and clothes, Xhosa hut 28429

Caledon

Caledon Museum, 22 Plein St, Caledon 7230 - T: (028) 2121511, Fax: 2141427, E-mail: calmuse@intekom.co.za. Head: Tizzie Mangiagalli
Decorative Arts Museum / Historical Museum - 1973
Victorian period furnishings, Peter E. Clarke art exhibition, textiles, arms, ceramics, glass, photographs, books, silver plate, agricultural machines, documents - Community archive 28430

Calvinia

Calvinia Regional Museum, 44 Church St, Calvinia 8190 - T: (0273) 411043. Head: Hugo
Local Museum - 1968
Local history exhibits housed in a former synagogue 28431

Cape Town

Bertram House Museum, Government Av and Orange St, Cape Town 8001, mail addr: POB 645, Cape Town 8000 - T: (021) 4249381, Fax: 4619592, Internet: http://www.museums.org.za/bertram. Head: Dr. Patricia Davison
Decorative Arts Museum - 1984
English furniture (18th c), silver, jewellery (19th c), ceramics 28432

Bo-Kaap Museum, S.A. Cultural History Museum, 71 Wale St, Cape Town 8001, mail addr: POB 645, Cape Town 8000 - T: (021) 4243846, Fax: 4619592. Head: Dr. Aron Mazel
Historical Museum 28433

Cape Town Holocaust Centre, 88 Hatfield St, Cape Town 8001 - T: (021) 4625553, Fax: 4625554, E-mail: ctholocaust@mweb.co.za, Internet: http://www.museums.org.za/ctholocaust
Historical Museum 28434

Castle Military Museum, Castle, Grand Parade, Cape Town 8001, mail addr: POB 1, Cape Town 8000 - T: (021) 4691153, Fax: 4691136, E-mail: casteel@cis.co.za. Head: I.B. Greeff
Military Museum - 1995
Militaria, Cape military hist (medals, uniforms, swords, weapons, badges, documents, paintings, maps 28435

Clock Tower Maritime Museum, Victoria Basin, Table Bay Harbour, Cape Town 8001, mail addr: POB 4379, Cape Town 8000 - T: (021) 7953966. Head: I.J. Temlett
Special Museum - 1978
Nautical exhibits, photo display of early local shipping, clock mechanism and tide gauge 28436

The Design Museum, The Foundry, Ebenezer Rd, Cape Town 8001 - T: (021) 4181154, E-mail: info@designmuseumsa.co.za, Internet: http://www.designmuseum.co.za
Decorative Arts Museum 28437

District Six Museum, 25a Buitenkant St, Cape Town 8001 - T: (021) 4618745, E-mail: info@districtsix.co.za, Internet: http://www.districtsix.co.za. Head: Linda Fortune
Local Museum - 1994 28438

Jewish Museum Old Synagogue → South African Jewish Museum

Koopmans-De Wet House Museum, 35 Strand St, Cape Town 8001, mail addr: POB 645, Cape Town 8000 - T: (021) 4242473, Fax: 4619592, Internet: http://www.museums.org.za/sachm. Head: Dr. Patricia Davison
Fine Arts Museum / Decorative Arts Museum - 1914
18th c Cape furniture and furnishings, Chinese porcelain, Japanese Imari ware, silver, glass and Dutch Delftware 28439

Michaelis Collection, Old Town House, Greenmarket Sq, Cape Town 8001 - T: (021) 4246367, Fax: 4619592, Internet: http://www.museums.org.za/michaelis. Head: Dr. H. Fransen
Fine Arts Museum / Decorative Arts Museum - 1914
16th-18th c Netherlandish paintings, 16th-19th c Netherlandish prints and drawings, Dutch and Cape colonial furniture, decorative art, local hist 28440

Museum Connection Die, Faurestr 3, Tuine, Cape Town 8001 - T: (021) 4238849
Local Museum 28441

Rust en Vreugd Museum, 78 Buitenkant St, Cape Town 8001 - T: (021) 4653628, Fax: 4619620, E-mail: wfehr@iafrica.com
Fine Arts Museum - 1965
Africana painting, water colors and drawings housed in 18th c house, historical rose and herb garden 28442

South African Cultural History Museum, 49 Adderley St, Cape Town 8001, mail addr: POB 645, Cape Town 8000 - T: (021) 4618280, Fax: 4619592, E-mail: agreyling@iziko.org.za, Internet: http://www.museums.org.za. Head: Dr. Aron Mazel
Historical Museum / Decorative Arts Museum / Archaeological Museum - 1966
Egyptian, Roman and Greek antiquities, Chinese and Japanese maritime arms and armour, South African coinage, Cape, Malay, Indonesian and European furniture and furnishings, Cape hist, Postal stores - library 28443

South African Jewish Museum, 88 Hatfield St, Gardens, Cape Town 8001 - T: (021) 4651546, Fax: 4650284, E-mail: vw@sajewishmuseum.co.za, Internet: http://www.sajewishmuseum.co.za. Head: Vivienne Anstey
Religious Arts Museum - 2000
Jewish ceremonial art and Judaica housed in first synagogue built in South Africa, 150 yrs SA jewish hist - archives 28444

South African Maritime Museum, V&A Waterfront, Dock Rd, Cape Town 8000 - T: (021) 4192505/06, Fax: 4197332, E-mail: museum@maritimemuseum.ac.za, Internet: http://www.maritimemuseum.ac.za. Head: Dr. D. Crous
Historical Museum / Science&Tech Museum - 1942 28445

South African Museum, 25 Queen Victoria St, Cape Town 8001, mail addr: POB 61, Cape Town 8000 - T: (021) 4243330, Fax: 4246716, E-mail: mcluver@samuseum.ac.za, Internet: http://museums.org.za/sam/index.htm. Head: Dr. M.A. Cluver
Natural History Museum / Ethnology Museum - 1825
Paleontology, entomology, ethnology, archaeology, marine biology, zoology (fishes, birds, reptiles, marine invertebrates, insects) 28446

South African National Gallery, Government Av, Cape Town 8001, mail addr: POB 2420, Cape Town 8000 - T: (021) 4651628, Fax: 4610045, E-mail: mmartin@iziko.org.za, Internet: http://www.museums.org.za/iziko/sang. Head: Marilyn Martin
Fine Arts Museum - 1871
Traditional African sculpture, Sir Abe Bailey coll of sporting and hunting pictures, African metal sculpture, Dutch, French and English painting (17th to 20th c), South African 19th and 20th c art 28447

William Fehr Collection, Castle of Good Hope, Buitenkant St, Cape Town 8000 - T: (021) 4623751, Fax: 4623750, Internet: http://www.museums.org.za/wfc. Head: J.L. Meltzer
Fine Arts Museum / Decorative Arts Museum / Historical Museum / Historic Site - 1964
Painting, furniture and furnishings, china, silver and copper - library 28448

Colenso

R.E. Stevenson Museum, Old Toll House, Colenso 3360, mail addr: POB 22, Colenso 3360 - T: (036) 4222111/112, Fax: 4222227
Military Museum - 1974
Weapons, badges, medals, personal relics, historical photographs 28449

Colesberg

Colesberg/Kemper Museum, Museum Sq, Murray St, Colesberg 9795 - T: (051) 7530678, Fax: 7530678, E-mail: belinda@mjvn.co.za, Internet: http://www.mjvn.co.za/anglo-boer. Head: B. Gordon
Local Museum - 1924
Hist of the Anglo Boer war, hist of Colesberg, Karoo Nomads 28450

Constantia

Groot Constantia Manor House and Wine Museum, Groot Constantia Estate, Constantia 7848 - T: (021) 7945067, Fax: 7947697, E-mail: HBrumfield@iziko.org.za, Internet: http://www.museums.org.za/grootcon/index.html. Head: Dr. M. Cluver
Fine Arts Museum / Decorative Arts Museum / Special Museum - 1926
17th-18th c Dutch painting, Cape furniture, Oriental ceramics, wine hist coll 28451

Cradock

Great Fish River Museum, 87 High St, Cradock 5880 - T: (048) 8814509, Fax: 8811421
Decorative Arts Museum / Agriculture Museum - 1979
English and Afrikaans furniture, furnishings, 19th c domestic and farming implements and equipment, early life of the Eastern Cape pioneers, 1820 settlers Anglo-Boer War, Afrikaans culture & heritage 28452

Olive Schreiner House, National English Literary Museum, 9 Cross St, Cradock 5880 - T: (048) 8815251, 8813210, Fax: 8813210, E-mail: heritagehouse@eastcape.net, Internet: http://www.places.co.za/html/schreiner.html. Head: Malcolm Hacksley
Special Museum
Literary works, life of Olive Schreiner, photographies 28453

Dundee

Talana Museum and Heritage Park, Private Bag 2024, Dundee 3000 - T: (034) 2122654, Fax: 2122376, E-mail: info@talana.co.za, Internet: http://www.talana.co.za. Head: P. McFadden
Local Museum / Military Museum - 1979
Local hist, military hist, geology, archeology, mining, glass gallery agriculture, African Bead gallery 28454

Durban

African Art Centre, 160 Pine St, Durban 4001 - T: (031) 3047915, Fax: 3047915, E-mail: afriart1@iafrica.com, Internet: http://www.afriart.org.za. Head: Anthea Martin
Public Gallery 28455

Campbell Collections, 220 Marriott Rd, Durban 4001 - T: (031) 2073432, Fax: 2073432, E-mail: harkness@un.ac.za. Head: Prof. Y. Seleli
University Museum / Ethnology Museum / Fine Arts Museum
Cape Dutch furniture, cultural relics, Africana pictures - Killie Campbell Africana library 28456

Durban Art Gallery, City Hall, Smith St, Durban 4001 - Internet: http://www.durban.gov.za/museums/artgallery
Fine Arts Museum / Decorative Arts Museum
European and South African painting, sculpture and graphic art, contemporary pottery, porcelain, bronze and glass, laces, ivory 28457

Durban Natural Science Museum, City Hall, Smith St, Durban 4001, mail addr: POB 4085, Durban 4000 - T: (031) 3112240/256, Fax: 3112242, E-mail: bretth@crsu.durban.gov.za. Head: Q.B. Hendey
Natural History Museum - 1887
Birds, mammals, fossils 28458

Geology Education Museum, c/o University of Natal, George Campbell Bldg, King George V Av, Durban 4001 - T: (031) 2602524, Fax: 2602280, E-mail: gem@geology.und.ac.za, Internet: http://www.und.ac.za/geology/gem1.html. Head: Sandra K. Gautier
Natural History Museum / University Museum - 1948
Minerals, rocks, fossils, Krantz coll - learning ressources lab 28459

Kwa Muhle Museum, 130-132 Ordnance Rd, Durban 4001 - T: (031) 3112223, Fax: 3112224, E-mail: lynnec@crsu.durban.gov.za. Head: R.H. Omar
Local Museum - 1994
20th c urban life with emphasis on the 'Durban system' of administering the African population 1908-1986 28460

Local History Museums → Old Court House Museum

Old Court House Museum, Old Court House, Aliwal St, Durban 4001 - T: (031) 3112223, Fax: 3112224, E-mail: lynnec@crsu.durban.gov.za. Head: R.H. Omar
Ethnology Museum / Historical Museum - 1887
Material relating to the settlement of Natal from 1497, hist of the Zulu and Boer wars, people of KwaZulu-Natal, Apartheid hist of Durban, Indian hist about these people in KwaZulu-Natal and the role of M.K. Gandhi in his 21 year stay in Durban 28461

Old House Museum, 31 Saint Andrew's St, Durban 4001 - T: (031) 3112261/223, Fax: 3112224, E-mail: lynnec@crsu.durban.gov.za. Head: R.H. Omar
Decorative Arts Museum / Fine Arts Museum - 1954
Furniture and domestic utensils, local works of art, period furnishings 28462

Port Natal Maritime Museum, Aliwal St, Durban 4001 - T: (031) 3112230, Fax: 3112224, E-mail: lynnec@crsu.durban.gov.za. Head: R.H. Omar
Historical Museum / Science&Tech Museum - 1988
Natal and Durban maritime hist, two tugs and a minesweeper 28463

SAAF Museum Durban, South African Air Force, Snell Parade, Durban 4001
Military Museum 28464

Sea World, Oceanographic Research Institute, 2 West St, Durban 4001, mail addr: POB 10712, Durban 4056 - T: (031) 3373536, Fax: 3372132, E-mail: seaworld@dbn.lia.net, Internet: http://www.seaworld.org.za. Head: Prof. Antonio J. de Freitas
Natural History Museum - 1959
Marine biology and ecology - library, education centre 28465

Technikon Natal Gallery, 51 Mansfield Pl, Berea, Durban 4000 - T: (031) 2042207, Fax: 2023405. Head: Frances van Melsen
Fine Arts Museum - 1984
South African art 28466

Westville Gallery, University of Durban, Private Bag X54001, Durban 4000 - T: (031) 8202548, Fax: 8202160. Head: Colin Sabapathy
Fine Arts Museum / University Museum - 1980
South African art 28467

East London

Ann Bryant Art Gallery, 9 Saint Marks Rd, East London 5201 - T: (043) 7224044, Fax: 7431729
Fine Arts Museum - 1947
South African painting, contemporary South African art, Eastern Cape focus 28468

East London Museum, 319 Oxford St, East London 5201 - T: (043) 7430686, Fax: 7433127, E-mail: elmuseum@mymail.net4u.co.za. Head: G.N. Vernon
Local Museum - 1921
Coelacanth type specimen, malacological, ornithological, cultural hist, beadwork 28469

Gately House, Park Gates Rd, East London 5201 - T: (0431) 22141, Fax: 433127. Head: R.M. Tietz
Decorative Arts Museum / Fine Arts Museum - 1963
Original period furnishings and objects d'art housed in former home of John Gates, 'father' of East London 28470

Eshowe

Zululand Historical Museum, Fort Nongquai, 37 Nongquai Rd, Eshowe 3815 - T: (0354) 41141, Fax: 74733. Head: Jenny Hawke
Historical Museum - 1961
Historical fort, Zulu lifestyle, natural history, Zulu art and crafts, missionaries, Anglo-Zulu war 28471

Estcourt

Bushman Site Museum, Main Caves, Giant's Castle Game Reserve, Estcourt 3310 - T: (03631) 24718
Open Air Museum - 1969
Pehistoric rock paintings, displays showing skills and crafts of Bushmen 28472

Florida Park

Roodepoort Museum, Civic Centre, Chrisiaan de Wet Rd, Florida Park 1709, mail addr: Private Bag X30, Roodepoort 1725 - T: (011) 7610225, Fax: 6744043, E-mail: aletts@wgt.org.za, Internet: http://www.museums.org.za/roodepoortmuseum. Head: A. Letts
Local Museum / Decorative Arts Museum - 1963
Domestic and farming implements, hand-made Transvaal pioneer furniture, relics from Witwatersand gold fields, Art Nouveau and Art Deco artefacts 28473

Fort Beaufort

Fort Beaufort Historical Museum, 44 Durban St, Fort Beaufort 5720 - T: 119. Head: A.T. Matthew
Historical Museum - 1938
Firearms, spears and arrows, costumes, old photographs, documents 28474

Franschhoek

Huguenot Memorial Museum, Lambrechts St, Franschhoek 7690, mail addr: POB 37, Franschhoek 7690 - T: (021) 8762532, Fax: 8763649, E-mail: huguenoot@museum.co.za, Internet: http://www.museum.co.za. Head: J.E. Malherbe
Historical Museum - 1960
Huguenot hist and genealogy 28475

Genadendal

Genadendal Museum, Church Sq, Genadendal 7234 - T: (028) 2518582, Fax: 2518582, E-mail: genadendalmuseum@xsinet.co.za. Head: Dr. Isaac Balie
Religious Arts Museum / Historical Museum
Documents of early missionary work housed on site of first South African missionary activity 28476

George

George Museum, Courtenay St, George 6530, mail addr: Posbus 564, George 6530 - T: (044) 8735343, Fax: 8740354, E-mail: mroux@pawc.wcape.gov.za. Head: Katy Abrahams
Local Museum - 1969
Local history, moutain passes and lakes district 28477

Outeniqua Railway Museum, Transnet Heritage Foundation, 2 Mission Street, George 6530, mail addr: POB 850, George 6530 - T: (044) 8018295, Fax: 8018252, E-mail: heritagefoundation@transnet.co.za. Head: V.B. MChuny
Science&Tech Museum - 1920
Custodian of almost 200 steam locomotives representing the S.A. steam heritage of over 135 years 28478

Graaff-Reinet

Graaf-Reinet Museum, Reinet House, Murray St, Graaff-Reinet 6280, mail addr: POB 104, Graaff-Reinet 6280 - T: (049) 8923801, Fax: 8925650, E-mail: graaffreinetmuseum@intekom.co.za, Internet: http://www.graaffreinet.co.za. Head: H. Baartman
Local Museum - 1948
Cape Dutch furniture, wooden agricultural implements, Cape silver, largest vine stem in the world, Laubscher or Graaff-Reinet doll coll, W. Roe photo coll, photographic equipment, costumes, bric-a-brac, Victorian furniture, cultural hist of town, Anglo-Boer War, Karoo fossils 28479

Hester Rupert Art Museum, 19 Church St, Graaff-Reinet 6280 - T: (049) 8922121, Fax: 8924319, E-mail: townclerkgrtmun@intekom.co.za. Head: Etienne du Pisani
Fine Arts Museum - 1966
Contemporary South African art (mostly 1960's) 28480

Grabouw

Elgin Apple Museum, Main Rd, Grabouw 7160, mail addr: POB 64, Elgin 7180 - T: (021) 8599126, Fax: 8599659, E-mail: country@nedclub.co.2a. Head: Norma Bridgman
Agriculture Museum - 1972
Hist of apple and pear industry in Elgin area, hist of Grabouw and Elgin valley 28481

Grahamstown

Albany Museum, Somerset St, Grahamstown 6139 - T: (046) 6222312, Fax: 6222398, E-mail: l.webley@ru.ac.za, Internet: http://www.ru.ac.za/albany-museum. Head: Dr. L. Webley
Local Museum / Natural History Museum - 1855
Fresh water ichthyology/invertebrates, entomology, hymenoptera, ornithology, archaeology, paleontology, botany, geology, anthropology, history - Natural Sciences Museum, History Museum, Observatory Museum 28482

Bathurst Agricultural Museum, Grahamstown 6140 - T: (0461) 23667
Agriculture Museum 28483

History Museum, Somerset St, Grahamstown 6139 - T: (046) 6222312, Fax: 6222398, E-mail: l.webley@ru.ac.za, Internet: http://www.ru.ac.za/albany-museum/history.html. Head: Dr. W. Webley
Historical Museum 28484

National English Literary Museum, 87 Beaufort St, Grahamstown 6140 - T: (046) 6227042, Fax: 6222582, E-mail: m.hacksley@ru.ac.za, Internet: http://www.rhodes.ac.za./nelm. Head: M.M. Hacksley
Special Museum - 1980
Literary manuscripts, press cuttings, rare Africana books, modern Southern African literature 28485

Observatory Museum, 10 Bathurst St, Grahamstown 6140 - T: (046) 6222312
Natural History Museum - 1982 28486

Rhodes Museum of Classical Antiquities, Grahamstown 6140, mail addr: c/o Department of Classics, Rhodes University, POB 94, Grahamstown 6140 - T: (0461) 22023. Head: Prof. D.B. Gain
Museum of Classical Antiquities
Greek and Roman vases, coins, various artifacts 28487

Temlett House, 53 Beaufort St, Grahamstown 6140
Decorative Arts Museum
Victorian furnishings housed in early 19th c dwelling, 19th c cottage (Scott's Farm Cottage) located in surrounding gardens 28488

Great Brak River

Great Brak River Museum, Amy Searle St, Great Brak River 6525, mail addr: POB 15, Great Brak River 6525
Local Museum
Local history, period furnishings and domestic utensils housed in typical late 19th c worker's cottage 28489

Green Point

Museum of Coast and Anti-Aircraft Artillery, Fort Wynyard, Green Point 8051, mail addr: POB 14068, Green Point 8051 - T: (021) 4191765
Military Museum - 1987
Coast and anti-aircraft guns and relics displayed in a restored coast artillery battery 28490

Greytown

Greytown Museum, 68 Scott St, Greytown 3250 - T: (033) 4139124, Fax: 4171393. Head: S. Rugunanau
Local Museum - 1961
Relics of pioneer families and the 1906 Bambatha rebellion, stone implements, Zulu artifacts 28491

Griquatown

Mary Moffat Museum, Main St, Griquatown 8365 - T: (053) 3430180. Head: H. Hager
Local Museum - 1956
Local history 28492

Hartenbos

Hartenbos Museum, Majuba Av, Hartenbos 6520 - T: (044) 6952183, Fax: 6950770. Head: Jeannette Geyer
Historical Museum - 1976
Displays depicting daily life of early Voortrekkers, authentic early equipment and utensils from the Great Trek started in 1835, preparation, lager forming, recreation and settlement, history of Hartenbos 28493

Heidelberg

Heidelberg Motor Museum, 126 Voortrekker St, Heidelberg 1441, mail addr: POB 320, Heidelberg 1438 - T: (016) 3416303, Fax: 3496265, E-mail: jalg@icon.co.za, Internet: http://www.heidelbergmotormuseum.com. Head: Judy Le Grange
Science&Tech Museum - 1974
Early bicycles, tricycles and motorcycles, antique motor vehicles, ancient transportation vehicles, railway cars and locomotives, racing cars 28494

Heilbron

Riemland Museum, c/o Municipality, Heilbron 9650 - T: (05889) 22014, Fax: 21764
Science&Tech Museum / Natural History Museum - 1983
Dairy industry, sorghum industry, wild life and hunting 28495

Hermanus

Old Harbour Museum, POB 118, Hermanus 7200 - T: (02831) 21475, Fax: 23810. Head: Elisabeth du Toit
Open Air Museum - 1973
Open-air, on-site coll of early harbour structures and boats, whales bones, and paraphernalia whale sound booth, historic photo coll, inter-tidal zone aquaria of local species - library 28496

Himeville

Settlers Museum, Loteni Nature Reserve, Himeville 3256 - T: (033) 7020560, Fax: 7020560, Internet: http://www.rhino.org.za. Head: Leo Khulani-Mkhize
Agriculture Museum
Victoriana, early farming machinery 28497

Howick

Howick Museum, Howick Falls Rd, Howick 3290, mail addr: POB 5, Howick 3290 - T: (0332) 306124, Fax: 304183. Head: M. Holland
Historical Museum / Agriculture Museum - 1977
Local cultural and agricultural hist 28498

Isandlwana

Saint Vincent Church Museum, Saint Vincent's Rectory, Isandlwana 3010
Local Museum
Local history, Battle of Isandlwana memorial 28499

Johannesburg

ABSA Group Museum, 187 Fox St, Johannesburg 2001 - T: (011) 3504167, 3506889, Fax: 3503435, E-mail: pietsn@absa.co.za, Internet: http://www.absa.co.za. Head: Dr. Pieter Snyman
Historical Museum
Banking, money - archives 28500

Adler Museum of Medicine, York Rd, Park Town, Johannesburg 2001, mail addr: c/o University of the Witwatersrand, Private Bag 3, Wits 2050 - T: (011) 7172000, Fax: 4899482, E-mail: 178wam@chiron.wits.ac.za, Internet: http://www.wits.ac.za/museums/adler.html
Special Museum / University Museum - 1962
Hist of medicine, traditional African, Asian and European medicine, folk medicine, pharmacy 28501

African Herbalist Shops, Museum for Man and Science, Diagonal Str 14, Johannesburg 2001 - T: (011) 8364470. Head: Peter Naidoo
Special Museum / Historical Museum
Herbal and traditional medicine of all Southern hemisphere tribes, cultural and ancestral need, Western and African medicine 28502

Anthropology Museum and Resource Centre, c/o University of Witwatersrand, Senate House, 1 Jan Smuts Av, Johannesburg 2001 - T: (011) 7171365, Fax: 7171369, E-mail: gallery@atlas.wits.ac.za, Internet: http://sunsite.wits.ac.za/mus/gpg
Ethnology Museum 28503

Bensusan Museum of Photography, MuseuMAfrica, 121 Bree St, Newtown, Johannesburg 2001, mail addr: POB 517, Newtown 2113 - T: (011) 8335624, Fax: 8335636, E-mail: photolib@mj.org.za, museum@mj.org.za
Special Museum - 1960
W.H. Fox Talbot coll, callotype photographs and camera, South African pictorialists, stereo cards, cabinet card portraits - library 28504

Bernard Price Institute Paleontology Museum, c/o University of the Witwatersrand, Van Riet Lowe Bldg, East Campus, Johannesburg 2001 - T: (011) 7176682, Fax: 4031423, E-mail: 106gar@cosmos.wits.ac.za. Head: Prof. Bruce Rubidge
Natural History Museum / University Museum - 1948
Paleontology, micro paleontology, paleoanthropology, Karroo vertebrates, mammalian fossils, bone artifacts 28505

Bernberg Fashion Museum, Museum Africa, Duncombe Rd and Jan Smuts Av, Forest Town, Johannesburg 2001, mail addr: POB 517, Newtown 2113 - T: (011) 6460716, 8335624, Fax: 8335636, E-mail: museum@mj.org.za
Special Museum - 1974
South African fashion from ca 1790 to date 28506

Bleloch Museum, c/o Dept. of Geology, University of Witwatersrand, 1 Jan Smuts Av, Johannesburg 2001 - T: (011) 7176569, Fax: 3391697, E-mail: 065matt@cosmos.wits.ac.za, Internet: http://www.sunsite.wits.ac.za. Head: Matthew Kitching
Natural History Museum / University Museum - 1922
Rocks, minerals and ores 28507

Brebner Surgical Museum, c/o Department of Surgery, Medical School, York Rd, Parktown, Johannesburg 2193 - T: (011) 7172080, Fax: 4842717, E-mail: 042susan@chiron.wits.ac.za, Internet: http://www.wits.ac.za/surgery. Head: Prof. Davies
Historical Museum - 1950 28508

Ethnological Museum, c/o University of the Witwatersrand, 1 Jan Smuts Av, Johannesburg 2000 - T: (011) 7162766. Head: Prof. W.D. Hammond-Tooke
Ethnology Museum / University Museum 28509

Geological Museum, Museum Africa, 121 Bree St, Newtown, Johannesburg 2001, mail addr: POB 517, Newtown 2113 - T: (011) 8335624, Fax: 8335636, E-mail: museum@mj.org.za
Natural History Museum - 1890
Geology, minerals, gold, gemstones 28510

Gertrude Posel Gallery, c/o University of Witwatersrand, Senate House, 1 Jan Smuts Av, Johannesburg 2001 - T: (011) 7171365, Fax: 7171369, E-mail: gallery@atlas.wits.ac.za, Internet: http://sunsite.wits.ac.za/mus/gpg. Head: Dr. Rayda Becker
Fine Arts Museum - 1977
South African beadwork, contemporary South African art 28511

James Hall Museum of Transport, MuseuMAfrica, Pioneer's Park, Rosettenville Rd, Johannesburg 2001, mail addr: POB 517, Johannesburg 2000 - T: (011) 4359718, Fax: 4359821, E-mail: museum@mj.org.za. Head: H.J. Bruce
Science&Tech Museum - 1964
Land transportation (fire engines, busses) 28512

Johannesburg Art Gallery, Klein Str, Joubertpark, Johannesburg 2044 - T: (011) 7253130/80/81, Fax: 7206000, E-mail: jburger@mj.org.za, Internet: http://www.sqevents.co.za/gallery.htm. Head: R. Keene
Fine Arts Museum - 1910
Dutch, French and British coll (17th to 20th c), classical and contemporary Southern African coll, modern international coll, lace, furniture, ceramics, print coll (15th c to present) - conservation dept, education dept, library, archives 28513

Museum Africa, 121 Bree St, Newtown, Johannesburg 2001, mail addr: POB 517, Newtown 2113 - T: (011) 8335624, Fax: 8335636, E-mail: museum@mj.org.za
Local Museum / Ethnology Museum - 1935
Traditional black culture, Cape silver, numismatics and philately, historic photographs, drawings and paintings, rock art 28514

Museum of Southern African Rock Art, Museum Africa, 121 Bree St, Newtown, Johannesburg 2001, mail addr: POB 517, Newtown 2113 - T: (011) 8335624, Fax: 8335636, E-mail: museum@mj.org.za
Archaeological Museum / Fine Arts Museum - 1935
Petroglyphs, rock engravings 28515

Reza Shah Museum, 41 Young Av, Mountain View, Johannesburg 2001
Fine Arts Museum - 1972
Ancient and modern Persian art - library 28516

SAB Centenary Centre, 15 President Str, Newtown, Johannesburg 2001 - T: (011) 8364900
Historical Museum 28517

South African Railway Museum, De Villiers St, Johannesburg 2001, mail addr: POB 1111, Johannesburg 2000
Science&Tech Museum - 1920
Early model locomotives used in South Africa 28518

Standard Bank Gallery, 6 Simmonds St, Johannesburg 2001 - T: (011) 6364231, Fax: 6367515
Special Museum 28519

Transnet Heritage Foundation Library, 96 Rissik St, Johannesburg 2000, mail addr: POB 3753, Johannesburg 2000 - T: (011) 7739523, Fax: 7743415, E-mail: eurikad@transnet.co.za. Head: V.B. MChuny
Library with Exhibitions - 1920
Photographs and documents, coll of 32 Johannesburg Station panels by J.H. Pierneef 28520

Zoology Museum, c/o University of the Witwatersrand, Old Education Bldg, East Campus, Johannesburg 2050 - T: (011) 7162307, E-mail: Museum@gecko.biol.wits.ac.za. Head: Caroline Crump
Natural History Museum 28521

Kimberley

Duggan-Cronin Gallery, Egerton Rd, Kimberley 8301, mail addr: POB 316, Kimberley 8300 - T: (053) 8420099, Fax: 8421433, E-mail: cfortune@museumsnc.co.za, Internet: http://www.museum.co.za. Head: C. Fortune
Ethnology Museum - 1937
Photographic coll covering Southern African tribes 28522

Dunluce House Museum, 9 Lodge Rd, Belgravia, Kimberley 8301 - T: (053) 8420099
Decorative Arts Museum 28523

Kimberley Mine Museum, c/o De Beers Consolidated Mines Ltd, Tucker St, Kimberley 8301 - T: (053) 8394901/03, E-mail: dschaefer@debeers.co.za. Head: D.E. Schaefer
Science&Tech Museum / Historical Museum
Diamond display, shops and dwellings of early Kimberley mining period, Kimberley 'Big Hole' open mine 28524

McGregor Museum and Duggan Cronin Gallery, Chapel St and Egerton Rd, Kimberley 8301, mail addr: POB 316, Kimberley 8300 - T: (053) 8420099, Fax: 8421433, E-mail: cfortune@museumsnc.co.za, Internet: http://www.museumsnc.co.za. Head: C. Fortune
Local Museum - 1907
Local history, anthropology, archaeology, botany, zoology, military history - archives 28525

Magersfontein Battlefields Museum, McGregor Museum, on Modder River Rd, km 47, Kimberley 8300, mail addr: POB 316, Kimberley 8301 - T: (053) 8337115, Fax: 8421433, E-mail: hist.cult@kimberley.co.za, Internet: http://www.museumsnc.co.za. Head: C.F. Fortune
Military Museum - 1973
Original defenses and memorials marking the Anglo-Boer War battle of 11 Dec. 1899, uniforms, equipment and weapons, relics and photos taken during the battle, trench battle scene, outlook post 28526

Pioneers of Aviation Museum, McGregor Museum, Airport Rd, Kimberley 8301, mail addr: POB 316, Kimberley 8300 - T: (053) 8420099, Fax: 8421433, E-mail: lizv@museumsnc.co.za, Internet: http://www.museumsnc.co.za. Head: C.F. Fortune
Science&Tech Museum
Replica of hangar of 1st flying school in South Africa, Patterson bi-plane replica 28527

Rudd House Museum, 4 Loch Rd, Belgravia, Kimberley 8301 - T: (053) 8420099
Decorative Arts Museum - 1970 28528

William Humphreys Art Gallery, Civic Centre, Cullinan Crescent, Kimberley 8301, mail addr: POB 885, Kimberley 8300 - T: (053) 8311724, Fax: 8322221. Head: A.F. Pretorius
Fine Arts Museum / Decorative Arts Museum - 1952
South African painting, sculpture, graphics, ceramics and rock art, European art incl British, French and 16th/17th c Dutch and Flemish Old Master prints and drawings, traditional African art, William Timlin 28529

King William's Town

Amathole Museum, Cnr Albert and Alexandra Rd, King William's Town 5600, mail addr: POB 1434, King William's Town 5600 - T: (043) 6424506, Fax: 6421569, E-mail: postmaster@amathole.org.za, Internet: http://www.amathole.org.za. Head: Lloyd R. Wingate
Local Museum / Natural History Museum - 1884
Hist of early German settlers, militaria, mammals, Xhosa ethnography, missionary hist, G.C. Shortridge - library, archive 28530

Missionary Museum, Amathole Museum, 27 Berkeley St, King William's Town 5600, mail addr: POB 1434, King William's Town 5600 - T: (043) 6424506, Fax: 6421569, E-mail: postmaster@amathole.org.za. Head: Lloyd R. Wingate
Religious Arts Museum - 1973
Photographs, documents and records relating to missionaries and missions stations (Eastern Cape) 28531

Klerksdorp

Klerksdorp Museum, Lombard and Magrietha Prinsloo Sts, Klerksdorp 2570, mail addr: POB 99, Klerksdorp 2570 - T: (018) 4623546, Fax: 4623546, Internet: http://www.koshinfo.co.za. Head: Prof. R. Marx
Local Museum / Open Air Museum - 1975
Prehist and hist of Klerksdorp and North West Province, geological and archaeological displays 28532

Knysna

Knysna Museum, Queen St, Knysna 6570, mail addr: POB 21, Knysna 6570 - T: (044) 3825066, Fax: 3825551. Head: M. Groenewald
Local Museum - 1972
Photos and relics related to Millwood goldrush of 1887, original furniture, Knysna's timber industrial hist 28533

Kroonstad

Sarel Cilliers Museum, Hill St, Kroonstad 9500 - T: (0562) 69249, Fax: 69122
Local Museum - 1983
Maize production, railways, gold mining industry, Anglo-Boer war, period furniture 28534

Kuils River

Marvol Museum, Hazendal Estate, Bottlery Rd, Kuils River 7579 - T: (021) 9062531, Fax: 9035112, E-mail: hazen@icon.co.za, Internet: http://www.museums.org.za/marvol. Head: Alexander Kononov
Fine Arts Museum
Russian art and culture 28535

Ladybrand

Heritage Collection Catherina Brand, 21 Church St, Ladybrand 9745 - T: (0561) 40654, Fax: 40305. Head: T.A. Lubbe
Local Museum - 1985
Old printing press, railways, mounted border police, Coakers pharmacy, wheat farming 28536

Lichtenburg

Lichtenburg Museums and Art Gallery, Kultuurhistories, Diamant Delwers en Landboumuseum, POB 7, Lichtenburg 2740 - T: (018) 6325051, Fax: 6325247, E-mail: museum@lichtenburg.co.za
Local Museum / Fine Arts Museum 28537

Louis Trichardt

Schoemansdal Museum, Eramus and Munnik Sts, Louis Trichardt 0920, mail addr: POB 2410, Louis Trichardt 0920 - T: (015) 5164937, Fax: 5163254. Head: C. Hartman
Open Air Museum - 1988 28538

Lwandle

Township Museum, Migrant Labour Museum and Arts and Crafts Centre, Vulindlela St, Lwandle 7143 - T: (021) 8456119, E-mail: township-webmaster@webmail.co.za, Internet: http://www.8ung.at/township
Local Museum / Fine Arts Museum 28539

Mafikeng

Mafikeng Museum, Martin St, Mafikeng 2745 - T: (018) 3816102, Fax: 3815090. Head: G.R. Phillips
Local Museum
Antique guns, local history exhibits, culture, arms, artillery, ammunition, geology 28540

Mariannhill

Africana Museum, Monastery, Mariannhill 3601, mail addr: POB 11077, Mariannhill 3601 - T: (031) 7004288, Fax: 7003113, E-mail: monastery@10net.co.za. Head: P. Superior
Ethnology Museum
Bantu ethnology, old African beadwork, musical instruments, domestic utensils, weapons, Bushmen paintings 28541

Matjiesfontein

Marie Rawdon Museum, Hotel Lord Milner, Matjiesfontein 6901 - T: (023) 5513011, Fax: 5513020, E-mail: milner2@mweb.co.za. Head: David D. Rawdon
Decorative Arts Museum - 1970
Victorian and Edwardian furnishings and domestic utensils housed in typical 19th c railway station, period costumes and dresses 28542

Messina

Messina Museum, National Rd, Messina 0900, mail addr: Private Bag X611, Messina 0900 - T: (015) 5340211/221, Fax: 5342513, E-mail: msnamanager@limpopo.co.za
Ethnology Museum / Historical Museum / Military Museum - 1971
Voortrekker firearms, mining equipment, copper ore, tribal weapons 28543

Middelburg Cape

P.W. Vorster Museum, c/o Grootfontein College of Agriculture, Middelburg Cape 5900 - T: 21113
Local Museum / University Museum
Local history displays housed in 1827 homestead, farm implements 28544

Molteno

Molteno Museum, Smith St, Molteno 5500 - T: (04572) 21, Fax: 467
Local Museum - 1968
Fossils, stone implements, arrowheads, pottery, beadwork 28545

Montagu

Montagu Museum, Long St, Montagu 6720, mail addr: POB 107, Montagu 6720 - T: (023) 6141950, Fax: 6141950, E-mail: museum@lando.co.za, Internet: http://www.museums.org.za/montaguemuseum. Head: J. Biesenbach
Local Museum - 1975
Photos and documents housed in 19th c dwelling, 18th c furniture, hist of Montagu, dolls, musical instruments - medicinical plant research 28546

Mossel Bay

Bartolomeu Dias Museum Complex, Market St, Mossel Bay 6500, mail addr: Private Bag X1, Mossel Bay 6500 - T: (044) 6911067, Fax: 6911915, E-mail: diasmuseum@mweb.co.za, Internet: http://www.gardenroute.net/mby/mbmuseums.htm. Head: L. Labuschagne
Local Museum / Historical Museum - 1961
Maps, photographs, maritime history of Mossel Bay, shells, Caravel ship, artefacts, flora 28547

Muizenberg

Natale Labia Museum, 192 Main Rd, Muizenberg 7951 - T: (021) 7884106/07, Fax: 7883908
Decorative Arts Museum - 1988
Italianate furnishings with 18th and 19th c British and European art 28548

Rhodes Cottage Museum, 246 Main Rd, Muizenberg 7945 - T: (021) 7881816. Head: E.O. Pahliney
Local Museum - 1953
Memorabilia of Cecil Rhodes, diamonds, British empire, education, war, agriculture, architecture 28549

Newlands

Rugby Museum, Newlands Rugby Grounds, Boundary Rd, Newlands 7700
Special Museum
History of rugby in South Africa, Rugby equipment - library 28550

Onderstepoort

Arnold Theiler Museum for African Diseases, c/o ARC-Onderstepoort Veterinary Institute, 100 Old Soutpan Rd, Onderstepoort 0110 - T: (012) 5299111, Fax: 565673, E-mail: liza@moon.ovi.ac.za. Head: Dr. St. Cornelius
Historical Museum 28551

Onderstepoort Veterinary History Museum, c/o ARC-Onderstepoort Veterinary Institute, 100 Old Soutpan Rd, Onderstepoort 0110 - T: (012) 5299111, Fax: 5299277, E-mail: sanette@moon.ovi.ac.za, Internet: http://www.onderstepoort.com. Head: Dr. S.T. Cornelius
Science&Tech Museum / Historical Museum - 1939
Historical veterinary and laboratory equipment, furniture from the Sir Arnold Theiler era 28552

Oudtshoorn

Arbeidsgenot, 217 Jan Van Riebeeck Rd, Oudtshoorn 6625 - T: (044) 2722968, Fax: 2722968. Head: Prof. J. Olivier
Special Museum / Historic Site
Former home of C.J. Langenhoven (1903-1932) - library 28553

Cango Caves Interpretive Centre, Voortrekker Rd, Oudtshoorn 6620, mail addr: POB 255, Oudtshoorn 6620 - T: (044) 2727410, Fax: 2728001, 2722755, E-mail: reservations@cangocaves.co.za. Head: M.C.T. Schultz
Natural History Museum / Archaeological Museum - 1967
Bushmen rock paintings, fossils, minerals, archaeology, paleontology, speleology 28554

C.P. Nel Museum, Baron Van Reede Rd, Oudtshoorn 6620 - T: (044) 2727306, Fax: 2727306, E-mail: cpnmuseum@pixie.co.za
Local Museum - 1953
Photographs, furniture, porcelain, musical instruments, firearms, household utensils, natural hist exhibits, old vehicles, hist of the Ostrich industry - library, archive 28555

Paarl

Afrikaans Language Museum, Gideon Malherbe House, Parsonage Ln, Paarl 7621, mail addr: POB 498, Paarl 7620 - T: (021) 8723441, Fax: 8723642, E-mail: afrmus@intekom.co.za, Internet: http://www.museums.org.za/. Head: J.P. Louvv
Special Museum - 1975
Exhibits related to development of Afrikaans as a written, national language, first editions of early Afrikaans publications, period furnishings 28556

The Paarl Museum, 303 Main St, Paarl 7646 - T: (021) 8722651, Fax: 8723642, E-mail: museum1@telkomsa.net. Head: M. Victor
Decorative Arts Museum - 1939
18th c Dutch furniture, Cape and English silver, Chinese, English and Dutch porcelain, glass, copper and brass kitchen utensils, coach house, farming implements, French Hugenot exhibits - library 28557

Parys

Parys Museum, Liebenbergstrek, Parys 9585, mail addr: Private Bag X20543, Parys 9585 - T: (01601) 2131, Fax: 2131
Local Museum
Development and local industries (nylon, basketry, colddrink s) 28558

Philippolis

Museum Transgariep, Private Bag X20543, Philippolis 9970 - T: (051) 772216, Fax: 7730213. Head: T.A. Lubbe
Historical Museum - 1982
Emily Hobhouse spinning and weaving school, local history, Griqua culture, witblits (moonshine) culture 28559

Pietermaritzburg

Jack Heath Art Gallery, University of Natal, Department of Fine Art and History of Art, PBag X01, Pietermaritzburg 3209 - T: (033) 32605170, Fax: 32605599
Fine Arts Museum / University Museum
South African and European art, ceramics, graphic prints 28560

Macrorie House Museum, 11 Loop St, Pietermaritzburg 3201 - T: (033) 3942161, Internet: http://www.zulu.org.za. Head: M. Rei
Decorative Arts Museum / Religious Arts Museum - 1975
Restored Victorian mansion of the 1870s, furniture and furnishings 28561

Natal Museum, 237 Loop St, Pietermaritzburg 3201, mail addr: Private Bag 9070, Pietermaritzburg 3200 - T: (033) 3451404/05, Fax: 3450561, E-mail: library@nmsa.org.za, Internet: http://www.nmsa.org.za. Head: Dr. Jason Londt
Local Museum / Natural History Museum - 1904
Afrotropical Diptera, Indopacific mollusks, African Arachnida, archeology, ethnology of Southern Africa, local hist, ungulate mammals of Africa - library 28562

Tatham Art Gallery, Commercial Rd, Pietermaritzburg 3201 - T: (033) 3421804, Fax: 3949831, E-mail: bell@tatham.org.za. Head: Brendan Bell
Fine Arts Museum - 1903
19th-20th c English and French works of art, graphic arts (19th c to present), objects d'art, oriental carpets, Southern African works of art 28563

Voortrekker Museum, Longmarket ands Boshoff Sts, Pietermaritzburg 3201, mail addr: POB 998, Pietermaritzburg 3200 - T: (033) 3946834/35, Fax: 3424100, E-mail: voortmus@iafrica.com. Head: Dr. Ivor Pols
Historical Museum / Local Museum - 1912
Voortrekker hist, homemade furniture, firearms, household utensils, costumes, wagons, Zulu and Indian culture, Zulu home, Stainbank coll of sculptures, replica of Indian temple 28564

Pietersburg

Pietersburg Art Museum, 70 Schoeman St, Pietersburg 0699, mail addr: POB 111, Pietersburg 0700 - T: (015) 2902177, Fax: 2902178, E-mail: anriet.vdev@pietersburg.org.za, Internet: http://www.pietersburg.org.za. Head: Anriët van Deventer
Fine Arts Museum - 1972
South african and Northern Province artists 28565

Pilgrim's Rest

Pilgrim's Rest Museum, Private Bag X519, Pilgrim's Rest 1290 - T: (013) 7681471/72, Fax: 7681469
Science&Tech Museum - 1974
Mining reduction works with original equipment, furnished miner's and mine manager's houses, robey steam engine 28566

Port Elizabeth

King George VI Art Gallery, 1 Park Dr, Port Elizabeth 6001 - T: (041) 5861030, Fax: 5863234, E-mail: kgg@kgg.gov.za, Internet: http://www.kgg.gov.za. Head: Dr. Melanie Hillebrand
Fine Arts Museum - 1956
South African art, Oriental art, British art, Chinese textiles, international printmaking 28567

Port Elizabeth Museum, Humewood, Beach Rd, Port Elizabeth 6013, mail addr: c/o Bayworld Inc., POB 13147, Port Elizabeth 6013 - T: (041) 5861051, Fax: 5862175, E-mail: pemdjp@zoo.upe.ac.za, Internet: http://www.bayworld.co.za. Head: S. Van Zyl
Local Museum / Natural History Museum - 1856
Oceanarium, snake park, local cultural history house museum, marine biology, marine archaeology, natural hist skulls, otolith coll, marine mammal skeleton coll, herpetology coll, costume coll, ichthyology - library 28568

SAAF Museum Port Elizabeth, South African Air Force, Airport Southside, Port Elizabeth 6013 - T: (041) 505129
Military Museum 28569

Potchefstroom

Goetz/Fleischack Museum, Gouws and Potgieter St, Potchefstroom 2520 - T: (018) 2995022, Internet: http://www.potch.co.za/tourism/museums.htm
Historical Museum - 1985
Home of A.M. Goetz (magistrate during the 1st Iniependence war 1880-81) and A.R. Fleischack (founder of the oldest firm of attorneys in town) 28570

Potchefstroom Museum, Gouws and Wolmarans Str, Potchefstroom 2520 - T: (018) 2995022, Fax: 2948203. Head: E. Weyers
Local Museum - 1960
Household utensils, furniture, clothing, weapons transport, artworks, local hist coll (artefacts, photogr, documents) - library 28571

President Pretorius Museum, Van der Hoff Av, Potchefstroom 2520 - T: (018) 2995022
Historical Museum
Home of the first President of the ZAR 28572

Totius House Museum, Molen and Esselen Sts, Potchefstroom 2520 - T: (018) 2995022
Special Museum - 1977
Rector's residence, J.D. Du Toit translated Bible into Afrikaans 28573

University Art Gallery, c/o University of Potchefstroom, Ferdinand Postma Library Bldg, Potchefstroom 2520 - T: (0148) 22112x2781. Head: Prof. Dr. G.M. Ballot
Fine Arts Museum / University Museum
Contemporary South African art 28574

Potgietersrus

Arend Dieperink Museum, 97 Voortrekker Rd, Potgietersrus 0600, mail addr: POB 34, Potgietersrus 0600 - T: (015) 4912244 ext 9735, Fax: 4915142, E-mail: arendmus@lantic.net, Internet: http://www.potgietersrus.co.za/museum
Local Museum / Archaeological Museum / Agriculture Museum - 1968
Relics of Voortrekker leader Piet Potgieter, farming implements and wagons, old music instruments, furniture and furnishings, photos and documents, Makapansgat caves 28575

Pretoria

Coert Steynbergmuseum, Bergln 465, Pretoria - T: (012) 5460404
Special Museum 28576

Edoardo Villa Museum, c/o University of Pretoria, Old Merensky Library, Main Campus, Pretoria 0002 - T: (012) 4204017, Fax: 4202262, E-mail: uwe@ccnet.up.ac.za
Historical Museum - 1995 28577

Engelenburg House Art Collection, 514 Ziervogel St, Arcadia, Pretoria 0007 - T: (012) 3285082, Fax: 3285091, E-mail: akademie@mweb.co.za, Internet: http://www.akademie.co.za. Head: Prof. Theuns Erasmus
Decorative Arts Museum - 1942
Oriental and Cape ceramics, Cape, English and Dutch furniture, tapestries, painting, carpets 28578

Ivan Solomon Gallery, c/o Pretoria Technikon, 420 Church St, Pretoria 0002 - T: (012) 283811 ext 316. Head: Carl Jeppe
Public Gallery 28579

Jansen Collection, 214 Struben St, Pretoria 0002, mail addr: POB 3300, Pretoria 0001
Decorative Arts Museum / Fine Arts Museum - 1964
18th and 19th c South African and imported furniture, Chinese and Japanese porcelain, ceramics and paintings by famous South African artists 28580

Kruger Museum, 60 Church St W, Pretoria 0002 - T: (012) 3269172, Fax: 3269595. Head: Anneke Lugtenburg
Historical Museum - 1934
Residence (1884-1900) of Paul Kruger (Pres. of Zuid- Afrikaansche Republiek, lifestyle at this time, Boer republic in SA against British imperialism 28581

Mapungubwe Museum, Sasol African Heritage Exhibition, c/o University of Pretoria, Old Arts Bldg, Main Campus, Lynnwood Rd, Pretoria 0002 - T: (027) 4203146, Fax: 4202262, E-mail: mapungubwe@postino.up.ac.za, Internet: http://mapungubwe.up.ac.za. Head: Sian L. Tiley
Archaeological Museum / University Museum
Archaeology on the farm Greefswald (Northern Province), 3 royal graves, coll of ceramic, bone, gold, ivory, glass and various metals 28582

Melrose House, 275 Jacob Maré St, Pretoria 0002 - T: (012) 3220420, Fax: 3202742. Head: E. Waldeck
Decorative Arts Museum - 1971
Late Victorian interior, dining room in which Peace Treaty of Vereeniging ending the Anglo-Boer War was signed - research library 28583

Museum of Anthropology and Archaeology, c/o Department of Anthropology and Archaeology, University of South Africa, Theo van Wijk Bldg, Muckleneuk Ridge, Pretoria 0003 - T: (012) 4296297, Fax: 4296297, E-mail: coetzfp@unisa.ac.za, Internet: http://www.unisa.ac.za/dept/vir/index.html. Head: F.P. Coetzee
Ethnology Museum / Archaeological Museum - 1957
Ethnography, folklore, archaeology of South Africa (Stone and Iron Age), anthropology (traditional artefacts of all natural groups of South Africa), fossils and replicas of Hominids, Xhose beadwrok coll 28584

Museum of Natural History, Transvaal Museum, Paul Kruger St, Pretoria 0002, mail addr: POB 413, Pretoria 0001 - T: (012) 3227632, Fax: 3227939, E-mail: kemp@nfi.co.za, Internet: http://

www.nfi.co.za. Head: Dr. Alan Kemp
Natural History Museum - 1893
South African fossil ape-men, mammals, birds, lower vertebrates, insects 28585

Museum of Science and Technology, 211 Skinner St, Pretoria 0002, mail addr: POB 1758, Pretoria 0001 - T: (012) 3226404, Fax: 3207803, E-mail: hanaue@fest.org.za. Head: E. Hanau
Science&Tech Museum - 1960
Hands-on science and educational models 28586

Museum of the Council for Geoscience, Paul Kruger St, Pretoria 0002, mail addr: Private Bag X112, Pretoria 0001 - T: (012) 3227122, Fax: 3200178, E-mail: pbender@nfi.co.za. Head: Dr. P. Bender
Natural History Museum - 1903
Rocks and minerals, Karroo reptiles, Gibeon meteorites, Alexander Bay marine diamonds, fossils, economic ores of South Africa 28587

National Cultural History Museum, 149 Visagie St, Sunnyside, Pretoria 0002 - T: (012) 3411320, Fax: 3416146, Internet: http://www.nchm.com. Head: Glyn Balkwill
Historical Museum - 1892
History od the area north of Vaal river, ceramics and glass, transport, textiles, art works, paper, organic materials, minerals, metals, weapons and arms, numismatics, photo coll - archives, library, mediatheque 28588

Old Art Gallery, c/o University of Pretoria, Old Arts Bldg, Main Campus, Pretoria 0002 - T: (012) 4203036, Fax: 4202262, E-mail: artcase@global.co.za. Head: Frieda Van Schalkwijy, Thea Van Schalkwijy
Fine Arts Museum / University Museum 28589

Pathology Museum, Beatrix St, Pretoria 0001, mail addr: c/o Institute of Pathology, University of Pretoria, POB 2034, Pretoria 0001 - T: (012) 3192614, Fax: 3214372, E-mail: ldreyer@medic.up.ac.za. Head: Prof. L. Dreyer
Natural History Museum / University Museum - 1945
Pathology exhibits 28590

Pretoria Art Museum, Arcadia Park, Wessels St, Pretoria 0083 - T: (012) 3441807/08, Fax: 3441809, E-mail: art.museum@tshwane.gov.za, Internet: http://www.pretoriaartmuseum.com. Head: D.C. Offringa
Fine Arts Museum - 1964
South African art from the 19th c to the present, graphic arts, African artifacts, international graphics, Lady Michaelis Bequest (17th c Dutch art) 28591

The Puppet Museum, c/o University of Pretoria, Education Law Bldg, Main Campus, Pretoria 0002 - T: (012) 4203031. Head: Melanie Gobler
Decorative Arts Museum / University Museum 28592

Sammy Marks Museum, East of Pretoria, N4 exit 11 to Witbank, Sunnyside, Pretoria 0002 - T: (012) 8021150, Fax: 8021292, E-mail: smarks@nfi.co.za, Internet: http://www.afsef.com/SammyMarks. Head: N. Walters
Decorative Arts Museum - 1986
A good example of Victoriana which belonged to the Marks family from the late-19th c until 1920 28593

South African Mint Museum, Coin World Tourist Centre, Pretoria 0002, mail addr: POB 464, Pretoria 0001 - T: (012) 6772342, Fax: 6772690. Head: E. Harbuz
Special Museum - 1923
Coins, tokens and medals, plaques and badges, history of the mint - library 28594

South African Police Service Museum, Kompol Bldg, Pretorius St and Volkstem Av, Pretoria 0002, mail addr: POB 4866, Pretoria 0001 - T: (012) 3536770, Fax: 3536771/75. Head: M. Smal
Special Museum - 1968
Uniforms, insignia, arms, and other artifacts showing the hist of the police force in South Africa, crime detection and prevention 28595

S.P. Engelbrecht Museum of the Nederduitsch Hervormde Kerk van Afrika, 224 Jacob Maré St, Pretoria 0002, mail addr: POB 2368, Pretoria 0001 - T: (012) 3228885, Fax: 3227909. Head: F.S. Van Rensburg
Religious Arts Museum - 1960
Artefacts relating to the history of the Dutch Reformed Church of Africa, coins and commemorative medals, painting, incunabula, cultural antiquities 28596

Stampwise Info Square, Church Sq, Pretoria 0002, mail addr: POB 800, Pretoria 0001 - T: (012) 3235078, Fax: 3211314, E-mail: deanb@sapo.co.za, Internet: http://www.sapo.co.za. Head: Nancy Moetlo
Special Museum - 1995
Postal equipment, postage stamps, postboxes - library 28597

UNISA Art Gallery, Theo van Wijk Bldg, B-Block, Pretoria 0003, mail addr: c/o University of South Africa, Posbus 392, Pretoria 0001 - T: (012) 4296255, 4296823, Fax: 4293221, E-mail: hattif@unisa.ac.za, Internet: http://www.unisa.ac.za
Fine Arts Museum / University Museum 28598

University of Pretoria Art Collection, Main Campus, Pretoria 0002 - T: (012) 4204017, Fax: 4202262, E-mail: uwe@ccnet.up.ac.za. Head: Uwe Gunther
Fine Arts Museum / University Museum 28599

Van Gybland-Oosterhoff Collection, c/o University of Pretoria, Old Arts Bldg, Main Campus, Pretoria 0002 - T: (012) 4203100, Fax: 4202262, E-mail: valerie@ccnet.up.ac.za, Internet: http://www.up.ac.za/services/marketing/van2.html. Head: Valerie Esterhuizen
Fine Arts Museum / Decorative Arts Museum / University Museum
Ceramics, silver, statuettes, medals, glasware, paintings, graphics, photographs 28600

Van Tilburg Collection, c/o University of Pretoria, Old Arts Bldg, Main Campus, Pretoria 0002 - T: (012) 4203100, Fax: 4202262, E-mail: valerie@ccnet.up.ac.za, Internet: http://www.up.ac.za/services/marketing/vantil_ge1.html. Head: Valerie Esterhuizen
Fine Arts Museum / Decorative Arts Museum / University Museum
Chinese and Japanese porcelain, Dutch Delft, furniture, paintings, graphic works 28601

Voortrekker Monument Heritage Site, Eeufees Rd, Pretoria 0002, mail addr: POB 1514, Groenkloof 0027 - T: (012) 3266770, Fax: 3268374, E-mail: vtm@voortrekkermon.org.za, Internet: http://www.voortrekkermon.org.za. Head: G. Opperman
Local Museum - 1957
Tapestries depicting the hist of the Great Trek, period rooms and displays depicting the Voortrekkers' lifestyle, Voortrekker memorabilia, maps of migrations in Africa, monument depicting the course of the pioneers 28602

Queenstown

Queenstown and Frontier Museum, 13 Shepstone St, Queenstown 5320 - T: (0451) 5860. Head: M. du Plessis
Local Museum - 1933
Lepidoptra, ethnic beadwork 28603

Rayton

Willem Prinsloo Museum, Kaalfontein, Rayton 1001 - T: (012) 7344171/72, Fax: 7344173, E-mail: nchm@nchm.co.za. Head: Etta Judson
Open Air Museum / Agriculture Museum - 1980
Late 19th c farm houses and outbuildings in the Cullinan district, between Pretoria and Bronkhorstspruit, horse-drawn vehicles, farming equipment and implements from Stone Age to 1945, indigerious animals 28604

Richmond

Richmond Museum, 19 Loop St, Richmond 7090 - T: (0536) 930023. Head: Chast Van der Heever
Decorative Arts Museum
Cape Dutch and Victorian furnishings in former (1863) school house, displays devoted to the American saddle horse 28605

Riversdale

Julius Gordon Africana Centre, Versveld House, Long St, Riversdale 6670 - T: (028) 7132418, Fax: 7133146, E-mail: riversdale@ezinet.co.za, Internet: http://www.riversdaler.co.za. Head: B. Burger
Fine Arts Museum / Decorative Arts Museum / Archaeological Museum - 1966
South African painting and antiques, furniture, domestic utensils, clocks, paintings by Thomas Bowler, ethnology, antiquities 28606

Robben Island

Robben Island Museum, Robben Island 7400 - T: (021) 4111006, Fax: 4111059, E-mail: info@robben-island.org.za, Internet: http://www.robben-island.org.za
Local Museum 28607

Rondebosch

Centre for African Studies Collection, University of Cape Town, Private Bag, Rondebosch 7700 - T: (021) 6502310. Head: Andrew Steyn
Fine Arts Museum / University Museum
Contemporary South African art, sculptures, paintings, West African textiles 28608

Wagner P.A. Museum, c/o Department of Geology, University of Cape Town, Rondebosch 7700 - T: 6502932. Head: P.J. Chadwick
Natural History Museum / University Museum 28609

Rosebank

Irma Stern Museum of the University of Cape Town, The Firs, Cecil Rd, Rosebank 7700 - T: (021) 6855686, Fax: 6867550, E-mail: bpettit@protem.uct.ac.za, Internet: http://www.museums.org.za/irma. Head:
Fine Arts Museum / Decorative Arts Museum / Archaeological Museum - 1972
African art and paintings of Irma Stern housed in former home of the artist, furnishings and objects d'art - library 28610

Works of Art Collection, University of Cape Town, Irma Stern House, Cecil Rd, Rosebank 7700 - T: (021) 6855686, Fax: 6867550, E-mail: cpeter@protem.uct.ac.za. Head: Christopher Peter
Fine Arts Museum / University Museum
South African and European art 28611

Saxonwold

South African National Museum of Military History, 22 Erlswold Way, Saxonwold 2196, mail addr: POB 52090, Saxonwold 2132 - T: (011) 6465513, Fax: 6465256, E-mail: milmus@icon.co.za. Head: John Keene
Military Museum - 1947
Military items, South African war art and photographs, aircraft, armored vehicles, small arms, artillery, medals, insignia, uniforms, flags, edged weapons - library 28612

Silverton

Pioneer Museum, Watermeyer St, Silverton 0127 - T: (012) 8036086/7, Fax: 8035639. Head: A.C. Van Vollenharen
Historical Museum - 1975
Pioneer cottage of 1848 with pioneer furniture and other articles situated on a period farmyard 28613

Simon's Town

Simon's Town Museum, Court Rd, Simon's Town 7975 - T: (021) 7863046, Fax: 7862391, E-mail: stmuseum@mweb.co.za, Internet: http://simonstown.com. Head: Cherry Dilley
Local Museum - 1977
Militaria and naval relics, Winifred and Llew Gay coll of cultural material, Willis coll of archival material, photographic glass plate negative coll, archaeological material from Khoisan site, cultural archaeology from site at the museum, artefacts from maritime archaeology on shipwrecks, early colonial hist (Dutch & British) of Simon's Town, the forced removal of 7,000 people under the Group Areas Act of the 1960's 28614

Skukuza

Stevenson-Hamilton Memorial Information Centre, Kruger National Park, Skukuza 1350, mail addr: POB 50, Skukuza 1350 - T: (013) 7355611 ext 2139, Fax: 7355138. Head: I. Grobler
Local Museum - 1961
Early, middle and late Stone Ages artifacts, local cultural hist, Africana coll, photographic and archival material, wildlife art - Africana library 28615

Smithfield

Museum Caledon River, 5 Douglas St, Smithfield 9966, mail addr: Private Bag X20543, Bloemfontein 9300 - T: (051) 6831105, Fax: 6831143. Head: T.A. Lubbe
Historical Museum - 1983
Smithfield commando, French missionary work, leading personalities of region, Gen. C. de Wet 28616

Somerset East

Somerset East Museum, Beaufort and McKay Sts, Somerset East 5850, mail addr: POB 151, Somerset East 5850
Decorative Arts Museum
Period furnishings in original setting, outbuildings and grounds 28617

Stellenbosch

Geology Museum of the University of Stellenbosch, c/o University of Stellenbosch, Chamber of Mines Building, Ryneveld St, Stellenbosch 7600 - T: (021) 8083219, Fax: 8083129, E-mail: ar@sun.ac.za, Internet: http://www.sun.ac.za. Head: Prof. A. Rozendaal
Natural History Museum / University Museum - 1911
Geology, mineralogy, gemmology, palaeontology 28618

Missionary Museum of the N.G. Kerk, 171 Dorp St, Stellenbosch 7600 - T: (021) 8083255, Fax: 8083251, E-mail: wriek@sun.ac.za, Internet: http://www.sun.ac.za/theology/. Head: Prof. D.J. Louw
Religious Arts Museum - 1982
Relics of early missionaries, photos and maps showing spread of missionary activity in Africa, artifacts related to Islam, Hinduism, Judaism, African traditional religions 28619

Rembrandt Van Rijn Art Gallery, 31 Dorp St, Stellenbosch 7600, mail addr: POB 456, Stellenbosch 7599 - T: (021) 8864340, Fax: 8883399. Head: D.E. Herselman
Fine Arts Museum - 1971
Sculptures of Anton van Wouw, panorama of Cape Town, 1808, by Josephus Jones, changing exhibitions of contemporary South African works of art owned by the Rembrandt van Rijn Art Foundation 28620

Sasol Art Museum and University Art Gallery, c/o Dept. of Creative Arts, University of Stellenbosch, Cnr Bird and Dorp Sts, Stellenbosch 7600 - T: (021) 8083693, Fax: 8083669, E-mail: usmuseum@maties.sun.ac.za
Fine Arts Museum / University Museum
Temporary exhibitions of works by university students and South African and overseas artists 28621

Stellenbosch Museum, 37 Ryneveld St, Stellenbosch 7600, mail addr: Private Bag X5048, Stellenbosch 7599 - T: (021) 8872937, Fax: 8832232, E-mail: stelmus@mweb.co.za, Internet: http://www.museums.org.za. Head: Marius Le Roux
Decorative Arts Museum / Historical Museum - 1962
Period furniture and furnishings, kitchen utensils, costume, textiles, historic gardens, weaponry, toys and miniatures 28622

Toy and Miniature Museum, Market St, Stellenbosch 7600 - T: (021) 8872948, E-mail: stelmus@mweb.co.za
Special Museum 28623

University Museum, 52 Ryneveld St, Stellenbosch 7600, mail addr: c/o University of Stellenbosch, Private Bag X1, Stellenbosch 7602 - T: (021) 8083693, Fax: 8083669, E-mail: usmuseum@maties.sun.ac.za, Internet: http://www.sun.ac.za/usmuseum. Head: Dr. Lydia M. De Waal
Fine Arts Museum / University Museum - 1991
Art, anthropology, cultural history 28624

University of Stellenbosch Art Gallery, Cnr Bird and Dorp Sts, 7600 Stellenbosch - T: (021) 8083524, Fax: 8083669, E-mail: usmuseum@adm.sun.ac.za. Head: Dr. Lydia M. De Waal
Fine Arts Museum / University Museum - 1968
South African artists and student works 28625

Village Museum, 18 Ryneveld St, Stellenbosch 7600 - T: (021) 8872902, Fax: 8832232, E-mail: stelmus@mweb.co.za
Local Museum 28626

Sterkstroom

Sterkstroom Museum, 34 Van Zyl St, Sterkstroom 5425 - T: (045) 9660188, Fax: 9660188. Head: Engela Beukes
Local Museum / Agriculture Museum - 1976
Local historical relics, agricultural implements, general store items, ceramics, embroidery, Anglo-Boer War artifacts, Khoza art, Xhoza beadwork 28627

Swartkop

SAAF Museum Swartkop, South African Air Force, Air Force Base, PO Valhalla, Swartkop 0137 - T: (012) 3512214, 3512153, Fax: 3512346
Military Museum 28628

Swellendam

Drostdy Museum, Swellengrebel St, Swellendam 6740 - T: (028) 5141138, Fax: 5142675, E-mail: drostdymuseum@sdm.dorea.co.za. Head: M. Van Hemert
Historical Museum / Agriculture Museum / Open Air Museum - 1939
Crafts, furniture, horsemill, interior, tools, trades, watermill 28629

Tulbagh

De Oude Drostdy, Drostdy Village, Tulbagh 6822 - T: (023) 2300203, Fax: 2300203. Head: M. Zelie
Decorative Arts Museum - 1974
Cape furniture, porcelain, glass and copperware 28630

Oude Kerk Volksmuseum, 4 Church St, Tulbagh 6820 - T: (023) 2301041, Fax: 2302950, E-mail: oudekerk@xpoint.co.za. Head: M.J. Potgieter
Folklore Museum / Decorative Arts Museum - 1925
Furniture and furnishings, dolls, kitchen utensils, weapons, books 28631

Uitenhage

Africana Museum, Town Hall, Market St, Uitenhage 6230, mail addr: POB 45, Uitenhage 6230 - T: 22011
Folklore Museum - 1960
Clothing, furniture and household utensils, personal relics of Gen. J.G. Cuyler (Landdrost 1806-1828) and Adriaan van Kervel (Cape governor 1737), 'De Mist Bible' 28632

Cuyler Manor, Uitenhage 6230 - T: 22011
Local Museum
Manor house and old water mill on grounds of farm founded in 1814 by American-born British officer Jacob Glen Cuyler 28633

Uitenhage Historical Museum, Market St, Uitenhage 6230 - T: 22011
Historical Museum - 1974
Railroad equipment from 1870 on 28634

Upington

Kalahari-Oranje Museum, Former Church, Upington 8800 - T: (054) 3326064
Local Museum
History of the Lower Orange River Valley 28635

Vereeniging

Vaal Teknorama Cultural and Industrial Museum, Skippie Botha Park, 1 Beethoven St, Duncanville, Vereeniging 1939, mail addr: POB 162, Vereeniging 1939 - T: (016) 4503136, Fax: 4212543, E-mail: renep@lekoa.co.za. Head: R. Pelser

Local Museum / Science&Tech Museum - 1966
Photos relating to the Anglo-Boer War, local hist, local fossils, F.W. de Klerk Presidential Museum 28636

Verulam

Mahatma Gandhi Museum, Phoenix Settlement, Inanda Rd, Verulam 4340, mail addr: POB 331, Verulam 4340 - T: (032) 5331166
Special Museum - 1969
Personal possessions of Mahatma Gandhi - library 28637

Victoria West

Victoria West Regional Museum, 47 Church St, Victoria West 7070 - T: (053) 6210413, Fax: 6210413, E-mail: rvlok@museumsnc.co.za. Head: Rochelle Vlok
Local Museum - 1969
Relics, photos and documents relating to hist of the town, local prehist (of the Karoo), cultural hist of Victoria West - fish fossil hall 28638

Vryburg

Vryburg Museum, POB 49, Vryburg 8600
Local Museum
Historic relics of the town 28639

Vryheid

Nieuwe Republiek Museums - Vryheid, 119 Landdrost, Vryheid 3100, mail addr: POB 57, Vryheid 3100 - T: (034) 9822133 ext 2287, Fax: 9823497, E-mail: information@ vhd.dorea.so.za. Head: S. Tustin
Historical Museum - 1938
Articles from the period of the Nieuwe Republiek (1884-1888) and the Zuid Afrikaanse Republiek (1888-1900) 28640

Weenen

Weenen Museum, POB 13, Weenen 3325
Local Museum
Costumes, firearms, relics from the Voortrekker period, period kitchen 28641

Welkom

Welkom Museum, Welkom 9460, mail addr: Private Bag X20543, Bloemfontein 9300 - T: (057) 3913133, Fax: 3532482. Head: T.A. Lubbe
Local Museum - 1987
Gold mining industry, bird life, leading personalities of mining industry, pioneers of region 28642

Westville

Bergtheil Museum, 16 Queens Av, Westville 3290 - T: (031) 2037107, Fax: 2037107. Head: A. Calboutin
Local Museum 28643

Winburg

Voortrekker Museum of the Orange Free State, Winburg 9420, mail addr: Private Bag X20543, Bloemfontein 9300 - T: (051) 8810130. Head: T.A. Lubbe
Historical Museum - 1979
Household articles used during Great Trek, State History ca. 1830-1860 28644

Worcester

Worcester Museum, 23 Traub St, Worcester 6850, mail addr: POB 557, Worcester 6850 - T: (023) 3422225/6, Fax: 3474134, E-mail: kleinplasie@ mweb.co.za. Head: I.H. Souris
Agriculture Museum / Historical Museum / Open Air Museum - 1941
19th c Cape furniture, domestic utensils, works by Worcester artist Hugo Naudé, documents and photographs, local history, farm outbuildings 28645

Ysterplaat

SAAF Museum Ysterplaat, South African Air Force, Koeberg Rd and Piet Grobler St, Ysterplaat 7425, mail addr: POB 100580, Ysterplaat 7425 - T: (021) 5086377, Internet: http://www.saafmuseum.co.za
Military Museum 28646

Spain

Abarca de Campos

Centro de Arte Contemporáneo, La Fábrica, 34338 Abarca de Campos - T: 979837560
Fine Arts Museum 28647

Agost

Centro Agost, Museo de Alfarería, Calle Teulería 11, 03698 Agost - T: 965691199, Fax: 965691199, E-mail: museoagost@dragonet.es. Head: Ilse Schütz
Ethnology Museum - 1983 28648

Agramunt

Espai Guinovart, Plaza del Mercat s/n, 25310 Agramunt - T: 973390904, Fax: 973390040
Fine Arts Museum 28649

Museu Municipal, Plaza del Mercat 1, 25310 Agramunt - T: 973390057, Fax: 973390040
Local Museum 28650

Agreda

Museo Sor María de Jesús de Agreda, Convento de la Concepción, Calle Vozmediano 29, 42100 Agreda - T: 975647095
Religious Arts Museum - 1965
Religious art, memorabilia on María Coronel y de Arana (1602-1665), her books, correspondence and personal objects 28651

Agüimes

Museo y Artesanía el Molino, Las Rosas, Calle Mozart 1, 35119 Agüimes - T: 928782439
Folklore Museum 28652

Aguilar de Campoo

Museo Parroquial Colegiata de San Miguel, Plaza España s/n, 34800 Aguilar de Campoo - T: 979122688
Religious Arts Museum - 1989 28653

Alaejos

Museo Interparroquial de Alaejos, Iglesia de Santa María, Plaza Santa María 1, 47510 Alaejos - T: 983867189
Religious Arts Museum 28654

Alba de Tormes

Museo Didáctico de Prehistoria, Seminario de San Jerónimo, Carretera de Galinduste s/n, 37800 Alba de Tormes - T: 923300135, Fax: 300808, E-mail: scjalba@planalja.es
Archaeological Museum 28655

Museo Teresiano, Plaza Santa Teresa 4, 37800 Alba de Tormes - T: 923300043
Religious Arts Museum 28656

Albacete

Museo de Albacete, Parque de Abelardo Sánchez, 02002 Albacete - T: 967228307, Fax: 967229515. Head: Rubi Sanz Gamo
Fine Arts Museum / Archaeological Museum / Local Museum - 1926
Archeology: ceramics, sculptures, inscriptions, numismatics, fine arts: 117 works of Benjamin Palecia, contemporary art - library 28657

Museo del Niño, Calle México s/n, 02006 Albacete - T: 967234035, E-mail: juanperalto@ono.com, Internet: http://www.museodelnino.es. Head: Juan Peralta Juárez
Ethnology Museum 28658

Albarracín

Museo Diocesano de Albarracín, Calle Catedral s/n, 44100 Albarracín - T: 978710084
Religious Arts Museum - 1961
Tapestry, goldsmith work, painting, sculpture, 13th c cathedral 28659

Albinyana

Aqualeon Parc de la Natura, Finca les Basses s/n, 43716 Albinyana - T: 977687656, Fax: 977687823, E-mail: comercial@aspro-ocio.com, Internet: http:// www.aspro-ocio.com
Natural History Museum 28660

Albocácer

Colleción Parroquial, Calle San Vicente 1, 12140 Albocácer - T: 964428033
Religious Arts Museum - 1968
Ecclesiastical art, painting, sculpture, goldsmith work 28661

Alcalá de Guadaira

Museo Taurino Conde de Colombi, c/o Hotel Oromana, Urbanización P. Oromana s/n, 41500 Alcalá de Guadaira - T: 955684202
Local Museum 28662

Alcalá de Henares

Casa Natal de Cervantes, Calle Mayor 48, 28801 Alcalá de Henares - T: 918899654, Fax: 918899654. Head: Charo Melero Tejerina
Special Museum - 1955
Memorial to and birthplace of the writer Miguel de Cervantes Saavedra (1547-1616), 16th c furniture, 17th c pottery - library 28663

Museo Arqueológico, Camino del Juncal s/n, 28802 Alcalá de Henares - T: 918813250
Archaeological Museum / Historical Museum 28664

Museo Específico de la Brigada Paracaidista, Carretera de Meco s/n, 28807 Alcalá de Henares - T: 918880300, Fax: 918880812
Military Museum 28665

Museo Histórico de la Administración Española, Antigua Universidad, 28801 Alcalá de Henares
Historical Museum - 1962
History of the Spanish administration 28666

Alcantarilla

Museo Municipal Etnológico de la Huerta, c/o Acequia Barreras, Desvío Carretera 340 Murcia-Granada, 30820 Alcantarilla - T: 968893866, Fax: 968800782
Ethnology Museum - 1963
Local ethnography, interiors, furniture, ceramics, glass, metalwork, textiles, Murciana - library 28667

Alcázar de San Juan

Casa Municipal de Cultura. Sala de Exposiciones, Calle Goya 1, 13600 Alcázar de San Juan - T: 926540707, Fax: 926540762
Fine Arts Museum 28668

Museo Ferroviario, Estación de Renfe, 13600 Alcázar de San Juan
Science&Tech Museum 28669

Museo Municipal, Antigua Posada Santo Domingo, Calle Santo Domingo 8-12, 13600 Alcázar de San Juan - T: 926540707, Fax: 926540762. Head: José Fernando Sánchez Ruiz
Archaeological Museum / Ethnology Museum - 1991
Roman mosaics, regional ethnography 28670

Sala de Exposiciones El Pasaje, Pasaje, Plaza España, 13600 Alcázar de San Juan - T: 926540707, Fax: 926540762
Fine Arts Museum 28671

Alcobendas

Acciona, Museo Interactivo de la Ciencia → Cosmolaixa

Cosmolaixa, Calle Pintor Velázquez s/n, 28100 Alcobendas - T: 914845200, Fax: 914845225
Science&Tech Museum 28672

Alcover

Museu Municipal, Calle La Costeta 1-3, 43460 Alcover - T: 977846452, Fax: 977760441, E-mail: museualcover@terra.es. Head: Laia Colomer
Local Museum 28673

Alcoy

Museo Arqueológico Municipal Camilo Visedo Molto, Calle San Miguel 27, 03800 Alcoy - T: 965540302, Fax: 96542376. Head: J.E. Aura Tortosa
Archaeological Museum - 1945
Prehistoric, Iberian, Roman finds, ceramics, terra cotta, painting, numismatics, local history, natural history 28674

Museu de la Festa, Casal de Sant Jordi, Calle Sant Miquel 60, 03801 Alcoy - T: 965540580
Special Museum 28675

Alcubilla del Marqués

Museo Etnográfico, Calle Ignacio Muga s/n, 42391 Alcubilla del Marqués
Ethnology Museum - 1984 28676

Alcúdia

Fundación Yannick y Ben Jakober, 07400 Alcúdia - T: 971549880, Fax: 971897163, E-mail: fuybjako@ arrakis.es, Internet: http://www.fundacionjakobe-r.arrakis.es. Head: Yannick Jakober
Fine Arts Museum - 1993
Portraits of children 14th-19th c, contemporary photography, sculptures 28677

Museo Arqueológico Municipal, Calle Goded 7, 07400 Alcúdia
Archaeological Museum - 1948
Roman finds from local excavations 28678

Museu Monografic de Pol Lèntia, Calle Sant Jaume 30, 07400 Alcúdia - T: 971577004, 971897102, E-mail: patrimoni@alcudia.net, Internet: http:// www.alcudia.net
Archaeological Museum 28679

Aldea del Rey

Sacro Convento Castillo de Calatrava la Nueva, Carretera Calzada-Puertollano km 7,200, 13380 Aldea del Rey - T: 926866910, Fax: 926865228, E-mail: ayto.aldeadelrey@cim.es, Internet: http:// www.cim.es/aldeadelrey/castillo.htm
Historic Site 28680

Alella

Masia Museu Can Magarola, Calle Riera Coma Clara 16, 08328 Alella - T: 935408210, 935400216, Fax: 935400328
Ethnology Museum 28681

Algaida

Museu del Vidre, Carretera Palma-Manacor, km 19, 07210 Algaida - T: 971665046, Fax: 971665374, E-mail: www.admon@gordiola.com, Internet: http:// www.gordiola.com. Head: Daniel Aldeguer Gordiola
Decorative Arts Museum 28682

Algeciras

Museo Municipal, Calle Ortega y Gasset s/n, 11207 Algeciras - T: 956570672, Fax: 956630477, E-mail: museoalgeciras@teleline.es. Head: Antonio Torremocha Silva
Local Museum - 1995 28683

Alicante

Museo Arqueológico Provincial-MARQ, Plaza Dr. Gómez Ulla s/n, 03013 Alicante - T: 965149000, Fax: 965149058, E-mail: musearqu@dip-alicante.es, Internet: http://www.marq-museo-arqueologico.com. Head: R. Azuar
Local Museum / Archaeological Museum - 1932
Prehist, archaeology, regional and local history, medieval pottery, Islamic bronzes from Egypt found at Denia (11th c) - library 28684

Museo de la Asegurada, Colección Arte Siglo XX, Plaza Santa María 3, 03002 Alicante - T: 965140768, 965140959, Fax: 965202557, E-mail: asegurada@ctv.es
Fine Arts Museum 28685

Allariz

Museo de Arte Sacro de Santa Clara, Convento de Santa Clara, 32660 Allariz - T: 988440702
Religious Arts Museum - 1989 28686

Museo Galego do Xoguete, Calle Portelo 4, 32660 Allariz - T: 988440859
Fine Arts Museum 28687

Parque Etnográfico do Río Arnoia, c/o Casa da Cultura de Allariz, 32660 Allariz - T: 988440001, 988440801, Fax: 988440078
Ethnology Museum 28688

Almagro

Museo del Teatro, Calle Villar 4, 13270 Almagro - T: 926882244, Fax: 926882533, E-mail: museoteatro@inaem.mcu.es, Internet: http://www.inaem.mcu.es. Head: Andrés Peláez Martín
Performing Arts Museum - 1989 28689

Almería

Estación Experimental de Zonas Áridas, Calle General Segura 1, 04001 Almería - T: 950276400, Fax: 950277100, Internet: http://www.eeza.csic.es
Natural History Museum - 1971 28690

Museo Catedralicio, Plaza Catedral, 04001 Almería - T: 950234848
Religious Arts Museum - 1965
Religious art, paintings, liturgical vestments 28691

Museo de Almería, Carretera de Ronda 91, 04006 Almería - T: 950225058
Local Museum - 1933 28692

Almoradi

Museo de la Huerta de Almoradi, Calle Cruz de Galindo, 03160 Almoradi - T: 965700101, 965700326, Fax: 965780104
Ethnology Museum 28693

Almuñécar

Museo Arqueológico, Calle Cueva de Siete Palacios s/n, 18690 Almuñécar - T: 958630426
Archaeological Museum - 1979 28694

La Almunia de Doña Godina

Museo Parroquial, Plaza Iglesia s/n, 50100 La Almunia de Doña Godina - T: 976600891
Religious Arts Museum - 1976 28695

Alquezar

Museo Parroquial, Antigua Colegiata, 22145 Alquezar
Religious Arts Museum - 1931
Ecclesiastical art, painting, sculpture, goldsmith work, liturgical vestments 28696

Altafulla

Museu Parroquial, Parròquia Sant Martí, Plaza Iglesia, 43893 Altafulla - T: 977650158
Religious Arts Museum 28697

Alzira

Museo Municipal, Calle Escoles Pies 4, 46600 Alzira - T: 962417407, E-mail: museo@tiscali.es. Head: Agustín Ferrer Ciari
Local Museum 28698

Ambrona

Museo de las Excavaciones de Torralba, Carretera II Madrid-Barcelona, km 146.2, 42230 Ambrona - T: 975834081. Head: José Luis Argente Oliver
Archaeological Museum - 1963
Local prehistory, fossils 28699

Amposta

Museo Municipal, c/o Ayuntamiento, Plaza de España, 43870 Amposta
Natural History Museum / Archaeological Museum - 1967
Prehistory, local archaeology, zoology from the Ebro delta 28700

Museu del Montsià, Calle Gran Capità 34, 43870 Amposta - T: 977702954. Head: Alex Farnós y Bel
Local Museum 28701

Ampudia

Collección Fontaneda, Castillo de Ampudia, Carretera León-Ampudia, por Villamartín de Campos, 34160 Ampudia - T: 988768023
Archaeological Museum / Fine Arts Museum - 1965
Prehistoric and ancient cultures, medieval art 28702

Amurrio

Museo Etnográfico de Amurrio Felix Murga, Calle Aldai 5, 01470 Amurrio - T: 945891450, Fax: 945891645
Ethnology Museum 28703

Anso

Museo Parroquial de Arte Sacro y Etnología, Iglesia Parroquial, Plaza San Pedro s/n, 22728 Anso - T: 974370022. Head: Damaso Lapetra
Ethnology Museum / Religious Arts Museum - 1973 28704

Antequera

Museo Municipal, Palacio Nájera, Plaza Guerrero Muñoz s/n, 29200 Antequera - T: 952704021, 952704051
Archaeological Museum / Historical Museum - 1966
Archaeology, especially Roman, 16th-18th c painting, sculpture and goldsmith work, history, local ethnography 28705

Museo Taurino Municipal, Plaza de la Constitución s/n, 29200 Antequera - T: 952700726, Fax: 952842908
Ethnology Museum 28706

Aracena

Museo Contemporáneo al Aire Libre, Calle Pozo de la Nieve 21, 21200 Aracena
Open Air Museum 28707

Aranjuez

Falúas Reales, Jardín del Príncipe, 28300 Aranjuez - T: 918911344, Fax: 918921532
Local Museum 28708

Palacio Real de Aranjuez, Plaza de Parejas s/n, 28300 Aranjuez - T: 918911344, 918924332, Fax: 918921532
Fine Arts Museum / Decorative Arts Museum
Former royal palace, 18th c art, decorative arts 28709

Real Casa del Labrador, Jardín del Príncipe s/n, 28300 Aranjuez - T: 918910305, Fax: 918921532
Religious Arts Museum - 1967
Ecclesiastical art 28710

L'Arboç

Museu-Arxiu Arbocenc, Calle Missers 8, 43720 L'Arboç - T: 977670282
Local Museum 28711

Arbúcies

Museu Etnològic del Montseny La Gabella, Carrer Major 6, 17401 Arbúcies - T: 972860908, Fax: 972860983, E-mail: memga@ddgi.es, Internet: http://www.palahi.es/memga/. Head: Jordi Tura
Ethnology Museum - 1983
Ethnological and archaeological coll - documentation center of Montseny, historical archive, library 28712

Arcienaga

Etnografi Museoa, Anexo al Santuario de Nuestra Señora de la Encina, 01474 Arcienaga - T: 945396001, Fax: 945396402
Ethnology Museum 28713

Arcos de la Frontera

Museo-Tesoro Parroquial, Plaza Modesto Gómez 8, 11630 Arcos de la Frontera - T: 956701608
Religious Arts Museum - 1962
Ecclesiastical art, painting, sculpture, goldsmith work, liturgical vestments, choral books 28714

L'Arenal

Collecció la Porciuncula, Av Fra Joan Llabres 1, 07600 L'Arenal - T: 971260002, Fax: 971743919. Head: Bartolomé Sans
Local Museum 28715

Arenas de San Pedro

Museo de la Real Capilla, c/o Convento de San Pedro de Alcántara, 05400 Arenas de San Pedro - T: 920370204
Religious Arts Museum - 1972 28716

Arenys de Mar

Museo-Archivo Municipal Fidel Fita, Plaza de la Villa 2, 08350 Arenys de Mar
Local Museum - 1918
Local archaeology, folk art, maritime history 28717

Museu Marès de la Punta, Calle Església 43, 08350 Arenys de Mar - T: 937921784
Local Museum 28718

Museu Mollfulleda de Mineralogía, Calle Església 39, 08350 Arenys de Mar - T: 937922626, Fax: 937957031, Internet: http://www.ictnet.es/minerals. Head: Joaquin Mollfulleda Borrell
Natural History Museum - 1988
Minerals around the world with special sections for Catalonian minerals and Spanish paragenesis 28719

Areu

Museu de la Fusta, Serradora d'Areu, 25575 Areu - T: 973624355, Fax: 973624388. Head: Josep Feliu Gabarra
Ethnology Museum 28720

Argentona

Museu del Càntir, Plaza de l'Església 9, 08310 Argentona - T: 937972152, Fax: 937970800, E-mail: correu@museucantir.org, Internet: http://www.museucantir.org. Head: Calvo Oriol
Decorative Arts Museum - 1975
Medieval pottery from Catalonia, Art Deco water vessels, Catalonian traditional pottery water vessels - workshop, library 28721

Arnedo

Museo del Calzado y Ciencias Naturales, Calle Palacio 10, 26580 Arnedo - T: 941381080
Local Museum 28722

Aroche

Collección del Santo Rosario, Calle Alférez Lobo 7, 21240 Aroche
Special Museum - 1960
Memorabilia on Santo Rosario 28723

Museo Municipal, Calle Portugal s/n, 21240 Aroche - T: 959140201, Fax: 959140226
Local Museum - 1958
Prehistory, Roman and Arab archaeology, mineralogy, zoology 28724

Arrecife

Museo Internacional de Arte Contemporáneo, Castillo de San José, Carretera de los Mármoles s/n, 35500 Arrecife - T: 928800616, Fax: 928802656. Head: César Manrique Cabrera
Fine Arts Museum 28725

Arsèguel

Museu de l'Acordió, 25722 Arsèguel
Ethnology Museum
Ethnological objects 28726

Artá

Museu Regional d'Artá, Calle Estreña 4, 07570 Artá - T: 971835017. Head: Joan Garcías y Truyols
Local Museum - 1927
Natural history, prehistory, Roman archaeology, folklore - library 28727

Artesa de Lleida

Museu Local Arqueològic, Calle Castell 3, 25150 Artesa de Lleida - T: 973167162, Fax: 973167162
Archaeological Museum 28728

Artesa de Segre

Museu del Montsec, Calle Carnisseries s/n, 25730 Artesa de Segre - T: 973400059
Local Museum 28729

Arucas

Museo Municipal de Arucas, Jardines de Gourie, 35400 Arucas
Fine Arts Museum 28730

Museo Ron Arehucas, Calle Era de San Pedro 2, 35402 Arucas - T: 928600050, Fax: 928603913
Local Museum 28731

Astorga

Museo de los Caminos, Glorieta Eduardo de Castro s/n, 24700 Astorga - T: 987616882
Local Museum - 1963
Art and history pertaining to the pilgrimage routes to Santiago de Compostela, Roman and medieval archaeology, regional ethnography 28732

Museo del Chocolate, Calle José María Goy 5, 24700 Astorga - T: 987616220
Science&Tech Museum 28733

Museo Diocesano-Catedralicio, Plaza de la Catedral s/n, 24700 Astorga - T: 987615820, Fax: 987619151. Head: Bernardo Velado Craña
Religious Arts Museum - 1945
14th-16th c sculpture, painting, 10th-16th c goldsmith work and ceramics, 16th c liturgical vestments, Romantic cathedral 28734

Astudillo

Museo Palacio de Don Pedro I, c/o Convento de Santa Clara, Calle Santa Clara 2, 34450 Astudillo - T: 979822134, Fax: 979822152
Archaeological Museum - 1931 28735

Atauta

Museo Etnográfico, 42345 Atauta - T: 975351163
Ethnology Museum 28736

Avila

Casa Natal de Santa Teresa de Jesús, Convento de Pp. Carmelitas, Plaza La Santa 2, 05001 Avila - T: 920211030
Religious Arts Museum - 1886 28737

Museo Catedralicio, Catedral, 05001 Avila - T: 920211641
Religious Arts Museum - 1947
12th-17th c paintings, 12th-17th c goldsmith art, 15th-18th c choral books, medieval documents, 14th-17th c wood sculptures 28738

Museo de Arte Oriental, Pl de Granada 1, 05003 Avila - T: 920220400, Fax: 920254162, E-mail: comavila@aplanalfa.es. Head: Vicente Eloy
Fine Arts Museum / Decorative Arts Museum - 1964
Art and crafts from China, Japan, the Philippines and Vietnam 28739

Museo de Avila, Casa de los Deanes, Plaza Nalvillos 3, 05001 Avila - T: 920211003, Fax: 920253701. Head: María Mariné Isidro
Local Museum - 1911
Archaeology, paintings, ceramics, folk arts and crafts - library, didactic department 28740

Museo Policial, Centro de Formación de la Policía, Carretera Nacional Avila-Madrid km 0,3, 05080 Avila - T: 920226200, Fax: 920254389
Military Museum - 1925 28741

Museo Teresiano, Convento de San José, Calle Las Madres 4, 05001 Avila - T: 920222127
Religious Arts Museum - 1970 28742

Museo Teresiano Monasterio de la Encarnación, Paseo de la Encarnación s/n, 05005 Avila - T: 920211212
Religious Arts Museum 28743

Museo Virgen de la Portería, Convento de San Antonio, Paseo San Antonio 5, 05005 Avila
Religious Arts Museum - 1943
Religious art, paintings, embroidery and lace 28744

Aya

Centro de Información e Interpretación del Parque de Pagoeta, 20809 Aya - T: 943835389
Ethnology Museum 28745

Conjunto de la Ferrería y Molinos de Agorregi, 20809 Aya - T: 943428842
Special Museum 28746

Ayegui

Museo Etnológico de Navarra Julio Caro Baroja, Monasterio de Irache, 31240 Ayegui - T: 948553556, Fax: 948553556, E-mail: - museo.etnologico.navarra@cfnavarra.es, Internet: http://www.cfnavarra.es/cultura/museoetnologico/
Ethnology Museum
Popular costumes, traditional workshops, traditional technology, popular Navarrese pottery 28747

Ayllón

Museo Municipal, c/o Edificio de Ayuntamiento, Calle Mayor 29, 40520 Ayllón - T: 921553000. Head: Miguel Gómez Arnanz
Fine Arts Museum - 1965
Art and hist, painting, sculpture 28748

Museo Obispo Vellosillo, Plaza Obispo Vellosillo 1, 40520 Ayllón - T: 921553000, Fax: 921553336
Fine Arts Museum / Archaeological Museum - 1965 28749

Azpeitia

Casa Natal de San Ignacio, Av de Loyola, 20730 Azpeitia - T: 943816508, Fax: 943813944. Head: P. Rector
Religious Arts Museum - 1954
Memorabilia of Iñigo López de Loyola (1491-1556), the founder of the Jesuit order and later (1622) sanctified San Ignacio 28750

Caserío de Errecarte, Casa Natal del Hermano Francisco Gárate, Barrio de Loyola 16, 20730 Azpeitia - T: 943816508, Fax: 943813944. Head: Ignacio M. Závala
Special Museum - 1929
Memorabilia of the blessed Hermano Francisco Gárate 28751

Ingurugiro Etxea (Enviromental Museum), Caserío Egibar, Carretera Vieja de Loyola 1, 20730 Azpeitia - T: 943812448, Fax: 943812448
Natural History Museum 28752

Museo Vasco del Ferrocarril (Basque Railway Museum), Calle Julian Elorza 6, 20730 Azpeitia - T: 943150677, Fax: 943150746, E-mail: museoa.euskotren@sarenet.es, Internet: http://www.geocities.com/euskalbml. Head: Juanjo Olaczola
Science&Tech Museum - 1991 28753

Azuaga

Museo Etnográfico de Azuaga de la Sierra y la Campiña, Calle Muñoz Crespo 19, 06920 Azuaga - T: 924892107, 924890400, Fax: 924891550, E-mail: azuaga@dip-badajoz.es
Ethnology Museum 28754

Badajoz

Museo Arqueológico Provincial, Pl José Alvárez y Saez de Buruaga, 06002 Badajoz - T: 924222314, Fax: 924222905, E-mail: museoba@pr.juntaex.es. Head: Guillermo S. Kurtz Schaefer
Archaeological Museum - 1938
Roman and Iberian antiquities, 6th-7th c Visigothic art, Islam art, calcholithic archaeology 28755

Museo Catedralicio, Calle José López Prudencio, 06002 Badajoz - T: 924223999
Religious Arts Museum
16th-18th c religious paintings, religious sculptures and documents, goldsmith work 28756

Museo de Bellas Artes, Calle Duque de San Germán, 06001 Badajoz - T: 924212469, 924248034, 9248483. Head: Román Hernández Nieves
Fine Arts Museum - 1919
19th-20th c regional painting and sculpture and graphic arts, especially from Estremadura, works by Francisco de Zurbarán and Juan de Avalos - library 28757

Museo Extremeño e Iberoamericano de Arte Contemporáneo, Calle Museo 2, 06002 Badajoz - T: 924140125, 924260384
Public Gallery - 1997 28758

Badalona

Museu de Badalona, Plaza de l'Assamblea de Catalunya 1, 08911 Badalona - T: 933841750, Fax: 933841662. Head: Joan Villarroya i Font
Local Museum - 1956
Roman archaeology, folk art, local history - observatory 'Baetulo' and meteorological service 28759

Baena

Museo de Semana Santa Baena, Calle Santo Domingo Henares 5, 14850 Baena - T: 957670000, Fax: 957671108
Religious Arts Museum 28760

Baeza

Museo Catedralicio, Plaza Santa María 1, 23440 Baeza - T: 953744157
Religious Arts Museum - 1976 28761

Balaguer

Museu Comarcal de la Noguera, Calle Sant Josep 2, 25600 Balaguer - T: 973445194, Fax: 973445053
Archaeological Museum 28762

Baldomar

Museu Arqueològic i Paleontològic, Calle La Font s/n, 25737 Baldomar - T: 973400943
Archaeological Museum 28763

Balsareny

Colección de Pintura y Recuerdos Históricos del Castell de Balsareny, Castell de Balsareny, 1,5 km Fuera de la Ciudad, 08660 Balsareny - T: 938396211
Fine Arts Museum / Historical Museum
Art and history, painting, furniture, books, heraldry 28764

Bande

Museo Monográfico Aquis Querquernis, Calle Porto Quintela, 32840 Bande - T: 988443387
Archaeological Museum 28765

Banyoles

Museu Arqueològic Comarcal, Plaza de la Font 11, 17820 Banyoles - T: 972572361, Fax: 972574917. Head: Erundino Sanz Sánchez
Archaeological Museum - 1933
Prehistory, Roman and Iberian finds, medieval architecture, numismatics, 14th-18th c ceramics, paleontology - restoration laboratory 28766

Museu Darder d'Història Natural, Plaza dels Estudis 2, 17820 Banyoles - T: 972574467, Fax: 972574467. Head: Mariona Juncà Bonal
Natural History Museum - 1916
Birds, human skulls, Francesc Darder i Llimona - library 28767

Barakaldo

Museo de la Técnica de Euskadi, Calle Andicollano s/n, 48903 Barakaldo - T: 944991634, Fax: 944998048
Science&Tech Museum 28768

Barbastro

Museo Diocesano-Catedralicio, Catedral y Antiguo Palacio Episcopal, Plaza Palacio s/n, 22300 Barbastro - T: 974311682
Religious Arts Museum - 1965/68
Ecclesiastical art, gothic cathedral 28769

Barca

Museo Etnológico, Calle Dehesa s/n, 42210 Barca - T: 975304014
Ethnology Museum 28770

Barcelona

Casa-Museu Gaudí, Parque Güell, Carretera Carmel 23, 08024 Barcelona - T: 932193811, 932106405, 933175221, Fax: 932846446. Head: Dr. J.M. Garrut
Decorative Arts Museum - 1963
Furniture and architectural projects designed by A. Gaudí and his collaborators, sentimental museum, house of the artist 28771

Centre d'Art Santa Mònica, Rambla de Santa Mònica 7, 08002 Barcelona - T: (093) 3162810, Fax: 3162817, Internet: http://www.cultura.gencat.es/casm
Fine Arts Museum 28772

Centro Cultural de la Fundació la Caixa, Passeig Sant Joan 108, 08037 Barcelona - T: 934588906/07, Fax: 934581308. Head: Jordi Ardid
Public Gallery 28773

Centro de Cultura Contemporània de Barcelona, Montalegre 5, 08001 Barcelona - T: 933064100, Fax: 933064101, E-mail: globalcccb@cccb.org, Internet: http://www.cccb.org. Head: Josep Ramoneda
Public Gallery 28774

Colecciones Biológicas de Referencia, Passeig Joan de Borbó, 08039 Barcelona - T: 932216450, 932216416, Fax: 932216416
Natural History Museum 28775

Collecio Thyssen-Bornemisza, Monasterio de Pedralbes, Baixada del Monestir 9, 08034 Barcelona - T: 932801434, Fax: 932041601, E-mail: museo.thyssen@offcampus.es
Fine Arts Museum 28776

Fundació Antoni Tàpies, Aragó 255, 08007 Barcelona - T: 934870315, Fax: 934870009, E-mail: museu@ftapies.com, Internet: http://www.fundaciotapies.com. Head: Miquel Tàpies
Fine Arts Museum 28777

Fundació Joan Miró, Parc de Montjuïc, 08038 Barcelona - T: 934439470, Fax: 933298609, E-mail: fjmiro@bcn.fjmiro.es, Internet: http://www.bcn.fjmiro.es. Head: Rosa María Malet Ybern
Fine Arts Museum 28778

Fundación Folch, Av Pearson 38, 08034 Barcelona - T: 932040923, Fax: 932040923
Ethnology Museum 28779

Gabinete de Física Experimental Mentora Alsina, Carretera de Vallvidrera al Tibidabo 56, 08023 Barcelona - T: 934175734, 933177775. Head: Ricard Gutiérrez Jodar
Natural History Museum 28780

Gabinete Numismático de Cataluña, Museu Nacional d'Art de Catalunya, Rambla de las Flores 99, 08002 Barcelona - T: 933017775, Fax: 933176077. Head: Marta Campo
Historical Museum - 1932
Numismatics, medals and coins 28781

Galerie de Catalans Illustres, Calle Bisbe Cacador 3, 08002 Barcelona - T: 933151111, 933150010
Fine Arts Museum 28782

Instituto Amatller de Arte Hispánico, Passeig de Gràcia 41, 08007 Barcelona - T: 932160175, Fax: 934875827, E-mail: amatller@amatller.com. Head: Santiago Alcolea Blanch
Fine Arts Museum - 1942
Art, medieval painting, Roman and Modern (16th-19th c) glass manufacture - library; photo archive 28783

Martorell Museum → Museu de Geología

Metrònom, Fundació Rafael Tous d'Art Contemporani, Carrer Fusina 9, 08003 Barcelona - T: 932684298, Fax: 932684298, E-mail: metronom@retemail.es
Public Gallery 28784

Museo de la Técnica, Escuela de Ingenieros Industriales, Av Diagonal 647, 08028 Barcelona
Science&Tech Museum - 1966
Industrial mechanical engineering 28785

Museo Geológico del Seminario, Calle Diputación 231, 08007 Barcelona - T: 934541600, Fax: 934525538, E-mail: jcarrasc@pie.xtec.es, Internet: http://mineral.geologia.uv.es/MGSB/. Head: S. Calzada
Natural History Museum - 1874
Paleontology (invertebrates) 28786

Museu Clarà, Calla Calatrava 27-29, 08017 Barcelona - T: 932034058. Head: María Alegría Manegat
Fine Arts Museum - 1969
Sculpture, painting, drawing, watercolor painting 28787

Museu d'Arqueologia de Catalunya, Passeig Santa Madrona 39, 08038 Barcelona - T: 934232149, Fax: 934254244, E-mail: mac@mac.es, Internet: http://www.mac.es. Head: Miguel Molist
Archaeological Museum - 1932
Prehistoric art from Catalunya and Baleares, Greek antiquities, esp from Ampurias, Roman antiquities, sculptures, mosaics, inscriptions, Iberian and Visigothic art, 7th c Byzantine bust - library 28788

Museu d'Arquitectura de la Real Càtedra Gaudí, Av Pedralbes 7, 08034 Barcelona - T: 932045250, Fax: 932048670, E-mail: joan.bassegoda@cda.upc.es. Head: Juan Bassegoda Nonell
Fine Arts Museum - 1817 28789

Museu d'Art Contemporani de Barcelona, Plaça dels Angels 1, 08001 Barcelona - T: 934120810, Fax: 934124602, E-mail: macba@macba.es. Head: Manuel J. Borja-Villel
Fine Arts Museum - 1988
Contemporary art from 2nd half of the 20th century 28790

Museu d'Art Modern del MNAC, Parc de la Ciutadella, Plaza de les Armes, 08003 Barcelona - T: 933195728, Fax: 933195965, E-mail: mnac@correu.gencat.es, Internet: http://www.mnac.es. Head: Cristina Mendoza Garriga
Fine Arts Museum - 1945
19th-20th c works of Catalan art, modernism and avant- garde, paintings, sculptures, decorative art - library 28791

Museu d'Arts Decoratives, Av Diagonal 686, 08034 Barcelona - T: 932805024, Fax: 932801874. Head: Marta Montmany
Decorative Arts Museum 28792

Museu d'Arts, Indústries i Tradicions Populars → Museu Etnològic de Barcelona

Museu de Carrosses Fúnebres, Calle Sancho de Avila 2, 08018 Barcelona - T: 934841700, Fax: 933004085, E-mail: sfsa@funerariabarcelona.com, Internet: http://www.funerariabarcelona.com. Head: Josep Cornet
Special Museum - 1970 28793

Museu de Cera, Passatge de la Banca 7, 08002 Barcelona - T: 933172649, Fax: 933185346. Head: Enrique Alarcón, Carmina Vall Petitpierre
Science&Tech Museum 28794

Museu de Cerámica, Palau de Pedralbes, Av Diagonal 686, 08034 Barcelona - T: 932801621, Fax: 932054518, E-mail: ceramica@intercom.es. Head: María Antonia Casanovas
Decorative Arts Museum - 1966
Medieval to modern Spanish ceramics - conservation dept, education dept, library 28795

Museu de Geología, Parc de la Ciutadella s/n, 08003 Barcelona - T: 933196895, Fax: 933199312, E-mail: museugeologia@mail.bcn.es. Head: Alicia Masriera
Natural History Museum - 1882
Geology, petrology, mineralogy, palentology - educational dept, library 28796

Museu de la Catedral, Plaza de la Seu s/n, 08002 Barcelona - T: 933153555, 933151554. Head: Josep A. Arenas i Sampera
Religious Arts Museum - 1932 28797

Museu de la Ciencia de la Fundació la Caixa, Calle Teodor Roviralta 55, 08022 Barcelona - T: 932126050, Fax: 932537457, E-mail: - musciencia.fundacio@lacaixa.es, Internet: http://www.fundacio.lacaixa.es. Head: Jorge Wagensberg
Science&Tech Museum 28798

Museu de la Farmàcia Catalana, c/o Facultat de Farmacia, Av Diagonal s/n, 08028 Barcelona - T: 934024555. Head: Prof. J.M. Suné, Prof. I. Figuerolar
Special Museum / University Museum 28799

Museu de la Música, Av Diagonal 373, 08008 Barcelona - T: 934161157, Fax: 932171106. Head: Román Escalas
Music Museum - 1946
1500 musical instruments from all over the world, coll of European instruments of the 16th - 20th c, documents - archive 28800

Museu de l'Automòbil, Via Augusta 182, 08021 Barcelona - T: 932095523
Science&Tech Museum 28801

Museu de les Arts Escèniques, Plaça Margarida Xirgu s/n, 08004 Barcelona - T: 932273910, Fax: 932273939, E-mail: it.mae@diba.es, Internet: http://www.diba.es/iteatre. Head: Montserrat Alvárez-Masso
Performing Arts Museum
Exhibition of scenery, lectures, etc. 28802

Museu de les Arts Gràfiques, Av Marqués de Comillas s/n, 08038 Barcelona - T: 934261999, 934247064, Fax: 934230196. Head: Pilar Vélez
Fine Arts Museum 28803

Museu de l'Institut de Criminología, c/o Facultat de Dret, Av Diagonal s/n, 08034 Barcelona - T: 932037507, 932051112
Special Museum / University Museum - 1960
Instruments of torture, means for execution, criminal history 28804

Museu de l'Instituto Botánico, Parc de Montjuïc, Av dels Muntanyans s/n, 08038 Barcelona - T: 933258050, Fax: 934269321, E-mail: i.botanic@ibb.csic.es, Internet: http://www.institutbotanic.bcn.es/home.htm. Head: Dr. J.M. Montserrat Martí
Natural History Museum - 1917
Iberian and North African flora, Salvador family natural hist coll (18th-19th c) - library, botanical garden, herbarium, research 28805

Museu de Zoologia de Barcelona, Passeig Picasso s/n, 08003 Barcelona - T: 933196950, Fax: 933104999, E-mail: museuzoologia@mail.bcn.es, Internet: http://www.bcn.es/icub. Head: Dr. Anna Omedes
Natural History Museum - 1882
Zoology, particularly Iberian and North African specimens, skeletons, insects, molluscs - wildlife sound library, library, preparation lab, archive 28806

Museu del Calcat Antic, Plaza Sant Felip Neri 5, 08002 Barcelona - T: 933022680, 933014533, Fax: 933022680
Ethnology Museum 28807

Museu del Perfum, Passeig de Gràcia 39, 08007 Barcelona - T: 932160146, Fax: 932160146. Head: Ramón Planas
Special Museum - 1961
History of perfume 28808

Museu del Temple Expiatori de la Sagrada Familia, Calle Mallorca 401, 08013 Barcelona - T: 934550247, Fax: 934358335
Religious Arts Museum 28809

Museu dels Autòmats (Automaton Museum), Pl Tibidabo 3-4, 08035 Barcelona - T: 932117942, Fax: 932112111, E-mail: p.a.tibidabo@catworld.net. Head: Santi Sardà
Science&Tech Museum - 1899
Automatons (1880-2000), machinery 28810

Museu d'Història de la Ciutat, Plaza del Rei s/n, 08002 Barcelona - T: 933151111, Fax: 933150957, E-mail: museuhistoria@mail.bcn.es. Head: Antoni Nicolau
Historical Museum - 1943
Prehistory, Roman antiquities, Islamic, Visigothic and Jewish art, medieval art, royal church (14th c), 7th c local maps, 15th-20th c history and cultural history of Barcelona, Roman and West Gothic ruins - library, educational center 28811

Museu Diocesà de Barcelona, Av de la Catedral 4, 08002 Barcelona - T: 933152213, Fax: 932701300, E-mail: dpcarqbcn@filnet.es. Head: José María Martí Bonet
Religious Arts Museum - 1916
Religious art 1st-20th c 28812

Museu Egipci de Barcelona, València 284, 08007 Barcelona - T: 934880188, Fax: 934878060, E-mail: infoclos@fundclos.com, Internet: http://www.fundclos.com. Head: Jordi Clos Llombart, Adolf Luna
Archaeological Museum 28813

Museu Etnogràfic Andino-Amazònic, Calle Cardenal Vives i Tutó 16, Caputxins de Sarrià, 08034 Barcelona - T: 932043458. Head: Valentí Serra de Manresa
Ethnology Museum 28814

Museu Etnològic de Barcelona, Parc de Montjuïc, Av Marqués de Comillas s/n, 08038 Barcelona - T: 934236954, Fax: 934230196, E-mail: maitp@intercom.es, Internet: http://www.museuetnologic.bcn.es. Head: Dr. Carmen Fauria
Folklore Museum 28815

Museu Etnològic de Barcelona, Parc de Montjuïc, Passeig de Santa Madrona s/n, 08038 Barcelona - T: 934246402, Fax: 934237364, E-mail: metno@intercom.es, Internet: http://www.museuetnologic.bcn.es. Head: Carmen Fauria
Ethnology Museum - 1948
Ethnological finds from Africa, America, Asia, Europe (esp. Spain) and Oceania, archaeological finds from America - library 28816

Museu Frederic Marès, Calle Comtes 10, 08002 Barcelona - T: 933105800, Fax: 933194116, E-mail: museumares@mail.bcn.es, Internet: http://www.museumares.bcn.es. Head: Pilar Vélez
Fine Arts Museum / Decorative Arts Museum - 1946
12th-17th c religious sculptures, 17th-19th c cultural hist, Roman and Hellenistic terracotta, medieval wood sculptures, decorative arts, ethnography 28817

Museu Futbol Club Barcelona President Núñez, c/o Estadi del F.C.B., Av d'Arístides Maillol s/n, 08028 Barcelona - T: 934963608, 934963600, Fax: 934112219, E-mail: museu@fcbarcelona.com, Internet: http://www.fcbarcelona.es. Head: Albert Pujol
Special Museum
documentation centre 28818

Museu Gabinet Postal, Palau de Pedralbes, Av Diagonal 686, 08034 Barcelona - T: 932801874
Special Museum
Postage stamps, letters, history of mail services 28819

Museu Historic Municipal de Ca l'Arra, Calle Les Acacies s/n, 08348 Barcelona - T: 937530884
Local Museum 28820

Museu i Centre d'Estudis de l'Esport Dr. Melcior Colet, Calle Buenos Aires 56-58, 08036 Barcelona - T: 932306118, Fax: 934106355. Head: Josep M. Sol i Bachs, Helena Blanco Sansa
Special Museum 28821

Museu Marítim de Barcelona, Av Drassanes s/n, 08001 Barcelona - T: 933429920, Fax: 933187876, E-mail: m.maritim@diba.es, Internet: http://www.diba.es/mmaritim. Head: Roger Marcet
Historical Museum - 1941
Marine archaeology, maritime history, cartography, ship models, figureheads, quay facilities, folk art, fishing, numismatics, ceramics - library, photographic archive, document archive 28822

Museu Militar, Castell de Montjuïc, Carretera de Montjuïc 66, 08038 Barcelona - T: 933298613, 934416829, Fax: 933298613. Head: Francisco Segovia Barrientos
Military Museum - 1963
Arms and weapons, military history 28823

Museu Nacional d'Art de Catalunya, Palau Nacional, Parc de Montjuïc, 08038 Barcelona - T: 936220360/375, Fax: 936220374, E-mail: mnac@mnac.es, Internet: http://www.mnac.es. Head: Eduard Carbonell i Esteller
Fine Arts Museum - 1934
11th-13th c Romanesque wall painting from Catalan churches, wood carvigs, sculptures, Gothic paintings and sculpture (14th-15th c), Renaissance and Baroque art - general library of hist of art 28824

Museu Picasso, Carrer de Montcada 15-23, 08003 Barcelona - T: 933196310, Fax: 933150102, E-mail: museupicasso@mail.bcn.es, Internet: http://www.museupicasso.bcn.es. Head: Maria Teresa Ocaña
Fine Arts Museum - 1963
Paintings, sculptures, drawings and engravings by Pablo Picasso (1890-1973), crafts - library 28825

Museu Taurí de la Monumental, Gran Vía de les Corts Catalanes 749, 08013 Barcelona - T: 932455802/03, Fax: 932152808
Historical Museum 28826

Museu Textil i d'Indumentaria, Palau del Marques de Llio, Calle Montcada 12, 08003 Barcelona - T: 933104516, Fax: 933150102
Fine Arts Museum 28827

Palacio de Pedralbes, Av Diagonal 686, 08034 Barcelona - T: 932035285
Fine Arts Museum / Decorative Arts Museum
19th c royal residence, art, furniture, decorative arts, 18th-20th c carriages and coaches 28828

La Pinacoteca, Passeig de Gràcia 34, 08007 Barcelona - T: 934877092
Fine Arts Museum 28829

Reial Academia Catalana Belles Arts Sant Jordi, Casa Lonja, Passeig Isabel II 1, 08003 Barcelona - T: 933192432, Fax: 933190216, E-mail: racbasj@suport.org, Internet: http://www.ba-stjordi.org. Head: Jordi Bonet Armengol
Fine Arts Museum 28830

Sala Montcada de la Fundació la Caixa, Calle Montcada 14, 08003 Barcelona - T: 933100699. Head: Imma Casas
Public Gallery 28831

Barco de Avila

Museo Parroquial, Iglesia de Nuestra Señora de la Asunción, Plaza las Acacias, 05600 Barco de Avila - T: 920340077
Religious Arts Museum - 1960
Religious art, painting, sculpture, 15th c goldsmith work 28832

Baza

Museo Arqueológico de Baza, Plaza Mayor 1, 18800 Baza - T: 958700691, Fax: 958700650, 958860092
Archaeological Museum / Historical Museum 28833

Béjar

Museo Municipal Mateo Hernández, Plaza Martín Mateos 49, 37700 Béjar - T: 923400738
Fine Arts Museum - 1966
Spanish, Flemish and Dutch painting, sculpture, decorative arts, Oriental art 28834

Bejis

Museo Etnológico, c/o Ayuntamiento, 12430 Bejis - T: 964120161, Fax: 964120224
Ethnology Museum 28835

Bellvís

Museu de Bellvís, Calle Domingo Cardenal 46, 25142 Bellvís - T: 973565000
Local Museum 28836

Belmonte

Museo de la Colegiata, Colegiata-Parroquia de San Bartolomé Apóstol, 16640 Belmonte - T: 969170208
Religious Arts Museum - 1931
Ecclesiastical art, painting, sculpture, goldsmith work, liturgical vestments, books and documents 28837

Bembibre

Museo Alto Bierzo, Paseo del Santo s/n, 24300 Bembibre - T: 987514072, Fax: 987511917
Ethnology Museum - 1987 28838

Benabarre

Museo Parroquial, Iglesia Nuestra Señora de Valdeflores, Plaza de la Iglesia s/n, 22580 Benabarre - T: 974543180
Religious Arts Museum - 1974 28839

Benalmádena

Museo Arqueológico Municipal Precolombino, Calle Felipe Orlando 1, 29639 Benalmádena - T: 952448593. Head: Felipe O. García Muriano
Archaeological Museum - 1970
Local and Mexican archaeology 28840

Benasal

Museo Arqueológico Alto Maestrazgo, Castillo la Mola, Calle La Mola 2, 12160 Benasal - T: 964431002, Fax: 964431411
Archaeological Museum 28841

Benissa

Museu Municipal, Calle Purísima 41, 03720 Benissa - T: 965731313, Fax: 965731496
Ethnology Museum 28842

Berga

Museu Municipal, Calle Angels 7, 08600 Berga - T: 938210100
Local Museum - 1955
Archaeology, natural history, palaeontology, local history, goldsmith work 28843

Bergara

Museo del Real Seminario de Bergara, Plaza San Martín de Aguirre s/n, 20570 Bergara - T: 943764446, Fax: 943779163
Local Museum 28844

Bermeo

Arrantzaleen Museoa (Fishermen's Museum), Ertzilla Dorrea-Torrontero 1, 48370 Bermeo - T: 946881171, Fax: 946186454. Head: Aingeru Astui
Historical Museum 28845

Besalú

Colección Arqueológica Municipal, Calle Portalet 4, 17850 Besalú
Archaeological Museum - 1962
Archaeology, painting 28846

Betancuria

Museo de Betancuria, Calle Vega de Río Palmas s/n, 35637 Betancuria - T: 928878241
Archaeological Museum 28847

Betanzos

Museo das Mariñas, Calle Emilio Romay 1, 15300 Betanzos - T: 981771946, Fax: 981771946. Head: Alfredo Erias Martinez
Local Museum 28848

Bielsa

Museo Etnológico, Plaza Mayor s/n, 22350 Bielsa - T: 974501000
Ethnology Museum 28849

Bilbao

Bilboko Arte Ederretako Museoa, Museo de Bellas Artes de Bilbao, Pl del Museo 2, 48011 Bilbao - T: 944396060, Fax: 944396145, E-mail: museobilbao@museobilbao.com, Internet: http://www.museobilbao.com. Head: Miguel Zugaza
Fine Arts Museum - 1914
13th-19th c Spanish painting, 15th-17th c Flemish painting, 15th-20th c European painting, 19th-20th modern sculpture, ceramics, Basque art - educational dept, library, restoring 28850

Centro del Diseño (Design Cerntre), Sabino de Arana 8, 48013 Bilbao - T: 944395622, Fax: 944278050, E-mail: centro@dzdesign.com, Internet: http://www.dzdesign.com
Public Gallery 28851

Euskal Arkeologia, Etnografia eta Kondaira Museoa, Calle Cruz 4, 48005 Bilbao - T: 944169246, Fax: 944790608, E-mail: museoa@euskal-museoa.org, Internet: http://www.euskal-museoa.org. Head: Dr. Amaia Basterretxea-Moreno
Archaeological Museum / Ethnology Museum / Historical Museum - 1920
Prehistory and archaeology of the territory of Bizkaia, ethnography and history of the Basque County - library, archives, photo-file 28852

Guggenheim Museum Bilbao, Av Abandoibarra 2, 48001 Bilbao - T: 944359020, 944359080, Fax: 944359010. Head: Juan Ignacio Vidarte
Fine Arts Museum - 1997 28853

Museo de Reproducciones Artísticas, Calle Conde de Mirasol 2, 48003 Bilbao - T: 944157673
Fine Arts Museum - 1930
Casts of sculptures and architectural fragments 28854

Museo Diocesano de Arte Sacro, Plaza Encarnación s/n, 48006 Bilbao - T: 944320125, Fax: 944320260
Religious Arts Museum 28855

Sala de Exposiciones Rekalde, Alameda de Recalde 30, 48009 Bilbao - T: 944208755, 944208532, Fax: 944208754, E-mail: salarekalde@bizkaia.net. Head: Pilar Mur
Public Gallery 28856

Binissalem

Museu de Cera, Carretera Palma-Inca km 25, 07350 Binissalem - T: 971511228, Fax: 971870352
Local Museum 28857

Blanes

Estación Internacional de Biología Mediterránea Carlos Faust, Jardín Botánico Mar y Murtra, Passeig Carles Faust 10, 17300 Blanes - T: 972330826, Fax: 972330826
Natural History Museum - 1951
Mediterranean and exotic plants, especially cacti 28858

Blecua

Museo Etnolólogico Anselmo Buil, Plaza Iglesia s/n, 22133 Blecua - T: 974240127, Fax: 974260150
Ethnology Museum 28859

Bocairente

Museo Parroquial, Calle Abadía s/n, 46880 Bocairente - T: 962350062
Religious Arts Museum - 1966
Ecclesiastical art, goldsmith work, painting, sculpture, ornamentation 28860

Bolívar

Museo Simón Bolívar, Caserío Rementería, Calle Beko Kale 4, 48279 Bolívar - T: 946164114, Fax: 946164114
Historical Museum 28861

Boltaña

Museo Etnológico, c/o Casa de Cultura, Calle Ramón y Cajal 28, 22340 Boltaña - T: 974502002, Fax: 974502380
Ethnology Museum - 1988 28862

Bornos

Museo de Artes y Costumbres Populares, c/o Casa Ordoñez, Calle Granada s/n, 11640 Bornos - T: 956712011
Folklore Museum 28863

Breda

Museu Municipal Josep Aragay, Calle Nou 2, 17400 Breda - T: 972870220
Fine Arts Museum - 1974 28864

El Bruc

Museu d'El Bruc, Calle Bruc del Mig 23, 08294 El Bruc - T: 937710006, Fax: 937710450
Local Museum 28865

Bueu

Museo Massó, c/o Massó Hermanos S.A., Av Montero Rios s/n, 36930 Bueu - T: 986544888, 986435402
Special Museum - 1928
Naval hist, fish canners industrie, fishing boats 28866

Buitrago del Lozoy

Museo Picasso, Plaza Picasso 1, 28730 Buitrago del Lozoy - T: 918680056, Fax: 918680630. Head: Pilar Navascués Benlloch
Fine Arts Museum - 1985 28867

Burgo de Osma

Museo Catedralicio, Plaza de San Pedro 2, 42300 Burgo de Osma - T: 975340288
Religious Arts Museum - 1928
Historical documents, miniature books, codices, 11th-13th c miniatures, 15th c painting, sculpture, goldsmith work, liturgical vestments, 14th c crafts 28868

Burgos

Monasterio de las Huelgas de Burgos, Museo de Ricas Telas, Calle Compases de Huelgas s/n, 09001 Burgos - T: 947201630, Fax: 947279729. Head: R.M. Abadesa
Religious Arts Museum - 1942
Art and history, medieval textiles, jewelry, religious art, Panteón de los Reyes de Castilla y León, monastery founded by Alfonso V in the 12th c 28869

Museo Catedralicio, Catedral, Plaza Rey San Fernando y Santa María, 09003 Burgos - T: 947204712, Fax: 947273950, E-mail: catedralburgos@planalfa.es, Internet: http://www3.planalfa.es/catedralburgos. Head: Agustin Lázaro López
Religious Arts Museum - 1930
13th-16th c religious painting, Romanesque architecture, 16th-17th c tapestry, 15th-18th c documents and codes, liturgical vestments, ivories, tombs, goldsmith work 28870

Museo de Burgos, Casa Miranda, Calle La Calera 25, 09002 Burgos - T: 947265875, Fax: 947276792. Head: Belén Castillo Iglesias
Local Museum / Fine Arts Museum / Museum of Classical Antiquities / Historical Museum - 1871
Prehistory, archaeology, fine arts 28871

Museo de Farmacia, Plaza Rey San Fernando s/n, 09003 Burgos - T: 947288868, Fax: 947288871, E-mail: imc@aytoburgos.es, Internet: http://www.aytoburgos.es. Head: Ignacio María Gonzalez de Santiago
Science&Tech Museum 28872

Museo del Retablo, Iglesia de San Esteban, Calle San Esteban 1, 09003 Burgos - T: 947273752. Head: Agustin Lázaro López
Local Museum 28873

Museo del Seminario Diocesano, Gabinete Ciencias Naturales, Paseo del Empecinado s/n, 09001 Burgos - T: 947207646
Natural History Museum - 1966
Natural Sciences 28874

Museo Marceliano Santa María, Antiguo Monasterio de San Juan, Plaza San Juan s/n, 09002 Burgos - T: 947205687. Head: Jesús del Olmo Fernández
Fine Arts Museum / Decorative Arts Museum - 1969
Art, 16th and 17th c painting and sculpture, furniture 28875

Museo Regional de Burgos, Acuartelamiento Diego Porcelos, Calle Glorieta Logroño 2, 09006 Burgos - T: 947221850, Fax: 947212602
Local Museum 28876

Real Cartuja de Miraflores, Carretera Burgos-Cardeña km 3, 09002 Burgos
Fine Arts Museum
15th c building, art and history, Gothic architecture, sculpture, painting, glass painting 28877

Burriana

Museo Arqueológico de la Plana Baja, Plaza Merced, 12530 Burriana - T: 964510010, Fax: 964517305
Archaeological Museum - 1967
Archaeology, ethnology 28878

Cabezón de la Sal

Museo de la Naturaleza de Cantabria, Carrejo, 39509 Cabezón de la Sal - T: 942701808
Natural History Museum 28879

Cabra

Museo Municipal, Calle Martín Belda 25, 14940 Cabra - T: 957520110
Local Museum - 1973 28880

Cacabelos

Museo Arqueológico, Calle Capitán Cortés 15, 24540 Cacabelos - T: 987546011
Archaeological Museum 28881

Cáceres

Museo de Cáceres, Plaza de las Veletas 1, 10003 Cáceres - T: 927247234, Fax: 927247277, E-mail: museocaceres@ctv.es, Internet: http://www.culturaextremadura.com/museocaceres. Head: Juan M. Valadés Sierra
Local Museum / Fine Arts Museum - 1917
Prehistory, archaeology, Roman, Iberian, Visigothic and Islamic antiquities, painting, Spanish pottery, religious art, numismatics, folklore and ethnology 28882

Museo de Historia y Cultura Casa Pedrilla, Ronda de San Francisco s/n, 10005 Cáceres - T: 927241633, Fax: 927240762, E-mail: m.pedrilla@brocente.com
Local Museum 28883

Cadaqués

Casa-Museu de Salvador Dalí de Cadaqués, Portlligat, 17488 Cadaqués - T: 972677500, E-mail: pllgrups@dali-estate.org, Internet: http://www.salvador-dali.org
Fine Arts Museum - 1997 28884

Museu d'Art, Calle Narcis Monturiol 15, 17488 Cadaqués - T: 972258194, Fax: 972258074
Fine Arts Museum 28885

Museu Perrot Moore d'Art Grafic Europeu, Calle Vigilant 1, 17488 Cadaqués - T: 972258076, Fax: 972258013
Fine Arts Museum 28886

Cádiz

Museo Catedralicio, Plaza Catedral, 11005 Cádiz - T: 956286154
Religious Arts Museum - 1931
Ecclesiastical art, painting, sculpture, goldsmith work, liturgical vestments 28887

Museo de Cádiz, Plaza Mina s/n, 11004 Cádiz - T: 956212281, 956214300, Fax: 956226215, E-mail: dpcadiz@ccul.junta-andalucia.es, Internet: http://www.junta-andalucia.es/cultura. Head: Cándida Garbarino Gaínza
Fine Arts Museum / Archaeological Museum / Ethnology Museum - 1887/1970
Museo Provincial de Bellas Artes: 15th-20th c Spanish, Italian and Flemish painting, 19th c sculpture, drawings, Baroque period, tapestry, jewellery; Museo Arqueológico: fossils, paleontology, Greek, Roman, Punic antiquities, early Christian archaeology, Visgothic and Islamic art, archaeological numismatics, ethnography 28888

Museo del Mar, Baluarte de la Candelaria, Paseo de Carlos III, 11005 Cádiz - T: 956222474, Fax: 956222051
Military Museum - 1971 28889

Museo Histórico Municipal, Calle Santa Inés 9-11, 11003 Cádiz - T: 956221788, Fax: 956222051
Historical Museum - 1909
Historical documents and letters, maps, 19th c paintings 28890

Calahorra

Museo Municipal de Calahorra, Calle Angel Oliván 8, 26500 Calahorra - T: 941135003, Fax: 941135016, E-mail: juventud@eniac.aniac.es
Archaeological Museum - 1984
Prehistory and archaeology 28891

Museo-Tesoro Catedralicio y Diocesano, Anejo a la Catedral, 26500 Calahorra - T: 941130098, 941131252
Religious Arts Museum - 1958
Painting: liturgical vestments, goldsmith work, 12th c miniature codices, documentation on the 11th-12th centuries 28892

Calasparra

Museo Municipal de Calasparra, c/o Edificio de la Encomiendа, Calle Lavador 13, 30420 Calasparra - T: 968720044
Local Museum 28893

Calatayud

Museo de Arte Sacro, Palacio Episcopal, Calle Baltasar Gracián 20, 50300 Calatayud
Religious Arts Museum - 1971 28894

Museo Municipal, c/o Casa de la Cultura, Plaza Comunidad s/n, 50300 Calatayud - T: 976881673
Local Museum
Local art and history 28895

Caldes de Montbui

Museo Arqueológico y Termas Romanas, Calle José Antonio 98, 08140 Caldes de Montbui. Head: Josep Palacios i Manuel
Archaeological Museum - 1949
Archaeology and local history, Roman hot springs 28896

Museo Thermalia, Museu d'Història, Plaza Font del Lleó 20, 08140 Caldes de Montbui - T: 938654140, Fax: 938653400. Head: Josep Palacios i Manuel
Historical Museum 28897

Museu Manolo Hugué, Mas Manolo, Calle Disseminat s/n, 08140 Caldes de Montbui - T: 938650243, Fax: 938653400. Head: Xavier Ballbé
Local Museum - 1994
Art, local hist 28898

Museu Romàntic Delger, Mossèn Joaquim Delger 12, 08140 Caldes de Montbui - T: 938654140, Fax: 938653400. Head: Josep Palacios i Manuel
Fine Arts Museum 28899

Calella

Museu-Arxiu Municipal de Calella, Calle Francesc Bartina 35, 08370 Calella - T: 937695102
Local Museum 28900

Callosa de Segura

Museo de Semana Santa Escultor José Noguera Valverde, Barrio del Palmeral, Carretera Callosa-Rafal s/n, 03360 Callosa de Segura - T: 966756767, 965310550
Religious Arts Museum / Historic Site 28901

Museo del Cañamo, Carretera Rafal s/n, 03360 Callosa de Segura - T: 966756767, Fax: 965310856
Special Museum 28902

Calonge de Mar

Museu Parroquial, Parroquia de Sant Martí, Plaza La Doma 1, 17251 Calonge de Mar - T: 972650064
Religious Arts Museum 28903

Caltojar

Ermita de San Baudelio de Berlanga, A 9 km de Berlanga de Duero, Carretera Local de Soria, 42367 Caltojar
Fine Arts Museum 28904

Camporrobles

Museo Etnográfico, Plaza Ayuntamiento 1, 46330 Camporrobles - T: 962181006, Fax: 962181341
Ethnology Museum 28905

Campos

Museu Parraquial, Calle Bisbe Tellades 17, 07630 Campos - T: 971650003
Fine Arts Museum 28906

Cañas

Monasterio de Santa María San Salvador, Calle Real 2, 26225 Cañas - T: 941379083
Religious Arts Museum 28907

Candás

Museo Antón, c/o Centro de Escultura de Candás, Plaza del Cueto s/n, 33430 Candás - T: 985871800, Fax: 985871901. Head: Angel Riego González
Fine Arts Museum 28908

Candelaria

Museo de la Basílica Nuestra Señora de la Candelaria, Plaza de la Patrona de Canarias 2, 38530 Candelaria - T: 922500100, Fax: 922502922
Religious Arts Museum 28909

Canduela

Museo Etnográfico de los Valles de Campoo, La Torrona, 500 m del Pueblo, 34811 Canduela
Ethnology Museum
Local ethnography 28910

Canet de Mar

Museu-Arxiu Parroquial, Plaza de l'Església 17, 08360 Canet de Mar - T: 937940394
Religious Arts Museum 28911

Cañete de las Torres

Museo Histórico Local, c/o Casa de Cultura, Plaza de España 8, 14660 Cañete de las Torres - T: 957183000, 957183001, Fax: 957183564
Archaeological Museum - 1983 28912

Cangas de Onis

Centro Parque Nacional Picos de Europa - Casa Dago, Av Covadonga 43, 33550 Cangas de Onis - T: 985848614, Fax: 985848699, E-mail: picos@mma.es. Head: Victoria Belgado Camblor
Natural History Museum / Ethnology Museum 28913

Museo Tesoro de la Santina, Plaza de la Basílica, 33550 Cangas de Onis - T: 985846035, Fax: 985846043
Religious Arts Museum 28914

Capellades

Museo Molino Papelero de Capellades, Moli de la Vila, Paseo Concepción 7, 08786 Capellades - T: 938012850, Fax: 938012850. Head: Victoria Rabal Merola
Science&Tech Museum
History of paper fabrication, Amador Romaní coll of prehistoric archaeology, local history, 16th c paper mill 28915

Capileira

Museo Costumbres Populares Pedro Antonio de Alarcón, Calle Escuelas y Mentidero, 18413 Capileira - T: 958763051
Ethnology Museum - 1972 28916

Caravaca de la Cruz

Museo Arqueológico Municipal, Iglesia de la Soledad, Calle Eugenio d'Ors s/n, 30400 Caravaca de la Cruz - T: 968702000, 968700512
Archaeological Museum - 1980 28917

Museo de la Vera Cruz, Real Alcázar Santuario de la Vera Cruz, 30400 Caravaca de la Cruz - T: 968707743, 968707528
Fine Arts Museum - 1978 28918

Cardedeu

Museu-Arxiu Tomàs Balvey i Bas, Plaza Sant Joan 1, 08440 Cardedeu - T: 938713070
Archaeological Museum / Folklore Museum / Historical Museum - 1965
Archaeology, Roman antiquities, 19th c weapons, numismatics, antique pharmacy including pharmacy pottery (18th c), folk art and costumes, 11th-19th c local history, 11th-19th c parchments 28919

Cardona

Museu de Sal de Josep Arnau, Calle Pompeu Fabra 4, 08261 Cardona - T: 938691000
Historical Museum 28920

Carmona

Conjunto Arqueológico de Carmona, Necrópolis y Anfiteatro Romano de Carmona, Av Jorge Bonsor 9, 41410 Carmona - T: 954140811, Fax: 954191476. Head: Soledad Gil de los Reyes
Archaeological Museum - 1881
Roman finds from Carmona 28921

Museo Municipal, San Ildefonso 1, 41410 Carmona - T: 954191226, E-mail: museocivdad@carmona.org, Internet: http://www.museocivdad.carmona.org. Head: Ricardo Lineros
Local Museum
Local prehistory and archaeology 28922

La Carolina

Museo Arqueológico, Centro 88, Calle Alfredo Calderón s/n, 23200 La Carolina - T: 953660034, 953660302
Archaeological Museum - 1980 28923

Carrión de Los Condes

Museo del Convento de Santa Clara, Calle Santa Clara 1, 34120 Carrión de Los Condes - T: 979880134
Religious Arts Museum 28924

Cartagena

Museo Arqueológico Municipal, Calle Santiago Ramón y Cajal 45, 30204 Cartagena - T: 968128881, Fax: 968128882. Head: Miguel Martínez Andreu
Archaeological Museum - 1943
Prehistory, Roman, Classical and submarine archaeology, Iberian and Islamic finds, architecture, sculpture, inscriptions, mining, 19th c crafts, 14th-18th c document coll 28925

Museo Nacional de Arqueología Marítima, Calle Dique de Navidad s/n, 30280 Cartagena - T: 968508415, 968101166, Fax: 968529692
Archaeological Museum 28926

Museo Naval de Cartagena, Calle Menéndez y Pelayo 8, 30290 Cartagena - T: 968127138
Special Museum 28927

Museo Yacimiento Romano, Calle Duque 29, 30202 Cartagena - T: 968502240, 968502400, Fax: 968101013
Archaeological Museum / Historical Museum 28928

Casalarreina

Monasterio de Nuestra Señora de la Piedad, Plaza Santo Domingo de Guzmán s/n, 26230 Casalarreina - T: 941324033
Religious Arts Museum 28929

Es Castell

Museu Militar de Menorca, Calle Explanada 19, 07720 Es Castell - T: 971365947
Military Museum 28930

Castellbisbal

Museu Municipal de la Pagesia, Calle Pi i Margall 13, 08755 Castellbisbal - T: 937720159. Head: Josep Mateu y Miró
Local Museum - 1985 28931

Castelldans

Museu del Pagès, Molí Vell, Calle L'Empit s/n, 25154 Castelldans - T: 973120002
Ethnology Museum 28932

Castellò d'Empúries

Museu Parroquial, Plaza de Mossèn Cinto Verdaguer s/n, 17486 Castellò d'Empúries - T: 972250519
Religious Arts Museum - 1967
Ecclesiastical art, goldsmith work, liturgical vestments, painting sculpture 28933

Castellón de la Plana

Museo de Bellas Artes de Castellón, Calle Caballeros 25, 12001 Castellón de la Plana - T: 964359711. Head: F. Olucha Montins
Fine Arts Museum 28934

Museo Etnológico de la Diputación, Calle Sanchis Abella s/n, 12001 Castellón de la Plana - T: 964359703
Ethnology Museum 28935

Museo Municipal de Etnología, Ermita San Jaime de Fadrell, Calle Partida Fadrell s/n, 12002 Castellón de la Plana - T: 964355100
Ethnology Museum 28936

Castellterçol

Casa-Museu Prat de la Riba, Plaza Prat de la Riba 7, 08183 Castellterçol - T: 938666362
Local Museum 28937

Castrillo del Val

Monasterio de San Pedro de Cardeña, A 10 km de Burgos, Carretera Local de la Cartuja de Miraflores, 09193 Castrillo del Val - T: 947290033, Fax: 947290075
Religious Arts Museum 28938

Castro de Rei

Museo Monográfico del Castro de Viladonga, Calle Castro de Viladonga, 27259 Castro de Rei - T: 982314255, Fax: 982314194
Archaeological Museum 28939

Castrojeriz

Museo de Arte Sacro, Iglesia de Santa María del Manzano, 09110 Castrojeriz - T: 947377036
Religious Arts Museum - 1974 28940

Museo Etnográfico, Calle Landelino Tardajos 8, 09110 Castrojeriz - T: 947377001, Fax: 947378520
Ethnology Museum 28941

Cazorla

Museo Artes y Costumbres Populares Alto Guadalquivir, Castillo de la Yedra, Camino Ángel s/n, 23470 Cazorla - T: 953710039
Ethnology Museum - 1971 28942

Cehegín

Museo Arqueológico Provincial, Antigua Casa Consistorial, Plaza Constitución 1, 30430 Cehegín - T: 968740922
Archaeological Museum 28943

Celanova

Casa Museo Curros Enríquez, 32800 Celanova - T: 988431481, Fax: 988451623
Historic Site - 1976 28944

Museo Parroquial, Monasterio de San Salvador, 32800 Celanova - T: 988431538. Head: Manuel Iglesias Grande
Religious Arts Museum - 1931
Ecclesiastical art 28945

Cerceda

Museo do Moucho, Av Mesón 21, 15185 Cerceda - T: 981685001, 981685036, Fax: 981685205
Fine Arts Museum 28946

Cervera

Museo Comarcal Durán y Sanpere, c/o Centro Comarcal de Cultura, Calle Mayor 15, 25200 Cervera - T: 973530488, Fax: 973531941
Archaeological Museum / Fine Arts Museum - 1914
Iberian and Roman finds, Gothic painting and sculpture 28947

Museu del Blat y de la Pagesia, c/o Centro Comarcal de Cultura, Calle Major 15, 25200 Cervera - T: 973530025, Fax: 973531941
Ethnology Museum - 1964
Ethnography 28948

Cervera de Pisuerga

Museo Etnográfico Piedad Isla, Plaza de la Cruz 4, 34840 Cervera de Pisuerga - T: 979870759
Ethnology Museum 28949

Museo Parroquial, Iglesia de Santa María del Castillo, 34840 Cervera de Pisuerga - T: 979870179
Religious Arts Museum - 1982 28950

Cervo

Real Patronato de Sargadelos, c/o Casa de Administración de Sargadelos, 27891 Cervo - T: 982557905, 982557922
Special Museum 28951

Ceuta

Museo Específico de la Legión de Ceuta, Calle Paseo Colón s/n, 51001 Ceuta - T: 956514057
Local Museum 28952

Chinchilla

Museo de Cerámica Nacional, Calle Peñuela 1, 02520 Chinchilla
Decorative Arts Museum - 1979 28953

Museo Parroquial Santa María del Salvador, Plus Ultra 2, 02520 Chinchilla - T: 967260039
Religious Arts Museum 28954

Chipiona

Museo Misional de Nuestra Señora de Regla, Colegio de Misioneros Franziscanos, 11550 Chipiona
Archaeological Museum - 1939
Early Roman Christian relics, ancient Egyptian and other North African objects, antique coins 28955

Cieza

Museo de Siyasa, Calle San Sebastian 17, 30530 Cieza - T: 968773153, Fax: 968773153, E-mail: museo.siyasa@ayuntamiento.cieza.net, Internet: http://www.ayuntamiento.cieza.net/culturaypatrimonio/museodesiyasa
Archaeological Museum - 1987 28956

Cisneros

Museo Parroquial San Pedro, Plaza España 2, 34320 Cisneros - T: 979844494
Religious Arts Museum - 1945 28957

Ciudad Real

Colección de Arqueología, c/o Casa de la Cultura, Calle Prado 7, 13002 Ciudad Real
Archaeological Museum - 1962
Local archaeology 28958

Colleción de Arte y Ciencias Naturales, Palacio de la Diputación, Calle Toledo 27, 13002 Ciudad Real
Fine Arts Museum / Natural History Museum
Local art, painting, sculpture, natural history, coleoptera 28959

Museo Catedralicio, Paseo del Prado, 13001 Ciudad Real
Religious Arts Museum - 1966
Ecclesiastical art and history, liturgical vestments, memorabilia on Concilio Vaticano II 28960

Museo de Ciudad Real, Calle Prado 4, 13001 Ciudad Real - T: 926226896, Fax: 926255304
Local Museum - 1976 28961

Museo Diocesano, Calle Cabelleros 5, 13001 Ciudad Real - T: 926250250, Fax: 926251258
Religious Arts Museum - 1983 28962

Museo Municipal Elisa Cendrero, Calle Toledo 11, 13001 Ciudad Real - T: 926227462, Fax: 926257035, E-mail: museosmunicipales-aytocr@hotmail.com. Head: Francisco Javier López Fernández
Local Museum 28963

Ciudad Rodrigo

Museo Catedralicio, Plaza Isabelina s/n, 37500 Ciudad Rodrigo - T: 923481424
Religious Arts Museum 28964

Ciudadela de Menorca

Museo Municipal de la Ciudadela, Batió de sa Font, Plaza sa Font s/n, 07760 Ciudadela de Menorca - T: 971380297
Local Museum 28965

Museu Diocesa de Menorca, Calle Seminari 7, 07760 Ciudadela de Menorca - T: 971380445
Religious Arts Museum - 1880
Art, local archaeology 28966

Coaña

Aula Didáctica del Castro de Coaña, Calle Castro de Coaña, 33795 Coaña - T: 985106700
Archaeological Museum 28967

Collbató

Museu de Coses del Poble, Calle Bonavista 2, 08293 Collbató - T: 937770100, Fax: 937770650
Local Museum - 1978 28968

Colmenar de Oreja

Museo Municipal Ulpiano Checa, Calle Costanilla de los Silleros 1, 28380 Colmenar de Oreja - T: 918944612
Local Museum - 1960
Local historical documents, memorabilia of the painter Ulpiano Checa (1860-1916) 28969

Colmenar Viejo

Colección Parroquial, Parroquia de la Asunción, Calle Cura s/n, 28770 Colmenar Viejo
Religious Arts Museum - 1954
Ecclesiastical art, goldsmith work, liturgical vestments, choral books 28970

Combarro

Museo de Artes y Costumbres Populares, 36993 Combarro
Folklore Museum - 1969
Local ethnology 28971

Comillas

Museo Cantábrico, Palacio del Marqués de Comillas, 39520 Comillas
Archaeological Museum / Fine Arts Museum / Decorative Arts Museum
Prehistory, Roman archaeology, medieval paintings, ceramics, numismatics 28972

Consuegra

Museo Municipal, Plaza España 1, 45700 Consuegra - T: 925480185, Fax: 925480288
Local Museum - 1964
Local archaeology 28973

Córdoba

Alcázar de los Reyes Cristianos, Campo Santo de los Mártires, 14004 Córdoba
Archaeological Museum / Historical Museum - 1960
Roman archaeology, 14th c residence of the Catholic kings 28974

Centro Cultural Torre de la Calahorra, Fundación Roger Garaudy, Calle Puente Romano s/n, 14009 Córdoba - T: 957293929, Fax: 957202677, E-mail: torrecalahorra@torrecalahorra.com, Internet: http://www.torrecalahorra.com. Head: Roger Garaudy, Balbino Povedano

Historical Museum - 1987
Magic model of the Alhambra (Granada), model of the Mosque as it was 500 yrs ago, multivision with 18 projectors 28975

Conjunto Arqueológico de Madinat Al Zahra, Carretera de Palma del Río km 8, 14071 Córdoba - T: 957329130, 957329118, Fax: 957330595. Head: Antonio Vallejo Triano
Archaeological Museum - 1911
Remains of the Islamic city Madinat Al Zahra 28976

Fundación Pública Municipal Jardín Botánico de Córdoba, Av Linneo s/n, 14004 Córdoba - T: 957200077, Fax: 957295333, E-mail: jardinbotcord@cod.servicom.es
Natural History Museum 28977

Museo Arqueológico Provincial, Pl Jerónimo Páez 7, 14003 Córdoba - T: 957474011, 957471076, Fax: 957474011. Head: Francisco Godoy Delgado
Archaeological Museum - 1867
Prehistoric coll, Roman archaeology, Iberian, Visigothic, Islamic, Mozarabian and Mudejar art, Gothic and Renaissance art, goldsmith work, ivory, ceramics and sculpture - library 28978

Museo de Bellas Artes, Plaza del Potro 1, 14002 Córdoba - T: 957473345, 957471314, Fax: 957470952
Fine Arts Museum - 1844
Paintings, sculptures, drawings since the end of the Middle Age till today, basic coll of works by artists from Cordoba - library 28979

Museo Diocesano de Bellas Artes, c/o Antiguo Palacio Episcopal, Calle Torrijos 10, 14004 Córdoba - T: 957479375
Religious Arts Museum 28980

Museo Julio Romero de Torres, Plaza del Potro 2, 14002 Córdoba - T: 957491909, 957201056. Head: Rafael Romero de Torres
Fine Arts Museum - 1931
Memorabilia of the painter Julio Romero de Torres 28981

Museo Municipal Taurino, Plaza Maimónides 5, 14003 Córdoba - T: 957201056, Fax: 957201056. Head: Ildefonso Montero Agüerz
Local Museum - 1954
Local crafts, jewelry, modern leatherwork, antique weights and measures, Portuguese sculptures, documents on famous bullfighters 28982

Museo-Tesoro Catedralicio, Catedral, 14003 Córdoba
Religious Arts Museum - 1882
Ecclesiastical art, goldsmith work, tapestry, liturgical vestments, painting, sculpture, miniature books 28983

Palacio de Viana, Calle Reja de Don Gome 2, 14001 Córdoba - T: 957482275, Fax: 957482268
Fine Arts Museum / Decorative Arts Museum - 1981
Art, painting, furniture, tapestry, leatherwork, special library on hunting, guns, crockery, glazed tile on heraldry 28984

Corella

Casa Museo de Arrese, Calle Vallejo 5, 31591 Corella - T: 948780024
Local Museum 28985

Museo de la Encarnación, Plaza Gobernador Don Pedro de Baygorri, 31591 Corella - T: 948780024
Religious Arts Museum - 1975 28986

A Coruña

Casa Museo de Doña Emilia Pardo Bazán, Real Academia Galega, Calle Tabernas 11, 15001 A Coruña - T: 981207308, Fax: 981207308
Historic Site - 1972 28987

Domus - Casa del Hombre, Calle Santa Teresa 1, 15002 A Coruña - T: 981217000, Fax: 981228934, E-mail: domus@casaciencias.org, Internet: http://www.casaciencias.org. Head: Ramón Núñez Centella
Science&Tech Museum 28988

Museo Casa de las Ciencias, Palacete de Santa Margarita, Parque de Santa Margarita, 15005 A Coruña - T: 81189844, Fax: 81189845, E-mail: marcos@casaciencias.org, Internet: http://www.casaciencias.org. Head: Ramon Nuñez
Science&Tech Museum 28989

Museo de Arte Sacro de Santa María do Campo, Plaza Santa María do Campo, 15001 A Coruña - T: 981203186
Religious Arts Museum 28990

Museo de Belas Artes da Coruña, Praza de Zalaeta, 15002 A Coruña - T: 981223723, Fax: 981223769, E-mail: mbaacoruna@retemail.es, Internet: http://www.amigosmuseo.com. Head: Angeles Penas Truque
Fine Arts Museum - 1922
Archaeology, Roman finds, 14th c Romanesque architecture, 16th-20th c regional and Spanish paintings, 17th c Flemish and Italian paintings, 13th-18th c Spanish sculptures, drawings and etchings, coll of Goya's engravings, musical compositions, numismatics, furnishings, porcelain, clocks 28991

Museo de la Colegiata de la Coruña, Calle Puerta de Aires 23, 15001 A Coruña - T: 981203186, Fax: 981203186
Religious Arts Museum 28992

Museo de Relojes, Palacio Municipal, Plaza María Pita 1, 15001 A Coruña - T: 981184200
Decorative Arts Museum - 1970
Horology, 17th-20th c English, French, German, Dutch and Spanish clocks 28993

Museo Histórico Arqueológico, Castillo de San Antón, 15001 A Coruña - T: 981210504, Fax: 981210504. Head: Felipe Senén López Gómez
Archaeological Museum - 1964
Archaeology and history, heraldry, Celtic treasure from Elviña, memorabilia of the explorer Sir Francis Drake - library 28994

Museo Militar Regional, Plaza Carlos I s/n, 15001 A Coruña - T: 981205300, 981206791, Fax: 981206791
Military Museum / Historical Museum 28995

Costitx

Museu de la Fauna Ibero-Balear, Calle Rafael Horrach s/n, 07144 Costitx - T: 971876070
Natural History Museum 28996

Covadonga

Museo-Tesoro de la Santina, Santuario, 33195 Covadonga
Religious Arts Museum - 1965
Ecclesiastical art, goldsmith work, liturgical vestments, history, royal tombs 28997

Covarrubias

Museo Parroquial de San Cosme y San Damián, Plaza Rey Chindasvinto 3, 09346 Covarrubias - T: 947406311
Religious Arts Museum - 1929
Art and history, medieval documents, treasures, costumes, 13th c tombs of the first Condes de Castilla e Infantas de Covarrubias, 14th-16th c religious sculpture and painting, 15th-18th c liturgical vestments, goldsmith work 28998

Crevillente

Museo Arqueológico Municipal, Casa del Parc Nou, Vial del Parque s/n, 03330 Crevillente - T: 966681478, Fax: 965404659
Archaeological Museum 28999

Museo Municipal Mariano Benlliure, Calle San Cayetano s/n, 03330 Crevillente - T: 965400534
Fine Arts Museum - 1967
Drawings and models of sculptures by Mariano Benlliure 29000

Cuacos de Yuste

Museo-Palacio del Emperador Carlos V, Monasterio de San Jerónimo de Yuste, 10430 Cuacos de Yuste - T: 927172130
Fine Arts Museum / Historical Museum - 1958
Art and history, palace of Carlos V when he retired to the monastery 29001

Cuadros

Museo Cultura Antigua Ribera del Bernesga, Calle Santiago Apóstol 3, 24122 Cuadros - T: 987251439
Ethnology Museum 29002

Cuenca

Museo Arqueológico Provincial El Almudi → Museo de Arte Abstracto Español

Museo Catedralicio, Plaza Mayor Pio XII s/n, 16001 Cuenca - T: 969212011
Religious Arts Museum - 1977 29003

Museo de Arte Abstracto Español, Fundación Juan March (Museum of Spanish Abstract Art), Casas Colgadas, 16001 Cuenca - T: 969212983, Fax: 969212285, E-mail: museocuenca@expo.march.es, Internet: http://www.march.es. Head: Dr. José Capa Eiriz
Fine Arts Museum
Spanish paintings and sculptures of the 20th c - library 29004

Museo de Cuenca, Calle Obispo Valero 12, 16001 Cuenca - T: 969213069, Fax: 969230629. Head: Concepciòn Rodríguez Ruza
Local Museum / Archaeological Museum / Fine Arts Museum - 1963
Paleontology, pre-history, Roman archaeology, fine arts 29005

Museo Diocesano-Catedralicio, Palacio Episcopal y Catedral, Calle Obispo Valero, 16001 Cuenca - T: 969224210
Religious Arts Museum - 1902
Art, goldsmith work, painting, sculpture, liturgical vestments, 12th c cathedral 29006

Daroca

Museo de los Corporales, Colegiata de Santa María, Plaza España s/n, 50360 Daroca - T: 976800761
Religious Arts Museum - 1929
Ecclesiastical art, painting, sculpture, goldsmith work, liturgical vestments 29007

Deià

Collecció Marroig, Calle Son Marroig, 07179 Deià - T: 971639158
Local Museum 29008

Deià Museo Arqueológico, Calle Clot s/n, 07179 Deià - T: 971639001, Fax: 971639152, E-mail: waldren@terra.es. Head: Dr. William Waldren
Archaeological Museum - 1963
Local archaeology, prehistory, paleontology 29009

Museu de Lluis Salvador d'Austria, Calle Son Marroig, 07179 Deià - T: 971639158
Fine Arts Museum 29010

Museu Parroquial, Calle Jeroni Pons 1, 07179 Deià - T: 971639172
Religious Arts Museum 29011

Dénia

Museo Arqueológico Municipal, Pl Constitución 10, 03700 Dénia - T: 965780100, Fax: 965789986, E-mail: museu@denia.net. Head: Josep Antoni Gisbert Santonja
Archaeological Museum - 1957
Local archaeology, fatimid bronzes (11th c) 29012

Museu Etnologic, Calle Cavallers 1, 03700 Dénia - T: 966420260, Fax: 965789986
Ethnology Museum 29013

Doña Mencia

Museo Arqueológico Municipal, c/o Casa de Cultura, Calle Juan Ramón Jiménez 5, 14860 Doña Mencia - T: 957676020, 957676152, Fax: 957676300
Archaeological Museum / Ethnology Museum - 1980 29014

Donostia-San Sebastián

Koldo Mitxelens Arts Centre, Kalea Urdaneta 9, 20006 Donostia-San Sebastián - T: 943482750, Fax: 943482755, E-mail: sala@kultura.gipuzkoa.net
Fine Arts Museum 29015

Museo de Cera de Igeldo, Parque de Atracciones Monte Igeldo, Paseo de Igeldo 183, 20008 Donostia-San Sebastián - T: 943311099
Special Museum 29016

Museo Diocesano de San Sebastián, Plaza La Sagrada Familia 11, 20010 Donostia-San Sebastián - T: 943472362
Religious Arts Museum 29017

Museo Municipal de San Telmo, Plaza Ignacio Zuloaga 1, 20003 Donostia-San Sebastián - T: 943424970, Fax: 943430693, E-mail: santelmo@donostia.org, Internet: http://www.donostiakultura.com. Head: Rafael Zulaika
Local Museum - 1899
15th-20th c painting, Basque ethnography, furniture, prehistory, tomb stelae 29018

Museo Naval - Untzi Museoa, Paseo Muelle 24, 20003 Donostia-San Sebastián - T: 943430051, Fax: 943431115, E-mail: mnaval@kultura.gipuzkoa.net, Internet: http://www.gipuzkoa.net/kultura/museos/um
Historical Museum - 1990 29019

Palacio del Mar/Aquarium, Plaza Carlos Blasco de Imaz s/n, 20003 Donostia-San Sebastián - T: 943440099, Fax: 943430092, E-mail: sog@aquariumss.com, Internet: http://www.aquariumss.com. Head: Vicente Zaragüeta
Natural History Museum - 1928
Marine zoology, natural history, navigation - library 29020

Durango

Durangaldeko Natur Zientzien Museoa, Calle Monagotorre Kalea 9, 48200 Durango - T: 629405740, Fax: 946814127, E-mail: museociencias@jet.es
Natural History Museum 29021

Museo de Arte e Historia, Calle San Agustinalde 16, 48200 Durango - T: 946200994
Fine Arts Museum 29022

Ecija

Museo Histórico Municipal de Écija, Palacio de Benamejí, Calle Cánovas del Castillo 4, 41400 Ecija - T: 955902919, Fax: 955902919, E-mail: museo@ecija.org, Internet: http://www.museo.ecija.org. Head: Antonio Fernández Ugalde
Historical Museum / Archaeological Museum 29023

Museo Parroquial, Plaza Santa María, 41400 Ecija - T: 954140811, Fax: 954191476
Religious Arts Museum - 1947
Local art, Roman and Islamic archaeology 29024

Eivissa

Museo Arqueológico d'Eivissa i Formentera, Plaza Catedral 3, 07800 Eivissa - T: 971301231, Fax: 971303263, E-mail: maef@jet.es. Head: Jorge H. Fernández
Archaeological Museum - 1907
Prehistory, Ibiza, Roman, Punic, Egyptian, Greek archaeological antiquities, Islamic art, 13th c sculpture, Gothic ceramics, 14th-16th c historical documents, ethnography and local crafts - library 29025

Museo Catedralicio, Catedral, 07800 Eivissa - T: 971312774
Religious Arts Museum - 1964
Religious art, goldsmith work, 14th-17th c paintings 29026

Museo Monográfico y Necrópolis Púnica de Puig des Molins, Vía Romana 31, 07800 Eivissa - T: 971301771, Fax: 971303263. Head: Jorge H. Fernández
Archaeological Museum - 1966
Carthagian and Roman relics from excavations, burial remains, necropolis - library 29027

Museu d'Art Contemporani d'Eivissa, Ronda Narcis Puvet, 07800 Eivissa - T: 971302723, Fax: 971302723. Head: Elena Ruiz Sastre
Fine Arts Museum - 1969
Etchings and paintings 29028

Elche

Esglesia de Santa María, Calle Obispo Tormo 16, 03202 Elche - T: 965451540
Religious Arts Museum 29029

Museo Arqueológico Municipal Alejandro Ramos Folqués, Palacio de Altamira, Diagonal del Palau s/n, 03202 Elche - T: 965453603, Fax: 965456611. Head: Dr. Rafael Ramos Fernández
Archaeological Museum - 1945
Archaeology, Greek, Roman and Iberian finds 29030

Museo de Arte Contemporáneo, Plaza Mayor del Raval, 03203 Elche - T: 965454982. Head: Sixio Marco
Fine Arts Museum 29031

Museo Escolar Agrícola de Pusol, Partida de Pusol 8, 03296 Elche - T: 966630478, Fax: 966630478
Ethnology Museum 29032

Museo Monográfico de la Alcudia, Partida Alzabaras Bajo P-1, 138, 03290 Elche - T: 966611506, Fax: 966611506
Archaeological Museum 29033

Elda

Museo Arqueológico Municipal, Calle Príncipe de Asturias 40, 03600 Elda - T: 965386816, Fax: 965399970
Archaeological Museum 29034

Museo del Calzado, c/o Instituto de Formación Profesional la Torreta, Calle Alemania s/n, 03600 Elda - T: 965383021, Fax: 965383021
Special Museum 29035

Elosu

Museo de Alfarería Tradicional Vasca, Calle Ollerías, 01510 Elosu - T: 945455145
Folklore Museum / Ethnology Museum 29036

Enguera

Casa de la Cultura, Plaza Manuel Tolsa s/n, 46810 Enguera - T: 962225524
Local Museum 29037

El Entrego

Museo de la Minería y de la Industria de Asturias, Calle El Trabanquín, 33940 El Entrego - T: 985663133, Fax: 985662676
Science&Tech Museum - 1986 29038

Epila

Colección de la Casa de Alba, Palacio de los Condes de Aranda, 50290 Epila
Historical Museum - 1808
Royal costumes, history 29039

L'Escala

Museu d'Arqueologia de Catalunya-Empúries, Calle del Museu s/n, 17130 L'Escala - T: 972770208, Fax: 972774260, E-mail: empuries@mac.es, Internet: http://www.mac.es. Head: Dr. Xavier Aquilué
Archaeological Museum 29040

Museu d'Arqueologia de Catalunya-Empúries, 17130 L'Escala - T: 972770208, Fax: 972774260, E-mail: empuries@mac.es, Internet: http://www.mac.es. Head: Xavier Aquilué
Archaeological Museum - 1908 29041

Eskoriatza

Eskoriatzako Museo Eskola, Calle Hidalga 5, 20540 Eskoriatza - T: 943714688, Fax: 943714042
Ethnology Museum 29042

Espejo

Museo Parroquial, Calle San Bartolomé 31, 14830 Espejo - T: 957376134
Religious Arts Museum - 1980 29043

L'Espluga de Francolí

Museo de la Vida Rural, Plaza Canós 18, 43440 L'Espluga de Francolí - T: 977870576, Fax: 977870430
Local Museum - 1963
History and archaeology, local arts and crafts 29044

Espot

Centre d'Interpretació p.n. d'Aigüestortes i Estany de Sant Maurici, Calle Prat del Guarda 2, 25597 Espot - T: 973624036, Fax: 973624036
Natural History Museum 29045

L'Estany

Museu del Monestir de Santa María, Plaza Monestir 1, 08189 L'Estany - T: 938300825, 938300801
Religious Arts Museum 29046

Estella

Museo Gustavo de Maeztu, Palacio de los Reyes de Navarra, Calle San Nicolás 1, 31200 Estella - T: 948546037, Fax: 948546037. Head: Francisco Beruete Calleja
Fine Arts Museum - 1949
Memorabilia on the painter Gustavo de Maeztu (1887-1947), 12th c palace - library, archive, documentation center 29047

Estepa

Museo Arqueológico Padre Martín Recio, Calle Ancha 14, 41560 Estepa - T: 955914088, Fax: 955914057, E-mail: estepa@dipusevilla.es
Archaeological Museum 29048

Museo del Mantecado, La Estepeña, Camino de las Piedras s/n, 41560 Estepa - T: 955912278
Local Museum 29049

Esterri d'Aneu

Ecomuseu de les Valls d'Aneu, Casa Gassia, Calle del Camp 22-24, 25580 Esterri d'Aneu - T: 973626436, Fax: 973626436, E-mail: ecomaneu@ecomuseu.com, Internet: http://www.ecomuseu.com. Head: Jordi Abella
Ethnology Museum
Ethnological objects 29050

Ezcaray

Museo Parroquial, Iglesia de Santa María la Mayor, 26280 Ezcaray - T: 941354059
Religious Arts Museum 29051

Falset

Museo-Archivo de Falset y Comarca, Calle Quartera 1, 43730 Falset - T: 977830873, Fax: 977830668. Head: Anton Vidal Inglès
Local Museum - 1965
History, art, local crafts and archaeology, wine growing 29052

Felanitx

Museu Cosme Bauça, Calle Sinia 20, 07200 Felanitx
Ethnology Museum 29053

Fene

Museo do Humor, c/o Casa da Cultura, Calle Fonte do Campo s/n, 15500 Fene - T: 981341451, 981342400, Fax: 981342400
Special Museum 29054

Ferrol

Museo Bello Piñeio, c/o Centro Cultural Antigo Hospital da Caridade, Plaza de España s/n, 15402 Ferrol - T: 981336700, Fax: 981354122
Local Museum 29055

Museo Naval de la Zona Marítima del Cantábrico, Arsenal Militar, 15490 Ferrol - T: 981336076
Military Museum / Historical Museum 29056

Figueres

Museu de l'Empordà, Calle Rambla 2, 17600 Figueres - T: 972502305, Fax: 972510765, E-mail: infome@museuemporda.org, Internet: http://www.museuemporda.org. Head: Anna Capella Molas
Fine Arts Museum / Local Museum - 1946
Local art and history, painting, watercolors 29057

Museu del Joguet de Catalunya, Antic Hotel París, Rambla 10, 17600 Figueres - T: 972504585, Fax: 972510765
Special Museum - 1982
Toy coll 29058

Teatre-Museu Dalí, Plaça de Gala i Salvador Dalí, 17600 Figueres - T: 972677505, Fax: 972501666, E-mail: t-mgrups@dali-estate.org, Internet: http://www.salvador-dali.org. Head: Antoni Pitxot
Fine Arts Museum - 1974
Wall painting by Salvador Dalí, town theatre (1850) - Dalí study centre 29059

Folgueroles

Casa-Museu del Poeta Verdaguer, Calle Major 7-9, 08519 Folgueroles - T: 938122157, Fax: 938887154
Special Museum 29060

La Fonsagrada

Museo Comarcal da Fonsagrada, Calle Rosalia de Castro s/n, 27100 La Fonsagrada - T: 982340008
Local Museum 29061

Forcall

Museo Municipal, Plaza Mayor 6, 12310 Forcall - T: 964171001, Fax: 964171001
Archaeological Museum 29062

Fornells de la Muntanya

Museu del Pastor, Cal Pastor, Km 128 Carretera Nacional 152, 17536 Fornells de la Muntanya - T: 972736163
Local Museum 29063

Foz

Museo Parroquial de San Martiño de Mondoñedo, San Martiño de Mondoñedo, 27780 Foz - T: 982132394, 982132607
Religious Arts Museum 29064

Fromista

Templo Románico de San Martín, Plaza San Martín, 34440 Fromista - T: 979810144
Religious Arts Museum - 1904
Art, architecture, sculpture 29065

Frontera

Ecomuseo de Guinea, 38046 Frontera
Ethnology Museum 29066

Fuendetodos

Casa Natal de Goya, Calle Zuloaga 3, 50142 Fuendetodos - T: 976143830, Fax: 976143857, E-mail: goya@dpz.es. Head: Elisa Picazo Verdejo
Fine Arts Museum - 1928
Memorial to Francisco de Goya in his birthplace 29067

Fuensanta

Museo Etnológico Popular, Santuario de la Fuensanta, 02637 Fuensanta - T: 967447808, 967447856
Ethnology Museum 29068

Fuente de Cantos

Casa-Museo de Zúrbaran, Calle Águila 6, 06240 Fuente de Cantos - T: 924500211
Special Museum 29069

Fuente Tojar

Museo Histórico Local, Calle Nueva s/n, 14815 Fuente Tojar
Local Museum 29070

Fuente Vaqueros

Casa Museo Federico García Lorca, Calle Poeta Federico García Lorca 4, 18340 Fuente Vaqueros - T: 958516453, Fax: 958516780, E-mail: lorca@valnet.es. Head: Juan de Loxa
Special Museum - 1986 29071

Galdar

Museo de Arte Sacro de Santiago de Galdar, Calle Fernando Guanarteme 2, 35460 Galdar - T: 928880721
Fine Arts Museum 29072

Parque Arqueológico Cueva Pintada, Calle Bentejui 23, 35460 Galdar - T: 928552402, Fax: 928552402
Archaeological Museum 29073

Gallarta

Museo Minero, c/o Casa de Cultura y del Matadero, Av del Minero, 48500 Gallarta
Local Museum 29074

Gandía

Museo Arqueológico Comarcal, Calle Colón 10, 46700 Gandía - T: 962872988, Fax: 962872988
Archaeological Museum 29075

Museo Municipal de Prehistoria, Plaza del Rey, 46700 Gandía
Local Museum
Local art and history 29076

Palau Ducal, Carrer Duc Alfons el Vell 1, 46700 Gandía - T: 962871465, 626753165, Fax: 962871465, E-mail: palauducal@infonegocis.com. Head: José Luis Ferrer Soria
Religious Arts Museum / Historic Site - 1893
Palace of the Jesuit duke Francisco de Borja y Aragón (1510-1572), 15th c portal 29077

Gando

Museo Aeronáutico Torre de Gando, c/o Base Aérea de Gando, 35219 Gando
Local Museum 29078

Garray

Yacimiento-Museo Arqueológico, A 7 km de Soria y Junto al Pueblo de Garray, 42162 Garray - T: 975114213
Archaeological Museum 29079

La Garriga

Museu Biblioteca Fundació Mauri, Calle Cardedeu 17, 08530 La Garriga - T: 938714900
Library with Exhibitions 29080

Gascueña

Colección Parroquial, 16532 Gascueña
Religious Arts Museum
Ecclesiastical art 29081

Gata de Gorgos

Museo Arqueológico, Calle Peñon 10, 03740 Gata de Gorgos - T: 965756089, Fax: 965756635
Archaeological Museum 29082

Gavà

Museu de Gavà, Plaza Dolors Clua 13-14, 08850 Gavà - T: 936382570, Fax: 936383596, E-mail: museu.gava@bcn.servicom.es
Local Museum - 1978
Prehistoric mines of Gava 29083

Gelida

Museu de Gelida, Casa del Senyor, Calle Angel Guimerà 12, 08790 Gelida - T: 937790437
Local Museum 29084

Gerena

Museo Taurino José Vega, Calle Pablo Picasso 19, 41860 Gerena
Ethnology Museum - 1970 29085

Gijón

Museo de la Gaita, Fundación Municipal de Cultura, Educación y Universidad Popular, Calle La Güelga s/n, 33203 Gijón - T: 985332244, Fax: 985332244. Head: Susana Asensio Llamas
Music Museum - 1966
Antique and modern bagpipes from Europe, Orient and Occident, and from Spain, traditional instruments from Asturias - documentation center, workshop 29086

Museo Etnográfico del Pueblo de Asturias, Calle Isabel la Católica s/n, 33203 Gijón - T: 985332244, 985373335, Fax: 985350709. Head: Joaquín López Álvarez
Folklore Museum 29087

Museo Evaristo Valle, La Redonda, Camino de Cabueñes s/n, Somió, 33203 Gijón - T: 985338092, Fax: 985338092, E-mail: museoevalle@teleline.es. Head: Guillermo Basagoiti
Fine Arts Museum
Work and personal belongings of the painter Evaristo Valle 29088

Museo Jovellanos, Pinacoteca Municipal, Plazoleta de Jovellanos s/n, 33201 Gijón - T: 985346313, Fax: 985350709, E-mail: museo@jovellanos.net. Head: Dr. Lucía Peláez Tremols
Fine Arts Museum / Local Museum - 1971
Paintings asturiana 19th and 20th c, memorabilia on Gaspar Melchor de Jovellanos (1833-1874) - library, archive 29089

Museo Nicanor Piñole, Plaza de Europa s/n, 33205 Gijón - T: 985359594, Fax: 985346313, E-mail: museo@jovellanos.net. Head: Dr. Lucía Peláez Tremols
Fine Arts Museum / Local Museum - 1991
Asturian paintings of the 20th c., memorabilia of Nicanor Piñole - Library, Archive 29090

Gilet

Monasterio Santo Espíritu, Carretera de Sant Esperit, 46149 Gilet - T: 962620011
Religious Arts Museum 29091

Girona

Centre Bonastruç ça Porta, Calle Força 8, 17004 Girona - T: 972216761, Fax: 972216761, E-mail: callgirona@grn.es, Internet: http://www.ajuntament.gi. Head: Assumpció Hosta y Rebés
Historical Museum / Ethnology Museum 29092

Museo Parroquial de San Félix, Subida de San Félix, 17004 Girona
Religious Arts Museum - 1962
Ecclesiastical art, painting, sculpture, jewelry and goldsmith work 29093

Museu Capitular de la Catedral de Girona, Plaza de la Catedral 12, 17004 Girona - T: 972214426, Fax: 972214426
Religious Arts Museum 29094

Museu d'Arqueologia de Catalunya Girona, Sant Pere de Galligant, Pujada de Santa Llúcia, 17007 Girona - T: 972202632, Fax: 972210454, E-mail: girona@mac.es, Internet: http://www.mac.es. Head: Aurora Martin
Archaeological Museum - 1846
Prehistoric coll, archaeological finds from Ampurias, Greek, Roman, Iberian, 13th-14th c Christian tombs, 12th c sculpture, 12th c Romanesque architecture 29095

Museu d'Art, Plaza de la Catedral 12, 17004 Girona - T: 972209536, Fax: 972227595. Head: Joan Surroca i Sens
Fine Arts Museum - 1979
19th-20th c art, 17th c visigothic inscripcions, 12th-13th c Islamic art, Romanesque art and codes, 12th-17th c church treasures, jewelry and goldsmith work, miniature codices, 16th-17th c sculpture, 14th-17th c religious painting, 15th-18th c textiles - documentation centre, library, educational workshops 29096

Museu d'Història de la Ciutat, Calle Força 27, 17004 Girona - T: 972209160, Fax: 972419401
Historical Museum - 1960
Local history and art - library, archive 29097

Museu Diocesà de Girona, Palau Episcopal, Pujada Catedral 12, 17004 Girona - T: 972201958, 972209536, Fax: 972201855, E-mail: BISBATGIRONA@PLANALFA.ES, Internet: http://www.palahi.es/bisat. Head: María Rosa Ferrer Dalgà
Religious Arts Museum - 1926
Medieval sculpture and painting - Museu d'Art 29098

Museu Farmàcia de l'Hospital de Santa Catarina, Plaza Pompeu Fabra 1, 17002 Girona - T: 972203834. Head: Joan Surroca
Historical Museum
Pottery 29099

Sala Girona de la Fundació la Caixa, Calle Sèquia 5, 17001 Girona - T: 972215408. Head: Enric Sagrera
Public Gallery 29100

Tresor de la Catedral, Plaza de la Catedral s/n, 17004 Girona - T: 972214426, Fax: 972215814. Head: Gabriel Roura Güibas
Religious Arts Museum - 1952
Art, tapestry, jewellery and goldsmith work, painting, sculpture, applied art, miniature books 29101

Godella

Casa Museo Pinazo, Calle Pintor Pinazo 31, 46110 Godella - T: 963631103
Fine Arts Museum 29102

Grado

Museo Etnográfico, Calle Alonso de Grado 3, 33820 Grado - T: 985750068
Ethnology Museum 29103

Granada

Cartuja de la Asunción, Carretera de Alcafar, Paseo Cartuja, 18011 Granada
Religious Arts Museum - 1931
Art, painting and sculpture, ceramics 29104

Casa de los Pisas, Calle Convalecencia 1, 18010 Granada - T: 958222144, Fax: 958227443
Religious Arts Museum 29105

Casa de los Tiros, Calle Pavaneras 19, 18009 Granada
Fine Arts Museum / Decorative Arts Museum - 1928
Painting, decorative arts, crafts, documents, folklore, local history 29106

Casa-Museo Manuel de Falla, Calle Antequeruela Alta 11, 18009 Granada - T: 958229421, Fax: 958228288. Head: Antonio Navarro Linares
Special Museum - 1965
Memorabilia of Manuel de Falla y Matheu (1876-1946) 29107

Colección de Arte Carmen Rodríguez Acosta, Plaza Torres Bermejas, 18009 Granada
Fine Arts Museum - 1934
Art, contemporary Spanish painting and Oriental art 29108

Colección del Observatorio de Cartuja, c/o Universidad, 18071 Granada - T: 958243000, 958243556
Science&Tech Museum / University Museum 29109

Colección Municipal, c/o Ayuntamiento, Plaza del Carmen, 18009 Granada
Local Museum - 1939
15th-17th c crafts and documents 29110

Huerta de San Vicente, Casa-Museo Federico García Lorca, Calle Virgen Blanca 6, 18004 Granada - T: 958258466, Fax: 958258466, E-mail: huerta-san-vicente@siapi.es, Internet: http://www.huertagarcialorca.es. Head: Laura Garcia-Lorca de los Rios
Historic Site - 1985 29111

Instituto Gómez-Moreno de la Fundación Rodríguez-Acosta, Callejón Niños del Rollo 10, 18009 Granada - T: 958227497
Archaeological Museum - 1982 29112

Museo Angel Barrios, Calle Real de la Alhambra s/n, 18009 Granada - T: 958227525, 958227526, Fax: 958226363, E-mail: sperez@alhambra-patronato.es, Internet: http://www.alhambra-patronato.es. Head: Mateo Revilla Uceda
Historic Site - 1978 29113

Museo Arqueológico Provincial, Carrera del Darro 43, 18010 Granada - T: 958225603. Head: Eduardo Fresneda Padilla
Archaeological Museum - 1876
Prehistoric art, Greek, Roman, Iberian, Punic, Celtic, Gothic and Visigothic antiquities, Islamic art and

architecture, archaeological and Islamic ceramic coll, Mozarabian art, 15th c art and architecture, inscriptions, numismatics, textiles, glass - library 29114

Museo Catedralicio, Plaza Alonso Cano, 18001 Granada - T: 958222959
Religious Arts Museum - 1929
Treasures, 16th c tapestry, 15th-17th c religious painting, 16th-18th c religious sculpture, liturgical vestments, miniature choral books, crafts 29115

Museo de Bellas Artes, Palacio de Carlos V, Alhambra, 18009 Granada - T: 958224843
Fine Arts Museum - 1839
15th-20th c art mainly of the Granada school, 15th-19th c painting, 16th c sculpture, 16th c enamels and painted glass, works by Sánchez Cotán, Alonso Cano and José de Mora - library 29116

Museo de la Alhambra, Palacio de Carlos V, Alhambra, 18009 Granada - T: 958226279. Head: Mateo Revilla Uceda
Fine Arts Museum / Decorative Arts Museum / Archaeological Museum / Ethnology Museum - 1942
Hispanic-Islamic ceramics, architectonical fragments, glass, inscriptions, archaeology and ethnology - conservation dept 29117

Museo de los Reyes Católicos, Capilla Real, Calle Oficios s/n, 18001 Granada - T: 958227848
Fine Arts Museum - 1945
14th-15th c Flemish painting and painting of Flemish schools, 15th c Spanish, German, Italian painting, 15th c crafts, sculpture, goldsmith work, liturgical vestments, miniature books, flags and banners, tombs of the Catholic Kings and of Donna Juana and Don Felipe el Hermoso 29118

Museo del Sacromonte, Abadía del Sacromonte, Camino del Sacromonte, 3 km from Granada, 18010 Granada - T: 958221445
Fine Arts Museum / Decorative Arts Museum - 1925
Sculpture, painting, goldsmith work, liturgical vestments, tapestry, Arabian codices 29119

Museo Nacional de Arte Hispanomusulmán, Palacio de Carlos V, Alhambra, 18009 Granada - T: 958226279. Head: Eduardo Fresneda Padilla
Fine Arts Museum 29120

Parque de las Ciencias de Granada, Museo Interactivo de Ciencias, Av Mediterráneo s/n, 18006 Granada - T: 958131900, Fax: 958133582, E-mail: cpciencias@parqueciencias.com, Internet: http://www.parqueciencias.com
Science&Tech Museum 29121

Real Monasterio de San Jerónimo, Calle Rector López Argüeta 9, 18001 Granada - T: 958279337
Religious Arts Museum - 1877 29122

Grandas de Salime

Museo Etnográfico, Av del Ferreiro s/n, 33730 Grandas de Salime - T: 985627243
Ethnology Museum 29123

Granollers

Centro Cultural de la Fundació la Caixa, Calle Joan Camps 1, 08400 Granollers - T: 938706467, Fax: 938707802. Head: Pruden Panadès
Public Gallery 29124

Museu de Granollers, Av Anselm Clavé 40-42, 08400 Granollers - T: 938706508, Fax: 938793919, E-mail: museu@ajuntament.granollers.org, Internet: http://www.museugranollers.org
Local Museum 29125

Museu de Granollers-Ciències Naturals, Calle Francesc Marcià 51, La Tela, 08400 Granollers - T: 938709651, Fax: 938709651, E-mail: m.granollers.cn@diba.es, Internet: http://museugranollers.org. Head: Josep Font Sentias
Natural History Museum - 1987
Small mammals of Spain - documentation centre 29126

Guadalajara

Museo de Guadalajara, Palacio del Infantado, Plaza de Los Caídos s/n, 19001 Guadalajara - T: 949213301, Fax: 949212773
Local Museum - 1973 29127

Guadalest

Museu Etnologic de Guadalest, Casa Típica del Segle XVIII, Calle Iglesia 1, 03517 Guadalest - T: 965885238
Ethnology Museum 29128

Guadelupe

Monasterio de Nuestra Señora de Guadelupe, Plaza Generalísimo Franco, 10140 Guadelupe
Religious Arts Museum - 1964
Art, painting, goldsmith work, choral books 29129

Guadix

Museo Catedralicio, Plaza de la Catedral, 18500 Guadix - T: 958661097
Religious Arts Museum - 1063
Ecclesiastical art, 15th c cathedral 29130

Guardamar de Segura

Museo Arqueológico Etnológico Municipal, Calle Colón 60, 03140 Guardamar de Segura - T: 965728610, Fax: 965727128
Local Museum 29131

La Guardia

Museo da Citania de Santa Tegra, Monte Santa Tegra, 36780 La Guardia - T: 986610000
Archaeological Museum / Historical Museum - 1914 29132

Güimar

Museo Arqueológico, Costumbrista y Naturalista, El Escobonal, Plaza de San José, 38591 Güimar
Local Museum 29133

Guernica y Luno

Museo Documental, Casa de Juntas de Guernica, Calle Allende Salazar 5, 48300 Guernica y Luno - T: 946255451
Historical Museum
History of the dominion in Vizcaya 29134

Guimerà

Museu de la Pedra i de l'Estable, c/o Ajuntament, 25341 Guimerà
Ethnology Museum 29135

Museu Municipal, Plaza Major s/n, Carrer Goleta, 25341 Guimerà - T: 973303038, Fax: 973303038
Local Museum 29136

Guissona

Museu Municipal Eduard Camps Cava, Plaza Vell Pla 1, 25210 Guissona - T: 973550005, Fax: 973550687
Local Museum - 1952
Local history and archaeology of Iesso, the present Guissona 29137

Gumiel de Hizán

Museo de Gomellano, Iglesia Santa María, Plaza Mayor 1, 09370 Gumiel de Hizán - T: 947544018. Head: Prof. Eutimio Herrero
Religious Arts Museum - 1962
Art, Romanesque architectural remains, painting 29138

Haro

Estación Enológica, Calle Bretón de los Herreros 4, 26200 Haro - T: 941310547, Fax: 941311800
Ethnology Museum 29139

Hellín

Museo Comercial, Calle Benito Toboso 12, 02400 Hellín - T: 967304630, 967300553
Local Museum 29140

Museo de Semana Santa, 02400 Hellín
Religious Arts Museum 29141

Hérvas

Museo Pérez Comendador-Leroux, Calle Asensió Neila 5, 10700 Hérvas - T: 927481655, Fax: 927481655
Fine Arts Museum - 1976 29142

Hondarribia

Museo Parroquial, Iglesia de Nuestra Señora de la Asunción y del Manzano, Calle Mayor s/n, 20280 Hondarribia - T: 943642666
Religious Arts Museum - 1973 29143

Horta de Sant Joan

Museu d'Art Popular, Plaza de l'Església 3, 43596 Horta de Sant Joan - T: 977435005
Folklore Museum 29144

L'Hospitalet de Llobregat

Museu de L'Hospitalet de Llobregat, Cantona Xipreret, Calle Joan Pallarès 38, 08901 L'Hospitalet de Llobregat - T: 933381396, Fax: 933381748. Head: Josep Solias i Aris
Local Museum - 1969
Contemporary Catalan art, 16th c panels 29145

Hoyo de Manzanares

Museo de la Academia de Ingenieros, Carretera Torrelodones-Colmenar s/n, 28240 Hoyo de Manzanares - T: 918566122, Fax: 918567795
Archaeological Museum / Historical Museum 29146

Huelva

Museo de Huelva, Alameda Sundheim 13, 21003 Huelva - T: 959259300, Fax: 959285547. Head: Manuel Osuna Ruíz
Archaeological Museum / Fine Arts Museum - 1973
Prehistoric coll, Roman, Christian archaeological and Islamic antiquities, painting (Vazquez, Diaz, 20th c), protohistory 29147

Huesca

Museo Arqueológico Provincial, c/o Universidad Sertoriana, Plaza Universidad 1, 22002 Huesca - T: 974220586, Fax: 974229388, E-mail: museohu@aragob.es. Head: Vicente Baldellou
Archaeological Museum - 1873
Prehistory, Iberian, Roman and Christian archaeology, 12th c architecture, sculptures, 15th-19th c painting, 17th c painting, Spanish ceramics, decorative arts - library 29148

Museo Diocesano de Huesca, Plaza Catedral, 22002 Huesca - T: 974231099, Fax: 974220679, E-mail: obhuesca@planalfa.es, Internet: http://www.museum.com/jb/museum?id= 15880. Head: Antonio Naval Mas
Religious Arts Museum / Archaeological Museum - 1950
14th-15th c Gothic wall painting, sculpture, 17th c painting, 12th-14th c crafts, goldsmith work, 11th c documents, medieval codices and miniature books 29149

Huete

Museo de Arte Sacro, Iglesia Parroquial de San Esteban, Plaza de la Merced s/n, 16500 Huete - T: 3469372081, Fax: 3469372081
Religious Arts Museum 29150

Museo Florencio de la Fuente, Plaza Merced s/n, 16500 Huete - T: 969372210, Fax: 969372084, 969372048
Fine Arts Museum - 1990 29151

Ibi

Museu Valencia del Joguet, Calle Aurora Pérez Caballero s/n, 03440 Ibi - T: 966550225, Fax: 966550226, E-mail: museujoguet@webhouse.es, Internet: http://www.cult.gva.es/museus/m00089/default.htm. Head: José Pascual, Manuel Tarancón
Ethnology Museum 29152

Ibiza → Eivissa

Igea

Museo de Fósiles y Minerales, Calle Mayor 6, 26525 Igea - T: 941194014, 941194001, Fax: 941176049
Natural History Museum 29153

Igualada

Museu Comarcal de l'Anoia, Calle Dr. Joan Mercader s/n, 08700 Igualada - T: 938046752, Fax: 938046752
Local Museum 29154

Museu de la Piel, Baixada Sant Nicolau 19, 08700 Igualada - T: 938046752
Local Museum 29155

Illescas

Hospital-Santuario de Nuestra Señora de la Caridad, Calle Cardenal Cisneros 2, 45200 Illescas - T: 925540035
Religious Arts Museum - 1966
Ecclesiastical art, painting, goldsmith work, liturgical vestments 29156

Ingenio

Museo de Piedra y Artesanía Canaria, Camino Real de Gando 1, 35250 Ingenio - T: 928781124
Local Museum 29157

Irún

Museo Ermita de Santa Elena, Necrópolis Romana Siglos I Y II, Calle Ermita 2, 20300 Irún - T: 943625500, 943630564, Fax: 943626007
Archaeological Museum 29158

Iruña de Oca

Museo del Oppidum de Iruña, Villodas-Tres Puentes, 01195 Iruña de Oca - T: 945231777, Fax: 945133804
Archaeological Museum / Historical Museum 29159

Jaca

Museo Diocesano, Catedral, 22700 Jaca - T: 974361841, Fax: 974355280
Religious Arts Museum
11th-12th c Romanesque art and architecture 29160

Museo Regional de la Escuela de Montaña → Sala de Recuerdos de la Escuela Militar de Montaña

Sala de Recuerdos de la Escuela Militar de Montaña (Memory Hall of the Military School of Montaña), Calle San Bernardo s/n, 22700 Jaca - T: 974356252, Fax: 974356224
Military Museum 29161

Jaén

Museo Catedralicio, Catedral, Plaza Santa María, 23002 Jaén - T: 953234233. Head: José Nelgares Raye
Religious Arts Museum - 1962
Ecclesiastical art, painting, sculpture, goldsmith work, choralbooks, manuscripts, liturgical vestments 29162

Museo de Artes y Costumbres Populares, Palacio Villardompardo, Plaza Santa Luisa de Marillac s/n, 23003 Jaén - T: 953236292, 953238103, Fax: 953238059
Ethnology Museum - 1980 29163

Museo Internacional de Arte "NAÏF", Palacio Villardompardo, Plaza Santa Luisa de Marillac s/n, 23003 Jaén - T: 953236292, 953238103, Fax: 953238059
Fine Arts Museum - 1990 29164

Museo Provincial, Paseo de la Estación 29, 23008 Jaén - T: 953250600, Fax: 953250320, E-mail: museojaen@yahoo.es. Head: José Luis Chicharro Chamorro
Local Museum - 1914
Prehistory, archaeology, Roman, Iberian, Islamic finds, Renaissance to 20th c art, painting and sculpture - library 29165

Jávea

Museo Arqueológico y Etnográfico Soler Blasco, Calle Primicias 1, 03730 Jávea - T: 965791098, Fax: 965795107
Archaeological Museum / Ethnology Museum 29166

Javier

Castillo de Javier, Plaza San Francisco Javier, 31411 Javier - T: 948884024, Fax: 948884259, E-mail: javier@2000.es. Head: Ricardo J. Sada
Archaeological Museum 29167

Jerez de la Frontera

Museo Arqueológico Municipal, Plaza del Mercado s/n, 11408 Jerez de la Frontera - T: 956333316, Fax: 956341350, E-mail: museoarq@aytojerez.es, Internet: http://www.ctv.es/users/jerezmuseoarq. Head: Rosalía González Rodríguez
Archaeological Museum - 1963
Prehistory, Roman, Greek, Punic, Visigothic, Islamic Iberian antiquities - library, educational dept 29168

Jérica

Museo Municipal, Calle Historiador Bayo, 12450 Jérica - T: 964129177
Local Museum / Archaeological Museum - 1946
Roman archaeology, art and local history 29169

Jijona

Museo de Escultura Octavio Vicent, Plaza Convent s/n, 03100 Jijona - T: 965611490
Fine Arts Museum 29170

Jumilla

Museo de la Vid y el Vino Juan Carcelén, Calle García Lorca 1, 30520 Jumilla - T: 968756064, 968780336, Fax: 968780145
Special Museum 29171

Museo Municipal Jerónimo Molina, Plaza de la Constitución 3, 30520 Jumilla - T: 968780740, Fax: 968783453. Head: Emiliano Hernández Carrión
Archaeological Museum - 1956
Local archaeology, Bronze Age, Iberian, Roman and Hispano-Arabian finds 29172

Juneda

Museu Etnològic i Arqueològic, Calle Dr. Cornudella 2, 25430 Juneda - T: 973150014
Ethnology Museum / Archaeological Museum 29173

Laguardia

Museo Arqueológico Poblado de la Hoya, Carretera el Villar-Villa de Laguardia, 01300 Laguardia - T: 945231777, Fax: 945143803
Archaeological Museum 29174

Museo de la Sociedad Amigos de Laguardia, Calle Mayor 66, 01300 Laguardia - T: 945100845
Local Museum - 1964
Local history, archaeology, ethnography, numismatics, ceramics, war items (Guerras Carlistas) 29175

La Laguna

Museo de Antropología de Tenerife - Casa de Carta, Carretera Tacoronte-Valle Guerra s/n, 38270 La Laguna - T: 922546000, Fax: 922544498, E-mail: mhenriquez.museostfe@cabtfe.es. Head: Fernando Estévez González
Ethnology Museum - 1983
Food, social anthropology, cultural studies 29176

Museo de Historia de Tenerife y Archivo Insular, Calle San Augustín 22, 38201 La Laguna - T: 92262594349, Fax: 922630013, Internet: http://www.museosdetenerife.com. Head: Fidencia Iglesias González
Historical Museum - 1993 29177

Museo de la Ciencia y el Cosmos, Calle Vía Láctea s/n, 38205 La Laguna - T: 922263454, Fax: 922263295. Head: Ignacio García de la Rosa
Natural History Museum - 1993
planetarium 29178

Lalín

Museo Municipal Ramón María Aller Ulloa, Calle Ramón Aller s/n, 36500 Lalín - T: 986784004
Local Museum 29179

Laspaules

Museo Geológico, Calle Jacinto Pere s/n, 22471 Laspaules - T: 974553141, Fax: 974553141
Natural History Museum - 1986 29180

Laudio

Museo Vasco de Gastronomía, Zubiko Etxea, Calle Maestro Elorza 11, 01400 Laudio - T: 946724330, Fax: 946724330. Head: Eva Gil de Prado
Special Museum 29181

Lebrija

Museo Tesoro Parroquial, Plaza del Rector Merina s/n, 41740 Lebrija - T: 955972337
Religious Arts Museum - 1978 29182

Leganés

Museo de Escultura al Aire Libre, Carretera de Villaverde, Calle Dr. Fleming, 28912 Leganés - T: 916944561
Open Air Museum 29183

Legazpia

Ferrería de Mirandaola, Calle Telleriarte 12, 20230 Legazpia - T: 943730428, Fax: 943733163, E-mail: mirandaola@lenbur.com. Head: Juan Ramón Larrañaga, Aurelio González
Special Museum 29184

Leioa

Museo Vasco de Historia de las Ciencias y de la Medicina, c/o Universidad del País Vasco, Campus de Leioa, 48940 Leioa - T: 944647700
Historical Museum 29185

León

Museo Catedralicio, Calle Cardenal Landazuri 2, 24003 León - T: 987230060, Fax: 987241216
Religious Arts Museum - 1932/1980
Romanesque Cathedral, 13th-17th c sculpture, medieval crafts, carvings, goldsmith work, liturgical vestments, 16th-17th c painting, 10th c Mozarabian Bible, medieval documents and missals 29186

Museo Catedralicio-Diocesano, Plaza de la Regla s/n, 24003 León - T: 987230060, Fax: 987241216, E-mail: catedral@catedraldelon.org, Internet: http://www.catedraldeleon.org. Head: Manuel Pérez Recio
Religious Arts Museum - 1948
10th-20th c ecclesiastical art 29187

Museo de la Comisión Provincial de Monumentos, Calle Navatejera s/n, 24008 León - T: 987236405, Fax: 987221602, E-mail: museodeleon@jet.es. Head: Luis A. Grau
Historical Museum - 1885 29188

Museo de León, Plaza de San Marcos, 24001 León - T: 987245061, 987236405, Fax: 987221602, E-mail: museodeleon@jet.es. Head: Luis A. Grau Lobo
Archaeological Museum / Fine Arts Museum / Archaeological Museum / Ethnology Museum - 1869
Regional prehistory, Roman Celtiberian, medieval architectural elements, 11th-13th c art and sculpture, 14th-16th c painting and sculpture, 15th c Flemish paintings, 13th-17th c ivory, goldsmith work and liturgical vestments, 10th c Mozarabian art, 15th-19th c Spanish paintings, regional ethnology, 1st-18th c inscriptions - library 29189

Museo Etnográfico Leones Ildefonso Fierro, Calle Puerta de la Reina 1, 24003 León - T: 987262799, Fax: 987250451, E-mail: dlilc@argored.com. Head: José Antonio Díaz Díaz
Ethnology Museum - 1971 29190

Museo Real Colegiata de San Isidoro, Panteón, Biblioteca, Museo, Claustro, Plaza San Isidoro 4, 24003 León - T: 987876161, Fax: 987876162, E-mail: sanisidoro@sanisidorodeleon.org, Internet: http://www.sanisidorodeleon.org. Head: Antonio Viñayo
Religious Arts Museum - 1910
Art and history from Romanesque: architecture, sculpture, royal tombs, wall paintings, goldsmith works, ivories, enamels, textiles, miniature codices, Islamic works, liturgical objects, textiles and choral books from other periods - archive, library 29191

Lérida → Lleida

Lietor

Colección Parroquial, Iglesia Santiago Apóstol, Plaza Mayor, 02410 Lietor - T: 967200024
Local Museum 29192

Linares

Centro de Documentación Musical, Casa Museo Andrés Segovia, Calle Canovas del Castillo 59, 23700 Linares - T: 953649100, Fax: 953649117
Historic Site 29193

Museo Arqueológico Monográfico de Cástulo Linares, Calle General Echagüe 2, 23700 Linares - T: 953692463
Archaeological Museum - 1957
Local history and archaeology, especially from the Iberic-Roman town of Cástulo 29194

La Línea de la Concepción

Archivo Museo Histórico Municipal, Av España s/n, 11300 La Línea de la Concepción - T: 956696222
Local Museum - 1984 29195

Museo Cruz Herrera, c/o Casa de Cultura, Av España s/n, 11300 La Línea de la Concepción - T: 956762576
Fine Arts Museum - 1969 29196

Museo Taurino, Calle San José 94, 11300 La Línea de la Concepción - T: 956172481
Historical Museum 29197

Linyola

Museu del Pagès, Calle Pi i Margall 19, 25240 Linyola - T: 973575248. Head: Antonio Más Vilaplana
Agriculture Museum - 1975
Agricultural implements 29198

Llaberia-Tivissa

Museu del Bast, Calle Forn 9, 43320 Llaberia-Tivissa
Ethnology Museum 29199

Llagostera

Fundació Emili Vilá, Calle Sant Pere 27, 17240 Llagostera - T: 972830253
Historic Site - 1968 29200

Museu Municipal, Calle Alt de Girona 4, 17240 Llagostera - T: 972830375
Local Museum 29201

Llança

Museu de l'Aquarella, Fundació J. Martínez Lozano, Calle Selva 17-19, 17490 Llança - T: 972380181
Fine Arts Museum 29202

Llanera de Ranes

Museu Parroquial, Plaza Santa Teresa s/n, 46814 Llanera de Ranes - T: 962254203
Local Museum 29203

Lleida

Centro Cultural de la Fundació la Caixa, Avinguda Blondel 3, 25002 Lleida - T: 973270788, Fax: 973274889, E-mail: info.fundacio@lacaixa.es, Internet: http://www.fundacio.lacaixa.es. Head: Mercè Freixinet
Public Gallery 29204

F.P. Institut d'Estudis Ilerdencs, Fons Bibliogràfic i Documental, Plaza Catedral, Av Blondel 62, 25002 Lleida - T: 973271500, Fax: 973274538. Head: Josep M. Gasset y Salafranca
Special Museum - 1969
Book art, rare books 29205

Museo Catedralicio, Plaza Catedral, 25002 Lleida
Religious Arts Museum - 1963
Tapestry, painting, liturgical vestments, goldsmith work, documents and miniature codices - archives, library 29206

Museo de la Paeria, c/o Ajuntament, Placa de la Paeria 1, 25003 Lleida - T: 973700223, Fax: 973238953
Historical Museum - 1963
Local history, heraldry, seals of documents, prints - archives 29207

Museo Diocesano, Jaime Conquistador 67, 25002 Lleida - T: 973268628, Fax: 973272972
Religious Arts Museum - 1893
13th-15th c Spanish painting and sculpture, local prehistoric archaeological finds, crafts, textiles, tapestry, numismatics, medals, incunabula and manuscripts 29208

Museu Arqueològic de l'Institut d'Estudis Ilerdencs, Plaza Catedral s/n, 25002 Lleida - T: 973271500, Fax: 973274538. Head: Montserrat Maciá y Gou
Archaeological Museum - 1954
Archaeology 29209

Museu Capitular, Plaza Catedral s/n, 25002 Lleida - T: 973269470
Religious Arts Museum 29210

Museu d'Art Modern 'Jaume Morera, Calle Cavallers 15, 25002 Lleida - T: 973273665, Fax: 973273665. Head: Jesús Navarro Guitart
Fine Arts Museum - 1917
Paintings of the 19th and 20th c 29211

Museu de Ciències Naturals, Carretera de Saragossa, 25194 Lleida
Natural History Museum
Natural sciences and geology 29212

Museu Numismàtic, Placa de la Catedral, 25002 Lleida - T: 973249200, E-mail: iei@fpiei.es
Special Museum 29213

Llinars del Vallés

Museu Monogràfic del Castell de Llinars, Can Bordoi, Carretera de Mataró, km 8, 08450 Llinars del Vallés - T: 938410875. Head: Teresa Roca
Archaeological Museum - 1978
14th-15th c archaeology 29214

Museu Municipal Joan Pal i Gras, Calle Ravalet s/n, 08450 Llinars del Vallés - T: 938410050
Local Museum 29215

Llivia

Museo de Farmacia, c/o Ayuntamiento, Plaza Mayor, 17527 Llivia
Special Museum - 1930
15th-19th c history of pharmacy, apothecary's shop (1415) with interiors 29216

Museu Municipal, Calle Forns 4, 17257 Llivia - T: 972896313, Fax: 972146155. Head: Josep Vinyet Estebanell
Local Museum 29217

Lloret de Mar

Museu de Lloret de Mar, Calle Sant Carles 16, 17310 Lloret de Mar - T: 972365398
Local Museum 29218

Llosa de Ranes

Museo Histórico Etnológico, Casa del Pou, Calle Cami Reial 88, 46815 Llosa de Ranes - T: 962230214
Ethnology Museum 29219

Lluc

Museo de Lluc, Santuario de Lluc, 07315 Lluc - T: 971871525 ext 229, Fax: 971517096, E-mail: info@lluc.net, Internet: http://www.lluc.net. Head: Dr. Elvira González
Religious Arts Museum / Archaeological Museum / Decorative Arts Museum / Folklore Museum - 1952
Prehistory, archaeology, Romanesque and Gothic art, 16th-18th c liturgical vestments, furnishings, numismatics, silverworks, tapestry, ceramics, 18th-19th c paintings tapestry, ceramics 29220

Museo del Monasterio, 07315 Lluc - T: 971517025, Fax: 971517054
Religious Arts Museum 29221

Lluchmajor

Moli d'en Gaspar, Carretera de Campos s/n, 07620 Lluchmajor - T: 971660837, Fax: 971660837
Ethnology Museum 29222

Loarre

Castillo de Loarre, A 5,5 km. de Loarre, Carretera Forestal, 22809 Loarre - T: 974380049
Archaeological Museum - 1906 29223

Logroño

Museo de la Rioja, Calle San Agustín 23, 26001 Logroño - T: 941291259, Fax: 941206821, E-mail: museo@larioja.org, Internet: http://www.museo.larioja.org. Head: Teresa Sánchez Trujillano
Local Museum - 1963
Archaeology, fine art and ethnology of La Rioja contemporary Spanish art - library, archive 29224

Lorca

Museo Arqueológico Municipal, Pl Juan Moreno s/n, 30800 Lorca - T: 968406267, Fax: 968406267. Head: Andrés Martínez Rodríguez
Archaeological Museum - 1992 29225

Museo de Bordados Paso Blanco, Conjunto Monumental Santo Domingo, 30800 Lorca - T: 968444233
Religious Arts Museum 29226

Luanco

Museo Marítimo de Asturias, Calle Gijón 6, 33440 Luanco - T: 985880101. Head: Dr. J.R. García López
Special Museum
Maritime history, marine cartography, maps and drawings, nautical instruments, ship models 29227

Lucena del Cid

Colección Museográfica Parroquial, Plaza Espanya 2, 12120 Lucena del Cid - T: 964380030
Religious Arts Museum 29228

Lugo

Museo Diocesano, Seminario, Calle Angel López Pérez 2, 27002 Lugo
Religious Arts Museum - 1918
Ecclesiastical art 29229

Museo Provincial, Plaza Soledad 6, 27001 Lugo - T: 982242112, Fax: 982242112. Head: Lucila Yáñez Anllo
Local Museum - 1932
Prehistory, Roman and Iberian finds, Mozarabian and Visigothic art, Romanesque architecture, 10th-15th c tombs, sculptures, paintings, crafts, furniture, folklore, marine history, numismatic and ceramic coll 29230

Museo-Tesoro Catedralicio, Catedral, Plaza Santa María, 27001 Lugo
Religious Arts Museum - 1931
11th c cathedral with Gothic, Renaissance, Baroque and neo-Classical annexes and interiors, religious art 29231

Madrid

Calcografía Nacional, Museo de la Real Academia de Bellas Artes, Calle Alcalá 13, 28014 Madrid - T: 915240883, Fax: 915240977
Decorative Arts Museum / Fine Arts Museum - 1790
Copper engraving, 18th-20th c copperplates and copper engravings, copperplate engravers' studios 29232

Casa-Museo de Lope de Vega, Calle Cervantes 11, 28014 Madrid - T: 914299216, Fax: 914299216
Historical Museum - 1935
Memorial to Lope de Vega (1562-1635), house where he had lived (1610-1635) - research center 29233

Centro de Mesonero Romanos, Casa de la Panadería, Plaza Villa 3, 28005 Madrid
Special Museum - 1942
Memorial to the writer Ramón Mesonero Romanos (1803-1882), 15th c building 29234

Centro Técnico de Intendencia, Paseo Extremadura 439, 28024 Madrid - T: 917111411, Fax: 917110927
Science&Tech Museum 29235

Colección Amazónica, Iglesia San Juan Crisostomo, Calle Domenico Scarlatti 2, 28003 Madrid - T: 915495328
Ethnology Museum 29236

Colección Anatomía, c/o Dpto. de Anatomía I, Facultad de Medicina, Ciudad Universitaria, 28040 Madrid - T: 913941374, Fax: 913941374, E-mail: secanat1@med.ucm.es, Internet: http://www.ucm.es/info/museoana. Head: Prof. J. Puerta
Natural History Museum / University Museum - 1834
Anatomical objects, human embryology, skeleton evolution, osteology, anatomical wax reproductions 29237

Colección Benedito, Calle Juan Bravo 4, 28006 Madrid - T: 915754687
Historic Site - 1975 29238

Colección de Arqueología y Etnografía Americana, c/o Facultad de Geografía e Historia, Ciudad Universitaria, Edificio B, 28040 Madrid - T: 913945785, Fax: 913945808
Archaeological Museum / Ethnology Museum / University Museum - 1966
Archaeology, ethnology from Tukuna and Cayapa - library 29239

Colección de la Biblioteca Musical, Calle Conde Duque 9-11, 28015 Madrid - T: 914296251. Head: Aurora Rodríguez Martín
Music Museum 29240

Colección de la Casa de Alba, Palacio de Liria, Calle Princesa 20, 28008 Madrid - T: 915475302
Archaeological Museum / Fine Arts Museum / Decorative Arts Museum - 1956
Roman and Greek sculpture, Italo-Greek pottery, 16th-19th c Spanish painting, 15th-17th c Italian painting, 17th c Dutch painting, 19th c paintings by Ingres, 19th c sculpture and furnishings, coll of miniatures and tapestry, porcelain, arms, codices and documents, history and paintings of the family of the Duke of Alba 29241

Colección de la Facultad de Filosofía y Letras, Ciudad Universitaria, 28004 Madrid
Fine Arts Museum / Archaeological Museum / University Museum
Spanish painting, works by Sorolla, Beruete, Inza and Sala, Phoenician and Roman archaeological objects 29242

Colección de la Real Academia de la Historia, Calle León 21, 28014 Madrid - T: 914290611
Historical Museum 29243

Colección de los Padres Escolapios, Calle Gaztambide 65, 28015 Madrid - T: 915435400, Fax: 915440527
Religious Arts Museum 29244

Colección de Mineralogía, c/o Facultad de Ciencias, Universidad Autónoma de Canto Blanco, 28049 Madrid - T: 913974132, Fax: 913974900
Natural History Museum - 1975 29245

Colección del Banco de España, Calle Alcalá 50, 28014 Madrid - T: 913385000, Fax: 913385398
Fine Arts Museum - 1856
19th c Spanish painting, tapestry and furniture 29246

Colección del Banco Exterior de España, Carrera de San Jerónimo 36, 28014 Madrid - T: 914294477. Head: Miguel Boyer
Fine Arts Museum - 1929
Painting, sculpture 29247

Colección del Observatorio Astronómico Nacional, Calle Alfonso XII 3, 28014 Madrid - T: 915270107, Fax: 915271925. Head: F. Lahulla
Science&Tech Museum - 1796
Scientific apparatuses, telescopes, chronographs, signal recording apparatuses, clocks, oscilloscopes, photometers, spectrographs 29248

Colección Municipal, c/o Ayuntamiento y Casa de Cisneros, Plaza de la Villa 4, 28005 Madrid
Fine Arts Museum / Decorative Arts Museum
Local art and history, goldsmith work, painting, tapestry, antique maps of Madrid 29249

Convento de San Plácido, Calle San Roque 9, 28004 Madrid - T: 915317999
Religious Arts Museum - 1943 29250

Ermita de San Antonio de la Florida, Calle Glorieta de la Florida 5, 28008 Madrid - T: 915420722
Religious Arts Museum 29251

Fundación Juan March, Calle Castelló 77, 28006 Madrid - T: 914354240, Fax: 915763420, E-mail: webmast@mail.march.es, Internet: http://www.march.es. Head: José Luis Yuste Grijalba
Public Gallery - 1955 29252

Gabinete de Antigüedades, c/o Real Academia de la Historia, Calle León 21, 28014 Madrid - T: 914290611
Archaeological Museum / Decorative Arts Museum / Fine Arts Museum - 1738
Art and history, prehistory, classical and paleo-Christian archaeology, Iberian and Visigothic finds, Islamic art, Mozarabian crafts, 4th c 'Silver dish of Theodosius', 4th c tombs, 15th-19th c painting, textiles, numismatics, 11th c documents 29253

Instituto de Valencia de Don Juan, Don Juan Institute of Valencia, Calle Fortuny 43, 28010 Madrid - T: 913081848, Fax: 913197848, E-mail: instvaldonjuan@terra.es. Head: Duque de Huescar
Fine Arts Museum / Decorative Arts Museum - 1916
Medieval crafts and sculptures, 14th-17th c textiles and costumes, Islamic inscriptions, ivory and other arts, 15th-18th c Islamic and Spanish ceramics, 15th c tapestry, 15th-16th c furnishings, porcelain, Celtic and Iberian jewelry, 15th, 17th, 19th c painting, 16th c miniatures, 14th c Koran, documents, Spanish numismatic coll, 15th-16th c arms, prehistoric archaeology and Visigothic finds, arms and armor - library; archive 29254

Monasterio de la Encarnación, Plaza de la Encarnación 1, 28013 Madrid - T: 915470510, Fax: 915426947, E-mail: juani.alises@patrimonionacional.es, Internet: http://www.patrimonionacional.es. Head: Leticia Sánchez Hernández
Religious Arts Museum - 1960
Monastic life in the 16th and 17th c, ecclesiastical art, painting, sculpture, furniture, reliquaries - library, archive 29255

Monasterio de las Descalzas Reales, Plaza de las Descalzas s/n, 28013 Madrid - T: 915485350, 914548700 ext 3234, Fax: 915426947. Head: Ana García Sanz
Religious Arts Museum - 1960
Monastic life in the 16th and 17th centuries, ecclesiastical art, painting, sculpture, tapestry, goldsmith work - library, musical archne 29256

Museo Africano Mundo Negro, Calle Arturo Soria 101, 28043 Madrid - T: 914152412, Fax: 915192550, E-mail: mundonegro@planalfa.es, Internet: http://www.planalfa.es/mcombonianos. Head: Julio Ocaña Iglesias
Ethnology Museum - 1985
Ethnology from Africa in general, Makonde art from Mozambique, masks of Africa (several countries), Ethopian crosses, African traditional musical instruments 29257

Museo Arqueológico Nacional, Calle Serrano 13, 28001 Madrid - T: 915777912, Fax: 914316840, Internet: http://www.man.es. Head: Miguel Angel Elvira Barba
Archaeological Museum - 1867
Prehistoric coll, Roman, Greek, Etruscan, Punic, Celtic, Iberian antiquities, archaeological finds from Balearic and Canary Islands' cultures, early Christian and Visigothic archaeology, Islamic archaeology, 12th-15th c Mudejar art, Modern art collection - library, photographical archives 29258

Museo Casa de la Moneda, Calle Doctor Esquerdo 36, 28071 Madrid, mail addr: Calle Jorge Juan 106, 28071 Madrid - T: 915666533, 915666544, Fax: 915666809, E-mail: museo@FNMT.es, Internet: http://www.FNMT.es/museo. Head: Dr. Rafael Feria, Tomás Sánchez
Special Museum / Science&Tech Museum - 1964
Hist of money and medals, Spanish numismatic coll, including European and Ibero-American issues of money related to Spain's political expansion, medals, etchings, stamps and machinery for coining, graphic arts - restoration laboratory 29259

Museo Cerralbo, Calle Ventura Rodríguez 17, 28008 Madrid - T: 915473646/47, Fax: 915591171. Head: Pilar de Navascués Benlloch
Fine Arts Museum / Decorative Arts Museum - 1922
Paintings, drawings, engravings and sculptures (15th-19th c), tapestry, furniture, ceramics, porcelain, numismatics - library 29260

Museo de Aeronáutica y Astronáutica, Carretera de Extremadura km 10,6, 28024 Madrid - T: 915091690, Fax: 917106847, Internet: http://www.mde.es/mde/cultura/patrim/museo4.htm. Head: Luis Castañón Albo
Military Museum - 1966
History of Spanish aviation, projects and models 29261

Museo de América, Av Reyes Católicos 6, 28040 Madrid - T: 915492641, 915439437, Fax: 915446742, E-mail: museo@mamerica.mcu.es. Head: Paz Cabello Carro
Ethnology Museum / Archaeological Museum / Fine Arts Museum - 1941
American archaeology and anthropology, art from former Spanish colonies, pre-Columbian goldwork, colonial painting, Ibero-American history 29262

Museo de Artes y Tradiciones Populares, c/o Facultad Filosofía y Letras, Universidad Autónoma Canto Blanco, 28049 Madrid - T: 913974270, 913974222, Fax: 913975544, E-mail: museo.arte@uam.es. Head: Guadalupe González-Hontoria y Allendesalazar
Ethnology Museum / Fine Arts Museum 29263

Museo de Bomberos, Vallecas, Calle Boada 4, 28038 Madrid - T: 914786572
Science&Tech Museum 29264

Museo de Carrozas (temporary closed), Palacio Real, Calle Bailén, 28071 Madrid - Fax: 9215426947
Science&Tech Museum - 1967
Carriages and coaches, saddles, litters (16th-20th centuries) 29265

Museo de Cera Colón, Paseo Recoletos 41, 28004 Madrid - T: 913192649, Fax: 913080825
Special Museum 29266

Museo de Farmacia Militar, Calle Embajadores 75, 28012 Madrid - T: 915274048, 915391006, Fax: 915302707
Science&Tech Museum / Military Museum - 1927 29267

Museo de la Bibliografía Española, c/o Biblioteca Nacional, Paseo de Recoletos 20-22, 28001 Madrid - T: 915807800
Library with Exhibitions - 1901
Bibliographical, documentary, artistic and musical coll, incunabula, rare books, book art, manuscripts and illuminations 29268

Museo de la Escuela General de Policía, Calle Miguel Angel 5, 28010 Madrid
Special Museum - 1943
History of the Spanish police, photo gallery, anthropometry, criminal weapons and utensils 29269

Museo de la Farmacia Hispana, c/o Facultad de Farmacia, Ciudad Universitaria, 28040 Madrid - T: 913941797, Fax: 913941797, E-mail: museofar@farm.ucm.es. Head: Dr. F. Javier Puerto
Special Museum / University Museum - 1951
Various pharmacies and reproductions (17th-18th c), reproduction of a Yatroquímico laboratory, 14th-19th c pharmaceutical ceramics, scales, weights and measures, apparatuses for the production of medicaments, microscopes, mortars, medicine-chests, paintings and drawings 29270

Museo de la Real Academia de Bellas Artes de San Fernando, Calle Alcalá 13, 28014 Madrid - T: 915240864, Fax: 915241034. Head: Antonio Bonet Correa
Fine Arts Museum - 1744
15th-20th c painting, 17th-20th c sculpture, 15-20th c Spanish, Italian, French, Flemish, Dutch drawing, musical section, decorative arts, Francisco de Goya - library and archive 29271

Museo de Regimiento de Ferrocarriles No 13, Av de la Aviación 6, Carretera de Extremadura, 28024 Madrid - T: 915092000, Fax: 915092376
Military Museum 29272

Museo de San Isidro, Pl de San Andrés 2, 28005 Madrid - T: 913667415, Fax: 913645149, E-mail: museosanisidro@munimadrid.es, Internet: http://www.munimadrid.es/museosanisidro. Head: Eduardo Salas Vázquez
Archaeological Museum / Historical Museum / Historic Site - 2000
Prehist, archaeology and paleontology of Madrid and the environs, Iranian ceramics, ancient and medieval coins, religious art, history and iconography of Madrid - library, research dept. 29273

Museo del Doctor Olavide, c/o Hospital Provincial Gregorio Marañon, Calle Doctor Esquerdo 46, 28007 Madrid - T: 915868000
Special Museum - 1903
Wax reproductions of lesions and diseased parts of the body for dermatological research 29274

Museo del Ejército, Calle Méndez Núñez 1, 28014 Madrid - T: 915314624, 915228977, Fax: 915314624, E-mail: josearivas@et.mde.es. Head: José A. Rivas Octavio
Military Museum - 1803
Military history and models of military equipment, uniforms and insignia of different branches of the service, exotical coll from Africa, America, Asia and Oceania 29275

Museo del Ferrocarril de Madrid, Paseo de las Delicias 61, 28045 Madrid - T: 902228822, Fax: 915068024, E-mail: fumuu21@ffe.es, Internet: http://www.ffe.es/delicias. Head: Rafael Ruiz Sanchidrián
Science&Tech Museum - 1984 29276

Museo Geominero, c/o Instituto Geológico y Minero de España, Calle Ríos Rosas 23, 28003 Madrid - T: 913495759, Fax: 913495830, E-mail: m.geominero@igme.es, Internet: http://www.igme.es. Head: Isabel Rabano
Natural History Museum - 1927
Mineralogy, palaeontology, section of vertebrates and invertebrates, petrology 29277

Museo Histórico-Minero Don Felipe de Borbón y Grecia, Calle Ríos Rosas 21, 28003 Madrid - T: 914423635, Fax: 913367070. Head: B. Calvo
Science&Tech Museum - 1777
Archaeology, shells, mining lamps and tools - library 29278

Museo Lázaro Galiano, Calle Serrano 122, 28006 Madrid - T: 915616084. Head: Alonso Araceli Pereda
Fine Arts Museum / Decorative Arts Museum - 1951
Painting, sculpture, enamels, ivory, furniture, bronzes, jewels, glass, textiles, medals, archeology, ceramics, keys, fans - library, archive 29279

Museo Municipal de Madrid, Calle Fuencarral 78, 28004 Madrid - T: 915888672, Fax: 915888679, E-mail: smuseosm@munimadrid.es, Internet: http://www.munimadrid.es/museos. Head: Carmen Priego Fernández del Campo
Historical Museum / Fine Arts Museum / Decorative Arts Museum / Folklore Museum - 1929
Hist (Middle Ages-20th c) and art from Madrid, 16th-20th c painting and sculpture, crafts and folk art, porcelain, ceramics, arms, numismatics and medals pertaining to the local mint, insignia, fans, furniture, silver, 17th-19th c maps, Madrid drawings and reproductions, photos, engravings, historical documents, military hist, theatre hist, Madrid bullfights 29280

Museo Nacional Centro de Arte Reina Sofía, Calle Santa Isabel 52, 28012 Madrid - T: 914675161, Fax: 914673163, E-mail: commicaciones.mncars@cars.mcu.es, Internet: http://www.museoreina-sofia.mcu.es. Head: Juan Manuel Bonet Planes
Fine Arts Museum - 1986/90
Refurbished 18th-c building, contemporary art - library, photography, record library, audio-visual archive 29281

Museo Nacional de Antropología, Av Juan de Herrera 2, 28040 Madrid - T: 915497150, 915492453, Fax: 915446970, E-mail: manuel.berges@mna.mcu.es, Internet: http://www.mec.es. Head: Manuel Berges Soriano
Ethnology Museum 29282

Museo Nacional de Antropología, Calle Alfonso XII 68, 28014 Madrid - T: 915306418, Fax: 914677098, E-mail: antropologico@mna.mcu.es, Internet: http://www.mcu.es/nmuseos/antropologica/Sede-Alfonso/. Head: Pilar Romero de Tejada
Ethnology Museum - 1910
Arts and crafts of Africa, America, Asia, Oceania, and Europa, physical anthropology - library, archive 29283

Museo Nacional de Arquitectura, c/o Escuela Superior de Arquitectura, Ciudad Universitaria, 28040 Madrid
Fine Arts Museum - 1943
Designs, models, drawings and prints, architectonical fragments 29284

Museo Nacional de Artes Decorativas, Calle Montalbán 12, 28014 Madrid - T: 915326845, Fax: 915232086. Head: Alberto Bartolomé Arraiza
Decorative Arts Museum - 1912
15th-19th c Spanish ceramics, 15th-19th c furniture, folk art, crafts, tapestry, 16th c paintings, porcelain, glass coll from prehistoric, Visigothic and medieval times to the 20th c, Oriental arts and crafts, leatherwork 29285

Museo Nacional de Ciencias Naturales, Calle José Gutiérrez Abascal 2, 28006 Madrid - T: 915618600, Fax: 915645078, Internet: http://www.mncn.csic.es. Head: Montserrat Gomendio Kindelán
Natural History Museum - 1776
Malacological objects from the Americas sent by the viceroys, geology, palaeontology, zoology, volcanology - library 29286

Museo Nacional de la Ciencia y la Tecnología, Antigua Estación de las Delicias, Paseo las Delicias 61, 28045 Madrid - T: 915303121, Fax: 914675119, E-mail: museo.mnct@mnct.mcu.es, Internet: http://mhct.dit.upm.es/mnct. Head: Dr. Amparo Sebastián
Science&Tech Museum - 1980 29287

Museo Nacional de Reproducciones Artísticas, Ciudad Universitaria, Av Juan de Herrera 2, 28040 Madrid - T: 915496618, Fax: 915496618, E-mail: Josefa.Almagro@mnra.mcu.es, Internet: http://www.mcu.es/nmuseos/reproducciones-artisticas/portada.html. Head: M.J. Almagro Gorbea
Fine Arts Museum - 1877
Plaster casts of important sculptures from oriental, greek, roman, medieval and renaissance, 17th-18th c art, numismatic, glass, photographical reproductions of paintings 29288

Museo Nacional del Ferrocarril → Museo del Ferrocarril de Madrid

Museo Nacional del Prado, Paseo del Prado, 28014 Madrid, mail addr: Calle de Ruiz de Alarcón 23, 28014 Madrid - T: 913302800, Fax: 913302856, E-mail: museo.nacional@prado.mcu.es, Internet: http://museoprado.mcu.es. Head: Eduardo Serra Rexach, Miguel Zugaza
Fine Arts Museum - 1819
12th-19th c painting of the Spanish school, 14th-18th c Italian painting, 15th-16th c German painting, 15th-17th c Flemish and Dutch painting, 17th-18th c French and English painting, 18th-19th c drawing and graphic arts, Spanish Romanesque wall painting, Greek and Roman sculpture, jewellery, "Tesoro de Delfín", decorative arts - library 29289

Museo Naval, Paseo del Prado 5, 28014 Madrid, mail addr: Calle de Montalbán 2, 28071 Madrid - T: 913795299, Fax: 913795056, E-mail: direccion@museonavalmadrid.com, Internet: http://www.museonavalmadrid.com. Head: Fernando Riaño Lozano
Historical Museum - 1843
Cartography, plans of vessels, manuscripts, nautical instruments, arms, models of vessels, drawings, engravings, decorations, uniforms 29290

Museo Parroquial, Iglesia de Santa Cruz, Calle Atocha 6, 28012 Madrid - T: 913691239
Religious Arts Museum 29291

Museo Pedagógico de Arte Infantil, c/o Facultad de Bellas Artes, Ciudad Universitaria, Calle Greco 2, 28040 Madrid - T: 913943571, 913943652, Fax: 913943653
Special Museum - 1980 29292

Museo Postal y Telegráfico, c/o Palacio de Comunicaciones, Calle Montalbán s/n, 28070 Madrid - T: 913962589, Fax: 913962129, E-mail: victoria.crespo@correos.es, Internet: http://www.correos.es. Head: Victoria Crespo Guliérrez
Special Museum
Postal and telegraphy gallery, phliatelic coll - library, graphic archive 29293

Museo Romántico, Calle San Mateo 13, 28004 Madrid - T: 914481071, Fax: 915942893. Head: Rosa Donoso Guerrero
Fine Arts Museum - 1924
Painting, sculpture, drawing, miniatures, tapestry, furnishings, domestic utensils, engravings of the Spanish Romantic period (1820-1868), books and graphic arts 29294

Museo Scout, Calle Donados 2, 28013 Madrid - T: 915412396, Fax: 915412396
Special Museum 29295

Museo Sorolla, Paseo General Martínez Campos 37, 28010 Madrid - T: 913101584, Fax: 913085925, E-mail: sorolla@museo.mec.es, Internet: http://mcu.es/nmuseos/sorolla. Head: Florencio de Santa Ana Alvárez Ossorio
Fine Arts Museum - 1932
Memorabilia of the painter Joaquín Sorolla y Bastida (1863-1923), furniture and decorative arts, ceramics, sculptures, archaeological objects, paintings and drawings by the artist 29296

Museo Taurino, Plaza de Toros de las Ventas, Calle Alcalá 237, 28028 Madrid - T: 917251857, Fax: 917259629
Special Museum - 1952
History and art of bullfighting 29297

Museo Thyssen-Bornemisza, Paseo del Prado 8, 28014 Madrid - T: 913690151, Fax: 914202780, E-mail: mtb@museothyssen.org, Internet: http://www.museothyssen.org. Head: Carlos Fernández de Henestrosa
Fine Arts Museum - 1992 29298

Palacio Real de Madrid, Calle Bailén s/n, 28071 Madrid - T: 9154200594, Fax: 9215426947
Fine Arts Museum / Decorative Arts Museum - 1950
Painting, 16th-18th c tapestry, sculpture, furniture, porcelain, crystal, clocks, miniatures, lamps, coaches, arms, musical instruments - library, archive, conservation area 29299

Panteón de Goya, San Antonio de la Florida, Paseo de la Florida, 28008 Madrid
Fine Arts Museum - 1905
Memorabilia of the royal painter Francisco José de Goya y Lucientes (1746-1828), frescos, tomb of the artist 29300

Patrimonio Nacional, Palacio Real, Calle Bailén s/n, 28071 Madrid - T: 914548720, Fax: 914548721, E-mail: daha@patrimonionacional.es. Head: Alvaro Fernández-Villaverde y de Silva Duque de San Carlos
Fine Arts Museum - 1940
library, archive 29301

La Quinta (temporary closed), Desvío km 3.500, Carretera el Pardo, 28048 Madrid - Fax: 913760452
Fine Arts Museum 29302

Real Armería (temporary closed), Palacio Nacional, Calle Bailén s/n, 28071 Madrid - T: 915475350, 914548700 ext 7234, Fax: 9215426947. Head: Alvaro Soler del Campo
Military Museum - 1893
Coll of 13th-19th c royal arms and armour, historical jewellery, military trophies, Kolman and Desiderius Helmschmid, Filippo Negroli 29303

Real Fábrica de Tapices, Calle Fuenterrabía 2, 28014 Madrid - T: 915513400, Fax: 915513409
Decorative Arts Museum - 1889
Tapestry, 18th c drawings and carpets 29304

Sala d'Exposiciones de la Fundació la Caixa, Calle Serrano 60, 28001 Madrid - T: 914354833, Fax: 915762253
Public Gallery 29305

San Antonio Abad, c/o Colegio de San Antón, Calle Hortaleza 63, 28004 Madrid
Fine Arts Museum - 1962
Painting, including two pieces by Goya 29306

Madrigal de las Altas Torres

Casa Natal de Isabel la Católica, Palacio de Juan II, Plaza del Cristo s/n, 05220 Madrigal de las Altas Torres - T: 920320050
Fine Arts Museum - 1942
15th-17th c art, paintings, sculptures and tapestry 29307

Mahón

Colecció Hernández Mora, Calle Claustre del Carme 5, 07701 Mahón - T: 971350597
Fine Arts Museum 29308

Museo de Bellas Artes, Plaza de la Conquista, 07701 Mahón
Fine Arts Museum - 1889
Prehistory, archaeology, local ethnology, Aztec artifacts, numismatics, ceramics 29309

Museo de Menorca, Av Dr. Guardia s/n, 07701 Mahón - T: 971350955, Fax: 9713505656. Head: Luis Plantalamor
Local Museum 29310

Mairena del Alcor

Casa Museo de Bonsor, Calle Castillo 1, 41510 Mairena del Alcor - T: 955942405
Historic Site 29311

Málaga

Cortijo Bacardi, Polígono Industrial Santa Teresa, 29196 Málaga - T: 952243100, Fax: 952243365
Special Museum 29312

Museo Catedralicio, Cister s/n, 29015 Málaga - T: 952215917, 952220345, Fax: 952220345, E-mail: catedralmalaga@planalfa.es, Internet: http://www3.planalfa.es/catedralmalaga. Head: Francisco García Mota
Religious Arts Museum - 1946
Ecclesiastical art, painting, textiles, manuscripts 29313

Museo de Artes y Costumbres Populares. Unicaja, Pasaje Santa Isabel 10, 29005 Málaga - T: 952217137
Ethnology Museum 29314

Museo de Málaga, Sección de Arqueología, Calle Alcazabilla s/n, 29015 Málaga - T: 952220443. Head: Rafael Puertas Tricas
Archaeological Museum - 1949
Prehistory, Roman, paleo-Christian and Arabian archaeology, Hispano-Arabian ceramics, finds from the excavations of Alcazaba - library, restoration area 29315

Museo de Málaga, Sección de Bellas Artes, Calle Alarcón Luján 8, 29005 Málaga - T: 952218382, Fax: 952218382. Head: Rafael Puertas Tricas
Fine Arts Museum - 1961
16th-20th c painting, sculpture, Roman archaeology - library 29316

Museo Loringiano, Finca de la Concepción, 29014 Málaga - T: 952250787, 952250745, Fax: 952257442, E-mail: botanic@microcad.es. Head: Francisco de la Torre Prados
Archaeological Museum 29317

Museo-Tesoro de la Cofradía de la Expiración, Plaza San Pedro s/n, 29008 Málaga - T: 952324916
Religious Arts Museum - 1968
Ecclesiastical art, goldsmith work, liturgical vestments 29318

Malla

Museu de Torrellebreta, Mas de Torrellebreta, Carrer de Balenyà, 08519 Malla - T: 938870227
Local Museum 29319

Malpartida de Cáceres

Museo Vostell-Malpartida de Cáceres, Carretera de los Barruecos s/n, 10910 Malpartida de Cáceres, mail addr: Apdo 20, 10910 Malpartida de Cáceres - T: 927276492, Fax: 927276491, E-mail: mvmoctv.es, Internet: http://www.museovostell.com. Head: José Antonio Agúndez García
Fine Arts Museum 29320

Manacor

Museo de Manacor, Carretera Son Forteza s/n, 07500 Manacor. Head: José Merino Santisteban
Archaeological Museum - 1925
Regional prehistory and archaeology, Roman finds, ceramics, mosaics, ethnology 29321

Torre dels Enagistes, Carretera Cales de Mallorca, km 1, 07500 Manacor - T: 971843065, Fax: 971849105. Head: Francisca Torres Orell
Archaeological Museum - 1926 29322

Manises

Museu de Ceràmica de Manises, Calle Sagrario 22, 46940 Manises - T: 961521044, Fax: 961520453, E-mail: mcm.manises@ayuntamiento.m400.gva.es. Head: Josep Pérez Camps
Decorative Arts Museum - 1967
Local ceramics (14th-20th c) - library, restoring 29323

Manlleu

Museu Municipal, Baixada de la Fidela s/n, 08560 Manlleu - T: 938506630
Local Museum 29324

Manresa

Museu Comarcal de Manresa, Vía de Sant Ignasi 40, 08240 Manresa - T: 938741155, Fax: 938782307, E-mail: m.manresa@diba.es, Internet: http://mcmmanresa.com. Head: Francesc Vilà Noguera
Decorative Arts Museum / Fine Arts Museum - 1896
Gothic pottery, Baroque sculpture 29325

Museu de Geología, Av Bases de Manresa 61, 08240 Manresa - T: 938772088, Fax: 938741607
Natural History Museum 29326

Museu Històric de la Seu, Baixada de la Seu s/n, 08240 Manresa - T: 938721512
Religious Arts Museum - 1934
Ecclesiastical art, painting, sculpture, textiles, goldsmith work, historical artifacts 29327

Manzanares El Real

Parque Regional de la Cuenca Alta del Manzanares, Carretera de Collado Villalba a Soto del Real, 28410 Manzanares El Real
Natural History Museum 29328

Marbella

Museo del Grabado Español Contemporáneo, Calle Hospital Bazán s/n, 29600 Marbella - T: 952825035, Fax: 952823443, E-mail: museograbado@terra.es, Internet: http://www.museodelgrabado.museum
Fine Arts Museum 29329

Marchena

Museo Arqueológico Municipal, Calle Carrera s/n, 41620 Marchena - T: 955846167
Archaeological Museum 29330

Museo de Zurbarán, Plaza Cardenal Spinola s/n, 41620 Marchena - T: 954843257, Fax: 954843257
Religious Arts Museum / Fine Arts Museum 29331

Museo Municipal Lorenzo Coullaut-Valera, Puerta de Morón, Calle San Francisco 33, 41620 Marchena - T: 955846167
Local Museum 29332

Museo Parroquial de Zurbarán, Iglesia de San Juan Bautista, Calle Cristóbal de Morales, 41620 Marchena
Religious Arts Museum - 1965
15th c Mudejar church, Gothic to 16th c paintings, goldsmith work, liturgical vestments, choral and miniature books 29333

Marín

Museo Municipal Manuel Torres, Av Orense 3, 36900 Marín - T: 986891186, Fax: 986890452, E-mail: oixmarin@terra.es, Internet: http://www.culturamarin.com. Head: Alberto Mallo Area
Fine Arts Museum
Monographies of painter Manuel Torres Martínez 29334

Marratxinet

Colección Veri, La Cabaneta, Son Veri, 07141 Marratxinet
Fine Arts Museum
Mudejár paintings and wainscots 29335

Martorell

L'Enrajolada Casa-Museu Santacana, Calle Francesc Santacana 15, 08760 Martorell - T: 937750795, Fax: 937740595, E-mail: m.martorell@diba.es, Internet: http://www.diba.es/museuslocals. Head: Ferran Balanza
Historical Museum - 1876
Architectural elements of decaying bldgs from Barcelona, art, 19th c painting, 14th-19th c ceramics, tiles 29336

Museu Municipal Vicenç Ros, Av de Vicenç Ros s/n, 08760 Martorell - T: 937740964, Fax: 937740595, E-mail: m.martorell.ros@diba.es, Internet: http://www.diba.es/museuslocals. Head: Ferran Balanza
Local Museum - 1945
Art, local archaeology, painting, 14th-18th c ceramics, tiles 29337

El Masnou

Museo Retrospectivo de Farmacia y Medicina, Laboratorios del Norte de España, Carretera a Francia, km 639, 08320 El Masnou - T: 935402100, Fax: 935558200. Head: Göran Lindgren
Natural History Museum - 1925
History of medicine and pharmacy, especially of Spain, rare books, 17th c apothecary's shop, including furnishings and laboratory - library 29338

Museu Municipal de Náutica, Calle San Francesc d'Assís 28, 08320 El Masnou - T: 935552055
Science&Tech Museum / Local Museum - 1957
Maritime history, archaeology, local history 29339

Mataró

Clos Arqueologic Torre Llauder, Av Roma s/n, 08302 Mataró - T: 937582401, Fax: 937582402, E-mail: cmarfa@infomataro.net, Internet: http://www.infomataro.net. Head: C. Marfà y Riera
Archaeological Museum 29340

Museu-Arxiu de Santa María de Mataró, Calle Sant Francesc d'Assis 23, 08301 Mataró - T: 937901528
Religious Arts Museum - 1946
Ecclesiastical art and local history, 18th c art work in Baroque style by Antoni Viladomat, 13th c documents, canonical files - library 29341

Museu de Mataró, Calle Carreró 17-19, 08301 Mataró - T: 937582401, Fax: 937582402, E-mail: cmarfa@infomataro.net, Internet: http://www.infomataro.net. Head: C. Marfà i Riera
Local Museum - 1942/1983
Art and history, archaeology, applied arts, modern painting 29342

Medina de Pomar

Museo Conventual, Calle Santa Clara 6, 09500 Medina de Pomar
Religious Arts Museum
Ecclesiastical art 29343

Museo de los Condestables de Castilla, Calle Santa Clara 8, 09500 Medina de Pomar - T: 947190160
Religious Arts Museum - 1973 29344

Medina de Rioseco

Museo Municipal, Calle Arco Ajujar s/n, 47800 Medina de Rioseco - T: 983700825
Ethnology Museum 29345

Museo Parroquial, Plaza Santa María s/n, 47800 Medina de Rioseco - T: 983700327
Religious Arts Museum - 1959
Ecclesiastical art, goldsmith work 29346

Medinaceli

Museo de la Colegiata, Plaza de la Colegiata, 42240 Medinaceli
Religious Arts Museum - 1968
Ecclesiastical art, painting, sculpture, goldsmith work, liturgical vestments, choral books 29347

Mediona

Museu de Sant Joan de Mediona, Calle Florenci Gustems s/n, 08773 Mediona - T: 938985071
Local Museum 29348

Melide

Museo da Terra de Melide, Calle Convento 3, 15800 Melide - T: 981505349
Ethnology Museum 29349

Melilla

Museo Municipal, Baluarte de la Concepción, Calle Concepción Alta, 52001 Melilla - T: 952684986
Local Museum - 1953
Local art and history 29350

Mendoza

Museo de Heráldica Alavesa, Torre de Mendoza, Carretera Nacional Madrid-Irún, a 11 km de Vitoria, 01191 Mendoza - T: 945231777, Fax: 945133804
Historical Museum - 1963
14th c castle, heraldry of Alava 29351

Mérida

Museo Nacional de Arte Romano, Calle José Ramón Mélida s/n, 06800 Mérida - T: 924311690, 924311912, Fax: 924302006, E-mail: e-mnar@mnar.es. Head: Dr. José María Alvárez Martínez
Archaeological Museum / Fine Arts Museum - 1838
Archaeology, Roman and Visigothic art 29352

Mijas

Carromato del Max, Av del Compás s/n, 29650 Mijas - T: 952485900, Fax: 952585199
Local Museum 29353

Museo Taurino de Mijas, Calle Algarrobo 6, 29650 Mijas - T: 952485548
Ethnology Museum 29354

Miño de Medinaceli

Museo Paleontológico, Carretera Nacional II Madrid-Barcelona km 146,2 ramal al Noreoste de Torralba, 42230 Miño de Medinaceli
Archaeological Museum 29355

Miranda del Castañar

Museo Parroquial, Iglesia Parroquial, 37660 Miranda del Castañar - T: 923432028
Religious Arts Museum - 1976 29356

Moguer

Casa-Museo Zenobia-Juan Ramón, Calle Juan Ramón Jiménez 10, 21800 Moguer - T: 959370156, Fax: 959372268. Head: Juan Cobos Wilkins
Special Museum - 1958
Memorabilia of the poet Juan Ramón Jiménez (1881-1958), partial library containing books and reviews 29357

Museo Diocesano de Arte Sacro, Plaza Monjas s/n, 21800 Moguer - T: 959370107
Religious Arts Museum - 1975 29358

Moià

Museu Arqueològic i Paleontològic, Plaza Sant Sebatià 7, 08180 Moià - T: 938300000
Archaeological Museum 29359

Museu Arxiu Comarcal, Calle Rafael Casanova 13, 08180 Moià - T: 938300223
Local Museum 29360

Molins de Rei

Museu Municipal, Calle Pintor Fortuny 55, 08750 Molins de Rei - T: 936682089. Head: Manuel Julia y Macias
Fine Arts Museum - 1953
Popular arts and crafts, ex libris, Iberian and Roman amphoras - library 29361

Moncada

Museu Etnografic Municipal, Centre Cultural Blasco Ibãez, Calle Lope de Vega 1, 46113 Moncada - T: 961390716, 961300163, Fax: 961395663
Ethnology Museum 29362

Mondoñedo

Museo Diocesano e Catedralicio de Mondoñedo, Catedral, Plaza España s/n, 27740 Mondoñedo - T: 982521006, 982521948
Religious Arts Museum - 1968 29363

Monestir de Poblet

Museu de Poblet, Plaza de la Corona d'Aragó 11, 43448 Monestir de Poblet - T: 977870089, Fax: 977870739
Religious Arts Museum - 1930
12th c monastery, 15th c palace of Martí l'Humà, local art, religion and prehistory 29364

Monforte de Lemos

Museo de Arte Sacro, Monasterio de Santa Clara, Calle Santa Clara s/n, 27400 Monforte de Lemos - T: 982401544
Religious Arts Museum - 1973
Religious art, goldsmith work, painting, 16th c sculpture, alabaster carving by Gregorio Fernández 29365

Museo de Nosa Señora da Antiga, Campo da Compañia 50, 27400 Monforte de Lemos - T: 982400450, Fax: 982410003
Fine Arts Museum 29366

Monistrol de Montserrat

Museu de Montserrat, Abadía de Montserrat, 08691 Monistrol de Montserrat - T: 938350251, Fax: 938284049. Head: Josep de C. Laplana
Fine Arts Museum - 1913
Art, biblical archaeology, Italian, French and Spanish painting since the 15th c 29367

Monóvar

Artes y Oficios, Av Constitución 11, 03640 Monóvar - T: 965470270
Local Museum 29368

Casa-Museo Azorín, c/o Caja de Ahorro del Mediterráneo, Calle Salamanca 6, 03640 Monóvar - T: 965470715, Fax: 965473034
Special Museum - 1969
Memorabilia of the poet José Martínez Ruiz 'Azorín' (1874-1967) and on other authors of his era 29369

Monreal del Campo

Museo Monográfico del Azafrán, Casa de la Cultura, Plaza Mayor s/n, 44300 Monreal del Campo - T: 978863236
Ethnology Museum - 1982 29370

Montblanc

Museu Comarcal de la Conca de Barberà, Calle Josa 6, 43400 Montblanc - T: 977860349, Fax: 977860349
Local Museum - 1958
History and arts of the region, prehistory, archaeology, painting, sculpture, palaeontology, documents 29371

Museu Frederic Marès, Plaza Sant Marçal 1, 43400 Montblanc - T: 977826341, Fax: 977860349
Local Museum 29372

Montbrió del Camp

Museu Els Cups, Av Sant Jordi 11, 43340 Montbrió del Camp - T: 977826341, Fax: 977180412
Local Museum 29373

Montcada i Reixac

Museu Municipal Les Maleses, Calle Juli García 2, 08110 Montcada i Reixac - T: 935648466, Fax: 935648648
Local Museum 29374

Montejo de Tiermes

Museo Monográfico de Tiermes, A 7 km del Pueblo, por Torresuso, 42341 Montejo de Tiermes - T: 975186156
Archaeological Museum 29375

Montemayor

Museo de Ulia, Iglesia Parroquial Nuestra Señora de la Asunción, 14530 Montemayor - T: 957384040
Archaeological Museum 29376

Monterroso

Museo Parroquial de Monterroso, Calle Ramón Díaz 7, 27560 Monterroso - T: 982377181
Local Museum 29377

Montesa

Museu Arxiu Parroquial, Plaza Vila 5, 46692 Montesa - T: 962299075
Religious Arts Museum 29378

Montilla

Museo Historico Munipal, c/o Casa de la Cultura, Calle Miguel de Molina 5, 14550 Montilla
Local Museum 29379

Montoro

Museo Antonio Rodríguez Luna, Plaza del Charco 18, 14600 Montoro
Local Museum 29380

Museo Histórico Local, Calle Sor Angela Artola, 14600 Montoro
Local Museum 29381

Morella

Museo Arciprestal, Basílica de Santa María la Mayor, Plaza Benedicto XV, 12300 Morella - T: 964160379. Head: Vicente F. Albiol Sampietro
Religious Arts Museum - 1951
Ecclesiastical art, goldsmith work, liturgical vestments, painting, archives including medieval documents, incunabula and choralbooks 29382

Museo Etnológico de Morella y del Meastrazgo, Real Convento de San Francisco, Plaza de San Francisco, 12300 Morella - T: 964173128
Ethnology Museum - 1962
Ethnography, 15th-19th c textile handicraft, folk and applied arts, farm implements, graphic and documentary material, archaeology, local art: painting, sculpture and goldsmith work 29383

Moyá

Casa-Museo Tomás Morales, Plaza de Tomás Morales 1, 35420 Moyá - T: 928620217, Fax: 928611217, E-mail: tomasmorales@step.es, Internet: http://www.cabgc.org/area-cultura. Head: Luisa Alonso Gens
Special Museum - 1976
Manuscripts, letters, photographs, first editions books, works of arts, pieces of furniture and personal things from Tomás Morales - library, archives, pedagogic dep 29384

Mula

Museo Monográfico del Cigarralejo, Palacio de Menahermosa, Calle Marqués 1, 30170 Mula - T: 968661422
Archaeological Museum 29385

Murcia

Centro de Estudios Árabes y Arqueológicos Ibn Arabi, Calle Selgas s/n, 30001 Murcia - T: 968239962, Fax: 968201866
Archaeological Museum 29386

Museo Catedralicio, Catedral, Plaza Cardenal Belluga s/n, 30001 Murcia - T: 968216344
Religious Arts Museum - 1956
Roman archaeology, sculpture, painting, goldsmith work, liturgical vestments, historical documents, choralbooks 29387

Museo de Murcia, Sección de Arqueología, Gran Vía Alfonso X El Sabio 5, 30008 Murcia - T: 968234602, (provisional 968277664), Fax: 968234602, (provisional 968215301), E-mail: pedrom.ballesta@carm.es. Head: Pedro Ballesta Gómiz
Archaeological Museum - 1910
Prehist, Bronze Age, Iberian, Roman, Arabian, Christian and Medieval archaeological finds, architecture, inscriptions, numismatics, 16th-18th c heraldry, medieval and modern crafts - library 29388

Museo de Murcia, Sección de Bellas Artes, Calle Obispo Frutos 8, 30003 Murcia - T: 968341060, Fax: 968342968, E-mail: angelesd.gutierrez@carm.es. Head: María Angeles Gutiérrez García
Fine Arts Museum - 1864/1910
17th-20th c painting, prints and drawings, sculpture - library 29389

Museo Hidráulico los Molinos del Río Segura, Calle Los Molinos 1, 30002 Murcia - T: 968220205
Science&Tech Museum 29390

Museo Ramón Gaya, Casa Palarea, Plaza Santa Catalina s/n, 30004 Murcia - T: 968221099, 968221180, Fax: 968221031
Historic Site - 1990 29391

Museo Salzillo, Calle San Agustín 1, 30005 Murcia - T: 968291893. Head: Dr. Cristóbal Belda Navarro
Fine Arts Museum - 1960
Sculptures and designs by Francisco Salzillo (1707-1783), memorabilia of the artist 29392

Muriedas

Museo Etnográfico de Cantabria, Casa de Velarde, Calle Héroes del Dos de Mayo s/n, 39600 Muriedas - T: 942251347, Fax: 942254862. Head: J.A. Jorrín García
Ethnology Museum - 1966
Regional ethnology, memorial to Pedro Velarde (1779-1808) - library 29393

Muro

Museu Etnologic de Muro, Secció Etnología Museu de Mallorca, Calle Major 15, 07440 Muro
Ethnology Museum 29394

Nájera

Monasterio de Santa María la Real, Calle Rey Don García, 26300 Nájera
Religious Arts Museum - 1889
11th c monastery with 15th-16th c annexes, art, history 29395

Museo Nájerillense, Pl de Navarra 12, 26300 Nájera - T: 941360101, E-mail: museonajera@aldonza.com. Head: Javier Ceniceros Herreros
Local Museum / Ethnology Museum / Archaeological Museum 29396

Naut Aran

Collecció Parroquial, Esglesia Parroquial de Gessa, 25598 Naut Aran - T: 973645042
Religious Arts Museum 29397

Las Navas de la Concepción

Museo de Cerámica Contemporánea Luis García Romo, Calle Recinto Ferial s/n, 41460 Las Navas de la Concepción - T: 954888010
Decorative Arts Museum 29398

Nerja

Museo Arqueológico, Carretera de Maro s/n, 29780 Nerja - T: 952529520, 952529635, Fax: 952529646, E-mail: cuevanerja@vnet.es, Internet: http://www.bd-andalucia.es/cuevanerja.html. Head: Luís Díaz García
Archaeological Museum - 1960
Local archaeology 29399

Nerva

Museo Municipal José María Labrador, c/o Ayuntamiento, 21670 Nerva
Local Museum 29400

As Neves (Capela)

Colección Etnográfica, Colexió Publicó Mosteiro de Caaveiro, 15613 As Neves (Capela) - T: 981459022
Ethnology Museum 29401

Novelda

Casa Museo Modernista, Calle Mayor 24, 03660 Novelda - T: 965600237, 965601062
Fine Arts Museum 29402

Museo Arqueológico, Calle Jaume II 3, 03660 Novelda - T: 965604650, Fax: 965605900
Archaeological Museum - 1983 29403

Nuevo Baztán

Colección Parroquial, Iglesia de San Francisco Javier, Plaza Palacio s/n, 28514 Nuevo Baztán - T: 918735164, Fax: 918732102
Religious Arts Museum - 1984 29404

Nules

Museu de Medallística Enrique Giner, Plaza Fort s/n, 12520 Nules - T: 964674361, Fax: 964674361
Special Museum 29405

Museu d'Història de Nules, Antigua Iglesia de la Sangre, Calle José Bartrina s/n, 12004 Nules - T: 964670001, 964674361, Fax: 964674361
Local Museum 29406

Ojacastro

Pajar Museo, Calle Iglesia s/n, 26270 Ojacastro - T: 941354160, 941291254
Ethnology Museum 29407

Olèrdola

Museu d'Arqueologia de Catalunya, Castell d'Olèrdola, Carretera Igualada-Sitges, km 40, 08734 Olèrdola - T: 938901420, Fax: 934254244, E-mail: mac@mac.es, Internet: http://www.mac.es/ole. Head: Francesc Tarrats Bou
Archaeological Museum / Historic Site - 1971 29408

Olesa de Montserrat

Collecció de la Unió Excursionista de Catalunya, Calle Sant Josep Oriol 3, 08640 Olesa de Montserrat - T: 937782952
Local Museum 29409

Oliva

Museu Arqueològico, Calle Les Moreres 38, 46780 Oliva - T: 962850250, Fax: 962839772
Archaeological Museum 29410

Parroquia de Santa María, Plaza España s/n, 46780 Oliva - T: 962850117
Religious Arts Museum 29411

Olivenza

Museo Etnografico Extremeño González Santana, Plaza Santa María del Castillo s/n, 06100 Olivenza - T: 924490222, Fax: 924490222, E-mail: museoliv@autovia.com, Internet: http://www.autovia.com. Head: Francisco González Santana
Ethnology Museum - 1982
Local pottery, toys, furniture, tools, musical instruments 29412

Olot

Museu Comarcal de la Garrotxa, Calle Sant Esteve 5, 17800 Olot - T: 972279130. Head: Gabriel Alcalde
Fine Arts Museum / Archaeological Museum - 1987
Modern and contemporary art (painting, sculpture) 29413

Museu del Volcans, Av Santa Coloma s/n, 17800 Olot - T: 972266762, Fax: 972270455. Head: Gabriel Alcalde
Natural History Museum
Volcamic Zone of la Garrotxa 29414

Museu-Tresor Parroquial, Esglesia de Sant Esteve, Calle Sant Esteve s/n, 17800 Olot - T: 972260474
Religious Arts Museum
Art, painting, carvings, goldsmith work, liturgical vestments 29415

Oña

Museo Iglesia del Salvador, Calle Iglesia s/n, 09530 Oña - T: 947300103
Religious Arts Museum - 1931 29416

Oncala

Museo de Tapices, Iglesia de San Millán, Calle Barrio de Arriba, 42172 Oncala - T: 975186156
Decorative Arts Museum
17th c Flemish tapestry and 18th c liturgical vestments 29417

Onda

Museo de Ciencias Naturales, Carretera de Tales, km 2, 12200 Onda - T: 964600730. Head: Rafael Artero Pamplona
Natural History Museum - 1955
Botany, mineralogy, fossils - library 29418

Museo del Azulejo, Calle Cervantes 8, 12200 Onda - T: 964770873, Fax: 964604133, E-mail: museu.onda@fump.es. Head: Vicent Estall i Poles
Special Museum
Tiles 13th-20th c 29419

Museo del Castillo de Odna, Castillo de Odna, 12200 Onda - T: 964766688, Fax: 964604133. Head: Vicent Estall i Poles
Local Museum - 1968
Local history and art, archaeology 29420

Museo Histórico Municipal → Museo del Castillo de Odna

Ontinyent

Museo del Colegio Padres Franciscanos, Av San Francisco 5, 46870 Ontinyent - T: 962380100, Fax: 962380120
Local Museum 29421

Orce

Museo Municipal, Castillo Alcazaba de las Siete Torres, 18858 Orce
Local Museum 29422

Orihuela

Casa Museo Miguel Hernández, Calle Miguel Hernández 73, 03300 Orihuela - T: 9653002747
Historic Site - 1985 29423

Museo Arqueológico Comarcal, Palacio de Rubalcaba, Calle Francisco Die 25, 03300 Orihuela - T: 965302747. Head: Emilio Diz Ardid
Archaeological Museum - 1970
Archaeology, art, local history 29424

Museo de la Reconquista, Calle Francisco die 25, 03300 Orihuela - T: 965302747, 965301977
Local Museum 29425

Museo de Semana Santa, Plaza Merced 1, 03300 Orihuela - T: 965302747
Religious Arts Museum 29426

Museo Diocesano Catedralicio de Arte Sacro, Calle Horno de San Miguel s/n, 03300 Orihuela - T: 965300140
Religious Arts Museum - 1944
Religious art, paintings, sculptures, goldsmith work, codices 29427

Museo-Tesoro Parroquial de Santiago, Plaza de Santiago 3, 03300 Orihuela
Religious Arts Museum - 1933
Religious art, sculptures from Salzillo, religious goldsmith work 29428

Palacio de la Granja, Calle Condesa V. Manuel 1, 03300 Orihuela - T: 965300296
Fine Arts Museum 29429

Oristà

Museu Rocaguinarda, Baixos de l'Església, 08519 Oristà - T: 938880330
Local Museum 29430

Ormaiztegi

Museo Zumalacárregui, Casa Iriarte-Erdikoa, 20216 Ormaiztegi - T: 943889900, Fax: 943880138
Archaeological Museum / Historical Museum 29431

Oropesa

Museu Municipal de Costums, Calle Ríos Portilla s/n, 12594 Oropesa - T: 964310100, Fax: 964310066
Ethnology Museum 29432

La Orotava

Museo de Artesanía Iberoamericana, Calle San Francisco 5, 38300 La Orotava - T: 922321746, Fax: 922335811
Ethnology Museum 29433

Oseira

Museo Etnográfico Liste, Calle San Cristovo de Cea, 32136 Oseira - T: 988880526, Fax: 988852789
Ethnology Museum 29434

Osuna

Monasterio de la Encarnación, Cuesta San Antón 15, 41640 Osuna - T: 954811121
Religious Arts Museum - 1969
Baroque church, painting, sculpture, goldsmith work, ceramics 29435

Museo Arqueológico, Cuesta de San Antón s/n, 41640 Osuna - T: 954811207
Archaeological Museum - 1971
Local archaeology, Roman and Iberian finds 29436

Museo de Arte Sacro, Iglesia Colegial, Calle Colegiata s/n, 41640 Osuna - T: 954810444
Religious Arts Museum - 1968
Ecclesiastical art, painting, sculpture, 15th-19th c goldsmith work, choralbooks, liturgical objects, documents, ducal pantheon 29437

Ourense

Museo Arqueológico Provincial, Antiguo Palacio Episcopal, Calle Obispo Carrascosa 1, 32005 Ourense - T: 988223884, Fax: 988223701. Head: Francisca Fariña Busto
Archaeological Museum - 1845
Prehistory, Roman and Iberian finds, Visigothic art (7th c), Mozarabian art (10th c), Romanesque architecture, Gothic art, sculptures, paintings (16th c), contemporary art, crafts, history 29438

Museo Diocesano, Calle Progreso 44, 32003 Ourense - T: 988220158
Religious Arts Museum 29439

Museo Diocesano-Catedralicio, Catedral, Plaza Trigo s/n, 32005 Ourense - T: 988220992
Religious Arts Museum - 1957
Ecclesiastical art, goldsmith work, painting, sculpture, liturgical vestments - library 29440

Museo Municipal, Calle Lepanto 6, 32005 Ourense - T: 988248970
Fine Arts Museum 29441

Oviedo

Cámara Santa, Museo Diocesano, Plaza Alfonso II el Casto s/n, 33003 Oviedo - T: 985221033
Religious Arts Museum - 1931
Liturgical goldsmith work, archives 29442

Museo Arqueológico de Asturias, Calle San Vicente 5, 33003 Oviedo - T: 985215405, Fax: 985219847. Head: Elisa Collado
Archaeological Museum - 1845
Prehistory, archaeology, pre-Romanic, Romanesque and Gothic art, inscriptions, numismatics 29443

Museo de Bellas Artes de Asturias, Palacio Verlarde, Calle Santa Ana 1, 33003 Oviedo - T: 985213061, 985226146, Fax: 985204232. Head: José A. Fernández Castañón, Emilio Marcos V.
Fine Arts Museum - 1980
Asturian art 19th c 29444

Museo de la Iglesia, Claustro alto de la Catedral, Corrada del Obispo, 33003 Oviedo - T: 985209715, 985203117, Fax: 985227976, 985216448, E-mail: arzovideovicgral@planalfa.es. Head: Ramon Platero, Agustin Hevia
Religious Arts Museum - 1985 29445

Sala de Exposiciones Edificio Historico, Universidad de Oviedo, San Francisco 1, 33003 Oviedo - T: 985210160, Internet: http://www.uniovi.es
Historical Museum / University Museum - 1963 29446

Oyón

Museo Etnográfico de Oyón, 01320 Oyón
Ethnology Museum 29447

Padrón

Casa-Museo Rosalía de Castro, Lugar de La Matanza s/n, 15900 Padrón - T: 981811204
Special Museum - 1971
Memorabilia of the poet Rosalía de Castro (1837-85) and of the poet and historian Manuel Martínez Murguía (1833-1923) - library 29448

Museo de Arte Sacro de la Colegiata de Iria Flavia, c/o Casa Rectoral de Iria, Calle Iria Flavia 18, 15900 Padrón - T: 981810802
Religious Arts Museum - 1947
Ecclesiastical art, 15th-18th c goldsmith work and liturgical vestments 29449

Palafrugell

Museu Municipal, Calle Cervantes 10, 17200 Palafrugell - T: 972303998, Fax: 972613158
Local Museum 29450

Palamós

Museu de la Pesca de Palamós (Fishing Museum of Palamós), Plaza dels Països Catalans s/n, 17230 Palamós - T: 972601244, Fax: 972312144, E-mail: museudelapesca@offcampus.net. Head: Miquel Martí i Llambrich
Local Museum / Ethnology Museum - 1920
Local prehistory and archaeology, numismatics, exlibris, 20th c painting - restauration, archives, documentation 29451

Palau de Plegamans

Museu Parroquial Palau Solitar, Masia Can Cortés, Camí Reial 56, 08184 Palau de Plegamans - T: 938649068
Religious Arts Museum 29452

Palencia

Museo Arqueológico Provincial, Plazuela del Cordón 1, 34001 Palencia - T: 979752328, Fax: 979700599. Head: Mariano del Amo y de la Hera
Archaeological Museum - 1845
Prehistory, archaeology, numismatics 29453

Museo Catedralicio, Catedral, Plaza Inmaculada Concepción, 34005 Palencia
Religious Arts Museum - 1965
Ecclesiastical art, painting, sculpture, goldsmith work, tapestry, liturgical vestments 29454

Museo Diocesano, Antiguo Palacio Episcopal, Calle General Mola s/n, 34005 Palencia - T: 979745900, Fax: 979745314
Religious Arts Museum 29455

Museo Municipal Victorio Macho, Calle Cristo del Otero, 34001 Palencia - T: 979718100, Fax: 979718138
Fine Arts Museum 29456

Pallejà

Museu Municipal de Pallejà, Edifici del Castell, Plaza Jacinto Verdaguer s/n, 08780 Pallejà - T: 936683500
Local Museum 29457

Palma de Mallorca

Banys Arabs, Calle Serra 3, 07001 Palma de Mallorca - T: 971721549
Archaeological Museum 29458

Casal Balaguer, c/o Cercle de Belles Arts, Calle Unió 3, 07001 Palma de Mallorca - T: 971712489
Fine Arts Museum 29459

Casal Solleric, Centre d'Exposicions i Documentació de l'Art Contemporai, Passeig del Born 27, 07012 Palma de Mallorca - T: 971722092, Fax: 971718498. Head: Luis G. Socias
Fine Arts Museum 29460

Centre de Cultura Sa Nostra, Calle Concepció 12, 07012 Palma de Mallorca - T: 971725210, Fax: 971713757, E-mail: cultura.palma@osic.sanostra.es, Internet: http://www.sanostra.es. Head: Albert Ribas Juan
Fine Arts Museum 29461

Colección Krekovic, Polígono del Levante, Calle Ciutat de Queretano 3, 07007 Palma de Mallorca - T: 971249409, Fax: 971249409
Fine Arts Museum
Paintings 29462

Colección Vivot, Calle Zavellá 4, 07001 Palma de Mallorca - T: 971221992
Fine Arts Museum
18th c building, furniture, paintings and sculptures - library 29463

Esglesia de Sant Francesc, Plaza Sant Francesc 7, 07001 Palma de Mallorca - T: 971712695, Fax: 971711886
Religious Arts Museum 29464

Fundació Barceló, Casa del Marques de Reguer, Calle Sant Jaume 4, 07012 Palma de Mallorca - T: 971722467
Fine Arts Museum 29465

Fundació la Caixa en las Islas Baleares, Plaza Weyler 3, 07002 Palma de Mallorca - T: 971720111, Fax: 971722120. Head: Jaume Martorell
Public Gallery 29466

Fundació Pilar i Joan Miró, Calle Joan de Saridakis 29, 07015 Palma de Mallorca - T: 971701420, Fax: 971702102, E-mail: fpjmiro@a-palma.es, Internet: http://www.a-palma.es/fpjmiro
Fine Arts Museum 29467

La Llonja, Plaza Llonja, 07012 Palma de Mallorca - T: 971711705
Local Museum 29468

Museo Catedral, Plaça de l'Almoina s/n, 07001 Palma de Mallorca - T: 971723130, Fax: 971719387
Religious Arts Museum - 1932
Religious art, paintings, goldsmith work, tapestry, liturgical vestments, documents and antique books 29469

Museo de la Iglesia de Mallorca → Museu Diocesà de Mallorca

Museu d'Art Espanyol Contemporani, Fundación Juan March, Calle Sant Miguel 11, 07002 Palma de Mallorca - T: 971713515, 971710428, Fax: 971712601, E-mail: museopalma@expo.march.es, Internet: http://www.march.es. Head: José Capa
Fine Arts Museum - 1990
Contemporary Spanish art: Pablo Picasso, Salvador Dalí, Joan Miró, Antoni Tapies, Barceló 29470

Museu de Mallorca, Calle Portella 5, 07001 Palma de Mallorca - T: 971724794, Fax: 971710483, E-mail: jperez@educacio.caib.es, Internet: http://www.mnct.mcu.es. Head: Guillermo Rosselló Bordoy
Local Museum / Archaeological Museum / Folklore Museum / Decorative Arts Museum / Ethnology Museum - 1961
Roman finds from excavations on Mallorca, Gothic paintings, folk art, applied art, old pharmacy, Islamic archaeology - secció Etnològica (Muro), museu monogràfic Pollentia (Alcúdia) 29471

Museu Diocesà de Mallorca, Carrer d'en Calders 2, 07001 Palma de Mallorca - T: 971213100, Fax: 971725847, E-mail: cetem@maptel.es. Head: Pere-Joan Llabrés
Religious Arts Museum - 1916
14th-18th c painting and sculpture, ceramics 29472

Museu Historic Militar del Castell de Sant Carles, Calle Dique de L'Oest s/n, 07015 Palma de Mallorca - T: 971402145
Military Museum 29473

Palacio Real la Almudaina, Calle Palau Reial s/n, 07001 Palma de Mallorca - T: 971727145, Fax: 971719145
Historical Museum
History of the city, local art 29474

Poble Espanyol, Calle Poble Espanyol 39, 07014 Palma de Mallorca - T: 971737070, Fax: 971731592
Ethnology Museum 29475

Palma del Río

Museo Municipal, Casa de la Cultura, Calle Gracia 15, 14700 Palma del Río - T: 957710245, Fax: 957644550
Local Museum 29476

Las Palmas de Gran Canaria

Casa Museo Pérez Galdós, Calle Cano 6, 35002 Las Palmas de Gran Canaria - T: 928366976, Fax: 928373734
Historic Site - 1964 29477

Centro Atlántico de Arte Moderno, Calle Los Balcones 9-11, 35001 Las Palmas de Gran Canaria - T: 928311824, Fax: 928333106. Head: Francisco Rivas
Fine Arts Museum 29478

Museo Canario, Calle Doctor Chil 25, 35001 Las Palmas de Gran Canaria - T: 928315600, Fax: 928314998
Ethnology Museum / Archaeological Museum - 1880
Anthropology, fossils, mineralogy, natural history, regional prehistory and archaeology - library 29479

Museo Casa de Colón, Calle Colón 1, 35001 Las Palmas de Gran Canaria - T: 928312373/384, Fax: 928331156, E-mail: casacolon@granca.step.es, Internet: http://www.cabgc.org/area-cultura/museos/. Head: Elena Acosta Guerrero
Historical Museum - 1951
Hist pertaining to Cristóbal Colón, 16th-19th c Spanish and Italian painting, town hist, pre-Columbian archaeology - research center, library 29480

Museo Diocesano de Arte Sacro, Calle Espíritu Santo 20, 35001 Las Palmas de Gran Canaria - T: 928314989, Fax: 928314989. Head: José Lavandera López
Religious Arts Museum - 1971
Painting, sculpture, goldsmith work, furniture, tapestry, ornamentation, incunabula and rare books 29481

Museo Néstor, Pueblo Canario, Parque de Doramas, 35005 Las Palmas de Gran Canaria - T: 928245135, Fax: 928243576. Head: Pedro Rosales Pedrero
Local Museum 29482

Palos de la Frontera

Monasterio de Santa María de la Rábida, Afuera de Palos de la Frontera, 21810 Palos de la Frontera
Historical Museum - 1856
Memorabilia of the explorer Christopher Columbus (Colón), room where he held conferences (1484/85), coll of flags and boxes with soil from all American countries, frescoes by the painter Daniel Vázquez Díaz 29483

Pals

Museu d'Arqueològia Submarina, Calle Creu 7, 17256 Pals - T: 972301700, Fax: 972667518
Archaeological Museum - 1981
Coll of Greek and Etruscan amphoras, South-Gallic 'campaniana sigillata' ceramics, leaden anchors, coll of conchs, winkles and mollusc shells, graphical documentation about the recovery process of the marine archeological objects 29484

Pamplona

Museo de Navarra, Calle Santo Domingo s/n, 31001 Pamplona - T: 948426492, Fax: 948426499, E-mail: museo@cfnavarra.es, Internet: http://www.cfnavarra.es/cultura/museo. Head: Francisco Javier Zubiaur Carreño
Fine Arts Museum / Archaeological Museum - 1956
Prehistory, archaeology, Gothic frescoes and paintings, architectural remains, Romanesque capitals, 16th-20th c paintings 29485

Museo Diocesano, Catedral, Calle Dormitalería s/n, 31001 Pamplona - T: 948210021, Fax: 948224667, E-mail: info@culture.com. Head: Juan Umeñaca
Religious Arts Museum - 1960
Ecclesiastical art, Gothic painting, goldsmith work, liturgical vestments, embroidery 29486

Paradas

Museo Parroquial, Parroquia de San Eutropio, Calle Padre Barea 33, 41610 Paradas - T: 954849039
Religious Arts Museum - 1968
Painting, ornamentation, goldsmith work, 'La Magdalena' by El Greco 29487

El Pardo

Casita del Príncipe (temporary closed), Paseo del Prado, 28048 El Pardo - Fax: 913761287
Decorative Arts Museum - 1976
Interior, tapestries, lamps, furniture, clocks 29488

Palacio Real de El Pardo, C Manuel Alonso s/n, 28048 El Pardo - T: 913761500, Fax: 913760452, 913761287
Decorative Arts Museum 29489

Paredes de Nava

Museo Parroquial de Santa Eulalia, Plaza España, 34300 Paredes de Nava - T: 979830469. Head: Manuel Zarzuelo Villaverde
Religious Arts Museum - 1964
Ecclesiastical art, painting, sculpture, goldsmith work, liturgical vestments, furniture 29490

Pasarón de la Vera

Museo Pecharromán, Calle Luis Garzón 37, 10411 Pasarón de la Vera - T: 927469130, Fax: 927469130, Internet: http://www.museopecharroman.arrakis.es. Head: Ricardo Pecharromán
Fine Arts Museum - 1996
Monographies, paintings, drawings 29491

El Paso

Parque Nacional de la Caldera de Taburiente, Carretera, 38750 El Paso - T: 922413141, 922420828, Fax: 922413448
Natural History Museum 29492

Pastrana

Museo Parroquial, Iglesia de Nuestra Señora de la Asunción, Calle Viento 1, 19100 Pastrana - T: 949390548
Religious Arts Museum - 1927
15th c tapestry, goldsmith work, wood and ivory carvings, 8th c crucifix, ornaments, parchments, 16th c tombs 29493

Paterna

Museo Municipal de Cerámica, Plaza Pueblo 1, 46980 Paterna - T: 961371197, Fax: 961370066
Archaeological Museum - 1980 29494

Pavias

Museo Municipal, Plaza s/n, 12449 Pavias - T: 964145542, Fax: 964145542
Local Museum 29495

Pedraza de la Sierra

Museo Ignacio Zuloaga, Castillo de Pedraza, 40172 Pedraza de la Sierra - T: 921509825
Fine Arts Museum - 1988 29496

Pego

Museu d'Art Contemporani, Calle Sant Domenec 5, 03780 Pego - T: 965572801, Fax: 965572583
Fine Arts Museum - 1983 29497

Museu d'Etnologia el Conreu de l'Arros, Calle Sant Domenec 5, 03780 Pego - T: 965572801, Fax: 965572583
Ethnology Museum 29498

Peñalba de Castro

Museo Monográfico de Clunia, 09454 Peñalba de Castro - T: 947388441
Archaeological Museum - 1931
Archaeology, excavations of the Roman colony Clunia Sulpicia 29499

Peñaranda de Duero

Museo de Farmacia, Calle José Grijalba 13, 09410 Peñaranda de Duero - T: 947552006
Special Museum - 1964
18th c pharmacy and laboratory, medicaments, utensils and instruments, medical library, garden with medical plants 29500

Peñiscola

Museo Castillo El Macho, Final de la Calle del Castillo, 12598 Peñiscola - T: 964480221, Fax: 964481636
Historical Museum - 1931
Art and history, medieval fort 29501

La Pera

Casa-Museu Castell Gala Dalí, Púbol, 17120 La Pera - T: 972677500, E-mail: pbgrups@dali-estate.org, Internet: http://www.salvador-dali.org
Fine Arts Museum - 1996 29502

Peralada

Museo del Castillo de Peralada, Plaza del Carmen s/n, 17491 Peralada - T: 972538125, Fax: 972538087. Head: Jaime Barrachina
Fine Arts Museum / Decorative Arts Museum - 1923
Painting, sculpture, numismatics, ceramics, glass, incunabula, Spanish history, 14th-15th c architectural elements - library, archive 29503

Petra

Museu i Centre d'Estudis Fray Juniper Serra, Calle Barracar, 07520 Petra
Local Museum 29504

Petrer

Depósito Arqueológico Municipal → Museo Municipal Sala Dámaso Navarro

Museo Municipal Sala Dámaso Navarro, Plaza Baix 10, 03610 Petrer - T: 966989400, Fax: 965376968, E-mail: petrercu@dip-alicante.es
Archaeological Museum 29505

Piedrafita de El Cebrero

Museo de Artes y Costumbres Populares, Pallozas en Santa María del Cebrero, 27670 Piedrafita de El Cebrero
Folklore Museum - 1969
Ethnology from the Galician mountains: interiors, domestic crafts, weaving, fowl breeding, painting, implements and utensils, architecture, ecclesiastical goldsmith work: chalices, reliquaries 29506

Piña de Campos

Museo Provincial y Parroquial, Iglesia de San Miguel, Calle Iglesia, 34430 Piña de Campos - T: 979810465
Religious Arts Museum - 1983 29507

Pizarra

Museo Municipal, Cortijo de Casablanca, Carretera Comarcal 337 de Cartama a Alora, 29560 Pizarra - T: 952483237, Fax: 952484244
Local Museum 29508

Plasencia

Museo Etnográfico Textil Pérez Enciso, Plaza Marqués de la Puebla s/n, 10600 Plasencia - T: 927421843, Fax: 927422002
Ethnology Museum 29509

Museo-Tesoro Catedralicio, Plazuela de la Catedral, 10600 Plasencia - T: 927414852
Religious Arts Museum - 1948
Ecclesiastical art, goldsmith work, painting, ornaments, antique hymnals 29510

Sala de Trofeos del Duque de Arión, Palacio de Mirahel, Plaza de San Nicolás, 10600 Plasencia - T: 927410701, Fax: 9274577593. Head: Dr. Hilda Fernández de Córdova Marquesa de Mirabel
Historical Museum - 1959
Hunting trophies of the late Duke of Arión 29511

Sa Pobla

Museu d'Art Contemporani de Mallorca, Calle Antoni Maura 6, 07420 Sa Pobla - T: 971540054, 971542389, Fax: 971862131
Fine Arts Museum 29512

La Poboa do Caramiñal

Casa Museo Valle Inclán, Torre Bermúdez, 15940 La Poboa do Caramiñal - T: 981831192
Historic Site 29513

Polinyà

Museu Historic Municipal de Polinyà, Calle Sant Salvador 14, 08213 Polinyà - T: 937130264. Head: Ramón Solà Turell
Local Museum / Historical Museum 29514

Pollença

Museu Municipal de Pollença, Calle Sant Domenec s/n, 07460 Pollença - T: 971530015
Natural History Museum 29515

El Pont de Claverol

Museu dels Raiers (Timber-rafting Museum), Calle Antigues Escoles s/n, 25517 El Pont de Claverol - T: 973680132, 973681493, Fax: 973680626, E-mail: raiers@ofimatica.net, Internet: http://www.goldenweb.es/museuraiers. Head: Àngel Portet
Ethnology Museum
Objects of traditional culture, wood-transport by water, log-rafts, raftsmen 29516

El Pont de Vilomara i Rocafort

Museu de Rocafort, Calle Major 18, 08254 El Pont de Vilomara i Rocafort - T: 932016320
Ethnology Museum 29517

Ponteareas

Museo Municipal, Calle Gabino Bugallal 57, 36860 Ponteareas - T: 986660765, Fax: 986660765
Local Museum - 1990 29518

Pontevedra

Museo de Ciencias Naturales, Av Reina Victoria s/n, 36001 Pontevedra - T: 986852026
Natural History Museum - 1890
Mineralogy, zoology 29519

Museo de Pontevedra, Plaza de la Leña, Calle de Pasantería y Ruinas de Santo Domingo, 36002 Pontevedra - T: 986851455, Fax: 986840693, E-mail: secretaria@muspontev.es. Head: Dr. José Carlos Valle Pérez
Local Museum - 1927
Local archaeology and prehist, sculpture, painting, prehistoric and medieval goldsmith work, jewellery, folk arts and crafts - library 29520

Ponts

Museu Arqueològic, c/o Ajuntament, 25740 Ponts
Archaeological Museum 29521

Porcuna

Museo Arqueológico Municipal de Obulco, Torreón de Boabdil, Calle José Moreno Torres, 23790 Porcuna - T: 953544004, Fax: 953544606
Archaeological Museum - 1976 29522

Porreres

Museu I Fons Artistic, Plaza Espanya 17, 07260 Porreres - T: 971647221, 971647187, Fax: 971168265
Fine Arts Museum 29523

Port de Pollença

Museo del Colegio Costa y Llobera, Calle Guillermo Cifre 13, 07470 Port de Pollença
Natural History Museum - 1949
Natural history, fossils and regional zoology 29524

Pozoblanco

Museo del Círculo de Bellas Artes, Calle Fernández Franco 50, 14400 Pozoblanco
Fine Arts Museum 29525

Museo Marcos Redondo, Calle Doctor Fleming 1, 14400 Pozoblanco
Local Museum 29526

Pozorrubio de Santiago

Museo Rural, Calle San Francisco 8, 16414 Pozorrubio de Santiago - T: 969127409
Ethnology Museum 29527

El Prat de Llobregat

Museu del Prat, Plaza Pau Casals s/n, 08820 El Prat de Llobregat - T: 933790050, Fax: 934785794
Local Museum 29528

Prats de Lluçanès

Museu Municipal Miquel Soldevila, Calle Bona Sort s/n, 08513 Prats de Lluçanès - T: 938560014
Local Museum 29529

Els Prats de Rei

Museu Arqueològic Municipal, Plaza Major 1, 08281 Els Prats de Rei - T: 938698192. Head: Josep Castellà Reial
Archaeological Museum - 1972 29530

Premià de Mar

Museu de l'Estampació de Premià de Mar, Esperança 19-21, 08330 Premià de Mar - T: 937529990
Science&Tech Museum 29531

Prioro

Museo Etnográfico Rural y Comarcal, c/o Centro Cultural, 24885 Prioro - T: 987715303
Ethnology Museum - 1985 29532

La Puebla de Cazalla

Museo de Arte Contemporáneo José María Moreno Galván, Calle Fábrica 27, 41540 La Puebla de Cazalla - T: 954847023, Fax: 955843035
Fine Arts Museum 29533

Puente Genil

Museo Arqueológico Municipal, Calle Contraalmirante s/n, 14500 Puente Genil - T: 957600025, Fax: 957602934
Archaeological Museum 29534

Puerto de la Cruz

Fundación Óxido, 38400 Puerto de la Cruz - T: 619978396
Fine Arts Museum 29535

Museo Arqueológico, Calle El Lomo 9a, 38400 Puerto de la Cruz - T: 922371465, Fax: 922374411
Archaeological Museum 29536

Museo Naval del Puerto de la Cruz, Casa Iriarte, Calle San Juan, 38400 Puerto de la Cruz
Military Museum 29537

El Puerto de Santa María

Casa Museo de Rafael Alberti, Calle Santo Domingo 25, 11550 El Puerto de Santa María - T: 956850711, Fax: 956852299, E-mail: fundacion@rafaelalberti.es, Internet: http://www.rafaelalberti.es. Head: María Asunción Mateo
Fine Arts Museum 29538

Museo Municipal, Calle Pagador 1, 11500 El Puerto de Santa María - T: 956542705, 956542775, Fax: 956542780
Archaeological Museum - 1982 29539

El Puig de Santa María

Real Monasterio de Santa María de El Puig, Carretera Nacional Valencia-Barcelona, km 14, 46540 El Puig de Santa María - T: 961470200, Fax: 961470200, E-mail: mercedpuig@ctv.es, Internet: http://www.ctv.es/users/mercedpuig
Religious Arts Museum - 1969
Painting, liturgical vestments, goldsmith work, ceramics, metalwork, numismatics 29540

Puigcerdà

Museu Cerdà, Calle Higini de Rivera 4, 17520 Puigcerdà - T: 972140817, Fax: 972140817, E-mail: museucerda@ctv.es, Internet: http://www.cerdanya.minorisa.es/museu/cmuseu.htm. Head: Oriol Mercadal i Fernández
Local Museum - 1993
Natural history, history, archaeology, art, ethnology 29541

Quejana

Monasterio de Dominicas, Calle Solar de los Ayala, 01478 Quejana
Religious Arts Museum - 1957
Religious art, paintings, goldsmith works, tomb of the chancelor of Ayala 29542

Quesada

Museo Zabaleta, Plaza Coronación 10, 23480 Quesada - T: 953733133, Fax: 953733707. Head: Manuel Vallejo Laso
Fine Arts Museum - 1960
Memorabilia of the painter Rafael Zabaleta (1907-60), his heritage consisting of oilpaintings, watercolors and drawings, friends of Zabaleta coll (oilpaintings, drawings, watercolours, sculptures) 29543

Quintana Redonda

Museo Etnográfico, Calle Las Peñas s/n, 42292 Quintana Redonda - T: 975181241
Ethnology Museum 29544

Rafelcofer

Museo Municipal, Calle La Pau 14, 46716 Rafelcofer - T: 962800368, Fax: 962800282
Archaeological Museum 29545

Randa

Monestir de Cura, Santuari de Cura, 07621 Randa - T: 971660994
Religious Arts Museum 29546

Real Bosque de Riofrío

Museo Nacional de Caza, Palacio Real Bosque de Riofrío, 40420 Real Bosque de Riofrío
Historical Museum - 1970
History of hunting in Spain, dioramas, arms, porcelain, tapestry, furniture, painting, sculpture, drawings, trophies 29547

El Real de la Jara

Museo Municipal de Ciencias Naturales, Torre del Reloj, Calle Cervantes 46, 41250 El Real de la Jara - T: 954733415
Science&Tech Museum 29548

Los Realejos

Centro de Visitantes del Parque Nacional del Teide, Portillo de la Villa, Carretera Comarcal C-821 km 32, 38002 Los Realejos - T: 922290129, Fax: 922244788
Natural History Museum 29549

Parque Museo el Catillo, Carretera a Icod de Los Vinos 1, 38410 Los Realejos - T: 922340327, Fax: 922340327
Local Museum 29550

Requena

Museo Histórico de Requena y su Comarca, Castillo, 46340 Requena - T: 962301400, Fax: 962303553
Historical Museum - 1968
Local art and history, archaeology, ethnology, historical books and documents 29551

Reus

Museo Comarcal Reus, Plaza de la Llibertat 15, 43201 Reus - T: 977344833
Local Museum 29552

Museo Municipal, Av Mártires 13, 43201 Reus - T: 977344833
Local Museum - 1961
Art and history of the region, prehistory, archaeology, painting, sculpture, heraldry, decorative and folk art 29553

Museu Comarcal Salvador Vilaseca, Raval de Santa Anna 59, 43201 Reus - T: 977345418, Fax: 977345249. Head: Jordi Suárez Baldrís
Local Museum - 1920
Art and hist, archaeology, ethnology - library, photo library, mineral workshop 29554

Sala de Exposiciones de la Fundació la Caixa, Plaza de la Llibertat 11-17, 43001 Reus - T: 977239212, Fax: 977218708. Head: Enric Sagrera
Public Gallery 29555

La Riba

Museo José Serra Farré, c/o Ayuntamiento, Plaza Major 1, 43450 La Riba - T: 977876087
Historical Museum
18th-19th c arms, tiles, documents - library 29556

Riba-Roja de Turia

Museu Municipal, Plaza País Valencia 9, 46190 Riba-Roja de Turia - T: 962770062, Fax: 962772462
Archaeological Museum 29557

Ribadavia

Museo de Artes y Costumbres Populares, Casa da la Fundación Martínez Vázquez, Travesia Santiago 10, 32400 Ribadavia - T: 988470961. Head: Francisco Fariña Busto
Folklore Museum - 1969
Local ethnography 29558

Ribadeo

Museo Municipal Forte de San Damián, Forte de San Damián, 27700 Ribadeo - T: 982110650, 982110662, Fax: 982110662
Local Museum / Historic Site 29559

Ribadesella

Aula Didáctica de Prehistoria de Tito Bustillo, Carretera la Piconera, 33560 Ribadesella - T: 985861118
Local Museum 29560

Real Bosque de Riofrío

Palacio Real de Riofrío, Bosque de Riofrío, a 10 km de Segovia, 40420 Real Bosque de Riofrío - T: 921470019, 921470020, Fax: 921471895
Local Museum 29561

Riotinto

Museo Minero de la Comarca de Riotinto, Plaza del Museo s/n, 21660 Riotinto - T: 959591915, 959590025, Fax: 959591074, 959590025, E-mail: aeg1657x@caymasa.es 29562

Ripoll

Monasterio de Santa María, Plaza del Abad Oliba, 17500 Ripoll
Religious Arts Museum - 1883
Art and history 29563

Museu Etnogràfic de Ripoll, Plaza de l'Abat Oliba s/n, 17500 Ripoll - T: 972703144
Ethnology Museum - 1929
Ethnography, local arms and smithwork, numismatic, folk costumes, antique religious parchments and documents 29564

Riudecanyes

Museu Municipal, Calle Dimarts s/n, 43771 Riudecanyes - T: 977834181
Local Museum 29565

Riudoms

Museu Històric Municipal, Calle Beat Bonaventura Gran 73, 43330 Riudoms - T: 977850350, Fax: 977851264
Historical Museum 29566

La Roda

Museo Antonio Martínez, Calle Antonio Martínez 6, 02630 La Roda - T: 967441820
Ethnology Museum 29567

Roda de Isábena

Museo Parroquial, Sala Capitular de la Antigua Catedral, 22482 Roda de Isábena
Religious Arts Museum - 1944
Art, furniture, 15th-16th c painting, sculpture, liturgical objects, liturgical vestments, medieval textiles 29568

Roda de Ter

Museu Arqueològic de l'Esquerda, Calle Bac de Roda 6, 08510 Roda de Ter - T: 938500075, Fax: 938540931
Archaeological Museum - 1971
Archeological coll of Iberian and Medieval cultures 29569

Rojales

Ecomuseo del Habitat Subterráneo de Rojales, Barrio del Rodeo, 03170 Rojales - T: 966715001, Fax: 966714742
Local Museum 29570

Museo Arqueológico y Paleontológico Municipal, Plaza Caudillo, 03170 Rojales - T: 966715001, Fax: 966714742
Natural History Museum / Archaeological Museum 29571

Museo Etnológico Aljibes de Gasparito, Av Justo Quesada, 03170 Rojales - T: 966715001, Fax: 966714742
Ethnology Museum 29572

Rollamienta

Museo Etnográfico, c/o Edificio de las Antiguas Escuelas, 42165 Rollamienta
Ethnology Museum 29573

Romanillos de Medinaceli

Museo Etnográfico, Calle Cruces s/n, 42295 Romanillos de Medinaceli
Ethnology Museum 29574

Roncal

Casa Museo Julián Gayarre, Calle Arana s/n, 31415 Roncal - T: 948475180
Historic Site - 1988 29575

Roncesvalles

Museo Artístico de Roncesvalles, Real Colegiata, 31650 Roncesvalles - T: 948760000, Fax: 948790450
Fine Arts Museum - 1925
Art and history, painting, goldsmith work, ornaments, royal pantheon of Sancho el Fuerte and Clemencia de Toulouse 29576

Museo de la Real Colegiata, Calle Real Colegiata, 31650 Roncesvalles - T: 948760000, Fax: 948790450
Fine Arts Museum / Historical Museum 29577

Ronda

Museo Taurino, Plaza de Toros, Calle Virgen de la Paz s/n, 29400 Ronda - T: 952874132
Ethnology Museum - 1986 29578

Rubí

Museu de Rubí, Calle Maximí Fornés s/n, 08191 Rubí - T: 935887574
Local Museum - 1924
Art, archaeology, local history - library 29579

Museu Vallhonrat, Passatge la Creu 6, 08191 Rubí - T: 936995499
Local Museum 29580

Rupit-Pruit

Colección Instrumentos Musicales Folklóricos y Cerámica Española, Finca la Fontana, 08569 Rupit-Pruit - T: 938522010
Folklore Museum 29581

Sabadell

Exposició Permanent d'Eines Agrícoles de la Masia de Can Deu → Museu d'Eines del Camp Masia de Can Deu

Museu d'Art Casa Turull, Calle Dr. Puig 16, 08202 Sabadell - T: 937257747, Fax: 937275507. Head: Dolors Forellad
Fine Arts Museum
Art 29582

Museu de l'Institut Paleontològic Miquel Crusafont, Calle Escola Industrial 23, 08201 Sabadell - T: 937266388, Fax: 937276641, E-mail: m.sabadell.pal@diba.es. Head: Jorge Agusti
Natural History Museum - 1969
Paleontology, esp mammals from the Tertiary and Quaternary in Spain, palaeontological philately - library, archive 29583

Museu d'Eines del Camp Masia de Can Deu, Carrer d'En Font 1-25, 08201 Sabadell - T: 937164781, Fax: 937164781, E-mail: candeu@ecodi.net, Internet: http://www.fcaixasabadell.org. Head: Fermí Pons-Pons
Agriculture Museum 29584

Museu d'Història, Calle Sant Antoni 13, 80020 Sabadell - T: 937278555. Head: Josep Serrano
Historical Museum - 1931
Prehistory, Iberian and Roman antiquities, local history (13th-17th c), local paintings, maps, textiles, pottery, furniture, coins, folklore 29585

Sabero

Museo Minero Ferrería de San Blas, Av 10 de Enero 37, 24810 Sabero - T: 987703122, Fax: 987703123
Science&Tech Museum 29586

Sabiñánigo

Museo Angel Orensanz y Artes de Serralbo, c/o Instituto de Cultura y Arte Contemporáneo, Barrio de El Puente, Calle San Nicolás s/n, 22600 Sabiñánigo - T: 974482240. Head: Prof. Domingo Buesa Conde
Fine Arts Museum 29587

Museo de Dibujo Castillo de Larrés, Calle Ramón y Cajal, Larrés, 22600 Sabiñánigo - T: 974482981. Head: Julio Gavin Moya
Fine Arts Museum - 1986
Exhibits the local architecture (plans, models, photos etc.) and design in general 29588

Sada

Museo Carlos Maside, Calle El Castro s/n, 15160 Sada - T: 981620937. Head: Isaac Diaz Pardo
Local Museum 29589

Saelices

Museo de Segóbriga, 16001 Saelices - T: 969132064
Archaeological Museum - 1974 29590

Sagunto

Museo Arqueológico, Castillo, 46500 Sagunto - T: 962665581, Fax: 962665581, E-mail: M00149@centres.cult.gva.es. Head: Emilia Hernández Hervás
Archaeological Museum - 1943
Castle and Roman theatre 29591

Sahagún

Monasterio de la Santa Cruz, Calle Alfonso VI, 24320 Sahagún
Religious Arts Museum - 1962
Art and history, sculpture, painting, goldsmith work, textiles 29592

Museo de las Madres Benedictinas, El Convento, San Benito, 24320 Sahagún - T: 987780078
Religious Arts Museum 29593

Salamanca

Casa-Museo de Unamuno, Antigua Casa Rectoral, Calle Libreros 25, 37008 Salamanca - T: 923294400, Fax: 923294503. Head: Ana Chaguaceda Toledano
Special Museum - 1952
Memorabilio on the author Miguel de Unamuno y Jugo (1864-1936) 29594

Claustro Conventual de Las Dueñas, Plaza Concilio de Trento s/n, 37001 Salamanca - T: 923215442
Religious Arts Museum 29595

Museo Conventual de Santa Clara, Calle Santa Clara 2, 37001 Salamanca - T: 923269623
Religious Arts Museum 29596

Museo de Salamanca, Patio Escuelas de Menores 2, 37008 Salamanca - T: 923212235, Fax: 923263765, E-mail: musal@helcom.es. Head: Dr. Manuel Santonja
Archaeological Museum / Fine Arts Museum / Ethnology Museum - 1848
Palaeolithic, Bronze Age and Roman finds, 15th-19th c painting, 15th-18th c stone and wood sculpture, folk art, ceramics, glass - library 29597

Museo del Convento de Santa Ursula, Calle Ursulas 2, 37002 Salamanca - T: 923219877
Fine Arts Museum - 1968
14th-16th c painting, sculpture, 16th c hymnal 29598

Museo Diocesano, Plaza Juan XXIII s/n, 37002 Salamanca - T: 923218205. Head: Marciano Sánchez Rodríguez
Religious Arts Museum
15th-16th c painting, 14th-18th c sculpture, goldsmith work, textiles, historical documents 29599

Museo Municipal, Plaza Mayor 29, 37002 Salamanca - T: 923402721
Local Museum 29600

Museo Municipal de Historia de la Ciudad de Salamanca, Plaza de Juan XXIII 15-17, 37008 Salamanca - T: 923213067, Fax: 923279774. Head: María José Frades Morera
Historical Museum 29601

Saldaña

Museo Monográfico de la Villa Romana de la Olmeda, Iglesia de San Pedro, Plaza San Pedro s/n, 34100 Saldaña
Archaeological Museum / Religious Arts Museum - 1984 29602

Sallent

Casa-Museu Torres Amat, Calle Pont 1, 08650 Sallent - T: 939371466
Local Museum 29603

Casa Natal de Sant Antoni María Claret, Calle Cós 4, 08650 Sallent - T: 938370396
Local Museum 29604

Collecions Municipals del Foment Arqueològic Excursionista Sallentí, Casal Municipal, Plaza Anselm Clavé s/na, 08650 Sallent - T: 938370200
Archaeological Museum 29605

Salteras

Museo de Cerámica de la Cartuja, c/o Fábrica de Cerámica la Cartuja, Carretera Sevilla-Extremadura km 80.5, 41909 Salteras - T: 955997083
Decorative Arts Museum 29606

La Salzadella

Collecció Parroquial, Calle Sant Antoni s/n, 12186 La Salzadella - T: 964419067
Religious Arts Museum 29607

San Ciprian-Concello de Cervo

Museo Provincial do Mar, Av da Mariña s/n, 27890 San Ciprian-Concello de Cervo - T: 982595081
Special Museum 29608

San Fernando

Museo Histórico Municipal, c/o Ayuntamiento, 11100 San Fernando - T: 956893702
Local Museum - 1988 29609

San Ildefonso o la Granja

Museo del Vidrio, c/o Real Fábrica Cristal San Ildefonso, Paseo Pocillo 1, 40100 San Ildefonso o la Granja - T: 921010700, Fax: 921010701, E-mail: rfc@fcnv.es, Internet: http://www.fcnv.es. Head: Paloma Pastor
Special Museum
Library, School of glass 29610

Palacio Real de la Granja, Plaza de España 17, 40100 San Ildefonso o la Granja - T: 921470019, 921470020, Fax: 921471895. Head: Angel Fernández
Historical Museum 29611

San José de la Rinconada

Museo Arqueológico I.B. Niguel de Mañara, Calle Cultura s/n, 41300 San José de la Rinconada - T: 954790288
Archaeological Museum 29612

San Juan de la Peña

Real Monasterio de San Juan de la Peña, 22711 San Juan de la Peña
Religious Arts Museum - 1889
Art and history, architectural fragments from different periods 29613

San Juan de Plan

Museo Etnológico, Calle Centro s/n, 22367 San Juan de Plan - T: 974506049
Ethnology Museum - 1982 29614

San Lorenzo de El Escorial

Monasterio de San Lorenzo de El Escorial, C Don Juan de Borbón y Battenberg s/n, 28200 San Lorenzo de El Escorial - T: 918905903 ext 214, Fax: 918907818, Internet: http://www.patrimonionacional.es. Head: Carmen García-Frías Checa
Fine Arts Museum
Royal palace of Philip II, 15th-18th c painting, 16th-17th c sculpture, liturgical vestments, religious crafts and treasures, ivory furniture 16th and 18th c, tapestries 16th and 18th c 29615

San Martín de Castañeda

Centro de Interpretación del P.N. del Lago de Sanabria, Monasterio de Santa María, 49361 San Martín de Castañeda - T: 980622063
Special Museum 29616

San Martiño de Mondoñedo-Foz

Museo Parroquial de San Martiño de Mondoñedo, Iglesia, Carretera Foz-Valle de Oro km 4, 27787 San Martiño de Mondoñedo-Foz - T: 982132394, 982132607
Local Museum 29617

San Mateo

Colección Museística de San Mateo, Calle Historiador Beti 4, 12170 San Mateo - T: 964416171, Fax: 964416129
Local Museum 29618

Colección Parroquial, Iglesia de San Mateo, Calle Sant Bernat 3, 12170 San Mateo
Religious Arts Museum
Art, liturgical goldsmith work, antique Gothic altar fragments, artifacts 29619

Museu Paleontologic Juna Cano Forner, Calle Arrabal de Barcelona 25, 12170 San Mateo - T: 964416590
Natural History Museum 29620

San Millán de Suso

Monasterio de San Millán de Suso, Carretera de Suso, 3 km from the Village, 26326 San Millán de Suso
Religious Arts Museum - 1931
Art and history, architecture, sculpture, tombs 29621

San Paio de Narla-Friol

Museo Etnográfico e da Historia de San Paio de Narla, 27226 San Paio de Narla-Friol - T: 982375156, 982242112, Fax: 982242112
Ethnology Museum 29622

San Pedro de Cardeña

Monasterio de San Pedro, Carretera Local de la Cartuja de Miraflores, 09193 San Pedro de Cardeña - T: 947290033
Religious Arts Museum - 1931
Art and history 29623

San Pedro del Pinatar

Museo del Mar, c/o Cofradía de Pescadores, Calle Ingeniero Lorenzo Morales 2, 30740 San Pedro del Pinatar - T: 968181920, 968181901, Fax: 968185181
Special Museum - 1980 29624

San Roque

Fundación Municipal de Cultura Luis Ortega Brú, c/o Museo Histórico de San Roque, Palacio de los Gobernadores, Calle Rubín de Celis 1, 11360 San Roque - T: 956781587, Fax: 956782634. Head: Juan Antonio Gómez Macías
Local Museum / Fine Arts Museum - 1969
Art and history, monographies, paintings, archaeology, entomology 29625

San Sebastián → Donostia-San Sebastián

San Sebastián de La Gomera

Casa de Colón, Calle Real s/n, 38800 San Sebastián de La Gomera
Historic Site 29626

Torre del Conde, Parque de la Torre, 38800 San Sebastián de La Gomera - T: 922140103, 922140106, Fax: 922140151
Archaeological Museum 29627

Sant Andreu de la Barca

Colleció de Sant Andreu de la Barca, Plaza Josep Anselm Clavé 2-4, 08740 Sant Andreu de la Barca - T: 936530413, Fax: 936822425
Local Museum 29628

Sant Andreu de Llavaneres

Museu de Llavaneres, Passeig Mare de Déu de Montserrat 27-33, 08392 Sant Andreu de Llavaneres. Head: Ferran Manau
Local Museum
Local hist, coll of cameras - archive 29629

Sant Celoni

Museu de Geología, c/o Casa de Cultura Can Ramis, Plaza la Villa 25, 08470 Sant Celoni - T: 938672213
Natural History Museum 29630

Sant Climent de Llobregat

Museu d'Eines del Pagès, Calle Església 20, 08849 Sant Climent de Llobregat - T: 936589906
Local Museum 29631

Sant Cugat del Vallès

Monasterio de Sant Cugat, Plaza Octaviano, 08190 Sant Cugat del Vallès
Religious Arts Museum - 1931
Art and history, architecture, painting, ecclesiastical artifacts 29632

Museu de Valldoreix, Plaza L'Esglesia 7, 08190 Sant Cugat del Vallès
Local Museum 29633

Sant Feliu de Codines

Museu Municipal Can Xifreda, Parc Xifreda s/n, 08182 Sant Feliu de Codines - T: 938662297, Fax: 938662297, E-mail: xifreda@sct.ictnet.es, Internet: http://www.ictnet.es/xifreda. Head: Francesc Garriga
Archaeological Museum / Local Museum
Archaeology, local hist, fossiles, arts, cartography 29634

Sant Feliu de Guíxols

Museu d'Història de la Ciutat, Calle Abadía s/n, 17220 Sant Feliu de Guíxols - T: 972821574, Fax: 972820119. Head: Angel Jiménez
Historical Museum - 1904
Archaeological copies of different origins, 18th-19th c Catalan and Valencian ceramics, 15th-18th c choral books - library 29635

Museu Municipal, Plaza del Monestir, Porta Ferrada, 17220 Sant Feliu de Guíxols - T: 972821575
Local Museum 29636

Sant Hilari Sacalm

Museu Municipal Guilleries, Calle Rectoria 17, 17403 Sant Hilari Sacalm - T: 972868101, Fax: 972868976. Head: Salvador Bosch i Cornellà
Local Museum - 1979 29637

Sant Joan de les Abadesses

Arxiu del Monestir, Plaza de l'Abadia, Calle Comte Guifré 8, 17860 Sant Joan de les Abadesses - T: 972720013
Religious Arts Museum
18th c, Ecclesiastical art, liturgical vestments, hymnals, sculpture, archives 29638

Sant Lluis

Museu Etnologic Moli del Dalt, Calle Sant Lluis 4, 07710 Sant Lluis - T: 971151084
Ethnology Museum 29639

Sant Lorenç de Morunys

Museu de la Vall de Lord, Calle Església 1, 25282 Sant Lorenç de Morunys - T: 973210912
Local Museum - 1946
Archaeology, painting, numismatics, folk arts and crafts, geology 29640

Sant Pol de Mar

Museo de Pintura, Plaza de la Villa 1, 08395 Sant Pol de Mar - T: 937600076
Fine Arts Museum 29641

Museu de Sant Pol de Mar, Plaza de la Vila 1, 08395 Sant Pol de Mar - T: 937600451
Local Museum 29642

Sant Sadurní d'Anoia

Museu Codorniú, Casa Codorniu, 08770 Sant Sadurní d'Anoia - T: 938183232
Local Museum 29643

Sant Vicenç dels Horts

Museu d'Art Matern, Calle Barcelona 302, 08620 Sant Vicenç dels Horts - T: 936560057
Fine Arts Museum 29644

Santa Coloma de Gramenet

Museu Torre Balldovina, Plaza Pau Casals s/n, 08922 Santa Coloma de Gramenet - T: 933857142, Fax: 934660974
Local Museum 29645

Santa Cruz de la Palma

Museo Insular de la Palma, Plaza de San Francisco s/n, 38700 Santa Cruz de la Palma - T: 922420558, Fax: 922420030
Local Museum 29646

Santa Cruz de Tenerife

Centro de Fotografía, Plaza Isla de la Madera s/n, 38003 Santa Cruz de Tenerife - T: 922290735, Fax: 922240553, E-mail: centrodefotografia@cabtfe.es. Head: Antonio Vela de la Torre
Fine Arts Museum 29647

Museo Arqueológico, Calle Fuente Morales s/n, 38003 Santa Cruz de Tenerife - T: 922224938, Fax: 922203363. Head: Rafael González Antón
Archaeological Museum - 1958
Archaeology, neolithic ceramics, local anthropology 29648

Museo de Ciencias Naturales de Tenerife, Calle Fuentes Morales s/n, 38003 Santa Cruz de Tenerife - T: 922209313/14, Fax: 922228753, E-mail: ana@museoscabtj.rcanaria.es, Internet: http://www.museosdetenerife.org. Head: Juan José Bacallado Aránega
Natural History Museum - 1962
Herbarium TFMC (vascular plants, lichens and mosses from Macronesia), entomology, marine biology (molluscs and fishes), geology and paleontology, ornithology 29649

Museo Militar Regional de Canarias, Calle San Isidro 2, 38001 Santa Cruz de Tenerife - T: 922271658, 922271662, Fax: 922286856
Military Museum 29650

Museo Municipal de Bellas Artes, Antiguo Convento de San Francisco, Calle José Murphy 12, 28002 Santa Cruz de Tenerife - T: 922244385
Fine Arts Museum - 1900
Painting, sculpture, arms, ethnology 29651

Santa Eulària des Riu

Museo Barrau, Puig de Missa, 07840 Santa Eulària des Riu - T: 971330072
Fine Arts Museum - 1963
Memorabilia on the Barcelona Impressionist Laureano Barrau y Buñol 29652

Museu Etnologic, Puig de Missa, 07840 Santa Eulària des Riu - T: 971332845
Ethnology Museum 29653

Santa Gadea del Cid

Museo Parroquial, Iglesia de San Pedro Apóstol, Plaza de la Fuentesanta, 09219 Santa Gadea del Cid - T: 947359141
Religious Arts Museum - 1932
Ecclesiastical art, goldsmith work, liturgical vestments, sculpture, prayer books, medieval documents 29654

Santa Lucía de Tirajana

Museo Castillo de la Fortaleza de Ansite, Calle Tomás Arroyo Cardoso s/n, 35280 Santa Lucía de Tirajana - T: 928798310
Local Museum 29655

Santa Margarida de Montbui

Colleció de la Tossa de Montbui, Castell i Ermita de la Tossa de Montbui, 08710 Santa Margarida de Montbui - T: 938030772
Local Museum 29656

Santa María de Huerta

Monasterio de Santa María, Plaza del Monasterio, 42260 Santa María de Huerta - T: 975327002
Religious Arts Museum - 1882
Art and history, 12th c monastery 29657

Santa María de Palautordera

Museu Comajoan Fauna del Montseny, Av Catalunya 23, 08460 Santa María de Palautordera - T: 938480579
Natural History Museum 29658

Santa María del Cami

Convent dels Minims, Plaza Hostals, 07320 Santa María del Cami - T: 971620174
Archaeological Museum 29659

Santa María del Campo

Museo Parroquial, Parroquia de la Asunción, Plaza Trinidad 5, 09342 Santa María del Campo - T: 947186185
Religious Arts Museum - 1931
Ecclesiastical art, painting, goldsmith work, tapestry from Bruxelles, 15th c church 29660

Santa Pau

Museu Parroquial, Plaza Major s/n, 17811 Santa Pau - T: 972260474
Religious Arts Museum 29661

Santa Perpètua de Mogoda

Museu la Granja, Espai Cultural, Passatge Mas Granollacs s/n, 08130 Santa Perpètua de Mogoda - T: 935600103, Fax: 935607656, E-mail: venturaap@diba.es
Archaeological Museum 29662

Museu Municipal → Museu la Granja, Espai Cultural

Santa Pola

Museo del Mar, Acuario, Plaza Castillo s/n, 03130 Santa Pola - T: 966692772, Fax: 965416388, E-mail: mooi55@centres.cult.gva.es, Internet: http://www.infoville.net. Head: Maria José Sanchez
Local Museum 29663

Santaella

Museo Arqueológico Municipal, Calle Antonio Palma 27, 14546 Santaella - T: 957313244
Local Museum 29664

Santander

Casa-Museo Menéndez Pelayo, Calle Gravina 4, 39007 Santander - T: 942234534, Fax: 942373766, E-mail: info@bibmp.com, Internet: http://www.bibmp.com. Head: Xavier Agenjo
Special Museum
Memorial to Marcelino Menéndez y Pelayo (1856-1912) 29665

Museo de Bellas Artes de Santander, Calle Rubio 6, 39007 Santander - T: 942239485, Fax: 942239487. Head: Salvador Carretero Rebes
Fine Arts Museum - 1907
Regional painting and sculpture 29666

Museo Marítimo del Cantábrico, Calle San Martín de Bajamar s/n, 39004 Santander - T: 942274962, Fax: 942281068. Head: José Luis Casado Soto
Natural History Museum - 1980
Maritime history of the Cantabrico Sea, fishing ethnography, Cetacea skeletons, skeleton of balaenoptery phisalus (24 m) - library; aquarium 29667

Museo Regional de Prehistoria y Arqueología de Cantabria, Calle Casimiro Sainz 4, 39003 Santander - T: 942207108, 942207109, Fax: 942207106, E-mail: mrpac@cantabria.org. Head: Amparo López Ortiz
Archaeological Museum - 1926
Prehist, archaeology - library 29668

Palacete del Embarcadero, Muelle del Embarcadero s/n, 39004 Santander - T: 942203600, Fax: 942203632, E-mail: carmelo@puertosantander.com, Internet: http://www.puertosantander.com. Head: Fernando García Pérez
Public Gallery 29669

Santes Creus

Monasterio de Santes Creus, Plaza San Bernardo s/n, 43815 Santes Creus - T: 977638329
Religious Arts Museum - 1835
Architectural elements of the antique monastery, royal tombs 29670

Santiago de Compostela

Centro Galego de Arte Contemporáneo, Calle Valle Inclán s/n, 15704 Santiago de Compostela - T: 981546629, Fax: 9815466225/33, E-mail: cgac@xunta.es, Internet: http://www.cgac.org. Head: Miguel Fernández Cid
Public Gallery 29671

Colección de Anestesioloxia e Reanimación, Calle San Pedro de Mezonzo 41, 15701 Santiago de Compostela - T: 981595562, 981599272
Science&Tech Museum 29672

Museo Casa de la Troya, Calle Troia 5, 15704 Santiago de Compostela - T: 981585159
Special Museum 29673

Museo das Peregrinacións, Calle San Miguel dos Agros 4, 15704 Santiago de Compostela - T: 981581558, Fax: 981581955, E-mail: informacion@mdperegrinacions.com, Internet: http://www.mdperegrinacions.com. Head: Bieito Pérez Outeiriño
Religious Arts Museum - 1951
Painting, sculpture, goldsmith work, drawings and popular art pertaining to the pilgrimage to Santiago 29674

Museo de Arte Sacro, Monasterio de San Pelayo, Calle Ante-Altares 23, 15704 Santiago de Compostela - T: 981583127, Fax: 981583127
Religious Arts Museum - 1971 29675

Museo de Colexiata do Sar, Calle Colexiata Do Sar, 15702 Santiago de Compostela - T: 981562891, Fax: 981562891
Religious Arts Museum 29676

Museo de Historia Natural, c/o Facultad de Química, Universidad de Santiago, Av de las Ciencias 1, 15706 Santiago de Compostela - T: 981593589. Head: Dr. Francisco Novoa
Natural History Museum / University Museum - 1900
Zoology and geology, especially specimens representing the Galician region 29677

Museo de la Catedral de Santiago de Compostela, Pl Platerías s/n, 15704 Santiago de Compostela - T: 981560527, Fax: 981563366. Head: Alejandro Barral Iglesias
Religious Arts Museum - 1930
Sculpture, tapestry, goldsmith work, ornaments, Roman archaeology and remnants of the original Roman cathedral, archives, miniature codices 29678

Museo de la Ciudad de Santiago de Compostela (closed) 29679

Museo de Terra Santa (Museum of the Holy Land), Calle Campiño de San Francisco 3, 15705 Santiago de Compostela - T: 981581600, Fax: 981571916. Head: José Rodriguez Carballo
Religious Arts Museum 29680

Museo del Colegio Médico de Santiago, Calle San Pedro de Mezonzo 41, 15701 Santiago de Compostela - T: 981595562
Science&Tech Museum 29681

Museo do Mosteiro de San Paio de Antealtares, Mosteiro de San Paio de Antealtares, 15704 Santiago de Compostela - T: 981583127
Religious Arts Museum 29682

Museo do Pobo Galego (Museum of the Galician People), Calle Santo Domingo de Bonaval, 15703 Santiago de Compostela - T: 981583620, Fax: 981554840, E-mail: museodopobo@interbook.net, Internet: http://www.museodopobo.es. Head: Carlos García Martinez
Ethnology Museum - 1977
Arts and crafts, folklife 29683

Museo Etnográfico Sotelo Blanco, Calle San Marcos s/n, 15000 Santiago de Compostela - T: 981582571
Ethnology Museum 29684

Santillana del Mar

Casa del Águila y la Parra, Museo Regional, Plaza Mayor s/n, 39330 Santillana del Mar - T: 942818398
Local Museum 29685

Museo de la Colegiata de Santa Juliana y Claustro, Calle Claustro Románico, 39330 Santillana del Mar - T: 942818004
Fine Arts Museum - 1889
Romanesque architecture, art, archive containing antique documents 29686

Museo Diocesano Regina Coeli, Monasterio de Regina Coeli, Av le Dorat 2, 39330 Santillana del Mar - T: 942818004
Religious Arts Museum - 1968
Religious folk art, furniture, photographs of regional Romanic architecture 29687

Museo Nacional y Centro de Investigación de Altamira, Calle Marcelino Sanz de Sautuola, 39330 Santillana del Mar - T: 942818005, Fax: 942840157, E-mail: altamira@museos.mec.es, Internet: http://www.mcu.es/nmuseos/altamira. Head: José Antonio Lasheras Corruchaga
Archaeological Museum - 1979
Altamira Cave, masterpiece of the upper palaeonthic art, people who made it possible 14,500 years ago 29688

Santiponce

Conjunto Arqueológico de Itálica, Av Extremadura 2, 41970 Santiponce - T: 955997376, Fax: 955996583, E-mail: italica@polifemo.us.es. Head: Javier Verdugo Santos
Archaeological Museum - 1989
Excavations of the Roman colony Aelia Augusta Itálica (founded by Publio Cornelio Escipión 'El Africano' 206 B.C.) 29689

Santisteban del Puerto

Museo Jacinto Higueras, Plaza Mayor 8, 23250 Santisteban del Puerto - T: 953402111, 953402112, Fax: 953402111, 953402112
Fine Arts Museum - 1963 29690

Santo Domingo de la Calzada

Museo Catedralicio, Catedral, 26250 Santo Domingo de la Calzada
Religious Arts Museum - 1931
Sculpture, painting, baroque goldsmith work, 16th-17th c vestments, archives: bulls, codices, incunabula, hymnals 29691

Santo Domingo de Silos

Museo Arqueológico y de Historia Natural, Monasterio de Santo Domingo, 09610 Santo Domingo de Silos - T: 947390068, Fax: 947390033
Archaeological Museum / Natural History Museum - 1905
17th c pharmacy, archaeological ceramics, goldsmith work, numismatics, manuscripts, Roman art, geology, local natural history 29692

Segorbe

Museo Diocesano-Catedralicio, Calle Santa María, 12400 Segorbe - T: 964110276. Head: Dr. Ramón Rodríguez Culebras
Religious Arts Museum - 1949
Ecclesiastical art, painting, goldsmith work, liturgical vestments, historical documents 29693

Museo Municipal de Arqueología y Etnología, Calle Colón 98, 12400 Segorbe - T: 964110626
Archaeological Museum / Ethnology Museum 29694

Segovia

Alcázar de Segovia, Pl del Alcázar, 40003 Segovia - T: 921460759, Fax: 921460755, E-mail: patronato@alcazarsesegovia.com, Internet: http://www.alcazarsesegovia.com. Head: José Antonio Ruiz Hernando
Historical Museum - 1951
Arms, furniture, painting 29695

Casa-Museo Antonio Machado, Calle Desamparados 5, 40003 Segovia - T: 921460377
Special Museum
Memorabilia of the poet Antonio Machado y Ruiz (1875-1939) 29696

Convento de San Antonio el Real, Calle San Antonio El Real 6, 40004 Segovia - T: 921420228
Religious Arts Museum - 1960
Painting, alto relievos, 15th c stucco, furnishing, liturgical vestments, carpets, hymnals 29697

Museo Catedralicio, Calle Marqués del Arco 1, 40003 Segovia - T: 921435325
Religious Arts Museum - 1924
Ecclesiastical art, painting, sculpture, goldsmith work, tapestry, ornamentation, miniature codices 29698

Museo de Segovia, Casa del Sol, Calle Socorro 11, 40003 Segovia - T: 921460613, Fax: 921460580, E-mail: museosegovia@interbook.net. Head: Alonso Zamora Canellada
Local Museum / Fine Arts Museum - 1844
Painting, sculpture, decorative arts, ceramics, crystal of La Granja, smithwork, archaeology, ethnology 29699

Museo Específico de la Academia de Artillería, Calle San Francisco 25, 40001 Segovia - T: 921420100, Fax: 921435464
Military Museum / Archaeological Museum 29700

Museo Parroquial, Iglesia San Martín, Calle Juan Bravo s/n, 40001 Segovia - T: 921443402
Religious Arts Museum 29701

Museo Zuloaga, Iglesia de San Juan, Plaza Colmenares s/n, 40001 Segovia - T: 921463348, Fax: 921460580, E-mail: museosegovia@interbook.net. Head: Alonso Zamora Canellada
Fine Arts Museum / Decorative Arts Museum - 1947
Painting, ceramics by Daniel Zuloaga 29702

Sepúlveda

Centro de Interpretación del P.N. de las Hoces del Río Duratón, Iglesia de Santiago, 40300 Sepúlveda - T: 921540586, Fax: 921540588
Natural History Museum 29703

La Seu d'Urgell

Museu Diocesá d'Urgell, Plaza del Deganat s/n, 25700 La Seu d'Urgell - T: 973353242, Fax: 973352230. Head: Antonio Cagigós i Soró
Religious Arts Museum - 1957
Ecclesiastical and folk art, Romanesque wallpaintings, sculpture, late Romanesque architectural elements, goldsmith work, ornaments, 13th c Oriental textiles, codices and miniature hymnbooks, Beato de Liébana (11th c) - library 29704

Sevilla

Alcázar, Plaza Triunfo, 41004 Sevilla - T: 954502324, Fax: 954502068, E-mail: actividades@patronato-alcazarsevilla.es, Internet: http://www.patronato-alcazarsevilla.es
Decorative Arts Museum / Fine Arts Museum - 10th century
Tapestry, painting, mosaics, fans and tiles 29705

Casa de las Dueñas, Calle Dueñas 5, 41003 Sevilla - T: 954220956
Religious Arts Museum - 1931
Ecclesiastical art 29706

Casa de Pilatos, Plaza Pilatos 1, 41003 Sevilla - T: 954225055, Fax: 954224677. Head: Dr. Antonio Sánchez González
Fine Arts Museum / Decorative Arts Museum / Archaeological Museum - 1931
Painting, ceramics, 16th c palace, classical Greek and Roman culture 29707

Casa Museo Murillo, Calle Santa Teresa 8, 41004 Sevilla - T: 954217535
Historic Site - 1972 29708

Centro Andaluz de Arte Contemporáneo, Av Américo Vespuccio 2, 41071 Sevilla - T: 955037070, Fax: 955037052, E-mail: admon@caac.junta-andalucia.es. Head: José Antonio Chacón Álvarez
Fine Arts Museum - 1989
20th c art - contemporary art library 29709

Colección Osuna, Calle Alfonso XII 48, 41002 Sevilla
Fine Arts Museum / Decorative Arts Museum - 1967
Paintings, furniture, tapestry, porcelain, fans 29710

Hospital de los Venerables, Pl Venerables 8, 41004 Sevilla - T: 954562696, Fax: 954564595, E-mail: focus@abengoa.com, Internet: http://www.focus.abengoa.es. Head: Morillo Leon Anabel
Historical Museum 29711

Monasterio de la Cartuja, Isla de la Cartuja, 41071 Sevilla - T: 954480611, Fax: 954480612
Local Museum 29712

Museo Arqueológico Provincial, Plaza América s/n, 41013 Sevilla - T: 954232401, Fax: 954629542, E-mail: marqsdir@cica.es. Head: Fernando Fernández Gómez
Archaeological Museum - 1880
Prehist, Iberian, Roman and medieval archaeology, finds from Roman town Italica, sculpture, culture, treasury of El Carambolo, anthropology - library 29713

Museo Catedralico y Giralda, Plaza Virgen de los Reyes, 41004 Sevilla - T: 954563321, 954564743
Religious Arts Museum 29714

Museo Conventual de Santa Paula, Calle Santa Paula 11, 41003 Sevilla - T: 954421307
Religious Arts Museum - 1968 29715

Museo de Artes y Costumbres Populares, Pabellón Mudéjar, Plaza América 3, 41013 Sevilla - T: 954232576, 954235540, Fax: 954232154
Ethnology Museum - 1972 29716

Museo de Bellas Artes de Sevilla, Plaza del Museo 9, 41001 Sevilla - T: 954220790, 954221829, Fax: 954224324, E-mail: museobase@navegalia.es. Head: Dr. Enrique Pareja López
Fine Arts Museum - 1841
15th-20th c painting and sculpture, drawings, ceramics, furniture, arms, Baroque painting from Sevilla, architecture - library 29717

Museo de la Real Plaza de Toros de Sevilla, Paseo Cristobal Colón 12, 41001 Sevilla - T: 954224577, Fax: 954220112
Ethnology Museum - 1983 29718

Museo Marítimo Torre del Oro, Paseo Cristóbal Colón s/n, 41001 Sevilla - T: 954222419, Fax: 954226159, E-mail: torreoro@teleline.es. Head: Cristóbal González-Aller Suevos
Science&Tech Museum / Military Museum - 1943
Antique nautical material, maritime history 29719

Museo Militar Regional, Puerta de Aragón, Plaza de España s/n, 41071 Sevilla - T: 954239909
Military Museum 29720

Museo-Tesoro de la Basílica de la Macarena, Calle Bécquer 1, 41002 Sevilla - T: 954901800, Fax: 954903177
Religious Arts Museum - 1949
Ecclesiastical art, 19th and 20th c lace, goldsmith work, liturgical vestments, cloister 29721

Museo-Tesoro del Templo del Cristo del Gran Poder, Plaza de San Lorenzo, 41002 Sevilla - T: 954385454
Religious Arts Museum
Ecclesiastical art, goldsmith work and ornamentation 29722

Palacio de Lebrija, Calle Cuna 18, 41004 Sevilla - T: 954463838, Fax: 954463333
Archaeological Museum - 1969
Roman, Islamic and Mudejar archaeology 29723

Torre de Don Fadrique, Compás del Convento de Santa Clara, Calle Santa Clara 40, 41003 Sevilla
Historic Site 29724

Siete Aguas

Museo de Arqueología, Calle Arrabal 2, 46392 Siete Aguas - T: 962340003, Fax: 962340300
Archaeological Museum 29725

Sigüenza

Museo Catedralicio, Pl Obispo Don Bernardo s/n, 19250 Sigüenza - T: 949391255, Fax: 949391911. Head: Felipe Gil Peces Rata
Religious Arts Museum - 1949
Sculpture, painting, tapestry, books and documents - archive, library 29726

Museo Diocesano de Arte Antiguo, Antigua Casa de los Barrenas, Plaza Obispo D. Bernardo s/n, 19250 Sigüenza - T: 949391255. Head: Felipe Gil Peces Rata
Religious Arts Museum / Archaeological Museum - 1967
Local archaeology and ecclesiastical art, painting, sculpture, goldsmith work, liturgical vestments, 12th-18th c architecural fragments - archive, library 29727

Sils

Colleció d'Autòbils de Salvador Claret Sargatal, Carretera Nacional II, km 706, 17410 Sils - T: 972853036, Fax: 972853502
Science&Tech Museum 29728

Sinarcas

Museo de Arqueología y Etnografía, Calle Eugenio Cañizares 44, 46320 Sinarcas - T: 962315411, Fax: 962315062, E-mail: sinarcas@gva.es, Internet: http://www.gva.es/sinarcas/sinarcas
Ethnology Museum / Archaeological Museum 29729

Sitges

Museu Cau Ferrat, Casa Rusiñol, Calle Fonollar 25, 08870 Sitges - T: 938940364, Fax: 938948529
Fine Arts Museum / Decorative Arts Museum - 1933
Wrought iron, painting, sculpture, furniture, ceramics, glass 29730

Museu Maricel de Mar, Calle Fonollar s/n, 08870 Sitges - T: 938940364, Fax: 938948529
Fine Arts Museum / Decorative Arts Museum - 1970
Art, painting, sculpture, furniture, ceramics, smithwork 29731

Museu Romàntic Can Llopis, Calle Sant Guadenci 1, 08870 Sitges - T: 938942969
Decorative Arts Museum - 1949
18th-19th c furniture and decorative arts, lamps, porcelain, clocks, crystal, musical instruments, Lola Anglada coll of 17th-19th c dolls, folklore and ethnology - library, garden 29732

Sobrado

Monasterio de Santa María, Calle Monasterio de Santa María, 15813 Sobrado - T: 981787509
Religious Arts Museum 29733

Sóller

Museo Balear de Ciencias Naturales, Carretera Palma-Port de Sóller, Km 30, 07100 Sóller - T: 971634064, Fax: 971633722
Natural History Museum 29734

Solsona

Museu Diocesà i Comarcal, Palacio Episcopal, Plaza Palau, 25280 Solsona - T: 973482101, Fax: 973480951. Head: Joaquín Calderer Serra
Religious Arts Museum - 1896
Regional prehistory and archaeology, 10th-15th c painting, Gothic and Renaissance sculpture 29735

Museu Diocesà i Comarcal, Secció Etnogràfica, Calle Castell 20, 25280 Solsona - T: 973480050. Head: Ramón Planes Torregassa
Ethnology Museum - 1969
Ethnology, art, history 29736

Sopuerta

Museo de las Encartaciones, Barrio Abellaneda s/n, 48190 Sopuerta - T: 946504488, 946104815, Fax: 946104990
Local Museum 29737

Soria

Museo Numantino, Paseo Espolón 8, 42001 Soria - T: 975221428, Fax: 975229872. Head: José Luis Argente Oliver
Archaeological Museum - 1916
Finds from the excavations of Numantia, ceramics, Museo Celtibérico: local prehistory and archaeology, Museo Epigráfico de San Juan: Roman art, mosaics and inscriptions, 13th c architectural elements, Ruinas de Numancia (12 km from Soria): pre-Roman, Iberian and Hispano-Roman finds from Numantia 29738

Museo San Juan de Duero, Sección Medieval del Museo Numantino, Paseo de las Animas s/n, 42002 Soria - T: 975221428, 975221397
Local Museum 29739

Tabar-Valle de Urraul Bajo

Museo de Tabar, Calle Mayorazgo, 31449 Tabar-Valle de Urraul Bajo - T: 948883046
Local Museum 29740

Talavera de la Reina

Museo de Cerámica Ruiz de Luna, Calle San Agustín el Viejo s/n, 45600 Talavera de la Reina - T: 925800149, Fax: 925225862
Decorative Arts Museum - 1963
Local ceramics 29741

Taradell

Museu del Blat, Masía El Colomer, Camí El Verinal, 08552 Taradell - T: 938870015
Local Museum 29742

Tarifa

Conjunto Arqueológico de Baelo Claudia, Calle Pedania de Bolonia s/n, 11391 Tarifa - T: 956688530, Fax: 956688560
Local Museum 29743

Tarragona

Museo Diocesà, Calle Claustre s/n, 43003 Tarragona - T: 977238685, Fax: 977233621, E-mail: mdt@tinet.fut.es, Internet: http://www.fut.es/~mdt. Head: Joseph Martí Aixalà
Fine Arts Museum / Decorative Arts Museum / Archaeological Museum - 1915
14th-18th c painting, folk paintings, 14th-18th c sculpture, tapestry, ornamentation, goldsmith work, decorative arts, 18th-19th c medals and coins, inscriptions, local archaeology and prehistorical finds from Escornalbou 29744

Museu d'Art Modern, Calle Santa Anna 8, 43003 Tarragona - T: 977235032, Fax: 977235137
Fine Arts Museum - 1976
Contemporary art 29745

Museu d'Història Casa Castellarnau, Palacio Castellarnau, Calle Cavallers 15, 43003 Tarragona - T: 977296232, Fax: 977236946. Head: Prof. Enric Olivé Serret
Historical Museum / Decorative Arts Museum - 1954
Roman world 29746

Museu d'Historia de Tarragona Pretori Romà, Pretorio Romano, Escales de Sant Hermenegild, 43003 Tarragona - T: 977296232, Fax: 977241110. Head: Prof. Enric Olivé Serret
Historical Museum / Archaeological Museum - 1981 29747

Museu i Necròpolis Paleocristians, Museu Nacional Arqueològic de Tarragona, Av de Ramón y Cajal 84, 43005 Tarragona - T: 977211175, 977251515, Fax: 977252286, E-mail: mnat@mnat.es, Internet: http://www.mnat.es. Head: Francesc Tarrats Bou
Archaeological Museum - 1928
Roman-Christian necropolis (3rd c), 4th-6th c sarcophagi, mosaics, burial grounds 29748

Museu Nacional Arqueològic de Tarragona, Plaça del Rei 5, 43003 Tarragona - T: 977251515, 977236209, Fax: 977252286, E-mail: mnat@mnat.es, Internet: http://www.mnat.es. Head: Francesc Tarrats Bou
Archaeological Museum - 1960
Roman archaeology 29749

Tárrega

Museo Municipal, Calle Picas 1, 25300 Tárrega - T: 973312960. Head: Jaume Espuiagosa Marsa
Local Museum - 1963
Prehistory, archaeology, palaeontology, art, local numismatics and ethnology - archives, library 29750

Museu Comarcal, Calle Major 11, 25300 Tárrega - T: 973312960, Fax: 973500552. Head: Jaume Espinagosa Marsà
Local Museum 29751

Teguise

Museo de la Fundación Cesar Manrique, Calle Taro de Tahiche s/n, 35530 Teguise - T: 928843138, Fax: 928843463, E-mail: fcm@fcmanrique.org, Internet: http://www.fcmanrique.org. Head: José Juan Ramírez
Fine Arts Museum 29752

Museo del Emigrante, Castillo de Guanapay, 35530 Teguise - T: 928845072, Fax: 928845059
Ethnology Museum 29753

Telde

Casa-Museo León y Castillo, Calle León y Castillo 43-45, 35200 Telde - T: 928691377, Fax: 928696653, E-mail: leonycastillo@step.es, Internet: http://www.cabgc.org/area-cultura. Head: Antonio María González Padrón
Historical Museum - 1954
Memorabilia of the politician Fernando de León y Castillo, spanish hist - library, archives 29754

Terrassa

Casa Museu Alegre de Sagrera, Calle Font Vella 29-31, 08221 Terrassa - T: 937316646, Fax: 937841788
Local Museum 29755

Castell Cartoixa Vallparadis, Museu de Terrassa, Calle Salmerón s/n, 08222 Terrassa - T: 937857144, Fax: 937368068, E-mail: museudeterrassa@terrassa.org, Internet: http://www.terrassa.org/museu
Historical Museum - 1959
Local art and history 29756

Centre de Documentació i Museu Tèxtil, Calle Salmerón 25, 08222 Terrassa - T: 937315202, 937314980, Fax: 937856170, E-mail: info@cdmt.es, Internet: http://www.cdmt.es. Head: Eulàlia Morral
Special Museum - 1946
European mediterranian textiles (15th-20th c), textiles from Al Andalus (13th-15th c), Egyptian textiles, religious and civil clothing from 17th to 20th c - library, restoration lab, IMATEX service for designers 29757

Conjunt Monumental de la Esglésias de Sant Pere, Museu de Terrassa, Pl del Rector Homs, 08222 Terrassa - T: 937833702, Fax: 937366068, E-mail: museudeterrassa@terrassa.org, Internet: http://www.terrassa.org/museu
Fine Arts Museum - 1931
Art, architecture, painting and architecture 29758

Museu de la Ciència i de la Tècnica de Catalunya, Rambla d'Ègara 270, 08221 Terrassa - T: 937368966, Fax: 937368960, E-mail: museu.mnactec@logiccontrol.es, Internet: http://cultura.gencat.es/museus/mctc.htm. Head: Eusebi Casanelles
Science&Tech Museum - 1984
Energy, textile, photography, science instruments - library, archive, restauration workshop 29759

Sala Muncunill, Plaça Didó 3, 08221 Terrassa - T: 937891615, Fax: 937397074, E-mail: imcet@terrassa.org, Internet: http://www.terrassa.org/cultura. Head: Pere Navarro i Morera
Public Gallery 29760

Teruel

Museo Diocesano de Arte Sacro, Palacio Episcopal, Plaza del Venerable Francés de Aranda, 44001 Teruel - T: 978601164, Fax: 9788603144
Religious Arts Museum
Ecclesiastical art 29761

Museo Provincial, Plaza Fray Anselmo Polanco 3, 44001 Teruel - T: 978600150, Fax: 978602832, E-mail: museo@dpteruel.es, Internet: http://www.dpteruel.es/museo.htm. Head: Jaime D. Vicente
Local Museum - 1956
library, archive, documentation 29762

Museo San Francisco, Convento de San Francisco, Av Zaragoza 6, 44001 Teruel - T: 978601612
Religious Arts Museum - 1978 29763

Tiana

Museu Sentronà, Carretera de la Conreria km 4, Can Sentronà, 08391 Tiana - T: 933950344
Local Museum 29764

Tivissa

Museu de Llaberia, Plaza de l'Església s/n, 43746 Tivissa
Local Museum 29765

El Toboso

Museo Casa de Dulcinea, Calle Don Quijote s/n, 45820 El Toboso - T: 925197288, Fax: 925225862. Head: Rafael García Serrano
Local Museum - 1967 29766

Toledo

Casa y Museo de El Greco, Calle Samuel Leví, 45002 Toledo - T: 925224046, Fax: 925224559. Head: Manuel Llanes
Fine Arts Museum - 1910
Furnishings and objects from the time of 'El Greco' Domenicos Theotocopoulos (1541-1614), paintings by the artist, 15th-17th c painting and sculpture 29767

Monasterio de San Juan de los Reyes, Calle Reyes Católicos 17, 45002 Toledo - T: 925223802
Fine Arts Museum - 1929
Art, architecture, painting, late Gothic monastery - library 29768

Monasterio de Santo Domingo el Antiguo, Plaza Santo Domingo el Antiguo s/n, 45002 Toledo - T: 925222930
Religious Arts Museum 29769

Museo de Arte Contemporáneo, Calle Bulas s/n, 45002 Toledo - T: 925227871. Head: Rafael García Serrano
Fine Arts Museum - 1973 29770

Museo de la Fundación Duque de Lerma, c/o Hospital Tavera, Calle Vega Baja s/n, 45003 Toledo - T: 925220451
Fine Arts Museum / Decorative Arts Museum - 1940
Painting, furniture, ecclesiastical art, antique pharmacy - library 29771

Museo de los Concilios y de la Cultura Visigoda, Iglesia de San Román, Calle San Román s/n, 45002 Toledo - T: 925227872, Fax: 925225862. Head: Rafael García Serrano
Religious Arts Museum / Archaeological Museum - 1969
Visigothic archaeology and art 29772

Museo de Santa Cruz, Calle Miguel de Cervantes 3, 45001 Toledo - T: 925221402, Fax: 925225862. Head: Rafael García Serrano
Fine Arts Museum / Archaeological Museum / Decorative Arts Museum - 1961
Archaeology, painting, sculpture, tapestry, textiles, goldsmith work, furniture, documents 29773

Museo del Alcázar, Cuesta Carlos V, 45001 Toledo - T: 925221673, Fax: 925256536, E-mail: sdmetoledo@terra.es, Internet: http://www.ejercito.mde.es/ihycm/museos/toledo. Head: D. Juan Mayorga Sanchón
Military Museum - 1940
Military history of Spain 29774

Museo Específico de la Academia de Infantería, c/o Castillo de San Servando, 45090 Toledo - T: 925226100
Local Museum 29775

Museo-Palacio de Fuensalida, Plaza del Conde, 45002 Toledo
Historical Museum - 1969
Art and history pertaining to the 'siglo de Oro' of Spanish culture 29776

Museo Sefardí, c/o Sinagoga de Samuel Ha Leví, Calle Alamillos del Tránsito, 45002 Toledo - T: 925223665, Fax: 925215831, E-mail: transito@mail.ddnet.es, Internet: http://www.ddnet.es/sefardi. Head: Ana María López
Ethnology Museum - 1964
Hebrew art and hist, liturgical lamps, documents, 14th c architecture 29777

Museo Sinagoga de Santa María la Blanca, Calle Reyes Católicos 2, 45002 Toledo - T: 925227257
Fine Arts Museum / Historical Museum - 1931
Art and history 29778

Museo Taller del Moro, Calle Taller del Moro 4, 45002 Toledo - T: 925227115
Archaeological Museum / Fine Arts Museum - 1963
Mudejar archaeology and art 29779

Museo-Tesoro Catedralicio, Catedral, Calle Arco del Palacio 2, 45001 Toledo - T: 925222241
Religious Arts Museum - 1900
Ecclesiastical art, painting, goldsmith work, liturgical vestments, miniature books 29780

WOL → Museo Taller del Moro

Tolosa

Gorrotxategi Konfiteri Museoa, Calle Lechuga 3, 20400 Tolosa - T: 943670727, Fax: 943675739
Special Museum 29781

Tomelloso

Museo del Carro y la Labranza, Carretera a Pedro Muñoz, entrada a la Ciudad, 13700 Tomelloso - T: 926510510, 926510068
Ethnology Museum - 1967
Ethnography 29782

Tona

Museu Municipal, Calle Font 8, 08551 Tona - T: 938870188, Fax: 938870498
Archaeological Museum - 1972
Iberian, Roman, medieval ceramics 29783

Tordesillas

Monasterio de Santa Clara de Tordesillas, 47100 Tordesillas - T: 983770071. Head: Pedro Criado Juárez
Religious Arts Museum - 1963
Architecture, painting, sculpture, textiles, furniture, hymnals 29784

Museo de San Antolín, Calle San Antolín s/n, 47100 Tordesillas - T: 983770980
Religious Arts Museum 29785

Torelló

Museu de l'Adet (temporary closed), Carrer Mossen Parassols s/n, 08570 Torelló - T: 938592457, E-mail: estudistorellonencs@yahoo.com, Internet: http://www.interausa.com/adet. Head: F. Xavier Viver
Local Museum 29786

Tornabous

Museu-Poblat Ibèric, Plaza Espígol, Clots de l'Infern, 25331 Tornabous
Archaeological Museum 29787

Toro

Colegiata de Santa María la Mayor, Plaza Colegiata, 49800 Toro - T: 980690388
Religious Arts Museum 29788

Madres Dominicanas - Monasterio Sancti Spiritus, Calle Canto 27, 49800 Toro - T: 980690304, Fax: 980691752, E-mail: dominicas@rolobe.com. Head: Dolores Pérez Mesuro
Religious Arts Museum - 1988 29789

Torreandaluz

Museo Etnográfico, c/o Edificio de las Antiguas Escuelas, 42293 Torreandaluz
Ethnology Museum 29790

Torrebesses

Museu de Torrebesses, Calle Museu 14, 25176 Torrebesses - T: 973126078
Local Museum 29791

Torrecampo

Casa Museo Posada del Moro, Calle Mudo 1, 14410 Torrecampo - T: 957155004
Local Museum - 1970 29792

Torregrossa

Museu d'Eines Antigues, Calle Sant Francesc 6, 25141 Torregrossa - T: 973170001
Archaeological Museum 29793

Torrejón de Ardoz

Colección de los Iconos, Calle Madrid 2, 28850 Torrejón de Ardoz - T: 916753900, Fax: 916750691
Fine Arts Museum 29794

Torrella

Museu Etnografic Municipal, Calle Mossen Ricard Climent 10, 46814 Torrella - T: 962244926
Ethnology Museum 29795

Torrente

Museu Municipal, Calle Sagra 17, 46900 Torrente - T: 961565821, Fax: 961575953
Local Museum 29796

Torroella de Fluvià

Museu del Pagès, Antigues Escoles, Calle Força 2, 17474 Torroella de Fluvià - T: 972520691
Local Museum 29797

Torroella de Montgrí

Museu de Montgrí i del Baix Ter, Calle Major 31, 17257 Torroella de Montgrí - T: 972757301, Fax: 972757437. Head: Enric Torrent í Bagudà
Local Museum 29798

Torroja del Priorat

Museu de Torroja, Calle Balandra s/n, 43737 Torroja del Priorat - T: 977839213
Local Museum 29799

Tortosa

Museo Catedralicio, Catedral, Plaza de la Olivera, 43500 Tortosa
Religious Arts Museum - 1931
Ecclesiastical art, tapestry, goldsmith work, enamels, manuscripts 29800

Museu-Arxiu Municipal, Calle Sant Domènec 12, 43500 Tortosa - T: 977441525, Fax: 977446514. Head: Albert Curto i Homedes
Local Museum - 1900
Local art and history, documents, Roman stone inscriptions and busts 29801

Museu de les Terres de l'Ebre i Museu Diocesa, c/o Colegio de San Jaime y San Matías, 43500 Tortosa
Religious Arts Museum 29802

Tossa de Mar

Museu Municipal, Plaza Pintor Roig i Soler 1, 17320 Tossa de Mar - T: 972340709, Fax: 972341834. Head: Vicente Esteban Darder
Archaeological Museum / Fine Arts Museum - 1930
Archaeological objects from excavations of a Roman Villa, contemporary painting and sculpture, especially Catalan 29803

Traiguera

Colección Parroquial, Parroquial de la Asunción, Plaza de la Iglesia 10, 12330 Traiguera - T: 964495004
Religious Arts Museum - 1964
Ecclesiastical art, 15th-17th c liturgical goldsmith work 29804

Trasalba-Amoeiro

Fundación Cultural Otero Pedrayo, Pazo de Trasalba-Amoeiro, 32172 Trasalba-Amoeiro - T: 988281139
Historic Site - 1980 29805

Tremp

Casa-Museu Pare Manyanet, Placeta de l'Església s/n, 25620 Tremp
Local Museum 29806

Tres Cantos

Museo de Metrología, Calle Alfar 2, 28760 Tres Cantos - T: 918074721, Fax: 918074807
Science&Tech Museum 29807

Tres Casas

Real Pinacoteca, Iglesia de la Inmaculada Concepción, 40194 Tres Casas - T: 921440225
Fine Arts Museum 29808

Trujillo

Museo de la Coria, Convento, Calle Santa María s/n, 10200 Trujillo - T: 927321898, Fax: 927321898, E-mail: fxdsalas@teleline.es. Head: Jaime de Salas
Historical Museum 29809

Tudanca

Museo Bilbioteca La Casona, Barrio Tudanca s/n, 39555 Tudanca - T: 942729025
Local Museum 29810

Tudela

Museo Diocesano, Catedral, Plaza de Santa María, 31500 Tudela
Religious Arts Museum - 1884
Art and history, painting, sculpture, archaeology, ornaments, books and documents 29811

Tui

Museo Catedralicio, Plaza San Fernando, 36700 Tui - T: 986600879. Head: Antonio Hernández Matias
Religious Arts Museum - 1976
Ecclesiastical art, archaeology, stone inscriptions, codices, 17th-18th c silver and goldsmith work 29812

Museo y Archivo Histórico Diocesano, Plaza San Fernando s/n, 36700 Tui, mail addr: Apdo 110, 36700 Tui - T: 986603107, Fax: 986603107. Head: Avelino Bouzón Gallego
Religious Arts Museum - 1976
archives 29813

Tulebras

Museo del Monasterio de Tulebras, Real Monasterio de Nuestra Señora de la Caridad, 31522 Tulebras - T: 948851475, Fax: 948850012
Religious Arts Museum 29814

Ubeda

Casa Museo Tito, Plaza del Ayuntamiento 12, 23400 Ubeda - T: 953751302, 953752024
Ethnology Museum 29815

Museo Arqueológico de Úbeda, Casa Mudéjar, Calle Cervantes 6, 23400 Ubeda - T: 953753702
Local Museum - 1972 29816

Museo San Juan de la Cruz, Calle Carmen 13, 23400 Ubeda - T: 953750615, Fax: 953750615
Religious Arts Museum / Historic Site - 1978 29817

Ucero

Centro de Interpretación del P.N. del Cañon del Río Lobos, Antigua Piscifactoría, 42317 Ucero - T: 975363564
Special Museum 29818

Ullastret

Museu d'Arqueología de Catalunya-Ullastret, Yacimiento Arqueológico, 17114 Ullastret - T: 972179058, Fax: 972179058, E-mail: ullastret@mac.es, Internet: http://www.mac.es. Head: Aurora Martín
Archaeological Museum - 1961
Archaeological material of Greek-Iberian excavations (7th-2nd c B.C.) - library 29819

La Unión

Museo Minero, c/o Centro Cultural Asensio Sáez, Plaza Asensio Sáez s/n, 30360 La Unión - T: 968541463, 968560660
Local Museum 29820

Urueña

Centro Etnográfico Joaquín Díaz, Calle Real 4, 47862 Urueña - T: 983717472, Fax: 983717014, E-mail: funjdiaz@funjdiaz.net, Internet: http://www.funjdiaz.net
Special Museum 29821

Utrera

Legado Alvárez Quintero, Calle Alvárez Quintero s/n, 41710 Utrera - T: 955860931, Fax: 954860181
Religious Arts Museum 29822

Museo de Ciencias Naturales, Colegio Salesiano Nuestra Señora del Carmen, Calle San Juan Bosco 13, 41710 Utrera - T: 954486110
Natural History Museum 29823

Val de Ollo

Museo Etnográfico del Reino de Pamplona, Casa Fantikorena, 31172 Val de Ollo - T: 948328034
Ethnology Museum 29824

Valdepeñas

Fundación Gregorio Prieto, Calle Pintor Mendoza 27, 13300 Valdepeñas - T: 926324965
Fine Arts Museum - 1990 29825

Molino-Museo Gregorio Prieto, Calle Francisco Megia s/n, 13300 Valdepeñas - T: 926323162, Fax: 926322808. Head: José Javier Pérez Aviles
Science&Tech Museum - 1954
Mill 29826

Museo Municipal, Calle Real 31, 13300 Valdepeñas - T: 926324815. Head: José Javier Pérez Aviles
Local Museum 29827

Valderrueda

Museo Etnográfico Rural, c/o Edificio del Granero Municipal, 42293 Valderrueda
Ethnology Museum 29828

Valencia

Biblioteca y Museo Histórico Médicos de Valencia, Av Blasco Ibañez 17, 46010 Valencia - T: 963864164, Fax: 963613975
Science&Tech Museum 29829

Casa de les Roques, Calle Roques 4, 46003 Valencia - T: 963525478, Fax: 963528670
Ethnology Museum 29830

Casa-Museo José Benlliure, Calle Blanquerías 23, 46002 Valencia - T: 963919103/04, Fax: 963529634. Head: Angel Català Gorgues
Fine Arts Museum
The museum is placed in the house of the artist José Benlliure. Furniture of 19th c and a wide collection of paintings of José Benlliure and his son Peppino and other contemporary artists as Sorolla, Rusiñol, Muñoz Degrain etc. 29831

Ciencias Naturales P. Ignacio Sala, Gran Vía Fernando el Católico 94, 46008 Valencia - T: 963913990
Natural History Museum 29832

Colección de la Caja de Ahorros, Caja de Ahorros, Calle General Tovar 3, 46003 Valencia
Fine Arts Museum
Painting, sculpture 29833

IVAM Centre Julio González, Calle Guillem de Castro 118, 46003 Valencia - T: 963863000, Fax: 963921094, E-mail: ivam@ivam.es, Internet: http://www.ivam.es. Head: Kosme de Barañano
Fine Arts Museum 29834

Museo Catedralicio-Diocesano, Santa Iglesia Catedral Basílica Metropolitana, Plaza Almoyna s/n, 46003 Valencia - T: 963918127. Head: Vicente Castell Maiques
Religious Arts Museum 29835

Museo de Bellas Artes, Calle San Pío V 9, 46010 Valencia - T: 963605793, Fax: 963697125, E-mail: lola.garcia@cultura.m400.gva.es, Internet: http://www.cult.gva.es/mbav. Head: Fernando Benito
Fine Arts Museum
Art from the 15th-20th c 29836

Museo de las Reales Atarazanas, Plaza Juan Antonio Benlliure s/n, 46011 Valencia - T: 963679046, Fax: 963529634
Historical Museum 29837

Museo de Prehistoria y Servicio de Investigación Prehistórica, Calle Corona 36, 46003 Valencia - T: 963883537, Fax: 963883536, E-mail: helena.bonet@diputacion.m400.gva.es. Head: Helena Bonet Rosado
Archaeological Museum - 1927
Prehistory, Greek, Roman and Iberian finds - library 29838

Museo del Medio Ambiente → Museo Valenciano de Historia Natural

Museo del Patriarca, Colegio Corpus Christi, Calle Nave 1, 46002 Valencia - T: 963514176, Fax: 963511351, E-mail: daniel.benito@uv.es. Head: Dr. Daniel Benito Goerlich
Fine Arts Museum / Decorative Arts Museum - 1954
Painting, goldsmith work, tapestry, furniture, sculpture 29839

Museo del Tejido Sedero Valenciano, Calle Hospital 7, 46001 Valencia - T: 963518233
Special Museum
Textile and silk manufacture - library 29840

Museo Fallero, Plaza Monteolivete 3, 46006 Valencia - T: 963525478, 963923336, Fax: 963920574
Special Museum 29841

Museo Histórico de la Ciudad, Palacio del Marqués de Campo, Plaza Arzobispo 3, 46009 Valencia - T: 963525478, Fax: 963529634
Historical Museum - 1928
History of Valencia 29842

Museo Nacional de Cerámica y de las Artes Suntuarias, Calle Poeta Querol 2, 46002 Valencia - T: 963516392, Fax: 963513512, E-mail: ceramica@museo.mec.es, Internet: http://www.mcu.es/nmuseos/ceramica. Head: Dr. Jaume Coll Conesa

Archaeological Museum / Decorative Arts Museum - 1954
Prehistoric, Greek, Roman, medieval and modern ceramics from Aragón, Cataluña, Valencia, Sevilla, Talavera, Toledo and Italy, silk, 18th c fans, arms, glass, engravings, bookplates - library 29843

Museo Ochoa, Calle Amadeo de Saboya 4, 46010 Valencia - T: 963698500, Fax: 963601453
Local Museum 29844

Museo Paleontológico Municipal, Plaza Ayuntamiento 1, 46002 Valencia - T: 963525478, Fax: 963529634
Natural History Museum - 1906
South American zoology and anthropology, Rodrigo Botet coll, paleontology 29845

Museo Taurino, County council of Valencia (Bullfighting Museum), Pasaje Dr. Serra 10, 46004 Valencia - T: 963511850
Special Museum - 1929
History and art of bullfighting 29846

Museo Valenciano de Historia Natural, Paseo Pechina 15, 46008 Valencia - T: 963910606, Fax: 963910606, E-mail: ftorressala@inforegicio.com, Internet: http://www.xarxamuseus.com/mvhn
Natural History Museum 29847

Museu de Prehitòria i de les Cultures de València, Calle Corona 36, 46003 Valencia - T: 963883619, Fax: 963883629, E-mail: jgregori@xarxamuseus.com, Internet: http://www.xarxamuseus.com. Head: Joan Gregori i Berenguer
Ethnology Museum / Archaeological Museum 29848

Museu d'Etnologia → Museu de Prehitòria i de les Cultures de València

La Vall d'Uixo

Museu Arqueologic Municipal, Av Jaume I 26, 12600 La Vall d'Uixo - T: 964690512, Fax: 964690512
Archaeological Museum 29849

Vallada

Museo de Arqueología, Calle Santísimo Cristo 6, 46691 Vallada - T: 962257009
Archaeological Museum 29850

Valladolid

Casa de Cervantes, Calle Rastro 7, 47001 Valladolid - T: 983308810, Fax: 983390703. Head: Jesús Urrea Fernández
Special Museum - 1948
Memorial to Don Miguel de Cervantes Saavedra, Biblioteca Cervantina, house where the poet lived in 1603 - library 29851

Casa de Zorrilla, Calle Fray Luis de Granada 2, 47003 Valladolid - T: 983258573, Fax: 983256880. Head: Christina Agudo Cadarso
Special Museum - 1918
Memorabilia on the writer José de Zorrilla (1817-1893), documents and furniture 29852

Casa-Museo de Colón, Calle Colón s/n, 47005 Valladolid - T: 983291353, Fax: 983426254
Historical Museum - 1965
Memorial to Cristóbal Colón, history of the American colonization 29853

Museo Anatómico, c/o Facultad de Medicina, Calle Ramón y Cajal 7, 47005 Valladolid - T: 983423570, Fax: 983423022, E-mail: juanpas@med.uva.es. Head: Prof. J.F. Pastor Vázquez
University Museum / Natural History Museum 29854

Museo de la Real Academia de Bellas Artes de la Purísima Concepción, Calle Rastro s/n, 47001 Valladolid - T: 983398004, Fax: 983390703
Fine Arts Museum 29855

Museo de Valladolid, Palacio de Fabio Nelli, Plaza Fabio Nelli s/n, 47003 Valladolid - T: 983351389, Fax: 983350422. Head: Eloisa Wattenberg García
Archaeological Museum / Fine Arts Museum / Decorative Arts Museum - 1875
Prehist, Roman, Iberian, Visigothic finds, Islamic and Mozarabian art, numismatic coll, 13th-16th c sculpture and painting, crafts, prehist to Renaissance Spanish ceramics, religious art - library 29856

Museo del Monasterio de San Joaquín y Santa Ana, Plaza de Santa Ana 4, 47001 Valladolid - T: 983357672
Fine Arts Museum - 1978
Paintings, sculpture, frescoes 29857

Museo del Monasterio de Santa Isabel, Plaza San Agustín s/n, 47003 Valladolid - T: 983352139
Religious Arts Museum 29858

Museo Diocesano-Catedralicio, Catedral, Calle Arribas 1, 47002 Valladolid - T: 983304362, Fax: 983290289
Religious Arts Museum - 1965
Ecclesiastical art, painting, sculpture, goldsmith work, liturgical vestments, Mudejar and Gothic architecture 29859

Museo Específico de la Academia de Caballería, Academia de Caballería, Paseo Zorrilla 2, 47006 Valladolid - T: 983350200, Fax: 983337585
Military Museum - 1976 29860

Museo Nacional de Escultura, Calle Cadenas de San Gregorio 1, 47011 Valladolid - T: 983250375, Fax: 983259300. Head: Luis Lunna Moreno
Fine Arts Museum - 1933
Spanish sculpture (13th-18th c), painting (15th-18th c) 29861

Museo Oriental, Paseo de Filipinos 7, 47007 Valladolid - T: 983306800, Fax: 983397896, E-mail: sestagus@adenet.es. Head: Blas Sierra de la Calle
Decorative Arts Museum - 1874
Chinese art, Philippine art 29862

Museo Pedagógico Ciencias Naturales Jesús María Hernando, Plaza España 7, 47001 Valladolid - T: 983211609, Fax: 983211609, E-mail: mcn.valladolid@uva.es. Head: Mercedes Buendía García
Natural History Museum 29863

Museo Pío del Río Ortega, c/o Facultad de Medicina, Calle Ramón y Cajal 7, 47005 Valladolid - T: 983423000
University Museum 29864

Vallbona de les Monges

Museu Monàstic, Monestir, Calle Mayor s/n, 25268 Vallbona de les Monges - T: 973330266, Fax: 973330491, E-mail: vallbona@vallbona.com, Internet: http://www.vallbona.com
Fine Arts Museum 29865

Valldemosa

Museu d'Art Contemporani, Conjunt Monumental la Cartoixa, Plaza Cartoixa s/n, 07170 Valldemosa - T: 971612106
Fine Arts Museum 29866

Real Cartuja, Plaza Cartuja, 07170 Valldemosa - T: 971612106, Fax: 971612106
Fine Arts Museum / Historical Museum / Archaeological Museum - 1924
Antique pharmacy (17th c), Chopin and George Sand Cabinet, wood engraving and prints from Mallorca, memorabilia of the Archduke Luis Salvador, Pinacoteca Municipal: painting, sculpture, archaeology, Palacio del Rey Sancho, local art and history 29867

Valle de Cuelgamuros

Valle de los Caídos, Carretera de Guadarrama, El Escorial, 28209 Valle de Cuelgamuros - T: 918905611, Fax: 918905544, Internet: http://www.patrimonionacional.es. Head: Carmen García-Frias Checa
Historic Site / Religious Arts Museum - 1940 29868

Valle de Hecho

Museo de Arte Contemporáneo Pajar de Agustín, Carretera de Hecho a Oza, 22720 Valle de Hecho - T: 974375002, Fax: 974375213
Fine Arts Museum 29869

Museo Etnológico Casa Mazo, Calle Aire 19, 22720 Valle de Hecho - T: 974375002, Fax: 974375213
Ethnology Museum 29870

Vallromanes

Rajoloteca Salvador Miquel, Can Ros, 08188 Vallromanes - T: 935681242
Fine Arts Museum 29871

Valls

Museu de la Ciutat, c/o Casa Municipal de Cultura, Passeig Caputxins 18, 43800 Valls - T: 977606654, Fax: 977613211
Local Museum / Fine Arts Museum - 1956
Local history and art, contemporary painting and sculpture 29872

Vallvidrera

Museu Verdaguer, Carretera de les Planes km 4.7, 08017 Vallvidrera - T: 932047805. Head: Dr. Margarita Tinto
Special Museum - 1902
Memorabilia of the poet Jacinto Verdaguer 29873

Valverde del Camino

Museo Mineralógico, c/o Casa de Cultura, Calle José Franco s/n, 21600 Valverde del Camino - T: 959550364, Fax: 959553341
Natural History Museum / Archaeological Museum - 1984 29874

Vélez-Málaga

Museo Municipal, Casa Cervantes, Calle Teniente Coronel Baturones 29, 29700 Vélez-Málaga
Local Museum - 1967
Art, history, ethnology 29875

Vélez Rubio

Museo Arqueológico y Etnográfico, c/o Hospital Real, Carrera del Caimán s/n, 04820 Vélez Rubio
Archaeological Museum / Local Museum 29876

Velilla de Ebro

Museo Monográfico Celsa. Centro de Investigación, 50760 Velilla de Ebro
Archaeological Museum - 1986 29877

El Vendrell

Museu Arqueològic Municipal Cal Guimerà, Calle Santa Anna 8, 43700 El Vendrell - T: 977665684, Fax: 977665685. Head: Gemma Sabaté i Piqué
Archaeological Museum - 1966/1991
Prehistory, archaeology 29878

Museu Pau Casals, Av Palfuriana 59-61, 43880 El Vendrell - T: 977684276, Fax: 977684783, E-mail: museu@paucasals.org, Internet: http://www.paucasals.org. Head: Narcis Castanyer Bachs
Music Museum - 1972
Souvenirs of Pablo Casals, universal cellist and musician 29879

Verdú

Casa Santuario de San Pedro Claver, Calle San Pedro Claver 30, 25340 Verdú - T: 973347084
Religious Arts Museum - 1888
Memorabilia of the Jesuit priest Pedro Claver (1580-1654) 29880

Museu Local d'Artesania Terrissaire, Plaza Major, 25340 Verdú - T: 973347007
Decorative Arts Museum 29881

Museu-Tresor Parroquial, Plaza Bisbe Comellas 6, 25340 Verdú - T: 973347033
Religious Arts Museum - 1942
Ecclesiastical art, especially goldsmith work - archive 29882

Vic

Centre Cultural de la Fundació La Caixa, Passeig de la Generalitat 46, 08500 Vic - T: 938894436, Fax: 938814544, E-mail: asegura.fundació@lacaixa.es, Internet: http://www.fundació.lacaixa.es. Head: Angela Segura
Public Gallery 29883

Museo Balmes, c/o Casa de la Cultura, Plaza Don Miguel de Clariana, 08500 Vic - T: 938861306
Special Museum - 1968
Memorabilia of the philosopher Jaime Balmes (1810-48) 29884

Museu Claretiano, Calle Sant Antoní María Claret 8, 08500 Vic - T: 938850242, Fax: 938895987
Religious Arts Museum 29885

Museu Episcopal de Vic, Plaça Bisbe Oliba 3, 08500 Vic - T: 938894417, Fax: 938894417, E-mail: informacio@museuepiscopalvic.com, Internet: http://www.museuepiscopalvic.com. Head: Miquel Tresseras
Archaeological Museum / Fine Arts Museum / Decorative Arts Museum / Religious Arts Museum - 1891
Medieval art, sculpture, 11th-15th c religious paintings and objects, Romanesque and Gothic art, archaeology, numismatics, coins and medals, decorative and applied arts 29886

La Vid

Museo del Monasterio de Santa María de la Vid, Carretera de Soria s/n, 09491 La Vid - T: 947530510, 947530514, Fax: 947530429
Religious Arts Museum 29887

Vielha

Museu Etnologic d'Era Val d'Aran, Calle Major 18, 25530 Vielha - T: 973641815, Fax: 973642351
Local Museum - 1984
History, art and ethnological coll of Valle de Arán 29888

Vigo

Pazo-Museo Municipal Quiñones de León, Parque de Quiñones de León, Calle Castrelos, 36213 Vigo
Fine Arts Museum - 1924
Painting, sculpture, miniatures 29889

La Vila Joiosa

Museo Municipal de Arqueología y Etnología, Calle Barranquet 4, 03570 La Vila Joiosa - T: 965890150, Fax: 966810040, E-mail: villajmu@dip-alicante.es. Head: Antonio Espinosa Ruiz
Ethnology Museum / Archaeological Museum 29890

Vilabella

Museu del Camp, Calle Roser 24, 43886 Vilabella - T: 977620236
Local Museum 29891

Vilafranca del Penedès

Museu del Vino, Museo de Vilafranca, Plaza Jaime I 1, 08720 Vilafranca del Penedès - T: 938900582, Fax: 938170036. Head: Enrique Regull, Dr. Antonio Comas Estatella, Luis Pure Via, Antonio Sabaté
Special Museum 29892

Museu de Vilafranca-Museu del Vi, Plaça Jaume I 1-5, 08720 Vilafranca del Penedès - T: 938900582, Fax: 938170036, E-mail: m.vilafranca@diba.es. Head: Montserrat Iniesta González
Ethnology Museum / Fine Arts Museum / Archaeological Museum / Natural History Museum - 1935
Winegrowing implements, local history, paintings, ceramics, archeology, geology, regional ornithology, musical archives, library specialised on winery and winegrowing 29893

Vilajüiga

Colección de Geología, Calle San Sebastián, 17493 Vilajüiga
Natural History Museum - 1902
Mineralogy, applied and folk arts, arms 29894

Collecció la Magrana, Calle Figueras 10, 17493 Vilajüiga - T: 972231171, 972240088
Special Museum - 1978
Spanish ceramic coll (14th-20th c) 29895

Vilalba

Museo de Prehistoria e Arqueoloxia de Vilalba, Plaza Suso Gayoso 1, 27800 Vilalba - T: 982511383
Local Museum 29896

Vilanova del Camí

Museu de l'Aigua Collecció Gavarró, Calle Molí de Rigat, 08788 Vilanova del Camí - T: 938031483, Fax: 938650952
Local Museum 29897

Vilanova i la Geltrú

Centre Aeri, Urbanització l'Aragai, Av l'Aragai, 08800 Vilanova i la Geltrú - T: 938156542, Fax: 938156745
Science&Tech Museum 29898

Museu de Curiositats Marineres, Calle Pintor Alexandre de Cabanyes 2, 08800 Vilanova i la Geltrú - T: 938154263, Internet: http://www.welcome.to/carpajuanita. Head: Francisco Roig Toqués
Special Museum - 1948
Ship models, instruments of navigation, arms, dissect fishes, maritime archaeology, tools, old books, shells 29899

Museu del Ferrocarril, Plaza Eduard Maristany s/n, 08800 Vilanova i la Geltrú - T: 938158491, Fax: 938158220. Head: Montserrat Illa i Vilà
Science&Tech Museum - 1972
Oldest locomotive in Spain - railway magazine and other publications 29900

Museu Romantic Can Papiol, Calle Mayor 32, 08800 Vilanova i la Geltrú - T: 938930382, Fax: 938142498. Head: Assumpta Gou Vernet
Decorative Arts Museum - 1961
18th-19th c furnishings and interiors, decorative arts, coaches - library 29901

Museu Víctor Balaguer, Av Víctor Balaguer s/n, 08800 Vilanova i la Geltrú - T: 938154202, Fax: 938153684. Head: Josep María Trullén i Thomàs
Special Museum - 1884
Prehistory, archaeology, 12th-17th c sculpture, 16th-20th c painting, decorative and applied arts, former residence of the poet and politician Victor Balaguer y Cirera (1826-1901) - library 29902

Vilar de Santos

Museo Etnográfico da Limia, 32650 Vilar de Santos - T: 988465883
Ethnology Museum 29903

Vilar-Rodona

Museu de la Vila, Calle Jacint Verdaguer 6, 43814 Vilar-Rodona - T: 977638038
Local Museum 29904

Vilassar de Dalt

Museu de Malacología Cau del Cargol, Calle Angel Guimerà 11, 08339 Vilassar de Dalt - T: 937530696. Head: Issa Bot Riera
Natural History Museum 29905

Museu Municipal, Calle Marquès de Barberà 9, 08339 Vilassar de Dalt - T: 937507488. Head: Josep Vilademunt y Corney
Local Museum 29906

Vilassar de Mar

Museu Enric Monjó, Calle Camí Ral 30, 08340 Vilassar de Mar - T: 937593639, Fax: 937593639. Head: Francesc Rodon
Special Museum 29907

Villaconejos

Museo del Melonero, c/o Edificio de la Cooperativa Campo, 28360 Villaconejos - T: 918938095
Local Museum 29908

Villadiego

Museo Municipal de Etnografía, Calle Vega 21, 09120 Villadiego - T: 947361700, Fax: 947361639, E-mail: turmodigos@arrzkis.es, Internet: http://www.arrzkis.es/~turmodigos/museos.htm
Ethnology Museum 29909

Museo Municipal de Pintura, Calle Vega 18, 09120 Villadiego - T: 947361700, Fax: 947361639, E-mail: turmodigos@arrzkis.es, Internet: http://www.arrzkis.es/~turmodigos/museos.htm
Fine Arts Museum 29910

Villafamés

Museo de Arte Contemporáneo de Villafamés, Palacio del Bayle, Calle Diputación 20, 12192 Villafamés - T: 964329152, Fax: 964329152. Head: Vicente Aquilera Cerni
Fine Arts Museum 29911

Museo del Vino, Calle Diputación 38, 12192 Villafamés - T: 964329001, Fax: 964329286
Special Museum 29912

Villafranca del Bierzo

Museo de Ciencias Naturales, Travesía de San Nicolás s/n, 24500 Villafranca del Bierzo - T: 987540027
Natural History Museum 29913

Villagarcía de Campos Valladolid

Museo de la Colegiata San Luis, Av Generalísimo s/n, 47840 Villagarcía de Campos Valladolid - T: 983717032, Fax: 983717423. Head: Angel Requejo
Fine Arts Museum / Decorative Arts Museum / Religious Arts Museum - 1959
Art and history, painting, sculpture, goldsmith work, liturgical vestments, local historical archives 29914

Villanueva de Lorenzana

Museo de Arte Sacro Antiguo, Iglesia de Santa María de Valdeflores, Plaza del Conde Santo, 27760 Villanueva de Lorenzana - T: 9821211073
Religious Arts Museum - 1978
Goldsmith work, sculpture, painting, 5th c sarcophagus, 9th c altar - Library 29915

Villarcayo

Museo Monasterio Santa María La Real de Vileña, Carretera de Medina de Pomar s/n, 09550 Villarcayo - T: 947100042
Religious Arts Museum 29916

Villasarracino

Museo del Centro Cultural de Villasarracino, Calle Fray Felix Cuadrado s/n, 34479 Villasarracino
Local Museum 29917

Villasobroso

Castillo de Sobroso, Carretera Madrid-Vigo, km 26, 36879 Villasobroso - T: 986656201
Fine Arts Museum / Historical Museum
Art and history 29918

Villena

Museo Arqueológico Municipal José María Soler, c/o Edificio de Ayuntamiento, Plaza Santiago 1, 03400 Villena - T: 965801150, Fax: 965806146. Head: José María Soler García
Archaeological Museum - 1957
Prehistory, archaeology, pre-Roman goldsmith work (Tesoro de Villena, Tesorillo del Cabezo Redondo), medieval ceramics 29919

Museo de Escultura Novarro Santafe, Calle Navarro Santafe 46, 03400 Villena - T: 965801150, Fax: 965806146
Fine Arts Museum 29920

Museo del Botijo, Calle Párroco Azorín 7, 03400 Villena - T: 965800571
Special Museum 29921

Museo del Festero, Plaza Santiago 6, 03400 Villena - T: 965802695
Ethnology Museum 29922

Vimbodí

Museu Parroquialí, Parroquia de Vimbodí, 43430 Vimbodí - T: 977878049
Religious Arts Museum 29923

Vinaixa

Museu Parroquial, Plaza Parroquial, 25440 Vinaixa - T: 973175319
Religious Arts Museum 29924

Vinaròs

Museo Municipal, Calle Santa Rita 2, 12500 Vinaròs - T: 964450200
Local Museum 29925

La Virgen del Camino

Museo de Ciencias Naturales, Convento Rr. Pp. Dominicos, Carretera de Astorga 87, 24198 La Virgen del Camino - T: 987300001
Natural History Museum 29926

Viso del Marqués

Archivo-Museo Don Alvaro de Bazán, Palacio del Marqués de Santa Cruz, Plaza del Pradillo 11, 13770 Viso del Marqués - T: 926336008, Fax: 926336743. Head: Fernando Riaño Lozano
Historical Museum - 1948
Documentation on the Spanish navy during 18th and 19th c - archive 29927

Vitoria-Gasteiz

Casa del Cordón, Calle Cuchillería 24, 01001 Vitoria-Gasteiz - T: 945259673, Fax: 945162190
Historical Museum
History, 15th c house and 13th c Gothic tower 29928

Colección de Numismática, Paseo de Fray Francisco 8, 01007 Vitoria-Gasteiz - T: 945181918, Fax: 945181919. Head: Dr. José Eguía
Special Museum - 1942
library 29929

Museo de Armería de Alava, Paseo Fray Francisco de Vitoria 3, 01007 Vitoria-Gasteiz - T: 945181925, Fax: 945181921. Head: Dr. José Eguía
Military Museum - 1942
History of arms - library 29930

Museo de Arqueología de Alava, Calle Correría 116, 01001 Vitoria-Gasteiz - T: 945181922, Fax: 945181923. Head: Dr. Amelia Baldeón
Archaeological Museum
Prehistory, archeology 29931

Museo de Bellas Artes de Alava, Palacio Augusti, Paseo Fray Francisco de Alava 8, 01007 Vitoria-Gasteiz - T: 945181918, Fax: 945181919
Fine Arts Museum - 1942
Basque Folkloric Art(19th-20th c) and Contemporary Art from the fifties to the present day 29932

Museo de Ciencias Naturales de Alava, Calle Siervas de Jésus 24, 01001 Vitoria-Gasteiz - T: 945181924, Fax: 945181932, E-mail: mcna@jet.es. Head: Jésus Alonso
Natural History Museum
Geology, botany, zoology, amber 29933

Museo de la Batalla de Vitoria, El Portalón, Calle Correría, 01001 Vitoria-Gasteiz
Military Museum - 1963
Memorabilia of the battle for independence (1813), 16th c early Renaissance building with Gothic and Mudejar elements 29934

Museo Fournier de Naipes de Alava, Palacio de Bendaña, Calle Cuchillería 54, 01001 Vitoria-Gasteiz - T: 945181920, Fax: 945181921. Head: Dr. José Eguía
Special Museum - 1916
Playing cards from all over the world XIVth to XX c - library 29935

Xàtiva

Esglesia de Sant Feliu, Carretera del Castell, 46800 Xàtiva - T: 962274469
Religious Arts Museum 29936

Museo del Almudín, Calle Corretgeria 46, 46800 Xàtiva - T: 962276597, Fax: 962289809
Local Museum
Archeological section with roman findings, islamic, ceramic toys and fine arts coll 29937

Museo Municipal, Calle Almundí s/n, 46800 Xàtiva - T: 962882802
Local Museum - 1918
Islamic art, Gothic architecture and sculpture, Roman inscriptions, 16th-20th c painting 29938

Museo Municipal de Bellas Artes, Calle Almundí s/n, 46800 Xàtiva - T: 962882802
Fine Arts Museum 29939

Xunqueira de Ambia

Museo Parroquial Santa María La Real, Antigua Colegiata, 32670 Xunqueira de Ambia - T: 988440738
Religious Arts Museum - 1931
Ecclesiastical art 29940

Yaiza

Museo de Rocas, Parque Nacional de Timanfaya, Carretera Yaiza-Tinajo, km 5 Echadero de los Camellos, 35560 Yaiza - T: 928840240, 928840238, Fax: 928840251, E-mail: timanfaya@mma.es, Internet: http://www.mma.es/timanfaya
Natural History Museum 29941

Yecla

Museo Arqueológico Municipal Cayetano Mergelina, c/o Casa Municipal de la Cultura, Calle España 37, 30150 Yecla - T: 968791899
Archaeological Museum - 1980
Archaeology, Iberic sculptures from Cerro de los Santos 29942

Museo de Reproducciones de El Greco, Calle San José 8, 30150 Yecla
Fine Arts Museum - 1980
73 replicas of famous pictures by El Greco 29943

Zafra

Monasterio de Santa Clara, Calle Sevilla 30, 06300 Zafra - T: 924551199
Religious Arts Museum - 1965
Religious art, paintings, sculptures, goldsmith work, 16th-18th c ornaments 29944

Zalduondo

Museo Comarcal, Palacio Lazarraga, 01208 Zalduondo - T: 945304393, Fax: 945304393, E-mail: elkartea@euskalnet.net. Head: Asun Ruiz de Azua Murua
Ethnology Museum 29945

Zamora

Museo Catedralicio, Catedral, Plaza Pío XII 2, 49001 Zamora - T: 980531802, Fax: 980531915. Head: Vitaliano Alfageme Sánchez
Religious Arts Museum - 1926
14th-16th c Flemish and French tapestry, sculpture, painting, goldsmith work, documents 29946

Museo de Semana Santa, Plaza Santa María la Nueva 1, 49004 Zamora - T: 980532295, Fax: 980536070, E-mail: junprosesaza@ssanta.zamoza.es, Internet: http://www.ssanta.zamoza.es. Head: Dionisio Alba Alvarez
Religious Arts Museum - 1963
Religious pictures, cloister 29947

Museo de Zamora, Palacio del Cordón, Plaza Santa Lucía 2, 49002 Zamora - T: 980516150, Fax: 980535064. Head: Rosario García Rozas
Local Museum - 1911
Painting, sculpture, prehistory, archaeology, numismatics, drawings, graphic arts, heraldry, reproductions 29948

Zaragoza

Basílica de Nuestra Señora del Pilar, Plaza del Pilar 19, 50003 Zaragoza - T: 976231355. Head: Eduardo Torra
Religious Arts Museum - 1904
Painting, sculpture, goldsmith work 29949

Casa de los Morlanes, Ayuntamiento de Zaragoza, Plaza de San Carlos 4, 50001 Zaragoza - T: 976721800, Fax: 976200260, E-mail: cultura-mye@ayto-zaragoza.es
Public Gallery 29950

La Lonja, Ayuntamiento de Zaragoza, Plaza del Pilar, 50003 Zaragoza - T: 976397239, Fax: 976397239, E-mail: cultura-mye@ayto-zaragoza.es
Public Gallery - 1985 29951

Museo Camón Aznar, Calle Expoz y Mina 23, 50003 Zaragoza - T: 976397328, Fax: 976397387
Performing Arts Museum - 1979 29952

Museo Catedralicio de la Seo, Catedral, Plaza de la Seo, 50001 Zaragoza - T: 976291231. Head: Eduardo Torra
Religious Arts Museum - 1940
Tapestry, ecclesiastical painting and goldsmith work 29953

Museo de Bellas Artes, Pl de los Sitios 6, 50001 Zaragoza - T: 976222181, 976225682, Fax: 976222378, E-mail: museoza@aragob.es. Head: Miguel Beltrán Lloris
Fine Arts Museum / Decorative Arts Museum / Archaeological Museum - 1844
French and Spanish prehist, Hallstatt culture finds, ceramics and bronzes, archaeology, Islamic art, Romanesque, Gothic, Mudejar art, 13th-16th c sculpture, 14th-20th c Spanish painting, Spanish crafts and ceramics, drawings and engravings, coll of Italian drawings, paintings of German and Flemish schools, ethnography coll, folklore - library, educational dept 29954

Museo de las Termas Públicas de Caesaraugusta, Calle San Juan y San Pedro 3-7, 50001 Zaragoza - T: 976399752, Fax: 976399752, E-mail: cultura-mye@ayto-zaragoza.es
Archaeological Museum - 1999 29955

Museo de Zaragoza, Pl de Los Sitios 6, 50001 Zaragoza - T: 976222181, 976225682, Fax: 976222378, E-mail: museoza@aragob.es. Head: Miguel Beltrán Lloris
Local Museum - 1908 29956

Museo de Zaragoza, Sección Cerámica, Parque Primo de Rivera, 50009 Zaragoza - T: 976351153, Fax: 976222378, E-mail: museoza@aragob.es. Head: Miguel Beltrán Lloris
Decorative Arts Museum - 1985 29957

Museo de Zaragoza, Sección de Etnología, Parque Primo de Rivera, 50009 Zaragoza - T: 976553726, Fax: 976222378, E-mail: museoza@aragob.es. Head: Miguel Beltrán Lloris
Ethnology Museum - 1957
Local costumes and ceramics 29958

Museo del Foro Caesaraugusta, Ayuntamiento de Zaragoza, Plaza de La Seo 2, 50001 Zaragoza - T: 976399752, Fax: 976399752, E-mail: cultura-mye@ayto-zaragoza.es
Archaeological Museum - 1995 29959

Museo Específico de la Academia General Militar, Carretera de Francia s/n, 50090 Zaragoza - T: 976517000
Military Museum 29960

Museo Pablo Gargallo, Ayuntamiento de Zaragoza, Plaza San Felipe 3, 50003 Zaragoza - T: 976392058, Fax: 976392076, E-mail: cultura-mye@ayto-zaragoza.es. Head: Maria Cristina Gil Imaz
Fine Arts Museum - 1985 29961

Museo Pablo Serrano, Calle María Agustín 20, 50004 Zaragoza - T: 976280659, 976280660, Fax: 976284370, E-mail: mpabloserrano@aragob.es
Fine Arts Museum 29962

Palacio de Montemuzo, Ayuntamiento de Zaragoza, Calle Santiago 36, 50003 Zaragoza - T: 976721800, Fax: 976200260, E-mail: cultura-mye@ayto-zaragoza.es
Public Gallery - 1985 29963

Torreón Fortea, Ayuntamiento de Zaragoza, Calle Torrenueva 25, 50003 Zaragoza - T: 976721400, Fax: 976200260, E-mail: cultura-mye@ayto-zaragoza.es. Head: Alejandro Salvador Zazurca
Public Gallery - 1985 29964

Zarautz

Museo Escuela del Mar Itxas Natura, Eguzki Lore, Eraikuntza s/n, 20800 Zarautz - T: 943131836
Special Museum 29965

Photomuseum, Calle San Ignazio 17, 20800 Zarautz - T: 943130906, Fax: 943831823
Fine Arts Museum 29966

Salas Municipales de Arte Sanz-Enea, Av Navarra-Villa Sanz-Enea, 20800 Zarautz - T: 943835950, Fax: 943134074, E-mail: erakus.zarauts@udal.gipuzkoa.net
Public Gallery 29967

Zerain

Museo Local de Zerain, Plaza Herriko s/n, 20214 Zerain - T: 943801724
Local Museum 29968

Zuheros

Museo Municipal, Plaza de la Paz 2, 14870 Zuheros - T: 957694545, Fax: 957694545. Head: Luis Rubio Pediata
Archaeological Museum 29969

Zumaia

Beobide Lantoki Museoa, Calle Beobide Ibilbidea s/n, 20750 Zumaia - T: 943860564, 943861608
Fine Arts Museum 29970

Casa Museo Ignacio Zuloaga, Calle Santiago Auzoa 50, 20750 Zumaia - T: 943862341
Local Museum 29971

Zumárraga

Casa Natal de Legazpi, Plaza Euskadi 1, 20700 Zumárraga - T: 943729022
Special Museum - 1945
Memorabilia of Miguel López de Legazpi, the conquistador of the Philippines, who died in Manila in 1572 29972

Museo de Minerales y Fósiles, c/o Casa de Cultura, Calle Jauregui 19, 20700 Zumárraga - T: 943724170, Fax: 943724754
Natural History Museum 29973

Sri Lanka

Ambalangoda

Ambalangoda Mask Museum, 426 Main St, Ambalangoda - T: (09) 58750, Fax: 58750. Head: Bandusena Wijesooriya
Folklore Museum - 1987
Masks and costumes of healing rituals of Sri Lanka 29974

Anuradhapura

Archaeological Museum, Anuradhapura - T: (025) 2589. Head: J.S.A. Uduwara
Archaeological Museum
Archeology, sculpture, jewelry, coins, pottery 29975

Folk Museum, Anuradhapura - T: (025) 2589
Folklore Museum - 1971
Folk art, handicraft 29976

Colombo

Archaeological Museum, c/o University, Colombo
Archaeological Museum / University Museum
Antiquities, ivory 29977

Art Gallery, Dr. Ananda Coomaraswamy Mawatha, Colombo 7
Fine Arts Museum 29978

Bandaranaike Museum, Bauddhaloka Mawatha, Colombo 7 - T: (01) 691139, Fax: 697420. Head: Sunethra Bandaranaike
Special Museum - 1974
Memorabilia of S.W.R.D. Bandaranaike (Prime Minister), filma and speeches of him, books 29979

Colombo National Museum, Sir Marcos Fernando
Mawatha, Colombo, mail addr: POB 854, Colombo 7
- T: (01) 692767/68, Fax: 695366, E-mail: nmdep@
slt.lk. Head: Dr. Nanda Wickramasinghe
Archaeological Museum / Ethnology Museum - 1877
Art, design, antiquities of Sri Lanca, local
archaeology, ethnology, anthropology -
library   29980

Dutch Period Museum, Prince St,Pettah, Colombo 11
- T: (01) 448466
Historical Museum - 1982
History (17th-18th c), furniture, maps   29981

Kalagaraya Art Gallery, Alliance Française de
Colombo, 54 Ward Pl, Colombo 7
Fine Arts Museum
Contemporary art   29982

Lionel Wendt Art Gallery, Guildford Crescent,
Colombo 7
Fine Arts Museum
Contemporary paintings   29983

National Museum of Natural History, Sir Marcos
Fernando Mawatha, Colombo 7, mail addr: POB 854,
Colombo - T: (01) 691399, Fax: 695366,
E-mail: nmdep@slt.lk. Head: Dr. Nanda
Wickramasinghe
Natural History Museum - 1985
Fauna and flora, rocks and minerals, entomology -
herbarium   29984

Sapumal Foundation Gallery, 32 Barnes Pl, Colombo
7
Fine Arts Museum
Sri Lankan paintings since 1920   29985

Dedigama

Archaeological Museum, Dedigama
Archaeological Museum
Local excavations   29986

Galle

Galle National Museum, Fort of Galle, Church St,
Galle - T: (09) 32051. Head: S. Senadheera
Local Museum - 1986
Art and culture of the Southern Province   29987

National Maritime Museum, Fort of Galle, Church St,
Galle - T: (09) 32051
Historical Museum
Fauna and flora of the sea, environment, traditional
methods of fishing, water archaeology   29988

Jaffna

Jaffna National Museum, Jaffna. Head: Dr. P.H.D.H.
de Silva
Historical Museum - 1978   29989

Kandy

Kandy National Museum, Dharmapala Mawatha,
Kandy - T: (08) 223867. Head: Senarath Panawatta
Local Museum - 1942
Ethnography, decorative arts, pottery, jewelry,
weapons   29990

Moratuwa

Weera Puran Appu Museum, New Galle Rd,
Moratuwa
Historical Museum
Life and times of this great hero   29991

Ratnapura

Museum of Ethnology and Folk Art, c/o Ratnapura
Gem Bureau and Laboratory, Getangama, Ratnapura
- T: (045) 22469, Fax: 23657. Head: P.B. Marapana
Ethnology Museum / Folklore Museum - 1980
Folk art, paintings, ancient palm leaf manuscripts,
ritual objects, Sri Lanka handicrafts, gems, and
minerals, gold jewelry   29992

Museum of Gems and Minerals, c/o Ratnapura Gem
Bureau and Laboratory, Getangama, Ratnapura -
T: (045) 22469, Fax: 23657. Head: P.B. Marapana
Natural History Museum - 1959   29993

Ratnapura National Museum, 8-14 Main St,
Colombo Rd, Ratnapura - T: (045) 2451. Head: Dr.
P.H.D.H. de Silva
Historical Museum / Local Museum - 1942
Archeology, prehistory, zoology, ethnography 29994

Sudan

El-Fasher

Sultan Ali Dianr Museum, Sudan National Museum,
El-Fasher, mail addr: POB 178, Khartoum
Local Museum   29995

El-Obeid

Sheikan Museum, Sudan National Museum, El-
Obeid, mail addr: POB 178, Khartoum
Ethnology Museum / Archaeological Museum
Archaeology, ethnography, Shiekan battle
weapons   29996

Khartoum

El-Barkai Museum, POB 178, Khartoum
Local Museum   29997

El-Ibied Regional Museum, POB 178, Khartoum.
Head: Prof. Osama A. El-Nur
Archaeological Museum / Ethnology Museum
Archeology, ethnography   29998

Ethographical Museum, Sudan National Museum,
POB 178, Khartoum - T: (011) 77052. Head:
Mohammed Hamed
Ethnology Museum - 1956
Ethnography, tools   29999

Geological Museum, Sharia Abu Sin, Khartoum, mail
addr: POB 410, Khartoum
Natural History Museum
Rocks and minerals, fossils, meteorites   30000

Khalif's House Museum, POB 178, Khartoum -
T: (11) 52968. Head: Prof. Osama A. El-Nur
Local Museum   30001

Sudan National Museum, El Neel Av, Khartoum, mail
addr: POB 178, Khartoum - T: (11) 70680. Head:
Hassan Hussein Idris
Museum of Classical Antiquities / Archaeological
Museum - 1905
Fossil skulls, statues of ancient kings, seals, golden
ornaments and utensils   30002

Sudan Natural History Museum, University of
Khartoum, Gama Av, Khartoum, mail addr: POB 321,
Khartoum - T: (011) 81873. Head: Dr. Dawi Musa
Hamed
Natural History Museum - 1920
Birds and wild game of Sudan - Library   30003

Medani

Natural History Museum, Medani
Natural History Museum   30004

Merowe

Merowe Museum, Pl Merowe, Merowe
Archaeological Museum / Ethnology Museum
Monumental granite statues of Napatan Kings,
archaeological and ethnographic coll   30005

Omdurman

Khalifa's House Museum, Omdurman
Historical Museum
Items from Mahdia period, weapons,
documents   30006

Port Sudan

Natural History Museum, Port Sudan
Natural History Museum   30007

Wadi Halfa

Halfa Museum, Wadi Halfa
Ethnology Museum / Archaeological Museum
Archaeology, ethnography and folklore   30008

Suriname

Nieuw Amsterdam

Openluchtmuseum Nieuw Amsterdam,
Wilhelminastr, Nieuw Amsterdam Commewijne, mail
addr: Postbus 2306, Nieuw Amsterdam
Commewijne - T: 0322225/27. Head: S. Mohan
Open Air Museum - 1734
18th c fort with barracks, powder houses, former
commanders house, brick sluice   30009

Paramaribo

Stichting Joden Savanna, Albergastr 28, Paramaribo
Historical Museum
Early Jewish settlement   30010

Surinaams Museum, Abraham Crijnssenweg 1,
Paramaribo, mail addr: Postbus 2306, Paramaribo -
T: 425871, Fax: 425881, E-mail: museum@cq-
link.sr, Internet: http://www.surinaamsmuseum.net.
Head: J.H.J. Van Putten
Local Museum - 1947
History of the Fort Zeelandia and the City of
Paramaribo, pre- and post-Columbian artifacts,
exhibitions about slaves, weapons, woodcarvings,
textiles, paintings, 19th c drawings, modern art,
maps, books, newspapers, 19th c. pharmacy,
colonial furniture, porcelain and antique glasscol l
(17-20th c.) - library   30011

Swaziland

Lobamba

Swaziland National Museums, Behind Parliament,
Lobamba H107, mail addr: POB 100, Lobamba H107
- T: 61178, Fax: 61875, E-mail: staff@
swazimus.org.sz. Head: Rosemary Andrade
Ethnology Museum - 1972
Displays illustrating material culture of Swaziland -
reference library   30012